TELEVISION & CABLE FACTBOOK
VOLUME 68

Publications & Services of Warren Communications News

TELEVISION & CABLE FACTBOOK
TELEVISION & CABLE FACTBOOK ON CD-ROM
CABLE & STATION COVERAGE ATLAS
Published Annually

TELEVISION & CABLE ACTION UPDATE
Published Weekly

TELEVISION DIGEST with CONSUMER ELECTRONICS
Published Weekly

AUDIO WEEK

COMMUNICATIONS DAILY

CONSUMER MULTIMEDIA REPORT
Published Biweekly

DAILY DOCUMENT SERVICE

FCC REPORT
Published Biweekly

LOCAL COMPETITION REPORT
Published Biweekly

LONG DISTANCE COMPETITION REPORT
Published Biweekly

MOBILE COMMUNICATIONS REPORT
Published Biweekly

PUBLIC BROADCASTING REPORT
Published Biweekly

SATELLITE WEEK

STATE TELEPHONE REGULATION REPORT
Published Biweekly

TELCO BUSINESS REPORT
Published Biweekly

TELECOM A.M.
Published Continually

VIDEO WEEK

WARREN'S CABLE REGULATION MONITOR
Published Weekly

WASHINGTON TELECOM NEWSWIRE
Published Continually

DATA BY DESIGN

Electronic Distribution via Dow Jones, Desktop Data, Information Access Co., Knight-Ridder Information, M.A.I.D. and Nexis

ISBN: 1-57696-032-3 Services Vol. ISBN: 1-57696-031-5
Cable Vol.1 ISBN: 1-57696-027-7 Cable Vol.2 ISBN: 1-57696-028-5
Stations Vol.1 ISBN: 1-57696-029-3 Stations Vol.2 ISBN: 1-57696-030-7
ISSN: 0732-8648

Index to Sections
Television & Cable Factbook No. 68

TV STATIONS VOLUME

Section A

Section B

Section C

CABLE SYSTEMS VOLUME

Section D

Section E

Section F

Cable Community Index

TV & CABLE SERVICES VOLUME

Section G

Section H

Section I

Professional Cards

ENGINEERING & CONSULTING SERVICES ▶

AFCCE
ASSOCIATION OF FEDERAL COMMUNICATIONS CONSULTING ENGINEERS
PO Box 19333
20th Street Station
Washington D.C. 20036
(703) 569-7704, Fax (703) 569-6417
http://www.afcce.org

CONSULTING ENGINEERS
7901 YARNWOOD COURT
SPRINGFIELD, VA 22153
(703) 569-7704
MEMBER AFCCE

COHEN, DIPPELL AND EVERIST, P C.
CONSULTING ENGINEERS
Since 1937
1300 "L" STREET, N.W., SUTE 1100
WASHINGTON, D.C. 20005
(202) 898-0111
FAX (202) 898-0895
cdepc@worldnet att.net
Member AFCCE

Denny & Associates, PC
Consulting Engineers
DENNY
PH 202 452 5630
FX 202 452 5620
Member AFCCE EM info@denny.com

du Treil, Lundin & Rackley, Inc.
Consulting Engineers
201 Fletcher Avenue
Sarasota, Florida 34236
Phone: (941) 329-6000
FAX: (941) 329-6030
www.dlr.com
MEMBER AFCCE

HAMMETT & EDISON, INC.
CONSULTING ENGINEERS
SAN FRANCISCO
707/996-5200
202/396-5200 DC
707/996-5280 facsimile

member AFCCE
www.h-e.com

Highlight your company by placing a professional card in the Television & Cable Factbook
For information, call
Warren Communications News
(800) 771-9202, Fax (202) 293-3535
e-mail: info@warren-news.com

Consulting Communications Engineers
WE ARE EXPERTS IN: AM, FM, TV, ITFS, PCS, FIBER
Transmitter Plant Design - Digital TV Transition
FCC Applications - RF Radiation - Field Engineering
Tower Detuning - Voice/Video/Data Networks
210 S. Main St., Thiensville, WI 53092, (414)242-6000, FAX (414)242-6045
http://www.evansassoc.com **Member AFCCE**

Index to Contents
Television & Cable Factbook No. 68

A

B

C

D

E

F

G

H

I

J

K

L

M

N

O

P

Q

R

S

T

U

V

W

X

Y

Z

Index to Advertisers Cable Volume

OHIO

Total Systems: **389**
Total Communities Served: **2,244**
Franchises Not Yet Operating: **7**
Applications Pending: **0**
Communities with Applications: **0**
Number of Basic Subscribers: **2,871,138**
Number of Expanded Basic Subscribers: **1,035,561**
Number of Pay Units: **1,570,202**

Top 100 Markets Represented: Cleveland-Lorain-Akron (8); Pittsburgh (10); Cincinnati, OH-Newport, KY (17); Columbus-Chillicothe (27); Charleston-Huntington (36); Dayton-Kettering (41); Toledo (52); Youngstown (79); Fort Wayne-Roanaoke, IN (82); Wheeling, WV-Steubenville, OH (90) .

For a list of all cable communities included in this section, see the Cable Community Index located in the back of this volume.
For explanation of terms used in cable system listings, see p. D-9.

ADA—FrontierVision, 220 N. Main St., Ada, OH 45810. Phone: 419-628-3423. Fax: 419-634-1245. Counties: Hancock & Hardin. Also serves Alger, Jenera, Liberty Twp. (Hardin County), McGuffey. ICA: OH0313.

TV Market Ranking: Below 100. Franchise award date: July 21, 1981. Franchise expiration date: July 21, 2006. Began: February 1, 1969.

Channel capacity: 37 (2-way capable; operating 2-way). Channels available but not in use: None.

Basic Service

Subscribers: 2,332.

Programming (received off-air): WBGU-TV (P) Bowling Green; WBNS-TV (C), WSYX (A) Columbus; WHIO-TV (C) Dayton; WLIO (N), WTLW (I) Lima; WGTE-TV (P), WNWO-TV (N), WTOL-TV (C), WTVG (A), WUPW (F) Toledo; allband FM.

Programming (via satellite): WGN-TV (W) Chicago; QVC; TBS Superstation; The Weather Channel.

Fee: $31.58 installation; $12.54 monthly.

Expanded Basic Service

Subscribers: 2,073.

Programming (via satellite): A & E; CNN; Country Music TV; Disney Channel; ESPN; Fox Family Channel; Headline News; Learning Channel; MTV; Nickelodeon; USA Network; VH1.

Fee: $9.12 monthly.

Expanded Basic Service 2

Subscribers: N.A.

Programming (via satellite): American Movie Classics; Discovery Channel; Nashville Network; Turner Network TV.

Fee: $3.75 monthly.

Pay Service 1

Pay Units: 258.

Programming (via satellite): HBO.

Fee: $11.95 monthly.

Pay Service 2

Pay Units: 275.

Programming (via satellite): Showtime.

Fee: $10.95 monthly.

Pay Service 3

Pay Units: 212.

Programming (via satellite): The Movie Channel.

Fee: N.A.

Pay Service 4

Pay Units: 138.

Programming (via satellite): Starz!

Fee: N.A.

Pay Service 5

Pay Units: 141.

Programming (via satellite): The New Encore.

Fee: N.A.

Miles of plant: 52.5 (coaxial); 133.0 (fiber optic). Homes passed: 3,369.

Manager: Steve Trippe. Chief technician: Bill Ricker.

Ownership: FrontierVision Partners LP (MSO). See Cable System Ownership.

ADENA—TCI Cablevision of Ohio Inc., Box 469, Bridgeport, OH 43912. Phone: 800-527-2222. Counties: Harrison & Jefferson. Also serves Dillonvale, Harrisville, Mount Pleasant Twp. (Jefferson County), Short Creek, Smithfield Twp. (Jefferson County). ICA: OH0181.

TV Market Ranking: 90. Franchise award date: N.A. Franchise expiration date: N.A. Began: June 1, 1978.

Channel capacity: 52. Channels available but not in use: 20.

Basic Service

Subscribers: 1,391.

Programming (received off-air): WOUC-TV (P) Cambridge; KDKA-TV (C), WCWB (W), WPGH-TV (F), WPXI (N), WQED (P), WTAE-TV (A) Pittsburgh; WTOV-TV (N) Steubenville-Wheeling; WTRF-TV (C) Wheeling-Steubenville.

Programming (via satellite): A & E; CNBC; CNN; Discovery Channel; Fox Family Channel; Knowledge TV; Lifetime; MTV; Nashville Network; Nickelodeon; Odyssey; QVC; TBS Superstation.

Fee: $60.00 installation; $8.94 monthly; $2.00 converter.

Expanded Basic Service

Subscribers: 1,299.

Programming (via satellite): American Movie Classics; Court TV; ESPN; Fox Sports Net Pittsburgh; Turner Network TV; USA Network.

Fee: $10.48 monthly.

Pay Service 1

Pay Units: 51.

Programming (via satellite): Disney Channel.

Fee: N.A.

Pay Service 2

Pay Units: 439.

Programming (via satellite): The New Encore.

Fee: N.A.

Pay Service 3

Pay Units: 231.

Programming (via satellite): HBO.

Fee: $11.95 monthly.

Pay Service 4

Pay Units: 157.

Programming (via satellite): Showtime.

Fee: N.A.

Equipment: C-COR headend; Kaiser amplifiers.

Miles of plant: 40.1 (coaxial). Homes passed: 1,774. Total homes in franchised area: 2,721.

Manager: Robert Weese. Chief technician: Earl Conway.

City fee: 3% of gross.

Ownership: AT&T Broadband & Internet Services (MSO). Purchased from Tele-Communications Inc., March 9, 1999.

AKRON—Time Warner Cable, 1655 Brittain Rd., Akron, OH 44310-3998. Phones: 330-633-9203; 800-950-2266. Fax: 330-633-0024. Counties: Medina, Portage, Summit & Wayne. Also serves Barberton, Cuyahoga Falls, Doylestown, Fairlawn, Lakemore, Mogadore, Munroe Falls, Norton, Silver Lake, Springfield Twp. (Summit County), Stow, Tallmadge, Wadsworth (Medina County), Wadsworth Twp. (Medina County). ICA: OH0005.

TV Market Ranking: 8. Franchise award date: N.A. Franchise expiration date: N.A. Began: August 1, 1969.

Channel capacity: 60 (not 2-way capable). Channels available but not in use: N.A.

Basic Service

Subscribers: 255,000.

Programming (received off-air): WAOH-LP (I), WBNX-TV (W,F), WEAO (P), WVPX (X) Akron; WNEO (P) Alliance; WDLI (T), WOAC (I) Canton; WEWS-TV (A), WJW (F), WKYC-TV (N), WQHS-TV (H), WVIZ-TV (P) Cleveland; WUAB (U) Lorain-Cleveland; WOIO (C) Shaker Heights.

Programming (via satellite): Discovery Channel.

Current originations: Automated time-weather.

Fee: $39.90 installation; $8.58 monthly.

Expanded Basic Service

Subscribers: N.A.

Programming (via satellite): WGN-TV (W) Chicago; A & E; American Movie Classics; BET; Bravo; C-SPAN; C-SPAN 2; CNBC; CNN; Country Music TV; Discovery Channel; E! Entertainment TV; ESPN; ESPN 2; EWTN; Fox Family Channel; Fox Sports Net Ohio; Headline News; Home & Garden Television; Learning Channel; Lifetime; MTV; Nashville Network; Nick at Nite's TV Land; Nickelodeon; Odyssey; QVC; TBS Superstation; TV Food Network; The Weather Channel; Travel Channel; Turner Classic Movies; Turner Network TV; USA Network; VH1.

Fee: $18.13 monthly.

A la Carte 1

Subscribers: N.A.

Programming (via satellite): Cartoon Network; Comedy Central; Court TV; ESPN Classic Sports; History Channel; Sci-Fi Channel; The New Encore.

Fee: $0.10 monthly (Court TV or History), $0.20 monthly (Comedy), $0.40 monthly (Cartoon or ESPN Classics Sports), $1.00 monthly (Encore or Sci-Fi).

Pay Service 1

Pay Units: 54,897.

Programming (via satellite): Cinemax; Disney Channel; HBO; Showtime; Starz!; The Movie Channel.

Fee: $4.95 installation; $10.95 monthly (TMC), $12.50 monthly (Disney), $13.55 monthly (Cinemax, HBO, Showtime or Starz).

Pay-Per-View

Addressable homes: 38,872.

Viewer's Choice.

Local advertising: Yes. Available in satellite distributed programming. Local sales manager: Barbara Steill. Regional interconnect: Northeast Ohio Interconnect.

Equipment: Scientific-Atlanta headend; Jerrold amplifiers; Times Fiber cable; Pioneer set top converters; Pioneer addressable set top converters; Comtech & Scientific-Atlanta satellite antenna; ChannelMatic commercial insert.

Miles of plant: 1527.0 (coaxial). Homes passed: 171,792. Total homes in franchised area: 173,825.

Manager: Stephen R. Fry. Chief technician: Robert P. Nyitray. Marketing director: Woody P. Woodward.

Ownership: Time Warner Cable (MSO).

ALBANY—FrontierVision, 32 Enterprise Dr., Chillicothe, OH 45601. Phones: 740-775-4288; 800-346-2288. Fax: 740-775-2195. County: Athens. Also serves Athens County, New Marshfield. ICA: OH0314.

TV Market Ranking: Below 100 (portions of Athens County); Outside TV Markets (Albany, portions of Athens County, New Marshfield). Franchise award date: June 1, 1980. Franchise expiration date: N.A. Began: June 1, 1980.

Channel capacity: 38 (not 2-way capable). Channels available but not in use: N.A.

Basic Service

Subscribers: 1,723.

Programming (received off-air): WOUB-TV (P) Athens; WCHS-TV (A), WOWK-TV (C), WPBY-TV (P), WSAZ-TV (N), WVAH-TV (F,U) Charleston-Huntington; WBNS-TV (C), WCMH-TV (N), WSYX (A), WTTE (F,U) Columbus; allband FM.

Programming (via satellite): WGN-TV (W) Chicago; Animal Planet; C-SPAN; CNN; Cartoon Network; Country Music TV; Discovery Channel; ESPN; ESPN 2; Fox Family Channel; Headline News; Home Shopping Network; MTV; Nashville Network; Nickelodeon; Odyssey; QVC; TBS Superstation; Turner Classic Movies; Turner Network TV; USA Network; VH1.

Current originations: Automated time-weather; public access.

Fee: $31.90 installation; $22.32 monthly.

Pay Service 1

Pay Units: 100.

Programming (via satellite): Disney Channel.

Fee: $10.00 installation; $5.95 monthly.

Pay Service 2

Pay Units: 250.

Programming (via satellite): Showtime.

Fee: $9.99 monthly.

Pay Service 3

Pay Units: 200.

Programming (via satellite): HBO.

Fee: $12.99 monthly.

Pay Service 4

Pay Units: 54.

Programming (via satellite): Cinemax.

Fee: $8.99 monthly.

Local advertising: Yes (insert only). Available in character-generated programming. Rates: $10.00/Week.

Program Guide: The Cable Guide.

Equipment: Blonder-Tongue headend; Gamco amplifiers; Comm/Scope & CCS Hatfield cable; Atari character generator; Standard Com-

ponents & Jerrold set top converters; Eagle & Vitek traps; AFC satellite antenna; DX Antenna, Microdyne & Gardiner satellite receivers.
Miles of plant: 17.0 (coaxial).
Manager: Steve Trippe. Technical supervisor: Jim Cavenda.
Ownership: FrontierVision Partners LP (MSO). See Cable System Ownership.

ALLEN TWP. (Ottawa County)—FrontierVision, Box 627, Chillicothe, OH 45601. Phones: 740-775-4300; 800-346-2288. Fax: 740-775-2915. Counties: Lucas, Ottawa, Sandusky & Wood. Also serves Bradner, Clay Center, Clay Twp. (Ottawa County), Curtice, Elmore, Freedom Twp. (Wood County), Genoa, Gibsonburg, Harris Twp. (Ottawa County), Hessville, Jerusalem Twp. (Lucas County), Lake Twp. (Wood County), Lindsey (Sandusky County), Luckey, Madison Twp. (Sandusky County), Millbury, Montgomery Twp. (Wood County), Pemberville, Perrysburg, Perrysburg Twp., Rising Sun, Walbridge, Wayne, Williston, Woodville. Plans service to Danbury Twp. (Ottawa County), Oak Harbor. ICA: OH0071.
TV Market Ranking: 52. Franchise award date: January 1, 1981. Franchise expiration date: July 1, 1999. Began: January 1, 1981.
Channel capacity: 36 (not 2-way capable). Channels available but not in use: None.
Basic Service
Subscribers: 5,911; Commercial subscribers: 13.
Programming (received off-air): WNWO-TV (N), WTOL-TV (C), WTVG (A), WUPW (F) Toledo.
Programming (via satellite): A & E; American Movie Classics; C-SPAN; CNBC; CNN; Country Music TV; Discovery Channel; ESPN; Fox Family Channel; Fox Sports Net Ohio; Headline News; Home Shopping Network; Lifetime; MTV; Nashville Network; Nick at Nite; Nickelodeon; TBS Superstation; TV Guide Channel; The Weather Channel; Turner Network TV; USA Network; VH1.
Fee: $19.95 installation; $10.95 monthly.
Pay Service 1
Pay Units: 6,698.
Programming (via satellite): Cinemax; Disney Channel; HBO; Showtime.
Fee: $9.50 monthly (each).
Local advertising: No.
Equipment: RCA & Scientific-Atlanta headend; Jerrold & Winegard amplifiers; Comm/Scope & Times Fiber cable; Atari character generator; Pioneer set top converters; Eagle & Pico traps; ChannelMaster, Hughes & Scientific-Atlanta satellite antenna; Scientific-Atlanta satellite receivers.
Miles of plant: 250.0 (coaxial). Homes passed: 10,441.
Manager: Richard Coplan. Chief technician: Sam Morabith. Program director: Chad Hume. Marketing director: Barbara Brewer.
City fee: 3% of gross.
Ownership: FrontierVision Partners LP (MSO). See Cable System Ownership.

AMELIA—Coaxial Communications of Southern Ohio Inc., 3416 State Rte. 132, Amelia, OH 45102. Phone: 513-797-4400. Fax: 513-797-8625. Counties: Brown, Butler South & Clermont. Also serves Batavia, Bethel, Clark Twp. (Brown County), Felicity, Franklin Twp. (Clermont County), Green Twp. (Brown County), Hamersville, Monroe Twp. (Clermont County), Moscow, New Richmond, Ohio Twp., Pierce Twp., Pike Twp. (Brown County), Ross, Sterling Twp., Tate Twp., Union Twp. (Clermont County), Washington Twp. (Clermont County), Williamsburg. ICA: OH0041.
TV Market Ranking: 17. Franchise award date: N.A. Franchise expiration date: N.A. Began: June 1, 1983.
Channel capacity: 44 (not 2-way capable). Channels available but not in use: 2.
Basic Service
Subscribers: 13,664.
Programming (received off-air): WCET (P), WCPO-TV (A), WKRC-TV (C), WLWT (N), WSTR-TV (W) Cincinnati; WXIX-TV (F) Cincinnati-Newport; WPTD (P) Dayton.
Programming (via satellite): WGN-TV (W) Chicago; A & E; American Movie Classics; C-SPAN; CNBC; CNN; Country Music TV; Discovery Channel; ESPN; Fox Family Channel; Goodlife TV Network; Headline News; Home Shopping Network; Learning Channel; Lifetime; MTV; Nashville Network; Nickelodeon; TBS Superstation; TV Guide Channel; The Weather Channel; Travel Channel; Turner Network TV; USA Network; VH1.
Fee: $31.95 installation; $6.24 monthly.
Pay Service 1
Pay Units: 2,462.
Programming (via satellite): Cinemax.
Fee: $11.95 monthly.
Pay Service 2
Pay Units: 2,310.
Programming (via satellite): Disney Channel.
Fee: $11.95 monthly.
Pay Service 3
Pay Units: 6,401.
Programming (via satellite): HBO.
Fee: $11.95 monthly.
Pay Service 4
Pay Units: 498.
Programming (via satellite): The Movie Channel.
Fee: $11.95 monthly.
Pay Service 5
Pay Units: 1,625.
Programming (via satellite): Showtime.
Fee: $11.95 monthly.
Pay-Per-View
Addressable homes: 13,664.
Action Pay-Per-View.
Fee: $4.95.
Local advertising: Yes. Available in satellite distributed programming.
Equipment: Scientific-Atlanta headend; Magnavox & Scientific-Atlanta amplifiers; Comm/Scope cable; Video Data Systems character generator; Hamlin set top converters; Pioneer & Regency addressable set top converters; Intercept traps; Prodelin & Scientific-Atlanta satellite antenna; Scientific-Atlanta satellite receivers.
Miles of plant: 617.0 (coaxial). Homes passed: 22,857.
Manager: Arthur P. Loescher.
City fee: 3% of basic gross.
Ownership: Coaxial Communications (MSO).

AMESVILLE—Riley Video Services, Box 5865, Athens, OH 45701-5865. Phone: 614-593-7023. County: Athens. ICA: OH0307.
TV Market Ranking: Below 100. Franchise award date: N.A. Franchise expiration date: N.A. Began: January 1, 1972.
Channel capacity: 12. Channels available but not in use: 1.
Basic Service
Subscribers: 83.
Programming (received off-air): WOUB-TV (P) Athens; WCHS-TV (A), WOWK-TV (C), WSAZ-TV (N), WVAH-TV (F,U) Charleston-Huntington; WBNS-TV (C), WCMH-TV (N), WSYX (A) Columbus; WTAP-TV (N) Parkersburg-Marietta; allband FM.
Programming (via satellite): TBS Superstation.
Fee: $15.00 installation; $9.00 monthly.
Pay Service 1
Pay Units: N.A.
Programming (via satellite): Showtime.
Fee: $8.00 installation; $7.00 monthly.
Equipment: Blonder-Tongue headend; Gamco amplifiers; Cerro cable; Vitek & Eagle traps; Microdyne satellite antenna.
Miles of plant: 3.0 (coaxial). Homes passed: 105.
Manager: David A. Riley.
Ownership: Riley Video Services.

AMHERST—MediaOne, 576 Ternes Ave., Elyria, OH 44035. Phone: 800-425-2225. County: Lorain. Also serves Amherst Twp., North Ridgeville, Russia Twp., South Amherst. ICA: OH0393.
TV Market Ranking: 8. Franchise award date: N.A. Franchise expiration date: N.A. Began: N.A.
Channel capacity: N.A. Channels available but not in use: N.A.
Basic Service
Subscribers: 3,147.
Programming (received off-air): WBNX-TV (W,F), WEAO (P), WVPX (X) Akron; WEWS-TV (A), WJW (F), WKYC-TV (N), WQHS-TV (H), WVIZ-TV (P) Cleveland; WUAB (U) Lorain-Cleveland; WGGN-TV (T) Sandusky; WOIO (C) Shaker Heights.
Programming (via satellite): C-SPAN; C-SPAN 2; EWTN; Learning Channel; QVC; TV Guide Channel; TV Guide Sneak Prevue.
Fee: N.A.
Expanded Basic Service
Subscribers: N.A.
Programming (via satellite): WGN-TV (W) Chicago; A & E; American Movie Classics; BET; CNBC; CNN; Cartoon Network; Comedy Central; Discovery Channel; Disney Channel; E! Entertainment TV; ESPN; Fox Family Channel; Fox Sports Net Ohio; Headline News; Home & Garden Television; Lifetime; MTV; Nashville Network; Nickelodeon; Odyssey; TBS Superstation; TV Food Network; The Weather Channel; Turner Network TV; USA Network; VH1.
Fee: N.A.
Pay Service 1
Pay Units: N.A.
Programming (via satellite): Cinemax; Golf Channel; HBO; Showtime; The Movie Channel.
Fee: N.A.
Pay-Per-View
Hot Choice; Viewer's Choice.
Ownership: MediaOne Group (MSO). See Cable System Ownership.

AMSTERDAM—TCI Cablevision of Ohio Inc., Box 347, 123 N. Market St., Minerva, OH 44657. Phone: 330-868-5413. Fax: 330-868-3731. County: Jefferson. Also serves Bergholz. ICA: OH0230.
TV Market Ranking: 90. Franchise award date: N.A. Franchise expiration date: N.A. Began: February 1, 1969.
Channel capacity: 57 (not 2-way capable). Channels available but not in use: 19.
Basic Service
Subscribers: 655.
Programming (received off-air): WNEO (P) Alliance; KDKA-TV (C), WPGH-TV (F), WPXI (N), WQED (P), WTAE-TV (A) Pittsburgh; WTOV-TV (N) Steubenville-Wheeling; WTRF-TV (C) Wheeling-Steubenville; WYTV (A,F) Youngstown; allband FM.
Programming (via satellite): Discovery Channel; QVC; TBS Superstation.
Fee: $37.50 installation; $8.85 monthly.
Expanded Basic Service
Subscribers: 610.
Programming (via satellite): A & E; American Movie Classics; Animal Planet; C-SPAN; CNBC; CNN; Cartoon Network; Comedy Central; ESPN; FX; Fox Family Channel; Fox News Channel; Lifetime; MTV; Nashville Network; Nickelodeon; Odyssey; The New Encore; Turner Network TV; USA Network.
Fee: $15.31 monthly.
Pay Service 1
Pay Units: 135.
Programming (via satellite): Cinemax; Disney Channel; HBO; Showtime; Starz!; The New Encore.
Fee: $1.95 monthly (Encore), $6.75 monthly (Starz), $12.50 monthly (Disney), $13.45 monthly (Cinemax), $14.95 monthly (HBO or Showtime).
Pay-Per-View
Special events.
Equipment: Blonder-Tongue headend; Jerrold amplifiers; Plastoid cable.
Miles of plant: 15.7 (coaxial). Homes passed: 910. Total homes in franchised area: 951.
Manager: Paul Liucart. Chief technician: Rodney Lentz.
City fee: 3% of gross.
Ownership: AT&T Broadband & Internet Services (MSO). Purchased from Tele-Communications Inc., March 9, 1999.

ANDOVER—CableVision Communications, Box 2200, 68 5th St., Buckhannon, WV 26201. Phone: 304-472-4193. Fax: 304-472-0756. County: Ashtabula. Also serves Andover Boro, Andover Twp. (Ashtabula County), Andover Village. ICA: OH0258.
TV Market Ranking: 79. Franchise award date: N.A. Franchise expiration date: N.A. Began: N.A.
Channel capacity: 34 (not 2-way capable). Channels available but not in use: None.
Basic Service
Subscribers: 391.
Programming (received off-air): WBNX-TV (W,F) Akron; WNEO (P) Alliance; WEWS-TV (A), WJW (F), WKYC-TV (N), WVIZ-TV (P) Cleveland; WICU-TV (N), WQLN (P) Erie; WUAB (U) Lorain-Cleveland; WOIO (C) Shaker Heights; WKBN-TV (C), WYTV (A,F) Youngstown.
Programming (via satellite): WGN-TV (W) Chicago; QVC; TBS Superstation.
Fee: $47.50 installation; $14.42 monthly.
Expanded Basic Service
Subscribers: N.A.
Programming (via satellite): American Movie Classics; CNN; Country Music TV; Discovery Channel; Disney Channel; E! Entertainment TV; ESPN; Fox Family Channel; Learning Channel; Lifetime; Nashville Network; Nickelodeon; The Inspirational Network; The Weather Channel; Turner Network TV; USA Network.
Fee: $14.74 monthly.
Pay Service 1
Pay Units: 188.
Programming (via satellite): Cinemax; Disney Channel; HBO.
Fee: $25.00 installation; $4.95 monthly (Disney), $7.95 monthly (Cinemax), $11.99 monthly (HBO).
Pay Service 2
Pay Units: N.A.
Programming (via satellite): Showtime; The Movie Channel.
Fee: $11.95 monthly (each).
Equipment: Blonder-Tongue headend; C-COR amplifiers; Jerrold set top converters; Microdyne satellite antenna; Microdyne satellite receivers.
Miles of plant: 15.3 (coaxial). Homes passed: 516.

Manager: Willie Critchfield. Chief technician: Bill Turner. Marketing Director: Kenny Phillips.
City fee: 3% of gross.
Ownership: Rifkin & Associates Inc. (MSO). See Cable System Ownership.

ANNA—Time Warner Entertainment Co. LP, 3100 Elida Rd., Lima, OH 45805. Phone: 419-331-3333. Fax: 419-331-1573. Counties: Logan & Shelby. Also serves Botkins, De Graff, Dinsmore Twp., Hardin, Jackson Center, Jackson Twp. (Shelby County), Lehmkuhl Landing, Maplewood, McCartyville, Montra, Pemberton, Pleasant Twp. (Logan County), Quincy, Sidney, Van Buren Twp. ICA: OH0140.
TV Market Ranking: Below 100. Franchise award date: January 1, 1983. Franchise expiration date: January 1, 1998. Began: February 1, 1983.
Channel capacity: 61. Channels available but not in use: 23.
Basic Service
Subscribers: 2,373; Commercial subscribers: 249.
Programming (received off-air): WBNS-TV (C), WCMH-TV (N) Columbus; WDTN (A), WHIO-TV (C), WKEF (N), WPTD (P), WRGT-TV (F,U) Dayton; WLIO (N), WTLW (I) Lima; WBDT (W) Springfield.
Programming (via satellite): WGN-TV (W) Chicago; A & E; C-SPAN; CNN; Cartoon Network; Country Music TV; Discovery Channel; ESPN; Fox Family Channel; Fox Sports Net Ohio; Headline News; Lifetime; MTV; Nashville Network; Nickelodeon; QVC; Sci-Fi Channel; TBS Superstation; The Weather Channel; Turner Network TV; USA Network; VH1.
Current originations: Public access.
Fee: $32.00 installation; $19.72 monthly; $1.10 converter.
Pay Service 1
Pay Units: 108.
Programming (via satellite): Cinemax.
Fee: $18.00 installation; $10.95 monthly.
Pay Service 2
Pay Units: 102.
Programming (via satellite): Disney Channel.
Fee: $18.00 installation; $10.95 monthly.
Pay Service 3
Pay Units: 195.
Programming (via satellite): HBO.
Fee: $18.00 installation; $10.95 monthly.
Pay Service 4
Pay Units: 112.
Programming (via satellite): Showtime.
Fee: $18.00 installation; $10.95 monthly.
Local advertising: Yes. Available in character-generated programming.
Equipment: Scientific-Atlanta headend; Scientific-Atlanta amplifiers; Scientific-Atlanta cable; Atari character generator; Scientific-Atlanta set top converters.
Miles of plant: 120.4 (coaxial). Additional miles planned: 15.0 (coaxial). Homes passed: 3,359. Total homes in franchised area: 3,500.
Manager: James D. Foust. Chief technician: Rick Steward. Marketing director: Keith Tyrell.
City fee: 3% of gross.
Ownership: Fanch Communications Inc. (MSO); Time Warner Cable (MSO). See Cable System Ownership.

ASHLAND—Armstrong Cable Services, 100 E. 2nd St., Ashland, OH 44805. Phone: 419-289-1343. Fax: 419-289-3508. Counties: Ashland & Richland. Also serves Blooming Grove Twp. (Richland County), Butler Twp. (Richland County), Hayesville, Mifflin Twp. (Ashland County), Milton Twp. (Ashland County), Montgomery Twp. (Ashland County), Nankin, Olivesburg, Orange Twp. (Ashland County), Sullivan Twp., Troy Twp. (Ashland County), Weller Twp. (Richland County). ICA: OH0079.
TV Market Ranking: Below 100. Franchise award date: December 1, 1968. Franchise expiration date: December 1, 2009. Began: August 20, 1969.
Channel capacity: 54 (not 2-way capable). Channels available but not in use: 14.
Basic Service
Subscribers: 8,580.
Programming (received off-air): WBNX-TV (W,F), WEAO (P), WVPX (X) Akron; WEWS-TV (A), WJW (F), WKYC-TV (N), WQHS-TV (H), WVIZ-TV (P) Cleveland; WBNS-TV (C) Columbus; WUAB (U) Lorain-Cleveland; WMFD-TV (I) Mansfield; WOIO (C) Shaker Heights.
Programming (via satellite): WGN-TV (W) Chicago; A & E; American Movie Classics; C-SPAN; CNBC; CNN; Comedy Central; Court TV; Discovery Channel; ESPN; ESPN 2; Fox Family Channel; Fox Sports Net Ohio; Headline News; Home Shopping Network; Lifetime; MTV; Nashville Network; Nick at Nite's TV Land; Nickelodeon; TBS Superstation; TV Guide Channel; TV Guide Sneak Prevue; The Inspirational Network; The Weather Channel; Turner Network TV; USA Network; VH1.
Fee: $35.00 installation; $25.34 monthly; $2.00 converter.
Expanded Basic Service
Subscribers: N.A.
Programming (via satellite): Bravo; Cartoon Network; Country Music TV; History Channel; Home & Garden Television; Learning Channel; Outdoor Channel; Sci-Fi Channel; TV Food Network; Turner Classic Movies.
Fee: $3.99 monthly.
Pay Service 1
Pay Units: 1,112.
Programming (via satellite): Cinemax.
Fee: $25.00 installation; $9.95 monthly.
Pay Service 2
Pay Units: 665.
Programming (via satellite): Disney Channel.
Fee: $25.00 installation; $7.95 monthly.
Pay Service 3
Pay Units: 1,569.
Programming (via satellite): HBO.
Fee: $25.00 installation; $11.95 monthly.
Pay Service 4
Pay Units: 497.
Programming (via satellite): Showtime.
Fee: $9.95 monthly.
Pay Service 5
Pay Units: N.A.
Programming (via satellite): DMX.
Fee: $7.95 monthly.
Pay-Per-View
Movies.
Local advertising: Yes. Available in satellite distributed & character-generated programming. Regional interconnect: Metrobase Cable Advertising.
Equipment: Scientific-Atlanta headend; Scientific-Atlanta amplifiers; Scientific-Atlanta cable; Pioneer & Scientific-Atlanta set top converters; Scientific-Atlanta satellite antenna; Scientific-Atlanta satellite receivers.
Miles of plant: 202.0 (coaxial). Homes passed: 11,478.
Manager: Dex R. Sedwick. Chief technician: Bill Stauffer. Marketing director: Jud D. Stewart.
City fee: $100 annually.
Ownership: Armstrong Group of Companies (MSO).

ASHLEY—Time Warner Cable, Box 787, 111 S. Mulberry St., Mount Vernon, OH 43050. Phones: 740-397-2288; 800-782-4118. Fax: 740-397-3730. County: Delaware. ICA: OH0272.
TV Market Ranking: 27. Franchise award date: N.A. Franchise expiration date: N.A. Began: December 1, 1983.
Channel capacity: 28. Channels available but not in use: None.
Basic Service
Subscribers: 337.
Programming (received off-air): WBNS-TV (C), WCMH-TV (N), WOSU-TV (P), WSYX (A), WTTE (F,U) Columbus; WXCB-LP (I) Delaware.
Programming (via satellite): WGN-TV (W) Chicago; A & E; C-SPAN; CNN; Country Music TV; Discovery Channel; E! Entertainment TV; ESPN; ESPN 2; Fox Family Channel; Headline News; History Channel; Lifetime; MTV; Nashville Network; Nickelodeon; QVC; Sci-Fi Channel; TBS Superstation; The Weather Channel; Turner Classic Movies; Turner Network TV; USA Network; VH1.
Fee: $32.00 installation; $18.95 monthly; $9.00 additional installation.
Pay Service 1
Pay Units: 30.
Programming (via satellite): Disney Channel.
Fee: $18.00 installation; $10.95 monthly.
Pay Service 2
Pay Units: 65.
Programming (via satellite): HBO.
Fee: $18.00 installation; $10.95 monthly.
Pay Service 3
Pay Units: 55.
Programming (via satellite): Cinemax.
Fee: $18.00 installation; $10.95 monthly.
Local advertising: No.
Miles of plant: 5.9 (coaxial). Homes passed: 422.
Manager: Paul S. Schonewolf. Technical operations manager: Dan Fessler. Field operations manager: Bill Schroeder. Marketing manager: Carl Bauer. Customer operations manager: Danielle Turner.
Ownership: Fanch Communications Inc. (MSO); Time Warner Cable (MSO). See Cable System Ownership.

ASHLEY CORNER—FrontierVision, Box 627, Chillicothe, OH 45601. Phones: 740-775-4288; 800-346-2288. Fax: 740-775-2915. County: Scioto. ICA: OH0377.
TV Market Ranking: Below 100. Franchise award date: N.A. Franchise expiration date: N.A. Began: N.A.
Channel capacity: 42 (not 2-way capable). Channels available but not in use: 5.
Basic Service
Subscribers: 515.
Programming (received off-air): WCHS-TV (A), WOWK-TV (C), WSAZ-TV (N), WVAH-TV (F,U) Charleston-Huntington; WBNS-TV (C) Columbus; WPBO-TV (P) Portsmouth.
Programming (via satellite): WGN-TV (W) Chicago; C-SPAN; QVC; TBS Superstation; The Weather Channel; Trinity Bcstg. Network.
Fee: $47.50 installation; $12.94 monthly.
Expanded Basic Service
Subscribers: 483.
Programming (via satellite): A & E; American Movie Classics; CNN; Country Music TV; Discovery Channel; Disney Channel; ESPN; Fox Family Channel; Headline News; Nashville Network; Nickelodeon; Turner Network TV; USA Network.
Fee: $47.50 installation; $14.40 monthly.
Pay Service 1
Pay Units: 27.
Programming (via satellite): Cinemax.
Fee: $6.95 monthly.
Pay Service 2
Pay Units: 29.
Programming (via satellite): The New Encore.
Fee: N.A.
Pay Service 3
Pay Units: 21.
Programming (via satellite): HBO.
Fee: $10.95 monthly.
Pay Service 4
Pay Units: 34.
Programming (via satellite): Showtime.
Fee: $11.99 monthly.
Pay Service 5
Pay Units: 29.
Programming (via satellite): Starz!
Fee: N.A.
Pay Service 6
Pay Units: 31.
Programming (via satellite): The Movie Channel.
Fee: N.A.
Miles of plant: 44.0 (coaxial). Homes passed: 608.
Manager: Richard Coplan. Chief technician: Sam Morabith. Program director: Chad Hume. Marketing director: Barbara Brewer.
Ownership: FrontierVision Partners LP (MSO). See Cable System Ownership.

ATHENS—Time Warner Cable, 28 Station St., Athens, OH 45701. Phone: 800-425-2225. Fax: 614-593-7999. County: Athens. Also serves Alexander Twp., Athens County, Athens Twp., Dover Twp., The Plains. ICA: OH0074.
TV Market Ranking: Below 100 (Alexander Twp., Athens, portions of Athens County, Athens Twp., Dover Twp., The Plains); Outside TV Markets (portions of Athens County). Franchise award date: N.A. Franchise expiration date: N.A. Began: January 1, 1952.
Channel capacity: 42 (not 2-way capable). Channels available but not in use: N.A.
Basic Service
Subscribers: 5,345.
Programming (received off-air): WOUB-TV (P) Athens; WCHS-TV (A), WOWK-TV (C), WSAZ-TV (N), WVAH-TV (F,U) Charleston-Huntington; WBNS-TV (C), WCMH-TV (N), WSYX (A) Columbus; WTAP-TV (N) Parkersburg-Marietta; 21 FMs.
Programming (via satellite): WGN-TV (W) Chicago; A & E; BET; C-SPAN; CNN; Discovery Channel; ESPN; Fox Family Channel; Home Shopping Network; Learning Channel; Lifetime; MTV; Nashville Network; Nickelodeon; TBS Superstation; Turner Network TV; USA Network.
Current originations: Public access; automated emergency alert.
Planned originations: Government access.
Fee: $30.00 installation; $18.20 monthly; $15.00 additional installation.
Pay Service 1
Pay Units: 3,450.
Programming (via satellite): Cinemax; Disney Channel; HBO.
Fee: $15.00 installation; $4.95 monthly (Disney), $8.95 monthly (Cinemax or HBO).
Local advertising: Yes (locally produced & insert). Available in satellite distributed, locally originated & taped programming.
Equipment: Scientific-Atlanta headend; Magnavox amplifiers; Comm/Scope cable; Sony & Panasonic cameras; Sony, JVC & Panasonic VTRs; Video Data Systems character generator; Jerrold set top converters; Eagle traps; Andrew & Scientific-Atlanta satellite antenna; Microdyne satellite receivers.
Miles of plant: 109.0 (coaxial); None (fiber optic). Homes passed: 10,255.
Manager: S. Diann Dunfee. Chief technician: Steven A. Hewitt.
City fee: 3% of gross.
Ownership: Time Warner Cable (MSO). Purchased from MediaOne Group, August 2, 1999.

ATTICA—Time Warner Cable, Box 369, 90 S. Washington St., Tiffin, OH 44883. Phone: 800-425-2225. Counties: Crawford & Seneca. Also serves Caroline, Carrothers, Chatfield, Chatfield Twp., Cranberry Twp., New Washington, Reed Twp., Siam, Venice Twp. ICA: OH0315.

TV Market Ranking: Below 100. Franchise award date: N.A. Franchise expiration date: April 1, 2004. Began: N.A.

Channel capacity: 52 (not 2-way capable). Channels available but not in use: 14.

Basic Service

Subscribers: 308.

Programming (received off-air): WBGU-TV (P) Bowling Green; W54AF (I) Bucyrus; WEWS-TV (A), WJW (F), WKYC-TV (N), WQHS-TV (H) Cleveland; WBNS-TV (C), WCMH-TV (N), WOSU-TV (P), WSYX (A) Columbus; WUAB (U) Lorain-Cleveland; WGGN-TV (T) Sandusky; WNWO-TV (N), WTOL-TV (C), WTVG (A), WUPW (F) Toledo.

Programming (via satellite): C-SPAN; C-SPAN 2; CNN; Discovery Channel; ESPN; Fox Family Channel; Headline News; Lifetime; MTV; Nashville Network; Nickelodeon; QVC; TBS Superstation; The Weather Channel; Turner Network TV; USA Network; VH1.

Current originations: Automated time-weather.

Fee: $15.00 installation; $17.50 monthly.

Pay Service 1

Pay Units: Included with Willard, OH.

Programming (via satellite): Cinemax; Disney Channel; HBO.

Fee: $10.95 monthly (each).

Equipment: Scientific-Atlanta headend; Magnavox & Texscan amplifiers; Comm/Scope cable; Atari character generator; RCA set top converters; Arcom & Eagle traps; Avantek satellite receivers.

Miles of plant & homes passed included with Willard, OH.

Manager: Pat McCauley.

Franchise fee: None.

Ownership: Time Warner Cable (MSO). Purchased from MediaOne Group, August 2, 1999.

ATWATER TWP.—Time Warner Cable, 5520 Whipple Ave. NW, Canton, OH 44720-7700. Phones: 330-494-0095; 800-245-8166. Fax: 330-663-7970. Counties: Mahoning, Portage & Stark. Also serves Charlestown Twp., Deerfield Twp. (Portage County), Edinburgh Twp., Marlboro Twp., Palmyra Twp. (portions), Randolph Twp. (Portage County), Smith Twp. (portions). ICA: OH0111.

TV Market Ranking: 8,79. Franchise award date: October 1, 1989. Franchise expiration date: October 1, 2004. Began: October 1, 1989.

Channel capacity: 33 (not 2-way capable). Channels available but not in use: 2.

Basic Service

Subscribers: 2,162.

Programming (received off-air): WBNX-TV (W,F), WEAO (P), WVPX (X) Akron; WDLI (T), WOAC (I) Canton; WEWS-TV (A), WJW (F), WKYC-TV (N), WQHS-TV (H) Cleveland; WUAB (U) Lorain-Cleveland; WOIO (C) Shaker Heights.

Programming (via satellite): WGN-TV (W) Chicago; A & E; C-SPAN; CNN; Country Music TV; Discovery Channel; ESPN; ESPN 2; Fox Family Channel; Fox Sports Net Ohio; Headline News; Home & Garden Television; Learning Channel; Lifetime; MTV; Nashville Network; Nick at Nite's TV Land; Nickelodeon; TBS Superstation; The Weather Channel; Turner Classic Movies; Turner Network TV; USA Network.

Current originations: Leased access.

Fee: $49.95 installation; $30.03 monthly.

Pay Service 1

Pay Units: 255.

Programming (via satellite): Disney Channel.

Fee: $7.95 monthly.

Pay Service 2

Pay Units: 463.

Programming (via satellite): HBO.

Fee: $12.95 monthly.

Pay Service 3

Pay Units: 355.

Programming (via satellite): Showtime.

Fee: $5.95 monthly.

Local advertising: No.

Miles of plant: 250.0 (coaxial). Homes passed: 5,085. Total homes in franchised area: 6,055.

Manager: Bill Farmer. Chief technician: Tod Dean. Marketing director: Jim Nicholas.

Franchise fee: 3%-5% of gross.

Ownership: Time Warner Cable (MSO); Fanch Communications Inc. (MSO). See Cable System Ownership.

AUBURN TWP.—Star Cable, Box 4478, 4720 Mahoning Ave., Youngstown, OH 44515. Phone: 330-792-9577. Fax: 330-792-9541. County: Geauga. Also serves Auburn Lakes, Burton (Geauga County), Burton Twp. (Geauga County), Newbury (Geauga County), Newbury Twp. (Geauga County), Punderson Lake. ICA: OH0198.

TV Market Ranking: 8 (Auburn Lakes, Auburn Twp., Burton, Burton Twp., Newbury, Newbury Twp., Punderson Lake); 79 (Auburn Lakes, Auburn Twp., Punderson Lake). Franchise award date: July 1, 1988. Franchise expiration date: N.A. Began: November 1, 1989.

Channel capacity: 62 (not 2-way capable). Channels available but not in use: 23.

Basic Service

Subscribers: 1,365; Commercial subscribers: 191.

Programming (received off-air): WBNX-TV (W,F) Akron; WEWS-TV (A), WJW (F), WKYCTV (N), WVIZ-TV (P) Cleveland; WUAB (U) Lorain-Cleveland; WOIO (C) Shaker Heights.

Programming (via satellite): QVC; TBS Superstation.

Fee: $25.00 installation; $10.50 monthly; $1.95 converter.

Expanded Basic Service

Subscribers: 1,290.

Programming (via satellite): A & E; American Movie Classics; C-SPAN; CNBC; CNN; Cartoon Network; Discovery Channel; ESPN; ESPN 2; Fox Family Channel; Fox News Channel; Fox Sports Net Ohio; Headline News; History Channel; Home & Garden Television; Learning Channel; Lifetime; MTV; Nashville Network; Nickelodeon; The Weather Channel; Turner Network TV; USA Network; VH1.

Fee: $20.00 monthly.

Pay Service 1

Pay Units: 158.

Programming (via satellite): Cinemax.

Fee: $15.00 installation; $11.00 monthly.

Pay Service 2

Pay Units: 178.

Programming (via satellite): Disney Channel.

Fee: $15.00 installation; $7.95 monthly.

Pay Service 3

Pay Units: 342.

Programming (via satellite): HBO.

Fee: $15.00 installation; $11.00 monthly.

Pay Service 4

Pay Units: 206.

Programming (via satellite): Showtime; The Movie Channel.

Fee: $15.00 installation; $12.95 monthly (Showtime or TMC).

Local advertising: No.

Equipment: Scientific-Atlanta & DX Engineering headend; Scientific-Atlanta amplifiers; Comm/Scope cable; Panasonic set top converters; Eagle traps; DH Satellite satellite antenna.

Miles of plant: 55.1 (coaxial); None (fiber optic). Homes passed: 1,970. Total homes in franchised area: 1,970.

Manager: Terry Dickerhoof. Chief technician: Tom Beat.

Franchise fee: 5% of gross.

Ownership: Star Cable Associates (MSO).

AUSTINTOWN TWP.—Armstrong Cable Services, 9328 Woodworth Rd., North Lima, OH 44452-9712. Phone: 330-758-6411. Fax: 330-726-0117. Counties: Mahoning & Trumbull. Also serves Canfield, Canfield Twp., Mahoning County, McDonald, Mineral Ridge, Trumbull County, Weathersfield Twp. (Trumbull County). ICA: OH0044.

TV Market Ranking: 8 (portions of Trumbull County); 79 (Austintown Twp., Canfield, Canfield Twp., Mahoning County, McDonald, Mineral Ridge, portions of Trumbull County, Weathersfield Twp.). Franchise award date: March 1, 1978. Franchise expiration date: March 25, 2006. Began: September 15, 1979.

Channel capacity: 78 (2-way capable; operating 2-way). Channels available but not in use: 4.

Basic Service

Subscribers: 18,230.

Programming (received off-air): WNEO (P) Alliance; WEWS-TV (A), WJW (F), WKYC-TV (N) Cleveland; WUAB (U) Lorain-Cleveland; WQED (P) Pittsburgh; WOIO (C) Shaker Heights; WFMJ-TV (N), WKBN-TV (C), WYTV (A,F) Youngstown.

Programming (via satellite): A & E; American Movie Classics; BET; C-SPAN; C-SPAN 2; CNBC; CNN; CNN/SI; Discovery Channel; ESPN; Fox Family Channel; Fox Sports Net Pittsburgh; Headline News; Home Shopping Network; Lifetime; MSNBC; MTV; Nashville Network; Nickelodeon; QVC; TBS Superstation; TV Guide Channel; TV Guide Sneak Prevue; Telemundo; The Health Network; The Weather Channel; Travel Channel; Turner Network TV; USA Network; VH1.

Current originations: Educational access; religious access; automated emergency alert.

Fee: $35.00 installation; $24.90 monthly; $2.95 converter.

Expanded Basic Service

Subscribers: 5,580.

Programming (via satellite): Bravo; Cartoon Network; Comedy Central; Country Music TV; ESPN 2; History Channel; Home & Garden Television; Learning Channel; Sci-Fi Channel; TV Food Network; Turner Classic Movies.

Fee: $7.95 monthly.

Expanded Basic Service 2

Subscribers: 709.

Programming (via satellite): CNN/SI; ESPN Classic Sports; Golf Channel; Outdoor Channel.

Fee: $5.95 monthly.

Pay Service 1

Pay Units: 2,340.

Programming (via satellite): Cinemax.

Fee: $19.95 installation; $9.95 monthly.

Pay Service 2

Pay Units: 1,405.

Programming (via satellite): Disney Channel.

Fee: $19.95 installation; $7.95 monthly.

Pay Service 3

Pay Units: 4,584.

Programming (via satellite): HBO.

Fee: $19.95 installation; $11.95 monthly.

Pay Service 4

Pay Units: 672.

Programming (via satellite): Flix.

Fee: $19.95 installation; $2.95 monthly.

Pay Service 5

Pay Units: 421.

Programming (via satellite): Showtime.

Fee: $19.95 installation; $7.95 monthly.

Pay Service 6

Pay Units: 430.

Programming (via satellite): Starz!; The New Encore.

Fee: $19.95 installation; $8.95 monthly.

Pay Service 7

Pay Units: N.A.

Programming (via satellite): DMX.

Fee: $35.00 installation; $7.95 monthly.

Pay-Per-View

Addressable homes: 12,718.

Movies; special events.

Fee: Varies.

Local advertising: Yes (insert only). Available in satellite distributed & character-generated programming.

Equipment: Scientific-Atlanta headend; Scientific-Atlanta amplifiers; Trilogy cable; Siecor fiber optic cable; Texscan character generator; Scientific-Atlanta addressable set top converters; LANcity modems; Eagle traps; Scientific-Atlanta satellite receivers.

Miles of plant: 343.0 (coaxial); 70.0 (fiber optic). Homes passed: 21,847. Total homes in franchised area: 22,000.

Manager: Paul R. Wachtel. Chief technician: Joe Battista. Customer service manager: Sharon Kosar.

City fee: 3% of gross.

Ownership: Armstrong Group of Companies (MSO).

AVA—CableVision Communications, Box 2200, 68 5th St., Buckhannon, WV 26201. Phone: 304-472-4193. Fax: 304-472-0756. County: Noble. ICA: OH0309.

TV Market Ranking: Below 100. Franchise award date: N.A. Franchise expiration date: N.A. Began: N.A.

Channel capacity: 12. Channels available but not in use: None.

Basic Service

Subscribers: 36.

Programming (received off-air): WOUC-TV (P) Cambridge; WSYX (A) Columbus; WTAP-TV (N) Parkersburg-Marietta; WTOV-TV (N) Steubenville-Wheeling; WTRF-TV (C) Wheeling-Steubenville; WHIZ-TV (N) Zanesville.

Programming (via satellite): ESPN; Fox Family Channel; Nashville Network; TBS Superstation.

Fee: $52.50 installation; $22.00 monthly; $1.24 converter.

Pay Service 1

Pay Units: 12.

Programming (via satellite): HBO.

Fee: $11.99 monthly.

Equipment: DX Engineering, Standard Communications & Blonder-Tongue headend; Jerrold amplifiers; Standard Communications satellite receivers.

Miles of plant: 2.0 (coaxial). Homes passed: 81. Total homes in franchised area: 81.

Manager: Willie Critchfield. Marketing director: Kenny Phillips.

City fee: None.

Ownership: Rifkin & Associates Inc. (MSO). See Cable System Ownership.

BAINBRIDGE—FrontierVision, Box 648, 102 Twin Oak Dr., Jackson, OH 45640. Phone: 614-345-4329. Fax: 614-286-1489. County: Ross. Also serves Bourneville, Paxton Twp., Twin Twp. (Ross County). ICA: OH0221.

TV Market Ranking: 27. Franchise award date: June 3, 1974. Franchise expiration date: December 17, 2002. Began: February 15, 1974.
Channel capacity: 37 (2-way capable; operating 2-way). Channels available but not in use: 1.
Basic Service
Subscribers: 669.
Programming (received off-air): WWHO (U) Chillicothe; WCPO-TV (A) Cincinnati; WXIX-TV (F) Cincinnati-Newport; WBNS-TV (C), WCMH-TV (N), WOSU-TV (P), WSYX (A), WTTE (F,U) Columbus; WHIO-TV (C) Dayton; allband FM.
Programming (via satellite): WGN-TV (W) Chicago; American Movie Classics; CNN; Country Music TV; Discovery Channel; ESPN; Fox Family Channel; Learning Channel; MTV; Nashville Network; Nickelodeon; QVC; TBS Superstation; The Weather Channel; Turner Network TV; USA Network; VH1.
Fee: $20.99 installation; $21.70 monthly; $15.12 additional installation.
Pay Service 1
Pay Units: 67.
Programming (via satellite): The New Encore.
Fee: N.A.
Pay Service 2
Pay Units: 67.
Programming (via satellite): HBO.
Fee: $11.95 monthly.
Pay Service 3
Pay Units: 99.
Programming (via satellite): Showtime.
Fee: N.A.
Pay Service 4
Pay Units: 63.
Programming (via satellite): Starz!
Fee: N.A.
Pay Service 5
Pay Units: 108.
Programming (via satellite): The Movie Channel.
Fee: N.A.
Equipment: Cadco headend; Triple Crown & Texscan amplifiers; Times Fiber cable; Arcom traps; M/A-Com satellite antenna; Drake satellite receivers.
Miles of plant: 44.5 (coaxial). Homes passed: 1,087. Total homes in franchised area: 1,250.
Manager: Steve Trippe. Chief technician: Bill Ricker.
City fee: None.
Ownership: FrontierVision Partners LP (MSO). See Cable System Ownership.

BAINBRIDGE TWP. (Geauga County)—Cablevision of Geauga County, 107 Water St., Chardon, OH 44024. Phone: 216-691-0800. Fax: 216-291-1631. County: Geauga. Also serves Russell Twp. (Geauga County), South Russell. ICA: OH0107.
TV Market Ranking: 8. Franchise award date: N.A. Franchise expiration date: N.A. Began: July 1, 1983.
Channel capacity: 54 (not 2-way capable). Channels available but not in use: 2.
Basic Service
Subscribers: N.A.
Programming (received off-air): WBNX-TV (W,F), WEAO (P), WVPX (X) Akron; WEWS-TV (A), WJW (F), WKYC-TV (N), WQHS-TV (H), WVIZ-TV (P) Cleveland; WUAB (U) Lorain-Cleveland; WOIO (C) Shaker Heights.
Programming (via satellite): A & E; C-SPAN; C-SPAN 2; CNBC; CNN; Country Music TV; Discovery Channel; ESPN; EWTN; Fox Family Channel; Fox Sports Net Ohio; Headline News; Knowledge TV; Learning Channel; Lifetime; MTV; Nashville Network; Nickelodeon; QVC; TBS Superstation; The Weather Channel; Trinity Bcstg. Network; Turner Network TV; USA Network; VH1.
Current originations: Automated time-weather; public access; educational access; government access; leased access; local sports.
Fee: N.A.
Pay Service 1
Pay Units: N.A.
Programming (via satellite): American Movie Classics; Bravo; Cinemax; Disney Channel; HBO; Showtime; The Movie Channel.
Fee: $10.00 monthly (each).
Local advertising: Yes. Available in satellite distributed & locally originated programming. Local sales manager: Jeff Smith. Regional interconnect: Northern Ohio Interconnect.
Program Guide: On Cablevision.
Equipment: Jerrold & Scientific-Atlanta headend; Jerrold amplifiers; Video Data Systems character generator; Jerrold set top converters; Jerrold addressable traps; Simulsat satellite antenna; Avantek & Scientific-Atlanta satellite receivers.
Miles of plant: 200.0 (coaxial). Additional miles planned: 5.0 (coaxial). Homes passed: 5,853. Total homes in franchised area: 11,000.
Manager: Richard Coplan. Chief technician: Richard Demarest. Program director: Kerry Paluscsak. Marketing director: William DeGraeve.
City fee: 3% of gross.
Ownership: Cablevision Systems Corp. (MSO).

BALTIMORE—Time Warner Cable, 1315 Granville Pike, Lancaster, OH 43130-0747. Phone: 740-653-9685. Fax: 740-653-1164. County: Fairfield. Also serves Liberty Twp. (Fairfield County), Millersport, Pleasantville, Thurston. ICA: OH0159.
TV Market Ranking: 27. Franchise award date: N.A. Franchise expiration date: N.A. Began: January 1, 1981.
Channel capacity: 30 (not 2-way capable). Channels available but not in use: 2.
Basic Service
Subscribers: 862.
Programming (received off-air): WBNS-TV (C), WCMH-TV (N), WOSU-TV (P), WSYX (A), WTTE (F,U) Columbus; WSFJ (I) Newark.
Programming (via satellite): WGN-TV (W) Chicago; A & E; C-SPAN; CNBC; CNN; Discovery Channel; ESPN; Lifetime; MTV; Nashville Network; Nickelodeon; TBS Superstation; The Weather Channel; Turner Classic Movies; Turner Network TV; USA Network.
Current originations: Automated time-weather; public access.
Fee: $35.00 installation; $18.30 monthly; $25.00 additional installation.
Pay Service 1
Pay Units: Included with Lancaster, OH.
Programming (via satellite): Disney Channel; HBO; Showtime; The Movie Channel.
Fee: $15.00 installation; $9.95 monthly (Disney, Showtime or TMC), $10.95 monthly (HBO).
Local advertising: Yes.
Equipment: Scientific-Atlanta headend; Scientific-Atlanta amplifiers; Texscan character generator; Panasonic set top converters; Intercept & Pico traps; Scientific-Atlanta satellite antenna; Scientific-Atlanta satellite receivers.
Miles of plant & homes passed included with Lancaster, OH.
Manager: David Johnston. Chief technician: Mike Bash. Marketing director: Cathy Schelb.
City fee: 3% of basic.
Ownership: Time Warner Cable (MSO). Purchased from MediaOne Group, August 2, 1999.

BARNESVILLE—TCI Cablevision of Ohio Inc., Box 469, Bridgeport, OH 43912. Phones: 740-633-2232; 800-527-2222. County: Belmont. Also serves Warren Twp. (Belmont County). ICA: OH0151.
TV Market Ranking: 90. Franchise award date: N.A. Franchise expiration date: N.A. Began: August 1, 1970.
Channel capacity: 22. Channels available but not in use: None.
Basic Service
Subscribers: 1,662.
Programming (received off-air): WVPX (X) Akron; WOUC-TV (P) Cambridge; KDKA-TV (C), WPGH-TV (F), WPXI (N) Pittsburgh; WTOV-TV (N) Steubenville-Wheeling; WTRF-TV (C) Wheeling-Steubenville; WHIZ-TV (N) Zanesville; allband FM.
Programming (via satellite): C-SPAN; CNN; Discovery Channel; Fox Family Channel; Lifetime; Nashville Network; TBS Superstation.
Fee: $60.00 installation; $15.96 monthly.
Expanded Basic Service
Subscribers: 1,625.
Programming (via satellite): American Movie Classics; ESPN; Fox Sports Net Pittsburgh; Headline News; QVC; Turner Network TV; USA Network.
Fee: $1.95 monthly.
Pay Service 1
Pay Units: 155.
Programming (via satellite): Disney Channel.
Fee: N.A.
Pay Service 2
Pay Units: 642.
Programming (via satellite): The New Encore.
Fee: N.A.
Pay Service 3
Pay Units: 381.
Programming (via satellite): HBO.
Fee: $20.00 installation; $10.95 monthly.
Equipment: Blonder-Tongue headend; Jerrold, Magnavox & Scientific-Atlanta amplifiers; AFC satellite antenna.
Miles of plant: 26.0 (coaxial). Homes passed: 2,801. Total homes in franchised area: 2,801.
Manager: Robert Weese. Chief technician: Earl Conway.
City fee: 3% of gross.
Ownership: AT&T Broadband & Internet Services (MSO). Purchased from Tele-Communications Inc., March 9, 1999.

BARTON—Powhaton Point Cable Co., Box 67, Powhaton Point, OH 43942. Phone: 614-795-5005. County: Belmont. Also serves Crescent. ICA: OH0212.
TV Market Ranking: 90. Franchise award date: N.A. Franchise expiration date: N.A. Began: December 1, 1965.
Channel capacity: N.A. Channels available but not in use: N.A.
Basic Service
Subscribers: 215.
Programming (received off-air): WBOY-TV (N), WDTV (C,A) Clarksburg-Weston; WNPB-TV (P) Morgantown; WTAP-TV (N) Parkersburg-Marietta; KDKA-TV (C), WPXI (N), WQED (P), WTAE-TV (A) Pittsburgh; WTOV-TV (N) Steubenville-Wheeling; WTRF-TV (C) Wheeling-Steubenville; allband FM.
Planned programming (received off-air): WOUB-TV (P) Athens; WPGH-TV (F) Pittsburgh.
Programming (via satellite): CNN; Discovery Channel; ESPN; Nashville Network; TBS Superstation; Turner Classic Movies; Turner Network TV; USA Network.
Fee: $12.00 monthly.
Equipment: Microdyne satellite antenna.
Miles of plant: 11.2 (coaxial). Homes passed: 1,166.
Manager: Kasmir Majewski.
Ownership: Walter Matkovich (MSO); Kasmir Majewski (MSO).

BATH TWP. (Summit County)—Cablevision Systems, 10270 Brecksville Rd., Brecksville, OH 44141. Phones: 216-691-0800; 216-575-8016. Fax: 216-291-1631. Counties: Medina & Summit. Also serves Copley Twp., Cuyahoga Falls, Granger, Northampton Twp. (Summit County), Richfield (village), Richfield Twp. (Summit County), Sharon Twp. (Medina County). ICA: OH0058.
TV Market Ranking: 8. Franchise award date: N.A. Franchise expiration date: N.A. Began: January 1, 1984.
Channel capacity: 54 (2-way capable). Channels available but not in use: 9.
Basic Service
Subscribers: 8,106; Commercial subscribers: 22.
Programming (received off-air): WBNX-TV (W,F), WEAO (P), WVPX (X) Akron; WOAC (I) Canton; WEWS-TV (A), WJW (F), WKYC-TV (N), WQHS-TV (H), WVIZ-TV (P) Cleveland; WUAB (U) Lorain-Cleveland; WOIO (C) Shaker Heights; 23 FMs.
Programming (via satellite): A & E; C-SPAN; CNBC; CNN; Discovery Channel; ESPN; EWTN; Fox Family Channel; Fox Sports Net Ohio; Headline News; Home Shopping Network; Knowledge TV; Learning Channel; Lifetime; MTV; Nashville Network; Nickelodeon; TBS Superstation; The Inspirational Network; The Weather Channel; Turner Network TV; USA Network; VH1.
Current originations: Automated time-weather; public access; educational access; government access; leased access; automated emergency alert; local news; local sports.
Fee: $25.00 installation; $18.95 monthly; $17.50 additional installation.
Commercial fee: $27.50 monthly.
Pay Service 1
Pay Units: N.A.
Programming (via satellite): American Movie Classics; Bravo; Cinemax; Disney Channel; HBO; Playboy TV; Showtime; The Movie Channel.
Fee: $5.00 installation; $9.95 monthly (each).
Pay-Per-View
Addressable homes: 6,283.
Viewer's Choice.
Fee: $5.00.
Local advertising: Yes. Available in satellite distributed & locally originated programming. Rates: $40.00/Minute; $25.00/30 Seconds. Local sales manager: Jeff Smith. Regional interconnect: Northern Ohio Interconnect.

Equipment: Scientific-Atlanta headend; Jerrold, Century III & Scientific-Atlanta amplifiers; Sony VTRs; Jerrold addressable set top converters; Eagle & Intercept traps; Scientific-Atlanta satellite antenna; Scientific-Atlanta satellite receivers; Spot Matic commercial insert.

Miles of plant: 450.0 (coaxial). Homes passed: 14,000. Total homes in franchised area: 14,000.

Manager: Kathleen Mayo. Chief technician: Bruce Smylie. Program director: John Stealey. Marketing director: Frank Naples.

City fee: 3% of gross.

Ownership: Cablevision Systems Corp. (MSO).

BAY VILLAGE—MediaOne, 27005 Knickerbocker Rd., Bay Village, OH 44140. Phones: 440-835-2291; 800-993-5538. Counties: Cuyahoga & Lorain. ICA: OH0063.

TV Market Ranking: 8. Franchise award date: January 1, 1980. Franchise expiration date: N.A. Began: October 1, 1980.

Channel capacity: 61 (not 2-way capable). Channels available but not in use: 8.

Basic Service

Subscribers: Included with Elyria, OH.

Programming (received off-air): WBNX-TV (W,F), WEAO (P), WVPX (X) Akron; WEWS-TV (A), WJW (F), WKYC-TV (N), WQHS-TV (H), WVIZ-TV (P) Cleveland; WUAB (U) Lorain-Cleveland; WGGN-TV (T) Sandusky; WOIO (C) Shaker Heights; 25 FMs.

Programming (via satellite): C-SPAN; C-SPAN 2; E! Entertainment TV; EWTN; Learning Channel; QVC; TV Food Network; TV Guide Channel; TV Guide Sneak Prevue.

Current originations: Public access; educational access; government access; automated emergency alert.

Fee: $41.00 installation; $9.61 monthly; $3.00 converter; $11.85 additional installation.

Expanded Basic Service

Subscribers: N.A.

Programming (via satellite): A & E; American Movie Classics; Animal Planet; BET; Bravo; CNBC; CNN; Cartoon Network; Comedy Central; Discovery Channel; ESPN; ESPN 2; Fox Family Channel; Fox News Channel; Fox Sports Net Ohio; Golf Channel; Headline News; History Channel; Home & Garden Television; Lifetime; MTV; Nashville Network; Nickelodeon; Odyssey; Outdoor Life Network; Sci-Fi Channel; Speedvision; The Weather Channel; USA Network; VH1.

Fee: $20.97 monthly.

Expanded Basic Service 2

Subscribers: N.A.

Programming (via satellite): WGN-TV (W) Chicago; Disney Channel; TBS Superstation; Turner Network TV.

Fee: $2.57 monthly.

Pay Service 1

Pay Units: Included with Elyria, OH.

Programming (via satellite): Cinemax; HBO (multiplexed); Independent Film Channel; Showtime; Starz!; The New Encore.

Fee: $15.00 installation; $4.95 monthly (IFC), $9.95 monthly (Encore & Starz), $11.50 monthly (Cinemax, HBO or Showtime).

Pay-Per-View

Hot Choice; Viewer's Choice; movies; special events.

Fee: $3.95 (movies).

Local advertising: Yes. Available in satellite distributed, locally originated & character-generated programming.

Equipment: Scientific-Atlanta headend; Magnavox amplifiers; Comm/Scope cable; Panasonic cameras; Sony VTRs; Video Data Systems character generator; Eagle addressable traps.

Miles of plant & homes passed included with Elyria, OH.

Manager: Larry Williamson. Chief technician: Bill Keslar. Program director: Joan Lowry.

Village fee: 3% of gross.

Ownership: MediaOne Group (MSO). See Cable System Ownership.

BAZETTA TWP.—TCI Cablevision of Ohio Inc., Suite 8, 7757 Auburn Rd., Painesville, OH 44077-9604. Phone: 440-942-0870. Fax: 440-639-6290. Counties: Mahoning & Trumbull. Also serves Bristol Twp. (Trumbull County), Champion, Farmington Twp., Fowler Twp. (Trumbull County), Johnston Twp. (Trumbull County), Lordstown, Mecca Twp. (Trumbull County), North Jackson, Southington Twp. (Trumbull County), Vienna Air Force Base, Weathersfield Twp. (Trumbull County), West Farmington. ICA: OH0082.

TV Market Ranking: 8 (Lordstown, Mecca Twp., Southington Twp.); 79 (Bazetta Twp., Bristol Twp., Champion, Farmington Twp., Fowler Twp., Johnston Twp., Lordstown, Mecca Twp., North Jackson, Southington Twp., Vienna Air Force Base, Weathersfield Twp., West Farmington). Franchise award date: September 21, 1983. Franchise expiration date: January 1, 1998. Began: February 19, 1985.

Channel capacity: 38. Channels available but not in use: N.A.

Basic Service

Subscribers: 7,156.

Programming (received off-air): WNEO (P) Alliance; WEWS-TV (A), WJW (F), WKYC-TV (N) Cleveland; WUAB (U) Lorain-Cleveland; WOIO (C) Shaker Heights; WFMJ-TV (N), WKBN-TV (C), WYTV (A,F) Youngstown.

Programming (via satellite): WGN-TV (W) Chicago; A & E; C-SPAN; CNN; Discovery Channel; Fox Family Channel; Headline News; Home Shopping Network; Lifetime; MTV; Nashville Network; Nickelodeon; Odyssey; TBS Superstation; The Weather Channel.

Fee: $60.00 installation; $9.73 monthly; $2.00 converter.

Expanded Basic Service

Subscribers: 6,326.

Programming (via satellite): American Movie Classics; ESPN; Fox Sports Net Pittsburgh; Turner Network TV; USA Network.

Fee: $11.04 monthly.

Pay Service 1

Pay Units: 603.

Programming (via satellite): Disney Channel.

Fee: $9.95 monthly.

Pay Service 2

Pay Units: 2,519.

Programming (via satellite): The New Encore.

Fee: N.A.

Pay Service 3

Pay Units: 1,960.

Programming (via satellite): HBO.

Fee: $11.40 monthly.

Pay Service 4

Pay Units: 996.

Programming (via satellite): Showtime.

Fee: $11.40 monthly.

Local advertising: Yes.

Equipment: Triple Crown headend; Comm/Scope cable; Jerrold set top converters; Harris satellite receivers.

Miles of plant: 340.5 (coaxial). Homes passed: 9,092. Total homes in franchised area: 11,000.

Manager: Ed Williams. Chief technician: Mike Drougovich.

City fee: 5% of gross.

Ownership: AT&T Broadband & Internet Services (MSO). Purchased from Tele-Communications Inc., March 9, 1999.

BELLAIRE—TCI Cablevision of Ohio Inc., 908 National Rd., Bridgeport, OH 43912. Phone: 800-527-2222. County: Belmont. Also serves Goshen Twp. (Belmont County), Neffs. ICA: OH0134.

TV Market Ranking: 90. Franchise award date: N.A. Franchise expiration date: N.A. Began: July 1, 1965.

Channel capacity: 60. Channels available but not in use: 25.

Basic Service

Subscribers: 2,285.

Programming (received off-air): WOUC-TV (P) Cambridge; WNPB-TV (P) Morgantown; KDKA-TV (C), WCWB (W), WPGH-TV (F), WPXI (N), WQED (P), WTAE-TV (A) Pittsburgh; WTOV-TV (N) Steubenville-Wheeling; WTRF-TV (C) Wheeling-Steubenville; WYTV (A,F) Youngstown; allband FM.

Programming (via satellite): A & E; BET; C-SPAN; CNBC; CNN; Discovery Channel; Fox Family Channel; Headline News; Knowledge TV; Lifetime; MTV; Nashville Network; Nickelodeon; Odyssey; QVC; TBS Superstation; The Weather Channel.

Current originations: Automated time-weather.

Fee: $60.00 installation; $18.16 monthly.

Expanded Basic Service

Subscribers: 2,193.

Programming (via satellite): American Movie Classics; ESPN; Fox Sports Net Pittsburgh; Turner Network TV; USA Network.

Fee: $1.95 monthly.

Pay Service 1

Pay Units: 139.

Programming (via satellite): Disney Channel.

Fee: $7.00 monthly.

Pay Service 2

Pay Units: 893.

Programming (via satellite): The New Encore.

Fee: N.A.

Pay Service 3

Pay Units: 522.

Programming (via satellite): HBO.

Fee: N.A.

Pay Service 4

Pay Units: 404.

Programming (via satellite): Showtime.

Fee: N.A.

Equipment: CAS headend; Ameco & Vikoa amplifiers; Times Fiber & Vikoa cable; AFC satellite antenna.

Miles of plant: 39.6 (coaxial). Homes passed: 3,557. Total homes in franchised area: 3,667.

Manager: Paul Luicart.

City fee: None.

Ownership: AT&T Broadband & Internet Services (MSO). Purchased from Tele-Communications Inc., March 9, 1999.

BELLE CENTER—Time Warner Cable, Box 787, 111 S. Mulberry St., Mount Vernon, OH 43050. Phones: 740-397-2288; 800-782-4118. Fax: 740-397-3730. County: Logan. Also serves Miami Twp. (Logan County), Rushsylvania. ICA: OH0252.

TV Market Ranking: Below 100 (Belle Center, Miami Twp.); Outside TV Markets (Rushsylvania). Franchise award date: January 1, 1983. Franchise expiration date: January 1, 2003. Began: December 1, 1983.

Channel capacity: 61. Channels available but not in use: 30.

Basic Service

Subscribers: 394.

Programming (received off-air): WBNS-TV (C), WCMH-TV (N), WOSU-TV (P), WSYX (A), WTTE (F,U) Columbus; WHIO-TV (C), WKEF (N) Dayton; WLIO (N) Lima.

Programming (via satellite): WGN-TV (W) Chicago; A & E; CNN; Country Music TV; Discovery Channel; ESPN; Fox Family Channel; Headline News; Lifetime; MTV; Nashville Network; Nickelodeon; QVC; TBS Superstation; Turner Network TV; USA Network; VH1.

Current originations: Local access.

Fee: $32.00 installation; $18.95 monthly; $4.50 converter; $9.00 additional installation.

Pay Service 1

Pay Units: 35.

Programming (via satellite): Disney Channel.

Fee: $18.00 installation; $10.95 monthly.

Pay Service 2

Pay Units: 94.

Programming (via satellite): HBO.

Fee: $18.00 installation; $10.95 monthly.

Pay Service 3

Pay Units: 28.

Programming (via satellite): Cinemax.

Fee: $18.00 installation; $10.95 monthly.

Local advertising: Yes. Available in character-generated programming.

Miles of plant: 21.8 (coaxial). Homes passed: 639.

Manager: Paul S. Schonewolf. Technical operations manager: Dan Fessler. Field operations manager: Bill Schroeder. Marketing manager: Carl Bauer. Customer operations manager: Danielle Turner.

Village fee: 3% of basic.

Ownership: Fanch Communications Inc. (MSO); Time Warner Cable (MSO). See Cable System Ownership.

BELLEFONTAINE—Scott Cable Communications Inc., 113 Northview Dr., Bellefontaine, OH 43311. Phone: 937-599-1884. Fax: 937-599-1884. County: Logan. Also serves Harrison Twp. (Logan County), Huntsville (village), Indian Lake Resort Area, Jefferson Twp. (Logan County), Lake Twp. (Logan County), Lakeview (Logan County), Liberty Twp. (Logan County), Russells Point, Stokes Twp. (Logan County), Union Twp. (Logan County), Washington Twp. (Logan County), Zanesfield (village). ICA: OH0117.

TV Market Ranking: Below 100. Franchise award date: N.A. Franchise expiration date: June 21, 2000. Began: September 1, 1966.

Channel capacity: 43 (2-way capable). Channels available but not in use: None.

Basic Service

Subscribers: 7,189; Commercial subscribers: 126.

Programming (received off-air): WBGU-TV (P) Bowling Green; WBNS-TV (C), WOSU-TV (P), WSYX (A), WTTE (F,U) Columbus; WDTN (A), WHIO-TV (C), WKEF (N) Dayton; WLIO (N), WTLW (I) Lima; WBDT (W) Springfield; 1 FM.

Programming (via satellite): WGN-TV (W) Chicago; TBS Superstation.

Current originations: Educational access.

Fee: $35.95 installation; $8.55 monthly; $1.04 converter.

Expanded Basic Service

Subscribers: 6,627.

Programming (via satellite): A & E; C-SPAN; CNN; Country Music TV; ESPN; EWTN; Fox Family Channel; Headline News; Lifetime; MTV; Nashville Network; Nick at Nite; Nickelodeon; QVC; Sci-Fi Channel; TV Guide Channel; The Weather Channel; Trinity Bcstg. Network; USA Network; VH1.

Fee: $35.95 installation; $14.42 monthly.

A la Carte 1
Subscribers: 5,925.
Programming (via satellite): American Movie Classics; Discovery Channel; Fox Sports Net Ohio; Turner Network TV.
Fee: $22.36 installation; $3.60 monthly (package).
Pay Service 1
Pay Units: 642.
Programming (via satellite): Showtime.
Fee: $9.00 monthly.
Pay Service 2
Pay Units: 343.
Programming (via satellite): Cinemax.
Fee: $9.00 monthly.
Pay Service 3
Pay Units: 634.
Programming (via satellite): Disney Channel.
Fee: $7.00 monthly.
Pay Service 4
Pay Units: 686.
Programming (via satellite): HBO.
Fee: $10.00 monthly.
Pay Service 5
Pay Units: 501.
Programming (via satellite): The Movie Channel.
Fee: $4.50 monthly.
Pay-Per-View
Addressable homes: 2,600.
Special events.
Fee: $2.19.
Local advertising: Yes. Available in satellite distributed programming.
Equipment: Scientific-Atlanta headend; Magnavox amplifiers; Comm/Scope & Times Fiber cable; Scientific-Atlanta & Standard Components set top converters; Jerrold addressable set top converters; Eagle & Pico traps; Gardiner & Scientific-Atlanta satellite antenna; Scientific-Atlanta satellite receivers.
Miles of plant: 144.0 (coaxial); None (fiber optic). Additional miles planned: 3.0 (coaxial). Homes passed: 10,263.
Manager: Chuck Rogers. Chief technician: Jim Post.
City fee: 3% of gross.
Ownership: American Cable Entertainment (MSO).

BELLEVUE—Time Warner Cable, 113 W. Main St., Bellevue, OH 44811-1329. Phone: 419-483-4762. Fax: 419-483-5319. Counties: Huron, Sandusky & Seneca. Also serves Adams Twp. (Seneca County), Ballville Twp., Clyde, Fremont, Green Creek Twp. (Sandusky County), Green Springs, Lyme Twp. (Huron County), Riley Twp. (Sandusky County), Sandusky Twp. (Sandusky County), Thompson Twp. (Seneca County), Townsend Twp., Vickery, York Twp. (Sandusky County). ICA: OH0086.
TV Market Ranking: 52 (Fremont, Vickery); Below 100 (Adams Twp., Ballville Twp., Bellevue, Clyde, Green Creek Twp., Green Springs, Lyme Twp., Riley Twp., Sandusky Twp., Thompson Twp., Townsend Twp., York Twp.). Franchise award date: August 29, 1969. Franchise expiration date: April 1, 2004. Began: September 1, 1970.
Channel capacity: 52. Channels available but not in use: 14.
Basic Service
Subscribers: 3,572.
Programming (received off-air): WVPX (X) Akron; WBGU-TV (P) Bowling Green; WEWS-TV (A), WJW (F), WKYC-TV (N), WVIZ-TV (P) Cleveland; WKBD-TV (U) Detroit; WUAB (U) Lorain-Cleveland; WGGN-TV (T) Sandusky; WGTE-TV (P), WNWO-TV (N), WTOL-TV (C), WTVG (A) Toledo; CBET Windsor; 14 FMs.
Programming (via satellite): A & E; C-SPAN; CNBC; CNN; Discovery Channel; ESPN; Fox Family Channel; Home Shopping Network; Lifetime; MTV; Nashville Network; Nickelodeon; TBS Superstation; The Weather Channel; Turner Network TV; USA Network; VH1.
Current originations: Public access; educational access; government access; leased access; automated emergency alert; local news; local sports.
Fee: N.A.
Pay Service 1
Pay Units: 3,979.
Programming (via satellite): Cinemax; Disney Channel; HBO; Showtime.
Fee: $15.00 installation; $6.95 monthly (Disney), $10.95 monthly (Cinemax, HBO or Showtime).
Local advertising: Yes. Available in satellite distributed & character-generated programming. Rates: $10.00/30 Seconds.
Equipment: Avantek & Phasecom headend; Texscan amplifiers; Comm/Scope cable; Video Data Systems character generator; RCA set top converters; Eagle traps; Microdyne satellite antenna; Microdyne satellite receivers.
Miles of plant: 92.0 (coaxial); 54.0 (fiber optic). Homes passed: 9,222.
Manager: Ike M. Mutlu. Chief technician: Dave Phillips. Marketing director: Susan St. Clair.
City fee: 3% of gross.
Ownership: Time Warner Cable (MSO). Purchased from MediaOne Group, August 2, 1999.

BELMONT—TCI Cablevision of Ohio Inc., Box 469, Bridgeport, OH 43912. Phone: 800-527-2222. County: Belmont. Also serves Bethesda. ICA: OH0241.
TV Market Ranking: 90. Franchise award date: N.A. Franchise expiration date: N.A. Began: August 1, 1971.
Channel capacity: 52. Channels available but not in use: N.A.
Basic Service
Subscribers: 759.
Programming (received off-air): WVPX (X) Akron; WOUC-TV (P) Cambridge; KDKA-TV (C), WPGH-TV (F), WPXI (N), WQED (P), WTAE-TV (A) Pittsburgh; WTOV-TV (N) Steubenville-Wheeling; WTRF-TV (C) Wheeling-Steubenville; WHIZ-TV (N) Zanesville.
Programming (via satellite): CNBC; CNN; Discovery Channel; Fox Family Channel; Lifetime; MTV; Nashville Network; Nick at Nite; Nickelodeon; Odyssey; QVC; TBS Superstation.
Fee: $60.00 installation; $9.07 monthly; $4.00 converter.
Expanded Basic Service
Subscribers: 672.
Programming (via satellite): A & E; American Movie Classics; ESPN; Turner Network TV; USA Network.
Fee: $9.77 monthly.
Pay Service 1
Pay Units: 250.
Programming (via satellite): The New Encore.
Fee: N.A.
Pay Service 2
Pay Units: 146.
Programming (via satellite): HBO.
Fee: $11.95 monthly.
Pay Service 3
Pay Units: 110.
Programming (via satellite): Showtime.
Fee: $11.95 monthly.
Equipment: Blonder-Tongue headend; Magnavox amplifiers.
Miles of plant: 14.2 (coaxial). Homes passed: 790. Total homes in franchised area: 1,492.
Manager: Robert Weese. Chief technician: Earl Conway.
City fee: $150 annually.
Ownership: AT&T Broadband & Internet Services (MSO). Purchased from Tele-Communications Inc., March 9, 1999.

BENTON RIDGE—B. R. Cablevision Co., 3225 W. Elm St., Lima, OH 45805. Phone: 419-227-2266. Fax: 419-999-2140.
E-mail: watchtmk@bright.net. County: Hancock. Also serves Blanchard Twp. (Hancock County), Liberty Twp. (Hancock County), Union Twp. (Hancock County). ICA: OH0287.
TV Market Ranking: Below 100. Franchise award date: N.A. Franchise expiration date: N.A. Began: December 1, 1983.
Channel capacity: 54 (not 2-way capable). Channels available but not in use: 17.
Basic Service
Subscribers: 234.
Programming (received off-air): WBGU-TV (P) Bowling Green; WBNS-TV (C) Columbus; WFFT-TV (F), WPTA (A) Fort Wayne; WLIO (N), WOHL-LP (F), WTLW (I) Lima; WGTE-TV (P), WNWO-TV (N), WTOL-TV (C), WTVG (A), WUPW (F) Toledo.
Programming (via satellite): WGN-TV (W) Chicago; CNN; Country Music TV; ESPN; Fox Family Channel; MTV; Nashville Network; Nickelodeon; TBS Superstation; The Weather Channel; USA Network.
Current originations: Public access; educational access; leased access.
Fee: $29.95 installation; $22.97 monthly.
Pay Service 1
Pay Units: 24.
Programming (via satellite): Disney Channel.
Fee: $25.00 installation; $8.95 monthly.
Pay Service 2
Pay Units: 52.
Programming (via satellite): HBO.
Fee: $25.00 installation; $9.95 monthly.
Pay Service 3
Pay Units: 31.
Programming (via satellite): Showtime.
Fee: $25.00 installation; $5.99 monthly.
Pay Service 4
Pay Units: 11.
Programming (via satellite): Cinemax.
Fee: $6.99 monthly.
Pay-Per-View
Addressable homes: 243.
Miles of plant: 11.0 (coaxial); None (fiber optic). Homes passed: 275.
Manager: Thomas N. Knippen. Chief technician: Mike Birkemeier.
City fee: None.
Ownership: Benton Ridge Telephone Co.

BEREA—Americast, 300 S. Riverside, Chicago, IL 60606. Phones: 312-526-8000; 800-848-2278. Fax: 312-526-8565. County: Cuyahoga. ICA: OH0410.
TV Market Ranking: 8. Franchise award date: June 1, 1996. Franchise expiration date: N.A. Began: N.A.
Channel capacity: N.A. Channels available but not in use: N.A.
Basic Service
Subscribers: N.A.
Programming (received off-air): WBNX-TV (W,F), WVPX (X) Akron; WOAC (I) Canton; WEWS-TV (A), WJW (F), WKYC-TV (N), WQHS-TV (H), WVIZ-TV (P) Cleveland; WUAB (U) Lorain-Cleveland; WOIO (C) Shaker Heights.
Programming (via satellite): WGN-TV (W) Chicago; QVC; TBS Superstation; TV Guide Channel; TV Guide Sneak Prevue.
Current originations: Public access; educational access; government access; leased access.
Fee: $39.95 installation; $9.95 monthly.
Expanded Basic Service
Subscribers: N.A.
Programming (via satellite): A & E; American Movie Classics; Animal Planet; BET; Bravo; C-SPAN; C-SPAN 2; CNBC; CNN; CNNfn; Cartoon Network; Comedy Central; Country Music TV; Court TV; Discovery Channel; Disney Channel; E! Entertainment TV; ESPN; ESPN 2; ESPN Classic Sports; ESPNews; Fox Family Channel; Fox Sports Net Ohio; Golf Channel; Goodlife TV Network; Headline News; History Channel; Home & Garden Television; Learning Channel; Lifetime; MTV; Nashville Network; Nickelodeon; Sci-Fi Channel; TV Food Network; The Health Network; The Inspirational Network; The Weather Channel; Travel Channel; Turner Classic Movies; Turner Network TV; USA Network; VH1.
Fee: $18.00 monthly.
Pay Service 1
Pay Units: N.A.
Programming (via satellite): Cinemax; Flix; HBO (multiplexed); Showtime (multiplexed); Starz!; The Movie Channel; The New Encore.
Fee: $5.95 monthly (Flix or Encore & Starz), $9.95 monthly (Cinemax, Showtime or TMC), $10.95 monthly (HBO).
Total homes in franchised area: 7,800.
Ownership: Ameritech New Media Inc. (MSO).

BERLIN TWP. (Mahoning County)—Star Cable, Box 4478, 4720 Mahoning Ave., Youngstown, OH 44515. Phone: 330-792-9577. Fax: 330-792-9541. County: Mahoning. Also serves Beaver Twp. (Mahoning County), Canfield Twp., Ellsworth Twp., Goshen Twp. (Mahoning County), Green Twp. (Mahoning County), Jackson Twp. (Mahoning County), Milton Twp. (Mahoning County), Smith Twp. (portions) (Mahoning County). ICA: OH0161.
TV Market Ranking: 79. Franchise award date: N.A. Franchise expiration date: N.A. Began: May 1, 1990.
Channel capacity: 62 (not 2-way capable). Channels available but not in use: 16.
Basic Service
Subscribers: 1,828.
Programming (received off-air): WBNX-TV (W,F) Akron; WNEO (P) Alliance; WJW (F) Cleveland; WUAB (U) Lorain-Cleveland; WOIO (C) Shaker Heights; WFMJ-TV (N), WKBN-TV (C), WYTV (A,F) Youngstown.
Programming (via satellite): QVC; TBS Superstation.
Current originations: Religious access.
Fee: $40.00 installation; $10.50 monthly; $1.95 converter.
Expanded Basic Service
Subscribers: 1,760.
Programming (via satellite): A & E; American Movie Classics; C-SPAN; CNBC; CNN; Cartoon Network; Country Music TV; Discovery Channel; ESPN; ESPN 2; Fox Family Channel; Fox News Channel; Fox Sports Net Ohio; Fox Sports Net Pittsburgh; Headline News; History Channel; Home & Garden Television; Learning Channel; Lifetime; MTV; Nashville Network; Nick at Nite's TV Land; Nickelodeon; Sci-Fi Channel; The Weather Channel; Turner Network TV; USA Network; VH1.
Fee: $20.00 monthly.
Pay Service 1
Pay Units: 148.
Programming (via satellite): Cinemax.
Fee: $11.00 monthly.
Pay Service 2
Pay Units: 161.

Programming (via satellite): Disney Channel.
Fee: $7.95 monthly.
Pay Service 3
Pay Units: 231.
Programming (via satellite): HBO.
Fee: $11.00 monthly.
Pay Service 4
Pay Units: 212.
Programming (via satellite): Showtime; The Movie Channel.
Fee: $12.95 monthly (Showtime or TMC).
Miles of plant: 136.6 (coaxial); None (fiber optic). Homes passed: 2,630. Total homes in franchised area: 2,630.
Manager: Terry Dickerhoof. Chief technician: Tom Beat.
Ownership: Star Cable Associates (MSO).

BETTSVILLE—Time Warner Entertainment Co. LP, 3100 Elida Rd., Lima, OH 45805. Phone: 419-331-3333. Fax: 419-331-1573. Counties: Sandusky & Seneca. Also serves Burgoon (village), Fort Seneca, Old Fort. ICA: OH0179.
TV Market Ranking: 52. Franchise award date: N.A. Franchise expiration date: N.A. Began: December 1, 1985.
Channel capacity: 42 (not 2-way capable). Channels available but not in use: 6.
Basic Service
Subscribers: 909.
Programming (received off-air): WBGU-TV (P) Bowling Green; WUAB (U) Lorain-Cleveland; WGTE-TV (P), WNWO-TV (N), WTOL-TV (C), WTVG (A), WUPW (F) Toledo.
Programming (via satellite): WGN-TV (W) Chicago; A & E; C-SPAN; C-SPAN 2; CNBC; CNN; Discovery Channel; ESPN; Fox Family Channel; Fox Sports Net Ohio; Headline News; Home Shopping Network; Lifetime; MTV; Nashville Network; Nickelodeon; TBS Superstation; The Weather Channel; Trinity Bcstg. Network; Turner Network TV; USA Network.
Fee: $39.95 installation; $19.50 monthly.
Pay Service 1
Pay Units: 129.
Programming (via satellite): Cinemax.
Fee: $9.95 monthly.
Pay Service 2
Pay Units: 75.
Programming (via satellite): Disney Channel.
Fee: $6.95 monthly.
Pay Service 3
Pay Units: 186.
Programming (via satellite): HBO.
Fee: $10.95 monthly.
Local advertising: No.
Miles of plant: 5.0 (coaxial). Homes passed: 1,800.
Manager: Larry K. Miller. Chief technician: Sean Gallagher.
Ownership: Fanch Communications Inc. (MSO); Time Warner Cable (MSO). See Cable System Ownership.

BIG ISLAND TWP.—Paxton Cable, Suite 280, 700 Ackerman Rd., Columbus, OH 43202. Phone: 614-263-6100. County: Marion. ICA: OH0317.
TV Market Ranking: Below 100. Franchise award date: N.A. Franchise expiration date: N.A. Began: November 1, 1991.
Channel capacity: N.A. Channels available but not in use: N.A.
Basic Service
Subscribers: N.A.
Programming (received off-air): WBNS-TV (C), WCMH-TV (N), WSYX (A), WTTE (F,U) Columbus.
Fee: N.A.
Director of operations: Lisa Collier.
Ownership: Paxton Cable Television Inc. (MSO).

BLADENSBURG—National Cable Inc., Suite 106A, 5151 Reed Rd., Columbus, OH 43220. Phone: 614-442-5890. Fax: 614-457-2567. County: Knox. ICA: OH0318.
TV Market Ranking: Below 100. Franchise award date: N.A. Franchise expiration date: N.A. Began: N.A.
Channel capacity: N.A. Channels available but not in use: N.A.
Basic Service
Subscribers: N.A.
Programming (received off-air): WBNS-TV (C), WCMH-TV (N), WSYX (A), WTTE (F,U) Columbus.
Programming (via satellite): WGN-TV (W) Chicago; TBS Superstation.
Fee: N.A.
System operations manager: Steve Miller.
Ownership: National Cable (MSO).

BLENDON TWP.—Americast, 300 S. Riverside, Chicago, IL 60606. Phones: 312-526-8000; 800-848-2278. Fax: 312-526-8565. County: Franklin. ICA: OH0411.
TV Market Ranking: 27. Franchise award date: December 1, 1996. Franchise expiration date: N.A. Began: N.A.
Channel capacity: N.A. Channels available but not in use: N.A.
Basic Service
Subscribers: N.A.
Programming (received off-air): WWHO (U) Chillicothe; WBNS-TV (C), WCMH-TV (N), WOSU-TV (P), WSYX (A), WTTE (F,U) Columbus; WSFJ (I) Newark.
Programming (via satellite): WGN-TV (W) Chicago; QVC; TBS Superstation; TV Guide Channel.
Current originations: Public access; educational access; government access; leased access.
Fee: $39.95 installation; $9.95 monthly.
Expanded Basic Service
Subscribers: N.A.
Programming (via satellite): A & E; American Movie Classics; BET; BET on Jazz; Bravo; C-SPAN; C-SPAN 2; CNBC; CNN; CNNfn; Cartoon Network; Comedy Central; Country Music TV; Court TV; Discovery Channel; Disney Channel; E! Entertainment TV; ESPN; ESPN 2; ESPN Classic Sports; Fox Family Channel; Fox Sports Net Ohio; Golf Channel; Headline News; History Channel; Home & Garden Television; Learning Channel; Lifetime; MTV; Nashville Network; Nickelodeon; Ohio News Network; Sci-Fi Channel; TV Food Network; The Health Network; The Inspirational Network; The Weather Channel; Travel Channel; Turner Classic Movies; Turner Network TV; USA Network; VH1.
Fee: $17.00 monthly.
Pay Service 1
Pay Units: N.A.
Programming (via satellite): Cinemax; Flix; HBO (multiplexed); Showtime (multiplexed); Starz!; Sundance Channel; The Movie Channel; The New Encore.
Fee: $5.95 monthly (Flix or Sundance), $7.95 monthly (Encore & Starz), $9.95 monthly (Cinemax, Showtime or TMC), $11.95 monthly (HBO).
Total homes in franchised area: 3,900.
Ownership: Ameritech New Media Inc. (MSO).

BLOOMINGDALE—Star Cable, Box 4478, 4720 Mahoning Ave., Youngstown, OH 44515. Phone: 330-792-9577. Fax: 330-792-9541. Counties: Harrison & Jefferson. Also serves German (village), Ross Twp. (Jefferson County), Salem Twp. (Jefferson County), Springfield Twp. (Jefferson County), Wayne Twp. (Jefferson County). ICA: OH0203.
TV Market Ranking: 10 (German); 90 (Bloomingdale, Ross Twp., Salem Twp., Springfield Twp., Wayne Twp.). Franchise award date: N.A. Franchise expiration date: N.A. Began: March 1, 1990.
Channel capacity: 62 (not 2-way capable). Channels available but not in use: 24.
Basic Service
Subscribers: 935; Commercial subscribers: 11.
Programming (received off-air): KDKA-TV (C), WCWB (W), WPGH-TV (F), WPXI (N), WQED (P), WQEX (P), WTAE-TV (A) Pittsburgh; WTOV-TV (N) Steubenville-Wheeling; WTRF-TV (C) Wheeling-Steubenville.
Programming (via satellite): QVC; TBS Superstation.
Fee: $30.00 installation; $10.50 monthly; $1.95 converter.
Expanded Basic Service
Subscribers: 904.
Programming (via satellite): A & E; American Movie Classics; C-SPAN; CNBC; CNN; Discovery Channel; ESPN; Fox Family Channel; Fox Sports Net Pittsburgh; Headline News; History Channel; Lifetime; MTV; Nashville Network; Nick at Nite's TV Land; Nickelodeon; Sci-Fi Channel; The Weather Channel; Turner Network TV; USA Network; VH1.
Fee: $20.00 monthly.
Pay Service 1
Pay Units: 83.
Programming (via satellite): Cinemax.
Fee: $11.00 monthly.
Pay Service 2
Pay Units: 79.
Programming (via satellite): Disney Channel.
Fee: $7.95 monthly.
Pay Service 3
Pay Units: 118.
Programming (via satellite): HBO.
Fee: $11.00 monthly.
Pay Service 4
Pay Units: 97.
Programming (via satellite): Showtime; The Movie Channel.
Fee: $12.95 monthly.
Miles of plant: 56.4 (coaxial); None (fiber optic). Homes passed: 1,345. Total homes in franchised area: 1,345.
Manager: Terry Dickerhoof.
Ownership: Star Cable Associates (MSO).

BLOOMVILLE—Time Warner Cable, Box 10, 105 Prospect St., Lodi, OH 44254. Phone: 330-633-9044. Fax: 330-948-1513. County: Seneca. ICA: OH0278.
TV Market Ranking: Below 100. Franchise award date: August 1, 1983. Franchise expiration date: August 1, 2003. Began: October 1, 1984.
Channel capacity: 36 (not 2-way capable). Channels available but not in use: 2.
Basic Service
Subscribers: 219.
Programming (received off-air): WBGU-TV (P) Bowling Green; WEWS-TV (A), WQHS-TV (H) Cleveland; WOSU-TV (P), WTTE (F,U) Columbus; WUAB (U) Lorain-Cleveland; WOIO (C) Shaker Heights; WGTE-TV (P), WNWO-TV (N), WTOL-TV (C), WTVG (A), WUPW (F) Toledo.
Programming (via satellite): WGN-TV (W) Chicago; CNN; Country Music TV; Discovery Channel; ESPN; Fox Family Channel; Headline News; Knowledge TV; MTV; Nashville Network; Odyssey; TBS Superstation; The Weather Channel; Turner Network TV; USA Network.
Fee: $30.00 installation; $12.95 monthly; $2.50 converter.
Pay Service 1
Pay Units: 30.
Programming (via satellite): Cinemax.
Fee: $8.95 installation; $8.95 monthly.
Pay Service 2
Pay Units: 32.
Programming (via satellite): Disney Channel.
Fee: $8.95 installation; $8.00 monthly.
Pay Service 3
Pay Units: 38.
Programming (via satellite): HBO.
Fee: $8.95 installation; $8.95 monthly.
Pay Service 4
Pay Units: 25.
Programming (via satellite): The Movie Channel.
Fee: $8.95 installation; $8.95 monthly.
Local advertising: No.
Equipment: DX Engineering headend; Jerrold amplifiers; Comm/Scope cable; Texscan character generator; Pioneer set top converters; Eagle traps; DX Engineering satellite receivers.
Miles of plant: 6.8 (coaxial). Additional miles planned: 1.0 (coaxial). Homes passed: 370.
Manager: Thomas Autry. Chief technician: Jim Parsons. Marketing director: Ray Kistler.
Ownership: Time Warner Cable (MSO).

BLUFFTON—FrontierVision, 220 N. Main St., Ada, OH 45810. Phones: 419-634-7160; 800-448-0013. Fax: 419-634-1245. County: Allen. ICA: OH0214.
TV Market Ranking: Below 100. Franchise award date: March 5, 1968. Franchise expiration date: October 6, 2006. Began: February 1, 1969.
Channel capacity: 60 (not 2-way capable). Channels available but not in use: N.A.
Basic Service
Subscribers: 1,445.
Programming (received off-air): WBGU-TV (P) Bowling Green; WBNS-TV (C) Columbus; WLIO (N), WTLW (I) Lima; WGTE-TV (P), WNWO-TV (N), WTVG (A), WUPW (F) Toledo.
Programming (via satellite): WGN-TV (W) Chicago; C-SPAN; TBS Superstation; VH1.
Fee: $32.56 installation; $12.80 monthly; $0.80 converter.
Expanded Basic Service
Subscribers: 1,194.
Programming (via satellite): A & E; American Movie Classics; CNN; Discovery Channel; ESPN; Fox Family Channel; Headline News; Learning Channel; Lifetime; Nashville Network; Nickelodeon; The Weather Channel; Turner Network TV; USA Network.
Fee: $32.56 installation; $9.32 monthly.
Pay Service 1
Pay Units: 67.
Programming (via satellite): Disney Channel.
Fee: $8.95 monthly.
Pay Service 2
Pay Units: 150.
Programming (via satellite): HBO.
Fee: $11.95 monthly.
Pay Service 3
Pay Units: 97.
Programming (via satellite): Showtime.
Fee: $10.95 monthly.
Miles of plant: 45.9 (coaxial). Homes passed: 1,983.
Manager: Weldon Feightner. Chief technician: Terry Pulley. Marketing director: Anna Hernandez. Customer service manager: Lenora Kelly.
Ownership: Cox Communications Inc. (MSO).

BOARDMAN—Armstrong Cable Services, 9328 Woodworth Rd., North Lima, OH 44452-9712. Phone: 330-758-6411. Fax: 330-726-0117. County: Mahoning. Also serves Beaver Twp. (Mahoning County), Campbell, New Springfield (portions), North Lima, Poland, Poland Twp. (Mahoning County), Springfield Twp. (Mahoning County). ICA: OH0024.

TV Market Ranking: 79. Franchise award date: December 4, 1972. Franchise expiration date: N.A. Began: October 1, 1974.

Channel capacity: 78 (2-way capable; operating 2-way). Channels available but not in use: 4.

Basic Service

Subscribers: 24,810; Commercial subscribers: 39.

Programming (received off-air): WNEO (P) Alliance; WUAB (U) Lorain-Cleveland; WQED (P) Pittsburgh; WFMJ-TV (N), WKBN-TV (C), WYTV (A,F) Youngstown.

Programming (via satellite): A & E; American Movie Classics; BET; C-SPAN; C-SPAN 2; CNBC; CNN; Discovery Channel; ESPN; Fox Family Channel; Fox Sports Net Ohio; Fox Sports Net Pittsburgh; Headline News; Home Shopping Network; Lifetime; MSNBC; MTV; Nashville Network; Nickelodeon; QVC; TBS Superstation; TV Guide Channel; TV Guide Sneak Prevue; Telemundo; The Health Network; The Weather Channel; Travel Channel; Turner Network TV; USA Network; VH1.

Current originations: Educational access; automated emergency alert.

Fee: $35.00 installation (aerial), $49.95 (underground); $24.90 monthly; $2.95 converter.

Expanded Basic Service

Subscribers: 7,138.

Programming (via satellite): Bravo; Cartoon Network; Comedy Central; Country Music TV; ESPN 2; History Channel; Home & Garden Television; Learning Channel; Sci-Fi Channel; TV Food Network; Turner Classic Movies.

Fee: $7.95 monthly.

Expanded Basic Service 2

Subscribers: 417.

Programming (via satellite): CNN/SI; ESPN Classic Sports; Golf Channel; Outdoor Channel.

Fee: $5.95 monthly.

Pay Service 1

Pay Units: 2,959.

Programming (via satellite): Cinemax.

Fee: $9.95 monthly.

Pay Service 2

Pay Units: 1,905.

Programming (via satellite): Disney Channel.

Fee: $7.95 monthly.

Pay Service 3

Pay Units: 1,084.

Programming (via satellite): Flix.

Fee: $0.99 monthly.

Pay Service 4

Pay Units: N.A.

Programming (via satellite): The New Encore.

Fee: N.A.

Pay Service 5

Pay Units: 5,825.

Programming (via satellite): HBO.

Fee: $11.95 monthly.

Pay Service 6

Pay Units: 716.

Programming (via satellite): Showtime.

Fee: $7.95 monthly.

Pay Service 7

Pay Units: 849.

Programming (via satellite): Starz!

Fee: $8.95 monthly.

Pay-Per-View

Addressable homes: 9,134.

Local advertising: Yes. Available in satellite distributed & character-generated programming.

Equipment: Scientific-Atlanta headend; Scientific-Atlanta amplifiers; Trilogy cable; Siecor fiber optic cable; Texscan character generator; Scientific-Atlanta set top converters; Scientific-Atlanta addressable set top converters; Eagle traps; Scientific-Atlanta satellite receivers.

Miles of plant: 478.0 (coaxial); 75.0 (fiber optic). Homes passed: 31,605. Total homes in franchised area: 32,000.

Manager: Paul R. Wachtel. Chief technician: Joe Battista. Customer service manager: Sharon Ferrante.

City fee: 3% of gross.

Ownership: Armstrong Group of Companies (MSO).

BOLIVAR—FrontierVision, Box 648, 102 Twin Oak Dr., Jackson, OH 45640. Phone: 614-345-4329. Fax: 614-286-1489. Counties: Stark & Tuscarawas. Also serves Beach City, Lawrence Twp. (Tuscarawas County), Wilkshire Hills, Wilmot, Zoar. ICA: OH0168.

TV Market Ranking: 8. Franchise award date: December 18, 1990. Franchise expiration date: December 18, 2005. Began: December 1, 1972.

Channel capacity: 62 (not 2-way capable). Channels available but not in use: 25.

Basic Service

Subscribers: 1,671.

Programming (received off-air): WBNX-TV (W,F), WVPX (X) Akron; WNEO (P) Alliance; WDLI (T), WOAC (I) Canton; WEWS-TV (A), WJW (F), WKYC-TV (N), WQHS-TV (H) Cleveland; WUAB (U) Lorain-Cleveland; WOIO (C) Shaker Heights; WTOV-TV (N) Steubenville-Wheeling.

Programming (via satellite): WGN-TV (W) Chicago; A & E; American Movie Classics; C-SPAN; CNN; Comedy Central; Country Music TV; Discovery Channel; ESPN; Fox Family Channel; Headline News; Lifetime; MTV; Nashville Network; Nickelodeon; QVC; TBS Superstation; The Weather Channel; Turner Network TV; USA Network; VH1.

Fee: $22.66 installation; $22.14 monthly.

Pay Service 1

Pay Units: 135.

Programming (via satellite): Disney Channel.

Fee: $13.22 installation; $10.95 monthly.

Pay Service 2

Pay Units: 272.

Programming (via satellite): HBO.

Fee: $13.22 installation; $11.95 monthly.

Pay Service 3

Pay Units: 93.

Programming (via satellite): Showtime.

Fee: $13.22 installation; $10.95 monthly.

Local advertising: No.

Program Guide: TV Entertainment.

Equipment: Blonder-Tongue, Jerrold & Scientific-Atlanta headend; Jerrold amplifiers; Times Fiber & Comm/Scope cable; NSC set top converters; Arcom & Gamco traps; Scientific-Atlanta satellite antenna; M/A-Com satellite receivers.

Miles of plant: 52.6 (coaxial). Homes passed: 2,221.

Manager: Steve Trippe. Chief technician: Bill Ricker.

Ownership: FrontierVision Partners LP (MSO). See Cable System Ownership.

BOWLING GREEN—Time Warner Entertainment Co. LP, 3100 Elida Rd., Lima, OH 45805. Phone: 419-331-3333. Fax: 419-331-1573. Counties: Henry & Wood. Also serves Custar (village), Dunbridge, McClure, McClure (village), Milton Center (village), Portage, Sugar Ridge, Weston. ICA: OH0054.

TV Market Ranking: 52. Franchise award date: N.A. Franchise expiration date: N.A. Began: December 1, 1965.

Channel capacity: 62 (not 2-way capable). Channels available but not in use: 17.

Basic Service

Subscribers: 6,740; Commercial subscribers: 566.

Programming (received off-air): WBGU-TV (P) Bowling Green; WJW (F) Cleveland; WDIV (N), WKBD-TV (U) Detroit; WGTE-TV (P), WNWO-TV (N), WTOL-TV (C), WTVG (A), WUPW (F) Toledo; CBET Windsor; 1 FM.

Programming (via satellite): A & E; C-SPAN; C-SPAN 2; CNBC; CNN; Comedy Central; Discovery Channel; ESPN; Electronic Program Guide; Fox Family Channel; Fox Sports Net Ohio; Headline News; Home Shopping Network; Lifetime; MTV; Nashville Network; Nickelodeon; QVC; TBS Superstation; The Inspirational Network; The Weather Channel; Turner Network TV; USA Network; VH1.

Current originations: Automated time-weather; public access; automated emergency alert.

Fee: $39.95 installation; $15.95 monthly; $25.00 additional installation.

Pay Service 1

Pay Units: 375.

Programming (via satellite): Cinemax.

Fee: $15.00 installation; $9.95 monthly.

Pay Service 2

Pay Units: 271.

Programming (via satellite): Disney Channel.

Fee: $15.00 installation; $9.95 monthly.

Pay Service 3

Pay Units: 946.

Programming (via satellite): HBO.

Fee: $15.00 installation; $9.95 monthly.

Pay Service 4

Pay Units: 257.

Programming (via satellite): The Movie Channel.

Fee: $15.00 installation; $9.95 monthly.

Pay Service 5

Pay Units: 174.

Programming (via satellite): Showtime.

Fee: $15.00 installation; $9.95 monthly.

Pay-Per-View

Addressable homes: 3,000.

Special events.

Local advertising: Yes. Available in satellite distributed & taped programming. Local sales manager: Randy Stasiak.

Program Guide: Prevue Guide.

Equipment: Scientific-Atlanta headend; Scientific-Atlanta & Jerrold amplifiers; Comm/Scope cable; ADS character generator; Jerrold set top converters; Scientific-Atlanta addressable set top converters; Scientific-Atlanta satellite antenna; Scientific-Atlanta satellite receivers.

Miles of plant: 170.0 (coaxial). Homes passed: 15,200.

Manager: Larry K. Miller. Chief technician: Sean Gallagher.

City fee: None.

Ownership: Fanch Communications Inc. (MSO); Time Warner Cable (MSO). See Cable System Ownership.

BRECKSVILLE—Cablevision Systems, 10270 Brecksville Rd., Brecksville, OH 44141. Phones: 216-575-8016; 800-686-2510. Fax: 216-291-1631. County: Cuyahoga. ICA: OH0122.

TV Market Ranking: 8. Franchise award date: July 1, 1982. Franchise expiration date: July 1, 1997. Began: April 1, 1983.

Channel capacity: 54 (2-way capable). Channels available but not in use: 4.

Basic Service

Subscribers: 2,300; Commercial subscribers: 10.

Programming (received off-air): WBNX-TV (W,F), WEAO (P), WVPX (X) Akron; WEWS-TV (A), WJW (F), WKYC-TV (N), WQHS-TV (H), WVIZ-TV (P) Cleveland; WUAB (U) Lorain-Cleveland; WOIO (C) Shaker Heights.

Programming (via satellite): TBS Superstation.

Current originations: Automated time-weather; public access; government access; religious access; local sports.

Fee: $25.00 installation; $12.50 monthly.

Commercial fee: $27.50 monthly.

Expanded Basic Service

Subscribers: N.A.

Programming (via satellite): A & E; American Movie Classics; BET; Bravo; C-SPAN; C-SPAN 2; CNBC; CNN; Court TV; Discovery Channel; ESPN; Fox Family Channel; Headline News; Home & Garden Television; Knowledge TV; Learning Channel; Lifetime; MTV; MuchMusic Network; Nashville Network; Nickelodeon; QVC; Sci-Fi Channel; TV Guide Channel; The Health Network; The Weather Channel; Turner Network TV; USA Network; VH1.

Fee: N.A.

Pay Service 1

Pay Units: N.A.

Programming (via satellite): Cinemax; Disney Channel; Flix; Fox Sports Net Ohio; HBO; Playboy TV; Showtime; The Movie Channel.

Fee: $5.00 installation; $10.45 monthly (Cinemax, Disney, HBO, Playboy, Showtime or TMC).

Pay-Per-View

Addressable homes: 2,300.

Movies; special events.

Local advertising: Yes. Available in satellite distributed, locally originated & taped programming. Rates: $40.00/Minute; $25.00/30 Seconds; $20.00/Month (video print channel). Local sales manager: Jeff Smith. Regional interconnect: Northern Ohio Interconnect.

Equipment: Scientific-Atlanta headend; Scientific-Atlanta amplifiers; JVC cameras; Sony, JVC & Panasonic VTRs; Scientific-Atlanta addressable set top converters; Eagle & Intercept traps; Scientific-Atlanta satellite antenna; Scientific-Atlanta satellite receivers.

Miles of plant: 89.0 (coaxial). Homes passed: 4,256. Total homes in franchised area: 4,256.

Manager: Kathleen Mayo. Chief technician: Bruce Smylie. Program director: John Stealey. Marketing director: Frank Naples.

City fee: 3% of gross.

Ownership: Cablevision Systems Corp. (MSO).

***BRICE**—Americast, 300 S. Riverside, Chicago, IL 60606. Phones: 312-526-8000; 800-848-2278. Fax: 312-526-8565. County: Franklin. ICA: OH0405.

TV Market Ranking: 27. Franchise award date: January 1, 1998. Franchise expiration date: N.A. Scheduled to begin: N.A.

Channel capacity: N.A.

Total homes in franchised area: 50.

Ownership: Ameritech New Media Inc. (MSO).

BRIDGEPORT—TCI Cablevision of Ohio, Box 469, Bridgeport, OH 43912. Phone: 800-527-2222. Fax: 614-633-2721. County: Belmont. Also serves Colerain, Mead Twp., Pultney Twp., Smith Twp. (Belmont County). ICA: OH0156.

TV Market Ranking: 90. Franchise award date: N.A. Franchise expiration date: N.A. Began: August 1, 1964.

Channel capacity: 30. Channels available but not in use: 2.

Basic Service
Subscribers: 2,535.
Programming (received off-air): WOUC-TV (P) Cambridge; KDKA-TV (C), WCWB (W), WPGH-TV (F), WPXI (N), WQED (P), WTAE-TV (A) Pittsburgh; WTOV-TV (N) Steubenville-Wheeling; WTRF-TV (C) Wheeling-Steubenville; WYTV (A,F) Youngstown; 16 FMs.
Programming (via satellite): A & E; C-SPAN; CNBC; CNN; Discovery Channel; Fox Family Channel; Lifetime; MTV; Nashville Network; Nickelodeon; TBS Superstation.
Fee: $60.00 installation; $18.16 monthly.
Expanded Basic Service
Subscribers: 2,483.
Programming (via satellite): American Movie Classics; ESPN; Fox Sports Net Pittsburgh; QVC; Turner Network TV; USA Network.
Fee: $1.95 monthly.
Pay Service 1
Pay Units: 145.
Programming (via satellite): Disney Channel.
Fee: N.A.
Pay Service 2
Pay Units: 851.
Programming (via satellite): The New Encore.
Fee: N.A.
Pay Service 3
Pay Units: 457.
Programming (via satellite): HBO.
Fee: N.A.
Pay Service 4
Pay Units: 340.
Programming (via satellite): Showtime.
Fee: N.A.
Miles of plant: 37.2 (coaxial). Homes passed: 2,682. Total homes in franchised area: 3,750.
Manager: Kim Ackerman. Chief technician: Jim Brown.
Ownership: AT&T Broadband & Internet Services (MSO). Purchased from Tele-Communications Inc., March 9, 1999.

BROOK PARK—Cablevision Systems Corp., 5127 W. 140th St., Brook Park, OH 44142. Phone: 216-575-8000. Fax: 216-291-1631. County: Cuyahoga. Also serves Berea, Brooklyn, Lakewood (Cuyahoga County). ICA: OH0046.
TV Market Ranking: 8. Franchise award date: N.A. Franchise expiration date: N.A. Began: May 1, 1981.
Channel capacity: 54. Channels available but not in use: N.A.
Basic Service
Subscribers: 10,443.
Programming (received off-air): WBNX-TV (W,F), WEAO (P), WVPX (X) Akron; WEWS-TV (A), WJW (F), WKYC-TV (N), WQHS-TV (H), WVIZ-TV (P) Cleveland; WUAB (U) Lorain-Cleveland; WOIO (C) Shaker Heights.
Programming (via satellite): A & E; C-SPAN; C-SPAN 2; CNBC; CNN; Discovery Channel; ESPN; EWTN; Fox Family Channel; Fox Sports Net Ohio; Headline News; Knowledge TV; Lifetime; MTV; Nashville Network; Nickelodeon; TBS Superstation; The Inspirational Network; The Weather Channel; Turner Network TV; USA Network; VH1.
Current originations: Government access.
Fee: $15.00 installation; $17.95monthly (Brook Park), $12.31 monthly (Berea).
Pay Service 1
Pay Units: N.A.
Programming (via satellite): American Movie Classics; Bravo; Cinemax; Disney Channel; HBO; Playboy TV; Showtime; The Movie Channel.
Fee: $9.95 monthly (each).
Pay-Per-View
Addressable homes: 7,510.
Local advertising: Yes. Available in satellite distributed, locally originated & taped programming. Local sales manager: Jeff Smith. Regional interconnect: Northern Ohio Interconnect.
Equipment: Scientific-Atlanta headend; Scientific-Atlanta amplifiers; Scientific-Atlanta cable; JVC & NEC VTRs; Jerrold & Oak set top converters; Jerrold addressable set top converters; Scientific-Atlanta satellite antenna.
Miles of plant: 151.9 (coaxial). Homes passed: 18,700.
Manager: Richard Coplan. Chief technician: Richard Demarest. Program director: Kerry Paluscsak. Marketing director: Bill DeGraeve.
City fee: 3% of gross.
Ownership: Cablevision Systems Corp. (MSO).

BROOKFIELD TWP. (Trumbull County)—Northeast Cable TV, Box 4095, Youngstown, OH 44515. Phone: 330-793-7434. Fax: 330-793-7434. County: Trumbull. ICA: OH0382.
TV Market Ranking: 79. Franchise award date: N.A. Franchise expiration date: N.A. Began: May 1, 1987.
Channel capacity: 60. Channels available but not in use: N.A.
Basic Service
Subscribers: N.A.
Programming (received off-air): WBNX-TV (W,F) Akron; WNEO (P) Alliance; WUAB (U) Lorain-Cleveland; WPGH-TV (F) Pittsburgh; WOIO (C) Shaker Heights; WFMJ-TV (N), WKBN-TV (C), WYTV (A,F) Youngstown.
Programming (via translator): WPCB-TV (I) Greensburg.
Programming (via satellite): Discovery Channel; ESPN; Fox Family Channel; Headline News; MOR Galleria; Nashville Network; Nickelodeon; TBS Superstation; Turner Network TV; USA Network.
Fee: $54.95 installation; $23.95 monthly.
Pay Service 1
Pay Units: N.A.
Programming (via satellite): HBO.
Fee: $12.95 monthly.
Miles of plant: 11.0 (coaxial). Homes passed: 235.
Manager: Al Pezzenti.
Ownership: Northeast Cable TV (MSO).

BRUNSWICK—Cablevision Systems Corp., 3400 Lakeside Ave., Cleveland, OH 44114. Phone: 216-575-8016. Fax: 216-575-0212. County: Medina. Also serves Brunswick Hills Twp., Hinckley Twp. ICA: OH0059.
TV Market Ranking: 8. Franchise award date: N.A. Franchise expiration date: N.A. Began: November 1, 1982.
Channel capacity: 54. Channels available but not in use: 3.
Basic Service
Subscribers: 7,208.
Programming (received off-air): WBNX-TV (W,F), WEAO (P), WVPX (X) Akron; WEWS-TV (A), WJW (F), WKYC-TV (N), WQHS-TV (H), WVIZ-TV (P) Cleveland; WUAB (U) Lorain-Cleveland; WOIO (C) Shaker Heights.
Programming (via satellite): A & E; Bravo; C-SPAN; C-SPAN 2; CNBC; CNN; Discovery Channel; ESPN; EWTN; Fox Family Channel; Fox Sports Net Ohio; Headline News; Knowledge TV; Lifetime; MTV; Nashville Network; Nickelodeon; QVC; TBS Superstation; The Weather Channel; Turner Network TV; USA Network; VH1.
Current originations: Public access; educational access; government access.
Fee: $36.25 installation; $23.35 monthly.
Pay Service 1
Pay Units: N.A.
Programming (via satellite): American Movie Classics; Cinemax; Disney Channel; HBO; Playboy TV; Showtime; The Movie Channel.
Fee: $10.45 monthly (each).
Pay-Per-View
Addressable homes: 4,000.
Local advertising: Yes. Available in satellite distributed programming. Local sales manager: Mark Dolan. Regional interconnect: Northern Ohio Interconnect.
Equipment: Jerrold headend; Jerrold set top converters; Simulsat satellite antenna; Scientific-Atlanta satellite receivers.
Miles of plant: 225.0 (coaxial). Homes passed: 12,928.
Manager: Kathleen R. Mayo. Chief technician: Bruce Smylie. Program director: John Stealey. Sales & marketing director: Frank Naples.
City fee: 3% of gross.
Ownership: Cablevision Systems Corp. (MSO).

BRYAN—FrontierVision, Box 627, Chillicothe, OH 45601. Phones: 740-775-4300; 800-346-2288. Fax: 740-775-2915. Counties: Fulton & Williams. Also serves Archbold, Center Twp. (Williams County), Edgerton, Jefferson Twp. (Williams County), Montpelier, Pulaski, Pulaski Twp. (Williams County), Springfield Twp. (Williams County), Stryker, West Jefferson, West Jefferson Twp. (Williams County), West Unity. Plans service to St. Joseph Twp. (Williams County). ICA: OH0078.
TV Market Ranking: 82 (Edgerton); Below 100 (Archbold, Bryan, Center Twp., Jefferson Twp., Montpelier, Pulaski, Pulaski Twp., Springfield Twp., Stryker, West Jefferson, West Jefferson Twp., West Unity). Franchise award date: N.A. Franchise expiration date: N.A. Began: August 1, 1974.
Channel capacity: 39 (2-way capable; operating 2-way). Channels available but not in use: None.
Basic Service
Subscribers: 8,027.
Programming (received off-air): WBGU-TV (P) Bowling Green; WDFM-LP (I) Defiance; WANE-TV (C), WFFT-TV (F), WKJG-TV (N), WPTA (A) Fort Wayne; WGTE-TV (P), WNWO-TV (N), WTOL-TV (C), WTVG (A), WUPW (F) Toledo; allband FM.
Programming (via satellite): WGN-TV (W) Chicago; A & E; C-SPAN; CNN; Discovery Channel; Fox Family Channel; Lifetime; MTV; Nashville Network; Nickelodeon; QVC; TBS Superstation; The Weather Channel.
Current originations: Automated time-weather.
Fee: $60.00 installation; $10.22 monthly; $30.00 additional installation.
Expanded Basic Service
Subscribers: 7,436.
Programming (via satellite): American Movie Classics; Court TV; Disney Channel; ESPN; Fox Sports Net Ohio; Turner Network TV; USA Network.
Fee: $11.49 monthly.
Pay Service 1
Pay Units: 653.
Programming (via satellite): Cinemax.
Fee: $15.00 installation; $9.95 monthly.
Pay Service 2
Pay Units: 1,880.
Programming (via satellite): The New Encore.
Fee: N.A.
Pay Service 3
Pay Units: 1,107.
Programming (via satellite): HBO.
Fee: $15.00 installation; $9.95 monthly.
Pay Service 4
Pay Units: 404.
Programming (via satellite): The Movie Channel.
Fee: $15.00 installation; $9.95 monthly.
Pay Service 5
Pay Units: 3.
Programming (via satellite): Showtime.
Fee: N.A.
Pay Service 6
Pay Units: 798.
Programming (via satellite): Starz!
Fee: N.A.
Pay-Per-View
Addressable homes: 232.
Program Guide: The Cable Guide.
Equipment: Scientific-Atlanta headend; C-COR, GTE Sylvania & Jerrold amplifiers; Comm/Scope & General cable; JVC VTRs; MSI character generator; Standard Components set top converters; AFC satellite antenna.
Miles of plant: 239.8 (coaxial). Homes passed: 11,796.
Manager: Richard Coplan. Chief technician: Sam Morabith. Program director: Chad Hume. Marketing director: Barbara Brewer.
City fee: 3% of gross.
Ownership: FrontierVision Partners LP (MSO). See Cable System Ownership.

BUCYRUS—Time Warner Cable, Box 787, 111 S. Mulberry St., Mount Vernon, OH 43050. Phones: 740-397-2288; 800-782-4118. Fax: 740-397-3730. County: Crawford. Also serves Bucyrus Twp., Holmes Twp. (Crawford County), Liberty Twp. (Crawford County), Sulphur Springs, Whetstone Twp. (Crawford County). ICA: OH0105.
TV Market Ranking: Below 100. Franchise award date: N.A. Franchise expiration date: N.A. Began: November 1, 1967.
Channel capacity: 52. Channels available but not in use: 11.
Basic Service
Subscribers: 5,383.
Programming (received off-air): WEWS-TV (A), WJW (F), WKYC-TV (N) Cleveland; WBNS-TV (C), WCMH-TV (N), WOSU-TV (P), WSYX (A) Columbus; WUAB (U) Lorain-Cleveland; WTOL-TV (C), WTVG (A) Toledo; 14 FMs.
Programming (via satellite): CNN; Country Music TV; Discovery Channel; ESPN; Fox Family Channel; Headline News; Home Shopping Network; Lifetime; MTV; Nickelodeon; TBS Superstation; The Weather Channel; Turner Classic Movies; USA Network; VH1.
Current originations: Automated time-weather; automated emergency alert.
Fee: $15.00 installation; $13.95 monthly; $15.00 additional installation.
Commercial fee: $10.50 monthly.
Pay Service 1
Pay Units: N.A.

Programming (via satellite): Cinemax; Disney Channel; HBO; Showtime; The Movie Channel.
Fee: $15.00 installation; $7.95 monthly (Disney), $9.95 monthly (Cinemax, Showtime or TMC), $10.95 monthly (HBO).
Local advertising: Yes. Available in taped programming.
Equipment: Scientific-Atlanta headend; Magnavox amplifiers; Comm/Scope cable; Scientific-Atlanta set top converters; Scientific-Atlanta addressable set top converters; Eagle traps; Scientific-Atlanta satellite receivers.
Miles of plant: 82.0 (coaxial). Homes passed: 5,900. Total homes in franchised area: 5,900.
Manager: Paul S. Schonewolf. Technical operations manager: Dan Fessler. Field operations manager: Bill Schroeder. Marketing manager: Carl Bauer. Customer operations manager: Danielle Turner.
City fee: 5% of gross.
Ownership: Time Warner Cable (MSO).

CADIZ—TCI Cablevision of Ohio Inc., Box 347, 123 N. Market St., Minerva, OH 44657. Phone: 330-868-5413. Fax: 330-868-3731. County: Harrison. ICA: OH0200.
TV Market Ranking: 90. Franchise award date: N.A. Franchise expiration date: N.A. Began: June 1, 1970.
Channel capacity: 57 (not 2-way capable). Channels available but not in use: 13.
Basic Service
Subscribers: 1,097.
Programming (received off-air): WOUC-TV (P) Cambridge; WDLI (T) Canton; WNPB-TV (P) Morgantown; KDKA-TV (C), WPGH-TV (F), WPXI (N), WQED (P), WTAE-TV (A) Pittsburgh; WTOV-TV (N) Steubenville-Wheeling; WTRF-TV (C) Wheeling-Steubenville.
Programming (via satellite): C-SPAN; Discovery Channel; QVC; TBS Superstation.
Fee: $37.50 installation; $10.58 monthly; $2.00 converter.
Expanded Basic Service
Subscribers: 1,048.
Programming (via satellite): A & E; American Movie Classics; Animal Planet; CNBC; CNN; Cartoon Network; Court TV; ESPN; FX; Fox Family Channel; Fox News Channel; Fox Sports Net Pittsburgh; Great American Country; Home Shopping Network; Knowledge TV; Lifetime; MTV; Nashville Network; Nickelodeon; Odyssey; The New Encore; The Weather Channel; Turner Network TV; USA Network.
Fee: $13.86 monthly.
Pay Service 1
Pay Units: 77.
Programming (via satellite): Disney Channel.
Fee: $12.50 monthly.
Pay Service 2
Pay Units: 345.
Programming (via satellite): The New Encore.
Fee: $1.95 monthly.
Pay Service 3
Pay Units: 174.
Programming (via satellite): HBO.
Fee: $14.95 monthly.
Pay Service 4
Pay Units: 136.
Programming (via satellite): Showtime.
Fee: $14.95 monthly.
Pay Service 5
Pay Units: N.A.
Programming (via satellite): Starz!
Fee: $6.75 monthly.
Miles of plant: 24.8 (coaxial). Homes passed: 1,446. Total homes in franchised area: 1,453.
Manager: Paul Liucart. Chief technician: Rodney Lentz.
City fee: 5% of gross.
Ownership: AT&T Broadband & Internet Services (MSO). Purchased from Tele-Communications Inc., March 9, 1999.

CALEDONIA—Paxton Cable, Suite 280, 700 Ackerman Rd., Columbus, OH 43202. Phone: 614-263-6100. County: Marion. Also serves Wood Valley. ICA: OH0257.
TV Market Ranking: Below 100. Franchise award date: January 1, 1985. Franchise expiration date: January 1, 2011. Began: August 1, 1985.
Channel capacity: 21 (not 2-way capable). Channels available but not in use: 7.
Basic Service
Subscribers: N.A.
Programming (received off-air): WBNS-TV (C), WCMH-TV (N), WOSU-TV (P), WSYX (A), WTTE (F,U) Columbus.
Programming (via satellite): ESPN; Fox Family Channel; Nashville Network; TBS Superstation; USA Network.
Fee: $25.00 installation; $9.95 monthly.
Pay Service 1
Pay Units: N.A.
Programming (via satellite): Disney Channel; Showtime.
Fee: $15.00 installation; $6.95 monthly (Disney), $9.95 monthly (Showtime).
Local advertising: No.
Equipment: Jerrold amplifiers; Comm/Scope cable; Pico traps.
Miles of plant: 4.9 (coaxial). Additional miles planned: 2.5 (coaxial). Homes passed: 530. Total homes in franchised area: 559.
Director of operations: Lisa Collier.
City fee: 1.5% of gross.
Ownership: Paxton Cable Television Inc. (MSO).

CAMBRIDGE—FrontierVision, Box 1297, 351 Highland Ave., Cambridge, OH 43725. Phone: 740-432-7321. Fax: 740-432-6465. Counties: Guernsey & Noble. Also serves Adams Twp. (Guernsey County), Belle Valley, Caldwell, Cambridge Twp., Noble County, Noble Twp. (Noble County), Olive Twp. (Noble County). ICA: OH0088.
TV Market Ranking: Below 100. Franchise award date: N.A. Franchise expiration date: January 2, 2004. Began: November 1, 1953.
Channel capacity: 62 (not 2-way capable). Channels available but not in use: 1.
Basic Service
Subscribers: 6,025; Commercial subscribers: 983.
Programming (received off-air): WOUC-TV (P) Cambridge; WTTE (F,U) Columbus; WSFJ (I) Newark; WTOV-TV (N) Steubenville-Wheeling; WTRF-TV (C) Wheeling-Steubenville; WHIZ-TV (N) Zanesville; 10 FMs.
Programming (via microwave): WBNS-TV (C), WCMH-TV (N), WSYX (A) Columbus; WUAB (U) Lorain-Cleveland.
Programming (via satellite): C-SPAN; CNBC; Home Shopping Network; Knowledge TV; TBS Superstation.
Fee: $31.55 installation; $11.97 monthly; $2.33 converter; $23.66 additional installation.
Expanded Basic Service
Subscribers: 5,572.
Programming (via satellite): A & E; CNN; Comedy Central; Country Music TV; Disney Channel; E! Entertainment TV; ESPN; FX; Fox Family Channel; Fox Sports Net Ohio; Golf Channel; Headline News; Knowledge TV; Lifetime; MSNBC; MTV; Nickelodeon; Outdoor Life Network; QVC; Sci-Fi Channel; TV Guide Channel; The Weather Channel; USA Network.
Fee: $14.25 monthly.
Expanded Basic Service 2
Subscribers: 6,292.
Programming (via satellite): American Movie Classics; Discovery Channel; Learning Channel; Nashville Network; Turner Network TV.
Fee: $2.50 monthly.
Pay Service 1
Pay Units: 507.
Programming (via satellite): Cinemax.
Fee: $8.00 monthly.
Pay Service 2
Pay Units: 944.
Programming (via satellite): HBO (multiplexed).
Fee: $10.95 monthly.
Pay Service 3
Pay Units: 550.
Programming (via satellite): Showtime.
Fee: $9.95 monthly.
Pay Service 4
Pay Units: 354.
Programming (via satellite): The Movie Channel.
Fee: $8.00 monthly.
Pay Service 5
Pay Units: 682.
Programming (via satellite): The New Encore.
Fee: $2.95 monthly.
Pay Service 6
Pay Units: 18.
Programming (via satellite): Starz!
Fee: N.A.
Pay-Per-View
Addressable homes: 2,461.
Hot Choice; Spice; Viewer's Choice.
Local advertising: Yes. Rates: $25.00/Month. Local sales manager: Charlie Jones.
Equipment: Jerrold headend; Jerrold amplifiers; Plastoid cable; Harris satellite antenna.
Miles of plant: 100.0 (coaxial); None (fiber optic). Homes passed: 8,860.
Manager: Judy Pierce. Technical supervisor: Chuck Gibson. Customer service supervisor: Rosa Robertson.
City fee: 5% of gross.
Ownership: FrontierVision Partners LP (MSO). See Cable System Ownership.

CAMERON—CableVision Communications, Box 2200, 68 5th St., Buckhannon, WV 26201. Phone: 304-472-4193. Fax: 304-472-0756. County: Monroe. ICA: OH0310.
TV Market Ranking: 90. Franchise award date: July 6, 1979. Franchise expiration date: July 6, 2004. Began: N.A.
Channel capacity: 21. Channels available but not in use: 6.
Basic Service
Subscribers: 34.
Programming (received off-air): WOUC-TV (P) Cambridge; KDKA-TV (C), WPGH-TV (F), WPXI (N), WTAE-TV (A) Pittsburgh; WTOV-TV (N) Steubenville-Wheeling; WTRF-TV (C) Wheeling-Steubenville.
Programming (via satellite): CNN; Discovery Channel; ESPN; Fox Family Channel; Nashville Network; TBS Superstation; USA Network.
Fee: $52.50 installation; $22.00 monthly; $0.73 converter; $25.00 additional installation.
Pay Service 1
Pay Units: 10.
Programming (via satellite): HBO.
Fee: $17.50 installation; $11.99 monthly.
Equipment: Blonder-Tongue headend; Jerrold amplifiers; Times Fiber cable; Eagle traps; DX Communications satellite receivers.
Miles of plant: 3.0 (coaxial). Homes passed: 63.
Manager: Willie Critchfield. Marketing director: Kenny Phillips.
City fee: None.
Ownership: Rifkin & Associates Inc. (MSO). See Cable System Ownership.

CANAAN TWP. (Madison County)—Paxton Cable, Suite 280, 700 Ackerman Rd., Columbus, OH 43202. Phone: 614-236-6100. Counties: Fayette, Franklin, Madison & Union. Also serves Bookwalter, Brown Twp. (Franklin County), Darby Twp. (Madison County), Fairfield Twp. (Madison County), Jefferson Twp. (Madison County), Jerome Twp. (Union County), Madison County (portions), Midway, Mill Creek Twp., Monroe Twp. (Madison County), Norwich Twp. (Franklin County), Paint Twp. (Madison County), Pike Twp. (Madison County), Pleasant Twp. (Franklin County), Range Twp., Washington Twp. (Franklin County). ICA: OH0131.
TV Market Ranking: 27. Franchise award date: N.A. Franchise expiration date: N.A. Began: December 1, 1985.
Channel capacity: 42 (2-way capable). Channels available but not in use: None.
Basic Service
Subscribers: 3,500.
Programming (received off-air): WBNS-TV (C), WCMH-TV (N), WOSU-TV (P), WSYX (A), WTTE (F,U) Columbus; WPTD (P) Dayton.
Programming (via satellite): WGN-TV (W) Chicago; A & E; American Movie Classics; C-SPAN; CNBC; CNN; Comedy Central; Country Music TV; Discovery Channel; ESPN; Fox Family Channel; Headline News; Home Shopping Network; Lifetime; MTV; Nashville Network; Nickelodeon; TBS Superstation; The Weather Channel; Trinity Bcstg. Network; Turner Network TV; USA Network; VH1.
Current originations: Automated timeweather.
Fee: $25.00 installation; $22.95 monthly.
Pay Service 1
Pay Units: 1,337.
Programming (via satellite): Cinemax; Disney Channel; HBO; Showtime.
Fee: $10.95 monthly (each).
Pay-Per-View
Addressable homes: 700.
Special events.
Local advertising: No.
Equipment: Scientific-Atlanta headend; Texscan amplifiers; Comm/Scope cable; Jerrold set top converters; Regency addressable set top converters; Scientific-Atlanta & Comtech satellite antenna; Scientific-Atlanta satellite receivers.
Miles of plant: 225.0 (coaxial); 16.5 (fiber optic). Homes passed: 5,551.
Director of operations: Lisa Collier. Chief technician: Tom Wehring.
Franchise fee: 3% of basic.
Ownership: Paxton Cable Television Inc.

CANTON—Time Warner Cable, 5520 Whipple Ave. NW, Canton, OH 44720-7700. Phones: 330-494-0095; 800-950-2266. Fax: 330-663-7970. Counties: Carroll, Mahoning, Stark & Tuscarawas. Also serves Alliance, Brown Twp. (Carroll County), Canton Twp., East Canton, East Sparta, Hartville, Hills & Dales (village), Jackson Twp. (Stark County), Lake Twp. (Stark County), Lexington Twp., Limaville, Louisville, Magnolia, Malvern (village), Marlboro Twp. (Stark County), Meyers Lake, Mineral City, Nimishillen, Nimishillen Twp. (Stark County), North Canton, Osnaburg Twp. (Stark County), Perry Twp. (Stark County), Pike Twp. (Stark County), Plain Twp. (Stark County), Sandy Twp. (Stark County), Sandy Twp. (Tuscarawas County), South Canton, Stark County (portions), Washington Twp. (Stark County), Waynesburg (village). ICA: OH0008.
TV Market Ranking: 8 (Alliance, Brown Twp., Canton, Canton Twp., East Canton, East

Sparta, Hartville, Hills & Dales, Jackson Twp., Lake Twp., Lexington Twp., Limaville, Louisville, Magnolia, Malvern, Marlboro Twp., Meyers Lake, Mineral City, Nimishillen, Nimishillen Twp., North Canton, Osnaburg Twp., Perry Twp., Pike Twp., Plain Twp., Sandy Twp., South Canton, portions of Stark County, Washington Twp., Waynesburg); 79 (Alliance, Lexington Twp., Marlboro Twp., portions of Stark County, Washington Twp.). Franchise award date: October 26, 1965. Franchise expiration date: October 27, 1997. Began: June 1, 1966.

Channel capacity: 81 (not 2-way capable). Channels available but not in use: N.A.

Basic Service

Subscribers: 82,500; Commercial subscribers: 1,325.

Programming (received off-air): WBNX-TV (W,F), WVPX (X) Akron; WNEO (P) Alliance; WDLI (T), WOAC (I) Canton; WEWS-TV (A), WJW (F), WKYC-TV (N), WQHS-TV (H), WVIZ-TV (P) Cleveland; WUAB (U) Lorain-Cleveland; WOIO (C) Shaker Heights; allband FM.

Current originations: Automated time-weather; public access; educational access; leased access; automated emergency alert.

Fee: $42.09 installation; $9.10 monthly; $25.00 additional installation.

Expanded Basic Service

Subscribers: N.A.

Programming (via satellite): A & E; American Movie Classics; BET; Bravo; C-SPAN; C-SPAN 2; CNBC; CNN; Cartoon Network; Country Music TV; Discovery Channel; E! Entertainment TV; ESPN; ESPN 2; EWTN; Fox Family Channel; Fox News Channel; Fox Sports Net Ohio; Headline News; Home & Garden Television; Learning Channel; Lifetime; MSNBC; MTV; Nashville Network; Nick at Nite's TV Land; Nickelodeon; QVC; TBS Superstation; TV Food Network; The Weather Channel; Travel Channel; Turner Network TV; USA Network; VH1.

Fee: $13.75 monthly.

Expanded Basic Service 2

Subscribers: N.A.

Programming (via satellite): WGN-TV (W) Chicago; Animal Planet; Discovery Channel; Turner Classic Movies.

Fee: $2.31 monthly.

A la Carte 1

Subscribers: N.A.

Programming (via satellite): Comedy Central; Court TV; ESPN Classic Sports; Golf Channel; History Channel; Sci-Fi Channel.

Fee: $3.59 monthly (package); $0.40 monthly (Comedy or Classic Sports), $1.00 monthly (Golf), $1.75 monthly (Sci-Fi).

Pay Service 1

Pay Units: 28,234.

Programming (via satellite): Cinemax; Disney Channel; Fox Sports Net Ohio; HBO (multiplexed); Playboy TV; Showtime (multiplexed); The Movie Channel.

Fee: $12.50 monthly (Cinemax, Disney, Playboy TV, Showtime or TMC), $13.60 monthly (HBO).

Pay Service 2

Pay Units: N.A.

Programming (via satellite): Music Choice; Starz!; The New Encore.

Fee: $1.95 monthly (Encore), $10.95 monthly (Starz).

Pay-Per-View

Addressable homes: 82,500.

Local advertising: Yes. Available in satellite distributed & locally originated programming. Rates: $50.00/Minute; $25.00/30 Seconds. Local sales manager: Barbara McCaffrey.

Regional interconnect: Northeast Ohio Interconnect.

Equipment: Scientific-Atlanta headend; Magnavox amplifiers; Comm/Scope cable; Hitachi cameras; Sony VTRs; Quanta character generator; Pioneer set top converters; Pioneer addressable set top converters; Scientific-Atlanta satellite antenna; Scientific-Atlanta satellite receivers.

Miles of plant: 1318.0 (coaxial). Additional miles planned: 60.0 (coaxial). Homes passed: 109,500. Total homes in franchised area: 110,500.

Manager: Bill Farmer. Chief technician: Tod Dean. Marketing director: Jim Nicholas.

City fee: 5% of gross.

Ownership: Time Warner Cable (MSO).

CAREY—FrontierVision, 220 N. Main St., Ada, OH 45810. Phone: 419-628-3423. County: Wyandot. ICA: OH0210.

TV Market Ranking: Outside TV Markets. Franchise award date: N.A. Franchise expiration date: N.A. Began: October 1, 1976.

Channel capacity: 37. Channels available but not in use: 7.

Basic Service

Subscribers: 1,276.

Programming (received off-air): WBGU-TV (P) Bowling Green; WEWS-TV (A), WKYC-TV (N) Cleveland; WBNS-TV (C), WCMH-TV (N), WSYX (A) Columbus; WLIO (N) Lima; WGTE-TV (P), WNWO-TV (N), WTOL-TV (C), WTVG (A) Toledo; allband FM.

Planned programming (via satellite): WGN-TV (W) Chicago; Fox Family Channel.

Current originations: Automated time-weather.

Fee: $50.00 installation; $16.25 monthly.

Pay Service 1

Pay Units: 143.

Programming (via satellite): HBO.

Fee: $10.95 monthly.

Pay Service 2

Pay Units: 230.

Programming (via satellite): Showtime.

Fee: $10.95 monthly.

Pay Service 3

Pay Units: 184.

Programming (via satellite): The Movie Channel.

Fee: N.A.

Equipment: AFC satellite antenna.

Miles of plant: 33.0 (coaxial). Homes passed: 1,950.

Manager: Steve Trippe. Chief technician: Bill Ricker.

City fee: None.

Ownership: FrontierVision Partners LP (MSO). See Cable System Ownership.

CARROLLTON—TCI Cablevision of Ohio Inc., Box 347, 123 N. Market St., Minerva, OH 44657. Phone: 330-868-5413. Fax: 330-868-3731. County: Carroll. ICA: OH0201.

TV Market Ranking: 90. Franchise award date: N.A. Franchise expiration date: N.A. Began: September 1, 1969.

Channel capacity: 57 (not 2-way capable). Channels available but not in use: 11.

Basic Service

Subscribers: 1,359.

Programming (received off-air): WVPX (X) Akron; WNEO (P) Alliance; WDLI (T), WOAC (I) Canton; WEWS-TV (A), WJW (F), WKYC-TV (N) Cleveland; WUAB (U) Lorain-Cleveland; KDKA-TV (C), WPGH-TV (F) Pittsburgh; WOIO (C) Shaker Heights; WTOV-TV (N) Steubenville-Wheeling; allband FM.

Programming (via satellite): C-SPAN; Discovery Channel; QVC; TBS Superstation.

Current originations: Automated time-weather.

Fee: $37.50 installation; $10.37 monthly; $3.00 converter.

Expanded Basic Service

Subscribers: 1,277.

Programming (via satellite): A & E; American Movie Classics; Animal Planet; C-SPAN 2; CNBC; CNN; Cartoon Network; Court TV; ESPN; FX; Fox Family Channel; Fox News Channel; Fox Sports Net Pittsburgh; Home Shopping Network; Knowledge TV; Lifetime; MTV; Nashville Network; Nickelodeon; Odyssey; The New Encore; The Weather Channel; Turner Network TV; USA Network.

Fee: $11.73 monthly.

Pay Service 1

Pay Units: 88.

Programming (via satellite): Cinemax.

Fee: $13.45 monthly.

Pay Service 2

Pay Units: 84.

Programming (via satellite): Disney Channel.

Fee: $12.50 monthly.

Pay Service 3

Pay Units: 403.

Programming (via satellite): The New Encore.

Fee: $1.95 monthly.

Pay Service 4

Pay Units: 203.

Programming (via satellite): HBO.

Fee: $14.95 monthly.

Pay Service 5

Pay Units: N.A.

Programming (via satellite): Starz!

Fee: $6.75 monthly.

Pay-Per-View

Special events.

Equipment: Ameco headend; Kaiser amplifiers; Vikoa cable.

Miles of plant: 29.0 (coaxial). Homes passed: 1,702. Total homes in franchised area: 1,711.

Manager: Paul Liucart. Chief technician: Rodney Lentz.

City fee: 3% of gross.

Ownership: AT&T Broadband & Internet Services (MSO). Purchased from Tele-Communications Inc., March 9, 1999.

CELINA—FrontierVision, Box 627, Chillicothe, OH 45601. Phones: 740-775-4300; 800-346-2288. Fax: 740-775-2915. County: Mercer. Also serves Butler Twp. (Mercer County), Carthagena, Coldwater, Cranberry Prairie, Franklin Twp. (Mercer County), Granville Twp. (Mercer County), Hopewell Twp. (Mercer County), Montezuma, St. Henry. ICA: OH0092.

TV Market Ranking: Below 100 (Carthagena, Celina, Coldwater, Cranberry Prairie, Franklin Twp., Hopewell Twp., Montezuma, St. Henry); Outside TV Markets (Butler Twp., Granville Twp.). Franchise award date: N.A. Franchise expiration date: N.A. Began: September 1, 1978.

Channel capacity: 54. Channels available but not in use: 2.

Basic Service

Subscribers: 6,544.

Programming (received off-air): WBGU-TV (P) Bowling Green; WDTN (A), WHIO-TV (C), WRGT-TV (F,U) Dayton; WANE-TV (C), WFFT-TV (F), WKJG-TV (N), WPTA (A) Fort Wayne; WLIO (N), WTLW (I) Lima; allband FM.

Programming (via satellite): WGN-TV (W) Chicago; C-SPAN; CNN; Discovery Channel; Fox Family Channel; Headline News; Lifetime; MTV; Nashville Network; Nickelodeon; Odyssey; QVC; TBS Superstation; The Weather Channel.

Current originations: Automated time-weather; public access; educational access.

Fee: $60.00 installation; $9.65 monthly; $30.00 additional installation.

Expanded Basic Service

Subscribers: 5,892.

Programming (via satellite): A & E; American Movie Classics; Disney Channel; ESPN; Fox Sports Net Ohio; Turner Network TV; USA Network.

Fee: $13.79 monthly.

Pay Service 1

Pay Units: 351.

Programming (via satellite): Cinemax.

Fee: $15.00 installation; $9.95 monthly.

Pay Service 2

Pay Units: 984.

Programming (via satellite): The New Encore.

Fee: N.A.

Pay Service 3

Pay Units: 694.

Programming (via satellite): HBO.

Fee: $15.00 installation; $9.95 monthly.

Pay Service 4

Pay Units: 169.

Programming (via satellite): The Movie Channel.

Fee: $15.00 installation; $9.95 monthly.

Pay Service 5

Pay Units: 400.

Programming (via satellite): Starz!

Fee: N.A.

Pay-Per-View

Addressable homes: 617.

Equipment: Tocom headend; C-COR amplifiers; General cable; JVC cameras; Panasonic & Sony VTRs; AFC satellite antenna.

Miles of plant: 144.5 (coaxial). Homes passed: 8,488. Total homes in franchised area: 9,000.

Manager: Richard Coplan. Chief technician: Sam Morabith. Program director: Chad Hume. Marketing director: Barbara Brewer.

City fee: $1.00 annually.

Ownership: FrontierVision Partners LP (MSO). See Cable System Ownership.

CENTERBURG—Time Warner Cable, Box 787, 111 S. Mulberry St., Mount Vernon, OH 43050. Phones: 740-397-2288; 800-782-4118. Fax: 740-397-3730. County: Knox. ICA: OH0256.

TV Market Ranking: 27. Franchise award date: N.A. Franchise expiration date: N.A. Began: N.A.

Channel capacity: 30. Channels available but not in use: 13.

Basic Service

Subscribers: 301.

Programming (received off-air): WBNS-TV (C), WCMH-TV (N), WOSU-TV (P), WSYX (A), WTTE (F,U) Columbus; WSFJ (I) Newark.

Programming (via satellite): WGN-TV (W) Chicago; CNN; Fox Family Channel; TBS Superstation.

Fee: $15.95 installation; $18.50 monthly; $1.00 converter.

Expanded Basic Service

Subscribers: N.A.

Programming (via satellite): ESPN; Lifetime; MTV; Nashville Network; Nickelodeon; USA Network.

Fee: $4.95 monthly.

Pay Service 1

Pay Units: 47.

Programming (via satellite): The Movie Channel.

Fee: $10.95 monthly.

Pay Service 2
Pay Units: 78.
Programming (via satellite): Showtime.
Fee: $10.95 monthly.
Homes passed: 532.
Manager: Paul S. Schonewolf. Technical operations manager: Dan Fessler. Field operations manager: Bill Schroeder. Marketing manager: Carl Bauer. Customer operations manager: Danielle Turner.
Ownership: Time Warner Cable (MSO).

CHARDON—Cablevision of Geauga County, 107 Water St., Chardon, OH 44024. Phone: 216-691-0800. Fax: 216-291-1631. County: Geauga. Also serves Aquilla (village), Burton Twp. (Geauga County), Chardon Twp., Claridon Twp. (Geauga County), Hambden Twp. (Geauga County), Hunting Valley, Middlefield, Munson Twp. (Geauga County), Newbury (Geauga County), Newbury Twp. (Geauga County). Plans service to Burton (Geauga County). ICA: OH0090.
TV Market Ranking: 8 (Aquilla, Burton Twp., Chardon, Chardon Twp., Claridon Twp., Hambden Twp., Hunting Valley, Middlefield, Munson Twp., Newbury, Newbury Twp.); 79 (Middlefield). Franchise award date: December 1, 1982. Franchise expiration date: N.A. Began: July 1, 1983.
Channel capacity: 54. Channels available but not in use: 2.
Basic Service
Subscribers: 4,399.
Programming (received off-air): WBNX-TV (W,F), WEAO (P), WVPX (X) Akron; WEWS-TV (A), WJW (F), WKYC-TV (N), WQHS-TV (H), WVIZ-TV (P) Cleveland; WUAB (U) Lorain-Cleveland; WOIO (C) Shaker Heights.
Programming (via satellite): A & E; C-SPAN; C-SPAN 2; CNBC; CNN; Country Music TV; Discovery Channel; ESPN; EWTN; Fox Family Channel; Fox Sports Net Ohio; Headline News; Knowledge TV; Learning Channel; Lifetime; MTV; Nashville Network; Nickelodeon; QVC; TBS Superstation; The Weather Channel; Trinity Bcstg. Network; Turner Network TV; USA Network; VH1.
Current originations: Automated time-weather; public access; educational access; government access; leased access; local sports.
Fee: $25.00 installation; $5.00 monthly.
Pay Service 1
Pay Units: N.A.
Programming (via satellite): American Movie Classics; Bravo; Cinemax; Disney Channel; HBO; Showtime; The Movie Channel.
Fee: $10.00 monthly (each).
Pay-Per-View
Addressable homes: 3,100.
Local advertising: Yes. Available in satellite distributed & locally originated programming. Local sales manager: Jeff Smith. Regional interconnect: Northern Ohio Interconnect.
Program Guide: On Cablevision.
Equipment: Jerrold & Scientific-Atlanta headend; Jerrold amplifiers; Video Data Systems character generator; Jerrold set top converters; Jerrold addressable traps; Scientific-Atlanta satellite receivers.
Miles of plant: 200.0 (coaxial). Additional miles planned: 5.0 (coaxial). Homes passed: 8,310.
Manager: Richard Coplan. Chief technician: Richard Demarest. Program director: Kerry Paluscsak. Marketing director: William DeGraeve.
City fee: 3% of gross.
Ownership: Cablevision Systems Corp. (MSO).

CHILLICOTHE—FrontierVision, Box 627, Chillicothe, OH 45601. Phones: 740-775-4300; 800-346-2288. Fax: 740-775-2915. Counties: Fairfield, Pickaway, Pike & Ross. Also serves Amanda Twp. (Fairfield County), Beaver, Benton Twp. (Pike County), Clear Creek Twp. (Fairfield County), Hocking Twp. (Fairfield County), Jasper Village, Liberty Twp. (Fairfield County), Madison Twp. (Fairfield County), Mifflin Twp. (Pike County), Newton Twp. (Pike County), Pebble Twp., Pickaway Twp. (Pickaway County), Ross County (portions), Salt Creek Twp. (Pickaway County), Stoutsville, Sunfish Twp., Tarlton. Plans service to Liberty Twp. (Ross County). ICA: OH0033.
TV Market Ranking: 27. Franchise award date: N.A. Franchise expiration date: N.A. Began: September 11, 1964.
Channel capacity: 43. Channels available but not in use: None.
Basic Service
Subscribers: 13,715.
Programming (received off-air): WOUB-TV (P) Athens; WOWK-TV (C), WSAZ-TV (N) Charleston-Huntington; WCPO-TV (A), WKRC-TV (C), WLWT (N) Cincinnati; WXIX-TV (F) Cincinnati-Newport; WBNS-TV (C), WCMH-TV (N), WOSU-TV (P), WSYX (A) Columbus; WHIO-TV (C), WKEF (N) Dayton; 14 FMs.
Programming (via satellite): WGN-TV (W) Chicago; American Movie Classics; CNN; ESPN; Fox Family Channel; Nickelodeon; TBS Superstation; The Weather Channel.
Planned programming (via satellite): C-SPAN.
Current originations: Automated time-weather; local news.
Fee: $50.00 installation; $24.94 monthly.
Pay Service 1
Pay Units: 484.
Programming (via satellite): The New Encore.
Fee: N.A.
Pay Service 2
Pay Units: 1,478.
Programming (via satellite): HBO.
Fee: $9.45 monthly.
Pay Service 3
Pay Units: 2,716.
Programming (via satellite): Showtime.
Fee: $9.45 monthly.
Pay Service 4
Pay Units: 482.
Programming (via satellite): Starz!
Fee: N.A.
Pay Service 5
Pay Units: 2,103.
Programming (via satellite): The Movie Channel.
Fee: $9.45 monthly.
Pay-Per-View
Addressable homes: 1,134.
Local advertising: Yes.
Program Guide: The Cable Guide.
Equipment: Jerrold headend; AEL amplifiers; Superior cable; Scientific-Atlanta satellite antenna.
Miles of plant: 363.0 (coaxial). Homes passed: 17,743.
Manager: Richard Coplan. Chief technician: Sam Morabith. Program director: Chad Hume. Marketing director: Barbara Brewer.
City fee: $5,000 annually.
Ownership: FrontierVision Partners LP (MSO). See Cable System Ownership.

CHIPPEWA TWP.—Warner Cable Communications, 1655 Brittain Rd., Akron, OH 44310-3998. Phone: 330-633-9203. Fax: 330-633-0024. County: Wayne. ICA: OH0173.
TV Market Ranking: 8. Franchise award date: N.A. Franchise expiration date: October 1, 2004. Began: October 1, 1989.
Channel capacity: 29 (not 2-way capable). Channels available but not in use: 5.
Basic Service
Subscribers: 1,144.
Programming (received off-air): WEAO (P), WVPX (X) Akron; WOAC (I) Canton; WXIX-TV (F) Cincinnati-Newport; WEWS-TV (A), WJW (F), WKYC-TV (N), WQHS-TV (H) Cleveland; WUAB (U) Lorain-Cleveland; WPTO (P) Oxford; WTOV-TV (N) Steubenville-Wheeling.
Programming (via satellite): WGN-TV (W) Chicago; A & E; CNN; Discovery Channel; ESPN; Fox Family Channel; Headline News; Lifetime; MTV; Nashville Network; Nickelodeon; TBS Superstation; The Weather Channel; Turner Network TV; USA Network.
Fee: $35.00 installation; $20.09 monthly.
Pay Service 1
Pay Units: 101.
Programming (via satellite): Disney Channel.
Fee: $7.95 monthly.
Pay Service 2
Pay Units: 163.
Programming (via satellite): Cinemax.
Fee: $9.95 monthly.
Pay Service 3
Pay Units: 212.
Programming (via satellite): HBO.
Fee: $9.95 monthly.
Local advertising: No.
Miles of plant: 46.5 (coaxial). Homes passed: 2,002.
Manager: Stephen Fry. Chief technician: Robert Nyitray. Marketing director: Woody Woodward.
Franchise fee: 3% of gross.
Ownership: Time Warner Cable (MSO); Fanch Communications Inc. (MSO). See Cable System Ownership.

CINCINNATI—Time Warner Cable of Greater Cincinnati, 11252 Cornell Park Dr., Cincinnati, OH 45242. Phones: 513-489-5000; 513-469-1112. Fax: 513-489-5065.
E-mail: cinci.mail@twcable.com. Web site: http://www.twcincy.com. Counties: Butler South, Clermont, Hamilton & Warren South. Also serves Amberley, Anderson Twp. (Hamilton County), Arlington Heights, Blue Ash, Butler County (portions), Clermont County (portions), Colerain Twp. (Hamilton County), Columbia Twp. (Hamilton County), Crosby Twp. (Hamilton County), Deer Park, Deerfield Twp. (Warren County), Delhi, Elmwood Place, Evendale, Fairfax, Fairfield (Butler County), Forest Park, Glendale, Golf Manor, Goshen (Clermont County), Green Twp. (Hamilton County), Greenhills, Hamilton Twp. (Warren County), Harrison, Harrison Twp. (Hamilton County), Indian Hill, Lebanon, Liberty Twp. (Butler County), Lincoln Heights, Lockland, Loveland, Madeira, Maineville (Warren County), Mariemont, Mason, Miami Twp. (Clermont County), Miami Twp. (Hamilton County), Milford, Montgomery, Mount Healthy, Newtown, North College Hill, Norwood, Reading, Sharonville, Silverton, South Lebanon, Springdale, Springfield Twp. (Hamilton County), St. Bernard, Sycamore Twp. (Hamilton County), Symmes Twp. (Hamilton County), Terrace Park, Turtle Creek Twp. (Warren County), Union Twp. (Butler County), Union Twp. (Clermont County), Warren County (portions), West Harrison, Woodlawn, Wyoming. ICA: OH0001.
TV Market Ranking: 17 (Amberley, Anderson Twp., Arlington Heights, Blue Ash, Butler County, Cincinnati, Clermont County, Colerain Twp., Columbia Twp., Crosby Twp., Deer Park, Deerfield Twp., Delhi, Elmwood Place, Evendale, Fairfax, Fairfield, Forest Park, Glendale, Golf Manor, Goshen, Green Twp., Greenhills, Hamilton Twp., Harrison, Harrison Twp., Indian Hill, Lebanon, Liberty Twp., Lincoln Heights, Lockland, Loveland, Madeira, Maineville, Mariemont, Mason, Miami Twp., Milford, Montgomery, Mount Healthy, Newtown, North College Hill, Norwood, Reading, Sharonville, Silverton, South Lebanon, Springdale, Springfield Twp., St. Bernard, Sycamore Twp., Symmes Twp., Terrace Park, Turtle Creek Twp., Union Twp., Warren County, West Harrison, Woodlawn, Wyoming); 41 (Blue Ash, Butler County, Crosby Twp., Deerfield Twp., Evendale, Forest Park, Glendale, Goshen, Hamilton Twp., Lebanon, Maineville, Mason, Miami Twp., Montgomery, Sharonville, South Lebanon, Springdale, Springfield Twp., Sycamore Twp., Symmes Twp., Turtle Creek Twp., Union Twp., Warren County, West Harrison, Woodlawn). Franchise award date: July 17, 1979. Franchise expiration date: N.A. Began: August 1, 1980.
Channel capacity: 76 (2-way capable; operating 2-way). Channels available but not in use: None.
Basic Service
Subscribers: 330,000; Commercial subscribers: 924.
Programming (received off-air): WCET (P), WCPO-TV (A), WKRC-TV (C), WLWT (N), WSTR-TV (W) Cincinnati; WXIX-TV (F) Cincinnati-Newport; WCVN (P) Covington; WDTN (A), WPTD (P) Dayton; WPTO (P) Oxford; allband FM.
Programming (via satellite): WGN-TV (W) Chicago; A & E; American Movie Classics; Animal Planet; BET; C-SPAN; C-SPAN 2; CNBC; CNN; Cartoon Network; Comedy Central; Court TV; Discovery Channel; E! Entertainment TV; ESPN; ESPN 2; EWTN; Fox Family Channel; Fox News Channel; Fox Sports Net Ohio; Great American Country; Headline News; Home & Garden Television; Home Shopping Network; Learning Channel; MSNBC; MTV; Nashville Network; Nickelodeon; Pax Net; Sci-Fi Channel; TBS Superstation; TV Guide Sneak Prevue; The Weather Channel; Travel Channel; Trinity Bcstg. Network; Turner Network TV; USA Network; VH1; ValueVision.
Current originations: Automated time-weather; public access; educational access; government access; religious access; leased access; automated emergency alert; local news.
Fee: $39.90 installation; $29.00 monthly; $2.00 converter; $30.01 additional installation.
Commercial fee: $40.10 monthly.
Expanded Basic Service
Subscribers: 201,070.
Programming (via satellite): Disney Channel; Golf Channel; History Channel; TV Food Network; The New Encore; Turner Classic Movies.
Fee: $2.90 monthly.
Pay Service 1
Pay Units: 31,382.
Programming (via satellite): Cinemax (multiplexed).
Fee: $11.99 monthly.
Pay Service 2
Pay Units: 30,356.
Programming (via satellite): Showtime.
Fee: $11.99 monthly.
Pay Service 3
Pay Units: 59,150.
Programming (via satellite): HBO (multiplexed).
Fee: $12.99 monthly.
Pay Service 4
Pay Units: 20,563.
Programming (via satellite): The Movie Channel.
Fee: $11.99 monthly.
Pay Service 5
Pay Units: 12,785.
Programming (via satellite): Starz!
Fee: $11.99 monthly.

Pay Service 6
Pay Units: 30,356.
Programming (via satellite): Showtime.
Fee: $11.99 monthly.

Pay-Per-View
Addressable homes: 155,000.
Action Pay-Per-View; Viewer's Choice; movies.
Fee: Varies.

Local advertising: Yes. Available in satellite distributed & locally originated programming. Rates: $2,400.00/Minute; $1,200.00/30 Seconds. Local sales manager: Douglas L. English.
Equipment: Scientific-Atlanta headend; C-COR amplifiers; Comm/Scope & Times Fiber cable; Siecor fiber optic cable; Ikegami cameras; Ampex & Sony VTRs; Video Data Systems character generator; General Instrument & Pioneer addressable set top converters; Arcom, Eagle & PPC traps; Hughes & Scientific-Atlanta satellite antenna; General Instrument & Scientific-Atlanta satellite receivers.
Miles of plant: 3450.0 (coaxial); 650.0 (fiber optic). Homes passed: 417,010. Total homes in franchised area: 445,748.
President: Virgil M. Reed. V.P., technical operations: Bill Spies. V.P., marketing: Dennis Holzmeier. Marketing director: Tom Dunley. Customer service director: Sue Coleman.
City fee: 3%-5% of gross.
Ownership: Time Warner Cable (MSO).

CIRCLEVILLE—Time Warner Cable, 1315 Granville Pike, Lancaster, OH 43130-0747. Phone: 740-653-9685. Fax: 740-653-0019. Counties: Fairfield & Pickaway. Also serves Ashville, Circleville Twp., Harrison Twp. (Pickaway County), Millersport, Pickaway Twp. (Pickaway County), South Bloomfield, Stoutsville, Walnut Twp. (Fairfield County), Walnut Twp. (Pickaway County), Washington Twp. (Pickaway County). ICA: OH0087.
TV Market Ranking: 27. Franchise award date: N.A. Franchise expiration date: N.A. Began: June 6, 1975.
Channel capacity: 30 (not 2-way capable). Channels available but not in use: None.

Basic Service
Subscribers: 3,710.
Programming (received off-air): WOUB-TV (P) Athens; WBNS-TV (C), WCMH-TV (N), WOSU-TV (P), WSYX (A), WTTE (F,U) Columbus.
Programming (via satellite): WGN-TV (W) Chicago; A & E; C-SPAN; CNBC; CNN; Discovery Channel; ESPN; Lifetime; MTV; Nashville Network; Nickelodeon; TBS Superstation; The Inspirational Network; The Weather Channel; Turner Network TV; USA Network.
Current originations: Automated time-weather; public access; automated emergency alert.
Fee: $35.00 installation; $18.30 monthly; $25.00 additional installation.

Pay Service 1
Pay Units: Included with Lancaster, OH.
Programming (via satellite): Disney Channel; HBO; Showtime; The Movie Channel.
Fee: $15.00 installation; $9.95 monthly (Disney, Showtime or TMC), $10.95 monthly (HBO).

Local advertising: Yes. Available in satellite distributed & character-generated programming. Rates: $20.00/Minute; $12.00/30 Seconds. Local sales manager: Greg Langemeir.
Equipment: Scientific-Atlanta headend; Scientific-Atlanta amplifiers; Comm/Scope cable; Texscan character generator; Panasonic set top converters; Intercept & Pico traps; AFC satellite antenna; Scientific-Atlanta satellite receivers; Texscan commercial insert.
Miles of plant & homes passed included with Lancaster, OH.
Manager: David Johnston. Chief technician: Mike Bash. Marketing director: Cathy Schelb.
City fee: 3% of gross.
Ownership: Time Warner Cable (MSO). Purchased from MediaOne Group, August 2, 1999.

CIRCLEVILLE (portions)—FrontierVision, 220 N. Main St., Ada, OH 45810. Phone: 419-628-3423. Fax: 419-775-2915. County: Pickaway. ICA: OH0320.
TV Market Ranking: 27. Franchise award date: September 1, 1989. Franchise expiration date: N.A. Began: September 1, 1989.
Channel capacity: 35 (not 2-way capable). Channels available but not in use: N.A.

Basic Service
Subscribers: 7,436.
Programming (received off-air): WOUB-TV (P) Athens; WWHO (U) Chillicothe; WBNS-TV (C), WCMH-TV (N), WOSU-TV (P), WSYX (A), WTTE (F,U) Columbus; WHIO-TV (C) Dayton.
Programming (via satellite): WGN-TV (W) Chicago; BET; C-SPAN; CNBC; Fox Family Channel; Knowledge TV; QVC; TBS Superstation; The Inspirational Network.
Current originations: Public access; educational access; government access; religious access; leased access; library access; local news; local sports.
Fee: $50.00 installation; $9.30 monthly.

Expanded Basic Service
Subscribers: N.A.
Programming (via satellite): A & E; American Movie Classics; CNN; Comedy Central; Country Music TV; Discovery Channel; Disney Channel; ESPN; Headline News; Lifetime; MTV; Nashville Network; Nickelodeon; The Weather Channel; Turner Network TV; USA Network; VH1.
Fee: N.A.

Pay Service 1
Pay Units: N.A.
Programming (via satellite): HBO; Showtime; The Movie Channel.
Fee: $9.95 monthly (HBO, Showtime or TMC).

Pay-Per-View
Viewer's Choice.
Fee: $3.95.

Local advertising: Yes.
Homes passed: 19,498.
Manager: Weldon Feightner. Chief technician: Tim Kinnard. Program director: Keith Alcorn. Marketing director: Anna Hernandez. Customer service manager: Lenora Kelly.
Ownership: FrontierVision Partners LP (MSO). See Cable System Ownership.

CLARINGTON—FrontierVision, Suite P-200, 1777 S. Harrison St., Denver, CO 80210. Phone: 303-757-1588. Fax: 303-757-6105. County: Monroe. ICA: OH0292.
TV Market Ranking: 90. Franchise award date: N.A. Franchise expiration date: N.A. Began: October 1, 1958.
Channel capacity: 80 (not 2-way capable). Channels available but not in use: 40.

Basic Service
Subscribers: 157.
Programming (received off-air): WOUC-TV (P) Cambridge; WNPB-TV (P) Morgantown; KDKA-TV (C), WPGH-TV (F), WPXI (N) Pittsburgh; WTOV-TV (N) Steubenville-Wheeling; WTRF-TV (C) Wheeling-Steubenville; allband FM.
Programming (via satellite): WABC-TV (A) New York; Country Music TV; Fox Family Channel.
Current originations: Public access.
Fee: $47.50 installation; $12.61 monthly; $0.73 converter.

Expanded Basic Service
Subscribers: 130.
Programming (via satellite): CNN; Discovery Channel; Disney Channel; ESPN; Nashville Network; TBS Superstation; USA Network.
Fee: $7.16 monthly.

Pay Service 1
Pay Units: 5.
Programming (via satellite): Cinemax.
Fee: N.A.

Pay Service 2
Pay Units: 8.
Programming (via satellite): The New Encore.
Fee: N.A.

Pay Service 3
Pay Units: 11.
Programming (via satellite): HBO.
Fee: $11.99 monthly.

Pay Service 4
Pay Units: 10.
Programming (via satellite): Showtime.
Fee: N.A.

Pay Service 5
Pay Units: 7.
Programming (via satellite): Starz!
Fee: N.A.

Pay Service 6
Pay Units: 8.
Programming (via satellite): The Movie Channel.
Fee: N.A.

Local advertising: Planned.
Miles of plant: 4.0 (coaxial). Homes passed: 226.
Manager: Steve Trippe. Chief technician: Bill Ricker.
City fee: $150.00 per year.
Ownership: FrontierVision Partners LP (MSO). See Cable System Ownership.

CLEVELAND—Cablevision of Ohio, 3400 Lakeside Ave., Cleveland, OH 44114. Phones: 216-575-8016; 216-771-1072. Fax: 216-575-0212. County: Cuyahoga. Also serves Bratenahl, Linndale. ICA: OH0003.
TV Market Ranking: 8. Franchise award date: August 1, 1986. Franchise expiration date: August 1, 2002. Began: December 23, 1987.
Channel capacity: 79 (2-way capable; operating 2-way). Channels available but not in use: 19.

Basic Service
Subscribers: 81,142; Commercial subscribers: 103.
Programming (received off-air): WBNX-TV (W,F), WEAO (P), WVPX (X) Akron; WEWS-TV (A), WJW (F), WKYC-TV (N), WQHS-TV (H), WVIZ-TV (P) Cleveland; WUAB (U) Lorain-Cleveland; WOIO (C) Shaker Heights; allband FM.
Programming (via satellite): WGN-TV (W) Chicago; Kaleidoscope; QVC; SCOLA; TBS Superstation; TV Guide Channel.
Current originations: Automated time-weather; public access; educational access; government access; religious access; leased access; automated emergency alert; local news.
Fee: $25.95 installation; $12.43 monthly.

Expanded Basic Service
Subscribers: N.A.
Programming (via satellite): A & E; American Movie Classics; BET; Bravo; C-SPAN; C-SPAN 2; CNBC; CNN; Cartoon Network; Comedy Central; Country Music TV; Court TV; Discovery Channel; E! Entertainment TV; ESPN; Fox Family Channel; Fox News Channel; Headline News; History Channel; Home & Garden Television; Home Shopping Network; Learning Channel; Lifetime; MSNBC; MTV; MuchMusic Network; Nashville Network; Nickelodeon; Sci-Fi Channel; Telemundo; The Health Network; The Weather Channel; Turner Network TV; USA Network; Univision; VH1.
Fee: $27.51 monthly.

A la Carte 1
Subscribers: N.A.
Programming (via satellite): ESPN 2; Flix; Fox Sports Net Ohio; Independent Film Channel; TV Food Network.
Fee: $1.95 monthly (each).

Pay Service 1
Pay Units: 17,201.
Programming (via satellite): Cinemax.
Fee: $10.95 installation; $10.95 monthly.

Pay Service 2
Pay Units: 10,482.
Programming (via satellite): Disney Channel.
Fee: $10.95 installation; $10.95 monthly.

Pay Service 3
Pay Units: 42,860.
Programming (via satellite): HBO.
Fee: $10.95 installation; $10.95 monthly.

Pay Service 4
Pay Units: 2,535.
Programming (via satellite): Playboy TV.
Fee: $10.95 installation; $10.95 monthly.

Pay Service 5
Pay Units: 31,167.
Programming (via satellite): Showtime (multiplexed).
Fee: $10.95 installation; $10.95 monthly.

Pay Service 6
Pay Units: 7,802.
Programming (via satellite): The Movie Channel.
Fee: $20.95 installation; $10.95 monthly.

Pay Service 7
Pay Units: N.A.
Programming (via satellite): Starz!; The New Encore.
Fee: $10.95 monthly (each).

Pay-Per-View
Addressable homes: 78,935.
Viewer's Choice.
Fee: $4.95.

Local advertising: Yes. Available in locally originated, character-generated, taped & automated programming. Rates: $35.00-$84.00/Minute; $17.50-$46.00/30 Seconds. Local sales manager: Vivian Goodman. Regional interconnect: Rainbow Advertising.
Program Guide: Choice.
Equipment: Catel headend; Magnavox amplifiers; Trilogy cable; Texscan character generator; Zenith set top converters; Zenith addressable set top converters; Simulsat satellite antenna; Standard Components satellite receivers; Texscan commercial insert.
Miles of plant: 1035.0 (coaxial); 22.0 (fiber optic). Homes passed: 221,276. Total homes in franchised area: 239,433.
Manager: Kathleen R. Mayo. Engineering director: Bruce Smylie. Program director: John Stealey. Sales & marketing director: Frank Naples.
City fee: 5% of gross.
Ownership: Cablevision Systems Corp. (MSO).

CLEVELAND HEIGHTS—Cablevision Systems Corp., 3400 Lakeside Ave., Cleveland, OH 44114. Phone: 216-575-8016. Fax: 216-575-0212. Counties: Cuyahoga, Geauga & Lake. Also serves Beachwood, Bedford, Bentleyville, Chagrin Falls, Euclid, Gates Mills, Highland Heights, Highland Hills, Hunting Valley, Lyndhurst, Maple Heights, Mayfield Heights, Mayfield Vil-

lage, Moreland Hills, North Randall, Orange, Pepper Pike, Richmond Heights, Shaker Heights, South Euclid, University Heights, Warrensville Heights, Willowick, Woodmere. ICA: OH0006.
TV Market Ranking: 8. Franchise award date: May 25, 1965. Franchise expiration date: N.A. Began: January 1, 1966.
Channel capacity: 77 (2-way capable; operating 2-way). Channels available but not in use: None.
Basic Service
Subscribers: 83,979; Commercial subscribers: 390.
Programming (received off-air): WBNX-TV (W,F), WEAO (P) Akron; WEWS-TV (A), WJW (F), WKYC-TV (N), WQHS-TV (H), WVIZ-TV (P) Cleveland; WUAB (U) Lorain-Cleveland; WOIO (C) Shaker Heights.
Current originations: Public access; educational access; government access; religious access; leased access; automated emergency alert; local sports.
Fee: $8.12 monthly.
Expanded Basic Service
Subscribers: N.A.
Programming (via satellite): A & E; American Movie Classics; BET; Bravo; C-SPAN; C-SPAN 2; CNBC; CNN; Discovery Channel; ESPN; Fox Family Channel; Fox Sports Net Ohio; Headline News; Home Shopping Network; Learning Channel; Lifetime; MTV; Nick at Nite; Nickelodeon; QVC; TBS Superstation; TV Guide Channel; The Inspirational Network; The Weather Channel; Turner Network TV; USA Network; VH1.
Fee: $47.05 installation; $26.68 monthly.
Pay Service 1
Pay Units: 83,394.
Programming (via satellite): Cinemax; Disney Channel; Flix; HBO; Playboy TV; Showtime; The Movie Channel.
Fee: $10.45 monthly (each).
Pay-Per-View
Addressable homes: 37,088.
Local advertising: Yes. Available in satellite distributed, locally originated, character-generated, taped & automated programming. Local sales manager: Mark Dolan. Regional interconnect: Northern Ohio Interconnect.
Program Guide: Preview Guide.
Equipment: Scientific-Atlanta headend; GTE Sylvania amplifiers; Texscan & Amiga character generator; Hamlin, Oak & Jerrold set top converters; Zenith addressable set top converters; Simulsat satellite antenna; Scientific-Atlanta satellite receivers; Texscan commercial insert.
Miles of plant: 1150.0 (coaxial); 27.0 (fiber optic). Homes passed: 137,353.
Manager: Kathleen R. Mayo. Chief technician: Bruce Smylie. Program director: John Stealey. Sales & marketing director: Frank Naples.
City fee: 3%-5% of gross.
Ownership: Cablevision Systems Corp. (MSO).

CLINTON TWP.—Americast, 300 S. Riverside, Chicago, IL 60606. Phones: 312-526-8000; 800-848-2278. Fax: 312-526-8565. County: Franklin. ICA: OH0412.
TV Market Ranking: 27. Franchise award date: October 1, 1996. Franchise expiration date: N.A. Began: N.A.
Channel capacity: N.A. Channels available but not in use: N.A.
Basic Service
Subscribers: N.A.
Programming (received off-air): WWHO (U) Chillicothe; WBNS-TV (C), WCMH-TV (N), WOSU-TV (P), WSYX (A), WTTE (F,U) Columbus; WSFJ (I) Newark.
Programming (via satellite): WGN-TV (W) Chicago; QVC; TBS Superstation; TV Guide Channel.
Current originations: Public access; educational access; government access; leased access.
Fee: $39.95 installation; $9.95 monthly.
Expanded Basic Service
Subscribers: N.A.
Programming (via satellite): A & E; American Movie Classics; BET; BET on Jazz; Bravo; C-SPAN; C-SPAN 2; CNBC; CNN; CNNfn; Cartoon Network; Comedy Central; Country Music TV; Court TV; Discovery Channel; Disney Channel; E! Entertainment TV; ESPN; ESPN 2; ESPN Classic Sports; Fox Family Channel; Fox Sports Net Ohio; Golf Channel; Headline News; History Channel; Home & Garden Television; Learning Channel; Lifetime; MTV; Nashville Network; Nickelodeon; Ohio News Network; Sci-Fi Channel; TV Food Network; The Health Network; The Inspirational Network; The Weather Channel; Travel Channel; Turner Classic Movies; Turner Network TV; USA Network; VH1.
Fee: $17.00 monthly.
Pay Service 1
Pay Units: N.A.
Programming (via satellite): Cinemax; Flix; HBO (multiplexed); Showtime (multiplexed); Starz!; Sundance Channel; The Movie Channel; The New Encore.
Fee: $5.95 monthly (Flix or Sundance), $7.95 monthly (Encore & Starz), $9.95 monthly (Cinemax, Showtime or TMC), $11.95 monthly (HBO).
Total homes in franchised area: 2,250.
Ownership: Ameritech New Media Inc. (MSO).

COITSVILLE TWP.—Star Cable, Box 4478, 4720 Mahoning Ave., Youngstown, OH 44515. Phone: 330-792-9577. Fax: 330-792-9541. Counties: Mahoning & Trumbull. Also serves Hubbard Twp. (Trumbull County). ICA: OH0233.
TV Market Ranking: 79. Franchise award date: N.A. Franchise expiration date: N.A. Began: N.A.
Channel capacity: 62 (not 2-way capable). Channels available but not in use: 23.
Basic Service
Subscribers: 575; Commercial subscribers: 38.
Programming (received off-air): WNEO (P) Alliance; WUAB (U) Lorain-Cleveland; WPGH-TV (F) Pittsburgh; WOIO (C) Shaker Heights; WFMJ-TV (N), WKBN-TV (C), WYTV (A,F) Youngstown.
Programming (via satellite): QVC; TBS Superstation.
Current originations: Educational access.
Fee: $10.50 monthly; $1.95 converter.
Expanded Basic Service
Subscribers: 555.
Programming (via satellite): A & E; American Movie Classics; C-SPAN; CNBC; CNN; Discovery Channel; ESPN; Fox Family Channel; Fox Sports Net Ohio; Fox Sports Net Pittsburgh; Headline News; History Channel; Learning Channel; Lifetime; MTV; Nashville Network; Nick at Nite's TV Land; Nickelodeon; Sci-Fi Channel; The Weather Channel; Turner Network TV; USA Network; VH1.
Fee: $20.00 monthly.
Pay Service 1
Pay Units: 48.
Programming (via satellite): Cinemax.
Fee: $11.00 monthly.
Pay Service 2
Pay Units: 51.
Programming (via satellite): Disney Channel.
Fee: $7.95 monthly.

Pay Service 3
Pay Units: 83.
Programming (via satellite): HBO.
Fee: $11.00 monthly.
Pay Service 4
Pay Units: 51.
Programming (via satellite): Showtime; The Movie Channel.
Fee: $12.95 monthly (Showtime or TMC).
Miles of plant: 31.6 (coaxial); None (fiber optic). Homes passed: 853. Total homes in franchised area: 853.
Manager: Terry Dickerhoof. Chief technician: Tom Beat.
Ownership: Star Cable Associates (MSO).

COLLINSVILLE—Coaxial Communications, 3416 State Rte. 132, Amelia, OH 45102. Phone: 513-797-4400. Fax: 513-797-8625. County: Butler North. Also serves Darrtown, Jacksonburg (village), Milford Twp. (Butler County), Oxford Twp. (Butler County), Reily Twp., Wayne Twp. (Butler County). ICA: OH0172.
TV Market Ranking: 17,41. Franchise award date: N.A. Franchise expiration date: N.A. Began: November 1, 1989.
Channel capacity: 36. Channels available but not in use: 2.
Basic Service
Subscribers: 1,474.
Programming (received off-air): WCPO-TV (A), WKRC-TV (C), WLWT (N) Cincinnati; WXIX-TV (F) Cincinnati-Newport; WDTN (A), WHIO-TV (C), WPTD (P) Dayton; WPTO (P) Oxford; WKOI (T) Richmond.
Programming (via satellite): WGN-TV (W) Chicago; A & E; CNN; Discovery Channel; ESPN; Fox Family Channel; Headline News; Learning Channel; Lifetime; MTV; Nashville Network; Nickelodeon; TBS Superstation; The Weather Channel; Turner Network TV; USA Network; VH1.
Fee: $31.95 installation; $8.44 monthly; $0.49 converter.
Pay Service 1
Pay Units: 138.
Programming (via satellite): Disney Channel.
Fee: $11.95 monthly.
Pay Service 2
Pay Units: 469.
Programming (via satellite): HBO.
Fee: $11.95 monthly.
Pay Service 3
Pay Units: 173.
Programming (via satellite): Showtime.
Fee: $11.95 monthly.
Local advertising: Yes. Available in satellite distributed programming.
Equipment: Scientific-Atlanta headend; Magnavox amplifiers; Comm/Scope cable; Video Data Systems character generator; Hamlin & Jerrold set top converters; ChannelMatic commercial insert.
Miles of plant: 140.0 (coaxial). Homes passed: 2,248.
Manager: Arthur P. Loescher.
City fee: 3%-5% of basic.
Ownership: Coaxial Communications (MSO).

COLUMBUS—Insight Communications, 3770 E. Livingston Ave., Columbus, OH 43227. Phone: 614-236-1292. Fax: 614-238-7023. Web site: http://www.insightcom.com. Counties: Delaware, Fairfield, Franklin, Licking & Pickaway. Also serves Berlin Twp. (Delaware County), Bloom Twp. (Fairfield County), Brice, Brown Twp. (Delaware County), Canal Winchester, Clinton Twp. (Franklin County), Delaware Twp. (Delaware County), Etna Twp., Gahanna (Franklin County), Genoa Twp. (Delaware County), Hamilton Twp. (Franklin County), Harlem Twp. (Delaware County), Harrison Twp. (Pickaway County), Jefferson Twp. (Franklin County), Jersey Twp., Liberty Twp. (Fairfield County), Lima Twp. (Licking County), Lithopolis, Lockbourne Village, Madison Twp. (Franklin County), Madison Twp. (Pickaway County), Mifflin Twp. (Franklin County), Monroe Twp. (Licking County), New Albany, Orange Twp. (Delaware County), Pickerington, Plain Twp. (Franklin County), Reynoldsburg, St. Albans Twp. (Licking County), Violet Twp., Westerville (Delaware & Franklin Counties), Whitehall. ICA: OH0007.
TV Market Ranking: 27. Franchise award date: May 1, 1973. Franchise expiration date: N.A. Began: May 1, 1973.
Channel capacity: 60 (2-way capable). Channels available but not in use: 1.
Basic Service
Subscribers: 86,041.
Programming (received off-air): WWHO (U) Chillicothe; WBNS-TV (C), WCMH-TV (N), WOSU-TV (P), WSYX (A), WTTE (F,U) Columbus; WSFJ (I) Newark; 28 FMs.
Programming (via microwave): WUAB (U) Lorain-Cleveland.
Programming (via satellite): WGN-TV (W) Chicago; A & E; American Movie Classics; BET; CNBC; CNN; Comedy Central; Country Music TV; Discovery Channel; ESPN; Electronic Program Guide; Fox Family Channel; Fox Sports Net Ohio; Fox Sports Net Pittsburgh; Headline News; Home Shopping Network; Learning Channel; Lifetime; MTV; Nashville Network; Nickelodeon; QVC; Sci-Fi Channel; TBS Superstation; The Box; The Weather Channel; Turner Classic Movies; Turner Network TV; USA Network; VH1.
Current originations: Public access; educational access; government access; leased access; local sports.
Fee: $20.30 installation; $10.64 monthly.
Pay Service 1
Pay Units: 11,930.
Programming (via satellite): Cinemax.
Fee: $10.00 installation; $11.95 monthly.
Pay Service 2
Pay Units: 6,867.
Programming (via satellite): Disney Channel.
Fee: $10.00 installation; $11.95 monthly.
Pay Service 3
Pay Units: 36,750.
Programming (via satellite): HBO.
Fee: $10.00 installation; $11.95 monthly.
Pay Service 4
Pay Units: 2,153.
Programming (via satellite): The Movie Channel.
Fee: $10.00 installation; $12.95 monthly.
Pay Service 5
Pay Units: 10,349.
Programming (via satellite): Showtime.
Fee: $10.00 installation; $11.95 monthly.

Pay-Per-View
Addressable homes: 82,008.
Action Pay-Per-View; Spice.
Fee: Varies.
Local advertising: Yes. Available in satellite distributed & automated programming. Rates: $2.00-$35.00/30 Seconds. Local sales manager: David Gettys.
Equipment: Catel, Microwave Assoc. & Microdyne headend; Magnavox amplifiers; Times Fiber, Capscan & Comm/Scope cable; Ikegami cameras; Panasonic & Sony VTRs; Jerrold set top converters; Regency & Jerrold addressable set top converters; Eagle traps; Comtech & Scientific-Atlanta satellite antenna; Microdyne & Scientific-Atlanta satellite receivers; Adams-Russell commercial insert.
Miles of plant: 2332.5 (coaxial); 115.4 (fiber optic). Additional miles planned: 60.0 (coaxial). Homes passed: 156,613.
Manager: Gregg Graff. Chief technician: Steve Crane.
City fee: 3% of gross service fees.
Ownership: Insight Communications Co. (MSO); Coaxial Communications (MSO). Insight Communications Co. purchased 75% from Coaxial Communications August 21, 1998.

COLUMBUS—Time Warner Communications, 1266 Dublin Rd., Columbus, OH 43215. Phone: 614-481-5000. Fax: 614-481-5044. Counties: Delaware, Franklin & Pickaway, OH; Delaware, NJ. Also serves Delaware, Delaware County (portions), NJ; Bexley, Clinton Twp. (Franklin County), Concord Twp. (Delaware County), Dublin, Gahanna (Franklin County), Grandview Heights, Grove City (Franklin County), Groveport, Hamilton Twp. (Franklin County), Hilliard, Jackson Twp. (Franklin County), Liberty Twp. (Delaware County), Marble Cliff, Mifflin Twp. (Franklin County), Minerva Park, Norwich Twp. (Franklin County), Obetz, Perry Twp. (Franklin County), Pickaway County, Pleasant Twp. (Franklin County), Powell (village), Prairie Twp. (Franklin County), Reese Station, Riverlea, Shawnee Hills, Upper Arlington, Urbancrest, Valleyview, Westerville (Franklin County), Worthington, OH. ICA: OH0002.
TV Market Ranking: 27. Franchise award date: N.A. Franchise expiration date: July 9, 2005. Began: December 1, 1971.
Channel capacity: 77 (2-way capable; operating 2-way). Channels available but not in use: 15.
Basic Service
Subscribers: 189,000.
Programming (received off-air): WWHO (U) Chillicothe; WBNS-TV (C), WCMH-TV (N), WOSU-TV (P), WSYX (A), WTTE (F,U) Columbus; WUAB (U) Lorain-Cleveland; WSFJ (I) Newark.
Programming (via satellite): WGN-TV (W) Chicago; C-SPAN; C-SPAN 2; Headline News; History Channel; International Channel; Learning Channel; Odyssey; QVC; TBS Superstation; TV Guide Channel; ValueVision.
Current originations: Automated time-weather; public access; educational access; government access; leased access.
Fee: $39.90 installation; $9.95 monthly.
Commercial fee: $30.00 monthly.
Expanded Basic Service
Subscribers: 175,000.
Programming (via satellite): A & E; American Movie Classics; Animal Planet; BET; Bravo; CNBC; CNN; Cartoon Network; Comedy Central; Country Music TV; Court TV; Discovery Channel; Disney Channel; E! Entertainment TV; ESPN; ESPN 2; Fox Family Channel; Fox Sports Net Ohio; Golf Channel; Home & Garden Television; Lifetime; MTV; Nashville Network; Nick at Nite's TV Land; Nickelodeon; Sci-Fi Channel; TV Food Network; TV Guide Sneak Prevue; The Weather Channel; Travel Channel; Turner Classic Movies; Turner Network TV; USA Network; VH1.
Fee: $26.95 monthly.
Pay Service 1
Pay Units: 23,601.
Programming (via satellite): Cinemax (multiplexed).
Fee: $10.00 monthly.
Pay Service 2
Pay Units: 64,107.
Programming (via satellite): HBO (multiplexed).
Fee: $10.00 monthly.
Pay Service 3
Pay Units: 22,305.
Programming (via satellite): Showtime (multiplexed).
Fee: $10.00 monthly.
Pay Service 4
Pay Units: 8,695.
Programming (via satellite): The Movie Channel.
Fee: $10.00 monthly.
Pay Service 5
Pay Units: N.A.
Programming (via satellite): Starz!; The New Encore.
Fee: $6.95 monthly.
Pay-Per-View
Addressable homes: 189,000.
Action Pay-Per-View; Playboy TV; Spice.
Fee: $4.50.
Local advertising: Yes. Available in character-generated & taped programming. Local sales manager: Laure Nordholt.
Equipment: Scientific-Atlanta headend; C-COR amplifiers; Ikegami cameras; Sony VTRs; Laird character generator; General Instrument set top converters; Scientific-Atlanta satellite antenna; Scientific-Atlanta satellite receivers; ChannelMatic & AFC commercial insert.
Miles of plant: 3000.0 (coaxial); 800.0 (fiber optic). Additional miles planned: 100.0 (fiber optic). Homes passed: 352,000.
Manager: Terry O'Connell. Chief technician: Randy Hall. Program director: Tom Dunlea. Marketing director: Cheryl Roller.
City fee: 3% of gross.
Ownership: Time Warner Cable (MSO).

COLUMBUS—Time Warner Entertainment Co. LP, 3100 Elida Rd., Lima, OH 45805. Phone: 419-331-3333. Fax: 419-333-1573. Counties: Franklin, Madison & Pickaway. Also serves Darby Twp. (Pickaway County), Darbydale, Derby, Era, Grove City (Franklin County), Harrisburg, Mount Sterling (Madison County), Orient, Pleasant Twp. (Franklin County), Sharon Twp. (Franklin County). ICA: OH0136.
TV Market Ranking: 27. Franchise award date: N.A. Franchise expiration date: N.A. Began: December 1, 1983.
Channel capacity: 30. Channels available but not in use: None.
Basic Service
Subscribers: 1,564.
Programming (received off-air): WWHO (U) Chillicothe; WBNS-TV (C), WCMH-TV (N), WOSU-TV (P), WSYX (A), WTTE (F,U) Columbus; WSFJ (I) Newark.
Programming (via satellite): WGN-TV (W) Chicago; A & E; CNN; Comedy Central; Country Music TV; Discovery Channel; ESPN; Fox Family Channel; Headline News; Home Shopping Network; Lifetime; MTV; Nashville Network; Nickelodeon; TBS Superstation; Turner Network TV; USA Network; VH1.
Current originations: Local news.
Fee: $32.00 installation; $19.76 monthly; $1.10 converter.
Pay Service 1
Pay Units: 245.
Programming (via satellite): Cinemax.
Fee: $18.00 installation; $10.95 monthly.
Pay Service 2
Pay Units: 95.
Programming (via satellite): Disney Channel.
Fee: $18.00 installation; $10.95 monthly.
Pay Service 3
Pay Units: 462.
Programming (via satellite): HBO.
Fee: $18.00 installation; $10.95 monthly.
Pay Service 4
Pay Units: 124.
Programming (via satellite): Showtime.
Fee: $18.00 installation; $10.95 monthly.
Local advertising: Yes. Available in character-generated programming.
Miles of plant: 56.8 (coaxial). Homes passed: 3,489.
Manager: James D. Foust. Chief technician: Rick Steward. Marketing director: Keith Tyrell.
Franchise fee: 3% of gross.
Ownership: Fanch Communications Inc. (MSO). See Cable System Ownership.

COLUMBUS—Americast, 300 S. Riverside, Chicago, IL 60606. Phones: 312-526-8000; 800-848-2278. Fax: 312-526-8565. County: Franklin. ICA: OH0426.
TV Market Ranking: 27. Franchise award date: April 1, 1996. Franchise expiration date: N.A. Began: N.A.
Channel capacity: N.A. Channels available but not in use: N.A.
Basic Service
Subscribers: N.A.
Programming (received off-air): WWHO (U) Chillicothe; WBNS-TV (C), WCMH-TV (N), WOSU-TV (P), WSYX (A), WTTE (F,U) Columbus; WSFJ (I) Newark.
Programming (via satellite): WGN-TV (W) Chicago; QVC; TBS Superstation; TV Guide Channel.
Current originations: Public access; educational access; government access; leased access.
Fee: $39.95 installation; $9.95 monthly.
Expanded Basic Service
Subscribers: N.A.
Programming (via satellite): A & E; American Movie Classics; BET; BET on Jazz; Bravo; C-SPAN; C-SPAN 2; CNBC; CNN; CNNfn; Cartoon Network; Comedy Central; Country Music TV; Court TV; Discovery Channel; Disney Channel; E! Entertainment TV; ESPN; ESPN 2; ESPN Classic Sports; Fox Family Channel; Fox Sports Net Ohio; Golf Channel; Headline News; History Channel; Home & Garden Television; Learning Channel; Lifetime; MTV; Nashville Network; Nickelodeon; Ohio News Network; Sci-Fi Channel; TV Food Network; The Health Network; The Inspirational Network; The Weather Channel; Travel Channel; Turner Classic Movies; Turner Network TV; USA Network; VH1.
Fee: $17.00 monthly.
Pay Service 1
Pay Units: N.A.
Programming (via satellite): Cinemax; Flix; HBO (multiplexed); Showtime (multiplexed); Starz!; Sundance Channel; The Movie Channel; The New Encore.
Fee: $5.95 monthly (Flix or Sundance), $7.95 monthly (Encore & Starz), $9.95 monthly (Cinemax, Showtime or TMC), $11.95 monthly (HBO).
Total homes in franchised area: 316,050.
Ownership: Ameritech New Media Inc. (MSO).

COLUMBUS GROVE (village)—Quality One Technologies Inc., 112 W. Sycamore St., Columbus Grove, OH 45830. Phone: 419-659-2111. Fax: 419-659-5001. County: Putnam. ICA: OH0402.
TV Market Ranking: Below 100. Franchise award date: September 9, 1996. Franchise expiration date: N.A. Began: May 1, 1997.
Channel capacity: N.A. Channels available but not in use: N.A.
Basic Service
Subscribers: N.A.
Programming (received off-air): WANE-TV (C) Fort Wayne; WLIO (N), WTLW (I) Lima; WNWO-TV (N), WTOL-TV (C), WTVG (A) Toledo.
Fee: $7.95 monthly.
Expanded Basic Service
Subscribers: N.A.
Programming (via satellite): Discovery Channel; Disney Channel; TBS Superstation.
Fee: $3.00 monthly.
Expanded Basic Service 2
Subscribers: N.A.
Programming (via satellite): American Movie Classics; CNBC; Cartoon Network; Country Music TV; ESPN; EWTN; Flix; Fox Family Channel; Fox Sports Net Ohio; Home & Garden Television; QVC; Sci-Fi Channel; TV Guide Channel; USA Network.
Fee: $7.95 monthly.
Expanded Basic Service 3
Subscribers: N.A.
Programming (via satellite): WGN-TV (W) Chicago; A & E; CNN; ESPN 2; Headline News; History Channel; Lifetime; MTV; Nashville Network; Nickelodeon; Speedvision; The New Encore; Turner Classic Movies; Turner Network TV; VH1.
Fee: $10.95 monthly.
Pay Service 1
Pay Units: N.A.
Programming (via satellite): Cinemax; HBO; Showtime; Starz!; The Movie Channel.
Fee: $5.95 monthly (Starz), $7.95 monthly (Cinemax, Showtime or TMC), $11.95 monthly (HBO).
Pay-Per-View
Playboy TV; Viewer's Choice.
Manager: Phil Maag. Chief technician: Scott Roach.
Ownership: Columbus Grove Telephone Co.

COMMERCIAL POINT—FrontierVision, Box 648, 102 Twin Oak Dr., Jackson, OH 45640. Phone: 614-345-4329. Fax: 614-286-1489. County: Pickaway. Also serves Darbyville, Jackson Twp. (Pickaway County), Muhlenberg Twp., Scioto Twp. (Pickaway County). ICA: OH0213.
TV Market Ranking: 27. Franchise award date: July 14, 1988. Franchise expiration date: July 14, 2003. Began: October 1, 1989.
Channel capacity: 62. Channels available but not in use: 22.
Basic Service
Subscribers: 727.
Programming (received off-air): WBNS-TV (C), WCMH-TV (N), WOSU-TV (P), WSYX (A), WTTE (F,U) Columbus.
Programming (via satellite): WGN-TV (W) Chicago; A & E; American Movie Classics; CNN; Cartoon Network; Comedy Central; Country Music TV; Discovery Channel; Disney Channel; ESPN; Fox Family Channel; Headline News; Lifetime; MTV; Nashville Network; Nickelodeon; QVC; TBS Superstation; The Weather Channel; Travel Channel; Turner Network TV; USA Network.
Fee: $21.62 installation; $23.70 monthly.
Pay Service 1
Pay Units: 46.
Programming (via satellite): Cinemax.
Fee: N.A.

Pay Service 2
Pay Units: 81.
Programming (via satellite): The New Encore.
Fee: N.A.
Pay Service 3
Pay Units: 119.
Programming (via satellite): HBO.
Fee: $11.95 monthly.
Pay Service 4
Pay Units: 132.
Programming (via satellite): Showtime.
Fee: $10.95 monthly.
Pay Service 5
Pay Units: 78.
Programming (via satellite): Starz!
Fee: N.A.
Pay Service 6
Pay Units: 111.
Programming (via satellite): The Movie Channel.
Fee: N.A.
Equipment: Scientific-Atlanta headend; Texscan amplifiers; Times Fiber cable; Panasonic set top converters; Eagle, Pico & Arcom traps; Prodelin satellite antenna; Scientific-Atlanta satellite receivers.
Miles of plant: 101.0 (coaxial). Homes passed: 1,204.
Manager: Steve Trippe. Chief technician: Bill Ricker.
Ownership: FrontierVision Partners LP (MSO). See Cable System Ownership.

CONCORD TWP. (Lake County)—Adelphia, Suite 8, 7757 Auburn Rd., Painesville, OH 44077-9604. Phone: 440-942-0870. Fax: 440-639-6290. Counties: Geauga & Lake. Also serves Chardon Twp., Chester Twp. (Geauga County), Kirtland, Kirtland Hills, Leroy Twp. (Lake County), Mentor-on-the-Lake, Munson Twp. (Geauga County), North Perry (village), Painesville Twp. (Lake County), Perry, Perry Twp. (Lake County), Waite Hill. ICA: OH0042.
TV Market Ranking: 8. Franchise award date: N.A. Franchise expiration date: October 1, 2000. Began: September 1, 1981.
Channel capacity: 52 (2-way capable; operating 2-way). Channels available but not in use: 9.
Basic Service
Subscribers: 17,940.
Programming (received off-air): WBNX-TV (W,F) Akron; WEWS-TV (A), WJW (F), WKYC-TV (N), WQHS-TV (H), WVIZ-TV (P) Cleveland; WUAB (U) Lorain-Cleveland; WOIO (C) Shaker Heights; allband FM.
Programming (via satellite): WGN-TV (W) Chicago; A & E; C-SPAN; CNBC; CNN; Comedy Central; Discovery Channel; Fox Family Channel; Headline News; Knowledge TV; Lifetime; MTV; Nashville Network; Nickelodeon; Odyssey; QVC; TBS Superstation; The Weather Channel; VH1.
Current originations: Automated time-weather; educational access.
Fee: $60.00 installation; $10.03 monthly; $2.00 converter.
Commercial fee: $6.49 monthly.
Expanded Basic Service
Subscribers: 15,533.
Programming (via satellite): American Movie Classics; Court TV; ESPN; Fox Sports Net Ohio; Turner Network TV; USA Network.
Fee: $13.31 monthly.
Pay Service 1
Pay Units: 1,949.
Programming (via satellite): Cinemax.
Fee: $15.00 installation; $11.70 monthly.
Pay Service 2
Pay Units: 1,319.
Programming (via satellite): Disney Channel.
Fee: $10.00 installation; $8.00 monthly.
Pay Service 3
Pay Units: 6,122.
Programming (via satellite): The New Encore.
Fee: N.A.
Pay Service 4
Pay Units: 5,038.
Programming (via satellite): HBO.
Fee: $15.00 installation; $11.70 monthly.
Pay Service 5
Pay Units: 1,209.
Programming (via satellite): The Movie Channel.
Fee: $15.00 installation; $11.70 monthly.
Pay Service 6
Pay Units: 1,536.
Programming (via satellite): Showtime.
Fee: $15.00 installation; $11.70 monthly.
Pay-Per-View
Addressable homes: 4,000.
Local advertising: Yes.
Program Guide: The Cable Guide.
Equipment: Scientific-Atlanta headend; C-COR amplifiers; Comm/Scope cable; Jerrold set top converters; Jerrold addressable set top converters; Scientific-Atlanta satellite antenna; Scientific-Atlanta satellite receivers.
Miles of plant: 440.0 (coaxial). Homes passed: 20,004. Total homes in franchised area: 21,471.
Manager: Ed Williams. Chief technician: Mike Drougovich.
City fee: 3% of gross.
Ownership: Adelphia Communications Corp. (MSO); AT&T Broadband & Internet Services (MSO). Purchased from Tele-Communications Inc., March 9, 1999.

CONGRESS—Time Warner Cable, Box 10, 105 Prospect St., Lodi, OH 44254. Phone: 330-633-9044. Fax: 330-948-1513. County: Wayne. ICA: OH0305.
TV Market Ranking: 8. Franchise award date: November 1, 1983. Franchise expiration date: January 1, 2003. Began: July 1, 1984.
Channel capacity: 35 (not 2-way capable). Channels available but not in use: 23.
Basic Service
Subscribers: 32.
Programming (received off-air): WVPX (X) Akron; WOAC (I) Canton; WEWS-TV (A), WJW (F), WKYC-TV (N), WQHS-TV (H), WVIZ-TV (P) Cleveland; WUAB (U) Lorain-Cleveland; WOIO (C) Shaker Heights.
Programming (via satellite): Nashville Network; TBS Superstation.
Fee: $30.00 installation; $13.07 monthly; $2.50 converter.
Pay Service 1
Pay Units: 15.
Programming (via satellite): The Movie Channel.
Fee: $10.00 installation; $10.50 monthly.
Local advertising: Planned.
Miles of plant: 1.2 (coaxial). Homes passed: 125.
Manager: Thomas P. Autry. Chief technician: Jim Parsons. Marketing director: Ray Kistler.
Ownership: Time Warner Cable (MSO).

CONNEAUT—Adelphia, Suite 8, 7757 Auburn Rd., Painesville, OH 44077-9604. Phone: 440-942-0870. Fax: 440-639-6290. Counties: Ashtabula, OH; Erie, PA. Also serves Ashtabula Twp. (Ashtabula County), Kingsville, North Kingsville, OH; Springfield Twp. (Erie County), PA. ICA: OH0093.
TV Market Ranking: Below 100 (Conneaut, Kingsville, North Kingsville, Springfield Twp.); Outside TV Markets (Ashtabula Twp.). Franchise award date: N.A. Franchise expiration date: N.A. Began: November 1, 1969.
Channel capacity: 39 (2-way capable; operating 2-way). Channels available but not in use: N.A.
Basic Service
Subscribers: 6,278.
Programming (received off-air): WVIZ-TV (P) Cleveland; WICU-TV (N), WJET-TV (A), WQLN (P), WSEE (C) Erie; WUAB (U) Lorain-Cleveland; WOIO (C) Shaker Heights; allband FM.
Programming (via microwave): WEWS-TV (A), WJW (F), WKYC-TV (N) Cleveland.
Programming (via satellite): WGN-TV (W) Chicago; BET; C-SPAN; C-SPAN 2; CNN; Discovery Channel; Fox Family Channel; Fox Sports Net Ohio; Headline News; Lifetime; MTV; Nashville Network; Nickelodeon; Odyssey; QVC; TBS Superstation; The Weather Channel.
Current originations: Automated time-weather; local news.
Fee: $60.00 installation; $9.39 monthly; $2.00 converter.
Expanded Basic Service
Subscribers: 6,028.
Programming (via satellite): A & E; American Movie Classics; ESPN; Turner Network TV; USA Network.
Fee: $11.78 monthly.
Pay Service 1
Pay Units: 243.
Programming (via satellite): Disney Channel.
Fee: $20.00 installation; $8.00 monthly.
Pay Service 2
Pay Units: 936.
Programming (via satellite): HBO.
Fee: $8.00 monthly.
Pay Service 3
Pay Units: 309.
Programming (via satellite): The Movie Channel.
Fee: $8.00 monthly.
Pay Service 4
Pay Units: 309.
Programming (via satellite): Showtime.
Fee: $8.00 monthly.
Local advertising: Yes.
Equipment: RCA headend; C-COR amplifiers; Comm/Scope cable; JVC VTRs; Jerrold set top converters; Microdyne satellite receivers.
Miles of plant: 142.6 (coaxial). Homes passed: 7,999. Total homes in franchised area: 8,619.
Manager: Ed Williams. Chief technician: Mike Drougovich.
City fee: 5% of gross (North Kingsville).
Ownership: Adelphia Communications Corp. (MSO); AT&T Broadband & Internet Services (MSO). Purchased from Tele-Communications Inc., March 9, 1999.

CORNING—Cablevision Communications, Box 2200, 68 5th St., Buckhannon, WV 26201. Phone: 304-472-4193. Fax: 304-472-0756. Counties: Hocking & Perry. Also serves Coal Twp. (Perry County), Hemlock, Hocking County, Monroe Twp. (Perry County), Moxahala, New Lexington (Perry County), New Straitsville, Oakfield, Pleasant Twp. (Perry County), Rendville, Salt Lick Twp., Shawnee. ICA: OH0193.
TV Market Ranking: 27 (portions of Hocking County); Below 100 (Coal Twp., Corning, Hemlock, portions of Hocking County, Monroe Twp., Moxahala, New Lexington, New Straitsville, Oakfield, Pleasant Twp., Rendville, Salt Lick Twp., Shawnee); Outside TV Markets (portions of Hocking County). Franchise award date: N.A. Franchise expiration date: N.A. Began: November 1, 1975.
Channel capacity: 37. Channels available but not in use: None.
Basic Service
Subscribers: 995.
Programming (received off-air): WOUB-TV (P) Athens; WBNS-TV (C), WCMH-TV (N), WOSU-TV (P), WSYX (A), WTTE (F,U) Columbus; WSFJ (I) Newark; WHIZ-TV (N) Zanesville.
Programming (via satellite): WGN-TV (W) Chicago; Animal Planet; C-SPAN; TBS Superstation.
Fee: $52.50 installation; $14.40 monthly; $1.24 converter; $17.50 additional installation.
Expanded Basic Service
Subscribers: N.A.
Programming (via satellite): A & E; American Movie Classics; CNN; Discovery Channel; Disney Channel; E! Entertainment TV; ESPN; Fox Family Channel; Great American Country; History Channel; Home Shopping Network; Lifetime; MSNBC; MTV; Nashville Network; Nickelodeon; Sci-Fi Channel; Trinity Bcstg. Network; Turner Network TV; USA Network; VH1.
Fee: $17.98 monthly.
Pay Service 1
Pay Units: N.A.
Programming (via satellite): Cinemax; HBO; Showtime; The Movie Channel; The New Encore.
Fee: $17.50 installation; $3.99 monthly (Encore), $7.95 monthly (Cinemax), $11.95 monthly (HBO, Showtime or TMC).
Equipment: Blonder-Tongue headend; Jerrold amplifiers; Times Fiber cable; Jerrold traps; Microdyne satellite antenna; Microdyne satellite receivers.
Miles of plant: 46.0 (coaxial). Homes passed: 1,572.
Manager: Willie Critchfield. Marketing director: Kenny Phillips.
City fee: $100 annually.
Ownership: Rifkin & Associates Inc. (MSO). See Cable System Ownership.

COSHOCTON—FrontierVision, 640 Walnut St., Coshocton, OH 43812. Phone: 740-622-6755. County: Coshocton. Also serves Bethlehem Twp. (Coshocton County), Conesville, Jackson Twp. (Coshocton County), Jefferson Twp. (Coshocton County), Keene Twp., Warsaw. ICA: OH0083.
TV Market Ranking: Below 100. Franchise award date: N.A. Franchise expiration date: N.A. Began: June 1, 1953.
Channel capacity: 62 (not 2-way capable). Channels available but not in use: 1.
Basic Service
Subscribers: 7,222; Commercial subscribers: 606.
Programming (received off-air): WOSU-TV (P), WTTE (F,U) Columbus; WSFJ (I) Newark; WTRF-TV (C) Wheeling-Steubenville; WHIZ-TV (N) Zanesville; 14 FMs.
Programming (via microwave): WEWS-TV (A) Cleveland; WBNS-TV (C), WCMH-TV (N), WSYX (A) Columbus; WUAB (U) Lorain-Cleveland.
Programming (via satellite): American Movie Classics; C-SPAN; Discovery Channel; TBS Superstation; The Weather Channel.
Current originations: Automated time-weather; educational access.
Fee: $35.09 installation; $12.94 monthly; $2.33 converter.
Expanded Basic Service
Subscribers: 6,876.
Programming (via satellite): A & E; Animal Planet; CNBC; CNN; Comedy Central; Coun-

try Music TV; Disney Channel; E! Entertainment TV; ESPN; ESPN 2; FX; Fox Family Channel; Fox Sports Net Ohio; Golf Channel; Headline News; History Channel; Home & Garden Television; Home Shopping Network; Lifetime; MTV; Nashville Network; Nickelodeon; Ole TV Network; QVC; Sci-Fi Channel; Speedvision; The Weather Channel; Turner Network TV; USA Network; VH1.
Fee: $13.41 monthly.

Pay Service 1
Pay Units: 702.
Programming (via satellite): Cinemax.
Fee: $30.00 installation; $8.95 monthly.

Pay Service 2
Pay Units: 1,188.
Programming (via satellite): The New Encore.
Fee: $30.00 installation; $2.95 monthly.

Pay Service 3
Pay Units: 1,325.
Programming (via satellite): HBO.
Fee: $30.00 installation; $10.95 monthly.

Pay Service 4
Pay Units: 899.
Programming (via satellite): Showtime.
Fee: $30.00 installation; $8.95 monthly.

Pay Service 5
Pay Units: 610.
Programming (via satellite): The Movie Channel.
Fee: $30.00 installation; $8.95 monthly.

Pay Service 6
Pay Units: 8.
Programming (via satellite): Starz!
Fee: N.A.

Pay-Per-View
Addressable homes: 3,386.
Spice; Viewer's Choice 1, 3, 4.
Fee: $3.95 (Viewer's Choice 1, 3, 4), $6.95 (Spice).

Local advertising: Yes. Available in locally originated programming.
Equipment: Scientific-Atlanta headend; C-COR & Jerrold amplifiers; Jerrold addressable set top converters.
Miles of plant: 155.4 (coaxial). Homes passed: 9,739.
Manager: Steve Trippe. Chief technician: Bill Ricker.
Ownership: FrontierVision Partners LP (MSO). See Cable System Ownership.

CRAIG BEACH—Time Warner Cable, 427 E. State St., Salem, OH 44460. Phone: 216-332-9607. Counties: Mahoning & Portage. Also serves Milton Twp. (Mahoning County), Palmyra Twp. (portions). ICA: OH0231.
TV Market Ranking: 8 (Craig Beach, Milton Twp.); 79 (Craig Beach, Milton Twp., Palmyra Twp.). Franchise award date: March 9, 1981. Franchise expiration date: N.A. Began: July 1, 1987.
Channel capacity: 35 (not 2-way capable). Channels available but not in use: 10.

Basic Service
Subscribers: 924.
Programming (received off-air): WVPX (X) Akron; WNEO (P) Alliance; WJW (F), WKYC-TV (N) Cleveland; WUAB (U) Lorain-Cleveland; WOIO (C) Shaker Heights; WFMJ-TV (N), WKBN-TV (C), WYTV (A,F) Youngstown.
Programming (via satellite): QVC.
Current originations: Automated time-weather; public access; educational access; government access; local news.
Fee: $34.75 installation (aerial), $43.75 (underground); $10.75 monthly; $1.50 converter.

Expanded Basic Service
Subscribers: 910.
Programming (via satellite): WGN-TV (W) Chicago; CNN; Comedy Central; Discovery Channel; ESPN; Fox Family Channel; Headline News; Nashville Network; TBS Superstation; Turner Network TV; USA Network.
Fee: $11.82 monthly.

Pay Service 1
Pay Units: 144.
Programming (via satellite): Cinemax.
Fee: $25.00 installation; $9.50 monthly.

Pay Service 2
Pay Units: 95.
Programming (via satellite): Disney Channel.
Fee: $25.00 installation; $7.50 monthly.

Pay Service 3
Pay Units: 228.
Programming (via satellite): HBO.
Fee: $25.00 installation; $9.50 monthly.

Local advertising: No.
Equipment: Scientific-Atlanta headend; C-COR amplifiers; Comm/Scope cable; Pioneer set top converters; Harris satellite antenna; Scientific-Atlanta satellite receivers.
Miles of plant: 43.5 (coaxial); None (fiber optic). Additional miles planned: 3.0 (coaxial). Homes passed: 1,747.
Manager: Daryl Morrison. Chief technician: Don Jugenheimer.
City fee: 5% of gross.
Ownership: Time Warner Cable (MSO).

CROOKSVILLE—Cablecomm, 37 E. Main St., Crooksville, OH 43731-1248. Phone: 888-229-4465. Counties: Morgan, Muskingum & Perry. Also serves Morgan County, Perry County, Roseville, York, York Twp. (Morgan County). ICA: OH0153.
TV Market Ranking: Below 100 (Crooksville, Morgan County, Perry County, Roseville, York Twp.); Outside TV Markets (York). Franchise award date: N.A. Franchise expiration date: N.A. Began: May 1, 1964.
Channel capacity: 31. Channels available but not in use: N.A.

Basic Service
Subscribers: 2,253.
Programming (received off-air): WOUB-TV (P) Athens; WBNS-TV (C), WCMH-TV (N), WSYX (A), WTTE (F,U) Columbus; WHIZ-TV (N) Zanesville; allband FM.
Programming (via satellite): WGN-TV (W) Chicago; CNN; Discovery Channel; Fox Family Channel; Lifetime; MTV; Nashville Network; Nickelodeon; QVC; TBS Superstation; The Weather Channel.
Current originations: Automated time-weather.
Fee: $60.00 installation; $9.43 monthly; $2.50 converter.

Expanded Basic Service
Subscribers: 2,170.
Programming (via satellite): American Movie Classics; ESPN; Fox Sports Net Pittsburgh; Odyssey; Turner Network TV; USA Network.
Fee: $11.12 monthly.

Pay Service 1
Pay Units: 301.
Programming (via satellite): Cinemax.
Fee: N.A.

Pay Service 2
Pay Units: 163.
Programming (via satellite): Disney Channel.
Fee: N.A.

Pay Service 3
Pay Units: 849.
Programming (via satellite): The New Encore.
Fee: N.A.

Pay Service 4
Pay Units: 458.
Programming (via satellite): HBO.
Fee: N.A.

Pay Service 5
Pay Units: 4.
Programming (via satellite): The Movie Channel.
Fee: N.A.

Equipment: Jerrold headend; Jerrold amplifiers; Times Fiber cable; Jerrold set top converters; Microdyne satellite antenna; Microdyne satellite receivers.
Miles of plant: 41.0 (coaxial). Homes passed: 2,747. Total homes in franchised area: 2,814.
Manager: Barney Printz.
Ownership: Fanch Communications Inc. (MSO); Time Warner Cable (MSO). Purchased from Tele-Communications Inc., February 25, 1999. See Cable System Ownership.

CROWN CITY—FrontierVision, Box 627, Chillicothe, OH 45601. Phones: 740-775-4300; 800-346-2288. Fax: 740-775-2915. Counties: Gallia & Lawrence. Also serves Athalia, Clay, Gallia County (unincorporated areas). ICA: OH0260.
TV Market Ranking: 36 (Clay, Crown City, portions of Gallia County); Below 100 (portions of Gallia County); Outside TV Markets (Athalia, portions of Gallia County). Franchise award date: N.A. Franchise expiration date: N.A. Began: January 1, 1983.
Channel capacity: 32 (not 2-way capable). Channels available but not in use: 2.

Basic Service
Subscribers: 253.
Programming (received off-air): WCHS-TV (A), WOWK-TV (C), WSAZ-TV (N), WVAH-TV (F,U) Charleston-Huntington.
Programming (via satellite): A & E; American Movie Classics; CNN; Country Music TV; Discovery Channel; Disney Channel; E! Entertainment TV; ESPN; ESPN 2; Fox Family Channel; Learning Channel; Lifetime; Nashville Network; QVC; Sci-Fi Channel; TBS Superstation; The Weather Channel; USA Network.
Fee: $26.00 monthly.

Pay Service 1
Pay Units: 21.
Programming (via satellite): Cinemax.
Fee: $8.99 monthly.

Pay Service 2
Pay Units: 22.
Programming (via satellite): HBO.
Fee: $11.99 monthly.

Pay Service 3
Pay Units: 15.
Programming (via satellite): Showtime.
Fee: $11.99 monthly.

Miles of plant: 18.0 (coaxial). Homes passed: 276.
Manager: Richard Coplan. Chief technician: Sam Morabith. Program director: Chad Hume. Marketing director: Barbara Brewer.
Ownership: FrontierVision Partners LP (MSO). See Cable System Ownership.

CUMBERLAND—Cablevision Communications, Box 2200, 68 5th St., Buckhannon, WV 26201. Phone: 304-472-4193. Fax: 304-472-0756. County: Guernsey. ICA: OH0294.
TV Market Ranking: Below 100. Franchise award date: N.A. Franchise expiration date: July 1, 2005. Began: July 1, 1968.
Channel capacity: 22 (not 2-way capable). Channels available but not in use: None.

Basic Service
Subscribers: 107.
Programming (received off-air): WOUC-TV (P) Cambridge; WBNS-TV (C), WSYX (A) Columbus; WTAP-TV (N) Parkersburg-Marietta; WTOV-TV (N) Steubenville-Wheeling; WTRF-TV (C) Wheeling-Steubenville; WHIZ-TV (N) Zanesville.
Programming (via satellite): American Movie Classics; CNN; Discovery Channel; ESPN; Fox Family Channel; FoxNet; Lifetime; Nashville Network; Nickelodeon; Sci-Fi Channel; TBS Superstation; Turner Network TV; USA Network.
Current originations: Automated time-weather.
Fee: $52.50 installation; $23.35 monthly; $1.24 converter; $17.50 additional installation.

Pay Service 1
Pay Units: 24.
Programming (via satellite): HBO.
Fee: $17.50 installation; $11.99 monthly.

Equipment: Blonder-Tongue & Olson headend; Jerrold amplifiers; Times Fiber cable; Eagle traps; Microdyne satellite antenna.
Miles of plant: 3.0 (coaxial). Homes passed: 195.
Manager: Willie Critchfield. Marketing director: Kenny Phillips.
Franchise fee: None.
Ownership: Rifkin & Associates Inc. (MSO). See Cable System Ownership.

DANVILLE—Time Warner Cable, Box 787, 111 S. Mulberry St., Mount Vernon, OH 43050. Phones: 740-397-2288; 800-782-4118. Fax: 740-397-3730. County: Knox. ICA: OH0263.
TV Market Ranking: Below 100. Franchise award date: N.A. Franchise expiration date: N.A. Began: September 1, 1970.
Channel capacity: 22 (not 2-way capable). Channels available but not in use: N.A.

Basic Service
Subscribers: 419.
Programming (received off-air): WEWS-TV (A), WJW (F), WKYC-TV (N) Cleveland; WBNS-TV (C), WCMH-TV (N), WOSU-TV (P), WSYX (A) Columbus; WUAB (U) Lorain-Cleveland.
Programming (via satellite): CNN; ESPN; Fox Family Channel; Home Shopping Network; MTV; Nashville Network; Nickelodeon; TBS Superstation; Turner Network TV; USA Network.
Current originations: Automated time-weather; automated emergency alert.
Fee: $15.00 installation; $15.95 monthly; $15.00 additional installation.

Pay Service 1
Pay Units: 64.
Programming (via satellite): Cinemax.
Fee: $10.95 monthly.

Pay Service 2
Pay Units: 94.
Programming (via satellite): HBO.
Fee: $15.00 installation; $10.95 monthly.

Local advertising: Yes. Available in character-generated programming.
Equipment: Jerrold headend; C-COR & Jerrold amplifiers; Comm/Scope cable; Texscan character generator; Scientific-Atlanta set top converters; Scientific-Atlanta addressable set top converters; Eagle traps; Eagle addressable traps; Microdyne satellite antenna; Microdyne satellite receivers.
Miles of plant: 8.0 (coaxial). Homes passed: 490.
Manager: Paul S. Schonewolf. Technical operations manager: Dan Fessler. Field operations manager: Bill Schroeder. Marketing manager: Carl Bauer. Customer operations manager: Danielle Turner.
Ownership: Time Warner Cable (MSO).

DAYTON—Time Warner Cable, 275 Leo St., Dayton, OH 45404-2830. Phone: 937-223-4077. Fax: 937-461-1838. County: Montgomery. Also serves Butler Twp. (Montgomery County), Mad River Twp. (Montgomery County), Riverside (Montgomery County). ICA: OH0011.

TV Market Ranking: 41. Franchise award date: N.A. Franchise expiration date: September 24, 2006. Began: September 24, 1976.

Channel capacity: 39 (2-way capable; operating 2-way). Channels available but not in use: N.A.

Basic Service

Subscribers: 46,000; Commercial subscribers: 24.

Programming (received off-air): WCPO-TV (A) Cincinnati; WXIX-TV (F) Cincinnati-Newport; WDTN (A), WHIO-TV (C), WKEF (N), WPTD (P), WRGT-TV (F,U) Dayton; WPTO (P) Oxford; WKOI (T) Richmond; WBDT (W) Springfield; 18 FMs.

Programming (via satellite): WGN-TV (W) Chicago; TBS Superstation.

Current originations: Educational access.

Fee: $31.13 installation; $10.63 monthly; $3.45 converter.

Expanded Basic Service

Subscribers: N.A.

Programming (via satellite): A & E; American Movie Classics; BET; C-SPAN; CNBC; CNN; Comedy Central; Court TV; Discovery Channel; E! Entertainment TV; ESPN; Fox Family Channel; Fox Sports Net Ohio; Headline News; Lifetime; MTV; Nashville Network; Nickelodeon; QVC; TV Guide Channel; TV Guide Sneak Prevue; The Weather Channel; Turner Network TV; USA Network; VH1.

Fee: N.A.

Expanded Basic Service 2

Subscribers: N.A.

Programming (via satellite): Cartoon Network; Court TV; History Channel; Learning Channel; Sci-Fi Channel.

Fee: $2.95 monthly.

Pay Service 1

Pay Units: N.A.

Programming (via satellite): Cinemax; Disney Channel; HBO; Playboy TV; Showtime; The Movie Channel.

Fee: $20.00 installation; $9.25 monthly (Disney), $12.25 monthly (Cinemax, HBO, Showtime or TMC).

Pay-Per-View

Viewer's Choice.

Local advertising: Yes (locally produced & insert). Rates: $35.00/30 Seconds. Local sales manager: Doug Wells. Regional interconnect: Greater Dayton Cable Advertising.

Equipment: Scientific-Atlanta headend; RCA amplifiers; Comm/Scope & General cable; System Concepts character generator; Hamlin set top converters; Scientific-Atlanta satellite receivers.

Miles of plant: 621.0 (coaxial). Homes passed: 93,900.

Manager: Stan Smith. Chief technician: Lyman Collins. Marketing director: Beverly Wall.

City fee: 5% of gross.

Ownership: Time Warner Cable (MSO). Purchased from AT&T Broadband & Internet Services, June 1, 1999.

DEFIANCE—FrontierVision, 310 Jefferson St., Defiance, OH 43512. Phone: 800-346-2288. Fax: 419-782-2640. Counties: Defiance, Fulton & Henry. Also serves Brunersburg, Defiance County (portions), Dover Twp. (Fulton County), Florida Twp. (Henry County), Liberty Center, Ney, Pettisville, Wauseon. ICA: OH0047.

TV Market Ranking: 52 (Dover Twp., Liberty Center, Pettisville, Wauseon); 82 (portions of Defiance County); Below 100 (portions of Defiance County, Ney); Outside TV Markets (Brunersburg, Defiance, portions of Defiance County, Florida Twp.). Franchise award date: May 1, 1964. Franchise expiration date: April 5, 1998. Began: May 1, 1964.

Channel capacity: 62 (not 2-way capable). Channels available but not in use: 4.

Basic Service

Subscribers: 7,452.

Programming (received off-air): WBGU-TV (P) Bowling Green; WGTE-TV (P), WNWO-TV (N), WTOL-TV (C), WTVG (A), WUPW (F) Toledo; 17 FMs.

Programming (via satellite): WGN-TV (W) Chicago; A & E; C-SPAN; CNN; Disney Channel; ESPN; Fox Family Channel; Headline News; Learning Channel; Lifetime; MTV; Nashville Network; Nickelodeon; TBS Superstation; The Weather Channel; USA Network; Univision.

Current originations: Automated time-weather; public access; educational access; government access; leased access; local news.

Planned originations: Automated emergency alert.

Fee: $45.35 installation; $10.97 monthly; $28.33 additional installation.

Pay Service 1

Pay Units: 504.

Programming (via satellite): Cinemax.

Fee: $10.95 monthly.

Pay Service 2

Pay Units: 286.

Programming (via satellite): The New Encore.

Fee: N.A.

Pay Service 3

Pay Units: 736.

Programming (via satellite): HBO.

Fee: $10.95 monthly.

Pay Service 4

Pay Units: 644.

Programming (via satellite): Showtime.

Fee: $9.95 monthly.

Pay Service 5

Pay Units: 284.

Programming (via satellite): Starz!

Fee: N.A.

Pay Service 6

Pay Units: 521.

Programming (via satellite): The Movie Channel.

Fee: $8.95 monthly.

Pay-Per-View

Addressable homes: 1,391.

Hot Choice; Viewer's Choice.

Local advertising: Yes. Available in locally originated programming.

Program Guide: The Cable Guide.

Equipment: Scientific-Atlanta headend; Jerrold amplifiers; Comm/Scope cable; Sony VTRs; MSI character generator; Jerrold & Oak set top converters; Harris satellite antenna.

Miles of plant: 169.1 (coaxial). Additional miles planned: 3.0 (coaxial). Homes passed: 10,650.

Manager: Steve Trippe. Chief technician: Bill Ricker.

City fee: 3% of gross.

Ownership: FrontierVision Partners LP (MSO). See Cable System Ownership.

DELHI TWP.—FrontierVision, Box 58339, 1272 Ebenezer Rd., Cincinnati, OH 45233. Phone: 513-941-7000. Fax: 513-941-1704. County: Hamilton. Also serves Addyston, Cleves, Miami Twp. (Hamilton County), North Bend, Whitewater Twp. (Hamilton County). ICA: OH0053.

TV Market Ranking: 17. Franchise award date: November 14, 1979. Franchise expiration date: November 14, 2009. Began: March 1, 1980.

Channel capacity: 80 (not 2-way capable). Channels available but not in use: 10.

Basic Service

Subscribers: 12,495.

Programming (received off-air): WBQC-LP (W), WCET (P), WCPO-TV (A), WKRC-TV (C), WLWT (N), WSTR-TV (W) Cincinnati; WXIX-TV (F) Cincinnati-Newport; WCVN (P) Covington; WPTD (P) Dayton; WPTO (P) Oxford; 20 FMs.

Programming (via satellite): Learning Channel; Lifetime; QVC.

Current originations: Automated time-weather; public access; educational access; government access; religious access; leased access; library access; automated emergency alert; local news; local sports.

Fee: $26.09 installation; $8.78 monthly; $3.48 converter; $17.93 additional installation.

Expanded Basic Service

Subscribers: 12,112.

Programming (via satellite): A & E; American Movie Classics; CNBC; CNN; Cartoon Network; Comedy Central; Country Music TV; Discovery Channel; Disney Channel; E! Entertainment TV; ESPN; ESPN 2; EWTN; FX; Fox Family Channel; Goodlife TV Network; Headline News; History Channel; Home & Garden Television; MTV; Nashville Network; Nickelodeon; Sci-Fi Channel; TV Food Network; TV Guide Channel; TV Guide Sneak Prevue; The Inspirational Network; The Weather Channel; Travel Channel; Turner Classic Movies; Turner Network TV; USA Network; VH1.

Fee: $17.93 installation; $16.21 monthly.

Pay Service 1

Pay Units: 836.

Programming (via satellite): Cinemax.

Fee: $19.56 installation; $11.95 monthly.

Pay Service 2

Pay Units: 457.

Programming (via satellite): The New Encore.

Fee: $7.95 monthly.

Pay Service 3

Pay Units: 984.

Programming (via satellite): Flix.

Fee: $2.95 monthly.

Pay Service 4

Pay Units: 1,737.

Programming (via satellite): HBO.

Fee: $11.95 monthly.

Pay Service 5

Pay Units: 1,015.

Programming (via satellite): Showtime.

Fee: $11.95 monthly.

Pay Service 6

Pay Units: 355.

Programming (via satellite): Starz!

Fee: $8.95 monthly.

Pay Service 7

Pay Units: 1,016.

Programming (via satellite): The Movie Channel.

Fee: $11.95 monthly.

Pay-Per-View

Addressable homes: 5,566.

Viewer's Choice.

Local advertising: Yes (locally produced & insert). Available in satellite distributed programming.

Equipment: RCA & Scientific-Atlanta headend; Scientific-Atlanta amplifiers; Times Fiber cable; Panasonic cameras; Panasonic VTRs; Scientific-Atlanta set top converters; Jerrold addressable set top converters; Arcom traps; Scientific-Atlanta & Microdyne satellite antenna; Standard Communications satellite receivers; Panasonic commercial insert.

Miles of plant: 279.4 (coaxial); 55.0 (fiber optic). Homes passed: 17,266.

Manager: Jim Underwood. Chief technician: Jerry Marnell. Marketing director: Keith Burt. Customer service manager: Lenora Kelly.

Ownership: FrontierVision Partners LP (MSO). See Cable System Ownership.

DELLROY—FrontierVision, Box 648, 102 Twin Oak Dr., Jackson, OH 45640. Phone: 614-345-4329. Fax: 614-286-1489. Counties: Carroll & Tuscarawas. Also serves Monroe, New Cumberland, Sherrodsville. ICA: OH0238.

TV Market Ranking: 90. Franchise award date: July 13, 1987. Franchise expiration date: July 13, 2002. Began: N.A.

Channel capacity: 37. Channels available but not in use: 3.

Basic Service

Subscribers: 670.

Programming (received off-air): WBNX-TV (W,F), WVPX (X) Akron; WNEO (P) Alliance; WDLI (T), WOAC (I) Canton; WJW (F), WQHS-TV (H) Cleveland; WUAB (U) Lorain-Cleveland; WOIO (C) Shaker Heights; WTOV-TV (N) Steubenville-Wheeling; WFMJ-TV (N), WKBN-TV (C) Youngstown.

Programming (via satellite): WGN-TV (W) Chicago; A & E; CNN; Comedy Central; Country Music TV; Discovery Channel; ESPN; Fox Family Channel; Lifetime; MTV; Nashville Network; TBS Superstation; The Weather Channel; USA Network.

Fee: $20.99 installation; $22.70 monthly; $15.12 additional installation.

Pay Service 1

Pay Units: 65.

Programming (via satellite): HBO.

Fee: $11.95 monthly.

Pay Service 2

Pay Units: 52.

Programming (via satellite): Showtime.

Fee: N.A.

Pay Service 3

Pay Units: 56.

Programming (via satellite): The Movie Channel.

Fee: N.A.

Equipment: Jerrold & Magnavox amplifiers; Comm/Scope cable; NSC set top converters; Arcom & Gamco traps; Scientific-Atlanta satellite antenna; Drake satellite receivers.

Miles of plant: 26.3 (coaxial). Homes passed: 821.

Manager: Steve Trippe. Chief technician: Bill Ricker.

Ownership: FrontierVision Partners LP (MSO). See Cable System Ownership.

DELPHOS—Warner Cable Communications Inc., 306 N. Main St., Delphos, OH 45833-1574. Phone: 419-692-3796. Counties: Allen & Van Wert. ICA: OH0143.

TV Market Ranking: Below 100. Franchise award date: N.A. Franchise expiration date: N.A. Began: January 1, 1968.

Channel capacity: 36. Channels available but not in use: 1.

Basic Service

Subscribers: 2,748.

Programming (received off-air): WBGU-TV (P) Bowling Green; WHIO-TV (C) Dayton; WANE-TV (C), WFFT-TV (F), WKJG-TV (N), WPTA (A) Fort Wayne; WLIO (N), WTLW (I) Lima; WNWO-TV (N), WUPW (F) Toledo; allband FM.

Programming (via satellite): WGN-TV (W) Chicago; A & E; C-SPAN; CNBC; CNN; Discovery Channel; E! Entertainment TV; ESPN; EWTN; Fox Family Channel; Headline News; Lifetime; MTV; Nashville Network; Nickelodeon; QVC; TBS Superstation; The Weather Channel; Turner Network TV; USA Network; VH1.

Current originations: Automated time-weather.

Fee: $25.00 installation; $9.95 monthly.

Pay Service 1

Pay Units: 615.

Programming (via satellite): Cinemax; HBO; Showtime; The Movie Channel.
Fee: $11.50 monthly (each).
Pay Service 2
Pay Units: 150.
Programming (via satellite): Disney Channel.
Fee: $7.95 monthly.
Pay-Per-View
Action Pay-Per-View.
Equipment: RCA & Scientific-Atlanta headend; Jerrold amplifiers; Comm/Scope cable; Sony cameras; Sony VTRs; Compuvid character generator; Vitek traps; Scientific-Atlanta satellite antenna; Scientific-Atlanta satellite receivers.
Miles of plant: 55.0 (coaxial). Homes passed: 3,209. Total homes in franchised area: 3,209.
Manager: Jeff Parker. Chief technician: Bill Lambert. Marketing director: Danny Schiffer.
City fee: 3% of gross.
Ownership: Time Warner Cable (MSO).

DENMARK TWP.—Star Cable, Box 4478, 4720 Mahoning Ave., Youngstown, OH 44515. Phone: 800-569-0200. County: Ashtabula. Also serves Ashtabula County (eastern portion), Dorset Twp., Jefferson Twp. (Ashtabula County), Monroe Twp. (Ashtabula County), Pierpont Twp., Plymouth Twp. (Ashtabula County), Sheffield Twp. (Ashtabula County). ICA: OH0228.
TV Market Ranking: 79 (portions of Ashtabula County); Below 100 (portions of Ashtabula County, Monroe Twp.); Outside TV Markets (portions of Ashtabula County, Denmark Twp., Dorset Twp., Jefferson Twp., Pierpont Twp., Plymouth Twp., Sheffield Twp.). Franchise award date: N.A. Franchise expiration date: N.A. Began: January 24, 1992.
Channel capacity: 36 (not 2-way capable). Channels available but not in use: 3.
Basic Service
Subscribers: 699.
Programming (received off-air): WEWS-TV (A), WJW (F), WKYC-TV (N) Cleveland; WICU-TV (N), WJET-TV (A), WQLN (P), WSEE (C) Erie; WUAB (U) Lorain-Cleveland; WOIO (C) Shaker Heights.
Programming (via satellite): A & E; American Movie Classics; CNN; Discovery Channel; ESPN; Fox Family Channel; Fox Sports Net Ohio; Nashville Network; Nickelodeon; QVC; TBS Superstation; The Weather Channel; Turner Classic Movies; Turner Network TV; USA Network; VH1.
Fee: $35.00 installation; $27.75 monthly; $3.00 converter.
Pay Service 1
Pay Units: 53.
Programming (via satellite): Cinemax.
Fee: $11.00 monthly.
Pay Service 2
Pay Units: 120.
Programming (via satellite): Disney Channel.
Fee: $4.95 monthly.
Pay Service 3
Pay Units: 96.
Programming (via satellite): HBO.
Fee: $11.50 monthly.
Pay Service 4
Pay Units: 79.
Programming (via satellite): Showtime; The Movie Channel.
Fee: $12.95 monthly.
Local advertising: Yes. Available in character-generated programming.
Equipment: Scientific-Atlanta headend; Scientific-Atlanta amplifiers; Trilogy cable; Scientific-Atlanta satellite receivers.
Miles of plant: 53.4 (coaxial); None (fiber optic). Additional miles planned: 15.0 (coaxial). Homes passed: 1,014. Total homes in franchised area: 1,014.
Manager: Terry Dickerhoof. Chief technician: Tom Beat.
Ownership: Star Cable Associates (MSO).

DESHLER—FrontierVision, Box 627, 32 Enterprise Dr., Chillicothe, OH 45601. Phones: 740-775-4300; 800-346-2288. Fax: 740-775-2915. County: Henry. Also serves Bartlow Twp., Hamler, Holgate, Marion Twp. (Henry County), Pleasant Twp. (Henry County). ICA: OH0191.
TV Market Ranking: Below 100 (Bartlow Twp., Deshler, Hamler, Marion Twp., Pleasant Twp.); Outside TV Markets (Holgate). Franchise award date: N.A. Franchise expiration date: N.A. Began: June 1, 1983.
Channel capacity: 38. Channels available but not in use: None.
Basic Service
Subscribers: 821.
Programming (received off-air): WBGU-TV (P) Bowling Green; WFFT-TV (F) Fort Wayne; WLIO (N) Lima; WGTE-TV (P), WNWO-TV (N), WTOL-TV (C), WTVG (A), WUPW (F) Toledo.
Programming (via satellite): WGN-TV (W) Chicago; A & E; C-SPAN; CNN; Disney Channel; ESPN; Fox Family Channel; Headline News; Home Shopping Network; Lifetime; MTV; Nashville Network; Nickelodeon; Showtime; TBS Superstation; The Weather Channel; USA Network; VH1.
Fee: $42.50 installation; $17.95 monthly.
Pay Service 1
Pay Units: 130.
Programming (via satellite): Cinemax.
Fee: N.A.
Pay Service 2
Pay Units: 160.
Programming (via satellite): HBO.
Fee: $10.95 monthly.
Miles of plant: 42.5 (coaxial). Homes passed: 1,601.
Manager: Richard Coplan. Chief technician: Sam Morabith. Program director: Chad Hume. Marketing director: Barbara Brewer.
Ownership: FrontierVision Partners LP (MSO). See Cable System Ownership.

DRESDEN—Cablecommm, Box 2249, 737 Howard St., Zanesville, OH 43702-2249. Phone: 888-229-4465. County: Muskingum. Also serves Trinway. ICA: OH0218.
TV Market Ranking: Below 100. Franchise award date: N.A. Franchise expiration date: N.A. Began: October 1, 1969.
Channel capacity: 33 (not 2-way capable). Channels available but not in use: 1.
Basic Service
Subscribers: 850.
Programming (received off-air): WOUC-TV (P) Cambridge; WBNS-TV (C), WCMH-TV (N), WOSU-TV (P), WSYX (A), WTTE (F,U) Columbus; WSFJ (I) Newark; WTRF-TV (C) Wheeling-Steubenville; WHIZ-TV (N) Zanesville; allband FM.
Programming (via satellite): Discovery Channel; QVC; TBS Superstation.
Fee: $44.85 installation; $10.13 monthly; $3.00 converter.
Expanded Basic Service
Subscribers: 818.
Programming (via satellite): A & E; American Movie Classics; Animal Planet; C-SPAN; CNN; Cartoon Network; ESPN; MTV; Nashville Network; Nickelodeon; The Weather Channel; Turner Network TV; USA Network.
Fee: $13.44 monthly.
Pay Service 1
Pay Units: 74.
Programming (via satellite): Disney Channel.
Fee: $20.00 installation; $11.95 monthly.
Pay Service 2
Pay Units: 326.
Programming (via satellite): The New Encore.
Fee: N.A.
Pay Service 3
Pay Units: 251.
Programming (via satellite): HBO.
Fee: $11.95 monthly.
Equipment: Blonder-Tongue & Scientific-Atlanta headend; Jerrold & Vikoa amplifiers; Times Fiber & Vikoa cable; Eagle traps; Scientific-Atlanta satellite antenna; Scientific-Atlanta satellite receivers.
Miles of plant: 10.0 (coaxial); None (fiber optic). Homes passed: 1,046. Total homes in franchised area: 1,050.
Manager: William F. Randles. Chief technician: John Barber.
Franchise fee: None.
Ownership: Fanch Communications Inc. (MSO); Time Warner Cable (MSO). Purchased from Tele-Communications Inc., February 25, 1999. See Cable System Ownership.

***DUBLIN**—Americast, 300 S. Riverside, Chicago, IL 60606. Phones: 312-526-8000; 800-848-2278. Fax: 312-526-8565. Counties: Delaware & Franklin. ICA: OH0406.
TV Market Ranking: 27. Franchise award date: December 1, 1997. Franchise expiration date: N.A. Scheduled to begin: N.A.
Channel capacity: N.A.
Total homes in franchised area: 7,500.
Ownership: Ameritech New Media Inc. (MSO).

DUNKIRK—FrontierVision, Box 627, Chillicothe, OH 45601. Phones: 740-775-4300; 800-346-2288. Fax: 740-775-2915. County: Hardin. ICA: OH0276.
TV Market Ranking: Below 100. Franchise award date: N.A. Franchise expiration date: March 3, 2005. Began: March 3, 1985.
Channel capacity: 37. Channels available but not in use: 5.
Basic Service
Subscribers: 234.
Programming (received off-air): WBGU-TV (P) Bowling Green; WTTE (F,U) Columbus; WLIO (N) Lima; WNWO-TV (N), WTOL-TV (C), WTVG (A), WUPW (F) Toledo.
Programming (via satellite): WGN-TV (W) Chicago; Fox Family Channel; Learning Channel; Nashville Network; Nickelodeon; Sci-Fi Channel; The Weather Channel; USA Network.
Fee: $43.75 installation; $18.95 monthly; $40.00 additional installation.
Expanded Basic Service
Subscribers: 212.
Programming (via satellite): C-SPAN; CNN; Country Music TV; Discovery Channel; Disney Channel; ESPN; MTV; TBS Superstation; Turner Classic Movies; Turner Network TV.
Fee: $4.50 monthly.
Pay Service 1
Pay Units: 50.
Programming (via satellite): Cinemax.
Fee: $10.00 monthly.
Pay Service 2
Pay Units: 54.
Programming (via satellite): HBO.
Fee: $10.00 monthly.
Miles of plant: 8.0 (coaxial). Homes passed: 398.
Manager: Richard Coplan. Chief technician: Sam Morabith. Program director: Chad Hume. Marketing director: Barbara Brewer.
Ownership: FrontierVision Partners LP (MSO). See Cable System Ownership.

EAST CLEVELAND—East Cleveland Cable TV & Communications LLC, 1395 Hayden Ave., East Cleveland, OH 44112. Phone: 216-851-2215. Fax: 216-851-0231. County: Cuyahoga. Also serves Bratenahl. ICA: OH0066.
TV Market Ranking: 8. Franchise award date: January 1, 1981. Franchise expiration date: January 1, 2008. Began: November 20, 1981.
Channel capacity: 46 (not 2-way capable). Channels available but not in use: None.
Basic Service
Subscribers: 3,708.
Programming (received off-air): WBNX-TV (W,F) Akron; WEWS-TV (A), WJW (F), WKYC-TV (N), WQHS-TV (H), WVIZ-TV (P) Cleveland; WUAB (U) Lorain-Cleveland; WOIO (C) Shaker Heights.
Programming (via satellite): WGN-TV (W) Chicago; A & E; American Movie Classics; Animal Planet; BET; BET on Jazz; CNBC; CNN; Cartoon Network; Comedy Central; Court TV; Discovery Channel; Disney Channel; E! Entertainment TV; ESPN; Fox Family Channel; Fox Sports Net Ohio; Headline News; History Channel; Learning Channel; Lifetime; MTV; Nickelodeon; Sci-Fi Channel; TBS Superstation; TV Guide Channel; The Weather Channel; Trinity Bcstg. Network; Turner Network TV; USA Network; VH1.
Current originations: Automated time-weather; public access; government access.
Fee: $25.00 installation; $26.85 monthly; $1.75 converter; $25.00 additional installation.
Pay Service 1
Pay Units: 449.
Programming (via satellite): Cinemax.
Fee: $7.95 monthly.
Pay Service 2
Pay Units: 1,167.
Programming (via satellite): HBO.
Fee: $10.95 monthly.
Pay Service 3
Pay Units: 707.
Programming (via satellite): Showtime; The Movie Channel.
Fee: $10.95 monthly.
Pay-Per-View
Addressable homes: 1,882.
Viewer's Choice.
Fee: $4.00.
Pay-per-view manager: James Gruttadaurio.
Local advertising: Yes. Available in locally originated programming. Local sales manager: Bill Fambrough.
Equipment: Magnavox headend; Magnavox amplifiers; Scientific-Atlanta cable; Pioneer ad-

dressable set top converters; Scientific-Atlanta satellite antenna.
Miles of plant: 50.0 (coaxial). Additional miles planned: 43.0 (coaxial). Homes passed: 12,000. Total homes in franchised area: 12,000.
Manager: Pamela Bryson. Chief technician: David Cook. Marketing director: James Gruttadaurio. Customer service manager: Angela Jackson.
City fee: 3% of gross.
Ownership: East Cleveland Cable TV LLC.

EAST LIVERPOOL—TCI Cablevision of Ohio Inc., 16808 St. Clair Ave., East Liverpool, OH 43920-3095. Phone: 800-421-3145. Fax: 330-385-0322. County: Columbiana. Also serves Liverpool Twp., Madison Twp. (Columbiana County), St. Clair Twp. (Columbiana County), Wellsville, Yellow Creek. ICA: OH0062.
TV Market Ranking: 10 (East Liverpool, portions of Liverpool Twp., Madison Twp.); 79 (East Liverpool, portions of Liverpool Twp., Madison Twp., St. Clair Twp., Wellsville, Yellow Creek); 90 (East Liverpool, portions of Liverpool Twp., Madison Twp., St. Clair Twp., Wellsville, Yellow Creek). Franchise award date: N.A. Franchise expiration date: N.A. Began: May 1, 1966.
Channel capacity: 41 (not 2-way capable). Channels available but not in use: N.A.
Basic Service
Subscribers: 9,897.
Programming (received off-air): WNEO (P) Alliance; KDKA-TV (C), WCWB (W), WPGH-TV (F), WPXI (N), WQED (P), WTAE-TV (A) Pittsburgh; WTOV-TV (N) Steubenville-Wheeling; WKBN-TV (C), WYTV (A,F) Youngstown; allband FM.
Programming (via microwave): Ecumenical TV Channel.
Programming (via satellite): WGN-TV (W) Chicago; A & E; BET; C-SPAN; CNBC; CNN; Discovery Channel; Fox Family Channel; Lifetime; MTV; Nashville Network; Nickelodeon; QVC; TBS Superstation; The Weather Channel.
Current originations: Automated time-weather; local news.
Fee: $60.00 installation; $10.54 monthly; $2.00 converter.
Expanded Basic Service
Subscribers: 8,906.
Programming (via satellite): American Movie Classics; ESPN; Fox Sports Net Pittsburgh; Turner Network TV; USA Network.
Fee: $8.54 monthly.
Pay Service 1
Pay Units: 455.
Programming (via satellite): Disney Channel.
Fee: $10.95 monthly.
Pay Service 2
Pay Units: 3,254.
Programming (via satellite): The New Encore.
Fee: N.A.
Pay Service 3
Pay Units: 2,132.
Programming (via satellite): HBO.
Fee: $10.95 monthly.
Pay Service 4
Pay Units: 572.
Programming (via satellite): Showtime.
Fee: $10.95 monthly.
Local advertising: Yes.
Program Guide: The Cable Guide.
Equipment: M/A-Com headend; Scientific-Atlanta amplifiers; Scientific-Atlanta cable; Jerrold addressable set top converters; Scientific-Atlanta satellite antenna.
Miles of plant: 175.0 (coaxial). Homes passed: 12,592. Total homes in franchised area: 14,457.
Manager: Jim Underwood. Chief technician: Donald S. Boyd.
City fee: 3% of gross; 5% of gross (Wellsville).
Ownership: AT&T Broadband & Internet Services (MSO). Purchased from Tele-Communications Inc., March 9, 1999.

EAST PALESTINE—TCI Cablevision of Ohio Inc., 2810 Darlington Rd., Beaver Falls, PA 15010-1028. Phone: 800-833-0901. County: Columbiana. Also serves Columbiana, Fairfield (Columbiana County), Leetonia, Middleton Twp. (Columbiana County), Negley, New Waterford, Salem, Unity, Unity Twp., Washingtonville. ICA: OH0099.
TV Market Ranking: 79 (Columbiana, East Palestine, Fairfield, Leetonia, Middleton Twp., Negley, New Waterford, Salem, Unity, Unity Twp., Washingtonville); 90 (East Palestine, Fairfield, Middleton Twp., Negley, New Waterford, Unity, Unity Twp.). Franchise award date: N.A. Franchise expiration date: January 1, 2005. Began: June 1, 1973.
Channel capacity: 55 (2-way capable; operating 2-way). Channels available but not in use: N.A.
Basic Service
Subscribers: 6,041.
Programming (received off-air): WNEO (P) Alliance; WJW (F) Cleveland; WUAB (U) Lorain-Cleveland; KDKA-TV (C), WPGH-TV (F), WPXI (N) Pittsburgh; WFMJ-TV (N), WKBN-TV (C), WYTV (A,F) Youngstown; allband FM.
Programming (via microwave): Ecumenical TV Channel.
Programming (via satellite): A & E; C-SPAN; CNBC; CNN; Discovery Channel; Fox Family Channel; Headline News; Knowledge TV; Lifetime; MTV; Nashville Network; Nickelodeon; QVC; TBS Superstation; The Weather Channel.
Current originations: Automated time-weather.
Fee: $60.00 installation; $8.39 monthly; $2.00 converter.
Expanded Basic Service
Subscribers: 5,211.
Programming (via satellite): American Movie Classics; Court TV; ESPN; Fox Sports Net Pittsburgh; Turner Network TV; USA Network.
Fee: $1.95 monthly.
Pay Service 1
Pay Units: 402.
Programming (via satellite): Disney Channel.
Fee: N.A.
Pay Service 2
Pay Units: 1,689.
Programming (via satellite): The New Encore.
Fee: N.A.
Pay Service 3
Pay Units: 1,105.
Programming (via satellite): HBO.
Fee: N.A.
Pay Service 4
Pay Units: 335.
Programming (via satellite): Showtime.
Fee: N.A.
Program Guide: The Cable Guide.
Equipment: Ameco headend; C-COR & Jerrold amplifiers; AFC satellite antenna.
Miles of plant: 125.5 (coaxial). Homes passed: 6,836. Total homes in franchised area: 15,948.
Manager: Terry Kelley. Chief technician: Carl Larkins.
City fee: 3% of gross.
Ownership: AT&T Broadband & Internet Services (MSO). Purchased from Tele-Communications Inc., March 9, 1999.

EDON—FrontierVision, Box 627, 32 Enterprise Dr., Chillicothe, OH 45601. Phones: 740-775-4300; 800-346-2288. Fax: 740-775-2915. County: Williams. ICA: OH0240.
TV Market Ranking: Below 100. Franchise award date: N.A. Franchise expiration date: N.A. Began: May 1, 1985.
Channel capacity: 37. Channels available but not in use: 6.
Basic Service
Subscribers: 166.
Programming (received off-air): WBGU-TV (P) Bowling Green; WANE-TV (C), WFFT-TV (F), WKJG-TV (N), WPTA (A) Fort Wayne; WILX-TV (N) Lansing; WNWO-TV (N), WTOL-TV (C), WTVG (A) Toledo.
Programming (via satellite): WGN-TV (W) Chicago; A & E; C-SPAN; CNN; Discovery Channel; Disney Channel; ESPN; Fox Family Channel; Home Shopping Network; Lifetime; MTV; Nashville Network; Nickelodeon; TBS Superstation; The Weather Channel; USA Network; VH1.
Fee: $42.50 installation; $17.95 monthly.
Pay Service 1
Pay Units: 21.
Programming (via satellite): Cinemax.
Fee: N.A.
Pay Service 2
Pay Units: 1.
Programming (via satellite): The New Encore.
Fee: N.A.
Pay Service 3
Pay Units: 25.
Programming (via satellite): HBO.
Fee: $10.00 installation; $10.00 monthly.
Pay Service 4
Pay Units: 1.
Programming (via satellite): Starz!
Fee: N.A.
Miles of plant: 10.0 (coaxial). Homes passed: 372.
Manager: Richard Coplan. Chief technician: Sam Morabith. Program director: Chad Hume. Marketing director: Barbara Brewer.
Ownership: FrontierVision Partners LP (MSO). See Cable System Ownership.

ELYRIA—MediaOne, 576 Ternes Ave., Elyria, OH 44035. Phone: 800-425-2225. County: Lorain. Also serves Avon Lake, Carlisle Twp. (Lorain County), Elyria Twp. (Lorain County). ICA: OH0026.
TV Market Ranking: 8. Franchise award date: January 1, 1979. Franchise expiration date: September 1, 1999. Began: September 15, 1980.
Channel capacity: 61 (2-way capable; operating 2-way). Channels available but not in use: None.
Note: Basic subscribers, pay units, miles of plant & homes passed include figures for Bay Village, OH.
Basic Service
Subscribers: 35,989.
Programming (received off-air): WBNX-TV (W,F), WEAO (P), WVPX (X) Akron; WEWS-TV (A), WJW (F), WKYC-TV (N), WQHS-TV (H), WVIZ-TV (P) Cleveland; WUAB (U) Lorain-Cleveland; WGGN-TV (T) Sandusky; WOIO (C) Shaker Heights; 21 FMs.
Programming (via satellite): C-SPAN; C-SPAN 2; EWTN; QVC; TV Guide Channel; TV Guide Sneak Prevue; The Inspirational Network.
Current originations: Public access; educational access; government access; automated emergency alert.
Fee: N.A.
Expanded Basic Service
Subscribers: N.A.
Programming (via satellite): WGN-TV (W) Chicago; A & E; American Movie Classics; BET; CNBC; CNN; Discovery Channel; Disney Channel; ESPN; Fox Family Channel; Fox Sports Net Ohio; Headline News; Lifetime; MTV; Nashville Network; Nickelodeon; TBS Superstation; The Weather Channel; Turner Network TV; USA Network; VH1.
Fee: N.A.
Pay Service 1
Pay Units: N.A.
Programming (via satellite): Cinemax; HBO; Showtime.
Fee: N.A.
Pay-Per-View
Hot Choice; Viewer's Choice.
Local advertising: Yes. Available in satellite distributed programming.
Equipment: Scientific-Atlanta headend; Magnavox amplifiers; Comm/Scope cable; Panasonic cameras; Sony VTRs; Video Data Systems character generator; Jerrold set top converters; Eagle traps; Scientific-Atlanta & Fort Worth Tower satellite antenna; Microdyne satellite receivers.
Miles of plant: 639.0 (coaxial); 62.0 (fiber optic). Homes passed: 55,882.
Program director: Joan Lowry.
City fee: 3% of basic.
Ownership: MediaOne Group (MSO). See Cable System Ownership.

ENTERPRISE—FrontierVision, Box 648, 102 Twin Oak Dr., Jackson, OH 45640. Phone: 614-345-4329. Fax: 614-286-1489. County: Hocking. Also serves Falls Twp. (Hocking County), Good Hope Twp., Laurel Twp., Logan, Rockbridge. ICA: OH0232.
TV Market Ranking: 27 (Enterprise, portions of Falls Twp., Good Hope Twp., Laurel Twp., Logan, Rockbridge); Below 100 (portions of Falls Twp.). Franchise award date: N.A. Franchise expiration date: N.A. Began: October 1, 1989.
Channel capacity: 32. Channels available but not in use: 2.
Basic Service
Subscribers: 664.
Programming (received off-air): WOUB-TV (P) Athens; WBNS-TV (C), WCMH-TV (N), WSYX (A), WTTE (F,U) Columbus; WSFJ (I) Newark.
Programming (via satellite): WGN-TV (W) Chicago; A & E; CNN; Country Music TV; Discovery Channel; ESPN; Fox Family Channel; MTV; Nashville Network; Nickelodeon; TBS Superstation; Turner Network TV; USA Network.
Fee: $20.99 installation; $23.70 monthly.
Pay Service 1
Pay Units: 65.
Programming (via satellite): The New Encore.
Fee: N.A.
Pay Service 2
Pay Units: 85.
Programming (via satellite): HBO.
Fee: $11.95 monthly.
Pay Service 3
Pay Units: 98.
Programming (via satellite): Showtime.
Fee: $10.95 monthly.
Pay Service 4
Pay Units: 64.
Programming (via satellite): Starz!
Fee: N.A.
Pay Service 5
Pay Units: 73.
Programming (via satellite): The Movie Channel.

Fee: N.A.
Equipment: Triple Crown headend; Texscan & Triple Crown amplifiers; Belden & Times Fiber cable; Hamlin & NSC set top converters; Arcom, Eagle & Pico traps; Prodelin satellite antenna; Standard Communications satellite receivers.
Miles of plant: 48.3 (coaxial). Homes passed: 891.
Manager: Steve Trippe. Chief technician: Bill Ricker.
Ownership: FrontierVision Partners LP (MSO). See Cable System Ownership.

EUREKA—FrontierVision, Box 627, Chillicothe, OH 45601. Phones: 740-775-4300; 800-346-2288. Fax: 740-775-2915. County: Gallia. ICA: OH0378.
TV Market Ranking: 36. Franchise award date: N.A. Franchise expiration date: N.A. Began: N.A.
Channel capacity: 29 (not 2-way capable). Channels available but not in use: None.
Basic Service
Subscribers: 261.
Programming (received off-air): WCHS-TV (A), WOWK-TV (C), WPBY-TV (P), WSAZ-TV (N), WVAH-TV (F,U) Charleston-Huntington.
Programming (via satellite): WGN-TV (W) Chicago; A & E; American Movie Classics; CNN; Country Music TV; Discovery Channel; Disney Channel; ESPN; Fox Family Channel; Headline News; Home Shopping Network; Lifetime; Nashville Network; Nickelodeon; TBS Superstation; Trinity Bcstg. Network; Turner Network TV; USA Network.
Fee: $26.00 monthly.
Pay Service 1
Pay Units: 24.
Programming (via satellite): Cinemax.
Fee: N.A.
Pay Service 2
Pay Units: 33.
Programming (via satellite): HBO.
Fee: N.A.
Pay Service 3
Pay Units: 21.
Programming (via satellite): Showtime.
Fee: N.A.
Miles of plant: 28.0 (coaxial). Homes passed: 400.
Manager: Richard Coplan. Chief technician: Sam Morabith. Program director: Chad Hume. Marketing director: Barbara Brewer.
Ownership: FrontierVision Partners LP (MSO). See Cable System Ownership.

FAIRBORN—MediaOne, One Herald Square, Fairborn, OH 45324. Phones: 937-294-6400; 800-425-2225. Fax: 937-294-3994. Web site: http://www.mediaone.com. County: Greene. Also serves Xenia. ICA: OH0432.
TV Market Ranking: 41. Franchise award date: N.A. Franchise expiration date: N.A. Began: N.A.
Channel capacity: N.A. Channels available but not in use: N.A.
Basic Service
Subscribers: 16,581.
Programming (received off-air): WCET (P), WCPO-TV (A), WKRC-TV (C) Cincinnati; WXIX-TV (F) Cincinnati-Newport; WDTN (A), WHIO-TV (C), WKEF (N), WPTD (P), WRGT-TV (F,U) Dayton; WPTO (P) Oxford; WKOI (T) Richmond; WBDT (W) Springfield.
Programming (via satellite): EWTN; Fox News Channel; Home Shopping Network; MSNBC; QVC; TV Food Network; TV Guide Channel; The Weather Channel; Travel Channel; ValueVision; Z Music Television.
Current originations: Public access; educational access; government access.
Fee: $41.00 installation; $10.38 monthly.
Expanded Basic Service
Subscribers: N.A.
Programming (via satellite): A & E; American Movie Classics; Animal Planet; BET; Bravo; C-SPAN; C-SPAN 2; CNBC; CNN; Cartoon Network; Comedy Central; Country Music TV; Court TV; Discovery Channel; E! Entertainment TV; ESPN; ESPN 2; Fox Family Channel; Fox Sports Net Ohio; Golf Channel; Headline News; History Channel; Home & Garden Television; Learning Channel; Lifetime; MTV; Nashville Network; Nick at Nite's TV Land; Nickelodeon; Outdoor Life Network; Sci-Fi Channel; Speedvision; USA Network; VH1.
Fee: $19.08 monthly.
Expanded Basic Service 2
Subscribers: N.A.
Programming (via satellite): WGN-TV (W) Chicago; TBS Superstation; Turner Network TV.
Fee: $1.61 monthly.
Pay Service 1
Pay Units: N.A.
Programming (via satellite): Cinemax; Disney Channel; HBO (multiplexed); Independent Film Channel; Showtime; Starz!; The New Encore.
Fee: $5.95 monthly (IFC), $10.95 monthly (Encore & Starz), $11.50 monthly (Disney), $11.95 monthly (Cinemax, HBO or Showtime).
Pay-Per-View
Hot Choice; Spice Hot; Viewer's Choice 1-4.
Ownership: MediaOne Group (MSO). Sale pends to Time Warner Cable.

FAIRFIELD (Butler County)—Coaxial Communications of Southern Ohio Inc., 3416 State Rte. 132, Amelia, OH 45102. Phone: 513-797-4400. Fax: 513-797-8625. County: Butler South. ICA: OH0376.
TV Market Ranking: 17,41. Franchise award date: December 1, 1992. Franchise expiration date: June 15, 2004. Began: December 1, 1992.
Channel capacity: 42. Channels available but not in use: 5.
Basic Service
Subscribers: 1,391.
Programming (received off-air): WCET (P), WCPO-TV (A), WKRC-TV (C), WLWT (N), WSTR-TV (W) Cincinnati; WXIX-TV (F) Cincinnati-Newport; WDTN (A), WHIO-TV (C), WKEF (N), WPTD (P), WRGT-TV (F,U) Dayton; WPTO (P) Oxford.
Programming (via satellite): WGN-TV (W) Chicago; A & E; American Movie Classics; BET; CNBC; CNN; Discovery Channel; ESPN; Fox Family Channel; Headline News; Lifetime; MTV; Nashville Network; Nickelodeon; Sci-Fi Channel; TBS Superstation; The Weather Channel; USA Network; VH1.
Fee: $31.95 installation; $7.13 monthly.
Pay Service 1
Pay Units: 174.
Programming (via satellite): Cinemax.
Fee: $11.00 monthly.
Pay Service 2
Pay Units: 127.
Programming (via satellite): Disney Channel.
Fee: $11.00 monthly.
Pay Service 3
Pay Units: 578.
Programming (via satellite): HBO.
Fee: $11.00 monthly.
Pay Service 4
Pay Units: 57.
Programming (via satellite): Playboy TV.
Fee: $10.00 monthly.
Pay Service 5
Pay Units: 105.
Programming (via satellite): Showtime.
Fee: $11.00 monthly.
Local advertising: Yes. Available in satellite distributed programming.
Equipment: Scientific-Atlanta headend; Magnavox amplifiers; Comm/Scope cable; Jerrold set top converters.
Miles of plant: 12.0 (coaxial). Homes passed: 2,113.
Manager: Arthur P. Loescher.
Ownership: Coaxial Communications (MSO).

FAIRFIELD TWP. (Butler County)—TCI Cablevision of Ohio Inc., Box 710, 341 City Centre Mall, Middletown, OH 45044. Phone: 513-424-2408. Fax: 513-896-5455. County: Butler South. Also serves Fairfield (Butler County), Indian Springs. ICA: OH0051.
TV Market Ranking: 17,41. Franchise award date: N.A. Franchise expiration date: N.A. Began: N.A.
Channel capacity: 60. Channels available but not in use: 14.
Basic Service
Subscribers: 13,048.
Programming (received off-air): WCET (P), WCPO-TV (A), WKRC-TV (C), WLWT (N), WSTR-TV (W) Cincinnati; WXIX-TV (F) Cincinnati-Newport; WDTN (A), WHIO-TV (C), WKEF (N), WPTD (P), WRGT-TV (F,U) Dayton; WPTO (P) Oxford; WKOI (T) Richmond.
Programming (via satellite): WGN-TV (W) Chicago; TBS Superstation; TV Guide Sneak Prevue.
Fee: $28.17 installation; $9.75 monthly; $0.53 converter.
Expanded Basic Service
Subscribers: 12,428.
Programming (via satellite): A & E; American Movie Classics; BET; C-SPAN; C-SPAN 2; CNBC; CNN; Court TV; Discovery Channel; ESPN; ESPN 2; FX; Fox Family Channel; Headline News; Intro TV; Knowledge TV; Lifetime; MTV; Nashville Network; Nickelodeon; Odyssey; QVC; TV Food Network; The Weather Channel; Turner Network TV; USA Network.
Fee: $12.11 monthly.
A la Carte 1
Subscribers: N.A.
Programming (via satellite): Cartoon Network; Country Music TV; E! Entertainment TV; Learning Channel.
Fee: $3.00 monthly (package); $0.85 monthly (each).
Pay Service 1
Pay Units: 1,908.
Programming (via satellite): Cinemax.
Fee: $13.12 monthly.
Pay Service 2
Pay Units: 1,102.
Programming (via satellite): Disney Channel.
Fee: $12.88 monthly.
Pay Service 3
Pay Units: 5,923.
Programming (via satellite): The New Encore.
Fee: $1.68 monthly.
Pay Service 4
Pay Units: 4,594.
Programming (via satellite): HBO.
Fee: $14.04 monthly.
Pay Service 5
Pay Units: 999.
Programming (via satellite): Showtime.
Fee: $14.04 monthly.
Pay Service 6
Pay Units: N.A.
Programming (via satellite): DMX; Starz!
Fee: $4.75 monthly (Starz), $4.95 monthly (DMX).
Pay-Per-View
Action Pay-Per-View; Spice; Viewer's Choice.
Miles of plant: 209.7 (coaxial). Homes passed: 16,690. Total homes in franchised area: 20,888.
Manager: Jeff Heinrich. Chief technician: Randy Senger.
Ownership: AT&T Broadband & Internet Services (MSO). Purchased from Tele-Communications Inc., March 9, 1999.

FAIRVIEW PARK—Americast, 300 S. Riverside, Chicago, IL 60606. Phones: 312-526-8000; 800-848-2278. Fax: 312-526-8565. County: Cuyahoga. ICA: OH0413.
TV Market Ranking: 8. Franchise award date: March 1, 1997. Franchise expiration date: N.A. Began: N.A.
Channel capacity: N.A. Channels available but not in use: N.A.
Basic Service
Subscribers: N.A.
Programming (received off-air): WBNX-TV (W,F), WVPX (X) Akron; WOAC (I) Canton; WEWS-TV (A), WJW (F), WKYC-TV (N), WQHS-TV (H), WVIZ-TV (P) Cleveland; WUAB (U) Lorain-Cleveland; WOIO (C) Shaker Heights.
Programming (via satellite): WGN-TV (W) Chicago; QVC; TBS Superstation; TV Guide Channel; TV Guide Sneak Prevue.
Current originations: Public access; educational access; government access; leased access.
Fee: $39.95 installation; $9.95 monthly.
Expanded Basic Service
Subscribers: N.A.
Programming (via satellite): A & E; American Movie Classics; Animal Planet; BET; Bravo; C-SPAN; C-SPAN 2; CNBC; CNN; CNNfn; Cartoon Network; Comedy Central; Country Music TV; Court TV; Discovery Channel; Disney Channel; E! Entertainment TV; ESPN; ESPN 2; ESPN Classic Sports; ESPNews; Fox Family Channel; Fox Sports Net Ohio; Golf Channel; Goodlife TV Network; Headline News; History Channel; Home & Garden Television; Learning Channel; Lifetime; MTV; Nashville Network; Nickelodeon; Sci-Fi Channel; TV Food Network; The Health Network; The Inspirational Network; The Weather Channel; Travel Channel; Turner Classic Movies; Turner Network TV; USA Network; VH1.
Fee: $17.00 monthly.
Pay Service 1
Pay Units: N.A.
Programming (via satellite): Cinemax; Flix; HBO (multiplexed); Showtime (multiplexed); Starz!; The Movie Channel; The New Encore.
Fee: $5.95 monthly (Flix or Encore & Starz), $9.95 monthly (Cinemax, Showtime or TMC), $10.95 monthly (HBO).
Total homes in franchised area: 8,150.
Ownership: Ameritech New Media Inc. (MSO).

FAYETTE—FrontierVision, Box 627, 32 Enterprise Dr., Chillicothe, OH 45601. Phones: 740-775-4300; 800-346-2288. Fax: 740-775-2915. Counties: Fulton, OH; Lenawee, MI. Also serves Morenci, MI. ICA: OH0194.
TV Market Ranking: Below 100 (Fayette); Outside TV Markets (Morenci). Franchise award date: N.A. Franchise expiration date: N.A. Began: December 1, 1983.

Channel capacity: 62. Channels available but not in use: 8.

Basic Service

Subscribers: 853.

Programming (received off-air): WKAR-TV (P) East Lansing; WILX-TV (N) Lansing; WGTE-TV (P), WNWO-TV (N), WTOL-TV (C), WTVG (A), WUPW (F) Toledo.

Programming (via satellite): WGN-TV (W) Chicago; A & E; CNN; Discovery Channel; Disney Channel; ESPN; Fox Family Channel; Headline News; Home Shopping Network; Lifetime; MTV; Nashville Network; Nickelodeon; TBS Superstation; The Weather Channel; Turner Network TV; USA Network; VH1.

Fee: $42.50 installation; $17.95 monthly.

Pay Service 1

Pay Units: 98.

Programming (via satellite): Cinemax.

Fee: N.A.

Pay Service 2

Pay Units: 84.

Programming (via satellite): The New Encore.

Fee: N.A.

Pay Service 3

Pay Units: 109.

Programming (via satellite): HBO.

Fee: $10.00 installation; $10.00 monthly.

Pay Service 4

Pay Units: 48.

Programming (via satellite): Showtime.

Fee: $10.00 installation; $10.00 monthly.

Pay Service 5

Pay Units: 84.

Programming (via satellite): Starz!

Fee: N.A.

Pay Service 6

Pay Units: 44.

Programming (via satellite): The Movie Channel.

Fee: N.A.

Miles of plant: 30.0 (coaxial). Homes passed: 1,511.

Manager: Richard Coplan. Chief technician: Sam Morabith. Program director: Chad Hume. Marketing director: Barbara Brewer.

Ownership: FrontierVision Partners LP (MSO). See Cable System Ownership.

FINDLAY—Time Warner Cable, 209 W. Main Cross St., Findlay, OH 45840. Phone: 419-423-8515. Fax: 419-423-5631. County: Hancock. Also serves Allen Twp. (Hancock County), Amanda Twp., Arlington, Biglick Twp., Blanchard Twp. (Hancock County), Delaware Twp., Eagle Twp. (Hancock County), Jackson Twp. (Hancock County), Liberty Twp. (Hancock County), Madison Twp. (Hancock County), Marion Twp. (Hancock County), McComb, Mount Blanchard, Mount Cory, Pleasant Twp. (Hancock County), Rawson, Union Twp. (Hancock County), Van Buren, Vanlue. ICA: OH0036.

TV Market Ranking: Below 100 (Allen Twp., portions of Amanda Twp., Arlington, portions of Biglick Twp., Blanchard Twp., Delaware Twp., Eagle Twp., Findlay, Jackson Twp., Liberty Twp., Madison Twp., Marion Twp., McComb, Mount Blanchard, Mount Cory, Pleasant Twp., Rawson); Outside TV Markets (portions of Amanda Twp., portions of Biglick Twp., Van Buren, Vanlue). Franchise award date: August 1, 1963. Franchise expiration date: August 1, 1999. Began: February 8, 1965.

Channel capacity: 60 (not 2-way capable). Channels available but not in use: N.A.

Basic Service

Subscribers: 15,853.

Programming (received off-air): WBGU-TV (P) Bowling Green; WLIO (N), WTLW (I) Lima; WGTE-TV (P), WNWO-TV (N), WTOL-TV (C), WTVG (A), WUPW (F) Toledo; 17 FMs.

Programming (via microwave): WEWS-TV (A) Cleveland; WBNS-TV (C) Columbus; WKBD-TV (U) Detroit; WUAB (U) Lorain-Cleveland; CBET Windsor.

Programming (via satellite): A & E; C-SPAN; C-SPAN 2; CNBC; CNN; Discovery Channel; ESPN; Electronic Program Guide; Fox Family Channel; Headline News; Home Shopping Network; Lifetime; MTV; Nashville Network; Nickelodeon; Odyssey; QVC; TBS Superstation; TV Guide Channel; The Weather Channel; Turner Network TV; USA Network; VH1.

Current originations: Automated time-weather; public access; educational access; automated emergency alert; local news.

Fee: $19.95 installation; $17.95 monthly; $9.50 additional installation.

Pay Service 1

Pay Units: 13,129.

Programming (via satellite): Cinemax; Disney Channel; HBO; Showtime.

Fee: N.A.

Local advertising: Yes (insert only). Available in satellite distributed & locally originated programming. Rates: $34.00/Minute; $17.00/30 Seconds. Local sales manager: Dick Callahan.

Equipment: Scientific-Atlanta headend; Magnavox amplifiers; Comm/Scope & Times Fiber cable; Hitachi cameras; Sony VTRs; Info/Soft & CACS character generator; RCA & Panasonic set top converters; Arcom & Eagle traps; Andrew, Scientific-Atlanta & RCA satellite antenna; Standard Components satellite receivers; Texscan commercial insert.

Miles of plant: 242.0 (coaxial); 29.0 (fiber optic). Homes passed: 22,588.

Manager: Pat McCauley.

City fee: 3% of gross (Findlay & McComb).

Ownership: Time Warner Cable (MSO). Purchased from MediaOne Group, August 2, 1999.

FLUSHING—TCI Cablevision of Ohio, Box 469, Bridgeport, OH 43912. Phones: 740-633-2232; 800-527-2222. County: Belmont. Also serves Holloway. ICA: OH0243.

TV Market Ranking: 90. Franchise award date: N.A. Franchise expiration date: N.A. Began: October 1, 1973.

Channel capacity: 35. Channels available but not in use: 6.

Basic Service

Subscribers: 547.

Programming (received off-air): WVPX (X) Akron; WOUC-TV (P) Cambridge; WDLI (T) Canton; KDKA-TV (C), WPGH-TV (F), WPXI (N), WQED (P), WTAE-TV (A) Pittsburgh; WTOV-TV (N) Steubenville-Wheeling; WTRF-TV (C) Wheeling-Steubenville.

Programming (via satellite): C-SPAN; CNBC; CNN; Discovery Channel; Fox Family Channel; Lifetime; MTV; Nashville Network; Nickelodeon; Odyssey; TBS Superstation.

Fee: $60.00 installation; $9.51 monthly; $4.00 converter.

Expanded Basic Service

Subscribers: 496.

Programming (via satellite): A & E; American Movie Classics; ESPN; Turner Network TV; USA Network.

Fee: $10.33 monthly.

Pay Service 1

Pay Units: 111.

Programming (via satellite): HBO.

Fee: N.A.

Pay Service 2

Pay Units: 62.

Programming (via satellite): Showtime.

Fee: N.A.

Pay Service 3

Pay Units: 232.

Programming (via satellite): The New Encore.

Fee: N.A.

Miles of plant: 10.6 (coaxial). Homes passed: 779. Total homes in franchised area: 895.

Manager: Robert Weese. Chief technician: Earl Conway.

Ownership: AT&T Broadband & Internet Services (MSO). Purchased from Tele-Communications Inc., March 9, 1999.

FOREST—Time Warner Cable, Box 787, 111 S. Mulberry St., Mount Vernon, OH 43050. Phones: 740-397-2288; 800-782-4118. Fax: 740-397-3730. Counties: Hardin & Wyandot. Also serves Patterson, Wharton. ICA: OH0222.

TV Market Ranking: Below 100. Franchise award date: N.A. Franchise expiration date: N.A. Began: December 1, 1983.

Channel capacity: 61. Channels available but not in use: 31.

Basic Service

Subscribers: 468.

Programming (received off-air): WBGU-TV (P) Bowling Green; WBNS-TV (C), WTTE (F,U) Columbus; WLIO (N), WTLW (I) Lima; WNWO-TV (N), WTVG (A) Toledo.

Programming (via satellite): WGN-TV (W) Chicago; A & E; CNBC; CNN; Comedy Central; Country Music TV; Discovery Channel; ESPN; Fox Family Channel; Headline News; Lifetime; MTV; Nashville Network; Nickelodeon; QVC; TBS Superstation; The Weather Channel; Turner Network TV; USA Network; VH1.

Fee: $32.00 installation; $19.95 monthly; $4.50 converter; $9.00 additional installation.

Pay Service 1

Pay Units: 71.

Programming (via satellite): Cinemax.

Fee: $18.00 installation; $10.95 monthly.

Pay Service 2

Pay Units: 36.

Programming (via satellite): Disney Channel.

Fee: $18.00 installation; $10.95 monthly.

Pay Service 3

Pay Units: 99.

Programming (via satellite): HBO.

Fee: $18.00 installation; $10.95 monthly.

Local advertising: No. Local sales manager: Jon Quatman.

Miles of plant: 22.7 (coaxial). Homes passed: 1,005.

Manager: Paul S. Schonewolf. Technical operations manager: Dan Fessler. Field operations manager: Bill Schroeder. Marketing manager: Carl Bauer. Customer operations manager: Danielle Turner.

City fee: 3% of gross.

Ownership: Time Warner Cable (MSO).

FORT JENNINGS—Fort Jennings Telephone Co., Box 146, 65 W. 3rd St., Fort Jennings, OH 45844. Phone: 419-286-2181. Fax: 419-286-2193. County: Putnam. ICA: OH0253.

TV Market Ranking: Below 100. Franchise award date: N.A. Franchise expiration date: N.A. Began: September 1, 1987.

Channel capacity: 36 (not 2-way capable). Channels available but not in use: 3.

Basic Service

Subscribers: 426.

Programming (received off-air): WBGU-TV (P) Bowling Green; WANE-TV (C), WFFT-TV (F), WPTA (A) Fort Wayne; WLIO (N) Lima; WNWO-TV (N), WTOL-TV (C), WTVG (A), WUPW (F) Toledo.

Programming (via satellite): WGN-TV (W) Chicago; A & E; CNN; Discovery Channel; ESPN; ESPN 2; EWTN; Fox Family Channel; Fox Sports Net Ohio; Lifetime; Nashville Network; Nickelodeon; TBS Superstation; The Weather Channel; Turner Classic Movies; Turner Network TV; USA Network.

Current originations: Automated time-weather.

Fee: $24.50 installation; $14.95 monthly.

Pay Service 1

Pay Units: 55.

Programming (via satellite): Disney Channel.

Fee: $7.95 monthly.

Pay Service 2

Pay Units: 47.

Programming (via satellite): HBO.

Fee: $10.45 monthly.

Pay Service 3

Pay Units: 107.

Programming (via satellite): Showtime.

Fee: $8.45 monthly.

Pay Service 4

Pay Units: 73.

Programming (via satellite): The Movie Channel.

Fee: $8.45 monthly.

Miles of plant: 39.0 (coaxial); 4.0 (fiber optic). Homes passed: 481. Total homes in franchised area: 660.

Manager: David Will. Chief technician: Mike Metzger.

Ownership: Fort Jennings Telephone Co.

FORT RECOVERY (village)—Americable International, 129 E. Water St., Portland, IN 47371. Phones: 219-726-8101; 800-347-3381. Fax: 219-726-6494. County: Mercer. ICA: OH0324.

TV Market Ranking: Outside TV Markets. Franchise award date: N.A. Franchise expiration date: September 19, 2005. Began: May 1, 1987.

Channel capacity: 63. Channels available but not in use: 5.

Basic Service

Subscribers: 275.

Programming (received off-air): WDTN (A), WHIO-TV (C), WRGT-TV (F,U) Dayton; WANE-TV (C), WFFT-TV (F), WKJG-TV (N), WPTA (A) Fort Wayne; WTTK (I) Kokomo; WLIO (N) Lima; WNDY-TV (U) Marion; WIPB (P) Muncie.

Programming (via satellite): WGN-TV (W) Chicago; A & E; American Movie Classics; C-SPAN; C-SPAN 2; CNBC; CNN; Comedy Central; Country Music TV; Discovery Channel; ESPN; EWTN; Electronic Program Guide; FX; fXM: Movies from Fox; Fox Family Channel; Fox Sports Net Ohio; Goodlife TV Network; Headline News; Home Shopping Network; Learning Channel; Lifetime; MOR Galleria; MTV; Nashville Network; Nickelodeon; QVC; Sci-Fi Channel; TBS Superstation; The Inspirational Network; The Weather Channel; Travel Channel; Trinity Bcstg. Network; Turner Classic Movies; Turner Network TV; USA Network; VH1.

Fee: $40.00 installation; $25.95 monthly.

Pay Service 1

Pay Units: N.A.

Programming (via satellite): Disney Channel; HBO; Showtime; The Movie Channel; The New Encore.

Fee: N.A.

Miles of plant: 13.0 (coaxial); 18.5 (fiber optic). Homes passed: 538. Total homes in franchised area: 538.

Manager: Rick Hensley. Chief technician: Ken Daniels.

Ownership: Americable International Inc. (MSO).

FORT SHAWNEE—Time Warner Entertainment Co. LP, 3100 Elida Rd., Lima, OH 45805. Phone: 419-331-3333. Fax: 419-331-1573. Counties: Allen & Auglaize. Also serves Allen County (portions), Auglaize County (portions), Cridersville. ICA: OH0120.

TV Market Ranking: Below 100. Franchise award date: N.A. Franchise expiration date: N.A. Began: January 28, 1968.

Channel capacity: 36. Channels available but not in use: 1.

Basic Service

Subscribers: 3,663.

Programming (received off-air): WBGU-TV (P) Bowling Green; WBNS-TV (C) Columbus; WHIO-TV (C) Dayton; WFFT-TV (F) Fort Wayne; WLIO (N), WTLW (I) Lima; WNWO-TV (N), WTVG (A), WUPW (F) Toledo; allband FM.

Programming (via satellite): A & E; BET; C-SPAN; CNBC; CNN; Comedy Central; Discovery Channel; ESPN; Fox Family Channel; Headline News; Lifetime; MTV; Nashville Network; Nickelodeon; QVC; TBS Superstation; The Weather Channel; Turner Network TV; USA Network; VH1.

Current originations: Automated time-weather.

Fee: $14.95 installation; $14.65 monthly.

Pay Service 1

Pay Units: 193.

Programming (via satellite): Cinemax.

Fee: $10.95 monthly.

Pay Service 2

Pay Units: 424.

Programming (via satellite): Disney Channel.

Fee: $6.95 monthly.

Pay Service 3

Pay Units: 477.

Programming (via satellite): HBO.

Fee: $10.95 monthly.

Pay Service 4

Pay Units: 319.

Programming (via satellite): Showtime.

Fee: $10.95 monthly.

Pay Service 5

Pay Units: 187.

Programming (via satellite): The Movie Channel.

Fee: $11.95 monthly.

Pay-Per-View

Addressable homes: 1,130.

Action Pay-Per-View.

Equipment: RCA headend; Jerrold amplifiers; Comm/Scope cable; Sony cameras; Sony VTRs; Compuvid character generator; Vitek traps; Scientific-Atlanta satellite antenna; Scientific-Atlanta satellite receivers.

Miles of plant: 92.0 (coaxial). Homes passed: 4,476. Total homes in franchised area: 4,496.

Manager: Jeff Parker. Chief technician: Ron Lamb. Marketing director: Sandy Bayliff.

City fee: 3% of gross.

Ownership: Time Warner Cable (MSO).

FOSTORIA—Time Warner Cable, 119 N. Main St., Fostoria, OH 44830. Phone: 800-425-2225. Counties: Hancock, Sandusky, Seneca & Wood. Also serves Arcadia, Bascom, Clinton Twp. (Seneca County), Eden Twp. (Seneca County), Hopewell Twp. (Seneca County), Jackson Twp. (Sandusky County), Jackson Twp. (Seneca County), Loudon Twp. (Seneca County), Perry Twp. (Wood County), Tiffin, Washington Twp. (Hancock County). ICA: OH0050.

TV Market Ranking: 52 (Fostoria, Jackson Twp., Perry Twp.); Below 100 (Bascom, Tiffin); Outside TV Markets (Arcadia, Clinton Twp., Eden Twp., Hopewell Twp., Loudon Twp., Washington Twp.). Franchise award date: N.A. Franchise expiration date: January 1, 2008. Began: December 1, 1964.

Channel capacity: 52 (not 2-way capable). Channels available but not in use: 8.

Basic Service

Subscribers: Included with Sycamore, OH.

Programming (received off-air): WBGU-TV (P) Bowling Green; W54AF (I) Bucyrus; WEWS-TV (A), WJW (F), WKYC-TV (N) Cleveland; WKBD-TV (U) Detroit; WLIO (N) Lima; WUAB (U) Lorain-Cleveland; WGGN-TV (T) Sandusky; WGTE-TV (P), WNWO-TV (N), WTOL-TV (C), WTVG (A), WUPW (F) Toledo; CBET Windsor; allband FM.

Programming (via satellite): A & E; C-SPAN; C-SPAN 2; CNBC; CNN; Discovery Channel; ESPN; Fox Family Channel; Headline News; Home Shopping Network; Lifetime; MTV; Nashville Network; Nickelodeon; QVC; TBS Superstation; The Weather Channel; Turner Network TV; USA Network; VH1.

Current originations: Public access; educational access; government access; automated emergency alert; local news.

Fee: $15.00 installation; $17.50 monthly; $2.95 converter.

Pay Service 1

Pay Units: Included with Sycamore, OH.

Programming (via satellite): Cinemax; Disney Channel; HBO; Showtime.

Fee: $15.00 installation; $10.95 monthly (each).

Local advertising: Yes. Available in locally originated, taped & automated programming. Rates: $100.00/Month.

Equipment: Scientific-Atlanta & Standard Components headend; Magnavox amplifiers; Comm/Scope & Times Fiber cable; Sony cameras; Panasonic & Sony VTRs; Atari character generator; RCA & Pioneer set top converters; Eagle & Arcom traps; Microdyne satellite antenna; Microdyne & Standard Components satellite receivers.

Miles of plant & homes passed included with Sycamore, OH.

Manager: Pat McCauley.

City fee: None.

Ownership: Time Warner Cable (MSO). Purchased from MediaOne Group, August 2, 1999.

FRANKFORT—FrontierVision, Box 648, 102 Twin Oak Dr., Jackson, OH 45640. Phone: 614-345-4329. Fax: 614-286-1489. County: Ross. Also serves South Salem. ICA: OH0227.

TV Market Ranking: 27. Franchise award date: January 13, 1986. Franchise expiration date: January 13, 2001. Began: January 1, 1977.

Channel capacity: 35 (not 2-way capable). Channels available but not in use: None.

Basic Service

Subscribers: 682.

Programming (received off-air): WWHO (U) Chillicothe; WXIX-TV (F) Cincinnati-Newport; WBNS-TV (C), WCMH-TV (N), WOSU-TV (P), WSYX (A), WTTE (F,U) Columbus; WHIO-TV (C) Dayton.

Programming (via satellite): WGN-TV (W) Chicago; A & E; CNN; Comedy Central; Country Music TV; Discovery Channel; ESPN; Fox Family Channel; Learning Channel; Lifetime; MTV; Nashville Network; Nickelodeon; QVC; TBS Superstation; Turner Network TV; USA Network.

Fee: $20.99 installation; $22.70 monthly; $15.12 additional installation.

Pay Service 1

Pay Units: 56.

Programming (via satellite): The New Encore.

Fee: N.A.

Pay Service 2

Pay Units: 61.

Programming (via satellite): HBO.

Fee: $15.95 installation; $11.95 monthly.

Pay Service 3

Pay Units: 124.

Programming (via satellite): Showtime.

Fee: $15.00 installation; $10.95 monthly.

Pay Service 4

Pay Units: 51.

Programming (via satellite): Starz!

Fee: N.A.

Pay Service 5

Pay Units: 95.

Programming (via satellite): The Movie Channel.

Fee: N.A.

Equipment: Scientific-Atlanta headend; Texscan amplifiers; Times Fiber cable; Pico traps; Harris satellite antenna; Standard Communications satellite receivers.

Miles of plant: 28.0 (coaxial). Homes passed: 940.

Manager: Steve Trippe. Chief technician: Bill Ricker.

Ownership: FrontierVision Partners LP (MSO). See Cable System Ownership.

FRANKLIN FURNACE—FrontierVision, Box 627, Chillicothe, OH 45601. Phones: 740-775-4300; 800-346-2288. Fax: 740-775-2915. Counties: Lawrence & Scioto. Also serves Green Twp. (Scioto County), Hanging Rock. ICA: OH0325.

TV Market Ranking: 36. Franchise award date: N.A. Franchise expiration date: N.A. Began: N.A.

Channel capacity: 32. Channels available but not in use: None.

Basic Service

Subscribers: 889.

Programming (received off-air): WCHS-TV (A), WOWK-TV (C), WSAZ-TV (N), WVAH-TV (F,U) Charleston-Huntington; WBNS-TV (C) Columbus; WPBO-TV (P) Portsmouth.

Programming (via satellite): WGN-TV (W) Chicago; Country Music TV; Discovery Channel; Disney Channel; ESPN; ESPN 2; Fox Family Channel; MTV; Nashville Network; Nickelodeon; Sci-Fi Channel; TBS Superstation; The Weather Channel; Turner Network TV; USA Network; VH1.

Fee: $47.50 installation; $26.34 monthly.

Pay Service 1

Pay Units: 37.

Programming (via satellite): Cinemax.

Fee: $8.99 monthly.

Pay Service 2

Pay Units: 67.

Programming (via satellite): The New Encore.

Fee: $6.99 monthly.

Pay Service 3

Pay Units: 36.

Programming (via satellite): HBO.

Fee: $11.99 monthly.

Pay Service 4

Pay Units: 28.

Programming (via satellite): Showtime.

Fee: N.A.

Pay Service 5

Pay Units: 41.

Programming (via satellite): Starz!

Fee: $6.99 monthly.

Miles of plant: 49.0 (coaxial). Homes passed: 1,029.

Manager: Richard Coplan. Chief technician: Sam Morabith. Program director: Chad Hume. Marketing director: Barbara Brewer.

Ownership: FrontierVision Partners LP (MSO). See Cable System Ownership.

FRANKLIN TWP.—Ameritech New Media, 300 S. Riverside, Chicago, IL 60606. Phones: 312-526-8000; 800-848-2278. Fax: 312-526-8565. County: Franklin. ICA: OH0415.

TV Market Ranking: 27. Franchise award date: April 1, 1997. Franchise expiration date: N.A. Began: N.A.

Channel capacity: N.A. Channels available but not in use: N.A.

Basic Service

Subscribers: N.A.

Programming (received off-air): WWHO (U) Chillicothe; WBNS-TV (C), WCMH-TV (N), WOSU-TV (P), WSYX (A), WTTE (F,U) Columbus; WSFJ (I) Newark.

Programming (via satellite): WGN-TV (W) Chicago; QVC; TBS Superstation; TV Guide Channel.

Current originations: Public access; educational access; government access; leased access.

Fee: $39.95 installation; $9.95 monthly.

Expanded Basic Service

Subscribers: N.A.

Programming (via satellite): A & E; American Movie Classics; BET; BET on Jazz; Bravo; C-SPAN; C-SPAN 2; CNBC; CNN; CNNfn; Cartoon Network; Comedy Central; Country Music TV; Court TV; Discovery Channel; Disney Channel; E! Entertainment TV; ESPN; ESPN 2; ESPN Classic Sports; Fox Family Channel; Fox Sports Net Ohio; Golf Channel; Headline News; History Channel; Home & Garden Television; Learning Channel; Lifetime; MTV; Nashville Network; Nickelodeon; Ohio News Network; Sci-Fi Channel; TV Food Network; The Health Network; The Inspirational Network; The Weather Channel; Travel Channel; Turner Classic Movies; Turner Network TV; USA Network; VH1.

Fee: $17.00 monthly.

Pay Service 1

Pay Units: N.A.

Programming (via satellite): Cinemax; Flix; HBO (multiplexed); Showtime (multiplexed); Starz!; Sundance Channel; The Movie Channel; The New Encore.

Fee: $5.95 monthly (Flix or Sundance), $7.95 monthly (Encore & Starz), $9.95 monthly (Cinemax, Showtime or TMC), $11.95 monthly (HBO).

Total homes in franchised area: 5,450.

Ownership: Ameritech New Media Inc. (MSO).

FRAZEYSBURG—Cablecomm, Box 2249, 737 Howard St., Zanesville, OH 43702-2249. Phone: 888-229-4465. County: Muskingum. ICA: OH0271.

TV Market Ranking: Below 100. Franchise award date: N.A. Franchise expiration date: N.A. Began: September 1, 1970.

Channel capacity: 33 (not 2-way capable). Channels available but not in use: 4.

Basic Service

Subscribers: 446.

Programming (received off-air): WVPX (X) Akron; WOUC-TV (P) Cambridge; WBNS-TV (C), WCMH-TV (N), WOSU-TV (P), WSYX (A), WTTE (F,U) Columbus; WHIZ-TV (N) Zanesville.

Programming (via satellite): QVC; TBS Superstation.

Fee: $44.95 installation; $10.13 monthly; $3.00 converter.

Expanded Basic Service

Subscribers: 408.

Programming (via satellite): A & E; American Movie Classics; Animal Planet; CNN; Cartoon Network; Discovery Channel; ESPN; Fox Family Channel; MTV; Nashville Network; Nickelodeon; Turner Network TV; USA Network.

Fee: $13.44 monthly.

Pay Service 1

Pay Units: 26.

Programming (via satellite): Disney Channel.

Fee: $20.00 installation; $11.95 monthly.

Pay Service 2

Pay Units: 79.

Programming (via satellite): HBO.

Fee: $11.95 monthly.

Pay Service 4

Pay Units: 176.

Programming (via satellite): The New Encore.

Fee: N.A.

Equipment: Blonder-Tongue & Jerrold headend; Vikoa amplifiers; Cerro & Vikoa cable; Scientific-Atlanta satellite antenna; Scientific-Atlanta satellite receivers.

Miles of plant: 6.4 (coaxial); None (fiber optic). Homes passed: 458. Total homes in franchised area: 458.

Manager: William F. Randles. Chief technician: John Barber.

City fee: None.

Ownership: Fanch Communications Inc. (MSO); Time Warner Cable (MSO). Purchased from Tele-Communications Inc., February 25, 1999. See Cable System Ownership.

FREDERICKTOWN—Time Warner Cable, Box 787, 111 S. Mulberry St., Mount Vernon, OH 43050. Phones: 740-397-2288; 800-782-4118. Fax: 740-397-3730. Counties: Knox & Richland. Also serves Bellville, Butler. ICA: OH0326.

TV Market Ranking: Below 100. Franchise award date: January 1, 1978. Franchise expiration date: N.A. Began: December 1, 1979.

Channel capacity: 21 (not 2-way capable). Channels available but not in use: None.

Basic Service

Subscribers: 2,576.

Programming (received off-air): WEWS-TV (A), WJW (F), WKYC-TV (N) Cleveland; WBNS-TV (C), WCMH-TV (N), WOSU-TV (P), WSYX (A), WTTE (F,U) Columbus.

Programming (via satellite): American Movie Classics; CNN; ESPN; Fox Family Channel; Home Shopping Network; MTV; Nashville Network; Nickelodeon; TBS Superstation; The Weather Channel; USA Network.

Current originations: Automated time-weather; automated emergency alert; local news; local sports.

Fee: $15.00 installation; $14.95 monthly; $15.00 additional installation.

Pay Service 1

Pay Units: 362.

Programming (via satellite): Cinemax.

Fee: $15.00 installation; $9.95 monthly.

Pay Service 2

Pay Units: 454.

Programming (via satellite): HBO.

Fee: $15.00 installation; $10.95 monthly.

Local advertising: Yes. Available in character-generated programming.

Equipment: Jerrold headend; C-COR & Jerrold amplifiers; Comm/Scope cable; Texscan character generator; Scientific-Atlanta set top converters; Scientific-Atlanta addressable set top converters; Eagle traps; Eagle addressable traps; Microdyne satellite antenna; Microdyne satellite receivers.

Miles of plant: 65.0 (coaxial).

Manager: Paul S. Schonewolf. Technical operations manager: Dan Fessler. Field operations manager: Bill Schroeder. Marketing manager: Carl Bauer. Customer operations manager: Danielle Turner.

City fee: None.

Ownership: Time Warner Cable (MSO).

FREEPORT TWP.—TCI Cablevision of Ohio Inc., Box 347, 123 N. Market St., Minerva, OH 44657. Phone: 330-868-5413. Fax: 330-868-3731. County: Harrison. Also serves Freeport. ICA: OH0295.

TV Market Ranking: 90. Franchise award date: N.A. Franchise expiration date: N.A. Began: June 1, 1972.

Channel capacity: 81 (not 2-way capable). Channels available but not in use: 56.

Basic Service

Subscribers: 145.

Programming (received off-air): WOUC-TV (P) Cambridge; KMGH-TV (A) Denver; WTOV-TV (N) Steubenville-Wheeling; WTRF-TV (C) Wheeling-Steubenville.

Programming (via satellite): American Movie Classics; Animal Planet; CNBC; CNN; Cartoon Network; Discovery Channel; ESPN; Fox Family Channel; Fox News Channel; FoxNet; Home & Garden Television; Nashville Network; Odyssey; QVC; TBS Superstation; The New Encore; Turner Network TV; USA Network.

Fee: $37.50 installation; $22.60 monthly; $1.50 converter.

Pay Service 1

Pay Units: 28.

Programming (via satellite): Showtime.

Fee: $14.95 monthly.

Pay Service 2

Pay Units: N.A.

Programming (via satellite): Starz!; The New Encore.

Fee: $1.95 monthly (Encore), $6.75 monthly (Starz).

Equipment: Jerrold headend; Vikoa amplifiers.

Miles of plant: 3.3 (coaxial). Homes passed: 221. Total homes in franchised area: 223.

Manager: Paul Liucart. Chief technician: Rodney Lentz.

City fee: $50 annually.

Ownership: AT&T Broadband & Internet Services (MSO). Purchased from Tele-Communications Inc., March 9, 1999.

FREMONT—Fremont CATV, 905 W. State St., Fremont, OH 43420. Phone: 419-332-7381. County: Sandusky. Also serves Ballville Twp., Sandusky Twp. (Sandusky County). ICA: OH0085.

TV Market Ranking: 52. Franchise award date: N.A. Franchise expiration date: January 1, 2004. Began: July 20, 1971.

Channel capacity: 40 (not 2-way capable). Channels available but not in use: 10.

Basic Service

Subscribers: 7,400.

Programming (received off-air): WBGU-TV (P) Bowling Green; WKBD-TV (U) Detroit; WUAB (U) Lorain-Cleveland; WGTE-TV (P), WNWO-TV (N), WTOL-TV (C), WTVG (A) Toledo.

Programming (via satellite): TBS Superstation.

Current originations: Automated time-weather.

Fee: $25.00 installation; $6.31 monthly.

Pay Service 1

Pay Units: N.A.

Programming (via satellite): Disney Channel.

Fee: $4.95 monthly.

Pay Service 2

Pay Units: 2,259.

Programming (via satellite): HBO.

Fee: $10.90 monthly.

Local advertising: No.

Equipment: Jerrold headend; Jerrold amplifiers; Times Fiber cable; Scientific-Atlanta satellite antenna.

Miles of plant: 103.0 (coaxial). Homes passed: 8,700. Total homes in franchised area: 9,100.

Manager: Tim Wolfe. Chief technician: Denny Sheren.

City fee: None.

Ownership: Wolfe Broadcasting Corp.

FRIENDSHIP—Warner Cable Communications, 180 Morgan Dr., Lucasville, OH 45648. Phone: 740-259-4170. Fax: 614-259-3266. County: Scioto. Also serves Nile Twp. ICA: OH0224.

TV Market Ranking: Below 100. Franchise award date: December 5, 1981. Franchise expiration date: N.A. Began: August 1, 1982.

Channel capacity: 35 (not 2-way capable). Channels available but not in use: N.A.

Basic Service

Subscribers: 508.

Programming (received off-air): WCHS-TV (A), WOWK-TV (C), WSAZ-TV (N), WVAH-TV (F,U) Charleston-Huntington; WPBO-TV (P) Portsmouth.

Programming (via satellite): WGN-TV (W) Chicago; CNN; Country Music TV; Discovery Channel; ESPN; Fox Family Channel; MTV; Nashville Network; Nickelodeon; QVC; TBS Superstation; Turner Network TV; USA Network.

Fee: $19.95 installation; $16.99 monthly.

Pay Service 1

Pay Units: 47.

Programming (via satellite): Cinemax.

Fee: $10.95 monthly.

Pay Service 2

Pay Units: 40.

Programming (via satellite): Disney Channel.

Fee: $7.95 monthly.

Pay Service 3

Pay Units: 68.

Programming (via satellite): HBO.

Fee: $10.95 monthly.

Equipment: GTE Sylvania amplifiers; Comm/Scope cable; AFC satellite antenna; Scientific-Atlanta satellite receivers.

Miles of plant: 32.0 (coaxial). Homes passed: 645. Total homes in franchised area: 1,313.

Manager: Michael Rector. Chief technician: Jack Lester.

City fee: 5% of gross.

Ownership: Time Warner Cable (MSO).

FULTON TWP.—FrontierVision, Box 627, Chillicothe, OH 45601. Phones: 740-775-4300; 800-346-2288. Fax: 740-775-2915. Counties: Fulton & Lucas. Also serves Amboy Twp., Richfield Twp. (Lucas County). ICA: OH0327.

TV Market Ranking: 52. Franchise award date: N.A. Franchise expiration date: N.A. Began: July 1, 1990.

Channel capacity: 37. Channels available but not in use: 5.

Basic Service

Subscribers: 249.

Programming (received off-air): WBGU-TV (P) Bowling Green; WKBD-TV (U) Detroit; WGTE-TV (P), WNWO-TV (N), WTOL-TV (C), WTVG (A), WUPW (F) Toledo.

Programming (via satellite): WGN-TV (W) Chicago; C-SPAN; CNN; Country Music TV; Discovery Channel; Disney Channel; ESPN; Fox Family Channel; MTV; Nashville Network; QVC; Sci-Fi Channel; TBS Superstation; The Weather Channel; Turner Classic Movies; Turner Network TV; USA Network.

Fee: $43.75 installation; $22.45 monthly.

Pay Service 1

Pay Units: 34.

Programming (via satellite): Cinemax.

Fee: $11.00 monthly.

Pay Service 2

Pay Units: 42.

Programming (via satellite): HBO.

Fee: $11.00 monthly.

Pay-Per-View

Addressable homes: 2.

Miles of plant: 32.0 (coaxial). Homes passed: 780.

Manager: Richard Coplan. Chief technician: Sam Morabith. Program director: Chad Hume. Marketing director: Barbara Brewer.

Ownership: FrontierVision Partners LP (MSO). See Cable System Ownership.

GALION—Time Warner Cable, 21 Public Square, Galion, OH 44833. Phones: 419-468-2000; 800-425-2225. Counties: Crawford, Morrow & Richland. Also serves Bloomfield, Crestline, Iberia, Jackson Twp. (Crawford County), Jefferson Twp. (Crawford County), Leesville, North Bloomfield Twp., North Robinson, Polk Twp., Sandusky Twp. (Richland County), Springfield Twp. (Richland County), Washington Twp. (Morrow County), Whetstone Twp. (Crawford County). ICA: OH0077.

TV Market Ranking: Below 100. Franchise award date: July 1, 1967. Franchise expiration date: September 21, 2003. Began: April 1, 1968.

Channel capacity: 52 (2-way capable; operating 2-way). Channels available but not in use: 14.

Basic Service

Subscribers: 6,044.

Programming (received off-air): W54AF (I) Bucyrus; WEWS-TV (A), WJW (F), WKYC-TV (N) Cleveland; WBNS-TV (C), WCMH-TV (N), WOSU-TV (P), WSYX (A), WTTE (F,U) Columbus; WUAB (U) Lorain-Cleveland; WOHZ-LP (I) Mansfield; WTOL-TV (C), WTVG (A) Toledo; 13 FMs.

Programming (via satellite): A & E; C-SPAN; C-SPAN 2; CNN; Discovery Channel; ESPN; EWTN; Fox Family Channel; Headline News; Home Shopping Network; Lifetime; MTV; Nashville Network; Nickelodeon; QVC; TBS Superstation; The Weather Channel; Turner Network TV; USA Network; VH1.

Current originations: Automated time-weather; public access; educational access; government access; automated emergency alert; local news; local sports.

Fee: $25.00 installation; $16.50 monthly; $2.75 converter; $12.00 additional installation.

Pay Service 1

Pay Units: 4,148.

Programming (via satellite): Cinemax; Disney Channel; HBO; Showtime.

Fee: $12.00 installation; $6.95 monthly (Disney), $11.95 monthly (Cinemax, HBO or Showtime).

Pay-Per-View

Hot Choice; Viewer's Choice.

Fee: Varies.

Local advertising: Yes. Available in satellite distributed & character-generated programming. Rates: $100.00/Month; $3.00/Day.

Equipment: Scientific-Atlanta headend; Texscan amplifiers; Comm/Scope cable; Sony & Panasonic VTRs; Video Data Systems & Texscan character generator; Pioneer & RCA set top converters; Eagle traps; Fort Worth Tower, M/A-Com & Prodelin satellite antenna; Microdyne satellite receivers.

Miles of plant: 134.0 (coaxial); 13.0 (fiber optic). Homes passed: 9,749.

Manager: Jane Kennard. Chief technician: John Fox.

Ownership: Time Warner Cable (MSO). Purchased from MediaOne Group, August 2, 1999.

GALLIPOLIS—Thompson Cable, Box 13309, Sissonville, WV 25360. Phone: 304-984-0025. County: Gallia. ICA: OH0178.

TV Market Ranking: 36. Franchise award date: N.A. Franchise expiration date: N.A. Began: January 1, 1984.

Channel capacity: 52. Channels available but not in use: N.A.

Basic Service

Subscribers: N.A.

Programming (received off-air): WCHS-TV (A), WOWK-TV (C), WPBY-TV (P), WSAZ-TV (N), WVAH-TV (F,U) Charleston-Huntington; WBNS-TV (C) Columbus.

Programming (via satellite): WGN-TV (W) Chicago; TBS Superstation.

Fee: N.A.

Miles of plant: 43.0 (coaxial). Homes passed: 1,870.

Manager: Dale Tachton.

Ownership: Thompson Cablevision Co. Inc. (MSO).

GAMBIER—Time Warner Cable, Box 787, 111 S. Mulberry St., Mount Vernon, OH 43050. Phones: 740-397-2288; 800-782-4118. Fax: 740-397-3730. County: Knox. Also serves Howard, Millwood. ICA: OH0250.

TV Market Ranking: Below 100. Franchise award date: N.A. Franchise expiration date: N.A. Began: N.A.

Channel capacity: 25. Channels available but not in use: None.

Basic Service

Subscribers: 544.

Programming (received off-air): WBNS-TV (C), WCMH-TV (N), WOSU-TV (P), WSYX (A), WTTE (F,U) Columbus; WSFJ (I) Newark; WHIZ-TV (N) Zanesville.

Programming (via satellite): A & E; C-SPAN; CNN; Discovery Channel; ESPN; Fox Family Channel; Headline News; Lifetime; MTV; Nashville Network; Nickelodeon; TBS Superstation; Turner Network TV; USA Network.

Fee: $40.00 installation; $18.50 monthly.

Pay Service 1

Pay Units: 85.

Programming (via satellite): HBO.

Fee: $10.95 monthly.

Pay Service 2

Pay Units: 56.

Programming (via satellite): The Movie Channel.

Fee: $10.95 monthly.

Pay Service 3

Pay Units: 76.

Programming (via satellite): Showtime.

Fee: $10.95 monthly.

Homes passed: 684.

Manager: Paul S. Schonewolf. Technical operations manager: Dan Fessler. Field operations manager: Bill Schroeder. Marketing manager: Carl Bauer. Customer operations manager: Danielle Turner.

Ownership: Time Warner Cable (MSO).

GARFIELD HEIGHTS—Cablevision of Ohio, 3400 Lakeside Ave., Cleveland, OH 44114. Phone: 216-575-8016. Fax: 216-575-0212. County: Cuyahoga. Also serves Cuyahoga Heights, Independence, Newburgh Heights, Valley View, Walton Hills. ICA: OH0049.

TV Market Ranking: 8. Franchise award date: October 1, 1983. Franchise expiration date: October 1, 1998. Began: August 1, 1984.

Channel capacity: 77. Channels available but not in use: 2.

Basic Service

Subscribers: 8,120.

Programming (received off-air): WBNX-TV (W,F), WEAO (P), WVPX (X) Akron; WEWS-TV (A), WJW (F), WKYC-TV (N), WQHS-TV (H), WVIZ-TV (P) Cleveland; WUAB (U) Lorain-Cleveland; WOIO (C) Shaker Heights.

Programming (via satellite): A & E; BET; Bravo; CNBC; CNN; Discovery Channel; ESPN; EWTN; Fox Family Channel; Fox Sports Net Ohio; Headline News; Learning Channel; Lifetime; MTV; Nashville Network; Nickelodeon; TBS Superstation; The Weather Channel; Trinity Bcstg. Network; Turner Network TV; USA Network; VH1.

Current originations: Public access; educational access; government access.

Fee: $36.25 installation; $25.85 monthly.

Pay Service 1

Pay Units: N.A.

Programming (via satellite): American Movie Classics; Cinemax; Disney Channel; HBO; Showtime; The Movie Channel.

Fee: $10.45 monthly (each).

Pay-Per-View

Addressable homes: 5,079.

Special events.

Fee: $2.95.

Local advertising: Yes. Available in satellite distributed programming. Local sales manager: Jeff Smith. Regional interconnect: Northern Ohio Interconnect.

Equipment: Scientific-Atlanta headend; Texscan character generator; Scientific-Atlanta set top converters; Scientific-Atlanta satellite antenna; Scientific-Atlanta satellite receivers.

Miles of plant: 165.0 (coaxial). Homes passed: 17,747.

Manager: Kathleen R. Mayo. Chief technician: Bruce Smylie. Program director: John Stealey. Sales & marketing director: Frank Naples.

City fee: 5% of annual gross.

Ownership: Cablevision Systems Corp. (MSO).

GENEVA—Adelphia, Box 1448, 2904 State Rd., Ashtabula, OH 44005. Phone: 440-998-2148. Counties: Ashtabula & Lake. Also serves Geneva Twp. (Ashtabula County), Geneva-on-the-Lake, Harpersfield Twp. (Ashtabula County), Madison, Madison Twp. (Lake County), Saybrook Twp. (Ashtabula County), Sheffield Twp. (Ashtabula County). ICA: OH0064.

TV Market Ranking: Below 100 (Madison, Madison Twp.); Outside TV Markets (Geneva, Geneva Twp., Geneva-on-the-Lake, Harpersfield Twp., Saybrook Twp., Sheffield Twp.). Franchise award date: N.A. Franchise expiration date: September 1, 1997. Began: April 1, 1973.

Channel capacity: 64 (2-way capable; operating 2-way). Channels available but not in use: N.A.

Basic Service

Subscribers: 11,211.

Programming (received off-air): WJW (F), WVIZ-TV (P) Cleveland; WICU-TV (N), WJET-TV (A), WQLN (P), WSEE (C) Erie; WUAB (U) Lorain-Cleveland; WOIO (C) Shaker Heights; allband FM.

Programming (via microwave): CNN; WEWS-TV (A), WKYC-TV (N) Cleveland.

Programming (via satellite): WGN-TV (W) Chicago; A & E; BET; C-SPAN; C-SPAN 2; CNBC; Comedy Central; Discovery Channel; EWTN; Fox Family Channel; Headline News; Knowledge TV; Lifetime; MTV; Nashville Network; Nickelodeon; Odyssey; QVC; TBS Superstation; The Weather Channel; VH1.

Current originations: Automated timeweather; public access; educational access; government access; local news.

Fee: $42.00 installation; $10.17 monthly; $3.25 converter.

Expanded Basic Service

Subscribers: 9,468.

Programming (via microwave): ESPN, USA Network.

Programming (via satellite): American Movie Classics; Court TV; Disney Channel; Fox Sports Net Ohio; Turner Network TV.

Fee: $19.73 monthly.

Pay Service 1

Pay Units: 2,090.

Programming (via satellite): HBO.

Fee: $20.00 installation; $8.00 monthly.

Pay Service 2

Pay Units: 410.

Programming (via satellite): The Movie Channel.

Fee: $8.00 monthly.

Pay Service 3

Pay Units: 666.

Programming (via satellite): Showtime.

Fee: $8.00 monthly.

Pay Service 4

Pay Units: 3,632.

Programming (via satellite): The New Encore.

Fee: N.A.

Local advertising: Yes.

Equipment: Tocom headend; C-COR amplifiers; General cable; Comtech satellite antenna.

Miles of plant: 244.0 (coaxial). Homes passed: 12,240. Total homes in franchised area: 14,750.

Manager: Edward R. Williams.

City fee: 3% of gross.

Ownership: Adelphia Communications Corp. (MSO); AT&T Broadband & Internet Services (MSO). Purchased from Tele-Communications Inc., March 9, 1999.

GERMANTOWN—Warner Cable Communications, 419 S. Barron St., Eaton, OH 45320. Phones: 937-456-1183; 800-762-2963. Fax: 937-456-9435. County: Montgomery. Also serves Farmersville, German Twp. (Montgomery County), Jefferson Twp. (Montgomery County). ICA: OH0158.

TV Market Ranking: 41. Franchise award date: July 12, 1982. Franchise expiration date: July 1, 1997. Began: February 15, 1983.

Channel capacity: 54. Channels available but not in use: 18.

Basic Service

Subscribers: 3,034.

Programming (received off-air): WCET (P), WCPO-TV (A), WKRC-TV (C), WLWT (N) Cincinnati; WXIX-TV (F) Cincinnati-Newport; WDTN (A), WHIO-TV (C), WKEF (N), WPTD (P), WRGT-TV (F,U) Dayton; WBDT (W) Springfield; 5 FMs.

Programming (via satellite): WGN-TV (W) Chicago; C-SPAN; CNN; Discovery Channel; ESPN; Fox Family Channel; Headline News; Lifetime; MTV; Nashville Network; Nickelodeon; QVC; TBS Superstation; The Weather Channel; Turner Network TV; USA Network; VH1.

Current originations: Automated timeweather; government access; automated emergency alert.

Fee: $19.95 installation; $20.25 monthly; $15.00 additional installation.

Pay Service 1

Pay Units: 62.

Programming (via satellite): Cinemax.

Fee: $10.00 installation; $10.45 monthly.

Pay Service 2

Pay Units: 140.

Programming (via satellite): Disney Channel.

Fee: $10.00 installation; $6.95 monthly.

Pay Service 3

Pay Units: 555.

Programming (via satellite): HBO.

Fee: $10.00 installation; $10.95 monthly.

Pay Service 4

Pay Units: 113.

Programming (via satellite): Showtime.

Fee: $10.45 monthly.

Pay Service 5

Pay Units: 70.

Programming (via satellite): The Movie Channel.

Fee: $10.45 monthly.

Local advertising: No.

Equipment: Scientific-Atlanta headend; Scientific-Atlanta & Jerrold amplifiers; Comm/Scope, Times Fiber & Scientific-Atlanta cable; Scientific-Atlanta & Pioneer set top converters; Microdyne satellite antenna; Microdyne satellite receivers.

Miles of plant: 58.0 (coaxial).

Manager: Mike Gray. Chief technician: Mike Ooten. Marketing director: Mike Weaver.

City fee: 3% of gross.

Ownership: Time Warner Cable (MSO).

GLENCOE—TCI Cablevision of Ohio Inc., Box 469, Bridgeport, OH 43912. Phone: 800-527-2222. County: Belmont. ICA: OH0298.

TV Market Ranking: 90. Franchise award date: N.A. Franchise expiration date: N.A. Began: August 1, 1976.

Channel capacity: 12. Channels available but not in use: 3.

Basic Service

Subscribers: 41.

Programming (received off-air): WOUC-TV (P) Cambridge; KDKA-TV (C), WCWB (W), WPGH-TV (F), WPXI (N), WQED (P), WTAE-TV (A) Pittsburgh; WTOV-TV (N) Steubenville-Wheeling; WTRF-TV (C) Wheeling-Steubenville.

Fee: $60.00 installation; $8.00 monthly.

Miles of plant: 4.0 (coaxial). Homes passed: 156. Total homes in franchised area: 156.

Manager: Robert Weese. Chief technician: Earl Conway.

Ownership: AT&T Broadband & Internet Services (MSO). Purchased from Tele-Communications Inc., March 9, 1999.

GLENMONT—FrontierVision, Box 648, 102 Twin Oak Dr., Jackson, OH 45640. Phone: 614-345-4329. Fax: 614-286-1489. County: Holmes. Also serves Richland Twp. (Holmes County). ICA: OH0300.

TV Market Ranking: Below 100. Franchise award date: December 8, 1986. Franchise expiration date: October 1, 2001. Began: December 1, 1955.

Channel capacity: 62. Channels available but not in use: 34.

Basic Service

Subscribers: 112.

Programming (received off-air): WVPX (X) Akron; WDLI (T) Canton; WEWS-TV (A), WJW (F), WKYC-TV (N), WVIZ-TV (P) Cleveland; WBNS-TV (C), WOSU-TV (P), WTTE

(F,U) Columbus; WUAB (U) Lorain-Cleveland; WTRF-TV (C) Wheeling-Steubenville; allband FM.
Programming (via satellite): WGN-TV (W) Chicago; CNN; Country Music TV; Discovery Channel; ESPN; Lifetime; MTV; Nashville Network; Nickelodeon; QVC; TBS Superstation; Turner Classic Movies; USA Network.
Fee: $20.99 installation; $22.70 monthly.
Pay Service 1
Pay Units: 10.
Programming (via satellite): HBO.
Fee: $15.00 installation; $11.95 monthly.
Equipment: Jerrold headend; Scientific-Atlanta amplifiers; Comm/Scope & Belden cable; NSC set top converters; AFC & Wilson satellite antenna; Microdyne satellite receivers.
Miles of plant: 5.7 (coaxial). Homes passed: 144.
Manager: Steve Trippe. Chief technician: Bill Ricker.
City fee: None.
Ownership: FrontierVision Partners LP (MSO). See Cable System Ownership.

GOLF MANOR—TCI Cablevision of Ohio Inc., Box 710, 341 City Centre Mall, Middletown, OH 45044. Phone: 513-424-2408. Fax: 513-896-5455. County: Hamilton. ICA: OH0180.
TV Market Ranking: 17. Franchise award date: N.A. Franchise expiration date: N.A. Began: September 1, 1979.
Channel capacity: 39. Channels available but not in use: N.A.
Basic Service
Subscribers: 895.
Programming (received off-air): WCET (P), WCPO-TV (A), WKRC-TV (C), WLWT (N), WSTR-TV (W) Cincinnati; WXIX-TV (F) Cincinnati-Newport; WCVN (P) Covington; WDTN (A), WHIO-TV (C), WKEF (N), WPTD (P), WRGT-TV (F,U) Dayton; WPTO (P) Oxford; 16 FMs.
Programming (via satellite): WGN-TV (W) Chicago; TBS Superstation.
Current originations: Government access.
Fee: $30.83 installation; $9.80 monthly; $2.00 converter; $5.14 additional installation.
Expanded Basic Service
Subscribers: 817.
Programming (via satellite): A & E; American Movie Classics; BET; C-SPAN; CNBC; CNN; Discovery Channel; ESPN; FX; Fox Family Channel; Headline News; Intro TV; Lifetime; MTV; Nickelodeon; QVC; The Weather Channel; Turner Network TV; USA Network.
Fee: $11.19 monthly.
Pay Service 1
Pay Units: 81.
Programming (via satellite): Disney Channel.
Fee: $13.10 monthly.
Pay Service 2
Pay Units: 434.
Programming (via satellite): HBO.
Fee: $13.78 monthly.
Pay Service 3
Pay Units: 227.
Programming (via satellite): Showtime.
Fee: $13.78 monthly.
Pay Service 4
Pay Units: 448.
Programming (via satellite): The New Encore.
Fee: $1.70 monthly.
Equipment: Scientific-Atlanta headend; GTE Sylvania amplifiers; Scientific-Atlanta satellite antenna.
Miles of plant: 9.2 (coaxial). Homes passed: 1,800. Total homes in franchised area: 1,800.
Manager: Jeff Heinrich. Chief technician: Randy Senger.
City fee: 3% of gross.
Ownership: AT&T Broadband & Internet Services (MSO). Purchased from Tele-Communications Inc., March 9, 1999.

GOSHEN TWP. (Clermont County)—Time Warner Cable, Box 823, 131 Catherine St., Hillsboro, OH 45133. Phone: 937-393-4217. Fax: 937-393-8022. County: Clermont. ICA: OH0129.
TV Market Ranking: 17,41. Franchise award date: June 11, 1984. Franchise expiration date: June 11, 1999. Began: July 1, 1985.
Channel capacity: 45 (not 2-way capable). Channels available but not in use: N.A.
Basic Service
Subscribers: 2,712.
Programming (received off-air): WCET (P), WCPO-TV (A), WKRC-TV (C), WLWT (N), WSTR-TV (W) Cincinnati; WXIX-TV (F) Cincinnati-Newport; WCVN (P) Covington; WDTN (A), WHIO-TV (C), WPTD (P), WRGT-TV (F,U) Dayton.
Programming (via satellite): WGN-TV (W) Chicago; A & E; American Movie Classics; Animal Planet; C-SPAN; CNBC; CNN; Comedy Central; Country Music TV; Discovery Channel; ESPN; ESPN 2; Fox Family Channel; Headline News; History Channel; Lifetime; MTV; Nashville Network; Nickelodeon; QVC; TBS Superstation; TV Guide Channel; The Inspirational Network; The Weather Channel; Trinity Bcstg. Network; Turner Network TV; USA Network; VH1.
Current originations: Public access.
Fee: $39.90 installation; $27.73 monthly.
Pay Service 1
Pay Units: 512.
Programming (via satellite): Cinemax.
Fee: $10.95 monthly.
Pay Service 2
Pay Units: 330.
Programming (via satellite): Disney Channel.
Fee: $7.95 monthly.
Pay Service 3
Pay Units: 671.
Programming (via satellite): HBO.
Fee: $10.95 monthly.
Pay Service 4
Pay Units: 334.
Programming (via satellite): The Movie Channel.
Fee: $10.95 monthly.
Pay Service 5
Pay Units: 481.
Programming (via satellite): Showtime.
Fee: $10.95 monthly.
Pay-Per-View
Addressable homes: 4,230.
Viewer's Choice.
Fee: $3.95.
Local advertising: Yes. Local sales manager: Gary Pitzer.
Equipment: Magnavox & Scientific-Atlanta headend; Scientific-Atlanta amplifiers; M/A-Com cable; Scientific-Atlanta satellite antenna; Scientific-Atlanta satellite receivers.
Miles of plant: 91.0 (coaxial); None (fiber optic). Homes passed: 3,238.
Manager: Michael Rector. Chief technician: Dale Zornes. Marketing director: Gary Pitzer.
City fee: 5% of gross.
Ownership: Time Warner Cable (MSO).

GRAFTON—Grafton Cable Communications, Box 67, 993 Commerce Dr., Grafton, OH 44044. Phone: 440-926-3230. Fax: 440-926-2889. County: Lorain. Also serves Eaton Twp. (Lorain County), Grafton Twp., Lagrange, Lagrange (village), Lagrange Twp. ICA: OH0133.
TV Market Ranking: 8. Franchise award date: N.A. Franchise expiration date: N.A. Began: May 25, 1981.
Channel capacity: 40 (2-way capable; operating 2-way partially). Channels available but not in use: 7.
Basic Service
Subscribers: 3,756; Commercial subscribers: 20.
Programming (received off-air): WBNX-TV (W,F), WVPX (X) Akron; WEWS-TV (A), WJW (F), WKYC-TV (N), WQHS-TV (H), WVIZ-TV (P) Cleveland; WUAB (U) Lorain-Cleveland; WOIO (C) Shaker Heights.
Programming (via satellite): WGN-TV (W) Chicago; CNBC; Country Music TV; Fox Family Channel; TBS Superstation; Travel Channel; USA Network.
Current originations: Automated time-weather; educational access; local sports.
Fee: $40.00 installation; $9.00 monthly; $2.83 converter; $15.00 additional installation.
Commercial fee: $20.00 monthly.
Expanded Basic Service
Subscribers: N.A.
Programming (via satellite): A & E; American Movie Classics; CNN; Discovery Channel; Disney Channel; E! Entertainment TV; ESPN; Fox Sports Net Ohio; Headline News; History Channel; Home & Garden Television; Learning Channel; Lifetime; MTV; Nashville Network; Nickelodeon; Sci-Fi Channel; TV Guide Channel; The Inspirational Network; The Weather Channel; Turner Classic Movies; Turner Network TV; VH1.
Fee: $16.35 monthly.
Pay Service 1
Pay Units: N.A.
Programming (via satellite): Cinemax; HBO; Showtime.
Fee: $10.95 monthly (each).
Local advertising: Yes (locally produced & insert). Available in locally originated & character-generated programming.
Program Guide: Premium Channels.
Equipment: Scientific-Atlanta, ISS & DX Engineering headend; Scientific-Atlanta amplifiers; Scientific-Atlanta, Times Fiber & Comm/Scope cable; Panasonic cameras; Panasonic VTRs; Telpar character generator; Scientific-Atlanta, Panasonic & Texscan set top converters; Arcom & Eagle traps; Scientific-Atlanta & Harris satellite antenna; Scientific-Atlanta, Sony & DX Antenna satellite receivers.
Miles of plant: 53.0 (coaxial). Additional miles planned: 3.0 (coaxial). Homes passed: 3,650.
Manager: Dale Durkee. Chief technician: George Michas.
City fee: 3% of gross.
Ownership: Kevin Flannigan (MSO).

GREEN COVE CONDOMINIUMS—Time Warner Entertainment Co. LP, 3100 Elida Rd., Lima, OH 45805. Phone: 419-331-3333. Fax: 419-331-1573. County: Ottawa. ICA: OH0289.
TV Market Ranking: 52. Franchise award date: N.A. Franchise expiration date: N.A. Began: September 1, 1988.
Channel capacity: 36 (not 2-way capable). Channels available but not in use: 5.
Basic Service
Subscribers: 44.
Programming (received off-air): WDIV (N), WKBD-TV (U) Detroit; WGTE-TV (P), WNWO-TV (N), WTOL-TV (C), WTVG (A), WUPW (F) Toledo.
Programming (via satellite): WGN-TV (W) Chicago; C-SPAN; CNBC; CNN; Discovery Channel; ESPN; Fox Family Channel; Home Shopping Network; Lifetime; Nashville Network; TBS Superstation; The Weather Channel; USA Network.
Fee: $25.00 installation; $14.50 monthly.
Pay Service 1
Pay Units: 9.
Programming (via satellite): Cinemax.
Fee: $10.95 monthly.
Pay Service 2
Pay Units: 11.
Programming (via satellite): HBO.
Fee: $10.95 monthly.
Pay Service 3
Pay Units: N.A.
Programming (via satellite): Disney Channel.
Fee: $6.95 monthly.
Local advertising: No.
Homes passed: 265. Total homes in franchised area: 265.
Manager: Larry K. Miller. Chief technician: Sean Gallagher.
Ownership: Fanch Communications Inc. (MSO); Time Warner Cable (MSO). See Cable System Ownership.

GREEN MEADOWS—Time Warner Entertainment Co. LP, 1266 Dublin Rd., Columbus, OH 43215. Phone: 614-481-5000. Fax: 614-481-5044. County: Clark. ICA: OH0286.
TV Market Ranking: 41. Franchise award date: N.A. Franchise expiration date: N.A. Began: July 1, 1986.
Channel capacity: 53. Channels available but not in use: 23.
Basic Service
Subscribers: 137.
Programming (received off-air): WBNS-TV (C), WCMH-TV (N), WOSU-TV (P), WSYX (A), WTTE (F,U) Columbus.
Programming (via satellite): WGN-TV (W) Chicago; A & E; CNN; Comedy Central; Country Music TV; Discovery Channel; ESPN; Fox Family Channel; Headline News; Nashville Network; Sci-Fi Channel; TBS Superstation; Turner Network TV; USA Network.
Fee: $32.00 installation; $18.95 monthly; $4.50 converter; $9.00 additional installation.
Pay Service 1
Pay Units: 11.
Programming (via satellite): Disney Channel.
Fee: $18.00 installation; $10.95 monthly.
Pay Service 2
Pay Units: 51.
Programming (via satellite): HBO.
Fee: $18.00 installation; $10.95 monthly.
Pay Service 3
Pay Units: 16.
Programming (via satellite): Cinemax.
Fee: $18.00 installation; $10.95 monthly.
Local advertising: No.
Miles of plant: 2.0 (coaxial). Homes passed: 288.
Manager: Terry O'Connell. Chief technician: Randy Hall. Marketing director: Cheryl Roller.
City fee: 10% of gross.
Ownership: Time Warner Cable (MSO).

GREEN TWP. (Hamilton County)—Time Warner Cable, 3290 Westbourne Dr., Cincinnati, OH 45248. Phone: 513-469-1112. County: Hamilton. ICA: OH0032.
TV Market Ranking: 17. Franchise award date: N.A. Franchise expiration date: N.A. Began: November 1, 1980.
Channel capacity: 36 (2-way capable; operating 2-way partially). Channels available but not in use: N.A.
Basic Service
Subscribers: 14,397.

Programming (received off-air): WCET (P), WCPO-TV (A), WKRC-TV (C), WLWT (N) Cincinnati; WXIX-TV (F) Cincinnati-Newport; WCVN (P) Covington; WPTO (P) Oxford; allband FM.
Programming (via satellite): WGN-TV (W) Chicago; TBS Superstation.
Current originations: Automated time-weather; public access; educational access; government access; automated emergency alert; local news.
Fee: $2.00 monthly; $3.00 converter.

Expanded Basic Service
Subscribers: 14,076.
Programming (via satellite): A & E; C-SPAN; CNBC; CNN; Discovery Channel; ESPN; EWTN; Fox Family Channel; Headline News; Home Shopping Network; Lifetime; MTV; Nashville Network; Nickelodeon; The Inspirational Network; The Weather Channel; Turner Network TV; USA Network.
Fee: $24.95 installation; $18.95 monthly.

Pay Service 1
Pay Units: 1,481.
Programming (via satellite): Disney Channel.
Fee: $10.00 installation; $9.00 monthly.

Pay Service 2
Pay Units: 4,791.
Programming (via satellite): HBO.
Fee: $10.00 installation; $9.00 monthly.

Pay Service 3
Pay Units: 1,406.
Programming (via satellite): The Movie Channel.
Fee: $10.00 installation; $9.00 monthly.

Pay Service 4
Pay Units: 2,199.
Programming (via satellite): Showtime.
Fee: $10.00 installation; $9.00 monthly.

Equipment: Scientific-Atlanta headend; Scientific-Atlanta amplifiers; Comm/Scope cable; Sony cameras; Sony VTRs; Jerrold, Regency & Scientific-Atlanta set top converters; Eagle traps; Scientific-Atlanta satellite antenna; Scientific-Atlanta satellite receivers.
Miles of plant: 250.0 (coaxial); 30.0 (fiber optic). Homes passed: 23,378.
Manager: Phil Lange. Chief technician: Rob Hauenstein.
City fee: 3% of gross.
Ownership: Time Warner Cable (MSO); Advance/Newhouse Partnership (MSO).

GREEN TWP. (Summit County)—Cable One, 535 E. Turkeyfoot Lake Rd., Akron, OH 44319-4188. Phone: 330-896-9088. Fax: 330-896-0022. Counties: Portage, Stark & Summit. Also serves Barberton, Clinton, Coventry Twp. (Summit County), Franklin Twp. (Summit County), Green Village (Summit County), Lake Twp. (Stark County), Suffield Twp. (Portage County). ICA: OH0031.
TV Market Ranking: 8 (Barberton, Clinton, Coventry Twp., Franklin Twp., Green Twp., Green Village, Lake Twp., Suffield Twp.); 79 (Suffield Twp.). Franchise award date: October 15, 1981. Franchise expiration date: N.A. Began: October 15, 1981.
Channel capacity: 53 (not 2-way capable). Channels available but not in use: 7.

Basic Service
Subscribers: 14,474.
Programming (received off-air): WBNX-TV (W,F), WEAO (P), WVPX (X) Akron; WDLI (T), WOAC (I) Canton; WEWS-TV (A), WJW (F), WKYC-TV (N), WQHS-TV (H), WVIZ-TV (P) Cleveland; WUAB (U) Lorain-Cleveland; WOIO (C) Shaker Heights; 18 FMs.
Programming (via satellite): A & E; CNBC; EWTN; Fox Family Channel.
Current originations: Automated time-weather; public access; educational access; leased access; automated emergency alert; local sports.
Fee: $63.83 installation; $19.25 monthly; $15.00 additional installation.

Expanded Basic Service
Subscribers: 11,983.
Programming (via satellite): C-SPAN; CNN; ESPN; Headline News; Home Shopping Network; MTV; Nashville Network; TBS Superstation; The Weather Channel; Turner Network TV; USA Network.
Fee: $15.00 installation; $4.95 monthly.

Expanded Basic Service 2
Subscribers: 8,113.
Programming (via satellite): American Movie Classics; C-SPAN 2; Discovery Channel; Learning Channel; Lifetime; Nickelodeon; Travel Channel; VH1.
Fee: $6.15 monthly.

Pay Service 1
Pay Units: 1,561.
Programming (via satellite): Cinemax.
Fee: $15.00 installation; $6.95 monthly.

Pay Service 2
Pay Units: 837.
Programming (via satellite): Disney Channel.
Fee: $15.00 installation; $6.95 monthly.

Pay Service 3
Pay Units: 4,709.
Programming (via satellite): HBO.
Fee: $15.00 installation; $6.95 monthly.

Pay Service 4
Pay Units: 1,022.
Programming (via satellite): The Movie Channel.
Fee: $15.00 installation; $6.95 monthly.

Pay Service 5
Pay Units: 2,313.
Programming (via satellite): Showtime.
Fee: $15.00 installation; $6.95 monthly.

Pay-Per-View
Addressable homes: 2,731.

Local advertising: Yes (locally produced & insert). Available in satellite distributed, locally originated, character-generated, taped & automated programming. Rates: $6.00-$20.00/Minute; $3.00-$10.00/30 Seconds.
Program Guide: The Cable Guide.
Equipment: Scientific-Atlanta headend; Scientific-Atlanta amplifiers; Scientific-Atlanta cable; Sony cameras; JVC & Sony VTRs; Compuvid & Atari character generator; Pioneer, Texscan & NSC set top converters; Zenith addressable set top converters; Eagle traps; Scientific-Atlanta satellite antenna; Scientific-Atlanta satellite receivers; ChannelMatic commercial insert.
Miles of plant: 434.0 (coaxial). Additional miles planned: 12.0 (coaxial). Homes passed: 24,224.
Manager: Lee Kosticki. Chief technician: Bob Kaye. Program director: Glenn W. Leech. Marketing director: Diana Russo.
City fee: 3% of gross.
Ownership: Cable One Inc. (MSO).

GREENFIELD—Cox Communications, Box 593, 218 E. Court House Rd., Washington Court House, OH 43160. Phone: 614-335-1202. County: Highland. ICA: OH0157.
TV Market Ranking: 27. Franchise award date: January 1, 1984. Franchise expiration date: January 1, 1999. Began: January 1, 1966.
Channel capacity: N.A. Channels available but not in use: N.A.

Basic Service
Subscribers: 1,849; Commercial subscribers: 93.
Programming (received off-air): WKRC-TV (C), WLWT (N) Cincinnati; WXIX-TV (F) Cincinnati-Newport; WBNS-TV (C), WCMH-TV (N), WOSU-TV (P), WSYX (A), WTTE (F,U) Columbus; WHIO-TV (C) Dayton; allband FM.
Programming (via satellite): A & E; C-SPAN; Fox Family Channel; Home Shopping Network; Lifetime; MTV; News Plus; Nickelodeon; The Weather Channel; USA Network.
Current originations: Automated time-weather.
Planned originations: Public access; educational access.
Fee: $50.00 installation; $20.08 monthly.

Expanded Basic Service
Subscribers: N.A.
Programming (via satellite): CNN; Discovery Channel; ESPN; Nashville Network; TBS Superstation; Turner Network TV.
Fee: $2.00 monthly.

Pay Service 1
Pay Units: N.A.
Programming (via satellite): Disney Channel; HBO; Showtime.
Fee: $20.00 installation; $9.66 monthly (Disney), $9.95 monthly (Showtime), $10.95 monthly (HBO).

Local advertising: Yes. Available in character-generated & automated programming.
Program Guide: The Cable Guide.
Equipment: Scientific-Atlanta headend; Jerrold & C-COR amplifiers; Times Fiber & Belden cable; System Concepts character generator; Tocom & Jerrold set top converters; Vitek & Northeast Filter traps; Scientific-Atlanta satellite antenna; Scientific-Atlanta satellite receivers.
Miles of plant: 19.0 (coaxial). Homes passed: 2,615. Total homes in franchised area: 2,615.
Manager: Dave Surgalski. Chief technician: Marion Whitley. Marketing director: Shelly Kline.
City fee: None.
Ownership: Cox Communications Inc. (MSO).

GREENFIELD ESTATES—The Greenfield Co., 630 Oak St., Mansfield, OH 44907. Phone: 419-526-4591. Fax: 419-526-1457. County: Richland. ICA: OH0328.
TV Market Ranking: Below 100. Franchise award date: N.A. Franchise expiration date: N.A. Began: October 1, 1986.
Channel capacity: N.A. Channels available but not in use: N.A.

Basic Service
Subscribers: N.A.
Programming (received off-air): WVPX (X) Akron; WJW (F), WKYC-TV (N) Cleveland; WBNS-TV (C), WOSU-TV (P) Columbus; WUAB (U) Lorain-Cleveland.
Programming (via satellite): Discovery Channel; ESPN; Nashville Network; TBS Superstation; USA Network.
Fee: N.A.

Pay Service 1
Pay Units: N.A.
Programming (via satellite): Showtime; The Movie Channel.
Fee: N.A.

Manager: Angela Thompson.
Ownership: Gilbert Macy.

GREENVILLE—Time Warner Cable, 632 Wagner Ave., Greenville, OH 45331-2649. Phone: 937-547-0445. Fax: 937-547-1768. Counties: Darke & Mercer. Also serves Adams Twp. (Darke County), Allen Twp. (Darke County), Ansonia, Ansonia (village), Brown Twp. (Darke County), Burketsville, Coletown, Gettysburg, Gettysburg (village), Greenville Twp. (Darke County), Harrison Twp. (Darke County), Hollansburg, Liberty Twp. (Darke County), Neave Twp. (Darke County), New Madison, New Madison (village), New Weston, Palestine, Rossburg, Washington Twp. (Darke County), Wayne Lakes (village), Woodington. ICA: OH0076.
TV Market Ranking: 41 (Adams Twp., Allen Twp., Gettysburg, Greenville, Greenville Twp., Harrison Twp., Liberty Twp., Neave Twp., New Madison, Rossburg, Washington Twp., Wayne Lakes, Woodington); Below 100 (Ansonia, Brown Twp., Burketsville, Coletown, Hollansburg, New Weston, Palestine). Franchise award date: May 6, 1975. Franchise expiration date: N.A. Began: May 15, 1977.
Channel capacity: 78 (2-way capable; operating 2-way). Channels available but not in use: 3.

Basic Service
Subscribers: 6,744.
Programming (received off-air): WCPO-TV (A) Cincinnati; WDTN (A), WHIO-TV (C), WKEF (N), WPTD (P), WRGT-TV (F,U) Dayton; WLIO (N) Lima; WIPB (P) Muncie; WKOI (T) Richmond; WBDT (W) Springfield; allband FM.
Programming (via satellite): TBS Superstation.
Current originations: Automated time-weather; public access; educational access; government access; automated emergency alert.
Fee: $10.44 monthly.

Expanded Basic Service
Subscribers: N.A.
Programming (via satellite): A & E; American Movie Classics; C-SPAN; CNBC; CNN; Cartoon Network; Discovery Channel; ESPN; Fox Family Channel; Fox News Channel; Headline News; Lifetime; MTV; Nashville Network; Nickelodeon; QVC; TV Guide Channel; TV Guide Sneak Prevue; The Weather Channel; Turner Network TV; USA Network.
Fee: $28.26 monthly.

Expanded Basic Service 2
Subscribers: N.A.
Programming (via satellite): Animal Planet; Comedy Central; Country Music TV; Court TV; E! Entertainment TV; ESPN 2; ESPN Classic Sports; Fox Sports Net Ohio; History Channel; Home & Garden Television; Learning Channel; Sci-Fi Channel; Turner Classic Movies.
Fee: N.A.

Pay Service 1
Pay Units: 527.
Programming (via satellite): Cinemax (multiplexed).
Fee: N.A.

Pay Service 2
Pay Units: 444.
Programming (via satellite): Disney Channel.
Fee: N.A.

Pay Service 3
Pay Units: 891.
Programming (via satellite): HBO (multiplexed).
Fee: N.A.

Pay Service 4
Pay Units: 496.
Programming (via satellite): Showtime (multiplexed).
Fee: N.A.

Pay Service 5
Pay Units: N.A.
Programming (via satellite): Flix; Playboy TV; The Movie Channel.
Fee: N.A.

Pay-Per-View
Action Pay-Per-View; Hot Choice; Viewer's Choice.

Local advertising: Yes. Rates: $28.00/Minute; $14.00/30 Seconds.
Equipment: RCA headend; C-COR amplifiers; Comm/Scope cable; AFC satellite antenna; Scientific-Atlanta satellite receivers.
Miles of plant: 208.0 (coaxial); 90.0 (fiber optic). Homes passed: 10,500. Total homes in franchised area: 10,500.
Manager: Steve Sullenberger. Chief technician: Mike Burns. Marketing director: Danny Schiffer.
City fee: 3% of gross.
Ownership: Time Warner Cable (MSO).

GREENWOOD (village)—Adelphia Cable Communications, 885 E. Highland Rd., Macedonia, OH 44056. Phone: 330-468-0307. County: Guernsey. ICA: OH0329.
TV Market Ranking: Below 100. Franchise award date: N.A. Franchise expiration date: N.A. Began: N.A.
Channel capacity: 36. Channels available but not in use: 7.
Basic Service
Subscribers: 531.
Fee: N.A.
Local advertising: No.
Equipment: Scientific-Atlanta headend.
Manager: Mitch Piskur. Chief technician: Rich Strebel.
Ownership: Adelphia Communications Corp. (MSO).

GUERNSEY COUNTY (portions)—FrontierVision, Box 1297, 351 Highland Ave., Cambridge, OH 43725. Phone: 740-432-7321. Fax: 740-432-6465. County: Guernsey. Also serves Cambridge (portions), Center Twp., Kimbolton. ICA: OH0396.
TV Market Ranking: 90 (portions of Guernsey County); Below 100 (Cambridge, Center Twp., portions of Guernsey County, Kimbolton). Franchise award date: N.A. Franchise expiration date: N.A. Began: N.A.
Channel capacity: 42. Channels available but not in use: 6.
Basic Service
Subscribers: 494.
Programming (received off-air): WOUC-TV (P) Cambridge; WTTE (F,U) Columbus; WTOV-TV (N) Steubenville-Wheeling; WTRF-TV (C) Wheeling-Steubenville.
Programming (via satellite): WGN-TV (W) Chicago; A & E; CNN; Comedy Central; Country Music TV; Discovery Channel; Disney Channel; ESPN; Fox Family Channel; Headline News; MTV; Nickelodeon; QVC; Sci-Fi Channel; TBS Superstation; Trinity Bcstg. Network; Turner Classic Movies; Turner Network TV; USA Network.
Fee: $25.95 monthly.
Pay Service 1
Pay Units: 57.
Programming (via satellite): HBO.
Fee: N.A.
Pay Service 2
Pay Units: 72.
Programming (via satellite): Showtime.
Fee: N.A.
Pay-Per-View
Addressable homes: 3.
Miles of plant: 35.0 (coaxial). Homes passed: 864.
Manager: Judy Pierce. Technical supervisor: Chuck Gibson. Customer service supervisor: Rosa Robertson.
Ownership: FrontierVision Partners LP (MSO). See Cable System Ownership.

GUILFORD LAKE—Time Warner Cable, 427 E. State St., Salem, OH 44460. Phone: 330-332-9607. County: Columbiana. Also serves Hanover Twp. (Columbiana County), Hanoverton, New Garden, Winona. ICA: OH0220.
TV Market Ranking: 79,90. Franchise award date: April 22, 1985. Franchise expiration date: April 22, 2000. Began: August 2, 1985.
Channel capacity: 35 (not 2-way capable). Channels available but not in use: 10.
Basic Service
Subscribers: 696.
Programming (received off-air): WNEO (P) Alliance; WJW (F) Cleveland; WUAB (U) Lorain-Cleveland; WPGH-TV (F) Pittsburgh; WFMJ-TV (N), WKBN-TV (C), WYTV (A,F) Youngstown.
Programming (via satellite): Fox Family Channel; Home Shopping Network; Nashville Network.
Current originations: Automated time-weather; public access; educational access; government access; local news.
Fee: $30.25 installation (aerial), $39.50 (underground); $11.75 monthly; $1.47 converter.
Expanded Basic Service
Subscribers: 659.
Programming (via satellite): CNN; Discovery Channel; ESPN; Headline News; Nickelodeon; The Weather Channel; Turner Network TV; VH1.
Fee: $8.65 monthly.
Expanded Basic Service 2
Subscribers: 655.
Programming (via satellite): WGN-TV (W) Chicago; TBS Superstation; USA Network.
Fee: $3.25 monthly.
Pay Service 1
Pay Units: 124.
Programming (via satellite): Cinemax.
Fee: $25.00 installation; $9.50 monthly.
Pay Service 2
Pay Units: 149.
Programming (via satellite): HBO.
Fee: $25.00 installation; $9.50 monthly.
Pay Service 3
Pay Units: 49.
Programming (via satellite): Disney Channel.
Fee: $25.00 installation; $7.50 monthly.
Local advertising: No.
Equipment: Cadco headend; Blonder-Tongue & Jerrold amplifiers; Times Fiber cable; Jerrold set top converters; Miralite satellite antenna; Miralite satellite receivers.
Miles of plant: 29.8 (coaxial); None (fiber optic). Homes passed: 870. Total homes in franchised area: 1,030.
Manager: Daryl Morrison. Chief technician: Don Jugenheimer.
City fee: 3% basic gross.
Ownership: Time Warner Cable (MSO); Fanch Communications Inc. (MSO). See Cable System Ownership.

GUYSVILLE—FrontierVision, Box 648, 102 Twin Oak Dr., Jackson, OH 45640. Phone: 614-345-4329. Fax: 614-286-1489. County: Athens. Also serves Lottridge, Rome Twp. (Athens County), Stewart. ICA: OH0265.
TV Market Ranking: Below 100. Franchise award date: August 1, 1988. Franchise expiration date: August 1, 2003. Began: October 1, 1989.
Channel capacity: 37. Channels available but not in use: 10.
Basic Service
Subscribers: 285.
Programming (received off-air): WOUB-TV (P) Athens; WCHS-TV (A), WOWK-TV (C), WSAZ-TV (N), WVAH-TV (F,U) Charleston-Huntington; WBNS-TV (C), WCMH-TV (N), WSYX (A) Columbus.
Programming (via satellite): WGN-TV (W) Chicago; CNN; Country Music TV; Discovery Channel; ESPN; Fox Family Channel; MTV; Nashville Network; Nickelodeon; TBS Superstation; Turner Network TV; USA Network.
Fee: $20.99 installation; $22.70 monthly.
Pay Service 1
Pay Units: 39.
Programming (via satellite): HBO.
Fee: $11.95 monthly.
Pay Service 2
Pay Units: 23.
Programming (via satellite): Showtime.
Fee: $10.95 monthly.
Equipment: Texscan & Jerrold headend; Jerrold amplifiers; Times Fiber & Belden cable; Hamlin & NSC set top converters; Eagle & Pico traps; Prodelin & ChannelMaster satellite antenna; Standard Communications satellite receivers.
Miles of plant: 23.5 (coaxial). Homes passed: 488. Total homes in franchised area: 1,260.
Manager: Steve Trippe. Chief technician: Bill Ricker.
Ownership: FrontierVision Partners LP (MSO). See Cable System Ownership.

HAMILTON—Time Warner Cable, Box 710, 341 City Centre Mall, Midldletown, OH 45044. Phones: 513-424-2408; 513-896-5455. Fax: 513-424-6555. County: Butler South. Also serves Butler County, Hanover Twp. (Butler County South), Madison Twp. (Butler County South), Millville, New Miami, Ross Twp. (Butler County), Seven Mile, St. Clair Twp. (Butler County), Trenton, Wayne Twp. (Butler County). ICA: OH0022.
TV Market Ranking: 17 (portions of Butler County, Hamilton, Hanover Twp., Madison Twp., Millville, New Miami, Ross Twp., Seven Mile, St. Clair Twp., Trenton, Wayne Twp.); 41 (portions of Butler County, Hamilton, Hanover Twp., Madison Twp., Millville, New Miami, Seven Mile, St. Clair Twp., Trenton, Wayne Twp.). Franchise award date: N.A. Franchise expiration date: N.A. Began: February 1, 1973.
Channel capacity: 63 (not 2-way capable). Channels available but not in use: N.A.
Basic Service
Subscribers: 38,597.
Programming (received off-air): WCET (P), WCPO-TV (A), WKRC-TV (C), WLWT (N), WSTR-TV (W) Cincinnati; WXIX-TV (F) Cincinnati-Newport; WDTN (A), WHIO-TV (C), WKEF (N), WPTD (P), WRGT-TV (F,U) Dayton; WPTO (P) Oxford; WKOI (T) Richmond; 12 FMs.
Programming (via satellite): WGN-TV (W) Chicago; TBS Superstation; TV Guide Sneak Prevue.
Fee: $30.89 installation; $9.62 monthly; $2.00 converter; $5.15 additional installation.
Expanded Basic Service
Subscribers: 21,439.
Programming (via satellite): A & E; American Movie Classics; BET; C-SPAN; C-SPAN 2; CNBC; CNN; Court TV; Discovery Channel; ESPN; ESPN 2; FX; Fox Family Channel; Headline News; Intro TV; Knowledge TV; Lifetime; MTV; Nashville Network; Nick at Nite; Nickelodeon; Odyssey; QVC; TV Food Network; The Weather Channel; Turner Network TV; USA Network.
Fee: $30.89 installation; $12.12 monthly.
A la Carte 1
Subscribers: N.A.
Programming (via satellite): Cartoon Network; Country Music TV; E! Entertainment TV; Learning Channel.
Fee: $3.00 monthly (package); $0.85 monthly (each).
Pay Service 1
Pay Units: 3,410.
Programming (via satellite): Cinemax.
Fee: $13.12 monthly.
Pay Service 2
Pay Units: 1,723.
Programming (via satellite): Disney Channel.
Fee: $12.88 monthly.
Pay Service 3
Pay Units: 7,180.
Programming (via satellite): HBO.
Fee: $14.04 monthly.
Pay Service 4
Pay Units: 1,654.
Programming (via satellite): Showtime.
Fee: $14.04 monthly.
Pay Service 5
Pay Units: 10,062.
Programming (via satellite): The New Encore.
Fee: $1.68 monthly.
Pay Service 6
Pay Units: N.A.
Programming (via satellite): DMX; Starz!
Fee: $4.75 monthly (Starz), $4.95 monthly (DMX).
Pay-Per-View
Action Pay-Per-View; Spice.
Local advertising: Yes (locally produced). Available in satellite distributed programming. Rates: $7.00/Minute. Local sales manager: Bob Pulley.
Program Guide: The Cable Guide.
Equipment: Jerrold & Scientific-Atlanta headend; Theta-Com & Scientific-Atlanta amplifiers; Belden, Plastoid & Theta-Com cable; Sony cameras; MSI character generator; Hamlin, Scientific-Atlanta & Jerrold set top converters; Jerrold addressable set top converters; Scientific-Atlanta & Anixter-Mark satellite receivers.
Miles of plant: 353.5 (coaxial).
Manager: Jeff Heinrich. Chief technician: Randy Senger.
City fee: 5% of gross ($7,500 minimum).
Ownership: Time Warner Cable (MSO). Purchased from AT&T Broadband & Internet Services, June 1, 1999.

HANNIBAL—FrontierVision, Suite P-200, 1777 S. Harrison St., Denver, CO 80210. Phone: 303-757-1588. Fax: 303-757-6105. County: Monroe. Also serves Duffy, Sardis. ICA: OH0251.
TV Market Ranking: 90. Franchise award date: N.A. Franchise expiration date: N.A. Began: September 1, 1959.
Channel capacity: 80 (not 2-way capable). Channels available but not in use: 40.
Basic Service
Subscribers: 588.
Programming (received off-air): WOUC-TV (P) Cambridge; WBOY-TV (N) Clarksburg-Weston; WNPB-TV (P) Morgantown; KDKA-TV (C), WPGH-TV (F), WPXI (N) Pittsburgh; WTOV-TV (N) Steubenville-Wheeling; WTRF-TV (C) Wheeling-Steubenville; allband FM.
Programming (via satellite): WGN-TV (W) Chicago; WABC-TV (A) New York; Country Music TV.
Fee: $47.50 installation; $11.21 monthly; $0.73 converter.
Expanded Basic Service
Subscribers: 516.
Programming (via satellite): A & E; CNN; Discovery Channel; Disney Channel; ESPN; Fox Family Channel; FoxNet; Nashville Network; TBS Superstation; USA Network.
Fee: $8.56 monthly.
Pay Service 1
Pay Units: 34.
Programming (via satellite): Cinemax.
Fee: $7.95 monthly.
Pay Service 2
Pay Units: 32.

For a list of all cable communities included in this section, see the **Cable Community Index** located in the back of this volume.

Programming (via satellite): The New Encore.
Fee: N.A.
Pay Service 3
Pay Units: 33.
Programming (via satellite): HBO.
Fee: $11.99 monthly.
Pay Service 4
Pay Units: 39.
Programming (via satellite): Showtime.
Fee: $11.95 monthly.
Pay Service 5
Pay Units: 29.
Programming (via satellite): Starz!
Fee: N.A.
Pay Service 6
Pay Units: 36.
Programming (via satellite): The Movie Channel.
Fee: $11.95 monthly.
Local advertising: No.
Equipment: Blonder-Tongue headend.
Miles of plant: 20.0 (coaxial). Homes passed: 673.
Manager: Steve Trippe. Chief technician: Bill Ricker.
City fee: None.
Ownership: FrontierVision Partners LP (MSO). See Cable System Ownership.

HANOVER (village)(Licking County)—FrontierVision, 111 N. 11th St., Newark, OH 43055. Phone: 740-454-2380. Fax: 740-345-7670. Counties: Licking & Muskingum. Also serves Muskingum Twp. (Muskingum County), Nashport, Toboso, Zanesville (northern portion). ICA: OH0330.
TV Market Ranking: Below 100. Franchise award date: N.A. Franchise expiration date: N.A. Began: March 1, 1978.
Channel capacity: 36. Channels available but not in use: 14.
Basic Service
Subscribers: N.A.
Programming (received off-air): WBNS-TV (C), WCMH-TV (N), WOSU-TV (P), WSYX (A) Columbus; WSFJ (I) Newark; WHIZ-TV (N) Zanesville.
Programming (via satellite): CNN; ESPN; Lifetime; TBS Superstation.
Fee: $9.50 monthly.
Expanded Basic Service
Subscribers: N.A.
Programming (received off-air): WTTE (F,U) Columbus.
Programming (via satellite): WGN-TV (W) Chicago; MTV; Nashville Network; Nickelodeon; USA Network.
Fee: $5.00 monthly.
Pay Service 1
Pay Units: N.A.
Programming (via satellite): Cinemax; Disney Channel; HBO; The Movie Channel.
Fee: N.A.
Local advertising: No.
Equipment: Microdyne headend.
Miles of plant: 15.0 (coaxial).
Regional manager: Judith Pierce. Marketing director: Rich Lutze.
Ownership: FrontierVision Partners LP (MSO). See Cable System Ownership.

HAYDEN HEIGHTS—Time Warner Cable, Box 823, 131 Catherine St., Hillsboro, OH 45133. Phone: 937-393-4217. Fax: 937-393-8022. County: Franklin. Also serves Amlin. ICA: OH0301.
TV Market Ranking: 27. Franchise award date: N.A. Franchise expiration date: N.A. Began: July 1, 1986.
Channel capacity: 41 (not 2-way capable). Channels available but not in use: 18.
Basic Service
Subscribers: 65.
Programming (received off-air): WBNS-TV (C), WCMH-TV (N), WOSU-TV (P), WSYX (A), WTTE (F,U) Columbus.
Programming (via satellite): WGN-TV (W) Chicago; A & E; Animal Planet; CNN; Comedy Central; Country Music TV; Discovery Channel; ESPN; Fox Family Channel; Headline News; Lifetime; Nashville Network; Nickelodeon; Sci-Fi Channel; TBS Superstation; The Weather Channel; Turner Network TV; USA Network.
Fee: $40.27 installation; $26.15 monthly; $0.44 converter.
Pay Service 1
Pay Units: 6.
Programming (via satellite): Disney Channel.
Fee: $18.00 installation; $10.95 monthly.
Pay Service 2
Pay Units: 26.
Programming (via satellite): HBO.
Fee: $18.00 installation; $10.95 monthly.
Miles of plant: 0.9 (coaxial). Homes passed: 142.
Manager: Mike Rector. Chief technician: Dale Zornes. Marketing director: Gary Pitzer.
City fee: 10% of gross.
Ownership: Fanch Communications Inc. (MSO); Time Warner Cable (MSO). See Cable System Ownership.

HICKSVILLE—Triax Cablevision, Box 334, 1102 N. 4th St., Chillicothe, OH 61523-0334. Phones: 309-274-4500; 800-874-2924. Fax: 309-274-3188. Counties: Defiance & Paulding. Also serves Antwerp. ICA: OH0169.
TV Market Ranking: 82. Franchise award date: N.A. Franchise expiration date: November 1, 2010. Began: March 4, 1981.
Channel capacity: 78 (2-way capable; operating 2-way). Channels available but not in use: 37.
Basic Service
Subscribers: 1,120.
Programming (received off-air): WINM (T) Angola; WBGU-TV (P) Bowling Green; WANE-TV (C), WFFT-TV (F), WFWA (P), WKJG-TV (N), WPTA (A) Fort Wayne; WLIO (N) Lima; WNWO-TV (N), WTVG (A) Toledo.
Programming (via satellite): TBS Superstation.
Current originations: Public access.
Fee: $45.00 installation; $12.31 monthly.
Expanded Basic Service
Subscribers: 1,052.
Programming (via satellite): WGN-TV (W) Chicago; A & E; American Movie Classics; C-SPAN; CNN; Discovery Channel; Disney Channel; E! Entertainment TV; ESPN; ESPN 2; Fox Family Channel; Headline News; History Channel; Home & Garden Television; Home Shopping Network; Learning Channel; Lifetime; MTV; Nashville Network; Nickelodeon; The Radar Channel; Turner Network TV; USA Network.
Fee: $18.91 monthly.
Pay Service 1
Pay Units: 576.
Programming (via satellite): Cinemax; HBO; Showtime; Starz!; The Movie Channel; The New Encore.
Fee: $3.99 monthly (Encore), $5.99 monthly (Encore & Starz), $7.99 monthly (Cinemax), $11.99 monthly (HBO, Showtime or TMC).
Equipment: Automation Techniques & Microdyne headend; Magnavox amplifiers; Times Fiber cable; Standard Electronics character generator; Microwave Assoc. satellite antenna.
Miles of plant: 46.0 (coaxial). Homes passed: 2,130.
Manager: Craig Grey. Chief technician: Joe Burelison.
Ownership: Triax Telecommunications Co. LLC (MSO). Purchased from FrontierVision Partners LP. See Cable System Ownership.

HIDE-A-WAY HILLS—FrontierVision, Box 648, 102 Twin Oak Dr., Jackson, OH 45640. Phone: 614-345-4329. Fax: 614-286-1489. Counties: Fairfield & Hocking. Also serves Berne, Marion, Rush Creek. ICA: OH0229.
TV Market Ranking: 27. Franchise award date: December 9, 1986. Franchise expiration date: N.A. Began: October 1, 1989.
Channel capacity: 62. Channels available but not in use: 33.
Basic Service
Subscribers: 627.
Programming (received off-air): WBNS-TV (C), WCMH-TV (N), WOSU-TV (P), WSYX (A), WTTE (F,U) Columbus.
Programming (via satellite): WGN-TV (W) Chicago; A & E; CNN; Country Music TV; Discovery Channel; ESPN; Fox Family Channel; Nashville Network; Nickelodeon; TBS Superstation; The Weather Channel; USA Network.
Current originations: Local access.
Fee: $20.99 installation; $22.95 monthly.
Pay Service 1
Pay Units: 99.
Programming (via satellite): HBO.
Fee: $11.95 monthly.
Pay Service 2
Pay Units: 114.
Programming (via satellite): Showtime.
Fee: $10.95 monthly.
Pay Service 3
Pay Units: 82.
Programming (via satellite): The Movie Channel.
Fee: N.A.
Equipment: Texscan amplifiers; Times Fiber & Belden cable; Hamlin & NSC set top converters; Eagle, Pico & Arcom traps; Prodelin satellite antenna; Standard Communications satellite receivers.
Miles of plant: 65.1 (coaxial). Homes passed: 940. Total homes in franchised area: 3,975.
Manager: Steve Trippe. Chief technician: Bill Ricker.
Ownership: FrontierVision Partners LP (MSO). See Cable System Ownership.

HILLIARD—Americast, 300 S. Riverside, Chicago, IL 60606. Phones: 312-526-8000; 800-848-2278. Fax: 312-526-8565. County: Franklin. ICA: OH0414.
TV Market Ranking: 27. Franchise award date: March 1, 1996. Franchise expiration date: N.A. Began: N.A.
Channel capacity: N.A. Channels available but not in use: N.A.
Basic Service
Subscribers: N.A.
Programming (received off-air): WWHO (U) Chillicothe; WBNS-TV (C), WCMH-TV (N), WOSU-TV (P), WSYX (A), WTTE (F,U) Columbus; WSFJ (I) Newark.
Programming (via satellite): WGN-TV (W) Chicago; QVC; TBS Superstation; TV Guide Channel.
Current originations: Public access; educational access; government access; leased access.
Fee: $39.95 installation; $9.95 monthly.
Expanded Basic Service
Subscribers: N.A.
Programming (via satellite): A & E; American Movie Classics; BET; BET on Jazz; Bravo; C-SPAN; C-SPAN 2; CNBC; CNN; CNNfn; Cartoon Network; Comedy Central; Country Music TV; Court TV; Discovery Channel; Disney Channel; E! Entertainment TV; ESPN; ESPN 2; ESPN Classic Sports; Fox Family Channel; Fox Sports Net Ohio; Golf Channel; Headline News; History Channel; Home & Garden Television; Learning Channel; Lifetime; MTV; Nashville Network; Nickelodeon; Ohio News Network; Sci-Fi Channel; TV Food Network; The Health Network; The Inspirational Network; The Weather Channel; Travel Channel; Turner Classic Movies; Turner Network TV; USA Network; VH1.
Fee: $17.00 monthly.
Pay Service 1
Pay Units: N.A.
Programming (via satellite): Cinemax; Flix; HBO (multiplexed); Showtime (multiplexed); Starz!; Sundance Channel; The Movie Channel; The New Encore.
Fee: $5.95 monthly (Flix or Sundance), $7.95 monthly (Encore & Starz), $9.95 monthly (Cinemax, Showtime or TMC), $11.95 monthly (HBO).
Total homes in franchised area: 8,100.
Ownership: Ameritech New Media Inc. (MSO).

HILLSBORO—Time Warner Cable, Box 823, 131 Catherine St., Hillsboro, OH 45133. Phone: 937-393-4217. Fax: 937-393-8022. County: Highland. Also serves Dodson Twp., Hamer Twp., Hillsboro Twp., Liberty Twp. (Highland County), Marshall Twp., New Market Twp., Penn Twp. (Highland County), Union Twp. (Highland County). ICA: OH0110.
TV Market Ranking: 27 (Hillsboro, portions of Hillsboro Twp., portions of Liberty Twp., Marshall Twp., portions of Penn Twp.); Below 100 (portions of Hillsboro Twp., portions of Liberty Twp.); Outside TV Markets (Dodson Twp., Hamer Twp., New Market Twp., portions of Penn Twp., Union Twp.). Franchise award date: February 21, 1983. Franchise expiration date: February 20, 1998. Began: August 1, 1971.
Channel capacity: 77 (not 2-way capable). Channels available but not in use: N.A.
Basic Service
Subscribers: 3,365.
Programming (received off-air): WCET (P), WCPO-TV (A), WKRC-TV (C), WLWT (N), WSTR-TV (W) Cincinnati; WXIX-TV (F) Cincinnati-Newport; WBNS-TV (C), WSYX (A) Columbus; WDTN (A), WHIO-TV (C), WRGT-TV (F,U) Dayton.
Programming (via satellite): A & E; American Movie Classics; C-SPAN; CNN; CNN/SI; Comedy Central; Country Music TV; Discovery Channel; ESPN; Fox Family Channel;

History Channel; Home & Garden Television; Lifetime; MTV; Nashville Network; Nickelodeon; QVC; TBS Superstation; TV Guide Channel; The Weather Channel; Trinity Bcstg. Network; Turner Network TV; USA Network; VH1.
Current originations: Public access; educational access; government access; religious access.
Fee: $39.90 installation; $26.00 monthly.

Expanded Basic Service
Subscribers: N.A.
Programming (via satellite): Animal Planet; Cartoon Network; Court TV; ESPN 2; Fox Sports Net Ohio; Nick at Nite's TV Land; Turner Classic Movies.
Fee: $2.95 monthly.

Pay Service 1
Pay Units: 451.
Programming (via satellite): Cinemax.
Fee: $10.95 monthly.

Pay Service 2
Pay Units: 306.
Programming (via satellite): Disney Channel.
Fee: $7.95 monthly.

Pay Service 3
Pay Units: 679.
Programming (via satellite): HBO.
Fee: $10.95 monthly.

Pay Service 4
Pay Units: 427.
Programming (via satellite): Showtime.
Fee: $10.95 monthly.

Pay Service 5
Pay Units: 262.
Programming (via satellite): The Movie Channel.
Fee: $10.95 monthly.

Pay-Per-View
Addressable homes: 4,827.
Viewer's Choice.
Fee: $3.95.

Local advertising: Yes. Local sales manager: Gary Pitzer.
Equipment: Ameco headend; Ameco amplifiers; General & Comm/Scope cable; Scientific-Atlanta satellite antenna; Scientific-Atlanta satellite receivers.
Miles of plant: 111.0 (coaxial). Additional miles planned: 1.0 (coaxial). Homes passed: 5,151. Total homes in franchised area: 5,480.
Manager: Michael Rector. Chief technician: Dale Zornes. Marketing director: Gary Pitzer.
City fee: 5% of gross.
Ownership: Time Warner Cable (MSO).

HOPEDALE—TCI Cablevision of Ohio Inc., Box 347, 123 N. Market St., Minerva, OH 44657. Phone: 330-868-5413. Fax: 330-868-3731. County: Harrison. ICA: OH0281.
TV Market Ranking: 90. Franchise award date: N.A. Franchise expiration date: N.A. Began: April 1, 1975.
Channel capacity: 40. Channels available but not in use: 9.

Basic Service
Subscribers: 300.
Programming (received off-air): WVPX (X) Akron; WOUC-TV (P) Cambridge; KDKA-TV (C), WPGH-TV (F), WPXI (N), WQED (P), WTAE-TV (A) Pittsburgh; WTOV-TV (N) Steubenville-Wheeling; WTRF-TV (C) Wheeling-Steubenville.
Programming (via satellite): A & E; American Movie Classics; Animal Planet; CNBC; CNN; Cartoon Network; Discovery Channel; ESPN; Fox Family Channel; Fox News Channel; Headline News; Home Shopping Network; Nashville Network; Odyssey; TBS Superstation; The New Encore; Turner Network TV; USA Network.
Fee: $37.50 installation; $21.84 monthly; $3.00 converter.

Pay Service 1
Pay Units: 71.
Programming (via satellite): HBO.
Fee: $14.95 monthly.

Pay Service 2
Pay Units: 57.
Programming (via satellite): Showtime.
Fee: $14.95 monthly.

Pay Service 3
Pay Units: 88.
Programming (via satellite): The New Encore.
Fee: $1.95 monthly.

Pay Service 4
Pay Units: N.A.
Programming (via satellite): Cinemax; Disney Channel; Starz!
Fee: $6.75 monthly (Starz), $12.50 monthly (Disney), $13.45 monthly (Cinemax).

Miles of plant: 7.3 (coaxial). Homes passed: 414. Total homes in franchised area: 417.
Manager: Paul Liucart. Chief technician: Rodney Lentz.
Ownership: AT&T Broadband & Internet Services (MSO). Purchased from Tele-Communications Inc., March 9, 1999.

HOWARD—FrontierVision, Box 4250, 111 N. 11th St., Newark, OH 43055. Phones: 740-454-2380; 888-293-1894. Fax: 740-345-7670. County: Knox. Also serves Knox County (portions). ICA: OH0397.
TV Market Ranking: 27 (portions of Knox County); Below 100 (Howard, portions of Knox County). Franchise award date: N.A. Franchise expiration date: N.A. Began: N.A.
Channel capacity: 36. Channels available but not in use: 7.

Basic Service
Subscribers: 403.
Programming (received off-air): WBNS-TV (C), WCMH-TV (N), WOSU-TV (P), WSYX (A), WTTE (F,U) Columbus.
Programming (via satellite): WGN-TV (W) Chicago; A & E; CNN; Cartoon Network; Country Music TV; Discovery Channel; ESPN; Fox Family Channel; Headline News; MTV; Nickelodeon; QVC; TBS Superstation; The Weather Channel; Turner Network TV; USA Network.
Fee: $25.95 monthly.

Pay Service 1
Pay Units: N.A.
Programming (via satellite): Cinemax; HBO.
Fee: N.A.

Regional manager: Judith Pierce. Marketing director: Rich Lutze.
Ownership: FrontierVision Partners LP (MSO). See Cable System Ownership.

HUBBARD TWP. (Trumbull County)—Northeast Cable TV, Box 4095, Youngstown, OH 44515. Phone: 330-793-7434. Fax: 330-793-7434. County: Trumbull. ICA: OH0383.
TV Market Ranking: 79. Franchise award date: N.A. Franchise expiration date: N.A. Began: May 1, 1985.
Channel capacity: 60. Channels available but not in use: N.A.

Basic Service
Subscribers: N.A.
Programming (received off-air): WBNX-TV (W,F) Akron; WNEO (P) Alliance; WEWS-TV (A), WJW (F), WKYC-TV (N) Cleveland; WUAB (U) Lorain-Cleveland; WOIO (C) Shaker Heights; WFMJ-TV (N), WKBN-TV (C), WYTV (A,F) Youngstown.
Programming (via satellite): CNN; ESPN; MOR Galleria; Nashville Network; Sci-Fi Channel; TBS Superstation; Turner Network TV; USA Network.
Fee: $29.95 installation; $22.50 monthly.

Pay Service 1
Pay Units: N.A.
Programming (via satellite): HBO.
Fee: $12.95 monthly.

Miles of plant: 5.0 (coaxial). Homes passed: 147.
Manager: Al Pezzenti.
Ownership: Northeast Cable TV (MSO).

HUNTINGTON TWP.—FrontierVision, Box 648, 102 Twin Oak Dr., Jackson, OH 45640. Phone: 614-345-4329. Fax: 614-286-1489. Counties: Pike & Ross. Also serves Franklin Twp. (Ross County), Pike County. ICA: OH0174.
TV Market Ranking: 27. Franchise award date: December 29, 1986. Franchise expiration date: December 29, 2001. Began: N.A.
Channel capacity: 37. Channels available but not in use: None.

Basic Service
Subscribers: 1,852.
Programming (received off-air): WOWK-TV (C), WVAH-TV (F,U) Charleston-Huntington; WBNS-TV (C), WCMH-TV (N), WOSU-TV (P), WSYX (A), WTTE (F,U) Columbus.
Programming (via satellite): WGN-TV (W) Chicago; A & E; C-SPAN; CNN; Comedy Central; Country Music TV; Discovery Channel; ESPN; Fox Family Channel; Learning Channel; Lifetime; MTV; Nashville Network; Nickelodeon; QVC; TBS Superstation; The Weather Channel; Turner Network TV; USA Network.
Fee: $22.21 installation; $22.95 monthly.

Pay Service 1
Pay Units: 199.
Programming (via satellite): The New Encore.
Fee: N.A.

Pay Service 2
Pay Units: 223.
Programming (via satellite): HBO.
Fee: $12.96 installation; $11.95 monthly.

Pay Service 3
Pay Units: 303.
Programming (via satellite): Showtime.
Fee: N.A.

Pay Service 4
Pay Units: 196.
Programming (via satellite): Starz!
Fee: N.A.

Pay Service 5
Pay Units: 337.
Programming (via satellite): The Movie Channel.
Fee: $12.96 installation; $10.95 monthly.

Equipment: Texscan & Triple Crown amplifiers; Times Fiber & Belden cable; Hamlin & NSC set top converters; Eagle & Pico traps; Scientific-Atlanta satellite antenna.
Miles of plant: 124.4 (coaxial). Homes passed: 2,044.
Manager: Steve Trippe. Chief technician: Bill Ricker.
Ownership: FrontierVision Partners LP (MSO). See Cable System Ownership.

IRONDALE—TCI Cablevision of Ohio Inc., 16808 St. Clair Ave., East Liverpool, OH 43920-3095. Phones: 330-385-4854; 800-421-3145. Fax: 330-385-0322. County: Jefferson. Also serves Hammondsville. ICA: OH0285.
TV Market Ranking: 90. Franchise award date: N.A. Franchise expiration date: January 1, 2001. Began: October 1, 1971.
Channel capacity: 35 (not 2-way capable). Channels available but not in use: 7.

Basic Service
Subscribers: 236.
Programming (received off-air): WOUC-TV (P) Cambridge; KDKA-TV (C), WCWB (W), WPGH-TV (F), WPXI (N), WQED (P), WTAE-TV (A) Pittsburgh; WTOV-TV (N) Steubenville-Wheeling; WTRF-TV (C) Wheeling-Steubenville; allband FM.
Programming (via satellite): WGN-TV (W) Chicago; C-SPAN; CNBC; CNN; Discovery Channel; Headline News; Lifetime; MTV; Nashville Network; Odyssey; QVC; TBS Superstation.
Fee: $9.70 monthly; $2.00 converter.

Expanded Basic Service
Subscribers: 133.
Programming (via satellite): A & E; American Movie Classics; ESPN; Turner Network TV; USA Network.
Fee: N.A.

Pay Service 1
Pay Units: 58.
Programming (via satellite): HBO.
Fee: N.A.

Equipment: M/A-Com headend; Jerrold amplifiers.
Miles of plant: 6.3 (coaxial). Homes passed: 308. Total homes in franchised area: 349.
Manager: Jim Underwood. Chief technician: Donald S. Boyd.
City fee: 2% of gross (Irondale).
Ownership: AT&T Broadband & Internet Services (MSO). Purchased from Tele-Communications Inc., March 9, 1999.

IRONTON—FrontierVision, Box 1357, Ashland, KY 41101. Phone: 800-346-2288. Fax: 614-532-1114. County: Lawrence. Also serves Coal Grove, Coryville, Deering, Forestdale, Heda, Kitts Hill. ICA: OH0073.
TV Market Ranking: 36. Franchise award date: January 1, 1965. Franchise expiration date: N.A. Began: October 15, 1965.
Channel capacity: 62 (2-way capable; operating 2-way). Channels available but not in use: None.

Basic Service
Subscribers: 7,487; Commercial subscribers: 956.
Programming (received off-air): WTSF (I) Ashland; WCHS-TV (A), WOWK-TV (C), WPBY-TV (P), WSAZ-TV (N), WVAH-TV (F,U) Charleston-Huntington; WLWT (N) Cincinnati; WBNS-TV (C) Columbus; WPBO-TV (P) Portsmouth; 16 FMs.
Programming (via microwave): TBS Superstation; WCPO-TV (A), WLWT (N) Cincinnati; WXIX-TV (F) Cincinnati-Newport; WBNS-TV (C) Columbus; WUAB (U) Lorain-Cleveland.
Programming (via satellite): C-SPAN; C-SPAN 2; Cartoon Network; Court TV; Fox Family Channel; History Channel; MTV; QVC; TBS Superstation; TV Guide Channel; Turner Classic Movies; VH1.
Current originations: Automated time-weather; educational access.
Fee: $41.34 installation; $22.25 monthly.

Expanded Basic Service
Subscribers: 7,279.
Programming (via satellite): A & E; CNN; Comedy Central; Country Music TV; E! Entertainment TV; ESPN; FX; Headline News; Home & Garden Television; Learning Channel; Lifetime; Nick at Nite; Nickelodeon; Outdoor Life Network; Sci-Fi Channel; TV Food Network; TV Guide Sneak Prevue; The Weather Channel; USA Network.
Fee: N.A.

Expanded Basic Service 2
Subscribers: N.A.
Programming (via satellite): American Movie Classics; Discovery Channel; Nashville Network; Turner Network TV.
Fee: N.A.

Pay Service 1
Pay Units: 680.
Programming (via satellite): Cinemax.
Fee: $5.00 installation; $9.35 monthly.

Pay Service 2
Pay Units: 304.
Programming (via satellite): The New Encore.
Fee: N.A.
Pay Service 3
Pay Units: 791.
Programming (via satellite): HBO.
Fee: N.A.
Pay Service 4
Pay Units: 840.
Programming (via satellite): Showtime.
Fee: N.A.
Pay Service 5
Pay Units: 299.
Programming (via satellite): Starz!
Fee: N.A.
Pay-Per-View
Addressable homes: 3,164.
Hot Choice; Spice; Viewer's Choice.
Pay-per-view manager: Tracee Tackett.
Local advertising: Yes. Available in satellite distributed programming.
Equipment: Scientific-Atlanta headend; C-COR & Jerrold amplifiers; Belden cable; RCA cameras; Sony VTRs; Standard Components set top converters.
Miles of plant: 151.0 (coaxial); 25.0 (fiber optic). Homes passed: 10,010.
Manager: Steve Trippe. Chief technician: Bill Ricker.
City fee: 3% of gross.
Ownership: FrontierVision Partners LP (MSO). See Cable System Ownership.

JACKSON—FrontierVision, 363 Marietta Rd., Chillicothe, OH 45601. Phones: 614-345-4329; 800-346-2288. Fax: 614-286-1489. Counties: Jackson & Vinton. Also serves Clinton Twp. (Vinton County), Coal Twp. (Jackson County), Coalton, Glen Roy, Hamden, Jackson County (portions), Lick Twp. (Jackson County), McArthur, Wellston. ICA: OH0098.
TV Market Ranking: 27 (Clinton Twp., Coal Twp., Coalton, Glen Roy, Hamden, Jackson, portions of Jackson County, Lick Twp., McArthur, Wellston); 36 (portions of Jackson County); Below 100 (portions of Jackson County). Franchise award date: June 9, 1968. Franchise expiration date: January 6, 1999. Began: March 1, 1969.
Channel capacity: 62 (not 2-way capable). Channels available but not in use: 11.
Basic Service
Subscribers: 6,708.
Programming (received off-air): WOUB-TV (P) Athens; WCHS-TV (A), WOWK-TV (C), WSAZ-TV (N), WVAH-TV (F,U) Charleston-Huntington; WBNS-TV (C), WCMH-TV (N), WOSU-TV (P), WSYX (A) Columbus; 16 FMs.
Programming (via satellite): WGN-TV (W) Chicago; WPIX (W) New York; A & E; American Movie Classics; CNN; Comedy Central; Country Music TV; Discovery Channel; Disney Channel; ESPN; Fox Family Channel; Lifetime; MTV; Nashville Network; Nickelodeon; QVC; Sci-Fi Channel; TBS Superstation; TV Guide Channel; The Weather Channel; Turner Network TV; USA Network.
Current originations: Automated time-weather; public access; religious access.
Fee: $22.21 installation; $23.50 monthly; $15.92 additional installation.
Pay Service 1
Pay Units: 189.
Programming (via satellite): Cinemax.
Fee: N.A.
Pay Service 2
Pay Units: 278.
Programming (via satellite): The New Encore.
Fee: N.A.
Pay Service 3
Pay Units: 840.
Programming (via satellite): HBO.
Fee: $15.00 installation; $11.95 monthly.
Pay Service 4
Pay Units: 585.
Programming (via satellite): Showtime.
Fee: $15.00 installation; $10.95 monthly.
Pay Service 5
Pay Units: 275.
Programming (via satellite): Starz!
Fee: N.A.
Pay Service 6
Pay Units: 319.
Programming (via satellite): The Movie Channel.
Fee: N.A.
Local advertising: Yes. Available in satellite distributed, locally originated & character-generated programming. Regional interconnect: Cabletime.
Program Guide: The Cable Guide.
Equipment: Scientific-Atlanta headend; Texscan amplifiers; Times Fiber cable; Video Data Systems character generator; Hamlin set top converters; Arcom traps; AFC & Prodelin satellite antenna; Standard Communications satellite receivers.
Miles of plant: 161.4 (coaxial). Homes passed: 8,001.
Manager: Steve Trippe. Chief technician: Bill Ricker.
City fee: $100 (Coalton); $300 (Hamden); $1,500 (Jackson & Wellston).
Ownership: FrontierVision Partners LP (MSO). See Cable System Ownership.

JACKSON TWP.—Americast, 300 S. Riverside, Chicago, IL 60606. Phones: 312-526-8000; 800-848-2278. Fax: 312-526-8565. County: Franklin. ICA: OH0416.
TV Market Ranking: 27. Franchise award date: November 1, 1997. Franchise expiration date: N.A. Began: N.A.
Channel capacity: N.A. Channels available but not in use: N.A.
Basic Service
Subscribers: N.A.
Programming (received off-air): WWHO (U) Chillicothe; WBNS-TV (C), WCMH-TV (N), WOSU-TV (P), WSYX (A), WTTE (F,U) Columbus; WSFJ (I) Newark.
Programming (via satellite): WGN-TV (W) Chicago; QVC; TBS Superstation; TV Guide Channel.
Current originations: Public access; educational access; government access; leased access.
Fee: $39.95 installation; $9.95 monthly.
Expanded Basic Service
Subscribers: N.A.
Programming (via satellite): A & E; American Movie Classics; BET; BET on Jazz; Bravo; C-SPAN; C-SPAN 2; CNBC; CNN; CNNfn; Cartoon Network; Comedy Central; Country Music TV; Court TV; Discovery Channel; Disney Channel; E! Entertainment TV; ESPN; ESPN 2; ESPN Classic Sports; Fox Family Channel; Fox Sports Net Ohio; Golf Channel; Headline News; History Channel; Home & Garden Television; Learning Channel; Lifetime; MTV; Nashville Network; Nickelodeon; Ohio News Network; Sci-Fi Channel; TV Food Network; The Health Network; The Inspirational Network; The Weather Channel; Travel Channel; Turner Classic Movies; Turner Network TV; USA Network; VH1.
Fee: $17.00 monthly.
Pay Service 1
Pay Units: N.A.
Programming (via satellite): Cinemax; Flix; HBO (multiplexed); Showtime (multiplexed); Starz!; Sundance Channel; The Movie Channel; The New Encore.
Fee: $5.95 monthly (Flix or Sundance), $7.95 monthly (Encore & Starz), $9.95 monthly (Cinemax, Showtime or TMC), $11.95 monthly (HBO).
Total homes in franchised area: 2,000.
Ownership: Ameritech New Media Inc. (MSO).

JEROMESVILLE—Time Warner Cable, Box 10, 105 Prospect St., Lodi, OH 44254. Phones: 330-633-9044; 800-821-7250. Fax: 330-948-1513. County: Ashland. Also serves Rowsburg. ICA: OH0266.
TV Market Ranking: Below 100. Franchise award date: N.A. Franchise expiration date: July 1, 1997. Began: June 1, 1978.
Channel capacity: 39 (not 2-way capable). Channels available but not in use: N.A.
Basic Service
Subscribers: 358.
Programming (received off-air): WBNX-TV (W,F), WVPX (X) Akron; WNEO (P) Alliance; WEWS-TV (A), WJW (F), WKYC-TV (N), WQHS-TV (H), WVIZ-TV (P) Cleveland; WUAB (U) Lorain-Cleveland; WMFD-TV (I) Mansfield; WOIO (C) Shaker Heights.
Programming (via satellite): A & E; American Movie Classics; Cartoon Network; Knowledge TV; The Inspirational Network.
Fee: $42.09 installation; $10.19 monthly; $2.50 converter; $15.00 additional installation.
Expanded Basic Service
Subscribers: N.A.
Programming (via satellite): WGN-TV (W) Chicago; C-SPAN; CNN; Country Music TV; Discovery Channel; ESPN; Fox Family Channel; Headline News; Lifetime; MTV; Nashville Network; Nickelodeon; TBS Superstation; The Weather Channel; Turner Network TV; USA Network.
Fee: $14.83 monthly.
Pay Service 1
Pay Units: 59.
Programming (via satellite): Disney Channel.
Fee: $8.95 installation; $8.95 monthly.
Pay Service 2
Pay Units: 108.
Programming (via satellite): HBO.
Fee: $8.95 installation; $8.95 monthly.
Pay Service 3
Pay Units: N.A.
Programming (via satellite): Cinemax; Showtime; The Movie Channel.
Fee: $8.95 monthly (each).
Local advertising: No.
Equipment: Toner headend; Jerrold amplifiers; Comm/Scope cable; Pioneer set top converters; Eagle & Vitek traps; Harris satellite antenna; Electrohome satellite receivers.
Miles of plant: 14.0 (coaxial). Homes passed: 480. Total homes in franchised area: 480.
Manager: Thomas P. Autry. Chief technician: Jim Parsons. Marketing director: Ray Kistler.
Ownership: Time Warner Cable (MSO).

JEWETT—TCI Cablevision of Ohio Inc., Box 347, 123 N. Market St., Minerva, OH 44657. Phone: 330-868-5413. Fax: 330-868-3731. County: Harrison. ICA: OH0283.
TV Market Ranking: 90. Franchise award date: N.A. Franchise expiration date: N.A. Began: August 1, 1971.
Channel capacity: 40 (not 2-way capable). Channels available but not in use: 7.
Basic Service
Subscribers: 242.
Programming (received off-air): WVPX (X) Akron; WOUC-TV (P) Cambridge; KDKA-TV (C), WPGH-TV (F), WPXI (N), WQED (P), WTAE-TV (A) Pittsburgh; WTOV-TV (N) Steubenville-Wheeling; WTRF-TV (C) Wheeling-Steubenville.
Programming (via satellite): Discovery Channel; QVC; TBS Superstation.
Fee: $37.50 installation; $10.40 monthly; $3.00 converter.
Expanded Basic Service
Subscribers: 236.
Programming (via satellite): A & E; American Movie Classics; Animal Planet; C-SPAN; CNBC; CNN; Cartoon Network; ESPN; Fox Family Channel; Fox News Channel; Lifetime; MTV; Nashville Network; Odyssey; The New Encore; Turner Network TV; USA Network.
Fee: $12.58 monthly.
Pay Service 1
Pay Units: 54.
Programming (via satellite): HBO.
Fee: $14.95 monthly.
Pay Service 2
Pay Units: 44.
Programming (via satellite): Showtime.
Fee: $14.95 monthly.
Pay Service 3
Pay Units: 90.
Programming (via satellite): The New Encore.
Fee: $1.95 monthly.
Pay Service 4
Pay Units: N.A.
Programming (via satellite): Cinemax; Disney Channel; Showtime; Starz!
Fee: $6.75 monthly (Starz), $12.50 monthly (Disney), $13.45 monthly (Cinemax), $14.95 monthly (Showtime).
Miles of plant: 5.0 (coaxial). Homes passed: 316. Total homes in franchised area: 327.
Manager: Paul Liucart. Chief technician: Rodney Lentz.
Ownership: AT&T Broadband & Internet Services (MSO). Purchased from Tele-Communications Inc., March 9, 1999.

JOHNSTOWN—Time Warner Cable, Box 191, 111 S. Mulberry St., Mt. Vernon, OH 43050. Phones: 740-397-2288; 800-282-2288. Fax: 740-397-3730. Counties: Delaware & Licking. Also serves Berkshire Twp., Croton, Galena, Hartford Twp. (Licking County), Monroe Twp. (Licking County), Porter Twp. (Delaware County), Sunbury, Trenton Twp. ICA: OH0370.
TV Market Ranking: 27. Franchise award date: January 1, 1975. Franchise expiration date: N.A. Began: August 1, 1979.
Channel capacity: 77 (not 2-way capable). Channels available but not in use: 41.
Basic Service
Subscribers: 1,411.
Programming (received off-air): WWHO (U) Chillicothe; WBNS-TV (C), WCMH-TV (N), WOSU-TV (P), WSYX (A), WTTE (F,U) Columbus; WXCB-LP (I) Delaware; WSFJ (I) Newark.
Programming (via satellite): WGN-TV (W) Chicago; A & E; American Movie Classics; C-SPAN; C-SPAN 2; CNBC; CNN; Cartoon Network; Comedy Central; Discovery Channel; E! Entertainment TV; ESPN; ESPN 2; Fox Family Channel; Headline News; Home Shopping Network; Knowledge TV; Learning Channel; Lifetime; MTV; Nashville Network; Nickelodeon; QVC; TBS Superstation; The Weather Channel; Travel Channel; Turner Network TV; USA Network; VH1.
Current originations: Automated time-weather.

Fee: $50.00 installation; $18.95 monthly; $45.00 additional installation.

Pay Service 1

Pay Units: 256.

Programming (via satellite): Cinemax.

Fee: $15.00 installation; $10.95 monthly.

Pay Service 2

Pay Units: 244.

Programming (via satellite): Disney Channel.

Fee: $15.00 installation; $10.95 monthly.

Pay Service 3

Pay Units: 503.

Programming (via satellite): HBO.

Fee: $15.00 installation; $10.95 monthly.

Pay Service 4

Pay Units: 217.

Programming (via satellite): Showtime.

Fee: $15.00 installation; $10.95 monthly.

Pay Service 5

Pay Units: 217.

Programming (via satellite): The Movie Channel.

Fee: $15.00 installation; $10.95 monthly.

Local advertising: Yes.

Equipment: Jerrold headend; C-COR & Jerrold amplifiers; Comm/Scope cable; Texscan character generator; Scientific-Atlanta set top converters; Scientific-Atlanta addressable set top converters; Eagle traps; Eagle addressable traps; Microdyne satellite antenna; Microdyne satellite receivers.

Miles of plant: 97.0 (coaxial).

Manager: Paul S. Schonewolf. Technical operations manager: Bill Schroeder.

Ownership: Time Warner Cable (MSO).

KALIDA—Kalida Telephone Co., Box 267, Kalida, OH 45853. Phone: 419-532-3218. Fax: 419-532-3300. E-mail: ktcinc@bright.net. County: Putnam. Also serves Greenburg Twp., Jackson Twp. (Putnam County), Sugar Creek Twp. (Putnam County), Union Twp. (Putnam County). ICA: OH0277.

TV Market Ranking: Below 100. Franchise award date: December 7, 1981. Franchise expiration date: N.A. Began: May 1, 1985.

Channel capacity: 36 (2-way capable; operating 2-way). Channels available but not in use: 4.

Basic Service

Subscribers: 835.

Programming (received off-air): WBGU-TV (P) Bowling Green; WANE-TV (C), WFFT-TV (F) Fort Wayne; WLIO (N) Lima; WNWO-TV (N), WTOL-TV (C), WTVG (A), WUPW (F) Toledo; 1 FM.

Programming (via satellite): WGN-TV (W) Chicago; CNN; ESPN; EWTN; Lifetime; TBS Superstation; The Weather Channel.

Current originations: Automated time-weather.

Fee: $24.50 installation; $14.95 monthly; $3.00 converter.

Expanded Basic Service

Subscribers: 200.

Programming (via satellite): A & E; Discovery Channel; ESPN 2; Fox Family Channel; Fox Sports Net Ohio; Nashville Network; Nickelodeon; Turner Classic Movies; Turner Network TV; USA Network.

Fee: N.A.

Pay Service 1

Pay Units: 131.

Programming (via satellite): Disney Channel.

Fee: $10.00 installation; $7.95 monthly.

Pay Service 2

Pay Units: 164.

Programming (via satellite): The Movie Channel.

Fee: $8.45 monthly.

Pay Service 3

Pay Units: 211.

Programming (via satellite): Showtime.

Fee: $8.45 monthly.

Local advertising: Planned.

Equipment: Texscan amplifiers; Times Fiber cable; Pioneer set top converters; Eagle traps.

Miles of plant: 24.5 (coaxial). Homes passed: 875.

Manager: Chris J. Phillips. Chief technician: Chris Hoffman.

City fee: 1% of basic gross.

Ownership: Kalida Telephone Co.

KENT—Time Warner Cable, Box 189, Kent, OH 44240-4174. Phone: 216-677-9692. County: Portage. Also serves Brady Lake Village, Brimfield Twp. (Portage County), Franklin Twp. (Portage County), Mantua, Randolph, Ravenna, Ravenna Twp. (Portage County), Rootstown Twp. (Portage County), Shalersville, Spring Lakes Mobile Home Park, Streetsboro, Suffield, Sugar Bush Knolls. ICA: OH0034.

TV Market Ranking: 8 (Brady Lake Village, Brimfield Twp., Franklin Twp., Kent, Mantua, Randolph, Ravenna, Ravenna Twp., Rootstown Twp., Shalersville, Spring Lakes Mobile Home Park, Streetsboro, Suffield, Sugar Bush Knolls); 79 (Brady Lake Village, Mantua, Randolph, Ravenna, Ravenna Twp., Rootstown Twp., Shalersville, Spring Lakes Mobile Home Park). Franchise award date: N.A. Franchise expiration date: N.A. Began: March 1, 1972.

Channel capacity: 63 (2-way capable; operating 2-way). Channels available but not in use: N.A.

Basic Service

Subscribers: 18,389.

Programming (received off-air): WBNX-TV (W,F), WVPX (X) Akron; WNEO (P) Alliance; WDLI (T), WOAC (I) Canton; WEWS-TV (A), WJW (F), WKYC-TV (N), WVIZ-TV (P) Cleveland; WUAB (U) Lorain-Cleveland; WOIO (C) Shaker Heights; 3 FMs.

Programming (via satellite): WGN-TV (W) Chicago; A & E; C-SPAN; C-SPAN 2; CNBC; CNN; Discovery Channel; Fox Family Channel; Headline News; Knowledge TV; Lifetime; MTV; Nashville Network; Nickelodeon; QVC; TBS Superstation; The Weather Channel; VH1.

Current originations: Automated time-weather; public access; educational access; government access; automated emergency alert.

Fee: $60.00 installation; $9.07 monthly; $1.50 converter; $30.00 additional installation.

Expanded Basic Service

Subscribers: 14,878.

Programming (via satellite): American Movie Classics; Court TV; ESPN; Fox Sports Net Pittsburgh; Turner Network TV; USA Network.

Fee: $13.48 monthly.

Pay Service 1

Pay Units: 920.

Programming (via satellite): Disney Channel.

Fee: N.A.

Pay Service 2

Pay Units: 3,842.

Programming (via satellite): HBO.

Fee: $12.20 monthly.

Pay Service 3

Pay Units: 782.

Programming (via satellite): The Movie Channel.

Fee: $12.20 monthly.

Pay Service 4

Pay Units: 1,139.

Programming (via satellite): Showtime.

Fee: $12.20 monthly.

Pay Service 5

Pay Units: 2,955.

Programming (via satellite): The New Encore.

Fee: N.A.

Local advertising: Yes.

Program Guide: The Cable Guide.

Equipment: Jerrold headend; C-COR & Jerrold amplifiers; Comm/Scope & Times Fiber cable; JVC & Panasonic cameras; JVC, Panasonic & RCA VTRs; Compuvid & Video Data Systems character generator; Jerrold & Oak set top converters; Microdyne satellite antenna; Microdyne satellite receivers.

Miles of plant: 415.0 (coaxial). Homes passed: 21,610. Total homes in franchised area: 21,610.

Manager: William Quinn. Chief technician: David Toth.

City fee: 5% of gross.

Ownership: Time Warner Cable (MSO). Purchased from AT&T Broadband & Internet Services, June 1, 1999.

KENTON—Time Warner Cable, Box 787, 111 S. Mulberry St., Mount Vernon, OH 43050. Phones: 740-397-2288; 800-782-4118. Fax: 740-397-3730. County: Hardin. Also serves Hardin County, Pleasant Twp. (Hardin County). ICA: OH0128.

TV Market Ranking: Below 100 (portions of Hardin County, Kenton, Pleasant Twp.); Outside TV Markets (portions of Hardin County). Franchise award date: N.A. Franchise expiration date: N.A. Began: May 8, 1966.

Channel capacity: 52. Channels available but not in use: 14.

Basic Service

Subscribers: 3,131.

Programming (received off-air): WBGU-TV (P) Bowling Green; WBNS-TV (C), WCMH-TV (N), WOSU-TV (P), WSYX (A), WTTE (F,U) Columbus; WLIO (N), WTLW (I) Lima; WNWO-TV (N) Toledo; 12 FMs.

Programming (via translator): WDLI (T) Canton.

Programming (via satellite): WGN-TV (W) Chicago.

Current originations: Automated time-weather; local news.

Fee: $15.00 installation; $13.95 monthly.

Expanded Basic Service

Subscribers: N.A.

Programming (via satellite): A & E; American Movie Classics; C-SPAN; C-SPAN 2; CNBC; CNN; Cartoon Network; Comedy Central; Country Music TV; Court TV; Discovery Channel; E! Entertainment TV; ESPN; EWTN; Fox Family Channel; Fox Sports Net Ohio; Headline News; History Channel; Learning Channel; Lifetime; MSNBC; MTV; Nashville Network; Nickelodeon; QVC; TBS Superstation; TV Guide Channel; The Weather Channel; Turner Network TV; USA Network; VH1.

Fee: N.A.

Expanded Basic Service 2

Subscribers: N.A.

Programming (via satellite): Animal Planet; ESPN 2; ESPN Classic Sports; Flix; Home & Garden Television; Nick at Nite's TV Land; Sci-Fi Channel; The New Encore; Turner Classic Movies.

Fee: N.A.

Pay Service 1

Pay Units: 927.

Programming (via satellite): Cinemax (multiplexed); HBO (multiplexed); Showtime (multiplexed).

Fee: $10.95 monthly (Cinemax or Showtime), $11.95 monthly (HBO).

Pay Service 2

Pay Units: 198.

Programming (via satellite): Disney Channel.

Fee: $6.95 monthly.

Equipment: Jerrold headend; Jerrold amplifiers; Scientific-Atlanta satellite antenna.

Miles of plant: 51.0 (coaxial). Homes passed: 4,071. Total homes in franchised area: 4,071.

Manager: Paul S. Schonewolf. Technical operations manager: Dan Fessler. Field operations manager: Bill Schroeder. Marketing manager: Carl Bauer. Customer operations manager: Danielle Turner.

City fee: None.

Ownership: Time Warner Cable (MSO).

KETTERING—Time Warner Cable, 4333 Display Lane, Kettering, OH 45429. Phones: 937-294-6400; 800-425-2225. Fax: 937-294-3994. Web site: http://www.mediaone.com. Counties: Clark, Greene, Madison, Miami, Montgomery & Warren North. Also serves Bath Twp. (Greene County), Beavercreek, Beavercreek Twp. (Greene County), Bellbrook, Bethel Twp. (Clark County), Bethel Twp. (Miami County), Butler Twp. (Montgomery County), Catawba (village), Cedarville, Cedarville Twp. (Greene County), Centerville, Clay Twp. (Montgomery County), Clayton, Clear Creek Twp. (Warren County), Clifton (village), Clifton Twp., Corwin Village, Donnelsville, Enon, Franklin Twp. (portions) (Warren County), Green Twp. (Clark County), Harmony Twp. (Clark County), Jamestown (village), Mad River Twp. (Greene County), Madison Twp. (Clark County), Madison Twp. (Montgomery County), Miami Twp. (Clark County), Miami Twp. (Greene County), Miami Twp. (Montgomery County), Miamisburg, Moorefield Twp. (Clark County), Moraine, New Carlisle, New Jasper Twp. (Greene County), Oakwood (Montgomery County), Pleasant Twp. (Clark County), Randolph Twp. (Montgomery County), Silver Creek Twp. (Greene County), South Solon, South Vienna, Spring Valley, Spring Valley Twp. (Greene County), Springboro, Springfield Twp. (Clark County), Sugar Creek Twp. (Greene County), Washington Twp. (Montgomery County), Wayne Twp. (Warren County), Waynesville, West Carrollton, Wilberforce, Xenia Twp. (Greene County). ICA: OH0010.

TV Market Ranking: 27 (Catawba, Harmony Twp., Pleasant Twp., South Solon, South Vienna, Springfield Twp.); 41 (Bath Twp., Beavercreek, Beavercreek Twp., Bellbrook, Bethel Twp., Butler Twp., Catawba, Cedarville, Cedarville Twp., Centerville, Clay Twp., Clayton, Clear Creek Twp., Clifton, Clifton Twp., Corwin Village, Donnelsville, Enon, Franklin Twp., Green Twp., Harmony Twp., Jamestown, Kettering, Mad River Twp., Madison Twp., Miami Twp., Miamisburg, Moorefield Twp., Moraine, New Carlisle, New Jasper Twp., Oakwood, Pleasant Twp., Randolph Twp., Silver Creek Twp., South Solon, South Vienna, Spring Valley, Spring Valley Twp., Springboro, Springfield Twp., Sugar Creek Twp., Washington Twp., Wayne Twp., Waynesville, West Carrollton, Wilberforce, Xenia Twp.). Franchise award date: January 1, 1975. Franchise expiration date: June 1, 2006. Began: January 1, 1978.

Channel capacity: 77 (2-way capable). Channels available but not in use: None.

Basic Service

Subscribers: 40,778.

Programming (received off-air): WCET (P), WCPO-TV (A), WKRC-TV (C) Cincinnati; WXIX-TV (F) Cincinnati-Newport; WDTN (A), WHIO-TV (C), WKEF (N), WPTD (P), WRGT-TV (F,U), WUCT-LP (W) Dayton; WPTO (P) Oxford; WKOI (T) Richmond; WBDT (W) Springfield.

Programming (via satellite): EWTN; Fox News Channel; Home Shopping Network; MSNBC;

QVC; TV Food Network; TV Guide Channel; The Weather Channel; Travel Channel; ValueVision; Z Music Television.
Current originations: Public access; educational access; government access; automated emergency alert.
Fee: $41.00 installation; $10.52 monthly; $20.00 additional installation.
Expanded Basic Service
Subscribers: N.A.
Programming (via satellite): A & E; American Movie Classics; Animal Planet; BET; Bravo; C-SPAN; C-SPAN 2; CNBC; CNN; Cartoon Network; Comedy Central; Country Music TV; Court TV; Discovery Channel; E! Entertainment TV; ESPN; ESPN 2; Fox Family Channel; Fox Sports Net Ohio; Golf Channel; Headline News; History Channel; Home & Garden Television; Independent Film Channel; Learning Channel; Lifetime; MTV; Nashville Network; Nick at Nite's TV Land; Nickelodeon; Outdoor Life Network; Sci-Fi Channel; Speedvision; USA Network; VH1.
Fee: $18.95 monthly.
Expanded Basic Service 2
Subscribers: N.A.
Programming (via satellite): WGN-TV (W) Chicago; TBS Superstation; Turner Network TV.
Fee: $1.72 monthly.
Pay Service 1
Pay Units: 100,941.
Programming (via satellite): Cinemax; Disney Channel; HBO (multiplexed); Showtime.
Fee: $15.00 installation; $11.50 monthly (Disney), $11.95 monthly (Cinemax, HBO or Showtime).
Pay Service 2
Pay Units: N.A.
Programming (via satellite): Independent Film Channel; Starz!; The New Encore.
Fee: $5.95 monthly (IFC), $10.95 monthly (Encore & Starz).
Pay-Per-View
Hot Choice; Spice; Viewer's Choice.
Local advertising: Yes. Available in locally originated programming. Local sales manager: John Stephenson. Regional interconnect: Greater Dayton Cable Advertising.
Equipment: RCA headend; Texscan amplifiers; Comm/Scope cable; Sony VTRs; Panasonic set top converters; Eagle traps; Microdyne, RCA & Scientific-Atlanta satellite antenna; Microdyne, Sony & Scientific-Atlanta satellite receivers.
Miles of plant: 2813.0 (coaxial); 474.0 (fiber optic). Homes passed: 250,618.
Manager: Robert E. Pugh. Chief technician: Randi Midkif. Program director: Jeff Forcon. Marketing director: Helen Brodie.
City fee: 5% of gross.
Ownership: Time Warner Cable (MSO). Purchased from MediaOne Group, August 2, 1999.

KINGSTON—FrontierVision, Box 648, 102 Twin Oak Dr., Jackson, OH 45640. Phone: 614-345-4329. Fax: 614-286-1489. Counties: Hocking, Pickaway & Ross. Also serves Adelphi, Colerain Twp. (Ross County), Hallsville, Laurelville, Salt Creek Twp. (Pickaway County), Whisler. ICA: OH0185.
TV Market Ranking: 27. Franchise award date: January 21, 1986. Franchise expiration date: January 21, 2001. Began: August 1, 1979.
Channel capacity: 37 (2-way capable). Channels available but not in use: N.A.
Basic Service
Subscribers: 1,263.
Programming (received off-air): WBNS-TV (C), WCMH-TV (N), WOSU-TV (P), WSYX (A), WTTE (F,U) Columbus.
Programming (via satellite): WGN-TV (W) Chicago; A & E; CNN; Comedy Central; Country Music TV; Discovery Channel; ESPN; Fox Family Channel; Goodlife TV Network; Learning Channel; Lifetime; MTV; Nashville Network; Nickelodeon; QVC; TBS Superstation; The Weather Channel; Trinity Bcstg. Network; Turner Network TV; USA Network; VH1.
Fee: $22.21 installation; $22.70 monthly; $15.92 additional installation.
Pay Service 1
Pay Units: 99.
Programming (via satellite): The New Encore.
Fee: N.A.
Pay Service 2
Pay Units: 156.
Programming (via satellite): HBO.
Fee: $12.96 installation; $11.95 monthly.
Pay Service 3
Pay Units: 245.
Programming (via satellite): Showtime.
Fee: $12.96 installation; $10.95 monthly.
Pay Service 4
Pay Units: 98.
Programming (via satellite): Starz!
Fee: N.A.
Pay Service 5
Pay Units: 183.
Programming (via satellite): The Movie Channel.
Fee: N.A.
Local advertising: No.
Equipment: Scientific-Atlanta headend; Magnavox amplifiers; Times Fiber cable; Hamlin set top converters; Pico & Eagle traps; Prodelin satellite antenna; Standard Communications satellite receivers.
Miles of plant: 69.7 (coaxial). Additional miles planned: 15.0 (coaxial). Homes passed: 1,677. Total homes in franchised area: 2,660.
Manager: Steve Trippe. Chief technician: Bill Ricker.
Ownership: FrontierVision Partners LP (MSO). See Cable System Ownership.

KINSMAN—CableVision Communications, Box 2200, 68 5th St., Buckhannon, WV 26201. Phone: 304-472-4193. Fax: 304-472-0756. County: Trumbull. Also serves Farmdale (Trumbull County), Kinsman Twp. ICA: OH0282.
TV Market Ranking: 79. Franchise award date: N.A. Franchise expiration date: September 8, 2001. Began: N.A.
Channel capacity: 22. Channels available but not in use: None.
Basic Service
Subscribers: 168.
Programming (received off-air): WNEO (P) Alliance; WJW (F), WKYC-TV (N), WQHS-TV (H) Cleveland; WUAB (U) Lorain-Cleveland; WOIO (C) Shaker Heights; WFMJ-TV (N), WKBN-TV (C), WYTV (A,F) Youngstown.
Programming (via satellite): WGN-TV (W) Chicago; A & E; CNN; Discovery Channel; Disney Channel; ESPN; Fox Family Channel; Nashville Network; TBS Superstation; Turner Network TV; USA Network.
Fee: $52.50 installation; $24.00 monthly; $1.24 converter; $26.25 additional installation.
Pay Service 1
Pay Units: 115.
Programming (via satellite): Cinemax; HBO.
Fee: $7.95 monthly (Cinemax), $11.99 monthly (HBO).
Equipment: Blonder-Tongue headend; Jerrold amplifiers; Times Fiber cable.
Miles of plant: 10.0 (coaxial). Homes passed: 339.
Manager: Willie Critchfield. Marketing director: Kenny Phillips.
Ownership: Rifkin & Associates Inc. (MSO). See Cable System Ownership.

KIRKERSVILLE—Time Warner Cable, Box 787, 111 S. Mulberry St., Mount Vernon, OH 43050. Phones: 740-397-2288; 800-782-4118. Fax: 740-397-3730. County: Licking. Also serves Alexandria, Outville, Pataskala. ICA: OH0170.
TV Market Ranking: 27. Franchise award date: N.A. Franchise expiration date: N.A. Began: N.A.
Channel capacity: 30. Channels available but not in use: 11.
Basic Service
Subscribers: 1,297.
Programming (received off-air): WBNS-TV (C), WCMH-TV (N), WOSU-TV (P), WSYX (A), WTTE (F,U) Columbus; WSFJ (I) Newark; WHIZ-TV (N) Zanesville.
Programming (via satellite): WGN-TV (W) Chicago; QVC; TBS Superstation.
Fee: $25.00 installation; $22.95 monthly.
Expanded Basic Service
Subscribers: N.A.
Programming (via satellite): A & E; CNN; Discovery Channel; ESPN; Fox Family Channel; Headline News; Lifetime; MTV; Nashville Network; Nickelodeon; Turner Network TV; USA Network.
Fee: $4.95 monthly.
Pay Service 1
Pay Units: 80.
Programming (via satellite): Disney Channel.
Fee: $10.95 monthly.
Pay Service 2
Pay Units: 334.
Programming (via satellite): HBO.
Fee: $10.95 monthly.
Pay Service 3
Pay Units: 94.
Programming (via satellite): The Movie Channel.
Fee: $10.95 monthly.
Pay Service 4
Pay Units: 276.
Programming (via satellite): Showtime.
Fee: $10.95 monthly.
Pay Service 5
Pay Units: N.A.
Programming (via satellite): Cinemax.
Fee: $10.95 monthly.
Homes passed: 2,066.
Manager: Paul S. Schonewolf. Technical operations manager: Dan Fessler. Field operations manager: Bill Schroeder. Marketing manager: Carl Bauer. Customer operations manager: Danielle Turner.
Ownership: Time Warner Cable (MSO).

KNOXVILLE—Star Cable, Box 4478, 4720 Mahoning Ave., Youngstown, OH 44515. Phone: 330-792-9577. Fax: 330-792-9541. County: Jefferson. Also serves Island Creek Twp. (Jefferson County), Knox Twp. (Jefferson County), Saline Twp. ICA: OH0239.
TV Market Ranking: 10 (Island Creek Twp., Knox Twp., Knoxville, Saline Twp.); 90 (Island Creek Twp., Knox Twp., Saline Twp.). Franchise award date: N.A. Franchise expiration date: N.A. Began: March 1, 1990.
Channel capacity: 62 (not 2-way capable). Channels available but not in use: 25.
Basic Service
Subscribers: 529.
Programming (received off-air): KDKA-TV (C), WCWB (W), WPGH-TV (F), WPXI (N), WQED (P), WTAE-TV (A) Pittsburgh; WTOV-TV (N) Steubenville-Wheeling; WTRF-TV (C) Wheeling-Steubenville.
Programming (via satellite): QVC; TBS Superstation.
Fee: $30.00 installation; $10.50 monthly; $1.95 converter.
Expanded Basic Service
Subscribers: 505.
Programming (via satellite): A & E; American Movie Classics; C-SPAN; CNBC; CNN; Discovery Channel; ESPN; Fox Family Channel; Fox Sports Net Pittsburgh; Headline News; History Channel; Lifetime; MTV; Nashville Network; Nick at Nite's TV Land; Nickelodeon; Sci-Fi Channel; The Weather Channel; Turner Network TV; USA Network; VH1.
Fee: $20.00 monthly.
Pay Service 1
Pay Units: 43.
Programming (via satellite): Cinemax.
Fee: $11.00 monthly.
Pay Service 2
Pay Units: 49.
Programming (via satellite): Disney Channel.
Fee: $7.95 monthly.
Pay Service 3
Pay Units: 76.
Programming (via satellite): HBO.
Fee: $11.00 monthly.
Pay Service 4
Pay Units: 64.
Programming (via satellite): Showtime; The Movie Channel.
Fee: $12.95 monthly.
Miles of plant: 33.3 (coaxial); None (fiber optic). Homes passed: 811. Total homes in franchised area: 811.
Manager: Terry Dickerhoof. Chief technician: Tom Beat.
Ownership: Star Cable Associates (MSO).

LA RUE—Time Warner Cable, Box 787, 111 S. Mulberry St., Mount Vernon, OH 43050. Phones: 740-397-2288; 800-782-4118. Fax: 740-397-3730. County: Marion. Also serves Marion Twp. (Marion County), New Bloomington. ICA: OH0242.
TV Market Ranking: Outside TV Markets. Franchise award date: May 2, 1983. Franchise expiration date: May 2, 2003. Began: December 1, 1983.
Channel capacity: 53. Channels available but not in use: 26.
Basic Service
Subscribers: 400.
Programming (received off-air): WBNS-TV (C), WCMH-TV (N), WOSU-TV (P), WSYX (A), WTTE (F,U) Columbus.
Programming (via satellite): WGN-TV (W) Chicago; A & E; CNBC; CNN; Comedy Central; Country Music TV; Discovery Channel; ESPN; Fox Family Channel; Headline News; Lifetime; Nashville Network; Nickelodeon; QVC; TBS Superstation; Turner Classic Movies; Turner Network TV; USA Network; VH1.
Fee: $32.00 installation; $18.95 monthly; $4.50 converter; $9.00 additional installation.
Pay Service 1
Pay Units: 27.
Programming (via satellite): Disney Channel.
Fee: $18.00 installation; $10.95 monthly.
Pay Service 2
Pay Units: 79.
Programming (via satellite): HBO.
Fee: $18.00 installation; $10.95 monthly.
Pay Service 3
Pay Units: 29.
Programming (via satellite): Cinemax.

Fee: $18.00 installation; $10.95 monthly.
Miles of plant: 14.8 (coaxial). Homes passed: 789.
Manager: Paul S. Schonewolf. Technical operations manager: Dan Fessler. Field operations manager: Bill Schroeder. Marketing manager: Carl Bauer. Customer operations manager: Danielle Turner.
City fee: 3% of gross.
Ownership: Fanch Communications Inc. (MSO); Time Warner Cable (MSO). See Cable System Ownership.

LAKE MOHAWK MOBILE HOME PARK—Warner Cable Communications, 1655 Brittain Rd., Akron, OH 44310-3998. Phone: 330-633-9203. Fax: 330-633-0024. County: Carroll. ICA: OH0249.
TV Market Ranking: 90. Franchise award date: January 1, 1987. Franchise expiration date: January 1, 2002. Began: January 1, 1987.
Channel capacity: 29. Channels available but not in use: 3.
Basic Service
Subscribers: 583.
Programming (received off-air): WVPX (X) Akron; WNEO (P) Alliance; WEWS-TV (A), WJW (F), WKYC-TV (N), WQHS-TV (H) Cleveland; WUAB (U) Lorain-Cleveland.
Programming (via satellite): WGN-TV (W) Chicago; A & E; CNN; Country Music TV; Discovery Channel; ESPN; Fox Family Channel; Headline News; Lifetime; MTV; Nashville Network; Nickelodeon; TBS Superstation; The Weather Channel; USA Network.
Fee: $35.00 installation; $20.09 monthly.
Pay Service 1
Pay Units: 68.
Programming (via satellite): Showtime.
Fee: $9.95 monthly.
Pay Service 2
Pay Units: 34.
Programming (via satellite): Disney Channel.
Fee: $7.95 monthly.
Pay Service 3
Pay Units: 58.
Programming (via satellite): HBO.
Fee: $9.95 monthly.
Local advertising: No.
Miles of plant: 17.3 (coaxial); 5.0 (fiber optic). Homes passed: 688. Total homes in franchised area: 710.
Manager: Stephen Fry. Chief technician: Robert Nyitray. Marketing director: Woody Woodward.
Franchise fee: 3% of gross.
Ownership: Time Warner Cable (MSO); Fanch Communications Inc. (MSO). See Cable System Ownership.

LANCASTER—Time Warner Cable, 1315 Granville Pike, Lancaster, OH 43130-0747. Phone: 740-653-9685. Fax: 740-653-0019. County: Fairfield. Also serves Berne Twp. (Fairfield County), Bloom Twp. (Fairfield County), Bremen, Carroll, Fairfield County, Greenfield Twp. (Fairfield County), Hocking Twp. (Fairfield County), Pleasant Twp. (Fairfield County), Rush Creek Twp. (Fairfield County), Sugar Grove. ICA: OH0039.
TV Market Ranking: 27. Franchise award date: N.A. Franchise expiration date: N.A. Began: August 1, 1974.
Channel capacity: 35 (not 2-way capable). Channels available but not in use: N.A.
Note: Pay units, miles of plant & homes passed include figures for Baltimore, Circleville & Pataskala, OH.
Basic Service
Subscribers: N.A.
Programming (received off-air): WOUB-TV (P) Athens; WBNS-TV (C), WCMH-TV (N), WOSU-TV (P), WSYX (A), WTTE (F,U) Columbus; WSFJ (I) Newark; WHIZ-TV (N) Zanesville.
Programming (via satellite): WGN-TV (W) Chicago; A & E; C-SPAN; CNBC; CNN; Discovery Channel; ESPN; Lifetime; MTV; Nashville Network; Nickelodeon; TBS Superstation; TV Guide Channel; The Weather Channel; Turner Network TV; USA Network.
Current originations: Public access.
Fee: $35.00 installation; $18.30 monthly; $25.00 additional installation.
Pay Service 1
Pay Units: 13,034.
Programming (via satellite): Disney Channel; HBO; Showtime; The Movie Channel.
Fee: $15.00 installation; $9.95 monthly (Disney, Showtime or TMC), $10.95 monthly (HBO).
Local advertising: Yes. Available in satellite distributed programming. Rates: $20.00/Minute; $12.00/30 Seconds. Local sales manager: Greg Langemeir.
Equipment: Scientific-Atlanta headend; Scientific-Atlanta amplifiers; Comm/Scope cable; Panasonic set top converters; Intercept & Pico traps; AFC satellite antenna; Scientific-Atlanta satellite receivers; Texscan commercial insert.
Miles of plant: 428.0 (coaxial); 103.0 (fiber optic). Homes passed: 37,534.
Manager: David Johnston. Chief technician: Mike Bash. Marketing director: Cathy Schelb.
City fee: 3% of gross.
Ownership: Time Warner Cable (MSO). Purchased from MediaOne Group, August 2, 1999.

LEBANON—Coaxial Communications, 3416 State Rte. 132, Amelia, OH 45102. Phone: 513-797-4400. Fax: 513-797-8625. Counties: Warren North & Warren South. Also serves Clear Creek Twp. (Warren County), Turtle Creek Twp. (Warren County). ICA: OH0171.
TV Market Ranking: 17,41. Franchise award date: July 1, 1987. Franchise expiration date: July 1, 2002. Began: October 19, 1987.
Channel capacity: 52 (not 2-way capable). Channels available but not in use: 15.
Basic Service
Subscribers: 1,465.
Programming (received off-air): WCET (P), WCPO-TV (A), WKRC-TV (C), WLWT (N) Cincinnati; WXIX-TV (F) Cincinnati-Newport; WDTN (A), WHIO-TV (C), WKEF (N), WPTD (P), WRGT-TV (F,U) Dayton; WPTO (P) Oxford.
Programming (via satellite): WGN-TV (W) Chicago; A & E; C-SPAN; CNBC; CNN; Country Music TV; Discovery Channel; ESPN; Fox Family Channel; Headline News; Lifetime; MTV; Nashville Network; Nickelodeon; Sci-Fi Channel; TBS Superstation; Turner Network TV; USA Network; VH1.
Fee: $31.95 installation; $8.51 monthly; $2.57 converter.
Pay Service 1
Pay Units: 122.
Programming (via satellite): Cinemax.
Fee: $11.95 monthly.
Pay Service 2
Pay Units: 128.
Programming (via satellite): Disney Channel.
Fee: $11.95 monthly.
Pay Service 3
Pay Units: 338.
Programming (via satellite): HBO.
Fee: $11.95 monthly.

Pay Service 4
Pay Units: 91.
Programming (via satellite): Showtime.
Fee: $11.95 monthly.
Pay-Per-View
Addressable homes: 665.
Local advertising: Yes. Available in satellite distributed programming.
Equipment: Nexus & Scientific-Atlanta headend; Magnavox amplifiers; Comm/Scope & Times Fiber cable; Jerrold set top converters; Eagle traps; Scientific-Atlanta satellite antenna; DX Antenna & Scientific-Atlanta satellite receivers.
Miles of plant: 108.0 (coaxial). Homes passed: 2,555. Total homes in franchised area: 2,800.
Manager: Arthur P. Loescher. Chief technician: Jeff Brown. Marketing director: William G. McNabb.
City fee: 3% of gross.
Ownership: Coaxial Communications (MSO).

LEESBURG—Time Warner Cable, Box 823, 131 Catherine St., Hillsboro, OH 45133. Phones: 937-393-4217; 800-677-9767. Fax: 937-393-8022. Counties: Clinton & Highland. Also serves Highland, New Vienna. ICA: OH0205.
TV Market Ranking: 27 (Highland, Leesburg); 41 (Highland, New Vienna). Franchise award date: March 1, 1978. Franchise expiration date: March 6, 1998. Began: March 1, 1979.
Channel capacity: 36 (not 2-way capable). Channels available but not in use: 7.
Basic Service
Subscribers: 1,030.
Programming (received off-air): WCET (P), WCPO-TV (A), WKRC-TV (C), WLWT (N) Cincinnati; WXIX-TV (F) Cincinnati-Newport; WBNS-TV (C), WOSU-TV (P), WSYX (A) Columbus; WDTN (A), WHIO-TV (C) Dayton.
Programming (via satellite): C-SPAN; Country Music TV; Discovery Channel; ESPN; Fox Family Channel; Headline News; MTV; Nashville Network; Nickelodeon; QVC; TBS Superstation; The Weather Channel; USA Network.
Fee: $39.90 installation; $24.79 monthly.
Pay Service 1
Pay Units: 172.
Programming (via satellite): Cinemax.
Fee: $10.95 monthly.
Pay Service 2
Pay Units: 80.
Programming (via satellite): Disney Channel.
Fee: $7.95 monthly.
Pay Service 3
Pay Units: 284.
Programming (via satellite): HBO.
Fee: $10.95 monthly.
Miles of plant: 42.0 (coaxial). Homes passed: 1,646.
Manager: Michael Rector. Chief technician: Dale Zornes.
City fee: 3% of gross (New Vienna).
Ownership: Time Warner Cable (MSO).

LEESVILLE—TCI Cable Television, Box 347, 123 N. Market St., Minerva, OH 44657. Phones: 330-868-5413; 800-421-3145. Fax: 330-868-3731. Counties: Carroll & Harrison. Also serves Bowerston. ICA: OH0404.
TV Market Ranking: Below 100. Franchise award date: N.A. Franchise expiration date: N.A. Began: N.A.
Channel capacity: N.A. Channels available but not in use: N.A.
Basic Service
Subscribers: 242.
Programming (received off-air): WVPX (X) Akron; WNEO (P) Alliance; WDLI (T), WOAC (I) Canton; WEWS-TV (A), WJW (F), WKYC-TV (N) Cleveland; WUAB (U) Lorain-Cleveland; WOIO (C) Shaker Heights; WTOV-TV (N) Steubenville-Wheeling; WTRF-TV (C) Wheeling-Steubenville.
Programming (via satellite): Home Shopping Network.
Fee: $44.95 installation; $10.59 monthly.
Expanded Basic Service
Subscribers: 223.
Programming (via satellite): Animal Planet; CNN; Cartoon Network; ESPN; Fox Family Channel; Headline News; MTV; Nashville Network; Nickelodeon; TBS Superstation; USA Network.
Fee: $10.13 monthly.
Pay Service 1
Pay Units: N.A.
Programming (via satellite): HBO; Showtime; Starz!; The New Encore.
Fee: $1.95 monthly (Encore), $6.75 monthly (Starz), $14.95 monthly (HBO or Showtime).
Miles of plant: 17.4 (coaxial).
Manager: Paul Liucart. Chief technician: Rodney Lentz.
Ownership: AT&T Broadband & Internet Services (MSO). Purchased from Tele-Communications Inc., March 9, 1999.

LEIPSIC—Orwell Cable TV Co., 22 Cherry St., Leipsic, OH 45856. Phones: 419-943-2109; 800-824-3620. Fax: 419-943-1000. Counties: Paulding & Putnam. Also serves Continental, Gilboa, Melrose, Miller City, Oakwood (Paulding County), Pandora, West Leipsic (village). ICA: OH0163.
TV Market Ranking: Below 100. Franchise award date: N.A. Franchise expiration date: N.A. Began: February 1, 1982.
Channel capacity: 30 (2-way capable). Channels available but not in use: 3.
Basic Service
Subscribers: 1,733.
Programming (received off-air): WBGU-TV (P) Bowling Green; WFFT-TV (F), WPTA (A) Fort Wayne; WLIO (N), WOHL-LP (F), WTLW (I) Lima; WGTE-TV (P), WTOL-TV (C), WTVG (A), WUPW (F) Toledo.
Programming (via satellite): A & E; CNN; CNN/SI; CNNfn; Cartoon Network; Discovery Channel; ESPN; Fox Family Channel; Fox Sports Net Ohio; Headline News; History Channel; Home & Garden Television; Learning Channel; Lifetime; Nashville Network; Odyssey; QVC; Sci-Fi Channel; TBS Superstation; The Weather Channel; Turner Classic Movies; Turner Network TV; USA Network.
Fee: $25.00 installation; $19.95 monthly; $25.00 additional installation.
Pay Service 1
Pay Units: 339.
Programming (via satellite): HBO.
Fee: $25.00 installation; $9.00 monthly.

Pay Service 2
Pay Units: 225.
Programming (via satellite): Showtime.
Fee: $25.00 installation; $9.00 monthly.
Local advertising: No.
Equipment: Microdyne headend; C-COR amplifiers; Times Fiber & Comm/Scope cable; Pico & Eagle traps; Microdyne satellite receivers.
Miles of plant: 55.0 (coaxial); 30.0 (fiber optic). Additional miles planned: 4.0 (coaxial). Homes passed: 2,400. Total homes in franchised area: 3,000.
Manager: James Holl. Chief technician: Paul Place. Marketing director: James Holl.
City fee: 3% of basic.
Ownership: Orwell Telephone Co. (MSO).

LEWISBURG—Time Warner Entertainment Co. LP, 419 S. Barron St., Eaton, OH 45320. Phones: 937-456-1183; 800-762-2963. Fax: 937-456-9435. Counties: Darke, Montgomery & Preble. Also serves Arcanum, Brookville, Camden, Castine, Dadsville, Eaton, Eldorado, Gordon, Gratis, Ithaca, Madison Twp. (Montgomery County), New Lebanon, New Lexington (Preble County), New Paris, Phillipsburg, Pitsburg, Verona, West Alexandria, West Elkton, West Manchester. ICA: OH0045.
TV Market Ranking: 41. Franchise award date: N.A. Franchise expiration date: N.A. Began: December 15, 1979.
Channel capacity: 36 (2-way capable; operating 2-way). Channels available but not in use: 7.
Basic Service
Subscribers: 12,518.
Programming (received off-air): WCPO-TV (A) Cincinnati; WXIX-TV (F) Cincinnati-Newport; WDTN (A), WHIO-TV (C), WKEF (N), WPTD (P), WRGT-TV (F,U) Dayton; WKOI (T) Richmond; 17 FMs.
Programming (via satellite): WGN-TV (W) Chicago; A & E; C-SPAN; CNN; Discovery Channel; ESPN; Fox Family Channel; Headline News; MTV; Nashville Network; Nickelodeon; Odyssey; QVC; TBS Superstation; Turner Network TV; USA Network.
Current originations: Automated time-weather.
Fee: $25.00 installation; $20.25 monthly.
Pay Service 1
Pay Units: 933.
Programming (via satellite): Cinemax.
Fee: $14.95 installation; $10.95 monthly.
Pay Service 2
Pay Units: 1,249.
Programming (via satellite): Disney Channel.
Fee: $14.95 installation; $6.95 monthly.
Pay Service 3
Pay Units: 2,011.
Programming (via satellite): HBO.
Fee: $14.95 installation; $10.95 monthly.
Pay Service 4
Pay Units: 2,301.
Programming (via satellite): Showtime.
Fee: $14.95 installation; $10.95 monthly.
Pay Service 5
Pay Units: 204.
Programming (via satellite): The Movie Channel.
Fee: $14.95 installation; $10.95 monthly.
Pay-Per-View
Addressable homes: 4,058.
Action Pay-Per-View.
Local advertising: Yes (locally produced). Available in satellite distributed & locally originated programming. Rates: $8.00/30 Seconds. Local sales manager: Norm Pytel.
Miles of plant: 388.0 (coaxial). Additional miles planned: 22.0 (coaxial). Homes passed: 19,662.
Manager: Mike Gray. Chief technician: Mike Ooten. Marketing manager: Mike Weaver.
Ownership: Time Warner Cable (MSO).

LIBERTY TWP. (Butler County)—Coaxial Communications, 3416 State Rte. 132, Amelia, OH 45102. Phone: 513-797-4400. Fax: 513-797-8625. Counties: Butler North & Butler South. Also serves Le Sourdsville Mobile Home Park, Union Twp. (Butler County). ICA: OH0142.
TV Market Ranking: 17 (Le Sourdsville Mobile Home Park, Liberty Twp., Union Twp.); 41 (Liberty Twp.). Franchise award date: N.A. Franchise expiration date: N.A. Began: N.A.
Channel capacity: 62. Channels available but not in use: 12.
Basic Service
Subscribers: 3,731.
Programming (received off-air): WCET (P), WCPO-TV (A), WKRC-TV (C), WLWT (N), WSTR-TV (W) Cincinnati; WXIX-TV (F) Cincinnati-Newport; WPTD (P), WRGT-TV (F,U) Dayton; WPTO (P) Oxford.
Fee: $31.95 installation; $7.35 monthly; $2.57 converter.
Expanded Basic Service
Subscribers: 3,680.
Programming (via satellite): A & E; American Movie Classics; C-SPAN; C-SPAN 2; CNBC; CNN; Comedy Central; Country Music TV; Discovery Channel; ESPN; Fox Family Channel; Headline News; Home Shopping Network; Lifetime; MTV; Nashville Network; Nickelodeon; QVC; Sci-Fi Channel; TBS Superstation; The Weather Channel; Travel Channel; Turner Network TV; USA Network; VH1.
Fee: $31.95 installation; $12.25 monthly.
Pay Service 1
Pay Units: 229.
Programming (via satellite): Cinemax.
Fee: $6.95 monthly.
Pay Service 2
Pay Units: 355.
Programming (via satellite): Disney Channel.
Fee: $6.95 monthly.
Pay Service 3
Pay Units: 914.
Programming (via satellite): HBO.
Fee: $12.95 monthly.
Pay Service 4
Pay Units: 16.
Programming (via satellite): The Movie Channel.
Fee: $6.95 monthly.
Pay Service 5
Pay Units: 434.
Programming (via satellite): Showtime.
Fee: $6.95 monthly.
Pay-Per-View
Addressable homes: 1,660.
Local advertising: Yes. Available in satellite distributed programming.
Equipment: Scientific-Atlanta headend; Magnavox amplifiers; Comm/Scope cable; Texscan character generator; Intercept traps; Prodelin & Scientific-Atlanta satellite antenna; Scientific-Atlanta satellite receivers.
Miles of plant: 136.6 (coaxial). Homes passed: 5,317.
Manager: Arthur P. Loescher. Chief technician: Michael Buckles. Marketing director: William G. McNabb.
Ownership: Coaxial Communications (MSO).

LIBERTY TWP. (Butler County)—Time Warner Cable, 11252 Cornell Park Dr., Cincinnati, OH 45242. Phone: 513-489-5000. Fax: 513-489-5065. County: Butler South. ICA: OH0332.
TV Market Ranking: 17,41. Franchise award date: N.A. Franchise expiration date: N.A. Began: January 1, 1988.
Channel capacity: 50. Channels available but not in use: 7.
Basic Service
Subscribers: 2,872.
Programming (received off-air): WCET (P), WCPO-TV (A), WKRC-TV (C), WLWT (N), WSTR-TV (W) Cincinnati; WXIX-TV (F) Cincinnati-Newport; WCVN (P) Covington; WDTN (A), WHIO-TV (C), WKEF (N), WPTD (P), WRGT-TV (F,U) Dayton; WPTO (P) Oxford; WKOI (T) Richmond.
Programming (via satellite): WGN-TV (W) Chicago; A & E; American Movie Classics; C-SPAN; C-SPAN 2; CNBC; CNN; Discovery Channel; ESPN; Fox Family Channel; Headline News; Home Shopping Network; Home Shopping Network 2; Lifetime; MTV; Nashville Network; Nickelodeon; TBS Superstation; The Weather Channel; USA Network; VH1.
Fee: $12.95 monthly.
Pay Service 1
Pay Units: N.A.
Programming (via satellite): Cinemax; Disney Channel; Showtime; The Movie Channel.
Fee: $9.95 monthly (each).
Manager: Virgil Reed. Chief technician: Bill Spies. Marketing director: Dennis Holzmeier. Customer service manager: Sue Coleman.
Ownership: Time Warner Cable (MSO).

LICK TWP. (Jackson County)—FrontierVision, Box 627, Chillicothe, OH 45601. Phones: 740-775-4300; 800-346-2288. Fax: 740-775-2915. County: Jackson. Also serves Green Acres. ICA: OH0311.
TV Market Ranking: 27. Franchise award date: N.A. Franchise expiration date: N.A. Began: May 1, 1986.
Channel capacity: 12. Channels available but not in use: N.A.
Basic Service
Subscribers: N.A.
Programming (received off-air): WOWK-TV (C), WSAZ-TV (N), WVAH-TV (F,U) Charleston-Huntington; WBNS-TV (C), WCMH-TV (N) Columbus; WPBO-TV (P) Portsmouth.
Programming (via satellite): WGN-TV (W) Chicago; TBS Superstation.
Fee: N.A.
Miles of plant: 3.0 (coaxial). Homes passed: 25.
Manager: Richard Coplan. Chief technician: Sam Morabith. Program director: Chad Hume. Marketing director: Barbara Brewer.
Ownership: FrontierVision Partners LP (MSO). See Cable System Ownership.

LICKING COUNTY (northeastern portion)—FrontierVision, 111 N. 11th St., Newark, OH 43055. Phones: 740-454-2380; 888-293-1894. Fax: 740-345-7670. County: Licking. Also serves Newark (portions), St. Louisville (portions). ICA: OH0398.
TV Market Ranking: 27 (portions of Licking County, Newark, St. Louisville); Below 100 (portions of Licking County). Franchise award date: N.A. Franchise expiration date: N.A. Began: N.A.
Channel capacity: 42 (not 2-way capable). Channels available but not in use: 9.
Basic Service
Subscribers: 407.
Programming (received off-air): WBNS-TV (C), WCMH-TV (N), WOSU-TV (P), WSYX (A), WTTE (F,U) Columbus.
Programming (via satellite): WGN-TV (W) Chicago; CNN; Country Music TV; Discovery Channel; Disney Channel; ESPN; Fox Family Channel; Headline News; MTV; Nickelodeon; QVC; Sci-Fi Channel; TBS Superstation; Turner Classic Movies; Turner Network TV; USA Network.
Fee: $25.95 monthly.
Pay Service 1
Pay Units: 55.
Programming (via satellite): HBO.
Fee: N.A.
Pay Service 2
Pay Units: 51.
Programming (via satellite): Showtime.
Fee: N.A.
Pay-Per-View
Addressable homes: 1.
Miles of plant: 32.0 (coaxial). Homes passed: 726.
Regional manager: Judith Pierce. Marketing director: Rich Lutze.
Ownership: FrontierVision Partners LP (MSO). See Cable System Ownership.

LICKING COUNTY (northwestern portion)—FrontierVision, 111 N. 11th St., Newark, OH 43055. Phones: 740-454-2380; 888-293-1894. Fax: 740-345-7670. County: Licking. Also serves Granville (portions), Johnstown (portions). ICA: OH0399.
TV Market Ranking: 27 (Granville, Johnstown, portions of Licking County); Below 100 (portions of Licking County). Franchise award date: N.A. Franchise expiration date: N.A. Began: N.A.
Channel capacity: 42 (not 2-way capable). Channels available but not in use: 8.
Basic Service
Subscribers: 382.
Programming (received off-air): WBNS-TV (C), WCMH-TV (N), WOSU-TV (P), WSYX (A), WTTE (F,U) Columbus.
Programming (via satellite): WGN-TV (W) Chicago; CNN; Comedy Central; Country Music TV; Discovery Channel; Disney Channel; ESPN; Fox Family Channel; Headline News; MTV; Nickelodeon; QVC; Sci-Fi Channel; TBS Superstation; Trinity Bcstg. Network; Turner Classic Movies; Turner Network TV; USA Network; VH1.
Fee: $25.95 monthly.
Pay Service 1
Pay Units: 63.
Programming (via satellite): HBO.
Fee: N.A.
Pay Service 2
Pay Units: 50.
Programming (via satellite): Showtime.
Fee: N.A.
Pay-Per-View
Addressable homes: 1.
Miles of plant: 43.0 (coaxial). Homes passed: 709.
Regional manager: Judith Pierce. Marketing director: Rich Lutze.
Ownership: FrontierVision Partners LP (MSO). See Cable System Ownership.

LIMA—Time Warner Entertainment Co. LP, 3100 Elida Rd., Lima, OH 45805. Phone: 419-331-3333. Fax: 419-331-1573. Counties: Allen & Putnam. Also serves Amanda Twp. (Allen County), American Twp. (Allen County), Auglaize Twp. (Allen County), Bath Twp. (Allen County), Beaverdam, Cairo, Elida, Gomer, Harrod, Jackson Twp. (Allen County), Lafayette, Marion Twp. (Allen County), Monroe Twp. (Allen County), Perry Twp. (Allen County), Richland Twp.

(Allen County), Shawnee Twp. (Allen County), Spencer Twp. (Allen County), Spencerville, Sugar Creek Twp. (Allen County), Vaughnsville, Westminster. ICA: OH0020.

TV Market Ranking: Below 100. Franchise award date: December 19, 1965. Franchise expiration date: N.A. Began: September 1, 1966.

Channel capacity: 36 (2-way capable; operating 2-way). Channels available but not in use: None.

Basic Service

Subscribers: 29,283.

Programming (received off-air): WBGU-TV (P) Bowling Green; WLWT (N) Cincinnati; WBNS-TV (C) Columbus; WDTN (A), WHIO-TV (C), WKEF (N) Dayton; WANE-TV (C), WFFT-TV (F) Fort Wayne; WLIO (N), WTLW (I) Lima; WNWO-TV (N), WTOL-TV (C), WTVG (A), WUPW (F) Toledo.

Programming (via satellite): A & E; BET; C-SPAN; CNBC; CNN; Comedy Central; Discovery Channel; ESPN; Fox Family Channel; Headline News; Lifetime; MTV; Nashville Network; Nickelodeon; QVC; TBS Superstation; The Weather Channel; Turner Network TV; USA Network; VH1.

Current originations: Automated time-weather; local news.

Fee: $19.95 installation; $13.95 monthly; $14.95 additional installation.

Pay Service 1

Pay Units: 2,343.

Programming (via satellite): Cinemax.

Fee: $10.00 installation; $12.55 monthly.

Pay Service 2

Pay Units: 3,212.

Programming (via satellite): Disney Channel.

Fee: $10.00 installation; $7.95 monthly.

Pay Service 3

Pay Units: 3,793.

Programming (via satellite): HBO.

Fee: $10.00 installation; $12.55 monthly.

Pay Service 4

Pay Units: 1,263.

Programming (via satellite): The Movie Channel.

Fee: $10.00 installation; $12.55 monthly.

Pay Service 5

Pay Units: 2,446.

Programming (via satellite): Showtime.

Fee: $10.00 installation; $12.55 monthly.

Pay-Per-View

Addressable homes: 13,998.

Action Pay-Per-View.

Fee: $4.95.

Local advertising: Yes (locally produced & insert). Available in satellite distributed & character-generated programming. Rates: $45.00/Week; $14.00/30 Seconds. Local sales manager: Jon Quatman.

Equipment: Scientific-Atlanta headend; Theta-Com & Jerrold amplifiers; Times Fiber, Scientific-Atlanta & Belden cable; Sony cameras; MSI & Texscan character generator; Zenith set top converters; Zenith addressable set top converters; Eagle & Vitek traps; Microdyne & Scientific-Atlanta satellite receivers.

Miles of plant: 441.0 (coaxial). Additional miles planned: 9.0 (coaxial). Homes passed: 33,635. Total homes in franchised area: 36,932.

Manager: Jeff Parker. Chief technician: Bill Lambert. Marketing director: Sandy Bayliff.

City fee: 3% of gross.

Ownership: Time Warner Cable (MSO).

LINDSEY (Sandusky County)—Time Warner Entertainment Co. LP, 3100 Elida Rd., Lima, OH 45805. Phone: 419-331-3333. Fax: 419-331-1573. County: Sandusky. Also serves Helena (village), Hessville. ICA: OH0333.

TV Market Ranking: 52. Franchise award date: N.A. Franchise expiration date: N.A. Began: May 1, 1986.

Channel capacity: 42 (not 2-way capable). Channels available but not in use: 6.

Basic Service

Subscribers: 383.

Programming (received off-air): WBGU-TV (P) Bowling Green; WGTE-TV (P), WNWO-TV (N), WTOL-TV (C), WTVG (A), WUPW (F) Toledo.

Programming (via satellite): WGN-TV (W) Chicago; A & E; C-SPAN; C-SPAN 2; CNBC; CNN; Discovery Channel; ESPN; Fox Family Channel; Headline News; Home Shopping Network; Lifetime; MTV; Nashville Network; Nickelodeon; TBS Superstation; The Inspirational Network; The Weather Channel; Turner Network TV; USA Network.

Current originations: Local news.

Fee: $39.95 installation; $19.00 monthly.

Pay Service 1

Pay Units: 51.

Programming (via satellite): Cinemax.

Fee: $9.95 monthly.

Pay Service 2

Pay Units: 105.

Programming (via satellite): HBO.

Fee: $9.95 monthly.

Pay Service 3

Pay Units: 51.

Programming (via satellite): Disney Channel.

Fee: $6.95 monthly.

Local advertising: No.

Manager: Larry K. Miller. Chief technician: Sean Gallagher.

Ownership: Fanch Communications Inc. (MSO); Time Warner Cable (MSO). See Cable System Ownership.

LISBON—Time Warner Cable, 427 E. State St., Salem, OH 44460. Phone: 330-332-9607. County: Columbiana. Also serves Center Twp. (Columbiana County). ICA: OH0182.

TV Market Ranking: 79,90. Franchise award date: May 14, 1984. Franchise expiration date: May 14, 1999. Began: March 23, 1968.

Channel capacity: 35 (not 2-way capable). Channels available but not in use: 4.

Basic Service

Subscribers: 1,602; Commercial subscribers: 11.

Programming (received off-air): WNEO (P) Alliance; WDLI (T) Canton; WJW (F) Cleveland; WUAB (U) Lorain-Cleveland; KDKA-TV (C), WPGH-TV (F) Pittsburgh; WFMJ-TV (N), WKBN-TV (C), WYTV (A,F) Youngstown.

Programming (via satellite): C-SPAN; Fox Family Channel; Home Shopping Network; Nashville Network.

Current originations: Automated time-weather; public access; educational access; government access.

Fee: $31.75 installation (aerial), $40.75 (underground); $10.00 monthly; $1.82 converter.

Expanded Basic Service

Subscribers: 1,540.

Programming (via satellite): American Movie Classics; CNN; Discovery Channel; ESPN; Lifetime; Nickelodeon; Sci-Fi Channel; The Weather Channel; Turner Network TV; USA Network; VH1.

Fee: $10.85 monthly.

Expanded Basic Service 2

Subscribers: 1,500.

Programming (via satellite): WGN-TV (W) Chicago; Fox Sports Net; TBS Superstation.

Fee: $2.95 monthly.

Pay Service 1

Pay Units: 219.

Programming (via satellite): Cinemax.

Fee: $25.00 installation; $9.50 monthly.

Pay Service 2

Pay Units: 107.

Programming (via satellite): Disney Channel.

Fee: $25.00 installation; $7.50 monthly.

Pay Service 3

Pay Units: 271.

Programming (via satellite): HBO.

Fee: $25.00 installation; $9.50 monthly.

Local advertising: No.

Equipment: Scientific-Atlanta headend; Texscan amplifiers; Perimeter 3 cable; Scientific-Atlanta set top converters; Magnavox traps; Scientific-Atlanta satellite antenna; Scientific-Atlanta satellite receivers.

Miles of plant: 27.8 (coaxial); None (fiber optic). Homes passed: 2,051.

Manager: Daryl Morrison. Chief technician: Don Jugenheimer.

City fee: 5% of gross.

Ownership: Time Warner Cable (MSO).

LODI—Time Warner Cable, Box 10, 105 Prospect St., Lodi, OH 44254. Phone: 330-633-9044. Fax: 330-948-1513. Counties: Medina & Wayne. Also serves Briarwood Village, Burbank, Chatham, Chippewa Lake, Chippewa Twp., Congress Twp. (Wayne County), Creston, Gloria Glen Village, Guilford Twp., Lafayette Twp. (Medina County), Montville Twp. (Medina County), Rittman, Seville, Spencer, Sterling, West Salem, Westfield Center, Westfield Twp. (Medina County). ICA: OH0068.

TV Market Ranking: 8. Franchise award date: N.A. Franchise expiration date: November 1, 2002. Began: November 1, 1970.

Channel capacity: 42 (not 2-way capable). Channels available but not in use: None.

Basic Service

Subscribers: 7,723; Commercial subscribers: 517.

Programming (received off-air): WBNX-TV (W,F), WVPX (X) Akron; WNEO (P) Alliance; WOAC (I) Canton; WEWS-TV (A), WJW (F), WKYC-TV (N), WQHS-TV (H), WVIZ-TV (P) Cleveland; WUAB (U) Lorain-Cleveland; WOIO (C) Shaker Heights; 9 FMs.

Programming (via satellite): WGN-TV (W) Chicago; A & E; American Movie Classics; C-SPAN; CNBC; CNN; Country Music TV; Discovery Channel; ESPN; Fox Family Channel; Headline News; Home Shopping Network; Knowledge TV; Lifetime; MTV; Nashville Network; Nickelodeon; TBS Superstation; The Inspirational Network; The Weather Channel; Turner Network TV; USA Network.

Fee: $30.00 installation; $12.95 monthly; $2.50 converter; $20.00 additional installation.

Pay Service 1

Pay Units: 1,037.

Programming (via satellite): Cinemax.

Fee: $8.95 monthly.

Pay Service 2

Pay Units: 1,143.

Programming (via satellite): Disney Channel.

Fee: $8.95 monthly.

Pay Service 3

Pay Units: 2,117.

Programming (via satellite): HBO.

Fee: $8.95 monthly.

Pay Service 4

Pay Units: 360.

Programming (via satellite): The Movie Channel.

Fee: $8.95 monthly.

Pay Service 5

Pay Units: 517.

Programming (via satellite): Showtime.

Fee: $8.95 monthly.

Local advertising: Yes. Available in satellite distributed & character-generated programming. Local sales manager: Charlie Jones.

Equipment: Avantek & Scientific-Atlanta headend; GTE Sylvania amplifiers; Times Fiber & Anixter cable; Pioneer set top converters; Eagle, Vitek & Arcom traps; Microdyne & Scientific-Atlanta satellite antenna; Avantek satellite receivers.

Miles of plant: 255.0 (coaxial); 10.0 (fiber optic). Homes passed: 11,068. Total homes in franchised area: 13,256.

Manager: Thomas P. Autry. Chief technician: Jim Parsons. Marketing director: Ray Kistler.

City fee: 5% of gross.

Ownership: Time Warner Cable (MSO).

LOGAN—FrontierVision, 205 W. 2nd St., Logan, OH 43138. Phone: 614-385-8535. County: Hocking. Also serves Falls Twp. (Hocking County). ICA: OH0130.

TV Market Ranking: 27. Franchise award date: N.A. Franchise expiration date: December 31, 2001. Began: January 1, 1961.

Channel capacity: 54. Channels available but not in use: 13.

Basic Service

Subscribers: 3,218; Commercial subscribers: 243.

Programming (received off-air): WOUB-TV (P) Athens; WBNS-TV (C), WCMH-TV (N), WOSU-TV (P), WSYX (A), WTTE (F,U) Columbus; WHIZ-TV (N) Zanesville; 14 FMs.

Programming (via satellite): WGN-TV (W) Chicago; A & E; American Movie Classics; C-SPAN; CNN; Discovery Channel; Disney Channel; ESPN; Fox Family Channel; Headline News; Lifetime; MTV; Nashville Network; Nickelodeon; QVC; TBS Superstation; Turner Network TV.

Current originations: Automated time-weather; educational access.

Fee: $40.00 installation; $12.95 monthly.

Pay Service 1

Pay Units: 190.

Programming (via satellite): Cinemax.

Fee: N.A.

Pay Service 2

Pay Units: 745.

Programming (via satellite): HBO.

Fee: N.A.

Pay Service 3

Pay Units: 288.

Programming (via satellite): Showtime.

Fee: $9.95 monthly.

Program Guide: The Cable Guide.

Equipment: Jerrold headend; Jerrold amplifiers; Hughes satellite antenna.

Miles of plant: 47.2 (coaxial). Homes passed: 4,401.

Manager: Steve Trippe. Chief technician: Bill Ricker.

City fee: 3% of basic.

Ownership: FrontierVision Partners LP (MSO). See Cable System Ownership.

LONDON—Time Warner Cable, Box 787, 111 S. Mulberry St., Mount Vernon, OH 43050. Phones: 740-397-2288; 800-782-4118. Fax: 740-397-3730. Counties: Franklin & Madison. Also serves Alton, Chocktaw Lake, Deer Creek Twp. (Madison County), Jefferson Twp. (Madison County), Pleasant Twp. (Franklin County), Prairie Twp. (Franklin County), Sumerford, Union Twp. (Madison County), West Jefferson. ICA: OH0089.

TV Market Ranking: 27. Franchise award date: June 19, 1976. Franchise expiration date: N.A. Began: December 6, 1980.

Channel capacity: 36 (2-way capable; operating 2-way). Channels available but not in use: None.

Basic Service
Subscribers: 5,201.
Programming (received off-air): WBNS-TV (C), WCMH-TV (N), WOSU-TV (P), WSYX (A), WTTE (F,U) Columbus; WKEF (N), WRGT-TV (F,U) Dayton; 23 FMs.
Programming (via satellite): WGN-TV (W) Chicago; BET; C-SPAN; C-SPAN 2; CNBC; CNN; Country Music TV; Discovery Channel; ESPN; Fox Family Channel; Headline News; Lifetime; MTV; Nashville Network; Nickelodeon; QVC; TBS Superstation; The Weather Channel; USA Network; VH1.
Current originations: Automated time-weather.
Fee: $29.95 installation; $13.65 monthly; $14.95 additional installation.
Pay Service 1
Pay Units: 2,890.
Programming (via satellite): Cinemax; HBO; Showtime; The Movie Channel.
Fee: $10.00 installation; $10.95 monthly (Cinemax, Showtime or TMC), $11.45 monthly (HBO).
Pay Service 2
Pay Units: 510.
Programming (via satellite): Disney Channel.
Fee: $6.95 monthly.
Pay-Per-View
Addressable homes: 1,550.
Action Pay-Per-View; Spice.
Local advertising: Yes (locally produced). Rates: $19.95/Week. Local sales manager: Norm Pytel.
Equipment: Scientific-Atlanta headend; Jerrold amplifiers; Comm/Scope, Times Fiber & Scientific-Atlanta cable; BEI character generator; GTE Sylvania, Oak & Jerrold set top converters; Eagle traps; Scientific-Atlanta satellite antenna.
Miles of plant: 141.0 (coaxial). Homes passed: 8,438. Total homes in franchised area: 8,438.
Manager: Paul S. Schonewolf. Technical operations manager: Dan Fessler. Field operations manager: Bill Schroeder. Marketing manager: Carl Bauer. Customer operations manager: Danielle Turner.
City fee: 3% of gross.
Ownership: Time Warner Cable (MSO).

LORAIN—Adelphia Communications, Box 178, 1801 Elyria Ave., Lorain, OH 44052-0178. Phone: 440-245-3535. Fax: 440-245-6094. County: Lorain. Also serves Sheffield Twp. (Lorain County). ICA: OH0025.
TV Market Ranking: 8. Franchise award date: N.A. Franchise expiration date: October 14, 1999. Began: July 1, 1981.
Channel capacity: 40. Channels available but not in use: None.
Basic Service
Subscribers: 19,100.
Programming (received off-air): WEAO (P), WVPX (X) Akron; WEWS-TV (A), WJW (F), WKYC-TV (N), WQHS-TV (H), WVIZ-TV (P) Cleveland; WUAB (U) Lorain-Cleveland; WGGN-TV (T) Sandusky; WOIO (C) Shaker Heights; 16 FMs.
Programming (via satellite): WGN-TV (W) Chicago; TBS Superstation; Univision.
Current originations: Automated time-weather; public access; educational access; government access; automated emergency alert.
Fee: $37.00 installation; $22.45 monthly; $28.00 additional installation.
Expanded Basic Service
Subscribers: 16,800.
Programming (via satellite): CNBC; CNN; ESPN; Fox Family Channel; Headline News; Lifetime; MTV; Nashville Network; The Inspirational Network; The Weather Channel; USA Network; VH1.
Fee: $28.00 installation; $9.25 monthly.
Pay Service 1
Pay Units: N.A.
Programming (via satellite): Cinemax; Disney Channel; HBO; The Movie Channel.
Fee: $15.95 installation; $11.95 monthly (each).
Pay-Per-View
Addressable homes: 13,500.
Local advertising: Yes. Available in satellite distributed, locally originated, character-generated & automated programming.
Equipment: Scientific-Atlanta headend; Magnavox & GTE Sylvania amplifiers; Comm/Scope cable; JVC cameras; JVC VTRs; Compuvid character generator; Jerrold & Scientific-Atlanta set top converters; Jerrold & Scientific-Atlanta addressable set top converters; PPC traps; Antenna Technology satellite antenna; Microdyne satellite receivers.
Miles of plant: 240.0 (coaxial). Homes passed: 29,000. Total homes in franchised area: 29,000.
Manager: Sebio DiLuciano. Chief technician: Kevin Alessio.
City fee: 3% of gross.
Ownership: Adelphia Communications Corp. (MSO); AT&T Broadband & Internet Services (MSO). Purchased from Tele-Communications Inc., March 9, 1999.

LOUDONVILLE—Time Warner Cable, Box 10, 105 Prospect St., Lodi, OH 44254. Phone: 330-633-9044. Fax: 330-948-1513. Counties: Ashland & Holmes. Also serves Perrysville. ICA: OH0334.
TV Market Ranking: Below 100. Franchise award date: January 1, 1987. Franchise expiration date: January 1, 2003. Began: November 24, 1968.
Channel capacity: 35 (not 2-way capable). Channels available but not in use: None.
Basic Service
Subscribers: 1,592.
Programming (received off-air): WBNX-TV (W,F) Akron; W59BP (I) Ashland; WEWS-TV (A), WJW (F), WKYC-TV (N), WVIZ-TV (P) Cleveland; WBNS-TV (C), WCMH-TV (N), WSYX (A) Columbus; WUAB (U) Lorain-Cleveland; WOIO (C) Shaker Heights.
Programming (via satellite): WGN-TV (W) Chicago; A & E; American Movie Classics; C-SPAN; CNN; Country Music TV; Discovery Channel; ESPN; Fox Family Channel; Headline News; Knowledge TV; Lifetime; MTV; Nashville Network; Nickelodeon; TBS Superstation; The Inspirational Network; The Weather Channel; Turner Network TV; USA Network.
Current originations: Automated time-weather; public access; educational access; local news; local sports.
Fee: $30.00 installation; $12.95 monthly; $2.50 converter; $20.00 additional installation.
Pay Service 1
Pay Units: 185.
Programming (via satellite): Cinemax.
Fee: $8.95 installation; $8.95 monthly.
Pay Service 2
Pay Units: 156.
Programming (via satellite): Disney Channel.
Fee: $8.95 monthly.
Pay Service 3
Pay Units: 379.
Programming (via satellite): HBO.
Fee: $8.95 monthly.
Local advertising: No.
Equipment: Jerrold headend; GTE Sylvania amplifiers; C-COR, Vikoa & Comm/Scope cable; Pioneer set top converters; Vitek, Eagle & Arcom traps; Microdyne & Scientific-Atlanta satellite antenna; Avantek satellite receivers.
Miles of plant: 32.0 (coaxial).
Manager: Thomas P. Autry. Chief technician: Jim Parsons. Marketing director: Ray Kistler.
City fee: None.
Ownership: Time Warner Cable (MSO).

LOWELL—Lowell Community TV Corp., Box 364, Water St., Lowell, OH 45744. Phone: 740-896-2626. County: Washington. ICA: OH0335.
TV Market Ranking: Below 100. Franchise award date: N.A. Franchise expiration date: N.A. Began: September 1, 1954.
Channel capacity: 12 (not 2-way capable). Channels available but not in use: None.
Basic Service
Subscribers: 315.
Programming (received off-air): WOUB-TV (P) Athens; WOWK-TV (C), WSAZ-TV (N), WVAH-TV (F,U) Charleston-Huntington; WTAP-TV (N) Parkersburg-Marietta; WTRF-TV (C) Wheeling-Steubenville; WHIZ-TV (N) Zanesville; allband FM.
Programming (via satellite): WGN-TV (W) Chicago; WABC-TV (A) New York; ESPN; Nashville Network; TBS Superstation.
Fee: $45.00 installation; $4.25 monthly.
Local advertising: No.
Equipment: Viking headend; Blonder-Tongue & Viking amplifiers; Viking cable.
Miles of plant: 5.0 (coaxial). Homes passed: 315. Total homes in franchised area: 315.
Manager: Dan Fliehman. Chief technician: Steve Weckbacher.
City fee: None.
Ownership: Lowell Community TV Corp.

LUCASVILLE—Warner Cable, 180 Morgan Dr., Lucasville, OH 45648. Phone: 614-259-4170. Fax: 614-259-3266. County: Scioto. Also serves Clay Twp. (Scioto County), Harrison Twp. (Scioto County), Jefferson Twp. (Scioto County), Minford Twp. (Scioto County), Morgan Twp. (Scioto County), Rush Twp. (Scioto County), Scioto County, Valley Twp. (Scioto County). ICA: OH0113.
TV Market Ranking: 27 (portions of Clay Twp., portions of Harrison Twp., Minford Twp., Morgan Twp., Rush Twp., portions of Scioto County, Valley Twp.); 36 (portions of Scioto County); Below 100 (portions of Clay Twp., portions of Harrison Twp., Jefferson Twp., Lucasville, portions of Scioto County). Franchise award date: May 24, 1976. Franchise expiration date: N.A. Began: January 1, 1974.
Channel capacity: 35 (not 2-way capable). Channels available but not in use: N.A.
Basic Service
Subscribers: 2,938.
Programming (received off-air): WCHS-TV (A), WOWK-TV (C), WSAZ-TV (N), WVAH-TV (F,U) Charleston-Huntington; WLWT (N) Cincinnati; WBNS-TV (C), WCMH-TV (N), WSYX (A) Columbus; WPBO-TV (P) Portsmouth.
Programming (via satellite): CNN; Country Music TV; ESPN; Fox Family Channel; MTV; Nashville Network; Nickelodeon; TBS Superstation; Turner Network TV; USA Network.
Fee: $25.00 installation; $12.00 monthly.
Pay Service 1
Pay Units: N.A.
Programming (via satellite): Cinemax; Disney Channel; HBO.
Fee: $25.00 installation; $7.95 monthly (Disney), $10.95 monthly (HBO or Cinemax).
Local advertising: No.
Equipment: Jerrold amplifiers; Comm/Scope cable; AFC satellite antenna; Scientific-Atlanta satellite receivers.
Miles of plant: 89.6 (coaxial). Additional miles planned: 2.0 (coaxial). Homes passed: 4,069.
Manager: Michael Rector. Chief technician: Jack Lester. Marketing director: Gary Pitzer.
City fee: 4% of gross.
Ownership: Time Warner Cable (MSO).

LUCKEY—FrontierVision, Box 627, Chillicothe, OH 45601. Phones: 740-775-4300; 800-346-2288. Fax: 740-775-2915. County: Wood. Also serves Lake Twp. (Wood County), Lemoyne, Stoney Ridge, Troy Twp. (Wood County). ICA: OH0216.
TV Market Ranking: 52. Franchise award date: N.A. Franchise expiration date: N.A. Began: N.A.
Channel capacity: 37. Channels available but not in use: 1.
Basic Service
Subscribers: 613.
Programming (received off-air): WBGU-TV (P) Bowling Green; WKBD-TV (U) Detroit; WGTE-TV (P), WNWO-TV (N), WTOL-TV (C), WTVG (A), WUPW (F) Toledo.
Programming (via satellite): WGN-TV (W) Chicago; A & E; C-SPAN; CNN; Discovery Channel; Disney Channel; ESPN; Fox Family Channel; Headline News; Home Shopping Network; Lifetime; MTV; Nashville Network; Nickelodeon; TBS Superstation; The Weather Channel; Turner Network TV; USA Network; VH1.
Fee: $42.50 installation; $17.95 monthly.
Pay Service 1
Pay Units: 68.
Programming (via satellite): Cinemax.
Fee: N.A.
Pay Service 2
Pay Units: 93.
Programming (via satellite): HBO.
Fee: $10.95 monthly.
Pay Service 3
Pay Units: 48.
Programming (via satellite): Showtime.
Fee: $10.95 monthly.
Pay Service 4
Pay Units: 47.
Programming (via satellite): The Movie Channel.
Fee: N.A.
Pay-Per-View
Addressable homes: 2.
Miles of plant: 26.0 (coaxial). Homes passed: 1,089.
Manager: Richard Coplan. Chief technician: Sam Morabith. Program director: Chad Hume. Marketing director: Barbara Brewer.
Ownership: FrontierVision Partners LP (MSO). See Cable System Ownership.

LYNCHBURG—Time Warner Cable, Box 823, 131 Catherine St., Hillsboro, OH 45133. Phone: 937-393-4217. Fax: 937-393-8022. County: Highland. ICA: OH0268.
TV Market Ranking: Outside TV Markets. Franchise award date: March 1, 1977. Franchise expiration date: N.A. Began: March 1, 1979.
Channel capacity: 77 (not 2-way capable). Channels available but not in use: 6.
Basic Service
Subscribers: 418.
Programming (received off-air): WCET (P), WCPO-TV (A), WKRC-TV (C), WLWT (N) Cincinnati; WXIX-TV (F) Cincinnati-Newport; WBNS-TV (C), WOSU-TV (P) Columbus; WDTN (A), WHIO-TV (C) Dayton; WKOI (T) Richmond.
Programming (via satellite): A & E; American Movie Classics; C-SPAN; CNN; Comedy Central; Country Music TV; Discovery Channel; ESPN; Fox Family Channel; Headline News; History Channel; Lifetime; MTV; Nashville Network; QVC; TBS Superstation;

TV Guide Channel; The Weather Channel; Turner Network TV; USA Network; VH1.
Fee: $39.90 installation; $26.81 monthly; $2.88 converter.

Expanded Basic Service
Subscribers: N.A.
Programming (via satellite): Animal Planet; CNN/SI; Cartoon Network; Court TV; ESPN 2; Fox Sports Net Ohio; Home & Garden Television; Nick at Nite's TV Land; Turner Classic Movies.
Fee: $2.95 monthly.

Pay Service 1
Pay Units: 96.
Programming (via satellite): HBO.
Fee: $10.95 monthly.

Pay Service 2
Pay Units: 88.
Programming (via satellite): Showtime.
Fee: $10.95 monthly.

Pay Service 3
Pay Units: 64.
Programming (via satellite): Cinemax.
Fee: $10.95 monthly.

Pay Service 4
Pay Units: 54.
Programming (via satellite): Disney Channel.
Fee: $7.95 monthly.

Pay Service 5
Pay Units: 39.
Programming (via satellite): The Movie Channel.
Fee: $10.95 monthly.

Pay-Per-View
Addressable homes: 776.
Viewer's Choice.
Fee: $3.95.

Equipment: Jerrold headend; Jerrold amplifiers; Comm/Scope cable; Scientific-Atlanta set top converters; Harris satellite antenna; Scientific-Atlanta satellite receivers.
Miles of plant: 12.5 (coaxial). Homes passed: 539.
Manager: Michael Rector. Chief technician: Dale Zornes.
Ownership: Time Warner Cable (MSO).

MACEDONIA—Adelphia Cable Communications, 885 E. Highland Rd., Macedonia, OH 44056. Phone: 330-468-0307. Counties: Portage & Summit. Also serves Aurora, Boston Heights, Hudson, Hudson Twp. (Summit County), Hudson Village, Northfield Center Twp. (Summit County), Reminderville, Sagamore Hills Twp. (Summit County), Twinsburg, Twinsburg Twp. (Summit County). ICA: OH0043.
TV Market Ranking: 8. Franchise award date: N.A. Franchise expiration date: N.A. Began: April 1, 1982.
Channel capacity: 45 (2-way capable; operating 2-way). Channels available but not in use: None.

Basic Service
Subscribers: 16,878.
Programming (received off-air): WEAO (P), WVPX (X) Akron; WNEO (P) Alliance; WOAC (I) Canton; WEWS-TV (A), WJW (F), WKYC-TV (N), WQHS-TV (H), WVIZ-TV (P) Cleveland; WUAB (U) Lorain-Cleveland; WOIO (C) Shaker Heights.
Programming (via satellite): C-SPAN; Fox Family Channel; Headline News; Learning Channel; TBS Superstation; The Weather Channel.
Current originations: Automated time-weather; public access; educational access; government access.
Fee: $15.00 installation; $8.50 monthly.

Expanded Basic Service
Subscribers: N.A.
Programming (via satellite): A & E; CNN; ESPN; Lifetime; MTV; Nashville Network; Nickelodeon; USA Network.
Fee: $15.00 installation; $3.50 monthly.

Pay Service 1
Pay Units: N.A.
Programming (via satellite): Cinemax; Disney Channel; HBO; The Movie Channel.
Fee: $10.00 installation; $8.95 monthly (Cinemax, HBO or TMC), $9.95 monthly (Disney).

Local advertising: Yes. Available in locally originated, taped & automated programming.
Equipment: Scientific-Atlanta headend; Scientific-Atlanta amplifiers; Comm/Scope cable; Video Data Systems character generator; Scientific-Atlanta set top converters; Scientific-Atlanta addressable set top converters; Scientific-Atlanta satellite antenna; Scientific-Atlanta satellite receivers.
Miles of plant: 500.0 (coaxial); 10.0 (fiber optic). Additional miles planned: 5.0 (coaxial). Homes passed: 20,000.
Manager: Rob Rosencrans. Chief technician: Rich Strebel.
Ownership: Adelphia Communications Corp. (MSO).

***MADISON TWP. (Franklin County)**—Americast, 300 S. Riverside, Chicago, IL 60606. Phones: 312-526-8000; 800-848-2278. Fax: 312-526-8565. County: Franklin. ICA: OH0407.
TV Market Ranking: 27. Franchise award date: October 1, 1997. Franchise expiration date: N.A. Scheduled to begin: N.A.
Channel capacity: N.A.
Total homes in franchised area: 5,000.
Ownership: Ameritech New Media Inc. (MSO).

MADISON TWP. (Lake County)—Adelphia, Suite 8, 7757 Auburn Rd., Painesville, OH 44077-9604. Phone: 440-942-0870. Fax: 440-639-6290. County: Lake. ICA: OH0336.
TV Market Ranking: Below 100. Franchise award date: N.A. Franchise expiration date: N.A. Began: March 1, 1990.
Channel capacity: N.A. Channels available but not in use: N.A.

Basic Service
Subscribers: N.A.
Programming (received off-air): WEWS-TV (A), WJW (F), WKYC-TV (N), WVIZ-TV (P) Cleveland; WUAB (U) Lorain-Cleveland; WOIO (C) Shaker Heights.
Programming (via satellite): TBS Superstation.
Fee: N.A.

Manager: Ed Williams. Chief technician: Mike Drougovich.
Ownership: Adelphia Communications Corp. (MSO); AT&T Broadband & Internet Services (MSO). Purchased from Tele-Communications Inc., August 1, 1998.

MALAGA TWP.—Richards Cable Inc., Drawer 2, Jerusalem, OH 43747. Phone: 740-926-1742. Counties: Belmont & Monroe. Also serves Beallsville, Jerusalem, Wilson. ICA: OH0270.
TV Market Ranking: 90. Franchise award date: N.A. Franchise expiration date: N.A. Began: October 15, 1977.
Channel capacity: 12. Channels available but not in use: N.A.

Basic Service
Subscribers: N.A.
Programming (received off-air): WVPX (X) Akron; WOUC-TV (P) Cambridge; WBOY-TV (N) Clarksburg-Weston; KDKA-TV (C), WPGH-TV (F), WPXI (N), WTAE-TV (A) Pittsburgh; WTOV-TV (N) Steubenville-Wheeling; WTRF-TV (C) Wheeling-Steubenville; WYTV (A,F) Youngstown; WHIZ-TV (N) Zanesville; allband FM.
Current originations: Automated time-weather.
Fee: $15.00 installation; $10.00 monthly.

Equipment: Blonder-Tongue headend; Jerrold amplifiers; Times Fiber cable.
Miles of plant: 13.6 (coaxial). Additional miles planned: 3.0 (coaxial). Homes passed: 454.
Manager: Paul E. Richards.
City fee: None.
Ownership: Paul E. Richards (MSO).

MANCHESTER—FrontierVision, Box 58339, 1272 Ebenezer Rd., Cincinnati, OH 45233. Phones: 513-941-7000; 800-272-2288. Fax: 513-941-1704. County: Adams. Also serves Bentonville. ICA: OH0209.
TV Market Ranking: Below 100. Franchise award date: April 2, 1984. Franchise expiration date: April 2, 1999. Began: January 1, 1966.
Channel capacity: 37 (not 2-way capable). Channels available but not in use: 4.

Basic Service
Subscribers: 941.
Programming (received off-air): WBGU-TV (P) Bowling Green; WCET (P), WCPO-TV (A), WKRC-TV (C), WLWT (N), WSTR-TV (W) Cincinnati; WXIX-TV (F) Cincinnati-Newport; WFFT-TV (F) Fort Wayne; WKYT-TV (C) Lexington.
Fee: $24.20 installation; $22.85 monthly; $2.18 converter.

Expanded Basic Service
Subscribers: 846.
Programming (via satellite): WGN-TV (W) Chicago; A & E; CNN; Country Music TV; Discovery Channel; Disney Channel; ESPN; Fox Family Channel; History Channel; Lifetime; MTV; Nashville Network; Nickelodeon; TBS Superstation; The Inspirational Network; The Weather Channel; Turner Network TV; USA Network.
Fee: $18.85 installation; $16.11 monthly.

Pay Service 1
Pay Units: 62.
Programming (via satellite): Cinemax.
Fee: $11.95 monthly.

Pay Service 2
Pay Units: 13.
Programming (via satellite): The New Encore.
Fee: N.A.

Pay Service 3
Pay Units: 91.
Programming (via satellite): HBO.
Fee: $11.95 monthly.

Pay Service 4
Pay Units: 51.
Programming (via satellite): Showtime.
Fee: N.A.

Pay Service 5
Pay Units: 13.
Programming (via satellite): Starz!
Fee: N.A.

Pay Service 6
Pay Units: 54.
Programming (via satellite): The Movie Channel.
Fee: N.A.

Local advertising: No.
Equipment: Scientific-Atlanta headend; GTE Sylvania amplifiers; Times Fiber & Belden cable; Standard Components set top converters; Arcom traps; Microdyne & Scientific-Atlanta satellite antenna; Scientific-Atlanta satellite receivers.
Miles of plant: 39.1 (coaxial); None (fiber optic). Homes passed: 1,228.
Manager: Jim Underwood. Chief technician: Jerry Marnell. Marketing director: Keith Burt.
Franchise fee: 3% of basic revenue.
Ownership: FrontierVision Partners LP (MSO). See Cable System Ownership.

MANSFIELD—Time Warner Cable, 3100 Elida Rd., Lima, OH 45085. Phones: 419-331-3333; 419-756-3333. Counties: Ashland, Delaware, Morrow & Richland. Also serves Ashland, Harlem Twp. (Delaware County), Johnsville, Kingston Twp., Lexington (Richland County), Lucas, Madison Twp. (Richland County), Mifflin, Mifflin Twp. (Ashland & Richland Counties), Monroe Twp. (Richland County), Ontario, Perry Twp. (Morrow County), Richland County, Sandusky Twp. (Richland County), Springfield Twp. (Richland County), Troy Twp. (Richland County), Washington Twp. (Richland County), Weller Twp. (Richland County). ICA: OH0023.
TV Market Ranking: 27 (Harlem Twp., Kingston Twp., Monroe Twp.); Below 100 (Ashland, Johnsville, Lexington, Lucas, Madison Twp., Mansfield, Mifflin, Mifflin Twp., Ontario, Perry Twp., Richland County, Sandusky Twp., Springfield Twp., Troy Twp., Washington Twp., Weller Twp.). Franchise award date: January 1, 1965. Franchise expiration date: N.A. Began: June 1, 1965.
Channel capacity: 43 (not 2-way capable). Channels available but not in use: N.A.

Basic Service
Subscribers: 31,843.
Programming (received off-air): WEWS-TV (A), WJW (F), WKYC-TV (N) Cleveland; WBNS-TV (C), WCMH-TV (N), WOSU-TV (P), WSYX (A) Columbus; WUAB (U) Lorain-Cleveland; WGGN-TV (T) Sandusky; WOIO (C) Shaker Heights.
Programming (via satellite): American Movie Classics; BET; CNBC; CNN; Country Music TV; Discovery Channel; ESPN; EWTN; Fox Family Channel; Headline News; Home Shopping Network; Lifetime; MTV; Music Choice; Nashville Network; Nickelodeon; TBS Superstation; The Weather Channel; Turner Network TV; USA Network; VH1.
Current originations: Automated time-weather; public access; automated emergency alert.
Fee: $25.00 installation; $15.95 monthly; $15.00 additional installation.

Pay Service 1
Pay Units: 1,920.
Programming (via satellite): Cinemax; Disney Channel; HBO; Showtime; The Movie Channel.
Fee: $25.00 installation; $7.95 monthly (Disney), $9.95 monthly (Cinemax, Showtime or TMC), $11.95 monthly (HBO).

Pay-Per-View
Special events.

Local advertising: Yes.
Program Guide: Premium Channels.
Equipment: RCA, Jerrold & Scientific-Atlanta headend; Texscan & Theta-Com amplifiers; Comm/Scope cable; Panasonic cameras; Compuvid character generator; Scientific-Atlanta set top converters; Scientific-Atlanta addressable set top converters; Eagle & PPC traps; Scientific-Atlanta satellite antenna; Scientific-Atlanta satellite receivers; CAS commercial insert.
Miles of plant: 476.9 (coaxial). Homes passed: 32,500. Total homes in franchised area: 34,000.
Manager: Erv Davis. Chief technician: Jim Shifferly. Marketing director: Sebio Diluciano.
City fee: 3% of gross.
Ownership: Time Warner Cable (MSO).

MANTUA—Adelphia Cable Communications, 885 E. Highland Rd., Macedonia, OH 44056. Phones: 330-468-0307; 800-451-9737. County: Portage. Also serves Mantua Twp., Shalersville. ICA: OH0337.
TV Market Ranking: 8,79. Franchise award date: N.A. Franchise expiration date: N.A. Began: N.A.

Channel capacity: 52. Channels available but not in use: 15.

Basic Service

Subscribers: 2,110.

Programming (received off-air): WBNX-TV (W,F), WEAO (P), WVPX (X) Akron; WNEO (P) Alliance; WEWS-TV (A), WJW (F), WKYC-TV (N), WQHS-TV (H), WVIZ-TV (P) Cleveland; WUAB (U) Lorain-Cleveland; WOIO (C) Shaker Heights; WFMJ-TV (N) Youngstown.

Programming (via satellite): WGN-TV (W) Chicago; TBS Superstation.

Current originations: Educational access.

Fee: $8.50 monthly.

Expanded Basic Service

Subscribers: N.A.

Programming (via microwave): Ecumenical TV Channel.

Programming (via satellite): A & E; American Movie Classics; C-SPAN; CNBC; CNN; Cartoon Network; Discovery Channel; ESPN; ESPN 2; EWTN; Electronic Program Guide; Fox Family Channel; Fox Sports Net Ohio; Home Shopping Network; Learning Channel; Lifetime; MTV; Nashville Network; Nickelodeon; The Weather Channel; Turner Network TV; USA Network; VH1.

Fee: N.A.

Equipment: Scientific-Atlanta headend; C-COR amplifiers; Comm/Scope cable; Scientific-Atlanta addressable set top converters; Microdyne satellite antenna; Microdyne & Standard Components satellite receivers.

Miles of plant: 61.0 (coaxial).

Manager: Mitch Piskur. Chief technician: Rich Strebel.

Ownership: Adelphia Communications Corp. (MSO).

MARENGO—Time Warner Cable, Box 787, 111 S. Mulberry St., Mount Vernon, OH 43050. Phones: 740-397-2288; 800-782-4118. Fax: 740-397-3730. County: Morrow. Also serves Bennington Twp., Cardington, Chester Twp. (Morrow County), Chesterville, Fulton, Harmony Twp. (Morrow County), Lincoln Twp., Peru Twp. (Morrow County), Sparta. ICA: OH0192.

TV Market Ranking: 27. Franchise award date: N.A. Franchise expiration date: N.A. Began: May 1, 1988.

Channel capacity: 41 (not 2-way capable). Channels available but not in use: 11.

Basic Service

Subscribers: 810.

Programming (received off-air): WBNS-TV (C), WCMH-TV (N), WOSU-TV (P), WSYX (A), WTTE (F,U) Columbus; WXCB-LP (I) Delaware.

Programming (via satellite): WGN-TV (W) Chicago; A & E; C-SPAN; CNN; Country Music TV; Discovery Channel; ESPN; ESPN 2; Fox Family Channel; Headline News; History Channel; Home Shopping Network; Learning Channel; Lifetime; MTV; Nashville Network; Nickelodeon; Sci-Fi Channel; TBS Superstation; The Weather Channel; Turner Classic Movies; Turner Network TV; USA Network; VH1.

Current originations: Local news.

Fee: $40.27 installation; $26.15 monthly; $0.44 converter.

Pay Service 1

Pay Units: 48.

Programming (via satellite): Disney Channel.

Fee: $18.00 installation; $10.95 monthly.

Pay Service 2

Pay Units: 147.

Programming (via satellite): HBO.

Fee: $18.00 installation; $10.95 monthly.

Pay Service 3

Pay Units: 51.

Programming (via satellite): Showtime.

Fee: $18.00 installation; $10.95 monthly.

Pay Service 4

Pay Units: 48.

Programming (via satellite): The Movie Channel.

Fee: $18.00 installation; $10.95 monthly.

Pay Service 5

Pay Units: 39.

Programming (via satellite): Cinemax.

Fee: $18.00 installation; $10.95 monthly.

Local advertising: Yes. Available in character-generated programming.

Miles of plant: 75.0 (coaxial). Homes passed: 1,596.

Manager: Paul S. Schonewolf. Technical operations manager: Dan Fessler. Field operations manager: Bill Schroeder. Marketing manager: Carl Bauer. Customer operations manager: Danielle Turner.

Ownership: Fanch Communications Inc. (MSO); Time Warner Cable (MSO). See Cable System Ownership.

MARGARETTA TWP.—FrontierVision, Box 627, Chillicothe, OH 45601. Phones: 740-775-4300; 800-346-2288. Fax: 740-775-2915. Counties: Erie & Sandusky. Also serves Castalia, Sandusky, Vickery. ICA: OH0338.

TV Market Ranking: 8 (Castalia, Margaretta Twp., Sandusky); Below 100 (Vickery). Franchise award date: N.A. Franchise expiration date: May 17, 2009. Began: June 8, 1990.

Channel capacity: 37. Channels available but not in use: 7.

Basic Service

Subscribers: 218.

Programming (received off-air): WGGN-TV (T) Sandusky; WOIO (C) Shaker Heights; WGTE-TV (P), WNWO-TV (N), WTOL-TV (C), WTVG (A), WUPW (F) Toledo.

Programming (via satellite): WGN-TV (W) Chicago; CNN; Country Music TV; Discovery Channel; Disney Channel; ESPN; Fox Family Channel; MTV; Nashville Network; Nickelodeon; Sci-Fi Channel; TBS Superstation; The Weather Channel; Turner Network TV; USA Network.

Fee: $43.75 installation; $21.95 monthly.

Pay Service 1

Pay Units: 29.

Programming (via satellite): HBO.

Fee: $11.00 monthly.

Pay Service 2

Pay Units: 38.

Programming (via satellite): Showtime.

Fee: $11.00 monthly.

Miles of plant: 23.0 (coaxial). Homes passed: 557.

Manager: Richard Coplan. Chief technician: Sam Morabith. Program director: Chad Hume. Marketing director: Barbara Brewer.

Ownership: FrontierVision Partners LP (MSO). See Cable System Ownership.

MARIETTA—TCI Cablevision of Ohio Inc., 37 E. Main St., Crooksville, OH 43731-1248. Phone: 888-229-4465. Counties: Washington, OH; Wood, WV. Also serves Reno, OH; Boaz, Briarwood Estates, Mulinex Addition, Oakwood Estates, Parkerstown, Waverly, Williamstown, WV. ICA: OH0339.

TV Market Ranking: Below 100. Franchise award date: N.A. Franchise expiration date: N.A. Began: March 1, 1959.

Channel capacity: 33. Channels available but not in use: N.A.

Basic Service

Subscribers: 12,675.

Programming (received off-air): WOUB-TV (P) Athens; WCHS-TV (A), WVAH-TV (F,U) Charleston-Huntington; WTAP-TV (N) Parkersburg-Marietta.

Programming (via microwave): WBNS-TV (C), WSYX (A) Columbus.

Programming (via satellite): CNBC; CNN; Discovery Channel; Fox Family Channel; Lifetime; MTV; Nashville Network; Nickelodeon; TBS Superstation; The Weather Channel.

Current originations: Automated time-weather; educational access.

Planned originations: Automated emergency alert.

Fee: $59.95 installation; $9.30 monthly; $2.00 converter.

Expanded Basic Service

Subscribers: 11,924.

Programming (via satellite): American Movie Classics; ESPN; Fox Sports Net Pittsburgh; QVC; Turner Network TV; USA Network.

Fee: $1.85 monthly.

Pay Service 1

Pay Units: 1,068.

Programming (via satellite): Cinemax.

Fee: $13.15 monthly.

Pay Service 2

Pay Units: 1,090.

Programming (via satellite): Disney Channel.

Fee: $10.00 monthly.

Pay Service 3

Pay Units: 2,477.

Programming (via satellite): HBO.

Fee: $13.15 monthly.

Pay Service 4

Pay Units: 1,354.

Programming (via satellite): Showtime.

Fee: $13.15 monthly.

Pay Service 5

Pay Units: 4,983.

Programming (via satellite): The New Encore.

Fee: N.A.

Local advertising: Yes.

Program Guide: The Cable Guide.

Equipment: Jerrold headend; Jerrold amplifiers; Jerrold cable; Microdyne satellite antenna; Microdyne satellite receivers.

Miles of plant: 177.6 (coaxial).

Manager: Frank Tacy. Chief technician: Ralph Palmer.

Ownership: AT&T Broadband & Internet Services (MSO). Purchased from Tele-Communications Inc., March 9, 1999.

MARION—Frontiervision, 160 N. Greenwood, Marion, OH 43302. Phone: 740-387-2288. County: Marion. Also serves Grand Prairie Twp., Marion County, Marion Twp. (Marion County), Pleasant Twp. (Marion County), Prospect Twp. (Marion County). ICA: OH0040.

TV Market Ranking: 27 (Prospect Twp.); Below 100 (Grand Prairie Twp., Marion, portions of Marion County, Marion Twp., Pleasant Twp.); Outside TV Markets (portions of Marion County). Franchise award date: N.A. Franchise expiration date: November 1, 2004. Began: September 19, 1966.

Channel capacity: 62 (not 2-way capable). Channels available but not in use: 6.

Basic Service

Subscribers: 15,397; Commercial subscribers: 996.

Programming (received off-air): WBNS-TV (C), WCMH-TV (N), WOSU-TV (P), WSYX (A), WTTE (F,U) Columbus; WUAB (U) Lorain-Cleveland.

Programming (via satellite): WGN-TV (W) Chicago; C-SPAN; CNN; Discovery Channel; ESPN; Fox Family Channel; Music Choice; Nashville Network; Nickelodeon; TBS Superstation; USA Network; VH1.

Current originations: Educational access.

Fee: $37.75 installation; $11.38 monthly; $30.00 additional installation.

Pay Service 1

Pay Units: 1,643.

Programming (via satellite): Cinemax.

Fee: $8.95 monthly.

Pay Service 2

Pay Units: 20.

Programming (via satellite): The New Encore.

Fee: N.A.

Pay Service 3

Pay Units: 61.

Programming (via satellite): Flix.

Fee: N.A.

Pay Service 4

Pay Units: 3,532.

Programming (via satellite): HBO.

Fee: $11.95 monthly.

Pay Service 5

Pay Units: 2,474.

Programming (via satellite): Showtime.

Fee: $10.95 monthly.

Pay Service 6

Pay Units: 29.

Programming (via satellite): Starz!

Fee: N.A.

Pay Service 7

Pay Units: 68.

Programming (via satellite): The Movie Channel.

Fee: N.A.

Pay-Per-View

Addressable homes: 1,351.

Spice; Viewer's Choice 1, 3, 4.

Fee: $3.95-$4.95.

Local advertising: Yes. Available in satellite distributed programming. Local sales manager: Lynn Wombacher.

Equipment: Scientific-Atlanta headend; Jerrold & Scientific-Atlanta amplifiers; M/A-Com cable; Sony VTRs; MSI character generator; Jerrold set top converters; Jerrold addressable set top converters; Pico & Eagle traps; Scientific-Atlanta & Anixter-Mark satellite antenna; Scientific-Atlanta satellite receivers.

Miles of plant: 227.1 (coaxial); 5.5 (fiber optic). Homes passed: 21,468. Total homes in franchised area: 21,468.

Manager: Steve Trippe. Chief technician: Bill Ricker.

City fee: 3% of gross.

Ownership: FrontierVision Partners LP (MSO). See Cable System Ownership.

***MARSEILLES**—Paxton Cable, Suite 280, 700 Ackerman Rd., Columbus, OH 43202. Phone:

614-263-6100. County: Wyandot. Plans service to Kirby, Marseilles Twp. ICA: OH0340.
TV Market Ranking: Outside TV Markets. Franchise award date: February 1, 1990. Franchise expiration date: February 1, 2015. Scheduled to begin: N.A.
Channel capacity: N.A.
Director of operations: Lisa Collier.
Ownership: Paxton Cable Television Inc. (MSO).

MARTINS FERRY—TCI Cablevision of Ohio Inc., Box 469, Bridgeport, OH 43912. Phone: 800-527-2222. Counties: Belmont & Jefferson. Also serves Colerain Twp. (Belmont County), Glen Robbins, Lansing Valley, Pease Twp. (Belmont County) (portions), Rayland, Tiltonsville, Yorkville. ICA: OH0102.
TV Market Ranking: 90. Franchise award date: N.A. Franchise expiration date: N.A. Began: November 1, 1965.
Channel capacity: 52. Channels available but not in use: 17.
Basic Service
Subscribers: 5,390.
Programming (received off-air): WOUC-TV (P) Cambridge; KDKA-TV (C), WCWB (W), WPGH-TV (F), WPXI (N), WQED (P), WTAE-TV (A) Pittsburgh; WTOV-TV (N) Steubenville-Wheeling; WTRF-TV (C) Wheeling-Steubenville; WKBN-TV (C), WYTV (A,F) Youngstown; allband FM.
Programming (via satellite): A & E; C-SPAN; CNBC; CNN; Discovery Channel; Fox Family Channel; Headline News; Lifetime; MTV; Nashville Network; Nickelodeon; Odyssey; QVC; TBS Superstation; The Weather Channel.
Current originations: Automated time-weather.
Fee: $60.00 installation; $9.44 monthly; $2.00 converter.
Expanded Basic Service
Subscribers: 5,213.
Programming (via satellite): American Movie Classics; ESPN; Fox Sports Net Pittsburgh; Turner Network TV; USA Network.
Fee: $11.72 monthly.
Pay Service 1
Pay Units: 473.
Programming (via satellite): Cinemax.
Fee: $13.15 monthly.
Pay Service 2
Pay Units: 259.
Programming (via satellite): Disney Channel.
Fee: N.A.
Pay Service 3
Pay Units: 1,077.
Programming (via satellite): HBO.
Fee: $13.15 monthly.
Pay Service 4
Pay Units: 266.
Programming (via satellite): Showtime.
Fee: $13.15 monthly.
Pay Service 5
Pay Units: 1,964.
Programming (via satellite): The New Encore.
Fee: N.A.
Local advertising: Yes.
Program Guide: The Cable Guide.
Equipment: Jerrold headend; Jerrold amplifiers; Scientific-Atlanta satellite antenna.
Miles of plant: 77.5 (coaxial). Homes passed: 6,117. Total homes in franchised area: 6,288.
Manager: Robert Weese. Chief technician: Earl Conway.
City fee: 3% of gross.
Ownership: AT&T Broadband & Internet Services (MSO). Purchased from Tele-Communications Inc., March 9, 1999.

MARTINSBURG—National Cable Inc., Suite 106A, 5151 Reed Rd., Columbus, OH 43220. Phone: 614-442-5890. Fax: 614-457-2567. County: Knox. ICA: OH0341.
TV Market Ranking: Below 100. Franchise award date: N.A. Franchise expiration date: N.A. Began: N.A.
Channel capacity: 40. Channels available but not in use: 20.
Basic Service
Subscribers: 155.
Programming (received off-air): WBNS-TV (C), WCMH-TV (N), WOSU-TV (P), WSYX (A), WTTE (F,U) Columbus.
Programming (via satellite): WGN-TV (W) Chicago; A & E; American Movie Classics; CNN; Country Music TV; Discovery Channel; ESPN; Fox Family Channel; Showtime; TBS Superstation; Turner Network TV; USA Network.
Fee: $26.00 monthly.
Miles of plant: 8.0 (coaxial). Homes passed: 200.
Manager: Mansell Nelson. Chief technician: Ron Enas. Marketing director: Dave Beasley.
Ownership: National Cable (MSO).

MARYSVILLE—Time Warner Cable, Box 787, 111 S. Mulberry St., Mount Vernon, OH 43050. Phones: 740-397-2288; 800-782-4118. Fax: 740-397-3730. Counties: Champaign, Delaware, Madison & Union. Also serves Darby Twp. (Madison & Union Counties), Dover Twp. (Union County), Jerome Twp. (Union County), Milford Center, North Lewisburg Village, Paris Twp. (Union County), Plain City, Radnor (town), Rush Twp. (Champaign County), Union Twp. (Union County). ICA: OH0097.
TV Market Ranking: 27. Franchise award date: October 1, 1978. Franchise expiration date: N.A. Began: August 28, 1980.
Channel capacity: 36 (2-way capable; operating 2-way). Channels available but not in use: 1.
Basic Service
Subscribers: 4,331.
Programming (received off-air): WBNS-TV (C), WCMH-TV (N), WOSU-TV (P), WSYX (A), WTTE (F,U) Columbus; WKEF (N) Dayton; allband FM.
Programming (via satellite): WGN-TV (W) Chicago; C-SPAN; C-SPAN 2; CNBC; CNN; Country Music TV; Discovery Channel; ESPN; Fox Family Channel; Headline News; Lifetime; MTV; Nashville Network; Nickelodeon; QVC; TBS Superstation; The Weather Channel; Turner Network TV; USA Network; VH1.
Current originations: Automated time-weather.
Planned originations: Public access; educational access.
Fee: $19.95 installation; $12.55 monthly; $14.95 additional installation.
Pay Service 1
Pay Units: 419.
Programming (via satellite): Cinemax.
Fee: $10.00 installation; $11.49 monthly.
Pay Service 2
Pay Units: 534.
Programming (via satellite): Disney Channel.
Fee: $14.95 installation; $7.30 monthly.
Pay Service 3
Pay Units: 1,551.
Programming (via satellite): HBO.
Fee: $14.95 installation; $12.00 monthly.
Pay Service 4
Pay Units: 314.
Programming (via satellite): Showtime.
Fee: $11.49 monthly.
Pay Service 5
Pay Units: 286.
Programming (via satellite): The Movie Channel.
Fee: $14.95 installation; $11.49 monthly.
Pay-Per-View
Spice.
Local advertising: Yes (locally produced). Rates: $19.95/Week. Local sales manager: Lori Nordholt.
Equipment: Scientific-Atlanta headend; Jerrold amplifiers; Comm/Scope, Times Fiber & Scientific-Atlanta cable; Sony VTRs; BEI character generator; GTE Sylvania, Jerrold & Oak set top converters; Eagle traps; Scientific-Atlanta satellite antenna; Scientific-Atlanta satellite receivers.
Miles of plant: 106.0 (coaxial). Homes passed: 7,244. Total homes in franchised area: 7,244.
Manager: Paul S. Schonewolf. Technical operations manager: Dan Fessler. Field operations manager: Bill Schroeder. Sales & marketing manager: Carl Bauer. Customer operations manager: Danielle Turner.
City fee: 3% of gross.
Ownership: Time Warner Cable (MSO).

MASSILLON—Massillon Cable TV Inc., Box 1000, 814 Cable Court NW, Massillon, OH 44648-1000. Phone: 330-833-4134. Fax: 330-833-7522. E-mail: rbgessner@sssnet.com. Counties: Stark, Summit & Wayne. Also serves Bethlehem Twp. (Stark County), Brewster, Canal Fulton, Jackson Twp. (Stark County), Lawrence Twp. (Stark County), Navarre, Perry Twp. (Stark County), Richville, Sugar Creek Twp. (Stark County), Summit County (southwestern portion), Tuscarawas Twp. (Stark County), Wayne County (eastern portion). ICA: OH0021.
TV Market Ranking: 8. Franchise award date: October 1, 1966. Franchise expiration date: October 18, 2000. Began: October 1, 1966.
Channel capacity: 110 (not 2-way capable). Channels available but not in use: 10.
Basic Service
Subscribers: 30,787.
Programming (received off-air): WBNX-TV (W,F), WVPX (X) Akron; WNEO (P) Alliance; WDLI (T), WOAC (I) Canton; WEWS-TV (A), WJW (F), WKYC-TV (N), WQHS-TV (H), WVIZ-TV (P) Cleveland; WUAB (U) Lorain-Cleveland; WOIO (C) Shaker Heights; WTOV-TV (N) Steubenville-Wheeling; WKBN-TV (C) Youngstown.
Programming (via satellite): WGN-TV (W) Chicago; A & E; American Movie Classics; BET; C-SPAN; C-SPAN 2; CNBC; CNN; Discovery Channel; ESPN; Fox Family Channel; Fox Sports Net; Headline News; Home & Garden Television; Home Shopping Network; Home Shopping Network 2; Lifetime; MTV; Nashville Network; Nickelodeon; QVC; TBS Superstation; TV Guide Channel; TV Guide Sneak Prevue; The Weather Channel; Trinity Bcstg. Network; Turner Network TV; USA Network; VH1.
Current originations: Automated time-weather; educational access; leased access.
Fee: $30.00 installation; $26.25 monthly; $3.00 converter.
Expanded Basic Service
Subscribers: 7,721.
Programming (via satellite): Bravo; CNN/SI; CNNfn; Cartoon Network; Comedy Central; Court TV; Disney Channel; E! Entertainment TV; ESPN 2; ESPN Classic Sports; EWTN; Fox News Channel; Great American Country; History Channel; Learning Channel; MSNBC; MuchMusic Network; Nick at Nite's TV Land; Romance Classics; Sci-Fi Channel; TV Food Network; The Health Network; Turner Classic Movies.
Fee: $10.00 installation; $4.95 monthly.
Pay Service 1
Pay Units: 1,269.
Programming (via satellite): Cinemax.
Fee: $15.00 installation; $9.50 monthly.
Pay Service 2
Pay Units: 985.
Programming (via satellite): The New Encore.
Fee: $8.00 monthly.
Pay Service 3
Pay Units: 1,572.
Programming (via satellite): Flix.
Fee: $15.00 installation; $13.00 monthly.
Pay Service 4
Pay Units: 4,474.
Programming (via satellite): HBO (multiplexed).
Fee: $15.00 installation; $11.00 monthly.
Pay Service 5
Pay Units: 1,572.
Programming (via satellite): The Movie Channel.
Fee: $13.00 monthly.
Pay Service 6
Pay Units: 1,623.
Programming (via satellite): Showtime (multiplexed).
Fee: $15.00 installation; $13.00 monthly.
Pay Service 7
Pay Units: 985.
Programming (via satellite): Starz!
Fee: $8.00 monthly.
Pay-Per-View
Addressable homes: 9,500.
Action Pay-Per-View; Spice2.
Fee: $4.95-$5.95.
Pay-per-view manager: Shannon Delaney.
Local advertising: Yes. Available in satellite distributed, locally originated, character-generated & automated programming. Rates: $18.00/Minute; $9.00/30 Seconds. Local sales manager: Elizabeth Gessner McAllister. Regional interconnect: Northern Ohio Interconnect.
Equipment: Jerrold & Scientific-Atlanta headend; Jerrold amplifiers; Comm/Scope cable; Hitachi cameras; JVC & Sony VTRs; Mycrotek character generator; Jerrold set top converters; Jerrold addressable set top converters; Vitek & Pico traps; Scientific-Atlanta & Simulsat satellite antenna; Scientific-Atlanta satellite receivers; ChannelMatic commercial insert.
Miles of plant: 560.0 (coaxial); 121.0 (fiber optic). Additional miles planned: 25.0 (coaxial). Homes passed: 34,000. Total homes in franchised area: 48,590.
Manager: Robert Gessner. Chief technician: Tom Mogus. Marketing director: Shannon Delaney. Customer service manager: Betty Humphreys.
City fee: 2.5% of gross.
Ownership: Massillon Cable TV Inc. (MSO).

MAYNARD—Powhaton Point Cable Co., Box 67, Powhaton Point, OH 43942. Phone: 614-795-5005. County: Belmont. ICA: OH0342.
TV Market Ranking: 90. Franchise award date: N.A. Franchise expiration date: N.A. Began: June 1, 1970.
Channel capacity: 21. Channels available but not in use: 7.
Basic Service
Subscribers: N.A.
Programming (received off-air): WOUB-TV (P) Athens; WDTV (C,A) Clarksburg-Weston; KDKA-TV (C), WPGH-TV (F), WPXI (N), WQED (P), WTAE-TV (A) Pittsburgh; WTOV-TV (N) Steubenville-Wheeling; WTRF-TV (C) Wheeling-Steubenville.
Programming (via satellite): CNN; Discovery Channel; ESPN; TBS Superstation; USA Network.
Fee: $6.00 monthly.
Manager: Kasmir Majewski.

Ownership: Kasmir Majewski (MSO); Walter Matkovich (MSO).

McCONNELSVILLE—FrontierVision, Suite P-200, 1777 S. Harrison St., Denver, CO 80210. Phone: 303-757-1588. Fax: 303-757-6105. County: Morgan. Also serves Malta, Stockport. ICA: OH0177.

TV Market Ranking: Below 100. Franchise award date: December 18, 1984. Franchise expiration date: N.A. Began: June 1, 1952.

Channel capacity: 42 (not 2-way capable). Channels available but not in use: 4.

Basic Service

Subscribers: 2,104.

Programming (received off-air): WOUB-TV (P) Athens; WBNS-TV (C), WSYX (A), WTTE (F,U) Columbus; WSFJ (I) Newark; WTAP-TV (N) Parkersburg-Marietta; WTRF-TV (C) Wheeling-Steubenville; WHIZ-TV (N) Zanesville; allband FM.

Programming (via satellite): WGN-TV (W) Chicago; WABC-TV (A) New York; TBS Superstation.

Fee: $29.95 installation; $26.17 monthly; $0.73 converter.

Expanded Basic Service

Subscribers: 1,845.

Programming (via satellite): A & E; American Movie Classics; CNN; Country Music TV; Discovery Channel; Disney Channel; E! Entertainment TV; ESPN; Fox Family Channel; Headline News; Home Shopping Network; Lifetime; Nashville Network; Nickelodeon; Sci-Fi Channel; The Inspirational Network; Trinity Bcstg. Network; Turner Network TV; USA Network.

Fee: $15.36 monthly.

Pay Service 1

Pay Units: 135.

Programming (via satellite): Cinemax.

Fee: $20.00 installation; $8.95 monthly.

Pay Service 2

Pay Units: 179.

Programming (via satellite): The New Encore.

Fee: $20.00 installation; $3.99 monthly.

Pay Service 3

Pay Units: 123.

Programming (via satellite): HBO.

Fee: $20.00 installation; $11.99 monthly.

Pay Service 4

Pay Units: 161.

Programming (via satellite): Showtime.

Fee: $20.00 installation; $11.95 monthly.

Pay Service 5

Pay Units: 147.

Programming (via satellite): The Movie Channel.

Fee: $20.00 installation; $11.95 monthly.

Local advertising: No.

Equipment: Blonder-Tongue & Scientific-Atlanta headend; AEL & Blonder-Tongue amplifiers; Times Fiber cable; Jerrold set top converters; AFC satellite antenna; Scientific-Atlanta satellite receivers.

Miles of plant: 89.0 (coaxial). Homes passed: 3,022.

Manager: Steve Trippe. Chief technician: Bill Ricker.

City fee: None.

Ownership: FrontierVision Partners LP (MSO). See Cable System Ownership.

MEDINA—Armstrong Cable Services, 1141 Lafayette Rd., Medina, OH 44256-2421. Phone: 330-723-3536. Fax: 330-725-3366. County: Medina. Also serves Litchfield Twp. (portions), Liverpool Twp., Medina Twp., Montville Twp., York Twp. ICA: OH0067.

TV Market Ranking: 8. Franchise award date: September 24, 1979. Franchise expiration date: April 10, 2010. Began: January 1, 1982.

Channel capacity: 61 (not 2-way capable). Channels available but not in use: None.

Basic Service

Subscribers: 11,202.

Programming (received off-air): WBNX-TV (W,F), WEAO (P), WVPX (X) Akron; WOAC (I) Canton; WEWS-TV (A), WJW (F), WKYC-TV (N), WQHS-TV (H), WVIZ-TV (P) Cleveland; WUAB (U) Lorain-Cleveland; WOIO (C) Shaker Heights.

Programming (via satellite): WGN-TV (W) Chicago; A & E; C-SPAN; CNBC; CNN; CNN/SI; Comedy Central; Discovery Channel; ESPN; ESPN 2; Fox Family Channel; Fox Sports Net Ohio; Golf Channel; Headline News; Home Shopping Network; Lifetime; MTV; Nashville Network; Nickelodeon; QVC; TBS Superstation; TV Guide Channel; TV Guide Sneak Prevue; The Inspirational Network; The Weather Channel; Turner Network TV; USA Network; VH1.

Current originations: Automated emergency alert.

Fee: $24.62 installation; $25.84 monthly; $2.95 converter.

Expanded Basic Service

Subscribers: 3,019.

Programming (via satellite): Cartoon Network; History Channel; Home & Garden Television; Learning Channel; Sci-Fi Channel; Travel Channel; Turner Classic Movies.

Fee: $6.95 monthly.

Pay Service 1

Pay Units: 1,509.

Programming (via satellite): Cinemax.

Fee: $7.50 installation; $8.95 monthly.

Pay Service 2

Pay Units: 716.

Programming (via satellite): DMX.

Fee: $7.95 monthly.

Pay Service 3

Pay Units: 841.

Programming (via satellite): Disney Channel.

Fee: $7.50 installation; $9.95 monthly.

Pay Service 4

Pay Units: 2,938.

Programming (via satellite): HBO.

Fee: $7.50 installation; $10.95 monthly.

Pay Service 5

Pay Units: 716.

Programming (via satellite): Showtime.

Fee: $7.50 installation; $9.50 monthly.

Pay-Per-View

Addressable homes: 3,623.

Viewer's Choice.

Fee: $3.95.

Local advertising: Yes. Available in taped & automated programming. Regional interconnect: Metrobase Cable Advertising.

Equipment: Scientific-Atlanta headend; Scientific-Atlanta amplifiers; Comm/Scope cable; Pioneer & Scientific-Atlanta set top converters; AFC satellite antenna.

Miles of plant: 368.0 (coaxial). Homes passed: 15,178.

Manager: John Cogley. Chief technician: Mike Bricker. Marketing director: Jud D. Stewart.

Franchise fee: 3% of gross.

Ownership: Armstrong Group of Companies (MSO).

MENTOR—MediaOne, 7820 Division Dr., Mentor, OH 44060. Phones: 440-974-3401; 800-425-2225. Fax: 440-974-3201. County: Lake. Also serves Eastlake, Fairport Harbor, Grand River, Lakeline, Painesville, Timberlake, Wickliffe, Willoughby, Willoughby Hills. ICA: OH0015.

TV Market Ranking: 8. Franchise award date: December 1, 1979. Franchise expiration date: January 26, 2005. Began: April 1, 1981.

Channel capacity: 77 (not 2-way capable). Channels available but not in use: N.A.

Basic Service

Subscribers: 40,456; Commercial subscribers: 6.

Programming (received off-air): WBNX-TV (W,F), WEAO (P), WVPX (X) Akron; WEWS-TV (A), WJW (F), WKYC-TV (N), WQHS-TV (H), WVIZ-TV (P) Cleveland; WUAB (U) Lorain-Cleveland; WOIO (C) Shaker Heights; 25 FMs.

Programming (via satellite): C-SPAN; C-SPAN 2; EWTN; Learning Channel; QVC; TV Guide Channel; TV Guide Sneak Prevue; The Inspirational Network.

Current originations: Automated time-weather; public access; educational access; government access; leased access; automated emergency alert.

Fee: $41.00 installation; $9.38 monthly; $3.10 converter; $10.70 additional installation.

Expanded Basic Service

Subscribers: N.A.

Programming (via satellite): A & E; American Movie Classics; Animal Planet; BET; Bravo; CNBC; CNN; Cartoon Network; Comedy Central; Discovery Channel; E! Entertainment TV; ESPN; ESPN 2; Fox Family Channel; Fox News Channel; Fox Sports Net Ohio; Golf Channel; Headline News; History Channel; Home & Garden Television; Lifetime; MTV; MuchMusic Network; Nashville Network; Nick at Nite's TV Land; Nickelodeon; Odyssey; Outdoor Life Network; Sci-Fi Channel; Speedvision; TV Food Network; The Weather Channel; USA Network; VH1.

Fee: $17.40 monthly.

A la Carte 1

Subscribers: N.A.

Programming (via satellite): WGN-TV (W) Chicago; Disney Channel; TBS Superstation; Turner Network TV.

Fee: $2.75 monthly (package).

Pay Service 1

Pay Units: 26,796.

Programming (via satellite): Cinemax; HBO (multiplexed); Independent Film Channel; Showtime; Starz!; The New Encore.

Fee: $4.95 monthly (IFC), $9.95 monthly (Encore & Starz), $11.50 monthly (Cinemax, HBO or Showtime).

Pay-Per-View

Hot Choice; Viewer's Choice; movies; special events.

Fee: $3.55 (movies).

Local advertising: Yes (locally produced). Available in satellite distributed, locally originated, character-generated, taped & automated programming. Rates: $50.00/Minute; $25.00/30 Seconds. Local sales manager: Tom McCormick.

Program Guide: TV Host.

Equipment: Scientific-Atlanta headend; Magnavox amplifiers; Comm/Scope cable; Panasonic cameras; Sony VTRs; Video Data Systems character generator; Jerrold, Panasonic & RCA set top converters; Eagle traps; Simulsat & Scientific-Atlanta satellite antenna; Standard Components satellite receivers; Sony & Wegener commercial insert.

Miles of plant: 557.0 (coaxial); 65.0 (fiber optic). Homes passed: 55,284.

Manager: Larry Williamson. Chief technician: Mike Beat.

City fee: 3% of gross; 5% of gross (Mentor).

Ownership: MediaOne Group (MSO). See Cable System Ownership.

METAMORA—FrontierVision, Box 627, Chillicothe, OH 45601. Phones: 740-775-4300; 800-346-2288. Fax: 740-775-2915. County: Fulton. Also serves Amboy Twp., Lyons, Royalton. ICA: OH0255.

TV Market Ranking: 52. Franchise award date: N.A. Franchise expiration date: N.A. Began: October 1, 1985.

Channel capacity: 37. Channels available but not in use: 2.

Basic Service

Subscribers: 233.

Programming (received off-air): WBGU-TV (P) Bowling Green; WKBD-TV (U) Detroit; WILX-TV (N) Lansing; WGTE-TV (P), WNWO-TV (N), WTOL-TV (C), WTVG (A), WUPW (F) Toledo.

Programming (via microwave): CBET Windsor.

Programming (via satellite): WGN-TV (W) Chicago; A & E; CNN; Discovery Channel; Disney Channel; ESPN; Fox Family Channel; Home Shopping Network; Lifetime; MTV; Nashville Network; Nickelodeon; Showtime; TBS Superstation; The Weather Channel; USA Network; VH1.

Fee: $42.50 installation; $17.95 monthly.

Pay Service 1

Pay Units: 37.

Programming (via satellite): HBO.

Fee: N.A.

Pay Service 2

Pay Units: 33.

Programming (via satellite): Cinemax.

Fee: N.A.

Pay-Per-View

Addressable homes: 1.

Miles of plant: 18.0 (coaxial). Homes passed: 605. Total homes in franchised area: 605.

Manager: Richard Coplan. Chief technician: Sam Morabith. Program director: Chad Hume. Marketing director: Barbara Brewer.

Ownership: FrontierVision Partners LP (MSO). See Cable System Ownership.

MIDDLEBURG (Noble County)—CableVision Communications, Box 218, Poplar Bluff, MO 63902. Phones: 573-686-0900; 573-686-6387. Fax: 573-686-3891. County: Noble. ICA: OH0312.

TV Market Ranking: Below 100. Franchise award date: N.A. Franchise expiration date: N.A. Began: N.A.

Channel capacity: 11. Channels available but not in use: 5.

Basic Service

Subscribers: 18.

Programming (received off-air): WOUC-TV (P) Cambridge; WBOY-TV (N), WDTV (C,A) Clarksburg-Weston; WTOV-TV (N) Steubenville-Wheeling; WTRF-TV (C) Wheeling-Steubenville; WHIZ-TV (N) Zanesville.

Fee: $47.50 installation; $22.00 monthly.

Pay Service 1

Pay Units: N.A.

Programming (via satellite): HBO.

Fee: $10.00 installation.

Equipment: Blonder-Tongue headend; Jerrold amplifiers; Times Fiber cable.

Miles of plant: 1.0 (coaxial). Homes passed: 18.

Manager: Willie Critchfield. Chief technician: Bill Turner. Marketing director: Kenny Phillips.

Ownership: Rifkin & Associates Inc. (MSO). Purchased from Triax Telecommunications Co. LLC, July 1, 1998. See Cable System Ownership.

MIDDLETOWN—Time Warner Cable, Box 710, 341 City Centre Mall, Middletown, OH 45044.

Phones: 513-424-2408; 513-896-5455. Fax: 513-424-6555. Counties: Butler North, Montgomery & Warren North. Also serves Carlisle, Franklin, Franklin Twp. (Warren County), Hanover Twp. (Butler County North), Lemon Twp. (Butler County), Madison Twp. (Butler County North), Miami Twp. (Montgomery County), Monroe, Turtle Creek Twp. (Warren County), Warren County, Wayne Twp. (Butler County). ICA: OH0018.

TV Market Ranking: 17,41. Franchise award date: N.A. Franchise expiration date: July 21, 2002. Began: May 1, 1973.

Channel capacity: 64. Channels available but not in use: N.A.

Basic Service

Subscribers: 25,544.

Programming (received off-air): WCET (P), WCPO-TV (A), WKRC-TV (C), WLWT (N), WSTR-TV (W) Cincinnati; WXIX-TV (F) Cincinnati-Newport; WDTN (A), WHIO-TV (C), WKEF (N), WPTD (P), WRGT-TV (F,U) Dayton; WPTO (P) Oxford; WKOI (T) Richmond; 13 FMs.

Programming (via satellite): WGN-TV (W) Chicago; Odyssey; TBS Superstation; TV Guide Sneak Prevue.

Fee: $56.34 installation; $10.07 monthly; $2.00 converter.

Expanded Basic Service

Subscribers: N.A.

Programming (via satellite): A & E; American Movie Classics; BET; C-SPAN; C-SPAN 2; CNBC; CNN; Court TV; Discovery Channel; ESPN; ESPN 2; FX; Fox Family Channel; Headline News; Intro TV; Knowledge TV; Lifetime; Nickelodeon; Odyssey; QVC; TV Food Network; The Weather Channel; Turner Network TV; USA Network.

Fee: $12.54 monthly.

A la Carte 1

Subscribers: N.A.

Programming (via satellite): Cartoon Network; Country Music TV; E! Entertainment TV; Learning Channel.

Fee: $3.00 monthly (package); $0.85 monthly (each).

Pay Service 1

Pay Units: 4,165.

Programming (via satellite): Cinemax.

Fee: $13.70 monthly.

Pay Service 2

Pay Units: 1,836.

Programming (via satellite): Disney Channel.

Fee: $13.45 monthly.

Pay Service 3

Pay Units: 8,484.

Programming (via satellite): HBO.

Fee: $14.65 monthly.

Pay Service 4

Pay Units: 2,002.

Programming (via satellite): Showtime.

Fee: $14.65 monthly.

Pay Service 5

Pay Units: 10,510.

Programming (via satellite): The New Encore.

Fee: $1.75 monthly.

Pay Service 6

Pay Units: N.A.

Programming (via satellite): DMX; Starz!

Fee: $4.75 monthly (Starz), $4.95 monthly (DMX).

Pay-Per-View

Action Pay-Per-View; Spice.

Local advertising: Yes.

Program Guide: The Cable Guide.

Equipment: Scientific-Atlanta headend; Theta-Com amplifiers; Times Fiber cable; Scientific-Atlanta satellite antenna.

Miles of plant: 464.7 (coaxial); None (fiber optic). Homes passed: 34,997. Total homes in franchised area: 38,755.

Manager: Jeff Heinrich. Chief technician: Randy Senger.

City fee: 3% of gross.

Ownership: Time Warner Cable (MSO). Purchased from AT&T Broadband & Internet Services, June 1, 1999.

MIFFLIN TWP.—Americast, 300 S. Riverside, Chicago, IL 60606. Phones: 312-526-8000; 800-848-2278. Fax: 312-526-8565. County: Franklin. ICA: OH0417.

TV Market Ranking: 27. Franchise award date: August 1, 1997. Franchise expiration date: N.A. Began: N.A.

Channel capacity: N.A. Channels available but not in use: N.A.

Basic Service

Subscribers: N.A.

Programming (received off-air): WWHO (U) Chillicothe; WBNS-TV (C), WCMH-TV (N), WOSU-TV (P), WSYX (A), WTTE (F,U) Columbus; WSFJ (I) Newark.

Programming (via satellite): WGN-TV (W) Chicago; QVC; TBS Superstation; TV Guide Channel.

Current originations: Public access; educational access; government access; leased access.

Fee: $39.95 installation; $9.95 monthly.

Expanded Basic Service

Subscribers: N.A.

Programming (via satellite): A & E; American Movie Classics; BET; BET on Jazz; Bravo; C-SPAN; C-SPAN 2; CNBC; CNN; CNNfn; Cartoon Network; Comedy Central; Country Music TV; Court TV; Discovery Channel; Disney Channel; E! Entertainment TV; ESPN; ESPN 2; ESPN Classic Sports; Fox Family Channel; Fox Sports Net Ohio; Golf Channel; Headline News; History Channel; Home & Garden Television; Learning Channel; Lifetime; MTV; Nashville Network; Nickelodeon; Ohio News Network; Sci-Fi Channel; TV Food Network; The Health Network; The Inspirational Network; The Weather Channel; Travel Channel; Turner Classic Movies; Turner Network TV; USA Network; VH1.

Fee: $17.00 monthly.

Pay Service 1

Pay Units: N.A.

Programming (via satellite): Cinemax; Flix; HBO (multiplexed); Showtime (multiplexed); Starz!; Sundance Channel; The Movie Channel; The New Encore.

Fee: $5.95 monthly (Flix or Sundance), $7.95 monthly (Encore & Starz), $9.95 monthly (Cinemax, Showtime or TMC), $11.95 monthly (HBO).

Total homes in franchised area: 300.

Ownership: Ameritech New Media Inc. (MSO).

MILLERSBURG—FrontierVision, Box 648, 102 Twin Oak Dr., Jackson, OH 45640. Phone: 614-345-4329. Fax: 614-286-1489. Counties: Holmes & Wayne. Also serves Berlin Twp. (Holmes County), Fredericksburg, Holmesville, Killbuck, Lake Buckhorn, Walnut Creek Twp. ICA: OH0144.

TV Market Ranking: Below 100. Franchise award date: November 24, 1986. Franchise expiration date: October 1, 2001. Began: December 1, 1951.

Channel capacity: 62. Channels available but not in use: 8.

Basic Service

Subscribers: 2,799.

Programming (received off-air): WBNX-TV (W,F), WVPX (X) Akron; WOUC-TV (P) Cambridge; WDLI (T), WOAC (I) Canton; WEWS-TV (A), WJW (F), WKYC-TV (N), WQHS-TV (H), WVIZ-TV (P) Cleveland; WBNS-TV (C), WTTE (F,U) Columbus; WUAB (U) Lorain-Cleveland; WOIO (C) Shaker Heights; WHIZ-TV (N) Zanesville; 4 FMs.

Programming (via satellite): WGN-TV (W) Chicago; C-SPAN; CNN; Comedy Central; Country Music TV; Discovery Channel; Disney Channel; ESPN; Fox Family Channel; Headline News; Lifetime; MTV; Nashville Network; Nickelodeon; QVC; TBS Superstation; The Weather Channel; Turner Network TV; USA Network; VH1.

Current originations: Public access; religious access.

Fee: $22.21 installation; $22.95 monthly; $0.96 converter.

Pay Service 1

Pay Units: 42.

Programming (via satellite): Cinemax.

Fee: N.A.

Pay Service 2

Pay Units: 118.

Programming (via satellite): The New Encore.

Fee: N.A.

Pay Service 3

Pay Units: 162.

Programming (via satellite): HBO.

Fee: $12.96 installation; $11.95 monthly.

Pay Service 4

Pay Units: 216.

Programming (via satellite): Showtime.

Fee: $12.96 installation; $10.95 monthly.

Pay Service 5

Pay Units: 111.

Programming (via satellite): Starz!

Fee: N.A.

Pay Service 6

Pay Units: 196.

Programming (via satellite): The Movie Channel.

Fee: $12.96 installation; $10.95 monthly.

Pay-Per-View

Addressable homes: 18.

Program Guide: The Cable Guide.

Equipment: Scientific-Atlanta headend; Scientific-Atlanta amplifiers; Comm/Scope & Times Fiber cable; NSC set top converters; Scientific-Atlanta satellite antenna; Scientific-Atlanta satellite receivers.

Miles of plant: 89.0 (coaxial). Homes passed: 3,143.

Manager: Steve Trippe. Chief technician: Bill Ricker.

City fee: None.

Ownership: FrontierVision Partners LP (MSO). See Cable System Ownership.

MINERVA—TCI Cablevision of Ohio Inc., Box 347, 123 N. Market St., Minerva, OH 44657. Phone: 330-868-5413. Fax: 330-868-3731. Counties: Carroll, Columbiana & Stark. Also serves Carroll County, Columbiana County, Lexington (Stark County), Malvern, Paris, Washington. ICA: OH0132.

TV Market Ranking: 8 (portions of Carroll County, portions of Columbiana County, Lexington, Malvern, Minerva, Paris, Washington); 79 (portions of Carroll County, portions of Columbiana County, Lexington, Minerva, Paris, Washington); 90 (portions of Columbiana County, Minerva). Franchise award date: N.A. Franchise expiration date: N.A. Began: May 1, 1971.

Channel capacity: 40 (not 2-way capable). Channels available but not in use: N.A.

Basic Service

Subscribers: 2,888.

Programming (received off-air): WBNX-TV (W,F), WVPX (X) Akron; WNEO (P) Alliance; WDLI (T), WOAC (I) Canton; WEWS-TV (A), WJW (F), WKYC-TV (N) Cleveland; WUAB (U) Lorain-Cleveland; WOIO (C) Shaker Heights; WFMJ-TV (N) Youngstown.

Programming (via satellite): Discovery Channel; QVC; TBS Superstation.

Current originations: Automated time-weather; government access.

Fee: $37.50 installation; $11.15 monthly; $3.00 converter.

Expanded Basic Service

Subscribers: 2,685.

Programming (via satellite): A & E; American Movie Classics; C-SPAN; C-SPAN 2; CNBC; CNN; Cartoon Network; ESPN; FX; Fox Family Channel; Fox News Channel; Fox Sports Net Pittsburgh; Learning Channel; Lifetime; MTV; Nashville Network; Nickelodeon; The New Encore; The Weather Channel; Turner Network TV; USA Network.

Fee: $13.62 monthly.

Pay Service 1

Pay Units: 279.

Programming (via satellite): Cinemax.

Fee: $13.45 monthly.

Pay Service 2

Pay Units: 227.

Programming (via satellite): Disney Channel.

Fee: $12.50 monthly.

Pay Service 3

Pay Units: 638.

Programming (via satellite): HBO.

Fee: $14.95 monthly.

Pay Service 4

Pay Units: 929.

Programming (via satellite): The New Encore.

Fee: $1.95 monthly.

Pay Service 5

Pay Units: N.A.

Programming (via satellite): Showtime; Starz!

Fee: $6.75 monthly (Starz), $14.95 monthly (Showtime).

Pay-Per-View

Addressable homes: 399.

Program Guide: The Cable Guide.

Equipment: Blonder-Tongue headend; Jerrold amplifiers; Plastoid cable.

Miles of plant: 70.6 (coaxial). Homes passed: 3,694. Total homes in franchised area: 3,811.

Manager: Paul Liucart. Chief technician: Rodney Lentz.

City fee: 3% of gross.

Ownership: AT&T Broadband & Internet Services (MSO). Purchased from Tele-Communications Inc., March 9, 1999.

MINSTER—FrontierVision, Box 7, 14 S. Hanover, Minster, OH 45865. Phone: 419-628-3423. Counties: Auglaize, Mercer & Shelby. Also serves Chickasaw, Fort Loramie, Kettlersville, New Bremen. ICA: OH0164.

TV Market Ranking: Below 100. Franchise award date: N.A. Franchise expiration date: N.A. Began: March 1, 1971.

Channel capacity: 62. Channels available but not in use: 5.

Basic Service

Subscribers: 2,676.

Programming (received off-air): WXIX-TV (F) Cincinnati-Newport; WCMH-TV (N) Columbus; WDTN (A), WHIO-TV (C), WKEF (N), WPTD (P) Dayton; WANE-TV (C), WKJG-TV (N), WPTA (A) Fort Wayne; WLIO (N) Lima; allband FM.

Programming (via satellite): Fox Family Channel.

Current originations: Automated time-weather.

Fee: $50.00 installation; $15.15 monthly.

Pay Service 1

Pay Units: 92.

Programming (via satellite): Cinemax.

Fee: N.A.

Pay Service 2
Pay Units: 151.
Programming (via satellite): The New Encore.
Fee: N.A.
Pay Service 3
Pay Units: 324.
Programming (via satellite): HBO.
Fee: N.A.
Pay Service 4
Pay Units: 394.
Programming (via satellite): Showtime.
Fee: N.A.
Pay Service 5
Pay Units: 150.
Programming (via satellite): Starz!
Fee: N.A.
Pay Service 6
Pay Units: 332.
Programming (via satellite): The Movie Channel.
Fee: N.A.
Miles of plant: 113.1 (coaxial). Homes passed: 4,667.
Manager: Steve Trippe. Chief technician: Bill Ricker.
Ownership: FrontierVision Partners LP (MSO). See Cable System Ownership.

MONROE TWP.—Time Warner Cable, 1450 Experiment Farm Rd., Troy, OH 45373, subsystem of Tipp City, Time Warner Cable. See listing for more details. Phone: 937-339-4974. Fax: 937-339-1844. County: Miami. ICA: OH0431.
TV Market Ranking: 41. Franchise award date: N.A. Franchise expiration date: N.A. Scheduled to begin: N.A.
Channel capacity: N.A.; Channels available but not in use: N.A.
Basic Service
Programming (received off-air): WCPO-TV (A) Cincinnati; WBNS-TV (C), WOSU-TV (P) Columbus; WDTN (A), WHIO-TV (C), WKEF (N), WPTD (P), WRGT-TV (F,U) Dayton; WLIO (N) Lima; WKOI (T) Richmond; WBDT (W) Springfield.
Programming (via satellite): WGN-TV (W) Chicago; QVC; TBS Superstation; TV Guide Channel.
Planned originations: Automated time-weather; public access.
Fee: $40.27 installation; $8.99 monthly; $0.44 converter; $22.51 additional installation.
Expanded Basic Service
Programming (via satellite): A & E; American Movie Classics; BET; C-SPAN; C-SPAN 2; CNBC; CNN; Cartoon Network; Comedy Central; Country Music TV; Court TV; Discovery Channel; E! Entertainment TV; ESPN; Fox Family Channel; Fox News Channel; Fox Sports Net Ohio; Headline News; History Channel; Learning Channel; Lifetime; MTV; Nashville Network; Nickelodeon; TV Food Network; TV Guide Sneak Prevue; The Weather Channel; Travel Channel; Turner Network TV; USA Network; VH1.
Fee: $19.37 monthly.
Expanded Basic Service 2
Programming (via satellite): Animal Planet; ESPN 2; ESPN Classic Sports; Golf Channel; Home & Garden Television; Nick at Nite's TV Land; Sci-Fi Channel; The New Encore; Turner Classic Movies.
Fee: $2.41 monthly.
Pay Service 1
Programming (via satellite): Cinemax (multiplexed); Disney Channel; Flix; HBO (multiplexed); Music Choice; Showtime (multiplexed); The Movie Channel.
Fee: $5.95 monthly (Music Choice), $7.30 monthly (Disney), $11.49 monthly (Cinemax, Showtime or TMC), $12.00 monthly (HBO).
Pay-Per-View
Action Pay-Per-View; Hot Choice; Playboy TV; Spice; Viewer's Choice.
Fee: $11.49 (Playboy or Spice).
Manager: Steve Sullenburger. Technical operations manager: Mike Burns. Chief technician: Tim Jackson.
Ownership: Time Warner Cable (MSO).

MORRAL—Paxton Cable, Suite 280, 700 Ackerman Rd., Columbus, OH 43202. Phone: 614-263-6100. County: Marion. Also serves Brush Ridge. ICA: OH0297.
TV Market Ranking: Outside TV Markets. Franchise award date: N.A. Franchise expiration date: May 1, 2014. Began: May 1, 1989.
Channel capacity: 18. Channels available but not in use: 5.
Basic Service
Subscribers: N.A.
Programming (received off-air): WBNS-TV (C), WCMH-TV (N), WOSU-TV (P), WSYX (A), WTTE (F,U) Columbus.
Programming (via satellite): ESPN; Fox Family Channel; Nashville Network; TBS Superstation; USA Network.
Fee: $25.00 installation; $10.95 monthly.
Pay Service 1
Pay Units: N.A.
Programming (via satellite): Disney Channel; Showtime.
Fee: $6.95 monthly (Disney), $9.95 monthly (Showtime).
Miles of plant: 3.1 (coaxial). Homes passed: 178.
Director of operations: Lisa Collier.
Ownership: Paxton Cable Television Inc. (MSO).

MORROW—Coaxial Communications of Southern Ohio Inc., 3416 State Rte. 132, Amelia, OH 45102. Phones: 513-797-4400; 800-686-4440. Fax: 513-797-8625. County: Warren South. Also serves Butlerville, Deerfield Twp. (Warren County), Hamilton Twp. (Warren County), Harlan Twp., Maineville (Warren County), Pleasant Plain, Salem Twp. (Warren County), South Lebanon, Union Twp. (Warren County). ICA: OH0115.
TV Market Ranking: 17,41. Franchise award date: November 21, 1986. Franchise expiration date: N.A. Began: N.A.
Channel capacity: 42 (not 2-way capable). Channels available but not in use: None.
Basic Service
Subscribers: 3,772.
Programming (received off-air): WCET (P), WCPO-TV (A), WKRC-TV (C), WLWT (N), WSTR-TV (W) Cincinnati; WXIX-TV (F) Cincinnati-Newport; WHIO-TV (C), WPTD (P) Dayton; WPTO (P) Oxford.
Programming (via satellite): WGN-TV (W) Chicago; TBS Superstation.
Fee: $28.93 installation; $6.94 monthly.
Expanded Basic Service
Subscribers: N.A.
Programming (via satellite): A & E; American Movie Classics; C-SPAN; CNBC; CNN; Comedy Central; Country Music TV; Discovery Channel; ESPN; Fox Family Channel; Headline News; Home Shopping Network; Learning Channel; Lifetime; MTV; Nashville Network; Nickelodeon; Sci-Fi Channel; The Weather Channel; Turner Network TV; USA Network; VH1.
Fee: $31.95 installation; $7.46 monthly.
Pay Service 1
Pay Units: 539.
Programming (via satellite): Cinemax.
Fee: $11.95 monthly.
Pay Service 2
Pay Units: 464.
Programming (via satellite): Disney Channel.
Fee: $11.95 monthly.
Pay Service 3
Pay Units: 1,354.
Programming (via satellite): HBO.
Fee: $11.95 monthly.
Pay Service 4
Pay Units: 347.
Programming (via satellite): Showtime.
Fee: $11.95 monthly.
Pay Service 5
Pay Units: 134.
Programming (via satellite): The Movie Channel.
Fee: $11.95 monthly.
Pay-Per-View
Addressable homes: 3,772.
Action Pay-Per-View.
Local advertising: Yes. Available in satellite distributed programming.
Equipment: Scientific-Atlanta headend; Magnavox amplifiers; Comm/Scope cable; Regency addressable set top converters; Intercept traps; Prodelin & Scientific-Atlanta satellite antenna; Scientific-Atlanta satellite receivers.
Miles of plant: 168.0 (coaxial). Homes passed: 6,300.
Manager: Arthur P. Loescher. Chief technician: Jeff Brown. Marketing director: William G. McNabb.
City fee: 3% of basic.
Ownership: Coaxial Communications (MSO).

MOUNT EATON—National Cable Inc., Suite 106A, 5151 Reed Rd., Columbus, OH 43220. Phone: 614-442-5890. Fax: 614-457-2567. County: Wayne. ICA: OH0344.
TV Market Ranking: 8. Franchise award date: N.A. Franchise expiration date: N.A. Began: February 28, 1991.
Channel capacity: 40. Channels available but not in use: 20.
Basic Service
Subscribers: 42.
Programming (received off-air): WBNX-TV (W,F), WEAO (P), WVPX (X) Akron; WJW (F), WKYC-TV (N) Cleveland.
Programming (via satellite): WGN-TV (W) Chicago; A & E; American Movie Classics; Country Music TV; Discovery Channel; ESPN; Fox Family Channel; Learning Channel; Nashville Network; Showtime; TBS Superstation; Turner Network TV; USA Network.
Fee: $50.00 installation; $26.00 monthly.
Miles of plant: 4.2 (coaxial). Homes passed: 126.
Manager: Mansell Nelson. Chief technician: Ron Enas. Marketing director: Dave Beasley.
Ownership: National Cable (MSO).

MOUNT GILEAD—Time Warner Cable, Box 787, 111 S. Mulberry St., Mount Vernon, OH 43050. Phones: 740-397-2288; 800-782-4118. Fax: 740-397-3730. County: Morrow. Also serves Cardington, Edison, Gilead Twp., Morrow County. ICA: OH0166.
TV Market Ranking: 27 (Gilead Twp., portions of Morrow County); Below 100 (Cardington, Edison, portions of Morrow County, Mount Gilead). Franchise award date: January 1, 1971. Franchise expiration date: December 16, 1999. Began: January 1, 1971.
Channel capacity: 77 (not 2-way capable). Channels available but not in use: 40.
Basic Service
Subscribers: 2,610.
Programming (received off-air): WBNS-TV (C), WCMH-TV (N), WOSU-TV (P), WSYX (A), WTTE (F,U) Columbus; WUAB (U) Lorain-Cleveland; WTVG (A) Toledo.
Programming (via satellite): American Movie Classics; CNN; ESPN; Fox Family Channel; Headline News; Home Shopping Network; MTV; Nashville Network; Nickelodeon; TBS Superstation; The Weather Channel; USA Network.
Fee: $50.00 installation; $18.95 monthly; $50.00 additional installation.
Pay Service 1
Pay Units: 217.
Programming (via satellite): Cinemax.
Fee: $10.00 installation; $10.95 monthly.
Pay Service 2
Pay Units: 307.
Programming (via satellite): HBO.
Fee: $10.00 installation; $10.95 monthly.
Pay Service 3
Pay Units: 147.
Programming (via satellite): Disney Channel.
Fee: $10.95 monthly.
Pay Service 4
Pay Units: 72.
Programming (via satellite): The Movie Channel.
Fee: $10.95 monthly.
Pay Service 5
Pay Units: 130.
Programming (via satellite): Showtime.
Fee: $10.95 monthly.
Local advertising: Yes. Available in character-generated programming.
Program Guide: The Entertainer.
Equipment: Scientific-Atlanta headend; C-COR & Jerrold amplifiers; Comm/Scope cable; Texscan character generator; Scientific-Atlanta set top converters; Scientific-Atlanta addressable set top converters; Eagle traps; Eagle addressable traps; Microdyne satellite antenna; Microdyne satellite receivers.
Miles of plant: 80.0 (coaxial).
Manager: Paul S. Schonewolf. Technical operations manager: Dan Fessler. Field operations manager: Bill Schroeder. Marketing manager: Carl Bauer. Customer operations manager: Danielle Turner.
Franchise fee: 3% of basic.
Ownership: Time Warner Cable (MSO).

MOUNT ORAB—Thompson Cable, Box 13309, Sissonville, WV 25360. Phone: 304-984-0025. County: Brown. ICA: OH0345.
TV Market Ranking: 17. Franchise award date: N.A. Franchise expiration date: N.A. Began: January 1, 1988.
Channel capacity: 36. Channels available but not in use: 6.
Basic Service
Subscribers: N.A.
Programming (received off-air): WCET (P), WCPO-TV (A), WKRC-TV (C), WLWT (N), WSTR-TV (W) Cincinnati; WXIX-TV (F) Cincinnati-Newport; WHIO-TV (C), WKEF (N), WPTD (P) Dayton; WTVQ-TV (A) Lexington.
Programming (via satellite): WGN-TV (W) Chicago; American Movie Classics; CNN; Country Music TV; Discovery Channel; ESPN; Fox Family Channel; Headline News; Home Shopping Network; Lifetime; MTV; Nashville Network; Nickelodeon; QVC; TBS Superstation; Turner Network TV; USA Network; VH1.
Fee: $25.00 installation; $16.95 monthly.
Pay Service 1
Pay Units: N.A.
Programming (via satellite): Disney Channel; Showtime.
Fee: $10.95 monthly (each).
Manager: Ron Peters.

Ownership: Thompson Cablevision Co. Inc. (MSO).

MOUNT PLEASANT TWP. (Jefferson County)—Community TV Systems Cable Co., Box 96, Martins Ferry, OH 43935. Phone: 740-635-9680. County: Jefferson. Also serves Connorville, Mount Pleasant, Warren Twp. (Jefferson County). ICA: OH0346.

TV Market Ranking: 90. Franchise award date: January 1, 1985. Franchise expiration date: January 1, 2005. Began: October 1, 1985.

Channel capacity: 60. Channels available but not in use: 13.

Basic Service

Subscribers: 562.

Programming (received off-air): WOUC-TV (P) Cambridge; WPCB-TV (I) Greensburg; KDKA-TV (C), WCWB (W), WPGH-TV (F), WQED (P), WTAE-TV (A) Pittsburgh; WTOV-TV (N) Steubenville-Wheeling; WTRF-TV (C) Wheeling-Steubenville.

Programming (via satellite): WGN-TV (W) Chicago; A & E; American Movie Classics; C-SPAN; CNN; Cartoon Network; Comedy Central; Country Music TV; Court TV; Discovery Channel; E! Entertainment TV; ESPN; ESPN 2; Fox Family Channel; Headline News; History Channel; Home Shopping Network; Learning Channel; Lifetime; MSNBC; MTV; Nashville Network; Nick at Nite's TV Land; Nickelodeon; QVC; Sci-Fi Channel; TBS Superstation; Trinity Bcstg. Network; Turner Network TV; USA Network; VH1.

Fee: $25.00 installation; $19.75 monthly.

Pay Service 1

Pay Units: N.A.

Programming (via satellite): HBO (multiplexed); Showtime; The Movie Channel.

Fee: $12.25 monthly (each).

Miles of plant: 14.0 (coaxial). Homes passed: 749.

Manager: Dom Cavicchia.

Ownership: Community TV Systems Cable Co. (MSO).

MOUNT STERLING (Muskingum County)—Time Warner Cable, Box 787, 111 S. Mulberry St., Mount Vernon, OH 43050. Phones: 740-397-2288; 800-782-4118. Fax: 740-397-3730. Counties: Licking & Muskingum. Also serves Brownsville, Gratiot (Muskingum County), Hopewell Twp. (Muskingum County), Zanesville. ICA: OH0237.

TV Market Ranking: Below 100. Franchise award date: N.A. Franchise expiration date: N.A. Began: N.A.

Channel capacity: 25. Channels available but not in use: 1.

Basic Service

Subscribers: 617.

Programming (received off-air): WBNS-TV (C), WCMH-TV (N), WOSU-TV (P), WSYX (A), WTTE (F,U) Columbus; WSFJ (I) Newark; WHIZ-TV (N) Zanesville.

Programming (via satellite): WGN-TV (W) Chicago; A & E; CNN; Discovery Channel; ESPN; Fox Family Channel; Headline News; Lifetime; MTV; Nashville Network; Nickelodeon; TBS Superstation; Turner Network TV; USA Network; VH1.

Fee: $40.00 installation; $22.95 monthly.

Pay Service 1

Pay Units: 85.

Programming (via satellite): HBO.

Fee: $10.95 monthly.

Pay Service 2

Pay Units: 61.

Programming (via satellite): The Movie Channel.

Fee: $10.95 monthly.

Pay Service 3

Pay Units: 130.

Programming (via satellite): Showtime.

Fee: $10.95 monthly.

Pay Service 4

Pay Units: N.A.

Programming (via satellite): Cinemax.

Fee: $10.95 monthly.

Homes passed: 820.

Manager: Paul S. Schonewolf. Technical operations manager: Dan Fessler. Field operations manager: Bill Schroeder. Marketing manager: Carl Bauer. Customer operations manager: Danielle Turner.

Ownership: Time Warner Cable (MSO).

MOUNT VERNON—Time Warner Cable, Box 787, 111 S. Mulberry St., Mount Vernon, OH 43050. Phones: 740-397-2288; 800-782-4118. Fax: 740-397-3730. County: Knox. ICA: OH0095.

TV Market Ranking: Below 100. Franchise award date: N.A. Franchise expiration date: N.A. Began: November 1, 1970.

Channel capacity: 40 (2-way capable; operating 2-way). Channels available but not in use: 5.

Basic Service

Subscribers: 6,602.

Programming (received off-air): WEWS-TV (A), WJW (F) Cleveland; WBNS-TV (C), WCMH-TV (N), WOSU-TV (P), WSYX (A), WTTE (F,U) Columbus; WUAB (U) Lorain-Cleveland; WSFJ (I) Newark; 1 FM.

Programming (via satellite): C-SPAN; QVC; TV Guide Channel.

Current originations: Automated time-weather.

Fee: $19.90 installation; $8.42 monthly.

Expanded Basic Service

Subscribers: 5,441.

Programming (via satellite): A & E; American Movie Classics; CNBC; CNN; Comedy Central; Country Music TV; Discovery Channel; ESPN; Fox Family Channel; Lifetime; MTV; Nashville Network; Nickelodeon; Sci-Fi Channel; The Weather Channel; Turner Network TV; USA Network.

Fee: $9.20 monthly.

Pay Service 1

Pay Units: N.A.

Programming (via satellite): Disney Channel; HBO; Showtime; The Movie Channel; The New Encore.

Fee: $10.00 monthly (Disney, HBO, Showtime or TMC).

Local advertising: No.

Program Guide: Premium Channels.

Equipment: Jerrold headend; Jerrold amplifiers; Jerrold cable; Scientific-Atlanta satellite antenna.

Miles of plant: 102.0 (coaxial). Additional miles planned: 30.0 (coaxial). Homes passed: 8,047.

Manager: Paul S. Schonewolf. Technical operations manager: Dan Fessler. Field operations manager: Bill Schroeder. Marketing manager: Carl Bauer. Customer operations manager: Danielle Turner.

City fee: None.

Ownership: Time Warner Cable (MSO).

MOWRYSTOWN—FrontierVision, Suite P-200, 1777 S. Harrison St., Denver, CO 80210. Phone: 303-757-1588. Fax: 303-757-6105. Counties: Brown & Highland. Also serves Sardinia, Washington Twp. (Brown County), White Oak Twp. ICA: OH0267.

TV Market Ranking: Outside TV Markets. Franchise award date: N.A. Franchise expiration date: N.A. Began: March 1, 1984.

Channel capacity: 37. Channels available but not in use: 11.

Basic Service

Subscribers: 373.

Programming (received off-air): WCET (P), WCPO-TV (A), WKRC-TV (C), WLWT (N) Cincinnati; WXIX-TV (F) Cincinnati-Newport; WDTN (A), WHIO-TV (C) Dayton.

Programming (via satellite): WGN-TV (W) Chicago; CNN; Disney Channel; ESPN; Fox Family Channel; MTV; Nashville Network; Nickelodeon; TBS Superstation.

Fee: N.A.

Pay Service 1

Pay Units: 104.

Programming (via satellite): HBO.

Fee: N.A.

Pay Service 2

Pay Units: 55.

Programming (via satellite): Showtime.

Fee: N.A.

Miles of plant: 25.0 (coaxial). Homes passed: 850.

Chief technician: Jerry Marnell. Marketing director: Keith Burt.

Ownership: FrontierVision Partners LP (MSO). Purchased from Paint Valley Cable Co. Inc., October 30, 1998. See Cable System Ownership.

MURRAY CITY—FrontierVision, Suite P-200, 1777 S. Harrison St., Denver, CO 80210. Phone: 303-757-1588. Fax: 303-757-6105. County: Hocking. Also serves Hocking County (unincorporated areas), Ward Twp. ICA: OH0284.

TV Market Ranking: 27 (portions of Hocking County); Below 100 (portions of Hocking County, Murray City, Ward Twp.); Outside TV Markets (portions of Hocking County). Franchise award date: N.A. Franchise expiration date: January 1, 1999. Began: November 1, 1951.

Channel capacity: 80. Channels available but not in use: 55.

Basic Service

Subscribers: 204.

Programming (received off-air): WOUB-TV (P) Athens; WCHS-TV (A), WOWK-TV (C), WSAZ-TV (N), WVAH-TV (F,U) Charleston-Huntington; WBNS-TV (C), WCMH-TV (N), WSYX (A) Columbus; WSFJ (I) Newark; WHIZ-TV (N) Zanesville; allband FM.

Current originations: Automated time-weather.

Fee: $47.50 installation; $10.94 monthly; $2.00 converter.

Expanded Basic Service

Subscribers: 197.

Programming (received off-air): WTTE (F,U) Columbus.

Programming (via satellite): WGN-TV (W) Chicago; CNN; ESPN; MOR Galleria; Nashville Network; TBS Superstation.

Fee: $5.01 monthly.

Pay Service 1

Pay Units: 47.

Programming (via satellite): Showtime.

Fee: $10.00 monthly.

Equipment: Blonder-Tongue headend; Jerrold amplifiers; Comm/Scope cable; Panasonic cameras; GTE Sylvania traps; Scientific-Atlanta & M/A-Com satellite antenna; Microdyne & Scientific-Atlanta satellite receivers.

Miles of plant: 3.0 (coaxial). Homes passed: 277. Total homes in franchised area: 330.

Manager: Steve Trippe. Chief technician: Bill Ricker.

City fee: None.

Ownership: FrontierVision Partners LP (MSO). See Cable System Ownership.

MUSKINGUM COUNTY (portions)—FrontierVision, 111 N. 11th St., Newark, OH 43055. Phones: 740-454-2380; 888-293-1894. Fax: 740-345-7670. County: Muskingum. Also serves Chandlersville, Duncan Falls (portions), Philo (portions), Zanesville (portions). ICA: OH0400.

TV Market Ranking: Below 100. Franchise award date: N.A. Franchise expiration date: N.A. Began: N.A.

Channel capacity: 42 (not 2-way capable). Channels available but not in use: 8.

Basic Service

Subscribers: 415.

Programming (received off-air): WBNS-TV (C), WCMH-TV (N), WOSU-TV (P), WSYX (A), WTTE (F,U) Columbus; WHIZ-TV (N) Zanesville.

Programming (via satellite): WGN-TV (W) Chicago; CNN; Comedy Central; Country Music TV; Discovery Channel; ESPN; Fox Family Channel; Headline News; MTV; Nickelodeon; QVC; Sci-Fi Channel; TBS Superstation; Trinity Bcstg. Network; Turner Network TV; USA Network; VH1.

Fee: $25.95 monthly.

Pay Service 1

Pay Units: 55.

Programming (via satellite): HBO.

Fee: N.A.

Pay Service 2

Pay Units: 38.

Programming (via satellite): Showtime.

Fee: N.A.

Pay-Per-View

Addressable homes: 1.

Miles of plant: 30.0 (coaxial). Homes passed: 723.

Regional manager: Judith Pierce. Marketing director: Rich Lutze.

Ownership: FrontierVision Partners LP (MSO). See Cable System Ownership.

NAPOLEON—FrontierVision, 310 Jefferson St., Defiance, OH 43512. Phone: 800-346-2288. Fax: 419-782-2640. County: Henry. Also serves Florida, Malinta. ICA: OH0121.

TV Market Ranking: 52 (Malinta, Napoleon); Outside TV Markets (Florida). Franchise award date: January 1, 1964. Franchise expiration date: N.A. Began: January 1, 1964.

Channel capacity: 41 (not 2-way capable). Channels available but not in use: None.

Basic Service

Subscribers: 3,719.

Programming (received off-air): WBGU-TV (P) Bowling Green; WDIV (N), WKBD-TV (U) Detroit; WGTE-TV (P), WNWO-TV (N), WTOL-TV (C), WTVG (A) Toledo; 16 FMs.

Planned programming (received off-air): WUPW (F) Toledo.

Programming (via satellite): WGN-TV (W) Chicago; CNN; Disney Channel; ESPN; Fox Family Channel; Lifetime; MTV; Nashville Network; TBS Superstation; USA Network.

Planned programming (via satellite): The Weather Channel.
Current originations: Automated time-weather; public access; educational access.
Fee: $45.35 installation; $12.37 monthly; $28.33 additional installation.

Pay Service 1
Pay Units: 186.
Programming (via satellite): Cinemax.
Fee: $7.95 monthly.

Pay Service 2
Pay Units: 227.
Programming (via satellite): HBO.
Fee: $10.95 monthly.

Pay Service 3
Pay Units: 307.
Programming (via satellite): Showtime.
Fee: $9.95 monthly.

Pay Service 4
Pay Units: 270.
Programming (via satellite): The Movie Channel.
Fee: $8.95 monthly.

Pay-Per-View
Addressable homes: 11.

Local advertising: No.
Equipment: Scientific-Atlanta headend; C-COR amplifiers; C-COR & Scientific-Atlanta cable; Jerrold set top converters; Oak addressable set top converters; Scientific-Atlanta satellite antenna; Scientific-Atlanta satellite receivers.
Miles of plant: 88.9 (coaxial). Homes passed: 5,793.
Manager: Steve Trippe. Chief technician: Bill Ricker.
city fee: 3% of gross.
Ownership: FrontierVision Partners LP (MSO). See Cable System Ownership.

NASHPORT—Cablecomm, Box 2249, 737 Howard St., Zanesville, OH 43702-2249. Phone: 888-229-4465. County: Muskingum. Also serves Licking Twp. (Muskingum County), Muskingum Twp. (Muskingum County). ICA: OH0247.
TV Market Ranking: Below 100. Franchise award date: October 1, 1981. Franchise expiration date: N.A. Began: July 1, 1985.
Channel capacity: 40 (not 2-way capable). Channels available but not in use: 8.

Basic Service
Subscribers: 559.
Programming (received off-air): WOUB-TV (P) Athens; WBNS-TV (C), WCMH-TV (N), WOSU-TV (P), WSYX (A), WTTE (F,U) Columbus; WSFJ (I) Newark; WHIZ-TV (N) Zanesville; allband FM.
Programming (via satellite): Discovery Channel; QVC; TBS Superstation.
Fee: $44.95 installation; $10.13 monthly; $3.00 converter.

Expanded Basic Service
Subscribers: 543.
Programming (via satellite): A & E; American Movie Classics; Animal Planet; C-SPAN; CNBC; CNN; Cartoon Network; ESPN; FX; Fox Family Channel; Fox News Channel; Lifetime; MTV; Nashville Network; Nickelodeon; Turner Network TV; USA Network.
Fee: $13.44 monthly.

Pay Service 1
Pay Units: 42.
Programming (via satellite): Disney Channel.
Fee: N.A.

Pay Service 2
Pay Units: 232.
Programming (via satellite): The New Encore.
Fee: N.A.

Pay Service 3
Pay Units: 157.
Programming (via satellite): HBO.
Fee: N.A.

Pay Service 4
Pay Units: N.A.
Programming (via satellite): Starz!
Fee: N.A.

Miles of plant: 28.4 (coaxial); None (fiber optic). Homes passed: 719. Total homes in franchised area: 1,754.
Manager: William F. Randles. Chief technician: John Barber.
Ownership: Fanch Communications Inc. (MSO); Time Warner Cable (MSO). Purchased from Tele-Communications Inc., February 25, 1999. See Cable System Ownership.

NELSON MOBILE HOME PARK—Warner Cable Communications, 1655 Brittain Rd., Akron, OH 44310-3998. Phone: 330-633-9203. Fax: 330-633-0024. County: Portage. ICA: OH0306.
TV Market Ranking: 79. Franchise award date: December 1, 1988. Franchise expiration date: December 1, 2003. Began: December 1, 1988.
Channel capacity: 18 (not 2-way capable). Channels available but not in use: 3.

Basic Service
Subscribers: 89.
Programming (received off-air): WEAO (P) Akron; WNEO (P) Alliance; WEWS-TV (A), WJW (F), WKYC-TV (N), WQHS-TV (H) Cleveland.
Programming (via satellite): WGN-TV (W) Chicago; A & E; Country Music TV; Discovery Channel; ESPN; Fox Family Channel; Headline News; Nashville Network; TBS Superstation; USA Network.
Fee: $35.00 installation; $18.12 monthly.
Commercial fee: $5.00 monthly.

Pay Service 1
Pay Units: 14.
Programming (via satellite): Disney Channel.
Fee: $7.95 monthly.

Pay Service 2
Pay Units: 38.
Programming (via satellite): The Movie Channel.
Fee: $9.95 monthly.

Local advertising: No.
Miles of plant: 1.0 (coaxial). Homes passed: 125. Total homes in franchised area: 125.
Manager: Stephen Fry. Chief technician: Robert Nyitray. Marketing director: Woody Woodward.
Franchise fee: 3% of gross.
Ownership: Time Warner Cable (MSO); Fanch Communications Inc. (MSO). See Cable System Ownership.

NELSON TWP.—Star Cable, Box 4478, 4720 Mahoning Ave., Youngstown, OH 44515. Phone: 330-792-9577. Fax: 330-792-9541. Counties: Geauga, Portage & Trumbull. Also serves Farmington, Freedom Twp. (Portage County), Mesopotamia, Mesopotamia Twp., Middlefield Twp., Parkman, Parkman Twp., Windham (Portage County), Windham Twp. ICA: OH0160.
TV Market Ranking: 8 (Freedom Twp., Mesopotamia, Mesopotamia Twp., Middlefield Twp., Nelson Twp., Parkman, Parkman Twp., Windham, Windham Twp.); 79 (Farmington, Freedom Twp., Mesopotamia, Mesopotamia Twp., Nelson Twp., Parkman, Parkman Twp., Windham, Windham Twp.). Franchise award date: June 25, 1988. Franchise expiration date: N.A. Began: November 1, 1989.
Channel capacity: 62 (not 2-way capable). Channels available but not in use: 17.

Basic Service
Subscribers: 1,718.
Programming (received off-air): WBNX-TV (W,F), WVPX (X) Akron; WNEO (P) Alliance; WDLI (T) Canton; WEWS-TV (A), WJW (F), WKYC-TV (N), WVIZ-TV (P) Cleveland; WUAB (U) Lorain-Cleveland; WOIO (C) Shaker Heights; WFMJ-TV (N) Youngstown.
Programming (via satellite): TBS Superstation.
Fee: $25.00 installation; $11.75 monthly; $1.95 converter.

Expanded Basic Service
Subscribers: 1,637.
Programming (via satellite): A & E; American Movie Classics; C-SPAN; CNN; Cartoon Network; Country Music TV; Discovery Channel; ESPN; ESPN 2; Fox Family Channel; Fox News Channel; Fox Sports Net Ohio; Headline News; History Channel; Home & Garden Television; Learning Channel; Lifetime; MTV; Nashville Network; Nick at Nite's TV Land; Nickelodeon; QVC; Sci-Fi Channel; The Weather Channel; Turner Network TV; USA Network; VH1.
Fee: $18.75 monthly.

Pay Service 1
Pay Units: 184.
Programming (via satellite): Cinemax.
Fee: $11.00 monthly.

Pay Service 2
Pay Units: 229.
Programming (via satellite): Disney Channel.
Fee: $7.95 monthly.

Pay Service 3
Pay Units: 260.
Programming (via satellite): HBO.
Fee: $11.00 monthly.

Pay Service 4
Pay Units: 256.
Programming (via satellite): Showtime; The Movie Channel.
Fee: $12.95 monthly.

Local advertising: No.
Equipment: DX Engineering & Scientific-Atlanta headend; Scientific-Atlanta amplifiers; Comm/Scope cable; Panasonic set top converters; Eagle traps; DH Satellite satellite antenna; DX Engineering satellite receivers.
Miles of plant: 131.7 (coaxial); None (fiber optic). Homes passed: 2,594. Total homes in franchised area: 2,594.
Manager: Terry Dickerhoof. Chief technician: Tom Beat.
Franchise fee: 5% of gross.
Ownership: Star Cable Associates (MSO).

NELSONVILLE—Nelsonville TV Cable, 1 W. Columbus St., Nelsonville, OH 45764. Phone: 614-753-2686. Counties: Athens & Hocking. Also serves Athens County, Buchtel, Carbon Hill, Chauncey, Glouster, Haydenville, Jacksonville, Millfield, The Plains, Trimble, Union Furnace. ICA: OH0347.
TV Market Ranking: Below 100 (portions of Athens County, Buchtel, Carbon Hill, Chauncey, Glouster, Jacksonville, Millfield, Trimble); Outside TV Markets (portions of Athens County, Haydenville, Nelsonville, Union Furnace). Franchise award date: N.A. Franchise expiration date: January 1, 2002. Began: December 8, 1952.
Channel capacity: 36. Channels available but not in use: 3.

Basic Service
Subscribers: 6,500.
Programming (received off-air): WOUB-TV (P) Athens; WCHS-TV (A), WOWK-TV (C), WSAZ-TV (N), WVAH-TV (F,U) Charleston-Huntington; WBNS-TV (C), WCMH-TV (N), WOSU-TV (P), WSYX (A), WTTE (F,U) Columbus; WHIZ-TV (N) Zanesville; allband FM.
Programming (via satellite): WGN-TV (W) Chicago; A & E; C-SPAN; C-SPAN 2; CNN; Discovery Channel; ESPN; Fox Family Channel; Headline News; Home Shopping Network; Nick at Nite; Nickelodeon; TBS Superstation; TV Guide Channel; USA Network.
Current originations: Automated time-weather; public access; religious access; local news; local sports.
Fee: $21.50 installation; $18.50 monthly.
Commercial fee: $1.00 monthly.

Pay Service 1
Pay Units: N.A.
Programming (via satellite): Disney Channel; HBO; Showtime.
Fee: $20.00 installation; $7.00 monthly (Disney or Showtime), $8.00 monthly (HBO).

Local advertising: Yes. Available in character-generated programming. Rates: $15.00/15 Seconds. Local sales manager: Eugene R. Edwards.
Program Guide: Premium Channels.
Equipment: Scientific-Atlanta headend; Triple Crown & C-COR amplifiers; Trilogy cable; Sharp cameras; JVC VTRs; MSI character generator; Jerrold & Pioneer set top converters; Eagle & Arcom traps; Blonder-Tongue addressable traps; Anixter-Mark, Comtech & Scientific-Atlanta satellite antenna; Standard Components & Scientific-Atlanta satellite receivers.
Miles of plant: 150.0 (coaxial). Additional miles planned: 5.0 (coaxial). Homes passed: 7,000.
Manager: Eugene R. Edwards.
City fee: None.
Ownership: Nelsonville TV Cable Inc.

NEW ATHENS—Richards & Sons Communications Co., Drawer 2, Jerusalem, OH 43747. Phone: 740-926-1742. Counties: Belmont & Harrison. Also serves Lloydsville. ICA: OH0348.
TV Market Ranking: 90. Franchise award date: N.A. Franchise expiration date: N.A. Began: N.A.
Channel capacity: 21. Channels available but not in use: 10.

Basic Service
Subscribers: N.A.
Programming (received off-air): KDKA-TV (C), WCWB (W), WPGH-TV (F), WQED (P), WTAE-TV (A) Pittsburgh; WTOV-TV (N) Steubenville-Wheeling; WTRF-TV (C) Wheeling-Steubenville.
Programming (via satellite): Nashville Network; TBS Superstation.
Fee: $15.00 installation; $10.00 monthly.

Manager: Paul E. Richards. Chief technician: Mark Richards.
Ownership: Paul E. Richards (MSO).

NEW CONCORD—Cablecomm, Box 2249, 737 Howard St., Zanesville, OH 43702-2249. Phone: 888-229-4465. County: Muskingum. ICA: OH0226.
TV Market Ranking: Below 100. Franchise award date: N.A. Franchise expiration date: April 14, 2004. Began: October 1, 1969.
Channel capacity: 33 (not 2-way capable). Channels available but not in use: 1.

Basic Service
Subscribers: 679.
Programming (received off-air): WOUB-TV (P) Athens; WBNS-TV (C), WCMH-TV (N), WOSU-TV (P), WSYX (A), WTTE (F,U) Columbus; WTRF-TV (C) Wheeling-Steubenville; WHIZ-TV (N) Zanesville; allband FM.
Programming (via satellite): Discovery Channel; QVC; TBS Superstation.
Current originations: Educational access.

Fee: $44.95 installation; $10.13 monthly; $3.00 converter.

Expanded Basic Service

Subscribers: 589.

Programming (via satellite): A & E; American Movie Classics; C-SPAN; CNBC; CNN; ESPN; Fox Sports Net Pittsburgh; Lifetime; MTV; Nashville Network; Nickelodeon; Turner Network TV; USA Network.

Fee: $13.44 monthly.

Pay Service 1

Pay Units: 41.

Programming (via satellite): Disney Channel.

Fee: $20.00 installation; $11.95 monthly.

Pay Service 2

Pay Units: 211.

Programming (via satellite): The New Encore.

Fee: N.A.

Pay Service 3

Pay Units: 155.

Programming (via satellite): HBO.

Fee: $11.95 monthly.

Equipment: Blonder-Tongue headend; Jerrold amplifiers; Vikoa cable; Eagle traps; Scientific-Atlanta satellite antenna; Scientific-Atlanta satellite receivers.

Miles of plant: 10.0 (coaxial); None (fiber optic). Homes passed: 964. Total homes in franchised area: 1,232.

Manager: William F. Randles. Chief technician: John Barber.

City fee: None.

Ownership: Fanch Communications Inc. (MSO); Time Warner Cable (MSO). Purchased from Tele-Communications Inc., February 25, 1999. See Cable System Ownership.

NEW HOLLAND—FrontierVision, Box 648, 102 Twin Oak Dr., Jackson, OH 45640. Phone: 614-345-4329. Fax: 614-286-1489. Counties: Fayette, Pickaway & Ross. Also serves Atlanta, Clarksburg, Deer Creek Twp. (Pickaway County), Perry Twp. (Pickaway County), Williamsport. ICA: OH0207.

TV Market Ranking: 27. Franchise award date: December 8, 1986. Franchise expiration date: December 8, 2001. Began: December 8, 1987.

Channel capacity: 37. Channels available but not in use: 4.

Basic Service

Subscribers: 718.

Programming (received off-air): WWHO (U) Chillicothe; WBNS-TV (C), WCMH-TV (N), WOSU-TV (P), WSYX (A), WTTE (F,U) Columbus; WHIO-TV (C), WKEF (N), WRGT-TV (F,U) Dayton.

Programming (via satellite): WGN-TV (W) Chicago; A & E; CNN; Comedy Central; Country Music TV; Discovery Channel; Disney Channel; ESPN; Fox Family Channel; Learning Channel; Lifetime; MTV; Nashville Network; Nickelodeon; QVC; TBS Superstation; The Weather Channel; Turner Network TV; USA Network.

Fee: $20.99 installation; $23.70 monthly.

Pay Service 1

Pay Units: 124.

Programming (via satellite): Cinemax.

Fee: N.A.

Pay Service 2

Pay Units: 190.

Programming (via satellite): HBO.

Fee: $15.00 installation; $11.95 monthly.

Pay Service 3

Pay Units: 1.

Programming (via satellite): Showtime.

Fee: N.A.

Pay Service 4

Pay Units: 1.

Programming (via satellite): The Movie Channel.

Fee: N.A.

Equipment: Triple Crown & Texscan amplifiers; Times Fiber & Belden cable; Hamlin & NSC set top converters; Eagle, Pico & Arcom traps; ChannelMaster satellite antenna; General & Standard Communications satellite receivers.

Miles of plant: 38.0 (coaxial). Homes passed: 1,264.

Manager: Steve Trippe. Chief technician: Bill Ricker.

Ownership: FrontierVision Partners LP (MSO). See Cable System Ownership.

NEW KNOXVILLE—New Knoxville Cable Systems, Box 219, 301 W. South St., New Knoxville, OH 45871. Phone: 419-753-5000. Fax: 419-753-2950. County: Auglaize. Also serves Minster, New Bremen. ICA: OH0275.

TV Market Ranking: Below 100. Franchise award date: May 5, 1985. Franchise expiration date: N.A. Began: February 1, 1986.

Channel capacity: 77 (not 2-way capable). Channels available but not in use: 6.

Basic Service

Subscribers: 1,170.

Programming (received off-air): WBGU-TV (P) Bowling Green; WBNS-TV (C) Columbus; WDTN (A), WHIO-TV (C), WKEF (N), WPTD (P), WRGT-TV (F,U) Dayton; WFFT-TV (F), WPTA (A) Fort Wayne; WLIO (N), WTLW (I) Lima.

Programming (via satellite): WGN-TV (W) Chicago; A & E; C-SPAN; CNN; Discovery Channel; ESPN; ESPN 2; Fox Family Channel; Fox Sports Net Ohio; Headline News; History Channel; Lifetime; Nashville Network; Nickelodeon; TBS Superstation; The Weather Channel; Turner Classic Movies; Turner Network TV; USA Network; VH1.

Current originations: Local News.

Fee: $24.95 installation; $14.95 monthly.

Expanded Basic Service

Subscribers: 1,002.

Programming (received off-air): WOHL-LP (F) Lima.

Programming (via satellite): American Movie Classics; Animal Planet; CNBC; CNNfn; Country Music TV; Disney Channel; ESPN Classic Sports; EWTN; Home & Garden Television; Learning Channel; MSNBC; MTV; Nick at Nite's TV Land; QVC; TV Guide Channel; Toon Disney; Trinity Bcstg. Network; Z Music Television.

Fee: $19.95 monthly.

Expanded Basic Service 2

Subscribers: 429.

Programming (via satellite): Comedy Central; E! Entertainment TV; Game Show Network; Golf Channel; Outdoor Life Network; Romance Classics; Sci-Fi Channel; Speedvision; The New Encore; ZDTV.

Fee: $24.95 monthly.

Pay Service 1

Pay Units: 45.

Programming (via satellite): Cinemax.

Fee: $9.50 monthly.

Pay Service 2

Pay Units: 90.

Programming (via satellite): HBO.

Fee: $9.50 monthly.

Pay Service 3

Pay Units: 74.

Programming (via satellite): Flix; Showtime; The Movie Channel.

Fee: $10.95 monthly.

Pay-Per-View

Addressable homes: 220.

Local advertising: Yes. Available in locally originated & character-generated programming. Rates: $5.00/Page/Day. Local sales manager: Preston Meyer.

Equipment: DX Engineering, ISS & Triple Crown headend; Jerrold amplifiers; Panasonic & Pioneer set top converters; DX Engineering, ISS & Triple Crown satellite receivers.

Miles of plant: 40.0 (coaxial); 15.0 (fiber optic). Homes passed: 2,300. Total homes in franchised area: 2,300.

Manager: Preston Meyer. Chief technician: Matt Slife. Customer service manager: Susan Quellhorst.

Ownership: New Knoxville Telephone Co.

NEW LEXINGTON (Perry County)—Time Warner Cable, Box 787, 111 S. Mulberry St., Mount Vernon, OH 43050. Phones: 740-397-2288; 800-782-4118. Fax: 740-397-3730. County: Perry. Also serves Junction City. ICA: OH0148.

TV Market Ranking: Below 100. Franchise award date: N.A. Franchise expiration date: N.A. Began: N.A.

Channel capacity: 12. Channels available but not in use: None.

Basic Service

Subscribers: 2,528.

Programming (received off-air): WOUB-TV (P) Athens; WBNS-TV (C), WCMH-TV (N), WOSU-TV (P), WSYX (A), WTTE (F,U) Columbus; WSFJ (I) Newark; WHIZ-TV (N) Zanesville; allband FM.

Programming (via satellite): WGN-TV (W) Chicago; A & E; CNN; Country Music TV; Discovery Channel; ESPN; Fox Family Channel; Lifetime; MTV; Nashville Network; Nickelodeon; QVC; TBS Superstation; The Weather Channel; Turner Network TV; USA Network.

Current originations: Automated time-weather; educational access; automated emergency alert; local news.

Fee: $10.00 installation; $21.81 monthly.

Pay Service 1

Pay Units: 139.

Programming (via satellite): Disney Channel.

Fee: $9.00 monthly.

Pay Service 2

Pay Units: 700.

Programming (via satellite): HBO.

Fee: $10.00 monthly.

Pay Service 3

Pay Units: 199.

Programming (via satellite): The Movie Channel.

Fee: $9.00 monthly.

Pay Service 4

Pay Units: N.A.

Programming (via satellite): Cinemax; Showtime.

Fee: $10.95 monthly (each).

Equipment: Cadco headend; Jerrold amplifiers; Times Fiber cable; Panasonic cameras; Sony VTRs; Pico traps; Scientific-Atlanta satellite antenna; Scientific-Atlanta satellite receivers.

Miles of plant: 40.0 (coaxial). Additional miles planned: 2.0 (coaxial). Homes passed: 2,890.

Manager: Paul S. Schonewolf. Technical operations manager: Dan Fessler. Field operations manager: Bill Schroeder. Marketing manager: Carl Bauer. Customer operations manager: Danielle Turner.

City fee: 3% of gross.

Ownership: Time Warner Cable (MSO).

NEW LONDON—Time Warner Cable, Box 10, 105 Prospect St., Lodi, OH 44254. Phone: 330-633-9044. Fax: 330-948-1513. Counties: Ashland & Huron. Also serves Bailey Lakes, Savannah. ICA: OH0202.

TV Market Ranking: 8. Franchise award date: N.A. Franchise expiration date: February 1, 2003. Began: March 1, 1973.

Channel capacity: 42. Channels available but not in use: 4.

Basic Service

Subscribers: 1,100.

Programming (received off-air): WBNX-TV (W,F), WVPX (X) Akron; WNEO (P) Alliance; WEWS-TV (A), WJW (F), WKYC-TV (N), WQHS-TV (H), WVIZ-TV (P) Cleveland; WUAB (U) Lorain-Cleveland; WMFD-TV (I) Mansfield; WGGN-TV (T) Sandusky; WOIO (C) Shaker Heights; WTOL-TV (C), WTVG (A) Toledo.

Programming (via satellite): Knowledge TV.

Fee: $30.00 installation; $7.99 monthly; $0.94 converter; $24.40 additional installation.

Expanded Basic Service

Subscribers: N.A.

Programming (via satellite): WGN-TV (W) Chicago; A & E; American Movie Classics; C-SPAN; CNBC; CNN; Country Music TV; Discovery Channel; ESPN; Fox Family Channel; Headline News; Lifetime; MTV; Nashville Network; Nickelodeon; TBS Superstation; The Weather Channel; Turner Network TV; USA Network.

Fee: $17.18 monthly.

Pay Service 1

Pay Units: 135.

Programming (via satellite): Cinemax.

Fee: $8.95 monthly.

Pay Service 2

Pay Units: 117.

Programming (via satellite): Disney Channel.

Fee: $8.95 monthly.

Pay Service 3

Pay Units: 274.

Programming (via satellite): HBO.

Fee: $8.95 monthly.

Pay Service 4

Pay Units: 80.

Programming (via satellite): Showtime.

Fee: $8.95 monthly.

Pay Service 5

Pay Units: N.A.

Programming (via satellite): The Movie Channel.

Fee: $8.95 monthly.

Local advertising: No.

Equipment: Jerrold & Scientific-Atlanta headend; GTE Sylvania amplifiers; Times Fiber cable; Pioneer set top converters; Eagle, Vitek & Arcom traps; Microdyne & Scientific-Atlanta satellite antenna; Avantek satellite receivers.

Miles of plant: 25.3 (coaxial). Homes passed: 1,346. Total homes in franchised area: 1,346.

Manager: Thomas P. Autry. Chief technician: Jim Parsons. Marketing director: Ray Kistler.

Ownership: Time Warner Cable (MSO).

NEW MATAMORAS—FrontierVision, Suite P-200, 1777 S. Harrison St., Denver, CO 80210. Phone: 303-757-1588. Fax: 303-757-6105. County: Washington. Also serves Beavertown. ICA: OH0245.

TV Market Ranking: Below 100. Franchise award date: N.A. Franchise expiration date: August 15, 1998. Began: November 1, 1966.

Channel capacity: 80 (not 2-way capable). Channels available but not in use: 40.

Basic Service

Subscribers: 484.

Programming (received off-air): WOUC-TV (P) Cambridge; WDTV (C,A) Clarksburg-Weston; WNPB-TV (P) Morgantown; WTAP-TV (N) Parkersburg-Marietta; WTOV-TV (N) Steubenville-Wheeling; WTRF-TV (C) Wheeling-Steubenville; allband FM.

Programming (via satellite): WGN-TV (W) Chicago; WABC-TV (A) New York; Country Music TV; Fox Family Channel; FoxNet.
Current originations: Automated time-weather.
Fee: $29.95 installation; $11.21 monthly; $0.73 converter.

Expanded Basic Service
Subscribers: 444.
Programming (via satellite): A & E; CNN; Discovery Channel; Disney Channel; ESPN; Nashville Network; TBS Superstation; USA Network.
Fee: $8.56 monthly.

Pay Service 1
Pay Units: 32.
Programming (via satellite): Cinemax.
Fee: $7.95 monthly.

Pay Service 2
Pay Units: 13.
Programming (via satellite): The New Encore.
Fee: N.A.

Pay Service 3
Pay Units: 36.
Programming (via satellite): HBO.
Fee: $11.99 monthly.

Pay Service 4
Pay Units: 22.
Programming (via satellite): Showtime.
Fee: $11.95 monthly.

Pay Service 5
Pay Units: 12.
Programming (via satellite): Starz!
Fee: N.A.

Pay Service 6
Pay Units: 23.
Programming (via satellite): The Movie Channel.
Fee: $11.95 monthly.

Local advertising: Planned.
Equipment: Jerrold headend; Coral amplifiers; Times Fiber cable; Scientific-Atlanta satellite antenna.
Miles of plant: 15.0 (coaxial); 15.0 (fiber optic). Homes passed: 709.
Manager: Steve Trippe. Chief technician: Bill Ricker.
City fee: $500 annually.
Ownership: FrontierVision Partners LP (MSO). See Cable System Ownership.

NEW PHILADELPHIA—FrontierVision, Box 506, New Philadelphia, OH 44663. Phone: 330-364-6634. Fax: 330-364-6796. County: Tuscarawas. Also serves Baltic, Barnhill, Columbia, Dennison, Dover, Gnadenhutton, Midvale, Newcomerstown, Oxford Twp. (Tuscarawas County), Parral, Port Washington, Roswell, Strasburg, Tuscarawas, Uhrichsville, Wainwright. ICA: OH0030.
TV Market Ranking: 8 (Parral, Strasburg); Below 100 (Baltic, Barnhill, Columbia, Dennison, Dover, Gnadenhutton, Midvale, New Philadelphia, Newcomerstown, Oxford Twp., Port Washington, Roswell, Tuscarawas, Uhrichsville, Wainwright). Franchise award date: January 1, 1951. Franchise expiration date: May 11, 2002. Began: May 1, 1982.
Channel capacity: 62 (not 2-way capable). Channels available but not in use: None.

Basic Service
Subscribers: 21,527; Commercial subscribers: 1,875.
Programming (received off-air): WBNX-TV (W,F), WEAO (P), WVPX (X) Akron; WOUC-TV (P) Cambridge; WDLI (T), WOAC (I) Canton; WEWS-TV (A), WJW (F), WKYC-TV (N) Cleveland; WUAB (U) Lorain-Cleveland; WOIO (C) Shaker Heights; WTOV-TV (N) Steubenville-Wheeling; WTRF-TV (C) Wheeling-Steubenville.
Programming (via microwave): WCMH-TV (N) Columbus.
Programming (via satellite): C-SPAN; TBS Superstation; Turner Classic Movies.
Current originations: Automated time-weather; automated emergency alert; local news.
Fee: $50.00 installation; $11.27 monthly.

Expanded Basic Service
Subscribers: 20,499.
Programming (via satellite): A & E; CNN; Comedy Central; Disney Channel; ESPN; FX; Fox Family Channel; Fox Sports Net Ohio; Golf Channel; Headline News; Home & Garden Television; Home Shopping Network; Knowledge TV; Lifetime; MSNBC; MTV; Music Choice; Nickelodeon; Outdoor Life Network; TV Food Network; TV Guide Channel; TV Guide Sneak Prevue; The Weather Channel; USA Network.
Fee: $12.28 monthly.

Expanded Basic Service 2
Subscribers: N.A.
Programming (via satellite): American Movie Classics; Discovery Channel; Learning Channel; Nashville Network; Turner Network TV.
Fee: $1.75 monthly.

A la Carte 1
Subscribers: N.A.
Programming (via satellite): Cartoon Network; Court TV; Sci-Fi Channel.
Fee: $1.95 monthly (package).

Pay Service 1
Pay Units: 1,395.
Programming (via satellite): Cinemax.
Fee: $6.95 monthly.

Pay Service 2
Pay Units: 1,877.
Programming (via satellite): The New Encore.
Fee: $2.95 monthly.

Pay Service 3
Pay Units: 2,439.
Programming (via satellite): HBO.
Fee: $10.95 monthly.

Pay Service 4
Pay Units: 1,381.
Programming (via satellite): Showtime.
Fee: $9.95 monthly.

Pay Service 5
Pay Units: 19.
Programming (via satellite): Starz!
Fee: N.A.

Pay Service 6
Pay Units: 945.
Programming (via satellite): The Movie Channel.
Fee: $6.95 monthly.

Pay-Per-View
Addressable homes: 10,732.
Hot Choice; Spice; Viewer's Choice.

Local advertising: Yes. Local sales manager: Charlie Jones.
Equipment: Scientific-Atlanta headend; Jerrold amplifiers; Comm/Scope cable; Hitachi cameras; Panasonic VTRs; MSI character generator; Standard Components set top converters; Scientific-Atlanta satellite antenna.
Miles of plant: 467.6 (coaxial). Homes passed: 27,432.
Manager: Steve Trippe. Chief technician: Bill Ricker.
City fee: 5% of gross.
Ownership: FrontierVision Partners LP (MSO). See Cable System Ownership.

***NEW ROME**—Americast, 300 S. Riverside, Chicago, IL 60606. Phones: 312-526-8000; 800-848-2278. Fax: 312-526-8565. County: Franklin. ICA: OH0408.
TV Market Ranking: 27. Franchise award date: January 1, 1998. Franchise expiration date: N.A. Scheduled to begin: N.A.
Channel capacity: N.A.
Total homes in franchised area: 50.
Ownership: Ameritech New Media Inc. (MSO).

NEWARK—FrontierVision, 111 N. 11th St., Newark, OH 43055. Phones: 740-345-4329; 740-454-2380. Fax: 740-345-7670. County: Licking. Also serves Buckeye Lake, Franklin Twp. (Licking County), Granville (village), Granville Twp. (Licking County), Hanover (portions), Heath, Hebron (Licking County), Licking Twp. (Licking County), Madison Twp. (Licking County), Newark Twp. (Licking County), Riverside (Licking County), St. Louisville, Union Twp. (Licking County). ICA: OH0019.
TV Market Ranking: 27 (Buckeye Lake, Franklin Twp., Granville, Granville Twp., Heath, Hebron, Licking Twp., Madison Twp., Newark, Newark Twp., Riverside, St. Louisville, Union Twp.); Below 100 (Hanover). Franchise award date: N.A. Franchise expiration date: N.A. Began: July 19, 1976.
Channel capacity: 80. Channels available but not in use: 7.

Basic Service
Subscribers: 27,072; Commercial subscribers: 1,621.
Programming (received off-air): WOUC-TV (P) Cambridge; WWHO (U) Chillicothe; WBNS-TV (C), WCMH-TV (N), WOSU-TV (P), WSYX (A), WTTE (F,U) Columbus; WSFJ (I) Newark; WHIZ-TV (N) Zanesville; 19 FMs.
Programming (via satellite): WGN-TV (W) Chicago; C-SPAN; Comedy Central; Discovery Channel; Learning Channel; TBS Superstation; TV Guide Channel; TV Guide Sneak Prevue.
Current originations: Automated time-weather; educational access; local sports.
Fee: $44.95 installation; $14.23 monthly.

Expanded Basic Service
Subscribers: 25,609.
Programming (via satellite): A & E; Animal Planet; BET; CNBC; CNN; Cartoon Network; Country Music TV; Disney Channel; ESPN; FX; Fox Family Channel; Fox Sports Net Ohio; Golf Channel; Headline News; Home & Garden Television; Lifetime; MSNBC; MTV; Music Choice; Nickelodeon; Outdoor Life Network; QVC; Sci-Fi Channel; Speedvision; TV Food Network; The Weather Channel; Turner Classic Movies; USA Network.
Fee: $14.09 monthly.

Expanded Basic Service 2
Subscribers: N.A.
Programming (via satellite): American Movie Classics; ESPN 2; History Channel; Nashville Network; Turner Network TV.
Fee: $2.50 monthly.

Pay Service 1
Pay Units: 2,526.
Programming (via satellite): Cinemax.
Fee: $8.95 monthly.

Pay Service 2
Pay Units: 3,710.
Programming (via satellite): The New Encore.
Fee: $2.95 monthly.

Pay Service 3
Pay Units: 401.
Programming (via satellite): Flix.
Fee: N.A.

Pay Service 4
Pay Units: 4,516.
Programming (via satellite): HBO (multiplexed).
Fee: $12.95 monthly.

Pay Service 5
Pay Units: 3,198.
Programming (via satellite): Showtime.
Fee: $10.95 monthly.

Pay Service 6
Pay Units: 158.
Programming (via satellite): Starz!
Fee: N.A.

Pay Service 7
Pay Units: 2,000.
Programming (via satellite): The Movie Channel.
Fee: $10.95 monthly.

Pay-Per-View
Addressable homes: 15,475.
Playboy TV; Spice; Viewer's Choice 1, 3, 4; Viewer's Choice 5.

Local advertising: Yes. Available in satellite distributed, locally originated & character-generated programming.
Program Guide: The Cable Guide.
Equipment: Jerrold headend; Jerrold amplifiers; Jerrold cable; Andrew satellite antenna.
Miles of plant: 499.3 (coaxial). Homes passed: 38,746. Total homes in franchised area: 57,000.
Regional manager: Judith Pierce. Marketing director: Rich Lutze.
City fee: 3% of gross.
Ownership: FrontierVision Partners LP (MSO). See Cable System Ownership.

NEWPORT—FrontierVision, Suite P-200, 1777 S. Harrison St., Denver, CO 80210. Phone: 303-757-1588. Fax: 303-757-6105. County: Washington. ICA: OH0264.
TV Market Ranking: Below 100. Franchise award date: N.A. Franchise expiration date: N.A. Began: November 1, 1965.
Channel capacity: 25 (not 2-way capable). Channels available but not in use: None.

Basic Service
Subscribers: 360.
Programming (received off-air): WOUB-TV (P) Athens; WCHS-TV (A), WOWK-TV (C), WSAZ-TV (N) Charleston-Huntington; WTAP-TV (N) Parkersburg-Marietta; WTRF-TV (C) Wheeling-Steubenville; WHIZ-TV (N) Zanesville; allband FM.
Programming (via satellite): C-SPAN; Country Music TV; Fox Family Channel; FoxNet.
Fee: $29.95 installation; $11.21 monthly; $0.73 converter.

Expanded Basic Service
Subscribers: 342.
Programming (via satellite): WGN-TV (W) Chicago; CNN; Discovery Channel; Disney Channel; ESPN; Lifetime; Nashville Network; TBS Superstation; USA Network.
Fee: $8.56 monthly.

Pay Service 1
Pay Units: 14.
Programming (via satellite): Cinemax.
Fee: $29.95 installation; $7.95 monthly.

Pay Service 2
Pay Units: 22.
Programming (via satellite): HBO.
Fee: $29.95 installation; $11.99 monthly.

Pay Service 3
Pay Units: 33.
Programming (via satellite): Showtime.
Fee: $29.95 installation; $11.95 monthly.

Pay Service 4
Pay Units: 32.
Programming (via satellite): The Movie Channel.
Fee: $29.95 installation; $11.95 monthly.

Local advertising: No.
Equipment: Jerrold headend; Coral amplifiers; Times Fiber cable.
Miles of plant: 12.0 (coaxial). Homes passed: 486.

Manager: Steve Trippe. Chief technician: Bill Ricker.
City fee: $250 annually.
Ownership: FrontierVision Partners LP (MSO). See Cable System Ownership.

NEWTON FALLS—TCI Cablevision of Ohio Inc., Box 189, Kent, OH 44240-4174. Phone: 216-677-9692. Counties: Mahoning, Portage & Trumbull. Also serves Braceville (Trumbull County), Craig Beach, Garrettsville, Hiram, Leavittsburg, Nelson, Warren Twp. (Trumbull County), Windham (Portage County). ICA: OH0114.
TV Market Ranking: 8,79. Franchise award date: N.A. Franchise expiration date: N.A. Began: September 1, 1975.
Channel capacity: 39. Channels available but not in use: N.A.
Basic Service
Subscribers: 4,181.
Programming (received off-air): WBNX-TV (W,F) Akron; WNEO (P) Alliance; WDLI (T) Canton; WEWS-TV (A), WJW (F), WKYC-TV (N) Cleveland; WUAB (U) Lorain-Cleveland; WOIO (C) Shaker Heights; WFMJ-TV (N), WKBN-TV (C), WYTV (A,F) Youngstown; allband FM.
Programming (via satellite): WGN-TV (W) Chicago; A & E; CNBC; CNN; Discovery Channel; Fox Family Channel; Headline News; Lifetime; MTV; Nashville Network; Nickelodeon; QVC; TBS Superstation; The Weather Channel.
Current originations: Automated time-weather; educational access; government access; local news.
Fee: $60.00 installation; $9.04 monthly; $2.00 converter.
Expanded Basic Service
Subscribers: 3,682.
Programming (via satellite): American Movie Classics; ESPN; Fox Sports Net Pittsburgh; Turner Network TV; USA Network.
Fee: $9.99 installation; $1.95 monthly.
Pay Service 1
Pay Units: 423.
Programming (via satellite): Cinemax.
Fee: $12.29 monthly.
Pay Service 2
Pay Units: 270.
Programming (via satellite): Disney Channel.
Fee: $10.00 monthly.
Pay Service 3
Pay Units: 1,245.
Programming (via satellite): The New Encore.
Fee: N.A.
Pay Service 4
Pay Units: 859.
Programming (via satellite): HBO.
Fee: $12.29 monthly.
Equipment: Blonder-Tongue headend; Jerrold amplifiers; Plastoid cable.
Miles of plant: 70.0 (coaxial). Homes passed: 5,040. Total homes in franchised area: 5,040.
Manager: William Quinn. Chief technician: David Toth.
City fee: 3% of gross.
Ownership: AT&T Broadband & Internet Services (MSO). Purchased from Tele-Communications Inc., March 9, 1999.

NEWTON TWP.—Star Cable, Box 4478, 4720 Mahoning Ave., Youngstown, OH 44515. Phone: 330-792-9577. Fax: 330-792-9541. Counties: Columbiana, Portage & Trumbull. Also serves Blue Water Manor, Paris Twp. (Portage County), Rogers. ICA: OH0187.
TV Market Ranking: 8,79. Franchise award date: N.A. Franchise expiration date: N.A. Began: N.A.
Channel capacity: 41 (not 2-way capable). Channels available but not in use: 1.
Basic Service
Subscribers: 1,351.
Programming (received off-air): WBNX-TV (W,F) Akron; WNEO (P) Alliance; WEWS-TV (A), WJW (F), WKYC-TV (N), WVIZ-TV (P) Cleveland; WUAB (U) Lorain-Cleveland; WOIO (C) Shaker Heights; WFMJ-TV (N), WKBN-TV (C), WYTV (A,F) Youngstown.
Programming (via satellite): TBS Superstation.
Fee: $40.00 installation; $12.25 monthly; $1.95 converter.
Expanded Basic Service
Subscribers: 1,304.
Programming (via satellite): WGN-TV (W) Chicago; A & E; American Movie Classics; CNN; Discovery Channel; ESPN; Fox Family Channel; Fox News Channel; Fox Sports Net Ohio; Headline News; History Channel; Home & Garden Television; Learning Channel; Lifetime; MTV; Nashville Network; Nickelodeon; QVC; The Weather Channel; Turner Network TV; USA Network; VH1.
Fee: $18.25 monthly.
Pay Service 1
Pay Units: 80.
Programming (via satellite): Cinemax.
Fee: $11.00 monthly.
Pay Service 2
Pay Units: 139.
Programming (via satellite): Disney Channel.
Fee: $7.95 monthly.
Pay Service 3
Pay Units: 235.
Programming (via satellite): HBO.
Fee: $11.00 monthly.
Pay Service 4
Pay Units: 154.
Programming (via satellite): Showtime; The Movie Channel.
Fee: $12.95 monthly.
Miles of plant: 57.4 (coaxial); None (fiber optic). Homes passed: 1,644. Total homes in franchised area: 1,644.
Manager: Terry Dickerhoof. Chief technician: Tom Beat.
Ownership: Star Cable Associates (MSO).

NORTH BALTIMORE—Americable USA Inc., 3630 S. Main St., Akron, OH 44319. Phone: 216-644-5459. County: Wood. Also serves Bloomdale, Cygnet. ICA: OH0349.
TV Market Ranking: 52. Franchise award date: N.A. Franchise expiration date: N.A. Began: September 1, 1982.
Channel capacity: 100. Channels available but not in use: N.A.
Basic Service
Subscribers: 1,550.
Programming (received off-air): WBGU-TV (P) Bowling Green; WKBD-TV (U) Detroit; WLIO (N) Lima; WUAB (U) Lorain-Cleveland; WGTE-TV (P), WNWO-TV (N), WTOL-TV (C), WTVG (A) Toledo.
Programming (via satellite): WGN-TV (W) Chicago; TBS Superstation.
Planned originations: Local news.
Fee: N.A.
Manager: Braughn Mckinney. Chief technician: Steve Cook.
Ownership: Americable USA Inc. (MSO).

NORTH OLMSTED—Cablevision of Ohio, 3400 Lakeside Ave., Cleveland, OH 44114. Phone: 216-575-8016. Fax: 216-575-0212. County: Cuyahoga. Also serves North Royalton, Westlake. ICA: OH0028.
TV Market Ranking: 8. Franchise award date: N.A. Franchise expiration date: N.A. Began: November 18, 1981.
Channel capacity: 78 (2-way capable; operating 2-way). Channels available but not in use: 8.
Basic Service
Subscribers: 15,050.
Programming (received off-air): WBNX-TV (W,F), WEAO (P), WVPX (X) Akron; WEWS-TV (A), WJW (F), WKYC-TV (N), WQHS-TV (H), WVIZ-TV (P) Cleveland; WUAB (U) Lorain-Cleveland; WOIO (C) Shaker Heights; 15 FMs.
Programming (via satellite): A & E; Bravo; C-SPAN; CNBC; CNN; ESPN; EWTN; Electronic Program Guide; Fox Family Channel; Fox Sports Net Ohio; Headline News; Lifetime; MTV; Nashville Network; Nickelodeon; TBS Superstation; The Weather Channel; Trinity Bcstg. Network; USA Network; VH1.
Current originations: Automated time-weather; public access; government access; leased access; automated emergency alert.
Fee: $36.25 installation; $23.99 monthly.
Pay Service 1
Pay Units: N.A.
Programming (via satellite): American Movie Classics; Cinemax; Disney Channel; HBO; Showtime; The Movie Channel.
Fee: $10.45 monthly (each).
Local advertising: Yes. Available in satellite distributed & locally originated programming. Local sales manager: Mark Dolan. Regional interconnect: Northern Ohio Interconnect.
Equipment: Scientific-Atlanta headend; Jerrold amplifiers; Comm/Scope cable; Panasonic cameras; JVC VTRs; Video Precision character generator; Jerrold set top converters; Scientific-Atlanta satellite antenna.
Miles of plant: 354.0 (coaxial). Additional miles planned: 10.0 (coaxial).
Manager: Kathleen R. Mayo. Chief technician: Bruce Smylie. Program director: John Stealey. Sales & marketing director: Frank Naples.
City fee: 5% of gross.
Ownership: Cablevision Systems Corp. (MSO).

NORTH OLMSTED—Americast, 300 S. Riverside, Chicago, IL 60606. Phones: 312-526-8000; 800-848-2278. Fax: 312-526-8565. County: Cuyahoga. ICA: OH0418.
TV Market Ranking: 8. Franchise award date: April 1, 1996. Franchise expiration date: N.A. Began: N.A.
Channel capacity: N.A. Channels available but not in use: N.A.
Basic Service
Subscribers: N.A.
Programming (received off-air): WBNX-TV (W,F), WVPX (X) Akron; WOAC (I) Canton; WEWS-TV (A), WJW (F), WKYC-TV (N), WQHS-TV (H), WVIZ-TV (P) Cleveland; WUAB (U) Lorain-Cleveland; WOIO (C) Shaker Heights.
Programming (via satellite): WGN-TV (W) Chicago; QVC; TBS Superstation; TV Guide Channel; TV Guide Sneak Prevue.
Current originations: Public access; educational access; government access; leased access.
Fee: $39.95 installation; $9.95 monthly.
Expanded Basic Service
Subscribers: N.A.
Programming (via satellite): A & E; American Movie Classics; Animal Planet; BET; Bravo; C-SPAN; C-SPAN 2; CNBC; CNN; CNNfn; Cartoon Network; Comedy Central; Country Music TV; Court TV; Discovery Channel; Disney Channel; E! Entertainment TV; ESPN; ESPN 2; ESPN Classic Sports; ESPNews; Fox Family Channel; Fox Sports Net Ohio; Golf Channel; Goodlife TV Network; Headline News; History Channel; Home & Garden Television; Learning Channel; Lifetime; MTV; Nashville Network; Nickelodeon; Sci-Fi Channel; TV Food Network; The Health Network; The Inspirational Network; The Weather Channel; Travel Channel; Turner Classic Movies; Turner Network TV; USA Network; VH1.
Fee: $18.00 monthly.
Pay Service 1
Pay Units: N.A.
Programming (via satellite): Cinemax; Flix; HBO (multiplexed); Showtime (multiplexed); Starz!; The Movie Channel; The New Encore.
Fee: $5.95 monthly (Flix or Encore & Starz), $9.95 monthly (Cinemax, Showtime or TMC), $10.95 monthly (HBO).
Total homes in franchised area: 13,900.
Ownership: Ameritech New Media Inc. (MSO).

NORTHWOOD—FrontierVision, Box 170, 105 S. 3rd St., Waterville, OH 43566. Phone: 800-346-2288. County: Wood. Also serves Cordoba, Eastpoint, Friendly Village, Lake Twp. (Wood County), Perrysburg, Troy Twp. (Wood County), Walbridge. ICA: OH0141.
TV Market Ranking: 52. Franchise award date: N.A. Franchise expiration date: N.A. Began: February 21, 1983.
Channel capacity: 54. Channels available but not in use: None.
Basic Service
Subscribers: 2,516.
Programming (received off-air): WBGU-TV (P) Bowling Green; WDIV (N), WJBK (F), WKBD-TV (U) Detroit; WGTE-TV (P), WNWO-TV (N), WTOL-TV (C), WTVG (A), WUPW (F) Toledo.
Programming (via satellite): WGN-TV (W) Chicago; A & E; American Movie Classics; C-SPAN; CNBC; CNN; Discovery Channel; Disney Channel; ESPN; Fox Family Channel; Headline News; Home Shopping Network; Learning Channel; Lifetime; MTV; Nashville Network; Nickelodeon; TBS Superstation; The Weather Channel; Turner Network TV; USA Network; VH1.
Fee: $42.50 installation; $17.95 monthly.
Pay Service 1
Pay Units: 207.
Programming (via satellite): Cinemax.
Fee: $10.95 monthly.
Pay Service 2
Pay Units: 260.
Programming (via satellite): The New Encore.
Fee: N.A.
Pay Service 3
Pay Units: 255.
Programming (via satellite): HBO.
Fee: $9.95 monthly.
Pay Service 4
Pay Units: 210.
Programming (via satellite): Showtime.
Fee: $9.95 monthly.
Pay Service 5
Pay Units: 199.
Programming (via satellite): The Movie Channel.
Fee: $10.95 monthly.
Pay-Per-View
Addressable homes: 50.
Miles of plant: 78.1 (coaxial). Homes passed: 3,938.
Manager: Steve Trippe. Chief technician: Bill Ricker.
Ownership: FrontierVision Partners LP (MSO). See Cable System Ownership.

NORWALK—Time Warner Cable, 29 E. Main St., Norwalk, OH 44857. Phone: 419-668-3776. Counties: Erie, Huron & Richland. Also serves Bronson Twp., Hartland Twp., Milan, Milan Twp. (Erie County), Monroeville, Norwalk Twp. (Huron County), Oxford Twp. (Erie County), Peru Twp. (Huron County), Plymouth, Ridgefield Twp. (Huron County). ICA: OH0075.

TV Market Ranking: 8 (Bronson Twp., Hartland Twp., Milan, Milan Twp., Monroeville, Norwalk, Norwalk Twp., Oxford Twp., Peru Twp., Ridgefield Twp.); Below 100 (Plymouth). Franchise award date: July 1, 1969. Franchise expiration date: N.A. Began: September 1, 1970.
Channel capacity: 52. Channels available but not in use: 10.
Basic Service
Subscribers: 7,630.
Programming (received off-air): WVPX (X) Akron; WEWS-TV (A), WJW (F), WKYC-TV (N), WQHS-TV (H), WVIZ-TV (P) Cleveland; WUAB (U) Lorain-Cleveland; WGGN-TV (T) Sandusky; WOIO (C) Shaker Heights; WGTE-TV (P), WNWO-TV (N), WTOL-TV (C), WTVG (A) Toledo; 14 FMs.
Programming (via satellite): A & E; C-SPAN; CNN; Discovery Channel; ESPN; Electronic Program Guide; Fox Family Channel; Learning Channel; Lifetime; MTV; Nashville Network; Nickelodeon; TBS Superstation; The Inspirational Network; The Weather Channel; Turner Network TV; USA Network.
Current originations: Public access; educational access; government access; automated emergency alert.
Fee: $17.20 installation; $10.95 monthly; $15.00 additional installation.
Pay Service 1
Pay Units: 5,478.
Programming (via satellite): Cinemax; Disney Channel; HBO.
Fee: $15.00 installation; $10.95 monthly (each).
Local advertising: Yes. Available in satellite distributed, locally originated & character-generated programming. Rates: $10.00/30 Seconds. Local sales manager: Dave Harris.
Equipment: Jerrold & Scientific-Atlanta headend; Magnavox amplifiers; Comm/Scope cable; Sony VTRs; Video Data Systems character generator; Jerrold set top converters; Eagle traps; Fort Worth Tower satellite antenna; Microdyne satellite receivers.
Miles of plant: 115.0 (coaxial); 25.0 (fiber optic). Homes passed: 10,130.
Manager: Ike M. Mutlu. Chief technician: David Phillips. Marketing director: Susan St. Clair.
City fee: 3% of gross (Milan, Monroeville, Norwalk).
Ownership: Time Warner Cable (MSO). Purchased from MediaOne Group, August 2, 1999.

NORWICH—Time Warner Cable, Box 823, 131 Catherine St., Hillsboro, OH 45133. Phone: 937-393-4217. Fax: 937-393-8022. County: Muskingum. Also serves Adamsville, New Concord, Perry Twp. (Muskingum County), Sonora, Union Twp. (Muskingum County), Washington Twp. (Muskingum County), Zanesville. ICA: OH0225.
TV Market Ranking: Below 100. Franchise award date: N.A. Franchise expiration date: N.A. Began: N.A.
Channel capacity: 41 (not 2-way capable). Channels available but not in use: 10.
Basic Service
Subscribers: 751; Commercial subscribers: 11.
Programming (received off-air): WBNS-TV (C), WCMH-TV (N), WOSU-TV (P), WSYX (A), WTTE (F,U) Columbus; WSFJ (I) Newark; WTOV-TV (N) Steubenville-Wheeling; WTRF-TV (C) Wheeling-Steubenville; WHIZ-TV (N) Zanesville.
Programming (via satellite): WGN-TV (W) Chicago; A & E; C-SPAN; CNN; Discovery Channel; ESPN; ESPN 2; Fox Family Channel; Headline News; Home Shopping Network; Lifetime; MTV; Nashville Network; Nickelodeon; Sci-Fi Channel; TBS Superstation; The Weather Channel; Turner Classic Movies; Turner Network TV; USA Network; VH1.
Fee: $40.27 installation; $26.15 monthly; $0.44 converter.
Pay Service 1
Pay Units: 43.
Programming (via satellite): Cinemax.
Fee: $18.00 installation; $9.95 monthly.
Pay Service 2
Pay Units: 55.
Programming (via satellite): Showtime.
Fee: $18.00 installation; $9.95 monthly.
Pay Service 3
Pay Units: 80.
Programming (via satellite): HBO.
Fee: $18.00 installation; $9.95 monthly.
Pay Service 4
Pay Units: 47.
Programming (via satellite): Showtime.
Fee: $18.00 installation; $9.95 monthly.
Local advertising: Yes. Available in character-generated programming.
Miles of plant: 41.7 (coaxial). Homes passed: 970.
Manager: Mike Rector. Chief technician: Dale Zornes. Marketing director: Gary Pitzer.
Ownership: Time Warner Cable (MSO).

NORWICH TWP.—Americast, 300 S. Riverside, Chicago, IL 60606. Phones: 312-526-8000; 800-848-2278. Fax: 312-526-8565. County: Franklin. ICA: OH0419.
TV Market Ranking: 27. Franchise award date: August 1, 1997. Franchise expiration date: N.A. Began: N.A.
Channel capacity: N.A. Channels available but not in use: N.A.
Basic Service
Subscribers: N.A.
Programming (received off-air): WWHO (U) Chillicothe; WBNS-TV (C), WCMH-TV (N), WOSU-TV (P), WSYX (A), WTTE (F,U) Columbus; WSFJ (I) Newark.
Programming (via satellite): WGN-TV (W) Chicago; QVC; TBS Superstation; TV Guide Channel.
Current originations: Public access; educational access; government access; leased access.
Fee: $39.95 installation; $9.95 monthly.
Expanded Basic Service
Subscribers: N.A.
Programming (via satellite): A & E; American Movie Classics; BET; BET on Jazz; Bravo; C-SPAN; C-SPAN 2; CNBC; CNN; CNNfn; Cartoon Network; Comedy Central; Country Music TV; Court TV; Discovery Channel; Disney Channel; E! Entertainment TV; ESPN; ESPN 2; ESPN Classic Sports; Fox Family Channel; Fox Sports Net Ohio; Golf Channel; Headline News; History Channel; Home & Garden Television; Learning Channel; Lifetime; MTV; Nashville Network; Nickelodeon; Ohio News Network; Sci-Fi Channel; TV Food Network; The Health Network; The Inspirational Network; The Weather Channel; Travel Channel; Turner Classic Movies; Turner Network TV; USA Network; VH1.
Fee: $17.00 monthly.
Pay Service 1
Pay Units: N.A.
Programming (via satellite): Cinemax; Flix; HBO (multiplexed); Showtime (multiplexed); Starz!; Sundance Channel; The Movie Channel; The New Encore.
Fee: $5.95 monthly (Flix or Sundance), $7.95 monthly (Encore & Starz), $9.95 monthly (Cinemax, Showtime or TMC), $11.95 monthly (HBO).
Total homes in franchised area: 1,900.
Ownership: Ameritech New Media Inc. (MSO).

OAK HARBOR—FrontierVision, Box 627, Chillicothe, OH 45601. Phones: 740-775-4300; 800-346-2288. Fax: 740-775-2915. Counties: Lucas, Ottawa & Sandusky. Also serves Benton Twp. (Ottawa County), Carroll Twp., Erie Twp. (Ottawa County), Graytown, Jerusalem Twp. (Lucas County), Lacarne, Portage Twp. (Sandusky County), Rice Twp., Riley Twp. (Sandusky County), Rocky Ridge Twp., Salem Twp. (Ottawa County), Sandusky Twp. (Sandusky County). ICA: OH0351.
TV Market Ranking: 52. Franchise award date: N.A. Franchise expiration date: N.A. Began: November 1, 1989.
Channel capacity: 54. Channels available but not in use: 6.
Basic Service
Subscribers: 3,142.
Programming (received off-air): WBGU-TV (P) Bowling Green; WKBD-TV (U) Detroit; WUAB (U) Lorain-Cleveland; WOIO (C) Shaker Heights; WGTE-TV (P), WNWO-TV (N), WTOL-TV (C), WTVG (A), WUPW (F) Toledo; CBET Windsor.
Programming (via satellite): Fox Sports Net Ohio; TBS Superstation.
Current originations: Automated time-weather.
Fee: $43.75 installation; $13.90 monthly; $1.50 converter.
Expanded Basic Service
Subscribers: 3,073.
Programming (via satellite): WGN-TV (W) Chicago; A & E; C-SPAN; CNN; Comedy Central; Country Music TV; Discovery Channel; Disney Channel; E! Entertainment TV; ESPN; Fox Family Channel; Headline News; Learning Channel; MTV; Nashville Network; Nickelodeon; QVC; Sci-Fi Channel; The Weather Channel; Turner Classic Movies; Turner Network TV; USA Network.
Fee: $9.25 monthly.
Pay Service 1
Pay Units: 258.
Programming (via satellite): Cinemax.
Fee: $15.00 installation; $11.00 monthly.
Pay Service 2
Pay Units: 306.
Programming (via satellite): HBO.
Fee: $15.00 installation; $11.00 monthly.
Pay Service 3
Pay Units: 385.
Programming (via satellite): Showtime.
Fee: $11.00 monthly.
Pay Service 4
Pay Units: 352.
Programming (via satellite): The Movie Channel.
Fee: N.A.
Pay-Per-View
WWF Wrestlemania.
Fee: $24.95.
Local advertising: No.
Equipment: Sony, General & Drake headend; C-COR amplifiers; Times Fiber cable; Jerrold & NSC set top converters.
Miles of plant: 193.0 (coaxial). Additional miles planned: 2.0 (coaxial). Homes passed: 5,395. Total homes in franchised area: 5,395.
Manager: Richard Coplan. Chief technician: Sam Morabith. Program director: Chad Hume. Marketing director: Barbara Brewer.
City fee: 3% gross.
Ownership: FrontierVision Partners LP (MSO). See Cable System Ownership.

OAK HILL—FrontierVision, Box 648, 102 Twin Oak Dr., Jackson, OH 45640. Phone: 614-345-4329. Fax: 614-286-1489. County: Jackson. ICA: OH0219.
TV Market Ranking: 36. Franchise award date: May 21, 1985. Franchise expiration date: May 21, 2000. Began: May 21, 1980.
Channel capacity: 33. Channels available but not in use: None.
Basic Service
Subscribers: 725.
Programming (received off-air): WOUB-TV (P) Athens; WCHS-TV (A), WOWK-TV (C), WSAZ-TV (N), WVAH-TV (F,U) Charleston-Huntington; WBNS-TV (C), WCMH-TV (N), WSYX (A) Columbus; WPBO-TV (P) Portsmouth.
Programming (via satellite): WGN-TV (W) Chicago; A & E; CNN; Comedy Central; Country Music TV; Discovery Channel; ESPN; Fox Family Channel; Lifetime; MTV; Nashville Network; Nickelodeon; QVC; TBS Superstation; The Weather Channel; Turner Network TV; USA Network.
Fee: $20.99 installation; $23.70 monthly; $0.63 converter.
Pay Service 1
Pay Units: 104.
Programming (via satellite): HBO.
Fee: $15.00 installation; $11.95 monthly.
Pay Service 2
Pay Units: 152.
Programming (via satellite): Showtime.
Fee: $15.00 installation; $10.95 monthly.
Pay Service 3
Pay Units: 112.
Programming (via satellite): The Movie Channel.
Fee: N.A.
Equipment: Magnavox amplifiers; Times Fiber & Belden cable; Hamlin & NSC set top converters; Eagle & Pico traps; Harris satellite antenna; Standard Communications satellite receivers.
Miles of plant: 16.5 (coaxial). Homes passed: 1,063.
Manager: Steve Trippe. Chief technician: Bill Ricker.
Ownership: FrontierVision Partners LP (MSO). See Cable System Ownership.

OAKLAND—FrontierVision, Box 627, Chillicothe, OH 45601. Phones: 740-775-4300; 800-346-2288. Fax: 740-775-2915. Counties: Fairfield & Pickaway. Also serves Amanda, Fairfield County (portions), Washington Twp. (Pickaway County). ICA: OH0352.
TV Market Ranking: 27. Franchise award date: N.A. Franchise expiration date: N.A. Began: N.A.
Channel capacity: 42. Channels available but not in use: 8.
Basic Service
Subscribers: 1,990.

Programming (received off-air): WOUB-TV (P) Athens; WBNS-TV (C), WCMH-TV (N), WOSU-TV (P), WSYX (A), WTTE (F,U) Columbus; WSFJ (I) Newark.
Programming (via satellite): WGN-TV (W) Chicago; CNN; Country Music TV; Discovery Channel; Disney Channel; ESPN; Fox Family Channel; MTV; Nashville Network; Nickelodeon; QVC; TBS Superstation; The Weather Channel; USA Network.
Fee: $40.00 installation; $16.45 monthly.

Pay Service 1
Pay Units: 204.
Programming (via satellite): The New Encore.
Fee: N.A.

Pay Service 2
Pay Units: 297.
Programming (via satellite): HBO.
Fee: $9.95 monthly.

Pay Service 3
Pay Units: 440.
Programming (via satellite): Showtime.
Fee: $9.95 monthly.

Pay Service 4
Pay Units: 201.
Programming (via satellite): Starz!
Fee: N.A.

Pay Service 5
Pay Units: 312.
Programming (via satellite): The Movie Channel.
Fee: N.A.

Miles of plant: 175.1 (coaxial). Homes passed: 3,154.
Manager: Richard Coplan. Chief technician: Sam Morabith. Program director: Chad Hume. Marketing director: Barbara Brewer.
Ownership: FrontierVision Partners LP (MSO). See Cable System Ownership.

OBERLIN—Cable Co-op Inc., 23 E. College St., Oberlin, OH 44074. Phone: 440-775-4001. Fax: 440-775-1635. County: Lorain. ICA: OH0147.
TV Market Ranking: 8. Franchise award date: June 27, 1986. Franchise expiration date: June 27, 2001. Began: January 25, 1988.
Channel capacity: 64 (2-way capable; operating 2-way partially). Channels available but not in use: 10.

Basic Service
Subscribers: 1,743; Commercial subscribers: 4.
Programming (received off-air): WBNX-TV (W,F), WEAO (P), WVPX (X) Akron; WEWS-TV (A), WJW (F), WKYC-TV (N), WQHS-TV (H), WVIZ-TV (P) Cleveland; WUAB (U) Lorain-Cleveland; WGGN-TV (T) Sandusky; WOIO (C) Shaker Heights; 20 FMs.
Programming (via satellite): WGN-TV (W) Chicago; A & E; American Movie Classics; BET; Bravo; C-SPAN; C-SPAN 2; CNBC; CNN; Comedy Central; Discovery Channel; Disney Channel; ESPN; ESPN 2; Fox Family Channel; Fox Sports Net Ohio; Headline News; History Channel; Home & Garden Television; Learning Channel; Lifetime; MTV; Nashville Network; Nickelodeon; Ovation; QVC; Sci-Fi Channel; TBS Superstation; TV Guide Channel; The Weather Channel; Travel Channel; Turner Classic Movies; Turner Network TV; USA Network; VH1.
Current originations: Public access; educational access; government access; religious access; leased access; automated emergency alert; local news; local sports.
Fee: $20.00 installation; $22.95 monthly; $10.00 additional installation.
Commercial fee: $16.00 monthly.

Pay Service 1
Pay Units: 181.
Programming (via satellite): Cinemax.
Fee: $9.95 monthly.

Pay Service 2
Pay Units: 366.
Programming (via satellite): HBO.
Fee: $10.95 monthly.

Pay Service 3
Pay Units: 113.
Programming (via satellite): Showtime.
Fee: $10.95 monthly.

Pay Service 4
Pay Units: 144.
Programming (via satellite): Independent Film Channel.
Fee: $2.00 monthly.

Local advertising: Yes. Available in locally originated, character-generated & taped programming. Rates: $5.00/30 Seconds. Local sales manager: Ralph L. Potts.
Equipment: Cadco & Standard Communications headend; Jerrold amplifiers; Comm/Scope cable; Sony cameras; Panasonic VTRs; Scientific-Atlanta set top converters; Eagle traps; Prodelin satellite antenna; Drake satellite receivers.
Miles of plant: 45.0 (coaxial); 42.0 (fiber optic). Additional miles planned: 2.0 (coaxial). Homes passed: 2,900. Total homes in franchised area: 2,900.
Manager: Ralph L. Potts. Chief technician: Engel Smit III. Customer service manager: Fran Downs.
Franchise fee: 5% of gross.
Ownership: Cable Cooperative Inc.

OLMSTED TWP.—Olmsted Cable Co. Corp., 7100 Columbia Rd., Olmsted Twp., OH 44138. Phone: 440-235-5300. County: Cuyahoga. ICA: OH0223.
TV Market Ranking: 8. Franchise award date: January 1, 1982. Franchise expiration date: N.A. Began: December 1, 1982.
Channel capacity: 52. Channels available but not in use: 22.

Basic Service
Subscribers: 800.
Programming (received off-air): WVPX (X) Akron; WEWS-TV (A), WJW (F), WKYC-TV (N), WQHS-TV (H), WVIZ-TV (P) Cleveland; WUAB (U) Lorain-Cleveland.
Programming (via satellite): WGN-TV (W) Chicago; TBS Superstation.
Fee: $20.25 monthly.

Pay Service 1
Pay Units: N.A.
Programming (via satellite): HBO; Showtime; The Movie Channel.
Fee: $10.95 monthly (each).

Miles of plant: 5.0 (coaxial). Homes passed: 1,000.
Manager: Bob Reed. Chief technician: Gregory Hausman.
Ownership: Olmsted Cable Co. Corp.

ORRVILLE—Armstrong Cable Services, 1141 Lafayette Rd., Medina, OH 44256-2421. Phone: 330-723-3536. Fax: 330-725-3366. County: Wayne. Also serves Baughman Twp., Burton City (portions), Dalton, Green Twp. (Wayne County), Marshallville, Sugar Creek Twp. (Wayne County). ICA: OH0109.
TV Market Ranking: 8. Franchise award date: September 7, 1965. Franchise expiration date: March 1, 2006. Began: March 1, 1967.
Channel capacity: 53 (not 2-way capable). Channels available but not in use: None.

Basic Service
Subscribers: 4,252.
Programming (received off-air): WBNX-TV (W,F), WEAO (P), WVPX (X) Akron; WDLI (T), WOAC (I) Canton; WEWS-TV (A), WJW (F), WKYC-TV (N), WQHS-TV (H), WVIZ-TV (P) Cleveland; WBNS-TV (C) Columbus; WUAB (U) Lorain-Cleveland; WOIO (C) Shaker Heights.
Programming (via satellite): WGN-TV (W) Chicago; A & E; American Movie Classics; C-SPAN; CNBC; CNN; CNN/SI; Cartoon Network; Comedy Central; Country Music TV; Discovery Channel; E! Entertainment TV; ESPN; ESPN 2; Fox Family Channel; Headline News; History Channel; Home & Garden Television; Home Shopping Network; Learning Channel; Lifetime; Nickelodeon; Outdoor Channel; TBS Superstation; TV Food Network; The Health Network; The Inspirational Network; The Weather Channel; Travel Channel; Turner Classic Movies; Turner Network TV; USA Network; VH1.
Current originations: Automated emergency alert.
Fee: $24.62 installation; $25.84 monthly; $2.95 converter.

Pay Service 1
Pay Units: 523.
Programming (via satellite): Cinemax.
Fee: $7.50 installation; $9.95 monthly.

Pay Service 2
Pay Units: 313.
Programming (via satellite): Disney Channel.
Fee: $7.50 installation; $7.95 monthly.

Pay Service 3
Pay Units: 726.
Programming (via satellite): HBO.
Fee: $7.50 installation; $11.95 monthly.

Pay Service 4
Pay Units: 187.
Programming (via satellite): Showtime.
Fee: $9.95 monthly.

Pay-Per-View
Addressable homes: 220.
Viewer's Choice.
Fee: $3.95.

Local advertising: Yes. Available in taped & automated programming. Regional interconnect: Metrobase Cable Advertising.
Equipment: Scientific-Atlanta headend; Scientific-Atlanta amplifiers; General cable; Pioneer & Scientific-Atlanta set top converters; AFC satellite antenna.
Miles of plant: 118.0 (coaxial). Homes passed: 5,806.
Manager: John Cogley. Chief technician: Mike Bricker. Marketing director: Jud D. Stewart.
City fee: 3% of gross.
Ownership: Armstrong Group of Companies (MSO).

ORWELL—Orwell Cable TV, Box 337, 70 S. Maple St., Orwell, OH 44076-0337. Phone: 440-437-6111. Fax: 440-437-1000. Counties: Ashtabula & Trumbull. Also serves Colebrook, North Bloomfield Twp., Rome Twp., Windsor. ICA: OH0195.
TV Market Ranking: 79. Franchise award date: N.A. Franchise expiration date: N.A. Began: October 1, 1982.
Channel capacity: 36 (2-way capable). Channels available but not in use: 9.

Basic Service
Subscribers: 1,155.
Programming (received off-air): WBNX-TV (W,F) Akron; WNEO (P) Alliance; WEWS-TV (A), WJW (F), WKYC-TV (N), WVIZ-TV (P) Cleveland; WUAB (U) Lorain-Cleveland; WOIO (C) Shaker Heights; WYTV (A,F) Youngstown; allband FM.
Programming (via satellite): A & E; CNN; CNN/SI; CNNfn; Cartoon Network; Discovery Channel; ESPN; Fox Family Channel; Fox Sports Net Ohio; Headline News; History Channel; Home & Garden Television; Learning Channel; Lifetime; Nashville Network; Odyssey; QVC; Sci-Fi Channel; Shop at Home; TBS Superstation; The Weather Channel; Turner Classic Movies; Turner Network TV; USA Network.
Fee: $25.00 installation; $20.95 monthly; $25.00 additional installation.

Pay Service 1
Pay Units: 347.
Programming (via satellite): HBO.
Fee: $25.00 installation; $9.00 monthly.

Pay Service 2
Pay Units: 493.
Programming (via satellite): Showtime.
Fee: $25.00 installation; $9.00 monthly.

Local advertising: No.
Equipment: Microdyne, Catel & Cadco headend; C-COR amplifiers; Times Fiber & Comm/Scope cable; Pico & Eagle traps; Microdyne satellite receivers.
Miles of plant: 62.0 (coaxial); 14.0 (fiber optic). Additional miles planned: 5.0 (coaxial). Homes passed: 1,500. Total homes in franchised area: 2,500.
Manager: Gwenn Maguire. Chief technician: Carl Barry. Marketing director: James L. Holl.
City fee: 3% of basic.
Ownership: Orwell Telephone Co. (MSO).

OTTAWA—Warner Cable Communications Inc., 228 N. Elm St., Ottawa, OH 45875. Phone: 419-523-4600. County: Putnam. Also serves Blanchard Twp. (Putnam County), Columbus Grove, Glandorf (village), Ottawa Twp. (Putnam County), Pleasant Twp. (Putnam County). ICA: OH0137.
TV Market Ranking: Below 100. Franchise award date: September 1, 1970. Franchise expiration date: N.A. Began: August 15, 1971.
Channel capacity: 42. Channels available but not in use: None.

Basic Service
Subscribers: 2,850.
Programming (received off-air): WBGU-TV (P) Bowling Green; WHIO-TV (C) Dayton; WANE-TV (C), WFFT-TV (F), WKJG-TV (N), WPTA (A) Fort Wayne; WLIO (N), WTLW (I) Lima; WNWO-TV (N), WTOL-TV (C), WTVG (A), WUPW (F) Toledo; 14 FMs.
Programming (via satellite): A & E; C-SPAN; C-SPAN 2; CNBC; CNN; Discovery Channel; ESPN; EWTN; Electronic Program Guide; Fox Family Channel; Headline News; Lifetime; MTV; Nashville Network; Nickelodeon; QVC; TBS Superstation; The Weather Channel; Turner Network TV; USA Network; VH1.
Fee: $19.95 installation; $12.35 monthly; $14.95 additional installation.

Pay Service 1
Pay Units: 132.
Programming (via satellite): Cinemax.
Fee: $10.00 installation; $11.49 monthly.

Pay Service 2
Pay Units: 270.
Programming (via satellite): Disney Channel.
Fee: $10.00 installation; $7.95 monthly.

Pay Service 3
Pay Units: 202.
Programming (via satellite): HBO.
Fee: $10.00 installation; $12.00 monthly.

Pay Service 4
Pay Units: 74.
Programming (via satellite): The Movie Channel.
Fee: $10.00 installation; $11.49 monthly.

Pay Service 5
Pay Units: 73.
Programming (via satellite): Showtime.
Fee: $10.00 installation; $11.49 monthly.

Pay-Per-View
Addressable homes: 1,531.
Action Pay-Per-View.
Fee: Varies.

Local advertising: Planned.
Equipment: Jerrold headend; Jerrold amplifiers; Times Fiber & Scientific-Atlanta cable;

Zenith set top converters; Zenith addressable set top converters.
Miles of plant: 60.0 (coaxial). Homes passed: 3,471. Total homes in franchised area: 3,471.
Manager: Jeff Parker. Chief technician: Bill Lambert. Marketing director: Danny Schiffer.
City fee: 3% of gross.
Ownership: Time Warner Cable (MSO).

OTTOVILLE—OTEC Communications Co., Box 427, Ottoville, OH 45876. Phone: 419-453-3324. Fax: 419-453-2468. Counties: Paulding, Putnam & Van Wert. Also serves Cloverdale, Groverhill, Hoaglin Twp. (Van Wert County), Jackson Twp. (Putnam County), Jackson Twp. (Van Wert County), Jennings Twp. (Putnam County), Latty Twp., Monterey Twp. (Putnam County), Perry Twp. (Putnam County), Washington Twp. (Paulding County). ICA: OH0211.
TV Market Ranking: 82 (Latty Twp.); Below 100 (Cloverdale, Groverhill, Hoaglin Twp., Jackson Twp., Jennings Twp., Monterey Twp., Ottoville, Perry Twp., Washington Twp.). Franchise award date: April 7, 1980. Franchise expiration date: April 6, 2000. Began: October 1, 1983.
Channel capacity: 25 (2-way capable; operating 2-way partially). Channels available but not in use: None.

Basic Service
Subscribers: 850.
Programming (received off-air): WBGU-TV (P) Bowling Green; WANE-TV (C), WFFT-TV (F), WPTA (A) Fort Wayne; WLIO (N) Lima; WNWO-TV (N), WTOL-TV (C), WTVG (A), WUPW (F) Toledo; allband FM.
Programming (via satellite): WGN-TV (W) Chicago; CNN; Discovery Channel; ESPN; EWTN; Fox Sports Net Ohio; Nashville Network; Nickelodeon; TBS Superstation; Turner Network TV; USA Network.
Current originations: Automated time-weather; public access; educational access; government access; religious access; local sports.
Fee: $24.50 installation; $14.95 monthly; $5.00 additional installation.

Pay Service 1
Pay Units: 80.
Programming (via satellite): Disney Channel.
Fee: $10.00 installation; $7.95 monthly.

Pay Service 2
Pay Units: 40.
Programming (via satellite): HBO.
Fee: $10.00 installation; $8.45 monthly.

Pay Service 3
Pay Units: 137.
Programming (via satellite): The Movie Channel.
Fee: $10.00 installation; $7.00 monthly.

Pay Service 4
Pay Units: 132.
Programming (via satellite): Showtime.
Fee: $7.00 monthly.

Local advertising: Yes (locally produced). Available in character-generated programming. Rates: $4.00/Week. Local sales manager: Don Hoersten.
Equipment: Scientific-Atlanta & Cadco headend; Texscan amplifiers; Comm/Scope & Times Fiber cable; Magnavox & RCA cameras; Magnavox VTRs; Texscan character generator; Pioneer set top converters; Pico traps; Anixter-Mark, Anixter-Pruzan & Scientific-Atlanta satellite antenna; Scientific-Atlanta satellite receivers.
Miles of plant: 93.0 (coaxial). Additional miles planned: 5.0 (coaxial). Homes passed: 1,175. Total homes in franchised area: 1,400.
Manager: Don Hoersten. Chief technician: Bill Honigford.
Ownership: OTEC Communications Co.

OWENSVILLE—Time Warner Cable, Box 823, 131 Catherine St., Hillsboro, OH 45133. Phone: 937-393-4217. Fax: 937-393-8022. Counties: Brown, Clermont & Clinton. Also serves Fayetteville, Green Twp. (Brown County), Jackson Twp. (Clermont County), Jefferson Twp. (Brown County), Martinsville, Midland, Newtonsville, Perry Twp. (Brown County), St. Martin, Stonelick Twp., Wayne Twp. (Clermont County), Westboro. ICA: OH0368.
TV Market Ranking: 17 (Fayetteville, Green Twp., Jackson Twp., Jefferson Twp., Martinsville, Midland, Newtonsville, Owensville, Perry Twp., St. Martin, Stonelick Twp., Wayne Twp., Westboro); 41 (Fayetteville, Jefferson Twp., Martinsville, Midland, Perry Twp., St. Martin, Stonelick Twp., Wayne Twp., Westboro). Franchise award date: July 6, 1983. Franchise expiration date: July 6, 2013. Began: N.A.
Channel capacity: 45 (not 2-way capable). Channels available but not in use: None.

Basic Service
Subscribers: 2,789.
Programming (received off-air): WCET (P), WCPO-TV (A), WKRC-TV (C), WLWT (N), WSTR-TV (W) Cincinnati; WXIX-TV (F) Cincinnati-Newport; WDTN (A), WHIO-TV (C), WKEF (N), WRGT-TV (F,U) Dayton.
Programming (via satellite): WGN-TV (W) Chicago; American Movie Classics; Animal Planet; C-SPAN; CNBC; CNN; Comedy Central; Country Music TV; Discovery Channel; ESPN; ESPN 2; Fox Family Channel; Headline News; History Channel; Lifetime; MTV; Nashville Network; Nickelodeon; QVC; TBS Superstation; TV Guide Channel; The Inspirational Network; The Weather Channel; Turner Network TV; USA Network; VH1.
Current originations: Public access; educational access; government access; religious access; automated emergency alert.
Fee: $39.90 installation; $27.73 monthly.

Pay Service 1
Pay Units: 448.
Programming (via satellite): Cinemax.
Fee: $10.95 monthly.

Pay Service 2
Pay Units: 340.
Programming (via satellite): Disney Channel.
Fee: $7.95 monthly.

Pay Service 3
Pay Units: 614.
Programming (via satellite): HBO.
Fee: $10.95 monthly.

Pay Service 4
Pay Units: 245.
Programming (via satellite): The Movie Channel.
Fee: $10.95 monthly.

Pay Service 5
Pay Units: 385.
Programming (via satellite): Showtime.
Fee: $10.95 monthly.

Pay-Per-View
Addressable homes: 4,517.
Viewer's Choice.
Fee: $3.95.

Equipment: Triple Crown headend; Jerrold & Scientific-Atlanta amplifiers; Comm/Scope & Times Fiber cable; Pico traps.
Miles of plant: 114.0 (coaxial); 13.0 (fiber optic).
Manager: Michael Rector. Chief technician: Dale Zornes. Marketing director: Gary Pitzer.
Ownership: Time Warner Cable (MSO).

OXFORD—Warner Cable Communications Inc., 114 S. Locust St., Oxford, OH 45056. Phone: 513-523-6333. Counties: Butler North, OH; Union, IN. Also serves College Corner, IN; College Corner, OH. ICA: OH0101.
TV Market Ranking: 17,41. Franchise award date: N.A. Franchise expiration date: N.A. Began: September 15, 1982.
Channel capacity: 36 (2-way capable; operating 2-way). Channels available but not in use: 2.

Basic Service
Subscribers: 3,329.
Programming (received off-air): WCET (P), WCPO-TV (A), WKRC-TV (C), WLWT (N) Cincinnati; WXIX-TV (F) Cincinnati-Newport; WDTN (A), WHIO-TV (C), WKEF (N), WRGT-TV (F,U) Dayton; WPTO (P) Oxford; WKOI (T) Richmond; 18 FMs.
Programming (via satellite): WGN-TV (W) Chicago; A & E; C-SPAN; CNBC; CNN; Discovery Channel; ESPN; Lifetime; MTV; Nashville Network; Nickelodeon; QVC; TBS Superstation; The Weather Channel; Turner Network TV; USA Network.
Current originations: Automated time-weather; educational access.
Fee: $19.95 installation; $20.25 monthly.

Pay Service 1
Pay Units: 103.
Programming (via satellite): Cinemax.
Fee: $14.95 installation; $10.45 monthly.

Pay Service 2
Pay Units: 182.
Programming (via satellite): Disney Channel.
Fee: $14.95 installation; $6.95 monthly.

Pay Service 3
Pay Units: 863.
Programming (via satellite): HBO.
Fee: $14.95 installation; $10.95 monthly.

Pay Service 4
Pay Units: 463.
Programming (via satellite): Showtime.
Fee: $14.95 installation; $10.45 monthly.

Local advertising: Yes (insert only). Available in satellite distributed programming. Rates: $8.00/30 Seconds. Local sales manager: Norm Pytel.
Equipment: Catel, Jerrold & Microdyne headend; GTE Sylvania, Jerrold & Scientific-Atlanta amplifiers; CCS Hatfield & Times Fiber cable; Sony cameras; Sony VTRs; Metrodata character generator; Pioneer set top converters; Eagle & Vitek traps; M/A-Com satellite antenna; Microdyne satellite receivers.
Miles of plant: 111.0 (coaxial). Homes passed: 6,731.
Manager: Mike Gray. Chief technician: Mike Ooten. Marketing director: Mike Weaver.
City fee: 3% of gross.
Ownership: Time Warner Cable (MSO).

PAINT TWP. (Highland County)—FrontierVision, Suite P-200, 1777 S. Harrison St., Denver, CO 80210. Phone: 303-757-1588. Fax: 303-757-6105. County: Highland. ICA: OH0196.
TV Market Ranking: 27. Franchise award date: N.A. Franchise expiration date: N.A. Began: June 1, 1983.
Channel capacity: 35. Channels available but not in use: 18.

Basic Service
Subscribers: N.A.
Programming (received off-air): WCET (P), WCPO-TV (A), WKRC-TV (C), WLWT (N) Cincinnati; WXIX-TV (F) Cincinnati-Newport; WBNS-TV (C), WCMH-TV (N), WSYX (A) Columbus; WHIO-TV (C), WKEF (N) Dayton.
Programming (via satellite): WGN-TV (W) Chicago; CNN; ESPN; Fox Family Channel; MTV; Nashville Network; Nickelodeon; TBS Superstation; USA Network.
Fee: N.A.

Pay Service 1
Pay Units: N.A.
Programming (via satellite): HBO; Showtime.
Fee: N.A.

Miles of plant: 39.0 (coaxial). Homes passed: 1,500.
Ownership: FrontierVision Partners LP (MSO). Purchased from Paint Valley Cable Co. Inc., October 30, 1998. See Cable System Ownership.

PARMA—Cox Communications, 12221 Plaza Dr., Parma, OH 44130. Phones: 216-676-8300; 216-676-8100. Fax: 216-676-8689. Web site: http://www.cox.com. County: Cuyahoga. Also serves Broadview Heights, Brooklyn Heights, Fairview Park, Lakewood (Cuyahoga County), Olmsted Falls, Olmsted Twp., Parma Heights, Rocky River, Seven Hills. ICA: OH0009.
TV Market Ranking: 8. Franchise award date: March 12, 1973. Franchise expiration date: March 11, 2003. Began: May 1, 1980.
Channel capacity: N.A. Channels available but not in use: N.A.

Basic Service
Subscribers: 60,000.
Programming (received off-air): WBNX-TV (W,F), WEAO (P), WVPX (X) Akron; WOAC (I) Canton; WEWS-TV (A), WJW (F), WKYC-TV (N), WQHS-TV (H), WVIZ-TV (P) Cleveland; WUAB (U) Lorain-Cleveland; WOIO (C) Shaker Heights; 3 FMs.
Programming (via satellite): WGN-TV (W) Chicago; A & E; Access Entertainment Network; American Movie Classics; Animal Planet; Bravo; C-SPAN; C-SPAN 2; CNBC; CNN; Cartoon Network; Comedy Central; Consumer Resource Network; Country Music TV; Court TV; Discovery Channel; Disney Channel; E! Entertainment TV; ESPN; ESPN 2; EWTN; FX; Fox Family Channel; Fox Sports Net Ohio; Game Show Network; Golf Channel; Headline News; History Channel; Home & Garden Television; Learning Channel; Lifetime; MSNBC; MTV; Nashville Network; Nick at Nite's TV Land; Nickelodeon; QVC; SCOLA; Sci-Fi Channel; Speedvision; TBS Superstation; TV Food Network; The Health Network; The Weather Channel; Trinity Bcstg. Network; Turner Classic Movies; Turner Network TV; USA Network; VH1.
Current originations: Automated time-weather; public access; educational access; government access; religious access; leased access; automated emergency alert; local news.
Fee: $23.85 installation (aerial), $50.00 (underground); $27.60 monthly; $0.50 converter; $10.50 additional installation.

Pay Service 1
Pay Units: 40,000.
Programming (via satellite): Cinemax (multiplexed); HBO (multiplexed); Showtime (multiplexed); The Movie Channel.
Fee: $5.00 installation; $9.50 monthly (each).

Pay Service 2
Pay Units: N.A.
Programming (via satellite): Starz! (multiplexed); The New Encore.
Fee: N.A.

Pay-Per-View
Addressable homes: 13,500.
Playboy TV; Spice; movies.

Local advertising: Yes (locally produced & insert). Available in satellite distributed, locally originated, taped & automated programming. Regional interconnect: Rainbow Advertising.
Equipment: Jerrold & Scientific-Atlanta headend; Jerrold & C-COR amplifiers; Comm/Scope & Times Fiber cable; Hitachi cameras; Panasonic & Sony VTRs; Quanta character generator; Oak set top converters; Pioneer addressable set top converters; Eagle traps; Andrew & Scientific-

Atlanta satellite antenna; Scientific-Atlanta satellite receivers; ChannelMatic & Texscan commercial insert.
Miles of plant: 770.0 (coaxial); 50.0 (fiber optic). Additional miles planned: 7.5 (coaxial); 150.0 (fiber optic). Homes passed: 98,321. Total homes in franchised area: 102,781.
Manager: Ron Hammaker. Chief technician: Tom Yenda. Marketing director: Laura Morabito.
City fee: 3% of gross.
Ownership: Cox Communications Inc. (MSO).

PATASKALA—Time Warner Cable, 1315 Granville Pike, Lancaster, OH 43130-0747. Phone: 740-653-9685. Fax: 740-653-1164. County: Licking. Also serves Lima Twp. (Licking County). ICA: OH0165.
TV Market Ranking: 27. Franchise award date: N.A. Franchise expiration date: N.A. Began: October 1, 1981.
Channel capacity: 35 (not 2-way capable). Channels available but not in use: 6.
Basic Service
Subscribers: N.A.
Programming (received off-air): WBNS-TV (C), WCMH-TV (N), WOSU-TV (P), WSYX (A), WTTE (F,U) Columbus; WSFJ (I) Newark.
Programming (via satellite): WGN-TV (W) Chicago; A & E; C-SPAN; CNBC; CNN; Discovery Channel; ESPN; Lifetime; MTV; Nashville Network; Nickelodeon; TBS Superstation; The Weather Channel; Turner Network TV; USA Network.
Current originations: Automated time-weather; public access.
Fee: $35.00 installation; $18.30 monthly; $25.00 additional installation.
Pay Service 1
Pay Units: Included with Lancaster, OH.
Programming (via satellite): Disney Channel; HBO; Showtime; The Movie Channel.
Fee: $15.00 installation; $9.95 monthly (Disney, Showtime or TMC), $10.95 monthly (HBO).
Local advertising: Yes. Available in character-generated programming.
Equipment: Scientific-Atlanta headend; Scientific-Atlanta amplifiers; Comm/Scope cable; Texscan character generator; Panasonic set top converters; Intercept & Pico traps; Scientific-Atlanta satellite antenna; Scientific-Atlanta satellite receivers.
Miles of plant & homes passed included with Lancaster, OH.
Manager: David Johnston. Chief technician: Mike Bash. Marketing director: Cathy Schelb.
City fee: 3% of gross.
Ownership: Time Warner Cable (MSO). Purchased from MediaOne Group, August 2, 1999.

PAULDING—FrontierVision, Box 627, Chillicothe, OH 45601. Phones: 740-775-4300; 800-346-2288. Fax: 740-775-2915. County: Paulding. Also serves Cecil, Emerald Twp., Paulding Twp. (Paulding County). ICA: OH0186.
TV Market Ranking: 82 (Cecil, portions of Emerald Twp., Paulding, Paulding Twp.); Outside TV Markets (portions of Emerald Twp.). Franchise award date: N.A. Franchise expiration date: N.A. Began: October 1, 1976.
Channel capacity: 42. Channels available but not in use: None.
Basic Service
Subscribers: 1,159.
Programming (received off-air): WINM (T) Angola; WBGU-TV (P) Bowling Green; WANE-TV (C), WFFT-TV (F), WFWA (P), WPTA (A) Fort Wayne; WLIO (N) Lima; WTOL-TV (C) Toledo; allband FM.
Programming (via satellite): WGN-TV (W) Chicago; C-SPAN; CNN; Country Music TV; Discovery Channel; Fox Family Channel; Headline News; Lifetime; MTV; Nashville Network; Nickelodeon; Odyssey; QVC; TBS Superstation; The Weather Channel.
Current originations: Automated time-weather; public access; educational access; automated emergency alert; local news.
Fee: $60.00 installation; $9.86 monthly.
Expanded Basic Service
Subscribers: 1,097.
Programming (via satellite): A & E; American Movie Classics; Disney Channel; ESPN; Fox Sports Net Ohio; Turner Network TV; USA Network.
Fee: $9.86 monthly.
Pay Service 1
Pay Units: 121.
Programming (via satellite): Cinemax.
Fee: N.A.
Pay Service 2
Pay Units: 284.
Programming (via satellite): The New Encore.
Fee: N.A.
Pay Service 3
Pay Units: 190.
Programming (via satellite): HBO.
Fee: N.A.
Pay Service 4
Pay Units: 13.
Programming (via satellite): Starz!
Fee: N.A.
Pay Service 5
Pay Units: 58.
Programming (via satellite): The Movie Channel.
Fee: N.A.
Pay-Per-View
Addressable homes: 2.
Equipment: Tocom headend; C-COR amplifiers; Comm/Scope cable; JVC & Shibaden cameras; Panasonic & Sony VTRs.
Miles of plant: 57.3 (coaxial). Homes passed: 1,728.
Manager: Richard Coplan. Chief technician: Sam Morabith. Program director: Chad Hume. Marketing director: Barbara Brewer.
City fee: 3% of gross.
Ownership: FrontierVision Partners LP (MSO). See Cable System Ownership.

PEDRO—FrontierVision, Box 627, Chillicothe, OH 45601. Phones: 740-775-4300; 800-346-2288. Fax: 740-775-2915. County: Lawrence. Also serves Decatur Twp. (Lawrence County), Elizabeth Twp. (Lawrence County). ICA: OH0244.
TV Market Ranking: 36. Franchise award date: February 1, 1989. Franchise expiration date: N.A. Began: N.A.
Channel capacity: 37. Channels available but not in use: 5.
Basic Service
Subscribers: 483.
Programming (received off-air): WKAS (P), WTSF (I) Ashland; WCHS-TV (A), WOWK-TV (C), WPBY-TV (P), WSAZ-TV (N), WVAH-TV (F,U) Charleston-Huntington.
Programming (via satellite): WGN-TV (W) Chicago; CNN; Country Music TV; Discovery Channel; Disney Channel; ESPN; Fox Family Channel; Nashville Network; Nickelodeon; TBS Superstation; USA Network; VH1.
Fee: $16.95 monthly.
Pay Service 1
Pay Units: 21.
Programming (via satellite): Cinemax.
Fee: N.A.
Pay Service 2
Pay Units: 31.
Programming (via satellite): HBO.
Fee: N.A.
Pay Service 3
Pay Units: 34.
Programming (via satellite): Showtime.
Fee: $7.95 monthly.
Pay Service 4
Pay Units: 28.
Programming (via satellite): The Movie Channel.
Fee: N.A.
Miles of plant: 31.0 (coaxial). Homes passed: 695. Total homes in franchised area: 775.
Manager: Richard Coplan. Chief technician: Sam Morabith. Program director: Chad Hume. Marketing director: Barbara Brewer.
Ownership: FrontierVision Partners LP (MSO). See Cable System Ownership.

PEEBLES—Time Warner Cable, Box 823, 131 Catherine St., Hillsboro, OH 45133. Phones: 937-393-4217; 800-677-9767. Fax: 937-393-8022. County: Adams. Also serves Franklin Twp. (Adams County), Meigs Twp. (Adams County). ICA: OH0197.
TV Market Ranking: 27 (Franklin Twp., portions of Meigs Twp., portions of Peebles); Below 100 (Meigs Twp., portions of Peebles). Franchise award date: July 18, 1972. Franchise expiration date: July 18, 1997. Began: April 1, 1974.
Channel capacity: 77 (not 2-way capable). Channels available but not in use: 5.
Basic Service
Subscribers: 815.
Programming (received off-air): WCPO-TV (A), WKRC-TV (C), WLWT (N), WSTR-TV (W) Cincinnati; WXIX-TV (F) Cincinnati-Newport; WPBO-TV (P) Portsmouth; W17AY (I) Seaman.
Programming (via satellite): A & E; American Movie Classics; CNN; Country Music TV; Discovery Channel; ESPN; Fox Family Channel; Fox Sports Net Ohio; Headline News; Home & Garden Television; Lifetime; MTV; Nashville Network; Nickelodeon; TBS Superstation; The Weather Channel; Trinity Bcstg. Network; Turner Network TV; USA Network.
Fee: $39.90 installation; $25.63 monthly.
Pay Service 1
Pay Units: 38.
Programming (via satellite): Disney Channel.
Fee: $9.95 installation; $7.95 monthly.
Pay Service 2
Pay Units: 108.
Programming (via satellite): HBO.
Fee: $9.95 installation; $10.95 monthly.
Pay Service 3
Pay Units: 125.
Programming (via satellite): Showtime.
Fee: $9.95 installation; $10.95 monthly.
Equipment: Ameco headend; Scientific-Atlanta amplifiers; Eagle traps; Scientific-Atlanta satellite antenna; Scientific-Atlanta satellite receivers.
Miles of plant: 21.0 (coaxial). Homes passed: 1,500.
Manager: Michael Rector. Chief technician: Dale Zornes. Marketing director: Gary Pitzer.
City fee: 3% of gross.
Ownership: Time Warner Cable (MSO).

PERRY TWP.—Americast, 300 S. Riverside, Chicago, IL 60606. Phones: 312-526-8000; 800-848-2278. Fax: 312-526-8565. County: Franklin. ICA: OH0420.
TV Market Ranking: 27. Franchise award date: July 1, 1996. Franchise expiration date: N.A. Began: N.A.
Channel capacity: N.A. Channels available but not in use: N.A.
Basic Service
Subscribers: N.A.
Programming (received off-air): WWHO (U) Chillicothe; WBNS-TV (C), WCMH-TV (N), WOSU-TV (P), WSYX (A), WTTE (F,U) Columbus; WSFJ (I) Newark.
Programming (via satellite): WGN-TV (W) Chicago; QVC; TBS Superstation; TV Guide Channel.
Current originations: Public access; educational access; government access; leased access.
Fee: $39.95 installation; $9.95 monthly.
Expanded Basic Service
Subscribers: N.A.
Programming (via satellite): A & E; American Movie Classics; BET; BET on Jazz; Bravo; C-SPAN; C-SPAN 2; CNBC; CNN; CNNfn; Cartoon Network; Comedy Central; Country Music TV; Court TV; Discovery Channel; Disney Channel; E! Entertainment TV; ESPN; ESPN 2; ESPN Classic Sports; Fox Family Channel; Fox Sports Net Ohio; Golf Channel; Headline News; History Channel; Home & Garden Television; Learning Channel; Lifetime; MTV; Nashville Network; Nickelodeon; Ohio News Network; Sci-Fi Channel; TV Food Network; The Health Network; The Inspirational Network; The Weather Channel; Travel Channel; Turner Classic Movies; Turner Network TV; USA Network; VH1.
Fee: $17.00 monthly.
Pay Service 1
Pay Units: N.A.
Programming (via satellite): Cinemax; Flix; HBO (multiplexed); Showtime (multiplexed); Starz!; Sundance Channel; The Movie Channel; The New Encore.
Fee: $5.95 monthly (Flix or Sundance), $7.95 monthly (Encore & Starz), $9.95 monthly (Cinemax, Showtime or TMC), $11.95 monthly (HBO).
Total homes in franchised area: 1,650.
Ownership: Ameritech New Media Inc. (MSO).

PHILO (portions)—Cablecomm, 37 E. Main St., Crooksville, OH 43731-1248. Phone: 888-229-4465. County: Muskingum. Also serves Duncan Falls, Muskingum County (southern portion), Wayne Twp. (Muskingum County). ICA: OH0354.
TV Market Ranking: Below 100. Franchise award date: N.A. Franchise expiration date: N.A. Began: December 1, 1968.
Channel capacity: 52. Channels available but not in use: 24.
Basic Service
Subscribers: 805.
Programming (received off-air): WOUC-TV (P) Cambridge; WBNS-TV (C), WCMH-TV (N), WOSU-TV (P), WSYX (A), WTTE (F,U) Columbus; WHIZ-TV (N) Zanesville; allband FM.
Programming (via satellite): C-SPAN; CNBC; CNN; Discovery Channel; Fox Family Channel; Lifetime; MTV; Nashville Network; Nickelodeon; QVC; TBS Superstation; The Weather Channel.
Current originations: Automated time-weather.
Fee: $60.00 installation; $8.75 monthly; $2.00 converter.
Expanded Basic Service
Subscribers: 790.
Programming (via satellite): American Movie Classics; ESPN; Fox Sports Net Pittsburgh; Turner Network TV; USA Network.
Fee: $10.35 monthly.
Pay Service 1
Pay Units: 20.
Programming (via satellite): Cinemax.
Fee: N.A.
Pay Service 2
Pay Units: 73.

Programming (via satellite): Disney Channel.
Fee: N.A.
Pay Service 3
Pay Units: 295.
Programming (via satellite): The New Encore.
Fee: N.A.
Pay Service 4
Pay Units: 182.
Programming (via satellite): HBO.
Fee: N.A.
Pay Service 5
Pay Units: 116.
Programming (via satellite): Showtime.
Fee: N.A.
Pay Service 6
Pay Units: 1.
Programming (via satellite): The Movie Channel.
Fee: N.A.
Equipment: Jerrold headend; Jerrold amplifiers; Times Fiber cable.
Miles of plant: 18.1 (coaxial). Total homes in franchised area: 895.
Manager: Barney Printz.
Ownership: Fanch Communications Inc. (MSO); Time Warner Cable (MSO). Purchased from Tele-Communications Inc., February 25, 1999. See Cable System Ownership

PIKETON—Time Warner Cable, 180 Morgan Dr., Lucasville, OH 45648. Phone: 800-866-9767. Fax: 614-259-3266. County: Pike. Also serves Seal Twp. (Pike County). ICA: OH0199.
TV Market Ranking: 27. Franchise award date: May 30, 1978. Franchise expiration date: N.A. Began: October 1, 1958.
Channel capacity: 35 (not 2-way capable). Channels available but not in use: 9.
Basic Service
Subscribers: 730.
Programming (received off-air): WCHS-TV (A), WOWK-TV (C), WSAZ-TV (N), WVAH-TV (F,U) Charleston-Huntington; WBNS-TV (C), WCMH-TV (N), WSYX (A) Columbus; WPBO-TV (P) Portsmouth.
Programming (via satellite): WGN-TV (W) Chicago; A & E; ESPN; Fox Family Channel; MTV; Nashville Network; Nickelodeon; QVC; TBS Superstation; Turner Network TV.
Fee: $19.95 installation; $16.99 monthly; $25.00 additional installation.
Pay Service 1
Pay Units: 95.
Programming (via satellite): Cinemax.
Fee: $25.00 installation; $10.95 monthly.
Pay Service 2
Pay Units: 52.
Programming (via satellite): Disney Channel.
Fee: $7.95 monthly.
Pay Service 3
Pay Units: 89.
Programming (via satellite): HBO.
Fee: $10.95 monthly.
Local advertising: No.
Equipment: Jerrold amplifiers; Times Fiber cable; AFC satellite antenna; Scientific-Atlanta satellite receivers.
Miles of plant: 25.0 (coaxial). Homes passed: 1,461.
Manager: Mike Rector. Chief technician: Jack Lester. Marketing director: Gary Pitzer.
City fee: 5% of gross.
Ownership: Time Warner Cable (MSO).

PINE LAKE TRAILER PARK—Marshall County Cable, Box 1696, 300 Chester Field Pkwy., Clarksburg, WV 26302-1696. Phones: 304-623-0150; 800-882-1206. County: Belmont. ICA: OH0355.
TV Market Ranking: 90. Franchise award date: N.A. Franchise expiration date: N.A. Began: N.A.
Channel capacity: 21. Channels available but not in use: 7.
Basic Service
Subscribers: 50.
Programming (received off-air): WOUB-TV (P) Athens; KDKA-TV (C), WCWB (W), WPGH-TV (F), WQED (P), WTAE-TV (A) Pittsburgh; WTOV-TV (N) Steubenville-Wheeling; WTRF-TV (C) Wheeling-Steubenville.
Programming (via satellite): Nashville Network; TBS Superstation.
Fee: $25.00 installation; $13.95 monthly.
Pay Service 1
Pay Units: N.A.
Programming (via satellite): HBO.
Fee: $12.50 monthly.
Miles of plant: 1.0 (coaxial).
Manager: Joe Nolan. Chief technician: Bill Martin.
Ownership: FinCom Corp. (MSO).

PIONEER—FrontierVision, Box 627, Chillicothe, OH 45601. Phones: 740-775-4300; 800-346-2288. Fax: 740-775-2915. County: Williams. ICA: OH0273.
TV Market Ranking: Below 100. Franchise award date: N.A. Franchise expiration date: N.A. Began: N.A.
Channel capacity: 37. Channels available but not in use: 1.
Basic Service
Subscribers: 309.
Programming (received off-air): WBGU-TV (P) Bowling Green; WANE-TV (C), WFFT-TV (F), WKJG-TV (N), WPTA (A) Fort Wayne; WILX-TV (N) Lansing; WNWO-TV (N), WTOL-TV (C), WTVG (A) Toledo.
Programming (via satellite): WGN-TV (W) Chicago; TBS Superstation.
Fee: $47.50 installation; $14.32 monthly.
Expanded Basic Service
Subscribers: 290.
Programming (via satellite): A & E; C-SPAN; CNN; Disney Channel; ESPN; Fox Family Channel; Headline News; Home Shopping Network; Lifetime; MTV; Nashville Network; Nickelodeon; The Weather Channel; USA Network; VH1.
Fee: $8.77 monthly.
Pay Service 1
Pay Units: 60.
Programming (via satellite): Cinemax.
Fee: $6.95 monthly.
Pay Service 2
Pay Units: 50.
Programming (via satellite): HBO.
Fee: $10.95 monthly.
Pay-Per-View
Addressable homes: 8.
Miles of plant: 11.1 (coaxial). Homes passed: 436.
Manager: Richard Coplan. Chief technician: Sam Morabith. Program director: Chad Hume. Marketing director: Barbara Brewer.
Ownership: FrontierVision Partners LP (MSO). See Cable System Ownership.

PIQUA—Warner Cable Communications Inc., 614 N. Main St., Piqua, OH 45356. Phones: 931-773-2288; 931-339-4770. Counties: Champaign, Darke & Miami. Also serves Adams Twp. (Champaign County), Bradford, Brown Twp. (Miami County), Covington, Fletcher, Johnson Twp. (Champaign County), Lockington (village), Newberry Twp., Newton Twp. (Miami County), Pleasant Hill (Miami County), Rosewood (village), Springcreek Twp. (Miami County), Washington Twp. (Miami County). ICA: OH0065.
TV Market Ranking: 41 (Bradford, Covington, Fletcher, Newberry Twp., Newton Twp., Piqua, Pleasant Hill, Springcreek Twp., Washington Twp.); Below 100 (Adams Twp., Brown Twp., Johnson Twp., Lockington, Rosewood). Franchise award date: N.A. Franchise expiration date: March 1, 2000. Began: February 27, 1965.
Channel capacity: 36 (2-way capable; operating 2-way). Channels available but not in use: None.
Basic Service
Subscribers: 9,931.
Programming (received off-air): WCPO-TV (A), WKRC-TV (C), WLWT (N) Cincinnati; WXIX-TV (F) Cincinnati-Newport; WBNS-TV (C), WCMH-TV (N), WOSU-TV (P), WSYX (A) Columbus; WDTN (A), WHIO-TV (C), WKEF (N), WPTD (P), WRGT-TV (F,U) Dayton; WLIO (N) Lima; allband FM.
Programming (via satellite): A & E; C-SPAN; C-SPAN 2; CNBC; CNN; Discovery Channel; ESPN; Fox Family Channel; Headline News; Lifetime; MTV; Nashville Network; Nickelodeon; QVC; TBS Superstation; The Weather Channel; Travel Channel; Turner Network TV; USA Network; VH1.
Current originations: Automated time-weather; public access; educational access; government access; automated emergency alert; local news.
Fee: $19.95 installation; $12.95 monthly; $14.95 additional installation.
Pay Service 1
Pay Units: 543.
Programming (via satellite): Cinemax.
Fee: $14.95 installation; $10.94 monthly.
Pay Service 2
Pay Units: 876.
Programming (via satellite): Disney Channel.
Fee: $14.95 installation; $6.95 monthly.
Pay Service 3
Pay Units: 982.
Programming (via satellite): HBO.
Fee: $14.95 installation; $11.45 monthly.
Pay Service 4
Pay Units: 616.
Programming (via satellite): Showtime.
Fee: $14.95 installation; $10.94 monthly.
Pay Service 5
Pay Units: 108.
Programming (via satellite): The Movie Channel.
Fee: $10.94 monthly.
Pay-Per-View
Addressable homes: 4,808.
Action Pay-Per-View; Spice.
Local advertising: Yes (locally produced & insert). Available in satellite distributed & locally originated programming. Rates: $8.00/30 Seconds; $1.50/Day (local origination). Local sales manager: Norm Pytel.
Equipment: Jerrold & Scientific-Atlanta headend; Jerrold amplifiers; Times Fiber cable; Ampex & Shibaden cameras; Sony VTRs; MSI character generator; GTE Sylvania & Tocom set top converters; Zenith addressable set top converters; Scientific-Atlanta satellite antenna.
Miles of plant: 226.0 (coaxial). Homes passed: 12,224.
Manager: Steve Sullenberger. Chief technician: Mike Burns. Marketing director: Danny Schiffer.
City fee: 3% of gross.
Ownership: Time Warner Cable (MSO).

PLYMOUTH TWP. (Ashtabula County)—Adelphia, Box 1448, 2904 State Rd., Ashtabula, OH 44005. Phone: 440-998-2148. County: Ashtabula. Also serves Ashtabula, Ashtabula Twp. (Ashtabula County), Austinburg Twp., Jefferson, Jefferson Twp. (Ashtabula County), Lenox, New Lyme Twp. (Ashtabula County), Plymouth (Ashtabula County), Saybrook Twp. (Ashtabula County). ICA: OH0052.
TV Market Ranking: Outside TV Markets. Franchise award date: N.A. Franchise expiration date: N.A. Began: March 1, 1969.
Channel capacity: 60 (2-way capable; operating 2-way). Channels available but not in use: 13.
Basic Service
Subscribers: 12,428.
Programming (received off-air): WEWS-TV (A), WJW (F), WKYC-TV (N), WVIZ-TV (P) Cleveland; WICU-TV (N), WJET-TV (A), WQLN (P), WSEE (C) Erie; WUAB (U) Lorain-Cleveland; WOIO (C) Shaker Heights; allband FM.
Programming (via satellite): WGN-TV (W) Chicago; A & E; BET; C-SPAN; C-SPAN 2; CNBC; CNN; Comedy Central; Discovery Channel; EWTN; Fox Family Channel; Headline News; Knowledge TV; Lifetime; MTV; Nashville Network; Nickelodeon; Odyssey; QVC; TBS Superstation; The Weather Channel; VH1.
Current originations: Automated time-weather; public access; educational access; government access; local news.
Fee: $42.00 installation; $10.17 monthly.
Expanded Basic Service
Subscribers: 11,757.
Programming (via satellite): American Movie Classics; Court TV; Disney Channel; ESPN; Fox Sports Net Ohio; Turner Network TV; USA Network.
Fee: $19.73 monthly.
Pay Service 1
Pay Units: 4,077.
Programming (via satellite): The New Encore.
Fee: N.A.
Pay Service 2
Pay Units: 2,093.
Programming (via satellite): HBO.
Fee: $8.00 monthly.
Pay Service 3
Pay Units: 698.
Programming (via satellite): Showtime.
Fee: $8.00 monthly.
Pay Service 4
Pay Units: 463.
Programming (via satellite): The Movie Channel.
Fee: $8.00 monthly.
Local advertising: Yes.
Program Guide: The Cable Guide.
Equipment: Entron headend; C-COR & Jerrold amplifiers; Anaconda cable; JVC cameras; System Concepts character generator; Comtech satellite antenna.
Miles of plant: 215.6 (coaxial). Homes passed: 15,844. Total homes in franchised area: 17,838.
Manager: Edward R. Williams.
City fee: 3% of gross.
Ownership: Adelphia Communications Corp. (MSO); AT&T Broadband & Internet Services (MSO). Purchased from Tele-Communications Inc., March 9, 1999.

POLK—Time Warner Cable, Box 10, 105 Prospect St., Lodi, OH 44254. Phone: 330-633-9044. Fax: 330-948-1513. County: Ashland. ICA: OH0304.
TV Market Ranking: 8. Franchise award date: November 1, 1984. Franchise expiration date: November 1, 2004. Began: September 1, 1985.
Channel capacity: 13. Channels available but not in use: None.

Basic Service

Subscribers: 200.

Programming (received off-air): WVPX (X) Akron; WOAC (I) Canton; WEWS-TV (A), WJW (F), WKYC-TV (N), WQHS-TV (H), WVIZ-TV (P) Cleveland; WUAB (U) Lorain-Cleveland; WOIO (C) Shaker Heights.

Programming (via satellite): CNN; ESPN; Headline News; Nashville Network; TBS Superstation; Turner Network TV.

Fee: $30.00 installation; $12.00 monthly; $2.50 converter.

Pay Service 1

Pay Units: 29.

Programming (via satellite): The Movie Channel.

Fee: $10.00 installation; $10.50 monthly.

Local advertising: Yes. Available in satellite distributed programming.

Miles of plant: 2.0 (coaxial).

Manager: Thomas P. Autry. Chief technician: Jim Parsons. Marketing director: Ray Kistler.

Ownership: Time Warner Cable (MSO).

PORT CLINTON—FrontierVision, Box 627, Chillicothe, OH 45601. Phones: 740-775-4300; 800-346-2288. Fax: 740-775-2915. County: Ottawa. Also serves Bay Twp., Catawba Island Twp. (Ottawa County), Danbury Twp. (Ottawa County), Erie Twp. (Ottawa County), Lakeside, Marblehead, Portage Twp. (Ottawa County). ICA: OH0060.

TV Market Ranking: 52 (Bay Twp., Erie Twp., Port Clinton, Portage Twp.); Below 100 (Catawba Island Twp., Danbury Twp., Lakeside, Marblehead). Franchise award date: N.A. Franchise expiration date: N.A. Began: February 1, 1974.

Channel capacity: 62 (2-way capable). Channels available but not in use: None.

Basic Service

Subscribers: 6,308.

Programming (received off-air): WBGU-TV (P) Bowling Green; WEWS-TV (A), WJW (F) Cleveland; WUAB (U) Lorain-Cleveland; WGGN-TV (T) Sandusky; WGTE-TV (P), WNWO-TV (N), WTOL-TV (C), WTVG (A), WUPW (F) Toledo; 12 FMs.

Programming (via satellite): CNN; Discovery Channel; Fox Family Channel; Lifetime; MTV; Nashville Network; Nickelodeon; TBS Superstation; The Weather Channel.

Current originations: Automated time-weather; local news.

Fee: N.A.

Expanded Basic Service

Subscribers: 5,596.

Programming (via satellite): A & E; American Movie Classics; Disney Channel; ESPN; QVC; Turner Network TV; USA Network.

Fee: $1.95 monthly.

Pay Service 1

Pay Units: 557.

Programming (via satellite): Cinemax.

Fee: $20.00 installation.

Pay Service 2

Pay Units: 1,147.

Programming (via satellite): The New Encore.

Fee: N.A.

Pay Service 3

Pay Units: 830.

Programming (via satellite): HBO.

Fee: N.A.

Pay Service 4

Pay Units: 114.

Programming (via satellite): Showtime.

Fee: N.A.

Pay Service 5

Pay Units: 695.

Programming (via satellite): Starz!

Fee: N.A.

Pay-Per-View

Addressable homes: 681.

Local advertising: Yes.

Program Guide: The Cable Guide.

Equipment: Jerrold headend; Jerrold & C-COR amplifiers; Times Fiber & Comm/Scope cable; Jerrold set top converters; Scientific-Atlanta satellite antenna; Scientific-Atlanta satellite receivers.

Miles of plant: 179.0 (coaxial). Homes passed: 11,131. Total homes in franchised area: 12,757.

Manager: Richard Coplan. Chief technician: Sam Morabith. Program director: Chad Hume. Marketing director: Barbara Brewer.

City fee: 3% of gross.

Ownership: FrontierVision Partners LP (MSO). See Cable System Ownership.

PORT WILLIAM—TCI Cablevision of Ohio Inc., 333 W. Clinton St., Wilmington, OH 45177. Phone: 800-284-1894. Counties: Clinton & Greene. Also serves Bowersville, Caesars Creek Twp., Jefferson Twp. (Greene County), Liberty Twp. (Clinton County), Lumerton, Paintersville. ICA: OH0259.

TV Market Ranking: 41. Franchise award date: August 1, 1988. Franchise expiration date: August 1, 2003. Began: December 1, 1988.

Channel capacity: 36. Channels available but not in use: 18.

Basic Service

Subscribers: 296.

Programming (received off-air): WDTN (A), WHIO-TV (C), WKEF (N), WPTD (P), WRGT-TV (F,U) Dayton.

Programming (via satellite): WGN-TV (W) Chicago; CNN; Country Music TV; Discovery Channel; ESPN; Fox Family Channel; Lifetime; Nashville Network; Nickelodeon; TBS Superstation; Turner Network TV; USA Network.

Fee: $25.00 installation (aerial), $50.00 (underground); $16.95 monthly; $15.00 additional installation.

Pay Service 1

Pay Units: 31.

Programming (via satellite): Cinemax.

Fee: $15.00 installation; $11.45 monthly.

Pay Service 2

Pay Units: 127.

Programming (via satellite): HBO.

Fee: $15.00 installation; $11.45 monthly.

Miles of plant: 20.0 (coaxial). Homes passed: 502.

Manager: Bob McElhaney.

Ownership: AT&T Broadband & Internet Services (MSO). Purchased from Tele-Communications Inc., March 9, 1999.

PORTERFIELD—FrontierVision, Suite P-200, 1777 S. Harrison St., Denver, CO 80210. Phone: 303-757-1588. Fax: 303-757-6105. Counties: Athens, Meigs & Washington. Also serves Chester, Coolville, Hockingport, Little Hocking, Olive Twp. (Meigs County), Orange Twp. (Meigs County), Pomeroy, Reedsville, Torch, Troy Twp. (Athens County), Tuppers Plains. ICA: OH0372.

TV Market Ranking: Below 100. Franchise award date: N.A. Franchise expiration date: N.A. Began: N.A.

Channel capacity: 38 (not 2-way capable). Channels available but not in use: None.

Basic Service

Subscribers: 1,749.

Programming (received off-air): WOUB-TV (P) Athens; WCHS-TV (A), WOWK-TV (C), WSAZ-TV (N), WVAH-TV (F,U) Charleston-Huntington; WTAP-TV (N) Parkersburg-Marietta.

Programming (via satellite): WGN-TV (W) Chicago; Home Shopping Network; Lifetime; TBS Superstation; Trinity Bcstg. Network.

Fee: $29.95 installation; $10.81 monthly; $0.73 converter.

Expanded Basic Service

Subscribers: 1,613.

Programming (via satellite): A & E; American Movie Classics; Bravo; CNN; Country Music TV; Discovery Channel; Disney Channel; E! Entertainment TV; ESPN; ESPN 2; Fox Family Channel; Headline News; Nashville Network; Nickelodeon; Sci-Fi Channel; The Inspirational Network; Turner Network TV; USA Network; VH1.

Fee: $15.36 monthly.

Pay Service 1

Pay Units: 128.

Programming (via satellite): Cinemax.

Fee: $8.95 monthly.

Pay Service 2

Pay Units: 139.

Programming (via satellite): The New Encore.

Fee: $3.99 monthly.

Pay Service 3

Pay Units: 119.

Programming (via satellite): HBO.

Fee: $11.99 monthly.

Pay Service 4

Pay Units: 126.

Programming (via satellite): Showtime.

Fee: $11.95 monthly.

Pay Service 5

Pay Units: 112.

Programming (via satellite): The Movie Channel.

Fee: $11.95 monthly.

Local advertising: No.

Miles of plant: 99.0 (coaxial). Homes passed: 2,500.

Manager: Steve Trippe. Chief technician: Bill Ricker.

Ownership: FrontierVision Partners LP (MSO). See Cable System Ownership.

PORTSMOUTH—Century Ohio Cable Television, 807 Washington St., Portsmouth, OH 45662-3942. Phone: 740-354-7733. Fax: 740-353-2364. Counties: Scioto, OH; Greenup & Lewis, KY. Also serves Greenup County, Lewis County, South Portsmouth, South Shore, KY; Bloom Twp. (Scioto County), Clay Twp. (Scioto County), Harrison Twp. (Scioto County), New Boston, Porter Twp. (Scioto County), Scioto Twp. (Scioto County), Sciotoville, South Webster (village), Valley Twp. (Scioto County), Washington Twp. (Scioto County), Wheelersburg, OH. ICA: OH0035.

TV Market Ranking: 27 (portions of Bloom Twp., portions of Clay Twp., Harrison Twp., portions of Portsmouth, Valley Twp.); 36 (portions of Bloom Twp., portions of Greenup County, New Boston, Porter Twp., Scioto Twp., Sciotoville, South Portsmouth, South Shore, South Webster, Wheelersburg); Below 100 (portions of Clay Twp., portions of Greenup County, portions of Lewis County, Portsmouth, Washington Twp.); Outside TV Markets (portions of Lewis County). Franchise award date: N.A. Franchise expiration date: N.A. Began: December 18, 1962.

Channel capacity: 38. Channels available but not in use: N.A.

Basic Service

Subscribers: 16,814.

Programming (received off-air): WTSF (I) Ashland; WCHS-TV (A), WOWK-TV (C), WSAZ-TV (N), WVAH-TV (F,U) Charleston-Huntington; WSYX (A) Columbus; WKMR (P) Morehead; WPBO-TV (P) Portsmouth; 12 FMs.

Programming (via microwave): WLWT (N) Cincinnati; WXIX-TV (F) Cincinnati-Newport; WBNS-TV (C) Columbus; WUAB (U) Lorain-Cleveland.

Programming (via satellite): A & E; American Movie Classics; C-SPAN; CNBC; CNN; ESPN; Fox Family Channel; Headline News; Home Shopping Network; Lifetime; MTV; Nashville Network; Nickelodeon; TBS Superstation; The Weather Channel; USA Network.

Current originations: Automated time-weather; government access; local news.

Fee: $25.00 installation; $12.95 monthly; $25.00 additional installation.

Pay Service 1

Pay Units: N.A.

Programming (via satellite): Cinemax; Disney Channel; HBO; Showtime.

Fee: $7.50 installation; $12.00 monthly (each).

Local advertising: Yes (locally produced). Available in satellite distributed programming. Rates: $300.00/30 Seconds. Local sales manager: Karen Kout.

Equipment: Scientific-Atlanta & Hughes headend; Jerrold & C-COR amplifiers; Times Fiber & Comm/Scope cable; Jerrold & Oak set top converters; Jerrold & Oak addressable set top converters; Andrew & Scientific-Atlanta satellite antenna; Standard Communications & Oraflex satellite receivers; ChannelMatic commercial insert.

Miles of plant: 359.0 (coaxial). Additional miles planned: 3.0 (coaxial). Homes passed: 21,450. Total homes in franchised area: 27,600.

Manager: Bob Nelsen. Chief technician: Jay Woodward.

City fee: 5% of gross.

Ownership: Century Communications Corp. (MSO). See Cable System Ownership.

POWHATON POINT—Powhaton Point Cable Co., Box 67, Powhaton Point, OH 43942. Phone: 614-795-5005. County: Belmont. ICA: OH0356.

TV Market Ranking: 90. Franchise award date: N.A. Franchise expiration date: N.A. Began: June 1, 1970.

Channel capacity: 36. Channels available but not in use: 8.

Basic Service

Subscribers: N.A.

Programming (received off-air): WOUB-TV (P) Athens; WDTV (C,A) Clarksburg-Weston; KDKA-TV (C), WPGH-TV (F), WPXI (N), WQED (P), WTAE-TV (A) Pittsburgh; WTOV-TV (N) Steubenville-Wheeling; WTRF-TV (C) Wheeling-Steubenville; WFMJ-TV (N) Youngstown.

Programming (via satellite): WGN-TV (W) Chicago; WABC-TV (A) New York; A & E; CNN; Discovery Channel; ESPN; Fox Family Channel; Fox Sports Net Ohio; Fox Sports Net Pittsburgh; Home Shopping Network;

Lifetime; MTV; Nashville Network; Nickelodeon; TBS Superstation; Turner Classic Movies; Turner Network TV; USA Network; VH1.
Fee: $8.00 monthly.
Pay Service 1
Pay Units: N.A.
Programming (via satellite): Disney Channel; HBO; Showtime.
Fee: $5.00 monthly (Disney or Showtime), $7.50 monthly (HBO).
Manager: Kasmir Majewski.
Ownership: Kasmir Majewski (MSO); Walter Matkovich (MSO).

***PRAIRIE TWP.**—Americast, 300 S. Riverside, Chicago, IL 60606. Phones: 312-526-8000; 800-848-2278. Fax: 312-526-8565. County: Franklin. ICA: OH0409.
TV Market Ranking: 27. Franchise award date: December 1, 1997. Franchise expiration date: N.A. Scheduled to begin: N.A.
Channel capacity: N.A.
Total homes in franchised area: 7,200.
Ownership: Ameritech New Media Inc. (MSO).

PROCTORVILLE—Green Tree Cable TV Inc., Box 85, Franklin Furnace, OH 45629. Phone: 614-354-9195. County: Lawrence. ICA: OH0291.
TV Market Ranking: 36. Franchise award date: N.A. Franchise expiration date: N.A. Began: N.A.
Channel capacity: 22. Channels available but not in use: N.A.
Basic Service
Subscribers: N.A.
Programming (received off-air): WKAS (P), WTSF (I) Ashland; WCHS-TV (A), WOWK-TV (C), WPBY-TV (P), WSAZ-TV (N), WVAH-TV (F,U) Charleston-Huntington.
Programming (via satellite): WGN-TV (W) Chicago; A & E; CNN; Country Music TV; Discovery Channel; ESPN; Fox Family Channel; Lifetime; Nashville Network; Nickelodeon; TBS Superstation; USA Network; VH1.
Fee: $13.50 monthly.
Pay Service 1
Pay Units: N.A.
Programming (via satellite): Disney Channel; Showtime.
Fee: $7.95 monthly (each).
Miles of plant: 10.0 (coaxial). Homes passed: 225.
Manager: Donna Lycans. Chief technician: Aaron Lycans.
Ownership: Green Tree Cable TV Inc. (MSO).

PUT-IN-BAY—FrontierVision, Box 627, Chillicothe, OH 45601. Phones: 740-775-4300; 800-346-2288. Fax: 740-775-2915. County: Ottawa. ICA: OH0357.
TV Market Ranking: 52. Franchise award date: N.A. Franchise expiration date: April 8, 2004. Began: April 8, 1989.
Channel capacity: 37. Channels available but not in use: 17.
Basic Service
Subscribers: 78.
Programming (received off-air): WUAB (U) Lorain-Cleveland; WGTE-TV (P), WNWO-TV (N), WTOL-TV (C), WTVG (A), WUPW (F) Toledo.
Programming (via satellite): WGN-TV (W) Chicago; CNN; Country Music TV; Discovery Channel; ESPN; Fox Family Channel; MTV; Nashville Network; Nickelodeon; QVC; TBS Superstation; The Weather Channel.
Fee: $43.75 installation; $22.25 monthly.
Pay Service 1
Pay Units: 13.
Programming (via satellite): Cinemax.
Fee: $11.00 monthly.
Pay Service 2
Pay Units: 19.
Programming (via satellite): HBO.
Fee: $11.00 monthly.
Miles of plant: 24.0 (coaxial). Homes passed: 778.
Manager: Richard Coplan. Chief technician: Sam Morabith. Program director: Chad Hume. Marketing director: Barbara Brewer.
Ownership: FrontierVision Partners LP (MSO). See Cable System Ownership.

RICHMOND DALE—FrontierVision, Box 648, 102 Twin Oak Dr., Jackson, OH 45640. Phone: 614-345-4329. Fax: 614-286-1489. Counties: Pike & Ross. Also serves Jackson Twp. (Pike County), Jefferson Twp. (Ross County). ICA: OH0262.
TV Market Ranking: 27. Franchise award date: May 2, 1983. Franchise expiration date: N.A. Began: January 1, 1983.
Channel capacity: 37. Channels available but not in use: 8.
Basic Service
Subscribers: 327.
Programming (received off-air): WVAH-TV (F,U) Charleston-Huntington; WBNS-TV (C), WCMH-TV (N), WSYX (A) Columbus; WPBO-TV (P) Portsmouth.
Programming (via satellite): WGN-TV (W) Chicago; A & E; CNN; Country Music TV; Discovery Channel; ESPN; Fox Family Channel; Learning Channel; Lifetime; Nashville Network; Nickelodeon; QVC; TBS Superstation; The Weather Channel; Turner Network TV; USA Network; VH1.
Fee: $20.99 installation; $22.70 monthly.
Pay Service 1
Pay Units: 74.
Programming (via satellite): HBO.
Fee: $15.00 installation; $11.95 monthly.
Equipment: Texscan & Triple Crown amplifiers; Times Fiber & Belden cable; Hamlin & NSC set top converters; Eagle & Pico traps; Harris & Prodelin satellite antenna; Standard Communications satellite receivers.
Miles of plant: 36.5 (coaxial). Homes passed: 523.
Manager: Steve Trippe. Chief technician: Bill Ricker.
Ownership: FrontierVision Partners LP (MSO). See Cable System Ownership.

RICHWOOD—Time Warner Cable, Box 787, 111 S. Mulberry St., Mount Vernon, OH 43050. Phones: 740-397-2288; 800-782-4118. Fax: 740-397-3730. Counties: Hardin, Logan, Marion & Union. Also serves Allen Twp. (Union County), Claiborne Twp., Green Camp, Hale Twp., Magnetic Springs, Mount Victory (village), Pleasant Twp. (Marion County), Prospect, Prospect Twp. (Marion County), Richland Twp. (Marion County), Ridgeway (village), Waldo. ICA: OH0150.
TV Market Ranking: 27 (Allen Twp., Claiborne Twp., Magnetic Springs, Prospect, Prospect Twp., Richwood, Waldo); Below 100 (portions of Pleasant Twp., Richland Twp., Ridgeway); Outside TV Markets (Green Camp, Hale Twp., Mount Victory, portions of Pleasant Twp.). Franchise award date: March 1, 1981. Franchise expiration date: March 1, 2001. Began: August 1, 1983.
Channel capacity: 36 (2-way capable; operating 2-way). Channels available but not in use: 1.
Basic Service
Subscribers: 1,516.
Programming (received off-air): WBNS-TV (C), WCMH-TV (N), WOSU-TV (P), WSYX (A), WTTE (F,U) Columbus; allband FM.
Programming (via satellite): WGN-TV (W) Chicago; C-SPAN; C-SPAN 2; CNN; Country Music TV; Discovery Channel; ESPN; Fox Family Channel; Headline News; Lifetime; MTV; Nashville Network; Nickelodeon; QVC; TBS Superstation; USA Network.
Current originations: Automated time-weather.
Fee: $19.95 installation; $22.50 monthly; $1.50 converter; $14.95 additional installation.
Pay Service 1
Pay Units: 201.
Programming (via satellite): Cinemax.
Fee: $10.00 installation; $11.49 monthly.
Pay Service 2
Pay Units: 226.
Programming (via satellite): Disney Channel.
Fee: $10.00 installation; $7.30 monthly.
Pay Service 3
Pay Units: 272.
Programming (via satellite): HBO.
Fee: $14.95 installation; $12.00 monthly.
Pay Service 4
Pay Units: 162.
Programming (via satellite): Showtime.
Fee: $10.00 installation; $11.49 monthly.
Pay Service 5
Pay Units: 126.
Programming (via satellite): The Movie Channel.
Fee: $10.00 installation; $11.49 monthly.
Local advertising: Yes (locally produced). Rates: $5.00/Day. Local sales manager: Lori Nordholt.
Equipment: Scientific-Atlanta headend; Jerrold amplifiers; Comm/Scope, Times Fiber & Scientific-Atlanta cable; BEI character generator; Oak set top converters; Eagle traps; Scientific-Atlanta satellite antenna.
Miles of plant: 60.0 (coaxial). Homes passed: 2,819. Total homes in franchised area: 2,819.
Manager: Paul S. Schonewolf. Technical operations manager: Dan Fessler. Field operations manager: Bill Schroeder. Sales & marketing manager: Carl Bauer. Customer operations manager: Danielle Turner.
Ownership: Time Warner Cable (MSO).

RIDGEVILLE TWP.—Ridgeville Telephone Co., Box A, Ridgeville Corners, OH 43555. Phone: 419-267-5185. County: Henry. ICA: OH0358.
TV Market Ranking: Outside TV Markets. Franchise award date: N.A. Franchise expiration date: N.A. Began: August 1, 1990.
Channel capacity: N.A. Channels available but not in use: N.A.
Basic Service
Subscribers: 139.
Programming (received off-air): WDFM-LP (I) Defiance; WLIO (N) Lima; WGTE-TV (P), WNWO-TV (N), WTOL-TV (C), WTVG (A), WUPW (F) Toledo.
Programming (via satellite): WGN-TV (W) Chicago; CNN; Discovery Channel; ESPN; Fox Family Channel; Lifetime; MTV; Nashville Network; Nickelodeon; TBS Superstation; Turner Network TV.
Fee: $20.00 installation; $16.95 monthly.
Pay Service 1
Pay Units: 12.
Programming (via satellite): Disney Channel.
Fee: $7.00 monthly.
Pay Service 2
Pay Units: 25.
Programming (via satellite): Showtime.
Fee: $7.00 monthly.
Pay Service 3
Pay Units: 23.
Programming (via satellite): The Movie Channel.
Fee: $7.00 monthly.
Manager: Ken Miller. Chief technician: Dave Gobrogge.
Ownership: Ridgeville Telephone Co.

RIO GRANDE—FrontierVision, Box 627, Chillicothe, OH 45601. Phones: 740-775-4300; 800-346-2288. Fax: 740-775-2915. County: Gallia. ICA: OH0379.
TV Market Ranking: 36. Franchise award date: N.A. Franchise expiration date: N.A. Began: N.A.
Channel capacity: 37. Channels available but not in use: 7.
Basic Service
Subscribers: 140.
Programming (received off-air): WOUB-TV (P) Athens; WCHS-TV (A), WOWK-TV (C), WSAZ-TV (N), WVAH-TV (F,U) Charleston-Huntington.
Programming (via satellite): WGN-TV (W) Chicago; A & E; CNN; Country Music TV; Discovery Channel; Disney Channel; ESPN; Fox Family Channel; Headline News; Lifetime; Nashville Network; Nickelodeon; QVC; TBS Superstation; Turner Network TV; USA Network; VH1.
Fee: $22.00 monthly.
Pay Service 1
Pay Units: 22.
Programming (via satellite): Cinemax.
Fee: $11.99 monthly.
Pay Service 2
Pay Units: 17.
Programming (via satellite): HBO.
Fee: $10.95 monthly.
Pay Service 3
Pay Units: 1.
Programming (via satellite): The Movie Channel.
Fee: N.A.
Miles of plant: 6.0 (coaxial). Homes passed: 248.
Manager: Richard Coplan. Chief technician: Sam Morabith. Program director: Chad Hume. Marketing director: Barbara Brewer.
Ownership: FrontierVision Partners LP (MSO). See Cable System Ownership.

RIPLEY (Brown County)—FrontierVision, Box 58339, 1272 Ebenezer Rd., Cincinnati, OH 45233. Phones: 513-941-7000; 800-272-2288. Fax: 513-941-1704. County: Brown. Also serves Aberdeen, Georgetown, Higginsport, Russellville. ICA: OH0167.
TV Market Ranking: 17 (Georgetown, Russellville); Outside TV Markets (Aberdeen, Higginsport, Ripley). Franchise award date: July 12, 1988. Franchise expiration date: July 12, 2003. Began: April 1, 1964.
Channel capacity: 38 (not 2-way capable). Channels available but not in use: N.A.
Basic Service
Subscribers: 3,349.
Programming (received off-air): WCET (P), WCPO-TV (A), WKRC-TV (C), WLWT (N), WSTR-TV (W) Cincinnati; WXIX-TV (F) Cincinnati-Newport; WRGT-TV (F,U) Dayton; WKYT-TV (C), WLEX-TV (N) Lexington; allband FM.
Programming (via satellite): WGN-TV (W) Chicago; TBS Superstation.
Current originations: Automated time-weather; public access; educational access.
Fee: $24.84 installation; $25.45 monthly; $2.45 converter; $17.08 additional installation.
Expanded Basic Service
Subscribers: 3,050.
Programming (via satellite): A & E; CNBC; CNN; Country Music TV; Discovery Chan-

nel; Disney Channel; ESPN; Fox Family Channel; Fox Sports Net Ohio; History Channel; Learning Channel; Lifetime; MTV; Nashville Network; Nickelodeon; The Inspirational Network; The Weather Channel; Turner Network TV; USA Network.
Fee: $14.08 monthly.
Pay Service 1
Pay Units: 83.
Programming (via satellite): The New Encore.
Fee: N.A.
Pay Service 2
Pay Units: 286.
Programming (via satellite): HBO.
Fee: $11.95 monthly.
Pay Service 3
Pay Units: 313.
Programming (via satellite): Showtime.
Fee: $11.95 monthly.
Pay Service 4
Pay Units: 137.
Programming (via satellite): Cinemax.
Fee: $11.95 monthly.
Pay Service 5
Pay Units: 250.
Programming (via satellite): The Movie Channel.
Fee: $11.95 monthly.
Pay Service 6
Pay Units: 84.
Programming (via satellite): Starz!
Fee: N.A.
Local advertising: Yes.
Equipment: Scientific-Atlanta & Jerrold headend; GTE Sylvania & Texscan amplifiers; Times Fiber cable; NSC set top converters; Arcom traps; Scientific-Atlanta satellite antenna.
Miles of plant: 74.1 (coaxial). Homes passed: 3,876.
Manager: Jim Underwood. Chief technician: Jerry Marnell. Marketing director: Keith Burt.
Ownership: FrontierVision Partners LP (MSO). See Cable System Ownership.

RISING SUN—Time Warner Entertainment Co. LP, 3100 Elida Rd., Lima, OH 45805. Phone: 419-331-3333. Fax: 419-331-1573. County: Wood. Also serves West Millgrove. ICA: OH0359.
TV Market Ranking: 52. Franchise award date: N.A. Franchise expiration date: N.A. Began: March 1, 1986.
Channel capacity: 42 (not 2-way capable). Channels available but not in use: 5.
Basic Service
Subscribers: 387.
Programming (received off-air): WBGU-TV (P) Bowling Green; WDIV (N) Detroit; WLIO (N), WTLW (I) Lima; WGTE-TV (P), WNWO-TV (N), WTOL-TV (C), WTVG (A), WUPW (F) Toledo.
Programming (via satellite): WGN-TV (W) Chicago; A & E; C-SPAN; C-SPAN 2; CNN; Discovery Channel; ESPN; Fox Family Channel; Headline News; Home Shopping Network; Lifetime; MTV; Nashville Network; Nickelodeon; TBS Superstation; The Weather Channel; Turner Network TV; USA Network.
Fee: $39.95 installation; $19.50 monthly.
Pay Service 1
Pay Units: 67.
Programming (via satellite): Cinemax.
Fee: $9.95 monthly.
Pay Service 2
Pay Units: 48.
Programming (via satellite): Disney Channel.
Fee: $6.95 monthly.
Pay Service 3
Pay Units: 101.
Programming (via satellite): HBO.
Fee: $9.95 monthly.
Local advertising: No.
Miles of plant: 19.2 (coaxial).
Manager: Larry K. Miller. Chief technician: Sean Gallagher.
Ownership: Fanch Communications Inc. (MSO); Time Warner Cable (MSO). See Cable System Ownership.

RIVERLEA—Americast, 300 S. Riverside, Chicago, IL 60606. Phones: 312-526-8000; 800-848-2278. Fax: 312-526-8565. County: Franklin. ICA: OH0421.
TV Market Ranking: 27. Franchise award date: October 1, 1996. Franchise expiration date: N.A. Began: N.A.
Channel capacity: N.A. Channels available but not in use: N.A.
Basic Service
Subscribers: N.A.
Programming (received off-air): WWHO (U) Chillicothe; WBNS-TV (C), WCMH-TV (N), WOSU-TV (P), WSYX (A), WTTE (F,U) Columbus; WSFJ (I) Newark.
Programming (via satellite): WGN-TV (W) Chicago; QVC; TBS Superstation; TV Guide Channel.
Current originations: Public access; educational access; government access; leased access.
Fee: $39.95 installation; $9.95 monthly.
Expanded Basic Service
Subscribers: N.A.
Programming (via satellite): A & E; American Movie Classics; BET; BET on Jazz; Bravo; C-SPAN; C-SPAN 2; CNBC; CNN; CNNfn; Cartoon Network; Comedy Central; Country Music TV; Court TV; Discovery Channel; Disney Channel; E! Entertainment TV; ESPN; ESPN 2; ESPN Classic Sports; Fox Family Channel; Fox Sports Net Ohio; Golf Channel; Headline News; History Channel; Home & Garden Television; Learning Channel; Lifetime; MTV; Nashville Network; Nickelodeon; Ohio News Network; Sci-Fi Channel; TV Food Network; The Health Network; The Inspirational Network; The Weather Channel; Travel Channel; Turner Classic Movies; Turner Network TV; USA Network; VH1.
Fee: $17.00 monthly.
Pay Service 1
Pay Units: N.A.
Programming (via satellite): Cinemax; Flix; HBO (multiplexed); Showtime (multiplexed); Starz!; Sundance Channel; The Movie Channel; The New Encore.
Fee: $5.95 monthly (Flix or Sundance), $7.95 monthly (Encore & Starz), $9.95 monthly (Cinemax, Showtime or TMC), $11.95 monthly (HBO).
Total homes in franchised area: 250.
Ownership: Ameritech New Media Inc. (MSO).

ROBBINS MOBILE HOME PARK—Warner Cable Communications, 1655 Brittain Rd., Akron, OH 44310-3998. Phone: 330-633-9203. Fax: 330-633-0024. County: Portage. ICA: OH0293.
TV Market Ranking: 8,79. Franchise award date: December 1, 1987. Franchise expiration date: December 1, 2002. Began: December 1, 1987.
Channel capacity: 18 (not 2-way capable). Channels available but not in use: 3.
Basic Service
Subscribers: 102.
Programming (received off-air): WEWS-TV (A), WJW (F), WKYC-TV (N) Cleveland; WUAB (U) Lorain-Cleveland; WKBN-TV (C) Youngstown.
Programming (via microwave): WXIX-TV (F) Cincinnati-Newport.
Programming (via satellite): WGN-TV (W) Chicago; A & E; Discovery Channel; ESPN; Fox Family Channel; Headline News; Nashville Network; TBS Superstation; USA Network.
Fee: $35.00 installation; $18.25 monthly.
Pay Service 1
Pay Units: 42.
Programming (via satellite): The Movie Channel.
Fee: $9.95 monthly.
Interactive Services Subscribers: 85.
Local advertising: No.
Miles of plant: 1.3 (coaxial). Homes passed: 215. Total homes in franchised area: 215.
Manager: Stephen Fry. Chief technician: Robert Nyitray. Marketing director: Woody Woodward.
Franchise fee: 7% of net.
Ownership: Time Warner Cable (MSO); Fanch Communications Inc. (MSO). See Cable System Ownership.

ROCK CREEK—Star Cable, Box 4478, 4720 Mahoning Ave., Youngstown, OH 44515. Phone: 330-792-9577. Fax: 330-792-9541. County: Ashtabula. ICA: OH0427.
TV Market Ranking: 13. Franchise award date: N.A. Franchise expiration date: N.A. Began: N.A.
Channel capacity: 36. Channels available but not in use: 4.
Basic Service
Subscribers: 784.
Programming (received off-air): WEWS-TV (A), WJW (F), WKYC-TV (N), WQHS-TV (H), WVIZ-TV (P) Cleveland; WICU-TV (N) Erie; WUAB (U) Lorain-Cleveland; WOIO (C) Shaker Heights.
Programming (via satellite): A & E; American Movie Classics; CNN; Comedy Central; Discovery Channel; ESPN; ESPN 2; Fox Family Channel; Fox Sports Net Ohio; Headline News; History Channel; MTV; Nashville Network; Nickelodeon; TBS Superstation; The Weather Channel; Turner Network TV; USA Network.
Fee: $24.75 monthly; $1.95 converter.
Pay Service 1
Pay Units: 87.
Programming (via satellite): Disney Channel.
Fee: $7.95 monthly.
Pay Service 2
Pay Units: 149.
Programming (via satellite): HBO.
Fee: $11.50 monthly.
Pay Service 3
Pay Units: 141.
Programming (via satellite): Showtime.
Fee: $12.95 monthly.
Miles of plant: 49.5 (coaxial). Homes passed: 1,077. Total homes in franchised area: 1,077.
Ownership: Star Cable Associates (MSO).

ROCKFORD—Time Warner Cable, 3100 Elida Rd., Lima, OH 45805. Phone: 419-331-3333. Fax: 419-331-1573. Counties: Mercer & Van Wert. Also serves Mendon, Mercer (portions), Willshire, Wren. ICA: OH0204.
TV Market Ranking: 82 (Willshire, Wren); Below 100 (Mendon, Mercer, Rockford). Franchise award date: July 1, 1984. Franchise expiration date: July 1, 2004. Began: November 1, 1985.
Channel capacity: 41. Channels available but not in use: 11.
Basic Service
Subscribers: 729.
Programming (received off-air): WBGU-TV (P) Bowling Green; WHIO-TV (C) Dayton; WANE-TV (C), WFFT-TV (F), WPTA (A) Fort Wayne; WLIO (N), WTLW (I) Lima.
Programming (via satellite): WGN-TV (W) Chicago; A & E; CNN; Country Music TV; Discovery Channel; ESPN; Fox Family Channel; Fox Sports Net Ohio; Headline News; Home Shopping Network; Lifetime; MTV; Nashville Network; Nickelodeon; TBS Superstation; Turner Classic Movies; Turner Network TV; USA Network; VH1.
Fee: $32.00 installation; $19.95 monthly; $4.50 converter; $9.00 additional installation.
Pay Service 1
Pay Units: 55.
Programming (via satellite): Cinemax.
Fee: $18.00 installation; $10.95 monthly.
Pay Service 2
Pay Units: 41.
Programming (via satellite): Disney Channel.
Fee: $18.00 installation; $10.95 monthly.
Pay Service 3
Pay Units: 103.
Programming (via satellite): HBO.
Fee: $18.00 installation; $10.95 monthly.
Pay Service 4
Pay Units: 55.
Programming (via satellite): Showtime.
Fee: $18.00 installation; $10.95 monthly.
Local advertising: Yes. Available in character-generated programming. Local sales manager: Jon Quatman.
Miles of plant: 44.8 (coaxial). Homes passed: 1,316.
Manager: Jeff Parker. Chief technician: Ron Lamb. Marketing director: Sandy Bayliff.
City fee: 3% of gross.
Ownership: Time Warner Cable (MSO).

ROSS TWP. (Butler County)—Coaxial Communications of Southern Ohio Inc., 3416 State Rte. 132, Amelia, OH 45102. Phone: 513-797-4400. Fax: 513-797-8625. Counties: Butler South & Hamilton. Also serves Colerain Twp. (Hamilton County), Crosby Twp. (Hamilton County), Hanover Twp. (Butler County), Morgan Twp. (Butler County). ICA: OH0127.
TV Market Ranking: 17. Franchise award date: N.A. Franchise expiration date: November 15, 2011. Began: May 1, 1986.
Channel capacity: 42 (not 2-way capable). Channels available but not in use: 8.
Basic Service
Subscribers: 3,021.
Programming (received off-air): WCET (P), WCPO-TV (A), WKRC-TV (C), WLWT (N) Cincinnati; WXIX-TV (F) Cincinnati-Newport; WDTN (A), WPTD (P), WRGT-TV (F,U) Dayton; WPTO (P) Oxford.
Programming (via satellite): WGN-TV (W) Chicago; A & E; C-SPAN; CNN; Discovery Channel; ESPN; Fox Family Channel; Headline News; Learning Channel; Lifetime; MTV; Nashville Network; Nickelodeon; TBS Superstation; The Weather Channel; Turner Network TV; USA Network; VH1.
Fee: $31.95 installation; $8.60 monthly; $0.49 converter.
Pay Service 1
Pay Units: 305.
Programming (via satellite): Cinemax.
Fee: $11.95 monthly.
Pay Service 2
Pay Units: 269.
Programming (via satellite): Disney Channel.
Fee: $11.95 monthly.
Pay Service 3
Pay Units: 944.
Programming (via satellite): HBO.
Fee: $11.95 monthly.
Pay Service 4
Pay Units: 326.
Programming (via satellite): Showtime.
Fee: $11.95 monthly.

Local advertising: Yes. Available in satellite distributed programming.
Equipment: Standard Communications headend; Scientific-Atlanta amplifiers; Scientific-Atlanta cable; Texscan character generator; Jerrold & Scientific-Atlanta set top converters; Pico traps; Standard Communications satellite receivers; ChannelMaster commercial insert.
Miles of plant: 161.0 (coaxial). Homes passed: 4,579.
Manager: Arthur P. Loescher. Chief technician: Jeff Brown. Marketing director: William G. McNabb.
City fee fee: 3% of gross.
Ownership: Coaxial Communications (MSO).

RUSH RUN—Jefferson County Cable Inc., 116 S. 4th St., Toronto, OH 43964. Phone: 740-537-2214. Fax: 740-537-2802. County: Jefferson. ICA: OH0360.
TV Market Ranking: 10,90. Franchise award date: N.A. Franchise expiration date: N.A. Began: N.A.
Channel capacity: 12. Channels available but not in use: N.A.
Basic Service
Subscribers: N.A.
Programming (received off-air): KDKA-TV (C), WCWB (W), WPGH-TV (F), WPXI (N), WQED (P), WTAE-TV (A) Pittsburgh; WTOV-TV (N) Steubenville-Wheeling; WTRF-TV (C) Wheeling-Steubenville.
Programming (via satellite): ESPN; TBS Superstation.
Fee: $75.00 installation; $9.00 monthly.
Pay Service 1
Pay Units: N.A.
Programming (via satellite): The Movie Channel.
Fee: $10.00 monthly.
Equipment: M/A-Com headend.
Miles of plant: 4.0 (coaxial).
Manager: David Bates.
Ownership: Jefferson County Cable Inc. (MSO).

SALEM—Time Warner Cable, 427 E. State St., Salem, OH 44460. Phone: 330-332-9607. Counties: Columbiana & Mahoning. Also serves Butler Twp. (Columbiana County), Goshen (Mahoning County) (portions), Perry Twp. (Columbiana County), Salem Twp. (Columbiana County). ICA: OH0096.
TV Market Ranking: 8 (Goshen, Perry Twp., Salem); 79 (Butler Twp., Salem, Salem Twp.). Franchise award date: April 15, 1986. Franchise expiration date: April 15, 2001. Began: February 7, 1970.
Channel capacity: 35 (not 2-way capable). Channels available but not in use: None.
Basic Service
Subscribers: 5,915; Commercial subscribers: 42.
Programming (received off-air): WNEO (P) Alliance; WDLI (T) Canton; WJW (F) Cleveland; WUAB (U) Lorain-Cleveland; KDKA-TV (C), WPGH-TV (F) Pittsburgh; WFMJ-TV (N), WKBN-TV (C), WYTV (A,F) Youngstown; 1 FM.
Programming (via microwave): Ecumenical TV Channel.
Programming (via satellite): C-SPAN; Fox Family Channel; Home Shopping Network; Nashville Network.
Current originations: Automated time-weather; public access; educational access; government access.
Fee: $28.75 installation (aerial), $37.75 (underground); $10.00 monthly; $1.82 converter.
Expanded Basic Service
Subscribers: 5,731.
Programming (via satellite): American Movie Classics; CNBC; CNN; Discovery Channel; ESPN; Headline News; Lifetime; Nickelodeon; Sci-Fi Channel; The Weather Channel; Turner Network TV; USA Network; VH1.
Fee: $10.95 monthly.
Expanded Basic Service 2
Subscribers: 5,546.
Programming (via satellite): WGN-TV (W) Chicago; Fox Sports Net; TBS Superstation.
Fee: $2.55 monthly.
Pay Service 1
Pay Units: 752.
Programming (via satellite): Cinemax.
Fee: $25.00 installation; $9.50 monthly.
Pay Service 2
Pay Units: 355.
Programming (via satellite): Disney Channel.
Fee: $25.00 installation; $7.50 monthly.
Pay Service 3
Pay Units: 953.
Programming (via satellite): HBO.
Fee: $25.00 installation; $9.50 monthly.
Local advertising: Yes (locally produced). Available in locally originated programming. Regional interconnect: Metrobase Cable Advertising.
Equipment: Scientific-Atlanta headend; Texscan amplifiers; Plastoid cable; Sony & Panasonic VTRs; Texscan character generator; Scientific-Atlanta set top converters; Scientific-Atlanta satellite antenna; Scientific-Atlanta satellite receivers.
Miles of plant: 95.5 (coaxial); None (fiber optic). Homes passed: 8,041.
Manager: Daryl Morrison. Chief technician: Don Jugenheimer.
City fee: 5% of basic ($500 minimum).
Ownership: Time Warner Cable (MSO); Fanch Communications Inc. (MSO). See Cable System Ownership.

SALINEVILLE—TCI Cablevision of Ohio Inc., Box 347, 123 N. Market St., Minerva, OH 44657. Phone: 330-868-5413. Fax: 330-868-3731. County: Columbiana. ICA: OH0254.
TV Market Ranking: 79,90. Franchise award date: N.A. Franchise expiration date: N.A. Began: September 1, 1968.
Channel capacity: 65 (not 2-way capable). Channels available but not in use: 29.
Basic Service
Subscribers: 471.
Programming (received off-air): WNEO (P) Alliance; KDKA-TV (C), WCWB (W), WPGH-TV (F), WPXI (N), WQED (P), WTAE-TV (A) Pittsburgh; WTOV-TV (N) Steubenville-Wheeling; WFMJ-TV (N), WKBN-TV (C), WYTV (A,F) Youngstown.
Programming (via satellite): Discovery Channel; TBS Superstation.
Current originations: Automated time-weather.
Fee: $37.50 installation; $10.59 monthly; $3.00 converter.
Expanded Basic Service
Subscribers: 447.
Programming (via satellite): A & E; American Movie Classics; Animal Planet; C-SPAN; CNBC; CNN; Cartoon Network; ESPN; Fox Family Channel; Fox News Channel; Lifetime; MTV; Nashville Network; Nickelodeon; Odyssey; QVC; The New Encore; Turner Network TV; USA Network.
Fee: $13.22 monthly.
Pay Service 1
Pay Units: N.A.
Programming (via satellite): Cinemax; Disney Channel; Showtime; Starz!; The New Encore.
Fee: $1.95 monthly (Encore), $6.75 monthly (Starz), $12.50 monthly (Disney), $13.45 monthly (Cinemax), $14.95 monthly (Showtime).
Pay Service 2
Pay Units: 111.
Programming (via satellite): HBO.
Fee: $14.95 monthly.
Equipment: Blonder-Tongue headend; Jerrold amplifiers; Plastoid cable.
Miles of plant: 10.6 (coaxial). Homes passed: 615. Total homes in franchised area: 619.
Manager: Paul Liucart. Chief technician: Rodney Lentz.
City fee: 3% of gross.
Ownership: AT&T Broadband & Internet Services (MSO). Purchased from Tele-Communications Inc., March 9, 1999.

SANDUSKY—Erie County Cablevision Inc., Box 5800, 105 W. Shoreline Dr., Sandusky, OH 44870. Phones: 419-627-0800; 419-627-1371. Fax: 419-627-0180.
Web site: http://www.thecablesystem.com.
Counties: Erie & Sandusky. Also serves Bay View, Berlin Twp. (Erie County), Castalia, Groton Twp. (Erie County), Huron, Huron Twp. (Erie County), Margaretta Twp., Milan Twp. (Erie County), Oxford Twp. (Erie County), Perkins Twp. (Erie County), Townsend Twp. ICA: OH0029.
TV Market Ranking: 8 (Bay View, Berlin Twp., Castalia, Groton Twp., Huron, Huron Twp., Margaretta Twp., Milan Twp., Oxford Twp., Perkins Twp., Sandusky); 52 (Townsend Twp.). Franchise award date: January 1, 1970. Franchise expiration date: January 1, 2003. Began: September 1, 1970.
Channel capacity: 57 (2-way capable; not operating 2-way). Channels available but not in use: 1.
Basic Service
Subscribers: 20,728; Commercial subscribers: 77.
Programming (received off-air): WBNX-TV (W,F) Akron; WEWS-TV (A), WJW (F), WKYC-TV (N), WVIZ-TV (P) Cleveland; WUAB (U) Lorain-Cleveland; WGGN-TV (T) Sandusky; WOIO (C) Shaker Heights; WGTE-TV (P), WNWO-TV (N), WTOL-TV (C), WTVG (A), WUPW (F) Toledo; CBET Windsor.
Programming (via satellite): C-SPAN 2; Home Shopping Network; TBS Superstation; TV Guide Channel.
Current originations: Public access; educational access; automated emergency alert.
Fee: $64.95 installation; $9.43 monthly; $1.44 converter; $18.00 additional installation.
Expanded Basic Service
Subscribers: 20,563.
Programming (via satellite): A & E; American Movie Classics; Animal Planet; BET; C-SPAN; CNBC; CNN; Comedy Central; Discovery Channel; Disney Channel; ESPN; ESPN 2; EWTN; Fox Family Channel; Fox Sports Net Ohio; Headline News; History Channel; Home & Garden Television; Learning Channel; Lifetime; MTV; Nashville Network; Nick at Nite's TV Land; Nickelodeon; Odyssey; QVC; The Weather Channel; Turner Network TV; USA Network; VH1; ValueVision.
Fee: $12.00 installation; $16.47 monthly.
A la Carte 1
Subscribers: 3,999.
Programming (via satellite): Cartoon Network; E! Entertainment TV; Flix; Sci-Fi Channel.
Fee: $5.00 installation; $3.95 monthly (package); $0.99 monthly (Cartoon, E! or Sci-Fi), $2.95 monthly (Flix).
Pay Service 1
Pay Units: 2,522.
Programming (via satellite): HBO.
Fee: $5.00 installation; $13.95 monthly.
Pay Service 2
Pay Units: 2,684.
Programming (via satellite): Showtime.
Fee: $5.00 installation; $8.95 monthly.
Pay Service 3
Pay Units: 2,394.
Programming (via satellite): The Movie Channel.
Fee: $5.00 installation; $9.95 monthly.
Pay-Per-View
Addressable homes: 15,264.
Hot Choice; Viewer's Choice 1 & 2.
Fee: $3.95.
Local advertising: Yes. Available in satellite distributed programming. Rates: $14.00/Minute; $7.00/30 Seconds. Local sales manager: Steve Piller.
Program Guide: TV Host.
Equipment: Scientific-Atlanta headend; C-COR amplifiers; Comm/Scope cable; AT&T & Comm/Scope fiber optic cable; Tocom & General Instrument set top converters; Tocom & General Instrument addressable set top converters; Scientific-Atlanta & Comtech satellite antenna; Scientific-Atlanta satellite receivers; Seachange commercial insert.
Miles of plant: 350.0 (coaxial); 30.0 (fiber optic). Homes passed: 28,160. Total homes in franchised area: 37,552.
Manager: Patrick Deville. Chief engineer: Robert Heim. Marketing director: Thomas Sample.
City fee: 3% of gross.
Ownership: Blade Communications Inc. (MSO).

SARAHSVILLE—CableVision Communications, Box 2200, 68 5th St., Buckhannon, WV 26201. Phone: 304-472-4193. Fax: 304-472-0756. County: Noble. ICA: OH0362.
TV Market Ranking: Below 100. Franchise award date: March 29, 1985. Franchise expiration date: N.A. Began: N.A.
Channel capacity: 21. Channels available but not in use: 3.
Basic Service
Subscribers: 63.
Programming (received off-air): WOUC-TV (P) Cambridge; WBNS-TV (C), WSYX (A) Columbus; WKRN-TV (A) Nashville; WTOV-TV (N) Steubenville-Wheeling; WTRF-TV (C) Wheeling-Steubenville; WHIZ-TV (N) Zanesville.
Programming (via satellite): CNN; Discovery Channel; Disney Channel; ESPN; Fox Family Channel; FoxNet; Nashville Network; TBS Superstation; USA Network.
Fee: $61.25 installation; $22.00 monthly; $1.24 converter.
Pay Service 1
Pay Units: 44.
Programming (via satellite): HBO.
Fee: $11.99 monthly.
Equipment: Blonder-Tongue & Olson headend; Jerrold amplifiers; Times Fiber cable.
Miles of plant: 6.0 (coaxial). Homes passed: 103.
Manager: Willie Critchfield. Marketing director: Kenny Phillips.
Ownership: Rifkin & Associates Inc. (MSO). See Cable System Ownership.

SCIO—TCI Cablevision of Ohio Inc., Box 347, 123 N. Market St., Minerva, OH 44657. Phone: 330-868-5413. Fax: 330-868-3731. County: Harrison. ICA: OH0269.
TV Market Ranking: 90. Franchise award date: N.A. Franchise expiration date: N.A. Began: December 1, 1976.

Channel capacity: 40 (not 2-way capable). Channels available but not in use: 6.

Basic Service

Subscribers: 359.

Programming (received off-air): WVPX (X) Akron; WNEO (P) Alliance; WOAC (I) Canton; KDKA-TV (C), WPGH-TV (F), WPXI (N) Pittsburgh; WTOV-TV (N) Steubenville-Wheeling; WTRF-TV (C) Wheeling-Steubenville; WYTV (A,F) Youngstown.

Programming (via satellite): C-SPAN; Discovery Channel; QVC; TBS Superstation.

Fee: $37.50 installation; $11.33 monthly; $3.00 converter.

Expanded Basic Service

Subscribers: 344.

Programming (via satellite): A & E; American Movie Classics; Animal Planet; CNBC; CNN; Cartoon Network; ESPN; Fox Family Channel; Fox News Channel; Lifetime; Nashville Network; Nickelodeon; Odyssey; The New Encore; The Weather Channel; Turner Network TV; USA Network.

Fee: $12.38 monthly.

Pay Service 1

Pay Units: 164.

Programming (via satellite): The New Encore.

Fee: $1.95 monthly.

Pay Service 2

Pay Units: 79.

Programming (via satellite): HBO.

Fee: $14.95 monthly.

Pay Service 3

Pay Units: 36.

Programming (via satellite): Showtime.

Fee: $14.95 monthly.

Pay Service 4

Pay Units: N.A.

Programming (via satellite): Cinemax; Disney Channel; Starz!

Fee: $6.75 monthly (Starz), $12.50 monthly (Disney), $13.45 monthly (Cinemax).

Miles of plant: 9.0 (coaxial). Homes passed: 461. Total homes in franchised area: 466.

Manager: Paul Liucart. Chief technician: Rodney Lentz.

Ownership: AT&T Broadband & Internet Services (MSO). Purchased from Tele-Communications Inc., March 9, 1999.

SCIPIO TWP. (Meigs County)—FrontierVision, Box 648, 102 Twin Oak Dr., Jackson, OH 45640. Phone: 614-345-4329. Fax: 614-286-1489. Counties: Athens & Meigs. Also serves Bedford Twp., Lodi Twp., Salisbury Twp. ICA: OH0274.

TV Market Ranking: Below 100. Franchise award date: March 4, 1989. Franchise expiration date: April 1, 2004. Began: January 1, 1990.

Channel capacity: 37. Channels available but not in use: 14.

Basic Service

Subscribers: 226.

Programming (received off-air): WOUB-TV (P) Athens; WCHS-TV (A), WOWK-TV (C), WSAZ-TV (N), WVAH-TV (F,U) Charleston-Huntington.

Programming (via satellite): WGN-TV (W) Chicago; CNN; Country Music TV; Discovery Channel; ESPN; Fox Family Channel; MTV; Nashville Network; Nickelodeon; TBS Superstation; Turner Classic Movies; Turner Network TV; USA Network.

Fee: $20.99 installation; $22.70 monthly.

Pay Service 1

Pay Units: 43.

Programming (via satellite): HBO.

Fee: $11.95 monthly.

Equipment: Texscan & Triple Crown amplifiers; Times Fiber cable; Hamlin & NSC set top converters; Eagle traps; Prodelin satellite antenna; Standard Communications satellite receivers.

Miles of plant: 33.0 (coaxial). Homes passed: 408.

Manager: Steve Trippe. Chief technician: Bill Ricker.

Franchise fee: 3% of gross.

Ownership: FrontierVision Partners LP (MSO). See Cable System Ownership.

SCOTT (village)—New Path Communications LC, Bldg. 6, 11260 Aurora Ave., Urbandale, IA 50322. Phones: 515-276-3174; 800-320-5581. Fax: 515-270-9181. Counties: Paulding & Van Wert. Also serves Haviland (village). ICA: OH0363.

TV Market Ranking: 82. Franchise award date: N.A. Franchise expiration date: N.A. Began: N.A.

Channel capacity: 36. Channels available but not in use: 13.

Basic Service

Subscribers: 23.

Programming (received off-air): WANE-TV (C), WFFT-TV (F), WFWA (P), WPTA (A) Fort Wayne; WLIO (N) Lima.

Programming (via satellite): WGN-TV (W) Chicago; A & E; American Movie Classics; CNN; Country Music TV; Discovery Channel; ESPN; Fox Family Channel; Showtime; TBS Superstation; Turner Network TV; USA Network.

Fee: $34.95 monthly.

Miles of plant: 3.6 (coaxial). Homes passed: 275.

Manager: Paul Scott. Chief technician: Rob Spiller. Marketing director: Josh Thackery.

Ownership: New Path Communications LC (MSO).

SEAMAN—Time Warner Cable, Box 823, 131 Catherine St., Hillsboro, OH 45133. Phones: 937-393-4217; 800-677-9767. Fax: 937-393-8022. County: Adams. Also serves Cherry Fork, Winchester. ICA: OH0208.

TV Market Ranking: Outside TV Markets. Franchise award date: March 1, 1982. Franchise expiration date: March 1, 2002. Began: August 1, 1983.

Channel capacity: 35 (not 2-way capable). Channels available but not in use: 5.

Basic Service

Subscribers: 777.

Programming (received off-air): WCPO-TV (A), WKRC-TV (C), WLWT (N) Cincinnati; WXIX-TV (F) Cincinnati-Newport; WPBO-TV (P) Portsmouth; WKOI (T) Richmond; W17AY (I) Seaman.

Programming (via satellite): American Movie Classics; CNN; Country Music TV; Discovery Channel; ESPN; Fox Family Channel; Headline News; MTV; Nashville Network; Nickelodeon; QVC; TBS Superstation; Trinity Bcstg. Network; Turner Network TV; USA Network.

Fee: $39.90 installation; $24.84 monthly; $0.29 converter.

Pay Service 1

Pay Units: 84.

Programming (via satellite): HBO.

Fee: $10.95 monthly.

Pay Service 2

Pay Units: 140.

Programming (via satellite): Showtime.

Fee: $10.95 monthly.

Local advertising: Yes. Local sales manager: Gary Pitzer.

Equipment: Jerrold amplifiers; Times Fiber cable; Harris satellite antenna; Scientific-Atlanta satellite receivers.

Miles of plant: 25.0 (coaxial). Homes passed: 1,285.

Manager: Michael Rector. Chief technician: Dale Zornes.

Ownership: Time Warner Cable (MSO).

SEBRING—TCI Cablevision of Ohio Inc., Suite 8, 7757 Auburn Rd., Painesville, OH 44077-9604. Phone: 440-942-0870. Fax: 440-639-6290. Counties: Columbiana & Mahoning. Also serves Beloit, Butler Twp. (Columbiana County), Goshen Twp. (Mahoning County), Knox Twp. (Columbiana County), Smith Twp. (Mahoning County). ICA: OH0126.

TV Market Ranking: 8,79. Franchise award date: N.A. Franchise expiration date: N.A. Began: February 1, 1974.

Channel capacity: 60. Channels available but not in use: 21.

Basic Service

Subscribers: 2,378.

Programming (received off-air): WBNX-TV (W,F) Akron; WNEO (P) Alliance; WDLI (T), WOAC (I) Canton; WEWS-TV (A), WJW (F), WKYC-TV (N) Cleveland; WUAB (U) Lorain-Cleveland; WOIO (C) Shaker Heights; WFMJ-TV (N), WKBN-TV (C), WYTV (A,F) Youngstown.

Programming (via satellite): A & E; C-SPAN; CNBC; CNN; Discovery Channel; Fox Family Channel; Headline News; Knowledge TV; Lifetime; MTV; Nashville Network; Nickelodeon; QVC; TBS Superstation; The Weather Channel.

Current originations: Automated timeweather.

Fee: $60.00 installation; $8.78 monthly; $2.00 converter.

Expanded Basic Service

Subscribers: 2,108.

Programming (via satellite): American Movie Classics; Court TV; ESPN; Fox Sports Net Pittsburgh; Turner Network TV; USA Network.

Fee: $10.43 monthly.

Pay Service 1

Pay Units: 178.

Programming (via satellite): Disney Channel.

Fee: N.A.

Pay Service 2

Pay Units: 843.

Programming (via satellite): The New Encore.

Fee: N.A.

Pay Service 3

Pay Units: 706.

Programming (via satellite): HBO.

Fee: N.A.

Pay Service 4

Pay Units: 155.

Programming (via satellite): Showtime.

Fee: N.A.

Equipment: Blonder-Tongue headend; Jerrold amplifiers; Plastoid cable; Andrew satellite antenna.

Miles of plant: 60.1 (coaxial). Homes passed: 4,090. Total homes in franchised area: 8,409.

Manager: Ed Williams. Chief technician: Mike Drougovich.

City fee: 3% of gross.

Ownership: AT&T Broadband & Internet Services (MSO). Purchased from Tele-Communications Inc., March 9, 1999.

SENECAVILLE—CableVision Communications, Box 2200, 68 5th St., Buckhannon, WV 26201. Phone: 304-472-4193. Fax: 304-472-0756. County: Guernsey. Also serves Buffalo, Byesville, Center Twp. (Guernsey County), Derwent, Jackson Twp. (Guernsey County), King Mines, Kipling, Lore City, Millwood Twp., Old Washington, Pleasant City, Quaker City, Richland Twp. (Guernsey County), Salesville, Valley Twp. (Guernsey County), Wills Twp. ICA: OH0124.

TV Market Ranking: 90 (Millwood Twp., Quaker City, Salesville); Below 100 (Buffalo, Byesville, Center Twp., Derwent, Jackson Twp., King Mines, Kipling, Lore City, Old Washington, Pleasant City, Richland Twp., Senecaville, Valley Twp., Wills Twp.). Franchise award date: N.A. Franchise expiration date: December 13, 1999. Began: N.A.

Channel capacity: 36. Channels available but not in use: None.

Basic Service

Subscribers: 2,946.

Programming (received off-air): WOUC-TV (P) Cambridge; WBNS-TV (C), WSYX (A), WTTE (F,U) Columbus; WKRN-TV (A) Nashville; WTOV-TV (N) Steubenville-Wheeling; WTRF-TV (C) Wheeling-Steubenville; WHIZ-TV (N) Zanesville.

Programming (via satellite): WGN-TV (W) Chicago; Bravo; Court TV; Home Shopping Network; Learning Channel; TBS Superstation; The Inspirational Network; Trinity Bcstg. Network.

Fee: $61.25 installation; $16.04 monthly; $1.24 converter.

Expanded Basic Service

Subscribers: 2,549.

Programming (via satellite): American Movie Classics; CNN; Discovery Channel; Disney Channel; E! Entertainment TV; ESPN; ESPN 2; Fox Family Channel; Great American Country; History Channel; Learning Channel; Lifetime; MuchMusic Network; Nashville Network; Nickelodeon; Sci-Fi Channel; Turner Network TV; USA Network.

Fee: $17.50 installation; $16.22 monthly.

Pay Service 1

Pay Units: N.A.

Programming (via satellite): Cinemax; HBO; Showtime; The Movie Channel; The New Encore.

Fee: $3.99 monthly (Encore), $7.95 monthly (Cinemax), $11.95 monthly (Showtime or TMC), $11.99 monthly (HBO).

Equipment: Blonder-Tongue, Catel & Electrohome headend; Scientific-Atlanta, Jerrold & Magnavox amplifiers; Times Fiber cable; Block set top converters; Intercept traps; M/A-Com satellite antenna; Standard Communications satellite receivers.

Miles of plant: 109.0 (coaxial). Homes passed: 4,123.

Manager: Willie Critchfield. Chief technician: Bill Turner. Marketing director: Kenny Phillips.

Ownership: Rifkin & Associates Inc. (MSO). See Cable System Ownership.

SHADYSIDE—TCI Cablevision of Ohio Inc., Box 469, Bridgeport, OH 43912. Phone: 800-527-2222. County: Belmont. ICA: OH0364.

TV Market Ranking: 90. Franchise award date: N.A. Franchise expiration date: N.A. Began: September 1, 1961.

Channel capacity: 52. Channels available but not in use: 24.

Basic Service

Subscribers: 1,804.

Programming (received off-air): 16 FMs.

Programming (via microwave): WOUC-TV (P) Cambridge; KDKA-TV (C), WCWB (W), WPGH-TV (F), WPXI (N), WQED (P), WTAE-TV (A) Pittsburgh; WTOV-TV (N) Steubenville-Wheeling; WTRF-TV (C) Wheeling-Steubenville; WYTV (A,F) Youngstown.

Programming (via satellite): A & E; C-SPAN; CNBC; CNN; Discovery Channel; Fox Family Channel; Lifetime; MTV; Nashville Network; Nickelodeon; Superaudio Cable Radio Service; TBS Superstation.

Current originations: Automated time-weather.
Fee: $60.00 installation; $18.16 monthly.

Expanded Basic Service
Subscribers: 1,727.
Programming (via satellite): American Movie Classics; ESPN; Fox Sports Net Pittsburgh; QVC; Turner Network TV; USA Network.
Fee: $1.95 monthly.

Pay Service 1
Pay Units: 97.
Programming (via satellite): Disney Channel.
Fee: N.A.

Pay Service 2
Pay Units: 528.
Programming (via satellite): The New Encore.
Fee: N.A.

Pay Service 3
Pay Units: 302.
Programming (via satellite): HBO.
Fee: N.A.

Pay Service 4
Pay Units: 235.
Programming (via satellite): Showtime.
Fee: N.A.

Equipment: Jerrold headend; Coral amplifiers; Times Fiber & Vikoa cable; Standard Components set top converters; Microdyne satellite antenna.
Miles of plant: 17.6 (coaxial). Total homes in franchised area: 1,850.
Manager: Robert Weese. Chief technician: Earl Conway.
City fee: None.
Ownership: AT&T Broadband & Internet Services (MSO). Purchased from Tele-Communications Inc., March 9, 1999.

SHARON TWP.—Americast, 300 S. Riverside, Chicago, IL 60606. Phones: 312-526-8000; 800-848-2278. Fax: 312-526-8565. County: Franklin. ICA: OH0423.
TV Market Ranking: 27. Franchise award date: January 1, 1997. Franchise expiration date: N.A. Began: N.A.
Channel capacity: N.A. Channels available but not in use: N.A.

Basic Service
Subscribers: N.A.
Programming (received off-air): WWHO (U) Chillicothe; WBNS-TV (C), WCMH-TV (N), WOSU-TV (P), WSYX (A), WTTE (F,U) Columbus; WSFJ (I) Newark.
Programming (via satellite): WGN-TV (W) Chicago; QVC; TBS Superstation; TV Guide Channel.
Current originations: Public access; educational access; government access; leased access.
Fee: $39.95 installation; $9.95 monthly.

Expanded Basic Service
Subscribers: N.A.
Programming (via satellite): A & E; American Movie Classics; BET; BET on Jazz; Bravo; C-SPAN; C-SPAN 2; CNBC; CNN; CNNfn; Cartoon Network; Comedy Central; Country Music TV; Court TV; Discovery Channel; Disney Channel; E! Entertainment TV; ESPN; ESPN 2; ESPN Classic Sports; Fox Family Channel; Fox Sports Net Ohio; Golf Channel; Headline News; History Channel; Home & Garden Television; Learning Channel; Lifetime; MTV; Nashville Network; Nickelodeon; Ohio News Network; Sci-Fi Channel; TV Food Network; The Health Network; The Inspirational Network; The Weather Channel; Travel Channel; Turner Classic Movies; Turner Network TV; USA Network; VH1.
Fee: $17.00 monthly.

Pay Service 1
Pay Units: N.A.
Programming (via satellite): Cinemax; Flix; HBO (multiplexed); Showtime (multiplexed); Starz!; Sundance Channel; The Movie Channel; The New Encore.
Fee: $5.95 monthly (Flix or Sundance), $7.95 monthly (Encore & Starz), $9.95 monthly (Cinemax, Showtime or TMC), $11.95 monthly (HBO).

Total homes in franchised area: 900.
Ownership: Ameritech New Media Inc. (MSO).

SHEFFIELD LAKE—Cablevision of Ohio, 3400 Lakeside Ave., Cleveland, OH 44114. Phone: 216-575-8016. Fax: 216-575-0212. County: Lorain. Also serves Avon, Sheffield (village). ICA: OH0100.
TV Market Ranking: 8. Franchise award date: May 4, 1982. Franchise expiration date: N.A. Began: December 31, 1982.
Channel capacity: 52. Channels available but not in use: 1.

Basic Service
Subscribers: 3,849.
Programming (received off-air): WBNX-TV (W,F), WEAO (P), WVPX (X) Akron; WEWS-TV (A), WJW (F), WKYC-TV (N), WQHS-TV (H), WVIZ-TV (P) Cleveland; WUAB (U) Lorain-Cleveland; WOIO (C) Shaker Heights.
Programming (via satellite): A & E; Bravo; C-SPAN; CNBC; CNN; Discovery Channel; ESPN; EWTN; Fox Family Channel; Fox Sports Net Ohio; Headline News; Learning Channel; Lifetime; MTV; Nashville Network; Nickelodeon; TBS Superstation; The Weather Channel; Turner Network TV; USA Network; VH1.
Current originations: Public access; educational access; government access.
Fee: $36.25 installation; $23.44 monthly.

Pay Service 1
Pay Units: 812.
Programming (via satellite): American Movie Classics; Cinemax; Disney Channel; HBO; Playboy TV; Showtime; The Movie Channel.
Fee: $10.45 monthly (each).

Pay-Per-View
Addressable homes: 2,258.

Local advertising: Yes (insert only). Available in satellite distributed programming. Local sales manager: Mark Dolan. Regional interconnect: Northern Ohio Interconnect.
Equipment: Scientific-Atlanta headend; Texscan character generator; Scientific-Atlanta set top converters.
Miles of plant: 111.0 (coaxial). Homes passed: 6,786.
Manager: Kathleen R. Mayo. Chief technician: Bruce Smylie. Program director: John Stealey. Sales & marketing director: Frank Naples.
City fee: 5% of gross.
Ownership: Cablevision Systems Corp. (MSO).

SHELBY—Time Warner Cable, 1575 Lexington Ave., Mansfield, OH 44907. Phone: 419-342-3286. Fax: 419-756-5319. Counties: Crawford & Richland. Also serves Jackson Twp. (Richland County), Plymouth Twp. (Richland County), Sharon Twp. (Richland County), Tiro, Vernon Twp. (Crawford County). ICA: OH0125.
TV Market Ranking: Below 100. Franchise award date: N.A. Franchise expiration date: N.A. Began: January 1, 1968.
Channel capacity: 52 (not 2-way capable). Channels available but not in use: 15.

Basic Service
Subscribers: 4,087.
Programming (received off-air): WEWS-TV (A), WJW (F), WKYC-TV (N) Cleveland; WBNS-TV (C), WCMH-TV (N), WOSU-TV (P), WSYX (A) Columbus; WUAB (U) Lorain-Cleveland; WOIO (C) Shaker Heights; WTVG (A) Toledo; 14 FMs.
Programming (via satellite): A & E; American Movie Classics; C-SPAN; CNBC; CNN; Country Music TV; Discovery Channel; ESPN; Fox Family Channel; Headline News; Lifetime; MTV; Nashville Network; Nickelodeon; QVC; TBS Superstation; The Weather Channel; Turner Classic Movies; Turner Network TV; USA Network; VH1.
Current originations: Automated time-weather; public access; educational access; government access; automated emergency alert.
Fee: $15.00 installation; $15.05 monthly; $15.00 additional installation.

Pay Service 1
Pay Units: N.A.
Programming (via satellite): Disney Channel; HBO; Showtime.
Fee: $15.00 installation; $7.95 monthly (Disney), $9.95 monthly (Showtime), $10.95 monthly (HBO).

Local advertising: Yes (insert only). Available in locally originated, character-generated & taped programming. Local sales manager: Mike Greene.
Program Guide: Premium Channels.
Equipment: Scientific-Atlanta headend; Magnavox amplifiers; Comm/Scope cable; Texscan character generator; Scientific-Atlanta set top converters; Eagle traps; Scientific-Atlanta satellite antenna; Scientific-Atlanta satellite receivers.
Miles of plant: 89.0 (coaxial). Homes passed: 4,100.
Manager: William Schroeder. Chief technician: Karl Mohn. Marketing director: Sebio Diluciano.
Franchise fee: None.
Ownership: Time Warner Cable (MSO).

SHERWOOD—Shertel Cable Inc., Box 4572, 105 W. Vine St., Sherwood, OH 43556. Phone: 419-899-2288. Fax: 419-899-4567. County: Defiance. ICA: OH0365.
TV Market Ranking: Below 100. Franchise award date: March 26, 1985. Franchise expiration date: March 26, 2010. Began: May 1, 1987.
Channel capacity: 52 (not 2-way capable). Channels available but not in use: 10.

Basic Service
Subscribers: 115.
Programming (received off-air): WBGU-TV (P) Bowling Green; WANE-TV (C), WFFT-TV (F), WKJG-TV (N), WPTA (A) Fort Wayne; WTLW (I) Lima; WTOL-TV (C), WTVG (A) Toledo.
Programming (via satellite): WGN-TV (W) Chicago; CNN; E! Entertainment TV; ESPN; Fox Family Channel; Learning Channel; MOR Galleria; Nashville Network; QVC; TBS Superstation; Trinity Bcstg. Network; Turner Network TV; USA Network.
Fee: $21.44 monthly.

Pay Service 1
Pay Units: N.A.
Programming (via satellite): Disney Channel; Showtime.
Fee: N.A.

Miles of plant: 3.3 (coaxial); None (fiber optic). Homes passed: 310.
Manager: Mike Woodring. Chief technician: Joe Woodring.
Ownership: Sherwood Telephone Co.

SHREVE—Time Warner Cable, Box 10, 105 Prospect St., Lodi, OH 44254. Phone: 330-633-9044. Fax: 330-948-1513. Counties: Holmes & Wayne. Also serves Big Prairie, Lakeville, Nashville, Nashville (village). ICA: OH0366.
TV Market Ranking: Below 100 (Nashville, Shreve); Outside TV Markets (Big Prairie, Lakeville). Franchise award date: N.A. Franchise expiration date: January 1, 2011. Began: June 1, 1972.
Channel capacity: 39 (not 2-way capable). Channels available but not in use: N.A.

Basic Service
Subscribers: 986.
Programming (received off-air): WVPX (X) Akron; WEWS-TV (A), WJW (F), WKYC-TV (N), WVIZ-TV (P) Cleveland; WBNS-TV (C), WCMH-TV (N), WSYX (A) Columbus; WUAB (U) Lorain-Cleveland; WOIO (C) Shaker Heights.
Programming (via satellite): WGN-TV (W) Chicago; C-SPAN; CNN; Country Music TV; Discovery Channel; ESPN; Fox Family Channel; Headline News; Home Shopping Network; Lifetime; MTV; Nashville Network; Nickelodeon; TBS Superstation; The Inspirational Network; The Weather Channel; Turner Network TV; USA Network.
Fee: $30.00 installation; $12.95 monthly; $2.50 converter; $20.00 additional installation.

Pay Service 1
Pay Units: 163.
Programming (via satellite): Cinemax.
Fee: $8.95 monthly.

Pay Service 2
Pay Units: 137.
Programming (via satellite): Disney Channel.
Fee: $8.95 monthly.

Pay Service 3
Pay Units: 219.
Programming (via satellite): HBO.
Fee: $8.95 monthly.

Local advertising: No.
Equipment: Jerrold headend; GTE Sylvania amplifiers; Times Fiber cable; Pioneer set top converters; Eagle, Vitek & Arcom traps; Microdyne, Scientific-Atlanta satellite antenna; Standard Components satellite receivers.
Miles of plant: 9.9 (coaxial). Additional miles planned: 12.0 (coaxial).
Manager: Thomas P. Autry. Chief technician: Jim Parsons. Marketing director: Ray Kistler.
City fee: None.
Ownership: Time Warner Cable (MSO).

SIDNEY—Time Warner Entertainment Co. LP, 3100 Elida Rd., Lima, OH 45805. Phone: 419-331-3333. Fax: 419-331-1573. Counties: Champaign & Shelby. Also serves Clinton Twp. (Shelby County), Franklin Twp. (Shelby County), Harrison Twp. (Champaign County), Orange Twp. (Shelby County), Port Jefferson, Salem Twp. (Shelby County), Tawawa (village), Washington Twp. (Shelby County). ICA: OH0080.
TV Market Ranking: Below 100. Franchise award date: February 11, 1966. Franchise expiration date: February 11, 2010. Began: February 11, 1966.

Channel capacity: 80 (2-way capable; operating 2-way). Channels available but not in use: 6.

Basic Service

Subscribers: 7,900; Commercial subscribers: 124.

Programming (received off-air): WBNS-TV (C), WOSU-TV (P) Columbus; WDTN (A), WHIO-TV (C), WKEF (N), WPTD (P), WRGT-TV (F,U) Dayton; WLIO (N) Lima; WBDT (W) Springfield.

Programming (via satellite): WGN-TV (W) Chicago; A & E; American Movie Classics; BET; C-SPAN; C-SPAN 2; CNBC; CNN; Cartoon Network; Comedy Central; Country Music TV; Court TV; Discovery Channel; E! Entertainment TV; ESPN; ESPN 2; Fox Family Channel; Golf Channel; Headline News; History Channel; Home & Garden Television; Home Shopping Network; Learning Channel; Lifetime; MTV; Nashville Network; Nickelodeon; QVC; Sci-Fi Channel; TBS Superstation; TV Food Network; TV Guide Channel; TV Guide Sneak Prevue; The Weather Channel; Travel Channel; Turner Classic Movies; Turner Network TV; USA Network; VH1.

Current originations: Automated time-weather; public access; educational access; government access; automated emergency alert; local news.

Fee: $19.95 installation; $9.95 monthly; $0.75 converter.

Pay Service 1

Pay Units: 4,324.

Programming (via satellite): Cinemax (multiplexed); Flix; HBO (multiplexed); Showtime (multiplexed).

Fee: N.A.

Pay Service 2

Pay Units: 512.

Programming (via satellite): Disney Channel.

Fee: N.A.

Pay-Per-View

Action Pay-Per-View; Hot Choice; Playboy TV.

Local advertising: Yes (locally produced). Available in locally originated programming. Local sales manager: Norm Pytel.

Equipment: Scientific-Atlanta & General Instrument headend; Augat amplifiers; Comm/Scope & Times Fiber cable; Sony cameras; Sony VTRs; MSI character generator; Scientific-Atlanta addressable set top converters; Scientific-Atlanta satellite antenna; Scientific-Atlanta & General Instrument satellite receivers.

Miles of plant: 193.0 (coaxial); 75.0 (fiber optic). Homes passed: 10,247. Total homes in franchised area: 10,247.

Manager: Steve Sullenberger. Chief technician: Tim Jackson. Program director: Norm Pytel. Marketing director: Carl Williams. Customer service manager: Barb Swarts.

Ownership: Time Warner Cable (MSO).

SOLON—Cablevision of Ohio, 3400 Lakeside Ave., Cleveland, OH 44114. Phone: 216-575-8016. Fax: 216-575-0212. Counties: Cuyahoga & Summit. Also serves Bedford Heights, Glenwillow (village), Northfield (village), Oakwood (village). ICA: OH0056.

TV Market Ranking: 8. Franchise award date: July 1, 1981. Franchise expiration date: N.A. Began: May 1, 1982.

Channel capacity: 77. Channels available but not in use: 3.

Basic Service

Subscribers: 11,899.

Programming (received off-air): WEAO (P), WVPX (X) Akron; WEWS-TV (A), WJW (F), WKYC-TV (N), WQHS-TV (H), WVIZ-TV (P) Cleveland; WUAB (U) Lorain-Cleveland; WOIO (C) Shaker Heights.

Programming (via satellite): TBS Superstation.

Current originations: Public access; educational access; government access.

Fee: $36.25 installation; $26.35 monthly.

Expanded Basic Service

Subscribers: 7,437.

Programming (via satellite): A & E; BET; Bravo; C-SPAN; CNBC; CNN; Discovery Channel; ESPN; Fox Family Channel; Fox Sports Net; Headline News; Lifetime; MTV; Nashville Network; Nickelodeon; The Weather Channel; Turner Network TV; USA Network; VH1.

Fee: N.A.

Pay Service 1

Pay Units: 6,125.

Programming (via satellite): American Movie Classics; Cinemax; Disney Channel; HBO; Showtime; The Movie Channel.

Fee: $10.45 monthly (each).

Pay-Per-View

Addressable homes: 10,400.

Local advertising: Yes. Available in satellite distributed programming. Local sales manager: Mark Dolan. Regional interconnect: Northern Ohio Interconnect.

Equipment: Scientific-Atlanta headend; Texscan character generator; Scientific-Atlanta set top converters.

Miles of plant: 190.0 (coaxial). Additional miles planned: 16.0 (coaxial). Homes passed: 14,236.

Manager: Kathleen R. Mayo. Chief technician: Bruce Smylie. Program director: John Stealey. Sales & marketing director: Frank Naples.

City fee: 5% of annual gross.

Ownership: Cablevision Systems Corp. (MSO).

SOMERSET—Time Warner Cable, Box 787, 111 S. Mulberry St., Mount Vernon, OH 43050. Phones: 740-397-2288; 800-782-4118. Fax: 740-397-3730. County: Fairfield. Also serves Rushville, West Rushville. ICA: OH0290.

TV Market Ranking: 27. Franchise award date: N.A. Franchise expiration date: N.A. Began: April 1, 1984.

Channel capacity: 24. Channels available but not in use: N.A.

Basic Service

Subscribers: 48.

Programming (received off-air): WOUB-TV (P) Athens; WBNS-TV (C), WCMH-TV (N), WOSU-TV (P), WSYX (A), WTTE (F,U) Columbus; WSFJ (I) Newark; WHIZ-TV (N) Zanesville.

Programming (via satellite): WGN-TV (W) Chicago; A & E; CNN; Country Music TV; Discovery Channel; ESPN; Fox Family Channel; Lifetime; MTV; Nashville Network; Nickelodeon; QVC; TBS Superstation; The Weather Channel; Turner Network TV; USA Network.

Fee: $25.00 installation; $20.95 monthly.

Pay Service 1

Pay Units: N.A.

Programming (via satellite): Cinemax; Disney Channel; HBO; Showtime; The Movie Channel.

Fee: $10.00 monthly (each).

Equipment: Cadco headend.

Miles of plant: 6.0 (coaxial). Homes passed: 232.

Manager: Paul S. Schonewolf. Technical operations manager: Dan Fessler. Field operations manager: Bill Schroeder. Marketing manager: Carl Bauer. Customer operations manager: Danielle Turner.

Ownership: Time Warner Cable (MSO).

SOUTH POINT—Armstrong Utilities Inc., 9651 County Rd. No. 1, South Point, OH 45680. Phone: 740-894-3886. Fax: 740-894-3270. Counties: Lawrence, OH; Boyd, KY; Wayne, WV. Also serves Catlettsburg, KY; Burlington, Chesapeake, Fayette Twp., Perry Twp. (Lawrence County), Proctorville, Rome Twp. (Lawrence County), Sheridan, Sybene, Union Twp. (Lawrence County), OH; Ceredo, Kenova, Spring Valley, Wayne County (northern portion), WV. ICA: WV0011.

TV Market Ranking: 36. Franchise award date: N.A. Franchise expiration date: April 1, 2005. Began: June 1, 1974.

Channel capacity: 35 (not 2-way capable). Channels available but not in use: None.

Basic Service

Subscribers: 13,112.

Programming (received off-air): WKAS (P), WTSF (I) Ashland; WCHS-TV (A), WOWK-TV (C), WPBY-TV (P), WSAZ-TV (N), WVAH-TV (F,U) Charleston-Huntington; WPBO-TV (P) Portsmouth.

Programming (via microwave): WXIX-TV (F) Cincinnati-Newport.

Programming (via satellite): WGN-TV (W) Chicago; A & E; American Movie Classics; C-SPAN; CNN; CNN/SI; Cartoon Network; Country Music TV; Discovery Channel; ESPN; Fox Family Channel; Headline News; Home Shopping Network; Lifetime; MTV; Nashville Network; Nickelodeon; TBS Superstation; The Inspirational Network; The Weather Channel; Turner Network TV; USA Network; VH1.

Current originations: Automated time-weather; local news.

Fee: $35.00 installation (aerial), $49.95 (underground); $23.90 monthly; $2.00 converter.

Pay Service 1

Pay Units: 1,935.

Programming (via satellite): Cinemax.

Fee: $25.00 installation; $9.95 monthly.

Pay Service 2

Pay Units: 759.

Programming (via satellite): Disney Channel.

Fee: $25.00 installation; $7.95 monthly.

Pay Service 3

Pay Units: 2,677.

Programming (via satellite): HBO.

Fee: $25.00 installation; $11.95 monthly.

Local advertising: Yes. Available in satellite distributed & character-generated programming.

Equipment: Scientific-Atlanta headend; Magnavox & Scientific-Atlanta amplifiers; Comm/Scope & Trilogy cable; Scientific-Atlanta set top converters; RCA & Scientific-Atlanta satellite antenna; Scientific-Atlanta satellite receivers.

Miles of plant: 254.0 (coaxial). Homes passed: 14,728. Total homes in franchised area: 17,000.

Manager: Melvin Yapp. Chief technician: Dave Wagner. Marketing director: Jud D. Stewart.

City fee: 5% of gross.

Ownership: Armstrong Group of Companies (MSO).

SPRINGFIELD—MediaOne, 75 W. Main St., Springfield, OH 45501. Phones: 937-325-7001; 800-425-2225. Fax: 937-294-3994. Web site: http://www.mediaone.com. County: Clark. Also serves South Charleston. ICA: OH0433.

TV Market Ranking: 41. Franchise award date: N.A. Franchise expiration date: N.A. Began: N.A.

Channel capacity: N.A. Channels available but not in use: N.A.

Basic Service

Subscribers: 19,279.

Programming (received off-air): WXIX-TV (F) Cincinnati-Newport; WBNS-TV (C), WCMH-TV (N), WOSU-TV (P), WSYX (A), WTTE (F,U) Columbus; WDTN (A), WHIO-TV (C), WKEF (N), WPTD (P), WRGT-TV (F,U) Dayton; WPTO (P) Oxford; WKOI (T) Richmond; WBDT (W) Springfield.

Programming (via satellite): EWTN; Fox News Channel; Home Shopping Network; MSNBC; QVC; TV Food Network; TV Guide Channel; The Weather Channel; Travel Channel; ValueVision; Z Music Television.

Current originations: Public access; educational access; government access.

Fee: $41.00 installation; $10.22 monthly.

Expanded Basic Service

Subscribers: N.A.

Programming (via satellite): A & E; American Movie Classics; Animal Planet; BET; Bravo; C-SPAN; C-SPAN 2; CNBC; CNN; Cartoon Network; Comedy Central; Country Music TV; Court TV; Discovery Channel; E! Entertainment TV; ESPN; ESPN 2; Fox Family Channel; Fox Sports Net Ohio; Golf Channel; Headline News; History Channel; Home & Garden Television; Learning Channel; Lifetime; MTV; Nashville Network; Nick at Nite's TV Land; Nickelodeon; Outdoor Life Network; Sci-Fi Channel; Speedvision; USA Network; VH1.

Fee: $18.57 monthly.

Expanded Basic Service 2

Subscribers: N.A.

Programming (via satellite): WGN-TV (W) Chicago; TBS Superstation; Turner Network TV.

Fee: $1.62 monthly.

Pay Service 1

Pay Units: N.A.

Programming (via satellite): Cinemax; Disney Channel; HBO (multiplexed); Independent Film Channel; Showtime; Starz!; The New Encore.

Fee: $5.95 monthly (IFC), $10.95 monthly (Encore & Starz), $11.50 monthly (Disney), $11.95 monthly (Cinemax, HBO or Showtime).

Pay-Per-View

Hot Choice; Spice Hot; Viewer's Choice 1-4.

Ownership: MediaOne Group (MSO). Sale pends to Time Warner Cable.

SPRINGFIELD TWP. (Mahoning County)—TCI Cablevision of Ohio Inc., Box 130, 516 E. Park, Columbiana, OH 44408-0130. Phone: 800-833-0901. Counties: Mahoning, OH; Lawrence, PA. Also serves New Middletown, OH; Bessemer, Mahoning Twp. (Lawrence County), North Beaver Twp. (Lawrence County), PA. ICA: OH0145.

TV Market Ranking: 79. Franchise award date: N.A. Franchise expiration date: N.A. Began: March 1, 1983.

Channel capacity: 35. Channels available but not in use: 1.

Basic Service

Subscribers: 2,474.

Programming (received off-air): WNEO (P) Alliance; WUAB (U) Lorain-Cleveland; KDKA-TV (C), WPGH-TV (F), WPXI (N) Pittsburgh; WFMJ-TV (N), WKBN-TV (C), WYTV (A,F) Youngstown; allband FM.

Programming (via microwave): Ecumenical TV Channel.

Programming (via satellite): WGN-TV (W) Chicago; A & E; C-SPAN; CNBC; CNN; Discovery Channel; Fox Family Channel; Lifetime; MTV; Nashville Network; Nickelodeon; QVC; TBS Superstation; The Weather Channel.

Current originations: Religious access.

Fee: $60.00 installation; $10.00 monthly.

Expanded Basic Service

Subscribers: 2,393.

Programming (via satellite): American Movie Classics; ESPN; Fox Sports Net Pittsburgh; Turner Network TV; USA Network.

Fee: $1.95 monthly.

Pay Service 1
Pay Units: 193.
Programming (via satellite): Disney Channel.
Fee: $20.00 installation; $8.95 monthly.
Pay Service 2
Pay Units: 797.
Programming (via satellite): The New Encore.
Fee: N.A.
Pay Service 3
Pay Units: 653.
Programming (via satellite): HBO.
Fee: $12.28 monthly.
Pay Service 4
Pay Units: 136.
Programming (via satellite): Showtime.
Fee: $12.28 monthly.
Miles of plant: 260.0 (coaxial). Homes passed: 7,300. Total homes in franchised area: 7,300.
Manager: Terry Kelley.
City fee: 3% of gross.
Ownership: AT&T Broadband & Internet Services (MSO). Purchased from Tele-Communications Inc., March 9, 1999.

ST. CLAIRSVILLE—TCI Cablevision of Ohio Inc., Box 469, Bridgeport, OH 43912. Phone: 800-527-2222. County: Belmont. Also serves Bannock, Belmont County, Fairpoint, Lafferty, Provident, Richland, Rustic Arms, Wheeling Twp. ICA: OH0367.
TV Market Ranking: 90. Franchise award date: N.A. Franchise expiration date: N.A. Began: August 1, 1970.
Channel capacity: 58. Channels available but not in use: N.A.
Basic Service
Subscribers: 12,226.
Programming (received off-air): WOUC-TV (P) Cambridge; KDKA-TV (C), WCWB (W), WPGH-TV (F), WPXI (N), WQED (P), WTAE-TV (A) Pittsburgh; WTOV-TV (N) Steubenville-Wheeling; WTRF-TV (C) Wheeling-Steubenville; WYTV (A,F) Youngstown; 16 FMs.
Programming (via satellite): A & E; BET; C-SPAN; CNBC; CNN; Discovery Channel; EWTN; Fox Family Channel; Headline News; Knowledge TV; Lifetime; MTV; Nashville Network; Nickelodeon; Odyssey; QVC; Superaudio Cable Radio Service; TBS Superstation; The Weather Channel; VH1.
Fee: $60.00 installation; $9.63 monthly; $2.00 converter.
Expanded Basic Service
Subscribers: 3,723.
Programming (via satellite): American Movie Classics; ESPN; Fox Sports Net Pittsburgh; Turner Network TV; USA Network.
Fee: $12.51 monthly.
Pay Service 1
Pay Units: 248.
Programming (via satellite): Disney Channel.
Fee: N.A.
Pay Service 2
Pay Units: 1,389.
Programming (via satellite): The New Encore.
Fee: N.A.
Pay Service 3
Pay Units: 704.
Programming (via satellite): HBO.
Fee: $13.15 monthly.
Pay Service 4
Pay Units: 546.
Programming (via satellite): Showtime.
Fee: $13.15 monthly.
Local advertising: Yes.
Equipment: Blonder-Tongue headend; C-COR amplifiers; Comm/Scope cable.
Miles of plant: 75.8 (coaxial).
Manager: Robert Weese. Chief technician: Earl Conway.
City fee: None.
Ownership: AT&T Broadband & Internet Services (MSO). Purchased from Tele-Communications Inc., March 9, 1999.

ST. MARYS—Warner Cable Communications Inc., 1592 Celina Rd., St. Marys, OH 45885. Phone: 419-394-2829. Fax: 419-738-8512. County: Auglaize. Also serves Celina, Southmoor Shores. ICA: OH0123.
TV Market Ranking: Below 100. Franchise award date: N.A. Franchise expiration date: N.A. Began: December 14, 1968.
Channel capacity: 36. Channels available but not in use: 1.
Basic Service
Subscribers: 4,522.
Programming (received off-air): WBGU-TV (P) Bowling Green; WBNS-TV (C) Columbus; WDTN (A), WHIO-TV (C), WKEF (N), WRGT-TV (F,U) Dayton; WFFT-TV (F), WKJG-TV (N), WPTA (A) Fort Wayne; WLIO (N), WTLW (I) Lima.
Programming (via satellite): A & E; C-SPAN; CNBC; CNN; Comedy Central; Discovery Channel; E! Entertainment TV; ESPN; EWTN; Headline News; Lifetime; MTV; Nashville Network; Nickelodeon; QVC; TBS Superstation; The Weather Channel; Turner Network TV; USA Network.
Current originations: Automated time-weather; local news.
Fee: $19.95 installation; $10.30 monthly.
Pay Service 1
Pay Units: 1,238.
Programming (via satellite): Cinemax; HBO; Showtime; The Movie Channel.
Fee: $9.95 installation; $10.95 monthly (each).
Pay Service 2
Pay Units: 226.
Programming (via satellite): Disney Channel.
Fee: $6.95 monthly.
Equipment: Jerrold & RCA headend; Jerrold amplifiers; Comm/Scope cable; Compuvid character generator; Jerrold set top converters; Vitek traps; Scientific-Atlanta satellite antenna; Scientific-Atlanta satellite receivers.
Miles of plant: 127.0 (coaxial). Homes passed: 5,977.
Manager: Jeffrey Parker. Chief technician: Larry Bryan. Program director: Jon Quatman. Marketing director: Danny Schiffer.
Ownership: Time Warner Cable (MSO); Fanch Communications Inc. (MSO). See Cable System Ownership.

ST. PARIS—Warner Cable Communications Inc., 614 N. Main St., Piqua, OH 45356. Phones: 931-773-2288; 931-339-4770. Counties: Champaign, Delaware & Union. Also serves Christiansburg, Jackson Twp. (Champaign County), Johnson Twp. (Champaign County), Ostrander (village), Scioto Twp. (Delaware County), Taylor Twp., Unionville Center, Woodstock. ICA: OH0176.
TV Market Ranking: 27 (Ostrander, Scioto Twp., Taylor Twp., Unionville Center, Woodstock); 41 (Christiansburg, Jackson Twp., Johnson Twp., St. Paris). Franchise award date: N.A. Franchise expiration date: N.A. Began: January 1, 1979.
Channel capacity: 54. Channels available but not in use: 14.
Basic Service
Subscribers: 1,151.
Programming (received off-air): WCPO-TV (A), WKRC-TV (C), WLWT (N) Cincinnati; WXIX-TV (F) Cincinnati-Newport; WBNS-TV (C), WCMH-TV (N), WOSU-TV (P), WSYX (A), WTTE (F,U) Columbus; WDTN (A), WHIO-TV (C), WKEF (N), WPTD (P), WRGT-TV (F,U) Dayton; WBDT (W) Springfield; 1 FM.
Programming (via satellite): WGN-TV (W) Chicago; A & E; C-SPAN; C-SPAN 2; CNBC; CNN; ESPN; Fox Family Channel; Headline News; Lifetime; MTV; Nashville Network; Nickelodeon; QVC; TBS Superstation; The Weather Channel; Turner Network TV; USA Network.
Current originations: Automated time-weather.
Fee: $19.95 installation; $21.25 monthly; $14.95 additional installation.
Pay Service 1
Pay Units: 90.
Programming (via satellite): Cinemax.
Fee: $14.95 installation; $11.49 monthly.
Pay Service 2
Pay Units: 158.
Programming (via satellite): Disney Channel.
Fee: $14.95 installation; $7.30 monthly.
Pay Service 3
Pay Units: 143.
Programming (via satellite): HBO.
Fee: $14.95 installation; $12.00 monthly.
Pay Service 4
Pay Units: 83.
Programming (via satellite): Showtime.
Fee: $14.95 installation; $11.49 monthly.
Pay Service 5
Pay Units: 18.
Programming (via satellite): The Movie Channel.
Fee: $14.95 installation; $11.49 monthly.
Pay-Per-View
Spice.
Fee: $11.49.
Local advertising: Planned. Available in satellite distributed & locally originated programming. Local sales manager: Norm Pytel.
Equipment: Scientific-Atlanta headend; Jerrold & Scientific-Atlanta amplifiers; Times Fiber cable; Zenith addressable set top converters; Vitek traps; Scientific-Atlanta satellite antenna.
Miles of plant: 34.0 (coaxial). Homes passed: 1,910. Total homes in franchised area: 1,910.
Manager: Steve Sullenberger. Chief technician: Mike Burns. Marketing director: Danny Schiffer.
Ownership: Time Warner Cable (MSO).

STEUBENVILLE—TCI Cablevision of Ohio Inc., Box 339, 2228 Sunset Blvd., Steubenville, OH 43952. Phone: 800-372-1599. Fax: 614-264-2097. Counties: Jefferson, OH; Brooke, WV. Also serves Brilliant, Cross Creek Twp. (Jefferson County), Island Creek Twp. (Jefferson County), Mingo Junction, New Alexandria, Richmond, Steubenville Twp. (Jefferson County), Wayne Twp. (Jefferson County), Wintersville, OH; Brooke County, Follansbee, WV. ICA: OH0048.
TV Market Ranking: 10 (Brilliant, portions of Brooke County, Follansbee, Mingo Junction, New Alexandria, Steubenville, Steubenville Twp.); 90 (Brilliant, portions of Brooke County, Cross Creek Twp., Follansbee, Island Creek Twp., Mingo Junction, New Alexandria, Richmond, Steubenville, Steubenville Twp., Wayne Twp., Wintersville). Franchise award date: N.A. Franchise expiration date: N.A. Began: December 1, 1965.
Channel capacity: 40 (not 2-way capable). Channels available but not in use: None.
Basic Service
Subscribers: 17,000.
Programming (received off-air): WOUC-TV (P) Cambridge; WNPB-TV (P) Morgantown; KDKA-TV (C), WCWB (W), WPGH-TV (F), WPXI (N), WQED (P), WTAE-TV (A) Pittsburgh; WTOV-TV (N) Steubenville-Wheeling; WTRF-TV (C) Wheeling-Steubenville; all-band FM.
Programming (via satellite): A & E; BET; C-SPAN; CNBC; CNN; Discovery Channel; EWTN; Fox Family Channel; Headline News; Lifetime; MTV; Nashville Network; Nickelodeon; Odyssey; QVC; TBS Superstation; The Weather Channel.
Current originations: Automated time-weather.
Fee: $27.69 installation; $9.83 monthly; $1.67 converter.
Expanded Basic Service
Subscribers: 16,050.
Programming (via satellite): American Movie Classics; ESPN; Fox Sports Net Pittsburgh; Turner Network TV; USA Network.
Fee: $11.26 monthly.
Pay Service 1
Pay Units: 1,469.
Programming (via satellite): Cinemax.
Fee: $20.00 installation; $12.70 monthly.
Pay Service 2
Pay Units: 838.
Programming (via satellite): Disney Channel.
Fee: $9.95 monthly.
Pay Service 3
Pay Units: 5,581.
Programming (via satellite): The New Encore.
Fee: N.A.
Pay Service 4
Pay Units: 3,621.
Programming (via satellite): HBO.
Fee: $12.70 monthly.
Pay Service 5
Pay Units: 968.
Programming (via satellite): Showtime.
Fee: $12.70 monthly.
Local advertising: Yes.
Program Guide: The Cable Guide.
Equipment: Jerrold headend; Jerrold amplifiers; Jerrold cable; Hughes satellite antenna.
Miles of plant: 273.0 (coaxial); 39.1 (fiber optic). Homes passed: 20,000. Total homes in franchised area: 26,000.
Chief technician: James Walker.
City fee: 3% of gross.
Ownership: AT&T Broadband & Internet Services (MSO). Purchased from Tele-Communications Inc., March 9, 1999.

STRONGSVILLE—Cablevision of Ohio, 3400 Lakeside Ave., Cleveland, OH 44114. Phone: 216-575-8016. Fax: 216-575-0212. Counties: Cuyahoga & Lorain. Also serves Columbia Station, Columbia Twp. (Lorain County), Middleburg Heights. ICA: OH0038.
TV Market Ranking: 8. Franchise award date: October 1, 1980. Franchise expiration date: N.A. Began: July 1, 1981.
Channel capacity: 54 (2-way capable; operating 2-way). Channels available but not in use: N.A.
Basic Service
Subscribers: 11,972.
Programming (received off-air): WBNX-TV (W,F), WEAO (P), WVPX (X) Akron; WEWS-TV (A), WJW (F), WKYC-TV (N), WQHS-TV (H), WVIZ-TV (P) Cleveland; WUAB (U) Lorain-Cleveland; WOIO (C) Shaker Heights.
Programming (via satellite): A & E; American Movie Classics; Bravo; C-SPAN; CNBC; CNN; Discovery Channel; ESPN; EWTN;

Fox Family Channel; Fox Sports Net Ohio; Headline News; Home Shopping Network; Learning Channel; Lifetime; MTV; Nashville Network; Nick at Nite; Nickelodeon; TBS Superstation; TV Guide Channel; The Inspirational Network; The Weather Channel; Trinity Bcstg. Network; Turner Network TV; USA Network; VH1.
Current originations: Public access; educational access; government access; automated emergency alert; local sports.
Fee: $35.00 installation; $23.44 monthly.
Pay Service 1
Pay Units: N.A.
Programming (via satellite): Cinemax; HBO; Playboy TV; Showtime; The Movie Channel.
Fee: $10.00 installation; $10.45 monthly (each).
Local advertising: Yes. Available in satellite distributed, locally originated, character-generated, taped & automated programming. Local sales manager: Mark Dolan. Regional interconnect: Northern Ohio Interconnect.
Equipment: Scientific-Atlanta headend; Siecor cable; Texscan character generator; Jerrold & Scientific-Atlanta set top converters; Jerrold & Scientific-Atlanta addressable set top converters; Eagle & Pico traps; Simulsat satellite antenna; Scientific-Atlanta satellite receivers; Texscan commercial insert.
Miles of plant: 314.0 (coaxial). Homes passed: 20,734.
Manager: Kathleen R. Mayo. Chief technician: Bruce Smylie. Program director: John Stealey. Sales & marketing director: Frank Naples.
City fee: 5% of gross.
Ownership: Cablevision Systems Corp. (MSO).

STRUTHERS—Century Communications Inc., Suite 101, 71 Terrace St., Struthers, OH 44471. Phone: 330-755-1486. County: Mahoning. Also serves Lowellville (village), Poland Twp. (Mahoning County). ICA: OH0116.
TV Market Ranking: 79. Franchise award date: January 1, 1973. Franchise expiration date: December 20, 2007. Began: January 1, 1974.
Channel capacity: 35 (2-way capable; operating 2-way). Channels available but not in use: None.
Basic Service
Subscribers: 4,177.
Programming (received off-air): WNEO (P) Alliance; WUAB (U) Lorain-Cleveland; WPGH-TV (F), WQED (P) Pittsburgh; WOIO (C) Shaker Heights; WFMJ-TV (N), WKBN-TV (C), WYTV (A,F) Youngstown.
Programming (via satellite): A & E; American Movie Classics; C-SPAN; Country Music TV; Discovery Channel; Disney Channel; ESPN; Fox Family Channel; Headline News; Home Shopping Network; Lifetime; MTV; Nickelodeon; QVC; The Weather Channel; USA Network.
Current originations: Automated timeweather; public access; educational access; government access.
Fee: $23.75 monthly; $0.31 converter.
A la Carte 1
Subscribers: N.A.
Programming (via satellite): CNN; Nashville Network; Sci-Fi Channel; TBS Superstation; Turner Network TV.
Fee: N.A.
Pay Service 1
Pay Units: N.A.
Programming (via satellite): Cinemax; HBO; Showtime.
Fee: $19.50 installation; $10.95 monthly (each).
Local advertising: Yes. Available in satellite distributed & character-generated programming. Regional interconnect: Cabletime.
Equipment: Scientific-Atlanta headend; C-COR amplifiers; composite cable; JVC cameras; Panasonic VTRs; Oak & Pioneer set top converters; Eagle & Vitek traps; Microdyne & Scientific-Atlanta satellite antenna; Avantek, Microdyne & Scientific-Atlanta satellite receivers.
Miles of plant: 58.0 (coaxial). Homes passed: 5,000. Total homes in franchised area: 5,590.
Manager: Steve Hervatine. Chief technician: Jerry T. Walsh.
City fee: 5% of gross.
Ownership: Century Communications Corp. (MSO). See Cable System Ownership.

SUGARCREEK—Cox Communications, 617 Tuscarawas Ave., New Philadelphia, OH 44663. Phone: 216-364-6634. County: Tuscarawas. ICA: OH0369.
TV Market Ranking: Below 100. Franchise award date: N.A. Franchise expiration date: N.A. Began: N.A.
Channel capacity: N.A. Channels available but not in use: N.A.
Basic Service
Subscribers: 738; Commercial subscribers: 17.
Programming (received off-air): WBNX-TV (W,F), WEAO (P), WVPX (X) Akron; WOUC-TV (P) Cambridge; WDLI (T), WOAC (I) Canton; WEWS-TV (A), WJW (F), WKYC-TV (N) Cleveland; WCMH-TV (N) Columbus; WUAB (U) Lorain-Cleveland; WOIO (C) Shaker Heights; WTOV-TV (N) Steubenville-Wheeling; WTRF-TV (C) Wheeling-Steubenville.
Programming (via satellite): C-SPAN; TBS Superstation.
Fee: $43.46 installation; $11.27 monthly; $0.86 converter; $32.59 additional installation.
Expanded Basic Service
Subscribers: N.A.
Programming (via satellite): A & E; CNN; ESPN; FX; Fox Family Channel; Fox Sports Net Ohio; Headline News; Lifetime; MTV; Nickelodeon; TV Guide Channel; The Weather Channel; USA Network.
Fee: $12.28 monthly.
Expanded Basic Service 2
Subscribers: N.A.
Programming (via satellite): American Movie Classics; Comedy Central; Discovery Channel; Disney Channel; Home & Garden Television; Home Shopping Network; Knowledge TV; Learning Channel; MSNBC; Nashville Network; Outdoor Life Network; TV Food Network; TV Guide Sneak Prevue; Turner Network TV.
Fee: $1.75 monthly.
A la Carte 1
Subscribers: N.A.
Programming (via satellite): Cartoon Network; Court TV; Sci-Fi Channel; Turner Classic Movies.
Fee: $1.95 monthly (package).
Pay Service 1
Pay Units: N.A.
Programming (via satellite): Cinemax; Golf Channel; HBO (multiplexed); Music Choice; Showtime; The Movie Channel; The New Encore.
Fee: $2.95 monthly (Encore), $6.95 monthly (Cinemax, Golf or TMC), $7.95 monthly (Music Choice), $9.95 monthly (Showtime), $10.95 monthly (HBO).
Pay-Per-View
Hot Choice; Spice; Viewer's Choice.
Miles of plant: 12.0 (coaxial).
Manager: Rich Lutze. Chief technician: Charlie Miller. Customer service manager: Sandra Wagner.
Ownership: Cox Communications Inc. (MSO).

SUMMERFIELD—CableVision Communications, Box 2200, 68 5th St., Buckhannon, WV 26201. Phone: 304-472-4193. Fax: 304-472-0756. County: Noble. ICA: OH0303.
TV Market Ranking: Outside TV Markets. Franchise award date: N.A. Franchise expiration date: N.A. Began: N.A.
Channel capacity: 21 (not 2-way capable). Channels available but not in use: 3.
Basic Service
Subscribers: 78.
Programming (received off-air): WOUC-TV (P) Cambridge; WDTV (C,A) Clarksburg-Weston; WKRN-TV (A) Nashville; WPGH-TV (F) Pittsburgh; WTOV-TV (N) Steubenville-Wheeling; WTRF-TV (C) Wheeling-Steubenville; WHIZ-TV (N) Zanesville.
Programming (via satellite): Discovery Channel; ESPN; Fox Family Channel; Great American Country; Nashville Network; Nickelodeon; TBS Superstation; Turner Network TV; USA Network.
Fee: $61.25 installation; $22.00 monthly; $1.24 converter.
Pay Service 1
Pay Units: 9.
Programming (via satellite): HBO.
Fee: $11.99 monthly.
Local advertising: No.
Equipment: Blonder-Tongue & Jerrold headend; Jerrold amplifiers; Times Fiber cable.
Miles of plant: 4.0 (coaxial). Homes passed: 131.
Manager: Willie Critchfield.
City fee: None.
Ownership: Rifkin & Associates Inc. (MSO). See Cable System Ownership.

SWANTON—FrontierVision, Box 170, 105 S. 3rd St., Waterville, OH 43566. Phone: 800-346-2288. Fax: 419-878-3837. Counties: Fulton & Lucas. Also serves Delta, Harding Twp., Neapolis, Providence, Spencer Twp. (Lucas County), Swan Creek, Swanton Twp. (Lucas County), York Twp. (Fulton County). ICA: OH0106.
TV Market Ranking: 52. Franchise award date: N.A. Franchise expiration date: N.A. Began: December 31, 1979.
Channel capacity: 62. Channels available but not in use: 8.
Basic Service
Subscribers: 4,387.
Programming (received off-air): WBGU-TV (P) Bowling Green; WDWB (W), WKBD-TV (U) Detroit; WGTE-TV (P), WNWO-TV (N), WTOL-TV (C), WTVG (A) Toledo; CBET Windsor; allband FM.
Programming (via satellite): WGN-TV (W) Chicago; A & E; C-SPAN; CNBC; CNN; Country Music TV; Discovery Channel; Disney Channel; ESPN; Fox Family Channel; Home Shopping Network; Lifetime; MTV; Nashville Network; Nickelodeon; TBS Superstation; The Weather Channel; Turner Network TV; USA Network; VH1.
Fee: $42.50 installation; $17.95 monthly.
Pay Service 1
Pay Units: 281.
Programming (via satellite): Cinemax.
Fee: $10.50 monthly.
Pay Service 2
Pay Units: 420.
Programming (via satellite): The New Encore.
Fee: N.A.
Pay Service 3
Pay Units: 328.
Programming (via satellite): HBO.
Fee: $10.50 monthly.
Pay Service 4
Pay Units: 276.
Programming (via satellite): Showtime.
Fee: $10.50 monthly.
Pay Service 5
Pay Units: 264.
Programming (via satellite): The Movie Channel.
Fee: $10.50 monthly.
Pay-Per-View
Addressable homes: 31.
Equipment: Blonder-Tongue headend; Magnavox amplifiers; Cerro cable; AFC & Hughes satellite antenna.
Miles of plant: 150.0 (coaxial). Homes passed: 6,460.
Manager: Steve Trippe. Chief technician: Bill Ricker.
City fee: 2% of gross.
Ownership: FrontierVision Partners LP (MSO). See Cable System Ownership.

SYCAMORE—Time Warner Cable, Box 369, 90 S. Washington St., Tiffin, OH 44883. Phone: 800-425-2225. Counties: Seneca & Wyandot. Also serves Adrian, Big Spring Twp., McCutchenville, Melmore, New Riegel, Republic, Scipio Twp. (Seneca County), Seneca Twp., Sycamore Twp., Tymochtee Twp. ICA: OH0215.
TV Market Ranking: Below 100 (Republic, Scipio Twp., portions of Sycamore Twp.); Outside TV Markets (Adrian, Big Spring Twp., McCutchenville, Melmore, New Riegel, Seneca Twp., Sycamore, portions of Sycamore Twp., Tymochtee Twp.). Franchise award date: N.A. Franchise expiration date: N.A. Began: August 1, 1984.
Channel capacity: 52 (not 2-way capable). Channels available but not in use: N.A.
Note: Basic subscribers, pay units, miles of plant & homes passed include figures for Fostoria, OH.
Basic Service
Subscribers: 13,681.
Programming (received off-air): WBGU-TV (P) Bowling Green; W54AF (I) Bucyrus; WQHS-TV (H) Cleveland; WBNS-TV (C) Columbus; WUAB (U) Lorain-Cleveland; WGTE-TV (P), WNWO-TV (N), WTOL-TV (C), WTVG (A), WUPW (F) Toledo.
Programming (via satellite): WGN-TV (W) Chicago; A & E; C-SPAN; C-SPAN 2; CNN; Discovery Channel; ESPN; EWTN; Fox Family Channel; Headline News; Lifetime; MTV; Nashville Network; Nickelodeon; QVC; TBS Superstation; The Inspirational Network; The Weather Channel; Turner Network TV; USA Network; VH1.
Current originations: Public access; educational access; government access.
Fee: $26.54 installation; $12.10 monthly.
Pay Service 1
Pay Units: 8,788.
Programming (via satellite): Cinemax; Disney Channel; HBO.
Fee: $10.95 monthly (each).
Local advertising: No.
Equipment: Scientific-Atlanta headend; Magnavox & Triple Crown amplifiers; Atari character generator; RCA set top converters; Arcom & Eagle traps; Standard Components satellite receivers.
Miles of plant: 270.0 (coaxial); None (fiber optic). Homes passed: 19,096.
Manager: Pat McCauley.
Ownership: Time Warner Cable (MSO). Purchased from MediaOne Group, August 2, 1999.

TAPPEN LAKE—TCI Cablevision of Ohio Inc., Box 347, 123 N. Market St., Minerva, OH 44657. Phone: 330-868-5413. Fax: 330-868-3731. Counties: Belmont & Jefferson. ICA: OH0308.
TV Market Ranking: 90. Franchise award date: N.A. Franchise expiration date: N.A. Began: May 1, 1979.

Channel capacity: 12 (not 2-way capable). Channels available but not in use: N.A.

Basic Service

Subscribers: 25.

Programming (received off-air): WVPX (X) Akron; WNEO (P) Alliance; KDKA-TV (C), WPXI (N), WTAE-TV (A) Pittsburgh; WTOV-TV (N) Steubenville-Wheeling; WTRF-TV (C) Wheeling-Steubenville.

Fee: $37.50 installation; $11.72 monthly; $3.00 converter.

Pay Service 1

Pay Units: N.A.

Programming (via satellite): Cinemax; Disney Channel; HBO; Showtime; Starz!; The New Encore.

Fee: $1.95 monthly (Encore), $6.75 monthly (Starz), $12.50 monthly (Disney), $13.45 monthly (Cinemax), $14.95 monthly (HBO or Showtime).

Miles of plant: 2.0 (coaxial). Homes passed: 91. Total homes in franchised area: 140.

Manager: Paul Liucart. Chief technician: Rodney Lentz.

Ownership: AT&T Broadband & Internet Services (MSO). Purchased from Tele-Communications Inc., March 9, 1999.

THOMPSON TWP. (Geauga County)—Star Cable Co., Box 4478, 4720 Mahoning Ave., Youngstown, OH 44515. Phone: 330-792-9577. Fax: 330-792-9541. Counties: Ashtabula, Geauga & Lake. Also serves Claridon, Hambden Twp. (Geauga County), Hartsgrove, Huntsburg Twp., Leroy Twp. (Lake County), Montville, Rustic Pines, Trumbull Twp., Windsor. ICA: OH0162.

TV Market Ranking: 8 (Claridon, Hambden Twp., Hartsgrove, Huntsburg Twp., Leroy Twp., Rustic Pines, Thompson Twp., Trumbull Twp., Windsor); 79 (Claridon, Hartsgrove, Montville, Rustic Pines, Thompson Twp., Windsor). Franchise award date: N.A. Franchise expiration date: N.A. Began: N.A.

Channel capacity: 62 (not 2-way capable). Channels available but not in use: 18.

Basic Service

Subscribers: 1,734; Commercial subscribers: 13.

Programming (received off-air): WBNX-TV (W,F) Akron; WEWS-TV (A), WJW (F), WKYC-TV (N), WQHS-TV (H), WVIZ-TV (P) Cleveland; WUAB (U) Lorain-Cleveland; WOIO (C) Shaker Heights.

Programming (via satellite): QVC; TBS Superstation.

Fee: $10.50 monthly; $1.95 converter.

Expanded Basic Service

Subscribers: 1,609.

Programming (via satellite): A & E; American Movie Classics; C-SPAN; CNBC; CNN; Cartoon Network; Country Music TV; Discovery Channel; ESPN; ESPN 2; Fox Family Channel; Fox News Channel; Fox Sports Net Ohio; Headline News; History Channel; Home & Garden Television; Learning Channel; Lifetime; MTV; Nashville Network; Nick at Nite's TV Land; Nickelodeon; Sci-Fi Channel; The Weather Channel; Turner Network TV; USA Network; VH1.

Fee: $20.00 monthly.

Pay Service 1

Pay Units: 172.

Programming (via satellite): Cinemax.

Fee: $11.00 monthly.

Pay Service 2

Pay Units: 209.

Programming (via satellite): Disney Channel.

Fee: $7.95 monthly.

Pay Service 3

Pay Units: 296.

Programming (via satellite): HBO.

Fee: $11.00 monthly.

Pay Service 4

Pay Units: 251.

Programming (via satellite): Showtime; The Movie Channel.

Fee: $12.95 monthly.

Miles of plant: 137.1 (coaxial); None (fiber optic). Homes passed: 2,595. Total homes in franchised area: 2,595.

Manager: Terry Dickerhoof. Chief technician: Tom Beat.

Ownership: Star Cable Associates (MSO).

THORNVILLE—Time Warner Cable, Box 787, 111 S. Mulberry St., Mount Vernon, OH 43050. Phones: 740-397-2288; 800-782-4118. Fax: 740-397-3730. Counties: Fairfield, Knox, Licking & Perry. Also serves Bowling Green Twp. (Licking County), Burlington Twp. (Licking County), Clinton Twp. (Knox County), Fairfield Beach, Harbor Hills, Hebron (Licking County), Jacksontown, Liberty Twp. (Licking County), Licking Twp. (Licking County), Linville, Monroe Twp. (Knox County), Morris Twp. (Knox County), New Salem, Newark Twp. (Licking County), Pike Twp. (Perry County), Pleasant Twp. (Knox County), Reading Twp. (Perry County), Richland Twp. (Fairfield County), St. Albans Twp. (Licking County), Thorn Twp. (Perry County), Union Twp. (Knox County). ICA: OH0154.

TV Market Ranking: 27 (Bowling Green Twp., Fairfield Beach, Harbor Hills, Hebron, Jacksontown, Liberty Twp., Licking Twp., Linville, New Salem, Newark Twp., St. Albans Twp., Thorn Twp., Thornville); Below 100 (Burlington Twp., Monroe Twp., Morris Twp., Union Twp.); Outside TV Markets (Clinton Twp., Pike Twp., Pleasant Twp., Reading Twp., Richland Twp.). Franchise award date: N.A. Franchise expiration date: N.A. Began: January 1, 1981.

Channel capacity: 30. Channels available but not in use: 12.

Basic Service

Subscribers: 1,412.

Programming (received off-air): WBNS-TV (C), WCMH-TV (N), WOSU-TV (P), WSYX (A), WTTE (F,U) Columbus; WSFJ (I) Newark; WHIZ-TV (N) Zanesville.

Programming (via satellite): WGN-TV (W) Chicago; A & E; CNN; Discovery Channel; ESPN; Fox Family Channel; Headline News; Lifetime; MTV; Nashville Network; Nickelodeon; QVC; TBS Superstation; Turner Network TV; USA Network.

Fee: $40.00 installation; $22.95 monthly.

Pay Service 1

Pay Units: 258.

Programming (via satellite): HBO.

Fee: $10.95 monthly.

Pay Service 2

Pay Units: 211.

Programming (via satellite): The Movie Channel.

Fee: $10.95 monthly.

Pay Service 3

Pay Units: 227.

Programming (via satellite): Showtime.

Fee: $10.95 monthly.

Pay Service 4

Pay Units: N.A.

Programming (via satellite): Cinemax; Disney Channel.

Fee: $10.95 monthly (each).

Local advertising: No.

Miles of plant: 13.6 (coaxial). Homes passed: 2,726.

Manager: Paul S. Schonewolf. Technical operations manager: Dan Fessler. Field operations manager: Bill Schroeder. Marketing manager: Carl Bauer. Customer operations manager: Danielle Turner.

Ownership: Time Warner Cable (MSO).

TIPP CITY—Time Warner Cable, 1450 Experiment Farm Rd., Troy, OH 45373. Phone: 937-339-4974. Fax: 937-339-1844. Counties: Miami & Montgomery. Also serves Butler Twp. (Montgomery County), Concord Twp. (Miami County), Laura, Ludlow Falls, Newton Twp. (Miami County), Potsdam, Union Twp. (Miami County), Washington Twp. (Miami County), West Milton Twp. (Miami County). ICA: OH0084.

Subsystems: Monroe Twp.

TV Market Ranking: 41. Franchise award date: July 1, 1980. Franchise expiration date: N.A. Began: August 31, 1981.

Channel capacity: 54 (2-way capable; operating 2-way). Channels available but not in use: 11.

Basic Service

Subscribers: 6,249.

Programming (received off-air): WCPO-TV (A) Cincinnati; WBNS-TV (C), WOSU-TV (P) Columbus; WDTN (A), WHIO-TV (C), WKEF (N), WPTD (P), WRGT-TV (F,U) Dayton; WLIO (N) Lima; WKOI (T) Richmond; WBDT (W) Springfield; allband FM.

Programming (via satellite): WGN-TV (W) Chicago; QVC; TBS Superstation; TV Guide Channel.

Current originations: Automated time-weather; public access; educational access; government access; automated emergency alert; local news.

Fee: $40.27 installation; $9.14 monthly; $0.44 converter; $22.51 additional installation.

Expanded Basic Service

Subscribers: N.A.

Programming (via satellite): A & E; American Movie Classics; BET; C-SPAN; C-SPAN 2; CNBC; CNN; Cartoon Network; Comedy Central; Country Music TV; Court TV; Discovery Channel; E! Entertainment TV; ESPN; Fox Family Channel; Fox News Channel; Fox Sports Net Ohio; Headline News; History Channel; Learning Channel; Lifetime; MTV; Nashville Network; Nickelodeon; TV Food Network; TV Guide Sneak Prevue; The Weather Channel; Travel Channel; Turner Network TV; USA Network; VH1.

Fee: $20.55 monthly.

Expanded Basic Service 2

Subscribers: N.A.

Programming (via satellite): Animal Planet; ESPN 2; ESPN Classic Sports; Golf Channel; Home & Garden Television; Nick at Nite's TV Land; Sci-Fi Channel; The New Encore; Turner Classic Movies.

Fee: $2.41 monthly.

Pay Service 1

Pay Units: 392.

Programming (via satellite): Cinemax (multiplexed).

Fee: $11.49 monthly.

Pay Service 2

Pay Units: 793.

Programming (via satellite): Disney Channel.

Fee: $7.30 monthly.

Pay Service 3

Pay Units: 1,000.

Programming (via satellite): HBO (multiplexed).

Fee: $12.00 monthly.

Pay Service 4

Pay Units: 99.

Programming (via satellite): The Movie Channel.

Fee: $11.49 monthly.

Pay Service 5

Pay Units: 522.

Programming (via satellite): Showtime (multiplexed).

Fee: $11.49 monthly.

Pay Service 6

Pay Units: N.A.

Programming (via satellite): Flix; Music Choice.

Fee: $5.95 monthly (Music Choice).

Pay-Per-View

Addressable homes: 3,506.

Action Pay-Per-View; Hot Choice; Playboy TV; Spice; Viewer's Choice.

Fee: $11.49 (Playboy TV or Spice).

Local advertising: Yes. Available in satellite distributed & locally originated programming. Rates: $60.00/Month (local origination); $8.00/30 Seconds. Local sales manager: Norm Pytel.

Equipment: Scientific-Atlanta headend; Scientific-Atlanta amplifiers; Times Fiber & Scientific-Atlanta cable; Sony cameras; Sony VTRs; Compuvid character generator; Jerrold set top converters; Zenith addressable set top converters; Vitek traps; Scientific-Atlanta satellite antenna; Scientific-Atlanta satellite receivers.

Miles of plant: 223.0 (coaxial). Homes passed: 8,775.

Manager: Steve Sullenberger. Technical operations manager: Mike Burns. Chief technician: Tim Jackson. Marketing director: Danny Schiffer.

Ownership: Time Warner Cable (MSO).

TOLEDO—Buckeye Cablevision Inc., 5566 Southwyck Blvd., Toledo, OH 43614. Phone: 419-724-9802. Fax: 419-724-7074. Counties: Lucas & Wood, OH; Monroe, MI. Also serves Erie Twp., Lost Peninsula, MI; Harbor View, Holland, Maumee, Middleton Twp., Monclova Twp. (Lucas County), Oregon, Ottawa Hills, Perrysburg, Perrysburg Twp., Rossford, Spencer Twp. (Lucas County), Springfield Twp. (Lucas County), Sylvania, Sylvania Twp. (Lucas County), Washington Twp. (Lucas County), Waterville Twp. (Lucas County), OH. ICA: OH0004.

TV Market Ranking: 52. Franchise award date: May 17, 1965. Franchise expiration date: December 31, 1999. Began: March 15, 1966.

Channel capacity: 60 (not 2-way capable). Channels available but not in use: None.

Basic Service

Subscribers: 128,603.

Programming (received off-air): WBGU-TV (P) Bowling Green; WDIV (N), WJBK (F), WKBD-TV (U), WXYZ-TV (A) Detroit; WGTE-TV (P), WNWO-TV (N), WTOL-TV (C), WTVG (A), WUPW (F) Toledo; CBET Windsor.

Programming (via satellite): C-SPAN; C-SPAN 2; Cartoon Network; Learning Channel; TBS Superstation; TV Guide Channel; TV5.

Current originations: Automated time-weather; leased access.

Fee: $15.00 installation; $25.95 monthly.

Expanded Basic Service

Subscribers: 128,326.

Programming (via satellite): A & E; American Movie Classics; BET; CNBC; CNN; Comedy Central; Court TV; Discovery Channel; E! Entertainment TV; ESPN; ESPN 2; ESPN Classic Sports; EWTN; Fox Family Channel; Headline News; History Channel; Lifetime; MTV; Nashville Network; Nick at Nite; Nick at Nite's TV Land; Nickelodeon; Odyssey; TV Guide Channel; The Health Network; The Weather Channel; Turner Network TV; USA Network; Univision; VH1; ValueVision.

Fee: $15.00 monthly.

A la Carte 1

Subscribers: 37,700.

Programming (via satellite): WGN-TV (W) Chicago; Flix; Golf Channel; Home & Garden Television; Sci-Fi Channel.
Fee: $3.49 monthly (package); $1.39 monthly (Flix).
Pay Service 1
Pay Units: 11,264.
Programming (via satellite): Disney Channel.
Fee: $5.00 installation; $4.95 monthly.
Pay Service 2
Pay Units: 15,666.
Programming (via satellite): HBO.
Fee: $5.00 installation; $12.95 monthly.
Pay Service 3
Pay Units: 18,345.
Programming (via satellite): Showtime.
Fee: $5.00 installation; $8.95 monthly.
Pay Service 4
Pay Units: 14,840.
Programming (via satellite): The Movie Channel.
Fee: $5.00 installation; $9.95 monthly.
Pay-Per-View
Addressable homes: 92,200.
Action Pay-Per-View; Playboy TV; special events.
Fee: $3.95.
Local advertising: Yes. Available in satellite distributed, locally originated & character-generated programming. Rates: $70.00/Minute; $35.00/30 Seconds. Local sales manager: Steve Piller.
Program Guide: TV Host.
Equipment: Scientific-Atlanta headend; C-COR & Jerrold amplifiers; Comm/Scope cable; Sony VTRs; Texscan character generator; Tocom set top converters; Tocom addressable set top converters; Scientific-Atlanta satellite antenna; Scientific-Atlanta satellite receivers; ChannelMatic commercial insert.
Miles of plant: 1780.0 (coaxial); 300.0 (fiber optic). Homes passed: 206,000. Total homes in franchised area: 208,000.
Manager: David G. Huey. Chief technician: Joseph Jensen. Marketing & program director: Ellen Jackson. Customer service manager: Bonnie Ask.
City fee: 4% of gross.
Ownership: Blade Communications Inc. (MSO).

TORONTO—Jefferson County Cable Inc., 116 S. 4th St., Toronto, OH 43964. Phone: 740-537-2214. Fax: 740-537-2802. County: Jefferson. Also serves Costonia, Empire, Pleasant Hill (Jefferson County), Pottery Addition, Smithfield, Stratton, Taylortown. ICA: OH0371.
TV Market Ranking: 10 (Costonia, Empire, Pleasant Hill, Pottery Addition, Taylortown, Toronto); 90 (Costonia, Empire, Pleasant Hill, Pottery Addition, Smithfield, Stratton, Taylortown, Toronto). Franchise award date: N.A. Franchise expiration date: N.A. Began: December 1, 1984.
Channel capacity: 36. Channels available but not in use: N.A.
Basic Service
Subscribers: N.A.
Programming (received off-air): KDKA-TV (C), WCWB (W), WPGH-TV (F), WPXI (N), WQED (P), WTAE-TV (A) Pittsburgh; WTOV-TV (N) Steubenville-Wheeling; WTRF-TV (C) Wheeling-Steubenville; WKBN-TV (C), WYTV (A,F) Youngstown.
Programming (via satellite): ESPN.
Fee: Free installation; $6.75 monthly.
Expanded Basic Service
Subscribers: N.A.
Programming (received off-air): WOUC-TV (P) Cambridge; WFMJ-TV (N) Youngstown.
Programming (via satellite): WGN-TV (W) Chicago; CNBC; CNN; Fox Family Channel; Lifetime; MTV; Nashville Network; Nickelodeon; TBS Superstation; USA Network.
Fee: $2.20 monthly.
Pay Service 1
Pay Units: N.A.
Programming (via satellite): Cinemax; Disney Channel; HBO; The Movie Channel.
Fee: $7.00 monthly (Disney), $8.60 monthly (Cinemax), $9.60 monthly (TMC), $9.95 monthly (HBO).
Program Guide: The Cable Guide.
Miles of plant: 15.0 (coaxial).
Manager: David Bates.
Ownership: Jefferson County Cable Inc. (MSO).

TROY—Warner Cable Communications Inc., 1450 Experiment Farm Rd., Troy, OH 45373. Phone: 937-339-4770. Fax: 937-339-1844. County: Miami. Also serves Casstown, Concord Twp. (Miami County), Elizabeth Twp. (Miami County), Lostcreek Twp., Newberry Twp., Staunton Twp. ICA: OH0069.
TV Market Ranking: 41. Franchise award date: October 19, 1978. Franchise expiration date: N.A. Began: October 14, 1979.
Channel capacity: 36 (2-way capable; operating 2-way). Channels available but not in use: None.
Basic Service
Subscribers: 7,700.
Programming (received off-air): WKRC-TV (C), WLWT (N) Cincinnati; WBNS-TV (C), WOSU-TV (P) Columbus; WDTN (A), WHIO-TV (C), WKEF (N), WPTD (P), WRGT-TV (F,U) Dayton; WLIO (N) Lima; allband FM.
Programming (via satellite): WGN-TV (W) Chicago; A & E; C-SPAN; C-SPAN 2; CNBC; CNN; ESPN; Fox Family Channel; Headline News; Lifetime; MTV; Nashville Network; Nickelodeon; QVC; TBS Superstation; The Weather Channel; Turner Network TV; USA Network.
Current originations: Automated time-weather; public access; educational access; government access; local news.
Fee: $19.95 installation; $13.65 monthly; $14.95 additional installation.
Pay Service 1
Pay Units: 481.
Programming (via satellite): Cinemax.
Fee: $10.00 installation; $10.94 monthly.
Pay Service 2
Pay Units: 768.
Programming (via satellite): Disney Channel.
Fee: $10.00 installation; $6.95 monthly.
Pay Service 3
Pay Units: 2,450.
Programming (via satellite): HBO.
Fee: $14.95 installation; $11.45 monthly.
Pay Service 4
Pay Units: 423.
Programming (via satellite): Showtime.
Fee: $10.00 installation; $10.94 monthly.
Pay-Per-View
Action Pay-Per-View; Spice.
Local advertising: Yes (locally produced & insert). Rates: $60.00/Month (local origination); $8.00/30 Seconds. Local sales manager: Norm Pytel.
Miles of plant: 176.0 (coaxial). Homes passed: 11,049.
Manager: Steve Sullenberger. Technical operations manager: Mike Burns. Chief technician: Tim Jackson. Marketing director: Danny Schiffer.
Ownership: Time Warner Cable (MSO).

UPPER ARLINGTON—Americast, 300 S. Riverside, Chicago, IL 60606. Phones: 312-526-8000; 800-848-2278. Fax: 312-526-8565. County: Franklin. ICA: OH0422.

TV Market Ranking: 27. Franchise award date: March 1, 1996. Franchise expiration date: N.A. Began: N.A.
Channel capacity: N.A. Channels available but not in use: N.A.
Basic Service
Subscribers: N.A.
Programming (received off-air): WWHO (U) Chillicothe; WBNS-TV (C), WCMH-TV (N), WOSU-TV (P), WSYX (A), WTTE (F,U) Columbus; WSFJ (I) Newark.
Programming (via satellite): WGN-TV (W) Chicago; QVC; TBS Superstation; TV Guide Channel.
Current originations: Public access; educational access; government access; leased access.
Fee: $39.95 installation; $9.95 monthly.
Expanded Basic Service
Subscribers: N.A.
Programming (via satellite): A & E; American Movie Classics; BET; BET on Jazz; Bravo; C-SPAN; C-SPAN 2; CNBC; CNN; CNNfn; Cartoon Network; Comedy Central; Country Music TV; Court TV; Discovery Channel; Disney Channel; E! Entertainment TV; ESPN; ESPN 2; ESPN Classic Sports; Fox Family Channel; Fox Sports Net Ohio; Golf Channel; Headline News; History Channel; Home & Garden Television; Learning Channel; Lifetime; MTV; Nashville Network; Nickelodeon; Ohio News Network; Sci-Fi Channel; TV Food Network; The Health Network; The Inspirational Network; The Weather Channel; Travel Channel; Turner Classic Movies; Turner Network TV; USA Network; VH1.
Fee: $17.00 monthly.
Pay Service 1
Pay Units: N.A.
Programming (via satellite): Cinemax; Flix; HBO (multiplexed); Showtime (multiplexed); Starz!; Sundance Channel; The Movie Channel; The New Encore.
Fee: $5.95 monthly (Flix or Sundance), $7.95 monthly (Encore & Starz), $9.95 monthly (Cinemax, Showtime or TMC), $11.95 monthly (HBO).
Total homes in franchised area: 14,950.
Ownership: Ameritech New Media Inc. (MSO).

UPPER SANDUSKY—Time Warner Cable, 114 N. Sandusky Ave., Upper Sandusky, OH 43351-1254. Phone: 800-425-2225. County: Wyandot. Also serves Antrim Twp., Crane Twp., Eden Twp., Harpster, Nevada, Pitt Twp. ICA: OH0138.
TV Market Ranking: Below 100 (portions of Antrim Twp., portions of Crane Twp., portions of Eden Twp.); Outside TV Markets (portions of Antrim Twp., portions of Crane Twp., portions of Eden Twp., Harpster, Nevada, Pitt Twp., Upper Sandusky). Franchise award date: January 1, 1967. Franchise expiration date: June 21, 2001. Began: September 1, 1967.
Channel capacity: 52 (2-way capable; operating 2-way). Channels available but not in use: 22.
Basic Service
Subscribers: 2,327.
Programming (received off-air): WBGU-TV (P) Bowling Green; W54AF (I) Bucyrus; WEWS-TV (A), WJW (F) Cleveland; WBNS-TV (C), WCMH-TV (N), WOSU-TV (P), WSYX (A) Columbus; WLIO (N) Lima; WNWO-TV (N), WTOL-TV (C), WTVG (A), WUPW (F) Toledo; 12 FMs.
Programming (via microwave): WUAB (U) Lorain-Cleveland.
Programming (via satellite): C-SPAN; CNN; Discovery Channel; ESPN; Fox Family Channel; Headline News; Home Shopping Network; Lifetime; Nashville Network; Odyssey; TBS Superstation; TV Guide Channel; The Weather Channel; Turner Network TV; USA Network.
Current originations: Automated time-weather; public access; educational access; government access; automated emergency alert; local news.
Fee: $41.50 installation; $12.06 monthly.
Pay Service 1
Pay Units: 1,685.
Programming (via satellite): Cinemax; Disney Channel; HBO.
Fee: $12.00 installation; $10.90 monthly (each).
Local advertising: Yes. Available in character-generated programming. Rates: $3.00/Day.
Equipment: Jerrold & Scientific-Atlanta headend; GTE Sylvania & Texscan amplifiers; Comm/Scope & Times Fiber cable; Info/Soft character generator; RCA set top converters; Eagle & Arcom traps; Microdyne, Scientific-Atlanta & RCA satellite antenna; Microdyne & Standard Communications satellite receivers.
Miles of plant: 44.0 (coaxial); 7.0 (fiber optic). Homes passed: 3,503.
Manager: Daniel Bemis. Chief technician: Paul Gross. Program director: J. Michael Quinlan.
City fee: $100 annually.
Ownership: Time Warner Cable (MSO). Purchased from MediaOne Group, August 2, 1999.

URBANA—Time Warner Entertainment Co. LP, Suites 7 & 8, 1512 State Rte. 68 S, Urbana, OH 43078. Phone: 937-653-5507. Counties: Champaign & Logan. Also serves Champaign County (portions), Liberty Twp. (Logan County), Logan County (portions), Mechanicsburg, Monroe Twp. (Logan County), Mutual, Springhill, West Liberty. ICA: OH0094.
TV Market Ranking: 27 (portions of Champaign County); 41 (portions of Champaign County, Urbana); Below 100 (portions of Champaign County, Liberty Twp., Logan County, Mechanicsburg, Monroe Twp., Mutual, Springhill, West Liberty). Franchise award date: N.A. Franchise expiration date: N.A. Began: January 1, 1979.
Channel capacity: 36 (2-way capable; operating 2-way). Channels available but not in use: None.
Basic Service
Subscribers: 5,318.
Programming (received off-air): WBNS-TV (C), WOSU-TV (P) Columbus; WDTN (A), WHIO-TV (C), WKEF (N), WPTD (P), WRGT-TV (F,U) Dayton; WLIO (N) Lima.
Programming (via satellite): WGN-TV (W) Chicago; A & E; C-SPAN; CNN; Cartoon Network; Comedy Central; Discovery Channel; ESPN; Fox Family Channel; Headline News;

Lifetime; MTV; Nashville Network; Nickelodeon; Odyssey; QVC; TBS Superstation; The Weather Channel; Turner Classic Movies; Turner Network TV; USA Network; VH1.
Current originations: Automated time-weather.
Fee: $19.95 installation; $20.40 monthly.
Pay Service 1
Pay Units: 2,475.
Programming (via satellite): Cinemax; HBO; Showtime; The Movie Channel.
Fee: $10.95 monthly (each).
Pay Service 2
Pay Units: 586.
Programming (via satellite): Disney Channel.
Fee: $6.95 monthly.
Equipment: Scientific-Atlanta satellite antenna.
Miles of plant: 131.0 (coaxial). Homes passed: 7,876. Total homes in franchised area: 7,876.
Manager: Steve Sullenberger. Chief technician: Todd Lutz. Marketing director: Danny Schiffer.
Ownership: Time Warner Cable (MSO).

UTICA—Time Warner Cable, Box 787, 111 S. Mulberry St., Mount Vernon, OH 43050. Phones: 740-397-2288; 800-782-4118. Fax: 740-397-3730. County: Licking. ICA: OH0217.
TV Market Ranking: 27. Franchise award date: N.A. Franchise expiration date: N.A. Began: August 1, 1982.
Channel capacity: 30. Channels available but not in use: 12.
Basic Service
Subscribers: 617.
Programming (received off-air): WBNS-TV (C), WCMH-TV (N), WOSU-TV (P), WSYX (A), WTTE (F,U) Columbus; WSFJ (I) Newark.
Programming (via satellite): WGN-TV (W) Chicago; CNN; ESPN; Fox Family Channel; MTV; Nashville Network; Nickelodeon; TBS Superstation; The Weather Channel; USA Network.
Fee: $25.00 installation; $18.50 monthly.
Pay Service 1
Pay Units: 64.
Programming (via satellite): HBO.
Fee: $10.95 monthly.
Pay Service 2
Pay Units: 49.
Programming (via satellite): The Movie Channel.
Fee: $10.95 monthly.
Pay Service 3
Pay Units: 101.
Programming (via satellite): Showtime.
Fee: $10.95 monthly.
Miles of plant: 9.9 (coaxial).
Manager: Paul S. Schonewolf. Technical operations manager: Dan Fessler. Field operations manager: Bill Schroeder. Marketing manager: Carl Bauer. Customer operations manager: Danielle Turner.
Ownership: Time Warner Cable (MSO).

VALLEYVIEW—Americast, 300 S. Riverside, Chicago, IL 60606. Phones: 312-526-8000; 800-848-2278. Fax: 312-526-8565. County: Franklin. ICA: OH0424.
TV Market Ranking: 27. Franchise award date: August 1, 1997. Franchise expiration date: N.A. Began: N.A.
Channel capacity: N.A. Channels available but not in use: N.A.
Basic Service
Subscribers: N.A.
Programming (received off-air): WWHO (U) Chillicothe; WBNS-TV (C), WCMH-TV (N), WOSU-TV (P), WSYX (A), WTTE (F,U) Columbus; WSFJ (I) Newark.
Programming (via satellite): WGN-TV (W) Chicago; QVC; TBS Superstation; TV Guide Channel.
Current originations: Public access; educational access; government access; leased access.
Fee: $39.95 installation; $9.95 monthly.
Expanded Basic Service
Subscribers: N.A.
Programming (via satellite): A & E; American Movie Classics; BET; BET on Jazz; Bravo; C-SPAN; C-SPAN 2; CNBC; CNN; CNNfn; Cartoon Network; Comedy Central; Country Music TV; Court TV; Discovery Channel; Disney Channel; E! Entertainment TV; ESPN; ESPN 2; ESPN Classic Sports; Fox Family Channel; Fox Sports Net Ohio; Golf Channel; Headline News; History Channel; Home & Garden Television; Learning Channel; Lifetime; MTV; Nashville Network; Nickelodeon; Ohio News Network; Sci-Fi Channel; TV Food Network; The Health Network; The Inspirational Network; The Weather Channel; Travel Channel; Turner Classic Movies; Turner Network TV; USA Network; VH1.
Fee: $17.00 monthly.
Pay Service 1
Pay Units: N.A.
Programming (via satellite): Cinemax; Flix; HBO (multiplexed); Showtime (multiplexed); Starz!; Sundance Channel; The Movie Channel; The New Encore.
Fee: $5.95 monthly (Flix or Sundance), $7.95 monthly (Encore & Starz), $9.95 monthly (Cinemax, Showtime or TMC), $11.95 monthly (HBO).
Total homes in franchised area: 250.
Ownership: Ameritech New Media Inc. (MSO).

VAN WERT—FrontierVision, Box 627, Chillicothe, OH 45601. Phones: 740-775-4300; 800-346-2288. Fax: 740-775-2915. Counties: Paulding & Van Wert. Also serves Crane Twp. (Paulding County), Hoaglin Twp. (Van Wert County), Liberty Twp. (Van Wert County), Ohio City, Ridge Twp. (Van Wert County), Union Twp. (Van Wert County), Van Wert Twp. (Van Wert County). ICA: OH0104.
TV Market Ranking: 82 (Ohio City, Van Wert, Van Wert Twp.); Below 100 (Crane Twp., Hoaglin Twp., Liberty Twp., Ridge Twp., Union Twp.). Franchise award date: N.A. Franchise expiration date: N.A. Began: October 1, 1974.
Channel capacity: 39 (2-way capable; operating 2-way). Channels available but not in use: None.
Basic Service
Subscribers: 3,923.
Programming (received off-air): WBGU-TV (P) Bowling Green; WANE-TV (C), WFFT-TV (F), WFWA (P), WKJG-TV (N), WPTA (A) Fort Wayne; WLIO (N), WTLW (I) Lima.
Programming (via satellite): WGN-TV (W) Chicago; C-SPAN; CNN; Discovery Channel; Fox Family Channel; Fox Sports Net Ohio; Headline News; Lifetime; MTV; Nashville Network; Nickelodeon; Odyssey; QVC; TBS Superstation; The Weather Channel.
Current originations: Automated time-weather; educational access; local news.
Fee: $60.00 installation; $9.86 monthly; $30.00 additional installation.
Expanded Basic Service
Subscribers: 3,679.
Programming (via satellite): A & E; Disney Channel; ESPN; Turner Network TV; USA Network.
Fee: $11.74 monthly.
Pay Service 1
Pay Units: 337.
Programming (via satellite): Cinemax.
Fee: $15.00 installation; $9.95 monthly.
Pay Service 2
Pay Units: 586.
Programming (via satellite): HBO.
Fee: $15.00 installation; $9.95 monthly.
Pay Service 3
Pay Units: 191.
Programming (via satellite): Starz!
Fee: N.A.
Pay Service 4
Pay Units: 180.
Programming (via satellite): The Movie Channel.
Fee: N.A.
Pay-Per-View
Addressable homes: 73.
Local advertising: Yes.
Equipment: Tocom headend; C-COR amplifiers; Comm/Scope cable; AFC satellite antenna.
Miles of plant: 114.6 (coaxial). Homes passed: 6,109.
Manager: Richard Coplan. Chief technician: Sam Morabith. Program director: Chad Hume. Marketing director: Barbara Brewer.
City fee: 3% of gross.
Ownership: FrontierVision Partners LP (MSO). See Cable System Ownership.

VANDALIA—MediaOne, 4166 Little York Rd., Dayton, OH 45414. Phones: 937-294-6400; 800-425-2225. Fax: 937-294-3994. Web site: http://www.mediaone.com. County: Montgomery. Also serves Englewood, Harrison Twp., Huber Heights, Trotwood, Union. ICA: OH0434.
TV Market Ranking: 41. Franchise award date: N.A. Franchise expiration date: N.A. Began: N.A.
Channel capacity: N.A. Channels available but not in use: N.A.
Basic Service
Subscribers: 34,498.
Programming (received off-air): WCET (P), WCPO-TV (A), WKRC-TV (C) Cincinnati; WXIX-TV (F) Cincinnati-Newport; WDTN (A), WHIO-TV (C), WKEF (N), WPTD (P), WRGT-TV (F,U), WUCT-LP (W) Dayton; WPTO (P) Oxford; WKOI (T) Richmond; WBDT (W) Springfield.
Programming (via satellite): EWTN; Fox News Channel; Home Shopping Network; MSNBC; QVC; TV Food Network; TV Guide Channel; The Weather Channel; Travel Channel; ValueVision; Z Music Television.
Current originations: Public access; educational access; government access.
Fee: $41.00 installation; $10.44 monthly.
Expanded Basic Service
Subscribers: N.A.
Programming (via satellite): A & E; American Movie Classics; Animal Planet; BET; Bravo; C-SPAN; C-SPAN 2; CNBC; CNN; Cartoon Network; Comedy Central; Country Music TV; Court TV; Discovery Channel; E! Entertainment TV; ESPN; ESPN 2; Fox Family Channel; Fox Sports Net Ohio; Golf Channel; Headline News; History Channel; Home & Garden Television; Learning Channel; Lifetime; MTV; Nashville Network; Nick at Nite's TV Land; Nickelodeon; Outdoor Life Network; Sci-Fi Channel; Speedvision; USA Network; VH1.
Fee: $19.29 monthly.
Expanded Basic Service 2
Subscribers: N.A.
Programming (via satellite): WGN-TV (W) Chicago; TBS Superstation; Turner Network TV.
Fee: $1.74 monthly.
Pay Service 1
Pay Units: N.A.
Programming (via satellite): Cinemax; Disney Channel; HBO (multiplexed); Independent Film Channel; Showtime; Starz!; The New Encore.
Fee: $5.95 monthly (IFC), $10.95 monthly (Encore & Starz), $11.50 monthly (Disney), $11.95 monthly (Cinemax HBO or Showtime).
Pay-Per-View
Hot Choice; Spice Hot; Viewer's Choice 1-4.
Ownership: MediaOne Group (MSO). Sale pends to Time Warner Cable.

VERMILION—Adelphia Cable, Box 178, 1801 Elyria Ave., Lorain, OH 44052-0178. Phone: 440-245-3535. Fax: 440-245-6094. Counties: Erie & Lorain. Also serves Brownhelm Twp., Florence Twp. (Erie County), Vermilion Twp. ICA: OH0118.
TV Market Ranking: 8. Franchise award date: N.A. Franchise expiration date: N.A. Began: March 1, 1983.
Channel capacity: 62 (2-way capable; operating 2-way). Channels available but not in use: 15.
Basic Service
Subscribers: 3,961.
Programming (received off-air): WBNX-TV (W,F), WEAO (P), WVPX (X) Akron; WNEO (P) Alliance; WEWS-TV (A), WJW (F), WKYC-TV (N), WQHS-TV (H), WVIZ-TV (P) Cleveland; WUAB (U) Lorain-Cleveland; WOIO (C) Shaker Heights; WNWO-TV (N), WTOL-TV (C), WTVG (A) Toledo.
Current originations: Public access; educational access; government access; leased access.
Fee: $2.95 monthly.
Expanded Basic Service
Subscribers: N.A.
Programming (via satellite): WGN-TV (W) Chicago; A & E; C-SPAN; CNN; Learning Channel; Nickelodeon.
Fee: $6.30 monthly.
Expanded Basic Service 2
Subscribers: N.A.
Programming (via satellite): Goodlife TV Network.
Fee: $2.95 monthly.
Expanded Basic Service 3
Subscribers: N.A.
Programming (via satellite): ESPN; Fox Family Channel; Lifetime; MTV; Nashville Network; TBS Superstation; USA Network.
Fee: $8.50 monthly.
Pay Service 1
Pay Units: N.A.
Programming (via satellite): Cinemax; Disney Channel; HBO; The Movie Channel.
Fee: $7.95 monthly (each).
Local advertising: Yes. Available in character-generated programming.
Equipment: Jerrold headend; Texscan amplifiers; Comm/Scope cable; Panasonic cameras; Panasonic VTRs; MSI character generator; Scientific-Atlanta set top converters; Scientific-Atlanta addressable set top converters; PPC traps; Simulsat satellite antenna; Jerrold satellite receivers.
Miles of plant: 130.0 (coaxial). Additional miles planned: 25.0 (coaxial). Homes passed: 4,560. Total homes in franchised area: 5,400.
Manager: Mitch Piskur. Chief technician: Kevin Alessio.
City fee: 5% of gross.
Ownership: Adelphia Communications Corp. (MSO).

VERNON—Star Cable, Box 4478, 4720 Mahoning Ave., Youngstown, OH 44515. Phone: 330-792-9577. Fax: 330-792-9541. Counties: Ashtabula & Trumbull. Also serves Andover Twp. (Ashtabula County), Braceville Twp., Kinsman (Trumbull County), Kinsman Twp., Pymatuning

State Park, Vernon Twp. (Trumbull County), Williamsfield. ICA: OH0246.
TV Market Ranking: 8 (Braceville Twp.); 79 (Andover Twp., Braceville Twp., Kinsman, Kinsman Twp., Pymatuning State Park, Vernon, Vernon Twp., Williamsfield). Franchise award date: July 13, 1989. Franchise expiration date: July 13, 2004. Began: July 1, 1990.
Channel capacity: 62 (not 2-way capable). Channels available but not in use: 23.

Basic Service

Subscribers: 574; Commercial subscribers: 60.
Programming (received off-air): WBNX-TV (W,F) Akron; WEWS-TV (A), WJW (F), WKYC-TV (N), WVIZ-TV (P) Cleveland; WUAB (U) Lorain-Cleveland; WOIO (C) Shaker Heights; WFMJ-TV (N), WKBN-TV (C), WYTV (A,F) Youngstown.
Programming (via satellite): TBS Superstation.
Fee: $10.50 monthly; $1.95 converter.

Expanded Basic Service

Subscribers: 553.
Programming (via satellite): WGN-TV (W) Chicago; A & E; American Movie Classics; C-SPAN; CNN; Discovery Channel; ESPN; Fox Family Channel; Fox Sports Net Ohio; Fox Sports Net Pittsburgh; Headline News; History Channel; Lifetime; MTV; Nashville Network; Nick at Nite's TV Land; Nickelodeon; QVC; Sci-Fi Channel; The Weather Channel; Turner Network TV; USA Network; VH1.
Fee: $18.75 monthly.

Pay Service 1

Pay Units: 53.
Programming (via satellite): Cinemax.
Fee: $11.00 monthly.

Pay Service 2

Pay Units: 61.
Programming (via satellite): Disney Channel.
Fee: $7.95 monthly.

Pay Service 3

Pay Units: 71.
Programming (via satellite): HBO.
Fee: $11.00 monthly.

Pay Service 4

Pay Units: 56.
Programming (via satellite): Showtime; The Movie Channel.
Fee: $12.95 monthly.

Local advertising: No.
Equipment: DX Antenna & Scientific-Atlanta headend; Scientific-Atlanta amplifiers; Comm/Scope cable; Panasonic set top converters; Eagle traps; DH Satellite satellite antenna; DX Antenna satellite receivers.
Miles of plant: 45.4 (coaxial); None (fiber optic). Homes passed: 894. Total homes in franchised area: 894.
Manager: Terry Dickerhoof. Chief technician: Tom Beat.
Franchise fee: 5% of gross.
Ownership: Star Cable Associates (MSO).

VERSAILLES—FrontierVision, Box 7, 14 S. Hanover, Minster, OH 45865. Phone: 419-628-3423. Counties: Darke & Shelby. Also serves North Star, Osgood, Russia, Wayne Twp. (Darke County), Yorkshire. ICA: OH0190.
TV Market Ranking: 41 (Russia, Versailles); Outside TV Markets (North Star, Osgood, Yorkshire). Franchise award date: N.A. Franchise expiration date: N.A. Began: October 1, 1975.
Channel capacity: 37. Channels available but not in use: 2.

Basic Service

Subscribers: 1,468.
Programming (received off-air): WCPO-TV (A), WKRC-TV (C), WLWT (N) Cincinnati; WXIX-TV (F) Cincinnati-Newport; WBNS-TV (C) Columbus; WDTN (A), WHIO-TV (C), WKEF (N), WPTD (P) Dayton; WFFT-TV (F) Fort Wayne; WLIO (N) Lima; allband FM.
Programming (via satellite): WGN-TV (W) Chicago; TBS Superstation.
Current originations: Automated time-weather.
Fee: $31.90 installation; $11.59 monthly.

Pay Service 1

Pay Units: 91.
Programming (via satellite): The New Encore.
Fee: N.A.

Pay Service 2

Pay Units: 155.
Programming (via satellite): HBO.
Fee: N.A.

Pay Service 3

Pay Units: 233.
Programming (via satellite): Showtime.
Fee: N.A.

Pay Service 4

Pay Units: 88.
Programming (via satellite): Starz!
Fee: N.A.

Pay Service 5

Pay Units: 148.
Programming (via satellite): The Movie Channel.
Fee: N.A.

Miles of plant: 57.6 (coaxial). Homes passed: 2,075.
Manager: Steve Trippe. Chief technician: Bill Ricker.
City fee: None.
Ownership: FrontierVision Partners LP (MSO). See Cable System Ownership.

WAKEMAN—FrontierVision, Box 627, Chillicothe, OH 45601. Phones: 740-775-4300; 800-346-2288. Fax: 740-775-2915. Counties: Erie, Huron & Lorain. Also serves Berlin Heights, Berlin Twp. (Erie County), Berlinville, Camden Twp., Collins, Huron, Milan. ICA: OH0373.
TV Market Ranking: 8. Franchise award date: February 1, 1985. Franchise expiration date: March 11, 2005. Began: March 11, 1985.
Channel capacity: 42 (not 2-way capable). Channels available but not in use: None.

Basic Service

Subscribers: 1,033.
Programming (received off-air): WBNX-TV (W,F) Akron; WEWS-TV (A), WJW (F), WKYC-TV (N), WQHS-TV (H), WVIZ-TV (P) Cleveland; WUAB (U) Lorain-Cleveland; WGGN-TV (T) Sandusky; WOIO (C) Shaker Heights; WNWO-TV (N), WTOL-TV (C), WTVG (A) Toledo.
Programming (via satellite): WGN-TV (W) Chicago; C-SPAN; Cartoon Network; Country Music TV; Discovery Channel; E! Entertainment TV; Fox Family Channel; Fox Sports Net Ohio; Learning Channel; MTV; Nashville Network; Nickelodeon; The Weather Channel; Trinity Bcstg. Network; USA Network; VH1.
Fee: $43.75 installation; $16.95 monthly.

Expanded Basic Service

Subscribers: 938.
Programming (via satellite): CNN; Disney Channel; ESPN; Sci-Fi Channel; TBS Superstation; Turner Classic Movies; Turner Network TV.
Fee: $4.50 monthly.

Pay Service 1

Pay Units: 195.
Programming (via satellite): Cinemax.
Fee: $10.00 monthly.

Pay Service 2

Pay Units: 204.
Programming (via satellite): HBO.
Fee: $10.00 monthly.

Pay-Per-View

Addressable homes: 6.

Local advertising: Yes. Available in character-generated programming. Local sales manager: John Finley.
Program Guide: CableView.
Equipment: Sony, General & Drake headend; Scientific-Atlanta amplifiers; Times Fiber cable; Hamlin, Jerrold & NSC set top converters.
Miles of plant: 59.0 (coaxial). Homes passed: 1,994.
Manager: Richard Coplan. Chief technician: Sam Morabith. Program director: Chad Hume. Marketing director: Barbara Brewer.
City fee: 3% of gross semi-annually.
Ownership: FrontierVision Partners LP (MSO). See Cable System Ownership.

WAPAKONETA—Time Warner Cable, 120 W. Auglaize St., Wapakoneta, OH 45895. Phone: 419-738-3020. County: Auglaize. Also serves Auglaize County, Duchoquet Twp. (southern portion), Moulton Twp., Noble Twp. (Auglaize County), St. Mary's Twp. (Auglaize County), Union Twp. (Auglaize County), Washington Twp. (Auglaize County). ICA: OH0119.
TV Market Ranking: Below 100. Franchise award date: N.A. Franchise expiration date: N.A. Began: January 20, 1967.
Channel capacity: 36. Channels available but not in use: 1.

Basic Service

Subscribers: 4,002; Commercial subscribers: 65.
Programming (received off-air): WBGU-TV (P) Bowling Green; WBNS-TV (C) Columbus; WDTN (A), WHIO-TV (C), WKEF (N), WRGT-TV (F,U) Dayton; WFFT-TV (F), WPTA (A) Fort Wayne; WLIO (N), WTLW (I) Lima; allband FM.
Programming (via satellite): TBS Superstation.
Current originations: Automated time-weather; local news.
Fee: $39.90 installation; $7.82 monthly; $2.71 converter.

Expanded Basic Service

Subscribers: 3,792.
Programming (via satellite): A & E; C-SPAN; CNN; Comedy Central; Discovery Channel; E! Entertainment TV; ESPN; Headline News; Lifetime; MTV; Nashville Network; Nickelodeon; QVC; TV Guide Channel; The Weather Channel; Turner Network TV; USA Network.
Fee: $17.29 monthly.

Pay Service 1

Pay Units: 204.
Programming (via satellite): Cinemax.
Fee: $10.00 installation; $11.50 monthly.

Pay Service 2

Pay Units: 201.
Programming (via satellite): Disney Channel.
Fee: $7.95 monthly.

Pay Service 3

Pay Units: 375.
Programming (via satellite): Flix.
Fee: N.A.

Pay Service 4

Pay Units: 402.
Programming (via satellite): HBO.
Fee: $11.50 monthly.

Pay Service 5

Pay Units: 375.
Programming (via satellite): The Movie Channel.
Fee: N.A.

Pay Service 6

Pay Units: 374.
Programming (via satellite): Showtime.
Fee: $12.55 monthly.

Pay-Per-View

Addressable homes: 998.
Viewer's Choice.
Fee: $3.95.

Equipment: Jerrold & RCA headend; Jerrold amplifiers; Comm/Scope cable; Compuvid character generator; Jerrold set top converters; Vitek traps; Scientific-Atlanta satellite antenna; Scientific-Atlanta satellite receivers.
Miles of plant: 91.0 (coaxial). Homes passed: 5,100. Total homes in franchised area: 5,100.
Manager: Jeff Parker. Chief technician: Bill Lambert. Marketing director: Danny Schiffer.
Ownership: Time Warner Cable (MSO).

WARNER—CableVision Communications, Box 2200, 68 5th St., Buckhannon, WV 26201. Phone: 304-472-4193. Fax: 304-472-0756. Counties: Noble & Washington. Also serves Aurelius Twp., Caldwell, Dexter City, Dudley, Elba, Jackson Twp. (Noble County), Lower Salem, Macksburg, Olive Twp. (Noble County), Salem Twp. (Washington County), South Drive, Whipple. ICA: OH0248.
TV Market Ranking: Below 100. Franchise award date: April 3, 1985. Franchise expiration date: June 1, 2000. Began: N.A.
Channel capacity: 31. Channels available but not in use: 8.

Basic Service

Subscribers: 445.
Programming (received off-air): WOUB-TV (P) Athens; WCHS-TV (A), WOWK-TV (C), WSAZ-TV (N) Charleston-Huntington; WDTV (C,A) Clarksburg-Weston; WKRN-TV (A) Nashville; WTAP-TV (N) Parkersburg-Marietta; WTOV-TV (N) Steubenville-Wheeling; WTRF-TV (C) Wheeling-Steubenville; WHIZ-TV (N) Zanesville.
Programming (via satellite): WGN-TV (W) Chicago; American Movie Classics; Animal Planet; CNN; Discovery Channel; Disney Channel; ESPN; Fox Family Channel; FoxNet; Great American Country; Home Shopping Network; Lifetime; Nashville Network; Nickelodeon; TBS Superstation; Trinity Bcstg. Network; Turner Network TV; USA Network; VH1.
Fee: $61.25 installation; $28.64 monthly; $1.24 converter; $17.50 additional installation.

Pay Service 1

Pay Units: N.A.
Programming (via satellite): Cinemax; HBO; Showtime; The Movie Channel.
Fee: $17.50 installation; $7.95 monthly (Cinemax), $11.95 monthly (Showtime or TMC), $11.99 monthly (HBO).

Equipment: Blonder-Tongue, Jerrold & Microdyne headend; Jerrold amplifiers; Times Fiber cable; ChannelMaster satellite antenna; Blonder-Tongue satellite receivers.
Miles of plant: 29.0 (coaxial). Homes passed: 689.
Manager: Willie Critchfield. Marketing director: Kenny Phillips.
City fee: None.
Ownership: Rifkin & Associates Inc. (MSO). See Cable System Ownership.

WARREN—Time Warner Cable, 2650 Weir Rd. NE, Warren, OH 44483. Phones: 330-372-1112; 800-826-2983. Fax: 330-372-9520. Web site: http://www.twcable.com. County: Trumbull. Also serves Bazetta, Champion Twp. (Trumbull County), Cortland, Girard, Howland Twp. (Trumbull County), Hubbard, Hubbard Twp. (Trumbull County), Liberty Twp. (Trumbull County), Niles, Vienna Twp., Warren Twp. (Trumbull County), Weathersfield Twp. (Trumbull County). ICA: OH0013.

TV Market Ranking: 79. Franchise award date: N.A. Franchise expiration date: N.A. Began: January 1, 1974.
Channel capacity: 78 (2-way capable). Channels available but not in use: N.A.

Basic Service
Subscribers: 44,233.
Programming (received off-air): WNEO (P) Alliance; WEWS-TV (A), WJW (F), WKYC-TV (N) Cleveland; WUAB (U) Lorain-Cleveland; WOIO (C) Shaker Heights; WFMJ-TV (N), WKBN-TV (C), WYTV (A,F) Youngstown; 4 FMs.
Programming (via microwave): Ecumenical TV Channel.
Programming (via satellite): Court TV; Discovery Channel; QVC; TBS Superstation; TV Guide Sneak Prevue.
Current originations: Automated time-weather; public access; educational access; government access; local news.
Fee: $39.95 installation; $11.04 monthly; $3.50 converter; $18.95 additional installation.

Digital Basic Service
Subscribers: N.A.
Programming (via satellite): BBC America; Bravo; Discovery Home & Leisure Channel; Discovery Kids Channel; Discovery People; Discovery Science Channel; Discovery Wings Channel; ESPN Classic Sports; ESPNews; Fox Sports World; Game Show Network; Golf Channel; History Channel; Independent Film Channel; Outdoor Life Network; Romance Classics; Sci-Fi Channel; Speedvision; Turner Classic Movies.
Fee: $10.00 monthly.

Expanded Basic Service
Subscribers: 41,032.
Programming (via satellite): A & E; American Movie Classics; Animal Planet; BET; C-SPAN; C-SPAN 2; CNBC; CNN; Disney Channel; ESPN; FX; Fox Family Channel; Fox News Channel; Fox Sports Net Ohio; Fox Sports Net Pittsburgh; Headline News; Home & Garden Television; Home Shopping Network; Learning Channel; Lifetime; MOVIEplex; MSNBC; MTV; Nashville Network; Nickelodeon; Odyssey; Ohio News Network; Pax Net; TV Guide Channel; The Weather Channel; Turner Network TV; USA Network.
Fee: $13.95 installation; $19.06 monthly.

A la Carte 1
Subscribers: N.A.
Programming (via satellite): Cartoon Network; Country Music TV; E! Entertainment TV; ESPN 2; Knowledge TV.
Fee: $3.85 monthly (package), $0.85 monthly (each).

Pay Service 1
Pay Units: 4,949.
Programming (via satellite): Cinemax.
Fee: $13.95 monthly.

Pay Service 2
Pay Units: 13,686.
Programming (via satellite): The New Encore (multiplexed).
Fee: $1.95 monthly.

Pay Service 3
Pay Units: 12,712.
Programming (via satellite): HBO.
Fee: $14.95 monthly.

Pay Service 4
Pay Units: N.A.
Programming (via satellite): Showtime; Starz!
Fee: $6.75 monthly (Starz), $14.95 monthly (Showtime).

Digital Pay Service 1
Pay Units: N.A.
Programming (via satellite): DMX; HBO (multiplexed); Showtime; Starz! Theater; The Movie Channel; The New Encore (multiplexed).
Fee: $9.95 monthly (DMX).

Pay-Per-View
Spice delivered digitally; Viewer's Choice Digital.
Fee: $4.99.

Local advertising: Yes. Rates: $56.00/Hour; $31.25/30 Minutes; $5.20/30 Seconds.
Program Guide: The Cable Guide.
Equipment: Phasecom headend; GTE Sylvania amplifiers; General cable; Scientific-Atlanta satellite antenna.
Miles of plant: 761.4 (coaxial); 175.6 (fiber optic). Homes passed: 63,373. Total homes in franchised area: 63,373.
Manager: Terry Kelley. Chief technician: Carl Larkins.
City fee: 3% of gross.
Ownership: Time Warner Cable (MSO). Purchased from AT&T Broadband & Internet Services, June 1, 1999.

WARREN TWP. (Trumbull County)—Northeast Cable TV, Box 4095, Youngstown, OH 44515. Phone: 330-793-7434. Fax: 330-793-7434. County: Trumbull. Also serves Warren. ICA: OH0380.
TV Market Ranking: 79. Franchise award date: N.A. Franchise expiration date: N.A. Began: May 1, 1991.
Channel capacity: 60. Channels available but not in use: N.A.

Basic Service
Subscribers: N.A.
Programming (received off-air): WBNX-TV (W,F), WEAO (P), WVPX (X) Akron; WDLI (T), WOAC (I) Canton; WEWS-TV (A), WJW (F), WKYC-TV (N), WVIZ-TV (P) Cleveland; WUAB (U) Lorain-Cleveland; WOIO (C) Shaker Heights; WFMJ-TV (N), WKBN-TV (C), WYTV (A,F) Youngstown.
Programming (via microwave): Catholic TV Network.
Programming (via translator): WPCB-TV (I) Greensburg.
Programming (via satellite): WGN-TV (W) Chicago; A & E; ESPN; Headline News; Home Shopping Network; Nashville Network; TBS Superstation; Turner Network TV; USA Network.
Current originations: Automated time-weather.
Fee: $34.95 installation; $23.95 monthly.

Miles of plant: 11.0 (coaxial). Homes passed: 515.
Manager: Al Pezzenti.
Ownership: Northeast Cable TV (MSO).

WASHINGTON COURT HOUSE—FrontierVision, 218 E. Court House Rd., Washington Court House, OH 43160. Phone: 800-346-2288. Counties: Clinton & Fayette. Also serves Bloomingburg, Jasper Twp., Jefferson Twp. (Fayette County), Jeffersonville, Milledgeville, Octa, Paint Twp. (Fayette County), Richland Twp. (Clinton County), Sabina, Union Twp. (Fayette County). ICA: OH0070.
TV Market Ranking: 27 (Bloomingburg, portions of Jasper Twp., Paint Twp., portions of Richland Twp., Washington Court House); 41 (portions of Jasper Twp., Jefferson Twp., Jeffersonville, Milledgeville, Octa, portions of Richland Twp., Sabina, Union Twp.). Franchise award date: N.A. Franchise expiration date: N.A. Began: December 15, 1968.
Channel capacity: 80 (2-way capable; not operating 2-way). Channels available but not in use: 28.

Basic Service
Subscribers: 7,690; Commercial subscribers: 320.
Programming (received off-air): WWHO (U) Chillicothe; WBNS-TV (C), WCMH-TV (N), WOSU-TV (P), WSYX (A), WTTE (F,U) Columbus; WDTN (A), WHIO-TV (C), WKEF (N), WPTD (P) Dayton; allband FM.
Programming (via satellite): WGN-TV (W) Chicago; C-SPAN; QVC; TBS Superstation; TV Guide Channel; VH1.
Current originations: Automated time-weather; local news.
Fee: $12.23 monthly.

Expanded Basic Service
Subscribers: 7,142.
Programming (via satellite): A & E; American Movie Classics; CNN; Comedy Central; Country Music TV; Discovery Channel; Disney Channel; E! Entertainment TV; ESPN; Fox Family Channel; Fox Sports Net Ohio; Headline News; Learning Channel; Lifetime; MTV; Nashville Network; Nickelodeon; The Weather Channel; Turner Network TV; USA Network.
Fee: $13.82 monthly.

Pay Service 1
Pay Units: 386.
Programming (via satellite): Cinemax.
Fee: N.A.

Pay Service 2
Pay Units: 404.
Programming (via satellite): The New Encore.
Fee: N.A.

Pay Service 3
Pay Units: 1,407.
Programming (via satellite): HBO.
Fee: N.A.

Pay Service 4
Pay Units: 1,479.
Programming (via satellite): Showtime.
Fee: N.A.

Pay Service 5
Pay Units: 402.
Programming (via satellite): Starz!
Fee: N.A.

Pay Service 6
Pay Units: 432.
Programming (via satellite): The Movie Channel.
Fee: N.A.

Pay-Per-View
Addressable homes: 1,025.
Viewer's Choice.

Program Guide: The Cable Guide.
Equipment: Jerrold headend; Kaiser amplifiers; Superior cable.
Miles of plant: 206.6 (coaxial); 8.5 (fiber optic). Homes passed: 11,366.
Manager: Steve Trippe. Chief technician: Bill Ricker.
City fee: $1,100 annually.
Ownership: FrontierVision Partners LP (MSO). See Cable System Ownership.

WATERTOWN—FrontierVision, Suite P-200, 1777 S. Harrison St., Denver, CO 80210. Phone: 303-757-1588. Fax: 303-757-6105. County: Washington. Also serves Adams Twp. (Washington County), Barlow, Beverly, Coal Run, Veto, Veto Lake, Vincent, Waterford. Plans service to Belpre Twp. (Washington County). ICA: OH0175.
TV Market Ranking: Below 100. Franchise award date: N.A. Franchise expiration date: N.A. Began: June 29, 1963.
Channel capacity: 35 (not 2-way capable). Channels available but not in use: 6.

Basic Service
Subscribers: 1,657.
Programming (received off-air): WOUB-TV (P) Athens; WCHS-TV (A), WSAZ-TV (N), WVAH-TV (F,U) Charleston-Huntington; WBNS-TV (C) Columbus; WTAP-TV (N) Parkersburg-Marietta; WTRF-TV (C) Wheeling-Steubenville; WHIZ-TV (N) Zanesville; allband FM.
Programming (via satellite): WGN-TV (W) Chicago; TBS Superstation; Trinity Bcstg. Network.
Fee: $29.95 installation; $10.57 monthly.

Expanded Basic Service
Subscribers: N.A.
Programming (via satellite): A & E; American Movie Classics; Bravo; CNN; Country Music TV; Discovery Channel; E! Entertainment TV; ESPN; Fox Family Channel; Headline News; Home Shopping Network; Learning Channel; Lifetime; Nashville Network; Nickelodeon; Sci-Fi Channel; The Inspirational Network; Turner Network TV; USA Network.
Fee: $15.60 monthly.

Pay Service 1
Pay Units: N.A.
Programming (via satellite): Cinemax; Disney Channel; HBO; Showtime; The Movie Channel; The New Encore.
Fee: $3.99 monthly (Encore), $5.95 monthly (Disney), $8.95 monthly (Cinemax), $11.95 monthly (Showtime or TMC), $11.99 monthly (HBO).

Local advertising: No.
Equipment: Blonder-Tongue & Jerrold headend; Vikoa amplifiers; Vikoa cable.
Miles of plant: 76.0 (coaxial). Homes passed: 1,959.
Manager: Willie Critchfield. Chief technician: Bill Turner.
Ownership: FrontierVision Partners LP (MSO). See Cable System Ownership.

WATERVILLE—FrontierVision, Box 627, Chillicothe, OH 45601. Phones: 740-775-4300; 800-346-2288. Fax: 740-775-2915. Counties: Lucas & Wood. Also serves Concordia, Garden Woods, Grand Rapids, Haskins, Lake Twp. (Wood County), Middleton Twp. (Lucas County), Middleton Twp. (Wood County), Monclova, Oakleaf, Perry Lake Village, Perrysburg, Spencer Twp. (Lucas County), Springfield Twp. (Lucas County), Tontogany, Washington Twp. (Wood County), Whitehouse, Woodland. ICA: OH0072.
TV Market Ranking: 52. Franchise award date: N.A. Franchise expiration date: July 2, 2015. Began: January 1, 1983.
Channel capacity: 54. Channels available but not in use: None.

Basic Service
Subscribers: 6,255.
Programming (received off-air): WBGU-TV (P) Bowling Green; WDIV (N), WJBK (F), WKBD-TV (U) Detroit; WGTE-TV (P), WNWO-TV (N), WTOL-TV (C), WTVG (A), WUPW (F) Toledo; CBET Windsor.
Programming (via satellite): WGN-TV (W) Chicago; A & E; American Movie Classics; C-SPAN; CNBC; CNN; Discovery Channel; Disney Channel; ESPN; Fox Family Channel; Headline News; Home Shopping Network; Learning Channel; Lifetime; MTV; Music Choice; Nashville Network; Nickelodeon; TBS Superstation; The Weather Channel; Turner Network TV; USA Network; VH1.
Fee: $42.50 installation; $17.95 monthly.

Pay Service 1
Pay Units: 330.
Programming (via satellite): Cinemax.
Fee: $10.95 monthly.

Pay Service 2
Pay Units: 779.
Programming (via satellite): The New Encore.
Fee: N.A.

Pay Service 3
Pay Units: 465.

Programming (via satellite): HBO.
Fee: $9.95 monthly.
Pay Service 4
Pay Units: 361.
Programming (via satellite): Showtime.
Fee: $9.95 monthly.
Pay Service 5
Pay Units: 342.
Programming (via satellite): The Movie Channel.
Fee: $10.95 monthly.
Pay-Per-View
Addressable homes: 63.
Program Guide: The Cable Guide.
Miles of plant: 163.3 (coaxial). Homes passed: 9,309.
Manager: Richard Coplan. Chief technician: Sam Morabith. Program director: Chad Hume. Marketing director: Barbara Brewer.
Ownership: FrontierVision Partners LP (MSO). See Cable System Ownership.

WAVERLY—FrontierVision, Box 67, Chillicothe, OH 45601. Phone: 800-346-2288. County: Pike. Also serves Lake White, Pee Pee Twp., Pike County. ICA: OH0139.
TV Market Ranking: 27. Franchise award date: N.A. Franchise expiration date: N.A. Began: August 1, 1953.
Channel capacity: 62. Channels available but not in use: 17.
Basic Service
Subscribers: 2,290; Commercial subscribers: 94.
Programming (received off-air): WBNS-TV (C), WCMH-TV (N), WSYX (A), WTTE (F,U) Columbus; WPBO-TV (P) Portsmouth; 14 FMs.
Programming (via satellite): A & E; American Movie Classics; C-SPAN; C-SPAN 2; CNBC; CNN; Discovery Channel; Disney Channel; ESPN; Fox Family Channel; Headline News; Lifetime; MTV; Nashville Network; Nickelodeon; QVC; TBS Superstation; The Weather Channel; Turner Network TV; USA Network.
Current originations: Automated time-weather.
Fee: $50.00 installation; $21.20 monthly.
Pay Service 1
Pay Units: 176.
Programming (via satellite): HBO.
Fee: $15.00 installation; $9.66 monthly.
Pay Service 2
Pay Units: 200.
Programming (via satellite): Showtime.
Fee: $15.00 installation; $9.66 monthly.
Pay Service 3
Pay Units: 92.
Programming (via satellite): The Movie Channel.
Fee: N.A.
Pay-Per-View
Addressable homes: 263.
Local advertising: Yes.
Program Guide: TV Times.
Equipment: Jerrold headend; Jerrold amplifiers; Plastoid cable; System Concepts character generator; Scientific-Atlanta satellite antenna; Scientific-Atlanta satellite receivers.
Miles of plant: 39.2 (coaxial). Homes passed: 3,657.
Manager: Steve Trippe. Chief technician: Bill Ricker.
City fee: None.
Ownership: FrontierVision Partners LP (MSO). See Cable System Ownership.

WAYNESFIELD—Time Warner Cable, 3100 Elida Rd., Lima, OH 45805. Phone: 419-331-3333. Fax: 419-331-1573. Counties: Auglaize, Hardin & Logan. Also serves Auglaize County (portions), Lakeview (Logan County), New Hampshire, Roundhead, St. Johns, Uniopolis. ICA: OH0146.
TV Market Ranking: Below 100. Franchise award date: April 3, 1984. Franchise expiration date: April 3, 1999. Began: N.A.
Channel capacity: 53. Channels available but not in use: 15.
Basic Service
Subscribers: 1,806; Commercial subscribers: 80.
Programming (received off-air): WBGU-TV (P) Bowling Green; WBNS-TV (C) Columbus; WDTN (A), WHIO-TV (C), WKEF (N), WRGT-TV (F,U) Dayton; WLIO (N), WTLW (I) Lima; WNWO-TV (N) Toledo.
Programming (via satellite): WGN-TV (W) Chicago; A & E; C-SPAN; CNBC; CNN; Cartoon Network; Comedy Central; Country Music TV; Discovery Channel; ESPN; Fox Family Channel; Headline News; Home Shopping Network; Lifetime; MTV; Nashville Network; Nickelodeon; TBS Superstation; The Weather Channel; Travel Channel; Turner Network TV; USA Network; VH1.
Current originations: Public access.
Fee: $32.00 installation; $19.72 monthly.
Pay Service 1
Pay Units: 80.
Programming (via satellite): Cinemax.
Fee: $18.00 installation; $10.95 monthly.
Pay Service 2
Pay Units: 43.
Programming (via satellite): Disney Channel.
Fee: $18.00 installation; $10.95 monthly.
Pay Service 3
Pay Units: 153.
Programming (via satellite): HBO.
Fee: $18.00 installation; $10.95 monthly.
Pay Service 4
Pay Units: 69.
Programming (via satellite): Showtime.
Fee: $18.00 installation; $10.95 monthly.
Local advertising: Yes (locally produced). Available in character-generated programming. Local sales manager: Jon Quatman.
Miles of plant: 59.2 (coaxial). Homes passed: 3,036.
Manager: Jeff Parker. Chief technician: Ron Lamb. Marketing director: Sandy Bayliff.
City fee: 3% of gross.
Ownership: Time Warner Cable (MSO); Fanch Communications Inc. (MSO). See Cable System Ownership.

WEATHERSFIELD TWP. (Trumbull County)—Northeast Cable TV, Box 4095, Youngstown, OH 44515. Phone: 330-793-7434. Fax: 330-793-7434. County: Trumbull. ICA: OH0384.
TV Market Ranking: 79. Franchise award date: N.A. Franchise expiration date: N.A. Began: May 1, 1987.
Channel capacity: 60. Channels available but not in use: N.A.
Basic Service
Subscribers: N.A.
Programming (received off-air): WBNX-TV (W,F) Akron; WNEO (P) Alliance; WEWS-TV (A), WJW (F) Cleveland; WUAB (U) Lorain-Cleveland; WOIO (C) Shaker Heights; WFMJ-TV (N), WKBN-TV (C), WYTV (A,F) Youngstown.
Programming (via satellite): ESPN; TBS Superstation; USA Network.
Fee: $54.95 installation; $17.95 monthly.
Miles of plant: 2.0 (coaxial). Homes passed: 105.
Manager: Al Pezzenti.
Ownership: Northeast Cable TV (MSO).

WELLINGTON—Wellington Cable Communications, Box 67, 993 Commerce Dr., Grafton, OH 44044. Phone: 440-926-3230. Fax: 440-926-2889. County: Lorain. Also serves Brighton Twp., Brownhelm Twp., Camden Twp., Henrietta Twp., Kipton (village), Penfield Twp., Pittsfield Twp., Rochester (village), Rochester Twp., Russia Twp., Wellington (village), Wellington Twp. ICA: OH0189.
TV Market Ranking: 8. Franchise award date: N.A. Franchise expiration date: N.A. Began: November 1, 1983.
Channel capacity: 52 (2-way capable; operating 2-way partially). Channels available but not in use: 18.
Basic Service
Subscribers: 3,085; Commercial subscribers: 5.
Programming (received off-air): WBNX-TV (W,F), WEAO (P), WVPX (X) Akron; WEWS-TV (A), WJW (F), WKYC-TV (N), WQHS-TV (H), WVIZ-TV (P) Cleveland; WUAB (U) Lorain-Cleveland; WOIO (C) Shaker Heights; allband FM.
Programming (via satellite): WGN-TV (W) Chicago; Fox Family Channel; TBS Superstation; The Inspirational Network; Travel Channel; USA Network.
Current originations: Automated time-weather; public access; educational access; automated emergency alert; local news; local sports.
Fee: $40.00 installation; $9.00 monthly; $2.83 converter; $15.00 additional installation.
Commercial fee: $20.00 monthly.
Expanded Basic Service
Subscribers: N.A.
Programming (via satellite): A & E; American Movie Classics; C-SPAN; CNN; Country Music TV; Discovery Channel; Disney Channel; E! Entertainment TV; ESPN; ESPN 2; Fox Sports Net Ohio; Headline News; History Channel; Home & Garden Television; Learning Channel; Lifetime; MTV; Nashville Network; Nickelodeon; Sci-Fi Channel; TV Guide Channel; The Weather Channel; Toon Disney; Turner Classic Movies; Turner Network TV; VH1.
Fee: $16.35 monthly.
Pay Service 1
Pay Units: N.A.
Programming (via satellite): Cinemax; HBO; Showtime.
Fee: $10.95 monthly (each).
Local advertising: Planned. Available in character-generated programming.
Program Guide: Premium Channels.
Equipment: Scientific-Atlanta headend; Scientific-Atlanta amplifiers; Scientific-Atlanta & Times Fiber cable; Panasonic cameras; Panasonic VTRs; Texscan, Panasonic & Scientific-Atlanta set top converters; Arcom & Eagle traps; Scientific-Atlanta & Harris satellite antenna; Scientific-Atlanta satellite receivers.
Miles of plant: 23.0 (coaxial). Additional miles planned: 3.0 (coaxial). Homes passed: 1,600. Total homes in franchised area: 1,600.
Manager: Dale Durkee. Chief technician: George Michas.
City fee: 5% of gross.
Ownership: Kevin Flannigan (MSO).

WEST LAFAYETTE—Time Warner Cable, 5520 Whipple Ave. NW, Canton, OH 44720-7700. Phones: 330-494-0095; 800-245-8166. Fax: 330-663-7970. County: Coshocton. Also serves Lafayette Twp. (Coshocton County), Plainfield Village. ICA: OH0374.
TV Market Ranking: Below 100. Franchise award date: N.A. Franchise expiration date: May 1, 2002. Began: October 1, 1967.
Channel capacity: 54 (2-way capable). Channels available but not in use: 19.
Basic Service
Subscribers: 1,547; Commercial subscribers: 2.
Programming (received off-air): WVPX (X) Akron; WOUC-TV (P) Cambridge; WEWS-TV (A) Cleveland; WBNS-TV (C), WTTE (F,U) Columbus; WTOV-TV (N) Steubenville-Wheeling; WTRF-TV (C) Wheeling-Steubenville; WHIZ-TV (N) Zanesville; allband FM.
Programming (via satellite): Home Shopping Network.
Current originations: Automated time-weather.
Fee: $33.53 installation; $5.96 monthly; $2.50 converter; $15.00 additional installation.
Expanded Basic Service
Subscribers: N.A.
Programming (via satellite): WGN-TV (W) Chicago; A & E; C-SPAN; CNBC; CNN; Country Music TV; Discovery Channel; ESPN; Fox Family Channel; Headline News; Knowledge TV; Lifetime; MTV; Nashville Network; Nickelodeon; TBS Superstation; The Inspirational Network; The Weather Channel; Turner Network TV; USA Network.
Fee: $20.84 monthly.
Pay Service 1
Pay Units: 164.
Programming (via satellite): Cinemax.
Fee: $10.00 installation; $8.95 monthly.
Pay Service 2
Pay Units: 119.
Programming (via satellite): Disney Channel.
Fee: $8.95 installation; $8.95 monthly.
Pay Service 3
Pay Units: 203.
Programming (via satellite): HBO.
Fee: $8.95 installation; $8.95 monthly.
Pay Service 4
Pay Units: 68.
Programming (via satellite): Showtime.
Fee: $8.95 monthly.
Pay Service 5
Pay Units: N.A.
Programming (via satellite): Starz!; The Movie Channel.
Fee: $8.95 monthly (each).
Pay-Per-View
Movies.
Fee: $3.95.
Local advertising: No.
Equipment: Jerrold headend; Jerrold amplifiers; Times Fiber cable; Sony VTRs; Pioneer set top converters; Eagle & Arcom traps; AFC, Scientific-Atlanta & Comtech satellite antenna; Electrohome satellite receivers.
Miles of plant: 37.2 (coaxial). Additional miles planned: 62.0 (coaxial); 8.0 (fiber optic).
Manager: Bill Farmer. Chief technician: Tod Dean. Marketing director: Jim Nicholas.
City fee: None.
Ownership: Time Warner Cable (MSO).

WEST MANSFIELD—Time Warner Cable, Box 787, 111 S. Mulberry St., Mount Vernon, OH 43050. Phones: 740-397-2288; 800-782-4118. Fax: 740-397-3730. County: Logan. Also serves East Liberty, Middleburg (Logan County), Valley Hi. ICA: OH0236.
TV Market Ranking: Below 100 (Middleburg, West Mansfield); Outside TV Markets (East Liberty, Valley Hi). Franchise award date: May 2, 1983. Franchise expiration date: May 3, 2003. Began: December 1, 1983.
Channel capacity: 61 (not 2-way capable). Channels available but not in use: 25.
Basic Service
Subscribers: 418; Commercial subscribers: 51.

Programming (received off-air): WBGU-TV (P) Bowling Green; WBNS-TV (C), WCMH-TV (N), WOSU-TV (P), WSYX (A), WTTE (F,U) Columbus; WDTN (A), WHIO-TV (C), WRGT-TV (F,U) Dayton; WLIO (N), WTLW (I) Lima; WBDT (W) Springfield.
Programming (via satellite): WGN-TV (W) Chicago; A & E; Animal Planet; C-SPAN; CNN; Comedy Central; Country Music TV; Discovery Channel; ESPN; Fox Family Channel; Headline News; Lifetime; MTV; Nashville Network; Nickelodeon; QVC; Sci-Fi Channel; TBS Superstation; The Weather Channel; Turner Classic Movies; Turner Network TV; USA Network; VH1.
Current originations: Public access.
Fee: $40.27 installation; $26.15 monthly; $0.44 converter.

Pay Service 1
Pay Units: 27.
Programming (via satellite): Cinemax.
Fee: $18.00 installation; $10.95 monthly.

Pay Service 2
Pay Units: 30.
Programming (via satellite): Disney Channel.
Fee: $18.00 installation; $10.95 monthly.

Pay Service 3
Pay Units: 62.
Programming (via satellite): HBO.
Fee: $18.00 installation; $10.95 monthly.

Pay Service 4
Pay Units: 34.
Programming (via satellite): Showtime.
Fee: $18.00 installation; $10.95 monthly.

Local advertising: Yes. Available in character-generated programming.
Miles of plant: 22.2 (coaxial). Homes passed: 822.
Manager: Paul S. Schonewolf. Technical operations manager: Dan Fessler. Field operations manager: Bill Schroeder. Marketing manager: Carl Bauer. Customer operations manager: Danielle Turner.
Village fee: 3% of gross.
Ownership: Time Warner Cable (MSO); Fanch Communications Inc. (MSO). See Cable System Ownership.

WEST UNION—Time Warner Cable, Box 823, 131 Catherine St., Hillsboro, OH 45133. Phone: 937-393-4217. Fax: 937-393-8022. County: Adams. Also serves Adams County (portions). ICA: OH0152.
TV Market Ranking: Below 100. Franchise award date: March 24, 1972. Franchise expiration date: March 24, 2012. Began: N.A.
Channel capacity: 35 (not 2-way capable). Channels available but not in use: 2.

Basic Service
Subscribers: 1,457.
Programming (received off-air): WCPO-TV (A), WKRC-TV (C), WLWT (N), WSTR-TV (W) Cincinnati; WXIX-TV (F) Cincinnati-Newport; WPBO-TV (P) Portsmouth; W17AY (I) Seaman.
Programming (via satellite): A & E; American Movie Classics; C-SPAN; CNN; Country Music TV; Discovery Channel; ESPN; Fox Family Channel; Headline News; Lifetime; MTV; Nashville Network; Nickelodeon; QVC; TBS Superstation; The Weather Channel; Trinity Bcstg. Network; Turner Network TV; USA Network.
Fee: $39.90 installation; $24.19 monthly.

Pay Service 1
Pay Units: 91.
Programming (via satellite): Cinemax.
Fee: $10.95 monthly.

Pay Service 2
Pay Units: 72.
Programming (via satellite): Disney Channel.
Fee: $7.95 monthly.

Pay Service 3
Pay Units: 282.
Programming (via satellite): HBO.
Fee: $10.95 monthly.

Pay Service 4
Pay Units: 74.
Programming (via satellite): Showtime.
Fee: $10.95 monthly.

Local advertising: No. Local sales manager: Gary Pitzer.
Equipment: Ameco headend; Ameco amplifiers; Ameco & Comm/Scope cable; Scientific-Atlanta satellite antenna; Scientific-Atlanta satellite receivers.
Miles of plant: 27.0 (coaxial). Homes passed: 1,970. Total homes in franchised area: 2,901.
Manager: Michael Rector. Chief technician: Dale Zornes. Marketing director: Gary Pitzer.
Ownership: Time Warner Cable (MSO).

***WESTLAKE**—Americast, 18th Floor, 300 S. Riverside Plaza, Chicago, IL 60606. Phones: 312-526-8000; 800-848-2278. Fax: 312-526-8565. County: Cuyahoga. ICA: OH0403.
TV Market Ranking: 8. Franchise award date: N.A. Franchise expiration date: N.A. Scheduled to begin: June 1, 1998.
Channel capacity: N.A.

Basic Service
Subscribers: N.A.
Planned programming (received off-air): WEWS-TV (A), WJW (F), WKYC-TV (N), WQHS-TV (H), WVIZ-TV (P) Cleveland; WUAB (U) Lorain-Cleveland; WOIO (C) Shaker Heights.
Fee: N.A.

Ownership: Ameritech New Media Inc.

WILLARD—Time Warner Cable, 207 Myrtle St., Willard, OH 44890. Phone: 800-425-2225. Counties: Huron & Richland. Also serves Cass Twp., Fairfield Twp. (Huron County), Greenfield Twp. (Huron County), Greenwich, Greenwich Village, New Haven, North Fairfield, Norwich Twp. (Huron County), Richmond Twp., Ripley Twp. (portions), Shiloh. ICA: OH0108.
TV Market Ranking: 8 (Fairfield Twp., Greenwich, Greenwich Village, North Fairfield); Below 100 (Cass Twp., Greenfield Twp., New Haven, Norwich Twp., Richmond Twp., Ripley Twp., Shiloh, Willard). Franchise award date: N.A. Franchise expiration date: N.A. Began: December 13, 1968.
Channel capacity: 52 (not 2-way capable). Channels available but not in use: 15.
Note: Basic subscribers, pay units, miles of plant & homes passed include figures for Attica, OH.

Basic Service
Subscribers: 5,139.
Programming (received off-air): W54AF (I) Bucyrus; WEWS-TV (A), WJW (F), WKYC-TV (N), WQHS-TV (H), WVIZ-TV (P) Cleveland; WUAB (U) Lorain-Cleveland; WGGN-TV (T) Sandusky; WOIO (C) Shaker Heights; WNWO-TV (N), WTOL-TV (C), WTVG (A) Toledo; 12 FMs.
Programming (via satellite): A & E; C-SPAN; C-SPAN 2; CNBC; CNN; Discovery Channel; ESPN; EWTN; Fox Family Channel; Learning Channel; Lifetime; MTV; Nashville Network; Nickelodeon; TBS Superstation; The Weather Channel; Turner Network TV; USA Network; VH1.
Current originations: Public access; educational access; government access; automated emergency alert; local sports.
Fee: $25.00 installation; $10.90 monthly; $2.75 converter; $15.00 additional installation.

Pay Service 1
Pay Units: 3,393.
Programming (via satellite): Cinemax; Disney Channel; HBO; Showtime; The Movie Channel.
Fee: $15.00 installation; $6.95 monthly (Disney), $11.95 monthly (Cinemax, HBO, Showtime or TMC).

Pay-Per-View
Hot Choice; Viewer's Choice.

Local advertising: Yes. Available in character-generated programming.
Equipment: Scientific-Atlanta headend; Texscan amplifiers; Comm/Scope cable; Video Data Systems character generator; Pioneer & RCA set top converters; Eagle traps; Microdyne satellite antenna; Microdyne satellite receivers.
Miles of plant: 158.0 (coaxial); 6.0 (fiber optic). Homes passed: 7,620.
Manager: Jane Kennard. Chief technician: John Fox.
Ownership: Time Warner Cable (MSO). Purchased from MediaOne Group, August 2, 1999.

WILLOWS MOBILE HOME PARK—Warner Cable Communications, 1655 Brittain Rd., Akron, OH 44310-3998. Phone: 330-633-9203. Fax: 330-633-0024. County: Summit. ICA: OH0302.
TV Market Ranking: 8. Franchise award date: February 1, 1987. Franchise expiration date: February 1, 2002. Began: February 1, 1987.
Channel capacity: 18 (not 2-way capable). Channels available but not in use: 3.

Basic Service
Subscribers: 124.
Programming (received off-air): WEAO (P) Akron; WEWS-TV (A), WJW (F), WKYC-TV (N) Cleveland; WUAB (U) Lorain-Cleveland.
Programming (via satellite): WGN-TV (W) Chicago; A & E; CNN; Discovery Channel; ESPN; Fox Family Channel; Nashville Network; TBS Superstation; USA Network.
Fee: $35.00 installation; $18.22 monthly.

Pay Service 1
Pay Units: 10.
Programming (via satellite): HBO.
Fee: $9.95 monthly.

Interactive Services Subscribers: 16.
Miles of plant: 1.0 (coaxial). Homes passed: 140. Total homes in franchised area: 140.
Manager: Stephen Fry. Chief technician: Robert Nyitray. Marketing director: Woody Woodward.
Franchise fee: 10% of gross.
Ownership: Time Warner Cable (MSO); Fanch Communications Inc. (MSO). See Cable System Ownership.

WILMINGTON—TCI Cablevision of Ohio Inc., 333 W. Clinton St., Wilmington, OH 45177. Phone: 800-284-1894. Counties: Clinton & Warren South. Also serves Adams Twp. (Clinton County), Blanchester, Clinton County (unincorporated areas), Marion Twp. (Clinton County), Union Twp. (Clinton County), Washington Twp. (Clinton County). ICA: OH0112.
TV Market Ranking: 17 (Blanchester, Marion Twp., Union Twp., Washington Twp.); 41 (Adams Twp., Blanchester, Clinton County, Marion Twp., Union Twp., Washington Twp., Wilmington). Franchise award date: May 1, 1971. Franchise expiration date: N.A. Began: March 20, 1972.
Channel capacity: 62 (not 2-way capable). Channels available but not in use: N.A.

Basic Service
Subscribers: 5,105.
Programming (received off-air): WCET (P), WCPO-TV (A), WKRC-TV (C), WLWT (N), WSTR-TV (W) Cincinnati; WXIX-TV (F) Cincinnati-Newport; WOSU-TV (P) Columbus; WDTN (A), WHIO-TV (C), WKEF (N), WPTD (P), WRGT-TV (F,U) Dayton; WPTO (P) Oxford; WBDT (W) Springfield; allband FM.
Programming (via satellite): WGN-TV (W) Chicago; TBS Superstation; TV Guide Sneak Prevue.
Current originations: Educational access; government access.
Fee: $30.86 installation; $10.34 monthly; $1.94 converter.

Expanded Basic Service
Subscribers: N.A.
Programming (via satellite): American Movie Classics; BET; C-SPAN; C-SPAN 2; CNBC; CNN; CNN International; Court TV; Discovery Channel; ESPN; FX; Fox Family Channel; Fox Sports Net Direct; Headline News; Intro TV; Knowledge TV; Lifetime; MTV; Nashville Network; Nickelodeon; Odyssey; QVC; The Health Network; The Weather Channel; Travel Channel; Turner Network TV; USA Network.
Fee: $11.99 monthly.

A la Carte 1
Subscribers: N.A.
Programming (via satellite): Cartoon Network; Country Music TV; Learning Channel.
Fee: $3.00 monthly (package); $0.85 monthly (each).

Pay Service 1
Pay Units: 520.
Programming (via satellite): HBO.
Fee: $10.00 installation; $14.07 monthly.

Pay Service 2
Pay Units: 466.
Programming (via satellite): Disney Channel.
Fee: $10.00 installation; $12.13 monthly.

Pay Service 3
Pay Units: 200.
Programming (via satellite): Showtime.
Fee: $10.00 installation; $13.13 monthly.

Pay Service 4
Pay Units: N.A.
Programming (via satellite): DMX; Starz!; The New Encore.
Fee: $1.70 monthly (Encore), $4.75 monthly (Starz), $4.95 monthly (DMX).

Pay-Per-View
Action Pay-Per-View; Spice.

Equipment: Scientific-Atlanta headend; AEL amplifiers; Comm/Scope cable; Arcom traps; Prodelin satellite antenna; Microdyne satellite receivers.
Miles of plant: 67.3 (coaxial).
Manager: Lowell Lindon. Chief technician: Jack Squire.
City fee: 3% of gross.

Ownership: AT&T Broadband & Internet Services (MSO). Purchased from Tele-Communications Inc., March 9, 1999.

WINESBURG—National Cable Inc., Suite 106A, 5151 Reed Rd., Columbus, OH 43220. Phone: 614-442-5890. Fax: 614-457-2567. County: Holmes. Also serves Walnut Creek. ICA: OH0375.
TV Market Ranking: Below 100. Franchise award date: N.A. Franchise expiration date: N.A. Began: N.A.
Channel capacity: 40. Channels available but not in use: 20.
Basic Service
Subscribers: 104.
Programming (received off-air): WBNX-TV (W,F), WVPX (X) Akron; WJW (F), WKYC-TV (N), WVIZ-TV (P) Cleveland.
Programming (via satellite): WGN-TV (W) Chicago; A & E; American Movie Classics; CNN; Country Music TV; Discovery Channel; ESPN; Fox Family Channel; Showtime; TBS Superstation; Turner Network TV; USA Network.
Fee: $22.00 monthly.
Miles of plant: 12.2 (coaxial). Homes passed: 200.
Systems operations manager: Steve Miller.
Ownership: National Cable (MSO).

WOODSFIELD—CableVision Communications, Box 2200, 68 5th St., Buckhannon, WV 26201. Phone: 304-472-4193. Fax: 304-472-0756. County: Monroe. Also serves Lewisville. ICA: OH0206.
TV Market Ranking: 90. Franchise award date: N.A. Franchise expiration date: N.A. Began: October 1, 1966.
Channel capacity: 43. Channels available but not in use: 2.
Basic Service
Subscribers: 1,167.
Programming (received off-air): WOUC-TV (P) Cambridge; WKRN-TV (A) Nashville; KDKA-TV (C), WPGH-TV (F), WTAE-TV (A) Pittsburgh; WTOV-TV (N) Steubenville-Wheeling; WTRF-TV (C) Wheeling-Steubenville; WHIZ-TV (N) Zanesville; allband FM.
Programming (via satellite): CNN; Fox Family Channel; Home Shopping Network; Nashville Network; TBS Superstation; The Weather Channel; Trinity Bcstg. Network; USA Network.
Fee: $61.25 installation; $15.98 monthly; $1.24 converter; $17.50 additional installation.
Expanded Basic Service
Subscribers: 817.
Programming (via satellite): A & E; American Movie Classics; C-SPAN; Discovery Channel; Disney Channel; ESPN; Great American Country; Headline News; Learning Channel; Lifetime; MTV; Nickelodeon; The Inspirational Network; Turner Network TV; VH1; WB 100+ Station Group.
Fee: $13.28 monthly.
Expanded Basic Service 2
Subscribers: N.A.
Programming (via satellite): Cartoon Network; Comedy Central; ESPN 2; Home & Garden Television; Sci-Fi Channel.
Fee: $3.99 monthly.
Pay Service 1
Pay Units: 601.
Programming (via satellite): Cinemax; HBO; Showtime; The Movie Channel; The New Encore.
Fee: $3.99 monthly (Encore), $7.95 monthly (Cinemax), $11.95 monthly (Showtime or TMC), $11.99 monthly (HBO).
Local advertising: Yes. Available in character-generated programming.
Equipment: Blonder-Tongue, Standard Communications & Catel headend; Jerrold & Magnavox amplifiers; Times Fiber cable; Eagle traps; AFC satellite antenna; Standard Communications satellite receivers.
Miles of plant: 23.0 (coaxial). Homes passed: 1,376.
Manager: Willie Critchfield. Chief technician: Bill Turner. Marketing director: Kenny Phillips.
Ownership: Rifkin & Associates Inc. (MSO). See Cable System Ownership.

WOOSTER—Clear Picture Inc., Box 917, 444 W. Milltown Rd., Wooster, OH 44691. Phone: 330-345-8114. Fax: 330-345-5265. Counties: Paulding & Wayne. Also serves Apple Creek, Canaan Twp. (Wayne County), Chester Twp. (Wayne County), Clinton Twp. (Wayne County), East Union Twp. (Wayne County), Franklin Twp. (Wayne County), Green Twp. (Wayne County), Melrose Mobile Home Park, Plain Twp. (Wayne County), Smithville, Sugar Creek Twp. (Wayne County), Wayne County (southeastern portion), Wayne Twp. (Wayne County), Wooster Twp. (Wayne County). ICA: OH0061.
TV Market Ranking: 8 (Apple Creek, Canaan Twp., Chester Twp., Clinton Twp., East Union Twp., Franklin Twp., Green Twp., Plain Twp., Smithville, Sugar Creek Twp., Wayne Twp., Wooster, Wooster Twp.); Below 100 (Melrose Mobile Home Park, Wayne County). Franchise award date: November 1, 1967. Franchise expiration date: N.A. Began: November 1, 1967.
Channel capacity: 52 (not 2-way capable). Channels available but not in use: 5.
Basic Service
Subscribers: 13,405.
Programming (received off-air): WBNX-TV (W,F), WEAO (P), WVPX (X) Akron; WNEO (P) Alliance; WDLI (T), WOAC (I) Canton; WEWS-TV (A), WJW (F), WKYC-TV (N), WQHS-TV (H), WVIZ-TV (P) Cleveland; WUAB (U) Lorain-Cleveland; WMFD-TV (I) Mansfield; WOIO (C) Shaker Heights.
Programming (via satellite): WGN-TV (W) Chicago; A & E; American Movie Classics; C-SPAN; C-SPAN 2; CNBC; CNN; Country Music TV; Discovery Channel; ESPN; Fox Family Channel; Fox Sports Net Ohio; Headline News; Home Shopping Network; Lifetime; MTV; Nashville Network; Nickelodeon; TBS Superstation; TV Guide Channel; The Weather Channel; Turner Network TV; USA Network; VH1.
Current originations: Automated time-weather; public access; educational access; government access; religious access; leased access; automated emergency alert; local sports.
Fee: $30.00 installation; $21.90 monthly; $20.00 additional installation.
Pay Service 1
Pay Units: 762.
Programming (via satellite): Cinemax.
Fee: $15.00 installation; $9.50 monthly.
Pay Service 2
Pay Units: 913.
Programming (via satellite): Disney Channel.
Fee: $5.00 monthly.
Pay Service 3
Pay Units: 1,132.
Programming (via satellite): HBO.
Fee: $15.00 installation; $11.50 monthly.
Pay Service 4
Pay Units: 1,826.
Programming (via satellite): Showtime.
Fee: $15.00 installation; $10.00 monthly.
Local advertising: Yes. Available in satellite distributed, locally originated, character-generated & automated programming. Rates: $50.00/30 Seconds. Local sales manager: Elizabeth Gessner.
Equipment: Jerrold & Scientific-Atlanta headend; Jerrold amplifiers; Trilogy cable; Panasonic cameras; Sony VTRs; Mycrotek character generator; Jerrold set top converters; Jerrold addressable set top converters; Vitek traps; Scientific-Atlanta & Simulsat satellite antenna; Scientific-Atlanta satellite receivers; ChannelMatic commercial insert.
Miles of plant: 524.0 (coaxial); None (fiber optic). Additional miles planned: 10.0 (coaxial).
Manager: Keith Chambers. Chief technician: Kelly Rehm. Customer service manager: Jack Henley.
City fee: 3% of gross.
Ownership: Massillon Cable TV Inc. (MSO).

WORTHINGTON—Americast, 300 S. Riverside, Chicago, IL 60606. Phones: 312-526-8000; 800-848-2278. Fax: 312-526-8565. County: Franklin. ICA: OH0425.
TV Market Ranking: 27. Franchise award date: September 1, 1996. Franchise expiration date: N.A. Began: N.A.
Channel capacity: N.A. Channels available but not in use: N.A.
Basic Service
Subscribers: N.A.
Programming (received off-air): WWHO (U) Chillicothe; WBNS-TV (C), WCMH-TV (N), WOSU-TV (P), WSYX (A), WTTE (F,U) Columbus; WSFJ (I) Newark.
Programming (via satellite): WGN-TV (W) Chicago; QVC; TBS Superstation; TV Guide Channel.
Current originations: Public access; educational access; government access; leased access.
Fee: $39.95 installation; $9.95 monthly.
Expanded Basic Service
Subscribers: N.A.
Programming (via satellite): A & E; American Movie Classics; BET; BET on Jazz; Bravo; C-SPAN; C-SPAN 2; CNBC; CNN; CNNfn; Cartoon Network; Comedy Central; Country Music TV; Court TV; Discovery Channel; Disney Channel; E! Entertainment TV; ESPN; ESPN 2; ESPN Classic Sports; Fox Family Channel; Fox Sports Net Ohio; Golf Channel; Headline News; History Channel; Home & Garden Television; Learning Channel; Lifetime; MTV; Nashville Network; Nickelodeon; Ohio News Network; Sci-Fi Channel; TV Food Network; The Health Network; The Inspirational Network; The Weather Channel; Travel Channel; Turner Classic Movies; Turner Network TV; USA Network; VH1.
Fee: $17.00 monthly.
Pay Service 1
Pay Units: N.A.
Programming (via satellite): Cinemax; Flix; HBO (multiplexed); Showtime (multiplexed); Starz!; Sundance Channel; The Movie Channel; The New Encore.
Fee: $5.95 monthly (Flix or Sundance), $7.95 monthly (Encore & Starz), $9.95 monthly (Cinemax, Showtime or TMC), $11.95 monthly (HBO).
Total homes in franchised area: 6,550.
Ownership: Ameritech New Media Inc. (MSO).

WORTHINGTON ARMS—Time Warner Entertainment Co. LP, 1266 Dublin Rd., Columbus, OH 43215. Phone: 614-481-5000. Fax: 614-481-5044. County: Delaware. ICA: OH0288.
TV Market Ranking: 27. Franchise award date: N.A. Franchise expiration date: N.A. Began: July 1, 1986.
Channel capacity: 41 (not 2-way capable). Channels available but not in use: 17.
Basic Service
Subscribers: 138.
Programming (received off-air): WBNS-TV (C), WCMH-TV (N), WOSU-TV (P), WSYX (A), WTTE (F,U) Columbus; WXCB-LP (I) Delaware.
Programming (via satellite): WGN-TV (W) Chicago; A & E; CNN; Country Music TV; Discovery Channel; ESPN; Fox Family Channel; Headline News; MTV; Nashville Network; Nickelodeon; TBS Superstation; Turner Network TV; USA Network.
Current originations: Public access.
Fee: $32.00 installation; $18.95 monthly; $4.50 converter; $9.00 additional installation.
Pay Service 1
Pay Units: 12.
Programming (via satellite): Disney Channel.
Fee: $18.00 installation; $10.95 monthly.
Pay Service 2
Pay Units: 41.
Programming (via satellite): HBO.
Fee: $18.00 installation; $10.95 monthly.
Local advertising: No.
Miles of plant: 1.3 (coaxial). Homes passed: 266.
Manager: Terry O'Connell. Chief technician: Randy Hall. Marketing director: Cheryl Roller.
Franchise fee: 3% of gross.
Ownership: Time Warner Cable (MSO).

YELLOW SPRINGS—Warner Cable Communications Inc., Suites 7 & 8, 1512 State Rte. 68 S, Urbana, OH 43078. Phone: 937-653-5507. Counties: Clark & Greene. Also serves German Twp. (Clark County), Green Twp. (Clark County), Lawrenceville, Mad River Twp. (Clark County), Miami Twp. (Greene County), Moorefield Twp. (Clark County), North Hampton, Pike Twp. (Clark County), Springfield Twp. (Clark County), Tremont City. ICA: OH0103.
TV Market Ranking: 41. Franchise award date: May 1, 1982. Franchise expiration date: N.A. Began: June 1, 1983.
Channel capacity: 54. Channels available but not in use: 17.
Basic Service
Subscribers: 3,200.
Programming (received off-air): WBNS-TV (C), WCMH-TV (N), WOSU-TV (P) Columbus; WDTN (A), WHIO-TV (C), WKEF (N), WPTD (P), WRGT-TV (F,U) Dayton; allband FM.
Programming (via satellite): WGN-TV (W) Chicago; A & E; BET; C-SPAN; C-SPAN 2; CNN; Cartoon Network; Comedy Central; Discovery Channel; ESPN; Headline News; Lifetime; MTV; Nashville Network; Nickelodeon; QVC; TBS Superstation; The Weather Channel; Turner Classic Movies; Turner Network TV; USA Network.
Fee: $19.95 installation; $12.05 monthly; $14.95 additional installation.
Pay Service 1
Pay Units: 460.
Programming (via satellite): Cinemax.
Fee: $10.00 installation; $10.94 monthly.
Pay Service 2
Pay Units: 560.
Programming (via satellite): Disney Channel.
Fee: $14.95 installation; $6.95 monthly.
Pay Service 3
Pay Units: 778.
Programming (via satellite): HBO.
Fee: $14.95 installation; $11.45 monthly.
Pay Service 4
Pay Units: 211.
Programming (via satellite): The Movie Channel.
Fee: $14.95 installation; $10.94 monthly.

Pay Service 5
Pay Units: 298.
Programming (via satellite): Showtime.
Fee: $14.95 installation; $10.94 monthly.
Pay-Per-View
Addressable homes: 1,838.
Action Pay-Per-View; Spice.
Local advertising: Planned. Local sales manager: Norm Pytel.
Equipment: Scientific-Atlanta headend; Jerrold amplifiers; Comm/Scope & Times Fiber cable; BEI character generator; GTE Sylvania & Oak set top converters; Eagle traps; Scientific-Atlanta satellite antenna.
Miles of plant: 171.0 (coaxial). Homes passed: 6,049. Total homes in franchised area: 6,049.
Manager: Steve Sullenberger. Chief technician: Todd Lutz. Marketing director: Danny Schiffer.
Ownership: Time Warner Cable (MSO).

YOUNGSTOWN—Time Warner Cable, 755 Wick Ave., Youngstown, OH 44505. Phones: 330-747-2550; 330-372-2522. Fax: 330-747-5003. Counties: Mahoning & Trumbull. ICA: OH0017.
TV Market Ranking: 79. Franchise award date: October 18, 1978. Franchise expiration date: N.A. Began: January 2, 1980.
Channel capacity: 38 (not 2-way capable). Channels available but not in use: N.A.
Basic Service
Subscribers: 22,458; Commercial subscribers: 421.
Programming (received off-air): WNEO (P) Alliance; WUAB (U) Lorain-Cleveland; WQED (P) Pittsburgh; WOIO (C) Shaker Heights; WFMJ-TV (N), WKBN-TV (C), WYTV (A,F) Youngstown.
Programming (via satellite): C-SPAN; Cartoon Network; Fox Family Channel; QVC; TV Guide Channel; The Weather Channel.
Current originations: Religious access.
Fee: $24.21 installation; $13.95 monthly.
Expanded Basic Service
Subscribers: N.A.
Programming (via satellite): A & E; American Movie Classics; BET; CNN; Cartoon Network; Discovery Channel; ESPN; Headline News; Knowledge TV; Lifetime; MTV; Nashville Network; Nick at Nite; Nickelodeon; TBS Superstation; Turner Network TV; USA Network; VH1.
Fee: N.A.
Pay Service 1
Pay Units: 17,817.
Programming (via satellite): Cinemax; Disney Channel; Fox Sports Net Ohio; HBO; Music Choice; Showtime; The Movie Channel.
Fee: $15.00 installation; $5.95 monthly (Fox Sports), $6.65 monthly (Music Choice), $11.50 monthly (Cinemax, Disney, Showtime or TMC), $12.55 monthly (HBO).
Pay-Per-View
Addressable homes: 10,000.
Action Pay-Per-View; Viewer's Choice.
Local advertising: Yes (locally produced & insert). Available in satellite distributed & locally originated programming. Rates: $8.75/30 Seconds. Local sales manager: Barb Steil. Regional interconnect: Northeast Ohio Interconnect.
Program Guide: TV Host.
Equipment: RCA & Scientific-Atlanta headend; Magnavox & Scientific-Atlanta amplifiers; Times Fiber cable; Sony VTRs; Compuvid character generator; Pioneer set top converters; Arcom, Eagle & Vitek traps; Scientific-Atlanta satellite antenna; Scientific-Atlanta satellite receivers; ChannelMatic commercial insert.
Miles of plant: 348.0 (coaxial); None (fiber optic). Homes passed: 36,000. Total homes in franchised area: 36,842.
Manager: Daryl Morrison. Chief technician: Kurt Hossman. Marketing director: Dan Bates.
Ownership: Time Warner Cable (MSO).

ZANESVILLE—Cablecomm, Box 2249, 737 Howard St., Zanesville, OH 43702-2249. Phone: 888-229-4465. County: Muskingum. Also serves Brush Creek Twp. (Muskingum County), East Fultonham, Falls Twp. (Muskingum County), Fultonham (village), Muskingum County, Newton Twp. (Muskingum County), Perry Twp. (Muskingum County), South Zanesville, Springfield Twp. (Muskingum County), Washington Twp. (Muskingum County), Wayne Twp. (Muskingum County), White Cottage. ICA: OH0037.
TV Market Ranking: Below 100. Franchise award date: N.A. Franchise expiration date: N.A. Began: January 1, 1968.
Channel capacity: 40 (not 2-way capable). Channels available but not in use: None.
Basic Service
Subscribers: 17,539.
Programming (received off-air): WOUB-TV (P) Athens; WBNS-TV (C), WCMH-TV (N), WOSU-TV (P), WSYX (A), WTTE (F,U) Columbus; WSFJ (I) Newark; WTRF-TV (C) Wheeling-Steubenville; WHIZ-TV (N) Zanesville; allband FM.
Programming (via satellite): Animal Planet; C-SPAN; Discovery Channel; TBS Superstation.
Current originations: Automated time-weather; public access.
Fee: $44.95 installation; $10.13 monthly; $3.00 converter.
Expanded Basic Service
Subscribers: 16,875.
Programming (via satellite): A & E; American Movie Classics; BET; CNBC; CNN; Cartoon Network; ESPN; FX; Fox Family Channel; Fox News Channel; Headline News; Lifetime; MTV; Nashville Network; Nickelodeon; QVC; The New Encore; The Weather Channel; Turner Network TV; USA Network.
Fee: $13.44 monthly.
Pay Service 1
Pay Units: 878.
Programming (via satellite): Cinemax.
Fee: $20.00 installation; $13.15 monthly.
Pay Service 2
Pay Units: 994.
Programming (via satellite): Disney Channel.
Fee: N.A.
Pay Service 3
Pay Units: 6,145.
Programming (via satellite): The New Encore.
Fee: N.A.
Pay Service 4
Pay Units: 2,495.
Programming (via satellite): HBO.
Fee: $13.15 monthly.
Pay Service 5
Pay Units: N.A.
Programming (via satellite): Starz!
Fee: N.A.
Pay Service 6
Pay Units: 713.
Programming (via satellite): Showtime.
Fee: $13.15 monthly.
Pay-Per-View
Addressable homes: 4,680.
Local advertising: Yes.
Program Guide: The Cable Guide.
Equipment: Jerrold & Scientific-Atlanta headend; GTE Sylvania amplifiers; Comm/Scope cable; Sony VTRs; MSI character generator; Jerrold set top converters; Scientific-Atlanta satellite antenna; Scientific-Atlanta satellite receivers.
Miles of plant: 300.9 (coaxial); None (fiber optic). Additional miles planned: 22.0 (coaxial). Homes passed: 20,795. Total homes in franchised area: 23,128.
Manager: William F. Randles. Chief technician: John Barber.
City fee: 3% of gross.
Ownership: Fanch Communications Inc. (MSO); Time Warner Cable (MSO). Purchased from Tele-Communications Inc., February 25, 1999. See Cable System Ownership.

OKLAHOMA

Total Systems: 355
Total Communities Served: 528
Franchises Not Yet Operating: 0
Applications Pending: 0
Communities with Applications: 0
Number of Basic Subscribers: 712,074
Number of Expanded Basic Subscribers: 537,743
Number of Pay Units: 304,143

Top 100 Markets Represented: Oklahoma City (39); Tulsa (54).

For a list of all cable communities included in this section, see the Cable Community Index located in the back of this volume.
For explanation of terms used in cable system listings, see p. D-9.

ACHILLE—CommuniComm Services, Box 597, 1501 W. Mississippi, Durant, OK 74702-0597. Phones: 580-924-2367; 800-752-4992. County: Bryan. ICA: OK0342.
TV Market Ranking: Below 100. Franchise award date: N.A. Franchise expiration date: N.A. Began: N.A.
Channel capacity: 52 (not 2-way capable). Channels available but not in use: 26.
Basic Service
Subscribers: 38.
Programming (received off-air): KTEN (A,N,F) Ada; KDAF (W), KDFW (F), KXAS-TV (N), KXTX-TV (I) Dallas-Fort Worth; KXII (C) Sherman.
Fee: $8.50 monthly.
Expanded Basic Service
Subscribers: N.A.
Programming (via satellite): WGN-TV (W) Chicago; A & E; CNN; Country Music TV; Discovery Channel; ESPN; Fox Family Channel; Nashville Network; TBS Superstation.
Fee: $15.00 monthly.
Pay Service 1
Pay Units: 7.
Programming (via satellite): HBO.
Fee: $12.95 monthly.
Miles of plant: 10.0 (coaxial); None (fiber optic).
Manager: Danny R. Neumann.
Ownership: James Cable Partners (MSO).

ADA—Cable One, 1610 Arlington, Ada, OK 74820. Phone: 580-332-8333. Fax: 580-332-4005. County: Pontotoc. Also serves Byng, Francis, Pontotoc County. ICA: OK0018.
TV Market Ranking: Below 100. Franchise award date: N.A. Franchise expiration date: January 1, 2003. Began: June 1, 1965.
Channel capacity: 78 (2-way capable; operating 2-way). Channels available but not in use: 4.
Basic Service
Subscribers: 7,541.
Programming (received off-air): KTEN (A,N,F) Ada; KETA (P), KFOR-TV (N), KOCB (W), KOCO-TV (A), KOKH-TV (F), KWTV (C) Oklahoma City; KXII (C) Sherman; 10 FMs.
Programming (via satellite): WGN-TV (W) Chicago; A & E; BET; C-SPAN; CNBC; CNN; Cartoon Network; Country Music TV; Discovery Channel; Disney Channel; E! Entertainment TV; ESPN; ESPN 2; ESPN Classic Sports; FX; Fox Family Channel; Fox Sports Net Southwest; Headline News; History Channel; Home & Garden Television; Home Shopping Network; Learning Channel; Lifetime; MSNBC; MTV; Nashville Network; Nick at Nite's TV Land; Nickelodeon; QVC; Sci-Fi Channel; TBS Superstation; TV Guide Channel; The Weather Channel; Travel Channel; Trinity Bcstg. Network; Turner Classic Movies; Turner Network TV; USA Network.
Current originations: Automated time-weather; educational access; automated emergency alert; CTV Video Marketplace.
Fee: $40.00 installation; $28.75 monthly.
Pay Service 1
Pay Units: 2,000.
Programming (via satellite): Cinemax (multiplexed).
Fee: $21.72 installation; $13.95 monthly.
Pay Service 2
Pay Units: 2,000.
Programming (via satellite): HBO (multiplexed).
Fee: $21.72 installation; $13.95 monthly.
Pay Service 3
Pay Units: 300.
Programming (via satellite): The Movie Channel.
Fee: $21.72 installation; $10.95 monthly.
Pay Service 4
Pay Units: 420.
Programming (via satellite): Showtime (multiplexed).
Fee: $21.72 installation; $10.95 monthly.
Pay-Per-View
Addressable homes: 3,400.
Hot Choice; Spice; Viewer's Choice.
Fee: $2.99.
Local advertising: Yes. Available in satellite distributed & character-generated programming. Rates: $100.00/Month (150 characters); $5.00/30 Seconds.
Program Guide: Premium Channels.
Equipment: Scientific-Atlanta headend; GTE Sylvania & C-COR amplifiers; Comm/Scope & Trilogy cable; Scientific-Atlanta addressable set top converters; Scientific-Atlanta satellite antenna; Scientific-Atlanta satellite receivers.
Miles of plant: 266.0 (coaxial); 133.0 (fiber optic). Homes passed: 10,000. Total homes in franchised area: 10,606.
Manager: Bill W. Dalton. Chief technician: Darren Flowers. Marketing manager: David Cobb.
City fee: 3% of gross.
Ownership: Cable One Inc. (MSO).

ADAIR—Oklahoma Cablecomm, Box 970, Fort Gibson, OK 74434-0970. Phones: 918-478-2100; 800-783-5701. Fax: 918-478-2355. County: Mayes. ICA: OK0219.
TV Market Ranking: 54. Franchise award date: June 1, 1981. Franchise expiration date: June 1, 2006. Began: January 1, 1983.
Channel capacity: 35 (not 2-way capable). Channels available but not in use: 13.
Basic Service
Subscribers: 91.
Programming (received off-air): KRSC-TV (E) Claremore; KJRH (N), KOED-TV (P), KOKI-TV (F), KOTV (C), KTFO (U), KTUL (A), KWHB (I) Tulsa.
Programming (via satellite): WGN-TV (W) Chicago; A & E; CNN; Discovery Channel; Fox Family Channel; Lifetime; Nashville Network; Nickelodeon; Sci-Fi Channel; TBS Superstation; Turner Network TV; USA Network.
Fee: $30.00 installation (aerial), $50.00 (underground); $20.95 monthly; $20.00 additional installation.
Pay Service 1
Pay Units: 23.
Programming (via satellite): HBO.
Fee: $20.00 installation; $11.95 monthly.
Pay Service 2
Pay Units: 10.
Programming (via satellite): The Movie Channel.
Fee: $20.00 installation; $10.95 monthly.
Pay Service 3
Pay Units: 10.
Programming (via satellite): Showtime.
Fee: $20.00 installation; $10.95 monthly.
Local advertising: No.
Program Guide: TV Host.
Equipment: Blonder-Tongue & Triple Crown headend; Magnavox amplifiers; Comm/Scope cable; Jerrold set top converters; Arcom, Eagle & Northeast Filter traps; Standard Communications satellite receivers.
Miles of plant: 6.0 (coaxial). Homes passed: 242.
Regional manager: Rick Wall. Chief technician: Leon Strain. Marketing & program director: Bruce Berkinshaw.
City fee: 2% of basic.
Ownership: Fanch Communications Inc. (MSO); Time Warner Cable (MSO). See Cable System Ownership.

AFTON—Oklahoma Cablecomm, Box 970, Fort Gibson, OK 74434-0970. Phones: 918-478-2100; 800-783-5701. Fax: 918-478-2355. County: Ottawa. Also serves Fairland. ICA: OK0102.
TV Market Ranking: Below 100 (Fairland); Outside TV Markets (Afton). Franchise award date: February 1, 1982. Franchise expiration date: April 1, 2005. Began: July 1, 1982.
Channel capacity: 36 (2-way capable; operating 2-way). Channels available but not in use: 15.
Basic Service
Subscribers: 430; Commercial subscribers: 32.
Programming (received off-air): KODE-TV (A), KSNF (N) Joplin-Pittsburg; KJRH (N), KOED-TV (P), KOKI-TV (F), KOTV (C), KTUL (A), KWHB (I) Tulsa.
Programming (via satellite): WGN-TV (W) Chicago; A & E; CNN; Cartoon Network; Discovery Channel; ESPN; Fox Family Channel; Lifetime; Nashville Network; Sci-Fi Channel; TBS Superstation; The Weather Channel; Turner Network TV; USA Network; VH1.
Fee: $40.00 installation; $20.95 monthly; $15.00 additional installation.
Pay Service 1
Pay Units: 30.
Programming (via satellite): Disney Channel.
Fee: $15.00 installation; $7.95 monthly.
Pay Service 2
Pay Units: 85.
Programming (via satellite): HBO.
Fee: $15.00 installation; $9.50 monthly.
Pay Service 3
Pay Units: 66.
Programming (via satellite): Showtime.
Fee: $15.00 installation; $7.00 monthly.
Local advertising: No.
Program Guide: TV Host.
Equipment: Blonder-Tongue, Drake & Scientific-Atlanta headend; Scientific-Atlanta amplifiers; Comm/Scope cable; Jerrold set top converters; Arcom & Northeast Filter traps; Anixter-Mark satellite antenna; Automation Techniques & Scientific-Atlanta satellite receivers.
Miles of plant: 37.0 (coaxial). Homes passed: 1,009. Total homes in franchised area: 1,009.
Regional manager: Rick Wall. Chief technician: Leon Strain. Marketing & program director: Bruce Berkinshaw.
City fee: 3% of basic.
Ownership: Fanch Communications Inc. (MSO); Time Warner Cable (MSO). See Cable System Ownership.

AGRA—Oklahoma Cablecomm, Box 970, Fort Gibson, OK 74434-0970. Phones: 918-478-2100; 800-783-5701. Fax: 918-478-2355. County: Lincoln. ICA: OK0260.
TV Market Ranking: Outside TV Markets. Franchise award date: January 1, 1989. Franchise expiration date: January 1, 2014. Began: September 1, 1990.
Channel capacity: 35 (not 2-way capable). Channels available but not in use: 17.
Basic Service
Subscribers: 48.
Programming (received off-air): KAUT-TV (U), KETA (P), KFOR-TV (N), KOCO-TV (A), KOKH-TV (F), KWTV (C) Oklahoma City.
Programming (via satellite): WGN-TV (W) Chicago; A & E; CNN; Discovery Channel; ESPN; Fox Family Channel; Nashville Network; TBS Superstation; USA Network.
Fee: $40.00 installation; $18.95 monthly.
Pay Service 1
Pay Units: 15.
Programming (via satellite): HBO.
Fee: $10.95 monthly.
Local advertising: No.
Program Guide: TV Host.
Equipment: Cadco headend; Scientific-Atlanta amplifiers; Comm/Scope cable; Arcom traps; Standard Communications satellite receivers.
Miles of plant: 3.0 (coaxial). Homes passed: 132. Total homes in franchised area: 132.
Regional manager: Rick Wall. Chief technician: Leon Strain. Marketing & program director: Bruce Berkinshaw.
City fee: 5% of basic gross.
Ownership: Fanch Communications Inc. (MSO); Time Warner Cable (MSO). See Cable System Ownership.

ALEX—Southwestern CATV Inc., Box 171, Medicine Park, OK 73557-0171. Phone: 580-529-2288. County: Grady. ICA: OK0334.
TV Market Ranking: Outside TV Markets. Franchise award date: N.A. Franchise expiration date: N.A. Began: January 1, 1992.
Channel capacity: 35. Channels available but not in use: N.A.
Basic Service
Subscribers: 125.
Programming (received off-air): KAUT-TV (U), KETA (P), KFOR-TV (N), KOCB (W),

KOCO-TV (A), KOKH-TV (F), KTBO-TV (T), KWTV (C) Oklahoma City.
Programming (via satellite): WGN-TV (W) Chicago; A & E; CNN; Country Music TV; Discovery Channel; ESPN; Fox Family Channel; Learning Channel; Nashville Network; TBS Superstation; Turner Network TV.
Fee: $15.00 installation; $16.50 monthly.

Pay Service 1
Pay Units: 12.
Programming (via satellite): The Movie Channel.
Fee: $10.00 monthly.
Manager: Douglas Joe Hillary.
Ownership: Southwestern CATV Inc. (MSO).

ALLEN—Peak Cablevision, 205 E. Cherokee, McAlester, OK 74502. Phone: 918-423-6661. Fax: 918-426-2809.
E-mail: ethayer@peakcable.com.
Counties: Hughes & Pontotoc. ICA: OK0351.
TV Market Ranking: Below 100. Franchise award date: N.A. Franchise expiration date: July 7, 2005. Began: N.A.
Channel capacity: 40 (not 2-way capable). Channels available but not in use: N.A.

Basic Service
Subscribers: 228.
Programming (received off-air): KTEN (A,N,F) Ada; KETA (P), KFOR-TV (N), KOCB (W), KOCO-TV (A), KOKH-TV (F), KWTV (C) Oklahoma City; KTUL (A) Tulsa.
Programming (via satellite): WGN-TV (W) Chicago; A & E; American Movie Classics; Animal Planet; C-SPAN; CNN; Country Music TV; Discovery Channel; Disney Channel; ESPN; Fox Family Channel; Fox Sports Net Southwest; History Channel; Home Shopping Network; Learning Channel; Lifetime; Nashville Network; Nick at Nite's TV Land; Nickelodeon; Sci-Fi Channel; TBS Superstation; The Weather Channel; Trinity Bcstg. Network; Turner Network TV; USA Network.
Fee: $25.87 monthly.

Pay Service 1
Pay Units: N.A.
Programming (via satellite): HBO; Showtime; Starz!; The Movie Channel; The New Encore.
Fee: $2.95 monthly (Encore), $6.95 monthly (Starz), $9.95 monthly (HBO), $11.00 monthly (Showtime or TMC).
Manager: Everett Thayer. Chief technician: Lynn Harrison. Marketing director: Terry Homesley. Customer service manager: Susan Moore.
Franchise fee: 2% of gross.
Ownership: Peak Cablevision LLC (MSO). See Cable System Ownership.

ALTUS—Cable One, Box 499, 618 N. Main St., Altus, OK 73521. Phone: 580-482-0523. Fax: 580-477-0911. County: Jackson. Also serves Altus AFB, Jackson County. ICA: OK0017.
TV Market Ranking: Outside TV Markets. Franchise award date: July 30, 1956. Franchise expiration date: May 22, 2001. Began: September 1, 1957.
Channel capacity: 60 (not 2-way capable). Channels available but not in use: None.

Basic Service
Subscribers: 8,334; Commercial subscribers: 151.
Programming (received off-air): KWET (P) Cheyenne; KFOR-TV (N), KOCB (W), KOCO-TV (A), KWTV (C) Oklahoma City; KAUZ-TV (C), KFDX-TV (N), KJTL (F,U), KSWO-TV (A) Wichita Falls-Lawton.
Programming (via satellite): WGN-TV (W) Chicago; A & E; American Movie Classics; BET; C-SPAN; CNN; Cartoon Network; Comedy Central; Country Music TV; Discovery Channel; Disney Channel; E! Entertainment TV; ESPN; ESPN 2; Electronic Program Guide; Fox Family Channel; Fox Sports Net Southwest; Headline News; History Channel; Home & Garden Television; Home Shopping Network; Inspirational Life; Learning Channel; Lifetime; MSNBC; MTV; Nashville Network; Nick at Nite's TV Land; Nickelodeon; QVC; Sci-Fi Channel; TBS Superstation; TV Guide Channel; The Inspirational Network; The Weather Channel; Turner Classic Movies; Turner Network TV; USA Network; Univision.
Current originations: Automated time-weather; educational access; government access; automated emergency alert.
Fee: $20.00 installation (aerial), $55.00 (underground); $32.40 monthly; $0.66 converter; $20.00 additional installation.

Pay Service 1
Pay Units: N.A.
Programming (via satellite): Cinemax (multiplexed); HBO (multiplexed); Showtime (multiplexed); The Movie Channel.
Fee: $12.95 monthly (Showtime & TMC), $15.95 monthly (Cinemax & HBO).

Pay-Per-View
Addressable homes: 1,975.
Hot Choice; Viewer's Choice 1 & 2.
Local advertising: Yes. Available in satellite distributed, locally originated & character-generated programming. Rates: $16.00/Minute; $8.00/30 Seconds. Local sales manager: Jimmy Young.
Equipment: Standard Agile Omni headend; Anaconda & Scientific-Atlanta cable; Texscan character generator; NSC set top converters; Zenith addressable set top converters; Andrew, Scientific-Atlanta & Prodelin satellite antenna; ChannelMatic commercial insert.
Miles of plant: 105.0 (coaxial); 8.0 (fiber optic). Homes passed: 9,196. Total homes in franchised area: 9,196.
Manager: George Wilburn. Chief technician: Bruce Copeland. Marketing director: Robin Graham.
City fee: 3% of gross.
Ownership: Cable One Inc. (MSO).

ALVA—Peak Cablevision, 131 E. Maine Ave., Enid, OK 73701. Phone: 580-237-7373. Fax: 580-242-4801. County: Woods. Also serves Woods County (eastern portion). ICA: OK0063.
TV Market Ranking: Outside TV Markets. Franchise award date: N.A. Franchise expiration date: N.A. Began: May 1, 1957.
Channel capacity: 78 (2-way capable; not operating 2-way). Channels available but not in use: 20.

Basic Service
Subscribers: 2,090.
Programming (received off-air): KETA (P), KFOR-TV (N), KOCO-TV (A), KWTV (C) Oklahoma City; KAKE-TV (A), KSNW (N), KWCH-TV (C) Wichita-Hutchinson; allband FM.
Programming (via satellite): WGN-TV (W) Chicago; CNN; Discovery Channel; Disney Channel; Fox Family Channel; FoxNet; MTV; Nashville Network; Nickelodeon; TBS Superstation; The Weather Channel.
Current originations: Automated time-weather; educational access.
Fee: $37.50 installation; $26.79 monthly; $18.75 additional installation.

A la Carte 1
Subscribers: 150.
Programming (via satellite): American Movie Classics; ESPN; Fox Sports Net Southwest; Turner Network TV; USA Network.
Fee: $3.00 monthly (package).

Pay Service 1
Pay Units: 214.
Programming (via satellite): Cinemax.
Fee: $12.50 installation; $12.94 monthly.

Pay Service 2
Pay Units: 1,131.
Programming (via satellite): The New Encore.
Fee: $12.50 installation; $1.75 monthly.

Pay Service 3
Pay Units: 478.
Programming (via satellite): HBO.
Fee: $12.50 installation; $12.46 monthly.

Pay-Per-View
Addressable homes: 200.
Viewer's Choice.
Local advertising: Yes.
Equipment: Jerrold headend; Jerrold amplifiers; Systems Wire cable; Hamlin set top converters; Scientific-Atlanta satellite antenna.
Miles of plant: 37.7 (coaxial); 5.2 (fiber optic). Homes passed: 2,312. Total homes in franchised area: 2,312.
Manager: Johnny Rosson. Chief technician: Tom Ritchie.
Ownership: Peak Cablevision LLC (MSO). See Cable System Ownership.

AMES—Classic Cable, Box 429, 605 N.W. 3rd St., Plainville, KS 67663-0429. Phones: 785-434-7620; 800-999-8876. Fax: 785-434-2614. Web site: http://www.classic-cable.com.
County: Major. ICA: OK0370.
TV Market Ranking: Outside TV Markets. Franchise award date: N.A. Franchise expiration date: N.A. Began: N.A.
Channel capacity: 36 (2-way capable). Channels available but not in use: N.A.

Basic Service
Subscribers: 37.
Programming (received off-air): KAUT-TV (U), KETA (P), KFOR-TV (N), KOCB (W), KOCO-TV (A), KOKH-TV (F), KWTV (C) Oklahoma City.
Programming (via satellite): WGN-TV (W) Chicago; CNN; Discovery Channel; Disney Channel; ESPN; Fox Family Channel; Nashville Network; TBS Superstation; Trinity Bcstg. Network; USA Network.
Current originations: Public access.
Fee: $35.00 installation; $27.95 monthly.

Pay Service 1
Pay Units: 3.
Programming (via satellite): HBO.
Fee: $11.00 monthly.
Miles of plant: 3.0 (coaxial). Homes passed: 120.
Region manager: Dave Walker. Chief technician: Jeff Smith. Marketing director: Jennifer Hauschild.
Ownership: Classic Cable (MSO).

ANADARKO—Classic Cable, Box 429, 605 N.W. 3rd St., Plainville, KS 67663-0429. Phones: 785-434-7620; 800-999-8876. Fax: 785-434-2614. Web site: http://www.classic-cable.com.
County: Caddo. ICA: OK0052.
TV Market Ranking: Outside TV Markets. Franchise award date: N.A. Franchise expiration date: N.A. Began: March 6, 1977.
Channel capacity: 41 (2-way capable). Channels available but not in use: N.A.

Basic Service
Subscribers: 1,936.
Programming (received off-air): KAUT-TV (U), KETA (P), KFOR-TV (N), KOCB (W), KOCO-TV (A), KOKH-TV (F), KTBO-TV (T), KWTV (C) Oklahoma City; KSWO-TV (A) Wichita Falls-Lawton; allband FM.
Programming (via satellite): WGN-TV (W) Chicago; A & E; C-SPAN; CNN; Comedy Central; Country Music TV; Discovery Channel; Disney Channel; ESPN; Fox Family Channel; Fox Sports Net Southwest; Headline News; Nashville Network; Nick at Nite's TV Land; Nickelodeon; QVC; Sci-Fi Channel; TBS Superstation; The Weather Channel; Turner Classic Movies; Turner Network TV; USA Network.
Current originations: Automated time-weather; automated emergency alert.
Fee: $35.00 installation; $28.95 monthly.

Pay Service 1
Pay Units: 283.
Programming (via satellite): HBO.
Fee: $10.95 monthly.

Pay Service 2
Pay Units: 232.
Programming (via satellite): Showtime.
Fee: $9.95 monthly.

Pay Service 3
Pay Units: 246.
Programming (via satellite): The Movie Channel.
Fee: $5.95 monthly.
Equipment: Scientific-Atlanta headend; Jerrold amplifiers; Times Fiber cable; Scientific-Atlanta satellite antenna.
Miles of plant: 65.0 (coaxial). Homes passed: 2,041. Total homes in franchised area: 3,176.
Region manager: Dave Walker. Chief technician: Roger Campbell. Marketing director: Jennifer Hauschild.
City fee: 3% of gross.
Ownership: Classic Cable (MSO).

ANTLERS—Peak Cablevision, 516 N. Lakeside Dr., DeQueen, AR 71832. Phone: 870-642-2441. Fax: 870-642-4259. County: Pushmataha. ICA: OK0101.
TV Market Ranking: Outside TV Markets. Franchise award date: N.A. Franchise expiration date: December 4, 2010. Began: November 1, 1963.
Channel capacity: 36 (not 2-way capable). Channels available but not in use: 8.

Basic Service
Subscribers: 1,052.
Programming (received off-air): KTEN (A,N,F) Ada; KOET (P) Eufaula; KHBS (A) Fort Smith; KTAL-TV (N) Shreveport-Texarkana; allband FM.
Programming (via microwave): KWTV (C) Oklahoma City.
Programming (via satellite): WGN-TV (W) Chicago; WDIV (N) Detroit; CNN; Country Music TV; Discovery Channel; ESPN; ESPN 2; Fox Family Channel; Home Shopping Network; Nashville Network; Nickelodeon; Sci-Fi Channel; Turner Classic Movies; Turner Network TV; USA Network; VH1.
Current originations: Automated time-weather; local news.
Fee: $35.00 installation; $20.95 monthly.

Pay Service 1
Pay Units: N.A.
Programming (via satellite): Disney Channel; HBO; Showtime; The Movie Channel; The New Encore.
Fee: N.A.
Equipment: U.S. Tower satellite antenna.
Miles of plant: 14.9 (coaxial).
Manager: Ron Beatty. Chief technician: Lynn Harrison. Marketing director: Terry Homesley. Customer service manager: Carol Litchford.
City fee: 2% of gross.
Ownership: Peak Cablevision LLC (MSO). See Cable System Ownership.

APACHE—Southwestern CATV Inc., Box 171, Medicine Park, OK 73557-0171. Phone: 580-529-2288. Fax: 580-529-5225. County: Caddo. ICA: OK0139.
TV Market Ranking: Below 100. Franchise award date: N.A. Franchise expiration date: N.A. Began: April 1, 1982.
Channel capacity: 35. Channels available but not in use: N.A.

Basic Service
Subscribers: N.A.
Programming (received off-air): KETA (P), KFOR-TV (N), KOCB (W), KOCO-TV (A), KOKH-TV (F), KTBO-TV (T), KWTV (C) Oklahoma City; KSWO-TV (A) Wichita Falls-Lawton.
Programming (via satellite): WGN-TV (W) Chicago; TBS Superstation.
Fee: $15.00 installation; $8.00 monthly.
Miles of plant: 14.9 (coaxial). Homes passed: 687.
City fee: 3% of gross.
Ownership: Southwestern CATV Inc. (MSO).

ARAPAHO—Classic Cable, Box 429, 605 N.W. 3rd St., Plainville, KS 67663-0429. Phones: 785-434-7620; 800-999-8876. Fax: 785-434-2614. Web site: http://www.classic-cable.com. County: Custer. ICA: OK0187.
TV Market Ranking: Outside TV Markets. Franchise award date: N.A. Franchise expiration date: N.A. Began: July 1, 1976.
Channel capacity: 43 (2-way capable). Channels available but not in use: N.A.
Basic Service
Subscribers: 175.
Programming (received off-air): KWET (P) Cheyenne; KFOR-TV (N), KOCB (W), KOCO-TV (A), KOKH-TV (F), KWTV (C) Oklahoma City; allband FM.
Programming (via satellite): WGN-TV (W) Chicago; A & E; CNN; Cartoon Network; Country Music TV; Discovery Channel; Disney Channel; E! Entertainment TV; ESPN; Fox Family Channel; Headline News; History Channel; Home & Garden Television; Learning Channel; Nashville Network; Nick at Nite's TV Land; Outdoor Channel; QVC; Sci-Fi Channel; TBS Superstation; Trinity Bcstg. Network; Turner Network TV; USA Network.
Current originations: Automated time-weather.
Fee: $35.00 installation; $29.95 monthly; $2.00 converter.
Pay Service 1
Pay Units: 19.
Programming (via satellite): HBO.
Fee: $9.95 monthly.
Pay Service 2
Pay Units: 8.
Programming (via satellite): Showtime.
Fee: $9.95 monthly.
Pay Service 3
Pay Units: 10.
Programming (via satellite): The Movie Channel.
Fee: $9.95 monthly.
Miles of plant: 9.0 (coaxial). Homes passed: 309.
Region manager: Dave Walker. Chief technician: Roger Campbell. Marketing director: Jennifer Hauschild.
City fee: 3% of gross.
Ownership: Classic Cable (MSO).

ARDMORE—Cable One, 811 W. Broadway, Ardmore, OK 73401. Phone: 405-223-9600. Fax: 405-226-4472. County: Carter. Also serves Carter County, Dickson, Lone Grove. ICA: OK0012.
TV Market Ranking: Outside TV Markets. Franchise award date: February 1, 1952. Franchise expiration date: February 13, 1999. Began: May 1, 1951.
Channel capacity: 62 (2-way capable; operating 2-way). Channels available but not in use: 3.
Basic Service
Subscribers: 10,346; Commercial subscribers: 18.
Programming (received off-air): KTEN (A,N,F) Ada; KETA (P) Oklahoma City; KXII (C) Sherman; 7 FMs.
Programming (via microwave): KXTX-TV (I), WFAA-TV (A) Dallas-Fort Worth; KFOR-TV (N), KWTV (C) Oklahoma City.
Programming (via satellite): A & E; American Movie Classics; BET; C-SPAN; C-SPAN 2; CNBC; CNN; Country Music TV; Discovery Channel; ESPN; Fox Family Channel; Fox Sports Net Southwest; Goodlife TV Network; Headline News; Home Shopping Network; Learning Channel; Lifetime; MTV; Nashville Network; Nickelodeon; Odyssey; Sci-Fi Channel; TBS Superstation; TV Guide Channel; The Weather Channel; Travel Channel; Trinity Bcstg. Network; Turner Network TV; USA Network; VH1.
Current originations: Automated time-weather; public access; educational access; government access; religious access; leased access; automated emergency alert.
Fee: $20.24 installation; $24.25 monthly; $20.24 additional installation.
Pay Service 1
Pay Units: 780.
Programming (via satellite): Cinemax.
Fee: $12.00 monthly.
Pay Service 2
Pay Units: 675.
Programming (via satellite): Disney Channel.
Fee: $8.00 monthly.
Pay Service 3
Pay Units: 1,246.
Programming (via satellite): HBO.
Fee: $12.00 monthly.
Pay Service 4
Pay Units: 264.
Programming (via satellite): The Movie Channel.
Fee: $10.00 monthly.
Pay Service 5
Pay Units: 764.
Programming (via satellite): Showtime.
Fee: $12.00 monthly.
Pay-Per-View
Addressable homes: 3,049.
Viewer's Choice.
Fee: $3.95.
Local advertising: Yes. Available in satellite distributed & character-generated programming. Rates: $12.00/Minute; $6.00/30 Seconds.
Program Guide: Premium Channels.
Equipment: Scientific-Atlanta headend; Scientific-Atlanta amplifiers; Comm/Scope & Scientific-Atlanta cable; Sony cameras; Sony VTRs; MSI character generator; Standard Components, Scientific-Atlanta & Hamlin set top converters; Eagle addressable set top converters; Hughes, Scientific-Atlanta & Prodelin satellite antenna; Scientific-Atlanta satellite receivers; ChannelMatic & Sony commercial insert.
Miles of plant: 308.3 (coaxial); 8.1 (fiber optic). Homes passed: 13,956. Total homes in franchised area: 15,291.
Manager: David H. Wall Jr. Chief technician: Bill Reynolds.
City fee: 3% of gross.
Ownership: Cable One Inc. (MSO).

ARNETT—Classic Cable, Box 429, 605 N.W. 3rd St., Plainville, KS 67663-0429. Phones: 785-434-7620; 800-999-8876. Fax: 785-434-2614. Web site: http://www.classic-cable.com. County: Ellis. ICA: OK0261.
TV Market Ranking: Outside TV Markets. Franchise award date: N.A. Franchise expiration date: N.A. Began: August 1, 1985.
Channel capacity: 36 (2-way capable). Channels available but not in use: N.A.
Basic Service
Subscribers: 140; Commercial subscribers: 24.
Programming (received off-air): KAMR-TV (N), KFDA-TV (C), KVII-TV (A) Amarillo; KWET (P) Cheyenne; KFOR-TV (N), KOCO-TV (A), KWTV (C) Oklahoma City; KOMI-LP (I) Woodward.
Programming (via satellite): WGN-TV (W) Chicago; A & E; CNN; Country Music TV; Discovery Channel; Disney Channel; ESPN; Fox Family Channel; Fox Sports Net Southwest; FoxNet; Home & Garden Television; Learning Channel; Lifetime; Nashville Network; Nickelodeon; Sci-Fi Channel; TBS Superstation; The Weather Channel; Trinity Bcstg. Network; Turner Network TV; USA Network; VH1.
Current originations: Automated time-weather; religious access.
Planned originations: Automated emergency alert.
Fee: $35.00 installation; $27.95 monthly.
Pay Service 1
Pay Units: 17.
Programming (via satellite): HBO.
Fee: $10.95 monthly.
Pay Service 2
Pay Units: 6.
Programming (via satellite): Showtime.
Fee: $9.95 monthly.
Local advertising: Yes. Available in character-generated programming.
Equipment: Scientific-Atlanta headend; Times Fiber cable; Tandy character generator; Scientific-Atlanta set top converters; Scientific-Atlanta satellite antenna; Scientific-Atlanta satellite receivers.
Miles of plant: 5.0 (coaxial). Homes passed: 293. Total homes in franchised area: 921.
Manager: Dave Walker. Chief technician: Jeff Smith. Marketing director: Jennifer Hauschild.
City fee: 2% of basic.
Ownership: Classic Cable (MSO).

ASHER—Westcom, Box 71279, Des Moines, IA 50325. Phone: 515-276-3174. Fax: 515-270-9181. County: Pottawatomie. ICA: OK0230.
TV Market Ranking: Below 100. Franchise award date: N.A. Franchise expiration date: N.A. Began: May 1, 1989.
Channel capacity: 35. Channels available but not in use: 17.
Basic Service
Subscribers: 24.
Programming (received off-air): KTEN (A,N,F) Ada; KAUT-TV (U), KETA (P), KFOR-TV (N), KOCB (W), KOCO-TV (A), KOKH-TV (F), KWTV (C) Oklahoma City.
Programming (via satellite): CNN; Country Music TV; Discovery Channel; ESPN; Nashville Network; TBS Superstation.
Fee: $21.50 monthly.
Pay Service 1
Pay Units: N.A.
Programming (via satellite): Cinemax; HBO.
Fee: N.A.
Homes passed: 194.
Ownership: Westcom LC (MSO).

ATOKA—CommuniComm Services, Box 597, 1501 W. Mississippi, Durant, OK 74702-4992. Phones: 580-924-2367; 800-752-4992. Fax: 580-924-5970. Counties: Atoka & Coal. Also serves Cottonwood, Tushka. ICA: OK0378.
TV Market Ranking: Below 100. Franchise award date: N.A. Franchise expiration date: N.A. Began: N.A.
Channel capacity: N.A. Channels available but not in use: N.A.
Basic Service
Subscribers: 950.
Programming (received off-air): KTEN (A,N,F) Ada; KETA (P), KFOR-TV (N), KOCO-TV (A), KWTV (C) Oklahoma City; KXII (C) Sherman.
Programming (via satellite): WGN-TV (W) Chicago; A & E; American Movie Classics; BET; C-SPAN; C-SPAN 2; CNBC; CNN; CNNfn; Cartoon Network; Country Music TV; Discovery Channel; Disney Channel; ESPN; ESPN 2; Fox Family Channel; Fox Sports Net Southwest; FoxNet; Headline News; History Channel; Learning Channel; Lifetime; MTV; Nashville Network; Nickelodeon; QVC; Sci-Fi Channel; TBS Superstation; The Radar Channel; The Weather Channel; Trinity Bcstg. Network; Turner Network TV; USA Network; VH1.
Fee: $49.95 installation; $34.95 monthly.
Pay Service 1
Pay Units: 265.
Programming (via satellite): Cinemax; HBO (multiplexed); Starz!; The New Encore.
Fee: $9.95 monthly (Cinemax, Encore or Starz), $12.95 monthly (HBO).
Miles of plant: 42.0 (coaxial). Homes passed: 1,737.
Manager: Danny R. Nuemann.
Ownership: James Cable Partners (MSO).

AVANT—Community Cablevision, Box 307, Skiatook, OK 74070-0307. Phone: 918-396-3019. County: Osage. ICA: OK0239.
TV Market Ranking: 54. Franchise award date: January 25, 1988. Franchise expiration date: January 25, 2013. Began: August 15, 1988.
Channel capacity: 35 (not 2-way capable). Channels available but not in use: 13.
Basic Service
Subscribers: 95.
Programming (received off-air): KJRH (N), KOED-TV (P), KOKI-TV (F), KOTV (C), KTUL (A), KWHB (I) Tulsa.
Programming (via satellite): WGN-TV (W) Chicago; CNN; Country Music TV; Discovery Channel; ESPN; Fox Family Channel; Headline News; Nashville Network; TBS Superstation; Turner Classic Movies; Turner Network TV; USA Network.
Current originations: Automated time-weather.
Fee: $25.00 installation; $16.25 monthly.
Pay Service 1
Pay Units: 22.
Programming (via satellite): Disney Channel.
Fee: $25.00 installation; $7.00 monthly.
Pay Service 2
Pay Units: 21.
Programming (via satellite): HBO.
Fee: $25.00 installation; $11.50 monthly.
Local advertising: No.
Equipment: Blonder-Tongue headend; Scientific-Atlanta cable; Standard Communications set top converters; Eagle traps; M/A-Com satellite antenna; Drake satellite receivers.
Miles of plant: 3.0 (coaxial). Homes passed: 178.
Manager: Ray Soule.
City fee: 2% of gross.
Ownership: Community Cablevision Co. (MSO).

BARNSDALL—Community Cablevision, Box 307, Skiatook, OK 74070-0307. Phone: 918-396-3019. County: Osage. ICA: OK0118.
TV Market Ranking: 54. Franchise award date: April 6, 1982. Franchise expiration date: April 6, 2007. Began: May 1, 1983.
Channel capacity: 35 (not 2-way capable). Channels available but not in use: 4.
Basic Service
Subscribers: 400.

Programming (received off-air): KDOR (T) Bartlesville; KJRH (N), KOED-TV (P), KOKI-TV (F), KOTV (C), KTUL (A), KWHB (I) Tulsa.
Programming (via satellite): WGN-TV (W) Chicago; A & E; CNN; Country Music TV; Discovery Channel; ESPN; Fox Family Channel; Headline News; Lifetime; MTV; Nashville Network; Nickelodeon; TBS Superstation; Turner Classic Movies; Turner Network TV; USA Network; VH1.
Current originations: Automated time-weather.
Fee: $25.00 installation; $16.25 monthly; $25.00 additional installation.

Pay Service 1
Pay Units: 91.
Programming (via satellite): Cinemax.
Fee: $25.00 installation; $11.50 monthly.

Pay Service 2
Pay Units: 60.
Programming (via satellite): Disney Channel.
Fee: $25.00 installation; $7.00 monthly.

Pay Service 3
Pay Units: 114.
Programming (via satellite): HBO.
Fee: $25.00 installation; $11.50 monthly.

Local advertising: Yes. Available in character-generated programming. Rates: $15.00/Week.
Equipment: Triple Crown, Jerrold & Blonder-Tongue headend; Scientific-Atlanta amplifiers; Comm/Scope cable; Texscan character generator; GTE Sylvania set top converters; Arcom traps; Scientific-Atlanta satellite antenna; Scientific-Atlanta satellite receivers.
Homes passed: 838.
Manager: Ray Soule.
City fee: 3% of gross.
Ownership: Community Cablevision Co. (MSO).

BARTLESVILLE—Cable One, Box 1028, Bartlesville, OK 74005. Phone: 918-335-0123. Fax: 918-333-6757. County: Washington. Also serves Dewey. ICA: OK0010.
TV Market Ranking: Below 100. Franchise award date: N.A. Franchise expiration date: April 13, 2010. Began: September 1, 1972.
Channel capacity: 38. Channels available but not in use: None.

Basic Service
Subscribers: 13,725.
Programming (received off-air): KDOR (T) Bartlesville; KRSC-TV (E) Claremore; KJRH (N), KOED-TV (P), KOKI-TV (F), KOTV (C), KTUL (A), KWHB (I) Tulsa; 14 FMs.
Programming (via satellite): C-SPAN.
Current originations: Automated time-weather.
Fee: $18.00 installation; $6.60 monthly; $2.05 converter; $10.00 additional installation.

Expanded Basic Service
Subscribers: 13,395.
Programming (via satellite): WGN-TV (W) Chicago; A & E; American Movie Classics; BET; CNBC; CNN; Discovery Channel; ESPN; Fox Family Channel; Fox Sports Net Southwest; Headline News; Home & Garden Television; Home Shopping Network; Learning Channel; Lifetime; MTV; Nashville Network; Nickelodeon; Odyssey; TBS Superstation; The Weather Channel; Turner Network TV; USA Network; VH1.
Fee: $13.35 monthly.

Pay Service 1
Pay Units: 573.
Programming (via satellite): Cinemax.
Fee: $10.00 installation; $9.85 monthly.

Pay Service 2
Pay Units: 657.
Programming (via satellite): Disney Channel.
Fee: $10.00 installation; $9.85 monthly.

Pay Service 3
Pay Units: 4,407.
Programming (via satellite): HBO.
Fee: $10.00 installation; $9.85 monthly.

Local advertising: Yes.
Equipment: Scientific-Atlanta headend; C-COR amplifiers; Comm/Scope cable; Hamlin set top converters; AFC satellite antenna.
Miles of plant: 211.0 (coaxial). Homes passed: 18,000.
Manager: Dick Marnell. Chief technician: Dennis Anderson.
City fee: 5% of gross.
Ownership: Cable One Inc. (MSO).

BEAVER—Classic Cable, Box 429, 605 N.W. 3rd St., Plainville, KS 67663-0429. Phones: 785-434-7620; 800-999-8876. Fax: 785-434-2614. Web Site: http://www.classic-cable.com. County: Beaver. Also serves Forgan. ICA: OK0114.
TV Market Ranking: Outside TV Markets. Franchise award date: N.A. Franchise expiration date: March 2, 2002. Began: April 19, 1962.
Channel capacity: 41 (2-way capable). Channels available but not in use: N.A.

Basic Service
Subscribers: 707.
Programming (received off-air): KAMR-TV (N), KFDA-TV (C), KVII-TV (A) Amarillo; KBSD-TV (C) Ensign; KUPK-TV (A) Garden City; KETA (P) Oklahoma City; 4 FMs.
Programming (via microwave): KAMR-TV (N), KFDA-TV (C), KVII-TV (A) Amarillo; KETA (P) Oklahoma City.
Programming (via satellite): WGN-TV (W) Chicago; A & E; CNN; Country Music TV; Discovery Channel; Disney Channel; E! Entertainment TV; ESPN; Fox Family Channel; Fox News Channel; Fox Sports Net Southwest; FoxNet; History Channel; Nashville Network; Nick at Nite's TV Land; Nickelodeon; QVC; Sci-Fi Channel; TBS Superstation; The Weather Channel; Turner Network TV; USA Network.
Current originations: Automated time-weather.
Fee: $35.00 installation; $28.95 monthly.

Pay Service 1
Pay Units: 105.
Programming (via satellite): HBO.
Fee: $10.95 monthly.

Pay Service 2
Pay Units: 106.
Programming (via satellite): Showtime.
Fee: $35.00 installation; $9.95 monthly.

Pay Service 3
Pay Units: 108.
Programming (via satellite): The Movie Channel.
Fee: $5.95 monthly.

Equipment: Jerrold headend; Jerrold & Starline amplifiers; Comm/Scope, Jerrold & Starline cable; R. H. Tyler satellite antenna.
Miles of plant: 20.0 (coaxial). Homes passed: 1,181.
Region manager: Dave Walker. Chief technician: Jeff Smith. Marketing director: Jennifer Hauschild.
City fee: 2% of gross.
Ownership: Classic Cable (MSO).

BEGGS—Oklahoma Cablecomm, Box 970, Fort Gibson, OK 74434-0970. Phones: 918-478-2100; 800-783-5701. Fax: 918-478-2355. County: Okmulgee. ICA: OK0154.
TV Market Ranking: 54. Franchise award date: February 1, 1980. Franchise expiration date: N.A. Began: October 1, 1982.
Channel capacity: 35 (not 2-way capable). Channels available but not in use: 15.

Basic Service
Subscribers: 275.
Programming (received off-air): KJRH (N), KOED-TV (P), KOKI-TV (F), KOTV (C), KTFO (U), KTUL (A), KWHB (I) Tulsa.
Programming (via satellite): WGN-TV (W) Chicago; A & E; CNN; Cartoon Network; Country Music TV; Discovery Channel; ESPN; Fox Family Channel; Nashville Network; Nickelodeon; TBS Superstation; Turner Classic Movies; Turner Network TV; USA Network.
Current originations: Automated time-weather; automated emergency alert.
Fee: $30.00 installation; $20.95 monthly.

Pay Service 1
Pay Units: 15.
Programming (via satellite): Disney Channel.
Fee: $20.00 installation; $8.95 monthly.

Pay Service 2
Pay Units: 106.
Programming (via satellite): HBO.
Fee: $20.00 installation; $8.95 monthly.

Local advertising: Yes. Available in character-generated programming.
Program Guide: TV Host.
Equipment: Scientific-Atlanta headend; Scientific-Atlanta amplifiers; Comm/Scope cable; BEI character generator; Hamlin & Jerrold set top converters; Anixter-Mark satellite antenna; Scientific-Atlanta satellite receivers.
Miles of plant: 13.0 (coaxial). Homes passed: 560. Total homes in franchised area: 560.
Regional manager: Rick Wall. Chief technician: Leon Strain. Marketing & program director: Bruce Berkinshaw.
City fee: 3% of gross.
Ownership: Fanch Communications Inc. (MSO); Time Warner Cable (MSO). See Cable System Ownership.

BENNINGTON—Peak Cablevision, 516 N. Lakeside Dr., DeQueen, AR 71832. Phone: 870-642-2441. Fax: 870-642-4259. County: Bryan. ICA: OK0352.
TV Market Ranking: Outside TV Markets. Franchise award date: N.A. Franchise expiration date: July 11, 2006. Began: N.A.
Channel capacity: 25 (not 2-way capable). Channels available but not in use: 12.

Basic Service
Subscribers: 48.
Programming (received off-air): KTEN (A,N,F) Ada; KETA (P) Oklahoma City; KXII (C) Sherman.
Programming (via satellite): WGN-TV (W) Chicago; CNN; Country Music TV; Discovery Channel; ESPN; Fox Family Channel; Nashville Network; TBS Superstation; Turner Network TV.
Fee: $25.00 installation; $15.00 monthly.

Pay Service 1
Pay Units: N.A.
Programming (via satellite): HBO.
Fee: N.A.

Manager: Ron Beatty. Chief technician: Lynn Harrison. Marketing director: Terry Homesley. Customer service manager: Carol Litchford.
Ownership: Peak Cablevision LLC (MSO). See Cable System Ownership.

BERNICE—Classic Cable, 315 N. Main St., Kingfisher, OK 73750. Phones: 405-375-6639; 800-783-5701. Fax: 405-375-6441. Web site: http://www.classic-cable.com. County: Delaware. ICA: OK0180.
TV Market Ranking: Outside TV Markets. Franchise award date: January 5, 1987. Franchise expiration date: September 3, 2005. Began: May 1, 1987.
Channel capacity: 21 (not 2-way capable). Channels available but not in use: 3.

Basic Service
Subscribers: 174.
Programming (received off-air): KOAM-TV (C), KODE-TV (A) Joplin-Pittsburg; KJRH (N), KOED-TV (P), KOKI-TV (F), KOTV (C), KTUL (A), KWHB (I) Tulsa.
Programming (via satellite): WGN-TV (W) Chicago; A & E; CNN; Cartoon Network; Country Music TV; ESPN; Fox Family Channel; Nashville Network; TBS Superstation; Turner Network TV; USA Network.
Fee: $30.00 installation; $19.95 monthly.

Pay Service 1
Pay Units: 20.
Programming (via satellite): HBO.
Fee: $20.00 installation; $11.95 monthly.

Local advertising: No.
Program Guide: TV Host.
Equipment: Blonder-Tongue, Drake & Triple Crown headend; Comm/Scope cable; Scientific-Atlanta satellite antenna; Automation Techniques satellite receivers.
Miles of plant: 9.0 (coaxial). Additional miles planned: 5.0 (coaxial). Homes passed: 415. Total homes in franchised area: 415.
Manager: Bob Bailey. Chief technician: Bill Thomison. Marketing & program director: Bruce Berkinshaw.
City fee: 3% of basic gross.
Ownership: Fanch Communications Inc. (MSO). See Cable System Ownership.

BESSIE—Classic Cable, Box 429, 605 N.W. 3rd St., Plainville, KS 67663-0429. Phones: 785-434-7620; 800-999-8876. Fax: 785-434-2614. Web site: http://www.classic-cable.com. County: Washita. ICA: OK0380.
TV Market Ranking: Outside TV Markets. Franchise award date: N.A. Franchise expiration date: N.A. Began: N.A.
Channel capacity: 36 (2-way capable). Channels available but not in use: N.A.

Basic Service
Subscribers: 40.
Programming (received off-air): KWET (P) Cheyenne; KAUT-TV (U), KFOR-TV (N), KOCB (W), KOCO-TV (A), KOKH-TV (F), KWTV (C) Oklahoma City; KJTL (F,U) Wichita Falls-Lawton.
Programming (via satellite): WGN-TV (W) Chicago; Discovery Channel; E! Entertainment TV; ESPN; Fox Family Channel; Nashville Network; Nick at Nite's TV Land; Sci-Fi Channel; TBS Superstation; Turner Network TV; USA Network.
Fee: $35.00 installation; $27.95 monthly.

Pay Service 1
Pay Units: 10.
Programming (via satellite): HBO.
Fee: $9.95 monthly.

Miles of plant: 4.0 (coaxial). Homes passed: 98.
Manager: Dave Walker. Chief technician: Roger Campbell. Marketing director: Jennifer Hauschild.
Ownership: Classic Cable (MSO).

BETHANY—Cablevision of Bethany, 6221 N.W. 39th Expressway, Bethany, OK 73008. Phone: 405-389-3549. County: Oklahoma. ICA: OK0020.
TV Market Ranking: 39. Franchise award date: August 1, 1978. Franchise expiration date: September 26, 1998. Began: December 1, 1979.

Channel capacity: 110 (2-way capable; operating 2-way). Channels available but not in use: 41.

Basic Service

Subscribers: 4,688.

Programming (received off-air): KAUT-TV (U), KETA (P), KFOR-TV (N), KOCB (W), KOCO-TV (A), KOKH-TV (F), KSBI (I), KTBO-TV (T), KWTV (C) Oklahoma City; 13 FMs.

Programming (via satellite): A & E; American Movie Classics; BET; C-SPAN; C-SPAN 2; CNBC; Discovery Channel; E! Entertainment TV; ESPN; Fox Sports Net Southwest; Home & Garden Television; Home Shopping Network; Learning Channel; Lifetime; MTV; Nick at Nite; Nickelodeon; QVC; TV Food Network; TV Guide Channel; The Weather Channel; USA Network; VH1.

Current originations: Public access; educational access; government access; local sports.

Planned originations: Automated emergency alert.

Fee: $17.47 installation; $18.72 monthly; $3.00 converter; $18.59 additional installation.

Expanded Basic Service

Subscribers: 4,745.

Programming (via satellite): WGN-TV (W) Chicago; CNN; Fox Family Channel; Headline News; Nashville Network; TBS Superstation; Turner Network TV.

Fee: $3.41 monthly.

Expanded Basic Service 2

Subscribers: 1,088.

Programming (via satellite): Bravo; Cartoon Network; Comedy Central; Country Music TV; Court TV; ESPN 2; History Channel; Sci-Fi Channel; TV Guide Sneak Prevue; Travel Channel; Turner Classic Movies.

Fee: $6.00 monthly.

Pay Service 1

Pay Units: 903.

Programming (via satellite): Cinemax.

Fee: $11.00 monthly.

Pay Service 2

Pay Units: 485.

Programming (via satellite): Disney Channel.

Fee: $7.95 monthly.

Pay Service 3

Pay Units: 1,430.

Programming (via satellite): HBO.

Fee: $11.00 monthly.

Pay Service 4

Pay Units: 822.

Programming (via satellite): Showtime.

Fee: $11.00 monthly.

Pay Service 5

Pay Units: 30.

Programming (via satellite): Music Choice.

Fee: $7.95 monthly.

Pay Service 6

Pay Units: 17.

Programming (via satellite): Golf Channel.

Fee: $6.95 monthly.

Pay-Per-View

Addressable homes: 1,244.

Special events.

Local advertising: Yes. Available in satellite distributed programming. Rates: $800.00/Hour; $400.00/30 Minutes; $160.00/Minute; $80.00/30 Seconds. Local sales manager: Mark Kanter.

Equipment: Scientific-Atlanta headend; RCA amplifiers; Comm/Scope cable; Jerrold fiber optic cable; Panasonic cameras; Panasonic VTRs; Jerrold, Oak & Hamlin set top converters; Scientific-Atlanta addressable set top converters; Eagle traps; Scientific-Atlanta satellite antenna; Scientific-Atlanta satellite receivers.

Miles of plant: 83.0 (coaxial). Homes passed: 8,322. Total homes in franchised area: 8,418.

Manager: David Cooper. Chief technician: Kurtis Gill. Marketing director: Jim Back. Customer service manager: Charitta Shelton.

City fee: 3% of gross.

Ownership: Multimedia Cablevision Inc. (MSO). See Cable System Ownership.

BILLINGS—Classic Cable, Box 429, 605 N.W. 3rd St., Plainville, KS 67663-0429. Phones: 785-434-7620; 800-999-8876. Fax: 785-434-2614. Web site: http://www.classic-cable.com. County: Noble. ICA: OK0235.

TV Market Ranking: Outside TV Markets. Franchise award date: March 1, 1984. Franchise expiration date: March 1, 2004. Began: June 17, 1985.

Channel capacity: 36 (2-way capable). Channels available but not in use: N.A.

Basic Service

Subscribers: 105; Commercial subscribers: 41.

Programming (received off-air): KAUT-TV (U), KETA (P), KFOR-TV (N), KOCB (W), KOCO-TV (A), KOKH-TV (F), KTBO-TV (T), KWTV (C) Oklahoma City.

Programming (via satellite): WGN-TV (W) Chicago; CNN; Country Music TV; Discovery Channel; Disney Channel; ESPN; Fox Family Channel; History Channel; Nashville Network; Nick at Nite's TV Land; Nickelodeon; Sci-Fi Channel; TBS Superstation; The Weather Channel; Turner Network TV; USA Network.

Fee: $35.00 installation; $27.95 monthly; $3.50 converter.

Pay Service 1

Pay Units: 27.

Programming (via satellite): HBO.

Fee: $20.00 installation; $9.95 monthly.

Pay Service 2

Pay Units: 14.

Programming (via satellite): Showtime.

Fee: $9.95 monthly.

Local advertising: No.

Equipment: Blonder-Tongue & Cadco headend; Magnavox amplifiers; Comm/Scope cable; Arcom, Eagle & Northeast Filter traps; Prodelin & Scientific-Atlanta satellite antenna; Standard Communications satellite receivers.

Miles of plant: 4.6 (coaxial). Homes passed: 191.

Region manager: Dave Walker. Chief technician: Jeff Smith. Marketing director: Jennifer Hauschild.

City fee: 2% of basic gross.

Ownership: Classic Cable (MSO).

BINGER—Classic Cable, Box 429, 605 N.W. 3rd St., Plainville, KS 67663-0429. Phones: 785-434-7620; 800-999-8876. Fax: 785-434-2614. Web site: http://www.classic-cable.com. County: Caddo. ICA: OK0262.

TV Market Ranking: Outside TV Markets. Franchise award date: N.A. Franchise expiration date: N.A. Began: N.A.

Channel capacity: 36 (2-way capable). Channels available but not in use: N.A.

Basic Service

Subscribers: 207.

Programming (received off-air): KAUT-TV (U), KETA (P), KFOR-TV (N), KOCB (W), KOCO-TV (A), KOKH-TV (F), KSBI (I), KTBO-TV (T), KWTV (C) Oklahoma City.

Programming (via satellite): WGN-TV (W) Chicago; CNN; Country Music TV; Discovery Channel; Disney Channel; E! Entertainment TV; ESPN; Fox Family Channel; History Channel; Home Shopping Network; Nashville Network; Nick at Nite's TV Land; Nickelodeon; TBS Superstation; The Weather Channel; Turner Network TV; USA Network.

Current originations: Public access.

Fee: $35.00 installation; $27.95 monthly.

Pay Service 1

Pay Units: 34.

Programming (via satellite): HBO.

Fee: $10.95 monthly.

Pay Service 2

Pay Units: 17.

Programming (via satellite): Showtime.

Fee: $9.95 monthly.

Miles of plant: 7.0 (coaxial). Homes passed: 330.

Region manager: Dave Walker. Chief technician: Roger Campbell. Marketing director: Jennifer Hauschild.

Ownership: Classic Cable (MSO).

BIXBY—TCI Cable of Kansas, 202 N. Armstrong, Bixby, OK 74008. Phone: 918-665-0200. County: Tulsa. ICA: OK0044.

TV Market Ranking: 54. Franchise award date: August 1, 1979. Franchise expiration date: N.A. Began: November 1, 1980.

Channel capacity: 35 (not 2-way capable). Channels available but not in use: None.

Basic Service

Subscribers: 2,420.

Programming (received off-air): KJRH (N), KOED-TV (P), KOKI-TV (F), KOTV (C), KTUL (A), KWHB (I) Tulsa; 11 FMs.

Programming (via satellite): A & E; American Movie Classics; C-SPAN; CNBC; Discovery Channel; ESPN; Fox Family Channel; Home Shopping Network; Learning Channel; Lifetime; MTV; Nashville Network; Nickelodeon; The Weather Channel; USA Network; VH1.

Current originations: Public access; educational access; government access; automated emergency alert.

Fee: $14.38 installation; $19.75 monthly; $6.15 additional installation.

A la Carte 1

Subscribers: N.A.

Programming (via satellite): WGN-TV (W) Chicago; CNN; Fox Sports Net Southwest; Headline News; TBS Superstation; Turner Network TV.

Fee: $3.07 monthly (package).

Pay Service 1

Pay Units: 663.

Programming (via satellite): Cinemax.

Fee: $11.00 monthly.

Pay Service 2

Pay Units: 358.

Programming (via satellite): Disney Channel.

Fee: $7.95 monthly.

Pay Service 3

Pay Units: 800.

Programming (via satellite): HBO.

Fee: $11.00 monthly.

Pay-Per-View

Special events.

Local advertising: No.

Equipment: Scientific-Atlanta headend; Scientific-Atlanta amplifiers; Comm/Scope cable; Panasonic cameras; Panasonic VTRs; Quanta character generator; Jerrold, Oak & RCA set top converters; Eagle traps; Scientific-Atlanta satellite antenna; Scientific-Atlanta satellite receivers.

Miles of plant: 82.8 (coaxial). Homes passed: 3,902. Total homes in franchised area: 3,902.

Manager: Ken Crouch. Chief technician: Lee Vardeman. Marketing director: Jim Back.

City fee: 3% of gross.

Ownership: AT&T Broadband & Internet Services (MSO). Purchased from Tele-Communications Inc., March 9, 1999.

BLACKWELL—TCA Cable Partners, Box 606, 1105 N. 9th St., Blackwell, OK 74831. Phones: 580-363-1870; 580-628-3298. County: Kay. Also serves Tonkawa. ICA: OK0036.

TV Market Ranking: Outside TV Markets. Franchise award date: N.A. Franchise expiration date: February 1, 2000. Began: October 1, 1964.

Channel capacity: 37 (2-way capable). Channels available but not in use: None.

Basic Service

Subscribers: 4,235.

Programming (received off-air): KAUT-TV (U), KETA (P), KFOR-TV (N), KOCB (W), KOCO-TV (A), KOKH-TV (F), KWTV (C) Oklahoma City; KSNW (N) Wichita-Hutchinson.

Programming (via satellite): WGN-TV (W) Chicago; TBS Superstation.

Current originations: Automated time-weather; educational access.

Fee: $30.00 installation; $5.99 monthly.

Expanded Basic Service

Subscribers: 4,085.

Programming (via satellite): A & E; C-SPAN; CNN; Country Music TV; Discovery Channel; ESPN; Fox Family Channel; Headline News; History Channel; Home Shopping Network; Lifetime; Nashville Network; Nickelodeon; Odyssey; Sci-Fi Channel; The Weather Channel; Trinity Bcstg. Network; Turner Classic Movies; Turner Network TV; USA Network.

Fee: $13.48 monthly.

Pay Service 1

Pay Units: 399.

Programming (via satellite): Cinemax.

Fee: $10.95 monthly.

Pay Service 2

Pay Units: 182.

Programming (via satellite): Disney Channel.

Fee: $9.95 monthly.

Pay Service 3

Pay Units: 945.

Programming (via satellite): HBO.

Fee: $10.95 monthly.

Pay Service 4

Pay Units: N.A.

Programming (via satellite): Showtime.

Fee: $5.95 monthly.

Local advertising: No.

Equipment: Scientific-Atlanta headend; Jerrold amplifiers; Superior cable; Hamlin set top converters; Microdyne satellite antenna.

Miles of plant: 85.0 (coaxial); 11.0 (fiber optic). Homes passed: 4,775. Total homes in franchised area: 4,775.

Manager: Jim Johnson. Chief technician: B. R. Kindred.

City fee: 3% of gross.

Ownership: TCA Cable Partners (MSO). See Cable System Ownership.

BLAIR—Rapid Cable, Box 6310, 310 Walnut Extension, Branson, MO 65615. Phones: 417-334-7897; 800-972-0962. Fax: 417-334-7899. E-mail: rcpcable@aol.com. County: Jackson. ICA: OK0181.

TV Market Ranking: Outside TV Markets. Franchise award date: N.A. Franchise expiration date: September 22, 2007. Began: January 1, 1972.

Channel capacity: 31 (2-way capable; not operating 2-way). Channels available but not in use: 3.

Basic Service

Subscribers: 295.

Programming (received off-air): KETA (P), KFOR-TV (N), KWTV (C) Oklahoma City; KJBO-LP (U) Wichita Falls; KAUZ-TV (C), KFDX-TV (N), KJTL (F,U), KSWO-TV (A) Wichita Falls-Lawton; allband FM.

Programming (via satellite): WGN-TV (W) Chicago; Animal Planet; CNN; Country Music TV; Discovery Channel; ESPN; Fox Family Channel; Fox News Channel; Home Shopping Network 2; Learning Channel; Nashville Network; TBS Superstation; The Weather Channel; Trinity Bcstg. Network; Turner Network TV; USA Network.

Fee: $29.95 installation; $22.95 monthly; $3.95 converter.

Pay Service 1

Pay Units: 26.

Programming (via satellite): Cinemax.

Fee: $9.00 monthly.

Pay Service 2

Pay Units: 26.

Programming (via satellite): HBO.

Fee: $10.00 monthly.

Pay Service 3

Pay Units: N.A.

Programming (via satellite): Showtime; The Movie Channel.

Fee: $10.00 monthly (Showtime), $10.95 monthly (TMC).

Pay Service 4

Pay Units: 33.

Programming (via satellite): Disney Channel.

Fee: $7.00 monthly.

Local advertising: No.

Miles of plant: 16.0 (coaxial). Homes passed: 552.

Manager: Belinda Murphy. Chief engineer: Steve Rice. Program director: Beth Semptimphelter. Marketing director: Bill Fischer.

Ownership: Rapid Communications Partners LP (MSO); TS Communications Inc. (MSO).

BLANCHARD—Classic Cable, 2820 N. Green Ave., Purcell, OK 73080-1707. Phone: 405-527-5651. Fax: 405-527-5392.

Web site: http://www.classic~cable.com.

Counties: Grady & McClain. ICA: OK0142.

TV Market Ranking: 39. Franchise award date: N.A. Franchise expiration date: N.A. Began: November 1, 1981.

Channel capacity: 40 (not 2-way capable). Channels available but not in use: None.

Basic Service

Subscribers: 377.

Programming (received off-air): KAUT-TV (U), KETA (P), KFOR-TV (N), KOCB (W), KOCO-TV (A), KOKH-TV (F), KSBI (I), KTBO-TV (T), KWTV (C) Oklahoma City.

Programming (via satellite): WGN-TV (W) Chicago; A & E; American Movie Classics; C-SPAN; CNN; Country Music TV; Discovery Channel; ESPN; Fox Family Channel; Lifetime; MTV; Nashville Network; Nickelodeon; QVC; TBS Superstation; The Weather Channel; Turner Network TV; USA Network.

Fee: $42.36 installation; $27.00 monthly; $21.22 additional installation.

Pay Service 1

Pay Units: N.A.

Programming (via satellite): Cinemax; HBO; The Movie Channel; Turner Classic Movies.

Fee: $1.75 monthly (TCM), $9.95 monthly (Cinemax), $12.84 monthly (TMC), $13.29 monthly (HBO).

Miles of plant: 8.2 (coaxial); None (fiber optic). Homes passed: 658. Total homes in franchised area: 723.

Manager: Kris Miller. Chief technician: Kurt Widmer.

Ownership: Classic Cable (MSO).

BOISE CITY—Classic Cable, Box 429, 605 N.W. 3rd St., Plainville, KS 67663-0429. Phones: 785-434-7620; 800-999-8876. Fax: 785-434-2614. Web site: http://www.classic-cable.com. County: Cimarron. ICA: OK0119.

TV Market Ranking: Outside TV Markets. Franchise award date: January 1, 1988. Franchise expiration date: January 1, 2013. Began: October 1, 1962.

Channel capacity: 36 (2-way capable). Channels available but not in use: N.A.

Basic Service

Subscribers: 558; Commercial subscribers: 80.

Programming (received off-air): 5 FMs.

Programming (via microwave): KAMR-TV (N), KCIT (F,U), KFDA-TV (C), KVII-TV (A) Amarillo.

Programming (via translator): KWET (P) Cheyenne.

Programming (via satellite): WGN-TV (W) Chicago; American Movie Classics; CNN; Country Music TV; Discovery Channel; Disney Channel; ESPN; Fox Family Channel; Fox Sports Net Southwest; Goodlife TV Network; Learning Channel; Lifetime; Nashville Network; Nick at Nite's TV Land; Nickelodeon; QVC; Sci-Fi Channel; TBS Superstation; The Weather Channel; Trinity Bcstg. Network; Turner Network TV; USA Network.

Current originations: Automated time-weather.

Fee: $35.00 installation; $25.95 monthly.

Pay Service 1

Pay Units: 144.

Programming (via satellite): HBO.

Fee: $10.00 installation; $9.95 monthly.

Pay Service 2

Pay Units: 50.

Programming (via satellite): Showtime.

Fee: $9.95 monthly.

Pay Service 3

Pay Units: 33.

Programming (via satellite): The Movie Channel.

Fee: $5.95 monthly.

Local advertising: Yes.

Equipment: Jerrold headend; Jerrold amplifiers; Cerro & Times Fiber cable; AFC satellite antenna.

Miles of plant: 11.0 (coaxial). Homes passed: 764. Total homes in franchised area: 800.

Region manager: Dave Walker. Chief technician: Jeff Smith. Marketing director: Jennifer Hauschild.

City fee: 2% of gross.

Ownership: Classic Cable (MSO).

BOKOSHE—Classic Cable, Box 429, 605 N.W. 3rd St., Plainville, KS 67663-0429. Phones: 785-434-7620; 800-999-8876. Fax: 785-434-2614. Web site: http://www.classic-cable.com. County: Le Flore. ICA: OK0263.

TV Market Ranking: Outside TV Markets. Franchise award date: N.A. Franchise expiration date: N.A. Began: July 1, 1988.

Channel capacity: 36 (2-way capable). Channels available but not in use: N.A.

Basic Service

Subscribers: 79.

Programming (received off-air): KFDF-LP (U), KFSM-TV (C), KHBS (A), KPBI-LP (F), KPOM-TV (N) Fort Smith; KETA (P) Oklahoma City; KOKI-TV (F), KTUL (A) Tulsa.

Programming (via satellite): WGN-TV (W) Chicago; CNN; ESPN; Fox Family Channel; Nashville Network; Nick at Nite's TV Land; TBS Superstation; The Weather Channel; Turner Classic Movies; USA Network.

Fee: $35.00 installation; $27.95 monthly.

Pay Service 1

Pay Units: 8.

Programming (via satellite): Showtime.

Fee: $11.00 monthly.

Pay Service 2

Pay Units: 2.

Programming (via satellite): The Movie Channel.

Fee: N.A.

Miles of plant: 6.4 (coaxial). Homes passed: 200.

Region manager: Dave Walker. Chief technician: Carl Miller. Marketing director: Jennifer Hauschild.

Ownership: Classic Cable (MSO).

BOSWELL—Peak Cablevision, 516 N. Lakeside Dr., DeQueen, AR 71832. Phone: 870-642-2441. Fax: 870-642-4259. County: Choctaw. Also serves Choctaw County (unincorporated areas). ICA: OK0199.

TV Market Ranking: Outside TV Markets. Franchise award date: N.A. Franchise expiration date: March 29, 2004. Began: March 1, 1984.

Channel capacity: 25 (not 2-way capable). Channels available but not in use: 8.

Basic Service

Subscribers: 197.

Programming (received off-air): KTEN (A,N,F) Ada; KXII (C) Sherman; KOED-TV (P) Tulsa.

Programming (via satellite): WGN-TV (W) Chicago; CNN; Country Music TV; Discovery Channel; ESPN; Fox Family Channel; Headline News; Nashville Network; TBS Superstation; Trinity Bcstg. Network; USA Network.

Fee: $25.00 installation; $15.95 monthly.

Pay Service 1

Pay Units: N.A.

Programming (via satellite): Cinemax; Disney Channel; HBO.

Fee: N.A.

Local advertising: No.

Miles of plant: 9.0 (coaxial). Homes passed: 301.

Manager: Ron Beatty. Chief technician: Lynn Harrison. Marketing director: Terry Homesley. Customer service manager: Carol Litchford.

City fee: 2% of gross.

Ownership: Peak Cablevision LLC (MSO). See Cable System Ownership.

BOYNTON—Oklahoma Cablecomm, Box 970, Fort Gibson, OK 74434-0970. Phones: 918-478-2100; 800-783-5701. Fax: 918-478-2355. County: Muskogee. ICA: OK0245.

TV Market Ranking: Outside TV Markets. Franchise award date: January 1, 1989. Franchise expiration date: January 1, 2014. Began: September 1, 1989.

Channel capacity: 45 (not 2-way capable). Channels available but not in use: N.A.

Basic Service

Subscribers: 37.

Programming (received off-air): KJRH (N), KOED-TV (P), KOKI-TV (F), KOTV (C), KTUL (A), KWHB (I) Tulsa.

Programming (via satellite): WGN-TV (W) Chicago; CNN; Country Music TV; Discovery Channel; ESPN; Fox Family Channel; Nashville Network; TBS Superstation; Turner Network TV.

Fee: $30.00 installation; $19.95 monthly.

Pay Service 1

Pay Units: 18.

Programming (via satellite): HBO.

Fee: $10.95 monthly.

Local advertising: No.

Equipment: Scientific-Atlanta amplifiers; Jerrold set top converters; Pico traps; Scientific-Atlanta satellite antenna; Cadco satellite receivers.

Miles of plant: 6.0 (coaxial). Homes passed: 159. Total homes in franchised area: 159.

Regional manager: Rick Wall. Chief technician: Leon Strain. Marketing & program director: Bruce Berkinshaw.

City fee: 5% of gross.

Ownership: Fanch Communications Inc. (MSO); Time Warner Cable (MSO). See Cable System Ownership.

BRAGGS—Peak Cablevision, 410 Eastside Blvd., Muskogee, OK 74403. Phone: 918-687-7511. Fax: 918-687-3291. County: Muskogee. ICA: OK0264.

TV Market Ranking: Outside TV Markets. Franchise award date: N.A. Franchise expiration date: N.A. Began: May 15, 1990.

Channel capacity: 36 (not 2-way capable). Channels available but not in use: 14.

Basic Service

Subscribers: 130.

Programming (received off-air): KOET (P) Eufaula; KHBS (A) Fort Smith; KJRH (N), KOED-TV (P), KOKI-TV (F), KOTV (C), KTUL (A) Tulsa.

Programming (via satellite): WGN-TV (W) Chicago; CNN; Country Music TV; Discovery Channel; ESPN; Fox Family Channel; Headline News; MTV; Nashville Network; Nickelodeon; TBS Superstation; Turner Network TV; USA Network.

Fee: $35.00 installation; $20.95 monthly.

Pay Service 1

Pay Units: 70.

Programming (via satellite): HBO.

Fee: $10.00 monthly.

Manager: Brad Mangum. Chief technician: Darrell Kimbrill. Marketing director: Terry Homesley.

Ownership: Peak Cablevision LLC (MSO). See Cable System Ownership.

BRECKENRIDGE—Classic Cable, Box 429, 605 N.W. 3rd St., Plainville, KS 67663-0429. Phones: 785-434-7620; 800-999-8876. Fax: 785-434-2614. Web site: http://www.classic-cable.com. County: Garfield. ICA: OK0265.

TV Market Ranking: Outside TV Markets. Franchise award date: January 1, 1989. Franchise expiration date: January 1, 2014. Began: September 1, 1989.

Channel capacity: 61 (2-way capable). Channels available but not in use: N.A.

Basic Service

Subscribers: 24.

Programming (received off-air): KAUT-TV (U), KETA (P), KFOR-TV (N), KOCB (W), KOCO-TV (A), KOKH-TV (F), KTBO-TV (T), KWTV (C) Oklahoma City.

Programming (via satellite): WGN-TV (W) Chicago; CNN; Country Music TV; Discovery Channel; ESPN; Fox Family Channel; Nashville Network; TBS Superstation; Turner Network TV.

Fee: $35.00 installation; $27.95 monthly; $3.50 converter.

Pay Service 1

Pay Units: 1.

Programming (via satellite): HBO.

Fee: $20.00 installation; $9.95 monthly.

Local advertising: No.
Equipment: Scientific-Atlanta amplifiers.
Miles of plant: 1.7 (coaxial). Homes passed: 77.
Region manager: Dave Walker. Chief technician: Jeff Smith. Marketing director: Jennifer Hauschild.
City fee: 5% of gross.
Ownership: Classic Cable (MSO).

BRISTOW—Peak Cablevision, 802 E. 6th St., Stillwater, OK 74074. Phone: 405-377-7785. Fax: 405-372-3980. County: Creek. ICA: OK0058.
TV Market Ranking: 54. Franchise award date: N.A. Franchise expiration date: July 29, 2005. Began: N.A.
Channel capacity: 44 (not 2-way capable). Channels available but not in use: None.
Basic Service
Subscribers: 1,226.
Programming (received off-air): KDOR (T) Bartlesville; KJRH (N), KOED-TV (P), KOKI-TV (F), KOTV (C), KTUL (A), KWHB (I) Tulsa.
Programming (via satellite): BET; Cartoon Network; Discovery Channel; FX; Home & Garden Television; Lifetime; QVC; TBS Superstation; TV Guide Channel; The Inspirational Network; The Weather Channel; VH1.
Current originations: Automated timeweather; local news.
Fee: $37.50 installation; $11.94 monthly.
Expanded Basic Service
Subscribers: 1,125.
Programming (via satellite): A & E; American Movie Classics; Animal Planet; Bravo; C-SPAN; C-SPAN 2; CNBC; CNN; Country Music TV; Disney Channel; ESPN; ESPN 2; Fox Family Channel; Fox News Channel; Fox Sports Net Southwest; Headline News; Learning Channel; MTV; Nashville Network; Nickelodeon; Turner Network TV; USA Network.
Fee: $14.68 monthly.
Pay Service 1
Pay Units: 222.
Programming (via satellite): Cinemax.
Fee: $11.00 monthly.
Pay Service 2
Pay Units: 444.
Programming (via satellite): The New Encore.
Fee: $1.75 monthly.
Pay Service 3
Pay Units: 335.
Programming (via satellite): HBO.
Fee: $11.00 monthly.
Pay Service 4
Pay Units: 114.
Programming (via satellite): Showtime.
Fee: $11.00 monthly.
Pay Service 5
Pay Units: 374.
Programming (via satellite): Starz!
Fee: $6.75 monthly.
Miles of plant: 30.6 (coaxial). Homes passed: 2,621. Total homes in franchised area: 2,621.
Manager: Ted Ramsey. Chief technician: Joe Goertz.
Ownership: Peak Cablevision LLC (MSO). See Cable System Ownership.

BROKEN BOW—Broken Bow TV Cable Co. Inc., Box 817, 108 N. Park Dr., Broken Bow, OK 74728. Phone: 405-584-3340. Fax: 405-584-3338. County: McCurtain. Also serves Eagletown, Haworth, Hochatowa, Idabel (Shultz Community), Lukfata, McCurtain County (portions), Oak Hill. ICA: OK0070.
TV Market Ranking: Outside TV Markets. Franchise award date: N.A. Franchise expiration date: N.A. Began: February 15, 1964.
Channel capacity: 30 (2-way capable; operating 2-way). Channels available but not in use: 2.
Basic Service
Subscribers: N.A.
Programming (received off-air): KTEN (A,N,F) Ada; KETG (P) Arkadelphia; KHBS (A) Fort Smith; KETA (P) Oklahoma City; KSLA-TV (C), KTAL-TV (N), KTBS-TV (A) Shreveport-Texarkana.
Programming (via microwave): WFAA-TV (A) Dallas-Fort Worth; KTUL (A) Tulsa.
Programming (via satellite): WGN-TV (W) Chicago; WPIX (W) New York; CNN; ESPN; Fox Family Channel; Lifetime; MTV; Nashville Network; Nickelodeon; TBS Superstation; The Weather Channel; USA Network.
Current originations: Automated timeweather; public access; educational access; local news; local sports.
Fee: $15.00 installation; $14.05 monthly; $3.00 converter; $5.00 additional installation.
Pay Service 1
Pay Units: N.A.
Programming (via satellite): Cinemax; Disney Channel; HBO; The Movie Channel.
Fee: $19.95 installation; $9.50 monthly (each).
Local advertising: Yes (locally produced). Available in satellite distributed programming. Local sales manager: Ken Wheeler.
Equipment: Scientific-Atlanta headend; GTE Sylvania amplifiers; Comm/Scope cable; Sony cameras; Hamlin set top converters; Anixter-Mark satellite antenna; Scientific-Atlanta satellite receivers.
Miles of plant: 200.0 (coaxial). Homes passed: 2,000.
Manager: Dale Fitzsimmons. Chief technician: Jerry Whisenhunt.
Ownership: Jewel B. Callaham Revocable Trust.

BUFFALO—Classic Cable, Box 429, 605 N.W. 3rd St., Plainville, KS 67663-0429. Phones: 785-434-7620; 800-999-8876. Fax: 785-434-2614. Web site: http://www.classic-cable.com. County: Harper. ICA: OK0151.
TV Market Ranking: Outside TV Markets. Franchise award date: N.A. Franchise expiration date: N.A. Began: March 1, 1962.
Channel capacity: 41 (2-way capable; operating 2-way). Channels available but not in use: N.A.
Basic Service
Subscribers: 480; Commercial subscribers: 63.
Programming (received off-air): KWET (P) Cheyenne; KOKH-TV (F) Oklahoma City.
Programming (via translator): KFOR-TV (N), KOCO-TV (A), KWTV (C) Oklahoma City.
Programming (via satellite): WGN-TV (W) Chicago; A & E; American Movie Classics; CNN; Cartoon Network; Country Music TV; Discovery Channel; Disney Channel; E! Entertainment TV; ESPN; Fox Family Channel; Fox Sports Net Southwest; Headline News; History Channel; Home & Garden Television; Learning Channel; Lifetime; Nashville Network; Nickelodeon; Outdoor Channel; QVC; Sci-Fi Channel; TBS Superstation; The Weather Channel; Trinity Bcstg. Network; Turner Network TV; USA Network; Univision.
Current originations: Public access; educational access; religious access.
Fee: $35.00 installation; $28.95 monthly.
Pay Service 1
Pay Units: 86.
Programming (via satellite): HBO.
Fee: $10.95 monthly.
Pay Service 2
Pay Units: 47.
Programming (via satellite): Showtime.
Fee: $9.95 monthly.
Pay Service 3
Pay Units: 52.
Programming (via satellite): The Movie Channel.
Fee: $5.95 monthly.
Equipment: Scientific-Atlanta headend; Magnavox amplifiers; Tandy character generator; Scientific-Atlanta set top converters; R. H. Tyler satellite antenna; Scientific-Atlanta satellite receivers.
Miles of plant: 14.4 (coaxial). Homes passed: 809.
Region manager: Dave Walker. Chief technician: Jeff Smith. Marketing director: Jennifer Hauschild.
City fee: 2% of gross.
Ownership: Classic Cable (MSO).

BURNS FLAT—Classic Cable, Box 429, 605 N.W. 3rd St., Plainville, KS 67663-0429. Phones: 785-434-7620; 800-999-8876. Fax: 785-434-2614. Web site: http://www.classic-cable.com. County: Washita. ICA: OK0098.
TV Market Ranking: Below 100. Franchise award date: N.A. Franchise expiration date: N.A. Began: N.A.
Channel capacity: 36 (2-way capable). Channels available but not in use: N.A.
Basic Service
Subscribers: 445; Commercial subscribers: 13.
Programming (received off-air): KWET (P) Cheyenne; KAUT-TV (U), KFOR-TV (N), KOCB (W), KOCO-TV (A), KOKH-TV (F), KWTV (C) Oklahoma City.
Programming (via satellite): WGN-TV (W) Chicago; American Movie Classics; CNN; Country Music TV; Discovery Channel; Disney Channel; E! Entertainment TV; ESPN; Fox Family Channel; Headline News; History Channel; Learning Channel; Lifetime; Nashville Network; Nick at Nite's TV Land; Nickelodeon; QVC; Sci-Fi Channel; TBS Superstation; The Weather Channel; Travel Channel; Trinity Bcstg. Network; Turner Network TV; USA Network.
Current originations: Automated timeweather.
Fee: $35.00 installation; $28.95 monthly.
Pay Service 1
Pay Units: 117.
Programming (via satellite): HBO.
Fee: $9.95 monthly.
Pay Service 2
Pay Units: 39.
Programming (via satellite): The Movie Channel.
Fee: $9.95 monthly.
Miles of plant: 11.0 (coaxial). Homes passed: 377. Total homes in franchised area: 1,100.
Region manager: Dave Walker. Chief technician: Roger Campbell. Marketing director: Jennifer Hauschild.
Ownership: Classic Cable (MSO).

BUTLER—Rapid Cable, Box 6310, 310 Walnut Extension, Branson, MO 65615. Phones: 417-334-7897; 800-972-0962. Fax: 417-334-7899. E-mail: rcpcable@aol.com. County: Custer. ICA: OK0240.
TV Market Ranking: Below 100. Franchise award date: September 2, 1997. Franchise expiration date: September 2, 2007. Began: February 1, 1983.
Channel capacity: 35 (2-way capable; not operating 2-way). Channels available but not in use: 14.
Basic Service
Subscribers: 89.
Programming (received off-air): KETA (P), KFOR-TV (N), KOCB (W), KOCO-TV (A), KOKH-TV (F), KWTV (C) Oklahoma City.
Programming (via satellite): WGN-TV (W) Chicago; CNN; Country Music TV; Discovery Channel; ESPN; Fox Family Channel; Home Shopping Network 2; Nashville Network; TBS Superstation; The Weather Channel; Turner Network TV; USA Network.
Fee: $29.95 installation; $22.95 monthly; $3.95 converter.
Pay Service 1
Pay Units: 11.
Programming (via satellite): HBO.
Fee: $10.00 monthly.
Pay Service 2
Pay Units: 2.
Programming (via satellite): Disney Channel.
Fee: $7.00 monthly.
Pay Service 3
Pay Units: N.A.
Programming (via satellite): Cinemax; HBO.
Fee: $15.95 monthly.
Local advertising: No.
Miles of plant: 4.0 (coaxial). Homes passed: 152.
Manager: Belinda Murphy. Chief engineer: Steve Rice. Program director: Beth Semptimphelter. Marketing director: Bill Fischer.
Ownership: Rapid Communications Partners LP (MSO).

BYARS—Classic Cable, Box 429, 605 N.W. 3rd St., Plainville, KS 67663-0429. Phones: 785-434-7620; 800-999-8876. Fax: 785-434-2614. Web site: http://www.classic-cable.com. County: McClain. ICA: OK0268.
TV Market Ranking: Below 100. Franchise award date: January 1, 1989. Franchise expiration date: January 1, 2014. Began: September 1, 1989.
Channel capacity: 36 (2-way capable). Channels available but not in use: N.A.
Basic Service
Subscribers: 26.
Programming (received off-air): KAUT-TV (U), KETA (P), KFOR-TV (N), KOCB (W), KOCO-TV (A), KOKH-TV (F), KWTV (C) Oklahoma City.
Programming (via satellite): WGN-TV (W) Chicago; CNN; Discovery Channel; ESPN; Fox Family Channel; Nashville Network; TBS Superstation; Trinity Bcstg. Network; Turner Network TV.
Fee: $35.00 installation; $27.95 monthly.
Pay Service 1
Pay Units: 2.
Programming (via satellite): HBO.
Fee: $9.95 monthly.
Equipment: Cadco headend; Scientific-Atlanta amplifiers; Jerrold set top converters; Drake satellite receivers.
Miles of plant: 3.3 (coaxial). Homes passed: 93.
Manager: Dave Walker. Chief technician: Roger Campbell. Marketing director: Jennifer Hauschild.
Ownership: Classic Cable (MSO).

CACHE—Classic Cable, Box 429, 605 N.W. 3rd St., Plainville, KS 67663-0429. Phones: 785-434-7620; 800-999-8876. Fax: 785-434-2614. Web site: http://www.classic-cable.com. County: Comanche. Also serves Indiahoma. ICA: OK0105.
TV Market Ranking: Below 100. Franchise award date: N.A. Franchise expiration date: N.A. Began: January 1, 1987.
Channel capacity: 41 (2-way capable). Channels available but not in use: N.A.

Basic Service
Subscribers: 702; Commercial subscribers: 4.
Programming (received off-air): KAUT-TV (U), KETA (P), KFOR-TV (N), KWTV (C) Oklahoma City; KAUZ-TV (C), KFDX-TV (N), KJTL (F,U), KSWO-TV (A) Wichita Falls-Lawton.
Programming (via satellite): WGN-TV (W) Chicago; A & E; American Movie Classics; C-SPAN; CNN; Country Music TV; Discovery Channel; Disney Channel; E! Entertainment TV; ESPN; Fox Family Channel; Fox News Channel; Fox Sports Net Southwest; Goodlife TV Network; Headline News; History Channel; Learning Channel; Lifetime; Nashville Network; Nick at Nite's TV Land; Nickelodeon; QVC; Sci-Fi Channel; TBS Superstation; The Weather Channel; Trinity Bcstg. Network; Turner Network TV; USA Network.
Current originations: Local Access.
Fee: $35.00 installation; $27.95 monthly.
Pay Service 1
Pay Units: 141.
Programming (via satellite): HBO.
Fee: $10.95 monthly.
Pay Service 2
Pay Units: 79.
Programming (via satellite): Showtime.
Fee: $9.95 monthly.
Pay Service 3
Pay Units: 79.
Programming (via satellite): The Movie Channel.
Fee: $5.95 monthly.
Local advertising: Yes. Available in character-generated programming. Rates: $5.00/Day.
Equipment: Drake & ISS headend; Jerrold amplifiers; Times Fiber cable; Jerrold set top converters.
Miles of plant: 45.0 (coaxial). Homes passed: 1,424.
Manager: Dave Walker. Chief technician: Roger Campbell. Marketing director: Jennifer Hauschild.
City fee: 2% of gross.
Ownership: Classic Cable (MSO).

CALUMET—Classic Cable, Box 429, 605 N.W. 3rd St., Plainville, KS 67663-0429. Phones: 785-434-7620; 800-999-8876. Fax: 785-434-2614. Web site: http://www.classic-cable.com.
County: Canadian. ICA: OK0238.
TV Market Ranking: 39. Franchise award date: N.A. Franchise expiration date: N.A. Began: June 1, 1988.
Channel capacity: 36 (2-way capable). Channels available but not in use: 18.
Basic Service
Subscribers: 80.
Programming (received off-air): KAUT-TV (U), KETA (P), KFOR-TV (N), KOCB (W), KOCO-TV (A), KOKH-TV (F), KTBO-TV (T), KWTV (C) Oklahoma City.
Programming (via satellite): WGN-TV (W) Chicago; A & E; CNN; Discovery Channel; Disney Channel; ESPN; Fox Family Channel; Home & Garden Television; Nashville Network; TBS Superstation; Turner Network TV; USA Network.
Fee: $35.00 installation; $27.95 monthly; $3.50 converter.
Pay Service 1
Pay Units: 10.
Programming (via satellite): Cinemax.
Fee: $20.00 installation; $9.95 monthly.
Pay Service 2
Pay Units: 23.
Programming (via satellite): HBO.
Fee: $20.00 installation; $9.95 monthly.
Equipment: Jerrold amplifiers; Jerrold set top converters.
Miles of plant: 4.5 (coaxial). Homes passed: 180.
Manager: Dave Walker. Chief technician: Jeff Smith. Marketing & program director: Sue Turner.
City fee: 5% of basic.
Ownership: Classic Cable (MSO).

CALVIN—Peak Cablevision, 205 E. Cherokee, McAlester, OK 74502. Phone: 918-423-6661. Fax: 918-426-2809.
E-mail: ethayer@peakcable.com.
County: Hughes. ICA: OK0254.
TV Market Ranking: Below 100. Franchise award date: N.A. Franchise expiration date: June 1, 2010. Began: January 1, 1985.
Channel capacity: 36 (not 2-way capable). Channels available but not in use: 9.
Basic Service
Subscribers: 64.
Programming (received off-air): KTEN (A,N,F) Ada; KETA (P), KFOR-TV (N), KOCB (W), KOKH-TV (F), KWTV (C) Oklahoma City; KTUL (A) Tulsa.
Programming (via satellite): A & E; C-SPAN; CNN; Country Music TV; Discovery Channel; ESPN; Fox Family Channel; Fox Sports Net Southwest; Learning Channel; Nashville Network; Nickelodeon; TBS Superstation; Trinity Bcstg. Network; Turner Network TV.
Fee: $20.00 installation; $23.14 monthly.
Pay Service 1
Pay Units: N.A.
Programming (via satellite): Showtime; Starz!; The New Encore.
Fee: $1.75 monthly (Encore), $6.75 monthly (Starz!), $11.00 monthly (Showtime).
Equipment: Jerrold headend; Jerrold amplifiers; Cerro & Times Fiber cable; Jerrold set top converters; Pico traps; AFC satellite antenna; Drake satellite receivers.
Miles of plant: 4.1 (coaxial). Homes passed: 153. Total homes in franchised area: 153.
Manager: Everett Thayer. Chief technician: Carl Simmons. Marketing director: Terry Homesley.
Franchise fee: 3% of gross.
Ownership: Peak Cablevision LLC (MSO). See Cable System Ownership.

CAMARGO—Classic Cable, Box 429, 605 N.W. 3rd St., Plainville, KS 67663-0429. Phones: 785-434-7620; 800-999-8876. Fax: 785-434-2614. Web site: http://www.classic-cable.com.
County: Dewey. ICA: OK0371.
TV Market Ranking: Outside TV Markets. Franchise award date: N.A. Franchise expiration date: N.A. Began: N.A.
Channel capacity: 36 (2-way capable). Channels available but not in use: N.A.
Basic Service
Subscribers: 48.
Programming (received off-air): KETA (P), KFOR-TV (N), KOCB (W), KOCO-TV (A), KOKH-TV (F), KWTV (C) Oklahoma City.
Programming (via satellite): WGN-TV (W) Chicago; CNN; Discovery Channel; Disney Channel; ESPN; Fox Family Channel; History Channel; Learning Channel; Nashville Network; Nick at Nite's TV Land; TBS Superstation; Trinity Bcstg. Network; Turner Classic Movies; Turner Network TV; USA Network.
Fee: $35.00 installation; $27.95 monthly.
Pay Service 1
Pay Units: 5.
Programming (via satellite): HBO.
Fee: $10.95 monthly.
Miles of plant: 2.8 (coaxial). Homes passed: 99.
Manager: Dave Walker. Chief technician: Jeff Smith. Marketing director: Jennifer Hauschild.
Ownership: Classic Cable (MSO).

CAMERON—Oklahoma Cablecomm, Box 970, Fort Gibson, OK 74434-0970. Phones: 918-478-2100; 800-783-5701. Fax: 918-478-2355.
County: Le Flore. ICA: OK0252.
TV Market Ranking: Below 100. Franchise award date: January 1, 1989. Franchise expiration date: January 1, 2014. Began: September 1, 1989.
Channel capacity: 45 (not 2-way capable). Channels available but not in use: 30.
Basic Service
Subscribers: 77.
Programming (received off-air): KOET (P) Eufaula; KFSM-TV (C), KHBS (A), KPOM-TV (N) Fort Smith.
Programming (via satellite): WGN-TV (W) Chicago; CNN; Country Music TV; Discovery Channel; ESPN; Fox Family Channel; Headline News; Nashville Network; TBS Superstation; Turner Network TV; USA Network.
Fee: $30.00 installation; $19.95 monthly.
Pay Service 1
Pay Units: 28.
Programming (via satellite): HBO.
Fee: $10.00 monthly.
Local advertising: No.
Equipment: Cadco headend; Scientific-Atlanta amplifiers; Jerrold set top converters; Pico traps; Scientific-Atlanta satellite antenna.
Miles of plant: 3.0 (coaxial). Homes passed: 117.
Regional manager: Rick Wall. Chief technician: Leon Strain. Marketing & program director: Bruce Berkinshaw.
City fee: 5% of gross.
Ownership: Fanch Communications Inc. (MSO); Time Warner Cable (MSO). See Cable System Ownership.

CANADIAN—Lakeland Cable TV Inc., Box 321, Crowder, OK 74430. Phone: 918-334-6200. Fax: 918-334-3202. County: Pittsburg. Also serves Crowder, Indianola. ICA: OK0269.
TV Market Ranking: Outside TV Markets. Franchise award date: N.A. Franchise expiration date: N.A. Began: April 1, 1982.
Channel capacity: N.A. Channels available but not in use: N.A.
Basic Service
Subscribers: 616.
Programming (received off-air): KOET (P) Eufaula; KJRH (N), KOKI-TV (F), KOTV (C), KTFO (U), KTUL (A), KWHB (I) Tulsa.
Programming (via satellite): WGN-TV (W) Chicago; A & E; CNN; Country Music TV; Discovery Channel; ESPN; Fox Family Channel; Nashville Network; Nickelodeon; TBS Superstation; The Weather Channel; Turner Network TV; USA Network; VH1.
Fee: $60.00 installation; $19.89 monthly.
Pay Service 1
Pay Units: 52.
Programming (via satellite): Disney Channel.
Fee: $9.18 monthly.
Pay Service 2
Pay Units: 61.
Programming (via satellite): The Movie Channel.
Fee: $11.00 monthly.
Pay Service 3
Pay Units: 198.
Programming (via satellite): Showtime.
Fee: $11.00 monthly.
Local advertising: No.
Equipment: GTE Sylvania headend; Anixter-Mark satellite antenna; Scientific-Atlanta satellite receivers.
Miles of plant: 10.0 (coaxial).
Manager: Charles O. Smith. Chief technician: Gary Brooks.
City fee: 2% of gross.
Ownership: Lakeland Cable TV Inc.

CANEY—Peak Cablevision, 516 N. Lakeside Dr., DeQueen, AR 71832. Phone: 870-642-2441. Fax: 870-642-4259. County: Atoka. ICA: OK0353.
TV Market Ranking: Outside TV Markets. Franchise award date: N.A. Franchise expiration date: June 21, 2010. Began: N.A.
Channel capacity: 20 (not 2-way capable). Channels available but not in use: 8.
Basic Service
Subscribers: 50.
Programming (received off-air): KTEN (A,N,F) Ada; KETA (P) Oklahoma City; KXII (C) Sherman.
Programming (via satellite): WGN-TV (W) Chicago; CNN; Discovery Channel; ESPN; Fox Family Channel; Nashville Network; TBS Superstation; Turner Network TV; USA Network.
Fee: $25.00 installation; $15.00 monthly.
Manager: Ron Beatty. Chief technician: Lynn Harrison. Marketing director: Terry Homesley. Customer service manager: Carol Litchford.
Franchise fee: 5% of gross.
Ownership: Peak Cablevision LLC (MSO). See Cable System Ownership.

CANTON—Rapid Cable, Box 6310, 310 Walnut Extension, Branson, MO 65615. Phones: 417-334-7897; 800-972-0962. Fax: 417-334-7899.
E-mail: rcpcable@ol.com.
Web site: http://www.classic-cable.com.
County: Blaine. ICA: OK0236.
TV Market Ranking: Outside TV Markets. Franchise award date: April 5, 1983. Franchise expiration date: April 5, 2008. Began: November 1, 1983.
Channel capacity: 35 (2-way capable; not operating 2-way). Channels available but not in use: 10.
Basic Service
Subscribers: 277; Commercial subscribers: 35.
Programming (received off-air): KETA (P), KFOR-TV (N), KOCB (W), KOCO-TV (A), KOKH-TV (F), KWTV (C) Oklahoma City.
Programming (via satellite): WGN-TV (W) Chicago; American Movie Classics; CNN; Country Music TV; Discovery Channel; ESPN; Fox Family Channel; Fox News Channel; Home Shopping Network 2; Learning Channel; Nashville Network; Sci-Fi Channel; TBS Superstation; The Weather Channel; Trinity Bcstg. Network; Turner Network TV; USA Network.
Fee: $29.95 installation; $21.95 monthly; $3.95 converter.
Pay Service 1
Pay Units: 37.
Programming (via satellite): Cinemax.
Fee: $9.00 monthly.
Pay Service 2
Pay Units: 42.
Programming (via satellite): HBO.
Fee: $10.00 monthly.
Pay Service 3
Pay Units: 37.
Programming (via satellite): Disney Channel.
Fee: $7.00 monthly.
Local advertising: No.
Miles of plant: 17.5 (coaxial). Homes passed: 635.

Manager: Belinda Murphy. Chief engineer: Steve Rice. Program director: Beth Semptimphelter. Marketing director: Bill Fischer.
Ownership: Rapid Communications Partners LP (MSO).

CANUTE—Classic Cable, Box 429, 605 N.W. 3rd St., Plainville, KS 67663-0429. Phones: 785-434-7620; 800-999-8876. Fax: 785-434-2614. County: Washita. ICA: OK0215.
TV Market Ranking: Below 100. Franchise award date: N.A. Franchise expiration date: N.A. Began: January 1, 1975.
Channel capacity: 36 (2-way capable). Channels available but not in use: N.A.
Basic Service
Subscribers: 134; Commercial subscribers: 7.
Programming (received off-air): KWET (P) Cheyenne; KFOR-TV (N), KOCO-TV (A), KOKH-TV (F), KWTV (C) Oklahoma City; allband FM.
Programming (via satellite): WGN-TV (W) Chicago; CNN; Discovery Channel; Disney Channel; E! Entertainment TV; ESPN; Fox Family Channel; Headline News; History Channel; Learning Channel; Nashville Network; Nick at Nite's TV Land; Nickelodeon; QVC; Sci-Fi Channel; TBS Superstation; Trinity Bcstg. Network; Turner Network TV; USA Network.
Current originations: Automated time-weather.
Fee: $35.00 installation; $27.95 monthly; $2.00 converter.
Pay Service 1
Pay Units: 31.
Programming (via satellite): HBO.
Fee: $9.95 monthly.
Pay Service 2
Pay Units: 12.
Programming (via satellite): Showtime.
Fee: $9.95 monthly.
Pay Service 3
Pay Units: 17.
Programming (via satellite): The Movie Channel.
Fee: $9.95 monthly.
Local advertising: Planned.
Equipment: Jerrold headend; Jerrold amplifiers; Jerrold cable; Jerrold set top converters.
Miles of plant: 12.0 (coaxial). Homes passed: 240.
Region manager: Dave Walker. Chief technician: Roger Campbell. Marketing director: Jennifer Hauschild.
City fee: 3% of gross.
Ownership: Classic Cable (MSO).

CARMEN—Classic Cable, Box 429, 605 N.W. 3rd St., Plainville, KS 67663-0429. Phones: 785-434-7620; 800-999-8876. Fax: 785-434-2614. Web site: http://www.classic-cable.com. County: Alfalfa. ICA: OK0234.
TV Market Ranking: Outside TV Markets. Franchise award date: N.A. Franchise expiration date: August 31, 1998. Began: February 1, 1977.
Channel capacity: 36 (2-way capable). Channels available but not in use: N.A.
Basic Service
Subscribers: 117.
Programming (received off-air): KAUT-TV (U), KETA (P), KFOR-TV (N), KOCB (W), KOCO-TV (A), KOKH-TV (F), KWTV (C) Oklahoma City; allband FM.
Programming (via satellite): A & E; CNN; Country Music TV; Discovery Channel; Disney Channel; ESPN; Fox Family Channel; Home Shopping Network; Nashville Network; Nick at Nite's TV Land; Sci-Fi Channel; TBS Superstation; The Weather Channel; USA Network.
Fee: $35.00 installation; $27.95 monthly.
Pay Service 1
Pay Units: 16.
Programming (via satellite): HBO.
Fee: $10.95 monthly.
Pay Service 2
Pay Units: 4.
Programming (via satellite): Showtime.
Fee: $9.95 monthly.
Local advertising: No.
Equipment: Automation Techniques & Blonder-Tongue headend; AEL amplifiers; Cerro cable; Harris satellite receivers.
Miles of plant: 6.0 (coaxial). Homes passed: 187.
Region manager: Dave Walker. Chief technician: Jeff Smith. Marketing director: Jennifer Hauschild.
City fee: None.
Ownership: Classic Cable (MSO).

CARNEGIE—SMS Cable Co., Box 1119, 30 W. Main, Carnegie, OK 73015. Phone: 580-654-1571. County: Caddo. ICA: OK0107.
TV Market Ranking: Outside TV Markets. Franchise award date: N.A. Franchise expiration date: N.A. Began: July 1, 1974.
Channel capacity: N.A. Channels available but not in use: N.A.
Basic Service
Subscribers: 850.
Programming (received off-air): KETA (P), KFOR-TV (N), KOCB (W), KOCO-TV (A), KOKH-TV (F), KWTV (C) Oklahoma City; KAUZ-TV (C), KFDX-TV (N), KSWO-TV (A) Wichita Falls-Lawton; allband FM.
Programming (via satellite): WGN-TV (W) Chicago; Fox Family Channel; TBS Superstation.
Current originations: Automated time-weather.
Fee: Free installation; $12.00 monthly.
Pay Service 1
Pay Units: 360.
Programming (via satellite): The Movie Channel.
Fee: $35.00 installation; $8.00 monthly.
Local advertising: No.
Program Guide: CableView.
Equipment: Blonder-Tongue, Cadco & Microdyne headend; Cadco & Jerrold amplifiers; Javelin cameras; Standard Components set top converters; Prodelin satellite antenna.
Miles of plant: 22.0 (coaxial). Homes passed: 950. Total homes in franchised area: 950.
Manager: H. S. Scott.
City fee: 2% of gross.
Ownership: SMS Cable Co.

CARNEY—Oklahoma Cablecomm, Box 970, Fort Gibson, OK 74434-0970. Phones: 918-478-2100; 800-783-5701. Fax: 918-478-2355. County: Lincoln. ICA: OK0270.
TV Market Ranking: Outside TV Markets. Franchise award date: January 1, 1988. Franchise expiration date: January 1, 2013. Began: September 1, 1990.
Channel capacity: 35 (not 2-way capable). Channels available but not in use: 18.
Basic Service
Subscribers: 57.
Programming (received off-air): KAUT-TV (U), KETA (P), KFOR-TV (N), KOCB (W), KOCO-TV (A), KOKH-TV (F), KWTV (C) Oklahoma City.
Programming (via satellite): WGN-TV (W) Chicago; A & E; CNN; Discovery Channel; ESPN; Fox Family Channel; Nashville Network; TBS Superstation; USA Network.
Fee: $40.00 installation; $20.95 monthly.
Pay Service 1
Pay Units: 12.
Programming (via satellite): HBO.
Fee: $20.00 installation; $10.95 monthly.
Local advertising: No.
Program Guide: TV Host.
Equipment: Cadco headend; Scientific-Atlanta amplifiers; Comm/Scope cable; Arcom traps; Standard Communications satellite receivers.
Miles of plant: 5.0 (coaxial). Homes passed: 220. Total homes in franchised area: 220.
Regional manager: Rick Wall. Chief technician: Leon Strain. Marketing & program director: Bruce Berkinshaw.
City fee: 5% of basic.
Ownership: Fanch Communications Inc. (MSO); Time Warner Cable (MSO). See Cable System Ownership.

CARTER—Rapid Cable, Box 6310, 310 Walnut Extension, Branson, MO 65615. Phones: 417-334-7897; 800-972-0962. Fax: 417-334-7899. E-mail: rcpcable@aol.com. County: Beckham. ICA: OK0242.
TV Market Ranking: Below 100. Franchise award date: N.A. Franchise expiration date: N.A. Began: April 17, 1990.
Channel capacity: 31 (2-way capable; not operating 2-way). Channels available but not in use: 12.
Basic Service
Subscribers: 49.
Programming (received off-air): KETA (P), KFOR-TV (N), KOCB (W), KOCO-TV (A), KOKH-TV (F), KWTV (C) Oklahoma City.
Programming (via satellite): WGN-TV (W) Chicago; CNN; Country Music TV; Discovery Channel; ESPN; Fox Family Channel; Nashville Network; TBS Superstation; The Weather Channel; Trinity Bcstg. Network; Turner Network TV.
Fee: $29.95 installation; $20.95 monthly; $3.95 converter.
Pay Service 1
Pay Units: 8.
Programming (via satellite): Cinemax.
Fee: $9.00 monthly.
Pay Service 2
Pay Units: 10.
Programming (via satellite): HBO.
Fee: $10.00 monthly.
Pay Service 3
Pay Units: 3.
Programming (via satellite): Disney Channel.
Fee: $7.00 monthly.
Local advertising: No.
Miles of plant: 5.2 (coaxial). Homes passed: 102.
Manager: Belinda Murphy. Chief engineer: Steve Rice. Program director: Beth Semptimphelter. Marketing director: Bill Fischer.
Ownership: Rapid Communications Partners LP (MSO).

CASHION—Classic Cable, Box 429, 605 N.W. 3rd St., Plainville, KS 67663-0429. Phones: 785-434-7620; 800-999-8876. Fax: 785-434-2614. Web site: http://www.classic-cable.com. Counties: Kingfisher & Logan. ICA: OK0233.
TV Market Ranking: 39. Franchise award date: N.A. Franchise expiration date: N.A. Began: N.A.
Channel capacity: 36 (2-way capable). Channels available but not in use: N.A.
Basic Service
Subscribers: 47.
Programming (received off-air): KAUT-TV (U), KETA (P), KFOR-TV (N), KOCB (W), KOCO-TV (A), KOKH-TV (F), KTBO-TV (T), KWTV (C) Oklahoma City.
Programming (via satellite): WGN-TV (W) Chicago; CNN; Discovery Channel; ESPN; Fox Family Channel; Nashville Network; TBS Superstation; Turner Network TV; USA Network.
Fee: $35.00 installation; $27.95 monthly; $3.50 converter.
Pay Service 1
Pay Units: 10.
Programming (via satellite): Cinemax.
Fee: $20.00 installation; $9.95 monthly.
Pay Service 2
Pay Units: 11.
Programming (via satellite): HBO.
Fee: $20.00 installation; $9.95 monthly.
Local advertising: No.
Equipment: Jerrold amplifiers; Times Fiber cable; Jerrold set top converters; Automation Techniques & Drake satellite receivers.
Miles of plant: 5.1 (coaxial). Homes passed: 192. Total homes in franchised area: 192.
Manager: Dave Walker. Chief technician: Jeff Smith. Marketing director: Jennifer Hauschild.
City fee: 3% of basic.
Ownership: Classic Cable (MSO).

CATOOSA—Blackstone Cable, Box 1729, Fairfield Glade, TN 38558. Phones: 334-937-0901; 800-388-6577. Counties: Rogers & Wagoner. Also serves Rogers County (portions), Wagoner County (portions). ICA: OK0271.
TV Market Ranking: 54. Franchise award date: N.A. Franchise expiration date: N.A. Began: May 1, 1990.
Channel capacity: 40. Channels available but not in use: 3.
Basic Service
Subscribers: 453.
Programming (received off-air): KRSC-TV (E) Claremore; KJRH (N), KOED-TV (P), KOKI-TV (F), KOTV (C), KTFO (U), KTUL (A), KWHB (I) Tulsa.
Programming (via satellite): C-SPAN; Cartoon Network; QVC; Trinity Bcstg. Network.
Fee: $29.95 installation; $11.95 monthly.
Expanded Basic Service
Subscribers: N.A.
Programming (via satellite): WGN-TV (W) Chicago; A & E; American Movie Classics; CNBC; CNN; Comedy Central; Country Music TV; Discovery Channel; ESPN; Fox Family Channel; Headline News; Learning Channel; Lifetime; MTV; Nashville Network; Nickelodeon; Sci-Fi Channel; TBS Superstation; The Weather Channel; Turner Network TV; USA Network; VH1.
Fee: $29.95 installation; $9.00 monthly.
Pay Service 1
Pay Units: 41.
Programming (via satellite): Disney Channel.
Fee: $9.95 monthly.
Pay Service 2
Pay Units: 122.
Programming (via satellite): HBO.
Fee: $10.95 monthly.
Pay Service 3
Pay Units: 50.
Programming (via satellite): Showtime.
Fee: $10.95 monthly.
Pay Service 4
Pay Units: 31.
Programming (via satellite): The Movie Channel.
Fee: $9.95 monthly.
Homes passed: 915.
Manager: Del Layne. Chief technician: Bill Cline.
Ownership: Bayside 1989-I LP (MSO).

CEMENT—Southwestern CATV, Box 171, Medicine Park, OK 73557-0171. Phone: 580-529-2288. Fax: 580-529-5225. County: Caddo. ICA: OK0195.
TV Market Ranking: Below 100. Franchise award date: N.A. Franchise expiration date: N.A. Began: December 1, 1981.

Channel capacity: 35. Channels available but not in use: N.A.
Basic Service
Subscribers: N.A.
Programming (received off-air): KETA (P), KFOR-TV (N), KOCB (W), KOCO-TV (A), KOKH-TV (F), KWTV (C) Oklahoma City; KSWO-TV (A) Wichita Falls-Lawton.
Programming (via satellite): WGN-TV (W) Chicago; TBS Superstation.
Fee: $15.00 installation; $8.00 monthly.
Miles of plant: 6.2 (coaxial). Homes passed: 340.
Ownership: Southwestern CATV Inc. (MSO).

CHANDLER—Peak Cablevision, 323 E. Broadway, Cushing, OK 74023. Phone: 800-547-8582. County: Lincoln. ICA: OK0112.
TV Market Ranking: Outside TV Markets. Franchise award date: N.A. Franchise expiration date: N.A. Began: May 1, 1981.
Channel capacity: 41 (not 2-way capable). Channels available but not in use: 4.
Basic Service
Subscribers: 522.
Programming (received off-air): KETA (P), KFOR-TV (N), KOCB (W), KOCO-TV (A), KOKH-TV (F), KTBO-TV (T), KWTV (C) Oklahoma City.
Programming (via satellite): A & E; American Movie Classics; Animal Planet; CNBC; CNN; Cartoon Network; Discovery Channel; Disney Channel; ESPN; FX; Fox Family Channel; Fox News Channel; Headline News; Home & Garden Television; Learning Channel; Lifetime; Nashville Network; Nickelodeon; TBS Superstation; The Weather Channel; Turner Network TV; USA Network.
Fee: $37.50 installation; $26.62 monthly; $1.50 converter; $12.50 additional installation.
Pay Service 1
Pay Units: 131.
Programming (via satellite): Starz!
Fee: $6.75 monthly.
Pay Service 2
Pay Units: 194.
Programming (via satellite): The New Encore.
Fee: $1.75 monthly.
Pay Service 3
Pay Units: 153.
Programming (via satellite): HBO.
Fee: $11.00 monthly.
Pay Service 4
Pay Units: 73.
Programming (via satellite): Showtime.
Fee: $11.00 monthly.
Miles of plant: 30.7 (coaxial). Homes passed: 908. Total homes in franchised area: 1,086.
Manager: Ted Ramsey. Chief technician: Joe Goertz.
Ownership: Peak Cablevision LLC (MSO). See Cable System Ownership.

CHATTANOOGA—Rapid Cable, Box 6310, 310 Walnut Extension, Branson, MO 65615. Phones: 417-334-7897; 800-972-0962. Fax: 417-334-7899. E-mail: rcpcable@aol.com. Counties: Comanche & Tillman. ICA: OK0272.
TV Market Ranking: Below 100. Franchise award date: November 8, 1982. Franchise expiration date: November 8, 2002. Began: August 1, 1984.
Channel capacity: 31 (2-way capable; not operating 2-way). Channels available but not in use: 7.
Basic Service
Subscribers: 95.
Programming (received off-air): KETA (P) Oklahoma City; KJBO-LP (U) Wichita Falls; KAUZ-TV (C), KFDX-TV (N), KJTL (F,U), KSWO-TV (A) Wichita Falls-Lawton.
Programming (via satellite): WGN-TV (W) Chicago; Animal Planet; CNN; Country Music TV; Discovery Channel; ESPN; Fox Family Channel; Home Shopping Network 2; Learning Channel; Nashville Network; TBS Superstation; The Weather Channel; Turner Network TV; USA Network.
Fee: $29.95 installation; $22.95 monthly; $3.95 converter.
Pay Service 1
Pay Units: 20.
Programming (via satellite): HBO.
Fee: $10.00 monthly.
Pay Service 2
Pay Units: 18.
Programming (via satellite): Cinemax.
Fee: $9.00 monthly.
Pay Service 3
Pay Units: 13.
Programming (via satellite): Disney Channel.
Fee: $7.00 monthly.
Local advertising: No.
Miles of plant: 6.0 (coaxial). Homes passed: 199.
Manager: Belinda Murphy. Chief engineer: Steve Rice. Program director: Beth Semptimphelter. Marketing director: Bill Fischer.
Ownership: Rapid Communications Partners LP (MSO).

CHELSEA—Oklahoma Cablecomm, Box 970, Fort Gibson, OK 74434-0970. Phones: 918-478-2100; 800-783-5701. Fax: 918-478-2355. County: Rogers. ICA: OK0127.
TV Market Ranking: Below 100. Franchise award date: July 2, 1980. Franchise expiration date: N.A. Began: N.A.
Channel capacity: 42 (not 2-way capable). Channels available but not in use: 4.
Basic Service
Subscribers: 459; Commercial subscribers: 34.
Programming (received off-air): KDOR (T) Bartlesville; KRSC-TV (E) Claremore; KJRH (N), KOED-TV (P), KOKI-TV (F), KOTV (C), KTFO (U), KTUL (A), KWHB (I) Tulsa.
Programming (via satellite): WGN-TV (W) Chicago; A & E; American Movie Classics; C-SPAN; CNBC; CNN; Cartoon Network; Country Music TV; Discovery Channel; Disney Channel; E! Entertainment TV; ESPN; ESPN 2; Fox Family Channel; Fox Sports Net; Headline News; History Channel; Learning Channel; Lifetime; Nashville Network; Nickelodeon; QVC; Sci-Fi Channel; TBS Superstation; The Inspirational Network; The Weather Channel; Turner Classic Movies; Turner Network TV; USA Network; VH1.
Fee: $29.95 installation; $23.45 monthly.
Pay Service 1
Pay Units: 36.
Programming (via satellite): Cinemax.
Fee: $20.00 installation; $11.95 monthly.
Pay Service 2
Pay Units: 70.
Programming (via satellite): HBO.
Fee: $20.00 installation; $11.95 monthly.
Local advertising: No.
Program Guide: TV Host.
Equipment: Olson, Scientific-Atlanta headend; Magnavox & Triple Crown amplifiers; Jerrold set top converters; Arcom traps; Scientific-Atlanta & Tru-Spec satellite antenna; ICM, Panasonic & Scientific-Atlanta satellite receivers.
Miles of plant: 15.0 (coaxial). Homes passed: 758. Total homes in franchised area: 758.
Manager: Rick Wall. Chief technician: Leon Strain. Marketing & program director: Bruce Berkinshaw.
City fee: 2% of basic.
Ownership: Fanch Communications Inc. (MSO); Time Warner Cable (MSO). See Cable System Ownership.

CHEROKEE—Classic Cable, Box 429, 605 N.W. 3rd St., Plainville, KS 67663-0429. Phones: 785-434-7620; 800-999-8876. Fax: 785-434-2614. Web site: http://www.classic-cable.com. County: Alfalfa. ICA: OK0110.
TV Market Ranking: Outside TV Markets. Franchise award date: N.A. Franchise expiration date: N.A. Began: March 1, 1964.
Channel capacity: 36 (2-way capable). Channels available but not in use: N.A.
Basic Service
Subscribers: 664; Commercial subscribers: 49.
Programming (received off-air): KAUT-TV (U), KETA (P), KFOR-TV (N), KOCB (W), KOCO-TV (A), KOKH-TV (F), KWTV (C) Oklahoma City; KAKE-TV (A) Wichita-Hutchinson; 2 FMs.
Programming (via satellite): WGN-TV (W) Chicago; A & E; American Movie Classics; CNN; Country Music TV; Discovery Channel; Disney Channel; E! Entertainment TV; ESPN; Fox Family Channel; Fox Sports Net Southwest; Headline News; History Channel; Learning Channel; Lifetime; MTV; Nashville Network; Nick at Nite's TV Land; Nickelodeon; QVC; Sci-Fi Channel; TBS Superstation; The Weather Channel; Trinity Bcstg. Network; Turner Network TV; USA Network.
Current originations: Automated time-weather; automated emergency alert.
Fee: $35.00 installation; $25.95 monthly; $3.50 converter.
Pay Service 1
Pay Units: 111.
Programming (via satellite): Showtime.
Fee: $20.00 installation; $9.95 monthly.
Pay Service 2
Pay Units: 39.
Programming (via satellite): HBO.
Fee: $20.00 installation; $10.95 monthly.
Pay Service 3
Pay Units: 59.
Programming (via satellite): The Movie Channel.
Fee: $20.00 installation; $5.95 monthly.
Local advertising: Yes. Available in character-generated programming. Rates: $10.00-$35.00/Week; $2.00/Day.
Equipment: Drake, ISS & Scientific-Atlanta headend; Century III, Dorate & Synchronics amplifiers; AFC, Microwave Assoc. & Scientific-Atlanta satellite antenna; Automation Techniques, ICM & Microdyne satellite receivers.
Miles of plant: 16.0 (coaxial). Homes passed: 950. Total homes in franchised area: 950.
Manager: Dave Walker. Chief technician: Jeff Smith. Marketing director: Jennifer Hauschild.
City fee: 3% of basic.
Ownership: Classic Cable (MSO).

CHEYENNE—James Mogg TV, Box 328, Cheyenne, OK 73628. Phone: 405-497-2182. County: Roger Mills. ICA: OK0147.
TV Market Ranking: Below 100. Franchise award date: N.A. Franchise expiration date: N.A. Began: N.A.
Channel capacity: 12. Channels available but not in use: N.A.
Basic Service
Subscribers: 404.
Programming (received off-air): KWET (P) Cheyenne; KOCB (W), KOCO-TV (A), KOKH-TV (F) Oklahoma City; KJTL (F,U) Wichita Falls-Lawton; 1 FM.
Programming (via microwave): KFOR-TV (N), KWTV (C) Oklahoma City.
Programming (via satellite): WGN-TV (W) Chicago; CNN; ESPN; Fox Family Channel; Nashville Network; TBS Superstation; Trinity Bcstg. Network; Turner Network TV; USA Network.
Planned originations: Automated time-weather.
Fee: $9.00 monthly.
Local advertising: Planned.
Equipment: Jerrold headend; Blonder-Tongue amplifiers.
Miles of plant: 6.0 (coaxial). Homes passed: 600.
City fee: None.
Ownership: James Mogg TV.

CHICKASHA—Multimedia Cablevision of Chickasha, 916 S. 4th St., Chickasha, OK 73018-4632. Phone: 405-359-3561. County: Grady. Also serves Grady County (portions). ICA: OK0023.
TV Market Ranking: 39 (portions of Grady County); Below 100 (portions of Grady County); Outside TV Markets (Chickasha, portions of Grady County). Franchise award date: N.A. Franchise expiration date: November 18, 2006. Began: March 1, 1978.
Channel capacity: 81 (not 2-way capable). Channels available but not in use: 43.
Basic Service
Subscribers: 4,860.
Programming (received off-air): KAUT-TV (U), KETA (P), KFOR-TV (N), KOCB (W), KOCO-TV (A), KOKH-TV (F), KSBI (I), KTBO-TV (T), KWTV (C) Oklahoma City; 18 FMs.
Programming (via satellite): A & E; American Movie Classics; BET; C-SPAN; Discovery Channel; ESPN; Fox Family Channel; Lifetime; MTV; Nickelodeon; The Weather Channel; USA Network; VH1.
Current originations: Public access; educational access; government access; automated emergency alert.
Fee: $15.39 installation; $17.73 monthly.
Expanded Basic Service
Subscribers: 4,557.
Programming (via satellite): WGN-TV (W) Chicago; CNN; Fox Sports Net Southwest; Headline News; Nashville Network; TBS Superstation; Turner Network TV.
Fee: $3.98 monthly.
Pay Service 1
Pay Units: 775.
Programming (via satellite): Cinemax.
Fee: $11.00 monthly.
Pay Service 2
Pay Units: 382.
Programming (via satellite): Disney Channel.
Fee: $7.95 monthly.
Pay Service 3
Pay Units: 1,227.
Programming (via satellite): HBO.
Fee: $11.00 monthly.

Pay Service 4
Pay Units: 838.
Programming (via satellite): Showtime.
Fee: $11.00 monthly.
Pay Service 5
Pay Units: 96.
Programming (via satellite): The Movie Channel.
Fee: $11.00 monthly.
Pay-Per-View
Special events.
Local advertising: Yes. Available in locally originated programming. Rates: $400.00/Month.
Equipment: Scientific-Atlanta headend; Scientific-Atlanta amplifiers; Comm/Scope cable; Quanta character generator; Oak & Hamlin set top converters; Scientific-Atlanta addressable set top converters; Eagle traps; Scientific-Atlanta satellite antenna; Standard Components satellite receivers.
Miles of plant: 89.4 (coaxial). Homes passed: 7,608. Total homes in franchised area: 7,760.
Manager: Steve Pool. Chief technician: Mark Harpole. Marketing director: Jim Back. Customer service manager: Charitta Shelton.
City fee: 3% of gross.
Ownership: Multimedia Cablevision Inc. (MSO). See Cable System Ownership.

CHICKEN CREEK—Quality Entertainment, Suite 512, Central Mall Plaza, Fort Smith, AR 72903. Phone: 501-452-1998. Fax: 501-452-6430. County: Cherokee. ICA: OK0368.
TV Market Ranking: Outside TV Markets. Franchise award date: N.A. Franchise expiration date: N.A. Began: N.A.
Channel capacity: 42 (not 2-way capable). Channels available but not in use: 13.
Basic Service
Subscribers: 64.
Programming (received off-air): KJRH (N), KOED-TV (P), KOKI-TV (F), KOTV (C), KTUL (A) Tulsa.
Programming (via satellite): WGN-TV (W) Chicago; A & E; Animal Planet; CNN; Discovery Channel; ESPN; Fox Family Channel; Learning Channel; Military Channel; Nashville Network; Nick at Nite's TV Land; Odyssey; Sci-Fi Channel; TBS Superstation; The Weather Channel; Travel Channel; Trinity Bcstg. Network; Turner Network TV; USA Network.
Fee: $40.00 installation; $24.00 monthly.
Pay Service 1
Pay Units: N.A.
Programming (via satellite): HBO.
Fee: $12.00 monthly.
Miles of plant: 5.0 (coaxial).
Manager: Brent Lewis.
Ownership: Quality Entertainment Corp. (MSO).

CHOCTAW—Multimedia Cablevision, Box 553, 14359 N.E. 23rd St., Choctaw, OK 73020. Phone: 405-309-8819. County: Oklahoma. Also serves Harrah, Nicoma Park. ICA: OK0027.
TV Market Ranking: 39. Franchise award date: N.A. Franchise expiration date: July 1, 2005. Began: September 30, 1980.
Channel capacity: 69 (2-way capable; not operating 2-way). Channels available but not in use: 8.
Basic Service
Subscribers: 4,076.
Programming (received off-air): KAUT-TV (U), KETA (P), KFOR-TV (N), KOCB (W), KOCO-TV (A), KOKH-TV (F), KSBI (I), KTBO-TV (T), KWTV (C) Oklahoma City.
Programming (via satellite): A & E; American Movie Classics; C-SPAN; CNBC; Discovery Channel; ESPN; Lifetime; MTV; Nickelodeon; QVC; The Weather Channel; USA Network; VH1.
Current originations: Automated time-weather; public access.
Fee: $16.85 installation; $16.88 monthly.
Expanded Basic Service
Subscribers: 3,987.
Programming (via satellite): WGN-TV (W) Chicago; CNN; Fox Family Channel; Headline News; Nashville Network; TBS Superstation; Turner Network TV.
Fee: $3.72 monthly.
Pay Service 1
Pay Units: 543.
Programming (via satellite): Disney Channel.
Fee: $7.95 monthly.
Pay Service 2
Pay Units: 1,401.
Programming (via satellite): HBO.
Fee: $11.00 monthly.
Pay Service 3
Pay Units: 94.
Programming (via satellite): The Movie Channel.
Fee: $11.00 monthly.
Pay Service 4
Pay Units: 1,160.
Programming (via satellite): Showtime.
Fee: $11.00 monthly.
Pay-Per-View
Special events.
Local advertising: Yes. Available in satellite distributed programming. Rates: $160.00/Minute; $80.00/30 Seconds. Local sales manager: Mark Kanter. Regional interconnect: Oklahoma Cable Advertising Interconnect.
Equipment: Scientific-Atlanta headend; Jerrold amplifiers; Comm/Scope & Trilogy cable; Texscan character generator; Hamlin set top converters; Tocom addressable set top converters; Scientific-Atlanta satellite antenna; Scientific-Atlanta satellite receivers.
Miles of plant: 229.3 (coaxial). Homes passed: 7,652.
Manager: Wayne Beikman. Chief technician: Darrell Low. Marketing director: Jim Back. Customer service manager: Charitta Shelton.
City fee: 3% of gross.
Ownership: Multimedia Cablevision Inc. (MSO). See Cable System Ownership.

CHOUTEAU—Oklahoma Cablecomm, Box 970, Fort Gibson, OK 74434-0970. Phone: 918-478-2100. Fax: 918-478-2355. County: Mayes. ICA: OK0358.
TV Market Ranking: 54. Franchise award date: N.A. Franchise expiration date: N.A. Began: N.A.
Channel capacity: N.A. Channels available but not in use: N.A.
Basic Service
Subscribers: N.A.
Programming (received off-air): KRSC-TV (E) Claremore; KJRH (N), KOED-TV (P), KOKI-TV (F), KOTV (C), KTFO (U), KTUL (A), KWHB (I) Tulsa.
Programming (via satellite): WGN-TV (W) Chicago; A & E; American Movie Classics; CNBC; CNN; Cartoon Network; Comedy Central; Country Music TV; Discovery Channel; Disney Channel; E! Entertainment TV; ESPN; ESPN 2; Fox Family Channel; Fox Sports Net Midwest; Headline News; History Channel; Learning Channel; Lifetime; MTV; Nashville Network; Nickelodeon; QVC; Sci-Fi Channel; TBS Superstation; The Inspirational Network; The Weather Channel; Turner Network TV; USA Network.
Fee: N.A.
Pay Service 1
Pay Units: N.A.
Programming (via satellite): Cinemax; HBO; Showtime.
Fee: N.A.
Manager: Rick Wall. Chief technician: Leon Strain. Marketing & program director: Bruce Berkinshaw.
Ownership: Fanch Communications Inc. (MSO); Time Warner Cable (MSO). See Cable System Ownership.

CLAREMORE—Tulsa Cable Television Inc., Box 470800, Tulsa, OK 74145. Phone: 918-665-1990. County: Rogers. ICA: OK0025.
TV Market Ranking: 54. Franchise award date: N.A. Franchise expiration date: N.A. Began: N.A.
Channel capacity: 40. Channels available but not in use: N.A.
Basic Service
Subscribers: N.A.
Programming (received off-air): KRSC-TV (E) Claremore; KJRH (N), KOED-TV (P), KOKI-TV (F), KOTV (C), KTUL (A) Tulsa.
Programming (via satellite): WGN-TV (W) Chicago; A & E; American Movie Classics; BET; Bravo; C-SPAN; C-SPAN 2; CNBC; CNN; Country Music TV; Discovery Channel; E! Entertainment TV; ESPN; Fox Family Channel; Fox Sports Net Southwest; Headline News; Learning Channel; Lifetime; MTV; Nashville Network; Nickelodeon; QVC; Sportsvue; TBS Superstation; TV Guide Channel; The Inspirational Network; The Weather Channel; Travel Channel; Turner Network TV; USA Network; VH1.
Current originations: Local news.
Fee: $49.95 installation.
Miles of plant: 68.8 (coaxial). Homes passed: 7,349. Total homes in franchised area: 7,349.
Manager: Bill Hoagland. Chief technician: Ernest Staten. Marketing director: Karen Hartley.
Ownership: AT&T Broadband & Internet Services (MSO). Purchased from Tele-Communications Inc., March 9, 1999.

CLAYTON—Peak Cablevision, Box 807, Pocola, OK 74902. Phone: 918-436-7488. Fax: 918-436-7151. County: Pushmataha. ICA: OK0273.
TV Market Ranking: Outside TV Markets. Franchise award date: N.A. Franchise expiration date: December 11, 2010. Began: July 1, 1977.
Channel capacity: 36 (not 2-way capable). Channels available but not in use: 6.
Basic Service
Subscribers: 123.
Programming (received off-air): KTEN (A,N,F) Ada; KOET (P) Eufaula; KFSM-TV (C), KPOM-TV (N) Fort Smith; KXII (C) Sherman; KJRH (N), KTUL (A) Tulsa.
Programming (via satellite): WGN-TV (W) Chicago; A & E; CNN; Country Music TV; Discovery Channel; ESPN; Fox Family Channel; Learning Channel; MTV; Nashville Network; Nickelodeon; Sci-Fi Channel; TBS Superstation; The Weather Channel; Trinity Bcstg. Network; Turner Network TV; USA Network; VH1.
Fee: $14.89 monthly.
Pay Service 1
Pay Units: N.A.
Programming (via satellite): Disney Channel; HBO; Showtime; The Movie Channel.
Fee: $10.00 monthly (each).
Miles of plant: 10.5 (coaxial). Homes passed: 456.
Manager: Dennis Moore. Chief technician: Rick Packard. Marketing director: Terry Homesley. Customer service manager: Susan Moore.
Franchise fee: 2% of basic subs.
Ownership: Peak Cablevision LLC (MSO). See Cable System Ownership.

CLEO SPRINGS—Rapid Cable, Box 6310, 310 Walnut Extension, Branson, MO 65615. Phones: 417-334-7897; 800-972-0962. Fax: 417-334-7899. E-mail: rcpcable@aol.com. County: Major. ICA: OK0227.
TV Market Ranking: Outside TV Markets. Franchise award date: October 15, 1982. Franchise expiration date: October 15, 2007. Began: August 1, 1985.
Channel capacity: 35 (2-way capable; not operating 2-way). Channels available but not in use: 12.
Basic Service
Subscribers: 96.
Programming (received off-air): KAUT-TV (U), KETA (P), KFOR-TV (N), KOCB (W), KOCO-TV (A), KOKH-TV (F), KWTV (C) Oklahoma City.
Programming (via satellite): WGN-TV (W) Chicago; CNN; Country Music TV; Discovery Channel; ESPN; Fox Family Channel; Home Shopping Network 2; Nashville Network; TBS Superstation; The Weather Channel; Trinity Bcstg. Network; Turner Network TV; USA Network.
Fee: $29.95 installation; $22.95 monthly; $3.95 converter.
Pay Service 1
Pay Units: 13.
Programming (via satellite): HBO.
Fee: $10.00 monthly.
Pay Service 2
Pay Units: 6.
Programming (via satellite): Cinemax.
Fee: $9.00 monthly.
Pay Service 3
Pay Units: 7.
Programming (via satellite): Disney Channel.
Fee: $7.00 monthly.
Local advertising: No.
Miles of plant: 4.3 (coaxial). Homes passed: 174.
Manager: Belinda Murphy. Chief engineer: Steve Rice. Program director: Beth Semptimphelter. Marketing director: Bill Fischer.
Ownership: Rapid Communications Partners LP (MSO); TS Communications Inc. (MSO).

CLEVELAND—Cim Tel Cable Inc., Box 266, 101 Cimarron St., Mannford, OK 74044. Phone: 918-865-3314. County: Pawnee. ICA: OK0097.
TV Market Ranking: 54. Franchise award date: N.A. Franchise expiration date: N.A. Began: January 1, 1982.
Channel capacity: 35. Channels available but not in use: N.A.
Basic Service
Subscribers: N.A.
Programming (received off-air): KJRH (N), KOED-TV (P), KOKI-TV (F), KOTV (C), KTUL (A) Tulsa.
Programming (via satellite): WGN-TV (W) Chicago; CNN; ESPN; Fox Family Channel; TBS Superstation.
Fee: $15.00 installation; $9.95 monthly.
Pay Service 1
Pay Units: N.A.
Programming (via satellite): Cinemax; HBO.
Fee: $9.50 monthly (each).
Equipment: Scientific-Atlanta headend; GTE Sylvania amplifiers; Comm/Scope cable; Anixter-Mark satellite antenna.
Miles of plant: 24.2 (coaxial). Homes passed: 1,125. Total homes in franchised area: 1,200.
Manager: H. Z. Goatcher.
City fee: 3% of gross.
Ownership: Cim Tel Cable Inc. (MSO).

CLINTON—Cable One, Box 367, 818 Frisco St., Clinton, OK 73601. Phone: 580-323-2225. Fax: 580-323-5869. County: Custer. ICA: OK0038.

TV Market Ranking: Outside TV Markets. Franchise award date: February 1, 1960. Franchise expiration date: August 1, 1999. Began: February 1, 1960.
Channel capacity: 42 (not 2-way capable). Channels available but not in use: None.
Basic Service
Subscribers: 3,350.
Programming (received off-air): KWET (P) Cheyenne; KFOR-TV (N), KOCB (W), KOCO-TV (A), KOKH-TV (F), KWTV (C) Oklahoma City; 11 FMs.
Programming (via satellite): WGN-TV (W) Chicago; C-SPAN; QVC; TBS Superstation; Trinity Bcstg. Network.
Current originations: Automated time-weather.
Fee: $35.00 installation (aerial), $60.00 (underground); $25.15 monthly; $3.25 converter; $20.00 additional installation.
Expanded Basic Service
Subscribers: 3,300.
Programming (via satellite): A & E; American Movie Classics; C-SPAN 2; CNBC; CNN; Country Music TV; Discovery Channel; E! Entertainment TV; ESPN; ESPN 2; Fox Family Channel; Fox Sports Net Southwest; Home & Garden Television; Learning Channel; Lifetime; MSNBC; Nashville Network; Nickelodeon; TV Food Network; TV Guide Channel; The Weather Channel; Turner Network TV; USA Network; Univision; VH1.
Fee: $35.00 installation; $25.15 monthly.
Pay Service 1
Pay Units: 197.
Programming (via satellite): Disney Channel.
Fee: $9.50 monthly.
Pay Service 2
Pay Units: 389.
Programming (via satellite): HBO (multiplexed).
Fee: $12.95 monthly.
Pay Service 3
Pay Units: 295.
Programming (via satellite): Showtime (multiplexed).
Fee: $12.95 monthly.
Pay-Per-View
Addressable homes: 700.
Viewer's Choice.
Fee: $2.99.
Local advertising: Yes. Available in taped programming. Local sales manager: Joe Englebrecht.
Equipment: Scientific-Atlanta headend; Jerrold amplifiers; Comm/Scope cable; Scientific-Atlanta satellite antenna; Scientific-Atlanta satellite receivers.
Miles of plant: 70.0 (coaxial). Homes passed: 4,337. Total homes in franchised area: 4,337.
Manager: Geary Stills. Chief technician: Don Davis. Office coordinator: Charla Loche.
City fee: 5% of gross.
Ownership: Cable One Inc. (MSO). Purchased from Marcus Cable, August 1, 1998.

COALGATE—CommuniComm Services, Box 597, 1501 W. Mississippi, Durant, OK 74702-0597. Phones: 580-924-2367; 800-752-4992. Fax: 580-924-5970. County: Coal. ICA: OK0120.
TV Market Ranking: Below 100. Franchise award date: N.A. Franchise expiration date: April 1, 1998. Began: February 1, 1974.
Channel capacity: 62 (not 2-way capable). Channels available but not in use: N.A.
Basic Service
Subscribers: 519.
Programming (received off-air): KTEN (A,N,F) Ada; KETA (P), KFOR-TV (N), KOCO-TV (A), KWTV (C) Oklahoma City; KXII (C) Sherman; allband FM.
Programming (via satellite): WGN-TV (W) Chicago; Cartoon Network; FoxNet; Sci-Fi Channel; TBS Superstation; Trinity Bcstg. Network.
Current originations: Automated time-weather; educational access; government access.
Fee: $49.95 installation; $10.75 monthly.
Expanded Basic Service
Subscribers: 1,723.
Programming (via satellite): A & E; American Movie Classics; BET; C-SPAN; C-SPAN 2; CNBC; CNN; CNNfn; Country Music TV; Discovery Channel; Disney Channel; ESPN; ESPN 2; Fox Family Channel; Fox Sports Net Southwest; Headline News; History Channel; Learning Channel; Lifetime; MTV; Nashville Network; Nickelodeon; QVC; The Radar Channel; The Weather Channel; Turner Network TV; USA Network; VH1.
Fee: $49.95 installation; $20.25 monthly.
Pay Service 1
Pay Units: 108.
Programming (via satellite): Cinemax; HBO (multiplexed); Starz!; The New Encore.
Fee: $20.00 installation; $9.95 monthly (Encore & Starz), $10.95 monthly (Cinemax), $12.95 monthly (HBO).
Equipment: Blonder-Tongue & Cadco headend; Cadco & C-COR amplifiers; Essex & Times Fiber cable; Scientific-Atlanta satellite antenna.
Miles of plant: 80.0 (coaxial); None (fiber optic). Homes passed: 936.
Manager: Danny R. Neumann.
City fee: 3% of gross.
Ownership: James Cable Partners (MSO).

COLBERT—CommuniComm Services, Box 597, 1501 W. Mississippi, Durant, OK 74702-0597. Phones: 580-924-2367; 800-752-4992. County: Bryan. Also serves Bokchito, Buncombe Creek, Caddo. ICA: OK0068.
TV Market Ranking: Below 100. Franchise award date: January 1, 1979. Franchise expiration date: N.A. Began: June 6, 1979.
Channel capacity: 42 (not 2-way capable). Channels available but not in use: 5.
Basic Service
Subscribers: 873.
Programming (received off-air): KTEN (A,N,F) Ada; KXAS-TV (N), WFAA-TV (A) Dallas-Fort Worth; KETA (P), KWTV (C) Oklahoma City; KXII (C) Sherman.
Programming (via satellite): WGN-TV (W) Chicago; A & E; American Movie Classics; CNBC; CNN; Cartoon Network; Country Music TV; Discovery Channel; Disney Channel; ESPN; ESPN 2; Fox Family Channel; Fox Sports Net Southwest; FoxNet; Headline News; Lifetime; MTV; Nashville Network; Nickelodeon; TBS Superstation; The Weather Channel; Trinity Bcstg. Network; Turner Network TV; USA Network.
Current originations: Public access; NEXRAD.
Fee: $49.95 installation; $31.00 monthly.
Pay Service 1
Pay Units: 101.
Programming (via satellite): Cinemax; HBO.
Fee: $9.95 (Cinemax), $12.95 monthly (HBO).
Local advertising: Yes. Local sales manager: Todd Tidwell.
Equipment: Tocom & Triple Crown headend; Magnavox amplifiers.
Miles of plant: 50.0 (coaxial); None (fiber optic). Homes passed: 1,605.
Manager: Danny R. Neumann.
Franchise fee: 3% of gross.
Ownership: James Cable Partners (MSO).

COLCORD—Oklahoma Cablecomm, Box 970, Fort Gibson, OK 74434-0970. Phones: 918-478-2100; 800-783-5701. Fax: 918-478-2355. County: Delaware. ICA: OK0204.
TV Market Ranking: Below 100. Franchise award date: N.A. Franchise expiration date: N.A. Began: January 1, 1983.
Channel capacity: 35 (not 2-way capable). Channels available but not in use: 16.
Basic Service
Subscribers: 114.
Programming (received off-air): KJRH (N), KOED-TV (P), KOKI-TV (F), KOTV (C), KTUL (A), KWHB (I) Tulsa.
Programming (via satellite): WGN-TV (W) Chicago; A & E; American Movie Classics; CNN; Country Music TV; Discovery Channel; ESPN; Fox Family Channel; Lifetime; Nashville Network; Nickelodeon; TBS Superstation; Turner Network TV; USA Network.
Fee: $40.00 installation; $20.95 monthly; $1.96 converter; $19.95 additional installation.
Pay Service 1
Pay Units: 14.
Programming (via satellite): Cinemax.
Fee: $9.95 monthly.
Pay Service 2
Pay Units: 25.
Programming (via satellite): HBO.
Fee: $9.95 monthly.
Pay Service 3
Pay Units: 13.
Programming (via satellite): Showtime.
Fee: $9.95 monthly.
Local advertising: No.
Program Guide: TV Host.
Equipment: Blonder-Tongue, Cadco & Pico headend; Magnavox amplifiers; Comm/Scope cable; Arco, Eagle & Northeast Filter traps; Prodelin & Scientific-Atlanta satellite antenna; Standard Communications satellite receivers.
Miles of plant: 6.0 (coaxial). Homes passed: 231.
Manager: Rick Wall. Chief technician: Leon Strain. Marketing & program director: Bruce Berkinshaw.
City fee: 2% of basic gross.
Ownership: Fanch Communications Inc. (MSO); Time Warner Cable (MSO). See Cable System Ownership.

COLLINSVILLE—Community Cablevision, Box 307, Skiatook, OK 74070-0307. Phone: 918-396-3019. County: Tulsa. ICA: OK0069.
TV Market Ranking: 54. Franchise award date: April 2, 1980. Franchise expiration date: April 2, 2005. Began: January 1, 1980.
Channel capacity: 35 (not 2-way capable). Channels available but not in use: 4.
Basic Service
Subscribers: 966.
Programming (received off-air): KDOR (T) Bartlesville; KRSC-TV (E) Claremore; KTPX (X) Okmulgee; KJRH (N), KOED-TV (P), KOKI-TV (F), KOTV (C), KTUL (A), KWHB (I) Tulsa; allband FM.
Programming (via satellite): WGN-TV (W) Chicago; A & E; C-SPAN; C-SPAN 2; CNN; Country Music TV; Discovery Channel; ESPN; Fox Family Channel; Headline News; Lifetime; MTV; Nashville Network; Nickelodeon; TBS Superstation; Turner Classic Movies; Turner Network TV; USA Network; VH1.
Current originations: Automated time-weather.
Fee: $25.00 installation; $16.25 monthly; $25.00 additional installation.
Pay Service 1
Pay Units: 196.
Programming (via satellite): Cinemax.
Fee: $25.00 installation; $11.50 monthly.
Pay Service 2
Pay Units: 143.
Programming (via satellite): Disney Channel.
Fee: $25.00 installation; $7.00 monthly.
Pay Service 3
Pay Units: 371.
Programming (via satellite): HBO.
Fee: $25.00 installation; $11.50 monthly.
Local advertising: Yes. Available in character-generated programming. Rates: $15.00/Week.
Equipment: Jerrold headend; Theta-Com amplifiers; Times Fiber cable; Texscan character generator; GTE Sylvania set top converters; Arcom traps; Comtech satellite antenna.
Miles of plant: 32.9 (coaxial). Homes passed: 2,019.
Manager: Ray Soule.
City fee: 4% of gross.
Ownership: Community Cablevision Co. (MSO).

COMANCHE—Classic Cable, Box 429, 605 N.W. 3rd St., Plainville, KS 67663-0429. Phones: 785-434-7620; 800-999-8876. Fax: 785-434-2614.
Web site: http://www.classic-cable.com.
Counties: Logan & Stephens. ICA: OK0177.
TV Market Ranking: 39 (Comanche); Below 100 (Comanche). Franchise award date: N.A. Franchise expiration date: N.A. Began: July 1, 1981.
Channel capacity: 41 (2-way capable). Channels available but not in use: N.A.
Basic Service
Subscribers: 775.
Programming (received off-air): KETA (P), KFOR-TV (N), KOCO-TV (A), KOKH-TV (F), KWTV (C) Oklahoma City; KAUZ-TV (C), KFDX-TV (N), KJTL (F,U), KSWO-TV (A) Wichita Falls-Lawton.
Programming (via satellite): WGN-TV (W) Chicago; A & E; American Movie Classics; C-SPAN; CNN; Cartoon Network; Country Music TV; Discovery Channel; Disney Channel; E! Entertainment TV; ESPN; Fox Family Channel; Fox News Channel; Fox Sports Net Southwest; Headline News; History Channel; Learning Channel; Lifetime; Nashville Network; Nick at Nite's TV Land; Nickelodeon; QVC; Sci-Fi Channel; TBS Superstation; The Weather Channel; Trinity Bcstg. Network; Turner Network TV; USA Network.
Current originations: Local news.
Fee: $35.00 installation; $28.95 monthly.
Pay Service 1
Pay Units: 116.
Programming (via satellite): HBO.
Fee: $10.95 monthly.
Pay Service 2
Pay Units: 53.
Programming (via satellite): Showtime.
Fee: $9.95 monthly.
Pay Service 3
Pay Units: 44.
Programming (via satellite): The Movie Channel.
Fee: $5.95 monthly.
Local advertising: Yes. Available in character-generated programming.
Equipment: ISS, Jerrold & Scientific-Atlanta headend; Broadband & Scientific-Atlanta amplifiers; Comm/Scope cable; Jerrold set top converters; Pico traps.
Miles of plant: 27.0 (coaxial). Homes passed: 822.
Manager: Dave Walker. Chief technician: Roger Campbell. Marketing director: Jennifer Hauschild.
Ownership: Classic Cable (MSO).

COOKSON—Quality Entertainment Corp., Suite 512, Central Mall Plaza, Fort Smith, AR 72903.

Phone: 501-452-1998. Fax: 501-452-6430. County: Cherokee. ICA: OK0367.
TV Market Ranking: Below 100. Franchise award date: N.A. Franchise expiration date: N.A. Began: N.A.
Channel capacity: 36 (not 2-way capable). Channels available but not in use: 10.
Basic Service
Subscribers: 40.
Programming (received off-air): KJRH (N), KOED-TV (P), KOKI-TV (F), KTUL (A) Tulsa.
Programming (via satellite): WGN-TV (W) Chicago; A & E; C-SPAN; CNN; Discovery Channel; ESPN; Fox Family Channel; History Channel; Learning Channel; Nashville Network; TBS Superstation; Trinity Bcstg. Network; USA Network.
Fee: $40.00 installation; $22.00 monthly.
Pay Service 1
Pay Units: N.A.
Programming (via satellite): Showtime.
Fee: $10.95 monthly.
Miles of plant: 5.0 (coaxial).
Manager: Brent Lewis.
Ownership: Quality Entertainment Corp. (MSO).

COPAN—Community Cablevision Co., Box 307, Skiatook, OK 74070. Phone: 918-535-2208. County: Washington. ICA: OK0168.
TV Market Ranking: Below 100. Franchise award date: N.A. Franchise expiration date: N.A. Began: N.A.
Channel capacity: 35 (not 2-way capable). Channels available but not in use: N.A.
Basic Service
Subscribers: 292.
Programming (received off-air): KJRH (N), KOED-TV (P), KOKI-TV (F), KOTV (C), KTUL (A), KWHB (I) Tulsa.
Programming (via satellite): WGN-TV (W) Chicago; A & E; CNN; Cartoon Network; Country Music TV; Discovery Channel; ESPN; Fox Family Channel; Headline News; MTV; Nashville Network; Nickelodeon; TBS Superstation; Turner Classic Movies; Turner Network TV.
Fee: $40.00 installation; $12.50 monthly; $7.50 additional installation.
Pay Service 1
Pay Units: 75.
Programming (via satellite): Cinemax.
Fee: $10.00 monthly.
Pay Service 2
Pay Units: 41.
Programming (via satellite): Disney Channel.
Fee: $9.95 monthly.
Pay Service 3
Pay Units: 93.
Programming (via satellite): HBO.
Fee: $12.50 monthly.
Local advertising: No.
Equipment: Scientific-Atlanta headend; Scientific-Atlanta amplifiers; Scientific-Atlanta cable; Texscan character generator; Scientific-Atlanta set top converters; Pico traps; Scientific-Atlanta satellite antenna; Scientific-Atlanta satellite receivers.
Miles of plant: 12.0 (coaxial). Homes passed: 466. Total homes in franchised area: 466.
City fee: 3% of gross.
Ownership: Community Cablevision Co. (MSO).

CORDELL—Cable One, 120 S. College St., Cordell, OK 73632-5208. Phone: 405-832-5311. Fax: 405-832-5112. County: Washita. ICA: OK0078.
TV Market Ranking: Outside TV Markets. Franchise award date: N.A. Franchise expiration date: N.A. Began: April 1, 1959.
Channel capacity: 25. Channels available but not in use: N.A.
Basic Service
Subscribers: 1,296.
Programming (received off-air): KWET (P) Cheyenne; KAUT-TV (U), KFOR-TV (N), KOCB (W), KOCO-TV (A), KOKH-TV (F), KWTV (C) Oklahoma City; 6 FMs.
Programming (via satellite): WGN-TV (W) Chicago; C-SPAN; CNBC; CNN; Discovery Channel; ESPN; Lifetime; MTV; Nashville Network; Odyssey; QVC; TBS Superstation; The Weather Channel; Trinity Bcstg. Network; Turner Network TV.
Current originations: Automated time-weather.
Fee: $60.00 installation; $19.14 monthly; $16.68 additional installation.
Pay Service 1
Pay Units: 101.
Programming (via satellite): Disney Channel.
Fee: $10.00 monthly.
Pay Service 2
Pay Units: 525.
Programming (via satellite): The New Encore.
Fee: N.A.
Pay Service 3
Pay Units: 51.
Programming (via satellite): Showtime.
Fee: $10.00 monthly.
Pay Service 4
Pay Units: 131.
Programming (via satellite): The Movie Channel.
Fee: $10.00 monthly.
Program Guide: The Cable Guide.
Equipment: AFC satellite antenna.
Miles of plant: 29.6 (coaxial). Homes passed: 1,758. Total homes in franchised area: 1,765.
Manager: Gary Stills. Office manager: Rhonda Maddox.
City fee: 2% of gross.
Ownership: Cable One Inc. (MSO).

CORN—Classic Cable, Box 429, 605 N.W. 3rd St., Plainville, KS 67663-0429. Phones: 785-434-7620; 800-999-8876. Fax: 785-434-2614. Web site: http://www.classic-cable.com. County: Washita. ICA: OK0274.
TV Market Ranking: Outside TV Markets. Franchise award date: November 1, 1979. Franchise expiration date: November 1, 2004. Began: N.A.
Channel capacity: 36 (2-way capable). Channels available but not in use: N.A.
Basic Service
Subscribers: 151.
Programming (received off-air): KAUT-TV (U), KETA (P), KFOR-TV (N), KOCB (W), KOCO-TV (A), KOKH-TV (F), KTBO-TV (T), KWTV (C) Oklahoma City.
Programming (via satellite): WGN-TV (W) Chicago; CNN; Discovery Channel; Disney Channel; E! Entertainment TV; ESPN; Fox Family Channel; Nashville Network; Nick at Nite's TV Land; Nickelodeon; TBS Superstation; The Weather Channel; Turner Network TV; USA Network.
Fee: $35.00 installation; $27.95 monthly.
Pay Service 1
Pay Units: 5.
Programming (via satellite): HBO.
Fee: $10.95 monthly.
Pay Service 2
Pay Units: 6.
Programming (via satellite): Showtime.
Fee: $9.95 monthly.
Miles of plant: 4.0 (coaxial). Homes passed: 200.
Region manager: Dave Walker. Chief technician: Roger Campbell. Marketing director: Jennifer Hauschild.
Franchise fee: 2% of gross.
Ownership: Classic Cable (MSO).

COVINGTON—Classic Cable, Box 429, 605 N.W. 3rd St., Plainville, KS 67663-0429. Phones: 785-434-7620; 800-999-8876. Fax: 785-434-2614. Web site: http://www.classic-cable.com. County: Garfield. ICA: OK0203.
TV Market Ranking: Outside TV Markets. Franchise award date: N.A. Franchise expiration date: N.A. Began: February 1, 1986.
Channel capacity: 41 (2-way capable). Channels available but not in use: N.A.
Basic Service
Subscribers: 93.
Programming (received off-air): KAUT-TV (U), KETA (P), KFOR-TV (N), KOCB (W), KOCO-TV (A), KOKH-TV (F), KTBO-TV (T), KWTV (C) Oklahoma City.
Programming (via satellite): WGN-TV (W) Chicago; A & E; American Movie Classics; CNN; Country Music TV; Discovery Channel; Disney Channel; E! Entertainment TV; ESPN; Fox Family Channel; Learning Channel; Lifetime; Nashville Network; Nick at Nite's TV Land; TBS Superstation; The Weather Channel; Trinity Bcstg. Network; Turner Network TV; USA Network.
Fee: $35.00 installation; $28.95 monthly; $3.50 converter; $15.00 additional installation.
Pay Service 1
Pay Units: 19.
Programming (via satellite): HBO.
Fee: $9.95 monthly.
Pay Service 2
Pay Units: 7.
Programming (via satellite): Showtime.
Fee: $9.95 monthly.
Local advertising: No.
Equipment: Cadco & DX Engineering headend; Magnavox amplifiers; Comm/Scope cable; Jerrold set top converters; DX Engineering satellite receivers.
Miles of plant: 5.2 (coaxial). Homes passed: 199. Total homes in franchised area: 291.
Manager: Dave Walker. Chief technician: Jeff Smith. Marketing director: Jennifer Hauschild.
City fee: 3% of basic.
Ownership: Classic Cable (MSO).

COWETA—Peak Cable, 410 East Side Blvd., Muskogee, OK 74403-4299. Phone: 918-687-7511. County: Wagoner. Also serves Wagoner County. ICA: OK0066.
TV Market Ranking: 54 (Coweta, portions of Wagoner County); Outside TV Markets (portions of Wagoner County). Franchise award date: N.A. Franchise expiration date: November 5, 1995. Began: March 1, 1980.
Channel capacity: 33. Channels available but not in use: N.A.
Basic Service
Subscribers: 896.
Programming (received off-air): KJRH (N), KOED-TV (P), KOKI-TV (F), KOTV (C), KTUL (A) Tulsa.
Programming (via satellite): WGN-TV (W) Chicago; C-SPAN; CNBC; CNN; Discovery Channel; Fox Family Channel; Headline News; Lifetime; MTV; Nashville Network; Nickelodeon; QVC; TBS Superstation; The Weather Channel.
Current originations: Automated time-weather.
Planned originations: Automated emergency alert.
Fee: $60.00 installation; $9.43 monthly; $6.03 additional installation.
Expanded Basic Service
Subscribers: 869.
Programming (via satellite): American Movie Classics; Court TV; ESPN; Fox Sports Net Southwest; Turner Network TV; USA Network.
Fee: $10.88 monthly.
Pay Service 1
Pay Units: 5.
Programming (via satellite): Cinemax.
Fee: N.A.
Pay Service 2
Pay Units: 381.
Programming (via satellite): The New Encore.
Fee: N.A.
Pay Service 3
Pay Units: 265.
Programming (via satellite): HBO.
Fee: $10.00 installation; $9.95 monthly.
Pay Service 4
Pay Units: 129.
Programming (via satellite): Showtime.
Fee: $9.95 monthly.
Pay Service 5
Pay Units: 66.
Programming (via satellite): The Movie Channel.
Fee: $9.95 monthly.
Local advertising: Planned.
Equipment: Scientific-Atlanta headend; C-COR, Scientific-Atlanta & Theta-Com amplifiers; Comm/Scope cable; Beston character generator; Jerrold & Oak set top converters; Eagle traps; Prodelin & Scientific-Atlanta satellite antenna; Gardiner & Scientific-Atlanta satellite receivers.
Miles of plant: 37.7 (coaxial). Homes passed: 2,080. Total homes in franchised area: 2,347.
Manager: Brad Mangum. Chief technician: Darrell Kimbrill.
City fee: 3% of gross.
Ownership: AT&T Broadband & Internet Services (MSO). Purchased from Tele-Communications Inc., March 9, 1999.

CRESCENT—Multimedia Cablevision Inc., Box 3027, 701 E. Douglas Ave., Wichita, KS 67201-3596. Phone: 316-262-4270. Fax: 316-262-2309. County: Logan. ICA: OK0124.
TV Market Ranking: Outside TV Markets. Franchise award date: March 16, 1980. Franchise expiration date: March 16, 2005. Began: October 19, 1981.
Channel capacity: 37 (not 2-way capable). Channels available but not in use: None.
Basic Service
Subscribers: 284.
Programming (received off-air): KAUT-TV (U), KETA (P), KFOR-TV (N), KOCB (W), KOCO-TV (A), KOKH-TV (F), KSBI (I), KTBO-TV (T), KWTV (C) Oklahoma City.
Programming (via satellite): A & E; American Movie Classics; C-SPAN; CNBC; Discovery Channel; ESPN; Home Shopping Network; Learning Channel; Lifetime; MTV; Nickelodeon; TV Guide Channel; The Weather Channel; Turner Network TV; USA Network; VH1.
Fee: $12.31 installation; $16.12 monthly; $13.10 additional installation.
Expanded Basic Service
Subscribers: 279.
Programming (via satellite): WGN-TV (W) Chicago; CNN; Fox Family Channel; Headline News; Nashville Network; TBS Superstation.
Fee: $3.22 monthly.
Pay Service 1
Pay Units: 79.
Programming (via satellite): Cinemax.
Fee: $11.00 monthly.
Pay Service 2
Pay Units: 94.
Programming (via satellite): HBO.
Fee: $11.00 monthly.

Pay-Per-View
Addressable homes: 2.
Local advertising: No.
Program Guide: The Cable Guide.
Equipment: Scientific-Atlanta headend; GTE Sylvania amplifiers; Comm/Scope cable; Oak set top converters; Eagle traps; Scientific-Atlanta satellite antenna.
Miles of plant: 38.9 (coaxial). Homes passed: 832. Total homes in franchised area: 832.
Manager: Ron Marnell. Chief technician: Richard Abraham. Program director: Mary Jobe. Marketing director: Jim Back. Customer service manager: Pat Belt.
City fee: 3% of gross.
Ownership: Multimedia Cablevision Inc. (MSO). See Cable System Ownership.

CROMWELL—Oklahoma Cablecomm, Box 970, Fort Gibson, OK 74434-0970. Phones: 918-478-2100; 800-783-5701. Fax: 918-478-2355. County: Seminole. ICA: OK0258.
TV Market Ranking: Outside TV Markets. Franchise award date: January 1, 1989. Franchise expiration date: January 1, 2014. Began: September 1, 1989.
Channel capacity: 45. Channels available but not in use: 30.
Basic Service
Subscribers: 34.
Programming (received off-air): KETA (P), KFOR-TV (N), KOCB (W), KOCO-TV (A), KOKH-TV (F), KWTV (C) Oklahoma City.
Programming (via satellite): WGN-TV (W) Chicago; CNN; Discovery Channel; Fox Family Channel; Nashville Network; TBS Superstation.
Fee: $30.00 installation; $19.95 monthly.
Pay Service 1
Pay Units: 12.
Programming (via satellite): HBO.
Fee: $10.00 monthly.
Local advertising: No.
Miles of plant: 3.0 (coaxial). Homes passed: 110.
Regional manager: Rick Wall. Chief technician: Leon Strain. Marketing & program director: Bruce Berkinshaw.
Ownership: Fanch Communications Inc. (MSO); Time Warner Cable (MSO). See Cable System Ownership.

CUMBERLAND—Quality Entertainment Corp., Suite 512, Central Mall Plaza, Fort Smith, AR 72903. Phone: 501-452-1998. Fax: 501-452-6430. County: Marshall. Also serves Cumberland Cove, Little City. ICA: OK0276.
TV Market Ranking: Below 100. Franchise award date: January 1, 1989. Franchise expiration date: January 1, 2004. Began: January 1, 1989.
Channel capacity: 35 (not 2-way capable). Channels available but not in use: 9.
Basic Service
Subscribers: 35.
Programming (received off-air): KTEN (A,N,F) Ada; KETA (P) Oklahoma City; KXII (C) Sherman.
Programming (via satellite): WGN-TV (W) Chicago; American Movie Classics; CNN; Country Music TV; Discovery Channel; Disney Channel; ESPN; Fox Family Channel; Nashville Network; TBS Superstation; Trinity Bcstg. Network; Turner Network TV; USA Network.
Fee: $40.00 installation; $22.00 monthly.
Miles of plant: 12.0 (coaxial); None (fiber optic). Homes passed: 200. Total homes in franchised area: 300.
Manager: Brent Lewis. Chief technician: Randall Hinton.
Ownership: Quality Entertainment Corp. (MSO).

CUSHING—Peak Cablevision, 802 E. 6th St., Stillwater, OK 74074. Phone: 405-377-7785. Fax: 405-372-3980. County: Payne. ICA: OK0037.
TV Market Ranking: Outside TV Markets. Franchise award date: August 28, 1978. Franchise expiration date: September 1, 1998. Began: March 5, 1980.
Channel capacity: 40 (not 2-way capable). Channels available but not in use: None.
Basic Service
Subscribers: 2,449.
Programming (received off-air): KAUT-TV (U), KETA (P), KFOR-TV (N), KOCB (W), KOCO-TV (A), KOKH-TV (F), KOPX (X), KTBO-TV (T), KWTV (C) Oklahoma City; KOTV (C) Tulsa.
Programming (via satellite): WGN-TV (W) Chicago; CNN; Discovery Channel; Fox News Channel; Headline News; TBS Superstation.
Current originations: Government access.
Fee: $37.50 installation; $11.96 monthly.
Expanded Basic Service
Subscribers: 2,255.
Programming (via satellite): A & E; American Movie Classics; Animal Planet; C-SPAN; Cartoon Network; Disney Channel; ESPN; Fox Family Channel; Fox Sports Net Southwest; History Channel; Home & Garden Television; Lifetime; MTV; Nashville Network; Nickelodeon; Sci-Fi Channel; The Weather Channel; Turner Network TV; USA Network.
Fee: $10.92 monthly.
Pay Service 1
Pay Units: 390.
Programming (via satellite): Cinemax.
Fee: $11.00 monthly.
Pay Service 2
Pay Units: 617.
Programming (via satellite): The New Encore.
Fee: $1.75 monthly.
Pay Service 3
Pay Units: 613.
Programming (via satellite): HBO.
Fee: $11.00 monthly.
Pay Service 4
Pay Units: 608.
Programming (via satellite): Starz!
Fee: $6.75 monthly.
Pay-Per-View
Special events.
Local advertising: Yes. Local sales manager: Steve Ray.
Program Guide: The Cable Guide.
Equipment: Scientific-Atlanta headend; Jerrold amplifiers; Comm/Scope & Trilogy cable; Sony cameras; Sony VTRs; Texscan character generator; Hamlin set top converters; Eagle traps; Scientific-Atlanta satellite antenna.
Miles of plant: 67.8 (coaxial). Homes passed: 4,685. Total homes in franchised area: 4,685.
Manager: Ted Ramsey. Chief technician: Joe Goertz.
City fee: 3% of gross.
Ownership: Peak Cablevision LLC (MSO). See Cable System Ownership.

CUSTER CITY—Classic Cable, Box 429, 605 N.W. 3rd St., Plainville, KS 67663-0429. Phones: 785-434-7620; 800-999-8876. Fax: 785-434-2614. Web site: http://www.classic-cable.com. County: Custer. ICA: OK0277.
TV Market Ranking: Below 100. Franchise award date: February 29, 1980. Franchise expiration date: February 29, 2020. Began: January 1, 1984.
Channel capacity: 36 (2-way capable). Channels available but not in use: N.A.
Basic Service
Subscribers: 93.
Programming (received off-air): KAUT-TV (U), KETA (P), KFOR-TV (N), KOCB (W), KOCO-TV (A), KOKH-TV (F), KTBO-TV (T), KWTV (C) Oklahoma City.
Programming (via satellite): WGN-TV (W) Chicago; CNN; Discovery Channel; ESPN; Fox Family Channel; Home Shopping Network; Nashville Network; Nick at Nite's TV Land; TBS Superstation; The Weather Channel; Turner Network TV; USA Network.
Fee: $35.00 installation; $27.95 monthly.
Pay Service 1
Pay Units: 6.
Programming (via satellite): HBO.
Fee: $11.00 monthly.
Pay Service 2
Pay Units: 10.
Programming (via satellite): Showtime.
Fee: $15.00 installation; $6.95 monthly.
Pay Service 3
Pay Units: 6.
Programming (via satellite): The Movie Channel.
Fee: $15.00 installation; $6.95 monthly.
Pay Service 4
Pay Units: 5.
Programming (via satellite): Disney Channel.
Fee: $7.95 monthly.
Miles of plant: 5.0 (coaxial). Homes passed: 200.
Region manager: Dave Walker. Chief technician: Roger Campbell. Marketing director: Jennifer Hauschild.
City fee: 2% of gross.
Ownership: Classic Cable (MSO).

CYRIL—Classic Cable, Box 429, 605 N.W. 3rd St., Plainville, KS 67663-0429. Phones: 785-434-7620; 800-999-8876. Fax: 785-434-2614. Web site: http://www.classic-cable.com. County: Caddo. ICA: OK0372.
TV Market Ranking: Below 100. Franchise award date: N.A. Franchise expiration date: N.A. Began: N.A.
Channel capacity: 36 (2-way capable). Channels available but not in use: N.A.
Basic Service
Subscribers: 316.
Programming (received off-air): KETA (P), KFOR-TV (N), KOCB (W), KOCO-TV (A), KOKH-TV (F), KSBI (I), KTBO-TV (T), KWTV (C) Oklahoma City; KJTL (F,U), KSWO-TV (A) Wichita Falls-Lawton.
Programming (via satellite): WGN-TV (W) Chicago; A & E; American Movie Classics; C-SPAN; CNN; Country Music TV; Discovery Channel; Disney Channel; ESPN; Fox Family Channel; Fox Sports Net Southwest; History Channel; Nashville Network; Nick at Nite's TV Land; Nickelodeon; QVC; TBS Superstation; The Weather Channel; Turner Network TV; USA Network.
Fee: $35.00 installation; $28.95 monthly.
Pay Service 1
Pay Units: 47.
Programming (via satellite): HBO.
Fee: $10.95 monthly.
Pay Service 2
Pay Units: 21.
Programming (via satellite): Showtime.
Fee: $9.95 monthly.
Miles of plant: 17.0 (coaxial). Homes passed: 482.
Region manager: Dave Walker. Chief technician: Roger Campbell. Marketing director: Jennifer Hauschild.
Ownership: Classic Cable (MSO).

DACOMA—Classic Cable, Box 429, 605 N.W. 3rd St., Plainville, KS 67663-0429. Phones: 785-434-7620; 800-999-8876. Fax: 785-434-2614. Web site: http://www.classic-cable.com. County: Woods. ICA: OK0278.
TV Market Ranking: Outside TV Markets. Franchise award date: January 1, 1989. Franchise expiration date: January 1, 2014. Began: September 1, 1989.
Channel capacity: 61 (2-way capable). Channels available but not in use: N.A.
Basic Service
Subscribers: 29.
Programming (received off-air): KAUT-TV (U), KETA (P), KFOR-TV (N), KOCB (W), KOCO-TV (A), KOKH-TV (F), KWTV (C) Oklahoma City.
Programming (via satellite): WGN-TV (W) Chicago; American Movie Classics; CNN; Country Music TV; Discovery Channel; ESPN; Fox Family Channel; Nashville Network; TBS Superstation.
Fee: $35.00 installation; $27.95 monthly; $3.50 converter.
Pay Service 1
Pay Units: 4.
Programming (via satellite): HBO.
Fee: $10.00 installation; $9.95 monthly.
Local advertising: No.
Equipment: Scientific-Atlanta amplifiers.
Miles of plant: 3.3 (coaxial). Homes passed: 86.
Region manager: Dave Walker. Chief technician: Jeff Smith. Marketing director: Jennifer Hauschild.
City fee: 5% of gross.
Ownership: Classic Cable (MSO).

DAVENPORT—Vi-Tel Inc., Box 789, 223 Broadway, Davenport, OK 74026-0789. Phone: 918-377-2347. Fax: 918-377-2506. County: Lincoln. ICA: OK0182.
TV Market Ranking: Outside TV Markets. Franchise award date: N.A. Franchise expiration date: N.A. Began: April 1, 1983.
Channel capacity: 36 (not 2-way capable). Channels available but not in use: 2.
Basic Service
Subscribers: 305.
Programming (received off-air): KETA (P), KFOR-TV (N), KOCB (W), KOCO-TV (A), KOKH-TV (F), KOPX (X), KWTV (C) Oklahoma City; KTUL (A) Tulsa.
Programming (via satellite): WGN-TV (W) Chicago; A & E; C-SPAN; CNN; Discovery Channel; Disney Channel; ESPN; Fox Family Channel; Fox Sports Net Southwest; History Channel; Home & Garden Television; Lifetime; Nashville Network; Nickelodeon; Sci-Fi Channel; TBS Superstation; The Weather Channel; Turner Classic Movies; Turner Network TV; USA Network.
Current originations: Automated time-weather; automated emergency alert.
Fee: $25.00 installation; $20.00 monthly.
Pay Service 1
Pay Units: 105.
Programming (via satellite): HBO.
Fee: $25.00 installation; $8.95 monthly.
Pay Service 2
Pay Units: 38.
Programming (via satellite): Showtime.
Fee: $25.00 installation; $8.95 monthly.
Local advertising: Yes. Available in character-generated programming.
Equipment: Scientific-Atlanta headend; Scientific-Atlanta amplifiers; Comm/Scope cable; Hamlin set top converters; Pico traps; Anixter-Mark satellite antenna; Scientific-Atlanta satellite receivers.
Miles of plant: 13.0 (coaxial); None (fiber optic). Homes passed: 450. Total homes in franchised area: 450.
Manager: Steven Guest. Chief technician: David Guest.

City fee: 3% of gross.
Ownership: Vi-Tel Inc.

DAVIDSON—Rapid Cable, Box 6310, 310 Walnut Extension, Branson, MO 65615. Phones: 417-334-7897; 800-972-0962. Fax: 417-334-7899. E-mail: rcpcable@aol.com. County: Tillman. ICA: OK0279.

TV Market Ranking: Outside TV Markets. Franchise award date: April 18, 1983. Franchise expiration date: April 18, 2003. Began: January 1, 1985.

Channel capacity: 31 (2-way capable; not operating 2-way). Channels available but not in use: 8.

Basic Service

Subscribers: 102.

Programming (received off-air): KETA (P) Oklahoma City; KJBO-LP (U) Wichita Falls; KAUZ-TV (C), KFDX-TV (N), KJTL (F,U), KSWO-TV (A) Wichita Falls-Lawton.

Programming (via satellite): WGN-TV (W) Chicago; Animal Planet; CNN; Country Music TV; Discovery Channel; ESPN; Fox Family Channel; GalaVision; Learning Channel; Nashville Network; TBS Superstation; The Weather Channel; Turner Network TV; USA Network.

Fee: $29.95 installation; $22.95 monthly; $3.95 converter.

Pay Service 1

Pay Units: 19.

Programming (via satellite): HBO.

Fee: $10.00 monthly.

Pay Service 2

Pay Units: 15.

Programming (via satellite): Cinemax.

Fee: $9.00 monthly.

Pay Service 3

Pay Units: 14.

Programming (via satellite): Disney Channel.

Fee: $7.00 monthly.

Miles of plant: 4.1 (coaxial). Homes passed: 219.

Manager: Belinda Murphy. Chief technician: Steve Rice. Program director: Beth Semptimphelter. Marketing director: Bill Fischer.

Ownership: Rapid Communications Partners LP (MSO); TS Communications Inc. (MSO).

DEER CREEK—Westcom, Box 71279, Des Moines, IA 50325. Phone: 515-276-3069. Fax: 515-270-9181. County: Grant. ICA: OK0280.

TV Market Ranking: Outside TV Markets. Franchise award date: N.A. Franchise expiration date: N.A. Began: N.A.

Channel capacity: 35. Channels available but not in use: 21.

Basic Service

Subscribers: 12.

Programming (received off-air): KFOR-TV (N), KWTV (C) Oklahoma City; KAKE-TV (A), KSAS-TV (F), KSNW (N) Wichita-Hutchinson.

Programming (via satellite): TBS Superstation.

Fee: $21.50 monthly.

Homes passed: 92.

Ownership: Westcom LC (MSO).

DEL CITY—Cablevision of Del City, 1304 N. Key Blvd., Midwest City, OK 73110. Phone: 405-733-1979. County: Oklahoma. Also serves Tinker AFB, Valley Brook. ICA: OK0015.

TV Market Ranking: 39. Franchise award date: January 16, 1978. Franchise expiration date: N.A. Began: November 1, 1979.

Channel capacity: 37 (2-way capable; operating 2-way). Channels available but not in use: None.

Basic Service

Subscribers: 6,809.

Programming (received off-air): KAUT-TV (U), KETA (P), KFOR-TV (N), KOCB (W), KOCO-TV (A), KOKH-TV (F), KSBI (I), KTBO-TV (T), KWTV (C) Oklahoma City; 24 FMs.

Programming (via satellite): A & E; American Movie Classics; BET; C-SPAN; CNBC; Discovery Channel; ESPN; Home Shopping Network; Learning Channel; Lifetime; MTV; Nickelodeon; The Weather Channel; USA Network; VH1.

Current originations: Public access; educational access; government access; religious access; leased access; automated emergency alert; local sports.

Fee: $13.95 installation; $17.41 monthly; $14.84 additional installation.

Expanded Basic Service

Subscribers: 6,799.

Programming (via satellite): WGN-TV (W) Chicago; CNN; Fox Family Channel; Headline News; Nashville Network; TBS Superstation; Turner Network TV.

Fee: $3.24 monthly.

Pay Service 1

Pay Units: 1,527.

Programming (via satellite): Cinemax.

Fee: $11.00 monthly.

Pay Service 2

Pay Units: 687.

Programming (via satellite): Disney Channel.

Fee: $7.95 monthly.

Pay Service 3

Pay Units: 2,433.

Programming (via satellite): HBO.

Fee: $11.00 monthly.

Pay Service 4

Pay Units: 1,480.

Programming (via satellite): Showtime.

Fee: $11.00 monthly.

Pay-Per-View

Addressable homes: 205.

Special events.

Fee: $1.95.

Local advertising: Yes (insert only). Available in satellite distributed programming. Rates: $800.00/Hour; $400.00/30 Minutes; $160.00/Minute; $80.00/30 Seconds. Local sales manager: Mark Kanter. Regional interconnect: Oklahoma Cable Advertising Interconnect.

Program Guide: The Cable Guide.

Equipment: Scientific-Atlanta headend; Scientific-Atlanta amplifiers; Comm/Scope cable; Panasonic cameras; Panasonic VTRs; Texscan character generator; Jerrold & Oak set top converters; Tocom addressable set top converters; Eagle traps; Scientific-Atlanta satellite antenna; Scientific-Atlanta satellite receivers.

Miles of plant: 126.9 (coaxial). Homes passed: 11,860. Total homes in franchised area: 14,068.

Manager: Wayne Beikman. Chief technician: Darrell Low. Marketing director: Jim Back. Customer service manager: Charitta Shelton.

City fee: 3% of gross.

Ownership: Multimedia Cablevision Inc. (MSO). See Cable System Ownership.

DELAWARE—Oklahoma Cablecomm, Box 970, Fort Gibson, OK 74434-0970. Phones: 918-478-2100; 800-783-5701. Fax: 918-478-2355. County: Nowata. Also serves Lenapah. ICA: OK0189.

TV Market Ranking: Below 100. Franchise award date: December 1, 1983. Franchise expiration date: December 1, 2003. Began: January 1, 1984.

Channel capacity: 35 (not 2-way capable). Channels available but not in use: 12.

Basic Service

Subscribers: 161.

Programming (received off-air): KDOR (T) Bartlesville; KRSC-TV (E) Claremore; KJRH (N), KOED-TV (P), KOKI-TV (F), KOTV (C), KTFO (U), KTUL (A), KWHB (I) Tulsa.

Programming (via satellite): WGN-TV (W) Chicago; A & E; CNN; Country Music TV; Discovery Channel; Disney Channel; ESPN; Fox Family Channel; Nashville Network; Nickelodeon; Sci-Fi Channel; TBS Superstation; Turner Network TV; USA Network.

Fee: $30.00 installation; $22.95 monthly.

Pay Service 1

Pay Units: N.A.

Programming (via satellite): Cinemax.

Fee: $20.00 installation; $9.95 monthly.

Pay Service 2

Pay Units: 25.

Programming (via satellite): HBO.

Fee: $20.00 installation; $9.95 monthly.

Pay Service 3

Pay Units: 8.

Programming (via satellite): Showtime.

Fee: $20.00 installation; $9.95 monthly.

Local advertising: No.

Program Guide: TV Host.

Equipment: Blonder-Tongue & Cadco headend; Magnavox amplifiers; Jerrold set top converters; Arcom & Northeast Filter traps; Prodelin & Scientific-Atlanta satellite antenna; Standard Communications satellite receivers.

Miles of plant: 16.0 (coaxial). Homes passed: 381. Total homes in franchised area: 381.

Manager: Rick Wall. Chief technician: Leon Strain. Marketing & program director: Bruce Berkinshaw.

City fee: 2% of basic gross.

Ownership: Fanch Communications Inc. (MSO); Time Warner Cable (MSO). See Cable System Ownership.

DEPEW—Oklahoma Cablecomm, Box 970, Fort Gibson, OK 74434-0970. Phones: 918-478-2100; 800-783-5701. Fax: 918-478-2355. County: Creek. ICA: OK0212.

TV Market Ranking: Below 100. Franchise award date: January 1, 1989. Franchise expiration date: January 1, 2014. Began: September 1, 1989.

Channel capacity: 35 (not 2-way capable). Channels available but not in use: 17.

Basic Service

Subscribers: 89.

Programming (received off-air): KAUT-TV (U), KOCB (W), KOKH-TV (F) Oklahoma City; KJRH (N), KOED-TV (P), KOTV (C), KTFO (U), KTUL (A), KWHB (I) Tulsa.

Programming (via satellite): WGN-TV (W) Chicago; A & E; CNN; Discovery Channel; ESPN; Fox Family Channel; Nashville Network; Sci-Fi Channel; TBS Superstation; Turner Network TV; USA Network.

Fee: $40.00 installation; $22.95 monthly; $1.96 converter; $19.95 additional installation.

Pay Service 1

Pay Units: 22.

Programming (via satellite): HBO.

Fee: $20.00 installation; $9.95 monthly.

Local advertising: No.

Program Guide: TV Host.

Equipment: Cadco headend; Scientific-Atlanta amplifiers; Comm/Scope cable; Jerrold set top converters; Standard Communications satellite receivers.

Miles of plant: 4.0 (coaxial). Homes passed: 257. Total homes in franchised area: 257.

Manager: Rick Wall. Chief technician: Leon Strain. Marketing & program director: Bruce Berkinshaw.

City fee: 5% of gross.

Ownership: Fanch Communications Inc. (MSO); Time Warner Cable (MSO). See Cable System Ownership.

DILL CITY—Classic Cable, Box 429, 605 N.W. 3rd St., Plainville, KS 67663-0429. Phones: 785-434-7620; 800-999-8876. Fax: 785-434-2614. Web site: http://www.classic-cable.com. County: Washita. ICA: OK0188.

TV Market Ranking: Below 100. Franchise award date: N.A. Franchise expiration date: N.A. Began: June 1, 1970.

Channel capacity: 41 (2-way capable). Channels available but not in use: N.A.

Basic Service

Subscribers: 157.

Programming (received off-air): KWET (P) Cheyenne; KAUT-TV (U), KFOR-TV (N), KOCB (W), KOCO-TV (A), KOKH-TV (F), KWTV (C) Oklahoma City; KSWO-TV (A) Wichita Falls-Lawton.

Programming (via satellite): WGN-TV (W) Chicago; American Movie Classics; CNN; Country Music TV; Discovery Channel; Disney Channel; ESPN; Fox Family Channel; Nashville Network; Nickelodeon; Sci-Fi Channel; TBS Superstation; Trinity Bcstg. Network; Turner Network TV; USA Network.

Fee: $35.00 installation; $28.95 monthly.

Pay Service 1

Pay Units: 35.

Programming (via satellite): HBO.

Fee: $9.95 monthly.

Equipment: Blonder-Tongue headend; Tocom amplifiers; Test traps; McCollough satellite antenna; McCollough satellite receivers.

Miles of plant: 6.0 (coaxial). Homes passed: 248. Total homes in franchised area: 390.

Region manager: Dave Walker. Chief technician: Roger Campbell. Marketing director: Jennifer Hauschild.

Ownership: Classic Cable (MSO).

DISNEY—Omni III Cable TV Inc., 226 S. 4th St., Jay, OK 74346. Phone: 918-253-4545. Fax: 918-253-3400. Counties: Delaware & Mayes. Also serves Jay. ICA: OK0216.

TV Market Ranking: Outside TV Markets. Franchise award date: N.A. Franchise expiration date: N.A. Began: March 1, 1983.

Channel capacity: 36. Channels available but not in use: 1.

Basic Service

Subscribers: 247.

Programming (received off-air): KDOR (T) Bartlesville; KOAM-TV (C), KSNF (N) Joplin-Pittsburg; KJRH (N), KOKI-TV (F), KOTV (C), KTUL (A) Tulsa.

Programming (via satellite): WGN-TV (W) Chicago; A & E; American Movie Classics; CNN; Cartoon Network; Country Music TV; Discovery Channel; ESPN; Fox Family Chan-

nel; Headline News; History Channel; Home Shopping Network; Nashville Network; Nickelodeon; QVC; TBS Superstation; The Weather Channel; Turner Classic Movies; Turner Network TV; USA Network.
Fee: $15.00 monthly.
Pay Service 1
Pay Units: 7.
Programming (via satellite): Cinemax.
Fee: $10.00 installation; $13.03 monthly.
Pay Service 2
Pay Units: 6.
Programming (via satellite): Disney Channel.
Fee: $10.00 installation; $13.03 monthly.
Pay Service 3
Pay Units: 22.
Programming (via satellite): HBO.
Fee: $10.00 installation; $13.03 monthly.
Pay Service 4
Pay Units: 6.
Programming (via satellite): Showtime.
Fee: $10.00 installation; $13.03 monthly.
Miles of plant: 7.0 (coaxial); 15.0 (fiber optic). Homes passed: 250.
Manager: Rex Brixey.
Ownership: Omni III Cable TV Inc.

DOVER—Classic Cable, Box 429, 605 N.W. 3rd St., Plainville, KS 67663-0429. Phones: 785-434-7620; 800-999-8876. Fax: 785-434-2614. Web site: http://www.classic-cable.com. County: Kingfisher. ICA: OK0250.
TV Market Ranking: Outside TV Markets. Franchise award date: N.A. Franchise expiration date: N.A. Began: July 1, 1988.
Channel capacity: 36 (2-way capable). Channels available but not in use: N.A.
Basic Service
Subscribers: 64.
Programming (received off-air): KAUT-TV (U), KETA (P), KFOR-TV (N), KOCB (W), KOCO-TV (A), KOKH-TV (F), KTBO-TV (T), KWTV (C) Oklahoma City.
Programming (via satellite): WGN-TV (W) Chicago; CNN; Discovery Channel; Disney Channel; ESPN; Fox Family Channel; Home & Garden Television; Nashville Network; Sci-Fi Channel; TBS Superstation; Turner Network TV; USA Network.
Current originations: Automated time-weather; public access; automated emergency alert; local news.
Fee: $35.00 installation; $27.95 monthly; $3.50 converter.
Pay Service 1
Pay Units: 15.
Programming (via satellite): Cinemax.
Fee: $9.95 monthly.
Pay Service 2
Pay Units: 24.
Programming (via satellite): HBO.
Fee: $9.95 monthly.
Local advertising: Yes. Available in character-generated programming. Rates: $35.00/Month; $10.00/Week; $2.00/Day. Local sales manager: Brenda Estep.
Equipment: Blonder-Tongue headend; Jerrold amplifiers; Jerrold set top converters; Drake satellite receivers.
Miles of plant: 3.2 (coaxial). Homes passed: 249. Total homes in franchised area: 249.
Region manager: Dave Walker. Chief technician: Jeff Smith. Marketing director: Jennifer Hauschild.
City fee: 3% of basic.
Ownership: Classic Cable (MSO).

DRUMMOND—Classic Cable, Box 429, 605 N.W. 3rd St., Plainville, KS 67663-0429. Phones: 785-434-7620; 800-999-8876. Fax: 785-434-2614. Web site: http://www.classic-cable.com. County: Garfield. ICA: OK0281.
TV Market Ranking: Outside TV Markets. Franchise award date: January 13, 1986. Franchise expiration date: N.A. Began: April 1, 1986.
Channel capacity: 36 (2-way capable). Channels available but not in use: N.A.
Basic Service
Subscribers: 56.
Programming (received off-air): KAUT-TV (U), KETA (P), KFOR-TV (N), KOCB (W), KOCO-TV (A), KOKH-TV (F), KTBO-TV (T), KWTV (C) Oklahoma City.
Programming (via satellite): WGN-TV (W) Chicago; CNN; Country Music TV; Discovery Channel; Disney Channel; ESPN; Fox Family Channel; Nashville Network; Sci-Fi Channel; TBS Superstation; Turner Network TV; USA Network.
Fee: $35.00 installation; $27.95 monthly; $3.50 converter.
Pay Service 1
Pay Units: 6.
Programming (via satellite): HBO.
Fee: $10.95 monthly.
Pay Service 2
Pay Units: 1.
Programming (via satellite): Showtime.
Fee: $9.95 monthly.
Local advertising: No.
Equipment: Cadco & Drake headend; Magnavox amplifiers; Jerrold set top converters; DX Engineering & Drake satellite receivers.
Miles of plant: 5.2 (coaxial). Homes passed: 204. Total homes in franchised area: 210.
Region manager: Dave Walker. Chief technician: Jeff Smith. Marketing director: Jennifer Hauschild.
City fee: 3% of basic gross.
Ownership: Classic Cable (MSO).

DRUMRIGHT—Peak Cablevision, 802 E. 6th St., Stillwater, OK 74074. Phone: 405-377-7785. Fax: 405-372-3980. County: Creek. ICA: OK0072.
TV Market Ranking: Outside TV Markets. Franchise award date: N.A. Franchise expiration date: December 4, 1999. Began: N.A.
Channel capacity: 44 (not 2-way capable). Channels available but not in use: None.
Basic Service
Subscribers: 856.
Programming (received off-air): KDOR (T) Bartlesville; KWTV (C) Oklahoma City; KTPX (X) Okmulgee; KJRH (N), KOED-TV (P), KOKI-TV (F), KOTV (C), KTUL (A), KWHB (I) Tulsa.
Programming (via satellite): WGN-TV (W) Chicago; Cartoon Network; Discovery Channel; FX; Home & Garden Television; QVC; TBS Superstation; TV Guide Channel; The Inspirational Network; The Weather Channel; VH1.
Fee: $37.50 installation; $11.58 monthly.
Expanded Basic Service
Subscribers: 810.
Programming (via satellite): A & E; American Movie Classics; Animal Planet; BET; Bravo; C-SPAN; CNBC; CNN; Country Music TV; Disney Channel; ESPN; ESPN 2; Fox Family Channel; Fox News Channel; Fox Sports Net Southwest; Headline News; Learning Channel; Lifetime; MTV; Nashville Network; Nickelodeon; Turner Network TV; USA Network.
Fee: $15.03 monthly.
Pay Service 1
Pay Units: 160.
Programming (via satellite): Cinemax.
Fee: $11.00 monthly.
Pay Service 2
Pay Units: 330.
Programming (via satellite): The New Encore.
Fee: $1.75 monthly.
Pay Service 3
Pay Units: 245.
Programming (via satellite): HBO.
Fee: $11.00 monthly.
Pay Service 4
Pay Units: 85.
Programming (via satellite): Showtime.
Fee: $11.00 monthly.
Pay Service 5
Pay Units: 270.
Programming (via satellite): Starz!
Fee: $6.75 monthly.
Miles of plant: 28.4 (coaxial). Homes passed: 1,757. Total homes in franchised area: 1,757.
Manager: Ted Ramsey. Chief technician: Joe Goertz.
Ownership: Peak Cablevision LLC (MSO). See Cable System Ownership.

DUKE—Rapid Cable, Box 6310, 310 Walnut Extension, Branson, MO 65615. Phones: 417-334-7897; 800-972-0962. Fax: 417-334-7899. E-mail: rcpcable@aol.com. County: Jackson. ICA: OK0224.
TV Market Ranking: Outside TV Markets. Franchise award date: October 4, 1982. Franchise expiration date: N.A. Began: December 1, 1985.
Channel capacity: 31 (2-way capable; not operating 2-way). Channels available but not in use: 5.
Basic Service
Subscribers: 107.
Programming (received off-air): KETA (P), KFOR-TV (N), KWTV (C) Oklahoma City; KJBO-LP (U) Wichita Falls; KFDX-TV (N), KJTL (F,U), KSWO-TV (A) Wichita Falls-Lawton.
Programming (via satellite): WGN-TV (W) Chicago; Animal Planet; CNN; Country Music TV; Discovery Channel; ESPN; Fox Family Channel; Home Shopping Network; Learning Channel; Nashville Network; Sci-Fi Channel; TBS Superstation; The Weather Channel; Turner Network TV; USA Network.
Fee: $29.95 installation; $22.95 monthly; $3.95 converter.
Pay Service 1
Pay Units: 17.
Programming (via satellite): HBO.
Fee: $10.00 monthly.
Pay Service 2
Pay Units: 9.
Programming (via satellite): Cinemax.
Fee: $9.00 monthly.
Pay Service 3
Pay Units: 8.
Programming (via satellite): Disney Channel.
Fee: $7.00 monthly.
Local advertising: No.
Miles of plant: 5.3 (coaxial). Homes passed: 217.
Manager: Belinda Murphy. Chief technician: Steve Rice. Program director: Beth Semptimphelter. Marketing director: Bill Fischer.
Ownership: Rapid Communications Partners LP (MSO); TS Communications Inc. (MSO).

DUNCAN—Cable One, Suite 30, Chisholm Mall, 1206 N. Hwy. 81, Duncan, OK 73533-1720. Phone: 580-252-0992. Fax: 580-252-9488. County: Stephens. Also serves Marlow. ICA: OK0013.
TV Market Ranking: Below 100. Franchise award date: January 1, 1970. Franchise expiration date: January 1, 2020. Began: July 1, 1971.
Channel capacity: 43 (not 2-way capable). Channels available but not in use: None.
Basic Service
Subscribers: 9,016.
Programming (received off-air): KETA (P), KFOR-TV (N), KOCO-TV (A), KOKH-TV (F), KWTV (C) Oklahoma City; KAUZ-TV (C), KFDX-TV (N), KJTL (F,U), KSWO-TV (A) Wichita Falls-Lawton; 6 FMs.
Programming (via satellite): C-SPAN; QVC; The Weather Channel; Trinity Bcstg. Network; Turner Classic Movies.
Current originations: Automated time-weather; public access; educational access; government access; religious access; automated emergency alert; local news.
Fee: $15.39 installation; $10.75 monthly; $1.60 converter.
Expanded Basic Service
Subscribers: 8,212.
Programming (via satellite): A & E; American Movie Classics; BET; CNBC; CNN; Comedy Central; Court TV; Discovery Channel; ESPN; fXM: Movies from Fox; Fox Family Channel; Fox Sports Net Southwest; Headline News; Learning Channel; Lifetime; MTV; Nashville Network; Nickelodeon; TBS Superstation; Turner Network TV; USA Network.
Fee: $15.39 installation; $17.00 monthly.
Pay Service 1
Pay Units: 845.
Programming (via satellite): Cinemax.
Fee: $25.00 installation; $13.00 monthly.
Pay Service 2
Pay Units: 1,649.
Programming (via satellite): HBO.
Fee: $25.00 installation; $13.59 monthly.
Pay Service 3
Pay Units: 198.
Programming (via satellite): Showtime.
Fee: $25.00 installation; $13.59 monthly.
Local advertising: Yes (insert only). Available in satellite distributed, locally originated, taped & automated programming. Rates: $50.00/Hour; $30.00/30 Minutes; $10.00/Minute; $6.00/30 Seconds. Local sales manager: Mickey Hawkins.
Program Guide: The Cable Guide.
Equipment: Jerrold, Monroe & Scientific-Atlanta headend; Jerrold & Magnavox amplifiers; Comm/Scope & Times Fiber cable; Sony cameras; JVC & Sony VTRs; Hamlin, Jerrold & Scientific-Atlanta set top converters; Jerrold addressable set top converters; Arcom & Pico traps; Scientific-Atlanta satellite antenna; Scientific-Atlanta satellite receivers.
Miles of plant: 219.4 (coaxial). Homes passed: 13,522. Total homes in franchised area: 14,330.
Manager: Adrian Loflin. Chief technician: Darrel Massie.
City fee: 3%-6% of gross.
Ownership: Cable One Inc. (MSO).

DURANT—CommuniComm Services, Box 597, 1501 W. Mississippi, Durant, OK 74702-0597. Phones: 580-924-2367; 800-752-4992. Fax: 580-924-5970. Counties: Bryan & Durant. Also serves Armstrong, Bryan County, Calera, Cartwright, Platter. ICA: OK0022.
TV Market Ranking: Below 100. Franchise award date: November 10, 1980. Franchise expiration date: November 10, 2005. Began: September 1, 1958.
Channel capacity: 77 (2-way capable; operating 2-way). Channels available but not in use: 15.
Basic Service
Subscribers: 4,862.
Programming (received off-air): KTEN (A,N,F) Ada; KXAS-TV (N), WFAA-TV (A) Dallas-Fort Worth; KETA (P), KWTV (C) Oklahoma City; KXII (C) Sherman; allband FM.

Programming (via satellite): WGN-TV (W) Chicago; A & E; American Movie Classics; Animal Planet; BET; C-SPAN; C-SPAN 2; CNBC; CNN; Cartoon Network; Country Music TV; Court TV; Discovery Channel; Disney Channel; E! Entertainment TV; ESPN; ESPN 2; ESPNews; FX; Fox Family Channel; Fox Sports Net Southwest; FoxNet; Headline News; History Channel; Home & Garden Television; Home Shopping Network; Learning Channel; Lifetime; MSNBC; MTV; Nashville Network; Nickelodeon; Outdoor Channel; Sci-Fi Channel; TBS Superstation; TV Guide Channel; The Weather Channel; Trinity Bcstg. Network; Turner Network TV; USA Network; VH1.

Current originations: Automated time-weather; religious access; automated emergency alert; local sports.

Fee: $49.95 installation; $34.95 monthly.

Pay Service 1

Pay Units: 505.

Programming (via satellite): Cinemax.

Fee: $9.95 monthly.

Pay Service 2

Pay Units: 780.

Programming (via satellite): HBO.

Fee: $12.95 monthly.

Pay Service 3

Pay Units: 270.

Programming (via satellite): Starz!

Fee: $9.95 monthly.

Pay-Per-View

Spice.

Fee: $2.95.

Local advertising: Yes (locally produced & insert). Available in satellite distributed programming. Local sales manager: Todd Tidwell.

Equipment: Scientific-Atlanta & Catel headend; Theta-Com amplifiers; Scientific-Atlanta cable; BEI character generator; Oak set top converters; Zenith modems; Pico & Eagle traps; Fort Worth Tower, Prodelin & Scientific-Atlanta satellite antenna; Scientific-Atlanta & Comtech satellite receivers.

Miles of plant: 150.0 (coaxial); 30.0 (fiber optic). Homes passed: 8,761. Total homes in franchised area: 9,000.

Manager: Danny R. Neumann. Chief technician: Dale Howard. Marketing director: Richard Curtis.

City fee: 3% of gross.

Ownership: James Cable Partners (MSO).

DUSTIN—Oklahoma Cablecomm, Box 970, Fort Gibson, OK 74434-0970. Phones: 918-478-2100; 800-783-5701. Fax: 918-478-2355. County: Hughes. ICA: OK0237.

TV Market Ranking: Outside TV Markets. Franchise award date: January 1, 1989. Franchise expiration date: January 1, 2014. Began: September 1, 1989.

Channel capacity: 45. Channels available but not in use: 30.

Basic Service

Subscribers: 74.

Programming (received off-air): KJRH (N), KOED-TV (P), KOKI-TV (F), KOTV (C), KTUL (A), KWHB (I) Tulsa.

Programming (via satellite): WGN-TV (W) Chicago; CNN; Country Music TV; Discovery Channel; ESPN; Fox Family Channel; Nashville Network; TBS Superstation; Turner Network TV; USA Network.

Fee: $40.00 installation; $22.00 monthly; $1.96 converter; $19.95 additional installation.

Pay Service 1

Pay Units: N.A.

Programming (via satellite): HBO.

Fee: $9.95 monthly.

Program Guide: TV Host.

Miles of plant: 6.0 (coaxial). Homes passed: 162.

Manager: Rick Wall. Chief technician: Leon Strain. Marketing & program director: Bruce Berkinshaw.

City fee: 5% of gross.

Ownership: Fanch Communications Inc. (MSO); Time Warner Cable (MSO). See Cable System Ownership.

EAKLY—Hinton CATV Co., Box 70, Hinton, OK 73047. Phone: 405-542-3211. Counties: Caddo & Washita. Also serves Colony. ICA: OK0282.

TV Market Ranking: Outside TV Markets. Franchise award date: N.A. Franchise expiration date: N.A. Began: July 1, 1983.

Channel capacity: 12. Channels available but not in use: N.A.

Basic Service

Subscribers: N.A.

Programming (received off-air): KAUT-TV (U), KETA (P), KFOR-TV (N), KOCB (W), KOCO-TV (A), KOKH-TV (F), KWTV (C) Oklahoma City.

Programming (via satellite): CNN; ESPN; TBS Superstation.

Fee: $25.00 installation; $8.50 monthly.

Pay Service 1

Pay Units: N.A.

Programming (via satellite): Cinemax; HBO.

Fee: $9.00 monthly (each).

Miles of plant: 3.1 (coaxial).

Manager: Kenneth Doughty.

Ownership: Hinton CATV Co. (MSO).

EARLSBORO—Falcon Cable Media, 707 W. Saratoga, Shawnee, OK 74801. Phone: 405-275-6923. Fax: 405-275-0276. County: Pottawatomie. ICA: OK0283.

TV Market Ranking: Outside TV Markets. Franchise award date: N.A. Franchise expiration date: N.A. Began: N.A.

Channel capacity: 54. Channels available but not in use: 34.

Basic Service

Subscribers: 74.

Programming (received off-air): KAUT-TV (U), KETA (P), KFOR-TV (N), KOCB (W), KOCO-TV (A), KOKH-TV (F), KTBO-TV (T), KWTV (C) Oklahoma City.

Programming (via satellite): WGN-TV (W) Chicago; CNN; ESPN; Fox Family Channel; Headline News; QVC.

Fee: $16.20 monthly.

Expanded Basic Service

Subscribers: 73.

Programming (via satellite): Discovery Channel; Sci-Fi Channel; TBS Superstation; USA Network.

Fee: $4.75 monthly.

Pay Service 1

Pay Units: 21.

Programming (via satellite): Cinemax.

Fee: $10.45 monthly.

Pay Service 2

Pay Units: 34.

Programming (via satellite): HBO.

Fee: $10.45 monthly.

Miles of plant: 8.0 (coaxial). Homes passed: 196.

Manager: Andrew Dearth.

Franchise fee: 5% of gross.

Ownership: Falcon Communications LP (MSO), joint venture formed September 30, 1998. See Cable System Ownership.

EDMOND—Edmond Cablevision, 820 W. Irish Lane, Edmond, OK 73003. Phone: 405-348-5750. Fax: 405-348-8059. County: Oklahoma. ICA: OK0007.

TV Market Ranking: 39. Franchise award date: October 1, 1976. Franchise expiration date: May 1, 2000. Began: November 14, 1978.

Channel capacity: 69 (2-way capable; operating 2-way). Channels available but not in use: 8.

Basic Service

Subscribers: 15,941.

Programming (received off-air): KAUT-TV (U), KETA (P), KFOR-TV (N), KOCB (W), KOCO-TV (A), KOKH-TV (F), KSBI (I), KTBO-TV (T), KWTV (C) Oklahoma City; 16 FMs.

Programming (via satellite): A & E; American Movie Classics; BET; C-SPAN; C-SPAN 2; CNBC; Discovery Channel; E! Entertainment TV; ESPN; Fox Sports Net Southwest; Home & Garden Television; Home Shopping Network; Learning Channel; Lifetime; MTV; Nick at Nite; Nickelodeon; QVC; TV Food Network; TV Guide Channel; TV Guide Sneak Prevue; The Weather Channel; USA Network; Univision; VH1.

Current originations: Public access; educational access; government access; leased access; automated emergency alert; local news; local sports.

Fee: $14.27 installation; $19.60 monthly; $3.00 converter.

Expanded Basic Service

Subscribers: 15,347.

Programming (via satellite): WGN-TV (W) Chicago; CNN; Fox Family Channel; Headline News; Nashville Network; TBS Superstation; Turner Network TV.

Fee: $4.24 monthly.

Expanded Basic Service 2

Subscribers: 4,311.

Programming (via satellite): Bravo; Cartoon Network; Comedy Central; Country Music TV; Court TV; ESPN 2; History Channel; Sci-Fi Channel; Travel Channel; Turner Classic Movies.

Fee: $6.00 monthly.

Pay Service 1

Pay Units: 3,162.

Programming (via satellite): Cinemax.

Fee: $11.00 monthly.

Pay Service 2

Pay Units: 2,463.

Programming (via satellite): Disney Channel.

Fee: $7.95 monthly.

Pay Service 3

Pay Units: 5,543.

Programming (via satellite): HBO.

Fee: $11.00 monthly.

Pay Service 4

Pay Units: 3,329.

Programming (via satellite): Showtime.

Fee: $11.00 monthly.

Pay Service 5

Pay Units: 74.

Programming (via satellite): Music Choice.

Fee: $7.95 monthly.

Pay Service 6

Pay Units: 187.

Programming (via satellite): Golf Channel.

Fee: $6.95 monthly.

Pay-Per-View

Addressable homes: 5,059.

Action Pay-Per-View.

Local advertising: Yes. Available in satellite distributed & taped programming. Rates: $800.00/Hour; $400.00/30 Minutes; $160.00/Minute; $80.00/30 Seconds. Local sales manager: Mark Kanter. Regional interconnect: Oklahoma Cable Advertising Interconnect.

Program Guide: The Cable Guide.

Equipment: Scientific-Atlanta headend; GTE Sylvania amplifiers; Comm/Scope cable; Jerrold fiber optic cable; Panasonic cameras; Panasonic VTRs; Gardiner character generator; GTE Sylvania, Jerrold & Oak set top converters; Scientific-Atlanta addressable set top converters; Eagle traps; Scientific-Atlanta addressable traps; Scientific-Atlanta satellite antenna.

Miles of plant: 372.6 (coaxial); 61.0 (fiber optic). Homes passed: 26,185.

Manager: Terry Gorsuch. Chief technician: Tom Heddlesten. Marketing director: Jim Back. Customer service manager: Charitta Shelton.

City fee: 3% of gross.

Ownership: Multimedia Cablevision Inc. (MSO). See Cable System Ownership.

EL RENO—El Reno Cablevision Inc., 115 W. Wade, El Reno, OK 73036. Phone: 405-262-7217. Fax: 405-348-8059. County: Canadian. ICA: OK0030.

TV Market Ranking: 39. Franchise award date: August 1, 1978. Franchise expiration date: August 10, 1998. Began: May 1, 1974.

Channel capacity: 38 (2-way capable; operating 2-way). Channels available but not in use: 3.

Basic Service

Subscribers: 3,684.

Programming (received off-air): KAUT-TV (U), KETA (P), KFOR-TV (N), KOCB (W), KOCO-TV (A), KOKH-TV (F), KSBI (I), KTBO-TV (T), KWTV (C) Oklahoma City; 10 FMs.

Programming (via satellite): A & E; American Movie Classics; C-SPAN; CNBC; Discovery Channel; ESPN; Home Shopping Network; Learning Channel; Lifetime; MTV; Nickelodeon; TV Guide Channel; The Weather Channel; USA Network; VH1.

Current originations: Public access; government access; automated emergency alert.

Planned originations: Educational access; local news.

Fee: $16.71 installation; $17.43 monthly.

Expanded Basic Service

Subscribers: 3,622.

Programming (via satellite): WGN-TV (W) Chicago; CNN; Fox Family Channel; Headline News; Nashville Network; TBS Superstation; Turner Network TV.

Fee: $3.59 monthly.

Pay Service 1

Pay Units: 725.

Programming (via satellite): Cinemax.

Fee: $11.00 monthly.

Pay Service 2

Pay Units: 310.

Programming (via satellite): Disney Channel.

Fee: $7.95 monthly.

Pay Service 3

Pay Units: 1,086.

Programming (via satellite): HBO.

Fee: $11.00 monthly.

Pay Service 4

Pay Units: 821.

Programming (via satellite): Showtime.

Fee: $11.00 monthly.

Pay-Per-View

Addressable homes: 101.

Special events.

Fee: $1.95.

Local advertising: Yes. Available in satellite distributed programming. Rates: $800.00/Hour; $400.00/30 Minutes; $160.00/Minute; $80.00/30 Seconds. Local sales manager: Mark Kanter. Regional interconnect: Oklahoma Cable Advertising Interconnect.

Program Guide: The Cable Guide.

Equipment: Scientific-Atlanta headend; Texscan amplifiers; Comm/Scope cable; Oak, Jerrold & RCA set top converters; Eagle traps; Scientific-Atlanta satellite antenna.

Miles of plant: 82.4 (coaxial). Homes passed: 6,433.

Manager: Terry Gorsuch. Chief technician: Kurtis Gill. Marketing director: Jim Back. Customer service manager: Charitta Shelton.

City fee: 3% of gross.
Ownership: Multimedia Cablevision Inc. (MSO). See Cable System Ownership.

ELDORADO—Rapid Cable, Box 6310, 310 Walnut Extension, Branson, MO 65615-6310. Phones: 417-334-7897; 800-972-0962. Fax: 417-334-7899. E-mail: rcpcable@aol.com. County: Jackson. ICA: OK0383.
TV Market Ranking: Outside TV Markets. Franchise award date: March 21, 1972. Franchise expiration date: March 21, 2002. Began: N.A.
Channel capacity: 22 (2-way capable; not operating 2-way). Channels available but not in use: 4.
Basic Service
Subscribers: 201.
Programming (received off-air): KETA (P), KFOR-TV (N), KOKH-TV (F), KWTV (C) Oklahoma City; KAUZ-TV (C), KFDX-TV (N), KJTL (F,U), KSWO-TV (A) Wichita Falls-Lawton.
Programming (via satellite): WGN-TV (W) Chicago; CNN; Country Music TV; Discovery Channel; ESPN; Fox Family Channel; Fox News Channel; Home Shopping Network 2; Learning Channel; Nashville Network; TBS Superstation; The Weather Channel; Turner Network TV; USA Network.
Fee: $29.95 installation; $20.95 monthly; $2.95 converter.
Pay Service 1
Pay Units: 13.
Programming (via satellite): Cinemax.
Fee: $9.00 monthly.
Pay Service 2
Pay Units: 20.
Programming (via satellite): Disney Channel.
Fee: $7.00 monthly.
Pay Service 3
Pay Units: 17.
Programming (via satellite): HBO.
Fee: $10.00 monthly.
Miles of plant: 5.0 (coaxial). Homes passed: 336.
Manager: Belinda Murphy. Chief technician: Steve Rice. Program director: Beth Semptimphelter. Marketing director: Bill Fischer.
Ownership: Rapid Communications Partners LP (MSO).

ELGIN—Classic Cable, Box 429, 605 N.W. 3rd St., Plainville, KS 67663-0429. Phones: 785-434-7620; 800-999-8876. Fax: 785-434-2614. Web site: http://www.classic-cable.com.
Counties: Caddo & Comanche. Also serves Cyril, Fletcher. ICA: OK0284.
TV Market Ranking: Below 100. Franchise award date: January 6, 1977. Franchise expiration date: N.A. Began: N.A.
Channel capacity: 22 (2-way capable). Channels available but not in use: N.A.
Basic Service
Subscribers: 526.
Programming (received off-air): KAUT-TV (U), KETA (P), KFOR-TV (N), KOCB (W), KOCO-TV (A), KOKH-TV (F), KTBO-TV (T), KWTV (C) Oklahoma City; KFDX-TV (N), KJTL (F,U), KSWO-TV (A) Wichita Falls-Lawton.
Programming (via satellite): WGN-TV (W) Chicago; A & E; CNN; Country Music TV; Discovery Channel; Disney Channel; ESPN; Fox Family Channel; Fox Sports Net Southwest; History Channel; Nashville Network; Nick at Nite's TV Land; Nickelodeon; QVC; TBS Superstation; The Weather Channel; Turner Network TV; USA Network.
Fee: $35.00 installation; $24.95 monthly.
Pay Service 1
Pay Units: 107.
Programming (via satellite): HBO.
Fee: $35.00 installation; $10.95 monthly.
Pay Service 2
Pay Units: 45.
Programming (via satellite): Showtime.
Fee: $35.00 installation; $9.95 monthly.
Local advertising: No.
Equipment: Motorola headend.
Miles of plant: 35.0 (coaxial). Homes passed: 1,044.
Manager: Dave Walker. Chief technician: Roger Campbell. Marketing director: Jennifer Hauschild.
City fee: 4% of gross.
Ownership: Classic Cable (MSO).

ELK CITY—Cable One, Box 863, 210 N. Oklahoma, Elk City, OK 73644. Phone: 580-225-3244. Fax: 580-225-5011. County: Beckham. ICA: OK0032.
TV Market Ranking: Below 100. Franchise award date: March 1, 1953. Franchise expiration date: July 1, 2000. Began: March 1, 1953.
Channel capacity: 78 (2-way capable). Channels available but not in use: 17.
Basic Service
Subscribers: 4,150.
Programming (received off-air): KWET (P) Cheyenne; K52AN (I) Elk City; KFOR-TV (N), KOCO-TV (A), KOKH-TV (F), KWTV (C) Oklahoma City.
Programming (via satellite): WGN-TV (W) Chicago; C-SPAN; C-SPAN 2; QVC; TBS Superstation.
Current originations: Automated time-weather; automated emergency alert.
Fee: $35.00 installation (aerial), $60.00 (underground); $9.02 monthly; $3.25 converter; $20.00 additional installation.
Expanded Basic Service
Subscribers: 3,900.
Programming (via satellite): A & E; American Movie Classics; BET; CNBC; CNN; Cartoon Network; Country Music TV; Discovery Channel; Disney Channel; E! Entertainment TV; ESPN; ESPN 2; FX; Fox Family Channel; Fox Sports Net Southwest; Gems Television; Headline News; History Channel; Home & Garden Television; Home Shopping Network; Learning Channel; Lifetime; MSNBC; MTV; Nashville Network; Nick at Nite's TV Land; Nickelodeon; Sci-Fi Channel; TV Food Network; TV Guide Channel; The Weather Channel; Trinity Bcstg. Network; Turner Classic Movies; Turner Network TV; USA Network; VH1.
Fee: $35.00 installation; $30.00 monthly.
Pay Service 1
Pay Units: 423.
Programming (via satellite): Cinemax (multiplexed); HBO (multiplexed).
Fee: N.A.
Pay Service 2
Pay Units: 341.
Programming (via satellite): Showtime (multiplexed); The Movie Channel.
Fee: N.A.
Pay-Per-View
Addressable homes: 900.
Viewer's Choice.
Fee: $3.95.
Local advertising: Yes. Available in satellite distributed programming. Local sales manager: Joe Englebredt.
Equipment: Scientific-Atlanta headend; Magnavox amplifiers; Comm/Scope cable.
Miles of plant: 100.0 (coaxial). Homes passed: 4,700. Total homes in franchised area: 5,109.
Manager: Geary Stills. Chief technician: Donnie Davis.
City fee: 5% of gross.
Ownership: Cable One Inc. (MSO).

ELK CREEK—Quality Entertainment Corp., Suite 512, Central Mall Plaza, Fort Smith, AR 72903. Phone: 501-452-1998. Fax: 501-452-6430. County: Cherokee. ICA: OK0364.
TV Market Ranking: Outside TV Markets. Franchise award date: N.A. Franchise expiration date: N.A. Began: N.A.
Channel capacity: 42 (not 2-way capable). Channels available but not in use: 8.
Basic Service
Subscribers: 135.
Programming (received off-air): KJRH (N), KOED-TV (P), KOKI-TV (F), KOTV (C), KTFO (U), KTUL (A) Tulsa.
Programming (via satellite): WGN-TV (W) Chicago; American Movie Classics; Animal Planet; CNN; Country Music TV; Discovery Channel; Disney Channel; ESPN; Fox Family Channel; Learning Channel; Military Channel; Nashville Network; Nick at Nite's TV Land; Odyssey; QVC; TBS Superstation; The Weather Channel; Travel Channel; Turner Network TV; USA Network.
Fee: $40.00 installation; $25.00 monthly.
Pay Service 1
Pay Units: N.A.
Programming (via satellite): HBO; Showtime.
Fee: $12.00 monthly.
Miles of plant: 18.0 (coaxial).
Manager: Brent Lewis.
Ownership: Quality Entertainment Corp. (MSO).

ELMORE CITY—Harmon Cable Communications, Box 340, 1218 W. Broadway, Sulphur, OK 73086. Phones: 580-622-2575; 800-858-1228. County: Garvin. ICA: OK0217.
TV Market Ranking: Outside TV Markets. Franchise award date: N.A. Franchise expiration date: N.A. Began: October 1, 1987.
Channel capacity: 61 (not 2-way capable). Channels available but not in use: N.A.
Basic Service
Subscribers: 220.
Programming (received off-air): KTEN (A,N,F) Ada; KAUT-TV (U), KETA (P), KFOR-TV (N), KOCB (W), KOCO-TV (A), KOKH-TV (F), KTBO-TV (T), KWTV (C) Oklahoma City; KXII (C) Sherman.
Programming (via satellite): WGN-TV (W) Chicago; CNN; Cartoon Network; Country Music TV; Discovery Channel; ESPN; History Channel; Home & Garden Television; Learning Channel; Nashville Network; Nick at Nite's TV Land; Nickelodeon; QVC; TBS Superstation; The Weather Channel; Turner Classic Movies; Turner Network TV; USA Network.
Fee: $27.50 installation (aerial), $40.00 (underground); $22.80 monthly; $1.10 converter; $10.00 additional installation.
Pay Service 1
Pay Units: N.A.
Programming (via satellite): Disney Channel; HBO; Showtime.
Fee: $10.00 monthly (each).
Homes passed: 250.
Manager: Nick Schwake. Chief technician: Jerry Lancaster.
Ownership: Harmon Cable Communications (MSO).

ENID—Peak Cablevision, 131 E. Maine, Enid, OK 73701. Phone: 580-237-7373. Fax: 580-242-4801. E-mail: jrosson.peakonline.com. Web site: http://www.enid.home2u.com. County: Garfield. Also serves Garfield County, North Enid, Vance AFB. ICA: OK0006.
TV Market Ranking: Outside TV Markets. Franchise award date: N.A. Franchise expiration date: N.A. Began: March 1, 1966.
Channel capacity: 111 (2-way capable; operating 2-way). Channels available but not in use: 50.
Basic Service
Subscribers: 14,870.
Programming (received off-air): KAUT-TV (U), KETA (P), KFOR-TV (N), KOCB (W), KOCO-TV (A), KOKH-TV (F), KOPX (X), KTBO-TV (T), KWTV (C) Oklahoma City.
Programming (via satellite): WGN-TV (W) Chicago; A & E; American Movie Classics; Animal Planet; BET; C-SPAN; CNBC; CNN; Cartoon Network; Comedy Central; Country Music TV; Discovery Channel; Disney Channel; ESPN 2; Fox Family Channel; Headline News; History Channel; Home & Garden Television; Home Shopping Network; Learning Channel; Lifetime; MTV; Nashville Network; Nickelodeon; Odyssey; QVC; Sci-Fi Channel; TBS Superstation; The Weather Channel; VH1.
Current originations: Automated time-weather; government access; local news.
Fee: $24.95 installation; $11.70 monthly; $1.50 converter; $12.50 additional installation.
Expanded Basic Service
Subscribers: 14,455.
Programming (via satellite): American Movie Classics; ESPN; Fox Sports Net Southwest; Turner Network TV; USA Network.
Fee: $14.95 monthly.
Pay Service 1
Pay Units: 1,524.
Programming (via satellite): Cinemax.
Fee: $13.00 monthly.
Pay Service 2
Pay Units: 6,552.
Programming (via satellite): The New Encore.
Fee: $1.67 monthly.
Pay Service 3
Pay Units: 3,720.
Programming (via satellite): HBO.
Fee: $12.95 installation; $13.00 monthly.
Pay Service 4
Pay Units: 868.
Programming (via satellite): Showtime.
Fee: $13.50 monthly.
Pay-Per-View
Addressable homes: 1,800.
Viewer's Choice.
Local advertising: Yes. Rates: $30.00/Hour; $18.00/30 Minutes; $12.00/15 Minutes; $7.50/5 Minutes; $6.00/Minute; $3.60/30 Seconds.
Program Guide: The Cable Guide.
Equipment: Jerrold & Scientific-Atlanta headend; Jerrold amplifiers; Times Fiber cable.
Miles of plant: 213.8 (coaxial); 55.0 (fiber optic). Homes passed: 22,706. Total homes in franchised area: 22,706.
Manager: Johnny Rosson.
City fee: 5% of gross.
Ownership: Peak Cablevision LLC (MSO). See Cable System Ownership.

ERICK—Classic Cable, Box 429, 605 N.W. 3rd St., Plainville, KS 67663-0429. Phones: 785-434-7620; 800-999-8876. Fax: 785-434-2614. Web site: http://www.classic-cable.com. County: Beckham. ICA: OK0150.
TV Market Ranking: Below 100. Franchise award date: N.A. Franchise expiration date: N.A. Began: January 1, 1955.
Channel capacity: 41 (2-way capable). Channels available but not in use: N.A.
Basic Service
Subscribers: 414; Commercial subscribers: 61.
Programming (received off-air): KVII-TV (A) Amarillo; KETA (P), KFOR-TV (N), KOCO-

TV (A), KOKH-TV (F), KWTV (C) Oklahoma City.
Programming (via microwave): KFOR-TV (N), KWTV (C) Oklahoma City.
Programming (via satellite): WGN-TV (W) Chicago; American Movie Classics; CNN; Cartoon Network; Country Music TV; Discovery Channel; Disney Channel; E! Entertainment TV; ESPN; Fox Family Channel; Goodlife TV Network; Headline News; History Channel; Home & Garden Television; Learning Channel; Lifetime; Nashville Network; Nick at Nite's TV Land; Nickelodeon; Outdoor Channel; QVC; TBS Superstation; The Weather Channel; Trinity Bcstg. Network; Turner Network TV; USA Network.
Current originations: Automated time-weather.
Fee: $35.00 installation; $27.95 monthly; $2.00 converter; $20.00 additional installation.
Pay Service 1
Pay Units: 24.
Programming (via satellite): Showtime.
Fee: $20.00 installation; $9.95 monthly.
Pay Service 2
Pay Units: 85.
Programming (via satellite): HBO.
Fee: $20.00 installation; $10.95 monthly.
Local advertising: No.
Equipment: Ameco headend; Ameco amplifiers; Belden cable; Jerrold set top converters; Eagle traps; Scientific-Atlanta satellite receivers.
Miles of plant: 12.8 (coaxial). Homes passed: 614.
Manager: Dave Walker. Chief technician: Roger Campbell. Marketing director: Jennifer Hauschild.
City fee: None.
Ownership: Classic Cable (MSO).

EUFAULA—Classic Cable, Box 429, 605 N.W. 3rd St., Plainville, KS 67663-0429. Phones: 785-434-7620; 800-999-8876. Fax: 785-434-2614. Web site: http://www.classic-cable.com. County: McIntosh. Also serves Checotah, McIntosh County. ICA: OK0054.
TV Market Ranking: Outside TV Markets. Franchise award date: N.A. Franchise expiration date: February 1, 2004. Began: July 1, 1973.
Channel capacity: 41 (2-way capable). Channels available but not in use: 3.
Basic Service
Subscribers: 1,744; Commercial subscribers: 73.
Programming (received off-air): KTPX (X) Okmulgee; KJRH (N), KOED-TV (P), KOKI-TV (F), KOTV (C), KTFO (U), KTUL (A), KWHB (I), KWMJ (I) Tulsa.
Programming (via satellite): WGN-TV (W) Chicago; A & E; American Movie Classics; BET; C-SPAN; CNN; Country Music TV; Discovery Channel; Disney Channel; ESPN; Electronic Program Guide Jr.; Fox Family Channel; Fox Sports Net Southwest; Headline News; History Channel; Learning Channel; Lifetime; Nashville Network; Nick at Nite's TV Land; Nickelodeon; Outdoor Channel; QVC; TBS Superstation; The Weather Channel; Turner Network TV; USA Network.
Current originations: Automated emergency alert.
Fee: $35.00 installation; $28.95 monthly; $1.11 converter.
Commercial fee: $22.05 monthly.
Pay Service 1
Pay Units: 209.
Programming (via satellite): HBO.
Fee: $10.95 monthly.
Pay Service 2
Pay Units: 218.
Programming (via satellite): The Movie Channel.
Fee: $5.95 monthly.
Pay Service 3
Pay Units: 228.
Programming (via satellite): Showtime.
Fee: $9.95 monthly.
Local advertising: No.
Equipment: Blonder-Tongue & Scientific-Atlanta headend; Magnavox amplifiers; Times Fiber cable; Atari character generator; Jerrold & Standard Components set top converters; AFC, Prodelin & Scientific-Atlanta satellite antenna; Standard Communications satellite receivers.
Miles of plant: 75.0 (coaxial). Homes passed: 3,482. Total homes in franchised area: 3,800.
Manager: Dave Walker. Chief technician: Carl Miller.
City fee: 3% of gross.
Ownership: Classic Cable (MSO).

FAIRFAX—Cim Tel Cable Inc., Box 266, 101 Cimarron St., Mannford, OK 74044. Phone: 918-865-3314. County: Osage. ICA: OK0133.
TV Market Ranking: Outside TV Markets. Franchise award date: N.A. Franchise expiration date: N.A. Began: December 20, 1981.
Channel capacity: 35. Channels available but not in use: N.A.
Basic Service
Subscribers: N.A.
Programming (received off-air): KJRH (N), KOED-TV (P), KOKI-TV (F), KOTV (C), KTUL (A) Tulsa.
Programming (via satellite): WGN-TV (W) Chicago; CNN; ESPN; Fox Family Channel; TBS Superstation.
Fee: $15.00 installation; $9.95 monthly.
Pay Service 1
Pay Units: N.A.
Programming (via satellite): Cinemax; HBO.
Fee: $9.50 monthly (each).
Equipment: Scientific-Atlanta headend; GTE Sylvania amplifiers; Comm/Scope cable; Anixter-Mark satellite antenna.
Miles of plant: 12.0 (coaxial). Homes passed: 708.
City fee: 3% of gross.
Ownership: Cim Tel Cable Inc. (MSO).

FAIRVIEW—Classic Cable, Box 429, 605 N.W. 3rd St., Plainville, KS 67663-0429. Phones: 785-434-7620; 800-999-8876. Fax: 785-434-2614. Web site: http://www.classic-cable.com. County: Major. ICA: OK0089.
TV Market Ranking: Outside TV Markets. Franchise award date: N.A. Franchise expiration date: N.A. Began: July 1, 1967.
Channel capacity: 61 (2-way capable). Channels available but not in use: N.A.
Basic Service
Subscribers: 907; Commercial subscribers: 207.
Programming (received off-air): KAUT-TV (U), KETA (P), KFOR-TV (N), KOCB (W), KOCO-TV (A), KOKH-TV (F), KTBO-TV (T), KWTV (C) Oklahoma City; KOMI-LP (I) Woodward.
Programming (via satellite): WGN-TV (W) Chicago; A & E; American Movie Classics; C-SPAN; CNN; Country Music TV; Court TV; Discovery Channel; Disney Channel; E! Entertainment TV; ESPN; Fox Family Channel; Fox News Channel; Fox Sports Net Southwest; Headline News; History Channel; Home & Garden Television; Learning Channel; Lifetime; MTV; Nashville Network; Nick at Nite's TV Land; Nickelodeon; Outdoor Channel; QVC; Sci-Fi Channel; TBS Superstation; The Weather Channel; Turner Network TV; USA Network; VH1.
Current originations: Automated time-weather; automated emergency alert.
Fee: $35.00 installation; $29.95 monthly; $3.50 converter; $15.00 additional installation.
Pay Service 1
Pay Units: 132.
Programming (via satellite): HBO.
Fee: $10.95 monthly.
Pay Service 2
Pay Units: 42.
Programming (via satellite): Showtime.
Fee: $9.95 monthly.
Pay Service 3
Pay Units: 35.
Programming (via satellite): Cinemax.
Fee: $9.95 monthly.
Pay Service 4
Pay Units: 46.
Programming (via satellite): The Movie Channel.
Fee: $5.95 monthly.
Local advertising: Yes. Available in character-generated programming. Rates: $35.00/Month; $10.00/Week; $2.00/Day.
Equipment: Blonder-Tongue, Drake & Scientific-Atlanta headend; Scientific-Atlanta amplifiers; Comm/Scope cable; Jerrold set top converters; M/A-Com & Prodelin satellite antenna; Automation Techniques, ICM & Microdyne satellite receivers.
Miles of plant: 30.0 (coaxial). Homes passed: 1,234. Total homes in franchised area: 1,308.
Manager: Dave Walker. Chief technician: Jeff Smith. Marketing director: Jennifer Hauschild.
City fee: 3% of basic.
Ownership: Classic Cable (MSO).

FARGO—Classic Cable, Box 429, 605 N.W. 3rd St., Plainville, KS 67663-0429. Phones: 785-434-7620; 800-999-8876. Fax: 785-434-2614. Web site: http://www.classic-cable.com. County: Ellis. ICA: OK0345.
TV Market Ranking: Outside TV Markets. Franchise award date: N.A. Franchise expiration date: N.A. Began: May 1, 1991.
Channel capacity: 41 (2-way capable). Channels available but not in use: N.A.
Basic Service
Subscribers: 44.
Programming (received off-air): KWET (P) Cheyenne; KFOR-TV (N), KOCB (W), KOCO-TV (A), KOKH-TV (F), KWTV (C) Oklahoma City; KOMI-LP (I) Woodward.
Programming (via satellite): WGN-TV (W) Chicago; American Movie Classics; CNN; Country Music TV; Discovery Channel; Disney Channel; ESPN; Fox Family Channel; Nashville Network; TBS Superstation; The Weather Channel; Trinity Bcstg. Network; Turner Network TV; USA Network.
Fee: $35.00 installation; $27.95 monthly.
Pay Service 1
Pay Units: 3.
Programming (via satellite): HBO.
Fee: $10.95 monthly.
Pay Service 2
Pay Units: 2.
Programming (via satellite): Showtime.
Fee: $9.95 monthly.
Miles of plant: 4.5 (coaxial). Homes passed: 103.
Manager: Dave Walker. Chief technician: Jeff Smith. Marketing director: Jennifer Hauschild.
Ownership: Classic Cable (MSO).

FORT COBB—Rapid Cable, Box 6310, 310 Walnut Extension, Branson, MO 65615. Phones: 417-334-7897; 800-972-0962. Fax: 417-334-7899. E-mail: rcpcable@aol.com. County: Caddo. ICA: OK0285.
TV Market Ranking: Outside TV Markets. Franchise award date: June 2, 1980. Franchise expiration date: June 2, 2005. Began: N.A.
Channel capacity: 23 (2-way capable; not operating 2-way). Channels available but not in use: None.
Basic Service
Subscribers: 150.
Programming (received off-air): KETA (P), KFOR-TV (N), KOCB (W), KOCO-TV (A), KOKH-TV (F), KWTV (C) Oklahoma City; KSWO-TV (A) Wichita Falls-Lawton.
Programming (via satellite): WGN-TV (W) Chicago; CNN; Country Music TV; Discovery Channel; ESPN; Fox Family Channel; Nashville Network; TBS Superstation; The Weather Channel; Trinity Bcstg. Network; USA Network.
Fee: $29.95 installation; $22.95 monthly; $2.95 converter.
Pay Service 1
Pay Units: 19.
Programming (via satellite): Cinemax.
Fee: $9.00 monthly.
Pay Service 2
Pay Units: 24.
Programming (via satellite): HBO.
Fee: $10.00 monthly.
Pay Service 3
Pay Units: 18.
Programming (via satellite): Disney Channel.
Fee: $7.00 monthly.
Miles of plant: 5.8 (coaxial). Homes passed: 357.
Manager: Belinda Murphy. Chief technician: Steve Rice. Program director: Beth Semptimphelter. Marketing director: Bill Fischer.
Ownership: Rapid Communications Partners LP (MSO); TS Communications Inc. (MSO).

FORT GIBSON—Oklahoma Cablecomm, Box 970, Fort Gibson, OK 74434-0970. Phones: 918-478-2100; 800-955-7028. Fax: 918-478-2355. County: Muskogee. ICA: OK0090.
TV Market Ranking: Outside TV Markets. Franchise award date: November 1, 1971. Franchise expiration date: N.A. Began: April 1, 1977.
Channel capacity: 42 (not 2-way capable). Channels available but not in use: 3.
Basic Service
Subscribers: 1,150; Commercial subscribers: 35.
Programming (received off-air): KRSC-TV (E) Claremore; KJRH (N), KOED-TV (P), KOKI-TV (F), KOTV (C), KTFO (U), KTUL (A), KWHB (I) Tulsa.
Programming (via satellite): WGN-TV (W) Chicago; A & E; American Movie Classics; C-SPAN; CNBC; CNN; Cartoon Network; Comedy Central; Country Music TV; Court TV; Discovery Channel; Disney Channel; E! Entertainment TV; ESPN; ESPN 2; FX; Fox Family Channel; Fox Sports Net Southwest; Headline News; History Channel; Home & Garden Television; Home Shopping Network; Learning Channel; Lifetime; MTV; Nashville Network; Nickelodeon; Outdoor Channel; QVC; Sci-Fi Channel; TBS Superstation; The Weather Channel; Turner Classic Movies; Turner Network TV; USA Network.
Fee: $40.00 installation; $24.95 monthly; $1.96 converter; $19.95 additional installation.
Pay Service 1
Pay Units: 70.
Programming (via satellite): Cinemax.
Fee: $9.95 monthly.
Pay Service 2
Pay Units: 171.
Programming (via satellite): HBO.
Fee: $9.95 monthly.

Pay Service 3
Pay Units: 65.
Programming (via satellite): Showtime.
Fee: $9.95 monthly.
Local advertising: No.
Program Guide: TV Host.
Equipment: Triple Crown headend; Jerrold amplifiers; Comm/Scope cable; Harris & Scientific-Atlanta satellite antenna; Scientific-Atlanta satellite receivers.
Miles of plant: 21.0 (coaxial). Additional miles planned: 15.0 (coaxial). Homes passed: 1,404.
Manager: Rick Wall. Chief technician: Leon Strain. Marketing & program director: Bruce Berkinshaw.
City fee: 3% of basic gross.
Ownership: Fanch Communications Inc. (MSO); Time Warner Cable (MSO). See Cable System Ownership.

FORT SILL—Classic Cable, Box 33278, 4636 Blair St., Fort Sill, OK 73503. Phone: 580-248-9954. Fax: 580-355-9114. County: Comanche. ICA: OK0031.
TV Market Ranking: Below 100. Franchise award date: January 1, 1980. Franchise expiration date: July 1, 2000. Began: September 1, 1980.
Channel capacity: 38 (not 2-way capable). Channels available but not in use: None.
Basic Service
Subscribers: 1,778.
Programming (received off-air): KETA (P), KWTV (C) Oklahoma City; KAUZ-TV (C), KFDX-TV (N), KJTL (F,U), KSWO-TV (A) Wichita Falls-Lawton.
Programming (via satellite): CNN; Disney Channel; FX; Headline News; Odyssey; Turner Classic Movies; Univision.
Current originations: Automated time-weather; public access; educational access; government access.
Fee: $16.08 installation; $9.02 monthly; $1.43 converter; $16.08 additional installation.
Expanded Basic Service
Subscribers: 1,713.
Programming (via satellite): WGN-TV (W) Chicago; A & E; American Movie Classics; BET; C-SPAN; Discovery Channel; Disney Channel; ESPN; Fox Family Channel; Fox News Channel; Fox Sports Net Southwest; Learning Channel; Lifetime; MTV; Nashville Network; Nickelodeon; TBS Superstation; The Weather Channel; Turner Network TV; USA Network.
Fee: $15.50 monthly.
Pay Service 1
Pay Units: 309.
Programming (via satellite): Cinemax.
Fee: N.A.
Pay Service 2
Pay Units: 709.
Programming (via satellite): HBO.
Fee: N.A.
Pay Service 3
Pay Units: 262.
Programming (via satellite): Showtime.
Fee: N.A.
Pay Service 4
Pay Units: 168.
Programming (via satellite): The Movie Channel.
Fee: N.A.
Pay Service 5
Pay Units: 773.
Programming (via satellite): Turner Classic Movies.
Fee: N.A.
Pay-Per-View
Fee: N.A.
Pay-per-view manager: Sue Whitaker.
Local advertising: Yes. Local sales manager: Debbi Jenson.
Program Guide: The Cable Guide.
Equipment: RCA headend; RCA amplifiers; Comm/Scope cable; Atari character generator; Regal set top converters; Jerrold addressable set top converters; Arcom traps; Scientific-Atlanta satellite antenna; Scientific-Atlanta satellite receivers.
Miles of plant: 60.0 (coaxial); None (fiber optic). Homes passed: 3,416. Total homes in franchised area: 5,417.
Manager: Sue Whitaker. Chief technician: Robert Duke. Marketing director: Jennifer Hauschild. Customer service manager: Sue Whitaker.
Ownership: Classic Cable (MSO). See Cable System Ownership.

FORT SUPPLY—Rapid Cable, Box 6310, 310 Walnut Extension, Branson, MO 65615. Phones: 417-334-7897; 800-972-0962. Fax: 417-334-7899. E-mail: rcpcable@aol.com. County: Woodward. ICA: OK0376.
TV Market Ranking:. Franchise award date: July 25, 1988. Franchise expiration date: July 25, 2003. Began: N.A.
Channel capacity: 31 (2-way capable; not operating 2-way). Channels available but not in use: 6.
Basic Service
Subscribers: 74.
Programming (received off-air): KETA (P), KFOR-TV (N), KOCO-TV (A), KOKH-TV (F), KWTV (C) Oklahoma City; KOMI-LP (I) Woodward.
Programming (via satellite): WGN-TV (W) Chicago; CNN; Country Music TV; Discovery Channel; E! Entertainment TV; ESPN; Fox Family Channel; Home Shopping Network 2; Learning Channel; Nashville Network; Sci-Fi Channel; TBS Superstation; The Weather Channel; Trinity Bcstg. Network; Turner Network TV; USA Network.
Fee: $29.95 installation; $21.95 monthly; $3.95 converter.
Pay Service 1
Pay Units: 13.
Programming (via satellite): Cinemax.
Fee: $9.00 monthly.
Pay Service 2
Pay Units: 12.
Programming (via satellite): Disney Channel.
Fee: $7.00 monthly.
Pay Service 3
Pay Units: 14.
Programming (via satellite): HBO.
Fee: $10.00 monthly.
Local advertising: No.
Miles of plant: 5.4 (coaxial). Homes passed: 276.
Manager: Belinda Murphy. Chief technician: Steve Rice. Program director: Beth Semptimphelter. Marketing director: Bill Fischer.
Ownership: Rapid Communications Partners LP (MSO); TS Communications Inc. (MSO).

FREDERICK—Cable One, Box 1014, Frederick, OK 73542. Phone: 580-335-7531. Fax: 580-335-2689. County: Tillman. Also serves Tillman County. ICA: OK0062.
TV Market Ranking: Below 100 (portions of Tillman County); Outside TV Markets (Frederick, portions of Tillman County). Franchise award date: November 1, 1976. Franchise expiration date: N.A. Began: November 1, 1976.
Channel capacity: 41 (not 2-way capable). Channels available but not in use: 3.
Basic Service
Subscribers: 1,710; Commercial subscribers: 10.
Programming (received off-air): KOKH-TV (F) Oklahoma City; KAUZ-TV (C), KFDX-TV (N), KJTL (F,U), KSWO-TV (A) Wichita Falls-Lawton.
Programming (via microwave): KETA (P), KFOR-TV (N), KOCO-TV (A), KWTV (C) Oklahoma City.
Programming (via satellite): WGN-TV (W) Chicago; A & E; BET; C-SPAN; CNN; Country Music TV; Discovery Channel; Disney Channel; E! Entertainment TV; ESPN; Fox Family Channel; Fox Sports Net Southwest; Lifetime; MSNBC; MTV; Nashville Network; Nickelodeon; Sci-Fi Channel; TBS Superstation; The Weather Channel; Trinity Bcstg. Network; Turner Classic Movies; Turner Network TV; USA Network; Univision.
Current originations: Automated time-weather.
Fee: $20.00 installation; $27.80 monthly; $0.99 converter; $20.00 additional installation.
Commercial fee: $7.00 monthly.
Pay Service 1
Pay Units: 294.
Programming (via satellite): Cinemax.
Fee: $11.95 monthly.
Pay Service 2
Pay Units: 401.
Programming (via satellite): HBO.
Fee: $9.50 installation; $11.95 monthly.
Local advertising: No.
Program Guide: Premium Channels.
Equipment: Scientific-Atlanta headend; GTE Sylvania amplifiers; Times Fiber cable; MSI character generator; Standard Components set top converters; Eagle & Pico traps; Fort Worth Tower & Scientific-Atlanta satellite antenna.
Miles of plant: 33.0 (coaxial); None (fiber optic). Homes passed: 2,192. Total homes in franchised area: 2,192.
Manager: Merlin Scott. Marketing director: Robin Graham.
City fee: 2.5% of gross.
Ownership: Cable One Inc. (MSO).

FREEDOM—Classic Cable, Box 429, 605 N.W. 3rd St., Plainville, KS 67663-0429. Phones: 785-434-7620; 800-999-8876. Fax: 785-434-2614. Web site: http://www.classic-cable.com. County: Woods. ICA: OK0247.
TV Market Ranking: Outside TV Markets. Franchise award date: N.A. Franchise expiration date: N.A. Began: January 1, 1972.
Channel capacity: 41 (2-way capable). Channels available but not in use: N.A.
Basic Service
Subscribers: 94.
Programming (received off-air): KBSD-TV (C) Ensign; KETA (P), KFOR-TV (N), KOCO-TV (A), KOKH-TV (F), KWTV (C) Oklahoma City; allband FM.
Programming (via satellite): WGN-TV (W) Chicago; CNN; Country Music TV; Discovery Channel; Disney Channel; ESPN; Fox Family Channel; History Channel; Nashville Network; Nick at Nite's TV Land; TBS Superstation; The Weather Channel; Trinity Bcstg. Network; Turner Network TV; USA Network.
Fee: $35.00 installation; $27.95 monthly.
Pay Service 1
Pay Units: 15.
Programming (via satellite): HBO.
Fee: $35.00 installation; $10.95 monthly.
Pay Service 2
Pay Units: 6.
Programming (via satellite): Showtime.
Fee: $9.95 monthly.
Equipment: Blonder-Tongue & ICM headend; Vikoa amplifiers; Vikoa cable; Scientific-Atlanta satellite receivers.
Miles of plant: 10.0 (coaxial). Homes passed: 142.
Manager: Dave Walker. Chief technician: Jeff Smith. Marketing director: Jennifer Hauschild.
City fee: None.
Ownership: Classic Cable (MSO).

GANS—Oklahoma Cablecomm, Box 970, Fort Gibson, OK 74434-0970. Phones: 918-478-2100; 800-783-5701. Fax: 918-478-2355. County: Sequoyah. Also serves Sequoyah County (unincorporated areas). ICA: OK0172.
TV Market Ranking: Below 100. Franchise award date: October 18, 1988. Franchise expiration date: October 18, 2003. Began: November 1, 1989.
Channel capacity: 35 (not 2-way capable). Channels available but not in use: 5.
Basic Service
Subscribers: 350.
Programming (received off-air): KOET (P) Eufaula; KFSM-TV (C), KHBS (A), KPBI-LP (F), KPOM-TV (N) Fort Smith; KJRH (N), KOKI-TV (F), KOTV (C), KTUL (A) Tulsa.
Programming (via satellite): WGN-TV (W) Chicago; A & E; American Movie Classics; C-SPAN; CNN; Cartoon Network; Country Music TV; Discovery Channel; Disney Channel; ESPN; ESPN 2; Fox Family Channel; Fox Sports Net; History Channel; Learning Channel; Lifetime; Nashville Network; Nickelodeon; Outdoor Channel; QVC; Sci-Fi Channel; TBS Superstation; The Weather Channel; Trinity Bcstg. Network; Turner Classic Movies; Turner Network TV; USA Network.
Fee: $30.00 installation; $19.95 monthly.
Pay Service 1
Pay Units: 52.
Programming (via satellite): Cinemax.
Fee: N.A.
Pay Service 2
Pay Units: 66.
Programming (via satellite): HBO.
Fee: $10.00 installation; $9.50 monthly.
Pay Service 3
Pay Units: 69.
Programming (via satellite): Showtime.
Fee: $10.00 installation; $6.95 monthly.
Local advertising: No.
Program Guide: Cabletime.
Equipment: M/A-Com headend; Jerrold & C-COR amplifiers; Trilogy cable; BEI character generator; Jerrold & RCA set top converters; Arcom traps; 3M & Scientific-Atlanta satellite antenna; M/A-Com satellite receivers.
Miles of plant: 25.0 (coaxial). Homes passed: 450. Total homes in franchised area: 450.

Manager: Rick Wall. Chief technician: Leon Strain. Marketing & program director: Bruce Berkinshaw.
City fee: 5% of basic.
Ownership: Fanch Communications Inc. (MSO); Time Warner Cable (MSO). See Cable System Ownership.

GARBER—Rapid Cable, Box 6310, Branson, MO 65615. Phone: 800-972-0962. County: Garfield. ICA: OK0169.
TV Market Ranking: Outside TV Markets. Franchise award date: N.A. Franchise expiration date: March 9, 2006. Began: March 9, 1981.
Channel capacity: 24. Channels available but not in use: 6.
Basic Service
Subscribers: N.A.
Programming (received off-air): KOET (P) Eufaula; KAUT-TV (U), KFOR-TV (N), KOCB (W), KOCO-TV (A), KOKH-TV (F), KTBO-TV (T), KWTV (C) Oklahoma City.
Programming (via satellite): WGN-TV (W) Chicago; CNN; Country Music TV; Discovery Channel; ESPN; Nashville Network; TBS Superstation; Turner Network TV; USA Network.
Fee: $35.00 installation; $18.00 monthly; $15.00 additional installation.
Pay Service 1
Pay Units: 81.
Programming (via satellite): Cinemax; HBO.
Fee: $10.00 installation; $10.00 monthly (each).
Local advertising: No.
Equipment: Cadco, Tocom & M/A-Com headend; Scientific-Atlanta, Tocom & GTE Sylvania amplifiers; Comm/Scope & Times Fiber cable; Scientific-Atlanta & Zenith set top converters; Arcom traps; Prodelin satellite antenna; Drake & Microdyne satellite receivers.
Miles of plant: 8.0 (coaxial). Additional miles planned: 1.0 (coaxial). Homes passed: 460. Total homes in franchised area: 460.
Manager: Eugene W. Kretchmar. Chief technician: Mark Kretchmar. Marketing director: Freda Kretchmar.
City fee: 3% of gross.
Ownership: Rapid Communications Partners LP (MSO).

GEARY—Classic Cable, Box 429, 605 N.W. 3rd St., Plainville, KS 67663-0429. Phones: 785-434-7620; 800-999-8876. Fax: 785-434-2614. Web site: http://www.classic-cable.com. Counties: Blaine & Canadian. ICA: OK0145.
TV Market Ranking: Outside TV Markets. Franchise award date: N.A. Franchise expiration date: N.A. Began: May 1, 1981.
Channel capacity: 41 (2-way capable). Channels available but not in use: N.A.
Basic Service
Subscribers: 224; Commercial subscribers: 4.
Programming (received off-air): KAUT-TV (U), KETA (P), KFOR-TV (N), KOCB (W), KOCO-TV (A), KOKH-TV (F), KTBO-TV (T), KWTV (C) Oklahoma City.
Programming (via satellite): WGN-TV (W) Chicago; A & E; CNN; Country Music TV; Discovery Channel; Disney Channel; ESPN; Fox Family Channel; Home & Garden Television; Nashville Network; Nickelodeon; TBS Superstation; The Weather Channel; Turner Classic Movies; Turner Network TV; USA Network.
Fee: $35.00 installation; $27.95 monthly; $3.50 converter; $15.00 additional installation.
Pay Service 1
Pay Units: 49.
Programming (via satellite): Cinemax.
Fee: $9.95 monthly.
Pay Service 2
Pay Units: 63.
Programming (via satellite): HBO.
Fee: $9.95 monthly.
Local advertising: No.
Equipment: ISS, Scientific-Atlanta & Triple Crown headend; Jerrold amplifiers; Prodelin & Scientific-Atlanta satellite antenna; ICM, Scientific-Atlanta & Triple Crown satellite receivers.
Miles of plant: 16.0 (coaxial). Homes passed: 481. Total homes in franchised area: 675.
Region manager: Dave Walker. Chief technician: Jeff Smith. Marketing director: Jennifer Hauschild.
City fee: 3% of basic.
Ownership: Classic Cable (MSO).

GERONIMO—Rapid Cable, Box 6310, 310 Walnut Extension, Branson, MO 65615. Phones: 417-334-7897; 800-972-0962. Fax: 417-334-7899. E-mail: rcpcable@aol.com. County: Comanche. ICA: OK0197.
TV Market Ranking: Below 100. Franchise award date: September 27, 1982. Franchise expiration date: September 27, 2007. Began: February 1, 1984.
Channel capacity: 31 (2-way capable; not operating 2-way). Channels available but not in use: 6.
Basic Service
Subscribers: 120.
Programming (received off-air): KETA (P) Oklahoma City; KJBO-LP (U) Wichita Falls; KAUZ-TV (C), KFDX-TV (N), KJTL (F,U), KSWO-TV (A) Wichita Falls-Lawton.
Programming (via satellite): WGN-TV (W) Chicago; Animal Planet; CNN; Country Music TV; Discovery Channel; ESPN; Fox Family Channel; Learning Channel; Nashville Network; Sci-Fi Channel; TBS Superstation; The Weather Channel; Trinity Bcstg. Network; Turner Network TV; USA Network.
Fee: $29.95 installation; $22.95 monthly; $3.95 converter.
Pay Service 1
Pay Units: 20.
Programming (via satellite): Cinemax.
Fee: $9.00 monthly.
Pay Service 2
Pay Units: 25.
Programming (via satellite): HBO.
Fee: $10.00 monthly.
Pay Service 3
Pay Units: 14.
Programming (via satellite): Disney Channel.
Fee: $7.00 monthly.
Local advertising: No.
Miles of plant: 7.7 (coaxial). Homes passed: 389.
Manager: Belinda Murphy. Chief technician: Steve Rice. Program director: Beth Semptimphelter. Marketing director: Bill Fischer.
Ownership: Rapid Communications Partners LP (MSO); TS Communications Inc. (MSO).

GLENCOE—Oklahoma Cablecomm, Box 970, Fort Gibson, OK 74434-0970. Phones: 918-478-2100; 800-783-5701. Fax: 918-478-2355. County: Payne. ICA: OK0221.
TV Market Ranking: Outside TV Markets. Franchise award date: December 1, 1985. Franchise expiration date: N.A. Began: March 1, 1988.
Channel capacity: 35 (not 2-way capable). Channels available but not in use: 13.
Basic Service
Subscribers: 114.
Programming (received off-air): KAUT-TV (U), KETA (P), KFOR-TV (N), KOCB (W), KOCO-TV (A), KOKH-TV (F), KTBO-TV (T), KWTV (C) Oklahoma City; KOKI-TV (F), KWHB (I) Tulsa.
Programming (via satellite): WGN-TV (W) Chicago; A & E; CNN; Country Music TV; Discovery Channel; ESPN; Fox Family Channel; Nashville Network; TBS Superstation; Turner Network TV; USA Network.
Fee: $40.00 installation; $22.00 monthly; $1.96 converter; $19.95 additional installation.
Pay Service 1
Pay Units: 29.
Programming (via satellite): Cinemax.
Fee: $20.00 installation; $9.95 monthly.
Pay Service 2
Pay Units: 29.
Programming (via satellite): HBO.
Fee: $20.00 installation; $9.95 monthly.
Local advertising: No.
Program Guide: TV Host.
Equipment: Jerrold amplifiers; Jerrold set top converters; Arcom traps; Antenna Technology satellite receivers.
Miles of plant: 3.0 (coaxial). Homes passed: 239. Total homes in franchised area: 239.
Manager: Rick Wall. Chief technician: Leon Strain. Marketing & program director: Bruce Berkinshaw.
City fee: 2% of gross.
Ownership: Fanch Communications Inc. (MSO); Time Warner Cable (MSO). See Cable System Ownership.

GOLTRY—Classic Cable, Box 429, 605 N.W. 3rd St., Plainville, KS 67663-0429. Phones: 785-434-7620; 800-999-8876. Fax: 785-434-2614. Web site: http://www.classic-cable.com. County: Alfalfa. ICA: OK0286.
TV Market Ranking: Outside TV Markets. Franchise award date: January 1, 1989. Franchise expiration date: January 1, 2014. Began: September 1, 1989.
Channel capacity: 31 (2-way capable). Channels available but not in use: N.A.
Basic Service
Subscribers: 33.
Programming (received off-air): KAUT-TV (U), KETA (P), KFOR-TV (N), KOCB (W), KOCO-TV (A), KOKH-TV (F), KWTV (C) Oklahoma City.
Programming (via satellite): WGN-TV (W) Chicago; CNN; Country Music TV; Discovery Channel; Disney Channel; ESPN; Fox Family Channel; Nashville Network; TBS Superstation; Turner Network TV.
Fee: $35.00 installation; $27.95 monthly; $3.50 converter.
Pay Service 1
Pay Units: 6.
Programming (via satellite): HBO.
Fee: $20.00 installation; $9.95 monthly.
Local advertising: No.
Equipment: Cadco headend; Scientific-Atlanta amplifiers; Jerrold set top converters.
Miles of plant: 3.3 (coaxial). Homes passed: 151.
Region manager: Dave Walker. Chief technician: Jeff Smith. Marketing director: Jennifer Hauschild.
Ownership: Classic Cable (MSO).

GOODWELL—Classic Cable, Box 429, 605 N.W. 3rd St., Plainville, KS 67663-0429. Phones: 785-434-7620; 800-999-8876. Fax: 913-434-2614. Web site: http://www.classic-cable.com. County: Texas. ICA: OK0183.
TV Market Ranking: Outside TV Markets. Franchise award date: N.A. Franchise expiration date: N.A. Began: May 1, 1983.
Channel capacity: 12. Channels available but not in use: N.A.
Basic Service
Subscribers: 256.
Programming (received off-air): KSNG (N), KUPK-TV (A) Garden City.
Programming (via microwave): KAMR-TV (N), KFDA-TV (C), KVII-TV (A) Amarillo.
Programming (via satellite): WGN-TV (W) Chicago; TBS Superstation.
Fee: $20.00 installation; $18.95 monthly.
Miles of plant: 6.2 (coaxial). Homes passed: 400.
Manager: Angie Remmel.
Ownership: Classic Cable (MSO).

GORE—Oklahoma Cablecomm, Box 970, Fort Gibson, OK 74434-0970. Phones: 918-478-2100; 800-783-5701. Fax: 918-478-2355. Counties: Muskogee & Sequoyah. Also serves Webbers Falls. ICA: OK0164.
TV Market Ranking: Outside TV Markets. Franchise award date: N.A. Franchise expiration date: N.A. Began: N.A.
Channel capacity: 42 (not 2-way capable). Channels available but not in use: 7.
Basic Service
Subscribers: 308; Commercial subscribers: 34.
Programming (received off-air): KOET (P) Eufaula; KFSM-TV (C), KHBS (A) Fort Smith; KJRH (N), KOKI-TV (F), KOTV (C), KTUL (A) Tulsa.
Programming (via satellite): WGN-TV (W) Chicago; A & E; American Movie Classics; C-SPAN; CNBC; CNN; Cartoon Network; Country Music TV; Discovery Channel; Disney Channel; ESPN; ESPN 2; Fox Family Channel; Fox Sports Net; Headline News; History Channel; Learning Channel; Lifetime; Nashville Network; Nickelodeon; Outdoor Channel; QVC; Sci-Fi Channel; TBS Superstation; The Weather Channel; Trinity Bcstg. Network; Turner Classic Movies; Turner Network TV; USA Network.
Fee: $30.00 installation; $21.95 monthly.
Pay Service 1
Pay Units: 63.
Programming (via satellite): Cinemax.
Fee: $9.50 monthly.
Pay Service 2
Pay Units: 49.
Programming (via satellite): HBO.
Fee: $10.95 monthly.
Local advertising: No.
Equipment: Blonder-Tongue, Drake & Triple Crown headend; C-COR amplifiers; Comm/Scope cable; Arcom & Northeast Filter traps; Prodelin satellite antenna; DX Engineering & Scientific-Atlanta satellite receivers.
Miles of plant: 17.0 (coaxial). Homes passed: 584.
Manager: Rick Wall. Chief technician: Leon Strang. Marketing & program director: Bruce Berkinshaw.
City fee: 2% of basic gross.
Ownership: Fanch Communications Inc. (MSO); Time Warner Cable (MSO). See Cable System Ownership.

GOTEBO—Rapid Cable, Box 6310, 310 Walnut Extension, Branson, MO 65615. Phones: 417-334-7897; 800-972-0962. Fax: 417-334-7899. E-mail: rcpcable@aol.com. County: Kiowa. ICA: OK0228.
TV Market Ranking: Outside TV Markets. Franchise award date: June 29, 1981. Franchise expiration date: June 29, 2001. Began: January 1, 1983.
Channel capacity: 35 (2-way capable; not operating 2-way). Channels available but not in use: 12.
Basic Service
Subscribers: 104.

Programming (received off-air): KETA (P), KFOR-TV (N), KWTV (C) Oklahoma City; KFDX-TV (N), KJTL (F,U), KSWO-TV (A) Wichita Falls-Lawton.
Programming (via satellite): WGN-TV (W) Chicago; Animal Planet; CNN; Country Music TV; Discovery Channel; ESPN; Fox Family Channel; Learning Channel; Nashville Network; TBS Superstation; The Weather Channel; Turner Network TV; USA Network.
Fee: $29.95 installation; $22.95 monthly; $3.95 converter.

Pay Service 1
Pay Units: 4.
Programming (via satellite): Cinemax.
Fee: $9.00 monthly.

Pay Service 2
Pay Units: 16.
Programming (via satellite): HBO.
Fee: $10.00 monthly.

Pay Service 3
Pay Units: 6.
Programming (via satellite): Disney Channel.
Fee: $7.00 monthly.

Miles of plant: 4.5 (coaxial). Homes passed: 296.
Manager: Belinda Murphy. Chief technician: Steve Rice. Program director: Beth Semptimphelter. Marketing director: Bill Fischer.
Ownership: Rapid Communications Partners LP (MSO); TS Communications Inc. (MSO).

GRACEMONT—Rapid Cable, Box 6310, 310 Walnut Extension, Branson, MO 65615. Phones: 417-334-7897; 800-972-0962. Fax: 417-334-7899. E-mail: rcpcable@aol.com. County: Caddo. ICA: OK0287.
TV Market Ranking: Outside TV Markets. Franchise award date: January 3, 1983. Franchise expiration date: January 3, 2005. Began: N.A.
Channel capacity: 31 (2-way capable; not operating 2-way). Channels available but not in use: 7.

Basic Service
Subscribers: 126.
Programming (received off-air): KETA (P), KFOR-TV (N), KOCB (W), KOCO-TV (A), KOKH-TV (F), KWTV (C) Oklahoma City.
Programming (via satellite): WGN-TV (W) Chicago; CNN; Country Music TV; Discovery Channel; ESPN; Fox Family Channel; Home Shopping Network 2; Nashville Network; Nickelodeon; TBS Superstation; The Weather Channel; Trinity Bcstg. Network; Turner Network TV; USA Network.
Fee: $29.95 installation; $22.95 monthly; $3.95 converter.

Pay Service 1
Pay Units: 8.
Programming (via satellite): Cinemax.
Fee: $9.00 monthly.

Pay Service 2
Pay Units: 16.
Programming (via satellite): HBO.
Fee: $10.00 monthly.

Pay Service 3
Pay Units: 12.
Programming (via satellite): Disney Channel.
Fee: $7.00 monthly.

Local advertising: No.
Miles of plant: 5.0 (coaxial). Homes passed: 221.
Manager: Belinda Murphy. Chief technician: Steve Rice. Program director: Beth Semptimphelter. Marketing director: Bill Fischer.
Ownership: Rapid Communications Partners LP (MSO); TS Communications Inc. (MSO).

GRAND LAKE-MONKEY ISLAND—Oklahoma Cablecomm, Box 970, Fort Gibson, OK 74434-0970. Phones: 918-478-2100; 800-783-5701. Fax: 918-478-2355. County: Delaware. ICA: OK0092.
TV Market Ranking: Outside TV Markets. Franchise award date: N.A. Franchise expiration date: N.A. Began: N.A.
Channel capacity: 35 (not 2-way capable). Channels available but not in use: 8.

Basic Service
Subscribers: 800.
Programming (received off-air): KOAM-TV (C), KODE-TV (A), KOZJ (P), KSNF (N) Joplin-Pittsburg; KJRH (N), KOED-TV (P), KOKI-TV (F), KOTV (C), KTFO (U), KTUL (A), KWHB (I) Tulsa.
Programming (via satellite): WGN-TV (W) Chicago; A & E; American Movie Classics; C-SPAN; CNBC; CNN; Cartoon Network; Country Music TV; Discovery Channel; Disney Channel; E! Entertainment TV; ESPN; ESPN 2; Fox Family Channel; Fox Sports Net; Headline News; History Channel; Learning Channel; Lifetime; Nashville Network; Nickelodeon; QVC; TBS Superstation; TV Food Network; The Inspirational Network; The Weather Channel; Travel Channel; Turner Network TV; USA Network.
Current originations: Local news.
Fee: $30.00 installation; $23.45 monthly.

Pay Service 1
Pay Units: 61.
Programming (via satellite): Cinemax.
Fee: $20.00 installation; $9.95 monthly.

Pay Service 2
Pay Units: 136.
Programming (via satellite): HBO.
Fee: $20.00 installation; $11.95 monthly.

Pay Service 3
Pay Units: 58.
Programming (via satellite): The Movie Channel.
Fee: $20.00 installation; $11.95 monthly.

Local advertising: No.
Program Guide: TV Host.
Equipment: Drake, Scientific-Atlanta & Triple Crown headend; Scientific-Atlanta & Triple Crown amplifiers; Comm/Scope cable; Eagle & Northeast Filter traps; Scientific-Atlanta satellite antenna; Scientific-Atlanta satellite receivers.
Miles of plant: 27.0 (coaxial). Homes passed: 1,255. Total homes in franchised area: 1,255.
Manager: Rick Wall. Chief technician: Leon Strang. Marketing & program director: Bruce Berkinshaw.
City fee: 2% of gross.
Ownership: Fanch Communications Inc. (MSO); Time Warner Cable (MSO). See Cable System Ownership.

GRANDFIELD—Southwestern CATV Inc., Box 171, Medicine Park, OK 73557-0171. Phone: 580-535-4663. Fax: 580-529-5225. County: Tillman. ICA: OK0143.
TV Market Ranking: Below 100. Franchise award date: N.A. Franchise expiration date: N.A. Began: October 1, 1982.
Channel capacity: 35. Channels available but not in use: N.A.

Basic Service
Subscribers: N.A.
Programming (received off-air): KAUZ-TV (C), KFDX-TV (N), KSWO-TV (A) Wichita Falls-Lawton.
Planned programming (via satellite): Fox Family Channel.
Fee: N.A.

Pay Service 1
Pay Units: N.A.
Planned programming (via satellite): HBO.
Fee: N.A.

Miles of plant: 11.8 (coaxial). Homes passed: 650.
City fee: 3% of gross.
Ownership: Southwestern CATV Inc. (MSO).

GRANITE—Rapid Cable, Box 6310, 310 Walnut Extension, Branson, MO 65615. Phones: 417-334-7897; 800-972-0962. Fax: 417-334-7899. E-mail: rcpcable@aol.com. Counties: Greer & Kiowa. Also serves Lone Wolf. ICA: OK0134.
TV Market Ranking: Below 100. Franchise award date: March 12, 1979. Franchise expiration date: March 12, 2004. Began: January 1, 1958.
Channel capacity: 31 (2-way capable; not operating 2-way). Channels available but not in use: None.

Basic Service
Subscribers: 396; Commercial subscribers: 75.
Programming (received off-air): KETA (P), KFOR-TV (N), KOCB (W), KOCO-TV (A), KOKH-TV (F), KWTV (C) Oklahoma City; KAUZ-TV (C), KFDX-TV (N), KJTL (F,U), KSWO-TV (A) Wichita Falls-Lawton; 1 FM.
Programming (via satellite): WGN-TV (W) Chicago; A & E; C-SPAN; CNN; Country Music TV; Discovery Channel; ESPN; ESPN 2; Fox Family Channel; Fox News Channel; Nashville Network; Nickelodeon; QVC; TBS Superstation; The Weather Channel; Trinity Bcstg. Network; Turner Classic Movies; Turner Network TV; USA Network.
Current originations: Automated time-weather; local news.
Fee: $29.95 installation; $21.95 monthly; $3.95 converter.

Pay Service 1
Pay Units: 34.
Programming (via satellite): Cinemax.
Fee: $9.00 monthly.

Pay Service 2
Pay Units: 44.
Programming (via satellite): HBO.
Fee: $10.00 monthly.

Pay Service 3
Pay Units: 23.
Programming (via satellite): Disney Channel.
Fee: $7.00 monthly.

Local advertising: No.
Equipment: CAS & Jerrold headend; CAS & Vikoa amplifiers; Plastoid cable; U.S. Tower satellite antenna.
Miles of plant: 17.8 (coaxial). Homes passed: 619.
Manager: Belinda Murphy. Chief technician: Steve Rice. Program director: Beth Semptimphelter. Marketing director: Bill Fischer.
Ownership: Rapid Communications Partners LP (MSO); TS Communications Inc. (MSO).

GROVE—Peak Cablevision, Suite B, 2800 W. Hudson, Rogers, AR 72756. Phone: 501-631-1650. Fax: 501-631-7831. County: Delaware. Also serves Delaware County (northern portion). ICA: OK0039.
TV Market Ranking: Below 100 (portions of Delaware County); Outside TV Markets (portions of Delaware County, Grove). Franchise award date: November 1, 1972. Franchise expiration date: N.A. Began: July 1, 1973.
Channel capacity: 42 (not 2-way capable). Channels available but not in use: 6.

Basic Service
Subscribers: 2,891.
Programming (received off-air): KOAM-TV (C), KODE-TV (A), KSNF (N) Joplin-Pittsburg; KJRH (N), KOED-TV (P), KOKI-TV (F), KOTV (C), KTUL (A) Tulsa; allband FM.
Programming (via satellite): WGN-TV (W) Chicago; A & E; American Movie Classics; CNN; Court TV; Discovery Channel; ESPN; Fox Family Channel; Headline News; MTV; Nashville Network; Nickelodeon; QVC; TBS Superstation; The Weather Channel; Turner Network TV; USA Network.
Current originations: Automated time-weather; automated emergency alert.
Fee: $18.75 installation; $23.44 monthly; $1.50 converter; $12.50 additional installation.

Pay Service 1
Pay Units: 90.
Programming (via satellite): Disney Channel.
Fee: $9.95 monthly.

Pay Service 2
Pay Units: 717.
Programming (via satellite): The New Encore.
Fee: N.A.

Pay Service 3
Pay Units: 275.
Programming (via satellite): HBO.
Fee: $9.95 monthly.

Pay Service 4
Pay Units: 158.
Programming (via satellite): Showtime.
Fee: $20.00 installation; $9.95 monthly.

Pay Service 5
Pay Units: 109.
Programming (via satellite): The Movie Channel.
Fee: $9.95 monthly.

Pay-Per-View
Addressable homes: 253.

Local advertising: Yes.
Program Guide: The Cable Guide.
Equipment: Blonder-Tongue headend; AEL amplifiers; Comm/Scope cable; Arcom traps; U.S. Tower satellite antenna; Scientific-Atlanta satellite receivers.
Miles of plant: 102.1 (coaxial); None (fiber optic). Homes passed: 4,619. Total homes in franchised area: 5,683.
Manager: Shane Bell. Chief technician: Lee A. Featherston. Marketing director: Tom Young.
City fee: 3% of gross.
Ownership: Peak Cablevision LLC (MSO). See Cable System Ownership.

GROVE—Oklahoma Cablecomm, Box 970, Fort Gibson, OK 74434-0970. Phones: 918-478-2100; 800-783-5701. Fax: 918-478-2355. County: Delaware. ICA: OK0128.
TV Market Ranking: Outside TV Markets. Franchise award date: N.A. Franchise expiration date: N.A. Began: November 1, 1984.
Channel capacity: N.A. Channels available but not in use: N.A.

Basic Service
Subscribers: 495; Commercial subscribers: 98.
Programming (received off-air): KRSC-TV (E) Claremore; KOAM-TV (C), KODE-TV (A), KSNF (N) Joplin-Pittsburg; KJRH (N), KOED-TV (P), KOKI-TV (F), KOTV (C), KTFO (U), KTUL (A) Tulsa.
Programming (via satellite): WGN-TV (W) Chicago; A & E; American Movie Classics; C-SPAN; CNBC; CNN; Cartoon Network; Comedy Central; Country Music TV; Discovery Channel; Disney Channel; E! Entertainment TV; ESPN; ESPN 2; Fox Family Channel; Fox Sports Net Southwest; Headline News; Home & Garden Television; Home Shopping Network; Learning Channel; Lifetime; Nashville Network; Nickelodeon; QVC; TBS Superstation; The Weather Channel; Trinity Bcstg. Network; Turner Network TV; USA Network.

Fee: $40.00 installation; $24.95 monthly; $1.96 converter; $19.95 additional installation.

Pay Service 1

Pay Units: 47.

Programming (via satellite): Cinemax.

Fee: $9.95 monthly.

Pay Service 2

Pay Units: 64.

Programming (via satellite): HBO.

Fee: $9.95 monthly.

Local advertising: No.

Program Guide: TV Host.

Miles of plant: 26.0 (coaxial). Homes passed: 751. Total homes in franchised area: 751.

Manager: Rick Wall. Chief technician: Leon Strain. Marketing & program director: Bruce Berkinshaw.

Ownership: Fanch Communications Inc. (MSO); Time Warner Cable (MSO). See Cable System Ownership

GUTHRIE—Cablevision of Guthrie, 220 E. Cleveland, Guthrie, OK 73044. Phone: 405-282-4272. County: Logan. ICA: OK0035.

TV Market Ranking: 39. Franchise award date: April 1, 1978. Franchise expiration date: November 5, 2006. Began: January 1, 1980.

Channel capacity: 60 (2-way capable; operating 2-way). Channels available but not in use: 8.

Basic Service

Subscribers: 2,634.

Programming (received off-air): KAUT-TV (U), KETA (P), KFOR-TV (N), KOCB (W), KOCO-TV (A), KOKH-TV (F), KSBI (I), KTBO-TV (T), KWTV (C) Oklahoma City; 15 FMs.

Programming (via satellite): A & E; American Movie Classics; BET; C-SPAN; CNBC; Discovery Channel; ESPN; Home Shopping Network; Lifetime; MTV; Nickelodeon; The Weather Channel; USA Network; VH1.

Current originations: Public access; educational access; government access; automated emergency alert; local sports.

Fee: $15.87 installation; $18.66 monthly; $16.89 additional installation.

Expanded Basic Service

Subscribers: 2,577.

Programming (via satellite): WGN-TV (W) Chicago; CNN; Fox Family Channel; Headline News; Nashville Network; TBS Superstation; Turner Network TV.

Fee: $3.62 monthly.

Expanded Basic Service 2

Subscribers: 597.

Programming (via satellite): Bravo; Cartoon Network; Comedy Central; Country Music TV; Court TV; ESPN 2; History Channel; Sci-Fi Channel; Travel Channel; Turner Classic Movies.

Fee: $6.00 monthly.

Pay Service 1

Pay Units: 706.

Programming (via satellite): Cinemax.

Fee: $11.00 monthly.

Pay Service 2

Pay Units: 334.

Programming (via satellite): Disney Channel.

Fee: $7.95 monthly.

Pay Service 3

Pay Units: 952.

Programming (via satellite): HBO.

Fee: $11.00 monthly.

Pay Service 4

Pay Units: 632.

Programming (via satellite): Showtime.

Fee: $11.00 monthly.

Pay Service 5

Pay Units: 7.

Programming (via satellite): Music Choice.

Fee: $6.35 monthly.

Pay Service 6

Pay Units: 15.

Programming (via satellite): Golf Channel.

Fee: $6.95 monthly.

Pay-Per-View

Addressable homes: 783.

Local advertising: Yes. Available in character-generated programming. Rates: $5.00/Week. Local sales manager: Mark Kanter.

Program Guide: The Cable Guide.

Equipment: Scientific-Atlanta headend; Magnavox & RCA amplifiers; Comm/Scope cable; Panasonic cameras; Panasonic VTRs; Quanta character generator; Jerrold, Oak & Hamlin set top converters; Scientific-Atlanta addressable set top converters; Eagle traps; Scientific-Atlanta satellite antenna.

Miles of plant: 116.8 (coaxial). Homes passed: 5,341. Total homes in franchised area: 5,341.

Manager: David Cooper. Chief technician: Tom Heddlesten. Marketing director: Jim Back. Customer service manager: Charitta Shelton.

City fee: 3% of gross.

Ownership: Multimedia Cablevision Inc. (MSO). See Cable System Ownership

GUYMON—TCA Cable Partners, 215 W. 5th, Guymon, OK 73942. Phone: 580-338-6730. County: Texas. ICA: OK0053.

TV Market Ranking: Outside TV Markets. Franchise award date: N.A. Franchise expiration date: N.A. Began: July 15, 1955.

Channel capacity: 35 (not 2-way capable). Channels available but not in use: 3.

Basic Service

Subscribers: 2,741.

Programming (received off-air): KSNG (N), KUPK-TV (A) Garden City; K53BE (I) Guymon; 5 FMs.

Programming (via microwave): KAMR-TV (N), KFDA-TV (C), KVII-TV (A) Amarillo; KETA (P) Oklahoma City.

Programming (via satellite): WGN-TV (W) Chicago; C-SPAN; CNN; Country Music TV; Discovery Channel; ESPN; Headline News; Home Shopping Network; Lifetime; MTV; Nashville Network; Nickelodeon; TBS Superstation; The Weather Channel; Turner Network TV; USA Network; Univision; VH1.

Current originations: Automated time-weather.

Fee: $8.00 installation; $17.00 monthly.

Pay Service 1

Pay Units: 430.

Programming (via satellite): Cinemax.

Fee: $9.95 monthly.

Pay Service 2

Pay Units: 198.

Programming (via satellite): Disney Channel.

Fee: $7.95 monthly.

Pay Service 3

Pay Units: 687.

Programming (via satellite): HBO.

Fee: $10.95 monthly.

Local advertising: No. Regional interconnect: Cabletime.

Equipment: Scientific-Atlanta headend; C-COR amplifiers; MSI character generator; Hamlin set top converters; Microdyne satellite antenna.

Miles of plant: 43.0 (coaxial). Homes passed: 3,050. Total homes in franchised area: 3,050.

Manager: Ryan Matzek. Chief technician: Jim Taylor.

City fee: 3% of gross.

Ownership: TCA Cable Partners (MSO).

HAMMON—Classic Cable, Box 429, 605 N.W. 3rd St., Plainville, KS 67663-0429. Phones: 785-434-7620; 800-999-8876. Fax: 785-434-2614. Web Site: http://www.classic-cable.com. County: Roger Mills. ICA: OK0220.

TV Market Ranking: Below 100. Franchise award date: N.A. Franchise expiration date: N.A. Began: January 1, 1955.

Channel capacity: 36 (2-way capable). Channels available but not in use: N.A.

Basic Service

Subscribers: 108; Commercial subscribers: 47.

Programming (received off-air): KWET (P) Cheyenne; KFOR-TV (N), KOCB (W), KOCO-TV (A), KOKH-TV (F), KWTV (C) Oklahoma City.

Programming (via satellite): WGN-TV (W) Chicago; CNN; Discovery Channel; Disney Channel; ESPN; Fox Family Channel; Headline News; History Channel; Learning Channel; Nashville Network; Nick at Nite's TV Land; Nickelodeon; QVC; Sci-Fi Channel; TBS Superstation; The Weather Channel; Trinity Bcstg. Network; Turner Network TV; USA Network.

Fee: $35.00 installation; $27.95 monthly; $2.00 converter.

Pay Service 1

Pay Units: 17.

Programming (via satellite): HBO.

Fee: $10.95 monthly.

Pay Service 2

Pay Units: 13.

Programming (via satellite): Showtime.

Fee: $9.95 monthly.

Local advertising: No.

Equipment: Jerrold headend; Jerrold amplifiers; Jerrold cable.

Miles of plant: 6.5 (coaxial). Homes passed: 237.

Manager: Dave Walker. Chief technician: Jeff Smith. Marketing director: Jennifer Hauschild.

Ownership: Classic Cable (MSO).

HARDESTY—Classic Cable, Box 429, 605 N.W. 3rd St., Plainville, KS 67663-0429. Phones: 785-434-7620; 800-999-8876. Fax: 785-434-2614. Web Site: http://www.classic-cable.com. County: Texas. ICA: OK0373.

TV Market Ranking: Outside TV Markets. Franchise award date: N.A. Franchise expiration date: N.A. Began: N.A.

Channel capacity: 36 (2-way capable). Channels available but not in use: N.A.

Basic Service

Subscribers: 42.

Programming (received off-air): KAMR-TV (N), KCIT (F,U), KFDA-TV (C), KVII-TV (A) Amarillo; KETA (P) Oklahoma City.

Programming (via satellite): WGN-TV (W) Chicago; CNN; Discovery Channel; ESPN; Nashville Network; TBS Superstation; Turner Network TV.

Fee: $35.00 installation; $23.95 monthly.

Pay Service 1

Pay Units: 21.

Programming (via satellite): HBO.

Fee: $9.95 monthly.

Miles of plant: 2.0 (coaxial). Homes passed: 101.

Region manager: Dave Walker. Chief technician: Jeff Smith. Marketing director: Jennifer Hauschild.

Ownership: Classic Cable (MSO).

HARTSHORNE—Oklahoma Cablecomm, Box 970, Fort Gibson, OK 74434-0970. Phones: 918-478-2100; 800-783-5701. Fax: 918-478-2355. County: Pittsburg. Also serves Haileyville. ICA: OK0083.

TV Market Ranking: Outside TV Markets. Franchise award date: N.A. Franchise expiration date: November 1, 2005. Began: July 1, 1965.

Channel capacity: 45. Channels available but not in use: 27.

Basic Service

Subscribers: 1,106.

Programming (received off-air): KTEN (A,N,F) Ada; KOET (P) Eufaula; KJRH (N), KOKI-TV (F), KOTV (C), KTFO (U), KTUL (A), KWHB (I) Tulsa; allband FM.

Programming (via satellite): WGN-TV (W) Chicago; A & E; American Movie Classics; C-SPAN; CNBC; CNN; Cartoon Network; Country Music TV; Court TV; Discovery Channel; Disney Channel; E! Entertainment TV; ESPN; ESPN 2; Fox Family Channel; Fox Sports Net Southwest; Headline News; History Channel; Home & Garden Television; Home Shopping Network; Learning Channel; Lifetime; Nashville Network; Nickelodeon; Outdoor Channel; QVC; Sci-Fi Channel; TBS Superstation; The Weather Channel; Turner Classic Movies; Turner Network TV; USA Network.

Planned originations: Automated time-weather.

Fee: $29.95 installation; $24.95 monthly; $1.96 converter; $19.95 additional installation.

Pay Service 1

Pay Units: 98.

Programming (via satellite): Cinemax.

Fee: $9.95 monthly.

Pay Service 2

Pay Units: 148.

Programming (via satellite): HBO.

Fee: $9.95 monthly.

Pay Service 3

Pay Units: N.A.

Programming (via satellite): Showtime.

Fee: $9.95 monthly.

Local advertising: No.

Program Guide: TV Host.

Equipment: Jerrold amplifiers; Jerrold set top converters; Pico traps; U.S. Tower satellite antenna.

Miles of plant: 45.0 (coaxial). Homes passed: 1,619. Total homes in franchised area: 1,619.

Manager: Rick Wall. Chief technician: Leon Strain. Marketing & program director: Bruce Berkinshaw.

Franchise fee: 2% of gross.

Ownership: Fanch Communications Inc. (MSO). See Cable System Ownership.

HASKELL—Peak Cablevision, 410 Eastside Blvd., Muskogee, OK 74403. Phone: 918-687-7511. Fax: 918-687-3291. Counties: Muskogee & Wagoner. Also serves Wagoner County (portions). ICA: OK0096.

TV Market Ranking: 54 (Haskell, portions of Wagoner County); Below 100 (portions of Wagoner County). Franchise award date: N.A. Franchise expiration date: N.A. Began: February 1, 1982.

Channel capacity: 35. Channels available but not in use: 13.

Basic Service

Subscribers: 255.

Programming (received off-air): KJRH (N), KOED-TV (P), KOKI-TV (F), KOTV (C), KTUL (A) Tulsa.

Programming (via satellite): WGN-TV (W) Chicago; CNBC; CNN; Discovery Channel; ESPN; Fox Family Channel; Lifetime; Nashville Network; Nickelodeon; QVC; TBS Superstation; Turner Network TV; USA Network.

Fee: $60.00 installation; $20.22 monthly; $6.27 additional installation.

Pay Service 1

Pay Units: 30.

Programming (via satellite): Cinemax.

Fee: N.A.

Pay Service 2

Pay Units: 91.

Programming (via satellite): The New Encore.
Fee: N.A.
Pay Service 3
Pay Units: 72.
Programming (via satellite): HBO.
Fee: N.A.
Pay Service 4
Pay Units: 28.
Programming (via satellite): Showtime.
Fee: N.A.
Miles of plant: 13.2 (coaxial). Homes passed: 1,186. Total homes in franchised area: 1,300.
Manager: Brad Mangum. Chief technician: Darrell Kimbrill.
City fee: 3% of gross.
Ownership: Peak Cablevision LLC (MSO). See Cable System Ownership.

HEALDTON—Classic Cable, Box 429, 605 N.W. 3rd St., Plainville, KS 67663-0429. Phones: 785-434-7620; 800-999-8876. Fax: 785-434-2614. Web Site: http://www.classic-cable.com. Counties: Carter, Jefferson & Ringling. Also serves Cornish, Ringling, Wilson. ICA: OK0055.
TV Market Ranking: Outside TV Markets. Franchise award date: N.A. Franchise expiration date: September 6, 2003. Began: September 1, 1974.
Channel capacity: 41 (2-way capable). Channels available but not in use: N.A.
Basic Service
Subscribers: 1,360.
Programming (received off-air): KTEN (A,N,F) Ada; KETA (P), KFOR-TV (N), KOCO-TV (A), KOKH-TV (F), KWTV (C) Oklahoma City; KXII (C) Sherman; KAUZ-TV (C), KFDX-TV (N), KJTL (F,U) Wichita Falls-Lawton.
Programming (via satellite): WGN-TV (W) Chicago; A & E; CNN; Country Music TV; Discovery Channel; Disney Channel; ESPN; Fox Family Channel; Fox Sports Net Southwest; Headline News; History Channel; Lifetime; Nashville Network; Nick at Nite's TV Land; Nickelodeon; QVC; TBS Superstation; The Weather Channel; Trinity Bcstg. Network; Turner Classic Movies; Turner Network TV; USA Network.
Fee: $35.00 installation; $28.95 monthly.
Pay Service 1
Pay Units: 131.
Programming (via satellite): HBO.
Fee: $10.95 monthly.
Pay Service 2
Pay Units: 126.
Programming (via satellite): Showtime.
Fee: $9.95 monthly.
Pay Service 3
Pay Units: 141.
Programming (via satellite): The Movie Channel.
Fee: $5.95 monthly.
Local advertising: No.
Equipment: Scientific-Atlanta headend; Scientific-Atlanta amplifiers; Comm/Scope cable; Scientific-Atlanta set top converters; Eagle & Pico traps; Scientific-Atlanta satellite antenna; Scientific-Atlanta satellite receivers.
Miles of plant: 42.0 (coaxial). Homes passed: 1,690. Total homes in franchised area: 2,885.
Manager: Dave Walker. Chief technician: Mark Jordan. Marketing director: Jennifer Hauschild.
City fee: 3% of gross.
Ownership: Classic Cable (MSO).

HEAVENER—Classic Cable, Box 429, 605 N.W. 3rd St., Plainville, KS 67663-0429. Phones: 785-434-7620; 800-999-8876. Fax: 785-434-2614. Web Site: http://www.classic-cable.com. County: Le Flore. ICA: OK0103.
TV Market Ranking: Outside TV Markets. Franchise award date: N.A. Franchise expiration date: September 1, 2014. Began: March 1, 1965.
Channel capacity: 41 (2-way capable). Channels available but not in use: N.A.
Basic Service
Subscribers: 677.
Programming (received off-air): KAFT (P) Fayetteville; KFSM-TV (C), KHBS (A), KPOM-TV (N) Fort Smith; KOKI-TV (F), KOTV (C), KTUL (A) Tulsa; allband FM.
Programming (via microwave): KETA (P) Oklahoma City.
Programming (via satellite): WGN-TV (W) Chicago; A & E; C-SPAN; CNN; Country Music TV; Discovery Channel; Disney Channel; ESPN; Fox Sports Net Southwest; Headline News; History Channel; Home & Garden Television; Lifetime; Nashville Network; Nick at Nite's TV Land; Nickelodeon; QVC; The Weather Channel; Turner Classic Movies; Turner Network TV; USA Network.
Planned programming (via satellite): Fox Family Channel; TBS Superstation.
Current originations: Automated time-weather; local news.
Fee: $35.00 installation; $25.95 monthly.
Pay Service 1
Pay Units: 108.
Programming (via satellite): HBO.
Fee: $35.00 installation; $10.95 monthly.
Pay Service 2
Pay Units: 57.
Programming (via satellite): Showtime.
Fee: $35.00 installation; $9.95 monthly.
Pay Service 3
Pay Units: 51.
Programming (via satellite): The Movie Channel.
Fee: $35.00 installation; $5.95 monthly.
Equipment: U.S. Tower satellite antenna.
Miles of plant: 25.0 (coaxial). Homes passed: 1,130.
Manager: Dave Walker. Chief technician: Carl Miller. Marketing director: Jennifer Hauschild.
City fee: 3% of gross revenue.
Ownership: Classic Cable (MSO).

HECTORVILLE—Quality Cablevision of Oklahoma Inc., Box 315, 816-D N. Date, Jenks, OK 74037. Phone: 918-299-0104. County: Okmulgee. ICA: OK0336.
TV Market Ranking: 54. Franchise award date: N.A. Franchise expiration date: N.A. Began: October 1, 1993.
Channel capacity: N.A. Channels available but not in use: N.A.
Basic Service
Subscribers: 493.
Programming (received off-air): KETA (P) Oklahoma City; KJRH (N), KOKI-TV (F), KOTV (C), KTFO (U), KTUL (A) Tulsa.
Programming (via satellite): Turner Classic Movies.
Fee: $29.95 installation; $19.95 monthly.
Pay Service 1
Pay Units: N.A.
Programming (via satellite): HBO; Showtime.
Fee: $11.95 monthly (each).
Miles of plant: 60.0 (coaxial). Homes passed: 800.
Manager: Curtis Scott. Chief technician: Bill Garrison.
Ownership: Quality Cablevision of Oklahoma Inc. (MSO).

HELENA—Classic Cable, Box 429, 605 N.W. 3rd St., Plainville, KS 67663-0429. Phones: 785-434-7620; 800-999-8876. Fax: 785-434-2614. Web Site: http://www.classic-cable.com. County: Alfalfa. ICA: OK0153.
TV Market Ranking: Outside TV Markets. Franchise award date: April 8, 1985. Franchise expiration date: N.A. Began: February 1, 1986.
Channel capacity: 41 (2-way capable). Channels available but not in use: N.A.
Basic Service
Subscribers: 149; Commercial subscribers: 1.
Programming (received off-air): KAUT-TV (U), KETA (P), KFOR-TV (N), KOCB (W), KOCO-TV (A), KOKH-TV (F), KTBO-TV (T), KWTV (C) Oklahoma City.
Programming (via satellite): WGN-TV (W) Chicago; A & E; CNN; Discovery Channel; Disney Channel; ESPN; Fox Family Channel; Learning Channel; Lifetime; Nashville Network; Nick at Nite's TV Land; TBS Superstation; The Weather Channel; Turner Network TV; USA Network.
Fee: $35.00 installation; $27.95 monthly; $3.50 converter.
Pay Service 1
Pay Units: 16.
Programming (via satellite): HBO.
Fee: $20.00 installation; $9.95 monthly.
Pay Service 2
Pay Units: 10.
Programming (via satellite): Showtime.
Fee: $20.00 installation; $9.95 monthly.
Local advertising: No.
Equipment: Cadco & DX Engineering headend; Magnavox amplifiers; Comm/Scope cable; Arcom & Northeast Filter traps; DX Engineering satellite receivers.
Miles of plant: 6.0 (coaxial). Homes passed: 255. Total homes in franchised area: 255.
Manager: Dave Walker. Chief technician: Jeff Smith. Marketing director: Jennifer Hauschild.
City fee: 3% of basic gross.
Ownership: Classic Cable (MSO).

HENNESSEY—Classic Cable, Box 429, 605 N.W. 3rd St., Plainville, KS 67663-0429. Phones: 785-434-7620; 800-999-8876. Fax: 785-434-2614. Web Site: http://www.classic-cable.com. County: Kingfisher. ICA: OK0113.
TV Market Ranking: Outside TV Markets. Franchise award date: N.A. Franchise expiration date: N.A. Began: October 15, 1979.
Channel capacity: 36 (2-way capable). Channels available but not in use: N.A.
Basic Service
Subscribers: 538; Commercial subscribers: 31.
Programming (received off-air): KAUT-TV (U), KETA (P), KFOR-TV (N), KOCB (W), KOCO-TV (A), KOKH-TV (F), KTBO-TV (T), KWTV (C) Oklahoma City; allband FM.
Programming (via satellite): WGN-TV (W) Chicago; A & E; American Movie Classics; CNN; Country Music TV; Discovery Channel; Disney Channel; ESPN; Fox Family Channel; Fox News Channel; Fox Sports Net Southwest; Goodlife TV Network; Headline News; History Channel; Home & Garden Television; Learning Channel; Lifetime; Nashville Network; Nick at Nite's TV Land; Nickelodeon; QVC; Sci-Fi Channel; TBS Superstation; The Weather Channel; Turner Network TV; USA Network.
Current originations: Automated time-weather; automated emergency alert.
Fee: $35.00 installation; $27.95 monthly; $3.50 converter; $15.00 additional installation.
Pay Service 1
Pay Units: 111.
Programming (via satellite): HBO.
Fee: $10.95 monthly.
Pay Service 2
Pay Units: 45.
Programming (via satellite): Showtime.
Fee: $9.95 monthly.
Pay Service 3
Pay Units: 48.
Programming (via satellite): The Movie Channel.
Fee: $5.95 monthly.
Local advertising: No.
Equipment: Blonder-Tongue, Scientific-Atlanta & Tocom headend; GTE Sylvania amplifiers; Comm/Scope cable; Jerrold set top converters; Eagle & PPC traps; AFC & Prodelin satellite antenna; ICM, Microdyne & Scientific-Atlanta satellite receivers.
Miles of plant: 20.9 (coaxial). Homes passed: 966. Total homes in franchised area: 966.
Manager: Dave Walker. Chief technician: Jeff Smith. Program director: Sue Turner. Marketing director: Jennifer Hauschild.
City fee: 3% of basic gross.
Ownership: Classic Cable (MSO).

HENRYETTA—Peak Cablevision, 410 Eastside Blvd., Muskogee, OK 74403. Phone: 918-687-7511. Fax: 918-687-3291. County: Okmulgee. Also serves Dewar. ICA: OK0049.
TV Market Ranking: Outside TV Markets. Franchise award date: N.A. Franchise expiration date: N.A. Began: December 1, 1972.
Channel capacity: 40. Channels available but not in use: 9.
Basic Service
Subscribers: 2,046.
Programming (received off-air): KFOR-TV (N), KOCO-TV (A), KWTV (C) Oklahoma City; KJRH (N), KOED-TV (P), KOKI-TV (F), KOTV (C), KTUL (A) Tulsa; allband FM.
Programming (via satellite): WGN-TV (W) Chicago; CNBC; CNN; Discovery Channel; Fox Family Channel; Headline News; Nashville Network; Nickelodeon; Odyssey; QVC; TBS Superstation.
Current originations: Automated time-weather.
Fee: $60.00 installation; $9.57 monthly; $4.71 additional installation.
Expanded Basic Service
Subscribers: 1,975.
Programming (via satellite): American Movie Classics; Court TV; ESPN; Fox Sports Net Southwest; Turner Network TV; USA Network.
Fee: $11.51 monthly.
Pay Service 1
Pay Units: 141.
Programming (via satellite): Disney Channel.
Fee: N.A.
Pay Service 2
Pay Units: 717.
Programming (via satellite): The New Encore.
Fee: N.A.
Pay Service 3
Pay Units: 214.
Programming (via satellite): HBO.
Fee: N.A.
Pay Service 4
Pay Units: 175.
Programming (via satellite): Showtime.
Fee: N.A.
Pay Service 5
Pay Units: 142.
Programming (via satellite): The Movie Channel.
Fee: N.A.
Program Guide: The Cable Guide.
Miles of plant: 68.9 (coaxial). Homes passed: 3,480. Total homes in franchised area: 4,805.
Manager: Brad Mangum. Chief technician: Darrell Kimbrill.
City fee: 4% of gross.
Ownership: Peak Cablevision LLC (MSO). See Cable System Ownership.

HINTON—Hinton CATV Co., Box 70, Hinton, OK 73047. Phone: 405-542-3211. County: Caddo. Also serves Bridgeport, Cedar Lake, Lookeba, Sickles. ICA: OK0140.

TV Market Ranking: Outside TV Markets. Franchise award date: N.A. Franchise expiration date: N.A. Began: July 1, 1983.

Channel capacity: 22. Channels available but not in use: N.A.

Basic Service

Subscribers: N.A.

Programming (received off-air): KAUT-TV (U), KETA (P), KFOR-TV (N), KOCB (W), KOCO-TV (A), KOKH-TV (F), KTBO-TV (T), KWTV (C) Oklahoma City.

Programming (via satellite): WGN-TV (W) Chicago; CNN; ESPN; Nashville Network; Odyssey; TBS Superstation.

Current originations: Local news.

Fee: $25.00 installation; $9.00 monthly.

Pay Service 1

Pay Units: N.A.

Programming (via satellite): Cinemax; Disney Channel; HBO; Showtime.

Fee: $9.00 monthly (each).

Miles of plant: 22.9 (coaxial). Homes passed: 686.

Manager: Kenneth Doughty.

Ownership: Hinton CATV Co. (MSO).

HOBART—Cable One, Box 720, 315 S. Washington St., Hobart, OK 73651. Phone: 580-726-2523. Fax: 580-726-5818. County: Kiowa. Also serves Kiowa County (portions). ICA: OK0067.

TV Market Ranking: Below 100 (portions of Kiowa County); Outside TV Markets (Hobart, portions of Kiowa County). Franchise award date: April 1, 1985. Franchise expiration date: February 25, 2000. Began: April 1, 1956.

Channel capacity: 53 (not 2-way capable). Channels available but not in use: 8.

Basic Service

Subscribers: 1,644; Commercial subscribers: 2.

Programming (received off-air): KWET (P) Cheyenne; KFOR-TV (N), KOCB (W), KOCO-TV (A), KOKH-TV (F), KWTV (C) Oklahoma City; KAUZ-TV (C), KFDX-TV (N), KJTL (F,U), KSWO-TV (A) Wichita Falls-Lawton; allband FM.

Programming (via satellite): WGN-TV (W) Chicago; A & E; BET; C-SPAN; CNN; Country Music TV; Discovery Channel; Disney Channel; E! Entertainment TV; ESPN; Fox Family Channel; Fox Sports Net Southwest; Headline News; History Channel; Home Shopping Network; Lifetime; MSNBC; MTV; Nashville Network; Nickelodeon; Odyssey; TBS Superstation; The Inspirational Network; The Weather Channel; Turner Network TV; USA Network; VH1.

Current originations: Public access; religious access; automated emergency alert.

Fee: $20.00 installation (aerial), $55.00 (underground); $30.50 monthly; $0.69 converter; $25.00 additional installation.

Pay Service 1

Pay Units: 162.

Programming (via satellite): Cinemax (multiplexed).

Fee: $20.00 installation; $11.65 monthly.

Pay Service 2

Pay Units: 218.

Programming (via satellite): HBO (multiplexed).

Fee: $20.00 installation; $11.65 monthly.

Pay Service 3

Pay Units: 43.

Programming (via satellite): Showtime.

Fee: $20.00 installation; $11.65 monthly.

Local advertising: Yes (insert only). Available in locally originated & character-generated programming. Rates: $50.00/Month. Local sales manager: Peggy Miller.

Equipment: Scientific-Atlanta headend; C-COR amplifiers; Comm/Scope cable; MSI & SpectraView character generator; NSC set top converters; Eagle traps; Scientific-Atlanta satellite antenna; Scientific-Atlanta satellite receivers.

Miles of plant: 29.0 (coaxial). Homes passed: 1,825. Total homes in franchised area: 1,825.

Manager: Rick Iliff. Office manager: Peggy Miller.

City fee: 4% of gross.

Ownership: Cable One Inc. (MSO).

HOLDENVILLE—Peak Cablevision, 205 E. Cherokee, McAlester, OK 74502. Phone: 918-423-6661. Fax: 918-426-2809. E-mail: ethayer@peakcable.com. County: Hughes. ICA: OK0061.

TV Market Ranking: Below 100. Franchise award date: N.A. Franchise expiration date: N.A. Began: September 1, 1967.

Channel capacity: 36 (not 2-way capable). Channels available but not in use: N.A.

Basic Service

Subscribers: 1,310.

Programming (received off-air): KTEN (A,N,F) Ada; KETA (P), KFOR-TV (N), KOCO-TV (A), KTBO-TV (T), KWTV (C) Oklahoma City; KOKI-TV (F), KOTV (C) Tulsa; allband FM.

Programming (via satellite): A & E; American Movie Classics; Animal Planet; CNBC; CNN; Cartoon Network; Comedy Central; Discovery Channel; Disney Channel; ESPN; FX; Fox Family Channel; Fox News Channel; Fox Sports Net Southwest; Home & Garden Television; Learning Channel; Lifetime; Nashville Network; QVC; TBS Superstation; Turner Network TV; USA Network; VH1.

Current originations: Automated time-weather; public access; educational access; government access; religious access; local sports.

Fee: $21.75 installation; $25.77 monthly; $14.50 additional installation.

Pay Service 1

Pay Units: 345.

Programming (via satellite): The New Encore.

Fee: $1.75 monthly.

Pay Service 2

Pay Units: 213.

Programming (via satellite): HBO.

Fee: $12.95 monthly.

Pay Service 3

Pay Units: 121.

Programming (via satellite): Showtime.

Fee: $12.95 monthly.

Pay Service 4

Pay Units: 131.

Programming (via satellite): Starz!

Fee: $6.75 monthly.

Local advertising: Planned.

Equipment: Phasecom headend; Texscan amplifiers; Amphenol cable; Prodelin satellite antenna.

Miles of plant: 24.0 (coaxial). Additional miles planned: 3.0 (coaxial). Homes passed: 2,373. Total homes in franchised area: 2,373.

Manager: Everett Thayer. Chief technician: Lynn Harrison. Marketing director: Terry Homesley. Customer service manager: Susan Moore.

City fee: 5% of gross.

Ownership: Peak Cablevision LLC (MSO). See Cable System Ownership.

HOLLIS—Classic Cable, Box 429, 605 N.W. 3rd St., Plainville, KS 67663-0429. Phones: 785-434-7620; 800-999-8876. Fax: 785-434-2614.

Web Site: http://www.classic-cable.com. County: Harmon. Also serves Gould. ICA: OK0087.

TV Market Ranking: Outside TV Markets. Franchise award date: N.A. Franchise expiration date: January 1, 1999. Began: February 1, 1958.

Channel capacity: 41 (2-way capable). Channels available but not in use: N.A.

Basic Service

Subscribers: 879; Commercial subscribers: 25.

Programming (received off-air): KAMR-TV (N) Amarillo; KWET (P) Cheyenne; KOCO-TV (A) Oklahoma City; KFDX-TV (N), KJTL (F,U), KSWO-TV (A) Wichita Falls-Lawton; allband FM.

Programming (via microwave): KFOR-TV (N), KWTV (C) Oklahoma City.

Programming (via satellite): WGN-TV (W) Chicago; A & E; American Movie Classics; BET; C-SPAN; CNN; Country Music TV; Discovery Channel; Disney Channel; E! Entertainment TV; ESPN; Fox Family Channel; Headline News; Home & Garden Television; Learning Channel; Lifetime; Nashville Network; Nick at Nite's TV Land; Nickelodeon; Outdoor Channel; QVC; TBS Superstation; The Weather Channel; Trinity Bcstg. Network; Turner Network TV; USA Network; Univision.

Current originations: Religious access; automated emergency alert.

Fee: $35.00 installation; $28.95 monthly.

Commercial fee: $24.00 monthly.

Pay Service 1

Pay Units: 45.

Programming (via satellite): The Movie Channel.

Fee: $5.95 monthly.

Pay Service 2

Pay Units: 56.

Programming (via satellite): HBO.

Fee: $10.95 monthly.

Pay Service 3

Pay Units: 52.

Programming (via satellite): Showtime.

Fee: $9.95 monthly.

Local advertising: No.

Equipment: Scientific-Atlanta & Standard Communications headend; Magnavox amplifiers; Times Fiber cable; Standard Communications set top converters; Scientific-Atlanta addressable set top converters; Eagle & Pico traps; AFC & Scientific-Atlanta satellite antenna; Scientific-Atlanta & Standard Communications satellite receivers.

Miles of plant: 27.0 (coaxial). Homes passed: 1,588.

Manager: Dave Walker. Chief technician: Rick Rattan. Marketing director: Jennifer Hauschild.

City fee: 2% of gross.

Ownership: Classic Cable (MSO).

HOMINY—Community Cablevision, Box 307, Skiatook, OK 74070-0307. Phone: 918-396-3019. County: Osage. ICA: OK0085.

TV Market Ranking: 54. Franchise award date: June 20, 1979. Franchise expiration date: June 20, 1999. Began: January 1, 1980.

Channel capacity: 35 (not 2-way capable). Channels available but not in use: 5.

Basic Service

Subscribers: 770.

Programming (received off-air): KDOR (T) Bartlesville; KTPX (X) Okmulgee; KJRH (N), KOED-TV (P), KOKI-TV (F), KOTV (C), KTUL (A), KWHB (I) Tulsa; allband FM.

Programming (via satellite): WGN-TV (W) Chicago; A & E; C-SPAN; C-SPAN 2; CNN; Country Music TV; Discovery Channel; ESPN; Fox Family Channel; Headline News; Lifetime; MTV; Nashville Network; Nickelodeon; TBS Superstation; Turner Classic Movies; Turner Network TV; USA Network; VH1.

Current originations: Automated time-weather; public access; educational access; government access; religious access; leased access; library access; local news; local sports.

Fee: $25.00 installation; $16.25 monthly; $25.00 additional installation.

Pay Service 1

Pay Units: 135.

Programming (via satellite): Cinemax.

Fee: $25.00 installation; $11.50 monthly.

Pay Service 2

Pay Units: 96.

Programming (via satellite): Disney Channel.

Fee: $25.00 installation; $7.00 monthly.

Pay Service 3

Pay Units: 231.

Programming (via satellite): HBO.

Fee: $25.00 installation; $11.50 monthly.

Local advertising: Yes. Available in character-generated programming. Rates: $15.00/Week.

Equipment: Jerrold headend; Theta-Com amplifiers; Times Fiber cable; RCA cameras; Zenith VTRs; Texscan character generator; GTE Sylvania & Pioneer set top converters; Comtech satellite antenna.

Miles of plant: 12.0 (coaxial). Additional miles planned: 4.0 (coaxial). Homes passed: 1,484.

Manager: Ray Soule.

City fee: 2% of gross.

Ownership: Community Cablevision Co. (MSO).

HOOKER—Classic Cable, Box 429, 605 N.W. 3rd St., Plainville, KS 67663-0429. Phones: 785-434-7620; 800-999-8876. Fax: 785-434-2614. Web Site: http://www.classic-cable.com. County: Texas. ICA: OK0125.

TV Market Ranking: Outside TV Markets. Franchise award date: N.A. Franchise expiration date: January 1, 2013. Began: July 15, 1957.

Channel capacity: 41 (2-way capable). Channels available but not in use: N.A.

Basic Service

Subscribers: 511; Commercial subscribers: 15.

Programming (received off-air): KCIT (F,U) Amarillo; KBSD-TV (C) Ensign; KSNG (N), KUPK-TV (A) Garden City; KETA (P) Oklahoma City; 7 FMs.

Programming (via microwave): KAMR-TV (N), KFDA-TV (C), KVII-TV (A) Amarillo.

Programming (via satellite): WGN-TV (W) Chicago; C-SPAN; CNN; Country Music TV; Discovery Channel; Disney Channel; E! Entertainment TV; ESPN; Fox Family Channel; Fox News Channel; Fox Sports Net Southwest; Goodlife TV Network; History Chan-

nel; Home & Garden Television; Lifetime; Nashville Network; Nick at Nite's TV Land; Nickelodeon; QVC; Sci-Fi Channel; TBS Superstation; The Weather Channel; Turner Network TV; USA Network.
Current originations: Automated time-weather.
Fee: $35.00 installation; $27.95 monthly.
Pay Service 1
Pay Units: 101.
Programming (via satellite): HBO.
Fee: $10.00 installation; $9.95 monthly.
Pay Service 2
Pay Units: 48.
Programming (via satellite): Showtime.
Fee: $10.00 installation; $9.95 monthly.
Pay Service 3
Pay Units: 33.
Programming (via satellite): The Movie Channel.
Fee: $5.95 monthly.
Local advertising: Yes. Available in character-generated programming. Local sales manager: Calvin J. Hammack.
Equipment: Jerrold, M/A-Com & Tocom headend; Jerrold, M/A-Com & Tocom amplifiers; Times Fiber cable; Sony cameras; Scientific-Atlanta set top converters; Eagle & Pico traps; AFC satellite antenna; Microdyne & Scientific-Atlanta satellite receivers.
Miles of plant: 10.0 (coaxial). Additional miles planned: 0.5 (coaxial). Homes passed: 829.
Manager: Dave Walker. Chief technician: Jeff Smith. Marketing director: Jennifer Hauschild.
City fee: 2% of gross.
Ownership: Classic Cable (MSO).

HOWE—Peak Cablevision, Box 807, Pocola, OK 74902. Phone: 918-436-7488. Fax: 918-436-7151. County: Le Flore. ICA: OK0243.
TV Market Ranking: Outside TV Markets. Franchise award date: N.A. Franchise expiration date: October 1, 2009. Began: January 1, 1985.
Channel capacity: 36 (not 2-way capable). Channels available but not in use: 20.
Basic Service
Subscribers: 107.
Programming (received off-air): KAFT (P) Fayetteville; KFSM-TV (C), KHBS (A), KPBI-LP (F), KPOM-TV (N) Fort Smith; KTUL (A) Tulsa.
Programming (via satellite): Discovery Channel; ESPN; Fox Family Channel; Nashville Network; TBS Superstation; USA Network.
Fee: $25.00 installation; $21.95 monthly.
Pay Service 1
Pay Units: 26.
Programming (via satellite): Disney Channel.
Fee: $25.00 installation; $7.95 monthly.
Pay Service 2
Pay Units: 27.
Programming (via satellite): HBO.
Fee: $13.00 monthly.
Pay Service 3
Pay Units: 31.
Programming (via satellite): Showtime.
Fee: $11.00 monthly.
Equipment: Blonder-Tongue & ISS headend; Jerrold amplifiers; Times Fiber cable; Jerrold set top converters; AFC satellite antenna; ISS satellite receivers.
Miles of plant: 5.0 (coaxial). Homes passed: 220.
Manager: Dennis Moore. Chief technician: Rick Packard. Marketing director: Terry Homesley. Customer service manager: Susan Moore.
Ownership: Peak Cablevision LLC (MSO). See Cable System Ownership.

HUGO—Classic Cable, Box 826, 206 N. 2nd St., Hugo, OK 74743. Phone: 580-326-7525. Fax: 580-326-2170. County: Choctaw. Also serves Choctaw County (portions). ICA: OK0050.
TV Market Ranking: Outside TV Markets. Franchise award date: June 1, 1976. Franchise expiration date: May 1, 2006. Began: August 1, 1976.
Channel capacity: 41 (not 2-way capable). Channels available but not in use: None.
Basic Service
Subscribers: 2,219.
Programming (received off-air): KTEN (A,N,F) Ada; KDFW (F), KTVT (C), KXAS-TV (N), WFAA-TV (A) Dallas-Fort Worth; KETA (P) Oklahoma City; KXII (C) Sherman; allband FM.
Programming (via satellite): WGN-TV (W) Chicago; American Movie Classics; BET; CNBC; CNN; Cartoon Network; Country Music TV; Court TV; Discovery Channel; Disney Channel; ESPN; FX; Fox Family Channel; Fox News Channel; Fox Sports Net Southwest; Headline News; Lifetime; MTV; Nashville Network; Nickelodeon; Odyssey; QVC; TBS Superstation; The Weather Channel; Trinity Bcstg. Network; Turner Classic Movies; Turner Network TV; USA Network.
Current originations: Automated time-weather; public access; educational access; religious access; leased access; automated emergency alert.
Planned originations: Local news.
Fee: $35.23 installation; $24.49 monthly; $1.24 converter; $16.12 additional installation.
Pay Service 1
Pay Units: 307.
Programming (via satellite): Cinemax.
Fee: N.A.
Pay Service 2
Pay Units: 245.
Programming (via satellite): HBO.
Fee: N.A.
Pay Service 3
Pay Units: 147.
Programming (via satellite): Showtime.
Fee: N.A.
Pay-Per-View
Special events.
Local advertising: No.
Program Guide: Premium Channels.
Equipment: Scientific-Atlanta headend; Texscan amplifiers; Comm/Scope & Times Fiber cable; Texscan/MSI character generator; Scientific-Atlanta set top converters; Jerrold addressable set top converters; AFC, Scientific-Atlanta & Comtech satellite antenna; Scientific-Atlanta satellite receivers.
Miles of plant: 59.2 (coaxial); None (fiber optic). Homes passed: 3,300. Total homes in franchised area: 3,300.
Manager: Lindy Loftin. Marketing director: Jennifer Hauschild.
City fee: 5% of gross.
Ownership: Classic Cable (MSO).

HULBERT—Oklahoma Cablecomm, Box 970, Fort Gibson, OK 74434-0970. Phones: 918-478-2100; 800-783-5701. Fax: 918-478-2355. County: Cherokee. ICA: OK0202.
TV Market Ranking: Outside TV Markets. Franchise award date: January 1, 1989. Franchise expiration date: January 1, 2014. Began: September 1, 1989.
Channel capacity: N.A. Channels available but not in use: N.A.
Basic Service
Subscribers: 102.
Programming (received off-air): KRSC-TV (E) Claremore; KJRH (N), KOED-TV (P), KOKI-TV (F), KOTV (C), KTFO (U), KTUL (A), KWHB (I) Tulsa.
Programming (via satellite): WGN-TV (W) Chicago; A & E; CNN; Country Music TV; Discovery Channel; ESPN; Fox Family Channel; Lifetime; Nashville Network; Nickelodeon; TBS Superstation; Turner Network TV; USA Network.
Fee: $40.00 installation; $21.05 monthly; $1.96 converter; $19.95 additional installation.
Pay Service 1
Pay Units: 22.
Programming (via satellite): HBO.
Fee: $9.95 monthly.
Local advertising: No.
Program Guide: TV Host.
Miles of plant: 5.0 (coaxial). Homes passed: 293. Total homes in franchised area: 293.
Manager: Rick Wall. Chief technician: Leon Strain. Marketing & program director: Bruce Berkinshaw.
City fee: 5% of gross.
Ownership: Fanch Communications Inc. (MSO). See Cable System Ownership.

HUNTER—Classic Cable, Box 429, 605 N.W. 3rd St., Plainville, KS 67663-0429. Phones: 785-434-7620; 800-999-8876. Fax: 785-434-2614. Web Site: http://www.classic-cable.com. County: Garfield. ICA: OK0288.
TV Market Ranking: Outside TV Markets. Franchise award date: N.A. Franchise expiration date: N.A. Began: January 1, 1989.
Channel capacity: 36 (2-way capable). Channels available but not in use: N.A.
Basic Service
Subscribers: 21.
Programming (received off-air): KAUT-TV (U), KETA (P), KFOR-TV (N), KOCB (W), KOCO-TV (A), KOKH-TV (F), KTBO-TV (T), KWTV (C) Oklahoma City.
Programming (via satellite): WGN-TV (W) Chicago; CNN; Discovery Channel; ESPN; Fox Family Channel; Nashville Network; TBS Superstation; Turner Network TV.
Fee: $35.00 installation; $27.95 monthly; $3.50 converter.
Pay Service 1
Pay Units: 2.
Programming (via satellite): HBO.
Fee: $20.00 installation; $10.95 monthly.
Local advertising: No.
Equipment: Jerrold amplifiers.
Miles of plant: 2.4 (coaxial). Homes passed: 96.
Manager: Dave Walker. Chief technician: Jeff Smith. Program director: Sue Turner. Marketing director: Jennifer Hauschild.
City fee: 2% of basic.
Ownership: Classic Cable (MSO).

IDABEL—Cable One, 404 S. Central, Idabel, OK 74745. Phone: 580-286-3335. Fax: 580-286-7165. County: McCurtain. ICA: OK0056.
TV Market Ranking: Outside TV Markets. Franchise award date: January 17, 1961. Franchise expiration date: October 20, 2000. Began: October 10, 1961.
Channel capacity: 40 (2-way capable; operating 2-way). Channels available but not in use: 1.
Basic Service
Subscribers: 2,324; Commercial subscribers: 53.
Programming (received off-air): KTEN (A,N,F) Ada; KSLA-TV (C), KTAL-TV (N), KTBS-TV (A) Shreveport-Texarkana.
Programming (via microwave): KDFW (F), KTVT (C) Dallas-Fort Worth; KTUL (A) Tulsa.
Programming (via translator): KOET (P) Eufaula.
Programming (via satellite): WGN-TV (W) Chicago; TBS Superstation.
Current originations: Automated emergency alert.
Fee: $15.31 installation; $8.54 monthly; $2.22 converter.
Expanded Basic Service
Subscribers: 37.
Programming (via satellite): A & E; American Movie Classics; BET; C-SPAN; CNBC; CNN; Discovery Channel; ESPN; Fox Family Channel; Headline News; Lifetime; MTV; Nashville Network; Nickelodeon; The Weather Channel; Trinity Bcstg. Network; Turner Network TV; USA Network; VH1.
Fee: $15.31 installation; $4.79 monthly.
Pay Service 1
Pay Units: 158.
Programming (via satellite): Cinemax.
Fee: $15.31 installation; $12.00 monthly.
Pay Service 2
Pay Units: 97.
Programming (via satellite): Disney Channel.
Fee: $15.31 installation; $8.00 monthly.
Pay Service 3
Pay Units: 365.
Programming (via satellite): HBO (multiplexed).
Fee: $15.31 installation; $12.00 monthly.
Pay Service 4
Pay Units: 32.
Programming (via satellite): The Movie Channel.
Fee: $15.31 installation; $10.00 monthly.
Pay Service 5
Pay Units: 110.
Programming (via satellite): Showtime.
Fee: $15.31 installation; $12.00 monthly.
Pay-Per-View
Addressable homes: 1,047.
Hot Choice; Viewer's Choice.
Fee: $3.95-$5.95.
Local advertising: Yes. Available in satellite distributed programming. Rates: $42.50/Minute. Local sales manager: Steve Pyburn.
Equipment: Scientific-Atlanta headend; Magnavox amplifiers; Comm/Scope cable; Pioneer & Oak set top converters; Oak addressable set top converters; Andrew satellite antenna; Scientific-Atlanta satellite receivers.
Miles of plant: 49.0 (coaxial); None (fiber optic). Additional miles planned: 10.0 (coaxial). Homes passed: 2,864. Total homes in franchised area: 2,864.
Manager: Lindy Loftin. Chief technician: Benny Strawn. Customer service manager: Jeanie Acker.
City fee: 3% of gross.
Ownership: Cable One Inc. (MSO).

INOLA—Oklahoma Cablecomm, Box 970, Fort Gibson, OK 74434-0970. Phones: 918-478-2100; 800-783-5701. Fax: 918-478-2355. County: Rogers. ICA: OK0129.
TV Market Ranking: 54. Franchise award date: December 2, 1980. Franchise expiration date: December 2, 2000. Began: February 1, 1982.
Channel capacity: 36 (not 2-way capable). Channels available but not in use: 6.
Basic Service
Subscribers: 402; Commercial subscribers: 40.
Programming (received off-air): KDOR (T) Bartlesville; KRSC-TV (E) Claremore; KJRH (N), KOED-TV (P), KOKI-TV (F), KOTV (C), KTFO (U), KTUL (A), KWHB (I) Tulsa.
Programming (via satellite): WGN-TV (W) Chicago; A & E; American Movie Classics; CNBC; CNN; Cartoon Network; Comedy Central; Country Music TV; Discovery Channel; Disney Channel; E! Entertainment TV; ESPN; ESPN 2; Fox Family Channel; Fox Sports Net Southwest; Headline News; His-

tory Channel; Learning Channel; Lifetime; MTV; Nashville Network; Nickelodeon; QVC; Sci-Fi Channel; TBS Superstation; The Weather Channel; Turner Network TV; USA Network.
Current originations: Automated time-weather.
Fee: $40.00 installation; $24.95 monthly; $1.96 converter; $19.95 additional installation.
Pay Service 1
Pay Units: N.A.
Programming (via satellite): Cinemax.
Fee: $20.00 installation; $9.95 monthly.
Pay Service 2
Pay Units: 71.
Programming (via satellite): HBO.
Fee: $20.00 installation; $9.95 monthly.
Pay Service 3
Pay Units: 59.
Programming (via satellite): Showtime.
Fee: $20.00 installation; $9.95 monthly.
Program Guide: TV Host.
Equipment: Scientific-Atlanta & Microdyne headend; Scientific-Atlanta amplifiers; Texscan character generator; Hamlin & Jerrold set top converters; Pico traps; Scientific-Atlanta satellite antenna; Scientific-Atlanta & Microdyne satellite receivers.
Miles of plant: 25.0 (coaxial). Homes passed: 730.
Manager: Rick Wall. Chief technician: Leon Strain. Marketing & program director: Bruce Berkinshaw.
City fee: 3% of gross.
Ownership: Fanch Communications Inc. (MSO); Time Warner Cable (MSO). See Cable System Ownership.

JENNINGS—Cim Tel Cable Inc., Box 266, 101 Cimarron St., Mannford, OK 74044. Phone: 918-865-3314. County: Pawnee. ICA: OK0289.
TV Market Ranking: 54. Franchise award date: N.A. Franchise expiration date: N.A. Began: February 1, 1989.
Channel capacity: N.A. Channels available but not in use: N.A.
Basic Service
Subscribers: N.A.
Programming (received off-air): KJRH (N), KOED-TV (P), KOKI-TV (F), KOTV (C), KTUL (A) Tulsa.
Programming (via satellite): WGN-TV (W) Chicago; CNN; ESPN; Fox Family Channel; TBS Superstation.
Fee: N.A.
Pay Service 1
Pay Units: N.A.
Programming (via satellite): Cinemax; Disney Channel; HBO.
Fee: N.A.
Ownership: Cim Tel Cable Inc. (MSO).

JET—Classic Cable, Box 429, 605 N.W. 3rd St., Plainville, KS 67663-0429. Phones: 785-434-7620; 800-999-8876. Fax: 785-434-2614. Web Site: http://www.classic-cable.com. County: Alfalfa. ICA: OK0290.
TV Market Ranking: Outside TV Markets. Franchise award date: N.A. Franchise expiration date: N.A. Began: April 1, 1986.
Channel capacity: 36 (2-way capable). Channels available but not in use: N.A.
Basic Service
Subscribers: 35.
Programming (received off-air): KAUT-TV (U), KETA (P), KFOR-TV (N), KOCB (W), KOCO-TV (A), KOKH-TV (F), KWTV (C) Oklahoma City.
Programming (via satellite): WGN-TV (W) Chicago; CNN; Discovery Channel; Disney Channel; ESPN; Fox Family Channel; Nashville Network; Nick at Nite's TV Land; TBS Superstation; Trinity Bcstg. Network; Turner Network TV; USA Network.
Fee: $35.00 installation; $27.95 monthly; $3.50 converter.
Pay Service 1
Pay Units: 4.
Programming (via satellite): Showtime.
Fee: $10.00 installation; $9.95 monthly.
Pay Service 2
Pay Units: 5.
Programming (via satellite): HBO.
Fee: $10.00 installation; $10.95 monthly.
Local advertising: No.
Equipment: Cadco & DX Engineering headend; Magnavox amplifiers; Comm/Scope cable; Arcom & Northeast Filter traps; DX Engineering satellite receivers.
Miles of plant: 5.4 (coaxial). Homes passed: 158.
Manager: Dave Walker. Chief technician: Jeff Smith. Program director: Sue Turner. Marketing director: Jennifer Hauschild.
Ownership: Classic Cable (MSO).

JONES—Classic Cable, Box 429, 605 N.W. 3rd St., Plainville, KS 67663-0429. Phones: 785-434-7620; 800-999-8876. Fax: 785-434-2614. Web Site: http://www.classic-cable.com. County: Oklahoma. ICA: OK0291.
TV Market Ranking: 39. Franchise award date: N.A. Franchise expiration date: April 1, 1998. Began: N.A.
Channel capacity: 36 (2-way capable). Channels available but not in use: N.A.
Basic Service
Subscribers: 198.
Programming (received off-air): KAUT-TV (U), KETA (P), KFOR-TV (N), KOCB (W), KOCO-TV (A), KOKH-TV (F), KSBI (I), KTBO-TV (T), KWTV (C) Oklahoma City.
Programming (via satellite): WGN-TV (W) Chicago; A & E; CNN; Country Music TV; Discovery Channel; Disney Channel; ESPN; Fox Family Channel; History Channel; Learning Channel; Nashville Network; Nickelodeon; QVC; TBS Superstation; The Weather Channel; Turner Network TV; USA Network.
Current originations: Local news.
Fee: $35.00 installation; $26.95 monthly.
Pay Service 1
Pay Units: 17.
Programming (via satellite): HBO.
Fee: $35.00 installation; $10.95 monthly.
Pay Service 2
Pay Units: 38.
Programming (via satellite): The Movie Channel.
Fee: $35.00 installation; $5.95 monthly.
Pay Service 3
Pay Units: 39.
Programming (via satellite): Showtime.
Fee: $35.00 installation; $9.95 monthly.
Miles of plant: 25.1 (coaxial). Homes passed: 360.
Manager: Dave Walker. Chief technician: Jeff Smith. Marketing director: Jennifer Hauschild.
City fee: 3% of basic gross.
Ownership: Classic Cable (MSO).

KANSAS—Oklahoma Cablecomm, Box 970, Fort Gibson, OK 74434-0970. Phones: 918-478-2100; 800-783-5701. Fax: 918-478-2355. County: Delaware. ICA: OK0292.
TV Market Ranking: Below 100. Franchise award date: January 1, 1989. Franchise expiration date: January 1, 2014. Began: June 1, 1989.
Channel capacity: N.A. Channels available but not in use: N.A.
Basic Service
Subscribers: 89.
Programming (received off-air): KRSC-TV (E) Claremore; KJRH (N), KOED-TV (P), KOKI-TV (F), KOTV (C), KTFO (U), KTUL (A), KWHB (I) Tulsa.
Programming (via satellite): WGN-TV (W) Chicago; A & E; American Movie Classics; CNN; Country Music TV; Discovery Channel; ESPN; Fox Family Channel; Lifetime; Nashville Network; TBS Superstation; Turner Network TV; USA Network.
Fee: $40.00 installation; $22.95 monthly; $1.96 converter; $19.95 additional installation.
Pay Service 1
Pay Units: 25.
Programming (via satellite): HBO.
Fee: $9.95 monthly.
Local advertising: No.
Program Guide: TV Host.
Miles of plant: 4.0 (coaxial). Homes passed: 188. Total homes in franchised area: 188.
Manager: Rick Wall. Chief technician: Leon Strain. Marketing & program director: Bruce Berkinshaw.
City fee: 4.9% of gross.
Ownership: Fanch Communications Inc. (MSO); Time Warner Cable (MSO). See Cable System Ownership.

KAW CITY—Community Cablevision Co., Box 307, Skiatook, OK 74070-0307. Phone: 918-396-3019. County: Kay. ICA: OK0231.
TV Market Ranking: Outside TV Markets. Franchise award date: N.A. Franchise expiration date: N.A. Began: N.A.
Channel capacity: 35. Channels available but not in use: 19.
Basic Service
Subscribers: 121.
Programming (received off-air): KETA (P), KFOR-TV (N) Oklahoma City; KJRH (N), KOKI-TV (F), KOTV (C), KTUL (A) Tulsa.
Programming (via satellite): WGN-TV (W) Chicago; CNN; Discovery Channel; Disney Channel; ESPN; Fox Family Channel; Nashville Network; TBS Superstation; The Weather Channel; USA Network.
Fee: $35.00 installation; $21.95 monthly.
Pay Service 1
Pay Units: 40.
Programming (via satellite): HBO.
Fee: $10.95 monthly.
Pay Service 2
Pay Units: N.A.
Programming (via satellite): Showtime.
Fee: $9.95 monthly.
Miles of plant: 5.7 (coaxial). Homes passed: 198.
Manager: Mark Livingston. Chief technician: Les Libal.
Ownership: Community Cablevision Co. (MSO).

KELLYVILLE—Oklahoma Cablecomm, Box 970, Fort Gibson, OK 74434-0970. Phones: 918-478-2100; 800-783-5701. Fax: 918-478-2355. County: Creek. ICA: OK0171.
TV Market Ranking: 54. Franchise award date: June 13, 1983. Franchise expiration date: June 13, 2003. Began: April 1, 1985.
Channel capacity: 35 (not 2-way capable). Channels available but not in use: 13.
Basic Service
Subscribers: 181.
Programming (received off-air): KDOR (T) Bartlesville; KJRH (N), KOED-TV (P), KOKI-TV (F), KOTV (C), KTFO (U), KTUL (A), KWHB (I) Tulsa.
Programming (via satellite): WGN-TV (W) Chicago; A & E; CNN; Country Music TV; Discovery Channel; Disney Channel; ESPN; Fox Family Channel; Nashville Network; Nickelodeon; TBS Superstation; The Weather Channel; Turner Network TV; USA Network.
Fee: $30.00 installation; $22.95 monthly.
Pay Service 1
Pay Units: N.A.
Programming (via satellite): Cinemax.
Fee: N.A.
Pay Service 2
Pay Units: 41.
Programming (via satellite): HBO.
Fee: $11.95 monthly.
Pay Service 3
Pay Units: 13.
Programming (via satellite): Showtime.
Fee: $10.95 monthly.
Local advertising: No.
Program Guide: TV Host.
Equipment: Blonder-Tongue, Cadco & Triple Crown headend; Magnavox amplifiers; Comm/Scope cable; Jerrold set top converters; Arcom & Northeast Filter traps; Prodelin & Scientific-Atlanta satellite antenna; Standard Communications satellite receivers.
Miles of plant: 7.0 (coaxial). Homes passed: 453. Total homes in franchised area: 453.
Manager: Rick Wall. Chief technician: Leon Strain. Marketing & program director: Bruce Berkinshaw.
City fee: 2% of basic gross.
Ownership: Fanch Communications Inc. (MSO); Time Warner Cable (MSO). See Cable System Ownership.

KEOTA—Oklahoma Cablecomm, Box 970, Fort Gibson, OK 74434-0970. Phones: 918-478-2100; 800-783-5701. Fax: 918-478-2355. County: Haskell. ICA: OK0218.
TV Market Ranking: Outside TV Markets. Franchise award date: April 1, 1982. Franchise expiration date: April 1, 1997. Began: April 15, 1982.
Channel capacity: 35 (not 2-way capable). Channels available but not in use: N.A.
Basic Service
Subscribers: 154.
Programming (received off-air): KOET (P) Eufaula; KFSM-TV (C), KHBS (A), KPOM-TV (N) Fort Smith; KOKI-TV (F), KTUL (A), KWHB (I) Tulsa.
Programming (via satellite): WGN-TV (W) Chicago; A & E; CNN; Country Music TV; Discovery Channel; Disney Channel; ESPN; Fox Family Channel; Goodlife TV Network; Nashville Network; QVC; TBS Superstation; Turner Classic Movies; Turner Network TV; USA Network.
Fee: $30.00 installation; $22.95 monthly; $1.00 converter.
Pay Service 1
Pay Units: N.A.
Programming (via satellite): Cinemax.
Fee: N.A.
Pay Service 2
Pay Units: 19.
Programming (via satellite): HBO.
Fee: $9.00 monthly.
Equipment: Blonder-Tongue, Catel & Jerrold headend; Times Fiber cable; Jerrold & RCA set top converters; Automation Techniques satellite receivers.
Miles of plant: 7.0 (coaxial). Homes passed: 238. Total homes in franchised area: 238.
Manager: Rick Wall. Chief technician: Leon Strain. Marketing & program director: Bruce Berkinshaw.
Ownership: Fanch Communications Inc. (MSO); Time Warner Cable (MSO). See Cable System Ownership.

KETCHUM—Oklahoma Cablecomm, Box 970, Fort Gibson, OK 74434-0970. Phones: 918-478-2100; 800-783-5701. Fax: 918-478-2355. County: Mayes. Also serves Langley. ICA: OK0179.

TV Market Ranking: Outside TV Markets. Franchise award date: October 4, 1979. Franchise expiration date: October 4, 2004. Began: January 1, 1983.
Channel capacity: 42 (2-way capable). Channels available but not in use: None.
Basic Service
Subscribers: 1,020; Commercial subscribers: 94.
Programming (received off-air): KDOR (T) Bartlesville; KRSC-TV (E) Claremore; KOZJ (P), KSNF (N) Joplin-Pittsburg; KJRH (N), KOED-TV (P), KOKI-TV (F), KOTV (C), KTFO (U), KTUL (A) Tulsa.
Programming (via satellite): WGN-TV (W) Chicago; A & E; American Movie Classics; C-SPAN; CNBC; CNN; Cartoon Network; Discovery Channel; Disney Channel; E! Entertainment TV; ESPN; ESPN 2; Fox Family Channel; Fox Sports Net Southwest; Headline News; History Channel; Home Shopping Network; Learning Channel; Lifetime; Nashville Network; Nickelodeon; QVC; Sci-Fi Channel; TBS Superstation; TV Food Network; The Inspirational Network; The Weather Channel; Travel Channel; Turner Network TV; USA Network; VH1.
Fee: $40.00 installation; $24.95 monthly; $1.96 converter; $19.95 additional installation.
Pay Service 1
Pay Units: N.A.
Programming (via satellite): Cinemax.
Fee: $20.00 installation; $9.95 monthly.
Pay Service 2
Pay Units: 129.
Programming (via satellite): HBO.
Fee: $20.00 installation; $9.95 monthly.
Local advertising: No.
Program Guide: TV Host.
Equipment: Blonder-Tongue, Drake & Scientific-Atlanta headend; Scientific-Atlanta amplifiers; Comm/Scope cable; Jerrold set top converters; Arcom & Northeast Filter traps; Scientific-Atlanta satellite antenna; Automation Techniques & Scientific-Atlanta satellite receivers.
Miles of plant: 27.0 (coaxial). Homes passed: 1,035.
Manager: Rick Wall. Chief technician: Leon Strain. Marketing & program director: Bruce Berkinshaw.
City fee: 1% of basic gross.
Ownership: Fanch Communications Inc. (MSO); Time Warner Cable (MSO). See Cable System Ownership.

KINGFISHER—Classic Cable, Box 429, 605 N.W. 3rd St., Plainville, KS 67663-0429. Phones: 785-434-7620; 800-999-8876. Fax: 785-434-2614. Web Site: http://www.classic-cable.com. County: Kingfisher. ICA: OK0080.
TV Market Ranking: Outside TV Markets. Franchise award date: N.A. Franchise expiration date: N.A. Began: September 1, 1979.
Channel capacity: 58 (2-way capable). Channels available but not in use: N.A.
Basic Service
Subscribers: 1,329; Commercial subscribers: 66.
Programming (received off-air): KAUT-TV (U), KETA (P), KFOR-TV (N), KOCB (W), KOCO-TV (A), KOKH-TV (F), KTBO-TV (T), KWTV (C) Oklahoma City.
Programming (via satellite): WGN-TV (W) Chicago; A & E; CNN; Country Music TV; Court TV; Discovery Channel; Disney Channel; E! Entertainment TV; ESPN; FX; Fox Family Channel; Fox News Channel; Fox Sports Net Southwest; Headline News; Home & Garden Television; Home Shopping Network; Learning Channel; Lifetime; Nashville Network; Nick at Nite's TV Land; Nickelodeon; QVC; Sci-Fi Channel; TBS Superstation; The Health Network; The Inspirational Network; The Weather Channel; Travel Channel; Turner Classic Movies; Turner Network TV; USA Network.
Current originations: Automated time-weather; public access; automated emergency alert.
Fee: $35.00 installation; $28.95 monthly; $3.50 converter; $15.00 additional installation.
Pay Service 1
Pay Units: 106.
Programming (via satellite): Cinemax.
Fee: $20.00 installation; $9.95 monthly.
Pay Service 2
Pay Units: 56.
Programming (via satellite): Showtime.
Fee: $20.00 installation; $9.95 monthly.
Pay Service 3
Pay Units: 325.
Programming (via satellite): HBO.
Fee: $20.00 installation; $9.95 monthly.
Pay Service 4
Pay Units: 3.
Programming (via satellite): The Movie Channel.
Fee: $20.00 installation; $5.95 monthly.
Local advertising: Yes. Available in locally originated, character-generated & taped programming. Rates: $35.00/Month; $10.00/Week; $2.00/Day.
Equipment: ISS, Jerrold & Scientific-Atlanta head end; Magnavox amplifiers; Comm/Scope & Times Fiber cable; Texscan character generator; Jerrold set top converters; Eagle & PPC traps; Prodelin & Scientific-Atlanta satellite antenna; ICM & Scientific-Atlanta satellite receivers.
Miles of plant: 40.0 (coaxial). Homes passed: 2,146. Total homes in franchised area: 2,146.
Manager: Dave Walker. Chief technician: Jeff Smith. Program director: Sue Turner. Marketing director: Jennifer Hauschild.
City fee: 3% of gross.
Ownership: Classic Cable (MSO).

KINGSTON—CommuniComm Services, Box 597, 1501 W. Mississippi, Durant, OK 74702-0597. Phones: 580-924-2367; 800-752-4992. County: Marshall. Also serves Caney Creek Resort, Marshall County (portions). ICA: OK0343.
TV Market Ranking: Below 100 (Kingston, Marshall County); Outside TV Markets (Caney Creek Resort). Franchise award date: N.A. Franchise expiration date: N.A. Began: N.A.
Channel capacity: 35 (not 2-way capable). Channels available but not in use: 1.
Basic Service
Subscribers: 565.
Programming (received off-air): KTEN (A,N,F) Ada; KDFW (F), KXAS-TV (N), KXTX-TV (I), WFAA-TV (A) Dallas-Fort Worth; KETA (P) Oklahoma City; KXII (C) Sherman.
Programming (via satellite): WGN-TV (W) Chicago; A & E; American Movie Classics; C-SPAN; CNN; Country Music TV; Discovery Channel; Disney Channel; ESPN; Fox Family Channel; Fox Sports Net Southwest; Headline News; MTV; Nashville Network; Nickelodeon; QVC; Sci-Fi Channel; TBS Superstation; The Weather Channel; Trinity Bcstg. Network; Turner Network TV; USA Network.
Fee: $49.95 installation; $31.00 monthly.
Pay Service 1
Pay Units: 10.
Programming (via satellite): Cinemax.
Fee: $9.95 monthly.
Pay Service 2
Pay Units: 15.
Programming (via satellite): HBO.
Fee: $12.95 monthly.
Miles of plant: 29.0 (coaxial); None (fiber optic).
Manager: Danny R. Neumann.
Ownership: James Cable Partners (MSO).

KONAWA—Peak Cablevision, 205 E. Cherokee, McAlester, OK 74502. Phone: 918-423-6661. Fax: 918-426-2809. County: Seminole. Also serves Seminole County (southern portion). ICA: OK0131.
TV Market Ranking: Below 100. Franchise award date: N.A. Franchise expiration date: N.A. Began: January 1, 1981.
Channel capacity: 36 (not 2-way capable). Channels available but not in use: N.A.
Basic Service
Subscribers: 328.
Programming (received off-air): KTEN (A,N,F) Ada; KETA (P), KFOR-TV (N), KOCB (W), KOCO-TV (A), KOKH-TV (F), KWTV (C) Oklahoma City.
Programming (via satellite): A & E; American Movie Classics; Animal Planet; CNBC; CNN; Cartoon Network; Country Music TV; Discovery Channel; Disney Channel; ESPN; FX; Fox Family Channel; Fox News Channel; Fox Sports Net Southwest; Headline News; Home & Garden Television; Learning Channel; MTV; Nashville Network; Nickelodeon; TBS Superstation; The Weather Channel; Turner Network TV; USA Network.
Fee: $21.75 installation; $25.96 monthly; $14.50 additional installation.
Pay Service 1
Pay Units: 35.
Programming (via satellite): Cinemax.
Fee: $12.05 installation; $12.25 monthly.
Pay Service 2
Pay Units: 88.
Programming (via satellite): The New Encore.
Fee: $1.75 monthly.
Pay Service 3
Pay Units: 52.
Programming (via satellite): HBO.
Fee: $12.95 installation; $12.70 monthly.
Pay Service 4
Pay Units: 39.
Programming (via satellite): Starz!
Fee: $6.75 monthly.
Miles of plant: 9.1 (coaxial). Homes passed: 720. Total homes in franchised area: 720.
Manager: Everett Thayer. Chief technician: Lynn Harrison. Marketing director: Terry Homesley. Customer service manager: Susan Moore.
Ownership: Peak Cablevision LLC (MSO). See Cable System Ownership.

KREMLIN—Classic Cable, Box 429, 605 N.W. 3rd St., Plainville, KS 67663-0429. Phones: 785-434-7620; 800-999-8876. Fax: 785-434-2614. Web Site: http://www.classic-cable.com. County: Garfield. ICA: OK0293.
TV Market Ranking: Outside TV Markets. Franchise award date: January 1, 1989. Franchise expiration date: January 1, 2014. Began: September 1, 1989.
Channel capacity: 61 (2-way capable). Channels available but not in use: N.A.
Basic Service
Subscribers: 38.
Programming (received off-air): KAUT-TV (U), KETA (P), KFOR-TV (N), KOCB (W), KOCO-TV (A), KOKH-TV (F), KWTV (C) Oklahoma City.
Programming (via satellite): WGN-TV (W) Chicago; CNN; Country Music TV; Discovery Channel; Disney Channel; ESPN; Fox Family Channel; Nashville Network; TBS Superstation; Turner Network TV.
Fee: $35.00 installation; $27.95 monthly; $3.50 converter.
Pay Service 1
Pay Units: 4.
Programming (via satellite): HBO.
Fee: $20.00 installation; $9.95 monthly.
Local advertising: No.
Equipment: Scientific-Atlanta amplifiers.
Miles of plant: 3.1 (coaxial). Homes passed: 120.
Manager: Dave Walker. Chief technician: Jeff Smith. Program director: Sue Turner. Marketing director: Jennifer Hauschild.
Ownership: Classic Cable (MSO).

LAHOMA—Classic Cable, Box 429, 605 N.W. 3rd St., Plainville, KS 67663-0429. Phones: 785-434-7620; 800-999-8876. Fax: 785-434-2614. Web Site: http://www.classic-cable.com. County: Garfield. ICA: OK0382.
TV Market Ranking: Outside TV Markets. Franchise award date: N.A. Franchise expiration date: N.A. Began: N.A.
Channel capacity: 36 (2-way capable). Channels available but not in use: N.A.
Basic Service
Subscribers: 159.
Programming (received off-air): KAUT-TV (U), KETA (P), KFOR-TV (N), KOCB (W), KOCO-TV (A), KOKH-TV (F), KTBO-TV (T), KWTV (C) Oklahoma City.
Programming (via satellite): WGN-TV (W) Chicago; CNN; Discovery Channel; Disney Channel; ESPN; Fox Family Channel; History Channel; Lifetime; Nashville Network; Nick at Nite's TV Land; Nickelodeon; QVC; TBS Superstation; The Weather Channel; Turner Network TV; USA Network.
Current originations: Local news.
Fee: $35.00 installation; $27.95 monthly.
Pay Service 1
Pay Units: 20.
Programming (via satellite): HBO.
Fee: $10.95 monthly.
Pay Service 2
Pay Units: 5.
Programming (via satellite): Showtime.
Fee: $9.95 monthly.
Miles of plant: 9.0 (coaxial). Homes passed: 352.
Manager: Dave Walker. Chief technician: Jeff Smith. Marketing director: Jennifer Hauschild.
Ownership: Classic Cable (MSO).

LAKE TENKILLER—Peak Cablevision, Box 471467, Tulsa, OK 74147-1467. Phone: 918-627-9406. Fax: 918-627-9407. County: Cherokee. ICA: OK0328.
TV Market Ranking: Outside TV Markets. Franchise award date: N.A. Franchise expiration date: N.A. Began: June 15, 1993.
Channel capacity: 34. Channels available but not in use: 21.
Basic Service
Subscribers: 48.
Programming (received off-air): KJRH (N), KOED-TV (P), KOKI-TV (F), KOTV (C), KTUL (A) Tulsa.
Programming (via satellite): WGN-TV (W) Chicago; CNN; ESPN; Nashville Network; TBS Superstation; The Weather Channel; Trinity Bcstg. Network.
Fee: $25.00 installation; $18.00 monthly.
Pay Service 1
Pay Units: 57.
Programming (via satellite): Showtime; The Movie Channel.
Fee: $10.95 monthly (each).
Miles of plant: 6.0 (coaxial). Homes passed: 244.
Manager: Dennis Moore. Chief technician: Lynn Harrison. Marketing director: Terry Homesley.

Ownership: Peak Cablevision LLC (MSO). See Cable System Ownership.

LAMONT—Rapid Cable, Box 117, 307 N. Main St., Granite, OK 73547. Phone: 800-972-0962. County: Grant. Also serves Medford. ICA: OK0211.
TV Market Ranking: Outside TV Markets. Franchise award date: N.A. Franchise expiration date: January 1, 2007. Began: N.A.
Channel capacity: 24. Channels available but not in use: N.A.
Basic Service
Subscribers: 131.
Programming (received off-air): KOET (P) Eufaula; KAUT-TV (U), KFOR-TV (N), KOCB (W), KOCO-TV (A), KOKH-TV (F), KWTV (C) Oklahoma City.
Programming (via satellite): WGN-TV (W) Chicago; CNN; ESPN; Nashville Network; TBS Superstation; Turner Network TV; USA Network.
Current originations: Public access; government access.
Fee: $35.00 installation; $14.50 monthly.
Pay Service 1
Pay Units: 29.
Programming (via satellite): The Movie Channel.
Fee: $10.00 installation; $10.00 monthly.
Pay Service 2
Pay Units: N.A.
Programming (via satellite): Disney Channel; Showtime.
Fee: $10.00 installation; $10.00 monthly (each).
Local advertising: No.
Equipment: Cadco, Drake & Microdyne headend; Scientific-Atlanta & Tocom amplifiers; Comm/Scope cable; Scientific-Atlanta & Zenith set top converters; Arcom traps; Drake, M/A-Com & Microdyne satellite receivers.
Miles of plant: 6.0 (coaxial). Homes passed: 260. Total homes in franchised area: 274.
Manager: Eugene W. Kretchmar. Chief technician: Mark Kretchmar. Marketing director: Freda Kretchmar.
City fee: 3% of basic.
Ownership: Rapid Communications Partners LP (MSO).

LANGSTON—Oklahoma Cablecomm, Box 970, Fort Gibson, OK 74434-0970. Phones: 918-478-2100; 800-783-5701. Fax: 918-478-2355. County: Logan. Also serves Coyle. ICA: OK0275.
TV Market Ranking: Outside TV Markets. Franchise award date: December 27, 1988. Franchise expiration date: December 27, 2013. Began: March 1, 1989.
Channel capacity: 35 (not 2-way capable). Channels available but not in use: 14.
Basic Service
Subscribers: 92.
Programming (received off-air): KAUT-TV (U), KETA (P), KFOR-TV (N), KOCB (W), KOCO-TV (A), KOKH-TV (F), KTBO-TV (T), KWTV (C) Oklahoma City.
Programming (via satellite): WGN-TV (W) Chicago; A & E; BET; CNN; Country Music TV; Discovery Channel; ESPN; Fox Family Channel; Nashville Network; TBS Superstation; Turner Network TV; USA Network.
Fee: $40.00 installation; $22.95 monthly; $1.96 converter; $19.95 additional installation.
Pay Service 1
Pay Units: 28.
Programming (via satellite): Cinemax.
Fee: $20.00 installation; $9.95 monthly.
Pay Service 2
Pay Units: 56.
Programming (via satellite): HBO.
Fee: $20.00 installation; $9.95 monthly.
Local advertising: No.
Program Guide: TV Host.
Equipment: Jerrold set top converters; Arcom traps.
Miles of plant: 9.0 (coaxial). Homes passed: 349.
Manager: Rick Wall. Chief technician: Leon Strain. Marketing & program director: Bruce Berkinshaw.
City fee: 5% of gross.
Ownership: Fanch Communications Inc. (MSO); Time Warner Cable (MSO). See Cable System Ownership.

LAVERNE—Classic Cable, Box 429, 605 N.W. 3rd St., Plainville, KS 67663-0429. Phones: 785-434-7620; 800-999-8876. Fax: 785-434-2614. Web Site: http://www.classic-cable.com. County: Harper. ICA: OK0132.
TV Market Ranking: Outside TV Markets. Franchise award date: N.A. Franchise expiration date: N.A. Began: February 15, 1962.
Channel capacity: 41 (2-way capable). Channels available but not in use: N.A.
Basic Service
Subscribers: 438.
Programming (received off-air): KETA (P), KOKH-TV (F) Oklahoma City; KOMI-LP (I) Woodward; 1 FM.
Programming (via microwave): KFOR-TV (N), KOCO-TV (A), KWTV (C) Oklahoma City.
Programming (via satellite): WGN-TV (W) Chicago; A & E; CNN; Discovery Channel; Disney Channel; ESPN; Fox Family Channel; Fox Sports Net Southwest; History Channel; Home & Garden Television; Nashville Network; Nick at Nite's TV Land; Nickelodeon; QVC; Sci-Fi Channel; TBS Superstation; The Weather Channel; Trinity Bcstg. Network; Turner Network TV; USA Network; Univision.
Current originations: Automated time-weather.
Fee: $35.00 installation; $28.95 monthly.
Pay Service 1
Pay Units: 74.
Programming (via satellite): HBO.
Fee: $10.95 monthly.
Pay Service 2
Pay Units: 30.
Programming (via satellite): Showtime.
Fee: $9.95 monthly.
Pay Service 3
Pay Units: 40.
Programming (via satellite): The Movie Channel.
Fee: $5.95 monthly.
Pay Service 4
Pay Units: 10.
Programming (via satellite): Cinemax.
Fee: $9.95 monthly.
Equipment: Drake & Jerrold headend; Tocom, Triple Crown & Viking amplifiers; Comsonics, Tocom & Triple Crown cable.
Miles of plant: 14.5 (coaxial). Homes passed: 712.
Manager: Dave Walker. Chief technician: Jeff Smith. Marketing director: Jennifer Hauschild.
City fee: 2% of gross.
Ownership: Classic Cable (MSO).

LAWTON—Lawton Cablevision Inc., 811 D Ave., Lawton, OK 73502. Phone: 580-353-2250. Fax: 580-355-7531. County: Comanche. Also serves Comanche County. ICA: OK0004.
TV Market Ranking: Below 100. Franchise award date: January 1, 1965. Franchise expiration date: January 1, 2006. Began: March 20, 1968.
Channel capacity: 35. Channels available but not in use: 4.
Basic Service
Subscribers: 25,000.
Programming (received off-air): KETA (P), KFOR-TV (N), KWTV (C) Oklahoma City; KAUZ-TV (C), KFDX-TV (N), KJTL (F,U), KSWO-TV (A) Wichita Falls-Lawton.
Programming (via satellite): WGN-TV (W) Chicago; TBS Superstation; The Weather Channel.
Current originations: Automated time-weather; educational access; government access.
Fee: $20.00 installation; $14.94 monthly; $11.00 additional installation.
Expanded Basic Service
Subscribers: 9,300.
Programming (via satellite): A & E; American Movie Classics; BET; C-SPAN; CNBC; CNN; Cartoon Network; Discovery Channel; Disney Channel; ESPN; Fox Family Channel; Headline News; Learning Channel; Lifetime; MTV; Nashville Network; Nickelodeon; QVC; Sci-Fi Channel; TV Guide Channel; Trinity Bcstg. Network; Turner Network TV; USA Network; VH1.
Fee: $11.00 installation; $12.37 monthly.
Pay Service 1
Pay Units: N.A.
Programming (via satellite): HBO; Showtime; The Movie Channel.
Fee: $20.00 installation; $10.00 monthly (Showtime or TMC), $11.00 monthly (HBO).
Equipment: Jerrold & Scientific-Atlanta headend; Jerrold amplifiers; Comm/Scope & Times Fiber cable; Sony VTRs; Compuvid & MSI character generator; Oak set top converters; Anixter-Mark, Harris & Scientific-Atlanta satellite antenna; Microdyne & Scientific-Atlanta satellite receivers.
Miles of plant: 350.0 (coaxial); None (fiber optic). Homes passed: 30,000. Total homes in franchised area: 30,000.
Manager: William T. Drewry. Chief technician: Herman Holland.
City fee: 5% of gross.
Ownership: Drewry Communications.

LEEDEY—Classic Cable, Box 429, 605 N.W. 3rd St., Plainville, KS 67663-0429. Phones: 785-434-7620; 800-999-8876. Fax: 785-434-2614. Web Site: http://www.classic-cable.com. County: Dewey. ICA: OK0381.
TV Market Ranking: Outside TV Markets. Franchise award date: N.A. Franchise expiration date: N.A. Began: N.A.
Channel capacity: 36 (2-way capable). Channels available but not in use: N.A.
Basic Service
Subscribers: 142.
Programming (received off-air): KETA (P), KFOR-TV (N), KOCB (W), KOCO-TV (A), KOKH-TV (F), KWTV (C) Oklahoma City.
Programming (via satellite): WGN-TV (W) Chicago; CNN; Discovery Channel; Disney Channel; ESPN; Fox Family Channel; Fox Sports Net Southwest; Learning Channel; Nashville Network; Nick at Nite's TV Land; Sci-Fi Channel; TBS Superstation; The Weather Channel; Trinity Bcstg. Network; Turner Network TV; USA Network.
Current originations: Local news.
Fee: $35.00 installation; $27.95 monthly.
Pay Service 1
Pay Units: 21.
Programming (via satellite): HBO.
Fee: $10.95 monthly.
Pay Service 2
Pay Units: 7.
Programming (via satellite): Showtime.
Fee: $9.95 monthly.
Miles of plant: 5.0 (coaxial). Homes passed: 238.
Manager: Dave Walker. Chief technician: Jeff Smith. Marketing director: Jennifer Hauschild.
Ownership: Classic Cable (MSO).

LINDSAY—Multimedia Cablevision, 1500 N.W. 4th St., Lindsay, OK 73052. Phone: 405-756-8163. Fax: 405-756-8477. County: Garvin. Also serves Erin Springs. ICA: OK0073.
TV Market Ranking: Outside TV Markets. Franchise award date: September 1, 1977. Franchise expiration date: January 11, 2008. Began: March 15, 1979.
Channel capacity: 81 (not 2-way capable). Channels available but not in use: N.A.
Basic Service
Subscribers: 1,225.
Programming (received off-air): KAUT-TV (U), KETA (P), KFOR-TV (N), KOCB (W), KOCO-TV (A), KOKH-TV (F), KTBO-TV (T), KWTV (C) Oklahoma City; KTBS-TV (A) Shreveport-Texarkana.
Programming (via satellite): WGN-TV (W) Chicago; A & E; American Movie Classics; C-SPAN; CNN; Discovery Channel; E! Entertainment TV; ESPN; Fox Family Channel; Fox Sports Net Southwest; Home Shopping Network; Lifetime; Nashville Network; Nick at Nite; Nickelodeon; QVC; TBS Superstation; The Weather Channel; Turner Network TV; USA Network; VH1.
Current originations: Automated time-weather; public access; automated emergency alert; local sports.
Planned originations: Educational access.
Fee: $21.05 installation; $18.28 monthly; $22.40 additional installation.
Expanded Basic Service
Subscribers: 50.
Programming (via satellite): Cartoon Network; Country Music TV; Court TV; ESPN 2; ESPN Classic Sports; History Channel; Sci-Fi Channel; Travel Channel; Turner Classic Movies.
Fee: $6.00 monthly.
Pay Service 1
Pay Units: 102.
Programming (via satellite): Disney Channel.
Fee: $7.95 monthly.
Pay Service 2
Pay Units: 255.
Programming (via satellite): HBO.
Fee: $11.00 monthly.
Pay Service 3
Pay Units: 130.
Programming (via satellite): Cinemax.
Fee: $11.00 monthly.
Pay Service 4
Pay Units: 106.
Programming (via satellite): Showtime.
Fee: $11.00 monthly.
Local advertising: Yes. Available in locally originated & character-generated programming. Rates: $25.00/Week.
Program Guide: The Cable Guide.
Equipment: Scientific-Atlanta headend; Scientific-Atlanta amplifiers; Trilogy cable; Quanta character generator; Oak set top converters; Eagle traps; Scientific-Atlanta satellite antenna.
Miles of plant: 29.2 (coaxial). Homes passed: 1,849. Total homes in franchised area: 1,849.
Manager: Wayne Beikmann. Chief technician: Mark Harpole. Technical supervisor: R. C. Lewis. Marketing director: Jim Back. Customer service manager: Charitta Shelton.
City fee: 3% of gross.
Ownership: Multimedia Cablevision Inc. (MSO).

LONE WOLF—Rapid Cable, Box 6310, 310 Walnut Extension, Branson, MO 65615. Phones:

417-334-7897; 800-972-0962. Fax: 417-334-7899. E-mail: rcpcable@aol.com. Counties: Branson & Kiowa. Also serves Granite. ICA: OK0377.
TV Market Ranking: Outside TV Markets. Franchise award date: January 31, 1977. Franchise expiration date: January 31, 2002. Began: N.A.
Channel capacity: 22 (2-way capable; not operating 2-way). Channels available but not in use: 4.
Basic Service
Subscribers: 177.
Programming (received off-air): KETA (P), KFOR-TV (N), KOCB (W), KOCO-TV (A), KOKH-TV (F), KWTV (C) Oklahoma City; KSWO-TV (A) Wichita Falls-Lawton; 1 FM.
Programming (via satellite): WGN-TV (W) Chicago; A & E; CNN; Discovery Channel; ESPN; Fox Family Channel; Home Shopping Network 2; Learning Channel; Lifetime; MOR Galleria; Nashville Network; Sci-Fi Channel; TBS Superstation; Trinity Bcstg. Network; Turner Network TV; USA Network.
Current originations: Local access.
Fee: $29.95 installation; $21.95 monthly; $3.95 converter.
Pay Service 1
Pay Units: 9.
Programming (via satellite): Cinemax.
Fee: $9.00 monthly.
Pay Service 2
Pay Units: 13.
Programming (via satellite): Disney Channel.
Fee: $7.00 monthly.
Pay Service 3
Pay Units: 12.
Programming (via satellite): HBO.
Fee: $10.00 monthly.
Local advertising: No.
Miles of plant: 8.0 (coaxial). Homes passed: 323.
Manager: Belinda Murphy. Chief technician: Steve Rice. Program director: Beth Semptimphelter. Marketing director: Bill Fischer.
Ownership: Rapid Communications Partners LP (MSO); TS Communications Inc. (MSO).

LONGDALE—Rapid Cable, Box 117, 307 N. Main St., Granite, OK 73547. Phone: 800-972-0962. County: Blaine. ICA: OK0257.
TV Market Ranking: Outside TV Markets. Franchise award date: N.A. Franchise expiration date: N.A. Began: November 1, 1983.
Channel capacity: 35. Channels available but not in use: N.A.
Basic Service
Subscribers: N.A.
Programming (received off-air): KETA (P), KFOR-TV (N), KOCB (W), KOCO-TV (A), KOKH-TV (F), KWTV (C) Oklahoma City.
Programming (via satellite): WGN-TV (W) Chicago; CNN; ESPN; TBS Superstation; The Inspirational Network.
Fee: $13.00 monthly.
Pay Service 1
Pay Units: N.A.
Programming (via satellite): HBO.
Fee: $13.00 monthly.
Miles of plant: 6.2 (coaxial). Homes passed: 80.
Manager: Steve P. Lowe.
Ownership: Rapid Communications Partners LP (MSO).

LONGTOWN—Oklahoma Cablecomm, Box 970, Fort Gibson, OK 74434-0970. Phones: 918-478-2100; 800-783-5701. Fax: 918-478-2355. County: Haskell. Also serves Brooken, Enterprise. ICA: OK0294.
TV Market Ranking: Outside TV Markets. Franchise award date: N.A. Franchise expiration date: N.A. Began: February 1, 1984.
Channel capacity: 35. Channels available but not in use: 9.
Basic Service
Subscribers: 641.
Programming (received off-air): KTEN (A,N,F) Ada; KOET (P) Eufaula; KJRH (N), KOKI-TV (F), KOTV (C), KTFO (U), KTUL (A), KWHB (I) Tulsa.
Programming (via satellite): WGN-TV (W) Chicago; A & E; American Movie Classics; CNBC; CNN; Cartoon Network; Country Music TV; Discovery Channel; Disney Channel; E! Entertainment TV; ESPN; ESPN 2; Fox Family Channel; Fox Sports Net Southwest; Goodlife TV Network; Headline News; History Channel; Home Shopping Network; Learning Channel; Lifetime; Nashville Network; Nickelodeon; Outdoor Channel; QVC; TBS Superstation; The Weather Channel; Turner Classic Movies; Turner Network TV; USA Network.
Fee: $40.00 installation; $24.95 monthly; $1.96 converter; $19.95 additional installation.
Pay Service 1
Pay Units: N.A.
Programming (via satellite): Cinemax.
Fee: $9.95 monthly.
Pay Service 2
Pay Units: 82.
Programming (via satellite): HBO.
Fee: $9.95 monthly.
Local advertising: No.
Program Guide: TV Host.
Equipment: C-COR & Jerrold amplifiers; Atari character generator; Jerrold set top converters; Pico traps; Automation Techniques satellite receivers.
Miles of plant: 61.0 (coaxial). Homes passed: 1,624. Total homes in franchised area: 1,624.
Manager: Rick Wall. Chief technician: Leon Strain. Marketing & program director: Bruce Berkinshaw.
Ownership: Fanch Communications Inc. (MSO); Time Warner Cable (MSO). See Cable System Ownership.

LUTHER—Oklahoma Cablecomm, Box 970, Fort Gibson, OK 74434-0970. Phones: 918-478-2100; 800-783-5701. Fax: 918-478-2355. County: Oklahoma. ICA: OK0225.
TV Market Ranking: 39. Franchise award date: January 1, 1988. Franchise expiration date: January 1, 2013. Began: June 1, 1988.
Channel capacity: 35 (not 2-way capable). Channels available but not in use: 15.
Basic Service
Subscribers: 93.
Programming (received off-air): KAUT-TV (U), KETA (P), KFOR-TV (N), KOCB (W), KOCO-TV (A), KOKH-TV (F), KTBO-TV (T), KWTV (C) Oklahoma City.
Programming (via satellite): WGN-TV (W) Chicago; A & E; BET; CNN; Discovery Channel; ESPN; Fox Family Channel; Nashville Network; Sci-Fi Channel; TBS Superstation; Turner Network TV; USA Network.
Fee: $29.95 installation; $22.95 monthly; $1.96 converter; $19.95 additional installation.
Pay Service 1
Pay Units: 14.
Programming (via satellite): Cinemax.
Fee: $20.00 installation; $9.95 monthly.
Pay Service 2
Pay Units: 31.
Programming (via satellite): HBO.
Fee: $20.00 installation; $9.95 monthly.
Local advertising: No.
Program Guide: TV Host.
Miles of plant: 5.0 (coaxial). Homes passed: 221. Total homes in franchised area: 221.
Manager: Rick Wall. Chief technician: Leon Strain. Marketing & program director: Bruce Berkinshaw.
City fee: 3% of basic.
Ownership: Fanch Communications Inc. (MSO); Time Warner Cable (MSO). See Cable System Ownership.

MADILL—Cable One, Box 39, Marietta, OK 73448-2832. Phone: 405-276-2168. County: Marshall. Also serves Marshall County (northern portion), Oakland. ICA: OK0074.
TV Market Ranking: Outside TV Markets. Franchise award date: N.A. Franchise expiration date: N.A. Began: August 1, 1962.
Channel capacity: 27. Channels available but not in use: None.
Basic Service
Subscribers: 1,020.
Programming (received off-air): KTEN (A,N,F) Ada; KETA (P) Oklahoma City; KXII (C) Sherman; 1 FM.
Programming (via microwave): KDFW (F), KTVT (C), KXAS-TV (N), KXTX-TV (I), WFAA-TV (A) Dallas-Fort Worth; KWTV (C) Oklahoma City.
Programming (via satellite): CNBC; CNN; Headline News; Lifetime; MTV; Nickelodeon; QVC; TBS Superstation.
Current originations: Automated time-weather.
Fee: $60.00 installation; $9.92 monthly.
Commercial fee: $9.70 monthly.
Expanded Basic Service
Subscribers: 923.
Programming (via satellite): American Movie Classics; ESPN; Fox Sports Net Southwest; Turner Network TV; USA Network.
Fee: $10.00 installation; $10.68 monthly.
Pay Service 1
Pay Units: 366.
Programming (via satellite): The New Encore.
Fee: N.A.
Pay Service 2
Pay Units: 152.
Programming (via satellite): HBO.
Fee: $10.00 installation; $11.95 monthly.
Pay Service 3
Pay Units: 115.
Programming (via satellite): Showtime.
Fee: $10.00 installation; $10.95 monthly.
Local advertising: No.
Program Guide: Premium Channels.
Equipment: Cadco, Jerrold & Scientific-Atlanta headend; Scientific-Atlanta amplifiers; Times Fiber cable; Fort Worth Tower satellite antenna; Scientific-Atlanta & Gardiner satellite receivers.
Miles of plant: 37.6 (coaxial). Homes passed: 1,857. Total homes in franchised area: 4,092.
Manager: Kris Miller. Chief technician: Cecil Holt.
City fee: 3% of gross.
Ownership: Cable One Inc. (MSO).

MANGUM—Cable One, Box 631, 211 E. Jefferson, Mangum, OK 73554. Phone: 580-782-3224. Fax: 580-782-5186. County: Greer. Also serves Greer County. ICA: OK0079.
TV Market Ranking: Below 100 (portions of Greer County, Mangum); Outside TV Markets (portions of Greer County). Franchise award date: September 3, 1957. Franchise expiration date: November 1, 2006. Began: April 1, 1958.
Channel capacity: 38 (not 2-way capable). Channels available but not in use: None.
Basic Service
Subscribers: 1,401; Commercial subscribers: 2.
Programming (received off-air): 6 FMs.
Programming (via microwave): KWET (P) Cheyenne; KFOR-TV (N), KOCB (U), KOCO-TV (A), KWTV (C) Oklahoma City; KAUZ-TV (C), KJTL (F,U), KSWO-TV (A) Wichita Falls-Lawton.
Programming (via satellite): WGN-TV (W) Chicago; A & E; BET; C-SPAN; CNN; Country Music TV; Discovery Channel; Disney Channel; E! Entertainment TV; ESPN; Fox Family Channel; Fox Sports Net Southwest; Headline News; History Channel; Learning Channel; Lifetime; MTV; Nashville Network; Nickelodeon; Odyssey; TBS Superstation; The Weather Channel; Trinity Bcstg. Network; Turner Classic Movies; Turner Network TV; USA Network.
Current originations: Automated time-weather; leased access; automated emergency alert.
Fee: $20.00 installation; $27.00 monthly; $0.78 converter.
Commercial fee: $137.78 monthly.
Pay Service 1
Pay Units: 137.
Programming (via satellite): Cinemax.
Fee: $11.40 monthly.
Pay Service 2
Pay Units: 153.
Programming (via satellite): HBO.
Fee: $20.00 installation; $11.40 monthly.
Local advertising: No.
Program Guide: Premium Channels.
Equipment: Scientific-Atlanta headend; Jerrold & GTE Sylvania amplifiers; Anaconda & Times Fiber cable; Texscan character generator; NSC set top converters; Eagle traps; Scientific-Atlanta satellite antenna; Scientific-Atlanta satellite receivers.
Miles of plant: 30.0 (coaxial). Homes passed: 1,615. Total homes in franchised area: 1,615.
Manager: George Wilburn. Office manager: Sue Underhill. Chief technician: Alexander Gary.
City fee: 5% of gross.
Ownership: Cable One Inc. (MSO).

MANNFORD—Cim Tel Cable Inc., Box 266, 101 Cimarron St., Mannford, OK 74044. Phone: 918-865-3314. County: Creek. ICA: OK0296.
TV Market Ranking: 54. Franchise award date: N.A. Franchise expiration date: N.A. Began: January 1, 1982.
Channel capacity: 35. Channels available but not in use: N.A.
Basic Service
Subscribers: 526.
Programming (received off-air): KJRH (N), KOED-TV (P), KOKI-TV (F), KOTV (C), KTUL (A) Tulsa.

Programming (via satellite): WGN-TV (W) Chicago; CNN; ESPN; Fox Family Channel; TBS Superstation.
Fee: $15.00 installation; $12.95 monthly.
Pay Service 1
Pay Units: 27.
Programming (via satellite): Cinemax.
Fee: $9.50 monthly.
Pay Service 2
Pay Units: 88.
Programming (via satellite): Disney Channel.
Fee: $9.50 monthly.
Pay Service 3
Pay Units: 232.
Programming (via satellite): HBO.
Fee: $9.50 monthly.
Equipment: Scientific-Atlanta headend; GTE Sylvania amplifiers; Comm/Scope cable; Anixter-Mark satellite antenna.
Manager: H. Z. Goatcher.
City fee: 3% of gross.
Ownership: Cim Tel Cable Inc. (MSO).

MARIETTA—Cable One, Box 39, Marietta, OK 73448-2832. Phone: 580-276-2168. County: Love. ICA: OK0091.
TV Market Ranking: Outside TV Markets. Franchise award date: N.A. Franchise expiration date: N.A. Began: July 1, 1966.
Channel capacity: 35. Channels available but not in use: 6.
Basic Service
Subscribers: 773.
Programming (received off-air): KTEN (A,N,F) Ada; KDFW (F), KTVT (C), KXAS-TV (N), WFAA-TV (A) Dallas-Fort Worth; KETA (P) Oklahoma City; KXII (C) Sherman; allband FM.
Programming (via satellite): C-SPAN; CNBC; CNN; Discovery Channel; Fox Family Channel; Headline News; Nashville Network; Nickelodeon; QVC; TBS Superstation; The Weather Channel.
Fee: $60.00 installation; $9.36 monthly.
Commercial fee: $9.90 monthly.
Expanded Basic Service
Subscribers: 686.
Programming (via satellite): American Movie Classics; Court TV; ESPN; Fox Sports Net Southwest; Turner Network TV; USA Network.
Fee: $10.00 installation; $10.92 monthly.
Pay Service 1
Pay Units: 72.
Programming (via satellite): Cinemax.
Fee: $10.00 installation; $10.95 monthly.
Pay Service 2
Pay Units: 34.
Programming (via satellite): Disney Channel.
Fee: N.A.
Pay Service 3
Pay Units: 278.
Programming (via satellite): The New Encore.
Fee: N.A.
Pay Service 4
Pay Units: 108.
Programming (via satellite): HBO.
Fee: $10.00 installation; $10.95 monthly.
Local advertising: No.
Program Guide: Premium Channels.
Equipment: Jerrold headend; Scientific-Atlanta amplifiers; Comm/Scope & Times Fiber cable; Fort Worth Tower satellite antenna.
Miles of plant: 26.8 (coaxial). Homes passed: 1,257. Total homes in franchised area: 2,494.
Manager: Kris Miller. Chief technician: Cecil Holt.
City fee: 2% of gross.
Ownership: Cable One Inc. (MSO).

MARLAND—Oklahoma Cablecomm, Box 970, Fort Gibson, OK 74434-0970. Phones: 918-478-2100; 800-783-5701. Fax: 918-478-2355. County: Noble. ICA: OK0297.
TV Market Ranking: Outside TV Markets. Franchise award date: January 1, 1989. Franchise expiration date: January 1, 2014. Began: September 1, 1989.
Channel capacity: 35 (not 2-way capable). Channels available but not in use: 18.
Basic Service
Subscribers: 38.
Programming (received off-air): KAUT-TV (U), KETA (P), KFOR-TV (N), KOCB (W), KOCO-TV (A), KOKH-TV (F), KWTV (C) Oklahoma City.
Programming (via satellite): WGN-TV (W) Chicago; A & E; CNN; Discovery Channel; ESPN; Fox Family Channel; Nashville Network; TBS Superstation; USA Network.
Fee: $30.00 installation; $20.95 monthly.
Pay Service 1
Pay Units: 21.
Programming (via satellite): HBO.
Fee: $30.00 installation; $10.95 monthly.
Local advertising: No.
Program Guide: TV Host.
Equipment: Cadco headend; Scientific-Atlanta amplifiers; Comm/Scope cable; Jerrold set top converters; Arcom traps; Standard Communications satellite receivers.
Miles of plant: 2.0 (coaxial).
Manager: Rick Wall. Chief technician: Leon Strain. Marketing & program director: Bruce Berkinshaw.
City fee: 5% of gross.
Ownership: Fanch Communications Inc. (MSO); Time Warner Cable (MSO). See Cable System Ownership.

MARSHALL—Classic Cable, Box 429, 605 N.W. 3rd St., Plainville, KS 67663-0429. Phones: 785-434-7620; 800-999-8876. Fax: 785-434-2614. Web Site: http://www.classic-cable.com. County: Logan. ICA: OK0298.
TV Market Ranking: Outside TV Markets. Franchise award date: N.A. Franchise expiration date: N.A. Began: January 1, 1989.
Channel capacity: 41 (2-way capable). Channels available but not in use: N.A.
Basic Service
Subscribers: 32.
Programming (received off-air): KAUT-TV (U), KETA (P), KFOR-TV (N), KOCB (W), KOCO-TV (A), KOKH-TV (F), KTBO-TV (T), KWTV (C) Oklahoma City.
Programming (via satellite): WGN-TV (W) Chicago; CNN; Discovery Channel; ESPN; Fox Family Channel; Nashville Network; Nick at Nite's TV Land; TBS Superstation; USA Network.
Current originations: Automated time-weather.
Fee: $35.00 installation; $27.95 monthly; $3.50 converter.
Pay Service 1
Pay Units: N.A.
Programming (via satellite): Showtime.
Fee: $9.95 monthly.
Pay Service 2
Pay Units: 6.
Programming (via satellite): HBO.
Fee: $10.95 monthly.
Local advertising: No.
Equipment: Blonder-Tongue headend; Jerrold amplifiers; Jerrold set top converters; Eagle & PPC traps.
Miles of plant: 2.8 (coaxial). Homes passed: 142.
Manager: Dave Walker. Chief technician: Jeff Smith. Program director: Sue Turner. Marketing director: Jennifer Hauschild.
City fee: 2% of basic.
Ownership: Classic Cable (MSO).

MARTHA—Rapid Cable, Box 6310, 310 Walnut Extension, Branson, MO 65615. Phones: 417-334-7897; 800-972-0962. Fax: 417-334-7899. E-mail: rcpcable@aol.com. County: Jackson. ICA: OK0299.
TV Market Ranking: Outside TV Markets. Franchise award date: N.A. Franchise expiration date: N.A. Began: May 1, 1990.
Channel capacity: 31 (2-way capable; not operating 2-way). Channels available but not in use: 15.
Basic Service
Subscribers: 46.
Programming (received off-air): KETA (P), KFOR-TV (N), KOCO-TV (A), KWTV (C) Oklahoma City; KJTL (F,U), KSWO-TV (A) Wichita Falls-Lawton.
Programming (via satellite): WGN-TV (W) Chicago; CNN; Country Music TV; ESPN; Fox Family Channel; Nashville Network; TBS Superstation.
Fee: $29.95 installation; $20.95 monthly; $3.95 converter.
Pay Service 1
Pay Units: 2.
Programming (via satellite): Cinemax.
Fee: $9.00 monthly.
Pay Service 2
Pay Units: 2.
Programming (via satellite): HBO.
Fee: $10.00 monthly.
Pay Service 3
Pay Units: 3.
Programming (via satellite): Disney Channel.
Fee: $7.00 monthly.
Local advertising: No.
Miles of plant: 1.9 (coaxial). Homes passed: 80.
Manager: Belinda Murphy. Chief technician: Steve Rice. Program director: Beth Semptimphelter. Marketing director: Bill Fischer.
Ownership: Rapid Communications Partners LP (MSO); TS Communications Inc. (MSO).

MAUD—Peak Cablevision, 205 E. Cherokee, McAlester, OK 74502. Phone: 918-423-6661. Fax: 918-426-2809. Counties: Pottawatomie & Seminole. ICA: OK0178.
TV Market Ranking: Below 100. Franchise award date: N.A. Franchise expiration date: N.A. Began: January 1, 1982.
Channel capacity: 35. Channels available but not in use: 9.
Basic Service
Subscribers: 242.
Programming (received off-air): KTEN (A,N,F) Ada; KETA (P), KFOR-TV (N), KOCB (W), KOCO-TV (A), KOKH-TV (F), KWTV (C) Oklahoma City.
Programming (via satellite): C-SPAN; CNBC; CNN; Discovery Channel; Fox Family Channel; Headline News; MTV; Nashville Network; TBS Superstation; The Weather Channel.
Fee: $60.00 installation; $20.70 monthly; $20.00 additional installation.
Commercial fee: $9.00 monthly.
Expanded Basic Service
Subscribers: 177.
Programming (via satellite): American Movie Classics; ESPN; Fox Sports Net Southwest; Turner Network TV; USA Network.
Fee: $3.00 monthly.
Pay Service 1
Pay Units: 29.
Programming (via satellite): Cinemax.
Fee: $20.00 installation; $10.00 monthly.
Pay Service 2
Pay Units: 20.
Programming (via satellite): Disney Channel.
Fee: $5.00 installation; $10.00 monthly.
Pay Service 3
Pay Units: 89.
Programming (via satellite): The New Encore.
Fee: N.A.
Pay Service 4
Pay Units: 57.
Programming (via satellite): HBO.
Fee: $20.00 installation; $10.00 monthly.
Local advertising: No.
Miles of plant: 10.9 (coaxial). Homes passed: 429. Total homes in franchised area: 429.
Manager: Everett Thayer. Chief technician: Lynn Harrison. Marketing director: Terry Homesley. Customer service manager: Susan Moore.
Ownership: Peak Cablevision LLC (MSO). See Cable System Ownership.

MAYSVILLE—Classic Cable, 2820 N. Green Ave., Purcell, OK 73080-1707. Phones: 405-527-5651; 800-324-5628. Fax: 405-527-5392. County: Garvin. ICA: OK0126.
TV Market Ranking: Outside TV Markets. Franchise award date: N.A. Franchise expiration date: N.A. Began: January 1, 1980.
Channel capacity: 32 (not 2-way capable). Channels available but not in use: None.
Basic Service
Subscribers: 376.
Programming (received off-air): KAUT-TV (U), KETA (P), KFOR-TV (N), KOCB (W), KOCO-TV (A), KOKH-TV (F), KSBI (I), KTBO-TV (T), KWTV (C) Oklahoma City.
Programming (via satellite): WGN-TV (W) Chicago; A & E; American Movie Classics; C-SPAN; CNN; Country Music TV; Discovery Channel; ESPN; Fox Family Channel; Home Shopping en Espanol; Lifetime; MTV; Nashville Network; Nickelodeon; QVC; TBS Superstation; The Weather Channel; Turner Network TV; USA Network.
Fee: $42.43 installation; $23.50 monthly; $21.22 additional installation.
Pay Service 1
Pay Units: N.A.
Programming (via satellite): Disney Channel; HBO; The Movie Channel; Turner Classic Movies.
Fee: $1.75 monthly (TCM), $12.37 monthly (TMC), $12.82 monthly (HBO), $13.00 monthly (Disney).
Miles of plant: 13.3 (coaxial); None (fiber optic). Homes passed: 759. Total homes in franchised area: 762.
Manager: Kris Miller. Chief technician: Kurt Widmer.
Ownership: Classic Cable (MSO).

McALESTER—Peak Cablevision, 205 E. Cherokee, McAlester, OK 74501. Phone: 918-423-6661. Fax: 918-426-2809. County: Pittsburg. Also serves Alderson, Krebs. ICA: OK0019.
TV Market Ranking: Outside TV Markets. Franchise award date: August 26, 1961. Franchise expiration date: N.A. Began: February 1, 1963.
Channel capacity: 40 (2-way capable; operating 2-way). Channels available but not in use: 4.
Basic Service
Subscribers: 6,996.
Programming (received off-air): KTEN (A,N,F) Ada; KOET (P) Eufaula; KJRH (N), KOKI-TV (F), KOTV (C), KTUL (A), KWHB (I) Tulsa; 12 FMs.
Programming (via microwave): KFOR-TV (N), KWTV (C) Oklahoma City.
Programming (via satellite): C-SPAN; Country Music TV; Discovery Channel; FX; Knowl-

edge TV; QVC; TBS Superstation; The Weather Channel.
Current originations: Educational access; government access; religious access; automated emergency alert.
Fee: $60.00 installation; $12.68 monthly; $2.00 converter; $18.34 additional installation.
Commercial fee: $1.30 monthly.
Expanded Basic Service
Subscribers: 5,852.
Programming (via satellite): A & E; American Movie Classics; Animal Planet; BET; CNBC; CNN; Cartoon Network; Disney Channel; ESPN; Fox Family Channel; Fox News Channel; Fox Sports Net Southwest; Headline News; MTV; Nashville Network; Nickelodeon; Turner Network TV; USA Network.
Fee: $13.28 monthly.
Pay Service 1
Pay Units: 1,547.
Programming (via satellite): Starz!
Fee: $6.75 monthly.
Pay Service 2
Pay Units: 2,455.
Programming (via satellite): The New Encore.
Fee: $1.75 monthly.
Pay Service 3
Pay Units: 1,605.
Programming (via satellite): HBO.
Fee: $10.50 installation; $12.59 monthly.
Pay Service 4
Pay Units: 946.
Programming (via satellite): Showtime.
Fee: $10.50 installation; $12.59 monthly.
Local advertising: Yes.
Program Guide: The Cable Guide.
Equipment: Scientific-Atlanta headend; Jerrold amplifiers; Times Fiber cable; Sony cameras; Panasonic VTRs; BEI character generator; Hamlin set top converters.
Miles of plant: 161.4 (coaxial). Homes passed: 8,879. Total homes in franchised area: 49,123.
Manager: Everett Thayer. Chief technician: Lynn Harrison. Marketing director: Terry Homesley. Customer service manager: Susan Moore.
City fee: 5% of gross.
Ownership: Peak Cablevision LLC (MSO). See Cable System Ownership.

McCURTAIN—Peak Cablevision, Box 807, Pocola, OK 74902. Phone: 918-436-7488. Fax: 918-436-7151. County: Haskell. ICA: OK0244.
TV Market Ranking: Outside TV Markets. Franchise award date: N.A. Franchise expiration date: September 11, 2010. Began: N.A.
Channel capacity: 36 (not 2-way capable). Channels available but not in use: 15.
Basic Service
Subscribers: 103.
Programming (received off-air): KOET (P) Eufaula; KFSM-TV (C), KHBS (A), KPOM-TV (N) Fort Smith; KOKI-TV (F), KTUL (A), KWHB (I) Tulsa.
Programming (via satellite): WGN-TV (W) Chicago; A & E; Country Music TV; Discovery Channel; ESPN; Fox Family Channel; Nashville Network; Sci-Fi Channel; TBS Superstation; Trinity Bcstg. Network; Turner Network TV; USA Network.
Fee: $22.61 monthly.
Pay Service 1
Pay Units: N.A.
Programming (via satellite): Disney Channel; HBO.
Fee: $7.95 monthly (Disney), $11.00 monthly (HBO).
Equipment: ISS & Drake headend; C-COR amplifiers; Times Fiber cable; Jerrold set top converters; Pico traps; Scientific-Atlanta satellite antenna; ISS & Drake satellite receivers.
Miles of plant: 3.0 (coaxial). Homes passed: 134. Total homes in franchised area: 160.
Manager: Dennis Moore. Chief technician: Rick Packard. Marketing director: Terry Homesley. Customer service manager: Susan Moore.
Franchise fee: 3% of basic subs.
Ownership: Peak Cablevision LLC (MSO). See Cable System Ownership.

MEDICINE PARK—Classic Cable, Box 429, 605 N.W. 3rd St., Plainville, KS 67663-0429. Phones: 785-434-7620; 800-999-8876. Fax: 785-434-2614. Web Site: http://www.classic-cable.com. County: Comanche. ICA: OK0116.
TV Market Ranking: Below 100. Franchise award date: N.A. Franchise expiration date: N.A. Began: September 1, 1977.
Channel capacity: N.A. Channels available but not in use: N.A.
Basic Service
Subscribers: 354.
Programming (received off-air): KAUT-TV (U), KETA (P), KFOR-TV (N), KOCB (W), KOCO-TV (A), KOKH-TV (F), KWTV (C) Oklahoma City; KFDX-TV (N), KJTL (F,U), KSWO-TV (A) Wichita Falls-Lawton; allband FM.
Programming (via satellite): WGN-TV (W) Chicago; CNN; Country Music TV; Discovery Channel; Disney Channel; ESPN; Fox Family Channel; Nashville Network; Nickelodeon; QVC; The Weather Channel; Trinity Bcstg. Network; Turner Network TV; USA Network.
Fee: $35.00 installation; $21.95 monthly.
Pay Service 1
Pay Units: N.A.
Programming (via satellite): HBO; Showtime.
Fee: $9.95 (Showtime), $10.95 monthly (HBO).
Miles of plant: 14.5 (coaxial). Additional miles planned: 7.0 (coaxial). Homes passed: 850.
Manager: Mark Livingston.
City fee: 3% of gross.
Ownership: Classic Cable (MSO).

MEEKER—Falcon Cable Media, 707 W. Saratoga, Shawnee, OK 74801. Phone: 405-275-6923. Fax: 405-275-0276. County: Lincoln. ICA: OK0186.
TV Market Ranking: Outside TV Markets. Franchise award date: May 1, 1982. Franchise expiration date: May 1, 2009. Began: May 1, 1985.
Channel capacity: 42 (2-way capable). Channels available but not in use: 15.
Basic Service
Subscribers: 232.
Programming (received off-air): KAUT-TV (U), KETA (P), KFOR-TV (N), KOCB (W), KOCO-TV (A), KOKH-TV (F), KTBO-TV (T), KWTV (C) Oklahoma City.
Programming (via satellite): CNN; Country Music TV; ESPN; Fox Family Channel; Headline News; MTV; Nickelodeon; QVC.
Current originations: Public access; educational access; government access.
Fee: $20.00 installation; $15.97 monthly; $10.00 additional installation.
Expanded Basic Service
Subscribers: 229.
Programming (via satellite): Sci-Fi Channel; The Weather Channel; USA Network.
Fee: $2.50 monthly.
Expanded Basic Service 2
Subscribers: 225.
Programming (via satellite): WGN-TV (W) Chicago; Disney Channel; Fox Sports Net Southwest; Nashville Network; TBS Superstation; Turner Network TV.
Fee: $7.75 monthly.
Pay Service 1
Pay Units: 22.
Programming (via satellite): Cinemax.
Fee: $20.00 installation; $10.45 monthly.
Pay Service 2
Pay Units: 69.
Programming (via satellite): HBO.
Fee: $20.00 installation; $10.45 monthly.
Local advertising: No.
Equipment: Jerrold, Phasecom & Scientific-Atlanta headend; Theta-Com amplifiers; Comm/Scope cable; Oak set top converters; Eagle traps; Scientific-Atlanta satellite antenna; Scientific-Atlanta satellite receivers.
Miles of plant: 16.0 (coaxial). Homes passed: 518.
Manager: Andrew Dearth.
Franchise fee: 3% of gross.
Ownership: Falcon Communications LP (MSO). See Cable System Ownership.

MENO—Westcom, Box 71279, Des Moines, IA 50325. Phone: 515-276-3174. Fax: 515-270-9181. County: Major. ICA: OK0255.
TV Market Ranking: Outside TV Markets. Franchise award date: N.A. Franchise expiration date: N.A. Began: August 1, 1989.
Channel capacity: 35. Channels available but not in use: 20.
Basic Service
Subscribers: 11.
Programming (received off-air): KAUT-TV (U), KFOR-TV (N), KOCB (W), KOCO-TV (A), KOKH-TV (F), KWTV (C) Oklahoma City.
Programming (via satellite): ESPN; Fox Family Channel; Nashville Network; TBS Superstation.
Fee: $21.50 monthly.
Pay Service 1
Pay Units: N.A.
Programming (via satellite): Cinemax.
Fee: $11.00 monthly.
Homes passed: 94.
Ownership: Westcom LC (MSO).

MERIDIAN—Classic Cable, Box 429, 605 N.W. 3rd St., Plainview, KS 67663-0429. Phones: 785-434-7620; 800-999-8876. Fax: 785-434-2614. Web Site: http://www.classic-cable.com. Counties: Logan & Stephens. Also serves Comanche. ICA: OK0384.
TV Market Ranking: Below 100. Franchise award date: N.A. Franchise expiration date: N.A. Began: July 1, 1981.
Channel capacity: 41 (2-way capable). Channels available but not in use: N.A.
Basic Service
Subscribers: 300.
Programming (received off-air): KETA (P), KFOR-TV (N), KOCO-TV (A), KOKH-TV (F), KWTV (C) Oklahoma City; KAUZ-TV (C), KFDX-TV (N), KJTL (F,U), KSWO-TV (A) Wichita Falls-Lawton.
Programming (via satellite): WGN-TV (W) Chicago; A & E; American Movie Classics; C-SPAN; CNN; Cartoon Network; Country Music TV; Discovery Channel; Disney Channel; E! Entertainment TV; ESPN; Fox Family Channel; Fox News Channel; Fox Sports Net Southwest; Headline News; History Channel; Learning Channel; Lifetime; Nashville Network; Nick at Nite's TV Land; Nickelodeon; QVC; Sci-Fi Channel; TBS Superstation; The Weather Channel; Trinity Bcstg. Network; Turner Network TV; USA Network.
Current originations: Local access.
Fee: $35.00 installation; $28.95 monthly.
Pay Service 1
Pay Units: 54.
Programming (via satellite): HBO.
Fee: $10.95 monthly.
Pay Service 2
Pay Units: 30.
Programming (via satellite): Showtime.
Fee: $9.95 monthly.
Pay Service 3
Pay Units: 21.
Programming (via satellite): The Movie Channel.
Fee: $5.95 monthly.
Local advertising: Yes. Available in satellite distributed programming.
Equipment: Jerrold & Scientific-Atlanta headend; Broadband & Scientific-Atlanta amplifiers; Comm/Scope cable; Jerrold set top converters; Pico traps.
Miles of plant: 27.0 (coaxial). Homes passed: 445.
Manager: Dave Walker. Chief technician: Roger Campbell. Marketing director: Jennifer Hauschild.
Ownership: Classic Cable (MSO).

MIAMI—Cable One, 136D Northeast, Miami, OK 74354. Phone: 918-542-1811. Fax: 918-542-6745. County: Ottawa. Also serves Commerce, North Miami, Ottawa County. ICA: OK0021.
TV Market Ranking: Below 100 (Commerce, Miami, North Miami, portions of Ottawa County); Outside TV Markets (portions of Ottawa County). Franchise award date: March 15, 1965. Franchise expiration date: June 20, 1997. Began: July 5, 1968.
Channel capacity: 62 (not 2-way capable). Channels available but not in use: 9.
Basic Service
Subscribers: 5,266.
Programming (received off-air): KODE-TV (A), KSNF (N) Joplin-Pittsburg; KJRH (N), KOED-TV (P), KOKI-TV (F), KOTV (C), KTUL (A) Tulsa; 10 FMs.
Programming (via satellite): WGN-TV (W) Chicago; A & E; C-SPAN; C-SPAN 2; CNBC; CNN; Cartoon Network; Comedy Central; Country Music TV; E! Entertainment TV; ESPN; EWTN; Electronic Program Guide; Fox Family Channel; Goodlife TV Network; Headline News; Knowledge TV; Learning Channel; Lifetime; MTV; Nashville Network; Nickelodeon; Odyssey; Sci-Fi Channel; TBS Superstation; TV Guide Channel; The Weather Channel; Trinity Bcstg. Network; Turner Classic Movies; Turner Network TV; USA Network; VH1.
Current originations: Automated time-weather; public access.
Fee: $33.70 installation; $21.75 monthly; $15.00 additional installation.
Pay Service 1
Pay Units: N.A.
Programming (via satellite): Cinemax; DMX; Disney Channel; HBO; Showtime; The Movie Channel.
Fee: $25.00 installation; $12.00 monthly (HBO or Showtime).
Pay-Per-View
Addressable homes: 4,800.
Local advertising: Yes. Available in satellite distributed programming. Rates: $9.00/30 Seconds. Local sales manager: Teddy Wood.
Equipment: Hughes, RCA & Scientific-Atlanta headend; GTE Sylvania, Century III & Texscan amplifiers; General & Times Fiber cable; Hitachi & Panasonic cameras; Sony & GTE Sylvania VTRs; Oak, Jerrold & Texscan set top converters; Oak addressable set top converters; Eagle traps; Scientific-Atlanta & Hughes satellite antenna; Scientific-Atlanta satellite receivers.

Miles of plant: 134.0 (coaxial). Homes passed: 8,265. Total homes in franchised area: 8,265.
Manager: Joel H. Durham. Chief technician: Danny Douthit. Marketing director: Rebecca Spaulding.
City fee: 3% of gross.
Ownership: Cable One Inc. (MSO).

MIDWEST CITY—Multimedia Cablevision Inc., 1304 N. Key Blvd., Midwest City, OK 73110. Phone: 405-733-4535. County: Oklahoma. Also serves Spencer. ICA: OK0005.
TV Market Ranking: 39. Franchise award date: February 23, 1978. Franchise expiration date: February 28, 2000. Began: November 1, 1979.
Channel capacity: 69 (2-way capable; operating 2-way). Channels available but not in use: 8.
Basic Service
Subscribers: 13,968.
Programming (received off-air): KAUT-TV (U), KETA (P), KFOR-TV (N), KOCB (W), KOCO-TV (A), KOKH-TV (F), KSBI (I), KTBO-TV (T), KWTV (C) Oklahoma City; 24 FMs.
Programming (via satellite): A & E; American Movie Classics; BET; C-SPAN; C-SPAN 2; CNBC; Discovery Channel; E! Entertainment TV; ESPN; Fox Sports Net Southwest; Home & Garden Television; Home Shopping Network; Learning Channel; Lifetime; MTV; Nick at Nite; Nickelodeon; QVC; TV Food Network; TV Guide Channel; The Weather Channel; USA Network; Univision; VH1.
Current originations: Public access; educational access; government access; religious access; automated emergency alert; local sports.
Fee: $13.67 installation; $19.34 monthly; $3.00 converter; $14.54 additional installation.
Expanded Basic Service
Subscribers: 13,844.
Programming (via satellite): WGN-TV (W) Chicago; CNN; Fox Family Channel; Headline News; Nashville Network; TBS Superstation; Turner Network TV.
Fee: $4.18 monthly.
Expanded Basic Service 2
Subscribers: 3,584.
Programming (via satellite): Bravo; Cartoon Network; Comedy Central; Country Music TV; Court TV; ESPN 2; History Channel; Sci-Fi Channel; TV Guide Sneak Prevue; Travel Channel; Turner Classic Movies.
Fee: $7.00 monthly.
Pay Service 1
Pay Units: 3,445.
Programming (via satellite): Cinemax.
Fee: $11.00 monthly.
Pay Service 2
Pay Units: 1,637.
Programming (via satellite): Disney Channel.
Fee: $7.95 monthly.
Pay Service 3
Pay Units: 5,835.
Programming (via satellite): HBO.
Fee: $11.00 monthly.
Pay Service 4
Pay Units: 3,559.
Programming (via satellite): Showtime.
Fee: $11.00 monthly.
Pay Service 5
Pay Units: 79.
Programming (via satellite): Music Choice.
Fee: $7.95 monthly.
Pay Service 6
Pay Units: 63.
Programming (via satellite): Golf Channel.
Fee: $6.95 monthly.
Pay-Per-View
Addressable homes: 4,335.
Local advertising: Yes. Available in satellite distributed programming. Rates: $800.00/Hour; $400.00/30 Minutes; $160.00/Minute; $80.00/30 Seconds. Local sales manager: Mark Kanter. Regional interconnect: Oklahoma Cable Advertising Interconnect.
Program Guide: The Cable Guide.
Equipment: Scientific-Atlanta headend; Jerrold amplifiers; Comm/Scope & Trilogy cable; Sony cameras; Sony VTRs; Texscan character generator; Hamlin set top converters; Scientific-Atlanta addressable set top converters; Scientific-Atlanta satellite antenna; Scientific-Atlanta satellite receivers.
Miles of plant: 268.2 (coaxial). Homes passed: 24,284. Total homes in franchised area: 24,504.
Manager: Wayne Beikman. Chief technician: Darrell Low. Marketing director: Jim Back. Customer service manager: Charitta Shelton.
City fee: 3% of gross.
Ownership: Multimedia Cablevision Inc. (MSO). See Cable System Ownership.

MILBURN—Oklahoma Cablecomm, Box 970, Fort Gibson, OK 74434-0970. Phones: 918-478-2100; 800-783-5701. Fax: 918-478-2355. County: Johnston. ICA: OK0253.
TV Market Ranking: Outside TV Markets. Franchise award date: January 17, 1989. Franchise expiration date: N.A. Began: September 1, 1990.
Channel capacity: 20. Channels available but not in use: 5.
Basic Service
Subscribers: 52.
Programming (received off-air): KTEN (A,N,F) Ada; KAUT-TV (U), KETA (P), KFOR-TV (N), KOCB (W), KOCO-TV (A), KOKH-TV (F), KWTV (C) Oklahoma City; KXII (C) Sherman.
Programming (via satellite): WGN-TV (W) Chicago; CNN; Country Music TV; Discovery Channel; ESPN; Fox Family Channel; Headline News; Nashville Network; TBS Superstation; USA Network.
Fee: $25.00 installation; $19.95 monthly.
Pay Service 1
Pay Units: 21.
Programming (via satellite): HBO.
Fee: $10.00 monthly.
Local advertising: No.
Program Guide: TV Host.
Miles of plant: 4.0 (coaxial). Homes passed: 104. Total homes in franchised area: 104.
Manager: Jim Stafford. Chief technician: Jacky Oliver. Marketing & program director: Bruce Berkinshaw.
Ownership: Fanch Communications Inc. (MSO); Time Warner Cable (MSO). See Cable System Ownership.

MOORE—Multimedia Cablevision, 820 W. Irish Lane, Edmond, OK 73003. Phone: 405-348-5750. Fax: 405-348-8059. County: Cleveland. ICA: OK0011.
TV Market Ranking: 39. Franchise award date: January 3, 1978. Franchise expiration date: January 3, 2000. Began: July 5, 1979.
Channel capacity: 78 (2-way capable; operating 2-way). Channels available but not in use: None.
Basic Service
Subscribers: 10,880.
Programming (received off-air): KETA (P), KFOR-TV (N), KOCB (W), KOCO-TV (A), KOKH-TV (F), KOPX (X), KSBI (I), KTBO-TV (T), KWTV (C) Oklahoma City.
Programming (via satellite): A & E; American Movie Classics; BET; C-SPAN; C-SPAN 2; CNBC; Discovery Channel; Disney Channel; E! Entertainment TV; ESPN; Fox Sports Net Southwest; Home & Garden Television; Home Shopping Network; Learning Channel; Lifetime; MSNBC; MTV; Nick at Nite's TV Land; Nickelodeon; QVC; TV Food Network; TV Guide Channel; TV Guide Sneak Prevue; The Weather Channel; USA Network; Univision; VH1.
Current originations: Public access; educational access; government access; religious access; automated emergency alert; local sports; local news.
Fee: $15.29 installation; $21.81 monthly; $3.00 converter.
Expanded Basic Service
Subscribers: 10,498.
Programming (via satellite): WGN-TV (W) Chicago; CNN; Fox Family Channel; Headline News; Nashville Network; TBS Superstation; Turner Network TV.
Fee: $4.18 monthly.
Expanded Basic Service 2
Subscribers: 5,679.
Programming (via satellite): Bravo; Cartoon Network; Comedy Central; Country Music TV; Court TV; ESPN 2; Golf Channel; History Channel; Sci-Fi Channel; Travel Channel; Turner Classic Movies.
Fee: $6.86 monthly.
Pay Service 1
Pay Units: 1,588.
Programming (via satellite): Cinemax (multiplexed).
Fee: $11.00 monthly.
Pay Service 2
Pay Units: 3,313.
Programming (via satellite): HBO (multiplexed).
Fee: $11.00 monthly.
Pay Service 3
Pay Units: 2,065.
Programming (via satellite): Showtime (multiplexed).
Fee: $11.00 monthly.
Pay Service 4
Pay Units: 42.
Programming (via satellite): Music Choice.
Fee: $7.95 monthly.
Pay-Per-View
Addressable homes: 3,662.
Viewer's Choice 1, 3, 4; Viewer's Choice 5; Hot Choice.
Fee: $3.95 (each).
Pay-per-view manager: Debra Smith.
Local advertising: Yes. Available in satellite distributed programming. Rates: $800.00/Hour; $400.00/30 Minutes; $160.00/Minute; $80.00/30 Seconds. Local sales manager: Mark Kanter. Regional interconnect: Oklahoma Cable Advertising Interconnect.
Equipment: Scientific-Atlanta headend; Scientific-Atlanta amplifiers; Trilogy cable; Jerrold fiber optic cable; Panasonic cameras; Panasonic VTRs; Texscan character generator; Jerrold, Oak & Hamlin set top converters; Scientific-Atlanta addressable set top converters; Eagle traps; Scientific-Atlanta satellite antenna; Scientific-Atlanta satellite receivers.
Miles of plant: 166.0 (coaxial). Homes passed: 16,139. Total homes in franchised area: 16,139.
Manager: Ken Crouch. Chief technician: Glenn Fuller. Marketing director: Jim Back. Customer service manager: Charitta Shelton.
City fee: 3% of gross.
Ownership: Multimedia Cablevision Inc. (MSO). See Cable System Ownership.

MORRIS—Oklahoma Cablecomm, Box 970, Fort Gibson, OK 74434-0970. Phones: 918-478-2100; 800-783-5701. Fax: 918-478-2355. County: Okmulgee. ICA: OK0152.
TV Market Ranking: Outside TV Markets. Franchise award date: N.A. Franchise expiration date: N.A. Began: March 1, 1982.
Channel capacity: 42 (not 2-way capable). Channels available but not in use: 10.
Basic Service
Subscribers: 337.
Programming (received off-air): KDOR (T) Bartlesville; KJRH (N), KOED-TV (P), KOKI-TV (F), KOTV (C), KTFO (U), KTUL (A), KWHB (I) Tulsa.
Programming (via satellite): WGN-TV (W) Chicago; A & E; American Movie Classics; CNN; Cartoon Network; Discovery Channel; Disney Channel; E! Entertainment TV; ESPN; ESPN 2; Fox Family Channel; Fox Sports Net Southwest; Headline News; History Channel; Learning Channel; Lifetime; Nashville Network; Nickelodeon; QVC; Sci-Fi Channel; TBS Superstation; The Inspirational Network; The Weather Channel; Turner Classic Movies; Turner Network TV; USA Network.
Current originations: Automated time-weather.
Fee: $40.00 installation; $24.95 monthly; $1.96 converter; $19.95 additional installation.
Pay Service 1
Pay Units: N.A.
Programming (via satellite): Cinemax.
Fee: $15.00 installation; $9.95 monthly.
Pay Service 2
Pay Units: 44.
Programming (via satellite): HBO.
Fee: $9.95 monthly.
Local advertising: No.
Program Guide: TV Host.
Equipment: Blonder-Tongue, RCA & Scientific-Atlanta headend; Theta-Com amplifiers; M/A-Com & Prodelin satellite antenna; Microdyne & Microwave Assoc. satellite receivers.
Miles of plant: 13.0 (coaxial). Homes passed: 529. Total homes in franchised area: 580.
Manager: Rick Wall. Chief technician: Leon Strain. Marketing & program director: Bruce Berkinshaw.
City fee: 2% of gross.
Ownership: Fanch Communications Inc. (MSO); Time Warner Cable (MSO). See Cable System Ownership.

MORRISON—Oklahoma Cablecomm, Box 970, Fort Gibson, OK 74434-0970. Phone: 918-478-2100. Fax: 918-478-2355. County: Noble. ICA: OK0357.
TV Market Ranking: Outside TV Markets. Franchise award date: N.A. Franchise expiration date: N.A. Began: N.A.
Channel capacity: N.A. Channels available but not in use: N.A.
Basic Service
Subscribers: 135.
Programming (received off-air): KAUT-TV (U), KETA (P), KFOR-TV (N), KOCB (W), KOCO-TV (A), KOKH-TV (F), KTBO-TV (T), KWTV (C) Oklahoma City; KOKI-TV (F), KWHB (I) Tulsa.
Programming (via satellite): WGN-TV (W) Chicago; A & E; American Movie Classics; CNN; Cartoon Network; Country Music TV; Discovery Channel; ESPN; Fox Family Channel; Fox Sports Net Southwest; History Channel; Nashville Network; Nickelodeon; TBS Superstation; The Weather Channel; Turner Network TV; USA Network.
Fee: $40.00 installation; $22.95 monthly; $1.96 converter; $19.95 additional installation.
Pay Service 1
Pay Units: N.A.
Programming (via satellite): Cinemax; HBO.
Fee: $9.95 monthly (each).
Manager: Rick Wall. Technician: Leon Strain. Marketing & program director: Bruce Berkinshaw.

Ownership: Fanch Communications Inc. (MSO); Time Warner Cable (MSO). See Cable System Ownership.

MOUNDS—Oklahoma Cablecomm, Box 970, Fort Gibson, OK 74434-0970. Phones: 918-478-2100; 800-783-5701. Fax: 918-478-2355. County: Creek. ICA: OK0175.

TV Market Ranking: 54. Franchise award date: February 1, 1980. Franchise expiration date: February 1, 2010. Began: January 1, 1983.

Channel capacity: 42 (not 2-way capable). Channels available but not in use: 4.

Basic Service

Subscribers: 160.

Programming (received off-air): KJRH (N), KOED-TV (P), KOKI-TV (F), KOTV (C), KTFO (U), KTUL (A), KWHB (I) Tulsa.

Programming (via satellite): WGN-TV (W) Chicago; A & E; American Movie Classics; BET; C-SPAN 2; CNN; Country Music TV; Discovery Channel; Disney Channel; E! Entertainment TV; ESPN; Fox Family Channel; Headline News; History Channel; Learning Channel; Lifetime; MTV; Nashville Network; Nickelodeon; QVC; Sci-Fi Channel; TBS Superstation; The Weather Channel; Turner Network TV; USA Network; VH1.

Fee: $30.00 installation; $20.95 monthly.

Pay Service 1

Pay Units: 24.

Programming (via satellite): Cinemax.

Fee: $20.00 installation; $10.00 monthly.

Pay Service 2

Pay Units: 34.

Programming (via satellite): HBO.

Fee: $20.00 installation; $10.00 monthly.

Pay Service 3

Pay Units: 10.

Programming (via satellite): The Movie Channel.

Fee: $20.00 installation; $10.00 monthly.

Local advertising: No.

Program Guide: TV Host.

Equipment: Blonder-Tongue, Drake & Triple Crown headend; Magnavox amplifiers; Automation Techniques satellite receivers.

Miles of plant: 7.0 (coaxial). Homes passed: 444. Total homes in franchised area: 444.

Manager: Rick Wall. Chief technician: Leon Strain. Marketing & program director: Bruce Berkinshaw.

City fee: 3% of gross.

Ownership: Fanch Communications Inc. (MSO); Time Warner Cable (MSO). See Cable System Ownership.

MOUNTAIN PARK—Rapid Cable, Box 117, 307 N. Main St., Granite, OK 73547. Phone: 800-972-0962. County: Kiowa. ICA: OK0300.

TV Market Ranking: Below 100. Franchise award date: N.A. Franchise expiration date: N.A. Began: N.A.

Channel capacity: N.A. Channels available but not in use: N.A.

Basic Service

Subscribers: N.A.

Programming (received off-air): KETA (P), KFOR-TV (N), KOCO-TV (A) Oklahoma City; KAUZ-TV (C), KFDX-TV (N), KJTL (F,U), KSWO-TV (A) Wichita Falls-Lawton.

Programming (via satellite): CNN; Discovery Channel; ESPN; Fox Family Channel; Nashville Network; TBS Superstation.

Fee: $25.00 installation; $13.00 monthly.

Pay Service 1

Pay Units: N.A.

Programming (via satellite): Cinemax.

Fee: $7.00 monthly.

Manager: Mike Stage.

Ownership: Rapid Communications Partners LP (MSO).

MOUNTAIN VIEW—Mountain View Cable TV, Box 237, 314 W. Main St., Mountain View, OK 73062. Phone: 585-347-2111. County: Kiowa. ICA: OK0166.

TV Market Ranking: Outside TV Markets. Franchise award date: March 19, 1969. Franchise expiration date: May 15, 2003. Began: May 1, 1969.

Channel capacity: 28. Channels available but not in use: 11.

Basic Service

Subscribers: 334.

Programming (received off-air): KAUT-TV (U), KETA (P), KFOR-TV (N), KOCB (W), KOCO-TV (A), KOKH-TV (F), KWTV (C) Oklahoma City; KSWO-TV (A) Wichita Falls-Lawton; 20 FMs.

Programming (via satellite): ESPN; TBS Superstation.

Current originations: Automated time-weather; public access; religious access.

Fee: $20.00 installation; $18.00 monthly.

Pay Service 1

Pay Units: 31.

Programming (via satellite): Cinemax.

Fee: $15.00 installation; $9.00 monthly.

Pay Service 2

Pay Units: 36.

Programming (via satellite): HBO.

Fee: $9.00 monthly.

Local advertising: Yes. Available in character-generated programming. Rates: $7.50/Week.

Equipment: Automation Techniques & Blonder-Tongue headend; Scientific-Atlanta amplifiers; Times Fiber cable; Mycrotek character generator; Jerrold set top converters; Eagle traps; Comtech satellite antenna; Automation Techniques satellite receivers.

Miles of plant: 9.0 (coaxial). Homes passed: 448. Total homes in franchised area: 448.

Manager: Mickey Davis.

City fee: 2% of gross.

Ownership: Mickey Davis.

MUSKOGEE—Peak Cablevision, 410 Eastside Blvd., Muskogee, OK 74403. Phone: 918-687-7511. Fax: 918-687-3291. County: Muskogee. Also serves Muskogee County. ICA: OK0009.

TV Market Ranking: 54 (portions of Muskogee County); Below 100 (Muskogee, portions of Muskogee County). Franchise award date: January 1, 1969. Franchise expiration date: September 20, 2000. Began: July 1, 1971.

Channel capacity: 40 (not 2-way capable). Channels available but not in use: N.A.

Basic Service

Subscribers: 9,612.

Programming (received off-air): KJRH (N), KOED-TV (P), KOKI-TV (F), KOTV (C), KTUL (A) Tulsa.

Programming (via satellite): WGN-TV (W) Chicago; A & E; BET; C-SPAN; CNBC; CNN; Comedy Central; Discovery Channel; Fox Family Channel; Headline News; Lifetime; MTV; Nashville Network; Nickelodeon; Odyssey; QVC; TBS Superstation; The Weather Channel; VH1.

Current originations: Automated time-weather; educational access; automated emergency alert; local news.

Fee: $60.00 installation; $18.45 monthly; $0.74 converter; $6.94 additional installation.

Expanded Basic Service

Subscribers: 9,369.

Programming (via satellite): American Movie Classics; Court TV; ESPN; Fox Sports Net Southwest; Turner Network TV; USA Network.

Fee: $1.43 monthly.

Pay Service 1

Pay Units: 792.

Programming (via satellite): Cinemax.

Fee: $12.59 monthly.

Pay Service 2

Pay Units: 354.

Programming (via satellite): Disney Channel.

Fee: $10.95 monthly.

Pay Service 3

Pay Units: 3,042.

Programming (via satellite): The New Encore.

Fee: N.A.

Pay Service 4

Pay Units: 1,465.

Programming (via satellite): HBO.

Fee: $12.59 monthly.

Pay Service 5

Pay Units: 728.

Programming (via satellite): Showtime.

Fee: $12.59 monthly.

Local advertising: Yes (insert only). Rates: $8.00/Minute; $4.80/30 Seconds; $40.00/Hour; $24.00/30 Minutes; $16.00/15 Minutes; $10.00/5 Minutes.

Program Guide: The Cable Guide.

Equipment: Jerrold headend; Jerrold amplifiers; Comm/Scope cable; Scientific-Atlanta set top converters; Jerrold addressable set top converters; Arcom traps; Scientific-Atlanta satellite antenna; Scientific-Atlanta satellite receivers; Sony commercial insert.

Miles of plant: 245.1 (coaxial). Homes passed: 17,228. Total homes in franchised area: 18,495.

Manager: Brad Mangum. Chief technician: Darrell Kimbrill.

City fee: 5% of gross.

Ownership: Peak Cablevision LLC (MSO). See Cable System Ownership.

MUSTANG—Multimedia Cablevision, 112 Armstrong Dr., Mustang, OK 73064. Phone: 405-376-4517. Fax: 405-376-4517. County: Canadian. ICA: OK0041.

TV Market Ranking: 39. Franchise award date: September 1, 1979. Franchise expiration date: August 21, 1999. Began: September 1, 1980.

Channel capacity: 69 (2-way capable; operating 2-way). Channels available but not in use: 8.

Basic Service

Subscribers: 2,902.

Programming (received off-air): KAUT-TV (U), KETA (P), KFOR-TV (N), KOCB (W), KOCO-TV (A), KOKH-TV (F), KSBI (I), KTBO-TV (T), KWTV (C) Oklahoma City; 11 FMs.

Programming (via satellite): A & E; American Movie Classics; C-SPAN; CNBC; Discovery Channel; ESPN; Home Shopping Network; Learning Channel; Lifetime; MTV; Nickelodeon; TV Guide Channel; The Weather Channel; USA Network; VH1.

Current originations: Public access; educational access; government access; automated emergency alert; local sports.

Fee: $18.31 installation; $17.97 monthly; $19.80 additional installation.

Expanded Basic Service

Subscribers: 2,860.

Programming (via satellite): WGN-TV (W) Chicago; CNN; Fox Family Channel; Headline News; Nashville Network; TBS Superstation; Turner Network TV.

Fee: $3.59 monthly.

Expanded Basic Service 2

Subscribers: 262.

Programming (via satellite): Bravo; Cartoon Network; Comedy Central; Country Music TV; Court TV; ESPN 2; History Channel; Sci-Fi Channel; Travel Channel; Turner Classic Movies.

Fee: $6.00 monthly.

Pay Service 1

Pay Units: 489.

Programming (via satellite): Cinemax.

Fee: $11.00 monthly.

Pay Service 2

Pay Units: 353.

Programming (via satellite): Disney Channel.

Fee: $7.95 monthly.

Pay Service 3

Pay Units: 819.

Programming (via satellite): HBO.

Fee: $11.00 monthly.

Pay Service 4

Pay Units: 685.

Programming (via satellite): Showtime.

Fee: $11.00 monthly.

Pay Service 5

Pay Units: 9.

Programming (via satellite): Music Choice.

Fee: $7.00 monthly.

Pay Service 6

Pay Units: 7.

Programming (via satellite): Golf Channel.

Fee: $6.95 monthly.

Pay-Per-View

Addressable homes: 581.

Local advertising: Yes. Available in satellite distributed programming. Rates: $800.00/Hour; $400.00/30 Minutes; $160.00/Minute; $80.00/30 Seconds. Local sales manager: Mark Kanter. Regional interconnect: Oklahoma Cable Advertising Interconnect.

Program Guide: The Cable Guide.

Equipment: RCA headend; Scientific-Atlanta amplifiers; Comm/Scope cable; Panasonic cameras; Panasonic VTRs; Jerrold & Oak set top converters; Scientific-Atlanta addressable set top converters; Eagle traps; Scientific-Atlanta satellite antenna; Scientific-Atlanta satellite receivers.

Miles of plant: 93.2 (coaxial). Homes passed: 4,288.

Vice president: Terry Gorsuch. Manager: David Cooper. Chief technician: Kurtis Gill. Marketing director: Jim Back. Customer service manager: Charitta Shelton.

City fee: 3% of gross.

Ownership: Multimedia Cablevision Inc. (MSO). See Cable System Ownership.

NASH—Classic Cable, Box 429, 605 N.W. 3rd St., Plainville, KS 67663-0429. Phones: 785-434-7620; 800-999-8876. Fax: 785-434-2614. Web site: http://www.classic-cable.com. County: Grant. ICA: OK0301.

TV Market Ranking: Outside TV Markets. Franchise award date: January 1, 1989. Franchise expiration date: January 1, 2014. Began: September 1, 1989.

Channel capacity: 61 (2-way capable). Channels available but not in use: N.A.

Basic Service

Subscribers: 46.

Programming (received off-air): KAUT-TV (U), KETA (P), KFOR-TV (N), KOCB (W), KOCO-TV (A), KOKH-TV (F), KWTV (C) Oklahoma City.

Programming (via satellite): WGN-TV (W) Chicago; CNN; Discovery Channel; Disney Channel; ESPN; Fox Family Channel; Nashville Network; TBS Superstation; Turner Network TV; USA Network.

Fee: $35.00 installation; $27.95 monthly; $3.50 converter.

Pay Service 1

Pay Units: 4.

Programming (via satellite): HBO.

Fee: $20.00 installation; $9.95 monthly.

Local advertising: No.

Equipment: Scientific-Atlanta amplifiers.

Miles of plant: 3.7 (coaxial). Homes passed: 139.
Manager: Dave Walker. Chief technician: Jeff Smith. Program director: Sue Turner. Marketing director: Jennifer Hauschild.
City fee: 5% of gross.
Ownership: Classic Cable (MSO).

NEWCASTLE—Classic Cable, Box 429, 605 N.W. 3rd St., Plainville, KS 67663-0429. Phones: 785-434-7620; 800-999-8876. Fax: 785-434-2614. Web site: http://www.classic-cable.com. County: McClain. ICA: OK0302.
TV Market Ranking: 39. Franchise award date: October 1, 1986. Franchise expiration date: October 1, 2001. Began: November 1, 1988.
Channel capacity: 41 (2-way capable). Channels available but not in use: N.A.
Basic Service
Subscribers: 203.
Programming (received off-air): KAUT-TV (U), KETA (P), KFOR-TV (N), KOCB (W), KOCO-TV (A), KOKH-TV (F), KSBI (I), KWTV (C) Oklahoma City.
Programming (via satellite): WGN-TV (W) Chicago; A & E; C-SPAN; CNN; Country Music TV; Discovery Channel; Disney Channel; E! Entertainment TV; ESPN; Fox Family Channel; Fox Sports Net Southwest; Headline News; Nashville Network; Nick at Nite's TV Land; Nickelodeon; QVC; Sci-Fi Channel; TBS Superstation; The Weather Channel; Trinity Bcstg. Network; Turner Network TV; USA Network.
Current originations: Local news.
Fee: $35.00 installation; $27.95 monthly.
Pay Service 1
Pay Units: 39.
Programming (via satellite): HBO.
Fee: $10.95 monthly.
Pay Service 2
Pay Units: 23.
Programming (via satellite): Showtime.
Fee: $9.95 monthly.
Pay Service 3
Pay Units: 24.
Programming (via satellite): The Movie Channel.
Fee: $5.95 monthly.
Equipment: Oak set top converters.
Miles of plant: 24.5 (coaxial). Homes passed: 450.
Manager: Dave Walker. Chief technician: Roger Campbell. Marketing director: Jennifer Hauschild.
Ownership: Classic Cable (MSO).

NEWKIRK—Multimedia Cablevision Inc., 101 N. Main, Newkirk, OK 74647. Phone: 405-362-3783. County: Kay. ICA: OK0303.
TV Market Ranking: Outside TV Markets. Franchise award date: N.A. Franchise expiration date: March 31, 1998. Began: February 1, 1969.
Channel capacity: 40 (not 2-way capable). Channels available but not in use: None.
Basic Service
Subscribers: 892.
Programming (received off-air): KETA (P), KFOR-TV (N), KOCO-TV (A), KWTV (C) Oklahoma City; allband FM.
Programming (via satellite): CNBC; Court TV; FoxNet; Lifetime; QVC; The Weather Channel.
Fee: $36.80 installation; $9.46 monthly.
Expanded Basic Service
Subscribers: 837.
Programming (via satellite): WGN-TV (W) Chicago; A & E; American Movie Classics; CNN; Discovery Channel; ESPN; Fox Family Channel; Headline News; MTV; Nashville Network; TBS Superstation; Turner Network TV; USA Network.
Fee: $11.18 monthly.
Pay Service 1
Pay Units: 76.
Programming (via satellite): Disney Channel.
Fee: $10.00 installation; $12.60 monthly.
Pay Service 2
Pay Units: 257.
Programming (via satellite): The New Encore.
Fee: $1.70 monthly.
Pay Service 3
Pay Units: 147.
Programming (via satellite): HBO.
Fee: $10.00 installation; $13.34 monthly.
Pay Service 4
Pay Units: 103.
Programming (via satellite): Showtime.
Fee: $10.00 installation; $13.34 monthly.
Pay-Per-View
Special events.
Fee: Varies.
Local advertising: No.
Program Guide: Premium Channels.
Equipment: Jerrold headend; Jerrold amplifiers; Times Fiber cable; Jerrold set top converters; Eagle traps; Scientific-Atlanta & Microdyne satellite antenna; Scientific-Atlanta & Microdyne satellite receivers.
Miles of plant: 19.4 (coaxial).
Systems manager: Allen Goff. Chief technician: John Ozbun.
City fee: 3% of gross.
Ownership: Multimedia Cablevision Inc. (MSO).

NICHOLS HILLS—Cablevision of Nichols Hills, 2109 1/2 W. Britton Rd., Oklahoma City, OK 73120-1505. Phone: 405-755-0312. County: Oklahoma. Also serves The Village. ICA: OK0028.
TV Market Ranking: 39. Franchise award date: October 10, 1978. Franchise expiration date: October 16, 1999. Began: March 15, 1980.
Channel capacity: 69 (not 2-way capable). Channels available but not in use: 8.
Basic Service
Subscribers: 4,163.
Programming (received off-air): KAUT-TV (U), KETA (P), KFOR-TV (N), KOCB (W), KOCO-TV (A), KOKH-TV (F), KSBI (I), KTBO-TV (T), KWTV (C) Oklahoma City; 15 FMs.
Programming (via satellite): A & E; American Movie Classics; C-SPAN; CNBC; Discovery Channel; ESPN; Home Shopping Network; Learning Channel; Lifetime; MTV; Nickelodeon; TV Guide Channel; The Weather Channel; USA Network; VH1.
Current originations: Public access; automated emergency alert; local news; local sports.
Fee: $13.21 installation; $24.75 monthly; $14.06 additional installation.
Expanded Basic Service
Subscribers: 4,052.
Programming (via satellite): WGN-TV (W) Chicago; CNN; Fox Family Channel; Headline News; Nashville Network; TBS Superstation; Turner Network TV.
Fee: $4.67 monthly.
Expanded Basic Service 2
Subscribers: 290.
Programming (via satellite): Bravo; Cartoon Network; Comedy Central; Country Music TV; Court TV; ESPN 2; History Channel; Sci-Fi Channel; Travel Channel; Turner Classic Movies.
Fee: $6.00 monthly.
Pay Service 1
Pay Units: 840.
Programming (via satellite): Cinemax.
Fee: $11.00 monthly.

Pay Service 2
Pay Units: 504.
Programming (via satellite): Disney Channel.
Fee: $7.95 monthly.
Pay Service 3
Pay Units: 1,557.
Programming (via satellite): HBO.
Fee: $11.00 monthly.
Pay Service 4
Pay Units: 1,052.
Programming (via satellite): Showtime.
Fee: $11.00 monthly.
Pay Service 5
Pay Units: 26.
Programming (via satellite): Music Choice.
Fee: $7.00 monthly.
Pay Service 6
Pay Units: 19.
Programming (via satellite): Golf Channel.
Fee: $6.95 monthly.
Pay-Per-View
Addressable homes: 475.
Local advertising: Yes. Available in satellite distributed programming. Rates: $800.00/Hour; $400.00/30 Minutes; $160.00/Minute; $80.00/30 Seconds. Local sales manager: Mark Kanter. Regional interconnect: Oklahoma Cable Advertising Interconnect.
Program Guide: The Cable Guide.
Equipment: Scientific-Atlanta headend; Scientific-Atlanta & RCA amplifiers; Comm/Scope cable; Panasonic cameras; Panasonic VTRs; Hamlin & Oak set top converters; Tocom addressable set top converters; Eagle traps.
Miles of plant: 77.7 (coaxial). Homes passed: 6,730. Total homes in franchised area: 6,730.
Manager: David Cooper. Chief technician: Tom Heddlesten. Marketing director: Jim Back. Customer service manager: Charitta Shelton.
City fee: 3% of gross.
Ownership: Multimedia Cablevision Inc. (MSO). See Cable System Ownership.

NINNEKAH—Rapid Cable, Box 6310, 310 Walnut Extension, Branson, MO 65615. Phones: 417-334-7897; 800-972-0962. Fax: 417-334-7899. E-mail: rcpcable@aol.com. County: Grady. ICA: OK0163.
TV Market Ranking: Outside TV Markets. Franchise award date: January 1, 1989. Franchise expiration date: May 23, 2008. Began: June 1, 1989.
Channel capacity: 53 (2-way capable; not operating 2-way). Channels available but not in use: N.A.
Basic Service
Subscribers: 185.
Programming (received off-air): KETA (P), KFOR-TV (N), KOCB (W), KOCO-TV (A), KOKH-TV (F), KTBO-TV (T), KWTV (C) Oklahoma City.
Programming (via satellite): WGN-TV (W) Chicago; A & E; CNN; Discovery Channel; ESPN; Fox Family Channel; Fox News Channel; Nashville Network; QVC; TBS Superstation; The Weather Channel; Turner Network TV; USA Network.
Fee: $29.95 installation; $21.95 monthly; $3.95 converter.
Pay Service 1
Pay Units: 59.
Programming (via satellite): HBO.
Fee: $10.00 monthly.
Pay Service 2
Pay Units: 32.
Programming (via satellite): Disney Channel.
Fee: $7.00 monthly.
Local advertising: No.
Equipment: C-COR amplifiers; Trilogy cable; Hamlin & Jerrold set top converters; Pico traps; Drake satellite receivers.
Miles of plant: 19.8 (coaxial). Homes passed: 450.
Manager: Belinda Murphy. Chief technician: Steve Rice. Program director: Beth Semptimphelter. Marketing director: Bill Fischer.
Ownership: Rapid Communications Partners LP (MSO); TS Communications Inc. (MSO).

NOBLE—Classic Cable, 2820 N. Green Ave., Purcell, OK 73080-1707. Phone: 405-527-5651. Fax: 405-527-5392. County: Cleveland. ICA: OK0084.
TV Market Ranking: 39. Franchise award date: N.A. Franchise expiration date: N.A. Began: December 1, 1980.
Channel capacity: 32 (not 2-way capable). Channels available but not in use: None.
Basic Service
Subscribers: 745.
Programming (received off-air): KAUT-TV (U), KETA (P), KFOR-TV (N), KOCB (W), KOCO-TV (A), KOKH-TV (F), KSBI (I), KTBO-TV (T), KWTV (C) Oklahoma City.
Programming (via satellite): WGN-TV (W) Chicago; A & E; American Movie Classics; C-SPAN; CNN; Country Music TV; Discovery Channel; ESPN; Fox Family Channel; Home Shopping en Espanol; Lifetime; MTV; Nashville Network; Nickelodeon; QVC; TBS Superstation; The Weather Channel; Turner Network TV; USA Network.
Fee: $42.36 installation; $22.78 monthly; $21.18 additional installation.
Pay Service 1
Pay Units: N.A.
Programming (via satellite): Disney Channel; HBO; The Movie Channel; Turner Classic Movies.
Fee: $1.75 monthly (TCM), $12.84 monthly (TMC), $13.29 monthly (HBO).
Miles of plant: 29.4 (coaxial); None (fiber optic). Homes passed: 1,513. Total homes in franchised area: 1,729.
Manager: Kris Miller. Chief technician: Kurt Widmer.
Ownership: Classic Cable (MSO).

NORMAN—Multimedia Cablevision, 1023 N. Flood St., Norman, OK 73069. Phone: 405-359-3555. Fax: 405-348-8059. County: Cleveland. Also serves Hall Park. ICA: OK0003.
TV Market Ranking: 39. Franchise award date: June 26, 1973. Franchise expiration date: December 4, 2008. Began: September 1, 1975.
Channel capacity: 78 (2-way capable; not operating 2-way). Channels available but not in use: 2.
Basic Service
Subscribers: 24,238.

Programming (received off-air): KAUT-TV (U), KETA (P), KFOR-TV (N), KOCB (W), KOCO-TV (A), KOKH-TV (F), KOPX (X), KSBI (I), KTBO-TV (T), KWTV (C) Oklahoma City; 14 FMs.
Programming (via satellite): A & E; American Movie Classics; BET; C-SPAN; C-SPAN 2; CNBC; Discovery Channel; Disney Channel; E! Entertainment TV; ESPN; Fox Sports Net Southwest; Home & Garden Television; Home Shopping Network; Learning Channel; Lifetime; MSNBC; MTV; Nick at Nite; Nickelodeon; Pax Net; QVC; TV Food Network; TV Guide Channel; The Weather Channel; USA Network; Univision; VH1.
Current originations: Public access; educational access; government access; religious access; automated emergency alert; local news; local sports.
Fee: $17.76 installation; $22.11 monthly; $3.00 converter.
Expanded Basic Service
Subscribers: 22,647.
Programming (via satellite): WGN-TV (W) Chicago; CNN; Fox Family Channel; Headline News; Nashville Network; TBS Superstation; Turner Network TV.
Fee: $4.41 monthly.
Expanded Basic Service 2
Subscribers: 12,362.
Programming (via satellite): Bravo; Cartoon Network; Comedy Central; Country Music TV; Court TV; ESPN 2; Golf Channel; History Channel; Sci-Fi Channel; Travel Channel; Turner Classic Movies.
Fee: $8.86 monthly.
Pay Service 1
Pay Units: 2,531.
Programming (via satellite): Cinemax (multiplexed).
Fee: $11.00 monthly.
Pay Service 2
Pay Units: 6,607.
Programming (via satellite): HBO (multiplexed).
Fee: $11.00 monthly.
Pay Service 3
Pay Units: 4,484.
Programming (via satellite): Showtime (multiplexed).
Fee: $11.00 monthly.
Pay Service 4
Pay Units: 287.
Programming (via satellite): Music Choice.
Fee: $7.95 monthly.
Pay-Per-View
Addressable homes: 7,140.
Action Pay-Per-View.
Local advertising: Yes. Available in satellite distributed programming. Rates: $800.00/Hour; $400.00/30 Minutes; $160.00/Minute; $80.00/30 Seconds. Local sales manager: Mark Kanter. Regional interconnect: Oklahoma Cable Advertising Interconnect.
Program Guide: The Cable Guide.
Equipment: Scientific-Atlanta headend; Jerrold amplifiers; Comm/Scope cable; Sony cameras; Sony VTRs; Quanta character generator; Hamlin & Jerrold set top converters; Scientific-Atlanta addressable set top converters; Eagle traps; Scientific-Atlanta satellite antenna; Scientific-Atlanta satellite receivers.
Miles of plant: 346.0 (coaxial). Homes passed: 41,261. Total homes in franchised area: 41,648.
Manager: Ken Crouch. Chief technician: Larry Dawson. Marketing director: Jim Back. Customer service manager: Charitta Shelton.
City fee: 5% of gross.
Ownership: Multimedia Cablevision Inc. (MSO). See Cable System Ownership.

NOWATA—Cable One, 105 W. Delaware, Vinita, OK 74301. Phone: 918-256-7871. Fax: 918-256-8275. County: Nowata. Also serves Nowata County. ICA: OK0075.
TV Market Ranking: Below 100. Franchise award date: N.A. Franchise expiration date: N.A. Began: July 1, 1976.
Channel capacity: 42 (not 2-way capable). Channels available but not in use: None.
Basic Service
Subscribers: 1,060.
Programming (received off-air): KDOR (T) Bartlesville; KRSC-TV (E) Claremore; KOAM-TV (C), KSNF (N) Joplin-Pittsburg; KTPX (X) Okmulgee; KJRH (N), KOED-TV (P), KOKI-TV (F), KOTV (C), KTFO (U), KTUL (A), KWHB (I), KWMJ (I) Tulsa.
Programming (via satellite): WGN-TV (W) Chicago; A & E; American Movie Classics; BET; CNN; Cartoon Network; Country Music TV; Discovery Channel; Disney Channel; ESPN; Fox Family Channel; History Channel; Home & Garden Television; Lifetime; Nashville Network; Nickelodeon; Outdoor Channel; Prime Sports Radio; QVC; Sci-Fi Channel; TBS Superstation; The Weather Channel; Turner Network TV; USA Network.
Current originations: Automated time-weather; public access; religious access.
Planned originations: Automated emergency alert.
Fee: $41.72 installation (aerial), $50.00 (underground); $26.50 monthly; $3.42 converter; $9.06 additional installation.
Pay Service 1
Pay Units: N.A.
Programming (via satellite): Cinemax; HBO; Showtime.
Fee: $12.00 monthly (each).
Local advertising: No.
Equipment: Block headend; GTE Sylvania amplifiers; Standard Communications, Oak & Hamlin set top converters; Eagle addressable set top converters; Eagle traps; Microdyne satellite receivers.
Miles of plant: 38.0 (coaxial); None (fiber optic). Homes passed: 1,828. Total homes in franchised area: 2,255.
Manager: Brook McDonald.
City fee: 2% of gross.
Ownership: Cable One Inc. (MSO).

OCHELATA—Community Cablevision Co., Box 307, Skiatook, OK 74070. Phone: 918-535-2770. County: Washington. ICA: OK0148.
TV Market Ranking: 54. Franchise award date: October 1, 1983. Franchise expiration date: October 1, 2003. Began: December 31, 1983.
Channel capacity: 35. Channels available but not in use: 17.
Basic Service
Subscribers: 312.
Programming (received off-air): KJRH (N), KOED-TV (P), KOKI-TV (F), KOTV (C), KTUL (A) Tulsa.
Programming (via satellite): WGN-TV (W) Chicago; CNN; Cartoon Network; ESPN; Fox Family Channel; Headline News; MTV; Nashville Network; Nickelodeon; TBS Superstation; Turner Classic Movies; Turner Network TV.
Current originations: Automated time-weather.
Fee: $25.00 installation; $10.00 monthly.
Pay Service 1
Pay Units: N.A.
Programming (via satellite): Cinemax; Disney Channel; HBO.
Fee: $9.95 monthly (Disney), $10.00 monthly (Cinemax or HBO).
Equipment: Scientific-Atlanta headend; Scientific-Atlanta amplifiers; Scientific-Atlanta cable; Texscan character generator; Scientific-Atlanta set top converters; Pico traps; Scientific-Atlanta satellite antenna; Scientific-Atlanta satellite receivers.
Miles of plant: 21.1 (coaxial). Homes passed: 600. Total homes in franchised area: 600.
City fee: 3% of gross.
Ownership: Community Cablevision Co. (MSO).

OILTON—Community Cablevision, Box 307, Skiatook, OK 74070-0307. Phone: 918-396-3019. County: Creek. ICA: OK0162.
TV Market Ranking: Outside TV Markets. Franchise award date: April 1, 1987. Franchise expiration date: April 1, 2012. Began: July 1, 1983.
Channel capacity: 35 (not 2-way capable). Channels available but not in use: 2.
Basic Service
Subscribers: 264.
Programming (received off-air): KAUT-TV (U), KFOR-TV (N), KOCB (W), KOCO-TV (A), KOKH-TV (F), KWTV (C) Oklahoma City; KJRH (N), KOED-TV (P), KOKI-TV (F), KOTV (C), KTUL (A), KWHB (I) Tulsa.
Programming (via satellite): WGN-TV (W) Chicago; A & E; CNN; Country Music TV; Discovery Channel; ESPN; Fox Family Channel; Headline News; MTV; Nashville Network; Nickelodeon; TBS Superstation; Turner Classic Movies; Turner Network TV; USA Network; VH1.
Current originations: Automated time-weather; public access; educational access; government access; religious access; leased access; library access; local news; local sports.
Fee: $25.00 installation; $16.25 monthly; $25.00 additional installation.
Pay Service 1
Pay Units: 41.
Programming (via satellite): Cinemax.
Fee: $25.00 installation; $11.50 monthly.
Pay Service 2
Pay Units: 47.
Programming (via satellite): Disney Channel.
Fee: $25.00 installation; $7.00 monthly.
Pay Service 3
Pay Units: 51.
Programming (via satellite): HBO.
Fee: $25.00 installation; $11.50 monthly.
Pay-Per-View
Addressable homes: 264.
Local advertising: Yes. Available in character-generated programming. Rates: $15.00/Week.
Equipment: Cadco & Blonder-Tongue headend; Texscan amplifiers; Comm/Scope cable; Zenith VTRs; Texscan character generator; Hamlin set top converters; Arcom traps; Scientific-Atlanta satellite antenna; Drake satellite receivers.
Miles of plant: 8.7 (coaxial). Homes passed: 538.
Manager: Ray Soule.
City fee: 2% of gross.
Ownership: Community Cablevision Co. (MSO).

OKARCHE—Classic Cable, Box 429, 605 N.W. 3rd St., Plainville, KS 67663-0429. Phones: 785-434-7620; 800-999-8876. Fax: 785-434-2614. Web site: http://www.classic-cable.com. Counties: Canadian & Kingfisher. ICA: OK0176.
TV Market Ranking: Outside TV Markets. Franchise award date: February 28, 1979. Franchise expiration date: N.A. Began: May 1, 1981.
Channel capacity: 36 (2-way capable). Channels available but not in use: N.A.
Basic Service
Subscribers: 295.
Programming (received off-air): KAUT-TV (U), KETA (P), KFOR-TV (N), KOCB (W), KOCO-TV (A), KOKH-TV (F), KTBO-TV (T), KWTV (C) Oklahoma City.
Programming (via satellite): WGN-TV (W) Chicago; American Movie Classics; CNN; Country Music TV; Discovery Channel; Disney Channel; ESPN; Fox Family Channel; Fox Sports Net Southwest; Home & Garden Television; Learning Channel; Lifetime; Nashville Network; Nick at Nite's TV Land; Nickelodeon; Sci-Fi Channel; TBS Superstation; The Weather Channel; Turner Network TV; USA Network.
Current originations: Automated time-weather.
Fee: $35.00 installation; $27.95 monthly; $3.50 converter.
Pay Service 1
Pay Units: 79.
Programming (via satellite): HBO.
Fee: $20.00 installation; $9.95 monthly.
Pay Service 2
Pay Units: 20.
Programming (via satellite): Showtime.
Fee: $20.00 installation; $9.95 monthly.
Local advertising: No.
Equipment: Drake, Scientific-Atlanta & Triple Crown headend; Jerrold amplifiers; Jerrold set top converters; Scientific-Atlanta satellite antenna; Scientific-Atlanta & Standard Communications satellite receivers.
Miles of plant: 8.0 (coaxial). Homes passed: 442. Total homes in franchised area: 732.
Manager: Dave Walker. Chief technician: Jeff Smith. Program director: Sue Turner. Marketing director: Jennifer Hauschild.
City fee: 3% of basic gross.
Ownership: Classic Cable (MSO).

OKAY—Oklahoma Cablecomm, Box 970, Fort Gibson, OK 74434-0970. Phones: 918-478-2100; 800-783-5701. Fax: 918-478-2355. County: Wagoner. ICA: OK0161.
TV Market Ranking: Outside TV Markets. Franchise award date: N.A. Franchise expiration date: N.A. Began: June 1, 1986.
Channel capacity: 35 (not 2-way capable). Channels available but not in use: 18.
Basic Service
Subscribers: 205.
Programming (received off-air): KJRH (N), KOED-TV (P), KOKI-TV (F), KOTV (C), KTUL (A), KWHB (I) Tulsa.
Programming (via satellite): WGN-TV (W) Chicago; A & E; CNN; Country Music TV; Discovery Channel; ESPN; Fox Family Channel; Nashville Network; Nickelodeon; TBS Superstation; The Weather Channel; Turner Network TV; USA Network.
Fee: $30.00 installation; $19.95 monthly; $15.00 additional installation.
Pay Service 1
Pay Units: 17.
Programming (via satellite): Disney Channel.
Fee: $7.95 monthly.
Pay Service 2
Pay Units: 65.
Programming (via satellite): HBO.
Fee: $10.95 monthly.
Pay Service 3
Pay Units: 18.
Programming (via satellite): Showtime.
Fee: $9.95 monthly.
Local advertising: No.
Program Guide: TV Host.
Equipment: Drake, Triple Crown headend; Magnavox amplifiers; Harris satellite antenna; DX

Engineering & Scientific-Atlanta satellite receivers.
Miles of plant: 12.0 (coaxial). Homes passed: 554. Total homes in franchised area: 554.
Manager: Dane Huston. Chief technician: Dale Yingst. Marketing & program director: Bruce Berkinshaw.
City fee: 5% of basic gross.
Ownership: Fanch Communications Inc. (MSO); Time Warner Cable (MSO). See Cable System Ownership.

OKEENE—Classic Cable, Box 429, 605 N.W. 3rd St., Plainville, KS 67663-0429. Phones: 785-434-7620; 800-999-8876. Fax: 785-434-2614. Web site: http://www.classic-cable.com. County: Blaine. ICA: OK0146.
TV Market Ranking: Outside TV Markets. Franchise award date: N.A. Franchise expiration date: N.A. Began: September 1, 1979.
Channel capacity: 41 (2-way capable). Channels available but not in use: N.A.

Basic Service
Subscribers: 326; Commercial subscribers: 122.
Programming (received off-air): KAUT-TV (U), KETA (P), KFOR-TV (N), KOCB (W), KOCO-TV (A), KOKH-TV (F), KTBO-TV (T), KWTV (C) Oklahoma City; allband FM.
Programming (via satellite): WGN-TV (W) Chicago; A & E; American Movie Classics; CNN; Cartoon Network; Country Music TV; Discovery Channel; Disney Channel; ESPN; Fox Family Channel; Fox Sports Net Southwest; Goodlife TV Network; Headline News; History Channel; Home & Garden Television; Lifetime; Nashville Network; Nick at Nite's TV Land; Nickelodeon; Outdoor Channel; QVC; Sci-Fi Channel; TBS Superstation; The Weather Channel; Turner Network TV; USA Network.
Current originations: Automated time-weather.
Fee: $35.00 installation; $28.95 monthly; $3.50 converter; $15.00 additional installation.

Pay Service 1
Pay Units: 13.
Programming (via satellite): Cinemax.
Fee: $9.95 monthly.

Pay Service 2
Pay Units: 62.
Programming (via satellite): HBO.
Fee: $10.95 monthly.

Pay Service 3
Pay Units: 9.
Programming (via satellite): Showtime.
Fee: $9.95 monthly.

Local advertising: No.
Equipment: ISS, Scientific-Atlanta & Tocom headend; GTE Sylvania amplifiers; Comm/Scope cable; AFC & Prodelin satellite antenna; Automation Techniques, ICM & Microdyne satellite receivers.
Miles of plant: 12.0 (coaxial). Homes passed: 636. Total homes in franchised area: 636.
Manager: Dave Walker. Chief technician: Jeff Smith. Program director: Sue Turner. Marketing director: Jennifer Hauschild.
City fee: 3% of gross.
Ownership: Classic Cable (MSO).

OKEMAH—Peak Cablevision, 410 Eastside Blvd., Muskogee, OK 74403. Phone: 918-687-7511. Fax: 918-687-3291. County: Okfuskee. ICA: OK0111.
TV Market Ranking: Below 100. Franchise award date: N.A. Franchise expiration date: September 1, 1998. Began: February 11, 1979.
Channel capacity: 34 (not 2-way capable). Channels available but not in use: 5.

Basic Service
Subscribers: 669.
Programming (received off-air): KAUT-TV (U), KETA (P), KFOR-TV (N), KOCB (W), KOCO-TV (A), KOKH-TV (F), KTBO-TV (T), KWTV (C) Oklahoma City; KJRH (N), KOKI-TV (F), KOTV (C), KTUL (A) Tulsa.
Programming (via satellite): WGN-TV (W) Chicago; C-SPAN; CNBC; CNN; Cartoon Network; Discovery Channel; ESPN; Lifetime; MTV; Nashville Network; Nickelodeon; TBS Superstation; Turner Network TV; USA Network.
Current originations: Local sports.
Fee: $60.00 installation; $9.70 monthly; $5.03 additional installation.

Pay Service 1
Pay Units: 32.
Programming (via satellite): Disney Channel.
Fee: $10.00 monthly.

Pay Service 2
Pay Units: 231.
Programming (via satellite): The New Encore.
Fee: N.A.

Pay Service 3
Pay Units: 60.
Programming (via satellite): Showtime.
Fee: $10.00 monthly.

Pay Service 4
Pay Units: 51.
Programming (via satellite): The Movie Channel.
Fee: $10.00 monthly.

Miles of plant: 21.9 (coaxial). Homes passed: 910. Total homes in franchised area: 1,635.
Manager: Brad Mangum. Chief technician: Darrell Kimbrill.
City fee: 3% of gross.
Ownership: Peak Cablevision LLC (MSO). See Cable System Ownership.

OKLAHOMA CITY—Cox Communications, 2312 N.W. 10th St., Oklahoma City, OK 73107. Phone: 405-600-2771. Fax: 405-600-9268. Counties: Canadian, Cleveland & Oklahoma. Also serves Forest Park. ICA: OK0002.
TV Market Ranking: 39. Franchise award date: May 4, 1980. Franchise expiration date: December 31, 2011. Began: May 4, 1980.
Channel capacity: 200 (2-way capable; not operating 2-way). Channels available but not in use: None.

Basic Service
Subscribers: 121,000.
Programming (received off-air): KAUT-TV (U) Oklahoma City, KETA (P), KFOR-TV (N), KOCB(W), KOCO-TV (A), KOKH-TV (F), KOPX (X), KSBI (I), KTBO-TV (T), KWTV (C) Oklahoma City.
Programming (via satellite): WGN-TV (W) Chicago; C-SPAN; C-SPAN 2; ESPN 2; Golf Channel; History Channel; Independent Film Channel; The New Encore; Turner Classic Movies.
Current originations: Public access; educational access; government access; religious access; leased access; local news; local sports.
Fee: $21.60 installation; $6.16 monthly.

Digital Basic Service
Subscribers: N.A.
Programming (via satellite): Discovery Civilization Channel; Discovery Health Channel; Discovery Home & Leisure Channel; Discovery Kids Channel; Discovery Science Channel; Discovery Wings Channel.
Fee: N.A.

Expanded Basic Service
Subscribers: 118,000.
Programming (via satellite): A & E; American Movie Classics; Animal Planet; BET; Bravo; CNBC; CNN; Cartoon Network; Comedy Central; Country Music TV; Discovery Channel; Disney Channel; E! Entertainment TV; ESPN; FX; Fox Family Channel; Fox Sports Net Southwest; Headline News; Home & Garden Television; Home Shopping Network; Learning Channel; Lifetime; MSNBC; MTV; Nashville Network; Nick at Nite's TV Land; Nickelodeon; Odyssey; Product Information Network; QVC; Sci-Fi Channel; Speedvision; TV Guide Channel; The Weather Channel; Travel Channel; Turner Network TV; USA Network; Univision; VH1.
Fee: $21.60 installation; $22.48 monthly.

Digital Expanded Basic Service
Subscribers: N.A.
Programming (via satellite): BBC America; BET on Jazz; ESPN 2; Encore Action; Encore Love Stories; Encore Mystery; Encore True Stories & Drama; Encore Westerns; Game Show Network; Golf Channel; History Channel; Independent Film Channel; Sundance Channel; The New Encore; Turner Classic Movies; WAM! America's Kidz Network.
Fee: N.A.

Digital Expanded Basic Service 2
Subscribers: N.A.
Programming (via satellite): Bloomberg Information TV; CNNfn; ESPN 2; ESPN Classic Sports; ESPNews; The Health Network; The Inspirational Network.
Fee: N.A.

Pay Service 1
Pay Units: 12,000.
Programming (via satellite): Cinemax (multiplexed).
Fee: $11.00 monthly.

Pay Service 2
Pay Units: 39,000.
Programming (via satellite): HBO (multiplexed).
Fee: $11.00 monthly.

Pay Service 3
Pay Units: 4,900.
Programming (via satellite): The Movie Channel.
Fee: $11.00 monthly.

Pay Service 4
Pay Units: 20,000.
Programming (via satellite): Showtime (multiplexed).
Fee: $11.00 monthly.

Digital Pay Service 1
Pay Units: N.A.
Programming (via satellite): Cinemax (multiplexed); HBO (multiplexed); Showtime (multiplexed); Starz! (multiplexed); The Movie Channel (multiplexed).
Fee: N.A.

Pay-Per-View
Addressable homes: 48,000.
Hot Choice; Viewer's Choice.
Fee: $$3.95 each.

Local advertising: Yes (locally produced & insert). Available in satellite distributed, character-generated & automated programming. Local sales manager: Mark Kanter. Regional interconnect: Oklahoma Cable Advertising Interconnect.
Program Guide: The Cable Guide.
Equipment: Scientific-Atlanta headend; Scientific-Atlanta amplifiers; Comm/Scope cable; Ikegami cameras; Sony VTRs; Quanta character generator; Scientific-Atlanta set top converters; Scientific-Atlanta addressable set top converters; Northeast Filter traps; Andrew, M/A-Com & Paraclipse satellite antenna; Scientific-Atlanta satellite receivers; ChannelMatic commercial insert.
Miles of plant: 2250.0 (coaxial); 450.0 (fiber optic). Additional miles planned: 15.0 (coaxial). Homes passed: 207,000. Total homes in franchised area: 215,000.
Manager: David Bialis. Marketing director: Meribeth Sloan.
City fee: 4% of gross.
Ownership: Cox Communications Inc. (MSO).

OKMULGEE—Peak Cablevision, 410 Eastside Blvd., Muskogee, OK 74403. Phone: 918-687-7511. Fax: 918-687-3291. County: Okmulgee. Also serves Okmulgee County (central portion). ICA: OK0026.
TV Market Ranking: 54 (portions of Okmulgee County); Below 100 (Okmulgee, portions of Okmulgee County). Franchise award date: January 1, 1977. Franchise expiration date: January 1, 1998. Began: January 1, 1974.
Channel capacity: 40 (not 2-way capable). Channels available but not in use: 2.

Basic Service
Subscribers: 3,193.
Programming (received off-air): KJRH (N), KOED-TV (P), KOKI-TV (F), KOTV (C), KTUL (A) Tulsa; allband FM.
Programming (via satellite): WGN-TV (W) Chicago; A & E; American Movie Classics; BET; CNBC; CNN; Cartoon Network; Court TV; Discovery Channel; ESPN; FX; Fox Family Channel; Fox Sports Net Southwest; Headline News; Home Shopping Network; Intro TV; Nashville Network; Nickelodeon; TBS Superstation; Turner Network TV; USA Network.
Current originations: Automated time-weather; automated emergency alert.
Fee: $34.82 installation; $20.75 monthly; $0.98 converter; $17.41 additional installation.

Pay Service 1
Pay Units: 1,227.
Programming (via satellite): The New Encore.
Fee: N.A.

Pay Service 2
Pay Units: 462.
Programming (via satellite): HBO.
Fee: $9.95 monthly.

Pay Service 3
Pay Units: 518.
Programming (via satellite): Showtime.
Fee: $9.95 monthly.

Pay Service 4
Pay Units: 150.
Programming (via satellite): The Movie Channel.
Fee: $9.95 monthly.

Pay Service 5
Pay Units: N.A.
Programming (via satellite): Disney Channel; Starz!
Fee: N.A.

Local advertising: Yes.
Program Guide: The Cable Guide.
Equipment: Scientific-Atlanta headend; AEL amplifiers; Comm/Scope cable; Scientific-Atlanta set top converters; Eagle & Arcom traps; Scientific-Atlanta satellite antenna; Scientific-Atlanta satellite receivers.
Miles of plant: 110.7 (coaxial); None (fiber optic). Homes passed: 6,983. Total homes in franchised area: 7,765.
Manager: Brad Mangum. Chief technician: Darrell Kimbrill.
City fee: 3% of gross.
Ownership: Peak Cablevision LLC (MSO). See Cable System Ownership.

OLUSTEE—Rapid Cable, Box 6310, 310 Walnut Extension, Branson, MO 65615. Phones: 417-334-7897; 800-972-0962. Fax: 417-334-7899. E-mail: rcpcable@aol.com. County: Jackson. ICA: OK0223.
TV Market Ranking: Outside TV Markets. Franchise award date: October 11, 1982. Fran-

chise expiration date: October 11, 2007. Began: April 1, 1985.
Channel capacity: 31 (2-way capable; not operating 2-way). Channels available but not in use: 8.
Basic Service
Subscribers: 157.
Programming (received off-air): KETA (P) Oklahoma City; KAUZ-TV (C), KFDX-TV (N), KJTL (F,U), KSWO-TV (A) Wichita Falls-Lawton.
Programming (via satellite): WGN-TV (W) Chicago; A & E; CNN; Country Music TV; Discovery Channel; ESPN; Fox Family Channel; Home Shopping Network 2; Nashville Network; TBS Superstation; Turner Network TV; USA Network.
Fee: $29.95 installation; $22.95 monthly; $2.95 converter.
Pay Service 1
Pay Units: 22.
Programming (via satellite): Cinemax.
Fee: $9.00 monthly.
Pay Service 2
Pay Units: 28.
Programming (via satellite): HBO.
Fee: $10.00 monthly.
Pay Service 3
Pay Units: 24.
Programming (via satellite): Disney Channel.
Fee: $7.00 monthly.
Local advertising: No.
Miles of plant: 7.0 (coaxial). Homes passed: 314.
Manager: Belinda Murphy. Chief technician: Steve Rice. Program director: Beth Semptimphelter. Marketing director: Bill Fischer.
Ownership: Rapid Communications Partners LP (MSO); TS Communications Inc. (MSO).

OOLOGAH—Oklahoma Cablecomm, Box 970, Fort Gibson, OK 74434-0970. Phones: 918-478-2100; 800-783-5701. Fax: 918-478-2355. County: Rogers. ICA: OK0144.
TV Market Ranking: 54. Franchise award date: June 1, 1980. Franchise expiration date: June 1, 2000. Began: May 1, 1982.
Channel capacity: 42 (not 2-way capable). Channels available but not in use: 10.
Basic Service
Subscribers: 290.
Programming (received off-air): KDOR (T) Bartlesville; KRSC-TV (E) Claremore; KJRH (N), KOED-TV (P), KOKI-TV (F), KOTV (C), KTFO (U), KTUL (A), KWHB (I) Tulsa.
Programming (via satellite): WGN-TV (W) Chicago; A & E; American Movie Classics; CNBC; CNN; Cartoon Network; Country Music TV; Discovery Channel; Disney Channel; ESPN; ESPN 2; Fox Family Channel; Fox Sports Net; Headline News; History Channel; Learning Channel; Lifetime; Nashville Network; Nickelodeon; QVC; TBS Superstation; The Weather Channel; Turner Classic Movies; Turner Network TV; USA Network; VH1.
Fee: $30.00 installation; $23.45 monthly.
Pay Service 1
Pay Units: N.A.
Programming (via satellite): Cinemax.
Fee: N.A.
Pay Service 2
Pay Units: 81.
Programming (via satellite): HBO.
Fee: $20.00 installation; $11.95 monthly.
Pay Service 3
Pay Units: 35.
Programming (via satellite): Showtime.
Fee: $20.00 installation; $10.95 monthly.
Local advertising: No.
Program Guide: TV Host.
Equipment: Blonder-Tongue, Catel & Drake headend; Scientific-Atlanta amplifiers; Arcom, Eagle & Northeast Filter traps; Scientific-Atlanta satellite antenna; Automation Techniques satellite receivers.
Miles of plant: 20.1 (coaxial). Homes passed: 630. Total homes in franchised area: 630.
Manager: Rick Wall. Chief technician: Leon Strain. Marketing & program director: Bruce Berkinshaw.
City fee: 2% of basic gross.
Ownership: Fanch Communications Inc. (MSO); Time Warner Cable (MSO). See Cable System Ownership.

ORLANDO—Westcom, Box 71279, Des Moines, IA 50325. Phone: 515-276-3069. Fax: 515-270-9181. County: Logan. Also serves Mulhall. ICA: OK0256.
TV Market Ranking: Outside TV Markets. Franchise award date: N.A. Franchise expiration date: N.A. Began: October 1, 1989.
Channel capacity: 35. Channels available but not in use: 21.
Basic Service
Subscribers: 12.
Programming (received off-air): KAUT-TV (U), KFOR-TV (N), KOCB (W), KOCO-TV (A), KOKH-TV (F), KWTV (C) Oklahoma City.
Programming (via satellite): ESPN; Fox Family Channel; Nashville Network; TBS Superstation.
Fee: $21.50 monthly.
Pay Service 1
Pay Units: 11.
Programming (via satellite): Cinemax.
Fee: $11.00 monthly.
Homes passed: 92.
Ownership: Westcom LC (MSO).

OSAGE—Cim Tel Cable Inc., Box 266, 101 Cimarron St., Mannford, OK 74044. Phone: 918-865-3314. County: Osage. ICA: OK0304.
TV Market Ranking: 54. Franchise award date: N.A. Franchise expiration date: N.A. Began: February 1, 1989.
Channel capacity: N.A. Channels available but not in use: N.A.
Basic Service
Subscribers: N.A.
Programming (received off-air): KJRH (N), KOED-TV (P), KOKI-TV (F), KOTV (C), KTUL (A) Tulsa.
Programming (via satellite): WGN-TV (W) Chicago; CNN; ESPN; Fox Family Channel; TBS Superstation.
Fee: N.A.
Pay Service 1
Pay Units: N.A.
Programming (via satellite): Cinemax; Disney Channel; HBO.
Fee: N.A.
Ownership: Cim Tel Cable Inc. (MSO).

PANAMA—Peak Cablevision, Box 807, Pocola, OK 74902. Phone: 918-436-7488. Fax: 918-436-7151. County: Le Flore. Also serves Le Flore County (unincorporated areas), Shady Point. ICA: OK0109.
TV Market Ranking: Below 100 (portions of Le Flore County, Panama, Shady Point); Outside TV Markets (portions of Le Flore County). Franchise award date: N.A. Franchise expiration date: October 22, 2010. Began: November 1, 1979.
Channel capacity: 36 (not 2-way capable). Channels available but not in use: 10.
Basic Service
Subscribers: 460.
Programming (received off-air): KOET (P) Eufaula; KFSM-TV (C), KHBS (A), KPBI-LP (F), KPOM-TV (N) Fort Smith; KTUL (A) Tulsa.
Programming (via satellite): WGN-TV (W) Chicago; A & E; American Movie Classics; CNN; Country Music TV; Discovery Channel; ESPN; Fox Family Channel; FoxNet; Nashville Network; Nick at Nite's TV Land; Nickelodeon; QVC; Sci-Fi Channel; TBS Superstation; The Weather Channel; Trinity Bcstg. Network; Turner Network TV; USA Network.
Fee: $25.00 installation; $21.74 monthly.
Pay Service 1
Pay Units: N.A.
Programming (via satellite): Disney Channel; HBO; Showtime; The Movie Channel.
Fee: $7.95 monthly (Disney), $10.00 monthly (HBO, Showtime or TMC).
Miles of plant: 24.8 (coaxial). Homes passed: 947.
Manager: Dennis Moore. Chief technician: Rick Packard. Marketing director: Terry Homesley. Customer service manager: Susan Moore.
Franchise fee: 2% of gross.
Ownership: Peak Cablevision LLC (MSO). See Cable System Ownership.

PAOLI—Classic Cable, Box 429, 605 N.W. 3rd St., Plainville, KS 67663-0429. Phones: 785-434-7620; 800-999-8876. Fax: 785-434-2614. Web site: http://www.classic-cable.com. County: Garvin. ICA: OK0210.
TV Market Ranking: Below 100. Franchise award date: March 22, 1984. Franchise expiration date: March 21, 1999. Began: September 1, 1988.
Channel capacity: 31 (2-way capable). Channels available but not in use: N.A.
Basic Service
Subscribers: 83.
Programming (received off-air): KAUT-TV (U), KETA (P), KFOR-TV (N), KOCB (W), KOCO-TV (A), KOKH-TV (F), KWTV (C) Oklahoma City.
Programming (via satellite): WGN-TV (W) Chicago; C-SPAN; CNN; Country Music TV; Discovery Channel; Disney Channel; ESPN; Fox Family Channel; Learning Channel; Nashville Network; Sci-Fi Channel; TBS Superstation; Trinity Bcstg. Network; Turner Network TV.
Fee: $35.00 installation; $27.95 monthly; $15.00 additional installation.
Pay Service 1
Pay Units: 20.
Programming (via satellite): HBO.
Fee: $9.95 monthly.
Pay Service 2
Pay Units: 0.
Programming (via satellite): Showtime.
Fee: $9.95 monthly.
Equipment: Blonder-Tongue, Triple Crown & Tru-Spec headend; C-COR & Texscan amplifiers; Northeast Filter traps; ICM & Scientific-Atlanta satellite receivers.
Miles of plant: 10.0 (coaxial). Homes passed: 264. Total homes in franchised area: 300.
Manager: Dave Walker. Chief technician: Roger Campbell. Marketing director: Jennifer Hauschild.
City fee: 3% of basic gross.
Ownership: Classic Cable (MSO).

PARADISE HILL—Quality Entertainment Corp., Suite 512, Central Mall Plaza, Fort Smith, AR 72903. Phone: 501-452-1998. Fax: 501-452-6430. County: Sequoyah. ICA: OK0366.
TV Market Ranking: Outside TV Markets. Franchise award date: N.A. Franchise expiration date: N.A. Began: N.A.
Channel capacity: 36 (not 2-way capable). Channels available but not in use: 7.
Basic Service
Subscribers: 221.
Programming (received off-air): KHBS (A) Fort Smith; KJRH (N), KOED-TV (P), KOKI-TV (F), KOTV (C), KTFO (U), KTUL (A), KWHB (I) Tulsa.
Programming (via satellite): WGN-TV (W) Chicago; A & E; American Movie Classics; CNN; Country Music TV; Discovery Channel; ESPN; Fox Family Channel; Nashville Network; Nick at Nite's TV Land; Odyssey; TBS Superstation; Trinity Bcstg. Network; Turner Network TV; USA Network.
Fee: $40.00 installation; $24.00 monthly.
Pay Service 1
Pay Units: N.A.
Programming (via satellite): Disney Channel; HBO; Showtime; The Movie Channel.
Fee: $10.00 monthly.
Miles of plant: 15.0 (coaxial).
Ownership: Quality Entertainment Corp. (MSO).

PARK HILL—Quality Entertainment Corp., Suite 512, Central Mall Plaza, Fort Smith, AR 72903. Phone: 501-452-1998. Fax: 501-452-6430. County: Cherokee. ICA: OK0350.
TV Market Ranking: Outside TV Markets. Franchise award date: N.A. Franchise expiration date: N.A. Began: N.A.
Channel capacity: 35 (not 2-way capable). Channels available but not in use: 7.
Basic Service
Subscribers: 211.
Programming (received off-air): KJRH (N), KOED-TV (P), KOKI-TV (F), KTUL (A) Tulsa.
Programming (via satellite): WGN-TV (W) Chicago; A & E; American Movie Classics; CNN; Country Music TV; Discovery Channel; ESPN; Fox Family Channel; Home Shopping Network; Learning Channel; Nashville Network; Nick at Nite's TV Land; Nickelodeon; Sci-Fi Channel; TBS Superstation; The Weather Channel; Trinity Bcstg. Network; Turner Network TV; USA Network.
Fee: $25.00 monthly.
Pay Service 1
Pay Units: N.A.
Programming (via satellite): HBO.
Fee: $12.00 monthly.
Miles of plant: 20.0 (coaxial); None (fiber optic). Homes passed: 450. Total homes in franchised area: 450.
Manager: Brent Lewis. Chief technician: Randall Hinton.
Ownership: Quality Entertainment Corp. (MSO).

PAULS VALLEY—Multimedia Cablevision of Pauls Valley, 509 S. Willow St., Pauls Valley, OK 73075. Phone: 405-238-7476. Fax: 405-238-3066. County: Garvin. Also serves Garvin County (unincorporated areas), Wynnewood. ICA: OK0033.
TV Market Ranking: Below 100 (portions of Garvin County, Pauls Valley, Wynnewood); Outside TV Markets (portions of Garvin County). Franchise award date: N.A. Franchise expiration date: March 21, 2004. Began: October 20, 1969.
Channel capacity: 45 (not 2-way capable). Channels available but not in use: 6.
Basic Service
Subscribers: 3,097.
Programming (received off-air): KTEN (A,N,F) Ada; KAUT-TV (U), KETA (P), KFOR-TV (N), KOCB (W), KOCO-TV (A), KOKH-TV (F), KSBI (I), KTBO-TV (T), KWTV (C) Oklahoma City; KXII (C) Sherman; 20 FMs.
Programming (via satellite): A & E; American Movie Classics; C-SPAN; CNBC; Discovery Channel; ESPN; Fox Family Channel; Home Shopping Network; Lifetime;

MTV; Nickelodeon; The Weather Channel; Travel Channel; USA Network; VH1.
Current originations: Public access; automated emergency alert; local sports.
Planned originations: Educational access.
Fee: $15.39 installation; $19.10 monthly; $8.12 additional installation.

Expanded Basic Service
Subscribers: 2,760.
Programming (via satellite): WGN-TV (W) Chicago; CNN; Fox Family Channel; Headline News; Nashville Network; TBS Superstation; Turner Network TV.
Fee: $4.23 monthly.

Pay Service 1
Pay Units: 421.
Programming (via satellite): Cinemax.
Fee: $9.00 monthly.

Pay Service 2
Pay Units: 212.
Programming (via satellite): Disney Channel.
Fee: $7.95 monthly.

Pay Service 3
Pay Units: 565.
Programming (via satellite): HBO.
Fee: $11.00 monthly.

Pay Service 4
Pay Units: 480.
Programming (via satellite): Showtime.
Fee: $8.00 monthly.

Pay Service 5
Pay Units: 68.
Programming (via satellite): The Movie Channel.
Fee: $11.00 monthly.

Pay-Per-View
Special events.

Local advertising: Yes. Available in locally originated & character-generated programming. Rates: $25.00/Week.
Program Guide: The Cable Guide.
Equipment: Scientific-Atlanta headend; Scientific-Atlanta amplifiers; Trilogy cable; Scientific-Atlanta set top converters; Eagle traps; Scientific-Atlanta satellite antenna; Scientific-Atlanta satellite receivers.
Miles of plant: 84.5 (coaxial). Homes passed: 4,933. Total homes in franchised area: 7,408.
Manager: Steve Pool. Chief technician: Mark Harpole. Marketing director: Jim Back. Customer service manager: Charitta Shelton. Office manager: Vera Gober.
City fee: 3% of basic.
Ownership: Multimedia Cablevision Inc. (MSO). See Cable System Ownership.

PAWHUSKA—Peak Cablevision, 131 E. Maine, Enid, OK 73701. Phone: 580-237-7373. Fax: 580-242-4801. County: Osage. ICA: OK0060.
TV Market Ranking: Below 100. Franchise award date: N.A. Franchise expiration date: N.A. Began: September 1, 1974.
Channel capacity: 36. Channels available but not in use: N.A.

Basic Service
Subscribers: 1,320.
Programming (received off-air): KWTV (C) Oklahoma City; KJRH (N), KOED-TV (P), KOKI-TV (F), KOTV (C), KTUL (A), KWHB (I) Tulsa; allband FM.
Programming (via satellite): CNBC; CNN; Discovery Channel; Fox Family Channel; MTV; Nashville Network; Nickelodeon; QVC; TBS Superstation.
Fee: $60.00 installation; $19.80 monthly; $10.00 additional installation.

Expanded Basic Service
Subscribers: 1,196.
Programming (via satellite): American Movie Classics; Court TV; ESPN; Turner Network TV; USA Network.
Fee: $1.50 monthly.

Pay Service 1
Pay Units: 58.
Programming (via satellite): Disney Channel.
Fee: N.A.

Pay Service 2
Pay Units: 530.
Programming (via satellite): The New Encore.
Fee: N.A.

Pay Service 3
Pay Units: 231.
Programming (via satellite): Showtime.
Fee: $10.00 installation; $11.50 monthly.

Pay Service 4
Pay Units: 69.
Programming (via satellite): The Movie Channel.
Fee: $10.00 installation; $11.50 monthly.

Local advertising: No.
Program Guide: Premium Channels.
Equipment: Jerrold headend; Jerrold amplifiers; Times Fiber cable; Jerrold set top converters; Eagle traps; Scientific-Atlanta satellite antenna.
Miles of plant: 36.8 (coaxial). Homes passed: 2,462. Total homes in franchised area: 2,506.
Manager: Johnny Rosson. Chief technician: Rick Gardner.
City fee: 3% of gross.
Ownership: Peak Cablevision LLC (MSO). See Cable System Ownership.

PAWNEE—Cim Tel Cable Inc., Box 266, 101 Cimarron St., Mannford, OK 74044. Phone: 918-865-3314. County: Pawnee. ICA: OK0117.
TV Market Ranking: Outside TV Markets. Franchise award date: N.A. Franchise expiration date: N.A. Began: June 1, 1982.
Channel capacity: 35. Channels available but not in use: N.A.

Basic Service
Subscribers: 506.
Programming (received off-air): KJRH (N), KOED-TV (P), KOKI-TV (F), KOTV (C), KTUL (A) Tulsa.
Programming (via satellite): WGN-TV (W) Chicago; CNN; ESPN; Fox Family Channel; TBS Superstation.
Fee: $15.00 installation; $9.95 monthly.

Pay Service 1
Pay Units: N.A.
Programming (via satellite): Cinemax.
Fee: $9.00 installation; $9.50 monthly.

Pay Service 2
Pay Units: 217.
Programming (via satellite): HBO.
Fee: $9.00 installation; $9.50 monthly.

Miles of plant: 16.1 (coaxial). Homes passed: 849.
Ownership: Cim Tel Cable Inc. (MSO).

PERRY—Peak Cablevision, 617 1/2 Delaware, Perry, OK 73077. Phone: 580-336-5559. County: Noble. Also serves Noble County (portions). ICA: OK0057.
TV Market Ranking: Outside TV Markets. Franchise award date: September 1, 1977. Franchise expiration date: N.A. Began: January 1, 1979.
Channel capacity: 47 (not 2-way capable). Channels available but not in use: 31.

Basic Service
Subscribers: 1,890.
Programming (received off-air): KAUT-TV (U), KETA (P), KFOR-TV (N), KOCB (W), KOCO-TV (A), KOKH-TV (F), KOPX (X), KTBO-TV (T), KWTV (C) Oklahoma City; 10 FMs.
Programming (via satellite): WGN-TV (W) Chicago; CNN; Discovery Channel; Home Shopping Network; TBS Superstation; The Weather Channel.
Current originations: Public access; government access.
Planned originations: Automated emergency alert.
Fee: $37.50 installation; $11.63 monthly; $1.50 converter.

Expanded Basic Service
Subscribers: 1,765.
Programming (via satellite): A & E; American Movie Classics; Animal Planet; C-SPAN; CNBC; Cartoon Network; Country Music TV; Disney Channel; ESPN; ESPN 2; Encore Movie Networks; Fox Family Channel; Fox News Channel; Fox Sports Net Southwest; Headline News; History Channel; Home & Garden Television; Learning Channel; Lifetime; Nashville Network; Nickelodeon; QVC; Sci-Fi Channel; Turner Network TV; USA Network; VH1.
Fee: $14.55 monthly.

Pay Service 1
Pay Units: 273.
Programming (via satellite): Cinemax.
Fee: $10.00 installation; $10.68 monthly.

Pay Service 2
Pay Units: 409.
Programming (via satellite): HBO.
Fee: $10.00 installation; $10.68 monthly.

Pay Service 3
Pay Units: 345.
Programming (via satellite): The New Encore.
Fee: $10.00 installation; $1.75 monthly.

Pay Service 4
Pay Units: 350.
Programming (via satellite): Starz!
Fee: $10.00 installation; $6.75 monthly.

Pay-Per-View
Special events.

Local advertising: Yes. Available in character-generated programming. Rates: $100.00/Month; $10.00/Minute; $5.00/30 Seconds. Local sales manager: Bill Fort.
Program Guide: The Cable Guide.
Equipment: Scientific-Atlanta headend; Texscan amplifiers; Comm/Scope cable; Panasonic cameras; Quanta character generator; Hamlin & Oak set top converters; Eagle traps; Scientific-Atlanta satellite antenna.
Miles of plant: 48.0 (coaxial); 5.0 (fiber optic). Homes passed: 3,063. Total homes in franchised area: 3,063.
Manager: Ted Ramsey. Chief technician: Joe Goertz.
City fee: 3% of gross.
Ownership: Peak Cablevision LLC (MSO). See Cable System Ownership.

PICHER—Mediacom, 115 N. Industrial Park Rd., Excelsior Springs, MO 64024. Phone: 816-637-4500. Fax: 816-637-1247. Counties: Cherokee, KS; Ottawa, OK. Also serves Treece, KS; Cardin, Quapaw, OK. ICA: OK0093.
TV Market Ranking: Below 100. Franchise award date: N.A. Franchise expiration date: October 9, 2005. Began: July 1, 1982.
Channel capacity: 35 (not 2-way capable). Channels available but not in use: None.

Basic Service
Subscribers: 701.
Programming (received off-air): KOAM-TV (C), KODE-TV (A), KOZJ (P), KSNF (N) Joplin-Pittsburg; KOED-TV (P), KOKI-TV (F), KTUL (A) Tulsa.
Programming (via satellite): WGN-TV (W) Chicago; A & E; CNN; Country Music TV; Discovery Channel; ESPN; ESPN 2; Fox Family Channel; Headline News; Learning Channel; Lifetime; MTV; Nashville Network; Nick at Nite's TV Land; Nickelodeon; QVC; TBS Superstation; The Weather Channel; Trinity Bcstg. Network; Turner Network TV; USA Network.
Current originations: Automated time-weather; local news.
Fee: $35.00 installation; $25.25 monthly.

Pay Service 1
Pay Units: 20.
Programming (via satellite): American Movie Classics.
Fee: $2.95 monthly.

Pay Service 2
Pay Units: 145.
Programming (via satellite): Cinemax.
Fee: $10.50 monthly.

Pay Service 3
Pay Units: 320.
Programming (via satellite): Disney Channel.
Fee: $5.95 monthly.

Pay Service 4
Pay Units: 317.
Programming (via satellite): HBO.
Fee: $10.50 monthly.

Pay Service 5
Pay Units: 314.
Programming (via satellite): Showtime.
Fee: $10.50 monthly.

Pay Service 6
Pay Units: 163.
Programming (via satellite): The Movie Channel.
Fee: $10.50 monthly.

Equipment: Blonder-Tongue, M/A-Com & Scientific-Atlanta headend; C-COR amplifiers; C-COR cable; Oak, Pioneer & Scientific-Atlanta set top converters; Scientific-Atlanta satellite receivers.
Miles of plant: 23.2 (coaxial). Homes passed: 1,622.
Regional manager: Arnold Cool. Manager: Roger Frederick. Chief technician: Steve Wilson.
City fee: 3% of basic.
Ownership: Mediacom LLC (MSO).

PIEDMONT—Classic Cable, Box 429, 605 N.W. 3rd St., Plainville, KS 67663-0429. Phones: 785-434-7620; 800-999-8876. Fax: 785-434-2614. Web site: http://www.classic-cable.com. Counties: Canadian & Kingfisher. ICA: OK0374.
TV Market Ranking: 39. Franchise award date: N.A. Franchise expiration date: N.A. Began: N.A.
Channel capacity: 41 (2-way capable). Channels available but not in use: N.A.

Basic Service
Subscribers: 259.
Programming (received off-air): KAUT-TV (U), KETA (P), KFOR-TV (N), KOCB (W), KOCO-TV (A), KOKH-TV (F), KSBI (I), KTBO-TV (T), KWTV (C) Oklahoma City.
Programming (via satellite): WGN-TV (W) Chicago; A & E; American Movie Classics; C-SPAN; CNN; Country Music TV; Discovery Channel; Disney Channel; E! Entertainment TV; ESPN; Fox Family Channel; Fox Sports Net Southwest; Headline News; Lifetime; MTV; Nashville Network; Nick at Nite's TV Land; Nickelodeon; QVC; Sci-Fi Channel; TBS Superstation; The Weather Channel; Turner Network TV; USA Network; VH1.
Current originations: Public access.
Fee: $35.00 installation; $28.95 monthly.

Pay Service 1
Pay Units: 53.
Programming (via satellite): HBO.
Fee: $10.95 monthly.

Pay Service 2
Pay Units: 34.
Programming (via satellite): Showtime.
Fee: $9.95 monthly.

Pay Service 3
Pay Units: 36.

Programming (via satellite): The Movie Channel.
Fee: $5.95 monthly.
Miles of plant: 37.2 (coaxial). Homes passed: 400.
Manager: Dave Walker. Chief technician: Jeff Smith. Marketing director: Jennifer Hauschild.
Ownership: Classic Cable (MSO).

POCASSET—Rapid Cable, Box 117, 307 N. Main St., Granite, OK 73547. Phone: 800-972-0962. County: Grady. ICA: OK0305.
TV Market Ranking: 39. Franchise award date: N.A. Franchise expiration date: N.A. Began: September 1, 1990.
Channel capacity: 15. Channels available but not in use: None.
Basic Service
Subscribers: 36.
Programming (received off-air): KFOR-TV (N), KOCO-TV (A), KWTV (C) Oklahoma City.
Programming (via satellite): WGN-TV (W) Chicago; CNN; Country Music TV; Discovery Channel; ESPN; Fox Family Channel; Nashville Network; TBS Superstation; USA Network.
Fee: $35.00 installation; $17.95 monthly.
Pay Service 1
Pay Units: N.A.
Programming (via satellite): Disney Channel; HBO; Showtime.
Fee: $9.00 monthly (each).
Manager: Marla Scarborough. Chief technician: Tom Wing.
Ownership: Rapid Communications Partners LP (MSO).

POCOLA—TCA Cable TV Inc., Box 3408, Fort Smith, AR 72913. Phones: 501-782-8941; 877-768-4873. Fax: 501-783-7892. E-mail: info@tca-cable.com. Web site: http://www.tca-cable.com. County: Le Flore. Also serves Le Flore County (unincorporated areas). ICA: OK0099.
TV Market Ranking: Below 100 (portions of Le Flore County, Pocola); Outside TV Markets (portions of Le Flore County). Franchise award date: N.A. Franchise expiration date: November 28, 2010. Began: April 1, 1982.
Channel capacity: 36 (not 2-way capable). Channels available but not in use: 6.
Basic Service
Subscribers: 910.
Programming (received off-air): KAFT (P) Fayetteville; KFSM-TV (C), KHBS (A), KPBI-LP (F), KPOM-TV (N) Fort Smith; KTUL (A) Tulsa.
Programming (via satellite): WGN-TV (W) Chicago; A & E; CNN; Discovery Channel; ESPN; Fox Family Channel; Fox Sports Net; Great American Country; History Channel; Home & Garden Television; Lifetime; Nashville Network; Nick at Nite's TV Land; Nickelodeon; QVC; TBS Superstation; The Weather Channel; Trinity Bcstg. Network; Turner Network TV; USA Network.
Fee: $25.00 installation; $23.97 monthly.
Pay Service 1
Pay Units: N.A.
Programming (via satellite): Cinemax; Disney Channel; HBO; Showtime; Starz!; The Movie Channel; The New Encore.
Fee: $2.00 (Encore), $7.95 monthly (Disney), $10.00 monthly (Cinemax, HBO, Showtime, Starz or TMC).
Miles of plant: 34.7 (coaxial); None (fiber optic). Homes passed: 1,084.
Manager: James Anderson. Chief technician: Mike Weiche. Marketing director: Michael Rogers. Customer service manager: Linda Savage.
Ownership: TCA Cable TV Inc. (MSO). Purchased from Peak Cablevision LLC, July 1, 1999.

PONCA CITY—Cable One, Box 2149, 303 N. 4th St., Ponca City, OK 74602. Phone: 580-762-6684. Fax: 580-762-0312. Counties: Kay & Osage. Also serves Kay County (portions), Osage County (portions), Tonkawa. ICA: OK0014.
TV Market Ranking: 54 (portions of Osage County); Below 100 (portions of Osage County); Outside TV Markets (Kay County, portions of Osage County, Ponca City, Tonkawa). Franchise award date: N.A. Franchise expiration date: N.A. Began: March 1, 1967.
Channel capacity: 70 (2-way capable). Channels available but not in use: None.
Basic Service
Subscribers: 12,589.
Programming (received off-air): KAUT-TV (U), KETA (P), KFOR-TV (N), KOCB (W), KOCO-TV (A), KOKH-TV (F), KWTV (C) Oklahoma City; K27DF (I) Ponca City; KJRH (N), KOKI-TV (F), KOTV (C), KTUL (A) Tulsa; KSNW (N) Wichita-Hutchinson.
Programming (via satellite): WGN-TV (W) Chicago; A & E; American Movie Classics; BET; Bravo; C-SPAN; C-SPAN 2; CNBC; CNN; Country Music TV; Discovery Channel; Disney Channel; E! Entertainment TV; ESPN; ESPN 2; FX; Fox Family Channel; Fox Sports Net Southwest; Headline News; History Channel; Home & Garden Television; Home Shopping Network; Learning Channel; Lifetime; MTV; Nashville Network; Nickelodeon; Odyssey; QVC; Sci-Fi Channel; TBS Superstation; TV Guide Channel; The Weather Channel; Travel Channel; Trinity Bcstg. Network; Turner Network TV; USA Network; Univision; VH1.
Current originations: Government access.
Fee: $25.00 installation (aerial), $80.00 (underground); $30.71 monthly.
Pay Service 1
Pay Units: 2,765.
Programming (via satellite): Cinemax.
Fee: $13.95 monthly.
Pay Service 2
Pay Units: 3,399.
Programming (via satellite): HBO.
Fee: $13.95 monthly.
Pay Service 3
Pay Units: 1,402.
Programming (via satellite): Showtime (multiplexed).
Fee: $10.95 monthly.
Pay Service 4
Pay Units: 1,393.
Programming (via satellite): The Movie Channel.
Fee: $10.95 monthly.
Pay-Per-View
Addressable homes: 1,981.
Hot Choice; Viewer's Choice.
Fee: $3.95 each.
Equipment: Scientific-Atlanta headend; GTE Sylvania amplifiers; Anaconda cable; Hitachi cameras; Sony VTRs; Video Data Systems character generator; Magnavox set top converters; Hughes satellite antenna.
Miles of plant: 235.0 (coaxial); 44.0 (fiber optic). Homes passed: 14,167. Total homes in franchised area: 15,344.
Manager: Gerald Stone. Plant manager: Phil Stajcar. Marketing director: Lois Payne. Office manager: Vicki Hardesty.
City fee: 4% of gross.
Ownership: Cable One Inc. (MSO).

POND CREEK—Classic Cable, Box 429, 605 N.W. 3rd St., Plainville, KS 67663-0429. Phones: 785-434-7620; 800-999-8876. Fax: 785-434-2614. Web site: http://www.classic-cable.com. County: Grant. ICA: OK0185.
TV Market Ranking: Outside TV Markets. Franchise award date: N.A. Franchise expiration date: N.A. Began: April 1, 1977.
Channel capacity: 36 (2-way capable). Channels available but not in use: N.A.
Basic Service
Subscribers: 218.
Programming (received off-air): KAUT-TV (U), KETA (P), KFOR-TV (N), KOCB (W), KOCO-TV (A), KOKH-TV (F), KWTV (C) Oklahoma City; allband FM.
Programming (via satellite): WGN-TV (W) Chicago; A & E; American Movie Classics; CNN; Country Music TV; Discovery Channel; Disney Channel; ESPN; Fox Family Channel; Fox Sports Net Southwest; History Channel; Lifetime; Nashville Network; Nick at Nite's TV Land; Nickelodeon; QVC; Sci-Fi Channel; TBS Superstation; The Weather Channel; Turner Network TV; USA Network.
Fee: $35.00 installation; $27.95 monthly.
Pay Service 1
Pay Units: 36.
Programming (via satellite): HBO.
Fee: $10.00 installation; $10.95 monthly.
Pay Service 2
Pay Units: 12.
Programming (via satellite): Showtime.
Fee: $9.95 monthly.
Pay Service 3
Pay Units: 11.
Programming (via satellite): Cinemax.
Fee: $9.95 monthly.
Equipment: Automation Techniques & Blonder-Tongue headend; RCA amplifiers; RCA & Vikoa cable; Andrew satellite antenna; Andrew satellite receivers.
Miles of plant: 17.0 (coaxial). Homes passed: 396.
Manager: Dave Walker. Chief technician: Jeff Smith. Marketing director: Jennifer Hauschild.
City fee: 3% of gross.
Ownership: Classic Cable (MSO).

PORTER—Oklahoma Cablecomm, Box 970, Fort Gibson, OK 74434-0970. Phones: 918-478-2100; 800-783-5701. Fax: 918-478-2355. County: Wagoner. ICA: OK0306.
TV Market Ranking: 54. Franchise award date: January 1, 1989. Franchise expiration date: January 1, 2014. Began: September 1, 1989.
Channel capacity: N.A. Channels available but not in use: N.A.
Basic Service
Subscribers: 71.
Programming (received off-air): KJRH (N), KOED-TV (P), KOKI-TV (F), KOTV (C), KTUL (A), KWHB (I) Tulsa.
Programming (via satellite): WGN-TV (W) Chicago; A & E; CNN; Country Music TV; Discovery Channel; ESPN; Fox Family Channel; Nashville Network; TBS Superstation; USA Network.
Fee: $30.00 installation; $18.95 monthly.
Pay Service 1
Pay Units: 23.
Programming (via satellite): HBO.
Fee: $10.95 monthly.
Local advertising: No.
Program Guide: TV Host.
Miles of plant: 6.0 (coaxial). Homes passed: 275. Total homes in franchised area: 275.
Manager: Bob Bailey. Chief technician: Bill Thomison. Marketing & program director: Bruce Berkinshaw.
Ownership: Fanch Communications Inc. (MSO); Time Warner Cable (MSO). See Cable System Ownership.

PORUM—Oklahoma Cablecomm, Box 970, Fort Gibson, OK 74434-0970. Phones: 918-478-2100; 800-783-5701. Fax: 918-478-2355. County: Muskogee. ICA: OK0196.
TV Market Ranking: Outside TV Markets. Franchise award date: July 1, 1981. Franchise expiration date: N.A. Began: January 1, 1982.
Channel capacity: 35. Channels available but not in use: 15.
Basic Service
Subscribers: 122.
Programming (received off-air): KOET (P) Eufaula; KJRH (N), KOKI-TV (F), KOTV (C), KTUL (A), KWHB (I) Tulsa.
Programming (via satellite): WGN-TV (W) Chicago; CNN; Discovery Channel; Disney Channel; ESPN; Fox Family Channel; Headline News; Nashville Network; Nickelodeon; QVC; TBS Superstation; Turner Network TV; USA Network.
Fee: $30.00 installation; $22.00 monthly.
Pay Service 1
Pay Units: N.A.
Programming (via satellite): Cinemax.
Fee: N.A.
Pay Service 2
Pay Units: 20.
Programming (via satellite): HBO.
Fee: $20.00 installation; $9.00 monthly.
Local advertising: No.
Program Guide: TV Host.
Equipment: Blonder-Tongue, Drake & Triple Crown headend; C-COR amplifiers; Comm/Scope cable; Jerrold set top converters; Arcom & Northeast Filter traps; Odom satellite antenna; DX Engineering satellite receivers.
Miles of plant: 6.0 (coaxial). Homes passed: 309.
Manager: Rick Wall. Chief technician: Leon Strain. Marketing & program director: Bruce Berkinshaw.
City fee: 5% of gross.
Ownership: Fanch Communications Inc. (MSO); Time Warner Cable (MSO). See Cable System Ownership.

PORUM LANDING—Peak Cablevision, Box 807, Pocola, OK 74902. Phone: 918-436-7488. Fax: 918-436-7151. County: McIntosh. ICA: OK0307.
TV Market Ranking: Outside TV Markets. Franchise award date: N.A. Franchise expiration date: N.A. Began: June 1, 1990.
Channel capacity: 36 (not 2-way capable). Channels available but not in use: 15.
Basic Service
Subscribers: 222.
Programming (received off-air): KJRH (N), KOED-TV (P), KOKI-TV (F), KOTV (C), KTUL (A) Tulsa.

Programming (via satellite): WGN-TV (W) Chicago; A & E; American Movie Classics; CNN; Country Music TV; Discovery Channel; ESPN; Fox Family Channel; History Channel; Nashville Network; Nickelodeon; QVC; TBS Superstation; The Weather Channel; Turner Network TV; USA Network.
Fee: $25.00 installation; $22.95 monthly.
Pay Service 1
Pay Units: N.A.
Programming (via satellite): Disney Channel; HBO; Showtime.
Fee: $7.95 monthly (Disney), $10.00 monthly (HBO or Showtime).
Miles of plant: 25.0 (coaxial). Homes passed: 771.
Manager: Dennis Moore. Chief technician: Rick Packard. Marketing director: Terry Homesley. Customer service manager: Susan Moore.
Ownership: Peak Cablevision LLC (MSO). See Cable System Ownership.

POTEAU—Classic Cable, Box 429, 605 N.W. 3rd St., Plainville, KS 67663-0429. Phones: 785-434-7620; 800-999-8876. Fax: 785-434-2614. Web site: http://www.classic-cable.com. County: Le Flore. ICA: OK0308.
TV Market Ranking: Below 100. Franchise award date: July 1, 1962. Franchise expiration date: July 1, 2010. Began: July 1, 1962.
Channel capacity: 41 (2-way capable). Channels available but not in use: N.A.
Basic Service
Subscribers: 2,447.
Programming (received off-air): KOET (P) Eufaula; KAFT (P) Fayetteville; KFDF-LP (U), KFSM-TV (C), KHBS (A), KPBI-LP (F), KPOM-TV (N) Fort Smith; KOTV (C), KTUL (A) Tulsa; allband FM.
Programming (via satellite): WGN-TV (W) Chicago; A & E; C-SPAN; CNN; Country Music TV; Discovery Channel; Disney Channel; ESPN; Fox Family Channel; Fox News Channel; Fox Sports Net Southwest; Headline News; History Channel; Learning Channel; Lifetime; Nashville Network; Nick at Nite's TV Land; Nickelodeon; QVC; Sci-Fi Channel; TBS Superstation; The Inspirational Network; The Weather Channel; Turner Classic Movies; Turner Network TV; USA Network.
Fee: $35.00 installation; $27.95 monthly.
Pay Service 1
Pay Units: 320.
Programming (via satellite): HBO.
Fee: $35.00 installation; $10.95 monthly.
Pay Service 2
Pay Units: 185.
Programming (via satellite): The Movie Channel.
Fee: $35.00 installation; $5.95 monthly.
Pay Service 3
Pay Units: 196.
Programming (via satellite): Showtime.
Fee: $35.00 installation; $9.95 monthly.
Pay-Per-View
Special events.
Local advertising: No.
Equipment: Blonder-Tongue headend; U.S. Tower satellite antenna.
Miles of plant: 125.0 (coaxial). Homes passed: 3,108.
Manager: Dave Walker. Chief technician: Carl Miller. Marketing director: Jennifer Hauschild.
City fee: 3% of gross.
Ownership: Classic Cable (MSO).

PRAGUE—Falcon Cable Media, 707 W. Saratoga, Shawnee, OK 74801. Phones: 405-275-6923; 405-275-0276. County: Lincoln. ICA: OK0115.
TV Market Ranking: Outside TV Markets. Franchise award date: July 1, 1979. Franchise expiration date: July 1, 2004. Began: May 31, 1982.
Channel capacity: 42 (2-way capable). Channels available but not in use: 10.
Basic Service
Subscribers: 478.
Programming (received off-air): KAUT-TV (U), KETA (P), KFOR-TV (N), KOCB (W), KOCO-TV (A), KOKH-TV (F), KTBO-TV (T), KWTV (C) Oklahoma City; 14 FMs.
Programming (via satellite): American Movie Classics; Bravo; CNN; Country Music TV; E! Entertainment TV; ESPN; Fox Family Channel; Headline News; Lifetime; MTV; Nickelodeon; QVC; The Weather Channel.
Current originations: Automated time-weather; public access; educational access; government access.
Fee: $20.00 installation (aerial), $45.00 (underground); $17.03 monthly; $10.00 additional installation.
Expanded Basic Service
Subscribers: 468.
Programming (via satellite): Discovery Channel; Sci-Fi Channel; USA Network.
Fee: $2.03 monthly.
Expanded Basic Service 2
Subscribers: 457.
Programming (via satellite): WGN-TV (W) Chicago; Disney Channel; Fox Sports Net Southwest; Nashville Network; TBS Superstation; Turner Network TV.
Fee: $7.75 monthly.
Pay Service 1
Pay Units: 80.
Programming (via satellite): Cinemax.
Fee: $20.00 installation; $10.45 monthly.
Pay Service 2
Pay Units: 119.
Programming (via satellite): HBO.
Fee: $20.00 installation; $10.45 monthly.
Local advertising: Yes. Available in locally originated & character-generated programming.
Equipment: Phasecom, Scientific-Atlanta headend; Theta-Com amplifiers; Comm/Scope cable; Hamlin & Scientific-Atlanta set top converters; Eagle traps; Anixter-Mark & Scientific-Atlanta satellite antenna; Microdyne & Standard Communications satellite receivers.
Miles of plant: 20.0 (coaxial). Homes passed: 1,073.
Manager: Andrew Dearth.
Franchise fee: 3% of gross.
Ownership: Falcon Communications LP (MSO), joint venture formed September 30, 1998. See Cable System Ownership.

PRESTON—Quality Cablevision of Oklahoma Inc., Box 315, 816-D N. Date, Jenks, OK 74037. Phone: 918-299-0104. County: Okmulgee. ICA: OK0338.
TV Market Ranking: 54. Franchise award date: N.A. Franchise expiration date: N.A. Began: February 12, 1993.
Channel capacity: N.A. Channels available but not in use: N.A.
Basic Service
Subscribers: 47.
Programming (received off-air): KETA (P) Oklahoma City; KJRH (N), KOKI-TV (F), KOTV (C), KTFO (U), KTUL (A) Tulsa.
Fee: $29.95 installation; $17.95 monthly.
Pay Service 1
Pay Units: N.A.
Programming (via satellite): HBO; Showtime.
Fee: $10.95 monthly (each).
Miles of plant: 14.0 (coaxial). Homes passed: 135.
Manager: Curtis Scott. Chief technician: Bill Garrison.
Ownership: Quality Cablevision of Oklahoma Inc. (MSO).

PRYOR—Peak Cablevision, Box 471467, Tulsa, OK 74147-1467. Phone: 918-627-9406. Fax: 918-627-9407. County: Mayes. Also serves Mayes County (portions). ICA: OK0046.
TV Market Ranking: 54 (portions of Mayes County); Outside TV Markets (portions of Mayes County, Pryor). Franchise award date: August 5, 1972. Franchise expiration date: N.A. Began: November 22, 1974.
Channel capacity: 35 (not 2-way capable). Channels available but not in use: 1.
Basic Service
Subscribers: 4,776; Commercial subscribers: 31.
Programming (received off-air): KDOR (T) Bartlesville; KRSC-TV (E) Claremore; KJRH (N), KOED-TV (P), KOKI-TV (F), KOTV (C), KTFO (U), KTUL (A), KWHB (I), KWMJ (I) Tulsa; allband FM.
Programming (via satellite): Fox Family Channel; Home Shopping Network.
Current originations: Automated emergency alert.
Fee: $50.00 installation; $9.69 monthly; $20.00 additional installation.
Expanded Basic Service
Subscribers: 2,489.
Programming (via satellite): WGN-TV (W) Chicago; American Movie Classics; Country Music TV; ESPN; ESPN 2; Headline News; Learning Channel; Lifetime; MTV; Nashville Network; Nickelodeon; Sci-Fi Channel; TBS Superstation; The Weather Channel; USA Network.
Fee: $50.00 installation; $23.65 monthly.
A la Carte 1
Subscribers: 2,180.
Programming (via satellite): CNN; Discovery Channel; Turner Network TV.
Fee: $2.35 monthly (package).
Pay Service 1
Pay Units: 163.
Programming (via satellite): Disney Channel.
Fee: $40.00 installation; $8.95 monthly.
Pay Service 2
Pay Units: 370.
Programming (via satellite): HBO.
Fee: $40.00 installation; $10.95 monthly.
Pay Service 3
Pay Units: 390.
Programming (via satellite): Showtime.
Fee: $40.00 installation; $9.95 monthly.
Local advertising: Yes (locally produced). Available in character-generated programming. Rates: $25.00/Month.
Equipment: Jerrold & Scientific-Atlanta headend; Texscan amplifiers; Times Fiber & Trilogy cable; Jerrold set top converters; Eagle & Pico traps; Andrew, Hughes & Scientific-Atlanta satellite antenna; Scientific-Atlanta satellite receivers.
Miles of plant: 62.0 (coaxial). Homes passed: 3,623. Total homes in franchised area: 3,708.
Manager: Mike Mavers.
City fee: 4% of gross.
Ownership: Time Warner Cable (MSO).

PRYOR (outside areas)—Peak Cablevision, Suite B, 2800 W. Hudson, Rogers, AR 72756. Phone: 501-631-1650. Fax: 501-631-7831. County: Mayes. Also serves Cherokee Heights, Sportsmen Acres. ICA: OK0354.
TV Market Ranking: Outside TV Markets. Franchise award date: N.A. Franchise expiration date: October 10, 2010. Began: N.A.
Channel capacity: 26 (2-way capable; not operating 2-way). Channels available but not in use: 11.
Basic Service
Subscribers: 25.
Programming (received off-air): KOET (P) Eufaula; KJRH (N), KOKI-TV (F), KOTV (C), KTUL (A), KWHB (I) Tulsa.
Programming (via satellite): WGN-TV (W) Chicago; CNN; Country Music TV; Discovery Channel; ESPN; Fox Family Channel; Nashville Network; TBS Superstation.
Fee: $35.00 installation; $19.95 monthly.
Pay Service 1
Pay Units: N.A.
Programming (via satellite): HBO.
Fee: $11.00 monthly.
Equipment: Pico headend; Jerrold amplifiers.
Manager: Shane Bell. Chief technician: Lynn Harrison. Marketing director: Terry Homseley.
Ownership: Peak Cablevision LLC (MSO). See Cable System Ownership.

PURCELL—Classic Cable, 2820 N. Green Ave., Purcell, OK 73080-1707. Phone: 405-527-5651. Fax: 405-527-5392. Counties: Cleveland & McClain. Also serves Lexington, McClain County. ICA: OK0048.
TV Market Ranking: 39 (Lexington, portions of McClain County, Purcell); Below 100 (portions of McClain County); Outside TV Markets (portions of McClain County). Franchise award date: N.A. Franchise expiration date: December 4, 1997. Began: November 1, 1976.
Channel capacity: 40 (not 2-way capable). Channels available but not in use: None.
Basic Service
Subscribers: 3,497.
Programming (received off-air): KAUT-TV (U), KETA (P), KFOR-TV (N), KOCB (W), KOCO-TV (A), KOKH-TV (F), KSBI (I), KTBO-TV (T), KWTV (C) Oklahoma City; allband FM.
Programming (via satellite): WGN-TV (W) Chicago; A & E; American Movie Classics; C-SPAN; CNBC; CNN; Cartoon Network; Country Music TV; Discovery Channel; Disney Channel; ESPN; FX; Fox Family Channel; Fox Sports Net Southwest; Headline News; History Channel; Learning Channel; Lifetime; MTV; Nashville Network; Nickelodeon; QVC; TBS Superstation; TV Food Network; The Weather Channel; Turner Classic Movies; Turner Network TV; USA Network.
Current originations: Automated time-weather.
Fee: $44.95 installation; $24.57 monthly; $24.95 additional installation.
Pay Service 1
Pay Units: 736.
Programming (via satellite): HBO.
Fee: N.A.
Pay Service 2
Pay Units: 249.
Programming (via satellite): The Movie Channel.
Fee: N.A.
Pay Service 3
Pay Units: 413.
Programming (via satellite): Cinemax.
Fee: N.A.
Program Guide: The Cable Guide.
Equipment: Scientific-Atlanta headend; RCA amplifiers; Times Fiber cable; U.S. Tower satellite antenna.
Miles of plant: 59.0 (coaxial); None (fiber optic). Homes passed: 3,573. Total homes in franchised area: 3,579.
Manager: Kris Miller. Chief technician: Kurt Widmer.
City fee: 3% of gross.
Ownership: Classic Cable (MSO).

QUINTON—Oklahoma Cablecomm, Box 970, Fort Gibson, OK 74434-0970. Phones: 918-478-2100; 800-783-5701. Fax: 918-478-2355.

Counties: Haskell & Pittsburg. Also serves Kinta. ICA: OK0156.
TV Market Ranking: Outside TV Markets. Franchise award date: N.A. Franchise expiration date: N.A. Began: January 1, 1977.
Channel capacity: 45 (not 2-way capable). Channels available but not in use: 18.
Basic Service
Subscribers: 443; Commercial subscribers: 39.
Programming (received off-air): KTEN (A,N,F) Ada; KOET (P) Eufaula; KJRH (N), KOKI-TV (F), KOTV (C), KTUL (A), KWHB (I) Tulsa.
Programming (via satellite): WGN-TV (W) Chicago; A & E; American Movie Classics; CNN; Cartoon Network; Country Music TV; Discovery Channel; Disney Channel; ESPN; ESPN 2; Fox Family Channel; Fox Sports Net Southwest; Goodlife TV Network; History Channel; Home & Garden Television; Learning Channel; Lifetime; Nashville Network; Nickelodeon; Outdoor Channel; QVC; Sci-Fi Channel; TBS Superstation; The Weather Channel; Turner Classic Movies; Turner Network TV; USA Network.
Fee: $30.00 installation; $23.45 monthly.
Pay Service 1
Pay Units: N.A.
Programming (via satellite): Cinemax.
Fee: N.A.
Pay Service 2
Pay Units: 56.
Programming (via satellite): HBO.
Fee: $9.00 monthly.
Local advertising: No.
Program Guide: TV Host.
Equipment: C-COR & Jerrold amplifiers; Atari character generator; Jerrold set top converters; Pico traps; Scientific-Atlanta satellite antenna; Scientific-Atlanta satellite receivers.
Miles of plant: 22.0 (coaxial). Homes passed: 643. Total homes in franchised area: 643.
Manager: Rick Wall. Chief technician: Leon Strain. Marketing & program director: Bruce Berkinshaw.
City fee: 2% of gross.
Ownership: Fanch Communications Inc. (MSO); Time Warner Cable (MSO). See Cable System Ownership.

RALSTON—Oklahoma Cablecomm, Box 970, Fort Gibson, OK 74434-0970. Phones: 918-478-2100; 800-783-5701. Fax: 918-478-2355. County: Pawnee. ICA: OK0241.
TV Market Ranking: Outside TV Markets. Franchise award date: January 1, 1988. Franchise expiration date: January 1, 2013. Began: April 1, 1988.
Channel capacity: 35 (not 2-way capable). Channels available but not in use: 17.
Basic Service
Subscribers: 103.
Programming (received off-air): KJRH (N), KOED-TV (P), KOKI-TV (F), KOTV (C), KTUL (A), KWHB (I) Tulsa.
Programming (via satellite): WGN-TV (W) Chicago; A & E; CNN; Country Music TV; Discovery Channel; ESPN; Fox Family Channel; Nashville Network; TBS Superstation; USA Network.
Fee: $30.00 installation; $20.95 monthly.
Pay Service 1
Pay Units: 22.
Programming (via satellite): Cinemax.
Fee: $10.00 monthly.
Pay Service 2
Pay Units: 28.
Programming (via satellite): HBO.
Fee: $10.00 monthly.
Local advertising: No.
Program Guide: TV Host.
Miles of plant: 3.0 (coaxial). Homes passed: 174. Total homes in franchised area: 174.
Manager: Rick Wall. Chief technician: Leon Strain. Marketing & program director: Bruce Berkinshaw.
City fee: 5% of gross.
Ownership: Fanch Communications Inc. (MSO); Time Warner Cable (MSO). See Cable System Ownership.

RAMONA—Community Cablevision Co., Box 307, Skiatook, OK 74070. Phone: 918-535-2770. County: Washington. ICA: OK0206.
TV Market Ranking: 54. Franchise award date: N.A. Franchise expiration date: January 1, 2009. Began: January 1, 1984.
Channel capacity: 35 (not 2-way capable). Channels available but not in use: 17.
Basic Service
Subscribers: 138.
Programming (received off-air): KJRH (N), KOED-TV (P), KOKI-TV (F), KOTV (C), KTUL (A) Tulsa.
Programming (via satellite): WGN-TV (W) Chicago; CNN; Cartoon Network; ESPN; Fox Family Channel; Headline News; MTV; Nashville Network; Nickelodeon; TBS Superstation; Turner Classic Movies.
Fee: $25.00 installation; $10.00 monthly.
Pay Service 1
Pay Units: N.A.
Programming (via satellite): Cinemax; Disney Channel; HBO.
Fee: $9.95 (Disney), $10.00 monthly (Cinemax or HBO).
Local advertising: No.
Equipment: Scientific-Atlanta headend; Scientific-Atlanta amplifiers; Scientific-Atlanta cable; Texscan character generator; Scientific-Atlanta set top converters; Pico traps; Scientific-Atlanta satellite antenna; Scientific-Atlanta satellite receivers.
Miles of plant: 8.0 (coaxial). Homes passed: 284. Total homes in franchised area: 284.
City fee: 3% of gross.
Ownership: Community Cablevision Co. (MSO).

RANDLETT—Cable Television Inc., Box 171, Medicine Park, OK 73557-0171. Phone: 580-529-2288. Fax: 580-529-5225. County: Cotton. ICA: OK0335.
TV Market Ranking: Below 100. Franchise award date: N.A. Franchise expiration date: N.A. Began: January 1, 1992.
Channel capacity: 35. Channels available but not in use: N.A.
Basic Service
Subscribers: 125.
Programming (received off-air): KETA (P) Oklahoma City; KAUZ-TV (C), KFDX-TV (N), KJTL (F,U), KSWO-TV (A) Wichita Falls-Lawton.
Programming (via satellite): WGN-TV (W) Chicago; A & E; CNN; Country Music TV; Discovery Channel; ESPN; Fox Family Channel; Learning Channel; Nashville Network; TBS Superstation; Turner Network TV.
Fee: $15.00 installation; $16.50 monthly.
Pay Service 1
Pay Units: 25.
Programming (via satellite): The Movie Channel.
Fee: $10.00 monthly.
Manager: Steven Hillary.
Ownership: Southwestern CATV Inc. (MSO).

RATTAN—Peak Cablevision, 516 N. Lakeside Dr., DeQueen, AR 71832. Phone: 870-642-2441. Fax: 870-642-4259. County: Pushmataha. ICA: OK0355.
TV Market Ranking: Outside TV Markets. Franchise award date: N.A. Franchise expiration date: May 25, 2005. Began: N.A.
Channel capacity: 20. Channels available but not in use: 5.
Basic Service
Subscribers: 83.
Programming (received off-air): KTEN (A,N,F) Ada; KOET (P) Eufaula; KXII (C) Sherman.
Programming (via satellite): WGN-TV (W) Chicago; Country Music TV; Discovery Channel; ESPN; Fox Family Channel; Nashville Network; Odyssey; TBS Superstation; USA Network.
Fee: $35.00 installation; $18.95 monthly.
Pay Service 1
Pay Units: N.A.
Programming (via satellite): Disney Channel; HBO; Showtime.
Fee: N.A.
Region manager: Ron Beatty. Chief technician: Lynn Harrison. Marketing director: Terry Homesley. Customer service manager: Carol Litchford.
Ownership: Peak Cablevision LLC (MSO). See Cable System Ownership.

RED ROCK—Westcom, Box 71279, Des Moines, IA 50325. Phone: 515-276-3069. Fax: 515-270-9181. County: Noble. ICA: OK0251.
TV Market Ranking: Outside TV Markets. Franchise award date: N.A. Franchise expiration date: N.A. Began: June 1, 1989.
Channel capacity: 35. Channels available but not in use: 22.
Basic Service
Subscribers: 26.
Programming (received off-air): KAUT-TV (U), KFOR-TV (N), KOCO-TV (A), KWTV (C) Oklahoma City.
Programming (via satellite): CNN; Country Music TV; Discovery Channel; ESPN; Nashville Network; TBS Superstation.
Fee: $8.00 installation; $15.95 monthly.
Pay Service 1
Pay Units: N.A.
Programming (via satellite): Cinemax.
Fee: N.A.
Homes passed: 120.
Ownership: Westcom LC (MSO).

RINGWOOD—Classic Cable, Box 429, 605 N.W. 3rd St., Plainville, KS 67663-0429. Phones: 785-434-7620; 800-999-8876. Fax: 785-434-2614. Web site: http://www.classic-cable.com. County: Major. ICA: OK0375.
TV Market Ranking: Outside TV Markets. Franchise award date: N.A. Franchise expiration date: N.A. Began: N.A.
Channel capacity: 36 (2-way capable). Channels available but not in use: N.A.
Basic Service
Subscribers: 46.
Programming (received off-air): KAUT-TV (U), KETA (P), KFOR-TV (N), KOCB (W), KOCO-TV (A), KOKH-TV (F), KTBO-TV (T), KWTV (C) Oklahoma City.
Programming (via satellite): WGN-TV (W) Chicago; CNN; Discovery Channel; Disney Channel; E! Entertainment TV; ESPN; Fox Family Channel; Nashville Network; TBS Superstation; Turner Network TV; USA Network.
Fee: $35.00 installation; $27.95 monthly.
Pay Service 1
Pay Units: 3.
Programming (via satellite): HBO.
Fee: $11.00 monthly.
Pay Service 2
Pay Units: 4.
Programming (via satellite): Showtime.
Fee: $6.95 monthly.
Pay Service 3
Pay Units: N.A.
Programming (via satellite): The Movie Channel.
Fee: $6.95 monthly.
Miles of plant: 4.0 (coaxial). Homes passed: 175.
Manager: Dave Walker. Chief technician: Jeff Smith. Marketing director: Jennifer Hauschild.
Ownership: Classic Cable (MSO).

RIPLEY—Westcom, Box 71279, Des Moines, IA 50325. Phones: 515-276-3174; 800-320-5581. Fax: 515-270-9181. County: Payne. ICA: OK0232.
TV Market Ranking: Outside TV Markets. Franchise award date: N.A. Franchise expiration date: N.A. Began: May 1, 1989.
Channel capacity: 35. Channels available but not in use: 18.
Basic Service
Subscribers: 18.
Programming (received off-air): KAUT-TV (U), KETA (P), KFOR-TV (N), KOCB (W), KOCO-TV (A), KTBO-TV (T), KWTV (C) Oklahoma City.
Programming (via satellite): CNN; Discovery Channel; ESPN; Fox Family Channel; Nashville Network; TBS Superstation.
Fee: $21.50 monthly.
Pay Service 1
Pay Units: N.A.
Programming (via satellite): Cinemax; HBO.
Fee: N.A.
Homes passed: 193.
Ownership: Westcom LC (MSO).

ROCKY—Rapid Cable, Box 6310, 310 Walnut Extension, Branson, MO 65615. Phones: 417-334-7897; 800-972-0962. Fax: 417-334-7899. E-mail: rcpcable@aol.com. County: Washita. ICA: OK0249.
TV Market Ranking: Outside TV Markets. Franchise award date: July 13, 1981. Franchise expiration date: July 13, 2001. Began: May 1, 1982.
Channel capacity: 36 (2-way capable; not operating 2-way). Channels available but not in use: 18.
Basic Service
Subscribers: 58.
Programming (received off-air): KETA (P), KFOR-TV (N), KWTV (C) Oklahoma City; KJTL (F,U), KSWO-TV (A) Wichita Falls-Lawton.
Programming (via satellite): WGN-TV (W) Chicago; CNN; Country Music TV; Discovery Channel; ESPN; Nashville Network; TBS Superstation; USA Network.
Fee: $29.95 installation; $22.95 monthly; $2.95 converter.
Pay Service 1
Pay Units: 1.
Programming (via satellite): Cinemax.
Fee: $9.00 monthly.
Pay Service 2
Pay Units: 6.
Programming (via satellite): HBO.
Fee: $10.00 monthly.
Pay Service 3
Pay Units: N.A.
Programming (via satellite): Disney Channel.
Fee: $7.00 monthly.
Local advertising: No.
Miles of plant: 3.0 (coaxial). Homes passed: 128.
Manager: Belinda Murphy. Chief technician: Steve Rice. Program director: Beth Semptimphelter. Marketing director: Bill Fischer.
Ownership: Rapid Communications Partners LP (MSO); TS Communications Inc. (MSO).

ROGERS COUNTY (northern portion)—Benchmark Communications, 16021 S. Hwy. 66, Claremore, OK 74017. Phone: 918-341-8441. Fax: 918-341-8443. Counties: Mayes, Rogers & Tulsa. Also serves Claremore, Mayes County (western portion), Tulsa (northwestern portion). ICA: OK0104.

TV Market Ranking: 54 (Claremore, portions of Mayes County, portions of Rogers County, Tulsa); Below 100 (portions of Rogers County); Outside TV Markets (portions of Mayes County, portions of Rogers County). Franchise award date: N.A. Franchise expiration date: N.A. Began: July 6, 1992.

Channel capacity: 77 (2-way capable; not operating 2-way). Channels available but not in use: 28.

Basic Service

Subscribers: 2,059.

Programming (received off-air): KDOR (T) Bartlesville; KRSC-TV (E) Claremore; KOET (P) Eufaula; KJRH (N), KOKI-TV (F), KOTV (C), KTFO (U), KTUL (A), KWHB (I) Tulsa.

Programming (via satellite): WGN-TV (W) Chicago; A & E; American Movie Classics; C-SPAN; C-SPAN 2; CNBC; CNN; Country Music TV; Discovery Channel; E! Entertainment TV; ESPN; Fox Family Channel; Headline News; Home Shopping Network; Lifetime; MTV; Nashville Network; Nickelodeon; QVC; Sci-Fi Channel; TBS Superstation; The Weather Channel; Travel Channel; Turner Network TV; USA Network; VH1.

Planned programming (via satellite): Cartoon Network.

Fee: $25.00 installation; $25.95 monthly.

Pay Service 1

Pay Units: 169.

Programming (via satellite): Cinemax.

Fee: $9.00 monthly.

Pay Service 2

Pay Units: 69.

Programming (via satellite): Disney Channel.

Fee: $9.00 monthly.

Pay Service 3

Pay Units: 326.

Programming (via satellite): HBO.

Fee: $10.95 monthly.

Pay Service 4

Pay Units: 95.

Programming (via satellite): Showtime.

Fee: $10.95 monthly.

Pay-Per-View

Addressable homes: 550.

Miles of plant: 220.0 (coaxial); 36.0 (fiber optic). Homes passed: 4,600.

Manager: Patsy Wrona. Chief technician: Tony Robbins.

Ownership: Benchmark Communications (MSO). Purchased from Genesis Cable Communications LLC, May 3, 1999.

ROOSEVELT—Classic Cable, Box 429, 605 N.W. 3rd St., Plainville, KS 67663-0429. Phones: 785-434-7620; 800-999-8876. Fax: 785-434-2614. County: Kiowa. ICA: OK0246.

TV Market Ranking: Outside TV Markets. Franchise award date: N.A. Franchise expiration date: N.A. Began: February 1, 1980.

Channel capacity: 36 (2-way capable). Channels available but not in use: N.A.

Basic Service

Subscribers: 91.

Programming (received off-air): KETA (P), KFOR-TV (N), KOKH-TV (F), KWTV (C) Oklahoma City; KAUZ-TV (C), KFDX-TV (N), KJTL (F,U), KSWO-TV (A) Wichita Falls-Lawton.

Programming (via satellite): A & E; American Movie Classics; CNN; Country Music TV; Discovery Channel; Disney Channel; ESPN; Fox Family Channel; Lifetime; Nashville Network; Sci-Fi Channel; TBS Superstation; Turner Network TV; USA Network.

Current originations: Automated time-weather; public access; local news.

Fee: $35.00 installation; $28.45 monthly.

Pay Service 1

Pay Units: 11.

Programming (via satellite): HBO.

Fee: $30.00 installation; $9.95 monthly.

Equipment: ISS headend; Jerrold amplifiers; Comm/Scope cable; Jerrold set top converters.

Miles of plant: 10.0 (coaxial). Homes passed: 139.

Manager: Dave Walker. Chief technician: Roger Campbell. Marketing director: Jennifer Hauschild.

City fee: 3% of gross.

Ownership: Classic Cable (MSO).

RUSH SPRINGS—Classic Cable, Box 429, 605 N.W. 3rd St., Plainville, KS 67663-0429. Phones: 785-434-7620; 800-999-8876. Fax: 785-434-2614. Web site: http://www.classic-cable.com. County: Grady. ICA: OK0121.

TV Market Ranking: Below 100. Franchise award date: N.A. Franchise expiration date: N.A. Began: November 1, 1982.

Channel capacity: 41 (2-way capable). Channels available but not in use: N.A.

Basic Service

Subscribers: 310.

Programming (received off-air): KAUT-TV (U), KETA (P), KFOR-TV (N), KOCB (W), KOCO-TV (A), KOKH-TV (F), KTBO-TV (T), KWTV (C) Oklahoma City; KSWO-TV (A) Wichita Falls-Lawton.

Programming (via satellite): WGN-TV (W) Chicago; A & E; American Movie Classics; C-SPAN; CNN; Country Music TV; Discovery Channel; Disney Channel; E! Entertainment TV; ESPN; Fox Family Channel; Headline News; History Channel; Learning Channel; Lifetime; Nashville Network; Nick at Nite's TV Land; QVC; Sci-Fi Channel; TBS Superstation; Turner Network TV; USA Network.

Fee: $35.00 installation; $28.95 monthly; $15.00 additional installation.

Pay Service 1

Pay Units: 66.

Programming (via satellite): HBO.

Fee: $9.95 monthly.

Pay Service 2

Pay Units: 21.

Programming (via satellite): Showtime.

Fee: $9.95 monthly.

Local advertising: Yes. Rates: $5.00/Day.

Equipment: Triple Crown headend; Jerrold amplifiers; Scientific-Atlanta satellite antenna; Scientific-Atlanta satellite receivers.

Miles of plant: 20.0 (coaxial). Homes passed: 684.

Manager: Dave Walker. Chief technician: Roger Campbell. Marketing director: Jennifer Hauschild.

City fee: 5% of basic gross.

Ownership: Classic Cable (MSO).

RYAN—Classic Cable, Box 429, 605 N.W. 3rd St., Plainville, KS 67663-0429. Phones: 785-434-7620; 800-999-8876. Fax: 785-434-2614. Web site: http://www.classic-cable.com. County: Jefferson. ICA: OK0184.

TV Market Ranking: Below 100. Franchise award date: N.A. Franchise expiration date: N.A. Began: April 1, 1982.

Channel capacity: 36 (2-way capable). Channels available but not in use: N.A.

Basic Service

Subscribers: 200.

Programming (received off-air): KTEN (A,N,F) Ada; KERA-TV (P) Dallas-Fort Worth; KXII (C) Sherman; KAUZ-TV (C), KFDX-TV (N), KJTL (F,U), KSWO-TV (A) Wichita Falls-Lawton.

Programming (via satellite): WGN-TV (W) Chicago; American Movie Classics; CNN; Country Music TV; Discovery Channel; Disney Channel; ESPN; Fox Family Channel; Fox Sports Net Southwest; Home & Garden Television; Nashville Network; Outdoor Channel; QVC; Sci-Fi Channel; TBS Superstation; Turner Network TV; Univision.

Current originations: Automated time-weather; public access.

Fee: $35.00 installation; $27.95 monthly.

Pay Service 1

Pay Units: 41.

Programming (via satellite): HBO.

Fee: $9.95 monthly.

Pay Service 2

Pay Units: 9.

Programming (via satellite): Showtime.

Fee: $9.95 monthly.

Pay Service 3

Pay Units: 22.

Programming (via satellite): Cinemax.

Fee: $9.95 monthly.

Local advertising: Yes. Rates: $5.00/Day.

Equipment: Triple Crown headend; Jerrold amplifiers; Times Fiber cable; Jerrold set top converters; Pico traps; Scientific-Atlanta satellite receivers.

Miles of plant: 8.5 (coaxial). Homes passed: 391.

Manager: Dave Walker. Chief technician: Roger Campbell. Marketing director: Jennifer Hauschild.

City fee: 5% of gross.

Ownership: Classic Cable (MSO).

SALINA—Oklahoma Cablecomm, Box 970, Fort Gibson, OK 74434-0970. Phones: 918-478-2100; 800-783-5701. Fax: 918-478-2355. County: Mayes. Also serves Locust Grove. ICA: OK0071.

TV Market Ranking: Outside TV Markets. Franchise award date: April 1, 1980. Franchise expiration date: April 1, 2005. Began: May 1, 1983.

Channel capacity: 35 (not 2-way capable). Channels available but not in use: 4.

Basic Service

Subscribers: 774; Commercial subscribers: 28.

Programming (received off-air): KRSC-TV (E) Claremore; KJRH (N), KOED-TV (P), KOKI-TV (F), KOTV (C), KTFO (U), KTUL (A), KWHB (I) Tulsa.

Programming (via satellite): WGN-TV (W) Chicago; A & E; CNBC; CNN; Cartoon Network; Comedy Central; Country Music TV; Discovery Channel; E! Entertainment TV; ESPN; Fox Family Channel; Fox Sports Net Southwest; Lifetime; MTV; Nashville Network; Nickelodeon; QVC; TBS Superstation; Turner Classic Movies; Turner Network TV; USA Network.

Fee: $30.00 installation; $20.95 monthly.

Pay Service 1

Pay Units: 87.

Programming (via satellite): Cinemax.

Fee: $20.00 installation; $9.00 monthly.

Pay Service 2

Pay Units: 48.

Programming (via satellite): Disney Channel.

Fee: $20.00 installation; $9.00 monthly.

Pay Service 3

Pay Units: 194.

Programming (via satellite): HBO.

Fee: $20.00 installation; $9.00 monthly.

Local advertising: No.

Program Guide: TV Host.

Miles of plant: 43.0 (coaxial). Homes passed: 1,967. Total homes in franchised area: 1,967.

Manager: Jim Stafford. Chief technician: Dale Yingst. Marketing & program director: Bruce Berkinshaw.

City fee: 3% of gross.

Ownership: Fanch Communications Inc. (MSO); Time Warner Cable (MSO). See Cable System Ownership.

SALLISAW—Classic Cable, 410 E. Cherokee, Sallisaw, OK 74955-4840. Phones: 918-775-3211; 918-775-6523. Fax: 918-775-7355. County: Sequoyah. ICA: OK0043.

TV Market Ranking: Below 100. Franchise award date: N.A. Franchise expiration date: N.A. Began: June 1, 1966.

Channel capacity: 40. Channels available but not in use: None.

Basic Service

Subscribers: 2,490.

Programming (received off-air): KFSM-TV (C), KHBS (A), KPOM-TV (N) Fort Smith; KETA (P) Oklahoma City; KJRH (N), KOKI-TV (F), KOTV (C), KTUL (A) Tulsa.

Programming (via satellite): C-SPAN; Knowledge TV; Odyssey; QVC; The Inspirational Network; The Weather Channel.

Fee: $16.54 installation; $10.83 monthly; $1.34 converter; $20.00 additional installation.

Expanded Basic Service

Subscribers: 2,340.

Programming (via satellite): A & E; American Movie Classics; CNBC; CNN; Discovery Channel; ESPN; FX; Fox Family Channel; Fox Sports Net Southwest; Headline News; Lifetime; MTV; Nashville Network; Nickelodeon; TBS Superstation; TV Guide Channel; Turner Network TV; USA Network.

Fee: $16.54 installation; $12.36 monthly.

Pay Service 1

Pay Units: 216.

Programming (via satellite): Cinemax.

Fee: $12.39 monthly.

Pay Service 2

Pay Units: 237.

Programming (via satellite): Disney Channel.

Fee: $10.00 installation; $13.00 monthly.

Pay Service 3

Pay Units: 820.

Programming (via satellite): The New Encore.

Fee: $1.75 monthly.

Pay Service 4

Pay Units: 583.

Programming (via satellite): HBO.

Fee: $10.00 installation; $12.83 monthly.

Pay Service 5

Pay Units: 213.

Programming (via satellite): Showtime.

Fee: $10.00 installation; $12.82 monthly.

Pay Service 6

Pay Units: 628.

Programming (via satellite): Starz!

Fee: $4.75 monthly.

Program Guide: The Cable Guide.

Miles of plant: 89.6 (coaxial). Homes passed: 3,740. Total homes in franchised area: 3,740.

Manager: Danny Keith. Marketing director: Dan Hobbs.

Ownership: Classic Cable (MSO).

SANDPOINT—CommuniComm Services, Box 597, 1501 W. Mississippi, Durant, OK 74702-0597. Phones: 580-924-2367; 800-752-4992. County: Bryan. ICA: OK0344.

TV Market Ranking: Below 100. Franchise award date: N.A. Franchise expiration date: N.A. Began: N.A.

Channel capacity: 35 (not 2-way capable). Channels available but not in use: 24.

Basic Service

Subscribers: 52.

Programming (received off-air): KTEN (A,N,F) Ada; KETA (P) Oklahoma City; KXII (C) Sherman.

Fee: $49.95 installation.

Expanded Basic Service

Subscribers: N.A.

Programming (via satellite): WGN-TV (W) Chicago; CNN; Country Music TV; ESPN; Nashville Network; TBS Superstation; USA Network.

Fee: N.A.

Pay Service 1

Pay Units: 49.

Programming (via satellite): HBO.

Fee: $12.95 monthly.

Miles of plant: 7.0 (coaxial); None (fiber optic).

Manager: Danny R. Neumann.

Ownership: James Cable Partners (MSO).

SAVANNA—Oklahoma Cablecomm, Box 970, Fort Gibson, OK 74434-0970. Phones: 918-478-2100; 800-783-5701. Fax: 918-478-2355. County: Pittsburg. Also serves Kiowa, McAlester Army Ammunition Plant. ICA: OK0310.

TV Market Ranking: Outside TV Markets. Franchise award date: N.A. Franchise expiration date: N.A. Began: January 1, 1988.

Channel capacity: 45. Channels available but not in use: 19.

Basic Service

Subscribers: 519; Commercial subscribers: 79.

Programming (received off-air): KTEN (A,N,F) Ada; KOET (P) Eufaula; KXII (C) Sherman; KJRH (N), KOTV (C), KTUL (A) Tulsa.

Programming (via satellite): WGN-TV (W) Chicago; A & E; American Movie Classics; C-SPAN; CNN; Cartoon Network; Country Music TV; Discovery Channel; Disney Channel; ESPN; ESPN 2; Fox Family Channel; Fox Sports Net; Fox Sports Net Southwest; Headline News; History Channel; Home & Garden Television; Learning Channel; Lifetime; Nashville Network; Nickelodeon; Outdoor Channel; QVC; Sci-Fi Channel; TBS Superstation; The Inspirational Network; The Weather Channel; Turner Classic Movies; Turner Network TV; USA Network.

Current originations: Automated time-weather; public access; local news.

Fee: $30.00 installation; $23.45 monthly.

Pay Service 1

Pay Units: N.A.

Programming (via satellite): Cinemax.

Fee: N.A.

Pay Service 2

Pay Units: 141.

Programming (via satellite): HBO.

Fee: $9.00 monthly.

Local advertising: No.

Equipment: C-COR amplifiers; Atari character generator; Jerrold set top converters; Pico traps; Scientific-Atlanta satellite antenna; Scientific-Atlanta satellite receivers.

Miles of plant: 36.0 (coaxial). Homes passed: 755. Total homes in franchised area: 755.

Manager: Rick Wall. Chief technician: Leon Strain. Marketing & program director: Bruce Berkinshaw.

City fee: 4% of gross.

Ownership: Fanch Communications Inc. (MSO); Time Warner Cable (MSO). See Cable System Ownership.

SAYRE—Cable One, 120 S. College St., Cordell, OK 73632-5208. Phone: 580-832-5311. Fax: 580-832-5112. County: Beckham. ICA: OK0086.

TV Market Ranking: Below 100. Franchise award date: N.A. Franchise expiration date: N.A. Began: January 1, 1954.

Channel capacity: 25 (not 2-way capable). Channels available but not in use: N.A.

Basic Service

Subscribers: 1,039.

Programming (received off-air): KWET (P) Cheyenne; KFOR-TV (N), KOCB (W), KOKH-TV (F), KWTV (C) Oklahoma City; KJTL (F,U) Wichita Falls-Lawton.

Programming (via satellite): WGN-TV (W) Chicago; CNBC; CNN; ESPN; MTV; Nashville Network; Odyssey; TBS Superstation; The Weather Channel; Trinity Bcstg. Network; Turner Network TV; USA Network.

Current originations: Automated time-weather; public access; educational access; religious access; leased access; automated emergency alert; local sports.

Fee: $16.70 installation; $22.01 monthly; $16.21 additional installation.

Pay Service 1

Pay Units: 46.

Programming (via satellite): Disney Channel.

Fee: $8.95 monthly.

Pay Service 2

Pay Units: 288.

Programming (via satellite): The New Encore.

Fee: N.A.

Pay Service 3

Pay Units: 65.

Programming (via satellite): HBO.

Fee: $10.00 monthly.

Pay Service 4

Pay Units: 76.

Programming (via satellite): The Movie Channel.

Fee: $8.95 monthly.

Pay Service 5

Pay Units: 48.

Programming (via satellite): Showtime.

Fee: $8.95 monthly.

Local advertising: Yes (locally produced). Available in character-generated programming. Rates: $6.00/Week; $1.75/Day.

Equipment: Dorate & Jerrold headend; Dorate & Jerrold amplifiers; Dorate & Jerrold cable; Texscan character generator; U.S. Tower satellite antenna; ICM satellite receivers.

Miles of plant: 27.0 (coaxial). Homes passed: 1,462. Total homes in franchised area: 1,462.

Manager: Gary Stills. Office manager: Rhonda Maddox.

City fee: None.

Ownership: Cable One Inc. (MSO).

SCHULTER—Oklahoma Cablecomm, Box 970, Fort Gibson, OK 74434. Phones: 918-478-2100; 800-783-5701. County: Okmulgee. ICA: OK0311.

TV Market Ranking: Below 100. Franchise award date: January 1, 1989. Franchise expiration date: January 1, 2014. Began: September 1, 1989.

Channel capacity: 45. Channels available but not in use: 30.

Basic Service

Subscribers: 109.

Programming (received off-air): KJRH (N), KOED-TV (P), KOKI-TV (F), KOTV (C), KTFO (U), KTUL (A), KWHB (I) Tulsa.

Programming (via satellite): WGN-TV (W) Chicago; CNN; Country Music TV; Discovery Channel; ESPN; Fox Family Channel; Nashville Network; TBS Superstation; Turner Network TV; USA Network.

Fee: $40.00 installation; $22.00 monthly; $1.96 converter; $19.95 additional installation.

Pay Service 1

Pay Units: 35.

Programming (via satellite): HBO.

Fee: $10.00 monthly.

Local advertising: No.

Program Guide: TV Host.

Miles of plant: 7.0 (coaxial). Homes passed: 204.

Manager: Rick Wall. Chief technician: Leon Strain. Marketing & program director: Bruce Berkinshaw.

Ownership: Fanch Communications Inc. (MSO); Time Warner Cable (MSO). See Cable System Ownership.

SEILING—Classic Cable, Box 429, 605 N.W. 3rd St., Plainville, KS 67663-0429. Phones: 785-434-7620; 800-999-8876. Fax: 785-434-2614. Web site: http://www.classic-cable.com. County: Dewey. ICA: OK0122.

TV Market Ranking: Outside TV Markets. Franchise award date: N.A. Franchise expiration date: N.A. Began: August 1, 1970.

Channel capacity: 41 (2-way capable). Channels available but not in use: N.A.

Basic Service

Subscribers: 289; Commercial subscribers: 79.

Programming (received off-air): KAUT-TV (U), KETA (P), KFOR-TV (N), KOCB (W), KOCO-TV (A), KOKH-TV (F), KWTV (C) Oklahoma City; KOMI-LP (I) Woodward; allband FM.

Programming (via satellite): WGN-TV (W) Chicago; A & E; American Movie Classics; CNN; Cartoon Network; Discovery Channel; Disney Channel; E! Entertainment TV; ESPN; Fox Family Channel; Fox Sports Net Southwest; Headline News; History Channel; Home & Garden Television; Learning Channel; Lifetime; Nashville Network; Nick at Nite's TV Land; Outdoor Channel; QVC; Sci-Fi Channel; TBS Superstation; The Weather Channel; Trinity Bcstg. Network; Turner Classic Movies; Turner Network TV.

Current originations: Automated time-weather.

Fee: $35.00 installation; $28.95 monthly.

Pay Service 1

Pay Units: 44.

Programming (via satellite): HBO.

Fee: $10.95 monthly.

Pay Service 2

Pay Units: 17.

Programming (via satellite): Showtime.

Fee: $9.95 monthly.

Pay Service 3

Pay Units: 4.

Programming (via satellite): Cinemax.

Fee: $9.95 monthly.

Equipment: Scientific-Atlanta headend; Jerrold amplifiers; Ameco cable; Scientific-Atlanta set top converters; Scientific-Atlanta satellite receivers.

Miles of plant: 17.9 (coaxial). Homes passed: 501.

Manager: Dave Walker. Chief technician: Jeff Smith. Marketing director: Jennifer Hauschild.

City fee: 3% of gross.

Ownership: Classic Cable (MSO).

SEMINOLE—Peak Cablevision, 205 E. Cherokee, McAlester, OK 74502. Phone: 918-423-6661. Fax: 918-426-2809. County: Seminole. ICA: OK0042.

TV Market Ranking: Below 100. Franchise award date: N.A. Franchise expiration date: October 13, 2002. Began: November 17, 1975.

Channel capacity: 30. Channels available but not in use: 3.

Basic Service

Subscribers: 2,227.

Programming (received off-air): KTEN (A,N,F) Ada; KETA (P), KFOR-TV (N), KOCB (W), KOCO-TV (A), KOKH-TV (F), KWTV (C) Oklahoma City; KTUL (A) Tulsa; allband FM.

Programming (via satellite): CNBC; CNN; Discovery Channel; Fox Family Channel; Headline News; MTV; Nashville Network; TBS Superstation; The Weather Channel.

Current originations: Automated time-weather.

Fee: $60.00 installation; $21.16 monthly; $20.00 additional installation.

Expanded Basic Service

Subscribers: 1,717.

Programming (via satellite): American Movie Classics; ESPN; Fox Sports Net Southwest; Turner Network TV; USA Network.

Fee: $3.00 monthly.

Pay Service 1

Pay Units: 182.

Programming (via satellite): Cinemax.

Fee: $20.00 installation; $10.00 monthly.

Pay Service 2

Pay Units: 151.

Programming (via satellite): Disney Channel.

Fee: $5.00 installation; $10.00 monthly.

Pay Service 3

Pay Units: 799.

Programming (via satellite): The New Encore.

Fee: N.A.

Pay Service 4

Pay Units: 355.

Programming (via satellite): HBO.

Fee: $20.00 installation; $10.00 monthly.

Local advertising: Yes (insert only). Available in automated programming.

Program Guide: The Cable Guide.

Equipment: Scientific-Atlanta headend; GTE Sylvania amplifiers; Systems Wire cable; AFC satellite antenna.

Miles of plant: 52.3 (coaxial). Additional miles planned: 1.0 (coaxial). Homes passed: 3,771. Total homes in franchised area: 3,771.

Manager: Everett Thayer. Chief technician: Lynn Harrison. Marketing director: Terry Homesley. Customer service manager: Susan Moore.

City fee: 3% of gross.

Ownership: Peak Cablevision LLC (MSO). See Cable System Ownership.

SENTINEL—Rapid Cable, Box 6310, 310 Walnut Extension, Branson, MO 65615. Phones: 417-334-7897; 800-972-0962. Fax: 417-334-7899. E-mail: rcpcable@aol.com. County: Washita. ICA: OK0157.

TV Market Ranking: Below 100. Franchise award date: January 2, 1979. Franchise expiration date: January 2, 2004. Began: June 1, 1955.

Channel capacity: 22 (2-way capable; not operating 2-way). Channels available but not in use: 4.

Basic Service

Subscribers: 248.

Programming (received off-air): KETA (P), KFOR-TV (N), KOCB (W), KOCO-TV (A), KOKH-TV (F), KWTV (C) Oklahoma City; KSWO-TV (A) Wichita Falls-Lawton.

Programming (via satellite): WGN-TV (W) Chicago; CNN; Country Music TV; Discovery Channel; ESPN; Fox Family Channel; Fox News Channel; Home Shopping Network 2; MOR Galleria; Nashville Network; Sci-Fi Channel; TBS Superstation; The Weather Channel; Trinity Bcstg. Network; USA Network.

Current originations: Automated time-weather.

Fee: $29.95 installation; $22.95 monthly; $3.95 converter.

Pay Service 1

Pay Units: 6.

Programming (via satellite): Cinemax.
Fee: $9.00 monthly.
Pay Service 2
Pay Units: 24.
Programming (via satellite): HBO.
Fee: $10.00 monthly.
Pay Service 3
Pay Units: 21.
Programming (via satellite): Disney Channel.
Fee: $7.00 monthly.
Miles of plant: 9.3 (coaxial). Homes passed: 511.
Manager: Belinda Murphy. Chief technician: Steve Rice. Program director: Beth Semptimphelter. Marketing director: Bill Fischer.
Ownership: TS Communications Inc. (MSO); Rapid Communications Partners LP (MSO).

SHATTUCK—Classic Cable, Box 429, 605 N.W. 3rd St., Plainville, KS 67663-0429. Phones: 785-434-7620; 800-999-8876. Fax: 785-434-2614. Web site: http://www.classic-cable.com. County: Ellis. Also serves Gage. ICA: OK0135.
TV Market Ranking: Outside TV Markets. Franchise award date: N.A. Franchise expiration date: N.A. Began: March 1, 1957.
Channel capacity: 41 (2-way capable; operating 2-way). Channels available but not in use: N.A.
Basic Service
Subscribers: 652; Commercial subscribers: 88.
Programming (received off-air): KVII-TV (A) Amarillo; KWET (P) Cheyenne; KFOR-TV (N), KOCO-TV (A), KOKH-TV (F), KWTV (C) Oklahoma City; KOMI-LP (I) Woodward.
Programming (via satellite): WGN-TV (W) Chicago; American Movie Classics; CNN; Cartoon Network; Country Music TV; Discovery Channel; Disney Channel; E! Entertainment TV; ESPN; Fox Family Channel; Fox Sports Net Southwest; Headline News; History Channel; Home & Garden Television; Learning Channel; Lifetime; Nashville Network; Nick at Nite's TV Land; Nickelodeon; Outdoor Channel; QVC; Sci-Fi Channel; TBS Superstation; The Weather Channel; Trinity Bcstg. Network; Turner Network TV; USA Network.
Current originations: Automated time-weather; religious access.
Fee: $35.00 installation; $28.95 monthly.
Pay Service 1
Pay Units: 22.
Programming (via satellite): Cinemax.
Fee: $9.95 monthly.
Pay Service 2
Pay Units: 83.
Programming (via satellite): HBO.
Fee: $10.95 monthly.
Pay Service 3
Pay Units: 45.
Programming (via satellite): Showtime.
Fee: $9.95 monthly.
Pay Service 4
Pay Units: 52.
Programming (via satellite): The Movie Channel.
Fee: $5.95 monthly.
Equipment: Scientific-Atlanta headend; Magnavox amplifiers; Scientific-Atlanta set top converters; Scientific-Atlanta satellite receivers.
Miles of plant: 12.8 (coaxial). Homes passed: 967.
Manager: Dave Walker. Chief technician: Jeff Smith. Marketing director: Jennifer Hauschild.
City fee: 2% of gross.
Ownership: Classic Cable (MSO).

SHAWNEE—Falcon Cable Media, 707 W. Saratoga, Shawnee, OK 74801. Phone: 405-275-6923. Fax: 405-275-0276. County: Pottawatomie. Also serves Dale, McLoud, Tecumseh. ICA: OK0016.
TV Market Ranking: 39 (Dale, McLoud); Outside TV Markets (Shawnee, Tecumseh). Franchise award date: October 1, 1978. Franchise expiration date: N.A. Began: October 1, 1979.
Channel capacity: 42 (2-way capable; operating 2-way). Channels available but not in use: 1.
Basic Service
Subscribers: 9,585; Commercial subscribers: 11.
Programming (received off-air): KAUT-TV (U), KETA (P), KFOR-TV (N), KOCB (W), KOCO-TV (A), KOKH-TV (F), KSBI (I), KTBO-TV (T), KWTV (C) Oklahoma City; 14 FMs.
Programming (via satellite): A & E; American Movie Classics; BET; C-SPAN; C-SPAN 2; CNBC; CNN; Country Music TV; ESPN; Fox Family Channel; Headline News; Lifetime; MTV; Nickelodeon; QVC; Sci-Fi Channel; Travel Channel.
Current originations: Public access; educational access; government access; religious access; leased access; automated emergency alert; local news; local sports.
Fee: $20.00 installation (aerial), $45.00 (underground); $20.27 monthly; $15.00 additional installation.
Commercial fee: $20.00 monthly.
Expanded Basic Service
Subscribers: 9,441.
Programming (via satellite): Discovery Channel; The Weather Channel; USA Network.
Fee: $1.81 monthly.
Expanded Basic Service 2
Subscribers: 9,212.
Programming (via satellite): WGN-TV (W) Chicago; Disney Channel; Nashville Network; TBS Superstation; Turner Network TV.
Fee: $7.00 monthly.
Pay Service 1
Pay Units: 526.
Programming (via satellite): Cinemax.
Fee: $20.00 installation; $10.45 monthly.
Pay Service 2
Pay Units: N.A.
Programming (via satellite): The New Encore.
Fee: N.A.
Pay Service 3
Pay Units: 2,856.
Programming (via satellite): HBO.
Fee: $20.00 installation; $10.45 monthly.
Pay Service 4
Pay Units: 466.
Programming (via satellite): Showtime.
Fee: $20.00 installation; $10.45 monthly.
Pay Service 5
Pay Units: 267.
Programming (via satellite): The Movie Channel.
Fee: $10.45 monthly.
Local advertising: Yes (locally produced). Available in satellite distributed, locally originated & character-generated programming. Rates: $300.00/Hour; $150.00/30 Minutes; $8.32/Minute; $4.16/30 Seconds. Local sales manager: Rick Hawkins.
Equipment: Phasecom, Scientific-Atlanta headend; Scientific-Atlanta, Texscan & Theta-Com amplifiers; Comm/Scope cable; Panasonic, Sony cameras; Panasonic & Sony VTRs; Video Data Systems character generator; Hamlin & Scientific-Atlanta set top converters; Eagle traps; Anixter-Mark & Scientific-Atlanta satellite antenna; Microdyne, Scientific-Atlanta & Standard Communications satellite receivers; Monroe commercial insert.

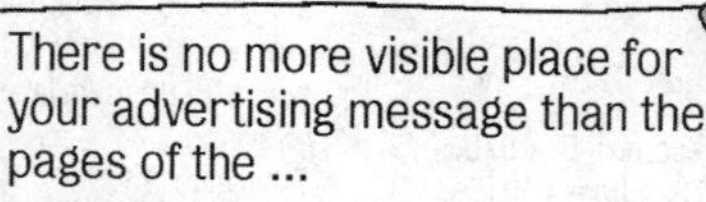

Miles of plant: 388.0 (coaxial). Homes passed: 14,401.
Manager: Andrew Dearth. Program director: Rick Hawkins. Marketing director: David Epley.
Franchise fee: 3%-5% of gross.
Ownership: Falcon Communications LP (MSO), joint venture formed September 30, 1998. See Cable System Ownership.

SKIATOOK—Community Cablevision, Box 307, Skiatook, OK 74070-0307. Phone: 918-396-3019. Counties: Osage & Tulsa. Also serves Sperry. ICA: OK0065.
TV Market Ranking: 54. Franchise award date: September 6, 1979. Franchise expiration date: September 6, 1999. Began: January 1, 1980.
Channel capacity: 35 (2-way capable; operating 2-way). Channels available but not in use: 4.
Basic Service
Subscribers: 1,209.
Programming (received off-air): KDOR (T) Bartlesville; KRSC-TV (E) Claremore; KTPX (X) Okmulgee; KJRH (N), KOED-TV (P), KOKI-TV (F), KOTV (C), KTUL (A), KWHB (I) Tulsa; allband FM.
Programming (via satellite): WGN-TV (W) Chicago; A & E; C-SPAN; C-SPAN 2; CNN; Country Music TV; Discovery Channel; ESPN; Fox Family Channel; Headline News; Lifetime; MTV; Nashville Network; Nickelodeon; TBS Superstation; Turner Classic Movies; Turner Network TV; USA Network; VH1.
Current originations: Automated time-weather; public access; educational access; government access; religious access; leased access; library access; local news; local sports.
Fee: $25.00 installation; $16.25 monthly; $25.00 additional installation.
Pay Service 1
Pay Units: 233.
Programming (via satellite): Cinemax.
Fee: $25.00 installation; $11.50 monthly.
Pay Service 2
Pay Units: 191.
Programming (via satellite): Disney Channel.
Fee: $25.00 installation; $7.00 monthly.
Pay Service 3
Pay Units: 399.
Programming (via satellite): HBO.
Fee: $25.00 installation; $11.50 monthly.
Pay-Per-View
Addressable homes: 1,209.
Local advertising: Yes. Available in character-generated programming. Rates: $15.00/Week.
Equipment: Jerrold headend; Theta-Com amplifiers; Times Fiber cable; RCA cameras; Texscan character generator; GTE Sylvania & Pioneer set top converters; Comtech satellite antenna; M/A-Com satellite receivers.
Miles of plant: 24.0 (coaxial). Homes passed: 2,221.
Manager: Ray Soule.
City fee: 3% of gross.
Ownership: Community Cablevision Co. (MSO).

SNYDER—Rapid Cable, Box 6310, 310 Walnut Extension, Branson, MO 65615. Phones: 417-334-7897; 800-972-0962. Fax: 417-334-7899. E-mail: rcpcable@aol.com. County: Kiowa. Also serves Mt. Park. ICA: OK0158.
TV Market Ranking: Below 100. Franchise award date: December 1, 1975. Franchise expiration date: November 15, 2012. Began: January 1, 1977.
Channel capacity: 22 (2-way capable; not operating 2-way). Channels available but not in use: 9.
Basic Service
Subscribers: 461.
Programming (received off-air): KETA (P), KFOR-TV (N), KOCO-TV (A) Oklahoma City; KJBO-LP (U) Wichita Falls; KAUZ-TV (C), KFDX-TV (N), KJTL (F,U), KSWO-TV (A) Wichita Falls-Lawton.
Programming (via satellite): WGN-TV (W) Chicago; A & E; Animal Planet; CNN; Country Music TV; Discovery Channel; ESPN; ESPN 2; Fox Family Channel; Fox News Channel; Home Shopping Network; Learning Channel; Nashville Network; Sci-Fi Channel; TBS Superstation; The Weather Channel; Trinity Bcstg. Network; Turner Network TV; USA Network.
Fee: $29.95 installation; $22.95 monthly; $3.95 converter.
Pay Service 1
Pay Units: 43.
Programming (via satellite): Cinemax.
Fee: $9.00 monthly.
Pay Service 2
Pay Units: 34.
Programming (via satellite): HBO.
Fee: $10.00 monthly.
Pay Service 3
Pay Units: 35.
Programming (via satellite): Disney Channel.
Fee: $7.00 monthly.
Local advertising: No.
Miles of plant: 17.2 (coaxial). Homes passed: 876.
Manager: Belinda Murphy. Chief technician: Steve Rice. Program director: Beth Semptimphelter. Marketing director: Bill Fischer.
Ownership: Rapid Communications Partners LP (MSO); TS Communications Inc. (MSO).

SOPER—Soper Cable TV, Box 22, Soper, OK 74759. Phone: 580-345-2898. County: Choctaw. ICA: OK0312.
TV Market Ranking: Outside TV Markets. Franchise award date: N.A. Franchise expiration date: N.A. Began: April 1, 1988.
Channel capacity: N.A. Channels available but not in use: N.A.
Basic Service
Subscribers: 98.
Programming (received off-air): KTEN (A,N,F) Ada; KETA (P) Oklahoma City; KXII (C) Sherman.
Programming (via satellite): WXIA-TV (N) Atlanta; WGN-TV (W) Chicago; Fox Family Channel; Nashville Network; TBS Superstation; Turner Network TV.
Fee: N.A.
Pay Service 1
Pay Units: N.A.
Programming (via satellite): HBO.
Fee: N.A.

Manager: Mary S. Loar.
Ownership: Mary S. Loar.

SPAVINAW—Oklahoma Cablecomm, Box 970, Fort Gibson, OK 74434-0970. Phones: 918-478-2100; 800-783-5701. Fax: 918-478-2355. County: Mayes. ICA: OK0205.
TV Market Ranking: Outside TV Markets. Franchise award date: March 1, 1983. Franchise expiration date: March 1, 2023. Began: January 1, 1984.
Channel capacity: 35 (not 2-way capable). Channels available but not in use: 14.
Basic Service
Subscribers: 92.
Programming (received off-air): KRSC-TV (E) Claremore; KJRH (N), KOED-TV (P), KOKI-TV (F), KOTV (C), KTFO (U), KTUL (A), KWHB (I) Tulsa.
Programming (via satellite): WGN-TV (W) Chicago; A & E; CNN; Country Music TV; Discovery Channel; ESPN; Fox Family Channel; Nashville Network; Nickelodeon; TBS Superstation; The Weather Channel; Turner Network TV; USA Network.
Fee: $40.00 installation; $22.95 monthly; $1.96 converter; $19.95 additional installation.
Pay Service 1
Pay Units: N.A.
Programming (via satellite): Cinemax.
Fee: $20.00 installation; $9.95 monthly.
Pay Service 2
Pay Units: 17.
Programming (via satellite): HBO.
Fee: $20.00 installation; $9.95 monthly.
Pay Service 3
Pay Units: 6.
Programming (via satellite): Showtime.
Fee: $20.00 installation; $9.95 monthly.
Local advertising: No.
Program Guide: TV Host.
Equipment: Blonder-Tongue & Triple Crown headend; Magnavox amplifiers; Comm/Scope cable; Arcom, Eagle & Northeast Filter traps; Prodelin & Scientific-Atlanta satellite antenna; Standard Communications satellite receivers.
Miles of plant: 5.0 (coaxial). Homes passed: 286. Total homes in franchised area: 286.
Manager: Rick Wall. Chief technician: Leon Strain. Marketing & program director: Bruce Berkinshaw.
City fee: 2% of gross.
Ownership: Fanch Communications Inc. (MSO); Time Warner Cable (MSO). See Cable System Ownership.

SPIRO—Classic Cable, Box 429, 605 N.W. 3rd St., Plainville, KS 67663-0429. Phones: 785-434-7620; 800-999-8876. Fax: 785-434-2614. Web site: http://www.classic-cable.com. County: Le Flore. ICA: OK0313.
TV Market Ranking: Below 100. Franchise award date: August 1, 1969. Franchise expiration date: August 1, 2005. Began: August 1, 1969.
Channel capacity: 78 (2-way capable). Channels available but not in use: N.A.
Basic Service
Subscribers: 595.
Programming (received off-air): KAFT (P) Fayetteville; KFSM-TV (C), KHBS (A), KPBI-LP (F), KPOM-TV (N) Fort Smith; KETA (P) Oklahoma City; KJRH (N), KOKI-TV (F), KTUL (A) Tulsa; allband FM.
Programming (via satellite): WGN-TV (W) Chicago; A & E; CNN; Country Music TV; Discovery Channel; Disney Channel; ESPN; Fox Family Channel; Headline News; History Channel; Nashville Network; Nick at Nite's TV Land; Nickelodeon; TBS Superstation; The Weather Channel; Turner Classic Movies; Turner Network TV; USA Network.
Fee: $35.00 installation; $27.95 monthly.
Pay Service 1
Pay Units: 71.
Programming (via satellite): HBO.
Fee: $11.00 monthly.
Pay Service 2
Pay Units: 44.
Programming (via satellite): Showtime.
Fee: $6.95 monthly.
Pay Service 3
Pay Units: 18.
Programming (via satellite): The Movie Channel.
Fee: $11.00 monthly.
Miles of plant: 38.0 (coaxial). Homes passed: 1,460.
Manager: Dave Walker. Chief technician: Carl Miller. Marketing director: Jennifer Hauschild.
City fee: 2% of gross.
Ownership: Classic Cable (MSO).

STERLING—Southwestern CATV Inc., Box 171, Medicine Park, OK 73557-0171. Phone: 580-529-2288. Fax: 580-529-5225. County: Comanche. ICA: OK0208.
TV Market Ranking: Below 100. Franchise award date: N.A. Franchise expiration date: N.A. Began: October 1, 1982.
Channel capacity: 35. Channels available but not in use: N.A.
Basic Service
Subscribers: N.A.
Programming (received off-air): KAUT-TV (U), KETA (P), KFOR-TV (N), KOCB (W), KOCO-TV (A), KOKH-TV (F), KTBO-TV (T), KWTV (C) Oklahoma City; KSWO-TV (A) Wichita Falls-Lawton; KSAS-TV (F), KSNW (N) Wichita-Hutchinson.
Programming (via satellite): WGN-TV (W) Chicago; ESPN; Nashville Network; TBS Superstation.
Fee: $15.00 installation; $8.00 monthly.
Pay Service 1
Pay Units: N.A.
Programming (via satellite): The Movie Channel.
Fee: $10.00 installation; $8.95 monthly.
Miles of plant: 6.2 (coaxial). Homes passed: 280.
Manager: Edward Hillary.
Ownership: Southwestern CATV Inc. (MSO).

STIGLER—Peak Cablevision, Box 807, Pocola, OK 74902. Phone: 918-436-7488. Fax: 918-436-7151. County: Haskell. Also serves Haskell County, Whitefield. ICA: OK0081.
TV Market Ranking: Below 100 (portions of Haskell County); Outside TV Markets (portions of Haskell County, Stigler, Whitefield). Franchise award date: November 18, 1968. Franchise expiration date: N.A. Began: August 1, 1970.
Channel capacity: 36 (not 2-way capable). Channels available but not in use: 1.
Basic Service
Subscribers: 1,082.
Programming (received off-air): KOET (P) Eufaula; KFSM-TV (C) Fort Smith; KJRH (N), KOKI-TV (F), KOTV (C), KTUL (A), KWHB (I) Tulsa; allband FM.
Programming (via satellite): A & E; C-SPAN; CNBC; CNN; Comedy Central; Discovery Channel; Disney Channel; Lifetime; Nashville Network; Nickelodeon; QVC; TBS Superstation; VH1.
Current originations: Automated time-weather; local sports.
Fee: $25.00 installation; $24.97 monthly.
Expanded Basic Service
Subscribers: 959.
Programming (via satellite): American Movie Classics; Court TV; ESPN; Turner Network TV; USA Network.
Fee: $1.50 monthly.
Pay Service 1
Pay Units: 68.
Programming (via satellite): Cinemax.
Fee: $7.95 monthly.
Pay Service 2
Pay Units: 278.
Programming (via satellite): The New Encore.
Fee: N.A.
Pay Service 3
Pay Units: 77.
Programming (via satellite): HBO.
Fee: $10.50 monthly.
Pay Service 4
Pay Units: 46.
Programming (via satellite): Showtime.
Fee: $10.00 installation; $9.95 monthly.
Local advertising: Yes. Available in automated programming. Rates: $21.75/Month. Local sales manager: Frank Kremer.
Equipment: Blonder-Tongue headend; Vikoa amplifiers; Scientific-Atlanta & Essex cable; MSI character generator; RCA & Jerrold set top converters; AFC & Prodelin satellite antenna; Microdyne & Scientific-Atlanta satellite receivers.
Miles of plant: 38.8 (coaxial). Homes passed: 1,645. Total homes in franchised area: 1,965.
Manager: Dennis Moore. Chief technician: Rick Gardner.
City fee: 2% of gross.
Ownership: Peak Cablevision LLC (MSO). See Cable System Ownership.

STILLWATER—Peak Cablevision, 802 E. 6th St., Stillwater, OK 74074. Phones: 405-377-7785; 800-348-1285. Fax: 405-372-3980. County: Payne. Also serves Perkins. ICA: OK0008.
TV Market Ranking: Outside TV Markets. Franchise award date: January 27, 1970. Franchise expiration date: January 27, 2000. Began: November 1, 1971.
Channel capacity: 77 (2-way capable; not operating 2-way). Channels available but not in use: None.
Basic Service
Subscribers: 11,477.
Programming (received off-air): KAUT-TV (U), KETA (P), KFOR-TV (N), KOCB (W), KOCO-TV (A), KOKH-TV (F), KOPX (X), KTBO-TV (T), KWTV (C) Oklahoma City; KOTV (C), KTUL (A) Tulsa; 39 FMs.
Programming (via satellite): WGN-TV (W) Chicago; CNN; Discovery Channel; Learning Channel; MTV; TBS Superstation.
Current originations: Public access; educational access; government access; religious access; automated emergency alert; local sports.
Fee: $44.95 installation; $10.68 monthly.
Digital Basic Service
Subscribers: N.A.
Programming (via satellite): BBC America; Bravo; Discovery Home & Leisure Channel; Discovery Kids Channel; Discovery Science Channel; ESPN Classic Sports; ESPNews; Fox Sports World; Game Show Network; History Channel; Home & Garden Television; Independent Film Channel; MuchMusic Network; Outdoor Life Network; Romance Classics; Sci-Fi Channel; Turner Classic Movies.
Fee: $10.00 monthly.
Expanded Basic Service
Subscribers: 10,356.
Programming (via satellite): A & E; American Movie Classics; C-SPAN; CNBC; Cartoon Network; Disney Channel; ESPN; ESPN 2; Encore Movie Networks; Fox Family Channel; Fox News Channel; Fox Sports Net Southwest; Headline News; Lifetime; Nashville Network; Nickelodeon; TV Guide Channel; The Weather Channel; Turner Network TV; USA Network; VH1.
Fee: $15.13 monthly.
Pay Service 1
Pay Units: 1,139.
Programming (via satellite): Cinemax.
Fee: $10.00 installation; $11.00 monthly.
Pay Service 2
Pay Units: 2,537.
Programming (via satellite): HBO.
Fee: $10.00 installation; $11.00 monthly.
Pay Service 3
Pay Units: 956.
Programming (via satellite): Showtime.
Fee: $10.00 installation; $11.00 monthly.
Pay Service 4
Pay Units: 1,950.
Programming (via satellite): The New Encore.
Fee: $1.75 monthly.
Pay Service 5
Pay Units: 1,929.
Programming (via satellite): Starz!
Fee: $6.75 monthly.
Digital Pay Service 1
Pay Units: N.A.
Programming (via satellite): HBO (multiplexed); Showtime; Starz!; The Movie Channel; The New Encore (multiplexed).
Fee: N.A.
Pay-Per-View
Addressable homes: 550.
Special events.
Local advertising: Yes. Available in satellite distributed programming. Rates: $891.00/Month. Local sales manager: Bill Fort.
Program Guide: The Cable Guide.
Equipment: Scientific-Atlanta headend; Jerrold amplifiers; Comm/Scope cable; Sony cameras; Hamlin set top converters; Tocom addressable set top converters; Eagle traps; Scientific-Atlanta satellite antenna; Scientific-Atlanta satellite receivers.
Miles of plant: 240.2 (coaxial). Homes passed: 19,441. Total homes in franchised area: 19,441.
Manager: Ted Ramsey. Chief technician: Joe Goertz.
City fee: 5% of gross.
Ownership: Peak Cablevision LLC (MSO). See Cable System Ownership.

STILWELL—Oklahoma Cablecomm, Box 970, Fort Gibson, OK 74434-0970. Phones: 918-478-2100; 800-783-5701. Fax: 918-478-2355. County: Mayes. ICA: OK0314.
TV Market Ranking: Below 100. Franchise award date: N.A. Franchise expiration date: N.A. Began: July 1, 1982.
Channel capacity: 36. Channels available but not in use: 16.
Basic Service
Subscribers: 818; Commercial subscribers: 85.
Programming (received off-air): KFSM-TV (C) Fort Smith; KJRH (N), KOED-TV (P), KOKI-TV (F), KOTV (C), KTUL (A) Tulsa.
Programming (via satellite): WGN-TV (W) Chicago; CNN; Cartoon Network; Discovery Channel; ESPN; Fox Family Channel; Nashville Network; Nickelodeon; TBS Superstation; VH1.
Fee: $30.00 installation; $17.95 monthly.
Pay Service 1
Pay Units: 210.
Programming (via satellite): The Movie Channel.
Fee: $10.00 installation; $10.00 monthly.

Pay Service 2
Pay Units: N.A.
Programming (via satellite): Cinemax; Disney Channel; HBO.
Fee: $10.00 installation; $10.00 monthly (each).
Miles of plant: 36.0 (coaxial).
Manager: Rick Wall. Chief technician: Richard Taapken. Marketing director: Rob Typer.
Ownership: Fanch Communications Inc. (MSO); Time Warner Cable (MSO). See Cable System Ownership.

STONEWALL—CommuniComm Services, Box 597, 1501 W. Mississippi, Durant, OK 74702-4992. Phones: 580-924-2367; 800-752-4992. Fax: 580-924-5970. Counties: Coal & Pontotoc. Also serves Tupelo. ICA: OK0379.
TV Market Ranking: Below 100. Franchise award date: N.A. Franchise expiration date: N.A. Began: N.A.
Channel capacity: N.A. Channels available but not in use: N.A.
Basic Service
Subscribers: 154.
Programming (received off-air): KTEN (A,N,F) Ada; KETA (P), KFOR-TV (N), KOCO-TV (A) Oklahoma City; KXII (C) Sherman.
Programming (via satellite): WGN-TV (W) Chicago; A & E; American Movie Classics; C-SPAN; CNBC; CNN; CNNfn; Cartoon Network; Country Music TV; Discovery Channel; Disney Channel; ESPN; ESPN 2; Fox Family Channel; Fox Sports Net Southwest; FoxNet; Headline News; History Channel; Lifetime; MTV; Nashville Network; Nickelodeon; Sci-Fi Channel; TBS Superstation; The Radar Channel; The Weather Channel; Trinity Bcstg. Network; Turner Network TV; USA Network; VH1.
Fee: $49.95 installation; $31.00 monthly.
Pay Service 1
Pay Units: 47.
Programming (via satellite): Cinemax; HBO (multiplexed); Starz!; The New Encore.
Fee: $9.95 monthly (Cinemax, Encore or Starz), $12.95 monthly (HBO).
Miles of plant: 17.0 (coaxial). Homes passed: 491.
Manager: Danny R. Nuemann.
Ownership: James Cable Partners (MSO).

STRANG—Oklahoma Cablecomm, Box 970, Fort Gibson, OK 74434-0970. Phones: 918-478-2100; 800-783-5701. Fax: 918-478-2355. County: Mayes. ICA: OK0259.
TV Market Ranking: Outside TV Markets. Franchise award date: November 1, 1991. Franchise expiration date: November 1, 2016. Began: November 28, 1991.
Channel capacity: 35 (not 2-way capable). Channels available but not in use: 20.
Basic Service
Subscribers: 42.
Programming (received off-air): KDOR (T) Bartlesville; KRSC-TV (E) Claremore; KJRH (N), KOED-TV (P), KOKI-TV (F), KOTV (C), KTUL (A), KWHB (I) Tulsa.
Programming (via satellite): WGN-TV (W) Chicago; A & E; CNN; Discovery Channel; ESPN; Fox Family Channel; Nashville Network; TBS Superstation; Turner Network TV; USA Network.
Fee: $40.00 installation; $22.95 monthly; $1.96 converter; $19.95 additional installation.
Pay Service 1
Pay Units: 15.
Programming (via satellite): HBO.
Fee: $20.00 installation; $9.95 monthly.
Local advertising: No.
Program Guide: TV Host.
Miles of plant: 4.0 (coaxial). Homes passed: 80.
Manager: Rick Wall. Chief technician: Leon Strain. Marketing & program director: Bruce Berkinshaw.
City fee: 5% of basic.
Ownership: Fanch Communications Inc. (MSO); Time Warner Cable (MSO). See Cable System Ownership.

STRATFORD—Falcon Cable Media, 707 W. Saratoga, Shawnee, OK 74801. Phone: 405-275-6923. Fax: 405-275-0276. County: Garvin. ICA: OK0315.
TV Market Ranking: Below 100. Franchise award date: June 3, 1980. Franchise expiration date: N.A. Began: June 1, 1981.
Channel capacity: 54. Channels available but not in use: 27.
Basic Service
Subscribers: 263.
Programming (received off-air): KTEN (A,N,F) Ada; KOKT-LP (U) Ardmore & Sulphur; KAUT-TV (U), KETA (P), KFOR-TV (N), KOCB (W), KOCO-TV (A), KOKH-TV (F), KTBO-TV (T), KWTV (C) Oklahoma City.
Programming (via satellite): A & E; American Movie Classics; CNN; Country Music TV; ESPN; Headline News; Learning Channel; QVC; Travel Channel.
Current originations: Public access; educational access; government access.
Fee: $15.58 monthly.
Expanded Basic Service
Subscribers: 256.
Programming (via satellite): Nashville Network; Sci-Fi Channel; USA Network.
Fee: $2.48 monthly.
Expanded Basic Service 2
Subscribers: 252.
Programming (via satellite): WGN-TV (W) Chicago; Discovery Channel; TBS Superstation.
Fee: $3.95 monthly.
Pay Service 1
Pay Units: 32.
Programming (via satellite): HBO.
Fee: $20.00 installation; $10.45 monthly.
Pay Service 2
Pay Units: 27.
Programming (via satellite): Showtime.
Fee: $20.00 installation; $10.45 monthly.
Miles of plant: 13.0 (coaxial). Homes passed: 805.
Manager: Andrew Dearth.
Franchise fee: 3% of gross.
Ownership: Falcon Communications LP (MSO), joint venture formed September 30, 1998. See Cable System Ownership.

STRINGTOWN—CommuniComm Services, Box 597, 1501 W. Mississippi, Durant, OK 74702-0597. Phones: 580-924-2367; 800-752-4992. County: Atoka. ICA: OK0339.
TV Market Ranking: Outside TV Markets. Franchise award date: N.A. Franchise expiration date: N.A. Began: January 1, 1988.
Channel capacity: 62 (not 2-way capable). Channels available but not in use: 50.
Basic Service
Subscribers: 40.
Programming (received off-air): KTEN (A,N,F) Ada; KXII (C) Sherman.
Programming (via satellite): WGN-TV (W) Chicago; A & E; CNN; Discovery Channel; ESPN; Fox Family Channel; Headline News; Nashville Network; TBS Superstation.
Fee: $49.95 installation; $3.80 monthly.
Pay Service 1
Pay Units: 15.
Programming (via satellite): Cinemax.
Fee: $9.95 monthly.
Miles of plant: 5.7 (coaxial); None (fiber optic). Homes passed: 120.
Manager: Danny R. Neumann. Chief technician: Dale Howard.
Ownership: James Cable Partners (MSO).

STROUD—Peak Cablevision, 323 E. Broadway, Cushing, OK 74023. Phone: 800-547-8582. County: Choctaw. ICA: OK0100.
TV Market Ranking: Outside TV Markets. Franchise award date: N.A. Franchise expiration date: N.A. Began: May 1, 1981.
Channel capacity: 40. Channels available but not in use: 12.
Basic Service
Subscribers: 661.
Programming (received off-air): KETA (P), KFOR-TV (N), KOCB (W), KOCO-TV (A), KOKH-TV (F), KTBO-TV (T), KWTV (C) Oklahoma City; KOTV (C) Tulsa.
Programming (via satellite): A & E; American Movie Classics; Animal Planet; CNBC; CNN; Cartoon Network; Discovery Channel; Disney Channel; ESPN; FX; Fox Family Channel; Fox News Channel; Headline News; Home & Garden Television; Learning Channel; Lifetime; Nashville Network; Nickelodeon; TBS Superstation; The Weather Channel; Turner Network TV; USA Network.
Fee: $37.50 installation; $24.66 monthly; $1.50 converter; $5.19 additional installation.
Pay Service 1
Pay Units: N.A.
Programming (via satellite): Starz!
Fee: $6.75 monthly.
Pay Service 2
Pay Units: 213.
Programming (via satellite): The New Encore.
Fee: $1.75 monthly.
Pay Service 3
Pay Units: 71.
Programming (via satellite): HBO.
Fee: $14.19 monthly.
Pay Service 4
Pay Units: 95.
Programming (via satellite): Showtime.
Fee: $14.19 monthly.
Miles of plant: 26.2 (coaxial). Homes passed: 1,073. Total homes in franchised area: 1,077.
Manager: Brad Mangum. Chief technician: Ron Diamond.
Ownership: Peak Cablevision LLC (MSO). See Cable System Ownership.

STUART—Peak Cablevision, 205 E. Cherokee, McAlester, OK 74502. Phone: 918-423-6661. Fax: 918-426-2809. Counties: Hughes & Pittsburg. Also serves Arpelar, Haywood. ICA: OK0356.
TV Market Ranking: Outside TV Markets. Franchise award date: N.A. Franchise expiration date: October 10, 2009. Began: N.A.
Channel capacity: 36 (not 2-way capable). Channels available but not in use: 6.
Basic Service
Subscribers: 254.
Programming (received off-air): KTEN (A,N,F) Ada; KOET (P) Eufaula; KFOR-TV (N), KOKH-TV (F) Oklahoma City; KXII (C) Sherman; KTUL (A) Tulsa.
Programming (via satellite): WGN-TV (W) Chicago; A & E; American Movie Classics; CNN; Country Music TV; Disney Channel; ESPN; Fox Family Channel; Lifetime; Nashville Network; Nick at Nite's TV Land; Sci-Fi Channel; TBS Superstation; The Weather Channel; Turner Network TV; USA Network.
Current originations: Community access.
Fee: $21.96 monthly.
Pay Service 1
Pay Units: N.A.
Programming (via satellite): HBO; Showtime; Starz!; The New Encore.
Fee: $10.00 monthly (each).
Miles of plant: 31.0 (coaxial). Homes passed: 436.
Manager: Everett Thayer. Chief technician: Lynn Harrison. Marketing director: Terry Homesley. Customer service manager: Susan Moore.
Franchise fee: 5% of basic subscibers.
Ownership: Peak Cablevision LLC (MSO). See Cable System Ownership.

SULPHUR—Harmon Cable Communications, Box 340, 1218 W. Broadway, Sulphur, OK 73086. Phones: 580-622-2575; 800-858-1228. Counties: Murray & Pontotoc. Also serves Davis, Roff. ICA: OK0051.
TV Market Ranking: Below 100. Franchise award date: N.A. Franchise expiration date: N.A. Began: October 10, 1969.
Channel capacity: 77 (not 2-way capable). Channels available but not in use: 20.
Basic Service
Subscribers: 3,120.
Programming (received off-air): KTEN (A,N,F) Ada; KOKT-LP (U) Ardmore & Sulphur; KETA (P), KFOR-TV (N), KOCO-TV (A), KOKH-TV (F), KTBO-TV (T), KWTV (C) Oklahoma City; KXII (C) Sherman; allband FM.
Programming (via satellite): WGN-TV (W) Chicago; A & E; American Movie Classics; Animal Planet; C-SPAN; CNBC; CNN; Cartoon Network; Country Music TV; Discovery Channel; E! Entertainment TV; ESPN; ESPN 2; Fox Family Channel; Fox Sports Net Southwest; Headline News; History Channel; Home & Garden Television; Home Shopping Network; Learning Channel; Lifetime; Nashville Network; Nick at Nite's TV Land; Nickelodeon; Odyssey; QVC; Sci-Fi Channel; TBS Superstation; The Weather Channel; Turner Classic Movies; Turner Network TV; USA Network; VH1.
Current originations: Automated time-weather.
Fee: $27.50 installation; $23.35 monthly; $1.10 converter; $10.00 additional installation.
Pay Service 1
Pay Units: 115.
Programming (via satellite): Disney Channel.
Fee: $20.00 installation; $9.95 monthly.
Pay Service 2
Pay Units: 738.
Programming (via satellite): HBO.
Fee: $20.00 installation; $9.95 monthly.
Pay Service 3
Pay Units: 382.
Programming (via satellite): Showtime.
Fee: $20.00 installation; $9.95 monthly.
Pay Service 4
Pay Units: 213.
Programming (via satellite): The New Encore.
Fee: $3.95 monthly.
Local advertising: Yes.
Program Guide: Premium Channels.
Equipment: Scientific-Atlanta amplifiers; AFC satellite antenna.
Miles of plant: 55.0 (coaxial); 15.0 (fiber optic). Additional miles planned: 5.0 (coaxial). Homes passed: 3,219.
Manager: Nick Schwake. Chief technician: Jerry Lancaster.
City fee: 2% of gross.
Ownership: Harmon Cable Communications (MSO).

TAHLEQUAH—Tahlequah Cable TV Inc., Box 1689, 110 E. Keetoowah, Tahlequah, OK 74464. Phone: 918-456-1102. Fax: 918-456-1172.

E-mail: tctvinc@netsites.net. County: Cherokee. ICA: OK0034.

TV Market Ranking: Outside TV Markets. Franchise award date: July 1, 1980. Franchise expiration date: July 1, 2004. Began: July 1, 1980.

Channel capacity: 30 (2-way capable; operating 2-way). Channels available but not in use: 1.

Basic Service

Subscribers: 4,500; Commercial subscribers: 890.

Programming (received off-air): KDOR (T) Bartlesville; KRSC-TV (E) Claremore; KTPX (X) Okmulgee; KJRH (N), KOED-TV (P), KOKI-TV (F), KOTV (C), KTFO (U), KTUL (A), KWHB (I), KWMJ (I) Tulsa; allband FM.

Programming (via satellite): WGN-TV (W) Chicago; C-SPAN; CNN; Discovery Channel; ESPN; Headline News; Lifetime; Nickelodeon; TBS Superstation; The Weather Channel.

Current originations: Public access; automated emergency alert.

Fee: $35.00 installation; $17.36 monthly; $20.00 additional installation.

Commercial fee: $6.00 monthly.

Expanded Basic Service

Subscribers: 4,021.

Programming (via satellite): A & E; American Movie Classics; Country Music TV; Disney Channel; Fox Family Channel; Fox News Channel; Headline News; History Channel; Home Shopping Network; Learning Channel; Lifetime; Nashville Network; Sci-Fi Channel; Turner Network TV; USA Network; VH1.

Fee: N.A.

Pay Service 1

Pay Units: 372.

Programming (via satellite): Cinemax.

Fee: $9.95 monthly.

Pay Service 2

Pay Units: 1,019.

Programming (via satellite): HBO.

Fee: $11.50 monthly.

Local advertising: Yes. Available in locally originated programming. Local sales manager: Kara Hayes.

Equipment: Scientific-Atlanta, Cadco & Drake headend; Texscan amplifiers; Comm/Scope & Times Fiber cable; MSI & Texscan character generator; RCA, Pioneer & Panasonic set top converters; Eagle, Arcom & Pico traps; Harris, Scientific-Atlanta & Odom satellite antenna; Panasonic, Gardiner & Drake satellite receivers.

Miles of plant: 136.0 (coaxial). Additional miles planned: 3.0 (coaxial). Homes passed: 5,000.

Manager: W. Mike Franke. Marketing director: Rebecca Smythe. Customer service manager: Shirley Little.

City fee: 3% of gross.

Ownership: WEHCO Video Inc. (MSO).

TALALA—Quality Cablevision of Oklahoma Inc., Box 315, 816-D N. Date, Jenks, OK 74037. Phone: 918-299-0104. County: Rogers. ICA: OK0340.

TV Market Ranking: 54. Franchise award date: N.A. Franchise expiration date: N.A. Began: May 15, 1993.

Channel capacity: N.A. Channels available but not in use: N.A.

Basic Service

Subscribers: 32.

Programming (received off-air): KETA (P) Oklahoma City; KJRH (N), KOKI-TV (F), KOTV (C), KTFO (U), KTUL (A) Tulsa.

Fee: $29.95 installation; $17.95 monthly.

Pay Service 1

Pay Units: N.A.

Programming (via satellite): HBO; Showtime.

Fee: $10.95 monthly (each).

Miles of plant: 4.0 (coaxial). Homes passed: 110.

Manager: Curtis Scott. Chief technician: Bill Garrison.

Ownership: Quality Cablevision of Oklahoma Inc. (MSO).

TALIHINA—Peak Cablevision, Box 807, Pocola, OK 74902. Phone: 918-436-7488. Fax: 918-436-7151. County: Le Flore. ICA: OK0136.

TV Market Ranking: Outside TV Markets. Franchise award date: N.A. Franchise expiration date: December 5, 2003. Began: February 1, 1972.

Channel capacity: 36 (not 2-way capable). Channels available but not in use: 6.

Basic Service

Subscribers: 619.

Programming (received off-air): KOET (P) Eufaula; KFSM-TV (C), KHBS (A), KPBI-LP (F) Fort Smith; KJRH (N), KOKI-TV (F), KOTV (C), KTUL (A) Tulsa; 1 FM.

Programming (via satellite): WGN-TV (W) Chicago; CNN; Country Music TV; Discovery Channel; ESPN; Fox Family Channel; Nashville Network; Nickelodeon; QVC; TBS Superstation; The Weather Channel; Trinity Bcstg. Network; Turner Network TV; USA Network.

Planned originations: Automated timeweather.

Fee: Free installation; $22.83 monthly.

Pay Service 1

Pay Units: N.A.

Programming (via satellite): Disney Channel; HBO; Showtime; The Movie Channel.

Fee: $7.95 monthly (Disney), $10.00 monthly (HBO, Showtime or TMC).

Miles of plant: 20.8 (coaxial). Homes passed: 921.

Manager: Dennis Moore. Chief technician: Rick Packard. Marketing director: Terry Homesley. Customer service manager: Susan Moore.

Franchise fee: 4% of basic subs.

Ownership: Peak Cablevision LLC (MSO). See Cable System Ownership.

TALOGA—Taloga Cable TV, Box 218, 109 S. Broadway, Taloga, OK 73667-0218. Phone: 580-328-5262. Fax: 580-328-5262. County: Dewey. ICA: OK0222.

TV Market Ranking: Outside TV Markets. Franchise award date: March 1, 1980. Franchise expiration date: January 1, 2001. Began: March 1, 1980.

Channel capacity: 36 (not 2-way capable). Channels available but not in use: None.

Basic Service

Subscribers: 143.

Programming (received off-air): KWET (P) Cheyenne; KAUT-TV (U), KFOR-TV (N), KOCB (W), KOCO-TV (A), KOKH-TV (F), KTBO-TV (T), KWTV (C) Oklahoma City; allband FM.

Programming (via satellite): WGN-TV (W) Chicago; A & E; C-SPAN; C-SPAN 2; CNN; Comedy Central; Country Music TV; Discovery Channel; ESPN; Fox Family Channel; Home & Garden Television; Learning Channel; Nashville Network; Nick at Nite; Nickelodeon; QVC; TV Food Network; The Weather Channel; Trinity Bcstg. Network; Turner Classic Movies; Turner Network TV; USA Network; Univision; VH1; Z Music Television.

Fee: $30.00 installation; $20.00 monthly; $3.00 converter.

Pay Service 1

Pay Units: 35.

Programming (via satellite): Disney Channel.

Fee: $15.00 installation; $8.00 monthly.

Pay Service 2

Pay Units: 59.

Programming (via satellite): HBO.

Fee: $15.00 installation; $9.00 monthly.

Pay Service 3

Pay Units: 39.

Programming (via satellite): Showtime.

Fee: $9.00 monthly.

Pay Service 4

Pay Units: 29.

Programming (via satellite): DMX.

Fee: $8.00 monthly.

Local advertising: No.

Equipment: Scientific-Atlanta headend; Scientific-Atlanta amplifiers; Times Fiber cable; Sony VTRs; Scientific-Atlanta set top converters; Eagle traps; Gardiner satellite receivers.

Miles of plant: 6.0 (coaxial); 3.0 (fiber optic). Homes passed: 170. Total homes in franchised area: 170.

Manager: Glenn Gore.

Ownership: Taloga Cable TV.

TERRAL—Classic Cable, Box 429, 605 N.W. 3rd St., Plainville, KS 67663-0429. Phones: 785-434-7620; 800-999-8876. Fax: 785-434-2614. Web Site: http://www.classic-cable.com. County: Jefferson. ICA: OK0229.

TV Market Ranking: Below 100. Franchise award date: N.A. Franchise expiration date: N.A. Began: July 1, 1984.

Channel capacity: 31 (2-way capable). Channels available but not in use: N.A.

Basic Service

Subscribers: 90.

Programming (received off-air): KAUZ-TV (C), KFDX-TV (N), KJTL (F,U), KSWO-TV (A) Wichita Falls-Lawton.

Programming (via microwave): KERA-TV (P) Dallas-Fort Worth.

Programming (via satellite): CNN; Discovery Channel; Disney Channel; ESPN; Fox Family Channel; Home & Garden Television; Nashville Network; Outdoor Channel; QVC; Sci-Fi Channel; TBS Superstation; Trinity Bcstg. Network; Turner Classic Movies; Turner Network TV; Univision.

Current originations: Automated timeweather; leased access.

Fee: $35.00 installation; $27.95 monthly.

Pay Service 1

Pay Units: 13.

Programming (via satellite): HBO.

Fee: $25.00 installation; $9.95 monthly.

Pay Service 2

Pay Units: 11.

Programming (via satellite): Cinemax.

Fee: $25.00 installation; $9.95 monthly.

Local advertising: Yes. Available in character-generated programming. Rates: $5.00/Day.

Equipment: Cadco headend; Scientific-Atlanta amplifiers; Comm/Scope cable; Microdyne satellite receivers.

Miles of plant: 5.0 (coaxial). Homes passed: 270.

Manager: Dave Walker. Chief technician: Roger Campbell. Marketing director: Jennifer Hauschild.

City fee: 5% of gross.

Ownership: Classic Cable (MSO).

THOMAS—Classic Cable, Box 429, 605 N.W. 3rd St., Plainville, KS 67663-0429. Phones: 785-434-7620; 800-999-8876. Fax: 785-434-2614. County: Custer. ICA: OK0155.

TV Market Ranking: Outside TV Markets. Franchise award date: N.A. Franchise expiration date: N.A. Began: March 1, 1976.

Channel capacity: 43 (2-way capable). Channels available but not in use: N.A.

Basic Service

Subscribers: 401; Commercial subscribers: 62.

Programming (received off-air): KAUT-TV (U), KETA (P), KFOR-TV (N), KOCB (W), KOCO-TV (A), KOKH-TV (F), KTBO-TV (T), KWTV (C) Oklahoma City; allband FM.

Programming (via satellite): WGN-TV (W) Chicago; A & E; American Movie Classics; CNN; Cartoon Network; Country Music TV; Discovery Channel; Disney Channel; E! Entertainment TV; ESPN; Fox Sports Net Southwest; Headline News; History Channel; Home & Garden Television; Learning Channel; Lifetime; Nashville Network; Nick at Nite's TV Land; QVC; Sci-Fi Channel; TBS Superstation; The Weather Channel; Travel Channel; Turner Network TV; USA Network.

Current originations: Automated timeweather; automated emergency alert.

Fee: $35.00 installation; $27.95 monthly; $2.00 converter.

Pay Service 1

Pay Units: 27.

Programming (via satellite): Showtime.

Fee: $9.95 monthly.

Pay Service 2

Pay Units: 56.

Programming (via satellite): HBO.

Fee: $10.95 monthly.

Miles of plant: 12.0 (coaxial). Homes passed: 537.

Manager: Dave Walker. Chief technician: Roger Campbell. Marketing director: Jennifer Hauschild.

City fee: 2% of gross.

Ownership: Classic Cable (MSO). Purchased from Fanch Communications Inc.

TIPTON—Rapid Cable, Box 6310, 310 Walnut Extension, Branson, MO 65615. Phones: 417-334-7897; 800-972-0962. Fax: 417-334-7899. E-mail: rcpcable@aol.com. County: Tillman. ICA: OK0191.

TV Market Ranking: Outside TV Markets. Franchise award date: May 5, 1980. Franchise expiration date: May 5, 2005. Began: August 1, 1981.

Channel capacity: 22 (2-way capable; not operating 2-way). Channels available but not in use: 2.

Basic Service

Subscribers: 241.

Programming (received off-air): KETA (P), KWTV (C) Oklahoma City; KAUZ-TV (C), KFDX-TV (N), KJTL (F,U), KSWO-TV (A) Wichita Falls-Lawton.

Programming (via satellite): WGN-TV (W) Chicago; CNN; Country Music TV; Discovery Channel; ESPN; Fox Family Channel; Fox News Channel; Home Shopping Network 2; Nashville Network; TBS Superstation; The Weather Channel; Trinity Bcstg. Network; Turner Network TV; USA Network.

Fee: $29.95 installation; $22.95 monthly; $3.95 converter.

Pay Service 1

Pay Units: 14.

Programming (via satellite): Cinemax.

Fee: $9.00 monthly.

Pay Service 2

Pay Units: 15.

Programming (via satellite): HBO.

Fee: $10.00 monthly.

Pay Service 3

Pay Units: 16.

Programming (via satellite): Disney Channel.

Fee: $7.00 monthly.

Local advertising: No.

Miles of plant: 9.0 (coaxial). Homes passed: 591.
Manager: Belinda Murphy. Chief technician: Steve Rice. Program director: Beth Semptimphelter. Marketing director: Bill Fischer.
Ownership: Rapid Communications Partners LP (MSO); TS Communications Inc. (MSO).

TISHOMINGO—CommuniComm Services, Box 597, 1501 W. Mississippi, Durant, OK 74702-0597. Phones: 580-924-2367; 800-752-4992. County: Johnston. Also serves Johnston County (portions), Ravia. ICA: OK0064.
TV Market Ranking: Below 100 (portions of Johnston County); Outside TV Markets (portions of Johnston County, Ravia, Tishomingo). Franchise award date: N.A. Franchise expiration date: N.A. Began: March 15, 1972.
Channel capacity: 42 (not 2-way capable). Channels available but not in use: None.
Basic Service
Subscribers: 786.
Programming (received off-air): KTEN (A,N,F) Ada; KOKT-LP (U) Ardmore & Sulphur; KETA (P), KFOR-TV (N) Oklahoma City; KXII (C) Sherman; allband FM.
Programming (via satellite): WGN-TV (W) Chicago; A & E; American Movie Classics; BET; C-SPAN; CNBC; CNN; Country Music TV; Discovery Channel; Disney Channel; ESPN; ESPN 2; Fox Family Channel; Fox Sports Net Southwest; FoxNet; Headline News; History Channel; Lifetime; MTV; Nashville Network; Nickelodeon; QVC; TBS Superstation; The Weather Channel; Trinity Bcstg. Network; Turner Network TV; USA Network.
Current originations: Automated time-weather.
Fee: $49.95 installation; $31.00 monthly.
Expanded Basic Service
Subscribers: 848.
Programming (via satellite): WGN-TV (W) Chicago; A & E; American Movie Classics; BET; C-SPAN; CNBC; CNN; Country Music TV; Discovery Channel; ESPN; Fox Family Channel; Fox Sports Net Southwest; Headline News; Lifetime; MTV; Nashville Network; Nickelodeon; Odyssey; QVC; TBS Superstation; The Weather Channel; Turner Network TV; USA Network.
Fee: N.A.
Pay Service 1
Pay Units: 176.
Programming (via satellite): Cinemax; Disney Channel; HBO (multiplexed); Starz!; The New Encore.
Fee: $11.00 monthly (each).
Equipment: Blonder-Tongue headend; Coral amplifiers; Comm/Scope cable; Scientific-Atlanta satellite antenna.
Miles of plant: 32.0 (coaxial); None (fiber optic). Homes passed: 1,637.
Manager: Danny R. Neumann.
City fee: 3% of gross.
Ownership: James Cable Partners (MSO).

TRYON—Oklahoma Cablecomm, Box 970, Fort Gibson, OK 74434-0970. Phones: 918-478-2100; 800-783-5701. Fax: 918-478-2355. County: Lincoln. ICA: OK0316.
TV Market Ranking: Outside TV Markets. Franchise award date: N.A. Franchise expiration date: N.A. Began: N.A.
Channel capacity: N.A. Channels available but not in use: N.A.
Basic Service
Subscribers: 54.
Programming (received off-air): KAUT-TV (U), KETA (P), KFOR-TV (N), KOCB (W), KOCO-TV (A), KOKH-TV (F), KWTV (C) Oklahoma City.
Programming (via satellite): WGN-TV (W) Chicago; A & E; CNN; Discovery Channel; ESPN; Fox Family Channel; Nashville Network; TBS Superstation; USA Network.
Fee: $30.00 installation; $18.95 monthly.
Pay Service 1
Pay Units: 13.
Programming (via satellite): HBO.
Fee: $10.50 monthly.
Local advertising: No.
Program Guide: TV Host.
Miles of plant: 5.0 (coaxial). Homes passed: 233. Total homes in franchised area: 233.
Manager: Jim Stafford. Chief technician: Dale Yingst. Marketing & program director: Bruce Berkinshaw.
City fee: 5% of gross.
Ownership: Fanch Communications Inc. (MSO); Time Warner Cable (MSO). See Cable System Ownership.

TULSA—TCI Cable Television Inc., Box 470800, Tulsa, OK 74145. Phone: 918-665-0200. Fax: 918-665-0590. Web Site: http://www.tci.com. Counties: Creek, Osage, Rogers, Tulsa & Wagoner. Also serves Broken Arrow, Catoosa, Creek County (portions), Glenpool, Jenks, Kiefer, Osage County (portions), Owasso, Rogers County (portions), Rolling Hills, Sand Springs, Sapulpa, Wagoner County (portions). ICA: OK0001.
TV Market Ranking: 54 (Broken Arrow, Catoosa, portions of Creek County, Glenpool, Jenks, Kiefer, portions of Osage County, Owasso, portions of Rogers County, Rolling Hills, Sand Springs, Sapulpa, Tulsa, portions of Wagoner County); Below 100 (portions of Osage County, portions of Rogers County); Outside TV Markets (portions of Creek County, portions of Osage County, portions of Rogers County, portions of Wagoner County). Franchise award date: June 1, 1971. Franchise expiration date: N.A. Began: January 18, 1974.
Channel capacity: 42. Channels available but not in use: N.A.
Basic Service
Subscribers: 153,703.
Programming (received off-air): KJRH (N), KOED-TV (P), KOKI-TV (F), KOTV (C), KTFO (U), KTUL (A) Tulsa.
Programming (via satellite): WGN-TV (W) Chicago; BET; C-SPAN; CNN; Country Music TV; Discovery Channel; E! Entertainment TV; Fox Family Channel; Headline News; Knowledge TV; Lifetime; MTV; Nashville Network; Nickelodeon; QVC; TBS Superstation; TV Guide Channel; The Inspirational Network; The Weather Channel; Travel Channel; Trinity Bcstg. Network; Univision; VH1.
Current originations: Educational access; government access; religious access; automated emergency alert; local news; local sports.
Fee: $49.95 installation; $9.55 monthly; $25.00 additional installation.
Expanded Basic Service
Subscribers: 149,490.
Programming (via satellite): A & E; American Movie Classics; Bravo; C-SPAN 2; CNBC; ESPN; Fox Sports Net Southwest; Turner Network TV; USA Network.
Fee: $10.99 monthly.
Pay Service 1
Pay Units: N.A.
Programming (via satellite): Cinemax; Disney Channel; HBO; Showtime; The New Encore.
Fee: $25.00 installation; $9.95 monthly (Cinemax, Disney, HBO or Showtime).
Pay-Per-View
Addressable homes: 20,000.
Playboy TV.
Interactive Services
Subscribers: 20,000.
Local advertising: Yes. Available in satellite distributed, locally originated, taped & automated programming. Rates: $90.00/Minute; $45.00/30 Seconds. Local sales manager: Ray Grimes.
Equipment: Scientific-Atlanta headend; Magnavox amplifiers; Times Fiber & Comm/Scope cable; IVC & Ikegami cameras; Panasonic & Sony VTRs; Jerrold & Scientific-Atlanta set top converters; Jerrold addressable set top converters; Eagle traps; Andrew & Anixter-Mark satellite antenna; Panasonic satellite receivers.
Miles of plant: 2984.0 (coaxial); 70.0 (fiber optic). Additional miles planned: 15.0 (fiber optic). Homes passed: 268,077. Total homes in franchised area: 268,077.
Manager: Bill Hoagland. Chief technician: Phil Koenig. Program director: Kent Doll. Marketing director: Kelly Schneider.
City fee: 3% of gross.
Ownership: AT&T Broadband & Internet Services (MSO). See Cable System Ownership.

TULSA COUNTY (western portion)—Blackstone Cable, Box 1729, Fairfield Glade, TN 38558. Phones: 334-937-0901; 800-388-6577. Counties: Creek, Osage & Tulsa. Also serves Candlestick Beach, Creek County (portions), Osage County (portions), Pretty Water. ICA: OK0341.
TV Market Ranking: 54. Franchise award date: N.A. Franchise expiration date: N.A. Began: N.A.
Channel capacity: 40. Channels available but not in use: 3.
Basic Service
Subscribers: 1,491.
Programming (received off-air): KRSC-TV (E) Claremore; KJRH (N), KOED-TV (P), KOKI-TV (F), KOTV (C), KTFO (U), KTUL (A), KWHB (I), KWMJ (I) Tulsa.
Programming (via satellite): Animal Planet; C-SPAN; Cartoon Network; Fox News Channel; Fox Sports Net Midwest; Home & Garden Television; QVC; Trinity Bcstg. Network.
Fee: $29.95 installation; $7.30 monthly.
Expanded Basic Service
Subscribers: 151.
Programming (via satellite): WGN-TV (W) Chicago; A & E; American Movie Classics; Animal Planet; CNBC; CNN; Cartoon Network; Comedy Central; Country Music TV; Discovery Channel; ESPN; ESPN 2; Fox Family Channel; Fox News Channel; Fox Sports Net Midwest; Headline News; Home & Garden Television; Learning Channel; Lifetime; MTV; Nashville Network; Nickelodeon; Sci-Fi Channel; TBS Superstation; The Weather Channel; Turner Network TV; USA Network; VH1.
Fee: $29.95 installation; $25.95 monthly.
Pay Service 1
Pay Units: 77.
Programming (via satellite): Disney Channel.
Fee: $9.95 monthly.
Pay Service 2
Pay Units: 485.
Programming (via satellite): HBO (multiplexed).
Fee: $7.25 monthly.
Pay Service 3
Pay Units: 104.
Programming (via satellite): Showtime.
Fee: $10.95 monthly.
Pay Service 4
Pay Units: 45.
Programming (via satellite): The Movie Channel.
Fee: $9.95 monthly.
Homes passed: 2,685.
Manager: Del Layne. Chief technician: Bill Cline.
Ownership: Bayside 1989-I LP (MSO).

TURPIN—Cable Systems Inc., Box 279, Meade, KS 67864. Phones: 316-873-7407; 800-480-7020. County: Beaver. ICA: OK0317.
TV Market Ranking: Outside TV Markets. Franchise award date: N.A. Franchise expiration date: N.A. Began: N.A.
Channel capacity: 36 (not 2-way capable). Channels available but not in use: 5.
Basic Service
Subscribers: 219.
Programming (received off-air): KAMR-TV (N), KCIT (F,U), KFDA-TV (C), KVII-TV (A) Amarillo; KBSD-TV (C) Ensign; KSNG (N), KUPK-TV (A) Garden City; KETA (P) Oklahoma City.
Programming (via satellite): WGN-TV (W) Chicago; A & E; American Movie Classics; Animal Planet; CNN; Country Music TV; Discovery Channel; ESPN; ESPN 2; Fox Family Channel; Headline News; Learning Channel; Lifetime; Nashville Network; Nick at Nite's TV Land; Nickelodeon; QVC; TBS Superstation; The Weather Channel; Turner Network TV; USA Network.
Fee: $39.95 installation; $25.45 monthly.
Pay Service 1
Pay Units: 59.
Programming (via satellite): Disney Channel.
Fee: $19.95 installation; $9.95 monthly.
Pay Service 2
Pay Units: 64.
Programming (via satellite): HBO.
Fee: $19.95 installation; $9.95 monthly.
Miles of plant: 16.0 (coaxial); None (fiber optic).
Manager: Mark Smith.
Ownership: Fanch Communications Inc. (MSO). See Cable System Ownership.

TUTTLE—Southwestern CATV Inc., Box 171, Medicine Park, OK 73557-0171. Phone: 580-529-2288. Fax: 580-529-5225. County: Grady. Also serves Minco. ICA: OK0137.
TV Market Ranking: 39. Franchise award date: N.A. Franchise expiration date: N.A. Began: March 1, 1982.
Channel capacity: 35. Channels available but not in use: 23.
Basic Service
Subscribers: N.A.
Programming (received off-air): KETA (P), KFOR-TV (N), KOCB (W), KOCO-TV (A), KOKH-TV (F), KTBO-TV (T), KWTV (C) Oklahoma City.
Programming (via satellite): WGN-TV (W) Chicago; ESPN; TBS Superstation; USA Network.
Fee: $8.00 monthly.
Pay Service 1
Pay Units: N.A.
Programming (via satellite): HBO.
Fee: $8.95 monthly.
Miles of plant: 16.1 (coaxial). Homes passed: 700.
City fee: 3% of gross.
Ownership: Southwestern CATV Inc. (MSO).

TYRONE—Cablecomm, Box 279, Meade, KS 67864. Phone: 316-873-7407. County: Texas. ICA: OK0318.
TV Market Ranking: Outside TV Markets. Franchise award date: N.A. Franchise expiration date: N.A. Began: September 1, 1982.
Channel capacity: 36 (not 2-way capable). Channels available but not in use: 3.
Basic Service
Subscribers: 236.
Programming (received off-air): KAMR-TV (N), KCIT (F,U), KFDA-TV (C), KVII-TV (A) Amarillo; KBSD-TV (C) Ensign; KSNG (N),

KUPK-TV (A) Garden City; KETA (P) Oklahoma City.
Programming (via satellite): WGN-TV (W) Chicago; A & E; American Movie Classics; Animal Planet; CNN; Country Music TV; Discovery Channel; ESPN; ESPN 2; Fox Family Channel; Headline News; History Channel; Home Shopping Network; Learning Channel; Lifetime; Nashville Network; Nick at Nite's TV Land; Nickelodeon; QVC; TBS Superstation; The Weather Channel; Turner Network TV; USA Network.
Fee: $19.95 installation; $23.50 monthly.

Pay Service 1
Pay Units: 61.
Programming (via satellite): Disney Channel.
Fee: $19.95 installation; $9.95 monthly.

Pay Service 2
Pay Units: 101.
Programming (via satellite): HBO.
Fee: $19.95 installation; $9.95 monthly.

Miles of plant: 11.0 (coaxial); None (fiber optic).
Manager: Mark Smith.
Ownership: Fanch Communications Inc. (MSO); Time Warner Cable (MSO). See Cable System Ownership.

UNION CITY—Classic Cable, Box 429, 605 N.W. 3rd St., Plainville, KS 67663-0429. Phones: 785-434-7620; 800-499-8876. Fax: 785-434-2614. Web Site: http://www.classic-cable.com. County: Canadian. ICA: OK0319.
TV Market Ranking: 39. Franchise award date: N.A. Franchise expiration date: N.A. Began: July 1, 1988.
Channel capacity: 36 (2-way capable). Channels available but not in use: 18.

Basic Service
Subscribers: 74.
Programming (received off-air): KAUT-TV (U), KETA (P), KFOR-TV (N), KOCB (W), KOCO-TV (A), KOKH-TV (F), KTBO-TV (T), KWTV (C) Oklahoma City.
Programming (via satellite): WGN-TV (W) Chicago; CNN; Discovery Channel; Disney Channel; ESPN; Fox Family Channel; Home & Garden Television; Nashville Network; Outdoor Channel; TBS Superstation; Turner Network TV; USA Network.
Current originations: Automated time-weather.
Fee: $35.00 installation; $27.95 monthly.

Pay Service 1
Pay Units: 16.
Programming (via satellite): HBO.
Fee: $20.00 installation; $9.95 monthly.

Pay Service 2
Pay Units: 14.
Programming (via satellite): Cinemax.
Fee: $20.00 installation; $9.95 monthly.

Equipment: Jerrold amplifiers; Jerrold set top converters.
Miles of plant: 4.4 (coaxial). Homes passed: 207.
Manager: Dave Walker. Chief technician: Roger Campbell. Program director: Glenn J. Chase. Marketing director: Jennifer Hauschild.
Ownership: Classic Cable (MSO).

VALLIANT—Peak Cablevision, 516 N. Lakeside Dr., DeQueen, AR 71832. Phone: 870-642-2441. Fax: 870-642-4259. County: McCurtain. ICA: OK0167.
TV Market Ranking: Outside TV Markets. Franchise award date: July 1, 1968. Franchise expiration date: January 28, 2005. Began: July 1, 1968.
Channel capacity: 35 (not 2-way capable). Channels available but not in use: 10.

Basic Service
Subscribers: 385.
Programming (received off-air): KTEN (A,N,F) Ada; KOET (P) Eufaula; KFSM-TV (C), KHBS (A) Fort Smith; KXII (C) Sherman; KTAL-TV (N) Shreveport-Texarkana.
Programming (via satellite): WGN-TV (W) Chicago; American Movie Classics; C-SPAN; CNBC; CNN; Comedy Central; Court TV; Discovery Channel; ESPN; FoxNet; Headline News; Lifetime; Nashville Network; Nickelodeon; Odyssey; Sci-Fi Channel; TBS Superstation; Trinity Bcstg. Network; Turner Network TV; USA Network; VH1.
Fee: $25.00 installation; $20.26 monthly.

Pay Service 1
Pay Units: 14.
Programming (via satellite): Disney Channel.
Fee: $10.00 installation; $10.95 monthly.

Pay Service 2
Pay Units: 80.
Programming (via satellite): The New Encore.
Fee: $1.75 monthly.

Pay Service 3
Pay Units: 98.
Programming (via satellite): HBO.
Fee: $12.20 monthly.

Local advertising: No.
Miles of plant: 17.9 (coaxial). Homes passed: 478. Total homes in franchised area: 500.
Manager: Ron Beatty. Chief technician: Lynn Harrison. Marketing director: Terry Homesley. Customer service manager: Carol Litchford.
City fee: 3% of gross.
Ownership: Peak Cablevision LLC (MSO). See Cable System Ownership.

VELMA—Classic Cable, Box 429, 605 N.W. 3rd St., Plainville, KS 67663-0429. Phones: 785-434-7620; 800-999-8876. Fax: 785-434-2614. Web Site: http://www.classic-cable.com. Counties: Carter & Stephens. Also serves Alma, Countyline, Fox, Pruitt City, Ratliff City. ICA: OK0320.
TV Market Ranking: Outside TV Markets. Franchise award date: N.A. Franchise expiration date: N.A. Began: February 1, 1983.
Channel capacity: 41 (2-way capable). Channels available but not in use: N.A.

Basic Service
Subscribers: 526.
Programming (received off-air): KAUT-TV (U), KETA (P), KFOR-TV (N), KOCB (W), KOCO-TV (A), KOKH-TV (F), KWTV (C) Oklahoma City; KXII (C) Sherman; KJTL (F,U), KSWO-TV (A) Wichita Falls-Lawton.
Programming (via satellite): WGN-TV (W) Chicago; A & E; American Movie Classics; CNN; Court TV; Discovery Channel; Disney Channel; E! Entertainment TV; ESPN; Fox Family Channel; Fox Sports Net Southwest; Goodlife TV Network; Headline News; History Channel; Home & Garden Television; Learning Channel; Lifetime; Nashville Network; Nick at Nite's TV Land; Nickelodeon; Outdoor Channel; QVC; Sci-Fi Channel; TBS Superstation; The Weather Channel; Travel Channel; Trinity Bcstg. Network; Turner Network TV; USA Network.
Current originations: Automated time-weather; public access; educational access; government access; religious access; automated emergency alert; local news.
Fee: $35.00 installation; $28.95 monthly.

Pay Service 1
Pay Units: 89.
Programming (via satellite): HBO.
Fee: $20.00 installation; $9.95 monthly.

Pay Service 2
Pay Units: 45.
Programming (via satellite): Showtime.
Fee: $9.95 monthly.

Pay Service 3
Pay Units: 76.
Programming (via satellite): The Movie Channel.
Fee: $9.95 monthly.

Local advertising: Yes. Available in character-generated programming. Rates: $5.00/Day.
Equipment: Scientific-Atlanta headend; Scientific-Atlanta amplifiers; Comm/Scope cable; Jerrold set top converters; Pico traps; Anixter-Mark satellite antenna; Scientific-Atlanta satellite receivers.
Miles of plant: 63.0 (coaxial). Homes passed: 971.
Region manager: Dave Walker. Chief technician: Roger Campbell. Marketing manager: Jennifer Hauschild.
City fee: 2% of gross.
Ownership: Classic Cable (MSO).

VERDEN—Rapid Cable, 310 Walnut Extension, Branson, MO 65616. Phones: 417-339-2200; 800-972-0962. Fax: 417-334-7899. E-mail: rcpcable@aol.com. County: Grady. ICA: OK0321.
TV Market Ranking: Outside TV Markets. Franchise award date: December 6, 1982. Franchise expiration date: December 6, 2007. Began: March 1, 1986.
Channel capacity: 31 (2-way capable; not operating 2-way). Channels available but not in use: 7.

Basic Service
Subscribers: 142.
Programming (received off-air): KETA (P), KFOR-TV (N), KOCB (W), KOCO-TV (A), KOKH-TV (F), KWTV (C) Oklahoma City.
Programming (via satellite): WGN-TV (W) Chicago; CNN; Country Music TV; Discovery Channel; ESPN; Fox Family Channel; Home Shopping Network; Nashville Network; TBS Superstation; The Weather Channel; Trinity Bcstg. Network; Turner Network TV; USA Network.
Fee: $29.95 installation; $22.95 monthly; $3.95 converter.

Pay Service 1
Pay Units: 27.
Programming (via satellite): Cinemax.
Fee: $9.00 monthly.

Pay Service 2
Pay Units: 27.
Programming (via satellite): HBO.
Fee: $10.00 monthly.

Pay Service 3
Pay Units: 17.
Programming (via satellite): Disney Channel.
Fee: $7.00 monthly.

Local advertising: No.
Miles of plant: 4.2 (coaxial). Homes passed: 288.
Manager: Tom Semptimphelter. Program director: Beth Semptimphelter. Marketing director: Bill Fischer.
Ownership: Rapid Communications Partners LP (MSO); TS Communications Inc. (MSO).

VERDIGRIS—Oklahoma Cablecomm, Box 970, Fort Gibson, OK 74434-0970. Phones: 918-478-2100; 800-783-5701. Fax: 918-478-2355. County: Rogers. ICA: OK0094.
TV Market Ranking: 54. Franchise award date: April 1, 1982. Franchise expiration date: April 1, 1997. Began: July 1, 1983.
Channel capacity: 42 (not 2-way capable). Channels available but not in use: None.

Basic Service
Subscribers: 710.
Programming (received off-air): KDOR (T) Bartlesville; KRSC-TV (E) Claremore; KJRH (N), KOED-TV (P), KOKI-TV (F), KOTV (C), KTFO (U), KTUL (A), KWHB (I) Tulsa.
Programming (via satellite): WGN-TV (W) Chicago; A & E; American Movie Classics; C-SPAN; CNBC; CNN; Cartoon Network; Court TV; Discovery Channel; Disney Channel; E! Entertainment TV; ESPN; ESPN 2; Fox Family Channel; Fox Sports Net; Headline News; History Channel; Home & Garden Television; Home Shopping Network; Learning Channel; Lifetime; Nashville Network; Nickelodeon; Sci-Fi Channel; TBS Superstation; TV Food Network; The Inspirational Network; The Weather Channel; Travel Channel; Turner Network TV; USA Network; VH1.
Fee: $60.00 installation; $23.45 monthly.

Pay Service 1
Pay Units: N.A.
Programming (via satellite): Cinemax.
Fee: N.A.

Pay Service 2
Pay Units: 162.
Programming (via satellite): HBO.
Fee: $20.00 installation; $11.95 monthly.

Pay Service 3
Pay Units: 73.
Programming (via satellite): Showtime.
Fee: $20.00 installation; $10.95 monthly.

Local advertising: No.
Program Guide: TV Host.
Equipment: Blonder-Tongue, Cadco & Triple Crown headend; Magnavox amplifiers; Comm/Scope cable; Jerrold set top converters; Arcom, Eagle & Northeast Filter traps; Standard Communications satellite receivers.
Miles of plant: 47.0 (coaxial). Homes passed: 1,103. Total homes in franchised area: 1,203.
Manager: Rick Wall. Chief technician: Leon Strain. Marketing & program director: Bruce Berkinshaw.
City fee: 2% of gross.
Ownership: Fanch Communications Inc. (MSO); Time Warner Cable (MSO). See Cable System Ownership.

VIAN—Oklahoma Cablecomm, Box 970, Fort Gibson, OK 74434-0970. Phones: 918-478-2100; 800-783-5701. Fax: 918-478-2355. County: Sequoyah. ICA: OK0130.
TV Market Ranking: Outside TV Markets. Franchise award date: January 28, 1980. Franchise expiration date: N.A. Began: N.A.
Channel capacity: 35 (not 2-way capable). Channels available but not in use: 15.

Basic Service
Subscribers: 442.
Programming (received off-air): KOET (P) Eufaula; KFSM-TV (C), KHBS (A) Fort Smith; KJRH (N), KOKI-TV (F), KTUL (A), KWHB (I) Tulsa.

Programming (via satellite): WGN-TV (W) Chicago; A & E; CNN; Cartoon Network; Country Music TV; Court TV; Discovery Channel; Disney Channel; E! Entertainment TV; ESPN; ESPN 2; Fox Family Channel; Fox Sports Net; Goodlife TV Network; Headline News; History Channel; Learning Channel; Lifetime; Nashville Network; Nickelodeon; QVC; Sci-Fi Channel; TBS Superstation; TV Food Network; The Inspirational Network; The Weather Channel; Turner Classic Movies; Turner Network TV; USA Network.
Fee: $30.00 installation; $23.45 monthly.

Pay Service 1
Pay Units: N.A.
Programming (via satellite): Cinemax.
Fee: N.A.

Pay Service 2
Pay Units: 77.
Programming (via satellite): HBO.
Fee: $20.00 installation; $9.00 monthly.

Local advertising: No.
Equipment: Blonder-Tongue, Drake & Triple Crown headend; C-COR & Scientific-Atlanta amplifiers; Comm/Scope cable; Jerrold set top converters; Northeast Filter traps; DX Engineering satellite receivers.
Miles of plant: 16.0 (coaxial). Homes passed: 750.
Manager: Rick Wall. Chief technician: Leon Strain. Marketing & program director: Bruce Berkinshaw.
City fee: 2% of gross.
Ownership: Fanch Communications Inc. (MSO); Time Warner Cable (MSO). See Cable System Ownership.

VICI—Classic Cable, Box 429, 605 N.W. 3rd St., Plainville, KS 67663-0429. Phones: 785-434-7620; 800-999-8876. Fax: 785-434-2614. Web Site: http://www.classic-cable.com. County: Dewey. ICA: OK0174.
TV Market Ranking: Outside TV Markets. Franchise award date: N.A. Franchise expiration date: N.A. Began: August 1, 1970.
Channel capacity: 41 (2-way capable). Channels available but not in use: N.A.

Basic Service
Subscribers: 230; Commercial subscribers: 30.
Programming (received off-air): KAUT-TV (U), KETA (P), KFOR-TV (N), KOCB (W), KOCO-TV (A), KOKH-TV (F), KWTV (C) Oklahoma City; KOMI-LP (I) Woodward; allband FM.
Programming (via satellite): WGN-TV (W) Chicago; American Movie Classics; CNN; Cartoon Network; Country Music TV; Discovery Channel; Disney Channel; E! Entertainment TV; ESPN; Fox Family Channel; Headline News; History Channel; Learning Channel; Lifetime; Nashville Network; Nick at Nite's TV Land; Outdoor Channel; QVC; Sci-Fi Channel; TBS Superstation; The Weather Channel; Travel Channel; Trinity Bcstg. Network; Turner Network TV; USA Network.
Current originations: Automated time-weather; automated emergency alert.
Fee: $35.00 installation; $27.95 monthly.

Pay Service 1
Pay Units: 22.
Programming (via satellite): HBO.
Fee: $10.95 monthly.

Pay Service 2
Pay Units: 10.
Programming (via satellite): Showtime.
Fee: $9.95 monthly.

Pay Service 3
Pay Units: 8.
Programming (via satellite): Cinemax.
Fee: $9.95 monthly.

Equipment: Scientific-Atlanta headend; Jerrold amplifiers; Scientific-Atlanta satellite receivers.
Miles of plant: 9.0 (coaxial). Homes passed: 356.
Manager: Dave Walker. Chief technician: Jeff Smith. Marketing director: Jennifer Hauschild.
City fee: 2% of gross.
Ownership: Classic Cable (MSO).

VINITA—Cable One, 105 W. Delaware, Vinita, OK 74301. Phone: 918-256-7871. Fax: 918-256-8275. County: Craig. Also serves Craig County. ICA: OK0322.
TV Market Ranking: Below 100 (portions of Craig County); Outside TV Markets (portions of Craig County, Vinita). Franchise award date: November 18, 1975. Franchise expiration date: N.A. Began: July 1, 1979.
Channel capacity: 53 (not 2-way capable). Channels available but not in use: None.

Basic Service
Subscribers: 2,180; Commercial subscribers: 1.
Programming (received off-air): KDOR (T) Bartlesville; KRSC-TV (E) Claremore; KOAM-TV (C), KODE-TV (A), KSNF (N) Joplin-Pittsburg; KTPX (X) Okmulgee; KJRH (N), KOED-TV (P), KOKI-TV (F), KOTV (C), KTFO (U), KTUL (A), KWHB (I), KWMJ (I) Tulsa; 2 FMs.
Programming (via satellite): WGN-TV (W) Chicago; A & E; American Movie Classics; C-SPAN; CNN; Cartoon Network; Comedy Central; Country Music TV; Discovery Channel; Disney Channel; ESPN; ESPN 2; Fox Family Channel; Headline News; History Channel; Home Shopping Network; Learning Channel; Lifetime; MSNBC; MTV; Nashville Network; Nickelodeon; Odyssey; QVC; Sci-Fi Channel; TBS Superstation; TV Food Network; TV Guide Channel; The Weather Channel; Travel Channel; Turner Network TV; USA Network.
Current originations: Automated time-weather; public access.
Planned originations: Automated emergency alert.
Fee: $41.64 installation (aerial), $50.00 (underground); $28.00 monthly; $1.56 converter; $9.04 additional installation.

Pay Service 1
Pay Units: N.A.
Programming (via satellite): Cinemax (multiplexed); HBO (multiplexed); Showtime (multiplexed).
Fee: $10.95 monthly (Showtime or TMC), $13.95 monthly (Cinemax or HBO), $24.95 monthly (Cinemax HBO, Showtime & TMC.

Pay-Per-View
Addressable homes: 2,000.
Hot Choice; Spice; Viewer's Choice; Viewer's Choice 5.

Local advertising: Yes. Available in satellite distributed & locally originated programming.
Equipment: Microdyne & Phasecom headend; Theta-Com amplifiers; Oak, Standard Components & Hamlin set top converters; Eagle addressable set top converters; Fort Worth Tower satellite antenna; Microdyne satellite receivers.
Miles of plant: 61.0 (coaxial); None (fiber optic). Additional miles planned: 10.0 (coaxial). Homes passed: 3,172. Total homes in franchised area: 3,400.
Manager, chief technician & program director: Brook McDonald.
City fee: 2% of gross.
Ownership: Cable One Inc. (MSO).

WAGONER—Peak Cablevision, 410 Eastside Blvd., Muskogee, OK 74403. Phone: 918-687-7511. Fax: 918-687-3291. Counties: Lincoln & Wagoner. Also serves Lincoln, Wagoner County (eastern portion), Wellston. ICA: OK0047.
TV Market Ranking: 54 (portions of Wagoner County); Below 100 (Wagoner, portions of Wagoner County, Wellson). Franchise award date: N.A. Franchise expiration date: N.A. Began: July 1, 1980.
Channel capacity: 35. Channels available but not in use: 6.

Basic Service
Subscribers: 1,679.
Programming (received off-air): KJRH (N), KOED-TV (P), KOKI-TV (F), KOTV (C), KTUL (A) Tulsa.
Programming (via satellite): WGN-TV (W) Chicago; CNBC; CNN; Discovery Channel; Fox Family Channel; Headline News; Lifetime; MTV; Nashville Network; Nickelodeon; Odyssey; QVC; TBS Superstation; The New Encore; The Weather Channel.
Fee: $60.00 installation; $20.58 monthly; $3.00 converter; $8.20 additional installation.

Expanded Basic Service
Subscribers: 1,341.
Programming (via satellite): American Movie Classics; Court TV; ESPN; Fox Sports Net Southwest; Turner Network TV; USA Network.
Fee: $1.50 monthly.

Pay Service 1
Pay Units: 169.
Programming (via satellite): Cinemax.
Fee: N.A.

Pay Service 2
Pay Units: 571.
Programming (via satellite): The New Encore.
Fee: N.A.

Pay Service 3
Pay Units: 410.
Programming (via satellite): HBO.
Fee: N.A.

Pay Service 4
Pay Units: 253.
Programming (via satellite): Showtime.
Fee: N.A.

Local advertising: No.
Miles of plant: 50.6 (coaxial). Homes passed: 3,619. Total homes in franchised area: 4,522.
Manager: Brad Mangum. Chief technician: Darrell Kimbrill.
Ownership: Peak Cablevision LLC (MSO). See Cable System Ownership.

WAKITA—Classic Cable, Box 429, 605 N.W. 3rd St., Plainville, KS 67663-0429. Phones: 785-434-7620; 800-999-8876. Fax: 785-434-2614. Web Site: http://www.classic-cable.com. County: Grant. ICA: OK0226.
TV Market Ranking: Outside TV Markets. Franchise award date: N.A. Franchise expiration date: N.A. Began: April 1, 1977.
Channel capacity: 36 (2-way capable). Channels available but not in use: N.A.

Basic Service
Subscribers: 81.
Programming (received off-air): KETA (P), KFOR-TV (N), KOCB (W), KOCO-TV (A), KOKH-TV (F), KWTV (C) Oklahoma City; KAKE-TV (A), KSNW (N) Wichita-Hutchinson; allband FM.
Programming (via satellite): WGN-TV (W) Chicago; A & E; CNN; Country Music TV; Discovery Channel; Disney Channel; ESPN; Fox Family Channel; Nashville Network; TBS Superstation; The Weather Channel; Trinity Bcstg. Network; USA Network.
Fee: $35.00 installation; $27.95 monthly.

Pay Service 1
Pay Units: 11.
Programming (via satellite): HBO.
Fee: $35.00 installation; $10.95 monthly.

Pay Service 2
Pay Units: 3.
Programming (via satellite): Showtime.
Fee: $35.00 installation; $9.95 monthly.

Equipment: Automation Techniques & Blonder-Tongue headend; RCA amplifiers; Comm/Scope & RCA cable; Harris satellite receivers.
Miles of plant: 4.0 (coaxial). Homes passed: 213.
Manager: Dave Walker. Chief technician: Jeff Smith. Marketing director: Jennifer Hauschild.
City fee: 3% of gross.
Ownership: Classic Cable (MSO).

WALTERS—Classic Cable, Box 429, 605 N.W. 3rd St., Plainville, KS 67663-0429. Phones: 785-434-7620; 800-999-8876. Fax: 785-434-2614. Web Site: http://www.classic-cable.com. County: Cotton. Also serves Temple. ICA: OK0108.
TV Market Ranking: Below 100. Franchise award date: N.A. Franchise expiration date: N.A. Began: January 1, 1978.
Channel capacity: 41 (2-way capable). Channels available but not in use: N.A.

Basic Service
Subscribers: 948; Commercial subscribers: 67.
Programming (received off-air): KETA (P), KFOR-TV (N), KWTV (C) Oklahoma City; KAUZ-TV (C), KFDX-TV (N), KJTL (F,U), KSWO-TV (A) Wichita Falls-Lawton.
Programming (via satellite): WGN-TV (W) Chicago; A & E; Animal Planet; C-SPAN; CNN; Country Music TV; Court TV; Discovery Channel; Disney Channel; E! Entertainment TV; ESPN; Fox Family Channel; Fox News Channel; Fox Sports Net Southwest; Headline News; History Channel; Home & Garden Television; Learning Channel; Lifetime; Nashville Network; Nick at Nite's TV Land; Nickelodeon; QVC; Sci-Fi Channel; TBS Superstation; The Weather Channel; Trinity Bcstg. Network; Turner Network TV; USA Network.
Current originations: Local Access.
Fee: $35.00 installation; $28.95 monthly.

Pay Service 1
Pay Units: 163.
Programming (via satellite): HBO.
Fee: $10.95 monthly.

Pay Service 2
Pay Units: 58.
Programming (via satellite): Showtime.
Fee: $9.95 monthly.

Pay Service 3
Pay Units: 63.
Programming (via satellite): The Movie Channel.
Fee: $5.95 monthly.

Pay-Per-View
Special events.

Local advertising: Yes. Available in character-generated programming. Rates: $5.00/Day.
Equipment: Drake & ISS headend; Scientific-Atlanta amplifiers; Comm/Scope cable; Jerrold set top converters; Fort Worth Tower satellite antenna; Drake satellite receivers.
Miles of plant: 35.0 (coaxial). Homes passed: 1,710.
Region manager: Dave Walker. Chief technician: Roger Campbell. Marketing director: Jennifer Hauschild.
City fee: 3% of gross.
Ownership: Classic Cable (MSO).

WANETTE—Classic Cable, Box 429, 605 N.W. 3rd St., Plainville, KS 67663-0429. Phones: 785-434-7620; 800-999-8876. Fax: 785-434-2614. Web Site: http://www.classic-cable.com. County: Pottawatomie. ICA: OK0323.

TV Market Ranking: Below 100. Franchise award date: January 1, 1989. Franchise expiration date: January 1, 2004. Began: September 1, 1989.
Channel capacity: 36 (2-way capable). Channels available but not in use: N.A.

Basic Service

Subscribers: 28.
Programming (received off-air): KAUT-TV (U), KETA (P), KFOR-TV (N), KOCB (W), KOCO-TV (A), KOKH-TV (F), KWTV (C) Oklahoma City.
Programming (via satellite): WGN-TV (W) Chicago; CNN; Discovery Channel; ESPN; Fox Family Channel; Nashville Network; TBS Superstation; Trinity Bcstg. Network; Turner Network TV.
Fee: $35.00 installation; $26.95 monthly.

Pay Service 1

Pay Units: 8.
Programming (via satellite): HBO.
Fee: $9.95 monthly.

Pay Service 2

Pay Units: 1.
Programming (via satellite): Showtime.
Fee: N.A.

Equipment: Cadco headend; Scientific-Atlanta amplifiers; Comm/Scope cable; Jerrold set top converters.
Miles of plant: 3.1 (coaxial). Homes passed: 143.
Manager: Dave Walker. Chief technician: Roger Campbell. Marketing director: Jennifer Hauschild.
Ownership: Classic Cable (MSO).

WAPANUCKA—CommuniComm Services, Box 597, 1501 W. Mississippi, Durant, OK 74702-0597. Phones: 580-924-2367; 800-752-4992. County: Johnston. ICA: OK0337.
TV Market Ranking: Below 100. Franchise award date: N.A. Franchise expiration date: N.A. Began: January 1, 1988.
Channel capacity: 62 (not 2-way capable). Channels available but not in use: 50.

Basic Service

Subscribers: 60.
Programming (received off-air): KTEN (A,N,F) Ada; KXII (C) Sherman.
Fee: $49.95 installation; $3.78 monthly.

Expanded Basic Service

Subscribers: N.A.
Programming (via satellite): WGN-TV (W) Chicago; A & E; CNN; Discovery Channel; ESPN; Fox Family Channel; Headline News; Nashville Network; TBS Superstation.
Fee: $19.22 monthly.

Pay Service 1

Pay Units: 23.
Programming (via satellite): Cinemax.
Fee: $9.95 monthly.

Miles of plant: 5.5 (coaxial); None (fiber optic). Homes passed: 180.
Manager: Danny Neumann. Chief technician: Dale Howard.
Ownership: James Cable Partners (MSO).

WARNER—Cross Cable TV, Box 509, 704 3rd Ave., Warner, OK 74469. Phone: 918-463-2921. Fax: 918-463-2551. County: Muskogee. ICA: OK0160.
TV Market Ranking: Outside TV Markets. Franchise award date: January 1, 1984. Franchise expiration date: January 1, 2009. Began: January 1, 1984.
Channel capacity: 35 (2-way capable; not operating 2-way). Channels available but not in use: 10.

Basic Service

Subscribers: 453.
Programming (received off-air): KDOR (T) Bartlesville; KJRH (N), KOED-TV (P), KOKI-TV (F), KOTV (C), KTFO (U), KTUL (A), KWHB (I) Tulsa.
Programming (via satellite): WGN-TV (W) Chicago; C-SPAN; CNN; Cartoon Network; Discovery Channel; Disney Channel; ESPN; Fox Family Channel; Headline News; Nashville Network; Nickelodeon; QVC; TBS Superstation; Turner Network TV; USA Network.
Fee: $15.00 installation; $15.95 monthly.

Pay Service 1

Pay Units: 79.
Programming (via satellite): Cinemax.
Fee: $15.00 installation; $9.50 monthly.

Pay Service 3

Pay Units: 123.
Programming (via satellite): HBO.
Fee: $15.00 installation; $9.50 monthly.

Local advertising: No.
Equipment: Scientific-Atlanta headend; Scientific-Atlanta & Texscan amplifiers; Comm/Scope cable; Scientific-Atlanta set top converters; Pico traps; Anixter satellite antenna; Scientific-Atlanta satellite receivers.
Miles of plant: 30.0 (coaxial); None (fiber optic). Homes passed: 650. Total homes in franchised area: 1,000.
Manager: Edward Smith. Chief technician & program director: Troy Duncan. Marketing director: V. David Miller. Customer service manager: Rexanna Pool.
City fee: 3% of gross.
Ownership: V. David & Billie Lynn Miller. Sale pends to Rexanna Pool.

WARR ACRES—Multimedia Cablevision of Warr Acres, 6221 N.W. 39th Expressway, Bethany, OK 73008. Phone: 405-389-3549. County: Oklahoma. ICA: OK0040.
TV Market Ranking: 39. Franchise award date: February 16, 1978. Franchise expiration date: N.A. Began: October 15, 1979.
Channel capacity: 69 (2-way capable; operating 2-way). Channels available but not in use: None.

Basic Service

Subscribers: 2,618.
Programming (received off-air): KAUT-TV (U), KETA (P), KFOR-TV (N), KOCB (W), KOCO-TV (A), KOKH-TV (F), KSBI (I), KTBO-TV (T), KWTV (C) Oklahoma City; 13 FMs.
Programming (via satellite): A & E; American Movie Classics; C-SPAN; CNBC; Discovery Channel; ESPN; Home Shopping Network; Knowledge TV; Learning Channel; Lifetime; MTV; Nickelodeon; TV Guide Channel; The Weather Channel; USA Network; VH1.
Current originations: Public access; educational access; government access; automated emergency alert; local sports.
Fee: $17.47 installation; $18.85 monthly; $18.59 additional installation.

Expanded Basic Service

Subscribers: 2,597.
Programming (via satellite): WGN-TV (W) Chicago; CNN; Fox Family Channel; Headline News; Nashville Network; TBS Superstation; Turner Network TV.
Fee: $3.41 monthly.

Expanded Basic Service 2

Subscribers: 563.
Programming (via satellite): Bravo; Cartoon Network; Comedy Central; Country Music TV; Court TV; ESPN 2; History Channel; Sci-Fi Channel; Travel Channel; Turner Classic Movies.
Fee: $6.00 monthly.

Pay Service 1

Pay Units: 514.
Programming (via satellite): Cinemax.
Fee: $11.00 monthly.

Pay Service 2

Pay Units: 306.
Programming (via satellite): Disney Channel.
Fee: $7.95 monthly.

Pay Service 3

Pay Units: 905.
Programming (via satellite): HBO.
Fee: $11.00 monthly.

Pay Service 4

Pay Units: 616.
Programming (via satellite): Showtime.
Fee: $11.00 monthly.

Pay Service 5

Pay Units: 14.
Programming (via satellite): Music Choice.
Fee: $7.95 monthly.

Pay Service 6

Pay Units: 9.
Programming (via satellite): Golf Channel.
Fee: $6.95 monthly.

Pay-Per-View

Addressable homes: 644.

Local advertising: Yes. Available in satellite distributed programming. Rates: $800.00/Hour; $400.00/30 Minutes; $160.00/Minute; $80.00/30 Seconds. Local sales manager: Mark Kanter. Regional interconnect: Oklahoma Cable Advertising Interconnect.
Program Guide: The Cable Guide.
Equipment: Scientific-Atlanta headend; RCA amplifiers; Comm/Scope cable; Panasonic cameras; Panasonic VTRs; Jerrold, Oak & Hamlin set top converters; Scientific-Atlanta addressable set top converters; Eagle traps; Scientific-Atlanta satellite antenna; Scientific-Atlanta satellite receivers.
Miles of plant: 54.0 (coaxial). Homes passed: 4,331. Total homes in franchised area: 4,331.
Manager: David Cooper. Chief technician: Kurtis Gill. Marketing director: Jim Back. Customer service manager: Charitta Shelton.
City fee: 3% of gross.
Ownership: Multimedia Cablevision Inc. (MSO). See Cable System Ownership.

WASHINGTON—Classic Cable, Box 429, 605 N.W. 3rd St., Plainville, KS 67663-0429. Phones: 785-434-7620; 800-999-8876. Fax: 785-434-2614. Web Site: http://www.classic-cable.com. County: McClain. ICA: OK0248.
TV Market Ranking: 39. Franchise award date: November 3, 1983. Franchise expiration date: N.A. Began: September 1, 1988.
Channel capacity: 36 (2-way capable). Channels available but not in use: N.A.

Basic Service

Subscribers: 38.
Programming (received off-air): KAUT-TV (U), KETA (P), KFOR-TV (N), KOCB (W), KOCO-TV (A), KOKH-TV (F), KWTV (C) Oklahoma City.
Programming (via satellite): WGN-TV (W) Chicago; CNN; Country Music TV; Discovery Channel; ESPN; Fox Family Channel; Nashville Network; TBS Superstation; Trinity Bcstg. Network; Turner Network TV.
Current originations: Automated time-weather; local news.
Fee: $35.00 installation; $26.95 monthly.

Pay Service 1

Pay Units: 7.
Programming (via satellite): HBO.
Fee: $9.95 monthly.

Local advertising: Yes. Available in character-generated programming. Rates: $5.00/Day.
Equipment: Blonder-Tongue, Triple Crown & Tru-Spec headend; C-COR & Texscan amplifiers; ICM & Scientific-Atlanta satellite receivers.
Miles of plant: 3.1 (coaxial). Homes passed: 146. Total homes in franchised area: 160.
Manager: Dave Walker. Chief technician: Roger Campbell. Marketing director: Jennifer Hauschild.
City fee: 2% of basic gross.
Ownership: Classic Cable (MSO).

WATONGA—Classic Cable, Box 429, 605 N.W. 3rd St., Plainville, KS 67663-0429. Phones: 785-434-7620; 800-999-8876. Fax: 785-434-2614. Web Site: http://www.classic-cable.com. County: Blaine. ICA: OK0082.
TV Market Ranking: Outside TV Markets. Franchise award date: N.A. Franchise expiration date: N.A. Began: August 1, 1979.
Channel capacity: 61 (2-way capable). Channels available but not in use: N.A.

Basic Service

Subscribers: 867; Commercial subscribers: 146.
Programming (received off-air): KAUT-TV (U), KETA (P), KFOR-TV (N), KOCB (W), KOCO-TV (A), KOKH-TV (F), KTBO-TV (T), KWTV (C) Oklahoma City; allband FM.
Programming (via satellite): WGN-TV (W) Chicago; American Movie Classics; BET; CNN; Country Music TV; Discovery Channel; Disney Channel; ESPN; Fox Family Channel; Fox News Channel; Fox Sports Net Southwest; Headline News; Home & Garden Television; Learning Channel; Lifetime; Nashville Network; Nick at Nite's TV Land; Nickelodeon; QVC; Sci-Fi Channel; TBS Superstation; Turner Network TV; USA Network; VH1.
Current originations: Automated time-weather; automated emergency alert.
Fee: $35.00 installation; $28.95 monthly; $3.50 converter; $20.00 additional installation.

Pay Service 1

Pay Units: 173.
Programming (via satellite): HBO.
Fee: $20.00 installation; $10.95 monthly.

Pay Service 2

Pay Units: 66.
Programming (via satellite): Showtime.
Fee: $20.00 installation; $9.95 monthly.

Pay Service 3

Pay Units: 54.
Programming (via satellite): Cinemax.
Fee: $9.95 monthly.

Pay Service 4

Pay Units: 68.
Programming (via satellite): The Movie Channel.
Fee: $20.00 installation; $5.95 monthly.

Local advertising: Yes. Available in character-generated programming. Rates: $35.00/Month; $10.00/Week; $2.00/Day.
Equipment: Scientific-Atlanta & Tocom headend; Scientific-Atlanta amplifiers; Times Fiber cable; Texscan character generator; AFC & Prodelin satellite antenna; ICM & Microdyne satellite receivers.
Miles of plant: 32.1 (coaxial). Homes passed: 1,452. Total homes in franchised area: 1,600.
Manager: Dave Walker. Chief technician: Jeff Smith. Program director: Sue Turner. Marketing director: Jennifer Hauschild.
City fee: 3% of gross.
Ownership: Classic Cable (MSO).

WATTS—Classic Cable, Box 429, 605 N.W. 3rd St., Plainville, KS 67663-0429. Phones: 785-434-7620; 800-999-8876. Fax: 919-434-2614. Web Site: http://www.classic-cable.com. County: Adair. ICA: OK0213.
TV Market Ranking: Below 100. Franchise award date: N.A. Franchise expiration date: N.A. Began: November 1, 1977.
Channel capacity: N.A. Channels available but not in use: N.A.

Basic Service
Subscribers: 152.
Programming (received off-air): KAFT (P), KHOG-TV (A) Fayetteville; KFSM-TV (C) Fort Smith; KSNF (N) Joplin-Pittsburg; KJRH (N), KOKI-TV (F), KOTV (C) Tulsa.
Programming (via satellite): TBS Superstation.
Fee: $30.00 installation; $16.95 monthly.
Pay Service 1
Pay Units: N.A.
Programming (via satellite): Showtime.
Fee: $15.00 installation; $10.00 monthly.
Miles of plant: 9.9 (coaxial). Homes passed: 257. Total homes in franchised area: 257.
Manager: Rick Wall. Chief technician: Richard Taapken. Marketing director: Rob Typer.
Ownership: Classic Cable (MSO).

WAUKOMIS—Classic Cable, Box 429, 605 N.W. 3rd St., Plainville, KS 67663-0429. Phones: 785-434-7620; 800-999-8876. Fax: 785-434-2614. Web Site: http://www.classic-cable.com. County: Garfield. ICA: OK0369.
TV Market Ranking: Outside TV Markets. Franchise award date: N.A. Franchise expiration date: N.A. Began: N.A.
Channel capacity: 41 (2-way capable). Channels available but not in use: N.A.
Basic Service
Subscribers: 229.
Programming (received off-air): KAUT-TV (U), KETA (P), KFOR-TV (N), KOCB (W), KOCO-TV (A), KOKH-TV (F), KTBO-TV (T), KWTV (C) Oklahoma City.
Programming (via satellite): WGN-TV (W) Chicago; A & E; American Movie Classics; CNN; Country Music TV; Discovery Channel; Disney Channel; ESPN; Fox Family Channel; Fox Sports Net Southwest; History Channel; Home & Garden Television; Nashville Network; Nick at Nite's TV Land; Nickelodeon; Sci-Fi Channel; TBS Superstation; The Weather Channel; Turner Network TV; USA Network.
Fee: $35.00 installation; $27.95 monthly.
Pay Service 1
Pay Units: 56.
Programming (via satellite): HBO.
Fee: $10.95 monthly.
Pay Service 2
Pay Units: 8.
Programming (via satellite): Showtime.
Fee: $9.95 monthly.
Pay Service 3
Pay Units: 14.
Programming (via satellite): Cinemax.
Fee: $9.95 monthly.
Miles of plant: 10.0 (coaxial). Homes passed: 475.
Manager: Dave Walker. Chief technician: Jeff Smith. Marketing director: Jennifer Hauschild.
Ownership: Classic Cable (MSO).

WAURIKA—Classic Cable, Box 429, 605 N.W. 3rd St., Plainville, KS 67663-0429. Phones: 785-434-7620; 800-999-8876. Fax: 785-434-2614. Web Site: http://www.classic-cable.com. County: Jefferson. ICA: OK0106.
TV Market Ranking: Below 100. Franchise award date: June 5, 1978. Franchise expiration date: June 5, 1998. Began: September 1, 1981.
Channel capacity: 41 (2-way capable). Channels available but not in use: N.A.
Basic Service
Subscribers: 487.
Programming (received off-air): KETA (P), KFOR-TV (N), KOCO-TV (A), KOKH-TV (F), KWTV (C) Oklahoma City; KAUZ-TV (C), KFDX-TV (N), KJTL (F,U), KSWO-TV (A) Wichita Falls-Lawton.
Programming (via satellite): WGN-TV (W) Chicago; A & E; CNN; Country Music TV; Discovery Channel; Disney Channel; ESPN; Fox Family Channel; Headline News; History Channel; Lifetime; Nashville Network; Nickelodeon; QVC; TBS Superstation; The Weather Channel; Trinity Bcstg. Network; Turner Classic Movies; Turner Network TV; USA Network.
Current originations: Automated time-weather.
Fee: $35.00 installation; $27.95 monthly.
Pay Service 1
Pay Units: 57.
Programming (via satellite): HBO.
Fee: $10.95 monthly.
Pay Service 2
Pay Units: 57.
Programming (via satellite): Showtime.
Fee: $9.95 monthly.
Pay Service 3
Pay Units: 76.
Programming (via satellite): The Movie Channel.
Fee: $5.95 monthly.
Equipment: Scientific-Atlanta amplifiers; Comm/Scope cable; Scientific-Atlanta set top converters; Eagle & Pico traps; Scientific-Atlanta & Weatherscan satellite antenna; M/A-Com & Scientific-Atlanta satellite receivers.
Miles of plant: 15.5 (coaxial). Homes passed: 1,030. Total homes in franchised area: 1,031.
Manager: Dave Walker. Chief technician: Roger Campbell. Marketing director: Jennifer Hauschild.
City fee: 3% of gross.
Ownership: Classic Cable (MSO).

WAYNE—Classic Cable, 2820 N. Green Ave., Purcell, OK 73080-1707. Phone: 405-527-5651. Fax: 405-527-5392. County: McClain. ICA: OK0209.
TV Market Ranking: Below 100. Franchise award date: N.A. Franchise expiration date: N.A. Began: October 1, 1981.
Channel capacity: 32 (not 2-way capable). Channels available but not in use: None.
Basic Service
Subscribers: 129.
Programming (received off-air): KAUT-TV (U), KETA (P), KFOR-TV (N), KOCB (W), KOCO-TV (A), KOKH-TV (F), KSBI (I), KTBO-TV (T), KWTV (C) Oklahoma City.
Programming (via satellite): WGN-TV (W) Chicago; A & E; American Movie Classics; C-SPAN; CNN; Country Music TV; Discovery Channel; ESPN; Fox Family Channel; Home Shopping en Espanol; Lifetime; MTV; Nashville Network; Nickelodeon; QVC; TBS Superstation; The Weather Channel; Turner Network TV; USA Network.
Fee: $42.43 installation; $23.50 monthly; $21.22 additional installation.
Pay Service 1
Pay Units: N.A.
Programming (via satellite): Disney Channel; HBO; The Movie Channel; Turner Classic Movies.
Fee: $1.75 monthly (TCM), $12.37 monthly (TMC), $12.82 monthly (HBO), $13.00 monthly (Disney).
Miles of plant: 4.7 (coaxial); None (fiber optic). Homes passed: 330.
Manager: Kris Miller. Chief technician: Kurt Widmer.
Ownership: Classic Cable (MSO).

WAYNOKA—Waynoka Community TV, Box 237, Waynoka, OK 73860. Phone: 580-824-9311. County: Woods. ICA: OK0149.
TV Market Ranking: Outside TV Markets. Franchise award date: N.A. Franchise expiration date: N.A. Began: June 1, 1958.
Channel capacity: 12. Channels available but not in use: None.
Basic Service
Subscribers: N.A.
Programming (received off-air): KETA (P), KFOR-TV (N), KOCO-TV (A), KOKH-TV (F), KWTV (C) Oklahoma City; allband FM.
Programming (via satellite): WGN-TV (W) Chicago; CNN; ESPN; TBS Superstation; USA Network.
Current originations: Automated time-weather.
Fee: $10.00 installation; $16.00 monthly.
Pay Service 1
Pay Units: N.A.
Programming (via satellite): HBO; Showtime.
Fee: $10.00 monthly (each).
Local advertising: Yes. Available in automated programming.
Equipment: Jerrold headend; Jerrold amplifiers; Texscan character generator; Eagle traps; Anixter & Prodelin satellite antenna; Microdyne satellite receivers.
Miles of plant: 14.0 (coaxial). Additional miles planned: 0.5 (coaxial). Homes passed: 600.
Manager: F. W. Marshall.
City fee: 3% of gross.
Ownership: Viola M. Shaffer & family.

WEATHERFORD—Classic Cable, Box 429, 605 N.W. 3rd St., Plainville, KS 67663-0429. Phones: 785-434-7620; 800-999-8876. Fax: 785-434-2614. E-mail: gmwood@nwoknet.net. Web Site: http://www.classic-cable.com. Counties: Blaine, Caddo & Custer. Also serves Hydro. ICA: OK0045.
TV Market Ranking: Outside TV Markets. Franchise award date: July 1, 1967. Franchise expiration date: July 1, 2008. Began: July 1, 1967.
Channel capacity: 45 (2-way capable). Channels available but not in use: N.A.
Basic Service
Subscribers: 3,811.
Programming (received off-air): KAUT-TV (U), KETA (P), KFOR-TV (N), KOCB (W), KOCO-TV (A), KOKH-TV (F), KWTV (C) Oklahoma City; allband FM.
Programming (via satellite): WGN-TV (W) Chicago; A & E; C-SPAN; CNN; Cartoon Network; Country Music TV; Discovery Channel; Disney Channel; E! Entertainment TV; ESPN; ESPN 2; EWTN; Fox Family Channel; Fox Sports Net Southwest; Headline News; History Channel; Home & Garden Television; Learning Channel; MTV; MuchMusic Network; Nashville Network; Nick at Nite's TV Land; Nickelodeon; Odyssey; QVC; Sci-Fi Channel; TBS Superstation; The Health Network; The Weather Channel; Trinity Bcstg. Network; Turner Classic Movies; Turner Network TV; USA Network.
Current originations: Automated time-weather; local news.
Fee: $35.00 installation; $24.95 monthly.
Pay Service 1
Pay Units: 624.
Programming (via satellite): HBO (multiplexed).
Fee: $35.00 installation; $10.95 monthly.
Pay Service 2
Pay Units: 267.
Programming (via satellite): Showtime.
Fee: $35.00 installation; $9.95 monthly.
Pay Service 3
Pay Units: 290.
Programming (via satellite): The Movie Channel.
Fee: $35.00 installation; $5.95 monthly.
Local advertising: No.
Equipment: SKL headend; Jerrold & SKL amplifiers; ITT & Times Fiber cable; U.S. Tower satellite antenna.
Miles of plant: 89.0 (coaxial). Homes passed: 4,900.
Manager: Dave Walker. Chief technician: Roger Campbell. Marketing director: Jennifer Hauschild.
City fee: 3.7% of basic net.
Ownership: Classic Cable (MSO).

WELCH—Oklahoma Cablecomm, Box 970, Fort Gibson, OK 74434-0970. Phones: 918-478-2100; 800-783-5701. Fax: 918-478-2355. County: Craig. ICA: OK0190.
TV Market Ranking: Outside TV Markets. Franchise award date: October 4, 1988. Franchise expiration date: October 4, 2013. Began: September 1, 1990.
Channel capacity: 35 (not 2-way capable). Channels available but not in use: 18.
Basic Service
Subscribers: 122.
Programming (received off-air): KRSC-TV (E) Claremore; KOAM-TV (C), KODE-TV (A), KSNF (N) Joplin-Pittsburg; KOED-TV (P), KTUL (A) Tulsa.
Programming (via satellite): WGN-TV (W) Chicago; A & E; CNN; Country Music TV; Discovery Channel; ESPN; FX; Fox Family Channel; Lifetime; Nashville Network; Nickelodeon; TBS Superstation; The Weather Channel; Turner Network TV; USA Network.
Fee: $40.00 installation; $22.00 monthly; $1.96 converter; $19.95 additional installation.
Pay Service 1
Pay Units: 28.
Programming (via satellite): HBO.
Fee: $9.95 monthly.
Local advertising: No.
Program Guide: TV Host.
Equipment: Cadco headend; Scientific-Atlanta amplifiers; Comm/Scope cable; Jerrold set top converters; Arcom traps; Standard Communications satellite receivers.
Miles of plant: 6.0 (coaxial). Homes passed: 357. Total homes in franchised area: 357.
Manager: Rick Wall. Chief technician: Leon Strain. Marketing & program director: Bruce Berkinshaw.
City fee: 5% of gross.
Ownership: Fanch Communications Inc. (MSO); Time Warner Cable (MSO). See Cable System Ownership.

WELEETKA—Oklahoma Cablecomm, Box 970, Fort Gibson, OK 74434. Phones: 918-478-2100; 800-783-5701. Fax: 918-478-2355. County: Okfuskee. ICA: OK0165.
TV Market Ranking: Outside TV Markets. Franchise award date: N.A. Franchise expiration date: N.A. Began: January 1, 1982.
Channel capacity: 35 (not 2-way capable). Channels available but not in use: 15.
Basic Service
Subscribers: 311; Commercial subscribers: 1.
Programming (received off-air): KJRH (N), KOED-TV (P), KOKI-TV (F), KOTV (C), KTUL (A), KWHB (I) Tulsa.
Programming (via satellite): WGN-TV (W) Chicago; A & E; American Movie Classics; CNN; Cartoon Network; Discovery Channel; Disney Channel; ESPN; ESPN 2; Fox Family Channel; Fox Sports Net; History Channel; Home & Garden Television; Learning Channel; Lifetime; Nashville Network; Nickelodeon; QVC; Sci-Fi Channel; TBS Superstation; The Inspirational Network; The Weather Channel; Turner Classic Movies; Turner Network TV; USA Network.
Current originations: Automated time-weather; local news.
Fee: $30.00 installation; $21.95 monthly.
Pay Service 1
Pay Units: N.A.

Programming (via satellite): Cinemax.
Fee: N.A.
Pay Service 2
Pay Units: 45.
Programming (via satellite): HBO.
Fee: $9.00 monthly.
Program Guide: TV Host.
Equipment: Blonder-Tongue & RCA headend; Theta-Com amplifiers; Atari character generator; Jerrold set top converters; Northeast Filter traps; M/A-Com & Microdyne satellite antenna; Microdyne & Microwave Assoc. satellite receivers.
Miles of plant: 11.0 (coaxial). Homes passed: 543.
Manager: Rick Wall. Chief technician: Leon Strain. Marketing & program director: Bruce Berkinshaw.
City fee: 2% of basic gross.
Ownership: Fanch Communications Inc. (MSO); Time Warner Cable (MSO). See Cable System Ownership.

WELLSTON—Peak Cablevision, 323 E. Broadway, Cushing, OK 74023. Phone: 800-547-8582. County: Lincoln. ICA: OK0192.
TV Market Ranking: 39. Franchise award date: N.A. Franchise expiration date: N.A. Began: January 1, 1981.
Channel capacity: 35. Channels available but not in use: 10.
Basic Service
Subscribers: 120.
Programming (received off-air): KETA (P), KFOR-TV (N), KOCB (W), KOCO-TV (A), KOKH-TV (F), KTBO-TV (T), KWTV (C) Oklahoma City.
Programming (via satellite): American Movie Classics; Animal Planet; CNBC; CNN; Cartoon Network; Discovery Channel; Disney Channel; ESPN; Fox Family Channel; Fox News Channel; Fox Sports Net Southwest; Headline News; Home & Garden Television; Learning Channel; MTV; Nashville Network; TBS Superstation; The Weather Channel; Turner Network TV; USA Network.
Fee: $37.50 installation; $24.62 monthly; $1.50 converter; $5.39 additional installation.
Commercial fee: $9.00 monthly.
Pay Service 1
Pay Units: 29.
Programming (via satellite): Cinemax.
Fee: $20.00 installation; $12.75 monthly.
Pay Service 2
Pay Units: 39.
Programming (via satellite): HBO.
Fee: $20.00 installation; $13.00 monthly.
Pay Service 3
Pay Units: 53.
Programming (via satellite): The New Encore.
Fee: $1.75 monthly.
Local advertising: No.
Miles of plant: 7.0 (coaxial). Homes passed: 350. Total homes in franchised area: 802.
Manager: Bud Gaither. Chief technician: Ron Diamond.
Ownership: Peak Cablevision LLC (MSO). See Cable System Ownership.

WESTPORT—Cim Tel Cable Inc., Box 266, 101 Cimarron St., Mannford, OK 74044. Phone: 918-865-3314. County: Pawnee. ICA: OK0324.
TV Market Ranking: 54. Franchise award date: N.A. Franchise expiration date: N.A. Began: February 1, 1989.
Channel capacity: N.A. Channels available but not in use: N.A.
Basic Service
Subscribers: N.A.
Programming (received off-air): KJRH (N), KOED-TV (P), KOKI-TV (F), KOTV (C), KTUL (A) Tulsa.
Programming (via satellite): WGN-TV (W) Chicago; CNN; ESPN; Fox Family Channel; TBS Superstation.
Fee: N.A.
Pay Service 1
Pay Units: N.A.
Programming (via satellite): Cinemax; Disney Channel; HBO.
Fee: N.A.
Ownership: Cim Tel Cable Inc. (MSO).

WESTVILLE—Oklahoma Cablecomm, Box 970, Fort Gibson, OK 74434-0970. Phones: 918-478-2100; 800-783-5701. Fax: 918-478-2355. County: Adair. ICA: OK0138.
TV Market Ranking: Below 100. Franchise award date: N.A. Franchise expiration date: August 28, 1997. Began: August 1, 1974.
Channel capacity: N.A. Channels available but not in use: N.A.
Basic Service
Subscribers: 415; Commercial subscribers: 51.
Programming (received off-air): KHOG-TV (A) Fayetteville; KFSM-TV (C), KHBS (A), KPOM-TV (N) Fort Smith; KOAM-TV (C) Joplin-Pittsburg; KJRH (N), KOED-TV (P), KOTV (C), KTUL (A) Tulsa; allband FM.
Programming (via satellite): WGN-TV (W) Chicago; Discovery Channel; Fox Family Channel; Nashville Network; Nickelodeon; TBS Superstation; VH1.
Fee: $30.00 installation; $16.95 monthly.
Pay Service 1
Pay Units: N.A.
Programming (via satellite): Showtime.
Fee: $10.00 installation; $10.00 monthly.
Equipment: Cadco headend; AEL amplifiers; Phelps-Dodge cable.
Miles of plant: 16.0 (coaxial). Homes passed: 700. Total homes in franchised area: 700.
Manager: Rick Wall. Chief technician: Richard Taapken. Marketing director: Rob Typer.
City fee: 3% of gross.
Ownership: Fanch Communications Inc. (MSO); Time Warner Cable (MSO). See Cable System Ownership.

WETUMKA—Peak Cablevision, Box 807, Pocola, OK 74502. Phone: 918-627-9906. Fax: 918-627-9407. County: Hughes. ICA: OK0325.
TV Market Ranking: Outside TV Markets. Franchise award date: N.A. Franchise expiration date: June 9, 2005. Began: June 1, 1981.
Channel capacity: 36 (not 2-way capable). Channels available but not in use: 3.
Basic Service
Subscribers: 388.
Programming (received off-air): KAUT-TV (U), KETA (P), KFOR-TV (N), KOCB (W), KOKH-TV (F), KWTV (C) Oklahoma City; KOKI-TV (F), KTUL (A), KWHB (I) Tulsa.
Programming (via satellite): WGN-TV (W) Chicago; A & E; American Movie Classics; CNN; Country Music TV; Discovery Channel; Disney Channel; ESPN; Fox Family Channel; History Channel; Home Shopping Network; Nashville Network; Nick at Nite's TV Land; Nickelodeon; TBS Superstation; The Weather Channel; Trinity Bcstg. Network; Turner Network TV; USA Network.
Fee: $23.45 monthly.
Pay Service 1
Pay Units: N.A.
Programming (via satellite): HBO; Showtime; Starz!; The Movie Channel; The New Encore.
Fee: $10.00 monthly (HBO or Showtime).
Miles of plant: 15.5 (coaxial). Homes passed: 710.
Manager: Everett Thayer. Chief technician: Rick Packard. Marketing director: Terry Homesley. Customer service manager: Susan Moore.
Franchise fee: 2% of gross.
Ownership: Peak Cablevision LLC (MSO). See Cable System Ownership.

WEWOKA—Peak Cablevision, 205 E. Cherokee, McAlester, OK 74502. Phone: 918-423-6661. Fax: 918-426-2809. County: Seminole. ICA: OK0077.
TV Market Ranking: Below 100. Franchise award date: N.A. Franchise expiration date: N.A. Began: September 1, 1976.
Channel capacity: 30. Channels available but not in use: 3.
Basic Service
Subscribers: 1,290.
Programming (received off-air): KTEN (A,N,F) Ada; KETA (P), KFOR-TV (N), KOCB (W), KOCO-TV (A), KOKH-TV (F), KWTV (C) Oklahoma City; KTUL (A) Tulsa; allband FM.
Programming (via satellite): CNBC; CNN; Discovery Channel; Fox Family Channel; Headline News; MTV; Nashville Network; TBS Superstation; The Weather Channel.
Current originations: Automated time-weather.
Fee: $60.00 installation; $20.59 monthly; $20.00 additional installation.
Expanded Basic Service
Subscribers: 1,112.
Programming (via satellite): American Movie Classics; ESPN; Fox Sports Net Southwest; Turner Network TV; USA Network.
Fee: $3.00 monthly.
Pay Service 1
Pay Units: 130.
Programming (via satellite): Cinemax.
Fee: $20.00 installation; $10.00 monthly.
Pay Service 2
Pay Units: 52.
Programming (via satellite): Disney Channel.
Fee: $5.00 installation; $10.00 monthly.
Pay Service 3
Pay Units: 624.
Programming (via satellite): The New Encore.
Fee: N.A.
Pay Service 4
Pay Units: 231.
Programming (via satellite): HBO.
Fee: $20.00 installation; $10.00 monthly.
Local advertising: Yes (insert only). Available in character-generated programming.
Program Guide: The Cable Guide.
Equipment: AFC satellite antenna.
Miles of plant: 24.9 (coaxial). Homes passed: 1,775. Total homes in franchised area: 1,775.
Manager: Everett Thayer. Chief technician: Lynn Harrison. Marketing director: Terry Homesley. Customer service manager: Susan Moore.
Ownership: Peak Cablevision LLC (MSO). See Cable System Ownership.

WHITE HORN COVE—TCA Cable, Box 3408, Fort Smith, AR 72913. Phone: 501-782-8941. County: Wagoner. Also serves Rocky Point. ICA: OK0095.
TV Market Ranking: Outside TV Markets. Franchise award date: N.A. Franchise expiration date: N.A. Began: March 1, 1988.
Channel capacity: 35. Channels available but not in use: 15.
Basic Service
Subscribers: 523.
Programming (received off-air): KJRH (N), KOED-TV (P), KOKI-TV (F), KOTV (C), KTUL (A), KWHB (I) Tulsa.
Programming (via satellite): WGN-TV (W) Chicago; American Movie Classics; CNN; Country Music TV; Discovery Channel; ESPN; Fox Family Channel; Home Shopping Network; MTV; TBS Superstation; The Weather Channel; Turner Network TV; USA Network.
Fee: $25.00 installation; $15.00 monthly.
Pay Service 1
Pay Units: 46.
Programming (via satellite): Disney Channel.
Fee: $10.00 installation; $6.95 monthly.
Pay Service 2
Pay Units: 141.
Programming (via satellite): HBO.
Fee: $10.00 installation; $9.50 monthly.
Pay Service 3
Pay Units: 127.
Programming (via satellite): Showtime.
Fee: $10.00 installation; $5.95 monthly.
Local advertising: No.
Equipment: Blonder-Tongue headend; Jerrold & C-COR amplifiers; Trilogy cable; RCA & Jerrold set top converters; Eagle & Arcom traps; Scientific-Atlanta & Prodelin satellite antenna; M/A-Com satellite receivers.
Miles of plant: 35.0 (coaxial). Homes passed: 1,200. Total homes in franchised area: 1,200.
Manager: Bob Griffith. Chief technician: Ron Bartell.
Ownership: Lake Area TV Cable.

WILBURTON—Oklahoma Cablecomm, Box 970, Fort Gibson, OK 74434-0970. Phones: 918-478-2100; 800-783-5701. Fax: 918-478-2355. County: Latimer. Also serves Red Oak. Plans service to Red Oak. ICA: OK0088.
TV Market Ranking: Outside TV Markets. Franchise award date: N.A. Franchise expiration date: N.A. Began: October 1, 1962.
Channel capacity: 45. Channels available but not in use: N.A.
Basic Service
Subscribers: 1,500; Commercial subscribers: 169.
Programming (received off-air): KTEN (A,N,F) Ada; KOET (P) Eufaula; KJRH (N), KOKI-TV (F), KOTV (C), KTFO (U), KTUL (A), KWHB (I) Tulsa; allband FM.
Programming (via satellite): WGN-TV (W) Chicago; A & E; American Movie Classics; C-SPAN; CNBC; CNN; Cartoon Network; Country Music TV; Discovery Channel; Disney Channel; E! Entertainment TV; ESPN; ESPN 2; Fox Family Channel; Fox Sports Net Southwest; Headline News; History Channel; Home & Garden Television; Home Shopping Network; Learning Channel; Lifetime; Nashville Network; Nickelodeon; Outdoor Channel; QVC; Sci-Fi Channel; TBS Superstation; The Weather Channel; Trinity Bcstg. Network; Turner Network TV; USA Network.
Current originations: Automated time-weather; local news.
Fee: $29.95 installation; $24.95 monthly; $1.96 converter; $19.95 additional installation.
Pay Service 1
Pay Units: 125.
Programming (via satellite): Cinemax.
Fee: $9.95 monthly.
Pay Service 2
Pay Units: 138.
Programming (via satellite): HBO.
Fee: $9.95 monthly.
Pay Service 3
Pay Units: 11.
Programming (via satellite): Showtime.
Fee: $9.95 monthly.
Program Guide: TV Host.

Equipment: Jerrold set top converters; Pico traps; U.S. Tower satellite antenna; Standard Communications satellite receivers.
Miles of plant: 80.0 (coaxial). Additional miles planned: 6.0 (coaxial). Homes passed: 1,950. Total homes in franchised area: 1,950.
Manager: Rick Wall. Chief technician: Leon Strain. Marketing & program director: Bruce Berkinshaw.
City fee: 2% of gross.
Ownership: Fanch Communications Inc. (MSO); Time Warner Cable (MSO). See Cable System Ownership.

WISTER—Peak Cablevision, Box 807, Pocola, OK 74902. Phone: 918-436-7488. Fax: 918-436-7151. County: Le Flore. ICA: OK0193.
TV Market Ranking: Outside TV Markets. Franchise award date: N.A. Franchise expiration date: December 4, 2003. Began: July 1, 1980.
Channel capacity: 36 (not 2-way capable). Channels available but not in use: 11.
Basic Service
Subscribers: 300.
Programming (received off-air): KOET (P) Eufaula; KFSM-TV (C), KHBS (A), KPOM-TV (N) Fort Smith; KOKI-TV (F), KTUL (A) Tulsa.
Programming (via satellite): WGN-TV (W) Chicago; American Movie Classics; CNN; Country Music TV; Discovery Channel; ESPN; Nashville Network; Nickelodeon; QVC; TBS Superstation; The Weather Channel; Trinity Bcstg. Network; Turner Network TV; USA Network.
Fee: $20.95 monthly.
Pay Service 1
Pay Units: N.A.
Programming (via satellite): Disney Channel; HBO; Showtime; The Movie Channel.
Fee: $7.95 monthly (Disney), $10.00 (HBO, Showtime or TMC).
Miles of plant: 15.0 (coaxial). Homes passed: 527.
Manager: Dennis Moore. Chief technician: Rick Packard. Marketing director: Terry Homesley. Customer service manager: Susan Moore.
Franchise fee: 5% of gross.
Ownership: Peak Cablevision LLC (MSO). See Cable System Ownership.

WOODALL—Quality Entertainment Corp., Suite 512, Central Mall Plaza, Fort Smith, AR 72903. Phone: 501-452-1998. Fax: 501-452-6430. County: Cherokee. ICA: OK0365.
TV Market Ranking: Outside TV Markets. Franchise award date: N.A. Franchise expiration date: N.A. Began: N.A.
Channel capacity: 36 (not 2-way capable). Channels available but not in use: 10.
Basic Service
Subscribers: 88.
Programming (received off-air): KJRH (N), KOED-TV (P), KOKI-TV (F), KOTV (C), KTFO (U), KTUL (A) Tulsa.
Programming (via satellite): WGN-TV (W) Chicago; A & E; American Movie Classics; CNN; Country Music TV; Discovery Channel; ESPN; Fox Family Channel; Learning Channel; Nashville Network; Nick at Nite's TV Land; QVC; Sci-Fi Channel; TBS Superstation; The Weather Channel; Trinity Bcstg. Network; Turner Network TV; USA Network.
Fee: $40.00 installation; $24.00 monthly.
Pay Service 1
Pay Units: N.A.
Programming (via satellite): HBO.
Fee: $12.00 monthly.
Miles of plant: 10.0 (coaxial).
Manager: Brent Lewis.
Ownership: Quality Entertainment Corp. (MSO).

WOODWARD—Classic Cable, Box 429, 605 N.W. 3rd St., Plainville, KS 67663-0429. Phones: 785-434-7620; 800-999-8876. Fax: 785-434-2614. County: Woodward. Also serves Mooreland. ICA: OK0029.
TV Market Ranking: Outside TV Markets. Franchise award date: March 18, 1956. Franchise expiration date: March 18, 2001. Began: April 1, 1956.
Channel capacity: 41 (2-way capable). Channels available but not in use: N.A.
Basic Service
Subscribers: 4,165; Commercial subscribers: 13.
Programming (received off-air): KETA (P), KOCB (W) Oklahoma City; KVDA (O) San Antonio; KOMI-LP (I) Woodward.
Programming (via microwave): KFOR-TV (N), KOCO-TV (A), KOKH-TV (F), KWTV (C) Oklahoma City.
Programming (via satellite): WGN-TV (W) Chicago; A & E; C-SPAN; C-SPAN 2; CNBC; CNN; Country Music TV; Discovery Channel; Disney Channel; E! Entertainment TV; ESPN; ESPN 2; Fox Family Channel; Fox Sports Net Southwest; Headline News; History Channel; Home & Garden Television; Learning Channel; Lifetime; MTV; Nashville Network; Nick at Nite's TV Land; Nickelodeon; QVC; Sci-Fi Channel; TBS Superstation; The Weather Channel; Toon Disney; Trinity Bcstg. Network; Turner Classic Movies; Turner Network TV; USA Network; VH1.
Current originations: Automated time-weather.
Fee: $35.00 installation; $26.95 monthly.
Digital Basic Service
Subscribers: N.A.
Programming (via satellite): BBC America; Discovery Home & Leisure Channel; Discovery Kids Channel; Discovery People; Discovery Science Channel; ESPN Classic Sports; ESPNews; Fox Sports World; Game Show Network; MuchMusic Network; Outdoor Life Network; Romance Classics.
Fee: $12.95 monthly.
Expanded Basic Service
Subscribers: N.A.
Programming (via satellite): Bravo; Encore Action; Encore Love Stories; Encore Mystery; Encore True Stories & Drama; Encore Westerns; Independent Film Channel.
Fee: $12.95 monthly.
Pay Service 1
Pay Units: 128.
Programming (via satellite): Cinemax.
Fee: $10.00 installation; $9.95 monthly.
Pay Service 2
Pay Units: 859.
Programming (via satellite): HBO.
Fee: $10.95 monthly.
Pay Service 3
Pay Units: 381.
Programming (via satellite): Showtime.
Fee: $9.95 monthly.
Pay Service 4
Pay Units: 368.
Programming (via satellite): The Movie Channel.
Fee: $5.95 monthly.
Digital Pay Service 1
Pay Units: N.A.
Programming (via satellite): Cinemax (multiplexed); DMX; Flix; HBO (multiplexed); Showtime (multiplexed); Starz! (multiplexed); Sundance Channel; The Movie Channel; The New Encore.
Fee: N.A.
Pay-Per-View
Spice delivered digitally.
Local advertising: Yes (locally produced & insert). Local sales manager: Dave Broughton.

Equipment: Microdyne, Scientific-Atlanta & RCA headend; Jerrold & Magnavox amplifiers; Comm/Scope cable; Sony VTRs; MSI character generator; Jerrold set top converters; Eagle traps; Scientific-Atlanta satellite antenna; Microdyne satellite receivers.
Miles of plant: 130.0 (coaxial). Homes passed: 6,026.
Manager: Dave Walker. Chief technician: Jeff Smith. Marketing director: Jennifer Houschild.
City fee: 5% of gross.
Ownership: Classic Cable (MSO). Purchased from Time Warner Cable.

WRIGHT CITY—Peak Cablevision, 516 N. Lakeside Dr., DeQueen, AR 71832. Phone: 870-642-2411. Fax: 870-642-4259. County: McCurtain. ICA: OK0198.
TV Market Ranking: Outside TV Markets. Franchise award date: N.A. Franchise expiration date: February 7, 2006. Began: December 1, 1965.
Channel capacity: 36 (not 2-way capable). Channels available but not in use: 12.
Basic Service
Subscribers: 235.
Programming (received off-air): KTEN (A,N,F) Ada; KOET (P) Eufaula; KXII (C) Sherman; KSLA-TV (C), KTAL-TV (N), KTBS-TV (A) Shreveport-Texarkana.
Programming (via satellite): WGN-TV (W) Chicago; American Movie Classics; CNBC; CNN; Comedy Central; Court TV; Discovery Channel; ESPN; FoxNet; Headline News; Lifetime; Nashville Network; Nickelodeon; Odyssey; Sci-Fi Channel; TBS Superstation; Trinity Bcstg. Network; Turner Network TV; USA Network; VH1.
Current originations: Local sports.
Fee: $25.00 installation; $20.29 monthly.
Pay Service 1
Pay Units: 14.
Programming (via satellite): Disney Channel.
Fee: $10.00 installation; $10.75 monthly.
Pay Service 2
Pay Units: 87.
Programming (via satellite): The New Encore.
Fee: $1.72 monthly.
Pay Service 3
Pay Units: 82.
Programming (via satellite): HBO.
Fee: $11.96 monthly.
Local advertising: No.
Miles of plant: 6.6 (coaxial). Homes passed: 308. Total homes in franchised area: 308.
Manager: Ron Beatty. Chief technician: Lynn Harrison. Marketing director: Terry Homesley. Customer service manager: Carol Litchford.
Ownership: Peak Cablevision LLC (MSO). See Cable System Ownership.

WYANDOTTE—Oklahoma Cablecomm, Box 970, Fort Gibson, OK 74434-0970. Phones: 918-478-2100; 800-783-5701. Fax: 918-478-2355. County: Ottawa. ICA: OK0327.
TV Market Ranking: Below 100. Franchise award date: January 1, 1989. Franchise expiration date: January 1, 2004. Began: September 1, 1989.
Channel capacity: N.A. Channels available but not in use: N.A.
Basic Service
Subscribers: 54.
Programming (received off-air): KOAM-TV (C), KODE-TV (A), KOZJ (P), KSNF (N) Joplin-Pittsburg; KTUL (A) Tulsa.
Programming (via satellite): WGN-TV (W) Chicago; A & E; CNN; Country Music TV; Discovery Channel; ESPN; Fox Family Channel; Nashville Network; TBS Superstation; Turner Network TV; USA Network.
Fee: $30.00 installation; $19.95 monthly.
Pay Service 1
Pay Units: 19.
Programming (via satellite): HBO.
Fee: $10.95 monthly.
Local advertising: No.
Program Guide: TV Host.
Miles of plant: 2.0 (coaxial). Homes passed: 143.
Manager: Rick Wall. Chief technician: Leon Strain. Marketing & program director: Bruce Berkinshaw.
City fee: 5% of gross.
Ownership: Fanch Communications Inc. (MSO); Time Warner Cable (MSO). See Cable System Ownership.

WYNONA—Community Cablevision, Box 307, Skiatook, OK 74070-0307. Phone: 918-396-3019. County: Osage. ICA: OK0214.
TV Market Ranking: Below 100. Franchise award date: October 15, 1986. Franchise expiration date: October 15, 2011. Began: February 1, 1987.
Channel capacity: 35 (not 2-way capable). Channels available but not in use: 13.
Basic Service
Subscribers: 119.
Programming (received off-air): KJRH (N), KOED-TV (P), KOKI-TV (F), KOTV (C), KTUL (A), KWHB (I) Tulsa.
Programming (via satellite): WGN-TV (W) Chicago; CNN; Country Music TV; Discovery Channel; ESPN; Fox Family Channel; Headline News; Nashville Network; TBS Superstation; Turner Classic Movies; Turner Network TV; USA Network.
Fee: $25.00 installation; $16.25 monthly.
Pay Service 1
Pay Units: 33.
Programming (via satellite): Cinemax.
Fee: $11.50 monthly.
Pay Service 2
Pay Units: 37.
Programming (via satellite): Disney Channel.
Fee: $7.00 monthly.
Pay Service 3
Pay Units: 35.
Programming (via satellite): HBO.
Fee: $11.50 monthly.
Pay-Per-View
Addressable homes: 119.
Local advertising: No.
Equipment: Blonder-Tongue headend; Scientific-Atlanta amplifiers; M/A-Com cable; Scientific-Atlanta set top converters; Pico traps; Weatherscan satellite antenna; Drake satellite receivers.

Miles of plant: 4.0 (coaxial). Homes passed: 254.
Manager: Ray Soule.
City fee: 2% of gross.
Ownership: Community Cablevision Co. (MSO).

YALE—Community Cablevision, Box 307, Skiatook, OK 74070-0307. Phone: 918-396-3019. County: Payne. ICA: OK0141.
TV Market Ranking: Outside TV Markets. Franchise award date: March 24, 1987. Franchise expiration date: March 24, 2012. Began: April 20, 1983.
Channel capacity: 35 (not 2-way capable). Channels available but not in use: 2.

Basic Service
Subscribers: 338.
Programming (received off-air): KAUT-TV (U), KFOR-TV (N), KOCB (W), KOCO-TV (A), KOKH-TV (F), KWTV (C) Oklahoma City; KJRH (N), KOED-TV (P), KOKI-TV (F), KOTV (C), KTUL (A), KWHB (I) Tulsa.
Programming (via satellite): WGN-TV (W) Chicago; A & E; CNN; Country Music TV; Discovery Channel; ESPN; Fox Family Channel; Headline News; MTV; Nashville Network; Nickelodeon; TBS Superstation; Turner Classic Movies; Turner Network TV; USA Network; VH1.
Current originations: Automated time-weather; public access; educational access; government access; religious access; leased access; library access; local sports.
Fee: $25.00 installation; $16.25 monthly; $25.00 additional installation.

Pay Service 1
Pay Units: 70.
Programming (via satellite): Cinemax.
Fee: $25.00 installation; $11.50 monthly.

Pay Service 2
Pay Units: 45.
Programming (via satellite): Disney Channel.
Fee: $25.00 installation; $7.00 monthly.

Pay Service 3
Pay Units: 83.
Programming (via satellite): HBO.
Fee: $25.00 installation; $11.50 monthly.

Pay-Per-View
Addressable homes: 338.
Local advertising: Yes. Available in character-generated programming. Rates: $15.00/Week.
Equipment: Cadco & Blonder-Tongue headend; Scientific-Atlanta amplifiers; Texscan character generator; Jerrold set top converters; Arcom traps; M/A-Com satellite antenna; Drake satellite receivers.
Miles of plant: 9.9 (coaxial). Homes passed: 659.
Manager: Ray Soule.
City fee: 2% of gross.
Ownership: Community Cablevision Co. (MSO).

YUKON—Cablevision of Yukon, 438 W. Main St., Yukon, OK 73099. Phone: 405-359-3556. County: Canadian. ICA: OK0024.
TV Market Ranking: 39. Franchise award date: October 1, 1974. Franchise expiration date: October 1, 2004. Began: August 1, 1976.
Channel capacity: 69 (not 2-way capable). Channels available but not in use: 8.

Basic Service
Subscribers: 5,321.
Programming (received off-air): KAUT-TV (U), KETA (P), KFOR-TV (N), KOCB (W), KOCO-TV (A), KOKH-TV (F), KSBI (I), KTBO-TV (T), KWTV (C) Oklahoma City; 15 FMs.
Programming (via satellite): A & E; American Movie Classics; C-SPAN; CNBC; Discovery Channel; ESPN; Home Shopping Network; Learning Channel; Lifetime; MTV; Nickelodeon; TV Guide Channel; The Weather Channel; USA Network; VH1.
Current originations: Public access; educational access; government access; religious access; automated emergency alert; local sports.
Fee: $15.98 installation; $19.47 monthly.

Expanded Basic Service
Subscribers: 5,183.
Programming (via satellite): WGN-TV (W) Chicago; CNN; Fox Family Channel; Headline News; Nashville Network; TBS Superstation; Turner Network TV.
Fee: $3.59 monthly.

Expanded Basic Service 2
Subscribers: 1,207.
Programming (via satellite): Bravo; Cartoon Network; Comedy Central; Country Music TV; Court TV; ESPN 2; History Channel; Sci-Fi Channel; Travel Channel; Turner Classic Movies.
Fee: $6.00 monthly.

Pay Service 1
Pay Units: 898.
Programming (via satellite): Cinemax.
Fee: $11.00 monthly.

Pay Service 2
Pay Units: 683.
Programming (via satellite): Disney Channel.
Fee: $7.95 monthly.

Pay Service 3
Pay Units: 1,513.
Programming (via satellite): HBO.
Fee: $11.00 monthly.

Pay Service 4
Pay Units: 1,006.
Programming (via satellite): Showtime.
Fee: $11.00 monthly.

Pay Service 5
Pay Units: 11.
Programming (via satellite): Music Choice.
Fee: $7.95 monthly.

Pay Service 6
Pay Units: 35.
Programming (via satellite): Golf Channel.
Fee: $6.95 monthly.

Pay-Per-View
Addressable homes: 1,401.
Special events.
Fee: $3.00.
Local advertising: Yes. Available in satellite distributed programming. Rates: $800.00/Hour; $400.00/30 Minutes; $160.00/Minute; $80.00/30 Seconds. Local sales manager: Mark Kanter. Regional interconnect: Oklahoma Cable Advertising Interconnect.
Program Guide: The Cable Guide.
Equipment: Scientific-Atlanta headend; Theta-Com amplifiers; Comm/Scope cable; Oak, Hamlin & Scientific-Atlanta set top converters; Scientific-Atlanta addressable set top converters; Eagle traps; Scientific-Atlanta satellite antenna; Scientific-Atlanta satellite receivers.
Miles of plant: 83.0 (coaxial). Homes passed: 7,882.
Manager: David Cooper. Chief technician: Kurtis Gill. Marketing director: Jim Back. Customer service manager: Charitta Shelton.
City fee: 5% of gross.
Ownership: Multimedia Cablevision Inc. (MSO). See Cable System Ownership.

OREGON

Total Systems: **141**
Total Communities Served: **411**
Franchises Not Yet Operating: **0**
Applications Pending: **0**
Communities with Applications: **0**
Number of Basic Subscribers: **743,997**
Number of Expanded Basic Subscribers: **515,317**
Number of Pay Units: **341,683**

Top 100 Markets Represented: Portland (29).

For a list of all cable communities included in this section, see the Cable Community Index located in the back of this volume.
For explanation of terms used in cable system listings, see p. D-9.

ADAMS—TCI Cablevision of Oregon Inc., Box 1577, 126 W. Poplar St., Walla Walla, WA 99362-2847. Phone: 509-529-9500. Fax: 509-522-1719. County: Umatilla. ICA: OR0118.
TV Market Ranking: Below 100. Franchise award date: N.A. Franchise expiration date: N.A. Began: N.A.
Channel capacity: 24. Channels available but not in use: N.A.
Basic Service
Subscribers: 69.
Programming (received off-air): KTVR (P) La Grande; KEPR-TV (C), KNDU (N), KVEW (A) Pasco-Kennewick-Richland; KPTV (U) Portland.
Fee: $36.34 installation; $18.75 monthly.
Miles of plant: 3.0 (coaxial). Homes passed: 111.
Manager: Tim Klinefelter. Chief technician: Tim Ream. Program director: Dinah Morrison. Marketing director: Marlene Ashby.
Ownership: AT&T Broadband & Internet Services (MSO). Purchased from Tele-Communications Inc., March 9, 1999.

ARLINGTON—Arlington TV Cooperative Inc., Box 184, Arlington, OR 97812. Phone: 541-454-2707. County: Gilliam. ICA: OR0106.
TV Market Ranking: Outside TV Markets. Franchise award date: N.A. Franchise expiration date: N.A. Began: December 1, 1955.
Channel capacity: 36 (2-way capable; not operating 2-way). Channels available but not in use: 20.
Basic Service
Subscribers: 170.
Programming (received off-air): KEPR-TV (C), KNDU (N), KVEW (A) Pasco-Kennewick-Richland; KPDX (F) Vancouver.
Programming (via microwave): KATU (A), KGW (N), KOAP-TV (P), KOIN (C), KPTV (U) Portland.
Programming (via satellite): CNN; Discovery Channel; ESPN; Fox Family Channel; Nashville Network; TBS Superstation; Turner Network TV.
Fee: $25.00 installation; $23.50 monthly.
Pay Service 1
Pay Units: 71.
Programming (via satellite): HBO.
Fee: $11.50 monthly.
Pay Service 2
Pay Units: N.A.
Programming (via satellite): Disney Channel.
Fee: N.A.
Pay-Per-View
Addressable homes: 78.
Equipment: Composite headend; composite amplifiers; composite cable.
Miles of plant: 8.0 (coaxial). Homes passed: 213.
Manager: Richard Rende. Chief technician: Steve Conlee.
Ownership: Arlington TV Cooperative Inc.

ASTORIA—Falcon Community Ventures I, 1241 Duane St., Astoria, OR 97103. Phone: 503-325-6114. Counties: Clatsop, OR; Pacific, WA. Also serves Clatsop County, Gearhart, Hammond, Lewis & Clark, Seaside, Walluski Loop, Warrenton, OR; Pacific County, WA. ICA: OR0012.
TV Market Ranking: Outside TV Markets. Franchise award date: January 1, 1971. Franchise expiration date: N.A. Began: November 25, 1948.
Channel capacity: 62 (not 2-way capable). Channels available but not in use: 2.
Basic Service
Subscribers: 10,780.
Programming (received off-air): KATU (A), KGW (N), KOIN (C), KOPB-TV (P), KPTV (U) Portland; KING-TV (N), KOMO-TV (A) Seattle-Tacoma; KPDX (F) Vancouver; 13 FMs.
Programming (via satellite): A & E; Blazer Vision; C-SPAN; CNN; FX; Goodlife TV Network; Home & Garden Television; Home Shopping Network; Learning Channel; MTV; Nickelodeon; QVC; TBS Superstation; TV Guide Channel; TV Guide Sneak Prevue; Trinity Bcstg. Network; USA Network.
Current originations: Automated time-weather; public access; educational access; local access.
Fee: $25.00 installation; $15.89 monthly.
Expanded Basic Service
Subscribers: 9,541.
Programming (via satellite): C-SPAN 2; ESPN; ESPN 2; Fox Sports Net Northwest; Headline News; Lifetime; Sci-Fi Channel; TV Food Network; VH1.
Fee: $10.00 installation; $7.05 monthly.
Expanded Basic Service 2
Subscribers: 4,999.
Programming (via satellite): American Movie Classics; Country Music TV; Discovery Channel; Disney Channel; Fox Family Channel; Nashville Network; Turner Network TV.
Fee: $7.00 monthly.
Expanded Basic Service 3
Subscribers: 1,674.
Programming (via satellite): Comedy Central; fXM: Movies from Fox; History Channel; The Weather Channel.
Fee: $5.00 monthly.
Pay Service 1
Pay Units: 601.
Programming (via satellite): Cinemax.
Fee: $10.00 installation; $10.95 monthly.
Pay Service 2
Pay Units: 1,332.
Programming (via satellite): HBO.
Fee: $10.00 installation; $11.95 monthly.
Pay Service 3
Pay Units: 1,071.
Programming (via satellite): Showtime.
Fee: $10.00 installation; $10.95 monthly.
Pay Service 4
Pay Units: 657.
Programming (via satellite): The Movie Channel.
Fee: $10.95 monthly.
Pay Service 5
Pay Units: N.A.
Programming (via satellite): The New Encore.
Fee: N.A.
Pay-Per-View
Action Pay-Per-View; Spice; Spice2; Viewer's Choice.
Local advertising: No.
Equipment: Catel, Hughes & Microwave Assoc. headend; Jerrold amplifiers; Comm/Scope & Times Fiber cable; Sony VTRs; Video Data Systems character generator; Oak set top converters; Eagle traps; Andrew & Scientific-Atlanta satellite antenna; Scientific-Atlanta satellite receivers.
Miles of plant: 251.0 (coaxial). Homes passed: 15,659. Total homes in franchised area: 18,718.
Manager: Ray Romine. Chief technician: Lowell Williams.
Franchise fee: 3%-5% of gross.
Ownership: Falcon Communications LP (MSO), joint venture formed September 30, 1998. See Cable System Ownership.

BAKER—TCI Cablevision of Oregon Inc., Box 1401, La Grande, OR 97850-2202. Phone: 541-963-4189. County: Baker. Also serves Baker County. ICA: OR0032.
TV Market Ranking: Outside TV Markets. Franchise award date: January 1, 1954. Franchise expiration date: N.A. Began: December 10, 1954.
Channel capacity: 37 (not 2-way capable). Channels available but not in use: N.A.
Basic Service
Subscribers: 3,472.
Programming (received off-air): KTVB (N) Boise; KTVR (P) La Grande.
Programming (via microwave): KATU (A), KGW (N), KOIN (C), KPTV (U) Portland; KPDX (F) Vancouver.
Programming (via satellite): A & E; C-SPAN; CNBC; CNN; Discovery Channel; ESPN; FX; Fox Family Channel; Fox Sports Net Northwest; Headline News; Lifetime; MTV; Nashville Network; Nickelodeon; Odyssey; QVC; TBS Superstation; The Weather Channel; Turner Network TV; USA Network; VH1.
Planned originations: Automated time-weather.
Fee: $41.00 installation; $23.19 monthly; $1.30 converter; $19.00 additional installation.
Pay Service 1
Pay Units: 190.
Programming (via satellite): Cinemax.
Fee: $11.45 monthly.
Pay Service 2
Pay Units: 181.
Programming (via satellite): Disney Channel.
Fee: $11.45 monthly.
Pay Service 3
Pay Units: 1,172.
Programming (via satellite): The New Encore.
Fee: $1.75 monthly.
Pay Service 4
Pay Units: 284.
Programming (via satellite): HBO.
Fee: $15.00 installation; $12.45 monthly.
Pay Service 5
Pay Units: 162.
Programming (via satellite): Showtime.
Fee: $12.45 monthly.
Pay Service 6
Pay Units: N.A.
Programming (via satellite): Starz!
Fee: $4.75 monthly.
Pay-Per-View
Addressable homes: 250.
Movies; special events.
Local advertising: No. Local sales manager: Alan Keffer.
Equipment: Scientific-Atlanta headend; Scientific-Atlanta amplifiers; Comm/Scope cable; Microdyne satellite antenna.
Miles of plant: 69.4 (coaxial). Homes passed: 4,805. Total homes in franchised area: 4,825.
Manager: Darrell Linklater. Customer service manager: Pam Hardwick.
City fee: 5% of gross.
Ownership: AT&T Broadband & Internet Services (MSO). Purchased from Tele-Communications Inc., March 9, 1999.

BANDON—Falcon Cable Systems Co., 1400 Newmark Ave., Coos Bay, OR 97420. Phone: 541-888-5712. Fax: 541-888-9292. County: Coos. ICA: OR0123.
TV Market Ranking: Below 100. Franchise award date: January 1, 1979. Franchise expiration date: N.A. Began: N.A.
Channel capacity: 61. Channels available but not in use: 26.
Basic Service
Subscribers: 1,532.
Programming (received off-air): KCBY-TV (C), KMTZ (N) Coos Bay; KOAC-TV (P) Corvallis; KEVU-LP (F), KEZI (A) Eugene; KOBI (N) Medford; KPTV (U) Portland; 14 FMs.
Programming (via satellite): WGN-TV (W) Chicago; Blazer Vision; Bravo; C-SPAN; CNN; Comedy Central; E! Entertainment TV; ESPN; FX; Fox Family Channel; Headline News; Home Shopping Network; QVC; TBS Superstation; VH1.
Fee: $25.00 installation; $18.28 monthly; $14.95 additional installation.
Expanded Basic Service
Subscribers: 1,465.
Programming (via satellite): A & E; American Movie Classics; ESPN 2; Lifetime; USA Network.
Fee: $3.08 monthly.
Expanded Basic Service 2
Subscribers: 1,330.
Programming (via satellite): Country Music TV; Discovery Channel; Disney Channel; Nashville Network; Sci-Fi Channel; Turner Network TV.
Fee: $5.46 monthly.
Pay Service 1
Pay Units: 56.
Programming (via satellite): HBO.
Fee: $11.95 monthly.

Pay Service 2
Pay Units: 135.
Programming (via satellite): Showtime.
Fee: $10.95 monthly.
Pay Service 3
Pay Units: 21.
Programming (via satellite): The Movie Channel.
Fee: $10.95 monthly.
Local advertising: No.
Equipment: Scientific-Atlanta headend; Jerrold amplifiers; Times Fiber cable; Compuvid character generator; Scientific-Atlanta satellite antenna; Scientific-Atlanta satellite receivers.
Miles of plant: 40.0 (coaxial). Homes passed: 2,173.
Manager: Bill Griffin. Chief technician: Norman Lacey. Marketing director: Joan Crabtree.
Franchise fee: 3% of gross.
Ownership: Falcon Communications LP (MSO), joint venture formed September 30, 1998. See Cable System Ownership.

BEAR MOUNTAIN—Falcon Cable Systems Co., Suite 5, 4739 Main St., Springfield, OR 97477. Phone: 503-746-4132. County: Lane. Also serves Coburg, Creswell, Dexter, Jasper, Lane County (portions), Leaburg, Lowell, Marcola, McKenzie, Mohawk, Oakridge, Pleasant Hill, Walterville, West Fir, Whitewater. ICA: OR0124.
TV Market Ranking: Below 100 (Bear Mountain, Coburg, Creswell, Dexter, Jasper, Lane County, Leaburg, Lowell, Marcola, McKenzie, Mohawk, Pleasant Hill, Walterville, Whitewater); Outside TV Markets (Oakridge, West Fir). Franchise award date: N.A. Franchise expiration date: N.A. Began: N.A.
Channel capacity: 40. Channels available but not in use: 5.
Basic Service
Subscribers: 6,641.
Programming (received off-air): KOAC-TV (P) Corvallis; KEVU-LP (F), KEZI (A), KLSR-TV (U), KMTR (N), KVAL-TV (C) Eugene.
Programming (via satellite): WGN-TV (W) Chicago; A & E; American Movie Classics; Blazer Vision; C-SPAN; Comedy Central; Fox Sports Net Northwest; MTV; QVC; TBS Superstation; VH1.
Current originations: Public access; educational access; government access.
Fee: $29.95 installation; $15.75 monthly.
Expanded Basic Service
Subscribers: 5,793.
Programming (via satellite): CNN; ESPN; Headline News; Lifetime; Sci-Fi Channel.
Fee: $7.61 monthly.
Expanded Basic Service 2
Subscribers: 3,485.
Programming (via satellite): Country Music TV; Discovery Channel; Disney Channel; Fox Family Channel; Nashville Network; Nickelodeon; USA Network.
Fee: $6.50 monthly.
Expanded Basic Service 3
Subscribers: 1,287.
Programming (via satellite): Cartoon Network; History Channel; Learning Channel; The Weather Channel.
Fee: $4.00 monthly.
Pay Service 1
Pay Units: 359.
Programming (via satellite): Cinemax.
Fee: $10.95 monthly.
Pay Service 2
Pay Units: 737.
Programming (via satellite): HBO.
Fee: $11.95 monthly.
Pay Service 3
Pay Units: 606.
Programming (via satellite): Showtime.
Fee: $10.95 monthly.
Pay Service 4
Pay Units: 326.
Programming (via satellite): The Movie Channel.
Fee: $10.95 monthly.
Miles of plant: 377.0 (coaxial). Homes passed: 12,172.
Manager: Derek White. Chief technician: James Gill.
Franchise fee: 5% of gross.
Ownership: Falcon Communications LP (MSO), joint venture formed September 30, 1998. See Cable System Ownership.

BEAVERCREEK—Beavercreek Telephone Co., Box 69, Beavercreek, OR 97004. Phone: 503-632-3113. Fax: 503-632-4159. County: Clackamas. Also serves Clackamas County (portions), Colton, Mulino. ICA: OR0167.
TV Market Ranking: 29. Franchise award date: N.A. Franchise expiration date: N.A. Began: March 15, 1994.
Channel capacity: 86 (not 2-way capable). Channels available but not in use: 41.
Basic Service
Subscribers: 2,550.
Programming (received off-air): KATU (A), KGW (N), KNMT (T), KOIN (C), KOPB-TV (P), KPTV (U) Portland; KPXG (X) Salem; KPDX (F) Vancouver.
Programming (via satellite): C-SPAN; Headline News; Home Shopping Network; TV Guide Channel; Univision.
Current originations: Public access; educational access.
Fee: $39.95 installation; $10.95 monthly.
Expanded Basic Service
Subscribers: 2,343.
Programming (via satellite): WGN-TV (W) Chicago; A & E; American Movie Classics; CNBC; CNN; Cartoon Network; Country Music TV; Discovery Channel; ESPN; Fox Sports Net Northwest; Learning Channel; Lifetime; MTV; Nashville Network; Nickelodeon; TBS Superstation; The Weather Channel; Turner Classic Movies; Turner Network TV; USA Network; VH1.
Fee: $12.00 monthly.
Pay Service 1
Pay Units: 132.
Programming (via satellite): Cinemax.
Fee: $7.95 monthly.
Pay Service 2
Pay Units: 63.
Programming (via satellite): Disney Channel.
Fee: $6.95 monthly.
Pay Service 3
Pay Units: 245.
Programming (via satellite): HBO.
Fee: $8.95 monthly.
Pay Service 4
Pay Units: 58.
Programming (via satellite): Showtime.
Fee: $7.95 monthly.
Pay Service 5
Pay Units: 58.
Programming (via satellite): The Movie Channel.
Fee: $7.95 monthly.
Pay-Per-View
Addressable homes: 2,295.
Blazer Vision.
Equipment: IVR PPV ordering system.
Miles of plant: 217.0 (coaxial); 1.0 (fiber optic). Homes passed: 3,910. Total homes in franchised area: 4,788.
Manager: Tom Linstrom. Chief technician: Jim Wilber. Marketing & program director: Tom Klotter.
Ownership: Beavercreek Cooperative Telephone Co.

BEAVERTON—TCI of Tualatin Valley Inc., 14200 S.W. Brigadoon Court, Beaverton, OR 97005. Phones: 503-605-4800; 503-605-4895. Fax: 503-646-8004. Counties: Clackamas & Washington. Also serves Aloha, Banks, Cornelius, Durham, Forest Grove, Gaston, Hillsboro, King City, Lake Oswego, North Plains, Reedville, Rivergrove, Sherwood, Tigard, Tualatin, Washington County, Wilsonville. ICA: OR0002.
TV Market Ranking: 29. Franchise award date: N.A. Franchise expiration date: December 1, 1999. Began: December 1, 1982.
Channel capacity: 62. Channels available but not in use: None.
Basic Service
Subscribers: 80,528.
Programming (received off-air): KATU (A), KGW (N), KNMT (T), KOIN (C), KOPB-TV (P), KPTV (U) Portland; KPXG (X), KWBP (W) Salem; KPDX (F) Vancouver.
Programming (via microwave): Northwest Cable News.
Programming (via satellite): Discovery Channel; TBS Superstation.
Current originations: Automated time-weather; public access; educational access; government access; leased access; library access; local sports.
Fee: $39.95 installation; $6.81 monthly.
Digital Basic Service
Subscribers: N.A.
Programming (via satellite): BBC America; Bravo; Discovery Civilization Channel; Discovery Home & Leisure Channel; Discovery Kids Channel; Discovery People; Discovery Science Channel; ESPN Classic Sports; ESPNews; Fox Sports World; Game Show Network; Golf Channel; Independent Film Channel; MuchMusic Network; Outdoor Life Network; Romance Classics; Speedvision; Turner Classic Movies.
Fee: $39.95 monthly; $3.25 converter.
Expanded Basic Service
Subscribers: N.A.
Programming (via satellite): A & E; American Movie Classics; C-SPAN; C-SPAN 2; CNBC; CNN; Cartoon Network; Comedy Central; Country Music TV; Disney Channel; ESPN; ESPN 2; FX; Fox Family Channel; Fox News Channel; Fox Sports Net Northwest; Headline News; History Channel; Home & Garden Television; Learning Channel; Lifetime; MTV; Nashville Network; Nickelodeon; QVC; Sci-Fi Channel; TV Guide Channel; The Inspirational Network; The Weather Channel; Turner Network TV; USA Network; Univision; VH1.
Fee: $22.73 monthly.
Pay Service 1
Pay Units: N.A.
Programming (via satellite): Cinemax; HBO; Showtime; Starz!; The Movie Channel; The New Encore.
Fee: $6.95 monthly (Showtime or TMC), $8.95 monthly (Cinemax), $9.95 monthly (HBO).
Digital Pay Service 1
Pay Units: N.A.
Programming (via satellite): DMX; Encore Love Stories; Encore Mystery; Encore Westerns; HBO (multiplexed); Showtime (multiplexed); Starz! (multiplexed).
Fee: N.A.
Pay-Per-View
Addressable homes: 50,000.
Blazer Vision; Spice delivered digitally.
Local advertising: Yes. Available in satellite distributed programming. Rates: $25.00/30 Seconds.
Program Guide: TV Host.
Equipment: Scientific-Atlanta headend; GTE Sylvania & Magnavox amplifiers; Times Fiber, Comm/Scope & Trilogy cable; Video Data Systems character generator; Scientific-Atlanta set top converters; Zenith addressable set top converters; Eagle traps; Scientific-Atlanta satellite antenna; Scientific-Atlanta satellite receivers; ChannelMatic commercial insert.
Miles of plant: 2375.0 (coaxial); 137.0 (fiber optic). Additional miles planned: 100.0 (coaxial); 25.0 (fiber optic). Homes passed: 99,036. Total homes in franchised area: 105,000.
Manager: Frank Settle. Chief technician: Harlan Cook. Marketing director: Bryon Allen.
City fee: 5% of gross.
Ownership: AT&T Broadband & Internet Services (MSO). Purchased from Tele-Communications Inc., March 9, 1999.

BEND—Bend Cable Communications LLC, Box 5067, 63090 Sherman Rd., Bend, OR 97701. Phones: 541-382-5551; 541-549-1911. Fax: 541-385-3271.
E-mail: manager@bendcable.com.
Web site: http://www.bendcable.com.
County: Deschutes. Also serves Black Butte Ranch, Sisters, Tumalo. ICA: OR0013.
TV Market Ranking: Below 100. Franchise award date: January 1, 1955. Franchise expiration date: January 1, 1999. Began: September 1, 1955.
Channel capacity: 36 (2-way capable; operating 2-way). Channels available but not in use: None.
Basic Service
Subscribers: 19,922.
Programming (received off-air): KFXO-LP (F), KOAB-TV (P), KTVZ (N) Bend; 12 FMs.
Programming (via microwave): KEZI (A), KVAL-TV (C) Eugene; KATU (A), KOIN (C), KPTV (U) Portland.
Programming (via satellite): A & E; C-SPAN; C-SPAN 2; CNBC; CNN; Cartoon Network; Country Music TV; Discovery Channel; ESPN; ESPN 2; Fox Family Channel; Fox Sports Net Northwest; Headline News; History Channel; Home & Garden Television; Home Shopping Network; Learning Channel; Lifetime; MTV; Nashville Network; Nick at Nite; Nickelodeon; QVC; Sci-Fi Channel; TBS Superstation; TV Guide Channel; The Weather Channel; Trinity Bcstg. Network; Turner Classic Movies; Turner Network TV; USA Network; VH1; Z Music Television.
Current originations: Automated time-weather; public access; government access; automated emergency alert; local news; local sports.
Fee: $50.00 installation; $27.45 monthly.
Pay Service 1
Pay Units: 101.
Programming (via satellite): Disney Channel.
Fee: $12.95 monthly.
Pay Service 2
Pay Units: 556.
Programming (via satellite): HBO.
Fee: $12.95 monthly.
Pay Service 3
Pay Units: 4.
Programming (via satellite): The Movie Channel.
Fee: $14.95 monthly.
Pay Service 4
Pay Units: 105.
Programming (via satellite): Showtime.
Fee: $9.95 monthly.
Local advertising: Yes (insert only). Available in satellite distributed & character-generated programming. Local sales manager: Mike Puckett.
Program Guide: Premium Channels.

Equipment: Scientific-Atlanta headend; GTE Sylvania amplifiers; Hitachi cameras; Sony VTRs; MSI & Texscan character generator; Pioneer set top converters; Eagle traps; Scientific-Atlanta & M/A-Com satellite antenna; Scientific-Atlanta satellite receivers.
Miles of plant: 600.0 (coaxial); 62.0 (fiber optic). Homes passed: 21,000. Total homes in franchised area: 25,000.
Manager: William P. Morton. Chief technician: Dan Heller. Marketing director: Femke van Velzen. Customer service manager: Lisa Littleton.
City fee: 5% of gross.
Ownership: Tykeson & Associates.

BLY—Bly Cable Co., 2809 Montelius St., Klamath Falls, OR 97601. County: Klamath. ICA: OR0110.
TV Market Ranking: Below 100. Franchise award date: N.A. Franchise expiration date: N.A. Began: June 1, 1964.
Channel capacity: 12. Channels available but not in use: 6.
Basic Service
Subscribers: 115.
Programming (received off-air): KOTI (N) Klamath Falls; KTVL (C) Medford.
Fee: N.A.
Miles of plant: 13.0 (coaxial). Homes passed: 150.
Manager: William J. Jones.
Ownership: Bly Cable Co.

BOARDMAN—Columbia Basin Cable, Box 490, 611 6th St., Umatilla, OR 97882. Phones: 541-922-5759; 800-521-3196. Fax: 541-922-3758. County: Morrow. ICA: OR0070.
TV Market Ranking: Below 100. Franchise award date: N.A. Franchise expiration date: N.A. Began: October 8, 1979.
Channel capacity: 52. Channels available but not in use: 2.
Basic Service
Subscribers: 574.
Programming (received off-air): KEPR-TV (C), KNDU (N), KVEW (A) Pasco-Kennewick-Richland; KATU (A), KGW (N), KOIN (C), KOPB-TV (P), KPTV (U) Portland; allband FM.
Programming (via satellite): WGN-TV (W) Chicago; TBS Superstation; TV Guide Channel.
Fee: $30.00 installation; $17.95 monthly.
Expanded Basic Service
Subscribers: 510.
Programming (via microwave): Northwest Cable News.
Programming (via satellite): A & E; American Movie Classics; Animal Planet; C-SPAN; CNN; Country Music TV; Discovery Channel; ESPN; ESPN 2; FX; fXM: Movies from Fox; Fox Family Channel; Fox News Channel; Fox Sports Net Northwest; GalaVision; Headline News; History Channel; Home & Garden Television; Lifetime; MTV; Nashville Network; Nickelodeon; The Inspirational Network; The Weather Channel; Trinity Bcstg. Network; Turner Network TV; USA Network; Univision; VH1.
Fee: $12.00 monthly.
Pay Service 1
Pay Units: 40.
Programming (via satellite): Disney Channel.
Fee: $9.95 monthly.
Pay Service 2
Pay Units: 147.
Programming (via satellite): HBO (multiplexed).
Fee: $10.95 monthly.
Pay Service 3
Pay Units: 84.
Programming (via satellite): MOVIEplex; Starz!; The New Encore.
Fee: $7.95 monthly.
Equipment: Blonder-Tongue & Phasecom headend; Coral amplifiers; Times Fiber cable.
Miles of plant: 17.0 (coaxial); None (fiber optic). Total homes in franchised area: 1,000.
Manager: Kerry Stratton. Chief technician: Darrell Johnson. Marketing director & customer service manager: Charlotte Winkler.
City fee: 3% of gross.
Ownership: USA Media Group LLC (MSO). Purchased from Cambridge Communications, May 15, 1999.

BONANZA—Blackstone Cable LLC, 1104 W. Ironwood Dr., Coeur d'Alene, ID 83814-2605. Phone: 208-664-3370. Fax: 208-664-5888. County: Klamath. ICA: OR0109.
TV Market Ranking: Below 100. Franchise award date: N.A. Franchise expiration date: December 31, 2011. Began: October 1, 1981.
Channel capacity: 19 (not 2-way capable). Channels available but not in use: 8.
Basic Service
Subscribers: 41.
Programming (received off-air): KDKF (A), KOTI (N) Klamath Falls; KMVU (F), KSYS (P), KTVL (C) Medford.
Programming (via satellite): WGN-TV (W) Chicago; CNN; Discovery Channel; Disney Channel; ESPN; Fox Family Channel; Nashville Network; TBS Superstation; Turner Network TV.
Fee: $43.50 installation; $21.00 monthly; $56.00 converter; $21.50 additional installation.
Commercial fee: $5.34 monthly.
Pay Service 1
Pay Units: 7.
Programming (via satellite): HBO.
Fee: $15.00 installation; $10.95 monthly.
Equipment: Microwave Assoc. headend; Blonder-Tongue amplifiers; Times Fiber cable; Metrodata character generator; Prodelin satellite antenna.
Miles of plant: 4.3 (coaxial); None (fiber optic). Homes passed: 139.
Manager: Ted Hughett.
City fee: 3% of basic.
Ownership: Blackstone Cable LLC (MSO).

BORING—Community Cable Inc., 13909 S.E. Stark St., Portland, OR 97233. County: Clackamas. Also serves Damascus, Pleasant Valley. ICA: OR0125.
TV Market Ranking: 29. Franchise award date: N.A. Franchise expiration date: N.A. Began: January 1, 1968.
Channel capacity: N.A. Channels available but not in use: N.A.
Basic Service
Subscribers: N.A.
Programming (received off-air): KATU (A), KGW (N), KOIN (C), KOPB-TV (P) Portland; KPDX (F) Vancouver.
Programming (via satellite): A & E; American Movie Classics; CNN; Discovery Channel; Fox Family Channel; Home Shopping Network; Nashville Network; Nickelodeon.
Fee: $16.50 monthly.
Pay Service 1
Pay Units: N.A.
Programming (via satellite): Disney Channel; HBO; Showtime; The Movie Channel.
Fee: $9.00 monthly (each).
Manager: Stan Turel.
Ownership: Oregon Community Cable TV Inc.

BRICKYARD ROAD—Falcon Telecable, 1344 N.E. Hwy. 101, Lincoln City, OR 97367. Phone: 541-994-6083. Fax: 541-994-7438. County: Tillamook. ICA: OR0171.
TV Market Ranking: Outside TV Markets. Franchise award date: N.A. Franchise expiration date: N.A. Began: N.A.
Channel capacity: 22. Channels available but not in use: 4.
Basic Service
Subscribers: 470.
Programming (received off-air): KATU (A), KGW (N), KOIN (C), KOPB-TV (P), KPTV (U) Portland; KPDX (F) Vancouver.
Programming (via satellite): A & E; Blazer Vision; CNN; Discovery Channel; ESPN; Fox Family Channel; Nashville Network; TBS Superstation; Turner Network TV; USA Network.
Fee: $17.23 monthly.
Pay Service 1
Pay Units: 52.
Programming (via satellite): Disney Channel.
Fee: $10.95 monthly.
Pay Service 2
Pay Units: 117.
Programming (via satellite): HBO.
Fee: $11.95 monthly.
Miles of plant: 25.0 (coaxial). Homes passed: 475.
Manager: Joel Billings. Chief technician: Charles Johnson.
Ownership: Falcon Communications LP (MSO), joint venture formed September 30, 1998. See Cable System Ownership.

BROOKINGS—Falcon Telecable, 1440 Parkway Dr., Crescent City, CA 95531. Phone: 707-464-4157. County: Curry. Also serves Curry County (portions). ICA: OR0173.
TV Market Ranking: Outside TV Markets. Franchise award date: N.A. Franchise expiration date: N.A. Began: N.A.
Channel capacity: 55 (2-way capable; not operating 2-way). Channels available but not in use: None.
Basic Service
Subscribers: 3,839.
Programming (received off-air): KBSC-LP (W) Brookings; KBVU (F,U), KIEM-TV (N) Eureka; KDRV (A), KOBI (N), KSYS (P), KTVL (C) Medford.
Programming (via satellite): WGN-TV (W) Chicago; A & E; American Movie Classics; Blazer Vision; C-SPAN; CNBC; Comedy Central; FX; Fox News Channel; Fox Sports Net Northwest; Home & Garden Television; Home Shopping Network; Learning Channel; Lifetime; MTV; Nickelodeon; Northwest Cable News; QVC; Sci-Fi Channel; TBS Superstation; TV Guide Channel; TV Guide Sneak Prevue; Travel Channel; Trinity Bcstg. Network; Univision; VH1.
Current originations: Local news.
Fee: $53.00 installation; $22.27 monthly; $2.24 converter.
Expanded Basic Service
Subscribers: 3,771.
Programming (via satellite): CNN; ESPN; Fox Family Channel; Headline News; Nashville Network.
Fee: $7.95 monthly.
Expanded Basic Service 2
Subscribers: 1,578.
Programming (via satellite): Country Music TV; Discovery Channel; Disney Channel; ESPN 2; Golf Channel; History Channel; The Weather Channel; Turner Network TV; USA Network.
Fee: $6.10 monthly.
Pay Service 1
Pay Units: 142.
Programming (via satellite): Cinemax.
Fee: $11.95 monthly.
Pay Service 2
Pay Units: 391.
Programming (via satellite): HBO.
Fee: $11.95 monthly.
Pay Service 3
Pay Units: 258.
Programming (via satellite): Showtime.
Fee: $11.95 monthly.
Pay Service 4
Pay Units: 166.
Programming (via satellite): The Movie Channel.
Fee: $11.95 monthly.
Pay Service 5
Pay Units: N.A.
Programming (via satellite): The New Encore.
Fee: $5.95 monthly.
Pay-Per-View
Action Pay-Per-View; Hot Choice; Spice; Viewer's Choice.
Fee: $3.95-$5.95.
Miles of plant: 202.0 (coaxial). Homes passed: 4,669.
Manager: Bob Pearson. Chief technician: Earl DeSomber.
Ownership: Falcon Communications LP (MSO), joint venture formed September 30, 1998. See Cable System Ownership.

BROOKS—Country Cablevision Ltd., Box 12038, Salem, OR 97309-0038. Phone: 503-588-8247. Fax: 503-588-0544. County: Marion. Also serves Lake Labish, Marion County (northern portion). ICA: OR0088.
TV Market Ranking: 29 (portions of Marion County); Below 100 (Brooks, Lake Labish, portions of Marion County). Franchise award date: January 1, 1982. Franchise expiration date: N.A. Began: June 1, 1982.
Channel capacity: 42 (not 2-way capable). Channels available but not in use: 12.
Basic Service
Subscribers: 371.
Programming (received off-air): KATU (A), KGW (N), KOIN (C), KOPB-TV (P), KPTV (U) Portland; KPXG (X) Salem; KPDX (F) Vancouver.
Programming (via satellite): WGN-TV (W) Chicago; American Movie Classics; CNN; Country Music TV; Discovery Channel; ESPN; Fox Family Channel; Headline News; Lifetime; Nashville Network; TBS Superstation; Turner Network TV; USA Network; Univision; VH1.
Current originations: Public access.
Fee: $49.95 installation; $21.95 monthly; $3.95 converter.
Pay Service 1
Pay Units: 160.
Programming (via satellite): Disney Channel; Showtime; The Movie Channel; The New Encore.
Fee: $4.95 monthly (Encore), $8.95 monthly (Showtime), $9.95 monthly (Disney), $10.95 monthly (TMC).
Local advertising: Yes. Available in locally originated programming.
Equipment: Trilogy cable.
Miles of plant: 32.0 (coaxial). Homes passed: 925. Total homes in franchised area: 1,500.
Manager: John P. Johnson. Chief technician: Veron L. Robinson.
Ownership: Country Cablevision Ltd. (MSO).

BROWNSVILLE—Falcon Cable Systems Co., Suite 5, 4739 Main St., Springfield, OR 97477. Phone: 503-746-4132. County: Linn. ICA: OR0079.
TV Market Ranking: Below 100. Franchise award date: N.A. Franchise expiration date: N.A. Began: January 1, 1971.
Channel capacity: 40 (not 2-way capable). Channels available but not in use: 8.
Basic Service
Subscribers: 548.

Programming (received off-air): KOAC-TV (P) Corvallis; KEVU-LP (F), KEZI (A), KMTR (N), KVAL-TV (C) Eugene; KATU (A), KGW (N), KOIN (C), KPTV (U) Portland; allband FM.
Programming (via satellite): American Movie Classics; Blazer Vision; ESPN; Fox Family Channel; Home & Garden Television; Home Shopping Network; Nickelodeon; QVC; TBS Superstation; Trinity Bcstg. Network.
Fee: $25.00 installation; $21.23 monthly.

Expanded Basic Service
Subscribers: 483.
Programming (via satellite): A & E; Lifetime; Sci-Fi Channel; USA Network.
Fee: $4.57 monthly.

Expanded Basic Service 2
Subscribers: 269.
Programming (via satellite): CNN; Country Music TV; Discovery Channel; Disney Channel; Nashville Network; Turner Network TV.
Fee: $5.35 monthly.

Pay Service 1
Pay Units: 60.
Programming (via satellite): HBO.
Fee: $11.95 monthly.

Pay Service 2
Pay Units: 68.
Programming (via satellite): Showtime.
Fee: $10.95 monthly.

Pay Service 3
Pay Units: 50.
Programming (via satellite): The Movie Channel.
Fee: $10.95 monthly.

Pay-Per-View
Addressable homes: 150.

Equipment: Scientific-Atlanta addressable set top converters; Scientific-Atlanta satellite receivers.
Miles of plant: 50.0 (coaxial). Homes passed: 1,163.
Manager: Derek White. Chief technician: James Gill.
Franchise fee: 5% of gross.
Ownership: Falcon Communications LP (MSO), joint venture formed September 30, 1998. See Cable System Ownership.

BURNS—TCI Cablevision of Oregon Inc., Box 1401, La Grande, OR 97850-2202. Phone: 541-963-4189. County: Harney. Also serves Harney County (portions), Hines. ICA: OR0045.
TV Market Ranking: Outside TV Markets. Franchise award date: N.A. Franchise expiration date: N.A. Began: June 1, 1956.
Channel capacity: 37 (not 2-way capable). Channels available but not in use: N.A.

Basic Service
Subscribers: 1,714; Commercial subscribers: 130.
Programming (received off-air): KOPB-TV (P) Portland.
Programming (via microwave): KATU (A), KGW (N), KOIN (C), KPTV (U) Portland.
Programming (via satellite): WGN-TV (W) Chicago; KCNC-TV (C), KMGH-TV (A), KUSA-TV (N) Denver; C-SPAN; CNN; Country Music TV; Discovery Channel; Fox Family Channel; Headline News; Home Shopping Network; Lifetime; Nashville Network; Nickelodeon; Odyssey; QVC; TBS Superstation; The Weather Channel.
Current originations: Automated timeweather.
Fee: $32.00 installation; $21.24 monthly; $19.00 additional installation.

Expanded Basic Service
Subscribers: 1,629.
Programming (via satellite): American Movie Classics; ESPN; Fox Sports Net Northwest; Turner Network TV; USA Network.
Fee: $1.80 monthly.

Pay Service 1
Pay Units: 143.
Programming (via satellite): Cinemax.
Fee: $20.00 installation; $7.95 monthly.

Pay Service 2
Pay Units: 117.
Programming (via satellite): Disney Channel.
Fee: $20.00 installation; $9.95 monthly.

Pay Service 3
Pay Units: 553.
Programming (via satellite): The New Encore.
Fee: N.A.

Pay Service 4
Pay Units: 205.
Programming (via satellite): HBO.
Fee: $20.00 installation; $8.95 monthly.

Pay Service 5
Pay Units: 95.
Programming (via satellite): Showtime.
Fee: $20.00 installation; $9.95 monthly.

Local advertising: Yes. Available in character-generated programming.
Equipment: Jerrold headend; Jerrold amplifiers; Jerrold cable; Scientific-Atlanta satellite antenna.
Miles of plant: 52.2 (coaxial). Homes passed: 2,493. Total homes in franchised area: 2,493.
Manager: Michael Vaughn.
City fee: 3% of gross.
Ownership: AT&T Broadband & Internet Services (MSO). Purchased from Tele-Communications Inc., March 9, 1999.

BUTTE FALLS—Phoenix Cablevision of Oregon Inc., Box 828, 6655 Rogue River Dr., Shady Cove, OR 97539. Phones: 541-878-3247; 800-827-3247. Fax: 541-878-2458. County: Jackson. ICA: OR0127.
TV Market Ranking: Below 100. Franchise award date: N.A. Franchise expiration date: August 13, 2002. Began: January 1, 1980.
Channel capacity: 36. Channels available but not in use: N.A.

Basic Service
Subscribers: 77.
Programming (received off-air): KDRV (A), KOBI (N), KSYS (P), KTVL (C) Medford.
Programming (via satellite): WGN-TV (W) Chicago; WWOR-TV (U) New York; American Movie Classics; CNN; Country Music TV; Discovery Channel; ESPN; Fox Family Channel; FoxNet; History Channel; Home Shopping Network; Learning Channel; Lifetime; Nashville Network; TBS Superstation; Turner Network TV; USA Network.
Fee: $23.13 installation; $23.13 monthly; $56.00 converter; $26.25 additional installation.
Commercial fee: $5.50 monthly.

Pay Service 1
Pay Units: 7.
Programming (via satellite): Cinemax.
Fee: $11.55 monthly.

Pay Service 2
Pay Units: 13.
Programming (via satellite): HBO.
Fee: $11.55 monthly.

Miles of plant: 1.0 (coaxial). Homes passed: 161.
Manager: Ted W. Hughett. Chief technician: Dan Middleton. Marketing & program director: John Finley.
City fee: 3% of gross.
Ownership: Phoenix Cable Inc. (MSO).

CANBY—North Willamette Telecom, Box 850, 190 S.E. 2nd Ave., Canby, OR 97013. Phones: 503-263-8080; 800-642-8464. Fax: 503-266-8207. Counties: Clackamas & Marion. Also serves Aurora, Barlow, Beavercreek, Clackamas, Clackamas County (portions), Colton, Donald, Hubbard, Marion County (northwestern portion), Molalla, Mulino, Needy, Oregon City (portions), Woodburn. ICA: OR0017.
TV Market Ranking: 29 (Aurora, Barlow, Beavercreek, Canby, Clackamas, portions of Clackamas County, Colton, Donald, Hubbard, portions of Marion County, Molalla, Mulino, Needy, Oregon City, Woodburn); Below 100 (portions of Clackamas County, portions of Marion County); Outside TV Markets (portions of Clackamas County). Franchise award date: N.A. Franchise expiration date: April 1, 1998. Began: October 1, 1983.
Channel capacity: 42 (2-way capable; operating 2-way partially). Channels available but not in use: 3.

Basic Service
Subscribers: N.A.
Programming (received off-air): KATU (A), KGW (N), KNMT (T), KOIN (C), KOPB-TV (P), KPTV (U) Portland; KPDX (F) Vancouver; 22 FMs.
Programming (via satellite): C-SPAN; CNBC; Fox Family Channel; Headline News; Home Shopping Network; TV Guide Channel; The Inspirational Network; Trinity Bcstg. Network; Univision.
Current originations: Automated timeweather; public access; educational access; government access; religious access; library access; local news; local sports.
Fee: $35.00 installation; $11.95 monthly; $15.00 additional installation.

Expanded Basic Service
Subscribers: N.A.
Programming (via satellite): WGN-TV (W) Chicago; A & E; American Movie Classics; CNN; Country Music TV; Discovery Channel; ESPN; Fox Sports Net Northwest; Goodlife TV Network; Knowledge TV; Learning Channel; Lifetime; MTV; Nashville Network; Nickelodeon; TBS Superstation; The Weather Channel; Turner Network TV; USA Network; VH1.
Fee: N.A.

Pay Service 1
Pay Units: N.A.
Programming (via satellite): Cinemax; Disney Channel; HBO; Showtime; The Movie Channel.
Fee: $8.00 installation; $7.95 monthly (Cinemax or Disney), $8.95 monthly (HBO, Showtime or TMC).

Local advertising: Yes (locally produced & insert). Local sales manager: Harry Lee Kwai.
Equipment: Scientific-Atlanta headend; Scientific-Atlanta & Texscan amplifiers; Times Fiber cable; JVC cameras; JVC VTRs; Fora character generator; Jerrold set top converters; Jerrold addressable set top converters; Antenna Technology & Simulsat satellite antenna; Scientific-Atlanta satellite receivers; ChannelMatic & Spot Matic commercial insert.
Miles of plant: 500.0 (coaxial). Additional miles planned: 15.0 (coaxial); 13.0 (fiber optic). Homes passed: 11,348.
Manager: Sandra K. Coleman. Chief technician: Jeff Herd.
City fee: 5% of gross.
Ownership: Canby Telephone Assn.

CASCADE LOCKS—City of Cascade Locks Cable TV, Box 308, Cascade Locks, OR 97014. Phone: 541-374-8484. Fax: 541-374-8752. County: Hood River. ICA: OR0087.
TV Market Ranking: Below 100. Franchise award date: N.A. Franchise expiration date: N.A. Began: January 1, 1971.
Channel capacity: 36. Channels available but not in use: 20.

Basic Service
Subscribers: 395.
Programming (received off-air): KATU (A), KGW (N), KOIN (C), KOPB-TV (P), KPTV (U) Portland; KPDX (F) Vancouver; allband FM.
Programming (via satellite): WGN-TV (W) Chicago; CNN; Discovery Channel; ESPN; Fox Family Channel; Nashville Network; Nickelodeon; TBS Superstation; Turner Network TV; USA Network.
Current originations: Automated timeweather; public access; educational access; local sports.
Fee: $60.00 installation; $14.50 monthly.

Pay Service 1
Pay Units: 149.
Programming (via satellite): Disney Channel.
Fee: $9.90 monthly.

Pay Service 2
Pay Units: 67.
Programming (via satellite): HBO.
Fee: $9.70 monthly.

Local advertising: Yes (locally produced & insert).
Equipment: Scientific-Atlanta headend; Magnavox amplifiers; General cable; RCA cameras; Hamlin set top converters; Eagle & Pico traps; Scientific-Atlanta & Hughes satellite antenna; Comsonics satellite receivers.
Miles of plant: 15.0 (coaxial). Homes passed: 438.
Manager: Tracy Hupp. Chief technician: Ed Winnett.
Ownership: City of Cascade Locks Cable TV.

CAVE JUNCTION—Falcon Cable Systems Co., Suite 5, 4739 Main St., Springfield, OR 97477. Phone: 503-746-4132. County: Josephine. Also serves Josephine County (portions), Kerby. ICA: OR0054.
TV Market Ranking: Below 100 (portions of Josephine County); Outside TV Markets (Cave Junction, portions of Josephine County, Kerby). Franchise award date: N.A. Franchise expiration date: N.A. Began: November 1, 1979.
Channel capacity: 33 (not 2-way capable). Channels available but not in use: None.

Basic Service
Subscribers: 818.
Programming (received off-air): KDRV (A), KOBI (N), KSYS (P), KTVL (C) Medford.
Programming (via satellite): A & E; Blazer Vision; ESPN; Fox Family Channel; FoxNet; Lifetime; Nickelodeon; QVC; TBS Superstation; Trinity Bcstg. Network.
Current originations: Automated timeweather; public access; educational access; government access.
Fee: $17.37 monthly.

Expanded Basic Service
Subscribers: 697.
Programming (via satellite): C-SPAN; C-SPAN 2; CNN; Discovery Channel; ESPN 2; ESPN Classic Sports; Headline News; Home Shopping Network; Sci-Fi Channel; Travel Channel; USA Network.
Fee: $9.94 monthly.

Expanded Basic Service 2
Subscribers: 539.
Programming (via satellite): American Movie Classics; Country Music TV; Disney Channel; Fox Sports Net Northwest; Nashville Network; Turner Network TV.
Fee: $6.50 monthly.

Expanded Basic Service 3
Subscribers: N.A.
Programming (via satellite): Cartoon Network; History Channel; Home & Garden

Television; Learning Channel; The Weather Channel.
Fee: N.A.
Pay Service 1
Pay Units: 45.
Programming (via satellite): Cinemax.
Fee: $25.00 installation; $10.95 monthly.
Pay Service 2
Pay Units: 93.
Programming (via satellite): HBO.
Fee: $11.95 monthly.
Pay Service 3
Pay Units: 45.
Programming (via satellite): Showtime.
Fee: $10.95 monthly.
Pay Service 4
Pay Units: 45.
Programming (via satellite): The Movie Channel.
Fee: $10.95 monthly.
Equipment: Scientific-Atlanta headend; Jerrold amplifiers; Scientific-Atlanta satellite antenna; Scientific-Atlanta satellite receivers.
Miles of plant: 27.0 (coaxial). Homes passed: 1,765.
Manager: Derek White. Chief technician: James Gill.
Franchise fee: 3% gross.
Ownership: Falcon Communications LP (MSO), joint venture formed September 30, 1998. See Cable System Ownership.

CHILOQUIN—Blackstone Cable LLC, 1104 W. Ironwood Dr., Coeur d'Alene, ID 83814-2605. Phone: 208-664-3370. Fax: 208-664-5888. County: Klamath. Plans service to Agency Lake. ICA: OR0090.
TV Market Ranking: Below 100. Franchise award date: N.A. Franchise expiration date: December 31, 2012. Began: October 15, 1981.
Channel capacity: 19 (not 2-way capable). Channels available but not in use: 5.
Basic Service
Subscribers: 118.
Programming (received off-air): KOTI (N) Klamath Falls; KDRV (A), KTVL (C) Medford.
Programming (via satellite): WGN-TV (W) Chicago; CNN; Discovery Channel; Disney Channel; ESPN; Fox Family Channel; FoxNet; Nashville Network; TBS Superstation; Turner Classic Movies; Turner Network TV.
Fee: $43.50 installation; $21.00 monthly; $56.00 converter; $21.50 additional installation.
Commercial fee: $5.34 monthly.
Pay Service 1
Pay Units: 30.
Programming (via satellite): HBO.
Fee: $15.00 installation; $10.95 monthly.
Equipment: Microwave Assoc. headend; Blonder-Tongue amplifiers; Times Fiber cable; Sony cameras; Sony VTRs; Metrodata character generator; Pioneer set top converters; Prodelin satellite antenna.
Miles of plant: 20.0 (coaxial); None (fiber optic). Homes passed: 320.
Manager: Ted Hughett.
City fee: 5% of basic.
Ownership: Blackstone Cable LLC (MSO).

CLATSKANIE—Falcon Cable TV, 3500 S.W. Bond St., Portland, OR 97201. Phone: 503-609-4800. County: Columbia. Also serves Columbia County (northern portion). ICA: OR0072.
TV Market Ranking: Outside TV Markets. Franchise award date: N.A. Franchise expiration date: N.A. Began: November 1, 1961.
Channel capacity: 35. Channels available but not in use: 11.
Basic Service
Subscribers: 719.
Programming (received off-air): KATU (A), KGW (N), KOIN (C), KOPB-TV (P), KPTV (U) Portland; allband FM.
Programming (via satellite): WGN-TV (W) Chicago; CNBC; CNN; Discovery Channel; Fox Family Channel; FoxNet; Nashville Network; Nickelodeon; TBS Superstation.
Fee: $49.00 installation; $9.67 monthly; $21.00 additional installation.
Expanded Basic Service
Subscribers: 672.
Programming (via satellite): American Movie Classics; ESPN; Turner Network TV; USA Network.
Fee: $11.07 monthly.
Pay Service 1
Pay Units: 93.
Programming (via satellite): Cinemax.
Fee: N.A.
Pay Service 2
Pay Units: 78.
Programming (via satellite): Disney Channel.
Fee: N.A.
Pay Service 3
Pay Units: 398.
Programming (via satellite): The New Encore.
Fee: N.A.
Pay Service 4
Pay Units: 189.
Programming (via satellite): HBO.
Fee: N.A.
Miles of plant: 20.0 (coaxial). Homes passed: 990. Total homes in franchised area: 1,030.
Manager: Bill Tierney. Marketing director: John Grismore.
Ownership: Falcon Communications LP (MSO). Purchased from Tele-Communications Inc., September 30, 1998. See Cable System Ownership.

CONDON—J & N Cable, 614 S. Columbus Ave., Goldendell, WA 98620. Phones: 509-773-5359; 800-752-9809. Fax: 509-773-7090. County: Gilliam. ICA: OR0093.
TV Market Ranking: Outside TV Markets. Franchise award date: N.A. Franchise expiration date: N.A. Began: January 1, 1955.
Channel capacity: 13. Channels available but not in use: 1.
Basic Service
Subscribers: N.A.
Programming (received off-air): KEPR-TV (C), KNDU (N), KVEW (A) Pasco-Kennewick-Richland; KATU (A), KOIN (C), KOPB-TV (P), KPTV (U) Portland; allband FM.
Programming (via satellite): ESPN; Fox Family Channel; TBS Superstation.
Fee: $20.00 installation; $8.75 monthly.
Pay Service 1
Pay Units: N.A.
Programming (via satellite): HBO.
Fee: $10.50 monthly.
Equipment: Blonder-Tongue headend; Blonder-Tongue amplifiers; Vikoa cable.
Miles of plant: 14.3 (coaxial). Homes passed: 320. Total homes in franchised area: 320.
Manager: John Kusky.
City fee: 3% of gross.
Ownership: J & N Cable Co. (MSO). Purchased from Telephone & Data Systems Inc.

COOS BAY—Falcon Cable Systems Co., 1400 Newmark Ave., Coos Bay, OR 97420. Phone: 541-888-5712. Fax: 541-888-9292. Counties: Coos & Curry. Also serves Coos County (northern portion), North Bend, Port Orford. ICA: OR0015.
TV Market Ranking: Below 100 (Coos Bay, Coos County, North Bend); Outside TV Markets (Port Orford). Franchise award date: N.A. Franchise expiration date: June 30, 2004. Began: October 1, 1954.
Channel capacity: 61. Channels available but not in use: None.
Basic Service
Subscribers: 10,193.
Programming (received off-air): KCBY-TV (C), KMTZ (N) Coos Bay; KOAC-TV (P) Corvallis; KEZI (A) Eugene; KOBI (N) Medford; KPTV (U) Portland; 14 FMs.
Programming (via satellite): A & E; American Movie Classics; C-SPAN; C-SPAN 2; CNBC; E! Entertainment TV; FX; Fox Sports Net Northwest; Home Shopping Network; Knowledge TV; Learning Channel; Lifetime; MTV; QVC; TV Guide Channel; TV Guide Sneak Prevue; The Weather Channel; Travel Channel; Trinity Bcstg. Network; VH1.
Current originations: Public access; educational access; government access.
Fee: $29.95 installation; $17.45 monthly.
Expanded Basic Service
Subscribers: 10,002.
Programming (via satellite): Blazer Vision; CNN; Discovery Channel; ESPN; Fox Family Channel; Headline News; Nickelodeon.
Fee: $5.70 monthly.
Expanded Basic Service 2
Subscribers: 4,660.
Programming (via satellite): Bravo; Comedy Central; Country Music TV; Disney Channel; Nashville Network; Sci-Fi Channel; Turner Network TV; USA Network.
Fee: $7.50 monthly.
Expanded Basic Service 3
Subscribers: 2,433.
Programming (via satellite): Cartoon Network; ESPN 2; fXM: Movies from Fox; History Channel; TBS Superstation.
Fee: $5.00 monthly.
Pay Service 1
Pay Units: 476.
Programming (via satellite): Cinemax.
Fee: $10.95 monthly.
Pay Service 2
Pay Units: 1,101.
Programming (via satellite): HBO.
Fee: $11.95 monthly.
Pay Service 3
Pay Units: 833.
Programming (via satellite): Showtime.
Fee: $10.95 monthly.
Pay Service 4
Pay Units: 530.
Programming (via satellite): The Movie Channel.
Fee: $10.95 monthly.
Pay Service 5
Pay Units: N.A.
Programming (via satellite): The New Encore.
Fee: N.A.
Pay-Per-View
Action Pay-Per-View; Spice; Viewer's Choice.
Local advertising: Yes. Available in satellite distributed programming. Local sales manager: Bruce Root.
Program Guide: The Cable Guide.
Equipment: Jerrold headend; C-COR, Delta-Benco-Cascade & Magnavox amplifiers; Comm/Scope & Superior cable; Sony VTRs; MSI character generator; Jerrold set top converters; Scientific-Atlanta satellite antenna; Scientific-Atlanta satellite receivers.
Miles of plant: 229.0 (coaxial). Homes passed: 14,045.
Manager: Bill Griffin. Chief technician: Norman Lacey. Marketing director: Joan Crabtree.
Franchise fee: 5% of gross.
Ownership: Falcon Communications LP (MSO), joint venture formed September 30, 1998. See Cable System Ownership.

COQUILLE—Falcon Cable Systems Co., 1400 Newmark Ave., Coos Bay, OR 97420. Phone: 541-888-5712. Fax: 541-888-9292. County: Coos. Also serves Coos County. ICA: OR0033.
TV Market Ranking: Below 100 (portions of Coos County, Coquille); Outside TV Markets (portions of Coos County). Franchise award date: N.A. Franchise expiration date: N.A. Began: July 1, 1954.
Channel capacity: 61 (not 2-way capable). Channels available but not in use: 25.
Basic Service
Subscribers: 1,756.
Programming (received off-air): KCBY-TV (C), KMTZ (N) Coos Bay; KOAC-TV (P) Corvallis; KEZI (A) Eugene; KOBI (N) Medford; KPTV (U) Portland; 14 FMs.
Programming (via satellite): WGN-TV (W) Chicago; Blazer Vision; Bravo; CNN; Comedy Central; E! Entertainment TV; ESPN; FX; Fox Family Channel; Headline News; Home Shopping Network; QVC; TBS Superstation; VH1.
Fee: $25.00 installation; $17.40 monthly.
Expanded Basic Service
Subscribers: 1,682.
Programming (via satellite): A & E; American Movie Classics; Lifetime; USA Network.
Fee: $3.97 monthly.
Expanded Basic Service 2
Subscribers: 1,586.
Programming (via satellite): C-SPAN; Country Music TV; Discovery Channel; Disney Channel; ESPN 2; Learning Channel; Nashville Network; Sci-Fi Channel.
Fee: $5.05 monthly.
Pay Service 1
Pay Units: 48.
Programming (via satellite): HBO.
Fee: $11.95 monthly.
Pay Service 2
Pay Units: 181.
Programming (via satellite): Showtime.
Fee: $10.95 monthly.
Pay Service 3
Pay Units: 15.
Programming (via satellite): The Movie Channel.
Fee: $10.95 monthly.
Equipment: Scientific-Atlanta headend; Jerrold amplifiers; Times Fiber cable; Hitachi & Magnavox cameras; Sony VTRs; Jerrold set top converters; Vitek traps; Andrew satellite antenna; Gardiner & Hughes satellite receivers.
Miles of plant: 45.0 (coaxial). Homes passed: 2,413.
Manager: Bill Griffin. Chief technician: Norman Lacey. Marketing director: Joan Crabtree.
Franchise fee: 5% of gross.

Ownership: Falcon Communications LP (MSO), joint venture formed September 30, 1998. See Cable System Ownership.

CORVALLIS—TCI Cablevision of Oregon Inc., Box T, Corvallis, OR 97330-4517. Phone: 541-758-8808. Fax: 541-758-8818. Counties: Benton & Linn. Also serves Adair Village, Albany, Benton County, Millersburg, North Albany, Philomath, Sodaville, Waterloo. ICA: OR0008.

TV Market Ranking: Below 100. Franchise award date: N.A. Franchise expiration date: N.A. Began: October 1, 1964.

Channel capacity: 38 (not 2-way capable). Channels available but not in use: N.A.

Basic Service

Subscribers: 36,057.

Programming (received off-air): KOAC-TV (P) Corvallis; KEZI (A), KLSR-TV (U), KMTR (N), KVAL-TV (C) Eugene; KATU (A), KGW (N), KOIN (C), KPTV (U) Portland; KWBP (W) Salem; 18 FMs.

Programming (via satellite): A & E; American Movie Classics; CNN; Discovery Channel; FX; Fox Family Channel; Learning Channel; Lifetime; MTV; Nashville Network; Nickelodeon; TBS Superstation; The Weather Channel.

Current originations: Automated time-weather; public access; educational access; local news.

Fee: $40.23 installation; $9.92 monthly; $17.24 additional installation.

Expanded Basic Service

Subscribers: 20,976.

Programming (via satellite): Disney Channel; ESPN; Fox Sports Net Northwest; Turner Network TV; USA Network.

Fee: $10.47 monthly.

Pay Service 1

Pay Units: N.A.

Programming (via satellite): Starz!; The New Encore.

Fee: N.A.

Pay Service 2

Pay Units: 4,071.

Programming (via satellite): HBO.

Fee: $9.95 monthly.

Pay Service 3

Pay Units: 2,673.

Programming (via satellite): Showtime.

Fee: $9.95 monthly.

Pay Service 4

Pay Units: 1,253.

Programming (via satellite): Cinemax.

Fee: $9.95 monthly.

Local advertising: Yes (locally produced & insert). Available in satellite distributed programming. Local sales manager: Brenda Roadhouse. Regional interconnect: TCI Cable Advertising-Oregon.

Program Guide: The Cable Guide.

Equipment: Scientific-Atlanta headend; GTE Sylvania & Jerrold amplifiers; Comm/Scope, Times Fiber & Magnavox cable; Sony VTRs; Jerrold & Hamlin set top converters; Arcom, Eagle & Vitek traps; Scientific-Atlanta satellite antenna; Scientific-Atlanta satellite receivers.

Miles of plant: 750.0 (coaxial); 12.0 (fiber optic). Additional miles planned: 12.0 (fiber optic). Homes passed: 38,222. Total homes in franchised area: 52,297.

Manager: Gary Hostetler. Chief technician: Frank Genio. Marketing director: Patrick McDonald.

City fee: 5% of gross.

Ownership: AT&T Broadband & Internet Services (MSO). Purchased from Tele-Communications Inc., March 9, 1999.

COTTAGE GROVE—Falcon Cable Systems Co., Suite 5, 4739 Main St., Springfield, OR 97477. Phones: 503-746-4132; 800-843-4500. County: Lane. ICA: OR0073.

TV Market Ranking: Below 100. Franchise award date: N.A. Franchise expiration date: N.A. Began: July 1, 1983.

Channel capacity: 52. Channels available but not in use: 8.

Basic Service

Subscribers: 1,855.

Programming (received off-air): KOAC-TV (P) Corvallis; KEVU-LP (F), KEZI (A), KLSR-TV (U), KMTR (N), KVAL-TV (C) Eugene; KOBI (N) Medford.

Programming (via satellite): WGN-TV (W) Chicago; A & E; American Movie Classics; Blazer Vision; Bravo; C-SPAN; ESPN; FX; Fox Family Channel; Goodlife TV Network; Home Shopping Network; Learning Channel; Lifetime; MTV; QVC; TBS Superstation; The Inspirational Network; Travel Channel; Trinity Bcstg. Network.

Current originations: Public access; educational access; government access.

Fee: $29.95 installation; $20.46 monthly.

Expanded Basic Service

Subscribers: 1,628.

Programming (via satellite): CNN; Headline News; Sci-Fi Channel; The Weather Channel.

Fee: $1.14 monthly.

Expanded Basic Service 2

Subscribers: 1,274.

Programming (via satellite): Country Music TV; Discovery Channel; Disney Channel; Nashville Network; Nickelodeon; USA Network.

Fee: $8.69 monthly.

Pay Service 1

Pay Units: 92.

Programming (via satellite): Cinemax.

Fee: $10.95 monthly.

Pay Service 2

Pay Units: 129.

Programming (via satellite): HBO.

Fee: $11.95 monthly.

Pay Service 3

Pay Units: 92.

Programming (via satellite): Showtime.

Fee: $10.95 monthly.

Pay Service 4

Pay Units: 35.

Programming (via satellite): The Movie Channel.

Fee: $10.95 monthly.

Pay Service 5

Pay Units: N.A.

Programming (via satellite): The New Encore.

Fee: N.A.

Miles of plant: 56.0 (coaxial). Homes passed: 3,412.

Manager: Derek White. Chief technician: James Gill.

Franchise fee: 5% of gross.

Ownership: Falcon Communications LP (MSO), joint venture formed September 30, 1998. See Cable System Ownership.

COVE—Blackstone Cable LLC, 1104 W. Ironwood Dr., Coeur d'Alene, ID 83814-2605. Phone: 208-664-3370. Fax: 208-664-5888. County: Union. ICA: OR0099.

TV Market Ranking: Outside TV Markets. Franchise award date: N.A. Franchise expiration date: May 15, 2006. Began: N.A.

Channel capacity: 19 (not 2-way capable). Channels available but not in use: 5.

Basic Service

Subscribers: 154.

Programming (received off-air): KTVB (N) Boise; KTVR (P) La Grande; KATU (A), KOIN (C), KPTV (U) Portland; KPDX (F) Vancouver.

Programming (via satellite): CNN; Discovery Channel; Disney Channel; ESPN; Fox Family Channel; Nashville Network; TBS Superstation; Turner Network TV; USA Network.

Fee: $43.50 installation; $21.00 monthly; $56.00 converter; $21.50 additional installation.

Commercial fee: $5.34 monthly.

Pay Service 1

Pay Units: 38.

Programming (via satellite): HBO.

Fee: $15.00 installation; $10.95 monthly.

Miles of plant: 9.8 (coaxial); None (fiber optic). Homes passed: 260.

Manager: Ted Hughett.

Franchise fee: 3% of basic.

Ownership: Blackstone Cable LLC (MSO).

CRABTREE—Interstate Cable Inc., Box 2687, Salina, KS 67402-2687. Phones: 785-452-9409; 800-888-4788. Fax: 785-238-7190. County: Linn. ICA: OR0132.

TV Market Ranking: Below 100. Franchise award date: N.A. Franchise expiration date: N.A. Began: N.A.

Channel capacity: N.A. Channels available but not in use: N.A.

Basic Service

Subscribers: 123.

Programming (received off-air): KOAC-TV (P) Corvallis; KVAL-TV (C) Eugene; KATU (A), KGW (N), KOIN (C), KPTV (U) Portland; KWBP (W) Salem; KPDX (F) Vancouver.

Programming (via satellite): WGN-TV (W) Chicago; A & E; CNN; Country Music TV; Discovery Channel; ESPN; Fox Family Channel; Headline News; Learning Channel; Nashville Network; QVC; Sci-Fi Channel; TBS Superstation; Trinity Bcstg. Network; Turner Network TV.

Fee: $50.00 installation; $19.95 monthly; $2.00 converter; $15.00 additional installation.

Pay Service 1

Pay Units: N.A.

Programming (via satellite): Cinemax; Disney Channel; HBO.

Fee: $7.95 monthly (Disney), $11.50 monthly (Cinemax or HBO).

Homes passed: 179.

Manager: Patti Lahey.

Ownership: Tristar Cable Inc. (MSO).

DALLAS—Falcon Cable Systems Co. II, Box 86, 1862 Godsey Rd., Dallas, OR 97338. Phone: 503-623-3241. Fax: 503-623-9446. Counties: Marion & Polk. Also serves Falls City, Independence, Jefferson, Marion County (southwestern portion), Monmouth, Polk County (portions). ICA: OR0039.

TV Market Ranking: Below 100. Franchise award date: N.A. Franchise expiration date: N.A. Began: April 1, 1966.

Channel capacity: 39 (2-way capable; operating 2-way). Channels available but not in use: None.

Basic Service

Subscribers: 6,762.

Programming (received off-air): KOAC-TV (P) Corvallis; KEZI (A), KVAL-TV (C) Eugene; KATU (A), KGW (N), KOIN (C), KPTV (U) Portland; KPXG (X), KWBP (W) Salem; KPDX (F) Vancouver; allband FM.

Programming (via satellite): WGN-TV (W) Chicago; A & E; Blazer Vision; C-SPAN; Home & Garden Television; MTV; QVC; TBS Superstation.

Current originations: Automated time-weather; public access; educational access; government access.

Fee: $65.00 installation; $17.96 monthly; $1.61 converter; $65.00 additional installation.

Expanded Basic Service

Subscribers: 5,233.

Programming (via satellite): Fox Sports Net Northwest; Headline News; Learning Channel; Nashville Network; Nickelodeon; Univision.

Fee: $65.00 installation; $6.68 monthly.

Expanded Basic Service 2

Subscribers: 3,462.

Programming (via satellite): CNN; Discovery Channel; Disney Channel; Fox Family Channel; Turner Network TV; USA Network.

Fee: $8.80 monthly.

Pay Service 1

Pay Units: 431.

Programming (via satellite): Cinemax.

Fee: $25.00 installation; $11.95 monthly.

Pay Service 2

Pay Units: 947.

Programming (via satellite): HBO.

Fee: $25.00 installation; $11.95 monthly.

Pay Service 3

Pay Units: 947.

Programming (via satellite): The New Encore.

Fee: $5.95 monthly.

Pay Service 4

Pay Units: 602.

Programming (via satellite): Showtime.

Fee: $25.00 installation; $11.95 monthly.

Pay Service 5

Pay Units: 406.

Programming (via satellite): The Movie Channel.

Fee: $25.00 installation; $11.95 monthly.

Pay Service 6

Pay Units: N.A.

Programming (via satellite): Playboy TV.

Fee: $11.95 monthly.

Pay-Per-View

Movies.

Fee: $3.95.

Equipment: Scientific-Atlanta headend; Scientific-Atlanta amplifiers; Comm/Scope cable; Scientific-Atlanta addressable set top converters; Scientific-Atlanta satellite antenna; Scientific-Atlanta satellite receivers.

Miles of plant: 179.8 (coaxial); 8.3 (fiber optic). Homes passed: 10,061.

Manager: Joel Billings.

Franchise fee: 5% of gross.

Ownership: Falcon Communications LP (MSO), joint venture formed September 30, 1998. See Cable System Ownership.

DAYVILLE—Blue Mountain TV Cable Co., Box 267, Mount Vernon, OR 97865. Phone: 541-932-4613. County: Grant. ICA: OR0120.

TV Market Ranking: Outside TV Markets. Franchise award date: N.A. Franchise expiration date: N.A. Began: October 1, 1956.

Channel capacity: 15 (not 2-way capable). Channels available but not in use: 8.

Basic Service

Subscribers: 45.

Programming (via satellite): KMGH-TV (A), KRMA-TV (P), KUSA-TV (N), KWGN-TV (W) Denver; Discovery Channel; FoxNet; Northwest Cable News.

Fee: $19.50 installation; $10.00 monthly.

Equipment: Standard Communications satellite receivers.

Miles of plant: 3.0 (coaxial). Homes passed: 60.

Manager: Chuck McKenna.

Ownership: Blue Mountain TV Cable Co. (MSO).

DEPOE BAY—Millennium Digital Media, Suite 107, 3633 136th Place SE, Bellevue, WA 98006. Phones: 425-747-4600; 800-829-2225. Fax: 425-644-4621. County: Lincoln. Also serves Gleneden Beach, Kernville, Lincoln Beach, Lin-

coln County (northern portion), Siletz River. ICA: OR0134.
TV Market Ranking: Outside TV Markets. Franchise award date: N.A. Franchise expiration date: N.A. Began: June 1, 1956.
Channel capacity: 35. Channels available but not in use: N.A.
Basic Service
Subscribers: 3,499.
Programming (received off-air): KATU (A), KGW (N), KOIN (C), KOPB-TV (P), KPTV (U) Portland; KPDX (F) Vancouver; allband FM.
Programming (via satellite): WGN-TV (W) Chicago; A & E; American Movie Classics; Blazer Vision; Bravo; C-SPAN; CNBC; CNN; Discovery Channel; Disney Channel; E! Entertainment TV; ESPN; Fox Family Channel; Fox Sports Net Northwest; Headline News; History Channel; Home & Garden Television; Learning Channel; Lifetime; Nashville Network; Nickelodeon; Northwest Cable News; QVC; TBS Superstation; TV Guide Channel; Trinity Bcstg. Network; Turner Classic Movies; Turner Network TV; USA Network.
Current originations: Local news.
Fee: $45.00 installation; $28.95 monthly.
Pay Service 1
Pay Units: 289.
Programming (via satellite): HBO.
Fee: $14.95 monthly.
Pay Service 2
Pay Units: 328.
Programming (via satellite): Showtime.
Fee: $20.00 installation; $14.95 monthly.
Pay Service 3
Pay Units: 110.
Programming (via satellite): The Movie Channel.
Fee: $14.95 monthly.
Local advertising: Yes.
Equipment: Ameco & Cadco headend; Ameco, Cadco & Magnavox amplifiers; composite cable; Scientific-Atlanta satellite antenna.
Miles of plant: 68.5 (coaxial).
Manager: Steve Weed. Chief technician: Gene Fry.
City fee: 2% of gross (Depoe Bay only).
Ownership: Millennium Digital Media LLC (MSO). Purchased from Summit Communications Inc., April 7, 1999.

DRAIN—Falcon Cable Systems Co., Suite 5, 4739 Main St., Springfield, OR 97477. Phone: 503-746-4132. County: Douglas. Also serves Douglas County (northern portion), Yoncalla. ICA: OR0066.
TV Market Ranking: Below 100 (portions of Douglas County, Drain, Yoncalla); Outside TV Markets (portions of Douglas County). Franchise award date: N.A. Franchise expiration date: N.A. Began: July 1, 1959.
Channel capacity: 40. Channels available but not in use: 5.
Basic Service
Subscribers: 748.
Programming (received off-air): KOAC-TV (P) Corvallis; KEVU-LP (F), KEZI (A), KLSR-TV (U), KMTR (N) Eugene; KOBI (N) Medford; KPIC (C) Roseburg.
Programming (via satellite): A & E; American Movie Classics; Blazer Vision; C-SPAN; Comedy Central; Fox Sports Net Northwest; MTV; QVC; TBS Superstation; VH1.
Current originations: Public access; educational access; government access.
Fee: $29.95 installation; $15.45 monthly.
Expanded Basic Service
Subscribers: 640.
Programming (via satellite): CNN; Disney Channel; ESPN; Headline News; Lifetime; Sci-Fi Channel.
Fee: $7.40 monthly.
Expanded Basic Service 2
Subscribers: 407.
Programming (via satellite): Country Music TV; Discovery Channel; Fox Family Channel; Nashville Network; Nickelodeon; USA Network.
Fee: $6.50 monthly.
Expanded Basic Service 3
Subscribers: 126.
Programming (via satellite): Cartoon Network; History Channel; Learning Channel; The Weather Channel.
Fee: $4.00 monthly.
Pay Service 1
Pay Units: 40.
Programming (via satellite): Cinemax.
Fee: $10.95 monthly.
Pay Service 2
Pay Units: 82.
Programming (via satellite): HBO.
Fee: $11.95 monthly.
Pay Service 3
Pay Units: 57.
Programming (via satellite): Showtime.
Fee: $10.95 monthly.
Pay Service 4
Pay Units: 31.
Programming (via satellite): The Movie Channel.
Fee: $10.95 monthly.
Equipment: Blonder-Tongue & Jerrold headend; Coral amplifiers; Times Fiber cable; Eagle traps; Andrew satellite antenna; Hughes satellite receivers.
Miles of plant: 31.0 (coaxial). Homes passed: 1,404.
Manager: Derek White. Chief technician: James Gill.
Ownership: Falcon Communications LP (MSO), joint venture formed September 30, 1998. See Cable System Ownership.

DUFUR—Northstate Cablevision, Box 609, Mount Vernon, OR 97865. Phone: 541-467-2409. County: Wasco. ICA: OR0097.
TV Market Ranking: Outside TV Markets. Franchise award date: April 16, 1984. Franchise expiration date: N.A. Began: June 1, 1955.
Channel capacity: 35 (not 2-way capable). Channels available but not in use: 26.
Basic Service
Subscribers: 278.
Programming (received off-air): KATU (A), KGW (N), KOIN (C), KOPB-TV (P), KPTV (U) Portland; allband FM.
Programming (via satellite): Fox Family Channel; Nashville Network; TBS Superstation.
Fee: $30.00 installation; $10.00 monthly.
Pay Service 1
Pay Units: 86.
Programming (via satellite): HBO.
Fee: $10.00 installation; $9.95 monthly.
Local advertising: No.
Equipment: Scientific-Atlanta headend; Scientific-Atlanta amplifiers; Superior cable; Scientific-Atlanta satellite antenna; Scientific-Atlanta satellite receivers.
Miles of plant: 5.0 (coaxial).
Manager: Gary E. Miller. Chief technician: Herb Watts.
Ownership: Northstate Cablevision Co.

ELGIN—Elgin TV Assn. Inc., Box 246, 830 Alder, Elgin, OR 97827. Phone: 541-437-4575. County: Union. ICA: OR0076.
TV Market Ranking: Below 100. Franchise award date: N.A. Franchise expiration date: January 1, 2000. Began: October 1, 1955.
Channel capacity: 36 (not 2-way capable). Channels available but not in use: 3.
Basic Service
Subscribers: 689.
Programming (received off-air): KTVB (N) Boise; KTVR (P) La Grande; KATU (A), KGW (N), KOIN (C), KPTV (U) Portland; KHQ-TV (N), KREM-TV (C), KXLY-TV (A) Spokane; KPDX (F) Vancouver.
Programming (via satellite): WGN-TV (W) Chicago; American Movie Classics; C-SPAN; CNN; Country Music TV; Discovery Channel; ESPN; Fox Family Channel; Fox Sports Net Northwest; Home & Garden Television; Learning Channel; Nashville Network; Nick at Nite's TV Land; Northwest Cable News; Outdoor Channel; Sci-Fi Channel; TBS Superstation; Turner Network TV; USA Network.
Current originations: Automated timeweather.
Fee: $10.00 installation; $12.00 monthly (members), $15.00 monthly (non-members); $50.00 membership.
Pay Service 1
Pay Units: 175.
Programming (via satellite): Disney Channel.
Fee: $10.00 installation; $7.00 monthly.
Pay Service 2
Pay Units: 275.
Programming (via satellite): HBO.
Fee: $10.00 installation; $8.00 monthly.
Local advertising: Yes. Available in locally originated programming. Rates: $1.00/Day.
Equipment: Blonder-Tongue & Jerrold headend; Scientific-Atlanta & Magnavox amplifiers; Times Fiber cable; Jerrold set top converters; Microdyne & Blonder-Tongue satellite receivers.
Miles of plant: 20.0 (coaxial); None (fiber optic). Homes passed: 750. Total homes in franchised area: 750.
Manager: Risa Hallgarth. Chief technician: Mike Rutherford.
Ownership: Elgin TV Assn. Inc.

ELKTON—Interstate Cable Inc., Box 2687, Salina, KS 67402-2687. Phones: 785-452-9409; 800-888-4788. Fax: 785-238-7190. County: Douglas. ICA: OR0136.
TV Market Ranking: Below 100. Franchise award date: N.A. Franchise expiration date: N.A. Began: July 1, 1991.
Channel capacity: N.A. Channels available but not in use: N.A.
Basic Service
Subscribers: 60.
Programming (received off-air): KOAC-TV (P) Corvallis; KEZI (A), KVAL-TV (C) Eugene; KDRV (A), KOBI (N) Medford.
Programming (via satellite): WGN-TV (W) Chicago; A & E; CNBC; CNN; Discovery Channel; ESPN; FX; Fox Family Channel; Lifetime; Nashville Network; QVC; TBS Superstation; Trinity Bcstg. Network; Turner Network TV.
Fee: $50.00 installation; $21.95 monthly; $2.00 converter; $15.00 additional installation.
Pay Service 1
Pay Units: N.A.
Programming (via satellite): Cinemax; Disney Channel; HBO; The New Encore.
Fee: $6.95 monthly (Encore), $7.95 monthly (Disney), $10.95 monthly (Cinemax or HBO).
Homes passed: 150.
Manager: Patti Lahey.
Franchise fee: 5% of gross.
Ownership: Tristar Cable Inc. (MSO).

ENTERPRISE—Crestview Cable TV, Suite 1-A, 103 Hwy. 82, Enterprise, OR 97828. Phone: 541-426-3636. Fax: 541-426-2091. County: Wallowa. Also serves Joseph, Lostine, Wallowa, Wallowa Lake. ICA: OR0048.
TV Market Ranking: Outside TV Markets. Franchise award date: N.A. Franchise expiration date: October 10, 1998. Began: June 1, 1955.
Channel capacity: 36 (not 2-way capable). Channels available but not in use: N.A.
Basic Service
Subscribers: 1,799.
Programming (received off-air): KTVR (P) La Grande; KHQ-TV (N), KREM-TV (C), KSPS-TV (P), KXLY-TV (A) Spokane; 14 FMs.
Programming (via microwave): KOIN (C), KPTV (U) Portland.
Programming (via satellite): A & E; CNBC; CNN; Discovery Channel; ESPN; Fox Family Channel; Headline News; Learning Channel; Nashville Network; QVC; TBS Superstation; Turner Network TV; ValueVision.
Current originations: Automated timeweather.
Fee: $25.00 installation; $13.95 monthly; $1.00 converter; $10.00 additional installation.
Commercial fee: $2.75 monthly.
Pay Service 1
Pay Units: 213.
Programming (via satellite): Cinemax.
Fee: $10.00 installation; $10.00 monthly.
Pay Service 2
Pay Units: 181.
Programming (via satellite): Disney Channel.
Fee: $10.00 monthly.
Pay Service 3
Pay Units: 362.
Programming (via satellite): HBO.
Fee: $10.00 monthly.
Local advertising: Yes. Available in character-generated programming. Rates: $20.00/Week/Page.
Equipment: Triple Crown headend; Triple Crown & Texscan amplifiers; Belden cable; Mycrotek character generator; Hamlin & NSC set top converters; Eagle, Pico & Arcom traps; Prodelin satellite antenna; Standard Communications satellite receivers.
Miles of plant: 60.0 (coaxial). Homes passed: 2,000.
Manager: Tony Ashcraft. Chief technician: Jerry Steele.
City fee: 3% of gross.
Ownership: California-Oregon Broadcasting Inc. (MSO).

ESTACADA—Cascade Cable TV Inc., Box 1283, 355 S.W. Broadway, Estacada, OR 97023. Phone: 503-630-2565. Fax: 503-630-6630. County: Clackamas. Also serves Clackamas County. ICA: OR0068.
TV Market Ranking: 29. Franchise award date: February 1, 1983. Franchise expiration date: October 1, 1997. Began: March 10, 1983.
Channel capacity: 35. Channels available but not in use: N.A.
Basic Service
Subscribers: 913.
Programming (received off-air): KATU (A), KGW (N), KOIN (C), KOPB-TV (P), KPTV (U) Portland; KPXG (X) Salem; KPDX (F) Vancouver.
Programming (via satellite): WGN-TV (W) Chicago; A & E; CNN; Cartoon Network; Discovery Channel; ESPN; Fox Family Channel; Goodlife TV Network; Nashville Network; Sci-Fi Channel; TBS Superstation; Turner Network TV; USA Network.
Current originations: Public access.
Fee: $35.00 installation; $9.00 monthly; $20.00 additional installation.
Pay Service 1
Pay Units: 320.

Programming (via satellite): Cinemax; Disney Channel; HBO.
Fee: $9.00 monthly (each).
Equipment: Scientific-Atlanta headend; Scientific-Atlanta amplifiers; Scientific-Atlanta cable; Scientific-Atlanta set top converters; Pico traps; United Satellite Systems satellite antenna; Scientific-Atlanta satellite receivers.
Miles of plant: 21.0 (coaxial). Additional miles planned: 2.0 (coaxial). Homes passed: 1,022. Total homes in franchised area: 3,150.
Manager: Bob Milliken. Chief technician: Ross Beecher.
City fee: 3% of gross.
Ownership: MasterTech Inc.

EUGENE—TCI Cablevision of Oregon Inc., 2897 Chad Dr., Eugene, OR 97408-7335. Phone: 541-484-3000. Fax: 541-343-5025. Web site: http://www.tci.com. Counties: Lane & Linn. Also serves Alvadore, Glenwood, Harrisburg, Junction City, Lane County, Santa Clara, Springfield. ICA: OR0004.
TV Market Ranking: Below 100 (Alvadore, Eugene, Glenwood, Harrisburg, Junction City, portions of Lane County, Santa Clara, Springfield); Outside TV Markets (portions of Lane County). Franchise award date: N.A. Franchise expiration date: June 1, 2008. Began: June 1, 1954.
Channel capacity: 40 (not 2-way capable). Channels available but not in use: None.
Basic Service
Subscribers: 59,000.
Programming (received off-air): KEPB-TV (P), KEVU-LP (F), KEZI (A), KLSR-TV (U), KMTR (N), KVAL-TV (C) Eugene; KTVC (X) Roseburg.
Programming (via satellite): C-SPAN; Discovery Channel; FX; Fox Family Channel; Fox News Channel; Headline News; Odyssey; QVC; The Weather Channel; Univision.
Current originations: Automated time-weather; public access; educational access; government access; leased access; local news.
Fee: $35.00 installation; $12.10 monthly; $11.65 additional installation.
Digital Basic Service
Subscribers: N.A.
Programming (via satellite): BBC America; Discovery Home & Leisure Channel; Discovery Kids Channel; Discovery People; Discovery Science Channel; ESPN Classic Sports; ESPNews; Fox Sports World; Game Show Network; History Channel; Home & Garden Television; Independent Film Channel; MuchMusic Network; Outdoor Life Network; Romance Classics; The Barker; Turner Classic Movies.
Fee: $12.80 monthly.
Expanded Basic Service
Subscribers: 54,500.
Programming (via satellite): A & E; Animal Planet; Blazer Vision; CNBC; CNN; Cartoon Network; Disney Channel; ESPN; Fox Sports Net Northwest; Learning Channel; MTV; Nashville Network; Nickelodeon; Superaudio Cable Radio Service; TBS Superstation; Turner Network TV; USA Network; WB 100+ Station Group.
Fee: $14.60 monthly.
Pay Service 1
Pay Units: 6,000.
Programming (via satellite): Cinemax.
Fee: $9.65 installation; $12.95 monthly.
Pay Service 2
Pay Units: 20,000.
Programming (via satellite): The New Encore.
Fee: $1.75 monthly.
Pay Service 3
Pay Units: 10,000.
Programming (via satellite): HBO.
Fee: $9.65 installation; $12.95 monthly.
Pay Service 4
Pay Units: 7,000.
Programming (via satellite): Showtime.
Fee: $9.65 installation; $12.95 monthly.
Pay Service 5
Pay Units: 16,000.
Programming (via satellite): Starz!
Fee: $6.75 monthly.
Digital Pay Service 1
Pay Units: N.A.
Programming (via satellite): DMX; Encore Love Stories; Encore Mystery; Encore Westerns; HBO Plus; HBO Signature; Showtime (multiplexed); Starz! (multiplexed); The Movie Channel.
Fee: N.A.
Pay-Per-View
Addressable homes: 1,200.
Local advertising: Yes. Available in satellite distributed programming. Rates: $180-$1350/Hour; $120-$750/30 Minutes; $15-$42/30 Seconds. Local sales manager: Randy Roman. Regional interconnect: Northwest Cable Advertising.
Program Guide: The Cable Guide.
Equipment: Scientific-Atlanta headend; Jerrold amplifiers; Times Fiber cable; Hitachi cameras; MPCS VTRs; Quanta character generator; Jerrold set top converters; Arcom addressable set top converters; Hughes satellite antenna; Hughes satellite receivers; ChannelMatic commercial insert.
Miles of plant: 1007.2 (coaxial); 30.0 (fiber optic). Homes passed: 99,000. Total homes in franchised area: 100,000.
Manager: Michael White. Operations manager: Bill Metcalf.
City fee: 5% of gross.
Ownership: AT&T Broadband & Internet Services (MSO). Purchased from Tele-Communications Inc., March 9, 1999.

FLORENCE—Falcon Cable Systems Co., 1400 Newmark Ave., Coos Bay, OR 97420. Phone: 541-888-5712. Fax: 541-888-9292. County: Lane. Also serves Dunes City, Lane County (portions). ICA: OR0030.
TV Market Ranking: Below 100 (portions of Lane County); Outside TV Markets (Dunes City, Florence, portions of Lane County). Franchise award date: May 1, 1965. Franchise expiration date: October 22, 2003. Began: July 1, 1965.
Channel capacity: 62. Channels available but not in use: 6.
Basic Service
Subscribers: 3,715; Commercial subscribers: 57.
Programming (received off-air): KOAC-TV (P) Corvallis; KEZI (A), KMTR (N), KVAL-TV (C) Eugene; KPTV (U) Portland; allband FM.
Programming (via satellite): WGN-TV (W) Chicago; A & E; American Movie Classics; Blazer Vision; C-SPAN; E! Entertainment TV; FX; Fox Family Channel; Headline News; Home & Garden Television; Home Shopping Network; Lifetime; Nashville Network; Nickelodeon; QVC; Sci-Fi Channel; TBS Superstation; TV Guide Channel; TV Guide Sneak Prevue; Travel Channel; Trinity Bcstg. Network; VH1.
Current originations: Automated time-weather; public access.
Fee: $25.00 installation; $25.87 monthly; $1.95 converter; $5.00 additional installation.
Expanded Basic Service
Subscribers: 3,466.
Programming (via satellite): CNN; Discovery Channel; ESPN; USA Network.
Fee: $4.49 monthly.
Expanded Basic Service 2
Subscribers: 967.
Programming (via satellite): Bravo; CNBC; Country Music TV; Disney Channel; Fox Sports Net Northwest; Learning Channel; Turner Network TV.
Fee: $5.00 monthly.
Expanded Basic Service 3
Subscribers: 409.
Programming (via satellite): Cartoon Network; fXM: Movies from Fox; History Channel; The Health Network; The Weather Channel.
Fee: $4.50 monthly.
Pay Service 1
Pay Units: 130.
Programming (via satellite): Cinemax.
Fee: $10.95 monthly.
Pay Service 2
Pay Units: 245.
Programming (via satellite): HBO.
Fee: $11.95 monthly.
Pay Service 3
Pay Units: 171.
Programming (via satellite): Showtime.
Fee: $10.95 monthly.
Pay Service 4
Pay Units: 131.
Programming (via satellite): The Movie Channel.
Fee: $10.95 monthly.
Pay Service 5
Pay Units: N.A.
Programming (via satellite): The New Encore.
Fee: N.A.
Pay-Per-View
Action Pay-Per-View; Spice; Spice2; Viewer's Choice.
Local advertising: Yes. Available in character-generated programming. Rates: $6.90/Day. Regional interconnect: Northwest Cable Advertising.
Program Guide: CableView.
Equipment: Scientific-Atlanta headend; Delta-Benco-Cascade, Magnavox & Century III amplifiers; Comm/Scope cable; Beston character generator; Hamlin set top converters; Scientific-Atlanta satellite antenna; Scientific-Atlanta satellite receivers.
Miles of plant: 130.0 (coaxial). Additional miles planned: 1.0 (coaxial). Homes passed: 7,521.
Manager: Bill Griffin. Chief technician: Norman Lacey. Marketing director: Joan Crabtree.
Franchise fee: 3%-5% of gross.
Ownership: Falcon Communications LP (MSO), joint venture formed September 30, 1998. See Cable System Ownership.

FOSSIL—Fossil Community TV Inc., Box 209, Fossil, OR 97830. County: Wheeler. ICA: OR0104.
TV Market Ranking: Outside TV Markets. Franchise award date: N.A. Franchise expiration date: N.A. Began: May 1, 1955.
Channel capacity: 12. Channels available but not in use: 4.
Basic Service
Subscribers: N.A.
Programming (received off-air): KEPR-TV (C), KNDU (N), KVEW (A) Pasco-Kennewick-Richland; KATU (A), KGW (N), KOIN (C), KOPB-TV (P), KPTV (U) Portland; allband FM.
Fee: $25.00 installation; $3.50 monthly.
Equipment: Amplivision & Benco headend; Blonder-Tongue amplifiers.
Miles of plant: 9.0 (coaxial). Homes passed: 240. Total homes in franchised area: 240.
Manager: Vern W. Kirby. Chief technician: LeRoy Stegner.
City fee: $84 per year.
Ownership: Fossil Community TV Inc.

GILCHRIST—Country Cablevision Ltd., Box 12038, Salem, OR 97309-0038. Phone: 503-588-8247. Fax: 503-588-0544. County: Klamath. Also serves Crescent. ICA: OR0137.
TV Market Ranking: Outside TV Markets. Franchise award date: January 1, 1988. Franchise expiration date: January 1, 2001. Began: January 1, 1990.
Channel capacity: 42 (2-way capable). Channels available but not in use: 12.
Basic Service
Subscribers: 275.
Programming (received off-air): KOAB-TV (P), KTVZ (N) Bend; KOTI (N) Klamath Falls; KTVL (C) Medford; KATU (A) Portland; KPDX (F) Vancouver.
Programming (via satellite): WGN-TV (W) Chicago; CNN; Country Music TV; Discovery Channel; ESPN; Fox Family Channel; Headline News; Lifetime; Nashville Network; TBS Superstation; Turner Network TV; USA Network.
Current originations: Public access.
Fee: $49.95 installation; $21.95 monthly.
Pay Service 1
Pay Units: 165.
Programming (via satellite): Disney Channel; Showtime; The Movie Channel; The New Encore.
Fee: $19.95 installation; $4.95 monthly (Encore), $8.95 monthly (Showtime), $9.95 monthly (Disney), $10.95 monthly (TMC).
Local advertising: Yes. Available in locally originated programming.
Equipment: Trilogy cable.
Miles of plant: 12.0 (coaxial). Homes passed: 400. Total homes in franchised area: 550.
Manager: John P. Johnson. Chief technician: Veron L. Robinson.
Ownership: Country Cablevision Ltd. (MSO).

GLENDALE—Phoenix Cablevision of Oregon Inc., Box 828, 6655 Rogue River Dr., Shady Cove, OR 97539. Phones: 541-878-3247; 800-827-3247. Fax: 541-878-2458. County: Douglas. Also serves Douglas County (unincorporated areas). ICA: OR0138.
TV Market Ranking: Below 100 (portions of Douglas County, Glendale); Outside TV Markets (portions of Douglas County). Franchise award date: August 1, 1981. Franchise expiration date: October 4, 2013. Began: January 1, 1985.
Channel capacity: 36 (not 2-way capable). Channels available but not in use: 9.
Basic Service
Subscribers: 346.
Programming (received off-air): KDRV (A), KOBI (N), KSYS (P) Medford; KPIC (C) Roseburg.
Programming (via satellite): WGN-TV (W) Chicago; WWOR-TV (U) New York; A & E; CNN; Cartoon Network; Country Music TV; Discovery Channel; Disney Channel; ESPN; Fox Family Channel; FoxNet; History Channel; Home & Garden Television; Home Shopping Network; Learning Channel; Lifetime; Nashville Network; Sci-Fi Channel; TBS Superstation; The Weather Channel; Trinity Bcstg. Network; Turner Classic Movies; Turner Network TV; USA Network.
Current originations: Local news.
Fee: $23.43 installation; $43.75 monthly; $56.00 converter; $26.25 additional installation.
Commercial fee: $5.50 monthly.
Pay Service 1
Pay Units: 27.

Programming (via satellite): Cinemax.
Fee: $15.00 installation; $11.55 monthly.

Pay Service 2
Pay Units: 47.
Programming (via satellite): HBO.
Fee: $15.00 installation; $11.55 monthly.

Equipment: Magnavox headend; Scientific-Atlanta satellite receivers.
Miles of plant: 19.3 (coaxial). Homes passed: 650.
Manager: Ted W. Hughett. Chief technician: Dan Middleton.
City fee: 3.5% of basic.
Ownership: Phoenix Cable Inc. (MSO).

GLIDE—Glide Cablevision, Box 609, 729 Grand View, Glide, OR 97433. Phone: 541-496-0515. Fax: 541-496-3499. County: Douglas. Also serves Idleyld Park. ICA: OR0139.
TV Market Ranking: Below 100. Franchise award date: N.A. Franchise expiration date: N.A. Began: January 1, 1989.
Channel capacity: 30. Channels available but not in use: N.A.

Basic Service
Subscribers: 325.
Programming (received off-air): KEZI (A) Eugene; KDRV (A), KOBI (N), KSYS (P) Medford; KPIC (C) Roseburg.
Programming (via satellite): WGN-TV (W) Chicago; WPIX (W) New York; A & E; CNBC; CNN; Country Music TV; Discovery Channel; ESPN; Fox Family Channel; Home Shopping Network; Knowledge TV; Learning Channel; Lifetime; MTV; Nashville Network; Nickelodeon; Odyssey; Sci-Fi Channel; TBS Superstation; Turner Classic Movies; Turner Network TV; USA Network; VH1.
Fee: $45.00 installation; $31.00 monthly.

Pay Service 1
Pay Units: 21.
Programming (via satellite): Disney Channel.
Fee: $7.95 monthly.

Pay Service 2
Pay Units: 42.
Programming (via satellite): HBO.
Fee: $8.50 monthly.

Pay Service 3
Pay Units: 14.
Programming (via satellite): Showtime.
Fee: $7.00 monthly.

Miles of plant: 11.0 (coaxial). Homes passed: 531.
Manager: Jean Marie Arwood. Chief technician: Rick Arwood.
Ownership: Glide Cablevision.

GOLD BEACH—Falcon Telecable, 1440 Parkway Dr., Crescent City, CA 95531. Phone: 707-464-4157. County: Curry. ICA: OR0044.
TV Market Ranking: Outside TV Markets. Franchise award date: N.A. Franchise expiration date: January 31, 2014. Began: March 1, 1964.
Channel capacity: 95 (2-way capable; not operating 2-way). Channels available but not in use: None.

Basic Service
Subscribers: 1,179.
Programming (received off-air): KCBY-TV (C) Coos Bay; KLSR-TV (U) Eugene; KDRV (A), KOBI (N) Medford; KOPB-TV (P) Portland; 5 FMs.
Programming (via satellite): A & E; C-SPAN; Discovery Channel; ESPN; Fox Family Channel; Nashville Network; QVC.
Current originations: Public access; educational access; government access.
Fee: $53.00 installation; $20.02 monthly.

Expanded Basic Service
Subscribers: 1,142.
Programming (via satellite): American Movie Classics; Country Music TV; Sci-Fi Channel; USA Network.
Fee: $5.97 monthly.

Expanded Basic Service 2
Subscribers: 1,132.
Programming (via satellite): WGN-TV (W) Chicago; CNN; Disney Channel; Headline News; TBS Superstation; Turner Network TV.
Fee: $7.25 monthly.

Pay Service 1
Pay Units: 82.
Programming (via satellite): Cinemax.
Fee: $11.95 monthly.

Pay Service 2
Pay Units: 191.
Programming (via satellite): HBO.
Fee: $11.95 monthly.

Pay Service 3
Pay Units: 153.
Programming (via satellite): Showtime.
Fee: $11.95 monthly.

Pay Service 4
Pay Units: 29.
Programming (via satellite): The Movie Channel.
Fee: $11.95 monthly.

Equipment: Phasecom headend; Magnavox amplifiers; Times Fiber cable; Magnavox set top converters; Eagle traps; AFC satellite antenna; Microwave Assoc. satellite receivers.
Miles of plant: 59.0 (coaxial). Additional miles planned: 5.0 (coaxial). Homes passed: 1,519. Total homes in franchised area: 3,500.
Manager: Bob Pearson. Chief technician: Ronald Simpson.
Franchise fee: 5% of gross.
Ownership: Falcon Communications LP (MSO), joint venture formed September 30, 1998. See Cable System Ownership.

GOVERNMENT CAMP—CharlieVision, Box 10, Government Camp, OR 97028. Phone: 503-272-3333. County: Clackamas. ICA: OR0168.
TV Market Ranking: Outside TV Markets. Franchise award date: N.A. Franchise expiration date: N.A. Began: N.A.
Channel capacity: 13. Channels available but not in use: 2.

Basic Service
Subscribers: 65.
Programming (received off-air): KATU (A), KGW (N), KOIN (C), KOPB-TV (P), KPTV (U) Portland.
Programming (via satellite): WGN-TV (W) Chicago; Discovery Channel; ESPN; TBS Superstation; Turner Network TV.
Fee: $25.00 monthly.

Pay Service 1
Pay Units: 65.
Programming (via satellite): HBO.
Fee: $2.50 monthly.

Miles of plant: 13.0 (coaxial). Homes passed: 178.
Manager: Charlie Sperr. Chief technician: Ed Winnett.
Ownership: Charlie Sperr.

GRANTS PASS—Falcon Cable TV, Box 1129, Grants Pass, OR 97526. Phone: 541-476-6606. Fax: 541-474-1570. Counties: Jackson & Josephine. Also serves Josephine County, Rogue River. ICA: OR0010.
TV Market Ranking: Below 100 (Grants Pass, portions of Josephine County); Outside TV Markets (portions of Josephine County, Rogue River). Franchise award date: November 20, 1957. Franchise expiration date: March 1, 1998. Began: January 1, 1954.
Channel capacity: 27 (2-way capable). Channels available but not in use: None.

Basic Service
Subscribers: 14,790; Commercial subscribers: 64.
Programming (received off-air): KDRV (A), KOBI (N), KSYS (P), KTVL (C) Medford; 13 FMs.
Programming (via microwave): KTVU (F) Oakland-San Francisco; KATU (A), KPTV (U) Portland; KPIX-TV (C) San Francisco.
Programming (via satellite): C-SPAN; CNN; Discovery Channel; Fox Family Channel; Headline News; Lifetime; MTV; Nashville Network; Nickelodeon; Odyssey; TBS Superstation.
Current originations: Automated time-weather.
Fee: $38.98 installation; $20.24 monthly; $2.00 converter; $25.98 additional installation.

Expanded Basic Service
Subscribers: 12,838.
Programming (via satellite): A & E; American Movie Classics; ESPN; Fox Sports Net Northwest; Turner Network TV; USA Network.
Fee: $1.85 monthly.

Pay Service 1
Pay Units: 480.
Programming (via satellite): Cinemax.
Fee: $12.90 monthly.

Pay Service 2
Pay Units: 824.
Programming (via satellite): Disney Channel.
Fee: N.A.

Pay Service 3
Pay Units: 6,893.
Programming (via satellite): The New Encore.
Fee: N.A.

Pay Service 4
Pay Units: 1,146.
Programming (via satellite): HBO.
Fee: $12.90 monthly.

Pay Service 5
Pay Units: 561.
Programming (via satellite): Showtime.
Fee: $12.90 monthly.

Pay-Per-View
Addressable homes: 1,976.
Special events.

Local advertising: Yes (locally produced & insert). Available in satellite distributed programming. Rates: $20.00/Minute; $10.00/30 Seconds. Local sales manager: Mike Dadaos. Regional interconnect: Northwest Cable Advertising.
Program Guide: The Cable Guide.
Equipment: Scientific-Atlanta headend; Century III & Texscan amplifiers; Comm/Scope cable; Sony VTRs; Microtek character generator; Jerrold & Texscan set top converters; Jerrold addressable set top converters; Andrew, Paraclipse & Prodelin satellite antenna; Scientific-Atlanta satellite receivers; ChannelMatic commercial insert.
Miles of plant: 350.0 (coaxial); 18.0 (fiber optic). Homes passed: 20,172. Total homes in franchised area: 21,675.
Manager: David Young. Chief technician: Mark McIntosh. Marketing director: Janis McTimmonds.
City fee: 5% of gross.
Ownership: Falcon Communications LP (MSO). Purchased from Tele-Communications Inc., September 30, 1998. See Cable System Ownership.

GREENACRES—Greenacres TV Cable, 85 Cordell Lane, Coos Bay, OR 97420. Phone: 541-267-4788. Fax: 541-267-4788. County: Coos. ICA: OR0163.
TV Market Ranking: Below 100. Franchise award date: N.A. Franchise expiration date: N.A. Began: August 1, 1993.
Channel capacity: 13 (2-way capable). Channels available but not in use: None.

Basic Service
Subscribers: 129.
Programming (received off-air): KCBY-TV (C), KMTZ (N) Coos Bay; KOAC-TV (P) Corvallis; KEZI (A), KLSR-TV (U) Eugene; KOBI (N) Medford.
Fee: $100.00 installation; $11.50 monthly.

Expanded Basic Service
Subscribers: 120.
Programming (via satellite): WGN-TV (W) Chicago; CNN; Discovery Channel; ESPN; Nashville Network; TBS Superstation; Trinity Bcstg. Network.
Fee: $8.50 monthly.

Miles of plant: 5.0 (coaxial). Homes passed: 140.
Manager: Wayne Morgan.
Ownership: Wayne E. Morgan.

HAINES—Blackstone Cable LLC, 1104 W. Ironwood Dr., Coeur d'Alene, ID 83814-2605. Phone: 208-664-3370. Fax: 208-664-5888. County: Baker. ICA: OR0108.
TV Market Ranking: Outside TV Markets. Franchise award date: September 15, 1987. Franchise expiration date: September 8, 2002. Began: December 1, 1988.
Channel capacity: 19 (not 2-way capable). Channels available but not in use: 5.

Basic Service
Subscribers: 68.
Programming (received off-air): KTVR (P) La Grande; KATU (A), KGW (N), KOIN (C), KPTV (U) Portland; KPDX (F) Vancouver.
Programming (via satellite): WGN-TV (W) Chicago; CNN; Discovery Channel; Disney Channel; ESPN; Fox Family Channel; Nashville Network; TBS Superstation; Turner Network TV.
Fee: $43.50 installation; $21.00 monthly; $56.00 converter; $21.50 additional installation.
Commercial fee: $5.24 monthly.

Pay Service 1
Pay Units: 11.
Programming (via satellite): HBO.
Fee: $15.00 installation; $10.95 monthly.

Miles of plant: 6.6 (coaxial); None (fiber optic). Homes passed: 166.
Manager: Wayne Morgan.
City fee: 5% of gross.
Ownership: Blackstone Cable LLC (MSO).

HALFWAY—Falcon Video Communications, 24 W. Idaho St., Weiser, ID 83672. Phone: 800-264-1572. County: Baker. ICA: OR0140.
TV Market Ranking: Outside TV Markets. Franchise award date: N.A. Franchise expiration date: N.A. Began: N.A.
Channel capacity: 37. Channels available but not in use: 14.

Basic Service
Subscribers: 136.
Programming (received off-air): KBCI-TV (C), KTVB (N) Boise; KIVI (A) Nampa; KOPB-TV (P) Portland.
Programming (via satellite): WGN-TV (W) Chicago; CNN; Country Music TV; ESPN; Fox Family Channel; FoxNet; Headline News; Home & Garden Television; Home Shopping Network; Nickelodeon; QVC; Sci-Fi Channel; TBS Superstation.
Fee: $17.25 installation; $18.71 monthly.

Expanded Basic Service
Subscribers: 134.

Programming (via satellite): Discovery Channel; Disney Channel; Nashville Network; USA Network.
Fee: $3.18 monthly.

Pay Service 1
Pay Units: 16.
Programming (via satellite): Cinemax.
Fee: $10.95 monthly.

Pay Service 2
Pay Units: 21.
Programming (via satellite): HBO.
Fee: $11.95 monthly.

Miles of plant: 6.0 (coaxial). Homes passed: 180.
Manager: John West.
Franchise fee: 5% of gross.
Ownership: Falcon Communications LP (MSO), joint venture formed September 30, 1998. See Cable System Ownership.

HALSEY—RTI Cable Television, Box 227, 705 W. 2nd St., Halsey, OR 97348. Phone: 541-369-2211. Fax: 541-369-2223. County: Linn. ICA: OR0100.
TV Market Ranking: Below 100. Franchise award date: July 22, 1981. Franchise expiration date: July 22, 2001. Began: October 1, 1983.
Channel capacity: 36 (2-way capable; operating 2-way). Channels available but not in use: 8.

Basic Service
Subscribers: 170.
Programming (received off-air): KOAC-TV (P) Corvallis; KEZI (A), KMTR (N), KVAL-TV (C) Eugene; KPTV (U) Portland; KPDX (F) Vancouver.
Programming (via satellite): WGN-TV (W) Chicago; A & E; CNN; Discovery Channel; ESPN; Fox Family Channel; Headline News; Lifetime; MTV; Nashville Network; Nickelodeon; TBS Superstation; The Inspirational Network; Turner Network TV; USA Network.
Fee: N.A.

Pay Service 1
Pay Units: N.A.
Programming (via satellite): HBO; Showtime.
Fee: $10.00 monthly (each).

Equipment: Blonder-Tongue headend; Scientific-Atlanta amplifiers; Comm/Scope cable; Scientific-Atlanta satellite receivers.
Miles of plant: 6.0 (coaxial). Homes passed: 254.
Manager: Randal L. Roome. Chief technician: Vince Emge.
City fee: 5% of gross.
Ownership: Roome Telecommunications Inc.

HAUSER—Falcon Cable Systems Co., 1400 Newmark Ave., Coos Bay, OR 97420. Phone: 541-888-5712. Fax: 541-888-9292. County: Coos. ICA: OR0089.
TV Market Ranking: Below 100. Franchise award date: N.A. Franchise expiration date: N.A. Began: January 1, 1972.
Channel capacity: 61. Channels available but not in use: None.

Basic Service
Subscribers: 478.
Programming (received off-air): KCBY-TV (C), KMTZ (N) Coos Bay; KOAC-TV (P) Corvallis; KEVU-LP (F), KEZI (A) Eugene; KOBI (N) Medford; KPTV (U) Portland; 16 FMs.
Programming (via satellite): WGN-TV (W) Chicago; A & E; American Movie Classics; C-SPAN; C-SPAN 2; CNBC; E! Entertainment TV; FX; Fox Sports Net Northwest; Home Shopping Network; Knowledge TV; Learning Channel; Lifetime; MTV; QVC; TV Guide Channel; TV Guide Sneak Prevue; The Weather Channel; Travel Channel; Trinity Bcstg. Network; VH1.
Current originations: Public access; educational access; government access.
Fee: $15.00 installation; $18.89 monthly; $10.00 additional installation.

Expanded Basic Service
Subscribers: 465.
Programming (via satellite): Blazer Vision; CNN; Discovery Channel; ESPN; Fox Family Channel; Headline News; Nickelodeon.
Fee: $4.48 monthly.

Expanded Basic Service 2
Subscribers: 212.
Programming (via satellite): Bravo; Comedy Central; Country Music TV; Disney Channel; Nashville Network; Sci-Fi Channel; Turner Network TV; USA Network.
Fee: $7.50 monthly.

Expanded Basic Service 3
Subscribers: 133.
Programming (via satellite): Cartoon Network; ESPN 2; fXM: Movies from Fox; History Channel; TBS Superstation.
Fee: $5.00 monthly.

Pay Service 1
Pay Units: 24.
Programming (via satellite): Cinemax.
Fee: $10.95 monthly.

Pay Service 2
Pay Units: 54.
Programming (via satellite): HBO.
Fee: $11.95 monthly.

Pay Service 3
Pay Units: 44.
Programming (via satellite): Showtime.
Fee: $10.95 monthly.

Pay Service 4
Pay Units: 26.
Programming (via satellite): The Movie Channel.
Fee: $10.95 monthly.

Pay Service 5
Pay Units: N.A.
Programming (via satellite): The New Encore.
Fee: N.A.

Pay-Per-View
Action Pay-Per-View; Spice; Viewer's Choice.

Equipment: Blonder-Tongue, Catel & Jerrold headend; Ameco, Vikoa & Jerrold amplifiers; Blonder-Tongue traps; Cadco satellite antenna.
Miles of plant: 26.0 (coaxial). Homes passed: 512.
Manager: Bill Griffin. Chief technician: Norman Lacey. Marketing director: Joan Crabtree.
Ownership: Falcon Communications LP (MSO), joint venture formed September 30, 1998. See Cable System Ownership.

HELIX—Helix Communications, Box 326, 200 Concord St., Helix, OR 97835. Phone: 541-457-6000. County: Umatilla. ICA: OR0119.
TV Market Ranking: Below 100. Franchise award date: N.A. Franchise expiration date: N.A. Began: December 1, 1977.
Channel capacity: 28. Channels available but not in use: N.A.

Basic Service
Subscribers: 54.
Programming (received off-air): KTVR (P) La Grande; KEPR-TV (C), KNDU (N), KVEW (A) Pasco-Kennewick-Richland.
Fee: $35.00 installation; $15.00 monthly.

Miles of plant: 2.0 (coaxial). Homes passed: 76. Total homes in franchised area: 76.
Manager: Gene Smith.
Ownership: Helix Communications.

HEPPNER—Heppner TV Inc., 162 N. Main St., Heppner, OR 97836. Phone: 541-676-9663. Fax: 541-676-9655. County: Morrow. ICA: OR0077.
TV Market Ranking: Outside TV Markets. Franchise award date: March 1, 1955. Franchise expiration date: March 1, 2002. Began: June 1, 1955.
Channel capacity: 35 (not 2-way capable). Channels available but not in use: None.

Basic Service
Subscribers: 637.
Programming (received off-air): KEPR-TV (C), KNDU (N), KVEW (A) Pasco-Kennewick-Richland; KOPB-TV (P) Portland; allband FM.
Programming (via microwave): KATU (A), KGW (N), KOIN (C), KPTV (U) Portland.
Programming (via translator): KOPB-TV (P) Portland; KPDX (F) Vancouver.
Programming (via satellite): WGN-TV (W) Chicago; A & E; CNN; Discovery Channel; ESPN; Fox Family Channel; Learning Channel; Nashville Network; Sci-Fi Channel; TBS Superstation; Turner Network TV; USA Network; VH1.
Current originations: Public access; local news.
Planned originations: Automated time-weather.
Fee: $15.00 installation; $21.00 monthly.

Pay Service 1
Pay Units: 244.
Programming (via satellite): Disney Channel; HBO.
Fee: $12.50 installation; $11.00 monthly (each).

Equipment: Jerrold headend; Jerrold amplifiers; Times Fiber cable; Eagle & Intercept traps; ISS & Sony satellite antenna; Hughes & Jerrold satellite receivers.
Miles of plant: 17.0 (coaxial); 4.0 (fiber optic). Homes passed: 700. Total homes in franchised area: 700.
Office manager: Judith Laughlin. Chief technician: Thomas Rawlins.
City fee: 3% of gross.
Ownership: Heppner TV Inc.

HERMISTON—TCI Cablevision of Northeastern Oregon, 152 S.W. Nye, Pendleton, OR 97801. Phone: 541-276-2821. Fax: 541-276-0134. County: Umatilla. Also serves Echo, Stanfield, Umatilla County. ICA: OR0029.
TV Market Ranking: Below 100 (Echo, Hermiston, Stanfield, portions of Umatilla County); Outside TV Markets (portions of Umatilla County). Franchise award date: N.A. Franchise expiration date: June 26, 1999. Began: June 1, 1969.
Channel capacity: 36 (not 2-way capable). Channels available but not in use: N.A.

Basic Service
Subscribers: 4,097; Commercial subscribers: 80.
Programming (received off-air): KTVR (P) La Grande; KEPR-TV (C), KNDU (N), KVEW (A) Pasco-Kennewick-Richland; KATU (A), KGW (N), KOIN (C), KPTV (U) Portland; 9 FMs.
Programming (via satellite): A & E; American Movie Classics; C-SPAN; CNBC; CNN; Discovery Channel; ESPN; Fox Family Channel; Fox Sports Net Northwest; Intro TV; MTV; Nashville Network; Nickelodeon; QVC; TBS Superstation; The Weather Channel; Turner Network TV; USA Network; Univision; VH1.
Fee: $30.00 installation; $9.79 monthly; $1.20 converter.

Pay Service 1
Pay Units: N.A.
Programming (via satellite): Cinemax; Disney Channel; HBO; Showtime; The New Encore.
Fee: $1.75 monthly (Encore), $10.95 monthly (Cinemax, Disney or Showtime), $12.45 monthly (HBO).

Pay-Per-View
Addressable homes: 200.
Special events.
Fee: Varies.

Local advertising: Yes. Available in locally originated & taped programming.
Equipment: Jerrold & Scientific-Atlanta headend; Jerrold amplifiers; Comm/Scope & Times Fiber cable; MSI & Texscan character generator; Hamlin & Standard Components set top converters; Eagle, Arcom traps; Andrew, Vertex & Scientific-Atlanta satellite antenna; Jerrold & Sony satellite receivers.
Miles of plant: 114.7 (coaxial); None (fiber optic). Homes passed: 5,902. Total homes in franchised area: 6,920.
Manager: Darrell Linklater. Office manager: Sandy Haley.
City fee: 3% of gross.
Ownership: AT&T Broadband & Internet Services (MSO). Purchased from Tele-Communications Inc., March 9, 1999.

HOOD RIVER—Falcon Cablevision, 1215 12th St., Hood River, OR 97031. Phone: 541-386-3100. Counties: Hood River, OR; Klickitat, WA. Also serves Hood River County, OR; Bingen, Klickitat, Klickitat County, White Salmon, WA. ICA: OR0034.
TV Market Ranking: Below 100 (portions of Hood River County); Outside TV Markets (Bingen, Hood River, portions of Hood River County, Klickitat, Klickitat County, White Salmon). Franchise award date: N.A. Franchise expiration date: N.A. Began: January 1, 1957.
Channel capacity: 42 (not 2-way capable). Channels available but not in use: None.

Basic Service
Subscribers: 4,160.
Programming (received off-air): KATU (A), KGW (N), KOIN (C), KOPB-TV (P), KPTV (U) Portland; KPDX (F) Vancouver; allband FM.
Programming (via satellite): WGN-TV (W) Chicago; A & E; Blazer Vision; C-SPAN; Comedy Central; ESPN; ESPN 2; Home & Garden Television; Home Shopping Network; MTV; QVC; TBS Superstation; Turner Network TV; VH1.
Fee: $29.95 installation; $16.02 monthly.

Expanded Basic Service
Subscribers: 2,684.
Programming (via satellite): Fox Family Channel; Fox Sports Net Northwest; Knowledge TV; Lifetime; Nickelodeon; Sci-Fi Channel; Travel Channel; Univision.
Fee: $10.93 monthly.

Expanded Basic Service 2
Subscribers: 1,643.
Programming (via satellite): American Movie Classics; CNN; Country Music TV; Discovery Channel; Disney Channel; Headline News; Nashville Network; USA Network.
Fee: $6.50 monthly.

Pay Service 1
Pay Units: 172.

Programming (via satellite): Cinemax.
Fee: N.A.
Pay Service 2
Pay Units: 414.
Programming (via satellite): HBO.
Fee: $11.95 monthly.
Pay Service 3
Pay Units: 329.
Programming (via satellite): Showtime.
Fee: $10.95 monthly.
Pay Service 4
Pay Units: 232.
Programming (via satellite): The Movie Channel.
Fee: $10.95 monthly.
Pay-Per-View
Addressable homes: 887.
Special events.
Program Guide: The Cable Guide.
Equipment: Scientific-Atlanta headend; Scientific-Atlanta amplifiers; Comm/Scope cable; Scientific-Atlanta addressable set top converters; Fort Worth Tower satellite antenna; Scientific-Atlanta satellite receivers.
Miles of plant: 138.0 (coaxial); 20.0 (fiber optic). Homes passed: 6,839.
Manager: H. H. Asher. Chief technician: Daniel Wallace.
Franchise fee: 3%-6% of gross.
Ownership: Falcon Communications LP (MSO), joint venture formed September 30, 1998. See Cable System Ownership.

HUNTINGTON—Chambers Cable of Oregon Inc., Box 398, 347 S.W. 19th St., Ontario, OR 97914. Phones: 541-889-3173; 800-962-6362. Fax: 541-889-4453. County: Baker. ICA: OR0098.
TV Market Ranking: Outside TV Markets. Franchise award date: N.A. Franchise expiration date: N.A. Began: January 1, 1974.
Channel capacity: 21 (not 2-way capable). Channels available but not in use: 5.
Basic Service
Subscribers: 196.
Programming (received off-air): KAID (P), KBCI-TV (C), KTVB (N) Boise; KIVI (A), KTRV (F) Nampa; allband FM.
Programming (via satellite): WGN-TV (W) Chicago; CNN; Discovery Channel; ESPN; Fox Family Channel; Nashville Network; Northwest Cable News; TBS Superstation; Turner Network TV; USA Network.
Fee: $36.00 installation; $20.26 monthly.
Pay Service 1
Pay Units: N.A.
Programming (via satellite): HBO.
Fee: $11.95 monthly.
Equipment: Blonder-Tongue headend; Blonder-Tongue amplifiers; Cerro & Theta-Com cable.
Miles of plant: 5.0 (coaxial); None (fiber optic). Homes passed: 276.
Manager: Ed Aronson. Chief technician: Kevin Smith.
City fee: 3% of gross.
Ownership: Chambers Communications Corp. (MSO).

IDANHA—North Santiam Communications, Box 517, 475 N. 2nd Ave., Stayton, OR 97383. Phone: 503-769-7898. Fax: 503-769-7398. County: Marion. Also serves Detroit. ICA: OR0101.
TV Market Ranking: Outside TV Markets. Franchise award date: November 1, 1976. Franchise expiration date: N.A. Began: January 1, 1954.
Channel capacity: 21 (not 2-way capable). Channels available but not in use: 4.
Basic Service
Subscribers: 261.
Programming (received off-air): KATU (A), KGW (N), KOIN (C), KPTV (U) Portland; 7 FMs.
Programming (via satellite): WGN-TV (W) Chicago; KMGH-TV (A), KRMA-TV (P), KUSA-TV (N) Denver; CNN; Country Music TV; Discovery Channel; ESPN; Fox Family Channel; Fox Sports Net Northwest; Nashville Network; TBS Superstation; Turner Network TV.
Current originations: Public access; local news.
Fee: $30.00 installation; $17.19 monthly.
Pay Service 1
Pay Units: 27.
Programming (via satellite): Cinemax.
Fee: $9.95 monthly.
Pay Service 2
Pay Units: 39.
Programming (via satellite): HBO.
Fee: $12.00 monthly.
Local advertising: Yes. Available in character-generated programming.
Equipment: Blonder-Tongue, ISS & Triple Crown headend; Magnavox & Jerrold amplifiers; Comm/Scope cable; Tandy character generator; Hamlin set top converters; Arcom & Eagle traps; ISS, Scientific-Atlanta & Drake satellite receivers.
Miles of plant: 20.0 (coaxial).
Manager: Curt Thornton. Chief technician: Scott Curtis. Program director: Sydney Gill. Marketing director: Stacey Smith.
City fee: 3% of gross.
Ownership: SCS Communications & Security (MSO).

IMBLER—Blackstone Cable LLC, 1104 W. Ironwood Dr., Coeur d'Alene, ID 83814-2605. Phone: 208-664-3370. Fax: 208-664-5888. County: Union. ICA: OR0116.
TV Market Ranking: Outside TV Markets. Franchise award date: July 6, 1988. Franchise expiration date: August 3, 2007. Began: November 1, 1988.
Channel capacity: 19 (not 2-way capable). Channels available but not in use: 5.
Basic Service
Subscribers: 56.
Programming (received off-air): KTVR (P) La Grande; KATU (A), KGW (N), KOIN (C), KPTV (U) Portland; KPDX (F) Vancouver.
Programming (via satellite): WGN-TV (W) Chicago; CNN; Discovery Channel; Disney Channel; ESPN; Fox Family Channel; Nashville Network; TBS Superstation; Turner Network TV.
Fee: $43.50 installation; $21.00 monthly; $56.00 converter; $21.50 additional installation.
Commercial fee: $5.34 monthly.
Pay Service 1
Pay Units: 17.
Programming (via satellite): HBO.
Fee: $15.00 installation; $10.95 monthly.
Miles of plant: 4.9 (coaxial); None (fiber optic). Homes passed: 123.
Manager: Ted Hughett.
City fee: 3% of basic.
Ownership: Blackstone Cable LLC (MSO).

IONE—Ione City TV Co-op, Box 154, Ione, OR 97843. Phone: 541-422-7456. County: Morrow. ICA: OR0114.
TV Market Ranking: Outside TV Markets. Franchise award date: N.A. Franchise expiration date: N.A. Began: February 1, 1955.
Channel capacity: 12. Channels available but not in use: 5.
Basic Service
Subscribers: N.A.
Programming (received off-air): KEPR-TV (C), KNDU (N), KVEW (A) Pasco-Kennewick-Richland; KATU (A), KGW (N), KOIN (C), KPTV (U) Portland; allband FM.
Fee: $10.00 installation; $6.00 monthly.
Miles of plant: 2.5 (coaxial). Homes passed: 130.
Ownership: Ione City TV Co-op.

KLAMATH FALLS—Falcon Cable TV, Box 8, Klamath Falls, OR 97601-3795. Phone: 541-882-5533. County: Klamath. Also serves Keno, Klamath County (unincorporated areas), Midland, Wocus. ICA: OR0011.
TV Market Ranking: Below 100. Franchise award date: N.A. Franchise expiration date: April 1, 2004. Began: January 1, 1953.
Channel capacity: 28 (not 2-way capable). Channels available but not in use: N.A.
Basic Service
Subscribers: 13,301; Commercial subscribers: 28.
Programming (received off-air): KDKF (A), KOTI (N) Klamath Falls; 11 FMs.
Programming (via microwave): KSYS (P), KTVL (C) Medford; KTVU (F) Oakland-San Francisco; KATU (A), KPTV (U) Portland; KPIX-TV (C) San Francisco.
Programming (via satellite): CNN; Discovery Channel; Fox Family Channel; Headline News; Lifetime; MTV; Nashville Network; Nickelodeon; Odyssey; QVC; TBS Superstation.
Current originations: Automated timeweather.
Fee: $49.70 installation; $9.79 monthly; $2.00 converter; $24.85 additional installation.
Expanded Basic Service
Subscribers: 12,714.
Programming (via satellite): A & E; American Movie Classics; ESPN; Fox Sports Net Northwest; Turner Network TV; USA Network.
Fee: $10.68 monthly.
Pay Service 1
Pay Units: 1,031.
Programming (via satellite): Disney Channel.
Fee: $25.00 installation; $9.00 monthly.
Pay Service 2
Pay Units: 6,353.
Programming (via satellite): The New Encore.
Fee: N.A.
Pay Service 3
Pay Units: 1,945.
Programming (via satellite): HBO.
Fee: $25.00 installation; $11.95 monthly.
Pay Service 4
Pay Units: 924.
Programming (via satellite): Showtime.
Fee: N.A.
Local advertising: Yes (insert only). Available in satellite distributed programming. Rates: $6.00-$10.00/30 Seconds. Local sales manager: Mike Dadaos.
Program Guide: The Cable Guide.
Equipment: Scientific-Atlanta headend; Century III & Texscan amplifiers; Comm/Scope cable; Sony VTRs; Video Data Systems character generator; Jerrold & Texscan set top converters; Jerrold addressable set top converters; Andrew & Prodelin satellite antenna; Scientific-Atlanta satellite receivers.
Miles of plant: 242.2 (coaxial). Homes passed: 19,428. Total homes in franchised area: 19,477.
Manager: John Storck.
City fee: 3% of gross.
Ownership: Falcon Communications LP (MSO). Purchased from Tele-Communications Inc., September 30, 1998. See Cable System Ownership.

KNAPPA—Pacific Sun Cable Partners LP, No. 404, 7901 Stoneridge Dr., Pleaston, CA 94588. Phone: 509-787-3543. County: Clatsop. Also serves Svensen. ICA: OR0071.
TV Market Ranking: Outside TV Markets. Franchise award date: N.A. Franchise expiration date: N.A. Began: January 1, 1965.
Channel capacity: 36. Channels available but not in use: 14.
Basic Service
Subscribers: 706.
Programming (received off-air): KATU (A), KGW (N), KOIN (C), KOPB-TV (P), KPTV (U) Portland; allband FM.
Programming (via satellite): WGN-TV (W) Chicago; A & E; CNN; Discovery Channel; ESPN; Fox Family Channel; Lifetime; MTV; Nashville Network; Nickelodeon; TBS Superstation; Turner Network TV; VH1.
Fee: $49.95 installation; $23.70 monthly.
Pay Service 1
Pay Units: 27.
Programming (via satellite): Cinemax.
Fee: $15.00 installation; $8.95 monthly.
Pay Service 2
Pay Units: 48.
Programming (via satellite): Disney Channel.
Fee: $15.00 installation; $8.95 monthly.
Pay Service 3
Pay Units: 78.
Programming (via satellite): HBO.
Fee: $15.00 installation; $11.50 monthly.
Equipment: Blonder-Tongue, Catel & Scientific-Atlanta headend; AEL, Jerrold & Magnavox amplifiers; Times Fiber cable; Pico traps; Anixter-Mark satellite antenna; Scientific-Atlanta satellite receivers.
Miles of plant: 40.0 (coaxial). Homes passed: 1,000.
Manager: Lance Barger.
Ownership: Sun Country Cable (MSO).

LA GRANDE—Falcon Cable TV, Box 1401, La Grande, OR 97850-2202. Phone: 541-963-4189. County: Union. Also serves Island City, Union County. ICA: OR0028.
TV Market Ranking: Outside TV Markets. Franchise award date: January 1, 1954. Franchise expiration date: January 1, 2005. Began: September 29, 1954.
Channel capacity: 36 (not 2-way capable). Channels available but not in use: 1.
Basic Service
Subscribers: 4,790.
Programming (received off-air): KTVB (N) Boise; KTVR (P) La Grande.
Programming (via microwave): KATU (A), KGW (N), KOIN (C), KPTV (U) Portland; KPDX (F) Vancouver.
Programming (via satellite): A & E; C-SPAN; CNBC; CNN; Discovery Channel; ESPN; FX; Fox Family Channel; Fox Sports Net Northwest; FoxNet; Headline News; Lifetime; MTV; Nashville Network; Nickelodeon; Odyssey; QVC; TBS Superstation; The Weather Channel; Turner Network TV; USA Network; VH1.
Current originations: Automated timeweather.
Fee: $41.00 installation; $23.19 monthly; $1.30 converter; $19.00 additional installation.
Pay Service 1
Pay Units: 297.
Programming (via satellite): Cinemax.
Fee: $11.45 monthly.
Pay Service 2
Pay Units: 313.
Programming (via satellite): Disney Channel.
Fee: $11.45 monthly.
Pay Service 3
Pay Units: 1,799.
Programming (via satellite): The New Encore.
Fee: $1.75 monthly.

Pay Service 4
Pay Units: 652.
Programming (via satellite): HBO.
Fee: $12.45 monthly.
Pay Service 5
Pay Units: 347.
Programming (via satellite): Showtime.
Fee: $12.45 monthly.
Pay Service 6
Pay Units: N.A.
Programming (via satellite): Starz!
Fee: $4.75 monthly.
Pay-Per-View
Addressable homes: 100.
Local advertising: No. Available in character-generated programming. Local sales manager: Alan Keffer.
Program Guide: The Cable Guide.
Equipment: Scientific-Atlanta headend; Scientific-Atlanta amplifiers; Comm/Scope cable; Scientific-Atlanta satellite antenna.
Miles of plant: 74.3 (coaxial); None (fiber optic). Homes passed: 6,490. Total homes in franchised area: 6,490.
Manager: Darrell Linklater. Customer service manager: Pam Hardwick.
City fee: 4% of gross.
Ownership: Falcon Communications LP (MSO). Purchased from Tele-Communications Inc., September 30, 1998. See Cable System Ownership.

LA PINE—Crestview Cable TV, 350 N. Durham, Prineville, OR 97754. Phones: 541-447-4342; 800-285-2330. Fax: 541-447-5987. County: Deschutes. ICA: OR0142.
TV Market Ranking: Below 100. Franchise award date: N.A. Franchise expiration date: N.A. Began: October 1, 1988.
Channel capacity: 30 (not 2-way capable). Channels available but not in use: 6.
Basic Service
Subscribers: 1,974.
Programming (received off-air): KOAB-TV (P), KTVZ (N) Bend; KEZI (A) Eugene; KOTI (N) Klamath Falls; KOIN (C), KPTV (U) Portland.
Programming (via satellite): KMGH-TV (A), KUSA-TV (N) Denver; A & E; CNBC; CNN; Discovery Channel; ESPN; Fox Family Channel; Nashville Network; TBS Superstation; Turner Network TV.
Current originations: Automated time-weather.
Fee: $30.50 installation; $18.30 monthly; $14.80 additional installation.
Pay Service 1
Pay Units: N.A.
Programming (via satellite): Cinemax; Disney Channel; HBO.
Fee: $10.00 monthly (each).
Local advertising: Planned (locally produced). Local sales manager: Kathy Buntain.
Miles of plant: 60.0 (coaxial). Additional miles planned: 40.0 (coaxial).
Manager: Tony Ashcraft. Chief technician: Ron Morgan. Office manager: Audrey Gautney.
Ownership: California-Oregon Broadcasting Inc. (MSO).

LACOMB—CVF Cablevision, Suite 212, 8301 Edgewater Dr., Oakland, CA 94621. Phones: 510-569-7537; 800-331-6832. County: Linn. ICA: OR0078.
TV Market Ranking: Below 100. Franchise award date: N.A. Franchise expiration date: N.A. Began: August 1, 1992.
Channel capacity: 60 (2-way capable; operating 2-way). Channels available but not in use: 21.
Basic Service
Subscribers: 279.
Programming (received off-air): KOAC-TV (P) Corvallis; KATU (A), KGW (N), KOIN (C), KPTV (U) Portland; KPDX (F) Vancouver.
Programming (via satellite): WGN-TV (W) Chicago; A & E; C-SPAN; CNBC; Cartoon Network; Fox Family Channel; Fox Sports Net Northwest; Learning Channel; Lifetime; MTV; Nickelodeon; QVC; Sci-Fi Channel; TBS Superstation; The Inspirational Network; Travel Channel; Trinity Bcstg. Network; Turner Network TV; USA Network; VH1.
Fee: $65.00 installation; $23.95 monthly; $4.95 converter.
Expanded Basic Service
Subscribers: 238.
Programming (via satellite): American Movie Classics; CNN; Country Music TV; Discovery Channel; ESPN; Nashville Network.
Fee: $65.00 installation; $2.00 monthly.
Pay Service 1
Pay Units: 202.
Programming (via satellite): Cinemax; Disney Channel; HBO.
Fee: $9.95 monthly (Cinemax or Disney), $11.95 monthly (HBO).
Pay Service 2
Pay Units: N.A.
Programming (via satellite): Flix; The Movie Channel.
Fee: $2.00 monthly (Flix), $9.95 monthly (TMC).
Miles of plant: 26.0 (coaxial); None (fiber optic). Homes passed: 575. Total homes in franchised area: 800.
Manager: Neil Schnog.
Ownership: CVF Cablevision. Purchased from Preferred Cable.

LAKEVIEW—TCI Cablevision of Oregon Inc., Box 8, Klamath Falls, OR 97601-3795. Phone: 541-947-3772. County: Lake. Also serves Lake County (portions). ICA: OR0051.
TV Market Ranking: Outside TV Markets. Franchise award date: N.A. Franchise expiration date: January 1, 1999. Began: August 1, 1956.
Channel capacity: 37 (not 2-way capable). Channels available but not in use: N.A.
Basic Service
Subscribers: 1,361; Commercial subscribers: 10.
Programming (received off-air): KOTI (N) Klamath Falls; KTVL (C) Medford; 7 FMs.
Programming (via microwave): KDKF (A) Klamath Falls; KGW (N), KOIN (C), KOPB-TV (P), KPTV (U) Portland.
Programming (via satellite): WGN-TV (W) Chicago; C-SPAN; C-SPAN 2; CNN; Country Music TV; Discovery Channel; FoxNet; Headline News; Home Shopping Network; Lifetime; Nashville Network; Nickelodeon; Odyssey; TBS Superstation; The Weather Channel.
Fee: $40.70 installation; $9.44 monthly; $2.00 converter; $20.35 additional installation.
Commercial fee: $5.00 monthly.
Expanded Basic Service
Subscribers: 1,276.
Programming (via satellite): American Movie Classics; ESPN; Fox Sports Net Northwest; Turner Network TV; USA Network.
Fee: $10.89 monthly.
Pay Service 1
Pay Units: 183.
Programming (via satellite): Cinemax.
Fee: N.A.
Pay Service 2
Pay Units: 161.
Programming (via satellite): Disney Channel.
Fee: N.A.
Pay Service 3
Pay Units: 500.
Programming (via satellite): The New Encore.
Fee: N.A.
Pay Service 4
Pay Units: 238.
Programming (via satellite): HBO.
Fee: N.A.
Local advertising: Yes. Available in character-generated programming. Rates: $1.00/Day.
Equipment: Catel & M/A-Com headend; Magnavox amplifiers; Times Fiber cable; Info/Soft character generator; Jerrold & Panasonic set top converters; Eagle traps; Prodelin satellite antenna; M/A-Com & DX Engineering satellite receivers.
Miles of plant: 25.0 (coaxial). Homes passed: 1,822. Total homes in franchised area: 1,827.
Manager: Dudley Steademan.
City fee: 3% of gross.
Ownership: AT&T Broadband & Internet Services (MSO). Purchased from Tele-Communications Inc., March 9, 1999.

LEBANON—TCI Cablevision of Oregon Inc., 2147 S. Santiam Hwy., Lebanon, OR 97355. Phone: 541-258-6090. County: Linn. Also serves Linn County (western portion), Oakville, Tangent. ICA: OR0024.
TV Market Ranking: Below 100 (Lebanon, portions of Linn County, Oakville, Tangent); Outside TV Markets (portions of Linn County). Franchise award date: N.A. Franchise expiration date: April 5, 2001. Began: August 1, 1967.
Channel capacity: 33 (not 2-way capable). Channels available but not in use: N.A.
Basic Service
Subscribers: 4,986.
Programming (received off-air): KOAC-TV (P) Corvallis; KVAL-TV (C) Eugene; KATU (A), KGW (N), KOIN (C), KPTV (U) Portland; KPXG (X) Salem; KPDX (F) Vancouver; 14 FMs.
Programming (via microwave): KEZI (A), KMTR (N) Eugene.
Programming (via satellite): C-SPAN; CNN; Discovery Channel; Fox Family Channel; Lifetime; MTV; Nashville Network; TBS Superstation; The Weather Channel.
Current originations: Public access; local news.
Fee: $33.56 installation; $10.23 monthly; $0.78 converter; $14.39 additional installation.
Expanded Basic Service
Subscribers: 4,337.
Programming (via satellite): American Movie Classics; ESPN; Fox Sports Net Northwest; QVC; Turner Network TV; USA Network.
Fee: $9.98 monthly.
Pay Service 1
Pay Units: 529.
Programming (via satellite): Disney Channel.
Fee: $10.00 installation; $10.95 monthly.
Pay Service 2
Pay Units: 2,564.
Programming (via satellite): The New Encore.
Fee: N.A.
Pay Service 3
Pay Units: 775.
Programming (via satellite): HBO.
Fee: $10.00 installation; $12.50 monthly.
Pay Service 4
Pay Units: 220.
Programming (via satellite): The Movie Channel.
Fee: $10.00 installation; $12.50 monthly.
Pay Service 5
Pay Units: 415.
Programming (via satellite): Showtime.
Fee: $10.00 installation; $12.50 monthly.
Local advertising: Yes. Available in satellite distributed programming. Regional interconnect: TCI Cable Advertising-Oregon.
Program Guide: The Cable Guide.
Equipment: Scientific-Atlanta headend; Theta-Com amplifiers; Scientific-Atlanta & Jerrold set top converters; Scientific-Atlanta satellite antenna; Scientific-Atlanta satellite receivers.
Miles of plant: 121.9 (coaxial). Homes passed: 7,069. Total homes in franchised area: 7,069.
Manager: Gary Hostetler. Chief technician: Jim Pace.
City fee: 3% of gross.
Ownership: AT&T Broadband & Internet Services (MSO). Purchased from Tele-Communications Inc., March 9, 1999.

LINCOLN CITY—Falcon Telecable, 1344 N.E. Hwy. 101, Lincoln City, OR 97367. Phone: 541-994-3111. Fax: 541-994-7438. County: Lincoln. Also serves Lincoln County (portions). ICA: OR0020.
TV Market Ranking: Below 100 (portions of Lincoln County); Outside TV Markets (Lincoln City, portions of Lincoln County). Franchise award date: January 1, 1955. Franchise expiration date: N.A. Began: October 22, 1954.
Channel capacity: 62 (not 2-way capable). Channels available but not in use: 5.
Basic Service
Subscribers: 5,608.
Programming (received off-air): KATU (A), KGW (N), KOIN (C), KOPB-TV (P), KPTV (U) Portland; KPDX (F) Vancouver; allband FM.
Programming (via satellite): WGN-TV (W) Chicago; A & E; C-SPAN; CNBC; Comedy Central; E! Entertainment TV; ESPN 2; FX; Home & Garden Television; Home Shopping Network; Learning Channel; MTV; QVC; TBS Superstation; TV Guide Channel; TV Guide Sneak Prevue; Trinity Bcstg. Network; VH1.
Current originations: Public access; educational access; government access; leased access.
Fee: $49.95 installation; $16.74 monthly; $15.00 additional installation.
Expanded Basic Service
Subscribers: 4,140.
Programming (via satellite): Blazer Vision; CNN; ESPN; Fox Family Channel; Fox Sports Net Northwest; Headline News; Lifetime; Nickelodeon; Sci-Fi Channel; Travel Channel.
Fee: $22.50 installation; $25.50 monthly.
Expanded Basic Service 2
Subscribers: 1,870.
Programming (via satellite): American Movie Classics; Country Music TV; Discovery Channel; Disney Channel; Nashville Network; The Weather Channel; Turner Network TV; USA Network.
Fee: $8.48 monthly.
Expanded Basic Service 3
Subscribers: 764.
Programming (via satellite): Cartoon Network; fXM: Movies from Fox; History Channel; Outdoor Life Network.
Fee: $7.56 monthly.
Pay Service 1
Pay Units: 282.
Programming (via satellite): Cinemax.
Fee: $11.95 monthly.
Pay Service 2
Pay Units: 518.
Programming (via satellite): HBO.
Fee: $11.95 monthly.

Pay Service 3
Pay Units: 359.
Programming (via satellite): Showtime.
Fee: $11.95 monthly.
Pay Service 4
Pay Units: 205.
Programming (via satellite): The Movie Channel.
Fee: $11.95 monthly.
Pay Service 5
Pay Units: N.A.
Programming (via satellite): The New Encore.
Fee: N.A.
Pay-Per-View
Addressable homes: 3,025.
Action Pay-Per-View; Spice; Viewer's Choice.
Local advertising: Planned.
Equipment: Scientific-Atlanta headend; Cascade, Jerrold & Magnavox amplifiers; Cerro, Times Fiber & Vikoa cable; MSI character generator; Scientific-Atlanta set top converters; Scientific-Atlanta addressable set top converters; Scientific-Atlanta satellite antenna; Scientific-Atlanta satellite receivers.
Miles of plant: 147.0 (coaxial). Homes passed: 7,767. Total homes in franchised area: 8,250.
Manager: Roberta Hogeland. Chief technician: Bruce Clark.
City fee: 5% of gross.
Ownership: Falcon Communications LP (MSO), joint venture formed September 30, 1998. See Cable System Ownership.

LOOKINGGLASS—Interstate Cable Inc., Box 2687, Salina, KS 67402-2687. Phones: 785-452-9409; 800-888-4788. Fax: 785-238-7190. County: Douglas. ICA: OR0082.
TV Market Ranking: Below 100. Franchise award date: N.A. Franchise expiration date: N.A. Began: September 1, 1990.
Channel capacity: 36. Channels available but not in use: N.A.
Basic Service
Subscribers: 270.
Programming (received off-air): KEZI (A) Eugene; KDRV (A), KOBI (N), KSYS (P) Medford; KPIC (C) Roseburg.
Programming (via satellite): WGN-TV (W) Chicago; A & E; C-SPAN; CNN; Comedy Central; Country Music TV; Discovery Channel; ESPN; FX; Fox Family Channel; Home Shopping Network; Nashville Network; QVC; Sci-Fi Channel; TBS Superstation; The Inspirational Network; Trinity Bcstg. Network; USA Network.
Fee: $50.00 installation; $23.95 monthly; $2.00 converter; $15.00 additional installation.
Pay Service 1
Pay Units: N.A.
Programming (via satellite): Cinemax; Disney Channel; HBO; Showtime.
Fee: $6.95 monthly (Encore), $7.95 monthly (Disney), $10.95 monthly (Cinemax, HBO or Showtime).
Miles of plant: 32.0 (coaxial). Homes passed: 615.
Manager: Patti Lahey.
Ownership: Tristar Cable Inc. (MSO).

MACLEAY—Country Cablevision Ltd., Box 12038, Salem, OR 97309-0038. Phone: 503-588-8247. Fax: 503-588-0544. County: Marion. Also serves Marion, Marion County (portions), Shaw, West Stayton. ICA: OR0064.
TV Market Ranking: 29 (portions of Marion County); Below 100 (Macleay, Marion, portions of Marion County, Shaw, West Stayton); Outside TV Markets (portions of Marion County). Franchise award date: January 1, 1987. Franchise expiration date: January 1, 1997. Began: August 1, 1987.
Channel capacity: 42 (2-way capable). Channels available but not in use: 12.
Basic Service
Subscribers: 930.
Programming (received off-air): KATU (A), KGW (N), KOIN (C), KOPB-TV (P), KPTV (U) Portland; KPDX (F) Vancouver.
Programming (via satellite): WGN-TV (W) Chicago; A & E; American Movie Classics; CNN; Country Music TV; Discovery Channel; ESPN; Fox Family Channel; Headline News; Lifetime; MTV; Nashville Network; Nickelodeon; QVC; TBS Superstation; Turner Network TV; USA Network; Univision; VH1.
Current originations: Public access.
Fee: $49.95 installation; $21.95 monthly.
Pay Service 1
Pay Units: 440.
Programming (via satellite): Disney Channel; Showtime; The Movie Channel; The New Encore.
Fee: $4.95 monthly (Encore), $8.95 monthly (Showtime), $9.95 monthly (Disney), $10.95 monthly (TMC).
Local advertising: Yes. Available in locally originated programming.
Equipment: Trilogy cable.
Miles of plant: 65.0 (coaxial). Homes passed: 2,100. Total homes in franchised area: 35,000.
Manager: John P. Johnson. Chief technician: Veron L. Robinson.
Ownership: Country Cablevision Ltd. (MSO).

MADRAS—Crestview Cable TV, Suite E, 35 S.E. C St., Madras, OR 97741. Phone: 541-475-2969. County: Jefferson. Also serves Culver, Metolius. ICA: OR0146.
TV Market Ranking: Below 100 (Metolius); Outside TV Markets (Culver, Madras). Franchise award date: January 1, 1955. Franchise expiration date: August 1, 2000. Began: June 1, 1955.
Channel capacity: 30 (not 2-way capable). Channels available but not in use: 5.
Basic Service
Subscribers: 2,161.
Programming (received off-air): KOAB-TV (P), KTVZ (N) Bend; KATU (A), KGW (N), KOIN (C), KPTV (U) Portland; KPDX (F) Vancouver; 14 FMs.
Current originations: Automated time-weather.
Fee: $25.00 installation (aerial), $30.00 (underground); $12.95 monthly; $1.00 converter; $10.00 additional installation.
Commercial fee: $2.20 monthly.
Expanded Basic Service
Subscribers: 2,130.
Programming (via satellite): A & E; CNBC; CNN; Discovery Channel; ESPN; Fox Family Channel; Lifetime; MTV; Nashville Network; Nickelodeon; TBS Superstation; Turner Network TV.
Fee: $2.95 monthly.
Pay Service 1
Pay Units: 323.
Programming (via satellite): Cinemax.
Fee: $10.00 monthly.
Pay Service 2
Pay Units: 240.
Programming (via satellite): Disney Channel.
Fee: $10.00 monthly.
Pay Service 3
Pay Units: 297.
Programming (via satellite): HBO.
Fee: $10.00 monthly.
Local advertising: Yes. Available in character-generated programming. Rates: $20.00/Week.
Local sales manager: Annette Hylton.
Program Guide: Premium Channels.
Equipment: Tocom headend; GTE Sylvania amplifiers; Anaconda & CCS Hatfield cable; Mycrotek character generator; Pioneer set top converters; Eagle traps; Scientific-Atlanta satellite antenna.
Miles of plant: 59.0 (coaxial). Total homes in franchised area: 3,500.
Manager: Roger Harris. Chief technician: Jerry R. Steele.
City fee: 3% of gross.
Ownership: California-Oregon Broadcasting Inc. (MSO).

MALIN—Blackstone Cable LLC, 1104 W. Ironwood Dr., Coeur d'Alene, ID 83814-2605. Phone: 208-664-3370. Fax: 208-664-5888. County: Klamath. ICA: OR0092.
TV Market Ranking: Below 100. Franchise award date: N.A. Franchise expiration date: June 9, 2010. Began: May 1, 1981.
Channel capacity: 19 (not 2-way capable). Channels available but not in use: 4.
Basic Service
Subscribers: 103.
Programming (received off-air): KDKF (A), KOTI (N) Klamath Falls; KMVU (F), KSYS (P), KTVL (C) Medford.
Programming (via satellite): WGN-TV (W) Chicago; CNN; Discovery Channel; Disney Channel; ESPN; Fox Family Channel; Nashville Network; TBS Superstation; The Inspirational Network; Turner Classic Movies; Turner Network TV; Univision.
Current originations: Automated time-weather.
Fee: $43.50 installation; $21.00 monthly; $56.00 converter; $21.50 additional installation.
Commercial fee: $5.34 monthly.
Pay Service 1
Pay Units: 12.
Programming (via satellite): HBO.
Fee: $15.00 installation; $10.95 monthly.
Miles of plant: 3.7 (coaxial); None (fiber optic). Homes passed: 270.
Manager: Ted Hughett.
City fee: 3% of basic.
Ownership: Blackstone Cable LLC (MSO).

MAPLETON—Falcon Cable Systems Co., 1400 Newmark Ave., Coos Bay, OR 97420. Phone: 541-888-5712. Fax: 541-888-9292. County: Lane. ICA: OR0161.
TV Market Ranking: Outside TV Markets. Franchise award date: N.A. Franchise expiration date: N.A. Began: N.A.
Channel capacity: 17. Channels available but not in use: None.
Basic Service
Subscribers: 176.
Programming (received off-air): KOAC-TV (P) Corvallis; KEVU-LP (F), KEZI (A), KMTR (N), KVAL-TV (C) Eugene; KATU (A) Portland.
Programming (via satellite): ESPN; Fox Family Channel; QVC; Sci-Fi Channel.
Fee: $14.01 monthly.
Expanded Basic Service
Subscribers: 169.
Programming (via satellite): Country Music TV; Discovery Channel; USA Network.
Fee: $1.73 monthly.
Expanded Basic Service 2
Subscribers: 155.
Programming (via satellite): WGN-TV (W) Chicago; Disney Channel; TBS Superstation.
Fee: $3.67 monthly.
Pay Service 1
Pay Units: 44.
Programming (via satellite): HBO.
Fee: $11.95 monthly.
Miles of plant: 7.0 (coaxial). Homes passed: 344.
Manager: Bill Griffin. Chief technician: Norman Lacey. Marketing director: Joan Crabtree.
Ownership: Falcon Communications LP (MSO), joint venture formed September 30, 1998. See Cable System Ownership.

MEDFORD—Falcon Cable, Box 399, 926 S. Grape St., Medford, OR 97501. Phone: 541-779-1851. Fax: 541-776-2278. County: Jackson. Also serves Ashland, Central Point, Eagle Point, Gold Hill, Jackson County, Jacksonville, Phoenix, Talent, White City. ICA: OR0006.
TV Market Ranking: Below 100. Franchise award date: N.A. Franchise expiration date: July 1, 2002. Began: January 1, 1958.
Channel capacity: 78 (2-way capable). Channels available but not in use: 10.
Basic Service
Subscribers: 34,877.
Programming (received off-air): KDRV (A), KMVU (F), KOBI (N), KSYS (P), KTVL (C) Medford; allband FM.
Programming (via satellite): C-SPAN; C-SPAN 2; Home Shopping Network; Knowledge TV; Learning Channel; Lifetime; Odyssey; QVC; Univision.
Current originations: Automated time-weather; public access; educational access; government access; leased access.
Fee: $34.16 installation; $11.02 monthly; $1.50 converter; $14.00 additional installation.
Commercial fee: $4.50 monthly.
Expanded Basic Service
Subscribers: 23,522.
Programming (via satellite): A & E; American Movie Classics; CNBC; CNN; Country Music TV; Discovery Channel; Disney Channel; E! Entertainment TV; ESPN; ESPN 2; FX; Fox Family Channel; Fox Sports Net Direct; Fox Sports Net Northwest; Headline News; History Channel; Intro TV; Lifetime; MTV; Nashville Network; Nick at Nite; Nickelodeon; Sci-Fi Channel; TBS Superstation; TV Food Network; The Health Network; The Weather Channel; Travel Channel; Turner Network TV; USA Network; VH1.
Fee: $11.39 installation; $18.35 monthly.
Pay Service 1
Pay Units: 1,038.
Programming (via satellite): Cinemax.
Fee: $13.83 installation; $12.95 monthly.
Pay Service 2
Pay Units: 11,859.
Programming (via satellite): The New Encore.
Fee: $1.75 monthly.
Pay Service 3
Pay Units: 3,494.
Programming (via satellite): HBO.
Fee: $12.95 monthly.
Pay Service 4
Pay Units: 1,797.
Programming (via satellite): Showtime.
Fee: $12.95 monthly.
Pay Service 5
Pay Units: 1,154.
Programming (via satellite): DMX.
Fee: $9.95 monthly.
Pay Service 6
Pay Units: 5,037.
Programming (via satellite): Starz!
Fee: $6.75 monthly.
Pay-Per-View
Addressable homes: 6,333.
Action Pay-Per-View; Playboy TV.
Fee: $2.99 (Action Pay-Per-View); $3.99 (Playboy TV).
Pay-per-view manager: Vince Zauskey.

Local advertising: Yes. Available in satellite distributed & character-generated programming. Rates: $49.00/Minute; $29.00/30 Seconds. Local sales manager: Lanny Guyer.
Program Guide: The Cable Guide.
Equipment: Scientific-Atlanta headend; Jerrold amplifiers; Comm/Scope cable; Sony VTRs; Jerrold set top converters; Jerrold addressable set top converters; Arcom traps; Microwave Assoc., Prodelin & Andrew satellite antenna; Microwave Assoc., Scientific-Atlanta & Jerrold satellite receivers.
Miles of plant: 697.5 (coaxial); 90.0 (fiber optic). Additional miles planned: 14.0 (coaxial); 2.0 (fiber optic). Homes passed: 61,994. Total homes in franchised area: 65,016.
Manager: Tom Coleman. Chief technician: Bob Thomas. Customer service manager: Ruth Burns.
City fee: 3%-5% of gross.
Ownership: Falcon Communications LP (MSO), joint venture formed September 30, 1998. See Cable System Ownership.

MERRILL—Blackstone Cable LLC, 1104 W. Ironwood Dr., Coeur d'Alene, ID 83814-2605. Phone: 208-664-3370. Fax: 208-664-5888. County: Klamath. ICA: OR0081.
TV Market Ranking: Below 100. Franchise award date: N.A. Franchise expiration date: N.A. Began: May 1, 1981.
Channel capacity: 19 (not 2-way capable). Channels available but not in use: 4.
Basic Service
Subscribers: 201.
Programming (received off-air): KDKF (A), KOTI (N) Klamath Falls; KMVU (F), KSYS (P), KTVL (C) Medford.
Programming (via satellite): WGN-TV (W) Chicago; CNN; Discovery Channel; Disney Channel; ESPN; Fox Family Channel; Nashville Network; TBS Superstation; The Inspirational Network; Turner Classic Movies; Turner Network TV; Univision.
Current originations: Automated timeweather.
Fee: $43.50 installation; $21.00 monthly; $56.00 converter; $21.50 additional installation.
Commercial fee: $5.50 monthly.
Pay Service 1
Pay Units: 23.
Programming (via satellite): HBO.
Fee: $15.00 installation; $10.95 monthly.
Equipment: Blonder-Tongue & Microwave Assoc. headend; MCE amplifiers; CCS Hatfield cable; Microwave Assoc. satellite antenna.
Miles of plant: 6.1 (coaxial); None (fiber optic). Homes passed: 350.
Manager: Ted Hughett.
Ownership: Blackstone Cable LLC (MSO).

MILTON-FREEWATER—TCI Cablevision of Oregon Inc., Box 1577, 126 W. Poplar St., Walla Walla, WA 99362-2847. Phone: 509-529-9500. Fax: 509-522-1719. County: Umatilla. Also serves Umatilla County (unincorporated areas). ICA: OR0043.
TV Market Ranking: Below 100 (Milton-Freewater, portions of Umatilla County); Outside TV Markets (portions of Umatilla County). Franchise award date: N.A. Franchise expiration date: N.A. Began: September 1, 1955.
Channel capacity: 40 (2-way capable). Channels available but not in use: None.
Basic Service
Subscribers: 1,960.
Programming (received off-air): KTVR (P) La Grande; KEPR-TV (C), KNDU (N), KVEW (A) Pasco-Kennewick-Richland; KPTV (U) Portland; KAYU-TV (F), KSPS-TV (P) Spokane.
Programming (via satellite): WGN-TV (W) Chicago; A & E; C-SPAN; CNN; Comedy Central; Discovery Channel; Fox Family Channel; Headline News; Lifetime; MTV; Nashville Network; Nickelodeon; TBS Superstation; The Weather Channel; Univision; VH1.
Current originations: Automated timeweather.
Fee: $36.34 installation; $10.11 monthly; $18.17 additional installation.
Expanded Basic Service
Subscribers: 1,800.
Programming (via satellite): A & E; American Movie Classics; CNN; Comedy Central; Discovery Channel; ESPN; FX; Fox Family Channel; Fox Sports Net Northwest; Headline News; Lifetime; MTV; Nashville Network; Nickelodeon; Turner Network TV; USA Network; Univision; VH1.
Fee: $12.01 monthly.
Pay Service 1
Pay Units: 132.
Programming (via satellite): Cinemax.
Fee: $11.70 monthly.
Pay Service 2
Pay Units: 139.
Programming (via satellite): Disney Channel.
Fee: $11.45 monthly.
Pay Service 3
Pay Units: 680.
Programming (via satellite): The New Encore.
Fee: N.A.
Pay Service 4
Pay Units: 255.
Programming (via satellite): HBO.
Fee: $12.00 monthly.
Pay Service 5
Pay Units: 115.
Programming (via satellite): Showtime.
Fee: $12.00 monthly.
Pay Service 6
Pay Units: 3.
Programming (via satellite): Xchange.
Fee: N.A.
Pay-Per-View
Addressable homes: 600.
Equipment: Scientific-Atlanta headend; RCA amplifiers; Times Fiber cable; Jerrold set top converters; Tocom addressable set top converters; Eagle traps; Scientific-Atlanta & Microdyne satellite antenna; Scientific-Atlanta & Microdyne satellite receivers.
Miles of plant: 40.5 (coaxial). Homes passed: 3,480.
Manager: Tim Klinefelter. Chief technician: Tim Ream. Program director: Dinah Morrison. Marketing director: Marlene Ashby.
City fee: 3% of gross.
Ownership: AT&T Broadband & Internet Services (MSO). Purchased from Tele-Communications Inc., March 9, 1999.

MILWAUKIE—TCI of Milwaukie, 5687 S.E. International Way, Milwaukie, OR 97222. Phone: 503-654-2266. Fax: 503-652-0464. County: Clackamas. ICA: OR0018.
TV Market Ranking: 29. Franchise award date: May 1, 1983. Franchise expiration date: April 3, 1998. Began: December 14, 1983.
Channel capacity: 61 (2-way capable; operating 2-way). Channels available but not in use: None.
Basic Service
Subscribers: 5,283; Commercial subscribers: 424.
Programming (received off-air): KATU (A), KGW (N), KNMT (T), KOIN (C), KOPB-TV (P), KPTV (U) Portland; KWBP (W) Salem; KPDX (F) Vancouver; 25 FMs.
Programming (via satellite): WGN-TV (W) Chicago; A & E; American Movie Classics; BET; C-SPAN; C-SPAN 2; CNBC; CNN; Comedy Central; Discovery Channel; Disney Channel; E! Entertainment TV; ESPN; ESPN 2; EWTN; FX; Fox Family Channel; Fox News Channel; Fox Sports Net Northwest; Great American Country; Headline News; History Channel; Home & Garden Television; Home Shopping Network; Knowledge TV; Learning Channel; Lifetime; MSNBC; MTV; Nashville Network; Nickelodeon; Northwest Cable News; Odyssey; Product Information Network; Sci-Fi Channel; TBS Superstation; TV Guide Channel; The Weather Channel; Trinity Bcstg. Network; Turner Network TV; USA Network; Univision; VH1.
Current originations: Public access; educational access; government access; automated emergency alert; local news.
Fee: $26.26 installation; $25.80 monthly; $3.42 converter.
Pay Service 1
Pay Units: 568.
Programming (via satellite): Cinemax.
Fee: $10.00 installation; $11.53 monthly.
Pay Service 2
Pay Units: 1,128.
Programming (via satellite): HBO.
Fee: $10.00 installation; $11.53 monthly.
Pay Service 3
Pay Units: 543.
Programming (via satellite): The Movie Channel.
Fee: $10.00 installation; $11.53 monthly.
Pay Service 4
Pay Units: 736.
Programming (via satellite): Showtime.
Fee: $10.00 installation; $11.53 monthly.
Pay Service 5
Pay Units: 515.
Programming (via satellite): The New Encore.
Fee: $1.84 monthly.
Pay Service 6
Pay Units: 504.
Programming (via satellite): Starz!
Fee: $7.11 monthly.
Local advertising: Yes. Available in satellite distributed programming.
Program Guide: TV Host.
Equipment: Scientific-Atlanta headend; Magnavox amplifiers; Comm/Scope cable; JVC cameras; Sony VTRs; Video Data Systems character generator; Scientific-Atlanta set top converters; Eagle traps; Simulsat satellite antenna; Scientific-Atlanta satellite receivers.
Miles of plant: 79.0 (coaxial); 79.0 (fiber optic). Homes passed: 9,749.
Manager: Ross Waggoner. Program director: Brad Nonler. Customer service manager: Virginia Meschi.
City fee: 5% of gross.
Ownership: AT&T Broadband & Internet Services (MSO). Purchased from Tele-Communications Inc., March 9, 1999.

MONROE—Monroe Area Communications Inc., Box 130, 575 Commercial St., Monroe, OR 97456. Phone: 541-847-5135. Fax: 541-847-9997. County: Benton. ICA: OR0105.
TV Market Ranking: Below 100. Franchise award date: N.A. Franchise expiration date: N.A. Began: October 15, 1983.
Channel capacity: 35. Channels available but not in use: 7.
Basic Service
Subscribers: 300.
Programming (received off-air): KOAC-TV (P) Corvallis; KEZI (A), KLSR-TV (U), KMTR (N), KVAL-TV (C) Eugene; KPTV (U) Portland; KTVC (X) Roseburg.
Programming (via satellite): WGN-TV (W) Chicago; A & E; American Movie Classics; C-SPAN; CNN; Discovery Channel; ESPN; Fox Family Channel; Fox Sports Net Northwest; Learning Channel; Lifetime; Nashville Network; Nickelodeon; QVC; Sci-Fi Channel; TBS Superstation; Turner Network TV; USA Network.
Fee: $10.00 installation; $19.95 monthly; $4.50 converter.
Pay Service 1
Pay Units: 71.
Programming (via satellite): HBO.
Fee: $10.00 installation; $10.00 monthly.
Pay Service 2
Pay Units: 21.
Programming (via satellite): Disney Channel.
Fee: $10.00 installation; $10.00 monthly.
Local advertising: Yes. Available in locally originated programming.
Equipment: Blonder-Tongue headend; Magnavox amplifiers; Scientific-Atlanta satellite antenna; Anixter-Mark satellite receivers.
Miles of plant: 13.0 (coaxial). Homes passed: 450.
Manager: John T. Dillard.
City fee: 3% of basic.
Ownership: Monroe Area Communications Inc.

MORO—Moro TV Club, Box 371, 603 Columbus St., Moro, OR 97039. Phone: 541-565-3353. County: Sherman. ICA: OR0111.
TV Market Ranking: Outside TV Markets. Franchise award date: November 3, 1954. Franchise expiration date: N.A. Began: January 1, 1955.
Channel capacity: 34 (not 2-way capable). Channels available but not in use: None.
Basic Service
Subscribers: 127.
Programming (received off-air): KBWU-LP (I) Pasco; KEPR-TV (C), KNDU (N), KVEW (A) Pasco-Kennewick-Richland.
Programming (via microwave): KATU (A), KGW (N), KOIN (C), KOPB-TV (P), KPTV (U) Portland; KPDX (F) Vancouver.
Programming (via satellite): WGN-TV (W) Chicago; A & E; C-SPAN; CNN; CNNfn; Cartoon Network; Discovery Channel; Disney Channel; ESPN; Fox Family Channel; Headline News; History Channel; Home & Garden Television; Learning Channel; Nashville Network; Nick at Nite's TV Land; Sci-Fi Channel; TBS Superstation; Trinity Bcstg. Network; Turner Classic Movies; Turner Network TV; USA Network.
Fee: $25.00 installation; $20.00 monthly; $15.00 converter.
Pay Service 1
Pay Units: 127.
Programming (via satellite): HBO.
Fee: N.A.
Local advertising: Yes. Available in locally originated programming. Local sales manager: Larry Hoctor.
Equipment: Blonder-Tongue & Drake headend; Blonder-Tongue amplifiers; Comm/Scope cable; Jerrold set top converters; ChannelMaster satellite antenna; ChannelMaster satellite receivers.
Miles of plant: 9.0 (coaxial); None (fiber optic). Additional miles planned: 1.0 (coaxial). Homes passed: 150. Total homes in franchised area: 173.
Manager: Larry Hoctor. Chief technicians: Larry Trickelhorn & Jim Roth.
Ownership: Moro TV Club.

MOUNT VERNON—Blue Mountain TV Cable Co., Box 267, Mount Vernon, OR 97865. Phone:

541-932-4613. County: Grant. Also serves Canyon City, John Day. ICA: OR0061.
TV Market Ranking: Outside TV Markets. Franchise award date: N.A. Franchise expiration date: N.A. Began: October 1, 1954.
Channel capacity: 15 (not 2-way capable). Channels available but not in use: None.
Basic Service
Subscribers: 1,270.
Programming (received off-air): KBCI-TV (C), KTVB (N) Boise; KIVI (A) Nampa; KOPB-TV (P) Portland; 4 FMs.
Programming (via microwave): KGW (N), KPTV (U) Portland.
Programming (via satellite): WGN-TV (W) Chicago; Discovery Channel; Fox Family Channel; Fox Sports Net Northwest; FoxNet; Nashville Network; TBS Superstation.
Current originations: Automated time-weather.
Fee: $12.50 installation; $9.50 monthly.
Pay Service 1
Pay Units: N.A.
Programming (via satellite): Cinemax; Disney Channel; HBO.
Fee: $8.80 monthly (Disney), $9.00 monthly (Cinemax), $10.00 monthly (HBO).
Equipment: Jerrold headend; Jerrold amplifiers; Plastoid & Times Fiber cable; Scientific-Atlanta satellite antenna.
Miles of plant: 30.0 (coaxial); None (fiber optic). Homes passed: 1,445.
Manager: Chuck McKenna.
Ownership: Blue Mountain TV Cable Co. (MSO).

MYRTLE CREEK—Falcon Cable, Box 1700, 650 N.E. Division St., Myrtle Creek, OR 97457. Phones: 541-863-4914; 541-673-2288. Fax: 541-863-6832.
Web site: http://www.falconcable.com.
County: Douglas. Also serves Canyonville, Dillard, Green, Riddle, Tri-City, Winston. ICA: OR0021.
TV Market Ranking: Below 100. Franchise award date: February 1, 1971. Franchise expiration date: February 1, 2001. Began: December 1, 1972.
Channel capacity: 41 (not 2-way capable). Channels available but not in use: None.
Basic Service
Subscribers: 6,500; Commercial subscribers: 17.
Programming (received off-air): KEVU-LP (F), KEZI (A), KLSR-TV (U) Eugene; KOBI (N), KSYS (P) Medford; KMTX-TV (N), KPIC (C), KTVC (X) Roseburg; 22 FMs.
Programming (via satellite): WGN-TV (W) Chicago; TBS Superstation.
Current originations: Public access; local sports.
Fee: $40.00 installation; $7.25 monthly; $2.00 converter; $25.00 additional installation.
Commercial fee: $106.00 monthly.
Expanded Basic Service
Subscribers: 6,038.
Programming (via satellite): A & E; American Movie Classics; C-SPAN; CNN; Comedy Central; Discovery Channel; ESPN; Fox Family Channel; Fox Sports Net Northwest; Great American Country; Headline News; Home Shopping Network; Knowledge TV; Lifetime; MSNBC; MTV; Nashville Network; Nickelodeon; Odyssey; Product Information Network; The Weather Channel; Turner Network TV; USA Network; VH1.
Fee: $25.00 installation; $17.54 monthly.
Pay Service 1
Pay Units: 647.
Programming (via satellite): Disney Channel.
Fee: $10.00 installation; $8.00 monthly.
Pay Service 2
Pay Units: 1,024.
Programming (via satellite): HBO.
Fee: $10.00 installation; $10.95 monthly.
Pay Service 3
Pay Units: 908.
Programming (via satellite): Showtime.
Fee: $10.00 installation; $9.00 monthly.
Pay Service 4
Pay Units: 1,317.
Programming (via satellite): The Movie Channel.
Fee: $10.00 installation; $9.00 monthly.
Pay-Per-View
Addressable homes: 352.
Action Pay-Per-View; Viewer's Choice.
Fee: Varies.
Pay-per-view manager: Charlene McCarit.
Local advertising: Yes (locally produced). Available in satellite distributed, locally originated, character-generated & taped programming. Rates: $10.00/Minute; $5.00/30 Seconds.
Local sales manager: Tom Fields.
Equipment: Scientific-Atlanta headend; Magnavox amplifiers; Comm/Scope cable; Texscan character generator; Hamlin set top converters; Pioneer addressable set top converters; Arcom & Eagle traps; Scientific-Atlanta satellite antenna; DX Communications satellite receivers; Logmatic commercial insert.
Miles of plant: 151.0 (coaxial); None (fiber optic). Additional miles planned: 2.0 (coaxial). Homes passed: 9,300.
Manager: Janis McTimmons. Chief technician: Michael Baldwin. Program & marketing director: Grant Sedawie.
City fee: 5% of gross (Myrtle Creek); 3% of gross (Riddle).
Ownership: Falcon Communications LP (MSO). Purchased from Jones Intercable Inc., August 1, 1999.

MYRTLE POINT—Falcon Cable Systems Co., 1400 Newmark Ave., Coos Bay, OR 97420. Phone: 541-888-5712. Fax: 541-888-9292. County: Coos. Also serves Coos County. ICA: OR0059.
TV Market Ranking: Below 100 (portions of Coos County, Myrtle Point); Outside TV Markets (portions of Coos County). Franchise award date: N.A. Franchise expiration date: N.A. Began: January 1, 1955.
Channel capacity: 37. Channels available but not in use: 3.
Basic Service
Subscribers: 752.
Programming (received off-air): KCBY-TV (C), KMTZ (N) Coos Bay; KOAC-TV (P) Corvallis; KEZI (A) Eugene; KOBI (N) Medford; KPTV (U) Portland.
Programming (via satellite): A & E; Blazer Vision; Bravo; C-SPAN; CNN; Comedy Central; E! Entertainment TV; ESPN; Fox Family Channel; Headline News; Home Shopping Network; Learning Channel; MTV; Nickelodeon; QVC; USA Network.
Current originations: Automated time-weather.
Fee: $20.19 monthly.
Expanded Basic Service
Subscribers: 737.
Programming (via satellite): Discovery Channel; Lifetime; Sci-Fi Channel; VH1.
Fee: $1.54 monthly.
Expanded Basic Service 2
Subscribers: 720.
Programming (via satellite): Disney Channel; Nashville Network; TBS Superstation; The Weather Channel; Turner Network TV.
Fee: $5.91 monthly.
Pay Service 1
Pay Units: 32.
Programming (via satellite): Cinemax.
Fee: $29.95 installation; $10.95 monthly.

Pay Service 2
Pay Units: 49.
Programming (via satellite): HBO.
Fee: $11.95 monthly.
Pay Service 3
Pay Units: 23.
Programming (via satellite): Showtime.
Fee: $10.95 monthly.
Pay Service 4
Pay Units: 11.
Programming (via satellite): The Movie Channel.
Fee: $10.95 monthly.
Equipment: Jerrold headend; Delta-Benco-Cascade amplifiers; Comm/Scope cable; Jerrold set top converters; Vitek traps; Scientific-Atlanta satellite antenna; Scientific-Atlanta satellite receivers.
Miles of plant: 28.0 (coaxial). Homes passed: 1,445. Total homes in franchised area: 1,475.
Manager: Bill Griffin. Chief technician: Norman Lacey. Marketing director: Joan Crabtree.
City fee: 5% of gross.
Ownership: Falcon Communications LP (MSO), joint venture formed September 30, 1998. See Cable System Ownership.

NEHALEM—Falcon Telecable, 1344 N.E. Hwy. 101, Lincoln City, OR 97367. Phone: 541-994-6083. Fax: 541-994-7438. Counties: Clatsop & Tillamook. Also serves Arch Cape, Bay City, Cannon Beach, Clatsop County, Falcon Cove, Garibaldi, Manzanita, Rockaway Beach, Tillamook County (portions), Wheeler, Wilson River. ICA: OR0056.
TV Market Ranking: Below 100 (portions of Tillamook County); Outside TV Markets (Arch Cape, Bay City, Cannon Beach, Clatsop County, Falcon Cove, Garibaldi, Manzanita, Nehalem, Rockaway Beach, portions of Tillamook County, Wheeler, Wilson River). Franchise award date: N.A. Franchise expiration date: September 8, 2001. Began: June 1, 1961.
Channel capacity: 35 (not 2-way capable). Channels available but not in use: None.
Basic Service
Subscribers: 4,630.
Programming (received off-air): KATU (A), KGW (N), KOIN (C), KOPB-TV (P), KPTV (U) Portland; KPDX (F) Vancouver; allband FM.
Programming (via satellite): WGN-TV (W) Chicago; Blazer Vision; C-SPAN; Comedy Central; QVC; TBS Superstation; VH1.
Current originations: Public access; educational access; government access.
Fee: $35.00 installation; $15.11 monthly; $15.00 additional installation.
Expanded Basic Service
Subscribers: 3,459.
Programming (via satellite): A & E; American Movie Classics; CNN; ESPN; Fox Family Channel; Headline News; Home Shopping Network; Lifetime; Turner Network TV.
Fee: $20.00 installation; $10.41 monthly.
Expanded Basic Service 2
Subscribers: 1,319.
Programming (via satellite): Country Music TV; Discovery Channel; Disney Channel; Nashville Network; Nickelodeon; USA Network.
Fee: $6.68 monthly.
Pay Service 1
Pay Units: 138.
Programming (via satellite): Cinemax.
Fee: $35.00 installation; $10.95 monthly.
Pay Service 2
Pay Units: 340.
Programming (via satellite): HBO.
Fee: $35.00 installation; $11.95 monthly.
Pay Service 3
Pay Units: 236.
Programming (via satellite): Showtime.
Fee: $35.00 installation; $10.95 monthly.
Pay Service 4
Pay Units: 154.
Programming (via satellite): The Movie Channel.
Fee: $35.00 installation; $10.95 monthly.
Pay Service 5
Pay Units: N.A.
Programming (via satellite): The New Encore.
Fee: N.A.
Pay-Per-View
Addressable homes: 2,150.
Playboy TV.
Equipment: Scientific-Atlanta headend; Scientific-Atlanta amplifiers; Comm/Scope cable; Scientific-Atlanta satellite antenna.
Miles of plant: 135.0 (coaxial). Homes passed: 6,384.
Manager: Joel Billings. Chief technician: Charles Johnson.
City fee: 3%-5% of gross.
Ownership: Falcon Communications LP (MSO), joint venture formed September 30, 1998. See Cable System Ownership.

NETARTS—Falcon Telecable, 1344 N.E. Hwy. 101, Lincoln City, OR 97367. Phone: 541-994-6083. Fax: 541-994-7438. County: Tillamook. Also serves Oceanside. ICA: OR0062.
TV Market Ranking: Outside TV Markets. Franchise award date: N.A. Franchise expiration date: N.A. Began: January 1, 1963.
Channel capacity: 22. Channels available but not in use: 4.
Basic Service
Subscribers: 829.
Programming (received off-air): KATU (A), KGW (N), KOIN (C), KOPB-TV (P), KPTV (U) Portland; KPDX (F) Vancouver; allband FM.
Programming (via satellite): A & E; Blazer Vision; CNN; Discovery Channel; ESPN; Fox Family Channel; Nashville Network; TBS Superstation; Turner Network TV; USA Network.
Fee: $25.00 installation; $17.23 monthly.
Pay Service 1
Pay Units: 47.
Programming (via satellite): Disney Channel.
Fee: $20.00 installation; $10.95 monthly.
Pay Service 2
Pay Units: 99.
Programming (via satellite): HBO.
Fee: $11.95 monthly.
Equipment: Scientific-Atlanta headend; Century III amplifiers; Times Fiber cable; Eagle traps; Scientific-Atlanta satellite antenna; Scientific-Atlanta satellite receivers.
Miles of plant: 17.0 (coaxial). Homes passed: 850.
Manager: Joel Billings. Chief technician: Charles Johnson.

Ownership: Falcon Communications LP (MSO), joint venture formed September 30, 1998. See Cable System Ownership.

NEWBERG—TCI Cablevision of Oregon Inc., 4025 Nimbus Loop, McMinnville, OR 97128. Phone: 503-472-1121. Fax: 503-472-0230. County: Yamhill. Also serves Carlton, Dayton, Dundee, Lafayette, McMinnville, Yamhill. ICA: OR0014.

TV Market Ranking: 29. Franchise award date: N.A. Franchise expiration date: N.A. Began: July 1, 1982.

Channel capacity: 54 (not 2-way capable). Channels available but not in use: None.

Basic Service

Subscribers: 12,400.

Programming (received off-air): KATU (A), KGW (N), KNMT (T), KOIN (C), KOPB-TV (P), KPTV (U) Portland; KPXG (X) Salem; 15 FMs.

Programming (via satellite): WGN-TV (W) Chicago; A & E; American Movie Classics; C-SPAN; C-SPAN 2; CNBC; CNN; Comedy Central; Discovery Channel; Fox Family Channel; Headline News; Lifetime; MTV; Nashville Network; Nickelodeon; Odyssey; QVC; TBS Superstation; The Weather Channel; Univision; VH1.

Current originations: Public access; government access.

Fee: $27.81 installation; $9.89 monthly; $2.18 converter; $20.25 additional installation.

Expanded Basic Service

Subscribers: 11,300.

Programming (via satellite): ESPN; Fox Sports Net Northwest; Knowledge TV; Turner Network TV; USA Network.

Fee: $10.97 monthly.

Pay Service 1

Pay Units: 1,025.

Programming (via satellite): Disney Channel.

Fee: N.A.

Pay Service 2

Pay Units: 4,485.

Programming (via satellite): The New Encore.

Fee: N.A.

Pay Service 3

Pay Units: 1,758.

Programming (via satellite): HBO.

Fee: $12.15 monthly.

Pay Service 4

Pay Units: 422.

Programming (via satellite): The Movie Channel.

Fee: $12.15 monthly.

Pay Service 5

Pay Units: 739.

Programming (via satellite): Showtime.

Fee: $12.15 monthly.

Pay-Per-View

Addressable homes: 3,019.

Local advertising: Yes. Regional interconnect: TCI Cable Advertising-Oregon.

Program Guide: The Cable Guide.

Equipment: Jerrold addressable set top converters; Simulsat satellite antenna; Scientific-Atlanta satellite receivers.

Miles of plant: 221.0 (coaxial); 27.0 (fiber optic). Homes passed: 17,119. Total homes in franchised area: 17,119.

Manager: Katherine McEneaney. Chief technician: Adam Keller. Marketing & program director: Mark Green.

City fee: 3% of gross.

Ownership: AT&T Broadband & Internet Services (MSO). Purchased from Tele-Communications Inc., March 9, 1999.

NEWPORT—Falcon Cable TV, Box 950, 355 NE 1st St., Newport, OR 97365. Phone: 541-265-2263. Fax: 541-265-5064. County: Lincoln. Also serves Lincoln County (portions), Otter Rock, Toledo. ICA: OR0022.

TV Market Ranking: Outside TV Markets. Franchise award date: N.A. Franchise expiration date: N.A. Began: March 1, 1965.

Channel capacity: 38. Channels available but not in use: N.A.

Basic Service

Subscribers: 5,398.

Programming (received off-air): 15 FMs.

Programming (via microwave): KEZI (A) Eugene; KATU (A), KGW (N), KOIN (C), KOPB-TV (P), KPTV (U) Portland; KPDX (F) Vancouver.

Programming (via satellite): C-SPAN; Fox Family Channel; Lifetime; MTV; TBS Superstation.

Current originations: Automated timeweather.

Fee: $29.24 installation; $11.24 monthly; $2.00 converter; $14.62 additional installation.

Expanded Basic Service

Subscribers: 5,020.

Programming (via satellite): WGN-TV (W) Chicago; A & E; American Movie Classics; CNBC; CNN; Discovery Channel; ESPN; Fox Sports Net Northwest; Headline News; Nashville Network; Nickelodeon; Odyssey; QVC; The Weather Channel; Turner Network TV; USA Network.

Fee: $10.03 monthly.

Pay Service 1

Pay Units: 542.

Programming (via satellite): Disney Channel.

Fee: $10.95 monthly.

Pay Service 2

Pay Units: 2,184.

Programming (via satellite): The New Encore.

Fee: N.A.

Pay Service 3

Pay Units: 1,071.

Programming (via satellite): HBO.

Fee: $12.90 monthly.

Pay Service 4

Pay Units: 358.

Programming (via satellite): The Movie Channel.

Fee: $12.90 monthly.

Pay Service 5

Pay Units: 561.

Programming (via satellite): Showtime.

Fee: $12.90 monthly.

Local advertising: Yes (locally produced). Available in satellite distributed & character-generated programming. Local sales manager: Rick Gibson. Regional interconnect: TCI Cable Advertising-Oregon.

Program Guide: The Cable Guide.

Equipment: Scientific-Atlanta headend; GTE Sylvania amplifiers; Times Fiber cable; Sony VTRs; Pioneer traps; Scientific-Atlanta satellite antenna; Scientific-Atlanta satellite receivers.

Miles of plant: 124.2 (coaxial). Homes passed: 7,130. Total homes in franchised area: 7,130.

Regional manager: Robert Smith. Manager: Tom Hansen. Chief technician: Doug Dahl.

City & state fee: 3% of gross.

Ownership: Falcon Communications LP (MSO). Purchased from Tele-Communications Inc., September 30, 1998. See Cable System Ownership.

NORTH POWDER—Blackstone Cable LLC, 1104 W. Ironwood Dr., Coeur d'Alene, ID 83814-2605. Phone: 208-664-3370. Fax: 208-664-5888. County: Union. ICA: OR0107.

TV Market Ranking: Outside TV Markets. Franchise award date: N.A. Franchise expiration date: September 8, 2006. Began: N.A.

Channel capacity: 19 (not 2-way capable). Channels available but not in use: 6.

Basic Service

Subscribers: 97.

Programming (received off-air): KTVB (N) Boise; KTVR (P) La Grande; KATU (A), KGW (N), KOIN (C), KPTV (U) Portland; KPDX (F) Vancouver.

Programming (via satellite): CNN; Discovery Channel; Disney Channel; ESPN; Fox Family Channel; Nashville Network; TBS Superstation; Turner Network TV; USA Network.

Fee: $43.50 installation; $21.00 monthly; $56.00 converter; $21.50 additional installation.

Commercial fee: $5.34 monthly.

Pay Service 1

Pay Units: 20.

Programming (via satellite): HBO.

Fee: $10.95 monthly.

Miles of plant: 3.5 (coaxial); None (fiber optic). Homes passed: 198.

Manager: Ted Hughett.

City fee: 3% of basic.

Ownership: Blackstone Cable LLC (MSO).

ODELL—Valley TV Co-op Inc., Box 450, Parkdale, OR 97041. Phone: 541-352-6760. County: Hood River. ICA: OR0102.

TV Market Ranking: Outside TV Markets. Franchise award date: N.A. Franchise expiration date: N.A. Began: April 1, 1955.

Channel capacity: 11. Channels available but not in use: N.A.

Basic Service

Subscribers: 150.

Programming (received off-air): KATU (A), KGW (N), KOIN (C), KOPB-TV (P), KPTV (U) Portland.

Programming (via satellite): WGN-TV (W) Chicago; Discovery Channel; ESPN; Nashville Network; Turner Network TV.

Fee: $25.00 installation; $13.00 monthly.

Pay Service 1

Pay Units: N.A.

Programming (via satellite): HBO.

Fee: $7.50 monthly.

Equipment: Blonder-Tongue headend; Blonder-Tongue amplifiers.

Miles of plant: 15.0 (coaxial). Homes passed: 250.

Chief technician: Paul Henne.

Ownership: Valley TV Co-op Inc. (MSO).

ONTARIO—Chambers Cable of Oregon Inc., Box 398, 347 S.W. 19th St., Ontario, OR 97914. Phones: 541-889-3173; 800-962-6362. Fax: 541-889-4453.

Web site: http://www.chamberscable.com.

County: Malheur. Also serves Nyssa, Vale. ICA: OR0026.

TV Market Ranking: Below 100. Franchise award date: N.A. Franchise expiration date: January 1, 2000. Began: September 1, 1981.

Channel capacity: 35 (not 2-way capable). Channels available but not in use: None.

Basic Service

Subscribers: 3,848.

Programming (received off-air): KAID (P), KBCI-TV (C), KTVB (N) Boise; KNIN-TV (U) Caldwell; KIVI (A), KTRV (F) Nampa; KGW (N) Portland.

Programming (via microwave): KOPB-TV (P) Portland.

Programming (via satellite): WGN-TV (W) Chicago; A & E; American Movie Classics; C-SPAN; CNN; Country Music TV; Discovery Channel; Disney Channel; ESPN; FX; Fox Family Channel; Fox Sports Net Northwest; Headline News; Lifetime; MTV; Nashville Network; Nickelodeon; Northwest Cable News; QVC; TBS Superstation; Turner Network TV; USA Network; Univision; VH1.

Fee: $27.35 monthly.

Pay Service 1

Pay Units: N.A.

Programming (via satellite): HBO; Showtime.

Fee: $15.00 installation; $12.50 monthly (each).

Local advertising: Yes. Available in locally originated & character-generated programming. Rates: $12.00/30 Seconds.

Equipment: Catel headend; Jerrold amplifiers; Times Fiber cable; Jerrold set top converters; Eagle traps; Prodelin satellite antenna; M/A-Com satellite receivers.

Miles of plant: 95.0 (coaxial). Additional miles planned: 5.0 (coaxial). Homes passed: 7,500.

Manager: Ed Aronson. Chief technician: Kevin Smith.

City fee: 5% of gross.

Ownership: Chambers Communications Corp. (MSO).

PARKDALE—Valley TV Co-op Inc., Box 450, Parkdale, OR 97041. Phone: 541-352-6760. County: Hood River. Also serves Mount Hood. ICA: OR0147.

TV Market Ranking: Outside TV Markets. Franchise award date: N.A. Franchise expiration date: N.A. Began: January 1, 1955.

Channel capacity: 12. Channels available but not in use: None.

Basic Service

Subscribers: 640.

Programming (received off-air): KATU (A), KGW (N), KOIN (C), KOPB-TV (P), KPTV (U) Portland.

Programming (via satellite): WGN-TV (W) Chicago; A & E; Discovery Channel; ESPN; Fox Family Channel; Turner Network TV.

Fee: $14.00 monthly.

Pay Service 1

Pay Units: N.A.

Programming (via satellite): Disney Channel; The Movie Channel.

Fee: $8.00 monthly (each).

Equipment: Jerrold headend; AEL amplifiers; Systems Wire & Times Fiber cable.

Miles of plant: 40.0 (coaxial).

Chief technician: Paul Henne.

Ownership: Valley TV Co-op Inc. (MSO).

PENDLETON—Falcon Cable TV, 152 S.W. Nye, Pendleton, OR 97801. Phone: 541-276-2821. Fax: 541-276-0134. County: Umatilla. Also serves Pilot Rock, Rieth, Umatilla County (portions), Umatilla Indian Reservation. ICA: OR0019.

TV Market Ranking: Outside TV Markets. Franchise award date: N.A. Franchise expiration date: September 18, 1999. Began: October 1, 1954.

Channel capacity: 36 (not 2-way capable). Channels available but not in use: N.A.

Basic Service

Subscribers: 6,345; Commercial subscribers: 228.

Programming (received off-air): KTVR (P) La Grande; KBWU-LP (I) Pasco; KEPR-TV (C), KNDU (N), KVEW (A) Pasco-Kennewick-Richland; KATU (A), KGW (N), KOIN (C), KPTV (U) Portland; 9 FMs.

Programming (via satellite): A & E; American Movie Classics; C-SPAN; CNBC; CNN; Discovery Channel; ESPN; Fox Family Channel; Fox Sports Net Northwest; Intro TV; MTV; Nashville Network; Nickelodeon; QVC; TBS Superstation; The Weather Channel; Turner Network TV; USA Network; Univision; VH1.

Fee: $30.00 installation; $9.29 monthly; $10.00 additional installation.

Pay Service 1
Pay Units: 476.
Programming (via satellite): Cinemax.
Fee: $10.95 monthly.

Pay Service 2
Pay Units: 321.
Programming (via satellite): Disney Channel.
Fee: $10.95 monthly.

Pay Service 3
Pay Units: N.A.
Programming (via satellite): Starz!; The New Encore.
Fee: $1.75 monthly (Encore), $4.95 monthly (Encore & Starz).

Pay Service 4
Pay Units: 1,494.
Programming (via satellite): HBO.
Fee: $12.45 monthly.

Pay Service 5
Pay Units: 217.
Programming (via satellite): Showtime.
Fee: $10.95 monthly.

Pay-Per-View
Addressable homes: 250.
Special events.
Fee: Varies.

Local advertising: Yes. Available in locally originated & taped programming.
Equipment: Jerrold, RCA & Scientific-Atlanta headend; Jerrold, Magnavox & Century III amplifiers; Comm/Scope & Times Fiber cable; MSI & Texscan character generator; Hamlin & Standard Components set top converters; Eagle & Arcom traps; Andrew, Anixter & Vertex satellite antenna; Jerrold, Sony & Scientific-Atlanta satellite receivers.
Miles of plant: 148.6 (coaxial). Homes passed: 9,913. Total homes in franchised area: 11,023.
Manager: Darrell Linklater. Office manager: Sandy Haley.
City fee: 5% of gross.
Ownership: Falcon Communications LP (MSO). Purchased from Tele-Communications Inc., September 30, 1998. See Cable System Ownership.

PIONEER MOBILE HOME PARK—Interstate Cable Inc., Box 2687, Salina, KS 67402-2687. Phones: 785-452-9409; 800-888-4788. Fax: 785-238-7190. County: Clackamas. ICA: OR0148.
TV Market Ranking: 29. Franchise award date: N.A. Franchise expiration date: N.A. Began: N.A.
Channel capacity: N.A. Channels available but not in use: N.A.

Basic Service
Subscribers: 26.
Programming (received off-air): KATU (A), KGW (N), KOIN (C), KOPB-TV (P), KPTV (U) Portland; KPDX (F) Vancouver.
Programming (via satellite): WGN-TV (W) Chicago; A & E; CNN; Discovery Channel; ESPN; Fox Family Channel; Goodlife TV Network; Nashville Network; Sci-Fi Channel; TBS Superstation; Trinity Bcstg. Network; Turner Classic Movies.
Fee: $50.00 installation; $21.95 monthly; $2.00 converter; $15.00 additional installation.

Pay Service 1
Pay Units: N.A.
Programming (via satellite): Cinemax; Disney Channel; HBO.
Fee: $7.95 monthly (Disney), $10.95 monthly (Cinemax or HBO).

Homes passed: 100.
Manager: Patti Lahey.
Franchise fee: 3% of basic.
Ownership: Tristar Cable Inc. (MSO).

PORTLAND—TCI Cablevision of Oregon Inc., 3500 S.W. Bond St., Portland, OR 97201. Phone: 503-609-4800. Fax: 503-243-7413. Counties: Clackamas, Multnomah & Washington. Also serves Dunthorpe, Gladstone, Multnomah County (portions), Oregon City, Riverdale, Sylvan, Washington County, West Linn. ICA: OR0009.
TV Market Ranking: 29. Franchise award date: July 1, 1993. Franchise expiration date: N.A. Began: July 1, 1993.
Channel capacity: 77 (not 2-way capable). Channels available but not in use: 1.

Basic Service
Subscribers: 84,000.
Programming (received off-air): KATU (A), KGW (N), KNMT (T), KOIN (C), KOPB-TV (P), KPTV (U) Portland; KPXG (X), KWBP (W) Salem; KPDX (F) Vancouver; allband FM.
Programming (via satellite): BET; C-SPAN; C-SPAN 2; EWTN; Odyssey; QVC; TV Guide Sneak Prevue; The Box.
Current originations: Public access; educational access; government access; leased access; local news.
Fee: $36.80 installation; $9.96 monthly; $0.81 converter; $17.00 additional installation.

Expanded Basic Service
Subscribers: 80,000.
Programming (via satellite): WGN-TV (W) Chicago; A & E; American Movie Classics; CNBC; CNN; Comedy Central; Court TV; Discovery Channel; ESPN; FX; Fox Family Channel; Fox Sports Net Direct; Fox Sports Net Northwest; Headline News; Intro TV; Learning Channel; Lifetime; MSNBC; MTV; Nashville Network; Nickelodeon; TBS Superstation; TV Food Network; TV Guide Channel; The Health Network; The Weather Channel; Travel Channel; Turner Network TV; USA Network; Univision; VH1.
Fee: $11.57 monthly.

A la Carte 1
Subscribers: N.A.
Programming (via satellite): Cartoon Network; Country Music TV; E! Entertainment TV; ESPN 2; International Channel.
Fee: N.A.

Pay Service 1
Pay Units: 2,600.
Programming (via satellite): DMX.
Fee: $12.95 monthly.

Pay Service 2
Pay Units: 6,700.
Programming (via satellite): Disney Channel.
Fee: $12.95 monthly.

Pay Service 3
Pay Units: 34,000.
Programming (via satellite): The New Encore.
Fee: $1.75 monthly.

Pay Service 4
Pay Units: 20,500.
Programming (via satellite): HBO.
Fee: $12.95 monthly.

Pay Service 5
Pay Units: 11,500.
Programming (via satellite): Showtime.
Fee: $12.95 monthly.

Pay Service 6
Pay Units: 5,200.
Programming (via satellite): The Movie Channel.
Fee: $12.95 monthly.

Pay Service 7
Pay Units: 1,400.
Programming (via satellite): Cinemax.
Fee: $10.95 monthly.

Pay Service 8
Pay Units: N.A.
Programming (via satellite): Starz!
Fee: N.A.

Pay-Per-View
Addressable homes: 18,000.
Action Pay-Per-View.
Fee: Varies.

Program Guide: The Cable Guide.
Miles of plant: 1354.1 (coaxial); 184.0 (fiber optic). Homes passed: 138,000. Total homes in franchised area: 138,000.
Manager: Ross Wagner. Chief technician: Dean Beseda. Program director: Randy Warren. Marketing director: Brad Nosler.
Ownership: AT&T Broadband & Internet Services (MSO). Purchased from Tele-Communications Inc., March 9, 1999.

PORTLAND (eastern portion)—TCI Cable, 3075 N.E. Sandy Blvd., Portland, OR 97232-2483. Phone: 503-230-2099. Fax: 503-230-2218. Counties: Clackamas & Multnomah. Also serves Clackamas County, Corbett, Eagle Creek, Fairview, Gresham, Happy Valley, Linnton, Maywood Park, Multnomah County (unincorporated areas), Orient, Springdale, Troutdale, Wood Village. ICA: OR0001.
TV Market Ranking: 29. Franchise award date: May 1, 1981. Franchise expiration date: December 31, 2010. Began: February 1, 1982.
Channel capacity: 58 (2-way capable; operating 2-way). Channels available but not in use: None.

Basic Service
Subscribers: 128,900; Commercial subscribers: 960.
Programming (received off-air): KATU (A), KGW (N), KNMT (T), KOIN (C), KOPB-TV (P), KPTV (U) Portland; KPXG (X), KWBP (W) Salem; KPDX (F) Vancouver.
Programming (via satellite): C-SPAN; CNBC; EWTN; QVC; TV Guide Channel; The Weather Channel; Univision; ValueVision.
Current originations: Automated time-weather; public access; educational access; government access; automated emergency alert; local news; local sports.
Fee: $32.00 installation; $11.38 monthly; $2.88 converter.

Expanded Basic Service
Subscribers: 106,730.
Programming (via satellite): A & E; American Movie Classics; BET; CNN; Comedy Central; Discovery Channel; ESPN; Fox Family Channel; Fox Sports Net Northwest; Headline News; History Channel; Learning Channel; Lifetime; MSNBC; MTV; Nashville Network; Nickelodeon; Sci-Fi Channel; Turner Network TV; USA Network; VH1.
Fee: $16.47 monthly.

A la Carte 1
Subscribers: N.A.
Programming (via satellite): WGN-TV (W) Chicago; Cartoon Network; TBS Superstation; Turner Classic Movies.
Fee: $1.89-$2.29 monthly (each); $3.75 monthly (package).

Pay Service 1
Pay Units: 7,561.
Programming (via satellite): Cinemax.
Fee: $5.25 installation; $10.45 monthly.

Pay Service 2
Pay Units: 5,461.
Programming (via satellite): Disney Channel.
Fee: $5.25 installation; $9.95 monthly.

Pay Service 3
Pay Units: 15,277.
Programming (via satellite): HBO (multiplexed).
Fee: $5.25 installation; $11.45 monthly.

Pay Service 4
Pay Units: 8,047.
Programming (via satellite): Showtime (multiplexed).
Fee: $5.25 installation; $10.45 monthly.

Pay Service 5
Pay Units: 7,452.
Programming (via satellite): The Movie Channel.
Fee: $5.25 installation; $6.95 monthly.

Pay-Per-View
Addressable homes: 82,000.
Blazer Vision; Spice; movies; special events.
Fee: Varies.
Pay-per-view manager: Jeff Henry.

Local advertising: Yes. Available in satellite distributed, locally originated & character-generated programming. Local sales manager: Lois Petrik.
Program Guide: TV Host.
Equipment: Scientific-Atlanta headend; Jerrold, C-COR & Scientific-Atlanta amplifiers; Comm/Scope cable; Siecor fiber optic cable; Scientific-Atlanta & Zenith addressable set top converters; Eagle & Pico traps; Scientific-Atlanta satellite antenna; Scientific-Atlanta satellite receivers.
Miles of plant: 2200.0 (coaxial); 67.0 (fiber optic). Additional miles planned: 50.0 (coaxial); 400.0 (fiber optic). Homes passed: 232,155.
Franchise fee: 8.5% of gross.
Ownership: AT&T Broadband & Internet Services (MSO). Purchased from Time Warner Cable, June 1, 1999.

POWERS 89—Falcon Cable Systems Co., 1400 Newmark Ave., Coos Bay, OR 97420. Phone: 541-888-5712. Fax: 541-888-9292. County: Coos. Also serves Coos County (southern portion). ICA: OR0094.
TV Market Ranking: Below 100 (portions of Coos County, Powers); Outside TV Markets (portions of Coos County). Franchise award date: N.A. Franchise expiration date: N.A. Began: January 1, 1956.
Channel capacity: 37. Channels available but not in use: 14.

Basic Service
Subscribers: 192.
Programming (received off-air): KCBY-TV (C), KMTZ (N) Coos Bay; KOAC-TV (P) Corvallis; KEZI (A) Eugene; KOBI (N) Medford; allband FM.
Programming (via satellite): Bravo; C-SPAN; CNN; Discovery Channel; ESPN; Fox Family Channel; Learning Channel; Nickelodeon; QVC.
Fee: $39.95 installation; $16.98 monthly.

Expanded Basic Service
Subscribers: 190.
Programming (via satellite): A & E; Nashville Network; USA Network.
Fee: $2.47 monthly.

Expanded Basic Service 2
Subscribers: 185.
Programming (via satellite): WGN-TV (W) Chicago; Disney Channel; TBS Superstation; Turner Network TV.
Fee: $4.80 monthly.

Pay Service 1
Pay Units: 14.
Programming (via satellite): HBO.
Fee: $29.95 installation; $11.95 monthly.

Equipment: Jerrold headend; Delta-Benco-Cascade amplifiers; Comm/Scope cable; Vitek traps; Scientific-Atlanta satellite antenna; Scientific-Atlanta satellite receivers.
Miles of plant: 7.0 (coaxial). Total homes in franchised area: 343.
Manager: Bill Griffin. Chief technician: Norman Lacey. Marketing director: Joan Crabtree.
City fee: 3% of gross.
Ownership: Falcon Communications LP (MSO), joint venture formed September 30, 1998. See Cable System Ownership.

PRAIRIE CITY—Blue Mountain TV Cable Co., Box 267, Mount Vernon, OR 97865. Phone: 541-932-4613. Fax: 541-932-4613. County: Grant. ICA: OR0084.
TV Market Ranking: Outside TV Markets. Franchise award date: N.A. Franchise expiration date: N.A. Began: October 1, 1962.
Channel capacity: 16 (not 2-way capable). Channels available but not in use: N.A.
Basic Service
Subscribers: 365.
Programming (received off-air): KBCI-TV (C), KTVB (N) Boise; KIVI (A) Nampa; allband FM.
Programming (via microwave): KGW (N), KOPB-TV (P) Portland.
Programming (via satellite): WGN-TV (W) Chicago; Discovery Channel; Fox Family Channel; Fox Sports Net Northwest; FoxNet; Nashville Network; Northwest Cable News; TBS Superstation.
Current originations: Automated time-weather.
Fee: $19.50 installation; $9.50 monthly.
Pay Service 1
Pay Units: N.A.
Programming (via satellite): Showtime.
Fee: N.A.
Miles of plant: 10.0 (coaxial). Homes passed: 400.
Manager: Chuck McKenna.
Ownership: Blue Mountain TV Cable Co. (MSO).

PRINEVILLE—Crestview Cable TV, 190 W. 4th, Prineville, OR 97754. Phones: 541-447-4342; 800-285-2330. Fax: 541-447-5987. County: Crook. ICA: OR0038.
TV Market Ranking: Below 100. Franchise award date: N.A. Franchise expiration date: N.A. Began: June 1, 1971.
Channel capacity: 36 (not 2-way capable). Channels available but not in use: 3.
Basic Service
Subscribers: 3,497.
Programming (received off-air): KOAB-TV (P), KTVZ (N) Bend; KEZI (A) Eugene; KATU (A), KGW (N), KOIN (C), KPTV (U) Portland; KPDX (F) Vancouver; 14 FMs.
Programming (via satellite): A & E; CNBC; CNN; Discovery Channel; ESPN; Fox Family Channel; Lifetime; MTV; Nashville Network; TBS Superstation; Turner Classic Movies; Turner Network TV.
Current originations: Automated time-weather.
Fee: $32.00 installation; $19.20 monthly; $0.86 converter; $10.00 additional installation.
Commercial fee: $2.20 monthly.
Pay Service 1
Pay Units: 517.
Programming (via satellite): Cinemax.
Fee: $10.00 monthly.
Pay Service 2
Pay Units: 431.
Programming (via satellite): Disney Channel.
Fee: $10.00 monthly.
Pay Service 3
Pay Units: 771.
Programming (via satellite): HBO.
Fee: $10.00 monthly.
Local advertising: Yes. Available in character-generated programming. Rates: $25.00/Week. Local sales manager: Annette Hylton.
Program Guide: Premium Channels.
Equipment: Tocom headend; GTE Sylvania amplifiers; CCS Hatfield cable; Mycrotek character generator; Pioneer set top converters; Eagle traps; Scientific-Atlanta satellite antenna.
Miles of plant: 80.0 (coaxial). Homes passed: 3,628.
Manager: Jerry Steele. Chief technician: Ron Morgan.
City fee: 5% of gross.
Ownership: California-Oregon Broadcasting Inc. (MSO).

PROSPECT—Phoenix Cablevision of Oregon Inc., Box 828, 6655 Rogue River Dr., Shady Cove, OR 97539. Phones: 541-878-3247; 800-827-3247. Fax: 541-878-2458. County: Jackson. ICA: OR0096.
TV Market Ranking: Below 100. Franchise award date: January 1, 1980. Franchise expiration date: N.A. Began: January 1, 1982.
Channel capacity: 36 (not 2-way capable). Channels available but not in use: 10.
Basic Service
Subscribers: 167.
Programming (received off-air): KDRV (A), KOBI (N), KSYS (P), KTVL (C) Medford.
Programming (via satellite): WGN-TV (W) Chicago; WWOR-TV (U) New York; A & E; CNN; Country Music TV; Discovery Channel; ESPN; ESPN 2; Fox Family Channel; FoxNet; History Channel; Home Shopping Network; Learning Channel; Lifetime; Nashville Network; Sci-Fi Channel; TBS Superstation; The Weather Channel; Turner Classic Movies; Turner Network TV; USA Network.
Fee: $43.75 installation; $43.75 monthly; $56.00 converter; $21.50 additional installation.
Commercial fee: $5.50 monthly.
Pay Service 1
Pay Units: 13.
Programming (via satellite): Cinemax.
Fee: $15.00 installation; $11.55 monthly.
Pay Service 2
Pay Units: 21.
Programming (via satellite): HBO.
Fee: $15.00 installation; $7.95 monthly.
Miles of plant: 14.0 (coaxial). Homes passed: 296.
Manager: Ted W. Hughett. Chief technician: Dan Middleton.
Ownership: Phoenix Cable Inc. (MSO).

RAINIER—Pacific Sun Cable Partners LP, No. 404, 7901 Stoneridge Dr., Pleaston, CA 94588. Phone: 509-787-3543. County: Columbia. ICA: OR0058.
TV Market Ranking: Below 100. Franchise award date: January 1, 1958. Franchise expiration date: N.A. Began: January 1, 1958.
Channel capacity: 36. Channels available but not in use: N.A.
Basic Service
Subscribers: 1,018.
Programming (received off-air): KATU (A), KGW (N), KOIN (C), KOPB-TV (P), KPTV (U) Portland; KSTW (U) Seattle-Tacoma; KPDX (F) Vancouver; allband FM.
Programming (via satellite): ESPN; Fox Family Channel; TBS Superstation.
Planned programming (via satellite): WGN-TV (W) Chicago; A & E; CNN; Discovery Channel; MTV; Nashville Network; Nickelodeon; VH1.
Current originations: Automated time-weather; public access.
Fee: $25.00 installation; $14.95 monthly.
Pay Service 1
Pay Units: 275.
Programming (via satellite): HBO.
Fee: $10.00 installation; $9.95 monthly.
Pay Service 2
Pay Units: 58.
Programming (via satellite): Disney Channel.
Fee: $10.00 installation; $8.95 monthly.
Pay Service 3
Pay Units: 75.
Programming (via satellite): Showtime.
Fee: $10.00 installation; $9.95 monthly.
Equipment: Jerrold headend; Cascade amplifiers; Times Fiber cable; Sony cameras; Eagle traps; AFC satellite antenna.
Miles of plant: 15.0 (coaxial). Homes passed: 1,500.
Manager: Tim Peck. Chief technician: Willard McCollam.
City fee: 3% of gross.
Ownership: Sun Country Cable (MSO).

REDMOND—Bend Cable Communications LLC, 741 S.W. 17th St., Redmond, OR 97756. Phone: 541-923-2263. Fax: 541-923-0241. E-mail: manager@bendcable.com.
Web site: http://www.bendcable.com.
County: Deschutes. Also serves Deschutes County. ICA: OR0031.
TV Market Ranking: Below 100 (portions of Deschutes County, Redmond); Outside TV Markets (portions of Deschutes County). Franchise award date: N.A. Franchise expiration date: February 1, 2002. Began: June 1, 1965.
Channel capacity: 36 (not 2-way capable). Channels available but not in use: 2.
Basic Service
Subscribers: 3,550; Commercial subscribers: 12.
Programming (received off-air): KOAB-TV (P), KTVZ (N) Bend; KEZI (A) Eugene; KATU (A), KOIN (C), KPTV (U) Portland; KPDX (F) Vancouver; 14 FMs.
Programming (via satellite): A & E; Blazer Vision; Bravo; Comedy Central; Discovery Channel; ESPN; Goodlife TV Network; Home & Garden Television; Lifetime; Nickelodeon; QVC; The Weather Channel.
Current originations: Automated time-weather; government access; local news.
Fee: $30.00 installation; $21.04 monthly; $2.00 converter; $15.00 additional installation.
Commercial fee: $5.00 monthly.
Expanded Basic Service
Subscribers: 2,902.
Programming (via satellite): Sci-Fi Channel; USA Network; VH1.
Fee: $1.88 monthly.
Expanded Basic Service 2
Subscribers: 3,269.
Programming (via satellite): CNN; Disney Channel; Fox Family Channel; Nashville Network; TBS Superstation; Turner Network TV.
Fee: $7.45 monthly.
Pay Service 1
Pay Units: 289.
Programming (via satellite): HBO.
Fee: $9.95 installation; $11.95 monthly.
Pay Service 2
Pay Units: 201.
Programming (via satellite): Showtime.
Fee: $9.95 installation; $10.95 monthly.
Pay Service 3
Pay Units: 173.
Programming (via satellite): The Movie Channel.
Fee: $9.95 installation; $10.95 monthly.
Pay Service 4
Pay Units: N.A.
Programming (via satellite): The New Encore.
Fee: N.A.
Local advertising: Yes (locally produced & insert). Available in satellite distributed & automated programming. Local sales manager: Don Booth.
Program Guide: Scene Magazine.
Equipment: Scientific-Atlanta & Jerrold headend; Magnavox & Century III amplifiers; Times Fiber cable; RCA cameras; Video Precision VTRs; Microtek character generator; Jerrold set top converters; Jerrold addressable set top converters; Microwave Assoc. & Scientific-Atlanta satellite antenna; Scientific-Atlanta satellite receivers.
Miles of plant: 162.0 (coaxial). Homes passed: 6,997.
Manager: William P. Morton. Chief technician: Dan Heller. Program director: Dave Jones. Marketing director: Femke van Velzen. Customer service manager: Lisa Littleton.
Franchise fee: 3% of gross.
Ownership: Tykeson & Associates (MSO). Purchased from Falcon Communications LP, March 1, 1999.

REEDSPORT—Falcon Cable Systems Co., 1400 Newmark Ave., Coos Bay, OR 97420. Phone: 541-888-5712. Fax: 541-888-9292. Counties: Coos & Douglas. Also serves Gardiner, Lakeside, Winchester Bay. ICA: OR0037.
TV Market Ranking: Below 100. Franchise award date: N.A. Franchise expiration date: May 1, 1998. Began: August 1, 1954.
Channel capacity: 34 (not 2-way capable). Channels available but not in use: None.
Basic Service
Subscribers: 2,672.
Programming (received off-air): KCBY-TV (C), KMTZ (N) Coos Bay; KOAC-TV (P) Corvallis; KEVU-LP (F), KEZI (A) Eugene; KOBI (N) Medford; KPTV (U) Portland; allband FM.
Programming (via satellite): Blazer Vision; Bravo; C-SPAN; CNN; E! Entertainment TV; ESPN; Fox Family Channel; Headline News; Home & Garden Television; Home Shopping Network; QVC; Sci-Fi Channel; USA Network.
Current originations: Public access; educational access; government access; local news.
Fee: $25.00 installation; $23.19 monthly.
Expanded Basic Service
Subscribers: 2,565.
Programming (via satellite): A & E; American Movie Classics; Lifetime; Nashville Network.
Fee: $2.31 monthly.
Expanded Basic Service 2
Subscribers: 2,506.
Programming (via satellite): WGN-TV (W) Chicago; Discovery Channel; Disney Channel; TBS Superstation; Turner Network TV.
Fee: $4.83 monthly.
Pay Service 1
Pay Units: 124.
Programming (via satellite): Cinemax.
Fee: $25.00 installation; $10.95 monthly.
Pay Service 2
Pay Units: 234.
Programming (via satellite): HBO.
Fee: $25.00 installation; $11.95 monthly.
Pay Service 3
Pay Units: 94.
Programming (via satellite): Showtime.
Fee: $25.00 installation; $10.95 monthly.
Pay Service 4
Pay Units: 46.
Programming (via satellite): The Movie Channel.
Fee: $10.95 monthly.
Local advertising: Yes. Available in locally originated programming.
Equipment: Cadco, Jerrold & Scientific-Atlanta headend; Magnavox amplifiers; Times Fiber & Comm/Scope cable; Sony VTRs; Info/Soft & Atari character generator; Scientific-Atlanta set top converters; Andrew & M/A-Com satellite antenna; Scientific-Atlanta, Harris & Standard

Communications satellite receivers; Wegener commercial insert.
Miles of plant: 71.0 (coaxial). Additional miles planned: 5.0 (coaxial). Homes passed: 3,650.
Manager: Bill Griffin. Chief technician: Norman Lacey. Marketing director: Joan Crabtree.
Franchise fee: 3% of gross.
Ownership: Falcon Communications LP (MSO), joint venture formed September 30, 1998. See Cable System Ownership.

RICHLAND—Eagle Valley Communications, Box 178, 109 Main St., Richland, OR 97870. Phone: 541-893-6111. Fax: 541-893-6202. County: Baker. ICA: OR0113.
TV Market Ranking: Outside TV Markets. Franchise award date: N.A. Franchise expiration date: N.A. Began: N.A.
Channel capacity: 19. Channels available but not in use: 7.
Basic Service
Subscribers: 140.
Programming (received off-air): KOAB-TV (P) Bend; KBCI-TV (C), KTVB (N) Boise; KTRV (F) Nampa; KATU (A), KPTV (U) Portland.
Programming (via satellite): CNN; Discovery Channel; ESPN; Fox Family Channel; Nashville Network; TBS Superstation; USA Network.
Fee: $30.00 installation; $13.95 monthly; $10.00 additional installation.
Pay Service 1
Pay Units: 22.
Programming (via satellite): HBO.
Fee: $15.00 installation; $9.95 monthly.
Manager: Pat Lattin. Plant manager: Mike Lattin.
Franchise fee: 5% of gross.
Ownership: Eagle Valley Communications (MSO).

ROSE LODGE—Millennium Digital Media, Suite 107, 3633 136th Place SE, Bellevue, WA 98006. Phones: 425-747-4600; 800-829-2225. Fax: 425-644-4621. County: Lincoln. Also serves Otis, Salmon River. ICA: OR0150.
TV Market Ranking: Outside TV Markets. Franchise award date: N.A. Franchise expiration date: N.A. Began: N.A.
Channel capacity: N.A. Channels available but not in use: N.A.
Basic Service
Subscribers: 808.
Programming (received off-air): KATU (A), KGW (N), KOIN (C), KOPB-TV (P), KPTV (U) Portland; KPDX (F) Vancouver.
Programming (via satellite): WGN-TV (W) Chicago; A & E; American Movie Classics; C-SPAN; CNBC; CNN; Discovery Channel; Disney Channel; ESPN; Fox Family Channel; Fox Sports Net Northwest; Headline News; Home & Garden Television; Learning Channel; Lifetime; Nashville Network; Nickelodeon; Northwest Cable News; QVC; TBS Superstation; Trinity Bcstg. Network; Turner Network TV; USA Network.
Current originations: Public access.
Fee: $45.00 installation; $26.95 monthly.
Pay Service 1
Pay Units: N.A.
Programming (via satellite): HBO; Showtime; The Movie Channel.
Fee: $14.95 monthly (each).
Manager: Steve Weed. Chief technician: Gene Fry.
Ownership: Millennium Digital Media LLC (MSO). Purchased from Summit Communications Inc., April 7, 1999.

ROSEBURG—Falcon Cable TV, 575 W. Harrison, Roseburg, OR 97470. Phone: 541-673-1267. Fax: 541-672-5193. County: Douglas. Also serves Douglas County (portions). ICA: OR0016.
TV Market Ranking: Below 100 (portions of Douglas County, Roseburg); Outside TV Markets (portions of Douglas County). Franchise award date: November 1, 1973. Franchise expiration date: December 31, 2005. Began: January 1, 1954.
Channel capacity: 27 (2-way capable). Channels available but not in use: None.
Basic Service
Subscribers: 7,494; Commercial subscribers: 41.
Programming (received off-air): KEVU-LP (F), KEZI (A), KLSR-TV (U) Eugene; KDRV (A), KOBI (N), KSYS (P) Medford; KMTX-TV (N), KPIC (C), KTVC (X) Roseburg; 12 FMs.
Programming (via satellite): American Movie Classics; Blazer Vision; ESPN; Fox Family Channel; Home Shopping Network; Nashville Network; Nickelodeon; QVC; TV Guide Channel; TV Guide Sneak Prevue.
Current originations: Automated time-weather.
Fee: $35.00 installation; $24.78 monthly; $15.00 additional installation.
Expanded Basic Service
Subscribers: 6,845.
Programming (via satellite): A & E; C-SPAN; ESPN 2; Fox News Channel; Game Show Network; Lifetime; MTV; USA Network.
Fee: $5.93 monthly.
Expanded Basic Service 2
Subscribers: 6,903.
Programming (via satellite): CNN; Discovery Channel; Disney Channel; Headline News; PandaAmerica Shopping Network; TBS Superstation; Trinity Bcstg. Network; Turner Network TV.
Fee: $8.75 monthly.
Expanded Basic Service 3
Subscribers: N.A.
Programming (via satellite): fXM: Movies from Fox; History Channel; Learning Channel; Sci-Fi Channel; The Weather Channel.
Fee: $6.00 monthly.
Expanded Basic Service 4
Subscribers: N.A.
Programming (via satellite): Animal Planet; Home & Garden Television; Outdoor Life Network; Romance Classics; Turner Classic Movies.
Fee: $6.00 monthly.
Pay Service 1
Pay Units: 569.
Programming (via satellite): HBO (multiplexed).
Fee: $25.00 installation; $11.95 monthly.
Pay Service 2
Pay Units: 438.
Programming (via satellite): Showtime.
Fee: $25.00 installation; $11.95 monthly.
Pay Service 3
Pay Units: 278.
Programming (via satellite): The Movie Channel.
Fee: $25.00 installation; $11.95 monthly.
Pay Service 4
Pay Units: N.A.
Programming (via satellite): Cinemax; The New Encore.
Fee: $5.95 monthly (Encore), $11.95 monthly (Cinemax).
Pay-Per-View
Spice; Spice2.
Local advertising: Yes (locally produced & insert). Available in character-generated & automated programming. Rates: $16.00/Minute; $8.00/30 Seconds. Local sales manager: Darell Rogers.
Program Guide: CableView.
Equipment: Scientific-Atlanta headend; Century III, C-COR & Jerrold amplifiers; Comm/Scope, Times Fiber & Trilogy cable; Sony VTRs; Texscan character generator; Jerrold & Texscan set top converters; Jerrold addressable set top converters; Microwave Assoc. & Prodelin satellite antenna; Microwave Assoc. & Scientific-Atlanta satellite receivers.
Miles of plant: 210.0 (coaxial). Homes passed: 14,441.
Manager: Edward Mosczynski. Chief technician: Wade Starbuck.
Franchise fee: 5% of gross.
Ownership: Falcon Communications LP (MSO), joint venture formed September 30, 1998. See Cable System Ownership.

RUCH—Sunnyside Cable TV Co., 5361 Hwy. 238, Jacksonville, OR 97530. Phone: 541-899-1341. County: Jackson. ICA: OR0091.
TV Market Ranking: Below 100. Franchise award date: N.A. Franchise expiration date: N.A. Began: N.A.
Channel capacity: 27 (2-way capable; operating 2-way). Channels available but not in use: N.A.
Basic Service
Subscribers: 350.
Programming (received off-air): KDRV (A), KOBI (N), KSYS (P), KTVL (C) Medford.
Programming (via satellite): WGN-TV (W) Chicago; A & E; CNN; Discovery Channel; ESPN; Fox Family Channel; Goodlife TV Network; Lifetime; MTV; Nashville Network; Nickelodeon; TBS Superstation; Turner Classic Movies; Turner Network TV; USA Network; VH1.
Fee: $20.95 monthly.
Pay Service 1
Pay Units: 31.
Programming (via satellite): Cinemax.
Fee: $7.50 monthly.
Pay Service 2
Pay Units: 20.
Programming (via satellite): Disney Channel.
Fee: $7.50 monthly.
Pay Service 3
Pay Units: 44.
Programming (via satellite): HBO.
Fee: $7.50 monthly.
Miles of plant: 30.0 (coaxial); None (fiber optic). Homes passed: 450.
Manager: Helene B. Johnson. Chief technician: David P. Johnson.
Ownership: Sunnyside Cable TV Co.

SALEM—TCI, 1710 Salem Industrial Dr. NE, Salem, OR 97303. Phone: 503-370-2770. Fax: 503-370-2571. Counties: Marion, Polk & Yamhill. Also serves Amity, Keizer, Marion County (portions), Polk County (portions). ICA: OR0005.
TV Market Ranking: 29 (portions of Marion County); Below 100 (Amity, Keizer, portions of Marion County, portions of Polk County, Salem); Outside TV Markets (portions of Marion County, portions of Polk County). Franchise award date: March 14, 1967. Franchise expiration date: N.A. Began: November 1, 1969.
Channel capacity: 40 (not 2-way capable). Channels available but not in use: None.
Basic Service
Subscribers: 51,620.
Programming (received off-air): KATU (A), KGW (N), KNMT (T), KOIN (C), KOPB-TV (P), KPTV (U) Portland; KPXG (X), KWBP (W) Salem; KPDX (F) Vancouver; 20 FMs.
Programming (via satellite): A & E; C-SPAN; C-SPAN 2; CNBC; CNN; Comedy Central; Fox Sports Net Northwest; Learning Channel; Nashville Network; Nickelodeon; TBS Superstation; Univision.
Current originations: Automated time-weather; public access; educational access; government access; leased access.
Fee: $20.45 installation; $22.82 monthly.
Expanded Basic Service
Subscribers: N.A.
Programming (via satellite): American Movie Classics; Discovery Channel; ESPN; Fox Family Channel; Lifetime; MTV; QVC; Sci-Fi Channel; The Weather Channel; Turner Network TV; USA Network; VH1.
Fee: N.A.
Pay Service 1
Pay Units: 19,532.
Programming (via satellite): Disney Channel; HBO; Playboy TV; Showtime; The Movie Channel.
Fee: $10.95 monthly (each).
Pay-Per-View
Addressable homes: 22,500.
Viewer's Choice.
Local advertising: Yes.
Equipment: Scientific-Atlanta headend; GTE Sylvania amplifiers; Cerro & Comm/Scope cable; Texscan character generator; Hamlin & Jerrold set top converters; Scientific-Atlanta satellite antenna; Hughes & Scientific-Atlanta satellite receivers; ChannelMatic commercial insert.
Miles of plant: 630.0 (coaxial); 230.0 (fiber optic). Homes passed: 76,200. Total homes in franchised area: 78,000.
Manager: Dave Ramsey. Technical operations manager: Dave Mingus. Chief technician: Max Shuck. Marketing director: Tim Ream. Office manager: Debbie Roberts.
City fee: 5% of basic revenue (Salem).
Ownership: AT&T Broadband & Internet Services (MSO). Purchased from Tele-Communications Inc., March 9, 1999.

SALEM (southeastern portion)—Mill Creek Cable TV Inc., 3100 Turner Rd. SE, Salem, OR 97302. Phone: 503-363-7717. Fax: 503-399-9978. County: Marion. ICA: OR0086.
TV Market Ranking: Below 100. Franchise award date: N.A. Franchise expiration date: N.A. Began: November 1, 1984.
Channel capacity: 35. Channels available but not in use: 13.
Basic Service
Subscribers: 395.
Programming (received off-air): KATU (A), KGW (N), KOIN (C), KOPB-TV (P), KPTV (U) Portland; KPDX (F) Vancouver; 1 FM.
Programming (via satellite): WGN-TV (W) Chicago; A & E; CNN; ESPN; Fox Family Channel; Nashville Network; TBS Superstation; USA Network.
Current originations: Automated time-weather; local news.
Fee: $10.95 monthly.
Pay Service 1
Pay Units: N.A.
Programming (via satellite): Showtime.
Fee: $10.95 monthly.
Miles of plant: 5.0 (coaxial). Homes passed: 434.
Manager: John Poole.
Ownership: Poole's Inc.

SANDY—Falcon Cablevision, 1215 12th St., Hood River, OR 97031. Phone: 541-386-3100. County: Clackamas. Also serves Clackamas County (portions), Wemme. ICA: OR0063.
TV Market Ranking: 29 (portions of Clackamas County, Sandy); Below 100 (portions of Clackamas County); Outside TV Markets (portions of Clackamas County, Wemme). Franchise award date: N.A. Franchise expiration date: N.A. Began: December 1, 1980.
Channel capacity: 42 (not 2-way capable). Channels available but not in use: 1.

Basic Service
Subscribers: 3,205.
Programming (received off-air): KATU (A), KGW (N), KOIN (C), KOPB-TV (P), KPTV (U) Portland; KPDX (F) Vancouver; 15 FMs.
Programming (via satellite): WGN-TV (W) Chicago; A & E; C-SPAN; Comedy Central; ESPN; ESPN 2; Fox Family Channel; Fox Sports Net Northwest; Home & Garden Television; Home Shopping Network; MTV; Nickelodeon; QVC; TBS Superstation; Trinity Bcstg. Network; VH1.
Current originations: Automated emergency alert.
Fee: $29.95 installation; $21.62 monthly.
Expanded Basic Service
Subscribers: 2,222.
Programming (via satellite): American Movie Classics; Lifetime; Sci-Fi Channel; Travel Channel; Univision.
Fee: $4.39 monthly.
Expanded Basic Service 2
Subscribers: 1,652.
Programming (via satellite): CNN; Country Music TV; Discovery Channel; Disney Channel; Headline News; Nashville Network; Turner Network TV; USA Network.
Fee: $5.45 monthly.
Pay Service 1
Pay Units: 364.
Programming (via satellite): HBO.
Fee: $29.95 installation; $11.95 monthly.
Pay Service 2
Pay Units: 432.
Programming (via satellite): Showtime.
Fee: $10.95 monthly.
Pay Service 3
Pay Units: 326.
Programming (via satellite): The Movie Channel.
Fee: $29.95 installation; $10.95 monthly.
Pay-Per-View
Special events.
Equipment: Scientific-Atlanta headend; Magnavox amplifiers; Comm/Scope cable; Scientific-Atlanta addressable set top converters; Scientific-Atlanta satellite antenna; Scientific-Atlanta satellite receivers.
Miles of plant: 148.0 (coaxial); 20.0 (fiber optic). Homes passed: 6,066.
Manager: H. H. Asher. Chief technician: Daniel Wallace.
Franchise fee: 3% of gross.
Ownership: Falcon Communications LP (MSO), joint venture formed September 30, 1998. See Cable System Ownership.

SCIO—Scio Cablevision Inc., Box 210, Scio, OR 97374. Phone: 503-394-2995. Fax: 503-394-3999. County: Linn. ICA: OR0151.
TV Market Ranking: Below 100. Franchise award date: N.A. Franchise expiration date: N.A. Began: December 1, 1982.
Channel capacity: 36 (not 2-way capable). Channels available but not in use: None.
Basic Service
Subscribers: 430.
Programming (received off-air): KATU (A), KGW (N), KOIN (C), KOPB-TV (P), KPTV (U) Portland; KPXG (X), KWBP (W) Salem; KPDX (F) Vancouver.
Programming (via satellite): WGN-TV (W) Chicago; A & E; American Movie Classics; C-SPAN; CNN; Cartoon Network; Country Music TV; Discovery Channel; Disney Channel; ESPN; Fox Family Channel; Fox Sports Net Northwest; Headline News; Home Shopping Network; Learning Channel; Lifetime; Nashville Network; Nickelodeon; Northwest Cable News; Sci-Fi Channel; TBS Superstation; Trinity Bcstg. Network; Turner Network TV; USA Network; VH1.
Fee: $50.00 installation; $21.00 monthly.
Pay Service 1
Pay Units: 84.
Programming (via satellite): HBO.
Fee: $15.00 installation; $10.00 monthly.
Pay Service 2
Pay Units: 38.
Programming (via satellite): The Movie Channel.
Fee: $15.00 installation; $10.00 monthly.
Local advertising: No.
Miles of plant: 40.0 (coaxial); 10.0 (fiber optic). Homes passed: 650.
Manager: Tom Barth.
Ownership: Scio Cablevision Inc.

SENECA—Blue Mountain TV Cable Co., Box 267, Mount Vernon, OR 97865. Phone: 541-932-4613. County: Grant. ICA: OR0122.
TV Market Ranking: Outside TV Markets. Franchise award date: N.A. Franchise expiration date: N.A. Began: October 1, 1956.
Channel capacity: 16 (not 2-way capable). Channels available but not in use: 8.
Basic Service
Subscribers: 35.
Programming (received off-air): KOPB-TV (P) Portland.
Programming (via satellite): WGN-TV (W) Chicago; KCNC-TV (C), KMGH-TV (A), KUSA-TV (N), KWGN-TV (W) Denver; Nashville Network; Northwest Cable News.
Fee: $19.50 installation; $11.00 monthly.
Equipment: Scientific-Atlanta satellite antenna; Scientific-Atlanta satellite receivers.
Miles of plant: 2.0 (coaxial). Homes passed: 70.
Manager: Chuck McKenna.
Ownership: Blue Mountain TV Cable Co. (MSO).

SHADY COVE—Phoenix Cablevision of Oregon Inc., Box 828, 6655 Rogue River Dr., Shady Cove, OR 97539. Phones: 541-878-3247; 800-827-3247. Fax: 541-878-2458. County: Jackson. Also serves Trail. ICA: OR0152.
TV Market Ranking: Below 100. Franchise award date: N.A. Franchise expiration date: April 30, 2000. Began: November 1, 1980.
Channel capacity: 42 (not 2-way capable). Channels available but not in use: 3.
Basic Service
Subscribers: 765.
Programming (received off-air): KDRV (A), KMVU (F), KOBI (N), KSYS (P), KTVL (C) Medford; 1 FM.
Programming (via satellite): WGN-TV (W) Chicago; C-SPAN; Country Music TV; Headline News; Home Shopping Network.
Fee: $26.95 installation; $43.75 monthly; $56.00 converter; $26.25 additional installation.
Commercial fee: $5.50 monthly.
Expanded Basic Service
Subscribers: 670.
Programming (via satellite): KTLA (W) Los Angeles; WPIX (W) New York; A & E; Animal Planet; CNN; Comedy Central; Discovery Channel; Disney Channel; ESPN; Fox Family Channel; Goodlife TV Network; Lifetime; MTV; Nashville Network; Nickelodeon; Turner Classic Movies; Turner Network TV; USA Network; VH1.
Fee: $11.25 monthly.
Expanded Basic Service 2
Subscribers: N.A.
Programming (via satellite): CNBC; Cartoon Network; E! Entertainment TV; ESPN 2; History Channel; Home & Garden Television; Learning Channel; Sci-Fi Channel; TBS Superstation; The Weather Channel; Travel Channel.
Fee: N.A.
Pay Service 1
Pay Units: 21.
Programming (via satellite): Cinemax.
Fee: $15.00 installation; $13.95 monthly.
Pay Service 2
Pay Units: 47.
Programming (via satellite): HBO.
Fee: $15.00 installation; $13.00 monthly.
Local advertising: Yes (insert only). Rates: $50.00/Week.
Program Guide: Premium Channels.
Equipment: Electrohome headend; RCA amplifiers; Jerrold & Comm/Scope cable; Hamlin set top converters; Arcom traps; Prodelin & M/A-Com satellite antenna; Electrohome satellite receivers.
Miles of plant: 28.0 (coaxial). Homes passed: 1,167.
Manager: Ted W. Hughett. Chief technician: Dan Middleton.
City fee: 3% of gross.
Ownership: Phoenix Cable Inc. (MSO).

SHERIDAN—Stuck Electric Inc., 147 W. Main, Sheridan, OR 97378. Phone: 503-843-2322. Fax: 503-843-2321. Counties: Polk & Yamhill. Also serves Grand Ronde, Willamina. ICA: OR0052.
TV Market Ranking: Below 100. Franchise award date: N.A. Franchise expiration date: N.A. Began: June 1, 1955.
Channel capacity: 12. Channels available but not in use: 2.
Basic Service
Subscribers: N.A.
Programming (received off-air): KOAB-TV (P) Bend; KOAC-TV (P) Corvallis; KEZI (A), KVAL-TV (C) Eugene; KATU (A), KGW (N), KOIN (C), KOPB-TV (P), KPTV (U) Portland; allband FM.
Fee: $37.00 installation; $6.50 monthly.
Equipment: Cadco headend; Ameco amplifiers; Vikoa cable.
Miles of plant: 32.0 (coaxial). Homes passed: 1,820.
Manager: Don Stuck. Chief technician: Dan Gutherie.
City fee: 3% of gross.
Ownership: Stuck Electric Inc.

SILETZ—Millennium Digital Media, Box 367, Depoe Bay, OR 97341. Phone: 425-747-4600. County: Lincoln. ICA: OR0080.
TV Market Ranking: Outside TV Markets. Franchise award date: N.A. Franchise expiration date: N.A. Began: June 1, 1965.
Channel capacity: 35 (not 2-way capable). Channels available but not in use: 1.
Basic Service
Subscribers: 497.
Programming (received off-air): KOAC-TV (P) Corvallis; KEZI (A) Eugene; KATU (A), KGW (N), KOIN (C), KPTV (U) Portland; KPDX (F) Vancouver.
Programming (via satellite): WGN-TV (W) Chicago; C-SPAN; CNN; ESPN; Fox Family Channel; Headline News; Home Shopping Network; TBS Superstation; Trinity Bcstg. Network.
Current originations: Local news.
Fee: $45.00 installation; $16.27 monthly.
Expanded Basic Service
Subscribers: N.A.
Programming (via satellite): A & E; CNBC; Discovery Channel; Nashville Network; Turner Network TV; USA Network.
Fee: $45.00 installation; $6.95 monthly.
Pay Service 1
Pay Units: N.A.
Programming (via satellite): Disney Channel; HBO; Showtime; The Movie Channel.
Fee: $8.95 monthly (Disney), $10.00 monthly (Showtime or TMC), $12.95 monthly (HBO).
Equipment: Blonder-Tongue & AML headend; Blonder-Tongue amplifiers; Comm/Scope cable; Hughes satellite antenna.
Miles of plant: 18.8 (coaxial). Homes passed: 540.
Manager: Steve Weed. Chief technician: Gene Fry. Marketing director: Cindy Linne.
City fee: 3% of gross.
Ownership: Millennium Digital Media LLC (MSO). Purchased from Summit Communications Inc., April 7, 1999.

SILVERTON—Falcon Cable Systems Co., Box 86, 1862 Godsey Rd., Dallas, OR 97338. Phone: 503-623-3241. Fax: 503-623-9446. County: Marion. Also serves Marion County (portions), Mount Angel. ICA: OR0047.
TV Market Ranking: 29 (portions of Marion County, Mount Angel, Silverton); Below 100 (portions of Marion County); Outside TV Markets (portions of Marion County). Franchise award date: March 3, 1980. Franchise expiration date: N.A. Began: September 1, 1980.
Channel capacity: 37 (2-way capable; operating 2-way). Channels available but not in use: None.
Basic Service
Subscribers: 1,804.
Programming (received off-air): KATU (A), KGW (N), KNMT (T), KOIN (C), KOPB-TV (P), KPTV (U) Portland; KPXG (X), KWBP (W) Salem; KPDX (F) Vancouver.
Programming (via satellite): C-SPAN; ESPN; Fox Family Channel; Home & Garden Television; MTV; Nickelodeon; QVC; TBS Superstation; Univision.
Current originations: Public access; educational access; government access.
Fee: $65.00 installation; $19.85 monthly; $1.61 converter; $65.00 additional installation.
Expanded Basic Service
Subscribers: 1,268.
Programming (via satellite): A & E; American Movie Classics; CNN; Headline News; Lifetime.
Fee: $5.37 monthly.
Expanded Basic Service 2
Subscribers: 860.
Programming (via satellite): Country Music TV; Discovery Channel; Disney Channel; Nashville Network; Turner Network TV; USA Network.
Fee: $8.80 monthly.
Pay Service 1
Pay Units: 131.
Programming (via satellite): Cinemax.
Fee: $25.00 installation; $11.95 monthly.
Pay Service 2
Pay Units: 260.

Programming (via satellite): HBO.
Fee: $25.00 installation; $11.95 monthly.
Pay Service 3
Pay Units: 180.
Programming (via satellite): Showtime.
Fee: $25.00 installation; $11.95 monthly.
Pay Service 4
Pay Units: 117.
Programming (via satellite): The Movie Channel.
Fee: $11.95 monthly.
Pay-Per-View
Blazer Vision.
Fee: $3.95.
Local advertising: Yes (locally produced). Available in satellite distributed, character-generated & automated programming.
Equipment: Scientific-Atlanta headend; GTE Sylvania amplifiers; Comm/Scope cable; Magnavox set top converters; Prodelin & Scientific-Atlanta satellite antenna.
Miles of plant: 57.7 (coaxial); None (fiber optic). Additional miles planned: 5.0 (coaxial). Homes passed: 3,814.
Manager: Joel Billings.
Franchise fee: 3%-5% of gross.
Ownership: Falcon Communications LP (MSO), joint venture formed September 30, 1998. See Cable System Ownership.

SOUTH SALEM—Country Cablevision Ltd., Box 12038, Salem, OR 97309-0038. Phone: 503-588-8247. Fax: 503-588-0544. County: Marion. Also serves Marion County (portions). ICA: OR0160.
TV Market Ranking: Below 100. Franchise award date: N.A. Franchise expiration date: N.A. Began: January 1, 1992.
Channel capacity: 54 (2-way capable). Channels available but not in use: 24.
Basic Service
Subscribers: 350.
Programming (received off-air): KATU (A), KGW (N), KOIN (C), KOPB-TV (P), KPTV (U) Portland; KPDX (F) Vancouver.
Programming (via satellite): WGN-TV (W) Chicago; A & E; American Movie Classics; CNN; Country Music TV; Discovery Channel; ESPN; Fox Family Channel; Headline News; Lifetime; MTV; Nashville Network; Nickelodeon; QVC; TBS Superstation; Turner Network TV; USA Network; Univision; VH1.
Current originations: Public access.
Fee: $49.95 installation; $21.95 monthly.
Pay Service 1
Pay Units: N.A.
Programming (via satellite): Disney Channel; Showtime; The Movie Channel; The New Encore.
Fee: $4.95 monthly (Encore), $8.95 monthly (Showtime), $9.95 monthly (Disney), $10.95 monthly (TMC).
Local advertising: Yes. Available in locally originated programming.
Equipment: Trilogy cable.
Miles of plant: 32.0 (coaxial). Homes passed: 800.
Manager: John P. Johnson. Chief technician: Veron L. Robinson.
Ownership: Country Cablevision Ltd. (MSO).

SOUTHBEACH—Millennium Digital Media, Box 367, Depoe Bay, OR 97341. Phone: 425-747-4600. County: Lincoln. Also serves Lincoln County (portions), Seal Rock. ICA: OR0153.
TV Market Ranking: Outside TV Markets. Franchise award date: N.A. Franchise expiration date: January 10, 1997. Began: May 1, 1972.
Channel capacity: 35. Channels available but not in use: 1.
Basic Service
Subscribers: 722.
Programming (received off-air): KOAC-TV (P) Corvallis; KEZI (A), KVAL-TV (C) Eugene; KATU (A), KGW (N), KOIN (C), KPTV (U) Portland; KPDX (F) Vancouver; allband FM.
Programming (via satellite): WGN-TV (W) Chicago; C-SPAN; CNN; ESPN; Fox Family Channel; Headline News; Home Shopping Network; TBS Superstation; Trinity Bcstg. Network.
Fee: $45.00 installation; $16.27 monthly.
Expanded Basic Service
Subscribers: N.A.
Programming (via satellite): A & E; CNBC; Discovery Channel; Nashville Network; Turner Network TV; USA Network.
Fee: $45.00 installation; $6.95 monthly.
Pay Service 1
Pay Units: N.A.
Programming (via satellite): Disney Channel; HBO; Showtime; The Movie Channel.
Fee: $8.95 monthly (Disney), $11.95 monthly (Showtime or TMC), $12.95 monthly (HBO).
Equipment: Blonder-Tongue & AML headend; Cascade amplifiers.
Miles of plant: 28.7 (coaxial).
Manager: Steve Weed. Chief technician: Gene Fry.
Ownership: Millennium Digital Media LLC (MSO). Purchased from Summit Communications Inc., April 7, 1999.

ST. HELENS—TCI Cablevision of Oregon Inc., 3500 S.W. Bond St., Portland, OR 97201. Phone: 503-609-4800. County: Columbia. Also serves Columbia City, Columbia County, Scappoose, Warren. ICA: OR0027.
TV Market Ranking: 29 (Columbia City, portions of Columbia County, Scappoose, St. Helens, Warren); Below 100 (portions of Columbia County); Outside TV Markets (portions of Columbia County). Franchise award date: N.A. Franchise expiration date: N.A. Began: December 1, 1981.
Channel capacity: 54 (2-way capable; operating 2-way). Channels available but not in use: 19.
Basic Service
Subscribers: N.A.
Programming (received off-air): KATU (A), KGW (N), KOIN (C), KOPB-TV (P), KPTV (U) Portland; KPDX (F) Vancouver; 15 FMs.
Programming (via satellite): C-SPAN; CNN; QVC; TBS Superstation.
Current originations: Automated time-weather; public access; automated emergency alert; local news.
Fee: $60.00 installation; $11.05 monthly; $0.81 converter; $22.79 additional installation.
Expanded Basic Service
Subscribers: 3,893.
Programming (via satellite): WGN-TV (W) Chicago; CNBC; Comedy Central; Discovery Channel; Fox Family Channel; Headline News; Lifetime; MTV; Nashville Network; Nickelodeon; VH1.
Fee: $53.17 installation; $9.52 monthly.
Expanded Basic Service 2
Subscribers: 3,671.
Programming (via satellite): A & E; American Movie Classics; ESPN; Fox Sports Net Northwest; Turner Network TV; USA Network.
Fee: $11.56 monthly.
Pay Service 1
Pay Units: 251.
Programming (via satellite): Cinemax.
Fee: $19.95 installation; $12.15 monthly.
Pay Service 2
Pay Units: 259.
Programming (via satellite): Disney Channel.
Fee: $19.95 installation; $9.95 monthly.
Pay Service 3
Pay Units: 1,941.
Programming (via satellite): The New Encore.
Fee: N.A.
Pay Service 4
Pay Units: 505.
Programming (via satellite): HBO.
Fee: $19.95 installation; $12.15 monthly.
Pay Service 5
Pay Units: 263.
Programming (via satellite): Showtime.
Fee: $19.95 installation; $12.15 monthly.
Local advertising: Planned.
Program Guide: The Cable Guide.
Equipment: Microwave Assoc. & Phasecom headend; Magnavox amplifiers; Times Fiber cable; Panasonic cameras; Panasonic VTRs; Compuvid character generator; Oak set top converters; Prodelin & Scientific-Atlanta satellite antenna; Microwave Assoc. satellite receivers.
Miles of plant: 156.0 (coaxial). Additional miles planned: 14.0 (coaxial). Homes passed: 6,359. Total homes in franchised area: 6,461.
Manager: Bill Tierney. Marketing director: John Grismore.
City fee: 5% of gross (St. Helens).
Ownership: AT&T Broadband & Internet Services (MSO). Purchased from Tele-Communications Inc., March 9, 1999.

ST. PAUL (town)—Interstate Cable Inc., Box 2687, Salina, KS 67402-2687. Phones: 785-452-9409; 800-888-4788. Fax: 785-238-7190. County: Marion. ICA: OR0154.
TV Market Ranking: 29. Franchise award date: N.A. Franchise expiration date: N.A. Began: December 1, 1991.
Channel capacity: N.A. Channels available but not in use: N.A.
Basic Service
Subscribers: 29.
Programming (received off-air): KATU (A), KGW (N), KNMT (T), KOIN (C), KOPB-TV (P), KPTV (U) Portland; KPDX (F) Vancouver.
Programming (via satellite): A & E; CNBC; CNN; Discovery Channel; EWTN; GalaVision; Headline News; Nashville Network; TBS Superstation; Turner Network TV; ValueVision.
Fee: $50.00 installation; $21.95 monthly; $2.00 converter; $15.00 additional installation.
Pay Service 1
Pay Units: N.A.
Programming (via satellite): Cinemax; Disney Channel; HBO; The New Encore.
Fee: $6.95 monthly (Encore), $7.95 monthly (Disney), $10.95 monthly (Cinemax or HBO).
Homes passed: 110.
Manager: Patti Lahey.
Franchise fee: 3%.
Ownership: Tristar Cable Inc. (MSO).

SUBLIMITY—North Santiam Communications, Box 517, 475 N. 2nd Ave., Stayton, OR 97383. Phones: 503-769-7898; 503-769-7898. Fax: 503-769-4567. Counties: Linn & Marion. Also serves Aumsville, Gates, Lyons, Mehama, Mill City, Stayton, Turner. ICA: OR0065.
TV Market Ranking: Below 100. Franchise award date: October 1, 1981. Franchise expiration date: N.A. Began: February 2, 1982.
Channel capacity: 40 (not 2-way capable). Channels available but not in use: None.
Basic Service
Subscribers: 5,500.
Programming (received off-air): KOAC-TV (P) Corvallis; KATU (A), KGW (N), KOIN (C), KPTV (U) Portland; KPXG (X) Salem; KPDX (F) Vancouver.
Programming (via satellite): WGN-TV (W) Chicago; A & E; CNN; Country Music TV; Discovery Channel; ESPN; EWTN; Fox Family Channel; Headline News; Home Shopping Network; Learning Channel; Lifetime; Nashville Network; Nickelodeon; TBS Superstation; Trinity Bcstg. Network; Turner Network TV; USA Network; VH1.
Fee: $30.00 installation; $23.25 monthly; $3.75 converter.
Pay Service 1
Pay Units: 111.
Programming (via satellite): Disney Channel.
Fee: $7.25 installation; $10.00 monthly.
Pay Service 2
Pay Units: 206.
Programming (via satellite): HBO.
Fee: $8.25 installation; $10.00 monthly.
Pay Service 3
Pay Units: 74.
Programming (via satellite): Showtime.
Fee: $6.50 installation; $10.00 monthly.
Local advertising: Yes. Local sales manager: Mason Dufield.
Equipment: Scientific-Atlanta & DX Engineering headend; Magnavox amplifiers; CCS Hatfield & Comm/Scope cable; Cable Text character generator; Hamlin set top converters; Eagle traps; Prodelin satellite antenna; DX Engineering satellite receivers.
Miles of plant: 180.0 (coaxial); 6.0 (fiber optic).
Manager: Curt Thornton. Chief technician: Marty Jones. Program director: Sydney Gill. Marketing director: Leslie Seaver.
City fee: 3% of gross.
Ownership: SCS Communications & Security (MSO).

SUMPTER—Blackstone Cable LLC, 1104 W. Ironwood Dr., Coeur d'Alene, ID 83814-2605. Phone: 208-664-3370. Fax: 208-664-5888. County: Baker. Also serves Baker County (portions). ICA: OR0112.
TV Market Ranking: Outside TV Markets. Franchise award date: N.A. Franchise expiration date: December 17, 2001. Began: December 1, 1974.
Channel capacity: 19 (not 2-way capable). Channels available but not in use: 7.
Basic Service
Subscribers: 76.
Programming (received off-air): KTVB (N) Boise; allband FM.
Programming (via translator): KTVR (P) La Grande; KATU (A), KGW (N), KOIN (C), KPTV (U) Portland; KPDX (F) Vancouver.
Programming (via satellite): CNN; Discovery Channel; Disney Channel; ESPN; Nashville Network; TBS Superstation; Turner Network TV; USA Network.
Fee: $43.50 installation; $21.00 monthly; $56.00 converter; $21.50 additional installation.
Commercial fee: $5.34 monthly.
Pay Service 1
Pay Units: 14.
Programming (via satellite): HBO.
Fee: $15.00 installation; $10.95 monthly.
Equipment: Blonder-Tongue headend; Blonder-Tongue amplifiers; Cerro & Theta-Com cable; Pico traps; DX Communications satellite receivers.
Miles of plant: 6.4 (coaxial); None (fiber optic). Homes passed: 145.
Manager: Ted Hughett.
City fee: 3% of basic.
Ownership: Blackstone Cable LLC (MSO).

SUNRIVER—Chambers Cable of Sunriver Inc., Box 3275, Sunriver, OR 97707. Phone: 541-593-1296. County: Deschutes. Also serves Spring River. ICA: OR0155.

TV Market Ranking: Below 100. Franchise award date: N.A. Franchise expiration date: N.A. Began: October 1, 1969.

Channel capacity: 59 (2-way capable; operating 2-way). Channels available but not in use: 36.

Basic Service

Subscribers: 3,514.

Programming (received off-air): KFXO-LP (F), KOAB-TV (P), KTVZ (N) Bend; KEZI (A) Eugene; KOIN (C), KPTV (U) Portland; 14 FMs.

Programming (via satellite): A & E; C-SPAN; CNBC; CNN; Discovery Channel; Disney Channel; E! Entertainment TV; ESPN; EWTN; FX; Fox Family Channel; Fox News Channel; Fox Sports Net Northwest; Golf Channel; Headline News; History Channel; Knowledge TV; Learning Channel; Lifetime; Nashville Network; Nickelodeon; TBS Superstation; TV Guide Channel; The Weather Channel; Turner Classic Movies; Turner Network TV; USA Network; VH1.

Current originations: Automated time-weather.

Fee: $39.95 installation; $29.81 monthly; $3.00 converter; $10.00 additional installation.

Pay Service 1

Pay Units: 110.

Programming (via satellite): Showtime.

Fee: $10.00 installation; $9.95 monthly.

Pay Service 2

Pay Units: 182.

Programming (via satellite): HBO.

Fee: $10.00 installation; $9.95 monthly.

Pay Service 3

Pay Units: 49.

Programming (via satellite): Sundance Channel.

Fee: $10.00 installation; $3.95 monthly.

Pay-Per-View

Addressable homes: 400.

Playboy TV.

Fee: $4.95.

Pay-per-view manager: Minnie Marshall.

Local advertising: Yes. Available in locally originated & character-generated programming.

Equipment: Jerrold & Scientific-Atlanta headend; Jerrold amplifiers; Comm/Scope cable; Mycrotek character generator; Jerrold set top converters; Arcom traps; Scientific-Atlanta satellite antenna; Scientific-Atlanta satellite receivers; Tele-Engineering commercial insert.

Miles of plant: 82.0 (coaxial). Homes passed: 3,902.

Manager: Michael McLain.

Ownership: Chambers Communications Corp. (MSO).

SUTHERLIN—Falcon Cable Systems Co., Suite 5, 4739 Main St., Springfield, OR 97477. Phone: 503-746-4132. County: Douglas. Also serves Douglas County (portions), Oakland. ICA: OR0046.

TV Market Ranking: Below 100 (portions of Douglas County, Oakland, Sutherlin); Outside TV Markets (portions of Douglas County). Franchise award date: N.A. Franchise expiration date: N.A. Began: November 1, 1974.

Channel capacity: 29 (not 2-way capable). Channels available but not in use: None.

Basic Service

Subscribers: 2,016.

Programming (received off-air): KOAC-TV (P) Corvallis; KEVU-LP (F), KEZI (A), KMTR (N) Eugene; KOBI (N) Medford; KPIC (C), KTVC (X) Roseburg; allband FM.

Programming (via satellite): A & E; American Movie Classics; E! Entertainment TV; ESPN; Fox Family Channel; Lifetime; Nickelodeon; QVC.

Current originations: Public access; educational access; government access.

Fee: $19.95 installation; $19.42 monthly; $2.50 converter.

Expanded Basic Service

Subscribers: 1,839.

Programming (via satellite): Country Music TV; Nashville Network; Sci-Fi Channel; USA Network.

Fee: $2.91 monthly.

Expanded Basic Service 2

Subscribers: 1,711.

Programming (via satellite): WGN-TV (W) Chicago; Blazer Vision; CNN; Disney Channel; Headline News; TBS Superstation; Turner Network TV.

Fee: $6.05 monthly.

Pay Service 1

Pay Units: 268.

Programming (via satellite): HBO.

Fee: $11.95 monthly.

Pay Service 2

Pay Units: 136.

Programming (via satellite): Showtime.

Fee: $10.95 monthly.

Pay Service 3

Pay Units: 136.

Programming (via satellite): The Movie Channel.

Fee: $10.95 monthly.

Equipment: Ameco headend; Coral amplifiers; Andrew satellite antenna.

Miles of plant: 52.0 (coaxial). Homes passed: 3,659.

Manager: Derek White. Chief technician: James Gill.

Franchise fee: 3% of gross.

Ownership: Falcon Communications LP (MSO), joint venture formed September 30, 1998. See Cable System Ownership.

SWEET HOME—TCI Cablevision of Oregon Inc., Box 428, Lebanon, OR 97355. Phone: 541-367-5511. County: Linn. ICA: OR0035.

TV Market Ranking: Below 100. Franchise award date: N.A. Franchise expiration date: N.A. Began: October 1, 1963.

Channel capacity: 40 (2-way capable; operating 2-way). Channels available but not in use: N.A.

Basic Service

Subscribers: 3,019.

Programming (received off-air): KOAC-TV (P) Corvallis; KEZI (A), KMTR (N), KVAL-TV (C) Eugene; KATU (A), KGW (N), KOIN (C), KPTV (U) Portland; KPXG (X) Salem; KPDX (F) Vancouver; 13 FMs.

Programming (via satellite): C-SPAN; CNN; Discovery Channel; Fox Family Channel; Headline News; Lifetime; MTV; Nashville Network; Nickelodeon; TBS Superstation; The Weather Channel.

Current originations: Public access.

Fee: $33.20 installation; $10.00 monthly; $14.23 additional installation.

Expanded Basic Service

Subscribers: 2,801.

Programming (via satellite): American Movie Classics; ESPN; Fox Sports Net Northwest; QVC; Turner Network TV; USA Network.

Fee: $12.45 monthly.

Pay Service 1

Pay Units: 251.

Programming (via satellite): Disney Channel.

Fee: N.A.

Pay Service 2

Pay Units: 1,425.

Programming (via satellite): The New Encore.

Fee: N.A.

Pay Service 3

Pay Units: 386.

Programming (via satellite): HBO.

Fee: $10.00 installation; $12.50 monthly.

Pay Service 4

Pay Units: 232.

Programming (via satellite): Showtime.

Fee: $10.00 installation; $12.50 monthly.

Local advertising: Yes. Regional interconnect: TCI Cable Advertising-Oregon.

Equipment: Scientific-Atlanta headend; Magnavox amplifiers; Comm/Scope & Times Fiber cable; Scientific-Atlanta set top converters; Eagle & Vitek traps; Scientific-Atlanta satellite antenna; Scientific-Atlanta satellite receivers.

Miles of plant: 64.3 (coaxial). Homes passed: 3,744. Total homes in franchised area: 3,761.

Manager: Donald T. Hostetler. Chief technician: Jim Gulliksen.

City fee: 4% of gross.

Ownership: AT&T Broadband & Internet Services (MSO). Purchased from Tele-Communications Inc., March 9, 1999.

TENMILE—Interstate Cable Inc., Box 2687, Salina, KS 67402-2687. Phones: 785-452-9409; 800-888-4788. Fax: 785-238-7190. County: Douglas. ICA: OR0156.

TV Market Ranking: Below 100. Franchise award date: N.A. Franchise expiration date: N.A. Began: February 1, 1991.

Channel capacity: N.A. Channels available but not in use: N.A.

Basic Service

Subscribers: 93.

Programming (received off-air): KEZI (A), KMTR (N) Eugene; KPIC (C) Roseburg.

Programming (via satellite): WGN-TV (W) Chicago; A & E; C-SPAN; Comedy Central; Discovery Channel; ESPN; FX; Fox Family Channel; Goodlife TV Network; Headline News; Nashville Network; TBS Superstation; The Inspirational Network; Turner Network TV; USA Network.

Fee: $50.00 installation; $23.95 monthly; $2.00 converter; $15.00 additional installation.

Pay Service 1

Pay Units: N.A.

Programming (via satellite): Cinemax; Disney Channel; HBO; Showtime; The New Encore.

Fee: $6.95 monthly (Encore), $7.95 monthly (Disney), $10.95 monthly (Cinemax, HBO or Showtime).

Homes passed: 250.

Manager: Patti Lahey.

Ownership: Tristar Cable Inc. (MSO).

THE DALLES—Falcon Community Ventures I, 1215 12th St., Hood River, OR 97031. Phone: 541-386-3100. Fax: 503-296-5088. Counties: Wasco, OR; Klickitat, WA. Also serves Wasco County, OR; Dallesport, Klickitat County (portions), Murdock, WA. ICA: OR0025.

TV Market Ranking: Outside TV Markets. Franchise award date: January 1, 1954. Franchise expiration date: March 15, 2004. Began: June 1, 1954.

Channel capacity: 56 (2-way capable). Channels available but not in use: None.

Basic Service

Subscribers: 5,022.

Programming (received off-air): KATU (A), KGW (N), KOIN (C), KOPB-TV (P), KPTV (U) Portland; KPDX (F) Vancouver; 10 FMs.

Programming (via satellite): Blazer Vision; C-SPAN; ESPN; ESPN 2; FX; Fox Family Channel; Fox Sports Net Northwest; Goodlife TV Network; Home & Garden Television; Home Shopping Network; Knowledge TV; MTV; QVC; TBS Superstation; TV Guide Channel; TV Guide Sneak Prevue; Travel Channel; Trinity Bcstg. Network; Univision; VH1.

Current originations: Public access; educational access; government access.

Fee: $25.00 installation; $22.91 monthly; $25.00 additional installation.

Expanded Basic Service

Subscribers: 4,449.

Programming (via satellite): Lifetime; Nickelodeon; Sci-Fi Channel; Turner Network TV.

Fee: $2.89 monthly.

Expanded Basic Service 2

Subscribers: 4,257.

Programming (via satellite): American Movie Classics; CNN; Country Music TV; Discovery Channel; Disney Channel; Headline News; Nashville Network; USA Network.

Fee: $7.75 monthly.

Expanded Basic Service 3

Subscribers: 636.

Programming (via satellite): A & E; Cartoon Network; fXM: Movies from Fox; History Channel; Learning Channel; The Weather Channel.

Fee: $4.75 monthly.

Pay Service 1

Pay Units: 253.

Programming (via satellite): Cinemax.

Fee: $10.00 installation; $10.95 monthly.

Pay Service 2

Pay Units: 453.

Programming (via satellite): HBO.

Fee: $10.00 installation; $11.95 monthly.

Pay Service 3

Pay Units: 345.

Programming (via satellite): Showtime.

Fee: $10.00 installation; $10.95 monthly.

Pay Service 4

Pay Units: 167.

Programming (via satellite): The Movie Channel.

Fee: $10.95 monthly.

Pay-Per-View

Action Pay-Per-View; Spice; Viewer's Choice.

Local advertising: Yes. Available in character-generated programming.

Program Guide: The Cable Guide.

Equipment: Scientific-Atlanta headend; Jerrold amplifiers; Comm/Scope cable; Sony VTRs; Jerrold set top converters; Eagle traps; Scientific-Atlanta satellite antenna; Scientific-Atlanta satellite receivers.

Miles of plant: 115.0 (coaxial); 60.0 (fiber optic). Homes passed: 7,912.

Manager: H. W. Asher. Chief technician: Daniel Wallace.

Franchise fee: 3% of gross.

Ownership: Falcon Communications LP (MSO), joint venture formed September 30, 1998. See Cable System Ownership.

TILLAMOOK—Falcon Telecable, 1344 N.E. Hwy. 101, Lincoln City, OR 97367. Phone: 541-994-6083. Fax: 541-994-7438. County: Tillamook. ICA: OR0040.

TV Market Ranking: Outside TV Markets. Franchise award date: N.A. Franchise expiration date: N.A. Began: March 1, 1957.

Channel capacity: 29. Channels available but not in use: None.

Basic Service

Subscribers: 2,443.

Programming (received off-air): KATU (A), KGW (N), KOIN (C), KOPB-TV (P), KPTV (U) Portland; KPDX (F) Vancouver; 8 FMs.

Programming (via satellite): American Movie Classics; Blazer Vision; Bravo; ESPN; Fox

Family Channel; Lifetime; QVC; Trinity Bcstg. Network; Turner Network TV; USA Network.
Current originations: Automated time-weather.
Fee: $40.00 installation; $20.27 monthly.
Expanded Basic Service
Subscribers: 1,974.
Programming (via satellite): A & E; CNN; Discovery Channel; Headline News; Nashville Network.
Fee: $5.49 monthly.
Expanded Basic Service 2
Subscribers: 964.
Programming (via satellite): WGN-TV (W) Chicago; Disney Channel; TBS Superstation.
Fee: $3.92 monthly.
Pay Service 1
Pay Units: 61.
Programming (via satellite): Cinemax.
Fee: $10.95 monthly.
Pay Service 2
Pay Units: 287.
Programming (via satellite): HBO.
Fee: $11.95 monthly.
Pay Service 3
Pay Units: 175.
Programming (via satellite): Showtime.
Fee: $10.95 monthly.
Pay Service 4
Pay Units: 109.
Programming (via satellite): The Movie Channel.
Fee: $10.95 monthly.
Equipment: Scientific-Atlanta headend; Jerrold & Magnavox amplifiers; Times Fiber cable; MSI character generator; Scientific-Atlanta satellite antenna; Scientific-Atlanta & ISS satellite receivers.
Miles of plant: 80.0 (coaxial). Additional miles planned: 1.0 (coaxial). Homes passed: 3,225.
Manager: Joel Billings. Chief technician: Charles Johnson.
Franchise fee: 5% of gross.
Ownership: Falcon Communications LP (MSO), joint venture formed September 30, 1998. See Cable System Ownership.

TILLAMOOK COUNTY (southwestern portion)—Falcon Telecable, 1344 N.E. Hwy. 101, Lincoln City, OR 97367. Phone: 541-994-3111. County: Tillamook. Also serves Beaver, Cloverdale, Hebo, Neskowin, Pacific City, Sand Lake. ICA: OR0129.
TV Market Ranking: Outside TV Markets. Franchise award date: N.A. Franchise expiration date: N.A. Began: N.A.
Channel capacity: 62 (2-way capable). Channels available but not in use: None.
Basic Service
Subscribers: 2,000.
Programming (received off-air): KATU (A), KGW (N), KOIN (C), KOPB-TV (P), KPTV (U) Portland; KPDX (F) Vancouver; allband FM.
Programming (via satellite): WGN-TV (W) Chicago; A & E; C-SPAN; CNBC; Comedy Central; E! Entertainment TV; ESPN 2; FX; Home & Garden Television; Home Shopping Network; Learning Channel; MTV; QVC; TBS Superstation; TV Guide Channel; TV Guide Sneak Prevue; Trinity Bcstg. Network; VH1.
Current originations: Public access; educational access; government access; leased access.
Fee: $17.71 monthly.
Expanded Basic Service
Subscribers: 1,345.
Programming (via satellite): Blazer Vision; CNN; ESPN; Fox Family Channel; Fox Sports Net Northwest; Headline News; Lifetime; Nickelodeon; Sci-Fi Channel; Travel Channel.
Fee: $9.62 monthly.
Expanded Basic Service 2
Subscribers: 1,335.
Programming (via satellite): American Movie Classics; Country Music TV; Discovery Channel; Disney Channel; Nashville Network; The Weather Channel; Turner Network TV; USA Network.
Fee: $7.56 monthly.
Expanded Basic Service 3
Subscribers: N.A.
Programming (via satellite): Cartoon Network; fXM: Movies from Fox; History Channel; Outdoor Life Network.
Fee: N.A.
Pay Service 1
Pay Units: 157.
Programming (via satellite): HBO.
Fee: $11.95 monthly.
Pay Service 2
Pay Units: 124.
Programming (via satellite): Showtime.
Fee: $11.95 monthly.
Pay Service 3
Pay Units: N.A.
Programming (via satellite): Cinemax; The Movie Channel.
Fee: $11.95 monthly (each).
Miles of plant: 96.0 (coaxial). Homes passed: 2,601.
Manager: Roberta Hogeland. Chief technician: Bruce Clark.
Ownership: Falcon Communications LP (MSO), joint venture formed September 30, 1998. See Cable System Ownership.

TYGH VALLEY—Cascade Cable Systems, Box 397, The Dalles, OR 97058. Phone: 541-298-4983. E-mail: jroth@gorge.net. County: Wasco. ICA: OR0117.
TV Market Ranking: Outside TV Markets. Franchise award date: N.A. Franchise expiration date: N.A. Began: January 1, 1978.
Channel capacity: 22 (not 2-way capable). Channels available but not in use: 9.
Basic Service
Subscribers: 97.
Programming (received off-air): KOAB-TV (P), KTVZ (N) Bend; KATU (A), KGW (N), KOIN (C), KPTV (U) Portland; KPDX (F) Vancouver; allband FM.
Programming (via satellite): Discovery Channel; ESPN; Nashville Network; Odyssey; TBS Superstation.
Fee: $25.00 installation; $15.00 monthly.
Pay Service 1
Pay Units: 20.
Programming (via satellite): The Movie Channel.
Fee: $10.00 installation; $10.00 monthly.
Miles of plant: 7.0 (coaxial); None (fiber optic). Homes passed: 110. Total homes in franchised area: 120.
Manager: James F. Roth.
Ownership: Cascade Cable Systems (MSO).

UMATILLA—Columbia Basin Cable, Box 490, 611 6th St., Umatilla, OR 97882. Phones: 541-922-5759; 800-521-3916. Fax: 541-922-3758. Counties: Morrow & Umatilla. Also serves Hermiston, Irrigon, Umatilla County (unincorporated areas). ICA: OR0053.
TV Market Ranking: Below 100 (Hermiston, Irrigon, Umatilla, portions of Umatilla County); Outside TV Markets (portions of Umatilla County). Franchise award date: N.A. Franchise expiration date: January 1, 2006. Began: February 1, 1981.
Channel capacity: 60 (not 2-way capable). Channels available but not in use: 1.
Basic Service
Subscribers: 1,922.
Programming (received off-air): KEPR-TV (C), KNDU (N), KVEW (A) Pasco-Kennewick-Richland; allband FM.
Programming (via microwave): KATU (A), KGW (N), KOIN (C), KOPB-TV (P), KPTV (U) Portland.
Programming (via satellite): WGN-TV (W) Chicago; WPIX (W) New York; TBS Superstation; TV Guide Channel; Trinity Bcstg. Network.
Current originations: Automated time-weather.
Fee: $35.00 installation; $17.95 monthly.
Expanded Basic Service
Subscribers: 1,704.
Programming (via microwave): Northwest Cable News.
Programming (via satellite): A & E; Animal Planet; C-SPAN; CNN; Country Music TV; Discovery Channel; ESPN; ESPN 2; FX; Fox Family Channel; Fox News Channel; Fox Sports Net Northwest; Goodlife TV Network; Headline News; History Channel; Home & Garden Television; Home Shopping Network; Lifetime; MTV; Nashville Network; Nickelodeon; QVC; Sci-Fi Channel; The Weather Channel; Turner Classic Movies; Turner Network TV; USA Network; Univision; VH1.
Fee: $29.95 monthly.
Pay Service 1
Pay Units: 110.
Programming (via satellite): Disney Channel.
Fee: $9.95 monthly.
Pay Service 2
Pay Units: 575.
Programming (via satellite): HBO (multiplexed).
Fee: $10.95 monthly.
Pay Service 3
Pay Units: 412.
Programming (via satellite): Starz!
Fee: $7.95 monthly.
Pay Service 4
Pay Units: N.A.
Programming (via satellite): The New Encore (multiplexed).
Fee: $7.95 monthly.
Pay-Per-View
Viewer's Choice 1-4; Spice.
Equipment: Blonder-Tongue headend; C-COR amplifiers; Times Fiber cable; Pioneer set top converters; Pioneer addressable set top converters; Standard Communications & Microdyne satellite receivers.
Miles of plant: 73.0 (coaxial); None (fiber optic). Additional miles planned: 1.0 (coaxial). Homes passed: 2,479.
Manager: Kerry Stratton. Chief technician: Darrell Johnson. Marketing director: Charlotte Winkler.
City fee: 3% of gross.
Ownership: USA Media Group LLC (MSO). Purchased from Cambridge Communications, May 15, 1999.

UNION—TCI Cablevision of Oregon Inc., Box 1401, La Grande, OR 97850-2202. Phone: 541-963-4189. County: Union. ICA: OR0074.
TV Market Ranking: Outside TV Markets. Franchise award date: N.A. Franchise expiration date: N.A. Began: July 1, 1956.
Channel capacity: 37 (not 2-way capable). Channels available but not in use: None.
Basic Service
Subscribers: 555.
Programming (received off-air): KTVB (N) Boise; KTVR (P) La Grande.
Programming (via microwave): KATU (A), KGW (N), KOIN (C), KPTV (U) Portland; KPDX (F) Vancouver.
Programming (via satellite): A & E; C-SPAN; CNBC; CNN; Discovery Channel; ESPN; FX; Fox Family Channel; Fox Sports Net Northwest; FoxNet; Headline News; Lifetime; MTV; Nashville Network; Nickelodeon; QVC; TBS Superstation; The Weather Channel; Turner Network TV; USA Network; Univision; VH1.
Current originations: Automated time-weather.
Fee: $41.00 installation; $23.19 monthly; $1.30 converter; $19.00 additional installation.
Pay Service 1
Pay Units: 42.
Programming (via satellite): Cinemax.
Fee: $11.45 monthly.
Pay Service 2
Pay Units: 60.
Programming (via satellite): Disney Channel.
Fee: $11.45 monthly.
Pay Service 3
Pay Units: 237.
Programming (via satellite): The New Encore.
Fee: $1.75 monthly.
Pay Service 4
Pay Units: 82.
Programming (via satellite): HBO.
Fee: $12.45 monthly.
Pay Service 5
Pay Units: 56.
Programming (via satellite): Showtime.
Fee: $12.45 monthly.
Pay Service 6
Pay Units: N.A.
Programming (via satellite): Starz!
Fee: $4.75 monthly.
Miles of plant: 10.3 (coaxial); None (fiber optic). Homes passed: 790. Total homes in franchised area: 790.
Manager: Darrell Linklater. Customer service manager: Pam Hardwick.
Ownership: AT&T Broadband & Internet Services (MSO). Purchased from Tele-Communications Inc., March 9, 1999.

VENETA—Falcon Cable Systems Co., Suite 5, 4739 Main St., Springfield, OR 97477. Phone: 503-746-4132. County: Lane. Also serves Elmira, Noti. ICA: OR0157.
TV Market Ranking: Below 100. Franchise award date: N.A. Franchise expiration date: N.A. Began: November 1, 1965.
Channel capacity: 30. Channels available but not in use: None.
Basic Service
Subscribers: 1,409.
Programming (received off-air): KOAC-TV (P) Corvallis; KEVU-LP (F), KEZI (A), KMTR (N), KVAL-TV (C) Eugene; KATU (A), KOIN (C) Portland.
Programming (via satellite): Blazer Vision; C-SPAN; Fox Family Channel; Goodlife TV Network; MTV.
Current originations: Public access; educational access; government access.
Fee: $15.72 monthly.
Expanded Basic Service
Subscribers: 1,338.
Programming (via satellite): ESPN; ESPN 2; ESPN Classic Sports; Fox Sports Net Northwest; Home Shopping Network; Nickelodeon; Sci-Fi Channel; TV Food Network; USA Network.
Fee: $4.91 monthly.
Expanded Basic Service 2
Subscribers: 1,196.
Programming (via satellite): A & E; CNN; Discovery Channel; Disney Channel; Headline News; Nashville Network; TBS Superstation.
Fee: $7.50 monthly.
Expanded Basic Service 3
Subscribers: N.A.

Programming (via satellite): Cartoon Network; Country Music TV; History Channel; Home & Garden Television; Learning Channel; The Weather Channel.
Fee: N.A.
Pay Service 1
Pay Units: 1.
Programming (via satellite): Cinemax.
Fee: $10.95 monthly.
Pay Service 2
Pay Units: 238.
Programming (via satellite): HBO.
Fee: $11.95 monthly.
Pay Service 3
Pay Units: 139.
Programming (via satellite): Showtime.
Fee: $10.95 monthly.
Pay Service 4
Pay Units: 73.
Programming (via satellite): The Movie Channel.
Fee: $10.95 monthly.
Miles of plant: 67.0 (coaxial). Homes passed: 2,780.
Manager: Derek White. Chief technician: James Gill.
Franchise fee: 3%-5% of gross.
Ownership: Falcon Communications LP (MSO), joint venture formed September 30, 1998. See Cable System Ownership.

VERNONIA—Vernonia CATV Inc., 536 S. First Ave., Vernonia, OR 97064. County: Columbia. ICA: OR0083.
TV Market Ranking: 29. Franchise award date: N.A. Franchise expiration date: N.A. Began: March 1, 1969.
Channel capacity: 5. Channels available but not in use: None.
Basic Service
Subscribers: 503.
Programming (received off-air): KATU (A), KGW (N), KOIN (C), KOPB-TV (P), KPTV (U) Portland; allband FM.
Programming (via satellite): Turner Network TV.
Fee: $25.00 installation; $6.00 monthly.
Pay Service 1
Pay Units: N.A.
Planned programming (via satellite): HBO.
Fee: N.A.
Equipment: Blonder-Tongue headend; Blonder-Tongue amplifiers; Comm/Scope & Essex cable; Scientific-Atlanta satellite antenna.
Miles of plant: 7.0 (coaxial).
Manager: V. E. Seager.
City fee: Less than 1% of gross.
Ownership: Vernonia CATV Inc.

WALDPORT—Alsea River Cable Co., Box 386, Waldport, OR 97394. Phone: 541-563-4807. Fax: 541-563-7341. County: Lincoln. Also serves Lincoln County (portions). ICA: OR0069.
TV Market Ranking: Outside TV Markets. Franchise award date: January 1, 1996. Franchise expiration date: N.A. Began: January 1, 1969.
Channel capacity: 36 (2-way capable). Channels available but not in use: 2.
Basic Service
Subscribers: 950.
Programming (received off-air): KOAC-TV (P) Corvallis; KEZI (A), KVAL-TV (C) Eugene; KATU (A), KGW (N), KOIN (C), KPTV (U) Portland; KPDX (F) Vancouver.
Programming (via satellite): WGN-TV (W) Chicago; A & E; C-SPAN 2; CNBC; CNN; Discovery Channel; ESPN; Fox Family Channel; Fox Sports Net Northwest; Learning Channel; Lifetime; MTV; Nashville Network; Nick at Nite; Nickelodeon; QVC; TBS Superstation; Turner Classic Movies; Turner Network TV; USA Network.
Current originations: Local access.
Fee: $15.00 installation; $14.00 monthly.
Pay Service 1
Pay Units: N.A.
Programming (via satellite): Cinemax; Disney Channel; Flix.
Fee: $7.00 monthly (Disney), $8.50 monthly (Cinemax or Flix).
Local advertising: No.
Equipment: Jerrold headend; Triple Crown amplifiers.
Miles of plant: 32.0 (coaxial). Homes passed: 1,010.
Manager: James Dale Haslett.
Ownership: James Dale Haslett.

WARM SPRINGS—American Telecasting, Box 5393, Bend, OR 97708. Phone: 541-382-4031. Fax: 541-382-6835. County: Jefferson. ICA: OR0085.
TV Market Ranking: Outside TV Markets. Franchise award date: N.A. Franchise expiration date: N.A. Began: June 1, 1955.
Channel capacity: 12. Channels available but not in use: 6.
Basic Service
Subscribers: N.A.
Programming (received off-air): KATU (A), KGW (N), KOIN (C), KOPB-TV (P), KPTV (U) Portland; allband FM.
Fee: Free installation; $5.50 monthly.
Equipment: Jerrold headend; Ameco amplifiers; Scientific-Atlanta satellite antenna.
Miles of plant: 8.0 (coaxial). Homes passed: 450.
Manager: Cathy Williams. Operations manager: Bruce Danielson.
Ownership: Dan Macy.

WASCO—J & N Cable Systems, 614 S. Columbus, Goldendale, WA 98620. Phone: 509-773-5359. Fax: 509-773-7090. County: Sherman. ICA: OR0159.
TV Market Ranking: Outside TV Markets. Franchise award date: N.A. Franchise expiration date: N.A. Began: January 1, 1989.
Channel capacity: N.A. Channels available but not in use: N.A.
Basic Service
Subscribers: 215.
Programming (received off-air): KATU (A), KGW (N), KOIN (C), KOPB-TV (P) Portland.
Programming (via satellite): WGN-TV (W) Chicago; CNN; ESPN; TBS Superstation.
Fee: $13.95 monthly.
Pay Service 1
Pay Units: N.A.
Programming (via satellite): HBO; Showtime.
Fee: $7.50 monthly (Showtime), $8.50 monthly (HBO).
Manager: John Kusky.
Ownership: J & N Cable Co. (MSO).

WESTON—TCI Cablevision of Oregon Inc., Box 1577, 126 W. Poplar St., Walla Walla, WA 99362-2847. Phone: 509-529-9500. Fax: 509-522-1719. County: Umatilla. Also serves Athena. ICA: OR0075.
TV Market Ranking: Below 100 (Weston); Outside TV Markets (Athena). Franchise award date: N.A. Franchise expiration date: N.A. Began: October 1, 1955.
Channel capacity: 30 (not 2-way capable). Channels available but not in use: N.A.
Basic Service
Subscribers: 588.
Programming (received off-air): KEPR-TV (C), KNDU (N), KVEW (A) Pasco-Kennewick-Richland; KSPS-TV (P) Spokane.
Programming (via satellite): A & E; CNN; Discovery Channel; ESPN; Fox Family Channel; Nashville Network; Nickelodeon; TBS Superstation; Turner Network TV; USA Network.
Fee: $36.34 installation; $18.43 monthly; $17.90 additional installation.
Pay Service 1
Pay Units: 68.
Programming (via satellite): Disney Channel.
Fee: $11.45 monthly.
Pay Service 2
Pay Units: 121.
Programming (via satellite): HBO.
Fee: N.A.
Miles of plant: 19.0 (coaxial). Homes passed: 820.
Manager: Tim Klinefelter. Chief technician: Tim Ream. Program director: Dinah Morrison. Marketing director: Marlene Ashby.
Ownership: AT&T Broadband & Internet Services (MSO). Purchased from Tele-Communications Inc., March 9, 1999.

WESTPORT—Sun Country Cable, Box 127, 7 D St. SW, Quincy, WA 98848. Phone: 509-787-3543. Fax: 509-787-3884. County: Clatsop. ICA: OR0170.
TV Market Ranking: Outside TV Markets. Franchise award date: N.A. Franchise expiration date: N.A. Began: N.A.
Channel capacity: 30. Channels available but not in use: 9.
Basic Service
Subscribers: 208.
Programming (received off-air): KATU (A), KGW (N), KOIN (C), KOPB-TV (P), KPTV (U) Portland.
Programming (via satellite): WGN-TV (W) Chicago; A & E; CNN; Country Music TV; Discovery Channel; ESPN; Fox Family Channel; FoxNet; Lifetime; MTV; Nashville Network; Nickelodeon; TBS Superstation; Turner Network TV; USA Network; VH1.
Fee: $39.95 installation; $26.20 monthly.
Pay Service 1
Pay Units: 15.
Programming (via satellite): Cinemax.
Fee: $8.95 monthly.
Pay Service 2
Pay Units: 14.
Programming (via satellite): Disney Channel.
Fee: $8.95 monthly.
Pay Service 3
Pay Units: 23.
Programming (via satellite): HBO.
Fee: $11.50 monthly.
Pay Service 4
Pay Units: 14.
Programming (via satellite): Cinemax; HBO.
Fee: $18.45 monthly.
Miles of plant: 3.0 (coaxial). Homes passed: 222.
Chief technician: Lance Barger.
Ownership: Sun Country Cable (MSO).

WOODBURN—Northland Cable TV, 635 Glatt Circle, Woodburn, OR 97071. Phone: 541-982-4085. Fax: 541-982-4804. County: Marion. Also serves Gervais, Hubbard, Marion County (portions). ICA: OR0023.
TV Market Ranking: 29. Franchise award date: October 12, 1992. Franchise expiration date: October 12, 2002. Began: March 7, 1983.
Channel capacity: 61 (2-way capable; operating 2-way partially). Channels available but not in use: 15.
Basic Service
Subscribers: 4,024.
Programming (received off-air): KATU (A), KGW (N), KNMT (T), KOIN (C), KOPB-TV (P), KPTV (U) Portland; KPXG (X), KWBP (W) Salem; KPDX (F) Vancouver.
Programming (via satellite): WGN-TV (W) Chicago; Electronic Program Guide; Headline News; TBS Superstation.
Current originations: Public access; government access; leased access; automated emergency alert; local news.
Fee: $50.00 installation; $12.50 monthly.
Expanded Basic Service
Subscribers: 3,919.
Programming (via microwave): Northwest Cable News.
Programming (via satellite): A & E; American Movie Classics; C-SPAN; CNBC; CNN; Country Music TV; Discovery Channel; ESPN; Fox Family Channel; Fox News Channel; Fox Sports Net Northwest; GalaVision; Goodlife TV Network; Knowledge TV; Learning Channel; Lifetime; MTV; Nashville Network; Nickelodeon; QVC; The Weather Channel; Turner Network TV; USA Network; Univision.
Fee: $50.00 installation; $12.50 monthly.
Pay Service 1
Pay Units: 312.
Programming (via satellite): Cinemax.
Fee: $30.00 installation; $7.50 monthly.
Pay Service 2
Pay Units: 135.
Programming (via satellite): Disney Channel.
Fee: $30.00 installation; $7.50 monthly.
Pay Service 3
Pay Units: 487.
Programming (via satellite): HBO.
Fee: $30.00 installation; $10.95 monthly.
Pay Service 4
Pay Units: 161.
Programming (via satellite): Showtime.
Fee: $30.00 installation; $7.95 monthly.
Pay Service 5
Pay Units: N.A.
Programming (via satellite): The New Encore.
Fee: $30.00 installation; $2.95 monthly.
Pay-Per-View
Viewer's Choice.
Pay-per-view manager: Donna Hendrick.
Local advertising: Yes. Available in satellite distributed, locally originated, character-generated, taped & automated programming. Rates: $4.50/30 Seconds. Local sales manager: Andrew Weathers.
Program Guide: Preview Guide.
Equipment: Scientific-Atlanta headend; Magnavox amplifiers; Comm/Scope cable; Hamlin, Regal & Scientific-Atlanta set top converters; Eagle & Arcom traps; Simulsat satellite antenna; M/A-Com, ISS & Scientific-Atlanta satellite receivers.
Miles of plant: 116.0 (coaxial); None (fiber optic). Additional miles planned: 5.0 (coaxial). Homes passed: 7,085. Total homes in franchised area: 7,085.
Manager: Pete Grigorieff. Chief technician: Kevin Worden. Marketing & customer service manager: Donna Hendrick.
City fee: 5% of gross.
Ownership: Northland Communications Corp. (MSO).

YACHATS—TCI Cablevision of Oregon Inc., Box 950, Newport, OR 97365. Phone: 541-563-4456. County: Lincoln. Also serves Lincoln County (southern portion), Seal Rock, Waldport. ICA: OR0041.
TV Market Ranking: Outside TV Markets. Franchise award date: N.A. Franchise expiration date: N.A. Began: June 1, 1969.
Channel capacity: 38. Channels available but not in use: N.A.

Basic Service

Subscribers: 1,978.

Programming (received off-air): 15 FMs.

Programming (via microwave): KEZI (A) Eugene; KATU (A), KGW (N), KOIN (C), KOPB-TV (P), KPTV (U) Portland; KPDX (F) Vancouver.

Programming (via satellite): WGN-TV (W) Chicago; A & E; C-SPAN; CNBC; CNN; Discovery Channel; Fox Family Channel; Headline News; Lifetime; MTV; Nickelodeon; Odyssey; QVC; TBS Superstation; The Weather Channel.

Current originations: Automated time-weather; public access.

Fee: $29.24 installation; $10.50 monthly; $14.62 additional installation.

Expanded Basic Service

Subscribers: 1,791.

Programming (via satellite): American Movie Classics; ESPN; Fox Sports Net Northwest; Nashville Network; Turner Network TV; USA Network.

Fee: $9.00 monthly.

Pay Service 1

Pay Units: 153.

Programming (via satellite): Disney Channel.

Fee: N.A.

Pay Service 2

Pay Units: 584.

Programming (via satellite): The New Encore.

Fee: N.A.

Pay Service 3

Pay Units: 351.

Programming (via satellite): HBO.

Fee: N.A.

Pay Service 4

Pay Units: 196.

Programming (via satellite): The Movie Channel.

Fee: N.A.

Pay Service 5

Pay Units: 222.

Programming (via satellite): Showtime.

Fee: N.A.

Equipment: Scientific-Atlanta headend; GTE Sylvania amplifiers; Times Fiber cable; Sony VTRs; Pioneer traps; Scientific-Atlanta satellite antenna; Scientific-Atlanta satellite receivers.

Miles of plant: 99.0 (coaxial). Homes passed: 2,959. Total homes in franchised area: 4,999.

Manager: Tom Hansen. Chief technician: Gene Brazel.

City & State fee: 3% of gross.

Ownership: AT&T Broadband & Internet Services (MSO). Purchased from Tele-Communications Inc., March 9, 1999.

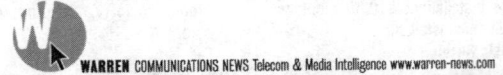

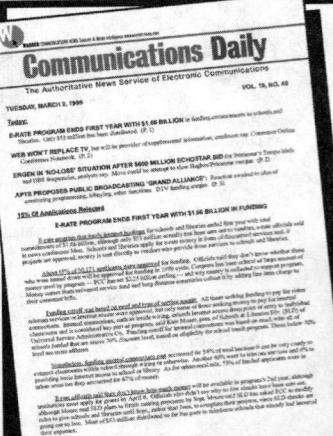

PENNSYLVANIA

Total Systems: **367**
Total Communities Served: **3,284**
Franchises Not Yet Operating: **0**
Applications Pending: **0**
Communities with Applications: **0**
Number of Basic Subscribers: **3,591,723**
Number of Expanded Basic Subscribers: **2,180,288**
Number of Pay Units: **1,543,565**

Top 100 Markets Represented: Philadelphia, PA-Burlington, NJ (4); Pittsburgh (10); Baltimore (14); Wilkes Barre-Scranton (49); Harrisburg-Lancaster-York (57); Johnstown-Altoona (74); Youngstown (79); Wheeling, WV-Steubenville, OH (90).

ADAMS TWP. (Cambria County)—Adelphia, One Adelphia Dr., Blairsville, PA 15717. Phone: 800-892-7300. County: Cambria. Also serves Beaverdale, Croyle Twp. (Cambria County), Elton, Lloydell, Salix, Sidman, South Fork, St. Michael, Summerhill Twp. ICA: PA0133.
TV Market Ranking: 74. Franchise award date: July 3, 1951. Franchise expiration date: September 23, 2006. Began: September 23, 1991.
Channel capacity: 43 (not 2-way capable). Channels available but not in use: N.A.
Basic Service
Subscribers: 6,087.
Programming (received off-air): WPSX-TV (P) Clearfield; WATM-TV (A), WJAC-TV (N), WKBS-TV (I), WTAJ-TV (C), WWCP-TV (F) Johnstown-Altoona; WCWB (W), WTAE-TV (A) Pittsburgh; allband FM.
Programming (via satellite): WGN-TV (W) Chicago; Home Shopping Network; TBS Superstation.
Current originations: Automated time-weather; public access.
Fee: $29.95 installation; $18.50 monthly.
Expanded Basic Service
Subscribers: 5,951.
Programming (via satellite): A & E; American Movie Classics; C-SPAN; CNN; Discovery Channel; Disney Channel; ESPN; ESPN 2; EWTN; Fox Family Channel; Fox Sports Net Pittsburgh; Headline News; History Channel; Learning Channel; Lifetime; MTV; Nashville Network; Nickelodeon; Pennsylvania Cable Network; Product Information Network; QVC; Sci-Fi Channel; TV Guide Channel; The Weather Channel; Turner Network TV; USA Network; VH1.
Fee: N.A.
Pay Service 1
Pay Units: 1,167.
Programming (via satellite): HBO.
Fee: $29.95 installation; $11.50 monthly.
Pay Service 2
Pay Units: 147.
Programming (via satellite): Showtime.
Fee: $29.95 installation; $11.50 monthly.
Pay Service 3
Pay Units: 83.
Programming (via satellite): The Movie Channel.
Fee: $29.95 installation; $8.95 monthly.
Local advertising: Yes. Available in taped & automated programming.
Equipment: Jerrold headend; Magnavox amplifiers; Comm/Scope & Essex cable; Hamlin, Oak & Scientific-Atlanta set top converters; Eagle traps; Scientific-Atlanta satellite antenna; Scientific-Atlanta satellite receivers.
Miles of plant: 87.1 (coaxial).
Manager: J. Francis Bradley Jr. Chief technician: Dave Bowen.
City fee: 5% of net basic.
Ownership: Adelphia Communications Corp. (MSO).

ADDISON TWP. (southern portion)—Somerfield Cable TV Co., 6511 National Pike, Addison, PA 15411. Phone: 814-395-3084. E-mail: mdiehl@qcol.net. Counties: Somerset, PA; Garrett, MD. Also serves Accident (unincorporated areas), Friendsville, Garrett County (portions), Grantsville, MD; Addison, PA. ICA: PA0307.
TV Market Ranking: Outside TV Markets. Franchise award date: N.A. Franchise expiration date: N.A. Began: April 1, 1989.
Channel capacity: 54 (not 2-way capable). Channels available but not in use: None.
Basic Service
Subscribers: 662.
Programming (received off-air): WPCB-TV (I) Greensburg; WJAC-TV (N), WWCP-TV (F) Johnstown-Altoona; WGPT (P) Oakland; KDKA-TV (C), WPGH-TV (F), WPXI (N), WQED (P), WTAE-TV (A) Pittsburgh.
Programming (via satellite): WGN-TV (W) Chicago; A & E; Animal Planet; C-SPAN; CNBC; CNN; Cartoon Network; Discovery Channel; Disney Channel; ESPN; ESPN 2; FX; fXM: Movies from Fox; Fox Family Channel; Fox News Channel; Fox Sports Net Pittsburgh; Great American Country; Headline News; History Channel; Home & Garden Television; Home Shopping Network; Learning Channel; Lifetime; Nashville Network; Nick at Nite's TV Land; Nickelodeon; Outdoor Life Network; QVC; Sci-Fi Channel; Speedvision; TBS Superstation; The Weather Channel; Trinity Bcstg. Network; Turner Classic Movies; Turner Network TV; USA Network; VH1; WB 100+ Station Group.
Fee: $25.00 installation (aerial), $30.00 (underground); $25.75 monthly; $3.00 converter; $8.00 additional installation.
Pay Service 1
Pay Units: 78.
Programming (via satellite): HBO.
Fee: $10.00 monthly.
Pay Service 2
Pay Units: 69.
Programming (via satellite): Showtime.
Fee: $7.50 monthly.
Miles of plant: 80.0 (coaxial); 10.0 (fiber optic). Additional miles planned: 5.0 (coaxial). Homes passed: 800. Total homes in franchised area: 800.
Manager: Michael J. Diehl.
Franchise fee: 3% of gross.
Ownership: Somerfield Cable TV Co.

ALIQUIPPA—AT&T Cable Services, 300 Corliss St., Pittsburgh, PA 15220-4815. Phones: 412-875-1100; 412-771-8100. County: Beaver. Also serves Center Twp. (Beaver County), Hopewell Twp. (Beaver County), South Heights. ICA: PA0069.
TV Market Ranking: 10,90. Franchise award date: N.A. Franchise expiration date: N.A. Began: October 1, 1967.
Channel capacity: 64 (not 2-way capable). Channels available but not in use: None.
Basic Service
Subscribers: 12,503.
Programming (received off-air): WPCB-TV (I) Greensburg; KDKA-TV (C), WCWB (W), WPGH-TV (F), WPXI (N), WQED (P), WQEX (P), WTAE-TV (A) Pittsburgh.
Programming (via microwave): Meadows Racing Network.
Programming (via satellite): BET; C-SPAN; Odyssey; Pennsylvania Cable Network; QVC; TV Guide Sneak Prevue.
Fee: $44.95 installation; $10.48 monthly; $1.50 converter; $24.95 additional installation.
Expanded Basic Service
Subscribers: 12,036.
Programming (via microwave): EWTN, Pittsburgh Cable News Channel.
Programming (via satellite): A & E; American Movie Classics; Animal Planet; C-SPAN 2; CNBC; CNN; Cartoon Network; Court TV; Discovery Channel; E! Entertainment TV; ESPN; ESPN 2; EWTN; FX; Fox Family Channel; Fox News Channel; Fox Sports Net Pittsburgh; Headline News; History Channel; Home Shopping Network; International Channel; Knowledge TV; Learning Channel; Lifetime; MOVIEplex; MTV; Nashville Network; Nickelodeon; Sci-Fi Channel; TBS Superstation; TV Guide Channel; The Weather Channel; Turner Network TV; USA Network; VH1.
Fee: $17.51 monthly.
Pay Service 1
Pay Units: 967.
Programming (via satellite): Cinemax.
Fee: $13.45 monthly.
Pay Service 2
Pay Units: 414.
Programming (via satellite): Disney Channel.
Fee: $12.50 monthly.
Pay Service 3
Pay Units: 1,993.
Programming (via satellite): HBO.
Fee: $14.95 monthly.
Pay Service 4
Pay Units: 589.
Programming (via satellite): Showtime.
Fee: $14.95 monthly.
Pay Service 5
Pay Units: 3,848.
Programming (via satellite): The New Encore.
Fee: $1.95 monthly.
Pay Service 6
Pay Units: N.A.
Programming (via satellite): DMX; Starz!
Fee: $12.95 installation; $6.75 monthly (Starz), $9.95 monthly (DMX).
Pay-Per-View
Action Pay-Per-View; Playboy TV; Spice.
Local advertising: Yes. Regional interconnect: TCI Media Services-Pittsburgh, PA.
Program Guide: The Cable Guide.
Miles of plant: 167.7 (coaxial). Homes passed: 14,453. Total homes in franchised area: 18,786.
Manager: Jeffrey C. Harshman. Chief technician: Fred Hamm. Marketing director: Glenn Ryerson.
Ownership: AT&T Broadband & Internet Services (MSO). Purchased from Tele-Communications Inc., March 9, 1999.

ALLENSVILLE—Valley Cable Systems, Box 78, Doylesburg, PA 17219. Phone: 717-349-7717. Counties: Huntingdon & Mifflin. Also serves Menno Twp. (Mifflin County), Miller Twp. (Huntingdon County). ICA: PA0285.
TV Market Ranking: 74. Franchise award date: January 1, 1972. Franchise expiration date: N.A. Began: N.A.
Channel capacity: 30 (not 2-way capable). Channels available but not in use: 16.
Basic Service
Subscribers: 90.
Programming (received off-air): WPSX-TV (P) Clearfield; WHTM-TV (A) Harrisburg; WJAC-TV (N), WKBS-TV (I), WTAJ-TV (C), WWCP-TV (F) Johnstown-Altoona; WGAL (N) Lancaster.
Programming (via satellite): CNN; ESPN; Fox Family Channel; Nashville Network; TBS Superstation; Turner Network TV.
Fee: $40.00 installation; $14.00 monthly.
Pay Service 1
Pay Units: 9.
Programming (via satellite): Disney Channel.
Fee: $7.42 monthly.
Equipment: GTE Sylvania amplifiers.
Miles of plant: 11.8 (coaxial). Homes passed: 125. Total homes in franchised area: 125.
Manager: Barry L. Kepner.
Ownership: Valley Cable Systems (MSO).

ALTOONA—CableCom, Box 2330, 2200 Beale Ave., Altoona, PA 16603-2330. Phone: 814-946-5491. Fax: 814-943-1721. Counties: Bedford & Blair. Also serves Allegheny Twp. (Blair County), Antis Twp., Bellwood, Blair Twp. (Blair County), Bloomfield Twp., Claysburg, Duncansville, Frankstown, Frankstown Twp. (Blair County), Freedom Twp. (Blair County), Greenfield Twp. (Blair County), Hollidaysburg, Huston Twp. (Blair County), Juniata Twp. (Blair County), Kimmell Twp., Logan Twp. (Blair County), Martinsburg, Newry, North Woodbury Twp., Pavia Twp., Roaring Spring, Taylor Twp. (Blair County), Tyrone Twp. (Blair County). ICA: PA0018.
TV Market Ranking: 74. Franchise award date: April 1, 1962. Franchise expiration date: February 1, 2003. Began: April 21, 1962.
Channel capacity: 62. Channels available but not in use: None.
Basic Service
Subscribers: 42,153.
Programming (received off-air): WPSX-TV (P) Clearfield; WATM-TV (A), WJAC-TV (N), WKBS-TV (I), WTAJ-TV (C), WWCP-TV (F) Johnstown-Altoona; KDKA-TV (C), WTAE-TV (A) Pittsburgh; allband FM.
Programming (via satellite): WPIX (W) New York; A & E; American Movie Classics; C-SPAN; CNBC; CNN; Cartoon Network; Comedy Central; Country Music TV; Court TV; Discovery Channel; E! Entertainment TV;

ESPN; Fox Family Channel; Fox Sports Net Pittsburgh; Headline News; Learning Channel; Lifetime; MTV; Nashville Network; Nickelodeon; Odyssey; QVC; TBS Superstation; TV Guide Channel; The Weather Channel; Travel Channel; Turner Network TV; USA Network; VH1.
Current originations: Automated time-weather; public access; educational access; automated emergency alert; local news.
Fee: $41.03 installation; $10.33 monthly.
Pay Service 1
Pay Units: 3,081.
Programming (via satellite): Cinemax.
Fee: $9.00 monthly.
Pay Service 2
Pay Units: 1,716.
Programming (via satellite): Disney Channel.
Fee: $9.00 monthly.
Pay Service 3
Pay Units: 6,780.
Programming (via satellite): HBO.
Fee: $9.00 monthly.
Pay Service 4
Pay Units: 2,437.
Programming (via satellite): Showtime.
Fee: $9.00 monthly.
Pay Service 5
Pay Units: 608.
Programming (via satellite): The Movie Channel.
Fee: $9.00 monthly.
Pay-Per-View
Addressable homes: 14,574.
Action Pay-Per-View; Viewer's Choice.
Fee: $3.95.
Local advertising: Yes. Available in satellite distributed & locally originated programming. Rates: $26.25/Minute; $17.50/30 Seconds. Regional interconnect: Cable AdNet-Johnstown/Altoona, PA.
Equipment: Catel, RCA & Scientific-Atlanta headend; Magnavox amplifiers; Comm/Scope, Phelps-Dodge & Times Fiber cable; Sony VTRs; Metrodata & Texscan character generator; Pioneer set top converters; Pioneer addressable set top converters; Hughes & Scientific-Atlanta satellite antenna; Scientific-Atlanta & Standard Components satellite receivers; JVC commercial insert.
Miles of plant: 785.0 (coaxial); 60.0 (fiber optic). Homes passed: 51,000. Total homes in franchised area: 52,000.
Manager: Dale Albright. Chief technician: Mike Thompson. Marketing director: Neill Jones.
Ownership: Fanch Communications Inc. (MSO); Time Warner Cable (MSO). See Cable System Ownership.

ANTHONY TWP.—Commuter Cable Television-East, 513 Jordan Ave., Montoursville, PA 17754. Phone: 570-368-3266. Fax: 570-368-8154. Counties: Columbia, Montour & Northumberland. Also serves Delaware Twp. (Northumberland County), Lewis Twp. (Northumberland County), Limestone Twp. (Montour County), Madison Twp. (Columbia County), Northumberland County (portions), Turbot Twp. (Northumberland County). ICA: PA0375.
TV Market Ranking: Below 100 (Anthony Twp., Limestone Twp., portions of Northumberland County); Outside TV Markets (Delaware Twp., Lewis Twp., portions of Northumberland County). Franchise award date: July 1, 1989. Franchise expiration date: July 1, 1999. Began: N.A.
Channel capacity: 40. Channels available but not in use: 2.
Basic Service
Subscribers: 650.
Programming (received off-air): WITF-TV (P) Harrisburg; WBRE-TV (N), WNEP-TV (A), WSWB (W), WVIA-TV (P), WYOU (C) Scranton & Wilkes-Barre.
Programming (via satellite): WGN-TV (W) Chicago; A & E; American Movie Classics; Animal Planet; C-SPAN; C-SPAN 2; CNBC; CNN; Country Music TV; Discovery Channel; Disney Channel; ESPN; ESPN 2; FX; Fox Family Channel; Fox News Channel; Headline News; History Channel; Learning Channel; Lifetime; MTV; Nashville Network; Nickelodeon; Pennsylvania Cable Network; QVC; TBS Superstation; The Weather Channel; Trinity Bcstg. Network; Turner Network TV; USA Network; VH1.
Fee: N.A.
Pay Service 1
Pay Units: N.A.
Programming (via satellite): HBO; Showtime; The Movie Channel.
Fee: $9.95 monthly (TMC), $10.95 monthly (Showtime), $11.95 monthly (HBO).
Miles of plant: 80.9 (coaxial); 2.0 (fiber optic). Homes passed: 1,005.
Manager: Roxanne Y. Criswell. Chief technician: Timothy J. Criswell.
Ownership: Criswell Group (MSO).

ARNOT—Blue Ridge Cable TV Inc., 15 Crafton St., Wellsboro, PA 16901. Phone: 717-724-4516. Fax: 570-724-2562. County: Tioga. ICA: PA0308.
TV Market Ranking: Below 100. Franchise award date: N.A. Franchise expiration date: N.A. Began: N.A.
Channel capacity: N.A. Channels available but not in use: N.A.
Basic Service
Subscribers: N.A.
Programming (received off-air): WBNG-TV (C) Binghamton; WPSX-TV (P) Clearfield; WENY-TV (A), WETM-TV (N) Elmira; WBRE-TV (N), WNEP-TV (A), WVIA-TV (P), WYOU (C) Scranton & Wilkes-Barre.
Programming (via satellite): WGN-TV (W) Chicago; CNN; ESPN; TBS Superstation.
Fee: $25.00 installation; $11.25 monthly.
Pay Service 1
Pay Units: N.A.
Programming (via satellite): HBO; The Movie Channel.
Fee: $9.00 monthly (TMC), $10.00 monthly (HBO).
Manager: Tom Freeman. Chief technician: Doug Patt.
Ownership: Leon Reed (MSO).

AULTMAN—Adelphia Cable, One Adelphia Dr., Blairsville, PA 15717. Phone: 800-892-7300. Fax: 724-459-0648. County: Indiana. Also serves Center Twp. (Indiana County), Clarksburg, Coal Run (Indiana County), Conemaugh Twp. (Indiana County), Iselin, Jacksonville (Indiana County), Kent, McIntyre, Young Twp. (Indiana County). ICA: PA0309.
TV Market Ranking: 74. Franchise award date: N.A. Franchise expiration date: N.A. Began: N.A.
Channel capacity: 52 (not 2-way capable). Channels available but not in use: 14.
Basic Service
Subscribers: 500.
Programming (received off-air): Allband FM.
Fee: $20.00 installation; $26.61 monthly; $30.00 additional installation.
Pay Service 1
Pay Units: 42.
Programming (via satellite): HBO.
Fee: $10.95 monthly.
Pay Service 2
Pay Units: 20.
Programming (via satellite): Showtime.
Fee: $6.95 monthly.
Equipment: Scientific-Atlanta, Cadco & Blonder-Tongue headend; AEL amplifiers; Times Fiber cable; Pioneer set top converters; Arcom traps; Scientific-Atlanta satellite receivers.
Miles of plant: 25.0 (coaxial); None (fiber optic). Additional miles planned: 12.0 (coaxial).
City fee: 3% of basic gross.
Ownership: Adelphia Communications Corp. (MSO). Purchased from Barry Electronics Inc., July 1, 1998.

AVELLA—Jefferson County Cable Inc., 116 S. 4th St., Toronto, OH 43964. Phone: 740-537-2214. Fax: 740-537-2802. County: Washington. ICA: PA0310.
TV Market Ranking: 10,90. Franchise award date: N.A. Franchise expiration date: N.A. Began: October 1, 1976.
Channel capacity: N.A. Channels available but not in use: N.A.
Basic Service
Subscribers: N.A.
Programming (received off-air): KDKA-TV (C), WCWB (W), WPGH-TV (F), WPXI (N), WQED (P), WTAE-TV (A) Pittsburgh; WTOV-TV (N) Steubenville-Wheeling; WTRF-TV (C) Wheeling-Steubenville.
Programming (via satellite): WGN-TV (W) Chicago; ESPN; Fox Family Channel.
Fee: $20.00 installation; $9.00 monthly.
Pay Service 1
Pay Units: N.A.
Programming (via satellite): HBO.
Fee: $9.60 monthly.
Miles of plant: 6.2 (coaxial).
Ownership: Jefferson County Cable Inc. (MSO).

AVIS—Susquehanna Communications, 330 Basin St., Williamsport, PA 17701. Phone: 717-753-3031. Fax: 717-753-8755. Counties: Clinton & Lycoming. Also serves Chapman Twp., Cummings Twp., Dunnstable Twp. (western portion), Jersey Shore, Mifflin Twp. (Lycoming County), Nippenose Twp. (Lycoming County), North Bend, Noyes Twp., Piatt Twp. (Lycoming County), Pine Creek Twp. (Lycoming County), Porter Twp. (Clinton County), Porter Twp. (Lycoming County), Rauchtown, Renovo, Salladasburg, South Renovo, Watson Twp. (Lycoming County), Wayne Twp. (Clinton County). ICA: PA0311.
TV Market Ranking: Below 100 (Avis, Chapman Twp., Cummings Twp., Dunnstable Twp., Jersey Shore, Mifflin Twp., Nippenose Twp., North Bend, Piatt Twp., Pine Creek Twp., Porter Twp., Rauchtown, Salladasburg, Watson Twp., Wayne Twp.); Outside TV Markets (Noyes Twp., Renovo, South Renovo). Franchise award date: N.A. Franchise expiration date: N.A. Began: December 1, 1954.
Channel capacity: 46 (not 2-way capable). Channels available but not in use: 1.
Basic Service
Subscribers: Included with Williamsport, PA.
Programming (received off-air): WPSX-TV (P) Clearfield; WBRE-TV (N), WNEP-TV (A), WVIA-TV (P), WYOU (C) Scranton & Wilkes-Barre; WILF (W,F) Williamsport; 8 FMs.
Programming (via microwave): WPHL-TV (W) Philadelphia.
Programming (via satellite): A & E; American Movie Classics; C-SPAN; CNN; Country Music TV; Discovery Channel; ESPN; ESPN 2; Fox Family Channel; Headline News; History Channel; Home Shopping Network; Learning Channel; Lifetime; MTV; Nashville Network; Nick at Nite; Nickelodeon; Odyssey; QVC; Sci-Fi Channel; TBS Superstation; The Weather Channel; Trinity Bcstg. Network; Turner Network TV; USA Network; VH1; ValueVision.
Current originations: Automated time-weather.
Fee: $35.50 installation; $22.30 monthly; $1.75 converter.
Pay Service 1
Pay Units: 1,947.
Programming (via satellite): Cinemax; Disney Channel; HBO; Showtime; The Movie Channel.
Fee: $8.50 monthly (Disney), $8.95 monthly (Cinemax), $9.95 monthly (Showtime & TMC), $10.50 monthly (HBO).
Pay-Per-View
Addressable homes: 1,882.
Action Pay-Per-View.
Fee: $3.95-$4.95.
Local advertising: Yes. Available in satellite distributed programming.
Equipment: AML satellite receivers.
Miles of plant: 182.0 (coaxial). Homes passed: 7,662.
Manager: Mike Loch. Chief technician: Tom Newlen. Customer service manager: Dawn Lupachino.
Ownership: Susquehanna Cable Co. (MSO).

BADEN—AT&T Cable Services, 300 Corliss St., Pittsburgh, PA 15220-4815. Phones: 412-875-1100; 412-771-8100. Counties: Allegheny, Beaver & Greene. Also serves Aleppo, Ambridge, Bell Acres, Conway, Conway Heights, Economy, Edgeworth, Glenfield, Harmony Twp. (Beaver County), Haysville, Leet Twp. (Allegheny County), Leetsdale, New Sewickley, Osborne, Sewickley, Sewickley Heights, Sewickley Hills. ICA: PA0064.
TV Market Ranking: 10,90. Franchise award date: N.A. Franchise expiration date: N.A. Began: October 1, 1967.
Channel capacity: 64 (not 2-way capable). Channels available but not in use: None.
Basic Service
Subscribers: 16,302.
Programming (received off-air): WPCB-TV (I) Greensburg; KDKA-TV (C), WCWB (W), WPGH-TV (F), WPXI (N), WQED (P), WQEX (P), WTAE-TV (A) Pittsburgh.
Programming (via microwave): Meadows Racing Network.
Programming (via satellite): BET; C-SPAN; Odyssey; Pennsylvania Cable Network; QVC; TV Guide Sneak Prevue.
Fee: $44.95 installation; $10.66 monthly; $1.50 converter; $24.95 additional installation.
Expanded Basic Service
Subscribers: 15,500.
Programming (via microwave): Pittsburgh Cable News Channel.
Programming (via satellite): A & E; American Movie Classics; Animal Planet; C-SPAN 2; CNBC; CNN; Cartoon Network; Court TV; Discovery Channel; E! Entertainment TV; ESPN; ESPN 2; EWTN; FX; Fox Family Channel; Fox News Channel; Fox Sports Net Pittsburgh; Headline News; History Channel; Home Shopping Network; International Channel; Knowledge TV; Learning Channel; Lifetime; MOVIEplex; MTV; Nashville Network; Nickelodeon; Sci-Fi Channel; TBS Superstation; TV Guide Channel; The Weather Channel; Turner Network TV; USA Network; VH1.
Fee: $17.68 monthly.
Pay Service 1
Pay Units: 1,029.
Programming (via satellite): Cinemax.

Fee: $13.45 monthly.
Pay Service 2
Pay Units: 537.
Programming (via satellite): Disney Channel.
Fee: $12.50 monthly.
Pay Service 3
Pay Units: 2,176.
Programming (via satellite): HBO (multiplexed).
Fee: $14.95 monthly.
Pay Service 4
Pay Units: 674.
Programming (via satellite): Showtime.
Fee: $14.95 monthly.
Pay Service 5
Pay Units: 4,755.
Programming (via satellite): The New Encore.
Fee: $1.95 monthly.
Pay Service 6
Pay Units: N.A.
Programming (via satellite): DMX; Starz!
Fee: $6.75 monthly (Starz), $9.95 monthly (DMX).
Pay-Per-View
Action Pay-Per-View; Playboy TV; Spice.
Fee: $3.99-$5.95.
Local advertising: Yes. Available in satellite distributed programming. Regional interconnect: TCI Media Services-Pittsburgh, PA.
Program Guide: The Cable Guide.
Equipment: Scientific-Atlanta headend; C-COR & GTE Sylvania amplifiers; General cable; Scientific-Atlanta satellite antenna; Scientific-Atlanta satellite receivers.
Miles of plant: 235.0 (coaxial). Homes passed: 16,678. Total homes in franchised area: 19,312.
Manager: Jeffrey C. Harshman. Chief technician: Fred Hamm. Marketing director: Glenn Ryerson.
City fee: 3% of gross.
Ownership: AT&T Broadband & Internet Services (MSO). Purchased from Tele-Communications Inc., March 9, 1999.

BARBOURS—Ralph Herr TV, Box 717, RR 4, Montoursville, PA 17754-9665. Phone: 717-435-2780. County: Lycoming. ICA: PA0264.
TV Market Ranking: Below 100. Franchise award date: N.A. Franchise expiration date: N.A. Began: January 1, 1955.
Channel capacity: 12. Channels available but not in use: N.A.
Basic Service
Subscribers: N.A.
Programming (received off-air): WHTM-TV (A) Harrisburg; WTAJ-TV (C) Johnstown-Altoona; WBRE-TV (N), WNEP-TV (A), WVIA-TV (P), WYOU (C) Scranton & Wilkes-Barre; allband FM.
Fee: $25.00 installation; $5.00 monthly.
Equipment: Blonder-Tongue headend; Coral amplifiers; Coral cable.
Miles of plant: 27.9 (coaxial). Additional miles planned: 2.0 (coaxial). Homes passed: 235.
Chief technician: Barry Herr.
City fee: None.
Ownership: Herr Cable Co. (MSO).

BASTRESS TWP.—Bastress TV Cable, Box 85, Loganton, PA 17747. Phone: 717-725-2733. County: Lycoming. ICA: PA0313.
TV Market Ranking: Below 100. Franchise award date: N.A. Franchise expiration date: N.A. Began: N.A.
Channel capacity: 12. Channels available but not in use: N.A.
Basic Service
Subscribers: 30.
Programming (received off-air): WPSX-TV (P) Clearfield; WTAJ-TV (C) Johnstown-Altoona; WBRE-TV (N), WNEP-TV (A), WSWB (W), WVIA-TV (P), WYOU (C) Scranton & Wilkes-Barre.
Fee: N.A.
Equipment: Blonder-Tongue headend.
Chief technician: Guy Bierly.
Ownership: Bastress TV Cable.

BEACH LAKE—Blue Ridge Cable TV, HC6 Box 6035, Hawley, PA 18428. Phone: 570-226-4914. County: Wayne. Also serves Berlin Twp. (Wayne County), Damascus Twp. ICA: PA0314.
TV Market Ranking: 49. Franchise award date: N.A. Franchise expiration date: N.A. Began: January 1, 1971.
Channel capacity: 42. Channels available but not in use: None.
Basic Service
Subscribers: 800.
Programming (received off-air): WBNG-TV (C), WSKG (P) Binghamton; WABC-TV (A), WCBS-TV (C), WNBC (N), WNYW (F), WPIX (W), WWOR-TV (U) New York; WBRE-TV (N), WNEP-TV (A), WSWB (W), WVIA-TV (P), WYOU (C) Scranton & Wilkes-Barre.
Programming (via satellite): WGN-TV (W) Chicago; A & E; C-SPAN; CNBC; CNN; Country Music TV; Discovery Channel; ESPN; Headline News; Home Shopping Network; Lifetime; MTV; Madison Square Garden Network; Nashville Network; Nickelodeon; QVC; TBS Superstation; The Weather Channel; Turner Network TV; USA Network; VH1.
Fee: $32.50 installation; $16.90 monthly.
Pay Service 1
Pay Units: N.A.
Programming (via satellite): Cinemax; HBO.
Fee: $10.00 monthly (each).
Equipment: Scientific-Atlanta headend; C-COR amplifiers; Comm/Scope cable.
Manager: Norman Bohs. Chief technician: Wayne Rogers.
Ownership: Pencor Services Inc. (MSO).

BEAVER FALLS—TCI of Pennsylvania, 2810 Darlington Rd., Beaver Falls, PA 15010. Phone: 724-843-8733. Fax: 724-843-7212. County: Beaver. Also serves Chippewa Twp., Daugherty Twp., Eastvale, Fallston, New Brighton, Patterson Heights, Patterson Twp., Pulaski Twp. (Beaver County), West Mayfield, White Twp. (Beaver County). ICA: PA0065.
TV Market Ranking: 10,79,90. Franchise award date: N.A. Franchise expiration date: N.A. Began: January 1, 1957.
Channel capacity: 54 (not 2-way capable). Channels available but not in use: 5.
Basic Service
Subscribers: 12,700; Commercial subscribers: 104.
Programming (received off-air): WNEO (P) Alliance; WPCB-TV (I) Greensburg; KDKA-TV (C), WCWB (W), WPGH-TV (F), WPXI (N), WQED (P), WQEX (P), WTAE-TV (A) Pittsburgh; WTOV-TV (N) Steubenville-Wheeling; WFMJ-TV (N), WKBN-TV (C), WYTV (A,F) Youngstown.
Programming (via satellite): A & E; American Movie Classics; BET; Bravo; C-SPAN; CNN; Comedy Central; Discovery Channel; ESPN; EWTN; Fox Family Channel; Fox Sports Net Pittsburgh; Headline News; Home Shopping Network; Lifetime; MTV; Nashville Network; Nickelodeon; Philadelphia Park Live; QVC; TBS Superstation; TV Guide Channel; The Weather Channel; Turner Network TV; USA Network; VH1.
Current originations: Automated time-weather; local news.
Fee: $38.00 installation; $22.57 monthly.
Pay Service 1
Pay Units: 952.
Programming (via satellite): Cinemax.
Fee: $9.95 monthly.
Pay Service 2
Pay Units: 520.
Programming (via satellite): Disney Channel.
Fee: $8.95 monthly.
Pay Service 3
Pay Units: 2,435.
Programming (via satellite): HBO.
Fee: $11.95 monthly.
Pay Service 4
Pay Units: 597.
Programming (via satellite): The Movie Channel.
Fee: $9.95 monthly.
Pay Service 5
Pay Units: 1,414.
Programming (via satellite): Showtime.
Fee: $10.95 monthly.
Pay-Per-View
Addressable homes: 200.
Viewer's Choice; movies; special events.
Fee: $4.95.
Local advertising: Yes.
Equipment: Scientific-Atlanta headend; C-COR amplifiers; Plastoid cable; Sony VTRs; Jerrold addressable set top converters; Scientific-Atlanta satellite antenna.
Miles of plant: 182.0 (coaxial); 5.0 (fiber optic). Homes passed: 16,470.
Manager: Joseph J. Rooney. Chief technician: Rob Mayer. Marketing director: Linda Walker.
City fee: 3% of gross.
Ownership: AT&T Broadband & Internet Services (MSO). Purchased from Tele-Communications Inc., March 9, 1999.

BEAVER SPRINGS—Beaver Springs Mutual TV Assn., Box 360, RR 1, Beaver Springs, PA 17812. Phone: 717-658-8403. Fax: 717-658-7413. County: Snyder. ICA: PA0259.
TV Market Ranking: Outside TV Markets. Franchise award date: N.A. Franchise expiration date: N.A. Began: April 1, 1954.
Channel capacity: N.A. Channels available but not in use: N.A.
Basic Service
Subscribers: 290.
Programming (received off-air): WHP-TV (C), WHTM-TV (A) Harrisburg; WKBS-TV (I), WTAJ-TV (C) Johnstown-Altoona; WGAL (N), WLYH-TV (U) Lancaster; WBRE-TV (N), WNEP-TV (A), WVIA-TV (P) Scranton & Wilkes-Barre; WPMT (F) York; allband FM.
Programming (via satellite): CNN; Discovery Channel; ESPN; ESPN 2; Fox Family Channel; Headline News; Nashville Network; TBS Superstation; Turner Network TV; USA Network.
Fee: $75.00 installation.
Pay Service 1
Pay Units: 95.
Programming (via satellite): The Movie Channel.
Fee: $5.00 monthly.
Local advertising: No.
Equipment: Blonder-Tongue headend; Ameco amplifiers; Belden cable; Eagle traps; Microwave Assoc. satellite antenna; Microdyne satellite receivers.
Miles of plant: 6.0 (coaxial). Additional miles planned: 1.5 (coaxial).
Manager: Paul W. Woodling.
City fee: None.
Ownership: Beaver Springs Mutual TV Assn.

BEAVER VALLEY—Adelphia, Box 1445, 215 E. North St., New Castle, PA 16103-1445. Phones: 614-246-4223; 800-782-4118. County: Beaver. Also serves Greene Twp. (Beaver County), Hanover Twp. (Beaver County), Hookstown, Hopewell Twp. (Beaver County), Independence Twp., Potter Twp. (Beaver County), Raccoon Twp. (southern portion). ICA: PA0157.
TV Market Ranking: 10 (Beaver Valley, Greene Twp., Hanover Twp., Hookstown, Hopewell Twp., Independence Twp., Potter Twp., Raccoon Twp.); 90 (Beaver Valley, Greene Twp., Hanover Twp., Hookstown, Hopewell Twp., Independence Twp., Raccoon Twp.). Franchise award date: N.A. Franchise expiration date: N.A. Began: April 1, 1983.
Channel capacity: 30. Channels available but not in use: 7.
Basic Service
Subscribers: 1,589.
Programming (received off-air): WPCB-TV (I) Greensburg; KDKA-TV (C), WCWB (W), WPGH-TV (F), WPXI (N), WQED (P), WTAE-TV (A) Pittsburgh; WTOV-TV (N) Steubenville-Wheeling; WTRF-TV (C) Wheeling-Steubenville; WFMJ-TV (N), WKBN-TV (C), WYTV (A,F) Youngstown.
Programming (via satellite): CNN.
Fee: $40.00 installation; $17.50 monthly.
Expanded Basic Service
Subscribers: 549.
Programming (via satellite): ESPN; Fox Family Channel; Lifetime; MTV; Nashville Network; Nickelodeon; USA Network.
Fee: $6.00 monthly.
Pay Service 1
Pay Units: 274.
Programming (via satellite): Showtime.
Fee: $10.95 monthly.
Pay Service 2
Pay Units: 127.
Programming (via satellite): Disney Channel.
Fee: $10.95 monthly.
Pay Service 3
Pay Units: 459.
Programming (via satellite): HBO.
Fee: $10.95 monthly.
Pay Service 4
Pay Units: 126.
Programming (via satellite): The Movie Channel.
Fee: $10.95 monthly.
Miles of plant: 130.2 (coaxial). Homes passed: 2,154.
Manager: Dave Campo. Chief technician: Bill Superak.
Ownership: Adelphia Communications Corp. (MSO).

BEAVERTOWN—Community TV, Box 111, Lewistown, PA 17044. Phone: 717-248-3733. County: Snyder. ICA: PA0315.
TV Market Ranking: Outside TV Markets. Franchise award date: N.A. Franchise expiration date: N.A. Began: January 30, 1963.
Channel capacity: 6. Channels available but not in use: N.A.
Basic Service
Subscribers: N.A.
Programming (received off-air): WTAJ-TV (C) Johnstown-Altoona; WGAL (N) Lancaster; WBRE-TV (N), WNEP-TV (A), WYOU (C) Scranton & Wilkes-Barre.
Current originations: Automated time-weather; educational access; government access.
Fee: $10.00 installation; $3.00 monthly.
Equipment: Blonder-Tongue headend; Blonder-Tongue amplifiers.
Chief technician: Michael Hain.
Ownership: Nittany Media Inc. (MSO).

BEDFORD—TCI of Pennsylvania Inc., Box 649, 410 E. Central Way, Bedford, PA 15522-1457.

Phone: 814-623-1128. County: Bedford. Also serves Alum Bank, Bedford Borough, Bedford Twp., Breezewood, Colerain Twp. (Bedford County), East Providence Twp., East St. Clair Twp. (Bedford County), Everett, Fishertown, Harrison Twp. (Bedford County), Lincoln Twp. (Bedford County), Manns Choice, Napier Twp. (Bedford County), New Paris, Rainsburg, Schellsburg, Snake Spring Valley Twp., Springhope, West Providence Twp., West St. Clair, Wolfsburg. ICA: PA0082.

TV Market Ranking: 74 (Alum Bank, Bedford, Bedford Borough, Bedford Twp., Breezewood, Colerain Twp., East Providence Twp., East St. Clair Twp., Fishertown, Harrison Twp., Lincoln Twp., Manns Choice, Napier Twp., New Paris, Schellsburg, Snake Spring Valley Twp., Springhope, West Providence Twp., West St. Clair, Wolfsburg); Outside TV Markets (Everett, Rainsburg). Franchise award date: N.A. Franchise expiration date: N.A. Began: October 1, 1958.

Channel capacity: 60. Channels available but not in use: N.A.

Basic Service

Subscribers: 7,140.

Programming (received off-air): WPSX-TV (P) Clearfield; WATM-TV (A), WJAC-TV (N), WKBS-TV (I), WTAJ-TV (C), WWCP-TV (F) Johnstown-Altoona; WTAE-TV (A) Pittsburgh; WTTG (F) Washington; 10 FMs.

Programming (via satellite): C-SPAN; C-SPAN 2; Home Shopping Network; Learning Channel; QVC; TV Guide Channel; Trinity Bcstg. Network.

Current originations: Public access.

Fee: $59.95 installation; $9.56 monthly; $2.00 converter; $49.95 additional installation.

Expanded Basic Service

Subscribers: 6,756.

Programming (via satellite): A & E; American Movie Classics; CNBC; CNN; Court TV; Discovery Channel; ESPN; FX; Fox Family Channel; Fox Sports Net Pittsburgh; Headline News; Intro TV; Knowledge TV; Lifetime; MTV; Nashville Network; Nickelodeon; Odyssey; TBS Superstation; The Weather Channel; Turner Network TV; USA Network.

Fee: $13.55 monthly.

Pay Service 1

Pay Units: 332.

Programming (via satellite): Cinemax.

Fee: $12.90 monthly.

Pay Service 2

Pay Units: 386.

Programming (via satellite): Disney Channel.

Fee: N.A.

Pay Service 3

Pay Units: 1,039.

Programming (via satellite): HBO.

Fee: $12.90 monthly.

Pay Service 4

Pay Units: 454.

Programming (via satellite): The Movie Channel.

Fee: $12.90 monthly.

Pay Service 5

Pay Units: 2,407.

Programming (via satellite): The New Encore.

Fee: N.A.

Pay Service 6

Pay Units: N.A.

Programming (via satellite): Starz!

Fee: N.A.

Pay-Per-View

Action Pay-Per-View; special events.

Local advertising: Yes.

Program Guide: The Cable Guide.

Equipment: Ameco & Entron headend; Ameco amplifiers; Ameco cable.

Miles of plant: 256.2 (coaxial). Homes passed: 9,085.

Manager: Kevan Whetstone.

City fee: None.

Ownership: AT&T Broadband & Internet Services (MSO). Purchased from Tele-Communications Inc., March 9, 1999.

BELLEVILLE—Belleville Area CATV System, Box 830, Lewistown, PA 17044. Phone: 717-248-1544. County: Mifflin. ICA: PA0316.

TV Market Ranking: Outside TV Markets. Franchise award date: N.A. Franchise expiration date: N.A. Began: N.A.

Channel capacity: 14. Channels available but not in use: N.A.

Basic Service

Subscribers: N.A.

Programming (received off-air): WPSX-TV (P) Clearfield; WHP-TV (C), WHTM-TV (A) Harrisburg; WJAC-TV (N), WTAJ-TV (C) Johnstown-Altoona; WGAL (N), WLYH-TV (U) Lancaster; WNEP-TV (A), WVIA-TV (P) Scranton & Wilkes-Barre; 1 FM.

Programming (via satellite): WGN-TV (W) Chicago; ESPN; TBS Superstation.

Fee: $25.00 installation; $10.75 monthly.

Pay Service 1

Pay Units: N.A.

Programming (via satellite): Disney Channel; The Movie Channel.

Fee: $7.95 monthly (Disney), $10.95 monthly (TMC).

Manager: Joe Zampelli.

Ownership: Zampelli TV (MSO).

BENSALEM TWP.—Suburban Cable, 1750 Byberry Rd., Bensalem, PA 19020. Phones: 215-638-7700; 800-222-1813. Web site: http://www.suburbancable.com. County: Bucks. Also serves Falls Twp. (Bucks County), Levittown, Lower Southampton, Morrisville, Tullytown, Upper Southampton, Warminster. ICA: PA0027.

TV Market Ranking: 4. Franchise award date: January 1, 1979. Franchise expiration date: N.A. Began: January 1, 1979.

Channel capacity: 35. Channels available but not in use: N.A.

Basic Service

Subscribers: 47,854.

Programming (received off-air): WGTW (I) Burlington; WPIX (W) New York; KYW-TV (C), WCAU (N), WPHL-TV (W), WPSG (U), WPVI-TV (A), WTXF-TV (F), WYBE (P) Philadelphia; WNJT (P) Trenton; WHSP-TV (H) Vineland; WHYY-TV (P), WPPX (X) Wilmington.

Programming (via microwave): Tri-State Media.

Programming (via satellite): QVC; TBS Superstation.

Current originations: Public access; educational access; government access; local news.

Fee: $18.00 installation; $10.07 monthly; $6.00 additional installation.

Expanded Basic Service

Subscribers: 45,886.

Programming (received off-air): WTVE (H) Reading.

Programming (via satellite): A & E; American Movie Classics; BET; Bravo; C-SPAN; C-SPAN 2; CNBC; CNN; Cartoon Network; Comedy Central; Discovery Channel; Disney Channel; E! Entertainment TV; ESPN; ESPN 2; EWTN; FX; Fox Family Channel; Goodlife TV Network; Headline News; History Channel; Home & Garden Television; Home Shopping Network; Learning Channel; Lifetime; MSNBC; MTV; Nashville Network; Nick at Nite; Nickelodeon; Pennsylvania Cable Network; Sci-Fi Channel; TV Food Network; TV Guide Channel; The Box; The Health Network; The Sports Network; The Weather Channel; Turner Classic Movies; Turner Network TV; USA Network; VH1; ValueVision.

Fee: $20.13 monthly.

Pay Service 1

Pay Units: 31,820.

Programming (via satellite): Cinemax; HBO (multiplexed); Showtime; Starz!; The Movie Channel.

Fee: $10.00 installation; $9.95 monthly (Cinemax or Starz), $11.95 monthly (HBO, Showtime or TMC).

Pay-Per-View

Playboy TV; Spice; movies; special events.

Local advertising: Yes. Regional interconnect: Metrobase Cable Advertising.

Miles of plant: 450.0 (coaxial). Homes passed: 64,095.

Manager: Mary Pat Headon. Chief technician: Bernie Miklos. Program director: George Ferrara. Marketing director: Jeff Underwood. Office manager: Jean Leon.

City fee: 5% of gross.

Ownership: Lenfest Communications Inc. (MSO).

BENTLEY CREEK—Mastervision, Box 518, Tioga, PA 16946. Phone: 570-827-2259. County: Bradford. Also serves Bradford County, Centerville (Bradford County), Fassett. ICA: PA0317.

TV Market Ranking: Below 100. Franchise award date: N.A. Franchise expiration date: N.A. Began: January 1, 1975.

Channel capacity: 12. Channels available but not in use: N.A.

Basic Service

Subscribers: N.A.

Programming (received off-air): WBNG-TV (C), WICZ-TV (F) Binghamton; WENY-TV (A), WETM-TV (N) Elmira; WBRE-TV (N), WNEP-TV (A), WVIA-TV (P), WYOU (C) Scranton & Wilkes-Barre; allband FM.

Programming (via satellite): ESPN; Fox Family Channel; USA Network.

Fee: $30.00 installation; $15.00 monthly.

Pay Service 1

Pay Units: N.A.

Programming (via satellite): Disney Channel; The Movie Channel.

Fee: $15.00 installation; $9.00 monthly (each).

Equipment: Blonder-Tongue headend; AEL amplifiers.

Miles of plant: 14.0 (coaxial).

Manager: Chris Caldwell.

City fee: None.

Ownership: Mastervision Cable Co.

BENTLEYVILLE—Bentleyville Telephone CATV, 608 Main St., Bentleyville, PA 15314. Phones: 724-239-2501; 800-239-2501. Fax: 724-239-1000.

E-mail: bentelco@navticom.net; twoweeks@nauticom.net.

Web site: http://www.bentelco.com.

County: Washington. Also serves Amwell Twp., North Bethlehem Twp., Scenery Hill, Somerset Twp. (Washington County), South Strabane Twp. ICA: PA0442.

TV Market Ranking: 10 (Amwell Twp., Bentleyville, North Bethlehem Twp., Scenery Hill, Somerset Twp., South Strabane Twp.); 90 (Amwell Twp., North Bethlehem Twp.). Franchise award date: January 1, 1992. Franchise expiration date: January 1, 2001. Began: N.A.

Channel capacity: 80 (2-way capable; not operating 2-way). Channels available but not in use: 33.

Basic Service

Subscribers: 1,136.

Programming (received off-air): WPCB-TV (I) Greensburg; KDKA-TV (C), WCWB (W), WPGH-TV (F), WPXI (N), WQED (P), WQEX (P), WTAE-TV (A) Pittsburgh.

Programming (via satellite): WGN-TV (W) Chicago; A & E; American Movie Classics; Animal Planet; C-SPAN; CNBC; CNN; Cartoon Network; Comedy Central; Country Music TV; Discovery Channel; E! Entertainment TV; ESPN; ESPN 2; EWTN; FX; Fox Family Channel; Fox Sports Net Pittsburgh; Golf Channel; Headline News; History Channel; Home & Garden Television; Home Shopping Network; Learning Channel; Lifetime; MSNBC; MTV; Nashville Network; Nickelodeon; QVC; Sci-Fi Channel; Superaudio Cable Radio Service; TBS Superstation; TV Food Network; TV Guide Channel; The Weather Channel; Trinity Bcstg. Network; Turner Classic Movies; Turner Network TV; USA Network; VH1.

Current originations: Public access; educational access; government access; religious access; automated emergency alert.

Fee: $20.00 installation; $24.00 monthly; $3.00 converter.

Pay Service 1

Pay Units: 85.

Programming (via satellite): Cinemax.

Fee: $9.50 monthly.

Pay Service 2

Pay Units: 69.

Programming (via satellite): Disney Channel.

Fee: $9.95 monthly.

Pay Service 3

Pay Units: 180.

Programming (via satellite): HBO.

Fee: $10.00 monthly.

Pay Service 4

Pay Units: 26.

Programming (via satellite): Playboy TV.

Fee: $10.00 monthly.

Pay Service 5

Pay Units: 84.

Programming (via satellite): Showtime.

Fee: $10.00 monthly.

Pay-Per-View

Addressable homes: 1,136.

Playboy TV; movies.

Fee: $3.95.

Pay-per-view manager: Patty Yoders.

Local advertising: Yes. Available in locally originated programming. Rates: $50.00/Month. Local sales manager: Dan DiDonato.

Equipment: Standard Components & Olson headend; C-COR amplifiers; Comm/Scope cable; Northern Telecom fiber optic cable; PPC character generator; Motorola modems; Comtech satellite antenna; Standard Components & Olson satellite receivers.

Miles of plant: 71.0 (coaxial); 15.0 (fiber optic). Homes passed: 1,500.

Manager: Walter P. Ziemba. Chief technician: John Conkle. Customer service manager & marketing director: Patty Yoders.

Franchise fee: 3% of gross.

Ownership: Bentleyville Telephone Co.

BERLIN BOROUGH—TCI of Pennsylvania Inc., Box 406, Rtes. 219 & 281, Somerset, PA 15501-0406. Phone: 814-443-4838. County: Somerset. Also serves Brothersvalley Twp., Shanksville, Somerset, Stonycreek Twp. (Somerset County). ICA: PA0169.

TV Market Ranking: 74. Franchise award date: N.A. Franchise expiration date: N.A. Began: September 1, 1978.
Channel capacity: 22 (not 2-way capable). Channels available but not in use: None.
Basic Service
Subscribers: 1,386.
Programming (received off-air): WJAC-TV (N), WWCP-TV (F) Johnstown-Altoona; KDKA-TV (C), WPGH-TV (F), WQED (P), WTAE-TV (A) Pittsburgh; WTRF-TV (C) Wheeling-Steubenville; allband FM.
Programming (via satellite): CNN; Cartoon Network; Discovery Channel; ESPN; Fox Family Channel; Fox Sports Net Pittsburgh; Headline News; Lifetime; Nashville Network; Nickelodeon; QVC; TBS Superstation; Turner Network TV; USA Network.
Current originations: Automated time-weather.
Fee: $59.95 installation; $19.40 monthly; $49.95 additional installation.
Pay Service 1
Pay Units: 45.
Programming (via satellite): Disney Channel.
Fee: $19.95 installation; $10.00 monthly.
Pay Service 2
Pay Units: 50.
Programming (via satellite): HBO.
Fee: $13.15 monthly.
Pay Service 3
Pay Units: 195.
Programming (via satellite): Showtime.
Fee: $13.15 monthly.
Pay Service 4
Pay Units: 2.
Programming (via satellite): Cinemax.
Fee: $12.50 monthly.
Pay Service 5
Pay Units: 14.
Programming (via satellite): The New Encore.
Fee: N.A.
Local advertising: Yes. Available in satellite distributed programming.
Program Guide: TV Entertainment.
Equipment: Microdyne & Scientific-Atlanta headend; C-COR & Jerrold amplifiers; Comm/Scope cable; Texscan character generator; Hamlin, Oak & Scientific-Atlanta set top converters; Eagle & Pico traps; AFC, Microdyne & Scientific-Atlanta satellite antenna; Microdyne & Scientific-Atlanta satellite receivers.
Miles of plant: 54.0 (coaxial). Homes passed: 1,726. Total homes in franchised area: 2,682.
Manager: Michael Berrier. Chief technician: Jeffrey Fassnacht.
City fee: 3% of gross.
Ownership: AT&T Broadband & Internet Services (MSO). Purchased from Tele-Communications Inc., March 9, 1999.

BERWICK—Cable TV Inc., 217 E. 9th St., Hazleton, PA 18201. Phone: 717-455-6851. Fax: 717-459-0963. Counties: Carbon, Columbia, Luzerne & Schuylkill. Also serves Beach Haven Twp., Benton Borough, Benton Twp. (Columbia County), Black Creek Twp., Blythe Twp., Briar Creek Borough, Briar Creek Twp., Brockton, Conyngham Twp. (Columbia County), Cumbola, Dorrance Twp., East Side Borough, Fishing Creek Twp., Hazle Twp., Hunlock Creek, Jackson Twp. (Columbia County), Kaska, Larksville, Lausanne Twp., Lehigh Twp. (Carbon County), Mary D, Middleport, Mifflin Twp. (Columbia County), Mifflinville, Millville, Millville Borough, Mocanaqua, Nescopeck Borough, Nescopeck Twp., New Philadelphia, Newport Twp., North Centre Twp. (Columbia County), North Union Twp. (Schuylkill County), Nuangola, Orange Twp. (Columbia County), Orangeville, Packer Twp. (Carbon County), Pine Twp. (Columbia County), Plymouth Twp. (Luzerne County), Rice, Salem Twp. (Luzerne County), Schuylkill Twp., Shavertown, Shickshinny Borough, Shickshinny Twp., Slocum, South Centre Twp. (Columbia County), Stillwater Borough, Tuscarora, Union Twp. (Luzerne County), Weatherly, West Nanticoke. ICA: PA0094.
TV Market Ranking: 49 (Beach Haven Twp., Benton Borough, Benton Twp., Berwick, Black Creek Twp., Briar Creek Borough, Briar Creek Twp., Conyngham Twp., Dorrance Twp., East Side Borough, Fishing Creek Twp., Hazle Twp., Hunlock Creek, Jackson Twp., Larksville, Lausanne Twp., Lehigh Twp., Mifflin Twp., Mifflinville, Millville, Millville Borough, Mocanaqua, Nescopeck Borough, Nescopeck Twp., Newport Twp., North Centre Twp., North Union Twp., Nuangola, Orange Twp., Orangeville, Packer Twp., portions of Pine Twp., Plymouth Twp., Rice, Salem Twp., Shavertown, Shickshinny Borough, Shickshinny Twp., Slocum, South Centre Twp., Stillwater Borough, Union Twp., Weatherly, West Nanticoke); Below 100 (Blythe Twp., Brockton, Cumbola, Kaska, Mary D, Middleport, New Philadelphia, portions of Pine Twp., Schuylkill Twp., Tuscarora). Franchise award date: January 1, 1947. Franchise expiration date: N.A. Began: December 1, 1950.
Channel capacity: 60 (2-way capable; operating 2-way). Channels available but not in use: 11.
Basic Service
Subscribers: 19,089; Commercial subscribers: 401.
Programming (received off-air): WBRE-TV (N), WNEP-TV (A), WSWB (W), WVIA-TV (P), WYOU (C) Scranton & Wilkes-Barre; allband FM.
Programming (via microwave): WPIX (W) New York; TBS Superstation.
Current originations: Automated time-weather; educational access; local news.
Fee: $42.95 installation; $7.92 monthly; $1.00 converter; $25.92 additional installation.
Expanded Basic Service
Subscribers: 18,557.
Programming (via microwave): WTXF-TV (F) Philadelphia.
Programming (via satellite): A & E; American Movie Classics; Animal Planet; C-SPAN; C-SPAN 2; CNBC; CNN; Country Music TV; Discovery Channel; Disney Channel; ESPN; ESPN 2; EWTN; Fox Family Channel; Goodlife TV Network; Headline News; History Channel; Learning Channel; Lifetime; MTV; Nashville Network; Nick at Nite's TV Land; Nickelodeon; QVC; Sci-Fi Channel; TV Food Network; The Weather Channel; Turner Network TV; USA Network; VH1.
Fee: $25.92 installation; $18.73 monthly.
Pay Service 1
Pay Units: 3,167.
Programming (via satellite): Cinemax.
Fee: $11.95 monthly.
Pay Service 2
Pay Units: 3,927.
Programming (via satellite): HBO.
Fee: $11.95 monthly.
Pay-Per-View
Addressable homes: 758.
Local advertising: Yes. Available in satellite distributed & locally originated programming. Local sales manager: Neil Rodina.
Equipment: Jerrold headend; Jerrold amplifiers; Anixter satellite antenna.
Miles of plant: 396.0 (coaxial); 70.6 (fiber optic). Homes passed: 23,783. Total homes in franchised area: 24,500.

Manager: Joseph W. Aman. Chief technician: Robert C. Jais. Marketing director: Mary Prokopovich. Customer service manager: Lori Wang.
City fee: 5% of gross.
Ownership: Gans Multimedia Partnership (MSO).

BETHEL—TCI, 655 Rodi Rd., Pittsburgh, PA 15235. Phone: 412-871-2900. Web site: http://www.tci.com. Counties: Armstrong & Westmoreland. Also serves Bethel Twp. (Armstrong County), Kiskiminetas Twp., Loyalhanna Twp., Mahoning Twp., Manor Twp. (Armstrong County), Pine Twp., Washington Twp. ICA: PA0388.
TV Market Ranking: 10 (Bethel, Bethel Twp., Kiskiminetas Twp., Loyalhanna Twp., Manor Twp.); 74 (Kiskiminetas Twp.); Outside TV Markets (Mahoning Twp., Pine Twp., Washington Twp.). Franchise award date: N.A. Franchise expiration date: N.A. Began: August 1, 1989.
Channel capacity: 40. Channels available but not in use: None.
Basic Service
Subscribers: N.A.
Programming (received off-air): WPCB-TV (I) Greensburg; WJAC-TV (N), WWCP-TV (F) Johnstown-Altoona; KDKA-TV (C), WCWB (W), WPGH-TV (F), WPXI (N), WQED (P), WTAE-TV (A) Pittsburgh.
Programming (via satellite): Fox Family Channel; Goodlife TV Network; Home & Garden Television; Outdoor Channel; QVC; TV Guide Channel.
Fee: $17.95 installation; $10.12 monthly.
Expanded Basic Service
Subscribers: N.A.
Programming (via satellite): WGN-TV (W) Chicago; A & E; American Movie Classics; Animal Planet; C-SPAN; CNBC; CNN; Cartoon Network; Comedy Central; Country Music TV; Discovery Channel; E! Entertainment TV; ESPN; ESPN 2; FX; Flix; Fox News Channel; Fox Sports Net Pittsburgh; History Channel; Home Shopping Network; Learning Channel; Lifetime; MOVIEplex; MSNBC; MTV; Nashville Network; Nick at Nite's TV Land; Nickelodeon; Sci-Fi Channel; TBS Superstation; The Weather Channel; Turner Classic Movies; Turner Network TV; USA Network; VH1.
Fee: $18.95 monthly.
Pay Service 1
Pay Units: N.A.
Programming (via satellite): Cinemax; Disney Channel; HBO; Showtime; Starz!; The Movie Channel.
Fee: $5.50 monthly (Starz), $7.00 monthly (TMC), $8.50 monthly (Disney), $9.50 monthly (Cinemax), $11.00 monthly (HBO or Showtime).
Manager: Mark Petretis. Chief technician: Jim Wynn.
Ownership: AT&T Broadband & Internet Services (MSO). Purchased from Tele-Communications Inc., March 9, 1999.

BETHEL PARK—Adelphia Cable Communications, 5335 Enterprise Blvd., Bethel Park, PA 15102. Phone: 800-892-7300. Fax: 412-835-2045. Counties: Allegheny & Washington. Also serves Finley Twp. (Washington County), Mount Lebanon, Peters Twp., South Hills (portions), Union Twp. (Washington County), Upper St. Clair Twp. ICA: PA0318.
TV Market Ranking: 10,90. Franchise award date: N.A. Franchise expiration date: N.A. Began: March 31, 1972.
Channel capacity: 60 (2-way capable; operating 2-way). Channels available but not in use: 7.
Basic Service
Subscribers: 10,677.
Programming (received off-air): WPCB-TV (I) Greensburg; KDKA-TV (C), WCWB (W), WPGH-TV (F), WPXI (N), WQED (P), WQEX (P), WTAE-TV (A) Pittsburgh; WTOV-TV (N) Steubenville-Wheeling; WTRF-TV (C) Wheeling-Steubenville.
Programming (via microwave): WUAB (U) Lorain-Cleveland.
Programming (via satellite): A & E; American Movie Classics; C-SPAN; C-SPAN 2; CNBC; CNN; Comedy Central; Discovery Channel; ESPN; EWTN; Fox Family Channel; Fox Sports Net Pittsburgh; Headline News; Home Shopping Network; Knowledge TV; Ladbroke Racing Channel/Meadows Racing Network; Lifetime; MTV; Music Choice; Nashville Network; Nickelodeon; QVC; TBS Superstation; TV Guide Channel; The Weather Channel; Travel Channel; Turner Network TV; USA Network; VH1.
Current originations: Automated time-weather.
Fee: $18.90 installation; $16.95 monthly.
Pay Service 1
Pay Units: N.A.
Programming (via satellite): Bravo; Cinemax; Disney Channel; HBO; Showtime; The Movie Channel.
Fee: $8.50 monthly (Bravo, Cinemax, Disney, Showtime or TMC), $10.50 monthly (HBO).
Local advertising: Yes. Available in satellite distributed programming. Regional interconnect: TCI Media Services-Pittsburgh, PA.
Program Guide: The Cable Guide.
Equipment: Scientific-Atlanta headend; Scientific-Atlanta amplifiers; Comm/Scope cable; Panasonic VTRs; Texscan character generator; Scientific-Atlanta set top converters; Scientific-Atlanta addressable set top converters; Eagle, Pico & PPC traps; Simulsat satellite antenna; Scientific-Atlanta satellite receivers; Metrodata commercial insert.
Miles of plant: 475.0 (coaxial).
Chief technician: Chuck Redpath.
City fee: 3% of gross.
Ownership: Adelphia Communications Corp. (MSO).

BIG POND—Barrett's TV Cable System, Box 197, RR 1, Troy, PA 16947. Phone: 570-297-3607. County: Bradford. ICA: PA0319.
TV Market Ranking: Below 100. Franchise award date: N.A. Franchise expiration date: N.A. Began: October 10, 1976.
Channel capacity: 13 (not 2-way capable). Channels available but not in use: N.A.
Basic Service
Subscribers: 35.

Programming (received off-air): WBNG-TV (C), WICZ-TV (F) Binghamton; WENY-TV (A), WETM-TV (N) Elmira; WYOU (C) Scranton & Wilkes-Barre; allband FM.
Programming (via translator): WVIA-TV (P) Scranton & Wilkes-Barre.
Fee: $35.00 installation; $8.00 monthly.
Equipment: Blonder-Tongue headend; AEL, Theta-Com & Jerrold amplifiers.
Miles of plant: 2.5 (coaxial).
Manager: Joseph K. Barrett.
Ownership: Barrett's TV Cable System (MSO).

BIGLER TWP.—TCI of Pennsylvania Inc., 1068 Pennsylvania Ave., Tyrone, PA 16686. Phone: 814-342-1370. County: Clearfield. Also serves Beccaria, Brisbin, Gulich Twp., Houtzdale, Ramey, Woodward Twp. (Clearfield County). ICA: PA0159.
TV Market Ranking: 74. Franchise award date: N.A. Franchise expiration date: N.A. Began: November 1, 1971.
Channel capacity: 23 (2-way capable; operating 2-way). Channels available but not in use: N.A.
Basic Service
Subscribers: 2,044.
Programming (received off-air): WPSX-TV (P) Clearfield; WATM-TV (A), WJAC-TV (N), WTAJ-TV (C), WWCP-TV (F) Johnstown-Altoona; allband FM.
Programming (via satellite): WGN-TV (W) Chicago; American Movie Classics; CNN; Discovery Channel; ESPN; Fox Family Channel; Fox Sports Net Pittsburgh; MTV; Nashville Network; QVC; TBS Superstation; USA Network.
Current originations: Automated timeweather.
Fee: $59.95 installation; $14.65 monthly.
Pay Service 1
Pay Units: 254.
Programming (via satellite): HBO.
Fee: N.A.
Pay Service 2
Pay Units: 150.
Programming (via satellite): Showtime.
Fee: N.A.
Local advertising: Yes. Rates: $15.00/Day.
Equipment: AFC satellite antenna.
Miles of plant: 69.6 (coaxial). Total homes in franchised area: 3,161.
Manager: Kim Yakich. Chief technician: Michael Catherine.
Ownership: AT&T Broadband & Internet Services (MSO). Purchased from Tele-Communications Inc., March 9, 1999.

BIRDSBORO—Service Electric Cablevision, Box 8, 6400 Perimoken Ave., Birdsboro, PA 19508. Phone: 610-582-5317. Fax: 610-582-3094. Counties: Berks, Chester & Lancaster. Also serves Amity Twp. (Berks County), Brecknock Twp. (Berks County), Caernarvon Twp. (Berks County), Caernarvon Twp. (Lancaster County), Cumru, Earl Twp. (Lancaster County), Elverson Borough, Exeter Twp. (Berks County), Honey Brook Borough, Honeybrook Twp. (Chester County), Oley, Robeson Twp., St. Lawrence, Union Twp. (Berks County), Warwick, Warwick Twp. (Berks County), Warwick Twp. (Chester County). ICA: PA0070.
TV Market Ranking: 4 (Elverson Borough, Warwick, Warwick Twp.); 57 (Amity Twp., Birdsboro, Brecknock Twp., Caernarvon Twp., Cumru, Earl Twp., Exeter Twp., Honey Brook Borough, Honeybrook Twp., Robeson Twp., St. Lawrence, Union Twp., Warwick Twp.); Below 100 (Oley). Franchise award date: N.A. Franchise expiration date: N.A. Began: January 1, 1956.
Channel capacity: 60 (2-way capable; operating 2-way). Channels available but not in use: 1.
Basic Service
Subscribers: 16,872.
Programming (received off-air): WFMZ-TV (I), WLVT-TV (P) Allentown; WGAL (N), WLYH-TV (U) Lancaster; KYW-TV (C), WCAU (N), WPHL-TV (W), WPSG (U), WPVI-TV (A), WTXF-TV (F) Philadelphia; WTVE (H) Reading; WHYY-TV (P) Wilmington; WPMT (F) York; allband FM.
Programming (via satellite): A & E; American Movie Classics; C-SPAN; CNBC; CNN; Cartoon Network; Comedy Central; Country Music TV; Discovery Channel; E! Entertainment TV; ESPN; ESPN 2; EWTN; Fox Family Channel; Headline News; Home Shopping Network; Learning Channel; Lifetime; MSNBC; MTV; Nashville Network; Nickelodeon; Philadelphia Park Live; QVC; Sci-Fi Channel; TBS Superstation; TV Food Network; The Weather Channel; Travel Channel; Turner Network TV; USA Network; VH1; ValueVision.
Current originations: Automated timeweather.
Fee: $32.00 installation; $24.16 monthly.
Pay Service 1
Pay Units: 9,042.
Programming (via satellite): Cinemax (multiplexed); Disney Channel; HBO (multiplexed); Showtime.
Fee: $31.00 installation; $8.00 monthly (Disney or Showtime), $10.00 monthly (Cinemax), $11.00 monthly (HBO).
Pay-Per-View
Addressable homes: 9,343.
Local advertising: Yes (insert only). Available in satellite distributed programming. Regional interconnect: Metrobase Cable Advertising.
Program Guide: TV Host.
Equipment: Scientific-Atlanta headend; Scientific-Atlanta cable; Scientific-Atlanta satellite antenna.
Miles of plant: 500.0 (coaxial); 50.0 (fiber optic). Homes passed: 32,000.
Manager: Karl Kowatch.
City fee: 3% of gross.
Ownership: Service Electric Cable TV Inc. (MSO).

BLAIRSVILLE—Adelphia, One Adelphia Dr., Blairsville, PA 15717. Phone: 412-459-5400. Fax: 412-459-0648. Counties: Allegheny, Indiana & Westmoreland. Also serves Armstrong Twp. (Indiana County), Black Lick Twp., Bolivar, Brenizer, Burrell Twp. (Indiana County), Center Twp. (Westmoreland County), Cherryhill Twp., Clymer, Commodore (Indiana County), Creekside, Derry, Derry Twp. (Westmoreland County), Dixonville (Indiana County), Ernest, Fairfield Twp. (Westmoreland County), Green Twp. (Indiana County), Homer City, Indiana, Indiana Twp. (Allegheny County), Latrobe, Laurel Mountain, Ligonier, Ligonier Twp., Lloydsville, Oakwood Hills, Payne, Rayne Twp. (portions), Starford, Unity Twp. (Westmoreland County), West Wheatfield Twp. (Indiana County), White Twp. (Indiana County), Youngstown. ICA: PA0320.
TV Market Ranking: 10 (Derry Twp., Indiana Twp., Latrobe, Lloydsville); 74 (Armstrong Twp., Black Lick Twp., Blairsville, Bolivar, Brenizer, Burrell Twp., Center Twp., Cherryhill Twp., Clymer, Commodore, Creekside, Derry, Derry Twp., Dixonville, Ernest, Fairfield Twp., Green Twp., Homer City, Indiana, Latrobe, Laurel Mountain, Ligonier, Ligonier Twp., Lloydsville, Oakwood Hills, Payne, Rayne Twp., Starford, Unity Twp., West Wheatfield Twp., White Twp., Youngstown). Franchise award date: N.A. Franchise expiration date: N.A. Began: March 1, 1965.
Channel capacity: 60 (not 2-way capable). Channels available but not in use: 16.
Basic Service
Subscribers: 27,244.
Programming (received off-air): WPSX-TV (P) Clearfield; WPCB-TV (I) Greensburg; WNPA (U) Jeanette; WJAC-TV (N), WTAJ-TV (C), WWCP-TV (F) Johnstown-Altoona; KDKA-TV (C), WCWB (W), WPGH-TV (F), WPXI (N), WQED (P), WQEX (P), WTAE-TV (A) Pittsburgh; allband FM.
Programming (via satellite): QVC; TBS Superstation.
Current originations: Automated timeweather.
Fee: N.A.
Expanded Basic Service
Subscribers: 25,556.
Programming (via satellite): A & E; American Movie Classics; Animal Planet; C-SPAN; C-SPAN 2; CNBC; CNN; Country Music TV; Discovery Channel; Disney Channel; ESPN; EWTN; FX; Fox Family Channel; Fox Sports Net Pittsburgh; Golf Channel; Headline News; History Channel; Home Shopping Network; Learning Channel; Lifetime; MSNBC; MTV; Nashville Network; Nick at Nite's TV Land; Nickelodeon; Product Information Network; QVC; Sci-Fi Channel; TV Food Network; TV Guide Channel; The Health Network; The Weather Channel; Turner Network TV; USA Network; VH1.
Fee: N.A.
Pay Service 1
Pay Units: 4,014.
Programming (via satellite): HBO.
Fee: $11.50 monthly.
Pay Service 2
Pay Units: 542.
Programming (via satellite): The Movie Channel.
Fee: $11.50 monthly.
Pay Service 3
Pay Units: 1,698.
Programming (via satellite): Cinemax.
Fee: $11.50 monthly.
Pay Service 4
Pay Units: 881.
Programming (via satellite): Showtime.
Fee: $11.50 monthly.
Pay-Per-View
Addressable homes: 4,178.
Viewer's Choice.
Fee: $3.95.
Local advertising: Yes. Regional interconnect: TCI Media Services-Pittsburgh, PA.
Program Guide: TV Guide.
Equipment: Jerrold headend; Scientific-Atlanta & Texscan amplifiers; Comm/Scope cable; Scientific-Atlanta set top converters; Scientific-Atlanta addressable set top converters; Eagle traps; Scientific-Atlanta satellite antenna; Scientific-Atlanta satellite receivers.
Miles of plant: 703.0 (coaxial).
Manager: J. Francis Bradley Jr. Chief technician: Dave Bowen.
City fee: 3% of gross.
Ownership: Adelphia Communications Corp. (MSO).

BLOOMSBURG—Service Electric Cablevision Inc., 500 Grant St., Sunbury, PA 17801. Phone: 717-286-5951. County: Columbia. Also serves Catawissa Borough, Catawissa Twp., Cleveland Twp., Franklin Twp. (Columbia County), Hemlock Twp., Locust Twp., Main Twp., Montour Twp. (Columbia County), Mount Pleasant Twp. (Columbia County), North Centre (portions), Orange Twp. (Columbia County), Roaring Creek Twp., Scott Twp. (Columbia County), South Centre Twp. (Columbia County). ICA: PA0088.
TV Market Ranking: 49 (Bloomsburg, Hemlock Twp., Main Twp., Montour Twp., Mount Pleasant Twp., North Centre, Orange Twp., Scott Twp., South Centre Twp.); Below 100 (Catawissa Borough, portions of Catawissa Twp., Cleveland Twp., Franklin Twp., Locust Twp., Roaring Creek Twp.); Outside TV Markets (portions of Catawissa Twp.). Franchise award date: N.A. Franchise expiration date: N.A. Began: May 1, 1953.
Channel capacity: 65 (2-way capable; operating 2-way). Channels available but not in use: None.
Basic Service
Subscribers: 7,300.
Programming (received off-air): WOLF-TV (F) Hazleton; WNYW (F), WPIX (W), WWOR-TV (U) New York; KYW-TV (C), WCAU (N), WPHL-TV (W), WPVI-TV (A), WTXF-TV (F) Philadelphia; WBRE-TV (N), WNEP-TV (A), WVIA-TV (P), WYOU (C) Scranton & Wilkes-Barre; allband FM.
Programming (via microwave): A & E, CNN, Country Music TV, Discovery Channel, ESPN, Fox Family Channel, Headline News, Lifetime, Nickelodeon, Travel Channel, USA Network.
Programming (via satellite): American Movie Classics; C-SPAN; CNBC; EWTN; Goodlife TV Network; Home Shopping Network; Learning Channel; MTV; Nashville Network; Philadelphia Park Live; QVC; Sci-Fi Channel; TBS Superstation; Telebet; The Weather Channel; Turner Network TV; VH1; ValueVision.
Current originations: Automated timeweather; educational access.
Fee: $32.00 installation; $24.45 monthly; $2.37 converter.
Pay Service 1
Pay Units: 1,513.
Programming (via microwave): Cinemax, Disney Channel, HBO, Showtime.
Fee: $31.00 installation; $8.00 monthly (Disney or Showtime), $10.00 monthly (Cinemax), $11.00 monthly (HBO).
Pay-Per-View
Addressable homes: 1,104.
Local advertising: Yes. Regional interconnect: Cabletime.
Program Guide: TV Host.
Equipment: Comm/Scope cable.
Miles of plant: 190.0 (coaxial). Additional miles planned: 15.0 (coaxial). Homes passed: 8,565. Total homes in franchised area: 11,275.
Manager: Dwight Walter. Chief technician & field manager: John Kurtz.
City fee: None.
Ownership: Service Electric Cable TV Inc. (MSO).

BLOSSBURG—Williamson Road TV Co. Inc., Box 45, Blossburg, PA 16912. Phones: 717-638-2490; 717-638-2582. County: Tioga. ICA: PA0321.
TV Market Ranking: Below 100. Franchise award date: June 1, 1955. Franchise expiration date: N.A. Began: June 1, 1955.
Channel capacity: N.A. Channels available but not in use: N.A.
Basic Service
Subscribers: 640.
Programming (received off-air): WBNG-TV (C), WSKG (P) Binghamton; WPSX-TV (P) Clearfield; WENY-TV (A), WETM-TV (N) Elmira; WBRE-TV (N), WNEP-TV (A), WSWB (W), WVIA-TV (P), WYOU (C) Scranton & Wilkes-Barre; 10 FMs.
Programming (via satellite): WGN-TV (W) Chicago; A & E; American Movie Classics;

CNN; Country Music TV; Discovery Channel; ESPN; Fox Family Channel; Headline News; MTV; Nashville Network; QVC; TBS Superstation; The Weather Channel; Turner Network TV; USA Network.
Fee: $109.00 installation; $16.00 monthly.
Pay Service 1
Pay Units: N.A.
Programming (via satellite): Disney Channel; HBO.
Fee: $15.00 installation; $13.00 monthly (each).
Equipment: Jerrold headend; Jerrold amplifiers; Jerrold cable; AFC satellite antenna.
Miles of plant: 18.0 (coaxial). Total homes in franchised area: 700.
Chief technician: Jim Rouppe.
City fee: None.
Ownership: Williamson Road TV Co. Inc.

BODINES—Ralph Herr TV, Box 717, RR 4, Montoursville, PA 17754-9665. Phone: 717-435-2780. County: Lycoming. Also serves Marsh Hill. ICA: PA0288.
TV Market Ranking: Below 100. Franchise award date: N.A. Franchise expiration date: N.A. Began: January 1, 1955.
Channel capacity: 12. Channels available but not in use: N.A.
Basic Service
Subscribers: N.A.
Programming (received off-air): WBNG-TV (C) Binghamton; WTAJ-TV (C) Johnstown-Altoona; WBRE-TV (N), WNEP-TV (A), WVIA-TV (P), WYOU (C) Scranton & Wilkes-Barre.
Fee: $25.00 installation; $5.00 monthly.
Equipment: Blonder-Tongue headend; Coral amplifiers; Coral cable.
Miles of plant: 8.1 (coaxial). Homes passed: 120.
Manager: Barry Herr.
City fee: None.
Ownership: Herr Cable Co. (MSO).

BOYERS—CableVision Communications, Box 2200, 68 5th St., Buckhannon, WV 26201. Phone: 304-472-4193. Fax: 304-472-0756. County: Butler. Also serves Hilliards. ICA: PA0276.
TV Market Ranking: Outside TV Markets. Franchise award date: N.A. Franchise expiration date: N.A. Began: N.A.
Channel capacity: 21. Channels available but not in use: N.A.
Basic Service
Subscribers: 76.
Programming (received off-air): KDKA-TV (C), WCWB (W), WPGH-TV (F), WPXI (N), WQED (P), WTAE-TV (A) Pittsburgh; WYTV (A,F) Youngstown.
Programming (via satellite): CNN; ESPN; Fox Family Channel; Nashville Network; TBS Superstation; Turner Network TV; USA Network.
Fee: $61.25 installation; $22.00 monthly; $0.73 converter.
Pay Service 1
Pay Units: 40.
Programming (via satellite): HBO.
Fee: $17.50 installation; $11.99 monthly.
Equipment: Blonder-Tongue, Olson & Triple Crown headend; Jerrold amplifiers; Comm/Scope & Standard Communications cable; Intercept & Pico traps; Triple Crown satellite receivers.
Miles of plant: 5.0 (coaxial). Homes passed: 156. Total homes in franchised area: 156.
Manager: Willie Critchfield. Marketing director: Kenny Phillips.
City fee: None.
Ownership: Rifkin & Associates Inc. (MSO). See Cable System Ownership.

BRADFORD—Cablecomm, 24 Main St., Bradford, PA 16701. Phone: 814-368-6991. Fax: 814-362-2190. County: McKean. Also serves Bradford Twp. (McKean County), Foster Twp. (McKean County), Lewis Run. ICA: PA0085.
TV Market Ranking: Below 100. Franchise award date: April 16, 1954. Franchise expiration date: N.A. Began: April 16, 1954.
Channel capacity: 53 (not 2-way capable). Channels available but not in use: 2.
Basic Service
Subscribers: 7,259; Commercial subscribers: 11.
Programming (received off-air): WGRZ-TV (N), WIVB-TV (C), WKBW-TV (A) Buffalo; WPSX-TV (P) Clearfield; WICU-TV (N), WSEE (C) Erie; allband FM.
Fee: $23.85 installation; $9.27 monthly; $1.60 converter.
Expanded Basic Service
Subscribers: 6,995.
Programming (via microwave): WNYW (F), WPIX (W) New York.
Programming (via satellite): A & E; C-SPAN; CNN; Discovery Channel; E! Entertainment TV; ESPN; Fox Family Channel; Lifetime; MTV; Nashville Network; Nickelodeon; QVC; TBS Superstation; The Weather Channel; Turner Network TV; USA Network; VH1.
Fee: $14.84 monthly.
Pay Service 1
Pay Units: 458.
Programming (via satellite): Cinemax.
Fee: $11.05 monthly.
Pay Service 2
Pay Units: 323.
Programming (via satellite): Disney Channel.
Fee: $11.05 monthly.
Pay Service 3
Pay Units: 1,105.
Programming (via satellite): Flix.
Fee: $1.69 monthly.
Pay Service 4
Pay Units: 765.
Programming (via satellite): HBO.
Fee: $11.05 monthly.
Pay Service 5
Pay Units: 102.
Programming (via satellite): The Movie Channel.
Fee: $11.05 monthly.
Pay Service 6
Pay Units: 306.
Programming (via satellite): Showtime.
Fee: $11.05 monthly.
Pay-Per-View
Addressable homes: 2,718.
Hot Choice; Playboy TV; Viewer's Choice.
Fee: $3.95-$6.95.
Local advertising: Yes.
Equipment: Scientific-Atlanta headend; C-COR amplifiers; Comm/Scope & Times Fiber cable; Scientific-Atlanta satellite antenna; Scientific-Atlanta satellite receivers.
Miles of plant: 130.0 (coaxial); None (fiber optic). Homes passed: 9,217.
Manager: Mike Papsrgi. Chief technician: Richard C. Himes.
City fee: 5% of gross.
Ownership: Fanch Communications Inc. (MSO); Time Warner Cable (MSO). See Cable System Ownership.

BRAVE—CableVision Communications, Box 2200, 68 5th St., Buckhannon, WV 26201. Phone: 304-472-4193. Fax: 304-472-0756. Counties: Greene, PA; Monongalia, WV. Also serves Spraggs (Greene County), PA; Daybrook, Macdale, Mooresville, Pentress, Wadestown, Wana, WV. ICA: PA0201.
TV Market Ranking: 90. Franchise award date: N.A. Franchise expiration date: N.A. Began: N.A.
Channel capacity: 39. Channels available but not in use: 4.
Basic Service
Subscribers: 788.
Programming (received off-air): WDTV (C,A) Clarksburg-Weston; WNPB-TV (P) Morgantown; KDKA-TV (C), WCWB (W), WPGH-TV (F), WPXI (N), WQED (P), WTAE-TV (A) Pittsburgh; WTRF-TV (C) Wheeling-Steubenville.
Programming (via satellite): WGN-TV (W) Chicago; C-SPAN; TBS Superstation.
Fee: $61.25 installation; $14.40 monthly; $1.24 converter; $17.50 additional installation.
Expanded Basic Service
Subscribers: 696.
Programming (via satellite): American Movie Classics; Animal Planet; CNN; Discovery Channel; Disney Channel; E! Entertainment TV; ESPN; Fox Family Channel; Great American Country; Home Shopping Network; Lifetime; Nashville Network; Nickelodeon; Sci-Fi Channel; The Weather Channel; Trinity Bcstg. Network; Turner Network TV; USA Network.
Fee: $16.93 monthly.
Pay Service 1
Pay Units: 574.
Programming (via satellite): Cinemax; HBO; Showtime.
Fee: $7.95 monthly (Cinemax), $11.95 monthly (Showtime), $11.99 monthly (HBO).
Pay Service 2
Pay Units: N.A.
Programming (via satellite): The Movie Channel; The New Encore.
Fee: $3.99 monthly (Encore), $11.95 monthly (TMC).
Equipment: Blonder-Tongue, Olson & Standard Communications headend; C-COR amplifiers; Capscan cable.
Miles of plant: 45.4 (coaxial). Homes passed: 1,034.
Manager: Willie Critchfield. Marketing director: Kenny Phillips.
Ownership: Rifkin & Associates Inc. (MSO). See Cable System Ownership.

BROAD TOP CITY—Broad Top Mountain Cable, 809 Lower Main St., Saxton, PA 16678. Phone: 814-635-2514. Counties: Bedford & Huntingdon. Also serves Coalmont, Dudley, Hopewell (Bedford County), Hopewell Twp. (Bedford County), Robertsdale, Wood. ICA: PA0224.
TV Market Ranking: 74. Franchise award date: N.A. Franchise expiration date: N.A. Began: January 1, 1972.
Channel capacity: 21 (not 2-way capable). Channels available but not in use: 8.
Basic Service
Subscribers: 695.
Programming (received off-air): WPSX-TV (P) Clearfield; WHTM-TV (A) Harrisburg; WJAC-TV (N), WTAJ-TV (C) Johnstown-Altoona; WTTG (F) Washington; WPMT (F) York; allband FM.
Programming (via satellite): WGN-TV (W) Chicago; Fox Family Channel; Nashville Network; TBS Superstation; USA Network.
Current originations: Automated time-weather.
Fee: $57.50 installation; $10.00 monthly.
Pay Service 1
Pay Units: N.A.
Programming (via satellite): Cinemax; Disney Channel; HBO.
Fee: $25.00 installation; $7.00 monthly (Cinemax or Disney), $10.00 monthly (HBO).
Local advertising: Yes.
Equipment: Blonder-Tongue headend; Magnavox amplifiers; Comm/Scope cable; Video Data Systems character generator; Standard Communications set top converters; Pico traps; Scientific-Atlanta satellite antenna; Scientific-Atlanta satellite receivers.
Miles of plant: 25.0 (coaxial).
Manager: John M. Zimmerman.
Ownership: SRW Inc. (MSO).

BROCKWAY—Brockway TV Inc., 501 Main St., Brockway, PA 15824. Phone: 814-268-6565. Fax: 814-265-1300. Counties: Elk & Jefferson. Also serves Horton Twp. (Elk County), Snyder Twp. (Jefferson County), Washington Twp. (Jefferson County). ICA: PA0182.
TV Market Ranking: Outside TV Markets. Franchise award date: N.A. Franchise expiration date: N.A. Began: April 1, 1952.
Channel capacity: 40 (2-way capable; operating 2-way). Channels available but not in use: 2.
Basic Service
Subscribers: 1,872.
Programming (received off-air): WPSX-TV (P) Clearfield; WJAC-TV (N), WTAJ-TV (C) Johnstown-Altoona; KDKA-TV (C), WCWB (W), WPGH-TV (F), WPXI (N), WQED (P), WTAE-TV (A) Pittsburgh; 18 FMs.
Programming (via satellite): WGN-TV (W) Chicago; ESPN; EWTN; Nashville Network; TBS Superstation.
Planned originations: Automated time-weather.
Fee: $16.50 monthly.
Pay Service 1
Pay Units: 134.
Programming (via satellite): Disney Channel.
Fee: $7.50 monthly.
Pay Service 2
Pay Units: 221.
Programming (via satellite): Showtime.
Fee: $10.25 monthly.
Local advertising: No. Regional interconnect: Cabletime.
Equipment: Jerrold & Scientific-Atlanta headend; Jerrold amplifiers; Comm/Scope & Times Fiber cable; Eagle traps; Scientific-Atlanta satellite antenna; Scientific-Atlanta satellite receivers.
Miles of plant: 36.0 (coaxial). Homes passed: 1,625.
Manager: Robert Fustine. Chief technician: Craig Manhart.
City fee: None.
Ownership: Brockway TV Inc.

BROOKSIDE—Ralph Herr TV, Box 717, RR 4, Montoursville, PA 17754-9665. Phone: 717-435-2780. County: Lycoming. ICA: PA0289.
TV Market Ranking: Below 100. Franchise award date: N.A. Franchise expiration date: N.A. Began: January 1, 1955.
Channel capacity: 12. Channels available but not in use: N.A.
Basic Service
Subscribers: N.A.
Programming (received off-air): WHP-TV (C) Harrisburg; WTAJ-TV (C) Johnstown-Altoona; WBRE-TV (N), WNEP-TV (A), WVIA-TV (P), WYOU (C) Scranton & Wilkes-Barre.
Fee: $25.00 installation; $6.00 monthly.
Equipment: Blonder-Tongue headend; Holt amplifiers; Holt cable.
Miles of plant: 12.0 (coaxial). Homes passed: 120.
Manager: Barry Herr.
City fee: None.
Ownership: Herr Cable Co. (MSO).

BRUSH VALLEY TWP.—TCI of Pennsylvania Inc., 535 E. Main St., Somerset, PA 15501. Phones: 814-443-4838; 800-535-7249. County: Indiana. Also serves Buffington, Center Twp. (Indiana County), East Wheatfield. ICA: PA0322.
TV Market Ranking: 74. Franchise award date: N.A. Franchise expiration date: N.A. Began: May 1, 1986.
Channel capacity: N.A. Channels available but not in use: N.A.
Basic Service
Subscribers: 370.
Programming (received off-air): WPCB-TV (I) Greensburg; WJAC-TV (N), WTAJ-TV (C), WWCP-TV (F) Johnstown-Altoona; KDKA-TV (C), WCWB (W), WPGH-TV (F), WPXI (N), WQED (P), WTAE-TV (A) Pittsburgh.
Programming (via satellite): CNN; Discovery Channel; ESPN; Fox Family Channel; MTV; Nashville Network; Nickelodeon; TBS Superstation; Turner Network TV; USA Network.
Fee: $20.00 installation; $15.00 monthly.
Pay Service 1
Pay Units: 22.
Programming (via satellite): Disney Channel.
Fee: $8.00 monthly.
Pay Service 2
Pay Units: 49.
Programming (via satellite): HBO.
Fee: $9.00 monthly.
Pay Service 3
Pay Units: 38.
Programming (via satellite): Showtime.
Fee: $9.00 monthly.
Miles of plant: 3.0 (coaxial). Additional miles planned: 8.0 (coaxial).
Manager: Rodney Weary. Chief technician: Tom Stratton.
Ownership: Brush Valley Cablevision Inc.

BURGETTSTOWN—Jefferson County Cable Inc., 116 S. 4th St., Toronto, OH 43964. Phone: 740-537-2214. Fax: 740-537-2802. County: Washington. Also serves Atlasburg, Bulger, Joffre, Langeloth, Slovan, Smith Twp. (Washington County). ICA: PA0323.
TV Market Ranking: 10,90. Franchise award date: N.A. Franchise expiration date: N.A. Began: October 1, 1974.
Channel capacity: 22. Channels available but not in use: 1.
Basic Service
Subscribers: N.A.
Programming (received off-air): KDKA-TV (C), WCWB (W), WPGH-TV (F), WPXI (N), WQED (P), WTAE-TV (A) Pittsburgh; WTOV-TV (N) Steubenville-Wheeling; WTRF-TV (C) Wheeling-Steubenville.
Programming (via satellite): WGN-TV (W) Chicago; CNN; ESPN; Fox Family Channel; Lifetime; MTV; Nashville Network; Nickelodeon; TBS Superstation; USA Network.
Fee: $20.00 installation; $13.00 monthly.
Pay Service 1
Pay Units: N.A.
Programming (via satellite): HBO; The Movie Channel.
Fee: $9.60 monthly (TMC), $10.00 monthly (HBO).
Equipment: Blonder-Tongue headend; AEL & Jerrold amplifiers; Comm/Scope cable; Scientific-Atlanta satellite antenna.
Miles of plant: 23.0 (coaxial). Additional miles planned: 15.0 (coaxial).
Manager: Melanie Cecchini.
Ownership: Jefferson County Cable Inc. (MSO).

BUTLER—Armstrong Cable Services, 660 S. Benbrook Rd., Butler, PA 16001. Phone: 724-482-4480. Fax: 724-482-4884. Web site: http://www.zbzoom.net. County: Butler. Also serves Buffalo Twp. (Butler County), Butler Twp. (Butler County), Center Twp. (Butler County), Clay Twp. (Butler County), Clearfield Twp. (Butler County), Connoquenessing Twp. (Butler County), Donegal Twp. (Butler County), East Butler, Jefferson Twp. (Butler County), Middlesex Twp. (Butler County), Oakland Twp. (Butler County), Penn Twp. (Butler County), Prospect, Saxonburg, Summit Twp. (Butler County), Winfield Twp. ICA: PA0044.
TV Market Ranking: 10 (Buffalo Twp., Butler, Butler Twp., Center Twp., Clearfield Twp., Connoquenessing Twp., Donegal Twp., East Butler, Jefferson Twp., Middlesex Twp., Oakland Twp., Penn Twp., Prospect, Saxonburg, Summit Twp., Winfield Twp.); Below 100 (Clay Twp.). Franchise award date: October 21, 1963. Franchise expiration date: October 21, 2001. Began: April 1, 1964.
Channel capacity: 54 (2-way capable; operating 2-way). Channels available but not in use: 10.
Basic Service
Subscribers: 24,325.
Programming (received off-air): WPCB-TV (I) Greensburg; WNPA (U) Jeanette; KDKA-TV (C), WCWB (W), WPGH-TV (F), WPXI (N), WQED (P), WQEX (P), WTAE-TV (A) Pittsburgh.
Programming (via satellite): WGN-TV (W) Chicago; A & E; American Movie Classics; C-SPAN; CNBC; CNN; Cartoon Network; Comedy Central; Court TV; Discovery Channel; ESPN; ESPN 2; Fox Family Channel; Fox Sports Net Pittsburgh; Headline News; Home Shopping Network; Learning Channel; Lifetime; MSNBC; MTV; Nashville Network; Nick at Nite's TV Land; Nickelodeon; QVC; TBS Superstation; TV Guide Channel; The Inspirational Network; The Weather Channel; Turner Network TV; USA Network; VH1.
Current originations: Automated time-weather; educational access; government access; religious access; leased access; automated emergency alert; local news.
Fee: $35.00 installation (aerial), $52.50 (underground); $24.95 monthly; $2.95 converter; $35.00 additional installation.
Expanded Basic Service
Subscribers: 8,500.
Programming (via satellite): Animal Planet; Country Music TV; E! Entertainment TV; History Channel; Home & Garden Television; Ovation; Romance Classics; Sci-Fi Channel; TV Food Network; Travel Channel; Turner Classic Movies; Z Music Television.
Fee: $19.95 installation; $3.99 monthly.
Expanded Basic Service 2
Subscribers: 23.
Programming (via satellite): CNN/SI; ESPN Classic Sports; Outdoor Channel; The Health Network.
Fee: $1.99 monthly.
Pay Service 1
Pay Units: 2,973.
Programming (via satellite): Cinemax.
Fee: $19.95 installation; $9.95 monthly.
Pay Service 2
Pay Units: 1,660.
Programming (via satellite): Disney Channel.
Fee: $19.95 installation; $7.95 monthly.
Pay Service 3
Pay Units: 5,004.
Programming (via satellite): HBO.
Fee: $19.95 installation; $11.95 monthly.
Pay Service 4
Pay Units: 1,049.
Programming (via satellite): Showtime.
Fee: $19.95 installation; $9.95 monthly.
Pay Service 5
Pay Units: 252.
Programming (via satellite): DMX.
Fee: $19.95 installation; $7.95 monthly.
Pay Service 6
Pay Units: 21.
Programming (via satellite): Starz!; The New Encore.
Fee: $19.95 installation; $8.95 monthly (package).
Pay Service 7
Pay Units: 13.
Programming (via satellite): Golf Channel.
Fee: $4.99 monthly.
Pay-Per-View
Addressable homes: 1,463.
Hot Choice; Viewer's Choice 1, 3, 4.
Local advertising: Yes (insert only). Available in satellite distributed, taped & automated programming.
Equipment: Scientific-Atlanta headend; Scientific-Atlanta amplifiers; Trilogy cable; Texscan character generator; Scientific-Atlanta set top converters; Lancity modems; Eagle traps; AFC satellite antenna; Scientific-Atlanta satellite receivers.
Miles of plant: 473.1 (coaxial). Additional miles planned: 15.0 (fiber optic). Homes passed: 27,127.
Manager: Richard L. Ross. Assistant manager: John Hayden. Chief technician: Pat Mills. Office supervisor: Connie Swartzfegger. Marketing director: Thomas E. Graham.
City fee: 5% of gross.
Ownership: Armstrong Group of Companies (MSO).

CALEDONIA—DuCom Inc., 50 Tipp St, Du Bois, PA 15801. Phone: 814-371-1925. Fax: 814-371-3052. E-mail: ducom@key-net.net. County: Elk. Also serves Jay Twp. ICA: PA0444.
TV Market Ranking: Outside TV Markets. Franchise award date: N.A. Franchise expiration date: N.A. Began: N.A.
Channel capacity: N.A. Channels available but not in use: N.A.
Basic Service
Subscribers: 65.
Programming (via satellite): WGN-TV (W) Chicago; CNN; Discovery Channel; Fox Family Channel; Nashville Network; TBS Superstation; Trinity Bcstg. Network; Turner Network TV.
Fee: $45.00 installation; $14.00 monthly; $2.50 converter.
Manager: Rodney Preston. Chief technician: Dave Kucenski.
Ownership: Dubois Communications Inc. (MSO).

CALIFORNIA—Armstrong Communications Inc., 259 E. Crawford Ave., Connellsville, PA 15425. Phone: 724-628-5462. Fax: 724-628-4963. Counties: Fayette & Washington. Also serves Allenport, Centerville (Washington County), Coal Center, Daisytown (Washington County), Dunlevy, Elco, Jefferson (Washington County), Long Branch, Newell, Roscoe, Stockdale, West Brownsville, West Pike Run Twp. ICA: PA0099.
TV Market Ranking: 10. Franchise award date: N.A. Franchise expiration date: April 1, 2000. Began: November 19, 1965.
Channel capacity: 54 (not 2-way capable). Channels available but not in use: 15.
Basic Service
Subscribers: 4,708.
Programming (received off-air): WPCB-TV (I) Greensburg; WJAC-TV (N) Johnstown-Altoona; KDKA-TV (C), WCWB (W), WPGH-TV (F), WPXI (N), WQED (P), WTAE-TV (A) Pittsburgh; WTRF-TV (C) Wheeling-Steubenville.
Programming (via satellite): WGN-TV (W) Chicago; A & E; American Movie Classics; C-SPAN; CNN; Discovery Channel; E! Entertainment TV; ESPN; Fox Family Channel; Headline News; Home Shopping Network; Lifetime; MTV; Nashville Network; Nickelodeon; TBS Superstation; The Weather Channel; Turner Network TV; USA Network; VH1.
Current originations: Automated time-weather.
Fee: $39.95 installation; $16.65 monthly.
Pay Service 1
Pay Units: 740.
Programming (via satellite): Cinemax.
Fee: $25.00 installation; $9.95 monthly.
Pay Service 2
Pay Units: 1,057.
Programming (via satellite): HBO.
Fee: $25.00 installation; $10.95 monthly.
Pay Service 3
Pay Units: 179.
Programming (via satellite): Disney Channel.
Fee: N.A.
Local advertising: Yes. Regional interconnect: Metrobase Cable Advertising.
Equipment: Scientific-Atlanta headend; Scientific-Atlanta amplifiers; M/A-Com cable; AFC satellite antenna; AFC satellite receivers.
Miles of plant: 112.5 (coaxial). Homes passed: 7,067. Total homes in franchised area: 8,000.
Manager: Joseph W. Taylor. Chief technician: Jack Thornton. Marketing director: Eric Baugh.
Ownership: Armstrong Group of Companies (MSO).

CALLENSBURG—CableVision Communications, Box 2200, 68 5th St., Buckhannon, WV 26201. Phone: 304-472-4193. Fax: 304-472-0756. County: Clarion. Also serves West Freedom. ICA: PA0258.
TV Market Ranking: Outside TV Markets. Franchise award date: N.A. Franchise expiration date: N.A. Began: N.A.
Channel capacity: 20. Channels available but not in use: 3.
Basic Service
Subscribers: 184.
Programming (received off-air): KDKA-TV (C), WCWB (W), WPGH-TV (F), WPXI (N), WQED (P), WTAE-TV (A) Pittsburgh.
Programming (via satellite): CNN; Discovery Channel; ESPN; Fox Family Channel; Nashville Network; Nickelodeon; TBS Superstation; Trinity Bcstg. Network; Turner Network TV; USA Network.
Fee: $61.25 installation; $22.00 monthly; $0.73 converter.
Pay Service 1
Pay Units: 70.
Programming (via satellite): Cinemax; HBO.
Fee: $7.95 monthly (Cinemax), $11.99 monthly (HBO).
Local advertising: No.
Equipment: Blonder-Tongue headend; Drake, Jerrold & Microdyne amplifiers; Intercept & Pico traps; Triple Crown & Microdyne satellite receivers.
Miles of plant: 10.3 (coaxial). Homes passed: 279.
Manager: Willie Critchfield. Marketing director: Kenny Phillips.
City fee: None.
Ownership: Rifkin & Associates Inc. (MSO). See Cable System Ownership.

CAMP HILL CORRECTIONAL INSTITUTE—Cosmic Cable TV Inc., Box 186, RR

4, Shickshinny, PA 18655. Phone: 570-256-3437. County: Cumberland. ICA: PA0324.
TV Market Ranking: 57. Franchise award date: October 1, 1985. Franchise expiration date: October 1, 2000. Began: October 1, 1985.
Channel capacity: 12 (not 2-way capable). Channels available but not in use: None.
Basic Service
Subscribers: 450.
Programming (received off-air): WHP-TV (C), WHTM-TV (A), WITF-TV (P) Harrisburg; WGAL (N), WLYH-TV (U) Lancaster.
Programming (via satellite): BET; ESPN; Fox Family Channel; TBS Superstation; Univision.
Fee: $10.45 monthly.
Pay Service 1
Pay Units: 200.
Programming (via satellite): The Movie Channel.
Fee: $8.95 monthly.
Miles of plant: 3.0 (coaxial); None (fiber optic).
Manager: Mark Reiber. Chief technician: Daniel Jamuscewski.
Ownership: June Hoover (MSO).

CANOE CREEK—Milestone Communications LP, Suite 200, 1850 Woodmoor Dr., Monument, CO 80132. Phone: 719-488-2916. Fax: 719-488-3629. County: Blair. Also serves Altoona, Catherine Twp., Hollidaysburg (unincorporated areas). ICA: PA0439.
TV Market Ranking: 74. Franchise award date: N.A. Franchise expiration date: September 1, 2008. Began: N.A.
Channel capacity: 27 (not 2-way capable). Channels available but not in use: 2.
Basic Service
Subscribers: 222.
Programming (received off-air): WPSX-TV (P) Clearfield; WATM-TV (A), WJAC-TV (N), WKBS-TV (I), WTAJ-TV (C), WWCP-TV (F) Johnstown-Altoona.
Programming (via satellite): WGN-TV (W) Chicago; A & E; CNN; Country Music TV; Discovery Channel; ESPN; ESPN 2; Fox Family Channel; Headline News; History Channel; Nashville Network; Nickelodeon; QVC; TBS Superstation; Trinity Bcstg. Network; Turner Network TV; USA Network.
Fee: $50.00 installation (aerial), $60.00 (underground); $22.75 monthly.
Pay Service 1
Pay Units: 33.
Programming (via satellite): Showtime; The Movie Channel.
Fee: $12.95 monthly (each).
Miles of plant: 15.5 (coaxial); None (fiber optic). Homes passed: 300.
Manager: Michael Drake. Engineering director: Randy Mock.
Ownership: Milestone Communications LP (MSO).

CANONSBURG—TCI, Box 360, Ridge Ave. Ext., Canonsburg, PA 15317. Phone: 724-745-4734. Fax: 724-745-0798. Counties: Allegheny & Washington. Also serves Cecil Twp., Chartiers Twp. (Washington County), Eighty Four, Fallowfield Twp., Hendersonville, Houston, McDonald, North Strabane Twp., Nottingham Twp., Oakdale, Somerset Twp. (Washington County), South Fayette Twp. (Allegheny County), Strabane. ICA: PA0057.
TV Market Ranking: 10 (Canonsburg, Cecil Twp., Chartiers Twp., Eighty Four, Fallowfield Twp., Hendersonville, Houston, McDonald, North Strabane Twp., Nottingham Twp., Oakdale, Somerset Twp., South Fayette Twp., Strabane); 90 (Canonsburg, Cecil Twp., Chartiers Twp., Eighty Four, Hendersonville, Houston, McDonald, North Strabane Twp., Oakdale, Somerset Twp., South Fayette Twp., Strabane). Franchise award date: January 1, 1968. Franchise expiration date: January 1, 1998. Began: July 1, 1969.
Channel capacity: 80 (not 2-way capable). Channels available but not in use: N.A.
Basic Service
Subscribers: 17,300.
Programming (received off-air): WPCB-TV (I) Greensburg; KDKA-TV (C), WCWB (W), WPGH-TV (F), WPXI (N), WQED (P), WQEX (P), WTAE-TV (A) Pittsburgh.
Programming (via satellite): Headline News; QVC; TBS Superstation; The Weather Channel; Turner Network TV; USA Network; VH1.
Planned originations: Automated emergency alert.
Fee: $23.64 installation; $7.09 monthly; $1.95 converter.
Expanded Basic Service
Subscribers: 16,850.
Programming (via satellite): A & E; C-SPAN; CNN; Cartoon Network; Discovery Channel; E! Entertainment TV; ESPN; EWTN; Fox Family Channel; Lifetime; MTV; Nashville Network; Nickelodeon; Odyssey.
Fee: $21.13 installation; $18.46 monthly.
Expanded Basic Service 2
Subscribers: 9,860.
Programming (via satellite): American Movie Classics; Fox Sports Net Pittsburgh; Ladbroke Racing Channel/Meadows Racing Network; Travel Channel.
Fee: $3.55 monthly.
Pay Service 1
Pay Units: 1,927.
Programming (via satellite): Cinemax.
Fee: $20.00 installation; $9.50 monthly.
Pay Service 2
Pay Units: 843.
Programming (via satellite): Disney Channel.
Fee: $20.00 installation; $9.50 monthly.
Pay Service 3
Pay Units: 5,740.
Programming (via satellite): HBO.
Fee: $20.00 installation; $10.50 monthly.
Pay Service 4
Pay Units: 1,222.
Programming (via satellite): Showtime.
Fee: $20.00 installation; $9.50 monthly.
Pay-Per-View
Addressable homes: 11,200.
Hot Choice; Viewer's Choice.
Local advertising: Yes. Available in satellite distributed programming. Regional interconnect: TCI Media Services-Pittsburgh, PA.
Equipment: Jerrold & Magnavox headend; Magnavox amplifiers; Times Fiber cable; Scientific-Atlanta set top converters; Scientific-Atlanta addressable set top converters; Eagle traps; Scientific-Atlanta satellite antenna.
Miles of plant: 377.0 (coaxial); 107.0 (fiber optic). Homes passed: 22,500.
Manager: Chuck Morrow. Chief technician: George Wakulik. Marketing director: Linda Walker. Customer service manager: Susan Zenaglio.
Ownership: AT&T Broadband & Internet Services (MSO). Purchased from Time Warner Cable, June 1, 1999.

CANTON—Retel TV Cable Co., 62 Troy St., Canton, PA 17724. Phone: 717-673-5326. County: Bradford. Also serves Alba, Canton Twp. (Bradford County), East Canton, Grover. ICA: PA0184.
TV Market Ranking: Below 100. Franchise award date: N.A. Franchise expiration date: N.A. Began: May 1, 1956.
Channel capacity: 40 (2-way capable; operating 2-way). Channels available but not in use: N.A.
Basic Service
Subscribers: 1,400.
Programming (received off-air): WBNG-TV (C) Binghamton; WENY-TV (A), WETM-TV (N) Elmira; WBRE-TV (N), WNEP-TV (A), WVIA-TV (P) Scranton & Wilkes-Barre; all-band FM.
Programming (via satellite): ESPN; Nashville Network.
Current originations: Educational access.
Fee: $30.00 installation; $20.00 monthly.
Pay Service 1
Pay Units: N.A.
Programming (via satellite): HBO.
Fee: $15.00 installation; $9.00 monthly.
Local advertising: Planned.
Equipment: Ameco headend; Gamco amplifiers; Times Fiber & Vikoa cable; Eagle & Vitek traps; Microdyne satellite antenna; Microdyne satellite receivers.
Miles of plant: 41.0 (coaxial); 70.0 (fiber optic). Additional miles planned: 3.0 (coaxial). Homes passed: 1,450. Total homes in franchised area: 1,450.
Manager: Terry W. Hughes.
City fee: 1% of gross.
Ownership: Retel TV Cable Co. Inc. (MSO).

CARBONDALE—Adams CATV Inc., 9 N. Main St., Carbondale, PA 18407. Phone: 717-282-6121. Fax: 717-282-3787. Counties: Lackawanna, Pike, Susquehanna & Wayne, PA; Broome, NY. Also serves Windsor (Broome County), NY; Aldenville, Archbald, Canaan Twp. (Lackawanna County), Carbondale Twp. (Lackawanna County), Cherry Ridge Twp. (Wayne County), Clifford Twp. (Susquehanna County), Clinton Twp. (Wayne County), Dyberry Twp., Farview State Hospital, Fell Twp. (Lackawanna County), Greene Twp. (Pike County), Greenfield Twp. (Lackawanna County), Hallstead (Susquehanna County), Hamlin, Herrick Twp., Hollisterville, Jefferson Twp. (Lackawanna County), Jermyn, Lake Ariel, Lake Twp. (Wayne County), Lakeville, Lenox Twp. (Susquehanna County), Madison Twp. (Lackawanna County), Mayfield, Moscow (Lackawanna County), Mount Pleasant Twp. (Wayne County), New Milford (Susquehanna County), Paupack Twp. (Wayne County), Pleasant Mount, Prompton, Salem Twp. (Wayne County), Scott Twp. (Wayne County), Seelyville (Wayne County), Simpson, South Canaan Twp., South Sterling, Sterling, Sterling Twp. (Wayne County), Texas Twp. (Wayne County), The Hideout, Uniondale, Wallenpaupack Lake Estates, Waymart, PA. ICA: PA0067.
TV Market Ranking: 49 (Aldenville, Archbald, Canaan Twp., Carbondale, Carbondale Twp., Cherry Ridge Twp., Clifford Twp., Clinton Twp., Dyberry Twp., Farview State Hospital, Fell Twp., Greene Twp., Greenfield Twp., Hamlin, Herrick Twp., Hollisterville, Jefferson Twp., Jermyn, Lake Ariel, Lake Twp., Lakeville, Lenox Twp., Madison Twp., Mayfield, Moscow, Mount Pleasant Twp., New Milford, Paupack Twp., Pleasant Mount, Prompton, Salem Twp., Scott Twp., Seelyville, Simpson, South Canaan Twp., South Sterling, Sterling, Sterling Twp., Texas Twp., The Hideout, Uniondale, Wallenpaupack Lake Estates, Waymart); Below 100 (Hallstead, Windsor). Franchise award date: February 1, 1965. Franchise expiration date: N.A. Began: July 1, 1962.
Channel capacity: 77 (2-way capable; operating 2-way). Channels available but not in use: None.
Basic Service
Subscribers: 22,000.
Programming (received off-air): WBRE-TV (N), WNEP-TV (A), WSWB (W), WVIA-TV (P), WYOU (C) Scranton & Wilkes-Barre.
Programming (via satellite): WPIX (W) New York; A & E; C-SPAN; CNBC; CNN; Country Music TV; Discovery Channel; Disney Channel; E! Entertainment TV; ESPN; EWTN; Fox Family Channel; Headline News; Learning Channel; Lifetime; MTV; Nashville Network; Nickelodeon; QVC; TBS Superstation; TV Guide Channel; The Weather Channel; Turner Network TV; USA Network; VH1.
Planned originations: Automated time-weather; public access; educational access; local sports.
Fee: $40.00 installation; $23.00 monthly.
Pay Service 1
Pay Units: 400.
Programming (via satellite): Cinemax.
Fee: $15.00 installation; $12.00 monthly.
Pay Service 2
Pay Units: 200.
Programming (via satellite): Showtime.
Fee: $15.00 installation; $9.95 monthly.
Pay Service 3
Pay Units: 2,000.
Programming (via satellite): HBO.
Fee: $15.00 installation; $12.00 monthly.
Pay Service 4
Pay Units: 200.
Programming (via satellite): The Movie Channel.
Fee: $15.00 installation; $9.95 monthly.
Pay Service 5
Pay Units: 50.
Programming (via satellite): Flix.
Fee: $15.00 installation; $4.95 monthly.
Pay-Per-View
Addressable homes: 2,000.
Viewer's Choice 1-4.
Fee: $3.99.
Local advertising: Yes. Available in locally originated & character-generated programming. Rates: $20.00/Week. Local sales manager: Doug Adams. Regional interconnect: Cabletime.
Equipment: Holt headend; Holt amplifiers; Comm/Scope & Trilogy cable; RCA cameras; RCA VTRs; Scientific-Atlanta set top converters; Scientific-Atlanta addressable set top converters; Arcom & PPC traps; Scientific-Atlanta satellite antenna; Scientific-Atlanta satellite receivers.
Miles of plant: 650.0 (coaxial); 120.0 (fiber optic). Homes passed: 25,000. Total homes in franchised area: 27,000.
Manager: Wendy White. Chief technician: John Wallis. Program director: Doug Adams.
City fee: 3% of gross.
Ownership: Adams CATV Inc. (MSO).

CARLISLE—TV Cable of Carlisle, 469 E. North St., Carlisle, PA 17013. Phone: 717-243-4918. Fax: 717-243-5965. Counties: Adams, Cumberland, Franklin & Perry, PA; Washington, MD. Also serves Cascade, Pen-Mar, Washington County (portions), MD; Antrim Twp., Blue Ridge Summit, Boiling Springs, Carlisle Barracks, Carroll Twp. (Perry County), Cumberland Twp. (Adams County), Dickinson Twp. (Cumberland County), Edenville, Guilford Twp., Hamilton Twp. (Franklin County), Lower Frankford Twp., Middlesex Twp. (Cumberland County), Monroe Twp. (Cumberland County), Mont Alto, Montgomery Twp. (Franklin County), Mount Holly Springs, North Middleton Twp. (Cumberland County), Penn Twp. (Cumberland County), Peters Twp., Quincy Twp., Rouzerville, Shady Grove, Shermans Dale, Silver Spring Twp. (Cumberland County), South

Middleton Twp. (Cumberland County), State Line, Washington Twp. (Franklin County), Wayne Heights, West Pennsboro Twp. (Cumberland County), Zullinger, PA. ICA: PA0047.

TV Market Ranking: 57 (Boiling Springs, Carlisle, Carlisle Barracks, Carroll Twp., Dickinson Twp., Lower Frankford Twp., Middlesex Twp., Monroe Twp., Mount Holly Springs, North Middleton Twp., Penn Twp., Shermans Dale, Silver Spring Twp., South Middleton Twp., West Pennsboro Twp.); Below 100 (Antrim Twp., Blue Ridge Summit, Cascade, Cumberland Twp., Edenville, Guilford Twp., Hamilton Twp., Mont Alto, Montgomery Twp., Pen-Mar, Peters Twp., Quincy Twp., Rouzerville, Shady Grove, State Line, Washington County, Washington Twp., Wayne Heights, Zullinger). Franchise award date: N.A. Franchise expiration date: January 15, 1999. Began: April 1, 1952.

Channel capacity: 64 (not 2-way capable). Channels available but not in use: 1.

Basic Service

Subscribers: 18,651.

Programming (received off-air): WHP-TV (C), WHTM-TV (A), WITF-TV (P) Harrisburg; WGAL (N), WLYH-TV (U) Lancaster; WPMT (F) York.

Programming (via satellite): BET; C-SPAN; C-SPAN 2; E! Entertainment TV; Fox Family Channel; Home Shopping Network; Knowledge TV; QVC; TBS Superstation; TV Guide Channel; TV Guide Sneak Prevue; Travel Channel.

Current originations: Automated time-weather.

Planned originations: Public access; educational access; government access; automated emergency alert.

Fee: $50.25 installation; $10.55 monthly; $2.00 converter.

Expanded Basic Service

Subscribers: 16,202.

Programming (via satellite): A & E; American Movie Classics; Bravo; CNBC; CNN; Cartoon Network; Comedy Central; Country Music TV; Court TV; Discovery Channel; ESPN; ESPN 2; Fox Sports Net Pittsburgh; Goodlife TV Network; Headline News; History Channel; Home & Garden Television; Home Team Sports; Learning Channel; Lifetime; MTV; NASA TV; Nashville Network; Nick at Nite; Nickelodeon; Odyssey; Pennsylvania Cable Network; Sci-Fi Channel; TV Food Network; The Weather Channel; Turner Network TV; USA Network; VH1.

Fee: $50.25 installation; $14.30 monthly.

Pay Service 1

Pay Units: 6,815.

Programming (via satellite): Cinemax; Disney Channel; HBO; Showtime; The Movie Channel.

Fee: N.A.

Pay-Per-View

Addressable homes: 4,947.

Action Pay-Per-View; Spice; TVN Entertainment; special events.

Local advertising: Yes. Available in satellite distributed & character-generated programming. Rates: On request. Regional interconnect: Central Pennsylvania Cable AdCom.

Equipment: Tocom addressable set top converters; Scientific-Atlanta satellite antenna.

Miles of plant: 456.0 (coaxial); None (fiber optic). Homes passed: 26,432. Total homes in franchised area: 26,432.

Manager: Hans Welch. Chief technician: Ron Pevoichi. Marketing director: Tim Horn. Customer service manager: Ginger McAllister.

City fee: 5% of gross.

Ownership: Lenfest Communications Inc. (MSO). Purchased from Raystay Co., July 30, 1999.

CARNEGIE—AT&T Cable Services, 300 Corliss St., Pittsburgh, PA 15220-4815. Phones: 412-875-1100; 412-771-8100. County: Allegheny. Also serves Bridgeville, Collier, Collier Twp., Green Tree, Heidelberg, Ingram, Pennsbury Village, Rosslyn Farms, Scott Twp. (Allegheny County), Thornburg. ICA: PA0045.

TV Market Ranking: 10,90. Franchise award date: N.A. Franchise expiration date: N.A. Began: December 1, 1969.

Channel capacity: 64 (not 2-way capable). Channels available but not in use: N.A.

Basic Service

Subscribers: 21,494.

Programming (received off-air): WPCB-TV (I) Greensburg; KDKA-TV (C), WCWB (W), WPGH-TV (F), WPXI (N), WQED (P), WQEX (P), WTAE-TV (A) Pittsburgh; 20 FMs.

Programming (via microwave): Meadows Racing Network.

Programming (via satellite): BET; C-SPAN; Odyssey; QVC; TV Guide Sneak Prevue; The Weather Channel.

Fee: $44.95 installation; $10.19 monthly; $1.50 converter; $24.95 additional installation.

Expanded Basic Service

Subscribers: 20,109.

Programming (via microwave): Pittsburgh Cable News Channel.

Programming (via satellite): A & E; American Movie Classics; Animal Planet; C-SPAN 2; CNBC; CNN; Cartoon Network; Court TV; Discovery Channel; E! Entertainment TV; ESPN; ESPN 2; EWTN; FX; Fox Family Channel; Fox News Channel; Fox Sports Net Pittsburgh; Headline News; History Channel; Home Shopping Network; Knowledge TV; Learning Channel; Lifetime; MOVIEplex; MTV; Nashville Network; Nickelodeon; Sci-Fi Channel; TBS Superstation; TV Guide Channel; Turner Network TV; USA Network; VH1.

Fee: $18.26 monthly.

Pay Service 1

Pay Units: 1,595.

Programming (via satellite): Cinemax.

Fee: $13.45 monthly.

Pay Service 2

Pay Units: 700.

Programming (via satellite): Disney Channel.

Fee: $12.50 monthly.

Pay Service 3

Pay Units: 3,610.

Programming (via satellite): HBO (multiplexed).

Fee: $14.95 monthly.

Pay Service 4

Pay Units: 1,089.

Programming (via satellite): Showtime.

Fee: $14.95 monthly.

Pay Service 5

Pay Units: 6,559.

Programming (via satellite): The New Encore.

Fee: $1.95 monthly.

Pay Service 6

Pay Units: N.A.

Programming (via satellite): DMX; Starz!

Fee: $6.75 monthly (Starz), $9.95 monthly (DMX).

Pay-Per-View

Action Pay-Per-View; Playboy TV; Spice.

Local advertising: Yes (locally produced & insert). Available in satellite distributed programming. Local sales manager: Dave McGlade. Regional interconnect: TCI Media Services-Pittsburgh, PA.

Program Guide: The Cable Guide.

Equipment: Benavac headend; C-COR amplifiers; Comm/Scope cable.

Miles of plant: 237.9 (coaxial). Homes passed: 25,910. Total homes in franchised area: 25,910.

Manager: Jeffrey Harshman. Chief technician: Fred Hamm. Marketing director: Glenn Ryerson.

City fee: 3% of gross.

Ownership: AT&T Broadband & Internet Services (MSO). Purchased from Tele-Communications Inc., March 9, 1999.

CARROLLTOWN BOROUGH—TCI of Pennsylvania Inc., Box 349, Rte. 219, Carrolltown, PA 15722. Phone: 814-344-6518. Counties: Cambria & Indiana. Also serves Barnesboro, Barr Twp., Burnside Twp. (Cambria County), Cambria Twp. (Cambria County), Carrolltown, Cherry Tree, Chest Twp. (Cambria County), Clearfield Twp. (Cambria County), East Carroll Twp. (Cambria County), Ebensburg, Elder Twp. (Cambria County), Hastings, Patton, Spangler, Susquehanna Twp. (Cambria County), West Carroll Twp. (Cambria County). ICA: PA0078.

TV Market Ranking: 74. Franchise award date: N.A. Franchise expiration date: N.A. Began: November 1, 1970.

Channel capacity: 48. Channels available but not in use: N.A.

Basic Service

Subscribers: 7,945.

Programming (received off-air): WPSX-TV (P) Clearfield; WATM-TV (A), WJAC-TV (N), WKBS-TV (I), WTAJ-TV (C), WWCP-TV (F) Johnstown-Altoona; KDKA-TV (C), WPXI (N), WTAE-TV (A) Pittsburgh; allband FM.

Programming (via satellite): C-SPAN; Ladbroke Racing Channel/Meadows Racing Network; Lifetime; QVC.

Current originations: Automated time-weather.

Fee: $59.95 installation; $9.06 monthly; $2.00 converter; $49.95 additional installation.

Expanded Basic Service

Subscribers: 7,498.

Programming (via satellite): A & E; American Movie Classics; CNBC; CNN; Court TV; Discovery Channel; ESPN; EWTN; Fox Family Channel; Fox Sports Net Pittsburgh; Headline News; MTV; Nashville Network; Nickelodeon; TBS Superstation; The Weather Channel; Turner Network TV; USA Network.

Fee: $13.33 monthly.

Pay Service 1

Pay Units: 1,447.

Programming (via satellite): HBO.

Fee: $13.15 monthly.

Pay Service 2

Pay Units: 351.

Programming (via satellite): Cinemax.

Fee: $13.15 monthly.

Pay Service 3

Pay Units: 663.

Programming (via satellite): Showtime.

Fee: $13.15 monthly.

Pay Service 4

Pay Units: 1,055.

Programming (via satellite): The New Encore.

Fee: N.A.

Pay Service 5

Pay Units: N.A.

Programming (via satellite): DMX; Disney Channel.

Fee: $9.95 monthly (DMX), $11.40 monthly (Disney).

Local advertising: Yes.

Program Guide: The Cable Guide.

Equipment: Benco headend; Jerrold & Vikoa amplifiers; Plastoid & Times Fiber cable; AFC satellite antenna; Microdyne satellite receivers.

Miles of plant: 166.5 (coaxial). Homes passed: 9,775. Total homes in franchised area: 9,775.

Manager: Randy Bender.

City fee: 4.5% of gross (Cambria Twp., Ebensburg & Ehrenfield); 3% of gross (Loretto).

Ownership: AT&T Broadband & Internet Services (MSO). Purchased from Tele-Communications Inc., March 9, 1999.

CASTLE SHANNON—AT&T Cable Services, 300 Corliss St., Pittsburgh, PA 15220-4815. Phones: 412-875-1100; 412-771-8100. County: Allegheny. Also serves Baldwin, Baldwin Twp., Brentwood, Clairton, Dormont, Jefferson (Allegheny County), South Hills, South Park, West Elizabeth, Whitehall. ICA: PA0021.

TV Market Ranking: 10 (Baldwin, Baldwin Twp., Brentwood, Castle Shannon, Clairton, Dormont, Jefferson, South Hills, South Park, West Elizabeth, Whitehall); 90 (Baldwin, Baldwin Twp., Brentwood, Castle Shannon, Dormont, Jefferson, South Hills, South Park, West Elizabeth, Whitehall). Franchise award date: N.A. Franchise expiration date: N.A. Began: September 1, 1970.

Channel capacity: 61 (not 2-way capable). Channels available but not in use: N.A.

Basic Service

Subscribers: 34,330.

Programming (received off-air): WPCB-TV (I) Greensburg; KDKA-TV (C), WCWB (W), WPGH-TV (F), WPXI (N), WQED (P), WQEX (P), WTAE-TV (A) Pittsburgh; allband FM.

Programming (via microwave): Meadows Racing Network.

Programming (via satellite): BET; C-SPAN; Odyssey; QVC; TV Guide Sneak Prevue; The Weather Channel.

Fee: $44.95 installation; $10.67 monthly; $1.50 converter; $24.95 additional installation.

Expanded Basic Service

Subscribers: 32,455.

Programming (via microwave): Pittsburgh Cable News Channel.

Programming (via satellite): A & E; American Movie Classics; Animal Planet; C-SPAN 2; CNBC; CNN; Cartoon Network; Court TV; Discovery Channel; E! Entertainment TV; ESPN; ESPN 2; EWTN; FX; Fox Family Channel; Fox News Channel; Fox Sports Net Pittsburgh; Headline News; History Channel; Home Shopping Network; International Channel; Knowledge TV; Learning Channel; Lifetime; MOVIEplex; MTV; Nash-

ville Network; Nickelodeon; Pennsylvania Cable Network; Sci-Fi Channel; TBS Superstation; TV Guide Channel; Turner Network TV; USA Network; VH1.
Fee: $18.50 monthly.

Pay Service 1
Pay Units: 2,843.
Programming (via satellite): Cinemax.
Fee: $13.45 monthly.

Pay Service 2
Pay Units: 1,261.
Programming (via satellite): Disney Channel.
Fee: $12.50 monthly.

Pay Service 3
Pay Units: 6,722.
Programming (via satellite): HBO.
Fee: $14.95 monthly.

Pay Service 4
Pay Units: 11,002.
Programming (via satellite): The New Encore.
Fee: $1.95 monthly.

Pay Service 5
Pay Units: 1,715.
Programming (via satellite): Showtime.
Fee: $14.95 monthly.

Pay Service 6
Pay Units: N.A.
Programming (via satellite): Starz!
Fee: $6.75 monthly.

Pay-Per-View
Addressable homes: 3,264.
Action Pay-Per-View; Playboy TV; Spice.

Local advertising: Yes (locally produced & insert). Available in satellite distributed programming. Rates: $50.00/Minute; $30.00/30 Seconds. Regional interconnect: TCI Media Services-Pittsburgh, PA.

Program Guide: The Cable Guide.

Equipment: Benavac headend; C-COR amplifiers; Times Fiber cable.

Miles of plant: 380.0 (coaxial). Homes passed: 43,541. Total homes in franchised area: 43,596.

Manager: Jeffrey C. Harshman. Chief technician: Fred Hamm. Marketing director: Glenn Ryerson.

Ownership: AT&T Broadband & Internet Services (MSO). Purchased from Tele-Communications Inc., March 9, 1999.

CENTRAL CITY BOROUGH—TCI Cablevision of Pennsylvania, Box 406, Rtes. 219 & 281, Somerset, PA 15501-0406. Phone: 814-443-4838. County: Somerset. Also serves Central City, Hooversville, Indian Lake, Paint Twp. (Somerset County), Quemahoning Twp. (Somerset County), Shade Twp. (Somerset County), Stonycreek Twp. (Somerset County), Stoystown. ICA: PA0132.

TV Market Ranking: 74. Franchise award date: N.A. Franchise expiration date: N.A. Began: June 1, 1973.

Channel capacity: 52. Channels available but not in use: 18.

Basic Service
Subscribers: 2,561.
Programming (received off-air): WPSX-TV (P) Clearfield; WPCB-TV (I) Greensburg; WATM-TV (A), WJAC-TV (N), WTAJ-TV (C), WWCP-TV (F) Johnstown-Altoona; KDKA-TV (C), WTAE-TV (A) Pittsburgh; allband FM.
Programming (via satellite): A & E; C-SPAN; CNN; Cartoon Network; Discovery Channel; EWTN; Fox Family Channel; Headline News; Lifetime; MTV; Nashville Network; Nickelodeon; Odyssey; QVC; TBS Superstation; The Weather Channel; Turner Classic Movies.
Current originations: Automated time-weather.
Fee: $59.95 installation; $9.36 monthly; $2.00 converter.

Expanded Basic Service
Subscribers: 2,347.
Programming (via satellite): American Movie Classics; Court TV; ESPN; Fox Sports Net Pittsburgh; Turner Network TV; USA Network.
Fee: $12.18 monthly.

Pay Service 1
Pay Units: 70.
Programming (via satellite): Disney Channel.
Fee: N.A.

Pay Service 2
Pay Units: 179.
Programming (via satellite): Cinemax.
Fee: N.A.

Pay Service 3
Pay Units: 354.
Programming (via satellite): HBO.
Fee: N.A.

Pay Service 4
Pay Units: 118.
Programming (via satellite): Showtime.
Fee: N.A.

Pay Service 5
Pay Units: 798.
Programming (via satellite): The New Encore.
Fee: N.A.

Local advertising: Yes. Rates: $15.00/Day; $1.00/Minute.

Equipment: AFC satellite antenna.

Miles of plant: 111.0 (coaxial). Homes passed: 3,308. Total homes in franchised area: 6,063.

Manager: Michael Berrier. Chief technician: Jeffrey Fassnacht.

City fee: 3% of gross. Twp. fee: 3% of gross.

Ownership: AT&T Broadband & Internet Services (MSO). Purchased from Tele-Communications Inc., March 9, 1999.

CHAMBERSBURG—TV Cable, Suite 2, 1108 Sheller Ave., Chambersburg, PA 17201. Phone: 717-263-8591. Fax: 717-263-6766. Counties: Cumberland & Franklin, PA; Washington, MD. Also serves Cascade, Washington County, MD; Chambersburg Twp., Cumberland County, Franklin County, Greencastle, Greene Twp. (Franklin County), Guilford Twp., Hamilton Twp. (Franklin County), Letterkenny Twp. (Franklin County), Lower Mifflin Twp., Mainsville, Mercersburg, Newville, North Newton Twp., Shippensburg, Southampton Twp. (Cumberland County), Southampton Twp. (Franklin County), St. Thomas Twp. (Franklin County), Waynesboro, West Pennsboro Twp. (Cumberland County), PA. ICA: PA0066.

TV Market Ranking: 57 (portions of Cumberland County, Lower Mifflin Twp., Newville, West Pennsboro Twp.); Below 100 (Cascade, Chambersburg, Chambersburg Twp., portions of Franklin County, Greencastle, Greene Twp., Guilford Twp., Hamilton Twp., Letterkenny Twp., Mainsville, Mercersburg, North Newton Twp., Shippensburg, Southampton Twp., St. Thomas Twp., Washington County, Waynesboro); Outside TV Markets (portions of Cumberland County, portions of Franklin County). Franchise award date: N.A. Franchise expiration date: N.A. Began: November 1, 1964.

Channel capacity: 64 (2-way capable; operating 2-way). Channels available but not in use: None.

Basic Service
Subscribers: 40,043.
Programming (received off-air): WHAG-TV (N), WJAL (W) Hagerstown; WHP-TV (C), WHTM-TV (A), WITF-TV (P) Harrisburg; WGAL (N), WLYH-TV (U) Lancaster; WWPX (I) Martinsburg; WDCA (U), WJLA-TV (A), WRC-TV (N), WTTG (F), WUSA (C) Washington; WPMT (F) York.
Programming (via satellite): Home Shopping Network; QVC; TBS Superstation; TV Guide Channel; TV Guide Sneak Prevue; Trinity Bcstg. Network.
Current originations: Public access.
Fee: $50.25 installation; $13.85 monthly; $1.94 converter.

Digital Basic Service
Subscribers: N.A.
Programming (via satellite): BBC America; DMX; Discovery Home & Leisure Channel; Discovery Kids Channel; Discovery People; Discovery Science Channel; ESPN Classic Sports; ESPNews; Fox Sports World; Game Show Network; History Channel; Home & Garden Television; MuchMusic Network; Outdoor Life Network; Sci-Fi Channel.
Fee: $23.80 monthly.

Expanded Basic Service
Subscribers: 38,000.
Programming (via satellite): A & E; American Movie Classics; BET; C-SPAN; C-SPAN 2; CNBC; CNN; Cartoon Network; Comedy Central; Country Music TV; Discovery Channel; E! Entertainment TV; ESPN; ESPN 2; FX; Fox Family Channel; Fox Sports Net Pittsburgh; Headline News; History Channel; Home Team Sports; Learning Channel; Lifetime; MSNBC; MTV; Nashville Network; Nick at Nite; Nickelodeon; Sci-Fi Channel; The Weather Channel; Travel Channel; Turner Network TV; USA Network; VH1.
Fee: $13.63 monthly.

Digital Expanded Basic Service
Subscribers: N.A.
Programming (via satellite): BET Movies/Starz!; Encore Movie Networks; Independent Film Channel; Romance Classics; Starz!; The New Encore; Turner Classic Movies.
Fee: $28.58 monthly.

Pay Service 1
Pay Units: 7,455.
Programming (via satellite): Cinemax; Disney Channel; HBO; Showtime; The Movie Channel.
Fee: $16.75 installation; $10.95 monthly (each).

Digital Pay Service 1
Pay Units: N.A.
Programming (via satellite): Cinemax (multiplexed); HBO (multiplexed); Showtime (multiplexed); The Movie Channel (multiplexed).
Fee: N.A.

Pay-Per-View
Addressable homes: 12,047.
Spice; Spice Hot; movies; special events.
Fee: $3.99-$7.99.

Local advertising: Yes. Available in satellite distributed programming. Local sales manager: Brad Hocker. Regional interconnect: Central Pennsylvania Cable AdCom.

Equipment: Scientific-Atlanta headend; Magnavox amplifiers; Times Fiber cable; Pioneer set top converters; Scientific-Atlanta satellite antenna; Scientific-Atlanta satellite receivers.

Miles of plant: 984.0 (coaxial); 200.0 (fiber optic). Additional miles planned: 100.0 (coaxial). Homes passed: 53,000.

Network manager: Ron Perocchi.

Franchise fee: 5% of gross.

Ownership: Lenfest Communications Inc. (MSO). Purchased from Raystay Co., July 30, 1999.

CHESTER COUNTY—Suburban Cable, 1375 Manor Rd., Coatesville, PA 19320. Phone: 610-466-1500. Web site: http://www.suburbancable.com. Counties: Chester & Delaware. Also serves Atglen (Chester County), Birmingham Twp. (Chester County), Caln Twp. (Chester County), Charlestown Twp. (portions), Coatesville, Downingtown, East Bradford Twp. (Chester County), East Brandywine Twp., East Caln Twp., East Fallowfield Twp. (Chester County), East Goshen Twp. (Chester County), East Nantmeal Twp., Honeybrook Twp. (Chester County), Modena, Parkesburg, Pocopson Twp., Sadsbury Twp. (Chester County), South Coatesville, Thornbury Twp. (Chester County), Thornbury Twp. (Delaware County), Upper Uwchlan Twp. (Chester County), Uwchlan Twp., Valley Twp. (Chester County), Wallace Twp., West Bradford Twp., West Brandywine Twp., West Caln Twp., West Chester, West Goshen, West Nantmeal, West Pikeland Twp. (portions), West Sadsbury Twp. (Chester County), West Vincent Twp., West Whitehead Twp. (Chester County), Westtown Twp. ICA: PA0014.

TV Market Ranking: 4 (Birmingham Twp., Caln Twp., Charlestown Twp., portions of Chester County, Coatesville, Downingtown, East Bradford Twp., East Brandywine Twp., East Caln Twp., East Fallowfield Twp., East Goshen Twp., East Nantmeal Twp., Thornbury Twp., Wallace Twp., West Vincent Twp.); 57 (Atglen, Caln Twp., portions of Chester County, Coatesville, Downingtown, East Bradford Twp., East Brandywine Twp., East Caln Twp., East Fallowfield Twp., East Goshen Twp., Honeybrook Twp., Modena, Parkesburg, Pocopson Twp., Sadsbury Twp., South Coatesville, Upper Uwchlan Twp., Uwchlan Twp., Valley Twp., Wallace Twp., West Bradford Twp., West Brandywine Twp., West Caln Twp., West Chester, West Goshen, West Nantmeal, West Pikeland Twp., West Sadsbury Twp., West Whitehead Twp., Westtown Twp.). Franchise award date: January 1, 1965. Franchise expiration date: N.A. Began: November 1, 1968.

Channel capacity: 62 (2-way capable; operating 2-way). Channels available but not in use: None.

Basic Service
Subscribers: 60,304; Commercial subscribers: 212.
Programming (received off-air): WGTW (I) Burlington; WNJS (P) Camden; WGAL (N) Lancaster; KYW-TV (C), WCAU (N), WPHL-TV (W), WPSG (U), WPVI-TV (A), WTXF-TV (F) Philadelphia; WTVE (H) Reading; WHYY-TV (P), WPPX (X) Wilmington; 1 FM.
Programming (via microwave): Tri-State Media.
Programming (via satellite): C-SPAN; Home Shopping Network; Knowledge TV; MSNBC; QVC; Univision.
Current originations: Automated time-weather; public access; educational access; government access; religious access; leased access; automated emergency alert; local sports.
Fee: $33.00 installation; $9.06 monthly.
Commercial fee: $30.00 monthly.

Expanded Basic Service
Subscribers: 57,397.
Programming (via satellite): A & E; American Movie Classics; BET; CNBC; CNN; Comedy Central; Discovery Channel; Disney Channel; E! Entertainment TV; ESPN; ESPN 2; EWTN; FX; Fox Family Channel; Headline News; History Channel; Learning Channel; Lifetime; MTV; Nashville Network; Nick at Nite; Nickelodeon; TBS Superstation; TV Food Network; The Sports Network; The Weather Channel; Travel Channel; Turner Network TV; USA Network; VH1.
Fee: N.A.

Expanded Basic Service 2
Subscribers: N.A.
Programming (via satellite): Cartoon Network; Court TV; MOVIEplex; Sci-Fi Channel.
Fee: N.A.
Pay Service 1
Pay Units: 5,500.
Programming (via satellite): Cinemax.
Fee: $15.00 installation; $7.95 monthly.
Pay Service 2
Pay Units: 256.
Programming (via satellite): Music Choice.
Fee: $6.95 monthly.
Pay Service 3
Pay Units: N.A.
Programming (via satellite): Starz!
Fee: N.A.
Pay Service 4
Pay Units: 16,589.
Programming (via satellite): HBO.
Fee: $15.00 installation; $9.00 monthly.
Pay Service 5
Pay Units: 3,953.
Programming (via satellite): Showtime.
Fee: $15.00 installation; $9.00 monthly.
Pay-Per-View
Addressable homes: 9,008.
Playboy TV; Spice; Viewer's Choice.
Local advertising: Yes. Available in satellite distributed & character-generated programming. Rates: $19.50/Spot. Regional interconnect: Philadelphia Cable Advertising.
Equipment: Scientific-Atlanta headend; Scientific-Atlanta amplifiers; Trilogy cable; Texscan character generator; Hamlin & Pioneer set top converters; Jerrold addressable set top converters; Eagle traps; Simulsat satellite antenna; Scientific-Atlanta satellite receivers; Sony commercial insert.
Miles of plant: 1430.0 (coaxial); 120.0 (fiber optic). Homes passed: 62,000. Total homes in franchised area: 80,000.
Manager: Bonnie Wallace. Chief technician: Chris Martin. Program director: George Ferrara. Marketing director: Lee Javens.
Ownership: Lenfest Communications Inc. (MSO).

CHICORA—CableVision Communications, Box 2200, 68 5th St., Buckhannon, WV 26201. Phone: 304-472-4193. Fax: 304-472-0756. Counties: Armstrong, Butler & Clarion. Also serves Bradys Bend Twp., Bruin, East Brady, Fairview (Butler County), Fairview Twp. (Butler County), Frogtown, Karns City, Kaylor, Parker Twp., Petrolia, Roseville, Seybertown, Sugarcreek Twp. ICA: PA0206.
TV Market Ranking: Outside TV Markets. Franchise award date: N.A. Franchise expiration date: N.A. Began: August 1, 1973.
Channel capacity: 46 (not 2-way capable). Channels available but not in use: None.
Basic Service
Subscribers: 2,247.
Programming (received off-air): WPCB-TV (I) Greensburg; WNPA (U) Jeanette; WWCP-TV (F) Johnstown-Altoona; KDKA-TV (C), WCWB (W), WPGH-TV (F), WPXI (N), WQED (P), WTAE-TV (A) Pittsburgh; WKBN-TV (C) Youngstown.
Programming (via satellite): WGN-TV (W) Chicago; Nashville Network; TBS Superstation; TV Guide Sneak Prevue.
Fee: $61.50 installation; $14.40 monthly; $1.24 converter; $26.25 additional installation.
Expanded Basic Service
Subscribers: N.A.
Programming (via satellite): American Movie Classics; CNN; Discovery Channel; Disney Channel; E! Entertainment TV; ESPN; ESPN 2; FX; Fox Family Channel; Fox Sports Net Pittsburgh; Great American Country; History Channel; Home & Garden Television; Home Shopping Network; Learning Channel; Lifetime; MTV; MuchMusic Network; Nickelodeon; QVC; Sci-Fi Channel; The Inspirational Network; The Weather Channel; Trinity Bcstg. Network; Turner Network TV; USA Network.
Fee: $11.68 monthly.
Pay Service 1
Pay Units: 977.
Programming (via satellite): Cinemax; HBO.
Fee: $17.50 installation; $7.95 monthly (Cinemax), $11.99 monthly (HBO).
Pay Service 2
Pay Units: N.A.
Programming (via satellite): Showtime; The Movie Channel; The New Encore; Turner Classic Movies.
Fee: $17.50 installation; $1.99 monthly, $3.99 monthly (Encore), $11.95 monthly (Showtime or TMC).
Local advertising: No.
Equipment: Blonder-Tongue & Olson headend; Jerrold amplifiers; Comm/Scope cable; Intercept & Pico traps; Harris satellite antenna; DX Engineering satellite receivers.
Miles of plant: 76.0 (coaxial). Homes passed: 2,557.
Manager: Willie Critchfield. Marketing director: Kenny Phillips.
City fee: None.
Ownership: Rifkin & Associates Inc. (MSO). See Cable System Ownership.

CLARENDON—Clarendon TV Association, Box 315, Clarendon, PA 16313. Phone: 814-723-4735. County: Warren. Also serves Clarendon Heights, Stoneham. ICA: PA0240.
TV Market Ranking: Below 100. Franchise award date: N.A. Franchise expiration date: N.A. Began: January 1, 1955.
Channel capacity: N.A. Channels available but not in use: N.A.
Basic Service
Subscribers: 395.
Programming (received off-air): WIVB-TV (C) Buffalo; WPSX-TV (P) Clearfield; WFXP (F), WICU-TV (N), WJET-TV (A) Erie; CHCH-TV Hamilton; allband FM.
Programming (via satellite): WGN-TV (W) Chicago; Discovery Channel; ESPN; Nashville Network; Nickelodeon; TBS Superstation; Turner Network TV; USA Network.
Fee: $225.00 installation; $8.33 monthly.
Equipment: Blonder-Tongue headend; Blonder-Tongue amplifiers; Times Fiber cable.
Miles of plant: 10.0 (coaxial). Homes passed: 450.
Manager: Robert Jones.
City fee: None.
Ownership: Clarendon TV Association.

CLARION BOROUGH—TCI of Pennsylvania Inc., 855 Main St., Clarion, PA 16214-1161. Phone: 814-226-6410. County: Clarion. Also serves Clarion, Clarion Twp., Monroe Twp. (Clarion County), Strattanville. ICA: PA0137.
TV Market Ranking: Outside TV Markets. Franchise award date: January 1, 1966. Franchise expiration date: N.A. Began: September 1, 1966.
Channel capacity: 37 (2-way capable; operating 2-way). Channels available but not in use: N.A.
Basic Service
Subscribers: 2,461.
Programming (received off-air): WPSX-TV (P) Clearfield; WPCB-TV (I) Greensburg; WJAC-TV (N), WTAJ-TV (C) Johnstown-Altoona; KDKA-TV (C), WCWB (W), WPGH-TV (F), WPXI (N), WQED (P), WTAE-TV (A) Pittsburgh; allband FM.
Programming (via satellite): C-SPAN; CNBC; CNN; Discovery Channel; Fox Family Channel; Headline News; Lifetime; MTV; Nashville Network; Nickelodeon; QVC; TBS Superstation.
Current originations: Automated time-weather.
Fee: $59.95 installation; $10.15 monthly; $2.00 converter.
Expanded Basic Service
Subscribers: 2,291.
Programming (via satellite): American Movie Classics; ESPN; Fox Sports Net Pittsburgh; Turner Network TV; USA Network.
Fee: $12.06 monthly.
Pay Service 1
Pay Units: 510.
Programming (via satellite): HBO.
Fee: $20.00 installation; $13.15 monthly.
Pay Service 2
Pay Units: 127.
Programming (via satellite): Disney Channel.
Fee: N.A.
Pay Service 3
Pay Units: 159.
Programming (via satellite): Cinemax.
Fee: $13.15 monthly.
Pay Service 4
Pay Units: 228.
Programming (via satellite): Showtime.
Fee: $13.15 monthly.
Pay Service 5
Pay Units: 860.
Programming (via satellite): The New Encore.
Fee: N.A.
Local advertising: Yes.
Program Guide: The Cable Guide.
Equipment: Entron headend; C-COR amplifiers; Times Fiber cable; MSI & Texscan character generator; Scientific-Atlanta set top converters; Scientific-Atlanta addressable set top converters; Pico traps; Scientific-Atlanta & Anixter-Pruzan satellite antenna; Scientific-Atlanta satellite receivers.
Miles of plant: 39.0 (coaxial). Homes passed: 3,005. Total homes in franchised area: 4,028.
Manager: W. Ben Call. Chief technician: Greg Allshouse.
City fee: 3% of basic.
Ownership: AT&T Broadband & Internet Services (MSO). Purchased from Tele-Communications Inc., March 9, 1999.

CLAYSVILLE—Jefferson County Cable Inc., 116 S. 4th St., Toronto, OH 43964. Phone: 740-537-2214. Fax: 740-537-2802. County: Washington. ICA: PA0265.
TV Market Ranking: 10,90. Franchise award date: N.A. Franchise expiration date: N.A. Began: March 1, 1978.
Channel capacity: N.A. Channels available but not in use: N.A.
Basic Service
Subscribers: N.A.
Programming (received off-air): WNPB-TV (P) Morgantown; KDKA-TV (C), WCWB (W), WPGH-TV (F), WPXI (N), WQED (P), WTAE-TV (A) Pittsburgh; WTOV-TV (N) Steubenville-Wheeling; WTRF-TV (C) Wheeling-Steubenville.
Programming (via satellite): WGN-TV (W) Chicago; ESPN; Fox Family Channel.
Fee: $20.00 installation; $9.00 monthly.
Pay Service 1
Pay Units: N.A.
Programming (via satellite): The Movie Channel.
Fee: $9.60 monthly.
Miles of plant: 6.2 (coaxial). Homes passed: 230.
Ownership: Jefferson County Cable Inc. (MSO).

CLEARFIELD—Cablecomm, 313-1/2 E. Cherry St., Clearfield, PA 16830. Phone: 814-765-5313. Fax: 814-765-7757. County: Clearfield. Also serves Boggs Twp. (Clearfield County), Bradford Twp. (Clearfield County), Curwensville (Clearfield County), Hyde, Lawrence Twp. (Clearfield County), Pike Twp. (Clearfield County). ICA: PA0084.
TV Market Ranking: 74 (Boggs Twp., Curwensville, Hyde); Outside TV Markets (Bradford Twp., Clearfield, Lawrence Twp., Pike Twp.). Franchise award date: N.A. Franchise expiration date: N.A. Began: February 1, 1952.
Channel capacity: 37 (not 2-way capable). Channels available but not in use: None.
Basic Service
Subscribers: 7,745.
Programming (received off-air): WPSX-TV (P) Clearfield; WATM-TV (A), WJAC-TV (N), WKBS-TV (I), WTAJ-TV (C), WWCP-TV (F) Johnstown-Altoona; KDKA-TV (C), WPXI (N), WTAE-TV (A) Pittsburgh; 11 FMs.
Programming (via satellite): C-SPAN; C-SPAN 2; EWTN; QVC; TV Guide Sneak Prevue.
Current originations: Automated time-weather.
Fee: $23.85 installation; $9.12 monthly; $1.60 converter.
Expanded Basic Service
Subscribers: 6,745.
Programming (via satellite): WPIX (W) New York; American Movie Classics; CNN; Country Music TV; Discovery Channel; ESPN; Fox Family Channel; Headline News; Lifetime; MTV; Nashville Network; Nickelodeon; TBS Superstation; The Weather Channel; Turner Network TV; USA Network.
Fee: $14.25 monthly.
A la Carte 1
Subscribers: N.A.
Programming (via satellite): WPIX (W) New York; TBS Superstation.
Fee: $0.24 monthly (package); $0.15 monthly (each).
Pay Service 1
Pay Units: 1,661.
Programming (via satellite): Cinemax; Disney Channel; Fox Sports Net Pittsburgh; HBO; Showtime; The Movie Channel.
Fee: $20.00 installation; $2.00 monthly (Fox Sports), $11.05 monthly (Cinemax, Disney, HBO, Showtime or TMC).
Pay-Per-View
Addressable homes: 1,500.
Action Pay-Per-View; Hot Choice; Viewer's Choice.
Fee: $3.95.
Local advertising: Yes. Local sales manager: Dale Manning. Regional interconnect: Cable AdNet-Johnstown/Altoona, PA.
Equipment: Scientific-Atlanta headend; C-COR amplifiers; Comm/Scope cable; Pioneer set top converters; Vitek traps; Scientific-Atlanta satellite antenna; Scientific-Atlanta satellite receivers.
Miles of plant: 122.0 (coaxial). Homes passed: 8,988. Total homes in franchised area: 9,033.
Operations manager: William Miller. Chief technician: Rick Himes.
City fee: 3% of gross.
Ownership: Fanch Communications Inc. (MSO); Time Warner Cable (MSO). See Cable System Ownership.

CLINTON TWP. (Lycoming County)—TCI of Pennsylvania Inc., 18 W. Houston Ave., Montgomery, PA 17752-1099. Phone: 717-547-2011. Counties: Lycoming, Northumberland & Union. Also serves Allenwood, Brady Twp. (Lycoming County), Delaware Twp. (Northumberland County), Elimsport, Gregg Twp. (Union County), Montgomery (Lycoming County), Washington Twp. (Lycoming County). ICA: PA0154.

TV Market Ranking: Below 100. Franchise award date: N.A. Franchise expiration date: July 6, 1997. Began: January 1, 1959.

Channel capacity: 22 (not 2-way capable). Channels available but not in use: None.

Basic Service

Subscribers: 2,096.

Programming (received off-air): WOLF-TV (F) Hazleton; WBRE-TV (N), WNEP-TV (A), WVIA-TV (P), WYOU (C) Scranton & Wilkes-Barre; allband FM.

Programming (via satellite): WPIX (W) New York; American Movie Classics; C-SPAN; CNN; Discovery Channel; ESPN; Fox Family Channel; Lifetime; MTV; Nashville Network; Nickelodeon; QVC; TBS Superstation; Turner Network TV; USA Network.

Current originations: Automated time-weather.

Fee: $59.95 installation; $15.70 monthly.

Pay Service 1

Pay Units: 391.

Programming (via satellite): Cinemax.

Fee: $19.95 installation; $9.95 monthly.

Pay Service 2

Pay Units: 530.

Programming (via satellite): HBO.

Fee: $19.95 installation; $11.95 monthly.

Pay-Per-View

Special events.

Fee: $24.95.

Local advertising: Yes (locally produced). Available in character-generated programming. Rates: $50.00/Week; $10.00/Day. Local sales manager: Gayle Decker.

Program Guide: The Cable Guide.

Equipment: Scientific-Atlanta & Microdyne headend; C-COR amplifiers; Comm/Scope cable; Compuvid character generator; Jerrold, Oak & Hamlin set top converters; Jerrold addressable set top converters; Pico traps; Scientific-Atlanta satellite antenna; Scientific-Atlanta satellite receivers.

Miles of plant: 80.8 (coaxial). Homes passed: 2,226. Total homes in franchised area: 2,991.

Manager: Gayle Decker.

City fee: 3% of gross.

Ownership: AT&T Broadband & Internet Services (MSO). Purchased from Tele-Communications Inc., March 9, 1999.

CLINTONVILLE—Multi-Tech Communications, Box 219, Sligo, PA 16255. Phone: 814-745-2426. Counties: Mercer & Venango. Also serves Barkeyville, Clinton Twp. (Venango County), Irwin Twp. (Venango County), Kennerdell, Pine Twp. (Mercer County), Rockland Twp. (Venango County). ICA: PA0325.

TV Market Ranking: 79 (portions of Pine Twp.); Outside TV Markets (Barkeyville, Clinton Twp., Clintonville, Irwin Twp., Kennerdell, portions of Pine Twp., Rockland Twp.). Franchise award date: N.A. Franchise expiration date: N.A. Began: April 1, 1983.

Channel capacity: 36 (not 2-way capable). Channels available but not in use: 3.

Basic Service

Subscribers: 650.

Programming (received off-air): WICU-TV (N), WJET-TV (A) Erie; WJAC-TV (N) Johnstown-Altoona; KDKA-TV (C), WPXI (N), WQED (P), WTAE-TV (A) Pittsburgh; WFMJ-TV (N), WKBN-TV (C) Youngstown.

Programming (via satellite): ESPN; TBS Superstation.

Fee: $35.00 installation; $23.00 monthly.

Pay Service 1

Pay Units: 24.

Programming (via satellite): The Movie Channel.

Fee: $11.00 monthly.

Miles of plant: 25.0 (coaxial).

Manager: Donald McCall. Chief technician: Rollie Miller.

Ownership: Multi-Tech Communications (MSO).

COALPORT—Cooney Cable, Box 69, Delbarton, WV 25670. Phones: 304-426-4609; 888-426-4609. Fax: 304-426-6726. Counties: Cambria & Clearfield. Also serves Beccaria Twp., Clearfield Twp. (Cambria County), Dean Twp. (Cambria County), Glen Hope, Irvona, Reade Twp. (Cambria County), White Twp. (Cambria County). ICA: PA0158.

TV Market Ranking: 74. Franchise award date: N.A. Franchise expiration date: N.A. Began: December 1, 1968.

Channel capacity: 36 (not 2-way capable). Channels available but not in use: 5.

Basic Service

Subscribers: 2,119.

Programming (received off-air): WPSX-TV (P) Clearfield; WATM-TV (A), WJAC-TV (N), WKBS-TV (I), WTAJ-TV (C), WWCP-TV (F) Johnstown-Altoona; WPXI (N) Pittsburgh.

Programming (via satellite): WGN-TV (W) Chicago; A & E; American Movie Classics; C-SPAN; CNN; Discovery Channel; ESPN; Fox Family Channel; Learning Channel; MTV; Nashville Network; Nickelodeon; TBS Superstation; Turner Network TV; USA Network.

Fee: $55.00 installation; $17.45 monthly; $1.06 converter.

Pay Service 1

Pay Units: 107.

Programming (via satellite): Disney Channel.

Fee: $17.50 installation; $8.95 monthly.

Pay Service 2

Pay Units: 245.

Programming (via satellite): HBO.

Fee: $17.50 installation; $9.95 monthly.

Pay Service 3

Pay Units: 198.

Programming (via satellite): The Movie Channel.

Fee: $17.50 installation; $9.95 monthly.

Local advertising: Yes (locally produced). Available in locally originated, character-generated & taped programming. Rates: $106.00/Page/Month; $7.50/Page/Day.

Equipment: Scientific-Atlanta, Jerrold & Triple Crown headend; Broadband, C-COR & Jerrold amplifiers; Times Fiber & Comm/Scope cable; Compucable character generator; Scientific-Atlanta set top converters; PPC & Vitek traps; AFC & Scientific-Atlanta satellite antenna; Microdyne satellite receivers.

Miles of plant: 93.5 (coaxial); None (fiber optic). Homes passed: 2,400.

Manager: John B. Cooney. Chief technician: Greg Goad.

City fee: $50.00 annually.

Ownership: Cooney Cable Assoc. Inc. (MSO). Purchased from C.P.S. Cable Vision Inc., March 1, 1999.

COGAN STATION—Retel TV Cable Co., 1836 Hays Ave., Williamsport, PA 17701. Phone: 717-494-1809. Fax: 717-673-7039. County: Lycoming. Also serves Hepburnville, Perryville, Quiggleville, Trout Run. ICA: PA0207.

TV Market Ranking: Below 100. Franchise award date: N.A. Franchise expiration date: N.A. Began: June 1, 1953.

Channel capacity: 40 (2-way capable; operating 2-way). Channels available but not in use: N.A.

Basic Service

Subscribers: 1,080.

Programming (received off-air): WTAJ-TV (C) Johnstown-Altoona; WBRE-TV (N), WNEP-TV (A), WVIA-TV (P) Scranton & Wilkes-Barre; allband FM.

Programming (via microwave): WNYW (F) New York.

Programming (via satellite): ESPN; Fox Family Channel; MTV; Nashville Network; TBS Superstation.

Current originations: Automated time-weather.

Fee: $50.00 installation; $9.50 monthly.

Pay Service 1

Pay Units: 200.

Programming (via satellite): HBO.

Fee: $15.00 installation; $9.00 monthly.

Equipment: Blonder-Tongue & Jerrold headend; Gamco & Jerrold amplifiers; Times Fiber & Vikoa cable; Eagle & Vitek traps; Microdyne satellite antenna; Microdyne satellite receivers.

Miles of plant: 35.0 (coaxial); 70.0 (fiber optic). Additional miles planned: 3.0 (coaxial). Homes passed: 1,050. Total homes in franchised area: 1,050.

Manager: Terry W. Hughes.

City fee: None.

Ownership: Retel TV Cable Co. Inc. (MSO).

CONNELLSVILLE—Armstrong Communications Inc., 259 E. Crawford Ave., Connellsville, PA 15425. Phone: 724-628-5462. Fax: 724-628-4963. Counties: Fayette & Westmoreland. Also serves Bullskin Twp., Connellsville Twp. (Fayette County), Donegal Twp. (Westmoreland County), Dunbar, Dunbar Twp., East Huntingdon Twp., Everson, Franklin Twp. (Westmoreland County), Mount Pleasant, Mount Pleasant Twp. (Westmoreland County), North Union Twp. (Fayette County), Scottdale, South Connellsville Twp. (Fayette County), South Huntingdon Twp. (portions), Springfield Twp. (Fayette County), Upper Tyrone Twp. (Fayette County), Vanderbilt. ICA: PA0046.

TV Market Ranking: 10 (Bullskin Twp., East Huntingdon Twp., Everson, Franklin Twp., Mount Pleasant, Mount Pleasant Twp., Scottdale, South Huntingdon Twp., Vanderbilt); 74 (Donegal Twp., Springfield Twp.); Below 100 (Connellsville, Connellsville Twp., Dunbar, Dunbar Twp., North Union Twp., South Connellsville Twp., Upper Tyrone Twp.). Franchise award date: N.A. Franchise expiration date: N.A. Began: July 1, 1967.

Channel capacity: N.A. Channels available but not in use: N.A.

Basic Service

Subscribers: 21,000.

Programming (received off-air): WPCB-TV (I) Greensburg; WJAC-TV (N) Johnstown-Altoona; KDKA-TV (C), WCWB (W), WPGH-TV (F), WPXI (N), WQED (P), WTAE-TV (A) Pittsburgh; WTRF-TV (C) Wheeling-Steubenville; allband FM.

Programming (via satellite): WGN-TV (W) Chicago; A & E; American Movie Classics; C-SPAN; CNN; Comedy Central; Discovery Channel; ESPN; Fox Family Channel; Fox Sports Net Pittsburgh; Headline News; Home & Garden Television; Home Shopping Network; Lifetime; MTV; Nashville Network; Nick at Nite; Nickelodeon; QVC; TBS Superstation; The Weather Channel; Turner Network TV; USA Network; VH1.

Current originations: Automated time-weather.

Fee: $39.95 installation; $19.45 monthly; $3.00 converter.

Expanded Basic Service

Subscribers: N.A.

Programming (via satellite): Bravo; CNBC; Cartoon Network; Country Music TV; E! Entertainment TV; ESPN 2; EWTN; History Channel; Learning Channel; Nick at Nite's TV Land; Sci-Fi Channel; TV Food Network; TV Guide Channel; Travel Channel; Turner Classic Movies.

Fee: N.A.

Pay Service 1

Pay Units: 2,987.

Programming (via satellite): Cinemax.

Fee: $9.95 monthly.

Pay Service 2

Pay Units: 5,020.

Programming (via satellite): HBO.

Fee: $10.95 monthly.

Pay Service 3

Pay Units: 1,350.

Programming (via satellite): Disney Channel.

Fee: $7.95 monthly.

Pay Service 4

Pay Units: 122.

Programming (via satellite): Showtime.

Fee: $10.95 monthly.

Local advertising: Yes. Regional interconnect: Metrobase Cable Advertising.

Equipment: Scientific-Atlanta satellite antenna.

Miles of plant: 505.7 (coaxial). Homes passed: 24,254. Total homes in franchised area: 28,000.

Manager: Joseph W. Taylor. Chief technician: Jack Thornton. Marketing director: Eric Baugh.

Ownership: Armstrong Group of Companies (MSO).

COOPERSTOWN—CableVision Communications, Box 2200, 68 5th St., Buckhannon, WV 26201. Phone: 304-472-4193. Fax: 304-472-0756. County: Venango. Also serves Canal Twp., Franklin (Venango County), Frenchcreek Twp. (Venango County), Jackson Twp. (Venango County), Sugarcreek (Venango County), Utica, Wyattville. ICA: PA0214.

TV Market Ranking: Outside TV Markets. Franchise award date: N.A. Franchise expiration date: May 9, 2000. Began: N.A.

Channel capacity: 36. Channels available but not in use: N.A.

Basic Service

Subscribers: 557.

Programming (received off-air): WJET-TV (A), WQLN (P), WSEE (C) Erie; KDKA-TV (C), WCWB (W), WPGH-TV (F), WPXI (N) Pittsburgh; WFMJ-TV (N), WKBN-TV (C), WYTV (A,F) Youngstown; allband FM.

Programming (via satellite): WGN-TV (W) Chicago; Animal Planet; C-SPAN; Home Shopping Network; Learning Channel; TBS Superstation.

Fee: $61.25 installation; $15.98 monthly; $1.24 converter; $17.50 additional installation.

Expanded Basic Service

Subscribers: 513.

Programming (via satellite): American Movie Classics; CNN; Discovery Channel; Disney Channel; E! Entertainment TV; ESPN; ESPN 2; FX; Fox Family Channel; Great American Country; History Channel; Lifetime; Nashville Network; Nickelodeon; Sci-Fi Channel; Turner Network TV; USA Network.

Fee: $16.29 monthly.

Pay Service 1

Pay Units: 392.

Programming (via satellite): Cinemax; HBO.

Fee: $17.50 installation; $7.95 monthly (Cinemax), $11.99 monthly (HBO).

Pay Service 2

Pay Units: N.A.

Programming (via satellite): Showtime; The Movie Channel.

Fee: $17.50 installation; $11.95 monthly (each).

Equipment: Blonder-Tongue & Olson headend; C-COR amplifiers.

Miles of plant: 22.0 (coaxial). Homes passed: 789.

Manager: Willie Critchfield. Marketing director: Kenny Phillips.

Ownership: Rifkin & Associates Inc. (MSO). See Cable System Ownership.

CORAOPOLIS—TCI, 644 Stoops Ferry Rd., Coraopolis, PA 15108. Phone: 412-264-6600. Fax: 412-264-8338. County: Allegheny. Also serves Crescent Twp., Findlay Twp. (Allegheny County), Moon Twp., Neville Twp., North Fayette Twp. (Allegheny County), Pittsburgh AFB. ICA: PA0061.

TV Market Ranking: 10,90. Franchise award date: N.A. Franchise expiration date: N.A. Began: November 1, 1967.

Channel capacity: 49 (not 2-way capable). Channels available but not in use: 1.

Basic Service

Subscribers: 15,200.

Programming (received off-air): WPCB-TV (I) Greensburg; KDKA-TV (C), WCWB (W), WPGH-TV (F), WPXI (N), WQED (P), WQEX (P), WTAE-TV (A) Pittsburgh.

Programming (via satellite): TBS Superstation.

Current originations: Automated time-weather; public access; leased access; local news; local sports.

Fee: $85.80 installation; $6.63 monthly; $23.60 additional installation.

Expanded Basic Service

Subscribers: 15,071.

Programming (via satellite): A & E; BET; C-SPAN; CNN; Discovery Channel; ESPN; ESPN 2; EWTN; FX; Fox Family Channel; Headline News; Ladbroke Racing Channel/Meadows Racing Network; Lifetime; MTV; Nashville Network; Nick at Nite; Nickelodeon; QVC; TV Guide Channel; TV Guide Sneak Prevue; The Weather Channel; Turner Network TV; USA Network; VH1.

Fee: $35.63 installation; $11.59 monthly.

Expanded Basic Service 2

Subscribers: 8,050.

Programming (via satellite): American Movie Classics; CNBC; E! Entertainment TV; Fox Sports Net Pittsburgh.

Fee: $12.58 installation; $2.14 monthly.

Pay Service 1

Pay Units: 1,454.

Programming (via satellite): Cinemax.

Fee: $10.50 monthly.

Pay Service 2

Pay Units: 800.

Programming (via satellite): Disney Channel.

Fee: $10.50 monthly.

Pay Service 3

Pay Units: 5,483.

Programming (via satellite): HBO.

Fee: $11.00 monthly.

Pay Service 4

Pay Units: 1,460.

Programming (via satellite): Showtime.

Fee: $10.50 monthly.

Pay-Per-View

Addressable homes: 8,304.

Hot Choice; Viewer's Choice.

Local advertising: Yes (locally produced). Available in satellite distributed programming. Regional interconnect: TCI Media Services-Pittsburgh, PA.

Equipment: Scientific-Atlanta headend; Magnavox amplifiers; Times Fiber cable; Scientific-Atlanta set top converters; Jerrold & Regency addressable set top converters; Eagle traps; Scientific-Atlanta satellite antenna; Scientific-Atlanta satellite receivers; Falcone International commercial insert.

Miles of plant: 216.0 (coaxial). Homes passed: 17,929.

Manager: Donna Gruseck. Chief technician: Dave Kane. Technical operations manager: Michael Flynn. Customer service manager: Judy Boley.

Ownership: AT&T Broadband & Internet Services (MSO). Purchased from Time Warner Cable, June 1, 1999.

CORRY—Cablevision, 122 N. Center St., Corry, PA 16407. Phone: 814-664-2411. Fax: 814-664-3031. Counties: Erie & Warren. Also serves Columbus Twp. (Warren County), Concord Twp. (Erie County), Elgin, Union City, Union Twp. (Erie County), Wayne Twp. (Erie County). ICA: PA0113.

TV Market Ranking: Below 100. Franchise award date: September 1, 1957. Franchise expiration date: N.A. Began: September 1, 1957.

Channel capacity: 62 (not 2-way capable). Channels available but not in use: 20.

Basic Service

Subscribers: 3,996.

Programming (received off-air): WFXP (F), WICU-TV (N), WJET-TV (A), WQLN (P), WSEE (C) Erie; 13 FMs.

Programming (via satellite): C-SPAN; TBS Superstation; WB 100+ Station Group.

Current originations: Automated time-weather; public access; educational access.

Fee: $19.24 installation; $4.49 monthly; $2.99 converter.

Expanded Basic Service

Subscribers: 3,891.

Programming (via satellite): A & E; American Movie Classics; Animal Planet; CNN; Cartoon Network; Country Music TV; Court TV; Discovery Channel; E! Entertainment TV; ESPN; ESPN 2; Fox Family Channel; Fox Sports Net Pittsburgh; Goodlife TV Network; Headline News; History Channel; Home Shopping Network; Knowledge TV; Learning Channel; Lifetime; MSNBC; MTV; Nashville Network; Nick at Nite's TV Land; Nickelodeon; Pax Net; Sci-Fi Channel; TV Food Network; The Weather Channel; Travel Channel; Turner Classic Movies; Turner Network TV; USA Network.

Fee: $23.92 monthly.

Pay Service 1

Pay Units: 350.

Programming (via satellite): Cinemax.

Fee: $9.95 monthly.

Pay Service 2

Pay Units: 268.

Programming (via satellite): Disney Channel.

Fee: $8.95 monthly.

Pay Service 3

Pay Units: 1,126.

Programming (via satellite): HBO (multiplexed).

Fee: $9.95 monthly.

Pay Service 4

Pay Units: 246.

Programming (via satellite): Showtime.

Fee: $9.95 monthly.

Pay Service 5

Pay Units: N.A.

Programming (via satellite): The Movie Channel.

Fee: $3.95 monthly.

Pay-Per-View

Addressable homes: 700.

Local advertising: Yes. Available in locally originated & character-generated programming. Rates: $25.00/Week; $5.00/Day.

Equipment: Scientific-Atlanta headend; Scientific-Atlanta amplifiers; Vikoa cable; Video Data Systems character generator; Scientific-Atlanta set top converters.

Miles of plant: 98.0 (coaxial); 13.0 (fiber optic). Homes passed: 5,565. Total homes in franchised area: 5,974.

Manager: William Wright. Chief technician: Michael Snow. Program & marketing director: Kevin Kick.

City fee: None.

Ownership: Time Warner Cable (MSO).

COUDERSPORT—Adelphia, 14 S. Main St., Coudersport, PA 16915. Phone: 800-892-7300. Fax: 814-274-6593. Counties: Cameron, McKean & Potter. Also serves Annin Twp., Austin Borough, Cameron (unincorporated areas), Emporium, Gardeau, Keating Twp. (Potter County), Liberty, Port Allegany, Portage Twp. (Cameron County), Potter (unincorporated areas), Roulette Twp., Shippen, Shippen Twp. (Cameron County). ICA: PA0121.

TV Market Ranking: Outside TV Markets. Franchise award date: January 1, 1952. Franchise expiration date: N.A. Began: March 1, 1953.

Channel capacity: 77 (2-way capable; operating 2-way partially). Channels available but not in use: None.

Basic Service

Subscribers: 6,210; Commercial subscribers: 160.

Programming (received off-air): WGRZ-TV (N), WIVB-TV (C), WKBW-TV (A) Buffalo; WPSX-TV (P) Clearfield; WETM-TV (N) Elmira; WJAC-TV (N), WTAJ-TV (C), WWCP-TV (F) Johnstown-Altoona.

Programming (via satellite): WGN-TV (W) Chicago; WPIX (W) New York; Animal Planet; TBS Superstation; TV Guide Channel.

Fee: N.A.

Expanded Basic Service

Subscribers: 6,049.

Programming (via satellite): A & E; American Movie Classics; C-SPAN; C-SPAN 2; CNBC; CNN; Cartoon Network; Country Music TV; Discovery Channel; Disney Channel; ESPN; ESPN 2; EWTN; Empire Sports Network; FX; Fox Family Channel; Fox Sports Net Pittsburgh; Headline News; History Channel; Home Shopping Network; Knowledge TV; Learning Channel; Lifetime; MSNBC; MTV; Nashville Network; Nickelodeon; Odyssey; Pennsylvania Cable Network; Product Information Network; QVC; TV Food Network; The Health Network; The Inspirational Network; The Weather Channel; Trinity Bcstg. Network; Turner Classic Movies; Turner Network TV; USA Network; Univision; VH1.

Fee: N.A.

Pay Service 1

Pay Units: 274.

Programming (via satellite): Cinemax.

Fee: $25.00 installation; $11.50 monthly.

Pay Service 2

Pay Units: 1,308.

Programming (via satellite): HBO (multiplexed).

Fee: $25.00 installation; $11.50 monthly.

Pay Service 3

Pay Units: 155.

Programming (via satellite): The Movie Channel.

Fee: $25.00 installation; $11.50 monthly.

Pay Service 4

Pay Units: 287.

Programming (via satellite): Showtime.

Fee: $25.00 installation; $11.50 monthly.

Pay-Per-View

Addressable homes: 1,438.

Viewer's Choice 1 & 2.

Fee: $3.95.

Local advertising: Yes. Available in locally originated programming. Regional interconnect: Cabletime.

Program Guide: TV Guide.

Equipment: Jerrold, Scientific-Atlanta & Standard Communications headend; C-COR amplifiers; Comm/Scope & Trilogy cable; MSI character generator; Scientific-Atlanta set top converters; Scientific-Atlanta addressable set top converters; Eagle traps; Simulsat satellite antenna; Standard Components satellite receivers; Sony commercial insert.

Miles of plant: 373.6 (coaxial). Homes passed: 7,841. Total homes in franchised area: 7,864.

Manager: Todd McManus. Program director: Leslie Easton. Marketing director: John Adduci. Customer service manager: Faye Furman.

City fee: $1,000 annually.

Ownership: Adelphia Communications Corp. (MSO).

CROSBY—County Cable, 217 E. 9th St., Hazelton, PA 18201. Phone: 717-455-6851. Fax: 717-459-0963. County: McKean. ICA: PA0301.

TV Market Ranking: Outside TV Markets. Franchise award date: N.A. Franchise expiration date: N.A. Began: January 1, 1982.

Channel capacity: N.A. Channels available but not in use: N.A.

Basic Service

Subscribers: 50.

Programming (received off-air): WPSX-TV (P) Clearfield.

Programming (via satellite): WXIA-TV (N) Atlanta; WGN-TV (W) Chicago; WRAL-TV (C) Raleigh-Durham; CNN; Country Music TV; Discovery Channel; ESPN; Fox Family Channel; FoxNet; Headline News; Lifetime; Nashville Network; Nickelodeon; QVC; TBS Superstation; Turner Network TV; USA Network.

Fee: $7.40 monthly.

Pay Service 1

Pay Units: N.A.

Programming (via satellite): HBO.

Fee: N.A.

Miles of plant: 3.7 (coaxial). Homes passed: 65.

Manager: Joe Aman. Chief technician: Roy Harbert.

Ownership: Gans Multimedia Partnership (MSO).

CURTIN TWP.—TCI of Pennsylvania Inc., 1155 Benner Pike, State College, PA 16801. Phone: 800-992-3515. County: Centre. Also serves Boggs Twp. (Centre County), Howard, Howard Twp., Jacksonville (Centre County), Marion Twp. (Centre County). ICA: PA0215.

TV Market Ranking: Outside TV Markets. Franchise award date: N.A. Franchise expiration date: N.A. Began: June 1, 1964.

Channel capacity: 21. Channels available but not in use: None.

Basic Service

Subscribers: 750.

Programming (received off-air): WPSX-TV (P) Clearfield; WATM-TV (A), WJAC-TV (N), WTAJ-TV (C) Johnstown-Altoona; WBRE-TV (N) Scranton & Wilkes-Barre; allband FM.

Programming (via satellite): WGN-TV (W) Chicago; CNN; Discovery Channel; ESPN;

Fox Family Channel; Fox Sports Net Pittsburgh; Lifetime; MTV; Nashville Network; QVC; TBS Superstation; Turner Network TV; USA Network.
Current originations: Automated time-weather.
Fee: $59.95 installation; $18.44 monthly.
Pay Service 1
Pay Units: 169.
Programming (via satellite): HBO.
Fee: $10.00 monthly.
Pay Service 2
Pay Units: 97.
Programming (via satellite): Showtime.
Fee: N.A.
Pay Service 3
Pay Units: 2.
Programming (via satellite): The New Encore.
Fee: N.A.
Equipment: C-COR headend; C-COR amplifiers; Microdyne satellite antenna.
Miles of plant: 41.4 (coaxial). Homes passed: 763. Total homes in franchised area: 1,905.
Manager: Jeff Fisher. Chief technician: Jim Cain.
Ownership: AT&T Broadband & Internet Services (MSO). Purchased from Tele-Communications Inc., March 9, 1999.

DALLAS—Tele-Media Co. of Luzerne County, Box 279, Rte. 415 N. Memorial Hwy., Dallas, PA 18612. Phone: 570-639-1171. Fax: 570-639-3195. Counties: Luzerne & Wyoming. Also serves Dallas Borough, Dallas Twp. (Luzerne County), Franklin Twp. (Luzerne County), Harveys Lake Borough, Kingston Twp., Lehman Twp. (Luzerne County), Northmoreland Twp. ICA: PA0087.
TV Market Ranking: 49. Franchise award date: N.A. Franchise expiration date: June 18, 2001. Began: August 31, 1976.
Channel capacity: 40 (not 2-way capable). Channels available but not in use: None.
Basic Service
Subscribers: 7,487; Commercial subscribers: 726.
Programming (received off-air): WBRE-TV (N), WNEP-TV (A), WSWB (W), WVIA-TV (P), WYOU (C) Scranton & Wilkes-Barre; allband FM.
Programming (via satellite): WPIX (W) New York; C-SPAN; Disney Channel; QVC; TBS Superstation.
Current originations: Automated time-weather; public access; local sports.
Fee: $34.35 installation; $10.00 monthly; $17.15 additional installation.
Expanded Basic Service
Subscribers: 7,722.
Programming (via satellite): A & E; American Movie Classics; CNBC; CNN; Comedy Central; Discovery Channel; ESPN; Fox Family Channel; Learning Channel; Lifetime; MTV; Nashville Network; Nickelodeon; The Weather Channel; Turner Network TV; USA Network; VH1.
Fee: $15.00 installation; $18.50 monthly.
Pay Service 1
Pay Units: 351.
Programming (via satellite): Cinemax.
Fee: $9.95 monthly.
Pay Service 2
Pay Units: 620.
Programming (via satellite): HBO.
Fee: $9.95 monthly.
Pay Service 3
Pay Units: 607.
Programming (via satellite): Showtime; The Movie Channel.
Fee: $9.95 monthly (package).
Pay Service 4
Pay Units: 542.
Programming (via satellite): Starz!
Fee: $6.95 monthly.
Pay-per-view manager: Deborah A. Vanderhoff.
Local advertising: Yes. Available in satellite distributed programming. Local sales manager: Kevin Edwards. Regional interconnect: Cabletime.
Program Guide: Premium Channels.
Equipment: Blonder-Tongue, Jerrold & Microdyne headend; Jerrold & C-COR amplifiers; Comm/Scope cable; Atari character generator; Scientific-Atlanta set top converters; Eagle traps; Scientific-Atlanta satellite receivers.
Miles of plant: 231.0 (coaxial). Additional miles planned: 8.0 (coaxial). Homes passed: 9,437.
Manager: Deborah Vanderhoff. Chief technician: Terry Borger. Marketing director: Tony Masella. Customer service manager: Brigitte Stark.
City fee: 3% of gross.
Ownership: Tele-Media Corp. (MSO).

DALLAS CORRECTIONAL INSTITUTE—Cosmic Cable TV Inc., Box 186, RR 4, Shickshinny, PA 18655. Phone: 570-256-3437. County: Luzerne. ICA: PA0200.
TV Market Ranking: 49. Franchise award date: November 1, 1983. Franchise expiration date: December 1, 2008. Began: May 1, 1983.
Channel capacity: 30 (not 2-way capable). Channels available but not in use: None.
Basic Service
Subscribers: 800.
Programming (received off-air): WBRE-TV (N), WNEP-TV (A), WVIA-TV (P), WYOU (C) Scranton & Wilkes-Barre.
Programming (via satellite): WGN-TV (W) Chicago; BET; CNN; Comedy Central; Discovery Channel; ESPN; ESPN 2; MTV; Sci-Fi Channel; TBS Superstation; Turner Classic Movies; Turner Network TV; USA Network; Univision.
Fee: $12.95 monthly.
Pay Service 1
Pay Units: 180.
Programming (via satellite): HBO.
Fee: $9.95 monthly.
Pay-Per-View
Addressable homes: 675.
Miles of plant: 3.0 (coaxial); None (fiber optic). Homes passed: 1,200. Total homes in franchised area: 1,200.
Manager: Mark Reiber. Chief technician: Daniel Jamuscewski.
Ownership: June Hoover (MSO).

DANVILLE—CATV Service Inc., 115 Mill St., Danville, PA 17821. Phone: 717-275-1431. Fax: 717-275-3888. Counties: Columbia, Montour, Northumberland & Union. Also serves Buffalo Twp. (Union County), Cooper Twp. (Montour County), Delaware Twp. (Northumberland County), Derry Twp. (Montour County), East Buffalo Twp., East Chillisquaque Twp., Kelly Twp. (Union County), Lewis Twp. (Northumberland County), Lewisburg, Liberty Twp. (Montour County), Limestone Twp. (Montour County), Mahoning Twp. (Montour County), Mayberry Twp. (Montour County), McEwensville, Milton, Montour County, Montour Twp. (Columbia County), Point Twp. (Northumberland County), Riverside (Northumberland County), Turbot Twp. (Northumberland County), Turbotville, Union Twp. (Union County), Valley Twp. (Montour County), Washingtonville, Watsontown, West Chillisquaque Twp. (portions), West Hemlock Twp., White Deer Twp. ICA: PA0054.

TV Market Ranking: Below 100. Franchise award date: N.A. Franchise expiration date: N.A. Began: May 1, 1953.
Channel capacity: 42. Channels available but not in use: 2.
Basic Service
Subscribers: 16,500; Commercial subscribers: 1,000.
Programming (received off-air): WHTM-TV (A), WITF-TV (P) Harrisburg; WBRE-TV (N), WNEP-TV (A), WSWB (W), WVIA-TV (P), WYOU (C) Scranton & Wilkes-Barre; allband FM.
Programming (via microwave): WPIX (W) New York; WPHL-TV (W), WTXF-TV (F) Philadelphia.
Programming (via satellite): CNBC; EWTN; Fox Family Channel; Home Shopping Network; TBS Superstation.
Current originations: Automated time-weather; public access; educational access; government access; religious access; leased access; local sports.
Fee: $35.00 installation (aerial), $87.50 (underground); $20.00 monthly.
Commercial fee: $4.00 monthly.
Expanded Basic Service
Subscribers: 15,800.
Programming (via satellite): A & E; American Movie Classics; C-SPAN; CNN; Discovery Channel; ESPN; FX; Headline News; Lifetime; MTV; Nashville Network; Nick at Nite; Nickelodeon; QVC; TV Food Network; The Weather Channel; Turner Network TV; USA Network; VH1.
Fee: $10.45 monthly.
Pay Service 1
Pay Units: 1,000.
Programming (via satellite): Cinemax.
Fee: $35.00 installation; $10.00 monthly.
Pay Service 2
Pay Units: 500.
Programming (via satellite): Disney Channel.
Fee: $35.00 installation; $8.00 monthly.
Pay Service 3
Pay Units: 1,700.
Programming (via satellite): HBO.
Fee: $25.00 installation; $11.00 monthly.
Local advertising: Yes (insert only). Available in satellite distributed, locally originated & taped programming. Rates: $100.00/Minute; $70.00/30 Seconds. Local sales manager: Joe Mauro.
Program Guide: TV Host.
Equipment: General headend; General amplifiers; Comm/Scope & Siecor cable; Texscan character generator; Panasonic set top converters; Eagle traps; Scientific-Atlanta satellite antenna; Scientific-Atlanta satellite receivers; Sony commercial insert.
Miles of plant: 330.0 (coaxial); 27.0 (fiber optic). Additional miles planned: 10.0 (coaxial); 30.0 (fiber optic). Homes passed: 20,000. Total homes in franchised area: 25,000.
Manager: Ron Podlesny. Chief technician: William Hause. Marketing & program director: Debra Bortel.
City fee: 3% of gross.
Ownership: CATV Service Inc.

DARLINGTON TWP. (Beaver County)—AT&T Cable Services, 300 Corliss St., Pittsburgh, PA 15220-4815. Phones: 412-875-1100; 412-771-8100. County: Beaver. Also serves Big Beaver (Beaver County), Darlington, Enon Valley, New Beaver Borough, New Galilee, South Beaver Twp. (Beaver County). ICA: PA0144.
TV Market Ranking: 10 (Big Beaver, Darlington, Darlington Twp., New Beaver Borough, New Galilee, South Beaver Twp.); 79 (Big Beaver, Darlington Twp., Enon Valley, New Beaver Borough, New Galilee, South Beaver Twp.); 90 (New Beaver Borough, New Galilee, South Beaver Twp.). Franchise award date: N.A. Franchise expiration date: N.A. Began: August 1, 1981.
Channel capacity: 40. Channels available but not in use: N.A.
Basic Service
Subscribers: 1,915.
Programming (received off-air): KDKA-TV (C), WCWB (W), WPGH-TV (F), WPXI (N), WQED (P), WQEX (P), WTAE-TV (A) Pittsburgh; WFMJ-TV (N), WKBN-TV (C) Youngstown.
Programming (via satellite): A & E; BET; C-SPAN; C-SPAN 2; CNN; Discovery Channel; EWTN; Fox Family Channel; Headline News; Ladbroke Racing Channel/Meadows Racing Network; Lifetime; MTV; Nashville Network; Nickelodeon; QVC; TBS Superstation; The Weather Channel.
Fee: $59.95 installation; $9.73 monthly.
Expanded Basic Service
Subscribers: 1,905.
Programming (via satellite): American Movie Classics; Court TV; ESPN; Fox Sports Net Pittsburgh; Turner Network TV; USA Network.
Fee: $9.73 monthly.
Pay Service 1
Pay Units: 253.
Programming (via satellite): Cinemax.
Fee: N.A.
Pay Service 2
Pay Units: 87.
Programming (via satellite): Disney Channel.
Fee: N.A.
Pay Service 3
Pay Units: 444.
Programming (via satellite): HBO.
Fee: N.A.
Pay Service 4
Pay Units: 92.
Programming (via satellite): Showtime.
Fee: N.A.
Pay Service 5
Pay Units: 619.
Programming (via satellite): The New Encore.
Fee: N.A.
Miles of plant: 91.3 (coaxial). Homes passed: 2,463. Total homes in franchised area: 3,735.
Manager: John Chapman. Chief technician: James Donegan.
Ownership: AT&T Broadband & Internet Services (MSO). Purchased from Tele-Communications Inc., March 9, 1999.

DILLSBURG—Dillsburg Cable, Box 3909, 2720 Baltimore Pike, Gettysburg, PA 17325-3909. Phones: 717-432-5919; 800-632-9026. Counties: Adams, Cumberland & York. Also serves Carroll Twp. (York County), Franklin Twp. (York County), Franklintown, Latimore Twp., Monaghan Twp., Monroe Twp. (Cumberland County). ICA: PA0326.

TV Market Ranking: 57. Franchise award date: N.A. Franchise expiration date: N.A. Began: September 1, 1973.

Channel capacity: 60 (not 2-way capable). Channels available but not in use: None.

Basic Service

Subscribers: 3,621.

Programming (received off-air): WBAL-TV (N), WJZ-TV (C) Baltimore; WHP-TV (C), WHTM-TV (A), WITF-TV (P) Harrisburg; WGAL (N), WLYH-TV (U) Lancaster; WGCB-TV (I) Red Lion; WDCA (U) Washington; WPMT (F) York.

Programming (via satellite): WGN-TV (W) Chicago; QVC; TBS Superstation.

Current originations: Educational access; government access.

Fee: $9.20 monthly; $1.37 converter.

Expanded Basic Service

Subscribers: 3,347.

Programming (via satellite): A & E; American Movie Classics; C-SPAN; CNBC; CNN; Cartoon Network; Discovery Channel; ESPN; ESPN 2; FX; Fox Family Channel; Great American Country; Headline News; History Channel; Home Team Sports; Learning Channel; Lifetime; MTV; Nashville Network; Nickelodeon; Sci-Fi Channel; The Weather Channel; Turner Network TV; USA Network; VH1.

Fee: $13.70 monthly.

Pay Service 1

Pay Units: 472.

Programming (via satellite): Cinemax.

Fee: $8.95 monthly.

Pay Service 2

Pay Units: 314.

Programming (via satellite): Disney Channel.

Fee: $8.95 monthly.

Pay Service 3

Pay Units: 611.

Programming (via satellite): HBO.

Fee: $10.95 monthly.

Local advertising: No.

Equipment: Scientific-Atlanta headend; Magnavox amplifiers; Times Fiber cable; Pioneer set top converters.

Miles of plant: 118.0 (coaxial); None (fiber optic).

Manager: Tim McCallister. Chief technician: Lloyd Mayhew.

Franchise fee: 3% of gross.

Ownership: Great Southern Printing & Manufacturing Co. (MSO).

DOYLESBURG—Valley Cable Systems, Box 78, Doylesburg, PA 17219. Phone: 717-349-7717. Counties: Franklin & Huntingdon. Also serves Blairs Mills, Fannett Twp. (Franklin County), Tell Twp. ICA: PA0286.

TV Market Ranking: 74 (Tell Twp.); Outside TV Markets (Blairs Mills, Doylesburg, Fannett Twp.). Franchise award date: January 1, 1982. Franchise expiration date: N.A. Began: February 1, 1981.

Channel capacity: 30 (not 2-way capable). Channels available but not in use: 4.

Basic Service

Subscribers: 50.

Programming (received off-air): WJZ-TV (C), WMPB (P) Baltimore; WHAG-TV (N), WJAL (W) Hagerstown; WATM-TV (A), WJAC-TV (N), WTAJ-TV (C) Johnstown-Altoona; WGAL (N) Lancaster; WTTG (F) Washington; WPMT (F) York.

Programming (via satellite): C-SPAN; Country Music TV; Discovery Channel; ESPN; Fox Family Channel; Nashville Network; QVC; Sci-Fi Channel; TBS Superstation; The Health Network; Trinity Bcstg. Network.

Current originations: Automated timeweather; religious access.

Fee: $40.00 installation; $17.95 monthly.

Local advertising: Yes.

Equipment: Jerrold, Blonder-Tongue & Drake headend; AEL & Gamco amplifiers; Comm/Scope cable; Atari & Info/Soft character generator; Jerrold set top converters; PPC traps; Scientific-Atlanta satellite antenna; Drake & Jerrold satellite receivers.

Miles of plant: 9.8 (coaxial). Additional miles planned: 3.0 (coaxial). Homes passed: 125. Total homes in franchised area: 400.

Manager: Barry L. Kepner.

Ownership: Valley Cable Systems (MSO).

DU BOIS—Adelphia Cable, Box 347, 129 Du Bois St., Du Bois, PA 15801. Phone: 814-371-2041. Fax: 814-371-6087. Counties: Clearfield & Jefferson. Also serves Brady Twp. (Clearfield County), Clearfield County, Falls Creek, Jefferson County, Sandy Twp. (Clearfield County), Troutville, Union Twp. (Jefferson County), Washington Twp. (Jefferson County), Winslow Twp. ICA: PA0093.

TV Market Ranking: 74 (portions of Clearfield County); Outside TV Markets (Brady Twp., Du Bois, Falls Creek, Jefferson County, Sandy Twp., Troutville, Washington Twp., Winslow Twp.). Franchise award date: October 22, 1962. Franchise expiration date: N.A. Began: February 1, 1964.

Channel capacity: 50 (not 2-way capable). Channels available but not in use: 3.

Basic Service

Subscribers: 6,902; Commercial subscribers: 25.

Programming (received off-air): WPSX-TV (P) Clearfield; WJAC-TV (N), WKBS-TV (I), WTAJ-TV (C), WWCP-TV (F) Johnstown-Altoona; KDKA-TV (C), WCWB (W), WPGH-TV (F), WQED (P), WTAE-TV (A) Pittsburgh; 12 FMs.

Programming (via satellite): WXYZ-TV (A) Detroit; C-SPAN; E! Entertainment TV; ESPN 2; Fox Sports Net Pittsburgh; Headline News; Ladbroke Racing Channel/Meadows Racing Network; QVC; The Weather Channel.

Current originations: Automated timeweather; public access; educational access; government access; religious access; automated emergency alert; local news.

Fee: $19.62 installation; $8.05 monthly; $1.75 converter.

Expanded Basic Service

Subscribers: 6,510.

Programming (via satellite): A & E; CNBC; CNN; Discovery Channel; ESPN; EWTN; Fox Family Channel; Lifetime; MTV; Nashville Network; Nickelodeon; Turner Network TV; USA Network.

Fee: $17.24 monthly.

A la Carte 1

Subscribers: 6,662.

Programming (via satellite): WGN-TV (W) Chicago; WPIX (W) New York; TBS Superstation; Turner Classic Movies.

Fee: $1.00 monthly (package).

Pay Service 1

Pay Units: N.A.

Programming (via satellite): Cinemax; Disney Channel; HBO; Showtime.

Fee: $19.62 installation; $4.95 monthly (Disney), $6.95 monthly (Cinemax or Showtime), $9.95 monthly (HBO).

Pay-Per-View

Addressable homes: 616.

Local advertising: Yes. Available in character-generated programming.

Equipment: Scientific-Atlanta headend; Jerrold amplifiers; Trilogy cable; Sony VTRs; Videotek character generator; Jerrold set top converters; Jerrold addressable set top converters; Eagle & Arcom traps; Arcom addressable traps; Scientific-Atlanta satellite antenna; Microwave General satellite receivers.

Miles of plant: 175.0 (coaxial). Homes passed: 8,599. Total homes in franchised area: 9,000.

Manager: Brian Frederick. Chief technician: Bernard A. Masonis. Marketing director: Kevin Kick. Customer service manager: Helen Ball.

City fee: 5% of gross.

Ownership: Adelphia Communications Corp. (MSO).

DUNCANNON—Blue Ridge CATV, 2800 Lewisberry Rd., York Haven, PA 17370. Phone: 717-938-6501. Fax: 717-834-9285. County: Perry. Also serves Carroll Twp. (Perry County), Miller Twp. (Perry County), New Buffalo (portions), Reed Twp. (Perry County), Rye Twp., Watts Twp., Wheatfield Twp. ICA: PA0117.

TV Market Ranking: 57. Franchise award date: N.A. Franchise expiration date: N.A. Began: January 1, 1971.

Channel capacity: 53 (not 2-way capable). Channels available but not in use: None.

Basic Service

Subscribers: 3,400.

Programming (received off-air): WBFF (F) Baltimore; WHP-TV (C), WHTM-TV (A), WITF-TV (P) Harrisburg; WGAL (N), WLYH-TV (U) Lancaster; WGCB-TV (I) Red Lion; WPMT (F) York.

Programming (via satellite): C-SPAN; Pennsylvania Cable Network.

Fee: $45.00 installation; $8.00 monthly.

Expanded Basic Service

Subscribers: 3,200.

Programming (via satellite): A & E; American Movie Classics; Animal Planet; CNBC; CNN; Cartoon Network; Comedy Central; Country Music TV; Discovery Channel; Disney Channel; E! Entertainment TV; ESPN; ESPN 2; FX; Fox Family Channel; Fox News Channel; Headline News; History Channel; Home & Garden Television; Home Shopping Network; Home Team Sports; Learning Channel; Lifetime; MSNBC; MTV; Nashville Network; Nick at Nite's TV Land; Nickelodeon; QVC; Sci-Fi Channel; TBS Superstation; The Weather Channel; Travel Channel; Turner Classic Movies; Turner Network TV; USA Network; VH1.

Fee: $17.25 monthly.

Pay Service 1

Pay Units: 436.

Programming (via satellite): HBO.

Fee: $10.00 monthly.

Pay Service 2

Pay Units: 272.

Programming (via satellite): Cinemax.

Fee: $9.00 monthly.

Pay Service 3

Pay Units: 412.

Programming (via satellite): Showtime.

Fee: $9.50 monthly.

Pay-Per-View

Movies; special events.

Fee: $3.95 (movies); Varies (special events).

Local advertising: Yes. Available in character-generated programming. Local sales manager: Michael Muniz.

Equipment: Scientific-Atlanta headend; Comm/Scope cable; RCA set top converters; Eagle traps; Scientific-Atlanta & Gardiner satellite antenna; Scientific-Atlanta satellite receivers.

Miles of plant: 181.0 (coaxial); None (fiber optic). Additional miles planned: 6.0 (coaxial). Homes passed: 5,300.

Manager: Michael Muniz.

Ownership: Pencor Services Inc. (MSO).

DUNMORE—Adelphia Cable TV, 1100 Clay Ave., Dunmore, PA 18512. Phone: 717-342-2270. Fax: 717-344-4573. Counties: Lackawanna, Luzerne & Wyoming. Also serves Abington Twp. (Lackawanna County), Archbald, Benton Twp. (Lackawanna County), Blakely, Chinchilla, Clarks Green, Clarks Summit, Clinton Twp. (Wyoming County), Covington Twp. (Lackawanna County), Dalton, Dupont, Duryea, Elmhurst Twp., Exeter Borough (portions), Exeter Twp. (Luzerne County), Exeter Twp. (Wyoming County), Eynon, Factoryville, Falls Twp. (Wyoming County), Falls Village, Glenburn Twp. (Lackawanna County), Hughestown, Jefferson Twp. (Lackawanna County), Jenkins Twp. (Luzerne County), Jessup, La Plume, Laflin Borough, Madison Twp. (Lackawanna County), Moscow (Lackawanna County), Newton Twp. (Lackawanna County), Nicholson Borough, Nicholson Twp. (Wyoming County), North Abington Twp., Olyphant, Peckville, Pittston, Pittston Twp., Roaring Brook Twp., Scott Twp. (Lackawanna County), South Abington Twp., Springbrook Twp. (Lackawanna County), West Pittston, Yatesville. ICA: PA0022.

TV Market Ranking: 49. Franchise award date: N.A. Franchise expiration date: N.A. Began: March 1, 1970.

Channel capacity: 36 (not 2-way capable). Channels available but not in use: None.

Basic Service

Subscribers: 39,199; Commercial subscribers: 800.

Programming (received off-air): WBRE-TV (N), WNEP-TV (A), WSWB (W), WVIA-TV (P), WYOU (C) Scranton & Wilkes-Barre.

Programming (via satellite): WWOR-TV (U) New York; TBS Superstation.

Fee: N.A.

Expanded Basic Service

Subscribers: 35,286.

Programming (via satellite): A & E; American Movie Classics; CNBC; CNN; Discovery Channel; E! Entertainment TV; ESPN; Fox Family Channel; Headline News; Home Shopping Network; Lifetime; MTV; Madison Square Garden Network; Nashville Network; Nickelodeon; The Weather Channel; Turner Network TV; USA Network; VH1.

Planned programming (via satellite): Animal Planet; C-SPAN; C-SPAN 2; Cartoon Network; ESPN 2; FX; History Channel; Learning Channel; MSNBC; Product Information Network; Sci-Fi Channel; TV Food Network; The Health Network.

Fee: N.A.

Pay Service 1

Pay Units: 2,063.

Programming (via satellite): Cinemax.

Fee: $11.50 monthly.

Pay Service 2

Pay Units: 9,586.

Programming (via satellite): HBO.

Fee: $11.50 monthly.

Pay Service 3

Pay Units: N.A.

Programming (via satellite): Starz!; The New Encore.

Fee: $11.50 monthly (each).

Pay-Per-View

Addressable homes: 4,720.

Viewer's Choice.
Fee: $3.95.
Local advertising: Yes. Available in taped programming. Local sales manager: Tom Keeler.
Program Guide: TV Guide.
Equipment: Jerrold & Hughes headend; Jerrold amplifiers; Comm/Scope cable; Standard Communications, RCA & Hamlin character generator; Hughes & Anixter set top converters; Scientific-Atlanta addressable set top converters; Eagle traps; Hughes & Anixter satellite antenna; Microdyne & Standard Communications satellite receivers.
Miles of plant: 913.0 (coaxial); 140.0 (fiber optic). Homes passed: 43,000.
City fee: 3% of gross.
Ownership: Adelphia Communications Corp. (MSO).

DUSHORE—Blue Ridge Cable TV, Box 141, Tunkhannock, PA 18657. Phone: 570-836-5422. Fax: 570-836-1659. Counties: Bradford, Columbia & Sullivan. Also serves Cherry Twp. (Sullivan County), Colley Twp. (Sullivan County), Jonestown (Columbia County), Muncy Valley, New Albany, Sonestown. ICA: PA0327.
TV Market Ranking: 49 (Cherry Twp., Colley Twp., Dushore, Jonestown, Sonestown); Below 100 (Muncy Valley, New Albany). Franchise award date: N.A. Franchise expiration date: N.A. Began: June 1, 1960.
Channel capacity: 42. Channels available but not in use: N.A.
Basic Service
Subscribers: 853.
Programming (received off-air): WBNG-TV (C), WICZ-TV (F), WIVT (A), WSKG (P) Binghamton; WBRE-TV (N), WNEP-TV (A), WSWB (W), WVIA-TV (P), WYOU (C) Scranton & Wilkes-Barre; allband FM.
Programming (via satellite): WGN-TV (W) Chicago; A & E; C-SPAN; Cartoon Network; Discovery Channel; ESPN; Fox Family Channel; Headline News; Home Shopping Network; Lifetime; MTV; Nashville Network; Nickelodeon; TBS Superstation; The Weather Channel; Turner Classic Movies; Turner Network TV; USA Network; VH1.
Fee: $30.00 installation; $16.90 monthly.
Pay Service 1
Pay Units: N.A.
Programming (via satellite): HBO.
Fee: $9.50 monthly.
Equipment: Scientific-Atlanta headend; C-COR amplifiers; Comm/Scope cable.
Manager: Ken Valentine.
Ownership: Pencor Services Inc. (MSO).

EAST CONEMAUGH—Adelphia, One Adelphia Dr., Blairsville, PA 15717. Phone: 800-892-7300. County: Cambria. ICA: PA0217.
TV Market Ranking: 74. Franchise award date: July 3, 1951. Franchise expiration date: N.A. Began: July 3, 1951.
Channel capacity: 77 (not 2-way capable). Channels available but not in use: None.
Basic Service
Subscribers: 596.
Programming (received off-air): WPSX-TV (P) Clearfield; WATM-TV (A), WJAC-TV (N), WKBS-TV (I), WTAJ-TV (C), WWCP-TV (F) Johnstown-Altoona; KDKA-TV (C), WPXI (N), WQED (P), WTAE-TV (A) Pittsburgh.
Programming (via satellite): WGN-TV (W) Chicago; A & E; American Movie Classics; Animal Planet; CNN; Discovery Channel; Disney Channel; ESPN; ESPN 2; EWTN; Fox Family Channel; Fox Sports Net Pittsburgh; Headline News; Lifetime; MSNBC; MTV; Nashville Network; Nickelodeon; QVC; TBS Superstation; Turner Classic Movies; Turner Network TV; USA Network; VH1.
Fee: N.A.
Pay Service 1
Pay Units: 130.
Programming (via satellite): HBO.
Fee: $29.50 installation; $11.50 monthly.
Local advertising: No.
Equipment: Jerrold, Scientific-Atlanta & Tocom headend; Magnavox amplifiers; Perimeter 3 cable; Hamlin, Oak & Scientific-Atlanta set top converters; Eagle traps; Scientific-Atlanta satellite antenna; Scientific-Atlanta satellite receivers.
Miles of plant: 6.6 (coaxial). Homes passed: 784.
Manager: J. Francis Bradley Jr. Chief technician: Dave Bowen.
City fee: 5% of basic gross.
Ownership: Adelphia Communications Corp. (MSO).

EAST HILLS—AT&T Cable Services, 300 Corliss St., Pittsburgh, PA 15220-4815. Phones: 412-875-1100; 412-771-8100. County: Allegheny. Also serves Braddock Hills, Chalfant, Edgewood, Forest Hills, Penn Hills Twp., Wilkinsburg. ICA: PA0030.
TV Market Ranking: 10. Franchise award date: N.A. Franchise expiration date: N.A. Began: December 1, 1968.
Channel capacity: 61 (not 2-way capable). Channels available but not in use: N.A.
Basic Service
Subscribers: 27,081.
Programming (received off-air): WPCB-TV (I) Greensburg; KDKA-TV (C), WCWB (W), WPGH-TV (F), WPXI (N), WQED (P), WQEX (P), WTAE-TV (A) Pittsburgh; allband FM.
Programming (via microwave): Meadows Racing Network.
Programming (via satellite): BET; C-SPAN; Odyssey; Pennsylvania Cable Network; QVC; TV Guide Sneak Prevue; The Weather Channel.
Current originations: Educational access; government access.
Fee: $44.95 installation; $10.60 monthly; $1.50 converter; $24.95 additional installation.
Expanded Basic Service
Subscribers: 25,537.
Programming (via microwave): Pittsburgh Cable News Channel.
Programming (via satellite): A & E; American Movie Classics; Animal Planet; C-SPAN 2; CNBC; CNN; Cartoon Network; Court TV; Discovery Channel; ESPN; ESPN 2; EWTN; FX; Fox Family Channel; Fox News Channel; Fox Sports Net Pittsburgh; Headline News; History Channel; Home Shopping Network; International Channel; Knowledge TV; Learning Channel; Lifetime; MOVIEplex; MTV; Nashville Network; Nickelodeon; Sci-Fi Channel; TBS Superstation; TV Guide Channel; Turner Network TV; USA Network; VH1.
Fee: $17.81 monthly.
Pay Service 1
Pay Units: 3,776.
Programming (via satellite): Cinemax.
Fee: $13.45 monthly.
Pay Service 2
Pay Units: 1,315.
Programming (via satellite): Disney Channel.
Fee: $12.50 monthly.
Pay Service 3
Pay Units: 8,200.
Programming (via satellite): HBO (multiplexed).
Fee: $14.95 monthly.
Pay Service 4
Pay Units: 2,492.
Programming (via satellite): Showtime.
Fee: $14.95 monthly.
Pay Service 5
Pay Units: 11,490.
Programming (via satellite): The New Encore.
Fee: $1.95 monthly.
Pay Service 6
Pay Units: N.A.
Programming (via satellite): DMX; Starz!
Fee: $6.75 monthly (Starz), $9.95 monthly (DMX).
Pay-Per-View
Action Pay-Per-View; Playboy TV; Spice.
Local advertising: Yes (locally produced & insert). Available in satellite distributed programming. Regional interconnect: TCI Media Services-Pittsburgh, PA.
Program Guide: The Cable Guide.
Equipment: Benavac headend; C-COR amplifiers; General cable; Hughes satellite antenna.
Miles of plant: 277.3 (coaxial). Homes passed: 37,941. Total homes in franchised area: 37,941.
Manager: Jeffrey C. Harshman. Chief technician: Fred Hamm. Marketing director: Glenn Ryerson.
City fee: 3% of gross.
Ownership: AT&T Broadband & Internet Services (MSO). Purchased from Tele-Communications Inc., March 9, 1999.

EAST SMITHFIELD—Community Cable Corp., Box 1560, RR 2, Mansfield, PA 16933. Phone: 717-549-3805. Fax: 717-549-2500. County: Bradford. ICA: PA0280.
TV Market Ranking: Below 100. Franchise award date: N.A. Franchise expiration date: N.A. Began: October 15, 1965.
Channel capacity: 17 (not 2-way capable). Channels available but not in use: None.
Basic Service
Subscribers: 134.
Programming (received off-air): WBNG-TV (C), WICZ-TV (F), WIVT (A), WSKG (P) Binghamton; WENY-TV (A), WETM-TV (N) Elmira; WBRE-TV (N), WNEP-TV (A), WSWB (W), WVIA-TV (P), WYOU (C) Scranton & Wilkes-Barre.
Programming (via satellite): CNN; Discovery Channel; ESPN; Nashville Network; TBS Superstation.
Fee: $25.00 installation; $10.00 monthly.
Local advertising: No.
Equipment: Ameco headend; Ameco amplifiers; Rome cable.
Miles of plant: 8.0 (coaxial). Homes passed: 150.
Manager: Robert Wagner. Chief technician: Joseph Gottwald.
City fee: None.
Ownership: Community Cable Corp. of Pennsylvania.

EAST WATERFORD—Valley Cable Systems, Box 78, Doylesburg, PA 17219. Phone: 717-349-7717. County: Juniata. ICA: PA0290.
TV Market Ranking: 57. Franchise award date: January 1, 1978. Franchise expiration date: N.A. Began: January 1, 1978.
Channel capacity: 36 (not 2-way capable). Channels available but not in use: 15.
Basic Service
Subscribers: 80.
Programming (received off-air): WJAL (W) Hagerstown; WHP-TV (C), WHTM-TV (A), WITF-TV (P) Harrisburg; WGAL (N), WLYH-TV (U) Lancaster.
Programming (via satellite): Country Music TV; Discovery Channel; ESPN; Fox Family Channel; Nashville Network; TBS Superstation; Trinity Bcstg. Network.
Current originations: Automated time-weather; religious access.
Fee: $40.00 installation; $13.95 monthly.
Local advertising: No.
Equipment: Blonder-Tongue, Scientific-Atlanta & Jerrold headend; GTE Sylvania & Jerrold amplifiers; Comm/Scope cable; Atari & Info/Soft character generator; Jerrold set top converters; PPC traps; Scientific-Atlanta satellite antenna; Drake satellite receivers.
Miles of plant: 6.0 (coaxial). Homes passed: 117. Total homes in franchised area: 300.
Manager: Barry L. Kepner.
Ownership: Valley Cable Systems (MSO).

EASTON—Service Electric Cable TV Inc., 2260 Ave. A, Bethlehem, PA 18017-2108. Phone: 610-865-9100. Fax: 610-865-5031.
E-mail: office@sectv.com.
Web site: http://www.sectv.com.
County: Northampton. Also serves Bethlehem Twp. (Northampton County), Forks Twp., Glendon (Northampton County), Lower Mount Bethel Twp., Palmer Twp. (Northampton County), Plainfield Twp. (Northampton County), Stockertown, West Easton, Williams Twp. (Northampton County), Wilson (Northampton County). ICA: PA0035.
TV Market Ranking: Below 100. Franchise award date: January 1, 1954. Franchise expiration date: November 1, 2001. Began: January 1, 1954.
Channel capacity: 85 (2-way capable; not operating 2-way). Channels available but not in use: None.
Basic Service
Subscribers: 12,711; Commercial subscribers: 2.
Programming (received off-air): WFMZ-TV (I), WLVT-TV (P) Allentown; WBPH-TV (I) Bethlehem; WGTW (I) Burlington; WABC-TV (A), WNBC (N), WNYW (F), WPIX (W), WWOR-TV (U) New York; KYW-TV (C), WCAU (N), WPHL-TV (W), WPSG (U), WPVI-TV (A), WTXF-TV (F) Philadelphia; WTVE (H) Reading; WNEP-TV (A) Scranton & Wilkes-Barre.
Programming (via satellite): BET; C-SPAN; C-SPAN 2; Discovery People; EWTN; Game Show Network; Goodlife TV Network; Home Shopping Network; NASA TV; Pennsylvania Cable Network; QVC; Style; TBS Superstation; TV Food Network; TV Guide Channel; The Inspirational Network; ValueVision.
Current originations: Automated time-weather; public access; educational access; government access; religious access; leased access; library access; automated emergency alert; local news; local sports.
Fee: $25.00 installation (aerial), $50.00 (underground); $11.82 monthly; $1.80 converter; $25.00 additional installation.
Expanded Basic Service
Subscribers: 12,495.
Programming (via microwave): Comcast SportsNet.
Programming (via satellite): A & E; American Movie Classics; CNBC; CNN; Cartoon Network; Comedy Central; Country Music TV; Discovery Channel; Disney Channel; E! Entertainment TV; ESPN; ESPN 2; FX; Fox Family Channel; Fox News Channel; Golf Channel; Headline News; History Channel; Home & Garden Television; International Channel; Learning Channel; Lifetime; MSNBC; MTV; Nashville Network; Nick at Nite's TV Land; Nickelodeon; Romance Classics; Sci-Fi Channel; Speedvision; The Weather Channel; Turner Classic Movies; Turner Network TV; USA Network; Univision; VH1.
Fee: $25.00 installation; $25.53 monthly.

Pay Service 1
Pay Units: 1,337.
Programming (via satellite): Cinemax (multiplexed).
Fee: $15.00 installation; $7.95 monthly.
Pay Service 2
Pay Units: 117.
Programming (via satellite): Music Choice.
Fee: $15.00 installation; $10.45 monthly.
Pay Service 3
Pay Units: 1,818.
Programming (via satellite): HBO (multiplexed).
Fee: $15.00 installation; $9.95 monthly.
Pay Service 4
Pay Units: 511.
Programming (via satellite): Showtime; The Movie Channel.
Fee: $9.95 monthly.
Pay Service 5
Pay Units: 148.
Programming (via satellite): Playboy TV.
Fee: $15.00 installation; $7.95 monthly.
Pay Service 6
Pay Units: 49.
Programming (via satellite): The New Encore.
Fee: $2.95 monthly.
Pay Service 7
Pay Units: 48.
Programming (via satellite): Starz!; The New Encore.
Fee: $7.95 monthly.
Pay-Per-View
Addressable homes: 2,089.
Viewer's Choice.
Fee: Varies.
Pay-per-view manager: Steve Salash.
Local advertising: Yes (locally produced & insert). Available in satellite distributed, locally originated & character-generated programming. Rates: On request. Local sales manager: Dan Walsh.
Program Guide: TV Host.
Equipment: Jerrold headend; GTE Sylvania & Philips amplifiers; Comm/Scope cable; Siecor fiber optic cable; Scientific-Atlanta set top converters; Jerrold addressable set top converters; Zenith modems; GTE Sylvania & Philips traps; Scientific-Atlanta satellite antenna; Jerrold satellite receivers; Sony commercial insert.
Miles of plant: 317.0 (coaxial); 73.3 (fiber optic). Homes passed: 25,036. Total homes in franchised area: 43,200.
Manager: John J. Capparell. Chief technician: Jeffrey Kelly. Program director: Don Hunt. Marketing director: Steve Salash. Customer service manager: MaryAnn Detweiler.
City fee: 3%-5% of gross.
Ownership: Service Electric Cable TV Inc. (MSO).

EASTVILLE—Eastville TV Cable, Box 85, Loganton, PA 17747. Phone: 717-725-2733. County: Clinton. ICA: PA0306.
TV Market Ranking: Outside TV Markets. Franchise award date: January 1, 1955. Franchise expiration date: N.A. Began: N.A.
Channel capacity: 12. Channels available but not in use: 8.
Basic Service
Subscribers: N.A.
Programming (received off-air): WTAJ-TV (C) Johnstown-Altoona; WBRE-TV (N), WNEP-TV (A), WVIA-TV (P) Scranton & Wilkes-Barre.
Fee: $3.00 monthly.
Equipment: Blonder-Tongue headend.
Miles of plant: 1.5 (coaxial). Homes passed: 28.
Chief technician: Guy Bierly.
Ownership: Eastville TV Cable.

EAU CLAIRE—CableVision Communications, Box 2200, 68 5th St., Buckhannon, WV 26201. Phone: 304-472-4193. Fax: 304-472-0756. County: Butler. Also serves Venango Twp. (Butler County). ICA: PA0269.
TV Market Ranking: Outside TV Markets. Franchise award date: N.A. Franchise expiration date: N.A. Began: N.A.
Channel capacity: 21 (not 2-way capable). Channels available but not in use: N.A.
Basic Service
Subscribers: 82.
Programming (received off-air): KDKA-TV (C), WCWB (W), WPGH-TV (F), WPXI (N), WQED (P), WTAE-TV (A) Pittsburgh; WYTV (A,F) Youngstown.
Programming (via satellite): CNN; ESPN; Fox Family Channel; Nashville Network; Nickelodeon; TBS Superstation; Turner Network TV; USA Network.
Fee: $61.25 installation; $22.00 monthly; $1.24 converter.
Pay Service 1
Pay Units: 22.
Programming (via satellite): HBO.
Fee: $17.50 installation; $11.99 monthly.
Local advertising: No.
Equipment: Drake headend; Jerrold amplifiers; Comm/Scope cable; Intercept traps; Drake satellite receivers.
Miles of plant: 5.0 (coaxial). Homes passed: 194.
Manager: Willie Critchfield. Marketing director: Kenny Phillips.
City fee: None.
Ownership: Rifkin & Associates Inc. (MSO). See Cable System Ownership.

EDINBORO—Coaxial Cable TV Corp., 105 Walker Dr., Edinboro, PA 16412. Phone: 814-734-1424. Fax: 814-734-8898. Web site: http://www.coaxialcabletv.com. Counties: Crawford & Erie. Also serves Cambridge Springs, Cambridge Twp. (Crawford County), Franklin Twp. (Erie County), Richmond Twp. (Crawford County), Rockdale Twp. (Crawford County), Townville, Venango, Venango Twp. (Crawford County), Washington Twp. (Erie County), Woodcock Borough. ICA: PA0115.
TV Market Ranking: Below 100. Franchise award date: July 1, 1967. Franchise expiration date: N.A. Began: July 1, 1967.
Channel capacity: 54 (not 2-way capable). Channels available but not in use: 11.
Basic Service
Subscribers: 4,800.
Programming (received off-air): WFXP (F), WICU-TV (N), WJET-TV (A), WQLN (P), WSEE (C) Erie; allband FM.
Programming (via satellite): WGN-TV (W) Chicago; A & E; American Movie Classics; Animal Planet; C-SPAN; CNBC; CNN; Cartoon Network; Country Music TV; Discovery Channel; E! Entertainment TV; ESPN; ESPN 2; Fox Family Channel; Fox Sports Net Ohio; Fox Sports Net Pittsburgh; Golf Channel; Headline News; History Channel; Home & Garden Television; Home Shopping Network; Learning Channel; Lifetime; MTV; NASA TV; Nashville Network; Nick at Nite's TV Land; Nickelodeon; Odyssey; Outdoor Channel; QVC; Sci-Fi Channel; TBS Superstation; TV Guide Channel; The Weather Channel; Travel Channel; Trinity Bcstg. Network; Turner Classic Movies; Turner Network TV; USA Network; VH1.
Current originations: Government access.
Fee: N.A.
Pay Service 1
Pay Units: 193.
Programming (via satellite): Disney Channel.
Fee: $7.95 monthly.
Pay Service 2
Pay Units: 594.
Programming (via satellite): HBO.
Fee: $11.95 monthly.
Pay Service 3
Pay Units: 208.
Programming (via satellite): Showtime.
Fee: $11.95 monthly.
Local advertising: Yes. Available in taped programming.
Equipment: Jerrold headend; Jerrold amplifiers; Comm/Scope cable; Panasonic set top converters; Arcom & Eagle traps; Scientific-Atlanta satellite antenna; Jerrold satellite receivers.
Miles of plant: 200.0 (coaxial); 60.0 (fiber optic). Additional miles planned: 10.0 (coaxial); 15.0 (fiber optic). Homes passed: 5,400. Total homes in franchised area: 5,400.
Manager: David K. Wescott.
City fee: 5% of gross.
Ownership: Coaxial Cable TV Corp.

ELDERTON BOROUGH—AT&T Cable Services, 300 Corliss St., Pittsburgh, PA 15220-4815. Phones: 412-875-1100; 412-771-8100. Counties: Armstrong & Indiana. Also serves Armstrong Twp. (Indiana County), Elderton, Plumcreek Twp., Shelocta. ICA: PA0229.
TV Market Ranking: 74. Franchise award date: N.A. Franchise expiration date: N.A. Began: February 1, 1984.
Channel capacity: 21 (not 2-way capable). Channels available but not in use: N.A.
Basic Service
Subscribers: 467.
Programming (received off-air): WPCB-TV (I) Greensburg; WJAC-TV (N) Johnstown-Altoona; KDKA-TV (C), WCWB (W), WPGH-TV (F), WPXI (N), WQED (P), WTAE-TV (A) Pittsburgh.
Programming (via satellite): Discovery Channel; Fox Family Channel; QVC.
Fee: $44.95 installation; $12.07 monthly; $1.50 converter; $24.95 additional installation.
Expanded Basic Service
Subscribers: 420.
Programming (via satellite): Animal Planet; CNN; Cartoon Network; ESPN; Fox Sports Net Pittsburgh; Lifetime; MTV; Nashville Network; TBS Superstation; Turner Network TV; USA Network.
Fee: $10.35 monthly.
Pay Service 1
Pay Units: 120.
Programming (via satellite): HBO.
Fee: $14.95 monthly.
Pay Service 2
Pay Units: N.A.
Programming (via satellite): Starz!; The New Encore.
Fee: $1.95 monthly (Encore), $6.75 monthly (Starz).
Program Guide: The Cable Guide.
Miles of plant: 19.2 (coaxial). Homes passed: 588. Total homes in franchised area: 2,443.
Manager: Jeffrey C. Harshman. Chief technician: Fred Hamm. Marketing director: Glenn Ryerson.
Ownership: AT&T Broadband & Internet Services (MSO). Purchased from Tele-Communications Inc., March 9, 1999.

ELDRED TWP. (Lycoming County)—Ralph Herr TV, Box 717, RR 4, Montoursville, PA 17754-9665. Phone: 717-435-2780. County: Lycoming. Also serves Quaker Hill. ICA: PA0212.
TV Market Ranking: Below 100. Franchise award date: N.A. Franchise expiration date: N.A. Began: January 1, 1973.
Channel capacity: 30. Channels available but not in use: N.A.
Basic Service
Subscribers: N.A.
Programming (received off-air): WHP-TV (C), WHTM-TV (A) Harrisburg; WTAJ-TV (C) Johnstown-Altoona; WBRE-TV (N), WNEP-TV (A), WYOU (C) Scranton & Wilkes-Barre.
Fee: N.A.
Miles of plant: 25.0 (coaxial). Homes passed: 800.
Manager: Ralph W. Herr.
Ownership: Herr Cable Co. (MSO).

ELIZABETHTOWN—AT&T Cable Services, Box 309, Elizabethtown, PA 17022. Phone: 717-361-0300. Fax: 717-361-0600. Counties: Lancaster, Mifflin & Perry. Also serves Armagh Twp., Brown Twp. (Mifflin County), Conoy Twp., East Donegal Twp., Greenwood Twp. (Perry County), Howe Twp., Juniata Twp. (Perry County), Marietta, Maytown, Millerstown, Mount Joy (Lancaster County), Mount Joy Twp. (Lancaster County), Mountville, Newport (Perry County), Oliver Twp. (Perry County), Rapho Twp. (Lancaster County), Tuscarora Twp. (Perry County), West Donegal Twp., West Hempfield Twp. (Lancaster County). ICA: PA0068.
TV Market Ranking: 57 (Conoy Twp., East Donegal Twp., Elizabethtown, Greenwood Twp., Howe Twp., Marietta, Maytown, Millerstown, Mount Joy, Mount Joy Twp., Mountville, Newport, Oliver Twp., Rapho Twp., Tuscarora Twp., West Donegal Twp., West Hempfield Twp.); Outside TV Markets (Armagh Twp., Brown Twp.). Franchise award date: N.A. Franchise expiration date: N.A. Began: June 1, 1967.
Channel capacity: 57 (2-way capable; operating 2-way). Channels available but not in use: N.A.
Basic Service
Subscribers: 22,196.
Programming (received off-air): WBAL-TV (N), WMAR-TV (A) Baltimore; WHP-TV (C), WHTM-TV (A), WITF-TV (P) Harrisburg; WGAL (N), WLYH-TV (U) Lancaster; KYW-TV (C), WCAU (N), WPHL-TV (W), WPSG (U), WPVI-TV (A), WTXF-TV (F) Philadelphia; WGCB-TV (I) Red Lion; WPMT (F) York; allband FM.
Programming (via satellite): A & E; American Movie Classics; Animal Planet; C-SPAN; C-SPAN 2; CNBC; CNN; Cartoon Network; Comedy Central; Country Music TV; Discovery Channel; ESPN; ESPN 2; Fox Family Channel; Fox News Channel; Fox Sports Net Pittsburgh; Headline News; History Channel; Home Shopping Network; Learning Channel; Lifetime; MTV; Nashville Network; Nickelodeon; QVC; TV Guide Channel; The New Encore; The Weather Channel; Turner Network TV; USA Network; VH1.
Fee: $5.31 installation; $21.16 monthly.
Pay Service 1
Pay Units: 2,123.
Programming (via satellite): Cinemax.
Fee: $10.02 monthly.
Pay Service 2
Pay Units: 729.
Programming (via satellite): Disney Channel.
Fee: $10.02 monthly.
Pay Service 3
Pay Units: 3,281.
Programming (via satellite): HBO.
Fee: $10.02 monthly.
Pay Service 4
Pay Units: 330.

Programming (via satellite): The Movie Channel.
Fee: $10.02 monthly.
Pay Service 5
Pay Units: 689.
Programming (via satellite): Showtime.
Fee: $10.02 monthly.
Pay-Per-View
Addressable homes: 10,891.
Action Pay-Per-View; Spice; Viewer's Choice.
Equipment: Scientific-Atlanta headend; C-COR amplifiers; Comm/Scope cable; MSI character generator; Pioneer set top converters; Pioneer addressable set top converters; Scientific-Atlanta satellite antenna; Scientific-Atlanta satellite receivers.
Miles of plant: 520.0 (coaxial); 16.0 (fiber optic). Additional miles planned: 28.0 (coaxial).
Manager: Ron Amick. Chief technician: Keith Pary. Operations manager: Karen Moad.
City fee: 5% of gross.
Ownership: AT&T Broadband & Internet Services (MSO). Purchased from Time Warner Cable, July 1, 1999.

ELKLAND—TW Fanch 2, Box 198, 176 Main St., Dansville, NY 14437. Phone: 716-335-2554. Fax: 716-335-8558. County: Tioga. Also serves Deerfield Twp. (Tioga County), Lawrence Twp. (Tioga County), Nelson, Nelson Twp., Osceola, Tioga Twp. ICA: PA0160.
TV Market Ranking: Below 100 (Elkland, Lawrence Twp., Nelson, Nelson Twp., Osceola, Tioga Twp.); Outside TV Markets (Deerfield Twp.). Franchise award date: N.A. Franchise expiration date: September 20, 2003. Began: November 1, 1952.
Channel capacity: 62 (2-way capable; not operating 2-way). Channels available but not in use: 29.
Basic Service
Subscribers: 1,220.
Programming (received off-air): WBNG-TV (C) Binghamton; WYDC (U,W) Corning; WENY-TV (A), WETM-TV (N) Elmira; WVIA-TV (P) Scranton & Wilkes-Barre; allband FM.
Programming (via satellite): WGN-TV (W) Chicago; WPIX (W) New York; C-SPAN; Fox Family Channel; FoxNet; Home Shopping Network; Nashville Network; Sci-Fi Channel; TBS Superstation.
Current originations: Automated time-weather; educational access.
Fee: $35.00 installation; $15.00 monthly.
Expanded Basic Service
Subscribers: 945.
Programming (via satellite): A & E; American Movie Classics; CNN; Country Music TV; Discovery Channel; ESPN; Fox Sports Net Pittsburgh; History Channel; Learning Channel; Lifetime; Nickelodeon; Turner Network TV; USA Network.
Fee: $15.95 installation; $6.50 monthly.
Pay Service 1
Pay Units: 155.
Programming (via satellite): Cinemax.
Fee: $10.95 monthly.
Pay Service 2
Pay Units: 92.
Programming (via satellite): Disney Channel.
Fee: $10.95 monthly.
Pay Service 3
Pay Units: 275.
Programming (via satellite): HBO.
Fee: $30.00 installation; $10.95 monthly.
Equipment: Scientific-Atlanta headend; Scientific-Atlanta & Vikoa amplifiers; Comm/Scope cable; Scientific-Atlanta set top converters; Scientific-Atlanta satellite antenna; Scientific-Atlanta satellite receivers.
Miles of plant: 30.0 (coaxial). Additional miles planned: 5.0 (coaxial). Homes passed: 2,000. Total homes in franchised area: 2,500.
Manager: Frank Gallagher. Chief technician: Mike Kane.
City fee: $250.00 annually.
Ownership: Fanch Communications Inc. (MSO); Time Warner Cable (MSO). See Cable System Ownership.

ELLWOOD CITY—Armstrong Cable Services, Box 40, 531 Perry Way, Zelienople, PA 16063. Phone: 724-452-5213. Fax: 724-452-8008. Counties: Beaver, Butler & Lawrence. Also serves Big Beaver (Beaver County), Daugherty Twp., Ellport, Franklin Twp. (Beaver County), Homewood, Koppel, Lawrence County, New Beaver, North Beaver Twp. (Lawrence County), North Sewickley Twp., Perry Twp. (Lawrence County), Shenango Twp. (Lawrence County), Slippery Rock Twp. (Lawrence County), Taylor Twp. (Lawrence County), Wampum, Wayne Twp. (Lawrence County), Worth Twp. ICA: PA0077.
TV Market Ranking: 10 (Big Beaver, Daugherty Twp., Ellport, Ellwood City, Franklin Twp., Homewood, Koppel, New Beaver, North Beaver Twp., North Sewickley Twp., Perry Twp., Slippery Rock Twp., Taylor Twp., Wampum, Wayne Twp.); 79 (Big Beaver, Ellport, Ellwood City, Franklin Twp., Homewood, Koppel, New Beaver, North Beaver Twp., North Sewickley Twp., Perry Twp., Shenango Twp., Taylor Twp., Wampum, Wayne Twp., Worth Twp.); 90 (Big Beaver, Homewood). Franchise award date: August 1, 1965. Franchise expiration date: August 1, 2009. Began: October 1, 1967.
Channel capacity: 50 (not 2-way capable). Channels available but not in use: 5.
Basic Service
Subscribers: 10,280.
Programming (received off-air): WPCB-TV (I) Greensburg; WNPA (U) Jeanette; KDKA-TV (C), WCWB (W), WPGH-TV (F), WPXI (N), WQED (P), WQEX (P), WTAE-TV (A) Pittsburgh.
Programming (via microwave): Pittsburgh Cable News Channel.
Programming (via satellite): WGN-TV (W) Chicago; A & E; American Movie Classics; C-SPAN; CNBC; CNN; Cartoon Network; Comedy Central; Court TV; Discovery Channel; ESPN; ESPN 2; Fox Family Channel; Fox Sports Net Pittsburgh; Headline News; Home Shopping Network; Learning Channel; Lifetime; MSNBC; MTV; Nashville Network; Nick at Nite's TV Land; Nickelodeon; Pennsylvania Cable Network; QVC; TBS Superstation; TV Guide Channel; The Inspirational Network; The Weather Channel; Turner Network TV; USA Network; VH1.
Current originations: Educational access.
Fee: $35.00 installation (aerial), $52.50 (underground); $25.95 monthly; $2.95 converter.
Pay Service 1
Pay Units: 1,025.
Programming (via satellite): Cinemax.
Fee: $9.95 monthly.
Pay Service 2
Pay Units: 582.
Programming (via satellite): Disney Channel.
Fee: $7.95 monthly.
Pay Service 3
Pay Units: 1,721.
Programming (via satellite): HBO.
Fee: $11.95 monthly.
Pay Service 4
Pay Units: 417.
Programming (via satellite): Showtime.
Fee: $9.95 monthly.
Pay Service 5
Pay Units: 91.
Programming (via satellite): DMX.
Fee: $7.95 monthly.
Pay-Per-View
Addressable homes: 500.
Local advertising: Yes. Available in satellite distributed & character-generated programming.
Equipment: Scientific-Atlanta headend; C-COR amplifiers; General cable; Scientific-Atlanta character generator; Scientific-Atlanta set top converters; Scientific-Atlanta addressable set top converters; Eagle & Pico traps; Scientific-Atlanta satellite antenna; Scientific-Atlanta satellite receivers; Texscan commercial insert.
Miles of plant: 283.5 (coaxial); 100.0 (fiber optic). Homes passed: 12,219. Total homes in franchised area: 13,000.
Manager: James R. Culver. Assistant manager: Carl Rose. Chief technician: Bruce Durbin. Marketing director: Aaron Call. Customer service manager: Melinda Schilling.
City fee: 0%-5% of gross.
Ownership: Armstrong Group of Companies (MSO).

EMMAUS—Service Electric Cable TV Inc., 2260 Ave. A, Bethlehem, PA 18017-2108. Phone: 610-865-9100. Fax: 610-865-5031.
E-mail: office@sectv.com.
Web site: http://www.sectv.com.
County: Lehigh. Also serves Lower Macungie Twp. (Lehigh County), Macungie, Salisbury Twp. (Lehigh County), Upper Milford Twp. ICA: PA0081.
TV Market Ranking: Below 100. Franchise award date: December 1, 1963. Franchise expiration date: N.A. Began: December 7, 1963.
Channel capacity: 74 (2-way capable; not operating 2-way). Channels available but not in use: None.
Basic Service
Subscribers: 8,985.
Programming (received off-air): WFMZ-TV (I), WLVT-TV (P) Allentown; WBPH-TV (I) Bethlehem; WGTW (I) Burlington; WABC-TV (A), WNBC (N), WNYW (F), WPIX (W), WWOR-TV (U) New York; KYW-TV (C), WCAU (N), WPHL-TV (W), WPSG (U), WPVI-TV (A), WTXF-TV (F) Philadelphia; WTVE (H) Reading; WBRE-TV (N), WNEP-TV (A) Scranton & Wilkes-Barre; 75 FMs.
Programming (via satellite): C-SPAN; EWTN; Home Shopping Network; Pennsylvania Cable Network; QVC; TBS Superstation; TV Food Network; TV Guide Channel.
Current originations: Automated time-weather; public access; educational access; government access; religious access; leased access; library access; automated emergency alert; local news; local sports.
Fee: $25.00 installation (aerial), $50.00 (underground); $11.82 monthly; $1.80 converter; $25.00 additional installation.
Expanded Basic Service
Subscribers: 8,851.
Programming (via microwave): Comcast SportsNet.
Programming (via satellite): A & E; American Movie Classics; C-SPAN 2; CNBC; CNN; Cartoon Network; Comedy Central; Country Music TV; Discovery Channel; Disney Channel; E! Entertainment TV; ESPN; ESPN 2; FX; Fox Family Channel; Fox News Channel; Golf Channel; Headline News; History Channel; Home & Garden Television; Learning Channel; Lifetime; MSNBC; MTV; Nashville Network; Nick at Nite's TV Land; Nickelodeon; Romance Classics; Sci-Fi Channel; Style; The Inspirational Network; The Weather Channel; Turner Network TV; USA Network; VH1; Z Music Television.
Fee: $25.00 installation; $24.83 monthly.
Pay Service 1
Pay Units: 907.
Programming (via satellite): Cinemax (multiplexed).
Fee: $7.95 monthly.
Pay Service 2
Pay Units: 1,201.
Programming (via satellite): HBO (multiplexed).
Fee: $9.95 monthly.
Pay Service 3
Pay Units: 346.
Programming (via satellite): Showtime; The Movie Channel.
Fee: $9.95 monthly.
Pay Service 4
Pay Units: 139.
Programming (via satellite): Playboy TV.
Fee: $7.95 monthly.
Pay-Per-View
Addressable homes: 3,573.
Viewer's Choice.
Fee: Varies.
Pay-per-view manager: Steve Salash.
Interactive Services
Subscribers: 31.
Games.
Fee: $12.95 monthly.
Local advertising: Yes (insert only). Available in satellite distributed, locally originated & character-generated programming. Rates: $5.00/Week. Local sales manager: Dan Walsh. Regional interconnect: Metrobase Cable Advertising.
Program Guide: TV Host.
Equipment: Jerrold headend; Philips & GTE Sylvania amplifiers; Comm/Scope cable; Siecor fiber optic cable; Scientific-Atlanta set top converters; Jerrold addressable set top converters; Zenith modems; GTE Sylvania & Philips traps; Scientific-Atlanta satellite antenna; Jerrold satellite receivers; Sony commercial insert.
Miles of plant: 167.0 (coaxial). Homes passed: 9,918.
Manager: John J. Capparell. Chief technician: Jeffrey Kelly. Program director: Don Hunt. Marketing director: Steve Salash. Customer service manager: MaryAnn Detweiler.
City fee: 5% of gross.
Ownership: Service Electric Cable TV Inc. (MSO).

EPHRATA—Blue Ridge Communications, Box 150, 804 Academy Heights Ave., Ephrata, PA 17522. Phone: 717-733-4111. Fax: 717-733-3245. Counties: Berks & Lancaster. Also serves Adamstown, Akron, Brecknock Twp. (Lancaster County), Caernarvon Twp. (Lancaster County), Clay Twp. (Lancaster County), Denver, Earl Twp. (Lancaster County), East Cocalico Twp., East Earl Twp. (portions), Elizabeth Twp. (Lancaster County), Ephrata Twp. (Lancaster County), Lititz, Manheim, Penn Twp. (Lancaster County), Rapho Twp. (Lancaster County), South Heidelberg Twp. (Berks County), Spring Twp. (Berks County), Terre Hill, Warwick Twp. (Lancaster County), West Cocalico Twp., West Earl Twp. (northern portion). ICA: PA0031.
TV Market Ranking: 57. Franchise award date: N.A. Franchise expiration date: N.A. Began: November 11, 1965.
Channel capacity: 62 (2-way capable). Channels available but not in use: None.

Basic Service
Subscribers: 30,000.
Programming (received off-air): WHP-TV (C), WHTM-TV (A), WITF-TV (P) Harrisburg; WGAL (N), WLYH-TV (U) Lancaster; KYW-TV (C), WCAU (N), WPHL-TV (W), WPVI-TV (A), WTXF-TV (F) Philadelphia; WGCB-TV (I) Red Lion; WPMT (F) York; allband FM.
Programming (via satellite): Cartoon Network.
Current originations: Automated time-weather; educational access; local news; local sports.
Fee: $45.00 installation; $7.75 monthly.
Expanded Basic Service
Subscribers: 29,106.
Programming (via satellite): C-SPAN 2; Learning Channel; TV Food Network; The Inspirational Network; Travel Channel; Turner Classic Movies; Z Music Television.
Fee: $23.50 monthly.
A la Carte 1
Subscribers: 863.
Programming (via satellite): Comedy Central; Court TV; ESPN 2.
Fee: N.A.
Pay Service 1
Pay Units: 2,002.
Programming (via satellite): Cinemax.
Fee: $10.00 installation; $10.00 monthly.
Pay Service 2
Pay Units: 1,675.
Programming (via satellite): Disney Channel.
Fee: $10.00 installation; $8.95 monthly.
Pay Service 3
Pay Units: 3,276.
Programming (via satellite): HBO.
Fee: $10.00 installation; $10.00 monthly.
Pay Service 4
Pay Units: 1,138.
Programming (via satellite): Showtime.
Fee: $10.00 installation; $10.00 monthly.
Pay-Per-View
Addressable homes: 7,000.
Viewer's Choice.
Local advertising: Yes. Rates: $20.00/Minute; $10.00/30 Seconds.
Equipment: Scientific-Atlanta headend; C-COR amplifiers; Amiga character generator; Tocom set top converters; Tocom addressable set top converters; Scientific-Atlanta satellite antenna.
Miles of plant: 627.0 (coaxial); 10.0 (fiber optic). Additional miles planned: 12.0 (coaxial); 50.0 (fiber optic). Homes passed: 40,250.
Manager: Bob Miller. Chief technician: Jeff Oberholtzer. Marketing director: Robin Eddy.
Ownership: Pencor Services Inc. (MSO).

ERIE—Erie Cablevision, 3627 Zimmerman Rd., Erie, PA 16510. Phone: 814-453-4553. Fax: 814-456-5162. County: Erie. ICA: PA0019.
TV Market Ranking: Below 100. Franchise award date: N.A. Franchise expiration date: October 1, 2001. Began: December 14, 1981.
Channel capacity: 84 (2-way capable; operating 2-way). Channels available but not in use: 20.
Basic Service
Subscribers: 30,400; Commercial subscribers: 206.
Programming (received off-air): WFXP (F), WICU-TV (N), WJET-TV (A), WQLN (P), WSEE (C) Erie; FMs.
Programming (via satellite): WGN-TV (W) Chicago; QVC; TBS Superstation.
Current originations: Public access; educational access; government access; automated emergency alert.
Fee: $52.86 installation; $4.33 monthly; $0.57 converter; $26.43 additional installation.
Commercial fee: $19.95 monthly.
Expanded Basic Service
Subscribers: N.A.
Programming (via satellite): A & E; American Movie Classics; Animal Planet; BET; C-SPAN; C-SPAN 2; CNBC; CNN; Cartoon Network; Comedy Central; Court TV; Discovery Channel; E! Entertainment TV; ESPN; ESPN 2; EWTN; Fox Family Channel; Fox Sports Net Ohio; Goodlife TV Network; Headline News; Home Shopping Network; Knowledge TV; Learning Channel; Lifetime; MTV; Nashville Network; Nick at Nite's TV Land; Nickelodeon; Pax Net; TV Food Network; TV Guide Channel; TV Guide Sneak Prevue; The Box; The Inspirational Network; The Weather Channel; Trinity Bcstg. Network; Turner Network TV; USA Network; Univision; VH1; ValueVision; WB 100+ Station Group.
Fee: $25.41 monthly.
A la Carte 1
Subscribers: N.A.
Programming (via satellite): Country Music TV; History Channel; Sci-Fi Channel; The New Encore; Turner Classic Movies.
Fee: $3.99 monthly (package); $0.99 monthly (CMT or History Channel), $1.29 monthly (Encore or Sci-Fi).
Pay Service 1
Pay Units: 3,900.
Programming (via satellite): Cinemax (multiplexed).
Fee: $11.91 monthly.
Pay Service 2
Pay Units: 1,630.
Programming (via satellite): Disney Channel.
Fee: $11.91 monthly.
Pay Service 3
Pay Units: 7,000.
Programming (via satellite): HBO (multiplexed).
Fee: $11.91 monthly.
Pay Service 4
Pay Units: 1,842.
Programming (via satellite): Showtime (multiplexed).
Fee: $11.91 monthly.
Pay Service 5
Pay Units: 363.
Programming (via satellite): The Movie Channel.
Fee: $5.05 monthly.
Pay Service 6
Pay Units: N.A.
Programming (via satellite): Fox Sports Net Pittsburgh; Playboy TV.
Fee: $4.95 monthly (FSP), $11.91 monthly (Playboy TV).
Pay-Per-View
Addressable homes: 10,696.
Action Pay-Per-View; Hot Choice; Playboy TV; Spice; Viewer's Choice.
Fee: Varies.
Local advertising: Yes. Available in satellite distributed, locally originated, character-generated & taped programming.
Equipment: Scientific-Atlanta headend; RCA amplifiers; Comm/Scope cable; Sony cameras; Sony VTRs; Hamlin set top converters; Scientific-Atlanta addressable set top converters; Arcom & Pico traps; Hughes satellite antenna; Jerrold & Hughes satellite receivers.
Miles of plant: 269.0 (coaxial). Additional miles planned: 40.0 (fiber optic). Homes passed: 49,000. Total homes in franchised area: 49,000.
Manager: William Wright. Chief technician: Keith Krueger. Marketing director: Kevin Kick.
City fee: 5% of gross.
Ownerhsip: Erie Cablevision.

ESTELLA—Beaver Valley Cable Co., Box 60-D, RR 2, Rome, PA 18837. Phone: 570-247-2512. Fax: 570-247-2494. County: Sullivan. Also serves Lincoln Falls, Millview. ICA: PA0329.
TV Market Ranking: Below 100 (Lincoln Falls, Millview); Outside TV Markets (Estella). Franchise award date: N.A. Franchise expiration date: N.A. Began: January 1, 1971.
Channel capacity: 45 (not 2-way capable). Channels available but not in use: 33.
Basic Service
Subscribers: 70.
Programming (received off-air): WBRE-TV (N), WNEP-TV (A), WVIA-TV (P), WYOU (C) Scranton & Wilkes-Barre.
Programming (via satellite): WGN-TV (W) Chicago; CNN; ESPN; Fox Family Channel; FoxNet; Nashville Network; TBS Superstation; USA Network.
Fee: $30.00 installation; $13.00 monthly.
Miles of plant: 9.2 (coaxial). Homes passed: 125.
Manager: Doug Soden. Chief technician: Gary Powers.
Ownership: Beaver Valley Cable Inc. (MSO).

FANNETTSBURG—Valley Cable Systems, Box 78, Doylesburg, PA 17219. Phone: 717-349-7717. County: Franklin. ICA: PA0330.
TV Market Ranking: Below 100. Franchise award date: January 1, 1987. Franchise expiration date: January 1, 2007. Began: January 1, 1987.
Channel capacity: 42 (not 2-way capable). Channels available but not in use: 13.
Basic Service
Subscribers: 150.
Programming (received off-air): WMPT (P) Annapolis; WHAG-TV (N), WJAL (W) Hagerstown; WHP-TV (C), WHTM-TV (A), WITF-TV (P) Harrisburg; WJAC-TV (N), WTAJ-TV (C) Johnstown-Altoona; WGAL (N), WLYH-TV (U) Lancaster; WDCA (U), WJLA-TV (A), WTTG (F) Washington; WPMT (F) York.
Programming (via satellite): WGN-TV (W) Chicago; CNBC; CNN; Country Music TV; Discovery Channel; Disney Channel; ESPN; ESPN 2; Fox Family Channel; MTV; Nashville Network; Nickelodeon; QVC; TBS Superstation; The Weather Channel; Turner Network TV; USA Network; VH1.
Fee: $40.00 installation; $17.95 monthly.
Pay Service 1
Pay Units: 14.
Programming (via satellite): The Movie Channel.
Fee: $9.54 monthly.
Local advertising: Yes. Available in character-generated programming.
Miles of plant: 10.0 (coaxial). Additional miles planned: 5.0 (coaxial). Total homes in franchised area: 500.
Manager: Barry L. Kepner.
City fee: None.
Ownership: Valley Cable Systems (MSO).

FANNETTSBURG—Fannettsburg Cable TV Co., Box 202, Fannettsburg, PA 17221. Phone: 717-349-7775. Counties: Franklin & Fulton. Also serves Burnt Cabins, Metal, Willow Hill. ICA: PA0331.
TV Market Ranking: Below 100. Franchise award date: N.A. Franchise expiration date: N.A. Began: September 16, 1976.
Channel capacity: 13 (2-way capable; operating 2-way). Channels available but not in use: N.A.
Basic Service
Subscribers: N.A.
Programming (received off-air): WHAG-TV (N) Hagerstown; WHP-TV (C), WHTM-TV (A), WITF-TV (P) Harrisburg; WJAC-TV (N), WTAJ-TV (C) Johnstown-Altoona; WGAL (N), WLYH-TV (U) Lancaster; WTTG (F) Washington; WPMT (F) York; allband FM.
Fee: $150.00 installation; $8.00 monthly.
Pay Service 1
Pay Units: N.A.
Programming (via satellite): The Movie Channel.
Fee: $6.00 monthly.
Equipment: Comm/Scope cable.
Manager: Alan McMullen.
Ownership: Fannettsburg Cable TV Co.

FAWN GROVE—Clearview Partners, 2242 Conowingo Rd., Bel Air, MD 21015. Phone: 410-838-7600. Fax: 410-838-8546. County: York. Also serves Chanceford Twp. (York County), Cross Roads, Cross Roads Borough, Delta Borough, East Hopewell Twp. (York County), Fawn Grove Borough, Fawn Twp. (York County), Hopewell Twp. (York County), Lower Chanceford Twp. (York County), Lower Windsor Twp., North Hopewell Twp. (York County), Peach Bottom Twp. (York County), Shrewsbury Twp. (York County), Stewartstown, Windsor Twp., Winterstown, Winterstown Borough. ICA: PA0152.
TV Market Ranking: 14 (Fawn Grove, Peach Bottom Twp.); 57 (Chanceford Twp., Cross Roads, Cross Roads Borough, Delta Borough, East Hopewell Twp., Fawn Grove Borough, Fawn Twp., Hopewell Twp., Lower Chanceford Twp., Lower Windsor Twp., North Hopewell Twp., Shrewsbury Twp., Stewartstown, Windsor Twp., Winterstown, Winterstown Borough). Franchise award date: April 25, 1989. Franchise expiration date: April 25, 2004. Began: July 1, 1989.
Channel capacity: 76 (2-way capable; not operating 2-way). Channels available but not in use: 21.
Basic Service
Subscribers: 3,784.
Programming (received off-air): WBAL-TV (N), WJZ-TV (C), WMAR-TV (A), WNUV (W) Baltimore; WHP-TV (C), WHTM-TV (A), WITF-TV (P) Harrisburg; WGAL (N), WLYH-TV (U) Lancaster; WGCB-TV (I) Red Lion; WPMT (F) York.
Fee: $35.00 installation; $11.88 monthly; $1.25 converter; $10.20 additional installation.
Expanded Basic Service
Subscribers: 3,709.

Programming (received off-air): WBFF (F) Baltimore.
Programming (via satellite): A & E; Animal Planet; C-SPAN; CNBC; CNN; Cartoon Network; Comedy Central; Country Music TV; Discovery Channel; Disney Channel; E! Entertainment TV; ESPN; ESPN 2; Fox Family Channel; Headline News; History Channel; Home & Garden Television; Home Shopping Network; Home Team Sports; Learning Channel; Lifetime; MSNBC; MTV; Nashville Network; Nickelodeon; Pennsylvania Cable Network; QVC; Sci-Fi Channel; Style; TBS Superstation; TV Guide Channel; The Weather Channel; Turner Classic Movies; Turner Network TV; USA Network; VH1.
Fee: $35.00 installation; $16.57 monthly.

Pay Service 1
Pay Units: 321.
Programming (via satellite): Cinemax (multiplexed).
Fee: $15.00 installation; $10.45 monthly.

Pay Service 2
Pay Units: 651.
Programming (via satellite): HBO (multiplexed).
Fee: $15.00 installation; $10.45 monthly.

Pay Service 3
Pay Units: 55.
Programming (via satellite): Showtime.
Fee: $10.75 monthly.

Pay-Per-View
Addressable homes: 717.

Local advertising: Yes. Available in satellite distributed & character-generated programming. Local sales manager: Bob Turk.
Equipment: Scientific-Atlanta headend; Magnavox amplifiers; Trilogy & Comm/Scope cable; Siecor fiber optic cable; Microtek character generator; Scientific-Atlanta set top converters; Scientific-Atlanta addressable set top converters; Eagle traps; Comtech satellite antenna; Standard Communications satellite receivers; Sony commercial insert.
Miles of plant: 209.0 (coaxial); 34.0 (fiber optic). Homes passed: 5,736.
Manager: Douglas Nace. Chief engineer: Mike Greer. Marketing director & customer service manager: Leah Micucci.
City fee: 3% of gross.
Ownership: Clearview Partners (MSO).

FLEETWOOD—Service Electric Cable TV, Box 8, 6400 Perkiomen Ave., Birdsboro, PA 19508. Phone: 610-944-7801. Fax: 610-944-3094. County: Berks. Also serves Maiden Creek, Richmond Twp. (Berks County), Ruscombmanor Twp. (Berks County). ICA: PA0122.
TV Market Ranking: Below 100. Franchise award date: May 1, 1965. Franchise expiration date: N.A. Began: May 1, 1965.
Channel capacity: 54 (not 2-way capable). Channels available but not in use: 25.

Basic Service
Subscribers: 3,655.
Programming (received off-air): WFMZ-TV (I), WLVT-TV (P) Allentown; WGAL (N) Lancaster; KYW-TV (C), WCAU (N), WPHL-TV (W), WPVI-TV (A), WTXF-TV (F) Philadelphia; WVIA-TV (P) Scranton & Wilkes-Barre.
Programming (via satellite): A & E; C-SPAN; C-SPAN 2; CNN; Discovery Channel; ESPN; Fox Family Channel; Headline News; Lifetime; MTV; Nashville Network; Nick at Nite; Nickelodeon; The Weather Channel; Turner Network TV; USA Network.
Fee: $32.00 installation; $19.74 monthly; $7.50 additional installation.

Pay Service 1
Pay Units: 1,449.
Programming (via satellite): Cinemax; Disney Channel; HBO; Showtime.
Fee: $5.00 installation; $8.70 monthly (Disney), $10.15 monthly (Cinemax), $10.70 monthly (Showtime), $10.80 monthly (HBO).

Pay-Per-View
Addressable homes: 1,449.
Special events.

Local advertising: Yes. Available in character-generated programming. Rates: $5.00/Week. Local sales manager: Curt Brown.
Equipment: Jerrold & Scientific-Atlanta headend; Texscan amplifiers; Comm/Scope cable; Jerrold addressable set top converters; Scientific-Atlanta satellite antenna; Standard Components & Scientific-Atlanta satellite receivers.
Miles of plant: 62.0 (coaxial); 10.0 (fiber optic). Homes passed: 3,840.
Manager: Karl E. Kowatch.
City fee: 3% of gross.
Ownership: Service Electric Cable TV Inc. (MSO).

FOREST CITY—Adams CATV Inc., 9 N. Main St., Carbondale, PA 18407-2303. Phone: 717-282-6121. Fax: 717-282-3787. Counties: Lackawanna, Susquehanna & Wayne. Also serves Browndale, Richmondale Village, Vandling. ICA: PA0179.
TV Market Ranking: 49. Franchise award date: N.A. Franchise expiration date: N.A. Began: November 1, 1961.
Channel capacity: 22. Channels available but not in use: N.A.

Basic Service
Subscribers: 1,286.
Programming (received off-air): WPIX (W), WWOR-TV (U) New York; WBRE-TV (N), WNEP-TV (A), WSWB (W), WVIA-TV (P), WYOU (C) Scranton & Wilkes-Barre; allband FM.
Programming (via satellite): CNN; Discovery Channel; ESPN; Goodlife TV Network; Nashville Network; TBS Superstation; Turner Network TV; USA Network.
Fee: $50.00 installation; $12.50 monthly.

Pay Service 1
Pay Units: 488.
Programming (via satellite): Disney Channel; HBO; Showtime.
Fee: $8.00 monthly (Disney), $9.00 monthly (Showtime), $11.00 monthly (HBO).

Equipment: Jerrold headend; Jerrold amplifiers.
Miles of plant: 31.0 (coaxial). Homes passed: 1,525.
Manager: Mark Haverkate.
City fee: None.
Ownership: Adams CATV Inc. (MSO).

FORT INDIANTOWN GAP—Gap Cable TV Inc., 3925 Hill Church Rd., Lebanon, PA 17042. Phone: 717-865-0511. County: Lebanon. Also serves East Hanover Twp. (Lebanon County), Union Twp. (Lebanon County). ICA: PA0332.
TV Market Ranking: 57. Franchise award date: December 5, 1991. Franchise expiration date: December 5, 2001. Began: August 15, 1992.
Channel capacity: 46. Channels available but not in use: None.

Basic Service
Subscribers: 300.
Programming (received off-air): WHP-TV (C), WHTM-TV (A), WITF-TV (P) Harrisburg; WGAL (N), WLYH-TV (U) Lancaster; WGCB-TV (I) Red Lion; WPMT (F) York.
Programming (via satellite): WGN-TV (W) Chicago; WPIX (W) New York; A & E; American Movie Classics; BET; C-SPAN; C-SPAN 2; CNBC; CNN; Cartoon Network; Comedy Central; Discovery Channel; ESPN; ESPN 2; Fox Family Channel; Headline News; Home Shopping Network; Learning Channel; Lifetime; MTV; Nashville Network; Nickelodeon; Sci-Fi Channel; TBS Superstation; The Health Network; The Weather Channel; Turner Network TV; USA Network; VH1.
Fee: $19.20 monthly; $3.40 converter.

Pay Service 1
Pay Units: 25.
Programming (via satellite): Cinemax; Disney Channel; HBO; Showtime; The Movie Channel.
Fee: $11.00 monthly (each).

Miles of plant: 18.0 (coaxial); None (fiber optic).
Manager: George Bryce.
Ownership: Gap Cable TV Inc.

FORT LOUDON—TV Cable, Suite 2, 1108 Sheller Ave., Chambersburg, PA 17201. Phone: 717-263-8591. Fax: 717-263-6766. County: Franklin. Also serves Peters Twp., St. Thomas Twp. (Franklin County). ICA: PA0333.
TV Market Ranking: Below 100. Franchise award date: N.A. Franchise expiration date: N.A. Began: N.A.
Channel capacity: 77 (not 2-way capable). Channels available but not in use: N.A.

Basic Service
Subscribers: 1,533.
Programming (received off-air): WJZ-TV (C) Baltimore; WHAG-TV (N), WJAL (W), WWPB (P) Hagerstown; WHTM-TV (A), WITF-TV (P) Harrisburg; WGAL (N) Lancaster; WWPX (I) Martinsburg; WDCA (U), WJLA-TV (A), WTTG (F), WUSA (C) Washington.
Programming (via satellite): C-SPAN; Home Shopping Network; Odyssey; QVC; TBS Superstation; TV Guide Channel; TV Guide Sneak Prevue; Trinity Bcstg. Network.
Current originations: Public access.
Fee: $50.25 installation; $13.85 monthly; $1.94 converter.

Digital Basic Service
Subscribers: N.A.
Programming (via satellite): BBC America; DMX; Discovery Home & Leisure; Discovery Kids Channel; Discovery People; Discovery Science Channel; ESPN Classic Sports; ESPNews; Fox Sports World; Game Show Network; History Channel; Home & Garden Television; MuchMusic Network; Outdoor Life Network; Sci-Fi Channel.
Fee: $19.95 monthly.

Expanded Basic Service
Subscribers: N.A.
Programming (via satellite): A & E; American Movie Classics; BET; C-SPAN 2; CNBC; CNN; Cartoon Network; Comedy Central; Country Music TV; Discovery Channel; E! Entertainment TV; ESPN; ESPN 2; FX; Fox Family Channel; Fox Sports Net Pittsburgh; Headline News; History Channel; Home Team Sports; Learning Channel; Lifetime; MSNBC; MTV; Nashville Network; Nick at Nite; Nickelodeon; Sci-Fi Channel; The Weather Channel; Travel Channel; Turner Network TV; USA Network; VH1; ValueVision.
Fee: $13.63 monthly.

Digital Expanded Basic Service
Subscribers: N.A.
Programming (via satellite): BET Movies/Starz!; Encore Movie Networks; Independent Film Channel; Romance Classics; Starz!; The New Encore; Turner Classic Movies.
Fee: $14.95 monthly.

Pay Service 1
Pay Units: 442.
Programming (via satellite): Cinemax; Disney Channel; HBO; Showtime; The Movie Channel.
Fee: $10.95 monthly (each).

Digital Pay Service 1
Pay Units: N.A.
Programming (via satellite): Cinemax (multiplexed); HBO (multiplexed); Showtime (multiplexed); The Movie Channel (multiplexed).
Fee: N.A.

Pay-Per-View
Spice; Spice Hot; movies; special events.
Fee: $3.99-$7.99.

Miles of plant: 56.0 (coaxial); None (fiber optic).
Manager: Hans Welch. Chief technician: David Fuchs. Customer service manager: Pam Ardery.
Ownership: Lenfest Communications Inc. (MSO). Purchased from Raystay Co., July 30, 1999.

FRANKLIN (Venango County)—Coaxial Cable Co., 503 13th St., Franklin, PA 16323. Phone: 814-432-5217. Fax: 814-437-2226. County: Venango. Also serves Cranberry Twp. (Venango County), Frenchcreek Twp. (Venango County), Mineral Twp., Polk, Polk Center, Sandy Creek Twp. (Venango County), Sugarcreek (Venango County). ICA: PA0100.
TV Market Ranking: Outside TV Markets. Franchise award date: N.A. Franchise expiration date: April 16, 1999. Began: October 1, 1954.
Channel capacity: 42 (2-way capable; operating 2-way). Channels available but not in use: 9.

Basic Service
Subscribers: 6,169.
Programming (received off-air): WICU-TV (N), WJET-TV (A), WQLN (P), WSEE (C) Erie; KDKA-TV (C), WCWB (W), WPGH-TV (F), WPXI (N), WQED (P), WTAE-TV (A) Pittsburgh; WKBN-TV (C) Youngstown; allband FM.
Programming (via satellite): C-SPAN; ESPN; Fox Family Channel; Learning Channel; Lifetime; Nashville Network; QVC; TBS Superstation; The Weather Channel; USA Network.
Current originations: Public access; religious access; automated emergency alert; local news.
Fee: $40.00 installation; $24.27 monthly; $15.00 additional installation.

Pay Service 1
Pay Units: N.A.
Programming (via satellite): Cinemax; Disney Channel; HBO.
Fee: $7.00 monthly (Disney), $12.95 monthly (Cinemax or HBO).

Local advertising: Yes (locally produced & insert). Available in satellite distributed programming. Local sales manager: Greg Faller.
Program Guide: Cable Watch.
Equipment: Scientific-Atlanta headend; C-COR amplifiers; Comm/Scope cable; Sony cameras; Sony VTRs; Texscan character generator; Hamlin set top converters; Eagle traps; Microdyne satellite antenna; Jerrold satellite receivers.
Miles of plant: 102.0 (coaxial). Additional miles planned: 1.0 (coaxial).
Manager: Brian Frederick.
City fee: 3% of gross.
Ownership: Time Warner Cable (MSO).

FREEPORT—Adelphia Communications Corp., One Adelphia Dr., Blairsville, PA 15717. Phone: 800-892-7300. Fax: 412-459-0648. County: Armstrong. ICA: PA0334.
TV Market Ranking: 10. Franchise award date: N.A. Franchise expiration date: N.A. Began: N.A.
Channel capacity: 52. Channels available but not in use: N.A.

Basic Service
Subscribers: 839.
Programming (received off-air): WPCB-TV (I) Greensburg; WNPA (U) Jeanette; WJAC-TV (N) Johnstown-Altoona; KDKA-TV (C), WPGH-TV (F), WPXI (N), WQED (P), WQEX (P), WTAE-TV (A) Pittsburgh.
Programming (via satellite): WGN-TV (W) Chicago; TBS Superstation.
Fee: N.A.
Expanded Basic Service
Subscribers: 821.
Programming (via satellite): A & E; Animal Planet; C-SPAN; CNN; Comedy Central; Country Music TV; Discovery Channel; Disney Channel; ESPN; ESPN 2; Fox Family Channel; Fox Sports Net Pittsburgh; Headline News; History Channel; Home Shopping Network; Lifetime; MTV; Nashville Network; Nickelodeon; QVC; The Weather Channel; Turner Network TV; USA Network; VH1.
Fee: N.A.
Pay Service 1
Pay Units: 97.
Programming (via satellite): Cinemax.
Fee: $11.50 monthly.
Pay Service 2
Pay Units: 100.
Programming (via satellite): HBO.
Fee: $11.50 monthly.
Pay Service 3
Pay Units: 24.
Programming (via satellite): Showtime.
Fee: $11.50 monthly.
Pay Service 4
Pay Units: 29.
Programming (via satellite): The Movie Channel.
Fee: $11.50 monthly.
Manager: J. Francis Bradley Jr. Chief technician: Dave Bowen.
Ownership: Adelphia Communications Corp. (MSO).

GAINES—Gaines-Watrous TV Inc., Box 30, RR 1, Gaines, PA 16921. Phone: 814-435-6578. Fax: 814-435-8585. Counties: Potter & Tioga. Also serves Gaines Twp. (Tioga County), Pike Twp. (Potter County). ICA: PA0266.
TV Market Ranking: Outside TV Markets. Franchise award date: N.A. Franchise expiration date: N.A. Began: January 1, 1954.
Channel capacity: 36 (not 2-way capable). Channels available but not in use: 11.
Basic Service
Subscribers: 317.
Programming (received off-air): WBNG-TV (C) Binghamton; WIVB-TV (C) Buffalo; WYDC (U,W) Corning; WENY-TV (A), WETM-TV (N) Elmira; WVIA-TV (P), WYOU (C) Scranton & Wilkes-Barre.
Programming (via satellite): WGN-TV (W) Chicago; C-SPAN; CNN; Country Music TV; Discovery Channel; Disney Channel; ESPN; ESPN 2; Fox Family Channel; Home Shopping Network; Learning Channel; Nashville Network; Nick at Nite's TV Land; Odyssey; Outdoor Channel; QVC; TBS Superstation; The Weather Channel; Trinity Bcstg. Network; Turner Network TV.
Fee: $35.00 installation; $15.00 monthly.
Pay Service 1
Pay Units: 60.
Programming (via satellite): Showtime.
Fee: $8.50 monthly.
Equipment: Pico & Jerrold headend; Jerrold amplifiers; Comm/Scope cable; Jerrold set top converters; Jerrold traps; Blonder-Tongue satellite antenna; Pico satellite receivers.
Miles of plant: 20.0 (coaxial). Homes passed: 330.
Manager: Melvin Lowrey.
Ownership: Gaines Watrous TV Association Inc.

GALETON—Blue Ridge Cable TV Inc., 46 N. Academy St., Mansfield, PA 16933. Phone: 570-662-2369. County: Potter. Also serves Pike Twp. (Potter County), West Branch Twp. (Potter County). ICA: PA0222.
TV Market Ranking: Outside TV Markets. Franchise award date: N.A. Franchise expiration date: N.A. Began: January 1, 1953.
Channel capacity: 35. Channels available but not in use: None.
Basic Service
Subscribers: 574.
Programming (received off-air): WIVB-TV (C) Buffalo; WPSX-TV (P) Clearfield; WENY-TV (A), WETM-TV (N) Elmira; WVIA-TV (P), WYOU (C) Scranton & Wilkes-Barre; allband FM.
Programming (via satellite): WGN-TV (W) Chicago; ESPN; Fox Family Channel; Nashville Network; TBS Superstation; Turner Classic Movies; USA Network.
Fee: $50.00 installation; $15.25 monthly.
Pay Service 1
Pay Units: 71.
Programming (via satellite): Disney Channel.
Fee: $15.00 installation; $8.00 monthly.
Pay Service 2
Pay Units: 186.
Programming (via satellite): HBO.
Fee: $15.00 installation; $11.00 monthly.
Equipment: Cascade & Jerrold headend; Cascade & Jerrold amplifiers; Times Fiber cable; Eagle traps; Scientific-Atlanta satellite antenna; Scientific-Atlanta & Jerrold satellite receivers.
Miles of plant: 12.0 (coaxial). Homes passed: 640. Total homes in franchised area: 640.
Manager: Tom Freeman. Chief technician: Tom O'Neill.
City fee: $200.00 annually.
Ownership: Pencor Services Inc. (MSO).

GALLITZIN TWP.—TCI of Pennsylvania Inc., Box 349, Rte. 219, Carrolltown, PA 15722. Phone: 814-344-6518. Counties: Cambria & Clearfield. Also serves Allegheny Twp. (Cambria County), Ashville, Cambria County, Cassandra, Clearfield County, Cresson Borough, Cresson Twp., Dean Twp. (Cambria County), Gallitzin Borough, Lilly, Loretto, Sankertown, Tunnelhill, Washington Twp. (Cambria County). ICA: PA0118.
TV Market Ranking: 74 (Allegheny Twp., Ashville, Cassandra, portions of Clearfield County, Cresson Borough, Cresson Twp., Dean Twp., Gallitzin Borough, Gallitzin Twp., Lilly, Loretto, Sankertown, Tunnelhill, Washington Twp.); Outside TV Markets (portions of Clearfield County). Franchise award date: N.A. Franchise expiration date: N.A. Began: October 1, 1970.
Channel capacity: 52. Channels available but not in use: 16.
Basic Service
Subscribers: 3,627.
Programming (received off-air): WPSX-TV (P) Clearfield; WATM-TV (A), WJAC-TV (N), WKBS-TV (I), WTAJ-TV (C), WWCP-TV (F) Johnstown-Altoona; KDKA-TV (C), WPXI (N), WTAE-TV (A) Pittsburgh; allband FM.
Programming (via satellite): A & E; C-SPAN; CNBC; CNN; Discovery Channel; EWTN; Fox Family Channel; Headline News; Ladbroke Racing Channel/Meadows Racing Network; Lifetime; MTV; Nashville Network; Nickelodeon; QVC; TBS Superstation; The Weather Channel.
Fee: $59.95 installation; $18.96 monthly.
Expanded Basic Service
Subscribers: 3,310.
Programming (via satellite): American Movie Classics; Court TV; ESPN; Fox Sports Net Pittsburgh; Turner Network TV; USA Network.
Fee: $2.50 monthly.
Pay Service 1
Pay Units: 153.
Programming (via satellite): Cinemax.
Fee: N.A.
Pay Service 2
Pay Units: 590.
Programming (via satellite): HBO.
Fee: $13.15 monthly.
Pay Service 3
Pay Units: 288.
Programming (via satellite): Showtime.
Fee: N.A.
Pay Service 4
Pay Units: 242.
Programming (via satellite): The New Encore.
Fee: N.A.
Local advertising: Yes.
Equipment: AFC satellite antenna.
Miles of plant: 85.4 (coaxial). Homes passed: 4,822. Total homes in franchised area: 4,822.
Manager: Randy Bender.
City fee: 4% of gross.
Ownership: AT&T Broadband & Internet Services (MSO). Purchased from Tele-Communications Inc., March 9, 1999.

GARLAND—CableVision Communications, Box 2200, 68 5th St., Buckhannon, WV 26201. Phone: 304-472-4193. Fax: 304-472-0756. County: Warren. ICA: PA0291.
TV Market Ranking: Below 100. Franchise award date: N.A. Franchise expiration date: N.A. Began: N.A.
Channel capacity: 13. Channels available but not in use: None.
Basic Service
Subscribers: 50.
Programming (received off-air): WIVB-TV (C), WKBW-TV (A) Buffalo; WICU-TV (N), WJET-TV (A), WQLN (P), WSEE (C) Erie.
Programming (via satellite): CNN; ESPN; FoxNet; Nashville Network; TBS Superstation; USA Network.
Fee: $61.25 installation; $22.00 monthly; $0.73 converter; $19.50 additional installation.
Pay Service 1
Pay Units: 7.
Programming (via satellite): HBO.
Fee: $11.99 monthly.
Equipment: Olson & M/A-Com headend; Jerrold amplifiers.
Miles of plant: 5.0 (coaxial). Homes passed: 116.
Manager: Willie Critchfield. Marketing director: Kenny Phillips.
Ownership: Rifkin & Associates Inc. (MSO). See Cable System Ownership.

GETTYSBURG—GS Communications, Box 3909, 2720 Baltimore Pike, Gettysburg, PA 17325-3909. Phone: 717-337-1630. Fax: 717-337-0992. Counties: Adams & York. Also serves Arendtsville, Bendersville, Biglerville, Bonneauville, Butler Twp. (Adams County), Carroll Valley, Codorus Twp., Cross Roads Borough, Cumberland Twp. (Adams County), Dover Twp., East Berlin, Fairfield, Franklin Twp., Freedom Twp., Germany Twp., Hamilton Twp., Hamiltonban Twp., Huntington Twp., Latimore Twp., Liberty Twp., Littlestown, Manheim Twp., Menallen Twp., Mount Joy Twp., Mount Pleasant Twp., New Oxford, North Codorus Twp., Oxford Twp., Paradise Twp., Reading Twp., Shrewsbury Twp., Springfield Twp., Straban Twp., Tyrone Twp., Union Twp., Warrington Twp., Washington Twp., West Manheim Twp., Winterstown Borough, York Springs. ICA: PA0106.
TV Market Ranking: 57. Franchise award date: N.A. Franchise expiration date: N.A. Began: April 1, 1966.
Channel capacity: 35 (2-way capable; operating 2-way). Channels available but not in use: N.A.
Basic Service
Subscribers: 3,596.
Programming (received off-air): WBAL-TV (N), WBFF (F), WJZ-TV (C), WMAR-TV (A), WMPB (P) Baltimore; WHAG-TV (N) Hagerstown; WHP-TV (C), WHTM-TV (A), WITF-TV (P) Harrisburg; WGAL (N), WLYH-TV (U) Lancaster; WGCB-TV (I) Red Lion; WDCA (U), WTTG (F) Washington; WPMT (F) York; allband FM.
Programming (via satellite): C-SPAN; C-SPAN 2; TBS Superstation.
Current originations: Automated time-weather.
Fee: $39.02 installation; $10.29 monthly; $1.00 converter.
Expanded Basic Service
Subscribers: N.A.
Programming (via satellite): A & E; American Movie Classics; CNN; Discovery Channel; ESPN; Fox Family Channel; Headline News; Lifetime; MTV; Nashville Network; Nickelodeon; QVC; The Weather Channel; Turner Network TV; USA Network.
Fee: $7.34 monthly.
Pay Service 1
Pay Units: 331.
Programming (via satellite): Cinemax.
Fee: $10.15 monthly.
Pay Service 2
Pay Units: 116.
Programming (via satellite): Disney Channel.
Fee: $9.50 monthly.
Pay Service 3
Pay Units: 457.
Programming (via satellite): HBO.
Fee: $12.45 monthly.
Pay Service 4
Pay Units: 261.
Programming (via satellite): Showtime.
Fee: $13.60 monthly.
Pay-Per-View
Special events.
Equipment: CAS & Jerrold headend; Coral & Vikoa amplifiers; Anaconda cable; Scientific-Atlanta satellite antenna; Hughes satellite receivers.
Miles of plant: 35.0 (coaxial). Additional miles planned: 7.0 (coaxial). Homes passed: 6,200. Total homes in franchised area: 6,200.
Manager: Ron DeForrest.
City fee: 3% of gross.
Ownership: Great Southern Printing & Manufacturing Co. (MSO).

GLASSPORT—AT&T Cable Services, 300 Corliss St., Pittsburgh, PA 15220-4815. Phones: 412-875-1100; 412-771-8100. County: Allegheny. Also serves Liberty, Lincoln (Allegheny County), Port Vue. ICA: PA0108.
TV Market Ranking: 10. Franchise award date: N.A. Franchise expiration date: N.A. Began: May 1, 1967.
Channel capacity: N.A. Channels available but not in use: N.A.
Basic Service
Subscribers: 4,705.

Programming (received off-air): WPCB-TV (I) Greensburg; KDKA-TV (C), WCWB (W), WPGH-TV (F), WPXI (N), WQED (P), WQEX (P), WTAE-TV (A) Pittsburgh.
Programming (via microwave): Meadows Racing Network.
Programming (via satellite): BET; C-SPAN; Pennsylvania Cable Network; QVC; TV Guide Sneak Prevue; The Weather Channel.
Fee: $44.95 installation; $10.48 monthly; $1.50 converter; $24.95 additional installation.

Expanded Basic Service
Subscribers: 4,496.
Programming (via microwave): Pittsburgh Cable News Channel.
Programming (via satellite): A & E; American Movie Classics; Animal Planet; C-SPAN 2; CNBC; CNN; Cartoon Network; Court TV; Discovery Channel; ESPN; ESPN 2; EWTN; FX; Fox Family Channel; Fox News Channel; Fox Sports Net Pittsburgh; Headline News; History Channel; Home & Garden Television; Home Shopping Network; Knowledge TV; Learning Channel; Lifetime; MOVIEplex; MTV; Nashville Network; Nickelodeon; Odyssey; Sci-Fi Channel; TBS Superstation; TV Guide Channel; Turner Network TV; USA Network.
Fee: $16.78 monthly.

Pay Service 1
Pay Units: 395.
Programming (via satellite): Cinemax.
Fee: $13.45 monthly.

Pay Service 2
Pay Units: 126.
Programming (via satellite): Disney Channel.
Fee: $12.50 monthly.

Pay Service 3
Pay Units: 754.
Programming (via satellite): HBO (multiplexed).
Fee: $14.95 monthly.

Pay Service 4
Pay Units: 215.
Programming (via satellite): Showtime.
Fee: $14.95 monthly.

Pay Service 5
Pay Units: 1,536.
Programming (via satellite): The New Encore.
Fee: $1.95 monthly.

Pay Service 6
Pay Units: 970.
Programming (via satellite): Starz!
Fee: $6.75 monthly.

Pay-Per-View
Action Pay-Per-View; Playboy TV; Spice; Viewer's Choice.

Program Guide: The Cable Guide.
Miles of plant: 55.5 (coaxial). Homes passed: 6,094. Total homes in franchised area: 6,161.
Manager: Jeffrey C. Harshman. Chief technician: Fred Hamm. Marketing director: Glenn S. Ryerson.
Ownership: AT&T Broadband & Internet Services (MSO). Purchased from Tele-Communications Inc., March 9, 1999.

GLEN RICHEY—Bud's Cable Service, Box 51, RD 3, Clearfield, PA 16830. Phone: 814-765-5018. Fax: 814-765-9831. County: Clearfield. Also serves Bloomington, Olanta, Oshanter. ICA: PA0250.
TV Market Ranking: 74. Franchise award date: N.A. Franchise expiration date: September 1, 1997. Began: September 1, 1977.
Channel capacity: 25 (not 2-way capable). Channels available but not in use: N.A.

Basic Service
Subscribers: 379.
Programming (received off-air): WPSX-TV (P) Clearfield; WNPA (U) Jeanette; WATM-TV (A), WJAC-TV (N), WKBS-TV (I), WTAJ-TV (C), WWCP-TV (F) Johnstown-Altoona.
Programming (via satellite): WGN-TV (W) Chicago; A & E; CNN; Discovery Channel; ESPN; Fox Family Channel; Lifetime; Nashville Network; Nickelodeon; QVC; Sci-Fi Channel; TBS Superstation; Turner Network TV; USA Network.
Fee: $45.00 installation; $20.25 monthly.

Pay Service 1
Pay Units: 70.
Programming (via satellite): HBO.
Fee: $10.00 monthly.

Equipment: C-COR amplifiers; Comm/Scope cable; Standard Communications satellite receivers.
Miles of plant: 22.0 (coaxial); None (fiber optic). Homes passed: 400. Total homes in franchised area: 400.
Manager: Alfred E. Swatsworth.
City fee: None.
Ownership: Bud's Electric Service Inc.

GLEN ROCK—GS Communications, Box 3909, 2720 Baltimore Pike, Gettysburg, PA 17325-3909. Phone: 800-632-9026. Fax: 717-337-0992. County: York. Also serves Codorus, Jefferson (York County), New Freedom, New Salem Borough, North Codorus Twp. (York County), Railroad, Seven Valleys, Shrewsbury, Shrewsbury Twp. (York County), Spring Grove, York/New Salem. ICA: PA0336.
TV Market Ranking: 14 (New Freedom, Railroad, Shrewsbury); 57 (Codorus, Glen Rock, Jefferson, New Freedom, New Salem Borough, North Codorus Twp., Railroad, Seven Valleys, Shrewsbury, Shrewsbury Twp., Spring Grove, York/New Salem). Franchise award date: N.A. Franchise expiration date: N.A. Began: March 1, 1973.
Channel capacity: 60 (not 2-way capable). Channels available but not in use: 8.

Basic Service
Subscribers: 6,757.
Programming (received off-air): WBFF (F), WJZ-TV (C), WMAR-TV (A), WMPB (P) Baltimore; WHP-TV (C), WHTM-TV (A), WITF-TV (P) Harrisburg; WGAL (N), WLYH-TV (U) Lancaster; WGCB-TV (I) Red Lion; WPMT (F) York.
Programming (via satellite): Electronic Program Guide; QVC; TBS Superstation.
Current originations: Educational access; government access.
Fee: $8.95 monthly; $1.37 converter.

Expanded Basic Service
Subscribers: 6,538.
Programming (via satellite): A & E; American Movie Classics; C-SPAN; CNN; Discovery Channel; ESPN; ESPN 2; FX; Fox Family Channel; Headline News; Home Team Sports; Lifetime; MTV; Nashville Network; Nickelodeon; Sci-Fi Channel; The Weather Channel; Turner Network TV; USA Network; VH1.
Fee: $13.70 monthly.

Pay Service 1
Pay Units: 1,012.
Programming (via satellite): Cinemax.
Fee: $8.95 monthly.

Pay Service 2
Pay Units: 767.
Programming (via satellite): Disney Channel.
Fee: $8.95 monthly.

Pay Service 3
Pay Units: 1,445.
Programming (via satellite): HBO.
Fee: $10.95 monthly.

Local advertising: No.
Equipment: Scientific-Atlanta headend; GTE Sylvania & Jerrold amplifiers; Times Fiber cable; Pioneer set top converters; AFC satellite antenna; Microdyne satellite receivers.
Miles of plant: 160.2 (coaxial); None (fiber optic). Additional miles planned: 5.0 (coaxial).
Manager: Tim McCallister. Chief technician: Lloyd Mayhew.
City fee: 3% of gross.
Ownership: Great Southern Printing & Manufacturing Co. (MSO).

GRAHAM TWP.—Ray's TV Cable, 100 Curtis St., Philipsburg, PA 16866. Phone: 814-238-3093. County: Clearfield. Also serves Boggs Twp. (Clearfield County), Wallaceton. ICA: PA0251.
TV Market Ranking: 74 (Boggs Twp., Wallaceton); Outside TV Markets (Graham Twp.). Franchise award date: N.A. Franchise expiration date: N.A. Began: April 1, 1983.
Channel capacity: 33 (not 2-way capable). Channels available but not in use: 3.

Basic Service
Subscribers: 392.
Programming (received off-air): WPSX-TV (P) Clearfield; WATM-TV (A), WJAC-TV (N), WTAJ-TV (C) Johnstown-Altoona; KDKA-TV (C), WTAE-TV (A) Pittsburgh.
Programming (via satellite): CNN; TBS Superstation.
Fee: $14.00 monthly.

Pay Service 1
Pay Units: 137.
Programming (via satellite): HBO.
Fee: N.A.

Miles of plant: 23.0 (coaxial). Homes passed: 400. Total homes in franchised area: 400.
Manager: Ray Smeal.
Ownership: Ray Smeal.

GRAMPIAN—CableVision Communications, Box 2200, 68 5th St., Buckhannon, WV 26201. Phone: 304-472-4193. Fax: 304-472-0756. County: Clearfield. Also serves Bells Landing, Bloom Twp., Curwensville (Clearfield County), Greenwood Twp. (Clearfield County), Hepburnia, Mahaffey, Penn Twp. (Clearfield County), Strawich. ICA: PA0236.
TV Market Ranking: 74 (Bells Landing, Curwensville, Grampian, Greenwood Twp., Hepburnia, Mahaffey, Penn Twp., Strawich); Outside TV Markets (Bloom Twp.). Franchise award date: N.A. Franchise expiration date: N.A. Began: January 1, 1982.
Channel capacity: 35 (not 2-way capable). Channels available but not in use: N.A.

Basic Service
Subscribers: 421.
Programming (received off-air): WPSX-TV (P) Clearfield; WATM-TV (A), WJAC-TV (N), WKBS-TV (I), WTAJ-TV (C), WWCP-TV (F) Johnstown-Altoona; KDKA-TV (C), WTAE-TV (A) Pittsburgh.
Programming (via satellite): WGN-TV (W) Chicago; Animal Planet; C-SPAN; Home Shopping Network; TBS Superstation; Trinity Bcstg. Network.
Fee: $61.25 installation; $14.40 monthly; $1.24 converter; $17.50 additional installation.

Expanded Basic Service
Subscribers: 373.
Programming (via satellite): A & E; American Movie Classics; CNN; Discovery Channel; Disney Channel; E! Entertainment TV; ESPN; ESPN 2; Fox Family Channel; Great American Country; History Channel; Lifetime; MTV; Nashville Network; Nickelodeon; Sci-Fi Channel; The Weather Channel; Turner Network TV; USA Network; VH1.
Fee: $18.13 monthly.

Pay Service 1
Pay Units: 210.
Programming (via satellite): Cinemax; HBO; Showtime.
Fee: $7.95 monthly (Cinemax), $11.95 monthly (Showtime), $11.99 monthly (HBO).

Pay Service 2
Pay Units: N.A.
Programming (via satellite): The Movie Channel.
Fee: $11.95 monthly.

Equipment: Olson & M/A-Com headend; Jerrold amplifiers.
Miles of plant: 28.0 (coaxial).
Manager: Willie Critchfield. Marketing director: Kenny Phillip.
City fee: $500.00 annually.
Ownership: Rifkin & Associates Inc. (MSO). See Cable System Ownership.

GRANVILLE TWP.—Nittany Media Inc., Box 111, Lewistown, PA 17044. Phone: 717-248-3733. County: Mifflin. Also serves Oliver Twp. (Mifflin County). ICA: PA0337.
TV Market Ranking: Outside TV Markets. Franchise award date: N.A. Franchise expiration date: N.A. Began: January 1, 1956.
Channel capacity: 12. Channels available but not in use: N.A.

Basic Service
Subscribers: N.A.
Programming (received off-air): WJZ-TV (C) Baltimore; WPSX-TV (P) Clearfield; WHTM-TV (A), WITF-TV (P) Harrisburg; WJAC-TV (N), WTAJ-TV (C) Johnstown-Altoona; WGAL (N), WLYH-TV (U) Lancaster; WPHL-TV (W) Philadelphia; WTTG (F) Washington.
Fee: N.A.

Manager: Anna H. Hain.
Ownership: Nittany Media Inc. (MSO).

GREEN TWP. (Indiana County)—Adelphia Cable, One Adelphia Dr., Blairsville, PA 15717. Phone: 800-892-7300. Fax: 724-459-0648. County: Indiana. Also serves Alverda, Cherryhill Twp., Commodore (Indiana County), Dixonville (Indiana County), Glen Campbell, Heilwood, Lovejoy, Marion Center, Montgomery Twp. (Indiana County), Pine Twp. (Indiana County), Starford. ICA: PA0338.
TV Market Ranking: 74. Franchise award date: N.A. Franchise expiration date: N.A. Began: February 1, 1987.
Channel capacity: 52 (not 2-way capable). Channels available but not in use: 14.

Basic Service
Subscribers: 1,040.
Programming (received off-air): WPSX-TV (P) Clearfield; WPCB-TV (I) Greensburg; WJAC-TV (N), WWCP-TV (F) Johnstown-Altoona; KDKA-TV (C), WCWB (W), WPGH-TV (F), WPXI (N), WQED (P), WTAE-TV (A) Pittsburgh.
Programming (via satellite): CNN; CNN International; Cartoon Network; Country Music TV; Discovery Channel; ESPN; ESPN 2; Fox Family Channel; Headline News; Ladbroke Racing Channel/Meadows Racing Network; Lifetime; Nashville Network; QVC; Sci-Fi Channel; TBS Superstation; Travel Channel; Turner Classic Movies; Turner Network TV; USA Network.
Fee: $30.00 installation; $23.54 monthly.

Pay Service 1
Pay Units: 208.
Programming (via satellite): HBO; Showtime.
Fee: $6.95 monthly (Showtime), $10.95 monthly (HBO).

Miles of plant: 21.0 (coaxial); None (fiber optic).
Franchise fee: 3%-5% of gross.

Ownership: Adelphia Communications Corp. (MSO). Purchased from Barry Electronics Inc., July 1, 1998.

GREENBURR—Greenburr TV Cable, Box 85, Loganton, PA 17747. Phone: 717-725-2733. County: Clinton. ICA: PA0339.

TV Market Ranking: Below 100. Franchise award date: N.A. Franchise expiration date: N.A. Began: January 1, 1955.

Channel capacity: 12. Channels available but not in use: 1.

Basic Service

Subscribers: 138.

Programming (received off-air): WPSX-TV (P) Clearfield; WHTM-TV (A) Harrisburg; WJAC-TV (N), WTAJ-TV (C) Johnstown-Altoona; WGAL (N) Lancaster; WPHL-TV (W) Philadelphia; WBRE-TV (N), WNEP-TV (A), WVIA-TV (P), WYOU (C) Scranton & Wilkes-Barre.

Fee: $3.00 monthly.

Equipment: Blonder-Tongue headend.

Miles of plant: 10.0 (coaxial).

Chief technician: Guy Bierly.

Ownership: Greenburr TV Cable.

GREENSBURG—AT&T Cable Services, 300 Corliss St., Pittsburgh, PA 15220-4815. Phones: 412-875-1100; 412-771-8100. Counties: Allegheny & Westmoreland. Also serves Adamsburg, Arona, Derry Twp. (Westmoreland County), East Huntingdon Twp. (portions), Hempfield Twp. (Westmoreland County), Hunker, Irwin, Jeannette, Madison, Manor, Mount Pleasant Twp. (Westmoreland County), New Alexandria, New Stanton, North Huntingdon (Westmoreland County), North Huntingdon Twp. (Westmoreland County), North Irwin, Penn, Penn Twp. (Westmoreland County), Salem Twp. (Westmoreland County), Sewickley Twp., South Greensburg, South Huntingdon (Westmoreland County), South Huntingdon Twp. (portions), South Versailles, South Versailles Twp. (portions), Southwest Greensburg, Unity Twp. (Westmoreland County), Youngwood. ICA: PA0015.

TV Market Ranking: 10 (Adamsburg, Arona, Derry Twp., East Huntingdon Twp., Greensburg, Hempfield Twp., Hunker, Irwin, Jeannette, Madison, Manor, Mount Pleasant Twp., New Alexandria, New Stanton, North Huntingdon, North Huntingdon Twp., North Irwin, Penn, Penn Twp., Salem Twp., Sewickley Twp., South Greensburg, South Huntingdon, South Huntingdon Twp., South Versailles, South Versailles Twp., Southwest Greensburg, Unity Twp., Youngwood); 74 (Greensburg, South Greensburg, Unity Twp., Youngwood). Franchise award date: January 1, 1966. Franchise expiration date: January 1, 2000. Began: March 1, 1966.

Channel capacity: N.A. Channels available but not in use: N.A.

Basic Service

Subscribers: 51,623.

Programming (received off-air): WPCB-TV (I) Greensburg; WJAC-TV (N), WWCP-TV (F) Johnstown-Altoona; KDKA-TV (C), WCWB (W), WPGH-TV (F), WPXI (N), WQED (P), WQEX (P), WTAE-TV (A) Pittsburgh; 19 FMs.

Programming (via microwave): Meadows Racing Network.

Programming (via satellite): C-SPAN; CNBC; EWTN; QVC.

Current originations: Automated time-weather; religious access.

Fee: $44.95 installation; $10.37 monthly; $1.50 converter; $24.95 additional installation.

Expanded Basic Service

Subscribers: 49,635.

Programming (via satellite): A & E; American Movie Classics; Animal Planet; CNN; Cartoon Network; Discovery Channel; ESPN; FX; Fox Family Channel; Fox News Channel; Fox Sports Net Pittsburgh; Headline News; Lifetime; MTV; Nashville Network; Nickelodeon; TBS Superstation; The Weather Channel; Travel Channel; Turner Network TV; USA Network; VH1.

Fee: $14.22 monthly.

Pay Service 1

Pay Units: 5,521.

Programming (via satellite): Cinemax.

Fee: $13.45 monthly.

Pay Service 2

Pay Units: 1,986.

Programming (via satellite): Disney Channel.

Fee: $12.50 monthly.

Pay Service 3

Pay Units: 9,421.

Programming (via satellite): HBO.

Fee: $14.95 monthly.

Pay Service 4

Pay Units: 13,213.

Programming (via satellite): The New Encore.

Fee: $1.95 monthly.

Pay Service 5

Pay Units: 1,737.

Programming (via satellite): Showtime.

Fee: $14.95 monthly.

Pay Service 6

Pay Units: 7,817.

Programming (via satellite): Starz!

Fee: $6.75 monthly.

Pay Service 7

Pay Units: N.A.

Programming (via satellite): DMX.

Fee: $9.95 monthly.

Local advertising: Yes. Available in satellite distributed programming. Rates: $5.00/Day; $10.00/Insert. Regional interconnect: TCI Media Services-Pittsburgh, PA.

Program Guide: The Cable Guide.

Equipment: Scientific-Atlanta headend; Scientific-Atlanta amplifiers; Times Fiber & Comm/Scope cable; Panasonic cameras; Sony & Panasonic VTRs; Knox & MSI character generator; Scientific-Atlanta set top converters; Arcom & Northeast Filter traps; Scientific-Atlanta satellite antenna; Scientific-Atlanta satellite receivers.

Miles of plant: 861.7 (coaxial). Homes passed: 57,415. Total homes in franchised area: 86,331.

Manager: Jeffrey C. Harshman. Chief technician: Fred Hamm. Marketing director: Glenn Ryerson.

Ownership: AT&T Broadband & Internet Services (MSO). Purchased from Tele-Communications Inc., March 9, 1999.

GREENTOWN—Blue Ridge Cable TV, HC6 Box 6035, Hawley, PA 18428. Phone: 570-226-4914. Counties: Pike & Wayne. Also serves Cherry Ridge Twp. (Wayne County), Greene Twp. (Pike County), Palmyra Twp. (Pike County). ICA: PA0177.

TV Market Ranking: 49. Franchise award date: N.A. Franchise expiration date: N.A. Began: January 1, 1981.

Channel capacity: 42. Channels available but not in use: None.

Basic Service

Subscribers: 511.

Programming (received off-air): WBNG-TV (C), WSKG (P) Binghamton; WABC-TV (A), WCBS-TV (C), WNBC (N), WNYW (F), WPIX (W), WWOR-TV (U) New York; WNET (P) New York-Newark; WBRE-TV (N), WNEP-TV (A), WSWB (W), WVIA-TV (P), WYOU (C) Scranton & Wilkes-Barre.

Programming (via satellite): WGN-TV (W) Chicago; A & E; CNBC; CNN; Discovery Channel; ESPN; Fox Family Channel; Headline News; Lifetime; MTV; Nashville Network; Nickelodeon; QVC; TBS Superstation; The Weather Channel; Turner Network TV; USA Network; VH1.

Fee: $32.50 installation; $16.90 monthly.

Pay Service 1

Pay Units: N.A.

Programming (via satellite): Cinemax; HBO.

Fee: $12.50 installation; $8.50 monthly (HBO), $9.50 monthly (Cinemax).

Equipment: Scientific-Atlanta headend; C-COR amplifiers; Comm/Scope cable.

Miles of plant: 51.0 (coaxial). Homes passed: 1,556.

Manager: Norman Bohs.

Ownership: Pencor Services Inc. (MSO).

GREENVILLE—Time Warner Cable, 6 S. High St., Greenville, PA 16125-2396. Phone: 724-588-8000. County: Mercer. Also serves Delaware Twp. (Mercer County), Fredonia, Greenville East, Hempfield Twp. (Mercer County), Sugar Grove Twp., West Salem Twp. ICA: PA0116.

TV Market Ranking: 79. Franchise award date: N.A. Franchise expiration date: N.A. Began: November 1, 1968.

Channel capacity: 25. Channels available but not in use: None.

Basic Service

Subscribers: 3,972.

Programming (received off-air): WNEO (P) Alliance; WQLN (P) Erie; WUAB (U) Lorain-Cleveland; KDKA-TV (C), WPGH-TV (F) Pittsburgh; WBDT (W) Springfield; WKBN-TV (C), WYTV (A,F) Youngstown; allband FM.

Programming (via satellite): Home Shopping Network; TBS Superstation.

Current originations: Automated time-weather.

Fee: $40.00 installation; $11.50 monthly.

Expanded Basic Service

Subscribers: 3,966.

Programming (via satellite): A & E; American Movie Classics; CNN; Discovery Channel; ESPN; Fox Family Channel; Headline News; Lifetime; MTV; Nashville Network; Nickelodeon; The Weather Channel; USA Network.

Fee: $59.95 installation; $21.45 monthly.

Pay Service 1

Pay Units: 296.

Programming (via satellite): Cinemax.

Fee: $19.95 installation; $9.95 monthly.

Pay Service 2

Pay Units: 199.

Programming (via satellite): Disney Channel.

Fee: $19.95 installation; $8.95 monthly.

Pay Service 3

Pay Units: 609.

Programming (via satellite): HBO.

Fee: $19.95 installation; $9.95 monthly.

Pay Service 4

Pay Units: 261.

Programming (via satellite): Showtime.

Fee: $19.95 installation; $9.95 monthly.

Local advertising: Yes. Available in locally originated programming. Local sales manager: Jim Baker. Regional interconnect: Cabletime.

Equipment: Jerrold headend; Jerrold amplifiers; Jerrold cable; Jerrold set top converters.

Miles of plant: 81.0 (coaxial). Homes passed: 5,343. Total homes in franchised area: 5,766.

Manager: Karen M. Nocera. Chief technician: Michael Snow. Marketing director: R. Susan Maha.

City fee: 3% of basic gross.

Ownership: Time Warner Cable (MSO).

GROVE CITY—Armstrong Cable Services, 1312 W. Main St., Grove City, PA 16127. Phone: 724-458-5460. Fax: 724-458-7404. Counties: Butler, Lawrence & Mercer. Also serves Brady Twp. (Butler County), Center Twp. (Butler County), Cherry Twp. (Butler County), Concord Twp. (Butler County), Coolspring Twp. (portions), East Lackawannock Twp. (portions), Findley Twp. (Mercer County), Harrisville, Jackson Twp. (Butler County), Lake Latonka Borough, Liberty Twp. (Mercer County), Mercer, Mercer Twp. (portions), Pine Twp. (Mercer County), Slippery Rock (Butler County), Slippery Rock Twp. (Butler County), Springfield Twp. (Mercer County), Volant Borough, Washington Twp. (Lawrence County), West Sunbury, Wolf Creek Twp. ICA: PA0089.

TV Market Ranking: 10 (Center Twp., Jackson Twp.); 79 (Brady Twp., Coolspring Twp., East Lackawannock Twp., Findley Twp., Grove City, Lake Latonka Borough, Liberty Twp., Mercer, Mercer Twp., portions of Pine Twp., Slippery Rock, Slippery Rock Twp., Springfield Twp., Volant Borough, Washington Twp., portions of Wolf Creek Twp.); Below 100 (Concord Twp.); Outside TV Markets (Cherry Twp., Harrisville, portions of Pine Twp., West Sunbury). Franchise award date: January 1, 1975. Franchise expiration date: January 1, 2004. Began: May 1, 1976.

Channel capacity: 54 (not 2-way capable). Channels available but not in use: None.

Basic Service

Subscribers: 8,678.

Programming (received off-air): WNEO (P) Alliance; KDKA-TV (C), WPGH-TV (F), WPXI (N), WQED (P), WTAE-TV (A) Pittsburgh; WFMJ-TV (N), WKBN-TV (C), WYTV (A,F) Youngstown.

Programming (via satellite): A & E; American Movie Classics; C-SPAN; CNBC; CNN; Comedy Central; Court TV; Discovery Channel; ESPN; Fox Family Channel; Fox Sports Net Pittsburgh; Goodlife TV Network; Headline News; Home Shopping Network; Lifetime; MTV; Nashville Network; Nick at Nite's TV Land; Nickelodeon; Odyssey; QVC; The Weather Channel; Travel Channel; Turner Network TV; USA Network; VH1.

Current originations: Automated time-weather; public access; government access; religious access; automated emergency alert; local news.

Fee: $35.00 installation; $24.95 monthly; $2.95 converter.

Pay Service 1

Pay Units: 994.

Programming (via satellite): Cinemax.

Fee: $20.00 installation; $9.95 monthly.

Pay Service 2

Pay Units: 710.

Programming (via satellite): Disney Channel.

Fee: $20.00 installation; $7.95 monthly.

Pay Service 3

Pay Units: 113.

Programming (via satellite): DMX.

Fee: $7.95 monthly.

Pay Service 4

Pay Units: 1,560.

Programming (via satellite): HBO.

Fee: $20.00 installation; $11.95 monthly.

Pay Service 5

Pay Units: N.A.

Programming (via satellite): Showtime.

Fee: $20.00 installation; $9.95 monthly.

Local advertising: Yes. Available in satellite distributed programming. Local sales manager: Sharon Stang.
Equipment: Scientific-Atlanta headend; Scientific-Atlanta amplifiers; Trilogy cable; Sony VTRs; Texscan character generator; Scientific-Atlanta set top converters; Eagle traps; AFC satellite antenna; Scientific-Atlanta satellite receivers.
Miles of plant: 310.2 (coaxial); 45.0 (fiber optic). Homes passed: 10,547.
Manager: Ike M. Mutlu.
City fee: 5% of gross.
Ownership: Armstrong Group of Companies (MSO).

HAMBURG—AT&T Cable Services, Suite A, 700 S. 4th St., Hamburg, PA 19526. Phone: 610-562-2572. Counties: Berks & Schuylkill. Also serves Bern Twp. (Berks County), Centerport, Centre Twp. (Berks County), Greenwich Twp. (Berks County), Leesport, Lenhartsville, Maidencreek Twp. (Berks County), Ontelaunee Twp. (Berks County), Perry Twp. (Berks County), Port Clinton, Shoemakersville, Tilden Twp., Windsor Twp. (Berks County). ICA: PA0102.
TV Market Ranking: 57 (Bern Twp., Centre Twp., Leesport, Maidencreek Twp., Ontelaunee Twp.); Below 100 (Centerport, Centre Twp., Greenwich Twp., Hamburg, Lenhartsville, Perry Twp., Port Clinton, Shoemakersville, Tilden Twp., Windsor Twp.). Franchise award date: N.A. Franchise expiration date: N.A. Began: October 1, 1951.
Channel capacity: 78 (not 2-way capable). Channels available but not in use: None.

Basic Service
Subscribers: 6,144; Commercial subscribers: 11.
Programming (received off-air): WFMZ-TV (I), WLVT-TV (P) Allentown; WHTM-TV (A) Harrisburg; WGAL (N), WLYH-TV (U) Lancaster; KYW-TV (C), WCAU (N), WPHL-TV (W), WPSG (U), WPVI-TV (A), WTXF-TV (F) Philadelphia; WTVE (H) Reading; WHYY-TV (P) Wilmington; WPMT (F) York; allband FM.
Programming (via satellite): TBS Superstation.
Current originations: Local news.
Fee: $5.31 installation; $23.23 monthly; $1.95 converter.
Commercial fee: $8.00 monthly.

Expanded Basic Service
Subscribers: 6,088.
Programming (via satellite): A & E; American Movie Classics; BET; C-SPAN; C-SPAN 2; CNBC; CNN; Cartoon Network; Comedy Central; Court TV; Discovery Channel; ESPN; Fox Family Channel; Fox News Channel; Goodlife TV Network; Headline News; Home Shopping Network; Lifetime; MTV; Nashville Network; Nickelodeon; Pennsylvania Cable Network; QVC; The Inspirational Network; The Weather Channel; Turner Network TV; USA Network; Univision; VH1; ValueVision.
Fee: N.A.

A la Carte 1
Subscribers: N.A.
Programming (via satellite): Animal Planet; Country Music TV; E! Entertainment TV; ESPN 2; History Channel; Learning Channel; Sci-Fi Channel; The New Encore.
Fee: N.A.

Pay Service 1
Pay Units: 3,477.
Programming (via satellite): Cinemax; Disney Channel; HBO (multiplexed); Showtime; Starz!
Fee: $5.31 installation; $7.80 monthly (Disney), $12.00 monthly (Cinemax, HBO or Showtime).

Pay-Per-View
Addressable homes: 3,876.
Action Pay-Per-View; Spice2; Viewer's Choice.
Local advertising: Yes. Available in satellite distributed, character-generated & automated programming. Regional interconnect: Metrobase Cable Advertising.
Program Guide: TVSM.
Equipment: Scientific-Atlanta headend; Jerrold & Scientific-Atlanta amplifiers; Comm/Scope & Trilogy cable; Texscan character generator; Hamlin & Scientific-Atlanta set top converters; Scientific-Atlanta addressable set top converters; Eagle & Arcom traps; Anixter-Mark satellite antenna; Scientific-Atlanta satellite receivers.
Miles of plant: 255.0 (coaxial); 73.0 (fiber optic). Additional miles planned: 11.0 (coaxial).
Manager: Doug Frank. Chief technician: Terry Dunbar. Customer service manager: Susan Gerner.
City fee: 5% of basic gross.
Ownership: AT&T Broadband & Internet Services (MSO). Purchased from Time Warner Cable, July 1, 1999.

HARBORCREEK TWP.—Adelphia, Box 7129, 5651 Jordan Rd., Erie, PA 16510-0129. Phone: 814-899-0625. Fax: 814-898-1540. County: Erie. Also serves Albion, Conneat Twp., Cranesville, Elk Creek Twp., Fairview (Erie County), Fairview Twp. (Erie County), Girard Borough, Girard Twp. (Erie County), Greene Twp. (Erie County), Lake City, Lawrence Park, McKean Borough, McKean Twp. (Erie County), Millcreek, Northeast, Northeast Twp. (Erie County), Platea Boro, Summit, Summit Twp. (Erie County), Waterford (Erie County), Waterford Twp. (Erie County), Wesleyville. Plans service to Lundys Lane. ICA: PA0025.
TV Market Ranking: Below 100. Franchise award date: N.A. Franchise expiration date: N.A. Began: April 1, 1976.
Channel capacity: 78 (2-way capable; not operating 2-way). Channels available but not in use: 2.

Basic Service
Subscribers: 37,000.
Programming (received off-air): WFXP (F), WICU-TV (N), WJET-TV (A), WQLN (P), WSEE (C) Erie; allband FM.
Programming (via microwave): WUAB (U) Lorain-Cleveland.
Programming (via satellite): C-SPAN; Discovery Channel; QVC; TBS Superstation.
Current originations: Automated time-weather; public access; educational access; government access.
Fee: $44.95 installation; $10.14 monthly; $3.00 converter.

Digital Basic Service
Subscribers: N.A.
Programming (via satellite): BBC America; Bravo; Discovery Home & Leisure Channel; Discovery Kids Channel; Discovery People; Discovery Science Channel; ESPN Classic Sports; ESPNews; Fox Sports World; Game Show Network; History Channel; Independent Film Channel; MuchMusic Network; Outdoor Life Network; Romance Classics; Sci-Fi Channel; The Barker; Turner Classic Movies.
Fee: N.A.

Expanded Basic Service
Subscribers: 32,748.
Programming (via satellite): A & E; America's Store; American Movie Classics; Animal Planet; BET; C-SPAN 2; CNBC; CNN; Cartoon Network; Country Music TV; Court TV; E! Entertainment TV; ESPN; ESPN 2; EWTN; Encore Movie Networks; FX; Fox Family Channel; Fox News Channel; Fox Sports Net; Fox Sports Net Pittsburgh; Headline News; Home & Garden Television; Home Shopping Network; Knowledge TV; Learning Channel; Lifetime; MSNBC; MTV; Nashville Network; Nickelodeon; Odyssey; TV Food Network; TV Guide Channel; TV Guide Sneak Prevue; The Health Network; The Weather Channel; Turner Network TV; USA Network; VH1.
Fee: $16.66 monthly.

Pay Service 1
Pay Units: 1,945.
Programming (via satellite): Cinemax.
Fee: N.A.

Pay Service 2
Pay Units: 1,547.
Programming (via satellite): Disney Channel.
Fee: N.A.

Pay Service 3
Pay Units: 8,296.
Programming (via satellite): HBO.
Fee: N.A.

Pay Service 4
Pay Units: 1,499.
Programming (via satellite): Showtime.
Fee: N.A.

Pay Service 5
Pay Units: 13,127.
Programming (via satellite): Starz!; The New Encore (multiplexed).
Fee: N.A.

Digital Pay Service 1
Pay Units: N.A.
Programming (via satellite): DMX; Encore Love Stories; Encore Mystery; Encore Westerns; HBO (multiplexed); Showtime (multiplexed); Starz! (multiplexed); The Movie Channel.
Fee: N.A.

Pay-Per-View
Addressable homes: 35,254.
Action Pay-Per-View; Spice; Spice delivered digitally.
Local advertising: Yes. Available in locally originated programming. Rates: $100.00/Month; $20.00-$30.00/Minute; $15.00-$25.00/30 Seconds.
Equipment: Scientific-Atlanta headend; Theta-Com amplifiers; Comm/Scope cable; JVC cameras; JVC VTRs; Metrodata character generator; Jerrold set top converters; Andrew satellite antenna; Microdyne satellite receivers.
Miles of plant: 933.2 (coaxial); 150.2 (fiber optic). Homes passed: 45,761. Total homes in franchised area: 52,134.
Manager: Tom Carey. Chief technician: Bob Westland.
City fee: 3% of gross.
Ownership: Adelphia Communications Corp. (MSO); AT&T Broadband & Internet Services (MSO). Purchased from Tele-Communications Inc., March 9, 1999.

HARRISBURG—Suburban Cable, 4601 Smith St., Harrisburg, PA 17109. Phones: 717-540-8900; 800-222-1813. Fax: 717-657-3926. Web site: http://www.suburbancable.com. Counties: Cumberland, Dauphin, Perry & York. Also serves Camp Hill, Carroll Twp. (Cumberland County), Dauphin, East Pennsboro Twp. (Cumberland County), Fairview Twp. (York County), Hampden Twp. (Cumberland County), Highspire, Lemoyne, Lower Allen Twp., Lower Paxton Twp. (Dauphin County), Lower Swatara Twp., Marysville, Mechanicsburg, Middle Paxton, Middletown, Monroe Twp. (Cumberland County), New Cumberland, New Cumberland Army Depot, Paxtang, Penbrook, Royalton, Shiremanstown, Silver Spring Twp. (Cumberland County), Steelton, Susquehanna Twp. (Dauphin County), Swatara, Upper Allen Twp., West Fairview, West Hanover Twp. (Dauphin County), Wormleysburg. ICA: PA0009.
TV Market Ranking: 57. Franchise award date: December 1, 1965. Franchise expiration date: July 1, 1999. Began: December 1, 1965.
Channel capacity: 42 (not 2-way capable). Channels available but not in use: None.

Basic Service
Subscribers: 108,529.
Programming (received off-air): WHP-TV (C), WHTM-TV (A), WITF-TV (P) Harrisburg; WGAL (N), WLYH-TV (U) Lancaster; WPHL-TV (W) Philadelphia; WGCB-TV (I) Red Lion; WPMT (F) York.
Programming (via satellite): WPIX (W) New York; C-SPAN; Pennsylvania Cable Network; QVC; TBS Superstation.
Current originations: Automated time-weather; public access; educational access; government access; religious access.
Fee: $25.00 installation; $9.73 monthly; $1.02 converter.

Expanded Basic Service
Subscribers: 105,386.
Programming (via microwave): Tri-State Media.
Programming (via satellite): A & E; American Movie Classics; BET; C-SPAN 2; CNBC; CNN; Comedy Central; Discovery Channel; Disney Channel; E! Entertainment TV; ESPN; ESPN 2; FX; Fox Family Channel; History Channel; Home Shopping Network; Learning Channel; Lifetime; MOVIEplex; MSNBC; MTV; Nashville Network; Nick at Nite; Nickelodeon; Sci-Fi Channel; TV Guide Channel; The Box; The Sports Network; The Weather Channel; Turner Network TV; USA Network; Univision; VH1.
Fee: $25.00 installation; $22.32 monthly.

Expanded Basic Service 2
Subscribers: N.A.
Programming (via satellite): Fox Sports Net Pittsburgh; Home Team Sports.
Fee: N.A.

Pay Service 1
Pay Units: 10,000.
Programming (via satellite): Cinemax.
Fee: $10.50 monthly.

Pay Service 2
Pay Units: N.A.
Programming (via satellite): Starz!
Fee: N.A.

Pay Service 3
Pay Units: 14,185.
Programming (via satellite): HBO.
Fee: $12.50 monthly.

Pay Service 4
Pay Units: 8,289.
Programming (via satellite): The Movie Channel.

Fee: $11.05 monthly.
Pay Service 5
Pay Units: 370.
Programming (via satellite): Music Choice.
Fee: $8.95 monthly.
Pay Service 6
Pay Units: 8,057.
Programming (via satellite): Showtime.
Fee: $12.08 monthly.
Pay-Per-View
Addressable homes: 38,955.
Special events.
Fee: $3.95.
Local advertising: Yes. Available in taped programming. Regional interconnect: Central Pennsylvania Cable AdCom.
Program Guide: TV Host.
Equipment: Scientific-Atlanta headend; Magnavox amplifiers; Siecor cable; Video Data Systems character generator; Jerrold set top converters; Jerrold addressable set top converters; Scientific-Atlanta satellite antenna; Scientific-Atlanta satellite receivers.
Miles of plant: 1623.0 (coaxial); 60.0 (fiber optic). Homes passed: 122,758. Total homes in franchised area: 136,000.
Manager: P. A. Bechtel. Chief technician: Clyde Fry.
City fee: 5% of gross.
Ownership: Lenfest Communications Inc. (MSO).

HARTSLOG—Milestone Communications LP, Suite 200, 1850 Woodmoor Dr., Monument, CO 80132. Phone: 719-488-2916. Fax: 719-488-3629. County: Huntingdon. Also serves Huntingdon County (unincorporated areas). ICA: PA0440.
TV Market Ranking: 74. Franchise award date: N.A. Franchise expiration date: December 1, 2009. Began: N.A.
Channel capacity: 24 (not 2-way capable). Channels available but not in use: 14.
Basic Service
Subscribers: 46.
Programming (received off-air): WPSX-TV (P) Clearfield; WHTM-TV (A) Harrisburg; WJAC-TV (N), WTAJ-TV (C), WWCP-TV (F) Johnstown-Altoona; WGAL (N) Lancaster; WPMT (F) York.
Programming (via satellite): WGN-TV (W) Chicago; CNN; TBS Superstation.
Fee: $50.00 installation (aerial), $60.00 (underground); $15.50 monthly; $10.00 additional installation.
Miles of plant: 2.2 (coaxial); None (fiber optic). Homes passed: 70. Total homes in franchised area: 70.
Manager: Michael Drake. Engineering director: Randy Mock.
Ownership: Milestone Communications LP (MSO).

HAWLEY—Blue Ridge Cable TV, HC6 Box 6035, Hawley, PA 18428. Phone: 570-226-4914. County: Wayne. Also serves Dreher Twp., Palmyra Twp. (Wayne County), Paupack Twp. (Wayne County). ICA: PA0342.
TV Market Ranking: 49. Franchise award date: N.A. Franchise expiration date: N.A. Began: June 1, 1955.
Channel capacity: 42. Channels available but not in use: N.A.
Basic Service
Subscribers: 2,532.
Programming (received off-air): WBNG-TV (C), WSKG (P) Binghamton; WABC-TV (A), WCBS-TV (C), WNBC (N), WNYW (F), WPIX (W), WWOR-TV (U) New York; WNET (P) New York-Newark; WBRE-TV (N), WNEP-TV (A), WSWB (W), WVIA-TV (P), WYOU (C) Scranton & Wilkes-Barre.
Programming (via satellite): WGN-TV (W) Chicago; A & E; C-SPAN; CNBC; CNN; Country Music TV; Discovery Channel; ESPN; Fox Family Channel; Headline News; Home Shopping Network; Lifetime; MTV; Madison Square Garden Network; Nashville Network; Nickelodeon; QVC; TBS Superstation; The Weather Channel; Turner Network TV; USA Network; VH1.
Fee: $32.50 installation; $16.90 monthly.
Pay Service 1
Pay Units: N.A.
Programming (via satellite): Cinemax; HBO.
Fee: $9.50 monthly (Cinemax), $10.50 monthly (HBO).
Local advertising: Yes. Regional interconnect: Cabletime.
Equipment: Scientific-Atlanta headend; C-COR amplifiers; Comm/Scope cable.
Miles of plant: 15.5 (coaxial).
Manager: Norman Bohs.
City fee: None.
Ownership: Pencor Services Inc. (MSO).

HAZEN—DuCom Cable TV, 50 Tipp St., Du Bois, PA 15801. Phone: 814-371-1925. Fax: 814-371-3052. E-mail: ducom@key-net.net. County: Jefferson. Also serves Pinecreek, Polk Twp. (Jefferson County), Snyder Twp. (Jefferson County), Warsaw Twp., Washington Twp. (Jefferson County). ICA: PA0223.
TV Market Ranking: Outside TV Markets. Franchise award date: November 12, 1989. Franchise expiration date: November 12, 1999. Began: August 1, 1990.
Channel capacity: 60 (not 2-way capable). Channels available but not in use: 13.
Basic Service
Subscribers: 686.
Programming (received off-air): WPSX-TV (P) Clearfield; WATM-TV (A), WJAC-TV (N), WKBS-TV (I), WTAJ-TV (C), WWCP-TV (F) Johnstown-Altoona; WCWB (W), WTAE-TV (A) Pittsburgh.
Programming (via satellite): WGN-TV (W) Chicago; A & E; C-SPAN; CNN; Cartoon Network; Country Music TV; Discovery Channel; Disney Channel; ESPN; ESPN 2; FX; Fox Family Channel; Fox Sports Net Pittsburgh; Headline News; Home & Garden Television; Home Shopping Network; Learning Channel; Lifetime; MSNBC; MTV; Nashville Network; Nick at Nite's TV Land; Nickelodeon; QVC; Sci-Fi Channel; TBS Superstation; The Weather Channel; Trinity Bcstg. Network; Turner Classic Movies; Turner Network TV; USA Network; VH1.
Fee: $45.00 installation; $28.95 monthly; $2.50 converter.
Pay Service 1
Pay Units: 67.
Programming (via satellite): Cinemax.
Fee: $5.00 installation; $9.00 monthly.
Pay Service 2
Pay Units: 83.
Programming (via satellite): HBO.
Fee: $5.00 installation; $10.95 monthly.
Pay Service 3
Pay Units: 29.
Programming (via satellite): Showtime.
Fee: $5.00 installation; $9.00 monthly.
Local advertising: Yes. Available in character-generated programming. Rates: $30.00/Month.
Equipment: Scientific-Atlanta headend; C-COR amplifiers; Comm/Scope & Trilogy cable; Amiga character generator; Scientific-Atlanta set top converters; Eagle traps; Scientific-Atlanta satellite receivers.
Miles of plant: 126.0 (coaxial). Additional miles planned: 68.0 (coaxial). Homes passed: 770. Total homes in franchised area: 1,000.
Manager: Rodney Preston. Chief engineer: David Kucenski.
Township fee: 3% of gross.
Ownership: Dubois Communications Inc. (MSO).

HAZLETON—Service Electric Cablevision Inc., Box R, 105 E. Broad St., Hazleton, PA 18201-0076. Phones: 570-454-3841; 610-432-2210. Fax: 570-454-3652. Counties: Carbon, Luzerne & Schuylkill. Also serves Banks Twp. (Carbon County), Beaver Meadows, Butler Twp. (Luzerne County), Conyngham Borough, Dorrance Twp., Foster Twp. (Luzerne County), Freeland, Hazle Twp., Jeddo, Kline Twp., McAdoo, Sugarloaf Twp., West Hazleton Borough. ICA: PA0050.
TV Market Ranking: 49. Franchise award date: January 1, 1952. Franchise expiration date: December 31, 2005. Began: January 1, 1952.
Channel capacity: 78 (2-way capable; operating 2-way). Channels available but not in use: N.A.
Basic Service
Subscribers: 21,576.
Programming (received off-air): WOLF-TV (F), WYLN-LP (W) Hazleton; KYW-TV (C), WPVI-TV (A) Philadelphia; WBRE-TV (N), WNEP-TV (A), WVIA-TV (P), WYOU (C) Scranton & Wilkes-Barre; allband FM.
Programming (via microwave): WPIX (W) New York.
Programming (via satellite): A & E; American Movie Classics; C-SPAN; CNBC; CNN; Country Music TV; Discovery Channel; ESPN; EWTN; Fox Family Channel; Goodlife TV Network; Headline News; Home Shopping Network; Learning Channel; Lifetime; MTV; Nashville Network; Nickelodeon; Pennsylvania Cable Network; QVC; Sci-Fi Channel; TBS Superstation; The Health Network; The Weather Channel; Travel Channel; Turner Network TV; USA Network; VH1; ValueVision.
Current originations: Automated time-weather.
Fee: $55.00 installation; $22.56 monthly; $2.56 converter.
Pay Service 1
Pay Units: 6,594.
Programming (via satellite): Cinemax; Disney Channel; HBO; Showtime.
Fee: $25.00 installation; $8.00 monthly (Showtime or Disney), $10.00 monthly (Cinemax), $11.00 monthly (HBO).
Pay-Per-View
Addressable homes: 5,291.
Local advertising: Yes.
Program Guide: TV Host.
Miles of plant: 285.5 (coaxial); 28.0 (fiber optic). Homes passed: 26,000. Total homes in franchised area: 26,600.
Manager: Robert Trently. Customer service manager: Kathleen Lutsky.
City fee: 5% of monthly gross.
Ownership: Service Electric Cable TV Inc. (MSO).

HEMLOCK FARMS DEVELOPMENT—Blue Ridge Cable TV, Box 215, 465 Delaware Ave., Palmerton, PA 18071-1908. Phone: 610-826-2551. County: Pike. ICA: PA0343.
TV Market Ranking: Below 100. Franchise award date: N.A. Franchise expiration date: N.A. Began: November 1, 1978.
Channel capacity: 36 (not 2-way capable). Channels available but not in use: None.
Basic Service
Subscribers: 1,200.
Programming (received off-air): WLVT-TV (P) Allentown; WABC-TV (A), WCBS-TV (C), WNBC (N), WNYW (F), WPIX (W) New York; WNET (P) New York-Newark; WPHL-TV (W), WTXF-TV (F) Philadelphia; WBRE-TV (N), WNEP-TV (A), WSWB (W), WVIA-TV (P), WYOU (C) Scranton & Wilkes-Barre.
Programming (via satellite): A & E; C-SPAN; CNBC; CNN; Discovery Channel; ESPN; Fox Family Channel; Headline News; Home Shopping Network; Lifetime; MTV; Madison Square Garden Network; Nashville Network; Nickelodeon; QVC; TBS Superstation; The Weather Channel; Turner Network TV; USA Network; VH1.
Fee: $75.00 installation; $16.90 monthly.
Pay Service 1
Pay Units: N.A.
Programming (via satellite): Cinemax; HBO.
Fee: $9.50 monthly (Cinemax), $10.50 monthly (HBO).
Equipment: Scientific-Atlanta headend; C-COR amplifiers; Comm/Scope cable; Arcom, Eagle & Pico traps.
Miles of plant: 69.4 (coaxial).
Ownership: Pencor Services Inc. (MSO).

HERNDON—Pike's Peak TV Association, General Delivery, Herndon, PA 17830. Phone: 717-758-1777. County: Northumberland. ICA: PA0344.
TV Market Ranking: Outside TV Markets. Franchise award date: N.A. Franchise expiration date: N.A. Began: January 1, 1952.
Channel capacity: 14. Channels available but not in use: 2.
Basic Service
Subscribers: N.A.
Programming (received off-air): WHP-TV (C), WHTM-TV (A), WITF-TV (P) Harrisburg; WGAL (N), WLYH-TV (U) Lancaster; WPVI-TV (A) Philadelphia; WBRE-TV (N), WNEP-TV (A), WVIA-TV (P), WYOU (C) Scranton & Wilkes-Barre; WPMT (F) York.
Programming (via satellite): USA Network.
Fee: $75.00 installation; $7.00 monthly.
Equipment: Jerrold headend; Jerrold amplifiers; Jerrold cable.
Miles of plant: 4.0 (coaxial).
Manager: Gene Dreibelbis.
City fee: None.
Ownership: Pike's Peak TV Assn.

HERSHEY—Suburban Cable, 441 W. Chocolate Ave., Hershey, PA 17033. Phone: 717-533-4433. Web site: http://www.suburbancable.com. Counties: Dauphin & Lebanon. Also serves Conewago Twp. (Dauphin County), Derry Twp. (Dauphin County), East Hanover Twp. (Dauphin County), Hummelstown, Londonderry Twp. (Dauphin County), North Londonderry Twp., Palmyra, South Annville Twp., South Hanover Twp., South Londonderry Twp. (Lebanon County). ICA: PA0052.
TV Market Ranking: 57. Franchise award date: May 31, 1967. Franchise expiration date: N.A. Began: October 1, 1967.
Channel capacity: 42 (not 2-way capable). Channels available but not in use: None.
Basic Service
Subscribers: 21,684; Commercial subscribers: 150.
Programming (received off-air): WHP-TV (C), WHTM-TV (A), WITF-TV (P) Harrisburg; WGAL (N), WLYH-TV (U) Lancaster; WPHL-TV (W), WPVI-TV (A) Philadelphia; WGCB-TV (I) Red Lion; WPMT (F) York.
Programming (via satellite): C-SPAN; Pennsylvania Cable Network; QVC; TBS Superstation.
Current originations: Automated time-weather; public access.
Fee: $33.00 installation; $8.54 monthly.
Expanded Basic Service
Subscribers: 20,672.

Programming (via microwave): Tri-State Media.

Programming (via satellite): A & E; American Movie Classics; C-SPAN 2; CNBC; CNN; Discovery Channel; Disney Channel; E! Entertainment TV; ESPN; ESPN 2; EWTN; FX; Fox Family Channel; Headline News; History Channel; Learning Channel; Lifetime; MOVIEplex; MSNBC; MTV; Nashville Network; Nick at Nite; Nickelodeon; Sci-Fi Channel; TV Guide Channel; The Box; The Sports Network; The Weather Channel; Turner Network TV; USA Network; VH1.

Fee: $13.80 monthly.

Expanded Basic Service 2

Subscribers: N.A.

Programming (via satellite): Fox Sports Net Pittsburgh; Home Team Sports.

Fee: N.A.

Pay Service 1

Pay Units: 1,638.

Programming (via satellite): Cinemax.

Fee: $10.00 installation; $8.95 monthly.

Pay Service 2

Pay Units: N.A.

Programming (via satellite): Starz!; The Movie Channel.

Fee: N.A.

Pay Service 3

Pay Units: 2,396.

Programming (via satellite): HBO.

Fee: $10.00 installation; $9.95 monthly.

Pay Service 4

Pay Units: 433.

Programming (via satellite): Showtime.

Fee: $10.00 installation; $9.95 monthly.

Pay-Per-View

Addressable homes: 6,500.

Viewer's Choice.

Local advertising: Yes. Available in satellite distributed, locally originated, character-generated & taped programming. Regional interconnect: Central Pennsylvania Cable AdCom.

Program Guide: TV Host.

Equipment: Scientific-Atlanta headend; Magnavox amplifiers; Comm/Scope cable; MSI & Texscan character generator; Scientific-Atlanta set top converters; Jerrold addressable set top converters; Arcom traps; Scientific-Atlanta satellite antenna; Scientific-Atlanta satellite receivers.

Miles of plant: 446.0 (coaxial); 48.0 (fiber optic). Additional miles planned: 8.0 (coaxial). Homes passed: 24,096. Total homes in franchised area: 24,096.

Regional manager: Sue Heinbach. Chief technician: Dan Cullison. Program director: George Ferrara.

City fee: 3% of gross.

Ownership: Lenfest Communications Inc. (MSO).

HILLSGROVE—Ralph Herr TV, Box 717, RR 4, Montoursville, PA 17754-9665. Phone: 717-435-2780. County: Sullivan. ICA: PA0299.

TV Market Ranking: Below 100. Franchise award date: N.A. Franchise expiration date: N.A. Began: January 1, 1974.

Channel capacity: 12. Channels available but not in use: N.A.

Basic Service

Subscribers: N.A.

Programming (received off-air): WBNG-TV (C) Binghamton; WTAJ-TV (C) Johnstown-Altoona; WBRE-TV (N), WNEP-TV (A), WVIA-TV (P), WYOU (C) Scranton & Wilkes-Barre.

Fee: $25.00 installation; $5.00 monthly.

Equipment: Blonder-Tongue headend; Coral amplifiers; Coral cable.

Miles of plant: 5.0 (coaxial). Additional miles planned: 5.0 (coaxial). Homes passed: 75.

Chief technician: Barry Herr.

City fee: None.

Ownership: Herr Cable Co. (MSO).

HOLLAND—Suburban Cable TV Co. Inc., 2319 York Rd., Jamison, PA 18929. Phone: 215-343-1211. Fax: 215-918-3101. County: Bucks. Also serves Ivyland (portions), Northampton Twp., Richboro. ICA: PA0345.

TV Market Ranking: 4. Franchise award date: April 15, 1981. Franchise expiration date: N.A. Began: April 15, 1981.

Channel capacity: 62 (not 2-way capable). Channels available but not in use: None.

Basic Service

Subscribers: 7,000; Commercial subscribers: 6.

Programming (received off-air): WFMZ-TV (I), WLVT-TV (P) Allentown; WGTW (I) Burlington; KYW-TV (C), WCAU (N), WPHL-TV (W), WPSG (U), WPVI-TV (A), WTXF-TV (F) Philadelphia; WNJT (P) Trenton; WHSP-TV (H) Vineland; WHYY-TV (P) Wilmington.

Programming (via satellite): C-SPAN; C-SPAN 2; Home Shopping Network; QVC.

Current originations: Public access; educational access; government access.

Fee: $33.00 installation; $9.15 monthly; $2.30 converter.

Commercial fee: $36.55 monthly.

Expanded Basic Service

Subscribers: 6,922.

Programming (via satellite): A & E; American Movie Classics; Bravo; CNBC; CNN; Cartoon Network; Comedy Central; Court TV; Discovery Channel; E! Entertainment TV; ESPN; Fox Family Channel; Headline News; Knowledge TV; Learning Channel; Lifetime; MTV; Nashville Network; Nickelodeon; Sci-Fi Channel; TBS Superstation; The Weather Channel; Turner Network TV; USA Network; VH1.

Fee: $10.00 installation; $12.55 monthly.

Pay Service 1

Pay Units: 706.

Programming (via satellite): Cinemax.

Fee: $8.95 monthly.

Pay Service 2

Pay Units: 12.

Programming (via satellite): Music Choice.

Fee: $9.95 monthly.

Pay Service 3

Pay Units: 821.

Programming (via satellite): Disney Channel.

Fee: $7.95 monthly.

Pay Service 4

Pay Units: 357.

Programming (via satellite): The New Encore.

Fee: $2.50 monthly.

Pay Service 5

Pay Units: 2,278.

Programming (via satellite): HBO.

Fee: $9.95 monthly.

Pay Service 6

Pay Units: 152.

Programming (via satellite): The Movie Channel.

Fee: $8.95 monthly.

Pay Service 7

Pay Units: 557.

Programming (via satellite): Showtime.

Fee: $9.95 monthly.

Pay-Per-View

Addressable homes: 2,000.

Playboy TV; Spice; Viewer's Choice.

Fee: $2.30.

Local advertising: Yes. Available in character-generated programming. Local sales manager: Deborah Stevens.

Program Guide: TV Host.

Equipment: Jerrold set top converters; Jerrold addressable set top converters.

Miles of plant: 13.0 (fiber optic).

Manager: Robert Pfeiffer. Chief technician: Tom Diehl. Program director: James Bunn. Marketing director: Julie Eble.

Franchise fee: 3% of gross.

Ownership: Lenfest Communications Inc. (MSO).

HONESDALE—Blue Ridge Cable TV, 444 Sunrise, Honesdale, PA 18431. Phone: 570-253-3451. Fax: 570-253-2355. County: Wayne. Also serves Berlin Twp. (Wayne County), Bethany, Cherry Ridge Twp. (Wayne County), Indian Orchard, Palmyra Twp. (Wayne County), Seelyville (Wayne County), Texas Twp. (Wayne County), White Mills. ICA: PA0346.

TV Market Ranking: 49. Franchise award date: N.A. Franchise expiration date: N.A. Began: January 1, 1950.

Channel capacity: 30. Channels available but not in use: N.A.

Basic Service

Subscribers: N.A.

Programming (received off-air): WWOR-TV (U) New York; WBRE-TV (N), WNEP-TV (A), WSWB (W), WVIA-TV (P), WYOU (C) Scranton & Wilkes-Barre; allband FM.

Programming (via satellite): CNN; Nashville Network; Trinity Bcstg. Network.

Current originations: Automated time-weather.

Fee: $35.00 installation.

Expanded Basic Service

Subscribers: N.A.

Programming (via satellite): WGN-TV (W) Chicago; A & E; C-SPAN; Discovery Channel; ESPN; Goodlife TV Network; Headline News; Home Shopping Network; Home Shopping Network 2; Home Team Sports; Lifetime; Nickelodeon; TBS Superstation; USA Network.

Fee: N.A.

Pay Service 1

Pay Units: N.A.

Programming (via satellite): Disney Channel; HBO; Showtime.

Fee: $35.00 installation; $10.00 monthly (Disney), $11.00 monthly (Showtime), $12.50 monthly (HBO).

Local advertising: Yes.

Equipment: Ameco headend; Ameco amplifiers; Plastoid cable.

Miles of plant: 30.0 (coaxial). Additional miles planned: 5.0 (coaxial).

Manager: Kathy Chrzan. Marketing director & customer service manager: Jennifer Schott.

City fee: None.

Ownership: Blue Ridge Communications.

HONEY GROVE—Nittany Media, Box 111, Lewistown, PA 17044. Phone: 717-248-3733. County: Juniata. ICA: PA0347.

TV Market Ranking: 57. Franchise award date: N.A. Franchise expiration date: N.A. Began: January 1, 1980.

Channel capacity: 12. Channels available but not in use: 1.

Basic Service

Subscribers: N.A.

Programming (received off-air): WHP-TV (C), WHTM-TV (A), WITF-TV (P) Harrisburg; WJAC-TV (N), WTAJ-TV (C) Johnstown-Altoona; WGAL (N), WLYH-TV (U) Lancaster; WBRE-TV (N), WSWB (W), WVIA-TV (P) Scranton & Wilkes-Barre; WPMT (F) York.

Fee: N.A.

Miles of plant: 8.0 (coaxial).

Manager: R. Edward Shields.

Ownership: R. Edward Shields (MSO).

HUNTINGDON—Huntingdon TV Cable Co. Inc., 170 Penn St., Huntingdon, PA 16652. Phone: 814-643-3498. Fax: 814-643-2830. Counties: Bedford & Huntingdon. Also serves Alexandria, Henderson Twp. (Huntingdon County), Hopewell Twp., Juniata Twp. (Huntingdon County), Liberty Twp., Lincoln Twp., Lincoln Twp. (Huntingdon County), Logan Twp. (Huntingdon County), Marklesburg, Miller Twp. (Huntingdon County), Oneida Twp., Penn Twp. (Huntingdon County), Petersburg, Porter Twp. (Huntingdon County), Saxton, Smithfield Twp. (Huntingdon County), Walker Twp. (Huntingdon County). ICA: PA0107.

TV Market Ranking: 74. Franchise award date: N.A. Franchise expiration date: N.A. Began: March 24, 1962.

Channel capacity: 77 (not 2-way capable). Channels available but not in use: 23.

Basic Service

Subscribers: 7,550.

Programming (received off-air): WPSX-TV (P) Clearfield; WATM-TV (A), WJAC-TV (N), WKBS-TV (I), WTAJ-TV (C), WWCP-TV (F) Johnstown-Altoona; allband FM.

Programming (via satellite): WPIX (W) New York; A & E; American Movie Classics; Animal Planet; C-SPAN; C-SPAN 2; CNBC; CNN; Cartoon Network; Country Music TV; Court TV; Discovery Channel; Disney Channel; E! Entertainment TV; ESPN; ESPN 2; ESPN Classic Sports; FX; Fox Family Channel; Fox News Channel; Fox Sports Net Pittsburgh; Game Show Network; Goodlife TV Network; Headline News; History Channel; Home & Garden Television; Home Shopping Network; Learning Channel; Lifetime; Nashville Network; Nick at Nite's TV Land; Nickelodeon; Pennsylvania Cable Network; QVC; Sci-Fi Channel; TBS Superstation; The Health Network; The Weather Channel; Travel Channel; Turner Network TV; USA Network.

Current originations: Automated time-weather.

Fee: $52.00 installation; $22.00 monthly.

Pay Service 1

Pay Units: N.A.

Programming (via satellite): Cinemax; HBO.

Fee: $10.00 installation; $10.95 monthly (each).

Local advertising: Yes. Available in satellite distributed & character-generated programming.

Equipment: Jerrold & Scientific-Atlanta headend; Magnavox amplifiers; Times Fiber & CCS Hatfield cable; MSI character generator; Scientific-Atlanta set top converters; Zenith addressable set top converters; Microdyne & Scientific-Atlanta satellite antenna.

Miles of plant: 200.0 (coaxial); 60.0 (fiber optic).

Manager: Chester P. Isett. Chief technician: Dan Cramer.

Ownership: Huntingdon TV Cable Co. Inc.

HUNTINGTON TWP. (Luzerne County)—Country Cable, Box 144-A, RR 3, Hunlock Creek, PA 18621. Phone: 717-477-3090. E-mail: dmartin@epix.net. County: Luzerne. ICA: PA0300.

TV Market Ranking: 49. Franchise award date: June 1, 1992. Franchise expiration date: June 1, 2007. Began: October 1, 1992.

Channel capacity: 54 (2-way capable; not operating 2-way). Channels available but not in use: 18.

Basic Service

Subscribers: 300.

Programming (received off-air): WBRE-TV (N), WNEP-TV (A), WSWB (W), WVIA-TV (P), WYOU (C) Scranton & Wilkes-Barre.

Programming (via satellite): WGN-TV (W) Chicago; C-SPAN; CNN; Country Music TV; Discovery Channel; ESPN; ESPN 2; Headline News; Learning Channel; MTV; Nashville Network; Nickelodeon; Pennsylvania Cable Network; QVC; Sci-Fi Channel; TBS Superstation; The Weather Channel; Travel Channel; Trinity Bcstg. Network; Turner Classic Movies; Turner Network TV; USA Network; VH1.
Current originations: Automated time-weather; public access.
Fee: $40.00 installation; $19.00 monthly.

Pay Service 1
Pay Units: 24.
Programming (via satellite): Cinemax.
Fee: $9.00 monthly.

Pay Service 2
Pay Units: 18.
Programming (via satellite): Disney Channel.
Fee: $8.00 monthly.

Pay Service 3
Pay Units: 50.
Programming (via satellite): HBO.
Fee: $11.00 monthly.

Local advertising: No.
Equipment: Drake, Blonder-Tongue & Nexus headend; C-COR & Jerrold amplifiers; Microwave Filter & Eagle traps; Drake satellite receivers.
Miles of plant: 30.0 (coaxial). Additional miles planned: 10.0 (coaxial). Homes passed: 450.
Manager: David Martin.
Ownership: Country Communications Inc.

HYNDMAN BOROUGH—TCI of Pennsylvania Inc., Box 649, 410 E. Central Way, Bedford, PA 15522-1457. Phone: 814-623-1128. Fax: 814-623-1055. County: Bedford. Also serves Hyndman, Londonderry Twp. (Bedford County). ICA: PA0227.
TV Market Ranking: Outside TV Markets. Franchise award date: N.A. Franchise expiration date: N.A. Began: June 1, 1964.
Channel capacity: 23. Channels available but not in use: None.

Basic Service
Subscribers: 572.
Programming (received off-air): WWPB (P) Hagerstown; WJAC-TV (N), WTAJ-TV (C), WWCP-TV (F) Johnstown-Altoona; WTAE-TV (A) Pittsburgh; WJLA-TV (A) Washington.
Programming (via satellite): Discovery Channel; FX; Lifetime; The Inspirational Network.
Current originations: Automated time-weather.
Fee: $59.95 installation; $9.67 monthly; $2.00 converter; $49.95 additional installation.

Expanded Basic Service
Subscribers: 563.
Programming (via satellite): CNN; ESPN; Fox Family Channel; Home Shopping Network; MTV; Nashville Network; Nickelodeon; TBS Superstation; USA Network.
Fee: $5.98 monthly.

Pay Service 1
Pay Units: 53.
Programming (via satellite): Cinemax.
Fee: $13.20 monthly.

Pay Service 2
Pay Units: 99.
Programming (via satellite): HBO.
Fee: $14.15 monthly.

Pay Service 3
Pay Units: 47.
Programming (via satellite): The Movie Channel.
Fee: $14.15 monthly.

Equipment: Magnavox amplifiers; Scientific-Atlanta satellite antenna.
Miles of plant: 16.9 (coaxial); None (fiber optic). Homes passed: 610. Total homes in franchised area: 2,912.
Manager: Dave Diehl.
Ownership: AT&T Broadband & Internet Services (MSO). Purchased from Tele-Communications Inc., March 9, 1999.

ICKESBURG—Nittany Media Inc., Box 111, Lewistown, PA 17044. Phone: 717-248-3733. County: Perry. ICA: PA0275.
TV Market Ranking: 57. Franchise award date: January 1, 1979. Franchise expiration date: N.A. Began: January 1, 1979.
Channel capacity: 30 (not 2-way capable). Channels available but not in use: 15.

Basic Service
Subscribers: 112.
Programming (received off-air): WHP-TV (C), WHTM-TV (A), WITF-TV (P) Harrisburg; WJAC-TV (N), WTAJ-TV (C) Johnstown-Altoona; WGAL (N), WLYH-TV (U) Lancaster; WPMT (F) York.
Programming (via satellite): Country Music TV; Discovery Channel; ESPN; Fox Family Channel; Nashville Network; TBS Superstation.
Fee: $40.00 installation; $13.95 monthly; $2.00 converter.

Pay Service 1
Pay Units: 29.
Programming (via satellite): Showtime.
Fee: $10.60 monthly.

Local advertising: No.
Equipment: Blonder-Tongue & Scientific-Atlanta headend; GTE Sylvania amplifiers; Comm/Scope cable; Jerrold set top converters; Pico traps; Scientific-Atlanta satellite antenna; Drake satellite receivers.
Miles of plant: 5.8 (coaxial). Homes passed: 164. Total homes in franchised area: 490.
Manager: Barry L. Kepner.
Ownership: Nittany Media Inc. (MSO).

INDIAN CREEK—Laurel Highland TV Co., Box 168, Rte. 130, Stahlstown, PA 15687. Phone: 724-593-2411. Fax: 724-593-2423. Counties: Fayette & Westmoreland. Also serves Champion, Cook Twp., Donegal, Donegal Twp. (Westmoreland County), Indian Head, Melcroft, Mill Run, Normalville, Saltlick Twp. (Fayette County), Stahlstown. ICA: PA0348.
TV Market Ranking: 74. Franchise award date: N.A. Franchise expiration date: N.A. Began: January 1, 1967.
Channel capacity: 24 (not 2-way capable). Channels available but not in use: 2.

Basic Service
Subscribers: 3,817.
Programming (received off-air): WPCB-TV (I) Greensburg; WNPA (U) Jeanette; WWCP-TV (F) Johnstown-Altoona; KDKA-TV (C), WCWB (W), WPGH-TV (F), WPXI (N), WQED (P), WQEX (P), WTAE-TV (A) Pittsburgh.
Programming (via satellite): American Movie Classics; CNN; Discovery Channel; E! Entertainment TV; ESPN; Fox Family Channel; Learning Channel; MSNBC; Nashville Network; Nick at Nite's TV Land; Nickelodeon; QVC.
Fee: $10.00 installation; $7.00 monthly.

Pay Service 1
Pay Units: 1,075.
Programming (via satellite): HBO.
Fee: $10.00 monthly.

Equipment: Ameco headend; Ameco amplifiers.
Miles of plant: 52.0 (coaxial); 20.0 (fiber optic). Homes passed: 5,883.
Manager: J. Paul Kalp. Chief technician: Jeffrey A. Stough.
Ownership: Laurel Highland TV Co.

JAMESTOWN—CableVision Communications, Box 2200, 68 5th St., Buckhannon, WV 26201. Phone: 304-472-4193. Fax: 304-472-0756. Counties: Crawford & Mercer. Also serves Greene Twp. (Mercer County), North Shenango, Shenango Twp. (Mercer County), South Shenango Twp., West Fallowfield Twp. Plans service to East Fallowfield Twp. (Crawford County), West Shenango Twp. ICA: PA0202.
TV Market Ranking: 79. Franchise award date: N.A. Franchise expiration date: N.A. Began: N.A.
Channel capacity: 37 (not 2-way capable). Channels available but not in use: N.A.

Basic Service
Subscribers: 606.
Programming (received off-air): WKYC-TV (N), WVIZ-TV (P) Cleveland; WFXP (F), WICU-TV (N), WJET-TV (A), WSEE (C) Erie; WUAB (U) Lorain-Cleveland; KDKA-TV (C) Pittsburgh; WFMJ-TV (N), WKBN-TV (C), WYTV (A,F) Youngstown.
Programming (via satellite): Home Shopping Network.
Fee: $61.25 installation; $14.40 monthly; $1.24 converter; $17.50 additional installation.

Expanded Basic Service
Subscribers: 567.
Programming (via satellite): WGN-TV (W) Chicago; A & E; American Movie Classics; C-SPAN; CNN; Discovery Channel; Disney Channel; E! Entertainment TV; ESPN; Fox Family Channel; Fox Sports Net Pittsburgh; Great American Country; History Channel; Lifetime; Nashville Network; Nickelodeon; Sci-Fi Channel; TBS Superstation; Trinity Bcstg. Network; Turner Network TV; USA Network.
Fee: $17.50 installation; $14.72 monthly.

Pay Service 1
Pay Units: 433.
Programming (via satellite): Cinemax; HBO; Showtime.
Fee: $17.50 installation; $7.95 monthly (Cinemax), $11.95 monthly (Showtime), $11.99 monthly (HBO).

Pay Service 2
Pay Units: N.A.
Programming (via satellite): The Movie Channel; The New Encore.
Fee: $17.50 installation; $11.95 monthly (TMC).

Local advertising: No.
Equipment: Blonder-Tongue & Olson headend; C-COR amplifiers; Intercept & Pico traps; ChannelMaster satellite antenna; Drake satellite receivers.
Miles of plant: 35.0 (coaxial). Homes passed: 1,022.
Manager: Willie Critchfield. Marketing director: Kenny Phillips.
City fee: 1% of gross.
Ownership: Rifkin & Associates Inc. (MSO). See Cable System Ownership.

JAMISON—Suburban Cable TV, 2319 York Rd., Jamison, PA 18929. Phone: 215-345-5151. Fax: 215-918-3101. County: Bucks. Also serves Buckingham, Buckingham Twp. (Bucks County), Chalfont, Doylestown, Holland, Ivyland (portions), New Britain, New Britain Twp. (Bucks County), Northampton Twp., Richboro, Solebury Twp., Tinicum Twp. (Bucks County), Warrington Twp. (Bucks County), Warwick Twp. (Bucks County). ICA: PA0033.
TV Market Ranking: 4. Franchise award date: May 24, 1982. Franchise expiration date: January 1, 1998. Began: July 1, 1982.
Channel capacity: 54 (2-way capable). Channels available but not in use: None.

Basic Service
Subscribers: 58,142; Commercial subscribers: 46.
Programming (received off-air): WFMZ-TV (I), WLVT-TV (P) Allentown; WGTW (I) Burlington; KYW-TV (C), WCAU (N), WPHL-TV (W), WPSG (U), WPVI-TV (A), WTXF-TV (F), WYBE (P) Philadelphia; WNJT (P) Trenton; WHSP-TV (H) Vineland; WHYY-TV (P), WPPX (X) Wilmington; allband FM.
Programming (via satellite): C-SPAN; C-SPAN 2; Home Shopping Network; Knowledge TV; QVC; TBS Superstation.
Current originations: Automated time-weather; public access; government access; leased access; local sports.
Fee: $30.00 installation; $11.95 monthly.

Expanded Basic Service
Subscribers: 52,667.
Programming (via satellite): A & E; American Movie Classics; Bravo; CNBC; CNN; Cartoon Network; Comedy Central; Court TV; Discovery Channel; E! Entertainment TV; ESPN; ESPN 2; Fox Family Channel; Headline News; History Channel; Home & Garden Television; Learning Channel; Lifetime; MSNBC; MTV; Nashville Network; Nick at Nite; Nickelodeon; Sci-Fi Channel; TV Food Network; The Weather Channel; Turner Network TV; USA Network; VH1.
Fee: $16.65 monthly.

Pay Service 1
Pay Units: 26,255.
Programming (via satellite): Cinemax; Disney Channel; HBO; Showtime; Starz!; The Movie Channel; The New Encore.
Fee: $15.00 installation; $7.95 monthly (each).

Pay-Per-View
Addressable homes: 7,600.
Playboy TV; Spice; Viewer's Choice; movies.
Fee: $3.95 (Viewer's Choice or movies), $4.95 (Spice).

Local advertising: Yes. Available in character-generated programming. Local sales manager: Deborah Stevens.
Program Guide: TV Host.
Equipment: Jerrold headend; Jerrold amplifiers; Trilogy cable; Sony VTRs; Texscan character generator; Jerrold set top converters; Jerrold addressable set top converters; Eagle traps; Microdyne & Scientific-Atlanta satellite antenna; Standard Components satellite receivers.
Miles of plant: 1000.0 (coaxial); 13.0 (fiber optic). Homes passed: 73,746.
Manager: Bob Pfeiffer. Chief technician: Jeff Burroughs. Program director: James Bunn. Marketing director: Julie Eble.
City fee: 3% of gross.
Ownership: Lenfest Communications Inc. (MSO).

JOHNSONBURG—Johnsonburg Community TV Co., 424 Center St., Johnsonburg, PA 15845. Phone: 814-965-4888. Fax: 814-965-4040. County: Elk. ICA: PA0174.
TV Market Ranking: Outside TV Markets. Franchise award date: October 1, 1953. Franchise expiration date: N.A. Began: October 1, 1953.
Channel capacity: 36 (not 2-way capable). Channels available but not in use: 2.

Basic Service
Subscribers: 1,577.
Programming (received off-air): WKBW-TV (A) Buffalo; WPSX-TV (P) Clearfield;

WICU-TV (N) Erie; WJAC-TV (N), WTAJ-TV (C), WWCP-TV (F) Johnstown-Altoona; KDKA-TV (C) Pittsburgh; allband FM.
Programming (via satellite): WGN-TV (W) Chicago; A & E; American Movie Classics; CNN; Discovery Channel; ESPN; EWTN; Fox Family Channel; Headline News; Home Shopping Network; Lifetime; Nashville Network; Nick at Nite; Nickelodeon; TBS Superstation; The Weather Channel; Turner Network TV; USA Network.
Current originations: Public access.
Fee: $125.00 installation; $11.55 monthly.
Pay Service 1
Pay Units: 1,841.
Programming (via satellite): Cinemax; Disney Channel; HBO.
Fee: $25.00 installation; $5.20 monthly (Cinemax), $7.80 monthly (Disney), $8.80 monthly (HBO).
Local advertising: No. Regional interconnect: Cabletime.
Equipment: RCA headend; RCA amplifiers; Times Fiber cable; Scientific-Atlanta satellite antenna; Scientific-Atlanta satellite receivers.
Miles of plant: 29.8 (coaxial).
Manager: Harry Horne. Chief technician: Jerry Muroski.
City fee: None.
Ownership: Johnsonburg Community TV Co. Inc.

JOHNSTOWN—Cablecomm, 120 Southmont Blvd., Johnstown, PA 15905-4591. Phone: 814-535-3506. Fax: 814-535-7749. Counties: Cambria & Somerset. Also serves Benson, Brownstown (Cambria County), Conemaugh Twp. (Cambria County), Conemaugh Twp. (Somerset County), Daisytown (Cambria County), Dale (Cambria County), Davidsville, East Taylor Twp., Ferndale (Cambria County), Franklin (Cambria County), Geistown, Hollsopple, Jackson Twp. (Cambria County), Jenner Twp. (Somerset County), Jerome, Lorain, Lower Yoder Twp., Middle Taylor Twp., Mineral Point, Paint Twp. (Somerset County), Quemahoning Twp. (Somerset County), Richland Twp. (Cambria County), Southmont, Stonycreek Twp. (Cambria County), Tire Hill, Upper Yoder Twp., West Taylor Twp., Westmont (Cambria County). ICA: PA0026.
TV Market Ranking: 74. Franchise award date: February 23, 1983. Franchise expiration date: N.A. Began: August 1, 1960.
Channel capacity: 78 (2-way capable; operating 2-way). Channels available but not in use: 10.
Basic Service
Subscribers: 30,750.
Programming (received off-air): WPSX-TV (P) Clearfield; WATM-TV (A), WJAC-TV (N), WKBS-TV (I), WTAJ-TV (C), WWCP-TV (F) Johnstown-Altoona; KDKA-TV (C), WPXI (N), WQED (P), WTAE-TV (A) Pittsburgh.
Programming (via satellite): C-SPAN; Country Music TV; E! Entertainment TV; EWTN; Fox Sports Net; Home Shopping Network; QVC; TV Guide Channel; Travel Channel.
Current originations: Public access; educational access; government access; religious access; leased access; local news; local sports.
Fee: $36.09 installation; $8.97 monthly.
Expanded Basic Service
Subscribers: 29,865.
Programming (via satellite): A & E; American Movie Classics; CNN; Comedy Central; Discovery Channel; ESPN; ESPN 2; Fox Family Channel; Fox Sports Net Pittsburgh; Headline News; Learning Channel; Lifetime; MTV; Nashville Network; Nickelodeon; TV Guide Sneak Prevue; The Weather Channel; Turner Classic Movies; Turner Network TV; USA Network; VH1.
Fee: $36.09 installation; $16.26 monthly.
A la Carte 1
Subscribers: 29,775.
Programming (via satellite): WGN-TV (W) Chicago; TBS Superstation.
Fee: $1.39 monthly (package); $0.89 monthly (each).
Pay Service 1
Pay Units: 1,906.
Programming (via satellite): Cinemax.
Fee: $12.96 monthly.
Pay Service 2
Pay Units: 1,190.
Programming (via satellite): Disney Channel.
Fee: $12.96 monthly.
Pay Service 3
Pay Units: 2,680.
Programming (via satellite): HBO.
Fee: $12.96 monthly.
Pay Service 4
Pay Units: 1,607.
Programming (via satellite): Showtime.
Fee: $12.96 monthly.
Pay-Per-View
Addressable homes: 8,534.
Hot Choice; Viewer's Choice.
Local advertising: Yes. Available in satellite distributed, locally originated, character-generated, taped & automated programming. Local sales manager: Dale Manning. Regional interconnect: Cable AdNet-Johnstown/Altoona, PA.
Equipment: Scientific-Atlanta, Catel & Zenith headend; Jerrold & Century III amplifiers; Times Fiber & Comm/Scope cable; Sony cameras; Sony & JVC VTRs; Video Data Systems character generator; Scientific-Atlanta set top converters; Zenith addressable set top converters; Scientific-Atlanta, Microdyne & Standard Communications satellite antenna; Scientific-Atlanta satellite receivers.
Miles of plant: 578.0 (coaxial); 140.0 (fiber optic). Homes passed: 40,672. Total homes in franchised area: 40,754.
Manager: Karen Broach. Technical operations manager: David Kuchenbrod. Business manager: Wanda Webb. Marketing & customer service manager: Ellen Holsinger.
City fee: 3% of gross.
Ownership: Fanch Communications Inc. (MSO); Time Warner Cable (MSO). See Cable System Ownership.

KANE—TCI of Pennsylvania Inc., 138 N. Fraley St., Kane, PA 16735-1386. Phone: 814-837-6272. Fax: 814-837-9701. Counties: Elk & McKean. Also serves East Kane, Hamlin Twp., Hazel Hurst, Highland Twp. (Elk County), James City, Mount Jewett, Westline, Wetmore Twp. ICA: PA0125.
TV Market Ranking: Outside TV Markets. Franchise award date: N.A. Franchise expiration date: N.A. Began: November 1, 1959.
Channel capacity: 36. Channels available but not in use: None.
Basic Service
Subscribers: 2,999.
Programming (received off-air): WIVB-TV (C), WKBW-TV (A) Buffalo; WPSX-TV (P) Clearfield; WICU-TV (N), WJET-TV (A) Erie; WJAC-TV (N), WTAJ-TV (C) Johnstown-Altoona; allband FM.
Programming (via satellite): WPIX (W) New York; EWTN; FoxNet; Odyssey; TBS Superstation; The Weather Channel.
Current originations: Automated timeweather.
Fee: $59.95 installation; $10.18 monthly; $2.00 converter; $49.95 additional installation.
Expanded Basic Service
Subscribers: 2,889.
Programming (via satellite): American Movie Classics; C-SPAN; CNBC; CNN; Discovery Channel; ESPN; FX; Fox Family Channel; Fox Sports Net Pittsburgh; Lifetime; MTV; Nashville Network; Nickelodeon; QVC; Turner Network TV; USA Network.
Fee: $11.34 monthly.
Pay Service 1
Pay Units: 188.
Programming (via satellite): Disney Channel.
Fee: $13.15 monthly.
Pay Service 2
Pay Units: 621.
Programming (via satellite): HBO.
Fee: $13.15 monthly.
Pay Service 3
Pay Units: 182.
Programming (via satellite): Showtime.
Fee: $13.15 monthly.
Pay Service 4
Pay Units: 91.
Programming (via satellite): The Movie Channel.
Fee: N.A.
Pay Service 5
Pay Units: 1,245.
Programming (via satellite): The New Encore.
Fee: N.A.
Pay-Per-View
Special events.
Local advertising: Yes. Regional interconnect: Cabletime.
Program Guide: The Cable Guide.
Equipment: Scientific-Atlanta headend; Jerrold amplifiers; General cable; Scientific-Atlanta & Anixter-Pruzan satellite antenna.
Miles of plant: 60.2 (coaxial).
Manager: Chuck Horner. Customer service manager: Pam Bizzak. Office manager: LuAnn Glenn.
City fee: $1,200 annually.
Ownership: AT&T Broadband & Internet Services (MSO). Purchased from Tele-Communications Inc., March 9, 1999.

KARTHAUS—CableVision Communications, Box 2200, 68 5th St., Buckhannon, WV 26201. Phone: 304-472-4193. Fax: 304-472-0756. County: Clearfield. Also serves Frenchville, Lacontes Mills. ICA: PA0231.
TV Market Ranking: Outside TV Markets. Franchise award date: April 20, 1988. Franchise expiration date: N.A. Began: N.A.
Channel capacity: 23. Channels available but not in use: None.
Basic Service
Subscribers: 397.
Programming (received off-air): WPSX-TV (P) Clearfield; WJAC-TV (N), WTAJ-TV (C) Johnstown-Altoona; WKRN-TV (A) Nashville; WPIX (W) New York.
Programming (via satellite): WGN-TV (W) Chicago; Animal Planet; CNN; Disney Channel; ESPN; Fox Family Channel; FoxNet; MTV; Nashville Network; Nickelodeon; TBS Superstation; Turner Network TV; USA Network; VH1.
Fee: $61.25 installation; $23.46 monthly; $1.24 converter; $17.50 additional installation.
Pay Service 1
Pay Units: 191.
Programming (via satellite): HBO; Showtime.
Fee: $11.95 monthly (Showtime), $11.99 (HBO).
Pay Service 2
Pay Units: N.A.
Programming (via satellite): Cinemax; The Movie Channel.
Fee: $7.95 monthly (Cinemax), $11.95 monthly (TMC).
Equipment: M/A-Com headend; C-COR amplifiers; Comm/Scope cable.
Miles of plant: 24.0 (coaxial). Homes passed: 564.
Manager: Willie Critchfield. Chief technician: Bill Turner. Marketing director: Kenny Phillips.
Ownership: Rifkin & Associates Inc. (MSO). See Cable System Ownership.

KELLETTVILLE—CableVision Communications, Box 2200, 68 5th St., Buckhannon, WV 26201. Phone: 304-472-4193. Fax: 304-472-0756. County: Forest. Also serves Fork Run, Wig Hill, Wilson Hill. ICA: PA0270.
TV Market Ranking: Outside TV Markets. Franchise award date: N.A. Franchise expiration date: N.A. Began: N.A.
Channel capacity: 36. Channels available but not in use: 24.
Basic Service
Subscribers: 26.
Programming (received off-air): WPSX-TV (P) Clearfield; WICU-TV (N), WJET-TV (A), WSEE (C) Erie; WJAC-TV (N) Johnstown-Altoona; KDKA-TV (C) Pittsburgh.
Programming (via satellite): Discovery Channel; ESPN; Fox Family Channel; Nashville Network; TBS Superstation; USA Network.
Fee: $61.25 installation; $24.00 monthly; $0.73 converter.
Equipment: Blonder-Tongue, Olson & Standard Communications headend; Jerrold amplifiers; Comm/Scope cable.
Miles of plant: 5.0 (coaxial). Homes passed: 194.
Manager: Willie Critchfield. Marketing director: Kenny Phillips.
Ownership: Rifkin & Associates Inc. (MSO). See Cable System Ownership.

KENNETT SQUARE—Harron Communications, Suite 400, 1220 Ward Ave., West Chester, PA 19380. Phone: 610-444-0796. Fax: 610-431-7782. Counties: Chester & Delaware. Also serves New London Twp., Avondale, Birmingham Twp. (Chester County), Chadds Ford Twp., East Marlborough Twp., Franklin Twp. (Chester County), London Britain Twp., London Grove Twp., New Garden Twp., Penn Twp. (Chester County), Pennsbury Twp. (Chester County), Pocopson, Pocopson Twp., Upper Oxford Twp., West Grove. ICA: PA0071.
TV Market Ranking: 4 (Avondale, Chadds Ford Twp., East Marlborough Twp., Franklin Twp., Kennett Square, London Britain Twp., London Grove Twp., New Garden Twp., Pennsbury Twp., Pocopson, Upper Oxford Twp.); 57 (Avondale, Birmingham Twp., East Marlborough Twp., Franklin Twp., Kennett Square, London Britain Twp., London Grove Twp., New Garden Twp., Penn Twp., Upper Oxford Twp., West Grove). Franchise award date: N.A. Franchise expiration date: December 3, 2010. Began: December 3, 1980.
Channel capacity: 57 (not 2-way capable). Channels available but not in use: 5.
Basic Service
Subscribers: 13,284.
Programming (received off-air): WGTW (I) Burlington; WGAL (N) Lancaster; KYW-TV (C), WCAU (N), WPHL-TV (W), WPSG (U), WPVI-TV (A), WTXF-TV (F), WYBE (P) Philadelphia; WTVE (H) Reading; WHSP-TV (H) Vineland; WHYY-TV (P), WPPX (X) Wilmington.

Programming (via satellite): C-SPAN; EWTN; QVC; TBS Superstation.
Current originations: Automated time-weather.
Planned originations: Public access; educational access.
Fee: $23.00 installation; $9.03 monthly.

Expanded Basic Service
Subscribers: 12,717.
Programming (via satellite): A & E; American Movie Classics; BET; Bravo; CNBC; CNN; Comedy Central; Discovery Channel; Disney Channel; E! Entertainment TV; ESPN; ESPN 2; Fox Family Channel; Fox Sports Net; Golf Channel; Headline News; History Channel; Home & Garden Television; Learning Channel; Lifetime; MSNBC; MTV; Nashville Network; Nickelodeon; Sci-Fi Channel; TV Food Network; TV Guide Channel; The Weather Channel; Turner Network TV; USA Network; Univision; VH1.
Fee: $21.58 monthly.

Pay Service 1
Pay Units: 1,190.
Programming (via satellite): Cinemax.
Fee: $9.95 monthly.

Pay Service 2
Pay Units: 2,386.
Programming (via satellite): HBO (multiplexed).
Fee: $11.95 monthly.

Pay Service 3
Pay Units: 1,166.
Programming (via satellite): The Movie Channel.
Fee: $9.95 monthly.

Pay Service 4
Pay Units: 741.
Programming (via satellite): Showtime.
Fee: $10.95 monthly.

Pay-Per-View
Addressable homes: 3,492.
Action Pay-Per-View; Spice Hot; Viewer's Choice 1-4; special events.

Local advertising: Yes. Available in satellite distributed programming.
Equipment: Scientific-Atlanta headend; Jerrold amplifiers; Comm/Scope cable; Compuvid character generator; Jerrold set top converters; Jerrold addressable set top converters; Microdyne & Prodelin satellite antenna; Microdyne satellite receivers.
Miles of plant: 454.6 (coaxial); 27.0 (fiber optic). Additional miles planned: 5.0 (coaxial). Homes passed: 18,832.
Manager: Patricia Sincavage. Technical operations manager: James Mellon.
Ownership: Harron Communications Corp. (MSO). See Cable System Ownership.

KING OF PRUSSIA—Suburban Cable, 202 Shoemaker Rd., Pottstown, PA 19464. Phone: 610-323-6400.
Web site: http://www.suburbancable.com.
Counties: Delaware & Montgomery. Also serves Collegeville, Graterford, Graterford Prison, Gulph Mills, Perkiomen, Rahns, Schwenksville, Skippack, Swedeland, Trappe, Upper Merion Twp., Upper Providence Twp. (Delaware County), Wayne. ICA: PA0059.
TV Market Ranking: 4. Franchise award date: N.A. Franchise expiration date: N.A. Began: November 1, 1981.
Channel capacity: 52 (not 2-way capable). Channels available but not in use: 2.

Basic Service
Subscribers: 17,692; Commercial subscribers: 71.
Programming (received off-air): WFMZ-TV (I), WLVT-TV (P) Allentown; WGTW (I) Burlington; KYW-TV (C), WCAU (N), WPHL-TV (W), WPSG (U), WPVI-TV (A), WTXF-TV (F), WYBE (P) Philadelphia; WTVE (H) Reading; WNJT (P) Trenton; WHYY-TV (P), WPPX (X) Wilmington.
Programming (via satellite): C-SPAN; EWTN; Fox Family Channel; Knowledge TV; MSNBC; QVC; TBS Superstation; The Box.
Current originations: Automated time-weather; public access; educational access; government access; local news.
Fee: $35.00 installation (aerial), $40.00 (underground); $21.95 monthly; $15.00 additional installation.
Commercial fee: $40.00 monthly.

Expanded Basic Service
Subscribers: 17,138.
Programming (via satellite): A & E; American Movie Classics; Bravo; CNBC; CNN; Comedy Central; Discovery Channel; Disney Channel; E! Entertainment TV; ESPN; ESPN 2; Headline News; History Channel; Learning Channel; Lifetime; MTV; Nashville Network; Nick at Nite; Nickelodeon; Sci-Fi Channel; The Sports Network; The Weather Channel; Turner Network TV; USA Network; VH1.
Fee: N.A.

Pay Service 1
Pay Units: 845.
Programming (via satellite): Cinemax.
Fee: $15.00 installation; $8.95 monthly.

Pay Service 2
Pay Units: N.A.
Programming (via satellite): Starz!
Fee: N.A.

Pay Service 3
Pay Units: 3,807.
Programming (via satellite): HBO.
Fee: $15.00 installation; $9.95 monthly.

Pay Service 4
Pay Units: 1,425.
Programming (via satellite): Showtime.
Fee: $15.00 installation; $8.95 monthly.

Pay-Per-View
Addressable homes: 2,300.
Playboy TV; Spice; Viewer's Choice.
Fee: $3.95 (Viewer's Choice), $4.95 (Spice), $5.95 (Playboy TV).

Local advertising: Yes (insert only). Available in satellite distributed & taped programming.
Program Guide: TV Host.
Equipment: Jerrold headend; Jerrold amplifiers; Times Fiber & Trilogy cable; JVC cameras; Sony VTRs; Texscan character generator; Jerrold & Hamlin set top converters; Jerrold addressable set top converters; Eagle traps; M/A-Com satellite antenna; Standard Communications satellite receivers; Sony commercial insert.
Miles of plant: 250.0 (coaxial). Additional miles planned: 6.0 (coaxial). Homes passed: 17,914. Total homes in franchised area: 18,464.
Manager: Daniel McMonigle. Chief technician: Chuck Laylon. Program director: George Ferrara. Marketing director: Sherri Radocaj.
City fee: 3% of gross.
Ownership: Lenfest Communications Inc. (MSO).

KISKIMINETAS TWP.—AT&T Cable Services, 300 Corliss St., Pittsburgh, PA 15220-4815. Phones: 412-875-1100; 412-771-8100.
Counties: Armstrong & Westmoreland. Also serves Allegheny Twp. (Westmoreland County), Apollo, East Vandergrift, Gilpin Twp., Hyde Park, Leechburg, North Apollo, Oklahoma, Parks Twp. (Armstrong County), Vandergrift, Washington Twp. (Westmoreland County), West Leechburg. ICA: PA0074.
TV Market Ranking: 10. Franchise award date: N.A. Franchise expiration date: N.A. Began: February 1, 1967.
Channel capacity: 54 (not 2-way capable). Channels available but not in use: N.A.

Basic Service
Subscribers: 10,687.
Programming (received off-air): WPCB-TV (I) Greensburg; WJAC-TV (N) Johnstown-Altoona; KDKA-TV (C), WCWB (W), WPGH-TV (F), WPXI (N), WQED (P), WQEX (P), WTAE-TV (A) Pittsburgh; allband FM.
Programming (via microwave): Meadows Racing Network.
Programming (via satellite): C-SPAN; C-SPAN 2; EWTN; Lifetime; QVC; TV Guide Sneak Prevue.
Current originations: Automated time-weather; public access; educational access; government access; automated emergency alert.
Fee: $44.95 installation; $8.79 monthly; $1.50 converter; $24.95 additional installation.

Expanded Basic Service
Subscribers: 9,994.
Programming (via satellite): A & E; American Movie Classics; Animal Planet; CNBC; CNN; Cartoon Network; Court TV; Discovery Channel; E! Entertainment TV; ESPN; ESPN 2; FX; Fox Family Channel; Fox News Channel; Fox Sports Net Pittsburgh; Headline News; Home & Garden Television; Home Shopping Network; Knowledge TV; Learning Channel; MOVIEplex; MTV; Nashville Network; Nickelodeon; TBS Superstation; The Weather Channel; Turner Network TV; USA Network; VH1.
Fee: $19.27 monthly.

Pay Service 1
Pay Units: 834.
Programming (via satellite): Cinemax.
Fee: $13.45 monthly.

Pay Service 2
Pay Units: 1,217.
Programming (via satellite): HBO.
Fee: $14.95 monthly.

Pay Service 3
Pay Units: 899.
Programming (via satellite): Showtime.
Fee: $14.95 monthly.

Pay Service 4
Pay Units: 2,771.
Programming (via satellite): The New Encore.
Fee: $1.95 monthly.

Pay Service 5
Pay Units: N.A.
Programming (via satellite): DMX; Disney Channel; Starz!
Fee: $6.75 monthly (Starz), $9.95 monthly (DMX), $12.50 monthly (Disney).

Pay-Per-View
Spice.

Local advertising: Yes. Regional interconnect: TCI Media Services-Pittsburgh, PA.
Program Guide: The Cable Guide.
Miles of plant: 201.0 (coaxial). Homes passed: 12,509. Total homes in franchised area: 35,775.
Manager: Jeffrey C. Harshman. Chief technician: Fred Hamm. Marketing director: Glenn Ryerson.
City fee: 5% of gross.
Ownership: AT&T Broadband & Internet Services (MSO). Purchased from Tele-Communications Inc., March 9, 1999.

KITTANNING—Adelphia, One Adelphia Dr., Blairsville, PA 15717. Phone: 800-892-7300. Fax: 412-459-0648. County: Armstrong. Also serves Applewold, Ford City, Ford Cliff, Garretts Run, Manor Twp. (Armstrong County), Manorville, McGrann, North Buffalo Twp., Pattonville, Rosston, South Buffalo Twp. (portions), West Kittanning, Worthington. ICA: PA0351.
TV Market Ranking: 10 (Applewold, Ford City, Ford Cliff, Manor Twp., Manorville, McGrann, North Buffalo Twp., Pattonville, Rosston, South Buffalo Twp.); Below 100 (Garretts Run, Kittanning, West Kittanning); Outside TV Markets (Worthington). Franchise award date: N.A. Franchise expiration date: N.A. Began: January 1, 1962.
Channel capacity: 54 (not 2-way capable). Channels available but not in use: N.A.

Basic Service
Subscribers: 8,425.
Programming (received off-air): WPCB-TV (I) Greensburg; WJAC-TV (N) Johnstown-Altoona; KDKA-TV (C), WPGH-TV (F), WPXI (N), WQED (P), WQEX (P), WTAE-TV (A) Pittsburgh; allband FM.
Programming (via microwave): WUAB (U) Lorain-Cleveland.
Planned programming (via microwave): WPIX (W) New York.
Programming (via satellite): WGN-TV (W) Chicago; TBS Superstation.
Current originations: Automated time-weather; public access.
Fee: N.A.

Expanded Basic Service
Subscribers: 8,171.
Programming (via satellite): A & E; C-SPAN; C-SPAN 2; CNN; Comedy Central; Country Music TV; Discovery Channel; Disney Channel; ESPN; ESPN 2; EWTN; FX; Fox Family Channel; Fox Sports Net Pittsburgh; Headline News; History Channel; Home Shopping Network; Learning Channel; Lifetime; MSNBC; MTV; Nashville Network; Nickelodeon; Product Information Network; QVC; Sci-Fi Channel; TV Food Network; TV Guide Channel; The Weather Channel; Turner Classic Movies; Turner Network TV; USA Network; VH1.
Fee: N.A.

Pay Service 1
Pay Units: 756.
Programming (via satellite): Cinemax.
Fee: $11.50 monthly.

Pay Service 2
Pay Units: 223.
Programming (via satellite): The New Encore.
Fee: $2.95 monthly.

Pay Service 3
Pay Units: 1,057.
Programming (via satellite): HBO.
Fee: $11.50 monthly.

Pay Service 4
Pay Units: 263.
Programming (via satellite): Showtime.
Fee: $11.50 monthly.

Pay Service 5
Pay Units: 162.
Programming (via satellite): The Movie Channel.
Fee: $11.50 monthly.
Local advertising: Yes. Regional interconnect: TCI Media Services-Pittsburgh, PA.
Equipment: Blonder-Tongue, Jerrold & Tocom headend; GTE Sylvania & Jerrold amplifiers; Times Fiber cable; Sony VTRs; Jerrold & Oak set top converters; Scientific-Atlanta satellite antenna.
Miles of plant: 136.0 (coaxial). Additional miles planned: 8.0 (coaxial).
Manager: J. Francis Bradley Jr. Chief technician: Dave Bowen.
Ownership: Adelphia Communications Corp. (MSO).

KUTZTOWN—Service Electric Cablevision, Box 8, 6400 Perkiomen Ave., Birdsboro, PA 19508. Phone: 610-582-5317. Fax: 610-582-3094. County: Berks. Also serves District Twp., Longswamp Twp., Lyons Station, Maidencreek Twp. (Berks County), Maxatawny Twp., Richmond Twp. (Berks County), Rockland Twp. (Berks County), Ruscombmanor Twp. (Berks County), Topton. ICA: PA0095.
TV Market Ranking: Below 100. Franchise award date: October 1, 1970. Franchise expiration date: N.A. Began: September 1, 1971.
Channel capacity: 50 (not 2-way capable). Channels available but not in use: N.A.
Basic Service
Subscribers: 6,652.
Programming (received off-air): WFMZ-TV (I), WLVT-TV (P) Allentown; WGAL (N) Lancaster; WPIX (W), WWOR-TV (U) New York; KYW-TV (C), WCAU (N), WPHL-TV (W), WPVI-TV (A), WTXF-TV (F) Philadelphia; WVIA-TV (P) Scranton & Wilkes-Barre; WPMT (F) York; 18 FMs.
Programming (via satellite): A & E; American Movie Classics; C-SPAN; CNBC; CNN; Cartoon Network; Country Music TV; Discovery Channel; ESPN; ESPN 2; Goodlife TV Network; Home Shopping Network; Learning Channel; Lifetime; MTV; Nashville Network; Nickelodeon; TBS Superstation; The Weather Channel; Travel Channel; Turner Classic Movies; Turner Network TV; USA Network; VH1.
Current originations: Educational access; local news; local sports.
Planned originations: Automated time-weather.
Fee: $32.00 installation; $22.90 monthly; $10.00 additional installation.
Pay Service 1
Pay Units: 1,818.
Programming (via satellite): Cinemax; Disney Channel; HBO.
Fee: $10.00 installation; $8.95 monthly (Disney), $9.95 monthly (Cinemax), $11.00 monthly (HBO).
Pay-Per-View
Addressable homes: 1,753.
Local advertising: Planned. Regional interconnect: Metrobase Cable Advertising.
Equipment: Jerrold headend; Jerrold amplifiers; Times Fiber cable; Jerrold set top converters; AFC satellite antenna; Microdyne satellite receivers.
Miles of plant: 242.0 (coaxial). Additional miles planned: 13.0 (coaxial). Homes passed: 7,400. Total homes in franchised area: 9,200.
Manager: Karl Kowatch. Chief technician: David Jones. Customer service manager: Donald Brandt.
City fee: 2% of gross; 5% of gross (Kutztown only).
Ownership: Service Electric Cable TV Inc. (MSO).

LAIRDSVILLE—Ralph Herr TV, Box 717, RR 4, Montoursville, PA 17754-9665. Phone: 717-435-2780. County: Lycoming. ICA: PA0305.
TV Market Ranking: Below 100. Franchise award date: N.A. Franchise expiration date: N.A. Began: N.A.
Channel capacity: 12. Channels available but not in use: 4.
Basic Service
Subscribers: 34.
Programming (received off-air): WHP-TV (C) Harrisburg; WBRE-TV (N), WNEP-TV (A), WSWB (W), WVIA-TV (P), WYOU (C) Scranton & Wilkes-Barre.
Fee: $20.00 installation; $8.00 monthly.
Miles of plant: 1.5 (coaxial). Homes passed: 36.
Chief technician: Ralph W. Herr.
Ownership: Herr Cable Co. (MSO).

LAKEWOOD—Lakewood Cable Co., Box 608, 6 Read St., Hancock, NY 13783-0608. Phones: 607-637-2568; 800-360-4664. Fax: 607-637-9999. County: Wayne. Also serves Lake Como (village), Preston Park (village), Starlight (village). ICA: PA0282.
TV Market Ranking: 49. Franchise award date: N.A. Franchise expiration date: N.A. Began: November 1, 1989.
Channel capacity: 28 (not 2-way capable). Channels available but not in use: 4.
Basic Service
Subscribers: 201.
Programming (received off-air): WBNG-TV (C), WICZ-TV (F), WIVT (A), WSKG (P) Binghamton; WBRE-TV (N), WNEP-TV (A), WSWB (W), WVIA-TV (P), WYOU (C) Scranton & Wilkes-Barre; 15 FMs.
Programming (via satellite): WGN-TV (W) Chicago; TBS Superstation.
Fee: $150.50 installation; $12.00 monthly.
Expanded Basic Service
Subscribers: 148.
Programming (via satellite): WPIX (W) New York; CNN; Discovery Channel; ESPN; ESPN 2; Nashville Network; QVC; Turner Network TV; USA Network.
Fee: $8.50 monthly.
Expanded Basic Service 2
Subscribers: 91.
Programming (via satellite): American Movie Classics; CNBC; Fox Family Channel; History Channel; Nickelodeon; Sci-Fi Channel; The Weather Channel.
Fee: $6.95 monthly.
Pay Service 1
Pay Units: 63.
Programming (via satellite): HBO.
Fee: $9.50 monthly.
Pay Service 2
Pay Units: 15.
Programming (via satellite): Disney Channel.
Fee: $8.00 monthly.
Miles of plant: 7.0 (coaxial). Homes passed: 240.
Manager: Beth Millar. Chief technician: Gary Schoonmaker. Customer service manager: Margaret Evanitsky.
Ownership: Hancel Inc. (MSO).

LANCASTER—Suburban Cable, 1131 S. Duke St., Lancaster, PA 17608. Phones: 717-291-3000; 800-336-4236. Fax: 717-392-4398. Web site: http://www.suburbancable.com. Counties: Chester, Lancaster & York. Also serves Bareville, Bart Twp., Blue Ball, Caernarvon Twp. (Lancaster County), Christiana (Lancaster County), Christiana Borough, Columbia, Columbia Borough, Conestoga, Drumore Twp., Earl Twp. (Lancaster County), East Drumore Twp., East Earl Twp. (southern portion), East Hempfield Twp. (Lancaster County), East Lampeter Twp. (Lancaster County), East Petersburg, Fulton Twp., Gap, Hellam (York County), Hellam Twp. (York County), Kinzers, Lancaster Twp. (Lancaster County), Leacock, Leacock Twp. (Lancaster County), Leola, Little Britain Twp., Manheim Twp. (Lancaster County), Manor Twp. (Lancaster County), Millersville, Mountville, Narvon, New Holland, Paradise, Paradise Twp. (Lancaster County), Pequea Twp. (Lancaster County), Providence Twp. (Lancaster County), Quarryville, Sadsbury Twp. (Lancaster County), Salisbury Twp. (Lancaster County), Strasburg, Strasburg Twp. (Lancaster County), Upper Leacock Twp., Washington Twp. (York County), West Earl Twp., West Hempfield Twp. (Lancaster County), West Lampeter Twp., Wrightsville. Plans service to Eden Twp., Martic Twp. ICA: PA0010.
TV Market Ranking: 57. Franchise award date: October 1, 1966. Franchise expiration date: N.A. Began: October 12, 1966.
Channel capacity: 52 (2-way capable; operating 2-way). Channels available but not in use: None.
Basic Service
Subscribers: 83,039; Commercial subscribers: 646.
Programming (received off-air): WHP-TV (C), WHTM-TV (A), WITF-TV (P) Harrisburg; WGAL (N), WLYH-TV (U) Lancaster; WCAU (N), WPHL-TV (W), WPVI-TV (A), WTXF-TV (F) Philadelphia; WGCB-TV (I) Red Lion; WPMT (F) York.
Programming (via microwave): Tri-State Media.
Programming (via satellite): WGN-TV (W) Chicago; C-SPAN; Home Shopping Network; Pennsylvania Cable Network; QVC.
Current originations: Public access; educational access; government access; religious access; local news; local sports.
Fee: $33.00 installation; $8.38 monthly.
Commercial fee: $23.45 monthly.
Expanded Basic Service
Subscribers: 77,807.
Programming (via satellite): A & E; American Movie Classics; BET; Bravo; CNBC; CNN; Comedy Central; Discovery Channel; Disney Channel; E! Entertainment TV; ESPN; ESPN 2; FX; Fox Family Channel; Headline News; History Channel; Home Team Sports; Learning Channel; Lifetime; MSNBC; MTV; Nashville Network; Nick at Nite; Nickelodeon; Odyssey; TBS Superstation; TV Guide Channel; The Box; The Sports Network; The Weather Channel; Travel Channel; Turner Network TV; USA Network; Univision; VH1.
Fee: $33.00 installation; $15.03 monthly.
A la Carte 1
Subscribers: N.A.
Programming (via satellite): Cartoon Network; Court TV; MOVIEplex; Sci-Fi Channel.
Fee: $3.50 monthly (package); $1.00-$2.50 monthly (each).
Pay Service 1
Pay Units: 4,239.
Programming (via satellite): Cinemax.
Fee: $25.00 installation; $7.95 monthly.
Pay Service 2
Pay Units: N.A.
Programming (via satellite): Starz!
Fee: N.A.
Pay Service 3
Pay Units: 8,763.
Programming (via satellite): HBO.
Fee: $10.00 installation; $9.95 monthly.
Pay Service 4
Pay Units: 2,595.
Programming (via satellite): Showtime.
Fee: $10.00 installation; $9.95 monthly.
Pay-Per-View
Addressable homes: 23,134.
Viewer's Choice.
Fee: $3.95.
Local advertising: Yes. Available in character-generated programming. Rates: $40.00/Minute; $20.00/30 Seconds. Local sales manager: Ray Marshall. Regional interconnect: Central Pennsylvania Cable AdCom.
Equipment: Jerrold headend; Jerrold & C-COR amplifiers; Comm/Scope cable; Sony cameras; Sony VTRs; Amiga character generator; Scientific-Atlanta set top converters; Tocom addressable set top converters; Microdyne satellite antenna; Scientific-Atlanta satellite receivers; Sony commercial insert.
Miles of plant: 1422.2 (coaxial); 145.0 (fiber optic). Homes passed: 103,407. Total homes in franchised area: 118,100.
Manager: Sue Heinbach. Chief technician: Bill Renninger. Program director: George Ferrara. Marketing director: Lee Javens.
City fee: 3% of gross.
Ownership: Lenfest Communications Inc. (MSO).

LANSDALE—Adelphia Cable, Box 198, One Apollo Rd., Plymouth Meeting, PA 19462. Phones: 610-943-5450; 814-274-9830. Fax: 610-941-9943.
Web site: http://www.adelphia.net.
Counties: Delaware & Montgomery. Also serves Broomall, Hatboro, Haverford Twp., Horsham Twp., Marple Twp. (Delaware County), Montgomery Twp. (Montgomery County), Montgomeryville, North Wales, Radnor Twp. (Delaware County), Towamencin, Upper Dublin Twp., Upper Gwynedd Twp. ICA: PA0352.
TV Market Ranking: 4. Franchise award date: November 1, 1978. Franchise expiration date: N.A. Began: September 1, 1979.
Channel capacity: 36 (not 2-way capable). Channels available but not in use: None.
Basic Service
Subscribers: 49,218.
Programming (received off-air): WLVT-TV (P) Allentown; WWOR-TV (U) New York; KYW-TV (C), WCAU (N), WPHL-TV (W), WPSG (U), WPVI-TV (A), WTXF-TV (F) Philadelphia; WHYY-TV (P) Wilmington.
Programming (via satellite): TBS Superstation.
Current originations: Automated time-weather; public access; educational access; government access; religious access; local news.
Fee: $35.00 installation (aerial), $50.00 (underground); $15.45 monthly; $25.00 additional installation.
Expanded Basic Service
Subscribers: N.A.
Programming (via satellite): A & E; American Movie Classics; C-SPAN; CNBC; CNN; Discovery Channel; ESPN; Fox Family Channel; Lifetime; MTV; Music Choice; Nashville Network; Nickelodeon; Philadelphia Park Live; QVC; The Weather Channel; Turner Classic Movies; Turner Network TV; USA Network; VH1.
Fee: $35.00 installation; $15.45 monthly.
Pay Service 1
Pay Units: 42,283.
Programming (via satellite): Cinemax; Disney Channel; HBO; Showtime; The Movie Channel.
Fee: $8.95 monthly (Disney), $10.95 monthly (Cinemax, HBO, Showtime or TMC).
Local advertising: Yes (insert only). Available in satellite distributed & automated programming. Local sales manager: Leeann Augustine.
Equipment: Scientific-Atlanta headend; C-COR amplifiers; Comm/Scope cable; JVC cam-

eras; Sony VTRs; Texscan character generator; Scientific-Atlanta set top converters; Pico & PPC traps; Scientific-Atlanta satellite antenna; Scientific-Atlanta satellite receivers.

Miles of plant: 570.6 (coaxial). Additional miles planned: 35.0 (coaxial).

Manager: Rick Conrad. Chief technician: Joe Ruff.

City fee: 3% of basic gross.

Ownership: Adelphia Communications Corp. (MSO).

LANSFORD—Blue Ridge Cable TV Inc., 20 W. Ridge St., Lansford, PA 18232. Phone: 717-645-5511.

Web site: http://www.blueridgecable.com.

Counties: Carbon & Schuylkill. Also serves Albrightsville, Coaldale, Jim Thorpe, Nesquehoning, Rush Twp. (Schuylkill County), Summit Hill. ICA: PA0097.

TV Market Ranking: 49. Franchise award date: N.A. Franchise expiration date: N.A. Began: October 1, 1950.

Channel capacity: 54 (2-way capable; operating 2-way). Channels available but not in use: N.A.

Basic Service

Subscribers: 7,300.

Programming (received off-air): WFMZ-TV (I), WLVT-TV (P) Allentown; WNYW (F) New York; KYW-TV (C), WCAU (N), WPHL-TV (W), WPVI-TV (A), WTXF-TV (F) Philadelphia; WBRE-TV (N), WNEP-TV (A), WSWB (W), WVIA-TV (P), WYOU (C) Scranton & Wilkes-Barre; allband FM.

Programming (via satellite): WPIX (W), WWOR-TV (U) New York; C-SPAN; Home Shopping Network.

Current originations: Automated time-weather; public access; leased access; local news; local sports.

Fee: $20.00 installation; $16.90 monthly.

Expanded Basic Service

Subscribers: 2,700.

Programming (via microwave): Comcast SportsNet.

Programming (via satellite): A & E; American Movie Classics; Animal Planet; CNBC; CNN; Cartoon Network; Comedy Central; Country Music TV; Court TV; Discovery Channel; E! Entertainment TV; ESPN; ESPN 2; ESPNews; EWTN; FX; Fox Family Channel; Golf Channel; Goodlife TV Network; Headline News; History Channel; Home & Garden Television; Knowledge TV; Learning Channel; Lifetime; MSNBC; MTV; Madison Square Garden Network; Nashville Network; Nick at Nite's TV Land; Nickelodeon; Pennsylvania Cable Network; QVC; Romance Classics; Sci-Fi Channel; Speedvision; TBS Superstation; TV Food Network; The Inspirational Network; The Weather Channel; Travel Channel; Turner Classic Movies; Turner Network TV; USA Network; VH1; ValueVision.

Fee: $25.77 monthly.

Pay Service 1

Pay Units: N.A.

Programming (via satellite): Cinemax; Disney Channel; HBO; Showtime; Spice; The Movie Channel.

Fee: $10.50 monthly.

Pay-Per-View

Addressable homes: 2,500.

Movies; special events.

Fee: $3.95 (movies); Varies (special events).

Equipment: Scientific-Atlanta headend; C-COR amplifiers; Comm/Scope cable; Zenith addressable set top converters; Scientific-Atlanta satellite receivers.

Miles of plant: 199.0 (coaxial); 50.0 (fiber optic). Homes passed: 5,000. Total homes in franchised area: 7,000.

Field supervisor: Lamar Semmel.

City fee: 3% of gross (Coaldale).

Ownership: Pencor Services Inc. (MSO).

LAPORTE BOROUGH—Eagles Mere/Laporte Cablevision Inc., 513 Jordan Ave., Montoursville, PA 17754. Phone: 570-368-3266. Fax: 570-368-8154. County: Sullivan. Also serves Eagles Mere Borough, Laporte Twp. (Sullivan County), Shrewsbury Twp. (Sullivan County). ICA: PA0413.

TV Market Ranking: 49 (Laporte Borough, Laporte Twp.); Below 100 (Eagles Mere Borough, Shrewsbury Twp.). Franchise award date: June 1, 1988. Franchise expiration date: June 1, 2003. Began: November 1, 1988.

Channel capacity: 40 (not 2-way capable). Channels available but not in use: 2.

Basic Service

Subscribers: 535.

Programming (received off-air): WBNG-TV (C), WSKG (P) Binghamton; WHTM-TV (A), WITF-TV (P) Harrisburg; WBRE-TV (N), WNEP-TV (A), WSWB (W), WVIA-TV (P), WYOU (C) Scranton & Wilkes-Barre.

Programming (via satellite): WGN-TV (W) Chicago; A & E; American Movie Classics; Animal Planet; C-SPAN; C-SPAN 2; CNBC; CNN; Country Music TV; Discovery Channel; Disney Channel; ESPN; ESPN 2; FX; Fox Family Channel; Fox News Channel; Headline News; History Channel; Learning Channel; Lifetime; MTV; Nashville Network; Nickelodeon; Pennsylvania Cable Network; QVC; TBS Superstation; The Weather Channel; Turner Network TV; USA Network; VH1.

Current originations: Automated time-weather.

Fee: $50.00 installation; $19.80 monthly.

Pay Service 1

Pay Units: N.A.

Programming (via satellite): HBO; Showtime; The Movie Channel.

Fee: $9.95 monthly (TMC), $10.95 monthly (Showtime), $11.95 monthly (HBO).

Equipment: Cadco & Drake headend; Texscan amplifiers; Trilogy & Comm/Scope cable; Scientific-Atlanta set top converters; Eagle & Production Products traps; Comtech satellite antenna; Drake & Scientific-Atlanta satellite receivers.

Miles of plant: 37.5 (coaxial). Homes passed: 800.

Manager: Roxanne Y. Criswell. Chief technician: Timothy J. Criswell.

Franchise fee: 3% of net basic.

Ownership: Criswell Group (MSO).

LAWRENCEVILLE—Cablecomm, 166 Main St., Hornell, NY 14843. Phone: 800-783-2839. County: Tioga. Also serves East Lawrence Twp. ICA: PA0354.

TV Market Ranking: Below 100. Franchise award date: N.A. Franchise expiration date: N.A. Began: October 1, 1967.

Channel capacity: 12. Channels available but not in use: N.A.

Basic Service

Subscribers: 1,487.

Programming (received off-air): WBNG-TV (C), WICZ-TV (F) Binghamton; WENY-TV (A), WETM-TV (N) Elmira; WVIA-TV (P) Scranton & Wilkes-Barre; allband FM.

Programming (via microwave): WPIX (W) New York.

Programming (via satellite): WGN-TV (W) Chicago; Cartoon Network; Fox Family Channel; TBS Superstation; Turner Classic Movies.

Current originations: Educational access.

Fee: $30.00 installation; $18.95 monthly.

Pay Service 1

Pay Units: 335.

Programming (via satellite): HBO.

Fee: $30.00 installation; $10.00 monthly.

Local advertising: Yes. Regional interconnect: Cabletime.

Equipment: Blonder-Tongue headend; Vikoa amplifiers; Times Fiber cable; Gamco traps; Scientific-Atlanta satellite antenna; Scientific-Atlanta satellite receivers.

Miles of plant: 50.0 (coaxial). Additional miles planned: 5.0 (coaxial).

Manager: Frank Gallagher.

City fee: $100.00 annually.

Ownership: Fanch Communications Inc. (MSO); Time Warner Cable (MSO). See Cable System Ownership.

LEBANON—AT&T Cable Services, 1555 Suzy St., Lebanon, PA 17046. Phone: 717-273-8511. Fax: 717-273-0702. Counties: Berks, Lancaster & Lebanon. Also serves Annville Twp., Bethel Twp. (Berks County), Bethel Twp. (Lebanon County), Cleona, Cornwall, East Hanover Twp. (Lebanon County), Elizabeth Twp. (Lancaster County), Heidelberg Twp. (Berks County), Heidelberg Twp. (Lebanon County), Jackson Twp. (Lebanon County), Jefferson Twp. (Berks County), Jonestown (Lebanon County), Marion Twp. (Berks County), Marion Twp. (Lebanon County), Millcreek Twp. (Lebanon County), Mount Gretna, Myerstown, North Annville Twp., North Cornwall Twp., North Lebanon Twp., Rapho Twp. (Lebanon County), Richland (Lebanon County), Robesonia, South Annville Twp., South Heidelberg Twp. (Berks County), South Lebanon Twp., South Londonderry Twp. (Lebanon County), Strausstown, Swatara Twp., Tulpehocken Twp., Union Twp. (Lebanon County), Upper Tulpehocken Twp. (portions), West Cornwall Twp., West Lebanon Twp., Womelsdorf (Berks County). ICA: PA0024.

TV Market Ranking: 57. Franchise award date: January 1, 1967. Franchise expiration date: January 1, 1999. Began: January 1, 1967.

Channel capacity: 70 (not 2-way capable). Channels available but not in use: None.

Basic Service

Subscribers: 33,365.

Programming (received off-air): WHP-TV (C), WHTM-TV (A), WITF-TV (P) Harrisburg; WGAL (N), WLYH-TV (U) Lancaster; KYW-TV (C), WPHL-TV (W), WPSG (U), WPVI-TV (A) Philadelphia; WGCB-TV (I) Red Lion; WVIA-TV (P) Scranton & Wilkes-Barre; WPMT (F) York; allband FM.

Programming (via satellite): C-SPAN 2; ValueVision.

Current originations: Automated time-weather; local news.

Fee: $5.31 installation; $8.53 monthly.

Expanded Basic Service

Subscribers: 32,680.

Programming (via microwave): Comcast SportsNet.

Programming (via satellite): A & E; Animal Planet; C-SPAN; CNBC; CNN; Cartoon Network; Comedy Central; Country Music TV; Court TV; E! Entertainment TV; ESPN; ESPN 2; EWTN; Fox Family Channel; Fox News Channel; Goodlife TV Network; Headline News; History Channel; Home & Garden Television; Home Shopping Network; Learning Channel; Lifetime; MTV; Nashville Network; Nick at Nite's TV Land; Nickelodeon; Odyssey; Pennsylvania Cable Network; QVC; Sci-Fi Channel; TV Food Network; TV Guide Sneak Prevue; The New Encore; The Weather Channel; Travel Channel; Turner Classic Movies; Turner Network TV; USA Network; Univision; VH1.

Fee: $5.31 installation; $12.87 monthly.

A la Carte 1

Subscribers: N.A.

Programming (via satellite): American Movie Classics; Discovery Channel; TBS Superstation.

Fee: N.A.

Pay Service 1

Pay Units: 2,882.

Programming (via satellite): Cinemax.

Fee: $5.31 installation; $11.00 monthly.

Pay Service 2

Pay Units: 2,150.

Programming (via satellite): Disney Channel.

Fee: $5.31 installation; $7.80 monthly.

Pay Service 3

Pay Units: 5,973.

Programming (via satellite): HBO.

Fee: $5.31 installation; $11.00 monthly.

Pay Service 4

Pay Units: 2,257.

Programming (via satellite): Starz!

Fee: $5.31 installation; $14.00 monthly.

Pay-Per-View

Addressable homes: 2,961.

Spice.

Fee: Varies.

Local advertising: Yes. Available in satellite distributed, character-generated & automated programming. Regional interconnect: Central Pennsylvania Cable AdCom.

Equipment: Scientific-Atlanta headend; Jerrold amplifiers; Comm/Scope cable; System Concepts character generator; Eagle traps; Harris, Prodelin & Scientific-Atlanta satellite antenna; Scientific-Atlanta satellite receivers.

Miles of plant: 653.0 (coaxial); 35.0 (fiber optic). Additional miles planned: 33.0 (coaxial). Homes passed: 40,233. Total homes in franchised area: 43,000.

Manager: Lee Glowacki. Chief technician: Bill Stahlman. Marketing director: Susanne Marshall. Customer service manager: Nancy Ristenbatt.

City fee: 5% of basic gross.

Ownership: AT&T Broadband & Internet Services (MSO). Purchased from Time Warner Cable, July 1, 1999.

LEHIGH VALLEY—Service Electric Cable TV Inc., 2260 Ave. A, Bethlehem, PA 18017-2108. Phone: 610-865-9100. Fax: 610-865-5031. E-mail: office@sectv.com. Web site: http://www.sectv.com. Counties: Berks, Bucks, Lehigh & Northampton, PA.; Hunterdon, NJ. Also serves Alexandria Twp., Frenchtown Boro, Holland Twp., Hunterdon County, Kingwood Twp., Milford Boro, NJ; Alburtis, Allen Twp., Allentown, Bangor Boro, Bath Boro, Bethlehem, Bethlehem Twp., Bridgeton Twp., Bushkill Twp., Catasauqua Boro, Chapman Boro, Coopersburg Boro, Coplay Boro, Durham Twp., East Allen Twp., East Bangor Boro, Fountain Hill Boro, Freemansburg Boro, Greenwich Twp., Hanover Twp. (Lehigh County), Hanover Twp. (Northampton County), Haycock Twp., Hellertown Boro, Hereford Twp., Longswamp Twp., Lower Macungie Twp., Lower Milford Twp., Lower Mount Bethel Twp., Lower Nazareth Twp., Lower Saucon Twp., Lowhill Twp., Moore Twp., Nazareth Boro, Nockamixon Twp., North Catasauqua Boro, North Whitehall Twp., Pen Argyl Boro, Plainfield Twp., Portland Boro, Richland Twp., Riegelsville Boro, Roseto Boro, Salisbury Twp., South Whitehall Twp., Springfield Twp., Tatamy Boro, Tinicum Twp., Upper Macungie Twp., Upper Mount Bethel Twp., Upper Nazareth Twp., Upper Saucon Twp.,

Washington Twp., Weisenberg Twp., Whitehall Twp., Williams Twp., Wind Gap Boro, PA. ICA: PA0006.
TV Market Ranking: 4 (Frenchtown Boro, Kingwood Twp., Upper Mount Bethel Twp.); Below 100 (Alburtis, Alexandria Twp., Allen Twp., Allentown, Bangor Boro, Bath Boro, Bethlehem, Bethlehem Twp., Bridgeton Twp., Bushkill Twp., Catasauqua Boro, Chapman Boro, Coopersburg Boro, Coplay Boro, Durham Twp., East Allen Twp., East Bangor Boro, Fountain Hill Boro, Freemansburg Boro, Greenwich Twp., Hanover Twp., Haycock Twp., Hellertown Boro, Hereford Twp., Holland Twp., Hunterdon County, Lehigh Valley, Longswamp Twp., Lower Macungie Twp., Lower Milford Twp., Lower Nazareth Twp., Lower Saucon Twp., Lowhill Twp., Milford Boro, Moore Twp., Nazareth Boro, Nockamixon Twp., North Catasauqua Boro, North Whitehall Twp., Pen Argyl Boro, Plainfield Twp., Portland Boro, Richland Twp., Riegelsville Boro, Roseto Boro, Salisbury Twp., South Whitehall Twp., Springfield Twp., Tatamy Boro, Tinicum Twp., Upper Macungie Twp., Upper Nazareth Twp., Upper Saucon Twp., Washington Twp., Weisenberg Twp., Whitehall Twp., Williams Twp., Wind Gap Boro). Franchise award date: January 1, 1951. Franchise expiration date: N.A. Began: January 1, 1951.
Channel capacity: 87 (2-way capable; operating 2-way partially). Channels available but not in use: None.

Basic Service

Subscribers: 91,396; Commercial subscribers: 7.
Programming (received off-air): WFMZ-TV (I), WLVT-TV (P) Allentown; WGTV (P) Athens; WBPH-TV (I) Bethlehem; WABC-TV (A), WNBC (N), WNYW (F), WPIX (W), WWOR-TV (U) New York; KYW-TV (C), WCAU (N), WPHL-TV (W), WPSG (U), WPVI-TV (A), WTXF-TV (F) Philadelphia; WTVE (H) Reading; WBRE-TV (N), WNEP-TV (A) Scranton & Wilkes-Barre; allband FM.
Programming (via satellite): BET; C-SPAN; EWTN; Home Shopping Network; Pennsylvania Cable Network; QVC; TBS Superstation; TV Food Network; TV Guide Channel; The Inspirational Network.
Current originations: Automated time-weather; public access; educational access; government access; religious access; leased access; library access; automated emergency alert; local news; local sports.
Fee: $25.00 installation; $11.82 monthly; $1.80 converter; $25.00 additional installation.

Expanded Basic Service

Subscribers: 88,693.
Programming (via microwave): Comcast SportsNet.
Programming (via satellite): A & E; American Movie Classics; Animal Planet; C-SPAN 2; CNBC; CNN; Cartoon Network; Comedy Central; Country Music TV; Discovery Channel; Disney Channel; E! Entertainment TV; ESPN; ESPN 2; FX; Fox Family Channel; Fox News Channel; Game Show Network; Golf Channel; Goodlife TV Network; Headline News; History Channel; Home & Garden Television; International Channel; Learning Channel; Lifetime; MSNBC; MTV; NASA TV; Nashville Network; Nick at Nite's TV Land; Nickelodeon; Odyssey; Outdoor Channel; Ovation; Romance Classics; Sci-Fi Channel; Speedvision; The Weather Channel; Travel Channel; Turner Classic Movies; Turner Network TV; USA Network; Univision; VH1; ValueVision.
Fee: $25.00 installation; $31.83 monthly.

Pay Service 1

Pay Units: 9,464.
Programming (via satellite): Cinemax (multiplexed).
Fee: $7.95 monthly.

Pay Service 2

Pay Units: 598.
Programming (via satellite): The New Encore.
Fee: $2.95 monthly.

Pay Service 3

Pay Units: 12,925.
Programming (via satellite): HBO (multiplexed).
Fee: $9.95 monthly.

Pay Service 4

Pay Units: 1,426.
Programming (via satellite): Showtime; The Movie Channel.
Fee: $9.95 monthly.

Pay Service 5

Pay Units: 191.
Programming (via satellite): Starz!; The New Encore.
Fee: $7.95 monthly.

Pay Service 6

Pay Units: 1,271.
Programming (via satellite): Playboy TV.
Fee: $7.95 monthly.

Pay-Per-View

Addressable homes: 31,698.
Viewer's Choice.
Fee: Varies.
Pay-per-view manager: Steve Salash.

Local advertising: Yes (locally produced & insert). Available in satellite distributed & locally originated programming. Rates: $500.00/ Week. Local sales manager: Dan Walsh. Regional interconnect: Metrobase Cable Advertising.
Program Guide: TV Host.
Equipment: Jerrold headend; Jerrold amplifiers; Times Fiber & Comm/Scope cable; Siecor fiber optic cable; Zenith addressable set top converters; Jerrold traps; Scientific-Atlanta satellite antenna; Jerrold satellite receivers; Sony commercial insert.
Miles of plant: 2601.0 (coaxial). Homes passed: 160,853. Total homes in franchised area: 195,000.
Manager: John J. Capparell. Chief technician: Jeffrey Kelly. Program director: Don Hunt. Marketing director: Steve Salash. Customer service manager: Mary Ann Detweiler.
Ownership: Service Electric Cable TV Inc. (MSO).

LEROY TWP.—Blue Ridge Cable Technologies Inc., 46 N. Academy St., Mansfield, PA 16933. Phones: 610-826-2551; 800-543-8128. Fax: 610-826-7626. County: Bradford. ICA: PA0302.
TV Market Ranking: Below 100. Franchise award date: N.A. Franchise expiration date: N.A. Began: July 1, 1977.
Channel capacity: 54 (2-way capable; not operating 2-way). Channels available but not in use: 2.

Basic Service

Subscribers: 41.
Programming (received off-air): WBNG-TV (C), WICZ-TV (F), WSKG (P) Binghamton; WENY-TV (A), WETM-TV (N) Elmira; WNEP-TV (A), WSWB (W), WVIA-TV (P), WYOU (C) Scranton & Wilkes-Barre; allband FM.
Programming (via satellite): WGN-TV (W) Chicago.
Fee: $50.00 installation; $10.00 monthly.

Expanded Basic Service

Subscribers: 39.
Programming (via satellite): A & E; American Movie Classics; Animal Planet; CNBC; CNN; Cartoon Network; Comedy Central; Country Music TV; Discovery Channel; E! Entertainment TV; ESPN; ESPN 2; Fox Family Channel; Fox Sports Net Pittsburgh; Headline News; History Channel; Home & Garden Television; Home Shopping Network; Learning Channel; Lifetime; MSNBC; MTV; Nashville Network; Nickelodeon; QVC; Sci-Fi Channel; TBS Superstation; TV Food Network; The Weather Channel; Travel Channel; Trinity Bcstg. Network; Turner Classic Movies; Turner Network TV; USA Network; VH1.
Fee: $25.95 monthly.

Pay Service 1

Pay Units: N.A.
Programming (via satellite): Cinemax; Disney Channel; HBO; Showtime.
Fee: N.A.

Pay-Per-View

Movies.

Equipment: Blonder-Tongue headend; Jerrold amplifiers; Times Fiber cable.
Miles of plant: 3.0 (coaxial). Additional miles planned: 1.0 (coaxial). Homes passed: 63.
Manager: Richard A. Semmel.
Ownership: Pencor Services Inc. (MSO).

LEVITTOWN—TCI, Box 850, 2320 Trenton Rd., Levittown, PA 19056. Phone: 215-943-5272. Fax: 215-943-2528. County: Bucks. Also serves Bristol, Bristol Twp., Hulmeville, Langhorne, Langhorne Manor, Lower Makefield Twp., Middletown Twp. (Bucks County), Penndel, Yardley. ICA: PA0016.
TV Market Ranking: 4. Franchise award date: December 1, 1965. Franchise expiration date: N.A. Began: April 10, 1967.
Channel capacity: 77 (2-way capable; operating 2-way). Channels available but not in use: None.

Basic Service

Subscribers: 42,526; Commercial subscribers: 173.
Programming (received off-air): WFMZ-TV (I), WLVT-TV (P) Allentown; WGTW (I) Burlington; KYW-TV (C), WCAU (N), WPHL-TV (W), WPSG (U), WPVI-TV (A), WTXF-TV (F), WYBE (P) Philadelphia; WTVE (H) Reading; WNJT (P) Trenton; WHSP-TV (H) Vineland; WHYY-TV (P), WPPX (X) Wilmington.
Programming (via satellite): C-SPAN; EWTN.
Current originations: Automated time-weather; public access; educational access; government access; leased access; local news; local sports.
Fee: $35.37 installation; $11.39 monthly; $0.57 converter; $17.99 additional installation.
Commercial fee: $35.00 monthly.

Expanded Basic Service

Subscribers: 40,450.
Programming (via microwave): Comcast SportsNet.
Programming (via satellite): A & E; American Movie Classics; Animal Planet; Bravo; CNBC; CNN; Cartoon Network; Discovery Channel; E! Entertainment TV; ESPN; FX; Fox Family Channel; Fox News Channel; Headline News; History Channel; Home & Garden Television; Learning Channel; Lifetime; MSNBC; MTV; Nashville Network; Nickelodeon; QVC; TBS Superstation; TV Food Network; TV Guide Channel; TV Guide Sneak Prevue; The Weather Channel; Travel Channel; Turner Network TV; USA Network; VH1.
Fee: $21.14 monthly.

Expanded Basic Service 2

Subscribers: 16,779.
Programming (via satellite): BET; Comedy Central; Court TV; ESPN 2; ESPN Classic Sports; Nick at Nite's TV Land; Sci-Fi Channel; The New Encore; Turner Classic Movies.
Fee: $6.52 monthly.

Pay Service 1

Pay Units: 5,643.
Programming (via satellite): Cinemax (multiplexed).
Fee: $11.00 monthly.

Pay Service 2

Pay Units: 1,952.
Programming (via satellite): Disney Channel.
Fee: $11.00 monthly.

Pay Service 3

Pay Units: 10,132.
Programming (via satellite): HBO (multiplexed).
Fee: $11.00 monthly.

Pay Service 4

Pay Units: 2,767.
Programming (via satellite): Showtime; The Movie Channel.
Fee: $11.00 monthly.

Pay Service 5

Pay Units: 271.
Programming (via satellite): Music Choice.
Fee: $6.95 monthly.

Pay-Per-View

Addressable homes: 21,652.
Action Pay-Per-View; Hot Choice; Spice; Viewer's Choice.
Fee: $3.95 (Action Pay-Per-View, Hot Choice or Viewer's Choice), $4.95 (Spice).

Local advertising: Yes (insert only). Available in satellite distributed, locally originated & character-generated programming. Local sales manager: Phil Salas. Regional interconnect: Metrobase Cable Advertising.
Equipment: Scientific-Atlanta headend; Jerrold amplifiers; Comm/Scope & Times Fiber cable; Sony VTRs; Jerrold set top converters; Microdyne & Scientific-Atlanta satellite antenna.
Miles of plant: 618.0 (coaxial). Additional miles planned: 5.0 (coaxial). Homes passed: 55,489. Total homes in franchised area: 55,489.
Manager: Brenda McCullough. Technical operations manager: Randy Strausbaugh. Public affairs & program manager: Mike Miller. Marketing manager: Jim Jenkinson.
City fee: 3% of gross.
Ownership: AT&T Broadband & Internet Services (MSO). Purchased from Time Warner Cable, June 1, 1999.

LEWISBURG—Lewisburg CATV, 216 Market, Lewisburg, PA 17837. Phone: 717-523-3875. County: Union. Also serves Kelly Twp. (Union County), New Columbia Twp., White Deer Twp. ICA: PA0356.
TV Market Ranking: Below 100. Franchise award date: N.A. Franchise expiration date: N.A. Began: November 1, 1989.
Channel capacity: 30. Channels available but not in use: None.

Basic Service

Subscribers: 625.
Programming (received off-air): WITF-TV (P) Harrisburg; WBRE-TV (N), WNEP-TV (A), WSWB (W), WVIA-TV (P), WYOU (C) Scranton & Wilkes-Barre.
Programming (via satellite): WGN-TV (W) Chicago; A & E; C-SPAN; CNN; Comedy Central; Country Music TV; Discovery Channel; ESPN; Fox Family Channel; Headline News; Lifetime; MTV; Nashville Network; Nick at Nite; Nickelodeon; QVC; TBS Superstation; Trinity Bcstg. Network; USA Network.
Current originations: Local news.
Fee: $25.00 installation; $14.50 monthly.

Pay Service 1

Pay Units: N.A.

Programming (via satellite): Disney Channel; HBO; Showtime.
Fee: $10.00 monthly (each).
Local advertising: Yes. Available in character-generated programming.
Equipment: Blonder-Tongue headend; Scientific-Atlanta amplifiers; Jerrold set top converters; Drake & Blonder-Tongue satellite receivers.
Miles of plant: 42.0 (coaxial).
Manager: Bob Gabey. Chief technician: Michael Siegfried.
Ownership: CATV Service Inc. (MSO).

LEWISTOWN—TCI of Pennsylvania Inc., Box 312, 130 W. Market St., Lewistown, PA 17044-2129. Phone: 717-248-0193. Fax: 717-248-5449. County: Mifflin. Also serves Burnham, Derry Twp. (Mifflin County), Granville Twp., Juniata Terrace. ICA: PA0092.
TV Market Ranking: Outside TV Markets. Franchise award date: N.A. Franchise expiration date: N.A. Began: January 1, 1951.
Channel capacity: 41 (2-way capable; not operating 2-way). Channels available but not in use: N.A.
Basic Service
Subscribers: 7,739.
Programming (received off-air): WPSX-TV (P) Clearfield; WHTM-TV (A) Harrisburg; WKBS-TV (I), WTAJ-TV (C), WWCP-TV (F) Johnstown-Altoona; WGAL (N), WLYH-TV (U) Lancaster; allband FM.
Programming (via satellite): A & E; C-SPAN; CNN; Comedy Central; Discovery Channel; EWTN; Fox Family Channel; Headline News; Lifetime; MTV; Nashville Network; Nickelodeon; Odyssey; QVC; TBS Superstation; The Weather Channel; VH1.
Current originations: Automated time-weather; public access; local news.
Fee: $59.95 installation; $9.77 monthly; $2.00 converter; $49.95 additional installation.
Expanded Basic Service
Subscribers: 5,822.
Programming (via satellite): American Movie Classics; Court TV; ESPN; Fox Sports Net Pittsburgh; Turner Network TV; USA Network.
Fee: $12.99 monthly.
Pay Service 1
Pay Units: 324.
Programming (via satellite): Cinemax.
Fee: $25.00 installation; $13.15 monthly.
Pay Service 2
Pay Units: 235.
Programming (via satellite): Disney Channel.
Fee: $25.00 installation; $10.95 monthly.
Pay Service 3
Pay Units: 568.
Programming (via satellite): HBO.
Fee: $25.00 installation; $13.15 monthly.
Pay Service 4
Pay Units: 175.
Programming (via satellite): The Movie Channel.
Fee: $25.00 installation; $13.15 monthly.
Pay Service 5
Pay Units: 209.
Programming (via satellite): Showtime.
Fee: $25.00 installation; $13.15 monthly.
Pay Service 6
Pay Units: N.A.
Programming (via satellite): The New Encore.
Fee: N.A.
Local advertising: Yes. Available in locally originated, character-generated & taped programming. Regional interconnect: Keynet Cable Advertising.
Program Guide: The Cable Guide.
Equipment: Scientific-Atlanta headend; C-COR amplifiers; Comm/Scope cable; NEC & Sony VTRs; Compuvid character generator; Oak set top converters; Scientific-Atlanta & Andrew satellite antenna; Scientific-Atlanta satellite receivers.
Miles of plant: 90.6 (coaxial). Homes passed: 8,096. Total homes in franchised area: 8,451.
Manager: Glenda Benoit. Chief technician: Dennis Turner.
City fee: 5% of gross.
Ownership: AT&T Broadband & Internet Services (MSO). Purchased from Tele-Communications Inc., March 9, 1999.

LEWISTOWN—Cablecomm, Box 272, 335 E. Chestnut St., Mifflinburg, PA 17844. Phones: 717-966-0662; 800-242-8093. County: Mifflin. Also serves Decatur Twp. (Mifflin County), Derry Twp. (Mifflin County). ICA: PA0175.
TV Market Ranking: Outside TV Markets. Franchise award date: January 1, 1972. Franchise expiration date: December 31, 1997. Began: January 1, 1956.
Channel capacity: 40 (not 2-way capable). Channels available but not in use: 2.
Basic Service
Subscribers: 1,218.
Programming (received off-air): WHP-TV (C), WHTM-TV (A), WITF-TV (P) Harrisburg; WJAC-TV (N), WTAJ-TV (C) Johnstown-Altoona; WGAL (N) Lancaster; WNEP-TV (A) Scranton & Wilkes-Barre; allband FM.
Programming (via microwave): WTTG (F) Washington.
Programming (via satellite): WGN-TV (W) Chicago; C-SPAN.
Current originations: Public access.
Fee: $58.60 installation; $8.10 monthly.
Expanded Basic Service
Subscribers: 1,207.
Programming (via satellite): A & E; CNN; Comedy Central; Country Music TV; Discovery Channel; ESPN; Fox Family Channel; Headline News; Lifetime; MTV; Nashville Network; Nickelodeon; QVC; TBS Superstation; The Weather Channel; Turner Network TV; USA Network; VH1.
Fee: $58.60 installation; $12.80 monthly.
Pay Service 1
Pay Units: 72.
Programming (via satellite): Cinemax.
Fee: $25.00 installation; $9.00 monthly.
Pay Service 2
Pay Units: 62.
Programming (via satellite): Disney Channel.
Fee: $25.00 installation; $7.00 monthly.
Pay Service 3
Pay Units: 24.
Programming (via satellite): The New Encore.
Fee: $4.95 monthly.
Pay Service 4
Pay Units: 73.
Programming (via satellite): HBO.
Fee: $25.00 installation; $10.00 monthly.
Pay Service 5
Pay Units: 68.
Programming (via satellite): The Movie Channel.
Fee: $25.00 installation; $9.00 monthly.
Pay Service 6
Pay Units: 68.
Programming (via satellite): Showtime.
Fee: $25.00 installation; $10.00 monthly.
Equipment: Scientific-Atlanta, M/A-Com & Cadco headend; Magnavox amplifiers; Times Fiber cable; Scientific-Atlanta & Harris satellite antenna; M/A-Com satellite receivers.
Miles of plant: 50.0 (coaxial). Homes passed: 1,610.
Manager: Charles Hilderbrand. Chief technician: Richard Fultz.
City fee: 2% of gross.
Ownership: Fanch Communications Inc. (MSO); Time Warner Cable (MSO). See Cable System Ownership.

LIMESTONE—Multi-Tech Communications, Box 219, Sligo, PA 16255. Phone: 814-745-2426. County: Clarion. Also serves Clarion, Monroe (Clarion County), Piney, Porter Twp. (Clarion County), Redbank Twp. (Clarion County). ICA: PA0197.
TV Market Ranking: Outside TV Markets. Franchise award date: N.A. Franchise expiration date: N.A. Began: January 1, 1986.
Channel capacity: 36 (not 2-way capable). Channels available but not in use: 3.
Basic Service
Subscribers: 950.
Programming (received off-air): WPSX-TV (P) Clearfield; WPCB-TV (I) Greensburg; WTAJ-TV (C), WWCP-TV (F) Johnstown-Altoona; KDKA-TV (C), WCWB (W), WPGH-TV (F), WPXI (N), WQED (P), WTAE-TV (A) Pittsburgh; WKBN-TV (C) Youngstown.
Programming (via satellite): A & E; CNN; Country Music TV; Discovery Channel; ESPN; Fox Sports Net Pittsburgh; Headline News; Lifetime; MTV; Nashville Network; Nickelodeon; QVC; TBS Superstation; The Weather Channel; VH1.
Fee: $35.00 installation; $23.00 monthly.
Pay Service 1
Pay Units: 176.
Programming (via satellite): Showtime.
Fee: $7.95 monthly.
Pay Service 2
Pay Units: 83.
Programming (via satellite): The Movie Channel.
Fee: $35.00 installation; $7.95 monthly.
Local advertising: Yes. Regional interconnect: Cabletime.
Miles of plant: 67.0 (coaxial). Homes passed: 1,100.
Manager: Richard McHenry. Chief technician: Donald McCall.
Ownership: Multi-Tech Communications (MSO).

LIMESTONE TWP. (Lycoming County)—TCI of Pennsylvania Inc., 18 W. Houston Ave., Montgomery, PA 17752-1099. Phone: 717-547-2011. County: Lycoming. ICA: PA0247.
TV Market Ranking: Below 100. Franchise award date: January 1, 1960. Franchise expiration date: N.A. Began: January 1, 1960.
Channel capacity: 12 (not 2-way capable). Channels available but not in use: None.
Basic Service
Subscribers: 383.
Programming (received off-air): WOLF-TV (F) Hazleton; WTAJ-TV (C) Johnstown-Altoona; WBRE-TV (N), WNEP-TV (A), WVIA-TV (P) Scranton & Wilkes-Barre; 8 FMs.
Programming (via satellite): CNN; ESPN; Fox Family Channel; Nashville Network; TBS Superstation.
Fee: $59.95 installation; $13.63 monthly; $49.95 additional installation.
Pay Service 1
Pay Units: 107.
Programming (via satellite): HBO.
Fee: $19.95 installation; $12.54 monthly.
Equipment: M/A-Com headend; Delta-Benco-Cascade & C-COR amplifiers; Pico traps; ChannelMaster satellite antenna; M/A-Com satellite receivers.
Miles of plant: 18.2 (coaxial). Homes passed: 396. Total homes in franchised area: 574.
Manager: Gayle Decker.
Franchise fee: 3% of basic gross.
Ownership: AT&T Broadband & Internet Services (MSO). Purchased from Tele-Communications Inc., March 9, 1999.

LINESVILLE—CableVision Communications, Box 2200, 68 5th St., Buckhannon, WV 26201. Phone: 304-472-4193. Fax: 304-472-0756. County: Crawford. Also serves Pine Twp. (Crawford County), Summit Twp. (Crawford County). ICA: PA0196.
TV Market Ranking: Below 100 (Summit Twp.); Outside TV Markets (Linesville, Pine Twp.). Franchise award date: N.A. Franchise expiration date: N.A. Began: January 1, 1968.
Channel capacity: 38 (not 2-way capable). Channels available but not in use: None.
Basic Service
Subscribers: 580.
Programming (received off-air): WEWS-TV (A), WJW (F) Cleveland; WFXP (F), WICU-TV (N), WJET-TV (A), WQLN (P), WSEE (C) Erie; WUAB (U) Lorain-Cleveland; KDKA-TV (C) Pittsburgh; WFMJ-TV (N) Youngstown; allband FM.
Programming (via satellite): C-SPAN; Home Shopping Network.
Fee: $61.25 installation; $14.40 monthly; $1.24 converter; $17.50 additional installation.
Expanded Basic Service
Subscribers: 517.
Programming (via satellite): WGN-TV (W) Chicago; A & E; American Movie Classics; Animal Planet; CNN; Discovery Channel; Disney Channel; E! Entertainment TV; ESPN; Fox Family Channel; Fox Sports Net Pittsburgh; Great American Country; Home & Garden Television; Lifetime; Nashville Network; Nickelodeon; Sci-Fi Channel; TBS Superstation; The Weather Channel; Trinity Bcstg. Network; Turner Network TV; USA Network.
Fee: $17.98 monthly.
Pay Service 1
Pay Units: 308.
Programming (via satellite): Cinemax; HBO; Showtime.
Fee: $7.95 monthly (Cinemax), $11.95 monthly (Showtime), $11.99 monthly (HBO).
Pay Service 2
Pay Units: N.A.
Programming (via satellite): The Movie Channel.
Fee: $11.95 monthly.
Equipment: Olson & M/A-Com headend; C-COR amplifiers; Intercept traps; DX Antenna satellite receivers.
Miles of plant: 19.0 (coaxial). Homes passed: 1,115.
Manager: Willie Critchfield. Marketing director: Kenny Phillips.
City fee: 3% of gross.
Ownership: Rifkin & Associates Inc. (MSO). See Cable System Ownership.

LITTLE MEADOWS—Beaver Valley Cable Co., Box 60-D, RR 2, Rome, PA 18837. Phone: 570-247-2512. Fax: 570-247-2494. Counties: Bradford & Susquehanna. Also serves Little Meadows Borough, Warren Center Twp. ICA: PA0358.
TV Market Ranking: 49 (Little Meadows); Below 100 (Little Meadows Borough, Warren Center Twp.). Franchise award date: N.A. Franchise expiration date: N.A. Began: N.A.
Channel capacity: 45 (2-way capable; not operating 2-way). Channels available but not in use: 10.

Basic Service
Subscribers: 239.
Programming (received off-air): WBNG-TV (C), WIVT (A), WSKG (P) Binghamton; WETM-TV (N) Elmira; WPIX (W) New York; WBRE-TV (N), WNEP-TV (A), WSWB (W), WVIA-TV (P), WYOU (C) Scranton & Wilkes-Barre.
Programming (via satellite): CNN; Discovery Channel; Disney Channel; ESPN; Fox Family Channel; Nashville Network; Nick at Nite; Nick at Nite's TV Land; TBS Superstation; USA Network.
Fee: $30.00 installation; $21.00 monthly.
Expanded Basic Service
Subscribers: 129.
Programming (via satellite): WGN-TV (W) Chicago; American Movie Classics; Country Music TV; ESPN 2; Home Shopping Network; Learning Channel; Lifetime; Outdoor Channel; Sci-Fi Channel; The Weather Channel; Trinity Bcstg. Network; Turner Network TV; VH1.
Fee: $8.50 monthly.
Pay Service 1
Pay Units: N.A.
Programming (via satellite): Cinemax; HBO.
Fee: $10.00 monthly (each).
Miles of plant: 25.0 (coaxial). Homes passed: 250.
Manager: Doug Soden. Chief technician: Gary Powers.
Ownership: Beaver Valley Cable Inc. (MSO).

LIVERPOOL—Zampelli TV, Box 830, Lewistown, PA 17044. Phone: 717-248-1544. County: Perry. ICA: PA0359.
TV Market Ranking: 57. Franchise award date: N.A. Franchise expiration date: N.A. Began: N.A.
Channel capacity: N.A. Channels available but not in use: N.A.
Basic Service
Subscribers: N.A.
Programming (received off-air): WHP-TV (C), WHTM-TV (A) Harrisburg; WGAL (N) Lancaster; WPMT (F) York.
Fee: N.A.
Ownership: Zampelli TV (MSO).

LOCK HAVEN—TCI of Pennsylvania Inc., Box 312, 130 W. Market St., Lewistown, PA 17044-2129. Phone: 717-248-0193. County: Clinton. Also serves Allison Twp., Bald Eagle Twp. (Clinton County), Castanea Twp., Colebrook Twp., Dunnstable Twp. (eastern portion), Flemington, Woodward Twp. (Clinton County). ICA: PA0111.
TV Market Ranking: Below 100. Franchise award date: N.A. Franchise expiration date: N.A. Began: January 1, 1950.
Channel capacity: 40 (not 2-way capable). Channels available but not in use: 11.
Basic Service
Subscribers: 5,193.
Programming (received off-air): WPSX-TV (P) Clearfield; WHP-TV (C) Harrisburg; WTAJ-TV (C), WWCP-TV (F) Johnstown-Altoona; WBRE-TV (N), WNEP-TV (A), WVIA-TV (P) Scranton & Wilkes-Barre.
Programming (via satellite): A & E; Fox Family Channel; Lifetime; QVC; TBS Superstation; The Weather Channel; VH1.
Current originations: Automated time-weather; educational access; automated emergency alert; local news.
Fee: $33.44 installation; $9.83 monthly.
Expanded Basic Service
Subscribers: 1,563.
Programming (via satellite): CNN; Discovery Channel; ESPN; MTV; Nashville Network; Nickelodeon; Turner Network TV; USA Network.
Fee: $9.94 monthly.
Pay Service 1
Pay Units: 319.
Programming (via satellite): Cinemax.
Fee: $8.95 monthly.
Pay Service 2
Pay Units: 266.
Programming (via satellite): Disney Channel.
Fee: $8.95 monthly.
Pay Service 3
Pay Units: 747.
Programming (via satellite): HBO.
Fee: $10.95 monthly.
Pay Service 4
Pay Units: 158.
Programming (via satellite): The Movie Channel.
Fee: $10.95 monthly.
Pay Service 5
Pay Units: 254.
Programming (via satellite): Showtime.
Fee: $10.95 monthly.
Pay Service 6
Pay Units: N.A.
Programming (via satellite): DMX.
Fee: $11.15 installation; $9.95 monthly.
Local advertising: Yes. Available in locally originated, character-generated & automated programming. Regional interconnect: Cabletime.
Equipment: Scientific-Atlanta headend; C-COR amplifiers; Comm/Scope cable; System Concepts character generator; Oak set top converters; Andrew & Scientific-Atlanta satellite antenna; Scientific-Atlanta satellite receivers.
Miles of plant: 84.0 (coaxial). Homes passed: 5,702. Total homes in franchised area: 6,754.
Manager: Dana Horner.
City fee: 3% of gross.
Ownership: AT&T Broadband & Internet Services (MSO). Purchased from Tele-Communications Inc., March 9, 1999.

LOGANTON—TV Cable Associates Inc., Box 101, Loganton, PA 17747. Phone: 717-725-2733. County: Clinton. ICA: PA0271.
TV Market Ranking: Below 100. Franchise award date: N.A. Franchise expiration date: N.A. Began: February 1, 1960.
Channel capacity: 20. Channels available but not in use: 5.
Basic Service
Subscribers: 165.
Programming (received off-air): WHTM-TV (A), WITF-TV (P) Harrisburg; WJAC-TV (N), WTAJ-TV (C) Johnstown-Altoona; WGAL (N), WLYH-TV (U) Lancaster; WBRE-TV (N), WNEP-TV (A), WSWB (W), WVIA-TV (P), WYOU (C) Scranton & Wilkes-Barre; allband FM.
Programming (via satellite): TBS Superstation; Turner Network TV.
Fee: $155.00 installation; $10.00 monthly.
Pay Service 1
Pay Units: 165.
Programming (via satellite): Disney Channel; HBO.
Fee: $7.00 monthly (Disney), $8.00 monthly (HBO).
Equipment: Blonder-Tongue headend; Jerrold amplifiers; Times Fiber cable.
Miles of plant: 2.0 (coaxial). Homes passed: 190.
Manager: Sheldon Miller. Chief technician: Guy F. Bierly.
City fee: None.
Ownership: TV Cable Associates Inc.

LONDONDERRY TWP. (Bedford County)—Leap Cable TV, Box 703, Hyndman, PA 15545. Phone: 814-842-3370. County: Bedford. ICA: PA0360.
TV Market Ranking: Outside TV Markets. Franchise award date: N.A. Franchise expiration date: N.A. Began: July 1, 1981.
Channel capacity: 21. Channels available but not in use: 11.
Basic Service
Subscribers: 130.
Programming (received off-air): WPSX-TV (P) Clearfield; WJAC-TV (N), WTAJ-TV (C) Johnstown-Altoona; KDKA-TV (C), WTAE-TV (A) Pittsburgh.
Programming (via satellite): Fox Family Channel; Nashville Network; TBS Superstation.
Fee: $21.00 monthly.
Pay Service 1
Pay Units: 30.
Programming (via satellite): HBO.
Fee: $10.00 monthly.
Manager: Don T. Leap.
Ownership: Don T. Leap.

LOOMIS LAKE—Adams CATV Inc., 9 N. Main St., Carbondale, PA 18407. Phone: 717-282-6121. Fax: 717-282-3787. County: Susquehanna. Also serves Acre Lake, Brooklyn Twp., Harford, Harford Twp., Hop Bottom, Kingsley, Lathrop Twp., Tingley Lake. ICA: PA0361.
TV Market Ranking: 49. Franchise award date: N.A. Franchise expiration date: N.A. Began: May 1, 1966.
Channel capacity: 40 (2-way capable). Channels available but not in use: 9.
Basic Service
Subscribers: 350.
Programming (received off-air): WBNG-TV (C), WICZ-TV (F), WIVT (A), WSKG (P) Binghamton; WBRE-TV (N), WNEP-TV (A), WSWB (W), WVIA-TV (P), WYOU (C) Scranton & Wilkes-Barre; allband FM.
Programming (via satellite): WPIX (W) New York; A & E; CNBC; CNN; Country Music TV; Discovery Channel; ESPN; Fox Family Channel; Headline News; Lifetime; Nashville Network; QVC; TBS Superstation; Turner Network TV; USA Network.
Fee: $40.00 installation; $19.00 monthly.
Pay Service 1
Pay Units: 50.
Programming (via satellite): Cinemax; Disney Channel; HBO; Playboy TV.
Fee: $7.00 monthly (Disney), $8.00 monthly (Playboy TV), $12.00 monthly (Cinemax or HBO).
Equipment: Holt headend; Holt amplifiers; Comm/Scope cable; Scientific-Atlanta set top converters; PPC traps; AFC satellite antenna; Scientific-Atlanta satellite receivers.
Miles of plant: 25.0 (coaxial); 12.0 (fiber optic). Homes passed: 425. Total homes in franchised area: 500.
Manager: Wendy White. Chief technician: John Wallis. Program director: Doug Adams.
Ownership: Adams CATV Inc. (MSO).

LOWER MERION TWP.—Comcast Cablevision of Montgomery County Inc., 205 E. Levering Mill Rd., Bala Cynwyd, PA 19004. Phone: 610-667-8880. Fax: 610-667-6146. County: Montgomery. Also serves Bala Cynwyd, Gladwyne, Narberth Borough. ICA: PA0048.
TV Market Ranking: 4. Franchise award date: N.A. Franchise expiration date: N.A. Began: June 1, 1981.
Channel capacity: 56. Channels available but not in use: N.A.
Basic Service
Subscribers: 17,827; Commercial subscribers: 355.
Programming (received off-air): WLVT-TV (P) Allentown; WNJS (P) Camden; KYW-TV (C), WCAU (N), WPHL-TV (W), WPSG (U), WPVI-TV (A), WTXF-TV (F), WYBE (P) Philadelphia; WHYY-TV (P), WPPX (X) Wilmington.
Programming (via satellite): American Movie Classics; Cartoon Network; Home Shopping Network 2.
Current originations: Automated time-weather; public access; educational access; government access; leased access; automated emergency alert; local news; local sports.
Fee: $54.57 installation; $7.84 monthly.
Expanded Basic Service
Subscribers: 16,152.
Programming (via satellite): TBS Superstation; Turner Network TV.
Fee: $1.09 monthly.
Expanded Basic Service 2
Subscribers: N.A.
Programming (via satellite): A & E; BET; C-SPAN; C-SPAN 2; CNBC; CNN; Discovery Channel; E! Entertainment TV; ESPN; ESPN 2; EWTN; Fox Family Channel; Fox Sports Net; Goodlife TV Network; Headline News; Learning Channel; Lifetime; MTV; Nashville Network; Nick at Nite; Nickelodeon; QVC; Sci-Fi Channel; TV Food Network; TV Guide Channel; The Weather Channel; Travel Channel; USA Network; VH1.
Fee: $13.48 monthly.
Pay Service 1
Pay Units: N.A.
Programming (via satellite): Cinemax; Disney Channel; HBO; Showtime; The New Encore.
Fee: $10.95 installation; $2.95 monthly (Encore), $13.05 monthly (Showtime), $14.05 monthly (Cinemax, Disney or HBO).
Pay-Per-View
Addressable homes: 5,400.
Viewer's Choice.
Fee: $3.99.
Local advertising: Yes. Available in satellite distributed, locally originated & character-generated programming. Rates: $10.00/30 Seconds. Regional interconnect: Philadelphia Cable Advertising.
Program Guide: The Cable Guide.
Equipment: Jerrold headend; Jerrold amplifiers; Times Fiber cable; JVC cameras; Sony VTRs; MSI character generator; Jerrold set top converters; Jerrold addressable set top converters; Eagle & Vitek traps; AFC satellite antenna; Microdyne satellite receivers; Texscan commercial insert.
Homes passed: 23,856. Total homes in franchised area: 23,856.

Manager: Roy Russell Jr. Chief technician: Mike Koller. Program director: Bernadette Everlof. Marketing director: Rosa Jackson.
Ownership: Comcast Cable Communications Inc. (MSO).

LYKENS—Century Lykens Cable Corp., Box 128, 609 N. 2nd St., Lykens, PA 17048. Phone: 717-453-7175. Counties: Dauphin & Schuylkill. Also serves Berrysburg, Elizabethville, Gratz, Hegins Twp., Hubley Twp., Lykens Twp., Mifflin Twp. (Dauphin County), Pillow, Porter Twp. (Schuylkill County), Rush Twp. (Dauphin County), Tower City, Upper Mahantango Twp., Upper Paxton Twp. (Dauphin County), Washington Twp. (Dauphin County), Wiconisco Twp., Williams Twp. (Dauphin County), Williamstown (Dauphin County). ICA: PA0096.
TV Market Ranking: 57. Franchise award date: N.A. Franchise expiration date: N.A. Began: June 6, 1951.
Channel capacity: 37 (2-way capable). Channels available but not in use: None.
Basic Service
Subscribers: 7,200.
Programming (received off-air): WHP-TV (C), WHTM-TV (A), WITF-TV (P) Harrisburg; WGAL (N), WLYH-TV (U) Lancaster; WPHL-TV (W) Philadelphia; WPMT (F) York; 20 FMs.
Programming (via satellite): A & E; American Movie Classics; C-SPAN; CNN; Comedy Central; Discovery Channel; E! Entertainment TV; ESPN; ESPN 2; Fox Family Channel; Headline News; History Channel; Home Shopping Network; Learning Channel; Lifetime; MTV; Nashville Network; Nick at Nite's TV Land; Nickelodeon; QVC; Sci-Fi Channel; TBS Superstation; The Inspirational Network; The Weather Channel; Turner Network TV; USA Network; VH1.
Current originations: Public access; religious access.
Fee: $25.00 installation; $22.66 monthly; $0.32 converter.
Pay Service 1
Pay Units: 1,300.
Programming (via satellite): Cinemax; Disney Channel; HBO; Showtime.
Fee: $15.00 installation; $8.00 monthly (Disney); $10.00 monthly (Cinemax or Showtime); $11.00 monthly (HBO).
Local advertising: No. Regional interconnect: Cabletime.
Equipment: Scientific-Atlanta headend; GTE Sylvania & Century III amplifiers; Times Fiber cable; Sony VTRs; Scientific-Atlanta satellite antenna.
Miles of plant: 172.0 (coaxial); 19.0 (fiber optic). Homes passed: 7,900. Total homes in franchised area: 8,300.
Manager: Ed Saterstad.
City fee: 3% of gross.
Ownership: Century Communications Corp. (MSO). See Cable System Ownership.

MAHAFFEY—Adelphia Cable, One Adelphia Dr., Blairsville, PA 15717. Phone: 800-892-7300. Fax: 724-459-0648. County: Clearfield. Also serves Bell Twp. (Clearfield County). ICA: PA0363.
TV Market Ranking: 74. Franchise award date: N.A. Franchise expiration date: N.A. Began: December 1, 1982.
Channel capacity: 52 (not 2-way capable). Channels available but not in use: 30.
Basic Service
Subscribers: 140.
Programming (received off-air): WPSX-TV (P) Clearfield; WJAC-TV (N), WTAJ-TV (C), WWCP-TV (F) Johnstown-Altoona; WCWB (W), WPGH-TV (F), WTAE-TV (A) Pittsburgh.
Programming (via satellite): ESPN; Nashville Network; TBS Superstation; Turner Network TV.
Fee: $30.00 installation; $23.54 monthly.
Pay Service 1
Pay Units: N.A.
Programming (via satellite): HBO; Showtime.
Fee: $6.95 monthly (Showtime), $10.95 monthly (HBO).
Miles of plant: 5.0 (coaxial); None (fiber optic).
Manager: Dan Barry. Chief technician: Carl Barry.
Ownership: Adelphia Communications Corp. (MSO). Purchased from Barry Electronics Inc., July 1, 1998.

MAHANOY CITY—Service Electric Cable TV, 201 W. Centre St., Mahanoy City, PA 17948. Phone: 717-773-2585. Fax: 717-773-0276. Counties: Columbia, Northumberland & Schuylkill. Also serves Ashland, Barry Twp., Butler Twp. (Schuylkill County), Centralia, Delano, East Brunswick Twp., East Cameron Twp., East Norwegian Twp. (Schuylkill County), Frackville, Gilberton, Girardville, Gordon, Mahanoy Twp., New Castle Twp. (Schuylkill County), New Ringgold, Norwegian Twp. (Schuylkill County), Ringtown, Rush Twp. (Schuylkill County), Ryan Twp., Schuylkill Twp. (Columbia County), St. Clair (Schuylkill County), Tamaqua, Union Twp. (Schuylkill County), Walker Twp. (Schuylkill County), West Mahanoy, West Penn Twp. (northwestern portion). ICA: PA0055.
TV Market Ranking: 49 (Butler Twp., Delano, East Cameron Twp., Mahanoy City, Mahanoy Twp., Rush Twp., Ryan Twp., Tamaqua); Below 100 (Ashland, Barry Twp., Centralia, East Brunswick Twp., East Norwegian Twp., Frackville, Gilberton, Girardville, Gordon, New Castle Twp., New Ringgold, Norwegian Twp., Ringtown, Schuylkill Twp., St. Clair, Union Twp., Walker Twp., West Mahanoy, West Penn Twp.). Franchise award date: N.A. Franchise expiration date: N.A. Began: June 1, 1948.
Channel capacity: 50. Channels available but not in use: None.
Basic Service
Subscribers: 17,250.
Programming (received off-air): WOLF-TV (F) Hazleton; KYW-TV (C), WCAU (N), WPHL-TV (W), WPVI-TV (A), WTXF-TV (F) Philadelphia; WBRE-TV (N), WNEP-TV (A), WVIA-TV (P), WYOU (C) Scranton & Wilkes-Barre; allband FM.
Programming (via microwave): WNYW (F), WPIX (W) New York.
Programming (via satellite): A & E; CNBC; CNN; Country Music TV; Discovery Channel; ESPN; EWTN; Fox Family Channel; Goodlife TV Network; Headline News; Home Shopping Network; Lifetime; MTV; Nashville Network; Nickelodeon; QVC; Telebet; The Weather Channel; Travel Channel; Turner Network TV; USA Network; VH1.
Current originations: Automated timeweather.
Planned originations: Local news.
Fee: $36.00 installation; $20.00 monthly.
Pay Service 1
Pay Units: 4,000.
Programming (via satellite): Cinemax; Disney Channel; HBO.
Fee: $25.00 installation; $10.00 monthly (Cinemax or Disney), $11.00 monthly (HBO).
Local advertising: Planned. Regional interconnect: Cabletime.
Equipment: Scientific-Atlanta headend; Scientific-Atlanta satellite antenna.
Miles of plant: 350.0 (coaxial). Homes passed: 20,000. Total homes in franchised area: 20,000.
Manager: William Brayford. Chief technician: Ron Debalko.
City fee: 3% of gross.
Ownership: Service Electric Cable TV Inc. (MSO).

MALVERN—Harron Communications Inc., Suite 400, 1220 Ward Ave., West Chester, PA 19380. Phone: 610-296-5100. Fax: 610-431-7782. Counties: Chester & Delaware. Also serves Charlestown Twp., East Goshen Twp. (Chester County), East Whiteland Twp., Easttown Twp., Edgmont Twp., Malvern Borough, Newtown Twp. (Delaware County), Tredyffrin Twp., West Whiteland Twp. (Chester County), Westtown Twp., Willistown Twp. ICA: PA0034.
TV Market Ranking: 4. Franchise award date: N.A. Franchise expiration date: N.A. Began: February 1, 1980.
Channel capacity: 57 (2-way capable; not operating 2-way). Channels available but not in use: None.
Basic Service
Subscribers: 29,797.
Programming (received off-air): WFMZ-TV (I), WLVT-TV (P) Allentown; WGTW (I) Burlington; KYW-TV (C), WCAU (N), WPHL-TV (W), WPSG (U), WPVI-TV (A), WTXF-TV (F), WYBE (P) Philadelphia; WTVE (H) Reading; WHSP-TV (H) Vineland; WHYY-TV (P), WPPX (X) Wilmington.
Programming (via satellite): A & E; American Movie Classics; Bravo; C-SPAN; CNBC; CNN; Comedy Central; Discovery Channel; Disney Channel; E! Entertainment TV; ESPN; ESPN 2; EWTN; Fox Family Channel; Fox Sports Net; Golf Channel; Headline News; History Channel; Home & Garden Television; Learning Channel; Lifetime; MSNBC; MTV; Nashville Network; Nickelodeon; QVC; Sci-Fi Channel; TBS Superstation; TV Food Network; TV Guide Channel; The Weather Channel; Turner Network TV; USA Network; VH1.
Fee: $25.00 installation; $32.19 monthly.
Pay Service 1
Pay Units: 3,173.
Programming (via satellite): Cinemax.
Fee: $9.95 monthly.
Pay Service 2
Pay Units: 6,438.
Programming (via satellite): HBO (multiplexed).
Fee: $11.95 monthly.
Pay Service 3
Pay Units: 4,480.
Programming (via satellite): The Movie Channel.
Fee: $9.95 monthly.
Pay Service 4
Pay Units: 2,712.
Programming (via satellite): Showtime.
Fee: $10.95 monthly.
Pay-Per-View
Addressable homes: 14,653.
Spice Hot; Viewer's Choice 1 & 2; special events.
Local advertising: Yes (locally produced & insert). Available in satellite distributed programming.
Equipment: Scientific-Atlanta headend; Jerrold amplifiers; Comm/Scope cable; Hitachi cameras; Sony VTRs; Metrodata character generator; Jerrold set top converters; Scientific-Atlanta addressable set top converters; Scientific-Atlanta satellite antenna; Scientific-Atlanta satellite receivers; Monroe commercial insert.
Miles of plant: 688.4 (coaxial); 34.0 (fiber optic). Homes passed: 40,262.
Manager: Patricia Sincavage. Technical operations manager: James L. Mellon. Program director: Dana L. Caterson.
City fee: 3%-5% of gross.
Ownership: Harron Communications Corp. (MSO). See Cable System Ownership.

MANSFIELD—Blue Ridge Cable TV Inc., 46 N. Academy St., Mansfield, PA 16933. Phone: 570-662-2369. County: Tioga. Also serves Covington Twp. (Tioga County), Lambs Creek, Mainesburg, Putnam Twp., Richmond Twp. (Tioga County), Sullivan Twp. (Tioga County). ICA: PA0156.
TV Market Ranking: Below 100. Franchise award date: January 1, 1953. Franchise expiration date: N.A. Began: April 1, 1953.
Channel capacity: 25 (not 2-way capable). Channels available but not in use: None.
Basic Service
Subscribers: 1,698; Commercial subscribers: 73.
Programming (received off-air): WBNG-TV (C), WSKG (P) Binghamton; WENY-TV (A), WETM-TV (N) Elmira; WVIA-TV (P), WYOU (C) Scranton & Wilkes-Barre; allband FM.
Programming (via satellite): WGN-TV (W) Chicago; WPIX (W) New York; A & E; CNN; Discovery Channel; ESPN; Fox Family Channel; Headline News; QVC; TBS Superstation; Turner Classic Movies; Turner Network TV; USA Network.
Current originations: Public access; educational access; local sports.
Fee: $35.00 installation; $15.25 monthly.
Pay Service 1
Pay Units: 117.
Programming (via satellite): Disney Channel.
Fee: $15.00 installation; $7.00 monthly.
Pay Service 2
Pay Units: 425.
Programming (via satellite): HBO.
Fee: $15.00 installation; $8.75 monthly.
Local advertising: Yes. Regional interconnect: Cabletime.
Equipment: Jerrold headend; Jerrold amplifiers; Times Fiber cable; Jerrold character generator; Jerrold set top converters; Microdyne & Scientific-Atlanta satellite antenna; Microdyne & Scientific-Atlanta satellite receivers.
Miles of plant: 60.0 (coaxial). Homes passed: 2,200. Total homes in franchised area: 2,200.
Manager: Tom Freeman.
City fee: $500 annually.
Ownership: Pencor Services Inc. (MSO).

MARIENVILLE—CableVision Communications, Box 2200, 68 5th St., Buckhannon, WV 26201. Phone: 304-472-4193. Fax: 304-472-0756. County: Forest. Also serves Jenks Twp., Roses. ICA: PA0221.
TV Market Ranking: Outside TV Markets. Franchise award date: N.A. Franchise expiration date: N.A. Began: N.A.
Channel capacity: N.A. Channels available but not in use: N.A.
Basic Service
Subscribers: 389.
Programming (received off-air): WPSX-TV (P) Clearfield; WICU-TV (N), WJET-TV (A) Erie; WJAC-TV (N), WTAJ-TV (C), WWCP-TV (F) Johnstown-Altoona; KDKA-TV (C), WCWB (W), WPGH-TV (F) Pittsburgh.
Programming (via satellite): WGN-TV (W) Chicago; TBS Superstation.
Current originations: Public access.
Fee: $61.25 installation; $14.40 monthly; $1.24 converter; $17.50 additional installation.
Expanded Basic Service
Subscribers: 312.

Programming (via satellite): American Movie Classics; CNN; Discovery Channel; Disney Channel; ESPN; Fox Family Channel; Fox Sports Net Pittsburgh; Home Shopping Network; Lifetime; MTV; Nashville Network; Nickelodeon; Trinity Bcstg. Network; Turner Network TV; USA Network; VH1.
Fee: $17.96 monthly.
Pay Service 1
Pay Units: 201.
Programming (via satellite): Cinemax; HBO; Showtime.
Fee: $7.95 monthly (Cinemax), $11.95 monthly (Showtime), $11.99 monthly (HBO).
Pay Service 2
Pay Units: N.A.
Programming (via satellite): The Movie Channel.
Fee: $11.95 monthly.
Local advertising: No.
Equipment: Blonder-Tongue, M/A-Com & Olson headend; Jerrold amplifiers; M/A-Com cable; Intercept & Pico traps; DX Engineering & Drake satellite receivers.
Miles of plant: 16.0 (coaxial). Homes passed: 663.
Manager: Willie Critchfield. Marketing manager: Kenny Phillips.
City fee: None.
Ownership: Rifkin & Associates Inc. (MSO). See Cable System Ownership.

MARKLEYSBURG—FrontierVision, Suite P-200, 1777 S. Harrison St., Denver, CO 80210. Phone: 303-757-1588. Fax: 303-757-6105. Counties: Fayette & Somerset, PA; Preston, WV. Also serves Addison Twp., Chalkhill, Confluence, Farmington (Fayette County), Fayette County (unincorporated areas), Henry Clay Twp., Lower Turkeyfoot Twp., Upper Turkeyfoot Twp. (Somerset County), Ursina, Wharton Twp., PA; Bruceton Mills, WV. ICA: PA0129.
TV Market Ranking: 10 (portions of Fayette County); 74 (portions of Fayette County); Below 100 (Chalkhill, portions of Fayette County, Lower Turkeyfoot Twp., Upper Turkeyfoot Twp., Ursina); Outside TV Markets (Addison Twp., Bruceton Mills, Confluence, Farmington, portions of Fayette County, Henry Clay Twp., Markleysburg, Wharton Twp.). Franchise award date: N.A. Franchise expiration date: N.A. Began: November 1, 1977.
Channel capacity: N.A. Channels available but not in use: N.A.
Basic Service
Subscribers: 1,986.
Programming (received off-air): WDTV (C,A) Clarksburg-Weston; WJAC-TV (N), WKBS-TV (I), WWCP-TV (F) Johnstown-Altoona; WNPB-TV (P) Morgantown; KDKA-TV (C), WCWB (W), WPGH-TV (F), WPXI (N), WQED (P), WTAE-TV (A) Pittsburgh.
Programming (via satellite): TBS Superstation.
Fee: $29.95 installation; $10.27 monthly; $3.50 converter.
Expanded Basic Service
Subscribers: N.A.
Programming (via satellite): A & E; American Movie Classics; CNN; Country Music TV; Discovery Channel; E! Entertainment TV; ESPN; ESPN 2; Fox Family Channel; Headline News; MTV; Nashville Network; Nickelodeon; Sci-Fi Channel; The Weather Channel; Trinity Bcstg. Network; Turner Network TV; USA Network.
Fee: $15.90 monthly.
Pay Service 1
Pay Units: 506.
Programming (via satellite): Cinemax; Disney Channel; HBO; Showtime.
Fee: $29.95 installation; $5.95 monthly (Disney), $8.95 monthly (Cinemax), $11.95 monthly (Showtime), $11.99 monthly (HBO).
Pay Service 2
Pay Units: N.A.
Programming (via satellite): The Movie Channel; The New Encore.
Fee: $3.99 monthly (Encore), $11.95 monthly (TMC).
Local advertising: No.
Equipment: Belden headend; GTE Sylvania amplifiers; Times Fiber cable.
Miles of plant: 152.0 (coaxial). Homes passed: 3,457.
Manager: William Critchfield. Chief technician: Bill Turner.
Ownership: FrontierVision Partners LP (MSO). See Cable System Ownership.

MATAMORAS—Matamoras Video Cable Corp., 605 Pennsylvania Ave., Matamoras, PA 18336. Phone: 717-491-4837. County: Pike. Also serves Westfall, Westfall Twp. (portions). ICA: PA0168.
TV Market Ranking: Below 100. Franchise award date: N.A. Franchise expiration date: N.A. Began: October 6, 1966.
Channel capacity: 60 (2-way capable; operating 2-way). Channels available but not in use: 10.
Basic Service
Subscribers: 1,550.
Programming (received off-air): WABC-TV (A), WCBS-TV (C), WNBC (N), WPIX (W), WWOR-TV (U) New York; WNET (P) New York-Newark; WMBC-TV (I) Newton; WBRE-TV (N), WSWB (W), WVIA-TV (P), WYOU (C) Scranton & Wilkes-Barre; 24 FMs.
Programming (via satellite): A & E; CNBC; CNN; Comedy Central; Discovery Channel; ESPN; Fox Family Channel; Lifetime; MTV; Nashville Network; Nickelodeon; QVC; TBS Superstation; The Weather Channel; Turner Network TV; USA Network.
Fee: $52.50 installation; $28.00 monthly.
Pay Service 1
Pay Units: N.A.
Programming (via satellite): Cinemax; Disney Channel; HBO; Showtime.
Fee: $8.00 monthly (Cinemax), $12.60 monthly (Disney, HBO or Showtime).
Pay-Per-View
Addressable homes: 225.
WWF Wrestlemania.
Program Guide: The Cable Guide.
Equipment: Scientific-Atlanta headend; Magnavox amplifiers; Scientific-Atlanta character generator; Scientific-Atlanta set top converters; Scientific-Atlanta addressable traps; Scientific-Atlanta satellite antenna; Scientific-Atlanta satellite receivers.
Miles of plant: 30.0 (coaxial). Homes passed: 1,750.
Manager: Teresa Gurdineer. Chief technician: Greg Simpson.
City fee: 2% of basic gross.
Ownership: Joseph R. Biondo (MSO).

McALEVYS FORT—Milestone Communications LP, Suite 200, 1850 Woodmoor Dr., Monument, CO 80132. Phone: 719-488-2916. Fax: 719-488-3629. County: Huntingdon. Also serves Huntingdon, Petersburg. ICA: PA0441.
TV Market Ranking: 74. Franchise award date: N.A. Franchise expiration date: March 5, 2005. Began: N.A.
Channel capacity: 27 (not 2-way capable). Channels available but not in use: 2.
Basic Service
Subscribers: 239.
Programming (received off-air): WPSX-TV (P) Clearfield; WATM-TV (A), WJAC-TV (N), WKBS-TV (I), WTAJ-TV (C), WWCP-TV (F) Johnstown-Altoona.
Programming (via satellite): WGN-TV (W) Chicago; A & E; CNN; Discovery Channel; ESPN; ESPN 2; Fox Family Channel; Headline News; History Channel; Nashville Network; Nickelodeon; QVC; Sci-Fi Channel; TBS Superstation; Trinity Bcstg. Network; Turner Network TV; USA Network.
Fee: $50.00 installation (aerial), $60.00 (underground); $23.25 monthly; $10.00 additional installation.
Pay Service 1
Pay Units: 39.
Programming (via satellite): Showtime; The Movie Channel.
Fee: $12.95 monthly.
Miles of plant: 21.0 (coaxial); None (fiber optic). Homes passed: 350.
Manager: Michael Drake. Engineering director: Randy Mock.
Ownership: Milestone Communications LP (MSO).

McALISTERVILLE—Nittany Media Inc., Box 111, Lewistown, PA 17044. Phone: 717-248-3733. County: Juniata. ICA: PA0365.
TV Market Ranking: Outside TV Markets. Franchise award date: N.A. Franchise expiration date: N.A. Began: N.A.
Channel capacity: N.A. Channels available but not in use: N.A.
Basic Service
Subscribers: N.A.
Programming (received off-air): WHP-TV (C), WHTM-TV (A), WITF-TV (P) Harrisburg; WGAL (N), WLYH-TV (U) Lancaster; WBRE-TV (N), WVIA-TV (P) Scranton & Wilkes-Barre.
Programming (via satellite): ESPN; TBS Superstation; The Inspirational Network.
Fee: N.A.
Pay Service 1
Pay Units: N.A.
Programming (via satellite): Nashville Network; The Movie Channel.
Fee: N.A.
Manager: Anna H. Hain. Chief technician: Michael Hain.
Ownership: Nittany Media Inc. (MSO).

McCLURE—McClure CATV Inc., Box 111, Lewistown, PA 17044. Phone: 717-248-3733. County: Snyder. ICA: PA0255.
TV Market Ranking: Outside TV Markets. Franchise award date: N.A. Franchise expiration date: N.A. Began: May 1, 1953.
Channel capacity: 12. Channels available but not in use: N.A.
Basic Service
Subscribers: 350.
Programming (received off-air): WHTM-TV (A) Harrisburg; WJAC-TV (N), WTAJ-TV (C) Johnstown-Altoona; WGAL (N) Lancaster; WYOU (C) Scranton & Wilkes-Barre; allband FM.
Programming (via satellite): Headline News.
Fee: $25.00 installation; $8.00 monthly.
Miles of plant: 3.0 (coaxial). Additional miles planned: 1.0 (coaxial).
Chief technician: Michael Hain.
Ownership: Nittany Media Inc. (MSO).

McCONNELLSBURG—TV Cable, Suite 2, 1108 Sheller Ave., Chambersburg, PA 17201. Phone: 717-263-8591. Fax: 717-263-6766. County: Fulton. Also serves Ayr Twp., Fulton County, Todd Twp. (Fulton County). ICA: PA0148.
TV Market Ranking: 74 (portions of Fulton County); Below 100 (Ayr Twp., portions of Fulton County, Mcconnellsburg, Todd Twp.). Franchise award date: May 10, 1971. Franchise expiration date: N.A. Began: October 1, 1971.
Channel capacity: 77 (2-way capable). Channels available but not in use: 12.
Basic Service
Subscribers: 2,004.
Programming (received off-air): WJZ-TV (C) Baltimore; WHAG-TV (N), WJAL (W), WWPB (P) Hagerstown; WHTM-TV (A), WITF-TV (P) Harrisburg; WGAL (N) Lancaster; WWPX (I) Martinsburg; WDCA (U), WJLA-TV (A), WTTG (F), WUSA (C) Washington.
Programming (via satellite): C-SPAN; Home Shopping Network; Odyssey; QVC; TBS Superstation; TV Guide Channel; TV Guide Sneak Prevue; Trinity Bcstg. Network.
Current originations: Public access.
Fee: $50.25 installation; $13.85 monthly; $1.94 converter.
Digital Basic Service
Subscribers: N.A.
Programming (via satellite): BBC America; DMX; Discovery Home & Leisure Channel; Discovery Kids Channel; Discovery People; Discovery Science Channel; ESPN Classic Sports; ESPNews; Fox Sports World; Game Show Network; History Channel; Home & Garden Television; MuchMusic Network; Outdoor Life Network; Sci-Fi Channel.
Fee: $23.80 monthly.
Expanded Basic Service
Subscribers: 1,603.
Programming (via satellite): A & E; American Movie Classics; BET; C-SPAN 2; CNBC; CNN; Cartoon Network; Comedy Central; Country Music TV; Discovery Channel; E! Entertainment TV; ESPN; ESPN 2; FX; Fox Family Channel; Fox Sports Net Pittsburgh; Headline News; History Channel; Home Team Sports; Learning Channel; Lifetime; MSNBC; MTV; Nashville Network; Nick at Nite; Nickelodeon; Sci-Fi Channel; The Weather Channel; Travel Channel; Turner Network TV; USA Network; VH1; ValueVision.
Fee: $13.63 monthly.
Digital Expanded Basic Service
Subscribers: N.A.
Programming (via satellite): BET Movies/Starz!; Encore Movie Networks; Independent Film Channel; Romance Classics; Starz!; The New Encore; Turner Classic Movies.
Fee: $28.58 monthly.
Pay Service 1
Pay Units: 100.
Programming (via satellite): Cinemax.
Fee: $10.95 monthly.
Pay Service 2
Pay Units: 92.
Programming (via satellite): Disney Channel.
Fee: $10.95 monthly.
Pay Service 3
Pay Units: 102.
Programming (via satellite): HBO.
Fee: $10.95 monthly.
Pay Service 4
Pay Units: N.A.
Programming (via satellite): Showtime; The Movie Channel.
Fee: $10.95 monthly.
Digital Pay Service 1
Pay Units: N.A.
Programming (via satellite): Cinemax (multiplexed); HBO (multiplexed); Showtime (multiplexed); The Movie Channel (multiplexed).
Fee: N.A.
Pay-Per-View
Spice; Spice Hot; movies; special events.
Fee: $3.99-$7.99.
Local advertising: No. Local sales manager: Brad Hocker.

Equipment: Microdyne & Scientific-Atlanta headend; Jerrold amplifiers; Comm/Scope cable; Pioneer set top converters; Microdyne & Scientific-Atlanta satellite antenna; Microdyne satellite receivers.
Miles of plant: 48.0 (coaxial); 10.0 (fiber optic). Homes passed: 3,600. Total homes in franchised area: 3,600.
Manager: Hans Welch. Chief technician: Ron Perocchi. Marketing director: Tim Horn.
Ownership: Lenfest Communications Inc. (MSO). Purchased from Raystay Co., July 30, 1999.

McDONALD—AT&T Cable Services, 300 Corliss St., Pittsburgh, PA 15220-4815. Phones: 412-875-1100; 412-771-8100. County: Allegheny. Also serves North Fayette Twp. (Allegheny County), Robinson Twp. (Allegheny County). ICA: PA0178.
TV Market Ranking: 10,90. Franchise award date: N.A. Franchise expiration date: N.A. Began: December 1, 1970.
Channel capacity: 66 (2-way capable; operating 2-way). Channels available but not in use: None.
Basic Service
Subscribers: 1,676.
Programming (received off-air): WPCB-TV (I) Greensburg; KDKA-TV (C), WCWB (W), WPGH-TV (F), WPXI (N), WQED (P), WQEX (P), WTAE-TV (A) Pittsburgh.
Programming (via microwave): Meadows Racing Network.
Programming (via satellite): C-SPAN; Odyssey; QVC; TV Guide Sneak Prevue.
Fee: $44.95 installation; $9.67 monthly; $1.50 converter; $24.95 additional installation.
Expanded Basic Service
Subscribers: 1,577.
Programming (via microwave): Pittsburgh Cable News Channel.
Programming (via satellite): A & E; American Movie Classics; Animal Planet; BET; C-SPAN 2; CNBC; CNN; Cartoon Network; Court TV; Discovery Channel; E! Entertainment TV; ESPN; ESPN 2; EWTN; FX; Fox Family Channel; Fox News Channel; Fox Sports Net; Fox Sports Net Pittsburgh; Headline News; History Channel; Home & Garden Television; Home Shopping Network; International Channel; Knowledge TV; Learning Channel; Lifetime; MOVIEplex; MTV; Nashville Network; Nickelodeon; Pennsylvania Cable Network; Sci-Fi Channel; TBS Superstation; TV Guide Channel; The Weather Channel; Turner Network TV; USA Network; VH1.
Fee: $16.78 monthly.
Pay Service 1
Pay Units: 139.
Programming (via satellite): Cinemax.
Fee: $13.45 monthly.
Pay Service 2
Pay Units: 67.
Programming (via satellite): Disney Channel.
Fee: $12.50 monthly.
Pay Service 3
Pay Units: 341.
Programming (via satellite): HBO (multiplexed).
Fee: $14.95 monthly.
Pay Service 4
Pay Units: 108.
Programming (via satellite): Showtime.
Fee: $14.95 monthly.
Pay Service 5
Pay Units: 552.
Programming (via satellite): The New Encore.
Fee: $1.95 monthly.
Pay Service 6
Pay Units: N.A.
Programming (via satellite): DMX; Starz!
Fee: $6.75 monthly (Starz), $9.95 monthly (DMX).
Pay-Per-View
Action Pay-Per-View; Playboy TV; Spice.
Fee: $4.99 (Spice).
Program Guide: The Cable Guide.
Miles of plant: 31.3 (coaxial). Total homes in franchised area: 5,483.
Manager: Jeffrey C. Harshman. Chief technician: Fred Hamm. Marketing director: Glenn Ryerson.
Ownership: AT&T Broadband & Internet Services (MSO). Purchased from Tele-Communications Inc., March 9, 1999.

McKEES ROCKS—AT&T Cable Services, 300 Corliss St., Pittsburgh, PA 15220-4815. Phones: 412-875-1100; 412-771-8100. County: Allegheny. Also serves Kennedy Twp., Stowe Twp. ICA: PA0080.
TV Market Ranking: 10,90. Franchise award date: N.A. Franchise expiration date: N.A. Began: April 1, 1967.
Channel capacity: 65 (not 2-way capable). Channels available but not in use: None.
Basic Service
Subscribers: 7,241.
Programming (received off-air): WPCB-TV (I) Greensburg; KDKA-TV (C), WCWB (W), WPGH-TV (F), WPXI (N), WQED (P), WQEX (P), WTAE-TV (A) Pittsburgh; allband FM.
Programming (via microwave): Meadows Racing Network.
Programming (via satellite): BET; C-SPAN; Pennsylvania Cable Network; QVC; TV Guide Sneak Prevue; The Weather Channel.
Fee: $44.95 installation; $10.48 monthly; $1.50 converter; $24.95 additional installation.
Expanded Basic Service
Subscribers: 6,903.
Programming (via microwave): Pittsburgh Cable News Channel.
Programming (via satellite): A & E; American Movie Classics; Animal Planet; C-SPAN 2; CNBC; CNN; Cartoon Network; Court TV; Discovery Channel; E! Entertainment TV; ESPN; ESPN 2; EWTN; FX; Fox Family Channel; Fox News Channel; Fox Sports Net Pittsburgh; Headline News; History Channel; Home & Garden Television; Home Shopping Network; International Channel; Knowledge TV; Learning Channel; Lifetime; MOVIEplex; MTV; Nashville Network; Nickelodeon; Odyssey; Sci-Fi Channel; TBS Superstation; TV Guide Channel; Turner Network TV; USA Network; VH1.
Fee: $12.03 monthly.
Pay Service 1
Pay Units: 691.
Programming (via satellite): Cinemax.
Fee: $13.45 monthly.
Pay Service 2
Pay Units: 282.
Programming (via satellite): Disney Channel.
Fee: $12.50 monthly.
Pay Service 3
Pay Units: 1,414.
Programming (via satellite): HBO (multiplexed).
Fee: $14.95 monthly.
Pay Service 4
Pay Units: 434.
Programming (via satellite): Showtime.
Fee: $14.95 monthly.
Pay Service 5
Pay Units: 2,314.
Programming (via satellite): The New Encore.
Fee: $1.95 monthly.
Pay Service 6
Pay Units: N.A.
Programming (via satellite): Starz!
Fee: $6.75 monthly.
Pay-Per-View
Action Pay-Per-View; Playboy TV; Spice; Viewer's Choice.
Fee: $4.99 (Spice).
Local advertising: Yes (locally produced & insert). Available in satellite distributed programming. Regional interconnect: TCI Media Services-Pittsburgh, PA.
Equipment: Jerrold headend; Kaiser amplifiers; Times Fiber cable; Scientific-Atlanta satellite antenna; Scientific-Atlanta satellite receivers.
Miles of plant: 72.3 (coaxial). Homes passed: 9,461. Total homes in franchised area: 9,461.
Manager: Jeffrey C. Harshman. Chief technician: Fred Hamm. Marketing director: Glenn Ryerson.
Ownership: AT&T Broadband & Internet Services (MSO). Purchased from Tele-Communications Inc., March 9, 1999.

McKEESPORT—AT&T Cable Services, 300 Corliss St., Pittsburgh, PA 15220-4815. Phones: 412-875-1100; 412-771-8100. County: Allegheny. Also serves Dravosburg, Duquesne, Elizabeth, Elizabeth Twp. (Allegheny County), Versailles, Wall, White Oak, Wilmerding. ICA: PA0039.
TV Market Ranking: 10. Franchise award date: N.A. Franchise expiration date: N.A. Began: December 1, 1967.
Channel capacity: 42 (not 2-way capable). Channels available but not in use: None.
Basic Service
Subscribers: 21,331.
Programming (received off-air): WPCB-TV (I) Greensburg; KDKA-TV (C), WCWB (W), WPGH-TV (F), WPXI (N), WQED (P), WQEX (P), WTAE-TV (A) Pittsburgh.
Programming (via microwave): Meadows Racing Network.
Programming (via satellite): BET; C-SPAN; Pennsylvania Cable Network; QVC; TV Guide Sneak Prevue; The Weather Channel.
Fee: $44.95 installation; $10.48 monthly; $1.50 converter; $24.95 additional installation.
Expanded Basic Service
Subscribers: 20,444.
Programming (via microwave): Pittsburgh Cable News Channel.
Programming (via satellite): A & E; American Movie Classics; Animal Planet; C-SPAN 2; CNBC; CNN; Cartoon Network; Court TV; Discovery Channel; E! Entertainment TV; ESPN; ESPN 2; EWTN; FX; Fox Family Channel; Fox News Channel; Fox Sports Net Pittsburgh; Headline News; History Channel; Home & Garden Television; Home Shopping Network; International Channel; Knowledge TV; Learning Channel; Lifetime; MOVIEplex; MTV; Nashville Network; Nickelodeon; Odyssey; Sci-Fi Channel; TBS Superstation; TV Guide Channel; Turner Network TV; USA Network; VH1.
Fee: $18.39 monthly.
Pay Service 1
Pay Units: 2,402.
Programming (via satellite): Cinemax.
Fee: $13.45 monthly.
Pay Service 2
Pay Units: 847.
Programming (via satellite): Disney Channel.
Fee: $12.50 monthly.
Pay Service 3
Pay Units: 4,551.
Programming (via satellite): HBO (multiplexed).
Fee: $14.95 monthly.
Pay Service 4
Pay Units: 1,494.
Programming (via satellite): Showtime.
Fee: $14.95 monthly.
Pay Service 5
Pay Units: 7,972.
Programming (via satellite): The New Encore.
Fee: $1.95 monthly.
Pay Service 6
Pay Units: N.A.
Programming (via satellite): DMX; Starz!
Fee: $6.75 monthly (Starz), $9.95 monthly (DMX).
Pay-Per-View
Action Pay-Per-View; Playboy TV; Spice; Viewer's Choice.
Local advertising: Yes (locally produced & insert). Available in satellite distributed programming. Regional interconnect: TCI Media Services-Pittsburgh, PA.
Program Guide: The Cable Guide.
Equipment: Jerrold headend; Kaiser amplifiers; Superior cable; Scientific-Atlanta satellite antenna; Scientific-Atlanta satellite receivers.
Miles of plant: 266.3 (coaxial). Homes passed: 30,123. Total homes in franchised area: 30,564.
Manager: Jeffrey C. Harshman. Chief technician: Fred Hamm. Marketing director: Glenn Ryerson.
City fee: 3% of gross.
Ownership: AT&T Broadband & Internet Services (MSO). Purchased from Tele-Communications Inc., March 9, 1999.

McVEYTOWN—Zampelli TV, Box 830, Lewistown, PA 17044. Phone: 717-248-1544. County: Mifflin. Also serves Mattawana. ICA: PA0366.
TV Market Ranking: 74. Franchise award date: N.A. Franchise expiration date: N.A. Began: N.A.
Channel capacity: 5. Channels available but not in use: N.A.
Basic Service
Subscribers: N.A.
Programming (received off-air): WHP-TV (C), WHTM-TV (A) Harrisburg; WTAJ-TV (C) Johnstown-Altoona; WGAL (N) Lancaster.
Fee: N.A.
Ownership: Zampelli TV (MSO).

MEADVILLE—Armstrong Cable Services, 160 Westview Dr., Meadville, PA 16335. Phones: 814-336-3171; 800-242-6307. Fax: 814-337-2510. Counties: Chester, Crawford & Mercer. Also serves Blooming Valley, Cochranton, Conneaut Lake, East Fairfield Twp., East Fallowfield Twp. (Crawford County), East Mead Twp., Fairfield Twp. (Crawford County), Greenwood Twp. (Crawford County), Guys Mills, Hayfield Twp., Otter Creek Twp., Perry Twp. (Mercer County), Randolph Twp. (Crawford County), Sadsbury Twp. (Crawford County), Saegertown, Sandy Creek Twp. (Mercer County), Sheakleyville Twp., Summit Twp. (Crawford County), Union Twp. (Crawford County), Vernon Twp., Wayne Twp. (Crawford County), West Fallowfield Twp., West Mead Twp., Woodcock Twp. ICA: PA0062.
TV Market Ranking: Below 100 (Blooming Valley, East Fallowfield Twp., East Mead Twp., Greenwood Twp., Guys Mills, Hayfield Twp., Meadville, Otter Creek Twp., Perry Twp., Randolph Twp., Saegertown, Sandy Creek

Twp., Sheakleyville Twp., Summit Twp., West Fallowfield Twp., West Mead Twp., Woodcock Twp.); Outside TV Markets (Cochranton, Conneaut Lake, East Fairfield Twp., Fairfield Twp., Sadsbury Twp., Union Twp., Vernon Twp., Wayne Twp., West Mead Twp.). Franchise award date: January 1, 1953. Franchise expiration date: January 1, 2005. Began: July 1, 1953.

Channel capacity: 54 (2-way capable; operating 2-way). Channels available but not in use: 6.

Basic Service

Subscribers: 14,546.

Programming (received off-air): WEWS-TV (A) Cleveland; WFXP (F), WICU-TV (N), WJET-TV (A), WQLN (P), WSEE (C) Erie; WUAB (U) Lorain-Cleveland; KDKA-TV (C) Pittsburgh; WFMJ-TV (N), WKBN-TV (C), WYTV (A,F) Youngstown; 14 FMs.

Programming (via satellite): A & E; American Movie Classics; C-SPAN; CNBC; CNN; Discovery Channel; ESPN; ESPN 2; EWTN; Fox Family Channel; Fox Sports Net Pittsburgh; Goodlife TV Network; Headline News; Home Shopping Network; Learning Channel; Lifetime; MTV; Nashville Network; Nickelodeon; Pennsylvania Cable Network; QVC; TBS Superstation; TV Guide Channel; The Inspirational Network; The Weather Channel; Travel Channel; Turner Network TV; USA Network; VH1.

Current originations: Automated time-weather; religious access; local news.

Fee: $35.00 installation; $24.45 monthly; $2.00 converter.

Pay Service 1

Pay Units: 975.

Programming (via satellite): Disney Channel.

Fee: $7.95 monthly.

Pay Service 2

Pay Units: N.A.

Programming (via satellite): Cinemax; DMX; HBO; Showtime.

Fee: $7.50 installation; $8.95 monthly (Showtime), $10.95 monthly (HBO).

Local advertising: Yes (locally produced & insert). Rates: $7.00/Day (alphanumeric); $20.00/Minute; $12.00/30 Seconds. Regional interconnect: Metrobase Cable Advertising.

Equipment: Scientific-Atlanta satellite antenna.

Miles of plant: 411.0 (coaxial); 35.0 (fiber optic). Additional miles planned: 25.0 (coaxial). Homes passed: 18,277. Total homes in franchised area: 23,000.

Manager: Ike M. Mutlu. Program director: James Cook.

City fee: None.

Ownership: Armstrong Group of Companies (MSO).

MESHOPPEN—Blue Ridge Cable TV Inc., Box 141, Tunkhannock, PA 18657. Phone: 570-836-5422. Fax: 570-836-1659. Counties: Bradford, Lackawanna & Wyoming. Also serves Albany Twp., Braintrim Twp., Camptown, Eaton Twp., Eatonville, Falls Twp. (Wyoming County), Forkston Twp., Laceyville, Lake Carey, Lake Winola, Lemon Twp., Mehoopany, Meshoppen Borough, Meshoppen Twp., Newton Twp. (Lackawanna County), Overfield Twp., Terry Twp., Tunkhannock Borough, Tunkhannock Twp. (Wyoming County), Tuscarora Twp. (Bradford County), Washington Twp. (Wyoming County), Wilmot Twp., Windham Twp., Wyalusing Borough, Wyalusing Twp. ICA: PA0367.

TV Market Ranking: 49 (Braintrim Twp., Camptown, Eaton Twp., Eatonville, Falls Twp., Forkston Twp., Laceyville, Lake Carey, Lake Winola, Lemon Twp., Mehoopany, Meshoppen, Meshoppen Borough, Meshoppen Twp., Newton Twp., Overfield Twp., Terry Twp., Tunkhannock Borough, Tunkhannock Twp., Tuscarora Twp., Washington Twp., Wilmot Twp., Windham Twp., Wyalusing Borough, Wyalusing Twp.); Outside TV Markets (Albany Twp.). Franchise award date: N.A. Franchise expiration date: N.A. Began: September 1, 1966.

Channel capacity: 42. Channels available but not in use: N.A.

Basic Service

Subscribers: 5,992.

Programming (received off-air): WBNG-TV (C), WICZ-TV (F), WIVT (A), WSKG (P) Binghamton; WBRE-TV (N), WNEP-TV (A), WSWB (W), WVIA-TV (P), WYOU (C) Scranton & Wilkes-Barre.

Planned programming (via microwave): WTXF-TV (F) Philadelphia.

Programming (via satellite): WPIX (W) New York; A & E; C-SPAN; CNBC; CNN; Cartoon Network; Discovery Channel; ESPN; Fox Family Channel; Headline News; Home Shopping Network; Lifetime; MTV; Madison Square Garden Network; Nashville Network; Nickelodeon; TBS Superstation; The Weather Channel; Turner Classic Movies; Turner Network TV; USA Network; VH1.

Fee: $30.00 installation; $16.90 monthly.

Pay Service 1

Pay Units: N.A.

Programming (via satellite): Cinemax; HBO.

Fee: $10.00 monthly (each).

Miles of plant: 58.3 (coaxial).

Manager: Ken Valentine.

City fee: 2% of gross.

Ownership: Pencor Services Inc. (MSO).

MEYERSDALE—FrontierVision, Box 1747, Greenville, TN 37745. Phone: 800-753-0778. Counties: Blair & Somerset. Also serves Grant, Summit Twp. (Somerset County). ICA: PA0192.

TV Market Ranking: Outside TV Markets. Franchise award date: N.A. Franchise expiration date: N.A. Began: January 1, 1951.

Channel capacity: 30. Channels available but not in use: None.

Basic Service

Subscribers: 1,418.

Programming (received off-air): WPCB-TV (I) Greensburg; WJAC-TV (N), WTAJ-TV (C), WWCP-TV (F) Johnstown-Altoona; KDKA-TV (C), WPGH-TV (F), WPXI (N), WQED (P), WTAE-TV (A) Pittsburgh.

Programming (via satellite): Fox Family Channel.

Fee: $39.30 installation; $11.74 monthly; $2.00 converter.

Expanded Basic Service

Subscribers: 1,286.

Programming (via satellite): CNN; Discovery Channel; Disney Channel; ESPN; ESPN 2; Fox Sports Net Pittsburgh; Learning Channel; Nashville Network; TBS Superstation; Turner Classic Movies; Turner Network TV; USA Network.

Fee: $39.30 installation; $19.05 monthly.

Pay Service 1

Pay Units: 110.

Programming (via satellite): Cinemax.

Fee: $9.45 monthly.

Pay Service 2

Pay Units: 113.

Programming (via satellite): HBO.

Fee: $9.95 monthly.

Equipment: Jerrold headend; Jerrold amplifiers; Microdyne satellite antenna.

Miles of plant: 35.9 (coaxial). Homes passed: 1,785.

Manager: Dan Callahan. Chief technician: Gary Shoemaker.

City fee: 3% of gross.

Ownership: FrontierVision Partners LP (MSO). See Cable System Ownership.

MIDLAND—TCI Cablevision of Ohio Inc., 16808 St. Clair Ave., East Liverpool, OH 43920-3095. Phone: 800-421-3145. County: Beaver. Also serves Brighton Twp., Glasgow, Industry, Ohioville. ICA: PA0110.

TV Market Ranking: 10,79,90. Franchise award date: N.A. Franchise expiration date: February 8, 1998. Began: November 1, 1965.

Channel capacity: 42 (not 2-way capable). Channels available but not in use: N.A.

Basic Service

Subscribers: 4,772.

Programming (received off-air): KDKA-TV (C), WCWB (W), WPGH-TV (F), WPXI (N), WQED (P), WQEX (P), WTAE-TV (A) Pittsburgh; WFMJ-TV (N), WKBN-TV (C) Youngstown.

Programming (via satellite): A & E; BET; C-SPAN; C-SPAN 2; CNN; Discovery Channel; EWTN; Fox Family Channel; Headline News; Ladbroke Racing Channel/Meadows Racing Network; Lifetime; MTV; Nashville Network; Nickelodeon; QVC; TBS Superstation; The Weather Channel.

Fee: $30.21 installation; $9.29 monthly.

Expanded Basic Service

Subscribers: 4,551.

Programming (via satellite): American Movie Classics; Court TV; ESPN; Fox Sports Net Pittsburgh; Turner Network TV; USA Network.

Fee: $10.00 monthly.

Pay Service 1

Pay Units: 632.

Programming (via satellite): Cinemax.

Fee: $13.70 monthly.

Pay Service 2

Pay Units: 235.

Programming (via satellite): Disney Channel.

Fee: $13.45 monthly.

Pay Service 3

Pay Units: 1,227.

Programming (via satellite): HBO.

Fee: $14.15 monthly.

Pay Service 4

Pay Units: 224.

Programming (via satellite): Showtime.

Fee: $14.15 monthly.

Pay Service 5

Pay Units: 1,454.

Programming (via satellite): The New Encore.

Fee: N.A.

Pay Service 6

Pay Units: N.A.

Programming (via satellite): Starz!

Fee: $4.75 monthly.

Pay-Per-View

Addressable homes: 153.

Miles of plant: 120.0 (coaxial). Homes passed: 5,705. Total homes in franchised area: 7,574.

Manager: Jim Unlenwood. Chief technician: Scott Boyd.

Ownership: AT&T Broadband & Internet Services (MSO). Purchased from Tele-Communications Inc., March 9, 1999.

MIDWAY—Adelphia Cable, Box 1445, 215 E. North St., New Castle, PA 16103-1445. Phones: 614-246-4223; 800-782-4118. Counties: Allegheny & Washington. Also serves McDonald (northern portion), Mount Pleasant Twp. (Washington County), Robinson Twp. (Washington County). ICA: PA0187.

TV Market Ranking: 10 (McDonald, Midway, Mount Pleasant Twp.); 90 (McDonald, Midway, Mount Pleasant Twp., Robinson Twp.). Franchise award date: N.A. Franchise expiration date: N.A. Began: August 1, 1981.

Channel capacity: N.A. Channels available but not in use: N.A.

Basic Service

Subscribers: 927.

Programming (received off-air): WDTV (C,A) Clarksburg-Weston; KDKA-TV (C), WCWB (W), WPGH-TV (F), WPXI (N), WQED (P), WTAE-TV (A) Pittsburgh; WTRF-TV (C) Wheeling-Steubenville.

Programming (via satellite): CNN; Nickelodeon; TBS Superstation.

Fee: $20.00 installation; $13.45 monthly.

Expanded Basic Service

Subscribers: N.A.

Programming (received off-air): WPCB-TV (I) Greensburg.

Programming (via satellite): WGN-TV (W) Chicago; ESPN; USA Network.

Fee: $3.95 monthly.

Pay Service 1

Pay Units: 144.

Programming (via satellite): Cinemax.

Fee: $9.95 monthly.

Pay Service 2

Pay Units: 47.

Programming (via satellite): Disney Channel.

Fee: $9.95 monthly.

Pay Service 3

Pay Units: 429.

Programming (via satellite): HBO.

Fee: $9.95 monthly.

Pay Service 4

Pay Units: 46.

Programming (via satellite): Showtime.

Fee: $9.95 monthly.

Equipment: Scientific-Atlanta satellite antenna.

Miles of plant: 54.6 (coaxial). Homes passed: 1,275.

Manager: Dave Campo. Chief technician: Terry Stanard.

Ownership: Adelphia Communications Corp. (MSO).

MIFFLINBURG—Cablecomm, Box 272, 335 E. Chestnut St., Mifflinburg, PA 17844. Phones: 717-966-0662; 800-242-8093. Fax: 717-966-1513. Counties: Mifflin & Union. Also serves Buffalo Twp. (Union County), Decatur Twp. (Mifflin County), Derry Twp. (Mifflin County), Glen Iron, Hartleton, Hartley Twp., Laurelton, Lewis Twp. (Union County), Limestone Twp. (Union County), Millmont, Swengel, Union County, Weikert, West Buffalo Twp. (portions). ICA: PA0131.

TV Market Ranking: Below 100 (Buffalo Twp., Glen Iron, Hartleton, Hartley Twp., Laurelton, Lewis Twp., Limestone Twp., Mifflinburg, Millmont, Swengel, Union County, Weikert, West Buffalo Twp.); Outside TV Markets (Decatur Twp., Derry Twp.). Franchise award date: N.A. Franchise expiration date: April 17, 2004. Began: October 17, 1962.

Channel capacity: 40 (not 2-way capable). Channels available but not in use: 3.

Basic Service

Subscribers: 1,803.

Programming (received off-air): WHTM-TV (A), WITF-TV (P) Harrisburg; WGAL (N), WLYH-TV (U) Lancaster; WBRE-TV (N), WNEP-TV (A), WSWB (W), WVIA-TV (P), WYOU (C) Scranton & Wilkes-Barre; allband FM.

Programming (via satellite): C-SPAN; QVC.

Current originations: Public access.

Fee: $46.20 installation; $8.15 monthly.

Expanded Basic Service

Subscribers: 1,777.

Programming (via satellite): WPIX (W) New York; A & E; CNN; Comedy Central; Country

Music TV; Discovery Channel; ESPN; Fox Family Channel; Headline News; Lifetime; MTV; Nashville Network; Nickelodeon; TBS Superstation; The Weather Channel; Turner Network TV; USA Network; VH1.
Fee: $46.20 installation; $12.85 monthly.

Pay Service 1
Pay Units: 65.
Programming (via satellite): Cinemax.
Fee: $9.00 monthly.

Pay Service 2
Pay Units: 99.
Programming (via satellite): Disney Channel.
Fee: $7.00 monthly.

Pay Service 3
Pay Units: 26.
Programming (via satellite): The New Encore.
Fee: $4.95 monthly.

Pay Service 4
Pay Units: 86.
Programming (via satellite): HBO.
Fee: $10.00 monthly.

Pay Service 5
Pay Units: 88.
Programming (via satellite): The Movie Channel.
Fee: $9.00 monthly.

Pay Service 6
Pay Units: 88.
Programming (via satellite): Showtime.
Fee: $10.00 monthly.

Local advertising: Yes. Available in satellite distributed programming. Rates: $1.00/Day.
Program Guide: Premium Channels.
Equipment: Scientific-Atlanta headend; Magnavox amplifiers; Times Fiber cable; Scientific-Atlanta & Prodelin satellite antenna; M/A-Com satellite receivers.
Miles of plant: 137.0 (coaxial). Homes passed: 3,315. Total homes in franchised area: 3,315.
Manager: Sam Andolina. Chief technician: Richard Fultz. Program director: R. E. Steffan III. Marketing director: Kevin Munnell.
City fee: 3% of basic gross.
Ownership: Fanch Communications Inc. (MSO); Time Warner Cable (MSO). See Cable System Ownership.

MIFFLINTOWN—Juniata CATV Inc., Box 111, Lewistown, PA 17044. Phone: 717-248-3733. County: Juniata. Also serves Fermanagh Twp., Mifflin, Milford Twp. (Juniata County). ICA: PA0368.
TV Market Ranking: Outside TV Markets. Franchise award date: N.A. Franchise expiration date: N.A. Began: January 1, 1963.
Channel capacity: N.A. Channels available but not in use: N.A.

Basic Service
Subscribers: N.A.
Programming (received off-air): WJZ-TV (C), WMAR-TV (A) Baltimore; WHAG-TV (N) Hagerstown; WHP-TV (C), WHTM-TV (A), WITF-TV (P) Harrisburg; WJAC-TV (N), WTAJ-TV (C) Johnstown-Altoona; WGAL (N), WLYH-TV (U) Lancaster; WPHL-TV (W), WTXF-TV (F) Philadelphia; WBRE-TV (N), WNEP-TV (A), WVIA-TV (P) Scranton & Wilkes-Barre; WPMT (F) York.
Fee: N.A.
Ownership: Nittany Media Inc. (MSO).

MILFORD—Blue Ridge Cable TV Inc., 204 4th St., Milford, PA 18337. Phone: 717-296-8200. County: Pike. Also serves Dingman Twp., Lackawaxen Twp., Milford Twp. (Pike County), Rowland, Shohola Twp. ICA: PA0369.
TV Market Ranking: 49 (Lackawaxen Twp., Rowland, Shohola Twp.); Below 100 (Dingman Twp., Milford, Milford Twp.). Franchise award date: N.A. Franchise expiration date: N.A. Began: December 1, 1965.
Channel capacity: 42. Channels available but not in use: None.

Basic Service
Subscribers: 3,500.
Programming (received off-air): WLVT-TV (P) Allentown; WABC-TV (A), WCBS-TV (C), WNBC (N), WNYW (F), WPIX (W), WWOR-TV (U) New York; WNET (P) New York-Newark; WPHL-TV (W), WTXF-TV (F) Philadelphia; WBRE-TV (N), WNEP-TV (A), WSWB (W), WVIA-TV (P), WYOU (C) Scranton & Wilkes-Barre; allband FM.
Programming (via satellite): A & E; C-SPAN; CNBC; CNN; Country Music TV; Discovery Channel; ESPN; Fox Family Channel; Headline News; Home Shopping Network; Lifetime; MTV; Madison Square Garden Network; Nashville Network; Nickelodeon; QVC; TBS Superstation; The Weather Channel; Turner Network TV; USA Network.
Fee: $30.00 installation; $16.90 monthly.

Pay Service 1
Pay Units: N.A.
Programming (via satellite): Cinemax; HBO.
Fee: $9.50 monthly (Cinemax), $10.50 monthly (HBO).

Local advertising: Yes. Regional interconnect: Cabletime.
Equipment: Scientific-Atlanta headend; C-COR amplifiers; Comm/Scope cable; AFC satellite antenna; Scientific-Atlanta satellite receivers.
Miles of plant: 18.0 (coaxial). Additional miles planned: 20.0 (coaxial).
Manager: Norman Bohs.
Ownership: Pencor Services Inc. (MSO).

MILL CREEK—Broad Top Mountain Cable, 809 Lower Main St., Saxton, PA 16678. Phone: 814-635-2514. County: Huntingdon. Also serves Brady Twp. (Huntingdon County), Henderson Twp. (Huntingdon County), Mill Creek Borough. ICA: PA0370.
TV Market Ranking: 74. Franchise award date: N.A. Franchise expiration date: N.A. Began: January 1, 1965.
Channel capacity: 21. Channels available but not in use: 8.

Basic Service
Subscribers: 380.
Programming (received off-air): WPSX-TV (P) Clearfield; WHTM-TV (A), WITF-TV (P) Harrisburg; WJAC-TV (N), WKBS-TV (I), WTAJ-TV (C) Johnstown-Altoona.
Programming (via satellite): WGN-TV (W) Chicago; ESPN; Fox Family Channel; Nashville Network; TBS Superstation; The Inspirational Network.
Fee: $50.00 installation; $14.75 monthly.

Pay Service 1
Pay Units: 50.
Programming (via satellite): Disney Channel; HBO.
Fee: $25.00 installation; $10.00 monthly (each).

Local advertising: No.
Miles of plant: 9.0 (coaxial).
Manager: Paul Whipple. Chief technician: John M. Zimmerman.
Ownership: SRW Inc. (MSO).

MILL HALL—River Valley Cable TV Inc., Box 205, Mill Hall, PA 17751. Phone: 717-726-4700. Fax: 717-726-7826. Counties: Centre & Clinton. Also serves Bald Eagle Twp. (Clinton County), Beech Creek Borough, Beech Creek Twp., Curtin Twp., Greene Twp. (Clinton County), Lamar Twp. (Clinton County), Liberty Twp. (Centre County), Loganton Borough, Mill Hall Borough, Porter Twp. (Clinton County), Walker Twp. (Centre County). ICA: PA0130.
TV Market Ranking: Below 100. Franchise award date: N.A. Franchise expiration date: N.A. Began: March 1, 1955.
Channel capacity: 36 (2-way capable). Channels available but not in use: None.

Basic Service
Subscribers: 3,900.
Programming (received off-air): WPSX-TV (P) Clearfield; WOLF-TV (F) Hazleton; WTAJ-TV (C) Johnstown-Altoona; WBRE-TV (N), WNEP-TV (A), WVIA-TV (P) Scranton & Wilkes-Barre.
Programming (via satellite): WGN-TV (W) Chicago; WPIX (W) New York; A & E; Animal Planet; Discovery Channel; Fox Family Channel; Lifetime; Nashville Network; Odyssey; TBS Superstation; Turner Network TV.
Current originations: Public access.
Fee: $33.00 installation; $23.85 monthly.

Expanded Basic Service
Subscribers: N.A.
Programming (via satellite): CNN; Country Music TV; ESPN; ESPN 2; Headline News; History Channel; Learning Channel; MTV; Nickelodeon; QVC; Sci-Fi Channel; The Weather Channel; USA Network; VH1.
Fee: N.A.

Pay Service 1
Pay Units: 475.
Programming (via satellite): Disney Channel; HBO; The Movie Channel.
Fee: $16.50 installation; $9.95 monthly (each).

Pay-Per-View
Addressable homes: 500.

Local advertising: Yes. Regional interconnect: Cabletime.
Equipment: Jerrold headend; Entron amplifiers; Scientific-Atlanta satellite antenna; Scientific-Atlanta satellite receivers.
Miles of plant: 160.0 (coaxial); 20.0 (fiber optic). Homes passed: 4,000. Total homes in franchised area: 4,000.
Manager: Diana Sayers. Chief technician: Blaine Kunes.
Ownership: River Valley Cable TV Inc.

MILL VILLAGE—CableVision Communications, Box 2200, 68 5th St., Buckhannon, WV 26201. Phone: 304-472-4193. Fax: 304-472-0756. County: Erie. Also serves Waterford (Erie County). ICA: PA0277.
TV Market Ranking: Below 100. Franchise award date: N.A. Franchise expiration date: N.A. Began: March 1, 1985.
Channel capacity: 21. Channels available but not in use: N.A.

Basic Service
Subscribers: 84.
Programming (received off-air): WFXP (F), WICU-TV (N), WJET-TV (A), WQLN (P), WSEE (C) Erie.
Programming (via satellite): WGN-TV (W) Chicago; Animal Planet; CNN; Country Music TV; Discovery Channel; Disney Channel; ESPN; Fox Family Channel; Lifetime; Nashville Network; Nickelodeon; TBS Superstation; Turner Network TV; USA Network.
Fee: $61.25 installation; $22.80 monthly; $1.24 converter; $17.50 additional installation.

Pay Service 1
Pay Units: 37.
Programming (via satellite): HBO.
Fee: $17.50 installation; $11.99 monthly.

Equipment: Blonder-Tongue headend; Jerrold amplifiers; Comm/Scope cable.
Miles of plant: 3.0 (coaxial). Homes passed: 153.
Manager: Willie Critchfield. Marketing director: Kenny Phillips.
Ownership: Rifkin & Associates Inc. (MSO). See Cable System Ownership.

MILLERSBURG—Millersburg TV Co., Box 66, 804 Plum St., Millersburg, PA 17061. Phone: 717-692-4772. Fax: 717-692-5654. Counties: Dauphin & Northumberland. Also serves Dalmatia, Halifax, Halifax Twp., Jackson Twp. (Dauphin County), Jefferson Twp. (Dauphin County), Reed Twp. (Dauphin County), Upper Paxton Twp. (Dauphin County), Wayne Twp. (Dauphin County). ICA: PA0373.
TV Market Ranking: 57. Franchise award date: N.A. Franchise expiration date: N.A. Began: September 1, 1953.
Channel capacity: 60 (not 2-way capable). Channels available but not in use: 11.

Basic Service
Subscribers: 4,620.
Programming (received off-air): WHP-TV (C), WHTM-TV (A), WITF-TV (P) Harrisburg; WGAL (N), WLYH-TV (U) Lancaster; WPHL-TV (W) Philadelphia; WGCB-TV (I) Red Lion; WPMT (F) York.
Programming (via satellite): A & E; American Movie Classics; Animal Planet; C-SPAN; CNBC; CNN; Country Music TV; Discovery Channel; ESPN; ESPN 2; Fox Family Channel; Fox Sports Net Pittsburgh; Goodlife TV Network; Headline News; History Channel; Home & Garden Television; Home Shopping Network; Lifetime; MSNBC; MTV; Nashville Network; Nick at Nite's TV Land; Nickelodeon; Odyssey; Outdoor Channel; QVC; Sci-Fi Channel; TBS Superstation; TV Food Network; The Weather Channel; Travel Channel; Turner Network TV; USA Network; VH1.
Current originations: Local news.
Fee: $35.00 installation; $25.00 monthly; $1.60 converter.

Pay Service 1
Pay Units: 178.
Programming (via satellite): Cinemax.
Fee: $8.00 monthly.

Pay Service 2
Pay Units: 70.
Programming (via satellite): Disney Channel.
Fee: $8.00 monthly.

Pay Service 3
Pay Units: 230.
Programming (via satellite): HBO.
Fee: $10.00 monthly.

Local advertising: Yes. Available in satellite distributed programming.
Equipment: Jerrold & Scientific-Atlanta headend; Jerrold amplifiers; Times Fiber cable; Jerrold set top converters; Arcom & Intercept

traps; Scientific-Atlanta satellite antenna; Scientific-Atlanta satellite receivers.
Miles of plant: 127.0 (coaxial); 29.0 (fiber optic).
Manager: Donald B. Herrold. Chief technician: Dennis Kratzer. Customer service manager: Janice Herrold.
Ownership: Millersburg TV Co.

MILLHEIM—Millheim TV Transmission Co., Box 365, Millheim, PA 16854. Phone: 814-349-8688. County: Centre. Also serves Aaronsburg, Coburn. ICA: PA0216.
TV Market Ranking: Outside TV Markets. Franchise award date: January 1, 1996. Franchise expiration date: N.A. Began: January 1, 1962.
Channel capacity: 36 (not 2-way capable). Channels available but not in use: 14.
Basic Service
Subscribers: 372.
Programming (received off-air): WPSX-TV (P) Clearfield; WHTM-TV (A) Harrisburg; WJAC-TV (N), WTAJ-TV (C) Johnstown-Altoona; WBRE-TV (N), WNEP-TV (A), WVIA-TV (P) Scranton & Wilkes-Barre; WPMT (F) York; allband FM.
Programming (via satellite): WGN-TV (W) Chicago; WPIX (W) New York; CNN; Discovery Channel; ESPN; Fox Family Channel; Nashville Network; Odyssey; TBS Superstation; Turner Network TV.
Fee: $135.00 installation; $10.50 monthly.
Pay Service 1
Pay Units: 342.
Programming (via satellite): HBO.
Fee: $10.00 installation; $7.50 monthly.
Pay-Per-View
Addressable homes: 863.
Equipment: Blonder-Tongue headend; C-COR amplifiers; Plastoid cable; Eagle traps; AFC satellite antenna.
Miles of plant: 30.0 (coaxial); None (fiber optic). Homes passed: 390. Total homes in franchised area: 390.
Manager: Wayne Rishel. Technical engineer: Earl Heckman.
Ownership: Millheim TV Transmission Co.

MON VALLEY—AT&T Cable Services, 300 Corliss St., Pittsburgh, PA 15220-4815. Phones: 412-875-1100; 412-771-8100. Counties: Allegheny, Fayette, Washington & Westmoreland. Also serves Belle Vernon, Carroll Twp. (Washington County), Charleroi, Donora, Fallowfield Twp., Forward Twp. (Allegheny County), Monessen, Monongahela, New Eagle, North Belle Vernon, North Charleroi, Rostraver Twp., Speers, Twilight, Washington Twp. (Allegheny County). ICA: PA0043.
TV Market Ranking: 10. Franchise award date: N.A. Franchise expiration date: N.A. Began: May 1, 1969.
Channel capacity: N.A. Channels available but not in use: N.A.
Basic Service
Subscribers: 21,247.
Programming (received off-air): WPCB-TV (I) Greensburg; KDKA-TV (C), WCWB (W), WPGH-TV (F), WPXI (N), WQED (P), WQEX (P), WTAE-TV (A) Pittsburgh; allband FM.
Programming (via satellite): BET; C-SPAN; Ladbroke Racing Channel/Meadows Racing Network; QVC; The Weather Channel.
Fee: $44.95 installation; $10.34 monthly; $1.50 converter; $24.95 additional installation.
Expanded Basic Service
Subscribers: 20,356.
Programming (via microwave): Pittsburgh Cable News Channel.
Programming (via satellite): A & E; American Movie Classics; Animal Planet; C-SPAN 2; CNBC; CNN; Cartoon Network; Court TV; Discovery Channel; E! Entertainment TV; ESPN; ESPN 2; EWTN; FX; Fox Family Channel; Fox News Channel; Fox Sports Net; Fox Sports Net Pittsburgh; Headline News; History Channel; Home & Garden Television; Home Shopping Network; International Channel; Knowledge TV; Learning Channel; Lifetime; MOVIEplex; MTV; Nashville Network; Nickelodeon; Odyssey; Sci-Fi Channel; TBS Superstation; TV Guide Sneak Prevue; Turner Network TV; USA Network; VH1.
Fee: $17.91 monthly.
Pay Service 1
Pay Units: 1,858.
Programming (via satellite): Cinemax.
Fee: $13.45 monthly.
Pay Service 2
Pay Units: 653.
Programming (via satellite): Disney Channel.
Fee: $12.50 monthly.
Pay Service 3
Pay Units: 3,627.
Programming (via satellite): HBO.
Fee: $14.95 monthly.
Pay Service 4
Pay Units: 994.
Programming (via satellite): Showtime.
Fee: $14.95 monthly.
Pay Service 5
Pay Units: 6,918.
Programming (via satellite): The New Encore.
Fee: $1.95 monthly.
Pay Service 6
Pay Units: N.A.
Programming (via satellite): DMX; Starz!
Fee: $6.75 monthly (Starz!), $9.95 monthly (DMX).
Pay-Per-View
Addressable homes: 2,000.
Action Pay-Per-View; Playboy TV; Spice.
Local advertising: Yes (insert only). Available in satellite distributed programming. Regional interconnect: TCI Media Services-Pittsburgh, PA.
Program Guide: The Cable Guide.
Equipment: Jerrold & Scientific-Atlanta headend; Jerrold amplifiers; Superior cable; Scientific-Atlanta set top converters; Jerrold addressable set top converters.
Miles of plant: 339.7 (coaxial). Homes passed: 26,209. Total homes in franchised area: 26,765.
Manager: Jeffrey C. Harshman. Chief technician: Fred A. Hamm. Marketing director: Glenn Ryerson.
City fee: 3% of gross.
Ownership: AT&T Broadband & Internet Services (MSO). Purchased from Tele-Communications Inc., March 9, 1999.

MONROEVILLE—Adelphia Cable, 200 James Place, Monroeville, PA 15146. Phone: 800-892-7300. Fax: 412-856-7650. Counties: Allegheny & Westmoreland. Also serves Braddock, Churchill, East McKeesport, East Pittsburgh, North Braddock, North Huntingdon (Westmoreland County), North Versailles Twp., Rankin, Swissvale, Trafford, Turtle Creek, Wilkins Twp. ICA: PA0023.
TV Market Ranking: 10. Franchise award date: N.A. Franchise expiration date: N.A. Began: January 1, 1966.
Channel capacity: 39 (2-way capable; operating 2-way). Channels available but not in use: N.A.
Basic Service
Subscribers: 31,675; Commercial subscribers: 300.
Programming (received off-air): WPCB-TV (I) Greensburg; WNPA (U) Jeanette; KDKA-TV (C), WPGH-TV (F), WPXI (N), WQED (P), WQEX (P), WTAE-TV (A) Pittsburgh.
Programming (via satellite): QVC.
Current originations: Public access; educational access; government access; leased access; automated emergency alert; local news.
Fee: N.A.
Expanded Basic Service
Subscribers: 29,616.
Programming (via microwave): Pittsburgh Cable News Channel.
Programming (via satellite): A & E; American Movie Classics; BET; C-SPAN; CNBC; CNN; Comedy Central; Discovery Channel; Disney Channel; E! Entertainment TV; ESPN; EWTN; Fox Family Channel; Fox Sports Net Pittsburgh; Headline News; History Channel; Home Shopping Network; Ladbroke Racing Channnel/Meadows Racing Network; Learning Channel; Lifetime; MTV; Nashville Network; Nickelodeon; TV Guide Channel; The Weather Channel; Turner Network TV; USA Network; VH1.
Fee: N.A.
Expanded Basic Service 2
Subscribers: N.A.
Programming (via satellite): Bravo; Cartoon Network; ESPN 2; MSNBC; Sci-Fi Channel; Travel Channel; Turner Classic Movies.
Fee: N.A.
A la Carte 1
Subscribers: 15,495.
Programming (via satellite): WGN-TV (W) Chicago; TBS Superstation; The New Encore.
Fee: $0.90 monthly (Encore).
Pay Service 1
Pay Units: 4,055.
Programming (via satellite): Cinemax (multiplexed).
Fee: $9.00 monthly.
Pay Service 2
Pay Units: 10,602.
Programming (via satellite): HBO (multiplexed).
Fee: $9.00 monthly.
Pay Service 3
Pay Units: 2,873.
Programming (via satellite): Showtime; The Movie Channel.
Fee: $9.00 monthly.
Pay Service 4
Pay Units: N.A.
Programming (via satellite): Playboy TV.
Fee: N.A.
Pay-Per-View
Hot Choice; Viewer's Choice.
Local advertising: Yes (locally produced & insert). Available in satellite distributed & character-generated programming. Regional interconnect: TCI Media Services-Pittsburgh, PA.
Equipment: Scientific-Atlanta headend; Century III & AEL amplifiers; Comm/Scope cable; Sony cameras; Sony VTRs; Video Data Systems character generator; Hamlin & Scientific-Atlanta set top converters; Scientific-Atlanta addressable set top converters; Eagle traps; Scientific-Atlanta, Superior & Uniden satellite antenna; Scientific-Atlanta satellite receivers.
Miles of plant: 347.4 (coaxial). Homes passed: 41,600. Total homes in franchised area: 41,600.
Manager: Fran Bradley. Program director: Jason Martin. Marketing director: Frank Polito.
City fee: 3% of gross.
Ownership: Adelphia Communications Corp. (MSO).

MONTEREY—Multi-Tech Communications, Box 219, Sligo, PA 16255. Phone: 814-745-2426. County: Clarion. Also serves Perry Twp. (Clarion County). ICA: PA0293.
TV Market Ranking: Outside TV Markets. Franchise award date: N.A. Franchise expiration date: N.A. Began: January 1, 1986.
Channel capacity: 36 (not 2-way capable). Channels available but not in use: 10.
Basic Service
Subscribers: 70.
Programming (received off-air): WPCB-TV (I) Greensburg; WJAC-TV (N) Johnstown-Altoona; KDKA-TV (C), WCWB (W), WPGH-TV (F), WPXI (N), WQED (P), WTAE-TV (A) Pittsburgh; WKBN-TV (C) Youngstown.
Programming (via satellite): CNN; Country Music TV; Discovery Channel; ESPN; Fox Sports Net Pittsburgh; Home Shopping Network; MTV; Nashville Network; QVC; TBS Superstation; The Weather Channel.
Fee: $35.00 installation; $23.00 monthly.
Pay Service 1
Pay Units: 22.
Programming (via satellite): Showtime.
Fee: $7.95 monthly.
Miles of plant: 6.0 (coaxial). Homes passed: 104.
Manager: Richard McHenry. Chief technician: Donald McCall.
Ownership: Multi-Tech Communications (MSO).

MONTGOMERY—Adelphia Cable, Box 198, One Apollo Rd., Plymouth Meeting, PA 19462. Phone: 610-828-8316. Fax: 610-941-9943. County: Montgomery. Also serves Ambler, Erdenheim, Flourtown, Laverock, Lower Gwynedd Twp. (Montgomery County), Oreland, Penllyn, Plymouth Twp. (Montgomery County), Springfield Twp. (Montgomery County), Whitemarsh Twp., Whitpain Twp. (portions), Wyndmoor. ICA: PA0056.
TV Market Ranking: 4. Franchise award date: N.A. Franchise expiration date: N.A. Began: August 5, 1978.
Channel capacity: 40 (2-way capable; operating 2-way). Channels available but not in use: None.
Basic Service
Subscribers: 15,042.
Programming (received off-air): WLVT-TV (P) Allentown; WNJS (P) Camden; KYW-TV (C), WCAU (N), WPHL-TV (W), WPSG (U), WPVI-TV (A), WTXF-TV (F) Philadelphia; WHYY-TV (P) Wilmington.
Programming (via satellite): Philadelphia Park Live; TBS Superstation.
Current originations: Automated time-weather; public access; educational access.
Fee: $74.95 installation; $6.00 monthly.
Expanded Basic Service
Subscribers: N.A.
Programming (via satellite): A & E; American Movie Classics; C-SPAN; CNBC; CNN; Discovery Channel; ESPN; Fox Family Channel; Headline News; Home Shopping Network; Lifetime; MTV; Nashville Network; Nickelodeon; QVC; The Weather Channel; Turner Network TV; USA Network.
Fee: $35.00 installation; $15.45 monthly.
Pay Service 1
Pay Units: 15,151.
Programming (via satellite): Bravo; Disney Channel; HBO; The Movie Channel.
Fee: $4.95 monthly (Bravo), $8.95 monthly (Disney), $10.95 monthly (HBO or TMC).
Local advertising: Yes. Available in satellite distributed & automated programming. Re-

gional interconnect: Metrobase Cable Advertising.
Program Guide: The Cable Guide.
Equipment: Scientific-Atlanta headend; C-COR amplifiers; Comm/Scope cable; Texscan character generator; Scientific-Atlanta set top converters; Scientific-Atlanta addressable set top converters; Eagle, Pico & PPC traps; Scientific-Atlanta satellite antenna; Scientific-Atlanta satellite receivers.
Miles of plant: 264.2 (coaxial). Additional miles planned: 5.0 (coaxial). Homes passed: 19,500. Total homes in franchised area: 19,500.
Manager: Rick Conrad. Chief technician: Joe Ruff.
City fee: 3% of gross.
Ownership: Adelphia Communications Corp. (MSO).

MONTROSE—Time Warner Cable, Box 2208, Binghamton, NY 13902. Phones: 607-798-8001; 800-955-0750. Fax: 607-770-8639. County: Susquehanna. Also serves Bridgewater Twp., Dimock Twp., Springville. ICA: PA0171.
TV Market Ranking: 49. Franchise award date: N.A. Franchise expiration date: N.A. Began: December 1, 1984.
Channel capacity: 36 (not 2-way capable). Channels available but not in use: 3.
Basic Service
Subscribers: 1,282.
Programming (received off-air): WBNG-TV (C), WICZ-TV (F), WIVT (A), WSKG (P) Binghamton; WBRE-TV (N), WNEP-TV (A), WSWB (W), WVIA-TV (P), WYOU (C) Scranton & Wilkes-Barre.
Programming (via satellite): TBS Superstation.
Fee: $149.00 installation; $7.00 monthly.
Expanded Basic Service
Subscribers: 1,276.
Programming (via satellite): A & E; American Movie Classics; C-SPAN; CNN; Discovery Channel; ESPN; Fox Family Channel; Headline News; Learning Channel; Lifetime; MTV; Nashville Network; Nickelodeon; QVC; Sci-Fi Channel; The Weather Channel; Turner Network TV; USA Network; VH1.
Fee: $82.54 installation; $7.14 monthly.
Pay Service 1
Pay Units: 376.
Programming (via satellite): Cinemax.
Fee: $10.00 monthly.
Pay Service 2
Pay Units: 418.
Programming (via satellite): HBO.
Fee: $10.00 monthly.
Equipment: Jerrold headend; Jerrold & Magnavox amplifiers; Times Fiber cable; Jerrold set top converters.
Miles of plant: 45.0 (coaxial). Homes passed: 1,698.
Manager: James Streevy. Chief technician: Kevin Tompkins.
Ownership: Time Warner Cable (MSO); Advance/Newhouse Partnership (MSO).

MONUMENT—Monument TV, Box 85, Loganton, PA 17747. Phone: 717-725-2733. County: Centre. ICA: PA0376.
TV Market Ranking: Outside TV Markets. Franchise award date: N.A. Franchise expiration date: N.A. Began: January 1, 1968.
Channel capacity: 12. Channels available but not in use: 5.
Basic Service
Subscribers: N.A.
Programming (received off-air): WPSX-TV (P) Clearfield; WTAJ-TV (C) Johnstown-Altoona; WBRE-TV (N), WNEP-TV (A), WSWB (W), WVIA-TV (P), WYOU (C) Scranton & Wilkes-Barre.
Fee: $5.00 monthly.
Equipment: Holt headend.
Miles of plant: 1.0 (coaxial).
Chief technician: Guy Bierly.
Ownership: Monument TV.

MOUNT MORRIS—AT&T Cable Services., 300 Corliss St., Pittsburgh, PA 15220-4815. Phones: 412-875-1100; 412-771-8100. Counties: Greene & Westmoreland. Also serves Perry Twp. (Greene County). ICA: PA0254.
TV Market Ranking: Below 100. Franchise award date: N.A. Franchise expiration date: N.A. Began: November 1, 1963.
Channel capacity: N.A. Channels available but not in use: N.A.
Basic Service
Subscribers: 268.
Programming (received off-air): KDKA-TV (C), WCWB (W), WPGH-TV (F), WPXI (N), WQED (P), WTAE-TV (A) Pittsburgh.
Programming (via satellite): Fox Family Channel; Nashville Network; TBS Superstation; USA Network.
Fee: $44.95 installation; $11.46 monthly; $1.50 converter; $24.95 additional installation.
Expanded Basic Service
Subscribers: 231.
Programming (via satellite): A & E; Animal Planet; C-SPAN; CNN; Cartoon Network; Court TV; Discovery Channel; ESPN; Fox Sports Net Pittsburgh; Headline News; Home & Garden Television; Learning Channel; Lifetime; MOVIEplex; MTV; Nickelodeon; The Weather Channel; Turner Network TV.
Fee: $12.13 monthly.
Pay Service 1
Pay Units: 44.
Programming (via satellite): HBO.
Fee: $13.75 monthly.
Pay Service 2
Pay Units: 14.
Programming (via satellite): Disney Channel.
Fee: $12.50 monthly.
Pay Service 3
Pay Units: 14.
Programming (via satellite): Cinemax.
Fee: $13.45 monthly.
Pay Service 4
Pay Units: N.A.
Programming (via satellite): The New Encore.
Fee: $1.95 monthly.
Program Guide: The Cable Guide.
Miles of plant: 6.0 (coaxial). Homes passed: 310. Total homes in franchised area: 590.
Manager: Jeffrey C. Harshman. Chief technician: Fred A. Hamm. Marketing director: Glenn Ryerson.
Ownership: AT&T Broadband & Internet Services (MSO). Purchased from Tele-Communications Inc., March 9, 1999.

MOUNT OLIVER—Mount Oliver TV Cable/Adelphia Cable, 5335 Enterprise Blvd., Bethel Park, PA 15102. Phone: 800-892-7300. Fax: 412-835-2045. County: Allegheny. ICA: PA0162.
TV Market Ranking: 10,90. Franchise award date: N.A. Franchise expiration date: N.A. Began: March 19, 1973.
Channel capacity: 30 (2-way capable; operating 2-way). Channels available but not in use: 7.
Basic Service
Subscribers: 1,166.
Programming (received off-air): WPCB-TV (I) Greensburg; KDKA-TV (C), WCWB (W), WPGH-TV (F), WPXI (N), WQED (P), WTAE-TV (A) Pittsburgh; WTOV-TV (N) Steubenville-Wheeling; WTRF-TV (C) Wheeling-Steubenville.
Programming (via satellite): ESPN; TBS Superstation.
Current originations: Government access.
Fee: $74.95 installation; $7.00 monthly.
Expanded Basic Service
Subscribers: N.A.
Programming (via satellite): CNN; Fox Sports Net Pittsburgh; Home Shopping Network; Ladbroke Racing Channnel/Meadows Racing Network; Lifetime; MTV; USA Network.
Fee: $29.95 installation; $13.95 monthly.
Pay Service 1
Pay Units: N.A.
Programming (via satellite): Cinemax; Disney Channel; HBO; The Movie Channel.
Fee: $8.50 monthly (Cinemax, Disney or TMC), $10.50 monthly (HBO).
Equipment: Scientific-Atlanta headend; Scientific-Atlanta amplifiers; Comm/Scope cable; Texscan character generator; Scientific-Atlanta set top converters; Scientific-Atlanta addressable set top converters; Eagle, Pico & PPC traps; Standard Communications satellite antenna; Scientific-Atlanta satellite receivers.
Miles of plant: 12.0 (coaxial). Homes passed: 1,900. Total homes in franchised area: 1,900.
Manager: J. Francis Bradley Jr. Chief technician: Chuck Redpath.
City fee: 3% of gross.
Ownership: Adelphia Communications Corp. (MSO).

MOUNT PLEASANT MILLS—R. J. Shelley CATV, Box 243, Mount Pleasant Mills, PA 17853. Phone: 717-539-8511. County: Snyder. Also serves Port Trevorton. ICA: PA0377.
TV Market Ranking: 57 (Mount Pleasant Mills); Outside TV Markets (Port Trevorton). Franchise award date: N.A. Franchise expiration date: N.A. Began: January 1, 1965.
Channel capacity: 18. Channels available but not in use: 1.
Basic Service
Subscribers: N.A.
Programming (received off-air): WHP-TV (C), WHTM-TV (A), WITF-TV (P) Harrisburg; WGAL (N), WLYH-TV (U) Lancaster; WPHL-TV (W), WTXF-TV (F) Philadelphia; WGCB-TV (I) Red Lion; WBRE-TV (N), WNEP-TV (A), WVIA-TV (P) Scranton & Wilkes-Barre; WPMT (F) York.
Programming (via satellite): WGN-TV (W) Chicago; Discovery Channel; ESPN; Nashville Network; USA Network.
Fee: N.A.
Miles of plant: 25.0 (coaxial).
Ownership: R. J. Shelley CATV (MSO).

MUNCY—Susquehanna Communications Co., 330 Basin St., Williamsport, PA 17701. Phone: 717-326-3384. Fax: 717-584-5092. County: Lycoming. Also serves Hughesville, Muncy Creek Twp., Muncy Twp., Penn Twp. (Lycoming County), Picture Rocks, Shrewsbury Twp. (Lycoming County), Wolf Twp. ICA: PA0119.
TV Market Ranking: Below 100. Franchise award date: January 1, 1950. Franchise expiration date: N.A. Began: January 1, 1954.
Channel capacity: 44 (not 2-way capable). Channels available but not in use: 2.
Basic Service
Subscribers: 4,323.
Programming (received off-air): WOLF-TV (F) Hazleton; WBRE-TV (N), WNEP-TV (A), WVIA-TV (P), WYOU (C) Scranton & Wilkes-Barre.
Programming (via microwave): WPIX (W) New York; WPHL-TV (W) Philadelphia.
Programming (via satellite): WGN-TV (W) Chicago; C-SPAN; MTV; Nashville Network; QVC; TBS Superstation; The Inspirational Network; VH1; ValueVision.
Fee: $34.75 installation; $11.90 monthly; $1.75 converter.
Expanded Basic Service
Subscribers: 4,170.
Programming (via satellite): A & E; American Movie Classics; CNN; Country Music TV; Discovery Channel; ESPN; ESPN 2; Fox Family Channel; Headline News; History Channel; Learning Channel; Lifetime; Nick at Nite; Nickelodeon; Sci-Fi Channel; The Weather Channel; Turner Network TV; USA Network.
Fee: $9.55 monthly.
Pay Service 1
Pay Units: 1,459.
Programming (via satellite): Cinemax; Disney Channel; HBO; Showtime; The Movie Channel.
Fee: $8.50 monthly (Disney), $8.95 monthly (Cinemax), $9.95 monthly (Showtime & TMC), $10.50 monthly (HBO).
Pay-Per-View
Addressable homes: 489.
Action Pay-Per-View.
Fee: $3.95-$4.95.
Equipment: Scientific-Atlanta headend; Scientific-Atlanta amplifiers; Comm/Scope cable; Compuvid character generator; Scientific-Atlanta & Tocom set top converters; Eagle & Vitek traps; Scientific-Atlanta satellite antenna; Scientific-Atlanta satellite receivers.
Miles of plant: 113.0 (coaxial). Homes passed: 4,692. Total homes in franchised area: 4,692.
Manager: Harland Bergstrom. Chief technician: Tom Newlen. Customer service manager: Dawn Lupachino.
City fee: 3% of basic gross.
Ownership: Susquehanna Cable Co. (MSO).

MURRYSVILLE—Adelphia Cablevision Association, One Adelphia Way, Blairsville, PA 15717. Phone: 412-459-5400. Fax: 412-459-0648. Counties: Allegheny & Westmoreland. Also serves Delmont, Export, Loyalhanna Twp. (Westmoreland County), Monroeville, Penn Twp. (Westmoreland County), Plum, Salem Twp. (Westmoreland County), Slickville, Upper Burrell Twp., Washington Twp. (Westmoreland County). ICA: PA0378.
TV Market Ranking: 10 (Delmont, Export, Loyalhanna Twp., Monroeville, Murrysville, Penn Twp., Plum, Salem Twp., Slickville, Upper Burrell Twp., Washington Twp.); 74 (Delmont, Export, Loyalhanna Twp., Murrysville, Penn Twp., Salem Twp., Slickville, Washington Twp.). Franchise award date: N.A. Franchise expiration date: N.A. Began: January 1, 1967.
Channel capacity: 56 (2-way capable; operating 2-way). Channels available but not in use: N.A.
Basic Service
Subscribers: 18,262.
Programming (received off-air): WPCB-TV (I) Greensburg; WNPA (U) Jeanette; WJAC-TV (N), WTAJ-TV (C), WWCP-TV (F) Johnstown-Altoona; KDKA-TV (C), WPGH-TV (F), WPXI (N), WQED (P), WQEX (P), WTAE-TV (A) Pittsburgh.
Programming (via satellite): TBS Superstation.
Fee: N.A.
Expanded Basic Service
Subscribers: 17,378.
Programming (via microwave): Meadows Racing Network.

Programming (via satellite): A & E; American Movie Classics; Animal Planet; C-SPAN; C-SPAN 2; CNBC; CNN; Cartoon Network; Comedy Central; Discovery Channel; Disney Channel; ESPN; ESPN 2; EWTN; FX; Fox Family Channel; Fox Sports Net Pittsburgh; Headline News; History Channel; Home Shopping Network; Learning Channel; Lifetime; MSNBC; MTV; Nashville Network; Nickelodeon; Product Information Network; QVC; Sci-Fi Channel; TV Guide Channel; The Weather Channel; Turner Network TV; USA Network; VH1.
Fee: N.A.

Pay Service 1
Pay Units: 1,005.
Programming (via satellite): Cinemax.
Fee: $11.50 monthly.

Pay Service 2
Pay Units: 4,582.
Programming (via satellite): HBO.
Fee: $11.50 monthly.

Pay Service 3
Pay Units: 723.
Programming (via satellite): Showtime.
Fee: $11.50 monthly.

Pay Service 4
Pay Units: 423.
Programming (via satellite): The Movie Channel.
Fee: $11.50 monthly.

Pay-Per-View
Addressable homes: 2,755.
Viewer's Choice 1 & 2.
Fee: $3.95.

Local advertising: Yes. Available in taped programming. Regional interconnect: TCI Media Services-Pittsburgh, PA.
Equipment: Scientific-Atlanta headend; Scientific-Atlanta & Texscan amplifiers; Comm/Scope cable; Scientific-Atlanta set top converters; Scientific-Atlanta addressable set top converters; Eagle traps; Scientific-Atlanta satellite antenna; Scientific-Atlanta satellite receivers.
Miles of plant: 285.7 (coaxial).
Manager: J. Francis Bradley Jr. Chief technician: Dave Bowen.
City fee: 5% of gross.
Ownership: Adelphia Communications Corp. (MSO).

NANTY GLO—Adelphia, One Adelphia Dr., Blairsville, PA 15717. Phone: 800-892-7300. Fax: 412-459-0648. Counties: Cambria & Indiana. Also serves Blacklick Twp., Jackson Twp. (Cambria County), Pine Twp. (Indiana County), Twin Rocks, Vintondale. ICA: PA0145.
TV Market Ranking: 74. Franchise award date: N.A. Franchise expiration date: N.A. Began: April 1, 1965.
Channel capacity: 41 (not 2-way capable). Channels available but not in use: 10.

Basic Service
Subscribers: 2,155.
Programming (received off-air): WPSX-TV (P) Clearfield; WPCB-TV (I) Greensburg; WATM-TV (A), WJAC-TV (N), WTAJ-TV (C), WWCP-TV (F) Johnstown-Altoona; WQED (P), WTAE-TV (A) Pittsburgh.
Programming (via satellite): QVC; TBS Superstation.
Fee: N.A.

Expanded Basic Service
Subscribers: 2,081.
Programming (via satellite): A & E; American Movie Classics; Animal Planet; C-SPAN; CNN; Discovery Channel; Disney Channel; ESPN; ESPN 2; EWTN; Fox Family Channel; Fox Sports Net Pittsburgh; Headline News; History Channel; Learning Channel; Lifetime; MTV; Nashville Network; Nickelodeon; Pennsylvania Cable Network; Product Information Network; Sci-Fi Channel; TV Guide Channel; The Weather Channel; Turner Network TV; USA Network; VH1.
Fee: N.A.

Pay Service 1
Pay Units: 420.
Programming (via satellite): HBO.
Fee: $11.50 monthly.

Pay Service 2
Pay Units: 63.
Programming (via satellite): Showtime.
Fee: $11.50 monthly.

Local advertising: Yes. Available in taped & automated programming.
Equipment: Tocom, Jerrold & Scientific-Atlanta headend; Magnavox amplifiers; Perimeter 3 & Trilogy cable; Oak, Hamlin & Scientific-Atlanta set top converters; Eagle traps; Scientific-Atlanta satellite antenna.
Miles of plant: 50.0 (coaxial). Homes passed: 2,858.
Manager: J. Francis Bradley Jr. Chief technician: Dave Bowen.
City fee: 5% of net basic.
Ownership: Adelphia Communications Corp. (MSO).

NEELYTON—Valley Cable Systems, Box 78, Doylesburg, PA 17219. Phone: 717-349-7717. County: Huntingdon. Also serves Dublin Twp. (Huntingdon County). ICA: PA0298.
TV Market Ranking: Outside TV Markets. Franchise award date: N.A. Franchise expiration date: N.A. Began: January 1, 1980.
Channel capacity: 30 (not 2-way capable). Channels available but not in use: 15.

Basic Service
Subscribers: 37.
Programming (received off-air): WJZ-TV (C) Baltimore; WPSX-TV (P) Clearfield; WHP-TV (C), WHTM-TV (A) Harrisburg; WJAC-TV (N), WTAJ-TV (C) Johnstown-Altoona; WGAL (N) Lancaster; WTTG (F) Washington.
Programming (via satellite): Country Music TV; Discovery Channel; ESPN; Fox Family Channel; Nashville Network; QVC; TBS Superstation; Trinity Bcstg. Network.
Fee: $40.00 installation; $17.95 monthly.

Local advertising: No.
Equipment: Blonder-Tongue headend; Times Fiber cable.
Miles of plant: 8.8 (coaxial). Homes passed: 83. Total homes in franchised area: 319.
Manager: Barry L. Kepner.
Ownership: Valley Cable Systems (MSO).

NEW BALTIMORE—Laurel Cable LP, Box 125, Berlin, PA 15530. Phones: 814-443-6250; 800-732-5604. County: Somerset. Also serves Allegheny Twp. (Somerset County). ICA: PA0292.
TV Market Ranking: 74. Franchise award date: N.A. Franchise expiration date: N.A. Began: July 1, 1979.
Channel capacity: N.A. Channels available but not in use: N.A.

Basic Service
Subscribers: 130.
Programming (received off-air): WPSX-TV (P) Clearfield; WHAG-TV (N), WWPB (P) Hagerstown; WNPA (U) Jeanette; WATM-TV (A), WJAC-TV (N), WKBS-TV (I), WTAJ-TV (C), WWCP-TV (F) Johnstown-Altoona; KDKA-TV (C), WTAE-TV (A) Pittsburgh.
Programming (via satellite): A & E; C-SPAN; CNN; Country Music TV; Discovery Channel; ESPN; ESPN 2; Fox Family Channel; Fox Sports Net Pittsburgh; Headline News; Home & Garden Television; Learning Channel; Lifetime; Nashville Network; QVC; TBS Superstation; The Weather Channel; Turner Classic Movies; Turner Network TV; USA Network.
Fee: $24.50 monthly.

Pay Service 1
Pay Units: 25.
Programming (via satellite): Disney Channel.
Fee: $7.95 monthly.

Pay Service 2
Pay Units: 15.
Programming (via satellite): HBO.
Fee: $10.50 monthly.

Miles of plant: 3.7 (coaxial).
Manager: Angie Miller. Chief technician: Kevin Custer.
Ownership: Laurel Cable LP.

NEW BETHLEHEM—Adelphia, 219 N. Findley St., Punxsutawney, PA 15767. Phone: 800-892-7300. Fax: 814-938-7622. Counties: Armstrong & Clarion. Also serves Alcoa Village, Fairmount City, Hawthorn, Oak Ridge Village, Porter Twp. (Clarion County), Redbank Twp. (Clarion County), South Bethlehem. ICA: PA0167.
TV Market Ranking: Outside TV Markets. Franchise award date: N.A. Franchise expiration date: N.A. Began: January 27, 1965.
Channel capacity: 52 (not 2-way capable). Channels available but not in use: N.A.

Basic Service
Subscribers: 1,255.
Programming (received off-air): WPSX-TV (P) Clearfield; WPCB-TV (I) Greensburg; WJAC-TV (N) Johnstown-Altoona; KDKA-TV (C), WCWB (W), WPGH-TV (F), WPXI (N), WQED (P), WTAE-TV (A) Pittsburgh.
Programming (via satellite): WGN-TV (W) Chicago; CNN; TBS Superstation.
Fee: $20.00 installation; $8.75 monthly.

Expanded Basic Service
Subscribers: 1,220.
Programming (via satellite): A & E; C-SPAN; Comedy Central; Country Music TV; Discovery Channel; Disney Channel; ESPN; ESPN 2; FX; Fox Family Channel; Fox Sports Net Pittsburgh; Headline News; History Channel; Home Shopping Network; Learning Channel; Lifetime; MSNBC; MTV; Nashville Network; Nick at Nite's TV Land; Nickelodeon; Pennsylvania Cable Network; Product Information Network; QVC; TV Food Network; The Weather Channel; Turner Network TV; USA Network; VH1.
Fee: N.A.

Pay Service 1
Pay Units: 111.
Programming (via satellite): HBO.
Fee: $11.50 monthly.

Pay Service 2
Pay Units: 102.
Programming (via satellite): Cinemax.
Fee: $11.50 monthly.

Pay Service 3
Pay Units: 18.
Programming (via satellite): The New Encore.
Fee: $2.95 monthly.

Pay Service 4
Pay Units: 33.
Programming (via satellite): Showtime.
Fee: $11.50 monthly.

Pay Service 5
Pay Units: 24.
Programming (via satellite): The Movie Channel.
Fee: $11.50 monthly.

Equipment: Blonder-Tongue & Jerrold headend; Jerrold amplifiers; Times Fiber cable; Oak set top converters; AFC satellite antenna.
Miles of plant: 23.0 (coaxial). Homes passed: 1,755.
Manager: Scott Brush. Chief technician: James Glatt.
Ownership: Adelphia Communications Corp. (MSO).

NEW BLOOMFIELD—Bloomfield Cablevision, Box 111, Lewistown, PA 17044. Phone: 717-248-3733. County: Perry. ICA: PA0380.
TV Market Ranking: 57. Franchise award date: N.A. Franchise expiration date: N.A. Began: N.A.
Channel capacity: 27. Channels available but not in use: N.A.

Basic Service
Subscribers: N.A.
Programming (received off-air): WHP-TV (C), WHTM-TV (A), WITF-TV (P) Harrisburg; WTAJ-TV (C) Johnstown-Altoona; WGAL (N), WLYH-TV (U) Lancaster; WNEP-TV (A), WVIA-TV (P) Scranton & Wilkes-Barre; WPMT (F) York; allband FM.
Programming (via satellite): WGN-TV (W) Chicago; CNN; ESPN; The Inspirational Network.
Current originations: Government access; automated emergency alert.
Fee: $15.00 installation; $10.25 monthly.

Pay Service 1
Pay Units: N.A.
Programming (via satellite): The Movie Channel.
Fee: $9.95 monthly.

Equipment: Blonder-Tongue & Jerrold headend; Magnavox amplifiers; Times Fiber cable; IVC VTRs.
Miles of plant: 12.0 (coaxial). Total homes in franchised area: 785.
Manager: Anna H. Hain. Chief technician: Michael Hain.
Ownership: Nittany Media Inc. (MSO).

NEW CASTLE—Adelphia Communications Corp., Box 1445, 215 E. North St., New Castle, PA 16103-1445. Phone: 800-892-7300. County: Lawrence. Also serves Hickory Twp. (Lawrence County), Mahoningtown Twp., Neshannock, Neshannock Twp., Plain Grove Twp., Scott Twp. (Lawrence County), Shenango Twp. (Lawrence County), South New Castle, Taylor Twp. (Lawrence County), Union Twp. (Lawrence County), Washington Twp. (Lawrence County), Wayne Twp. (Lawrence County), Wilmington Twp. ICA: PA0041.
TV Market Ranking: 79. Franchise award date: N.A. Franchise expiration date: N.A. Began: November 1, 1966.
Channel capacity: 64 (2-way capable; operating 2-way). Channels available but not in use: 12.

Basic Service
Subscribers: 13,280.
Programming (received off-air): WUAB (U) Lorain-Cleveland; KDKA-TV (C), WCWB (W), WPGH-TV (F), WPXI (N), WQED (P), WTAE-TV (A) Pittsburgh; WFMJ-TV (N), WKBN-TV (C), WYTV (A,F) Youngstown.
Programming (via satellite): American Movie Classics; C-SPAN; CNBC; CNN; E! Entertainment TV; ESPN; EWTN; Fox Family Channel; Home Shopping Network; Learning Channel; Nashville Network; QVC; TBS Superstation; TV Guide Channel; The Weather Channel.
Current originations: Automated time-weather; local news.
Fee: $50.00 installation; $21.95 monthly.

Expanded Basic Service
Subscribers: N.A.
Programming (via satellite): A & E; BET; C-SPAN 2; Discovery Channel; Fox Sports Net; Fox Sports Net Pittsburgh; Goodlife TV Net-

work; Headline News; Ladbroke Racing Channel/Meadows Racing Network; Lifetime; MTV; Nickelodeon; Philadelphia Park Live; Turner Network TV; USA Network; VH1.
Fee: $20.00 installation; $7.95 monthly.

Pay Service 1
Pay Units: 7,500.
Programming (via satellite): Cinemax; Disney Channel; HBO; Showtime; The Movie Channel.
Fee: $20.00 installation; $7.95 monthly (Disney), $11.00 monthly (Cinemax, HBO, Showtime or TMC).

Pay-Per-View
Addressable homes: 9,200.
Special events.

Local advertising: Yes. Available in taped programming. Rates: $4.00-$15.00/Spot. Regional interconnect: TCI Media Services-Pittsburgh, PA.
Equipment: Scientific-Atlanta headend; C-COR amplifiers; Comm/Scope cable; Scientific-Atlanta set top converters; Scientific-Atlanta addressable set top converters; Scientific-Atlanta satellite antenna; Scientific-Atlanta satellite receivers.
Miles of plant: 464.2 (coaxial); 82.0 (fiber optic). Additional miles planned: 15.0 (coaxial). Homes passed: 29,366. Total homes in franchised area: 29,366.
Manager: Lou Abraham. Chief technician: John Ayers.
City fee: 2% of gross.
Ownership: Adelphia Communications Corp. (MSO).

NEW FREEPORT—DuCom Cable TV, 50 Tipp St., Du Bois, PA 15801. Phone: 814-371-1925. Fax: 814-371-3052.
E-mail: ducom@key-net.net.
County: Greene. Also serves Freeport Twp., Gilmore Twp. (Greene County). ICA: PA0432.
TV Market Ranking: 90 (Freeport Twp., New Freeport); Below 100 (Gilmore Twp.). Franchise award date: August 1, 1994. Franchise expiration date: August 1, 2014. Began: July 30, 1994.
Channel capacity: 41 (not 2-way capable). Channels available but not in use: 15.

Basic Service
Subscribers: 68.
Programming (received off-air): WKBS-TV (I) Johnstown-Altoona; KDKA-TV (C), WCWB (W), WPGH-TV (F), WPXI (N), WQED (P), WTAE-TV (A) Pittsburgh; WTOV-TV (N) Steubenville-Wheeling; WTRF-TV (C) Wheeling-Steubenville.
Programming (via satellite): CNN; Country Music TV; Discovery Channel; Disney Channel; ESPN; ESPN 2; Fox Sports Net Pittsburgh; Nashville Network; Nickelodeon; QVC; TBS Superstation; Trinity Bcstg. Network; Turner Network TV; USA Network; VH1.
Fee: $45.00 installation; $23.00 monthly.

Pay Service 1
Pay Units: 10.
Programming (via satellite): HBO.
Fee: $10.95 monthly.

Miles of plant: 31.0 (coaxial). Homes passed: 80. Total homes in franchised area: 400.
Manager: Rodney Preston. Chief engineer: David Kucenski.
Ownership: Dubois Communications Inc. (MSO).

NEW MILFORD TWP.—Adams Cable, 9 N. Main St., Carbondale, PA 18407-2303. Phone: 717-282-6121. Fax: 717-282-3787. County: Susquehanna. Also serves Great Bend, Great Bend Borough, Great Bend Twp., Hallstead, New Milford Borough. ICA: PA0381.
TV Market Ranking: 49 (New Milford Borough, New Milford Twp.); Below 100 (Great Bend, Great Bend Borough, Great Bend Twp., Hallstead). Franchise award date: N.A. Franchise expiration date: N.A. Began: May 1, 1962.
Channel capacity: 60 (2-way capable). Channels available but not in use: 28.

Basic Service
Subscribers: 1,882.
Programming (received off-air): WBNG-TV (C), WICZ-TV (F), WSKG (P) Binghamton; WBRE-TV (N), WNEP-TV (A), WSWB (W), WVIA-TV (P), WYOU (C) Scranton & Wilkes-Barre.
Programming (via satellite): TBS Superstation; TV Guide Channel.
Current originations: Public access; educational access; government access.
Fee: $10.15 monthly.

Expanded Basic Service
Subscribers: 1,619.
Programming (via satellite): A & E; American Movie Classics; C-SPAN; CNBC; CNN; Discovery Channel; ESPN; ESPN 2; Fox Family Channel; Fox Sports Net; Home Shopping Network; Learning Channel; Nashville Network; Nick at Nite; Nickelodeon; TV Food Network; The Weather Channel; Turner Network TV; USA Network.
Fee: $12.50 monthly.

Pay Service 1
Pay Units: N.A.
Programming (via satellite): Cinemax.
Fee: N.A.

Pay Service 2
Pay Units: 29.
Programming (via satellite): Disney Channel.
Fee: $12.50 installation; $10.00 monthly.

Pay Service 3
Pay Units: 175.
Programming (via satellite): HBO.
Fee: $12.50 installation; $10.00 monthly.

Pay Service 4
Pay Units: 24.
Programming (via satellite): Showtime.
Fee: $12.50 installation; $10.00 monthly.

Local advertising: Yes.
Program Guide: The Cable Guide.
Equipment: Blonder-Tongue, Jerrold & Scientific-Atlanta headend; C-COR amplifiers; Trilogy cable; Tandy character generator; Scientific-Atlanta & Pioneer set top converters; Gamco & Eagle traps; Scientific-Atlanta satellite antenna; Scientific-Atlanta & Microdyne satellite receivers.
Miles of plant: 55.8 (coaxial); None (fiber optic). Homes passed: 2,508.
Manager: Terry Womack. Chief technician: Mark Graham. Marketing director: Will Keubler.
City fee: $1.00 annually.
Ownership: Adams CATV Inc. (MSO).

NEW WILMINGTON—New Wilmington Borough Cable TV, 134 High St., New Wilmington, PA 16142. Phone: 724-946-8167. Fax: 724-946-8841. County: Lawrence. ICA: PA0382.
TV Market Ranking: 79. Franchise award date: N.A. Franchise expiration date: N.A. Began: June 1, 1979.
Channel capacity: N.A. Channels available but not in use: N.A.

Basic Service
Subscribers: 900.
Programming (received off-air): WNEO (P) Alliance; WUAB (U) Lorain-Cleveland; KDKA-TV (C), WCWB (W), WPGH-TV (F), WPXI (N), WQED (P), WTAE-TV (A) Pittsburgh; WFMJ-TV (N), WKBN-TV (C), WYTV (A,F) Youngstown.
Programming (via satellite): WGN-TV (W) Chicago; A & E; C-SPAN; CNN; ESPN; Fox Sports Net Pittsburgh; Nashville Network; TBS Superstation; Turner Network TV; USA Network.
Fee: $25.00 installation; $12.00 monthly; $15.00 additional installation.

Pay Service 1
Pay Units: 198.
Programming (via satellite): Showtime.
Fee: $8.00 monthly.

Local advertising: No.
Equipment: Microdyne headend; GTE Sylvania amplifiers; Pioneer set top converters.
Miles of plant: 8.0 (coaxial).
Manager: Fred Garrett.
Ownership: New Wilmington Borough Cable TV.

NEWBERRY TWP.—Blue Ridge CATV, 2800 Lewisberry Rd., York Haven, PA 17370. Phone: 717-938-6501. Fax: 717-938-8734. County: York. Also serves Fairview Twp. (York County), Lewisberry, Warrington Twp. (York County), Wellsville, York Haven (York County). ICA: PA0105.
TV Market Ranking: 57. Franchise award date: N.A. Franchise expiration date: N.A. Began: May 1, 1982.
Channel capacity: 63 (not 2-way capable). Channels available but not in use: 6.

Basic Service
Subscribers: 5,300.
Programming (received off-air): WHP-TV (C), WHTM-TV (A), WITF-TV (P) Harrisburg; WGAL (N), WLYH-TV (U) Lancaster; WPHL-TV (W), WTXF-TV (F) Philadelphia; WGCB-TV (I) Red Lion; WPMT (F) York; allband FM.
Programming (via satellite): Cartoon Network; Disney Channel; TBS Superstation.
Fee: $45.00 installation; $6.99 monthly.

Expanded Basic Service
Subscribers: 5,100.
Programming (via satellite): A & E; C-SPAN; CNBC; CNN; Comedy Central; Country Music TV; Discovery Channel; ESPN; ESPN 2; Fox Family Channel; Home Shopping Network; Learning Channel; Lifetime; MTV; Nashville Network; Nickelodeon; QVC; Sci-Fi Channel; The Weather Channel; Travel Channel; Turner Network TV; USA Network; VH1.
Fee: $17.76 monthly.

Pay Service 1
Pay Units: 562.
Programming (via satellite): Cinemax.
Fee: $9.50 monthly.

Pay Service 2
Pay Units: 1,185.
Programming (via satellite): HBO.
Fee: $10.50 monthly.

Pay Service 3
Pay Units: 507.
Programming (via satellite): Showtime.
Fee: $9.50 monthly.

Pay-Per-View
Addressable homes: 350.
WWF Wrestlemania.
Fee: $19.95-$29.95.

Local advertising: Yes. Available in character-generated programming. Local sales manager: Michael Muniz.
Equipment: Scientific-Atlanta, M/A-Com & Gardiner headend; Texscan & C-COR amplifiers; Comm/Scope & Belden cable; Texscan character generator; Pioneer, RCA & Jerrold set top converters; Eagle traps; Scientific-Atlanta & Gardiner satellite antenna; M/A-Com & Scientific-Atlanta satellite receivers.
Miles of plant: 173.0 (coaxial); 11.0 (fiber optic). Additional miles planned: 6.0 (coaxial). Homes passed: 6,000. Total homes in franchised area: 8,000.
Manager: Michael Muniz.
Ownership: Pencor Services Inc. (MSO).

NEWBURG—Kuhn Communications, Box 277, Walnut Bottom, PA 17266-0277. Phone: 717-532-8857. Fax: 717-532-5563. County: Cumberland. Also serves Hopewell Twp. (Cumberland County). ICA: PA0272.
TV Market Ranking: Outside TV Markets. Franchise award date: N.A. Franchise expiration date: N.A. Began: January 1, 1981.
Channel capacity: 35. Channels available but not in use: 20.

Basic Service
Subscribers: N.A.
Programming (received off-air): WBAL-TV (N), WBFF (F), WJZ-TV (C) Baltimore; WHAG-TV (N) Hagerstown; WHP-TV (C), WHTM-TV (A), WITF-TV (P) Harrisburg; WGAL (N), WLYH-TV (U) Lancaster; WGCB-TV (I) Red Lion; WTTG (F) Washington; WPMT (F) York.
Programming (via satellite): ESPN; Nashville Network.
Fee: $20.00 installation; $6.75 monthly.

Pay Service 1
Pay Units: N.A.
Programming (via satellite): Showtime.
Fee: $9.60 monthly.

Equipment: Blonder-Tongue headend.
Miles of plant: 5.0 (coaxial). Homes passed: 190.
Manager: Earl Kuhn. Office manager: Tracy Reath.
Ownership: Kuhn Communications (MSO).

NEWTOWN—Suburban Cable, 2319 York Rd., Jamison, PA 18929. Phone: 800-222-1813. Web site: http://www.suburbancable.com. County: Bucks. Also serves Makefield Twp., Milford Square, New Hope (Bucks County), Newtown Twp. (Bucks County), Penns Park, Pineville, Pipersville, Upper Makefield Twp., Wrightstown, Wrightstown Twp. ICA: PA0083.
TV Market Ranking: 4. Franchise award date: N.A. Franchise expiration date: N.A. Began: October 26, 1983.
Channel capacity: 52. Channels available but not in use: 11.

Basic Service
Subscribers: 6,908.
Programming (received off-air): WFMZ-TV (I), WLVT-TV (P) Allentown; WGTW (I) Burlington; KYW-TV (C), WCAU (N), WPHL-TV (W), WPSG (U), WPVI-TV (A), WTXF-TV (F), WYBE (P) Philadelphia; WTVE (H) Reading; WNJT (P) Trenton; WHSP-TV (H) Vineland; WHYY-TV (P), WPPX (X) Wilmington.
Programming (via satellite): C-SPAN; C-SPAN 2; Home Shopping Network; Knowledge TV; QVC; TBS Superstation; The Box.
Current originations: Educational access; government access.
Planned originations: Public access.
Fee: $10.55 installation; $8.45 monthly.

Expanded Basic Service
Subscribers: N.A.
Programming (via microwave): Tri-State Media.
Programming (via satellite): A & E; American Movie Classics; Bravo; CNBC; CNN; Comedy Central; Discovery Channel; Disney Channel; E! Entertainment TV; ESPN; ESPN 2; Fox Family Channel; Headline News; History Channel; Learning Channel; Lifetime; MOVIEplex; MSNBC; MTV; Nashville Network; Nick at Nite; Nickelodeon; TV Food Network; The Sports Network; The

Weather Channel; Turner Network TV; USA Network; VH1.
Fee: N.A.
Pay Service 1
Pay Units: N.A.
Programming (via satellite): Cinemax; HBO; Showtime; Starz!; The Movie Channel.
Fee: $10.55 installation; $8.00 monthly (Cinemax), $9.45 monthly (HBO).
Pay-Per-View
Addressable homes: 6,908.
Equipment: Jerrold headend; GTE Sylvania amplifiers; Comm/Scope cable; Jerrold addressable set top converters.
Miles of plant: 166.6 (coaxial). Homes passed: 8,973.
Manager: Nancy Keys. Chief technician: Randy Thompson. Program director: George Ferrara. Marketing director: Rose McFlynn.
City fee: 5% of gross.
Ownership: Lenfest Communications Inc. (MSO).

NINEVAH—Multi-Tech Communications, Box 219, Sligo, PA 16255. Phone: 814-745-2426. Counties: Clarion & Venango. Also serves Ashland Twp., Beaver Twp. (Clarion County), Elk Twp. (Clarion County), Richland Twp. (Clarion County), Rockland, Salem Twp. (Clarion County). ICA: PA0198.
TV Market Ranking: Outside TV Markets. Franchise award date: N.A. Franchise expiration date: N.A. Began: January 1, 1988.
Channel capacity: 36 (not 2-way capable). Channels available but not in use: 3.
Basic Service
Subscribers: 625.
Programming (received off-air): WPSX-TV (P) Clearfield; WPCB-TV (I) Greensburg; WTAJ-TV (C), WWCP-TV (F) Johnstown-Altoona; KDKA-TV (C), WCWB (W), WPGH-TV (F), WPXI (N), WQED (P), WTAE-TV (A) Pittsburgh; WKBN-TV (C) Youngstown.
Programming (via satellite): A & E; CNN; Country Music TV; Discovery Channel; ESPN; Fox Sports Net Pittsburgh; Headline News; Lifetime; MTV; Nashville Network; Nickelodeon; QVC; TBS Superstation; The Weather Channel; VH1.
Fee: $35.00 installation; $23.00 monthly.
Pay Service 1
Pay Units: 125.
Programming (via satellite): Showtime.
Fee: $7.95 monthly.
Pay Service 2
Pay Units: 107.
Programming (via satellite): The Movie Channel.
Fee: $7.95 monthly.
Local advertising: Yes. Regional interconnect: Cabletime.
Miles of plant: 65.0 (coaxial). Homes passed: 1,100.
Manager: Richard McHenry. Chief technician: Donald McCall.
Ownership: Multi-Tech Communications (MSO).

NORRISTOWN—Suburban Cable, 202 Shoemaker Rd., Pottstown, PA 19464. Phone: 610-323-6400. Fax: 610-943-5487. Web site: http://www.suburbancable.com. County: Montgomery. Also serves Bridgeport, Conshohocken, East Norriton Twp., Lower Gwynedd Twp. (Montgomery County), Lower Providence Twp., West Conshohocken, West Norriton Twp., Whitemarsh Twp. (southern portion), Whitpain Twp., Worcester Twp. (Montgomery County). ICA: PA0028.
TV Market Ranking: 4. Franchise award date: N.A. Franchise expiration date: N.A. Began: October 6, 1975.
Channel capacity: N.A. Channels available but not in use: N.A.
Basic Service
Subscribers: 35,160.
Programming (received off-air): WFMZ-TV (I), WLVT-TV (P) Allentown; WGTW (I) Burlington; KYW-TV (C), WCAU (N), WPHL-TV (W), WPSG (U), WPVI-TV (A), WTXF-TV (F), WYBE (P) Philadelphia; WTVE (H) Reading; WNJT (P) Trenton; WHYY-TV (P), WPPX (X) Wilmington.
Programming (via satellite): BET; Bravo; C-SPAN; EWTN; Fox Family Channel; MOVIEplex; MSNBC; QVC; TBS Superstation; TV Food Network; The Box; Travel Channel; Univision.
Current originations: Automated time-weather; public access; educational access; government access.
Fee: $22.50 installation; $8.30 monthly.
Expanded Basic Service
Subscribers: 33,380.
Programming (via satellite): A & E; American Movie Classics; CNBC; CNN; Comedy Central; Discovery Channel; Disney Channel; E! Entertainment TV; ESPN; ESPN 2; Headline News; History Channel; Learning Channel; Lifetime; MTV; Nashville Network; Nickelodeon; Sci-Fi Channel; The Sports Network; The Weather Channel; Turner Network TV; USA Network; VH1.
Fee: $11.94 monthly.
Pay Service 1
Pay Units: 6,250.
Programming (via satellite): HBO.
Fee: $12.00 monthly.
Pay Service 2
Pay Units: 3,252.
Programming (via satellite): Showtime.
Fee: $14.95 monthly.
Pay Service 3
Pay Units: N.A.
Programming (via satellite): Cinemax; Starz!
Fee: N.A.
Pay-Per-View
Playboy TV; Spice; Viewer's Choice.
Local advertising: Yes. Available in satellite distributed, locally originated & taped programming. Regional interconnect: Philadelphia Cable Advertising.
Program Guide: The Cable Guide.
Equipment: Jerrold headend; Jerrold amplifiers; Times Fiber cable; Sony cameras; Panasonic VTRs; Hamlin set top converters; Vitek traps; Microdyne, Prodelin & Scientific-Atlanta satellite antenna; Microdyne & Scientific-Atlanta satellite receivers.
Miles of plant: 450.0 (coaxial). Additional miles planned: 50.0 (coaxial). Homes passed: 38,000. Total homes in franchised area: 41,000.
Manager: Tom C. Stowell. Chief technician: Steve S. Contorno.
City fee: 3% of gross.
Ownership: Lenfest Communications Inc. (MSO).

NORTH CLARION—CableVision Communications, Box 2200, 68 5th St., Buckhannon, WV 26201. Phone: 304-472-4193. Fax: 304-472-0756. Counties: Clarion, Forest & Venango. Also serves Crown, Farmington Twp. (Clarion County), Fryburg, Huefner, Hunter Station, Knox Twp. (Clarion County), Lake Lucy, Leeper, Licking Twp. (Clarion County), Lickingville, Lucinda, Marble, Newmansville, North Pine Grove, Perry Twp. (Clarion County), President Twp., Snydersburg, Tionesta, Tionesta Twp., Tylersburg, Venus, Vowinckel, Washington Twp. (Clarion County). ICA: PA0142.
TV Market Ranking: Outside TV Markets. Franchise award date: N.A. Franchise expiration date: N.A. Began: May 1, 1957.
Channel capacity: 36 (not 2-way capable). Channels available but not in use: N.A.

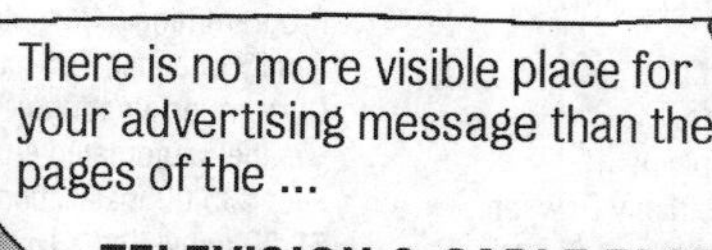

Basic Service
Subscribers: 1,820.
Programming (received off-air): WPSX-TV (P) Clearfield; WICU-TV (N), WJET-TV (A) Erie; WNPA (U) Jeanette; WTAJ-TV (C) Johnstown-Altoona; KDKA-TV (C), WCWB (W), WPGH-TV (F), WPXI (N), WTAE-TV (A) Pittsburgh; 18 FMs.
Programming (via satellite): Disney Channel; TBS Superstation.
Current originations: Public access.
Fee: $10.56 monthly; $1.24 converter.
Expanded Basic Service
Subscribers: 1,349.
Programming (via satellite): A & E; American Movie Classics; CNBC; CNN; Discovery Channel; E! Entertainment TV; ESPN; Fox Family Channel; Fox Sports Net Pittsburgh; Great American Country; Home Shopping Network; Lifetime; MTV; Nashville Network; Nickelodeon; Sci-Fi Channel; Trinity Bcstg. Network; Turner Network TV; USA Network; VH1.
Fee: $17.50 installation; $17.30 monthly.
Pay Service 1
Pay Units: 845.
Programming (via satellite): Cinemax; HBO; Showtime.
Fee: $10.00 installation; $7.95 monthly (Cinemax), $11.95 monthly (Showtime), $11.99 monthly (HBO).
Pay Service 2
Pay Units: N.A.
Programming (via satellite): The Movie Channel; The New Encore.
Fee: $3.99 monthly (Encore), $11.95 monthly (TMC).
Local advertising: Planned. Available in character-generated programming. Regional interconnect: Cabletime.
Equipment: Blonder-Tongue headend; Scientific-Atlanta, C-COR & Jerrold amplifiers; Magnavox cable; Intercept & Pico traps; M/A-Com & Scientific-Atlanta satellite antenna; M/A-Com satellite receivers.
Miles of plant: 98.0 (coaxial). Homes passed: 2,755. Total homes in franchised area: 3,500.
Manager: Willie Critchfield. Marketing director: Kenny Phillips.
City fee: None.
Ownership: Rifkin & Associates Inc. (MSO). See Cable System Ownership.

NORTHAMPTON—RCN, 105 Carnegie Center, Princeton, NJ 08540. Phone: 609-734-3700. Fax: 609-734-3713. Counties: Lehigh & Northampton. Also serves Allen Twp., Allentown, Bangor (Northampton County), Bath, Bethlehem (Northampton County), Bethlehem Twp. (Northampton County), Bushkill Twp. (Northampton County), Catasauqua, Chapman, Coplay (Lehigh County), East Allen Twp. (Northampton County), Easton, Forks Twp., Fountain Hill (Lehigh County), Freemansburg, Glendon (Northampton County), Hanover Twp. (Lehigh County), Hanover Twp. (Northampton County), Heidelberg Twp. (Lehigh County), Hellertown (Northampton County), Lehigh Twp. (Northampton County), Lower Macungie Twp. (Lehigh County), Lower Nazareth Twp. (Northampton County), Lower Saucon Twp. (Northampton County), Lowhill Twp. (Lehigh County), Moore Twp. (Northampton County), Nazareth (Northampton County), North Catasauqua (Lehigh County), North Whitehall Twp. (Lehigh County), Palmer Twp. (Northampton County), Pen Argyl, Plainfield Twp. (Northampton County), Portland, Roseto, Salisbury Twp. (Lehigh County), South Whitehall Twp. (Lehigh County), Stockertown, Tatamy, Upper Macungie Twp. (Lehigh County), Upper Mount Bethel, Upper Nazareth Twp. (Northampton County), Upper Saucon Twp. (Lehigh County), Washington Twp. (Northampton County), Weisenberg Twp. (Lehigh County), West Easton, Whitehall Twp. (Lehigh County), Williams Twp. (Northampton County), Wilson (Northampton County), Wind Gap (rural areas). ICA: PA0008.
TV Market Ranking: Below 100. Franchise award date: N.A. Franchise expiration date: N.A. Began: December 1, 1963.
Channel capacity: 78 (not 2-way capable). Channels available but not in use: 1.
Basic Service
Subscribers: 83,274.
Programming (received off-air): WFMZ-TV (I), WLVT-TV (P) Allentown; WBPH-TV (I) Bethlehem; WGTW (I) Burlington; WABC-TV (A), WCBS-TV (C), WNBC (N), WNYW (F), WPIX (W), WWOR-TV (U) New York; KYW-TV (C), WCAU (N), WPHL-TV (W), WPSG (U), WPVI-TV (A), WTXF-TV (F) Philadelphia; WTVE (H) Reading; WBRE-TV (N), WNEP-TV (A) Scranton & Wilkes-Barre; all-band FM.
Programming (via satellite): NASA TV.
Current originations: Public access; educational access; government access; religious access; leased access.
Fee: $25.00 installation; $25.00 monthly; $2.00 converter.
Expanded Basic Service
Subscribers: 79,522.
Programming (via satellite): A & E; American Movie Classics; BET; C-SPAN; C-SPAN 2; CNBC; CNN; Cartoon Network; Comedy Central; Country Music TV; Discovery Channel; Disney Channel; E! Entertainment TV; ESPN; ESPN 2; ESPN Classic Sports; EWTN; FX; Fox Family Channel; Fox News Channel; Fox Sports Net; Game Show Network; Golf Channel; Headline News; History Channel; Home & Garden Television; International Channel; Learning Channel; Lifetime; MSNBC; MTV; Nashville Network; Nick at Nite's TV Land; Nickelodeon; QVC; RAI-USA; Romance Classics; Sci-Fi Channel; Speedvision; TBS Superstation; TV Food Network; The Health Network; The Inspirational Network; The Weather Channel; Turner Network TV; USA Network; Univision; VH1; ValueVision.
Fee: N.A.
Pay Service 1
Pay Units: 17,340.
Programming (via satellite): Cinemax (multiplexed); HBO (multiplexed); Showtime; The Movie Channel; The New Encore.
Fee: $25.00 installation; $2.95 monthly (Encore), $12.95 monthly (Showtime & TMC), $14.95 monthly (Cinemax & HBO).
Pay Service 2
Pay Units: N.A.
Programming (via satellite): Starz!
Fee: N.A.

Pay-Per-View
Addressable homes: 14,039.
Playboy TV; Spice; movies.
Fee: $5.95 (Playboy or Spice).
Pay-per-view manager: Bethany Dawson.
Local advertising: Yes (locally produced). Available in satellite distributed & locally originated programming. Rates: $30.00/30 Seconds.
Program Guide: TV Host.
Equipment: Scientific-Atlanta headend; Magnavox amplifiers; Times Fiber cable; Siecor fiber optic cable; Sony cameras; Sony VTRs; Dubner & Chyron character generator; General Instrument set top converters; General Instrument addressable set top converters; Eagle & Microwave Filter traps; AFC & Scientific-Atlanta satellite antenna; General Instrument satellite receivers; ChannelMatic commercial insert.
Miles of plant: 2500.0 (coaxial); 128.7 (fiber optic). Additional miles planned: 300.0 (coaxial). Homes passed: 125,000. Total homes in franchised area: 150,000.
Manager: Ed Kuczma. Marketing director: Michael Steinkirchner. Customer service director: Jeanne Daniels.
City fee: 5% of gross.
Ownership: RCN Corp. (MSO).

NOXEN—Blue Ridge Cable TV Inc., Box 141, Tunkhannock, PA 18657. Phone: 570-836-5422. Fax: 570-836-1659. Counties: Luzerne & Wyoming. Also serves Dallas, Dallas Twp. (Luzerne County), Kunkle, Monroe Twp. (Wyoming County), Wyoming County. ICA: PA0384.
TV Market Ranking: 49. Franchise award date: N.A. Franchise expiration date: N.A. Began: February 1, 1976.
Channel capacity: 36. Channels available but not in use: 9.
Basic Service
Subscribers: N.A.
Programming (received off-air): WBNG-TV (C), WICZ-TV (F), WSKG (P) Binghamton; WBRE-TV (N), WNEP-TV (A), WVIA-TV (P), WYOU (C) Scranton & Wilkes-Barre.
Programming (via satellite): WGN-TV (W) Chicago; TBS Superstation.
Fee: $30.00 installation; $16.90 monthly.
Pay Service 1
Pay Units: N.A.
Programming (via satellite): Cinemax; Disney Channel; HBO.
Fee: $8.95 monthly (Disney), $9.50 monthly (Cinemax), $10.50 monthly (HBO).
Equipment: Scientific-Atlanta headend; C-COR amplifiers; Comm/Scope cable.
Miles of plant: 29.8 (coaxial).
Manager: Ken Valentine.
Ownership: Pencor Services Inc. (MSO).

OIL CITY—TCI of Pennsylvania, 286 Elm St., Oil City, PA 16301. Phone: 814-677-3011. County: Venango. Also serves Complanter Twp. (Venango County), Cranberry Twp. (Venango County), Oakland Twp. (Venango County), Rouseville, Sugarcreek (Venango County). ICA: PA0086.
TV Market Ranking: Outside TV Markets. Franchise award date: October 1, 1951. Franchise expiration date: September 1, 1997. Began: October 1, 1951.
Channel capacity: 54 (not 2-way capable). Channels available but not in use: 20.
Basic Service
Subscribers: 7,366.
Programming (received off-air): WICU-TV (N), WJET-TV (A), WQLN (P), WSEE (C) Erie; KDKA-TV (C), WPGH-TV (F), WPXI (N), WTAE-TV (A) Pittsburgh; allband FM.
Programming (via satellite): ESPN; Fox Family Channel; TBS Superstation.
Current originations: Automated time-weather; automated emergency alert.
Fee: $35.00 installation; $15.00 monthly; $3.00 converter; $15.00 additional installation.
Expanded Basic Service
Subscribers: 840.
Programming (received off-air): WCWB (W), WQED (P) Pittsburgh.
Programming (via satellite): WGN-TV (W) Chicago; A & E; American Movie Classics; C-SPAN; C-SPAN 2; CNN; Discovery Channel; Lifetime; MTV; Nashville Network; Nickelodeon; QVC; Turner Network TV; USA Network; VH1.
Fee: $20.00 installation; $3.00 monthly.
Pay Service 1
Pay Units: 534.
Programming (via satellite): Cinemax.
Fee: $20.00 installation; $10.20 monthly.
Pay Service 2
Pay Units: 224.
Programming (via satellite): Disney Channel.
Fee: $20.00 installation; $8.50 monthly.
Pay Service 3
Pay Units: 507.
Programming (via satellite): HBO.
Fee: $20.00 installation; $11.80 monthly.
Pay Service 4
Pay Units: 262.
Programming (via satellite): Showtime.
Fee: $20.00 installation; $11.40 monthly.
Local advertising: Yes (insert only). Available in satellite distributed programming. Local sales manager: Terry Myers. Regional interconnect: Metrobase Cable Advertising.
Program Guide: TV Host.
Equipment: Scientific-Atlanta headend; Scientific-Atlanta amplifiers; Comm/Scope cable; Ampex & Sony VTRs; Video Data Systems character generator; Oak & Hamlin set top converters; Microdyne, Scientific-Atlanta & Prodelin satellite antenna; Scientific-Atlanta, Microdyne & Standard Communications satellite receivers; Sony commercial insert.
Miles of plant: 111.0 (coaxial). Homes passed: 8,624. Total homes in franchised area: 9,225.
Manager: Day Beren. Chief technician: Edward Land.
City fee: 5% of gross.
Ownership: AT&T Broadband & Internet Services (MSO). Purchased from Tele-Communications Inc., March 9, 1999.

OLD PORT—Nittany Media Inc., Box 111, Lewistown, PA 17044. Phone: 717-248-3733. County: Juniata. Also serves Turbett Twp. ICA: PA0287.
TV Market Ranking: 57 (Old Port); Outside TV Markets (Turbett Twp.). Franchise award date: January 1, 1974. Franchise expiration date: January 1, 2004. Began: January 1, 1974.
Channel capacity: 30 (not 2-way capable). Channels available but not in use: 15.
Basic Service
Subscribers: 95.
Programming (received off-air): WHP-TV (C), WHTM-TV (A) Harrisburg; WTAJ-TV (C) Johnstown-Altoona; WGAL (N), WLYH-TV (U) Lancaster; WPMT (F) York.
Programming (via satellite): Country Music TV; Discovery Channel; ESPN; Fox Family Channel; Nashville Network; TBS Superstation; USA Network.
Fee: $40.00 installation; $13.60 monthly.
Local advertising: Planned (locally produced & insert).
Equipment: Blonder-Tongue headend; AEL amplifiers; Times Fiber cable.
Miles of plant: 9.0 (coaxial). Homes passed: 125. Total homes in franchised area: 320.
Manager: Barry L. Kepner.
Ownership: Nittany Media Inc. (MSO).

ORRSTOWN—Kuhn Communications Cable TV Service, Box 277, Walnut Bottom, PA 17266-0277. Phone: 717-532-8857. Fax: 717-532-5563. County: Franklin. Also serves Letterkenny Twp. (Franklin County), Southampton Twp. (Franklin County). ICA: PA0218.
TV Market Ranking: Below 100. Franchise award date: N.A. Franchise expiration date: N.A. Began: January 1, 1981.
Channel capacity: 30. Channels available but not in use: N.A.
Basic Service
Subscribers: N.A.
Programming (received off-air): WBAL-TV (N), WBFF (F), WJZ-TV (C) Baltimore; WHAG-TV (N) Hagerstown; WHP-TV (C), WHTM-TV (A), WITF-TV (P) Harrisburg; WGAL (N) Lancaster; WGCB-TV (I) Red Lion; WDCA (U) Washington; WPMT (F) York.
Programming (via satellite): ESPN.
Fee: $6.75 monthly.
Pay Service 1
Pay Units: N.A.
Programming (via satellite): Nashville Network; The Movie Channel.
Fee: $9.60 monthly.
Miles of plant: 18.0 (coaxial). Homes passed: 750.
Manager: Earl W. Kuhn. Office manager: Tracy Reath.
Ownership: Kuhn Communications (MSO).

ORVISTON—Orviston TV, Box 85, Loganton, PA 17747. Phone: 717-725-2733. County: Centre. ICA: PA0385.
TV Market Ranking: Outside TV Markets. Franchise award date: N.A. Franchise expiration date: N.A. Began: January 1, 1967.
Channel capacity: 12. Channels available but not in use: 6.
Basic Service
Subscribers: N.A.
Programming (received off-air): WPSX-TV (P) Clearfield; WJAC-TV (N), WTAJ-TV (C) Johnstown-Altoona; WBRE-TV (N), WNEP-TV (A), WVIA-TV (P) Scranton & Wilkes-Barre.
Fee: N.A.
Equipment: Holt headend.
Chief technician: Guy Bierly.
Ownership: Orviston TV.

OSWAYO—Kellogg Communications, Box 774, RD 1, Shinglehouse, PA 16748. Phone: 814-697-7163. County: Potter. ICA: PA0386.
TV Market Ranking: Outside TV Markets. Franchise award date: N.A. Franchise expiration date: N.A. Began: N.A.
Channel capacity: N.A. Channels available but not in use: N.A.
Basic Service
Subscribers: N.A.
Programming (received off-air): WGRZ-TV (N), WIVB-TV (C), WKBW-TV (A) Buffalo; WPSX-TV (P) Clearfield.
Programming (via satellite): TBS Superstation.
Fee: N.A.
Manager: Gerald Kellogg. Customer service manager: Laurie Kellogg.
Ownership: Kellogg Communications.

OXFORD—Armstrong Cable, 122 S. Queen St., Rising Sun, MD 21911. Phone: 800-524-5505. Fax: 410-658-4777. Counties: Chester, PA; Cecil, MD. Also serves Cecil County (portions), Rising Sun, MD; East Nottingham Twp., Elk Twp. (Chester County), Highland Twp. (Chester County), Londonderry Twp. (Chester County), Lower Oxford Twp., Upper Oxford Twp., West Fallowfield Twp., West Nottingham Twp., PA. ICA: PA0098.
TV Market Ranking: 57. Franchise award date: N.A. Franchise expiration date: N.A. Began: June 1, 1982.
Channel capacity: 61 (not 2-way capable). Channels available but not in use: 17.
Basic Service
Subscribers: 7,091.
Programming (received off-air): WBAL-TV (N), WBFF (F), WJZ-TV (C), WMAR-TV (A), WMPB (P), WNUV (W) Baltimore; WGTW (I) Burlington; WHP-TV (C) Harrisburg; WGAL (N), WLYH-TV (U) Lancaster; KYW-TV (C), WCAU (N), WPVI-TV (A), WTXF-TV (F) Philadelphia; WHYY-TV (P) Wilmington.
Programming (via satellite): WGN-TV (W) Chicago; A & E; American Movie Classics; C-SPAN; CNN; Cartoon Network; Comedy Central; Discovery Channel; ESPN; ESPN 2; Fox Family Channel; Headline News; Home Shopping Network; Home Team Sports; Lifetime; MTV; Nashville Network; Nickelodeon; TBS Superstation; The Weather Channel; Turner Network TV; USA Network; VH1.
Current originations: Educational access; government access.
Fee: $35.00 installation (aerial), $49.95 (underground); $22.31 monthly; $2.00 converter; $20.00 additional installation.
Pay Service 1
Pay Units: 2,060.
Programming (via satellite): Cinemax.
Fee: $7.50 installation; $7.00 monthly.
Pay Service 2
Pay Units: 898.
Programming (via satellite): Disney Channel.
Fee: $7.50 installation; $7.95 monthly.
Pay Service 3
Pay Units: 3,385.
Programming (via satellite): HBO.
Fee: $7.50 installation; $8.00 monthly.
Pay Service 4
Pay Units: N.A.
Programming (via satellite): Showtime.
Fee: N.A.
Local advertising: Yes. Available in character-generated programming. Regional interconnect: Metrobase Cable Advertising.
Equipment: Scientific-Atlanta headend; Scientific-Atlanta amplifiers; Trilogy cable; MSI & Texscan character generator; Scientific-Atlanta set top converters; Eagle traps; Scientific-Atlanta satellite antenna; Scientific-Atlanta satellite receivers.
Miles of plant: 380.0 (coaxial); 54.0 (fiber optic). Additional miles planned: 30.0 (coaxial). Homes passed: 8,594. Total homes in franchised area: 14,000.
Manager: Gary D. Davis Jr. Marketing & program director: Jud D. Stewart.
Ownership: Armstrong Group of Companies (MSO).

PAINT TWP. (Clarion County)—Helicon Cable Communications, 320 Bailey Ave., Uniontown, PA 15401. Phone: 724-437-9875. Fax: 724-437-6910. County: Clarion. Also serves Elk Twp. (Clarion County), Knox, Shippenville. ICA: PA0387.
TV Market Ranking: Outside TV Markets. Franchise award date: N.A. Franchise expiration date: N.A. Began: April 1, 1973.

Channel capacity: 61 (not 2-way capable). Channels available but not in use: 11.

Basic Service

Subscribers: 1,572.

Programming (received off-air): WPSX-TV (P) Clearfield; WPCB-TV (I) Greensburg; WJAC-TV (N) Johnstown-Altoona; KDKA-TV (C), WCWB (W), WPGH-TV (F), WPXI (N), WQED (P), WTAE-TV (A) Pittsburgh; WKBN-TV (C), WYTV (A,F) Youngstown.

Programming (via satellite): A & E; American Movie Classics; CNBC; CNN; Country Music TV; Court TV; Discovery Channel; ESPN; ESPN 2; Fox Family Channel; Fox Sports Net; Headline News; History Channel; Home Shopping Network; Home Shopping Network 2; Ladbroke Racing Channel/Meadows Racing Network; Learning Channel; Lifetime; MTV; Nashville Network; Nick at Nite; Nick at Nite's TV Land; Nickelodeon; QVC; Sci-Fi Channel; TV Food Network; The Weather Channel; Trinity Bcstg. Network; Turner Network TV; USA Network; VH1.

Current originations: Automated time-weather.

Fee: $35.00 installation; $27.82 monthly.

Expanded Basic Service

Subscribers: 1,572.

Programming (via satellite): Animal Planet; C-SPAN; Cartoon Network; TBS Superstation.

Fee: $4.50 monthly.

Pay Service 1

Pay Units: 54.

Programming (via satellite): Disney Channel.

Fee: $20.00 installation; $9.50 monthly.

Pay Service 2

Pay Units: 144.

Programming (via satellite): HBO.

Fee: $20.00 installation; $9.50 monthly.

Pay Service 3

Pay Units: 108.

Programming (via satellite): Showtime.

Fee: $20.00 installation; $9.50 monthly.

Pay-Per-View

Addressable homes: 275.

Local advertising: Yes. Available in character-generated programming. Rates: $25.00/Month.

Program Guide: CableView.

Equipment: Scientific-Atlanta headend; Texscan amplifiers; Comm/Scope cable; Atari character generator; Jerrold set top converters; Prodelin & Scientific-Atlanta satellite antenna; Scientific-Atlanta satellite receivers.

Miles of plant: 47.4 (coaxial). Additional miles planned: 10.0 (fiber optic). Homes passed: 1,737. Total homes in franchised area: 2,072.

Regional manager: Craig S. Tomchik. Plant manager: Fred Davies. Marketing director: Megan Wheeler.

City fee: 3% of gross.

Ownership: Helicon Corp. (MSO). See Cable System Ownership.

PALMERTON—Blue Ridge Communications, Box 316, 465 Delaware Ave., Palmerton, PA 18071-1908. Phone: 610-826-2551. Counties: Carbon, Lehigh, Northampton & Schuylkill. Also serves Bowmanstown, East Penn Twp., Eldred Twp. (Schuylkill County), Franklin Twp. (Carbon County), Heidelberg Twp. (Lehigh County), Jim Thorpe, Kidder Twp. (Carbon County), Lehigh Twp. (Northampton County), Lehighton, Lower Towamensing Twp., Lynn Twp. (Lehigh County), Mahoning Twp. (Carbon County), Parryville, Penn Forest Twp. (Carbon County), Reynolds, Slatington, Towamensing Twp., Walker Twp. (Schuylkill County), Walnutport, Washington Twp. (Carbon County), Weissport, West Penn Twp. (southeastern portion). ICA: PA0042.

TV Market Ranking: 49 (Bowmanstown, East Penn Twp., Franklin Twp., Jim Thorpe, Kidder Twp., Lehighton, Lower Towamensing Twp., Mahoning Twp., Palmerton, Parryville, Penn Forest Twp., Towamensing Twp., Washington Twp., Weissport); Below 100 (Eldred Twp., Heidelberg Twp., Lehigh Twp., Lynn Twp., Palmerton, Reynolds, Slatington, Walker Twp., Walnutport, West Penn Twp.). Franchise award date: N.A. Franchise expiration date: N.A. Began: September 14, 1951.

Channel capacity: 54. Channels available but not in use: 2.

Basic Service

Subscribers: 27,946.

Programming (received off-air): WFMZ-TV (I), WLVT-TV (P) Allentown; WNYW (F), WPIX (W), WWOR-TV (U) New York; KYW-TV (C), WCAU (N), WPHL-TV (W), WPVI-TV (A), WTXF-TV (F) Philadelphia; WBRE-TV (N), WNEP-TV (A), WSWB (W), WVIA-TV (P), WYOU (C) Scranton & Wilkes-Barre; allband FM.

Programming (via satellite): A & E; American Movie Classics; C-SPAN; CNBC; CNN; Cartoon Network; Comedy Central; Discovery Channel; ESPN; EWTN; Fox Family Channel; Headline News; Home Shopping Network; Lifetime; MTV; Madison Square Garden Network; Nashville Network; Nickelodeon; Odyssey; QVC; TBS Superstation; The Weather Channel; Turner Classic Movies; Turner Network TV; USA Network; VH1.

Current originations: Automated time-weather; public access; leased access; local news; local sports.

Fee: $30.00 installation; $16.90 monthly.

Pay Service 1

Pay Units: N.A.

Programming (via satellite): Cinemax; Disney Channel; HBO; Showtime.

Fee: $15.00 installation; $8.95 monthly (Disney), $9.50 monthly (Cinemax or Showtime), $10.50 monthly (HBO).

Pay-Per-View

Addressable homes: 8,467.

Viewer's Choice.

Local advertising: Yes. Regional interconnect: Metrobase Cable Advertising.

Equipment: Composite & Scientific-Atlanta headend; composite & C-COR amplifiers; composite & Comm/Scope cable; Zenith addressable set top converters; AFC satellite antenna; Scientific-Atlanta satellite receivers.

Miles of plant: 666.4 (coaxial). Additional miles planned: 20.0 (coaxial).

Manager: Richard A. Semmel. Chief technician: Randy Semmel. Program director: Paula Patterson. Marketing director: Jeff Reinhard.

Ownership: Pencor Services Inc. (MSO).

PHILADELPHIA (area 1)—Greater Media Cable, 1351 S. Columbus Blvd., Philadelphia, PA 19147. Phone: 215-468-2222. Fax: 215-463-2330. E-mail: gmcnotes@aol.com. County: Philadelphia. ICA: PA0003.

TV Market Ranking: 4. Franchise award date: October 8, 1985. Franchise expiration date: October 8, 2000. Began: February 1, 1972.

Channel capacity: 80 (2-way capable; operating 2-way). Channels available but not in use: None.

Basic Service

Subscribers: 78,126; Commercial subscribers: 512.

Programming (received off-air): WFMZ-TV (I), WLVT-TV (P) Allentown; WGTW (I) Burlington; WNJS (P) Camden; KYW-TV (C), WCAU (N), WPHL-TV (W), WPSG (U), WPVI-TV (A), WTXF-TV (F), WYBE (P) Philadelphia; WTVE (H) Reading; WHYY-TV (P) Wilmington.

Programming (via satellite): C-SPAN; C-SPAN 2; EWTN; Home Shopping Network; International Channel; Learning Channel; MSNBC; Pax Net; Pennsylvania Cable Network; QVC; TBS Superstation; TV Food Network; TV Guide Channel; The Health Network; Trinity Bcstg. Network; Univision.

Current originations: Public access; educational access; government access; leased access; local news.

Fee: $46.46 installation; $15.00 monthly; $17.79 additional installation.

Commercial fee: $55.00 monthly.

Expanded Basic Service

Subscribers: 73,174.

Programming (via microwave): Comcast SportsNet.

Programming (via satellite): A & E; American Movie Classics; BET; CNBC; CNN; Cartoon Network; Comedy Central; Court TV; Discovery Channel; E! Entertainment TV; ESPN; ESPN 2; ESPN Classic Sports; FX; Fox Family Channel; Headline News; History Channel; Lifetime; MTV; Nashville Network; Nick at Nite's TV Land; Nickelodeon; The Weather Channel; Turner Classic Movies; Turner Network TV; USA Network; VH1.

Fee: $25.00 installation; $16.25 monthly.

A la Carte 1

Subscribers: 3,107.

Programming (via satellite): Bravo; fXM: Movies from Fox; Independent Film Channel; Sci-Fi Channel; Sundance Channel.

Fee: $1.50 monthly (each).

Pay Service 1

Pay Units: 12,684.

Programming (via satellite): Cinemax.

Fee: $10.00 monthly.

Pay Service 2

Pay Units: 30,413.

Programming (via satellite): HBO (multiplexed).

Fee: $12.00 monthly.

Pay Service 3

Pay Units: 9,556.

Programming (via satellite): The Movie Channel.

Fee: $10.00 monthly.

Pay Service 4

Pay Units: 3,624.

Programming (via satellite): Disney Channel.

Fee: $7.00 monthly.

Pay Service 5

Pay Units: 11,272.

Programming (via satellite): Showtime.

Fee: $10.00 monthly.

Pay-Per-View

Addressable homes: 73,574.

Hot Choice; Playboy TV; Spice2; movies; special events.

Fee: $5.99 (Playboy TV); $6.99 (Spice2); $7.99 (Hot Choice).

Pay-per-view manager: John DiSanto.

Local advertising: Yes. Available in satellite distributed programming. Rates: $184.00/Minute; $92.00/30 Seconds. Local sales manager: Mike Wall.

Program Guide: CableView.

Equipment: Scientific-Atlanta headend; Antec amplifiers; Comm/Scope cable; Alcatel fiber optic cable; Video Data Systems character generator; Tocom set top converters; Tocom addressable set top converters; Scientific-Atlanta satellite antenna; Scientific-Atlanta satellite receivers; Star commercial insert.

Miles of plant: 460.0 (coaxial); 120.0 (fiber optic). Homes passed: 160,000. Total homes in franchised area: 160,000.

Manager: Joe Neff. Chief technician: Jack Clayton. Program director: David Schwartz. Marketing director: Kathy Banco. Customer service manager: Luis Tubins.

City fee: 5% of gross.

Ownership: Greater Media Inc. (MSO). Sale pends to Comcast Cable Communications Inc.

PHILADELPHIA (area 2)—Wade Cable, 1700 N. 49th St., Philadelphia, PA 19131. Phone: 215-581-6700. Fax: 215-871-5140. County: Philadelphia. ICA: PA0004.

TV Market Ranking: 4. Franchise award date: November 1, 1984. Franchise expiration date: January 1, 2001. Began: December 15, 1987.

Channel capacity: 82. Channels available but not in use: 1.

Basic Service

Subscribers: 60,000; Commercial subscribers: 150.

Programming (received off-air): WLVT-TV (P) Allentown; WGTW (I) Burlington; WNJS (P) Camden; KYW-TV (C), WCAU (N), WPHL-TV (W), WPSG (U), WPVI-TV (A), WTXF-TV (F), WYBE (P) Philadelphia; WNJT (P) Trenton; WHSP-TV (H) Vineland; WHYY-TV (P), WPPX (X) Wilmington.

Programming (via satellite): A & E; American Movie Classics; BET; Bravo; C-SPAN; C-SPAN 2; CNBC; CNN; Cartoon Network; Comedy Central; Country Music TV; Discovery Channel; E! Entertainment TV; ESPN; ESPN 2; EWTN; Electronic Program Guide; Fox Family Channel; Fox Sports Net; Goodlife TV Network; Headline News; Home Shopping Network; Learning Channel; Lifetime; MTV; Nashville Network; Nickelodeon; Pennsylvania Cable Network; QVC; Sci-Fi Channel; TBS Superstation; TV Food Network; TV Guide Channel; The Weather Channel; Travel Channel; Turner Network TV; USA Network; Univision; VH1.

Current originations: Public access; educational access; religious access.

Fee: $57.00 installation; $26.35 monthly.

Commercial fee: $39.95 monthly.

Pay Service 1

Pay Units: 12,848.

Programming (via satellite): Cinemax.

Fee: $10.19 monthly.

Pay Service 2

Pay Units: 5,342.

Programming (via satellite): Disney Channel.

Fee: $10.19 monthly.

Pay Service 3

Pay Units: 32,934.

Programming (via satellite): HBO.

Fee: $10.19 monthly.

Pay Service 4

Pay Units: 15,007.

Programming (via satellite): Showtime.

Fee: $10.19 monthly.

Pay Service 5

Pay Units: 7,441.

Programming (via satellite): The Movie Channel.

Fee: $10.19 monthly.

Pay Service 6

Pay Units: 1,113.

Programming (via satellite): Playboy TV.

Fee: $10.19 monthly.

Pay-Per-View

Addressable homes: 19,000.

Spice.

Local advertising: Yes. Regional interconnect: Philadelphia Cable Advertising.

Program Guide: TV Host.

Miles of plant: 596.0 (coaxial). Additional miles planned: 1.0 (coaxial). Homes passed:

161,800. Total homes in franchised area: 166,503.
Manager: Maurice Brody. Chief technician: Don Jones. Program director: Jan Wierczerzak. Marketing director: Martin Wills.
City fee: 5% of gross.
Ownership: Time Warner Cable (MSO).

PHILADELPHIA (area 3)—Comcast Cablevision of Philadelphia, 4400 Wayne Ave., Philadelphia, PA 19140. Phone: 215-329-4039. County: Philadelphia. ICA: PA0007.
TV Market Ranking: 4. Franchise award date: November 1, 1984. Franchise expiration date: N.A. Began: December 9, 1986.
Channel capacity: 84 (not 2-way capable). Channels available but not in use: 2.
Basic Service
Subscribers: Included with Philadelphia (area 4), PA.
Programming (received off-air): WLVT-TV (P) Allentown; WNJS (P) Camden; KYW-TV (C), WCAU (N), WPHL-TV (W), WPSG (U), WPVI-TV (A), WTXF-TV (F) Philadelphia; WHYY-TV (P), WPPX (X) Wilmington.
Programming (via satellite): A & E; BET; C-SPAN; C-SPAN 2; CNBC; CNN; Country Music TV; Discovery Channel; E! Entertainment TV; ESPN; EWTN; Fox Family Channel; Goodlife TV Network; Headline News; Home Shopping Network; Learning Channel; Lifetime; MTV; Nashville Network; News Plus; Nickelodeon; Odyssey; QVC; Storyvision Network; TBS Superstation; TV Guide Channel; The Weather Channel; Travel Channel; Trinity Bcstg. Network; Turner Network TV; USA Network; Univision; VH1.
Current originations: Public access; educational access; government access; leased access; automated emergency alert; local news; local sports.
Fee: $58.56 installation; $19.00 monthly; $2.76 converter.
Pay Service 1
Pay Units: N.A.
Programming (via satellite): American Movie Classics; Bravo; Cinemax; Disney Channel; GalaVision; HBO; Showtime; The Movie Channel.
Fee: $10.00 installation; $6.20 monthly (AMC), $7.25 monthly (GalaVision), $10.25 monthly (Bravo, Cinemax, Disney, HBO, Showtime or TMC).
Pay-Per-View
Hot Choice; Viewer's Choice.
Local advertising: Yes. Available in satellite distributed & character-generated programming. Local sales manager: Larry Simons. Regional interconnect: Philadelphia Cable Advertising.
Equipment: Jerrold headend; Jerrold amplifiers; Times Fiber cable; Sony VTRs; Tocom set top converters; Standard Communications satellite antenna; Simulsat satellite receivers; Texscan commercial insert.
Homes passed: 140,000. Total homes in franchised area: 149,000.
Manager: Sanford Ames. Chief technician: Randy Cicatello. Program director: Jim Riesenbach. Marketing director: Paul Fitzgerald.
Ownership: Comcast Cable Communications Inc. (MSO).

PHILADELPHIA (area 4)—Comcast Cablevision of Philadelphia, 11400 Northeast Ave., Philadelphia, PA 19116. Phones: 215-961-3800; 215-673-6600. Fax: 215-961-3875. County: Philadelphia. ICA: PA0005.
TV Market Ranking: 4. Franchise award date: November 1, 1984. Franchise expiration date: N.A. Began: September 1, 1986.
Channel capacity: 83 (not 2-way capable). Channels available but not in use: N.A.
Basic Service
Subscribers: 173,200; Commercial subscribers: 2,342. Includes figures for Philadelphia (area 3), PA.
Programming (received off-air): WLVT-TV (P) Allentown; WNJS (P) Camden; KYW-TV (C), WCAU (N), WPHL-TV (W), WPSG (U), WPVI-TV (A), WTXF-TV (F) Philadelphia; WHYY-TV (P), WPPX (X) Wilmington.
Programming (via satellite): A & E; BET; C-SPAN; CNBC; CNN; Country Music TV; Discovery Channel; E! Entertainment TV; ESPN; EWTN; Fox Family Channel; Goodlife TV Network; Headline News; Learning Channel; Lifetime; MTV; Nashville Network; Nickelodeon; Odyssey; TBS Superstation; The Weather Channel; Trinity Bcstg. Network; Turner Network TV; USA Network; VH1.
Current originations: Public access; educational access; government access; leased access; automated emergency alert; local news; local sports.
Fee: $30.00 installation; $23.99 monthly; $2.46 converter.
Commercial fee: $21.57 monthly.
Pay Service 1
Pay Units: N.A.
Programming (via satellite): Bravo; Cinemax; Disney Channel; GalaVision; HBO; The Movie Channel.
Fee: $10.25 monthly (each).
Pay-Per-View
Hot Choice; Viewer's Choice.
Local advertising: Yes. Available in satellite distributed & character-generated programming. Local sales manager: Larry Simons. Regional interconnect: Philadelphia Cable Advertising.
Program Guide: The Cable Guide.
Equipment: Jerrold headend; Jerrold amplifiers; Times Fiber cable; Jerrold set top converters; Jerrold addressable set top converters; Jerrold addressable traps; Scientific-Atlanta satellite receivers; Texscan commercial insert.
Manager: Ed Pardini. Program & marketing director: Chip Goodman.
Ownership: Comcast Cable Communications Inc. (MSO).

PHILIPSBURG BOROUGH—TCI of Pennsylvania Inc., 1068 Pennnsylvania Ave., Tyrone, PA 16686. Phone: 814-342-1370. Counties: Centre & Clearfield. Also serves Boggs Twp. (Clearfield County), Chester Hill, Decatur Twp. (Clearfield County), Morris Twp., Osceola Mills, Philipsburg, Rush Twp. (Clearfield County), South Philipsburg. ICA: PA0109.
TV Market Ranking: 74. Franchise award date: N.A. Franchise expiration date: January 1, 2004. Began: December 1, 1958.
Channel capacity: 52. Channels available but not in use: 19.
Basic Service
Subscribers: 5,359.
Programming (received off-air): WPSX-TV (P) Clearfield; WATM-TV (A), WJAC-TV (N), WKBS-TV (I), WTAJ-TV (C), WWCP-TV (F) Johnstown-Altoona; WTAE-TV (A) Pittsburgh; 14 FMs.
Programming (via satellite): A & E; C-SPAN; CNBC; CNN; Discovery Channel; Fox Family Channel; Headline News; Lifetime; MTV; Nashville Network; Nickelodeon; QVC; TBS Superstation; The Weather Channel.
Fee: $59.95 installation; $8.94 monthly; $2.00 converter; $49.99 additional installation.
Expanded Basic Service
Subscribers: 5,078.
Programming (via satellite): American Movie Classics; Court TV; ESPN; Fox Sports Net Pittsburgh; Turner Network TV; USA Network.
Fee: $13.46 monthly.
Pay Service 1
Pay Units: 266.
Programming (via satellite): Disney Channel.
Fee: $20.00 installation; $9.50 monthly.
Pay Service 2
Pay Units: 1,969.
Programming (via satellite): The New Encore.
Fee: N.A.
Pay Service 3
Pay Units: 895.
Programming (via satellite): HBO.
Fee: $20.00 installation; $13.15 monthly.
Pay Service 4
Pay Units: 397.
Programming (via satellite): Showtime.
Fee: $20.00 installation; $13.15 monthly.
Local advertising: Yes.
Program Guide: The Cable Guide.
Equipment: Jerrold headend; Jerrold amplifiers; Times Fiber cable; Magnavox set top converters; Hughes satellite antenna; Hughes satellite receivers.
Miles of plant: 139.1 (coaxial). Total homes in franchised area: 6,659.
Manager: Kim Yakich. Chief technician: Michael Catherine.
City fee: 4% of gross.
Ownership: AT&T Broadband & Internet Services (MSO). Purchased from Tele-Communications Inc., March 9, 1999.

PINOAK—CableVision Communications, Box 2200, 68 5th St., Buckhannon, WV 26201. Phone: 304-472-4193. Fax: 304-472-0756. County: Venango. Also serves Pinegrove Twp. (Venango County), Pinoak Village. ICA: PA0284.
TV Market Ranking: Outside TV Markets. Franchise award date: N.A. Franchise expiration date: N.A. Began: N.A.
Channel capacity: 21 (not 2-way capable). Channels available but not in use: 3.
Basic Service
Subscribers: 64.
Programming (received off-air): WJET-TV (A) Erie; KDKA-TV (C), WCWB (W), WPGH-TV (F), WPXI (N), WQED (P), WTAE-TV (A) Pittsburgh; WKBN-TV (C) Youngstown.
Programming (via satellite): A & E; CNN; Discovery Channel; Disney Channel; E! Entertainment TV; ESPN; Fox Family Channel; Great American Country; Learning Channel; Lifetime; Nashville Network; Nickelodeon; TBS Superstation; The Weather Channel; Turner Network TV; USA Network.
Fee: $61.50 installation; $19.42 monthly; $1.24 converter.
Pay Service 1
Pay Units: N.A.
Programming (via satellite): Cinemax; HBO; Showtime; The Movie Channel.
Fee: $17.50 installation; $7.95 monthly (Cinemax), $11.95 monthly (Showtime or TMC), $11.99 monthly (HBO).
Local advertising: No.
Equipment: Blonder-Tongue headend; GTE Sylvania amplifiers; Comm/Scope cable; Intercept & Pico traps; Standard Communications satellite receivers.
Miles of plant: 2.0 (coaxial). Homes passed: 130.
Manager: Willie Critchfield. Chief technician: Bill Turner. Marketing director: Kenny Phillips.
City fee: None.
Ownership: Rifkin & Associates Inc. (MSO). See Cable System Ownership.

PITCAIRN—Pitcairn Community Cable, 582 6th St., Pitcairn, PA 15140. Phone: 412-372-6500. Fax: 412-373-1464. County: Allegheny. ICA: PA0166.
TV Market Ranking: 10. Franchise award date: N.A. Franchise expiration date: N.A. Began: November 1, 1952.
Channel capacity: 40 (not 2-way capable). Channels available but not in use: 4.
Basic Service
Subscribers: 1,554.
Programming (received off-air): WPCB-TV (I) Greensburg; KDKA-TV (C), WCWB (W), WPGH-TV (F), WPXI (N), WQED (P), WQEX (P), WTAE-TV (A) Pittsburgh.
Programming (via satellite): WGN-TV (W) Chicago; A & E; American Movie Classics; CNN; Country Music TV; Discovery Channel; Disney Channel; ESPN; ESPN 2; EWTN; Fox Family Channel; Fox Sports Net Pittsburgh; Lifetime; MTV; Nashville Network; Nickelodeon; QVC; TBS Superstation; Turner Network TV; USA Network.
Current originations: Educational access.
Fee: $75.00 installation; $16.00 monthly.
Pay Service 1
Pay Units: 500.
Programming (via satellite): HBO.
Fee: $10.17 monthly.
Pay Service 2
Pay Units: 255.
Programming (via satellite): Showtime.
Fee: $10.17 monthly.
Pay-Per-View
Addressable homes: 1,555.
Local advertising: Yes. Available in locally originated programming.
Equipment: Jerrold headend; Magnavox amplifiers; Times Fiber cable; Scientific-Atlanta set top converters; Scientific-Atlanta satellite antenna; Standard Communications satellite receivers.
Miles of plant: 10.0 (coaxial). Homes passed: 1,750. Total homes in franchised area: 1,750.
Manager: Josephine Higgins. Chief technician: Marshall S. Kelley.
Ownership: Pitcairn Community Antenna System.

PITTSBURGH—AT&T Cable Services, 300 Corliss St., Pittsburgh, PA 15220-4815. Phones: 412-875-1100; 412-771-8100. County: Allegheny. ICA: PA0001.
TV Market Ranking: 10. Franchise award date: N.A. Franchise expiration date: October 25, 1999. Began: December 1, 1980.
Channel capacity: 80 (not 2-way capable). Channels available but not in use: N.A.
Basic Service
Subscribers: 103,902.
Programming (received off-air): WPCB-TV (I) Greensburg; WNPA (U) Jeanette; KDKA-TV (C), WCWB (W), WPGH-TV (F), WPXI (N), WQED (P), WQEX (P), WTAE-TV (A) Pittsburgh.
Programming (via microwave): Pittsburgh Cable News Channel.
Programming (via satellite): WGN-TV (W) Chicago; Electronic Program Guide; GRTV Network; Knowledge TV; Odyssey; QVC; TV Guide Channel; ValueVision.
Current originations: Automated time-weather; public access; educational access; government access; religious access; automated emergency alert.
Fee: $44.95 installation; $11.43 monthly; $1.50 converter; $24.95 additional installation.

Digital Basic Service
Subscribers: N.A.
Programming (via satellite): BBC America; Box Classic; Box Pulse; Bravo; Discovery Civilization Channel; Discovery Health Channel; Discovery Home & Leisure Channel; Discovery Kids Channel; Discovery People; Discovery Science Channel; Discovery Wings Channel; ESPN Classic Sports; ESPNews; Fox Sports World; Game Show Network; Golf Channel; Independent Film Channel; MuchMusic Network; Outdoor Life Network; Romance Classics; Speedvision; The Barker; Turner Classic Movies.
Fee: N.A.
Expanded Basic Service
Subscribers: 95,000.
Programming (via microwave): Meadows Racing Network.
Programming (via satellite): A & E; American Movie Classics; Animal Planet; BET; C-SPAN; C-SPAN 2; CNBC; CNN; Cartoon Network; Comedy Central; Court TV; Discovery Channel; Disney Channel; E! Entertainment TV; ESPN; ESPN 2; EWTN; FX; Fox Family Channel; Fox News Channel; Fox Sports Net Pittsburgh; Headline News; History Channel; Home & Garden Television; Home Shopping Network; International Channel; Learning Channel; Lifetime; MOVIEplex; MTV; Nashville Network; Nick at Nite's TV Land; Nickelodeon; Sci-Fi Channel; Shop at Home; TBS Superstation; The Weather Channel; Travel Channel; Turner Network TV; USA Network; VH1.
Fee: $12.85 monthly.
Pay Service 1
Pay Units: 12,779.
Programming (via satellite): Cinemax.
Fee: $13.45 monthly.
Pay Service 2
Pay Units: N.A.
Programming (via satellite): Starz!
Fee: $6.75 monthly.
Pay Service 3
Pay Units: 44,990.
Programming (via satellite): The New Encore.
Fee: $1.95 monthly.
Pay Service 4
Pay Units: 32,416.
Programming (via satellite): HBO.
Fee: $14.95 monthly.
Pay Service 5
Pay Units: 9,776.
Programming (via satellite): The Movie Channel.
Fee: $13.45 monthly.
Pay Service 6
Pay Units: 12,022.
Programming (via satellite): Showtime.
Fee: N.A.
Digital Pay Service 1
Pay Units: N.A.
Programming (via satellite): DMX; Encore Love Stories; Encore Mystery; Encore Westerns; HBO Plus; HBO Signature; Showtime (multiplexed); Starz! Theater.
Fee: N.A.
Pay-Per-View
Action Pay-Per-View; Playboy TV; Spice; Spice delivered digitally; Viewer's Choice Digital; special events.
Local advertising: Yes. Available in character-generated programming. Rates: $25.00/ Month. Regional interconnect: TCI Media Services-Pittsburgh, PA.
Program Guide: The Cable Guide.
Equipment: Scientific-Atlanta headend; C-COR amplifiers; Times Fiber cable; Ikegami cameras; JVC & Sony VTRs; Video Data Systems character generator; Pioneer set top converters; Eagle traps; Hughes satellite antenna; Hughes satellite receivers.
Miles of plant: 2085.5 (coaxial). Homes passed: 181,000. Total homes in franchised area: 181,000.
Manager: Jeffrey C. Harshman. Chief technician: Fred A. Hamm. Marketing director: Glenn Ryerson.
City fee: 5% of gross.
Ownership: AT&T Broadband & Internet Services (MSO). Purchased from Tele-Communications Inc., March 9, 1999.

PLUMER—CableVision Communications, Box 2200, 68 5th St., Buckhannon, WV 26201. Phone: 304-472-4193. Fax: 304-472-0756. County: Venango. Also serves Ahrensville, Cornplanter Twp. (Venango County), Henry's Bend, Oleopolis, Walnut Bend. ICA: PA0238.
TV Market Ranking: Outside TV Markets. Franchise award date: December 6, 1984. Franchise expiration date: N.A. Began: N.A.
Channel capacity: 24 (not 2-way capable). Channels available but not in use: N.A.
Basic Service
Subscribers: 252.
Programming (received off-air): WPSX-TV (P) Clearfield; WICU-TV (N), WJET-TV (A), WSEE (C) Erie; WJAC-TV (N) Johnstown-Altoona; KDKA-TV (C), WCWB (W), WPGH-TV (F) Pittsburgh.
Programming (via satellite): WGN-TV (W) Chicago; A & E; American Movie Classics; Animal Planet; CNN; Country Music TV; Discovery Channel; Disney Channel; ESPN; Fox Family Channel; Nashville Network; TBS Superstation; Trinity Bcstg. Network; USA Network.
Fee: $61.25 installation; $26.49 monthly; $1.24 converter; $17.50 additional installation.
Pay Service 1
Pay Units: 69.
Programming (via satellite): HBO.
Fee: $17.50 installation; $11.99 monthly.
Local advertising: No.
Equipment: Blonder-Tongue & Olson headend; Jerrold, GTE Sylvania & Scientific-Atlanta amplifiers; Comm/Scope cable; Intercept & Pico traps; Standard Communications & DX Antenna satellite receivers.
Miles of plant: 15.0 (coaxial). Homes passed: 475.
Manager: Willie Critchfield. Chief technician: Bill Turner. Marketing director: Kenny Phillips.
City fee: None.
Ownership: Rifkin & Associates Inc. (MSO). See Cable System Ownership.

POCONO—Pocono CATV Inc., 217 E. 9th St., Hazleton, PA 18201. Phone: 717-455-6851. Fax: 717-459-0963. Counties: Carbon, Lackawanna, Luzerne, Monroe & Wayne. Also serves Bear Creek, Big Bass (Clifton Twp.), Blakeslee, Clifton Twp., Coolbaugh Twp., Dennison Twp., East Side, Foster Twp. (Luzerne County), Gouldsboro, Indian County Campsite, Kidder Twp. (Luzerne County), Lake Harmony, Lehigh Twp. (Wayne County), Penn Lake Borough, Pocono Mobile Manor, Pocono Ranchettes, Pocono Springs, Tobyhanna Twp. (Monroe County), Tunkhannock Twp. (Monroe County), White Haven. ICA: PA0141.
TV Market Ranking: 49. Franchise award date: January 1, 1972. Franchise expiration date: March 21, 1998. Began: March 22, 1973.
Channel capacity: 60 (not 2-way capable). Channels available but not in use: 7.
Basic Service
Subscribers: 5,400.
Programming (received off-air): WPIX (W), WWOR-TV (U) New York; KYW-TV (C), WCAU (N), WPVI-TV (A), WTXF-TV (F) Philadelphia; WBRE-TV (N), WNEP-TV (A), WSWB (W), WVIA-TV (P), WYOU (C) Scranton & Wilkes-Barre; allband FM.
Programming (via satellite): A & E; C-SPAN; CNBC; CNN; Country Music TV; Discovery Channel; Disney Channel; ESPN; EWTN; Fox Family Channel; Goodlife TV Network; Headline News; Lifetime; MTV; Nashville Network; Nickelodeon; QVC; Sci-Fi Channel; TBS Superstation; TV Guide Channel; The Weather Channel; Turner Network TV; USA Network; VH1.
Current originations: Automated time-weather.
Fee: $42.95 installation; $11.21 monthly; $1.00 converter; $25.92 additional installation.
Pay Service 1
Pay Units: 876.
Programming (via satellite): Cinemax.
Fee: $11.95 monthly.
Pay Service 2
Pay Units: 1,259.
Programming (via satellite): HBO.
Fee: $11.95 monthly.
Equipment: Jerrold headend.
Miles of plant: 112.2 (coaxial); None (fiber optic).
Ownership: Gans Multimedia Partnership (MSO).

PORT ROYAL—Nittany Media Inc., Box 111, Lewistown, PA 17044. Phone: 717-248-3733. County: Juniata. ICA: PA0392.
TV Market Ranking: 57. Franchise award date: N.A. Franchise expiration date: N.A. Began: N.A.
Channel capacity: N.A. Channels available but not in use: N.A.
Basic Service
Subscribers: N.A.
Programming (received off-air): WHP-TV (C), WHTM-TV (A), WITF-TV (P) Harrisburg; WTAJ-TV (C) Johnstown-Altoona; WGAL (N) Lancaster; WNEP-TV (A) Scranton & Wilkes-Barre; WPMT (F) York.
Programming (via satellite): WGN-TV (W) Chicago; CNN; ESPN; The Inspirational Network.
Fee: N.A.
Pay Service 1
Pay Units: N.A.
Programming (via satellite): Nashville Network; The Movie Channel.
Fee: N.A.
Manager: Anna H. Hain. Chief technician: Michael Hain.
Ownership: Nittany Media Inc. (MSO).

PORTAGE—Adelphia, One Adelphia Dr., Blairsville, PA 15717. Phone: 800-892-7300. Counties: Cambria & Somerset. Also serves Ogle Twp., Paint, Paint Twp. (Somerset County), Portage (borough), Portage Twp. (Cambria County), Scalp Level, Washington Twp. (Cambria County), Windber. ICA: PA0146.
TV Market Ranking: 74. Franchise award date: July 1, 1969. Franchise expiration date: August 14, 2006. Began: July 1, 1969.
Channel capacity: 41 (not 2-way capable). Channels available but not in use: None.
Basic Service
Subscribers: 2,297.
Programming (received off-air): WPSX-TV (P) Clearfield; WJAC-TV (N), WTAJ-TV (C), WWCP-TV (F) Johnstown-Altoona; KDKA-TV (C), WCWB (W), WPGH-TV (F), WPXI (N), WQED (P), WTAE-TV (A) Pittsburgh; allband FM.
Programming (via satellite): A & E; American Movie Classics; CNN; Discovery Channel; ESPN; EWTN; Fox Family Channel; Fox Sports Net Pittsburgh; Headline News; Lifetime; MTV; Nashville Network; Nickelodeon; TBS Superstation; The Weather Channel; Turner Network TV; USA Network; VH1.
Fee: $25.00 installation; $18.50 monthly.
Expanded Basic Service
Subscribers: 2,208.
Programming (via satellite): A & E; American Movie Classics; C-SPAN; CNN; Discovery Channel; Disney Channel; ESPN; ESPN 2; EWTN; Fox Family Channel; Fox Sports Net Pittsburgh; Headline News; History Channel; Learning Channel; Lifetime; MTV; Nashville Network; Nickelodeon; Pennsylvania Cable Network; Product Information Network; QVC; Sci-Fi Channel; TV Guide Channel; The Weather Channel; Turner Network TV; USA Network; VH1.
Fee: N.A.
Pay Service 1
Pay Units: 395.
Programming (via satellite): HBO.
Fee: $11.50 monthly.
Pay Service 2
Pay Units: 26.
Programming (via satellite): Showtime.
Fee: $11.50 monthly.
Pay Service 3
Pay Units: 32.
Programming (via satellite): The Movie Channel.
Fee: $11.50 monthly.
Local advertising: Yes. Available in taped & automated programming.
Equipment: Scientific-Atlanta headend; Magnavox amplifiers; Essex cable; Hamlin, Oak & Scientific-Atlanta set top converters; Eagle traps; Scientific-Atlanta satellite antenna; Scientific-Atlanta satellite receivers.
Miles of plant: 43.6 (coaxial). Homes passed: 2,869.
Manager: J. Francis Bradley Jr. Chief technician: Dave Bowen.
City fee: 5% of net basic.
Ownership: Adelphia Communications Corp. (MSO).

POTTSTOWN—Suburban Cable, 202 Shoemaker Rd., Pottstown, PA 19464. Phone: 610-323-6400. Fax: 610-943-5487. Web site: http://www.suburbancable.com. Counties: Berks, Chester & Montgomery. Also serves Bally, Bechtelsville, Boyertown Borough, Charlestown, Colebrookdale Twp., Douglass Twp. (Berks County), Douglass Twp. (Montgomery County), Earl Twp. (Berks County), East Coventry Twp., East Greenville, East Pikeland Twp., East Vincent Twp., Hereford Twp. (Berks County), Limerick Twp., Lower Pottsgrove Twp., New Hanover Twp. (Montgomery County), North Coventry Twp., Oley Twp. (Berks County), Pennsburg, Phoenixville, Red Hill, Royersford, Schuylkill Twp. (Chester County), Spring City, Upper Hanover Twp., Upper Pottsgrove, Upper Providence Twp. (Montgomery County), Washington Twp. (Berks County), West Pottsgrove Twp. ICA: PA0394.
TV Market Ranking: 4 (Charlestown, Colebrookdale Twp., Douglass Twp., East Coventry Twp., East Greenville, East Pikeland Twp., East Vincent Twp., Limerick Twp., Lower Pottsgrove Twp., New Hanover Twp., North Coventry Twp., Pennsburg, Phoenixville, Pottstown, Red Hill, Royersford, Schuylkill Twp., Spring City, Upper Hanover Twp., Upper Pottsgrove, Upper Providence Twp., West Pottsgrove Twp.); Below 100 (Bally, Boyertown Borough, Earl Twp., Hereford

Twp., Oley Twp., Washington Twp.); Outside TV Markets (Bechtelsville). Franchise award date: May 1, 1977. Franchise expiration date: N.A. Began: February 14, 1979.

Channel capacity: 42 (2-way capable; operating 2-way). Channels available but not in use: None.

Basic Service

Subscribers: 51,658; Commercial subscribers: 238.

Programming (received off-air): WFMZ-TV (I), WLVT-TV (P) Allentown; WGTW (I) Burlington; KYW-TV (C), WCAU (N), WPHL-TV (W), WPSG (U), WPVI-TV (A), WTXF-TV (F) Philadelphia; WTVE (H) Reading; WNJT (P) Trenton; WHYY-TV (P), WPPX (X) Wilmington.

Programming (via satellite): BET; Bravo; C-SPAN; E! Entertainment TV; Fox Family Channel; Home Shopping Network; Knowledge TV; MOVIEplex; MSNBC; QVC; TBS Superstation; The Box; Travel Channel; Univision.

Current originations: Automated time-weather; public access; local sports.

Fee: $33.00 installation; $9.26 monthly; $2.51 converter.

Commercial fee: $27.94 monthly.

Expanded Basic Service

Subscribers: 49,508.

Programming (via microwave): Tri-State Media.

Programming (via satellite): A & E; American Movie Classics; CNBC; CNN; Comedy Central; Discovery Channel; Disney Channel; ESPN; ESPN 2; Headline News; History Channel; Learning Channel; Lifetime; MTV; Nashville Network; Nick at Nite; Nickelodeon; Sci-Fi Channel; TV Food Network; The Sports Network; The Weather Channel; Turner Network TV; USA Network; VH1.

Fee: $33.00 installation; $11.99 monthly.

Pay Service 1

Pay Units: 1,648.

Programming (via satellite): Cinemax.

Fee: $8.95 monthly.

Pay Service 2

Pay Units: N.A.

Programming (via satellite): Starz!

Fee: N.A.

Pay Service 3

Pay Units: 14,120.

Programming (via satellite): HBO.

Fee: $9.95 monthly.

Pay Service 4

Pay Units: 1,472.

Programming (via satellite): Showtime.

Fee: $9.95 monthly.

Pay-Per-View

Addressable homes: 7,605.

Viewer's Choice.

Local advertising: Yes. Available in satellite distributed programming.

Equipment: Jerrold & Scientific-Atlanta headend; C-COR & Jerrold amplifiers; Comm/Scope cable; Jerrold addressable set top converters; Prodelin & Scientific-Atlanta satellite antenna.

Miles of plant: 915.9 (coaxial); 59.7 (fiber optic). Homes passed: 78,343.

Manager: Robert Lawrence. Chief technician: Henry Petri. Program director: George Ferrara.

Ownership: Lenfest Communications Inc. (MSO).

POTTSVILLE—AT&T Cable Services, 2323 W. End Ave., Pottsville, PA 17901. Phone: 570-622-2161. Counties: Montour & Schuylkill. Also serves Branch Twp., Cass Twp. (Schuylkill County), Cressona, East Norwegian Twp. (Schuylkill County), Friedensburg, Landingville, Llewellyn, Mar Lin, Mechanicsville, Minersville, Mount Carbon, New Castle Twp. (Schuylkill County), North Manheim Twp., Norwegian Twp. (Schuylkill County), Orwigsburg, Pine Grove (Schuylkill County), Pine Grove Twp. (Schuylkill County), Schuylkill County, Schuylkill Haven, Seltzer, South Manheim Twp., Tremont Twp., Washington Twp. (Schuylkill County), Wayne Twp. (Schuylkill County), West Brunswick Twp. ICA: PA0060.

TV Market Ranking: 49 (portions of Schuylkill County); 57 (Mount Carbon, New Castle Twp., Pine Grove, Pine Grove Twp., portions of Schuylkill County, Tremont Twp., Washington Twp.); Below 100 (Branch Twp., Cass Twp., Cressona, East Norwegian Twp., Friedensburg, Landingville, Llewellyn, Mar Lin, Mechanicsville, Minersville, North Manheim Twp., Norwegian Twp., Orwigsburg, Pottsville, portions of Schuylkill County, Schuylkill Haven, Seltzer, South Manheim Twp., Wayne Twp., West Brunswick Twp.). Franchise award date: N.A. Franchise expiration date: N.A. Began: February 1, 1951.

Channel capacity: 60 (not 2-way capable). Channels available but not in use: N.A.

Basic Service

Subscribers: 17,923.

Programming (received off-air): WOLF-TV (F) Hazleton; WGAL (N) Lancaster; WNYW (F) New York; WPHL-TV (W), WPVI-TV (A), WTXF-TV (F) Philadelphia; WBRE-TV (N), WNEP-TV (A), WVIA-TV (P), WYOU (C) Scranton & Wilkes-Barre; allband FM.

Programming (via satellite): C-SPAN; E! Entertainment TV; QVC.

Fee: $5.31 installation; $8.36 monthly.

Expanded Basic Service

Subscribers: N.A.

Programming (via satellite): WPIX (W), WWOR-TV (U) New York; A & E; American Movie Classics; C-SPAN; C-SPAN 2; CNBC; CNN; Cartoon Network; Comedy Central; Country Music TV; Discovery Channel; E! Entertainment TV; ESPN; ESPN 2; EWTN; Fox Family Channel; Goodlife TV Network; Headline News; History Channel; Home & Garden Television; Home Shopping Network; Learning Channel; Lifetime; MTV; Nashville Network; Nickelodeon; QVC; Sci-Fi Channel; TBS Superstation; TV Guide Channel; The Inspirational Network; The New Encore; The Weather Channel; Travel Channel; Turner Network TV; USA Network; VH1; ValueVision.

Fee: $12.12 monthly.

Pay Service 1

Pay Units: 6,380.

Programming (via satellite): Cinemax; Disney Channel; HBO; Showtime; Starz!; The Movie Channel.

Fee: $5.31 installation; $11.77 monthly (each).

Pay-Per-View

Addressable homes: 7,202.

Hot Choice; Spice; Viewer's Choice; Viewer's Choice 6.

Fee: Varies.

Local advertising: Yes. Available in taped programming.

Equipment: Scientific-Atlanta headend; Jerrold & C-COR amplifiers; Comm/Scope cable; Sony VTRs; Texscan character generator; Scientific-Atlanta set top converters; Pioneer addressable set top converters; Vitek traps; Hughes & Scientific-Atlanta satellite antenna; Scientific-Atlanta satellite receivers.

Miles of plant: 388.0 (coaxial); 25.0 (fiber optic). Additional miles planned: 16.0 (coaxial). Total homes in franchised area: 18,185.

Manager: Doug Frank. Chief technician: Michael Brinich.

City fee: 5%.

Ownership: AT&T Broadband & Internet Services (MSO). Purchased from Time Warner Cable, July 1, 1999.

POTTSVILLE—Wire Tele-View Corp., 603 E. Market St., Pottsville, PA 17901. Phone: 570-622-4501. County: Schuylkill. Also serves Palo Alto, Port Carbon. ICA: PA0123.

TV Market Ranking: Below 100. Franchise award date: N.A. Franchise expiration date: N.A. Began: June 11, 1951.

Channel capacity: 20. Channels available but not in use: N.A.

Basic Service

Subscribers: 1,625.

Programming (received off-air): WGAL (N), WLYH-TV (U) Lancaster; WNYW (F), WPIX (W), WWOR-TV (U) New York; WPHL-TV (W), WTXF-TV (F) Philadelphia; WBRE-TV (N), WNEP-TV (A), WVIA-TV (P), WYOU (C) Scranton & Wilkes-Barre; allband FM.

Fee: $15.00 installation; $14.00 monthly.

Pay Service 1

Pay Units: N.A.

Programming (via satellite): Disney Channel; HBO.

Fee: $9.00 monthly (Disney), $12.00 monthly (HBO).

Equipment: Jerrold headend; Jerrold amplifiers; Jerrold cable; Microdyne satellite antenna; Microdyne satellite receivers.

Miles of plant: 16.0 (coaxial). Homes passed: 3,750.

Manager: Margaret Davenport.

Ownership: Wire Tele-View Corp. (MSO).

PRIMROSE—J. B. Cable, Box 268, Minersville, PA 17954. Phone: 717-544-5582. County: Schuylkill. Also serves Branch Twp., Cass Twp. (Schuylkill County), Foster Twp. (Schuylkill County), Reilly Twp. ICA: PA0395.

TV Market Ranking: Below 100. Franchise award date: N.A. Franchise expiration date: N.A. Began: January 1, 1950.

Channel capacity: 36 (not 2-way capable). Channels available but not in use: 17.

Basic Service

Subscribers: 591.

Programming (received off-air): WOLF-TV (F) Hazleton; WGAL (N) Lancaster; KYW-TV (C), WCAU (N), WPHL-TV (W), WPVI-TV (A), WTXF-TV (F) Philadelphia; WNEP-TV (A), WVIA-TV (P), WYOU (C) Scranton & Wilkes-Barre; WPMT (F) York.

Programming (via satellite): CNN; Country Music TV; Discovery Channel; ESPN; Nashville Network; TBS Superstation; USA Network.

Fee: $40.00 installation; $13.50 monthly.

Equipment: Jerrold headend; Jerrold amplifiers; General & Times Fiber cable; Jerrold set top converters; Microdyne, Scientific-Atlanta & Jerrold satellite receivers.

Miles of plant: 34.0 (coaxial).

Manager: Thomas O'Brien.

Ownership: J. B. Cable.

PULASKI—Ward Communications, Box 3393, Williamsport, PA 17701. Phones: 717-435-2035; 800-257-2288. Fax: 717-435-2035. County: Lawrence. Also serves Mahoning Twp. (Lawrence County), Pulaski Twp. (Lawrence County). ICA: PA0396.

TV Market Ranking: 79. Franchise award date: N.A. Franchise expiration date: N.A. Began: May 1, 1988.

Channel capacity: 68 (2-way capable; not operating 2-way). Channels available but not in use: 24.

Basic Service

Subscribers: 840.

Programming (received off-air): WNEO (P) Alliance; KDKA-TV (C), WPGH-TV (F), WPXI (N), WQED (P), WTAE-TV (A) Pittsburgh; WFMJ-TV (N), WKBN-TV (C), WYTV (A,F) Youngstown.

Programming (via satellite): WGN-TV (W) Chicago; A & E; American Movie Classics; CNN; Cartoon Network; Comedy Central; Country Music TV; Discovery Channel; ESPN; Fox Family Channel; Fox Sports Net Pittsburgh; Headline News; History Channel; Home & Garden Television; Home Shopping Network; Learning Channel; Lifetime; MTV; Nashville Network; Nick at Nite; Nickelodeon; QVC; Sci-Fi Channel; TBS Superstation; The Weather Channel; Travel Channel; Turner Network TV; USA Network.

Fee: $35.00 installation; $26.40 monthly; $35.00 additional installation.

Pay Service 1

Pay Units: 100.

Programming (via satellite): Cinemax.

Fee: $9.95 monthly.

Pay Service 2

Pay Units: 45.

Programming (via satellite): Disney Channel.

Fee: $7.50 monthly.

Pay Service 3

Pay Units: 100.

Programming (via satellite): HBO.

Fee: $10.95 monthly.

Pay Service 4

Pay Units: N.A.

Programming (via satellite): The Movie Channel.

Fee: N.A.

Equipment: Scientific-Atlanta & Jerrold headend; Jerrold amplifiers; Pico traps; Scientific-Atlanta satellite antenna.

Miles of plant: 55.0 (coaxial); None (fiber optic). Homes passed: 1,160. Total homes in franchised area: 1,400.

Manager: Neal W. Kimberling.

Franchise fee: .02% of gross.

Ownership: Ward Communications.

PUNXSUTAWNEY—Punxsutawney TV Cable Co., 234 N. Findley St., Punxsutawney, PA 15767. Phone: 800-892-7300. Counties: Indiana & Jefferson. Also serves Bell Twp. (Jefferson County), Big Run, Big Soldier, Canoe Twp., Cloe, Gaskill Twp., Henderson Twp. (Jefferson County), McCalmont Twp., Oliver Twp. (Indiana County), Perry Twp. (Indiana County), Rathmel, Reynoldsville, Rossiter, Sykesville, Walston, Winslow Twp. (portions), Wishan Twp., Young Twp. (Jefferson County). ICA: PA0397.

TV Market Ranking: Outside TV Markets. Franchise award date: N.A. Franchise expiration date: N.A. Began: December 1, 1964.
Channel capacity: 62. Channels available but not in use: 17.
Basic Service
Subscribers: 7,174.
Programming (received off-air): WPSX-TV (P) Clearfield; WATM-TV (A), WJAC-TV (N), WKBS-TV (I), WTAJ-TV (C), WWCP-TV (F) Johnstown-Altoona; KDKA-TV (C), WCWB (W), WPGH-TV (F), WPXI (N), WQED (P), WTAE-TV (A) Pittsburgh; 20 FMs.
Programming (via satellite): A & E; American Movie Classics; C-SPAN; CNBC; CNN; Discovery Channel; ESPN; EWTN; Fox Family Channel; Fox Sports Net; Home Shopping Network; Lifetime; MTV; Nashville Network; Nickelodeon; QVC; TBS Superstation; The Weather Channel; Turner Classic Movies; Turner Network TV; USA Network; VH1.
Current originations: Educational access.
Planned originations: Automated time-weather.
Fee: $15.00 installation; $13.95 monthly; $2.00 converter.
Pay Service 1
Pay Units: N.A.
Programming (via satellite): Cinemax; Disney Channel; Fox Sports Net Pittsburgh; HBO; Showtime; The Movie Channel.
Fee: $19.95 installation; $3.95 monthly (Fox Sports), $8.95 monthly (Disney), $9.95 monthly (Cinemax, HBO, Showtime or TMC).
Local advertising: No. Regional interconnect: Cable AdNet-Johnstown/Altoona, PA.
Program Guide: The Cable Guide.
Equipment: Scientific-Atlanta headend; C-COR amplifiers; Comm/Scope cable; PPC & Eagle traps; Scientific-Atlanta satellite antenna; Scientific-Atlanta satellite receivers.
Miles of plant: 116.0 (coaxial). Additional miles planned: 10.0 (coaxial).
Manager: James Brush. Chief technician: Ivan Glatt.
City fee: 3% of gross.
Ownership: Adelphia Communications Corp. (MSO).

RALSTON—Retel TV Cable Co. Inc., 62 Troy St., Canton, PA 17724. Phone: 717-673-5326. County: Lycoming. Also serves Roaring Branch. ICA: PA0253.
TV Market Ranking: Below 100. Franchise award date: N.A. Franchise expiration date: N.A. Began: January 1, 1952.
Channel capacity: 40 (2-way capable; operating 2-way). Channels available but not in use: N.A.
Basic Service
Subscribers: 205.
Programming (received off-air): WHP-TV (C), WHTM-TV (A) Harrisburg; WBRE-TV (N), WNEP-TV (A), WVIA-TV (P), WYOU (C) Scranton & Wilkes-Barre; allband FM.
Programming (via satellite): ESPN; TBS Superstation.
Fee: $40.00 installation; $20.00 monthly.
Pay Service 1
Pay Units: N.A.
Programming (via satellite): Showtime.
Fee: N.A.
Equipment: Blonder-Tongue headend; Ameco & Gamco amplifiers; Plastoid cable; Eagle & Vitek traps; Microdyne satellite antenna; Microdyne satellite receivers.
Miles of plant: 15.0 (coaxial). Additional miles planned: 1.0 (coaxial). Homes passed: 230. Total homes in franchised area: 230.
Manager: Terry W. Hughes.
City fee: None.
Ownership: Retel TV Cable Co. Inc. (MSO).

RAYNE TWP.—Satterlee Leasing Inc., Box 173, RD 1, Rochester Mills, PA 15771. Phone: 724-397-2400. County: Indiana. ICA: PA0399.
TV Market Ranking: 74. Franchise award date: N.A. Franchise expiration date: N.A. Began: May 1, 1986.
Channel capacity: 12. Channels available but not in use: N.A.
Basic Service
Subscribers: N.A.
Programming (received off-air): WPSX-TV (P) Clearfield; WJAC-TV (N) Johnstown-Altoona; KDKA-TV (C), WTAE-TV (A) Pittsburgh.
Fee: N.A.
Manager: Dan Satterlee.
Ownership: Satterlee Leasing Corp. (MSO).

READING—TCI, Suite 102, 875 Berkshire Blvd., Wyomissing, PA 19610. Phones: 610-376-9770; 610-376-9375. Fax: 610-376-9472. Counties: Berks & Lancaster. Also serves Alsace Twp., Bern Twp. (Berks County), Bernville, Brecknock Twp. (Lancaster County), Centre, Cumru Twp., Exeter Twp. (Berks County), Heidelberg Twp. (Berks County), Jefferson Twp. (Berks County), Kenhorst, Laureldale, Lower Alsace Twp., Lower Heidelberg Twp. (Berks County), Maidencreek Twp. (Berks County), Mohnton, Mount Penn, Muhlenberg Twp., North Heidelberg, Oley Twp. (Berks County), Ontelaunee (Berks County), Penn Twp. (Berks County), Ruscombmanor Twp. (Berks County), Shartlesville, Shillington, Sinking Spring, South Heidelberg Twp. (Berks County), Spring Twp. (Berks County), Temple, Wernersville, West Lawn, West Reading, Wyomissing, Wyomissing Hills. ICA: PA0012.
TV Market Ranking: 57. Franchise award date: January 1, 1963. Franchise expiration date: December 1, 2005. Began: May 1, 1964.
Channel capacity: 62 (2-way capable; operating 2-way). Channels available but not in use: None.
Basic Service
Subscribers: 73,983; Commercial subscribers: 45.
Programming (received off-air): WFMZ-TV (I), WLVT-TV (P) Allentown; WGTW (I) Burlington; WITF-TV (P) Harrisburg; WGAL (N) Lancaster; KYW-TV (C), WCAU (N), WPHL-TV (W), WPSG (U), WPVI-TV (A), WTXF-TV (F) Philadelphia; WTVE (H) Reading; WVIA-TV (P) Scranton & Wilkes-Barre; WHYY-TV (P) Wilmington; WPMT (F) York.
Current originations: Public access; educational access; government access; religious access; leased access; local news; local sports.
Fee: $5.31 installation; $9.18 monthly; $15.00 additional installation.
Expanded Basic Service
Subscribers: N.A.
Programming (via satellite): A & E; BET; C-SPAN; C-SPAN 2; CNBC; CNN; Comedy Central; Court TV; E! Entertainment TV; ESPN; EWTN; Fox Family Channel; Goodlife TV Network; Headline News; Home Shopping Network; Learning Channel; Lifetime; MTV; Nashville Network; Nickelodeon; Pennsylvania Cable Network; Philadelphia Park Live; QVC; TV Guide Channel; The Weather Channel; Travel Channel; Turner Network TV; USA Network; Univision; VH1; ValueVision.
Fee: $14.57 monthly.
Expanded Basic Service 2
Subscribers: N.A.
Programming (via satellite): American Movie Classics; Discovery Channel; TBS Superstation.
Fee: $1.95 monthly.
Pay Service 1
Pay Units: 40,059.
Programming (via satellite): Cinemax; Disney Channel; HBO; Showtime; Starz!
Fee: $5.31 installation; $12.00 monthly (each).
Pay-Per-View
Addressable homes: 22,009.
Hot Choice; Spice; Viewer's Choice.
Fee: $3.95 (Hot Choice or Viewer's Choice), $6.95 (Spice).
Local advertising: Yes. Available in satellite distributed, locally originated, character-generated & automated programming.
Program Guide: TVSM.
Equipment: Scientific-Atlanta headend; Scientific-Atlanta amplifiers; Comm/Scope cable; Sony cameras; Sony VTRs; 3M character generator; Scientific-Atlanta set top converters; Scientific-Atlanta addressable set top converters; Pico, Eagle & PPC traps; Microdyne, RCA & Superior satellite antenna; Standard Communications satellite receivers.
Miles of plant: 1024.0 (coaxial); 70.0 (fiber optic). Additional miles planned: 46.0 (coaxial). Homes passed: 94,137. Total homes in franchised area: 94,137.
Manager: Carolyn Orlando. Chief technician: Dennis Quinter. Program director: Bruce Shaak. Marketing director: Greg Wells.
City fee: 5% of gross.
Ownership: AT&T Broadband & Internet Services (MSO). Purchased from Time Warner Cable, June 1, 1999.

REEDSVILLE—Warner Cable of Reedsville, Box 517, Reedsville, PA 17084. Phone: 800-272-7749. County: Mifflin. Also serves Armagh Twp., Brown Twp. (Mifflin County), Milroy. ICA: PA0150.
TV Market Ranking: Outside TV Markets. Franchise award date: N.A. Franchise expiration date: N.A. Began: December 1, 1953.
Channel capacity: 30 (not 2-way capable). Channels available but not in use: 5.
Basic Service
Subscribers: 2,105.
Programming (received off-air): WPSX-TV (P) Clearfield; WHP-TV (C), WHTM-TV (A) Harrisburg; WJAC-TV (N), WTAJ-TV (C) Johnstown-Altoona; WGAL (N), WLYH-TV (U) Lancaster; WTTG (F) Washington; WPMT (F) York; allband FM.
Programming (via satellite): A & E; CNN; ESPN; Fox Family Channel; Lifetime; MTV; Nashville Network; Nickelodeon; TBS Superstation; Turner Network TV; USA Network.
Fee: $25.00 installation; $17.95 monthly.
Pay Service 1
Pay Units: 75.
Programming (via satellite): Disney Channel.
Fee: $15.00 installation; $9.95 monthly.
Pay Service 2
Pay Units: 175.
Programming (via satellite): HBO.
Fee: $15.00 installation; $11.00 monthly.
Pay Service 3
Pay Units: 100.
Programming (via satellite): The Movie Channel.
Fee: $15.00 installation; $11.00 monthly.
Equipment: Scientific-Atlanta headend; C-COR amplifiers; Times Fiber cable; Jerrold set top converters; Scientific-Atlanta satellite antenna; Scientific-Atlanta satellite receivers.
Miles of plant: 63.0 (coaxial). Homes passed: 2,295. Total homes in franchised area: 3,170.
Manager: Ron Amick. Chief technician: John Riley.
Ownership: Time Warner Cable (MSO).

RENO—Reno Cable Co., 111 2nd St., Reno, PA 16343. Phone: 814-676-3115. County: Venango. ICA: PA0273.
TV Market Ranking: Outside TV Markets. Franchise award date: N.A. Franchise expiration date: N.A. Began: January 1, 1953.
Channel capacity: 22. Channels available but not in use: N.A.
Basic Service
Subscribers: N.A.
Programming (received off-air): WICU-TV (N), WJET-TV (A), WQLN (P) Erie; WPCB-TV (I) Greensburg; KDKA-TV (C), WCWB (W), WPGH-TV (F), WPXI (N), WQED (P), WTAE-TV (A) Pittsburgh; WKBN-TV (C), WYTV (A,F) Youngstown.
Programming (via satellite): ESPN; Fox Family Channel; MTV; Nashville Network; Nickelodeon; TBS Superstation.
Fee: $5.50 monthly.
Pay Service 1
Pay Units: N.A.
Programming (via satellite): HBO.
Fee: $5.50 monthly.
Miles of plant: 6.0 (coaxial). Homes passed: 184.
Manager: Walter Ebbert. Chief technician: Charles Stormer.
City fee: 3% of gross.
Ownership: Reno Cable Co.

RETREAT CORRECTIONAL INSTITUTION—Cosmic Cable TV, Box 186, RR 4, Shickshinny, PA 18655. Phone: 570-256-3437. Fax: 570-542-4190. County: Luzerne. ICA: PA0445.
TV Market Ranking: 49. Franchise award date: January 1, 1989. Franchise expiration date: January 1, 2004. Began: N.A.
Channel capacity: 12 (not 2-way capable). Channels available but not in use: None.
Basic Service
Subscribers: 386.
Programming (received off-air): WBRE-TV (N), WNEP-TV (A), WVIA-TV (P), WYOU (C) Scranton & Wilkes-Barre.
Programming (via satellite): WGN-TV (W) Chicago; BET; ESPN; TBS Superstation; Turner Network TV.
Fee: $9.70 monthly.
Pay Service 1
Pay Units: 159.
Programming (via satellite): The Movie Channel.
Fee: $7.95 monthly.
Miles of plant: 3.0 (coaxial).
Manager: Mark Reiber. Chief technician: Daniel Jamuscewski.
Ownership: June Hoover (MSO).

RICHFIELD—R. J. Shelley CATV, Box 243, Mount Pleasant Mills, PA 17853. Phone: 717-539-8511. Counties: Juniata & Snyder. Also serves Monroe (Juniata County), West Perry Twp. ICA: PA0225.
TV Market Ranking: 57. Franchise award date: N.A. Franchise expiration date: N.A. Began: July 1, 1953.
Channel capacity: 12. Channels available but not in use: N.A.
Basic Service
Subscribers: N.A.
Programming (received off-air): WHP-TV (C), WHTM-TV (A), WITF-TV (P) Harrisburg; WTAJ-TV (C) Johnstown-Altoona; WGAL (N), WLYH-TV (U) Lancaster; WBRE-TV (N), WNEP-TV (A), WVIA-TV (P) Scranton & Wilkes-Barre; WPMT (F) York; allband FM.
Fee: $35.00 installation; $4.25 monthly.
Equipment: Blonder-Tongue headend; Ameco amplifiers.

Miles of plant: 9.9 (coaxial). Homes passed: 625.
City fee: None.
Ownership: R. J. Shelley CATV (MSO).

RIDGWAY BOROUGH—TCI of Pennsylvania Inc., 12 S. Mill St., Ridgway, PA 15853-1022. Phone: 800-734-8099. Counties: Elk & Jefferson. Also serves Brockport, Fox Twp. (Elk County), Horton Twp. (Elk County), Ridgway, Ridgway Twp. (Elk County), Snyder Twp. (Jefferson County). ICA: PA0124.
TV Market Ranking: Outside TV Markets. Franchise award date: N.A. Franchise expiration date: N.A. Began: November 1, 1950.
Channel capacity: 36. Channels available but not in use: N.A.
Basic Service
Subscribers: 3,355.
Programming (received off-air): WKBW-TV (A) Buffalo; WPSX-TV (P) Clearfield; WJET-TV (A) Erie; WJAC-TV (N), WKBS-TV (I), WTAJ-TV (C) Johnstown-Altoona; KDKA-TV (C), WPGH-TV (F), WPXI (N), WTAE-TV (A) Pittsburgh; allband FM.
Programming (via satellite): C-SPAN; CNBC; CNN; Discovery Channel; EWTN; Fox Family Channel; Headline News; Lifetime; MTV; Nashville Network; Nickelodeon; Odyssey; QVC; TBS Superstation; The Weather Channel.
Planned originations: Automated time-weather.
Fee: $59.95 installation; $10.25 monthly; $2.00 converter; $49.95 additional installation.
Expanded Basic Service
Subscribers: 3,222.
Programming (via satellite): American Movie Classics; ESPN; Fox Sports Net Pittsburgh; Turner Network TV; USA Network.
Fee: $12.17 monthly.
Pay Service 1
Pay Units: 306.
Programming (via satellite): Cinemax.
Fee: N.A.
Pay Service 2
Pay Units: 184.
Programming (via satellite): Disney Channel.
Fee: N.A.
Pay Service 3
Pay Units: 1,059.
Programming (via satellite): The New Encore.
Fee: N.A.
Pay Service 4
Pay Units: 736.
Programming (via satellite): HBO.
Fee: $13.15 monthly.
Pay Service 5
Pay Units: 111.
Programming (via satellite): The Movie Channel.
Fee: $13.15 monthly.
Local advertising: Planned. Regional interconnect: Cabletime.
Equipment: Scientific-Atlanta headend; AEL & Theta-Com amplifiers.
Miles of plant: 80.0 (coaxial). Homes passed: 3,719. Total homes in franchised area: 4,503.
Manager: W. Ben Call.
City fee: None.
Ownership: AT&T Broadband & Internet Services (MSO). Purchased from Tele-Communications Inc., March 9, 1999.

ROBINSON TWP. (Allegheny County)—Adelphia Cable, 5335 Enterprise Blvd., Bethel Park, PA 15102. Phone: 800-892-7300. Fax: 412-835-2045. County: Allegheny. ICA: PA0401.
TV Market Ranking: 10,90. Franchise award date: N.A. Franchise expiration date: N.A. Began: N.A.
Channel capacity: 52. Channels available but not in use: 1.
Basic Service
Subscribers: 3,720.
Programming (received off-air): WPCB-TV (I) Greensburg; KDKA-TV (C), WCWB (W), WPGH-TV (F), WPXI (N), WQED (P), WQEX (P), WTAE-TV (A) Pittsburgh; WTOV-TV (N) Steubenville-Wheeling; WTRF-TV (C) Wheeling-Steubenville.
Programming (via satellite): WGN-TV (W) Chicago; A & E; American Movie Classics; C-SPAN; CNBC; CNN; Comedy Central; Discovery Channel; ESPN; EWTN; Fox Family Channel; Fox Sports Net Pittsburgh; Headline News; Ladbroke Racing Channel/Meadows Racing Network; Learning Channel; Lifetime; MTV; Nashville Network; Nickelodeon; QVC; Sci-Fi Channel; TBS Superstation; TV Guide Channel; The Weather Channel; Travel Channel; Turner Classic Movies; Turner Network TV; USA Network; VH1.
Fee: $29.95 installation; $20.50 monthly.
Pay Service 1
Pay Units: 61.
Programming (via satellite): Cinemax.
Fee: $8.95 monthly.
Pay Service 2
Pay Units: 167.
Programming (via satellite): Disney Channel.
Fee: $7.95 monthly.
Pay Service 3
Pay Units: 1,198.
Programming (via satellite): HBO.
Fee: $8.95 monthly.
Pay Service 4
Pay Units: 198.
Programming (via satellite): Showtime.
Fee: $8.95 monthly.
Pay Service 5
Pay Units: 249.
Programming (via satellite): The Movie Channel.
Fee: $8.95 monthly.
Pay-Per-View
Addressable homes: 1,498.
Action Pay-Per-View.
Miles of plant: 65.3 (coaxial). Homes passed: 4,549.
Ownership: Adelphia Communications Corp. (MSO).

ROCHESTER—Adelphia Communications Corp., 367 Cleveland St., Rochester, PA 15074. Phones: 724-775-2800; 800-892-7300. County: Beaver. Also serves Beaver, Bridgewater, East Rochester, Freedom, Monaca, Rochester Borough, Rochester Twp., Vanport Twp. ICA: PA0076.
TV Market Ranking: 10,79,90. Franchise award date: N.A. Franchise expiration date: N.A. Began: November 1, 1967.
Channel capacity: 54. Channels available but not in use: None.
Basic Service
Subscribers: 7,943.
Programming (received off-air): WPCB-TV (I) Greensburg; KDKA-TV (C), WCWB (W), WPGH-TV (F), WPXI (N), WQED (P), WTAE-TV (A) Pittsburgh; WTOV-TV (N) Steubenville-Wheeling; WTRF-TV (C) Wheeling-Steubenville; WKBN-TV (C), WYTV (A,F) Youngstown.
Programming (via satellite): TBS Superstation.
Fee: $50.00 installation; $7.00 monthly; $2.00 converter.
Expanded Basic Service
Subscribers: N.A.
Programming (via satellite): A & E; American Movie Classics; CNN; ESPN; EWTN; Home Shopping Network; MTV; Nashville Network; Nickelodeon; Philadelphia Park Live; QVC; Turner Network TV; USA Network.
Fee: $29.95 installation; $15.45 monthly.
Pay Service 1
Pay Units: 3,600.
Programming (via satellite): Cinemax; Disney Channel; HBO; Showtime.
Fee: $20.00 installation; $8.50 monthly (Cinemax, Disney or Showtime), $10.95 monthly (HBO).
Pay-Per-View
Addressable homes: 3,800.
Special events.
Local advertising: Yes. Available in taped programming.
Program Guide: The Cable Guide.
Equipment: Scientific-Atlanta headend; Jerrold & Gamco amplifiers; Comm/Scope cable; Scientific-Atlanta & Pioneer set top converters; Scientific-Atlanta addressable set top converters; Eagle, Pico & PPC traps; Scientific-Atlanta satellite antenna; Scientific-Atlanta satellite receivers.
Miles of plant: 20.0 (coaxial). Homes passed: 11,500. Total homes in franchised area: 11,500.
Manager: Lou L. Abraham. Chief technician: John Ayers.
City fee: 3% of gross.
Ownership: Adelphia Communications Corp. (MSO).

ROCKMERE—CableVision Communications, Box 218, Poplar Bluff, MO 63902. Phones: 573-686-0900; 573-686-6387. Fax: 573-686-3891. County: Venango. Also serves Coal Hill, Cranberry Twp. (Venango County), Fertigs, Hampton Station, Heckathorne Church, Kahles Corners, Oakwood, Pinegrove Twp. (Venango County), Sawtown, Stanleys Corners, Tippery. ICA: PA0237.
TV Market Ranking: Outside TV Markets. Franchise award date: N.A. Franchise expiration date: N.A. Began: N.A.
Channel capacity: 35 (not 2-way capable). Channels available but not in use: N.A.
Basic Service
Subscribers: 435.
Programming (received off-air): WJET-TV (A), WSEE (C) Erie; KDKA-TV (C), WCWB (W), WPGH-TV (F), WPXI (N), WQED (P), WTAE-TV (A) Pittsburgh.
Programming (via satellite): WGN-TV (W) Chicago; C-SPAN; Fox Family Channel; TBS Superstation.
Fee: $47.50 installation; $11.82 monthly; $0.73 converter.
Expanded Basic Service
Subscribers: 388.
Programming (via satellite): American Movie Classics; Bravo; CNBC; CNN; Country Music TV; Discovery Channel; E! Entertainment TV; ESPN; ESPN 2; Home Shopping Network; Lifetime; MTV; Nashville Network; Nickelodeon; RAI-USA; Sci-Fi Channel; The Inspirational Network; Trinity Bcstg. Network; Turner Network TV; USA Network.
Fee: $16.04 monthly.
Pay Service 1
Pay Units: 151.
Programming (via satellite): Cinemax; Disney Channel; HBO; Showtime.
Fee: $4.95 monthly (Disney), $7.95 monthly (Cinemax), $11.95 monthly (Showtime), $11.99 monthly (HBO).
Pay Service 2
Pay Units: N.A.
Programming (via satellite): The Movie Channel.
Fee: $11.95 monthly.
Local advertising: No.
Equipment: Blonder-Tongue & Olson headend; GTE Sylvania, Jerrold & Magnavox amplifiers; M/A-Com cable; Intercept traps; Scientific-Atlanta satellite antenna; M/A-Com satellite receivers.
Miles of plant: 26.0 (coaxial). Homes passed: 484.
Manager: Willie Critchfield. Chief technician: Bill Turner. Marketing director: Kenny Phillips.
Ownership: Rifkin & Associates Inc. (MSO). Purchased from Triax Telecommunications Co. LLC, July 1, 1998. See Cable System Ownership.

ROCKWOOD—FrontierVision, Suite P-200, 1777 S. Harrison St., Denver, CO 80210. Phone: 303-757-1588. Fax: 303-757-6105. County: Somerset. Also serves Black Twp., Casselman, Milford (Somerset County). ICA: PA0402.
TV Market Ranking: 74. Franchise award date: N.A. Franchise expiration date: June 1, 1998. Began: January 1, 1968.
Channel capacity: N.A. Channels available but not in use: N.A.
Basic Service
Subscribers: 512.
Programming (received off-air): WJAC-TV (N), WTAJ-TV (C), WWCP-TV (F) Johnstown-Altoona; KDKA-TV (C), WCWB (W), WPXI (N), WQED (P), WTAE-TV (A) Pittsburgh; allband FM.
Programming (via satellite): WGN-TV (W) Chicago; TBS Superstation; Trinity Bcstg. Network.
Current originations: Automated time-weather.
Fee: $29.95 installation; $10.27 monthly; $0.73 converter.
Expanded Basic Service
Subscribers: 449.
Programming (via satellite): A & E; American Movie Classics; CNN; Country Music TV; Discovery Channel; E! Entertainment TV; ESPN; ESPN 2; Fox Family Channel; Headline News; Home Shopping Network; Lifetime; Nashville Network; Nickelodeon; Sci-Fi Channel; The Inspirational Network; The Weather Channel; Turner Network TV; USA Network.
Fee: $15.90 monthly.
Pay Service 1
Pay Units: 117.
Programming (via satellite): Cinemax; Disney Channel; HBO; Showtime.
Fee: $5.95 monthly (Disney), $8.95 monthly (Cinemax), $11.95 monthly (Showtime), $11.99 monthly (HBO).
Pay Service 2
Pay Units: N.A.
Programming (via satellite): The Movie Channel.
Fee: $11.95 monthly.
Equipment: Ameco headend; Ameco amplifiers; Ameco cable.
Miles of plant: 28.0 (coaxial). Homes passed: 720.
Manager: Willie Critchfield. Chief technician: Bill Turner.
City fee: $100.00 annually.
Ownership: FrontierVision Partners LP (MSO). Purchased from Triax Telecommunications Co. LLC.

ROGERSVILLE—DuCom Cable TV, 50 Tipp St, Du Bois, PA 15801. Phone: 814-371-1925. Fax:

814-371-3052. E-mail: ducom@key-net.net. County: Greene. Also serves Center Twp. (Greene County), Franklin Twp. (Greene County). ICA: PA0433.
TV Market Ranking: 90. Franchise award date: July 15, 1994. Franchise expiration date: N.A. Began: June 15, 1994.
Channel capacity: 41 (not 2-way capable). Channels available but not in use: 15.
Basic Service
Subscribers: 243.
Programming (received off-air): KDKA-TV (C), WCWB (W), WPGH-TV (F), WPXI (N), WQED (P), WTAE-TV (A) Pittsburgh; WTOV-TV (N) Steubenville-Wheeling; WTRF-TV (C) Wheeling-Steubenville.
Programming (via satellite): CNN; Country Music TV; Discovery Channel; Disney Channel; ESPN; ESPN 2; Fox Sports Net Pittsburgh; Nashville Network; Nickelodeon; QVC; TBS Superstation; Trinity Bcstg. Network; Turner Network TV; USA Network; VH1.
Fee: $45.00 installation; $23.00 monthly.
Pay Service 1
Pay Units: 38.
Programming (via satellite): HBO.
Fee: $10.95 monthly.
Miles of plant: 16.0 (coaxial). Homes passed: 260.
Manager: Rodney Preston. Chief engineer: David Kucenski.
Ownership: Dubois Communications Inc. (MSO).

ROME—Beaver Valley Cable Co., Box 60-D, RR#2, Rome, PA 18837. Phone: 570-247-2512. Fax: 570-247-2494. County: Bradford. Also serves Le Raysville, Le Raysville Borough, North Orwell, North Rome, Potterville, Rome Borough. ICA: PA0403.
TV Market Ranking: Below 100. Franchise award date: N.A. Franchise expiration date: N.A. Began: N.A.
Channel capacity: 45 (2-way capable; not operating 2-way). Channels available but not in use: 10.
Basic Service
Subscribers: 585.
Programming (received off-air): WBNG-TV (C), WIVT (A), WSKG (P) Binghamton; WETM-TV (N) Elmira; WPIX (W) New York; WBRE-TV (N), WNEP-TV (A), WSWB (W), WVIA-TV (P), WYOU (C) Scranton & Wilkes-Barre.
Programming (via satellite): CNN; Discovery Channel; Disney Channel; ESPN; Fox Family Channel; Nashville Network; Nick at Nite's TV Land; Nickelodeon; TBS Superstation; USA Network.
Fee: $30.00 installation; $21.00 monthly.
Expanded Basic Service
Subscribers: 348.
Programming (via satellite): WGN-TV (W) Chicago; American Movie Classics; Country Music TV; ESPN 2; Home Shopping Network; Learning Channel; Lifetime; Outdoor Channel; Sci-Fi Channel; The Weather Channel; Trinity Bcstg. Network; Turner Network TV; VH1.
Fee: $8.50 monthly.
Pay Service 1
Pay Units: N.A.
Programming (via satellite): Cinemax; HBO.
Fee: $10.00 monthly (each).
Miles of plant: 45.9 (coaxial).
Manager: Doug Soden. Chief technician: Gary Powers.
Ownership: Beaver Valley Cable Inc. (MSO).

ROSE TWP.—TCI of Pennsylvania Inc., 855 Main St., Clarion, PA 16214-1161. Phone: 800-692-6205. County: Jefferson. Also serves Brookville, Corsica, Eldred Twp. (Jefferson County), Knox Twp. (Jefferson County), Pinecreek Twp. (Jefferson County), Union Twp. (Jefferson County). ICA: PA0135.
TV Market Ranking: Outside TV Markets. Franchise award date: January 1, 1963. Franchise expiration date: July 27, 1998. Began: December 1, 1963.
Channel capacity: 60. Channels available but not in use: 25.
Basic Service
Subscribers: 2,627.
Programming (received off-air): WPSX-TV (P) Clearfield; WPCB-TV (I) Greensburg; WJAC-TV (N), WTAJ-TV (C), WWCP-TV (F) Johnstown-Altoona; KDKA-TV (C), WPXI (N), WQED (P), WTAE-TV (A) Pittsburgh; allband FM.
Programming (via satellite): WGN-TV (W) Chicago; A & E; C-SPAN; CNBC; CNN; Discovery Channel; Fox Family Channel; Headline News; Lifetime; MTV; Nashville Network; Nickelodeon; QVC; TBS Superstation; The Weather Channel.
Current originations: Public access.
Fee: $59.95 installation; $10.02 monthly; $49.95 additional installation.
Expanded Basic Service
Subscribers: 2,298.
Programming (via satellite): American Movie Classics; Court TV; ESPN; Fox Sports Net Pittsburgh; Turner Network TV; USA Network.
Fee: $12.62 monthly.
Pay Service 1
Pay Units: 184.
Programming (via satellite): Disney Channel.
Fee: N.A.
Pay Service 2
Pay Units: 790.
Programming (via satellite): The New Encore.
Fee: N.A.
Pay Service 3
Pay Units: 502.
Programming (via satellite): HBO.
Fee: N.A.
Pay Service 4
Pay Units: 186.
Programming (via satellite): The Movie Channel.
Fee: N.A.
Equipment: Ameco headend; Coral amplifiers.
Miles of plant: 91.3 (coaxial). Homes passed: 3,207. Total homes in franchised area: 4,633.
Manager: W. Ben Call. Chief technician: Greg Allshouse.
City fee: 3% of basic & pay (Corsica).
Ownership: AT&T Broadband & Internet Services (MSO). Purchased from Tele-Communications Inc., March 9, 1999.

ROSS TWP. (Allegheny County)—AT&T Cable Services, 300 Corliss St., Pittsburgh, PA 15220-4815. Phones: 412-875-1100; 412-771-8100. County: Allegheny. Also serves Aspinwall, Avalon, Bellevue, Ben Avon, Ben Avon Heights, Emsworth, Etna, Fox Chapel, Franklin Park, Kilbuck, McCandless, Millvale, O'Hara, Ohio, Reserve Twp. (Allegheny County), Shaler Twp., Sharpsburg, West View. ICA: PA0032.
TV Market Ranking: 10 (Aspinwall, Avalon, Bellevue, Ben Avon, Ben Avon Heights, Emsworth, Etna, Fox Chapel, Franklin Park, Kilbuck, McCandless, Millvale, O'Hara, Ohio, Reserve Twp., Ross Twp., Shaler Twp., Sharpsburg, West View); 90 (Avalon, Bellevue, Ben Avon, Ben Avon Heights, Emsworth, Franklin Park, Kilbuck, McCandless, Ohio, Ross Twp., West View). Franchise award date: N.A. Franchise expiration date: N.A. Began: December 1, 1970.
Channel capacity: 54 (not 2-way capable). Channels available but not in use: None.
Basic Service
Subscribers: 53,719.
Programming (received off-air): WPCB-TV (I) Greensburg; KDKA-TV (C), WCWB (W), WPGH-TV (F), WPXI (N), WQED (P), WQEX (P), WTAE-TV (A) Pittsburgh.
Programming (via microwave): Meadows Racing Network.
Programming (via satellite): BET; C-SPAN; Odyssey; QVC; TV Guide Sneak Prevue; The Weather Channel.
Fee: $44.95 installation; $11.10 monthly; $1.50 converter; $24.95 additional installation.
Expanded Basic Service
Subscribers: 51,385.
Programming (via microwave): Pittsburgh Cable News Channel.
Programming (via satellite): A & E; American Movie Classics; Animal Planet; CNBC; CNN; Cartoon Network; Court TV; Discovery Channel; E! Entertainment TV; ESPN; ESPN 2; EWTN; FX; Fox Family Channel; Fox News Channel; Fox Sports Net Pittsburgh; Headline News; History Channel; Home Shopping Network; Learning Channel; Lifetime; MOVIEplex; MTV; Nashville Network; Nickelodeon; Pennsylvania Cable Network; TBS Superstation; Turner Network TV; USA Network; VH1.
Fee: $16.95 monthly.
Pay Service 1
Pay Units: 4,608.
Programming (via satellite): Cinemax.
Fee: $13.45 monthly.
Pay Service 2
Pay Units: 2,315.
Programming (via satellite): Disney Channel.
Fee: $12.50 monthly.
Pay Service 3
Pay Units: 16,387.
Programming (via satellite): The New Encore.
Fee: $1.95 monthly.
Pay Service 4
Pay Units: 10,386.
Programming (via satellite): HBO.
Fee: $14.95 monthly.
Pay Service 5
Pay Units: 2,458.
Programming (via satellite): Showtime.
Fee: $14.95 monthly.
Pay Service 6
Pay Units: N.A.
Programming (via satellite): Starz!
Fee: $6.75 monthly.
Pay-Per-View
Playboy TV; Spice.
Fee: $4.95-$4.99.
Local advertising: Yes. Regional interconnect: TCI Media Services-Pittsburgh, PA.
Program Guide: The Cable Guide.
Miles of plant: 463.6 (coaxial).
Manager: Jeffrey C. Harshman. Chief technician: Fred A. Hamm. Marketing director: Glenn Ryerson.
Ownership: AT&T Broadband & Internet Services (MSO). Purchased from Tele-Communications Inc., March 9, 1999.

RURAL VALLEY—AT&T Cable Services, 300 Corliss St., Pittsburgh, PA 15220-4815. Phones: 412-875-1100; 412-771-8100. Counties: Allegheny, Armstrong & Indiana. Also serves Cowanshannock Twp., Dayton Borough, Plumville, South Mahoning Twp. ICA: PA0199.
TV Market Ranking: 74 (Plumville, South Mahoning Twp.); Outside TV Markets (Cowanshannock Twp., Dayton Borough, Rural Valley). Franchise award date: N.A. Franchise expiration date: N.A. Began: October 1, 1984.
Channel capacity: 37 (not 2-way capable). Channels available but not in use: N.A.
Basic Service
Subscribers: 1,198.
Programming (received off-air): WPCB-TV (I) Greensburg; WJAC-TV (N) Johnstown-Altoona; KDKA-TV (C), WCWB (W), WPGH-TV (F), WPXI (N), WQED (P), WTAE-TV (A) Pittsburgh.
Fee: $44.95 installation; $11.90 monthly; $1.50 converter; $24.95 additional installation.
Expanded Basic Service
Subscribers: 1,054.
Programming (via microwave): Meadows Racing Network.
Programming (via satellite): American Movie Classics; Animal Planet; CNN; Cartoon Network; Discovery Channel; ESPN; FX; Fox Family Channel; Fox News Channel; Fox Sports Net Pittsburgh; Headline News; History Channel; Home & Garden Television; Learning Channel; Lifetime; MOVIEplex; MTV; Nashville Network; Nickelodeon; QVC; Sci-Fi Channel; TBS Superstation; The Weather Channel; Turner Network TV; USA Network.
Fee: $12.74 monthly.
Pay Service 1
Pay Units: 50.
Programming (via satellite): Showtime.
Fee: $13.75 monthly.
Pay Service 2
Pay Units: N.A.
Programming (via satellite): Cinemax; Disney Channel; HBO; Starz!; The New Encore.
Fee: $1.95 monthly (Encore), $6.75 monthly (Starz), $12.50 monthly (Disney), $13.45 monthly (Cinemax), $14.95 monthly (HBO).
Equipment: Scientific-Atlanta headend; C-COR amplifiers; Plastoid cable; Eagle & Pico traps; Scientific-Atlanta satellite receivers.
Miles of plant: 33.4 (coaxial). Total homes in franchised area: 2,538.
Manager: Jeffrey C. Harshman. Chief technician: Fred A. Hamm. Marketing director: Glenn Ryerson.
City fee: 3% of gross.
Ownership: AT&T Broadband & Internet Services (MSO). Purchased from Tele-Communications Inc., March 9, 1999.

SABULA—DuCom Communications Inc., 50 Tipp St., Du Bois, PA 15801. Phone: 814-371-1925. Fax: 814-371-3052.
E-mail: ducom@key-net.net.
County: Clearfield. Also serves Huston Twp. (Clearfield County), Penfield, Sandy Twp. (Clearfield County). ICA: PA0249.
TV Market Ranking: Outside TV Markets. Franchise award date: August 1, 1989. Franchise expiration date: August 1, 1999. Began: August 1, 1990.
Channel capacity: 60 (not 2-way capable). Channels available but not in use: 13.
Basic Service
Subscribers: 631.
Programming (received off-air): WPSX-TV (P) Clearfield; WATM-TV (A), WJAC-TV (N), WKBS-TV (I), WTAJ-TV (C), WWCP-TV (F) Johnstown-Altoona; WCWB (W), WTAE-TV (A) Pittsburgh.
Programming (via satellite): WGN-TV (W) Chicago; A & E; C-SPAN; CNN; Cartoon Network; Country Music TV; Discovery Channel; Disney Channel; ESPN; ESPN 2; FX; Fox Family Channel; Fox Sports Net Pittsburgh; Headline News; Home & Garden Television; Home Shopping Network; Learning Channel; Lifetime; MSNBC; MTV; Nashville Net-

work; Nick at Nite's TV Land; Nickelodeon; QVC; Sci-Fi Channel; TBS Superstation; The Weather Channel; Trinity Bcstg. Network; Turner Classic Movies; Turner Network TV; USA Network; VH1.
Current originations: Public access; educational access; government access.
Fee: $45.00 installation; $28.95 monthly; $2.50 converter.
Pay Service 1
Pay Units: 41.
Programming (via satellite): Cinemax.
Fee: $5.00 installation; $9.00 monthly.
Pay Service 2
Pay Units: 123.
Programming (via satellite): HBO.
Fee: $5.00 installation; $10.95 monthly.
Pay Service 3
Pay Units: 22.
Programming (via satellite): Showtime.
Fee: $5.00 installation; $9.00 monthly.
Interactive Services
Home shopping.
Local advertising: Yes. Available in character-generated programming.
Equipment: Scientific-Atlanta headend; C-COR amplifiers; Comm/Scope & Trilogy cable; Amiga character generator; Scientific-Atlanta set top converters; Eagle traps; Comtech satellite antenna; Scientific-Atlanta satellite receivers.
Miles of plant: 28.0 (coaxial). Additional miles planned: 50.0 (coaxial). Homes passed: 330. Total homes in franchised area: 330.
Manager: David Kucenski.
Ownership: Dubois Communications Inc. (MSO).

SALTILLO—Saltillo TV Cable Corp., Box 176, Saltillo, PA 17253. Phone: 814-448-3553. County: Huntingdon. ICA: PA0404.
TV Market Ranking: 74. Franchise award date: N.A. Franchise expiration date: N.A. Began: January 1, 1964.
Channel capacity: 12. Channels available but not in use: N.A.
Basic Service
Subscribers: 180.
Programming (received off-air): WJAC-TV (N), WTAJ-TV (C) Johnstown-Altoona; WGAL (N) Lancaster; WTAE-TV (A) Pittsburgh.
Programming (via satellite): WGN-TV (W) Chicago; CNN; Discovery Channel; ESPN; MTV; Nashville Network; Odyssey; Turner Network TV.
Fee: $100.00 installation; $6.00 monthly.
Pay Service 1
Pay Units: 100.
Programming (via satellite): HBO.
Fee: $6.50 monthly.
Ownership: Saltillo TV Cable Corp.

SALTSBURG—AT&T Cable Services, 300 Corliss St., Pittsburgh, PA 15220-4815. Phones: 412-875-1100; 412-771-8100. Counties: Indiana & Westmoreland. Also serves Avonmore, Bell Twp. (Westmoreland County), Conemaugh Twp. (Indiana County), Loyalhanna Twp. (Westmoreland County). ICA: PA0173.
TV Market Ranking: 10,74. Franchise award date: N.A. Franchise expiration date: N.A. Began: August 1, 1982.
Channel capacity: 32 (not 2-way capable). Channels available but not in use: None.
Basic Service
Subscribers: 1,260.
Programming (received off-air): WPCB-TV (I) Greensburg; WJAC-TV (N) Johnstown-Altoona; KDKA-TV (C), WCWB (W), WPGH-TV (F), WPXI (N), WQED (P), WTAE-TV (A) Pittsburgh.
Programming (via satellite): C-SPAN; CNBC; Discovery Channel; Lifetime; QVC; The Weather Channel.
Fee: $44.95 installation; $11.61 monthly; $1.50 converter; $24.95 additional installation.
Expanded Basic Service
Subscribers: 1,189.
Programming (via satellite): American Movie Classics; Animal Planet; CNN; Cartoon Network; ESPN; Fox Family Channel; Fox News Channel; Fox Sports Net Pittsburgh; Headline News; MOVIEplex; MTV; Nashville Network; Nickelodeon; TBS Superstation; Turner Network TV; USA Network.
Fee: $12.32 monthly.
Pay Service 1
Pay Units: 405.
Programming (via satellite): The New Encore.
Fee: $1.95 monthly.
Pay Service 2
Pay Units: 247.
Programming (via satellite): HBO.
Fee: $14.95 monthly.
Pay Service 3
Pay Units: 177.
Programming (via satellite): Showtime.
Fee: $14.95 monthly.
Pay Service 4
Pay Units: N.A.
Programming (via satellite): Starz!
Fee: $6.75 monthly.
Program Guide: The Cable Guide.
Equipment: Scientific-Atlanta headend; C-COR amplifiers; Comm/Scope cable; Jerrold set top converters; Scientific-Atlanta satellite antenna; Scientific-Atlanta satellite receivers.
Miles of plant: 36.1 (coaxial). Homes passed: 1,628. Total homes in franchised area: 3,047.
Manager: Jeffrey C. Harshman. Chief technician: Fred A. Hamm. Marketing director: Glenn Ryerson.
City fee: 3% of gross.
Ownership: AT&T Broadband & Internet Services (MSO). Purchased from Tele-Communications Inc., March 9, 1999.

SANDY LAKE—CableVision Communications, Box 2200, 68 5th St., Buckhannon, WV 26201. Phone: 304-472-4193. Fax: 304-472-0756. County: Mercer. Also serves Jackson Center, Jackson Center Borough, Lake Twp. (Mercer County), Sandy Lake Twp., Stoneboro. ICA: PA0176.
TV Market Ranking: 79 (Jackson Center, Lake Twp., Stoneboro); Outside TV Markets (Sandy Lake). Franchise award date: N.A. Franchise expiration date: December 4, 2001. Began: N.A.
Channel capacity: 36. Channels available but not in use: N.A.
Basic Service
Subscribers: 895.
Programming (received off-air): WICU-TV (N) Erie; KDKA-TV (C), WPGH-TV (F), WPXI (N), WQED (P), WTAE-TV (A) Pittsburgh; WFMJ-TV (N), WKBN-TV (C), WYTV (A,F) Youngstown.
Programming (via satellite): WGN-TV (W) Chicago; C-SPAN; TBS Superstation.
Fee: $61.25 installation; $14.40 monthly; $1.24 converter; $17.50 additional installation.
Expanded Basic Service
Subscribers: 747.
Programming (via satellite): A & E; American Movie Classics; CNN; Discovery Channel; Disney Channel; E! Entertainment TV; ESPN; ESPN 2; Fox Family Channel; Fox Sports Net Pittsburgh; Great American Country; Home Shopping Network; Lifetime; Nashville Network; Nickelodeon; Sci-Fi Channel; The Inspirational Network; The Weather Channel; Trinity Bcstg. Network; Turner Network TV; USA Network.
Fee: $15.06 monthly.
Pay Service 1
Pay Units: 549.
Programming (via satellite): Cinemax; HBO.
Fee: $17.50 installation; $7.95 monthly (Cinemax), $11.99 monthly (HBO).
Pay Service 2
Pay Units: N.A.
Programming (via satellite): Showtime; The Movie Channel; The New Encore.
Fee: $3.99 monthly (Encore), $11.95 monthly (Showtime or TMC).
Local advertising: Yes. Available in locally originated programming.
Equipment: Blonder-Tongue & Olson headend; C-COR amplifiers; M/A-Com cable; Eagle traps; M/A-Com satellite antenna.
Miles of plant: 17.0 (coaxial). Homes passed: 1,824.
Manager: Willie Critchfield. Marketing director: Kenny Phillips.
City fee: None.
Ownership: Rifkin & Associates Inc. (MSO). See Cable System Ownership.

SANDY TWP. (Clearfield County)—Satterlee Leasing Inc., Box 173, RD 1, Rochester Mills, PA 15771. Phone: 724-397-2400. County: Clearfield. ICA: PA0405.
TV Market Ranking: Outside TV Markets. Franchise award date: N.A. Franchise expiration date: N.A. Began: August 1, 1982.
Channel capacity: N.A. Channels available but not in use: N.A.
Basic Service
Subscribers: N.A.
Programming (received off-air): WPSX-TV (P) Clearfield; WJAC-TV (N), WTAJ-TV (C) Johnstown-Altoona; WTAE-TV (A) Pittsburgh.
Programming (via satellite): WGN-TV (W) Chicago; TBS Superstation.
Fee: N.A.
Manager: Dan Satterlee.
Ownership: Satterlee Leasing Corp. (MSO).

SAYRE—Time Warner Cable, 142 W. Lockhart St., Sayre, PA 18840. Phone: 570-888-9331. Counties: Bradford & Tioga, PA; Chemung & Tioga, NY. Also serves Barton (town), Chemung (town), Nichols (town), Waverly (village), NY; Athens (borough), Athens Twp., Litchfield (town), Nichols (village), South Waverly (borough), Ulster (town), PA. ICA: PA0079.
TV Market Ranking: Below 100. Franchise award date: N.A. Franchise expiration date: N.A. Began: November 1, 1958.
Channel capacity: 60. Channels available but not in use: N.A.
Basic Service
Subscribers: 8,404.
Programming (received off-air): WBNG-TV (C), WICZ-TV (F), WIVT (A), WSKG (P) Binghamton; WENY-TV (A), WETM-TV (N) Elmira; WSWB (W), WVIA-TV (P), WYOU (C) Scranton & Wilkes-Barre; allband FM.
Programming (via satellite): WPIX (W) New York; FX; MSNBC; QVC; TBS Superstation.
Current originations: Public access; educational access; government access.
Fee: $56.50 installation; $7.65 monthly.
Expanded Basic Service
Subscribers: N.A.
Programming (via satellite): A & E; American Movie Classics; C-SPAN; CNBC; Cartoon Network; Comedy Central; Court TV; Discovery Channel; E! Entertainment TV; ESPN; ESPN 2; EWTN; Fox Family Channel; Headline News; History Channel; Home & Garden Television; Home Shopping Network; Learning Channel; Lifetime; MTV; Nickelodeon; Sci-Fi Channel; TV Food Network; TV Guide Channel; The Weather Channel; Turner Classic Movies; USA Network; VH1.
Fee: N.A.
Expanded Basic Service 2
Subscribers: N.A.
Programming (via satellite): CNN; Nashville Network; Turner Network TV.
Fee: N.A.
Pay Service 1
Pay Units: 2,911.
Programming (via satellite): Cinemax; Disney Channel; HBO; Showtime.
Fee: $9.95 monthly (Disney), $10.95 monthly (Cinemax, HBO or Showtime).
Local advertising: Yes. Rates: $4.00/Day. Regional interconnect: Cabletime.
Equipment: DX Engineering, Jerrold & Scientific-Atlanta headend; Texscan amplifiers; Comm/Scope cable; Jerrold set top converters; Scientific-Atlanta satellite antenna.
Miles of plant: 143.0 (coaxial). Homes passed: 9,469. Total homes in franchised area: 10,185.
Manager: Robert Rickert. Chief technician: David Dugan. Marketing director: Sue Maha.
City fee: 5% of gross.
Ownership: Time Warner Cable (MSO); Advance/Newhouse Partnership (MSO).

SCRANTON—Adelphia Cable, Box 710, Pittston, PA 18640. Phone: 570-451-4300. Fax: 570-451-4333. Counties: Lackawanna & Luzerne. Also serves Avoca, Dickson City, Edwardsville, Exeter, Forty Fort, Luzerne, Moosic, Nanticoke, Old Forge, Plains Twp. (Luzerne County), Plymouth, Swoyersville, Taylor, Throop, West Wyoming, Wyoming. ICA: PA0011.
TV Market Ranking: 49. Franchise award date: June 1, 1973. Franchise expiration date: December 31, 2010. Began: October 7, 1973.
Channel capacity: 38 (2-way capable). Channels available but not in use: N.A.
Basic Service
Subscribers: 58,060.
Programming (received off-air): WBRE-TV (N), WNEP-TV (A), WSWB (W), WVIA-TV (P), WYOU (C) Scranton & Wilkes-Barre.
Programming (via microwave): WPIX (W) New York; WPHL-TV (W) Philadelphia; Catholic TV Network.
Programming (via satellite): TBS Superstation.
Current originations: Automated time-weather; educational access; religious access.
Fee: $49.95 installation; $10.00 monthly; $15.00 additional installation.
Expanded Basic Service
Subscribers: 57,650.
Programming (via satellite): A & E; American Movie Classics; C-SPAN; CNBC; CNN; Discovery Channel; ESPN; Fox Family Channel; Headline News; Home Shopping Network; Lifetime; MTV; Nashville Network; Nickelodeon; QVC; The Weather Channel; Turner Network TV; USA Network; VH1.
Fee: $28.00 installation; $19.99 monthly.
Pay Service 1
Pay Units: 24,821.
Programming (via satellite): Cinemax; Disney Channel; HBO.
Fee: $8.00 monthly (Disney), $8.99 monthly (Cinemax), $11.49 monthly (HBO).
Pay-Per-View
Addressable homes: 3,800.
Viewer's Choice.
Fee: $3.95.

Local advertising: Yes. Available in satellite distributed programming. Local sales manager: Harry Wahl. Regional interconnect: Cabletime.

Equipment: Jerrold headend; Jerrold amplifiers; Comm/Scope & Times Fiber cable; Oak & Pioneer set top converters; Jerrold addressable set top converters; Jerrold addressable traps; Scientific-Atlanta satellite antenna; Scientific-Atlanta satellite receivers.

Miles of plant: 635.0 (coaxial); 23.0 (fiber optic). Homes passed: 78,950. Total homes in franchised area: 79,120.

Manager: Mark DeStefano. Chief technician: James Peters. Marketing director: John T. Kennedy. Customer service manager: M. Miller.

City fee: 5% of gross.

Ownership: Adelphia Communications Corp. (MSO). Purchased from Verto Communications, January 21, 1999.

SELLERSVILLE—Suburban Cable, 114 Ridge Rd., Sellersville, PA 18960-1521. Phone: 800-222-1813.

Web site: http://www.suburbancable.com.

Counties: Bucks & Montgomery. Also serves Bedminster Twp., Dublin Borough, East Rockhill Twp., Franconia, Green Lane Borough, Hatfield, Hatfield Twp., Hilltown Twp., Lower Frederick, Lower Salford, Marlborough Twp., Milford Twp. (Bucks County), Perkasie, Quakertown, Richland Twp. (Bucks County), Richlandtown, Salford, Silverdale, Souderton, Telford, Trumbauersville, Upper Frederick Twp., Upper Salford, West Rockhill Twp. ICA: PA0017.

TV Market Ranking: 4. Franchise award date: N.A. Franchise expiration date: N.A. Began: February 1, 1975.

Channel capacity: 52 (not 2-way capable). Channels available but not in use: None.

Basic Service

Subscribers: 39,954; Commercial subscribers: 129.

Programming (received off-air): WFMZ-TV (I), WLVT-TV (P) Allentown; WGTW (I) Burlington; KYW-TV (C), WCAU (N), WPHL-TV (W), WPSG (U), WPVI-TV (A), WTXF-TV (F) Philadelphia; WTVE (H) Reading; WNJT (P) Trenton; WHSP-TV (H) Vineland; WHYY-TV (P), WPPX (X) Wilmington; allband FM.

Programming (via satellite): Bravo; C-SPAN; Fox Family Channel; Home Shopping Network; Knowledge TV; MOVIEplex; MSNBC; QVC; TBS Superstation; The Box.

Current originations: Automated time-weather; public access; educational access; government access; religious access; local news.

Fee: $33.00 installation; $8.99 monthly.

Expanded Basic Service

Subscribers: 37,585.

Programming (via satellite): A & E; American Movie Classics; CNBC; CNN; Comedy Central; Country Music TV; Discovery Channel; Disney Channel; E! Entertainment TV; ESPN; ESPN 2; History Channel; Learning Channel; Lifetime; MTV; Nashville Network; Nick at Nite; Nickelodeon; TV Food Network; The Sports Network; The Weather Channel; Turner Network TV; USA Network; VH1.

Fee: N.A.

Pay Service 1

Pay Units: 1,289.

Programming (via satellite): Cinemax.

Fee: $6.95 monthly.

Pay Service 2

Pay Units: N.A.

Programming (via satellite): Starz!

Fee: N.A.

Pay Service 3

Pay Units: 10,470.

Programming (via satellite): HBO (multiplexed).

Fee: $9.50 monthly.

Pay Service 4

Pay Units: 1,114.

Programming (via satellite): Showtime.

Fee: $6.95 monthly.

Pay-Per-View

Addressable homes: 6,742.

Playboy TV; Spice; Viewer's Choice; movies; special events.

Fee: $3.95 (Viewer's Choice); $5.95 (Playboy TV).

Local advertising: Yes. Available in satellite distributed & character-generated programming. Regional interconnect: Philadelphia Cable Advertising.

Program Guide: TV Host.

Equipment: Jerrold headend; C-COR & Jerrold amplifiers; Comm/Scope & Trilogy cable; MSI character generator; Tocom set top converters; Jerrold addressable set top converters; Eagle traps; Harris & Prodelin satellite antenna.

Miles of plant: 1009.0 (coaxial); 43.0 (fiber optic). Additional miles planned: 20.0 (coaxial). Homes passed: 53,302.

Manager: Marc Lockard. Chief technician: Greg Siewert. Program director: George Ferrara. Marketing director: Joanne Carter.

City fee: 3% of gross.

Ownership: Lenfest Communications Inc. (MSO).

SHADE GAP—Shade Gap TV Assn., HC 83 Box 398, Shade Gap, PA 17255. Phone: 814-259-3673. County: Huntingdon. Also serves Dublin Twp. (Huntingdon County). ICA: PA0283.

TV Market Ranking: Outside TV Markets. Franchise award date: N.A. Franchise expiration date: N.A. Began: January 1, 1953.

Channel capacity: 14. Channels available but not in use: 2.

Basic Service

Subscribers: 120.

Programming (received off-air): WPSX-TV (P) Clearfield; WHAG-TV (N) Hagerstown; WHTM-TV (A) Harrisburg; WJAC-TV (N), WTAJ-TV (C) Johnstown-Altoona; WGAL (N), WLYH-TV (U) Lancaster; WPMT (F) York; allband FM.

Programming (via satellite): American Movie Classics; Country Music TV; Discovery Channel; Disney Channel; ESPN; Nashville Network; TBS Superstation; Trinity Bcstg. Network; Turner Network TV; USA Network.

Fee: $9.00 monthly.

Pay Service 1

Pay Units: 29.

Programming (via satellite): Cinemax.

Fee: $5.50 monthly.

Miles of plant: 4.0 (coaxial). Homes passed: 133. Total homes in franchised area: 133.

Manager: Richard Price.

Ownership: Shade Gap TV Assn.

SHARON—Century Communications, 155 Snyder Rd., Hermitage, PA 16148. Phones: 724-347-5543; 800-686-2728. Fax: 724-347-2886.

Web site: http://www.centurycomm.net. Counties: Mercer, PA; Trumbull, OH. Also serves Brookfield Twp. (Trumbull County), Hartford Twp. (Trumbull County), Hubbard Twp. (Trumbull County), Masury, Orangeville, Yankee Lake, OH; Clark, Farrell, Hermitage, Pymatuning Twp., Sharpsville, South Pymatuning Twp., West Middlesex, Wheatland, Wilmington Twp., PA. ICA: PA0038.

TV Market Ranking: 79. Franchise award date: N.A. Franchise expiration date: N.A. Began: March 1, 1966.

Channel capacity: 38 (not 2-way capable). Channels available but not in use: None.

Basic Service

Subscribers: 20,500.

Programming (received off-air): WNEO (P) Alliance; WUAB (U) Lorain-Cleveland; KDKA-TV (C), WQED (P) Pittsburgh; W50BF (I) Sharon; WFMJ-TV (N), WKBN-TV (C), WYTV (A,F) Youngstown.

Programming (via microwave): Ecumenical TV Channel.

Programming (via satellite): A & E; American Movie Classics; BET; C-SPAN; C-SPAN 2; CNBC; Country Music TV; Discovery Channel; E! Entertainment TV; ESPN; Fox Family Channel; FoxNet; Headline News; History Channel; Lifetime; MTV; Nickelodeon; QVC; The Weather Channel; Turner Network TV; USA Network; VH1.

Current originations: Public access.

Fee: $28.53 installation; $24.12 monthly; $0.21 converter; $10.06 additional installation.

Expanded Basic Service

Subscribers: N.A.

Programming (via satellite): CNN; Disney Channel; Fox Sports Net Pittsburgh; Nashville Network; TBS Superstation.

Fee: $6.71 monthly.

Pay Service 1

Pay Units: 7,800.

Programming (via satellite): Cinemax; HBO.

Fee: $9.00 monthly (Cinemax), $10.00 monthly (HBO).

Pay Service 2

Pay Units: N.A.

Programming (via satellite): Showtime.

Fee: $9.00 monthly.

Pay-Per-View

Addressable homes: 7,600.

Special events.

Fee: Varies.

Local advertising: Yes. Available in satellite distributed & character-generated programming. Regional interconnect: Cabletime.

Equipment: Jerrold headend; GTE Sylvania & Jerrold amplifiers; Belden & Times Fiber cable; Shibaden cameras; Sony VTRs; Telemation character generator; Jerrold set top converters; Oak addressable set top converters; Microdyne satellite antenna; Microdyne satellite receivers.

Miles of plant: 468.0 (coaxial); 28.0 (fiber optic). Homes passed: 31,300. Total homes in franchised area: 32,500.

Manager: Steve Hervatine. Chief technician: Ron Brown. Marketing director: Tony McLusky.

City fee: 3% of gross.

Ownership: Century Communications Corp. (MSO). See Cable System Ownership.

SHEFFIELD—West Side TV Corp., Box 812, Sheffield, PA 16347. Phone: 814-968-3346. County: Warren. Also serves Saybrook. ICA: PA0242.

TV Market Ranking: Below 100. Franchise award date: N.A. Franchise expiration date: N.A. Began: December 1, 1953.

Channel capacity: 12. Channels available but not in use: N.A.

Basic Service

Subscribers: 420.

Programming (received off-air): WIVB-TV (C), WKBW-TV (A) Buffalo; WPSX-TV (P) Clearfield; WICU-TV (N), WJET-TV (A) Erie; WJAC-TV (N), WTAJ-TV (C) Johnstown-Altoona; KDKA-TV (C) Pittsburgh; allband FM.

Fee: $225.00 installation.

Equipment: Blonder-Tongue headend; Jerrold amplifiers; Times Fiber cable.

Miles of plant: 12.0 (coaxial). Homes passed: 425.

Manager: Charles Culbertson. Chief technician: Gary Fitzgerald.

Ownership: West Side TV Corp.

SHEFFIELD—South Side TV Assn., Pickering St., Sheffield, PA 16347. Phone: 814-968-5493. County: Warren. ICA: PA0246.

TV Market Ranking: Below 100. Franchise award date: N.A. Franchise expiration date: N.A. Began: May 1, 1953.

Channel capacity: 12. Channels available but not in use: N.A.

Basic Service

Subscribers: 350.

Programming (received off-air): WGRZ-TV (N), WIVB-TV (C), WKBW-TV (A) Buffalo; WPSX-TV (P) Clearfield; WICU-TV (N), WSEE (C) Erie; WJAC-TV (N), WTAJ-TV (C) Johnstown-Altoona.

Programming (via satellite): Turner Network TV.

Fee: $80.00 installation.

Equipment: Ameco & Blonder-Tongue headend; Ameco amplifiers.

Miles of plant: 8.0 (coaxial). Homes passed: 400.

Ownership: South Side TV Assn.

SHENANDOAH—Shen-Heights TV Assoc. Inc., 38 N. Main St., Shenandoah, PA 17976. Phone: 570-462-1911. Fax: 570-462-1948. County: Schuylkill. Also serves Brandonville, East Union Twp., Oneida, Sheppton, Union Twp. (Schuylkill County), West Mahanoy Twp. ICA: PA0114.

TV Market Ranking: 49. Franchise award date: October 1, 1951. Franchise expiration date: October 1, 2001. Began: October 1, 1950.

Channel capacity: 60 (not 2-way capable). Channels available but not in use: 10.

Basic Service

Subscribers: 3,900.

Programming (received off-air): WOLF-TV (F), WYLN-LP (W) Hazleton; KYW-TV (C), WCAU (N), WPSG (U), WPVI-TV (A) Philadelphia; WBRE-TV (N), WNEP-TV (A), WSWB (W), WVIA-TV (P), WYOU (C) Scranton & Wilkes-Barre; allband FM.

Programming (via satellite): WGN-TV (W) Chicago; WPIX (W) New York; Home Shopping Network; Pennsylvania Cable Network; QVC.

Current originations: Automated time-weather.

Fee: $20.00 installation; $9.50 monthly.

Expanded Basic Service

Subscribers: 3,875.

Programming (via satellite): A & E; American Movie Classics; C-SPAN; CNBC; CNN; Cartoon Network; Comedy Central; Country Music TV; Discovery Channel; Disney Channel; E! Entertainment TV; ESPN; ESPN 2; EWTN; Fox Family Channel; Fox Sports Net; History Channel; Home & Garden Television; Learning Channel; Lifetime; MSNBC; MTV; Nashville Network; Nickelodeon; Sci-Fi Channel; TBS Superstation; The Weather Channel; Travel Channel; Trinity Bcstg. Network; Turner Network TV; USA Network; VH1.

Fee: $20.00 installation; $20.45 monthly.

Pay Service 1

Pay Units: N.A.

Programming (via satellite): Cinemax; HBO; Showtime.

Fee: $20.00 installation; $10.00 monthly (each).

Pay-Per-View

Addressable homes: 600.

Action Pay-Per-View; Playboy TV.

Local advertising: Yes. Available in satellite distributed, character-generated & automated programming. Rates: $25.00/Week.

Equipment: Jerrold headend; Jerrold amplifiers; Times Fiber cable; Sony cameras; Sony VTRs; MSI & Texscan character generator; Jerrold set top converters; Scientific-Atlanta satellite antenna; Microdyne & Scientific-Atlanta satellite receivers.

Miles of plant: 42.0 (coaxial). Additional miles planned: 5.0 (coaxial). Homes passed: 6,500.

Manager: Martin Brophy. Chief technician: Anthony Brophy.

Ownership: Martin P. Brophy.

SHIPPINGPORT BOROUGH—TCI Cablevision of Ohio Inc., 2650 Weir Rd. NE, Warren, OH 44483. Phone: 330-372-1112. County: Beaver. Also serves Shippingport. ICA: PA0296.

TV Market Ranking: 10,90. Franchise award date: N.A. Franchise expiration date: N.A. Began: December 1, 1977.

Channel capacity: 24. Channels available but not in use: 1.

Basic Service

Subscribers: 90.

Programming (received off-air): WNEO (P) Alliance; WPCB-TV (I) Greensburg; KDKA-TV (C), WCWB (W), WPGH-TV (F), WPXI (N), WQED (P), WQEX (P), WTAE-TV (A) Pittsburgh; WTOV-TV (N) Steubenville-Wheeling; WTRF-TV (C) Wheeling-Steubenville; WFMJ-TV (N), WKBN-TV (C), WYTV (A,F) Youngstown.

Programming (via satellite): WGN-TV (W) Chicago; CNN; ESPN; Fox Family Channel; Nashville Network; TBS Superstation; Turner Network TV; USA Network.

Fee: $60.00 installation; $11.45 monthly.

Equipment: Blonder-Tongue headend; C-COR amplifiers; Comm/Scope cable; Microdyne satellite antenna.

Miles of plant: 7.0 (coaxial). Homes passed: 98.

Manager: Terry Kelley. Chief technician: Carl Larkins.

City fee: None.

Ownership: AT&T Broadband & Internet Services (MSO). Purchased from Tele-Communications Inc., March 9, 1999.

SHIRLEY TWP.—TCI of Pennsylvania Inc., Box 312, 130 W. Market St., Lewistown, PA 17044-2129. Phone: 717-248-0193. Counties: Huntingdon & Mifflin. Also serves Kistler, Mount Union, Newton Hamilton, Shirleysburg, Wayne Twp. (Mifflin County). ICA: PA0139.

TV Market Ranking: 74. Franchise award date: N.A. Franchise expiration date: N.A. Began: January 1, 1953.

Channel capacity: 21 (not 2-way capable). Channels available but not in use: None.

Basic Service

Subscribers: 2,468.

Programming (received off-air): WPSX-TV (P) Clearfield; WATM-TV (A), WJAC-TV (N), WTAJ-TV (C) Johnstown-Altoona; WGAL (N) Lancaster; WPMT (F) York; allband FM.

Programming (via satellite): WGN-TV (W) Chicago; CNN; Discovery Channel; ESPN; Fox Family Channel; MTV; Nashville Network; Nickelodeon; QVC; TBS Superstation; USA Network.

Fee: $59.95 installation; $15.70 monthly.

Pay Service 1

Pay Units: 68.

Programming (via satellite): Disney Channel.

Fee: N.A.

Pay Service 2

Pay Units: 430.

Programming (via satellite): HBO.

Fee: N.A.

Pay Service 3

Pay Units: 122.

Programming (via satellite): The Movie Channel.

Fee: N.A.

Local advertising: Planned.

Program Guide: The Cable Guide.

Equipment: Jerrold headend; Coral & Scientific-Atlanta amplifiers; Times Fiber cable; Jerrold set top converters; Pico traps; Microdyne satellite antenna; Drake & Scientific-Atlanta satellite receivers.

Miles of plant: 67.4 (coaxial). Homes passed: 2,792. Total homes in franchised area: 4,629.

Manager: Chuck Horner. Chief technician: Dennis Treaster.

Ownership: AT&T Broadband & Internet Services (MSO). Purchased from Tele-Communications Inc., March 9, 1999.

SIX MILE RUN—Six Mile Run TV Corp., c/o Dale Roarbaugh, Six Mile Run, PA 16679. Phone: 814-928-4897. County: Bedford. ICA: PA0295.

TV Market Ranking: 74. Franchise award date: N.A. Franchise expiration date: N.A. Began: April 20, 1951.

Channel capacity: 12. Channels available but not in use: None.

Basic Service

Subscribers: 64.

Programming (received off-air): WPSX-TV (P) Clearfield; WJAC-TV (N), WTAJ-TV (C) Johnstown-Altoona; KDKA-TV (C), WTAE-TV (A) Pittsburgh; allband FM.

Programming (via satellite): TBS Superstation; Turner Classic Movies.

Fee: $40.00 installation; $7.00 monthly.

Pay Service 1

Pay Units: N.A.

Programming (via satellite): HBO.

Fee: $7.00 monthly.

Equipment: Coral amplifiers; CCS Hatfield & Comm/Scope cable.

Miles of plant: 3.0 (coaxial). Homes passed: 100.

Manager: Dale Roarbaugh. Chief technician: Harold Colbert.

City fee: None.

Ownership: Six Mile Run TV Corp.

SMETHPORT—TCI of Pennsylvania Inc., 138 N. Fraley St., Kane, PA 16735-1386. Phone: 814-837-6272. Fax: 814-837-9701. County: McKean. Also serves Coryville, Duke Center, Eldred, Farmers Valley, Foster Twp. (McKean County), Keating Twp. (McKean County), Otto, Rixford. ICA: PA0147.

TV Market Ranking: Outside TV Markets. Franchise award date: N.A. Franchise expiration date: N.A. Began: June 1, 1953.

Channel capacity: 40. Channels available but not in use: N.A.

Basic Service

Subscribers: 2,123.

Programming (received off-air): WGRZ-TV (N), WIVB-TV (C), WKBW-TV (A) Buffalo; WPSX-TV (P) Clearfield; WICU-TV (N) Erie; WTAJ-TV (C) Johnstown-Altoona; allband FM.

Programming (via satellite): WGN-TV (W) Chicago; C-SPAN; FoxNet; Odyssey; QVC; TBS Superstation; TV Guide Channel.

Current originations: Automated time-weather.

Fee: $59.95 installation; $10.25 monthly; $2.00 converter; $49.95 additional installation.

Expanded Basic Service

Subscribers: 1,872.

Programming (via satellite): American Movie Classics; CNBC; CNN; Court TV; Discovery Channel; ESPN; FX; Fox Family Channel; Fox Sports Net Pittsburgh; Headline News; Lifetime; MTV; Nashville Network; Nickelodeon; The Weather Channel; Turner Network TV; USA Network.

Fee: $11.42 monthly.

Pay Service 1

Pay Units: 298.

Programming (via satellite): HBO.

Fee: $19.95 installation; $13.15 monthly.

Pay Service 2

Pay Units: 286.

Programming (via satellite): Showtime.

Fee: $19.95 installation; $13.15 monthly.

Pay Service 3

Pay Units: 921.

Programming (via satellite): The New Encore.

Fee: N.A.

Pay Service 4

Pay Units: N.A.

Programming (via satellite): Starz!

Fee: N.A.

Pay-Per-View

Action Pay-Per-View; special events.

Equipment: Jerrold headend; Jerrold amplifiers; Times Fiber cable; Sony cameras; Sony VTRs; Video Data Systems character generator; Scientific-Atlanta satellite antenna.

Miles of plant: 76.7 (coaxial). Homes passed: 2,339. Total homes in franchised area: 2,339.

Manager: Chuck Horner. Customer service manager: Pam Bizzak. Office manager: LuAnn Glenn.

City fee: None.

Ownership: AT&T Broadband & Internet Services (MSO). Purchased from Tele-Communications Inc., March 9, 1999.

SNOW SHOE—CableVision Communications, Box 2200, 68 5th St., Buckhannon, WV 26201. Phone: 304-472-4193. Fax: 304-472-0756. Counties: Centre & Clearfield. Also serves Burnside Twp. (Centre County), Clarence, Cooper Twp. (Clearfield County), Covington Twp. (Clearfield County), Girard Twp. (Clearfield County), Grassflat, Karthaus Twp., Snow Shoe Borough, Snow Shoe Twp. ICA: PA0188.

TV Market Ranking: Outside TV Markets. Franchise award date: N.A. Franchise expiration date: N.A. Began: May 1, 1957.

Channel capacity: 23. Channels available but not in use: N.A.

Basic Service

Subscribers: 695.

Programming (received off-air): WPSX-TV (P) Clearfield; WJAC-TV (N), WTAJ-TV (C) Johnstown-Altoona; WPIX (W) New York; WNEP-TV (A) Scranton & Wilkes-Barre; allband FM.

Programming (via satellite): WGN-TV (W) Chicago; WPIX (W) New York; Animal Planet; CNN; Discovery Channel; Disney Channel; ESPN; Fox Family Channel; FoxNet; MTV; Nashville Network; Nickelodeon; TBS Superstation; Turner Network TV; USA Network.

Fee: $61.25 installation; $19.76 monthly; $1.24 converter.

Pay Service 1

Pay Units: 427.

Programming (via satellite): HBO; Showtime.

Fee: $11.95 monthly (Showtime), $11.99 monthly (HBO).

Pay Service 2

Pay Units: N.A.

Programming (via satellite): Cinemax; The Movie Channel.

Fee: $7.95 monthly (Cinemax), $11.95 monthly (TMC).

Local advertising: Yes. Available in locally originated programming.

Equipment: Blonder-Tongue & Olson headend; C-COR amplifiers; Comm/Scope cable; AFC satellite antenna.

Miles of plant: 34.0 (coaxial). Additional miles planned: 1.0 (coaxial). Homes passed: 1,213.

Manager: Willie Critchfield. Chief technician: Bill Turner.

Ownership: Rifkin & Associates Inc. (MSO). See Cable System Ownership.

SOMERSET—CableVision Communications, Box 2200, 68 5th St., Buckhannon, WV 26201. Phone: 304-472-4193. Fax: 304-472-0756. Counties: Fayette & Somerset. Also serves Acosta, Allanvale, Alpine Heights, Bakersville, Barionville, Boswell, Champion, Chickentown, Edie, Friedens, Gray, Hidden Valley, Jefferson Twp. (Somerset County), Jenner Twp. (Somerset County), Jennerstown (Somerset County), Kingwood, Levansville, Lincoln Twp. (Somerset County), Listie, Markleton, Middle Creek Twp., New Centerville, New Lexington, Pioneer Park Camp Ground, Posey Corners, Poverty Hollow, Quecreek, Quemahoning Twp. (Somerset County), Rockwood Borough, Roytown, Saltlick Twp. (Fayette County), Scottyland, Scullton, Seven Springs, Sipesville, Somerset County, Somerset Twp. (Somerset County), Swiss Mountain, Trent, Upper Turkeyfoot Twp. (Somerset County). ICA: PA0128.

TV Market Ranking: 74 (Acosta, Allanvale, Alpine Heights, Bakersville, Barionville, Boswell, Champion, Chickentown, Edie, Friedens, Gray, Hidden Valley, Jefferson Twp., Jenner Twp., Jennerstown, Kingwood, Levansville, Lincoln Twp., Listie, Middle Creek Twp., New Centerville, New Lexington, Pioneer Park Camp Ground, Posey Corners, Poverty Hollow, Quecreek, Quemahoning Twp., Rockwood Borough, Roytown, Saltlick Twp., Scottyland, Scullton, Seven Springs, Sipesville, Somerset, portions of Somerset County, Somerset Twp., Swiss Mountain, Trent, Upper Turkeyfoot Twp.); Below 100 (Markleton, portions of Somerset County); Outside TV Markets (portions of Somerset County). Franchise award date: N.A. Franchise expiration date: N.A. Began: N.A.

Channel capacity: 30. Channels available but not in use: N.A.

Basic Service

Subscribers: 1,783.

Programming (received off-air): WPCB-TV (I) Greensburg; WNPA (U) Jeanette; WJAC-TV (N), WTAJ-TV (C), WWCP-TV (F) Johnstown-Altoona; WNPB-TV (P) Morgantown; KDKA-TV (C), WCWB (W), WPGH-TV (F),

WPXI (N), WQED (P), WTAE-TV (A) Pittsburgh.
Programming (via satellite): WGN-TV (W) Chicago; Discovery Channel; Fox Family Channel; TBS Superstation; The Weather Channel.
Fee: $61.25 installation; $16.70 monthly; $1.24 converter.

Expanded Basic Service
Subscribers: 1,385.
Programming (via satellite): American Movie Classics; CNN; Disney Channel; ESPN; Fox Sports Net Pittsburgh; MTV; Nashville Network; Nickelodeon; Trinity Bcstg. Network; Turner Network TV; USA Network.
Fee: $17.50 installation; $11.16 monthly.

Pay Service 1
Pay Units: 724.
Programming (via satellite): Cinemax; HBO; Showtime.
Fee: $10.00 installation; $7.95 monthly (Cinemax), $11.95 monthly (Showtime), $11.99 monthly (HBO).

Pay Service 2
Pay Units: N.A.
Programming (via satellite): The Movie Channel.
Fee: $11.95 monthly.

Local advertising: Yes.
Equipment: M/A-Com & Olson headend; Jerrold amplifiers; Comm/Scope cable.
Miles of plant: 101.0 (coaxial). Homes passed: 3,497.
Manager: Willie Critchfield. Chief technician: Bill Turner. Marketing director: Kenny Phillips.
Ownership: Rifkin & Associates Inc. (MSO). See Cable System Ownership.

SOMERSET BOROUGH—TCI of Pennsylvania Inc., Box 406, Rtes. 219 & 281, Somerset, PA 15501-0406. Phone: 814-443-4838. County: Somerset. Also serves Boswell, Jenners, Jennerstown (Somerset County), Lincoln (Somerset County), Milford (Somerset County), Quemahoning (Somerset County), Somerset Twp. (Somerset County). ICA: PA0091.
TV Market Ranking: 74. Franchise award date: N.A. Franchise expiration date: N.A. Began: December 1, 1965.
Channel capacity: 60. Channels available but not in use: 25.

Basic Service
Subscribers: 6,365.
Programming (received off-air): WPSX-TV (P) Clearfield; WPCB-TV (I) Greensburg; WATM-TV (A), WJAC-TV (N), WTAJ-TV (C), WWCP-TV (F) Johnstown-Altoona; KDKA-TV (C), WQED (P), WTAE-TV (A) Pittsburgh.
Programming (via satellite): A & E; C-SPAN; CNN; Discovery Channel; EWTN; Fox Family Channel; Headline News; Lifetime; MTV; Nashville Network; Nickelodeon; Odyssey; QVC; TBS Superstation; The Weather Channel.
Fee: $59.95 installation; $9.32 monthly; $2.00 converter; $49.95 additional installation.

Expanded Basic Service
Subscribers: 6,002.
Programming (via satellite): American Movie Classics; Court TV; ESPN; Fox Sports Net Pittsburgh; Turner Network TV; USA Network.
Fee: $12.78 monthly.

Pay Service 1
Pay Units: 166.
Programming (via satellite): Cinemax.
Fee: $13.15 monthly.

Pay Service 2
Pay Units: 287.
Programming (via satellite): Disney Channel.
Fee: $10.95 monthly.

Pay Service 3
Pay Units: 779.
Programming (via satellite): HBO.
Fee: $13.15 monthly.

Pay Service 4
Pay Units: 725.
Programming (via satellite): Showtime.
Fee: $13.15 monthly.

Pay Service 5
Pay Units: 1,953.
Programming (via satellite): The New Encore.
Fee: N.A.

Program Guide: The Cable Guide.
Miles of plant: 189.9 (coaxial). Homes passed: 8,158. Total homes in franchised area: 12,229.
Manager: Michael Berrier. Chief technician: Jeffrey Fassnacht.
Ownership: AT&T Broadband & Internet Services (MSO). Purchased from Tele-Communications Inc., March 9, 1999.

SOUTH BUFFALO TWP.—South Buffalo Cablevision, 259 Horseshoe Dr., Freeport, PA 16229. Phone: 724-295-3466. County: Armstrong. ICA: PA0257.
TV Market Ranking: 10. Franchise award date: N.A. Franchise expiration date: N.A. Began: January 1, 1988.
Channel capacity: N.A. Channels available but not in use: N.A.

Basic Service
Subscribers: 162.
Programming (received off-air): WPCB-TV (I) Greensburg; WJAC-TV (N) Johnstown-Altoona; KDKA-TV (C), WCWB (W), WPGH-TV (F), WPXI (N), WQED (P), WQEX (P) Pittsburgh.
Programming (via satellite): WGN-TV (W) Chicago; CNN; Discovery Channel; ESPN; Nashville Network; TBS Superstation.
Fee: $27.00 installation; $12.95 monthly.

Pay Service 1
Pay Units: N.A.
Programming (via satellite): Disney Channel; HBO.
Fee: $7.95 monthly (Disney), $9.95 monthly (HBO).

Miles of plant: 11.0 (coaxial). Homes passed: 285. Total homes in franchised area: 365.
Manager: Richard P. Koglman.
Ownership: South Buffalo Cablevision.

SOUTH FORK—TCI of Pennsylvania Inc., Box 349, Rte. 219, Carrolltown, PA 15722. Phone: 814-344-6518. County: Cambria. Also serves Croyle Twp. (Cambria County), Ehrenfeld, Summerhill, Wilmore. ICA: PA0189.
TV Market Ranking: 74. Franchise award date: N.A. Franchise expiration date: N.A. Began: August 1, 1971.
Channel capacity: 52. Channels available but not in use: 16.

Basic Service
Subscribers: 1,011.
Programming (received off-air): WPSX-TV (P) Clearfield; WATM-TV (A), WJAC-TV (N), WKBS-TV (I), WTAJ-TV (C), WWCP-TV (F) Johnstown-Altoona; KDKA-TV (C), WPGH-TV (F), WPXI (N), WQED (P), WTAE-TV (A) Pittsburgh.
Programming (via satellite): WGN-TV (W) Chicago; C-SPAN; CNBC; CNN; Discovery Channel; Fox Family Channel; Headline News; Ladbroke Racing Channel/Meadows Racing Network; Lifetime; MTV; Nashville Network; Nickelodeon; QVC; TBS Superstation; The Weather Channel.
Fee: $59.95 installation; $10.36 monthly; $0.43 converter; $49.95 additional installation.

Expanded Basic Service
Subscribers: 926.
Programming (via satellite): American Movie Classics; Court TV; ESPN; Fox Sports Net Pittsburgh; Turner Network TV; USA Network.
Fee: $12.21 monthly.

Pay Service 1
Pay Units: 48.
Programming (via satellite): Cinemax.
Fee: $13.15 monthly.

Pay Service 2
Pay Units: 130.
Programming (via satellite): HBO.
Fee: $13.15 monthly.

Pay Service 3
Pay Units: 84.
Programming (via satellite): Showtime.
Fee: $13.15 monthly.

Pay Service 4
Pay Units: 36.
Programming (via satellite): The New Encore.
Fee: N.A.

Miles of plant: 23.4 (coaxial). Homes passed: 1,207. Total homes in franchised area: 1,207.
Manager: Randy Bender.
Ownership: AT&T Broadband & Internet Services (MSO). Purchased from Tele-Communications Inc., March 9, 1999.

SPARTANSBURG—DuCom Cable TV, 50 Tipp St., Du Bois, PA 15801. Phone: 814-371-1925. Fax: 814-371-3052.
E-mail: ducom@key-net.net.
County: Crawford. Also serves Sparta Twp. (Crawford County). ICA: PA0438.
TV Market Ranking: Below 100. Franchise award date: N.A. Franchise expiration date: N.A. Began: N.A.
Channel capacity: 41 (not 2-way capable). Channels available but not in use: 13.

Basic Service
Subscribers: 123.
Programming (received off-air): WFXP (F), WICU-TV (N), WJET-TV (A), WQLN (P), WSEE (C) Erie.
Programming (via satellite): WGN-TV (W) Chicago; A & E; C-SPAN 2; CNN; Country Music TV; Discovery Channel; Disney Channel; ESPN; ESPN 2; Fox Family Channel; Headline News; Lifetime; Nashville Network; Nickelodeon; QVC; Sci-Fi Channel; TBS Superstation; Trinity Bcstg. Network; Turner Network TV; USA Network; VH1.
Fee: $45.00 installation; $23.00 monthly; $2.50 converter.

Pay Service 1
Pay Units: 29.
Programming (via satellite): HBO.
Fee: $10.95 monthly.

Local advertising: No.
Miles of plant: 5.0 (coaxial). Additional miles planned: 5.0 (coaxial). Homes passed: 150.
Manager: Rodney Preston. Chief engineer: David Kucenski.
Ownership: Dubois Communications Inc. (MSO).

SPRING MILLS—Spring Mills TV Co., Box 241, RD 3, Spring Mills, PA 16875. Phones: 814-422-8460; 814-422-8453. County: Centre. ICA: PA0268.
TV Market Ranking: Outside TV Markets. Franchise award date: N.A. Franchise expiration date: N.A. Began: January 1, 1968.
Channel capacity: 16 (not 2-way capable). Channels available but not in use: None.

Basic Service
Subscribers: 192.
Programming (received off-air): WPSX-TV (P) Clearfield; WATM-TV (A), WKBS-TV (I), WTAJ-TV (C) Johnstown-Altoona; WBRE-TV (N), WNEP-TV (A), WVIA-TV (P) Scranton & Wilkes-Barre; allband FM.
Programming (via satellite): CNN; Discovery Channel; Disney Channel; ESPN; Fox Family Channel; FoxNet; Nashville Network; TBS Superstation; Turner Network TV.
Fee: $50.00 installation; $9.00 monthly.

Local advertising: No.
Miles of plant: 4.0 (coaxial). Homes passed: 200. Total homes in franchised area: 204.
Manager: Schenley Johnson. Chief technician: Lynn McCool.
Ownership: Spring Mills TV Co.

SPRING TWP. (Crawford County)—TCI of Pennsylvania Inc., Box 7129, 5651 Jordan Rd., Erie, PA 16510-0129. Phones: 814-899-0625; 800-321-4451. Fax: 814-898-1540. County: Crawford. Also serves Conneautville, Spring, Springboro. ICA: PA0230.
TV Market Ranking: Below 100. Franchise award date: N.A. Franchise expiration date: N.A. Began: January 1, 1961.
Channel capacity: 35 (not 2-way capable). Channels available but not in use: None.

Basic Service
Subscribers: 522.
Programming (received off-air): WEWS-TV (A), WJW (F) Cleveland; WFXP (F), WICU-TV (N), WJET-TV (A), WQLN (P), WSEE (C) Erie; WFMJ-TV (N), WKBN-TV (C) Youngstown; allband FM.
Programming (via satellite): Discovery Channel; Odyssey; QVC; TBS Superstation.
Fee: $44.95 installation; $10.76 monthly.

Expanded Basic Service
Subscribers: 482.
Programming (via satellite): Animal Planet; C-SPAN; CNBC; CNN; Cartoon Network; ESPN; Fox Family Channel; Fox News Channel; Headline News; Lifetime; MTV; Nashville Network; Nickelodeon; The Weather Channel; Turner Network TV; USA Network.
Fee: $12.01 monthly.

Pay Service 1
Pay Units: 106.
Programming (via satellite): HBO.
Fee: $20.00 installation; $7.00 monthly.

Pay Service 2
Pay Units: N.A.
Programming (via satellite): Disney Channel; Starz!; The New Encore (multiplexed).
Fee: N.A.

Equipment: Jerrold headend; Jerrold amplifiers.
Miles of plant: 13.0 (coaxial). Homes passed: 588. Total homes in franchised area: 588.
Manager: Tom Carey. Chief technician: Bob Westland.
City fee: $1.00 annually.
Ownership: AT&T Broadband & Internet Services (MSO). Purchased from Tele-Communications Inc., March 9, 1999.

SPRUCE CREEK TWP.—County Cable Inc., 217 E. 9th St., Hazleton, PA 18201. Phone: 717-455-6851. Fax: 717-459-0963. County: Huntingdon. Also serves Franklin Twp. (Huntingdon County). ICA: PA0274.
TV Market Ranking: 74. Franchise award date: N.A. Franchise expiration date: N.A. Began: November 1, 1984.
Channel capacity: 42 (not 2-way capable). Channels available but not in use: 20.

Basic Service
Subscribers: 137.
Programming (received off-air): WPSX-TV (P) Clearfield; WATM-TV (A), WJAC-TV (N),

WKBS-TV (I), WTAJ-TV (C), WWCP-TV (F) Johnstown-Altoona; allband FM.
Programming (via translator): WWOR-TV (U) New York.
Programming (via satellite): CNN; Discovery Channel; ESPN; FX; Fox Family Channel; Lifetime; Nashville Network; Nickelodeon; QVC; TBS Superstation; Turner Network TV; USA Network.
Fee: $42.95 installation; $23.50 monthly.

Pay Service 1
Pay Units: 16.
Programming (via satellite): HBO.
Fee: $12.95 monthly.

Pay Service 2
Pay Units: 8.
Programming (via satellite): Cinemax.
Fee: $12.95 monthly.

Equipment: Blonder-Tongue headend; C-COR amplifiers.
Miles of plant: 10.5 (coaxial). Homes passed: 171.
Manager: Joseph W. Aman.
Twp. fee: $1.00 annually.
Ownership: Gans Multimedia Partnership (MSO).

ST. MARYS—St. Marys TV, 314 S. Michael St., St. Marys, PA 15857. Phone: 814-781-1466. Fax: 814-834-1706. County: Elk. Also serves Benzinger Twp., Daguscahonda, Fox Twp. (Elk County), Kersey, Toby. ICA: PA0101.
TV Market Ranking: Outside TV Markets. Franchise award date: N.A. Franchise expiration date: N.A. Began: May 1, 1953.
Channel capacity: 45 (2-way capable; operating 2-way). Channels available but not in use: 6.

Basic Service
Subscribers: 6,810.
Programming (received off-air): WPSX-TV (P) Clearfield; WICU-TV (N) Erie; WATM-TV (A), WJAC-TV (N), WKBS-TV (I), WTAJ-TV (C), WWCP-TV (F) Johnstown-Altoona; WQED (P), WTAE-TV (A) Pittsburgh.
Programming (via satellite): WGN-TV (W) Chicago; WPIX (W) New York; A & E; C-SPAN; CNBC; CNN; Comedy Central; Country Music TV; Discovery Channel; E! Entertainment TV; ESPN; ESPN 2; ESPNews; EWTN; Fox Family Channel; Fox Sports Net Pittsburgh; Headline News; Home Shopping Network; Learning Channel; MTV; Nashville Network; Nick at Nite's TV Land; Nickelodeon; TBS Superstation; TV Guide Channel; The Weather Channel; Turner Classic Movies; Turner Network TV; USA Network; VH1.
Current originations: Automated time-weather; public access; educational access; automated emergency alert.
Fee: $50.00 installation; $17.25 monthly; $1.75 converter.

Pay Service 1
Pay Units: 667.
Programming (via satellite): Disney Channel.
Fee: $9.00 installation; $7.00 monthly.

Pay Service 2
Pay Units: 1,013.
Programming (via satellite): HBO.
Fee: $9.00 installation; $10.00 monthly.

Pay Service 3
Pay Units: 838.
Programming (via satellite): The Movie Channel.
Fee: $9.00 installation; $2.95 monthly.

Pay Service 4
Pay Units: 524.
Programming (via satellite): Showtime.
Fee: $9.00 installation; $10.00 monthly.

Local advertising: Yes (insert only). Available in locally originated & taped programming.
Equipment: Jerrold headend; Ameco amplifiers; Jerrold set top converters; Scientific-Atlanta satellite antenna; Scientific-Atlanta satellite receivers.
Miles of plant: 187.0 (coaxial); 8.3 (fiber optic). Additional miles planned: 9.0 (coaxial); 12.0 (fiber optic). Homes passed: 7,000. Total homes in franchised area: 7,000.
Manager: Cletas Heller. Chief technician: Ronald Snelick.
Franchise fee: $0.50 per subscriber (Benzinger Twp. & St. Marys).
Ownership: St. Marys TV.

ST. PETERSBURG—TCI of Pennsylvania Inc., 855 Main St., Clarion, PA 16214-1161. Phone: 800-692-6205. Counties: Armstrong, Clarion & Venango. Also serves Emlenton, Foxburg, Hovey Twp., Parker, Perry Twp. (Clarion County), Richland Twp. (Clarion County). ICA: PA0195.
TV Market Ranking: Outside TV Markets. Franchise award date: N.A. Franchise expiration date: N.A. Began: October 1, 1968.
Channel capacity: 31. Channels available but not in use: None.

Basic Service
Subscribers: 1,030.
Programming (received off-air): WPSX-TV (P) Clearfield; WJAC-TV (N), WTAJ-TV (C) Johnstown-Altoona; KDKA-TV (C), WCWB (W), WPGH-TV (F), WPXI (N), WQED (P), WTAE-TV (A) Pittsburgh; allband FM.
Programming (via satellite): WGN-TV (W) Chicago; C-SPAN; CNN; Discovery Channel; Fox Family Channel; Lifetime; MTV; Nashville Network; Nickelodeon; QVC; TBS Superstation; The Weather Channel.
Fee: $59.95 installation; $16.59 monthly.

Expanded Basic Service
Subscribers: 444.
Programming (via satellite): American Movie Classics; ESPN; Fox Sports Net Pittsburgh; Turner Network TV; USA Network.
Fee: $1.95 monthly.

Pay Service 1
Pay Units: 137.
Programming (via satellite): Cinemax.
Fee: N.A.

Pay Service 2
Pay Units: 380.
Programming (via satellite): The New Encore.
Fee: N.A.

Pay Service 3
Pay Units: 227.
Programming (via satellite): HBO.
Fee: N.A.

Equipment: Blonder-Tongue headend; AEL amplifiers; Times Fiber cable.
Miles of plant: 27.8 (coaxial). Homes passed: 1,137. Total homes in franchised area: 1,488.
Manager: W. Ben Call. Chief technician: Greg Allshouse.
City fee: $450.00 annually.
Ownership: AT&T Broadband & Internet Services (MSO). Purchased from Tele-Communications Inc., March 9, 1999.

STATE COLLEGE—AT&T Cable Services, 1155 Benner Pike, State College, PA 16801. Phones: 814-238-3096; 800-992-3515. Counties: Centre & Huntingdon. Also serves Bellefonte, Benner Twp., Boggs Twp. (Centre County), Centre Hall, College Twp. (Centre County), Ferguson Twp., Franklin Twp. (Huntingdon County), Halfmoon Twp., Harris Twp. (Centre County), Milesburg, Patton Twp. (Centre County), Port Matilda, Potter Twp. (Centre County), Spring Twp. (Centre County), Stormstown, Worth Twp. Plans service to Linden Hall. ICA: PA0037.
TV Market Ranking: 74 (portions of Benner Twp., College Twp., Ferguson Twp., Franklin Twp., Halfmoon Twp., portions of Harris Twp., Patton Twp., Port Matilda, State College, Stormstown, Worth Twp.); Outside TV Markets (Bellefonte, portions of Benner Twp., Boggs Twp., Centre Hall, portions of Harris Twp., Milesburg, Potter Twp., Spring Twp.). Franchise award date: N.A. Franchise expiration date: N.A. Began: February 1, 1952.
Channel capacity: 53. Channels available but not in use: N.A.

Basic Service
Subscribers: 23,408.
Programming (received off-air): WATM-TV (A), WKBS-TV (I), WTAJ-TV (C), WWCP-TV (F) Johnstown-Altoona.
Programming (via microwave): WPSX-TV (P) Clearfield; WJAC-TV (N) Johnstown-Altoona; WPIX (W) New York; WNEP-TV (A) Scranton & Wilkes-Barre.
Programming (via satellite): C-SPAN; C/Net: The Computer Network; Discovery Channel; EWTN; Odyssey; Pennsylvania Cable Network; QVC; TBS Superstation; TV Guide Channel.
Current originations: Educational access; government access; leased access; local news.
Fee: $59.95 installation; $8.95 monthly; $2.00 converter; $49.95 additional installation.

Digital Basic Service
Subscribers: N.A.
Programming (via satellite): BBC America; Bravo; Discovery Civilization Channel; Discovery Health Channel; Discovery Home & Leisure Channel; Discovery Kids Channel; Discovery People; Discovery Science Channel; Discovery Wings Channel; ESPN Classic Sports; ESPNews; Fox Sports World; Game Show Network; Golf Channel; History Channel; Home & Garden Television; Independent Film Channel; Outdoor Life Network; Romance Classics; Sci-Fi Channel; Speedvision; Turner Classic Movies.
Fee: N.A.

Expanded Basic Service
Subscribers: 21,061.
Programming (via satellite): A & E; American Movie Classics; Animal Planet; BET; C-SPAN 2; CNBC; CNN; Cartoon Network; Comedy Central; Court TV; Disney Channel; E! Entertainment TV; ESPN; ESPN 2; FX; Fox Family Channel; Fox News Channel; Fox Sports Net Pittsburgh; Headline News; Home Shopping Network; Knowledge TV; Learning Channel; Lifetime; MSNBC; MTV; Nashville Network; Nick at Nite's TV Land; Nickelodeon; Pax Net; TV Food Network; The Health Network; The Weather Channel; Travel Channel; Turner Network TV; USA Network; VH1.
Fee: $13.69 monthly.

Pay Service 1
Pay Units: 2,114.
Programming (via satellite): Cinemax.
Fee: $13.15 monthly.

Pay Service 2
Pay Units: 5,390.
Programming (via satellite): HBO.
Fee: $13.15 monthly.

Pay Service 3
Pay Units: 994.
Programming (via satellite): Showtime.
Fee: $13.15 monthly.

Pay Service 4
Pay Units: 8,089.
Programming (via satellite): The New Encore.
Fee: N.A.

Pay Service 5
Pay Units: N.A.
Programming (via satellite): Starz!
Fee: N.A.

Digital Pay Service 1
Pay Units: N.A.
Programming (via satellite): DMX; Encore Love Stories; Encore Mystery; Encore Westerns; HBO Plus; HBO Signature; Showtime Beyond; Starz! Theater; The Movie Channel.
Fee: N.A.

Pay-Per-View
Action Pay-Per-View; Spice delivered digitally; movies delivered digitally; special events.

Local advertising: Yes.
Program Guide: The Cable Guide.
Equipment: CAS headend; C-COR amplifiers; General cable; Jerrold addressable set top converters; Hughes satellite antenna.
Miles of plant: 424.4 (coaxial); 77.0 (fiber optic). Homes passed: 31,966. Total homes in franchised area: 39,562.
Manager: Jeff Fisher. Chief technician: Curt Kosko. Marketing director: Neill Jones.
City fee: 3% of gross ($2,000 minimum).
Ownership: AT&T Broadband & Internet Services (MSO). Purchased from Tele-Communications Inc., March 9, 1999.

STROUDSBURG—Blue Ridge Communications, 920 Ehler St., Stroudsburg, PA 18360. Phone: 570-421-0780. Counties: Monroe & Pike. Also serves Barrett Twp., Buck Hill Falls, Bushkill, Chestnut Hill Twp., Coolbaugh Twp., Delaware Water Gap, East Stroudsburg, Hamilton Twp. (Monroe County), Jackson Twp. (Monroe County), Lehman Twp. (Pike County), Middle Smithfield, Middle Smithfield Twp., Mount Pocono, Paradise Twp. (Monroe County), Pine Ridge, Pocono Lake, Pocono Twp., Polk Twp. (Monroe County), Price Twp. (Monroe County), Ross Twp. (Monroe County), Saw Creek, Saw Creek Estates, Smithfield Twp. (Monroe County), Stroud Twp. (Monroe County), The Falls, Timothy Lake, Tobyhanna Twp. (Monroe County), Winona Lakes (Monroe & Pike Counties). ICA: PA0411.
TV Market Ranking: 49 (Barrett Twp., Buck Hill Falls, Chestnut Hill Twp., Coolbaugh Twp., Jackson Twp., Middle Smithfield, Mount Pocono, Paradise Twp., Pine Ridge, Pocono Lake, Pocono Twp., Polk Twp., Price Twp., Saw Creek, Smithfield Twp., Stroud Twp., Stroudsburg, The Falls, Timothy Lake, Tobyhanna Twp.); Below 100 (Delaware Water Gap, East Stroudsburg, Hamilton Twp., Ross Twp.); Outside TV Markets (Bushkill, Lehman Twp., Middle Smithfield Twp., Saw Creek Estates, Winona Lakes). Franchise award date: N.A. Franchise expiration date: N.A. Began: March 31, 1952.
Channel capacity: 54. Channels available but not in use: 1.

Basic Service
Subscribers: 44,000.
Programming (received off-air): WFMZ-TV (I), WLVT-TV (P) Allentown; WCBS-TV (C), WNBC (N), WNYW (F), WPIX (W), WWOR-TV (U) New York; KYW-TV (C), WCAU (N), WPHL-TV (W), WPVI-TV (A) Philadelphia; WBRE-TV (N), WNEP-TV (A), WSWB (W), WVIA-TV (P), WYOU (C) Scranton & Wilkes-Barre; allband FM.
Programming (via satellite): C-SPAN.
Planned programming (via satellite): CNN; ESPN; Fox Family Channel; Nickelodeon; TBS Superstation.
Current originations: Public access; local news.
Fee: $30.00 installation; $16.90 monthly.

Pay Service 1
Pay Units: 8,500.
Programming (via satellite): Cinemax; Disney Channel; HBO; Showtime.
Fee: $15.00 installation; $8.95 monthly (Disney), $9.50 monthly (Cinemax or Showtime), $10.50 monthly (HBO).
Local advertising: Yes.
Equipment: Scientific-Atlanta headend; C-COR amplifiers; Comm/Scope cable; Zenith addressable set top converters; Andrew satellite antenna; Scientific-Atlanta satellite receivers.
Miles of plant: 150.0 (coaxial); 12.9 (fiber optic). Additional miles planned: 15.0 (coaxial).
Manager: John Kintner.
Ownership: Pencor Services Inc. (MSO).

SUGAR GROVE—County Cable Inc., 217 E. 9th St., Hazleton, PA 18201. Phone: 717-455-6851. Fax: 717-459-0963. County: Warren. ICA: PA0412.
TV Market Ranking: Below 100. Franchise award date: N.A. Franchise expiration date: N.A. Began: October 1, 1977.
Channel capacity: 42 (not 2-way capable). Channels available but not in use: 19.
Basic Service
Subscribers: 199.
Programming (received off-air): WGRZ-TV (N), WIVB-TV (C), WKBW-TV (A), WNED-TV (P), WUTV (F,U) Buffalo; WICU-TV (N), WJET-TV (A), WSEE (C) Erie.
Programming (via translator): WWOR-TV (U) New York.
Programming (via satellite): CNN; Country Music TV; Discovery Channel; Fox Family Channel; Lifetime; Nashville Network; Nickelodeon; QVC; TBS Superstation; Turner Network TV.
Fee: $42.95 installation; $23.10 monthly.
Pay Service 1
Pay Units: 24.
Programming (via satellite): The Movie Channel.
Fee: $12.95 monthly.
Pay Service 2
Pay Units: 26.
Programming (via satellite): HBO.
Fee: $12.95 monthly.
Manager: Joseph W. Aman.
Ownership: Gans Multimedia Partnership (MSO).

SUGARLOAF TWP.—4 City Cable TV Inc., Box 100, Sweet Valley, PA 18656. Phone: 717-925-5720. County: Columbia. ICA: PA0256.
TV Market Ranking: 49. Franchise award date: June 1, 1991. Franchise expiration date: June 1, 2001. Began: June 1, 1991.
Channel capacity: 21. Channels available but not in use: 5.
Basic Service
Subscribers: 208.
Programming (received off-air): WBRE-TV (N), WNEP-TV (A), WSWB (W), WVIA-TV (P), WYOU (C) Scranton & Wilkes-Barre.
Programming (via satellite): CNN; Country Music TV; Discovery Channel; ESPN; Fox Family Channel; Nashville Network; Nickelodeon; TBS Superstation; USA Network.
Current originations: Public access; religious access; local news.
Fee: $25.00 installation; $14.00 monthly.
Pay Service 1
Pay Units: 50.
Programming (via satellite): HBO.
Fee: $11.00 monthly.
Local advertising: Yes. Available in locally originated & character-generated programming.
Miles of plant: 5.0 (coaxial). Homes passed: 300. Total homes in franchised area: 613.
Chief technician: Murph Hislop.
Franchise fee: 2% of gross.
Ownership: Donald Wesley.

SUMMERVILLE—Summerville Cablevision Inc., 513 Jordan Ave., Montoursville, PA 17754. Phone: 570-368-3266. Fax: 570-368-8154. Counties: Clarion & Jefferson. Also serves Baxter, Beaver Twp. (Jefferson County), Clover Twp., Heathville, Limestone Twp. (Clarion County), Mayport, Ohl, Redbank Twp. (Clarion County), Shannondale, Summerville Borough. ICA: PA0232.
TV Market Ranking: Outside TV Markets. Franchise award date: N.A. Franchise expiration date: January 1, 2003. Began: January 1, 1984.
Channel capacity: 40 (not 2-way capable). Channels available but not in use: 2.
Basic Service
Subscribers: 524.
Programming (received off-air): WPSX-TV (P) Clearfield; WJAC-TV (N), WKBS-TV (I), WTAJ-TV (C), WWCP-TV (F) Johnstown-Altoona; KDKA-TV (C), WPGH-TV (F), WPXI (N), WQED (P), WTAE-TV (A) Pittsburgh.
Programming (via satellite): WGN-TV (W) Chicago; A & E; American Movie Classics; Animal Planet; C-SPAN; CNBC; CNN; Country Music TV; Discovery Channel; Disney Channel; ESPN; ESPN 2; FX; Fox Family Channel; Fox News Channel; Fox Sports Net Pittsburgh; Headline News; Lifetime; MTV; Nashville Network; Nickelodeon; QVC; TBS Superstation; The Weather Channel; Turner Network TV; USA Network; VH1.
Current originations: Automated time-weather; public access; educational access; government access.
Fee: N.A.
Pay Service 1
Pay Units: N.A.
Programming (via satellite): HBO; Showtime; The Movie Channel.
Fee: $9.95 monthly (TMC), $10.95 monthly (Showtime), $11.95 monthly (HBO).
Miles of plant: 33.0 (coaxial). Homes passed: 600.
Manager: Roxanne Criswell. Chief technician: Timothy Criswell.
Ownership: Criswell Group (MSO).

SUNBURY—Service Electric Cablevision Inc., 500 Grant St., Sunbury, PA 17801. Phone: 717-286-2607. Fax: 717-286-9710. Counties: Columbia, Montour, Northumberland, Snyder & Union. Also serves Aristes, Beaver Twp. (Snyder County), Beavertown Borough, Centre Twp. (Snyder County), Coal, Coal Twp. (Northumberland County), Conyngham Twp. (Columbia County), East Cameron Twp., Elysburg, Franklin Twp. (Columbia County), Franklin Twp. (Northumberland County), Franklin Twp. (Snyder County), Freeburg, Green Ridge, Jackson Twp. (Northumberland County), Jackson Twp. (Snyder County), Jordan, Kreamer, Kulpmont (Northumberland County), Limestone Twp. (Union County), Little Mahanoy Twp., Lower Mahanoy Twp., Marion Heights, Middleburg, Middleburg Borough, Middlecreek Twp., Monroe Twp. (Snyder County), Mount Carmel Borough, Mount Carmel Twp. (Northumberland County), New Berlin, Northumberland, Paxinos, Paxtonville, Penn Twp. (Snyder County), Penns Creek, Point Twp. (Montour County), Ralpho Twp., Rockefeller Twp., Selinsgrove, Shamokin, Shamokin Dam, Shamokin Twp., Snydertown (Northumberland County), Strong, Union Twp. (Union County), Upper Augusta Twp., Upper Mahanoy Twp., Washington Twp. (Northumberland County), Washington Twp. (Snyder County), West Cameron Twp., Zerbe Twp. ICA: PA0029.
TV Market Ranking: 57 (Jordan, Lower Mahanoy Twp.); Below 100 (Aristes, Beavertown Borough, Centre Twp., Coal, Coal Twp., Conyngham Twp., East Cameron Twp., Elysburg, Franklin Twp., Freeburg, Green Ridge, Jackson Twp., Kreamer, Kulpmont, Limestone Twp., Marion Heights, Middleburg, Middleburg Borough, Middlecreek Twp., Monroe Twp., Mount Carmel Borough, Mount Carmel Twp., New Berlin, Northumberland, Penn Twp., Penns Creek, Point Twp., Ralpho Twp., Rockefeller Twp., Selinsgrove, Shamokin, Shamokin Dam, Shamokin Twp., Snydertown, Strong, Sunbury, Union Twp., Upper Mahanoy Twp., Washington Twp., West Cameron Twp., Zerbe Twp.); Outside TV Markets (Beaver Twp., Little Mahanoy Twp., Paxinos, Paxtonville, Upper Augusta Twp.). Franchise award date: N.A. Franchise expiration date: N.A. Began: May 1, 1953.
Channel capacity: 65 (2-way capable; operating 2-way). Channels available but not in use: None.
Basic Service
Subscribers: 32,200.
Programming (received off-air): WHP-TV (C), WHTM-TV (A), WITF-TV (P) Harrisburg; WOLF-TV (F) Hazleton; WGAL (N) Lancaster; WPIX (W), WWOR-TV (U) New York; WPHL-TV (W) Philadelphia; WBRE-TV (N), WNEP-TV (A), WVIA-TV (P), WYOU (C) Scranton & Wilkes-Barre; allband FM.
Programming (via satellite): A & E; American Movie Classics; C-SPAN; CNBC; CNN; Country Music TV; Discovery Channel; ESPN; EWTN; Fox Family Channel; Headline News; Home Shopping Network; Lifetime; MTV; Nashville Network; Nickelodeon; QVC; Sci-Fi Channel; TBS Superstation; The Weather Channel; Travel Channel; Turner Network TV; USA Network; VH1; ValueVision.
Current originations: Automated time-weather.
Fee: $32.00 installation; $24.45 monthly; $2.37 converter.
Pay Service 1
Pay Units: 8,912.
Programming (via satellite): Cinemax; Disney Channel; HBO (multiplexed).
Fee: $31.00 installation; $8.00 monthly (Disney), $10.00 monthly (Cinemax), $11.00 monthly (HBO).
Pay-Per-View
Addressable homes: 6,910.
Local advertising: Yes (insert only). Available in satellite distributed programming. Regional interconnect: Cabletime.
Program Guide: TV Host.
Equipment: Scientific-Atlanta headend; Scientific-Atlanta satellite antenna.
Miles of plant: 190.0 (coaxial); 100.0 (fiber optic). Homes passed: 38,000. Total homes in franchised area: 45,000.
Manager: Dwight Walter. Chief technician: John Kurtz.
Ownership: Service Electric Cable TV Inc. (MSO).

SWEET VALLEY—Blue Ridge Cable TV, Box 141, Tunkhannock, PA 18657. Phone: 570-836-5422. Fax: 570-836-1659. County: Luzerne. Also serves Hunlock Creek, Muhlenberg, Union Twp. (Luzerne County). ICA: PA0181.
TV Market Ranking: 49. Franchise award date: N.A. Franchise expiration date: N.A. Began: March 1, 1985.
Channel capacity: 52. Channels available but not in use: N.A.
Basic Service
Subscribers: N.A.
Programming (received off-air): WBRE-TV (N), WNEP-TV (A), WSWB (W), WVIA-TV (P), WYOU (C) Scranton & Wilkes-Barre.
Programming (via microwave): WPIX (W) New York; WTXF-TV (F) Philadelphia.
Programming (via satellite): CNN; Discovery Channel; ESPN; Fox Family Channel; Learning Channel; Lifetime; MTV; Nashville Network; TBS Superstation; USA Network.
Current originations: Automated time-weather; educational access; government access; leased access.
Fee: $15.00 installation; $10.00 monthly; $10.00 additional installation.
Pay Service 1
Pay Units: N.A.
Programming (via satellite): Cinemax; Disney Channel; HBO; Playboy TV; The Movie Channel.
Fee: $15.00 installation; $8.00 monthly (Disney or Playboy), $8.95 monthly (TMC), $9.50 monthly (Cinemax), $10.50 monthly (HBO).
Local advertising: No. Regional interconnect: Cabletime.
Equipment: Scientific-Atlanta headend; Jerrold amplifiers; Panasonic cable; Eagle addressable set top converters; Arcom, Eagle & Pico traps; Scientific-Atlanta satellite receivers.
Miles of plant: 90.0 (coaxial). Homes passed: 1,500. Total homes in franchised area: 2,000.
Manager: Ken Valentine.
Ownership: Pencor Services Inc. (MSO).

TARENTUM BOROUGH—Comcast Cablevision of Westmoreland, 890 Constitution Blvd., New Kensington, PA 15068. Phone: 724335-9188. Fax: 724-335-6648. Web site: http://www.comcast.com. Counties: Allegheny, Butler & Westmoreland. Also serves Arnold, Blawnox Borough, Brackenridge Borough, Buffalo Twp. (Butler County), Cheswick, Clinton Twp., East Deer Twp., Fawn Twp. (Allegheny County), Fox Chapel, Frazer Twp., Hampton Twp. (Allegheny County), Harmar Twp., Harrison Twp. (Allegheny County), Indiana Twp. (Allegheny County), Lower Burrell, New Kensington, O'Hara Twp. (Allegheny County), Oakmont, Richland Twp. (Allegheny County), Springdale Borough, Springdale Twp. (Allegheny County), Verona Borough, West Deer Twp., Westmoreland. ICA: PA0424.
TV Market Ranking: 10. Franchise award date: N.A. Franchise expiration date: N.A. Began: September 1, 1966.
Channel capacity: 54 (not 2-way capable). Channels available but not in use: None.
Basic Service
Subscribers: 42,996.
Programming (received off-air): WPCB-TV (I) Greensburg; WNPA (U) Jeanette; KDKA-TV (C), WCWB (W), WPGH-TV (F), WPXI (N), WQED (P), WQEX (P), WTAE-TV (A) Pittsburgh.
Programming (via satellite): FX; News Plus.
Fee: $46.46 installation; $6.20 monthly; $0.51 converter; $15.49 additional installation.
Expanded Basic Service
Subscribers: N.A.
Programming (via satellite): A & E; BET; C-SPAN; C-SPAN 2; CNBC; CNN; Comedy Central; Country Music TV; Discovery Channel; E! Entertainment TV; ESPN; EWTN; Fox Family Channel; Fox Sports Net Pittsburgh; Headline News; History Channel; Knowledge TV; Ladbroke Racing Channel/Meadows Racing Network; Learning Channel; Lifetime; MSNBC; Nick at Nite's TV Land; Pennsylvania Cable Network; QVC; Sci-Fi Channel; Speedvision; TBS Superstation; TV Food Network; TV Guide Channel; TV

Guide Sneak Prevue; The Weather Channel; VH1.
Fee: $15.49 installation; $20.01 monthly.

Expanded Basic Service 2
Subscribers: 22,000.
Programming (via satellite): WGN-TV (W) Chicago; ESPN 2; Home & Garden Television; Nashville Network; TBS Superstation; Turner Network TV.
Fee: $15.49 installation; $3.99 monthly.

Expanded Basic Service 3
Subscribers: N.A.
Programming (via satellite): American Movie Classics; Golf Channel; Goodlife TV Network; MTV; Nickelodeon; USA Network.
Fee: $2.75 monthly.

Pay Service 1
Pay Units: N.A.
Programming (via satellite): Cinemax; Disney Channel; HBO; Playboy TV; Showtime; The Movie Channel; The New Encore.
Fee: $39.95 installation; $12.45 monthly (each).

Pay-Per-View
Addressable homes: 21,200.
Playboy TV; Viewer's Choice.

Local advertising: Yes. Available in satellite distributed, locally originated, character-generated, taped & automated programming. Regional interconnect: TCI Media Services-Pittsburgh, PA.
Program Guide: The Cable Guide.
Equipment: Jerrold headend; Jerrold amplifiers; Times Fiber cable; Shibaden cameras; Sony VTRs; Video Data Systems character generator; Jerrold set top converters; Jerrold addressable set top converters; Vitek traps; Anixter-Mark satellite antenna; Microdyne satellite receivers.
Miles of plant: 681.0 (coaxial); 30.0 (fiber optic). Total homes in franchised area: 50,000.
Manager: Rick Ricchuito. Plant manager: Jim Moore. Program director: Robert Tatin. Marketing director: Virginia Buffone.
City fee: 3% of gross.
Ownership: Comcast Cable Communications Inc. (MSO).

THOMPSON TWP.—Adams CATV Inc., 9 N. Main St., Carbondale, PA 18407. Phone: 717-282-6121. Fax: 717-282-3787. Counties: Susquehanna & Wayne. Also serves Ararat Twp., Coxton Lake, Gibson Twp., Great Bend Twp., Harmony Twp. (Susquehanna County), Independent Lake, Jackson Twp. (Susquehanna County), Lake Lorain, Lanesboro, Oakland Borough, Oakland Twp. (Susquehanna County), Orson, Poyntelle, Preston Twp., Spruce Lake, Starrucca, Summit Lake, Susquehanna Depot Borough, Thompson Borough, Wrighter Lake. ICA: PA0414.
TV Market Ranking: 49 (Coxton Lake, Gibson Twp., Independent Lake, Jackson Twp., Lake Lorain, Orson, Poyntelle, Preston Twp., Spruce Lake, Starrucca, Summit Lake, Susquehanna Depot Borough, Thompson Borough, Thompson Twp., Wrighter Lake); Below 100 (Ararat Twp., Great Bend Twp., Harmony Twp., Lanesboro, Oakland Borough, Oakland Twp.). Franchise award date: N.A. Franchise expiration date: N.A. Began: N.A.
Channel capacity: 40 (2-way capable). Channels available but not in use: None.

Basic Service
Subscribers: 1,400.
Programming (received off-air): WBNG-TV (C), WICZ-TV (F), WIVT (A), WSKG (P) Binghamton; WBRE-TV (N), WNEP-TV (A), WSWB (W), WVIA-TV (P), WYOU (C) Scranton & Wilkes-Barre.
Programming (via satellite): WPIX (W) New York; A & E; CNBC; CNN; Country Music TV; Discovery Channel; ESPN; Fox Family Channel; Headline News; Lifetime; Nashville Network; QVC; TBS Superstation; Turner Network TV; USA Network.
Fee: $20.00 monthly.

Pay Service 1
Pay Units: N.A.
Programming (via satellite): Cinemax; Disney Channel; HBO; Playboy TV.
Fee: $10.00 installation; $7.00 monthly (Disney), $8.00 monthly (Playboy), $12.00 monthly (Cinemax or HBO).

Pay-Per-View
Addressable homes: 150.

Miles of plant: 80.0 (coaxial); 20.0 (fiber optic). Homes passed: 1,800. Total homes in franchised area: 2,200.
Manager: Wendy White. Chief technician: John Wallis. Program director: Doug Adams.
Ownership: Adams CATV Inc. (MSO).

THOMPSONTOWN—Nittany Media Inc., Box 111, Lewistown, PA 17044. Phone: 717-248-3733. County: Juniata. ICA: PA0415.
TV Market Ranking: 57. Franchise award date: N.A. Franchise expiration date: N.A. Began: N.A.
Channel capacity: N.A. Channels available but not in use: N.A.

Basic Service
Subscribers: N.A.
Programming (received off-air): WHP-TV (C), WHTM-TV (A), WITF-TV (P) Harrisburg; WTAJ-TV (C) Johnstown-Altoona; WGAL (N) Lancaster; WBRE-TV (N) Scranton & Wilkes-Barre; WPMT (F) York.
Programming (via satellite): WGN-TV (W) Chicago; CNN; ESPN; The Inspirational Network.
Fee: N.A.

Pay Service 1
Pay Units: N.A.
Programming (via satellite): Nashville Network; The Movie Channel.
Fee: N.A.

Manager: Anna H. Hain. Chief technician: Michael Hain.
Ownership: Nittany Media Inc. (MSO).

THREE SPRINGS—County Cable Inc., 217 E. 9th St., Hazleton, PA 18201. Phone: 717-455-6851. Fax: 717-459-0963. County: Huntingdon. Also serves Clay Twp. (Huntingdon County), Cromwell. ICA: PA0233.
TV Market Ranking: 74. Franchise award date: N.A. Franchise expiration date: N.A. Began: November 1, 1984.
Channel capacity: 42 (not 2-way capable). Channels available but not in use: 23.

Basic Service
Subscribers: 378.
Programming (received off-air): WPSX-TV (P) Clearfield; WHAG-TV (N) Hagerstown; WHTM-TV (A) Harrisburg; WATM-TV (A), WTAJ-TV (C) Johnstown-Altoona; WGAL (N) Lancaster; allband FM.
Programming (via translator): WWOR-TV (U) New York.
Programming (via satellite): A & E; Country Music TV; Discovery Channel; ESPN; Fox Family Channel; Nashville Network; Nickelodeon; TBS Superstation; USA Network.
Fee: $42.95 installation; $22.50 monthly.

Pay Service 1
Pay Units: 29.
Programming (via satellite): HBO.
Fee: $12.95 monthly.

Pay Service 2
Pay Units: 19.
Programming (via satellite): Cinemax.
Fee: $12.95 monthly.

Local advertising: Yes.
Equipment: AFC satellite antenna.
Miles of plant: 30.0 (coaxial). Homes passed: 536. Total homes in franchised area: 600.
Chief operating officer: Joseph W. Aman.
City fee: None.
Ownership: Gans Multimedia Partnership (MSO).

TIDIOUTE—CableVision Communications, Box 2200, 68 5th St., Buckhannon, WV 26201. Phone: 304-472-4193. Fax: 304-472-0756. Counties: Forest & Warren. Also serves Althom, Brokenstraw Twp. (portions), Deerfield Twp. (Warren County), Dunns Eddie, East Hickory, Endeavor, Hickory Twp. (Warren County), Irvine, Kingsley Twp., Limestone Twp. (Warren County), Pleasant Twp. (Warren County), Watson Twp. (Warren County), West Hickory. ICA: PA0183.
TV Market Ranking: Below 100 (Althom, Brokenstraw Twp., Deerfield Twp., Dunns Eddie, Endeavor, Hickory Twp., Irvine, Limestone Twp., Pleasant Twp., Tidioute, Watson Twp.); Outside TV Markets (East Hickory, Kingsley Twp., West Hickory). Franchise award date: N.A. Franchise expiration date: April 2, 2004. Began: February 1, 1952.
Channel capacity: 36 (not 2-way capable). Channels available but not in use: N.A.

Basic Service
Subscribers: 1,052.
Programming (received off-air): WPSX-TV (P) Clearfield; WICU-TV (N), WJET-TV (A), WQLN (P), WSEE (C) Erie; WJAC-TV (N) Johnstown-Altoona.
Programming (via satellite): WGN-TV (W) Chicago; CNN; E! Entertainment TV; Fox-Net; Learning Channel; QVC; TBS Superstation; The Weather Channel; Trinity Bcstg. Network.
Fee: $61.25 installation; $14.58 monthly; $1.24 converter; $17.50 additional installation.

Expanded Basic Service
Subscribers: 735.
Programming (via satellite): American Movie Classics; Discovery Channel; Disney Channel; ESPN; ESPN 2; Fox Family Channel; Fox Sports Net Pittsburgh; Great American Country; Headline News; History Channel; Lifetime; MTV; Nashville Network; Nickelodeon; Sci-Fi Channel; Turner Network TV; USA Network; VH1.
Fee: $17.73 monthly.

Pay Service 1
Pay Units: 479.
Programming (via satellite): Cinemax; HBO; Showtime.
Fee: $7.95 monthly (Cinemax), $11.95 monthly (Showtime), $11.99 monthly (HBO).

Pay Service 2
Pay Units: N.A.
Programming (via satellite): The Movie Channel; The New Encore.
Fee: $3.99 monthly (Encore), $11.95 monthly (TMC).

Equipment: Blonder-Tongue, Scientific-Atlanta & Olson headend; Jerrold, Scientific-Atlanta & Magnavox amplifiers; Pico & Intercept traps; ChannelMaster & Scientific-Atlanta satellite antenna; Drake satellite receivers.
Miles of plant: 46.0 (coaxial). Additional miles planned: 18.1 (coaxial). Homes passed: 1,380.
Manager: Willie Critchfield. Marketing director: Kenny Phillips.
City fee: $1.00 per year.
Ownership: Rifkin & Associates Inc. (MSO). See Cable System Ownership.

TIMBLIN BOROUGH—Commuter Cable Television-West, 513 Jordan Ave., Montoursville, PA 17754. Phone: 570-368-3266. Fax: 570-368-8154. County: Jefferson. Also serves Knox Twp. (Jefferson County), Oliver Twp. (Jefferson County), Ringgold Twp., Rose Twp., Worthville Borough. ICA: PA0349.
TV Market Ranking: Outside TV Markets. Franchise award date: November 1, 1989. Franchise expiration date: November 1, 2005. Began: January 1, 1990.
Channel capacity: 40 (not 2-way capable). Channels available but not in use: 2.

Basic Service
Subscribers: 530.
Programming (received off-air): WPSX-TV (P) Clearfield; WJAC-TV (N), WKBS-TV (I), WTAJ-TV (C), WWCP-TV (F) Johnstown-Altoona; KDKA-TV (C), WPGH-TV (F), WTAE-TV (A) Pittsburgh.
Programming (via satellite): WGN-TV (W) Chicago; A & E; American Movie Classics; Animal Planet; C-SPAN; CNBC; CNN; Country Music TV; Discovery Channel; Disney Channel; ESPN; ESPN 2; FX; Fox Family Channel; Fox News Channel; Fox Sports Net; Headline News; Lifetime; MTV; Nashville Network; Nickelodeon; Pennsylvania Cable Network; QVC; TBS Superstation; The Weather Channel; Turner Network TV; USA Network; VH1.
Fee: N.A.

Pay Service 1
Pay Units: N.A.
Programming (via satellite): HBO; Showtime; The Movie Channel.
Fee: $9.95 monthly (TMC), $10.95 monthly (Showtime), $11.95 monthly (HBO).

Miles of plant: 57.3 (coaxial). Homes passed: 818.
Manager: Roxanne Y. Criswell. Chief technician: Timothy J. Criswell.
Ownership: Criswell Group (MSO).

TIOGA—Cablecomm, 166 Main St., Hornell, NY 14843. Phone: 800-783-2839. County: Tioga. ICA: PA0219.
TV Market Ranking: Below 100. Franchise award date: N.A. Franchise expiration date: N.A. Began: January 1, 1953.
Channel capacity: 12. Channels available but not in use: N.A.

Basic Service
Subscribers: 537.
Programming (received off-air): WBNG-TV (C), WICZ-TV (F), WIVT (A), WSKG (P) Binghamton; WENY-TV (A), WETM-TV (N) Elmira; WVIA-TV (P) Scranton & Wilkes-Barre; allband FM.
Fee: $30.00 installation; $13.00 monthly.

Pay Service 1
Pay Units: 184.

Programming (via satellite): HBO.
Fee: $30.00 installation; $10.00 monthly.
Local advertising: No.
Miles of plant: 44.0 (coaxial). Homes passed: 700.
Manager: Frank Gallagher.
City fee: $100.00 annually.
Ownership: Fanch Communications Inc. (MSO). See Cable System Ownership.

TITUSVILLE—CableVision Communications, Box 2200, 68 5th St., Buckhannon, WV 26201. Phone: 304-472-4193. Fax: 304-472-0756. Counties: Crawford, Venango & Warren. Also serves Centerville (Crawford County), Cherrytree Twp., Dempseytown, Enterprise (Warren County), Hydetown, Kaneville, Pleasantville, Plum Twp., Rome Twp., Rynd Farm, Steuben Twp. ICA: PA0416.
TV Market Ranking: Below 100 (Enterprise, Rome Twp., Steuben Twp.); Outside TV Markets (Centerville, Cherrytree Twp., Dempseytown, Hydetown, Kaneville, Pleasantville, Plum Twp., Rynd Farm, Titusville). Franchise award date: N.A. Franchise expiration date: N.A. Began: March 1, 1953.
Channel capacity: 60. Channels available but not in use: N.A.
Basic Service
Subscribers: 3,877.
Programming (received off-air): WFXP (F), WICU-TV (N), WJET-TV (A), WQLN (P), WSEE (C) Erie; KDKA-TV (C), WPXI (N) Pittsburgh; WKBN-TV (C), WYTV (A,F) Youngstown; allband FM.
Programming (via satellite): WGN-TV (W) Chicago; Animal Planet; Disney Channel; Fox Family Channel; Home Shopping Network; TBS Superstation; Trinity Bcstg. Network.
Current originations: Automated time-weather; local news.
Fee: $61.25 installation; $14.18 monthly; $1.24 converter.
Expanded Basic Service
Subscribers: 3,414.
Programming (via satellite): A & E; American Movie Classics; C-SPAN; CNBC; CNN; Discovery Channel; Disney Channel; E! Entertainment TV; ESPN; Fox Sports Net Pittsburgh; Great American Country; Home & Garden Television; Lifetime; MTV; Nashville Network; Nickelodeon; Sci-Fi Channel; The Weather Channel; Turner Network TV; USA Network; VH1.
Fee: $17.50 installation; $14.56 monthly.
Pay Service 1
Pay Units: 2,650.
Programming (via satellite): Cinemax; HBO; Showtime; The New Encore.
Fee: $3.99 monthly (Encore), $7.95 monthly (Cinemax), $11.95 monthly (Showtime), $11.99 monthly (HBO).
Pay Service 2
Pay Units: N.A.
Programming (via satellite): The Movie Channel.
Fee: $11.95 monthly.
Local advertising: Yes. Available in character-generated programming. Regional interconnect: Metrobase Cable Advertising.
Equipment: Blonder-Tongue & Scientific-Atlanta headend; Jerrold & GTE Sylvania amplifiers; Scientific-Atlanta satellite antenna.
Miles of plant: 105.4 (coaxial). Homes passed: 4,614.
Manager: Willie Critchfield. Marketing director: Kenny Phillips.
Ownership: Rifkin & Associates Inc. (MSO). See Cable System Ownership.

TOBY TWP.—TCI of Pennsylvania Inc., 855 Main St., Clarion, PA 16214-1161. Phone: 814-226-6410. Counties: Clarion & Venango. Also serves Huey, Madison Twp. (Clarion County), Piney Twp., Richland Twp. (Venango County), Rimersburg, Sligo. ICA: PA0186.
TV Market Ranking: Outside TV Markets. Franchise award date: January 1, 1968. Franchise expiration date: October 10, 2001. Began: June 1, 1968.
Channel capacity: 52 (not 2-way capable). Channels available but not in use: 17.
Basic Service
Subscribers: 974.
Programming (received off-air): WPSX-TV (P) Clearfield; WJAC-TV (N), WTAJ-TV (C) Johnstown-Altoona; KDKA-TV (C), WCWB (W), WPGH-TV (F), WPXI (N), WQED (P), WTAE-TV (A) Pittsburgh; WYTV (A,F) Youngstown; allband FM.
Programming (via satellite): A & E; C-SPAN; CNBC; CNN; Discovery Channel; Fox Family Channel; Headline News; Lifetime; MTV; Nashville Network; Nickelodeon; Odyssey; QVC; TBS Superstation; The Weather Channel.
Fee: $59.95 installation; $17.45 monthly.
Expanded Basic Service
Subscribers: 907.
Programming (via satellite): American Movie Classics; Court TV; ESPN; Fox Sports Net Pittsburgh; Turner Network TV; USA Network.
Fee: $1.95 monthly.
Pay Service 1
Pay Units: 165.
Programming (via satellite): HBO.
Fee: N.A.
Pay Service 2
Pay Units: 84.
Programming (via satellite): Showtime.
Fee: N.A.
Pay Service 3
Pay Units: 329.
Programming (via satellite): The New Encore.
Fee: N.A.
Equipment: Scientific-Atlanta headend; C-COR amplifiers; Texscan character generator; Scientific-Atlanta set top converters.
Miles of plant: 25.6 (coaxial). Homes passed: 1,280. Total homes in franchised area: 1,983.
Manager: W. Ben Call. Chief technician: Greg Allshouse.
Franchise fee: 1% of gross (Rimersburg & Sligo).
Ownership: AT&T Broadband & Internet Services (MSO). Purchased from Tele-Communications Inc., March 9, 1999.

TOWANDA—TCI of Pennsylvania Inc., Box 368, 212 Main St., Towanda, PA 18848. Phone: 717-265-3914. Fax: 717-265-3040. County: Bradford. Also serves Asylum Twp., Monroe (Bradford County), Monroe Twp. (Bradford County), Monroeton Borough, North Towanda Twp., Towanda Twp., Wysox Twp. ICA: PA0138.
TV Market Ranking: Below 100. Franchise award date: N.A. Franchise expiration date: N.A. Began: April 1, 1961.
Channel capacity: 36. Channels available but not in use: N.A.
Basic Service
Subscribers: 2,511.
Programming (received off-air): WBNG-TV (C), WIVT (A), WSKG (P) Binghamton; WETM-TV (N) Elmira; WBRE-TV (N), WNEP-TV (A), WSWB (W), WVIA-TV (P), WYOU (C) Scranton & Wilkes-Barre; allband FM.
Programming (via satellite): C-SPAN; CNBC; CNN; Discovery Channel; EWTN; Fox Family Channel; Headline News; Lifetime; MTV; Nashville Network; Nickelodeon; Odyssey; QVC; TBS Superstation; The Weather Channel.
Current originations: Automated time-weather.
Fee: $20.10 installation; $10.77 monthly; $2.00 converter.
Expanded Basic Service
Subscribers: 2,410.
Programming (via satellite): A & E; American Movie Classics; ESPN; Turner Network TV; USA Network.
Fee: $12.64 monthly.
Pay Service 1
Pay Units: 281.
Programming (via satellite): Cinemax.
Fee: $13.15 monthly.
Pay Service 2
Pay Units: 224.
Programming (via satellite): Disney Channel.
Fee: N.A.
Pay Service 3
Pay Units: 653.
Programming (via satellite): HBO.
Fee: $13.15 monthly.
Pay Service 4
Pay Units: 271.
Programming (via satellite): Showtime.
Fee: $13.15 monthly.
Pay Service 5
Pay Units: 1,073.
Programming (via satellite): The New Encore.
Fee: N.A.
Pay-Per-View
Addressable homes: 177.
Local advertising: Yes. Regional interconnect: Cabletime.
Program Guide: The Cable Guide.
Equipment: Blonder-Tongue headend; C-COR amplifiers; General cable; Scientific-Atlanta satellite antenna.
Miles of plant: 61.4 (coaxial). Homes passed: 3,059.
Manager: Dana Horner.
City fee: None.
Ownership: AT&T Broadband & Internet Services (MSO). Purchased from Tele-Communications Inc., March 9, 1999.

TOWNVILLE—CableVision Communications, Box 2200, 68 5th St., Buckhannon, WV 26201. Phone: 304-472-4193. Fax: 304-472-0756. County: Crawford. ICA: PA0278.
TV Market Ranking: Below 100. Franchise award date: N.A. Franchise expiration date: N.A. Began: June 1, 1984.
Channel capacity: 30. Channels available but not in use: N.A.
Basic Service
Subscribers: 67.
Programming (received off-air): WFXP (F), WICU-TV (N), WJET-TV (A), WQLN (P), WSEE (C) Erie.
Programming (via satellite): WGN-TV (W) Chicago; A & E; American Movie Classics; Animal Planet; CNN; Cartoon Network; Discovery Channel; Disney Channel; ESPN; ESPN 2; Fox Family Channel; Great American Country; Home Shopping Network; Lifetime; MTV; Nashville Network; Nickelodeon; Sci-Fi Channel; TBS Superstation; The Weather Channel; Turner Network TV; USA Network; VH1.
Fee: $61.25 installation; $8.85 monthly; $1.24 converter; $17.50 additional installation.
Pay Service 1
Pay Units: 52.
Programming (via satellite): Cinemax.
Fee: $5.95 monthly.
Pay Service 2
Pay Units: N.A.
Programming (via satellite): HBO.
Fee: $6.95 monthly.
Equipment: M/A-Com & Olson headend; Jerrold amplifiers; Comm/Scope cable; Jerrold set top converters.
Miles of plant: 3.0 (coaxial). Homes passed: 153.
Manager: Willie Critchfield. Marketing director: Kenny Phillips.
Ownership: Rifkin & Associates Inc. (MSO). See Cable System Ownership.

TREMONT—Wire Tele-View Corp., 603 E. Market St., Pottsville, PA 17901. Phone: 717622-4501. Fax: 717-622-8340. County: Schuylkill. Also serves Frailey Twp., Zerbe. ICA: PA0204.
TV Market Ranking: Below 100. Franchise award date: N.A. Franchise expiration date: N.A. Began: June 18, 1952.
Channel capacity: 36 (not 2-way capable). Channels available but not in use: 4.
Basic Service
Subscribers: 900.
Programming (received off-air): WITF-TV (P) Harrisburg; WGAL (N), WLYH-TV (U) Lancaster; WCAU (N), WPHL-TV (W), WPSG (U), WTXF-TV (F) Philadelphia; WBRE-TV (N), WNEP-TV (A) Scranton & Wilkes-Barre; WHYY-TV (P) Wilmington; WPMT (F) York; allband FM.
Programming (via satellite): A & E; CNN; Discovery Channel; ESPN; Fox Family Channel; Goodlife TV Network; Lifetime; MTV; Nashville Network; QVC; TBS Superstation; Turner Network TV; USA Network.
Fee: $37.50 installation; $14.50 monthly.
Pay Service 1
Pay Units: 160.
Programming (via satellite): Cinemax; HBO.
Fee: $15.00 installation; $10.00 monthly (each).
Local advertising: No.
Equipment: Microdyne satellite antenna; Scientific-Atlanta & Sony satellite receivers.
Miles of plant: 8.1 (coaxial). Homes passed: 980.
Manager: Thelma Crepack. Chief technician: Brian Brennan.
Ownership: Wire Tele-View Corp. (MSO).

TROY—Blue Ridge Cable TV Inc., 46 N. Academy St., Mansfield, PA 16933. Phone: 570-662-2369. County: Bradford. Also serves Austinville Twp., Burlington, Burlington Borough, Columbia Crossroads, Columbia Crossroads Twp., Columbia Twp. (Bradford County), East Troy, Franklindale Twp., Powell, Powell Twp., Sylvania, Sylvania Borough, Troy Twp. ICA: PA0165.
TV Market Ranking: Below 100 (Austinville Twp., Burlington Borough, Columbia Crossroads, Columbia Crossroads Twp., Columbia Twp., East Troy, Franklindale Twp., Powell Twp., Sylvania, Sylvania Borough, Troy, Troy Twp.); Outside TV Markets (Burlington, Powell). Franchise award date: N.A. Franchise expiration date: February 1, 1999. Began: June 1, 1958.
Channel capacity: 35 (not 2-way capable). Channels available but not in use: None.
Basic Service
Subscribers: 924.
Programming (received off-air): WBNG-TV (C) Binghamton; WETM-TV (N) Elmira; WNEP-TV (A), WSWB (W), WVIA-TV (P), WYOU (C) Scranton & Wilkes-Barre; allband FM.
Programming (via satellite): CNN; Discovery Channel; ESPN; Fox Family Channel;

Nashville Network; QVC; TBS Superstation; USA Network; VH1.
Current originations: Automated time-weather; educational access.
Fee: $35.00 installation; $15.25 monthly.

Pay Service 1
Pay Units: 341.
Programming (via satellite): HBO.
Fee: $15.00 installation; $10.50 monthly.

Local advertising: Yes. Regional interconnect: Cabletime.
Equipment: Scientific-Atlanta headend; Jerrold amplifiers; Times Fiber cable.
Miles of plant: 25.0 (coaxial). Homes passed: 1,800. Total homes in franchised area: 1,800.
Manager: Tom Freeman. Chief technician: Jeff Brewer.
City fee: 3% of gross.
Ownership: Pencor Services Inc. (MSO).

TYLERSVILLE—Community TV, Box 85, Loganton, PA 17747. Phone: 717-725-2733. County: Clinton. ICA: PA0417.
TV Market Ranking: Below 100. Franchise award date: N.A. Franchise expiration date: N.A. Began: January 1, 1972.
Channel capacity: 12. Channels available but not in use: 5.

Basic Service
Subscribers: N.A.
Programming (received off-air): WPSX-TV (P) Clearfield; WTAJ-TV (C) Johnstown-Altoona; WGAL (N) Lancaster; WBRE-TV (N), WSWB (W), WVIA-TV (P), WYOU (C) Scranton & Wilkes-Barre.
Fee: $3.00 monthly.

Equipment: Blonder-Tongue headend.
Chief technician: Guy Bierly.
Ownership: Community TV.

TYRONE—TCI of Pennsylvania Inc., 1068 Pennsylvania Ave., Tyrone, PA 16686. Phone: 814-684-2151. County: Blair. Also serves Snyder Twp. (Blair County), Taylor Twp. (Blair County). ICA: PA0418.
TV Market Ranking: 74. Franchise award date: September 24, 1959. Franchise expiration date: N.A. Began: January 1, 1961.
Channel capacity: 30. Channels available but not in use: 5.

Basic Service
Subscribers: 3,223.
Programming (received off-air): WPSX-TV (P) Clearfield; WATM-TV (A), WJAC-TV (N), WTAJ-TV (C), WWCP-TV (F) Johnstown-Altoona; WTAE-TV (A) Pittsburgh; all-band FM.
Programming (via satellite): A & E; CNN; Discovery Channel; ESPN; Fox Family Channel; MTV; Nashville Network; Nickelodeon; TBS Superstation; Turner Network TV; USA Network; VH1.
Current originations: Automated time-weather; local news.
Fee: $30.00 installation; $9.85 monthly; $15.00 additional installation.

Pay Service 1
Pay Units: 100.
Programming (via satellite): Cinemax.
Fee: $5.00 installation; $13.15 monthly.

Pay Service 2
Pay Units: 118.
Programming (via satellite): Disney Channel.
Fee: $5.00 installation; $8.95 monthly.

Pay Service 3
Pay Units: 247.
Programming (via satellite): HBO.
Fee: $5.00 installation; $13.15 monthly.

Pay Service 4
Pay Units: 66.
Programming (via satellite): The Movie Channel.
Fee: $5.00 installation; $13.15 monthly.

Pay Service 5
Pay Units: 90.
Programming (via satellite): Showtime.
Fee: $5.00 installation; $13.15 monthly.

Local advertising: Yes. Available in locally originated, character-generated & taped programming.
Program Guide: CableView.
Equipment: Scientific-Atlanta headend; Jerrold amplifiers; Comm/Scope cable; JVC VTRs; System Concepts character generator; Oak set top converters; Andrew & Scientific-Atlanta satellite antenna; Andrew & Scientific-Atlanta satellite receivers.
Miles of plant: 67.8 (coaxial). Total homes in franchised area: 3,499.
Manager: Kim Yakich. Chief technician: Michael Catherine.
City fee: 2% of gross.
Ownership: AT&T Broadband & Internet Services (MSO). Purchased from Tele-Communications Inc., March 9, 1999.

ULSTER—Beaver Valley Cable Co., Box 60-D, RR2, Rome, PA 18837. Phone: 570-247-2512. Fax: 570-247-2494. County: Bradford. ICA: PA0252.
TV Market Ranking: Below 100. Franchise award date: N.A. Franchise expiration date: N.A. Began: February 1, 1961.
Channel capacity: 45 (2-way capable; not operating 2-way). Channels available but not in use: 10.

Basic Service
Subscribers: 400.
Programming (received off-air): WBNG-TV (C), WIVT (A), WSKG (P) Binghamton; WETM-TV (N) Elmira; WPIX (W) New York; WBRE-TV (N), WNEP-TV (A), WSWB (W), WVIA-TV (P), WYOU (C) Scranton & Wilkes-Barre.
Programming (via satellite): CNN; Discovery Channel; Disney Channel; ESPN; Fox Family Channel; Nashville Network; Nick at Nite's TV Land; Nickelodeon; TBS Superstation; USA Network.
Fee: $30.00 installation; $21.00 monthly.

Expanded Basic Service
Subscribers: 240.
Programming (via satellite): WGN-TV (W) Chicago; American Movie Classics; Country Music TV; ESPN 2; Home Shopping Network; Learning Channel; Lifetime; Outdoor Channel; Sci-Fi Channel; The Weather Channel; Trinity Bcstg. Network; Turner Network TV; VH1.
Fee: $8.50 monthly.

Pay Service 1
Pay Units: 120.
Programming (via satellite): Cinemax.
Fee: $10.00 monthly.

Pay Service 2
Pay Units: 300.
Programming (via satellite): HBO.
Fee: $10.00 monthly.

Program Guide: CableView.
Equipment: Blonder-Tongue & Cadco headend; C-COR & Magnavox amplifiers; Plastoid cable; Scientific-Atlanta, Harris & M/A-Com satellite antenna; Drake & Olson satellite receivers.
Miles of plant: 25.9 (coaxial). Additional miles planned: 20.0 (coaxial); 10.0 (fiber optic). Homes passed: 450.
Manager: Doug Soden. Chief technician: Gary Powers.
Ownership: Doug Soden.

ULYSSES—Cablecomm, 166 Main St., Hornell, NY 14843. Phone: 800-783-2839. County: Potter. ICA: PA0419.
TV Market Ranking: Outside TV Markets. Franchise award date: N.A. Franchise expiration date: N.A. Began: July 1, 1982.
Channel capacity: 12. Channels available but not in use: N.A.

Basic Service
Subscribers: 207.
Programming (received off-air): WGRZ-TV (N), WIVB-TV (C), WKBW-TV (A) Buffalo; WPSX-TV (P) Clearfield.
Programming (via satellite): TBS Superstation.
Fee: $35.00 installation; $17.95 monthly.

Ownership: Fanch Communications Inc. (MSO). See Cable System Ownership.

UNION TWP. (Centre County)—Country Cable, 196 S. Main St., Pleasant Gap, PA 16823. Phone: 814-359-3161. Fax: 814-359-2145. County: Centre. Also serves Fleming Borough, Huston Twp. (Centre County), Julian. ICA: PA0209.
TV Market Ranking: Outside TV Markets. Franchise award date: N.A. Franchise expiration date: N.A. Began: June 1, 1974.
Channel capacity: 36 (2-way capable; not operating 2-way). Channels available but not in use: 2.

Basic Service
Subscribers: 894.
Programming (received off-air): WPSX-TV (P) Clearfield; WATM-TV (A), WJAC-TV (N), WKBS-TV (I), WTAJ-TV (C), WWCP-TV (F) Johnstown-Altoona; WBRE-TV (N), WNEP-TV (A), WVIA-TV (P) Scranton & Wilkes-Barre.
Programming (via satellite): WGN-TV (W) Chicago; CNN; Discovery Channel; ESPN; Electronic Program Guide Jr.; Fox Family Channel; Fox Sports Net Pittsburgh; Nashville Network; Nickelodeon; TBS Superstation; Turner Network TV; USA Network.
Fee: $35.00 installation; $18.50 monthly.

Pay Service 1
Pay Units: 205.
Programming (via satellite): HBO.
Fee: $20.00 installation; $13.00 monthly.

Local advertising: Yes. Available in character-generated programming.
Equipment: Triple Crown headend; C-COR & Triple Crown amplifiers; Pioneer set top converters; Eagle traps; Triple Crown satellite receivers.
Miles of plant: 70.0 (coaxial); None (fiber optic). Homes passed: 925. Total homes in franchised area: 965.
Manager: Lee Dorman.
Ownership: Lee C. Dorman.

UNION TWP. (Huntingdon County)—Calvin Cable System Inc., Box 96, Lakeway Manor, Calvin, PA 16622. Phone: 814-643-0438. Fax: 814-643-0438. County: Huntingdon. Also serves Calvin, Cass Twp. (Huntingdon County), Cassville Borough, Todd, Todd Twp. (Huntingdon County). ICA: PA0208.
TV Market Ranking: 74. Franchise award date: N.A. Franchise expiration date: January 1, 1999. Began: November 1, 1984.
Channel capacity: 40 (not 2-way capable). Channels available but not in use: 10.

Basic Service
Subscribers: 900.
Programming (received off-air): WPSX-TV (P) Clearfield; WHTM-TV (A) Harrisburg; WATM-TV (A), WJAC-TV (N), WKBS-TV (I), WTAJ-TV (C), WWCP-TV (F) Johnstown-Altoona.
Programming (via satellite): CNN; Country Music TV; Discovery Channel; ESPN; Fox Family Channel; Learning Channel; Nashville Network; QVC; TBS Superstation; The Weather Channel; Turner Network TV; USA Network.
Current originations: Automated time-weather; public access; government access.
Fee: $75.00 installation; $16.48 monthly.

Expanded Basic Service
Subscribers: 294.
Programming (via satellite): ESPN 2; MTV; Nickelodeon.
Fee: $5.00 monthly.

Pay Service 1
Pay Units: N.A.
Programming (via satellite): Cinemax; Disney Channel; Fox Sports Net Pittsburgh; HBO.
Fee: $2.00 monthly (Fox Sports), $7.00 monthly (Disney), $8.00 monthly (Cinemax), $10.00 monthly (HBO).

Local advertising: Yes. Available in character-generated programming. Rates: $3.00/30 Seconds. Local sales manager: Judy A. Colbert.
Equipment: Blonder-Tongue, Drake & Jerrold headend; Texscan amplifiers; Times Fiber cable; SpectraView character generator; Scientific-Atlanta set top converters; PPC traps; ChannelMaster satellite antenna; Drake satellite receivers.
Miles of plant: 100.0 (coaxial); None (fiber optic). Homes passed: 1,100. Total homes in franchised area: 1,125.
Manager: Judy A. Colbert. Chief technician: Harold L. Colbert.
Franchise fee: 3% of basic (Cass Twp.).
Ownership: Calvin Cable System Inc.

UNIONTOWN—Helicon Cablevision, 320 Bailey Ave., Uniontown, PA 15401. Phone: 412-437-9875. Fax: 412-437-6910. Counties: Fayette, Greene, Washington & Westmoreland. Also serves Allison I, Allison II, Beallsville, Bentleyville, Besco, Bobtown, Braden Plan, Braznell, Brownsville, Brownsville Twp. (Fayette County), Burson Plan, Cardale, Carmichaels, Centerville (Fayette County), Chartiers, Clarksville, Cokeburg, Colonial IV, Crucible, Cumberland Twp. (Greene County), Dawson, Dry Tavern, Dunkard Twp., Dunlap Creek Village, Dutch Hill (Fayette County), East Bethlehem Twp. (Washington County), Ellsworth, Fairbank, Fairchance, Fayette City (Fayette County), Filbert, Fredericktown, Georges Twp. (Fayette County), German Twp. (Fayette County), Glassworks, Greensboro, Grindstone, Herbert, Hiller, Hopwood, Isabella (portions), Jefferson (Greene County), Jefferson Twp. (Fayette County), Keisterville, Knoxville (Fayette County), La Belle, Linn, Linn Road, Luzerne Twp. (Fayette County), Mapletown (portions), Marianna, Masontown, Mather, Maxwell, McClellandtown, Menallen Twp. (Fayette County), Merrittstown, Milfred Terrace, Millsboro, Monongahela Twp., Morgan Twp. (Greene County), Nemacolin, New Salem, Nicholson Twp. (Fayette County), North Bethlehem Twp. (portions), North Union Twp. (Fayette County), Orient, Perry Twp. (Fayette County), Perryopolis, Pike Mine, Pitt Gas, Point Marion, Redstone Twp. (Fayette County), Republic, Rices Landing, Rostraver (Westmoreland County), Rowes Run, Smithfield, Smithton, Smock (portions), South Union Twp., Springhill Twp. (Fayette County), Springhill Twp. (Greene County), Taylor Patch, Teagarden Homes, Vesta Heights, Vestaburg, Washington Twp. (Fayette County), Williamstown (Washington County). ICA: PA0020.

TV Market Ranking: 10 (Allison I, Allison II, Beallsville, Bentleyville, Besco, Braden Plan, Braznell, Brownsville, Brownsville Twp., Burson Plan, Cardale, Centerville, Chartiers, Cokeburg, Colonial IV, Crucible, Dawson, Dry Tavern, Dunlap Creek Village, Dutch Hill, East Bethlehem Twp., Ellsworth, Fairbank, Fairchance, Fayette City, Filbert, Fredericktown, Georges Twp., German Twp., Grindstone, Herbert, Hiller, Hopwood, Isabella, Jefferson Twp., Keisterville, Knoxville, La Belle, Linn, Linn Road, Luzerne Twp., Mapletown, Marianna, Masontown, Mather, Maxwell, McClellandtown, Menallen Twp., Merrittstown, Milfred Terrace, Millsboro, Morgan Twp., New Salem, Nicholson Twp., North Bethlehem Twp., North Union Twp., Orient, Perry Twp., Perryopolis, Pike Mine, Pitt Gas, Point Marion, Redstone Twp., Republic, Rices Landing, Rostraver, Rowes Run, Smithton, Smock, Taylor Patch, Teagarden Homes, Vesta Heights, Vestaburg, Washington Twp., Williamstown); 90 (Chartiers, Clarksville, Cokeburg, Glassworks, Jefferson); Below 100 (Bobtown, Dunkard Twp., South Union Twp., Uniontown); Outside TV Markets (Carmichaels, Cumberland Twp., Greensboro, Monongahela Twp., Nemacolin, Smithfield, Springhill Twp.). Franchise award date: January 1, 1966. Franchise expiration date: N.A. Began: January 1, 1966.

Channel capacity: 82 (2-way capable; operating 2-way). Channels available but not in use: N.A.

Basic Service

Subscribers: 39,479.

Programming (received off-air): WPCB-TV (I) Greensburg; WNPB-TV (P) Morgantown; KDKA-TV (C), WCWB (W), WPGH-TV (F), WPXI (N), WQED (P), WQEX (P), WTAE-TV (A) Pittsburgh; WTRF-TV (C) Wheeling-Steubenville.

Programming (via satellite): A & E; American Movie Classics; BET; C-SPAN; CNBC; CNN; Comedy Central; Country Music TV; Court TV; Discovery Channel; E! Entertainment TV; ESPN; ESPN 2; ESPNews; EWTN; FX; Fox Family Channel; Fox News Channel; Headline News; History Channel; Home Shopping Network; Ladbroke Racing Channel/Meadows Racing Network; Learning Channel; Lifetime; MSNBC; MTV; Nashville Network; Nick at Nite; Nick at Nite's TV Land; Nickelodeon; Pennsylvania Cable Network; QVC; Sci-Fi Channel; TV Food Network; TV Guide Channel; The Box; The Weather Channel; Trinity Bcstg. Network; Turner Network TV; USA Network; VH1; ValueVision.

Current originations: Public access; educational access.

Fee: $35.00 installation; $27.29 monthly.

Expanded Basic Service

Subscribers: 39,479.

Programming (via satellite): Animal Planet; Cartoon Network; Fox Sports Net; TBS Superstation.

Fee: $1.86 monthly.

Pay Service 1

Pay Units: 822.

Programming (via satellite): Cinemax.

Fee: $20.00 installation; $9.95 monthly.

Pay Service 2

Pay Units: 774.

Programming (via satellite): Disney Channel.

Fee: $20.00 installation; $9.95 monthly.

Pay Service 3

Pay Units: 3,187.

Programming (via satellite): HBO (multiplexed).

Fee: $20.00 installation; $10.95 monthly.

Pay Service 4

Pay Units: 3,353.

Programming (via satellite): The Movie Channel.

Fee: $20.00 installation; $9.95 monthly.

Pay Service 5

Pay Units: 3,338.

Programming (via satellite): Showtime.

Fee: $20.00 installation; $9.95 monthly.

Pay Service 6

Pay Units: N.A.

Programming (via satellite): fXM: Movies from Fox.

Fee: N.A.

Pay-Per-View

Addressable homes: 8,400.

Action Pay-Per-View; Hot Choice; Spice; Viewer's Choice.

Fee: $5.95.

Local advertising: Yes. Available in satellite distributed programming. Rates: $12.00/30 Seconds. Regional interconnect: TCI Media Services-Pittsburgh, PA.

Program Guide: CableView.

Equipment: Scientific-Atlanta headend; Jerrold amplifiers; Times Fiber cable; Jerrold set top converters; Jerrold addressable set top converters; Eagle & Pico traps; Comtech satellite antenna; Microdyne & Scientific-Atlanta satellite receivers; Sony commercial insert.

Miles of plant: 1017.0 (coaxial); 231.0 (fiber optic). Additional miles planned: 4.0 (fiber optic). Homes passed: 50,000. Total homes in franchised area: 52,000.

Manager: Craig S. Tomchik. Plant manager: Fred Davies. Program director: David Baum. Marketing director: Mark LaMarche.

City fee: 3% of gross.

Ownership: Helicon Corp. (MSO). See Cable System Ownership.

WALKER TWP. (Centre County)—Tele-Media Co. of Zion, Box 39, 804 Jacksonville Rd., Bellefonte, PA 16823. Phone: 814-353-2025. Fax: 814-359-5391. County: Centre. Also serves Hublersburg (Centre County), Jacksonville (Centre County), Marion Twp. (Centre County), Mingoville, Nittany, Snydertown (Centre County), Spring Twp. (Centre County), Zion. ICA: PA0193.

TV Market Ranking: Outside TV Markets. Franchise award date: N.A. Franchise expiration date: October 6, 2002. Began: January 1, 1974.

Channel capacity: 35 (not 2-way capable). Channels available but not in use: 2.

Basic Service

Subscribers: 1,106.

Programming (received off-air): WPSX-TV (P) Clearfield; WHTM-TV (A) Harrisburg; WJAC-TV (N), WTAJ-TV (C) Johnstown-Altoona; WGAL (N) Lancaster; WNEP-TV (A) Scranton & Wilkes-Barre; WPMT (F) York; allband FM.

Programming (via satellite): WGN-TV (W) Chicago; Fox Family Channel; TBS Superstation.

Current originations: Automated time-weather; public access.

Fee: $48.40 installation; $10.80 monthly.

Expanded Basic Service

Subscribers: 1,054.

Programming (via satellite): A & E; American Movie Classics; CNN; Discovery Channel; ESPN; ESPN 2; Home & Garden Television; MTV; Nashville Network; Nickelodeon; QVC; The Weather Channel; Turner Network TV; USA Network.

Fee: $11.95 monthly.

Pay Service 1

Pay Units: 155.

Programming (via satellite): Cinemax.

Fee: $15.00 installation; $9.95 monthly.

Pay Service 2

Pay Units: 65.

Programming (via satellite): Disney Channel.

Fee: $15.00 installation; $7.00 monthly.

Pay Service 3

Pay Units: 145.

Programming (via satellite): HBO.

Fee: $15.00 installation; $12.00 monthly.

Local advertising: No.

Program Guide: Premium Channels.

Equipment: Blonder-Tongue, Jerrold & Scientific-Atlanta headend; Broadband & C-COR amplifiers; CCS Hatfield & Times Fiber cable; Jerrold set top converters; AFC & Harris satellite antenna; Microdyne, Scientific-Atlanta & M/A-Com satellite receivers.

Miles of plant: 54.0 (coaxial); None (fiber optic). Additional miles planned: 2.0 (coaxial). Homes passed: 1,196.

Manager: Charles J. Hilderbrand. Chief technician: Randy Boone. Program director: Judy Steinen. Marketing director: Lesley Strouse. Customer service manager: Marge Frazier.

City fee: 3% of gross.

Ownership: Tele-Media Corp. (MSO).

WALLINGFORD—Suburban Cable, 3 Moore Rd., Wallingford, PA 19086. Phones: 610-499-2472; 800-222-1813. Fax: 610-876-8577. Web site: http://www.suburbancable.com. County: Delaware. Also serves Aldan, Aston, Aston Twp., Bethel Twp. (Delaware County), Brookhaven, Chester, Chester Heights, Chester Twp. (Delaware County), Clifton Heights, Collingdale, Colwyn, Concord, Concord Twp. (Delaware County), Darby, Darby Twp., East Lansdowne, Eddystone (Delaware County), Folcroft, Glenolden, Lansdowne, Lower Chichester Twp., Marcus Hook, Media (Delaware County), Middletown Twp. (Delaware County), Millbourne (Delaware County), Morton, Morton Twp., Nether Providence Twp., Norwood, Parkside, Prospect Park, Ridley Park (Delaware County), Ridley Twp., Rose Valley, Rutledge (Delaware County), Sharon Hill, Springfield Twp. (Delaware County), Swarthmore, Tinicum Twp. (Delaware County), Trainer, Upland, Upper Chichester Twp., Upper Darby, Upper Darby Twp., Upper Providence Twp. (Delaware County), Yeadon. ICA: PA0002.

TV Market Ranking: 4. Franchise award date: N.A. Franchise expiration date: N.A. Began: November 1, 1979.

Channel capacity: 82 (2-way capable; operating 2-way). Channels available but not in use: None.

Basic Service

Subscribers: 123,598.

Programming (received off-air): WLVT-TV (P) Allentown; WGTW (I) Burlington; WNJS (P) Camden; KYW-TV (C), WCAU (N), WPHL-TV (W), WPSG (U), WPVI-TV (A), WTXF-TV (F), WYBE (P) Philadelphia; WHSP-TV (H) Vineland; WHYY-TV (P), WPPX (X) Wilmington.

Programming (via satellite): C-SPAN; Knowledge TV; Pennsylvania Cable Network; TBS Superstation.

Current originations: Public access; educational access; government access.

Fee: $33.00 installation; $11.05 monthly; $24.00 additional installation.

Expanded Basic Service

Subscribers: 118,860.

Programming (via satellite): A & E; American Movie Classics; BET; Bravo; C-SPAN 2; CNBC; CNN; Comedy Central; Discovery Channel; E! Entertainment TV; ESPN; ESPN 2; EWTN; FX; Fox Family Channel; Headline News; Home Shopping Network; Learning Channel; Lifetime; MSNBC; MTV; Nashville Network; Nick at Nite; Nickelodeon; QVC; TV Food Network; TV Guide Channel; The Box; The Health Network; The Sports Network; The Weather Channel; Turner Network TV; USA Network; Univision; VH1.

Fee: $18.45 monthly.

A la Carte 1

Subscribers: N.A.

Programming (via satellite): Cartoon Network; Court TV; fXM: Movies from Fox; History Channel; Home & Garden Television; MOVIEplex; Sci-Fi Channel; Travel Channel; Turner Classic Movies.

Fee: N.A.

Pay Service 1

Pay Units: 18,900.

Programming (via satellite): Cinemax.

Fee: $9.95 monthly.

Pay Service 2

Pay Units: 6,800.

Programming (via satellite): Disney Channel.

Fee: $8.95 monthly.

Pay Service 3

Pay Units: 34,600.

Programming (via satellite): HBO (multiplexed).

Fee: $11.95 monthly.

Pay Service 4

Pay Units: 16,700.

Programming (via satellite): Showtime.

Fee: $11.95 monthly.

Pay Service 5

Pay Units: 18,700.

Programming (via satellite): Starz!

Fee: $9.95 monthly.

Pay Service 6

Pay Units: N.A.

Programming (via satellite): The Movie Channel.

Fee: N.A.

Pay-Per-View

Addressable homes: 58,700.

Playboy TV; Spice; movies; special events.

Fee: Varies.

Local advertising: Yes. Available in satellite distributed, locally originated & character-generated programming. Local sales manager: Lou Perrotta.

Program Guide: TV Host.

Equipment: Scientific-Atlanta headend; AEL, Scientific-Atlanta & Jerrold amplifiers; Comm/Scope cable; Sony cameras; Sony VTRs; Texscan & Amiga character generator; Hamlin & Jerrold set top converters; Scientific-Atlanta addressable set top converters; Arcom traps; Scientific-Atlanta satellite antenna; Scientific-Atlanta satellite receivers.

Miles of plant: 1670.0 (coaxial); 392.0 (fiber optic). Homes passed: 185,900.

Technical operations manager: Keith Boyd. Chief technician: Mike Hance. Program director: George Ferrara. Marketing director: John M. Murawski.

City fee: 3% of gross.

Ownership: Lenfest Communications Inc. (MSO).

WALNUT—Penn CATV of Walnut, Box 87-B, RD 1, McClure, PA 17841. Phone: 717-543-5972. County: Juniata. ICA: PA0281.

TV Market Ranking: Outside TV Markets. Franchise award date: N.A. Franchise expiration date: N.A. Began: December 1, 1983.

Channel capacity: 12. Channels available but not in use: 2.

Basic Service

Subscribers: N.A.

Programming (received off-air): WHP-TV (C), WHTM-TV (A), WITF-TV (P) Harrisburg; WTAJ-TV (C) Johnstown-Altoona; WGAL (N), WLYH-TV (U) Lancaster; WBRE-TV (N),

WNEP-TV (A), WVIA-TV (P) Scranton & Wilkes-Barre; WPMT (F) York.
Fee: N.A.
Miles of plant: 8.0 (coaxial). Homes passed: 138. Total homes in franchised area: 138.
Manager: R. Edward Shields.
Ownership: R. Edward Shields (MSO).

WALNUT BOTTOM—Kuhn Communications, Box 277, Walnut Bottom, PA 17266-0277. Phone: 717-532-8857. Fax: 717-532-5563. County: Cumberland. Also serves Newton (Cumberland County), Penn Twp. (Cumberland County). ICA: PA0220.
TV Market Ranking: 57. Franchise award date: N.A. Franchise expiration date: N.A. Began: January 1, 1978.
Channel capacity: 35. Channels available but not in use: N.A.
Basic Service
Subscribers: N.A.
Programming (received off-air): WNUV (W) Baltimore; WHAG-TV (N), WJAL (W) Hagerstown; WHP-TV (C), WHTM-TV (A), WITF-TV (P) Harrisburg; WTAJ-TV (C) Johnstown-Altoona; WGAL (N), WLYH-TV (U) Lancaster; WDCA (U) Washington; WPMT (F) York.
Programming (via satellite): ESPN; MTV; Nashville Network; USA Network.
Fee: $20.00 installation; $6.75 monthly.
Pay Service 1
Pay Units: N.A.
Programming (via satellite): HBO; The Movie Channel.
Fee: $9.60 monthly (each).
Miles of plant: 14.0 (coaxial). Homes passed: 700.
Manager: Earl Kuhn. Office manager: Tracy Reath.
Ownership: Kuhn Communications (MSO).

WARREN—TW Fanch-One, 14 Biddle St., Warren, PA 16365. Phone: 814-723-7900. Fax: 814-723-3283. County: Warren. Also serves Conewango Twp. (Warren County), Glade Twp. (Warren County), Mead Twp. (Warren County), Pine Grove Twp. (Warren County), Pleasant Twp. (Warren County), Warren County. ICA: PA0090.
TV Market Ranking: Below 100. Franchise award date: March 1, 1952. Franchise expiration date: July 16, 2004. Began: February 1, 1953.
Channel capacity: 54. Channels available but not in use: 11.
Basic Service
Subscribers: 7,767.
Programming (received off-air): WGRZ-TV (N), WIVB-TV (C), WKBW-TV (A) Buffalo; WPSX-TV (P) Clearfield; WFXP (F), WICU-TV (N), WJET-TV (A), WSEE (C) Erie; allband FM.
Programming (via microwave): WNYW (F), WPIX (W) New York.
Programming (via satellite): C-SPAN; C-SPAN 2; EWTN; QVC; TBS Superstation; TV Guide Channel; Trinity Bcstg. Network.
Current originations: Automated time-weather.
Fee: $45.24 installation; $9.77 monthly; $1.77 converter; $18.10 additional installation.
Expanded Basic Service
Subscribers: N.A.
Programming (via satellite): A & E; American Movie Classics; Animal Planet; CNBC; CNN; Cartoon Network; Country Music TV; Court TV; Discovery Channel; E! Entertainment TV; ESPN; ESPN 2; Fox Family Channel; Fox News Channel; Headline News; History Channel; Home & Garden Television; Learning Channel; Lifetime; MOVIEplex; MTV; Nashville Network; Nick at Nite's TV Land; Nickelodeon; The Weather Channel; Travel Channel; Turner Network TV; USA Network; VH1.
Fee: $20.96 monthly.
A la Carte 1
Subscribers: N.A.
Programming (via satellite): Fox Sports Net Pittsburgh.
Fee: $1.99 monthly.
Pay Service 1
Pay Units: 2,147.
Programming (via satellite): Cinemax; Disney Channel; HBO; Showtime; The Movie Channel.
Fee: $15.00 installation; $11.60 monthly (each).
Pay-Per-View
Action Pay-Per-View; Playboy TV; Viewer's Choice 1 & 2.
Fee: $2.99-$4.95.
Local advertising: Yes.
Equipment: Scientific-Atlanta headend; C-COR amplifiers; Capscan cable; Texscan character generator; Scientific-Atlanta & Harris satellite antenna; Scientific-Atlanta & Harris satellite receivers.
Miles of plant: 127.0 (coaxial). Homes passed: 8,395. Total homes in franchised area: 8,462.
Manager: Linda Sinons. Chief technician: Mike Papasergi.
City fee: 3% of gross.
Ownership: Fanch Communications Inc. (MSO); Time Warner Cable (MSO). See Cable System Ownership.

WARRIORS MARK—Milestone Communications LP, Suite 200, 1850 Woodmoor Dr., Monument, CO 80132. Phone: 719-488-2916. Fax: 719-488-3629. Counties: Blair & Huntingdon. Also serves Birmingham Borough, Snyder, Tyrone. ICA: PA0434.
TV Market Ranking: 74. Franchise award date: N.A. Franchise expiration date: February 5, 2010. Began: N.A.
Channel capacity: 27 (not 2-way capable). Channels available but not in use: 2.
Basic Service
Subscribers: 399.
Programming (received off-air): WPSX-TV (P) Clearfield; WATM-TV (A), WJAC-TV (N), WKBS-TV (I), WTAJ-TV (C), WWCP-TV (F) Johnstown-Altoona.
Programming (via satellite): WGN-TV (W) Chicago; A & E; CNN; Country Music TV; Discovery Channel; ESPN; ESPN 2; Fox Family Channel; Headline News; History Channel; Nashville Network; Nickelodeon; QVC; TBS Superstation; Trinity Bcstg. Network; Turner Network TV; USA Network.
Current originations: Public access.
Fee: $50.00 installation (aerial), $60.00 (underground); $23.25 monthly; $2.50 converter; $10.00 additional installation.
Pay Service 1
Pay Units: 70.
Programming (via satellite): Showtime; The Movie Channel.
Fee: $10.00 installation; $12.95 monthly (each).
Local advertising: No.
Miles of plant: 23.4 (coaxial); None (fiber optic). Homes passed: 550.
Manager: Michael Drake. Engineering director: Randy Mock.
Ownership: Milestone Communications LP (MSO).

WASHINGTON—TCI of Pennsylvania, 140 Park Ave., Washington, PA 15301. Phone: 724-225-6534. Fax: 724-222-9363. County: Washington. Also serves Amwell Twp., Buffalo Twp. (Washington County), Canton Twp. (Washington County), Chartiers Twp. (Washington County), East Washington, North Franklin Twp., South Franklin Twp., South Strabane Twp. ICA: PA0058.
TV Market Ranking: 10,90. Franchise award date: N.A. Franchise expiration date: N.A. Began: December 18, 1968.
Channel capacity: 35 (not 2-way capable). Channels available but not in use: None.
Basic Service
Subscribers: 16,227; Commercial subscribers: 1,589.
Programming (received off-air): WPCB-TV (I) Greensburg; KDKA-TV (C), WCWB (W), WPGH-TV (F), WPXI (N), WQED (P), WQEX (P), WTAE-TV (A) Pittsburgh; WTOV-TV (N) Steubenville-Wheeling; WTRF-TV (C) Wheeling-Steubenville.
Programming (via satellite): C-SPAN; Fox Family Channel; TBS Superstation; The Weather Channel.
Current originations: Public access; educational access; government access.
Fee: $30.34 installation; $11.93 monthly; $0.17 converter; $7.58 additional installation.
Expanded Basic Service
Subscribers: 15,772.
Programming (via satellite): A & E; CNN; ESPN; Fox Sports Net Pittsburgh; Headline News; Ladbroke Racing Channel/Meadows Racing Network; Lifetime; MTV; Nickelodeon; QVC; Sci-Fi Channel; TV Guide Channel; USA Network; VH1.
Fee: $9.06 monthly.
Expanded Basic Service 2
Subscribers: N.A.
Programming (via satellite): American Movie Classics; Discovery Channel; Nashville Network; Turner Network TV.
Fee: $2.00 monthly.
Pay Service 1
Pay Units: 881.
Programming (via satellite): Cinemax.
Fee: $9.95 monthly.
Pay Service 2
Pay Units: 881.
Programming (via satellite): Disney Channel.
Fee: $8.95 monthly.
Pay Service 3
Pay Units: 2,645.
Programming (via satellite): HBO.
Fee: $11.95 monthly.
Pay Service 4
Pay Units: 435.
Programming (via satellite): The Movie Channel.
Fee: $9.95 monthly.
Pay Service 5
Pay Units: 2,257.
Programming (via satellite): Showtime.
Fee: $10.95 monthly.
Pay-Per-View
Addressable homes: 3,837.
Viewer's Choice.
Local advertising: Yes.
Equipment: Scientific-Atlanta headend; Jerrold amplifiers; Comm/Scope cable; Scientific-Atlanta satellite antenna.
Miles of plant: 203.9 (coaxial). Homes passed: 21,771.
Manager: Denise Furley. Chief technician: Danny Starr. Marketing director: Linda Walker.
City fee: 3% of gross.
Ownership: AT&T Broadband & Internet Services (MSO). Purchased from Tele-Communications Inc., March 9, 1999.

WATERFALL—Waterfall Community TV, Box 3, Waterfall, PA 16689. Phone: 814-685-3464. County: Fulton. Also serves New Grenada, Wells Tannery. ICA: PA0260.
TV Market Ranking: 74. Franchise award date: N.A. Franchise expiration date: N.A. Began: January 1, 1973.
Channel capacity: 21. Channels available but not in use: 8.
Basic Service
Subscribers: 288.
Programming (received off-air): WPSX-TV (P) Clearfield; WGAL (N), WLYH-TV (U) Lancaster; WDCA (U), WTTG (F) Washington; WPMT (F) York.
Programming (via satellite): CNN; Cartoon Network; Country Music TV; Discovery Channel; ESPN; Fox Family Channel; Nashville Network; TBS Superstation; Turner Classic Movies.
Current originations: Public access.
Fee: $50.00 installation; $9.50 monthly.
Equipment: Blonder-Tongue headend; Gamco, Blonder-Tongue & Triple Crown amplifiers; Plastoid & Trilogy cable; Jerrold set top converters.
Miles of plant: 15.0 (coaxial).
Manager: Tom Newman.
Ownership: Tom Newman.

WATERVILLE—Ralph Herr TV, Box 717, RR 4, Montoursville, PA 17754-9665. Phone: 717-435-2780. County: Lycoming. Also serves Harrison Flats, Jersey Mills. ICA: PA0279.
TV Market Ranking: Below 100. Franchise award date: N.A. Franchise expiration date: N.A. Began: January 1, 1955.
Channel capacity: 12. Channels available but not in use: N.A.
Basic Service
Subscribers: N.A.
Programming (received off-air): WHP-TV (C), WHTM-TV (A) Harrisburg; WTAJ-TV (C) Johnstown-Altoona; WBRE-TV (N), WNEP-TV (A), WVIA-TV (P), WYOU (C) Scranton & Wilkes-Barre; allband FM.
Fee: $25.00 installation; $5.00 monthly.
Equipment: Blonder-Tongue headend; Coral amplifiers; Coral cable.
Miles of plant: 10.0 (coaxial). Additional miles planned: 3.0 (coaxial). Homes passed: 145.
Manager: Barry Herr.
City fee: None.
Ownership: Herr Cable Co. (MSO).

WATTSBURG—CableVision Communications, Box 2200, 68 5th St., Buckhannon, WV 26201. Phone: 304-472-4193. Fax: 304-472-0756. County: Erie. Also serves Lowville, Venango Twp. (Erie County). ICA: PA0248.
TV Market Ranking: Below 100. Franchise award date: N.A. Franchise expiration date: N.A. Began: October 1, 1984.
Channel capacity: 31. Channels available but not in use: N.A.
Basic Service
Subscribers: 239.
Programming (received off-air): WFXP (F), WICU-TV (N), WJET-TV (A), WQLN (P), WSEE (C) Erie.
Programming (via satellite): WGN-TV (W) Chicago; American Movie Classics; CNN; Country Music TV; Discovery Channel; Disney Channel; ESPN; Fox Family Channel; Lifetime; Nashville Network; Nickelodeon; TBS Superstation; The Inspirational Network; Turner Network TV; USA Network.
Fee: $61.25 installation; $24.00 monthly; $1.24 converter; $17.50 additional installation.

Pay Service 1
Pay Units: 176.
Programming (via satellite): Cinemax; HBO.
Fee: $7.95 monthly (Cinemax), $11.99 monthly (HBO).
Equipment: Blonder-Tongue headend; Jerrold amplifiers; Comm/Scope cable; Scientific-Atlanta set top converters.
Miles of plant: 10.0 (coaxial). Homes passed: 337.
Manager: Willie Critchfield. Marketing director: Kenny Phillips.
Ownership: Rifkin & Associates Inc. (MSO). See Cable System Ownership.

WAYNESBURG—AT&T Cable Services, 300 Corliss St., Pittsburgh, PA 15220-4815. Phones: 412-875-1100; 412-771-8100. County: Greene. Also serves Franklin (Greene County), Franklin Twp. (Greene County), Greene County, Wayne Twp. (Greene County). ICA: PA0134.
TV Market Ranking: 10 (portions of Greene County); 90 (Franklin, Franklin Twp., portions of Greene County, Wayne Twp., Waynesburg); Below 100 (portions of Greene County); Outside TV Markets (portions of Greene County). Franchise award date: N.A. Franchise expiration date: N.A. Began: November 1, 1963.
Channel capacity: 33 (not 2-way capable). Channels available but not in use: N.A.
Basic Service
Subscribers: 3,381.
Programming (received off-air): WPCB-TV (I) Greensburg; KDKA-TV (C), WCWB (W), WPGH-TV (F), WPXI (N), WQED (P), WTAE-TV (A) Pittsburgh; allband FM.
Programming (via satellite): C-SPAN; Discovery Channel; Fox Family Channel; Lifetime; QVC.
Current originations: Automated time-weather; public access; educational access; government access; local news.
Fee: $44.95 installation; $12.13 monthly; $1.50 converter; $24.95 additional installation.
Expanded Basic Service
Subscribers: 3,154.
Programming (via satellite): A & E; American Movie Classics; Animal Planet; CNN; ESPN; Fox News Channel; Fox Sports Net Pittsburgh; Headline News; Learning Channel; MOVIEplex; MTV; Nashville Network; Nickelodeon; TBS Superstation; The Weather Channel; Turner Network TV; USA Network.
Fee: $14.80 monthly.
Pay Service 1
Pay Units: 213.
Programming (via satellite): Cinemax.
Fee: $13.45 monthly.
Pay Service 2
Pay Units: 84.
Programming (via satellite): Disney Channel.
Fee: $12.50 monthly.
Pay Service 3
Pay Units: 443.
Programming (via satellite): HBO.
Fee: $14.95 monthly.
Pay Service 4
Pay Units: 56.
Programming (via satellite): The Movie Channel.
Fee: $13.45 monthly.
Pay Service 5
Pay Units: 875.
Programming (via satellite): The New Encore.
Fee: $1.95 monthly.
Pay Service 6
Pay Units: 452.
Programming (via satellite): Starz!
Fee: $6.75 monthly.
Local advertising: Yes. Rates: $15.00/Day.
Program Guide: The Cable Guide.
Equipment: RCA headend; C-COR amplifiers; Comm/Scope cable; Panasonic cameras; Panasonic VTRs; Jerrold set top converters; AFC satellite antenna; Microdyne satellite receivers.
Miles of plant: 36.1 (coaxial). Total homes in franchised area: 3,448.
Manager: Jeffrey C. Harshman. Chief technician: Fred A. Hamm. Marketing director: Glenn Ryerson.
Ownership: AT&T Broadband & Internet Services (MSO). Purchased from Tele-Communications Inc., March 9, 1999.

WEEDVILLE—DuCom Inc., 50 Tipp St., DuBois, PA 15801. Phone: 814-371-0334. County: Elk. Also serves Jay Twp. ICA: PA0234.
TV Market Ranking: Outside TV Markets. Franchise award date: N.A. Franchise expiration date: N.A. Began: January 1, 1959.
Channel capacity: 13. Channels available but not in use: None.
Basic Service
Subscribers: 581.
Programming (received off-air): WPSX-TV (P) Clearfield; WJAC-TV (N), WTAJ-TV (C), WWCP-TV (F) Johnstown-Altoona; KDKA-TV (C), WTAE-TV (A) Pittsburgh.
Programming (via satellite): WGN-TV (W) Chicago; ESPN; Fox Family Channel; Nashville Network; TBS Superstation; USA Network.
Fee: N.A.
Pay Service 1
Pay Units: N.A.
Programming (via satellite): The Movie Channel.
Fee: N.A.
Miles of plant: 8.0 (coaxial).
Manager: David Kucenski.
Ownership: Dubois Communications Inc. (MSO). Purchased from Rudy L. Cadori.

WELLSBORO—Blue Ridge Cable TV Inc., 15 Crafton St., Wellsboro, PA 16901. Phone: 570-724-4516. Fax: 570-724-2562. County: Tioga. Also serves Catlin Hollow, Kennedyville, Middlebury, Shippen Twp. (Tioga County). ICA: PA0421.
TV Market Ranking: Outside TV Markets. Franchise award date: N.A. Franchise expiration date: N.A. Began: October 1, 1951.
Channel capacity: N.A. Channels available but not in use: N.A.
Basic Service
Subscribers: 3,000.
Programming (received off-air): WBNG-TV (C), WICZ-TV (F), WIVT (A), WSKG (P) Binghamton; WENY-TV (A), WETM-TV (N) Elmira; 2 FMs.
Programming (via microwave): WPIX (W) New York.
Programming (via satellite): WGN-TV (W) Chicago; CNN; Cartoon Network; ESPN; Fox Family Channel; MTV; Nashville Network; TBS Superstation; USA Network.
Current originations: Automated time-weather.
Fee: $20.00 installation; $9.00-$9.50 monthly.
Pay Service 1
Pay Units: N.A.
Programming (via satellite): Disney Channel; HBO.
Fee: $15.00 installation; $8.00 monthly (Disney), $9.00 monthly (HBO).
Equipment: Entron headend; Entron amplifiers; Times Fiber & Vikoa cable; Scientific-Atlanta satellite antenna; Scientific-Atlanta satellite receivers.
Miles of plant: 93.6 (coaxial).
Manager: Tom Freeman. Chief technician: Doug Patt.
City fee: None.
Ownership: Leon Reed (MSO).

WEST ALEXANDER—Community TV Systems Cable Co., Box 96, Martins Ferry, OH 43935. Phone: 740-635-9680. County: Washington. Also serves Donegal Twp. (Washington County). ICA: PA0235.
TV Market Ranking: 10,90. Franchise award date: August 1, 1988. Franchise expiration date: August 1, 2004. Began: January 1, 1989.
Channel capacity: 60 (not 2-way capable). Channels available but not in use: 17.
Basic Service
Subscribers: 456.
Programming (received off-air): WOUC-TV (P) Cambridge; WPCB-TV (I) Greensburg; WNPA (U) Jeanette; KDKA-TV (C), WCWB (W), WPGH-TV (F), WPXI (N), WQED (P), WTAE-TV (A) Pittsburgh; WTRF-TV (C) Wheeling-Steubenville.
Programming (via satellite): WGN-TV (W) Chicago; A & E; American Movie Classics; C-SPAN; CNN; Cartoon Network; Comedy Central; Country Music TV; Court TV; Discovery Channel; E! Entertainment TV; ESPN; ESPN 2; Fox Family Channel; Headline News; History Channel; Home & Garden Television; Home Shopping Network; Learning Channel; Lifetime; MSNBC; MTV; Nashville Network; Nick at Nite's TV Land; Nickelodeon; QVC; Sci-Fi Channel; TBS Superstation; Trinity Bcstg. Network; Turner Network TV; USA Network; VH1.
Fee: $10.00 installation; $20.50 monthly.
Pay Service 1
Pay Units: 245.
Programming (via satellite): HBO (multiplexed); Showtime (multiplexed); The Movie Channel.
Fee: $12.25 monthly (each).
Equipment: Blonder-Tongue & DX Engineering headend; Jerrold amplifiers; Trilogy cable; Jerrold set top converters; Eagle traps; Comtech satellite antenna; DX Engineering satellite receivers.
Miles of plant: 21.0 (coaxial); None (fiber optic). Homes passed: 613.
Manager: Dom Cavicchia. Chief technician: Tom Duke.
Ownership: Community TV Systems Cable Co. (MSO).

WEST BURLINGTON TWP.—Barrett's TV Cable System, Box 197, RR 1, Troy, PA 16947. Phone: 570-297-3607. Fax: 570-297-4074. County: Bradford. ICA: PA0303.
TV Market Ranking: Below 100. Franchise award date: N.A. Franchise expiration date: N.A. Began: January 1, 1980.
Channel capacity: 13. Channels available but not in use: None.
Basic Service
Subscribers: 35.
Programming (received off-air): WBNG-TV (C), WICZ-TV (F) Binghamton; WENY-TV (A), WETM-TV (N) Elmira; WVIA-TV (P), WYOU (C) Scranton & Wilkes-Barre.
Fee: $35.00 installation; $8.00 monthly.
Equipment: Blonder-Tongue headend; Jerrold & Theta-Com amplifiers.
Miles of plant: 4.0 (coaxial).
Manager: Joseph K. Barrett.
Ownership: Barrett's TV Cable System (MSO).

WEST MIFFLIN—Adelphia Cable Communications, 5335 Enterprise Blvd., Bethel Park, PA 15102. Phone: 800-892-7300. Fax: 412-835-2045. County: Allegheny. Also serves Homestead, Munhall, Pleasant Hills, West Homestead, Whitaker. ICA: PA0422.
TV Market Ranking: 10. Franchise award date: N.A. Franchise expiration date: N.A. Began: January 1, 1967.
Channel capacity: 32 (2-way capable; operating 2-way). Channels available but not in use: None.
Basic Service
Subscribers: 16,724.
Programming (received off-air): WPCB-TV (I) Greensburg; WJAC-TV (N) Johnstown-Altoona; KDKA-TV (C), WCWB (W), WPGH-TV (F), WPXI (N), WQED (P), WQEX (P), WTAE-TV (A) Pittsburgh; WTRF-TV (C) Wheeling-Steubenville; 14 FMs.
Programming (via satellite): C-SPAN; CNN; ESPN; Fox Family Channel; Fox Sports Net; Fox Sports Net Pittsburgh; Home Shopping Network; Ladbroke Racing Channel/Meadows Racing Network; Lifetime; MTV; Nashville Network; Nickelodeon; TBS Superstation; The Weather Channel; Turner Network TV; USA Network; VH1.
Current originations: Public access; educational access; government access.
Fee: $29.95 installation; $17.95 monthly; $2.00 converter.
Pay Service 1
Pay Units: 10,371.
Programming (via satellite): Cinemax; HBO; Showtime; The Movie Channel.
Fee: $20.00 installation; $8.00 monthly (each).
Pay Service 2
Pay Units: N.A.
Programming (via satellite): Disney Channel.
Fee: $20.00 installation; $8.00 monthly.
Local advertising: Yes. Available in satellite distributed & taped programming. Rates: $25.00/30 Seconds. Regional interconnect: TCI Media Services-Pittsburgh, PA.
Equipment: Scientific-Atlanta headend; Scientific-Atlanta amplifiers; Comm/Scope cable; JVC cameras; JVC VTRs; Texscan character generator; Scientific-Atlanta set top converters; Scientific-Atlanta addressable set top converters; Eagle, Pico & PPC traps; Simulsat satellite antenna; Scientific-Atlanta satellite receivers.
Miles of plant: 209.0 (coaxial).
Chief technician: Chuck Redpath.
City fee: 3%-7% of gross.
Ownership: Adelphia Communications Corp. (MSO).

WEST NEWTON—Adelphia Communications Corp., 5335 Enterprise Blvd., Bethel Park, PA 15102. Phone: 800-892-7300. Fax: 412-835-2045. County: Westmoreland. Also serves Lowber, Rostraver (Westmoreland County), South Huntingdon (Westmoreland County), South Huntingdon Twp. (portions), Sutersville. ICA: PA0423.

TV Market Ranking: 10. Franchise award date: N.A. Franchise expiration date: N.A. Began: November 1, 1971.

Channel capacity: 35. Channels available but not in use: N.A.

Basic Service

Subscribers: 2,019.

Programming (received off-air): WPCB-TV (I) Greensburg; WJAC-TV (N) Johnstown-Altoona; KDKA-TV (C), WCWB (W), WPGH-TV (F), WPXI (N), WQED (P), WTAE-TV (A) Pittsburgh; allband FM.

Programming (via satellite): A & E; American Movie Classics; CNN; Discovery Channel; ESPN; Fox Family Channel; Fox Sports Net; Fox Sports Net Pittsburgh; Home Shopping Network; Lifetime; MTV; Nashville Network; Nickelodeon; TBS Superstation; The Weather Channel; Turner Network TV; USA Network.

Current originations: Automated time-weather; government access.

Fee: $19.95 installation; $14.95 monthly; $2.00 converter.

Pay Service 1

Pay Units: N.A.

Programming (via satellite): Cinemax; Disney Channel; HBO; Showtime; The Movie Channel.

Fee: $8.00 monthly (Cinemax, Disney, Showtime or TMC), $14.99 monthly (HBO).

Local advertising: Yes. Available in taped programming.

Equipment: Scientific-Atlanta headend; Scientific-Atlanta amplifiers; Comm/Scope cable; Texscan character generator; Scientific-Atlanta set top converters; Scientific-Atlanta addressable set top converters; Eagle, Pico & PPC traps; Simulsat satellite antenna; Scientific-Atlanta satellite receivers.

Miles of plant: 45.0 (coaxial).

Manager: Allen Brundagi. Chief technician: Chuck Redpath.

City fee: 3% of gross.

Ownership: Adelphia Communications Corp. (MSO).

WEST WHEATFIELD TWP. (Indiana County)—TCI of Pennsylvania Inc., Box 349, Rte. 219, Carrolltown, PA 15722. Phone: 814-344-6518. Counties: Indiana & Westmoreland. Also serves Armagh, East Wheatfield Twp., Fairfield Twp. (Westmoreland County), New Florence, Seward, St. Clair (Westmoreland County). ICA: PA0153.

TV Market Ranking: 74. Franchise award date: N.A. Franchise expiration date: N.A. Began: October 1, 1982.

Channel capacity: 37. Channels available but not in use: N.A.

Basic Service

Subscribers: 1,833.

Programming (received off-air): WPCB-TV (I) Greensburg; WATM-TV (A), WJAC-TV (N), WTAJ-TV (C), WWCP-TV (F) Johnstown-Altoona; KDKA-TV (C), WPGH-TV (F), WPXI (N), WQED (P), WTAE-TV (A) Pittsburgh.

Programming (via satellite): WGN-TV (W) Chicago; C-SPAN; CNN; Discovery Channel; Fox Family Channel; Headline News; Ladbroke Racing Channel/Meadows Racing Network; Lifetime; MTV; Nashville Network; Nickelodeon; QVC; TBS Superstation; The Weather Channel.

Fee: $59.95 installation; $10.16 monthly; $49.95 additional installation.

Expanded Basic Service

Subscribers: 1,654.

Programming (via satellite): American Movie Classics; Court TV; ESPN; Fox Sports Net Pittsburgh; Turner Network TV; USA Network.

Fee: $12.79 monthly.

Pay Service 1

Pay Units: 105.

Programming (via satellite): Cinemax.

Fee: N.A.

Pay Service 2

Pay Units: 379.

Programming (via satellite): HBO.

Fee: N.A.

Pay Service 3

Pay Units: 156.

Programming (via satellite): Showtime.

Fee: N.A.

Pay Service 4

Pay Units: 366.

Programming (via satellite): The New Encore.

Fee: N.A.

Miles of plant: 63.0 (coaxial). Homes passed: 2,232. Total homes in franchised area: 4,266.

Manager: Randy Bender.

Ownership: AT&T Broadband & Internet Services (MSO). Purchased from Tele-Communications Inc., March 9, 1999.

WESTFIELD—Westfield Community Antenna, 121 Strang St., Westfield, PA 16950. Phone: 814-367-5190. Fax: 814-367-5586. County: Tioga. Also serves Cowanesque, Westfield Twp. ICA: PA0185.

TV Market Ranking: Outside TV Markets. Franchise award date: N.A. Franchise expiration date: N.A. Began: September 1, 1952.

Channel capacity: 45 (not 2-way capable). Channels available but not in use: 7.

Basic Service

Subscribers: 1,055.

Programming (received off-air): WBNG-TV (C) Binghamton; WIVB-TV (C), WKBW-TV (A) Buffalo; WPSX-TV (P) Clearfield; WENY-TV (A), WETM-TV (N) Elmira; WVIA-TV (P) Scranton & Wilkes-Barre; allband FM.

Programming (via satellite): WSBK-TV (U) Boston; WGN-TV (W) Chicago; KTLA (W) Los Angeles; WPIX (W) New York; A & E; CNN; Country Music TV; Discovery Channel; ESPN; ESPN 2; Fox Family Channel; FoxNet; Headline News; History Channel; Nashville Network; Nick at Nite's TV Land; QVC; Sci-Fi Channel; TBS Superstation; The Weather Channel; Trinity Bcstg. Network; Turner Classic Movies; Turner Network TV; USA Network.

Current originations: Educational access.

Fee: $13.00 monthly.

Pay Service 1

Pay Units: 362.

Programming (via satellite): Disney Channel; HBO.

Fee: N.A.

Equipment: Jerrold headend; Jerrold amplifiers; Times Fiber cable; Scientific-Atlanta satellite antenna.

Miles of plant: 22.9 (coaxial); None (fiber optic). Homes passed: 1,450.

Manager: Linda Bisel. Chief technician: C. Stanley Taft.

Ownership: Westfield Community Antenna Assn. Inc.

WESTLINE—Keystone Wilcox Cable TV Inc., Box 134, Ridgway, PA 15853. Phone: 814-371-2939. Fax: 814-371-2939. County: McKean. ICA: PA0427.

TV Market Ranking: Below 100. Franchise award date: N.A. Franchise expiration date: N.A. Began: June 1, 1990.

Channel capacity: 30 (not 2-way capable). Channels available but not in use: 13.

Basic Service

Subscribers: 51.

Programming (received off-air): WGRZ-TV (N), WIVB-TV (C), WKBW-TV (A) Buffalo; WPSX-TV (P) Clearfield; WICU-TV (N) Erie; WJAC-TV (N), WTAJ-TV (C), WWCP-TV (F) Johnstown-Altoona; allband FM.

Programming (via satellite): CNN; TBS Superstation; Turner Network TV; USA Network.

Current originations: Educational access.

Fee: $20.00 installation; $18.00 monthly.

Miles of plant: 4.0 (coaxial). Homes passed: 60. Total homes in franchised area: 65.

Manager: Shirley W. McCoy. Chief technician: Edward Hulings.

Ownership: Keystone Wilcox Cable TV Inc. (MSO).

WILCOX—Keystone Wilcox Cable TV Inc., Box 134, Ridgway, PA 15853. Phone: 814-371-2939. County: McKean. ICA: PA0241.

TV Market Ranking: Outside TV Markets. Franchise award date: October 1, 1978. Franchise expiration date: N.A. Began: October 1, 1978.

Channel capacity: 36 (2-way capable; operating 2-way). Channels available but not in use: 4.

Basic Service

Subscribers: 430.

Programming (received off-air): WIVB-TV (C), WKBW-TV (A) Buffalo; WPSX-TV (P) Clearfield; WICU-TV (N) Erie; WNPA (U) Jeanette; WATM-TV (A), WJAC-TV (N), WTAJ-TV (C), WWCP-TV (F) Johnstown-Altoona; allband FM.

Programming (via satellite): CNN; Country Music TV; Discovery Channel; ESPN; Fox Family Channel; Headline News; Nashville Network; Nickelodeon; QVC; TBS Superstation; The Weather Channel; Turner Network TV; USA Network.

Fee: $20.00 installation; $21.00 monthly.

Pay Service 1

Pay Units: 60.

Programming (via satellite): Disney Channel.

Fee: $9.00 monthly.

Pay Service 2

Pay Units: 180.

Programming (via satellite): HBO.

Fee: $8.00 monthly.

Equipment: Blonder-Tongue, Olson & Standard Components headend; U.S. Tower amplifiers; Times Fiber cable; Pioneer set top converters; Eagle traps.

Miles of plant: 38.0 (coaxial); None (fiber optic). Homes passed: 460. Total homes in franchised area: 500.

Manager: Shirley W. McCoy. Chief technician: Edward Hulings.

City fee: None.

Ownership: Keystone Wilcox Cable TV Inc. (MSO).

WILKES-BARRE—Service Electric Cable TV Inc., 15 J. Campbell Collin Dr., Wilkes-Barre, PA 18702. Phone: 717-825-8508. Fax: 717-822-2601. County: Luzerne. Also serves Ashley, Bear Creek Twp., Buck Twp., Courtdale, Fairview Twp. (Luzerne County), Hanover Twp. (Luzerne County), Kingston (Luzerne County), Laurel Run, Mountain Top, Pringle, Rice Twp., Sugar Notch, Warrior Run Borough, Wilkes-Barre Twp., Wright Twp. ICA: PA0036.

TV Market Ranking: 49. Franchise award date: N.A. Franchise expiration date: N.A. Began: January 1, 1951.

Channel capacity: 80 (2-way capable). Channels available but not in use: 28.

Basic Service

Subscribers: 28,000.

Programming (received off-air): WLYH-TV (U) Lancaster; KYW-TV (C), WCAU (N) Philadelphia; WBRE-TV (N), WNEP-TV (A), WSWB (W), WVIA-TV (P), WYOU (C) Scranton & Wilkes-Barre; allband FM.

Programming (via satellite): WPIX (W) New York; A & E; American Movie Classics; C-SPAN; C-SPAN 2; CNBC; CNN; Cartoon Network; Comedy Central; Country Music TV; Court TV; Discovery Channel; ESPN; ESPN 2; EWTN; Fox Family Channel; Headline News; Home Shopping Network; Learning Channel; Lifetime; MTV; NASA TV; Nashville Network; Nickelodeon; Penn National Racing Alive (Telebet); Pennsylvania Cable Network; QVC; Sci-Fi Channel; TBS Superstation; TV Food Network; TV Guide Channel; The Weather Channel; Travel Channel; Turner Network TV; USA Network; VH1.

Current originations: Automated time-weather.

Fee: $36.00 installation; $22.50 monthly.

Pay Service 1

Pay Units: 8,200.

Programming (via satellite): Cinemax; Disney Channel; HBO.

Fee: $25.00 installation; $10.00 monthly (Cinemax or Disney), $11.00 monthly (HBO).

Pay-Per-View

Addressable homes: 9,000.

Special events.

Local advertising: Yes. Regional interconnect: Cabletime.

Program Guide: TV Host.

Equipment: Scientific-Atlanta headend; composite cable; Scientific-Atlanta satellite antenna.

Miles of plant: 640.0 (coaxial); 46.0 (fiber optic). Homes passed: 42,000.

Manager: Edward Ganc. Chief technician: Ron Debalko.

Ownership: Service Electric Cable TV Inc. (MSO).

WILLIAMSBURG (Blair County)—Broad Top Mountain Cable, 809 Lower Main St., Saxton, PA 16678. Phone: 814-635-2305. County: Blair. Also serves Catherine Twp., Frankstown Twp. (Blair County), Woodbury Twp. (Blair County). ICA: PA0205.

TV Market Ranking: 74. Franchise award date: N.A. Franchise expiration date: N.A. Began: December 1, 1959.

Channel capacity: 21. Channels available but not in use: 8.

Basic Service

Subscribers: 892.

Programming (received off-air): WPSX-TV (P) Clearfield; WATM-TV (A), WJAC-TV (N), WTAJ-TV (C) Johnstown-Altoona; allband FM.

Programming (via satellite): WGN-TV (W) Chicago; WXYZ-TV (A) Detroit; ESPN; Fox Family Channel; Nashville Network; TBS

Superstation; The Inspirational Network; USA Network.
Fee: $50.00 installation; $13.50 monthly; $15.00 additional installation.

Pay Service 1
Pay Units: N.A.
Programming (via satellite): Cinemax; Disney Channel; HBO.
Fee: $25.00 installation; $10.00 monthly (each).

Equipment: Blonder-Tongue headend; Magnavox amplifiers; Comm/Scope cable; GTE Sylvania VTRs; MSI character generator; Standard Components set top converters; Scientific-Atlanta satellite receivers.
Miles of plant: 22.9 (coaxial). Additional miles planned: 1.0 (coaxial). Homes passed: 950.
Manager: Connie Weirmert. Chief technician: John M. Zimmerman.
City fee: None.
Ownership: SRW Inc. (MSO).

WILLIAMSPORT—Susquehanna Communications Co., 330 Basin St., Williamsport, PA 17701. Phone: 717-753-3031. Fax: 717-753-8755. County: Lycoming. Also serves Armstrong Twp. (Lycoming County), Duboistown, Fairfield Twp. (Lycoming County), Hepburn Twp., Hughesville, Loyalsock Twp., Lycoming Twp., Montoursville, Old Lycoming Twp., Piatt Twp. (Lycoming County), South Williamsport, Susquehanna Twp. (Lycoming County), Woodward Twp. (Lycoming County). ICA: PA0040.
TV Market Ranking: Below 100. Franchise award date: N.A. Franchise expiration date: N.A. Began: April 1, 1952.
Channel capacity: 30. Channels available but not in use: N.A.

Basic Service
Subscribers: 35,000; Commercial subscribers: 1,682. Includes figures for Avis, PA.
Programming (received off-air): WPSX-TV (P) Clearfield; WHP-TV (C), WHTM-TV (A), WITF-TV (P) Harrisburg; WGAL (N) Lancaster; WBRE-TV (N), WNEP-TV (A), WSWB (W), WVIA-TV (P), WYOU (C) Scranton & Wilkes-Barre; 14 FMs.
Programming (via microwave): WNYW (F), WPIX (W) New York; WPHL-TV (W), WTXF-TV (F) Philadelphia.
Programming (via satellite): WGN-TV (W) Chicago; Fox Family Channel; TBS Superstation.
Fee: $50.00 installation; $21.95 monthly.

Pay Service 1
Pay Units: N.A.
Programming (via microwave): HBO.
Fee: $10.95 monthly.

Local advertising: Yes. Regional interconnect: Metrobase Cable Advertising.
Program Guide: The Cable Guide.
Equipment: C-COR cable; Harris satellite antenna.
Miles of plant: 272.0 (coaxial); None (fiber optic). Homes passed: 29,532.
Manager: Mike Loch. Chief technician: John Quay.
City fee: 1% of gross.
Ownership: Susquehanna Cable Co. (MSO).

WILLOW GROVE—Comcast Cablevision Corp., 11400 NE Ave., Philadelphia, PA 19116. Phone: 215-657-6990. Fax: 215-961-3871. County: Montgomery. Also serves Abington Twp. (Montgomery County), Bryn Athyn Borough, Cheltenham Twp., Jenkintown Borough, Lower Moreland Twp., Rockledge Borough, Upper Moreland Twp. ICA: PA0425.
TV Market Ranking: 4. Franchise award date: N.A. Franchise expiration date: N.A. Began: July 1, 1979.
Channel capacity: 37 (not 2-way capable). Channels available but not in use: None.

Basic Service
Subscribers: 148,039; Commercial subscribers: 520.
Programming (received off-air): WLVT-TV (P) Allentown; WNJS (P) Camden; KYW-TV (C), WCAU (N), WPHL-TV (W), WPSG (U), WPVI-TV (A), WTXF-TV (F) Philadelphia; WTVE (H) Reading; WHYY-TV (P) Wilmington.
Programming (via satellite): A & E; BET; C-SPAN; C-SPAN 2; CNBC; CNN; ESPN; EWTN; Electronic Program Guide; Fox Family Channel; Headline News; Kaleidoscope; Lifetime; MTV; Music Choice; Nickelodeon; QVC; TBS Superstation; The Weather Channel; Turner Network TV; USA Network; VH1.
Current originations: Public access; educational access; government access.
Fee: $62.66 installation; $21.92 monthly; $2.39 converter.
Commercial fee: $18.00 monthly.

Pay Service 1
Pay Units: N.A.
Programming (via satellite): Disney Channel; HBO; Showtime.
Fee: $30.00 installation; $7.53 monthly (Disney), $14.99 monthly (HBO or Showtime).

Local advertising: Yes. Available in satellite distributed, locally originated, character-generated & automated programming. Rates: $52.50/Minute; $30.00/30 Seconds. Local sales manager: Dave Minkoff.
Program Guide: The Cable Guide.
Equipment: Jerrold headend; Jerrold amplifiers; Times Fiber cable; Hitachi cameras; Sony VTRs; Video Data Systems character generator; Jerrold set top converters; Jerrold addressable set top converters; Eagle traps; Scientific-Atlanta satellite antenna; Microdyne & Standard Communications satellite receivers; Texscan commercial insert.
Miles of plant: 472.0 (coaxial).
Manager: Ed Pardini. Chief technician: Celio DaCosta.
City fee: 3%-5% of gross.
Ownership: Comcast Cable Communications Inc. (MSO).

WIND RIDGE—DuCom Cable TV, 50 Tipp St, Du Bois, PA 15801. Phone: 814-371-1925. Fax: 814-371-3052. E-mail: ducom@key-net.net. County: Greene. Also serves Gray Twp., Richhill Twp. ICA: PA0437.
TV Market Ranking: 90. Franchise award date: November 1, 1994. Franchise expiration date: October 31, 2004. Began: March 27, 1995.
Channel capacity: 41 (not 2-way capable). Channels available but not in use: 15.

Basic Service
Subscribers: 107.
Programming (received off-air): WKBS-TV (I) Johnstown-Altoona; KDKA-TV (C), WCWB (W), WPGH-TV (F), WPXI (N), WQED (P), WTAE-TV (A) Pittsburgh; WTOV-TV (N) Steubenville-Wheeling; WTRF-TV (C) Wheeling-Steubenville.
Programming (via satellite): CNN; Country Music TV; Discovery Channel; Disney Channel; ESPN; ESPN 2; Fox Sports Net Pittsburgh; Nashville Network; Nickelodeon; QVC; TBS Superstation; Trinity Bcstg. Network; Turner Network TV; USA Network; VH1.
Fee: $45.00 installation; $23.00 monthly.

Pay Service 1
Pay Units: N.A.

Programming (via satellite): HBO.
Fee: $10.95 monthly.

Homes passed: 177.
Manager: Rodney Preston. Chief engineer: David Kucenski.
Ownership: Dubois Communications Inc. (MSO).

WOODBURY—Detwiler Golden Rule Communications, 880 Golden Rule Dr., New Enterprise, PA 16664. Phone: 814-766-2614. Fax: 814-766-2619. County: Bedford. Also serves East St. Clair Twp. (Bedford County), King Twp., South Woodbury Twp., St. Clair (Bedford County), St. Clairsville, Woodbury Twp. (Bedford County). ICA: PA0426.
TV Market Ranking: 74. Franchise award date: January 1, 1977. Franchise expiration date: N.A. Began: June 1, 1977.
Channel capacity: 35. Channels available but not in use: 19.

Basic Service
Subscribers: N.A.
Programming (received off-air): WPSX-TV (P) Clearfield; WPCB-TV (I) Greensburg; WJAC-TV (N), WTAJ-TV (C) Johnstown-Altoona; WGAL (N) Lancaster; KDKA-TV (C), WTAE-TV (A) Pittsburgh.
Programming (via satellite): WGN-TV (W) Chicago; CNN; ESPN; TBS Superstation.
Fee: $30.00 installation; $12.00 monthly.

Pay Service 1
Pay Units: N.A.
Programming (via satellite): Disney Channel; HBO.
Fee: $8.00 monthly (Disney), $10.00 monthly (HBO).

Local advertising: Yes. Rates: $5.00/Week.
Manager: Alan Detwiler.
Ownership: Allen Detwiler.

YORK—Cable TV of York, Box 1787, 1050 E. King St., York, PA 17405-1787. Phones: 717-521-9966; 717-846-4551. Fax: 717-843-5400. Counties: Adams & York. Also serves Abbottstown, Berwick Twp., Canadochly, Chanceford Twp. (York County), Conewago Twp. (Adams County), Conewago Twp. (York County), Dallastown, Dover, Dover Twp. (York County), East Manchester Twp. (York County), East Prospect, Felton, Goldsboro, Hallam Borough, Hamilton Twp., Hanover, Heidelberg Twp., Hellam (York County), Hellam Twp. (York County), Jackson Twp. (York County), Jacobus, Littlestown, Loganville, Lower Windsor Twp. (York County), Manchester, Manchester Twp., Manheim Twp., McSherrystown, Mount Wolf, Newberry Twp., North York, Oxford Twp., Paradise Twp., Penn Twp., Red Lion, Spring Garden Twp., Springettsbury Twp., Springfield Twp. (York County), Union Twp., West Manchester Twp., West Manheim Twp., West York, Windsor, Windsor Twp. (York County), Yoe, York Haven (York County), York Twp. (York County), Yorkana. ICA: PA0013.
TV Market Ranking: 57. Franchise award date: N.A. Franchise expiration date: November 1, 2004. Began: November 27, 1967.
Channel capacity: 77 (2-way capable; operating 2-way). Channels available but not in use: 6.

Basic Service
Subscribers: 89,000.
Programming (received off-air): WBAL-TV (N), WMAR-TV (A), WMPB (P) Baltimore; WHP-TV (C), WHTM-TV (A), WITF-TV (P) Harrisburg; WGAL (N), WLYH-TV (U) Lancaster; WPHL-TV (W) Philadelphia; WGCB-TV (I) Red Lion; WPMT (F) York.
Programming (via satellite): WGN-TV (W) Chicago; C-SPAN; Learning Channel; QVC; TBS Superstation; TV Guide Channel; The Weather Channel.
Current originations: Automated time-weather; public access; educational access; government access; religious access; automated emergency alert; local news; local sports.
Fee: $35.00 installation (aerial), $50.00 (underground); $9.55 monthly; $1.30 converter.

Expanded Basic Service
Subscribers: 66,353.
Programming (via satellite): A & E; American Movie Classics; Animal Planet; BET; Bravo; CNBC; CNN; Cartoon Network; Comedy Central; Consumer Resource Network; Country Music TV; Discovery Channel; E! Entertainment TV; ESPN; ESPN 2; ESPNews; Fox Family Channel; Fox Sports Net Pittsburgh; Headline News; History Channel; Home & Garden Television; Home Shopping Network; Home Team Sports; Lifetime; MTV; Nashville Network; Nick at Nite's TV Land; Nickelodeon; Odyssey; Sci-Fi Channel; Turner Network TV; USA Network; Univision; VH1.
Fee: $11.80 monthly.

Pay Service 1
Pay Units: 10,001.
Programming (via satellite): Cinemax.
Fee: $11.24 monthly.

Pay Service 2
Pay Units: 3,504.
Programming (via satellite): Disney Channel.
Fee: $7.95 monthly.

Pay Service 3
Pay Units: 12,805.
Programming (via satellite): HBO.
Fee: $11.24 monthly.

Pay Service 4
Pay Units: 5,840.
Programming (via satellite): Showtime.
Fee: $11.24 monthly.

Pay-Per-View
Addressable homes: 31,137.
Hot Choice; Viewer's Choice.
Fee: $3.95 (Viewer's Choice).

Local advertising: Yes (locally produced & insert). Available in satellite distributed, locally originated & character-generated programming. Local sales manager: Kathy Henry. Regional interconnect: Central Pennsylvania Cable AdCom.
Equipment: Scientific-Atlanta headend; Jerrold amplifiers; Comm/Scope cable; Microgen character generator; Panasonic set top converters; Jerrold addressable set top converters.

Miles of plant: 1222.0 (coaxial); 206.0 (fiber optic). Additional miles planned: 20.0 (fiber optic). Homes passed: 87,229.
Manager: Bruce D. Abbott. Chief technician: Matt Galli. Program director: Debra Bruner. Customer service manager: Brenda Winter.
City fee: 5% of gross.
Ownership: Susquehanna Cable Co. (MSO).

YOUNGSVILLE—Youngsville TV Corp., 3 W. Main St., Youngsville, PA 16371. Phone: 814-563-3336. Fax: 814-563-7299. County: Warren. Also serves Brokenstraw Twp., Pittsfield. ICA: PA0190.
TV Market Ranking: Below 100. Franchise award date: N.A. Franchise expiration date: September 13, 2005. Began: N.A.
Channel capacity: 22 (2-way capable). Channels available but not in use: None.

Basic Service
Subscribers: 1,200.
Programming (received off-air): WIVB-TV (C), WKBW-TV (A), WUTV (F,U) Buffalo; WPSX-TV (P) Clearfield; WICU-TV (N), WJET-TV (A), WSEE (C) Erie; allband FM.
Programming (via satellite): WGN-TV (W) Chicago; CNN; Discovery Channel; ESPN; Fox Family Channel; Lifetime; MTV; Nashville Network; Nickelodeon; TBS Superstation; The Weather Channel; Turner Network TV; USA Network.
Current originations: Automated time-weather.
Fee: $135.00 installation; $10.00 monthly.

Pay Service 1
Pay Units: 601.
Programming (via satellite): HBO.
Fee: $7.00 monthly.

Equipment: Triple Crown, M/A-Com & ISS headend; C-COR amplifiers; Vikoa & Belden cable; Sony cameras; Standard Communications, RCA & Oak set top converters; Eagle & Arcom traps; KES & Paraclipse satellite antenna; Triple Crown, M/A-Com & Jerrold satellite receivers.
Miles of plant: 40.0 (coaxial).
Manager: William H. Myers Jr. Chief technician: Robert Mourer.
City fee: None.
Ownership: Youngsville TV Corp.

ZELIENOPLE—Armstrong Cable Services, Box 40, 531 Perry Way, Zelienople, PA 16063. Phones: 724-452-5213; 412-776-4200. Fax: 724-452-8008. Counties: Allegheny, Beaver & Butler. Also serves Adams Twp. (Butler County), Bradford Woods, Callery, Clinton Twp. (Butler County), Cranberry Twp. (Butler County), Evans City, Forward, Hampton Twp. (Allegheny County), Harmony, Jackson Twp. (Butler County), Lancaster Twp. (Butler County), Marion Twp. (Butler County), Mars, Marshall Twp., Muddycreek Twp., New Sewickley Twp., Pine Twp. (Allegheny County), Pine Twp. (Butler County), Portersville, Richland Twp. (Allegheny County), Seven Fields, Treesdale, Valencia, West Deer Twp. (portions). ICA: PA0053.
TV Market Ranking: 10 (Adams Twp., Bradford Woods, Callery, Clinton Twp., Cranberry Twp., Evans City, Forward, Hampton Twp., Harmony, Jackson Twp., Lancaster Twp., Marion Twp., Mars, Marshall Twp., Muddycreek Twp., Pine Twp., Portersville, Richland Twp., Seven Fields, Treesdale, Valencia, West Deer Twp., Zelienople); 79 (New Sewickley Twp.). Franchise award date: February 1, 1983. Franchise expiration date: February 1, 2008. Began: January 1, 1969.
Channel capacity: 50 (not 2-way capable). Channels available but not in use: 3.

Basic Service
Subscribers: 33,000.
Programming (received off-air): WPCB-TV (I) Greensburg; KDKA-TV (C), WCWB (W), WPGH-TV (F), WPXI (N), WQED (P), WQEX (P), WTAE-TV (A) Pittsburgh.
Programming (via microwave): Pittsburgh Cable News Channel.
Programming (via satellite): WGN-TV (W) Chicago; A & E; American Movie Classics; C-SPAN; CNBC; CNN; Cartoon Network; Comedy Central; Court TV; Discovery Channel; ESPN; ESPN 2; Fox Family Channel; Fox Sports Net Pittsburgh; Headline News; Home Shopping Network; Learning Channel; Lifetime; MSNBC; MTV; Nashville Network; Nick at Nite's TV Land; Nickelodeon; QVC; TBS Superstation; TV Guide Channel; The Inspirational Network; The Weather Channel; Turner Network TV; USA Network; VH1.
Current originations: Educational access.
Fee: $35.00 installation; $25.95 monthly; $2.95 converter; $17.50 additional installation.

Pay Service 1
Pay Units: 3,413.
Programming (via satellite): Cinemax.
Fee: $9.95 monthly.

Pay Service 2
Pay Units: 2,625.
Programming (via satellite): Disney Channel.
Fee: $7.95 monthly.

Pay Service 3
Pay Units: 6,868.
Programming (via satellite): HBO.
Fee: $11.95 monthly.

Pay Service 4
Pay Units: 1,567.
Programming (via satellite): Showtime.
Fee: $9.95 monthly.

Pay Service 5
Pay Units: 485.
Programming (via satellite): DMX.
Fee: $7.95 monthly.

Pay-Per-View
Addressable homes: 2,142.
Viewer's Choice 1-4.
Fee: $3.95.

Local advertising: Yes. Available in satellite distributed & character-generated programming.
Equipment: Scientific-Atlanta headend; C-COR amplifiers; General cable; Scientific-Atlanta character generator; Scientific-Atlanta set top converters; Scientific-Atlanta addressable set top converters; Eagle & Pico traps; Scientific-Atlanta satellite antenna; Scientific-Atlanta satellite receivers; Texscan commercial insert.
Miles of plant: 1100.0 (coaxial); 400.0 (fiber optic). Homes passed: 40,306. Total homes in franchised area: 44,000.
Manager: James R. Culver. Chief technician: Bruce Durbin. Assistant manager: Carl Rose. Marketing director: Aaron Call. Customer service manager: Melinda Schilling.
City fee: 4% of gross.
Ownership: Armstrong Group of Companies (MSO).

RHODE ISLAND

Total Systems: 8
Total Communities Served: 54
Franchises Not Yet Operating: 0
Applications Pending: 0
Communities with Applications: 0
Number of Basic Subscribers: 272,266
Number of Expanded Basic Subscribers: 153,219
Number of Pay Units: 255,446

Top 100 Markets Represented: Boston-Cambridge-Worcester-Lawrence (6); Hartford-New Haven-New Britain-Waterbury-New London (19); Providence, RI-New Bedford, MA(33).

**For a list of all cable communities included in this section, see the Cable Community Index located in the back of this volume.
For explanation of terms used in cable system listings, see p. D-9.**

CRANSTON—Cox Cable Rhode Island Inc., 111 Comstock Pkwy., Cranston, RI 02921. Phone: 401-943-6993. Fax: 401-946-3830. County: Providence. ICA: RI0004.

TV Market Ranking: 33. Franchise award date: November 1, 1974. Franchise expiration date: N.A. Began: October 22, 1981.

Channel capacity: 58 (not 2-way capable). Channels available but not in use: None.

Basic Service

Subscribers: 39,615.

Programming (received off-air): WBZ-TV (C), WCVB-TV (A), WFXT (F), WGBH-TV (P), WHDH-TV (N), WSBK-TV (U) Boston; WLVI-TV (W) Cambridge-Boston; WJAR (N), WLNE-TV (A), WNAC-TV (F), WPRI-TV (C), WSBE-TV (P) Providence; WUNI (S) Worcester.

Programming (via satellite): WPIX (W) New York; Radio Television Portugal International; TBS Superstation.

Current originations: Public access; leased access.

Fee: $15.91 installation; $9.19 monthly; $1.76 converter.

Expanded Basic Service

Subscribers: 38,610.

Programming (via satellite): A & E; Animal Planet; BET; Bravo; C-SPAN; C-SPAN 2; CNBC; CNN; Comedy Central; Disney Channel; E! Entertainment TV; ESPN; EWTN; FX; Fox Family Channel; Headline News; Home & Garden Television; Home Shopping Network; Learning Channel; Lifetime; MSNBC; MTV; Nick at Nite's TV Land; Nickelodeon; QVC; Sci-Fi Channel; TV Guide Channel; The Inspirational Network; The Weather Channel; Travel Channel; USA Network; VH1.

Fee: $14.68 monthly.

Expanded Basic Service 2

Subscribers: N.A.

Programming (via satellite): American Movie Classics; Discovery Channel; Nashville Network; Turner Network TV.

Fee: $3.19 monthly.

Expanded Basic Service 3

Subscribers: N.A.

Programming (via satellite): Cartoon Network; ESPN 2; History Channel; Turner Classic Movies.

Fee: $4.95 monthly.

Pay Service 1

Pay Units: 32,731.

Programming (via satellite): Cinemax (multiplexed); Fox Sports Net New England; HBO (multiplexed); Music Choice; New England Sports Network; Showtime (multiplexed); The Movie Channel.

Fee: $9.95 monthly (Cinemax, FSNE, Music Choice, NESN, Showtime or TMC), $10.95 monthly (HBO).

Pay-Per-View

Addressable homes: 38,610.

Spice; Viewer's Choice; movies; special events.

Fee: $5.95 (Spice or Viewer's Choice).

Local advertising: Yes. Available in satellite distributed & character-generated programming.

Equipment: Jerrold headend; Jerrold amplifiers; Times Fiber cable; JVC cameras; JVC VTRs; System Concepts character generator; Jerrold set top converters; Jerrold addressable set top converters; Scientific-Atlanta satellite antenna; Scientific-Atlanta satellite receivers.

Miles of plant: 834.5 (coaxial); 26.0 (fiber optic). Homes passed: 55,524. Total homes in franchised area: 55,824.

Manager: Gary M. Perrelli. Chief technician: James M. Kelly. Program director: Patricia Bordeleau. Marketing director: Genny L. Plas.

Franchise fee: None.

Ownership: Cox Communications Inc. (MSO). Sale pends to AT&T Broadband & Internet Services.

JOHNSTON—Cox Cable, 9 J. P. Murphy Hwy., West Warwick, RI 02893. Phone: 401-821-1919. Fax: 401-828-3835. County: Providence. Also serves Burrillville (town), Glocester (town), Scituate (town). ICA: RI0015.

TV Market Ranking: 33. Franchise award date: N.A. Franchise expiration date: N.A. Began: N.A.

Channel capacity: N.A. Channels available but not in use: N.A.

Basic Service

Subscribers: N.A.

Programming (received off-air): WBZ-TV (C), WCVB-TV (A), WFXT (F), WGBH-TV (P), WHDH-TV (N), WSBK-TV (U) Boston; WLVI-TV (W) Cambridge-Boston; WJAR (N), WLNE-TV (A), WNAC-TV (F), WPRI-TV (C), WSBE-TV (P) Providence; WUNI (S) Worcester.

Programming (via satellite): WPIX (W) New York; Radio Television Portugal International; TBS Superstation.

Current originations: Public access; leased access.

Fee: $15.91 installation; $9.19 monthly; $1.76 converter.

Expanded Basic Service

Subscribers: N.A.

Programming (via satellite): A & E; C-SPAN; C-SPAN 2; CNBC; CNN; Comedy Central; Disney Channel; E! Entertainment TV; ESPN; EWTN; FX; Fox Family Channel; Headline News; Home Shopping Network; Learning Channel; Lifetime; MTV; Nickelodeon; QVC; Sci-Fi Channel; TV Guide Channel; The Inspirational Network; The Weather Channel; Travel Channel; USA Network; VH1.

Fee: $13.70 monthly.

Expanded Basic Service 2

Subscribers: N.A.

Programming (via satellite): American Movie Classics; Discovery Channel; Nashville Network; Turner Network TV.

Fee: $3.19 monthly.

Pay Service 1

Pay Units: N.A.

Programming (via satellite): Cinemax; Fox Sports Net New England; HBO; Music Choice; New England Sports Network; Showtime; The Movie Channel.

Fee: $9.95 monthly (Cinemax, Fox Sports, Music Choice, NESN, Showtime or TMC), $10.95 monthly (HBO).

Pay-Per-View

Spice; movies; special events.

Fee: Varies.

Ownership: Cox Communications Inc. (MSO).

NEW SHOREHAM—Block Island Cable TV, Drawer A2, Block Island, RI 02807. Phone: 401-466-2479. Fax: 401-596-7366. County: Washington. ICA: RI0013.

TV Market Ranking: Below 100. Franchise award date: N.A. Franchise expiration date: N.A. Began: February 1, 1980.

Channel capacity: 21. Channels available but not in use: N.A.

Basic Service

Subscribers: 495.

Programming (received off-air): WBZ-TV (C), WCVB-TV (A), WFXT (F), WGBH-TV (P), WHDH-TV (N), WSBK-TV (U) Boston; WFSB (C) Hartford; WTNH-TV (A) New Haven; WEDN (P) Norwich; WJAR (N), WLNE-TV (A), WPRI-TV (C), WSBE-TV (P) Providence; WUNI (S) Worcester.

Fee: N.A.

Local advertising: Yes.

Miles of plant: 45.3 (coaxial).

Ownership: Block Island Cable TV.

NEWPORT—Newport Cable TV Inc., Box 6001, 61 Myrock Ave., Waterford, CT 06385. Phone: 203-442-5616. Fax: 203-443-6031. County: Newport. Also serves Newport Naval Base. ICA: RI0011.

TV Market Ranking: 33. Franchise award date: N.A. Franchise expiration date: N.A. Began: December 1, 1986.

Channel capacity: 62 (2-way capable; operating 2-way). Channels available but not in use: 19.

Basic Service

Subscribers: 1,669.

Programming (received off-air): WBZ-TV (C), WCVB-TV (A), WFXT (F), WGBH-TV (P), WGBX-TV (P), WHDH-TV (N), WSBK-TV (U) Boston; WLVI-TV (W) Cambridge-Boston; WJAR (N), WLNE-TV (A), WNAC-TV (F), WPRI-TV (C), WSBE-TV (P) Providence.

Programming (via satellite): WGN-TV (W) Chicago; WPIX (W) New York; A & E; C-SPAN; CNBC; CNN; Discovery Channel; ESPN; Nashville Network; Nickelodeon; TBS Superstation; The Weather Channel; Turner Network TV; Univision; VH1.

Current originations: Government access.

Fee: $35.00 installation; $17.00 monthly.

Pay Service 1

Pay Units: 87.

Programming (via satellite): Cinemax.

Fee: $10.00 monthly.

Pay Service 2

Pay Units: 237.

Programming (via satellite): Disney Channel.

Fee: $7.95 monthly.

Pay Service 3

Pay Units: 252.

Programming (via satellite): HBO.

Fee: $10.00 monthly.

Pay Service 4

Pay Units: 215.

Programming (via satellite): The Movie Channel.

Fee: $10.00 monthly.

Pay Service 5

Pay Units: 25.

Programming (via satellite): New England Sports Network.

Fee: $7.95 monthly.

Pay Service 6

Pay Units: 228.

Programming (via satellite): Showtime.

Fee: $10.00 monthly.

Pay-Per-View

Addressable homes: 1,669.

Local advertising: No.

Equipment: Scientific-Atlanta headend; Scientific-Atlanta amplifiers; Times Fiber cable; Sony cameras; Jerrold addressable set top converters; Scientific-Atlanta satellite antenna; Scientific-Atlanta satellite receivers.

Miles of plant: 36.0 (coaxial). Homes passed: 2,048. Total homes in franchised area: 2,048.

Manager: Hugh O'Brien. Chief technician: Russell Dipallaria.

Franchise fee: None.

Ownership: Eastern Connecticut Cable TV Inc. (MSO).

NEWPORT & LINCOLN—Cox Cable, 9 J.P. Murphy Hwy., West Warwick, RI 02893. Phone: 401-821-1919. Fax: 401-828-3835. Counties: Kent, Newport, Providence & Washington, RI; Bristol, Norfolk & Worcester, MA. Also serves Blackstone, Franklin, Mills, Norton, Plainville, Somerset, Swansea, MA; Boon Lake, Exeter (town), Jamestown, Little Compton, Middletown, Narragansett, Newport County, North Kingstown, Portsmith, Richmond (portions), South Kingstown, Tiverton, West Greenwich, RI. ICA: RI0002.

TV Market Ranking: 6 (Blackstone, Franklin, Mills, Newport & Lincoln, Norton, Plainville, Somerset, Swansea); 19 (Exeter, Narragansett, South Kingstown, West Greenwich); 33 (Blackstone, Boon Lake, Exeter, Jamestown, Little Compton, Middletown, Narragansett, Newport & Lincoln, Newport County, North Kingstown, Norton, Plainville, Portsmith, Richmond, Somerset, South Kingstown, Swansea, Tiverton, West Greenwich). Franchise award date: November 1, 1974. Franchise expiration date: N.A. Began: July 1, 1982.

Channel capacity: 60 (not 2-way capable). Channels available but not in use: None.

Basic Service

Subscribers: 102,593.

Programming (received off-air): WBZ-TV (C), WCVB-TV (A), WFXT (F), WGBH-TV (P), WGBX-TV (P), WHDH-TV (N), WSBK-TV (U) Boston; WLVI-TV (W) Cambridge-Boston;

WJAR (N), WLNE-TV (A), WNAC-TV (F), WPRI-TV (C), WSBE-TV (P) Providence.
Programming (via satellite): EWTN; FX; QVC; TBS Superstation; TV Guide Channel.
Current originations: Automated time-weather; public access; educational access; government access; leased access; automated emergency alert; local news; local sports.
Fee: $60.00 installation; $23.20 monthly; $10.00 additional installation.

Expanded Basic Service
Subscribers: N.A.
Programming (via satellite): A & E; American Movie Classics; BET; Bravo; C-SPAN; C-SPAN 2; CNBC; CNN; Comedy Central; Country Music TV; Discovery Channel; E! Entertainment TV; ESPN; Fox Family Channel; Headline News; Home Shopping Network; Lifetime; MSNBC; MTV; Nashville Network; Nickelodeon; Radio Television Portugal International; TV Guide Channel; The Weather Channel; Turner Network TV; USA Network; Univision; VH1.
Fee: N.A.

Pay Service 1
Pay Units: 6,237.
Programming (via satellite): Cinemax.
Fee: $10.95 monthly.

Pay Service 2
Pay Units: 5,186.
Programming (via satellite): Disney Channel.
Fee: $10.95 monthly.

Pay Service 3
Pay Units: 15,069.
Programming (via satellite): The New Encore.
Fee: N.A.

Pay Service 4
Pay Units: 14,368.
Programming (via satellite): HBO.
Fee: $10.95 monthly.

Pay Service 5
Pay Units: N.A.
Programming (via satellite): Starz!
Fee: N.A.

Pay Service 6
Pay Units: 7,136.
Programming (via satellite): New England Sports Network.
Fee: N.A.

Pay Service 7
Pay Units: 4,938.
Programming (via satellite): Showtime.
Fee: $10.95 monthly.

Pay Service 8
Pay Units: 5,339.
Programming (via satellite): Fox Sports Net New England.
Fee: $10.88 monthly.

Pay-Per-View
Addressable homes: 101,000.
Spice; movies; special events.
Fee: Varies.
Pay-per-view manager: Joyce Arcand.

Local advertising: Yes (locally produced). Available in satellite distributed programming.
Program Guide: The Cable Guide.
Equipment: Hughes, Jerrold & Scientific-Atlanta headend; Jerrold & General Instrument amplifiers; Comm/Scope & Times Fiber cable; Siecor fiber optic cable; JVC cameras; JVC VTRs; Video Data Systems character generator; Jerrold & General Instrument set top converters; Jerrold & General Instrument addressable set top converters; Motorola modems; Eagle traps; Scientific-Atlanta & Simulsat satellite antenna; Scientific-Atlanta & General Instrument satellite receivers.
Miles of plant: 535.4 (coaxial). Additional miles planned: 42.0 (coaxial).
Manager: Gary Perrelli. Chief engineer: Mark Scott. Marketing director: Fred Bristol. Customer service manager: Gary McCollum.
Ownership: Cox Communications Inc. (MSO).

PROVIDENCE—Cox Cable, 9 J.P. Murphy Hwy., West Warwick, RI 02893. Phone: 401-821-1919. Fax: 401-828-3835. Counties: Kent & Providence. Also serves Central Falls, Coventry, Cumberland, East Greenwich, East Providence, East Warwick, North Providence, North Smithfield, Pawtucket, Providence County, Smithfield, Warwick, West Warwick, Woonsocket. ICA: RI0001.
TV Market Ranking: 6 (Central Falls, Cumberland, North Providence, North Smithfield, Pawtucket, Providence County, Smithfield); 33 (Coventry, East Greenwich, East Providence, East Warwick, North Providence, North Smithfield, Pawtucket, Providence, Smithfield, Warwick, West Warwick, Woonsocket). Franchise award date: November 1, 1974. Franchise expiration date: N.A. Began: August 18, 1982.
Channel capacity: 60 (2-way capable; operating 2-way). Channels available but not in use: 1.

Basic Service
Subscribers: 99,399.
Programming (received off-air): WBZ-TV (C), WCVB-TV (A), WGBH-TV (P), WHDH-TV (N), WSBK-TV (U) Boston; WLVI-TV (W) Cambridge-Boston; WJAR (N), WLNE-TV (A), WNAC-TV (F), WPRI-TV (C), WSBE-TV (P) Providence.
Programming (via satellite): WPIX (W) New York; Home Shopping Network; QVC; TBS Superstation; TV Guide Channel.
Current originations: Public access; educational access; government access; religious access; leased access; local news.
Fee: $12.75 installation; $9.32 monthly.

Expanded Basic Service
Subscribers: 89,777.
Programming (via satellite): WSBK-TV (U) Boston; A & E; Animal Planet; BET; C-SPAN 2; CNBC; CNN; Cartoon Network; E! Entertainment TV; ESPN; ESPN 2; EWTN; FX; Fox Family Channel; Goodlife TV Network; Headline News; History Channel; Home & Garden Television; Learning Channel; Lifetime; MSNBC; MTV; Nick at Nite's TV Land; Nickelodeon; Outdoor Life Network; Radio Television Portugal International; Sci-Fi Channel; Speedvision; TV Food Network; TV Guide Sneak Prevue; The Weather Channel; Turner Classic Movies; USA Network; Univision; VH1.
Fee: $10.56 monthly.

A la Carte 1
Subscribers: 88,165.
Programming (via satellite): American Movie Classics; Discovery Channel; Nashville Network; Turner Network TV.
Fee: $3.10 monthly (package); $1.55 monthly (each).

Pay Service 1
Pay Units: 10,209.
Programming (via satellite): Cinemax.
Fee: $50.00 installation; $7.95 monthly.

Pay Service 2
Pay Units: 9,425.
Programming (via satellite): Disney Channel.
Fee: $7.95 monthly.

Pay Service 3
Pay Units: 23,486.
Programming (via satellite): HBO.
Fee: $10.95 monthly.

Pay Service 4
Pay Units: 17,126.
Programming (via satellite): Showtime.
Fee: $9.95 monthly.

Pay Service 5
Pay Units: N.A.
Programming (via satellite): Fox Sports Net New England; New England Sports Network.
Fee: N.A.

Pay Service 6
Pay Units: 6,458.
Programming (via satellite): The Movie Channel.
Fee: $8.95 monthly.

Pay-Per-View
Addressable homes: 54,631.
Action Pay-Per-View; Playboy TV; Spice2.
Pay-per-view manager: Joyce Arcand.

Equipment: RCA & Scientific-Atlanta headend; Magnavox & General Instrument amplifiers; Comm/Scope cable; Siecor fiber optic cable; System Concepts & Video Data Systems character generator; Texscan & General Instrument set top converters; Pioneer & General Instrument addressable set top converters; Motorola modems; Eagle traps; Harris, Scientific-Atlanta & Simulsat satellite antenna; Harris, Scientific-Atlanta & General Instrument satellite receivers.
Miles of plant: 1150.0 (coaxial); 100.0 (fiber optic). Additional miles planned: 50.0 (coaxial); 27.0 (fiber optic). Homes passed: 154,479.
Manager: Gary Perrelli. Chief Engineer: Mark Scott. Marketing director: Fred Bristol. Customer service manager.: Gary McCollum.
Ownership: Cox Communications Inc. (MSO). Sale pends to AT&T Broadband & Internet Services.

WARREN—Full Channel TV Inc., 57 Everett St., Warren, RI 02885. Phones: 401-247-2250; 401-247-1250. Fax: 401-247-0191. County: Bristol. Also serves Barrington, Bristol, Bristol County. ICA: RI0009.
TV Market Ranking: 33. Franchise award date: November 1, 1974. Franchise expiration date: N.A. Began: February 2, 1984.
Channel capacity: 52 (2-way capable; operating 2-way). Channels available but not in use: None.

Basic Service
Subscribers: 12,600.
Programming (received off-air): WBZ-TV (C), WFXT (F), WGBH-TV (P), WGBX-TV (P), WHDH-TV (N), WSBK-TV (U) Boston; WJAR (N), WLNE-TV (A), WNAC-TV (F), WPRI-TV (C), WSBE-TV (P) Providence; WLWC (U,W) Providence-New Bedford; allband FM.
Programming (via satellite): A & E; Access Entertainment Network; American Movie Classics; Animal Planet; C-SPAN; C-SPAN 2; CNBC; CNN; Comedy Central; Discovery Channel; ESPN; ESPN 2; EWTN; Fox Family Channel; Fox News Channel; Goodlife TV Network; Headline News; History Channel; Home Shopping Network; Learning Channel; Lifetime; MSNBC; MTV; Nashville Network; Nick at Nite; Nick at Nite's TV Land; Nickelodeon; QVC; TBS Superstation; The Weather Channel; Travel Channel; Trinity Bcstg. Network; Turner Network TV; USA Network; Univision; VH1.
Current originations: Public access; educational access; government access; religious access; leased access; library access; local news.
Fee: $40.00 installation; $33.75 monthly; $3.00 converter.

Pay Service 1
Pay Units: N.A.
Programming (via satellite): Cinemax; Disney Channel; HBO (multiplexed); New England Sports Network; Showtime; The Movie Channel.
Fee: $10.00 installation; $8.95 monthly (NESN), $9.95 monthly (Disney), $10.95 monthly (Cinemax), $12.95 monthly (HBO, Showtime or TMC).

Pay-Per-View
Addressable homes: 11,200.
Viewer's Choice.

Local advertising: Yes (locally produced & insert). Available in satellite distributed, locally originated, character-generated, taped & automated programming.
Program Guide: CableView.
Equipment: Jerrold headend; Jerrold amplifiers; General cable; Ikegami cameras; Sony VTRs; Chyron character generator; Jerrold set top converters; Jerrold addressable set top converters; Jerrold traps; Scientific-Atlanta & Harris satellite antenna; Tele-Engineering commercial insert.
Miles of plant: 360.0 (coaxial). Homes passed: 18,900. Total homes in franchised area: 18,900.
Manager: Mike Davis. Chief technician: Brian I. Frasier. Program director: Valerie Bain.
Ownership: John Donofrio Jr.

WESTERLY—MediaOne, 7 Canal St., Westerly, RI 02891. Phone: 401-596-0156. Fax: 401-596-2119. County: Washington. Also serves Ashaway, Bradford, Charlestown, Hopkinton, Richmond. ICA: RI0008.
TV Market Ranking: 19 (Ashaway, Bradford, Charlestown, Hopkinton, Richmond, Westerly); 33 (Ashaway, Bradford, Charlestown, Hopkinton, Richmond). Franchise award date: December 1, 1965. Franchise expiration date: N.A. Began: December 1, 1965.
Channel capacity: 64 (2-way capable; not operating 2-way). Channels available but not in use: 4.

Basic Service
Subscribers: 15,895.
Programming (received off-air): WGBH-TV (P) Boston; WLVI-TV (W) Cambridge-Boston; WFSB (C) Hartford; WHPX (I) New London; WEDN (P) Norwich; WJAR (N), WLNE-TV (A), WNAC-TV (F), WPRI-TV (C), WSBE-TV (P) Providence.
Programming (via satellite): A & E; C-SPAN; C-SPAN 2; CNBC; Country Music TV; E! Entertainment TV; EWTN; Fox Family Channel; Headline News; Home Shopping Network; Learning Channel; MTV; Nashville Network; QVC; Sci-Fi Channel; TV Food Network; TV Guide Channel; The Weather Channel; Travel Channel; VH1.
Current originations: Public access; educational access; government access; leased access; local sports; local access.
Fee: $36.98 installation; $19.06 monthly; $2.19 converter.

Expanded Basic Service
Subscribers: 12,985.
Programming (via satellite): CNN; Discovery Channel; ESPN; FX; Fox Sports Net

New England; Lifetime; Nickelodeon; The Health Network; USA Network.
Fee: $36.98 installation; $8.79 monthly.

Expanded Basic Service 2
Subscribers: 11,847.
Programming (via satellite): WSBK-TV (U) Boston; ESPN 2; Fox News Channel; Turner Classic Movies; Turner Network TV.
Fee: $36.98 installation; $2.80 monthly.

Pay Service 1
Pay Units: 1,654.
Programming (via satellite): Cinemax.
Fee: $25.00 installation; $9.95 monthly.

Pay Service 2
Pay Units: 1,754.
Programming (via satellite): Disney Channel.
Fee: $25.00 installation; $9.95 monthly.

Pay Service 3
Pay Units: 2,330.
Programming (via satellite): HBO.
Fee: $25.00 installation; $10.95 monthly.

Pay Service 4
Pay Units: 1,301.
Programming (via satellite): The Movie Channel.
Fee: $25.00 installation; $9.95 monthly.

Pay Service 5
Pay Units: 1,490.
Programming (via satellite): Showtime.
Fee: $25.00 installation; $9.95 monthly.

Pay Service 6
Pay Units: N.A.
Programming (via satellite): New England Sports Network.
Fee: N.A.

Pay-Per-View
Addressable homes: 13,057.
Movies.

Local advertising: Yes. Available in satellite distributed & automated programming. Rates: $50.00/Minute; $25.00/30 Seconds. Local sales manager: Mike O'Brian.
Program Guide: The Cable Guide.
Equipment: Scientific-Atlanta headend; Philips amplifiers; Times Fiber cable; AT&T & Comm/Scope fiber optic cable; Hitachi & Sony cameras; Sony VTRs; Amiga character generator; Eagle, Pico & Arcom traps; Hughes & Scientific-Atlanta satellite antenna; Scientific-Atlanta satellite receivers; Arvis commercial insert.
Miles of plant: 488.8 (coaxial); 38.0 (fiber optic). Homes passed: 22,346. Total homes in franchised area: 24,600.
Manager: Richard I. Adams. Technical manager: George Randeau. Program director: Chiara Vicente. Marketing & customer service manager: Alda Nye.
Ownership: MediaOne Group (MSO). See Cable System Ownership.

Become a subscriber to the biweekly business publication focusing on U.S. telephone company strategies at home and abroad...

...from the publishers of the daily record of telecommunications, *Communications Daily*...

Telco Business REPORT

Analyzing U.S. telephone company strategies at home and abroad

Vol. 16, No. 12 June 7, 1999

FCC Moves Closer to Completing High-Cost Subsidy Reform

The FCC took a major step toward completing its reform of the subsidy program for high-cost universal service — a process that has dragged out over two years and has brought much criticism onto the agency.

The Commission, at its May 27 agenda meeting, decided to seek one last round of comments on a new cost model before the agency approves the entire process in the fall. At an unusually acrimonious meeting, Commissioner Harold Furchtgott-Roth compared the Commission's dependence on a model to the old Soviet Union, leading other commissioners to refer to each other as "comrade" or "Vladimir."

The agency took two related actions on the high-cost non-rural program: (1) It voted 4-1 to issue a further notice of proposed rulemaking to obtain comments on a cost model, this time reviewing the so-called input values such as the cost of buried cable versus cable on phone poles. Furchtgott-Roth voted against the item, saying he was opposed to using a model to determine costs. Comments are due July 2, with replies July 16. (2) It tweaked the 1997 universal service order by adopting many of the Federal-State Joint Board's proposed changes.

Congress Reviews FCC Merger Authority — Page 3

Appeals Court Reverses FCC Price Cap Rules — Page 4

IXCs, Incumbent LECs Near Access Charge Pact — Page 6

WARREN 100 % GUARANTEED PUBLISHING, INC.

Telco Business Report provides you—in one easy-to-read issue every other week—analysis of U.S. telephone company strategies, with an eye on federal legislation that would allow other telcos into the long-distance market, while giving careful scrutiny to the game plans of the Bell operating companies. ***Telco Business Report***, delivers accurate detail and expert analysis of stories that affect you and your business. You get reliable briefings at a very affordable price.

Increase your competitive advantage...
Whatever your interest in telecom, ***Telco Business Report*** offers you information to help you craft a profit-making strategy. You'll find coverage of events that affect you, illustrated with easy-to-use strategic business charts and thoughtful analysis. ***TBR*** will help you discover emerging technologies and services that actually sell, , markets that are vulnerable and opportunities that could affect your plans. And because the telecom industry is global, you'll find excellent international coverage. All tailored to fit the hectic pace of telecommunications professionals. ***TBR*** is designed to be read quickly—to help you spend less time gathering information and more time using what you've found. ***TBR's*** extensive business coverage offers revealing insights for marketing executives searching for new markets for their products and services. In a sentence, ***Telco Business Report*** is a concise, bottom-line oriented source of telco business and marketing intelligence. Each issue looks at:

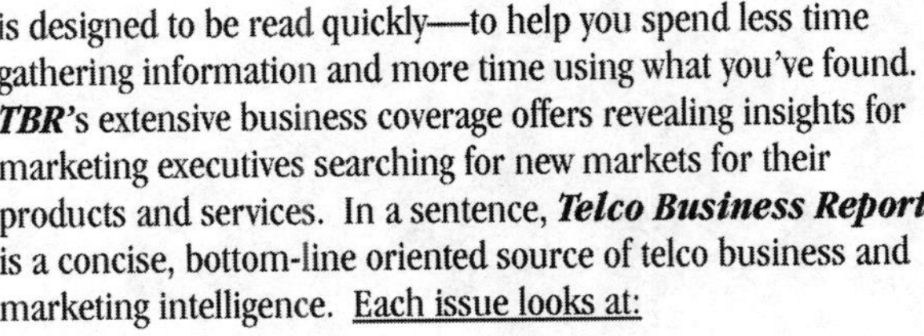

- telco, cable and telecom company analysis, marketing plans and trends
- effects of significant state and federal legislation and regulations
- new products, technologies and services...and how they're selling
- inside word of marketing and advertising budgets
- breaking news on BOC's main competitors: the CLECs

Become a subscriber NOW...
Important events are taking place as you read this--there's no time like the present to sign on for ***Telco Business Report***. Order today!

(clip and return order certificate below)

Order Certificate *TELCO BUSINESS REPORT*

Sign me up. ***Telco Business Report*** sounds like *the* publication I need. I understand I will receive ***Telco Business Report*** on a biweekly basis for $782 per year (Washington, D.C. subscribers add 5.75% sales tax). Subscribers outside the U.S. and Canada add $44 for delivery and handling.

NO-RISK GUARANTEE:

I understand that If I am not 100% satisfied with ***Telco Business Report*** at any time during the lifetime of my subscription, I may cancel my subscription and receive a full refund on all unmailed copies (no questions asked).

☐ Bill me. ☐ Check enclosed. ☐ Credit card authorization

(Make Check Payable to ***Warren Publishing, Inc.****)*

☐ MasterCard. ☐ Visa. ☐ American Express.

Card number ______

Expires ______ Signature ______

Name ______ (please print)

Title ______

Organization ______

Address ______

City ______ State ______ Zip ______

Warren Communications News
Reporting the Future Since 1945
2115 Ward Court, NW/ Washington DC 20037
PHONE: 800-771-9202/FAX: 202-293-3435

SOUTH CAROLINA

Total Systems: 128
Total Communities Served: 461
Franchises Not Yet Operating: 0
Applications Pending: 0
Communities with Applications: 0
Number of Basic Subscribers: 850,512
Number of Expanded Basic Subscribers: 511,590
Number of Pay Units: 328,562

Top 100 Markets Represented: Charlotte (42); Greenville-Spartanburg-Anderson, SC-Asheville, NC (46); Columbia (100).

For a list of all cable communities included in this section, see the Cable Community Index located in the back of this volume.
For explanation of terms used in cable system listings, see p. D-9.

ABBEVILLE—Charter Communications Inc., 306 S. Main St., Abbeville, SC 29620. Phone: 864-459-9646. Fax: 864-459-5963. County: Abbeville. Also serves Abbeville County. ICA: SC0041.

TV Market Ranking: 46. Franchise award date: November 1, 1985. Franchise expiration date: November 1, 1999. Began: January 1, 1971.

Channel capacity: 60 (2-way capable; operating 2-way). Channels available but not in use: 9.

Basic Service

Subscribers: 2,445.

Programming (received off-air): WJBF (A), WRDW-TV (C) Augusta; WIS (N) Columbia; WGGS-TV (I), WNTV (P) Greenville; WHNS (F,U), WLOS (A), WSPA-TV (C), WYFF (N) Greenville-Spartanburg-Asheville; WNEH (P) Greenwood; WCES-TV (P) Wrens.

Programming (via satellite): WGN-TV (W) Chicago; A & E; BET; CNN; Cartoon Network; Discovery Channel; ESPN; Fox Family Channel; Headline News; Lifetime; MTV; Nashville Network; Nickelodeon; TBS Superstation; The Inspirational Network; The Weather Channel; USA Network.

Current originations: Automated time-weather; public access; educational access; government access; religious access; automated emergency alert; local news.

Fee: $35.00 installation; $22.95 monthly; $25.00 additional installation.

Pay Service 1

Pay Units: 54.

Programming (via satellite): Disney Channel.

Fee: $15.00 installation; $7.95 monthly.

Pay Service 2

Pay Units: 260.

Programming (via satellite): HBO.

Fee: $15.00 installation; $10.95 monthly.

Pay Service 3

Pay Units: 104.

Programming (via satellite): The Movie Channel.

Fee: $15.00 installation; $9.95 monthly.

Local advertising: Yes. Available in character-generated programming.

Equipment: Scientific-Atlanta headend; Scientific-Atlanta amplifiers; Times Fiber & Scientific-Atlanta cable; Texscan character generator; Panasonic & Pioneer set top converters; Eagle traps; Scientific-Atlanta addressable traps; AFC satellite antenna; Scientific-Atlanta satellite receivers.

Miles of plant: 50.0 (coaxial). Additional miles planned: 2.0 (coaxial). Homes passed: 2,800. Total homes in franchised area: 3,000.

Manager: Kay Lewis. Chief technician: Terry Cromer.

City fee: 3% of gross.

Ownership: Charter Communications Inc. (MSO).

AIKEN—Northland Cable TV, Box 151, 3060 Cablevision Rd., Aiken, SC 29801-2906. Phones: 803-648-8361; 800-922-1635. Fax: 803-649-1002. Counties: Aiken & Barnwell. Also serves Barnwell County (portions), Burnettown, Jackson, New Ellenton. ICA: SC0106.

TV Market Ranking: Below 100 (Aiken, portions of Barnwell County, Burnettown, Jackson, New Ellenton); Outside TV Markets (portions of Barnwell County). Franchise award date: June 7, 1977. Franchise expiration date: July 1, 2008. Began: December 1, 1968.

Channel capacity: 78 (2-way capable; not operating 2-way). Channels available but not in use: 28.

Basic Service

Subscribers: 22,787; Commercial subscribers: 524.

Programming (received off-air): WEBA-TV (P) Allendale; WAGT (N), WBEK-LP (W), WFXG (F), WJBF (A), WRDW-TV (C) Augusta; WIS (N), WOLO-TV (A) Columbia; WCES-TV (P) Wrens.

Programming (via satellite): TV Guide Channel; The Inspirational Network.

Current originations: Automated time-weather; public access; educational access; government access.

Fee: $42.98 installation; $10.41 monthly; $3.95 converter; $10.00 additional installation.

Commercial fee: $5.50 monthly.

Expanded Basic Service

Subscribers: 12,993.

Programming (via satellite): A & E; BET; C-SPAN; C-SPAN 2; CNBC; Discovery Channel; E! Entertainment TV; ESPN; Fox Family Channel; Fox News Channel; Great American Country; Home & Garden Television; Home Shopping Network; Learning Channel; QVC; TBS Superstation; TV Food Network; The Weather Channel; Travel Channel; Turner Network TV; USA Network.

Fee: $17.54 monthly.

Expanded Basic Service 2

Subscribers: N.A.

Programming (via satellite): American Movie Classics; Animal Planet; Bravo; CNN; Cartoon Network; Comedy Central; Court TV; ESPN 2; fXM: Movies from Fox; FX; Fox Sports Net South; Golf Channel; Headline News; History Channel; Lifetime; MTV; Nashville Network; Nick at Nite's TV Land; Nickelodeon; Outdoor Channel; Sci-Fi Channel; Speedvision; Turner Classic Movies; VH1.

Fee: $7.83 monthly.

Pay Service 1

Pay Units: 1,904.

Programming (via satellite): Cinemax (multiplexed).

Fee: $10.95 monthly.

Pay Service 2

Pay Units: 1,194.

Programming (via satellite): Disney Channel.

Fee: $8.95 monthly.

Pay Service 3

Pay Units: 4,321.

Programming (via satellite): HBO (multiplexed).

Fee: $10.95 monthly.

Pay Service 4

Pay Units: 2,048.

Programming (via satellite): The Movie Channel.

Fee: $10.95 monthly.

Pay Service 5

Pay Units: 2,348.

Programming (via satellite): Showtime (multiplexed).

Fee: $10.95 monthly.

Pay Service 6

Pay Units: 268.

Programming (via satellite): Starz!

Fee: $10.95 monthly.

Pay Service 7

Pay Units: 571.

Programming (via satellite): The New Encore.

Fee: $6.95 monthly.

Pay-Per-View

Addressable homes: 4,755.

Viewer's Choice 1 & 2; movies.

Fee: $3.95.

Pay-per-view manager: Kim Vine.

Local advertising: Yes (locally produced & insert). Available in satellite distributed programming. Rates: $7.00/Minute; $5.50/30 Seconds. Local sales manager: Chuck Field.

Equipment: Jerrold headend; Jerrold amplifiers; Comm/Scope cable; Panasonic VTRs; Jerrold & Pioneer addressable set top converters; Scientific-Atlanta satellite antenna; Jerrold & Scientific-Atlanta satellite receivers.

Miles of plant: 581.0 (coaxial); 19.0 (fiber optic). Additional miles planned: 20.0 (coaxial); 20.0 (fiber optic). Homes passed: 26,114. Total homes in franchised area: 59,000.

Manager: Bruce Tipi. Chief technician: Bobby Vine. Marketing director: Kim Vine. Customer service manager: Frances Nicholson.

City fee: 3% of gross. County fee: 3% of gross.

Ownership: Northland Communications Corp. (MSO).

ANCHOR POINT—Charter Communications, 202 Campbell St., Belton, SC 29627. Phone: 864-338-9975. County: Anderson. Also serves Anderson County (unincorporated areas), La France, Portman Marina, Sandy Springs, Townville. ICA: SC0107.

TV Market Ranking: 46. Franchise award date: N.A. Franchise expiration date: N.A. Began: N.A.

Channel capacity: N.A. Channels available but not in use: N.A.

Basic Service

Subscribers: 1,629.

Programming (received off-air): WNTV (P) Greenville; WHNS (F,U), WLOS (A), WSPA-TV (C), WYFF (N) Greenville-Spartanburg-Asheville.

Programming (via satellite): WGN-TV (W) Chicago; ESPN; Fox Family Channel; QVC; TBS Superstation; The Weather Channel.

Fee: $40.00 installation; $9.86 monthly.

Expanded Basic Service

Subscribers: 1,608.

Programming (via satellite): CNN; Country Music TV; Discovery Channel; Electronic Program Guide; Fox Sports Net South; Goodlife TV Network; Headline News; MTV; Nashville Network; Nickelodeon; Turner Network TV; USA Network; VH1.

Fee: $11.76 monthly.

Pay Service 1

Pay Units: 177.

Programming (via satellite): Cinemax.

Fee: $9.95 monthly.

Pay Service 2

Pay Units: 57.

Programming (via satellite): Disney Channel.

Fee: $8.95 monthly.

Pay Service 3

Pay Units: 235.

Programming (via satellite): HBO.

Fee: $11.95 monthly.

Pay Service 4

Pay Units: 131.

Programming (via satellite): Showtime.

Fee: $9.95 monthly.

Miles of plant: 174.0 (coaxial). Homes passed: 4,151.

Manager: Joe Haight. Marketing & program director: Tim Morrison.

Ownership: Charter Communications Inc. (MSO).

ANDERSON—Helicon Cable Communications, 520 Hwy. 29 Bypass, Anderson, SC 29621. Phone: 864-225-3156. Fax: 864-225-3301. County: Anderson. Also serves Anderson County. ICA: SC0011.

TV Market Ranking: 46. Franchise award date: N.A. Franchise expiration date: January 30, 2000. Began: February 1, 1972.

Channel capacity: 77 (2-way capable; operating 2-way). Channels available but not in use: 7.

Basic Service

Subscribers: 16,500.

Programming (received off-air): WFBC-TV (W) Anderson; WASV-TV (I) Asheville; WGGS-TV (I), WNTV (P) Greenville; WHNS (F,U), WLOS (A), WSPA-TV (C), WYFF (N) Greenville-Spartanburg-Asheville; WNEG-TV (I) Toccoa; 1 FM.

Programming (via satellite): WGN-TV (W) Chicago; EWTN; Home Shopping Network; Product Information Network; QVC; TBS Superstation; Travel Channel; Z Music Television.

Current originations: Automated time-weather.

Fee: $35.00 installation; $22.50 monthly.

Expanded Basic Service

Subscribers: 15,120.

Programming (via satellite): A & E; American Movie Classics; BET; C-SPAN; CNBC; CNN; Country Music TV; Discovery Channel; ESPN; ESPN 2; FX; Fox Family Channel; Fox Sports Net South; Goodlife TV Network; Headline News; History Channel; Home & Garden Television; Learning Channel; Lifetime; MSNBC; MTV; Nashville Network; Nick at Nite's TV Land; Nickelodeon; Odyssey; Sci-Fi Channel; TV Guide Sneak Prevue; The Weather Channel; Turner Network TV; USA Network; VH1.

Fee: $15.88 monthly.

Pay Service 1
Pay Units: 985.
Programming (via satellite): Cinemax.
Fee: $9.95 monthly.
Pay Service 2
Pay Units: 506.
Programming (via satellite): Disney Channel.
Fee: $8.05 monthly.
Pay Service 3
Pay Units: 3,145.
Programming (via satellite): HBO (multiplexed).
Fee: $9.95 monthly.
Pay Service 4
Pay Units: 783.
Programming (via satellite): Showtime.
Fee: $9.95 monthly.
Pay Service 5
Pay Units: 783.
Programming (via satellite): The Movie Channel.
Fee: N.A.
Pay-Per-View
Addressable homes: 4,720.
Action Pay-Per-View.
Local advertising: Yes.
Equipment: Scientific-Atlanta headend; Magnavox amplifiers; Comm/Scope cable; BEI character generator; Pioneer set top converters; Pioneer addressable set top converters; Scientific-Atlanta satellite antenna.
Miles of plant: 449.0 (coaxial); 120.0 (fiber optic). Homes passed: 25,520. Total homes in franchised area: 25,960.
Manager: John Brinker. Chief technician: Mike Wood. Marketing manager: Sharon Nicometo.
City fee: 3% of gross.
Ownership: Helicon Corp. (MSO). See Cable System Ownership.

AWENDAW—US Cable Coastal Properties, Box 469, Johns Island, SC 29457. Phone: 843-559-2424. County: Charleston. ICA: SC0094.
TV Market Ranking: Below 100. Franchise award date: N.A. Franchise expiration date: N.A. Began: January 1, 1983.
Channel capacity: N.A. Channels available but not in use: N.A.
Basic Service
Subscribers: 1,055.
Programming (received off-air): WCBD-TV (N), WCIV (A), WCSC-TV (C), WITV (P), WMMP (U), WTAT-TV (F,U) Charleston.
Programming (via satellite): C-SPAN; C-SPAN 2; Country Music TV; Home Shopping Network; Trinity Bcstg. Network; VH1.
Fee: $75.51 installation; $12.22 monthly.
Expanded Basic Service
Subscribers: 944.
Programming (via satellite): A & E; BET; CNBC; CNN; Disney Channel; ESPN; ESPN 2; FX; Fox Family Channel; Fox Sports Net South; Golf Channel; Headline News; History Channel; Home & Garden Television; Learning Channel; Lifetime; MSNBC; MTV; Nashville Network; Nick at Nite's TV Land; Nickelodeon; Outdoor Channel; Romance Classics; Sci-Fi Channel; Speedvision; The Weather Channel; Travel Channel; Turner Classic Movies; Turner Network TV; USA Network.
Fee: $15.38 monthly.
Expanded Basic Service 2
Subscribers: N.A.
Programming (via satellite): WGN-TV (W) Chicago; American Movie Classics; Discovery Channel; TBS Superstation.
Fee: $2.45 monthly.
Pay Service 1
Pay Units: N.A.
Programming (via satellite): Cinemax; HBO; Showtime.
Fee: $9.50 monthly (each).
Miles of plant: 64.7 (coaxial). Homes passed: 1,887.
Manager: Randy Houser. Chief technician: Ray Kirkendall.
Ownership: US Cable Corp. (MSO).

BARNWELL—Northland Cable, 1706 Patterson St., Barnwell, SC 29812. Phone: 803-541-3354. Counties: Aiken, Allendale, Bamberg, Barnwell & Hampton. Also serves Aiken County (portions), Allendale, Allendale County, Bamberg, Bamberg County, Barnwell County, Blackville, Denmark, Elko, Fairfax, Snelling, Williston. ICA: SC0018.
TV Market Ranking: 100 (portions of Aiken County); Below 100 (portions of Aiken County, portions of Allendale County, portions of Barnwell County, Snelling, Williston); Outside TV Markets (portions of Aiken County, Allendale, portions of Allendale County, Bamberg, Bamberg County, Barnwell, portions of Barnwell County, Blackville, Denmark, Elko, Fairfax). Franchise award date: December 14, 1965. Franchise expiration date: October 1, 2006. Began: December 1, 1966.
Channel capacity: 30. Channels available but not in use: None.
Basic Service
Subscribers: 2,659; Commercial subscribers: 529.
Programming (received off-air): WEBA-TV (P) Allendale; WAGT (N), WFXG (F), WJBF (A), WRDW-TV (C) Augusta; WIS (N), WLTX (C), WOLO-TV (A) Columbia; allband FM.
Programming (via satellite): WGN-TV (W) Chicago; A & E; BET; CNN; Discovery Channel; ESPN; Fox Family Channel; Fox Sports Net South; Goodlife TV Network; Home Shopping Network; Lifetime; MTV; Nashville Network; Nickelodeon; QVC; TBS Superstation; The Weather Channel; Turner Network TV; USA Network.
Fee: $42.98 installation; $9.74 monthly; $24.56 additional installation.
Commercial fee: $3.45 monthly.
Pay Service 1
Pay Units: 2,597.
Programming (via satellite): Disney Channel; HBO; Showtime; The Movie Channel.
Fee: $7.50 installation; $8.95 monthly (Disney, HBO or Showtime), $10.95 monthly (TMC).
Local advertising: Yes (locally produced & insert). Available in satellite distributed programming. Rates: $7.00/Minute; $5.50/30 Seconds. Local sales manager: Chuck Field.
Equipment: Jerrold & Scientific-Atlanta headend; Jerrold & Magnavox amplifiers; Belden & Times Fiber cable; Jerrold set top converters; Eagle & Arcom traps; Scientific-Atlanta satellite antenna; Scientific-Atlanta satellite receivers.
Miles of plant: 338.0 (coaxial). Additional miles planned: 12.0 (coaxial). Homes passed: 43,978. Total homes in franchised area: 57,500.
Manager: Bruce Tipi.
City fee: 2% of gross. County fee: 3% of gross.
Ownership: Northland Communications Corp. (MSO). Purchased from InterMedia Partners.

BATESBURG—Alert Cable TV of South Carolina Inc., Box 631, U.S. 1 & Hwy. 47, Batesburg, SC 29006. Phone: 803-532-3814. Counties: Lexington & Saluda. Also serves Leesville, Lexington County, Saluda County. ICA: SC0049.
TV Market Ranking: 100 (Batesburg, Leesville, Lexington County, portions of Saluda County); Below 100 (portions of Saluda County); Outside TV Markets (portions of Saluda County). Franchise award date: July 15, 1981. Franchise expiration date: N.A. Began: January 1, 1982.
Channel capacity: 35 (not 2-way capable). Channels available but not in use: 3.
Basic Service
Subscribers: 1,285.
Programming (received off-air): WACH (F), WIS (N), WLTX (C), WOLO-TV (A), WRLK-TV (P) Columbia.
Programming (via satellite): WGN-TV (W) Chicago; A & E; BET; CNBC; CNN; Comedy Central; Discovery Channel; ESPN; Fox Family Channel; Headline News; Lifetime; MTV; Nashville Network; Nickelodeon; QVC; TBS Superstation; The Weather Channel; Turner Network TV; USA Network; VH1.
Fee: $50.00 installation; $21.45 monthly.
Pay Service 1
Pay Units: 225.
Programming (via satellite): Cinemax.
Fee: $40.00 installation; $10.95 monthly.
Pay Service 2
Pay Units: 168.
Programming (via satellite): Disney Channel.
Fee: $40.00 installation; $9.95 monthly.
Pay Service 3
Pay Units: 359.
Programming (via satellite): HBO.
Fee: $40.00 installation; $11.95 monthly.
Pay Service 4
Pay Units: 208.
Programming (via satellite): Showtime.
Fee: $40.00 installation; $10.95 monthly.
Pay Service 5
Pay Units: 156.
Programming (via satellite): The Movie Channel.
Fee: $40.00 installation; $10.95 monthly.
Local advertising: Yes. Available in locally originated & taped programming.
Equipment: Scientific-Atlanta headend; Scientific-Atlanta & Jerrold amplifiers; Times Fiber cable; Panasonic, Jerrold & Hamlin set top converters; Eagle traps; Scientific-Atlanta satellite antenna; Avantek, DX Antenna & Scientific-Atlanta satellite receivers.
Miles of plant: 64.0 (coaxial). Homes passed: 2,142.
Manager: Jim Carey. Chief technician: John Griggs. Marketing director: Dale Ordoyne.
City fee: 3% of gross.
Ownership: Time Warner Cable (MSO); Advance/Newhouse Partnership (MSO).

BEAUFORT—Falcon Video Communications, 700 Paris Ave., Port Royal, SC 29935. Phone: 843-525-1131. Fax: 843-525-6277. County: Beaufort. Also serves Beaufort County, Beaufort Naval Hospital, Parris Island, Port Royal. ICA: SC0020.
TV Market Ranking: Below 100. Franchise award date: N.A. Franchise expiration date: February 13, 1999. Began: June 1, 1979.
Channel capacity: 53 (2-way capable; not operating 2-way). Channels available but not in use: None.
Basic Service
Subscribers: 9,625; Commercial subscribers: 631.
Programming (received off-air): WJWJ-TV (P) Beaufort; WCBD-TV (N), WCIV (A), WCSC-TV (C) Charleston; WTGS (F) Hardeeville; WJCL (A), WSAV-TV (N), WTOC-TV (C), WVAN-TV (P) Savannah.
Programming (via satellite): A & E; American Movie Classics; BET; C-SPAN; CNBC; ESPN; Fox Family Channel; Home Shopping Network; Knowledge TV; Lifetime; MTV; Nickelodeon; QVC; Sci-Fi Channel; Trinity Bcstg. Network.
Current originations: Public access; educational access; government access.
Fee: $18.70 monthly; $2.90 converter; $20.00 additional installation.
Expanded Basic Service
Subscribers: 9,518.
Programming (via satellite): C-SPAN 2; Discovery Channel; Fox Sports Net South; Headline News; Nashville Network; TV Food Network; TV Guide Channel; USA Network; VH1; Z Music Television.
Fee: $3.17 monthly.
Expanded Basic Service 2
Subscribers: 9,502.
Programming (via satellite): CNN; Disney Channel; ESPN 2; TBS Superstation; The Weather Channel; Turner Network TV.
Fee: $6.50 monthly.
Pay Service 1
Pay Units: 1,366.
Programming (via satellite): Cinemax.
Fee: $20.00 installation; $10.95 monthly.
Pay Service 2
Pay Units: 2,484.
Programming (via satellite): HBO.
Fee: $20.00 installation; $11.95 monthly.
Pay Service 3
Pay Units: 1,191.
Programming (via satellite): Showtime.
Fee: $20.00 installation; $10.95 monthly.
Pay Service 4
Pay Units: 687.
Programming (via satellite): The Movie Channel.
Fee: $10.95 monthly.
Pay-Per-View
Addressable homes: 3,800.
Local advertising: Yes. Available in satellite distributed programming. Rates: $3.89/30 Seconds.
Equipment: Jerrold headend; Jerrold amplifiers; CCS Hatfield & Comm/Scope cable; Microdyne satellite antenna.
Miles of plant: 273.0 (coaxial); 80.0 (fiber optic). Additional miles planned: 20.0 (coaxial). Homes passed: 13,590. Total homes in franchised area: 15,000.
Manager: Sharon Lewis. Chief technician: Wilfredo Rivera. Marketing director: Katie Creel.
Franchise fee: 3%-5% of gross.
Ownership: Falcon Communications LP (MSO), joint venture formed September 30, 1998. See Cable System Ownership.

BELTON—Charter Communications, 202 Campbell St., Belton, SC 29627. Phone: 803-338-9975. Fax: 803-487-5075. Counties: Abbeville & Anderson. Also serves Anderson County (eastern portion), Honea Path. ICA: SC0028.
TV Market Ranking: 46. Franchise award date: January 17, 1974. Franchise expiration date: N.A. Began: June 12, 1979.
Channel capacity: 60 (not 2-way capable). Channels available but not in use: N.A.
Basic Service
Subscribers: 3,379.
Programming (received off-air): WGGS-TV (I), WNTV (P) Greenville; WHNS (F,U), WLOS (A), WSPA-TV (C), WYFF (N) Greenville-Spartanburg-Asheville; WNEG-TV (I) Toccoa.
Programming (via satellite): WGN-TV (W) Chicago; Electronic Program Guide; Home Shopping Network; TBS Superstation.
Fee: $44.19 installation; $7.82 monthly; $3.50 converter.
Expanded Basic Service
Subscribers: 3,333.
Programming (via satellite): CNN; Headline News; Nashville Network; USA Network.
Fee: $2.84 monthly.

Pay Service 1
Pay Units: 227.
Programming (via satellite): Cinemax.
Fee: $14.73 installation; $9.95 monthly.
Pay Service 2
Pay Units: 115.
Programming (via satellite): Disney Channel.
Fee: $14.73 installation; $8.95 monthly.
Pay Service 3
Pay Units: 464.
Programming (via satellite): HBO.
Fee: $14.73 installation; $11.95 monthly.
Pay Service 4
Pay Units: 423.
Programming (via satellite): Showtime.
Fee: $14.73 installation; $11.95 monthly.
Equipment: Scientific-Atlanta headend; Scientific-Atlanta amplifiers; Systems Wire cable; Atari character generator; Jerrold set top converters; Pico traps; Andrew & Harris satellite antenna; Scientific-Atlanta & Microdyne satellite receivers.
Miles of plant: 210.0 (coaxial). Homes passed: 6,567.
Manager: Joe Haight. Marketing & program director: Tim Morrison.
City fee: 3% of gross.
Ownership: Charter Communications Inc. (MSO).

BENNETTSVILLE—Northland Cable TV, Box 1073, Bennettsville, SC 29512. Phone: 803-479-4063. Fax: 803-479-7115. County: Marlboro. Also serves Clio, Marlboro County, McColl, Tatum. ICA: SC0037.
TV Market Ranking: Below 100 (Bennettsville, Clio, portions of Marlboro County, McColl, Tatum); Outside TV Markets (portions of Marlboro County). Franchise award date: September 1, 1990. Franchise expiration date: September 1, 2005. Began: May 15, 1991.
Channel capacity: 77. Channels available but not in use: 29.
Basic Service
Subscribers: 5,100.
Programming (received off-air): WSOC-TV (A) Charlotte; WIS (N) Columbia; WBTW (C), WJPM-TV (P), WPDE-TV (A), WWMB (U) Florence; WFXB (F) Myrtle Beach; WECT (N) Wilmington.
Programming (via satellite): TV Guide Channel.
Fee: Free installation; $7.00 monthly.
Expanded Basic Service
Subscribers: N.A.
Programming (via satellite): A & E; BET; C-SPAN; CNBC; CNN; CNN/SI; Country Music TV; ESPN; Fox Family Channel; Home & Garden Television; Learning Channel; QVC; TBS Superstation; The Inspirational Network; The Weather Channel; Travel Channel; Trinity Bcstg. Network; Turner Network TV.
Fee: N.A.
Expanded Basic Service 2
Subscribers: N.A.
Programming (via satellite): American Movie Classics; Cartoon Network; Court TV; Discovery Channel; ESPN 2; FX; Fox News Channel; Fox Sports Net South; Headline News; History Channel; Lifetime; MuchMusic Network; Nashville Network; Nickelodeon; Sci-Fi Channel; Turner Classic Movies; USA Network.
Fee: N.A.
Pay Service 1
Pay Units: N.A.
Programming (via satellite): Cinemax; Disney Channel; HBO; Showtime; The Movie Channel; The New Encore.
Fee: $10.00 monthly (each).
Pay-Per-View
Special events.
Miles of plant: 90.0 (coaxial). Homes passed: 3,660.
Manager: Shirley McCormack. Chief technician: Leroy Henry.
Ownership: Northland Communications Corp. (MSO).

BETHUNE—Pine Tree Cablevision, 2628 Millwood Ave., Columbia, SC 29205. Phone: 803-799-6226. Fax: 803-799-8804. County: Kershaw. ICA: SC0110.
TV Market Ranking: Below 100. Franchise award date: N.A. Franchise expiration date: N.A. Began: May 1, 1985.
Channel capacity: 36. Channels available but not in use: N.A.
Basic Service
Subscribers: 376.
Programming (received off-air): WCCB (F), WSOC-TV (A) Charlotte; WACH (F), WIS (N), WOLO-TV (A) Columbia; WBTW (C), WJPM-TV (P) Florence.
Programming (via satellite): TBS Superstation.
Fee: N.A.
Manager: Tony Wilson.
Ownership: Pine Tree Cablevision (MSO). Purchased from Bay Cable Inc., February 1, 1999.

BISHOPVILLE—Alert Cable TV of South Carolina Inc., Drawer 1479, 116 Epps St., Lake City, SC 29560. Phone: 803-394-8231. Fax: 803-394-3722. County: Lee. Also serves Lee County. ICA: SC0111.
TV Market Ranking: 100 (portions of Lee County); Below 100 (Bishopville, portions of Lee County). Franchise award date: July 1, 1969. Franchise expiration date: October 16, 2000. Began: July 1, 1971.
Channel capacity: 61 (not 2-way capable). Channels available but not in use: 17.
Basic Service
Subscribers: 964.
Programming (received off-air): WACH (F), WIS (N), WLTX (C), WOLO-TV (A) Columbia; WBTW (C), WPDE-TV (A) Florence; WRJA-TV (P) Sumter.
Programming (via satellite): WGN-TV (W) Chicago; A & E; American Movie Classics; BET; C-SPAN; CNBC; CNN; Cartoon Network; Comedy Central; Country Music TV; Court TV; Discovery Channel; ESPN; Fox Family Channel; Headline News; History Channel; Home Shopping Network; Lifetime; MSNBC; MTV; Nashville Network; Nickelodeon; QVC; TBS Superstation; TV Food Network; The Weather Channel; Turner Classic Movies; Turner Network TV; USA Network; VH1.
Planned originations: Automated time-weather; public access.
Fee: $49.95 installation (aerial), $69.95 (underground); $27.88 monthly; $2.00 converter; $19.95 additional installation.
Pay Service 1
Pay Units: 34.
Programming (via satellite): Disney Channel.
Fee: $19.95 installation; $9.95 monthly.
Pay Service 2
Pay Units: 208.
Programming (via satellite): HBO.
Fee: $19.95 installation; $12.95 monthly.
Pay Service 3
Pay Units: 56.
Programming (via satellite): Showtime.
Fee: $19.95 installation; $10.95 monthly.
Local advertising: Yes. Local sales manager: Missy Worthington.
Program Guide: Premium Channels.
Equipment: Scientific-Atlanta, DX Engineering & Jerrold headend; Scientific-Atlanta amplifiers; Times Fiber cable; Oak, Intercept & Panasonic set top converters; Eagle, Pico & Northeast Filter traps; Scientific-Atlanta & Harris satellite antenna; Scientific-Atlanta & DX Antenna satellite receivers.
Miles of plant: 33.0 (coaxial); None (fiber optic).
Manager: Kurt Newber. Chief technician: Tommy Martin. Marketing director: Donna Waller. Customer service manager: Robin Hewitt.
City fee: 3% of gross.
Ownership: Time Warner Cable (MSO).

BLUFFTON—Bluffton Cablevision, Box 818, Bluffton, SC 29910. Phone: 803-757-3707. Fax: 803-757-7337. County: Beaufort. Also serves Beaufort County (southern portion). ICA: SC0042.
TV Market Ranking: Below 100. Franchise award date: March 1, 1984. Franchise expiration date: January 1, 1998. Began: August 1, 1984.
Channel capacity: 36 (2-way capable; operating 2-way). Channels available but not in use: 5.
Basic Service
Subscribers: 1,700.
Programming (received off-air): WJWJ-TV (P) Beaufort; WCSC-TV (C) Charleston; WTGS (F) Hardeeville; WJCL (A), WSAV-TV (N), WTOC-TV (C), WVAN-TV (P) Savannah.
Programming (via satellite): WGN-TV (W) Chicago; A & E; C-SPAN; CNN; Country Music TV; Discovery Channel; ESPN; Fox Family Channel; Headline News; Home Shopping Network; MTV; Nashville Network; Nickelodeon; TBS Superstation; The Weather Channel; Turner Network TV; USA Network; VH1.
Current originations: Public access; government access; automated emergency alert.
Fee: $25.00 installation; $18.95 monthly.
Pay Service 1
Pay Units: N.A.
Programming (via satellite): Cinemax; Disney Channel; HBO; Showtime.
Fee: $10.00 installation; $9.00 monthly (each).
Local advertising: Yes. Available in locally originated programming.
Program Guide: Premium Channels.
Equipment: Scientific-Atlanta headend; Scientific-Atlanta amplifiers; Times Fiber cable; Jerrold & Scientific-Atlanta set top converters; Pico traps; Scientific-Atlanta satellite antenna; Scientific-Atlanta satellite receivers.
Miles of plant: 110.0 (coaxial). Homes passed: 2,650. Total homes in franchised area: 4,000.
Manager: Pat Holloway.
City fee: 3% of gross.
Ownership: Hargray Telephone Co. (MSO).

BRANCHVILLE—Blackstone Cable LLC, 10 S. Franklin Turnpike, Ramsey, NJ 07446. Phone: 201-825-9090. Fax: 201-825-8794. County: Orangeburg. Also serves Bowman. ICA: SC0112.
TV Market Ranking: Below 100 (Bowman); Outside TV Markets (Branchville). Franchise award date: April 1, 1982. Franchise expiration date: April 1, 1997. Began: January 1, 1985.
Channel capacity: 45 (not 2-way capable). Channels available but not in use: 17.
Basic Service
Subscribers: 406.
Programming (received off-air): WRDW-TV (C) Augusta; WCBD-TV (N), WCSC-TV (C) Charleston; WIS (N) Columbia.
Programming (via satellite): WGN-TV (W) Chicago; BET; CNN; Discovery Channel; ESPN; Fox Family Channel; Headline News; Nashville Network; QVC; Sci-Fi Channel; TBS Superstation; Trinity Bcstg. Network; Turner Classic Movies; Turner Network TV; USA Network.
Current originations: Educational access.
Fee: $22.50 monthly.
Pay Service 1
Pay Units: N.A.
Programming (via satellite): Disney Channel; HBO; Showtime; The Movie Channel.
Fee: $9.00 monthly (each).
Manager: Maryanne Lyman.
Ownership: Blackstone Cable LLC (MSO). Purchased from Milestone Media Management Inc., July 1, 1998.

BRIARCLIFF ACRES—Cablevision Industries Inc., 9261 Hwy. 707, Myrtle Beach, SC 29575. Phone: 843-650-7450. Fax: 843-650-1150. Counties: Georgetown & Horry. Also serves Horry County (eastern portion), Litchfield Beach. ICA: SC0027.
TV Market Ranking: Below 100. Franchise award date: N.A. Franchise expiration date: January 1, 2000. Began: January 1, 1980.
Channel capacity: 80 (2-way capable; not operating 2-way). Channels available but not in use: 5.
Basic Service
Subscribers: 4,800.
Programming (received off-air): WCIV (A), WCSC-TV (C), WTAT-TV (F,U) Charleston; WIS (N) Columbia; WHMC (P) Conway; WBTW (C), WPDE-TV (A), WWMB (U) Florence; WFXB (F) Myrtle Beach; WECT (N), WSFX-TV (F), WUNJ-TV (P) Wilmington.
Programming (via satellite): WGN-TV (W) Chicago; A & E; American Movie Classics; Animal Planet; BET; Bravo; C-SPAN; C-SPAN 2; CNBC; CNN; Cartoon Network; Comedy Central; Country Music TV; Discovery Channel; Disney Channel; E! Entertainment TV; ESPN; ESPN 2; EWTN; FX; Fox Family Channel; Fox News Channel; Golf Channel; Goodlife TV Network; Great American Country; Headline News; History Channel; Home & Garden Television; Home Shopping Network; Learning Channel; Lifetime; MTV; Nashville Network; Nick at Nite's TV Land; Nickelodeon; Odyssey; Outdoor Channel; QVC; Romance Classics; Sci-Fi Channel; Speedvision; Superaudio Cable Radio Service; TBS Superstation; TV Guide Channel; TV Guide Sneak Prevue; The Inspirational Network; The Weather Channel; Travel Channel; Trinity Bcstg. Network; Turner Classic Movies; Turner Network TV; USA Network; VH1.
Current originations: Public access; educational access; government access.
Fee: $31.25 installation; $22.84 monthly; $2.50 converter.
Pay Service 1
Pay Units: 765.
Programming (via satellite): Cinemax; Disney Channel; HBO (multiplexed); Showtime; The Movie Channel.
Fee: $5.95 monthly (Cinemax, Disney, Showtime or TMC), $9.75 monthly (HBO).
Pay-Per-View
Addressable homes: 1,200.
Action Pay-Per-View; Hot Choice; Playboy TV; Viewer's Choice.
Fee: $3.95-$6.95.
Pay-per-view manager: Megan Tressler.
Local advertising: Yes. Available in locally originated programming. Local sales manager: Bob Scarborough.
Equipment: Philips amplifiers; Comm/Scope cable; Comm/Scope fiber optic cable; Phasecom character generator; General Instrument set top converters; General Instrument addressable set top converters; Eagle traps; Odom

satellite antenna; Standard Components satellite receivers.
Miles of plant: 70.0 (coaxial); 34.0 (fiber optic). Homes passed: 30,000. Total homes in franchised area: 30,000.
Ownership: Ray V. Miller Group (MSO).

BROWNS FERRY—Benchmark Communications, 2511 Highmarket St., Georgetown, SC 29440. Phone: 843-527-2447. Fax: 843-527-2034. County: Georgetown. Also serves Choppee, Dunbar. ICA: SC0089.
TV Market Ranking: Below 100. Franchise award date: December 1, 1989. Franchise expiration date: N.A. Began: June 1, 1990.
Channel capacity: 55 (2-way capable; operating 2-way). Channels available but not in use: 15.
Basic Service
Subscribers: 563.
Programming (received off-air): WCBD-TV (N), WCIV (A), WCSC-TV (C), WITV (P), WTAT-TV (F,U) Charleston; WBTW (C), WPDE-TV (A) Florence.
Programming (via satellite): WGN-TV (W) Chicago; A & E; American Movie Classics; Animal Planet; BET; C-SPAN; CNN; Cartoon Network; Country Music TV; Discovery Channel; ESPN; Fox Family Channel; Fox News Channel; Headline News; Home & Garden Television; Lifetime; MTV; Nashville Network; Nickelodeon; QVC; Sci-Fi Channel; TBS Superstation; TV Guide Channel; The Weather Channel; Trinity Bcstg. Network; Turner Network TV; USA Network; VH1.
Fee: $25.00 installation; $24.92 monthly; $2.00 converter.
Pay Service 1
Pay Units: 2.
Programming (via satellite): Cinemax.
Fee: $9.50 monthly.
Pay Service 2
Pay Units: 4.
Programming (via satellite): Disney Channel.
Fee: $9.50 monthly.
Pay Service 3
Pay Units: 4.
Programming (via satellite): HBO.
Fee: $9.50 monthly.
Pay Service 4
Pay Units: 2.
Programming (via satellite): Showtime.
Fee: $9.50 monthly.
Equipment: Scientific-Atlanta headend; GTE Sylvania amplifiers; Trilogy cable; Scientific-Atlanta character generator; Scientific-Atlanta set top converters; Pico traps; ChannelMaster satellite antenna; Scientific-Atlanta satellite receivers.
Miles of plant: 61.0 (coaxial); None (fiber optic). Homes passed: 987. Total homes in franchised area: 1,100.
Manager: Kenneth Koch. Program director: Kim Angus.
Ownership: Benchmark Communications (MSO). Purchased from Genesis Cable Communications LLC, May 3, 1999.

CALHOUN FALLS—Comcast Cablevision of the South, 105A E. Villanow St., La Fayette, GA 30728-2518. Phone: 706-638-5900. County: Abbeville. Also serves Abbeville County (portions). ICA: SC0075.
TV Market Ranking: 46. Franchise award date: February 8, 1982. Franchise expiration date: February 8, 1997. Began: September 1, 1982.
Channel capacity: 36. Channels available but not in use: N.A.
Basic Service
Subscribers: 446.
Programming (received off-air): WJBF (A), WRDW-TV (C) Augusta; WNTV (P) Greenville; WLOS (A), WSPA-TV (C), WYFF (N) Greenville-Spartanburg-Asheville.
Programming (via satellite): WGN-TV (W) Chicago; CNN; Fox Family Channel; MTV; Nashville Network; Nickelodeon; QVC; TBS Superstation; USA Network.
Fee: $20.00 installation; $15.95 monthly.
Pay Service 1
Pay Units: 119.
Programming (via satellite): Cinemax.
Fee: $9.95 monthly.
Pay Service 2
Pay Units: 117.
Programming (via satellite): HBO.
Fee: $10.95 monthly.
Miles of plant: 19.1 (coaxial). Homes passed: 933.
Manager: Kim Rueckert. Chief technician: Guy Lee. Marketing director: Martin O'Keeffe.
Ownership: Comcast Cable Communications Inc. (MSO).

CAMDEN—Charter Communications, Box 2042, 2629 Broad St., Camden, SC 29020. Phones: 803-432-1406; 800-955-0488. Fax: 803-425-4772. Web site: http://www.chartercom.com. County: Kershaw. Also serves Cassatt, Kershaw County, Lugoff. ICA: SC0113.
TV Market Ranking: 100 (Camden, Cassatt, portions of Kershaw County, Lugoff); Below 100 (portions of Kershaw County); Outside TV Markets (portions of Kershaw County). Franchise award date: N.A. Franchise expiration date: N.A. Began: December 15, 1978.
Channel capacity: 37 (not 2-way capable). Channels available but not in use: None.
Basic Service
Subscribers: 5,034.
Programming (received off-air): WACH (F), WIS (N), WLTX (C), WOLO-TV (A) Columbia; WBTW (C) Florence; WRJA-TV (P) Sumter.
Programming (via satellite): WGN-TV (W) Chicago; QVC; TBS Superstation; TV Guide Channel.
Current originations: Automated time-weather; public access.
Fee: $35.00 installation; $10.95 monthly; $1.45 converter.
Expanded Basic Service
Subscribers: 4,830.
Programming (via satellite): A & E; American Movie Classics; BET; C-SPAN; CNBC; CNN; Comedy Central; Country Music TV; Discovery Channel; Disney Channel; E! Entertainment TV; ESPN; ESPN 2; FX; Fox Family Channel; Fox Sports Net South; Headline News; History Channel; Home & Garden Television; Home Shopping Network; Learning Channel; Lifetime; MTV; Nashville Network; Nickelodeon; Sci-Fi Channel; TV Guide Channel; The Weather Channel; Turner Network TV; USA Network; VH1.
Fee: $15.00 installation; $31.30 monthly.
Pay Service 1
Pay Units: N.A.
Programming (via satellite): Cinemax.
Fee: $15.00 installation.
Pay Service 2
Pay Units: 329.
Programming (via satellite): HBO.
Fee: $11.45 monthly.
Pay Service 3
Pay Units: 559.
Programming (via satellite): Showtime.
Fee: $11.45 monthly.
Pay Service 4
Pay Units: 199.
Programming (via satellite): The Movie Channel.
Fee: $11.45 monthly.
Pay-Per-View
Addressable homes: 500.
Hot Choice; Viewer's Choice.
Local advertising: Yes. Available in character-generated programming.
Program Guide: The Cable Guide.
Equipment: Scientific-Atlanta headend; Scientific-Atlanta amplifiers; Times Fiber cable; Texscan character generator; Jerrold set top converters; Northeast Filter traps; Scientific-Atlanta satellite antenna; Scientific-Atlanta satellite receivers.
Miles of plant: 200.0 (coaxial). Total homes in franchised area: 6,900.
Manager: Buddy Timmons. Chief technician: Phillip Bennett.
City fee: 3% of gross.
Ownership: Charter Communications Inc. (MSO).

CHARLESTON—Comcast Cable of Carolina Inc., Box 63407, North Charleston, SC 29419-3407. Phones: 843-747-1403; 843-554-4100. Fax: 843-529-6190. Counties: Beaufort, Berkeley, Charleston & Dorchester. Also serves Beaufort USMC Air Station, Berkeley County, Charleston Air Force Base, Charleston County (northern portion), Charleston Naval Base, Goose Creek, Hanahan, Hunley Park, Isle of Palms, James Island, Laurel Bay, Mount Pleasant, North Charleston, Sullivan's Island, Summerville. ICA: SC0001.
TV Market Ranking: Below 100 (Beaufort USMC Air Station, portions of Berkeley County, Charleston, Charleston Air Force Base, Charleston County, Charleston Naval Base, Goose Creek, Hanahan, Hunley Park, Isle of Palms, James Island, Laurel Bay, Mount Pleasant, North Charleston, Sullivan's Island, Summerville); Outside TV Markets (portions of Berkeley County). Franchise award date: N.A. Franchise expiration date: N.A. Began: January 1, 1973.
Channel capacity: 53 (2-way capable; operating 2-way). Channels available but not in use: N.A.
Basic Service
Subscribers: 81,362; Commercial subscribers: 1,893.
Programming (received off-air): WCBD-TV (N), WCIV (A), WCSC-TV (C), WITV (P), WMMP (U), WTAT-TV (F,U) Charleston.
Programming (via satellite): FX; Fox Sports Net South.
Current originations: Educational access; government access; leased access; local originations.
Fee: $55.51 installation; $4.76 monthly; $0.74 converter.
Expanded Basic Service
Subscribers: 66,450.
Programming (via satellite): A & E; Animal Planet; BET; Bravo; C-SPAN; C-SPAN 2; CNBC; CNN; Cartoon Network; Comedy Central; Country Music TV; E! Entertainment TV; ESPN; ESPN 2; ESPN Classic Sports; Fox Family Channel; Game Show Network; Golf Channel; Headline News; History Channel; Home & Garden Television; Home Shopping Network; Knowledge TV; Learning Channel; Lifetime; MSNBC; MTV; Nashville Network; Nick at Nite's TV Land; Nickelodeon; Odyssey; Pax Net; QVC; Sci-Fi Channel; Speedvision; TV Food Network; TV Guide Channel; TV Guide Sneak Prevue; The Inspirational Network; The Weather Channel; Travel Channel; Trinity Bcstg. Network; Turner Classic Movies; USA Network; Univision; VH1.
Fee: $23.46 monthly.
A la Carte 1
Subscribers: 66,450.
Programming (via satellite): WGN-TV (W) Chicago; American Movie Classics; Discovery Channel; Outdoor Life Network; Speedvision; TBS Superstation; Turner Network TV.
Fee: $0.49 monthly (each), $2.48 monthly (package).
Pay Service 1
Pay Units: N.A.
Programming (via satellite): Cinemax; Disney Channel; HBO (multiplexed); Showtime; The Movie Channel; The New Encore.
Fee: $35.00 installation; $1.95 monthly (Encore), $11.45 monthly (Disney), $11.95 monthly (Showtime or TMC), $12.45 monthly (Cinemax), $13.95 monthly (HBO).
Pay-Per-View
Addressable homes: 27,872.
Hot Choice; Playboy TV; Viewer's Choice; special events.
Fee: $4.95.
Local advertising: Yes. Available in satellite distributed & locally originated programming. Local sales manager: Preston E. Oliver.
Equipment: Scientific-Atlanta headend; GTE Sylvania amplifiers; Times Fiber cable; Sony cameras; Sony VTRs; MSI character generator; Jerrold set top converters; Fort Worth Tower & Scientific-Atlanta satellite antenna.
Miles of plant: 1583.1 (coaxial); None (fiber optic). Additional miles planned: 27.7 (coaxial). Homes passed: 131,800. Total homes in franchised area: 163,000. Miles of plant, homes passed & total homes in franchised area include figures for Beaufort & Walterboro, SC.
Manager: Gary Waterfield. Chief technician: Tom Jacobs.
Ownership: Comcast Cable Communications Inc. (MSO).

CHERAW—Century Communications, Box 1109, 1741 Hwy. 9 W, Dillon, SC 29536. Phones: 843-774-2461; 800-822-0861. Fax: 843-774-2035. E-mail: kspruill@centurycomm.com. Web site: http://www.centurycomm.com. County: Chesterfield. Also serves Chesterfield County. ICA: SC0038.
TV Market Ranking: Below 100 (Cheraw, portions of Chesterfield County); Outside TV Markets (portions of Chesterfield County). Franchise award date: N.A. Franchise expiration date: N.A. Began: January 1, 1968.
Channel capacity: 36 (not 2-way capable). Channels available but not in use: 1.
Basic Service
Subscribers: 2,770.
Programming (received off-air): WBTV (C), WCCB (F), WCNC-TV (N), WSOC-TV (A) Charlotte; WIS (N) Columbia; WBTW (C), WJPM-TV (P), WPDE-TV (A) Florence.
Programming (via satellite): C-SPAN; Home Shopping Network; QVC; Turner Network TV.
Fee: $60.00 installation; $17.75 monthly.

Expanded Basic Service
Subscribers: N.A.
Programming (via satellite): American Movie Classics; BET; Country Music TV; Discovery Channel; Fox Family Channel; Headline News; Lifetime; MTV; Nickelodeon; The Weather Channel; Trinity Bcstg. Network; VH1.
Fee: $10.00 installation; $3.20 monthly.
Expanded Basic Service 2
Subscribers: N.A.
Programming (via satellite): A & E; CNN; ESPN; Nashville Network; TBS Superstation; USA Network.
Fee: $2.00 monthly.
Pay Service 1
Pay Units: N.A.
Programming (via satellite): Cinemax; Disney Channel; HBO.
Fee: $7.00 monthly (Disney), $9.00 monthly (Cinemax or HBO).
Equipment: Jerrold headend; Jerrold amplifiers; Times Fiber cable; Scientific-Atlanta satellite antenna.
Miles of plant: 59.2 (coaxial). Additional miles planned: 3.0 (coaxial). Homes passed: 3,400.
Manager: Kevine Barrett. Chief technician: Tim Bourgoin. Marketing & program director: Betty Jackson.
City fee: 3% of gross.
Ownership: Century Communications Corp. (MSO). See Cable System Ownership.

CHESTER—Charter Communications, 101 Cestrian Square, Chester, SC 29706. Phone: 803-377-1181. Fax: 803-488-4410. County: Chester. Also serves Chester County (unincorporated areas). ICA: SC0034.
TV Market Ranking: Below 100. Franchise award date: December 4, 1978. Franchise expiration date: December 4, 2004. Began: October 1, 1978.
Channel capacity: 36 (not 2-way capable). Channels available but not in use: 1.
Basic Service
Subscribers: 3,347.
Programming (received off-air): WJZY (U) Belmont; WBTV (C), WCCB (F), WCNC-TV (N), WSOC-TV (A) Charlotte; WIS (N), WLTX (C) Columbia; WSPA-TV (C) Greenville-Spartanburg-Asheville; WNSC-TV (P) Rock Hill.
Programming (via satellite): WGN-TV (W) Chicago; TBS Superstation.
Fee: $47.07 installation; $7.30 monthly; $3.50 converter.
Expanded Basic Service
Subscribers: 3,154.
Programming (via satellite): A & E; BET; C-SPAN; CNN; Country Music TV; Discovery Channel; ESPN; Electronic Program Guide; Fox Family Channel; Headline News; Home Shopping Network; Learning Channel; MTV; Nashville Network; Nickelodeon; The Weather Channel; Turner Network TV; USA Network.
Fee: $13.72 monthly.
Pay Service 1
Pay Units: 264.
Programming (via satellite): Cinemax.
Fee: $15.69 installation; $9.95 monthly.
Pay Service 2
Pay Units: 72.
Programming (via satellite): Disney Channel.
Fee: $15.69 installation; $8.95 monthly.
Pay Service 3
Pay Units: 389.
Programming (via satellite): HBO.
Fee: $15.69 installation; $11.95 monthly.
Pay Service 4
Pay Units: 384.
Programming (via satellite): Showtime.
Fee: $15.69 installation; $11.95 monthly.
Equipment: Scientific-Atlanta & Olson headend; RCA amplifiers; Times Fiber cable; Jerrold set top converters; Pico traps; Harris & Scientific-Atlanta satellite antenna; Scientific-Atlanta & Microdyne satellite receivers.
Miles of plant: 95.2 (coaxial). Homes passed: 5,068.
Manager: Buddy Timmons. Marketing director: Tim Morrison.
City fee: 3% of gross.
Ownership: Charter Communications Inc. (MSO).

CHESTERFIELD—Enstar Cable TV, 310 10th St., North Wilkesboro, NC 28697. Phone: 910-667-4151. Fax: 910-667-0261. County: Chesterfield. Also serves Chesterfield County (portions), Ruby. ICA: SC0087.
TV Market Ranking: Below 100 (portions of Chesterfield County); Outside TV Markets (Chesterfield, portions of Chesterfield County, Ruby). Franchise award date: N.A. Franchise expiration date: May 25, 2003. Began: January 1, 1984.
Channel capacity: 37 (not 2-way capable). Channels available but not in use: 1.
Basic Service
Subscribers: 483.
Programming (received off-air): WJZY (U) Belmont; WBTV (C), WCCB (F), WCNC-TV (N), WSOC-TV (A) Charlotte; WIS (N) Columbia; WBTW (C), WJPM-TV (P), WPDE-TV (A) Florence; WFVT (W) Rock Hill.
Programming (via satellite): American Movie Classics; Bravo; CNN; Country Music TV; Discovery Channel; E! Entertainment TV; ESPN; Fox Family Channel; Headline News; MTV; QVC; Sci-Fi Channel; The Weather Channel; Turner Network TV.
Fee: $25.00 installation; $20.00 monthly; $7.50 additional installation.
Expanded Basic Service
Subscribers: 479.
Programming (via satellite): Lifetime; Nickelodeon; USA Network.
Fee: $1.99 monthly.
Expanded Basic Service 2
Subscribers: 468.
Programming (via satellite): WGN-TV (W) Chicago; Disney Channel; History Channel; Home Shopping Network; Nashville Network; TBS Superstation.
Fee: $6.00 monthly.
Pay Service 1
Pay Units: 25.
Programming (via satellite): Cinemax.
Fee: $10.95 monthly.
Pay Service 2
Pay Units: 76.
Programming (via satellite): HBO.
Fee: $11.95 monthly.
Pay Service 3
Pay Units: 44.
Programming (via satellite): Showtime.
Fee: $10.95 monthly.
Equipment: Scientific-Atlanta & Blonder-Tongue headend; Scientific-Atlanta amplifiers; Comm/Scope cable; Pico, Eagle & Intercept traps; Scientific-Atlanta satellite antenna; Scientific-Atlanta satellite receivers.
Miles of plant: 26.0 (coaxial). Homes passed: 894.
Manager: Larry Ott. Chief technician: Eddie Collins.
Franchise fee: 3% of gross.
Ownership: Falcon Communications LP (MSO), joint venture formed September 30, 1998. See Cable System Ownership.

CLOVER—Time Warner Cable, 4027 E. Franklin Blvd., Gastonia, NC 28056. Phones: 704-824-9856; 704-228-7248. Fax: 704-824-5738. Counties: York, SC; Gaston, NC. Also serves Gaston County, NC; Bowling Green, Lake Wylie (north central portion), York County (portions), SC. ICA: SC0045.
TV Market Ranking: 42 (Bowling Green, Clover, Lake Wylie, portions of York County); 46 (portions of York County); Below 100 (Gaston County, portions of York County). Franchise award date: N.A. Franchise expiration date: N.A. Began: N.A.
Channel capacity: 38 (not 2-way capable). Channels available but not in use: None.
Basic Service
Subscribers: 1,330; Commercial subscribers: 31.
Programming (received off-air): WJZY (U) Belmont; WBTV (C), WCCB (F), WCNC-TV (N), WSOC-TV (A) Charlotte; WIS (N) Columbia; WSPA-TV (C) Greenville-Spartanburg-Asheville; WNSC-TV (P) Rock Hill.
Programming (via satellite): WGN-TV (W) Chicago; A & E; American Movie Classics; BET; C-SPAN; CNBC; Country Music TV; Discovery Channel; Fox Family Channel; Home Shopping Network; Knowledge TV; Lifetime; MTV; Nashville Network; Nickelodeon; Odyssey; TBS Superstation; The Weather Channel; Trinity Bcstg. Network; USA Network.
Fee: $27.12 installation; $9.21 monthly; $2.10 converter; $20.00 additional installation.
Expanded Basic Service
Subscribers: 1,241.
Programming (via satellite): CNN; ESPN; Fox Sports Net South; Headline News; Turner Network TV.
Fee: $11.50-$13.07 monthly.
Pay Service 1
Pay Units: 177.
Programming (via satellite): Cinemax.
Fee: $11.55 installation; $11.00 monthly.
Pay Service 2
Pay Units: 127.
Programming (via satellite): Disney Channel.
Fee: $11.55 installation; $7.95 monthly.
Pay Service 3
Pay Units: 225.
Programming (via satellite): HBO.
Fee: $11.55 installation; $11.00 monthly.
Pay Service 4
Pay Units: 179.
Programming (via satellite): Showtime.
Fee: $11.55 installation; $11.00 monthly.
Local advertising: No.
Equipment: Scientific-Atlanta headend; Scientific-Atlanta amplifiers; Belden, Comm/Scope & Times Fiber cable; Hamlin & Scientific-Atlanta set top converters; Eagle & Intercept traps; Scientific-Atlanta satellite antenna; Scientific-Atlanta satellite receivers.
Miles of plant: 70.6 (coaxial). Homes passed: 2,700.
Manager: Rob Bridges. Chief technician: James Loren Evans. Marketing director: Margaret Loren Wilkins.
City fee: 3% of gross. County fee: 3% of gross.
Ownership: Time Warner Cable (MSO); Advance/Newhouse Partnership (MSO).

COLUMBIA—Time Warner Cable, 293 Greystone Blvd., Columbia, SC 29210. Phone: 803-252-2253. Fax: 803-251-2920. Counties: Lancaster, Lexington, Newberry & Richland. Also serves Arcadia Lakes, Blythewood, Cayce, Chapin, Dentsville, Eastover, Elgin, Forest Acres, Fort Jackson, Harbison, Irmo, Lake Murry, Lexington, Lexington County, Little Mountain, Lost Creek, Newberry, Pelion, Pineridge, Ravenwwod, Richland County, Riverhill, South Congaree, Springdale, Waterford, West Columbia. ICA: SC0002.
TV Market Ranking: (Blythewood, Dentsville, Lake Murry, Lost Creek, Pelion, Ravenwwod, Riverhill, Waterford); 100 (Arcadia Lakes, Cayce, Chapin, Columbia, Eastover, Forest Acres, Harbison, Irmo, Lexington, Lexington County, Little Mountain, Newberry, Pineridge, Richland County, South Congaree, Springdale, West Columbia); Below 100 (Elgin, Fort Jackson). Franchise award date: November 2, 1977. Franchise expiration date: October 18, 2003. Began: December 1, 1977.
Channel capacity: 78 (2-way capable; not operating 2-way). Channels available but not in use: 2.
Basic Service
Subscribers: 109,800.
Programming (received off-air): WACH (F), WIS (N), WLTX (C), WOLO-TV (A), WRLK-TV (P) Columbia.
Programming (via satellite): WGN-TV (W) Chicago; C-SPAN; Knowledge TV; QVC; TV Guide Channel.
Current originations: Educational access; government access; leased access.
Fee: $51.00 installation; $8.15 monthly; $2.63 converter; $17.00 additional installation.
Expanded Basic Service
Subscribers: N.A.
Programming (via satellite): A & E; American Movie Classics; Animal Planet; BET; CNBC; CNN; Cartoon Network; Comedy Central; Country Music TV; Court TV; Discovery Channel; E! Entertainment TV; ESPN; Fox Family Channel; Headline News; History Channel; Home & Garden Television; Home Shopping Network; Learning Channel; Lifetime; MSNBC; MTV; Nashville Network; Nick at Nite's TV Land; Nickelodeon; Odyssey; Pax Net; TBS Superstation; TV Food Network; The Inspirational Network; The Weather Channel; Travel Channel; Turner Classic Movies; Turner Network TV; USA Network; VH1.
Fee: $2.00 installation; $27.01 monthly.
Expanded Basic Service 2
Subscribers: N.A.
Programming (via satellite): Bravo; Disney Channel; Goodlife TV Network; Sci-Fi Channel.
Fee: $2.00 installation; $4.50 monthly.
Expanded Basic Service 3
Subscribers: N.A.
Programming (via satellite): CNN/SI; ESPN 2; ESPN Classic Sports; Fox Sports Net South; Golf Channel.
Fee: $2.00 installation; $3.20 monthly.
Pay Service 1
Pay Units: 9,725.
Programming (via satellite): Cinemax (multiplexed).
Fee: $2.00 installation; $10.95 monthly.
Pay Service 2
Pay Units: 22,550.
Programming (via satellite): HBO (multiplexed).
Fee: $2.00 installation; $11.95 monthly.
Pay Service 3
Pay Units: 1,800.
Programming (via satellite): The Movie Channel.
Fee: $2.00 installation; $10.95 monthly.
Pay Service 4
Pay Units: 6,000.
Programming (via satellite): Showtime (multiplexed).
Fee: $2.00 installation; $9.95 monthly.
Pay Service 5
Pay Units: N.A.
Programming (via satellite): BET Movies/Starz!; Encore Movie Networks; Flix; Independent Film Channel; Music Choice; Starz!; Sundance Channel.
Fee: $4.95 monthly (Music Choice).
Pay-Per-View
Addressable homes: 47,450.
Action Pay-Per-View; Playboy TV; Spice; Viewer's Choice.

Pay-per-view manager: Diana Smith.
Local advertising: No. Local sales manager: Cable Vantage.
Equipment: Jerrold headend; Jerrold & Scientific-Atlanta amplifiers; Times Fiber & Comm/Scope cable; System Concepts & Texscan character generator; GTE Sylvania, Scientific-Atlanta & Panasonic set top converters; Jerrold & Scientific-Atlanta addressable set top converters; Eagle traps; Scientific-Atlanta satellite antenna; Jerrold & Scientific-Atlanta satellite receivers.
Miles of plant: 2650.0 (coaxial); 1718.0 (fiber optic). Additional miles planned: 60.0 (coaxial). Homes passed: 221,500.
Manager: Tim Hartman. Chief technician: Rhett Stokes. Division marketing manager: Diana Smith.
City fee: 5% of gross.
Ownership: Time Warner Cable (MSO); Advance/Newhouse Partnership (MSO).

COTTAGEVILLE—Pine Tree Cablevision, Box 1060, 3931 Byrnes Dr., St. Stephen, SC 29479. Phone: 843-567-3289. Fax: 843-567-2089. County: Colleton. Also serves Colleton County. ICA: SC0114.
TV Market Ranking: Below 100. Franchise award date: N.A. Franchise expiration date: N.A. Began: N.A.
Channel capacity: 35 (not 2-way capable). Channels available but not in use: 9.
Basic Service
Subscribers: 356.
Programming (received off-air): WCBD-TV (N), WCIV (A), WCSC-TV (C), WITV (P), WTAT-TV (F,U) Charleston.
Programming (via satellite): WGN-TV (W) Chicago; A & E; BET; CNN; Country Music TV; Discovery Channel; ESPN; Fox Family Channel; Lifetime; Nashville Network; Nickelodeon; QVC; TBS Superstation; Trinity Bcstg. Network; Turner Network TV; USA Network.
Fee: $22.70 monthly.
Pay Service 1
Pay Units: 83.
Programming (via satellite): Cinemax.
Fee: N.A.
Pay Service 2
Pay Units: 115.
Programming (via satellite): HBO.
Fee: N.A.
Manager: Walter Kemmerer.
Ownership: Pine Tree Cablevision (MSO). Purchased from Bay Cable Inc., February 1, 1999.

COWARD—Galaxy Cablevision, 1899 S.E. 58th Ave., Ocala, FL 34471-5847. Phone: 352-624-1117. County: Florence. Also serves Florence County (portions). ICA: SC0084.
TV Market Ranking: Below 100. Franchise award date: December 23, 1988. Franchise expiration date: December 23, 2003. Began: N.A.
Channel capacity: 31. Channels available but not in use: None.
Basic Service
Subscribers: 166.
Programming (received off-air): WIS (N) Columbia; WBTW (C), WJPM-TV (P), WPDE-TV (A) Florence.
Programming (via satellite): WGN-TV (W) Chicago; A & E; American Movie Classics; CNBC; CNN; Country Music TV; Discovery Channel; ESPN; Fox Family Channel; Headline News; Lifetime; Nashville Network; Nickelodeon; QVC; TBS Superstation; The Weather Channel; Turner Network TV; USA Network; VH1.
Fee: $30.00 installation; $26.75 monthly; $3.00 converter.
Pay Service 1
Pay Units: 79.
Programming (via satellite): Cinemax.
Fee: $10.95 monthly.
Pay Service 2
Pay Units: 33.
Programming (via satellite): Disney Channel.
Fee: $10.95 monthly.
Pay Service 3
Pay Units: 91.
Programming (via satellite): HBO.
Fee: $10.95 monthly.
Local advertising: No.
Miles of plant: 38.0 (coaxial). Homes passed: 760.
State manager: Dan Labbe. Technical manager: Joe Ferrell.
Ownership: Galaxy Cablevision (MSO).

CROSS—Pine Tree Cablevision, Box 1060, 3931 Byrnes Dr., St. Stephen, SC 29479. Phone: 843-567-3289. Fax: 843-567-2089. County: Berkeley. ICA: SC0115.
TV Market Ranking: Outside TV Markets. Franchise award date: N.A. Franchise expiration date: N.A. Began: N.A.
Channel capacity: 36 (not 2-way capable). Channels available but not in use: 5.
Basic Service
Subscribers: 387.
Programming (received off-air): WCBD-TV (N), WCIV (A), WCSC-TV (C), WITV (P), WTAT-TV (F,U) Charleston.
Programming (via satellite): WGN-TV (W) Chicago; A & E; BET; CNN; Country Music TV; Discovery Channel; ESPN; Fox Family Channel; Home Shopping Network; Lifetime; MTV; Nashville Network; Nickelodeon; TBS Superstation; Trinity Bcstg. Network; Turner Network TV; USA Network; VH1.
Fee: $40.00 installation; $22.70 monthly.
Pay Service 1
Pay Units: 37.
Programming (via satellite): Cinemax.
Fee: N.A.
Pay Service 2
Pay Units: 78.
Programming (via satellite): HBO.
Fee: N.A.
Pay Service 3
Pay Units: 71.
Programming (via satellite): Showtime.
Fee: N.A.
Manager: Walter Kemmerer.
Ownership: Pine Tree Cablevision (MSO). Purchased from Bay Cable Inc., February 1, 1999.

CROSS HILL—Galaxy Cablevision, 1899 S.E. 58th Ave., Ocala, FL 34471-5847. Phone: 352-624-1117. County: Laurens. Also serves Laurens County (portions). ICA: SC0040.
TV Market Ranking: 46. Franchise award date: July 25, 1989. Franchise expiration date: July 11, 2009. Began: N.A.
Channel capacity: 33. Channels available but not in use: None.
Basic Service
Subscribers: 967.
Programming (received off-air): WHNS (F,U), WLOS (A), WSPA-TV (C), WYFF (N) Greenville-Spartanburg-Asheville; WNEH (P) Greenwood.
Programming (via satellite): WGN-TV (W) Chicago; A & E; BET; CNN; Country Music TV; Discovery Channel; E! Entertainment TV; ESPN; Fox Family Channel; Lifetime; Nashville Network; Nickelodeon; QVC; TBS Superstation; The Weather Channel; USA Network; VH1.
Fee: $20.00 installation; $26.25 monthly.
Pay Service 1
Pay Units: 196.
Programming (via satellite): Cinemax.
Fee: $10.95 monthly.
Pay Service 2
Pay Units: 44.
Programming (via satellite): Disney Channel.
Fee: $10.95 monthly.
Pay Service 3
Pay Units: 308.
Programming (via satellite): HBO.
Fee: $10.95 monthly.
Local advertising: No.
Miles of plant: 148.0 (coaxial). Homes passed: 2,869.
State manager: Dan Labbe. Technical manager: Joe Ferrell.
Ownership: Galaxy Cablevision (MSO).

DAUFUSKIE ISLAND—Falcon Cable TV, 5026 S. Hwy. 27, Somerset, KY 42501. Phone: 606-678-3035. County: Beaufort. ICA: SC0116.
TV Market Ranking: Below 100. Franchise award date: N.A. Franchise expiration date: N.A. Began: September 1, 1989.
Channel capacity: 36 (not 2-way capable). Channels available but not in use: 24.
Pay Service 1
Pay Units: N.A.
Programming (via satellite): HBO.
Fee: $10.00 monthly.
Manager: David Hudson. Chief technician: Larry Gregory.
Ownership: Falcon Communications LP (MSO), joint venture formed September 30, 1998. See Cable System Ownership.

DEBORDIEU COLONY—Benchmark Communications, 2511 Highmarket St., Georgetown, SC 29440. Phone: 843-527-2447. Fax: 843-527-2034. County: Georgetown. ICA: SC0047.
TV Market Ranking: Below 100. Franchise award date: January 1, 1986. Franchise expiration date: January 1, 2001. Began: November 1, 1986.
Channel capacity: 36 (2-way capable; operating 2-way). Channels available but not in use: 3.
Basic Service
Subscribers: 333.
Programming (received off-air): WCBD-TV (N), WCIV (A), WCSC-TV (C), WITV (P), WTAT-TV (F,U) Charleston; WIS (N) Columbia; WBTW (C), WPDE-TV (A) Florence.
Programming (via satellite): WGN-TV (W) Chicago; A & E; American Movie Classics; Animal Planet; C-SPAN; C-SPAN 2; CNBC; CNN; Country Music TV; Discovery Channel; ESPN; Fox Family Channel; Fox News Channel; Golf Channel; Headline News; Home & Garden Television; Learning Channel; Lifetime; MTV; Nashville Network; Nickelodeon; QVC; Sci-Fi Channel; TBS Superstation; TV Guide Channel; The Weather Channel; Trinity Bcstg. Network; Turner Network TV; USA Network; VH1.
Planned originations: Automated emergency alert.
Fee: $25.00 installation; $24.95 monthly; $2.00 converter.
Pay Service 1
Pay Units: 7.
Programming (via satellite): Cinemax.
Fee: $10.50 monthly.
Pay Service 2
Pay Units: 20.
Programming (via satellite): Disney Channel.
Fee: $9.50 monthly.
Pay Service 3
Pay Units: 6.
Programming (via satellite): HBO.
Fee: $10.50 monthly.
Pay Service 4
Pay Units: 14.
Programming (via satellite): Showtime.
Fee: $10.50 monthly.
Local advertising: Yes.
Equipment: Scientific-Atlanta headend; Jerrold amplifiers; Trilogy cable; Scientific-Atlanta character generator; Scientific-Atlanta set top converters; Pico traps; Scientific-Atlanta satellite receivers.
Miles of plant: 13.0 (coaxial); None (fiber optic). Additional miles planned: 10.0 (coaxial). Homes passed: 389. Total homes in franchised area: 500.
Manager: Kenneth Koch.
Ownership: Benchmark Communications (MSO). Purchased from Genesis Cable Communications LLC, May 3, 1999.

DILLON—Century Communications, Box 1109, 1741 Hwy. 9W, Dillon, SC 29536. Phone: 843-774-2461. Fax: 843-774-2035. E-mail: kspruill@centurycomm.com. Web site: http://www.centurycomm.com. County: Dillon. Also serves Dillon County, Latta. ICA: SC0036.
TV Market Ranking: Below 100. Franchise award date: N.A. Franchise expiration date: N.A. Began: May 1, 1969.
Channel capacity: 36 (not 2-way capable). Channels available but not in use: 1.
Basic Service
Subscribers: 3,720.
Programming (received off-air): WIS (N) Columbia; WBTW (C), WJPM-TV (P), WPDE-TV (A) Florence; WECT (N), WWAY (A) Wilmington.
Programming (via satellite): C-SPAN; Home Shopping Network; QVC.
Fee: $60.00 installation; $24.19 monthly; $8.53 additional installation.
Expanded Basic Service
Subscribers: N.A.
Programming (via satellite): A & E; American Movie Classics; Discovery Channel; Fox Family Channel; Headline News; The Weather Channel; Trinity Bcstg. Network; VH1.
Fee: $10.00 installation; $3.20 monthly.
Expanded Basic Service 2
Subscribers: N.A.
Programming (via satellite): CNN; ESPN; Nashville Network; TBS Superstation; Turner Network TV; USA Network.
Fee: $2.00 monthly.
Pay Service 1
Pay Units: 850.
Programming (via satellite): Cinemax; Disney Channel; HBO.
Fee: $10.00 installation; $7.00 monthly (Disney), $9.00 monthly (Cinemax or HBO).
Local advertising: No. Local sales manager: Betty Jackson.
Equipment: Scientific-Atlanta headend; Century III & Kaiser amplifiers; Comm/Scope & Superior cable; Oak set top converters; Scientific-Atlanta satellite antenna.
Miles of plant: 90.6 (coaxial). Additional miles planned: 12.0 (coaxial). Homes passed: 4,730.
Manager: Kraig Spruill. Chief technician: Tim Bourgoin. Marketing & program director: Bertha Casey.
City fee: 3% of gross.
Ownership: Century Communications Corp. (MSO). See Cable System Ownership.

DOVESVILLE—Galaxy Cablevision, 1899 S.E. 58th Ave., Ocala, FL 34471-5847. Phone: 352-624-1117. County: Darlington. ICA: SC0070.
TV Market Ranking: Below 100. Franchise award date: March 31, 1989. Franchise expiration date: March 31, 2004. Began: December 1, 1989.

Channel capacity: 32. Channels available but not in use: None.

Basic Service

Subscribers: 539.

Programming (received off-air): WIS (N) Columbia; WBTW (C), WJPM-TV (P), WPDE-TV (A) Florence.

Programming (via satellite): WGN-TV (W) Chicago; A & E; American Movie Classics; BET; CNBC; CNN; Discovery Channel; E! Entertainment TV; ESPN; Fox Family Channel; Headline News; Lifetime; Nashville Network; Nickelodeon; QVC; TBS Superstation; The Weather Channel; Turner Network TV; USA Network; VH1.

Fee: $30.00 installation; $26.75 monthly.

Pay Service 1

Pay Units: 115.

Programming (via satellite): Cinemax.

Fee: $10.95 monthly.

Pay Service 2

Pay Units: 36.

Programming (via satellite): Disney Channel.

Fee: $10.95 monthly.

Pay Service 3

Pay Units: 181.

Programming (via satellite): HBO.

Fee: $10.95 monthly.

Miles of plant: 53.0 (coaxial). Homes passed: 1,030.

State manager: Dan Labbe. Technical manager: Joe Ferrell.

Ownership: Galaxy Cablevision (MSO).

DUE WEST—Due West Cablevision, Box 156, Due West, SC 29639. Phone: 864-379-2174. County: Abbeville. Also serves Donalds. ICA: SC0117.

TV Market Ranking: 46. Franchise award date: December 1, 1985. Franchise expiration date: December 1, 2000. Began: March 1, 1986.

Channel capacity: 35. Channels available but not in use: 2.

Basic Service

Subscribers: 574.

Programming (received off-air): WFBC-TV (W) Anderson; WGGS-TV (I), WNTV (P) Greenville; WHNS (F,U), WLOS (A), WSPA-TV (C), WYFF (N) Greenville-Spartanburg-Asheville.

Programming (via satellite): Fox Family Channel; Headline News; Home Shopping Network; TBS Superstation.

Current originations: Automated time-weather; educational access; local news; local sports.

Fee: $25.00 installation; $10.00 monthly.

Expanded Basic Service

Subscribers: 530.

Programming (via satellite): WGN-TV (W) Chicago; A & E; BET; C-SPAN; CNN; Country Music TV; Discovery Channel; ESPN; MTV; Nashville Network; Nick at Nite; Nickelodeon; The Weather Channel; Turner Classic Movies; Turner Network TV; USA Network.

Fee: $12.00 monthly.

Pay Service 1

Pay Units: 35.

Programming (via satellite): The Movie Channel.

Fee: $10.00 monthly.

Pay Service 2

Pay Units: 61.

Programming (via satellite): Showtime.

Fee: $10.00 monthly.

Local advertising: No.

Equipment: Pico & Jerrold headend; Jerrold amplifiers; Comm/Scope cable; Jerrold & Microdyne satellite receivers.

Miles of plant: 55.0 (coaxial); None (fiber optic). Additional miles planned: 10.0 (coaxial). Homes passed: 875. Total homes in franchised area: 1,575.

Manager: Travis Payne.

Ownership: Travis Payne.

DUNES WEST—Southern Cable Communications, Box 1998, Georgetown, SC 29442-1998. Phone: 843-556-2200. Fax: 803-527-2314. County: Charleston. Also serves Cypress Point, Mount Pleasant. ICA: SC0149.

TV Market Ranking: Below 100. Franchise award date: June 18, 1992. Franchise expiration date: January 1, 2007. Began: August 31, 1992.

Channel capacity: 64. Channels available but not in use: 27.

Basic Service

Subscribers: 51.

Programming (received off-air): WCBD-TV (N), WCIV (A), WCSC-TV (C), WITV (P), WMMP (U), WTAT-TV (F,U) Charleston.

Programming (via satellite): WGN-TV (W) Chicago; A & E; CNBC; CNN; Discovery Channel; ESPN; Fox Family Channel; Headline News; Knowledge TV; Lifetime; MOR Galleria; MTV; Nashville Network; Nickelodeon; QVC; Sci-Fi Channel; TBS Superstation; The Weather Channel; Travel Channel; Trinity Bcstg. Network; Turner Network TV; USA Network; VH1.

Fee: $35.00 installation; $18.95 monthly.

Pay Service 1

Pay Units: 25.

Programming (via satellite): Cinemax; Disney Channel; HBO; Showtime; The Movie Channel.

Fee: $9.50 monthly (each).

Miles of plant: 5.0 (coaxial). Homes passed: 75. Total homes in franchised area: 3,000.

Manager: Robert Atkinson. Chief technician: Ken Charlton.

Ownership: Southern Cable Communications (MSO).

EDGEFIELD—Aiken Cablevision Inc., Box 518, 109 W. Church St., Saluda, SC 29138. County: Edgefield. Also serves Edgefield County, Johnston. ICA: SC0044.

TV Market Ranking: Below 100 (Edgefield, portions of Edgefield County, Johnston); Outside TV Markets (portions of Edgefield County). Franchise award date: January 1, 1981. Franchise expiration date: N.A. Began: July 1, 1981.

Channel capacity: 36 (not 2-way capable). Channels available but not in use: 8.

Basic Service

Subscribers: 1,198; Commercial subscribers: 17.

Programming (received off-air): WAGT (N), WFXG (F), WJBF (A), WRDW-TV (C) Augusta; WIS (N), WRLK-TV (P) Columbia.

Programming (via satellite): WGN-TV (W) Chicago; A & E; BET; C-SPAN; CNN; Country Music TV; Discovery Channel; ESPN; Fox Family Channel; Fox Sports Net South; Headline News; Home Shopping Network; MTV; Nashville Network; Nickelodeon; TBS Superstation; The Weather Channel; Turner Network TV; USA Network; VH1.

Current originations: Automated time-weather; public access; educational access; government access.

Fee: $25.00 installation; $18.95 monthly; $10.00 additional installation.

Commercial fee: $5.50 monthly.

Pay Service 1

Pay Units: 585.

Programming (via satellite): Cinemax; Disney Channel; HBO; Showtime.

Fee: $7.50 installation; $7.95 monthly (Disney), $8.95 monthly (Cinemax, HBO or Showtime).

Local advertising: No.

Equipment: Jerrold headend; Jerrold amplifiers; Comm/Scope cable; Jerrold set top converters; Eagle & Arcom traps; Scientific-Atlanta satellite antenna; Jerrold & Scientific-Atlanta satellite receivers.

Miles of plant: 56.5 (coaxial). Additional miles planned: 3.0 (coaxial). Homes passed: 1,837. Total homes in franchised area: 7,000.

Manager: Lee A. Perron. Chief technician: Tony Urban.

City fee: 3% of gross.

Ownership: InterMedia Partners (MSO).

EDISTO BEACH—US Cable Coastal Properties, Box 469, Johns Island, SC 29457. Phone: 843-559-2424. County: Colleton. ICA: SC0059.

TV Market Ranking: Below 100. Franchise award date: January 1, 1983. Franchise expiration date: January 1, 2001. Began: June 1, 1984.

Channel capacity: N.A. Channels available but not in use: N.A.

Basic Service

Subscribers: 1,385.

Programming (received off-air): WCBD-TV (N), WCIV (A), WCSC-TV (C), WITV (P), WMMP (U), WTAT-TV (F,U) Charleston.

Programming (via satellite): C-SPAN; C-SPAN 2; Home Shopping Network; MuchMoreMusic; Trinity Bcstg. Network; VH1.

Fee: $75.51 installation; $11.43 monthly.

Expanded Basic Service

Subscribers: 1,255.

Programming (via satellite): A & E; CNBC; CNN; Disney Channel; ESPN; ESPN 2; Fox Family Channel; Fox Sports Net South; Headline News; History Channel; Home & Garden Television; Learning Channel; Lifetime; MSNBC; MTV; Nashville Network; Nickelodeon; Outdoor Channel; Romance Classics; Speedvision; The Weather Channel; Travel Channel; Turner Classic Movies; Turner Network TV; USA Network.

Fee: $15.83 monthly.

Expanded Basic Service 2

Subscribers: N.A.

Programming (via satellite): WGN-TV (W) Chicago; American Movie Classics; Discovery Channel; TBS Superstation.

Fee: $2.45 monthly.

Pay Service 1

Pay Units: N.A.

Programming (via satellite): Cinemax; HBO.

Fee: $9.50 monthly (each).

Miles of plant: 34.9 (coaxial). Homes passed: 1,775.

Manager: Randy Houser. Chief technician: Ray Kirkendall.

Ownership: US Cable Corp. (MSO).

ELLOREE—Pine Tree Cablevision, 2628 Millwood Ave., Columbia, SC 29205. Phone: 803-799-6226. Fax: 803-799-8804. County: Orangeburg. ICA: SC0099.

TV Market Ranking: Below 100. Franchise award date: February 1, 1985. Franchise expiration date: February 1, 2000. Began: October 1, 1986.

Channel capacity: 22. Channels available but not in use: 10.

Basic Service

Subscribers: 190.

Programming (received off-air): WRDW-TV (C) Augusta; WCIV (A) Charleston; WIS (N), WOLO-TV (A), WRLK-TV (P) Columbia.

Programming (via satellite): CNN; ESPN; Fox Family Channel; Nashville Network; TBS Superstation.

Fee: $30.00 installation; $12.00 monthly.

Pay Service 1

Pay Units: N.A.

Programming (via satellite): Disney Channel; Showtime.

Fee: $8.00 monthly (each).

Homes passed: 530.

Manager: Tony Wilson.

Ownership: Pine Tree Cablevision (MSO). Purchased from South Carolina Cable TV LP, October 1, 1998.

ESTILL—Hargray CATV Co. Inc., Box 700, Ridgeland, SC 29936. Phone: 843-784-6411. County: Hampton. ICA: SC0118.

TV Market Ranking: Below 100. Franchise award date: N.A. Franchise expiration date: N.A. Began: August 1, 1984.

Channel capacity: 36. Channels available but not in use: 21.

Basic Service

Subscribers: 409.

Programming (received off-air): WJWJ-TV (P) Beaufort; WCSC-TV (C) Charleston; WJCL (A), WSAV-TV (N), WTOC-TV (C) Savannah.

Programming (via satellite): WGN-TV (W) Chicago; CNN; ESPN; Fox Family Channel; Nashville Network; Nickelodeon; TBS Superstation; USA Network.

Fee: $13.65 monthly.

Pay Service 1

Pay Units: N.A.

Programming (via satellite): Cinemax; HBO.

Fee: $9.95 monthly (each).

Equipment: Triple Crown headend.

Miles of plant: Included with Ridgeland, SC.

Manager: Frank Semken. Chief technician: Kerry Asher.

Ownership: Hargray Telephone Co. (MSO).

FIVE POINTS—Galaxy Cablevision, 1899 S.E. 58th Ave., Ocala, FL 34471-5847. Phone: 352-624-1117. County: Oconee. Also serves Oconee County (portions). ICA: SC0081.

TV Market Ranking: 46. Franchise award date: October 3, 1989. Franchise expiration date: October 3, 2004. Began: January 1, 1991.

Channel capacity: 28. Channels available but not in use: None.

Basic Service

Subscribers: 314.

Programming (received off-air): WNTV (P) Greenville; WHNS (F,U), WLOS (A), WSPA-TV (C), WYFF (N) Greenville-Spartanburg-Asheville.

Programming (via satellite): WGN-TV (W) Chicago; A & E; CNN; Country Music TV; Discovery Channel; ESPN; Fox Family Channel; Headline News; Nashville Network; Nickelodeon; TBS Superstation; The Weather Channel; USA Network; VH1.

Fee: $30.00 installation; $25.75 monthly.

Pay Service 1

Pay Units: 68.

Programming (via satellite): Cinemax.

Fee: $10.95 monthly.

Pay Service 2

Pay Units: 36.

Programming (via satellite): Disney Channel.

Fee: $7.95 monthly.

Pay Service 3

Pay Units: 73.

Programming (via satellite): HBO.

Fee: $10.95 monthly.

Local advertising: No.

Miles of plant: 30.0 (coaxial). Homes passed: 728.

State manager: Dan Labbe. Technical manager: Joe Ferrell.

Ownership: Galaxy Cablevision (MSO).

FLORENCE—Time Warner Cable, 3232 Bryson Dr., Florence, SC 29501. Phone: 843-662-8191. Fax: 843-665-5483. Counties: Darlington & Florence. Also serves Darlington, Darlington County, Florence County, Pamplico, Quinby, Timmonsville. ICA: SC0005.

TV Market Ranking: Below 100. Franchise award date: December 1, 1962. Franchise expiration date: December 1, 2012. Began: December 16, 1963.

Channel capacity: 63 (2-way capable; operating 2-way). Channels available but not in use: 2.

Basic Service

Subscribers: 35,000.

Programming (received off-air): WIS (N) Columbia; WBTW (C), WEYB-LP (I), WPDE-TV (A), WWMB (U) Florence; WFXB (F) Myrtle Beach; WRJA-TV (P) Sumter.

Programming (via satellite): WGN-TV (W) Chicago.

Current originations: Automated timeweather; government access.

Fee: $48.00 installation; $4.58 monthly; $16.00 additional installation.

Expanded Basic Service

Subscribers: 29,655.

Programming (via satellite): Learning Channel; TBS Superstation; Turner Network TV.

Fee: $1.49 monthly.

Expanded Basic Service 2

Subscribers: 31,638.

Programming (via satellite): A & E; American Movie Classics; BET; C-SPAN; CNBC; CNN; Court TV; Discovery Channel; E! Entertainment TV; ESPN; ESPN 2; FX; Fox Family Channel; Headline News; Lifetime; MTV; Nashville Network; Nickelodeon; Odyssey; QVC; The Weather Channel; USA Network; VH1.

Fee: $24.79 monthly.

Expanded Basic Service 3

Subscribers: 9,793.

Programming (via satellite): fXM: Movies from Fox; Fox Sports Net South; Golf Channel; History Channel.

Fee: $1.92 monthly.

Pay Service 1

Pay Units: 4,322.

Programming (via satellite): Cinemax.

Fee: $2.00 installation; $7.49 monthly.

Pay Service 2

Pay Units: 1,819.

Programming (via satellite): Disney Channel.

Fee: $6.95 monthly.

Pay Service 3

Pay Units: 9,640.

Programming (via satellite): HBO.

Fee: $10.95 monthly.

Pay Service 4

Pay Units: 2,712.

Programming (via satellite): Showtime.

Fee: $7.49 monthly.

Pay-Per-View

Addressable homes: 15,793.

Hot Choice; Viewer's Choice.

Fee: $4.95 (each).

Local advertising: Yes (insert only). Available in satellite distributed & automated programming. Local sales manager: Peggy Baker.

Program Guide: The Cable Guide.

Equipment: RCA & Scientific-Atlanta headend; Jerrold amplifiers; General & Times Fiber cable; Sony VTRs; Comtech character generator; Jerrold set top converters; Jerrold & Octagon addressable set top converters; Eagle & Vitek traps; Scientific-Atlanta satellite antenna; Microdyne satellite receivers; Sony commercial insert.

Miles of plant: 1129.0 (coaxial); 220.0 (fiber optic). Homes passed: 47,171. Total homes in franchised area: 70,000.

Manager: Kurt A. Newber. Chief technician: Tommy L. Martin.

City fee: 4% of gross.

Ownership: Time Warner Cable (MSO); Advance/Newhouse Partnership (MSO).

FOLLY BEACH—US Cable Coastal Properties, Box 469, Johns Island, SC 29457. Phone: 843-559-2424. County: Charleston. ICA: SC0052.

TV Market Ranking: Below 100. Franchise award date: N.A. Franchise expiration date: N.A. Began: June 1, 1983.

Channel capacity: N.A. Channels available but not in use: N.A.

Basic Service

Subscribers: 1,336.

Programming (received off-air): WCBD-TV (N), WCIV (A), WCSC-TV (C), WITV (P), WMMP (U), WTAT-TV (F,U) Charleston.

Programming (via satellite): BET; C-SPAN; C-SPAN 2; Home Shopping Network; Trinity Bcstg. Network; VH1.

Fee: $75.51 installation; $11.78 monthly.

Expanded Basic Service

Subscribers: 1,252.

Programming (via satellite): A & E; CNBC; CNN; Comedy Central; Disney Channel; ESPN; Fox Family Channel; Fox Sports Net South; Headline News; History Channel; Home & Garden Television; Learning Channel; Lifetime; MSNBC; MTV; Nashville Network; Nickelodeon; Outdoor Channel; Speedvision; The Weather Channel; Travel Channel; Turner Classic Movies; Turner Network TV; USA Network.

Fee: $15.57 monthly.

Expanded Basic Service 2

Subscribers: N.A.

Programming (via satellite): WGN-TV (W) Chicago; American Movie Classics; Discovery Channel; TBS Superstation.

Fee: $2.45 monthly.

Pay Service 1

Pay Units: N.A.

Programming (via satellite): Cinemax; HBO; Showtime.

Fee: $9.50 monthly (each).

Local advertising: No.

Equipment: M/A-Com headend; Texscan amplifiers; Times Fiber cable; Atari character generator; Jerrold set top converters; M/A-Com & Scientific-Atlanta satellite antenna; M/A-Com satellite receivers.

Miles of plant: 36.5 (coaxial). Homes passed: 2,708.

Manager: Randy Houser. Chief technician: Ray Kirkendall.

Ownership: US Cable Corp. (MSO).

FORT MILL—Palmetto Cable TV, Box 1418, 404 Springcrest Dr., Fort Mill, SC 29715. Phone: 803-548-6000. Fax: 803-547-6655. Counties: Lancaster & York. Also serves Lancaster County (portions), Tega Cay, York County (portions). ICA: SC0120.

TV Market Ranking: 42. Franchise award date: N.A. Franchise expiration date: November 1, 1997. Began: March 1, 1983.

Channel capacity: 77 (not 2-way capable). Channels available but not in use: 15.

Basic Service

Subscribers: 7,344.

Programming (received off-air): WJZY (U) Belmont; WBTV (C), WCCB (F), WCNC-TV (N), WSOC-TV (A), WTVI (P) Charlotte; WSPA-TV (C) Greenville-Spartanburg-Asheville; WAXN (I) Kannapolis; WFVT (W), WNSC-TV (P) Rock Hill; allband FM.

Programming (via satellite): A & E; American Movie Classics; BET; C-SPAN; C-SPAN 2; CNN; CNNfn; Cartoon Network; Comedy Central; Country Music TV; Discovery Channel; ESPN; ESPN 2; FX; Fox Family Channel; Fox Sports Net South; Headline News; Home & Garden Television; Home Shopping Network; Learning Channel; Lifetime; Nashville Network; Nick at Nite's TV Land; Nickelodeon; Sci-Fi Channel; TBS Superstation; TV Guide Channel; The Weather Channel; Trinity Bcstg. Network; Turner Network TV; USA Network; VH1.

Current originations: Automated timeweather; public access; educational access; government access; religious access; automated emergency alert.

Fee: $45.00 installation; $23.55 monthly.

Expanded Basic Service

Subscribers: 6,556.

Programming (via satellite): A & E; American Movie Classics; BET; CNN; CNNfn; Cartoon Network; Country Music TV; Discovery Channel; ESPN; ESPN 2; ESPN Classic Sports; FX; Fox Family Channel; Fox Sports Net South; FoxNet; Headline News; History Channel; Home & Garden Television; Learning Channel; Lifetime; Nashville Network; Nick at Nite's TV Land; Nickelodeon; Sci-Fi Channel; Turner Network TV.

Fee: $14.55 monthly.

Pay Service 1

Pay Units: 557.

Programming (via satellite): Cinemax (multiplexed).

Fee: $9.95 monthly.

Pay Service 2

Pay Units: 388.

Programming (via satellite): Disney Channel.

Fee: $7.95 monthly.

Pay Service 3

Pay Units: 1,399.

Programming (via satellite): HBO (multiplexed).

Fee: $9.95 monthly.

Pay Service 4

Pay Units: 451.

Programming (via satellite): Showtime; The Movie Channel.

Fee: $9.95 monthly.

Pay Service 5

Pay Units: 897.

Programming (via satellite): The New Encore.

Fee: $9.95 monthly.

Pay Service 6

Pay Units: 899.

Programming (via satellite): Starz!

Fee: $9.95 monthly.

Pay-Per-View

Addressable homes: 6,556.

Viewer's Choice 1, 3, 4; special events.

Fee: $3.95.

Pay-per-view manager: John Barnes Jr.

Local advertising: Yes. Local sales manager: John Burnett.

Equipment: C-COR amplifiers; Comm/Scope cable; Siecor fiber optic cable; System Concepts character generator; Scientific-Atlanta set top converters; Scientific-Atlanta addressable set top converters.

Miles of plant: 29.1 (coaxial). Additional miles planned: 30.0 (coaxial). Homes passed: 800.

Manager: William C. Beaty Jr. Marketing & program director: John Barnes Jr. Customer service manager: Sherri Parrish.

City fee: 3.5% of gross.

Ownership: Palmetto Cable TV Inc. (MSO).

FRIPP ISLAND—US Cable, Box 70193, Beaufort, SC 29902. Phone: 843-522-0784. County: Beaufort. Also serves Harbour Island, Hunting Town. ICA: SC0067.

TV Market Ranking: Below 100. Franchise award date: N.A. Franchise expiration date: N.A. Began: January 1, 1981.

Channel capacity: 36. Channels available but not in use: N.A.

Basic Service

Subscribers: N.A.

Programming (received off-air): WJWJ-TV (P) Beaufort; WCIV (A), WCSC-TV (C) Charleston; WCCB (F) Charlotte; WSAV-TV (N) Savannah.

Programming (via satellite): WGN-TV (W) Chicago; A & E; CNN; ESPN; Nickelodeon; TBS Superstation.

Current originations: Automated timeweather.

Fee: $25.00 installation; $11.45 monthly.

Pay Service 1

Pay Units: N.A.

Programming (via satellite): Showtime.

Fee: $7.95 monthly.

Equipment: Scientific-Atlanta headend; Comm/Scope & Times Fiber cable; Scientific-Atlanta satellite antenna; Scientific-Atlanta satellite receivers.

Miles of plant: 38.4 (coaxial). Homes passed: 1,185.

Manager: Wally Davidson. Chief technician: Don Mizell.

City fee: 3% of gross.

Ownership: US Cable Corp. (MSO).

GAFFNEY—Charter Communications, 124 Willis St., Gaffney, SC 29340. Phone: 864-489-3186. Fax: 864-488-4407. County: Cherokee. Also serves Blacksburg, Cherokee County (unincorporated areas). ICA: SC0021.

TV Market Ranking: 46. Franchise award date: September 6, 1966. Franchise expiration date: September 5, 2006. Began: October 4, 1968.

Channel capacity: 36 (not 2-way capable). Channels available but not in use: None.

Basic Service

Subscribers: 6,629.

Programming (received off-air): WJZY (U) Belmont; WBTV (C), WSOC-TV (A) Charlotte; WGGS-TV (I), WNTV (P) Greenville; WHNS (F,U), WLOS (A), WSPA-TV (C), WYFF (N) Greenville-Spartanburg-Asheville; allband FM.

Programming (via satellite): WGN-TV (W) Chicago; Cartoon Network; TBS Superstation.

Fee: $47.07 installation; $8.12 monthly; $3.39 converter.

Expanded Basic Service

Subscribers: 6,006.

Programming (via satellite): A & E; BET; C-SPAN; CNN; Comedy Central; Country Music TV; Discovery Channel; Fox Family Channel; Headline News; Home Shopping Network; Lifetime; MTV; Nashville Network; Nickelodeon; TV Guide Channel; The Weather Channel; Turner Network TV; USA Network.

Fee: $12.50 monthly.

Pay Service 1

Pay Units: 368.

Programming (via satellite): Cinemax.

Fee: $11.95 monthly.

Pay Service 2

Pay Units: 115.

Programming (via satellite): Disney Channel.

Fee: $8.95 monthly.

Pay Service 3

Pay Units: 406.

Programming (via satellite): HBO.

Fee: $13.95 monthly.

Pay Service 4
Pay Units: 84.
Programming (via satellite): The Movie Channel.
Fee: $11.95 monthly.
Pay Service 5
Pay Units: 241.
Programming (via satellite): Showtime.
Fee: $11.95 monthly.
Pay-Per-View
Addressable homes: 539.
Viewer's Choice.
Fee: $4.95.
Local advertising: Yes. Available in taped programming. Local sales manager: Myra Byars.
Program Guide: Prevue Guide.
Equipment: Scientific-Atlanta headend; Kaiser & Magnavox amplifiers; Comm/Scope cable; Atari character generator; Jerrold set top converters; Jerrold addressable set top converters; Scientific-Atlanta satellite antenna; Microdyne & Scientific-Atlanta satellite receivers.
Miles of plant: 262.0 (coaxial). Homes passed: 10,159.
Manager: Buddy Timmons. Chief technician: Larry Camp.
City fee: 3% of gross.
Ownership: Charter Communications Inc. (MSO).

GASTON—Pine Tree Cablevision, 2628 Millwood Ave., Columbia, SC 29205. Phone: 803-799-6226. Fax: 803-799-8804. County: Lexington. Also serves Lexington County (unincorporated areas). ICA: SC0080.
TV Market Ranking: 100. Franchise award date: N.A. Franchise expiration date: N.A. Began: June 1, 1989.
Channel capacity: 36. Channels available but not in use: N.A.
Basic Service
Subscribers: 327.
Programming (received off-air): WACH (F), WIS (N), WLTX (C), WOLO-TV (A), WRLK-TV (P) Columbia.
Programming (via satellite): C-SPAN; CNN; ESPN; Fox Family Channel; Headline News; Home Shopping Network; Lifetime; Nashville Network; Nickelodeon; TBS Superstation; USA Network.
Fee: $14.95 monthly.
Pay Service 1
Pay Units: 111.
Programming (via satellite): Disney Channel; HBO; Showtime.
Fee: $9.95 monthly (each).
Homes passed: 850.
Manager: Tony Wilson.
Ownership: Pine Tree Cablevision (MSO). Purchased from Cable Synergy TV LP, October 1, 1998.

GEORGETOWN—Alert Cable TV of South Carolina Inc., Box 615, N. Georgetown Plaza, Hwy. 701, Georgetown, SC 29440. Phone: 843-546-2475. Fax: 843-546-1851. County: Georgetown. Also serves Andrews, Georgetown County. ICA: SC0029.
TV Market Ranking: Below 100 (Georgetown, portions of Georgetown County); Outside TV Markets (Andrews, portions of Georgetown County). Franchise award date: February 15, 1968. Franchise expiration date: N.A. Began: May 1, 1969.
Channel capacity: 36 (not 2-way capable). Channels available but not in use: N.A.
Basic Service
Subscribers: 4,505; Commercial subscribers: 40.
Programming (received off-air): WCBD-TV (N), WCIV (A), WCSC-TV (C), WITV (P), WTAT-TV (F,U) Charleston; WIS (N) Columbia; WBTW (C), WPDE-TV (A) Florence.
Programming (via satellite): A & E; American Movie Classics; BET; C-SPAN; CNBC; CNN; Country Music TV; Discovery Channel; ESPN; Fox Family Channel; Home Shopping Network; Lifetime; MTV; Nashville Network; Nickelodeon; Odyssey; TBS Superstation; The Weather Channel; Trinity Bcstg. Network; Turner Network TV; USA Network; VH1.
Current originations: Leased access.
Fee: $50.00 installation; $20.50 monthly; $3.00 converter; $25.00 additional installation.
Pay Service 1
Pay Units: 152.
Programming (via satellite): Disney Channel.
Fee: $40.00 installation; $9.95 monthly.
Pay Service 2
Pay Units: 876.
Programming (via satellite): HBO.
Fee: $40.00 installation; $12.95 monthly.
Pay Service 3
Pay Units: 72.
Programming (via satellite): Playboy TV.
Fee: $40.00 installation; $10.50 monthly.
Pay Service 4
Pay Units: 212.
Programming (via satellite): Showtime.
Fee: $40.00 installation; $9.95 monthly.
Pay Service 5
Pay Units: 245.
Programming (via satellite): The Movie Channel.
Fee: $40.00 installation; $10.95 monthly.
Local advertising: Yes. Rates: $2.00/Month/Line.
Equipment: Scientific-Atlanta headend; GTE Sylvania amplifiers; Times Fiber & Belden cable; GTE Sylvania, Jerrold & Panasonic set top converters; Arcom traps; Scientific-Atlanta & Microdyne satellite antenna; Scientific-Atlanta satellite receivers.
Miles of plant: 136.0 (coaxial). Homes passed: 6,093.
Manager: Dennis Davis. Chief technician: Larry Brothers. Marketing director: Dale Ordoyne.
City fee: 3% of gross.
Ownership: Time Warner Cable (MSO).

GILBERT—Pond Branch Cable, 121 Centerville Rd., Gilbert, SC 29054. Phone: 803-892-6600. Fax: 803-892-5592. Counties: Aiken, Lexington & Saluda. Also serves Aiken County (portions), Lake Murray, Lexington County (northwestern portion), Ridge Spring, Saluda County (eastern portion), Summit. ICA: SC0148.
TV Market Ranking: 100 (Aiken County, Gilbert, Lake Murray, Lexington County, Saluda County, Summit); Below 100 (Aiken County, Ridge Spring). Franchise award date: N.A. Franchise expiration date: N.A. Began: November 29, 1991.
Channel capacity: N.A. Channels available but not in use: N.A.
Basic Service
Subscribers: 647.
Programming (received off-air): WACH (F), WIS (N), WLTX (C), WOLO-TV (A), WRLK-TV (P) Columbia.
Programming (via satellite): WGN-TV (W) Chicago; CNN; Discovery Channel; ESPN; Fox Family Channel; Nashville Network; TBS Superstation; Turner Network TV; USA Network.
Fee: $25.00 installation; $15.75 monthly.
Pay Service 1
Pay Units: 52.
Programming (via satellite): Cinemax.
Fee: $11.55 monthly.

Pay Service 2
Pay Units: 77.
Programming (via satellite): Disney Channel.
Fee: $7.35 monthly.
Pay Service 3
Pay Units: 150.
Programming (via satellite): HBO.
Fee: $11.55 monthly.
Miles of plant: 40.0 (coaxial). Homes passed: 750.
Manager: Tim Martin. Chief technician: Sandy Harmon.
Ownership: Pond Branch Cable. Purchased from Community Cable Services Inc.

GRAY COURT—Charter Communications, Box 367, Simpsonville, SC 29681. Phone: 864-963-3676. Fax: 864-963-2673. Counties: Greenville, Laurens & Spartanburg. Also serves Clinton, Enoree, Fountain Inn, Greenville County, Laurens County, Mauldin, Owings, Simpsonville, Woodruff. ICA: SC0013.
TV Market Ranking: 46 (Clinton, Enoree, Fountain Inn, Gray Court, Greenville County, portions of Laurens County, Mauldin, Owings, Simpsonville, Woodruff); Outside TV Markets (portions of Laurens County). Franchise award date: N.A. Franchise expiration date: N.A. Began: N.A.
Channel capacity: 60 (2-way capable; not operating 2-way). Channels available but not in use: 7.
Basic Service
Subscribers: 25,909; Commercial subscribers: 125.
Programming (received off-air): WFBC-TV (W) Anderson; WGGS-TV (I), WNTV (P) Greenville; WHNS (F,U), WLOS (A), WSPA-TV (C), WYFF (N) Greenville-Spartanburg-Asheville.
Programming (via satellite): WGN-TV (W) Chicago; TBS Superstation; TV Guide Channel.
Current originations: Public access; educational access; leased access.
Fee: $40.00 installation.
Expanded Basic Service
Subscribers: 23,483.
Programming (via satellite): A & E; American Movie Classics; BET; C-SPAN; CNBC; CNN; Cartoon Network; Comedy Central; Country Music TV; Court TV; Discovery Channel; E! Entertainment TV; ESPN; ESPN 2; FX; Fox Family Channel; Fox Sports Net South; Golf Channel; Headline News; History Channel; Home Shopping Network; Learning Channel; Lifetime; MTV; Nashville Network; Nickelodeon; QVC; Sci-Fi Channel; The Weather Channel; Turner Network TV; USA Network; VH1.
Fee: $15.00 installation; $5.50 monthly.
Pay Service 1
Pay Units: 2,197.
Programming (via satellite): Cinemax.
Fee: $10.00 installation; $10.95 monthly.
Pay Service 2
Pay Units: 1,713.
Programming (via satellite): Disney Channel.
Fee: $7.95 monthly.
Pay Service 3
Pay Units: 4,705.
Programming (via satellite): HBO.
Fee: $10.00 installation; $10.95 monthly.
Pay Service 4
Pay Units: 1,159.
Programming (via satellite): The Movie Channel.
Fee: $10.95 monthly.
Pay Service 5
Pay Units: 1,955.
Programming (via satellite): Showtime.
Fee: $10.95 monthly.
Pay-Per-View
Addressable homes: 5,912.
Hot Choice; Playboy TV; Viewer's Choice.
Local advertising: Yes. Available in locally originated, character-generated & taped programming. Local sales manager: John Hood.
Program Guide: The Cable Guide.
Equipment: Scientific-Atlanta headend; Scientific-Atlanta amplifiers; Comm/Scope cable; Texscan character generator; Panasonic set top converters; Zenith addressable set top converters; Eagle, Northeast Filter & Pico traps; Zenith addressable traps; Scientific-Atlanta satellite antenna; Scientific-Atlanta satellite receivers; Sony commercial insert.
Miles of plant: 750.0 (coaxial); 195.0 (fiber optic). Additional miles planned: 100.0 (coaxial). Homes passed: 37,000.
V.P., Operations: Buddy Timmons. Plant manager: Jeff Berger. Marketing & program director: Tim Morrison.
Franchise fee: 5% of gross.
Ownership: Charter Communications Inc. (MSO).

GREAT FALLS—Great Falls Cable TV, 905 N. Main St., Lancaster, SC 29720. Phone: 803-482-2222. Fax: 803-285-3383. Counties: Chester & Fairfield. Also serves Chester County, Fairfield County (portions). ICA: SC0121.
TV Market Ranking: Below 100. Franchise award date: N.A. Franchise expiration date: January 1, 1997. Began: January 1, 1982.
Channel capacity: 77 (not 2-way capable). Channels available but not in use: 15.
Basic Service
Subscribers: 955.
Programming (received off-air): WJZY (U) Belmont; WBTV (C), WCCB (F), WCNC-TV (N), WSOC-TV (A), WTVI (P) Charlotte; WIS (N) Columbia; WAXN (I) Kannapolis; WFVT (W), WNSC-TV (P) Rock Hill.
Programming (via satellite): ESPN; TBS Superstation; The Weather Channel.
Current originations: Automated time-weather; local sports.
Fee: $25.00 installation (aerial), $45.00 (underground); $10.50 monthly; $1.00 converter.
Expanded Basic Service
Subscribers: 803.
Programming (via satellite): A & E; American Movie Classics; American Sports Classics; BET; C-SPAN; C-SPAN 2; CNN; CNNfn; Cartoon Network; Comedy Central; Country Music TV; Discovery Channel; ESPN 2; FX; Fox Family Channel; Fox Sports Net South; Headline News; History Channel; Home & Garden Television; Home Shopping Network; Learning Channel; Lifetime; Nashville Network; Nick at Nite's TV Land; Nickelodeon; Sci-Fi Chan-

nel; TV Guide Channel; Trinity Bcstg. Network; Turner Network TV; USA Network; VH1.
Fee: $14.55 monthly.
Pay Service 1
Pay Units: 83.
Programming (via satellite): Cinemax (multiplexed).
Fee: $9.95 monthly.
Pay Service 2
Pay Units: 42.
Programming (via satellite): Disney Channel.
Fee: $7.95 monthly.
Pay Service 3
Pay Units: 163.
Programming (via satellite): HBO (multiplexed).
Fee: $9.95 monthly.
Pay Service 4
Pay Units: 74.
Programming (via satellite): Showtime; The Movie Channel.
Fee: $9.95 monthly.
Pay Service 5
Pay Units: 47.
Programming (via satellite): The New Encore.
Fee: $5.95 monthly.
Pay Service 6
Pay Units: 49.
Programming (via satellite): Starz!
Fee: $9.95 monthly.
Pay-Per-View
Addressable homes: 803.
Viewer's Choice 1 & 2; Viewer's Choice 1, 3, 4.
Fee: $3.95 (each).
Local advertising: Yes. Available in satellite distributed, locally originated, character-generated, taped & automated programming. Rates: $9.12/30 Seconds. Local sales manager: John Burnette.
Equipment: C-COR amplifiers; Comm/Scope cable; Scientific-Atlanta set top converters; Scientific-Atlanta addressable set top converters.
Miles of plant: 88.8 (coaxial).
Manager: William C. Beaty Jr. Chief technician: Jim Ghent. Marketing & program director: John M. Barnes Jr. Customer service manager: Sherri Parrish.
City fee: 3% of basic.
Ownership: Catawba Services Inc. (MSO).

GREENVILLE—InterMedia, 17 Lindsay Ave., Greenville, SC 29607-2916. Phone: 864-271-8526. Fax: 864-242-4029. Counties: Greenville, Pickens & Spartanburg. Also serves City View, Easley, Greenville County, Pickens, Spartanburg County (unincorporated areas). ICA: SC0003.
TV Market Ranking: 46. Franchise award date: March 1, 1968. Franchise expiration date: July 25, 2001. Began: March 23, 1972.
Channel capacity: 42. Channels available but not in use: N.A.
Basic Service
Subscribers: 69,136.
Programming (received off-air): WGGS-TV (I), WNTV (P) Greenville; WHNS (F,U), WLOS (A), WSPA-TV (C), WYFF (N) Greenville-Spartanburg-Asheville; allband FM.
Programming (via satellite): WGN-TV (W) Chicago; C-SPAN; Fox Family Channel; TBS Superstation; The Weather Channel.
Current originations: Local news.
Fee: $21.76 installation; $12.31 monthly.
Expanded Basic Service
Subscribers: 55,982.
Programming (via satellite): A & E; American Movie Classics; BET; CNBC; CNN; Country Music TV; ESPN; Goodlife TV Network; Headline News; Lifetime; MTV; Nashville Network; Nickelodeon; USA Network.
Fee: $21.76 installation; $9.83 monthly.
Pay Service 1
Pay Units: N.A.
Programming (via satellite): Cinemax; Disney Channel; HBO; Showtime; The Movie Channel.
Fee: $15.00 installation; $10.95 monthly (Cinemax, Disney, HBO or Showtime).
Local advertising: Yes. Available in satellite distributed programming. Local sales manager: Jeff Carter.
Equipment: Scientific-Atlanta headend; GTE Sylvania, Jerrold & Magnavox amplifiers; Times Fiber cable; GTE Sylvania cameras; Sony VTRs; Jerrold set top converters; Zenith addressable set top converters; Eagle traps; Scientific-Atlanta satellite antenna.
Miles of plant: 1558.4 (coaxial); 128.4 (fiber optic). Additional miles planned: 83.0 (coaxial). Homes passed: 78,780.
Manager: Vic Nicholls. Chief technician: Sam Sullivan. Marketing director: Kirby Brooks.
City fee: 5% of gross.
Ownership: InterMedia Partners (MSO).

GREENWOOD—Northland Cable TV, Box 8069, 235 N. Creek Blvd., Greenwood, SC 29646. Phone: 864-229-5421. Fax: 864-229-6609. Counties: Greenwood & Laurens. Also serves Greenwood County, Laurens County (portions), Ninety-Six. ICA: SC0014.
TV Market Ranking: 46 (Greenwood, portions of Greenwood County, portions of Laurens County); Outside TV Markets (portions of Greenwood County, portions of Laurens County, Ninety-Six). Franchise award date: N.A. Franchise expiration date: June 1, 1997. Began: March 1, 1968.
Channel capacity: 44 (not 2-way capable). Channels available but not in use: 4.
Basic Service
Subscribers: 16,400.
Programming (received off-air): WFBC-TV (W) Anderson; WFXG (F) Augusta; WGGS-TV (I) Greenville; WHNS (F,U), WLOS (A), WSPA-TV (C), WYFF (N) Greenville-Spartanburg-Asheville; WNEH (P) Greenwood; allband FM.
Programming (via satellite): BET; Learning Channel.
Fee: $35.95 installation; $26.45 monthly; $1.03 converter.
Expanded Basic Service
Subscribers: N.A.
Programming (via satellite): WGN-TV (W) Chicago; A & E; American Movie Classics; C-SPAN; C-SPAN 2; CNBC; CNN; Cartoon Network; Country Music TV; Court TV; Discovery Channel; ESPN; ESPN 2; FX; Fox Family Channel; Fox News Channel; Fox Sports Net South; Headline News; History Channel; Home & Garden Television; Home Shopping Network; Lifetime; MSNBC; MTV; Nashville Network; Nick at Nite's TV Land; Nickelodeon; QVC; TBS Superstation; TV Guide Channel; The Inspirational Network; The Weather Channel; Turner Network TV; USA Network; VH1.
Fee: N.A.
Pay Service 1
Pay Units: 8,000.
Programming (via satellite): Cinemax; Disney Channel; HBO (multiplexed); Showtime; The Movie Channel; The New Encore.
Fee: $14.95 installation; $8.95 monthly (Encore), $10.95 monthly (Cinemax, Disney, Showtime or TMC), $12.45 monthly (HBO).
Local advertising: Yes. Regional interconnect: Cable Advertising Sales.
Equipment: Jerrold headend; Theta-Com amplifiers; Comm/Scope cable; Sony VTRs; Jerrold character generator; Vitek traps; Andrew satellite antenna; Hughes satellite receivers.
Miles of plant: 449.0 (coaxial). Additional miles planned: 4.0 (coaxial). Homes passed: 20,277.
Manager: Kevin Barrett. Chief technician: Harold Mathis. Marketing coordinator: Kim Vine.
Ownership: Northland Communications Corp. (MSO).

GREER—Charter Communications, Box 1750, Greer, SC 29652-1750. Phone: 864-877-9683. Counties: Greenville & Spartanburg. Also serves Blue Ridge, Greenville County, Marietta, Spartanburg County. ICA: SC0030.
TV Market Ranking: 46. Franchise award date: N.A. Franchise expiration date: N.A. Began: September 21, 1977.
Channel capacity: 36 (not 2-way capable). Channels available but not in use: None.
Basic Service
Subscribers: 3,385.
Programming (received off-air): WGGS-TV (I), WNTV (P) Greenville; WHNS (F,U), WLOS (A), WSPA-TV (C), WYFF (N) Greenville-Spartanburg-Asheville.
Programming (via satellite): WGN-TV (W) Chicago; A & E; American Movie Classics; C-SPAN; CNBC; CNN; Discovery Channel; ESPN; Fox Family Channel; Headline News; Lifetime; MTV; Nashville Network; Nickelodeon; QVC; TBS Superstation; The Weather Channel; Turner Network TV; USA Network; VH1.
Current originations: Automated time-weather.
Fee: $25.00 installation; $26.45 monthly.
Pay Service 1
Pay Units: 295.
Programming (via satellite): Cinemax.
Fee: $15.00 installation; $9.95 monthly.
Pay Service 2
Pay Units: 150.
Programming (via satellite): Disney Channel.
Fee: $15.00 installation; $7.95 monthly.
Pay Service 3
Pay Units: 1,175.
Programming (via satellite): HBO.
Fee: $15.00 installation; $9.95 monthly.
Pay Service 4
Pay Units: 100.
Programming (via satellite): Showtime.
Fee: $15.00 installation; $9.95 monthly.
Pay Service 5
Pay Units: 185.
Programming (via satellite): The Movie Channel.
Fee: $15.00 installation; $9.95 monthly.
Local advertising: Yes. Available in satellite distributed & character-generated programming.
Program Guide: The Cable Guide.
Equipment: Scientific-Atlanta headend; AEL amplifiers; Comm/Scope cable; Sony cameras; Scientific-Atlanta satellite antenna.
Miles of plant: 93.0 (coaxial). Homes passed: 5,800.
Manager: Buddy Timmons. Chief technician: Barry Green. Marketing director: Tim Morrison.
City fee: 5% of gross.
Ownership: Charter Communications Inc. (MSO).

HAMPTON—Jones Communications, 5515 Abercorn St., Savannah, GA 31405. Phones: 912-354-2813; 800-843-0728. Fax: 912-353-6045. Web site: http://www.jii.com. Counties: Aiken & Hampton. Also serves Brunson, Burnettown, Hampton County (portions), Varnville. ICA: SC0154.
TV Market Ranking: Below 100 (Burnettown); Outside TV Markets (Brunson, Hampton, Varnville). Franchise award date: N.A. Franchise expiration date: N.A. Began: N.A.
Channel capacity: N.A. Channels available but not in use: N.A.
Basic Service
Subscribers: 1,712.
Programming (received off-air): WJBF (A) Augusta; WJWJ-TV (P) Beaufort; WCIV (A), WCSC-TV (C) Charleston; WIS (N) Columbia; WTGS (F) Hardeeville; WJCL (A), WSAV-TV (N), WTOC-TV (C) Savannah.
Programming (via satellite): Court TV; E! Entertainment TV; QVC.
Fee: $52.43 installation; $8.45 monthly.
Expanded Basic Service
Subscribers: 1,681.
Programming (via satellite): WGN-TV (W) Chicago; A & E; BET; CNBC; CNN; Comedy Central; Country Music TV; ESPN; Fox Family Channel; Headline News; Nashville Network; Nickelodeon; The Weather Channel; Trinity Bcstg. Network; Turner Network TV; USA Network.
Fee: $11.25 monthly.
A la Carte 1
Subscribers: N.A.
Programming (via satellite): American Movie Classics; Discovery Channel; TBS Superstation.
Fee: N.A.
Pay Service 1
Pay Units: N.A.
Programming (via satellite): Disney Channel; HBO; The Movie Channel.
Fee: N.A.
Ownership: Jones Intercable Inc. (MSO). Purchased from Time Warner Cable.

HARDEEVILLE—Hargray CATV Co. Inc., Box 700, Ridgeland, SC 29936. Phone: 843-784-6411. County: Jasper. ICA: SC0122.
TV Market Ranking: Below 100. Franchise award date: N.A. Franchise expiration date: N.A. Began: April 1, 1983.
Channel capacity: 36. Channels available but not in use: 21.
Basic Service
Subscribers: 581.
Programming (received off-air): WJWJ-TV (P) Beaufort; WCSC-TV (C) Charleston; WJCL (A), WSAV-TV (N), WTOC-TV (C) Savannah.
Programming (via satellite): WGN-TV (W) Chicago; CNN; ESPN; Fox Family Channel; Nashville Network; Nickelodeon; TBS Superstation; USA Network.
Fee: $13.65 monthly.
Pay Service 1
Pay Units: N.A.
Programming (via satellite): Cinemax; HBO.
Fee: $9.95 monthly (each).
Equipment: Scientific-Atlanta headend; Scientific-Atlanta cable; Scientific-Atlanta satellite antenna; Scientific-Atlanta satellite receivers.
Miles of plant included with Ridgeland, SC.
Manager: Frank Semken. Chief technician: Kerry Asher.
Ownership: Hargray Telephone Co. (MSO).

HARTSVILLE—Century Cable, Box 1069, 1920 W. BoBo Newsome Hwy., Hartsville, SC 29550. Phone: 803-332-0195. Fax: 843-383-6253. County: Darlington. Also serves Darlington County (unincorporated areas), Kellytown, Pineridge. ICA: SC0025.

TV Market Ranking: Below 100. Franchise award date: N.A. Franchise expiration date: May 12, 2005. Began: June 1, 1967.
Channel capacity: 62 (not 2-way capable). Channels available but not in use: 8.
Basic Service
Subscribers: 6,764.
Programming (received off-air): WCNC-TV (N), WSOC-TV (A) Charlotte; WACH (F), WIS (N) Columbia; WBTW (C), WJPM-TV (P), WPDE-TV (A), WWMB (U) Florence; 12 FMs.
Programming (via satellite): A & E; American Movie Classics; BET; C-SPAN; CNBC; CNN; Cartoon Network; Country Music TV; ESPN; ESPN 2; FX; Fox Family Channel; Headline News; Home Shopping Network; Learning Channel; Lifetime; MTV; Nickelodeon; QVC; Sci-Fi Channel; TV Guide Channel; The Inspirational Network; The Weather Channel; Turner Classic Movies; Turner Network TV; USA Network; VH1.
Fee: $23.14 installation; $27.09 monthly.
Expanded Basic Service
Subscribers: 6,508.
Programming (via satellite): Discovery Channel; History Channel; Nashville Network; TBS Superstation.
Fee: $5.75 monthly.
Pay Service 1
Pay Units: 305.
Programming (via satellite): Cinemax.
Fee: $10.00 installation; $11.50 monthly.
Pay Service 2
Pay Units: 116.
Programming (via satellite): Disney Channel.
Fee: $10.50 monthly.
Pay Service 3
Pay Units: 545.
Programming (via satellite): HBO.
Fee: $12.50 monthly.
Pay Service 4
Pay Units: 189.
Programming (via satellite): Showtime.
Fee: $11.50 monthly.
Local advertising: No.
Equipment: Scientific-Atlanta headend; Theta-Com amplifiers; Comm/Scope cable; Hamlin set top converters; Anixter-Mark & Scientific-Atlanta satellite antenna; Scientific-Atlanta satellite receivers.
Miles of plant: 210.0 (coaxial). Homes passed: 11,791. Total homes in franchised area: 12,000.
Manager: Kevin S. Barrett. Chief technician: Oscar A. Herringdine. Customer service manager: Caroljean Abbott.
City fee: 3% of gross.
Ownership: Century Communications Corp. (MSO). See Cable System Ownership.

HARTWELL VILLAS—Charter Communications, 202 Campbell St., Belton, SC 29627. Phone: 803-338-9975. Fax: 803-487-5075. County: Anderson. Also serves Anderson County (unincorporated areas). ICA: SC0123.
TV Market Ranking: 46. Franchise award date: N.A. Franchise expiration date: N.A. Began: N.A.
Channel capacity: N.A. Channels available but not in use: N.A.
Basic Service
Subscribers: 65.
Programming (received off-air): WGGS-TV (I), WNTV (P) Greenville; WHNS (F,U), WLOS (A), WSPA-TV (C), WYFF (N) Greenville-Spartanburg-Asheville.
Programming (via satellite): CNN; ESPN; Nashville Network; TBS Superstation; Turner Network TV; USA Network.
Fee: $40.00 installation; $15.95 monthly.
Pay Service 1
Pay Units: 19.
Programming (via satellite): HBO.
Fee: $11.95 monthly.
Miles of plant: 1.0 (coaxial). Homes passed: 69.
Manager: Joe Haight. Marketing & program director: Tim Morrison.
Ownership: Charter Communications Inc. (MSO).

HILDA—Galaxy Cablevision, 1899 S.E. 58th Ave., Ocala, FL 34471-5847. Phone: 352-624-1117. Counties: Bamberg & Barnwell. Also serves Bamberg County (portions), Barnwell County (portions), Olar. ICA: SC0091.
TV Market Ranking: Outside TV Markets. Franchise award date: N.A. Franchise expiration date: June 3, 2004. Began: N.A.
Channel capacity: 30. Channels available but not in use: None.
Basic Service
Subscribers: 258.
Programming (received off-air): WEBA-TV (P) Allendale; WAGT (N), WJBF (A), WRDW-TV (C) Augusta; WIS (N) Columbia.
Programming (via satellite): WGN-TV (W) Chicago; A & E; BET; CNN; Discovery Channel; E! Entertainment TV; ESPN; Fox Family Channel; Lifetime; Nashville Network; Nickelodeon; QVC; TBS Superstation; The Weather Channel; Turner Network TV; USA Network; VH1.
Fee: $30.00 installation; $27.00 monthly.
Pay Service 1
Pay Units: 72.
Programming (via satellite): Cinemax.
Fee: $10.95 monthly.
Pay Service 2
Pay Units: 30.
Programming (via satellite): Disney Channel.
Fee: $10.95 monthly.
Pay Service 3
Pay Units: 86.
Programming (via satellite): HBO.
Fee: $10.95 monthly.
Local advertising: No.
Miles of plant: 29.1 (coaxial). Homes passed: 611.
State manager: Dan Labbe. Technical manager: Joe Ferrell.
Ownership: Galaxy Cablevision (MSO).

HILTON HEAD ISLAND—Adelphia Cable, 12 Pope Ave., Hilton Head Island, SC 29928-4708. Phone: 843-785-5175. Fax: 843-686-6474. County: Beaufort. Also serves Beaufort County. ICA: SC0010.
TV Market Ranking: Below 100. Franchise award date: N.A. Franchise expiration date: N.A. Began: March 29, 1972.
Channel capacity: 35 (2-way capable; operating 2-way partially). Channels available but not in use: None.
Basic Service
Subscribers: 16,498; Commercial subscribers: 3,466.
Programming (received off-air): WJWJ-TV (P) Beaufort; WCSC-TV (C) Charleston; WTGS (F) Hardeeville; WJCL (A), WSAV-TV (N), WTOC-TV (C), WVAN-TV (P) Savannah.
Programming (via satellite): C-SPAN; QVC; TBS Superstation.
Current originations: Automated time-weather; government access; leased access; automated emergency alert.
Fee: $30.00 installation; $18.95 monthly; $3.00 converter; $15.00 additional installation.
Commercial fee: $2.25 monthly.
Expanded Basic Service
Subscribers: N.A.
Programming (via satellite): A & E; American Movie Classics; Animal Planet; BET; Bravo; C-SPAN 2; CNNfn; Country Music TV; Discovery Channel; ESPN; ESPN 2; EWTN; FX; Fox Sports Net South; History Channel; Home & Garden Television; Home Shopping Network; Learning Channel; Lifetime; MSNBC; MTV; Nashville Network; Nick at Nite's TV Land; Nickelodeon; Product Information Network; Sci-Fi Channel; TV Food Network; TV Guide Channel; The Health Network; The Inspirational Network; Turner Network TV; USA Network; VH1.
Fee: N.A.
A la Carte 1
Subscribers: N.A.
Programming (via satellite): WGN-TV (W) Chicago; CNBC; CNN; Fox Family Channel; Headline News; The Weather Channel.
Fee: N.A.
Pay Service 1
Pay Units: N.A.
Programming (via satellite): Cinemax; Golf Channel.
Fee: $25.00 installation; $12.50 monthly (Cinemax).
Pay Service 2
Pay Units: 530.
Programming (via satellite): Disney Channel.
Fee: $10.00 monthly.
Pay Service 3
Pay Units: 3,325.
Programming (via satellite): HBO.
Fee: $12.50 monthly.
Pay Service 4
Pay Units: 715.
Programming (via satellite): Showtime.
Fee: $12.50 monthly.
Local advertising: Yes. Rates: $29.00/Minute; $17.00/30 Seconds.
Equipment: Scientific-Atlanta headend; C-COR, GTE Sylvania & Jerrold amplifiers; Comm/Scope & Times Fiber cable; JVC cameras; JVC & Sony VTRs; MSI character generator; Hamlin set top converters; Simulsat satellite antenna; Microdyne & Scientific-Atlanta satellite receivers.
Miles of plant: 535.0 (coaxial). Additional miles planned: 22.0 (coaxial). Homes passed: 23,111. Total homes in franchised area: 23,111.
Manager: Donna Tuggle.
City fee: 3% of gross.
Ownership: Adelphia Communications Corp. (MSO).

HOLLY HILL—Phoenix Cable, Box 1729, Fairfield Glade, TN 38558. Phone: 800-228-8296. Fax: 931-456-1913. County: Orangeburg. Also serves Eutawville, Orangeburg County (unincorporated areas). ICA: SC0088.
TV Market Ranking: 100 (portions of Orangeburg County); Outside TV Markets (Eutawville, Holly Hill, portions of Orangeburg County). Franchise award date: January 1, 1981. Franchise expiration date: N.A. Began: January 1, 1983.
Channel capacity: 35. Channels available but not in use: N.A.
Basic Service
Subscribers: N.A.
Programming (received off-air): WCBD-TV (N), WCIV (A), WCSC-TV (C), WITV (P), WMMP (U), WTAT-TV (F,U) Charleston; WIS (N), WLTX (C) Columbia.
Programming (via satellite): WGN-TV (W) Chicago; A & E; BET; CNN; Discovery Channel; ESPN; ESPN 2; Fox Family Channel; History Channel; Home & Garden Television; Learning Channel; Lifetime; Nashville Network; Nickelodeon; QVC; TBS Superstation; The Weather Channel; Trinity Bcstg. Network; Turner Classic Movies; Turner Network TV; USA Network.
Fee: $22.44 monthly.
Pay Service 1
Pay Units: N.A.
Programming (via satellite): Cinemax; Disney Channel; HBO; Showtime; The Movie Channel.
Fee: $9.00 monthly (Cinemax, Disney or TMC), $12.00 monthly (HBO).
Equipment: Scientific-Atlanta headend; Scientific-Atlanta cable; Scientific-Atlanta satellite antenna; Scientific-Atlanta satellite receivers.
Miles of plant: 16.0 (coaxial). Homes passed: 700.
Manager: Helen P. Belisle. Chief technician: Clarence Roberts.
Ownership: Phoenix Cable Inc. (MSO).

HOLLYWOOD—US Cable Coastal Properties, Box 469, Johns Island, SC 29457. Phone: 843-559-2424. County: Charleston. Also serves Ravenel. ICA: SC0061.
TV Market Ranking: Below 100. Franchise award date: N.A. Franchise expiration date: N.A. Began: N.A.
Channel capacity: N.A. Channels available but not in use: N.A.
Basic Service
Subscribers: 1,064.
Programming (received off-air): WCBD-TV (N), WCIV (A), WCSC-TV (C), WITV (P), WMMP (U), WTAT-TV (F,U) Charleston.
Programming (via satellite): BET; C-SPAN; C-SPAN 2; Home Shopping Network; MuchMoreMusic; Trinity Bcstg. Network.
Fee: $75.51 installation; $10.92 monthly.
Expanded Basic Service
Subscribers: 1,025.
Programming (via satellite): A & E; CNBC; CNN; Comedy Central; Disney Channel; ESPN; Fox Family Channel; Fox Sports Net South; Headline News; History Channel; Home & Garden Television; Learning Channel; Lifetime; MSNBC; MTV; Nashville Network; Nick at Nite's TV Land; Nickelodeon; The Weather Channel; Travel Channel; Turner Classic Movies; Turner Network TV; USA Network; VH1.
Fee: $15.11 monthly.
Expanded Basic Service 2
Subscribers: N.A.
Programming (via satellite): WGN-TV (W) Chicago; American Movie Classics; Discovery Channel; TBS Superstation.
Fee: $2.45 monthly.
Pay Service 1
Pay Units: N.A.
Programming (via satellite): Cinemax; Disney Channel; HBO; Showtime.
Fee: $9.50 monthly (each).
Equipment: Scientific-Atlanta headend; Texscan amplifiers; Times Fiber cable; Jerrold set top converters; Intercept traps; Scientific-Atlanta satellite antenna; Scientific-Atlanta satellite receivers.
Miles of plant: 102.2 (coaxial). Homes passed: 2,659.
Manager: Randy Houser. Chief technician: Ray Kirkendall.
Ownership: US Cable Corp. (MSO).

HOMEWOOD—Horry Telephone Cablevision, Box 1820, 3480 Hwy. 701 N, Conway, SC 29528-1820. Phones: 843-365-2151; 843-365-2154. Fax: 843-365-1111. Web site: http://www.sccoast.net. Counties: Georgetown & Horry. Also serves Aynor, Bucksport, Conway (rural portions), Longs, Loris, Murrells Inlet, North Myrtle Beach, Socastee, Wampee. ICA: SC0016.

TV Market Ranking: Below 100. Franchise award date: January 1, 1980. Franchise expiration date: January 1, 2005. Began: October 11, 1983.
Channel capacity: N.A. Channels available but not in use: None.
Basic Service
Subscribers: 25,206.
Programming (received off-air): WCSC-TV (C) Charleston; WIS (N) Columbia; WHMC (P) Conway; WBTW (C), WPDE-TV (A), WWMB (U) Florence; WFXB (F) Myrtle Beach; WECT (N) Wilmington.
Programming (via satellite): WGN-TV (W) Chicago; Fox Family Channel; Headline News; QVC; TBS Superstation; TV Guide Channel.
Current originations: Educational access; government access.
Fee: $35.00 installation; $10.00 monthly; $2.50 converter.
Expanded Basic Service
Subscribers: 24,558.
Programming (via satellite): A & E; American Movie Classics; BET; C-SPAN; CNBC; CNN; Cartoon Network; Comedy Central; Country Music TV; Court TV; Discovery Channel; Disney Channel; E! Entertainment TV; ESPN; ESPN 2; Fox Sports Net South; Golf Channel; Goodlife TV Network; History Channel; Home & Garden Television; Learning Channel; Lifetime; MTV; Nashville Network; Nick at Nite's TV Land; Nickelodeon; Sci-Fi Channel; Speedvision; The Weather Channel; Trinity Bcstg. Network; Turner Classic Movies; Turner Network TV; USA Network; VH1.
Fee: $15.00 monthly.
Pay Service 1
Pay Units: 3,373.
Programming (via satellite): HBO (multiplexed).
Fee: $5.00 installation; $9.50 monthly.
Pay Service 2
Pay Units: 1,787.
Programming (via satellite): Showtime (multiplexed).
Fee: $5.00 installation; $9.50 monthly.
Pay Service 3
Pay Units: N.A.
Programming (via satellite): DMX; Flix; The Movie Channel.
Fee: $3.95 monthly (Flix), $9.50 monthly (TMC), $9.95 monthly (DMX).
Pay-Per-View
Addressable homes: 11,700.
Hot Choice; Viewer's Choice 1 & 2; movies; special events.
Varies.
Local advertising: Planned.
Program Guide: Premium Channels.
Equipment: Jerrold, M/A-Com & Microdyne headend; C-COR amplifiers; Comm/Scope cable; Scientific-Atlanta addressable set top converters; Microdyne satellite antenna; Microdyne satellite receivers.
Miles of plant: 1500.0 (coaxial); None (fiber optic). Additional miles planned: 70.0 (coaxial). Homes passed: 28,000. Total homes in franchised area: 28,000.
Manager: Curley Huggins. Chief technician: Jim Morgan. Marketing director: Debby Broles.
County fee: 3% of gross.
Ownership: Horry Telephone Cooperative Inc.

HOPKINS—Pine Tree Cablevision, 2628 Millwood Ave., Columbia, SC 29205. Phone: 803-799-6226. Fax: 803-799-8804. County: Richland. Also serves Eastover, Gadsden. ICA: SC0156.
TV Market Ranking: 100. Franchise award date: N.A. Franchise expiration date: N.A. Began: April 1, 1993.
Channel capacity: N.A. Channels available but not in use: N.A.
Basic Service
Subscribers: 734.
Programming (received off-air): WACH (F), WIS (N), WLTX (C), WOLO-TV (A), WRLK-TV (P) Columbia.
Programming (via satellite): WGN-TV (W) Chicago; A & E; BET; C-SPAN; CNN; Cartoon Network; Country Music TV; Discovery Channel; ESPN; ESPN 2; Fox Family Channel; Fox Sports Net South; Headline News; Home Shopping Network; Learning Channel; Lifetime; MTV; Nashville Network; Nickelodeon; Sci-Fi Channel; TBS Superstation; The Weather Channel; Trinity Bcstg. Network; Turner Classic Movies; Turner Network TV; USA Network; VH1.
Current originations: Public access.
Fee: $35.00 installation; $26.10 monthly.
Pay Service 1
Pay Units: N.A.
Programming (via satellite): Disney Channel; HBO; Showtime; The Movie Channel.
Fee: $7.85 monthly (Disney), $9.95 monthly (HBO or Showtime), $12.95 monthly (Showtime & TMC).
Manager: Tony Wilson.
Ownership: Pine Tree Cablevision (MSO).

IVA—Charter Communications, 202 Campbell St., Belton, SC 29627. Phone: 803-338-9975. County: Anderson. Also serves Anderson County (portions), Chambert Forest, Starr. ICA: SC0125.
TV Market Ranking: 46. Franchise award date: N.A. Franchise expiration date: N.A. Began: July 1, 1983.
Channel capacity: 30 (2-way capable; operating 2-way). Channels available but not in use: N.A.
Basic Service
Subscribers: 1,205.
Programming (received off-air): WGGS-TV (I), WNTV (P) Greenville; WHNS (F,U), WLOS (A), WSPA-TV (C), WYFF (N) Greenville-Spartanburg-Asheville; WNEG-TV (I) Toccoa.
Programming (via satellite): WGN-TV (W) Chicago; ESPN; TBS Superstation; The Weather Channel.
Fee: $9.86 monthly.
Expanded Basic Service
Subscribers: 1,190.
Programming (via satellite): Country Music TV; Discovery Channel; Electronic Program Guide; Fox Sports Net South; Goodlife TV Network; Headline News; MTV; Nashville Network; Nickelodeon; Turner Network TV; USA Network.
Fee: $44.19 installation; $11.20 monthly.
Pay Service 1
Pay Units: 129.
Programming (via satellite): Cinemax.
Fee: $14.73 installation; $9.95 monthly.
Pay Service 2
Pay Units: 59.
Programming (via satellite): Disney Channel.
Fee: $8.95 monthly.
Pay Service 3
Pay Units: 176.
Programming (via satellite): HBO.
Fee: $11.95 monthly.
Pay Service 4
Pay Units: 104.
Programming (via satellite): Showtime.
Fee: $9.95 monthly.
Local advertising: No.
Equipment: Blonder-Tongue headend; Jerrold amplifiers; Comm/Scope cable; Eagle & Pico traps; Anixter satellite antenna; M/A-Com & Prodelin satellite receivers.
Miles of plant: 110.0 (coaxial). Homes passed: 2,600.
Manager: Joe Haight. Marketing director: Tim Morrison.
City fee: 3% of gross.
Ownership: Charter Communications Inc. (MSO).

JEFFERSON—Pine Tree Cablevision, 2628 Millwood Ave., Columbia, SC 29205. Phone: 803-799-6226. Fax: 803-799-8804. County: Chesterfield. ICA: SC0126.
TV Market Ranking: Outside TV Markets. Franchise award date: N.A. Franchise expiration date: N.A. Began: December 1, 1986.
Channel capacity: 36. Channels available but not in use: N.A.
Basic Service
Subscribers: 250.
Programming (received off-air): WBTV (C), WCCB (F), WSOC-TV (A) Charlotte; WIS (N) Columbia; WBTW (C), WPDE-TV (A) Florence; WNTV (P) Greenville; WNSC-TV (P) Rock Hill.
Fee: N.A.
Manager: Tony Wilson.
Ownership: Pine Tree Cablevision (MSO). Purchased from Cable Synergy TV LP, October 1, 1998.

JOHNS ISLAND—US Cable Coastal Properties, Box 469, Johns Island, SC 29455-0469. Phone: 843-559-2424. Counties: Beaufort & Charleston. Also serves Kiawah Island, Seabrook Island, Wadmalaw Island. ICA: SC0054.
TV Market Ranking: Below 100. Franchise award date: January 1, 1983. Franchise expiration date: January 1, 2004. Began: December 1, 1983.
Channel capacity: N.A. Channels available but not in use: N.A.
Basic Service
Subscribers: 5,363.
Programming (received off-air): WCBD-TV (N), WCIV (A), WCSC-TV (C), WITV (P), WMMP (U), WTAT-TV (F,U) Charleston.
Programming (via satellite): BET; C-SPAN; C-SPAN 2; Learning Channel; TV Guide Channel; Trinity Bcstg. Network.
Fee: $75.51 installation; $10.69 monthly.
Expanded Basic Service
Subscribers: 4,956.
Programming (via satellite): A & E; Bravo; CNBC; CNN; Comedy Central; Disney Channel; E! Entertainment TV; ESPN; ESPN 2; FX; Fox Family Channel; Fox Sports Net South; Golf Channel; Headline News; History Channel; Home Shopping Network; Lifetime; MSNBC; MTV; Nashville Network; Nickelodeon; Speedvision; The Weather Channel; Travel Channel; Turner Classic Movies; Turner Network TV; USA Network; VH1.
Fee: $18.32 monthly.
Expanded Basic Service 2
Subscribers: N.A.
Programming (via satellite): WGN-TV (W) Chicago; American Movie Classics; Discovery Channel; TBS Superstation.
Fee: $2.45 monthly.
Pay Service 1
Pay Units: N.A.
Programming (via satellite): Cinemax; HBO; Showtime.
Fee: $5.00 installation; $9.50 monthly (each).
Local advertising: Yes. Available in character-generated programming.
Program Guide: TV Blue Print.
Equipment: Scientific-Atlanta headend; Scientific-Atlanta amplifiers; Times Fiber cable; Texscan character generator; Jerrold set top converters; Arcom traps; Scientific-Atlanta satellite antenna.
Miles of plant: 275.1 (coaxial). Homes passed: 8,189.
Manager: Randy Houser. Chief technician: Ray Kirkendall.
Ownership: US Cable Corp. (MSO).

JOHNSONVILLE—Time Warner Cable, Drawer 1479, 116 Epps St., Lake City, SC 29560. Phone: 843-394-8231. Fax: 843-394-3722. Counties: Florence & Williamsburg. Also serves Florence County, Hemingway, Williamsburg County. ICA: SC0057.
TV Market Ranking: Below 100 (Florence County, Hemingway, Johnsonville, portions of Williamsburg County); Outside TV Markets (portions of Williamsburg County). Franchise award date: April 1, 1980. Franchise expiration date: March 6, 2005. Began: November 1, 1981.
Channel capacity: 60 (not 2-way capable). Channels available but not in use: 14.
Basic Service
Subscribers: 1,196.
Programming (received off-air): WCBD-TV (N), WCIV (A), WCSC-TV (C), WTAT-TV (F,U) Charleston; WIS (N) Columbia; WBTW (C), WPDE-TV (A), WWMB (U) Florence; WRJA-TV (P) Sumter.
Programming (via satellite): WGN-TV (W) Chicago; A & E; American Movie Classics; BET; C-SPAN; CNBC; CNN; Cartoon Network; Comedy Central; Country Music TV; Court TV; Discovery Channel; ESPN; ESPN 2; Fox Family Channel; Headline News; History Channel; Home Shopping Network; Lifetime; MSNBC; MTV; Nashville Network; Nickelodeon; TBS Superstation; TV Food Network; The Inspirational Network; The Weather Channel; Turner Classic Movies; Turner Network TV; USA Network; VH1.
Fee: $49.95 installation (aerial), $69.95 (underground); $27.88 monthly; $2.00 converter; $19.95 additional installation.
Pay Service 1
Pay Units: 29.
Programming (via satellite): Disney Channel.
Fee: $19.95 installation; $9.95 monthly.
Pay Service 2
Pay Units: 106.
Programming (via satellite): HBO.
Fee: $19.95 installation; $12.95 monthly.
Pay Service 3
Pay Units: 68.
Programming (via satellite): Showtime.
Fee: $19.95 installation; $10.95 monthly.
Local advertising: Yes.
Program Guide: Premium Channels.
Equipment: Scientific-Atlanta, DX Engineering & Jerrold headend; Scientific-Atlanta amplifiers; Times Fiber cable; Monroe character generator; Oak, Intercept & Jerrold set top converters; Eagle, Pico & Northeast Filter traps; Scientific-Atlanta & Harris satellite antenna; Scientific-Atlanta & DX Antenna satellite receivers.
Miles of plant: 53.2 (coaxial); None (fiber optic). Homes passed: 1,558. Total homes in franchised area: 2,000.
Manager: Kurt Newber. Chief technician: Tommy Martin. Marketing director: Donna Waller. Customer service manager: Robin Hewitt.
City fee: 3% of gross.
Ownership: Time Warner Cable (MSO).

KERSHAW—Enstar Cable TV, 310 10th St., North Wilkesboro, NC 28659-4112. Phone: 910-667-4151. Counties: Kershaw & Lancaster. Also serves Heath Springs, Lancaster County (portions). ICA: SC0127.
TV Market Ranking: 42 (portions of Lancaster County); Below 100 (Heath Springs, por-

tions of Lancaster County); Outside TV Markets (Kershaw, portions of Lancaster County). Franchise award date: N.A. Franchise expiration date: November 15, 2002. Began: March 1, 1984.
Channel capacity: 35 (not 2-way capable). Channels available but not in use: None.
Basic Service
Subscribers: 878.
Programming (received off-air): WJZY (U) Belmont; WBTV (C), WCCB (F), WCNC-TV (N), WSOC-TV (A) Charlotte; WIS (N), WLTX (C), WOLO-TV (A) Columbia; WBTW (C), WJPM-TV (P) Florence; WFVT (W) Rock Hill.
Programming (via satellite): American Movie Classics; Bravo; Country Music TV; ESPN; Learning Channel; MTV; Nickelodeon; QVC; Sci-Fi Channel; The Weather Channel; Turner Network TV; USA Network.
Fee: $25.00 installation; $20.27 monthly; $7.50 additional installation.
Expanded Basic Service
Subscribers: 870.
Programming (via satellite): CNN; Discovery Channel; Headline News; Nashville Network.
Fee: $1.69 monthly.
Expanded Basic Service 2
Subscribers: 863.
Programming (via satellite): WGN-TV (W) Chicago; Disney Channel; Fox Family Channel; Home Shopping Network; TBS Superstation.
Fee: $5.25 monthly.
Pay Service 1
Pay Units: 91.
Programming (via satellite): Cinemax.
Fee: $10.95 monthly.
Pay Service 2
Pay Units: 129.
Programming (via satellite): HBO.
Fee: $11.95 monthly.
Pay Service 3
Pay Units: 64.
Programming (via satellite): Showtime.
Fee: $10.95 monthly.
Equipment: Scientific-Atlanta, Jerrold & Blonder-Tongue headend; Scientific-Atlanta amplifiers; Scientific-Atlanta set top converters; Eagle & Intercept traps.
Miles of plant: 59.0 (coaxial). Homes passed: 1,545.
Manager: Wanda Parsons. Chief technician: Eddie Collins.
Franchise fee: 3% of gross.
Ownership: Falcon Communications LP (MSO), joint venture formed September 30, 1998. See Cable System Ownership.

KINGSTREE—Time Warner Cable, 1170 N. Guignard Dr., Sumter, SC 29150. Phone: 803-469-2200. Fax: 803-469-2423. County: Williamsburg. Also serves Williamsburg County. ICA: SC0043.
TV Market Ranking: Below 100 (portions of Williamsburg County); Outside TV Markets (Kingstree, portions of Williamsburg County). Franchise award date: April 19, 1977. Franchise expiration date: February 19, 1999. Began: September 1, 1977.
Channel capacity: 41 (not 2-way capable). Channels available but not in use: None.
Basic Service
Subscribers: 2,100.
Programming (received off-air): WCBD-TV (N), WCIV (A), WCSC-TV (C), WTAT-TV (F,U) Charleston; WIS (N) Columbia; WBTW (C), WPDE-TV (A) Florence; WRJA-TV (P) Sumter.
Programming (via satellite): WGN-TV (W) Chicago; Home Shopping Network; MSNBC; QVC.
Fee: $48.00 installation; $29.50 monthly.
Expanded Basic Service
Subscribers: N.A.
Programming (via satellite): A & E; American Movie Classics; BET; C-SPAN; CNBC; Cartoon Network; Comedy Central; Country Music TV; Court TV; Discovery Channel; ESPN; Fox Family Channel; Goodlife TV Network; Headline News; Lifetime; Nashville Network; Nick at Nite; Nickelodeon; TV Food Network; The Weather Channel; Turner Network TV; USA Network; VH1.
Fee: N.A.
A la Carte 1
Subscribers: N.A.
Programming (via satellite): CNN; ESPN 2; TBS Superstation.
Fee: N.A.
Pay Service 1
Pay Units: 400.
Programming (via satellite): HBO.
Fee: $10.95 monthly.
Pay Service 2
Pay Units: 230.
Programming (via satellite): Showtime.
Fee: $6.95 monthly.
Pay Service 3
Pay Units: N.A.
Programming (via satellite): Disney Channel.
Fee: N.A.
Local advertising: No.
Equipment: Scientific-Atlanta headend; Scientific-Atlanta amplifiers; Times Fiber cable; Jerrold & Scientific-Atlanta set top converters; Eagle, Pico & Northeast Filter traps; Scientific-Atlanta satellite antenna.
Miles of plant: 55.0 (coaxial). Homes passed: 2,435.
Manager: James Mott. Chief technician: Glenn Washington. Marketing director: J. J. Jonas.
City fee: 3% of gross.
Ownership: Time Warner Cable (MSO); Advance/Newhouse Partnership (MSO).

LADY'S ISLAND—US Cable Coastal Properties, Box 70193, Beaufort, SC 29902. Phone: 843-522-0784. County: Beaufort. Also serves Dataw Island, St. Helena Island. ICA: SC0056.
TV Market Ranking: Below 100. Franchise award date: N.A. Franchise expiration date: N.A. Began: N.A.
Channel capacity: 42 (2-way capable; operating 2-way partially). Channels available but not in use: 1.
Basic Service
Subscribers: 3,847.
Programming (received off-air): WJWJ-TV (P) Beaufort; WCBD-TV (N), WCIV (A), WCSC-TV (C) Charleston; WTGS (F) Hardeeville; WJCL (A), WSAV-TV (N), WTOC-TV (C) Savannah.
Programming (via satellite): BET; C-SPAN; Home Shopping Network; Trinity Bcstg. Network.
Fee: $75.51 installation; $11.31 monthly; $15.00 additional installation.
Expanded Basic Service
Subscribers: 3,558.
Programming (via satellite): A & E; Bravo; CNBC; CNN; ESPN; FX; Fox Family Channel; Fox Sports Net Southwest; Headline News; History Channel; Learning Channel; Lifetime; MTV; Nashville Network; Nickelodeon; Romance Classics; The Weather Channel; Turner Classic Movies; Turner Network TV; USA Network; VH1.
Fee: $15.37 monthly.
Expanded Basic Service 2
Subscribers: N.A.
Programming (via satellite): WGN-TV (W) Chicago; American Movie Classics; Discovery Channel; TBS Superstation.
Fee: $2.25 monthly.
Pay Service 1
Pay Units: N.A.
Programming (via satellite): Cinemax; HBO; Showtime.
Fee: $9.50 monthly (each).
Local advertising: Yes. Regional interconnect: Southern Cable Advertising.
Equipment: Scientific-Atlanta headend; Scientific-Atlanta amplifiers; Times Fiber cable; Jerrold set top converters; Intercept & Arcom traps; Scientific-Atlanta satellite antenna; Scientific-Atlanta satellite receivers.
Miles of plant: 192.4 (coaxial). Homes passed: 6,351.
Manager: Randy Houser. Chief technician: Ray Kirkendall.
Ownership: US Cable Corp. (MSO).

LAKE CITY—Time Warner Cable, Drawer 1479, 116 Epps St., Lake City, SC 29560. Phone: 843-394-8231. Fax: 843-394-3722. County: Florence. Also serves Florence County, Scranton. ICA: SC0128.
TV Market Ranking: Below 100. Franchise award date: March 11, 1969. Franchise expiration date: March 10, 2001. Began: August 1, 1970.
Channel capacity: 53 (not 2-way capable). Channels available but not in use: 13.
Basic Service
Subscribers: 2,405.
Programming (received off-air): WTAT-TV (F,U) Charleston; WIS (N), WLTX (C) Columbia; WBTW (C), WPDE-TV (A), WWMB (U) Florence; WRJA-TV (P) Sumter.
Programming (via satellite): WGN-TV (W) Chicago; A & E; American Movie Classics; BET; C-SPAN; CNBC; CNN; Cartoon Network; Comedy Central; Country Music TV; Court TV; Discovery Channel; ESPN; ESPN 2; Fox Family Channel; Fox Sports Net South; Headline News; History Channel; Home Shopping Network; Lifetime; MSNBC; MTV; Nashville Network; Nickelodeon; Odyssey; QVC; TBS Superstation; TV Food Network; The Weather Channel; Turner Network TV; USA Network; VH1.
Current originations: Automated timeweather; public access.
Fee: $49.95 installation (aerial), $69.95 (underground); $27.88 monthly; $2.00 converter.
Pay Service 1
Pay Units: 95.
Programming (via satellite): Disney Channel.
Fee: $19.95 installation; $9.95 monthly.
Pay Service 2
Pay Units: 340.
Programming (via satellite): HBO.
Fee: $19.95 installation; $12.95 monthly.
Pay Service 3
Pay Units: 148.
Programming (via satellite): Showtime.
Fee: $19.95 installation; $10.95 monthly.
Local advertising: Yes. Local sales manager: Missy Worthington.
Program Guide: Premium Channels.
Equipment: Scientific-Atlanta, DX Antenna & Jerrold headend; Scientific-Atlanta amplifiers; Times Fiber cable; Oak, Intercept & Panasonic set top converters; Eagle, Pico & Northeast Filter traps; Scientific-Atlanta & Harris satellite antenna; Hughes, Scientific-Atlanta & DX Antenna satellite receivers.
Miles of plant: 79.5 (coaxial); None (fiber optic).
Manager: Kurt Newber. Chief technician: Tommy Martin. Marketing director: Donna Waller. Customer service manager: Robin Hewitt.
City fee: 3% of gross.
Ownership: Time Warner Cable (MSO); Advance/Newhouse Partnership (MSO).

LAKE VIEW—Southern Cable, Box 1998, Georgetown, SC 29442-1998. Phone: 843-546-2200. Fax: 803-280-1735. Counties: Dillon & Marion. Also serves Marion County (northern portion), Nichols. ICA: SC0066.
TV Market Ranking: Below 100. Franchise award date: N.A. Franchise expiration date: N.A. Began: August 1, 1988.
Channel capacity: 36. Channels available but not in use: 8.
Basic Service
Subscribers: 707.
Programming (received off-air): WHMC (P) Conway; WFPX (X) Fayetteville; WBTW (C), WPDE-TV (A) Florence; WECT (N) Wilmington.
Programming (via satellite): WGN-TV (W) Chicago; BET; CNN; ESPN; Fox Family Channel; Headline News; Home Shopping Network; MTV; Nashville Network; Nickelodeon; TBS Superstation; The Weather Channel; Turner Network TV; USA Network; VH1.
Current originations: Automated timeweather.
Fee: $17.95 monthly.
Pay Service 1
Pay Units: 165.
Programming (via satellite): Cinemax.
Fee: $10.00 installation; $9.95 monthly.
Pay Service 2
Pay Units: 46.
Programming (via satellite): Disney Channel.
Fee: $9.95 monthly.
Pay Service 3
Pay Units: 174.
Programming (via satellite): HBO.
Fee: $9.95 monthly.
Local advertising: Yes. Available in character-generated programming. Rates: $30/month.
Equipment: Scientific-Atlanta headend; Scientific-Atlanta amplifiers; Times Fiber cable; Scientific-Atlanta satellite receivers.
Miles of plant: 81.0 (coaxial). Homes passed: 1,200.
Manager: Rita Wilson. Chief technician: Greg Williams.
Franchise fee: 3% of gross (Lake View, Nichols).
Ownership: Southern Cable Communications (MSO).

LAMAR—Pine Tree Cablevision, 2628 Millwood Ave., Columbia, SC 29205. Phone: 803-799-6226. Fax: 803-799-8804. County: Darlington. ICA: SC0129.
TV Market Ranking: Below 100. Franchise award date: N.A. Franchise expiration date: N.A. Began: June 1, 1987.
Channel capacity: 36. Channels available but not in use: N.A.
Basic Service
Subscribers: N.A.
Programming (received off-air): WIS (N) Columbia; WBTW (C), WJPM-TV (P), WPDE-TV (A) Florence.
Programming (via satellite): WGN-TV (W) Chicago; TBS Superstation.
Fee: N.A.
Manager: Tony Wilson.
Ownership: Pine Tree Cablevision (MSO). Purchased from Cable Synergy TV LP, October 1, 1998.

LANCASTER—Lancaster Cable TV, 905 N. Main St., Lancaster, SC 29720. Phone: 803-283-1000. Counties: Chester & Lancaster. Also serves Fort Lawn, Lancaster County. ICA: SC0023.
TV Market Ranking: Below 100. Franchise award date: N.A. Franchise expiration date: N.A. Began: August 1, 1967.
Channel capacity: 77 (not 2-way capable). Channels available but not in use: 15.

Basic Service
Subscribers: 10,257.
Programming (received off-air): WJZY (U) Belmont; WBTV (C), WCCB (F), WCNC-TV (N), WSOC-TV (A), WTVI (P) Charlotte; WIS (N) Columbia; WAXN (I) Kannapolis; WFVT (W), WNSC-TV (P) Rock Hill.
Programming (via satellite): ESPN; TBS Superstation; The Weather Channel.
Fee: $45.00 installation; $13.95 monthly; $1.60 converter.
Expanded Basic Service
Subscribers: 8,375.
Programming (via satellite): A & E; American Movie Classics; American Sports Classics; BET; C-SPAN; CNN; Cartoon Network; Comedy Central; Country Music TV; Discovery Channel; ESPN 2; FX; Fox Family Channel; Fox Sports Net South; Headline News; History Channel; Home Shopping Network; Learning Channel; Lifetime; Nashville Network; Nick at Nite's TV Land; Nickelodeon; Sci-Fi Channel; TV Guide Channel; TV Guide Sneak Prevue; Trinity Bcstg. Network; Turner Network TV; USA Network; VH1.
Fee: $14.40 monthly.
Pay Service 1
Pay Units: 875.
Programming (via satellite): Cinemax (multiplexed).
Fee: $9.95 monthly.
Pay Service 2
Pay Units: 403.
Programming (via satellite): Disney Channel.
Fee: $7.95 monthly.
Pay Service 3
Pay Units: 2,079.
Programming (via satellite): HBO (multiplexed).
Fee: $9.95 monthly.
Pay Service 4
Pay Units: 630.
Programming (via satellite): Showtime; The Movie Channel.
Fee: $9.95 monthly.
Pay Service 5
Pay Units: 356.
Programming (via satellite): The New Encore.
Fee: $5.95 monthly.
Pay Service 6
Pay Units: 365.
Programming (via satellite): Starz!
Fee: $9.95 monthly.
Pay-Per-View
Addressable homes: 8,375.
Viewer's Choice.
Local advertising: Yes. Local sales manager: John Barnes Jr.
Equipment: Jerrold headend; C-COR & Scientific-Atlanta amplifiers; Comm/Scope cable; Siecor fiber optic cable; Scientific-Atlanta set top converters; Scientific-Atlanta satellite antenna; Scientific-Atlanta satellite receivers.
Miles of plant: 220.7 (coaxial). Additional miles planned: 60.0 (coaxial). Homes passed: 10,000.
Manager: William C. Beaty Jr. Chief technician: Jim Ghent. Marketing & program director: John Barnes Jr. Customer service manager: Sherri Parrish.
City fee: 3% of gross.
Ownership: Video Vision Inc.

LANE—Time Warner Cable, 1170 N. Guignard Dr., Sumter, SC 29150. Phone: 803-469-2200. Fax: 803-469-2423. County: Williamsburg. ICA: SC0155.
TV Market Ranking: Outside TV Markets. Franchise award date: N.A. Franchise expiration date: N.A. Began: N.A.
Channel capacity: N.A. Channels available but not in use: N.A.
Basic Service
Subscribers: 99.
Programming (received off-air): WCBD-TV (N), WCIV (A), WCSC-TV (C), WTAT-TV (F,U) Charleston; WIS (N) Columbia; WBTW (C), WPDE-TV (A) Florence; WRJA-TV (P) Sumter.
Programming (via satellite): WGN-TV (W) Chicago; Home Shopping Network; MSNBC; QVC.
Fee: $49.95 installation; $7.30 monthly.
Expanded Basic Service
Subscribers: 99.
Programming (via satellite): A & E; American Movie Classics; BET; C-SPAN; CNBC; Cartoon Network; Comedy Central; Country Music TV; Court TV; Discovery Channel; ESPN; Fox Family Channel; Goodlife TV Network; Headline News; Lifetime; Nashville Network; Nick at Nite; Nickelodeon; TV Food Network; The Weather Channel; Turner Network TV; USA Network; VH1.
Fee: $1.55 monthly.
A la Carte 1
Subscribers: N.A.
Programming (via satellite): CNN; ESPN 2; TBS Superstation.
Fee: N.A.
Pay Service 1
Pay Units: N.A.
Programming (via satellite): Disney Channel; HBO; Showtime.
Fee: N.A.
Manager: James Mott. Chief techician: Glenn Washington. Marketing director: Dan Santelle.
Ownership: Time Warner Cable (MSO).

LAURENS—Charter Communications, Box 850, Laurens, SC 29360. Phone: 803-682-2222. County: Laurens. Also serves Joanna, Laurens County. ICA: SC0022.
TV Market Ranking: 46 (Laurens, portions of Laurens County); Outside TV Markets (Joanna, portions of Laurens County). Franchise award date: July 1, 1973. Franchise expiration date: N.A. Began: November 1, 1975.
Channel capacity: 80 (not 2-way capable). Channels available but not in use: 38.
Basic Service
Subscribers: 7,500; Commercial subscribers: 400.
Programming (received off-air): WGGS-TV (I), WNTV (P) Greenville; WHNS (F,U), WLOS (A), WSPA-TV (C), WYFF (N) Greenville-Spartanburg-Asheville; allband FM.
Programming (via satellite): WGN-TV (W) Chicago; C-SPAN; QVC; TBS Superstation.
Planned originations: Public access; educational access; government access; leased access; automated emergency alert.
Fee: $35.00 installation; $11.86 monthly.
Expanded Basic Service
Subscribers: 6,700.
Programming (via satellite): A & E; American Movie Classics; BET; CNBC; CNN; Comedy Central; Country Music TV; Discovery Channel; E! Entertainment TV; ESPN; Fox Family Channel; Fox Sports Net South; Headline News; Learning Channel; Lifetime; MTV; Nashville Network; Nickelodeon; TV Guide Channel; The Weather Channel; Turner Network TV; USA Network; VH1.
Fee: $15.00 installation; $15.09 monthly.
Pay Service 1
Pay Units: 3,000.
Programming (via satellite): Cinemax; Disney Channel; HBO; Showtime; The Movie Channel.
Fee: $15.00 installation; $12.02 monthly (each).
Pay-Per-View
Addressable homes: 400.
Hot Choice; Viewer's Choice.
Local advertising: Yes. Available in satellite distributed, locally originated, character-generated & taped programming. Local sales manager: John Hood.
Program Guide: The Cable Guide.
Equipment: Scientific-Atlanta headend; Jerrold & Scientific-Atlanta amplifiers; Comm/Scope cable; Texscan character generator; Panasonic set top converters; Zenith addressable set top converters; Pico, Northeast Filter & Eagle traps; Zenith addressable traps; Scientific-Atlanta satellite antenna; Scientific-Atlanta satellite receivers; Sony commercial insert.
Miles of plant: 220.0 (coaxial); 30.0 (fiber optic). Homes passed: 11,194.
Manager: Carl Naes. Chief technician: Eugene Collins. Marketing & program director: Tim Morrison.
City fee: 3% of gross ($250 minimum).
Ownership: Charter Communications Inc. (MSO).

LIBERTY—Northland Cable TV, Box 718, 206 Anderson Dr., Liberty, SC 29657. Phone: 864-882-0002. Fax: 803-843-2724. County: Pickens. Also serves Norris, Pickens, Pickens County, Six Mile. ICA: SC0024.
TV Market Ranking: 46. Franchise award date: August 20, 1979. Franchise expiration date: N.A. Began: August 1, 1979.
Channel capacity: 27 (not 2-way capable). Channels available but not in use: None.
Basic Service
Subscribers: 2,675; Commercial subscribers: 1.
Programming (received off-air): WGGS-TV (I), WNTV (P) Greenville; WHNS (F,U), WLOS (A), WSPA-TV (C), WYFF (N) Greenville-Spartanburg-Asheville; WNEG-TV (I) Toccoa.
Programming (via satellite): WGN-TV (W) Chicago; A & E; C-SPAN; CNN; Country Music TV; Discovery Channel; ESPN; Fox Family Channel; MTV; Nashville Network; QVC; TBS Superstation; The Weather Channel; Turner Network TV; USA Network.
Fee: $45.00 installation; $20.45 monthly.
Pay Service 1
Pay Units: 390.
Programming (via satellite): Cinemax.
Fee: $25.00 installation; $9.95 monthly.
Pay Service 2
Pay Units: 239.
Programming (via satellite): Disney Channel.
Fee: $25.00 installation; $8.95 monthly.
Pay Service 3
Pay Units: 409.
Programming (via satellite): HBO.
Fee: $25.00 installation; $12.95 monthly.
Pay Service 4
Pay Units: 155.
Programming (via satellite): The Movie Channel.
Fee: $25.00 installation; $10.95 monthly.
Local advertising: No.
Equipment: Scientific-Atlanta headend; Scientific-Atlanta amplifiers; Microtek character generator; Jerrold set top converters; Scientific-Atlanta satellite antenna; Scientific-Atlanta satellite receivers.
Miles of plant: 138.3 (coaxial). Additional miles planned: 20.0 (coaxial). Homes passed: 8,396.
Manager: Ken Strickland.
City fee: 3% of gross.
Ownership: Northland Communications Corp. (MSO).

LITTLE RIVER—Savannah River Cable, 1616 Calhoun Rd., Greenwood, SC 29649. Phone: 803-229-3638. County: Horry. ICA: SC0130.
TV Market Ranking: Below 100. Franchise award date: N.A. Franchise expiration date: N.A. Began: April 1, 1990.
Channel capacity: N.A. Channels available but not in use: N.A.
Basic Service
Subscribers: N.A.
Programming (received off-air): WAGT (N), WJBF (A), WRDW-TV (C) Augusta; WHNS (F,U), WLOS (A), WSPA-TV (C), WYFF (N) Greenville-Spartanburg-Asheville; WNEH (P) Greenwood.
Programming (via satellite): WGN-TV (W) Chicago; C-SPAN; CNN; ESPN; Fox Family Channel; Headline News; Home Shopping Network; MTV; Nashville Network; Nickelodeon; TBS Superstation; The Weather Channel; USA Network.
Fee: Free installation; $12.95 monthly.
Pay Service 1
Pay Units: N.A.
Programming (via satellite): Cinemax; Disney Channel; HBO; Showtime.
Fee: $6.95 monthly (Disney or Showtime), $8.50 monthly (Cinemax), $9.50 monthly (HBO).
Manager: Bill Quarles.
Ownership: Bill Quarles.

LOCKHART—Charter Communications, 101 Cestrian Square, Chester, SC 29706. Phone: 803-377-1181. Fax: 803-487-5075. Counties: Chester & Union. Also serves Chester County (unincorporated areas), Union County (unincorporated areas). ICA: SC0098.
TV Market Ranking: 46 (portions of Chester County, Lockhart, Union County); Below 100 (portions of Chester County). Franchise award date: June 2, 1988. Franchise expiration date: June 2, 2003. Began: January 1, 1988.
Channel capacity: 35 (not 2-way capable). Channels available but not in use: N.A.
Basic Service
Subscribers: 364.
Programming (received off-air): WJZY (U) Belmont; WBTV (C), WCCB (F) Charlotte; WNTV (P) Greenville; WLOS (A), WSPA-TV (C), WYFF (N) Greenville-Spartanburg-Asheville.
Programming (via satellite): CNN; ESPN; Home Shopping Network; Nashville Network; TBS Superstation.
Fee: $40.00 installation; $10.38 monthly; $3.50 converter.
Expanded Basic Service
Subscribers: 358.

Programming (via satellite): Headline News; Nickelodeon; The Weather Channel; Turner Network TV; USA Network.
Fee: $9.86 monthly.
Pay Service 1
Pay Units: 12.
Programming (via satellite): Disney Channel.
Fee: $15.00 installation; $8.95 monthly.
Pay Service 2
Pay Units: 51.
Programming (via satellite): HBO.
Fee: $15.00 installation; $11.95 monthly.
Pay Service 3
Pay Units: 23.
Programming (via satellite): Showtime.
Fee: $15.00 installation; $9.95 monthly.
Program Guide: TV Host.
Equipment: Scientific-Atlanta headend; Scientific-Atlanta amplifiers; Times Fiber cable; Atari character generator; Jerrold set top converters; Pico traps; Harris & Scientific-Atlanta satellite antenna; Scientific-Atlanta satellite receivers.
Miles of plant: 33.0 (coaxial). Homes passed: 782.
Manager: Joe Haight. Marketing director: Kemp Delo.
City fee: 2% of gross.
Ownership: Charter Communications Inc. (MSO).

LYNCHBURG—Galaxy Cablevision, 1899 S.E. 58th Ave., Ocala, FL 34471-5847. Phone: 352-624-1117. County: Lee. Also serves Lee County (portions). ICA: SC0096.
TV Market Ranking: Below 100. Franchise award date: N.A. Franchise expiration date: March 28, 2004. Began: N.A.
Channel capacity: 29. Channels available but not in use: None.
Basic Service
Subscribers: 87.
Programming (received off-air): WACH (F), WIS (N) Columbia; WBTW (C), WPDE-TV (A) Florence; WRJA-TV (P) Sumter.
Programming (via satellite): WGN-TV (W) Chicago; A & E; American Movie Classics; BET; CNBC; CNN; Discovery Channel; ESPN; Fox Family Channel; Lifetime; Nashville Network; Nickelodeon; QVC; TBS Superstation; The Weather Channel; Turner Network TV; USA Network; VH1.
Fee: $30.00 installation; $25.75 monthly.
Pay Service 1
Pay Units: 34.
Programming (via satellite): Cinemax.
Fee: $10.95 monthly.
Pay Service 2
Pay Units: 14.
Programming (via satellite): Disney Channel.
Fee: $10.95 monthly.
Pay Service 3
Pay Units: 64.
Programming (via satellite): HBO.
Fee: $10.95 monthly.
Miles of plant: 23.0 (coaxial). Homes passed: 728.
State manager: Dan Labbe. Technical manager: Joe Ferrell.
Ownership: Galaxy Cablevision (MSO).

MANNING—Time Warner Cable, 1170 N. Guignard Dr., Sumter, SC 29150. Phone: 803-469-2200. Fax: 803-469-2423. County: Clarendon. Also serves Clarendon County, Summerton. ICA: SC0131.
TV Market Ranking: Below 100. Franchise award date: December 19, 1977. Franchise expiration date: December 18, 1997. Began: N.A.
Channel capacity: 36 (not 2-way capable). Channels available but not in use: 4.
Basic Service
Subscribers: 2,900.
Programming (received off-air): WCIV (A), WCSC-TV (C), WTAT-TV (F,U) Charleston; WIS (N), WLTX (C), WOLO-TV (A) Columbia; WBTW (C) Florence; WRJA-TV (P) Sumter.
Programming (via satellite): WGN-TV (W) Chicago; A & E; BET; CNBC; CNN; Comedy Central; Country Music TV; Discovery Channel; ESPN; Fox Family Channel; Lifetime; MTV; Nashville Network; Nickelodeon; QVC; TBS Superstation; The Weather Channel; Turner Network TV; USA Network; VH1.
Planned originations: Automated time-weather.
Fee: $25.00 installation; $21.45 monthly.
Pay Service 1
Pay Units: N.A.
Programming (via satellite): Disney Channel; HBO; Showtime.
Fee: $40.00 installation; $9.95 monthly (Disney), $10.95 monthly (Showtime), $12.95 monthly (HBO).
Equipment: Scientific-Atlanta headend; Scientific-Atlanta amplifiers; Comm/Scope cable; Intercept, Oak & Pioneer set top converters; Pico, Eagle & Northeast Filter traps; Scientific-Atlanta satellite antenna; Scientific-Atlanta & DX Antenna satellite receivers.
Miles of plant: 123.0 (coaxial). Additional miles planned: 20.0 (coaxial). Total homes in franchised area: 14,517.
Manager: Jim Mott. Chief technician: Tom Perry. Marketing director: J. J. Jonas.
City fee: 3% of gross.
Ownership: Time Warner Cable (MSO); Advance/Newhouse Partnership (MSO).

McCLELLANVILLE—Benchmark Communications, 2511 Highmarket St., Georgetown, SC 29440. Phone: 843-527-2447. Fax: 843-527-2034. County: Charleston. Also serves Charleston County (unincorporated areas), South Santee. ICA: SC0101.
TV Market Ranking: Below 100. Franchise award date: January 1, 1988. Franchise expiration date: January 1, 2003. Began: January 1, 1988.
Channel capacity: 36 (not 2-way capable). Channels available but not in use: 8.
Basic Service
Subscribers: 198.
Programming (received off-air): WCBD-TV (N), WCIV (A), WCSC-TV (C), WITV (P), WMMP (U), WTAT-TV (F,U) Charleston.
Programming (via satellite): WGN-TV (W) Chicago; A & E; American Movie Classics; Animal Planet; BET; CNN; Cartoon Network; Discovery Channel; ESPN; Fox Family Channel; Fox News Channel; Headline News; MTV; Nashville Network; Nickelodeon; QVC; Sci-Fi Channel; TBS Superstation; The Weather Channel; Trinity Bcstg. Network; Turner Network TV; USA Network; VH1.
Fee: $25.00 installation; $24.92 monthly; $2.00 converter.
Pay Service 1
Pay Units: 22.
Programming (via satellite): Cinemax.
Fee: $9.95 monthly.
Pay Service 2
Pay Units: 4.
Programming (via satellite): Disney Channel.
Fee: $9.95 monthly.
Pay Service 3
Pay Units: 39.
Programming (via satellite): HBO.
Fee: $9.95 monthly.
Program Guide: CableView.
Equipment: Scientific-Atlanta headend; Jerrold amplifiers; Scientific-Atlanta set top converters; Prodelin satellite antenna; Scientific-Atlanta satellite receivers.
Miles of plant: 17.0 (coaxial); None (fiber optic). Homes passed: 450. Total homes in franchised area: 840.
Manager: Kenneth Koch.
City fee: 3% of basic.
Ownership: Benchmark Communications (MSO). Purchased from Genesis Cable Communications LLC, May 3, 1999.

McCORMICK—Robin Cable Systems LP, Box 151, 3060 Cablevision Rd., Aiken, SC 29801-2906. Phone: 864-445-8018. Fax: 864-456-3412. County: McCormick. Also serves McCormick County (portions). ICA: SC0079.
TV Market Ranking: 46 (portions of McCormick County); Below 100 (portions of McCormick County); Outside TV Markets (portions of McCormick County, McCormick). Franchise award date: April 15, 1984. Franchise expiration date: April 1, 1999. Began: December 23, 1985.
Channel capacity: 36 (not 2-way capable). Channels available but not in use: 8.
Basic Service
Subscribers: 426; Commercial subscribers: 17.
Programming (received off-air): WAGT (N), WFXG (F), WJBF (A), WRDW-TV (C) Augusta; WHNS (F,U), WYFF (N) Greenville-Spartanburg-Asheville; WNEH (P) Greenwood; WCES-TV (P) Wrens.
Programming (via satellite): WGN-TV (W) Chicago; A & E; BET; C-SPAN; CNN; Discovery Channel; ESPN; Fox Family Channel; Fox Sports Net South; Headline News; Home Shopping Network; MTV; Nashville Network; Nickelodeon; QVC; TBS Superstation; The Weather Channel; Turner Network TV; USA Network; VH1.
Fee: $49.95 installation; $24.37 monthly; $10.00 additional installation.
Commercial fee: $5.50 monthly.
Pay Service 1
Pay Units: 230.
Programming (via satellite): Cinemax; Disney Channel; HBO; Showtime.
Fee: $4.50 installation; $8.95 monthly (Disney), $9.00 monthly (Cinemax, HBO or Showtime).
Local advertising: No.
Equipment: Jerrold headend; Jerrold amplifiers; Comm/Scope cable; Jerrold & Oak set top converters; Eagle & Arcom traps; Scientific-Atlanta satellite antenna; Scientific-Atlanta & Jerrold satellite receivers.
Miles of plant: 23.0 (coaxial). Additional miles planned: 1.0 (coaxial). Homes passed: 608.
Manager: Lee A. Perron. Chief technician: Tony Urban.
City fee: 3% of basic; 1% of pay gross.
Ownership: InterMedia Partners (MSO).

MONCKS CORNER—Berkeley Cable TV, Box 1257, Moncks Corner, SC 29461. Phone: 803-761-8188. Fax: 803-899-9200. Web site: http://www.hometelco.com/html/berkeleyctv. Counties: Berkeley & Dorchester. Also serves Berkeley County (unincorporated areas), Harleyville. ICA: SC0132.
TV Market Ranking: Below 100 (portions of Berkeley County, Moncks Corner); Outside TV Markets (portions of Berkeley County, Harleyville). Franchise award date: N.A. Franchise expiration date: October 1, 2007. Began: October 1, 1980.
Channel capacity: 78 (2-way capable; operating 2-way). Channels available but not in use: N.A.
Basic Service
Subscribers: 6,055.
Programming (received off-air): WCBD-TV (N), WCIV (A), WCSC-TV (C), WITV (P), WMMP (U), WTAT-TV (F,U) Charleston.
Programming (via satellite): WGN-TV (W) Chicago; C-SPAN; C-SPAN 2; Home Shopping Network; The Weather Channel.
Current originations: Automated time-weather; automated emergency alert.
Fee: $35.00 installation; $25.65 monthly; $2.25 converter; $25.00 additional installation.
Expanded Basic Service
Subscribers: 5,447.
Programming (via satellite): A & E; BET; CNN; Country Music TV; Discovery Channel; Disney Channel; ESPN; ESPN 2; Fox Family Channel; Fox Sports Net; Great American Country; Headline News; History Channel; Learning Channel; Nashville Network; Nick at Nite; Nickelodeon; Sci-Fi Channel; Turner Classic Movies; Turner Network TV; USA Network; VH1.
Fee: $25.65 monthly.
Pay Service 1
Pay Units: 1,556.
Programming (via satellite): HBO.
Fee: $5.00 installation; $10.95 monthly.
Pay Service 2
Pay Units: 494.
Programming (via satellite): Cinemax.
Fee: $5.00 installation; $9.95 monthly.
Pay Service 3
Pay Units: 641.
Programming (via satellite): Showtime.
Fee: $5.00 installation; $9.95 monthly.
Pay-Per-View
Addressable homes: 5,447.
Viewer's Choice.
Fee: $3.95.
Local advertising: Yes. Available in satellite distributed programming.
Equipment: Scientific-Atlanta headend; Texscan amplifiers; Comm/Scope cable; Texscan character generator; Scientific-Atlanta set top converters; Scientific-Atlanta addressable set top converters; Scientific-Atlanta satellite antenna; Scientific-Atlanta satellite receivers.
Miles of plant: 296.4 (coaxial); 50.0 (fiber optic). Homes passed: 6,390. Total homes in franchised area: 7,953.
Manager: Robert L. Helmly. Program director: Rob L. Helmly.
Franchise fee: 5% of gross.
Ownership: Berkeley Cable TV Co. Inc. (MSO).

MULLINS—Century Communications, Box 1109, 1741 Hwy. 9 W, Dillon, SC 29536. Phone: 843-774-2461. Fax: 843-774-2035. E-mail: kspruill@centurycomm.com. Web site: http://www.centurycomm.com. County: Marion. Also serves Marion, Marion County (portions). ICA: SC0032.
TV Market Ranking: Below 100. Franchise award date: N.A. Franchise expiration date: N.A. Began: September 1, 1967.
Channel capacity: 36 (not 2-way capable). Channels available but not in use: 2.
Basic Service
Subscribers: 4,153.
Programming (received off-air): WIS (N) Columbia; WBTW (C), WJPM-TV (P), WPDE-TV (A) Florence; WECT (N), WWAY (A) Wilmington; 1 FM.
Programming (via satellite): C-SPAN; Home Shopping Network; QVC.
Current originations: Automated time-weather.
Fee: $60.00 installation; $18.32 monthly; $7.50 additional installation.
Expanded Basic Service
Subscribers: N.A.

Programming (via satellite): American Movie Classics; BET; Country Music TV; Discovery Channel; Fox Family Channel; Headline News; The Weather Channel; Trinity Bcstg. Network; VH1.
Fee: $10.00 installation; $3.20 monthly.

Expanded Basic Service 2
Subscribers: N.A.
Programming (via satellite): A & E; CNN; ESPN; Lifetime; MTV; Nashville Network; Nickelodeon; TBS Superstation; Turner Network TV; USA Network.
Fee: N.A.

Pay Service 1
Pay Units: N.A.
Programming (via satellite): Cinemax; Disney Channel.
Fee: $10.00 installation; $7.00 monthly (Disney), $9.00 monthly (Cinemax).

Pay Service 2
Pay Units: 984.
Programming (via satellite): HBO.
Fee: $9.00 monthly.

Local advertising: No.
Equipment: Scientific-Atlanta headend; Jerrold & Scientific-Atlanta amplifiers; Oak set top converters; Scientific-Atlanta satellite antenna.
Miles of plant: 79.1 (coaxial). Additional miles planned: 10.0 (coaxial). Homes passed: 5,270.
Manager: Kraig Spruill. Chief technician: Tim Bourgoin. Marketing & program director: Bertha Casey.
City fee: 3% of gross.
Ownership: Century Communications Corp. (MSO). See Cable System Ownership.

MYRTLE BEACH—Time Warner Cable, 1901 Oak St., Myrtle Beach, SC 29577. Phone: 803-448-7858. Fax: 803-626-2922. Counties: Georgetown, Horry & Williamsburg. Also serves Atlantic Beach, Briarcliff Acres, Conway, Forestbrook, Georgetown County, Horry County, Little River, North Myrtle Beach, Williamsburg County. ICA: SC0007.
TV Market Ranking: Below 100 (Atlantic Beach, Briarcliff Acres, Conway, Forestbrook, portions of Georgetown County, Horry County, Little River, Myrtle Beach, North Myrtle Beach, portions of Williamsburg County); Outside TV Markets (portions of Georgetown County, portions of Williamsburg County). Franchise award date: January 1, 1961. Franchise expiration date: August 17, 2001. Began: September 17, 1962.
Channel capacity: 63 (not 2-way capable). Channels available but not in use: None.

Basic Service
Subscribers: 32,207; Commercial subscribers: 16,055.
Programming (received off-air): WHMC (P) Conway; WBTW (C), WPDE-TV (A), WWMB (U) Florence; WFXB (F) Myrtle Beach; WECT (N), WSFX-TV (F), WUNJ-TV (P) Wilmington.
Programming (via microwave): WIS (N) Columbia.
Programming (via satellite): WGN-TV (W) Chicago; TBS Superstation.
Current originations: Public access; educational access; government access; religious access; leased access; automated emergency alert; local news; local news.
Fee: $28.00 installation; $6.61 monthly; $1.63 converter.

Expanded Basic Service
Subscribers: 39,501.
Programming (via satellite): A & E; American Movie Classics; BET; C-SPAN; CNBC; CNN; Comedy Central; Country Music TV; Discovery Channel; Disney Channel; E! Entertainment TV; ESPN; EWTN; FX; Fox Family Channel; Fox Sports Net South; Headline News; Learning Channel; Lifetime; MTV; Nashville Network; Nickelodeon; Odyssey; QVC; TV Guide Channel; TV Guide Sneak Prevue; The Weather Channel; Turner Network TV; USA Network; VH1.
Fee: $28.00 installation; $19.92 monthly.

Pay Service 1
Pay Units: 3,806.
Programming (via satellite): Cinemax.
Fee: $5.00 installation; $6.45 monthly.

Pay Service 2
Pay Units: 10,815.
Programming (via satellite): HBO.
Fee: $15.00 installation; $9.95 monthly.

Pay Service 3
Pay Units: 4,266.
Programming (via satellite): Showtime.
Fee: $5.00 installation; $9.50 monthly.

Pay-Per-View
Addressable homes: 11,000.
Hot Choice; Viewer's Choice.
Fee: $3.95.
Pay-per-view manager: Lori White.

Local advertising: Yes. Available in satellite distributed, locally originated, character-generated, taped & automated programming. Rates: $150.00/Week; $180.00/Minute; $100.00/30 Seconds. Local sales manager: Linda Kohlhagen.
Program Guide: TV Blue Print.
Equipment: Scientific-Atlanta headend; Scientific-Atlanta amplifiers; Comm/Scope cable; Hitachi cameras; Sony VTRs; Texscan character generator; Scientific-Atlanta set top converters; Scientific-Atlanta addressable set top converters; Eagle traps; Scientific-Atlanta satellite antenna; Scientific-Atlanta satellite receivers; Texscan commercial insert.
Miles of plant: 700.0 (coaxial); 110.0 (fiber optic). Additional miles planned: 100.0 (coaxial); 100.0 (fiber optic). Homes passed: 61,000. Total homes in franchised area: 61,000.
Manager: Darrell Wells. Chief technician: Jim Streets. Marketing director: Mary Anne Moore.
City fee: 5% of gross.
Ownership: Time Warner Cable (MSO); Advance/Newhouse Partnership (MSO).

NEWBERRY—Comcast Cablevision of the South, Box 674, 2335 College St., Newberry, SC 29108. Phone: 803-276-2343. County: Newberry. Also serves Newberry County. Plans service to Prosperity. ICA: SC0035.
TV Market Ranking: 100 (portions of Newberry County); Outside TV Markets (Newberry, portions of Newberry County). Franchise award date: March 9, 1968. Franchise expiration date: N.A. Began: June 1, 1968.
Channel capacity: N.A. Channels available but not in use: N.A.

Basic Service
Subscribers: 4,748.
Programming (received off-air): WJZY (U) Belmont; WACH (F), WIS (N), WLTX (C), WOLO-TV (A), WRLK-TV (P) Columbia; WLOS (A), WSPA-TV (C), WYFF (N) Greenville-Spartanburg-Asheville; 17 FMs.
Planned programming (received off-air): WHNS (F,U) Greenville-Spartanburg-Asheville.
Programming (via satellite): WGN-TV (W) Chicago; QVC.
Current originations: Automated time-weather; educational access.
Fee: $40.00 installation; $7.06 monthly; $2.00 converter; $23.25 additional installation.

Expanded Basic Service
Subscribers: N.A.
Programming (via satellite): A & E; BET; C-SPAN; C-SPAN 2; CNBC; CNN; Cartoon Network; Country Music TV; Court TV; E! Entertainment TV; ESPN; ESPN 2; Fox Family Channel; Fox Sports Net South; Game Show Network; Golf Channel; Headline News; Home & Garden Television; Home Shopping Network; Learning Channel; Lifetime; MTV; Nick at Nite's TV Land; Nickelodeon; Outdoor Life Network; Pax Net; Sci-Fi Channel; TV Food Network; The Weather Channel; Travel Channel; Trinity Bcstg. Network; Turner Classic Movies; USA Network.
Fee: $19.28 monthly.

Expanded Basic Service 2
Subscribers: N.A.
Programming (via satellite): Discovery Channel; Nashville Network; TBS Superstation; Turner Network TV.
Fee: $3.16 monthly.

Pay Service 1
Pay Units: 328.
Programming (via satellite): Cinemax.
Fee: $10.00 installation; $11.95 monthly.

Pay Service 2
Pay Units: 173.
Programming (via satellite): Disney Channel.
Fee: $10.00 installation; $10.95 monthly.

Pay Service 3
Pay Units: 715.
Programming (via satellite): HBO.
Fee: $10.00 installation; $12.95 monthly.

Pay Service 4
Pay Units: 170.
Programming (via satellite): Showtime.
Fee: $11.95 monthly.

Equipment: Jerrold headend; Vikoa amplifiers; Vikoa cable; Gardiner satellite antenna.
Miles of plant: 107.0 (coaxial). Additional miles planned: 10.0 (coaxial). Homes passed: 4,999.
Manager: Kim Rueckert. Chief technician: Guy Lee. Marketing director: Martin O'Keefe.
City fee: 3% of gross.
Ownership: Comcast Cable Communications Inc. (MSO).

NORTH—Pine Tree Cablevision, 2628 Millwood Ave., Columbia, SC 29205. Phone: 803-799-6226. Fax: 803-799-8804. County: Orangeburg. ICA: SC0092.
TV Market Ranking: 100. Franchise award date: November 1, 1985. Franchise expiration date: November 1, 2000. Began: October 1, 1986.
Channel capacity: 22. Channels available but not in use: 10.

Basic Service
Subscribers: N.A.
Programming (received off-air): WJBF (A), WRDW-TV (C) Augusta; WIS (N), WOLO-TV (A), WRLK-TV (P) Columbia.
Programming (via satellite): CNN; ESPN; Fox Family Channel; Nashville Network; TBS Superstation.
Fee: $30.00 installation; $12.00 monthly.

Pay Service 1
Pay Units: N.A.
Programming (via satellite): Disney Channel; Showtime.
Fee: $8.00 monthly (each).

Miles of plant: 9.9 (coaxial). Homes passed: 600.
Manager: Tony Wilson.
Ownership: Pine Tree Cablevision (MSO). Purchased from South Carolina Cable TV LP, October 1, 1998.

ORANGEBURG—Time Warner Cable, Box 1485, 987 Broughton St. SW, Orangeburg, SC 29115. Phone: 803-534-7373. Fax: 803-534-5119. Counties: Calhoun & Orangeburg. Also serves Cordova (southwestern portion), Orangeburg County, St. Mathews. ICA: SC0017.
TV Market Ranking: 100 (portions of Orangeburg County, St. Mathews); Outside TV Markets (Cordova, Orangeburg, portions of Orangeburg County). Franchise award date: May 16, 1967. Franchise expiration date: May 30, 2004. Began: September 1, 1968.
Channel capacity: 36 (2-way capable; operating 2-way). Channels available but not in use: None.

Basic Service
Subscribers: 13,664; Commercial subscribers: 1,850.
Programming (received off-air): WCIV (A), WCSC-TV (C) Charleston; WACH (F), WIS (N), WLTX (C), WOLO-TV (A), WRLK-TV (P) Columbia; allband FM.
Programming (via satellite): WGN-TV (W) Chicago; A & E; American Movie Classics; BET; C-SPAN; CNBC; CNN; Discovery Channel; ESPN; Fox Family Channel; Fox Sports Net South; Headline News; Home Shopping Network; Knowledge TV; Lifetime; MTV; Nashville Network; Nickelodeon; TBS Superstation; TV Guide Channel; The Weather Channel; Turner Network TV; USA Network; VH1.
Current originations: Religious access; leased access; automated emergency alert; local news; local sports.
Fee: $25.50 installation; $20.06 monthly; $17.00 additional installation.
Commercial fee: $7.50 monthly.

Pay Service 1
Pay Units: 2,410.
Programming (via satellite): Cinemax (multiplexed).
Fee: $5.00 installation; $9.00 monthly.

Pay Service 2
Pay Units: 746.
Programming (via satellite): Disney Channel (multiplexed).
Fee: $5.00 installation; $6.95 monthly.

Pay Service 3
Pay Units: 3,167.
Programming (via satellite): HBO (multiplexed).
Fee: $5.00 installation; $10.00 monthly.

Pay Service 4
Pay Units: 1,106.
Programming (via satellite): Showtime (multiplexed).
Fee: $5.00 installation; $9.00 monthly.

Pay Service 5
Pay Units: 718.
Programming (via satellite): The Movie Channel (multiplexed).
Fee: $5.00 installation; $9.00 monthly.

Pay Service 6
Pay Units: 290.
Programming (via satellite): The New Encore.
Fee: $1.95 monthly.

Pay-Per-View
Addressable homes: 7,052.
Action Pay-Per-View; Playboy TV; Spice; Viewer's Choice.
Fee: $3.99 (Action Pay-Per-View or Viewer's Choice); $5.99 (Playboy TV or Spice).
Pay-per-view manager: Roy Haigler.

Local advertising: Yes. Available in locally originated & taped programming. Rates: $16.00/30 Seconds; Senior Account Manager: Lynda Hunter.
Program Guide: Prevue Guide.
Equipment: Scientific-Atlanta headend; Texscan & C-COR amplifiers; Comm/Scope & Belden cable; Sony & JVC cameras; Sony & JVC VTRs; Jerrold set top converters; Jerrold & Scientific-Atlanta addressable set top converters; Eagle traps; Scientific-Atlanta satellite antenna; Scientific-Atlanta satellite receivers; Falcone International commercial insert.
Miles of plant: 430.0 (coaxial); 110.0 (fiber optic). Additional miles planned: 25.4 (coaxial). Homes passed: 22,482. Total homes in franchised area: 45,000.

Manager: Terry Roberson. Chief technician: Marty Kinard. Customer service manager: Roy Haigler.
City fee: 5% of gross. County fee: 5% of gross.
Ownership: Time Warner Cable (MSO); Advance/Newhouse Partnership (MSO).

PAGELAND—Enstar Cable TV, 310 10th St., North Wilkesboro, NC 28659-4112. Phone: 910-667-4151. County: Chesterfield. ICA: SC0082.
TV Market Ranking: Outside TV Markets. Franchise award date: N.A. Franchise expiration date: N.A. Began: July 1, 1983.
Channel capacity: 35 (not 2-way capable). Channels available but not in use: None.
Basic Service
Subscribers: 760.
Programming (received off-air): WJZY (U) Belmont; WBTV (C), WCCB (F), WCNC-TV (N), WSOC-TV (A) Charlotte; WIS (N) Columbia; WUNG-TV (P) Concord; WBTW (C) Florence; WFVT (W) Rock Hill.
Programming (via satellite): American Movie Classics; Bravo; C-SPAN; CNN; Country Music TV; E! Entertainment TV; ESPN; Headline News; Learning Channel; MTV; Nickelodeon; Sci-Fi Channel; The Weather Channel; Turner Network TV.
Fee: $25.00 installation; $21.10 monthly; $7.50 additional installation.
Expanded Basic Service
Subscribers: 756.
Programming (via satellite): Discovery Channel; Lifetime; USA Network.
Fee: $1.54 monthly.
Expanded Basic Service 2
Subscribers: 753.
Programming (via satellite): WGN-TV (W) Chicago; Fox Family Channel; Nashville Network; TBS Superstation.
Fee: $4.50 monthly.
Pay Service 1
Pay Units: 59.
Programming (via satellite): Cinemax.
Fee: $10.95 monthly.
Pay Service 2
Pay Units: 235.
Programming (via satellite): HBO.
Fee: $11.95 monthly.
Pay Service 3
Pay Units: 49.
Programming (via satellite): Showtime.
Fee: $10.95 monthly.
Pay Service 4
Pay Units: 41.
Programming (via satellite): The Movie Channel.
Fee: $10.95 monthly.
Local advertising: No.
Equipment: Scientific-Atlanta headend; Scientific-Atlanta amplifiers; Comm/Scope cable; Pico, Eagle & Intercept traps; Scientific-Atlanta satellite antenna; Scientific-Atlanta satellite receivers.
Miles of plant: 40.0 (coaxial). Homes passed: 1,297.
Manager: Wanda Parsons. Chief technician: Eddie Collins.
Franchise fee: 5% of gross.
Ownership: Falcon Communications LP (MSO), joint venture formed September 30, 1998. See Cable System Ownership.

PAWLEYS ISLAND—Jones Intercable Inc., 11546 Hwy. 17 Bypass S, Murrells Inlet, SC 29576. Phone: 864-237-8018. Counties: Georgetown & Horry. Also serves Georgetown County (eastern portion), Litchfield, Waccamawneck. ICA: SC0093.
TV Market Ranking: Below 100. Franchise award date: May 1, 1990. Franchise expiration date: May 1, 2015. Began: June 1, 1990.
Channel capacity: 70 (2-way capable; operating 2-way). Channels available but not in use: 20.
Basic Service
Subscribers: 400; Commercial subscribers: 1.
Programming (received off-air): WCBD-TV (N), WCIV (A), WCSC-TV (C), WTAT-TV (F,U) Charleston; WIS (N) Columbia; WHMC (P) Conway; WBTW (C), WPDE-TV (A) Florence; WFXB (F) Myrtle Beach; WECT (N), WWAY (A) Wilmington.
Programming (via satellite): WGN-TV (W) Chicago; A & E; American Movie Classics; Bravo; C-SPAN; C-SPAN 2; CNBC; CNN; Comedy Central; Country Music TV; Discovery Channel; ESPN; Electronic Program Guide; Fox Family Channel; Fox Sports Net South; Goodlife TV Network; Headline News; Home Shopping Network; Knowledge TV; Learning Channel; Lifetime; MTV; Nashville Network; Nickelodeon; QVC; TBS Superstation; TV Guide Channel; The Weather Channel; Travel Channel; Trinity Bcstg. Network; Turner Network TV; USA Network; VH1.
Current originations: Local access.
Fee: $19.50 monthly.
Pay Service 1
Pay Units: 19.
Programming (via satellite): Disney Channel.
Fee: $9.00 monthly.
Pay Service 2
Pay Units: 34.
Programming (via satellite): HBO.
Fee: $9.00 monthly.
Pay Service 3
Pay Units: 14.
Programming (via satellite): The Movie Channel.
Fee: $9.00 monthly.
Pay Service 4
Pay Units: N.A.
Programming (via satellite): Playboy TV; Showtime.
Fee: N.A.
Pay-Per-View
Addressable homes: 400.
Special events.
Local advertising: Yes. Available in satellite distributed, locally originated, character-generated & taped programming. Rates: $30.00/Minute.
Equipment: Drake headend; Jerrold amplifiers; Comm/Scope cable; Panasonic set top converters; Pico traps; Drake satellite antenna; ChannelMaster satellite receivers.
Miles of plant: 10.0 (coaxial). Additional miles planned: 40.0 (coaxial). Homes passed: 600. Total homes in franchised area: 6,000.
Manager: V. Miller. Chief technician: John L. Dumas.
Franchise fee: 3% of gross.
Ownership: Private Cable Communities Inc.

PICKENS—Charter Communications, Box 69, Pickens, SC 29671-0069. Phones: 864-878-0023; 800-878-0023. Fax: 864-963-2673. County: Pickens. Also serves Pickens County (portions). ICA: SC0135.
TV Market Ranking: 46. Franchise award date: N.A. Franchise expiration date: N.A. Began: April 2, 1991.
Channel capacity: 43. Channels available but not in use: 2.
Basic Service
Subscribers: 4,302.
Programming (received off-air): WFBC-TV (W) Anderson; WGGS-TV (I), WNTV (P) Greenville; WHNS (F,U), WLOS (A), WSPA-TV (C), WYFF (N) Greenville-Spartanburg-Asheville; WNEG-TV (I) Toccoa.
Programming (via satellite): WGN-TV (W) Chicago; TBS Superstation.
Current originations: Public access.
Fee: $30.00 installation; $21.85 monthly.
Expanded Basic Service
Subscribers: N.A.
Programming (via satellite): A & E; American Movie Classics; C-SPAN; CNBC; CNN; Cartoon Network; Comedy Central; Country Music TV; Discovery Channel; ESPN; ESPN 2; Fox Family Channel; Fox Sports Net South; Headline News; History Channel; Home & Garden Television; Home Shopping Network; Learning Channel; Lifetime; MTV; Nashville Network; Nick at Nite's TV Land; Nickelodeon; QVC; Sci-Fi Channel; TV Food Network; TV Guide Channel; The Inspirational Network; The Weather Channel; Turner Network TV; USA Network; VH1; Z Music Television.
Fee: $4.05 monthly.
Pay Service 1
Pay Units: 311.
Programming (via satellite): Cinemax.
Fee: $11.45 monthly.
Pay Service 2
Pay Units: 156.
Programming (via satellite): Disney Channel.
Fee: $8.45 monthly.
Pay Service 3
Pay Units: 433.
Programming (via satellite): HBO.
Fee: $11.45 monthly.
Pay Service 4
Pay Units: N.A.
Programming (via satellite): The Movie Channel.
Fee: N.A.
Pay Service 5
Pay Units: 177.
Programming (via satellite): Showtime.
Fee: $11.45 monthly.
Pay-Per-View
Addressable homes: 150.
Hot Choice; Playboy TV; Viewer's Choice.
Miles of plant: 340.0 (coaxial); None (fiber optic).
Manager: Buddy Timmons. Plant manager: Danny Walters. Marketing & program director: Tim Morrison.
Ownership: Charter Communications Inc. (MSO).

PINE GROVE—Galaxy Cablevision, 1899 S.E. 58th Ave., Ocala, FL 34471-5847. Phone: 352-624-1117. County: Kershaw. Also serves Kershaw County (western portion), Lugoff. ICA: SC0076.
TV Market Ranking: 100. Franchise award date: May 16, 1989. Franchise expiration date: May 14, 2004. Began: N.A.
Channel capacity: 30. Channels available but not in use: None.
Basic Service
Subscribers: 497.
Programming (received off-air): WACH (F), WIS (N), WLTX (C), WOLO-TV (A), WRLK-TV (P) Columbia.
Programming (via satellite): WGN-TV (W) Chicago; A & E; CNN; Country Music TV; Discovery Channel; ESPN; Fox Family Channel; Headline News; Lifetime; Nashville Network; Nickelodeon; QVC; TBS Superstation; The Weather Channel; Turner Network TV; USA Network; VH1.
Fee: $30.00 installation; $28.25 monthly.
Pay Service 1
Pay Units: 81.
Programming (via satellite): Cinemax.
Fee: $10.95 monthly.
Pay Service 2
Pay Units: 18.
Programming (via satellite): Disney Channel.
Fee: $10.95 monthly.
Pay Service 3
Pay Units: 90.
Programming (via satellite): HBO.
Fee: $10.95 monthly.
Miles of plant: 46.0 (coaxial). Homes passed: 1,035.
State manager: Dan Labbe. Technical manager: Joe Ferrell.
Ownership: Galaxy Cablevision (MSO).

PLUM BRANCH—Galaxy Cablevision, 1899 S.E. 58th Ave., Ocala, FL 34471-5847. Phone: 352-624-1117. County: McCormick. Also serves McCormick County (portions), Parksville. ICA: SC0100.
TV Market Ranking: Below 100. Franchise award date: April 1, 1990. Franchise expiration date: April 26, 2005. Began: August 27, 1990.
Channel capacity: 28 (not 2-way capable). Channels available but not in use: None.
Basic Service
Subscribers: 269.
Programming (received off-air): WTBS (I) Atlanta; WAGT (N), WFXG (F), WJBF (A), WRDW-TV (C) Augusta; WCES-TV (P) Wrens.
Programming (via satellite): WGN-TV (W) Chicago; CNN; Cartoon Network; Discovery Channel; ESPN; Fox Family Channel; Headline News; MTV; Nashville Network; Nickelodeon; QVC; USA Network.
Current originations: Public access.
Fee: $30.00 installation; $19.00 monthly.
Pay Service 1
Pay Units: 55.
Programming (via satellite): Disney Channel.
Fee: $6.94 monthly.
Pay Service 2
Pay Units: 108.
Programming (via satellite): HBO.
Fee: $9.72 monthly.
Pay Service 3
Pay Units: 86.
Programming (via satellite): Showtime.
Fee: $9.72 monthly.
Miles of plant: 26.5 (coaxial). Homes passed: 539.
State manager: Dan Labbe. Technical manager: Joe Ferrell.
Franchise fee: 3% of gross.
Ownership: Galaxy Cablevision (MSO).

REGENT PARK—Palmetto Cable, Box 1418, 101 Allison St., Fort Mill, SC 29715. Phone: 803-548-6000. County: York. ICA: SC0150.
TV Market Ranking: 42. Franchise award date: N.A. Franchise expiration date: N.A. Began: April 1, 1992.
Channel capacity: 37. Channels available but not in use: 8.
Basic Service
Subscribers: 315.
Programming (received off-air): WJZY (U) Belmont; WBTV (C), WCCB (F), WCNC-TV (N), WSOC-TV (A), WTVI (P) Charlotte; WIS (N) Columbia; WFVT (W), WNSC-TV (P) Rock Hill.
Programming (via satellite): WGN-TV (W) Chicago; A & E; C-SPAN; CNN; Discovery Channel; ESPN; Fox Family Channel; Goodlife TV Network; Headline News; Home Shopping Network; Learning Channel; Lifetime; Nashville Network; Odyssey; TBS Superstation; TV Guide Channel; Trinity Bcstg. Network; Turner Network TV; USA Network.
Fee: $20.00 installation; $17.95 monthly.
Pay Service 1
Pay Units: 19.

Programming (via satellite): Disney Channel.
Fee: $9.00 monthly.
Local advertising: Yes. Available in locally originated programming.
Equipment: Drake & Scientific-Atlanta satellite receivers.
Additional miles planned: 3.0 (coaxial). Homes passed: 450. Total homes in franchised area: 450.
Ownership: Palmetto Cable TV Inc.

RIDGELAND—Hargray CATV Co. Inc., Box 700, Ridgeland, SC 29936. Phone: 843-784-6411. County: Jasper. ICA: SC0137.
TV Market Ranking: Below 100. Franchise award date: N.A. Franchise expiration date: N.A. Began: March 1, 1983.
Channel capacity: 36. Channels available but not in use: N.A.
Basic Service
Subscribers: 916.
Programming (received off-air): WJWJ-TV (P) Beaufort; WCSC-TV (C) Charleston; WJCL (A), WSAV-TV (N), WTOC-TV (C) Savannah.
Programming (via satellite): WGN-TV (W) Chicago; CNN; ESPN; Fox Family Channel; Nashville Network; Nickelodeon; TBS Superstation; USA Network.
Fee: $13.65 monthly.
Pay Service 1
Pay Units: N.A.
Programming (via satellite): Cinemax; HBO.
Fee: $9.95 monthly (each).
Equipment: Scientific-Atlanta headend; Scientific-Atlanta cable; Scientific-Atlanta satellite antenna; Scientific-Atlanta satellite receivers.
Miles of plant: 100.0 (coaxial). Includes figures for Estill & Hardeeville, SC.
Manager: Frank Semken. Chief technician: Kerry Asher.
Ownership: Hargray Telephone Co. (MSO).

RIDGEVILLE—Time Warner Cable, Box 2080, 410 Trolley Rd., Summerville, SC 29484. Phone: 843-871-7000. Fax: 843-875-7600. County: Dorchester. ICA: SC0151.
TV Market Ranking: Below 100. Franchise award date: N.A. Franchise expiration date: N.A. Began: April 30, 1991.
Channel capacity: 54. Channels available but not in use: 17.
Basic Service
Subscribers: 307.
Programming (received off-air): WCBD-TV (N), WCIV (A), WCSC-TV (C), WITV (P), WMMP (U), WTAT-TV (F,U) Charleston.
Programming (via satellite): C-SPAN; CNBC; Home Shopping Network; MTV; QVC; Trinity Bcstg. Network.
Fee: $69.95 installation; $8.38 monthly.
Expanded Basic Service
Subscribers: 301.
Programming (via satellite): A & E; BET; Comedy Central; Court TV; Discovery Channel; ESPN; Fox Family Channel; Headline News; Knowledge TV; Lifetime; Nashville Network; Nickelodeon; Sci-Fi Channel; The Weather Channel; USA Network; VH1.
Fee: $11.87 monthly.
Expanded Basic Service 2
Subscribers: 301.
Programming (via satellite): CNN; TBS Superstation; Turner Network TV.
Fee: $2.95 monthly.
Pay Service 1
Pay Units: 134.
Programming (via satellite): Cinemax; Disney Channel; HBO; Playboy TV; Showtime; The Movie Channel.
Fee: $9.95 monthly (Disney), $10.50 monthly (Playboy), $10.95 monthly (Cinemax, Showtime or TMC), $11.95 monthly (HBO).
Miles of plant: 30.0 (coaxial); None (fiber optic). Homes passed: 650.
Manager: Tim Hartman. Chief technician: Mike Murray.
Ownership: Time Warner Cable (MSO).

RIVER HILLS—Enstar Cable TV, 310 10th St., North Wilkesboro, NC 28659-4112. Phone: 910-667-4151. County: York. Also serves Lake Wylie Woods, York County (portions). ICA: SC0073.
TV Market Ranking: 42 (Lake Wylie Woods, River Hills, portions of York County); 46 (portions of York County); Outside TV Markets (portions of York County). Franchise award date: N.A. Franchise expiration date: January 6, 2002. Began: June 1, 1982.
Channel capacity: 36 (not 2-way capable). Channels available but not in use: None.
Basic Service
Subscribers: 1,303.
Programming (received off-air): WJZY (U) Belmont; WBTV (C), WCCB (F), WCNC-TV (N), WSOC-TV (A) Charlotte; WIS (N) Columbia; WFVT (W), WNSC-TV (P) Rock Hill.
Programming (via satellite): A & E; American Movie Classics; C-SPAN; CNBC; CNN; ESPN; Fox Family Channel; Fox Sports Net South; Headline News; Learning Channel; QVC; Sci-Fi Channel; The Weather Channel; Trinity Bcstg. Network; Turner Network TV.
Current originations: Public access; educational access; government access.
Fee: $15.00 installation; $22.79 monthly; $7.50 additional installation.
Expanded Basic Service
Subscribers: 1,287.
Programming (via satellite): Discovery Channel; Lifetime; Nickelodeon; USA Network.
Fee: $1.90 monthly.
Expanded Basic Service 2
Subscribers: 1,113.
Programming (via satellite): WGN-TV (W) Chicago; Nashville Network; TBS Superstation.
Fee: $4.05 monthly.
Pay Service 1
Pay Units: 108.
Programming (via satellite): Cinemax.
Fee: $10.95 monthly.
Pay Service 2
Pay Units: 316.
Programming (via satellite): HBO.
Fee: $11.95 monthly.
Pay Service 3
Pay Units: 148.
Programming (via satellite): Showtime.
Fee: $10.95 monthly.
Pay Service 4
Pay Units: 116.
Programming (via satellite): The Movie Channel.
Fee: $10.95 monthly.
Local advertising: No.
Equipment: Scientific-Atlanta headend; Scientific-Atlanta amplifiers; Comm/Scope cable; Scientific-Atlanta set top converters; Scientific-Atlanta satellite antenna; Scientific-Atlanta satellite receivers.
Miles of plant: 50.0 (coaxial). Homes passed: 1,661.
Manager: Wanda Parsons. Chief technician: Eddie Collins.
Franchise fee: 5% of gross.
Ownership: Falcon Communications LP (MSO), joint venture formed September 30, 1998. See Cable System Ownership.

ROCK HILL—Rock Hill Cable TV, Box 11703, 249 E. Main St., Rock Hill, SC 29730. Phone: 803-329-9000. Fax: 803-324-2600. Counties: Chester & York. Also serves Chester County (unincorporated areas), Richburg, York County. ICA: SC0138.
TV Market Ranking: 42 (portions of Chester County, Rock Hill, portions of York County); 46 (portions of Chester County, portions of York County); Below 100 (portions of Chester County, Richburg, portions of York County). Franchise award date: January 1, 1965. Franchise expiration date: March 1, 2007. Began: January 1, 1967.
Channel capacity: 77 (not 2-way capable). Channels available but not in use: 15.
Basic Service
Subscribers: 22,475.
Programming (received off-air): WJZY (U) Belmont; WBTV (C), WCCB (F), WCNC-TV (N), WSOC-TV (A), WTVI (P) Charlotte; WSPA-TV (C) Greenville-Spartanburg-Asheville; WAXN (I) Kannapolis; WFVT (W), WNSC-TV (P) Rock Hill; allband FM.
Programming (via satellite): C-SPAN; C-SPAN 2; Home Shopping Network; TV Guide Channel; Trinity Bcstg. Network.
Current originations: Automated time-weather; religious access; local news.
Fee: $45.00 installation; $13.95 monthly; $2.10 converter.
Expanded Basic Service
Subscribers: 20,421.
Programming (via satellite): A & E; American Movie Classics; BET; CNN; CNNfn; Cartoon Network; Comedy Central; Country Music TV; Discovery Channel; ESPN; ESPN 2; ESPN Classic Sports; FX; Fox Family Channel; Fox Sports Net South; Headline News; History Channel; Home & Garden Television; Learning Channel; Lifetime; Nashville Network; Nick at Nite's TV Land; Nickelodeon; Sci-Fi Channel; TBS Superstation; TV Guide Sneak Prevue; The Weather Channel; Turner Network TV; USA Network; VH1.
Fee: $16.70 monthly.
Pay Service 1
Pay Units: 2,104.
Programming (via satellite): Cinemax (multiplexed).
Fee: $9.95 monthly.
Pay Service 2
Pay Units: 1,078.
Programming (via satellite): Disney Channel.
Fee: $7.95 monthly.
Pay Service 3
Pay Units: 4,949.
Programming (via satellite): HBO (multiplexed).
Fee: $9.95 monthly.
Pay Service 4
Pay Units: 1,741.
Programming (via satellite): Showtime; The Movie Channel.
Fee: $9.95 monthly.
Pay Service 5
Pay Units: 3,135.
Programming (via satellite): The New Encore.
Fee: $5.95 monthly.
Pay Service 6
Pay Units: 3,158.
Programming (via satellite): Starz!
Fee: $9.95 monthly.
Pay-Per-View
Addressable homes: 19,434.
Viewer's Choice.
Local advertising: Yes. Rates: Vary. Local sales manager: John Burnett. Regional interconnect: Cable Adcast-North Carolina.
Equipment: Jerrold headend; C-COR & Scientific-Atlanta amplifiers; Siecor cable; Sony cameras; Sony VTRs; Scientific-Atlanta set top converters; Scientific-Atlanta addressable set top converters; Eagle traps; Scientific-Atlanta satellite antenna; Scientific-Atlanta satellite receivers.
Miles of plant: 427.8 (coaxial). Additional miles planned: 100.0 (coaxial). Homes passed: 32,039.
Manager: William C. Beaty Jr. Chief technician: Danny Ghent. Marketing & program director: John Barnes Jr. Customer service manager: Sherri Parrish.
City fee: 5% of gross.
Ownership: Catawba Services Inc. (MSO).

SALEM—Charter Communications, 1202 Stamp Creek Rd., Salem, SC 29676. Phone: 843-944-1043. Fax: 843-944-7655. County: Oconee. Also serves Ebenezer, Fairfield, Keowee Key, Oconee County (unincorporated areas), Pickett Post. ICA: SC0139.
TV Market Ranking: 46 (Ebenezer, Fairfield, Keowee Key, portions of Oconee County, Pickett Post, Salem); Below 100 (portions of Oconee County); Outside TV Markets (portions of Oconee County). Franchise award date: N.A. Franchise expiration date: N.A. Began: January 1, 1987.
Channel capacity: 36. Channels available but not in use: 12.
Basic Service
Subscribers: 1,428.
Programming (received off-air): WNTV (P) Greenville; WHNS (F,U), WLOS (A), WSPA-TV (C), WYFF (N) Greenville-Spartanburg-Asheville.
Programming (via satellite): WGN-TV (W) Chicago; A & E; American Movie Classics; C-SPAN; CNBC; CNN; Comedy Central; Country Music TV; Discovery Channel; E! Entertainment TV; ESPN; Fox Family Channel; Headline News; Learning Channel; Lifetime; Nashville Network; Nickelodeon; QVC; TBS Superstation; The Weather Channel; Travel Channel; Turner Network TV; USA Network; VH1.
Current originations: Automated time-weather.
Fee: $40.00 installation; $26.95 monthly.
Pay Service 1
Pay Units: 86.
Programming (via satellite): Disney Channel.
Fee: $7.95 monthly.
Pay Service 2
Pay Units: 224.
Programming (via satellite): HBO.
Fee: $15.00 installation; $10.95 monthly.
Pay Service 3
Pay Units: 115.
Programming (via satellite): Showtime.
Fee: $15.00 installation; $10.95 monthly.
Equipment: Scientific-Atlanta headend; Scientific-Atlanta amplifiers; Comm/Scope cable; Texscan character generator; Eagle traps; Scientific-Atlanta satellite antenna; Scientific-Atlanta satellite receivers.
Miles of plant: 130.0 (coaxial).
Manager: Ron Johnson. Chief technician: Mark Medlin.
Ownership: Charter Communications Inc. (MSO).

SALUDA—Robin Cable Systems LP, Box 151, 3060 Cablevision Rd., Aiken, SC 29801-2906. Phone: 864-445-8018. Fax: 864-445-7935. County: Saluda. Also serves Saluda County. ICA: SC0074.
TV Market Ranking: 100 (portions of Saluda County); Below 100 (portions of Saluda County); Outside TV Markets (Saluda, portions of Saluda County). Franchise award

date: July 1, 1981. Franchise expiration date: N.A. Began: December 1, 1981.
Channel capacity: 36 (not 2-way capable). Channels available but not in use: 9.
Basic Service
Subscribers: 698; Commercial subscribers: 15.
Programming (received off-air): WFXG (F), WJBF (A) Augusta; WIS (N), WLTX (C), WOLO-TV (A), WRLK-TV (P) Columbia.
Programming (via satellite): WGN-TV (W) Chicago; A & E; BET; C-SPAN; CNN; Country Music TV; Discovery Channel; ESPN; Fox Family Channel; Fox Sports Net South; Headline News; Home Shopping Network; Lifetime; MTV; Nashville Network; Nickelodeon; TBS Superstation; The Weather Channel; Turner Network TV; USA Network; VH1.
Fee: $49.95 installation; $25.66 monthly; $10.00 additional installation.
Commercial fee: $5.50 monthly.
Pay Service 1
Pay Units: 400.
Programming (via satellite): Disney Channel; HBO; Showtime.
Fee: $7.50 installation; $8.50 monthly (Disney), $8.95 monthly (HBO or Showtime).
Equipment: Jerrold headend; Jerrold amplifiers; Comm/Scope cable; Jerrold set top converters; Scientific-Atlanta satellite antenna; Jerrold & Scientific-Atlanta satellite receivers.
Miles of plant: 25.0 (coaxial). Additional miles planned: 2.0 (coaxial). Homes passed: 906.
Manager: Lee A. Perron. Chief technician: Tony Urban.
City fee: 3% of gross.
Ownership: InterMedia Partners (MSO).

SAMPIT—Benchmark Communications, 2511 Highmarket St., Georgetown, SC 29440. Phone: 843-527-2447. Fax: 843-527-2034. County: Georgetown. Also serves Lambertown, North Santee, North Stone. ICA: SC0090.
TV Market Ranking: Below 100. Franchise award date: N.A. Franchise expiration date: N.A. Began: March 1, 1989.
Channel capacity: 36 (not 2-way capable). Channels available but not in use: 3.
Basic Service
Subscribers: 779.
Programming (received off-air): WCBD-TV (N), WCIV (A), WCSC-TV (C), WITV (P), WTAT-TV (F,U) Charleston; WBTW (C), WPDE-TV (A) Florence.
Programming (via satellite): WGN-TV (W) Chicago; A & E; American Movie Classics; Animal Planet; BET; C-SPAN; CNN; Cartoon Network; Country Music TV; Discovery Channel; ESPN; Fox Family Channel; Fox News Channel; Headline News; Home & Garden Television; Learning Channel; Lifetime; MTV; Nashville Network; Nickelodeon; QVC; Sci-Fi Channel; TBS Superstation; TV Guide Channel; The Weather Channel; Trinity Bcstg. Network; Turner Network TV; USA Network; VH1.
Fee: $25.00 installation; $24.92 monthly; $2.00 converter.
Pay Service 1
Pay Units: 9.
Programming (via satellite): Cinemax.
Fee: $9.50 monthly.
Pay Service 2
Pay Units: 28.
Programming (via satellite): Disney Channel.
Fee: $9.50 monthly.
Pay Service 3
Pay Units: 9.
Programming (via satellite): HBO.
Fee: $9.50 monthly.
Pay Service 4
Pay Units: 7.
Programming (via satellite): Showtime.
Fee: $9.50 monthly.
Equipment: Scientific-Atlanta headend; Texscan amplifiers; Trilogy cable; Scientific-Atlanta character generator; Scientific-Atlanta set top converters; Pico traps; ChannelMaster satellite antenna.
Miles of plant: 78.0 (coaxial); None (fiber optic). Additional miles planned: 24.0 (coaxial). Homes passed: 1,348. Total homes in franchised area: 5,000.
Manager: Kenneth Koch.
County fee: 3% of basic.
Ownership: Benchmark Communications (MSO). Purchased from Genesis Cable Communications LLC, May 3, 1999.

SANTEE—Blackstone Cable LLC, 10 S. Franklin Turnpike, Ramsey, NJ 07446. Phone: 201-825-9090. Fax: 201-825-8794. County: Orangeburg. Also serves Vance. ICA: SC0140.
TV Market Ranking: Outside TV Markets. Franchise award date: April 1, 1982. Franchise expiration date: N.A. Began: January 1, 1985.
Channel capacity: 45 (not 2-way capable). Channels available but not in use: 12.
Basic Service
Subscribers: 740.
Programming (received off-air): WRDW-TV (C) Augusta; WCBD-TV (N), WCSC-TV (C) Charleston; WIS (N) Columbia.
Programming (via satellite): WGN-TV (W) Chicago; A & E; BET; CNN; Country Music TV; Discovery Channel; ESPN; Fox Family Channel; Golf Channel; Headline News; Nashville Network; QVC; Sci-Fi Channel; TBS Superstation; The Weather Channel; Trinity Bcstg. Network; Turner Classic Movies; Turner Network TV; USA Network.
Current originations: Educational access.
Fee: $23.50 monthly.
Pay Service 1
Pay Units: N.A.
Programming (via satellite): Cinemax; Disney Channel; HBO; Showtime; The Movie Channel.
Fee: $9.00 monthly.
Manager: Maryanne Lyman.
Ownership: Blackstone Cable LLC (MSO). Purchased from Milestone Media Management Inc., July 1, 1998.

SENECA—Northland Cable Television, Box 833, Seneca, SC 29679. Phone: 864-882-0002. Fax: 864-882-4490. Counties: Anderson, Oconee & Pickens. Also serves Anderson County (unincorporated areas), Central, Clemson (unincorporated areas), Oconee County (unincorporated areas), Pendleton, Walhalla, West Union, Westminster. ICA: SC0019.
TV Market Ranking: 46. Franchise award date: April 11, 1977. Franchise expiration date: September 22, 2017. Began: June 1, 1979.
Channel capacity: 43 (not 2-way capable). Channels available but not in use: 1.
Basic Service
Subscribers: 9,900.
Programming (received off-air): WFBC-TV (W) Anderson; WGGS-TV (I), WNTV (P) Greenville; WHNS (F,U), WSPA-TV (C), WYFF (N) Greenville-Spartanburg-Asheville; WNEG-TV (I) Toccoa.
Programming (via satellite): C-SPAN; Home Shopping Network; TV Guide Channel.
Fee: $50.00 installation; $10.40 monthly.
Expanded Basic Service
Subscribers: 9,850.
Programming (via satellite): WGN-TV (W) Chicago; A & E; BET; CNN; Country Music TV; Discovery Channel; ESPN; Fox Family Channel; Headline News; Nashville Network; TBS Superstation; The Weather Channel.

Fee: $11.23 monthly.
Expanded Basic Service 2
Subscribers: 9,750.
Programming (via satellite): American Movie Classics; Fox Sports Net South; MTV; Nickelodeon; Turner Network TV; USA Network.
Fee: $5.15 monthly.
Pay Service 1
Pay Units: 587.
Programming (via satellite): Cinemax.
Fee: $30.00 installation; $10.45 monthly.
Pay Service 2
Pay Units: 338.
Programming (via satellite): Disney Channel.
Fee: $30.00 installation; $8.95 monthly.
Pay Service 3
Pay Units: 899.
Programming (via satellite): HBO.
Fee: $30.00 installation; $12.55 monthly.
Pay Service 4
Pay Units: 232.
Programming (via satellite): The Movie Channel.
Fee: $30.00 installation; $9.40 monthly.
Local advertising: Yes. Available in locally originated programming.
Equipment: Scientific-Atlanta headend; Scientific-Atlanta amplifiers; Comm/Scope cable; Jerrold set top converters; Pico traps; Scientific-Atlanta satellite antenna; Scientific-Atlanta satellite receivers.
Miles of plant: 396.0 (coaxial); 18.0 (fiber optic). Additional miles planned: 12.0 (coaxial). Homes passed: 15,700.
Manager: Jim Carr. Chief technician: Alan Boggs.
City fee: 5% of gross.
Ownership: Northland Communications Corp. (MSO).

SOCIETY HILL—Galaxy Cablevision, 1899 S.E. 58th Ave., Ocala, FL 34471-5847. Phone: 352-624-1117. County: Darlington. Also serves Darlington County (unincorporated areas). ICA: SC0086.
TV Market Ranking: Below 100. Franchise award date: N.A. Franchise expiration date: N.A. Began: September 1, 1989.
Channel capacity: 35. Channels available but not in use: 10.
Basic Service
Subscribers: 407.
Programming (received off-air): WIS (N) Columbia; WBTW (C), WJPM-TV (P), WPDE-TV (A) Florence.
Programming (via satellite): WGN-TV (W) Chicago; A & E; American Movie Classics; BET; CNBC; CNN; Discovery Channel; ESPN; Headline News; Lifetime; Nashville Network; Nickelodeon; QVC; TBS Superstation; The Weather Channel; Turner Network TV; USA Network; VH1.
Fee: $20.00 installation; $19.95 monthly.
Pay Service 1
Pay Units: 30.
Programming (via satellite): Disney Channel.
Fee: $10.95 monthly.
Pay Service 2
Pay Units: 166.
Programming (via satellite): HBO.
Fee: $10.95 monthly.
Pay Service 3
Pay Units: 115.
Programming (via satellite): Showtime.
Fee: $10.95 monthly.
Miles of plant: 11.0 (coaxial). Homes passed: 701.
State manager: Dan Labbe. Technical manager: Joe Ferrell.
Ownership: Galaxy Cablevision (MSO).

SPARTANBURG—InterMedia of Spartanburg, Box 2944, Spartanburg, SC 29304. Phone: 864-585-0354. Fax: 864-585-7701. Counties: Cherokee, Greenville, Spartanburg & Union. Also serves Campobello, Central Pacolet, Cherokee County (western portion), Chesnee, Cowpens, Duncan, Greenville County, Greer, Inman, Jonesville, Landrum, Lyman, Pacolet, Pacolet Mills, Spartanburg County, Union County, Wellford. ICA: SC0004.
TV Market Ranking: 46 (Campobello, Central Pacolet, Cherokee County, Chesnee, Cowpens, Duncan, Greenville County, Greer, Inman, Jonesville, Landrum, Lyman, Pacolet, Pacolet Mills, Spartanburg, Spartanburg County, portions of Union County, Wellford); Below 100 (portions of Union County); Outside TV Markets (portions of Union County). Franchise award date: January 1, 1971. Franchise expiration date: January 1, 2004. Began: November 1, 1972.
Channel capacity: 47. Channels available but not in use: None.
Basic Service
Subscribers: 42,821.
Programming (received off-air): WGGS-TV (I) Greenville; WHNS (F,U), WLOS (A), WSPA-TV (C), WYFF (N) Greenville-Spartanburg-Asheville; WRET-TV (P) Spartanburg; allband FM.
Programming (via satellite): WGN-TV (W) Chicago; A & E; BET; C-SPAN; C-SPAN 2; CNBC; Comedy Central; Country Music TV; Fox Family Channel; Learning Channel; QVC; TBS Superstation; TV Guide Channel; The Weather Channel; Travel Channel; VH1; ValueVision.
Current originations: Automated time-weather; local news.
Fee: $37.33 installation; $13.18 monthly; $21.83 additional installation.
Expanded Basic Service
Subscribers: 34,785.
Programming (via satellite): American Movie Classics; CNN; Discovery Channel; ESPN; FX; Fox Sports Net South; Headline News; Lifetime; MTV; Nashville Network; Nickelodeon; Sci-Fi Channel; Turner Network TV; USA Network.
Fee: $37.33 installation; $9.05 monthly.
Pay Service 1
Pay Units: N.A.
Programming (via satellite): Cinemax (multiplexed); Disney Channel; HBO (multiplexed); Showtime (multiplexed); The Movie Channel.
Fee: $10.00 monthly (each).
Local advertising: Yes. Available in satellite distributed programming. Local sales manager: John Hood.
Equipment: Scientific-Atlanta headend; Jerrold amplifiers; Comm/Scope cable; Sony VTRs; Jerrold & Pioneer set top converters; Zenith

addressable set top converters; Eagle traps; Scientific-Atlanta satellite antenna; Scientific-Atlanta satellite receivers.
Miles of plant: 1025.4 (coaxial); 25.0 (fiber optic). Homes passed: 55,000.
Manager: Kirby Brooks. Chief technician: Johnnie Turner.
Ownership: InterMedia Partners (MSO). See Cable System Ownership.

ST. GEORGE—Phoenix Concept Cablevision of Indiana, 106 S. Main St., Sheridan, IN 46069. Phone: 317-758-4474. County: Dorchester. Also serves Dorchester County (unincorporated areas), Reevesville. ICA: SC0078.
TV Market Ranking: Below 100 (portions of Dorchester County); Outside TV Markets (portions of Dorchester County, Reevesville, St. George). Franchise award date: January 1, 1981. Franchise expiration date: N.A. Began: August 8, 1983.
Channel capacity: 35. Channels available but not in use: N.A.
Basic Service
Subscribers: N.A.
Programming (received off-air): WCBD-TV (N), WCIV (A), WCSC-TV (C), WITV (P), WTAT-TV (F,U) Charleston.
Programming (via satellite): BET; CNN; ESPN; Fox Family Channel; Nashville Network; Nickelodeon; TBS Superstation; USA Network.
Fee: $8.25 monthly.
Pay Service 1
Pay Units: N.A.
Programming (via satellite): Cinemax; Disney Channel; HBO; Playboy TV; Showtime; The Movie Channel.
Fee: $9.00 monthly (each).
Equipment: Scientific-Atlanta headend; Scientific-Atlanta cable; Scientific-Atlanta satellite antenna; Scientific-Atlanta satellite receivers.
Miles of plant: 18.0 (coaxial). Homes passed: 900.
Manager: Helen P. Belisle. Chief technician: Clarence Roberts.
Ownership: Phoenix Cable Inc. (MSO).

ST. MATTHEWS—Alert Cable TV of South Carolina Inc., 125 E. Bridge St., St. Matthews, SC 29135. Phone: 803-655-5703. Fax: 803-655-7870. County: Calhoun. Also serves Calhoun County (portions). ICA: SC0072.
TV Market Ranking: 100 (portions of Calhoun County, St. Matthews); Outside TV Markets (portions of Calhoun County). Franchise award date: October 13, 1981. Franchise expiration date: N.A. Began: N.A.
Channel capacity: 32 (not 2-way capable). Channels available but not in use: 11.
Basic Service
Subscribers: 567.
Programming (received off-air): WACH (F), WIS (N), WLTX (C), WOLO-TV (A), WRLK-TV (P) Columbia.
Programming (via satellite): WGN-TV (W) Chicago; CNN; Discovery Channel; ESPN; Fox Family Channel; Nashville Network; Nickelodeon; QVC; TBS Superstation; The Weather Channel; USA Network; VH1.
Current originations: Automated time-weather; public access; educational access; government access; religious access; leased access; automated emergency alert; local news; local sports.
Fee: $10.00 installation; $18.00 monthly.
Pay Service 1
Pay Units: 75.
Programming (via satellite): Cinemax.
Fee: $40.00 installation; $8.95 monthly.
Pay Service 2
Pay Units: 50.
Programming (via satellite): Disney Channel.
Fee: $40.00 installation; $8.95 monthly.
Pay Service 3
Pay Units: 125.
Programming (via satellite): HBO.
Fee: $40.00 installation; $9.95 monthly.
Interactive Services
Home shopping.
Local advertising: No.
Program Guide: Premium Channels.
Equipment: Scientific-Atlanta & DX Engineering headend; Scientific-Atlanta & Jerrold amplifiers; Times Fiber cable; Jerrold set top converters; Eagle traps; Scientific-Atlanta & Microdyne satellite antenna; Scientific-Atlanta & DX Engineering satellite receivers.
Miles of plant: 23.0 (coaxial). Additional miles planned: 1.0 (coaxial). Homes passed: 985. Total homes in franchised area: 1,000.
Manager: Terry Roberson. Chief technician: Marty Kinard. Marketing director: Dale Ordoyne.
City fee: 5% of gross.
Ownership: Time Warner Cable (MSO); Advance/Newhouse Partnership (MSO).

ST. STEPHEN—Pine Tree Cablevision, Box 1060, 3931 Byrnes Dr., St. Stephen, SC 29479. Phone: 843-567-3289. Fax: 843-567-2089. County: Berkeley. Also serves Alvin, Berkeley County (unincorporated areas), Bonneau, Bonneau Beach, Macedonia, Pineville, Russellville. ICA: SC0141.
TV Market Ranking: Below 100 (portions of Berkeley County); Outside TV Markets (Alvin, portions of Berkeley County, Bonneau, Bonneau Beach, Macedonia, Pineville, Russellville, St. Stephen). Franchise award date: January 1, 1986. Franchise expiration date: N.A. Began: January 1, 1989.
Channel capacity: 42 (not 2-way capable). Channels available but not in use: 3.
Basic Service
Subscribers: 1,600.
Programming (received off-air): WCBD-TV (N), WCIV (A), WCSC-TV (C), WITV (P), WTAT-TV (F,U) Charleston; WIS (N) Columbia.
Programming (via satellite): WGN-TV (W) Chicago; A & E; BET; CNN; Country Music TV; Discovery Channel; ESPN; Fox Family Channel; Home Shopping Network; Lifetime; MTV; Nashville Network; Nickelodeon; TBS Superstation; Trinity Bcstg. Network; Turner Network TV; USA Network; VH1.
Fee: $40.00 installation; $24.65 monthly.
Pay Service 1
Pay Units: 272.
Programming (via satellite): Cinemax.
Fee: $9.95 monthly.
Pay Service 2
Pay Units: 502.
Programming (via satellite): HBO.
Fee: $9.95 monthly.
Pay Service 3
Pay Units: 263.
Programming (via satellite): Showtime.
Fee: $9.95 monthly.
Equipment: Scientific-Atlanta amplifiers.
Manager: Walter Kemmerer.
Ownership: Pine Tree Cablevision (MSO). Purchased from Bay Cable Inc., February 1, 1999.

SUMMERTON—Blackstone Cable LLC, 10 S. Franklin Turnpike, Ramsey, NJ 07446. Phone: 201-825-9090. Fax: 201-825-8794. County: Clarendon. Also serves Davis Station, Goat Island, Manning, Potato Creek, Taw Caw. ICA: SC0077.
TV Market Ranking: Below 100. Franchise award date: November 1, 1988. Franchise expiration date: November 1, 2008. Began: March 1, 1989.
Channel capacity: 46 (not 2-way capable). Channels available but not in use: 1.
Basic Service
Subscribers: 1,021.
Programming (received off-air): WCBD-TV (N), WCIV (A), WCSC-TV (C), WITV (P), WTAT-TV (F,U) Charleston; WIS (N), WLTX (C) Columbia.
Programming (via satellite): WGN-TV (W) Chicago; A & E; C-SPAN; CNBC; CNN; Country Music TV; Discovery Channel; ESPN; ESPN 2; Fox Family Channel; Golf Channel; Headline News; History Channel; Home Shopping Network; Knowledge TV; Learning Channel; Lifetime; MTV; Nashville Network; Nickelodeon; QVC; Sci-Fi Channel; TBS Superstation; The Weather Channel; Travel Channel; Trinity Bcstg. Network; Turner Classic Movies; Turner Network TV; USA Network; VH1.
Current originations: Automated emergency alert.
Planned originations: Public access.
Fee: $35.00 installation; $23.50 monthly; $3.00 converter.
Pay Service 1
Pay Units: 11.
Programming (via satellite): Disney Channel.
Fee: $10.00 installation; $7.95 monthly.
Pay Service 2
Pay Units: 71.
Programming (via satellite): HBO.
Fee: $10.00 installation; $9.95 monthly.
Pay Service 3
Pay Units: 36.
Programming (via satellite): Showtime.
Fee: $10.00 installation; $9.95 monthly.
Pay Service 4
Pay Units: N.A.
Programming (via satellite): Cinemax; The Movie Channel.
Fee: N.A.
Local advertising: Planned.
Program Guide: CableView.
Equipment: Scientific-Atlanta headend; Scientific-Atlanta set top converters; Eagle traps; Prodelin satellite antenna; DX Antenna satellite receivers.
Miles of plant: 73.0 (coaxial).
County fee: 5% of gross.
Ownership: Blackstone Cable LLC (MSO). Purchased from Milestone Media Management Inc., July 1, 1998.

SUMMERVILLE—Time Warner Cable, Box 2080, 410 Trolley Rd., Summerville, SC 29484. Phone: 843-871-7000. Fax: 843-875-7600. Counties: Berkeley & Dorchester. Also serves Berkeley County (portions), Dorchester County (portions), North Charleston (western portion). ICA: SC0012.
TV Market Ranking: Below 100 (portions of Berkeley County, portions of Dorchester County, North Charleston, Summerville); Outside TV Markets (portions of Berkeley County, portions of Dorchester County). Franchise award date: December 12, 1979. Franchise expiration date: N.A. Began: February 28, 1980.
Channel capacity: 37 (2-way capable; operating 2-way). Channels available but not in use: None.
Basic Service
Subscribers: 18,900.
Programming (received off-air): WCBD-TV (N), WCIV (A), WCSC-TV (C), WITV (P), WMMP (U), WTAT-TV (F,U) Charleston.
Programming (via satellite): C-SPAN; CNBC; Home Shopping Network; MTV; QVC; Trinity Bcstg. Network.
Current originations: Automated time-weather; public access; educational access.
Fee: $69.95 installation; $8.38 monthly; $3.00 converter.
Expanded Basic Service
Subscribers: 18,522.
Programming (via satellite): A & E; American Movie Classics; BET; Comedy Central; Court TV; Discovery Channel; ESPN; Fox Family Channel; Headline News; Knowledge TV; Lifetime; Nashville Network; Nickelodeon; Sci-Fi Channel; The Weather Channel; USA Network; VH1.
Fee: $11.87 monthly.
A la Carte 1
Subscribers: 18,522.
Programming (via satellite): CNN; TBS Superstation; Turner Network TV.
Fee: $2.95 monthly (package).
Pay Service 1
Pay Units: 9,086.
Programming (via satellite): Cinemax; Disney Channel; HBO; Playboy TV; Showtime; The Movie Channel.
Fee: $40.00 installation; $9.95 monthly (Disney), $10.50 monthly (Playboy), $10.95 monthly (Cinemax, Showtime or TMC), $11.95 monthly (HBO).
Pay-Per-View
Special events.
Fee: Varies.
Local advertising: Yes. Available in satellite distributed & character-generated programming. Rates: $2.00/30 Seconds.
Equipment: Scientific-Atlanta & DX Engineering headend; Jerrold & Scientific-Atlanta amplifiers; Cerro, Times Fiber & Comm/Scope cable; Sony cameras; Sony VTRs; Video Data Systems character generator; Oak set top converters; Gardiner & Scientific-Atlanta satellite antenna; Scientific-Atlanta satellite receivers.
Miles of plant: 600.0 (coaxial); 9.0 (fiber optic). Homes passed: 30,440.
Manager: Tim Hartman. Chief technician: Mike Murray. Marketing director: Dale Ordoyne.
City fee: 3% of gross.
Ownership: Time Warner Cable (MSO).

SUMTER—Time Warner Cable, 1170 N. Guignard Dr., Sumter, SC 29150. Phone: 803-469-3700. Fax: 803-469-2423. County: Sumter. Also serves Dalzell, Mayesville, Pinewood, Shaw AFB, Sumter County. ICA: SC0008.
TV Market Ranking: 100 (Dalzell, Shaw AFB, portions of Sumter County); Below 100 (Mayesville, Pinewood, portions of Sumter County); Outside TV Markets (Sumter, portions of Sumter County). Franchise award date: N.A. Franchise expiration date: N.A. Began: February 1, 1964.
Channel capacity: 53 (not 2-way capable). Channels available but not in use: N.A.
Basic Service
Subscribers: 24,000; Commercial subscribers: 10.
Programming (received off-air): WACH (F), WIS (N), WLTX (C), WOLO-TV (A) Columbia; WBTW (C), WPDE-TV (A) Florence; WQHB (U), WRJA-TV (P) Sumter.
Current originations: Public access.
Fee: $48.00 installation; $35.40 monthly.
Expanded Basic Service
Subscribers: N.A.
Programming (via satellite): WGN-TV (W) Chicago; A & E; American Movie Classics; Animal Planet; BET; C-SPAN; CNBC; CNN; Cartoon Network; Country Music TV; Court TV; Discovery Channel; E! Entertainment TV; ESPN; ESPN 2; FX; Fox Family Channel; Headline News; History Channel; Home & Garden Television; Learning Channel; Lifetime; MSNBC; MTV; Nashville Network; Nickelodeon; Odyssey; QVC; TBS Superstation;

TV Guide Channel; TV Guide Sneak Prevue; The Weather Channel; Trinity Bcstg. Network; Turner Network TV; USA Network; VH1.
Fee: N.A.
Expanded Basic Service 2
Subscribers: N.A.
Programming (via satellite): fXM: Movies from Fox; Fox Sports Net South; Golf Channel; Sci-Fi Channel; Turner Classic Movies.
Fee: N.A.
Pay Service 1
Pay Units: N.A.
Programming (via satellite): Cinemax (multiplexed); Disney Channel; HBO (multiplexed); Showtime.
Fee: $8.39 installation; $6.95 monthly (Cinemax, Disney or Showtime), $10.95 monthly (HBO).
Pay-Per-View
Addressable homes: 12,500.
Hot Choice; Viewer's Choice.
Local advertising: Yes (digital insertion). Available in satellite distributed programming. Local sales manager: Susan Trantsch.
Equipment: Scientific-Atlanta headend; Jerrold amplifiers; Tribeyey Cable cable; Jerrold addressable set top converters.
Miles of plant: 750.0 (coaxial); 30.0 (fiber optic). Homes passed: 29,000. Total homes in franchised area: 30,000.
Manager: Jim Mott. Chief technician: Glenn Washington. Marketing director: J. J. Jonas.
City fee: 5% of gross.
Ownership: Time Warner Cable (MSO); Advance/Newhouse Partnership (MSO).

SURFSIDE BEACH—Jones Intercable, 1901 Oak St., Myrtle Beach, SC 29577. Phone: 843-651-6699. Fax: 843-651-0757. Counties: Georgetown & Horry. Also serves Garden City Beach, Georgetown County, Horry County, Murrells Inlet, Myrtle Beach (portions), Pawleys Island, Socastee. ICA: SC0006.
TV Market Ranking: Below 100 (Garden City Beach, portions of Georgetown County, portions of Horry County, Murrells Inlet, Myrtle Beach, Pawleys Island, Socastee, Surfside Beach); Outside TV Markets (portions of Georgetown County, portions of Horry County). Franchise award date: N.A. Franchise expiration date: February 2, 2013. Began: January 1, 1971.
Channel capacity: 77 (2-way capable; operating 2-way). Channels available but not in use: 6.
Basic Service
Subscribers: 22,000; Commercial subscribers: 12,500.
Programming (received off-air): WCBD-TV (N), WCIV (A), WCSC-TV (C), WTAT-TV (F,U) Charleston; WIS (N) Columbia; WHMC (P) Conway; WBTW (C), WPDE-TV (A), WWMB (U) Florence; WFXB (F) Myrtle Beach; WECT (N) Wilmington.
Programming (via satellite): Knowledge TV; TBS Superstation; TV Guide Channel.
Current originations: Automated timeweather.
Fee: $25.00 installation; $18.50 additional installation.
Expanded Basic Service
Subscribers: N.A.
Programming (via satellite): A & E; American Movie Classics; Animal Planet; BET; Bravo; C-SPAN; C-SPAN 2; CNBC; CNN; Cartoon Network; Comedy Central; Discovery Channel; E! Entertainment TV; ESPN; ESPN 2; FX; Fox Family Channel; Fox Sports Net South; Golf Channel; Goodlife TV Network; Great American Country; Headline News; History Channel; Home & Garden Television; Home Shopping Network; Learning Channel; Lifetime; MSNBC; MTV; Nashville Network; Nickelodeon; Odyssey; Product Information Network; QVC; TV Guide Sneak Prevue; The Weather Channel; Turner Network TV; USA Network; VH1.
Fee: $16.30 monthly.
Pay Service 1
Pay Units: 3,328.
Programming (via satellite): Disney Channel.
Fee: $1.99 installation; $5.95 monthly.
Pay Service 2
Pay Units: 5,538.
Programming (via satellite): HBO.
Fee: $1.99 installation; $9.95 monthly.
Pay Service 3
Pay Units: 243.
Programming (via satellite): Playboy TV.
Fee: $1.99 installation; $9.95 monthly.
Pay Service 4
Pay Units: 3,142.
Programming (via satellite): Showtime; The Movie Channel.
Fee: $1.99 installation; $9.95 monthly.
Pay Service 5
Pay Units: 3,865.
Programming (via satellite): Cinemax.
Fee: $1.99 installation; $5.95 monthly.
Pay-Per-View
Addressable homes: 13,250.
Playboy TV; Spice.
Fee: $3.95.
Local advertising: Yes. Available in satellite distributed programming. Local sales manager: Jeff Hesla.
Equipment: Scientific-Atlanta headend; Scientific-Atlanta amplifiers; Trilogy cable; Sony VTRs; Chyron character generator; Scientific-Atlanta & Tocom set top converters; Tocom addressable set top converters; Scientific-Atlanta satellite antenna; Scientific-Atlanta satellite receivers.
Miles of plant: 550.0 (coaxial). Additional miles planned: 80.0 (coaxial); 14.0 (fiber optic). Homes passed: 32,918. Total homes in franchised area: 38,600.
Manager: Darrell Wells. Chief technician: Roger Cleveland. Marketing director: Jim Doolittle. Customer service manager: Jeanette Craig.
City fee: 3% of gross.
Ownership: Time Warner Cable (MSO); Advance/Newhouse Partnership (MSO). Purchased from Jones Intercable Inc., October 1, 1998.

SWANSEA—Pine Tree Cablevision, 2628 Millwood Ave., Columbia, SC 29205. Phone: 803-799-6226. Fax: 803-799-8804. County: Lexington. ICA: SC0097.
TV Market Ranking: 100. Franchise award date: August 10, 1985. Franchise expiration date: August 1, 2000. Began: October 1, 1986.
Channel capacity: 22. Channels available but not in use: 10.
Basic Service
Subscribers: N.A.
Programming (received off-air): WJBF (A), WRDW-TV (C) Augusta; WIS (N), WOLO-TV (A), WRLK-TV (P) Columbia.
Programming (via satellite): CNN; ESPN; Fox Family Channel; Nashville Network; TBS Superstation.
Fee: $30.00 installation; $12.00 monthly.
Pay Service 1
Pay Units: N.A.
Programming (via satellite): Disney Channel; Showtime.
Fee: $8.00 monthly (each).
Miles of plant: 8.1 (coaxial). Homes passed: 550.
Manager: Tony Wilson.
Ownership: Pine Tree Cablevision (MSO). Purchased from South Carolina Cable TV LP, October 1, 1998.

THE SUMMIT—Benchmark Communications, 2511 Highmarket St., Georgetown, SC 29440. Phone: 843-527-2447. Fax: 843-527-2034. County: Richland. ICA: SC0142.
TV Market Ranking: 100. Franchise award date: N.A. Franchise expiration date: N.A. Began: September 1, 1990.
Channel capacity: 54. Channels available but not in use: 14.
Basic Service
Subscribers: 430.
Programming (received off-air): WACH (F), WIS (N), WLTX (C), WOLO-TV (A), WRLK-TV (P) Columbia.
Programming (via satellite): WGN-TV (W) Chicago; A & E; American Movie Classics; Animal Planet; BET; C-SPAN; CNBC; CNN; Cartoon Network; Country Music TV; Discovery Channel; ESPN; ESPN 2; Fox Family Channel; Fox News Channel; Headline News; History Channel; Home & Garden Television; Learning Channel; Lifetime; MTV; Nashville Network; Nickelodeon; QVC; Sci-Fi Channel; TBS Superstation; The Weather Channel; Trinity Bcstg. Network; Turner Network TV; USA Network; VH1.
Current originations: Public access.
Fee: $25.00 installation; $24.92 monthly; $2.00 converter.
Pay Service 1
Pay Units: N.A.
Programming (via satellite): Cinemax; Disney Channel; HBO; Showtime.
Fee: $6.95 monthly (Disney), $8.95 monthly (Cinemax, HBO or Showtime).
Miles of plant: 7.0 (coaxial); None (fiber optic).
Manager: Kenneth Koch.
Ownership: Benchmark Communications (MSO). Purchased from Genesis Cable Communications LLC, May 3, 1999.

TRAVELERS REST—Charter Communications, Box 396, 18 Holliday St., West Pelzer, SC 29669. Phones: 864-947-1328; 803-947-9084. Fax: 864-947-1940. County: Greenville. Also serves Greenville County. ICA: SC0143.
TV Market Ranking: 46. Franchise award date: N.A. Franchise expiration date: N.A. Began: March 1, 1982.
Channel capacity: 35 (not 2-way capable). Channels available but not in use: 4.
Basic Service
Subscribers: 5,102.
Programming (received off-air): WGGS-TV (I), WNTV (P) Greenville; WLOS (A), WSPA-TV (C), WYFF (N) Greenville-Spartanburg-Asheville.
Programming (via satellite): WGN-TV (W) Chicago; ESPN; Fox Family Channel; Lifetime; TBS Superstation; USA Network.
Current originations: Automated timeweather.
Fee: $40.00 installation; $26.95 monthly.
Expanded Basic Service
Subscribers: N.A.
Programming (via satellite): CNN; MTV; Nashville Network.
Fee: $2.00-$4.00 monthly.
Pay Service 1
Pay Units: 666.
Programming (via satellite): Cinemax.
Fee: $11.45 monthly.
Pay Service 2
Pay Units: 523.
Programming (via satellite): Disney Channel.
Fee: $8.45 monthly.
Pay Service 3
Pay Units: 994.
Programming (via satellite): HBO.
Fee: $11.45 monthly.
Pay Service 4
Pay Units: 224.
Programming (via satellite): Showtime.
Fee: $11.45 monthly.
Pay-Per-View
Addressable homes: 200.
Viewer's Choice; Hot Choice; Playboy TV.
Local advertising: Yes. Available in character-generated & taped programming.
Equipment: Comtech & Scientific-Atlanta headend; Magnavox & Scientific-Atlanta amplifiers; Comm/Scope cable; Texscan character generator; Pioneer set top converters; Eagle traps; Comtech satellite antenna; Comtech & Scientific-Atlanta satellite receivers; Sony commercial insert.
Miles of plant: 286.0 (coaxial). Additional miles planned: 5.0 (coaxial).
Plant manager: Danny Walters.
City fee: 3% of gross.
Ownership: Charter Communications Inc. (MSO).

TURBEVILLE—Farmers Telephone Co-op Inc., Box 588, 1101 E. Main St., Kingstree, SC 29556. Phone: 843-382-2333. Fax: 843-382-3909. Counties: Clarendon & Florence. Also serves Olanta. ICA: SC0085.
TV Market Ranking: Below 100. Franchise award date: N.A. Franchise expiration date: N.A. Began: January 1, 1983.
Channel capacity: 25 (not 2-way capable). Channels available but not in use: None.
Basic Service
Subscribers: 585.
Programming (received off-air): WCSC-TV (C), WTAT-TV (F,U) Charleston; WIS (N) Columbia; WBTW (C), WPDE-TV (A), WWMB (U) Florence; WRJA-TV (P) Sumter.
Programming (via satellite): WGN-TV (W) Chicago; CNN; Comedy Central; Country Music TV; Discovery Channel; ESPN; Fox Family Channel; Headline News; Nashville Network; Nickelodeon; QVC; TBS Superstation; The Weather Channel; USA Network.
Fee: $40.00 installation; $19.00 monthly.
Pay Service 1
Pay Units: 109.
Programming (via satellite): Cinemax.
Fee: $25.00 installation; $9.00 monthly.
Pay Service 2
Pay Units: 51.
Programming (via satellite): Disney Channel.
Fee: $25.00 installation; $9.00 monthly.
Pay Service 3
Pay Units: 160.
Programming (via satellite): HBO.
Fee: $25.00 installation; $11.00 monthly.
Local advertising: Yes (insert only). Available in locally originated programming. Local sales manager: Robin Rogers.
Equipment: Scientific-Atlanta headend; Scientific-Atlanta amplifiers; Compuvid character generator; Microdyne satellite antenna.
Miles of plant: 40.0 (coaxial). Homes passed: 750.
Manager: J. L. McDaniel. Chief technician: Don Bryant. Marketing director: Guy D. Adams Jr.
City fee: 3% of gross.
Ownership: Farmers Telephone Co-op Inc.

UNION—Charter Communications, 124 Willis St., Gaffney, SC 29340. Phone: 864-489-3186. Fax: 864-448-4407. County: Union. Also serves Buffalo, Union County (portions). ICA: SC0033.
TV Market Ranking: 46 (Buffalo, Union, portions of Union County); Below 100 (portions of Union County); Outside TV Markets (portions of Union County). Franchise award

date: May 2, 1978. Franchise expiration date: N.A. Began: December 10, 1968.
Channel capacity: 36 (not 2-way capable). Channels available but not in use: 3.

Basic Service
Subscribers: 4,055.
Programming (received off-air): WJZY (U) Belmont; WBTV (C) Charlotte; WIS (N) Columbia; WGGS-TV (I), WNTV (P) Greenville; WHNS (F,U), WLOS (A), WSPA-TV (C), WYFF (N) Greenville-Spartanburg-Asheville; allband FM.
Programming (via satellite): WGN-TV (W) Chicago; ESPN; TBS Superstation.
Fee: $47.07 installation; $7.11 monthly; $3.39 converter.

Expanded Basic Service
Subscribers: 3,955.
Programming (via satellite): A & E; BET; C-SPAN; CNN; Comedy Central; Country Music TV; Discovery Channel; Fox Family Channel; Headline News; Home Shopping Network; Lifetime; MTV; Nashville Network; Nickelodeon; TV Guide Channel; The Weather Channel; Turner Network TV; USA Network.
Fee: $10.86 monthly.

Pay Service 1
Pay Units: 207.
Programming (via satellite): Cinemax.
Fee: $15.69 installation; $11.95 monthly.

Pay Service 2
Pay Units: 40.
Programming (via satellite): Disney Channel.
Fee: $15.69 installation; $8.95 monthly.

Pay Service 3
Pay Units: 192.
Programming (via satellite): HBO.
Fee: $15.69 installation; $13.95 monthly.

Pay Service 4
Pay Units: 25.
Programming (via satellite): The Movie Channel.
Fee: $15.69 installation; $11.95 monthly.

Pay Service 5
Pay Units: 101.
Programming (via satellite): Showtime.
Fee: $15.69 installation; $11.95 monthly.

Pay-Per-View
Addressable homes: 278.
Viewer's Choice.
Fee: $4.95.

Local advertising: Yes. Available in taped programming. Local sales manager: Myra Byars.
Program Guide: Prevue Guide.
Equipment: Scientific-Atlanta headend; Kaiser & Magnavox amplifiers; Comm/Scope cable; Atari character generator; Jerrold set top converters; Jerrold addressable set top converters; Scientific-Atlanta satellite antenna; Microdyne & Scientific-Atlanta satellite receivers.
Miles of plant: 165.0 (coaxial). Additional miles planned: 2.0 (coaxial). Homes passed: 6,866.
Manager: Buddy Timmons. Chief technician: Larry Camp.
City fee: 3% of gross.
Ownership: Charter Communications Inc. (MSO).

WAGENER—Pine Tree Cablevision, 2628 Millwood Ave., Columbia, SC 29205. Phone: 803-799-6226. Fax: 803-799-8804. County: Aiken. ICA: SC0102.
TV Market Ranking: 100. Franchise award date: November 1, 1985. Franchise expiration date: November 1, 2000. Began: October 1, 1986.
Channel capacity: 22. Channels available but not in use: 10.

Basic Service
Subscribers: N.A.
Programming (received off-air): WJBF (A), WRDW-TV (C) Augusta; WIS (N), WOLO-TV (A), WRLK-TV (P) Columbia.
Programming (via satellite): CNN; ESPN; Fox Family Channel; Nashville Network; TBS Superstation.
Fee: $30.00 installation; $12.00 monthly.

Pay Service 1
Pay Units: N.A.
Programming (via satellite): Disney Channel; Showtime.
Fee: $8.00 monthly (each), $11.00 monthly (package).

Miles of plant: 8.1 (coaxial). Homes passed: 500.
Manager: Tony Wilson.
Ownership: Pine Tree Cablevision (MSO). Purchased from South Carolina Cable TV LP, October 1, 1998.

WALLACE—Galaxy Cablevision, 1899 S.E. 58th Ave., Ocala, FL 34471-5847. Phone: 352-624-1117. County: Marlboro. Also serves Marlboro County (unincorporated areas). ICA: SC0071.
TV Market Ranking: Below 100 (portions of Marlboro County, Wallace); Outside TV Markets (portions of Marlboro County). Franchise award date: February 9, 1989. Franchise expiration date: February 9, 2004. Began: September 1, 1989.
Channel capacity: 33. Channels available but not in use: None.

Basic Service
Subscribers: 572.
Programming (received off-air): WCCB (F) Charlotte; WIS (N) Columbia; WBTW (C), WJPM-TV (P), WPDE-TV (A) Florence.
Programming (via satellite): WGN-TV (W) Chicago; A & E; American Movie Classics; BET; CNBC; CNN; Discovery Channel; E! Entertainment TV; ESPN; Fox Family Channel; Headline News; Lifetime; Nashville Network; Nickelodeon; QVC; TBS Superstation; The Weather Channel; Turner Network TV; USA Network; VH1.
Fee: $20.00 installation; $27.17 monthly.

Pay Service 1
Pay Units: 29.
Programming (via satellite): Disney Channel.
Fee: $10.95 monthly.

Pay Service 2
Pay Units: 181.
Programming (via satellite): HBO.
Fee: $10.95 monthly.

Pay Service 3
Pay Units: 113.
Programming (via satellite): Showtime.
Fee: $10.95 monthly.

Miles of plant: 53.0 (coaxial). Homes passed: 1,055.
State manager: Dan Labbe. Technical manager: Joe Ferrell.
Ownership: Galaxy Cablevision (MSO).

WALTERBORO—Comcast Cablevision of Carolina Inc., 332 Walter St., Walterboro, SC 29488. Phone: 843-549-9561. County: Colleton. Also serves Colleton County. ICA: SC0145.
TV Market Ranking: Below 100 (portions of Colleton County); Outside TV Markets (portions of Colleton County, Walterboro). Franchise award date: N.A. Franchise expiration date: N.A. Began: N.A.
Channel capacity: 35 (2-way capable; operating 2-way). Channels available but not in use: N.A.

Basic Service
Subscribers: 3,848; Commercial subscribers: 224.
Programming (received off-air): WJWJ-TV (P) Beaufort; WCBD-TV (N), WCIV (A), WCSC-TV (C), WITV (P), WTAT-TV (F,U) Charleston; WIS (N) Columbia; WJCL (A), WSAV-TV (N) Savannah.
Programming (via satellite): WGN-TV (W) Chicago; A & E; BET; C-SPAN; CNN; Discovery Channel; ESPN; Fox Family Channel; Headline News; Home Shopping Network; Lifetime; MTV; Music Choice; Nashville Network; Nickelodeon; TBS Superstation; The Inspirational Network; The Weather Channel; USA Network.
Fee: $52.64 installation; $22.71 monthly; $23.39 additional installation.
Commercial fee: $9.95 monthly.

Pay Service 1
Pay Units: N.A.
Programming (via satellite): Disney Channel; HBO; Showtime; The Movie Channel.
Fee: $25.00 installation; $8.50 monthly (TMC or Showtime), $10.00 monthly (Disney), $10.50 monthly (HBO).

Local advertising: Yes. Available in satellite distributed & locally originated programming.
Miles of plant, homes passed & total homes in franchised area included with Charleston, SC.
Manager: Gary Waterfield. Chief technician: Bob Bradshaw. Marketing director: Bernie Sisko.
Ownership: Comcast Cable Communications Inc. (MSO).

WARE PLACE—Galaxy Cablevision, 1899 S.E. 58th Ave., Ocala, FL 34471-5847. Phone: 352-624-1117. Counties: Greenville & Laurens. Also serves Greenville County (southeastern portion), Laurens County (northwestern portion). ICA: SC0063.
TV Market Ranking: 46. Franchise award date: N.A. Franchise expiration date: N.A. Began: N.A.
Channel capacity: 35. Channels available but not in use: 9.

Basic Service
Subscribers: 770.
Programming (received off-air): WGGS-TV (I), WNTV (P) Greenville; WHNS (F,U), WLOS (A), WSPA-TV (C), WYFF (N) Greenville-Spartanburg-Asheville.
Programming (via satellite): WGN-TV (W) Chicago; A & E; BET; CNN; Cartoon Network; Discovery Channel; E! Entertainment TV; ESPN; Fox Family Channel; Lifetime; Nashville Network; Nickelodeon; QVC; TBS Superstation; The Weather Channel; USA Network; VH1.
Fee: $18.95 monthly.

Pay Service 1
Pay Units: 123.
Programming (via satellite): Cinemax.
Fee: $10.95 monthly.

Pay Service 2
Pay Units: 52.
Programming (via satellite): Disney Channel.
Fee: $10.95 monthly.

Pay Service 3
Pay Units: 172.
Programming (via satellite): HBO.
Fee: $10.95 monthly.

Miles of plant: 65.0 (coaxial). Homes passed: 1,317.
State manager: Dan Labbe. Technical manager: Joe Ferrell.
Ownership: Galaxy Cablevision (MSO).

WARE SHOALS—Ware Shoals Cablevision, Box 148, 42A N. Greenwood Ave., Ware Shoals, SC 29692. Phone: 803-456-2626. Fax: 803-456-3412. Counties: Abbeville, Greenwood & Laurens. Also serves Abbeville County, Greenwood County, Hodges, Laurens County. ICA: SC0053.
TV Market Ranking: 46 (portions of Abbeville County, portions of Greenwood County, Hodges, portions of Laurens County, Ware Shoals); Outside TV Markets (portions of Abbeville County, portions of Greenwood County, portions of Laurens County). Franchise award date: May 1, 1981. Franchise expiration date: N.A. Began: July 30, 1982.
Channel capacity: 33 (not 2-way capable). Channels available but not in use: None.

Basic Service
Subscribers: 1,254; Commercial subscribers: 17.
Programming (received off-air): WFBC-TV (W) Anderson; WIS (N) Columbia; WGGS-TV (I), WNTV (P) Greenville; WHNS (F,U), WLOS (A), WSPA-TV (C), WYFF (N) Greenville-Spartanburg-Asheville.
Programming (via satellite): WGN-TV (W) Chicago; A & E; BET; C-SPAN; CNN; Country Music TV; Discovery Channel; ESPN; Fox Family Channel; Fox Sports Net South; Headline News; Home Shopping Network; Lifetime; MTV; Nashville Network; Nickelodeon; TBS Superstation; The Weather Channel; Turner Network TV; USA Network; VH1.
Fee: $25.00 installation; $17.95 monthly; $10.00 additional installation.
Commercial fee: $5.50 monthly.

Pay Service 1
Pay Units: 569.
Programming (via satellite): Cinemax; Disney Channel; HBO; Showtime.
Fee: $8.00 monthly (Cinemax), $8.95 monthly (Disney or HBO).

Local advertising: No.
Equipment: Avantek & Scientific-Atlanta headend; GTE Sylvania amplifiers; Scientific-Atlanta & Comm/Scope cable; Pioneer & Jerrold set top converters; Eagle & Arcom traps; Scientific-Atlanta satellite antenna; Avantek & Scientific-Atlanta satellite receivers.
Miles of plant: 36.0 (coaxial). Additional miles planned: 30.0 (coaxial). Homes passed: 1,620. Total homes in franchised area: 2,875.
Manager: Lee A. Perron. Chief technician: Tony Urban.
Franchise fee: 3% of basic gross; 1% of pay gross.
Ownership: InterMedia Partners (MSO).

WEST PELZER—Charter Communications, Box 396, 18 Holliday St., West Pelzer, SC 29669. Phones: 803-947-9084; 803-947-1328. Fax: 803-947-1940. Counties: Anderson, Greenville & Pickens. Also serves Anderson County, Centerville, Greenville County, Pelzer, Pickens County, Piercetown. ICA: SC0009.
TV Market Ranking: 46. Franchise award date: January 1, 1981. Franchise expiration date: N.A. Began: July 13, 1981.
Channel capacity: 35 (not 2-way capable). Channels available but not in use: None.

Basic Service
Subscribers: 14,212.
Programming (received off-air): WFBC-TV (W) Anderson; WGGS-TV (I), WNTV (P)

Greenville; WHNS (F,U), WLOS (A), WSPA-TV (C), WYFF (N) Greenville-Spartanburg-Asheville; WNEG-TV (I) Toccoa.

Programming (via satellite): WGN-TV (W) Chicago; A & E; American Movie Classics; BET; C-SPAN; CNBC; CNN; Comedy Central; Country Music TV; Discovery Channel; ESPN; Fox Family Channel; Fox Sports Net South; Headline News; Lifetime; MTV; Nashville Network; Nickelodeon; QVC; TBS Superstation; TV Guide Channel; The Weather Channel; Turner Network TV; USA Network; VH1.

Current originations: Automated time-weather.

Fee: $40.00 installation; $26.69 monthly.

Pay Service 1

Pay Units: 671.

Programming (via satellite): Cinemax.

Fee: $4.95 installation; $11.45 monthly.

Pay Service 2

Pay Units: 1,352.

Programming (via satellite): Disney Channel.

Fee: $4.95 installation; $8.45 monthly.

Pay Service 3

Pay Units: 2,087.

Programming (via satellite): HBO.

Fee: $4.95 installation; $11.45 monthly.

Pay Service 4

Pay Units: 764.

Programming (via satellite): Showtime.

Fee: $4.95 installation; $11.45 monthly.

Pay Service 5

Pay Units: 469.

Programming (via satellite): The Movie Channel.

Fee: $4.95 installation; $11.45 monthly.

Pay-Per-View

Addressable homes: 6,980.

Playboy TV.

Fee: Varies.

Local advertising: Yes. Available in character-generated & taped programming.

Equipment: Scientific-Atlanta headend; Scientific-Atlanta amplifiers; Comm/Scope & Scientific-Atlanta cable; Texscan character generator; Pioneer set top converters; Tocom addressable set top converters; Arcom & Eagle traps; Scientific-Atlanta satellite antenna; Scientific-Atlanta satellite receivers; Sony commercial insert.

Miles of plant: 649.8 (coaxial); 36.0 (fiber optic). Additional miles planned: 100.0 (coaxial). Homes passed: 24,793.

Plant manager: Danny Walters. Marketing director: Tim Morrison.

City fee: 3% of gross.

Ownership: Charter Communications Inc. (MSO).

WHITMIRE—Charter Communications, 101 Cestrian Square, Chester, SC 29706. Phone: 803-377-1181. Fax: 803-487-5075. Counties: Newberry & Union. Also serves Newberry County (unincorporated areas), Union County (unincorporated areas). ICA: SC0065.

TV Market Ranking: 46 (portions of Newberry County, portions of Union County); 100 (portions of Newberry County); Below 100 (portions of Union County); Outside TV Markets (portions of Newberry County, portions of Union County, Whitmire). Franchise award date: April 14, 1980. Franchise expiration date: N.A. Began: February 1, 1982.

Channel capacity: 62 (not 2-way capable). Channels available but not in use: 38.

Basic Service

Subscribers: 725.

Programming (received off-air): WBTV (C), WCCB (F) Charlotte; WIS (N), WLTX (C), WOLO-TV (A), WRLK-TV (P) Columbia; WGGS-TV (I) Greenville; WLOS (A), WSPA-TV (C), WYFF (N) Greenville-Spartanburg-Asheville.

Programming (via satellite): WGN-TV (W) Chicago; TBS Superstation.

Fee: $40.00 installation; $9.09 monthly; $3.50 converter.

Expanded Basic Service

Subscribers: 689.

Programming (via satellite): BET; C-SPAN; CNN; Comedy Central; Discovery Channel; ESPN; Fox Family Channel; Headline News; Home Shopping Network; MTV; Nashville Network; Nickelodeon; The Weather Channel; Turner Network TV; USA Network.

Fee: $11.86 monthly.

Pay Service 1

Pay Units: 29.

Programming (via satellite): Disney Channel.

Fee: $15.00 installation; $8.95 monthly.

Pay Service 2

Pay Units: 83.

Programming (via satellite): HBO.

Fee: $13.95 monthly.

Pay Service 3

Pay Units: 84.

Programming (via satellite): Showtime.

Fee: $11.95 monthly.

Program Guide: The Entertainer.

Equipment: Scientific-Atlanta headend; RCA amplifiers; Times Fiber cable; Atari character generator; RCA & Scientific-Atlanta set top converters; Pico traps; Harris satellite antenna; Microdyne & Scientific-Atlanta satellite receivers.

Miles of plant: 19.2 (coaxial). Homes passed: 1,206.

Manager: Joe Haight. Marketing director: Kemp Delo.

City fee: 3% of gross.

Ownership: Charter Communications Inc. (MSO).

WILD DUNES—TriTek Communications, 5759 Palm Blvd., Isle of Palms, GA 29451-2734. Phone: 843-886-2400. Fax: 843-886-2892. County: Charleston. ICA: SC0064.

TV Market Ranking: Below 100. Franchise award date: January 1, 1988. Franchise expiration date: January 1, 2003. Began: January 1, 1982.

Channel capacity: 35 (not 2-way capable). Channels available but not in use: 1.

Basic Service

Subscribers: 1,057.

Programming (received off-air): WCBD-TV (N), WCIV (A), WCSC-TV (C), WITV (P), WTAT-TV (F,U) Charleston.

Programming (via satellite): WGN-TV (W) Chicago; A & E; C-SPAN; CNBC; CNN; Comedy Central; Discovery Channel; ESPN; Fox Family Channel; Headline News; Home Shopping Network; Lifetime; MTV; Nashville Network; Nickelodeon; TBS Superstation; The Inspirational Network; The Weather Channel; Turner Network TV; USA Network; VH1.

Current originations: Automated time-weather; public access.

Planned originations: Automated emergency alert.

Fee: $19.95 installation; $20.45 monthly.

Pay Service 1

Pay Units: 23.

Programming (via satellite): Cinemax.

Fee: $9.95 installation; $9.95 monthly.

Pay Service 2

Pay Units: 28.

Programming (via satellite): Disney Channel.

Fee: $9.95 monthly.

Pay Service 3

Pay Units: 137.

Programming (via satellite): HBO.

Fee: $9.95 monthly.

Pay Service 4

Pay Units: 41.

Programming (via satellite): Showtime.

Fee: $9.95 monthly.

Pay Service 5

Pay Units: 31.

Programming (via satellite): The Movie Channel.

Fee: $9.95 monthly.

Pay-Per-View

Addressable homes: 1,057.

Viewer's Choice.

Fee: $4.95.

Local advertising: Yes. Available in character-generated programming.

Program Guide: CableView.

Equipment: Scientific-Atlanta headend; Scientific-Atlanta amplifiers; Times Fiber cable; Scientific-Atlanta addressable set top converters; Scientific-Atlanta satellite antenna; Scientific-Atlanta satellite receivers.

Miles of plant: 30.0 (coaxial). Additional miles planned: 7.0 (coaxial). Homes passed: 1,300. Total homes in franchised area: 2,100.

Manager: Lionel Snipes. Chief technician: Harry Holmes.

Ownership: US Cable Corp. (MSO).

WILLIAMSTON—Charter Communications, Box 396, 18 Holliday St., West Pelzer, SC 29669. Phone: 803-947-9084. County: Anderson. ICA: SC0062.

TV Market Ranking: 46. Franchise award date: N.A. Franchise expiration date: N.A. Began: June 1, 1979.

Channel capacity: 21 (not 2-way capable). Channels available but not in use: 1.

Basic Service

Subscribers: N.A.

Programming (received off-air): WFBC-TV (W) Anderson; WGGS-TV (I), WNTV (P) Greenville; WHNS (F,U), WLOS (A), WSPA-TV (C), WYFF (N) Greenville-Spartanburg-Asheville; WNEG-TV (I) Toccoa; 1 FM.

Programming (via satellite): WGN-TV (W) Chicago; A & E; American Movie Classics; BET; C-SPAN; CNBC; CNN; Comedy Central; Country Music TV; Discovery Channel; ESPN; Fox Family Channel; Headline News; Lifetime; MTV; Nashville Network; Nickelodeon; QVC; TBS Superstation; TV Guide Channel; The Weather Channel; Turner Network TV; USA Network; VH1.

Fee: $40.00 installation; $26.95 monthly.

Pay Service 1

Pay Units: 64.

Programming (via satellite): Cinemax.

Fee: $4.95 installation; $11.45 monthly.

Pay Service 2

Pay Units: 71.

Programming (via satellite): Disney Channel.

Fee: $4.95 installation; $8.45 monthly.

Pay Service 3

Pay Units: 146.

Programming (via satellite): HBO.

Fee: $4.95 installation; $11.45 monthly.

Pay Service 4

Pay Units: 25.

Programming (via satellite): The Movie Channel.

Fee: $11.45 monthly.

Pay Service 6

Pay Units: 61.

Programming (via satellite): Showtime.

Fee: $11.45 monthly.

Pay-Per-View

Playboy TV.

Local advertising: Yes (insert only). Available in satellite distributed programming. Rates: $0.20/Subscriber.

Equipment: Scientific-Atlanta headend; Scientific-Atlanta amplifiers; Comm/Scope cable; Jerrold set top converters; Pico traps; Scientific-Atlanta satellite antenna; Scientific-Atlanta satellite receivers.

Miles of plant: 24.0 (coaxial); None (fiber optic). Homes passed: 1,319. Total homes in franchised area: 1,319.

Manager: Jack Bradshaw. Chief technician: Robert Etheredge.

City fee: 3% of gross.

Ownership: Charter Communications Inc. (MSO).

WINNSBORO—Winnsboro/Ridgeway Cable TV, Box 1117, Rte. 3, Winnsboro, SC 29180. Phones: 803-635-6459; 803-337-8388. Fax: 803-635-3988. County: Fairfield. Also serves Fairfield County (portions), Ridgeway. ICA: SC0048.

TV Market Ranking: 100. Franchise award date: N.A. Franchise expiration date: N.A. Began: October 15, 1980.

Channel capacity: 36. Channels available but not in use: 6.

Basic Service

Subscribers: 2,178.

Programming (received off-air): WACH (F), WIS (N), WLTX (C), WOLO-TV (A), WRLK-TV (P) Columbia; WQHB (U) Sumter; WCTV (C) Tallahassee-Thomasville.

Programming (via satellite): WGN-TV (W) Chicago; A & E; American Movie Classics; BET; C-SPAN; CNN; Country Music TV; Discovery Channel; ESPN; Fox Family Channel; Fox Sports Net South; Headline News; History Channel; Home Shopping Network; Lifetime; MTV; Nashville Network; Nickelodeon; TBS Superstation; TV Guide Channel; The Weather Channel; Trinity Bcstg. Network; Turner Network TV; USA Network.

Fee: $45.00 installation; $23.90 monthly.

Pay Service 1

Pay Units: 14.

Programming (via satellite): Disney Channel.

Fee: $7.95 monthly.

Pay Service 2

Pay Units: 384.

Programming (via satellite): HBO.

Fee: $10.95 monthly.

Pay Service 3

Pay Units: 253.

Programming (via satellite): The Movie Channel.

Fee: $9.95 monthly.

Pay Service 4

Pay Units: N.A.

Programming (via satellite): Cinemax; Showtime.

Fee: $9.95 monthly (each).

Equipment: Scientific-Atlanta headend; Scientific-Atlanta amplifiers; Times Fiber cable; Fort Worth Tower & Scientific-Atlanta satellite antenna; Scientific-Atlanta satellite receivers.

Miles of plant: 47.7 (coaxial). Homes passed: 2,196. Total homes in franchised area: 2,300.

Manager: William C. Beaty. Chief technician: Ricky Inman.

City fee: 3% of gross.

Ownership: Catawba Services Inc. (MSO).

YORK—York Cable TV, 416C E. Liberty St., York, SC 29745. Phone: 803-684-1012. Fax: 803-684-9833. County: York. Also serves Hickory Grove, Sharon, York County (unincorporated areas). ICA: SC0146.

TV Market Ranking: 42 (York, portions of York County); 46 (Hickory Grove, Sharon, portions of York County). Franchise award date: N.A. Franchise expiration date: May 1, 2023. Began: September 6, 1965.

Channel capacity: 42. Channels available but not in use: None.

Basic Service

Subscribers: 2,800.

Programming (received off-air): WJZY (U) Belmont; WBTV (C), WCCB (F), WCNC-TV (N), WSOC-TV (A) Charlotte; WSPA-TV (C) Greenville-Spartanburg-Asheville; WAXN (I) Kannapolis; WNSC-TV (P) Rock Hill; all-band FM.

Programming (via satellite): WGN-TV (W) Chicago; ESPN; TBS Superstation; The Weather Channel.

Current originations: Automated time-weather; local news.

Fee: $45.00 installation; $9.00 monthly.

Expanded Basic Service

Subscribers: 2,500.

Programming (via satellite): A & E; BET; C-SPAN; CNN; Cartoon Network; Country Music TV; Discovery Channel; Fox Family Channel; Fox Sports Net South; Headline News; Home Shopping Network; Learning Channel; Lifetime; Nashville Network; Nick at Nite; Nickelodeon; TV Guide Channel; TV Guide Sneak Prevue; The Inspirational Network; Turner Network TV; USA Network; VH1.

Fee: $12.90 monthly.

Pay Service 1

Pay Units: 313.

Programming (via satellite): Cinemax.

Fee: $9.95 monthly.

Pay Service 2

Pay Units: 157.

Programming (via satellite): Disney Channel.

Fee: $7.95 monthly.

Pay Service 3

Pay Units: 641.

Programming (via satellite): HBO.

Fee: $9.95 monthly.

Pay Service 4

Pay Units: 227.

Programming (via satellite): Showtime.

Fee: $9.95 monthly.

Pay Service 5

Pay Units: 93.

Programming (via satellite): The Movie Channel.

Fee: $9.95 monthly.

Pay-Per-View

Addressable homes: 2,153.

Viewer's Choice; special events.

Fee: $3.95.

Local advertising: Yes. Available in satellite distributed, locally originated, character-generated, taped & automated programming. Rates: $9.12/30 Seconds. Local sales manager: John M. Barnes Jr.

Equipment: Scientific-Atlanta headend; Scientific-Atlanta amplifiers; Times Fiber cable; Scientific-Atlanta addressable set top converters.

Miles of plant: 211.8 (coaxial).

Manager: William C. Beaty Jr. Chief technician: Danny Ghent. Marketing director: John M. Barnes Jr.

City fee: 3% gross (York). County fee: $5.04.

Ownership: Catawba Services Inc. (MSO).

SOUTH DAKOTA

Total Systems: **191**
Total Communities Served: **268**
Franchises Not Yet Operating: **0**
Applications Pending: **0**
Communities with Applications: **0**
Number of Basic Subscribers: **150,349**
Number of Expanded Basic Subscribers: **32,174**
Number of Pay Units: **66,376**

Top 100 Markets Represented: Sioux Falls-Mitchell (85).

For a list of all cable communities included in this section, see the Cable Community Index located in the back of this volume.
For explanation of terms used in cable system listings, see p. D-9.

ABERDEEN—Midcontinent Cable Co., Box 910, Aberdeen, SD 57402-0910. Phone: 605-229-1775. County: Brown. Also serves Brown County. ICA: SD0003.
TV Market Ranking: Below 100 (Aberdeen, portions of Brown County); Outside TV Markets (portions of Brown County). Franchise award date: August 16, 1968. Franchise expiration date: November 5, 2001. Began: July 1, 1970.
Channel capacity: 76 (2-way capable; operating 2-way). Channels available but not in use: N.A.
Basic Service
Subscribers: 9,613.
Programming (received off-air): KABY-TV (A), KDSD-TV (P) Aberdeen; KDLO-TV (C) Florence-Watertown; KTTM (F) Huron; 5 FMs.
Programming (via translator): KDLT (N) Sioux Falls-Mitchell.
Programming (via satellite): WGN-TV (W) Chicago; A & E; American Movie Classics; Animal Planet; Bravo; C-SPAN; C-SPAN 2; CNBC; CNN; Cartoon Network; Comedy Central; Country Music TV; DMX; Discovery Channel; Disney Channel; E! Entertainment TV; ESPN; ESPN 2; ESPNews; EWTN; FX; fXM: Movies from Fox; Flix; Fox Family Channel; Golf Channel; Headline News; History Channel; Learning Channel; Lifetime; MTV; Midwest Sports Channel; Nashville Network; Nick at Nite's TV Land; Nickelodeon; Outdoor Channel; QVC; Sci-Fi Channel; Starz!; TBS Superstation; TV Guide Channel; The Health Network; The Inspirational Network; The New Encore; The Weather Channel; Travel Channel; Turner Classic Movies; Turner Network TV; USA Network; VH1.
Current originations: Public access; educational access; automated emergency alert; local news; local sports.
Fee: $50.00 installation; $25.00 monthly.
Pay Service 1
Pay Units: 351.
Programming (via satellite): Cinemax (multiplexed).
Fee: $20.00 installation; $11.00 monthly.
Pay Service 2
Pay Units: 1,144.
Programming (via satellite): HBO (multiplexed).
Fee: $20.00 installation; $11.00 monthly.
Pay Service 3
Pay Units: 1,166.
Programming (via satellite): Showtime (multiplexed).
Fee: $20.00 installation; $11.00 monthly.
Pay Service 4
Pay Units: 1,093.
Programming (via satellite): The Movie Channel.
Fee: $20.00 installation; $11.00 monthly.
Local advertising: No.
Equipment: Scientific-Atlanta headend; Scientific-Atlanta amplifiers; Times Fiber cable; Eagle traps; Simulsat satellite antenna; Scientific-Atlanta satellite receivers.
Miles of plant: 109.7 (coaxial); 42.0 (fiber optic). Homes passed: 11,534.
Manager: Lonnie Schumacher. Marketing director: Fred Jamieson. Customer service manager: Chris VanDover.
City fee: 3% of gross.
Ownership: Midcontinent Communications (MSO).

ALCESTER—Telecom Inc., Box 127, Irene, SD 57037-0127. Phone: 800-239-7501. Fax: 605-766-7695. E-mail: jeanniejohnson@dtg.com. County: Union. ICA: SD0066.
TV Market Ranking: 85. Franchise award date: N.A. Franchise expiration date: January 1, 2011. Began: June 4, 1983.
Channel capacity: 36 (not 2-way capable). Channels available but not in use: 10.
Basic Service
Subscribers: 278.
Programming (received off-air): KCAU-TV (A), KMEG (C), KTIV (N) Sioux City; KDLV-TV (N), KELO-TV (C), KSFY-TV (A), KTTW (F) Sioux Falls-Mitchell; KUSD-TV (P) Vermillion.
Programming (via satellite): WGN-TV (W) Chicago; CNN; Country Music TV; Discovery Channel; Disney Channel; ESPN; ESPN 2; Fox Family Channel; Midwest Sports Channel; Nashville Network; Nickelodeon; TBS Superstation; Turner Network TV; USA Network; VH1.
Fee: $35.00 installation; $24.95 monthly.
Pay Service 1
Pay Units: 12.
Programming (via satellite): Cinemax.
Fee: $13.00 installation; $7.95 monthly.
Pay Service 2
Pay Units: 41.
Programming (via satellite): Showtime.
Fee: $13.00 installation; $7.95 monthly.
Pay Service 3
Pay Units: 49.
Programming (via satellite): HBO.
Fee: $13.00 installation; $7.95 monthly.
Pay Service 4
Pay Units: 15.
Programming (via satellite): Starz!; The New Encore.
Fee: $13.00 installation; $7.95 monthly.
Pay-Per-View
Viewer's Choice 1-4.
Local advertising: No.
Program Guide: Premium Channels.
Equipment: Scientific-Atlanta headend; Scientific-Atlanta amplifiers; Pioneer set top converters; Pico & Eagle traps; Scientific-Atlanta satellite antenna; Scientific-Atlanta satellite receivers.
Miles of plant: 7.0 (coaxial). Homes passed: 367. Total homes in franchised area: 411.
Manager: Thomas W. Hertz. Chief technician: Jerry Andersen. Program director: Jeannie Johnson. Marketing director: Marshall Damgaard.
City fee: 3% of gross.
Ownership: Dakota Telecom Inc. (MSO).

ALEXANDRIA—Central Cableland TV, Box 217, Alexandria, SD 57311-0217. Phone: 605-239-4302. Fax: 605-239-4301. County: Hanson. ICA: SD0097.
TV Market Ranking: 85. Franchise award date: N.A. Franchise expiration date: N.A. Began: November 1, 1983.
Channel capacity: N.A. Channels available but not in use: N.A.
Basic Service
Subscribers: 194.
Programming (received off-air): KESD-TV (P) Brookings; KDLV-TV (N), KELO-TV (C), KSFY-TV (A), KTTW (F) Sioux Falls-Mitchell.
Programming (via satellite): WGN-TV (W) Chicago; CNN; Country Music TV; Discovery Channel; ESPN; EWTN; Fox Family Channel; Nashville Network; TBS Superstation; Turner Network TV.
Fee: $20.00 installation; $14.00 monthly.
Pay Service 1
Pay Units: 63.
Programming (via satellite): HBO.
Fee: $9.50 monthly.
Miles of plant: 3.5 (coaxial). Homes passed: 215.
Manager: Bryan Roth. Chief technician: Tim Wenande. Customer service manager: Carla Bambas.
Ownership: Hanson Communications (MSO).

ARMOUR—Cable TV Services, 510 West Haven, Mitchell, SD 57301. Phone: 605-996-7683. County: Douglas. ICA: SD0149.
TV Market Ranking: 85. Franchise award date: January 1, 1981. Franchise expiration date: N.A. Began: March 1, 1982.
Channel capacity: 22. Channels available but not in use: 5.
Basic Service
Subscribers: 296.
Programming (received off-air): KTSD-TV (P) Pierre; KDLV-TV (N), KELO-TV (C), KSFY-TV (A) Sioux Falls-Mitchell.
Programming (via satellite): WGN-TV (W) Chicago; CNN; Country Music TV; Discovery Channel; ESPN; Fox Family Channel; FoxNet; Headline News; Nashville Network; TBS Superstation; Turner Network TV; USA Network.
Fee: $28.27 installation; $19.38 monthly.
Pay Service 1
Pay Units: 48.
Programming (via satellite): HBO.
Fee: $11.43 monthly.
Local advertising: No.
Miles of plant: 6.8 (coaxial).
Manager: Jeannette Lemke. Chief technician: Jay Shank.
City fee: 3% of gross.
Ownership: Kevin Johnson. Purchased from Jack W. Schaefer.

ASHTON—Satellite Cable Services Inc., Box 106, Brookings, SD 57006-0106. Phone: 605-692-5508. Fax: 605-692-6496. County: Spink. ICA: SD0150.
TV Market Ranking: Below 100. Franchise award date: N.A. Franchise expiration date: N.A. Began: N.A.
Channel capacity: 36 (2-way capable; not operating 2-way). Channels available but not in use: N.A.
Basic Service
Subscribers: 33.
Programming (via satellite): WGN-TV (W) Chicago; KCNC-TV (C), KWGN-TV (W) Denver; CNN; Discovery Channel; ESPN; Midwest Sports Channel; Nashville Network; TBS Superstation; Turner Network TV.
Fee: $25.79 monthly.
Pay Service 1
Pay Units: N.A.
Programming (via satellite): HBO.
Fee: $11.95 monthly.
Manager: Doug Bierschbach. Chief technician: Paul Schmidt.
Ownership: Satellite Cable Services Inc. (MSO).

ASTORIA—Satellite Cable Services Inc., Box 106, Brookings, SD 57006-0106. Phone: 605-692-5508. Fax: 605-692-6496. County: Deuel. ICA: SD0151.
TV Market Ranking: Below 100. Franchise award date: N.A. Franchise expiration date: N.A. Began: N.A.
Channel capacity: 36 (2-way capable; not operating 2-way). Channels available but not in use: N.A.
Basic Service
Subscribers: N.A.
Programming (received off-air): KESD-TV (P) Brookings; KDLV-TV (N), KELO-TV (C), KSFY-TV (A) Sioux Falls-Mitchell.
Programming (via satellite): WGN-TV (W) Chicago; CNN; ESPN; Midwest Sports Channel; Nashville Network; TBS Superstation; Turner Network TV.
Fee: $26.32 monthly.
Pay Service 1
Pay Units: N.A.
Programming (via satellite): HBO.
Fee: $11.95 monthly.
Manager: Doug Bierschbach. Chief technician: Paul Schmidt.
Ownership: Satellite Cable Services Inc. (MSO).

AVON—Village Cable Inc., Box 270, 124 E. 7th Ave., Redfield, SD 57469. Phone: 605-472-3415. County: Bon Homme. ICA: SD0079.
TV Market Ranking: Outside TV Markets. Franchise award date: N.A. Franchise expiration date: N.A. Began: April 1, 1982.
Channel capacity: 36. Channels available but not in use: N.A.
Basic Service
Subscribers: 215.
Programming (received off-air): KCAU-TV (A) Sioux City; KDLV-TV (N), KELO-TV (C), KSFY-TV (A) Sioux Falls-Mitchell; KUSD-TV (P) Vermillion.
Programming (via satellite): WGN-TV (W) Chicago; TBS Superstation.
Fee: $30.00 installation; $16.95 monthly.

Pay Service 1
Pay Units: 89.
Programming (via satellite): HBO.
Fee: $10.00 monthly.
Miles of plant: 9.9 (coaxial). Homes passed: 296.
Manager: Terry Thomas. Chief technician: Jerry Neu.
Ownership: Cable TV Assoc. Inc. (MSO).

BATH—Midcontinent Cable Systems of South Dakota, Box 910, Aberdeen, SD 57402-0910. Phones: 605-229-1775; 800-456-0564. Fax: 605-229-0478. County: Brown. ICA: SD0245.
TV Market Ranking: Below 100. Franchise award date: N.A. Franchise expiration date: N.A. Began: N.A.
Channel capacity: N.A. Channels available but not in use: N.A.
Basic Service
Subscribers: 12.
Programming (received off-air): KABY-TV (A), KDSD-TV (P) Aberdeen; KDLO-TV (C) Florence-Watertown; KTTM (F) Huron; KDLV-TV (N) Sioux Falls-Mitchell.
Programming (via satellite): WGN-TV (W) Chicago; American Movie Classics; Animal Planet; Bravo; C-SPAN; C-SPAN 2; CNBC; CNN; Cartoon Network; Comedy Central; DMX; Discovery Channel; Disney Channel; E! Entertainment TV; ESPN; ESPN 2; ESPNews; EWTN; Encore Movie Networks; FX; fXM: Movies from Fox; Flix; Golf Channel; Headline News; History Channel; Learning Channel; Midwest Sports Channel; Nick at Nite's TV Land; Nickelodeon; Outdoor Channel; QVC; Sci-Fi Channel; Starz!; TBS Superstation; TV Guide Channel; The Health Network; The Inspirational Network; The New Encore; The Weather Channel; Travel Channel; Turner Classic Movies.
Current originations: Educational access.
Fee: $50.00 installation; $25.00 monthly.
Expanded Basic Service
Subscribers: 6.
Programming (via satellite): A & E; Country Music TV; Fox Family Channel; Lifetime; MTV; Nashville Network; Turner Network TV; USA Network; VH1.
Fee: $3.00 monthly.
Pay Service 1
Pay Units: N.A.
Programming (via satellite): Cinemax (multiplexed).
Fee: $11.00 monthly.
Pay Service 2
Pay Units: 1.
Programming (via satellite): HBO (multiplexed).
Fee: $12.00 monthly.
Pay Service 3
Pay Units: 1.
Programming (via satellite): The Movie Channel.
Fee: $11.00 monthly.
Pay Service 4
Pay Units: 1.
Programming (via satellite): Showtime (multiplexed).
Fee: $11.00 monthly.
Pay-Per-View
Addressable homes: 2.
Viewer's Choice.
Fee: $3.95.
Pay-per-view manager: Dawn Vaux.
Equipment: Times Fiber cable; Siecor fiber optic cable; Zenith set top converters.
Homes passed: 82.
System manager: Clay Stephens. Marketing director: Fred Jamieson. Customer service manager: Kathy Fuhrmann.
Ownership: Midcontinent Communications (MSO).

BELLE FOURCHE—TCI Cablevision, Box 309, 842 Short Track Rd., Sturgis, SD 57785. Phone: 605-347-3090. Fax: 605-347-3499. County: Butte. ICA: SD0019.
TV Market Ranking: Below 100. Franchise award date: N.A. Franchise expiration date: N.A. Began: August 1, 1969.
Channel capacity: 35. Channels available but not in use: N.A.
Basic Service
Subscribers: 1,500.
Programming (received off-air): KPSD-TV (P) Eagle Butte; KCLO-TV (C), KEVN-TV (F), KNBN-LP (N), KOTA-TV (A) Rapid City; allband FM.
Programming (via satellite): KWGN-TV (W) Denver; A & E; C-SPAN; CNBC; CNN; Cartoon Network; Country Music TV; Discovery Channel; ESPN; ESPN 2; EWTN; Fox Family Channel; Fox Sports Net; Headline News; History Channel; Lifetime; MTV; Nashville Network; Nickelodeon; QVC; TBS Superstation; TV Guide Channel; The Weather Channel; Trinity Bcstg. Network; Turner Network TV; USA Network.
Current originations: Automated timeweather; educational access.
Fee: $40.00 installation; $25.52 monthly; $10.00 additional installation.
Pay Service 1
Pay Units: N.A.
Programming (via satellite): Cinemax; Disney Channel; HBO; Showtime; The Movie Channel.
Fee: N.A.
Local advertising: No.
Equipment: Scientific-Atlanta & Jerrold headend; Scientific-Atlanta amplifiers; Times Fiber cable; Arco traps; Scientific-Atlanta satellite antenna; Scientific-Atlanta satellite receivers.
Miles of plant and homes passed included with Custer, SD.
Manager: Dale Hodgkins. Chief technician: Gary Reimer.
City fee: 3% of gross.
Ownership: AT&T Broadband & Internet Services (MSO). Purchased from South Dakota Cable Inc., April 1, 1999.

BERESFORD—Beresford Cablevision Inc., 101 N. 3rd St., Beresford, SD 57004. Phone: 605-763-2500. Fax: 605-763-7112. Counties: Lincoln & Union. ICA: SD0032.
TV Market Ranking: 85. Franchise award date: N.A. Franchise expiration date: N.A. Began: January 1, 1983.
Channel capacity: 60 (not 2-way capable). Channels available but not in use: 11.
Basic Service
Subscribers: 743.
Programming (received off-air): KCAU-TV (A), KTIV (N) Sioux City; KDLV-TV (N), KELO-TV (C), KSFY-TV (A) Sioux Falls-Mitchell; KUSD-TV (P) Vermillion.
Programming (via satellite): C-SPAN; Fox Family Channel.
Current originations: Automated timeweather; public access; educational access; automated emergency alert; local sports.
Fee: $25.00 installation; $11.95 monthly; $1.00 converter.
Expanded Basic Service
Subscribers: 654.
Programming (via satellite): WGN-TV (W) Chicago; A & E; CNN; Country Music TV; Discovery Channel; Disney Channel; ESPN; History Channel; Learning Channel; Lifetime; MTV; Midwest Sports Channel; Nashville Network; Nickelodeon; TBS Superstation; Turner Network TV; USA Network.
Fee: $25.00 installation; $8.95 monthly.
Pay Service 1
Pay Units: 152.
Programming (via satellite): Showtime.
Fee: $25.00 installation; $18.95 monthly.
Pay Service 2
Pay Units: 206.
Programming (via satellite): HBO.
Fee: $25.00 installation; $18.95 monthly.
Local advertising: Yes. Local sales manager: Wayne Akland.
Equipment: Scientific-Atlanta headend; Jerrold amplifiers; Comm/Scope & Times Fiber cable; RCA cameras; JVC VTRs; Texscan character generator; RCA & Scientific-Atlanta set top converters; Arcom traps; Scientific-Atlanta satellite antenna; Scientific-Atlanta satellite receivers.
Miles of plant: 41.0 (coaxial). Additional miles planned: 4.0 (coaxial). Homes passed: 810. Total homes in franchised area: 830.
Manager: Wayne Akland. Chief technician: Steve Volden. Marketing director: Dean Jacobson.
City fee: None.
Ownership: Beresford Cablevision Inc.

BISON—West River CATV, Box 39, Bison, SD 57620. Phone: 605-244-5213. Fax: 605-244-7288. County: Perkins. ICA: SD0103.
TV Market Ranking: Outside TV Markets. Franchise award date: May 12, 1982. Franchise expiration date: May 12, 2002. Began: December 1, 1982.
Channel capacity: 14 (not 2-way capable). Channels available but not in use: None.
Basic Service
Subscribers: 168.
Programming (received off-air): KPSD-TV (P) Eagle Butte; KEVN-TV (F), KOTA-TV (A) Rapid City.
Programming (via satellite): WGN-TV (W) Chicago; CNN; Discovery Channel; ESPN; Fox Family Channel; Nashville Network; TBS Superstation; The Weather Channel; Turner Network TV.
Fee: $35.00 installation; $14.50 monthly.
Pay Service 1
Pay Units: 54.
Programming (via satellite): Disney Channel.
Fee: $21.00 installation; $6.00 monthly.
Pay Service 2
Pay Units: 56.
Programming (via satellite): Showtime.
Fee: $21.00 installation; $6.95 monthly.
Pay-Per-View
Addressable homes: 185.
Local advertising: No.
Equipment: Scientific-Atlanta headend; Scientific-Atlanta amplifiers; Comm/Scope cable; Scientific-Atlanta cameras; Pico traps; Anixter satellite antenna; Cushcraft satellite receivers.
Miles of plant: 7.0 (coaxial). Homes passed: 200. Total homes in franchised area: 200.
Manager: Darrell Henderson. Chief technician: Colle Nash. Marketing director: Jerry Reisenauer.
City fee: None.
Ownership: West River Cooperative Telephone Co.

BLACK HAWK—TCI Cablevision, Box 309, 842 Short Track Rd., Sturgis, SD 57785. Phones: 605-347-3090; 800-658-3456. Fax: 605-347-3499. Counties: Meade & Pennington. Also serves Pennington County (portions), Piedmont. ICA: SD0015.
TV Market Ranking: Below 100. Franchise award date: N.A. Franchise expiration date: N.A. Began: N.A.
Channel capacity: 22. Channels available but not in use: None.
Basic Service
Subscribers: 1,230.
Programming (received off-air): KBHE-TV (P), KCLO-TV (C), KEVN-TV (F), KNBN-LP (N), KOTA-TV (A) Rapid City.
Programming (via satellite): A & E; Animal Planet; C-SPAN; C-SPAN 2; CNN; Cartoon Network; Comedy Central; Country Music TV; Discovery Channel; ESPN; ESPN 2; Fox Family Channel; Fox Sports Net; Fox-Net; Headline News; History Channel; Home & Garden Television; Learning Channel; Lifetime; MTV; Nashville Network; Nickelodeon; Outdoor Channel; QVC; Sci-Fi Channel; TBS Superstation; TV Guide Channel; The Weather Channel; Turner Classic Movies; Turner Network TV; USA Network; VH1.
Current originations: Automated timeweather.
Fee: $32.00 installation; $24.95 monthly.
Pay Service 1
Pay Units: N.A.
Programming (via satellite): Disney Channel; HBO; Showtime; The Movie Channel.
Fee: $10.95 monthly (each).
Miles of plant: 25.0 (coaxial). Homes passed: 2,000.
Manager: Dale Hodgkins. Chief technician: Gary Reimer.
Ownership: AT&T Broadband & Internet Services (MSO). Purchased from South Dakota Cable Inc., April 1, 1999.

BLUNT—Sully Buttes Telephone Cooperative Inc., Box 157, Highmore, SD 57345. Phone: 605-852-2224. Fax: 605-852-2404. County: Hughes. ICA: SD0125.
TV Market Ranking: Below 100. Franchise award date: N.A. Franchise expiration date: N.A. Began: November 1, 1985.
Channel capacity: 15 (not 2-way capable). Channels available but not in use: None.
Basic Service
Subscribers: 143.
Programming (received off-air): KTTM (F) Huron; KPRY-TV (A), KTSD-TV (P) Pierre; KPLO-TV (C) Reliance.
Programming (via satellite): WGN-TV (W) Chicago; American Movie Classics; CNN; Disney Channel; ESPN; Fox Family Channel; Nashville Network; TBS Superstation; The Weather Channel; USA Network.
Fee: $20.00 installation; $20.00 monthly.
Pay Service 1
Pay Units: 46.
Programming (via satellite): Showtime.
Fee: $15.00 installation; $9.50 monthly.
Local advertising: No.
Equipment: Scientific-Atlanta headend; Jerrold amplifiers; Times Fiber cable; Compucable character generator; Pico traps; Scientific-Atlanta satellite antenna; Scientific-Atlanta satellite receivers.
Miles of plant: 5.1 (coaxial); None (fiber optic). Homes passed: 150.
Manager: Randy Hoydek. Chief technician: Randy Olson.
Ownership: Sully Buttes Telephone Cooperative Inc. (MSO).

BOULDER CANYON—Galaxy Cablevision, 203 S. Lincoln Ave., York, NE 68467. Phones: 402-362-1705; 800-365-6988. Fax: 402-362-3698. County: Lawrence. ICA: SD0132.

TV Market Ranking: Below 100. Franchise award date: N.A. Franchise expiration date: February 26, 2001. Began: September 1, 1983.
Channel capacity: 41 (not 2-way capable). Channels available but not in use: 19.
Basic Service
Subscribers: 102.
Programming (received off-air): KMGH-TV (A), KUSA-TV (N) Denver; KPSD-TV (P) Eagle Butte; KEVN-TV (F), KOTA-TV (A) Rapid City.
Programming (via satellite): WGN-TV (W) Chicago; Bravo; CNN; Discovery Channel; Disney Channel; ESPN; Fox Family Channel; Lifetime; Nashville Network; Nickelodeon; QVC; TBS Superstation; The Weather Channel; Turner Network TV; USA Network.
Fee: $28.50 monthly.
Pay Service 1
Pay Units: 11.
Programming (via satellite): HBO.
Fee: $12.95 monthly.
Pay Service 2
Pay Units: 10.
Programming (via satellite): Showtime.
Fee: $7.95 monthly.
Local advertising: No.
Miles of plant: 6.5 (coaxial). Homes passed: 147.
District vice president: John M. Dixon III. State manager: Steve Jordan. Technical manager: Van De Vries.
Ownership: Galaxy Cablevision (MSO).

BOWDLE—Midcontinent Cable Systems Co. of South Dakota, Box 910, Aberdeen, SD 57402-0910. Phones: 605-229-1775; 800-456-0564. Fax: 605-229-0478. County: Edmunds. ICA: SD0152.
TV Market Ranking: Outside TV Markets. Franchise award date: January 11, 1989. Franchise expiration date: January 11, 2011. Began: April 1, 1984.
Channel capacity: 75 (not 2-way capable). Channels available but not in use: 2.
Basic Service
Subscribers: 199.
Programming (received off-air): KABY-TV (A), KDSD-TV (P) Aberdeen; KDLO-TV (C) Florence-Watertown; KTTM (F) Huron; KDLV-TV (N) Sioux Falls-Mitchell.
Programming (via satellite): WGN-TV (W) Chicago; A & E; American Movie Classics; Animal Planet; Bravo; C-SPAN; C-SPAN 2; CNBC; CNN; Cartoon Network; Comedy Central; Country Music TV; Discovery Channel; Disney Channel; E! Entertainment TV; ESPN; ESPN 2; ESPNews; EWTN; FX; fXM: Movies from Fox; Flix; Fox Family Channel; Golf Channel; Headline News; History Channel; Learning Channel; Lifetime; MTV; Midwest Sports Channel; Nashville Network; Nick at Nite's TV Land; Nickelodeon; Outdoor Channel; QVC; Sci-Fi Channel; Starz!; TBS Superstation; TV Guide Channel; The Health Network; The Inspirational Network; The New Encore; The Weather Channel; Travel Channel; Turner Classic Movies; Turner Network TV; USA Network; VH1.
Current originations: Automated time-weather; public access; local news.
Fee: $50.00 installation; $26.50 monthly.
Pay Service 1
Pay Units: 13.
Programming (via satellite): Showtime (multiplexed).
Fee: $20.00 installation; $12.00 monthly.
Pay Service 2
Pay Units: 6.
Programming (via satellite): HBO (multiplexed).
Fee: $20.00 installation; $12.00 monthly.
Pay Service 3
Pay Units: 9.
Programming (via satellite): The Movie Channel.
Fee: $20.00 installation; $12.00 monthly.
Pay Service 4
Pay Units: N.A.
Programming (via satellite): Cinemax (multiplexed).
Fee: $20.00 installation; $12.00 monthly.
Local advertising: No.
Miles of plant: 3.9 (coaxial); None (fiber optic). Homes passed: 278.
Manager: Lonnie Schumacher. Marketing director: Fred Jamieson. Customer service manager: Kathy Furhmann.
Ownership: Midcontinent Communications (MSO).

BRISTOL—Midcontinent Cable Systems Co. of South Dakota, Box 910, Aberdeen, SD 57402-0910. Phones: 605-229-1775; 800-456-0564. Fax: 605-229-0478. County: Day. ICA: SD0099.
TV Market Ranking: Outside TV Markets. Franchise award date: May 29, 1994. Franchise expiration date: May 29, 2009. Began: December 7, 1983.
Channel capacity: 75 (not 2-way capable). Channels available but not in use: 2.
Basic Service
Subscribers: 143.
Programming (received off-air): KABY-TV (A), KDSD-TV (P) Aberdeen; KDLO-TV (C) Florence-Watertown; KTTM (F) Huron.
Programming (via microwave): KDLT-TV (N) Sioux Falls.
Programming (via satellite): WGN-TV (W) Chicago; A & E; American Movie Classics; Animal Planet; Bravo; C-SPAN; C-SPAN 2; CNBC; CNN; Cartoon Network; Comedy Central; Country Music TV; DMX; Discovery Channel; Disney Channel; E! Entertainment TV; ESPN; ESPN 2; ESPNews; EWTN; FX; fXM: Movies from Fox; Flix; Fox Family Channel; Golf Channel; Headline News; History Channel; Learning Channel; Lifetime; MTV; Midwest Sports Channel; Nashville Network; Nick at Nite's TV Land; Nickelodeon; Outdoor Channel; QVC; Sci-Fi Channel; TBS Superstation; TV Guide Channel; The Health Network; The Inspirational Network; The Weather Channel; Travel Channel; Turner Classic Movies; Turner Network TV; USA Network; VH1.
Current originations: Educational access; local access.
Fee: $50.00 installation; $25.00 monthly.
Pay Service 1
Pay Units: 19.
Programming (via satellite): HBO (multiplexed).
Fee: $20.00 installation; $12.00 monthly.
Pay Service 2
Pay Units: 1.
Programming (via satellite): Cinemax (multiplexed).
Fee: $20.00 installation; $11.00 monthly.
Pay Service 3
Pay Units: 10.
Programming (via satellite): Showtime (multiplexed).
Fee: $20.00 installation; $11.00 monthly.
Pay Service 4
Pay Units: 9.
Programming (via satellite): The Movie Channel.
Fee: $20.00 installation; $11.00 monthly.
Pay Service 5
Pay Units: N.A.
Programming (via satellite): Starz!; The New Encore.
Fee: N.A.
Pay-Per-View
Addressable homes: 35.
Hot Choice; Viewer's Choice 1, 3, 4.
Local advertising: No.
Equipment: Magnavox amplifiers; Times Fiber cable.
Miles of plant: 3.3 (coaxial); None (fiber optic). Homes passed: 224. Total homes in franchised area: 224.
Manager: Lonnie Schumacher. Marketing director: Fred Jamieson. Customer service manager: Kathy Fuhrmann.
City fee: 3% of gross.
Ownership: Midcontinent Communications (MSO).

BRITTON—Britton Community Cable TV, Box 111, Redfield, SD 57469. Phone: 605-472-3415. County: Marshall. ICA: SD0041.
TV Market Ranking: Outside TV Markets. Franchise award date: N.A. Franchise expiration date: N.A. Began: May 1, 1979.
Channel capacity: 23. Channels available but not in use: N.A.
Basic Service
Subscribers: N.A.
Programming (received off-air): KABY-TV (A), KDSD-TV (P) Aberdeen; KVLY-TV (N), WDAY-TV (A) Fargo; KXJB-TV (C) Valley City; allband FM.
Programming (via satellite): WGN-TV (W) Chicago; Fox Family Channel; TBS Superstation.
Fee: N.A.
Pay Service 1
Pay Units: N.A.
Programming (via satellite): HBO.
Fee: $9.00 monthly.
Equipment: Hughes & Scientific-Atlanta headend; Scientific-Atlanta amplifiers; Andrew satellite antenna.
Miles of plant: 11.2 (coaxial). Homes passed: 625.
Ownership: Cable TV Assoc. Inc. (MSO).

BROOKINGS—Brookings Cablevision, 1027 S. Main Ave., Brookings, SD 57006. Phone: 605-692-5508. Fax: 605-692-6496. Counties: Brookings, Kingsbury & Moody. Also serves Arlington, Aurora, Colman, De Smet, Egan, Elkton, Flandreau, Lake Preston, Volga. ICA: SD0005.
TV Market Ranking: 85 (Colman, Egan, Flandreau); Below 100 (De Smet); Outside TV Markets (Arlington, Aurora, Brookings, Elkton, Lake Preston, Volga). Franchise award date: June 1, 1989. Franchise expiration date: June 1, 2004. Began: July 1, 1970.
Channel capacity: 60 (2-way capable; operating 2-way). Channels available but not in use: 3.
Basic Service
Subscribers: 2,080; Commercial subscribers: 610.
Programming (received off-air): KESD-TV (P) Brookings; KDLT-TV (N), KELO-TV (C) Sioux Falls; KDLV-TV (N), KSFY-TV (A), KTTW (F) Sioux Falls-Mitchell; allband FM.
Programming (via satellite): WGN-TV (W) Chicago; A & E; American Movie Classics; C-SPAN; C-SPAN 2; CNBC; CNN; Cartoon Network; Comedy Central; Country Music TV; Discovery Channel; Disney Channel; E! Entertainment TV; ESPN; ESPN 2; Fox Family Channel; Fox News Channel; Headline News; History Channel; Home & Garden Television; Knowledge TV; Learning Channel; Lifetime; MTV; Midwest Sports Channel; Nashville Network; Nickelodeon; Odyssey; QVC; Sci-Fi Channel; TBS Superstation; TV Guide Channel; The Weather Channel; Travel Channel; Turner Network TV; USA Network; VH1; WB 100+ Station Group.
Current originations: Automated time-weather; local news.
Fee: $44.30 installation; $26.28 monthly.
Pay Service 1
Pay Units: 520.
Programming (via satellite): Cinemax (multiplexed).
Fee: $10.95 monthly.
Pay Service 2
Pay Units: 870.
Programming (via satellite): HBO (multiplexed).
Fee: $10.95 monthly.
Pay Service 3
Pay Units: 490.
Programming (via satellite): Starz!
Fee: $6.75 monthly.
Pay Service 4
Pay Units: 960.
Programming (via satellite): Showtime (multiplexed).
Fee: $10.95 monthly.
Pay Service 5
Pay Units: N.A.
Programming (via satellite): Golf Channel.
Fee: $6.75 monthly.
Pay Service 6
Pay Units: N.A.
Programming (via satellite): The New Encore.
Fee: N.A.
Pay-Per-View
Addressable homes: 1,590.
Special events.
Local advertising: Yes (locally produced). Available in satellite distributed, locally originated & character-generated programming. Rates: $2.50/30 Seconds. Local sales manager: Paul Schmidt.
Program Guide: TV Guide.
Equipment: Scientific-Atlanta headend; Scientific-Atlanta amplifiers; Times Fiber cable; Texscan character generator; Scientific-Atlanta set top converters; Scientific-Atlanta addressable set top converters; Scientific-Atlanta addressable traps; Microdyne satellite antenna; Scientific-Atlanta satellite receivers; Sony commercial insert.
Miles of plant: 620.0 (coaxial); 5.0 (fiber optic). Homes passed: 7,500. Total homes in franchised area: 7,500.
Manager: Doug Bierschbach. Chief technician: Paul Schmidt. Marketing director: Kristi Kindt.
City fee: 3% of gross.
Ownership: Satellite Cable Services Inc. (MSO). Purchased 50% from AT&T Broadband & Internet Services, February 16, 1999, 50% from Tele-Communications Inc., March 9, 1999.

BRUCE—Satellite Cable Services Inc., Box 106, Brookings, SD 57006-0106. Phone: 605-692-5508. Fax: 605-692-6496. County: Brookings. ICA: SD0153.
TV Market Ranking: Outside TV Markets. Franchise award date: N.A. Franchise expiration date: N.A. Began: N.A.
Channel capacity: 36 (2-way capable; not operating 2-way). Channels available but not in use: None.
Basic Service
Subscribers: 70.
Programming (received off-air): KESD-TV (P) Brookings; KDLV-TV (N), KELO-TV (C), KSFY-TV (A) Sioux Falls-Mitchell.
Programming (via satellite): WGN-TV (W) Chicago; CNN; ESPN; Fox Family Channel; Nashville Network; TBS Superstation.
Fee: $27.38 monthly.

Pay Service 1
Pay Units: N.A.
Programming (via satellite): HBO.
Fee: $11.95 monthly.
Manager: Doug Bierschbach. Chief technician: Paul Schmidt.
Ownership: Satellite Cable Services Inc. (MSO).

BRYANT—Satellite Cable Services Inc., Box 106, Brookings, SD 57006-0106. Phone: 605-692-5508. Fax: 605-692-6496. County: Hamlin. ICA: SD0100.
TV Market Ranking: Below 100. Franchise award date: N.A. Franchise expiration date: N.A. Began: August 1, 1984.
Channel capacity: 36 (2-way capable; not operating 2-way). Channels available but not in use: None.
Basic Service
Subscribers: 130.
Programming (received off-air): KABY-TV (A) Aberdeen; KESD-TV (P) Brookings; KDLO-TV (C) Florence-Watertown; KDLV-TV (N) Sioux Falls-Mitchell.
Programming (via satellite): WGN-TV (W) Chicago; CNN; ESPN; Fox Family Channel; Nashville Network; TBS Superstation; USA Network.
Fee: $24.95 installation; $26.32 monthly.
Pay Service 1
Pay Units: N.A.
Programming (via satellite): HBO.
Fee: $11.95 monthly.
Miles of plant: 4.0 (coaxial). Homes passed: 225.
Manager: Doug Bierschbach. Chief technician: Paul Schmidt.
Ownership: Satellite Cable Services Inc. (MSO).

BUFFALO—Midcontinent Cable Systems Co. of South Dakota, Box 910, Aberdeen, SD 57402-0910. Phones: 605-229-1775; 800-456-0564. Fax: 605-229-0478. County: Harding. ICA: SD0106.
TV Market Ranking: Outside TV Markets. Franchise award date: October 31, 1989. Franchise expiration date: October 31, 2011. Began: June 1, 1984.
Channel capacity: 40 (not 2-way capable). Channels available but not in use: 4.
Basic Service
Subscribers: 169.
Programming (received off-air): KPSD-TV (P) Eagle Butte; KHSD-TV (A), KIVV-TV (F) Lead; KARE (N) Minneapolis-St. Paul.
Programming (via satellite): WGN-TV (W) Chicago; KCNC-TV (C) Denver; A & E; American Movie Classics; C-SPAN; CNBC; CNN; Cartoon Network; Country Music TV; Discovery Channel; Disney Channel; ESPN; FX; Fox Family Channel; Headline News; Learning Channel; Lifetime; Midwest Sports Channel; Nashville Network; Nick at Nite's TV Land; Nickelodeon; QVC; TBS Superstation; TV Guide Channel; The Inspirational Network; The Weather Channel; Turner Network TV; USA Network; VH1.
Fee: $50.00 installation; $26.50 monthly.
Pay Service 1
Pay Units: 24.
Programming (via satellite): HBO.
Fee: $20.00 installation; $12.00 monthly.
Pay Service 2
Pay Units: 5.
Programming (via satellite): Showtime.
Fee: $20.00 installation; $11.00 monthly.
Pay Service 3
Pay Units: 5.
Programming (via satellite): The Movie Channel.
Fee: $20.00 installation; $11.00 monthly.
Local advertising: No.
Miles of plant: 4.6 (coaxial); None (fiber optic). Homes passed: 201.
Manager: Darrell Wrege. Marketing director: Fred Jamieson. Customer service manager: Kathy Fuhrmann.
City fee: 3% of gross.
Ownership: Midcontinent Communications (MSO).

BUFFALO GAP—Golden West Cablevision, Box 9159, 2727 N. Plaza Dr., Rapid City, SD 57709. Phone: 605-348-6529. Fax: 605-342-1160. County: Custer. ICA: SD0154.
TV Market Ranking: Below 100. Franchise award date: May 4, 1992. Franchise expiration date: May 4, 2012. Began: N.A.
Channel capacity: 36 (not 2-way capable). Channels available but not in use: 22.
Basic Service
Subscribers: 59.
Programming (received off-air): KBHE-TV (P), KEVN-TV (F), KOTA-TV (A) Rapid City.
Programming (via translator): K28DP (C) Custer.
Programming (via satellite): WGN-TV (W) Chicago; CNN; Discovery Channel; ESPN; Nashville Network; TBS Superstation; The Weather Channel; Turner Network TV.
Programming (via fiber optic cable): KNBN-LP (N) Rapid City.
Fee: $16.95 monthly.
Pay Service 1
Pay Units: 19.
Programming (via satellite): Disney Channel.
Fee: $7.95 monthly.
Pay Service 2
Pay Units: 25.
Programming (via satellite): Showtime.
Fee: $7.95 monthly.
Manager: Dwight Flatt. Chief technician: Ross Whitley. Marketing director: Greg Oleson.
Ownership: Golden West Cablevision.

BURKE—Rosebud Community Cable TV, Box 111, Redfield, SD 57469. Phone: 605-472-3415. County: Gregory. ICA: SD0062.
TV Market Ranking: Outside TV Markets. Franchise award date: N.A. Franchise expiration date: N.A. Began: September 1, 1980.
Channel capacity: N.A. Channels available but not in use: N.A.
Basic Service
Subscribers: N.A.
Programming (received off-air): KMNE-TV (P) Bassett; KPRY-TV (A), KTSD-TV (P) Pierre; KPLO-TV (C) Reliance; KDLV-TV (N) Sioux Falls-Mitchell.
Programming (via satellite): WGN-TV (W) Chicago; TBS Superstation.
Fee: N.A.
Miles of plant: 8.1 (coaxial). Homes passed: 387.
Manager: Mike McClure.
Ownership: Cable TV Assoc. Inc. (MSO).

CANOVA—Communications Enterprises Inc., Box 67, Woonsocket, SD 57385. Phone: 605-796-4411. Fax: 605-796-4419. County: Miner. ICA: SD0182.
TV Market Ranking: 85. Franchise award date: N.A. Franchise expiration date: N.A. Began: January 1, 1985.
Channel capacity: 17 (not 2-way capable). Channels available but not in use: None.
Basic Service
Subscribers: 42.
Programming (received off-air): KESD-TV (P) Brookings; KDLV-TV (N), KELO-TV (C), KSFY-TV (A) Sioux Falls-Mitchell.
Programming (via satellite): WGN-TV (W) Chicago; CNN; ESPN; Nashville Network; Nickelodeon; TBS Superstation.
Fee: $30.00 installation; $21.15 monthly.
Pay Service 1
Pay Units: N.A.
Programming (via satellite): Showtime.
Fee: $8.00 monthly.
Manager: Gene Kroell.
Ownership: Sanborn Telephone Cooperative (MSO).

CANTON—Midcontinent Communications, 3507 S. Duluth Ave., Sioux Falls, SD 57105-6415. Phones: 605-339-3339; 800-456-0564. County: Lincoln. ICA: SD0022.
TV Market Ranking: 85. Franchise award date: January 1, 1981. Franchise expiration date: N.A. Began: August 1, 1981.
Channel capacity: 36 (not 2-way capable). Channels available but not in use: 1.
Basic Service
Subscribers: 849.
Programming (received off-air): KCAU-TV (A), KMEG (C), KSIN (P), KTIV (N) Sioux City; KDLV-TV (N), KELO-TV (C), KSFY-TV (A), KTTW (F) Sioux Falls-Mitchell; KUSD-TV (P) Vermillion.
Programming (via satellite): WGN-TV (W) Chicago; A & E; CNN; Discovery Channel; Disney Channel; ESPN; ESPN 2; EWTN; Fox Family Channel; Headline News; History Channel; Learning Channel; Lifetime; Nashville Network; Nick at Nite's TV Land; Nickelodeon; TBS Superstation; The Weather Channel; Travel Channel; Turner Classic Movies; Turner Network TV; USA Network.
Current originations: Automated time-weather; public access; automated emergency alert.
Fee: $15.00 installation; $25.52 monthly.
Pay Service 1
Pay Units: 96.
Programming (via satellite): Cinemax.
Fee: $9.95 monthly.
Pay Service 2
Pay Units: 158.
Programming (via satellite): HBO.
Fee: $9.95 monthly.
Equipment: Scientific-Atlanta headend; Scientific-Atlanta amplifiers; Times Fiber cable; Sony cameras; Compuvid character generator; Jerrold set top converters; Scientific-Atlanta satellite antenna; Scientific-Atlanta satellite receivers.
Miles of plant: 22.0 (coaxial). Additional miles planned: 1.0 (coaxial). Homes passed: 1,278. Total homes in franchised area: 1,278.
Manager: Lonnie Schumacher. Chief technician: Tim Anglin.
City fee: 3% of gross.
Ownership: Midcontinent Communications (MSO). Purchased from Zylstra Communications Corp., May 1, 1999.

CARTHAGE—Satellite Cable Services Inc., Box 106, Brookings, SD 57006-0106. Phone: 605-692-5508. Fax: 605-692-6496. County: Miner. ICA: SD0244.
TV Market Ranking: 85. Franchise award date: N.A. Franchise expiration date: N.A. Began: N.A.
Channel capacity: 36 (2-way capable; not operating 2-way). Channels available but not in use: N.A.
Basic Service
Subscribers: 84.
Programming (received off-air): KESD-TV (P) Brookings; KDLV-TV (N), KELO-TV (C), KSFY-TV (A) Sioux Falls-Mitchell.
Programming (via satellite): WGN-TV (W) Chicago; C-SPAN; CNN; Discovery Channel; ESPN; Fox Family Channel; Nashville Network; QVC; TBS Superstation; Turner Network TV; USA Network.
Fee: $24.95 installation; $26.32 monthly.
Pay Service 1
Pay Units: 13.
Programming (via satellite): HBO.
Fee: $10.50 monthly.
Manager: Doug Bierschbach. Chief technician: Paul Schmidt.
Ownership: Satellite Cable Services Inc. (MSO).

CASTLEWOOD—Satellite Cable Services Inc., Box 106, Brookings, SD 57006-0106. Phone: 605-692-5508. Fax: 605-692-6496. County: Hamlin. ICA: SD0098.
TV Market Ranking: Below 100. Franchise award date: N.A. Franchise expiration date: January 1, 1998. Began: August 1, 1983.
Channel capacity: 35 (2-way capable; operating 2-way). Channels available but not in use: N.A.
Basic Service
Subscribers: 190.
Programming (received off-air): KABY-TV (A) Aberdeen; KESD-TV (P) Brookings; KDLO-TV (C) Florence-Watertown; KDLV-TV (N) Sioux Falls-Mitchell.
Programming (via satellite): WGN-TV (W) Chicago; CNN; ESPN; Fox Family Channel; TBS Superstation; USA Network.
Fee: $24.95 installation; $27.38 monthly.
Pay Service 1
Pay Units: N.A.
Programming (via satellite): HBO.
Fee: $9.45 installation; $11.95 monthly.
Equipment: Scientific-Atlanta headend; Magnavox amplifiers; Scientific-Atlanta cable; Eagle traps; Anixter-Mark satellite antenna; Scientific-Atlanta satellite receivers.
Miles of plant: 5.0 (coaxial). Homes passed: 230. Total homes in franchised area: 230.
Manager: Doug Bierschbach. Chief technician: Paul Schmidt.
City fee: 3% of gross.
Ownership: Satellite Cable Services Inc. (MSO).

CAVOUR—Satellite Cable Services Inc., Box 106, Brookings, SD 57006-0106. Phone: 605-692-5508. Fax: 605-692-6496. County: Beadle. ICA: SD0155.
TV Market Ranking: Below 100. Franchise award date: N.A. Franchise expiration date: N.A. Began: N.A.
Channel capacity: 36. Channels available but not in use: N.A.
Basic Service
Subscribers: 40.
Programming (received off-air): KABY-TV (A), KDSD-TV (P) Aberdeen; KDLV-TV (N), KELO-TV (C) Sioux Falls-Mitchell.

Programming (via satellite): WGN-TV (W) Chicago; CNN; ESPN; Midwest Sports Channel; Nashville Network; TBS Superstation; Turner Network TV.
Fee: $26.32 monthly.
Pay Service 1
Pay Units: N.A.
Programming (via satellite): HBO.
Fee: $11.95 monthly.
Manager: Doug Bierschbach. Chief technician: Paul Schmidt.
Ownership: Satellite Cable Services Inc. (MSO).

CHAMBERLAIN—Satellite Cable Services Inc., Box 106, Brookings, SD 57006-0106. Phone: 605-692-5508. Fax: 605-692-6496. County: Brule. ICA: SD0026.
TV Market Ranking: Below 100. Franchise award date: December 7, 1988. Franchise expiration date: December 7, 2003. Began: N.A.
Channel capacity: 150 (2-way capable; operating 2-way). Channels available but not in use: N.A.
Basic Service
Subscribers: 760.
Programming (received off-air): KELO-TV (C), KSFY-TV (A) Sioux Falls-Mitchell; KUSD-TV (P) Vermillion.
Programming (via satellite): WGN-TV (W) Chicago; KCNC-TV (C) Denver; American Movie Classics; CNN; Discovery Channel; ESPN; Fox Family Channel; Headline News; Nashville Network; TBS Superstation; The Weather Channel; Turner Network TV; USA Network.
Fee: $27.96 monthly.
Pay Service 1
Pay Units: N.A.
Programming (via satellite): HBO; Showtime.
Fee: $10.95 monthly (Showtime), $11.45 monthly (HBO).
Homes passed: 1,075.
Manager: Doug Bierschbach. Chief technician: Paul Schmidt.
Ownership: Satellite Cable Services Inc. (MSO).

CHERRY CREEK—Cheyenne River Sioux Tribe Telephone Cable, Box 810, Eagle Butte, SD 57625. Phone: 605-964-2600. Fax: 605-964-1003. County: Ziebach. ICA: SD0157.
TV Market Ranking: Below 100. Franchise award date: N.A. Franchise expiration date: N.A. Began: March 1, 1993.
Channel capacity: 14. Channels available but not in use: 5.
Basic Service
Subscribers: 42.
Programming (via satellite): WGN-TV (W) Chicago; CNN; Country Music TV; Discovery Channel; ESPN; Nashville Network; TBS Superstation; USA Network.
Fee: $25.00 installation; $16.00 monthly.
Pay Service 1
Pay Units: N.A.
Programming (via satellite): HBO.
Fee: $10.00 monthly.
Miles of plant: 0.2 (coaxial).
Manager: J. D. Williams. Chief technician: Ellen B. Brown.
Ownership: Cheyenne River Sioux Tribe Telephone Authorit (MSO).

CHESTER—Satellite Cable Services Inc., Box 106, Brookings, SD 57006-0106. Phone: 605-692-5508. Fax: 605-692-6496. County: Lake. ICA: SD0158.
TV Market Ranking: 85. Franchise award date: N.A. Franchise expiration date: N.A. Began: October 1, 1989.
Channel capacity: 36 (2-way capable; not operating 2-way). Channels available but not in use: N.A.
Basic Service
Subscribers: 60.
Programming (received off-air): KDLV-TV (N), KELO-TV (C), KSFY-TV (A) Sioux Falls-Mitchell; KUSD-TV (P) Vermillion.
Programming (via satellite): WGN-TV (W) Chicago; TBS Superstation.
Fee: $26.32 monthly.
Miles of plant: 2.0 (coaxial).
Manager: Doug Bierschbach. Chief technician: Paul Schmidt.
Ownership: Satellite Cable Services Inc. (MSO).

CLARK—Clark Community Cable TV, Box 111, Redfield, SD 57469. Phone: 605-472-3415. County: Clark. ICA: SD0160.
TV Market Ranking: Below 100. Franchise award date: N.A. Franchise expiration date: N.A. Began: February 1, 1981.
Channel capacity: 13. Channels available but not in use: 3.
Basic Service
Subscribers: N.A.
Programming (received off-air): KABY-TV (A), KDSD-TV (P) Aberdeen; KDLO-TV (C) Florence-Watertown; KDLV-TV (N) Sioux Falls-Mitchell.
Programming (via satellite): WGN-TV (W) Chicago; ESPN; TBS Superstation.
Fee: $30.00 installation; $9.95 monthly.
Pay Service 1
Pay Units: N.A.
Programming (via satellite): HBO.
Fee: $10.00 installation; $9.95 monthly.
Miles of plant: 11.2 (coaxial).
Manager: Mike McClure. Chief technician: Terry Thomas.
City fee: None.
Ownership: Cable TV Assoc. Inc. (MSO).

CLEAR LAKE—Village Cable, Box 111, Redfield, SD 57469. Phone: 605-472-3415. County: Deuel. ICA: SD0047.
TV Market Ranking: Below 100. Franchise award date: N.A. Franchise expiration date: N.A. Began: May 1, 1978.
Channel capacity: N.A. Channels available but not in use: N.A.
Basic Service
Subscribers: N.A.
Programming (received off-air): KABY-TV (A) Aberdeen; KCCO-TV (C) Alexandria; KWCM-TV (P) Appleton; KESD-TV (P) Brookings; KDLV-TV (N), KELO-TV (C) Sioux Falls-Mitchell; allband FM.
Programming (via translator): KSTP-TV (A), WCCO-TV (C) Minneapolis-St. Paul.
Programming (via satellite): WGN-TV (W) Chicago; CNN; ESPN; TBS Superstation; USA Network.
Current originations: Automated time-weather.
Fee: $25.00 installation; $11.00 monthly.
Pay Service 1
Pay Units: N.A.
Programming (via satellite): HBO; Showtime.
Fee: $10.00 monthly (Showtime), $10.50 monthly (HBO).
Equipment: Blonder-Tongue headend; Jerrold amplifiers.
Miles of plant: 8.1 (coaxial). Homes passed: 554. Total homes in franchised area: 554.
Manager: Bruce Reuber. Chief technician: Richard Brewer.
City fee: None.
Ownership: Cable TV Assoc. Inc.

COLMAN—Satellite Cable Services Inc., Box 106, Brookings, SD 57006-0106. Phone: 605-692-5508. Fax: 605-692-6496. County: Moody. ICA: SD0093.
TV Market Ranking: 85. Franchise award date: N.A. Franchise expiration date: N.A. Began: November 1, 1982.
Channel capacity: 80 (2-way capable; operating 2-way). Channels available but not in use: N.A.
Basic Service
Subscribers: 135.
Programming (received off-air): KESD-TV (P) Brookings; KDLV-TV (N), KELO-TV (C), KSFY-TV (A) Sioux Falls-Mitchell; KUSD-TV (P) Vermillion.
Programming (via satellite): WGN-TV (W) Chicago; CNN; Discovery Channel; ESPN; Fox Family Channel; Nashville Network; TBS Superstation; USA Network.
Fee: $24.95 installation; $28.96 monthly.
Pay Service 1
Pay Units: 13.
Programming (via satellite): Disney Channel.
Fee: $25.00 installation; $10.00 monthly.
Pay Service 2
Pay Units: 78.
Programming (via satellite): HBO.
Fee: $9.45 installation; $10.95 monthly.
Miles of plant: 4.0 (coaxial). Homes passed: 245.
Manager: Doug Bierschbach. Chief technician: Paul Schmidt.
Ownership: Satellite Cable Services Inc. (MSO).

COLTON—Telecom Inc., Box 127, Irene, SD 57037-0127. Phone: 800-239-7501. Fax: 605-766-7695. E-mail: jeanniejohnson@dtg.com. County: Minnehaha. ICA: SD0161.
TV Market Ranking: 85. Franchise award date: N.A. Franchise expiration date: February 1, 2006. Began: November 1, 1982.
Channel capacity: 36 (not 2-way capable). Channels available but not in use: 7.
Basic Service
Subscribers: 183.
Programming (received off-air): K53EG (I) Sioux Falls; KCSD-TV (P), KDLV-TV (N), KELO-TV (C), KSFY-TV (A), KTTW (F) Sioux Falls-Mitchell; KUSD-TV (P) Vermillion.
Programming (via satellite): WGN-TV (W) Chicago; A & E; CNN; Country Music TV; Discovery Channel; Disney Channel; ESPN; ESPN 2; Fox Family Channel; History Channel; Lifetime; Midwest Sports Channel; Nashville Network; Nickelodeon; Sci-Fi Channel; TBS Superstation; The Weather Channel; Turner Network TV; USA Network; VH1.
Fee: $35.00 installation; $21.27 monthly.
Pay Service 1
Pay Units: 36.
Programming (via satellite): HBO.
Fee: $13.00 installation; $7.95 monthly.
Pay Service 2
Pay Units: 6.
Programming (via satellite): Showtime.
Fee: $13.00 installation; $7.95 monthly.
Miles of plant: 4.7 (coaxial). Homes passed: 259. Total homes in franchised area: 291.
Manager: Thomas W. Hertz. Chief technician: Jerry Andersen. Program director: Jeannie Johnson. Marketing director: Marshall Damgaard.
Franchise fee: 3% of gross.
Ownership: Dakota Telecom Inc. (MSO).

CONDE—Satellite Cable Services Inc., Box 106, Brookings, SD 57006-0106. Phone: 605-692-5508. Fax: 605-692-6496. County: Spink. ICA: SD0163.
TV Market Ranking: Below 100. Franchise award date: N.A. Franchise expiration date: N.A. Began: February 1, 1988.
Channel capacity: 36 (2-way capable; not operating 2-way). Channels available but not in use: N.A.
Basic Service
Subscribers: 60.
Programming (via satellite): KCNC-TV (C), KWGN-TV (W) Denver; CNN; Country Music TV; ESPN; Fox Family Channel; TBS Superstation.
Fee: $25.79 monthly.
Pay Service 1
Pay Units: N.A.
Programming (via satellite): HBO.
Fee: N.A.
Manager: Doug Bierschbach. Chief technician: Paul Schmidt.
Ownership: Satellite Cable Services Inc. (MSO).

CORSICA—Ollig Cablevision, Box 98, 525 E. 4th St., Dell Rapids, SD 57022. Phone: 605-428-5421. Fax: 605-428-3132. County: Douglas. ICA: SD0094.
TV Market Ranking: 85. Franchise award date: January 1, 1983. Franchise expiration date: January 1, 1998. Began: July 1, 1983.
Channel capacity: 12 (not 2-way capable). Channels available but not in use: None.
Basic Service
Subscribers: 162.
Programming (received off-air): KTTM (F) Huron; KTSD-TV (P) Pierre; KPLO-TV (C) Reliance; KDLV-TV (N), KSFY-TV (A) Sioux Falls-Mitchell.
Programming (via satellite): WGN-TV (W) Chicago; CNN; ESPN; Fox Family Channel; Nashville Network; TBS Superstation.
Fee: $35.00 installation; $13.50 monthly.
Pay Service 1
Pay Units: 27.
Programming (via satellite): HBO.
Fee: $10.95 monthly.
Local advertising: No.
Equipment: Jerrold headend; Magnavox amplifiers; Times Fiber cable; Harris & Scientific-Atlanta satellite antenna; Jerrold satellite receivers.
Miles of plant: 4.0 (coaxial). Homes passed: 240. Total homes in franchised area: 256.
Manager: Denny Law. Chief technician: Mike Bures.
City fee: 2% of gross.
Ownership: Ollig Utilities Co. (MSO).

COUNTRY VILLAGE/PRAIRIE ACRES MOBILE HOME PARK—Galaxy Cablevision, 203 S. Lincoln Ave., York, NE 68467. Phones: 402-362-1705; 800-365-6988. Fax: 402-362-3698. County: Pennington. ICA: SD0222.
TV Market Ranking: Below 100. Franchise award date: N.A. Franchise expiration date: N.A. Began: N.A.
Channel capacity: N.A. Channels available but not in use: N.A.
Basic Service
Subscribers: 63.
Programming (received off-air): KWGN-TV (W) Denver; KBHE-TV (P), KCLO-TV (C), KEVN-TV (F), KNBN-LP (N), KOTA-TV (A) Rapid City.
Programming (via satellite): WGN-TV (W) Chicago; A & E; American Movie Classics; CNN; Discovery Channel; Disney Channel; ESPN; ESPN 2; Fox Family Channel; Headline News; Learning Channel; Lifetime; Nashville Network; Nickelodeon; QVC; TBS Superstation; The Weather Channel; Turner Network TV; USA Network; VH1.
Fee: $28.95 monthly.

Pay Service 1
Pay Units: 14.
Programming (via satellite): HBO.
Fee: $12.95 monthly.
Miles of plant: 5.5 (coaxial). Homes passed: 326.
District vice president: John M. Dixon III. State manager: Steve Jordan. Technical manager: Van De Vries.
Ownership: Galaxy Cablevision (MSO).

COUNTRYSIDE MOBILE HOME PARK—Galaxy Cablevision, 203 S. Lincoln Ave., York, NE 68467. Phones: 402-362-1705; 800-365-6988. Fax: 402-362-3698. County: Pennington. Also serves Rapid City (portions). ICA: SD0223.
TV Market Ranking: Below 100. Franchise award date: N.A. Franchise expiration date: N.A. Began: N.A.
Channel capacity: 41. Channels available but not in use: 12.
Basic Service
Subscribers: 184.
Programming (received off-air): KWGN-TV (W) Denver; KBHE-TV (P), KCLO-TV (C), KEVN-TV (F), KNBN-LP (N), KOTA-TV (A) Rapid City.
Programming (via satellite): WGN-TV (W) Chicago; A & E; American Movie Classics; CNN; Discovery Channel; Disney Channel; ESPN; ESPN 2; Fox Family Channel; Headline News; Home & Garden Television; Learning Channel; Lifetime; Nashville Network; Nickelodeon; QVC; TBS Superstation; The Weather Channel; Turner Network TV; USA Network; VH1.
Fee: $28.95 monthly.
Pay Service 1
Pay Units: 33.
Programming (via satellite): HBO.
Fee: $12.95 monthly.
Pay Service 2
Pay Units: 5.
Programming (via satellite): Showtime.
Fee: $7.95 monthly.
Miles of plant: 9.1 (coaxial). Homes passed: 482.
District vice president: John M. Dixon III. State manager: Steve Jordan. Technical manager: Van De Vries.
Ownership: Galaxy Cablevision (MSO).

CUSTER—TCI Cablevision, Box 309, 842 Short Track Rd., Sturgis, SD 57785. Phone: 605-347-3090. Fax: 605-347-3499. County: Custer. Also serves Custer County (unincorporated areas). ICA: SD0034.
TV Market Ranking: Below 100 (Custer, portions of Custer County); Outside TV Markets (portions of Custer County). Franchise award date: N.A. Franchise expiration date: N.A. Began: September 1, 1980.
Channel capacity: 35. Channels available but not in use: 1.
Note: Miles of plant & homes passed include figures for Belle Fourche, Deadwood, Hot Springs, Spearfish & Sturgis, SD.
Basic Service
Subscribers: 720.
Programming (received off-air): KBHE-TV (P), KCLO-TV (C), KEVN-TV (F), KNBN-LP (N), KOTA-TV (A) Rapid City; allband FM.
Programming (via satellite): KWGN-TV (W) Denver; A & E; C-SPAN; CNBC; CNN; Cartoon Network; Country Music TV; Discovery Channel; ESPN; ESPN 2; EWTN; Fox Family Channel; Fox Sports Net; Headline News; History Channel; Lifetime; MTV; Nashville Network; Nickelodeon; QVC; TBS Superstation; TV Guide Channel; The Weather Channel; Trinity Bcstg. Network; Turner Network TV; USA Network.
Current originations: Automated time-weather; public access; educational access.
Fee: $40.00 installation; $25.52 monthly; $10.00 additional installation.
Pay Service 1
Pay Units: N.A.
Programming (via satellite): Cinemax; Disney Channel; HBO; Showtime; The Movie Channel.
Fee: N.A.
Local advertising: No.
Equipment: Scientific-Atlanta headend; Scientific-Atlanta amplifiers; Times Fiber cable; Video Data Systems character generator; Arcom traps; Scientific-Atlanta satellite antenna; Scientific-Atlanta satellite receivers.
Miles of plant: 250.0 (coaxial). Homes passed: 19,000.
Manager: Dale Hodgkins. Chief technician: Gary Reimer.
City fee: 3% of gross.
Ownership: AT&T Broadband & Internet Services (MSO). Purchased from South Dakota Cable Inc., April 1, 1999.

DEADWOOD—TCI Cablevision, Box 309, 842 Short Track Rd., Sturgis, SD 57785. Phone: 605-347-3090. Fax: 605-347-3499. County: Lawrence. Also serves Central City, Lawrence County, Lead. ICA: SD0011.
TV Market Ranking: Below 100. Franchise award date: N.A. Franchise expiration date: N.A. Began: March 1, 1969.
Channel capacity: 35 (2-way capable; operating 2-way). Channels available but not in use: N.A.
Basic Service
Subscribers: 1,940.
Programming (received off-air): KPSD-TV (P) Eagle Butte; KCLO-TV (C), KEVN-TV (F), KNBN-LP (N), KOTA-TV (A) Rapid City; allband FM.
Programming (via satellite): KWGN-TV (W) Denver; A & E; C-SPAN; CNBC; CNN; Cartoon Network; Country Music TV; Discovery Channel; ESPN; ESPN 2; EWTN; Fox Family Channel; Fox Sports Net; Headline News; History Channel; Lifetime; MTV; Nashville Network; Nickelodeon; QVC; TBS Superstation; TV Guide Channel; The Weather Channel; Trinity Bcstg. Network; Turner Network TV; USA Network.
Current originations: Automated time-weather; public access; educational access.
Fee: $40.00 installation; $24.28 monthly; $10.00 additional installation.
Pay Service 1
Pay Units: N.A.
Programming (via satellite): Cinemax; Disney Channel; HBO; Showtime; The Movie Channel.
Fee: N.A.
Local advertising: No.
Equipment: Scientific-Atlanta headend; Scientific-Atlanta amplifiers; Times Fiber cable; Arcom traps; Scientific-Atlanta satellite antenna; Scientific-Atlanta satellite receivers.
Note: Miles of plant and homes passed included with Custer, SD.
Manager: Dale Hodgkins. Chief technician: Gary Reimer.
City fee: 3% of gross.
Ownership: AT&T Broadband & Internet Services (MSO). Purchased from South Dakota Cable Inc., April 1, 1999.

DELL RAPIDS—Valley Cablevision, Box 98, 525 E. 4th St., Dell Rapids, SD 57022. Phone: 605-428-5421. Fax: 605-428-3132. County: Minnehaha. Also serves Minnehaha County. ICA: SD0028.
TV Market Ranking: 85. Franchise award date: August 1, 1982. Franchise expiration date: N.A. Began: August 1, 1982.
Channel capacity: 35 (not 2-way capable). Channels available but not in use: 10.
Basic Service
Subscribers: 451.
Programming (received off-air): KDLV-TV (N), KELO-TV (C), KSFY-TV (A), KTTW (F) Sioux Falls-Mitchell; KUSD-TV (P) Vermillion.
Fee: $35.00 installation; $10.45 monthly.
Expanded Basic Service
Subscribers: 431.
Programming (via satellite): WGN-TV (W) Chicago; American Movie Classics; CNN; Discovery Channel; ESPN; Fox Family Channel; Headline News; Midwest Sports Channel; Nashville Network; Nickelodeon; Odyssey; QVC; Sci-Fi Channel; TBS Superstation; Turner Network TV; USA Network.
Fee: $35.00 installation; $13.00 monthly.
Pay Service 1
Pay Units: 185.
Programming (via satellite): Disney Channel.
Fee: $4.95 monthly.
Pay Service 2
Pay Units: 200.
Programming (via satellite): HBO.
Fee: $9.00 monthly.
Pay Service 3
Pay Units: 137.
Programming (via satellite): Showtime.
Fee: $9.00 monthly.
Local advertising: Yes (locally produced). Available in character-generated programming. Rates: $2.00/Day.
Program Guide: Premium Channels.
Equipment: Scientific-Atlanta headend; GTE Sylvania amplifiers; Times Fiber cable; Comtech character generator; Pioneer, Scientific-Atlanta & Standard Components set top converters; Vitek traps; Scientific-Atlanta satellite antenna; Scientific-Atlanta satellite receivers.
Miles of plant: 29.0 (coaxial). Homes passed: 964. Total homes in franchised area: 964.
Manager: Denny Law. Chief technician: Mike Bures.
City fee: 3% of gross.
Ownership: Ollig Utilities Co. (MSO).

DOLAND—Midcontinent Cable, Box 910, Aberdeen, SD 57402-0910. Phones: 605-229-1775; 800-456-0564. Fax: 605-229-0478. County: Spink. ICA: SD0118.
TV Market Ranking: Outside TV Markets. Franchise award date: October 12, 1983. Franchise expiration date: May 1, 2011. Began: December 1, 1983.
Channel capacity: 41 (not 2-way capable). Channels available but not in use: 2.
Basic Service
Subscribers: 101.
Programming (received off-air): KABY-TV (A), KDSD-TV (P) Aberdeen; KDLO-TV (C) Florence-Watertown; KTTM (F) Huron.
Programming (via microwave): KDLT-TV (N) Sioux Falls.
Programming (via satellite): WGN-TV (W) Chicago; A & E; American Movie Classics; C-SPAN; CNBC; CNN; Cartoon Network; Country Music TV; Discovery Channel; Disney Channel; ESPN; ESPN 2; ESPNews; EWTN; FX; Fox Family Channel; Headline News; Learning Channel; Lifetime; MTV; Midwest Sports Channel; Nashville Network; Nick at Nite's TV Land; Nickelodeon; QVC; TBS Superstation; TV Guide Channel; The Weather Channel; Turner Network TV; USA Network; VH1.
Fee: $50.00 installation; $26.50 monthly.
Pay Service 1
Pay Units: 13.
Programming (via satellite): HBO.
Fee: $20.00 installation; $12.00 monthly.
Pay Service 2
Pay Units: 8.
Programming (via satellite): Showtime.
Fee: $20.00 installation; $11.00 monthly.
Pay Service 3
Pay Units: 8.
Programming (via satellite): The Movie Channel.
Fee: $20.00 installation; $11.00 monthly.
Pay Service 4
Pay Units: N.A.
Programming (via satellite): Cinemax.
Fee: N.A.
Local advertising: No.
Equipment: Magnavox amplifiers; Times Fiber cable; Eagle traps.
Miles of plant: 3.2 (coaxial); None (fiber optic). Homes passed: 172. Total homes in franchised area: 172.
Manager: Lonnie Schumacher. Marketing director: Fred Jamieson. Customer service manager: Kathy Fuhrmann.
City fee: 3% of basic gross.
Ownership: Midcontinent Communications (MSO).

EAGLE BUTTE—Cheyenne River Sioux Tribe Telephone Cable, Box 810, Eagle Butte, SD 57625. Phone: 605-964-2600. Fax: 605-964-1003. Counties: Dewey & Ziebach. Also serves Dupree. ICA: SD0164.
TV Market Ranking: Outside TV Markets. Franchise award date: N.A. Franchise expiration date: N.A. Began: January 1, 1982.
Channel capacity: 12. Channels available but not in use: N.A.
Basic Service
Subscribers: N.A.
Programming (received off-air): KPSD-TV (P) Eagle Butte; KPRY-TV (A) Pierre; KCLO-TV (C) Rapid City.
Programming (via satellite): KCNC-TV (C) Denver; CNN; ESPN; TBS Superstation.
Fee: $25.00 installation; $13.00 monthly.
Pay Service 1
Pay Units: 330.
Programming (via satellite): HBO.
Fee: $11.00 monthly.
Manager: J. D. Williams. Chief technician: Kim Peterson.
Ownership: Cheyenne River Sioux Tribe Telephone Authority (MSO).

EDEN—Satellite Cable Services Inc., Box 106, Brookings, SD 57006-0106. Phone: 605-692-5508. Fax: 605-692-6496. County: Marshall. ICA: SD0165.
TV Market Ranking: Outside TV Markets. Franchise award date: N.A. Franchise expiration date: N.A. Began: N.A.
Channel capacity: 36. Channels available but not in use: N.A.
Basic Service
Subscribers: 30.
Programming (via satellite): KCNC-TV (C), KWGN-TV (W) Denver; CNN; ESPN; Nashville Network; TBS Superstation.
Fee: $25.79 monthly.
Pay Service 1
Pay Units: N.A.
Programming (via satellite): HBO.
Fee: $11.95 monthly.
Manager: Doug Bierschbach. Chief technician: Paul Schmidt.
Ownership: Satellite Cable Services Inc. (MSO).

EDGEMONT—Wy-Dak Inc., Box 111, Redfield, SD 57469. Phone: 605-472-3415. County: Fall River. ICA: SD0043.

TV Market Ranking: Outside TV Markets. Franchise award date: N.A. Franchise expiration date: N.A. Began: May 1, 1978.

Channel capacity: 23. Channels available but not in use: N.A.

Basic Service

Subscribers: N.A.

Programming (received off-air): KBHE-TV (P), KEVN-TV (F), KOTA-TV (A) Rapid City; KDUH-TV (A) Scottsbluff.

Programming (via satellite): Fox Family Channel; TBS Superstation.

Current originations: Automated time-weather.

Fee: $8.75 monthly.

Equipment: Hughes & Jerrold headend; Magnavox amplifiers; Comm/Scope cable; Andrew satellite antenna.

Miles of plant: 9.0 (coaxial). Homes passed: 600.

City fee: 3% of gross.

Ownership: Cable TV Assoc. Inc. (MSO).

ELK POINT—TelePartners, Bldg. 12, 11260 Aurora Ave., Urbandale, IA 50322. Phone: 515-276-3069. Fax: 515-270-9181. County: Union. ICA: SD0061.

TV Market Ranking: Below 100. Franchise award date: N.A. Franchise expiration date: December 23, 2004. Began: N.A.

Channel capacity: 41 (not 2-way capable). Channels available but not in use: 10.

Basic Service

Subscribers: 384.

Programming (received off-air): KCAU-TV (A), KMEG (C), KSIN (P), KTIV (N) Sioux City; KDLV-TV (N), KELO-TV (C), KSFY-TV (A) Sioux Falls-Mitchell; KUSD-TV (P) Vermillion.

Programming (via satellite): WGN-TV (W) Chicago; A & E; CNN; Discovery Channel; Disney Channel; ESPN; FX; Fox Family Channel; Fox News Channel; Fox Sports Net; FoxNet; Headline News; MTV; Nashville Network; Nickelodeon; QVC; TBS Superstation; The Weather Channel; Turner Network TV; USA Network.

Fee: $35.00 installation; $29.50 monthly.

Pay Service 1

Pay Units: 47.

Programming (via satellite): HBO.

Fee: $12.95 monthly.

Pay Service 2

Pay Units: 67.

Programming (via satellite): Showtime.

Fee: $7.95 monthly.

Pay Service 3

Pay Units: 64.

Programming (via satellite): The Movie Channel.

Fee: $6.95 monthly.

Local advertising: No.

Equipment: Scientific-Atlanta satellite antenna; Scientific-Atlanta satellite receivers.

Miles of plant: 8.6 (coaxial). Homes passed: 712.

Manager: Russ Gifford. Technical manager: Van De Vries.

City fee: 3% of gross.

Ownership: TelePartners (MSO). Purchased from Galaxy Cablevision, September 1, 1998.

EMERY—Emery Cable Vision Inc., Box 304, Emery, SD 57332. Phone: 605-449-4203. Fax: 605-449-4329. County: Hanson. ICA: SD0107.

TV Market Ranking: 85. Franchise award date: April 11, 1983. Franchise expiration date: April 11, 1998. Began: November 1, 1984.

Channel capacity: 16 (not 2-way capable). Channels available but not in use: None.

Basic Service

Subscribers: 155; Commercial subscribers: 4.

Programming (received off-air): KESD-TV (P) Brookings; KTTM (F) Huron; KDLV-TV (N), KELO-TV (C), KSFY-TV (A) Sioux Falls-Mitchell.

Programming (via satellite): WGN-TV (W) Chicago; CNN; Discovery Channel; ESPN; Fox Family Channel; Nashville Network; QVC; TBS Superstation; Trinity Bcstg. Network; USA Network.

Fee: $15.00 installation (aerial), $30.00 (underground); $14.50 monthly.

Commercial fee: $14.50 monthly.

Pay Service 1

Pay Units: 40.

Programming (via satellite): HBO.

Fee: $5.00 installation; $9.50 monthly.

Local advertising: No.

Equipment: Scientific-Atlanta headend.

Miles of plant: 7.0 (coaxial). Homes passed: 200. Total homes in franchised area: 200.

Manager: John Pudwill.

City fee: 3% of gross.

Ownership: Richard Ekstrand.

ESTELLINE—Satellite Cable Services Inc., Box 106, Brookings, SD 57006-0106. Phone: 605-692-5508. Fax: 605-692-6496. County: Hamlin. ICA: SD0076.

TV Market Ranking: Below 100. Franchise award date: N.A. Franchise expiration date: January 1, 1998. Began: August 1, 1983.

Channel capacity: 35 (2-way capable; operating 2-way). Channels available but not in use: N.A.

Basic Service

Subscribers: 200.

Programming (received off-air): KABY-TV (A) Aberdeen; KESD-TV (P) Brookings; KDLO-TV (C) Florence-Watertown; KDLV-TV (N) Sioux Falls-Mitchell.

Programming (via satellite): WGN-TV (W) Chicago; CNN; ESPN; Fox Family Channel; Nashville Network; TBS Superstation; USA Network.

Fee: $24.95 installation; $27.38 monthly.

Pay Service 1

Pay Units: N.A.

Programming (via satellite): HBO.

Fee: $10.00 installation; $11.95 monthly.

Equipment: Scientific-Atlanta headend; Magnavox amplifiers; Scientific-Atlanta cable; Eagle traps; Anixter-Mark satellite antenna; Scientific-Atlanta satellite receivers.

Miles of plant: 5.0 (coaxial). Homes passed: 308. Total homes in franchised area: 308.

Manager: Doug Bierschbach. Chief technician: Paul Schmidt.

City fee: 3% of gross.

Ownership: Satellite Cable Services Inc. (MSO).

ETHAN—Communications Enterprises Inc., Box 67, Woonsocket, SD 57385. Phone: 605-796-4411. Fax: 605-796-4419. County: Davison. ICA: SD0167.

TV Market Ranking: 85. Franchise award date: N.A. Franchise expiration date: N.A. Began: January 1, 1984.

Channel capacity: 15 (not 2-way capable). Channels available but not in use: None.

Basic Service

Subscribers: 92.

Programming (received off-air): KESD-TV (P) Brookings; KDLV-TV (N), KELO-TV (C), KSFY-TV (A) Sioux Falls-Mitchell.

Programming (via satellite): WGN-TV (W) Chicago; CNN; Nashville Network; Nickelodeon; TBS Superstation.

Fee: $30.00 installation; $21.30 monthly.

Pay Service 1

Pay Units: N.A.

Programming (via satellite): HBO.

Fee: $9.00 monthly.

Manager: Gene Kroell.

Ownership: Sanborn Telephone Cooperative (MSO).

EUREKA—Village Cable Inc., Box 270, 124 E. 7th Ave., Redfield, SD 57469. Phone: 605-472-3415. County: McPherson. ICA: SD0040.

TV Market Ranking: Outside TV Markets. Franchise award date: N.A. Franchise expiration date: N.A. Began: April 1, 1983.

Channel capacity: 36. Channels available but not in use: N.A.

Basic Service

Subscribers: 457.

Programming (received off-air): KFYR-TV (N), KXMB-TV (C) Bismarck; KDLO-TV (C) Florence-Watertown; KPRY-TV (A) Pierre; KDLV-TV (N) Sioux Falls-Mitchell; KUSD-TV (P) Vermillion.

Programming (via satellite): WGN-TV (W) Chicago; Headline News; TBS Superstation; Turner Network TV.

Fee: N.A.

Miles of plant: 9.9 (coaxial). Homes passed: 629.

Ownership: Cable TV Assoc. Inc. (MSO).

EVERGREEN HOUSING—Golden West Cablevision, Box 9159, 2727 N. Plaza Dr., Rapid City, SD 57709. Phone: 605-348-6529. Fax: 605-342-1160. County: Shannon. ICA: SD0168.

TV Market Ranking: Below 100. Franchise award date: May 6, 1992. Franchise expiration date: May 6, 2012. Began: N.A.

Channel capacity: 36 (not 2-way capable). Channels available but not in use: 22.

Basic Service

Subscribers: 49.

Programming (received off-air): KBHE-TV (P), KCLO-TV (C), KEVN-TV (F), KOTA-TV (A) Rapid City.

Programming (via satellite): WGN-TV (W) Chicago; CNN; Discovery Channel; ESPN; Nashville Network; TBS Superstation; The Weather Channel; Turner Network TV.

Programming (via fiber optic cable): KNBN-LP (N) Rapid City.

Fee: $16.95 monthly.

Pay Service 1

Pay Units: 47.

Programming (via satellite): Disney Channel.

Fee: N.A.

Pay Service 2

Pay Units: 49.

Programming (via satellite): Showtime.

Fee: $7.95 monthly.

Manager: Dwight Flatt. Chief technician: Ross Whitley. Marketing director: Greg Oleson.

Ownership: Golden West Cablevision.

FAIRFAX—Sky Scan Cable Co. Inc., Box 57, 713 Main St., Creighton, NE 68729. Phone: 402-358-3510. County: Gregory. Also serves Bonesteel. ICA: SD0169.

TV Market Ranking: Outside TV Markets. Franchise award date: N.A. Franchise expiration date: N.A. Began: April 1, 1987.

Channel capacity: 36. Channels available but not in use: N.A.

Basic Service

Subscribers: 176.

Programming (received off-air): KMNE-TV (P) Bassett; KPRY-TV (A), KTSD-TV (P) Pierre; KPLO-TV (C) Reliance; KDLV-TV (N), KTTW (F) Sioux Falls-Mitchell.

Programming (via satellite): WGN-TV (W) Chicago; A & E; CNN; Discovery Channel; ESPN; Fox Family Channel; Nashville Network; Sci-Fi Channel; TBS Superstation; Turner Network TV; USA Network.

Fee: $35.00 installation; $23.95 monthly.

Pay Service 1

Pay Units: 25.

Programming (via satellite): HBO.

Fee: $12.95 monthly.

Pay Service 2

Pay Units: 9.

Programming (via satellite): Cinemax.

Fee: $10.95 monthly.

Manager: Gelvin Stevens. Chief technician: Kenny Bartos.

Ownership: Sky Scan Cable Co. (MSO).

FAITH—Midcontinent Cable Systems Co. of South Dakota, Box 910, Aberdeen, SD 57402-0910. Phones: 605-229-1775; 800-456-0564. Fax: 605-229-0478. County: Meade. ICA: SD0102.

TV Market Ranking: Outside TV Markets. Franchise award date: April 1, 1986. Franchise expiration date: April 1, 2001. Began: March 1, 1983.

Channel capacity: 42 (not 2-way capable). Channels available but not in use: 20.

Basic Service

Subscribers: 155.

Programming (received off-air): KPSD-TV (P) Eagle Butte; KCLO-TV (C), KEVN-TV (F), KOTA-TV (A) Rapid City.

Programming (via satellite): WGN-TV (W) Chicago; KARE (N) Minneapolis-St. Paul; CNN; Discovery Channel; Disney Channel; ESPN; ESPN 2; Fox Family Channel; Nashville Network; Nickelodeon; TBS Superstation; Turner Network TV; USA Network.

Current originations: Religious access.

Fee: $50.00 installation; $24.37 monthly.

Pay Service 1

Pay Units: 38.

Programming (via satellite): HBO.

Fee: $20.00 installation; $11.00 monthly.

Local advertising: No.

Equipment: Scientific-Atlanta headend; Scientific-Atlanta amplifiers; Miralite satellite antenna; Blonder-Tongue satellite receivers.

Miles of plant: 3.6 (coaxial); None (fiber optic). Homes passed: 211.

Manager: Lonnie Schumacher. Marketing director: Fred Jamieson. Customer service manager: Kathy Fuhrmann.

City fee: 3% of gross.

Ownership: Midcontinent Communications (MSO).

FAULKTON—Faulkton Cable TV, Box 111, Redfield, SD 57469. Phone: 605-472-3415. County: Faulk. ICA: SD0170.

TV Market Ranking: Outside TV Markets. Franchise award date: N.A. Franchise expiration date: N.A. Began: February 1, 1981.

Channel capacity: 13. Channels available but not in use: 3.

Basic Service

Subscribers: 342.

Programming (received off-air): KABY-TV (A), KDSD-TV (P) Aberdeen; KDLO-TV (C) Florence-Watertown; KDLV-TV (N) Sioux Falls-Mitchell.

Programming (via satellite): WGN-TV (W) Chicago; ESPN; TBS Superstation; Turner Network TV.

Fee: $30.00 installation; $9.95 monthly.

Pay Service 1

Pay Units: N.A.

Programming (via satellite): HBO.

Fee: $10.00 installation; $9.95 monthly.

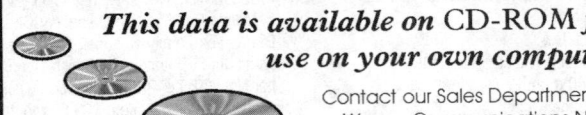

Equipment: Nexus headend; Magnavox amplifiers; Times Fiber cable; Oak set top converters; Nexus satellite receivers.
Manager: Mike McClure.
City fee: None.
Ownership: Cable TV Assoc. Inc. (MSO).

FLORENCE—Satellite Cable Services Inc., Box 106, Brookings, SD 57006-0106. Phone: 605-692-5508. Fax: 605-692-6496. County: Codington. ICA: SD0171.
TV Market Ranking: Below 100. Franchise award date: N.A. Franchise expiration date: N.A. Began: N.A.
Channel capacity: 36 (2-way capable; not operating 2-way). Channels available but not in use: N.A.
Basic Service
Subscribers: 60.
Programming (via satellite): KCNC-TV (C), KWGN-TV (W) Denver; CNN; ESPN; Nashville Network; TBS Superstation.
Fee: $25.79 monthly.
Pay Service 1
Pay Units: N.A.
Programming (via satellite): HBO.
Fee: $11.95 monthly.
Manager: Doug Bierschbach. Chief technician: Paul Schmidt.
Ownership: Satellite Cable Services Inc. (MSO).

FORT PIERRE—Midcontinent Cable Systems Co. of South Dakota, Box 910, Aberdeen, SD 57402-0910. Phone: 605-229-1775; 800-456-0564; Fax: 605-229-0478. County: Stanley. ICA: SD0172.
TV Market Ranking: Below 100. Franchise award date: June 17, 1985. Franchise expiration date: June 17, 2000. Began: N.A.
Channel capacity: 40 (not 2-way capable). Channels available but not in use: None.
Basic Service
Subscribers: 731.
Programming (received off-air): KTTM (F) Huron; KPRY-TV (A), KTSD-TV (P) Pierre; KPLO-TV (C) Reliance; KDLV-TV (N) Sioux Falls-Mitchell; 5 FMs.
Programming (via satellite): WGN-TV (W) Chicago; A & E; American Movie Classics; C-SPAN; CNBC; CNN; Cartoon Network; Country Music TV; Discovery Channel; Disney Channel; ESPN; ESPN 2; ESPNews; EWTN; FX; Fox Family Channel; Headline News; Lifetime; MTV; Midwest Sports Channel; Nashville Network; Nick at Nite's TV Land; Nickelodeon; QVC; TBS Superstation; TV Guide Channel; The Health Network; The Weather Channel; Turner Network TV; USA Network; VH1.
Current originations: Educational access.
Fee: $50.00 installation; $23.18 monthly.
Pay Service 1
Pay Units: 55.
Programming (via satellite): Cinemax.
Fee: $11.00 monthly.
Pay Service 2
Pay Units: 158.
Programming (via satellite): HBO.
Fee: $11.00 monthly.
Pay Service 3
Pay Units: 108.
Programming (via satellite): Showtime.
Fee: $11.00 monthly.
Pay Service 4
Pay Units: 99.
Programming (via satellite): The Movie Channel.
Fee: $20.00 installation; $11.00 monthly.
Equipment: Simulsat headend; C-COR amplifiers; Times Fiber cable; Scientific-Atlanta satellite receivers.
Miles of plant: 19.1 (coaxial); 1.5 (fiber optic). Homes passed: 796.
Manager: Lonnie Schumacher. Marketing director: Fred Jamieson. Customer service manager: Kathy Fuhrmann.
Ownership: Midcontinent Communications (MSO).

FRANKFORT—Village Cable, Box 111, Redfield, SD 57469. Phone: 605-472-3415. County: Spink. ICA: SD0173.
TV Market Ranking: Below 100. Franchise award date: N.A. Franchise expiration date: N.A. Began: N.A.
Channel capacity: 36. Channels available but not in use: N.A.
Basic Service
Subscribers: N.A.
Programming (received off-air): KABY-TV (A) Aberdeen; KESD-TV (P) Brookings; KDLO-TV (C) Florence-Watertown; KDLV-TV (N) Sioux Falls-Mitchell.
Programming (via satellite): WGN-TV (W) Chicago; CNN; ESPN; Nashville Network; TBS Superstation.
Fee: $15.00 monthly.
Pay Service 1
Pay Units: N.A.
Programming (via satellite): Showtime.
Fee: $11.00 monthly.
Manager: Terry Thomas. Chief technician: Jerry Neu.
Ownership: Cable TV Assoc. Inc. (MSO).

FREDERICK—Midcontinent Cable Systems Co. of South Dakota, Box 910, Aberdeen, SD 57402-0910. Phones: 605-229-1775; 800-456-0564. Fax: 605-229-0478. County: Brown. ICA: SD0131.
TV Market Ranking: Below 100. Franchise award date: May 1, 1996. Franchise expiration date: May 1, 2011. Began: December 1, 1983.
Channel capacity: 38 (not 2-way capable). Channels available but not in use: 2.
Basic Service
Subscribers: 86.
Programming (received off-air): KABY-TV (A), KDSD-TV (P) Aberdeen; KDLO-TV (C) Florence-Watertown; KTTM (F) Huron.
Programming (via microwave): KDLT-TV (N) Sioux Falls.
Programming (via satellite): WGN-TV (W) Chicago; A & E; American Movie Classics; C-SPAN; CNBC; CNN; Cartoon Network; Country Music TV; Discovery Channel; Disney Channel; ESPN; FX; Fox Family Channel; Headline News; Learning Channel; Lifetime; Midwest Sports Channel; Nashville Network; Nick at Nite's TV Land; Nickelodeon; QVC; TBS Superstation; TV Guide Channel; The Inspirational Network; The Weather Channel; Turner Network TV; USA Network; VH1.
Fee: $50.00 installation; $26.50 monthly.
Pay Service 1
Pay Units: 13.
Programming (via satellite): HBO.
Fee: $20.00 installation; $12.00 monthly.
Pay Service 2
Pay Units: 2.
Programming (via satellite): The Movie Channel.
Fee: $20.00 installation; $11.00 monthly.
Pay Service 3
Pay Units: 2.
Programming (via satellite): Showtime.
Fee: $20.00 installation; $11.00 monthly.
Local advertising: No.
Equipment: Scientific-Atlanta headend; Magnavox amplifiers; Times Fiber cable; Eagle traps; Scientific-Atlanta satellite antenna.
Miles of plant: 2.8 (coaxial); None (fiber optic). Homes passed: 125. Total homes in franchised area: 125.
Manager: Lonnie Schumacher. Marketing director: Fred Jamieson. Customer service manager: Kathy Fuhrmann.
City fee: 3% of basic gross.
Ownership: Midcontinent Communications (MSO).

FREEMAN—Satellite Cable Services Inc., Box 106, Brookings, SD 57006-0106. Phone: 605-692-5508. Fax: 605-692-6496. Counties: Bon Homme, Hutchinson, McCook & Turner. Also serves Bridgewater, Canistota, Marion, Menno, Olivet, Parkston, Salem, Scotland. ICA: SD0038.
TV Market Ranking: 85 (Bridgewater, Canistota, Marion, Parkston, Salem); Outside TV Markets (Freeman, Menno, Olivet, Scotland). Franchise award date: N.A. Franchise expiration date: N.A. Began: December 9, 1981.
Channel capacity: 150. Channels available but not in use: 11.
Basic Service
Subscribers: 2,455.
Programming (received off-air): KESD-TV (P) Brookings; KDLT-TV (N) Sioux Falls; KELO-TV (C), KSFY-TV (A), KTTW (F) Sioux Falls-Mitchell.
Programming (via satellite): WGN-TV (W) Chicago; A & E; American Movie Classics; C-SPAN; C-SPAN 2; CNBC; CNN; Comedy Central; Country Music TV; Discovery Channel; Disney Channel; E! Entertainment TV; ESPN; ESPN 2; Fox Family Channel; Fox News Channel; History Channel; Home & Garden Television; Knowledge TV; Learning Channel; Lifetime; MTV; Midwest Sports Channel; Nashville Network; Nick at Nite's TV Land; Nickelodeon; Odyssey; QVC; TBS Superstation; The Weather Channel; Turner Network TV; USA Network; VH1.
Fee: $24.95 installation; $27.38 monthly.
Pay Service 1
Pay Units: N.A.
Programming (via satellite): Cinemax (multiplexed); Golf Channel; HBO; Showtime (multiplexed); Starz!; The New Encore.
Fee: $9.45 installation; $11.95 monthly (HBO).
Equipment: Scientific-Atlanta headend; Scientific-Atlanta amplifiers; Scientific-Atlanta cable; Pioneer set top converters; Eagle traps; Scientific-Atlanta satellite antenna; Scientific-Atlanta satellite receivers.
Miles of plant: 9.0 (coaxial). Additional miles planned: 1.0 (coaxial). Homes passed: 2,455. Total homes in franchised area: 2,455.
Manager: Doug Bierschbach. Chief technician: Paul Schmidt.
City fee: 3% of gross.
Ownership: Satellite Cable Services Inc. (MSO).

GARRETSON—Splitrock Telecom Cooperative Inc., 612 3rd St., Garretson, SD 57030. Phone: 605-594-3411. Fax: 605-594-6776. County: Minnehaha. Also serves Brandon, Corson, Sherman. ICA: SD0016.
TV Market Ranking: 85. Franchise award date: N.A. Franchise expiration date: N.A. Began: December 10, 1981.
Channel capacity: 34 (not 2-way capable). Channels available but not in use: 3.
Basic Service
Subscribers: 1,941.
Programming (received off-air): KDLV-TV (N), KELO-TV (C), KSFY-TV (A), KTTW (F) Sioux Falls-Mitchell; KUSD-TV (P) Vermillion.
Programming (via satellite): WGN-TV (W) Chicago; A & E; C-SPAN; CNN; Discovery Channel; Disney Channel; ESPN; Fox Family Channel; Headline News; Lifetime; MTV; Midwest Sports Channel; Nashville Network; Nickelodeon; TBS Superstation; The Weather Channel; Turner Network TV; USA Network.
Fee: $12.50 monthly.
Pay Service 1
Pay Units: 609.
Programming (via satellite): HBO.
Fee: $9.00 installation; $9.00 monthly.
Pay Service 2
Pay Units: 372.
Programming (via satellite): Showtime.
Fee: $9.00 installation; $8.00 monthly.
Local advertising: No.
Program Guide: Premium Channels.
Miles of plant: 54.0 (coaxial). Homes passed: 2,234.
Manager: Don Snyders. Chief technician: Bob Stietvater.
Ownership: Splitrock Telecom Cooperative Inc.

GARY—Satellite Cable Services Inc., Box 106, Brookings, SD 57006-0106. Phone: 605-692-5508. Fax: 605-692-6496. County: Deuel. ICA: SD0174.
TV Market Ranking: Below 100. Franchise award date: N.A. Franchise expiration date: N.A. Began: N.A.
Channel capacity: 36 (2-way capable; not operating 2-way). Channels available but not in use: N.A.
Basic Service
Subscribers: 100.
Programming (received off-air): KWCM-TV (P) Appleton; KDLO-TV (C) Florence-Watertown; KDLV-TV (N), KSFY-TV (A) Sioux Falls-Mitchell.
Programming (via satellite): WGN-TV (W) Chicago; CNN; Discovery Channel; ESPN; Fox Family Channel; Midwest Sports Channel; Nashville Network; TBS Superstation.
Fee: $27.38 monthly.
Pay Service 1
Pay Units: N.A.
Programming (via satellite): HBO.
Fee: $11.95 monthly.
Manager: Doug Bierschbach. Chief technician: Paul Schmidt.
Ownership: Satellite Cable Services Inc. (MSO).

GEDDES—Sky Scan Cable Co. Inc., Box 57, 713 Main St., Creighton, NE 68729. Phone: 402-358-3510. County: Charles Mix. ICA: SD0175.
TV Market Ranking: Outside TV Markets. Franchise award date: N.A. Franchise expiration date: N.A. Began: November 1, 1986.
Channel capacity: 36. Channels available but not in use: N.A.

Basic Service
Subscribers: 106.
Programming (received off-air): KMGH-TV (A), KUSA-TV (N) Denver; KTSD-TV (P) Pierre; KPLO-TV (C) Reliance; KDLV-TV (N), KSFY-TV (A) Sioux Falls-Mitchell.
Programming (via satellite): WGN-TV (W) Chicago; CNN; Discovery Channel; ESPN; ESPN 2; Fox Family Channel; FoxNet; Nashville Network; TBS Superstation; Turner Network TV; USA Network.
Fee: $35.00 installation; $23.95 monthly.
Pay Service 1
Pay Units: 6.
Programming (via satellite): Cinemax.
Fee: $10.95 monthly.
Pay Service 2
Pay Units: 10.
Programming (via satellite): HBO.
Fee: $12.95 monthly.
Miles of plant: 3.1 (coaxial).
Manager: Gelvin Stevens. Chief technician: Kenny Bartos.
Ownership: Sky Scan Cable Co. (MSO).

GETTYSBURG—Midcontinent Cable Systems Co. of South Dakota, Box 910, Aberdeen, SD 57402-0910. Phones: 605-229-1775; 800-456-0564. Fax: 605-229-0478. County: Potter. ICA: SD0036.
TV Market Ranking: Outside TV Markets. Franchise award date: January 6, 1992. Franchise expiration date: January 6, 2007. Began: February 1, 1980.
Channel capacity: 38 (not 2-way capable). Channels available but not in use: None.
Basic Service
Subscribers: 531.
Programming (received off-air): KQSD-TV (P) Lowry; KPRY-TV (A) Pierre; KPLO-TV (C) Reliance; KDLV-TV (N) Sioux Falls-Mitchell.
Programming (via satellite): WGN-TV (W) Chicago; A & E; American Movie Classics; C-SPAN; CNBC; CNN; Cartoon Network; Country Music TV; Discovery Channel; Disney Channel; ESPN; FX; Fox Family Channel; FoxNet; Headline News; Learning Channel; Lifetime; Midwest Sports Channel; Nashville Network; Nick at Nite's TV Land; Nickelodeon; QVC; TBS Superstation; TV Guide Channel; The Inspirational Network; The New Encore; The Weather Channel; Turner Network TV; USA Network; VH1.
Current originations: Leased access.
Fee: $50.00 installation; $26.50 monthly.
Pay Service 1
Pay Units: 57.
Programming (via satellite): HBO.
Fee: $20.00 installation; $12.00 monthly.
Pay Service 2
Pay Units: 61.
Programming (via satellite): Showtime.
Fee: $20.00 installation; $11.00 monthly.
Pay Service 3
Pay Units: 61.
Programming (via satellite): The Movie Channel.
Fee: $20.00 installation; $11.00 monthly.
Pay Service 4
Pay Units: 36.
Programming (via satellite): The New Encore.
Fee: $20.00 installation; $7.95 monthly.
Local advertising: No.
Equipment: Scientific-Atlanta headend; Scientific-Atlanta amplifiers; Times Fiber cable; Eagle traps; Scientific-Atlanta satellite antenna.
Miles of plant: 11.2 (coaxial); None (fiber optic). Homes passed: 699. Total homes in franchised area: 704.
Manager: Lonnie Schumacher. Marketing director: Fred Jamieson. Customer service manager: Kathy Fuhrmann.
City fee: 3% of gross.
Ownership: Midcontinent Communications (MSO).

GLENHAM—Valley Telecommunication, Box 7, 102 S. Main, Herreid, SD 57632. Phone: 605-437-2615. Fax: 605-437-2220. Web site: http://www.valleytel.net. County: Walworth. ICA: SD0143.
TV Market Ranking: Outside TV Markets. Franchise award date: July 1, 1987. Franchise expiration date: July 1, 2007. Began: January 1, 1988.
Channel capacity: 24 (not 2-way capable). Channels available but not in use: N.A.
Basic Service
Subscribers: 39.
Programming (received off-air): KFYR-TV (N) Bismarck; KQSD-TV (P) Lowry; KPRY-TV (A) Pierre; KELO-TV (C) Sioux Falls-Mitchell; 1 FM.
Programming (via satellite): WGN-TV (W) Chicago; CNN; Country Music TV; Discovery Channel; ESPN; Fox Family Channel; Nashville Network; TBS Superstation; Turner Network TV; USA Network.
Current originations: Automated time-weather.
Fee: $25.00 installation; $18.00 monthly; $1.00 converter; $25.00 additional installation.
Pay Service 1
Pay Units: 3.
Programming (via satellite): HBO.
Fee: $21.00 installation; $10.00 monthly.
Local advertising: Yes. Available in character-generated programming. Rates: $5.00/Week.
Equipment: Triple Crown headend; Magnavox amplifiers; Times Fiber cable; Mycrotek character generator; Hamlin set top converters; Prodelin satellite antenna; Triple Crown satellite receivers.
Miles of plant: 1.4 (coaxial); None (fiber optic). Homes passed: 61. Total homes in franchised area: 65.
Manager: Dianna Quaschnick. Chief technician: Bob Schuetzle. Marketing director: Cindy Schick.
Ownership: Valley Cable & Satellite Communications (MSO).

GREGORY—Rosebud Community Cable TV, Box 111, Redfield, SD 57469. Phone: 605-472-3415. County: Spink. ICA: SD0042.
TV Market Ranking: Outside TV Markets. Franchise award date: N.A. Franchise expiration date: N.A. Began: January 1, 1980.
Channel capacity: N.A. Channels available but not in use: N.A.
Basic Service
Subscribers: N.A.
Programming (received off-air): KMNE-TV (P) Bassett; KTSD-TV (P) Pierre; KPLO-TV (C) Reliance; KDLV-TV (N), KSFY-TV (A) Sioux Falls-Mitchell.
Programming (via satellite): WGN-TV (W) Chicago; A & E; CNN; Discovery Channel; ESPN; Fox Family Channel; Nashville Network; Nickelodeon; TBS Superstation; USA Network.
Fee: $30.00 installation; $16.00 monthly.
Pay Service 1
Pay Units: N.A.
Programming (via satellite): Cinemax; Disney Channel; HBO.
Fee: $10.00 installation; $10.00 monthly (each).
Miles of plant: 11.8 (coaxial). Homes passed: 620.
Manager: Mike McClure.
City fee: None.
Ownership: Cable TV Assoc. Inc. (MSO).

GROTON—James Valley Cooperative Telephone Co., Box 260, 235 First Ave. E, Groton, SD 57445-0260. Phone: 605-397-2323. Fax: 605-397-2350. Counties: Brown & Day. Also serves Andover, Claremont, Columbia, Hecla, Stratford, Turton. ICA: SD0030.
TV Market Ranking: Below 100. Franchise award date: July 1, 1981. Franchise expiration date: N.A. Began: May 1, 1982.
Channel capacity: 54 (not 2-way capable). Channels available but not in use: 31.
Basic Service
Subscribers: 778.
Programming (received off-air): KABY-TV (A), KDSD-TV (P) Aberdeen; KDLO-TV (C) Florence-Watertown; KTTM (F) Huron.
Programming (via satellite): WGN-TV (W) Chicago; WDIV (N) Detroit; CNN; Country Music TV; Discovery Channel; Disney Channel; ESPN; Fox Family Channel; MTV; Midwest Sports Channel; Nashville Network; Nickelodeon; TBS Superstation; The Weather Channel; Turner Network TV; USA Network.
Current originations: Automated time-weather; public access; educational access; government access; religious access; local sports.
Fee: $40.00 installation; $20.95 monthly.
Pay Service 1
Pay Units: 107.
Programming (via satellite): HBO.
Fee: $9.00 monthly.
Pay Service 2
Pay Units: 51.
Programming (via satellite): The Movie Channel.
Fee: $8.00 installation; $8.00 monthly.
Local advertising: No.
Equipment: Scientific-Atlanta headend; Jerrold amplifiers; Times Fiber cable; BEI character generator; Standard Components set top converters; Vitek & Pico traps; Scientific-Atlanta satellite antenna; Scientific-Atlanta satellite receivers.
Miles of plant: 56.0 (coaxial); 120.0 (fiber optic). Homes passed: 900. Total homes in franchised area: 900.
Manager: Clinton Hanson. Chief technician: Bill Ewart.
City fee: None.
Ownership: James Valley Cooperative Telephone Co.

HARROLD—Sully Buttes Telephone Cooperative Inc., Box 157, Highmore, SD 57345. Phone: 605-852-2224. Fax: 605-852-2404. County: Hughes. ICA: SD0139.
TV Market Ranking: Below 100. Franchise award date: N.A. Franchise expiration date: N.A. Began: September 15, 1989.
Channel capacity: 13 (not 2-way capable). Channels available but not in use: None.
Basic Service
Subscribers: 65.
Programming (received off-air): KPRY-TV (A), KTSD-TV (P) Pierre; KPLO-TV (C) Reliance.
Programming (via satellite): WDIV (N) Detroit; CNN; Discovery Channel; ESPN; ESPN 2; Nashville Network; TBS Superstation.
Fee: $20.00 installation; $19.50 monthly.
Pay Service 1
Pay Units: 21.
Programming (via satellite): Showtime.
Fee: $9.00 installation; $9.50 monthly.
Equipment: Jerrold amplifiers; Comm/Scope cable; Pico traps; Winegard satellite antenna; Drake satellite receivers.
Miles of plant: 1.8 (coaxial); None (fiber optic). Homes passed: 80.
Manager: Randy Hoydek. Chief technician: Randy Olson.
Ownership: Sully Buttes Telephone Cooperative Inc. (MSO).

HARTFORD—WMW Cable TV, Box 460, 116 N. Main Ave., Hartford, SD 57033. Phone: 605-528-3270. Fax: 605-528-2266. E-mail: uniontel@unitelsd.com. County: Minnehaha. Also serves Minnehaha County (southern portion). ICA: SD0057.
TV Market Ranking: 85. Franchise award date: January 1, 1983. Franchise expiration date: January 1, 2012. Began: December 1, 1983.
Channel capacity: 36 (not 2-way capable). Channels available but not in use: 3.
Basic Service
Subscribers: 640.
Programming (received off-air): KDLT-TV (N) Sioux Falls; KELO-TV (C), KSFY-TV (A), KTTW (F) Sioux Falls-Mitchell; KUSD-TV (P) Vermillion.
Programming (via satellite): WGN-TV (W) Chicago; A & E; American Movie Classics; CNN; Discovery Channel; Disney Channel; ESPN; Fox Family Channel; Headline News; History Channel; Learning Channel; Lifetime; MTV; Midwest Sports Channel; Nashville Network; Nickelodeon; QVC; Sci-Fi Channel; TBS Superstation; The Weather Channel; Turner Network TV; USA Network; VH1.
Current originations: Automated time-weather; public access; educational access; government access; religious access; local sports.
Fee: $16.50 monthly.
Pay Service 1
Pay Units: N.A.
Programming (via satellite): HBO; Showtime; The Movie Channel.
Fee: $10.00 monthly (HBO), $11.95 monthly (Showtime or TMC).
Miles of plant: 25.0 (coaxial); 5.0 (fiber optic).
Manager: Richard T. Freemark.
Rural fee: 3% of basic.
Ownership: WMW Cable TV.

HAYTI—Satellite Cable Services Inc., Box 106, Brookings, SD 57006-0106. Phone: 605-692-5508. Fax: 605-692-6496. County: Hamlin. ICA: SD0120.
TV Market Ranking: Below 100. Franchise award date: N.A. Franchise expiration date: N.A. Began: June 1, 1984.
Channel capacity: 36. Channels available but not in use: N.A.
Basic Service
Subscribers: 100.
Programming (received off-air): KABY-TV (A) Aberdeen; KESD-TV (P) Brookings; KDLO-TV (C) Florence-Watertown; KDLV-TV (N) Sioux Falls-Mitchell.
Programming (via satellite): WGN-TV (W) Chicago; CNN; ESPN; Fox Family Channel; Nashville Network; TBS Superstation.
Fee: $24.95 installation; $27.38 monthly.
Pay Service 1
Pay Units: N.A.
Programming (via satellite): HBO.
Fee: $11.95 monthly.
Miles of plant: 3.0 (coaxial). Homes passed: 167.
Manager: Doug Bierschbach. Chief technician: Paul Schmidt.
Ownership: Satellite Cable Services Inc. (MSO).

HENRY—Satellite Cable Services Inc., Box 106, Brookings, SD 57006-0106. Phone: 605-692-5508. Fax: 605-692-6496. County: Codington. ICA: SD0176.

TV Market Ranking: Below 100. Franchise award date: N.A. Franchise expiration date: N.A. Began: N.A.
Channel capacity: 36 (2-way capable; not operating 2-way). Channels available but not in use: N.A.
Basic Service
Subscribers: 60.
Programming (via satellite): KCNC-TV (C), KWGN-TV (W) Denver; CNN; ESPN; Nashville Network; TBS Superstation.
Fee: $27.38 monthly.
Pay Service 1
Pay Units: N.A.
Programming (via satellite): HBO.
Fee: $11.95 monthly.
Manager: Doug Bierschbach. Chief technician: Paul Schmidt.
Ownership: Satellite Cable Services Inc. (MSO).

HERREID—Valley Telco, Box 7, 102 S. Main, Herreid, SD 57632. Phone: 605-437-2615. Fax: 605-437-2220.
Web site: http://www.valleytel.net.
County: Campbell. ICA: SD0091.
TV Market Ranking: Outside TV Markets. Franchise award date: January 1, 1985. Franchise expiration date: January 1, 2005. Began: March 1, 1984.
Channel capacity: 24 (not 2-way capable). Channels available but not in use: N.A.
Basic Service
Subscribers: 176.
Programming (received off-air): KFYR-TV (N) Bismarck; KQSD-TV (P) Lowry; KPRY-TV (A) Pierre; KELO-TV (C) Sioux Falls-Mitchell; 1 FM.
Programming (via satellite): WGN-TV (W) Chicago; CNN; Country Music TV; Discovery Channel; ESPN; Fox Family Channel; Nashville Network; TBS Superstation; Turner Network TV; USA Network.
Current originations: Automated time-weather.
Fee: $25.00 installation; $18.00 monthly; $1.00 converter.
Pay Service 1
Pay Units: 16.
Programming (via satellite): HBO.
Fee: $21.00 installation; $10.00 monthly.
Local advertising: Yes. Available in character-generated programming. Rates: $5.00/Week.
Equipment: Triple Crown headend; Magnavox amplifiers; Times Fiber cable; BEI character generator; Hamlin set top converters; M/A-Com & Prodelin satellite antenna; Triple Crown satellite receivers.
Miles of plant: 4.0 (coaxial); None (fiber optic). Homes passed: 250.
Manager: Dianna Quaschnick. Chief technician: Bob Schuetzle. Marketing director: Cindy Schick.
Ownership: Valley Cable & Satellite Communications (MSO).

HIGHMORE—Sully Buttes Telephone Cooperative, Box 157, Highmore, SD 57345. Phone: 605-852-2224. Fax: 605-852-2404. County: Hyde. ICA: SD0060.
TV Market Ranking: Outside TV Markets. Franchise award date: N.A. Franchise expiration date: N.A. Began: May 1, 1982.
Channel capacity: 18 (not 2-way capable). Channels available but not in use: None.
Basic Service
Subscribers: 352.
Programming (received off-air): KTTM (F) Huron; KPRY-TV (A), KTSD-TV (P) Pierre; KPLO-TV (C) Reliance.
Programming (via satellite): WGN-TV (W) Chicago; WDIV (N) Detroit; American Movie Classics; CNN; Discovery Channel; Disney Channel; ESPN; ESPN 2; Fox Family Channel; Headline News; History Channel; Nashville Network; Nickelodeon; TBS Superstation; The Weather Channel; Turner Network TV; USA Network.
Current originations: Automated time-weather.
Fee: $20.00 installation; $20.00 monthly.
Pay Service 1
Pay Units: 48.
Programming (via satellite): Showtime.
Fee: $15.00 installation; $8.50 monthly.
Pay Service 2
Pay Units: 28.
Programming (via satellite): The Movie Channel.
Fee: $8.50 monthly.
Local advertising: No.
Equipment: Scientific-Atlanta headend; Jerrold amplifiers; Times Fiber cable; Mycrotek character generator; Standard Components set top converters; Pico traps; Scientific-Atlanta satellite antenna; Scientific-Atlanta satellite receivers.
Miles of plant: 10.3 (coaxial). Homes passed: 400.
Manager: Randy Hoydek. Chief technician: Randy Olson.
Ownership: Sully Buttes Telephone Cooperative Inc. (MSO).

HILL CITY—Galaxy Cablevision, 203 S. Lincoln Ave., York, NE 68467. Phones: 402-362-1705; 800-365-6988. Fax: 402-362-3698. County: Pennington. ICA: SD0088.
TV Market Ranking: Below 100. Franchise award date: March 1, 1983. Franchise expiration date: December 23, 2004. Began: July 1, 1983.
Channel capacity: 41 (not 2-way capable). Channels available but not in use: 16.
Basic Service
Subscribers: 183.
Programming (received off-air): KBHE-TV (P), KCLO-TV (C), KEVN-TV (F), KNBN-LP (N), KOTA-TV (A) Rapid City.
Programming (via satellite): WGN-TV (W) Chicago; American Movie Classics; CNN; Country Music TV; Discovery Channel; Disney Channel; ESPN; ESPN 2; Fox Family Channel; Learning Channel; Lifetime; Nashville Network; Nickelodeon; QVC; TBS Superstation; The Weather Channel; Turner Network TV; USA Network.
Fee: $28.95 monthly.
Pay Service 1
Pay Units: 24.
Programming (via satellite): HBO.
Fee: $12.95 monthly.
Pay Service 2
Pay Units: 20.
Programming (via satellite): Showtime.
Fee: $7.95 monthly.
Local advertising: No.
Miles of plant: 5.0 (coaxial). Homes passed: 299.
District vice president: John M. Dixon III. State manager: Steve Jordan. Technical manager: Van De Vries.
City fee: 3% of gross.
Ownership: Galaxy Cablevision (MSO).

HITCHCOCK—Sully Buttes Telephone Cooperative, Box 157, Highmore, SD 57345. Phone: 605-852-2224. Fax: 605-852-2404. County: Beadle. ICA: SD0140.
TV Market Ranking: Below 100. Franchise award date: N.A. Franchise expiration date: N.A. Began: October 1, 1989.
Channel capacity: 12 (not 2-way capable). Channels available but not in use: None.
Basic Service
Subscribers: 49.
Programming (received off-air): KABY-TV (A) Aberdeen; KDLO-TV (C) Florence-Watertown; KTSD-TV (P) Pierre.
Programming (via satellite): WDIV (N) Detroit; CNN; ESPN; ESPN 2; Fox Family Channel; Nashville Network; TBS Superstation.
Fee: $20.00 installation; $19.50 monthly.
Pay Service 1
Pay Units: 16.
Programming (via satellite): Showtime.
Fee: $9.50 monthly.
Equipment: Jerrold amplifiers; Comm/Scope cable; Pico traps; Winegard satellite antenna; Drake satellite receivers.
Miles of plant: 2.3 (coaxial). Homes passed: 80.
Manager: Randy Hoydek. Chief technician: Randy Olson.
Ownership: Sully Buttes Telephone Cooperative Inc. (MSO).

HOSMER—Valley Telco Cooperative Assn. Inc., Box 7, 102 S. Main, Herreid, SD 57632. Phone: 605-437-2615. Fax: 605-437-2220. Web site: http://www.valleytel.net. County: Edmunds. ICA: SD0117.
TV Market Ranking: Outside TV Markets. Franchise award date: January 1, 1984. Franchise expiration date: January 1, 2004. Began: February 1, 1985.
Channel capacity: 24 (not 2-way capable). Channels available but not in use: N.A.
Basic Service
Subscribers: 100.
Programming (received off-air): KABY-TV (A) Aberdeen; KQSD-TV (P) Lowry; KDLV-TV (N), KELO-TV (C) Sioux Falls-Mitchell; 1 FM.
Programming (via satellite): WGN-TV (W) Chicago; CNN; Country Music TV; Discovery Channel; ESPN; Fox Family Channel; Nashville Network; TBS Superstation; Turner Network TV; USA Network.
Current originations: Automated time-weather.
Fee: $25.00 installation; $18.00 monthly; $1.00 converter.
Pay Service 1
Pay Units: 12.
Programming (via satellite): HBO.
Fee: $21.00 installation; $10.00 monthly.
Local advertising: Yes. Available in character-generated programming. Rates: $5.00/Week.
Equipment: Triple Crown headend; Magnavox amplifiers; BEI character generator; Hamlin set top converters; M/A-Com & Prodelin satellite antenna; Triple Crown satellite receivers.
Miles of plant: 4.0 (coaxial); None (fiber optic). Homes passed: 175. Total homes in franchised area: 175.
Manager: Dianna Quaschnick. Chief technician: Bob Schuetzle. Marketing director: Cindy Schick.
City fee: 1% of gross.
Ownership: Valley Cable & Satellite Communications (MSO).

HOT SPRINGS—TCI Cablevision, Box 309, 842 Short Track Rd., Sturgis, SD 57785. Phone: 605-347-3090. Fax: 605-347-3499. County: Fall River. Also serves Fall River County. ICA: SD0018.
TV Market Ranking: Outside TV Markets. Franchise award date: N.A. Franchise expiration date: N.A. Began: December 1, 1969.
Channel capacity: 35 (2-way capable; operating 2-way). Channels available but not in use: 14.
Basic Service
Subscribers: 1,437.
Programming (received off-air): KBHE-TV (P), KCLO-TV (C), KEVN-TV (F), KNBN-LP (N), KOTA-TV (A) Rapid City; allband FM.
Programming (via satellite): KWGN-TV (W) Denver; A & E; C-SPAN; CNBC; CNN; Cartoon Network; Country Music TV; Discovery Channel; ESPN; ESPN 2; EWTN; Fox Family Channel; Fox Sports Net; Headline News; History Channel; Lifetime; MTV; Nashville Network; Nickelodeon; QVC; TBS Superstation; TV Guide Channel; The Weather Channel; Trinity Bcstg. Network; Turner Network TV; USA Network.
Current originations: Public access.
Fee: $40.00 installation; $25.52 monthly; $10.00 additional installation.
Pay Service 1
Pay Units: N.A.
Programming (via satellite): Cinemax; Disney Channel; HBO; Showtime; The Movie Channel.
Fee: N.A.
Local advertising: No.
Equipment: Scientific-Atlanta headend; Scientific-Atlanta amplifiers; Times Fiber cable; Arcom traps; Scientific-Atlanta satellite antenna; Scientific-Atlanta satellite receivers.
Note: Miles of plant and homes passed included with Custer, SD.
Manager: Dale Hodgkins. Chief technician: Gary Reimer.
City fee: 3% of gross.
Ownership: AT&T Broadband & Internet Services (MSO). Purchased from South Dakota Cable Inc., April 1, 1999.

HOVEN—Sully Buttes Telephone Cooperative, Box 157, Highmore, SD 57345. Phone: 605-852-2224. Fax: 605-852-2404. County: Potter. ICA: SD0082.
TV Market Ranking: Outside TV Markets. Franchise award date: N.A. Franchise expiration date: N.A. Began: May 1, 1983.
Channel capacity: 16 (not 2-way capable). Channels available but not in use: None.
Basic Service
Subscribers: 201.
Programming (received off-air): KQSD-TV (P) Lowry; KELO-TV (C), KSFY-TV (A) Sioux Falls-Mitchell.
Programming (via satellite): WGN-TV (W) Chicago; WDIV (N) Detroit; American Movie Classics; CNN; Discovery Channel; Disney Channel; ESPN; Fox Family Channel; Nashville Network; Nickelodeon; TBS Superstation; Turner Network TV; USA Network.
Current originations: Automated time-weather.
Fee: $20.00 installation; $19.50 monthly.
Pay Service 1
Pay Units: 52.
Programming (via satellite): Showtime.
Fee: $15.00 installation; $9.50 monthly.
Equipment: Scientific-Atlanta headend; Jerrold amplifiers; Times Fiber cable; BEI character generator; Pico traps; Scientific-Atlanta satellite antenna; Scientific-Atlanta satellite receivers.
Miles of plant: 4.2 (coaxial). Homes passed: 285.
Manager: Randy Hoydek. Chief technician: Randy Olson.
Ownership: Sully Buttes Telephone Cooperative Inc. (MSO).

HOWARD—Satellite Cable Services Inc., Box 106, Brookings, SD 57006-0106. Phone: 605-692-5508. Fax: 605-692-6496. County: Miner. ICA: SD0052.

TV Market Ranking: 85. Franchise award date: N.A. Franchise expiration date: N.A. Began: April 1, 1981.
Channel capacity: 35 (2-way capable; not operating 2-way). Channels available but not in use: N.A.
Basic Service
Subscribers: 350.
Programming (received off-air): KESD-TV (P) Brookings; KDLV-TV (N), KELO-TV (C), KSFY-TV (A) Sioux Falls-Mitchell.
Programming (via satellite): WGN-TV (W) Chicago; ESPN; Fox Family Channel; Nickelodeon; TBS Superstation; USA Network.
Fee: $24.95 installation; $27.38 monthly.
Pay Service 1
Pay Units: N.A.
Programming (via satellite): HBO.
Fee: $9.45 installation; $11.95 monthly.
Equipment: Scientific-Atlanta headend; Scientific-Atlanta amplifiers; Times Fiber cable; Scientific-Atlanta satellite antenna; Scientific-Atlanta satellite receivers.
Miles of plant: 8.0 (coaxial). Homes passed: 529.
Manager: Doug Bierschbach. Chief technician: Paul Schmidt.
City fee: 3% of gross.
Ownership: Satellite Cable Services Inc. (MSO).

HUDSON—American Telecasting Inc., 210 N. Main St., Mitchell, SD 57301. Phone: 605-996-1300. County: Lincoln. ICA: SD0142.
TV Market Ranking: 85. Franchise award date: N.A. Franchise expiration date: N.A. Began: N.A.
Channel capacity: N.A. Channels available but not in use: N.A.
Basic Service
Subscribers: 40.
Programming (received off-air): KESD-TV (P) Brookings; KDLV-TV (N), KELO-TV (C), KSFY-TV (A) Sioux Falls-Mitchell.
Programming (via satellite): WGN-TV (W) Chicago; CNN; ESPN; Fox Family Channel; Nashville Network; Nickelodeon; TBS Superstation; USA Network.
Fee: $29.00 installation; $17.95 monthly.
Pay Service 1
Pay Units: 18.
Programming (via satellite): Showtime.
Fee: $9.95 monthly.
Miles of plant: 2.0 (coaxial). Homes passed: 75.
Manager: Bill Mauszycki. Chief technician: Kevin Johnson.
Ownership: American Telecasting Inc. (MSO). Sale pends to Sprint Corp.

HUMBOLDT—Telecom Inc., Box 127, Irene, SD 57037-0127. Phone: 605-766-7600. Fax: 605-766-7695.
E-mail: jeanniejohnson@dtg.com.
County: Minnehaha. ICA: SD0177.
TV Market Ranking: 85. Franchise award date: November 14, 1983. Franchise expiration date: February 1, 2011. Began: N.A.
Channel capacity: 36 (not 2-way capable). Channels available but not in use: 10.
Basic Service
Subscribers: 131.
Programming (received off-air): KDLV-TV (N), KELO-TV (C), KSFY-TV (A), KTTW (F) Sioux Falls-Mitchell; KUSD-TV (P) Vermillion.
Programming (via satellite): WGN-TV (W) Chicago; A & E; CNN; Country Music TV; Discovery Channel; Disney Channel; ESPN; Fox Family Channel; History Channel; Lifetime; Midwest Sports Channel; Nashville Network; Nickelodeon; Sci-Fi Channel; TBS Superstation; The Weather Channel; Turner Network TV; USA Network; VH1.
Fee: $35.00 installation; $21.27 monthly.
Pay Service 1
Pay Units: 32.
Programming (via satellite): HBO.
Fee: $13.00 installation; $7.95 monthly.
Pay Service 2
Pay Units: 8.
Programming (via satellite): Showtime.
Fee: $13.00 installation; $7.95 monthly.
Miles of plant: 4.7 (coaxial). Homes passed: 159. Total homes in franchised area: 195.
Manager: Thomas W. Hertz. Chief technician: Jerry Andersen. Program director: Jeannie Johnson. Marketing director: Marshall Damgaard.
Ownership: Dakota Telecom Inc. (MSO).

HURON—Midcontinent Cable Systems Co. of South Dakota, Box 910, Aberdeen, SD 57402-0910. Phones: 605-229-1775; 800-456-0564. Fax: 605-229-0478. Counties: Beadle & Hand. Also serves Miller, St. Lawrence, Wolsey. Plans service to Beadle County. ICA: SD0006.
TV Market Ranking: Below 100. Franchise award date: December 1, 1984. Franchise expiration date: August 22, 2012. Began: December 1, 1968.
Channel capacity: 68 (not 2-way capable). Channels available but not in use: 9.
Basic Service
Subscribers: 4,668.
Programming (received off-air): KABY-TV (A) Aberdeen; KESD-TV (P) Brookings; KDLO-TV (C) Florence-Watertown; KTTM (F) Huron; KDLV-TV (N) Sioux Falls-Mitchell; 5 FMs.
Programming (via satellite): WGN-TV (W) Chicago; A & E; American Movie Classics; C-SPAN; C-SPAN 2; CNBC; CNN; Cartoon Network; Country Music TV; Discovery Channel; Disney Channel; ESPN; ESPN 2; ESPNews; EWTN; FX; Flix; Fox Family Channel; Headline News; Learning Channel; Lifetime; MTV; Midwest Sports Channel; Nashville Network; Nick at Nite's TV Land; Nickelodeon; QVC; Starz!; TBS Superstation; TV Guide Channel; The Health Network; The Weather Channel; Trinity Bcstg. Network; Turner Network TV; USA Network; VH1.
Current originations: Automated time-weather; educational access.
Fee: $50.00 installation; $25.00 monthly.
Expanded Basic Service
Subscribers: N.A.
Programming (via satellite): Animal Planet; Comedy Central; E! Entertainment TV; fXM: Movies from Fox; History Channel; Outdoor Channel; Sci-Fi Channel; Speedvision; Travel Channel; Turner Classic Movies.
Fee: N.A.
Pay Service 1
Pay Units: 163.
Programming (via satellite): Cinemax (multiplexed).
Fee: $20.00 installation; $11.00 monthly.
Pay Service 2
Pay Units: 549.
Programming (via satellite): HBO (multiplexed).
Fee: $20.00 installation; $12.00 monthly.
Pay Service 3
Pay Units: 389.
Programming (via satellite): Showtime (multiplexed).
Fee: $20.00 installation; $11.00 monthly.
Pay Service 4
Pay Units: 336.
Programming (via satellite): The Movie Channel.
Fee: $20.00 installation; $11.00 monthly.
Pay Service 5
Pay Units: N.A.
Programming (via satellite): Golf Channel; The New Encore.
Fee: $20.00 installation; $5.95 monthly (Golf), $7.95 monthly (Encore).
Pay-Per-View
Addressable homes: 968.
Hot Choice; Viewer's Choice 1, 3, 4.
Local advertising: No.
Equipment: Scientific-Atlanta headend; Scientific-Atlanta amplifiers; Times Fiber cable; Eagle traps; Simulsat satellite antenna; Scientific-Atlanta satellite receivers.
Miles of plant: 54.0 (coaxial); 13.8 (fiber optic). Homes passed: 5,200. Total homes in franchised area: 5,200.
Manager: Lonnie Schumacher. Marketing director: Fred Jamieson. Customer service manager: Kathy Fuhrmann.
City fee: 3% of gross or $3,000 annually.
Ownership: Midcontinent Communications (MSO).

IPSWICH—Midcontinent Cable Systems, Box 910, Aberdeen, SD 57402-0910. Phones: 605-229-1775; 800-456-0564. Fax: 605-229-0478. County: Edmunds. ICA: SD0059.
TV Market Ranking: Below 100. Franchise award date: May 3, 1994. Franchise expiration date: May 3, 2009. Began: September 1, 1980.
Channel capacity: 38 (not 2-way capable). Channels available but not in use: 2.
Basic Service
Subscribers: 335.
Programming (received off-air): KABY-TV (A), KDSD-TV (P) Aberdeen; KDLO-TV (C) Florence-Watertown; KTTM (F) Huron; KDLV-TV (N) Sioux Falls-Mitchell; allband FM.
Programming (via satellite): WGN-TV (W) Chicago; A & E; American Movie Classics; Bravo; C-SPAN; C-SPAN 2; CNBC; CNN; Cartoon Network; Country Music TV; Discovery Channel; Disney Channel; ESPN; ESPN 2; ESPNews; EWTN; FX; Flix; Fox Family Channel; Headline News; Learning Channel; Lifetime; MTV; Midwest Sports Channel; Nashville Network; Nick at Nite's TV Land; Nickelodeon; QVC; Starz!; TBS Superstation; TV Guide Channel; The Health Network; The Inspirational Network; The Weather Channel; Turner Network TV; USA Network; VH1.
Current originations: Educational access; government access; local access.
Fee: $50.00 installation; $26.50 monthly.
Expanded Basic Service
Subscribers: N.A.
Programming (via satellite): Animal Planet; Comedy Central; E! Entertainment TV; fXM: Movies from Fox; History Channel; Outdoor Channel; Sci-Fi Channel; Travel Channel; Turner Classic Movies.
Fee: N.A.
Pay Service 1
Pay Units: 23.
Programming (via satellite): HBO (multiplexed).
Fee: $20.00 installation; $11.00 monthly.
Pay Service 2
Pay Units: 16.
Programming (via satellite): Showtime (multiplexed).
Fee: $20.00 installation; $11.00 monthly.
Pay Service 3
Pay Units: 15.
Programming (via satellite): The Movie Channel.
Fee: $20.00 installation; $11.00 monthly.
Pay Service 4
Pay Units: 126.
Programming (via satellite): Cinemax (multiplexed).
Fee: $20.00 installation; $11.00 monthly.
Pay Service 5
Pay Units: N.A.
Programming (via satellite): Golf Channel; The New Encore.
Fee: $20.00 installation; $5.95 monthly (Golf), $7.95 monthly (Encore).
Pay-Per-View
Addressable homes: 24.
Hot Choice; Viewer's Choice 1, 3, 4.
Local advertising: No.
Equipment: Magnavox amplifiers; Times Fiber cable; Eagle traps.
Miles of plant: 7.5 (coaxial); None (fiber optic). Homes passed: 408. Total homes in franchised area: 408.
Manager: Lonnie Schumacher. Marketing director: Fred Jamieson. Customer service manager: Kathy Fuhrmann.
City fee: 3% of gross.
Ownership: Midcontinent Communications (MSO).

IROQUOIS—Satellite Cable Services Inc., Box 106, Brookings, SD 57006-0106. Phone: 605-692-5508. Fax: 605-692-6496. Counties: Beadle & Kingsbury. ICA: SD0128.
TV Market Ranking: Below 100. Franchise award date: N.A. Franchise expiration date: N.A. Began: December 1, 1984.
Channel capacity: 36 (2-way capable; not operating 2-way). Channels available but not in use: N.A.
Basic Service
Subscribers: 100.
Programming (received off-air): KABY-TV (A) Aberdeen; KESD-TV (P) Brookings; KDLO-TV (C) Florence-Watertown; KDLV-TV (N) Sioux Falls-Mitchell.
Programming (via satellite): WGN-TV (W) Chicago; CNN; ESPN; Fox Family Channel; Nashville Network; TBS Superstation; USA Network.
Fee: $24.95 installation; $26.32 monthly.
Pay Service 1
Pay Units: N.A.
Programming (via satellite): HBO.
Fee: $11.95 monthly.
Miles of plant: 3.0 (coaxial). Homes passed: 141.
Manager: Doug Bierschbach. Chief technician: Paul Schmidt.
Ownership: Satellite Cable Services Inc. (MSO).

JAVA—Midcontinent Cable Systems of South Dakota, Box 910, Aberdeen, SD 57402-0910. Phones: 605-229-1775; 800-456-0564. Fax: 605-229-0478. County: Walworth. ICA: SD0178.
TV Market Ranking: Outside TV Markets. Franchise award date: March 31, 1988. Franchise expiration date: March 31, 2011. Began: June 7, 1988.
Channel capacity: 38 (not 2-way capable). Channels available but not in use: 3.
Basic Service
Subscribers: 62.
Programming (received off-air): KABY-TV (A), KDSD-TV (P) Aberdeen; KDLO-TV (C) Florence-Watertown; KTTM (F) Huron; KDLV-TV (N) Sioux Falls-Mitchell.
Programming (via satellite): WGN-TV (W) Chicago; A & E; American Movie Classics; C-SPAN; C-SPAN 2; CNBC; CNN; Cartoon Network; Country Music TV; Discovery Channel; Disney Channel; ESPN; ESPN 2; ESPNews; EWTN; FX; Flix; Fox Family Channel; Headline News; Learning Channel; Lifetime; MTV; Midwest Sports Channel; Nashville Network; Nick at Nite's TV Land; Nickelodeon; QVC; Starz!; TBS Superstation; TV Guide Channel; The Health Network; The In-

spirational Network; The Weather Channel; Turner Network TV; USA Network; VH1.
Current originations: Public access; educational access.
Fee: $50.00 installation; $26.50 monthly.

Expanded Basic Service
Subscribers: N.A.
Programming (via satellite): Animal Planet; Bravo; Comedy Central; E! Entertainment TV; fXM: Movies from Fox; History Channel; Outdoor Channel; Sci-Fi Channel; Travel Channel; Turner Classic Movies.
Fee: N.A.

Pay Service 1
Pay Units: 9.
Programming (via satellite): HBO (multiplexed).
Fee: $20.00 installation; $12.00 monthly.

Pay Service 2
Pay Units: 5.
Programming (via satellite): Showtime (multiplexed).
Fee: $20.00 installation; $11.00 monthly.

Pay Service 3
Pay Units: 5.
Programming (via satellite): The Movie Channel.
Fee: $20.00 installation; $11.00 monthly.

Pay Service 4
Pay Units: N.A.
Programming (via satellite): Cinemax (multiplexed); Golf Channel; The New Encore.
Fee: $20.00 installation; $5.95 monthly (Golf), $7.95 monthly (Encore), $11.00 monthly (Cinemax).

Pay-Per-View
Addressable homes: 8.
Hot Choice; Viewer's Choice 1, 3, 4.

Miles of plant: 2.3 (coaxial); None (fiber optic). Homes passed: 111.
Manager: Lonnie Schumacher. Marketing director: Fred Jamieson. Customer service manager: Kathy Fuhrmann.
Ownership: Midcontinent Communications (MSO).

JEFFERSON—Jefferson Satellite Telecommunications Inc., Box 26, 311 Main St., Jefferson, SD 57038. Phone: 605-966-5631. Fax: 605-966-5340. County: Union. ICA: SD0179.
TV Market Ranking: Below 100. Franchise award date: N.A. Franchise expiration date: N.A. Began: January 1, 1985.
Channel capacity: N.A. Channels available but not in use: N.A.

Basic Service
Subscribers: 125.
Programming (received off-air): KCAU-TV (A), KMEG (C), KTIV (N) Sioux City; KELO-TV (C) Sioux Falls-Mitchell; KUSD-TV (P) Vermillion.
Programming (via satellite): WGN-TV (W) Chicago; CNN; Discovery Channel; ESPN; Fox Family Channel; Nashville Network; Nickelodeon; TBS Superstation; USA Network.
Fee: $15.00 installation; $12.50 monthly.

Pay Service 1
Pay Units: N.A.
Programming (via satellite): Cinemax; HBO.
Fee: $9.85 monthly (Cinemax), $9.95 monthly (HBO).

Manager: Tom Connors. Chief technician: Patrick Connors.
Ownership: Jefferson Telephone Co. Inc.

KADOKA—Golden West Cablevision, Box 9159, 2727 N. Plaza Dr., Rapid City, SD 57709. Phone: 605-348-6529. Fax: 605-342-1160. County: Jackson. ICA: SD0180.
TV Market Ranking: Outside TV Markets. Franchise award date: N.A. Franchise expiration date: February 1, 2003. Began: January 1, 1983.
Channel capacity: 36 (not 2-way capable). Channels available but not in use: 19.

Basic Service
Subscribers: 293.
Programming (received off-air): KIVV-TV (F) Lead; KZSD-TV (P) Martin; KOTA-TV (A) Rapid City.
Programming (via translator): K69DJ (C) Philip & Kadoka.
Programming (via satellite): WGN-TV (W) Chicago; A & E; CNN; Discovery Channel; ESPN; Fox Family Channel; Nashville Network; TBS Superstation; The Weather Channel; Turner Network TV; USA Network.
Programming (via fiber optic cable): KNBN-LP (N) Rapid City.
Fee: $25.00 installation; $14.00 monthly.

Pay Service 1
Pay Units: 46.
Programming (via satellite): Disney Channel.
Fee: $10.00 installation; $7.95 monthly.

Pay Service 2
Pay Units: 75.
Programming (via satellite): Showtime.
Fee: $7.95 monthly.

Local advertising: No.
Program Guide: Video Viewing.
Equipment: Scientific-Atlanta headend; Scientific-Atlanta amplifiers; Scientific-Atlanta cable; Scientific-Atlanta set top converters; Arcom traps; Scientific-Atlanta satellite antenna.
Miles of plant: 14.0 (coaxial).
Manager: Dwight Flatt. Chief technician: Ross Whitley. Marketing director: Greg Oleson.
City fee: None.
Ownership: Golden West Cablevision (MSO).

KENNEBEC—Kennebec CATV Co., Box 158, Main St., Kennebec, SD 57544. Phone: 605-869-2229. Fax: 605-869-2221. County: Lyman. ICA: SD0130.
TV Market Ranking: Below 100. Franchise award date: April 1, 1980. Franchise expiration date: N.A. Began: November 1, 1982.
Channel capacity: 36 (not 2-way capable). Channels available but not in use: 23.

Basic Service
Subscribers: 90.
Programming (received off-air): KPRY-TV (A), KTSD-TV (P) Pierre; KPLO-TV (C) Reliance.
Programming (via satellite): WGN-TV (W) Chicago; WDIV (N) Detroit; CNN; Cartoon Network; Discovery Channel; Disney Channel; ESPN; Fox Family Channel; Nashville Network; Nickelodeon; TBS Superstation; Turner Network TV.
Fee: $30.00 installation; $20.00 monthly.

Pay Service 1
Pay Units: 40.
Programming (via satellite): HBO.
Fee: $10.00 installation; $9.50 monthly.

Equipment: Scientific-Atlanta headend; Scientific-Atlanta amplifiers; Scientific-Atlanta cable; Oak set top converters; Pico traps; Scientific-Atlanta satellite antenna; Scientific-Atlanta satellite receivers.
Miles of plant: 12.0 (coaxial). Homes passed: 126. Total homes in franchised area: 126.
Manager: Delores Johnstone. Chief technician: Rod Bowar.
Ownership: Kennebec CATV Co.

KIMBALL—WCENet Inc., Box 17, Murdo, SD 57559. Phone: 605-669-2472. Fax: 605-669-2358. County: Brule. ICA: SD0077.
TV Market Ranking: Below 100. Franchise award date: N.A. Franchise expiration date: N.A. Began: August 1, 1983.
Channel capacity: 41 (not 2-way capable). Channels available but not in use: N.A.

Basic Service
Subscribers: 127.
Programming (received off-air): KPRY-TV (A), KTSD-TV (P) Pierre; KPLO-TV (C) Reliance; KDLV-TV (N) Sioux Falls-Mitchell.
Programming (via satellite): WGN-TV (W) Chicago; CNN; CNNfn; Country Music TV; Discovery Channel; Disney Channel; ESPN; ESPN 2; Fox Family Channel; Home & Garden Television; Learning Channel; Lifetime; Nashville Network; Nick at Nite's TV Land; Nickelodeon; Outdoor Channel; QVC; TBS Superstation; The Weather Channel; Turner Classic Movies; Turner Network TV; USA Network.
Fee: $23.45 monthly.

Pay Service 1
Pay Units: N.A.
Programming (via satellite): HBO.
Fee: $9.95 monthly.

Miles of plant: 6.2 (coaxial). Homes passed: 308.
Manager: Steve Reed. Marketing director: Joe Connot.
Ownership: West Central Electric Cooperative Inc. (MSO).

KYLE—Golden West Cablevision, Box 9159, 2727 N. Plaza Dr., Rapid City, SD 57709. Phone: 605-348-6529. Fax: 605-342-1160. County: Shannon. ICA: SD0121.
TV Market Ranking: Outside TV Markets. Franchise award date: N.A. Franchise expiration date: N.A. Began: November 1, 1984.
Channel capacity: 36 (not 2-way capable). Channels available but not in use: 19.

Basic Service
Subscribers: 203.
Programming (received off-air): KIVV-TV (F) Lead; KZSD-TV (P) Martin; KCLO-TV (C), KOTA-TV (A) Rapid City.
Programming (via satellite): WGN-TV (W) Chicago; CNN; Discovery Channel; ESPN; Fox Family Channel; MTV; Nashville Network; TBS Superstation; The Weather Channel; Turner Network TV; USA Network.
Programming (via fiber optic cable): KNBN-LP (N) Rapid City.
Fee: $25.00 installation; $14.00 monthly.

Pay Service 1
Pay Units: 93.
Programming (via satellite): Disney Channel.
Fee: $7.95 monthly.

Pay Service 2
Pay Units: 162.
Programming (via satellite): Showtime.
Fee: $7.95 monthly.

Miles of plant: 8.7 (coaxial).
Manager: Dwight Flatt. Chief technician: Ross Whitley. Marketing director: Greg Oleson.
Ownership: Golden West Cablevision (MSO).

LAKE ANDES—Village Cable, Box 111, Redfield, SD 57469. Phone: 605-472-3415. County: Charles Mix. ICA: SD0072.
TV Market Ranking: Outside TV Markets. Franchise award date: N.A. Franchise expiration date: N.A. Began: June 1, 1986.
Channel capacity: 36. Channels available but not in use: N.A.

Basic Service
Subscribers: 307.
Programming (received off-air): KPLO-TV (C) Reliance; KDLV-TV (N), KELO-TV (C), KSFY-TV (A) Sioux Falls-Mitchell.
Programming (via satellite): WGN-TV (W) Chicago; TBS Superstation; Turner Network TV.
Fee: N.A.

Pay Service 1
Pay Units: N.A.
Programming (via satellite): HBO.
Fee: N.A.

Miles of plant: 6.2 (coaxial). Homes passed: 340.
Manager: Terry Thomas.
Ownership: Cable TV Assoc. Inc. (MSO).

LAKE NORDEN—Satellite Cable Services Inc., Box 106, Brookings, SD 57006-0106. Phone: 605-692-5508. Fax: 605-692-6496. County: Hamlin. ICA: SD0114.
TV Market Ranking: Below 100. Franchise award date: N.A. Franchise expiration date: N.A. Began: July 1, 1984.
Channel capacity: 36 (2-way capable; not operating 2-way). Channels available but not in use: None.

Basic Service
Subscribers: 120.
Programming (received off-air): KABY-TV (A) Aberdeen; KESD-TV (P) Brookings; KDLO-TV (C) Florence-Watertown; KDLV-TV (N) Sioux Falls-Mitchell.
Programming (via satellite): WGN-TV (W) Chicago; CNN; ESPN; Fox Family Channel; Nashville Network; TBS Superstation; USA Network.
Fee: $24.95 installation; $27.38 monthly.

Pay Service 1
Pay Units: N.A.
Programming (via satellite): HBO.
Fee: $11.95 monthly.

Miles of plant: 3.1 (coaxial). Homes passed: 184.
Manager: Doug Bierschbach. Chief technician: Paul Schmidt.
Ownership: Satellite Cable Services Inc. (MSO).

LANGFORD—Sully Buttes Telephone Cooperative Inc., Box 157, Highmore, SD 57345. Phone: 605-852-2225. Fax: 605-852-2404. County: Marshall. ICA: SD0095.
TV Market Ranking: Below 100. Franchise award date: N.A. Franchise expiration date: N.A. Began: December 15, 1985.
Channel capacity: 15 (not 2-way capable). Channels available but not in use: None.

Basic Service
Subscribers: 139.
Programming (received off-air): KABY-TV (A), KDSD-TV (P) Aberdeen; KDLO-TV (C) Florence-Watertown; KTTM (F) Huron.
Programming (via satellite): WGN-TV (W) Chicago; CNN; ESPN; Fox Family Channel; Nashville Network; TBS Superstation; USA Network.
Fee: $17.00 installation; $15.00 monthly.

Pay Service 1
Pay Units: 42.

Programming (via satellite): Showtime.
Fee: $15.00 installation; $9.50 monthly.
Equipment: Scientific-Atlanta headend; Jerrold amplifiers; Times Fiber cable; Pico traps; Scientific-Atlanta satellite antenna; Scientific-Atlanta satellite receivers.
Miles of plant: 3.7 (coaxial). Homes passed: 240.
Manager: Randy Hoydek. Chief technician: Randy Olson.
City fee: None.
Ownership: Sully Buttes Telephone Cooperative Inc. (MSO).

LEMMON—Midcontinent Cable Systems of South Dakota, Box 910, Aberdeen, SD 57402-0910. Phones: 605-229-1775; 800-456-0564. Fax: 605-229-0478. County: Perkins. ICA: SD0033.
TV Market Ranking: Outside TV Markets. Franchise award date: January 2, 1994. Franchise expiration date: January 2, 2011. Began: January 1, 1979.
Channel capacity: 40 (not 2-way capable). Channels available but not in use: None.
Basic Service
Subscribers: 552.
Programming (received off-air): KFYR-TV (N), KXMB-TV (C) Bismarck; KPSD-TV (P) Eagle Butte; allband FM.
Programming (via microwave): KOTA-TV (A) Rapid City.
Programming (via satellite): WGN-TV (W) Chicago; KMGH-TV (A) Denver; A & E; American Movie Classics; Animal Planet; C-SPAN; CNBC; CNN; Cartoon Network; Country Music TV; Discovery Channel; Disney Channel; ESPN; FX; Fox Family Channel; FoxNet; Headline News; Learning Channel; Lifetime; Midwest Sports Channel; Nashville Network; Nick at Nite's TV Land; Nickelodeon; QVC; TBS Superstation; TV Guide Channel; The Inspirational Network; The Weather Channel; Turner Network TV; USA Network; VH1.
Current originations: Local access.
Fee: $50.00 installation; $26.50 monthly.
Pay Service 1
Pay Units: 74.
Programming (via satellite): HBO.
Fee: $20.00 installation; $11.00 monthly.
Pay Service 2
Pay Units: 51.
Programming (via satellite): Showtime.
Fee: $11.00 monthly.
Pay Service 3
Pay Units: 51.
Programming (via satellite): The Movie Channel.
Fee: $11.00 monthly.
Pay Service 4
Pay Units: 39.
Programming (via satellite): The New Encore.
Fee: $7.95 monthly.
Local advertising: No.
Equipment: Standard Components & Scientific-Atlanta headend; Magnavox amplifiers; Times Fiber cable; Eagle traps; Gardiner & Prodelin satellite antenna; Standard Components satellite receivers.
Miles of plant: 10.0 (coaxial); None (fiber optic). Homes passed: 824.
Manager: Darrell Wrege. Marketing director: Fred Jamieson. Customer service manager: Kathy Fuhrmann.
City fee: 3% of gross.
Ownership: Midcontinent Communications (MSO).

LEOLA—Valley Telco, Box 7, 102 S. Main, Herreid, SD 57632. Phone: 605-437-2615. Fax: 605-437-2220.
Web site: http://www.valleytel.net.
County: McPherson. ICA: SD0065.
TV Market Ranking: Below 100. Franchise award date: January 1, 1981. Franchise expiration date: January 1, 2001. Began: February 1, 1981.
Channel capacity: 16 (not 2-way capable). Channels available but not in use: None.
Basic Service
Subscribers: 195.
Programming (received off-air): KABY-TV (A), KDSD-TV (P) Aberdeen; KDLO-TV (C) Florence-Watertown; KDLV-TV (N), KTTW (F) Sioux Falls-Mitchell; 1 FM.
Programming (via satellite): WGN-TV (W) Chicago; CNN; Country Music TV; Discovery Channel; ESPN; Fox Family Channel; Nashville Network; TBS Superstation; Turner Network TV; USA Network.
Current originations: Automated time-weather.
Fee: $25.00 installation; $18.00 monthly; $1.00 converter; $25.00 additional installation.
Pay Service 1
Pay Units: 31.
Programming (via satellite): HBO.
Fee: $21.00 installation; $10.00 monthly.
Local advertising: Yes. Available in character-generated programming. Rates: $5.00/Week.
Equipment: Microdyne & Scientific-Atlanta headend; Jerrold & Magnavox amplifiers; Mycrotek character generator; Hamlin set top converters; Microdyne satellite antenna; Microdyne satellite receivers.
Miles of plant: 4.0 (coaxial); None (fiber optic). Homes passed: 375.
Manager: Dianna Quaschnick. Chief technician: Bob Schuetzle. Marketing director: Cindy Schick.
Ownership: Valley Cable & Satellite Communications (MSO).

LESTERVILLE—American Telecasting Inc., 210 N. Main St., Mitchell, SD 57301. Phone: 605-996-1300. County: Yankton. ICA: SD0181.
TV Market Ranking: Outside TV Markets. Franchise award date: N.A. Franchise expiration date: N.A. Began: N.A.
Channel capacity: N.A. Channels available but not in use: N.A.
Basic Service
Subscribers: N.A.
Programming (received off-air): KESD-TV (P) Brookings; KCAU-TV (A), KTIV (N) Sioux City; KELO-TV (C), KSFY-TV (A) Sioux Falls-Mitchell.
Programming (via satellite): WGN-TV (W) Chicago; CNN; ESPN; Fox Family Channel; Nashville Network; TBS Superstation; USA Network.
Fee: $24.50 installation; $17.95 monthly.
Pay Service 1
Pay Units: N.A.
Programming (via satellite): Showtime.
Fee: $9.95 monthly.
Manager: Bill Mauszycki. Chief technician: Kevin Johnson.
Ownership: American Telecasting Inc. (MSO). Sale pends to Sprint Corp.

MADISON—TCI Cablevision, Box 309, 842 Short Track Rd., Sturgis, SD 57785. Phone: 605-347-3090. Fax: 605-347-3499. County: Lake. ICA: SD0014.
TV Market Ranking: Outside TV Markets. Franchise award date: April 25, 1977. Franchise expiration date: N.A. Began: November 15, 1978.
Channel capacity: 35 (not 2-way capable). Channels available but not in use: N.A.
Basic Service
Subscribers: 2,100.
Programming (received off-air): KESD-TV (P) Brookings; KDLT-TV (N) Sioux Falls; KELO-TV (C), KSFY-TV (A), KTTW (F) Sioux Falls-Mitchell; 3 FMs.
Programming (via satellite): WGN-TV (W) Chicago; A & E; American Movie Classics; C-SPAN; CNBC; CNN; Cartoon Network; Country Music TV; Discovery Channel; ESPN; ESPN 2; Fox Family Channel; Headline News; History Channel; Home & Garden Television; Knowledge TV; Lifetime; MTV; Midwest Sports Channel; Nashville Network; Nickelodeon; QVC; Sci-Fi Channel; TBS Superstation; TV Guide Channel; The Weather Channel; Turner Network TV; USA Network; VH1.
Current originations: Public access.
Fee: $50.00 installation; $25.22 monthly; $20.00 additional installation.
Pay Service 1
Pay Units: 204.
Programming (via satellite): Cinemax.
Fee: $20.00 installation; $11.00 monthly.
Pay Service 2
Pay Units: 91.
Programming (via satellite): Disney Channel.
Fee: $20.00 installation; $10.50 monthly.
Pay Service 3
Pay Units: 457.
Programming (via satellite): HBO.
Fee: $20.00 installation; $11.00 monthly.
Pay Service 4
Pay Units: N.A.
Programming (via satellite): Showtime; The Movie Channel.
Fee: N.A.
Local advertising: No.
Equipment: Jerrold headend; Jerrold amplifiers; Times Fiber cable; Eagle traps; Scientific-Atlanta satellite antenna.
Miles of plant: 25.0 (coaxial). Homes passed: 2,484. Total homes in franchised area: 2,484.
Manager: Dale Hodgkins. Chief technician: Gary Reimer. Marketing director: Colleen Goodman.
City fee: 3% of gross.
Ownership: AT&T Broadband & Internet Services (MSO). Purchased from South Dakota Cable Inc., April 1, 1999.

MANDERSON-WHITE HORSE CREEK—Golden West Cablevision, Box 9159, 2727 N. Plaza Dr., Rapid City, SD 57709. Phone: 605-348-6529. Fax: 605-342-1160. County: Shannon. ICA: SD0183.
TV Market Ranking: Outside TV Markets. Franchise award date: May 18, 1992. Franchise expiration date: May 18, 2012. Began: N.A.
Channel capacity: 36 (not 2-way capable). Channels available but not in use: 22.
Basic Service
Subscribers: 69.
Programming (received off-air): KBHE-TV (P), KCLO-TV (C), KEVN-TV (F), KOTA-TV (A) Rapid City.
Programming (via satellite): WGN-TV (W) Chicago; CNN; Discovery Channel; ESPN; MTV; Nashville Network; TBS Superstation; The Weather Channel.
Programming (via fiber optic cable): KNBN-LP (N) Rapid City.
Fee: $25.00 installation; $16.95 monthly.
Pay Service 1
Pay Units: 78.
Programming (via satellite): Disney Channel.
Fee: N.A.
Pay Service 2
Pay Units: 74.
Programming (via satellite): Showtime.
Fee: $7.95 monthly.
Manager: Dwight Flatt. Chief technician: Ross Whitley. Marketing director: Greg Oleson.
Ownership: Golden West Cablevision (MSO).

MARTIN—Golden West Cablevision, Box 9159, 2727 N. Plaza Dr., Rapid City, SD 57709. Phone: 605-348-6529. Fax: 605-342-1160. County: Bennett. ICA: SD0184.
TV Market Ranking: Outside TV Markets. Franchise award date: N.A. Franchise expiration date: February 1, 2002. Began: December 14, 1982.
Channel capacity: 36 (2-way capable). Channels available but not in use: 19.
Basic Service
Subscribers: 514.
Programming (received off-air): KIVV-TV (F) Lead; KZSD-TV (P) Martin; KCLO-TV (C), KOTA-TV (A) Rapid City.
Programming (via satellite): WGN-TV (W) Chicago; CNN; Discovery Channel; ESPN; Fox Family Channel; Nashville Network; Nickelodeon; TBS Superstation; The Weather Channel; Turner Network TV; USA Network.
Programming (via fiber optic cable): KNBN-LP (N) Rapid City.
Fee: $25.00 installation; $14.00 monthly.
Pay Service 1
Pay Units: 161.
Programming (via satellite): Disney Channel.
Fee: $7.95 monthly.
Pay Service 2
Pay Units: 231.
Programming (via satellite): Showtime.
Fee: $7.95 monthly.
Local advertising: No.
Program Guide: Video Viewing.
Equipment: Scientific-Atlanta headend; Scientific-Atlanta amplifiers; Scientific-Atlanta cable; Scientific-Atlanta satellite antenna.
Miles of plant: 27.0 (coaxial).
Manager: Dwight Flatt. Chief technician: Ross Whitley. Marketing director: Greg Oleson.
City fee: None.
Ownership: Golden West Cablevision (MSO).

McINTOSH—Midcontinent Cable Systems Co. of South Dakota, Box 910, Aberdeen, SD 57402-0910. Phones: 605-229-1775; 800-456-0564. Fax: 605-229-0478. County: Corson. ICA: SD0138.
TV Market Ranking: Outside TV Markets. Franchise award date: January 11, 1989. Franchise expiration date: January 11, 2011. Began: December 1, 1984.
Channel capacity: 41 (not 2-way capable). Channels available but not in use: 5.
Basic Service
Subscribers: 77.
Programming (received off-air): KBMY (A), KFYR-TV (N), KXMB-TV (C) Bismarck; KPSD-TV (P) Eagle Butte.
Programming (via satellite): WGN-TV (W) Chicago; A & E; American Movie Classics; C-SPAN; CNBC; CNN; Cartoon Network; Country Music TV; Discovery Channel; Disney Channel; ESPN; FX; Fox Family Channel; FoxNet; Headline News; Learning Channel; Lifetime; Midwest Sports Channel; Nashville Network; Nick at Nite's TV Land; Nickelodeon; QVC; TBS Superstation; TV Guide Channel; The Inspirational Network; The Weather Channel; Turner Network TV; USA Network; VH1.
Current originations: Automated time-weather.
Fee: $50.00 installation; $23.34 monthly.

Pay Service 1
Pay Units: 11.
Programming (via satellite): Showtime.
Fee: $20.00 installation; $11.00 monthly.
Pay Service 2
Pay Units: 1.
Programming (via satellite): HBO.
Fee: $20.00 installation; $12.00 monthly.
Pay Service 3
Pay Units: N.A.
Programming (via satellite): The Movie Channel.
Fee: N.A.
Miles of plant: 2.4 (coaxial); None (fiber optic). Homes passed: 147.
Manager: Lonnie Schumacher. Marketing director: Fred Jamieson. Customer service manager: Kathy Fuhrmann.
Franchise fee: 3% of gross.
Ownership: Midcontinent Communications (MSO).

McLAUGHLIN—Midcontinent Cable Systems of South Dakota, Box 910, Aberdeen, SD 57402-0910. Phones: 605-229-1775; 800-456-0564. Fax: 605-229-0478. County: Corson. ICA: SD0185.
TV Market Ranking: Outside TV Markets. Franchise award date: April 5, 1989. Franchise expiration date: April 5, 1999. Began: December 1, 1981.
Channel capacity: 22 (not 2-way capable). Channels available but not in use: 3.
Basic Service
Subscribers: 285.
Programming (received off-air): KBMY (A), KFYR-TV (N), KXMB-TV (C) Bismarck; KQSD-TV (P) Lowry; KPLO-TV (C) Reliance.
Programming (via satellite): WGN-TV (W) Chicago; CNN; Country Music TV; Discovery Channel; ESPN; EWTN; Fox Family Channel; Nashville Network; Nickelodeon; TBS Superstation; Turner Network TV; USA Network; VH1.
Current originations: Automated time-weather; public access.
Fee: $50.00 installation; $22.61 monthly.
Pay Service 1
Pay Units: 87.
Programming (via satellite): Showtime.
Fee: $20.00 installation; $10.00 monthly.
Miles of plant: 5.4 (coaxial); None (fiber optic). Homes passed: 425.
Manager: Lonnie Schumacher. Marketing director: Fred Jamieson. Customer service manager: Kathy Fuhrmann.
Ownership: Midcontinent Communications (MSO).

MELLETTE—Village Cable, Box 111, Redfield, SD 57469. Phone: 605-472-3415. Counties: Faulk & Spink. Also serves Cresbard. ICA: SD0086.
TV Market Ranking: Below 100. Franchise award date: N.A. Franchise expiration date: N.A. Began: June 1, 1986.
Channel capacity: 36 (not 2-way capable). Channels available but not in use: N.A.
Basic Service
Subscribers: N.A.
Programming (received off-air): KABY-TV (A), KDSD-TV (P) Aberdeen; KDLO-TV (C) Florence-Watertown; KTTM (F) Huron.
Programming (via satellite): WXIA-TV (N) Atlanta; WGN-TV (W) Chicago; CNN; Discovery Channel; ESPN; Fox Family Channel; Nashville Network; TBS Superstation; USA Network.
Fee: N.A.
Pay Service 1
Pay Units: N.A.
Programming (via satellite): HBO.
Fee: N.A.
Equipment: Scientific-Atlanta satellite antenna; Scientific-Atlanta satellite receivers.
Miles of plant: 2.5 (coaxial). Homes passed: 270.
Manager: Terry Thomas.
Ownership: Cable TV Assoc. Inc.

MIDLAND—Golden West Cablevision, Box 9159, 2727 N. Plaza Dr., Rapid City, SD 57709. Phone: 605-348-6529. Fax: 605-342-1160. County: Haakon. ICA: SD0136.
TV Market Ranking: Outside TV Markets. Franchise award date: N.A. Franchise expiration date: N.A. Began: December 1, 1983.
Channel capacity: 36 (2-way capable; operating 2-way). Channels available but not in use: 18.
Basic Service
Subscribers: 88.
Programming (received off-air): KZSD-TV (P) Martin; KPRY-TV (A) Pierre; KEVN-TV (F) Rapid City.
Programming (via translator): K69DJ (C) Philip & Kadoka.
Programming (via satellite): WGN-TV (W) Chicago; WNBC (N) New York; CNN; Discovery Channel; ESPN; Fox Family Channel; FoxNet; Nashville Network; TBS Superstation; Turner Network TV; USA Network.
Fee: $25.00 installation; $14.00 monthly.
Pay Service 1
Pay Units: 21.
Programming (via satellite): Disney Channel.
Fee: $7.95 monthly.
Pay Service 2
Pay Units: 26.
Programming (via satellite): Showtime.
Fee: $7.95 monthly.
Equipment: Scientific-Atlanta headend; Scientific-Atlanta amplifiers.
Miles of plant: 8.1 (coaxial). Homes passed: 104.
Manager: Dwight Flatt. Chief technician: Ross Whitley. Marketing director: Greg Oleson.
Ownership: Golden West Cablevision (MSO).

MILBANK—TCI Cablevision of South Dakota, Box 144, Milbank, SD 57252-0144. Phone: 605-432-6776. Fax: 605-432-4661. County: Grant. Also serves Grant County. ICA: SD0017.
TV Market Ranking: Below 100 (portions of Grant County, Milbank); Outside TV Markets (portions of Grant County). Franchise award date: June 1, 1984. Franchise expiration date: June 1, 1999. Began: December 1, 1984.
Channel capacity: 37. Channels available but not in use: N.A.
Basic Service
Subscribers: 1,288.
Programming (received off-air): KABY-TV (A), KDSD-TV (P) Aberdeen; KCCO-TV (C) Alexandria; KWCM-TV (P) Appleton; KDLO-TV (C) Florence-Watertown.
Programming (via microwave): KARE (N), KMSP-TV (U) Minneapolis-St. Paul.
Programming (via satellite): WGN-TV (W) Chicago; C-SPAN; CNN; Discovery Channel; EWTN; Fox Family Channel; FoxNet; Headline News; Lifetime; MTV; Nashville Network; Nickelodeon; Odyssey; QVC; TBS Superstation; The Weather Channel.
Current originations: Automated time-weather.
Fee: $10.50 monthly; $2.50 converter; $24.95 additional installation.
Expanded Basic Service
Subscribers: 974.
Programming (via satellite): American Movie Classics; Court TV; ESPN; Midwest Sports Channel; Turner Network TV; USA Network.
Fee: $1.25 monthly.
Pay Service 1
Pay Units: 180.
Programming (via satellite): Cinemax.
Fee: $9.95 monthly.
Pay Service 2
Pay Units: 75.
Programming (via satellite): Disney Channel.
Fee: $9.95 monthly.
Pay Service 3
Pay Units: 211.
Programming (via satellite): HBO.
Fee: $9.95 monthly.
Pay Service 4
Pay Units: 407.
Programming (via satellite): The New Encore.
Fee: N.A.
Local advertising: No.
Program Guide: The Cable Guide.
Equipment: Scientific-Atlanta headend; Scientific-Atlanta amplifiers; Scientific-Atlanta cable; Scientific-Atlanta traps; Scientific-Atlanta satellite antenna; Scientific-Atlanta satellite receivers.
Miles of plant: 24.1 (coaxial). Homes passed: 1,802. Total homes in franchised area: 1,802.
Manager: Joe Villella. Chief technician: Ray Olson.
Ownership: AT&T Broadband & Internet Services (MSO). Purchased from Tele-Communications Inc., March 9, 1999.

MILLER—Midcontinent Cable Systems of South Dakota, Box 910, Aberdeen, SD 57402-0910. Phones: 605-229-1775; 800-456-0564. Fax: 605-229-0478. County: Hand. ICA: SD0031.
TV Market Ranking: Outside TV Markets. Franchise award date: August 1, 1985. Franchise expiration date: August 1, 2000. Began: January 1, 1972.
Channel capacity: 68 (not 2-way capable). Channels available but not in use: 2.
Basic Service
Subscribers: 714.
Programming (received off-air): KABY-TV (A) Aberdeen; KESD-TV (P) Brookings; KDLO-TV (C) Florence-Watertown; KTTM (F) Huron; allband FM.
Programming (via microwave): KDLT-TV (N) Sioux Falls.
Programming (via satellite): WGN-TV (W) Chicago; A & E; American Movie Classics; C-SPAN; CNBC; CNN; Cartoon Network; Country Music TV; Discovery Channel; Disney Channel; ESPN; ESPN 2; ESPNews; EWTN; FX; Fox Family Channel; Headline News; Lifetime; MTV; Midwest Sports Channel; Nashville Network; Nick at Nite's TV Land; Nickelodeon; QVC; TBS Superstation; TV Guide Channel; The Health Network; The Weather Channel; Turner Network TV; USA Network; VH1.
Current originations: Automated time-weather.
Fee: $50.00 installation; $26.50 monthly.
Expanded Basic Service
Subscribers: N.A.
Programming (via satellite): Animal Planet; Comedy Central; E! Entertainment TV; fXM: Movies from Fox; History Channel; Outdoor Channel; Sci-Fi Channel; Speedvision; Travel Channel; Turner Classic Movies.
Fee: N.A.
Pay Service 1
Pay Units: 75.
Programming (via satellite): HBO.
Fee: $20.00 installation; $12.00 monthly.
Pay Service 2
Pay Units: 55.
Programming (via satellite): Showtime.
Fee: $20.00 installation; $11.00 monthly.
Pay Service 3
Pay Units: 18.
Programming (via satellite): Cinemax; The Movie Channel.
Fee: $20.00 installation; $11.00 monthly.
Pay-Per-View
Viewer's Choice.
Fee: Varies.
Local advertising: No.
Equipment: Scientific-Atlanta headend; Scientific-Atlanta amplifiers; Times Fiber cable; Eagle traps.
Miles of plant: 15.5 (coaxial); None (fiber optic). Homes passed: 934.
Manager: Lonnie Schumacher. Marketing director: Fred Jamieson. Customer service manager: Kathy Fuhrmann.
City fee: 3% of gross.
Ownership: Midcontinent Communications (MSO).

MINA—Midcontinent Cable Systems of South Dakota, Box 910, Aberdeen, SD 57402-0910. Phones: 605-229-1775; 800-456-0564. Fax: 605-229-0478. County: Edmunds. ICA: SD0246.
TV Market Ranking: Below 100. Franchise award date: N.A. Franchise expiration date: N.A. Began: N.A.
Channel capacity: N.A. Channels available but not in use: N.A.
Basic Service
Subscribers: 55.
Programming (received off-air): KABY-TV (A), KDSD-TV (P) Aberdeen; KDLO-TV (C) Florence-Watertown; KTTM (F) Huron; KDLV-TV (N) Sioux Falls-Mitchell.
Programming (via satellite): WGN-TV (W) Chicago; American Movie Classics; Animal Planet; Bravo; C-SPAN; C-SPAN 2; CNBC; CNN; Cartoon Network; Comedy Central; DMX; Discovery Channel; Disney Channel; E! Entertainment TV; ESPN; ESPN 2; ESPNews; EWTN; FX; fXM: Movies from Fox; Golf Channel; Headline News; History Channel; Learning Channel; Midwest Sports Channel; Nick at Nite's TV Land; Outdoor Channel; QVC; Sci-Fi Channel; Starz!; TBS Superstation; TV Guide Channel; The Health Network; The Inspirational Network; The Weather Channel; Travel Channel; Turner Classic Movies.
Current originations: Educational access.
Fee: $50.00 installation; $25.00 monthly.
Expanded Basic Service
Subscribers: 14.
Programming (via satellite): A & E; Country Music TV; Flix; Fox Family Channel; Lifetime; MTV; Nashville Network; Nickelodeon; Turner Network TV; USA Network; VH1.
Fee: $3.00 monthly.
Pay Service 1
Pay Units: N.A.
Programming (via satellite): Cinemax (multiplexed).
Fee: $11.00 monthly.
Pay Service 2
Pay Units: 4.
Programming (via satellite): HBO (multiplexed).
Fee: $12.00 monthly.
Pay Service 3
Pay Units: 1.
Programming (via satellite): The Movie Channel.
Fee: $11.00 monthly.

Pay Service 4
Pay Units: 2.
Programming (via satellite): Showtime (multiplexed).
Fee: $11.00 monthly.
Pay Service 5
Pay Units: N.A.
Programming (via satellite): Encore Movie Networks.
Fee: N.A.
Pay-Per-View
Addressable homes: 16.
Viewer's Choice.
Fee: $3.95.
Pay-per-view manager: Dawn Vaux.
Equipment: Magnavox amplifiers; Times Fiber cable; Zenith set top converters.
Miles of plant: 4.0 (coaxial). Homes passed: 296.
Manager: Lonnie Schumacher. Marketing director: Fred Jamieson. Customer service manager: Kathy Fuhrmann.
Ownership: Midcontinent Communications (MSO).

MISSION—Savage Communications, Box 810, Hinckley, MN 55037. Phone: 320-384-7442. Fax: 320-384-7446. County: Todd. ICA: SD0048.
TV Market Ranking: Outside TV Markets. Franchise award date: January 1, 1983. Franchise expiration date: April 1, 2003. Began: January 1, 1984.
Channel capacity: 54 (2-way capable; not operating 2-way). Channels available but not in use: 14.
Basic Service
Subscribers: 449.
Programming (received off-air): KPRY-TV (A), KTSD-TV (P) Pierre; KPLO-TV (C) Reliance.
Programming (via satellite): WGN-TV (W) Chicago; KCNC-TV (C), KMGH-TV (A), KWGN-TV (W) Denver; A & E; CNN; Country Music TV; Discovery Channel; ESPN; Fox Family Channel; Headline News; History Channel; Learning Channel; MTV; Nashville Network; Nickelodeon; Sci-Fi Channel; TBS Superstation; The Weather Channel; Turner Classic Movies; Turner Network TV; USA Network; VH1.
Fee: $37.50 installation; $25.00 monthly.
Pay Service 1
Pay Units: 378.
Programming (via satellite): The Movie Channel.
Fee: $10.00 monthly.
Pay Service 2
Pay Units: N.A.
Programming (via satellite): Disney Channel; HBO.
Fee: $8.00 monthly (Disney), $11.00 monthly (HBO).
Miles of plant: 12.0 (coaxial); 1.0 (fiber optic). Homes passed: 649.
Manager: Mike Danielson. Chief technician: Chuck Wilson.
Ownership: Savage Communications Inc. (MSO).

MITCHELL—Communications Enterprises Inc., Box 67, Woonsocket, SD 57385. Phone: 605-796-4411. Fax: 605-796-4419. Counties: Aurora, Douglas, Jerauld & Miner. Also serves Delmont, Lane, Stickney. ICA: SD0141.
TV Market Ranking: 85. Franchise award date: September 1, 1987. Franchise expiration date: N.A. Began: January 1, 1988.
Channel capacity: 12 (not 2-way capable). Channels available but not in use: None.
Basic Service
Subscribers: 1,611.
Programming (received off-air): KESD-TV (P) Brookings; KDLV-TV (N), KELO-TV (C), KSFY-TV (A) Sioux Falls-Mitchell.
Programming (via satellite): WGN-TV (W) Chicago; CNN; ESPN; Fox Family Channel; Nashville Network; Nickelodeon; TBS Superstation.
Fee: $50.00 installation; $22.00 monthly.
Pay Service 1
Pay Units: N.A.
Programming (via satellite): Showtime.
Fee: $9.95 monthly.
Pay-Per-View
Addressable homes: 1,611.
Miles of plant: 3.0 (coaxial).
Manager: Gene Kroell.
Ownership: Sanborn Telephone Cooperative (MSO).

MITCHELL—Mitchell Cable Television, 1101 N. Main, Mitchell, SD 57301-0609. Phone: 605-996-6362. Fax: 605-996-6821. County: Davison. ICA: SD0007.
TV Market Ranking: 85. Franchise award date: N.A. Franchise expiration date: March 21, 2001. Began: January 1, 1952.
Channel capacity: 76 (2-way capable; operating 2-way). Channels available but not in use: 16.
Basic Service
Subscribers: 4,708.
Programming (received off-air): KESD-TV (P) Brookings; KDLV-TV (N), KELO-TV (C), KSFY-TV (A), KTTW (F) Sioux Falls-Mitchell.
Programming (via satellite): WGN-TV (W) Chicago; A & E; American Movie Classics; Animal Planet; Bravo; C-SPAN; C-SPAN 2; C-SPAN Extra; CNBC; CNN; Discovery Channel; Disney Channel; ESPN; EWTN; Fox Family Channel; Fox News Channel; Headline News; Home Shopping Network; Learning Channel; Lifetime; MTV; Midwest Sports Channel; Nashville Network; Nick at Nite's TV Land; Nickelodeon; QVC; TBS Superstation; The Health Network; The Inspirational Network; The Weather Channel; Turner Network TV; USA Network; VH1; WB 100+ Station Group.
Current originations: Automated time-weather; educational access; automated emergency alert.
Fee: $30.00 installation; $21.00 monthly.
Expanded Basic Service
Subscribers: 1,020.
Programming (via satellite): Cartoon Network; Comedy Central; Country Music TV; ESPN 2; History Channel; Home & Garden Television; Independent Film Channel; Sci-Fi Channel; Turner Classic Movies.
Fee: $3.95 monthly.
Pay Service 1
Pay Units: 829.
Programming (via satellite): HBO (multiplexed).
Fee: $15.00 installation; $11.00 monthly.
Pay Service 2
Pay Units: 460.
Programming (via satellite): Showtime.
Fee: $15.00 installation; $11.00 monthly.
Pay Service 3
Pay Units: 415.
Programming (via satellite): The Movie Channel.
Fee: $15.00 installation; $11.00 monthly.
Pay-Per-View
Movies; special events.
Local advertising: Planned (insert only). Available in satellite distributed & locally originated programming. Local sales manager: Tim Evans.
Equipment: Scientific-Atlanta headend; Scientific-Atlanta amplifiers; Comm/Scope cable; Scientific-Atlanta set top converters; Pico traps; Scientific-Atlanta satellite antenna; Scientific-Atlanta satellite receivers.
Miles of plant: 90.8 (coaxial); 14.0 (fiber optic). Additional miles planned: 10.0 (coaxial). Homes passed: 6,652. Total homes in franchised area: 6,652.
Chief technician: Tom Bechen. Marketing director: Lee Johnson.
City fee: 5% of gross.
Ownership: Midcontinent Communications (MSO); AT&T Broadband & Internet Services (MSO). Purchased from Tele-Communications Inc., March 9, 1999.

MOBRIDGE—TCI Cablevision, Box 309, 842 Short Track Rd., Sturgis, SD 57785. Phone: 605-347-3090. Fax: 605-347-3499. County: Walworth. Also serves Walworth County. ICA: SD0186.
TV Market Ranking: Outside TV Markets. Franchise award date: November 1, 1976. Franchise expiration date: November 1, 2005. Began: November 29, 1979.
Channel capacity: N.A. Channels available but not in use: N.A.
Basic Service
Subscribers: 1,440; Commercial subscribers: 9.
Programming (received off-air): KFYR-TV (N), KXMB-TV (C) Bismarck; KDLO-TV (C) Florence-Watertown; KQSD-TV (P) Lowry; KPRY-TV (A) Pierre; KDLT-TV (N) Sioux Falls; 1 FM.
Programming (via satellite): WGN-TV (W) Chicago; KMGH-TV (A) Denver; A & E; CNN; Cartoon Network; Country Music TV; Discovery Channel; ESPN; ESPN 2; EWTN; Fox Family Channel; FoxNet; Headline News; History Channel; Home & Garden Television; Midwest Sports Channel; Nashville Network; Nickelodeon; QVC; Sci-Fi Channel; TBS Superstation; The Weather Channel; Turner Classic Movies; Turner Network TV; USA Network; VH1.
Current originations: Automated time-weather.
Fee: $15.00 installation; $21.95 monthly; $15.00 additional installation.
Commercial fee: $17.80 monthly.
Pay Service 1
Pay Units: 38.
Programming (via satellite): Cinemax.
Fee: $8.00 monthly.
Pay Service 2
Pay Units: 242.
Programming (via satellite): Disney Channel.
Fee: $5.00 monthly.
Pay Service 3
Pay Units: 222.
Programming (via satellite): HBO.
Fee: $10.50 monthly.
Local advertising: Yes (locally produced). Available in character-generated programming.
Equipment: Scientific-Atlanta & Hughes headend; Magnavox amplifiers; Comm/Scope cable; MSI character generator; Scientific-Atlanta set top converters; Eagle traps; Prodelin satellite antenna; Scientific-Atlanta satellite receivers.
Miles of plant: 30.0 (coaxial).
Manager: Dale Hodgkins. Chief technician: Gary Reimer. Marketing director: Dianna Aman.
Ownership: AT&T Broadband & Internet Services (MSO). Purchased from South Dakota Cable Inc., April 1, 1999.

MONROE—Dakota Telecommunications Inc., Box 66, 29705 453rd Ave., Irene, SD 57037-0066. Phone: 605-263-3301. County: Turner. ICA: SD0187.
TV Market Ranking: 85. Franchise award date: N.A. Franchise expiration date: N.A. Began: N.A.
Channel capacity: N.A. Channels available but not in use: N.A.
Basic Service
Subscribers: N.A.
Programming (received off-air): KESD-TV (P) Brookings; KCAU-TV (A), KTIV (N) Sioux City; KELO-TV (C), KSFY-TV (A) Sioux Falls-Mitchell.
Programming (via satellite): WGN-TV (W) Chicago; CNN; ESPN; Fox Family Channel; Nashville Network; TBS Superstation; USA Network.
Fee: $24.50 installation; $17.95 monthly.
Pay Service 1
Pay Units: N.A.
Programming (via satellite): Showtime.
Fee: $9.95 monthly.
Manager: Bill Mauszycki. Chief technician: Kevin Johnson.
Ownership: American Telecasting Inc. (MSO). Sale pends to Sprint Corp.

MONTROSE—Ollig Cablevision, Box 98, 525 E. 4th St., Dell Rapids, SD 57022. Phone: 605-428-5421. Fax: 605-428-3132. County: McCook. ICA: SD0224.
TV Market Ranking: 85. Franchise award date: N.A. Franchise expiration date: N.A. Began: N.A.
Channel capacity: 21. Channels available but not in use: 7.
Basic Service
Subscribers: 123.
Programming (received off-air): KESD-TV (P) Brookings; KDLV-TV (N), KELO-TV (C), KSFY-TV (A) Sioux Falls-Mitchell.
Programming (via satellite): WGN-TV (W) Chicago; CNN; Discovery Channel; ESPN; Fox Family Channel; TBS Superstation; Turner Network TV.
Fee: $15.00 installation; $12.50 monthly.
Pay Service 1
Pay Units: 26.
Programming (via satellite): Disney Channel.
Fee: $7.50 monthly.
Pay Service 2
Pay Units: 30.
Programming (via satellite): Showtime.
Fee: $9.50 monthly.
Miles of plant: 3.0 (coaxial). Homes passed: 189.
Manager: Denny Law. Chief technician: Mike Bures.
Ownership: Ollig Utilities Co.

MOUNT VERNON—Communications Enterprises Inc., Box 67, Woonsocket, SD 57385. Phone: 605-796-4411. Fax: 605-796-4419. County: Davison. ICA: SD0188.
TV Market Ranking: 85. Franchise award date: N.A. Franchise expiration date: N.A. Began: January 1, 1983.
Channel capacity: 15 (not 2-way capable). Channels available but not in use: None.
Basic Service
Subscribers: 120.
Programming (received off-air): KESD-TV (P) Brookings; KDLV-TV (N), KELO-TV (C), KSFY-TV (A) Sioux Falls-Mitchell.
Programming (via satellite): WGN-TV (W) Chicago; CNN; ESPN; Nashville Network; Nickelodeon; TBS Superstation; Turner Network TV.
Fee: $30.00 installation; $20.05 monthly.
Pay Service 1
Pay Units: N.A.

Programming (via satellite): HBO.
Fee: $9.00 monthly.
Manager: Gene Kroell.
Ownership: Sanborn Telephone Cooperative (MSO).

MURDO—WCENet Inc., Box 17, Murdo, SD 57559. Phone: 605-669-2472. Fax: 605-669-2358. County: Jones. ICA: SD0075.
TV Market Ranking: Outside TV Markets. Franchise award date: N.A. Franchise expiration date: N.A. Began: May 1, 1983.
Channel capacity: 41 (not 2-way capable). Channels available but not in use: N.A.
Basic Service
Subscribers: 207.
Programming (received off-air): KPRY-TV (A), KTSD-TV (P) Pierre; KPLO-TV (C) Reliance.
Programming (via microwave): KELO-TV (C) Sioux Falls-Mitchell.
Programming (via satellite): WGN-TV (W) Chicago; WDIV (N) Detroit; A & E; CNN; CNNfn; Country Music TV; Discovery Channel; Disney Channel; ESPN; ESPN 2; Fox Family Channel; Headline News; History Channel; Home & Garden Television; Learning Channel; Lifetime; Nashville Network; Nick at Nite's TV Land; Nickelodeon; Outdoor Channel; QVC; TBS Superstation; The Weather Channel; Trinity Bcstg. Network; Turner Classic Movies; Turner Network TV; USA Network.
Fee: $23.45 monthly.
Pay Service 1
Pay Units: N.A.
Programming (via satellite): Cinemax; HBO.
Fee: $9.95 monthly (each).
Miles of plant: 6.2 (coaxial). Homes passed: 310.
Manager: Steve Reed. Marketing manager: Joe Connot.
Ownership: West Central Electric Cooperative Inc. (MSO).

NEW EFFINGTON—Satellite Cable Services Inc., Box 106, Brookings, SD 57006-0106. Phone: 605-692-5508. Fax: 605-692-6496. County: Roberts. ICA: SD0189.
TV Market Ranking: Outside TV Markets. Franchise award date: N.A. Franchise expiration date: N.A. Began: N.A.
Channel capacity: 36 (2-way capable; not operating 2-way). Channels available but not in use: N.A.
Basic Service
Subscribers: 60.
Programming (via satellite): KCNC-TV (C), KWGN-TV (W) Denver; CNN; ESPN; Nashville Network; TBS Superstation.
Fee: $25.79 monthly.
Pay Service 1
Pay Units: N.A.
Programming (via satellite): HBO.
Fee: $11.95 monthly.
Manager: Doug Bierschbach. Chief technician: Paul Schmidt.
Ownership: Satellite Cable Services Inc. (MSO).

NEW UNDERWOOD—Golden West Cablevision, Box 9159, 2727 N. Plaza Dr., Rapid City, SD 57709. Phone: 605-348-6529. Fax: 605-342-1160. County: Pennington. ICA: SD0126.
TV Market Ranking: Below 100. Franchise award date: N.A. Franchise expiration date: August 15, 2003. Began: August 15, 1983.
Channel capacity: 36 (not 2-way capable). Channels available but not in use: 19.
Basic Service
Subscribers: 171.
Programming (received off-air): KIVV-TV (F) Lead; KBHE-TV (P), KCLO-TV (C), KOTA-TV (A) Rapid City.
Programming (via satellite): WGN-TV (W) Chicago; CNN; Discovery Channel; ESPN; Fox Family Channel; Nashville Network; Nickelodeon; TBS Superstation; The Weather Channel; Turner Network TV; USA Network.
Programming (via fiber optic cable): KNBN-LP (N) Rapid City.
Fee: $25.00 installation; $14.00 monthly.
Pay Service 1
Pay Units: 38.
Programming (via satellite): Disney Channel.
Fee: $7.95 monthly.
Pay Service 2
Pay Units: 56.
Programming (via satellite): Showtime.
Fee: $7.95 monthly.
Local advertising: No.
Equipment: Scientific-Atlanta headend; Scientific-Atlanta amplifiers; Scientific-Atlanta cable; Arcom traps; Scientific-Atlanta satellite antenna.
Miles of plant: 18.0 (coaxial).
Manager: Dwight Flatt. Chief technician: Ross Whitley. Marketing director: Greg Oleson.
City fee: None.
Ownership: Golden West Cablevision (MSO).

NEWELL—Galaxy Cablevision, 203 S. Lincoln Ave., York, NE 68467. Phones: 402-362-1705; 800-365-6988. Fax: 402-362-3698. County: Butte. ICA: SD0078.
TV Market Ranking: Below 100. Franchise award date: N.A. Franchise expiration date: December 23, 2004. Began: May 1, 1983.
Channel capacity: 41 (not 2-way capable). Channels available but not in use: 17.
Basic Service
Subscribers: 138.
Programming (received off-air): KUSA-TV (N) Denver; KPSD-TV (P) Eagle Butte; KCLO-TV (C), KEVN-TV (F), KOTA-TV (A) Rapid City.
Programming (via satellite): WGN-TV (W) Chicago; American Movie Classics; CNN; Country Music TV; Discovery Channel; Disney Channel; ESPN; ESPN 2; Fox Family Channel; Lifetime; Nashville Network; Nickelodeon; QVC; TBS Superstation; The Weather Channel; Turner Network TV; USA Network.
Fee: $28.95 monthly.
Pay Service 1
Pay Units: 21.
Programming (via satellite): HBO.
Fee: $12.95 monthly.
Pay Service 2
Pay Units: 9.
Programming (via satellite): Showtime.
Fee: $7.95 monthly.
Local advertising: No.
Miles of plant: 5.0 (coaxial). Homes passed: 325.
District vice president: John M. Dixon III. State manager: Steve Jordan. Technical manager: Van De Vries.
City fee: 3% of gross.
Ownership: Galaxy Cablevision (MSO).

OACOMA—WCENet Inc., Box 17, Murdo, SD 57559. Phone: 605-669-2472. Fax: 605-669-2358. County: Lyman. ICA: SD0135.
TV Market Ranking: Below 100. Franchise award date: N.A. Franchise expiration date: N.A. Began: November 1, 1988.
Channel capacity: 41 (not 2-way capable). Channels available but not in use: N.A.
Basic Service
Subscribers: 80.
Programming (received off-air): KPRY-TV (A), KTSD-TV (P) Pierre; KPLO-TV (C) Reliance; KDLV-TV (N) Sioux Falls-Mitchell.
Programming (via satellite): WGN-TV (W) Chicago; CNBC; CNN; Country Music TV; Discovery Channel; Disney Channel; ESPN; ESPN 2; Fox Family Channel; Home & Garden Television; Learning Channel; Lifetime; Nashville Network; Nick at Nite's TV Land; Nickelodeon; Outdoor Channel; QVC; TBS Superstation; The Weather Channel; Turner Network TV; USA Network.
Fee: $23.45 monthly.
Pay Service 1
Pay Units: N.A.
Programming (via satellite): HBO.
Fee: $6.95 monthly.
Equipment: DX Antenna headend; Magnavox amplifiers; Times Fiber cable; Scientific-Atlanta satellite antenna; Scientific-Atlanta satellite receivers.
Miles of plant: 5.0 (coaxial). Homes passed: 110. Total homes in franchised area: 110.
Manager: Steve Reed. Marketing manager: Joe Connot.
Ownership: West Central Electric Cooperative Inc. (MSO).

OELRICHS—Golden West Cablevision, Box 9159, 2727 N. Plaza Dr., Rapid City, SD 57709. Phone: 605-348-6529. Fax: 605-342-1160. County: Fall River. ICA: SD0190.
TV Market Ranking: Outside TV Markets. Franchise award date: November 9, 1990. Franchise expiration date: November 9, 2010. Began: N.A.
Channel capacity: 36 (not 2-way capable). Channels available but not in use: 22.
Basic Service
Subscribers: 52.
Programming (received off-air): KBHE-TV (P), KCLO-TV (C), KEVN-TV (F), KOTA-TV (A) Rapid City.
Programming (via satellite): WGN-TV (W) Chicago; KMGH-TV (A) Denver; CNN; Discovery Channel; ESPN; Nashville Network; TBS Superstation; The Weather Channel; Turner Network TV.
Programming (via fiber optic cable): KNBN-LP (N) Rapid City.
Fee: $25.00 installation; $16.95 monthly.
Pay Service 1
Pay Units: 17.
Programming (via satellite): Disney Channel.
Fee: $7.95 monthly.
Pay Service 2
Pay Units: 24.
Programming (via satellite): Showtime.
Fee: $7.95 monthly.
Local advertising: No.
Miles of plant: 4.0 (coaxial).
Manager: Dwight Flatt. Chief technician: Ross Whitley. Marketing director: Greg Oleson.
Franchise fee: None.
Ownership: Golden West Cablevision (MSO).

OLDHAM—Satellite Cable Services Inc., Box 106, Brookings, SD 57006-0106. Phone: 605-692-5508. Fax: 605-692-6496. County: Kingsbury. ICA: SD0191.
TV Market Ranking: Outside TV Markets. Franchise award date: N.A. Franchise expiration date: N.A. Began: December 1, 1987.
Channel capacity: 36 (2-way capable; not operating 2-way). Channels available but not in use: N.A.
Basic Service
Subscribers: 50.
Programming (received off-air): KESD-TV (P) Brookings; KDLV-TV (N), KELO-TV (C), KSFY-TV (A) Sioux Falls-Mitchell.
Programming (via satellite): WGN-TV (W) Chicago; CNN; ESPN; Nashville Network; TBS Superstation; USA Network.
Fee: $24.95 installation; $27.38 monthly.
Pay Service 1
Pay Units: N.A.
Programming (via satellite): HBO.
Fee: $11.95 monthly.
Manager: Doug Bierschbach. Chief technician: Paul Schmidt.
Ownership: Satellite Cable Services Inc. (MSO).

ONAKA—Sully Buttes Telephone Cooperative Inc., Box 157, Highmore, SD 57345. Phone: 605-852-2224. Fax: 605-852-2404. County: Faulk. ICA: SD0146.
TV Market Ranking: Outside TV Markets. Franchise award date: N.A. Franchise expiration date: N.A. Began: November 13, 1989.
Channel capacity: 13 (not 2-way capable). Channels available but not in use: None.
Basic Service
Subscribers: 23.
Programming (received off-air): KABY-TV (A), KDSD-TV (P) Aberdeen; KDLO-TV (C) Florence-Watertown.
Programming (via satellite): WDIV (N) Detroit; CNN; ESPN; Fox Family Channel; Nashville Network; TBS Superstation; Turner Network TV.
Fee: $20.00 installation; $17.00 monthly.
Pay Service 1
Pay Units: 3.
Programming (via satellite): Showtime.
Fee: $9.50 monthly.
Equipment: Drake headend; Jerrold amplifiers; Comm/Scope cable; Pico traps; Winegard satellite antenna; Drake satellite receivers.
Miles of plant: 1.1 (coaxial). Homes passed: 35.
Manager: Randy Hoydek. Chief technician: Randy Olson.
Ownership: Sully Buttes Telephone Cooperative Inc. (MSO).

ONIDA—Onida Cable TV, Box 285, 124 E. 7th Ave., Onida, SD 57564. Phone: 605-258-2874. County: Sully. ICA: SD0092.
TV Market Ranking: Below 100. Franchise award date: N.A. Franchise expiration date: N.A. Began: May 1, 1982.
Channel capacity: 9 (not 2-way capable). Channels available but not in use: N.A.
Basic Service
Subscribers: 210.
Programming (received off-air): KPRY-TV (A), KTSD-TV (P) Pierre; KPLO-TV (C) Reliance; KDLV-TV (N) Sioux Falls-Mitchell.
Programming (via satellite): WGN-TV (W) Chicago; CNN; ESPN; TBS Superstation; Turner Network TV.
Fee: $35.00 installation; $15.00 monthly.

Pay Service 1
Pay Units: 108.
Programming (via satellite): HBO.
Fee: $10.00 monthly.
Local advertising: No.
Equipment: Scientific-Atlanta headend; Scientific-Atlanta amplifiers; Eagle traps; Scientific-Atlanta satellite antenna; Scientific-Atlanta satellite receivers.
Miles of plant: 5.0 (coaxial). Homes passed: 250. Total homes in franchised area: 250.
Manager: Michael Miles.
City fee: None.
Ownership: Onida Cable TV.

PHILIP—Golden West Cablevision, Box 9159, 2727 N. Plaza Dr., Rapid City, SD 57709. Phone: 605-348-6529. Fax: 605-342-1160. County: Haakon. Also serves Lake Waggoner, Rhode Addition. ICA: SD0054.
TV Market Ranking: Outside TV Markets. Franchise award date: N.A. Franchise expiration date: N.A. Began: September 15, 1982.
Channel capacity: 36 (2-way capable). Channels available but not in use: 18.
Basic Service
Subscribers: 488.
Programming (received off-air): KIVV-TV (F) Lead; KZSD-TV (P) Martin; KOTA-TV (A) Rapid City; KPLO-TV (C) Reliance.
Programming (via satellite): WGN-TV (W) Chicago; CNN; Discovery Channel; ESPN; EWTN; Fox Family Channel; Nashville Network; Nickelodeon; TBS Superstation; Turner Network TV; USA Network.
Programming (via fiber optic cable): KNBN-LP (N) Rapid City.
Fee: $25.00 installation; $14.00 monthly.
Pay Service 1
Pay Units: 86.
Programming (via satellite): Disney Channel.
Fee: $7.95 monthly.
Pay Service 2
Pay Units: 119.
Programming (via satellite): Showtime.
Fee: $7.95 monthly.
Local advertising: No.
Equipment: Scientific-Atlanta headend; Scientific-Atlanta amplifiers; Scientific-Atlanta cable; Arcom traps; Scientific-Atlanta satellite antenna.
Miles of plant: 27.0 (coaxial). Homes passed: 500.
Manager: Dwight Flatt. Chief technician: Ross Whitley. Marketing director: Greg Oleson.
City fee: None.
Ownership: Golden West Cablevision (MSO).

PICKSTOWN—Sky Scan Cable Co., Box 57, 713 Main St., Creighton, NE 68729. Phone: 402-358-3510. County: Charles Mix. ICA: SD0193.
TV Market Ranking: Outside TV Markets. Franchise award date: N.A. Franchise expiration date: N.A. Began: N.A.
Channel capacity: 36. Channels available but not in use: N.A.
Basic Service
Subscribers: 45.
Programming (received off-air): KMNE-TV (P) Bassett; KPRY-TV (A) Pierre; KPLO-TV (C) Reliance; KDLV-TV (N) Sioux Falls-Mitchell.
Programming (via satellite): WGN-TV (W) Chicago; CNN; Discovery Channel; ESPN; ESPN 2; Fox Family Channel; Nashville Network; TBS Superstation; Turner Network TV; USA Network.
Fee: $35.00 installation; $23.95 monthly.
Pay Service 1
Pay Units: 13.
Programming (via satellite): HBO.
Fee: $12.95 installation; $12.95 monthly.
Manager: Gelvin Stevens. Chief technician: Kenny Bartos.
Ownership: Sky Scan Cable Co. (MSO).

PIERPONT—Satellite Cable Services Inc., Box 106, Brookings, SD 57006-0106. Phone: 605-692-5508. Fax: 605-692-6496. County: Day. ICA: SD0194.
TV Market Ranking: Below 100. Franchise award date: N.A. Franchise expiration date: N.A. Began: N.A.
Channel capacity: 36 (2-way capable; not operating 2-way). Channels available but not in use: N.A.
Basic Service
Subscribers: 20.
Programming (via satellite): KCNC-TV (C), KWGN-TV (W) Denver; CNN; ESPN; Nashville Network; TBS Superstation.
Fee: $25.27 monthly.
Pay Service 1
Pay Units: N.A.
Programming (via satellite): HBO.
Fee: $11.95 monthly.
Manager: Doug Bierschbach. Chief technician: Paul Schmidt.
Ownership: Satellite Cable Services Inc. (MSO).

PIERRE—Midcontinent Cable Systems of South Dakota, Box 910, Aberdeen, SD 57402-0910. Phones: 605-229-1775; 800-456-0564. Fax: 605-229-0478. County: Hughes. ICA: SD0008.
TV Market Ranking: Below 100. Franchise award date: September 27, 1985. Franchise expiration date: September 27, 2000. Began: October 1, 1968.
Channel capacity: 40 (not 2-way capable). Channels available but not in use: N.A.
Basic Service
Subscribers: 5,003.
Programming (received off-air): KTTM (F) Huron; KPRY-TV (A), KTSD-TV (P) Pierre; KPLO-TV (C) Reliance; KDLV-TV (N) Sioux Falls-Mitchell; 5 FMs.
Programming (via satellite): WGN-TV (W) Chicago; A & E; American Movie Classics; C-SPAN; CNBC; CNN; Cartoon Network; Country Music TV; Discovery Channel; Disney Channel; ESPN; ESPN 2; ESPNews; EWTN; FX; Fox Family Channel; Headline News; Lifetime; MTV; Midwest Sports Channel; Nashville Network; Nick at Nite's TV Land; Nickelodeon; QVC; TBS Superstation; TV Guide Channel; The Health Network; The Weather Channel; Turner Network TV; USA Network; VH1.
Current originations: Educational access.
Fee: $50.00 installation; $24.34 monthly.
Pay Service 1
Pay Units: 277.
Programming (via satellite): Cinemax.
Fee: $20.00 installation; $11.00 monthly.
Pay Service 2
Pay Units: 752.
Programming (via satellite): HBO.
Fee: $20.00 installation; $11.00 monthly.
Pay Service 3
Pay Units: 440.
Programming (via satellite): Showtime.
Fee: $20.00 installation; $11.00 monthly.
Pay Service 4
Pay Units: 386.
Programming (via satellite): The Movie Channel.
Fee: $20.00 installation; $11.00 monthly.
Local advertising: No.
Equipment: C-COR headend; C-COR amplifiers; Times Fiber cable; Eagle traps.
Miles of plant: 57.4 (coaxial); 1.0 (fiber optic). Homes passed: 5,783.
Manager: Lonnie Schumacher. Marketing director: Fred Jamieson. Customer service manager: Kathy Fuhrmann.
City fee: 3% of gross.
Ownership: Midcontinent Communications (MSO).

PINE RIDGE—Pine Ridge Cable TV, Box 420, Billy Mills Hall, Pine Ridge, SD 57770. Phone: 605-867-1166. County: Shannon. ICA: SD0037.
TV Market Ranking: Outside TV Markets. Franchise award date: N.A. Franchise expiration date: N.A. Began: N.A.
Channel capacity: 52 (2-way capable). Channels available but not in use: 27.
Basic Service
Subscribers: 470.
Programming (received off-air): KBHE-TV (P), KEVN-TV (F), KOTA-TV (A) Rapid City; KPLO-TV (C) Reliance.
Programming (via satellite): WGN-TV (W) Chicago; CNN; Country Music TV; ESPN; Fox Family Channel; TBS Superstation; USA Network.
Fee: $20.00 installation; $25.00 monthly.
Pay Service 1
Pay Units: N.A.
Programming (via satellite): HBO.
Fee: $10.00 monthly.
Miles of plant: 7.5 (coaxial); None (fiber optic). Homes passed: 650. Total homes in franchised area: 700.
Manager: Heather Janis. Chief technician: Warren L. Chord.
Ownership: Pine Ridge Cable TV.

PLATTE—Platte Community Cable TV, Box 111, Redfield, SD 57469. Phone: 605-472-3415. County: Charles Mix. ICA: SD0049.
TV Market Ranking: Outside TV Markets. Franchise award date: N.A. Franchise expiration date: N.A. Began: January 1, 1981.
Channel capacity: 12 (not 2-way capable). Channels available but not in use: 2.
Basic Service
Subscribers: N.A.
Programming (received off-air): KMNE-TV (P) Bassett; KPRY-TV (A), KTSD-TV (P) Pierre; KPLO-TV (C) Reliance; KDLV-TV (N), KELO-TV (C) Sioux Falls-Mitchell.
Programming (via satellite): WGN-TV (W) Chicago; ESPN; TBS Superstation.
Fee: $30.00 installation; $9.25 monthly.
Pay Service 1
Pay Units: N.A.
Programming (via satellite): HBO.
Fee: $10.00 installation; $9.00 monthly.
Equipment: Scientific-Atlanta headend; Comm/Scope cable; Anixter-Pruzan satellite antenna.
Miles of plant: 11.3 (coaxial). Homes passed: 550.
Manager: Mike McClure.
City fee: None.
Ownership: Cable TV Assoc. Inc. (MSO).

POLLOCK—Valley Telco Cooperative Assn. Inc., Box 7, 102 S. Main, Herreid, SD 57632. Phone: 605-437-2615. Fax: 605-437-2220. Web site: http://www.valleytel.net. County: Campbell. ICA: SD0195.
TV Market Ranking: Outside TV Markets. Franchise award date: January 1, 1984. Franchise expiration date: January 1, 2004. Began: March 1, 1985.
Channel capacity: 24 (not 2-way capable). Channels available but not in use: None.
Basic Service
Subscribers: 126.
Programming (received off-air): KFYR-TV (N) Bismarck; KQSD-TV (P) Lowry; KELO-TV (C), KSFY-TV (A) Sioux Falls-Mitchell; 1 FM.
Programming (via satellite): WGN-TV (W) Chicago; CNN; Country Music TV; Discovery Channel; ESPN; Fox Family Channel; Nashville Network; TBS Superstation; Turner Network TV; USA Network.
Current originations: Automated time-weather.
Fee: $25.00 installation; $18.00 monthly; $1.00 converter; $25.00 additional installation.
Pay Service 1
Pay Units: 13.
Programming (via satellite): HBO.
Fee: $21.00 installation; $10.00 monthly.
Local advertising: Yes. Available in character-generated programming. Rates: $5.00/Week.
Equipment: Triple Crown headend; Magnavox amplifiers; BEI character generator; Hamlin set top converters; M/A-Com & Prodelin satellite antenna; Triple Crown satellite receivers.
Miles of plant: 4.0 (coaxial); None (fiber optic).
Manager: Dianna Quaschnick. Chief technician: Bob Schuetzle. Marketing director: Cindy Schick.
City fee: None.
Ownership: Valley Cable & Satellite Communications (MSO).

PRAIRIEWOOD VILLAGE—Satellite Cable Services Inc., Box 106, Brookings, SD 57006-0106. Phone: 605-692-5508. Fax: 605-692-6496. County: Brown. ICA: SD0196.
TV Market Ranking: Below 100. Franchise award date: N.A. Franchise expiration date: N.A. Began: N.A.
Channel capacity: 36 (2-way capable; not operating 2-way). Channels available but not in use: N.A.
Basic Service
Subscribers: 50.
Programming (received off-air): KABY-TV (A), KDSD-TV (P) Aberdeen; KDLO-TV (C) Florence-Watertown; KDLV-TV (N) Sioux Falls-Mitchell.
Programming (via satellite): WGN-TV (W) Chicago; KCNC-TV (C) Denver; CNN; Discovery Channel; ESPN; Fox Family Channel; Midwest Sports Channel; Nashville Network; TBS Superstation.
Fee: $27.95 monthly.
Pay Service 1
Pay Units: N.A.
Programming (via satellite): HBO.
Fee: $11.95 monthly.
Manager: Doug Bierschbach. Chief technician: Paul Schmidt.
Ownership: Satellite Cable Services Inc. (MSO).

PRESHO—WCENet Inc., Box 17, Murdo, SD 57559. Phone: 605-669-2472. Fax: 605-669-2358. County: Lyman. ICA: SD0073.
TV Market Ranking: Below 100. Franchise award date: N.A. Franchise expiration date: N.A. Began: July 1, 1984.
Channel capacity: 41. Channels available but not in use: N.A.
Basic Service
Subscribers: 154.
Programming (received off-air): KPRY-TV (A), KTSD-TV (P) Pierre; KPLO-TV (C) Reliance.
Programming (via satellite): WGN-TV (W) Chicago; KARE (N) Minneapolis-St. Paul; A & E; CNN; Discovery Channel; Disney Channel; ESPN; ESPN 2; Fox Family Channel; FoxNet; Headline News; History Channel; Home & Garden Television; Learning Channel; Lifetime; Nashville Network; Nick at Nite's TV Land; Outdoor Channel; QVC; TBS Superstation; The Weather Channel; Turner Clas-

sic Movies; Turner Network TV; USA Network.
Fee: $23.45 monthly.
Pay Service 1
Pay Units: N.A.
Programming (via satellite): Cinemax; HBO.
Fee: $9.95 monthly (each).
Miles of plant: 5.0 (coaxial). Homes passed: 318.
Manager: Steve Reed. Marketing manager: Joe Connot.
Ownership: West Central Electric Cooperative Inc. (MSO).

PUKWANA—Satellite Cable Services Inc., Box 106, Brookings, SD 57006-0106. Phone: 605-692-5508. Fax: 605-692-6496. County: Brule. ICA: SD0197.
TV Market Ranking: Below 100. Franchise award date: N.A. Franchise expiration date: N.A. Began: N.A.
Channel capacity: 36 (2-way capable; operating 2-way). Channels available but not in use: N.A.
Basic Service
Subscribers: 75.
Programming (received off-air): KDLT-TV (N) Sioux Falls; KELO-TV (C), KSFY-TV (A) Sioux Falls-Mitchell; KUSD-TV (P) Vermillion.
Programming (via satellite): WGN-TV (W) Chicago; TBS Superstation.
Fee: $28.96 monthly.
Miles of plant: 2.0 (coaxial).
Manager: Doug Bierschbac. Chief technician: Paul Schmidt.
Ownership: Satellite Cable Services Inc. (MSO).

RAMONA—Satellite Cable Services Inc., Box 106, Brookings, SD 57006-0106. Phone: 605-692-5508. Fax: 605-692-6496. County: Lake. ICA: SD0198.
TV Market Ranking: Outside TV Markets. Franchise award date: N.A. Franchise expiration date: N.A. Began: September 1, 1988.
Channel capacity: 36 (2-way capable; not operating 2-way). Channels available but not in use: N.A.
Basic Service
Subscribers: 50.
Programming (received off-air): KESD-TV (P) Brookings; KDLV-TV (N), KELO-TV (C), KSFY-TV (A) Sioux Falls-Mitchell.
Programming (via satellite): WGN-TV (W) Chicago; TBS Superstation.
Fee: $27.38 monthly.
Manager: Doug Bierschbach. Chief technician: Paul Schmidt.
Ownership: Satellite Cable Services Inc. (MSO).

RAPID CITY—TCI Cablevision of South Dakota, Box 537, Rapid City, SD 57709. Phone: 605-343-3402. Fax: 605-343-6380. Web site: http://www.tci.com. Counties: Meade & Pennington. Also serves Box Elder, Ellsworth AFB, Meade County (portions), Pennington County. ICA: SD0002.
TV Market Ranking: Below 100 (Box Elder, Ellsworth AFB, portions of Meade County, Rapid City); Outside TV Markets (portions of Meade County). Franchise award date: N.A. Franchise expiration date: N.A. Began: October 6, 1958.
Channel capacity: 54 (2-way capable; not operating 2-way). Channels available but not in use: None.
Basic Service
Subscribers: 15,055.
Programming (received off-air): KBHE-TV (P), KCLO-TV (C), KEVN-TV (F), KNBN-LP (N), KOTA-TV (A) Rapid City.
Programming (via satellite): Discovery Channel; FX; TBS Superstation; The Weather Channel; WB 100+ Station Group.
Current originations: Automated time-weather; educational access; government access.
Fee: $43.50 installation; $11.40 monthly; $3.25 converter; $21.75 additional installation.
Digital Basic Service
Subscribers: N.A.
Programming (via satellite): BBC America; Discovery Home & Leisure Channel; Discovery Kids Channel; Discovery People; Discovery Science Channel; ESPN Classic Sports; ESPNews; Fox Sports World; Game Show Network; History Channel; Independent Film Channel; MuchMusic Network; Outdoor Life Network; Romance Classics; Sci-Fi Channel; The Barker.
Fee: $13.50 monthly.
Expanded Basic Service
Subscribers: 14,211.
Programming (via satellite): A & E; American Movie Classics; Animal Planet; BET; C-SPAN; C-SPAN 2; CNBC; CNN; Cartoon Network; Comedy Central; Country Music TV; Disney Channel; ESPN; ESPN 2; Encore Movie Networks; Fox Family Channel; Fox News Channel; Fox Sports Net Rocky Mountain; Headline News; Home & Garden Television; Learning Channel; Lifetime; MTV; Nashville Network; Nickelodeon; QVC; Turner Classic Movies; Turner Network TV; USA Network; VH1.
Fee: $16.93 monthly.
Pay Service 1
Pay Units: 1,542.
Programming (via satellite): Cinemax.
Fee: $14.50 installation; $10.95 monthly.
Pay Service 2
Pay Units: 3,573.
Programming (via satellite): HBO.
Fee: $13.40 monthly.
Pay Service 3
Pay Units: 1,134.
Programming (via satellite): Showtime.
Fee: $12.50 monthly.
Pay Service 4
Pay Units: 9,219.
Programming (via satellite): The New Encore.
Fee: $1.75 monthly.
Pay Service 5
Pay Units: N.A.
Programming (via satellite): Starz!
Fee: $6.75 monthly.
Digital Pay Service 1
Pay Units: N.A.
Programming (via satellite): Bravo; DMX; Encore Love Stories; Encore Mystery; Encore Westerns; HBO Plus; HBO Signature; Showtime (multiplexed); Starz! (multiplexed); The Movie Channel.
Fee: N.A.
Pay-Per-View
Addressable homes: 2,200.
Spice delivered digitally; Viewer's Choice Digital.
Fee: Varies.
Local advertising: Yes (insert only). Available in satellite distributed programming.
Program Guide: The Cable Guide.
Equipment: Jerrold headend; Scientific-Atlanta amplifiers; Comm/Scope & Times Fiber cable; Scientific-Atlanta satellite antenna.
Miles of plant: 307.9 (coaxial); None (fiber optic). Homes passed: 20,511. Total homes in franchised area: 21,922.
Manager: Dale Hodgkins. Chief technician: Dave Gorsuch.
Ownership: AT&T Broadband & Internet Services (MSO). Purchased from Tele-Communications Inc., March 9, 1999.

RAYMOND—Satellite Cable Services Inc., Box 106, Brookings, SD 57006-0106. Phone: 605-692-5508. Fax: 605-692-6496. County: Clark. ICA: SD0199.
TV Market Ranking: Outside TV Markets. Franchise award date: N.A. Franchise expiration date: N.A. Began: N.A.
Channel capacity: 36. Channels available but not in use: N.A.
Basic Service
Subscribers: 25.
Programming (via satellite): KCNC-TV (C), KWGN-TV (W) Denver; CNN; ESPN; Nashville Network; TBS Superstation.
Fee: $25.79 monthly.
Pay Service 1
Pay Units: N.A.
Programming (via satellite): HBO.
Fee: $11.95 monthly.
Manager: Doug Bierschbach. Chief technician: Paul Schmidt.
Ownership: Satellite Cable Services Inc. (MSO).

REDFIELD—Midcontinent Cable Systems of South Dakota, Box 910, Aberdeen, SD 57402-0910. Phones: 605-229-1775; 800-456-0564. Fax: 605-229-0478. County: Spink. ICA: SD0020.
TV Market Ranking: Outside TV Markets. Franchise award date: October 5, 1988. Franchise expiration date: October 5, 2011. Began: December 15, 1971.
Channel capacity: 41 (not 2-way capable). Channels available but not in use: 2.
Basic Service
Subscribers: 810.
Programming (received off-air): KABY-TV (A), KDSD-TV (P) Aberdeen; KDLO-TV (C) Florence-Watertown; KTTM (F) Huron; all-band FM.
Programming (via microwave): KDLT-TV (N) Sioux Falls.
Programming (via satellite): WGN-TV (W) Chicago; A & E; American Movie Classics; C-SPAN; CNBC; CNN; Cartoon Network; Country Music TV; Discovery Channel; Disney Channel; ESPN; ESPN 2; ESPNews; EWTN; FX; Fox Family Channel; Headline News; Learning Channel; Lifetime; MTV; Midwest Sports Channel; Nashville Network; Nick at Nite's TV Land; Nickelodeon; QVC; TBS Superstation; TV Guide Channel; The Weather Channel; Turner Network TV; USA Network; VH1.
Current originations: Automated time-weather.
Fee: $50.00 installation; $26.50 monthly.
Pay Service 1
Pay Units: 45.
Programming (via satellite): Cinemax.
Fee: $20.00 installation; $11.00 monthly.
Pay Service 2
Pay Units: 144.
Programming (via satellite): HBO.
Fee: $20.00 installation; $12.00 monthly.
Pay Service 3
Pay Units: 68.
Programming (via satellite): Showtime.
Fee: $20.00 installation; $11.00 monthly.
Pay Service 4
Pay Units: 66.
Programming (via satellite): The Movie Channel.
Fee: $11.00 monthly.
Local advertising: No.
Equipment: Scientific-Atlanta headend; Jerrold amplifiers; Times Fiber cable; Eagle traps; Scientific-Atlanta satellite antenna.
Miles of plant: 21.9 (coaxial); None (fiber optic). Homes passed: 1,392. Total homes in franchised area: 1,392.
Manager: Lonnie Schumacher. Marketing director: Fred Jamieson. Customer service manager: Kathy Fuhrmann.
City fee: 3% of gross.
Ownership: Midcontinent Communications (MSO).

REE HEIGHTS—Sully Buttes Telephone Cooperative Inc., Box 157, Highmore, SD 57345. Phone: 605-852-2224. Fax: 605-852-2404. County: Hand. ICA: SD0144.
TV Market Ranking: Outside TV Markets. Franchise award date: N.A. Franchise expiration date: N.A. Began: November 1, 1989.
Channel capacity: 12 (not 2-way capable). Channels available but not in use: None.
Basic Service
Subscribers: 33.
Programming (received off-air): KPRY-TV (A), KTSD-TV (P) Pierre; KPLO-TV (C) Reliance.
Programming (via satellite): WDIV (N) Detroit; CNN; ESPN; Nashville Network; TBS Superstation.
Fee: $20.00 installation; $17.00 monthly.
Pay Service 1
Pay Units: 10.
Programming (via satellite): Showtime.
Fee: $15.00 installation; $9.50 monthly.
Equipment: Jerrold amplifiers; Comm/Scope cable; Pico traps; Winegard satellite antenna; Drake satellite receivers.
Homes passed: 40.
Manager: Randy Hoydek. Chief technician: Randy Olson.
Ownership: Sully Buttes Telephone Cooperative Inc. (MSO).

RELIANCE—WCENet Inc., Box 17, Murdo, SD 57559. Phone: 605-669-2472. Fax: 605-669-2358. County: Lyman. ICA: SD0200.
TV Market Ranking: Below 100. Franchise award date: N.A. Franchise expiration date: N.A. Began: July 1, 1990.
Channel capacity: 41 (not 2-way capable). Channels available but not in use: N.A.
Basic Service
Subscribers: 33.
Programming (received off-air): KPRY-TV (A), KTSD-TV (P) Pierre; KPLO-TV (C) Reliance.
Programming (via satellite): WGN-TV (W) Chicago; WDIV (N) Detroit; CNN; Country Music TV; Discovery Channel; ESPN; Fox Family Channel; Lifetime; Nashville Network; QVC; TBS Superstation; The Weather Channel; Turner Network TV.
Fee: $21.45 monthly.
Pay Service 1
Pay Units: N.A.
Programming (via satellite): HBO.
Fee: $6.95 monthly.
Manager: Steve Reed. Marketing manager: Joe Connot.
Ownership: West Central Electric Cooperative Inc. (MSO).

REVILLO—Satellite Cable Services Inc., Box 106, Brookings, SD 57006-0106. Phone: 605-692-5508. Fax: 605-692-6496. County: Grant. ICA: SD0202.
TV Market Ranking: Below 100. Franchise award date: June 6, 1990. Franchise expiration date: June 6, 2005. Began: January 1, 1991.
Channel capacity: 36 (2-way capable; operating 2-way). Channels available but not in use: N.A.

Basic Service
Subscribers: 45.
Programming (received off-air): KABY-TV (A) Aberdeen; KWCM-TV (P) Appleton; KDLO-TV (C) Florence-Watertown.
Programming (via satellite): WGN-TV (W) Chicago; KCNC-TV (C) Denver; CNN; Discovery Channel; ESPN; Midwest Sports Channel; Nashville Network; TBS Superstation; Turner Network TV.
Fee: $26.32 monthly.
Pay Service 1
Pay Units: N.A.
Programming (via satellite): HBO.
Fee: $11.95 monthly.
Manager: Doug Bierschbach. Chief technician: Paul Schmidt.
Ownership: Satellite Cable Services Inc. (MSO).

RIMROCK—Galaxy Cablevision, 203 S. Lincoln Ave., York, NE 68467. Phones: 402-362-1705; 800-365-6988. Fax: 402-362-3698. County: Pennington. Also serves Rapid City (portions). ICA: SD0221.
TV Market Ranking: Below 100. Franchise award date: N.A. Franchise expiration date: N.A. Began: N.A.
Channel capacity: 41. Channels available but not in use: 11.
Basic Service
Subscribers: 405.
Programming (received off-air): KBHE-TV (P), KCLO-TV (C), KEVN-TV (F), KNBN-LP (N), KOTA-TV (A) Rapid City.
Programming (via satellite): WGN-TV (W) Chicago; KWGN-TV (W) Denver; A & E; American Movie Classics; CNN; Country Music TV; Discovery Channel; Disney Channel; ESPN; ESPN 2; Fox Family Channel; Headline News; Home & Garden Television; Learning Channel; Lifetime; Nashville Network; Nickelodeon; QVC; TBS Superstation; The Weather Channel; Turner Network TV; USA Network; VH1.
Fee: $28.95 monthly.
Pay Service 1
Pay Units: 12.
Programming (via satellite): Showtime.
Fee: $7.95 monthly.
Pay Service 2
Pay Units: 65.
Programming (via satellite): HBO.
Fee: $12.95 monthly.
Miles of plant: 22.0 (coaxial). Homes passed: 446.
District vice president: John M. Dixon III. State manager: Steve Jordan. Technical manager: Van De Vries.
Ownership: Galaxy Cablevision (MSO).

ROSCOE—Midcontinent Cable Systems of South Dakota, Box 910, Aberdeen, SD 57402-0910. Phones: 605-229-1775; 800-456-0564. Fax: 605-229-0478. County: Edmunds. ICA: SD0119.
TV Market Ranking: Outside TV Markets. Franchise award date: August 2, 1995. Franchise expiration date: August 2, 2010. Began: June 1, 1983.
Channel capacity: 75 (not 2-way capable). Channels available but not in use: None.
Basic Service
Subscribers: 113.
Programming (received off-air): KABY-TV (A), KDSD-TV (P) Aberdeen; KDLO-TV (C) Florence-Watertown; KTTM (F) Huron; KDLV-TV (N) Sioux Falls-Mitchell.
Programming (via satellite): WGN-TV (W) Chicago; A & E; American Movie Classics; C-SPAN; C-SPAN 2; CNBC; CNN; Cartoon Network; Country Music TV; Discovery Channel; Disney Channel; ESPN; ESPN 2; ESPNews; EWTN; FX; Flix; Fox Family Channel; Headline News; Learning Channel; Lifetime; MTV; Midwest Sports Channel; Nashville Network; Nick at Nite's TV Land; Nickelodeon; QVC; TBS Superstation; TV Guide Channel; The Health Network; The Inspirational Network; The Weather Channel; Turner Network TV; USA Network; VH1.
Current originations: Public access; educational access; local access.
Fee: $50.00 installation; $26.50 monthly.
Expanded Basic Service
Subscribers: N.A.
Programming (via satellite): Animal Planet; Bravo; Comedy Central; E! Entertainment TV; fXM: Movies from Fox; History Channel; Outdoor Channel; Sci-Fi Channel; Travel Channel; Turner Classic Movies.
Fee: N.A.
Pay Service 1
Pay Units: 4.
Programming (via satellite): HBO (multiplexed).
Fee: $20.00 installation; $12.00 monthly.
Pay Service 2
Pay Units: 16.
Programming (via satellite): Showtime (multiplexed).
Fee: $20.00 installation; $11.00 monthly.
Pay Service 3
Pay Units: 16.
Programming (via satellite): The Movie Channel.
Fee: $20.00 installation; $11.00 monthly.
Pay Service 4
Pay Units: N.A.
Programming (via satellite): Cinemax (multiplexed); Golf Channel; Starz!; The New Encore (multiplexed).
Fee: $20.00 installation; $5.95 monthly (Golf), $7.95 monthly (Encore & Starz), $11.00 monthly (Cinemax).
Local advertising: No.
Equipment: Magnavox amplifiers; Times Fiber cable; Eagle traps.
Miles of plant: 3.5 (coaxial); None (fiber optic). Homes passed: 172.
Manager: Lonnie Schumacher. Marketing director: Fred Jamieson. Customer service manager: Kathy Fuhrmann.
City fee: 3% of gross.
Ownership: Midcontinent Communications (MSO).

ROSEBUD—Savage Communications, Box 810, Hinckley, MN 55037. Phone: 320-384-7442. Fax: 320-384-7446. County: Todd. ICA: SD0203.
TV Market Ranking: Outside TV Markets. Franchise award date: April 1, 1987. Franchise expiration date: April 1, 2003. Began: January 1, 1988.
Channel capacity: 54 (2-way capable; not operating 2-way). Channels available but not in use: 14.
Basic Service
Subscribers: 243.
Programming (received off-air): KCNC-TV (C), KMGH-TV (A), KWGN-TV (W) Denver; KPRY-TV (A), KTSD-TV (P) Pierre; KPLO-TV (C) Reliance.
Programming (via satellite): WGN-TV (W) Chicago; A & E; CNN; Country Music TV; Discovery Channel; ESPN; Fox Family Channel; History Channel; Learning Channel; MTV; Nashville Network; Nickelodeon; Sci-Fi Channel; TBS Superstation; The Weather Channel; Turner Classic Movies; Turner Network TV; USA Network; VH1.
Fee: $37.50 installation; $25.00 monthly.
Pay Service 1
Pay Units: 93.
Programming (via satellite): The Movie Channel.
Fee: $10.00 monthly.
Pay Service 2
Pay Units: N.A.
Programming (via satellite): Disney Channel; HBO.
Fee: $8.00 monthly (Disney), $11.00 monthly (HBO).
Miles of plant: 15.5 (coaxial). Homes passed: 342.
Manager: Mike Danielson. Chief technician: Pat McCabe.
Ownership: Savage Communications Inc. (MSO).

ROSHOLT—TCI Cablevision of South Dakota, Box 144, Milbank, SD 57252-0144. Phone: 605-432-6776. Fax: 605-432-4661. County: Roberts. ICA: SD0115.
TV Market Ranking: Outside TV Markets. Franchise award date: N.A. Franchise expiration date: N.A. Began: December 1, 1979.
Channel capacity: 35. Channels available but not in use: 15.
Basic Service
Subscribers: 164.
Programming (received off-air): KABY-TV (A), KDSD-TV (P) Aberdeen; KVRR (F) Fargo; KDLO-TV (C) Florence-Watertown; 1 FM.
Programming (via microwave): KVLY-TV (N) Fargo.
Programming (via satellite): WGN-TV (W) Chicago; CNN; Discovery Channel; Fox Family Channel; Lifetime; TBS Superstation.
Fee: $29.95 installation; $20.69 monthly; $24.95 additional installation.
Expanded Basic Service
Subscribers: 159.
Programming (via satellite): American Movie Classics; Court TV; ESPN; Nashville Network; Turner Network TV; USA Network.
Fee: N.A.
Pay Service 1
Pay Units: 14.
Programming (via satellite): Disney Channel.
Fee: N.A.
Pay Service 2
Pay Units: 27.
Programming (via satellite): HBO.
Fee: N.A.
Pay Service 3
Pay Units: 66.
Programming (via satellite): The New Encore.
Fee: N.A.
Miles of plant: 2.9 (coaxial). Homes passed: 183. Total homes in franchised area: 183.
Manager: Joe Villella. Chief technician: Ray Olson.
City fee: None.
Ownership: AT&T Broadband & Internet Services (MSO). Purchased from Tele-Communications Inc., March 9, 1999.

ROSLYN—Midcontinent Cable Systems of South Dakota, Box 910, Aberdeen, SD 57402-0910. Phones: 605-229-1775; 800-456-0564. Fax: 605-229-0478. County: Day. ICA: SD0134.
TV Market Ranking: Outside TV Markets. Franchise award date: May 9, 1994. Franchise expiration date: May 9, 2009. Began: October 18, 1984.
Channel capacity: 75 (not 2-way capable). Channels available but not in use: N.A.
Basic Service
Subscribers: 84.
Programming (received off-air): KABY-TV (A), KDSD-TV (P) Aberdeen; KDLO-TV (C) Florence-Watertown; KTTM (F) Huron.
Programming (via microwave): KDLT-TV (N) Sioux Falls.
Programming (via satellite): WGN-TV (W) Chicago; A & E; American Movie Classics; C-SPAN; C-SPAN 2; CNBC; CNN; Cartoon Network; Country Music TV; DMX; Discovery Channel; Disney Channel; ESPN; ESPN 2; ESPNews; EWTN; FX; Flix; Fox Family Channel; Headline News; Learning Channel; Lifetime; MTV; Midwest Sports Channel; Nashville Network; Nick at Nite's TV Land; Nickelodeon; QVC; TBS Superstation; TV Guide Channel; The Health Network; The Inspirational Network; The Weather Channel; Turner Network TV; USA Network; VH1.
Current originations: Public access; educational access; local access.
Fee: $50.00 installation; $25.00 monthly.
Expanded Basic Service
Subscribers: N.A.
Programming (via satellite): Animal Planet; Bravo; Comedy Central; E! Entertainment TV; fXM: Movies from Fox; History Channel; Outdoor Channel; Sci-Fi Channel; Travel Channel; Turner Classic Movies.
Fee: N.A.
Pay Service 1
Pay Units: 7.
Programming (via satellite): HBO (multiplexed).
Fee: $20.00 installation; $12.00 monthly.
Pay Service 2
Pay Units: 3.
Programming (via satellite): Cinemax (multiplexed).
Fee: $20.00 installation; $11.00 monthly.
Pay Service 3
Pay Units: 2.
Programming (via satellite): Showtime (multiplexed).
Fee: $20.00 installation; $11.00 monthly.
Pay Service 4
Pay Units: N.A.
Programming (via satellite): The Movie Channel.
Fee: $20.00 installation; $11.00 monthly.
Pay Service 5
Pay Units: N.A.
Programming (via satellite): Golf Channel; Starz!; The New Encore (multiplexed).
Fee: $20.00 installation; $5.95 monthly (Golf), $7.95 monthly (Encore & Starz).
Local advertising: No.
Equipment: Magnavox amplifiers; Times Fiber cable; Eagle traps; Scientific-Atlanta satellite antenna.
Miles of plant: 1.7 (coaxial); None (fiber optic). Homes passed: 124.
Manager: Lonnie Schumacher. Marketing director: Fred Jamieson. Customer service manager: Kathy Fuhrmann.
City fee: 3% of gross.
Ownership: Midcontinent Communications (MSO).

SELBY—Midcontinent Cable Systems Co. of South Dakota, Box 910, Aberdeen, SD 57402-0910. Phones: 605-229-1775; 800-456-0564. Fax: 605-229-0478. County: Walworth. ICA: SD0204.
TV Market Ranking: Outside TV Markets. Franchise award date: January 11, 1989. Franchise expiration date: January 11, 2011. Began: December 1, 1983.
Channel capacity: 75 (not 2-way capable). Channels available but not in use: N.A.
Basic Service
Subscribers: 244.
Programming (received off-air): KABY-TV (A), KDSD-TV (P) Aberdeen; KDLO-TV (C) Florence-Watertown; KTTM (F) Huron; KDLV-TV (N) Sioux Falls-Mitchell.

Programming (via satellite): WGN-TV (W) Chicago; A & E; American Movie Classics; C-SPAN; C-SPAN 2; CNBC; CNN; Cartoon Network; Country Music TV; Discovery Channel; Disney Channel; ESPN; ESPN 2; ESPNews; EWTN; FX; Flix; Fox Family Channel; Headline News; Learning Channel; Lifetime; MTV; Midwest Sports Channel; Nashville Network; Nick at Nite's TV Land; Nickelodeon; QVC; TBS Superstation; TV Guide Channel; The Health Network; The Inspirational Network; The Weather Channel; Turner Network TV; USA Network; VH1.
Current originations: Public access; educational access; local access.
Fee: $50.00 installation; $26.50 monthly.

Expanded Basic Service
Subscribers: N.A.
Programming (via satellite): Animal Planet; Bravo; Comedy Central; E! Entertainment TV; fXM: Movies from Fox; History Channel; Outdoor Channel; Sci-Fi Channel; Travel Channel; Turner Classic Movies.
Fee: N.A.

Pay Service 1
Pay Units: 25.
Programming (via satellite): Showtime (multiplexed).
Fee: $20.00 installation; $11.00 monthly.

Pay Service 2
Pay Units: 6.
Programming (via satellite): HBO (multiplexed).
Fee: $20.00 installation; $12.00 monthly.

Pay Service 3
Pay Units: 11.
Programming (via satellite): The Movie Channel.
Fee: $20.00 installation; $11.00 monthly.

Pay Service 4
Pay Units: N.A.
Programming (via satellite): Cinemax (multiplexed).
Fee: $20.00 installation; $11.00 monthly.

Pay Service 5
Pay Units: N.A.
Programming (via satellite): Golf Channel; Starz!; The New Encore (multiplexed).
Fee: $20.00 installation; $7.95 monthly (package).

Pay-Per-View
Addressable homes: 48.
Hot Choice; Viewer's Choice 1, 3, 4.

Miles of plant: 4.4 (coaxial); None (fiber optic). Homes passed: 323.
Region manager: Lonnie Schumacher. Marketing director: Fred Jamieson. Customer service manager: Kathy Fuhrmann.
Ownership: Midcontinent Communications (MSO).

SENECA—Sully Buttes Telephone Cooperative Inc., Box 157, Highmore, SD 57345. Phone: 605-852-2224. Fax: 605-852-2404. County: Faulk. ICA: SD0145.
TV Market Ranking: Outside TV Markets. Franchise award date: N.A. Franchise expiration date: N.A. Began: October 16, 1989.
Channel capacity: 13. Channels available but not in use: None.

Basic Service
Subscribers: 24.
Programming (received off-air): KABY-TV (A), KDSD-TV (P) Aberdeen; KDLO-TV (C) Florence-Watertown.
Programming (via satellite): WDIV (N) Detroit; CNN; ESPN; Nashville Network; TBS Superstation.
Fee: $20.00 installation; $17.00 monthly.

Pay Service 1
Pay Units: 3.
Programming (via satellite): Showtime.
Fee: $9.50 monthly.

Equipment: Jerrold amplifiers; Comm/Scope cable; Pico traps; Winegard satellite antenna; Drake satellite receivers.
Homes passed: 40.
Manager: Randy Hoydek. Chief technician: Randy Olson.
Ownership: Sully Buttes Telephone Cooperative Inc. (MSO).

SIOUX FALLS—Sioux Falls Cable, 3507 S. Duluth Ave., Sioux Falls, SD 57105-6415. Phone: 605-339-3339. Fax: 605-335-1987. Counties: Lincoln & Minnehaha. Also serves Baltic, Crooks, Renner. ICA: SD0001.
TV Market Ranking: 85. Franchise award date: May 30, 1969. Franchise expiration date: December 29, 2004. Began: December 29, 1969.
Channel capacity: 78 (2-way capable). Channels available but not in use: 17.

Basic Service
Subscribers: 35,727.
Programming (received off-air): KDLV-TV (N), KELO-TV (C), KSFY-TV (A), KTTW (F) Sioux Falls-Mitchell; KSMN (P) Worthington.
Programming (via microwave): KUSD-TV (P) Vermillion.
Programming (via satellite): WGN-TV (W) Chicago; A & E; American Movie Classics; Bravo; C-SPAN; C-SPAN 2; CNBC; CNN; Discovery Channel; Disney Channel; ESPN; Fox Family Channel; Fox News Channel; Headline News; Home Shopping Network; Learning Channel; Lifetime; MTV; Midwest Sports Channel; Nashville Network; Nick at Nite's TV Land; Nickelodeon; QVC; TBS Superstation; TV Guide Channel; The Weather Channel; Turner Network TV; USA Network; VH1.
Current originations: Automated time-weather; educational access; government access; religious access; automated emergency alert.
Fee: $15.00 installation; $23.60 monthly; $2.00 converter.

Expanded Basic Service
Subscribers: 8,634.
Programming (via satellite): Cartoon Network; Comedy Central; Country Music TV; ESPN 2; History Channel; Home & Garden Television; Sci-Fi Channel; Turner Classic Movies.
Fee: $3.95 monthly.

Pay Service 1
Pay Units: 1,422.
Programming (via satellite): Cinemax.
Fee: $25.00 installation; $11.35 monthly.

Pay Service 2
Pay Units: 8,240.
Programming (via satellite): HBO.
Fee: $25.00 installation; $11.35 monthly.

Pay Service 3
Pay Units: 5,015.
Programming (via satellite): Showtime.
Fee: $25.00 installation; $11.35 monthly.

Pay Service 4
Pay Units: 4,777.
Programming (via satellite): The Movie Channel.
Fee: $25.00 installation; $11.35 monthly.

Pay-Per-View
Addressable homes: 9,500.
Playboy TV.
Fee: Varies.

Local advertising: Yes. Available in locally originated programming. Rates: $120.00/Minute; $60.00/30 Seconds. Local sales manager: Josh Houk.
Equipment: Scientific-Atlanta headend; Texscan amplifiers; Comm/Scope cable; Siecor & AT&T fiber optic cable; Sony cameras; Sony VTRs; Scientific-Atlanta set top converters; Scientific-Atlanta addressable set top converters; Pico & Eagle traps; Simulsat satellite antenna; Scientific-Atlanta & General satellite receivers; Sony commercial insert.
Miles of plant: 626.0 (coaxial); 98.4 (fiber optic). Additional miles planned: 50.0 (coaxial). Homes passed: 51,601. Total homes in franchised area: 51,601.
Manager: Rod Carlson. System engineer: Michael Schmit. Program director: Lee Johnson.
City fee: 3% of gross.
Ownership: Midcontinent Communications (MSO); AT&T Broadband & Internet Services (MSO). Purchased from Tele-Communications Inc., March 9, 1999.

SISSETON—TCI Cablevision of South Dakota, Box 144, Milbank, SD 57252-0144. Phone: 605-432-6776. Fax: 605-432-4661. County: Roberts. ICA: SD0023.
TV Market Ranking: Outside TV Markets. Franchise award date: N.A. Franchise expiration date: N.A. Began: February 1, 1977.
Channel capacity: 31. Channels available but not in use: N.A.

Basic Service
Subscribers: 837.
Programming (received off-air): KABY-TV (A), KDSD-TV (P) Aberdeen; KCCO-TV (C) Alexandria; KWCM-TV (P) Appleton; KVLY-TV (N), KVRR (F), WDAY-TV (A) Fargo; KDLO-TV (C) Florence-Watertown; allband FM.
Programming (via satellite): WGN-TV (W) Chicago; C-SPAN; CNN; Discovery Channel; Fox Family Channel; Lifetime; MTV; Nickelodeon; QVC; TBS Superstation.
Fee: $29.95 installation; $20.04 monthly; $24.95 additional installation.

Expanded Basic Service
Subscribers: 792.
Programming (via satellite): American Movie Classics; ESPN; EWTN; Midwest Sports Channel; Nashville Network; Turner Network TV; USA Network.
Fee: N.A.

Pay Service 1
Pay Units: N.A.
Programming (via satellite): Cinemax.
Fee: N.A.

Pay Service 2
Pay Units: 98.
Programming (via satellite): Disney Channel.
Fee: N.A.

Pay Service 3
Pay Units: 379.
Programming (via satellite): The New Encore.
Fee: N.A.

Pay Service 4
Pay Units: 188.
Programming (via satellite): HBO.
Fee: N.A.

Equipment: Ameco headend; Ameco amplifiers; Comm/Scope cable; Scientific-Atlanta satellite antenna.
Miles of plant: 17.2 (coaxial). Homes passed: 1,188. Total homes in franchised area: 1,188.
Manager: Joe Villella. Chief technician: Ray Olson.
City fee: None.
Ownership: AT&T Broadband & Internet Services (MSO). Purchased from Tele-Communications Inc., March 9, 1999.

SOUTH SHORE—Satellite Cable Services Inc., Box 106, Brookings, SD 57006-0106. Phone: 605-692-5508. Fax: 605-692-6496. County: Codington. ICA: SD0205.
TV Market Ranking: Below 100. Franchise award date: N.A. Franchise expiration date: N.A. Began: N.A.
Channel capacity: 36 (2-way capable; not operating 2-way). Channels available but not in use: N.A.

Basic Service
Subscribers: 60.
Programming (via satellite): KCNC-TV (C), KWGN-TV (W) Denver; CNN; ESPN; Nashville Network; TBS Superstation.
Fee: $25.79 monthly.

Pay Service 1
Pay Units: N.A.
Programming (via satellite): HBO.
Fee: $11.95 monthly.

Manager: Doug Bierschbach. Chief technician: Paul Schmidt.
Ownership: Satellite Cable Services Inc. (MSO).

SPEARFISH—TCI Cablevision, Box 309, 842 Short Track Rd., Sturgis, SD 57785. Phone: 605-347-3090. Fax: 605-347-3499. County: Lawrence. ICA: SD0010.
TV Market Ranking: Below 100. Franchise award date: N.A. Franchise expiration date: N.A. Began: June 1, 1969.
Channel capacity: 35. Channels available but not in use: N.A.

Basic Service
Subscribers: 3,600.
Programming (received off-air): KPSD-TV (P) Eagle Butte; KCLO-TV (C), KEVN-TV (F), KNBN-LP (N), KOTA-TV (A) Rapid City; allband FM.
Programming (via satellite): KWGN-TV (W) Denver; A & E; C-SPAN; CNBC; CNN; Cartoon Network; Country Music TV; Discovery Channel; ESPN; ESPN 2; EWTN; Fox Family Channel; Fox Sports Net; Headline News; History Channel; Lifetime; MTV; Nashville Network; Nickelodeon; QVC; TBS Superstation; TV Guide Channel; The Weather Channel; Trinity Bcstg. Network; Turner Network TV; USA Network.
Current originations: Automated time-weather; public access; automated emergency alert.
Fee: $40.00 installation; $24.28 monthly; $10.00 additional installation.

Pay Service 1
Pay Units: N.A.
Programming (via satellite): Cinemax; Disney Channel; HBO; Showtime; The Movie Channel.
Fee: N.A.

Local advertising: No.
Equipment: Scientific-Atlanta headend; Scientific-Atlanta amplifiers; Times Fiber cable;

Video Data Systems character generator; Arcom traps; Scientific-Atlanta satellite antenna; Scientific-Atlanta satellite receivers.
Miles of plant & homes passed included with Custer, SD.
Manager: Dale Hodgkins. Chief technician: Gary Reimer.
City fee: 3% of gross.
Ownership: AT&T Broadband & Internet Services (MSO). Purchased from South Dakota Cable Inc., April 1, 1999.

SPENCER—Central Cableland TV, Box 217, Alexandria, SD 57311-0217. Phone: 605-239-4302. Fax: 605-239-4301. County: McCook. ICA: SD0225.
TV Market Ranking: 85. Franchise award date: N.A. Franchise expiration date: N.A. Began: N.A.
Channel capacity: N.A. Channels available but not in use: N.A.
Basic Service
Subscribers: 90.
Programming (received off-air): KESD-TV (P) Brookings; KDLV-TV (N), KELO-TV (C), KSFY-TV (A), KTTW (F) Sioux Falls-Mitchell.
Programming (via satellite): WGN-TV (W) Chicago; CNN; Country Music TV; ESPN; Fox Family Channel; Nashville Network; TBS Superstation; Turner Network TV.
Fee: $20.00 installation; $13.50 monthly.
Pay Service 1
Pay Units: 16.
Programming (via satellite): Disney Channel.
Fee: $7.50 monthly.
Pay Service 2
Pay Units: 17.
Programming (via satellite): Showtime.
Fee: $9.50 monthly.
Miles of plant: 3.0 (coaxial). Homes passed: 156.
Manager: Bryan Roth. Chief technician: Tim Wenande. Customer service manager: Carla Bambas.
Ownership: Hanson Communications (MSO).

SPRINGFIELD—Springfield Cable Inc., Box 434, Springfield, SD 57062. Phone: 605-369-5585. County: Bon Homme. ICA: SD0070.
TV Market Ranking: Outside TV Markets. Franchise award date: April 9, 1985. Franchise expiration date: April 9, 2000. Began: October 1, 1985.
Channel capacity: 36. Channels available but not in use: 13.
Basic Service
Subscribers: 250.
Programming (received off-air): KDLV-TV (N), KELO-TV (C), KSFY-TV (A) Sioux Falls-Mitchell; KUSD-TV (P) Vermillion.
Programming (via satellite): WGN-TV (W) Chicago; CNN; Discovery Channel; ESPN; EWTN; Fox Family Channel; FoxNet; Lifetime; Nashville Network; Nickelodeon; TBS Superstation; Turner Network TV; USA Network.
Fee: $12.95 installation; $19.00 monthly.
Pay Service 1
Pay Units: 30.
Programming (via satellite): Cinemax.
Fee: $10.00 monthly.
Pay Service 2
Pay Units: 24.
Programming (via satellite): The Movie Channel.
Fee: $10.00 monthly.
Miles of plant: 7.1 (coaxial). Homes passed: 350.
Manager: Jim Libis. Marketing director: Di Ann Schelske.
Ownership: Golden West Cablevision (MSO). Purchased from Springfield Cable Inc., July 1, 1998.

ST. FRANCIS—Savage Communications, Box 810, Hinckley, MN 55037. Phone: 320-384-7442. Fax: 320-384-7446. County: Todd. ICA: SD0050.
TV Market Ranking: Outside TV Markets. Franchise award date: July 1, 1989. Franchise expiration date: July 1, 2004. Began: September 1, 1989.
Channel capacity: 54 (2-way capable; not operating 2-way). Channels available but not in use: 14.
Basic Service
Subscribers: 154.
Programming (received off-air): KPRY-TV (A), KTSD-TV (P) Pierre; KPLO-TV (C) Reliance.
Programming (via satellite): WGN-TV (W) Chicago; KCNC-TV (C), KMGH-TV (A), KWGN-TV (W) Denver; A & E; CNN; Country Music TV; Discovery Channel; ESPN; Fox Family Channel; History Channel; Learning Channel; MTV; Nashville Network; Nickelodeon; Sci-Fi Channel; TBS Superstation; The Weather Channel; Turner Classic Movies; Turner Network TV; USA Network; VH1.
Fee: $37.50 installation; $25.00 monthly.
Pay Service 1
Pay Units: 60.
Programming (via satellite): The Movie Channel.
Fee: $10.00 monthly.
Pay Service 2
Pay Units: N.A.
Programming (via satellite): Disney Channel; HBO.
Fee: $8.00 monthly (Disney), $11.00 monthly (HBO).
Miles of plant: 8.5 (coaxial). Homes passed: 289.
Manager: Mike Danielson. Chief technician: Pat McCabe.
Ownership: Savage Communications Inc. (MSO).

ST. LAWRENCE—Midcontinent Cable Systems, Box 910, Aberdeen, SD 57402-0910. Phones: 605-229-1775; 800-456-0564. Fax: 605-229-0478. County: Hand. ICA: SD0137.
TV Market Ranking: Below 100. Franchise award date: January 3, 1984. Franchise expiration date: April 28, 2011. Began: June 12, 1984.
Channel capacity: 27 (not 2-way capable). Channels available but not in use: 2.
Basic Service
Subscribers: 82.
Programming (received off-air): KABY-TV (A) Aberdeen; KDLO-TV (C) Florence-Watertown; KTTM (F) Huron; KTSD-TV (P) Pierre.
Programming (via microwave): KDLT-TV (N) Sioux Falls.
Programming (via satellite): WGN-TV (W) Chicago; A & E; C-SPAN; CNN; Country Music TV; Discovery Channel; ESPN; ESPN 2; EWTN; Fox Family Channel; Midwest Sports Channel; Nashville Network; Nickelodeon; TBS Superstation; The Weather Channel; Turner Network TV; USA Network; VH1.
Fee: $50.00 installation; $22.68 monthly.
Pay Service 1
Pay Units: 8.
Programming (via satellite): HBO.
Fee: $20.00 installation; $12.00 monthly.
Pay Service 2
Pay Units: 10.
Programming (via satellite): Showtime.
Fee: $20.00 installation; $7.00 monthly.
Local advertising: No.
Equipment: Scientific-Atlanta headend; Magnavox amplifiers; Times Fiber cable; Eagle traps; Scientific-Atlanta satellite antenna.
Miles of plant: 3.0 (coaxial); None (fiber optic). Homes passed: 100.
Manager: Lonnie Schumacher. Marketing director: Fred Jamieson. Customer service manager: Kathy Fuhrmann.
City fee: 3% of gross.
Ownership: Midcontinent Communications (MSO).

STURGIS—TCI Cablevision, Box 309, 842 Short Track Rd., Sturgis, SD 57785. Phone: 605-347-3090. Fax: 605-347-3499. County: Meade. Also serves Meade County (portions). ICA: SD0013.
TV Market Ranking: Below 100 (portions of Meade County, Sturgis); Outside TV Markets (portions of Meade County). Franchise award date: N.A. Franchise expiration date: N.A. Began: August 1, 1969.
Channel capacity: 35. Channels available but not in use: N.A.
Basic Service
Subscribers: 2,487.
Programming (received off-air): KPSD-TV (P) Eagle Butte; KCLO-TV (C), KEVN-TV (F), KNBN-LP (N), KOTA-TV (A) Rapid City; allband FM.
Programming (via satellite): KWGN-TV (W) Denver; A & E; C-SPAN; C-SPAN 2; CNBC; CNN; Cartoon Network; Comedy Central; Country Music TV; Discovery Channel; ESPN; ESPN 2; ESPNews; EWTN; Fox Family Channel; Fox Sports Net; Headline News; History Channel; Home & Garden Television; Learning Channel; Lifetime; MTV; Nashville Network; Nickelodeon; Outdoor Channel; QVC; Sci-Fi Channel; TBS Superstation; TV Guide Channel; The Weather Channel; Trinity Bcstg. Network; Turner Classic Movies; Turner Network TV; USA Network; VH1.
Current originations: Automated time-weather; public access.
Fee: $40.00 installation; $25.95 monthly; $10.00 additional installation.
Pay Service 1
Pay Units: N.A.
Programming (via satellite): Cinemax; Disney Channel; HBO; Showtime; The Movie Channel.
Fee: N.A.
Local advertising: No.
Equipment: Scientific-Atlanta headend; Scientific-Atlanta amplifiers; Times Fiber cable; Video Data Systems character generator; Arcom traps; Scientific-Atlanta satellite antenna; Scientific-Atlanta satellite receivers.
Miles of plant and homes passed included with Custer, SD.
Manager: Dale Hodgkins. Chief technician: Gary Reimer.
City fee: 3% of gross.
Ownership: AT&T Broadband & Internet Services (MSO). Purchased from South Dakota Cable Inc., April 1, 1999.

SUMMIT—Satellite Cable Services Inc., Box 106, Brookings, SD 57006-0106. Phone: 605-692-5508. Fax: 605-692-6496. County: Roberts. ICA: SD0207.
TV Market Ranking: Below 100. Franchise award date: N.A. Franchise expiration date: N.A. Began: N.A.
Channel capacity: 40 (2-way capable; not operating 2-way). Channels available but not in use: N.A.
Basic Service
Subscribers: 60.
Programming (via satellite): KCNC-TV (C), KWGN-TV (W) Denver; CNN; ESPN; Nashville Network; TBS Superstation.
Fee: $25.79 monthly.
Pay Service 1
Pay Units: N.A.
Programming (via satellite): HBO.
Fee: $11.95 monthly.
Manager: Doug Bierschbach. Chief technician: Paul Schmidt.
Ownership: Satellite Cable Services Inc. (MSO).

TABOR—Telecom Inc., Box 127, Irene, SD 57037-0127. Phone: 800-239-7501. Fax: 605-766-7695. E-mail: jeanniejohnson@dtg.com. County: Bon Homme. ICA: SD0208.
TV Market Ranking: Outside TV Markets. Franchise award date: May 21, 1987. Franchise expiration date: January 1, 2011. Began: November 1, 1987.
Channel capacity: 36 (not 2-way capable). Channels available but not in use: 11.
Basic Service
Subscribers: 115.
Programming (received off-air): KDLV-TV (N), KELO-TV (C), KSFY-TV (A), KTTW (F) Sioux Falls-Mitchell; KUSD-TV (P) Vermillion.
Programming (via satellite): WGN-TV (W) Chicago; A & E; American Movie Classics; CNN; Country Music TV; Discovery Channel; Disney Channel; ESPN; ESPN 2; Fox Family Channel; Headline News; Lifetime; Nashville Network; Nickelodeon; Sci-Fi Channel; TBS Superstation; Turner Network TV; USA Network; VH1.
Fee: $35.00 installation; $18.31 monthly.
Pay Service 1
Pay Units: 20.
Programming (via satellite): HBO.
Fee: $7.95 monthly.
Miles of plant: 2.9 (coaxial). Homes passed: 193. Total homes in franchised area: 248.
Manager: Thomas W. Hertz. Chief technician: Jerry Andersen. Program director: Jeannie Johnson. Marketing director: Marshall Damgaard.
City fee: None.
Ownership: Dakota Telecom Inc. (MSO).

TAKINI—Cheyenne River Sioux Tribe Telephone Authority, Box 810, Eagle Butte, SD 57625. Phone: 605-964-2600. Fax: 605-964-1003. County: Ziebach. ICA: SD0209.
TV Market Ranking: Below 100. Franchise award date: N.A. Franchise expiration date: N.A. Began: March 1, 1993.
Channel capacity: 14. Channels available but not in use: 5.
Basic Service
Subscribers: 16.
Programming (via satellite): WGN-TV (W) Chicago; CNN; Country Music TV; Discovery Channel; ESPN; Nashville Network; TBS Superstation; USA Network.
Fee: $25.00 installation; $16.00 monthly.
Pay Service 1
Pay Units: 16.
Programming (via satellite): HBO.
Fee: $10.00 monthly.
Miles of plant: 0.1 (coaxial).
Manager: J. D. Williams. Chief technician: Ellen B. Brown.
Ownership: Cheyenne River Sioux Tribe Telephone Authority (MSO).

TIMBER LAKE—Midcontinent Cable Systems of South Dakota, Box 910, Aberdeen, SD 57402-0910. Phones: 605-229-1775; 800-456-0564. Fax: 605-229-0478. County: Dewey. ICA: SD0085.

TV Market Ranking: Outside TV Markets. Franchise award date: January 16, 1986. Franchise expiration date: January 16, 2011. Began: November 1, 1982.

Channel capacity: 38 (not 2-way capable). Channels available but not in use: 3.

Basic Service

Subscribers: 151.

Programming (received off-air): KXMB-TV (C) Bismarck; KPSD-TV (P) Eagle Butte; KARE (N) Minneapolis-St. Paul; KPRY-TV (A) Pierre; KPLO-TV (C) Reliance; allband FM.

Programming (via satellite): WGN-TV (W) Chicago; A & E; American Movie Classics; C-SPAN; CNBC; CNN; Cartoon Network; Country Music TV; Discovery Channel; Disney Channel; ESPN; FX; Fox Family Channel; FoxNet; Headline News; Learning Channel; Lifetime; Midwest Sports Channel; Nashville Network; Nick at Nite's TV Land; Nickelodeon; QVC; TBS Superstation; TV Guide Channel; The Inspirational Network; The Weather Channel; Turner Network TV; USA Network; VH1.

Current originations: Automated time-weather.

Fee: $50.00 installation; $26.50 monthly.

Pay Service 1

Pay Units: 41.

Programming (via satellite): HBO.

Fee: $20.00 installation; $12.00 monthly.

Pay Service 2

Pay Units: 13.

Programming (via satellite): Showtime.

Fee: $20.00 installation; $11.00 monthly.

Pay Service 3

Pay Units: 12.

Programming (via satellite): The Movie Channel.

Fee: $20.00 installation; $11.00 monthly.

Local advertising: No.

Equipment: Scientific-Atlanta headend; Scientific-Atlanta amplifiers; Times Fiber cable; Eagle traps; M/A-Com satellite antenna; M/A-Com satellite receivers.

Miles of plant: 3.9 (coaxial); None (fiber optic). Homes passed: 258. Total homes in franchised area: 278.

Manager: Lonnie Schumacher. Marketing director: Fred Jamieson. Customer service manager: Kathy Fuhrmann.

City fee: 3% of gross.

Ownership: Midcontinent Communications (MSO).

TOLSTOY—Sully Buttes Telephone Cooperative Inc., Box 157, Highmore, SD 57345. Phone: 605-852-2224. Fax: 605-852-2404. County: Potter. ICA: SD0147.

TV Market Ranking: Outside TV Markets. Franchise award date: N.A. Franchise expiration date: N.A. Began: November 13, 1989.

Channel capacity: 13 (not 2-way capable). Channels available but not in use: None.

Basic Service

Subscribers: 30.

Programming (received off-air): KABY-TV (A), KDSD-TV (P) Aberdeen; KDLO-TV (C) Florence-Watertown.

Programming (via satellite): WDIV (N) Detroit; CNN; ESPN; Nashville Network; TBS Superstation.

Fee: $20.00 installation; $17.00 monthly.

Pay Service 1

Pay Units: 10.

Programming (via satellite): Showtime.

Fee: $9.50 monthly.

Equipment: Jerrold amplifiers; Comm/Scope cable; Pico traps; Winegard satellite antenna; Drake satellite receivers.

Miles of plant: 1.1 (coaxial). Homes passed: 35.

Manager: Randy Hoydek. Chief technician: Randy Olson.

Ownership: Sully Buttes Telephone Cooperative Inc. (MSO).

TORONTO—Satellite Cable Services Inc., Box 106, Brookings, SD 57006-0106. Phone: 605-692-5508. Fax: 605-692-6496. County: Deuel. ICA: SD0210.

TV Market Ranking: Below 100. Franchise award date: N.A. Franchise expiration date: N.A. Began: May 1, 1988.

Channel capacity: 40 (2-way capable; not operating 2-way). Channels available but not in use: N.A.

Basic Service

Subscribers: 65.

Programming (received off-air): KESD-TV (P) Brookings; KDLV-TV (N), KELO-TV (C), KSFY-TV (A) Sioux Falls-Mitchell.

Programming (via satellite): WGN-TV (W) Chicago; CNN; Discovery Channel; ESPN; Midwest Sports Channel; Nashville Network; TBS Superstation.

Fee: $24.95 installation; $27.38 monthly.

Pay Service 1

Pay Units: N.A.

Programming (via satellite): HBO.

Fee: $11.95 monthly.

Manager: Doug Bierschbach. Chief technician: Paul Schmidt.

Ownership: Satellite Cable Services Inc. (MSO).

TRENT—Satellite Cable Services Inc., Box 106, Brookings, SD 57006-0106. Phone: 605-692-5508. Fax: 605-692-6496. County: Moody. ICA: SD0211.

TV Market Ranking: 85. Franchise award date: N.A. Franchise expiration date: N.A. Began: N.A.

Channel capacity: 36 (2-way capable; not operating 2-way). Channels available but not in use: N.A.

Basic Service

Subscribers: 25.

Programming (received off-air): KDLV-TV (N), KELO-TV (C), KSFY-TV (A) Sioux Falls-Mitchell; KUSD-TV (P) Vermillion.

Programming (via satellite): WGN-TV (W) Chicago; TBS Superstation.

Fee: $25.27 monthly.

Miles of plant: 2.0 (coaxial).

Manager: Doug Bierschbach. Chief technician: Paul Schmidt.

Ownership: Satellite Cable Services Inc. (MSO).

TRIPP—Village Cable Inc., Box 270, 124 E. 7th Ave., Redfield, SD 57469. Phone: 605-472-3415. County: Hutchinson. ICA: SD0087.

TV Market Ranking: 85. Franchise award date: N.A. Franchise expiration date: N.A. Began: September 1, 1983.

Channel capacity: 36. Channels available but not in use: 25.

Basic Service

Subscribers: N.A.

Programming (received off-air): KDLV-TV (N), KELO-TV (C), KSFY-TV (A) Sioux Falls-Mitchell; KUSD-TV (P) Vermillion.

Programming (via satellite): WGN-TV (W) Chicago; CNN; ESPN; Fox Family Channel; TBS Superstation; USA Network.

Fee: N.A.

Pay Service 1

Pay Units: N.A.

Programming (via satellite): HBO.

Fee: N.A.

Miles of plant: 6.8 (coaxial). Homes passed: 265.

Ownership: Cable TV Assoc. Inc. (MSO).

TULARE—Sully Buttes Telephone Cooperative Inc., Box 157, Highmore, SD 57345. Phone: 605-852-2224. Fax: 605-852-2404. County: Spink. ICA: SD0124.

TV Market Ranking: Below 100. Franchise award date: N.A. Franchise expiration date: N.A. Began: October 1, 1985.

Channel capacity: 14 (not 2-way capable). Channels available but not in use: None.

Basic Service

Subscribers: 94.

Programming (received off-air): KTTM (F) Huron; KPRY-TV (A), KTSD-TV (P) Pierre; KPLO-TV (C) Reliance.

Programming (via satellite): WGN-TV (W) Chicago; WDIV (N) Detroit; CNN; Disney Channel; ESPN; ESPN 2; Fox Family Channel; Nashville Network; TBS Superstation; Turner Network TV; USA Network.

Current originations: Automated time-weather.

Fee: $20.00 installation; $19.50 monthly.

Pay Service 1

Pay Units: 23.

Programming (via satellite): Showtime.

Fee: $15.00 installation; $9.50 monthly.

Local advertising: No.

Equipment: Scientific-Atlanta headend; Jerrold amplifiers; Times Fiber cable; BEI character generator; Pico traps; Scientific-Atlanta satellite antenna; Scientific-Atlanta satellite receivers.

Miles of plant: 1.9 (coaxial). Homes passed: 160.

Manager: Randy Hoydek. Chief technician: Randy Olson.

Ownership: Sully Buttes Telephone Cooperative Inc. (MSO).

TYNDALL—Village Cable Inc., Box 270, 124 E. 7th Ave., Redfield, SD 57469. Phone: 605-472-3415. County: Bon Homme. ICA: SD0045.

TV Market Ranking: Outside TV Markets. Franchise award date: N.A. Franchise expiration date: N.A. Began: August 1, 1983.

Channel capacity: 36. Channels available but not in use: N.A.

Basic Service

Subscribers: N.A.

Programming (received off-air): KPRY-TV (A), KTSD-TV (P) Pierre; KPLO-TV (C) Reliance; KDLV-TV (N), KELO-TV (C), KSFY-TV (A) Sioux Falls-Mitchell; KUSD-TV (P) Vermillion.

Programming (via satellite): WGN-TV (W) Chicago; CNN; ESPN; Fox Family Channel; Nashville Network; TBS Superstation; USA Network.

Fee: N.A.

Pay Service 1

Pay Units: N.A.

Programming (via satellite): HBO.

Fee: N.A.

Miles of plant: 8.7 (coaxial). Homes passed: 580.

City fee: 1% of gross.

Ownership: Cable TV Assoc. Inc. (MSO).

VALLEY SPRINGS—Telecom Inc., Box 127, Irene, SD 57037-0127. Phone: 800-239-7501. Fax: 605-766-7695.

E-mail: jeanniejohnson@dtg.com.

County: Minnehaha. ICA: SD0084.

TV Market Ranking: 85. Franchise award date: December 27, 1982. Franchise expiration date: February 1, 2011. Began: October 20, 1983.

Channel capacity: 36 (not 2-way capable). Channels available but not in use: 13.

Basic Service

Subscribers: 172.

Programming (received off-air): KDLV-TV (N), KELO-TV (C), KSFY-TV (A), KTTW (F) Sioux Falls-Mitchell; KUSD-TV (P) Vermillion.

Programming (via satellite): WGN-TV (W) Chicago; A & E; American Movie Classics; CNN; Country Music TV; Discovery Channel; Disney Channel; ESPN; Fox Family Channel; Lifetime; Midwest Sports Channel; Nashville Network; Nickelodeon; Sci-Fi Channel; TBS Superstation; The Weather Channel; Turner Network TV; USA Network; VH1.

Fee: $35.00 installation; $21.27 monthly.

Pay Service 1

Pay Units: 54.

Programming (via satellite): HBO.

Fee: $13.00 installation; $7.95 monthly.

Pay Service 2

Pay Units: 9.

Programming (via satellite): Showtime.

Fee: $13.00 installation; $7.95 monthly.

Miles of plant: 4.5 (coaxial). Homes passed: 275. Total homes in franchised area: 310.

Manager: Thomas W. Hertz. Chief technician: Jerry Andersen. Program director: Jeannie Johnson. Marketing director: Marshall Damgaard.

Ownership: Dakota Telecom Inc. (MSO).

VERMILLION—Vermillion Cable TV Ltd., Box 178, Yankton, SD 57078. Phone: 605-624-5553. Fax: 605-624-6712. County: Clay. ICA: SD0012.

TV Market Ranking: Below 100. Franchise award date: N.A. Franchise expiration date: N.A. Began: December 18, 1980.

Channel capacity: 36 (2-way capable; operating 2-way). Channels available but not in use: 5.

Basic Service

Subscribers: 2,746.

Programming (received off-air): KXNE-TV (P) Norfolk; KCAU-TV (A), KMEG (C), KSIN (P), KTIV (N) Sioux City; KDLV-TV (N), KELO-TV (C), KSFY-TV (A) Sioux Falls-Mitchell; KUSD-TV (P) Vermillion.

Programming (via satellite): WGN-TV (W) Chicago; A & E; Fox Family Channel; Nickelodeon; TBS Superstation; USA Network.

Current originations: Automated time-weather.

Fee: $25.00 installation; $11.95 monthly.

Expanded Basic Service

Subscribers: 1,709.

Programming (via satellite): C-SPAN; CNN; ESPN; Learning Channel; Lifetime; MTV; Nashville Network; The Weather Channel; Turner Classic Movies.

Fee: $25.00 installation; $5.80 monthly.

Pay Service 1

Pay Units: 242.

Programming (via satellite): Cinemax.

Fee: $8.95 monthly.

Pay Service 2

Pay Units: 71.

Programming (via satellite): Disney Channel.

Fee: $8.95 monthly.

Pay Service 3

Pay Units: 464.

Programming (via satellite): HBO.

Fee: $8.95 monthly.

Pay Service 4

Pay Units: 176.

Programming (via satellite): The Movie Channel.

Fee: $8.95 monthly.

Equipment: Scientific-Atlanta headend; Scientific-Atlanta amplifiers; Times Fiber cable; Compuvid character generator; Jerrold set top converters; Microdyne & Scientific-At-

lanta satellite antenna; Scientific-Atlanta satellite receivers.
Miles of plant: 33.0 (coaxial). Homes passed: 3,043. Total homes in franchised area: 3,043.
Manager: Jim Abbott. Chief technician: Bill Lokken.
City fee: 3% of gross.
Ownership: Zylstra Communications Corp. (MSO). Sale pends to Mediacom LLC.

VIBORG—Dakota Telecom Inc., Box 127, Irene, SD 57037-0127. Phone: 800-239-7501. Fax: 605-766-7695.
E-mail: jeanniejohnson@dtg.com.
Counties: Clay, Lincoln, Turner & Yankton. Also serves Canton (portions), Centerville, Chancellor, Gayville, Harrisburg, Hurley, Irene, Lennox, Parker, Tea, Wakonda, Worthing. ICA: SD0071.
TV Market Ranking: 85 (Canton, Centerville, Chancellor, Harrisburg, Hurley, Lennox, Parker, Tea, Viborg, Worthing); Below 100 (Gayville); Outside TV Markets (Irene, Wakonda). Franchise award date: February 7, 1983. Franchise expiration date: February 4, 2013. Began: July 1, 1983.
Channel capacity: 77 (not 2-way capable). Channels available but not in use: 13.
Basic Service
Subscribers: 4,176.
Programming (received off-air): KDLV-TV (N), KELO-TV (C), KSFY-TV (A), KTTW (F) Sioux Falls-Mitchell; KUSD-TV (P) Vermillion.
Programming (via satellite): WGN-TV (W) Chicago; A & E; American Movie Classics; C-SPAN; CNBC; CNN; Cartoon Network; Country Music TV; Discovery Channel; Disney Channel; ESPN; ESPN 2; EWTN; FX; fXM: Movies from Fox; Fox Family Channel; Golf Channel; Headline News; History Channel; Home & Garden Television; Learning Channel; Lifetime; MTV; Midwest Sports Channel; Nashville Network; Nick at Nite's TV Land; Nickelodeon; Sci-Fi Channel; TBS Superstation; TV Guide Channel; The Inspirational Network; The Weather Channel; Turner Network TV; USA Network; VH1.
Fee: $35.00 installation; $24.95 monthly.
Pay Service 1
Pay Units: 882.
Programming (via satellite): HBO (multiplexed).
Fee: $7.95 monthly.
Pay Service 2
Pay Units: 372.
Programming (via satellite): Cinemax (multiplexed).
Fee: $7.95 monthly.
Pay Service 3
Pay Units: 882.
Programming (via satellite): Showtime (multiplexed).
Fee: $7.95 monthly.
Pay Service 4
Pay Units: 239.
Programming (via satellite): Starz!; The New Encore (multiplexed).
Fee: $7.95 monthly (package).
Pay-Per-View
Addressable homes: 865.
Viewer's Choice 1-4.
Local advertising: Yes.
Equipment: Blonder-Tongue headend; Scientific-Atlanta amplifiers; Pioneer set top converters; Eagle traps; Sceptor satellite antenna; Automation Techniques satellite receivers.
Miles of plant: 53.8 (coaxial). Homes passed: 5,001. Total homes in franchised area: 5,446.
Manager: Thomas W. Hertz. Chief technician: Jerry Andersen. Program director: Jeannie Johnson. Marketing director: Marshall Damgaard.
City fee: 3% of gross.
Ownership: Dakota Telecom Inc. (MSO).

VOLIN—Dakota Telecommunications Inc., Box 66, 29705 453rd Ave., Irene, SD 57037-0066. Phone: 605-263-3301. County: Yankton. ICA: SD0213.
TV Market Ranking: Outside TV Markets. Franchise award date: N.A. Franchise expiration date: N.A. Began: N.A.
Channel capacity: N.A. Channels available but not in use: N.A.
Basic Service
Subscribers: N.A.
Programming (received off-air): KESD-TV (P) Brookings; KCAU-TV (A), KTIV (N) Sioux City; KELO-TV (C), KSFY-TV (A) Sioux Falls-Mitchell.
Programming (via satellite): WGN-TV (W) Chicago; CNN; ESPN; Fox Family Channel; Nashville Network; TBS Superstation; USA Network.
Fee: $24.50 installation; $17.95 monthly; $15.00 additional installation.
Pay Service 1
Pay Units: N.A.
Programming (via satellite): Showtime.
Fee: $9.95 monthly.
Manager: Bill Mauszycki. Chief technician: Kevin Johnson.
Ownership: American Telecasting Inc. (MSO). Sale pends to Sprint Corp.

WALL—Golden West Cablevision, Box 9159, 2727 N. Plaza Dr., Rapid City, SD 57709. Phone: 605-348-6529. Fax: 605-342-1160. County: Pennington. ICA: SD0068.
TV Market Ranking: Outside TV Markets. Franchise award date: October 15, 1982. Franchise expiration date: October 15, 2002. Began: October 15, 1982.
Channel capacity: 36 (not 2-way capable). Channels available but not in use: 18.
Basic Service
Subscribers: 334.
Programming (received off-air): KIVV-TV (F) Lead; KZSD-TV (P) Martin; KCLO-TV (C), KOTA-TV (A) Rapid City.
Programming (via satellite): WGN-TV (W) Chicago; CNN; Discovery Channel; ESPN; Fox Family Channel; Nashville Network; TBS Superstation; The Weather Channel; Turner Network TV; USA Network.
Fee: $25.00 installation; $14.00 monthly.
Pay Service 1
Pay Units: 81.
Programming (via satellite): Disney Channel.
Fee: $7.95 monthly.
Pay Service 2
Pay Units: 116.
Programming (via satellite): Showtime.
Fee: $7.95 monthly.
Equipment: Scientific-Atlanta headend; Scientific-Atlanta amplifiers; Scientific-Atlanta cable; Arcom traps; Scientific-Atlanta satellite antenna.
Miles of plant: 16.0 (coaxial). Homes passed: 365.
Manager: Dwight Flatt. Chief technician: Ross Whitley. Marketing director: Greg Oleson.
City fee: None.
Ownership: Golden West Cablevision (MSO).

WANBLEE—Golden West Cablevision, Box 9159, 2727 N. Plaza Dr., Rapid City, SD 57709. Phone: 605-348-6529. Fax: 605-342-1160. County: Jackson. ICA: SD0133.
TV Market Ranking: Outside TV Markets. Franchise award date: N.A. Franchise expiration date: N.A. Began: December 1, 1984.
Channel capacity: 36 (not 2-way capable). Channels available but not in use: 19.
Basic Service
Subscribers: 105.
Programming (received off-air): KIVV-TV (F) Lead; KZSD-TV (P) Martin; KCLO-TV (C), KOTA-TV (A) Rapid City.
Programming (via satellite): WGN-TV (W) Chicago; CNN; Discovery Channel; ESPN; Fox Family Channel; MTV; Nashville Network; TBS Superstation; The Weather Channel; Turner Network TV; USA Network.
Fee: $25.00 installation; $14.00 monthly.
Pay Service 1
Pay Units: 60.
Programming (via satellite): Disney Channel.
Fee: $7.95 monthly.
Pay Service 2
Pay Units: 102.
Programming (via satellite): Showtime.
Fee: $7.95 monthly.
Miles of plant: 8.1 (coaxial). Homes passed: 129.
Manager: Dwight Flatt. Chief technician: Ross Whitley. Marketing director: Greg Oleson.
Ownership: Golden West Cablevision (MSO).

WARNER—Midcontinent Cable Systems of South Dakota, Box 910, Aberdeen, SD 57402-0910. Phones: 605-229-1775; 800-456-0564. Fax: 605-229-0478. County: Brown. ICA: SD0214.
TV Market Ranking: Below 100. Franchise award date: October 12, 1983. Franchise expiration date: March 6, 2011. Began: December 2, 1983.
Channel capacity: 75 (not 2-way capable). Channels available but not in use: 2.
Basic Service
Subscribers: 138.
Programming (received off-air): KABY-TV (A), KDSD-TV (P) Aberdeen; KDLO-TV (C) Florence-Watertown; KTTM (F) Huron; KDLV-TV (N) Sioux Falls-Mitchell; 4 FMs.
Programming (via microwave): KDLT-TV (N) Sioux Falls.
Programming (via satellite): WGN-TV (W) Chicago; A & E; American Movie Classics; C-SPAN; C-SPAN 2; CNBC; CNN; Cartoon Network; Country Music TV; DMX; Discovery Channel; Disney Channel; ESPN; ESPN 2; ESPNews; EWTN; FX; Flix; Fox Family Channel; Golf Channel; Headline News; Learning Channel; Lifetime; MTV; Midwest Sports Channel; Nashville Network; Nick at Nite's TV Land; Nickelodeon; QVC; TBS Superstation; TV Guide Channel; The Health Network; The Inspirational Network; The Weather Channel; Turner Network TV; USA Network; VH1.
Current originations: Public access; educational access; local acccess.
Fee: $50.00 installation; $25.00 monthly.
Expanded Basic Service
Subscribers: N.A.
Programming (via satellite): Animal Planet; Bravo; Comedy Central; E! Entertainment TV; fXM: Movies from Fox; History Channel; Outdoor Channel; Sci-Fi Channel; Travel Channel; Turner Classic Movies.
Fee: N.A.
Pay Service 1
Pay Units: 13.
Programming (via satellite): HBO (multiplexed).
Fee: $20.00 installation; $12.00 monthly.
Pay Service 2
Pay Units: 1.
Programming (via satellite): Cinemax (multiplexed).
Fee: $20.00 installation; $11.00 monthly.
Pay Service 3
Pay Units: 8.
Programming (via satellite): The Movie Channel.
Fee: $20.00 installation; $11.00 monthly.
Pay Service 4
Pay Units: 8.
Programming (via satellite): Showtime (multiplexed).
Fee: $20.00 installation; $11.00 monthly.
Pay Service 5
Pay Units: N.A.
Programming (via satellite): Starz!; The New Encore (multiplexed).
Fee: $20.00 installation; $7.95 monthly (package).
Local advertising: No.
Equipment: Magnavox amplifiers; Times Fiber cable.
Miles of plant: 3.8 (coaxial); None (fiber optic). Homes passed: 148.
Manager: Lonnie Schumacher. Marketing director: Fred Jamieson. Customer service manager: Kathy Fuhrmann.
City fee: 3% of gross.
Ownership: Midcontinent Communications (MSO).

WATERTOWN—TCI of Watertown Inc., Box 1234, 15 S. Broadway St., Watertown, SD 57201. Phone: 605-886-7990. Fax: 605-886-9327. County: Codington. Also serves Codington County (portions). ICA: SD0004.
TV Market Ranking: Below 100. Franchise award date: N.A. Franchise expiration date: N.A. Began: June 29, 1973.
Channel capacity: 42 (2-way capable; operating 2-way). Channels available but not in use: 7.
Basic Service
Subscribers: 7,252.
Programming (received off-air): KABY-TV (A) Aberdeen; KESD-TV (P) Brookings; KDLO-TV (C) Florence-Watertown; KDLV-TV (N) Sioux Falls-Mitchell; allband FM.
Programming (via microwave): KMSP-TV (U) Minneapolis-St. Paul.
Programming (via satellite): A & E; American Movie Classics; Bravo; C-SPAN; CNBC; CNN; Country Music TV; Discovery Channel; E! Entertainment TV; ESPN; EWTN; Fox Family Channel; FoxNet; Headline News; Home Shopping Network; Lifetime; MTV; Midwest Sports Channel; Nashville Network; Nickelodeon; QVC; TBS Superstation; The Weather Channel; Travel Channel; Turner Network TV; USA Network; VH1.
Current originations: Government access.
Fee: $29.95 installation; $9.82 monthly; $0.43 converter; $15.00 additional installation.
Pay Service 1
Pay Units: 398.
Programming (via satellite): Cinemax.
Fee: $15.00 installation; $9.95 monthly.
Pay Service 2
Pay Units: 190.
Programming (via satellite): Disney Channel.
Fee: $15.00 installation; $8.69 monthly.
Pay Service 3
Pay Units: 837.
Programming (via satellite): HBO.
Fee: $15.00 installation; $9.95 monthly.
Pay Service 4
Pay Units: 261.
Programming (via satellite): Showtime.
Fee: $15.00 installation; $9.95 monthly.

Pay-Per-View
Addressable homes: 1,200.
Local advertising: Yes.
Equipment: Scientific-Atlanta headend; Magnavox amplifiers; Capscan & Comm/Scope cable; MSI character generator; Pioneer set top converters; Pioneer addressable set top converters; Scientific-Atlanta satellite antenna; Scientific-Atlanta satellite receivers.
Miles of plant: 107.0 (coaxial). Homes passed: 8,456. Total homes in franchised area: 9,302.
Manager: Steve Schirber. Chief technician: Bob Spilde.
City fee: 3% of gross.
Ownership: AT&T Broadband & Internet Services (MSO). Purchased from Tele-Communications Inc., March 9, 1999.

WAUBAY—Midcontinent Cable Systems of South Dakota, Box 910, Aberdeen, SD 57402-0910. Phones: 605-229-1775; 800-456-0564. Fax: 605-229-0478. County: Day. ICA: SD0080.
TV Market Ranking: Below 100. Franchise award date: May 22, 1994. Franchise expiration date: May 22, 2009. Began: December 28, 1983.
Channel capacity: 75 (not 2-way capable). Channels available but not in use: 2.
Basic Service
Subscribers: 203.
Programming (received off-air): KABY-TV (A), KDSD-TV (P) Aberdeen; KDLO-TV (C) Florence-Watertown; KTTM (F) Huron.
Programming (via microwave): KDLT-TV (N) Sioux Falls.
Programming (via satellite): WGN-TV (W) Chicago; A & E; American Movie Classics; C-SPAN; C-SPAN 2; CNBC; CNN; Cartoon Network; Country Music TV; DMX; Discovery Channel; Disney Channel; ESPN; ESPN 2; ESPNews; EWTN; FX; Fox Family Channel; Golf Channel; Headline News; Learning Channel; Lifetime; MTV; Midwest Sports Channel; Nashville Network; Nick at Nite's TV Land; Nickelodeon; QVC; TBS Superstation; TV Guide Channel; The Health Network; The Inspirational Network; The Weather Channel; Turner Network TV; USA Network; VH1.
Current originations: Public access; educational access; local access.
Fee: $50.00 installation; $25.00 monthly.
Expanded Basic Service
Subscribers: N.A.
Programming (via satellite): Animal Planet; Bravo; Comedy Central; E! Entertainment TV; fXM: Movies from Fox; History Channel; Outdoor Channel; Sci-Fi Channel; Travel Channel; Turner Classic Movies.
Fee: N.A.
Pay Service 1
Pay Units: 46.
Programming (via satellite): HBO (multiplexed).
Fee: $20.00 installation; $12.00 monthly.
Pay Service 2
Pay Units: 14.
Programming (via satellite): Cinemax (multiplexed).
Fee: $20.00 installation; $11.00 monthly.
Pay Service 3
Pay Units: 7.
Programming (via satellite): Showtime (multiplexed).
Fee: $20.00 installation; $11.00 monthly.
Pay Service 4
Pay Units: 5.
Programming (via satellite): Starz!; The New Encore (multiplexed).
Fee: $20.00 installation; $7.95 monthly (package).
Pay Service 5
Pay Units: N.A.
Programming (via satellite): The Movie Channel.
Fee: $20.00 installation.
Pay-Per-View
Addressable homes: 70.
Hot Choice; Viewer's Choice 1, 3, 4.
Local advertising: No.
Equipment: Magnavox amplifiers; Times Fiber cable.
Miles of plant: 7.2 (coaxial); None (fiber optic). Homes passed: 289. Total homes in franchised area: 289.
Manager: Lonnie Schumacher. Marketing director: Fred Jamieson. Customer service manager: Kathy Fuhrmann.
City fee: 3% of gross.
Ownership: Midcontinent Communications (MSO).

WEBSTER—Midcontinent Cable Systems of South Dakota, Box 910, Aberdeen, SD 57402-0910. Phones: 605-229-1775; 800-456-0564. Fax: 605-229-0478. County: Day. ICA: SD0027.
TV Market Ranking: Outside TV Markets. Franchise award date: August 1, 1988. Franchise expiration date: August 1, 2003. Began: December 30, 1977.
Channel capacity: 76 (not 2-way capable). Channels available but not in use: 26.
Basic Service
Subscribers: 762.
Programming (received off-air): KABY-TV (A), KDSD-TV (P) Aberdeen; KDLO-TV (C) Florence-Watertown; KTTM (F) Huron; all-band FM.
Programming (via microwave): KDLT-TV (N) Sioux Falls.
Programming (via satellite): WGN-TV (W) Chicago; A & E; American Movie Classics; C-SPAN; C-SPAN 2; CNBC; CNN; Cartoon Network; Country Music TV; Discovery Channel; Disney Channel; ESPN; ESPN 2; ESPNews; EWTN; FX; Flix; Fox Family Channel; Golf Channel; Headline News; Learning Channel; Lifetime; MTV; Midwest Sports Channel; Nashville Network; Nick at Nite's TV Land; Nickelodeon; QVC; TBS Superstation; TV Guide Channel; The Health Network; The Inspirational Network; The Weather Channel; Turner Network TV; USA Network; VH1.
Current originations: Automated time-weather; public access; educational access; local access.
Fee: $50.00 installation; $25.00 monthly.
Expanded Basic Service
Subscribers: N.A.
Programming (via satellite): Animal Planet; Bravo; Comedy Central; E! Entertainment TV; fXM: Movies from Fox; History Channel; Outdoor Channel; Sci-Fi Channel; Travel Channel; Turner Classic Movies.
Fee: N.A.
Pay Service 1
Pay Units: 70.
Programming (via satellite): HBO (multiplexed).
Fee: $20.00 installation; $11.00 monthly.
Pay Service 2
Pay Units: 10.
Programming (via satellite): Cinemax (multiplexed).
Fee: $20.00 installation; $11.00 monthly.
Pay Service 3
Pay Units: 35.
Programming (via satellite): Showtime (multiplexed).
Fee: $20.00 installation; $11.00 monthly.
Pay Service 4
Pay Units: 7.
Programming (via satellite): The Movie Channel.
Fee: $20.00 installation; $11.00 monthly.
Pay Service 5
Pay Units: 4.
Programming (via satellite): Starz!; The New Encore (multiplexed).
Fee: $7.95 monthly (package).
Pay-Per-View
Addressable homes: 135.
Hot Choice; Viewer's Choice 1, 3, 4.
Local advertising: No.
Equipment: Magnavox headend; Magnavox amplifiers; Times Fiber cable; Eagle traps.
Miles of plant: 15.2 (coaxial); None (fiber optic). Homes passed: 966. Total homes in franchised area: 966.
Manager: Lonnie Schumacher. Marketing director: Fred Jamieson. Customer service manager: Kathy Fuhrmann.
City fee: 3% of gross.
Ownership: Midcontinent Communications (MSO).

WENTWORTH—Satellite Cable Services Inc., Box 106, Brookings, SD 57006-0106. Phone: 605-692-5508. Fax: 605-692-6496. County: Lake. ICA: SD0215.
TV Market Ranking: Outside TV Markets. Franchise award date: N.A. Franchise expiration date: N.A. Began: N.A.
Channel capacity: 36. Channels available but not in use: N.A.
Basic Service
Subscribers: 40.
Programming (received off-air): KESD-TV (P) Brookings; KDLV-TV (N), KELO-TV (C), KSFY-TV (A) Sioux Falls-Mitchell.
Programming (via satellite): WGN-TV (W) Chicago; CNN; ESPN; Midwest Sports Channel; Nashville Network; TBS Superstation; Turner Network TV.
Fee: $27.38 monthly.
Pay Service 1
Pay Units: N.A.
Programming (via satellite): HBO.
Fee: $10.95 monthly.
Manager: Doug Bierschbach. Chief technician: Paul Schmidt.
Ownership: Satellite Cable Services Inc. (MSO).

WESSINGTON—Sully Buttes Telephone Cooperative Inc., Box 157, Highmore, SD 57345. Phone: 605-852-2224. Fax: 605-852-2404. Counties: Beadle & Hand. ICA: SD0109.
TV Market Ranking: Below 100. Franchise award date: N.A. Franchise expiration date: N.A. Began: September 1, 1985.
Channel capacity: 15 (not 2-way capable). Channels available but not in use: None.
Basic Service
Subscribers: 108.
Programming (received off-air): KABY-TV (A) Aberdeen; KTSD-TV (P) Pierre; KPLO-TV (C) Reliance.
Programming (via satellite): WGN-TV (W) Chicago; WDIV (N) Detroit; CNN; Disney Channel; ESPN; ESPN 2; Fox Family Channel; Nashville Network; TBS Superstation; Turner Network TV; USA Network.
Current originations: Automated time-weather.
Fee: $20.00 installation; $19.50 monthly.
Pay Service 1
Pay Units: 28.
Programming (via satellite): Showtime.
Fee: $15.00 installation; $9.50 monthly.
Local advertising: No.
Equipment: Scientific-Atlanta headend; Jerrold amplifiers; Times Fiber cable; BEI character generator; Pico traps; Scientific-Atlanta satellite antenna; Scientific-Atlanta satellite receivers.
Miles of plant: 6.8 (coaxial). Homes passed: 200.
Manager: Randy Hoydek. Chief technician: Randy Olson.
Ownership: Sully Buttes Telephone Cooperative Inc. (MSO).

WESSINGTON SPRINGS—Satellite Cable Services Inc., Box 106, Brookings, SD 57006-0106. Phone: 605-692-5508. Fax: 605-692-6496. County: Jerauld. ICA: SD0051.
TV Market Ranking: Below 100. Franchise award date: N.A. Franchise expiration date: N.A. Began: December 15, 1980.
Channel capacity: 40 (2-way capable; not operating 2-way). Channels available but not in use: N.A.
Basic Service
Subscribers: 390.
Programming (received off-air): KABY-TV (A) Aberdeen; KESD-TV (P) Brookings; KDLO-TV (C) Florence-Watertown; KDLV-TV (N) Sioux Falls-Mitchell.
Programming (via satellite): WGN-TV (W) Chicago; C-SPAN; CNN; ESPN; Fox Family Channel; Lifetime; MTV; Nashville Network; Nickelodeon; TBS Superstation; USA Network.
Fee: $24.95 installation; $27.38 monthly.
Pay Service 1
Pay Units: N.A.
Programming (via satellite): Disney Channel; HBO.
Fee: $9.45 installation; $11.95 monthly (each).
Equipment: Scientific-Atlanta headend; Scientific-Atlanta amplifiers; Times Fiber cable; Scientific-Atlanta satellite antenna; Scientific-Atlanta satellite receivers.
Miles of plant: 9.0 (coaxial). Homes passed: 548. Total homes in franchised area: 548.
Manager: Doug Bierschbach. Chief technician: Paul Schmidt.
City fee: 3% of basic gross.
Ownership: Satellite Cable Services Inc. (MSO).

WEST WHITLOCK—Village Cable, Box 111, Redfield, SD 57469. Phone: 605-472-3415. County: Potter. ICA: SD0216.
TV Market Ranking: Outside TV Markets. Franchise award date: N.A. Franchise expiration date: N.A. Began: N.A.
Channel capacity: 36. Channels available but not in use: N.A.
Basic Service
Subscribers: N.A.
Programming (received off-air): KABY-TV (A) Aberdeen; KESD-TV (P) Brookings; KDLO-TV (C) Florence-Watertown; KDLV-TV (N) Sioux Falls-Mitchell.

Programming (via satellite): WGN-TV (W) Chicago; CNN; Discovery Channel; ESPN; Nashville Network; TBS Superstation.
Fee: $17.00 monthly.
Manager: Terry Thomas. Chief technician: Jerry Neu.
Ownership: Cable TV Assoc. Inc. (MSO).

WHITE—Satellite Cable Services Inc., Box 106, Brookings, SD 57006-0106. Phone: 605-692-5508. Fax: 605-692-6496. County: Brookings. ICA: SD0105.
TV Market Ranking: Outside TV Markets. Franchise award date: N.A. Franchise expiration date: N.A. Began: August 1, 1984.
Channel capacity: 40. Channels available but not in use: None.
Basic Service
Subscribers: 140.
Programming (received off-air): KESD-TV (P) Brookings; KDLV-TV (N), KELO-TV (C), KSFY-TV (A) Sioux Falls-Mitchell.
Programming (via satellite): WGN-TV (W) Chicago; CNN; ESPN; Fox Family Channel; Nashville Network; TBS Superstation; USA Network.
Fee: $24.95 installation; $27.38 monthly.
Pay Service 1
Pay Units: N.A.
Programming (via satellite): HBO.
Fee: $11.45 monthly.
Miles of plant: 4.0 (coaxial). Homes passed: 208.
Manager: Doug Bierschbach. Chief technician: Paul Schmidt.
Ownership: Satellite Cable Services Inc. (MSO).

WHITE LAKE—Satellite Cable Services Inc., Box 106, Brookings, SD 57006-0106. Phone: 605-692-5508. Fax: 605-692-6496. County: Aurora. ICA: SD0217.
TV Market Ranking: 85. Franchise award date: N.A. Franchise expiration date: N.A. Began: January 1, 1987.
Channel capacity: 120 (2-way capable; operating 2-way). Channels available but not in use: N.A.
Basic Service
Subscribers: 195.
Programming (received off-air): KPRY-TV (A), KTSD-TV (P) Pierre; KPLO-TV (C) Reliance; KDLV-TV (N) Sioux Falls-Mitchell.
Programming (via satellite): WGN-TV (W) Chicago; CNN; ESPN; Fox Family Channel; TBS Superstation; USA Network.
Fee: $24.95 installation; $27.96 monthly.
Pay Service 1
Pay Units: N.A.
Programming (via satellite): HBO.
Fee: $11.95 monthly.
Manager: Doug Bierschbach. Chief technician: Paul Schmidt.
Ownership: Satellite Cable Services Inc. (MSO).

WHITE RIVER—Golden West Cablevision, Box 9159, 2727 N. Plaza Dr., Rapid City, SD 57709. Phone: 605-348-6529. Fax: 605-342-1160. County: Mellette. Also serves Horse Creek Housing. ICA: SD0218.
TV Market Ranking: Outside TV Markets. Franchise award date: N.A. Franchise expiration date: February 1, 2003. Began: February 1, 1983.
Channel capacity: 36 (not 2-way capable). Channels available but not in use: 18.
Basic Service
Subscribers: 288.
Programming (received off-air): KPRY-TV (A), KTSD-TV (P) Pierre; KPLO-TV (C) Reliance.
Programming (via satellite): WGN-TV (W) Chicago; WNBC (N) New York; CNN; Discovery Channel; ESPN; Fox Family Channel; FoxNet; Nashville Network; Nickelodeon; TBS Superstation; Turner Network TV; USA Network.
Fee: $25.00 installation; $14.00 monthly.
Pay Service 1
Pay Units: 77.
Programming (via satellite): Disney Channel.
Fee: $7.95 monthly.
Pay Service 2
Pay Units: 146.
Programming (via satellite): Showtime.
Fee: $7.95 monthly.
Local advertising: No.
Program Guide: Video Viewing.
Equipment: Scientific-Atlanta headend; Scientific-Atlanta amplifiers; Scientific-Atlanta cable; Arcom traps; Scientific-Atlanta satellite antenna.
Miles of plant: 11.0 (coaxial).
Manager: Dwight Flatt. Chief technician: Ross Whitley. Marketing director: Greg Oleson.
City fee: None.
Ownership: Golden West Cablevision (MSO).

WHITEWOOD—Galaxy Cablevision, 203 S. Lincoln Ave., York, NE 68467. Phones: 402-362-1705; 800-365-6988. Fax: 402-362-3698. County: Lawrence. ICA: SD0219.
TV Market Ranking: Below 100. Franchise award date: N.A. Franchise expiration date: December 23, 2004. Began: April 1, 1983.
Channel capacity: 41 (not 2-way capable). Channels available but not in use: 16.
Basic Service
Subscribers: 223.
Programming (received off-air): KPSD-TV (P) Eagle Butte; KEVN-TV (F), KOTA-TV (A) Rapid City.
Programming (via satellite): WGN-TV (W) Chicago; KMGH-TV (A), KUSA-TV (N) Denver; American Movie Classics; CNN; Country Music TV; Discovery Channel; Disney Channel; ESPN; ESPN 2; Fox Family Channel; Learning Channel; Lifetime; Nashville Network; Nickelodeon; QVC; TBS Superstation; The Weather Channel; Turner Network TV; USA Network.
Fee: $28.95 monthly.
Pay Service 1
Pay Units: 43.
Programming (via satellite): HBO.
Fee: $12.95 monthly.
Pay Service 2
Pay Units: 27.
Programming (via satellite): Showtime.
Fee: $7.95 monthly.
Miles of plant: 6.0 (coaxial). Homes passed: 364.
District vice president: John M. Dixon III. State manager: Steve Jordan. Technical manager: Van De Vries.
City fee: 3% of gross.
Ownership: Galaxy Cablevision (MSO).

WILLOW LAKE—Satellite Cable Services Inc., Box 106, Brookings, SD 57006-0106. Phone: 605-692-5508. Fax: 605-692-6496. County: Clark. ICA: SD0112.
TV Market Ranking: Below 100. Franchise award date: N.A. Franchise expiration date: N.A. Began: December 1, 1984.
Channel capacity: 40 (2-way capable; not operating 2-way). Channels available but not in use: None.
Basic Service
Subscribers: 100.
Programming (received off-air): KABY-TV (A) Aberdeen; KESD-TV (P) Brookings; KDLO-TV (C) Florence-Watertown; KDLV-TV (N) Sioux Falls-Mitchell.
Programming (via satellite): WGN-TV (W) Chicago; CNN; ESPN; Fox Family Channel; Nashville Network; TBS Superstation; USA Network.
Fee: $24.95 installation; $27.38 monthly.
Pay Service 1
Pay Units: N.A.
Programming (via satellite): HBO.
Fee: $11.95 monthly.
Miles of plant: 3.0 (coaxial). Homes passed: 189.
Manager: Doug Bierschbach. Chief technician: Paul Schmidt.
Ownership: Satellite Cable Services Inc. (MSO).

WILMOT—TCI Cablevision of South Dakota, Box 144, Milbank, SD 57252-0144. Phone: 605-432-6776. Fax: 605-432-4661. County: Roberts. ICA: SD0089.
TV Market Ranking: Outside TV Markets. Franchise award date: N.A. Franchise expiration date: N.A. Began: December 1, 1979.
Channel capacity: 35. Channels available but not in use: 15.
Basic Service
Subscribers: 206.
Programming (received off-air): KABY-TV (A), KDSD-TV (P) Aberdeen; KVRR (F) Fargo; KDLO-TV (C) Florence-Watertown; 1 FM.
Programming (via microwave): KVLY-TV (N) Fargo.
Programming (via satellite): WGN-TV (W) Chicago; CNN; Discovery Channel; Fox Family Channel; Lifetime; TBS Superstation.
Fee: $29.95 installation; $20.67 monthly; $24.95 additional installation.
Expanded Basic Service
Subscribers: 198.
Programming (via satellite): American Movie Classics; Court TV; ESPN; Nashville Network; Turner Network TV; USA Network.
Fee: N.A.
Pay Service 1
Pay Units: 15.
Programming (via satellite): Disney Channel.
Fee: N.A.
Pay Service 2
Pay Units: 34.
Programming (via satellite): HBO.
Fee: N.A.
Pay Service 3
Pay Units: 93.
Programming (via satellite): The New Encore.
Fee: N.A.
Miles of plant: 3.9 (coaxial). Homes passed: 258. Total homes in franchised area: 258.
Manager: Joe Villella. Chief technician: Ray Olson.
City fee: None.
Ownership: AT&T Broadband & Internet Services (MSO). Purchased from Tele-Communications Inc., March 9, 1999.

WINNER—Midcontinent Cable Systems of South Dakota, Box 910, Aberdeen, SD 57402-0910. Phones: 605-229-1775; 800-456-0564. Fax: 605-229-0478. County: Tripp. Also serves Colome. ICA: SD0021.
TV Market Ranking: Below 100 (Colome); Outside TV Markets (Winner). Franchise award date: October 19, 1987. Franchise expiration date: October 19, 2011. Began: November 1, 1968.
Channel capacity: 60 (not 2-way capable). Channels available but not in use: 20.
Basic Service
Subscribers: 1,181.
Programming (received off-air): KPRY-TV (A), KTSD-TV (P) Pierre; KPLO-TV (C) Reliance; allband FM.
Programming (via microwave): KDLT-TV (N) Sioux Falls.
Programming (via satellite): WGN-TV (W) Chicago; KWGN-TV (W) Denver; A & E; American Movie Classics; C-SPAN; CNBC; CNN; Cartoon Network; Country Music TV; Discovery Channel; Disney Channel; ESPN; ESPN 2; ESPNews; FX; Fox Family Channel; FoxNet; Headline News; Learning Channel; Lifetime; MTV; Midwest Sports Channel; Nashville Network; Nick at Nite's TV Land; Nickelodeon; QVC; TBS Superstation; TV Guide Channel; The Weather Channel; Trinity Bcstg. Network; Turner Network TV; USA Network; VH1.
Fee: $50.00 installation; $26.50 monthly.
Pay Service 1
Pay Units: 77.
Programming (via satellite): Cinemax.
Fee: $20.00 installation; $11.00 monthly.
Pay Service 2
Pay Units: 181.
Programming (via satellite): HBO.
Fee: $20.00 installation; $12.00 monthly.
Pay Service 3
Pay Units: 121.
Programming (via satellite): Showtime.
Fee: $20.00 installation; $11.00 monthly.
Pay Service 4
Pay Units: 116.
Programming (via satellite): The Movie Channel.
Fee: $20.00 installation; $11.00 monthly.
Local advertising: No.
Equipment: Scientific-Atlanta headend; Scientific-Atlanta amplifiers; Eagle traps; Scientific-Atlanta satellite antenna.
Miles of plant: 19.3 (coaxial); None (fiber optic). Homes passed: 1,388. Total homes in franchised area: 1,388.
Manager: Lonnie Schumacher. Marketing director: Fred Jamieson. Customer service manager: Kathy Fuhrmann.
City fee: 3% of gross.
Ownership: Midcontinent Communications (MSO).

WOLSEY—Midcontinent Cable Systems of South Dakota, Box 910, Aberdeen, SD 57402-0910. Phones: 605-229-1775; 800-456-0564. Fax: 605-229-0478. County: Beadle. ICA: SD0116.
TV Market Ranking: Below 100. Franchise award date: January 18, 1996. Franchise expiration date: January 18, 2011. Began: December 15, 1983.
Channel capacity: 35 (not 2-way capable). Channels available but not in use: 9.
Basic Service
Subscribers: 145.
Programming (received off-air): KABY-TV (A) Aberdeen; KESD-TV (P) Brookings; KDLO-TV (C) Florence-Watertown; KTTM (F) Huron; KDLV-TV (N) Sioux Falls-Mitchell.
Programming (via satellite): WGN-TV (W) Chicago; A & E; American Movie Classics; C-SPAN; C-SPAN 2; CNBC; CNN; Cartoon Network; Country Music TV; Discovery Channel; Disney Channel; ESPN; ESPN 2; ESPNews; EWTN; FX; Flix; Fox Family Channel; Headline News; Learning Channel; Lifetime; MTV; Midwest Sports Channel; Nashville Network; Nick at Nite's TV Land; Nickelodeon; QVC; Speedvision; TBS Superstation; TV Guide Channel; The Health Network; The Weather Channel; Trinity Bcstg. Network; Turner Network TV; USA Network; VH1.

Current originations: Educational access; local access.
Fee: $50.00 installation; $26.50 monthly.
Expanded Basic Service
Subscribers: N.A.
Programming (via satellite): Animal Planet; Comedy Central; E! Entertainment TV; fXM: Movies from Fox; History Channel; Outdoor Channel; Sci-Fi Channel; Speedvision; Travel Channel; Turner Classic Movies.
Fee: N.A.
Pay Service 1
Pay Units: 25.
Programming (via satellite): HBO (multiplexed).
Fee: $20.00 installation; $12.00 monthly.
Pay Service 2
Pay Units: 11.
Programming (via satellite): Showtime (multiplexed).
Fee: $20.00 installation; $11.00 monthly.
Pay Service 3
Pay Units: 12.
Programming (via satellite): The Movie Channel.
Fee: $20.00 installation; $11.00 monthly.
Pay Service 4
Pay Units: 7.
Programming (via satellite): Cinemax (multiplexed).
Fee: $20.00 installation; $11.00 monthly.
Pay Service 5
Pay Units: 1.
Programming (via satellite): Starz!; The New Encore (multiplexed).
Fee: $20.00 installation; $7.95 monthly (package).
Pay-Per-View
Addressable homes: 17.
Hot Choice; Viewer's Choice 1, 3, 4.
Local advertising: No.
Equipment: Magnavox amplifiers; Times Fiber cable.
Miles of plant: 4.3 (coaxial); None (fiber optic). Homes passed: 181. Total homes in franchised area: 181.
Manager: Lonnie Schumacher. Marketing director: Fred Jamieson. Customer service manager: Kathy Fuhrmann.
City fee: 3% of gross.
Ownership: Midcontinent Communications (MSO).

WOONSOCKET—Communications Enterprises Inc., Box 67, Woonsocket, SD 57385. Phone: 605-796-4411. Fax: 605-796-4419. Counties: Jerauld & Sanborn. Also serves Alpena, Artesian, Letcher. ICA: SD0096.
TV Market Ranking: 85 (Artesian, Letcher, Woonsocket); Outside TV Markets (Alpena). Franchise award date: N.A. Franchise expiration date: N.A. Began: February 15, 1983.
Channel capacity: 17 (not 2-way capable). Channels available but not in use: None.
Basic Service
Subscribers: 417.
Programming (received off-air): KABY-TV (A) Aberdeen; KESD-TV (P) Brookings; KDLO-TV (C) Florence-Watertown; KDLV-TV (N) Sioux Falls-Mitchell.
Programming (via satellite): WGN-TV (W) Chicago; CNN; ESPN; Nashville Network; Nickelodeon; TBS Superstation; Turner Network TV; USA Network.
Fee: $30.00 installation; $18.30 monthly.
Pay Service 1
Pay Units: N.A.
Programming (via satellite): HBO.
Fee: $7.95 monthly.
Miles of plant: 6.8 (coaxial).
Manager: Gene Kroell.
Ownership: Sanborn Telephone Cooperative (MSO).

YALE—Satellite Cable Services Inc., Box 106, Brookings, SD 57006-0106. Phone: 605-692-5508. Fax: 605-692-6496. County: Beadle. ICA: SD0220.
TV Market Ranking: Below 100. Franchise award date: N.A. Franchise expiration date: N.A. Began: N.A.
Channel capacity: 36 (2-way capable; not operating 2-way). Channels available but not in use: N.A.
Basic Service
Subscribers: 38.
Programming (received off-air): KESD-TV (P) Brookings; KDLV-TV (N), KELO-TV (C), KSFY-TV (A) Sioux Falls-Mitchell.
Programming (via satellite): WGN-TV (W) Chicago; CNN; ESPN; Midwest Sports Channel; Nashville Network; TBS Superstation; Turner Network TV.
Fee: $26.32 monthly.
Pay Service 1
Pay Units: N.A.
Programming (via satellite): HBO.
Fee: $11.95 monthly.
Manager: Doug Bierschbach. Chief technician: Paul Schmidt.
Ownership: Satellite Cable Services Inc. (MSO).

YANKTON—Yankton Cable TV Ltd., Box 178, Yankton, SD 57078. Phone: 605-624-5553. Fax: 605-624-6712. County: Yankton. ICA: SD0009.
TV Market Ranking: Outside TV Markets. Franchise award date: N.A. Franchise expiration date: N.A. Began: April 1, 1980.
Channel capacity: 36 (2-way capable; operating 2-way). Channels available but not in use: 5.
Basic Service
Subscribers: 4,151.
Programming (received off-air): KXNE-TV (P) Norfolk; KCAU-TV (A), KMEG (C), KSIN (P), KTIV (N) Sioux City; KDLV-TV (N), KELO-TV (C), KSFY-TV (A) Sioux Falls-Mitchell; KUSD-TV (P) Vermillion.
Programming (via satellite): WGN-TV (W) Chicago; A & E; Fox Family Channel; Nickelodeon; TBS Superstation; USA Network.
Current originations: Automated time-weather.
Fee: $25.00 installation; $13.95 monthly.
Expanded Basic Service
Subscribers: 3,372.
Programming (via satellite): C-SPAN; CNN; ESPN; Learning Channel; Lifetime; MTV; Nashville Network; The Weather Channel.
Fee: $6.50 monthly.
Pay Service 1
Pay Units: 505.
Programming (via satellite): Cinemax.
Fee: $25.00 installation; $8.95 monthly.
Pay Service 2
Pay Units: 167.
Programming (via satellite): Disney Channel.
Fee: $8.95 monthly.
Pay Service 3
Pay Units: 808.
Programming (via satellite): HBO.
Fee: $8.95 monthly.
Pay Service 4
Pay Units: 371.
Programming (via satellite): The Movie Channel.
Fee: $8.95 monthly.
Equipment: Scientific-Atlanta headend; Scientific-Atlanta amplifiers; Times Fiber cable; Sony cameras; Sony & JVC VTRs; Compuvid character generator; Jerrold set top converters; Scientific-Atlanta satellite antenna; Scientific-Atlanta satellite receivers.
Miles of plant: 57.7 (coaxial). Homes passed: 4,800. Total homes in franchised area: 4,800.
Manager: Jim Abbott. Chief technician: Bill Lokken.
City fee: 3% of gross.
Ownership: Zylstra Communications Corp. (MSO). Sale pends to Mediacom LLC.

TENNESSEE

Total Systems: **143**
Total Communities Served: **574**
Franchises Not Yet Operating: **0**
Applications Pending: **0**
Communities with Applications: **0**
Number of Basic Subscribers: **1,272,257**
Number of Expanded Basic Subscribers: **671,249**
Number of Pay Units: **677,642**

Top 100 Markets Represented: Memphis (26); Greenville-Spartanburg-Anderson, SC-Asheville, NC (46); Knoxville (71); Chattanooga (78); Huntsville-Decatur (96).

For a list of all cable communities included in this section, see the Cable Community Index located in the back of this volume.
For explanation of terms used in cable system listings, see p. D-9.

ALAMO—Time Warner Cable, 2177 Christmasville Rd., Jackson, TN 38305. Phone: 800-997-8204. Fax: 615-424-4257. County: Crockett. Also serves Bells, Crockett County (portions), Maury City. ICA: TN0069.
TV Market Ranking: Below 100. Franchise award date: April 1, 1976. Franchise expiration date: N.A. Began: August 1, 1977.
Channel capacity: 39 (not 2-way capable). Channels available but not in use: N.A.
Basic Service
Subscribers: 1,612; Commercial subscribers: 74.
Programming (received off-air): WBBJ-TV (A), WMTU (U) Jackson; WLJT (P) Lexington; WHBQ-TV (F), WKNO (P), WMC-TV (N), WPTY-TV (A), WREG-TV (C) Memphis; allband FM.
Programming (via satellite): WGN-TV (W) Chicago; CNN; ESPN; Home Shopping Network; MTV; Nashville Network; Nickelodeon; QVC; TBS Superstation; The Weather Channel; USA Network.
Current originations: Automated time-weather; local news.
Fee: $40.00 installation; $11.50 monthly; $40.00 additional installation.
Pay Service 1
Pay Units: 180.
Programming (via satellite): Cinemax.
Fee: $40.00 installation; $9.95 monthly.
Pay Service 2
Pay Units: 350.
Programming (via satellite): HBO.
Fee: $40.00 installation; $9.95 monthly.
Pay Service 3
Pay Units: 135.
Programming (via satellite): Disney Channel.
Fee: $40.00 installation; $9.95 monthly.
Pay Service 4
Pay Units: 110.
Programming (via satellite): Showtime.
Fee: $40.00 installation; $9.95 monthly.
Local advertising: Yes.
Equipment: Scientific-Atlanta headend; Scientific-Atlanta amplifiers; Cerro & Comm/Scope cable; Ampex, Panasonic & Sony cameras; Panasonic & Sony VTRs; AFC & Scientific-Atlanta satellite antenna; Microdyne satellite receivers.
Miles of plant: 52.5 (coaxial). Additional miles planned: 12.0 (coaxial). Homes passed: 2,125. Total homes in franchised area: 2,500.
Manager: Jerry W. Creasy. Chief technician: Ron Crowder.
City fee: 3% of annual gross.
Ownership: Time Warner Cable (MSO).

ALCOA—InterMedia, 725 Louisville Rd., Alcoa, TN 37701-1846. Phone: 423-984-1400. Fax: 423-982-4974. County: Blount. Also serves Blount County (portions), Maryville, Rockford. ICA: TN0151.
TV Market Ranking: 71. Franchise award date: January 1, 1979. Franchise expiration date: March 10, 2016. Began: January 1, 1979.
Channel capacity: 53 (not 2-way capable). Channels available but not in use: None.
Basic Service
Subscribers: 60,206.
Programming (received off-air): WATE-TV (A), WBIR-TV (N), WKOP-TV (P), WTNZ (F), WVLT-TV (C) Knoxville; WSJK (P) Sneedville.
Programming (via satellite): C-SPAN.
Current originations: Religious access; automated emergency alert; local news.
Fee: $46.42 installation; $7.46 monthly.
Expanded Basic Service
Subscribers: 57,140.
Programming (via satellite): A & E; American Movie Classics; BET; C-SPAN 2; CNBC; CNN; Cartoon Network; Country Music TV; Discovery Channel; ESPN; EWTN; Fox Sports Net South; Headline News; History Channel; Home Shopping Network; Learning Channel; Lifetime; MTV; Nashville Network; Nickelodeon; QVC; The Weather Channel; Turner Network TV; USA Network; VH1.
Fee: $16.46 monthly.
Pay Service 1
Pay Units: 32,231.
Programming (via satellite): Cinemax; Disney Channel; HBO; Showtime; The Movie Channel.
Fee: N.A.
Pay-Per-View
Addressable homes: 1,400.
Special events.
Note: Miles of plant & homes passed include figures for Crossville, Gatlinburg, Loudon, Madisonville & Seymour, TN.
Miles of plant: 1900.0 (coaxial); 243.0 (fiber optic). Homes passed: 89,743.
Office manager: Paul Maynard. Technical operations manager: Mark Haley. Chief engineer: Dale Taylor. Business manager: Cathy Dunford.
City fee: 5% of gross.
Ownership: InterMedia Partners (MSO). See Cable System Ownership.

ALEXANDRIA—Alexandria Cablevision, Box 999, 223 S. College St., Lebanon, TN 37087. Phone: 615-444-2288. Fax: 615-449-4252. Counties: DeKalb & Smith. Also serves Dowelltown, Gordonsville, Liberty, Smith County (unincorporated areas). ICA: TN0125.
TV Market Ranking: Below 100. Franchise award date: N.A. Franchise expiration date: N.A. Began: N.A.
Channel capacity: N.A. Channels available but not in use: N.A.
Basic Service
Subscribers: 848.
Programming (received off-air): WCTE (P) Cookeville; WHTN (I) Murfreesboro; WDCN (P), WKRN-TV (A), WNAB (W), WSMV (N), WTVF (C), WUXP (U), WZTV (F) Nashville.
Programming (via satellite): WGN-TV (W) Chicago; Fox Family Channel; Home Shopping Network; Learning Channel; TBS Superstation; The Weather Channel; USA Network.
Fee: $32.05 installation; $18.95 monthly.
Expanded Basic Service
Subscribers: N.A.
Programming (via satellite): A & E; American Movie Classics; Animal Planet; C-SPAN; CNBC; CNN; Comedy Central; Discovery Channel; E! Entertainment TV; ESPN; Fox News Channel; Fox Sports Net South; Great American Country; Headline News; Home & Garden Television; Lifetime; Nashville Network; Nick at Nite; Nick at Nite's TV Land; Nickelodeon; The Health Network; Turner Network TV; VH1.
Fee: N.A.
Pay Service 1
Pay Units: N.A.
Programming (via satellite): Cinemax; Disney Channel; HBO; Showtime; Starz!; The New Encore.
Fee: N.A.
Manager: Andy Blume. Chief technician: Dwayne Salts.
Ownership: Rifkin & Associates Inc. (MSO). See Cable System Ownership.

ALTAMONT—HDC Cable, 8518 Linwood Dr., Catlettsburg, KY 41129. Phone: 606-739-6445. County: Grundy. Also serves Beersheba Springs, Grundy County (unincorporated areas). ICA: TN0126.
TV Market Ranking: Outside TV Markets. Franchise award date: March 1, 1989. Franchise expiration date: N.A. Began: January 1, 1990.
Channel capacity: N.A. Channels available but not in use: N.A.
Basic Service
Subscribers: 315.
Programming (received off-air): WDEF-TV (C), WDSI-TV (F), WRCB-TV (N), WTCI (P), WTVC (A) Chattanooga; WZTV (F) Nashville.
Programming (via satellite): WGN-TV (W) Chicago; A & E; Cartoon Network; Discovery Channel; ESPN; Fox Family Channel; Nashville Network; QVC; TBS Superstation; USA Network.
Fee: $29.95 installation; $17.00 monthly.
Pay Service 1
Pay Units: 51.
Programming (via satellite): Cinemax; Disney Channel; HBO; Showtime.
Fee: $9.95 monthly (each).
Miles of plant: 30.0 (coaxial).
Manager: Doug Jones. Chief technician: Herman Marr.
Ownership: HDC Cable.

ANTHONY HILL—Charter Communications, 530 Sparkman St. SW, Hartselle, AL 35640. Phone: 205-773-6537. Fax: 205-773-4209. County: Giles. Also serves Giles County (unincorporated areas), Minor Hill. ICA: TN0111.
TV Market Ranking: 96 (Anthony Hill, portions of Giles County, Minor Hill); Below 100 (portions of Giles County); Outside TV Markets (portions of Giles County). Franchise award date: N.A. Franchise expiration date: January 1, 2002. Began: N.A.
Channel capacity: 32 (not 2-way capable). Channels available but not in use: 6.
Basic Service
Subscribers: 331.
Programming (received off-air): WYLE (W) Florence; WAAY-TV (A), WAFF (N), WHNT-TV (C), WZDX (F) Huntsville-Decatur; WDCN (P), WKRN-TV (A), WSMV (N), WTVF (C) Nashville.
Programming (via satellite): Country Music TV; TBS Superstation; USA Network.
Current originations: Religious access.
Fee: $40.00 installation; $10.95 monthly.
Expanded Basic Service
Subscribers: N.A.
Programming (via satellite): American Movie Classics; CNN; Cartoon Network; Discovery Channel; ESPN; ESPN 2; Fox Family Channel; History Channel; MTV; Nashville Network; Nickelodeon; The Weather Channel; Turner Network TV.
Fee: $13.00 monthly.
Pay Service 1
Pay Units: 30.
Programming (via satellite): Disney Channel.
Fee: $8.45 monthly.
Pay Service 2
Pay Units: 61.
Programming (via satellite): Showtime.
Fee: $11.45 monthly.
Miles of plant: 22.0 (coaxial). Homes passed: 518.
Manager: Tom Salters. Chief technician: Doc Collins. Program director: Sheri Smith.
Ownership: Charter Communications Inc. (MSO).

ASHLAND CITY—Charter Communications, Box 908, Clarksville, TN 37041-0908. Phone: 615-645-8840. Fax: 615-552-6144. County: Cheatham. Plans service to Cheatham County. ICA: TN0052.
TV Market Ranking: 30. Franchise award date: January 1, 1981. Franchise expiration date: N.A. Began: June 1, 1981.
Channel capacity: 36 (not 2-way capable). Channels available but not in use: 6.
Basic Service
Subscribers: 1,600.
Programming (received off-air): WDCN (P), WKRN-TV (A), WSMV (N), WTVF (C), WUXP (U), WZTV (F) Nashville.
Programming (via satellite): WGN-TV (W) Chicago; American Movie Classics; CNN; Country Music TV; ESPN; Fox Family Channel; Headline News; Lifetime; MTV; Nashville Network; Nickelodeon; QVC; TBS Superstation; The Weather Channel; USA Network.
Fee: $23.65 monthly.
Pay Service 1
Pay Units: 138.
Programming (via satellite): Disney Channel.
Fee: $10.00 monthly.
Pay Service 2
Pay Units: 480.

Programming (via satellite): HBO.
Fee: $10.00 monthly.
Pay Service 3
Pay Units: 288.
Programming (via satellite): Showtime.
Fee: $10.00 monthly.
Pay Service 4
Pay Units: 246.
Programming (via satellite): The Movie Channel.
Fee: $10.00 monthly.
Local advertising: Yes. Regional interconnect: Intermedia Television Advertising.
Program Guide: Premium Channels.
Equipment: Scientific-Atlanta & Jerrold headend; Scientific-Atlanta amplifiers; Comm/Scope cable; Scientific-Atlanta set top converters; Eagle traps; Scientific-Atlanta satellite receivers.
Miles of plant: 110.0 (coaxial). Additional miles planned: 3.0 (coaxial). Homes passed: 3,500.
Manager: Chris Ginn. Chief technician: John Viehland. Program director: John Moseley. Marketing director: Christy Poole.
City fee: 3% of gross.
Ownership: Charter Communications Inc. (MSO).

ATHENS—Comcast Cablevision of the South, 408 S. White St., Athens, TN 37303. Phone: 423-745-6480. Fax: 423-745-6402. Counties: McMinn & Polk. Also serves Delano, Englewood, Etowah, McMinn County (portions), Polk County (portions), Riceville. ICA: TN0024.
TV Market Ranking: 78 (portions of McMinn County, portions of Polk County); Below 100 (Athens, Delano, Englewood, Etowah, portions of McMinn County, portions of Polk County, Riceville). Franchise award date: N.A. Franchise expiration date: N.A. Began: March 1, 1967.
Channel capacity: 42 (not 2-way capable). Channels available but not in use: N.A.
Basic Service
Subscribers: 34,015. Includes figures for Harriman, TN.
Programming (received off-air): WDEF-TV (C), WDSI-TV (F), WRCB-TV (N), WTCI (P), WTVC (A) Chattanooga; WFLI-TV (U) Cleveland; WATE-TV (A), WBIR-TV (N), WKOP-TV (P), WVLT-TV (C) Knoxville; allband FM.
Programming (via satellite): WGN-TV (W) Chicago; American Movie Classics; C-SPAN; C-SPAN 2; CNN; Country Music TV; Discovery Channel; ESPN; ESPN 2; Fox Family Channel; Fox Sports Net South; Headline News; Home Shopping Network; Learning Channel; MTV; Nashville Network; Nickelodeon; TBS Superstation; The Weather Channel; Trinity Bcstg. Network; Turner Network TV; USA Network; VH1.
Fee: $25.73 installation; $24.18 monthly.
Pay Service 1
Pay Units: 1,537.
Programming (via satellite): Cinemax.
Fee: $10.00 installation; $9.00 monthly.
Pay Service 2
Pay Units: 794.
Programming (via satellite): Disney Channel.
Fee: $10.00 installation; $6.95 monthly.
Pay Service 3
Pay Units: 2,242.
Programming (via satellite): HBO.
Fee: $20.00 installation; $9.00 monthly.
Pay Service 4
Pay Units: N.A.
Programming (via satellite): Showtime.
Fee: N.A.
Local advertising: Yes.
Miles of plant: 300.0 (coaxial); None (fiber optic). Homes passed: 11,000. Total homes in franchised area: 16,000.
Manager: Marilyn Powers. Chief technician: Sam Wattenbarger. Marketing director: Paul Maynard.
City fee: 3% of gross.
Ownership: Comcast Cable Communications Inc. (MSO).

BEAN STATION—FrontierVision, Suite P-200, 1777 S. Harrison St., Denver, CO 80210. Phone: 303-757-1588. Fax: 303-757-6105. Counties: Grainger & Hawkins. Also serves Grainger County (northeastern portion), Mooresburg, Rutledge. ICA: TN0053.
TV Market Ranking: 71 (Rutledge); Below 100 (Bean Station, Grainger County, Mooresburg). Franchise award date: April 9, 1984. Franchise expiration date: April 9, 1999. Began: September 1, 1984.
Channel capacity: 42 (not 2-way capable). Channels available but not in use: 19.
Basic Service
Subscribers: 1,971.
Programming (received off-air): WATE-TV (A), WBIR-TV (N), WTNZ (F), WVLT-TV (C) Knoxville; WSJK (P) Sneedville.
Programming (via satellite): WGN-TV (W) Chicago; WPIX (W) New York; CNN; Comedy Central; Discovery Channel; ESPN; Fox Family Channel; Headline News; MTV; Nashville Network; Nickelodeon; QVC; TBS Superstation; Turner Network TV; USA Network.
Fee: $40.00 installation; $14.95 monthly; $3.00 converter.
Pay Service 1
Pay Units: 297.
Programming (via satellite): Cinemax.
Fee: $15.00 installation; $9.95 monthly.
Pay Service 2
Pay Units: 332.
Programming (via satellite): HBO.
Fee: $15.00 installation; $10.95 monthly.
Local advertising: No.
Program Guide: CableView.
Equipment: Cadco, Electrohome & Scientific-Atlanta headend; Magnavox amplifiers; Comm/Scope & Times Fiber cable; Scientific-Atlanta set top converters; Intercept traps; Channel-Master satellite antenna; Electrohome & Triple Crown satellite receivers.
Miles of plant: 146.0 (coaxial). Homes passed: 3,468.
President: James Vaugh. Vice president, engineering: David Heyrend. Executive vice president: John Koo.
County fee: 3% of gross.
Ownership: FrontierVision Partners LP (MSO). See Cable System Ownership.

BENTON—Comcast Cablevision of the South, 408 S. White St., Athens, TN 37303. Phone: 615-745-6480. County: Polk. Also serves Ocoee, Oldfort, Polk County (portions). ICA: TN0127.
TV Market Ranking: 78 (Ocoee, Oldfort, portions of Polk County); Below 100 (Benton, portions of Polk County). Franchise award date: N.A. Franchise expiration date: N.A. Began: N.A.
Channel capacity: 42 (not 2-way capable). Channels available but not in use: N.A.
Basic Service
Subscribers: 1,350.
Programming (received off-air): WDEF-TV (C), WDSI-TV (F), WRCB-TV (N), WTCI (P), WTVC (A) Chattanooga; WFLI-TV (U) Cleveland; WVLT-TV (C) Knoxville.
Programming (via satellite): WGN-TV (W) Chicago; C-SPAN; C-SPAN 2; Home Shopping Network; Learning Channel; TBS Superstation.
Fee: $10.13 monthly.
Expanded Basic Service
Subscribers: 924.
Programming (via satellite): A & E; American Movie Classics; CNN; Country Music TV; Discovery Channel; ESPN; ESPN 2; Fox Family Channel; Headline News; Lifetime; MTV; Nashville Network; Nickelodeon; QVC; The Weather Channel; Trinity Bcstg. Network; Turner Network TV; USA Network; VH1; ValueVision.
Fee: $25.73 installation; $14.58 monthly.
Pay Service 1
Pay Units: N.A.
Programming (via satellite): Cinemax; Disney Channel; HBO; Showtime.
Fee: $7.47 monthly (Disney), $9.68 monthly (Cinemax or HBO).
Miles of plant: 82.0 (coaxial); None (fiber optic). Homes passed: 2,075. Total homes in franchised area: 4,000.
Manager: Marilyn Powers. Chief technician: Sam Wattenbarger.
Ownership: Comcast Cable Communications Inc. (MSO).

BOLIVAR—Enstar Cable TV, 312 E. Center St., Sikeston, MO 63801. Phone: 573-472-0244. Fax: 573-472-1559. County: Hardeman. Also serves Hardeman County (portions). ICA: TN0051.
TV Market Ranking: Below 100. Franchise award date: April 8, 1980. Franchise expiration date: N.A. Began: August 1, 1981.
Channel capacity: 36 (not 2-way capable). Channels available but not in use: None.
Basic Service
Subscribers: 1,722.
Programming (received off-air): WBBJ-TV (A), WMTU (U) Jackson; WLJT (P) Lexington; WHBQ-TV (F), WKNO (P), WLMT (U), WMC-TV (N), WPTY-TV (A), WREG-TV (C) Memphis.
Programming (via satellite): A & E; American Movie Classics; BET; ESPN; Fox Family Channel; Fox Sports Net South; Home & Garden Television; MTV; Nashville Network; Nickelodeon; QVC; Trinity Bcstg. Network.
Current originations: Public access.
Fee: $21.11 monthly; $10.00 additional installation.
Expanded Basic Service
Subscribers: 1,703.
Programming (via satellite): Discovery Channel; Lifetime; USA Network.
Fee: $1.73 monthly.
Expanded Basic Service 2
Subscribers: 1,675.
Programming (via satellite): WGN-TV (W) Chicago; CNN; Disney Channel; Headline News; TBS Superstation; Turner Network TV.
Fee: $7.95 monthly.
Pay Service 1
Pay Units: 178.
Programming (via satellite): Cinemax.
Fee: $10.95 monthly.
Pay Service 2
Pay Units: 389.
Programming (via satellite): HBO.
Fee: $11.95 monthly.
Pay Service 3
Pay Units: 150.
Programming (via satellite): Showtime.
Fee: $10.95 monthly.
Pay Service 4
Pay Units: 165.
Programming (via satellite): The Movie Channel.
Fee: $10.95 monthly.
Equipment: Catel, Jerrold & Scientific-Atlanta headend; Jerrold & Scientific-Atlanta amplifiers; Comm/Scope cable; Jerrold & Scientific-Atlanta set top converters; Eagle, Intercept & Pico traps; Microdyne & ScientificAtlanta satellite antenna; Microdyne & Scientific-Atlanta satellite receivers.
Miles of plant: 72.0 (coaxial). Homes passed: 2,989. Total homes in franchised area: 3,600.
Manager: Dave Huntsman. Chief technician: Kevin Goetz.
Franchise fee: 3%-5% of gross.
Ownership: Falcon Communications LP (MSO), joint venture formed September 30, 1998. See Cable System Ownership.

BRADEN—Time Warner Communications, Box 610, 12935 S. Main St., Somerville, TN 38068. Phone: 901-259-2225. Counties: Fayette & Tipton. Also serves Tipton County (southeastern portion). ICA: TN0128.
TV Market Ranking: 26. Franchise award date: N.A. Franchise expiration date: N.A. Began: N.A.
Channel capacity: 35. Channels available but not in use: 2.
Basic Service
Subscribers: 487; Commercial subscribers: 1.
Programming (received off-air): WHBQ-TV (F), WKNO (P), WLMT (U), WMC-TV (N), WPTY-TV (A), WREG-TV (C) Memphis.
Programming (via satellite): WGN-TV (W) Chicago; A & E; American Movie Classics; BET; C-SPAN; CNN; Country Music TV; Court TV; Discovery Channel; ESPN; Fox Family Channel; Headline News; Home Shopping Network; Lifetime; MTV; Nashville Network; Nickelodeon; QVC; TBS Superstation; The Weather Channel; Turner Network TV; USA Network.
Fee: $39.00 installation; $19.05 monthly.
Pay Service 1
Pay Units: N.A.
Programming (via satellite): Cinemax; Disney Channel; HBO; Showtime.
Fee: $7.00 monthly (Disney), $9.95 monthly (Cinemax, HBO or Showtime).
Manager: Bob Moss. Chief technician: Art Brown.
Ownership: Time Warner Cable (MSO).

BRADFORD—Enstar Cable TV, 312 E. Center St., Sikeston, MO 63801. Phone: 573-472-0244. Fax: 573-472-1559. County: Gibson. ICA: TN0178.
TV Market Ranking: Below 100. Franchise award date: N.A. Franchise expiration date: N.A. Began: N.A.
Channel capacity: 35. Channels available but not in use: 4.
Basic Service
Subscribers: 468.
Programming (received off-air): WBBJ-TV (A), WMTU (U) Jackson; WLJT (P) Lexington; WHBQ-TV (F), WKNO (P), WMC-TV (N), WPTY-TV (A), WREG-TV (C) Memphis; WPSD-TV (N) Paducah.
Programming (via satellite): American Movie Classics; ESPN; Headline News; Home & Garden Television; Home Shopping Network; QVC; Sci-Fi Channel; The Weather Channel; Trinity Bcstg. Network; Turner Network TV.
Fee: $18.51 monthly.
Expanded Basic Service
Subscribers: 466.
Programming (via satellite): Discovery Channel; Fox Family Channel; Lifetime; USA Network.
Fee: $2.76 monthly.
Expanded Basic Service 2
Subscribers: 462.
Programming (via satellite): WGN-TV (W) Chicago; CNN; Disney Channel; ESPN 2; Nashville Network; TBS Superstation.
Fee: $6.81 monthly.
Pay Service 1
Pay Units: 42.
Programming (via satellite): Cinemax.
Fee: $10.95 monthly.

Pay Service 2
Pay Units: 66.
Programming (via satellite): HBO.
Fee: $11.95 monthly.
Miles of plant: 12.0 (coaxial). Homes passed: 615.
Manager: Dave Huntsman. Chief technician: Kevin Goetz.
Ownership: Falcon Communications LP (MSO), joint venture formed September 30, 1998. See Cable System Ownership.

BRISTOL—Charter Communications Inc., 204 Bluff City Hwy., Bristol, TN 37620-4215. Phone: 423-968-2141. Fax: 423-968-1945. Counties: Sullivan, TN; Washington, VA. Also serves Blountville, Sullivan County, TN; Washington County, VA. ICA: TN0014.
TV Market Ranking: Below 100. Franchise award date: N.A. Franchise expiration date: N.A. Began: June 26, 1965.
Channel capacity: 30 (not 2-way capable). Channels available but not in use: None.
Basic Service
Subscribers: 19,691.
Programming (received off-air): WCYB-TV (N) Bristol-Kingsport; WEMT (F) Greeneville; WJHL-TV (C) Johnson City; WKPT-TV (A) Kingsport; WMSY-TV (P) Marion; WSJK (P) Sneedville; 15 FMs.
Programming (via satellite): WGN-TV (W) Chicago; C-SPAN; C-SPAN 2; E! Entertainment TV; QVC; TBS Superstation; TV Guide Channel; TV Guide Sneak Prevue.
Current originations: Automated time-weather; educational access; religious access.
Fee: $25.00 installation (aerial), $35.00 (underground); $13.50 monthly; $25.00 additional installation.
Expanded Basic Service
Subscribers: N.A.
Programming (via satellite): A & E; American Movie Classics; BET; CNBC; CNN; Country Music TV; Discovery Channel; ESPN; ESPN 2; Fox Family Channel; Fox Sports Net South; Headline News; Learning Channel; Lifetime; MTV; Nashville Network; Nickelodeon; Odyssey; TV Food Network; The Box; The Weather Channel; Travel Channel; Turner Network TV; USA Network; Z Music Television.
Fee: N.A.
Expanded Basic Service 2
Subscribers: 400.
Programming (via satellite): Cartoon Network; ESPN Classic Sports; Home & Garden Television; Outdoor Life Network; Sci-Fi Channel; Speedvision; Turner Classic Movies.
Fee: $6.95 monthly.
Pay Service 1
Pay Units: 1,140.
Programming (via satellite): Cinemax.
Fee: $25.00 installation; $7.95 monthly.
Pay Service 2
Pay Units: 1,110.
Programming (via satellite): Disney Channel.
Fee: $25.00 installation; $7.95 monthly.
Pay Service 3
Pay Units: 1,603.
Programming (via satellite): HBO.
Fee: $25.00 installation; $10.95 monthly.
Pay Service 4
Pay Units: 1,622.
Programming (via satellite): Showtime.
Fee: $25.00 installation; $10.95 monthly.
Pay-Per-View
Addressable homes: 3,200.
Special events.
Local advertising: Yes (locally produced & insert). Available in satellite distributed programming. Regional interconnect: Cabletime.
Equipment: RCA & Scientific-Atlanta headend; Magnavox amplifiers; Anaconda, Comm/Scope & Cerro cable; Video Data Systems character generator; Oak set top converters; Jerrold addressable set top converters; Scientific-Atlanta satellite antenna; Scientific-Atlanta, Microdyne & Standard Communications satellite receivers.
Miles of plant: 412.0 (coaxial). Additional miles planned: 38.0 (coaxial); 55.0 (fiber optic). Homes passed: 23,000. Total homes in franchised area: 27,000.
Manager: Steve Pollock. Chief technician: Larry Wilson. Marketing director: Linda Houser. Marketing director: Georgia Page.
City fee: 3% of gross.
Ownership: Charter Communications Inc. (MSO). Purchased from Marcus Cable, April 1, 1999.

BROWNSVILLE—Enstar Cable TV, 312 E. Center St., Sikeston, MO 63801. Phone: 573-472-0244. Fax: 572-472-1559. County: Haywood. Also serves Haywood County (portions). ICA: TN0054.
TV Market Ranking: Below 100. Franchise award date: N.A. Franchise expiration date: N.A. Began: March 1, 1981.
Channel capacity: 37 (not 2-way capable). Channels available but not in use: None.
Basic Service
Subscribers: 2,813.
Programming (received off-air): WBBJ-TV (A), WMTU (U) Jackson; WHBQ-TV (F), WKNO (P), WLMT (U), WMC-TV (N), WPTY-TV (A), WREG-TV (C) Memphis.
Programming (via satellite): A & E; American Movie Classics; BET; C-SPAN; ESPN; Fox Family Channel; Fox Sports Net South; Home & Garden Television; MTV; Nashville Network; Nickelodeon; QVC; Sci-Fi Channel; The Weather Channel.
Current originations: Public access.
Fee: $25.00 installation; $21.45 monthly; $10.00 additional installation.
Expanded Basic Service
Subscribers: 2,788.
Programming (via satellite): Discovery Channel; Lifetime; USA Network.
Fee: $1.47 monthly.
Expanded Basic Service 2
Subscribers: 2,739.
Programming (via satellite): WGN-TV (W) Chicago; CNN; Disney Channel; ESPN 2; Headline News; TBS Superstation; Turner Network TV.
Fee: $8.11 monthly.
Pay Service 1
Pay Units: 306.
Programming (via satellite): Cinemax.
Fee: $10.95 monthly.
Pay Service 2
Pay Units: 665.
Programming (via satellite): HBO.
Fee: $11.95 monthly.
Pay Service 3
Pay Units: 249.
Programming (via satellite): Showtime.
Fee: $10.95 monthly.
Pay Service 4
Pay Units: 253.
Programming (via satellite): The Movie Channel.
Fee: $10.95 monthly.
Local advertising: Yes.
Equipment: Blonder-Tongue, Jerrold & Microdyne headend; Jerrold amplifiers; Comm/Scope cable; Jerrold & Scientific-Atlanta set top converters; Microdyne & Scientific-Atlanta satellite antenna; Microdyne & Scientific-Atlanta satellite receivers.
Miles of plant: 100.0 (coaxial). Homes passed: 4,467.
Manager: Dave Huntsman. Chief technician: Kevin Goetz.
Franchise fee: 3% of gross.
Ownership: Falcon Communications LP (MSO), joint venture formed September 30, 1998. See Cable System Ownership.

BYRDSTOWN—CommuniComm Cable, Box 465, 1106 Hwy. 62, Wartburg, TN 37887. Phone: 423-346-6674. County: Pickett. Also serves Pickett County. ICA: TN0109.
TV Market Ranking: Below 100 (Byrdstown, portions of Pickett County); Outside TV Markets (portions of Pickett County). Franchise award date: N.A. Franchise expiration date: January 1, 2007. Began: January 1, 1968.
Channel capacity: 36 (not 2-way capable). Channels available but not in use: 8.
Basic Service
Subscribers: 470.
Programming (received off-air): WBKO (A) Bowling Green; WCTE (P) Cookeville; WDCN (P), WKRN-TV (A), WSMV (N), WTVF (C), WZTV (F) Nashville.
Programming (via satellite): WGN-TV (W) Chicago; A & E; C-SPAN; C-SPAN 2; CNBC; CNN; Country Music TV; Discovery Channel; ESPN; Fox Family Channel; Lifetime; Nashville Network; Nickelodeon; QVC; TBS Superstation; The Weather Channel; Turner Network TV; USA Network.
Fee: $50.00 installation; $22.90 monthly.
Pay Service 1
Pay Units: 50.
Programming (via satellite): Cinemax.
Fee: $9.95 monthly.
Pay Service 2
Pay Units: 30.
Programming (via satellite): Disney Channel.
Fee: $8.95 monthly.
Pay Service 3
Pay Units: 100.
Programming (via satellite): HBO.
Fee: $11.95 monthly.
Equipment: Scientific-Atlanta headend; Scientific-Atlanta amplifiers; Comm/Scope cable; Scientific-Atlanta set top converters; Arcom traps; Scientific-Atlanta satellite receivers.
Miles of plant: 23.0 (coaxial). Homes passed: 560.
Manager: Mike Adams. Chief technician: Faron Jackson.
City fee: 1% of gross.
Ownership: James Cable Partners (MSO).

CALHOUN—Helicon Cable, Box 307, 71332 Hwy. 41S, Jasper, TN 37347-0307. Phones: 423-336-2513; 800-845-9937. Fax: 423-942-2851. Counties: Bradley & McMinn. Also serves Charleston. Plans service to Bradley County, McMinn County. ICA: TN0129.
TV Market Ranking: 78. Franchise award date: N.A. Franchise expiration date: N.A. Began: N.A.
Channel capacity: 12. Channels available but not in use: N.A.
Basic Service
Subscribers: 300.
Programming (received off-air): WDEF-TV (C), WRCB-TV (N), WTVC (A) Chattanooga; WATE-TV (A) Knoxville.
Fee: $15.00 installation; $9.00 monthly.
Equipment: Scientific-Atlanta satellite antenna.
Manager: Anthony Pope. Chief technician: Ricky Brown.
City fee: 3% of gross.
Ownership: Helicon Corp. See Cable System Ownership.

CAMDEN—Time Warner Cable, 2177 Christmasville Rd., Jackson, TN 38305. Phone: 800-997-8204. Fax: 901-424-4257. County: Benton. ICA: TN0130.
TV Market Ranking: Outside TV Markets. Franchise award date: November 1, 1968. Franchise expiration date: November 1, 2008. Began: September 27, 1969.
Channel capacity: 60 (2-way capable). Channels available but not in use: 27.
Basic Service
Subscribers: 1,831; Commercial subscribers: 120.
Programming (received off-air): WBBJ-TV (A), WMTU (U) Jackson; WDCN (P), WKRN-TV (A), WSMV (N), WTVF (C), WZTV (F) Nashville; WPSD-TV (N) Paducah.
Programming (via satellite): WGN-TV (W) Chicago; A & E; American Movie Classics; CNBC; CNN; Discovery Channel; ESPN; Fox Family Channel; Goodlife TV Network; Home Shopping Network; Lifetime; MTV; Nashville Network; Nickelodeon; Odyssey; QVC; TBS Superstation; The Weather Channel; Turner Network TV; USA Network.
Current originations: Automated time-weather.
Fee: $50.00 installation; $11.50 monthly; $1.50 converter; $40.00 additional installation.
Pay Service 1
Pay Units: 210.
Programming (via satellite): Cinemax.
Fee: $40.00 installation; $9.95 monthly.
Pay Service 2
Pay Units: 172.
Programming (via satellite): Disney Channel.
Fee: $40.00 installation; $9.95 monthly.
Pay Service 3
Pay Units: 425.
Programming (via satellite): HBO.
Fee: $40.00 installation; $9.95 monthly.
Pay Service 4
Pay Units: 158.
Programming (via satellite): Showtime.
Fee: $40.00 installation; $9.95 monthly.
Equipment: Scientific-Atlanta headend; Magnavox amplifiers; Times Fiber cable; Scientific-Atlanta satellite antenna.
Miles of plant: 62.0 (coaxial). Additional miles planned: 10.0 (coaxial). Total homes in franchised area: 2,000.
Manager: Jerry Creasy. Chief technician: Ron Crowder. Marketing director: Judy Phelps.
City fee: 3% of gross.
Ownership: Time Warner Cable (MSO).

CARTHAGE—Intermedia, 660 Main Stream Dr., Nashville, TN 37208. Phone: 800-883-6786. Web site: http://www.intermediamtn.com. County: Smith. Also serves Elmwood, Monoville, Rock City, Rome, Smith County, South Carthage, Tanglewood, Turkey Creek. ICA: TN0131.
TV Market Ranking: Below 100. Franchise award date: N.A. Franchise expiration date: N.A. Began: March 27, 1982.
Channel capacity: 39. Channels available but not in use: 12.
Basic Service
Subscribers: 1,778.
Programming (received off-air): WDCN (P), WKRN-TV (A), WSMV (N), WTVF (C), WZTV (F) Nashville.
Current originations: Automated time-weather.
Fee: $60.00 installation; $10.00 monthly; $10.00 additional installation.
Expanded Basic Service
Subscribers: 1,766.
Programming (via satellite): WGN-TV (W) Chicago; CNBC; CNN; Country Music TV; Discovery Channel; ESPN; Fox Family Channel; Nashville Network; Nickelodeon; TBS Superstation; The Weather Channel; Turner Network TV; USA Network.
Fee: $60.00 installation; $6.65 monthly.
Pay Service 1
Pay Units: 84.

Programming (via satellite): Disney Channel.
Fee: $9.95 monthly.

Pay Service 2
Pay Units: 259.
Programming (via satellite): The New Encore.
Fee: $1.50 monthly.

Pay Service 3
Pay Units: 292.
Programming (via satellite): HBO.
Fee: $9.95 monthly.

Pay Service 4
Pay Units: 152.
Programming (via satellite): Showtime.
Fee: $9.95 monthly.

Equipment: Scientific-Atlanta & Catel headend; Magnavox amplifiers; Comm/Scope cable; Oak set top converters; Scientific-Atlanta satellite antenna; Scientific-Atlanta satellite receivers.
Miles of plant: 111.3 (coaxial). Additional miles planned: 2.0 (coaxial). Homes passed: 2,461.
Manager: Kathy Harris. Chief technician: Raymond Strait.
City fee: 3% of gross.
Ownership: InterMedia Partners (MSO). See Cable System Ownership.

CELINA—Mid South Cable TV Inc., 538 Cedar St., McKenzie, TN 38201. Phones: 901-352-2980; 800-541-4208. Fax: 901-352-3533. County: Clay. Also serves Clay County (unincorporated areas). ICA: TN0096.
TV Market Ranking: Below 100 (Celina); Outside TV Markets (Clay County). Franchise award date: N.A. Franchise expiration date: N.A. Began: July 1, 1988.
Channel capacity: 36 (not 2-way capable). Channels available but not in use: 2.

Basic Service
Subscribers: 922.
Programming (received off-air): WBKO (A) Bowling Green; WGRB (F) Campbellsville; WCTE (P) Cookeville; WDCN (P), WKRN-TV (A), WSMV (N), WTVF (C), WZTV (F) Nashville.
Programming (via satellite): WGN-TV (W) Chicago; C-SPAN; CNBC; CNN; Comedy Central; Country Music TV; Discovery Channel; ESPN; Fox Family Channel; Headline News; Home Shopping Network; MTV; Nashville Network; Nickelodeon; QVC; TBS Superstation; The Weather Channel; Travel Channel; Turner Network TV; USA Network; VH1.
Current originations: Automated time-weather.
Fee: $40.00 installation; $17.95 monthly.

Pay Service 1
Pay Units: N.A.
Programming (via satellite): Cinemax; Disney Channel; HBO.
Fee: $8.25 monthly (Disney), $11.18 monthly (Cinemax or HBO).

Equipment: Jerrold & Scientific-Atlanta headend; Jerrold amplifiers; Times Fiber cable; Jerrold set top converters; Pico traps.
Miles of plant: 35.2 (coaxial). Homes passed: 1,050.
Ownership: Mid South Cable TV Inc. (MSO).

CHAPEL HILL—Small Town Cable, 225 Highland Villa, Nashville, TN 37211. Phone: 877-368-2110. Counties: Bedford & Marshall. Also serves Bedford County (unincorporated areas), El Bethel, Holt's Corner, Rover, Unionville. ICA: TN0089.
TV Market Ranking: Below 100. Franchise award date: April 11, 1985. Franchise expiration date: April 11, 2000. Began: April 1, 1985.
Channel capacity: 36. Channels available but not in use: 10.

Basic Service
Subscribers: 852.
Programming (received off-air): WHTN (I) Murfreesboro; WDCN (P), WKRN-TV (A), WSMV (N), WTVF (C), WUXP (U), WZTV (F) Nashville.
Programming (via satellite): WGN-TV (W) Chicago; TBS Superstation.
Fee: $40.00 installation; $10.95 monthly.

Expanded Basic Service
Subscribers: 806.
Programming (via satellite): American Movie Classics; CNN; Cartoon Network; Country Music TV; Discovery Channel; ESPN; ESPN 2; Fox Family Channel; History Channel; Lifetime; MTV; Nashville Network; Nickelodeon; The Weather Channel; Turner Network TV; USA Network.
Fee: $13.00 monthly.

Pay Service 1
Pay Units: 60.
Programming (via satellite): Disney Channel.
Fee: $8.45 monthly.

Pay Service 2
Pay Units: 230.
Programming (via satellite): HBO.
Fee: $11.45 monthly.

Program Guide: The Cable Guide.
Equipment: Cadco headend; Magnavox amplifiers; Times Fiber cable; Hamlin set top converters; Pico traps; Harris satellite antenna; Sony satellite receivers.
Miles of plant: 54.3 (coaxial). Homes passed: 1,303.
Manager: Tom Salters. Chief technician: Doc Collins. Program director: Sheri Smith.
City fee: 3% of basic.
Ownership: Small Town Cable Corp. (MSO). Purchased from Charter Communications Inc., January 1, 1999.

CHATTANOOGA—Comcast Communications, Box 182249, 2030 E. Polymer Dr., Chattanooga, TN 37421. Phone: 423-855-3900. Fax: 423-892-5893. Counties: Hamilton & Sequatchie, TN; Walker, GA. Also serves Lookout Mountain, GA; Collegedale, East Ridge, Hamilton County, Lakesite, Lookout Mountain, Red Bank, Ridgeside, Sequatchie County (unincorporated areas), Signal Mountain, Soddy Daisy, Walden, TN. ICA: TN0003.
TV Market Ranking: 78 (Chattanooga, Collegedale, East Ridge, Hamilton County, Lakesite, Lookout Mountain, Red Bank, Ridgeside, portions of Sequatchie County, Signal Mountain, Soddy Daisy, Walden); Outside TV Markets (portions of Sequatchie County). Franchise award date: October 6, 1970. Franchise expiration date: January 1, 2006. Began: May 25, 1977.
Channel capacity: 78 (not 2-way capable). Channels available but not in use: N.A.

Basic Service
Subscribers: 90,178.
Programming (received off-air): WDEF-TV (C), WDSI-TV (F), WRCB-TV (N), WTCI (P), WTVC (A) Chattanooga.
Programming (via microwave): WCLP-TV (P) Chatsworth.
Programming (via satellite): WGN-TV (W) Chicago; CNN; Headline News; TBS Superstation.
Current originations: Educational access; government access; leased access; automated emergency alert.
Fee: $44.08 installation; $6.46 monthly; $3.52 converter; $20.00 additional installation.

Expanded Basic Service
Subscribers: 83,840.
Programming (via satellite): A & E; American Movie Classics; BET; C-SPAN; C-SPAN 2; CNBC; Cartoon Network; Country Music TV; Discovery Channel; E! Entertainment TV; ESPN; FX; Fox Family Channel; Fox News Channel; Fox Sports Net South; Home & Garden Television; Home Shopping Network; Knowledge TV; Learning Channel; Lifetime; MTV; Nashville Network; Nick at Nite; Nickelodeon; Odyssey; Outdoor Life Network; QVC; Shop at Home; TV Food Network; TV Guide Channel; TV Guide Sneak Prevue; The Health Network; The Weather Channel; Travel Channel; Turner Network TV; USA Network; VH1.
Fee: $44.08 installation; $18.43 monthly.

A la Carte 1
Subscribers: 10,489.
Programming (via satellite): Bravo; Comedy Central; Court TV; ESPN 2; Goodlife TV Network; History Channel; Sci-Fi Channel; Turner Classic Movies; Z Music Television.
Fee: $3.95 monthly (package).

Pay Service 1
Pay Units: 4,405.
Programming (via satellite): Cinemax.
Fee: $20.00 installation; $10.50 monthly.

Pay Service 2
Pay Units: 4,175.
Programming (via satellite): Disney Channel.
Fee: $20.00 installation; $10.50 monthly.

Pay Service 3
Pay Units: 20,248.
Programming (via satellite): HBO.
Fee: $20.00 installation; $11.50 monthly.

Pay Service 4
Pay Units: 8,708.
Programming (via satellite): Showtime.
Fee: $20.00 installation; $10.50 monthly.

Pay Service 5
Pay Units: 2,540.
Programming (via satellite): The Movie Channel.
Fee: $10.50 monthly.

Pay Service 6
Pay Units: 1,566.
Programming (via satellite): DMX.
Fee: $6.95 monthly.

Pay Service 7
Pay Units: 941.
Programming (via satellite): The New Encore.
Fee: $2.00 monthly.

Pay-Per-View
Addressable homes: 37,705.
Action Pay-Per-View; Viewer's Choice.
Fee: $3.95-$4.95.

Local advertising: Yes (insert only). Available in satellite distributed & locally originated programming. Rates: $50.00/30 Seconds. Local sales manager: Bill Thornton. Regional interconnect: Knoxville Interconnect.
Program Guide: CableView.
Equipment: Scientific-Atlanta headend; Scientific-Atlanta amplifiers; Comm/Scope cable; Jerrold & Scientific-Atlanta addressable set top converters; Eagle traps; Scientific-Atlanta satellite antenna; Scientific-Atlanta satellite receivers; ChannelMatic commercial insert.
Miles of plant: 2300.0 (coaxial); 60.0 (fiber optic). Additional miles planned: 60.0 (coaxial); 90.0 (fiber optic). Homes passed: 200,235. Total homes in franchised area: 200,235.
Manager: Gene Shatlock. Chief technician: Hal Dickey.
City fee: 3%-5% of gross.
Ownership: Comcast Cable Communications Inc. (MSO).

CLARKSVILLE—Charter Communications, Box 908, Clarksville, TN 37041-0908. Phone: 931-552-2288. Fax: 931-552-6144. County: Montgomery. Plans service to Montgomery County. ICA: TN0009.
TV Market Ranking: Outside TV Markets. Franchise award date: January 1, 1978. Franchise expiration date: June 1, 2005. Began: October 2, 1978.
Channel capacity: 34 (not 2-way capable). Channels available but not in use: None.

Basic Service
Subscribers: 25,681.
Programming (received off-air): WDCN (P), WKRN-TV (A), WSMV (N), WTVF (C), WUXP (U), WZTV (F) Nashville; allband FM.
Programming (via satellite): WGN-TV (W) Chicago; C-SPAN; Cartoon Network; Fox Family Channel; Home Shopping Network; TBS Superstation; Turner Classic Movies.
Current originations: Automated time-weather; public access; leased access; local sports.
Fee: $39.95 installation; $24.00 monthly.

Expanded Basic Service
Subscribers: 21,400.
Programming (via satellite): American Movie Classics; BET; CNBC; CNN; ESPN; Headline News; Lifetime; MTV; Nashville Network; Nickelodeon; QVC; TV Guide Channel; The Weather Channel; Turner Network TV; USA Network; VH1.
Fee: $9.95 monthly.

Pay Service 1
Pay Units: 4,682.
Programming (via satellite): HBO.
Fee: $20.00 installation; $10.50 monthly.

Pay Service 2
Pay Units: 2,071.
Programming (via satellite): Cinemax.
Fee: $10.50 monthly.

Pay Service 3
Pay Units: 1,731.
Programming (via satellite): Disney Channel.
Fee: $7.95 monthly.

Pay Service 4
Pay Units: 2,477.
Programming (via satellite): Showtime.
Fee: $10.50 monthly.

Pay Service 5
Pay Units: 187.
Programming (via satellite): The Movie Channel.
Fee: $10.00 monthly.

Pay-Per-View
Addressable homes: 18,000.

Local advertising: Yes. Available in locally originated, character-generated, taped & automated programming. Rates: $8.00/30 Seconds. Local sales manager: Robert Belvin. Regional interconnect: Intermedia Television Advertising.
Program Guide: Premium Channels.

Equipment: Jerrold & Scientific-Atlanta headend; Jerrold & Scientific-Atlanta amplifiers; Comm/Scope cable; Scientific-Atlanta set top converters; Scientific-Atlanta addressable set top converters; Eagle traps; Comtech satellite antenna; Scientific-Atlanta & Standard Communications satellite receivers; Channel-Matic commercial insert.
Miles of plant: 57.0 (coaxial). Additional miles planned: 50.0 (coaxial). Homes passed: 30,000.
Manager: Chris Ginn. Chief technician: John Viehland. Program director: John Moseley. Marketing director: Christy Poole.
City fee: 5% of gross.
Ownership: Charter Communications Inc. (MSO).

CLEVELAND—InterMedia, 1235 King St. SE, Cleveland, TN 37323-0656. Phone: 423-479-9743. County: Bradley. Also serves Bradley County, Charleston, McDonald. ICA: TN0013.
TV Market Ranking: 78. Franchise award date: N.A. Franchise expiration date: N.A. Began: October 1, 1976.
Channel capacity: 46. Channels available but not in use: N.A.
Basic Service
Subscribers: 18,263; Commercial subscribers: 33.
Programming (received off-air): WCLP-TV (P) Chatsworth; WDEF-TV (C), WDSI-TV (F), WRCB-TV (N), WTCI (P), WTVC (A) Chattanooga; 14 FMs.
Programming (via satellite): WGN-TV (W) Chicago; Discovery Channel; Fox Family Channel; QVC; TBS Superstation; The Weather Channel.
Current originations: Automated time-weather.
Fee: $25.54 installation; $12.96 monthly.
Expanded Basic Service
Subscribers: 11,314.
Programming (via satellite): A & E; American Movie Classics; Bravo; C-SPAN; CNN; Country Music TV; ESPN; Goodlife TV Network; Headline News; Lifetime; MTV; Nashville Network; Nickelodeon; Odyssey; USA Network; VH1.
Fee: $15.00 installation; $10.00 monthly.
Pay Service 1
Pay Units: 3,019.
Programming (via satellite): Cinemax.
Fee: $10.95 monthly.
Pay Service 2
Pay Units: 1,672.
Programming (via satellite): Disney Channel.
Fee: $15.00 installation; $10.95 monthly.
Pay Service 3
Pay Units: 5,075.
Programming (via satellite): HBO.
Fee: $15.00 installation; $10.95 monthly.
Pay Service 4
Pay Units: 2,465.
Programming (via satellite): Showtime.
Fee: $15.00 installation; $10.95 monthly.
Pay-Per-View
Addressable homes: 13,900.
Hot Choice; Viewer's Choice.
Local advertising: Yes.
Equipment: Jerrold headend; Jerrold amplifiers; Comm/Scope, Times Fiber & General cable; General cameras; Zenith set top converters; Zenith addressable set top converters; Eagle traps; Scientific-Atlanta satellite antenna; Scientific-Atlanta satellite receivers.
Miles of plant: 500.0 (coaxial). Homes passed: 24,000.
Manager: Ron Moore. Chief technician: Bob Compton.
City fee: 3% of gross.
Ownership: InterMedia Partners (MSO). See Cable System Ownership.

CLIFTON—InterMedia Partners, Box 250, 24 Circle Dr., McKenzie, TN 38201. Phone: 901-352-2273. Fax: 901-352-3164. Web site: http://www.intermediamtn.com. County: Wayne. ICA: TN0120.
TV Market Ranking: Outside TV Markets. Franchise award date: N.A. Franchise expiration date: N.A. Began: N.A.
Channel capacity: 42 (not 2-way capable). Channels available but not in use: 16.
Basic Service
Subscribers: 267.
Programming (received off-air): W18BL (I) Adamsville; WOWL-TV (N) Florence; WBBJ-TV (A), WMTU (U) Jackson; WLJT (P) Lexington; WKRN-TV (A), WSMV (N), WTVF (C) Nashville.
Programming (via satellite): FoxNet.
Fee: $39.00 installation; $10.47 monthly.
Expanded Basic Service
Subscribers: 231.
Programming (via satellite): A & E; American Movie Classics; C-SPAN; CNN; Country Music TV; Discovery Channel; Disney Channel; ESPN; ESPN 2; Headline News; Lifetime; Nashville Network; TBS Superstation; Turner Network TV; USA Network.
Fee: $12.00 monthly.
Pay Service 1
Pay Units: 52.
Programming (via satellite): HBO.
Fee: $11.95 monthly.
Local advertising: No.
Equipment: Scientific-Atlanta, Blonder-Tongue & Cadco headend; Jerrold amplifiers; Eagle traps; Scientific-Atlanta satellite antenna; M/A-Com & Scientific-Atlanta satellite receivers.
Miles of plant: 15.1 (coaxial); None (fiber optic). Homes passed: 468.
Manager: Robert L. Pace. Chief technician: Benny Jackson.
City fee: 1% of gross.
Ownership: InterMedia Partners (MSO). See Cable System Ownership.

COLUMBIA—Columbia Cablevision, Box 1039, 2008 S. Main St., Columbia, TN 38401. Phone: 931-388-3550. Fax: 931-381-4446. Counties: Lawrence, Maury & Williamson. Also serves Lawrence County (unincorporated areas), Maury County (portions), Mount Pleasant, Spring Hill, Williamson County (portions). ICA: TN0017.
TV Market Ranking: 30 (portions of Maury County, Spring Hill, Williamson County); Below 100 (portions of Lawrence County, portions of Maury County); Outside TV Markets (Columbia, portions of Lawrence County, portions of Maury County, Mount Pleasant). Franchise award date: N.A. Franchise expiration date: N.A. Began: October 15, 1967.
Channel capacity: 60. Channels available but not in use: 12.
Basic Service
Subscribers: 15,750.
Programming (received off-air): WDCN (P), WKRN-TV (A), WSMV (N), WTVF (C), WZTV (F) Nashville.
Programming (via satellite): WGN-TV (W) Chicago; C-SPAN; C-SPAN 2; Home Shopping Network; Knowledge TV; Learning Channel; QVC; TBS Superstation; ValueVision.
Current originations: Automated time-weather.
Fee: $34.32 installation; $8.48 monthly.
Expanded Basic Service
Subscribers: 14,451.
Programming (via satellite): A & E; American Movie Classics; BET; CNBC; CNN; Cartoon Network; Comedy Central; Country Music TV; Discovery Channel; E! Entertainment TV; ESPN; ESPN 2; Fox Family Channel; Fox Sports Net South; Headline News; Lifetime; MTV; Nashville Network; Nickelodeon; Odyssey; TV Guide Channel; The Weather Channel; Travel Channel; Trinity Bcstg. Network; Turner Classic Movies; Turner Network TV; USA Network; VH1.
Fee: $16.44 monthly.
Pay Service 1
Pay Units: 9,120.
Programming (via satellite): Cinemax; Disney Channel; HBO; Showtime; The Movie Channel.
Fee: $20.00 installation; $9.95 monthly (each).
Pay Service 2
Pay Units: 637.
Programming (via satellite): DMX.
Fee: $20.00 installation; $8.95 monthly.
Pay-Per-View
Special events.
Fee: Varies.
Local advertising: Yes. Regional interconnect: Intermedia Television Advertising.
Equipment: Jerrold headend; Anaconda amplifiers; Comm/Scope cable; Comtech satellite antenna.
Miles of plant: 444.0 (coaxial); 100.0 (fiber optic). Homes passed: 20,680.
Manager: Chris Karn. Chief technician: Gary Powell.
City fee: 3%-6% of gross.
Ownership: Rifkin & Associates Inc. (MSO). See Cable System Ownership.

COOKEVILLE—Cookeville Cablevision, Box 1250, Cookeville, TN 38503-1250. Phone: 615-5285436. Fax: 615-528-9324. Counties: Putnam & White. Also serves Algood, Baxter, Putnam County (portions), White County (portions). ICA: TN0020.
TV Market Ranking: Below 100. Franchise award date: N.A. Franchise expiration date: N.A. Began: January 1, 1968.
Channel capacity: 37 (not 2-way capable). Channels available but not in use: 2.
Basic Service
Subscribers: 13,700.
Programming (received off-air): WCTE (P), WNPX (X) Cookeville; WDCN (P), WKRN-TV (A), WSMV (N), WTVF (C), WZTV (F) Nashville.
Programming (via satellite): WGN-TV (W) Chicago; C-SPAN; Fox Family Channel; Home Shopping Network; TBS Superstation.
Current originations: Automated time-weather; local news.
Fee: $28.17 installation; $8.66 monthly; $1.95 converter.
Expanded Basic Service
Subscribers: 11,700.
Programming (via satellite): A & E; American Movie Classics; CNN; Comedy Central; Country Music TV; Discovery Channel; ESPN; Fox Sports Net South; Goodlife TV Network; Headline News; Lifetime; MTV; Nashville Network; Nickelodeon; The Weather Channel; Trinity Bcstg. Network; Turner Network TV; USA Network; VH1.
Fee: $16.22 monthly.
Pay Service 1
Pay Units: 6,600.
Programming (via satellite): Cinemax; Disney Channel; HBO; Showtime; The Movie Channel.
Fee: $10.00 installation; $4.95 monthly (TMC), $5.95 monthly (Showtime), $9.95 monthly (Cinemax, Disney or HBO).
Pay Service 2
Pay Units: 300.
Programming (via satellite): DMX.
Fee: $10.00 installation; $8.95 monthly.
Pay-Per-View
Special events.
Fee: Varies.
Local advertising: Yes. Regional interconnect: Intermedia Television Advertising.
Equipment: AFC satellite antenna.
Miles of plant: 421.0 (coaxial); None (fiber optic). Homes passed: 16,600.
Manager: Jay Bradshaw. Chief technician: Jerry Frazier.
Ownership: Rifkin & Associates Inc. (MSO). See Cable System Ownership.

CORNERSVILLE—Small Town Cable, 225 Highland Villa, Nashville, TN 37211. Phone: 877-368-2110. County: Marshall. ICA: TN0133.
TV Market Ranking: Outside TV Markets. Franchise award date: July 18, 1988. Franchise expiration date: July 18, 2003. Began: N.A.
Channel capacity: 24. Channels available but not in use: 1.
Basic Service
Subscribers: 240.
Programming (received off-air): WAAY-TV (A) Huntsville-Decatur; WDCN (P), WKRN-TV (A), WSMV (N), WTVF (C), WZTV (F) Nashville.
Fee: $40.00 installation; $10.95 monthly.
Expanded Basic Service
Subscribers: 228.
Programming (via satellite): WGN-TV (W) Chicago; American Movie Classics; CNN; Cartoon Network; Country Music TV; Discovery Channel; ESPN; ESPN 2; Fox Family Channel; History Channel; Lifetime; MTV; Nashville Network; Nickelodeon; TBS Superstation; Turner Network TV; USA Network.
Fee: $13.00 monthly.
Pay Service 1
Pay Units: 12.
Programming (via satellite): Disney Channel.
Fee: $8.45 monthly.
Pay Service 2
Pay Units: 47.
Programming (via satellite): HBO.
Fee: $11.45 monthly.
Miles of plant: 6.0 (coaxial). Homes passed: 335.
Manager: Tom Salters. Chief technician: Doc Collins. Program director: Sheri Smith.
Ownership: Small Town Cable Corp. (MSO). Purchased from Charter Communications Inc., January 1, 1999.

COUNCE—Pickwick Cablevision, Box 12, 18455 Old St. Rd. 57, Pickwick Dam, TN 38365-0012. Phone: 901-689-5722. Fax: 901-689-3632. County: Hardin. Also serves Hardin County (portions), Pickwick. ICA: TN0100.
TV Market Ranking: Below 100 (portions of Hardin County, Pickwick); Outside TV Markets (Counce, portions of Hardin County). Franchise award date: N.A. Franchise expiration date: N.A. Began: July 1, 1978.
Channel capacity: 19 (not 2-way capable). Channels available but not in use: None.
Basic Service
Subscribers: 840.
Programming (received off-air): WOWL-TV (N), WYLE (W) Florence; WBBJ-TV (A) Jackson; WHBQ-TV (F), WKNO (P), WMC-TV (N), WREG-TV (C) Memphis.
Programming (via satellite): WGN-TV (W) Chicago; CNN; Discovery Channel; ESPN; Fox Family Channel; Nashville Network; Nick at Nite; Nickelodeon; TBS Superstation; The Weather Channel; Turner Classic Movies; Turner Network TV; USA Network.
Fee: $30.00 installation; $16.75 monthly.
Pay Service 1
Pay Units: N.A.
Programming (via satellite): HBO.
Fee: $30.00 installation; $10.44 monthly.
Local advertising: No.
Miles of plant: 40.0 (coaxial). Homes passed: 900.
Manager: Robert Campbell Sr.
Ownership: Pickwick Cablevision.

COVINGTON—Enstar Cable TV, 312 E. Center St., Sikeston, MO 63801. Phone: 573-472-0244. Fax: 573-472-1559. County: Tipton. Also serves Brighton, Burlison, Garland, Gilt Edge, Tipton County. ICA: TN0066.

TV Market Ranking: 26 (Brighton, Burlison, Covington, Garland, Gilt Edge, portions of Tipton County); Outside TV Markets (portions of Gilt Edge, portions of Tipton County). Franchise award date: N.A. Franchise expiration date: N.A. Began: January 1, 1981.

Channel capacity: 36 (not 2-way capable). Channels available but not in use: None.

Basic Service

Subscribers: 3,090.

Programming (received off-air): WBBJ-TV (A) Jackson; WHBQ-TV (F), WKNO (P), WLMT (U), WMC-TV (N), WPTY-TV (A), WPXX-TV (X), WREG-TV (C) Memphis.

Programming (via satellite): A & E; American Movie Classics; BET; C-SPAN; ESPN; Fox Family Channel; Fox Sports Net South; Home & Garden Television; MTV; Nashville Network; Nickelodeon; QVC; The Inspirational Network; The Weather Channel.

Current originations: Public access.

Fee: $25.00 installation; $21.03 monthly; $10.00 additional installation.

Expanded Basic Service

Subscribers: 3,062.

Programming (via satellite): Discovery Channel; Lifetime; USA Network.

Fee: $1.25 monthly.

Expanded Basic Service 2

Subscribers: 3,027.

Programming (via satellite): WGN-TV (W) Chicago; CNN; Disney Channel; Headline News; TBS Superstation; Turner Network TV.

Fee: $7.94 monthly.

Pay Service 1

Pay Units: 273.

Programming (via satellite): Cinemax.

Fee: $10.95 monthly.

Pay Service 2

Pay Units: 763.

Programming (via satellite): HBO.

Fee: $11.95 monthly.

Pay Service 3

Pay Units: 291.

Programming (via satellite): Showtime.

Fee: $10.95 monthly.

Pay Service 4

Pay Units: 273.

Programming (via satellite): The Movie Channel.

Fee: $10.95 monthly.

Local advertising: Yes. Available in character-generated programming.

Equipment: Electrohome, Jerrold & Scientific-Atlanta headend; Delta-Benco-Cascade & Scientific-Atlanta amplifiers; Comm/Scope cable; Jerrold & Scientific-Atlanta set top converters; Eagle, Intercept & Pico traps; Microdyne satellite antenna; Electrohome satellite receivers.

Miles of plant: 180.0 (coaxial). Homes passed: 6,334.

Manager: Dave Huntsman. Chief technician: Kevin Goetz.

Franchise fee: 3% of gross.

Ownership: Falcon Communications LP (MSO), joint venture formed September 30, 1998. See Cable System Ownership.

CROSSVILLE—InterMedia, 725 Louisville Rd., Alcoa, TN 37701-1846. Phone: 1400. Fax: 423-983-0383. County: Cumberland. Also serves Cumberland County, Lake Tansi. ICA: TN0134.

TV Market Ranking: Below 100. Franchise award date: N.A. Franchise expiration date: September 12, 2001. Began: July 21, 1979.

Channel capacity: 62. Channels available but not in use: 26.

Basic Service

Subscribers: 5,058.

Programming (received off-air): WCTE (P) Cookeville; WATE-TV (A), WBIR-TV (N), WTNZ (F), WVLT-TV (C) Knoxville.

Programming (via satellite): C-SPAN; C-SPAN 2; Headline News; QVC; Trinity Bcstg. Network.

Current originations: Local news.

Fee: $19.95 installation; $9.37 monthly.

Expanded Basic Service

Subscribers: N.A.

Programming (via satellite): WGN-TV (W) Chicago; A & E; American Movie Classics; CNBC; CNN; Country Music TV; Discovery Channel; ESPN; Fox Family Channel; Fox Sports Net South; Lifetime; MTV; Nashville Network; Nick at Nite; Nickelodeon; TBS Superstation; The Weather Channel; Turner Network TV; USA Network.

Fee: $8.04 monthly.

Pay Service 1

Pay Units: 2,292.

Programming (via satellite): Cinemax; Disney Channel; HBO; Showtime; The Movie Channel.

Fee: $4.95 monthly (Disney), $9.95 monthly (Cinemax, HBO, Showtime or TMC).

Equipment: AFC satellite antenna.

Miles of plant & homes passed included with Alcoa, TN.

Office manager: Paul Maynard. Technical operations manager: Mark Haley. Chief engineer: Dale Taylor. Business manager: Cathy Dunford.

City fee: 3% of gross.

Ownership: InterMedia Partners (MSO). Sale pends to Rifkin & Associates Inc.

DAYTON—Helicon Communications, 101 N. Commerce St., Summerville, GA 30747. Phone: 706-857-2551. County: Rhea. ICA: TN0064.

TV Market Ranking: 78. Franchise award date: N.A. Franchise expiration date: N.A. Began: July 1, 1980.

Channel capacity: N.A. Channels available but not in use: N.A.

Basic Service

Subscribers: N.A.

Programming (received off-air): WDEF-TV (C), WRCB-TV (N), WTCI (P), WTVC (A) Chattanooga; WBIR-TV (N), WVLT-TV (C) Knoxville.

Programming (via satellite): WGN-TV (W) Chicago; TBS Superstation.

Fee: N.A.

Equipment: Scientific-Atlanta satellite antenna.

Miles of plant: 19.9 (coaxial). Homes passed: 2,500.

Ownership: Helicon Corp. (MSO). See Cable System Ownership.

DECATUR—Helicon Communications, 101 N. Commerce St., Summerville, GA 30747. Phone: 706-857-2551. County: Meigs. ICA: TN0117.

TV Market Ranking: Below 100. Franchise award date: N.A. Franchise expiration date: N.A. Began: July 1, 1983.

Channel capacity: N.A. Channels available but not in use: N.A.

Basic Service

Subscribers: N.A.

Programming (received off-air): WDEF-TV (C), WDSI-TV (F), WRCB-TV (N), WTCI (P), WTVC (A) Chattanooga; WTNZ (F) Knoxville.

Programming (via satellite): WGN-TV (W) Chicago; TBS Superstation.

Fee: N.A.

Miles of plant: 13.0 (coaxial). Homes passed: 300.

Ownership: Helicon Corp. (MSO). See Cable System Ownership.

DICKSON—InterMedia Partners, 660 Mainstream Dr., Nashville, TN 37228. Phone: 615-244-5900. Fax: 615-255-6528.

Web site: http://www.intermediamtn.com.

Counties: Cheatham, Davidson & Dickson. Also serves Burns, Charlotte, Cheatham County (portions), Davidson County (western portion), Dickson County, Kingston Springs, Pegram, White Bluff. ICA: TN0039.

TV Market Ranking: 30 (Burns, Charlotte, Cheatham County, Western portion of Davidson County, Dickson, portions of Dickson County, Kingston Springs, Pegram, White Bluff); Outside TV Markets (portions of Dickson County). Franchise award date: August 31, 1982. Franchise expiration date: N.A. Began: July 1, 1983.

Channel capacity: 200 (not 2-way capable). Channels available but not in use: None.

Basic Service

Subscribers: 6,000.

Programming (received off-air): WPGD (I) Hendersonville; WJFB (I) Lebanon; WHTN (I) Murfreesboro; WDCN (P), WKRN-TV (A), WNAB (W), WSMV (N), WTVF (C), WUXP (U), WZTV (F) Nashville.

Current originations: Public access; educational access; government access; leased access.

Fee: $39.00 installation; $33.54 monthly.

Digital Basic Service

Subscribers: N.A.

Programming (via satellite): BBC America; BET on Jazz; CNN/SI; DMX; Discovery Civilization Channel; Discovery Health Channel; Discovery Home & Leisure Channel; Discovery Kids Channel; Discovery People; Discovery Science Channel; Discovery Wings Channel; ESPN Classic Sports; ESPNews; Fox Sports World; Game Show Network; Golf Channel; Goodlife TV Network; Independent Film Channel; International Channel; Kaleidoscope; Lifetime; MuchMusic Network; Outdoor Channel; Outdoor Life Network; Ovation; Romance Classics; Speedvision; The Barker; The Inspirational Network; Turner Classic Movies; Weatherscan by the Weather Channel; ZDTV.

Fee: N.A.

Expanded Basic Service

Subscribers: 5,800.

Programming (via satellite): WGN-TV (W) Chicago; A & E; American Movie Classics; Animal Planet; BET; Bravo; C-SPAN; CNBC; CNN; Cartoon Network; Comedy Central; Country Music TV; Discovery Channel; Disney Channel; E! Entertainment TV; ESPN; ESPN 2; FX; fXM: Movies from Fox; Fox Family Channel; Fox News Channel; Fox Sports Net South; Headline News; History Channel; Home & Garden Television; Home Shopping Network; Learning Channel; Lifetime; MSNBC; MTV; Nashville Network; Nick at Nite; Nick at Nite's TV Land; Nickelodeon; Odyssey; QVC; Sci-Fi Channel; TBS Superstation; TV Guide Channel; TV Guide Sneak Prevue; The Weather Channel; Trinity Bcstg. Network; Turner Network TV; USA Network; Univision; VH1.

Fee: N.A.

Pay Service 1

Pay Units: 3,081.

Programming (via satellite): Cinemax (multiplexed); HBO (multiplexed); Showtime (multiplexed); Starz!; The New Encore.

Fee: N.A.

Digital Pay Service 1

Pay Units: N.A.

Programming (via satellite): BET Movies/Starz!; Cinemax (multiplexed); Encore Action; Encore Love Stories; Encore Mystery; Encore True Stories & Drama; Encore Westerns; Flix (multiplexed); HBO; HBO Comedy; HBO Family; HBO Plus; HBO Signature; HBO Zone; Showtime (multiplexed); Starz!; Starz! Theater; Sundance Channel (multiplexed); The Movie Channel (multiplexed); The New Encore.

Fee: N.A.

Pay-Per-View

Action Pay-Per-View; Playboy TV; movies; special events.

Local advertising: Yes. Local sales manager: Sanjiv Moore. Regional interconnect: Intermedia Television Advertising.

Equipment: Triple Crown headend; Scientific-Atlanta amplifiers; CommScope cable; Video Data Systems character generator; Scientific-Atlanta set top converters; Eagle traps; Scientific-Atlanta satellite antenna; Automation Techniques satellite receivers.

Miles of plant: 259.0 (coaxial); 36.0 (fiber optic). Homes passed: 11,665. Total homes in franchised area: 18,135.

Manager: Robert L. Pace. Chief technician: Benny Jackson.

City fee: 5% of gross.

Ownership: InterMedia Partners (MSO). See Cable System Ownership.

DOVER—Mediacom, 90 N. Main St., Benton, KY 42025. Phone: 502-527-9939. Fax: 502-527-0813. County: Stewart. Also serves Stewart County. ICA: TN0092.

TV Market Ranking: Outside TV Markets. Franchise award date: N.A. Franchise expiration date: N.A. Began: October 1, 1982.

Channel capacity: 41. Channels available but not in use: 12.

Basic Service

Subscribers: 1,018.

Programming (received off-air): WDCN (P), WKRN-TV (A), WSMV (N), WTVF (C), WUXP (U), WZTV (F) Nashville.

Programming (via satellite): WGN-TV (W) Chicago; American Movie Classics; C-SPAN; CNN; Country Music TV; Discovery Channel; ESPN; Fox Family Channel; Headline News; MTV; Nashville Network; Nickelodeon; QVC; TBS Superstation; The Inspirational Network; The Weather Channel; Turner Network TV; USA Network.

Fee: $36.95 installation; $19.23 monthly.

Pay Service 1

Pay Units: 99.

Programming (via satellite): Cinemax.

Fee: $10.50 monthly.

Pay Service 2

Pay Units: 293.

Programming (via satellite): Disney Channel.

Fee: $9.00 monthly.

Pay Service 3

Pay Units: 273.

Programming (via satellite): HBO.

Fee: $10.50 monthly.

Pay Service 4

Pay Units: 278.

Programming (via satellite): Showtime.

Fee: $10.50 monthly.

Pay Service 5

Pay Units: 126.

Programming (via satellite): The Movie Channel.

Fee: N.A.

Equipment: Drake, DX Engineering & Scientific-Atlanta headend; Magnavox & Scientific-Atlanta amplifiers; Comm/Scope, Magnavox & Scientific-Atlanta cable; Scientific-Atlanta set top

converters; Scientific-Atlanta satellite receivers.
Miles of plant: 78.0 (coaxial). Homes passed: 1,205. Total homes in franchised area: 4,478.
Manager: Gene Brock. Chief technician: Bruce Sears.
Ownership: Mediacom LLC (MSO).

DRESDEN—Dresden Cable Inc., 106 W. Maple, Dresden, TN 38225. Phone: 901-364-5259. County: Weakley. ICA: TN0102.
TV Market Ranking: Outside TV Markets. Franchise award date: N.A. Franchise expiration date: N.A. Began: April 1, 1981.
Channel capacity: 17. Channels available but not in use: N.A.
Basic Service
Subscribers: N.A.
Programming (received off-air): KFVS-TV (C) Cape Girardeau; WBBJ-TV (A) Jackson; WLJT (P) Lexington; WHBQ-TV (F) Memphis; WKRN-TV (A), WSMV (N) Nashville; WPSD-TV (N) Paducah.
Programming (via satellite): WGN-TV (W) Chicago; TBS Superstation.
Fee: $20.00 installation; $9.50 monthly.
Pay Service 1
Pay Units: N.A.
Programming (via satellite): HBO; The Movie Channel.
Fee: $9.50 monthly (each).
Miles of plant: 11.8 (coaxial). Homes passed: 800.
Manager: Kathleen Walden. Chief technician: Richard Hutcherson.
Ownership: Dresden Cable Inc.

DUNLAP—Bledsoe Telephone Co-op/CATV, Box 609, Cumberland Ave., Pikeville, TN 37367. Phone: 423-447-2121. Fax: 423-447-2498. County: Sequatchie. Also serves Cartwright, Sequatchie County (central portion). ICA: TN0040.
TV Market Ranking: 78. Franchise award date: N.A. Franchise expiration date: January 1, 2000. Began: January 1, 1983.
Channel capacity: 22 (not 2-way capable). Channels available but not in use: None.
Basic Service
Subscribers: 2,472.
Programming (received off-air): WDEF-TV (C), WDSI-TV (F), WRCB-TV (N), WTCI (P), WTVC (A) Chattanooga.
Programming (via satellite): WGN-TV (W) Chicago; A & E; CNN; Country Music TV; Discovery Channel; ESPN; Fox Sports Net South; Headline News; Home Shopping Network; Learning Channel; Nashville Network; TBS Superstation; The Weather Channel; Trinity Bcstg. Network; Turner Network TV; USA Network.
Fee: $40.00 installation; $16.00 monthly.
Pay Service 1
Pay Units: 299.
Programming (via satellite): The Movie Channel.
Fee: $10.00 installation; $10.50 monthly.
Equipment: Scientific-Atlanta headend; C-COR amplifiers; Comm/Scope cable; Beston character generator; Oak & Scientific-Atlanta set top converters; Eagle traps; Scientific-Atlanta satellite antenna; Scientific-Atlanta satellite receivers.
Miles of plant: 194.0 (coaxial). Additional miles planned: 42.0 (coaxial). Homes passed: 4,291. Total homes in franchised area: 8,057.
Manager: Greg Anderson. Chief technician: Edward Harmon.
City fee: 3% of gross.
Ownership: Bledsoe Telephone Co. (MSO).

DYER—Enstar Cable TV, 312 E. Center St., Sikeston, MO 63801. Phone: 573-472-0244. Fax: 573-472-1559. Counties: Gibson & Obion. Also serves Gibson County, Kenton, Obion County, Rutherford. ICA: TN0057.
TV Market Ranking: Below 100 (Dyer, portions of Gibson County, Rutherford); Outside TV Markets (portions of Gibson County, Kenton, Obion County). Franchise award date: N.A. Franchise expiration date: N.A. Began: March 19, 1974.
Channel capacity: 60. Channels available but not in use: 24.
Basic Service
Subscribers: 2,174.
Programming (received off-air): KFVS-TV (C) Cape Girardeau; WBBJ-TV (A), WMTU (U) Jackson; WLJT (P) Lexington; WHBQ-TV (F), WKNO (P), WMC-TV (N), WPTY-TV (A), WREG-TV (C) Memphis; WPSD-TV (N) Paducah.
Programming (via satellite): C-SPAN; CNN; ESPN; FX; Fox Family Channel; Headline News; Home & Garden Television; Home Shopping Network; QVC; Sci-Fi Channel; Trinity Bcstg. Network; Turner Network TV.
Fee: $15.00 installation; $19.16 monthly.
Expanded Basic Service
Subscribers: 2,149.
Programming (via satellite): Discovery Channel; Lifetime; Nashville Network; USA Network.
Fee: $2.48 monthly.
Expanded Basic Service 2
Subscribers: 2,013.
Programming (via satellite): WGN-TV (W) Chicago; American Movie Classics; Disney Channel; ESPN 2; TBS Superstation; The Weather Channel.
Fee: $6.82 monthly.
Pay Service 1
Pay Units: 135.
Programming (via satellite): Cinemax.
Fee: $20.00 installation; $10.95 monthly.
Pay Service 2
Pay Units: 332.
Programming (via satellite): HBO.
Fee: $11.95 monthly.
Pay Service 3
Pay Units: 101.
Programming (via satellite): Showtime.
Fee: $10.95 monthly.
Pay Service 4
Pay Units: 65.
Programming (via satellite): The Movie Channel.
Fee: $10.95 monthly.
Equipment: Jerrold headend; Jerrold amplifiers; Times Fiber cable; Comtech satellite antenna.
Miles of plant: 84.0 (coaxial). Homes passed: 2,913. Total homes in franchised area: 3,500.
Manager: Dave Huntsman. Chief technician: Kevin Goetz.
Franchise fee: 3%-5% of gross.
Ownership: Falcon Communications LP (MSO), joint venture formed September 30, 1998. See Cable System Ownership.

DYERSBURG—Cable One, Box 888, 416 W. Court, Dyersburg, TN 38024. Phones: 901-285-4174; 800-696-6923. Fax: 901-287-8040. Counties: Crockett & Dyer. Also serves Dyer County, Finley, Friendship, Lennox, Roellen, Tigrett. ICA: TN0025.
TV Market Ranking: Below 100 (portions of Dyer County, Dyersburg, Finley, Friendship, Roellen, Tigrett); Outside TV Markets (portions of Dyer County, Dyersburg, Lennox). Franchise award date: May 24, 1966. Franchise expiration date: September 9, 2001. Began: April 1, 1967.

Channel capacity: 70 (2-way capable; operating 2-way). Channels available but not in use: 2.
Basic Service
Subscribers: 10,069; Commercial subscribers: 27.
Programming (received off-air): KFVS-TV (C) Cape Girardeau; WBBJ-TV (A) Jackson; WLJT (P) Lexington; WHBQ-TV (F), WKNO (P), WLMT (U), WMC-TV (N), WPTY-TV (A), WREG-TV (C) Memphis; WPSD-TV (N) Paducah.
Programming (via satellite): WGN-TV (W) Chicago; A & E; American Movie Classics; BET; C-SPAN; C-SPAN 2; CNBC; CNN; Cartoon Network; Comedy Central; Country Music TV; Court TV; Discovery Channel; Disney Channel; ESPN; FX; Fox Family Channel; Headline News; History Channel; Home & Garden Television; Home Shopping Network; Learning Channel; Lifetime; MTV; Nashville Network; Nickelodeon; Odyssey; QVC; Sci-Fi Channel; TBS Superstation; TV Guide Channel; The Weather Channel; Travel Channel; Trinity Bcstg. Network; Turner Classic Movies; Turner Network TV; USA Network; VH1.
Current originations: Automated time-weather; educational access; government access; automated emergency alert.
Planned originations: Public access.
Fee: $35.77 installation; $27.57 monthly; $0.90 converter.
Pay Service 1
Pay Units: 2,251.
Programming (via satellite): Cinemax (multiplexed).
Fee: $5.00 installation; $13.95 monthly.
Pay Service 2
Pay Units: 2,339.
Programming (via satellite): HBO (multiplexed).
Fee: $5.00 installation; $13.95 monthly.
Pay Service 3
Pay Units: 822.
Programming (via satellite): The Movie Channel.
Fee: $5.00 installation; $10.95 monthly.
Pay Service 4
Pay Units: 819.
Programming (via satellite): Showtime (multiplexed).
Fee: $5.00 installation; $10.95 monthly.
Pay Service 5
Pay Units: 149.
Programming (via satellite): DMX.
Fee: $5.00 installation; $7.95 monthly.
Pay-Per-View
Addressable homes: 4,838.
Action Pay-Per-View; Hot Choice; Spice; Viewer's Choice.
Fee: Varies.
Local advertising: Yes (insert only). Available in satellite distributed, locally originated & character-generated programming. Rates: $4.00/30 Seconds. Local sales manager: Charles Dawson.
Program Guide: Premium Channels.
Equipment: Scientific-Atlanta headend; Scientific-Atlanta amplifiers; Comm/Scope & Trilogy cable; Standard Components set top converters; Zenith addressable set top converters; Eagle traps; Andrew satellite antenna; Scientific-Atlanta satellite receivers.
Miles of plant: 270.0 (coaxial); 36.0 (fiber optic). Homes passed: 13,500.
Manager: Jim Duck. Chief technician: James Eudaley. Marketing director: Kim Carman.
City fee: 5% of gross.
Ownership: Cable One Inc. (MSO).

EAGLEVILLE—Mid South Cable TV Inc., Box 910, 538 Cedar St., McKenzie, TN 38201. Phone: 901-352-2980. Fax: 901-352-3533. Counties: Rutherford & Williamson. Also serves Kirkland, Williamson County (unincorporated areas). ICA: TN0136.
TV Market Ranking: Below 100. Franchise award date: N.A. Franchise expiration date: N.A. Began: N.A.
Channel capacity: 27. Channels available but not in use: 5.
Basic Service
Subscribers: N.A.
Programming (received off-air): WDCN (P), WKRN-TV (A), WSMV (N), WTVF (C), WUXP (U), WZTV (F) Nashville.
Programming (via satellite): WGN-TV (W) Chicago; A & E; CNN; Country Music TV; Discovery Channel; ESPN; Fox Family Channel; Lifetime; MTV; Nashville Network; Nickelodeon; TBS Superstation; USA Network.
Fee: $12.95 monthly.
Pay Service 1
Pay Units: N.A.
Programming (via satellite): Disney Channel; HBO; Showtime.
Fee: $9.95 monthly (each).
Manager: Gary Blount.
Ownership: Mid South Cable TV Inc. (MSO).

FAIRFIELD GLADE—Phoenix Cable, Box 1729, 27 Druid Circle, Fairfield Glade, TN 38558. Phones: 931-456-0550; 800-228-8296. Fax: 931-456-1913. County: Cumberland. Also serves Crossville (unincorporated areas), Cumberland County (portions). ICA: TN0081.
TV Market Ranking: Below 100. Franchise award date: April 20, 1981. Franchise expiration date: N.A. Began: December 1, 1981.
Channel capacity: 35. Channels available but not in use: 6.
Basic Service
Subscribers: 2,516.
Programming (received off-air): WCTE (P) Cookeville; WATE-TV (A), WBIR-TV (N), WKOP-TV (P), WTNZ (F), WVLT-TV (C) Knoxville; allband FM.
Programming (via satellite): WGN-TV (W) Chicago; A & E; C-SPAN; CNBC; CNN; Discovery Channel; ESPN; Fox Family Channel; Fox Sports Net South; Golf Channel; History Channel; Home & Garden Television; Lifetime; Nashville Network; QVC; TBS Superstation; The Inspirational Network; The Weather Channel; Travel Channel; Turner Classic Movies; Turner Network TV; USA Network.
Current originations: Automated time-weather; local news.
Fee: $43.75 installation; $25.67 monthly; $1.50 converter; $26.25 additional installation.
Pay Service 1
Pay Units: 233.
Programming (via satellite): HBO.
Fee: $26.25 installation; $11.69 monthly.

Pay Service 2
Pay Units: 137.
Programming (via satellite): Showtime.
Fee: $26.25 installation; $11.69 monthly.
Pay Service 3
Pay Units: 55.
Programming (via satellite): Disney Channel.
Fee: $10.05 monthly.
Equipment: Scientific-Atlanta headend; Jerrold amplifiers; Comm/Scope & Scientific-Atlanta cable; BEI character generator; Vitek traps; Scientific-Atlanta satellite antenna; Scientific-Atlanta satellite receivers.
Miles of plant: 78.5 (coaxial). Homes passed: 3,268. Total homes in franchised area: 3,300.
Manager: Diane Bilbery. Chief technician: Charles Himelrick. Marketing & program director: John E. Finley.
City fee: 3% of basic gross.
Ownership: Phoenix Cable Inc. (MSO).

FAYETTEVILLE—Cablevision Communications, Box 686, Columbia, TN 38402. Phone: 888-307-0800. Fax: 931-381-4446. County: Lincoln. ICA: TN0185.
TV Market Ranking: 96. Franchise award date: January 1, 1989. Franchise expiration date: January 1, 2009. Began: March 1, 1992.
Channel capacity: 61. Channels available but not in use: 7.
Basic Service
Subscribers: 500.
Programming (received off-air): WAAY-TV (A), WAFF (N), WHNT-TV (C), WZDX (F) Huntsville-Decatur; WDCN (P), WKRN-TV (A), WSMV (N), WTVF (C), WZTV (F) Nashville.
Programming (via satellite): Headline News; TBS Superstation.
Fee: $8.95 monthly.
Expanded Basic Service
Subscribers: 495.
Programming (via satellite): WGN-TV (W) Chicago; A & E; American Movie Classics; BET; C-SPAN; CNBC; CNN; Comedy Central; Country Music TV; Discovery Channel; ESPN; Fox Family Channel; Fox Sports Net; Learning Channel; Lifetime; MTV; Nashville Network; Nickelodeon; QVC; The New Encore; The Weather Channel; Travel Channel; Trinity Bcstg. Network; USA Network; VH1.
Fee: $6.00 monthly.
Pay Service 1
Pay Units: N.A.
Programming (via satellite): Cinemax; Disney Channel; HBO; Showtime; The Movie Channel.
Fee: $5.00 monthly (Showtime), $5.95 monthly (Disney), $8.95 monthly (Cinemax, HBO or TMC).
Pay-Per-View
Special events.
Fee: Varies.
Miles of plant: 45.0 (coaxial); None (fiber optic). Homes passed: 1,200.
Manager: Bill Mashburn.
Ownership: Rifkin & Associates Inc. (MSO). See Cable System Ownership.

FRIENDSVILLE—FrontierVision, Suite P-200, 1777 S. Harrison St., Denver, CO 80210. Phone: 303-757-1588. Fax: 303-757-6105. Counties: Blount & Loudon. Also serves Greenback, Loudon County (portions). ICA: TN0062.
TV Market Ranking: 71 (Friendsville, Greenback, portions of Loudon County); Below 100 (portions of Loudon County). Franchise award date: December 23, 1983. Franchise expiration date: December 23, 1998. Began: N.A.
Channel capacity: 42 (not 2-way capable). Channels available but not in use: 11.
Basic Service
Subscribers: 1,190.
Programming (received off-air): WATE-TV (A), WBIR-TV (N), WTNZ (F), WVLT-TV (C) Knoxville; WSJK (P) Sneedville.
Programming (via satellite): WGN-TV (W) Chicago; A & E; CNN; Country Music TV; Discovery Channel; ESPN; Fox Family Channel; Headline News; Home Shopping Network; Lifetime; Nashville Network; Nickelodeon; TBS Superstation; Turner Network TV; VH1.
Fee: $40.00 installation; $16.95 monthly; $2.00 converter.
Pay Service 1
Pay Units: 69.
Programming (via satellite): HBO.
Fee: $15.00 installation; $10.95 monthly.
Pay Service 2
Pay Units: 194.
Programming (via satellite): Showtime.
Fee: $15.00 installation; $10.00 monthly.
Pay Service 3
Pay Units: 188.
Programming (via satellite): The Movie Channel.
Fee: N.A.
Local advertising: No.
Program Guide: CableView.
Equipment: Magnavox amplifiers; Comm/Scope & Times Fiber cable; Scientific-Atlanta set top converters; Eagle & PPC traps; Microdyne satellite antenna; Microdyne satellite receivers.
Miles of plant: 79.4 (coaxial). Homes passed: 1,759.
President: James Vaugh. Vice president, engineering: David Heyrend. Executive vice president: John Koo.
City fee: 2% of gross.
Ownership: FrontierVision Partners LP (MSO). See Cable System Ownership.

GALLATIN—InterMedia Partners, 660 Mainstream Dr., Nashville, TN 37228. Phone: 615-244-5900. Fax: 615-255-6528.
Web site: http://www.intermediamtn.com.
County: Sumner. Also serves Sumner County (portions). ICA: TN0033.
TV Market Ranking: 30 (Gallatin, portions of Sumner County); Below 100 (portions of Sumner County). Franchise award date: January 1, 1980. Franchise expiration date: August 15, 2010. Began: January 1, 1982.
Channel capacity: N.A. Channels available but not in use: N.A.
Basic Service
Subscribers: 8,225.
Programming (received off-air): WPGD (I) Hendersonville; WJFB (I) Lebanon; WHTN (I) Murfreesboro; WDCN (P), WKRN-TV (A), WNAB (W), WSMV (N), WTVF (C), WUXP (U), WZTV (F) Nashville.
Current originations: Public access; educational access; government access; leased access; local news.
Fee: $35.00 installation; $12.95 monthly; $25.00 additional installation.
Digital Basic Service
Subscribers: N.A.
Programming (via satellite): BBC America; BET on Jazz; CNN/SI; DMX; Discovery Civilization Channel; Discovery Health Channel; Discovery Home & Leisure Channel; Discovery Kids Channel; Discovery People; Discovery Science Channel; Discovery Wings Channel; ESPN Classic Sports; ESPNews; Fox Sports World; Game Show Network; Golf Channel; Goodlife TV Network; Independent Film Channel; International Channel; Kaleidoscope; Lifetime; MuchMusic Network; Outdoor Channel; Outdoor Life Network; Ovation; Romance Classics; Speedvision; The Barker; The Inspirational Network; Turner Classic Movies; Weatherscan by the Weather Channel; ZDTV.
Fee: N.A.
Expanded Basic Service
Subscribers: 8,000.
Programming (via satellite): WGN-TV (W) Chicago; A & E; American Movie Classics; Animal Planet; BET; Bravo; C-SPAN; C-SPAN 2; CNBC; CNN; Cartoon Network; Comedy Central; Country Music TV; Discovery Channel; Disney Channel; E! Entertainment TV; ESPN; ESPN 2; FX; fXM: Movies from Fox; Fox Family Channel; Fox News Channel; Fox Sports Net South; Headline News; History Channel; Home & Garden Television; Home Shopping Network; Learning Channel; Lifetime; MSNBC; MTV; Nashville Network; Nick at Nite; Nick at Nite's TV Land; Nickelodeon; Odyssey; QVC; Sci-Fi Channel; TBS Superstation; TV Guide Channel; TV Guide Sneak Prevue; The Weather Channel; Turner Network TV; USA Network; Univision; VH1.
Fee: N.A.
Pay Service 1
Pay Units: 821.
Programming (via satellite): Showtime (multiplexed).
Fee: $2.09 installation; $9.50 monthly.
Pay Service 2
Pay Units: 617.
Programming (via satellite): Cinemax (multiplexed).
Fee: $2.09 installation; $9.50 monthly.
Pay Service 3
Pay Units: N.A.
Programming (via satellite): Starz!; The Movie Channel; The New Encore.
Fee: N.A.
Pay Service 4
Pay Units: 1,444.
Programming (via satellite): HBO (multiplexed).
Fee: $2.09 installation; $9.50 monthly.
Digital Pay Service 1
Pay Units: N.A.
Programming (via satellite): BET Movies/Starz!; Cinemax (multiplexed); Encore Action; Encore Love Stories; Encore Mystery; Encore True Stories & Drama; Encore Westerns; Flix (multiplexed); HBO; HBO Comedy; HBO Family; HBO Plus; HBO Signature; HBO Zone; Showtime (multiplexed); Starz!; Starz! Theater; Sundance Channel (multiplexed); The Movie Channel (multiplexed); The New Encore.
Fee: N.A.
Pay-Per-View
Action Pay-Per-View; Playboy TV; movies; special events.
Local advertising: Yes (locally produced & insert). Available in satellite distributed, locally originated, character-generated & automated programming. Rates: $6.50/30 Seconds. Local sales manager: Doug Roberts. Regional interconnect: Intermedia Television Advertising.
Equipment: Scientific-Atlanta headend; Magnavox amplifiers; Comm/Scope cable; JVC cameras; Sony VTRs; RCA character generator; Jerrold set top converters; Eagle traps; Scientific-Atlanta satellite antenna; Scientific-Atlanta satellite receivers.
Miles of plant: 163.0 (coaxial). Additional miles planned: 10.0 (coaxial). Total homes in franchised area: 12,000.
Manager: Robert Pace. Chief technician: Benny Jackson.
City fee: 3% of basic gross.
Ownership: InterMedia Partners (MSO). See Cable System Ownership.

GATLINBURG—InterMedia, 725 Louisville Rd., Alcoa, TN 37701-1846. Phone: 423-984-1400. Fax: 423-983-0383. County: Sevier. Also serves Pigeon Forge, Sevierville. ICA: TN0140.
TV Market Ranking: 71. Franchise award date: February 1, 1973. Franchise expiration date: January 1, 2002. Began: March 1, 1973.
Channel capacity: 52. Channels available but not in use: 14.
Basic Service
Subscribers: 6,658.
Programming (received off-air): WATE-TV (A), WBIR-TV (N), WKOP-TV (P), WTNZ (F), WVLT-TV (C) Knoxville; WSJK (P) Sneedville.
Programming (via satellite): WGN-TV (W) Chicago; ESPN; Headline News; TBS Superstation; Trinity Bcstg. Network.
Current originations: Government access.
Fee: $19.95 installation; $9.37 monthly.
Expanded Basic Service
Subscribers: N.A.
Programming (via satellite): A & E; American Movie Classics; C-SPAN; CNBC; CNN; Country Music TV; Discovery Channel; Fox Family Channel; Fox Sports Net South; MTV; Nashville Network; Nickelodeon; The Weather Channel; Turner Network TV; USA Network.
Fee: $8.04 monthly.
Pay Service 1
Pay Units: 1,524.
Programming (via satellite): Cinemax; Disney Channel; HBO; Showtime; The Movie Channel.
Fee: N.A.
Pay-Per-View
Special events.
Fee: Varies.
Equipment: Scientific-Atlanta headend; AEL amplifiers; Comm/Scope cable; Sony VTRs; AEL set top converters; Arcom traps; AFC & Anixter-Mark satellite antenna; Microdyne satellite receivers.
Miles of plant & homes passed included with Alcoa, TN.
Office manager: Paul Maynard. Technical operations manager: Mark Haley. Chief engineer: Dale Taylor. Business manager: Cathy Dunford.
City fee: 3% of gross.
Ownership: InterMedia Partners (MSO). See Cable System Ownership.

GRAND JUNCTION—Time Warner Communications, Box 610, 12935 S. Main St., Somerville, TN 38068. Phone: 901-259-2225. Counties: Fayette & Hardeman. Also serves La Grange, Saulsbury. ICA: TN0141.
TV Market Ranking: Below 100. Franchise award date: N.A. Franchise expiration date: N.A. Began: N.A.
Channel capacity: 35. Channels available but not in use: 2.
Basic Service
Subscribers: 265.
Programming (received off-air): WHBQ-TV (F), WKNO (P), WLMT (U), WMC-TV (N), WPTY-TV (A), WREG-TV (C) Memphis.
Programming (via satellite): WGN-TV (W) Chicago; A & E; American Movie Classics; BET; C-SPAN; CNN; Country Music TV; Court TV; Discovery Channel; ESPN; Fox Family Channel; Headline News; Home Shopping Network; Lifetime; MTV; Nashville Network; Nickelodeon; QVC; TBS Superstation; The Weather Channel; Turner Network TV; USA Network.
Fee: $39.00 installation; $19.05 monthly.
Pay Service 1
Pay Units: N.A.
Programming (via satellite): Cinemax; Disney Channel; HBO; Showtime.

Fee: $7.00 monthly (Disney), $9.00 monthly (HBO), $9.95 monthly (Cinemax or Showtime).
Manager: Bob Moss. Chief technician: Art Brown.
Ownership: Time Warner Cable (MSO).

GRAY—Comcast Communciations, Box 3988, 1794 Old Gray Station Rd., Gray, TN 37615. Phone: 423-282-1370. Fax: 423-283-4855. Web site: http://www.comcast.com. Counties: Carter, Greene, Johnson, Unicoi & Washington. Also serves Braemar, Carter County, Erwin, Fall Branch, Hampton, Harmony, Johnson City (southwestern portion), Jonesboro, Mountain City, Unicoi County, Valley Forge, Washington County. ICA: TN0142.
TV Market Ranking: 46 (portions of Unicoi County); Below 100 (Braemar, Carter County, Erwin, Fall Branch, Gray, Hampton, Harmony, Johnson City, Jonesboro, Mountain City, portions of Unicoi County, Valley Forge, Washington County). Franchise award date: N.A. Franchise expiration date: N.A. Began: October 1, 1954.
Channel capacity: 75 (not 2-way capable). Channels available but not in use: 20.
Basic Service
Subscribers: 21,101; Commercial subscribers: 106.
Programming (received off-air): WCYB-TV (N) Bristol-Kingsport; WEMT (F) Greeneville; WLFG (I) Grundy; WJHL-TV (C) Johnson City; WKPT-TV (A) Kingsport; WSJK (P) Sneedville.
Programming (via satellite): WGN-TV (W) Chicago; C-SPAN; CNBC; CNN; Country Music TV; ESPN; Fox Family Channel; Headline News; Lifetime; MTV; Nashville Network; Nickelodeon; TBS Superstation; The Weather Channel; USA Network.
Current originations: Government access; leased access; automated emergency alert.
Fee: $45.00 installation; $23.40 monthly; $2.77 converter; $14.46 additional installation.
Pay Service 1
Pay Units: 2,238.
Programming (via satellite): Cinemax (multiplexed).
Fee: $10.00 installation; $12.88 monthly.
Pay Service 2
Pay Units: 1,117.
Programming (via satellite): Disney Channel.
Fee: $10.00 installation; $12.88 monthly.
Pay Service 3
Pay Units: 3,190.
Programming (via satellite): HBO (multiplexed).
Fee: $10.00 installation; $13.87 monthly.
Pay Service 4
Pay Units: 1,802.
Programming (via satellite): Showtime (multiplexed).
Fee: $10.00 installation; $12.88 monthly.
Pay Service 5
Pay Units: 636.
Programming (via satellite): The Movie Channel.
Fee: $10.00 installation; $12.88 monthly.
Pay-Per-View
Addressable homes: 7,080.
Playboy TV; Viewer's Choice.
Fee: $3.95 (Viewer's Choice), $9.95 (Playboy TV).
Pay-per-view manager: Sandra Munsey.
Local advertising: Yes. Available in locally originated programming. Regional interconnect: Cabletime.
Equipment: C-COR amplifiers; Comm/Scope cable; Scientific-Atlanta set top converters; Scientific-Atlanta addressable set top converters; Scientific-Atlanta satellite antenna.
Miles of plant: 433.5 (coaxial). Additional miles planned: 28.0 (fiber optic). Homes passed: 34,850.
Manager: James Scott. Area engineer: Lynn McMahan. Marketing manager: Sandra Munsey. Customer service manager: Lisa Hughes.
City fee: 5% of gross.
Ownership: Comcast Cable Communications Inc. (MSO).

GREENBRIER—Tennessee Valley CableVision, 6940 Moores Lane, Brentwood, TN 37027-2908. Phone: 615-244-5900. Fax: 615-377-3683. Counties: Davidson & Robertson. Also serves Baggettsville, Chestnut Grove, Chestnut Orchard, Coopertown, Owens, Ridgetop, Robertson County (portions), Springfield. ICA: TN0170.
TV Market Ranking: 30. Franchise award date: N.A. Franchise expiration date: December 2, 2000. Began: July 1, 1980.
Channel capacity: 46 (2-way capable; operating 2-way). Channels available but not in use: 4.
Basic Service
Subscribers: 4,831.
Programming (received off-air): WDCN (P), WKRN-TV (A), WSMV (N), WTVF (C), WUXP (U), WZTV (F) Nashville.
Programming (via satellite): WGN-TV (W) Chicago; Home Shopping Network; Knowledge TV; QVC; TBS Superstation.
Current originations: Government access.
Fee: $40.00 installation; $20.95 monthly; $10.00 additional installation.
Commercial fee: $29.95 monthly.
Expanded Basic Service
Subscribers: 482.
Programming (via satellite): BET; CNN; Country Music TV; Discovery Channel; ESPN; Fox Family Channel; Headline News; Lifetime; MTV; Nashville Network; Nickelodeon; The Weather Channel; Turner Network TV; USA Network.
Fee: $30.00 installation; $14.95 monthly.
Pay Service 1
Pay Units: 2,474.
Programming (via satellite): Cinemax; Disney Channel; HBO.
Fee: $6.95 monthly (Disney), $9.95 monthly (Cinemax or HBO).
Local advertising: Yes. Regional interconnect: Intermedia Television Advertising.
Program Guide: TV Host.
Equipment: Scientific-Atlanta headend; Scientific-Atlanta amplifiers; Comm/Scope cable; AFC satellite antenna; Sony commercial insert.
Miles of plant: 125.0 (coaxial). Homes passed: 7,952.
Manager: Alan Taylor. Chief technician: Dan Winkler.
City fee: 3% of gross.
Ownership: InterMedia Partners (MSO). See Cable System Ownership.

GREENEVILLE—FrontierVision, Box 1747, Greeneville, TN 37744. Phone: 423-639-4321. Fax: 423-639-0145. County: Greene. Also serves Afton, Baileyton, Chuckey, Greene County, Midway, Mosheim, Rheatown, Tusculum, Tusculum College. ICA: TN0022.
TV Market Ranking: 46 (portions of Greene County); Below 100 (Afton, Baileyton, Chuckey, portions of Greene County, Greeneville, Midway, Mosheim, Rheatown, Tusculum, Tusculum College). Franchise award date: November 25, 1985. Franchise expiration date: N.A. Began: N.A.
Channel capacity: 54 (not 2-way capable). Channels available but not in use: 4.
Basic Service
Subscribers: 15,751.
Programming (received off-air): WCYB-TV (N) Bristol-Kingsport; WEMT (F) Greeneville; WLOS (A) Greenville-Spartanburg-Asheville; WJHL-TV (C) Johnson City; WKPT-TV (A) Kingsport; WATE-TV (A), WBIR-TV (N) Knoxville; WSJK (P) Sneedville.
Programming (via satellite): WGN-TV (W) Chicago; A & E; C-SPAN; CNBC; CNN; Country Music TV; Discovery Channel; Disney Channel; ESPN; Fox Family Channel; Headline News; Lifetime; MTV; Nashville Network; Nickelodeon; TBS Superstation; TV Guide Channel; The Weather Channel; Turner Network TV; USA Network; VH1.
Current originations: Public access; government access.
Fee: $25.00 installation; $11.50 monthly.
Pay Service 1
Pay Units: 772.
Programming (via satellite): Cinemax.
Fee: $5.00 installation; $7.26 monthly.
Pay Service 2
Pay Units: 131.
Programming (via satellite): The New Encore.
Fee: N.A.
Pay Service 3
Pay Units: 252.
Programming (via satellite): Flix.
Fee: N.A.
Pay Service 4
Pay Units: 1,056.
Programming (via satellite): HBO.
Fee: $9.26 monthly.
Pay Service 5
Pay Units: 770.
Programming (via satellite): Showtime.
Fee: $9.26 monthly.
Pay Service 6
Pay Units: 130.
Programming (via satellite): Starz!
Fee: N.A.
Pay Service 7
Pay Units: 455.
Programming (via satellite): The Movie Channel.
Fee: N.A.
Pay-Per-View
Addressable homes: 78.
Viewer's Choice.
Fee: $3.95.
Local advertising: No. Regional interconnect: Cabletime.
Equipment: Scientific-Atlanta amplifiers; Comm/Scope & Times Fiber cable; Scientific-Atlanta set top converters; Scientific-Atlanta & Comtech satellite antenna; Scientific-Atlanta satellite receivers.
Miles of plant: 580.8 (coaxial). Homes passed: 18,735.
Manager: Dan Callahan. Chief technician: Gary Shoemaker.
City fee: 3% of gross.
Ownership: FrontierVision Partners LP (MSO). See Cable System Ownership.

HARRIMAN—Comcast Cablevision of the South, Box 1169, Hwy. 27S, Harriman, TN 37748. Phone: 423-637-5411. Counties: Anderson, Cumberland & Roane. Also serves Anderson County (portions), Cumberland County (portions), Kingston, Roane County. ICA: TN0021.
TV Market Ranking: 71 (Anderson County, Kingston, portions of Roane County); Below 100 (Cumberland County, Harriman, portions of Roane County). Franchise award date: N.A. Franchise expiration date: N.A. Began: January 1, 1966.
Channel capacity: N.A. Channels available but not in use: N.A.
Basic Service
Subscribers: Included with Athens, TN.
Programming (received off-air): WDEF-TV (C), WTVC (A) Chattanooga; WATE-TV (A), WBIR-TV (N), WKOP-TV (P), WTNZ (F), WVLT-TV (C) Knoxville; allband FM.
Programming (via satellite): WGN-TV (W) Chicago; A & E; American Movie Classics; C-SPAN; C-SPAN 2; CNN; Comedy Central; Country Music TV; Discovery Channel; ESPN; Fox Family Channel; Headline News; Home Shopping Network; Kaleidoscope; Learning Channel; Lifetime; MTV; Nashville Network; Nickelodeon; Odyssey; Sci-Fi Channel; TBS Superstation; The Weather Channel; Turner Network TV; USA Network; VH1; ValueVision.
Current originations: Automated time-weather.
Fee: $29.95 installation; $17.95 monthly; $10.00 additional installation.
Pay Service 1
Pay Units: 1,156.
Programming (via satellite): Cinemax.
Fee: $10.00 installation; $9.00 monthly.
Pay Service 2
Pay Units: 1,978.
Programming (via satellite): HBO.
Fee: $10.00 installation; $9.00 monthly.
Pay Service 3
Pay Units: 195.
Programming (via satellite): Showtime.
Fee: $9.00 monthly.
Equipment: Jerrold headend; Kaiser amplifiers; Times Fiber cable.
Miles of plant: 221.0 (coaxial). Homes passed: 14,029. Total homes in franchised area: 16,918.
Manager: Roger Rule. Chief technician: Don Alford.
City fee: 3% of gross.
Ownership: Comcast Cable Communications Inc. (MSO).

HARTSVILLE—InterMedia Partners, Box 250, 307 Circle Dr., McKenzie, TN 38201. Phone: 901-352-2273. Fax: 901-352-3164. Web site: http://www.intermediamtn.com. County: Trousdale. ICA: TN0099.
TV Market Ranking: 30. Franchise award date: N.A. Franchise expiration date: N.A. Began: July 1, 1981.
Channel capacity: N.A. Channels available but not in use: N.A.
Basic Service
Subscribers: 722.
Programming (received off-air): WJFB (I) Lebanon; WHTN (I) Murfreesboro; WDCN (P), WKRN-TV (A), WNAB (W), WSMV (N), WTVF (C), WUXP (U), WZTV (F) Nashville.
Current originations: Automated time-weather.
Fee: $60.00 installation; $10.00 monthly; $10.00 additional installation.
Digital Basic Service
Subscribers: N.A.
Programming (via satellite): BBC America; BET on Jazz; CNN/SI; DMX; Discovery Civilization Channel; Discovery Health Channel; Discovery Home & Leisure Channel; Discovery Kids Channel; Discovery People; Discovery Science Channel; Discovery Wings Channel; ESPN Classic Sports; ESPNews; Fox Sports World; Game Show Network; Golf Channel; Goodlife TV Network; Independent Film Channel; International Channel; Kaleidoscope; Lifetime; MuchMusic Network; Outdoor Channel; Outdoor Life Network; Ovation; Romance Classics; Speedvision; The Barker; The Inspirational Network; Turner Classic Movies; Weatherscan by the Weather Channel; ZDTV.
Fee: N.A.
Expanded Basic Service
Subscribers: 583.

Programming (received off-air): WPGD (I) Hendersonville.
Programming (via satellite): WGN-TV (W) Chicago; A & E; C-SPAN; CNN; Discovery Channel; ESPN; ESPN 2; Fox Family Channel; Headline News; Lifetime; Nashville Network; Nick at Nite; Nickelodeon; TBS Superstation; Turner Classic Movies; Turner Network TV; USA Network.
Fee: N.A.

Pay Service 1
Pay Units: 83.
Programming (via satellite): HBO.
Fee: $9.95 monthly.

Pay Service 2
Pay Units: 61.
Programming (via satellite): Showtime.
Fee: $9.95 monthly.

Pay Service 3
Pay Units: 58.
Programming (via satellite): The New Encore.
Fee: $1.50 monthly.

Digital Pay Service 1
Pay Units: N.A.
Programming (via satellite): BET Movies/Starz!; Cinemax (multiplexed); Encore Action; Encore Love Stories; Encore Mystery; Encore True Stories & Drama; Encore Westerns; Flix (multiplexed); HBO; HBO Comedy; HBO Family; HBO Plus; HBO Signature; HBO Zone; Showtime (multiplexed); Starz!; Starz! Theater; Sundance Channel (multiplexed); The Movie Channel (multiplexed); The New Encore.
Fee: N.A.

Equipment: Scientific-Atlanta headend; Magnavox amplifiers; Comm/Scope cable; Oak set top converters; Scientific-Atlanta satellite antenna; Scientific-Atlanta satellite receivers.
Miles of plant: 24.5 (coaxial). Homes passed: 941.
Manager: Robert Pace. Chief technician: Benny Jackson.
Ownership: InterMedia Partners (MSO). See Cable System Ownership.

HENDERSON—InterMedia Partners, Box 250, 24 Circle Dr., McKenzie, TN 38201. Phone: 901-352-2273. Fax: 901-352-3164. Web site: http://www.intermediamtn.com. County: Chester. Also serves Chester County. ICA: TN0074.
TV Market Ranking: Below 100. Franchise award date: February 8, 1968. Franchise expiration date: N.A. Began: November 1, 1969.
Channel capacity: 60 (not 2-way capable). Channels available but not in use: 12.

Basic Service
Subscribers: 1,792.
Programming (received off-air): WBBJ-TV (A), WMTU (U) Jackson; WLJT (P) Lexington; WHBQ-TV (F), WMC-TV (N), WPTY-TV (A), WREG-TV (C) Memphis.
Programming (via satellite): WGN-TV (W) Chicago; Fox Family Channel; FoxNet; Learning Channel.
Current originations: Automated time-weather; educational access.
Fee: $12.01 monthly.

Expanded Basic Service
Subscribers: 1,638.
Programming (via satellite): A & E; American Movie Classics; BET; C-SPAN; CNBC; CNN; Comedy Central; Country Music TV; Discovery Channel; Disney Channel; ESPN; ESPN 2; FX; Fox Sports Net South; Headline News; History Channel; Home & Garden Television; Home Shopping Network; Lifetime; MTV; Nashville Network; Nick at Nite's TV Land; Nickelodeon; QVC; TBS Superstation; The Weather Channel; Trinity Bcstg. Network; Turner Classic Movies; Turner Network TV; USA Network.
Fee: $16.34 monthly.

Pay Service 1
Pay Units: 600.
Programming (via satellite): Cinemax; HBO; Showtime; The New Encore.
Fee: $11.95 monthly.

Pay-Per-View
Addressable homes: 657.

Local advertising: Yes. Local sales manager: Sharon Nicholson.
Equipment: Scientific-Atlanta headend; Scientific-Atlanta amplifiers; Comm/Scope cable; Texscan & MSI character generator; Scientific-Atlanta set top converters; Scientific-Atlanta addressable set top converters; Eagle traps; Scientific-Atlanta satellite antenna; Scientific-Atlanta satellite receivers.
Miles of plant: 70.0 (coaxial); None (fiber optic). Homes passed: 2,599.
Manager: Robert L. Pace. Chief technician: Benny Jackson.
City fee: 2% of gross.
Ownership: InterMedia Partners (MSO). See Cable System Ownership.

HENDERSONVILLE—InterMedia Partners, 393 Johnny Cash Pkwy., Hendersonville, TN 37075. Phone: 615-824-8543. Fax: 615-822-0555. County: Sumner. Also serves Sumner County. ICA: TN0143.
TV Market Ranking: 30 (Hendersonville, portions of Sumner County); Below 100 (portions of Sumner County). Franchise award date: December 13, 1977. Franchise expiration date: December 31, 2007. Began: June 1, 1980.
Channel capacity: 35 (not 2-way capable). Channels available but not in use: 1.

Basic Service
Subscribers: 13,718.
Programming (received off-air): WHTN (I) Murfreesboro; WDCN (P), WKRN-TV (A), WSMV (N), WTVF (C), WUXP (U), WZTV (F) Nashville; allband FM.
Programming (via satellite): WGN-TV (W) Chicago; A & E; C-SPAN; CNBC; CNN; Country Music TV; Discovery Channel; ESPN; Fox Family Channel; Goodlife TV Network; Headline News; Lifetime; MTV; Nashville Network; Nickelodeon; QVC; TBS Superstation; The Weather Channel; Turner Network TV; USA Network; VH1.
Current originations: Government access; automated emergency alert.
Fee: $25.00 installation; $16.95 monthly.

Pay Service 1
Pay Units: 1,295.
Programming (via satellite): Cinemax.
Fee: $10.00 installation; $10.50 monthly.

Pay Service 2
Pay Units: 812.
Programming (via satellite): Disney Channel.
Fee: $10.00 installation; $10.50 monthly.

Pay Service 3
Pay Units: 2,578.
Programming (via satellite): HBO.
Fee: $10.00 installation; $10.95 monthly.

Pay Service 4
Pay Units: 1,113.
Programming (via satellite): Showtime.
Fee: $10.00 installation; $10.50 monthly.

Local advertising: Yes. Available in satellite distributed, locally originated & character-generated programming. Rates: Vary. Local sales manager: Stan Sellers. Regional interconnect: Intermedia Television Advertising.
Program Guide: CableView.
Miles of plant: 271.0 (coaxial).
Manager: Keith Walker. Chief technician: Bob Etheridge. Marketing director: Glen Dowe.
City fee: 3% of gross.
Ownership: InterMedia Partners (MSO). See Cable System Ownership.

HENRY—Peoples CATV Inc., Box 310, Rte. 1, Erin, TN 37061. Phone: 615-289-4221. Fax: 615-289-4220. County: Henry. ICA: TN0144.
TV Market Ranking: Outside TV Markets. Franchise award date: April 12, 1983. Franchise expiration date: April 12, 2003. Began: January 1, 1985.
Channel capacity: 36 (not 2-way capable). Channels available but not in use: 24.

Basic Service
Subscribers: 144.
Programming (received off-air): WBBJ-TV (A) Jackson; WLJT (P) Lexington; WSMV (N) Nashville; WPSD-TV (N) Paducah.
Programming (via satellite): WGN-TV (W) Chicago; CNN; ESPN; Nashville Network; TBS Superstation; USA Network.
Fee: $25.00 installation; $12.95 monthly.

Pay Service 1
Pay Units: 66.
Programming (via satellite): Cinemax.
Fee: $7.75 monthly.

Pay Service 2
Pay Units: 28.
Programming (via satellite): HBO.
Fee: $10.15 monthly.

Local advertising: No.
Equipment: Scientific-Atlanta headend; Scientific-Atlanta amplifiers; Times Fiber & Comm/Scope cable; Pico & Arcom traps; Scientific-Atlanta satellite antenna; Scientific-Atlanta satellite receivers.
Miles of plant: 11.0 (coaxial); None (fiber optic). Homes passed: 250. Total homes in franchised area: 250.
Manager: James H. Coakley. Chief technician: Steve Hall. Program director: Irene Wilbanks. Marketing director: Fay Lair.
Ownership: Peoples Telephone Co. Inc. (Tennessee) (MSO).

HOHENWALD—Tennessee Valley CableVision, 6940 Moores Lane, Brentwood, TN 37027-2908. Phone: 615-244-5900. Fax: 615-377-3683. Counties: Hickman, Lewis, Marshall, Maury & Williamson. Also serves Centerville, Centerville Two, College Grove, Farmington, Hickman County, Lewis County (portions), Lyles, Mount Pleasant. ICA: TN0055.
TV Market Ranking: 30 (College Grove, portions of Hickman County, Lyles); Outside TV Markets (Centerville, Centerville Two, Farmington, portions of Hickman County, Hohenwald, Lewis County, Mount Pleasant). Franchise award date: N.A. Franchise expiration date: N.A. Began: January 1, 1980.
Channel capacity: 39. Channels available but not in use: 7.

Basic Service
Subscribers: 3,555; Commercial subscribers: 550.
Programming (received off-air): WDCN (P), WKRN-TV (A), WSMV (N), WTVF (C), WUXP (U), WZTV (F) Nashville.
Programming (via satellite): WGN-TV (W) Chicago; Fox Family Channel; Headline News; Knowledge TV; QVC; TBS Superstation.
Current originations: Local news.
Fee: $40.00 installation; $20.95 monthly; $3.50 converter; $10.00 additional installation.
Commercial fee: $29.95 monthly.

Expanded Basic Service
Subscribers: N.A.
Programming (via satellite): A & E; American Movie Classics; Country Music TV; Discovery Channel; ESPN; Fox Sports Net South; Lifetime; Nashville Network; Nickelodeon; The Weather Channel; Turner Network TV; USA Network; VH1.
Fee: N.A.

Pay Service 1
Pay Units: 1,440.
Programming (via satellite): Cinemax; Disney Channel; HBO; Showtime.
Fee: $9.95 monthly (Cinemax, HBO or Showtime).

Equipment: Scientific-Atlanta headend; Scientific-Atlanta amplifiers; Comm/Scope cable.
Miles of plant: 965.0 (coaxial). Homes passed: 6,063.
Manager: Dan Yates. Chief technician: Dan Winkler. Marketing director: Sandra Staggs.
Ownership: InterMedia Partners (MSO). Sale pends to Rifkin & Associates Inc.

HUMBOLDT—Humboldt Cable Co. Inc., Box 760, 2606 E. End Dr., Humboldt, TN 38343. Phone: 901-784-5000. Fax: 901-784-7474. County: Gibson. Also serves Medina. ICA: TN0046.
TV Market Ranking: Below 100. Franchise award date: N.A. Franchise expiration date: N.A. Began: January 1, 1970.
Channel capacity: 30 (not 2-way capable). Channels available but not in use: None.

Basic Service
Subscribers: 4,483.
Programming (received off-air): WBBJ-TV (A), WMTU (U) Jackson; WLJT (P) Lexington; WHBQ-TV (F), WMC-TV (N), WPTY-TV (A), WREG-TV (C) Memphis.
Programming (via satellite): WGN-TV (W) Chicago; C-SPAN; QVC; TBS Superstation.
Fee: $25.00 installation; $24.86 monthly; $1.25 converter; $12.50 additional installation.

Expanded Basic Service
Subscribers: 3,913.
Programming (via satellite): A & E; BET; CNN; Cartoon Network; Country Music TV; Discovery Channel; ESPN; ESPN 2; Fox Family Channel; Fox Sports Net South; Headline News; Home & Garden Television; Learning Channel; Lifetime; MTV; Nashville Network; Nickelodeon; Sci-Fi Channel; The Weather Channel; Trinity Bcstg. Network; Turner Classic Movies; Turner Network TV; USA Network; VH1.
Fee: N.A.

Pay Service 1
Pay Units: 901.
Programming (via satellite): Showtime.
Fee: $9.95 monthly.

Local advertising: No.
Equipment: Jerrold & Scientific-Atlanta headend; Jerrold amplifiers; Times Fiber & Comm/Scope cable; Mycrotek character generator; Jerrold set top converters; Eagle traps; Scientific-Atlanta satellite antenna; Scientific-Atlanta satellite receivers.
Miles of plant: 105.0 (coaxial).
Manager: Frank Warmath. Chief technician: Mark Love.
City fee: 3% of gross.
Ownership: Warmath Communications Inc.

HUNTLAND—Mediacom, 123 Ware Dr., Huntsville, AL 35811. Phone: 205-852-6490. Fax: 205-851-7708. County: Franklin. ICA: TN0116.
TV Market Ranking: 96. Franchise award date: April 26, 1982. Franchise expiration date: N.A. Began: January 1, 1984.
Channel capacity: 36 (not 2-way capable). Channels available but not in use: 6.

Basic Service
Subscribers: 326.
Programming (received off-air): WAAY-TV (A), WAFF (N), WHIQ (P), WHNT-TV (C),

WZDX (F) Huntsville-Decatur; WKRN-TV (A), WSMV (N) Nashville.
Fee: $5.11 monthly; $1.00 converter.

Expanded Basic Service
Subscribers: N.A.
Programming (via satellite): WGN-TV (W) Chicago; American Movie Classics; CNN; Discovery Channel; ESPN; Fox Family Channel; Lifetime; MTV; Nashville Network; Nick at Nite; Nickelodeon; QVC; TBS Superstation; Turner Network TV; USA Network.
Fee: $15.68 monthly.

Pay Service 1
Pay Units: 68.
Programming (via satellite): Cinemax.
Fee: $9.95 monthly.

Pay Service 2
Pay Units: 73.
Programming (via satellite): HBO.
Fee: $9.95 monthly.

Pay Service 3
Pay Units: 65.
Programming (via satellite): Showtime.
Fee: $9.95 monthly.

Pay Service 4
Pay Units: 68.
Programming (via satellite): Flix.
Fee: $2.95 monthly.

Equipment: Scientific-Atlanta amplifiers; Times Fiber cable.
Miles of plant: 10.0 (coaxial); None (fiber optic). Homes passed: 423. Total homes in franchised area: 423.
Manager: Bill Barbour. Chief technician: Steve Dozier. Marketing director: Tammy Warren.
City fee: 3% of gross.
Ownership: Mediacom LLC (MSO).

JACKSON—Charter Communications Inc., 2177 Christmasville Rd., Jackson, TN 38305. Phones: 901-424-3290; 800-372-8348. Fax: 901-424-4257. Web site: http://www.chartercom.com. County: Madison. Also serves Bemis, Madison County, Malesus. ICA: TN0008.
TV Market Ranking: Below 100. Franchise award date: December 1, 1965. Franchise expiration date: December 1, 2005. Began: October 1, 1968.
Channel capacity: 60 (2-way capable; operating 2-way partially). Channels available but not in use: 15.

Basic Service
Subscribers: 31,782; Commercial subscribers: 29.
Programming (received off-air): WBBJ-TV (A), WMTU (U) Jackson; WLJT (P) Lexington; WHBQ-TV (F), WKNO (P), WMC-TV (N), WPTY-TV (A), WREG-TV (C) Memphis; 14 FMs.
Programming (via microwave): WSMV (N), WTVF (C) Nashville.
Programming (via satellite): TV Guide Sneak Prevue.
Current originations: Automated time-weather; religious access; leased access.
Fee: $50.00 installation; $5.70 monthly; $2.00 converter; $40.00 additional installation.
Commercial fee: $2.42 monthly.

Expanded Basic Service
Subscribers: N.A.
Programming (via satellite): A & E; American Movie Classics; BET; C-SPAN; CNBC; CNN; Comedy Central; Country Music TV; Discovery Channel; Disney Channel; E! Entertainment TV; ESPN; ESPN 2; Encore Movie Networks; FX; Fox Family Channel; Fox Sports Net South; Headline News; Home & Garden Television; Home Shopping Network; Learning Channel; Lifetime; MTV; Nashville Network; Nickelodeon; Odyssey; QVC; Sci-Fi Channel; TV Guide Channel; The Weather Channel; Travel Channel; Turner Network TV; USA Network; VH1.
Fee: $26.06 monthly.

Expanded Basic Service 2
Subscribers: N.A.
Programming (via satellite): WGN-TV (W) Chicago; TBS Superstation.
Fee: $1.39 monthly.

Pay Service 1
Pay Units: N.A.
Programming (via satellite): Cinemax (multiplexed); HBO (multiplexed); Showtime (multiplexed); Starz! (multiplexed); The Movie Channel.
Fee: $40.00 installation; $5.95 monthly (Starz), $9.95 monthly (Cinemax, HBO, Showtime or TMC).

Pay-Per-View
Addressable homes: 7,500.
Movies.

Local advertising: Yes. Available in satellite distributed, locally originated, character-generated, taped & automated programming. Rates: $7.20/Day. Local sales manager: Bill Way.
Equipment: Magnavox headend; Magnavox amplifiers; Comm/Scope cable; Jerrold set top converters; Jerrold addressable set top converters.
Miles of plant: 444.3 (coaxial). Additional miles planned: 15.0 (coaxial). Homes passed: 33,900. Total homes in franchised area: 35,000.
Manager: Kim Kersey. Chief technician: Ron Crowder.
City fee: 3% of basic.
Ownership: Charter Communications Inc. (MSO). Purchased from Renaissance Media Holdings LLC, April 30, 1999.

JASPER—Helicon Cable Communications, Box 307, 71332 Hwy. 41S, Jasper, TN 37347-0307. Phones: 423-336-2513; 800-845-9937. Fax: 423-942-2851. Counties: Marion, TN; Jackson, AL. Also serves Bridgeport, Cedar Grove, Stevenson, AL; Haletown-Ladds, Kimball, New Hope, Powells Crossroads, Sequatchie, South Pittsburg, Whiteside, Whitwell, TN. ICA: TN0070.
TV Market Ranking: 78. Franchise award date: March 1, 1983. Franchise expiration date: N.A. Began: July 1, 1983.
Channel capacity: 35 (2-way capable; operating 2-way). Channels available but not in use: 9.

Basic Service
Subscribers: N.A.
Programming (received off-air): WDEF-TV (C), WDSI-TV (F), WRCB-TV (N), WTCI (P), WTVC (A) Chattanooga.
Programming (via satellite): WGN-TV (W) Chicago; CNN; Electronic Program Guide Jr.; Nickelodeon; TBS Superstation; USA Network.
Current originations: Automated time-weather; public access; educational access; local news; local sports.
Fee: $25.00 installation; $9.05 monthly.

Expanded Basic Service
Subscribers: N.A.
Programming (via satellite): Country Music TV; Discovery Channel; ESPN; Fox Family Channel; Lifetime; MTV; Nashville Network.
Fee: $3.50 monthly.

Pay Service 1
Pay Units: N.A.
Programming (via satellite): Disney Channel; HBO; Playboy TV; Showtime.
Fee: $7.95 monthly (each).

Local advertising: Yes (locally produced & insert). Available in satellite distributed & locally originated programming. Rates: $120.00/Minute; $75.00/30 Seconds; $20.00/Month (character-generated page). Local sales manager: Juanita Greene.
Equipment: Blonder-Tongue & Catel headend; Magnavox amplifiers; CCS Hatfield & Scientific-Atlanta cable; RCA cameras; Panasonic & Sony VTRs; Atari character generator; Scientific-Atlanta set top converters; Scientific-Atlanta addressable set top converters; Microwave Filter traps; Odom & Prodelin satellite antenna; Scientific-Atlanta & Arcom satellite receivers; Vista commercial insert.
Miles of plant: 62.0 (coaxial). Additional miles planned: 12.0 (coaxial). Homes passed: 2,100. Total homes in franchised area: 2,500.
Manager: Anthony Pope. Chief technician: Ricky Brown.
County fee: None.
Ownership: Helicon Corp. (MSO). Purchased from Paradign Communications Inc. See Cable System Ownership.

JELLICO—Falcon Cable TV, 5026 S. Hwy. 27, Somerset, KY 42501. Phone: 606-678-3035. Counties: Campbell, TN; Whitley, KY. Also serves Emlyn, Whitley County (southern portion), KY; Newcomb, Oswego, TN. ICA: TN0056.
TV Market Ranking: Below 100. Franchise award date: N.A. Franchise expiration date: N.A. Began: April 1, 1979.
Channel capacity: 35 (not 2-way capable). Channels available but not in use: None.

Basic Service
Subscribers: 1,918; Commercial subscribers: 11.
Programming (received off-air): WPXK (X) Jellico; WATE-TV (A), WBIR-TV (N), WTNZ (F), WVLT-TV (C) Knoxville; WKYT-TV (C) Lexington; WSJK (P) Sneedville; WKSO-TV (P) Somerset.
Programming (via satellite): American Movie Classics; Bravo; CNN; Country Music TV; Discovery Channel; E! Entertainment TV; ESPN; Headline News; Learning Channel; MTV; Nickelodeon; QVC; Sci-Fi Channel; Trinity Bcstg. Network; VH1.
Current originations: Public access.
Fee: $25.00 installation; $20.55 monthly; $3.00 converter; $15.00 additional installation.

Expanded Basic Service
Subscribers: 706.
Programming (via satellite): Fox Family Channel; Lifetime; The Weather Channel; USA Network.
Fee: $1.59 monthly.

Expanded Basic Service 2
Subscribers: 649.
Programming (via satellite): WGN-TV (W) Chicago; Disney Channel; Nashville Network; TBS Superstation; Turner Network TV.
Fee: $7.00 monthly.

Pay Service 1
Pay Units: 44.
Programming (via satellite): Cinemax.
Fee: $10.95 monthly.

Pay Service 2
Pay Units: 54.
Programming (via satellite): HBO.
Fee: $11.95 monthly.

Local advertising: Yes. Available in locally originated & character-generated programming. Rates: $20.00/Month.
Equipment: Catel, Phasecom & Scientific-Atlanta headend; Jerrold, Scientific-Atlanta & GTE Sylvania amplifiers; Comm/Scope, Times Fiber & Trilogy cable; Texscan character generator; Jerrold & Scientific-Atlanta set top converters; Eagle & Production Products traps; Microdyne & Scientific-Atlanta satellite antenna; Scientific-Atlanta satellite receivers.
Miles of plant: 61.0 (coaxial). Additional miles planned: 8.0 (coaxial). Homes passed: 2,938.
Manager: Dave Hudson. Chief technician: Larry Gregory.
Franchise fee: 3%-5% of gross.
Ownership: Falcon Communications LP (MSO), joint venture formed September 30, 1998. See Cable System Ownership.

JOELTON—InterMedia Partners, Box 250, 307 Circle Dr., McKenzie, TN 38201. Phone: 901-352-2273. Fax: 901-352-3164.
Web site: http://www.intermediamtn.com.
County: Davidson. Also serves Whites Creek. ICA: TN0082.
TV Market Ranking: 30. Franchise award date: August 5, 1986. Franchise expiration date: August 1, 2011. Began: N.A.
Channel capacity: N.A. Channels available but not in use: N.A.

Basic Service
Subscribers: 1,600.
Programming (received off-air): WNPX (X) Cookeville; WUPN-TV (U) Greensboro-High Point; WPGD (I) Hendersonville; WJFB (I) Lebanon; WHTN (I) Murfreesboro; WDCN (P), WKRN-TV (A), WNAB (W), WSMV (N), WTVF (C), WZTV (F) Nashville.
Programming (via satellite): WGN-TV (W) Chicago; A & E; American Movie Classics; Animal Planet; BET; Bravo; C-SPAN; C-SPAN 2; CNBC; CNN; Cartoon Network; Comedy Central; Country Music TV; Discovery Channel; Disney Channel; E! Entertainment TV; ESPN; ESPN 2; FX; fXM: Movies from Fox; Fox Family Channel; Fox News Channel; Fox Sports Net South; Headline News; History Channel; Home & Garden Television; Home Shopping Network; Learning Channel; Lifetime; MSNBC; MTV; Nashville Network; Nick at Nite's TV Land; Nickelodeon; Odyssey; QVC; TBS Superstation; TV Guide Channel; TV Guide Sneak Prevue; The Weather Channel; Turner Network TV; USA Network; Univision.
Current originations: Public access; educational access; government access; leased access.
Fee: $39.00 installation; $13.50 monthly.

Digital Basic Service
Subscribers: N.A.
Programming (via satellite): BBC America; BET on Jazz; CNN/SI; DMX; Discovery Civilization Channel; Discovery Health Channel; Discovery Home & Leisure Channel; Discovery Kids Channel; Discovery People; Discovery Science Channel; Discovery Wings Channel; ESPN Classic Sports; ESPNews; Fox Sports World; Game Show Network; Golf Channel; Goodlife TV Network; Independent Film Channel; International Channel; Kaleidoscope; Lifetime; MuchMusic Network; Outdoor Channel; Outdoor Life Network; Ovation; Romance Classics; Speedvision; The Barker; The Inspirational Network; Turner Classic Movies; Weatherscan by the Weather Channel; ZDTV.
Fee: N.A.

Pay Service 1
Pay Units: 800.
Programming (via satellite): Cinemax; HBO; Showtime; The New Encore.
Fee: $10.00 installation; $10.00 monthly (Cinemax, HBO or Showtime).

Digital Pay Service 1
Pay Units: N.A.
Programming (via satellite): BET Movies/Starz!; Cinemax (multiplexed); Encore Action; Encore Love Stories; Encore Mystery; Encore True Stories & Drama; Encore Westerns; Flix (multiplexed); HBO; HBO Comedy; HBO Family; HBO Plus; HBO Signature; HBO Zone; Showtime (multiplexed); Starz!; Starz! Theater; Sundance Channel (multiplexed);

The Movie Channel (multiplexed); The New Encore.
Fee: N.A.
Equipment: Scientific-Atlanta headend; Scientific-Atlanta amplifiers; Times Fiber cable; DX Engineering satellite receivers.
Miles of plant: 70.0 (coaxial). Homes passed: 1,690.
Manager: Robert Pace. Chief technician: Benny Jackson.
County fee: 5% of gross.
Ownership: InterMedia Partners (MSO). See Cable System Ownership.

JOHNSON CITY—Charter Communications Inc., Box 1737, Johnson City, TN 37605-1737. Phone: 423-929-2101. Fax: 423-929-7230. Counties: Carter & Washington. Also serves Elizabethton. ICA: TN0010.
TV Market Ranking: Below 100. Franchise award date: January 1, 1962. Franchise expiration date: December 31, 2001. Began: January 1, 1952.
Channel capacity: 60 (not 2-way capable). Channels available but not in use: 4.
Basic Service
Subscribers: 22,293.
Programming (received off-air): WCYB-TV (N) Bristol-Kingsport; WEMT (F) Greeneville; WLFG (I) Grundy; WJHL-TV (C) Johnson City; WAPK-LP (U), WKPT-TV (A) Kingsport; WSJK (P) Sneedville.
Programming (via satellite): WGN-TV (W) Chicago; C-SPAN; C-SPAN 2; E! Entertainment TV; MSNBC; QVC; TBS Superstation; TV Guide Channel.
Current originations: Automated time-weather; religious access.
Fee: $25.00 installation; $8.05 monthly; $2.27 converter.
Expanded Basic Service
Subscribers: 21,999.
Programming (via satellite): A & E; American Movie Classics; BET; CNBC; CNN; Country Music TV; Discovery Channel; ESPN; ESPN 2; Fox Family Channel; Headline News; Learning Channel; Lifetime; MTV; Nashville Network; Nick at Nite; Nickelodeon; Odyssey; TV Food Network; TV Guide Sneak Prevue; The Box; The Weather Channel; Travel Channel; Turner Network TV; USA Network; Z Music Television.
Fee: $25.00 installation; $12.94 monthly.
Expanded Basic Service 2
Subscribers: 400.
Programming (via satellite): Cartoon Network; ESPN Classic Sports; Home & Garden Television; Sci-Fi Channel; Turner Classic Movies.
Fee: $21.95 monthly.
Pay Service 1
Pay Units: 1,803.
Programming (via satellite): Cinemax.
Fee: $25.00 installation; $9.15 monthly.
Pay Service 2
Pay Units: 1,262.
Programming (via satellite): Disney Channel.
Fee: $25.00 installation; $9.50 monthly.
Pay Service 3
Pay Units: 2,276.
Programming (via satellite): HBO.
Fee: $25.00 installation; $12.50 monthly.
Pay Service 4
Pay Units: 1,177.
Programming (via satellite): Showtime.
Fee: $25.00 installation; $12.20 monthly.
Pay Service 5
Pay Units: 569.
Programming (via satellite): Music Choice.
Fee: $9.95 monthly.
Pay-Per-View
Addressable homes: 6,126.
Hot Choice; movies; special events.
Fee: Varies.
Local advertising: Yes (locally produced). Available in satellite distributed & character-generated programming. Regional interconnect: Cabletime.
Equipment: Scientific-Atlanta headend; Magnavox amplifiers; Comm/Scope cable; Info/Soft character generator; Oak set top converters; Jerrold addressable set top converters; Simulsat satellite antenna; Standard Components & Microdyne satellite receivers.
Miles of plant: 475.0 (coaxial); 24.0 (fiber optic). Additional miles planned: 10.0 (coaxial). Homes passed: 28,900.
Office manager: Debbie Cassell. Chief technician: Larry Sparks. Marketing director: Georgia Page.
City fee: 5% of gross.
Ownership: Charter Communications Inc. (MSO). Purchased from Marcus Cable, April 1, 1999.

KENTUCKY LAKE—Paris Cablevision, Box 220, 508 E. Washington St., Paris, TN 38242. Phone: 901-642-7028. Fax: 901-642-5512. County: Henry. Also serves Buchanan, Henry County (unincorporated areas), Mansard Island, Russwood Shores, Springville. ICA: TN0145.
TV Market Ranking: Outside TV Markets. Franchise award date: N.A. Franchise expiration date: N.A. Began: N.A.
Channel capacity: 41 (not 2-way capable). Channels available but not in use: 27.
Basic Service
Subscribers: 859.
Programming (received off-air): WBBJ-TV (A) Jackson; WLJT (P) Lexington; WKRN-TV (A), WSMV (N), WTVF (C), WZTV (F) Nashville; WPSD-TV (N) Paducah.
Programming (via satellite): WGN-TV (W) Chicago; Home Shopping Network; Odyssey; TBS Superstation.
Fee: $26.25 installation; $10.00 monthly.
Expanded Basic Service
Subscribers: 675.
Programming (via satellite): A & E; American Movie Classics; C-SPAN; CNN; Comedy Central; Country Music TV; Discovery Channel; Disney Channel; E! Entertainment TV; ESPN; Fox Family Channel; Headline News; Lifetime; MTV; Nashville Network; Nickelodeon; The Weather Channel; Turner Network TV; USA Network; VH1.
Fee: $30.05 monthly.
Pay Service 1
Pay Units: 241.
Programming (via satellite): Cinemax; HBO; Showtime; The Movie Channel.
Fee: $7.95 monthly (TMC), $10.95 monthly (Cinemax, HBO or Showtime).
Miles of plant: 28.0 (coaxial); None (fiber optic). Homes passed included with Paris, TN.
Plant manager: Duane Lear. Customer service manager: Dana Owens.
Ownership: Rifkin & Associates Inc. (MSO). See Cable System Ownership.

KINGSPORT—InterMedia Partners, 6940 Moores Lane, Brentwood, TN 37027-2908. Phone: 615-244-5900. Fax: 615-577-3683. Counties: Hawkins & Sullivan. Also serves Church Hill, Colonial Heights, Hawkins County, Lynn Garden, Mount Carmel, Sullivan County, Sullivan Gardens. ICA: TN0007.
TV Market Ranking: Below 100. Franchise award date: May 17, 1966. Franchise expiration date: January 20, 2007. Began: December 1, 1980.
Channel capacity: 52. Channels available but not in use: None.
Basic Service
Subscribers: 31,162; Commercial subscribers: 26.
Programming (received off-air): WCYB-TV (N) Bristol-Kingsport; WEMT (F) Greeneville; WJHL-TV (C) Johnson City; WAPK-LP (U), WKPT-TV (A) Kingsport; WSBN-TV (P) Norton; WSJK (P) Sneedville; 16 FMs.
Programming (via satellite): WGN-TV (W) Chicago; C-SPAN; TBS Superstation; TV Guide Channel.
Current originations: Automated time-weather; public access; educational access; government access; local news.
Fee: $39.95 installation; $13.95 monthly.
Expanded Basic Service
Subscribers: 31,100.
Programming (via satellite): A & E; American Movie Classics; BET; C-SPAN 2; CNBC; CNN; Comedy Central; Country Music TV; Discovery Channel; E! Entertainment TV; ESPN; Electronic Program Guide; Fox Family Channel; Fox Sports Net South; Headline News; Lifetime; MTV; Nashville Network; News Plus; Nickelodeon; QVC; The Weather Channel; Trinity Bcstg. Network; Turner Network TV; USA Network; VH1.
Fee: $19.95 monthly.
Pay Service 1
Pay Units: 2,377.
Programming (via satellite): Cinemax.
Fee: $5.00 installation; $11.00 monthly.
Pay Service 2
Pay Units: 1,243.
Programming (via satellite): Disney Channel.
Fee: $5.00 installation; $9.95 monthly.
Pay Service 3
Pay Units: 3,690.
Programming (via satellite): HBO.
Fee: $5.00 installation; $11.00 monthly.
Pay Service 4
Pay Units: 2,709.
Programming (via satellite): Showtime.
Fee: $5.00 installation; $11.00 monthly.
Pay Service 5
Pay Units: 524.
Programming (via satellite): The Movie Channel.
Fee: $5.00 installation; $11.95 monthly.
Local advertising: Yes (locally produced & insert). Available in satellite distributed programming. Local sales manager: Ray Walker. Regional interconnect: Cabletime.
Equipment: Scientific-Atlanta headend; C-COR amplifiers; Capscan cable; Sony VTRs; MSI character generator; Jerrold set top converters; Pioneer addressable set top converters; Gamco & Microwave Filter traps; Anixter-Mark satellite antenna; Sony commercial insert.
Miles of plant: 656.0 (coaxial). Additional miles planned: 10.0 (coaxial). Homes passed: 40,797. Total homes in franchised area: 100,000.
Manager: Craig Perica. Chief technician: Grant Evans. Marketing director: Tim Miller.
City fee: 3% of gross.
Ownership: InterMedia Partners (MSO). See Cable System Ownership.

KINGSTON—Helicon Cable Communications, Box 307, 71332 Hwy. 41S, Jasper, TN 37347-0307. Phones: 423-336-2513; 800-845-9937. Fax: 423-942-2851. Counties: Meigs & Roane. Also serves Midway (Roane County), Ten Mile. ICA: TN0073.
TV Market Ranking: 71 (portions of Kingston); Below 100 (portions of Kingston, Midway, Ten Mile). Franchise award date: N.A. Franchise expiration date: N.A. Began: October 1, 1989.
Channel capacity: 40. Channels available but not in use: N.A.
Basic Service
Subscribers: 1,339.
Programming (received off-air): WDEF-TV (C), WDSI-TV (F), WRCB-TV (N), WTCI (P), WTVC (A) Chattanooga; WFLI-TV (U) Cleveland; WATE-TV (A), WBIR-TV (N), WTNZ (F), WVLT-TV (C) Knoxville.
Programming (via satellite): WGN-TV (W) Chicago; A & E; C-SPAN; CNBC; CNN; Comedy Central; Country Music TV; Discovery Channel; E! Entertainment TV; ESPN; Fox Family Channel; Learning Channel; Lifetime; MTV; Nashville Network; Nickelodeon; QVC; TBS Superstation; Travel Channel; Trinity Bcstg. Network; Turner Network TV; USA Network.
Fee: $51.71 installation; $22.95 monthly; $0.78 converter.
Pay Service 1
Pay Units: 47.
Programming (via satellite): Cinemax.
Fee: $11.34 monthly.
Pay Service 2
Pay Units: 17.
Programming (via satellite): Disney Channel.
Fee: $11.34 monthly.
Pay Service 3
Pay Units: 65.
Programming (via satellite): HBO.
Fee: $11.34 monthly.
Pay Service 4
Pay Units: 30.
Programming (via satellite): Showtime.
Fee: $11.34 monthly.
Pay Service 5
Pay Units: 15.
Programming (via satellite): The Movie Channel.
Fee: $11.34 monthly.
Miles of plant: 100.0 (coaxial); None (fiber optic). Homes passed: 2,084.
Manager: Anthony Pope. Chief technician: Ricky Brown.
Ownership: Helicon Corp. (MSO). Purchased from Mid South Cable TV Inc. See Cable System Ownership.

KNOXVILLE—Comcast Cablevision of the South, 614 N. Central Ave., Knoxville, TN 37917-7389. Phone: 423-637-5411. Fax: 423-637-8805. Counties: Blount & Knox. Also serves Blount County (portions), Halls, Knox County, Powell, Rockford. ICA: TN0004.
TV Market Ranking: 71. Franchise award date: June 17, 1973. Franchise expiration date: N.A. Began: March 1, 1975.
Channel capacity: 78 (not 2-way capable). Channels available but not in use: 21.
Basic Service
Subscribers: 107,334.
Programming (received off-air): WPXK (X) Jellico; WATE-TV (A), WBIR-TV (N), WKOP-

TV (P), WTNZ (F), WVLT-TV (C) Knoxville; 2 FMs.
Programming (via satellite): WGN-TV (W) Chicago; TBS Superstation.
Current originations: Automated time-weather; public access; educational access; local news.
Fee: $29.25 installation (aerial), $55.25 (underground); $6.35 monthly.

Expanded Basic Service
Subscribers: 105,333.
Programming (via satellite): A & E; American Movie Classics; BET; C-SPAN; C-SPAN 2; CNN; Court TV; Discovery Channel; ESPN; Fox Family Channel; Headline News; Home Shopping Network; Lifetime; MTV; Nashville Network; Nickelodeon; Odyssey; QVC; TV Guide Channel; The Weather Channel; Travel Channel; Turner Network TV; USA Network.
Fee: $17.71 monthly.

A la Carte 1
Subscribers: 15,000.
Programming (via satellite): CNBC; Cartoon Network; Comedy Central; Country Music TV; Learning Channel; Sci-Fi Channel.
Fee: $2.98 monthly (package).

Pay Service 1
Pay Units: 5,736.
Programming (via satellite): Cinemax.
Fee: $16.00 installation; $11.62 monthly.

Pay Service 2
Pay Units: 9,060.
Programming (via satellite): Disney Channel.
Fee: $16.00 installation; $6.77 monthly.

Pay Service 3
Pay Units: 19,397.
Programming (via satellite): HBO.
Fee: $16.00 installation; $11.62 monthly.

Pay Service 4
Pay Units: 6,653.
Programming (via satellite): The Movie Channel.
Fee: $16.00 installation; $6.77 monthly.

Pay Service 5
Pay Units: 11,860.
Programming (via satellite): Showtime.
Fee: $16.00 installation; $6.77 monthly.

Pay Service 6
Pay Units: 1,245.
Programming (via satellite): DMX.
Fee: $10.62 monthly.

Pay Service 7
Pay Units: 10,000.
Programming (via satellite): The New Encore.
Fee: $2.50 monthly.

Pay-Per-View
Addressable homes: 49,000.
Action Pay-Per-View; Hot Choice; Viewer's Choice.
Fee: $2.50.

Local advertising: Yes (insert only). Available in satellite distributed programming. Rates: $150.00/Minute; $75.00/30 Seconds. Local sales manager: Tim Kiser. Regional interconnect: Knoxville Interconnect.
Program Guide: CableView.
Equipment: Scientific-Atlanta headend; C-COR amplifiers; Comm/Scope cable; Texscan & MSI character generator; Jerrold & Scientific-Atlanta addressable set top converters; Eagle & Pico traps; Scientific-Atlanta & Microdyne satellite antenna; Scientific-Atlanta & Jerrold satellite receivers; ChannelMatic commercial insert.
Miles of plant: 2350.0 (coaxial); 1090.0 (fiber optic). Additional miles planned: 200.0 (coaxial). Homes passed: 150,765.
Manager: Mona Mead. Chief technician: Mike Davis.
City fee: 3%-5% of gross.
Ownership: Comcast Cable Communications Inc. (MSO).

LA FOLLETTE—Comcast Cablevision of the South, Box 457, Jacksboro, TN 37757. Phone: 423-566-0760. Fax: 423-566-5501. Counties: Anderson & Campbell. Also serves Campbell County, Caryville, Jacksboro, Lake City, Rogers Dock. ICA: TN0035.
TV Market Ranking: 71 (portions of Campbell County, Caryville, Jacksboro, La Follette, Lake City); Below 100 (portions of Campbell County). Franchise award date: May 11, 1965. Franchise expiration date: N.A. Began: September 20, 1966.
Channel capacity: 36 (not 2-way capable). Channels available but not in use: 2.

Basic Service
Subscribers: 9,400.
Programming (received off-air): WCYB-TV (N) Bristol-Kingsport; WTVC (A) Chattanooga; WLOS (A) Greenville-Spartanburg-Asheville; WJHL-TV (C) Johnson City; WATE-TV (A), WBIR-TV (N), WTNZ (F), WVLT-TV (C) Knoxville; WSJK (P) Sneedville; allband FM.
Programming (via satellite): WGN-TV (W) Chicago; CNN; ESPN; Lifetime; MTV; Nashville Network; Nickelodeon; USA Network; VH1.
Planned programming (via satellite): Fox Family Channel; TBS Superstation.
Current originations: Automated time-weather.
Fee: $28.87 installation; $13.95 monthly.

Pay Service 1
Pay Units: 166.
Programming (via satellite): Disney Channel.
Fee: $19.95 installation; $16.95 monthly.

Pay Service 2
Pay Units: 1,201.
Programming (via satellite): HBO.
Fee: $19.95 installation; $16.95 monthly.

Pay Service 3
Pay Units: 291.
Programming (via satellite): Showtime.
Fee: $19.95 installation; $16.95 monthly.

Pay-Per-View
Addressable homes: 1,500.

Equipment: Comtech satellite antenna.
Miles of plant: 280.0 (coaxial); 48.0 (fiber optic). Homes passed: 12,000.
Manager: Mona Meade. Chief technician: Tony Miller.
City fee: 3% of gross.
Ownership: Comcast Cable Communications Inc. (MSO).

LAFAYETTE—InterMedia, 6940 Moores Lane, Brentwood, TN 37027-2908. Phone: 615-244-5900. County: Macon. Also serves Macon County, Webbtown. ICA: TN0085.
TV Market Ranking: Below 100 (Lafayette, Macon County); Outside TV Markets (Webbtown). Franchise award date: N.A. Franchise expiration date: January 9, 2011. Began: May 1, 1981.
Channel capacity: 39. Channels available but not in use: 11.

Basic Service
Subscribers: 1,282.
Programming (received off-air): WDCN (P), WKRN-TV (A), WSMV (N), WTVF (C), WUXP (U), WZTV (F) Nashville.
Current originations: Automated time-weather; public access.
Fee: $60.00 installation; $10.00 monthly; $10.00 additional installation.

Expanded Basic Service
Subscribers: 1,058.
Programming (via satellite): CNN; Country Music TV; ESPN; Fox Family Channel; MTV; Nashville Network; Nickelodeon; TBS Superstation; Turner Network TV; USA Network.
Fee: $60.00 installation; $6.65 monthly.

Pay Service 1
Pay Units: 131.
Programming (via satellite): Cinemax.
Fee: $10.00 installation; $9.95 monthly.

Pay Service 2
Pay Units: 40.
Programming (via satellite): Disney Channel.
Fee: $9.95 monthly.

Pay Service 3
Pay Units: 179.
Programming (via satellite): The New Encore.
Fee: $1.50 monthly.

Pay Service 4
Pay Units: 206.
Programming (via satellite): HBO.
Fee: $9.95 monthly.

Equipment: Scientific-Atlanta headend; Scientific-Atlanta amplifiers.
Miles of plant: 58.4 (coaxial). Homes passed: 1,661.
Manager: Kathy Harris. Chief technician: Raymond Strait.
City fee: 3% of gross.
Ownership: InterMedia Partners (MSO). See Cable System Ownership.

LAUREL BLOOMERY—FrontierVision, 12089 Hwy. 421 N, Zionville, NC 28698. Phone: 704-297-4090. County: Johnson. Also serves Johnson County (unincorporated areas). ICA: TN0146.
TV Market Ranking: Below 100. Franchise award date: N.A. Franchise expiration date: N.A. Began: N.A.
Channel capacity: N.A. Channels available but not in use: N.A.

Basic Service
Subscribers: N.A.
Programming (received off-air): WCYB-TV (N) Bristol-Kingsport; WBTV (C), WCCB (F), WSOC-TV (A) Charlotte; WJHL-TV (C) Johnson City; WKPT-TV (A) Kingsport; WSJK (P) Sneedville.
Programming (via satellite): WGN-TV (W) Chicago; CNN; ESPN; Fox Family Channel; Nashville Network; TBS Superstation; USA Network.
Fee: $13.00 monthly.

Pay Service 1
Pay Units: N.A.
Programming (via satellite): HBO.
Fee: $9.95 monthly.

Manager: Bob Blevins. Chief technician: Jimmy Phipps.
Ownership: FrontierVision Partners LP (MSO). See Cable System Ownership.

LAWRENCEBURG—Cablevision Communications, Box 1039, 2008 S. Main St., Columbia, TN 38401. Phone: 931-388-3550. Fax: 931-381-4446. County: Lawrence. Also serves Dunn. ICA: TN0147.
TV Market Ranking: Outside TV Markets. Franchise award date: N.A. Franchise expiration date: N.A. Began: N.A.
Channel capacity: N.A. Channels available but not in use: N.A.

Basic Service
Subscribers: 4,952.
Programming (received off-air): WOWL-TV (N) Florence; WAAY-TV (A), WHNT-TV (C) Huntsville-Decatur; WDCN (P), WKRN-TV (A), WSMV (N), WTVF (C), WZTV (F) Nashville.
Programming (via satellite): C-SPAN; Home Shopping Network; Learning Channel; Lifetime; TBS Superstation.
Fee: N.A.

Expanded Basic Service
Subscribers: 4,907.
Programming (via translator): WYLE (W) Florence.
Programming (via satellite): A & E; American Movie Classics; BET; CNBC; CNN; Comedy Central; Country Music TV; Court TV; Discovery Channel; ESPN; Fox Family Channel; Fox Sports Net South; Headline News; MTV; Nashville Network; Nickelodeon; Odyssey; The Weather Channel; Turner Network TV; USA Network; VH1.
Fee: N.A.

Pay Service 1
Pay Units: N.A.
Programming (via satellite): Cinemax; Disney Channel; HBO; Showtime.
Fee: N.A.

Local advertising: Yes. Regional interconnect: Intermedia Television Advertising.
Manager: Chris Karn. Chief technician: Gary Powell.
Ownership: Rifkin & Associates Inc. (MSO). See Cable System Ownership.

LEBANON—Lebanon Cablevision, Box 999, 223 S. College St., Lebanon, TN 37087. Phone: 615-444-2288. County: Wilson. Also serves Watertown, Wilson County (portions). ICA: TN0029.
TV Market Ranking: 30 (Lebanon, portions of Wilson County); Below 100 (Watertown, portions of Wilson County). Franchise award date: N.A. Franchise expiration date: N.A. Began: April 6, 1981.
Channel capacity: 35. Channels available but not in use: 4.

Basic Service
Subscribers: 8,984.
Programming (received off-air): WPGD (I) Hendersonville; WHTN (I) Murfreesboro; WDCN (P), WKRN-TV (A), WSMV (N), WTVF (C), WUXP (U), WZTV (F) Nashville; allband FM.
Programming (via satellite): WGN-TV (W) Chicago; C-SPAN; TBS Superstation; ValueVision.
Fee: N.A.

Expanded Basic Service
Subscribers: 6,398.
Programming (via satellite): A & E; American Movie Classics; BET; CNN; Comedy Central; Country Music TV; Discovery Channel; ESPN; Fox Family Channel; Headline News; Home Shopping Network; Lifetime; MTV; Nashville Network; Nickelodeon; Turner Network TV; USA Network; VH1.
Fee: $29.95 installation; $16.95 monthly.

Pay Service 1
Pay Units: 950.
Programming (via satellite): Cinemax.
Fee: $10.00 installation; $9.50 monthly.

Pay Service 2
Pay Units: 463.
Programming (via satellite): Disney Channel.
Fee: $10.00 installation; $6.95 monthly.

Pay Service 3
Pay Units: 1,554.
Programming (via satellite): HBO.
Fee: $10.00 installation; $9.50 monthly.

Pay Service 4
Pay Units: 580.
Programming (via satellite): Showtime.
Fee: $10.00 installation; $9.50 monthly.

Pay Service 5
Pay Units: N.A.
Programming (via satellite): The Movie Channel.
Fee: N.A.

Local advertising: Yes. Regional interconnect: Intermedia Television Advertising.
Equipment: Scientific-Atlanta headend; Scientific-Atlanta amplifiers; Times Fiber cable;

Sony cameras; JVC VTRs; MSI & Texscan character generator; Oak set top converters; Scientific-Atlanta satellite antenna.
Miles of plant: 158.0 (coaxial). Homes passed: 9,411.
Manager: Andy Blume. Chief technician: Dwayne Salts.
City fee: 3% of gross.
Ownership: Rifkin & Associates Inc. (MSO). See Cable System Ownership.

LEWISBURG—InterMedia Partners, Box 250, 24 Circle Dr., McKenzie, TN 38201. Phone: 901-352-2273. Fax: 901-352-3164. Web site: http://www.intermediamtn.com. Counties: Bedford & Marshall. Also serves Bedford County (portions), Marshall County (portions). ICA: TN0049.
TV Market Ranking: Below 100 (Bedford County, Lewisburg, portions of Marshall County); Outside TV Markets (portions of Marshall County). Franchise award date: December 6, 1967. Franchise expiration date: December 31, 2007. Began: April 1, 1974.
Channel capacity: 61 (not 2-way capable). Channels available but not in use: 16.
Basic Service
Subscribers: 3,172.
Programming (received off-air): WAAY-TV (A), WAFF (N), WHNT-TV (C) Huntsville-Decatur; WDCN (P), WKRN-TV (A), WNAB (W), WSMV (N), WTVF (C), WZTV (F) Nashville; 14 FMs.
Programming (via satellite): WGN-TV (W) Chicago; Fox Family Channel.
Fee: N.A.
Expanded Basic Service
Subscribers: 3,023.
Programming (via satellite): A & E; American Movie Classics; BET; C-SPAN; CNBC; CNN; Comedy Central; Country Music TV; Discovery Channel; Disney Channel; ESPN; ESPN 2; FX; Fox News Channel; Fox Sports Net South; Headline News; History Channel; Home Shopping Network; Learning Channel; Lifetime; MTV; Nashville Network; Nickelodeon; QVC; TBS Superstation; The Weather Channel; Trinity Bcstg. Network; Turner Classic Movies; Turner Network TV; USA Network.
Fee: N.A.
Pay Service 1
Pay Units: 1,521.
Programming (via satellite): Cinemax; HBO; Showtime; The New Encore.
Fee: N.A.
Local advertising: Yes. Regional interconnect: Intermedia Television Advertising.
Equipment: Jerrold headend; C-COR & Magnavox amplifiers; Comm/Scope cable; Telemation cameras; Sony VTRs; Pioneer set top converters; AFC & Microdyne satellite antenna; Scientific-Atlanta & Standard Components satellite receivers.
Miles of plant: 230.0 (coaxial); 40.0 (fiber optic). Homes passed: 4,678.
Manager: Robert L. Pace. Chief technician: Benny Jackson.
City fee: 5% of gross.
Ownership: InterMedia Partners (MSO). Sale pends to Rifkin & Associates Inc.

LEXINGTON—InterMedia Partners, Box 250, 24 Circle Dr., McKenzie, TN 38201. Phone: 901-352-2273. Fax: 901-352-3164. Web site: http://www.intermediamtn.com. County: Henderson. Also serves Henderson County. ICA: TN0047.
TV Market Ranking: Below 100. Franchise award date: October 10, 1964. Franchise expiration date: October 10, 2014. Began: January 1, 1965.
Channel capacity: 42 (not 2-way capable). Channels available but not in use: None.
Basic Service
Subscribers: 3,401.
Programming (received off-air): WBBJ-TV (A), WMTU (U) Jackson; WLJT (P) Lexington; WMC-TV (N), WREG-TV (C) Memphis; WSMV (N), WTVF (C) Nashville.
Programming (via satellite): WGN-TV (W) Chicago; C-SPAN; FoxNet; Learning Channel.
Current originations: Automated time-weather.
Fee: $11.11 monthly.
Expanded Basic Service
Subscribers: 3,131.
Programming (via satellite): A & E; American Movie Classics; BET; CNBC; CNN; Comedy Central; Country Music TV; Discovery Channel; Disney Channel; ESPN; ESPN 2; Fox Family Channel; Fox News Channel; Fox Sports Net South; Headline News; History Channel; Lifetime; MTV; Nashville Network; Nickelodeon; QVC; TBS Superstation; The Weather Channel; Trinity Bcstg. Network; Turner Network TV; USA Network.
Fee: $14.96 monthly.
Pay Service 1
Pay Units: 1,470.
Programming (via satellite): Cinemax; HBO; Showtime; The New Encore.
Fee: $11.95 monthly.
Local advertising: Yes. Local sales manager: Andy Atkinson.
Equipment: Scientific-Atlanta headend; Jerrold & Scientific-Atlanta amplifiers; Times Fiber & Comm/Scope cable; Jerrold addressable set top converters; Scientific-Atlanta satellite antenna; Jerrold, Microdyne & Scientific-Atlanta satellite receivers.
Miles of plant: 150.2 (coaxial); None (fiber optic). Homes passed: 5,356.
Manager: Robert L. Pace. Chief technician: Benny Jackson.
City fee: 5% of gross.
Ownership: InterMedia Partners (MSO). See Cable System Ownership.

LINDEN—Pat's Cable TV, Box 555, Linden, TN 37096. Phone: 931-589-2696. County: Perry. ICA: TN0098.
TV Market Ranking: Outside TV Markets. Franchise award date: N.A. Franchise expiration date: N.A. Began: June 16, 1981.
Channel capacity: 12 (2-way capable; operating 2-way). Channels available but not in use: N.A.
Basic Service
Subscribers: N.A.
Programming (received off-air): WBBJ-TV (A) Jackson; WDCN (P), WKRN-TV (A), WSMV (N), WTVF (C), WZTV (F) Nashville; allband FM.
Programming (via satellite): WGN-TV (W) Chicago; ESPN; Nashville Network; TBS Superstation; Turner Network TV.
Fee: $20.00 installation; $13.00 monthly.
Pay Service 1
Pay Units: N.A.
Programming (via satellite): HBO.
Fee: $9.00 monthly.
Equipment: Cadco headend; Magnavox amplifiers; Comm/Scope cable; Gardiner satellite antenna.
Additional miles planned: 21.0 (coaxial). Homes passed: 922. Total homes in franchised area: 1,820.
Manager: Dorothy Patterson. Chief technician: Bert Patterson.
Ownership: Pat's Inc. (MSO).

LIVINGSTON—Comcast Cablevision of the South, Box 69, 407 University Dr., Livingston, TN 38570. Phone: 931-823-1331. Fax: 931-823-7991. County: Overton. ICA: TN0078.
TV Market Ranking: Below 100. Franchise award date: November 4, 1963. Franchise expiration date: November 4, 2003. Began: May 1, 1966.
Channel capacity: 36 (not 2-way capable). Channels available but not in use: N.A.
Basic Service
Subscribers: 930.
Programming (received off-air): WCTE (P) Cookeville; WDCN (P), WKRN-TV (A), WSMV (N), WTVF (C), WZTV (F) Nashville; 1 FM.
Programming (via satellite): WGN-TV (W) Chicago; CNN; Country Music TV; Discovery Channel; ESPN; Fox Family Channel; Goodlife TV Network; Headline News; Lifetime; MTV; Nashville Network; Nickelodeon; TBS Superstation; The Weather Channel; Turner Network TV; USA Network.
Current originations: Automated time-weather; public access; local news; local sports.
Fee: $20.00 installation; $9.00 monthly; $20.00 additional installation.
Pay Service 1
Pay Units: 143.
Programming (via satellite): Cinemax.
Fee: $20.00 installation; $9.00 monthly.
Pay Service 2
Pay Units: 48.
Programming (via satellite): Disney Channel.
Fee: $20.00 installation; $7.95 monthly.
Pay Service 3
Pay Units: 184.
Programming (via satellite): HBO.
Fee: $20.00 installation; $9.00 monthly.
Equipment: Scientific-Atlanta & Jerrold headend; Jerrold amplifiers; Times Fiber cable; Jerrold, Scientific-Atlanta & RCA set top converters; Pico traps; Scientific-Atlanta & Comtech satellite antenna; Microdyne satellite receivers.
Miles of plant: 49.5 (coaxial). Homes passed: 1,791.
Manager: Shirley Webb. Chief technician: Jimmy Copeland.
City fee: 2% of gross.
Ownership: Comcast Cable Communications Inc. (MSO).

LIVINGSTON—Overton County Cable TV, 1034 E. Main St., Livingston, TN 38570. Phones: 931-823-1114; 931-823-1123. County: Overton. Also serves Overton County (portions). ICA: TN0184.
TV Market Ranking: Below 100. Franchise award date: N.A. Franchise expiration date: N.A. Began: N.A.
Channel capacity: 40. Channels available but not in use: 3.
Basic Service
Subscribers: 2,572.
Programming (received off-air): WCTE (P) Cookeville; WDCN (P), WKRN-TV (A), WSMV (N), WTVF (C), WUXP (U), WZTV (F) Nashville.
Programming (via satellite): WGN-TV (W) Chicago; A & E; American Movie Classics; C-SPAN; CNBC; CNN; Cartoon Network; Comedy Central; Country Music TV; Discovery Channel; ESPN; Fox Family Channel; Fox Sports Net South; Home Shopping Network; Lifetime; MTV; Nashville Network; Nickelodeon; Sci-Fi Channel; TBS Superstation; Trinity Bcstg. Network; Turner Network TV; USA Network; VH1.
Fee: $10.78 installation; $12.50 monthly.
Pay Service 1
Pay Units: 137.
Programming (via satellite): Cinemax.
Fee: $10.31 monthly.
Pay Service 2
Pay Units: 59.
Programming (via satellite): Disney Channel.
Fee: $9.77 monthly.
Pay Service 3
Pay Units: 325.
Programming (via satellite): HBO.
Fee: $10.31 monthly.
Pay Service 4
Pay Units: 55.
Programming (via satellite): Showtime.
Fee: $10.31 monthly.
Miles of plant: 187.0 (coaxial).
Manager: Cliff Bilbrey. Chief technician: Kenneth Allen.
Ownership: Cliff Bilbrey.

LOBELVILLE—Pat's Cable TV, Box 555, Linden, TN 37096. Phone: 931-589-2696. County: Perry. ICA: TN0149.
TV Market Ranking: Outside TV Markets. Franchise award date: N.A. Franchise expiration date: N.A. Began: N.A.
Channel capacity: 12. Channels available but not in use: N.A.
Basic Service
Subscribers: N.A.
Programming (received off-air): WBBJ-TV (A) Jackson; WDCN (P), WKRN-TV (A), WSMV (N), WTVF (C), WZTV (F) Nashville.
Programming (via satellite): WGN-TV (W) Chicago; ESPN; Nashville Network; TBS Superstation; Turner Network TV.
Fee: $13.00 monthly.
Pay Service 1
Pay Units: N.A.
Programming (via satellite): HBO.
Fee: $9.00 monthly.
Manager: Dorothy Patterson. Chief technician: Bert Patterson.
Ownership: Pat's Inc. (MSO).

LORETTO—InterMedia Partners, Box 250, 24 Circle Dr., McKenzie, TN 38201. Phone: 901-352-2273. Fax: 901-352-3164. Web site: http://www.intermediamtn.com. Counties: Lawrence & Wayne, TN; Lauderdale, AL. Also serves Lauderdale County (portions), AL; Iron City, Lawrence County (portions), St. Joseph, TN. ICA: TN0068.
TV Market Ranking: 96 (portions of Lawrence County); Below 100 (Iron City, Lauderdale County, portions of Lawrence County, Loretto, St. Joseph); Outside TV Markets (portions of Lawrence County). Franchise award date: N.A. Franchise expiration date: August 1, 2006. Began: November 1, 1970.
Channel capacity: 61. Channels available but not in use: 19.
Basic Service
Subscribers: 2,020.
Programming (received off-air): WOWL-TV (N) Florence; WAAY-TV (A), WHNT-TV (C), WZDX (F) Huntsville-Decatur; WDCN (P), WKRN-TV (A), WSMV (N) Nashville; allband FM.
Programming (via satellite): WGN-TV (W) Chicago; C-SPAN; Fox Family Channel; Learning Channel.
Fee: N.A.
Expanded Basic Service
Subscribers: 1,939.
Programming (via satellite): A & E; American Movie Classics; CNBC; CNN; Comedy Central; Country Music TV; Discovery Channel; Disney Channel; ESPN; ESPN 2; FX; Fox Sports Net South; Headline News; History Channel; Home Shopping Network; MTV; Nashville Network; Nickelodeon; QVC; TBS Superstation; The Weather Channel; Turner

Classic Movies; Turner Network TV; USA Network; VH1.
Fee: N.A.
Pay Service 1
Pay Units: 591.
Programming (via satellite): Cinemax; HBO; Showtime; The New Encore.
Fee: N.A.
Equipment: Scientific-Atlanta headend; Scientific-Atlanta amplifiers; Comm/Scope cable; Scientific-Atlanta set top converters; Pico traps; Scientific-Atlanta satellite antenna; Scientific-Atlanta satellite receivers.
Miles of plant: 95.0 (coaxial); 25.2 (fiber optic). Homes passed: 3,008.
Manager: Robert L. Pace. Chief technician: Benny Jackson.
City fee: 4% of gross.
Ownership: InterMedia Partners (MSO). See Cable System Ownership.

LOUDON—InterMedia, 725 Louisville Rd., Alcoa, TN 37701-1846. Phone: 423-984-1400. Fax: 423-983-0383. Counties: Knox & Loudon. Also serves Concord, Farragut, Knox County, Lenoir City, Loudon County, Philadelphia. ICA: TN0148.
TV Market Ranking: 71 (Concord, Farragut, Knox County, Lenoir City, Loudon, portions of Loudon County, Philadelphia); Below 100 (portions of Loudon County). Franchise award date: N.A. Franchise expiration date: November 1, 2007. Began: August 1, 1977.
Channel capacity: 61. Channels available but not in use: 15.
Basic Service
Subscribers: N.A.
Programming (received off-air): WATE-TV (A), WBIR-TV (N), WKOP-TV (P), WTNZ (F), WVLT-TV (C) Knoxville; W38AQ (I) Lenoir City; WSJK (P) Sneedville; allband FM.
Programming (via satellite): WGN-TV (W) Chicago; C-SPAN; Fox Family Channel; Headline News; TBS Superstation.
Current originations: Local news.
Fee: $19.95 installation; $9.37 monthly.
Expanded Basic Service
Subscribers: N.A.
Programming (via satellite): A & E; American Movie Classics; BET; CNBC; CNN; Comedy Central; Country Music TV; Discovery Channel; ESPN; Fox Sports Net South; Learning Channel; Lifetime; MTV; Nashville Network; Nickelodeon; QVC; The Weather Channel; Trinity Bcstg. Network; Turner Network TV; USA Network; VH1.
Fee: $8.04 monthly.
Pay Service 1
Pay Units: 3,731.
Programming (via satellite): Cinemax; Disney Channel; HBO; Showtime; The Movie Channel.
Fee: $7.50 monthly (HBO).
Pay-Per-View
Special events.
Fee: Varies.
Equipment: RCA headend; RCA amplifiers; General cable; AFC satellite antenna.
Miles of plant & homes passed included with Alcoa, TN.
Office manager: Paul Maynard. Technical operations manager: Mark Haley. Chief engineer: Dale Taylor. Business manager: Cathy Dunford.
City fee: 3% of gross.
Ownership: InterMedia Partners (MSO). See Cable System Ownership.

LYNCHBURG—InterMedia Partners, Box 250, 24 Circle Dr., McKenzie, TN 38201. Phone: 901-352-2273. Fax: 901-352-3164. Web site: http://www.intermediamtn.com. County: Moore. Also serves Moore County (portions). ICA: TN0119.
TV Market Ranking: 96 (portions of Moore County); Below 100 (portions of Moore County); Outside TV Markets (Lynchburg, portions of Moore County). Franchise award date: May 3, 1976. Franchise expiration date: May 3, 2006. Began: September 1, 1976.
Channel capacity: 37 (not 2-way capable). Channels available but not in use: 6.
Basic Service
Subscribers: 209.
Programming (received off-air): WAAY-TV (A), WAFF (N), WHNT-TV (C), WZDX (F) Huntsville-Decatur; WHTN (I) Murfreesboro; WDCN (P), WKRN-TV (A), WSMV (N), WTVF (C), WZTV (F) Nashville.
Programming (via satellite): Fox Family Channel; QVC.
Fee: N.A.
Expanded Basic Service
Subscribers: 130.
Programming (via satellite): WGN-TV (W) Chicago; A & E; American Movie Classics; CNN; Country Music TV; Discovery Channel; Disney Channel; ESPN; ESPN 2; Lifetime; MTV; Nashville Network; Nickelodeon; TBS Superstation; The Weather Channel; Turner Network TV; USA Network.
Fee: N.A.
Pay Service 1
Pay Units: 48.
Programming (via satellite): Cinemax; HBO.
Fee: N.A.
Local advertising: Yes. Local sales manager: Andy Atkinson.
Equipment: Blonder-Tongue headend; Scientific-Atlanta amplifiers.
Miles of plant: 8.0 (coaxial); None (fiber optic). Additional miles planned: 1.0 (coaxial). Homes passed: 336.
Manager: Robert L. Pace. Chief technician: Benny Jackson.
City fee: 3% of gross.
Ownership: InterMedia Partners (MSO). See Cable System Ownership.

LYNNVILLE—Small Town Cable, 225 Highland Villa, Nashville, TN 37211. Phone: 877-368-2110. County: Giles. Also serves Giles County (unincorporated areas), Waco. ICA: TN0123.
TV Market Ranking: Outside TV Markets. Franchise award date: July 18, 1988. Franchise expiration date: July 18, 2001. Began: N.A.
Channel capacity: 32. Channels available but not in use: 14.
Basic Service
Subscribers: 107.
Programming (received off-air): WZDX (F) Huntsville-Decatur; WDCN (P), WKRN-TV (A), WSMV (N), WTVF (C), WUXP (U), WZTV (F) Nashville.
Programming (via satellite): Country Music TV; TBS Superstation.
Fee: $40.00 installation; $10.95 monthly.
Expanded Basic Service
Subscribers: N.A.
Programming (via satellite): CNN; Discovery Channel; ESPN; ESPN 2; Fox Family Channel; History Channel; Nashville Network; Nickelodeon.
Fee: $13.00 monthly.
Pay Service 1
Pay Units: 6.
Programming (via satellite): Disney Channel.
Fee: $8.45 monthly.
Pay Service 2
Pay Units: 19.
Programming (via satellite): Showtime.

Fee: $11.45 monthly.
Miles of plant: 5.0 (coaxial). Homes passed: 196.
Manager: Tom Salters. Chief technician: Doc Collins. Program director: Sheri Smith.
Ownership: Small Town Cable Corp. (MSO). Purchased from Charter Communications Inc., January 1, 1999.

MADISONVILLE—InterMedia, 725 Louisville Rd., Alcoa, TN 37701-1846. Phone: 423-984-1400. Fax: 423-983-0383. County: Monroe. Also serves Monroe County, Sweetwater. ICA: TN0176.
TV Market Ranking: Below 100 (portions of Monroe County); Outside TV Markets (Madisonville, portions of Monroe County, Sweetwater). Franchise award date: N.A. Franchise expiration date: April 1, 2002. Began: N.A.
Channel capacity: 61. Channels available but not in use: 21.
Basic Service
Subscribers: 1,220.
Programming (received off-air): WATE-TV (A), WBIR-TV (N), WKOP-TV (P), WTNZ (F), WVLT-TV (C) Knoxville; WSJK (P) Sneedville.
Programming (via satellite): WGN-TV (W) Chicago; A & E; Discovery Channel; Fox Family Channel; Headline News; Nickelodeon; TBS Superstation.
Fee: $19.95 installation; $9.37 monthly.
Expanded Basic Service
Subscribers: N.A.
Programming (via satellite): CNN; ESPN; MTV; Nashville Network; Turner Network TV; USA Network.
Fee: $8.04 monthly.
Pay Service 1
Pay Units: 590.
Programming (via satellite): Disney Channel; HBO; Showtime.
Fee: N.A.
Miles of plant & homes passed included with Alcoa, TN.
Office manager: Paul Maynard. Technical operations manager: Mark Haley. Chief engineer: Dale Taylor. Business manager: Cathy Dunford.
Ownership: InterMedia Partners (MSO). See Cable System Ownership.

MANCHESTER—Charter Communications, 215 Industrial Blvd., Tullahoma, TN 37388-4076. Phone: 931-455-2672. Fax: 931-455-5392. County: Coffee. Also serves Coffee County (portions). ICA: TN0150.
TV Market Ranking: Below 100 (portions of Coffee County, Manchester); Outside TV Markets (portions of Coffee County). Franchise award date: N.A. Franchise expiration date: N.A. Began: December 1, 1967.
Channel capacity: 38. Channels available but not in use: N.A.
Basic Service
Subscribers: 4,924.
Programming (received off-air): WDCN (P), WKRN-TV (A), WSMV (N), WTVF (C), WZTV (F) Nashville.
Programming (via satellite): WGN-TV (W) Chicago; C-SPAN; Country Music TV; QVC; TBS Superstation.
Current originations: Automated time-weather; public access.
Fee: $49.99 installation; $10.33 monthly; $24.95 additional installation.
Expanded Basic Service
Subscribers: 3,450.
Programming (via satellite): A & E; American Movie Classics; BET; CNBC; CNN; Comedy Central; Discovery Channel; ESPN; Fox Family Channel; Fox Sports Net South; Goodlife TV Network; Headline News; Lifetime; MTV; Nashville Network; Nickelodeon; The Weather Channel; Turner Network TV; USA Network; VH1.
Fee: $10.83 monthly.
Pay Service 1
Pay Units: N.A.
Programming (via satellite): Cinemax; Disney Channel; HBO; Showtime.
Fee: N.A.
Local advertising: Yes. Regional interconnect: Intermedia Television Advertising.
Equipment: Microdyne & Phasecom headend; Jerrold amplifiers; Jerrold cable; Microdyne satellite antenna.
Miles of plant: 40.0 (coaxial).
Manager: Earl Hines. Chief technician: Rex Ferguson.
City fee: 3% of gross.
Ownership: Rifkin & Associates Inc. (MSO). See Cable System Ownership.

MARTIN—InterMedia Partners, Box 250, 24 Circle Dr., McKenzie, TN 38201. Phone: 901-352-2273. Fax: 901-352-3164. Web site: http://www.intermediamtn.com. Counties: Obion & Weakley. Also serves Rives, Union City, Weakley County (portions), Woodland Mills. ICA: TN0042.
TV Market Ranking: Outside TV Markets. Franchise award date: August 1, 1970. Franchise expiration date: N.A. Began: N.A.
Channel capacity: 41 (not 2-way capable). Channels available but not in use: 2.
Basic Service
Subscribers: 8,208.
Programming (received off-air): KBSI (F), KFVS-TV (C) Cape Girardeau; WBBJ-TV (A) Jackson; WLJT (P) Lexington; WMC-TV (N) Memphis; WTVF (C) Nashville; WPSD-TV (N) Paducah; 1 FM.
Programming (via satellite): WGN-TV (W) Chicago; C-SPAN; Fox Family Channel.
Current originations: Automated time-weather.
Fee: $11.61 monthly.
Expanded Basic Service
Subscribers: 7,644.
Programming (via satellite): A & E; American Movie Classics; BET; CNBC; CNN; Comedy Central; Country Music TV; Discovery Channel; Disney Channel; ESPN; ESPN 2; FX; Fox News Channel; Fox Sports Net South; Headline News; History Channel; Learning Channel; Lifetime; MTV; Nashville Network; Nickelodeon; QVC; TBS Superstation; The Weather Channel; Trinity Bcstg. Network; Turner Network TV; USA Network.
Fee: $15.68 monthly.
Pay Service 1
Pay Units: 3,659.
Programming (via satellite): Cinemax; HBO; Showtime; The New Encore.
Fee: $11.95 monthly.

Pay-Per-View
Special events.
Local advertising: Yes.
Equipment: Scientific-Atlanta headend; Scientific-Atlanta amplifiers; Comm/Scope cable; Texscan & MSI character generator; Panasonic set top converters; Eagle traps; Scientific-Atlanta satellite antenna; Scientific-Atlanta satellite receivers.
Miles of plant: 195.0 (coaxial); 17.5 (fiber optic). Homes passed: 12,732.
Manager: Robert L. Pace. Chief technician: Benny Jackson.
City fee: 5% of gross.
Ownership: InterMedia Partners (MSO). See Cable System Ownership.

MAYNARDVILLE—Comcast Cablevision of the South, 614 N. Central Ave., Knoxville, TN 37917-7389. Phone: 615-637-5411. Fax: 615-637-8805. Counties: Grainger & Union. Also serves Blaine, Luttrell, Union County (portions). ICA: TN0077.
TV Market Ranking: 71. Franchise award date: N.A. Franchise expiration date: N.A. Began: October 1, 1986.
Channel capacity: 31. Channels available but not in use: N.A.
Basic Service
Subscribers: 142.
Programming (received off-air): WATE-TV (A), WBIR-TV (N), WTNZ (F), WVLT-TV (C) Knoxville; WSJK (P) Sneedville.
Programming (via satellite): WGN-TV (W) Chicago; A & E; BET; C-SPAN; CNN; Discovery Channel; ESPN; Fox Family Channel; Headline News; Learning Channel; Lifetime; MTV; Nashville Network; News Plus; Nickelodeon; Odyssey; QVC; TBS Superstation; The Weather Channel; Turner Network TV; USA Network; VH1.
Fee: $15.99 monthly.
Pay Service 1
Pay Units: N.A.
Programming (via satellite): Cinemax; Disney Channel; HBO; Showtime; The Movie Channel.
Fee: $7.95 monthly (Disney), $10.95 monthly (Cinemax, HBO, Showtime or TMC).
Local advertising: Planned. Local sales manager: Tim Kiser.
Miles of plant: 74.5 (coaxial). Homes passed: 1,925.
Manager: Mona Mead. Plant supervisor: Mike Davis.
Ownership: Comcast Cable Communications Inc. (MSO).

McEWEN—InterMedia Partners, Box 250, 24 Circle Dr., McKenzie, TN 38201. Phone: 901-352-2273. Fax: 901-352-3164. Web site: http://www.intermediamtn.com. County: Humphreys. ICA: TN0107.
TV Market Ranking: Outside TV Markets. Franchise award date: February 10, 1983. Franchise expiration date: February 9, 1998. Began: December 1, 1984.
Channel capacity: 42 (not 2-way capable). Channels available but not in use: 7.
Basic Service
Subscribers: 452.
Programming (received off-air): WHTN (I) Murfreesboro; WDCN (P), WKRN-TV (A), WNAB (W), WSMV (N), WTVF (C), WUXP (U), WZTV (F) Nashville.
Programming (via satellite): C-SPAN; Fox Family Channel; Lifetime; QVC.
Fee: $15.15 monthly.
Expanded Basic Service
Subscribers: 446.
Programming (via satellite): WGN-TV (W) Chicago; A & E; American Movie Classics; CNBC; CNN; Country Music TV; Discovery Channel; Disney Channel; ESPN; ESPN 2; FX; Fox Sports Net South; History Channel; MTV; Nashville Network; Nickelodeon; TBS Superstation; Turner Network TV; USA Network.
Fee: $10.18 monthly.
Pay Service 1
Pay Units: 206.
Programming (via satellite): Cinemax; HBO; Showtime; The New Encore.
Fee: $11.95 monthly.
Local advertising: Yes. Local sales manager: Andy Atkinson.
Equipment: DX Engineering & Triple Crown headend; Scientific-Atlanta amplifiers; Scientific-Atlanta satellite antenna; DX Engineering satellite receivers.
Miles of plant: 30.5 (coaxial); None (fiber optic). Homes passed: 916.
Manager: Robert L. Pace. Chief technician: Benny Jackson.
City fee: 3% of gross.
Ownership: InterMedia Partners (MSO). See Cable System Ownership.

McKENZIE—InterMedia Partners, Box 250, 24 Circle Dr., McKenzie, TN 38201. Phone: 901-352-2273. Fax: 901-352-3164. Web site: http://www.intermediamtn.com. Counties: Carroll, Gibson, Henry & Weakley. Also serves Atwood, Bruceton, Clarksburg, Gibson, Gibson County, Gleason, Greenfield, Hollow Rock, Huntingdon, McLemoresville, Milan, Sharon, Trezevant. ICA: TN0063.
TV Market Ranking: Below 100 (Atwood, Clarksburg, Gibson, portions of Gibson County, Huntingdon, McLemoresville, Milan, Trezevant); Outside TV Markets (Bruceton, portions of Gibson County, Gleason, Greenfield, Hollow Rock, Mckenzie, Sharon). Franchise award date: November 24, 1964. Franchise expiration date: December 5, 2006. Began: October 1, 1965.
Channel capacity: 78 (2-way capable). Channels available but not in use: None.
Basic Service
Subscribers: 11,678.
Programming (received off-air): WBBJ-TV (A), WMTU (U) Jackson; WLJT (P) Lexington; WMC-TV (N), WREG-TV (C) Memphis; WSMV (N), WTVF (C) Nashville; WPSD-TV (N) Paducah; 1 FM.
Programming (via satellite): WGN-TV (W) Chicago; FoxNet.
Fee: $11.31 monthly.
Expanded Basic Service
Subscribers: 10,122.
Programming (via satellite): A & E; American Movie Classics; Animal Planet; BET; C-SPAN; CNBC; CNN; Cartoon Network; Comedy Central; Country Music TV; Discovery Channel; Disney Channel; ESPN; ESPN 2; FX; Fox Family Channel; Fox News Channel; Fox Sports Net South; Headline News; History Channel; Home & Garden Television; Learning Channel; Lifetime; MTV; Nashville Network; Nickelodeon; QVC; TBS Superstation; TV Guide Channel; The Weather Channel; Trinity Bcstg. Network; Turner Network TV; USA Network; VH1.
Fee: N.A.
Pay Service 1
Pay Units: 4,392.
Programming (via satellite): Cinemax; HBO; Showtime; The New Encore.
Fee: $14.95 installation; $11.95 monthly.
Pay-Per-View
Addressable homes: 428.
Local advertising: Yes. Local sales manager: Sharon Nicholson.
Equipment: Scientific-Atlanta headend; Jerrold amplifiers; Comm/Scope cable; Pioneer set top converters; Arcom traps; Scientific-Atlanta satellite antenna; Scientific-Atlanta satellite receivers.
Miles of plant: 321.1 (coaxial); None (fiber optic). Homes passed: 11,816.
Manager: Robert L. Pace. Chief technician: Benny Jackson.
City fee: 5% of quarterly gross.
Ownership: InterMedia Partners (MSO). See Cable System Ownership.

McMINNVILLE—McMinnville Cablevision, Box 328, McMinnville, TN 37110. Phone: 931-668-5343. Fax: 931-668-2470. Counties: Franklin, Grundy, Van Buren, Warren & White. Also serves Centertown, Coalmont, Doyle, Gruetli-Laager, Grundy County (portions), Monteagle, Morrison, Palmer, Sewanee, Sparta, Spencer, Tracy City, Van Buren County (portions), Viola, Warren County (portions), White County (portions). ICA: TN0016.
TV Market Ranking: 78 (Coalmont, Gruetli-Laager, portions of Grundy County, Monteagle, Palmer, Tracy City); Below 100 (Centertown, Doyle, Morrison, Sparta, Spencer, Van Buren County, Viola, portions of Warren County, White County); Outside TV Markets (portions of Grundy County, McMinnville, Sewanee, portions of Warren County). Franchise award date: N.A. Franchise expiration date: November 1, 2001. Began: July 1, 1968.
Channel capacity: 42 (not 2-way capable). Channels available but not in use: None.
Basic Service
Subscribers: 16,246.
Programming (received off-air): WCTE (P) Cookeville; WDCN (P), WKRN-TV (A), WSMV (N), WTVF (C), WZTV (F) Nashville; allband FM.
Programming (via satellite): WGN-TV (W) Chicago; A & E; American Movie Classics; C-SPAN; C-SPAN 2; CNN; Comedy Central; Country Music TV; Discovery Channel; ESPN; Fox Family Channel; Fox Sports Net South; Headline News; Home Shopping Network; Learning Channel; Lifetime; MTV; Nashville Network; Nickelodeon; Odyssey; TBS Superstation; The Weather Channel; Travel Channel; Turner Network TV; USA Network; VH1.
Current originations: Automated time-weather.
Fee: $29.95 installation; $11.95 monthly.
Pay Service 1
Pay Units: 990.
Programming (via satellite): Cinemax.
Fee: $10.00 installation; $9.25 monthly.
Pay Service 2
Pay Units: 450.
Programming (via satellite): Disney Channel.
Fee: $10.00 installation; $9.25 monthly.
Pay Service 3
Pay Units: 1,400.
Programming (via satellite): HBO.
Fee: $10.00 installation; $9.25 monthly.
Pay Service 4
Pay Units: N.A.
Programming (via satellite): DMX; Showtime; The Movie Channel.
Fee: N.A.
Local advertising: Yes. Regional interconnect: Intermedia Television Advertising.
Equipment: Jerrold headend; Jerrold amplifiers; Times Fiber cable; Comtech satellite antenna.
Miles of plant: 644.0 (coaxial); None (fiber optic).
Manager: Earl Hines. Plant manager: Joe Hunter.
City fee: 5% of gross.
Ownership: Rifkin & Associates Inc. (MSO). See Cable System Ownership.

MEMPHIS—Time Warner Entertainment Co., 5450 Winchester Rd., Memphis, TN 38115. Phone: 901-365-1770. Fax: 901-369-4515. Counties: Shelby, TN; DeSoto, MS. Also serves De Soto County, Maywood, MS; Bartlett, Collierville, Germantown, Lakeland, Rossville, Shelby County, TN. ICA: TN0001.
TV Market Ranking: 26. Franchise award date: N.A. Franchise expiration date: N.A. Began: February 1, 1976.
Channel capacity: 90 (2-way capable; operating 2-way). Channels available but not in use: N.A.
Basic Service
Subscribers: 227,000; Commercial subscribers: 1,422.
Programming (received off-air): WBUY (T) Holly Springs; WHBQ-TV (F), WKNO (P), WLMT (U), WMC-TV (N), WPTY-TV (A), WPXX-TV (X), WREG-TV (C) Memphis.
Programming (via satellite): C-SPAN; C-SPAN 2; EWTN; Home Shopping Network; QVC.
Current originations: Public access; educational access; government access; library access; automated emergency alert; local news.
Fee: $43.00 installation; $21.00 monthly.
Expanded Basic Service
Subscribers: N.A.
Programming (via satellite): WGN-TV (W) Chicago; A & E; American Movie Classics; Animal Planet; BET; CNBC; CNN; Cartoon Network; Comedy Central; Discovery Channel; E! Entertainment TV; ESPN; Fox Family Channel; Fox Sports Net South; Headline News; Lifetime; MTV; Nashville Network; Nick at Nite's TV Land; Nickelodeon; Odyssey; TBS Superstation; TV Food Network; The Weather Channel; Travel Channel; Turner Network TV; USA Network; VH1; ValueVision.
Fee: $17.50 monthly.
Expanded Basic Service 2
Subscribers: N.A.
Programming (via satellite): Country Music TV; Court TV; DMX; ESPN 2; Home & Garden Television; MSNBC; Sci-Fi Channel; Sundance Channel; TV Guide Channel; TV Guide Sneak Prevue; Turner Classic Movies.
Fee: N.A.
Pay Service 1
Pay Units: 153,000.
Programming (via satellite): Cinemax (multiplexed); Disney Channel; HBO (multiplexed); Showtime (multiplexed).
Fee: $9.99 monthly (Disney); $11.49 monthly (Cinemax, HBO, or Showtime).
Pay Service 2
Pay Units: N.A.
Programming (via satellite): BET Movies/Starz!; Starz!; The New Encore.
Fee: N.A.
Pay-Per-View
Addressable homes: 155,000.
Playboy TV; Spice; Viewer's Choice.
Fee: $4.95.
Local advertising: Yes (insert only). Available in satellite distributed, locally originated & character-generated programming. Local sales manager: Chris Bailey.
Equipment: Scientific-Atlanta headend; Scientific-Atlanta amplifiers; Comm/Scope cable; JVC cameras; Sony VTRs; Chyron character generator; Hamlin set top converters; Scientific-Atlanta addressable set top converters; Hughes & Scientific-Atlanta satellite antenna; Hughes satellite receivers; Microdyne commercial insert.

Miles of plant: 3150.0 (coaxial); 65.0 (fiber optic). Additional miles planned: 40.0 (coaxial). Homes passed: 320,000.
Manager: Dean Deyo. Chief engineer: Don Shackelford. Marketing director: Linda Brashear.
City fee: 5% of gross.
Ownership: Time Warner Cable (MSO).

MIDDLETON—Time Warner Communications, Box 610, 12935 S. Main St., Somerville, TN 38068. Phone: 901-259-2225. Counties: Hardeman, TN; Tippah, MS. Also serves Walnut, MS. ICA: MS0187.
TV Market Ranking: Below 100. Franchise award date: N.A. Franchise expiration date: N.A. Began: October 1, 1986.
Channel capacity: 35. Channels available but not in use: 2.
Basic Service
Subscribers: 1,072.
Programming (received off-air): WHBQ-TV (F), WKNO (P), WLMT (U), WMC-TV (N), WPTY-TV (A), WREG-TV (C) Memphis.
Programming (via satellite): WGN-TV (W) Chicago; A & E; American Movie Classics; BET; C-SPAN; CNN; Country Music TV; Court TV; Discovery Channel; ESPN; Fox Family Channel; Headline News; Home Shopping Network; Lifetime; MTV; Nashville Network; Nickelodeon; QVC; TBS Superstation; The Weather Channel; Turner Network TV; USA Network.
Fee: $39.00 installation; $19.05 monthly.
Pay Service 1
Pay Units: N.A.
Programming (via satellite): Cinemax; Disney Channel; HBO; Showtime.
Fee: $7.00 monthly (Disney), $9.00 monthly (Cinemax, HBO or Showtime).
Manager: Bob Moss. Chief technician: Art Brown.
Ownership: Time Warner Cable (MSO).

MILLINGTON—Millington CATV Inc., Box 399, 5115 Easley St., Millington, TN 38083-0399. Phone: 901-872-3600. Fax: 901-872-6703. Counties: Shelby & Tipton. Also serves Atoka, Drummonds, Munford, Northaven. ICA: TN0027.
TV Market Ranking: 26. Franchise award date: June 1, 1982. Franchise expiration date: January 1, 2008. Began: May 1, 1982.
Channel capacity: 36 (2-way capable; operating 2-way). Channels available but not in use: None.
Basic Service
Subscribers: 7,700.
Programming (received off-air): WBUY (T) Holly Springs; WHBQ-TV (F), WKNO (P), WLMT (U), WMC-TV (N), WPTY-TV (A), WREG-TV (C) Memphis; 1 FM.
Programming (via satellite): WGN-TV (W) Chicago; A & E; American Movie Classics; BET; CNN; Comedy Central; Country Music TV; Discovery Channel; ESPN; Fox Family Channel; Headline News; Home Shopping Network; Learning Channel; Lifetime; MTV; Nashville Network; Nick at Nite; Nickelodeon; TBS Superstation; The Weather Channel; Turner Network TV; USA Network.
Current originations: Automated time-weather; government access.
Planned originations: Local news; local sports.
Fee: $30.00 installation; $45.50 monthly.
Pay Service 1
Pay Units: 1,488.
Programming (via satellite): Cinemax.
Fee: $12.50 installation; $9.95 monthly.
Pay Service 2
Pay Units: 693.
Programming (via satellite): Disney Channel.
Fee: $12.50 installation; $8.95 monthly.
Pay Service 3
Pay Units: 2,326.
Programming (via satellite): HBO.
Fee: $12.50 installation; $9.95 monthly.
Pay-Per-View
Addressable homes: 7,700.
Special events.
Fee: Varies.
Local advertising: Yes (locally produced). Available in locally originated, character-generated, taped & automated programming. Local sales manager: Rex Moody.
Program Guide: TV Host.
Equipment: Scientific-Atlanta headend; Texscan amplifiers; Times Fiber cable; Panasonic character generator; Oak set top converters; Oak addressable set top converters; Scientific-Atlanta satellite antenna; Scientific-Atlanta satellite receivers.
Miles of plant: 400.0 (coaxial); 17.0 (fiber optic).
Manager: Holly Starnes. Chief technician: Gene Berry.
City fee: 3% of gross.
Ownership: Millington CATV Inc.

MONTEREY—InterMedia Cable, Box 260, Jackson, MS 39205-0260. Phone: 601-355-1522. County: Putnam. Also serves Putnam County. ICA: TN0091.
TV Market Ranking: Below 100. Franchise award date: January 6, 1978. Franchise expiration date: January 16, 2008. Began: November 23, 1979.
Channel capacity: 30 (not 2-way capable). Channels available but not in use: 5.
Basic Service
Subscribers: 1,118.
Programming (received off-air): WBKO (A) Bowling Green; WCTE (P) Cookeville; WBIR-TV (N) Knoxville; WHTN (I) Murfreesboro; WDCN (P), WKRN-TV (A), WSMV (N), WTVF (C), WUXP (U), WZTV (F) Nashville; 18 FMs.
Programming (via satellite): WGN-TV (W) Chicago; A & E; C-SPAN; CNN; Country Music TV; Discovery Channel; ESPN; Fox Family Channel; Headline News; Nashville Network; Nickelodeon; QVC; TBS Superstation; The Weather Channel; Turner Network TV; USA Network.
Fee: $25.00 installation; $19.25 monthly; $0.50 converter.
Pay Service 1
Pay Units: 206.
Programming (via satellite): HBO.
Fee: $10.00 installation; $10.00 monthly.
Pay Service 2
Pay Units: 80.
Programming (via satellite): Showtime.
Fee: $10.00 installation; $10.00 monthly.
Local advertising: Yes.
Program Guide: CableView.
Miles of plant: 23.0 (coaxial). Homes passed: 1,240.
Manager: Hazel Walker. Chief technician: Johnnie Gentry. Marketing director: Starr Latimer.
City fee: 3% of gross.
Ownership: InterMedia Partners (MSO). See Cable System Ownership.

MONTGOMERY COUNTY—Charter Communications, Box 31269, 1850 Business Park Dr., Clarksville, TN 37040. Phones: 931-552-2288; 800-232-1449. Fax: 931-648-9255. Counties: Cheatham & Montgomery. Also serves Cheap Hill, Cunningham, Henrietta, Hilltop, Liverwort, Oak Plains, Oakplain, Round Pond, Salem, Shady Grove, Southside. ICA: TN0152.
TV Market Ranking: 30 (Cheap Hill, Cunningham, Henrietta, portions of Montgomery County, Oak Plains, Oakplain, Shady Grove, Southside); Outside TV Markets (Hilltop, Liverwort, portions of Montgomery County, Round Pond, Salem). Franchise award date: N.A. Franchise expiration date: N.A. Began: N.A.
Channel capacity: 54. Channels available but not in use: 4.
Basic Service
Subscribers: 3,200.
Programming (received off-air): WPGD (I) Hendersonville; WDCN (P), WKRN-TV (A), WNAB (W), WSMV (N), WTVF (C), WUXP (U), WZTV (F) Nashville.
Programming (via satellite): QVC.
Current originations: Educational access.
Fee: $20.00 installation; $13.00 monthly.
Expanded Basic Service
Subscribers: N.A.
Programming (via satellite): WGN-TV (W) Chicago; A & E; American Movie Classics; C-SPAN; C-SPAN 2; CNBC; CNN; Cartoon Network; Comedy Central; Country Music TV; Discovery Channel; ESPN; ESPN 2; EWTN; Fox Family Channel; Fox Sports Net South; Headline News; History Channel; Home & Garden Television; Learning Channel; Lifetime; MTV; Nashville Network; Nick at Nite's TV Land; Nickelodeon; Sci-Fi Channel; TBS Superstation; TV Food Network; The Inspirational Network; The Weather Channel; Turner Network TV; USA Network; VH1.
Fee: $17.10 monthly.
Pay Service 1
Pay Units: 1,000.
Programming (via satellite): Disney Channel; HBO (multiplexed); Showtime (multiplexed); The Movie Channel.
Fee: $6.55 monthly (Disney), $10.95 monthly (Showtime or TMC), $11.50 monthly (HBO).
Pay-Per-View
Viewer's Choice.
Miles of plant: 125.1 (coaxial).
Manager: Chris Ginn.
Ownership: Charter Communications Inc. (MSO). Purchased from Annox Inc., September 30, 1998.

MORRISTOWN—Charter Communications Inc., 2491 Old Hwy. 25 E, Morristown, TN 37816. Phone: 423-586-8700. Fax: 423-586-9065. Web site: http://www.chartercom.com. Counties: Cocke, Grainger, Hamblen & Jefferson. Also serves Baneberry, Cocke County, Dandridge, Hamblen County, Jefferson City, Jefferson County, New Market, Newport, Rutledge, Talbott, White Pine. ICA: TN0154.
TV Market Ranking: 71 (Baneberry, Dandridge, portions of Hamblen County, Jefferson City, portions of Jefferson County, New Market, Rutledge, Talbott); Below 100 (Cocke County, portions of Hamblen County, portions of Jefferson County, Morristown, Newport, White Pine). Franchise award date: N.A. Franchise expiration date: March 1, 1999. Began: February 23, 1964.
Channel capacity: 40. Channels available but not in use: 1.
Basic Service
Subscribers: 17,669.
Programming (received off-air): WBXX-TV (W) Crossville; WATE-TV (A), WBIR-TV (N), WTNZ (F), WVLT-TV (C) Knoxville; WSJK (P) Sneedville; allband FM.
Programming (via satellite): WGN-TV (W) Chicago; C-SPAN; C-SPAN 2; Home Shopping Network; Lifetime; Pax Net; QVC; TV Food Network; TV Guide Channel; The Weather Channel.
Current originations: Automated time-weather; leased access; local news.
Fee: $54.68 installation; $9.65 monthly; $25.00 additional installation.
Expanded Basic Service
Subscribers: N.A.
Programming (via satellite): A & E; American Movie Classics; Animal Planet; BET; Bravo; CNBC; CNN; Cartoon Network; Comedy Central; Country Music TV; Discovery Channel; Disney Channel; E! Entertainment TV; ESPN; ESPN 2; ESPNews; Fox Family Channel; Fox Sports Net South; Game Show Network; Golf Channel; Headline News; History Channel; Home & Garden Television; Learning Channel; MSNBC; MTV; Nashville Network; Nick at Nite's TV Land; Nickelodeon; Outdoor Life Network; Romance Classics; Sci-Fi Channel; Speedvision; TBS Superstation; Toon Disney; Trinity Bcstg. Network; Turner Network TV; USA Network; VH1; ZDTV.
Fee: $20.60 monthly.
Pay Service 1
Pay Units: N.A.
Programming (via satellite): Cinemax (multiplexed); HBO (multiplexed); Showtime (multiplexed); The Movie Channel.
Fee: $12.95 monthly (each).
Digital Pay Service 1
Pay Units: N.A.
Programming (via satellite): Cinemax (multiplexed); DMX; Encore Action; Encore Love Stories; Encore Mystery; Encore True Stories & Drama; Flix (multiplexed); HBO (multiplexed); Showtime (multiplexed); Starz! (multiplexed); The Movie Channel (multiplexed); The New Encore (multiplexed).
Fee: N.A.
Pay-Per-View
Hot Choice; Hot Choice delivered digitally; Spice; Spice delivered digitally; Viewer's Choice 1 & 2; movies delivered digitally; special events.
Fee: Varies.
Equipment: Scientific-Atlanta headend; AEL & Scientific-Atlanta amplifiers; Comm/Scope cable; Scientific-Atlanta satellite antenna.
Miles of plant: 204.0 (coaxial).
Manager: Jim Steet. Technical manager: Wes Hudson. Chief technician: Kelly Moore. Marketing director: Janie Beck.
City fee: 3% of gross.
Ownership: Charter Communications Inc. (MSO). Purchased from Marcus Cable, April 1, 1999.

MOUNT JULIET—Central Tennessee Cablevision, 4056 N. Mount Juliet Rd., Mount Juliet, TN 37122. Phone: 615-754-2288. Counties: Davidson & Wilson. Also serves Gladeville, Hermitage, Old Hickory, Wilson County (western portion). ICA: TN0037.
TV Market Ranking: 30 (Gladeville, Hermitage, Mount Juliet, Old Hickory, portions of Wilson County); Below 100 (portions of Wilson County). Franchise award date: N.A. Franchise expiration date: July 18, 2004. Began: September 14, 1981.
Channel capacity: 43 (not 2-way capable). Channels available but not in use: 4.
Basic Service
Subscribers: 7,071.
Programming (received off-air): WHTN (I) Murfreesboro; WDCN (P), WKRN-TV (A), WSMV (N), WTVF (C), WZTV (F) Nashville; 4 FMs.
Current originations: Automated time-weather; government access.
Fee: $60.00 installation; $10.00 monthly; $2.50 converter; $10.00 additional installation.
Expanded Basic Service
Subscribers: 7,057.
Programming (via satellite): WGN-TV (W) Chicago; A & E; American Movie Classics; BET; C-SPAN; CNBC; CNN; Country Music TV; Discovery Channel; ESPN; Fox Family Channel; Fox Sports Net South; Headline News; Lifetime; MTV; Nashville Network;

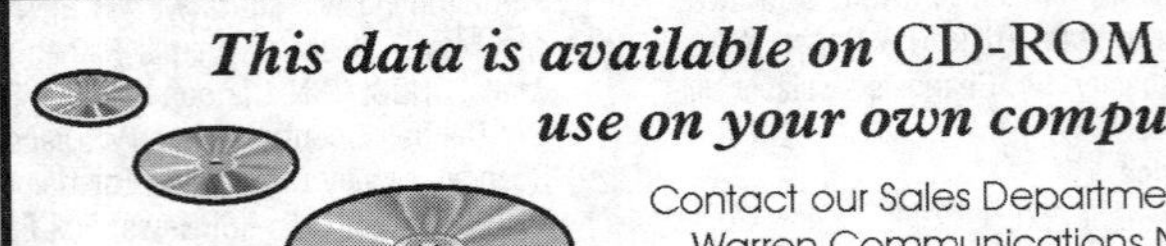

Nickelodeon; QVC; TBS Superstation; The Weather Channel; Turner Network TV; USA Network.
Fee: $60.00 installation; $11.80 monthly.

Pay Service 1
Pay Units: 653.
Programming (via satellite): Cinemax.
Fee: $9.95 monthly.

Pay Service 2
Pay Units: 718.
Programming (via satellite): Disney Channel.
Fee: $9.95 monthly.

Pay Service 3
Pay Units: 1,588.
Programming (via satellite): HBO.
Fee: $9.95 monthly.

Pay Service 4
Pay Units: 877.
Programming (via satellite): Showtime.
Fee: $9.95 monthly.

Pay Service 5
Pay Units: 888.
Programming (via satellite): The New Encore.
Fee: $1.50 monthly.

Local advertising: Yes (locally produced & insert). Available in satellite distributed programming. Local sales manager: Doug Roberts. Regional interconnect: Intermedia Television Advertising.
Equipment: Scientific-Atlanta headend; Scientific-Atlanta amplifiers; Comm/Scope & Scientific-Atlanta cable; Panasonic cameras; Cable Text character generator; Oak set top converters; Scientific-Atlanta satellite antenna.
Miles of plant: 301.0 (coaxial). Additional miles planned: 200.0 (coaxial). Homes passed: 9,529.
Manager: Kathy Harris. Chief technician: Raymond Strait.
City fee: 3% of gross.
Ownership: InterMedia Partners (MSO). See Cable System Ownership.

MOUNTAIN CITY—Cablevision Communications, Box 699, 105 N. Main St., Lebanon, VA 24266. Phones: 540-889-0669; 800-654-7619. Fax: 540-889-3382. County: Johnson. Also serves Johnson County. ICA: TN0067.
TV Market Ranking: Below 100. Franchise award date: N.A. Franchise expiration date: N.A. Began: July 1, 1963.
Channel capacity: 36 (not 2-way capable). Channels available but not in use: None.

Basic Service
Subscribers: 1,906.
Programming (received off-air): WCYB-TV (N) Bristol-Kingsport; WBTV (C) Charlotte; WEMT (F) Greeneville; WLFG (I) Grundy; WJHL-TV (C) Johnson City; WKPT-TV (A) Kingsport; WSJK (P) Sneedville.
Programming (via satellite): WGN-TV (W) Chicago; Fox Family Channel; QVC; The Weather Channel.
Fee: $53.64 installation; $11.75 monthly.

Expanded Basic Service
Subscribers: 1,656.
Programming (via satellite): A & E; C-SPAN; CNN; Cartoon Network; Country Music TV; Discovery Channel; ESPN; ESPN 2; Fox Sports Net South; Headline News; History Channel; Home & Garden Television; Lifetime; MTV; Nashville Network; Nick at Nite's TV Land; Nickelodeon; TBS Superstation; Turner Classic Movies; Turner Network TV; USA Network; VH1.
Fee: $14.90 monthly.

Pay Service 1
Pay Units: 112.
Programming (via satellite): Cinemax.
Fee: $8.95 monthly.

Pay Service 2
Pay Units: 154.
Programming (via satellite): Disney Channel.
Fee: $8.95 monthly.

Pay Service 3
Pay Units: 201.
Programming (via satellite): HBO.
Fee: $10.95 monthly.

Pay Service 4
Pay Units: 157.
Programming (via satellite): Showtime.
Fee: $8.95 monthly.

Equipment: Scientific-Atlanta satellite antenna.
Miles of plant: 53.0 (coaxial). Homes passed: 2,155.
Manager: Dave Burke. Plant manager: Daryl Boyd. Customer service manager: Nickie Ketron.
City fee: 3% of gross.
Ownership: Cablevision Communications Inc. (MSO).

MURFREESBORO—InterMedia Partners, Box 250, 307 Circle Dr., McKenzie, TN 38201. Phone: 901-352-2273. Fax: 901-352-3164. Web site: http://www.intermediamtn.com. County: Rutherford. Also serves Rutherford County. ICA: TN0011.
TV Market Ranking: 30 (Murfreesboro, portions of Rutherford County); Below 100 (portions of Rutherford County). Franchise award date: January 1, 1973. Franchise expiration date: April 16, 2001. Began: November 1, 1978.
Channel capacity: 39 (2-way capable; operating 2-way). Channels available but not in use: 3.

Basic Service
Subscribers: 28,806.
Programming (received off-air): WDCN (P), WKRN-TV (A), WSMV (N), WTVF (C), WZTV (F) Nashville.
Programming (via satellite): WGN-TV (W) Chicago; A & E; American Movie Classics; BET; C-SPAN; CNBC; CNN; Comedy Central; Country Music TV; Discovery Channel; ESPN; Fox Family Channel; Fox Sports Net South; Headline News; Lifetime; MTV; Nashville Network; Nickelodeon; QVC; TBS Superstation; The Weather Channel; Turner Network TV; USA Network; VH1.
Current originations: Automated timeweather; public access; educational access; government access; local news.
Fee: $35.00 installation; $20.95 monthly; $1.00 converter; $25.00 additional installation.

Pay Service 1
Pay Units: 1,961.
Programming (via satellite): Showtime.
Fee: $25.00 installation; $9.50 monthly.

Pay Service 2
Pay Units: 1,467.
Programming (via satellite): Cinemax.
Fee: $25.00 installation; $9.50 monthly.

Pay Service 3
Pay Units: 1,183.
Programming (via satellite): Disney Channel.
Fee: $25.00 installation; $9.50 monthly.

Pay Service 4
Pay Units: 6,425.
Programming (via satellite): HBO.
Fee: $25.00 installation; $9.50 monthly.

Local advertising: Yes (locally produced & insert). Available in satellite distributed, locally originated, character-generated & automated programming. Rates: $6.50/30 Seconds. Local sales manager: Doug Roberts. Regional interconnect: Intermedia Television Advertising.
Equipment: Scientific-Atlanta headend; RCA amplifiers; Comm/Scope cable; Sony VTRs; Video Data Systems character generator; Jerrold set top converters; Eagle traps; Scientific-Atlanta satellite antenna; Scientific-Atlanta satellite receivers; ChannelMatic commercial insert.
Miles of plant: 465.0 (coaxial). Additional miles planned: 55.0 (coaxial). Total homes in franchised area: 42,000.
Manager: Robert Pace. Chief technician: Benny Jackson.
City fee: 3% of gross.
Ownership: InterMedia Partners (MSO). See Cable System Ownership.

NASHVILLE—InterMedia, Box 280570, 660 Mainstream Dr., Nashville, TN 37228-1204. Phone: 615-244-7462. Fax: 615-255-6528. Web site: http://www.intermediamtn.com. Counties: Davidson, Hickman, Sumner & Williamson. Also serves Bellevue, Bon Aqua, Brentwood, Brentwood Pointe I, Brentwood Pointe II, Brentwood Two, Davidson County, Fairview, Franklin, Goodlettsville, Lyles, Nolensville, Williamson County (portions). ICA: TN0002.
TV Market Ranking: 30. Franchise award date: February 1, 1979. Franchise expiration date: May 4, 2010. Began: February 1, 1979.
Channel capacity: 77 (2-way capable; operating 2-way). Channels available but not in use: 15.

Basic Service
Subscribers: 140,146; Commercial subscribers: 176.
Programming (received off-air): WPGD (I) Hendersonville; WHTN (I) Murfreesboro; WDCN (P), WKRN-TV (A), WSMV (N), WTVF (C), WUXP (U), WZTV (F) Nashville.
Programming (via satellite): WGN-TV (W) Chicago; TBS Superstation; TV Guide Channel; TV Guide Sneak Prevue; The Weather Channel.
Fee: $33.02 installation; $8.69 monthly.
Commercial fee: $29.95 monthly.

Expanded Basic Service
Subscribers: 139,356.
Programming (via satellite): A & E; American Movie Classics; BET; C-SPAN; C-SPAN 2; CNBC; CNN; Comedy Central; Country Music TV; Discovery Channel; E! Entertainment TV; ESPN; FX; Fox Family Channel; Fox Sports Net South; Headline News; Learning Channel; Lifetime; MTV; Nashville Network; Nick at Nite; Nickelodeon; Odyssey; QVC; Sci-Fi Channel; TV Guide Channel; Turner Network TV; USA Network; VH1; ValueVision.
Fee: $14.01 monthly.

Expanded Basic Service 2
Subscribers: 6,553.
Programming (via satellite): Bravo; Cartoon Network; Court TV; fXM: Movies from Fox; History Channel.
Fee: $1.95 monthly.

Pay Service 1
Pay Units: 17,305.
Programming (via satellite): Cinemax.
Fee: $8.00 monthly.

Pay Service 2
Pay Units: 23,026.
Programming (via satellite): Disney Channel.
Fee: $8.00 monthly.

Pay Service 3
Pay Units: 44,746.
Programming (via satellite): HBO.
Fee: $8.00 monthly.

Pay Service 4
Pay Units: 38,563.
Programming (via satellite): Showtime.
Fee: $8.00 monthly.

Pay Service 5
Pay Units: 13,466.
Programming (via satellite): The Movie Channel.
Fee: $8.00 monthly.

Pay-Per-View
Addressable homes: 88,616.
Hot Choice; Playboy TV; Viewer's Choice.

Local advertising: Yes. Available in satellite distributed programming. Rates: $150.00/Minute; $75.00/30 Seconds. Local sales manager: John Walser. Regional interconnect: Intermedia Television Advertising.
Program Guide: Nashville's Entertainment.
Equipment: Scientific-Atlanta headend; C-COR, GTE Sylvania & Texscan amplifiers; Comm/Scope cable; Panasonic & Sharp cameras; Panasonic & Sony VTRs; Oak & Zenith set top converters; Oak & Zenith addressable set top converters; Eagle traps; Scientific-Atlanta satellite antenna; Microdyne & Scientific-Atlanta satellite receivers; Texscan & Video Data Systems commercial insert.
Miles of plant: 2300.0 (coaxial); 140.0 (fiber optic). Homes passed: 235,000. Total homes in franchised area: 258,000.
Manager: Wayne Vowell. Chief technician: George Hale. Marketing director: D.J. Saugars.
City fee: 5% of gross.
Ownership: InterMedia Partners (MSO). See Cable System Ownership.

NEW TAZEWELL—Fannon Cable TV, Box 1526, 120 Main St., New Tazewell, TN 37825. Phone: 423-626-9107. Fax: 423-626-6304. Counties: Claiborne & Scott. Also serves Arthur, Cumberland Gap, Harrogate, Lone Mountain, Shawanee, Speedwell, Tazewell. ICA: TN0038.
TV Market Ranking: 71 (Lone Mountain, New Tazewell, Speedwell); Below 100 (Arthur, Cumberland Gap, Harrogate, Tazewell). Franchise award date: January 1, 1977. Franchise expiration date: January 1, 2018. Began: August 1, 1978.
Channel capacity: 36 (not 2-way capable). Channels available but not in use: 9.

Basic Service
Subscribers: 5,746.
Programming (received off-air): W18AN (I) Harrogate; WATE-TV (A), WBIR-TV (N), WTNZ (F), WVLT-TV (C) Knoxville; WSJK (P) Sneedville.
Programming (via satellite): WGN-TV (W) Chicago; CNN; Country Music TV; Discovery Channel; ESPN; ESPN 2; Fox Family Channel; Headline News; Home Shopping Network; Learning Channel; MTV; Nashville Network; Nickelodeon; TBS Superstation; Turner Network TV; USA Network; VH1.
Current originations: Automated timeweather; local news.
Fee: $17.70 installation; $20.00 monthly.

Pay Service 1
Pay Units: 291.
Programming (via satellite): Cinemax.
Fee: $10.95 monthly.

Pay Service 2
Pay Units: 125.
Programming (via satellite): Disney Channel.
Fee: $7.00 monthly.
Pay Service 3
Pay Units: 403.
Programming (via satellite): HBO.
Fee: $10.95 monthly.
Pay Service 4
Pay Units: 272.
Programming (via satellite): The Movie Channel.
Fee: $10.95 monthly.
Pay Service 5
Pay Units: 218.
Programming (via satellite): Showtime.
Fee: $10.95 monthly.
Pay Service 6
Pay Units: N.A.
Programming (via satellite): Flix.
Fee: $5.00 monthly.
Pay-Per-View
Addressable homes: 5,746.
Local advertising: Yes. Available in character-generated programming.
Program Guide: Premium Channels.
Equipment: Cadco, Microdyne & DX Engineering headend; Magnavox amplifiers; Times Fiber & Comm/Scope cable; Tocom set top converters; Microdyne & Scientific-Atlanta satellite antenna.
Miles of plant: 200.0 (coaxial). Additional miles planned: 12.0 (coaxial). Homes passed: 8,100. Total homes in franchised area: 29,000.
Manager: Grant Jorgensen. Chief technician: Bill Kelly.
Ownership: Fannon Cable TV Co.

NEWBERN—Tennessee Cablevision Inc., Grove Center, Oak Ridge, TN 37830. Phone: 423-482-4444. Fax: 423-482-6553. Counties: Dyer & Obion. Also serves Obion, Obion County (unincorporated areas), Trimble, Troy. ICA: TN0072.
TV Market Ranking: Below 100 (Obion, Trimble, Troy); Outside TV Markets (Newbern, Obion County). Franchise award date: February 1, 1977. Franchise expiration date: N.A. Began: December 1, 1977.
Channel capacity: 60 (not 2-way capable). Channels available but not in use: 26.
Basic Service
Subscribers: 982.
Programming (received off-air): KFVS-TV (C) Cape Girardeau; WBBJ-TV (A), WMTU (U) Jackson; WLJT (P) Lexington; WHBQ-TV (F), WKNO (P), WMC-TV (N), WPTY-TV (A), WREG-TV (C) Memphis; WPSD-TV (N) Paducah.
Programming (via satellite): American Movie Classics; CNBC; CNN; Country Music TV; Discovery Channel; ESPN; Fox Family Channel; Home Shopping Network; Lifetime; Nashville Network; Nickelodeon; QVC; TBS Superstation; The Weather Channel; Turner Network TV; USA Network; VH1.
Fee: $15.00 installation; $11.50 monthly; $40.00 additional installation.
Pay Service 1
Pay Units: 150.
Programming (via satellite): Cinemax.
Fee: $40.00 installation; $9.95 monthly.
Pay Service 2
Pay Units: 125.
Programming (via satellite): Disney Channel.
Fee: $40.00 installation; $9.95 monthly.
Pay Service 3
Pay Units: 300.
Programming (via satellite): HBO.
Fee: $40.00 installation; $9.95 monthly.
Pay Service 4
Pay Units: 75.
Programming (via satellite): Showtime.
Fee: $40.00 installation; $9.95 monthly.
Equipment: Jerrold headend; Jerrold amplifiers; Times Fiber & Trilogy cable.
Miles of plant: 53.3 (coaxial). Homes passed: 2,091.
Manager: Kim W. Kersey. Chief technician: Ron Crowder. Marketing director: Judy Phelps.
City fee: 3% of gross.
Ownership: Time Warner Cable (MSO).

NIOTA—Rapid Cable, 1106 Knoxville Hwy., Wartburg, TN 37887. Phone: 800-228-8836. Fax: 423-346-7451. County: McMinn. ICA: TN0115.
TV Market Ranking: Below 100. Franchise award date: N.A. Franchise expiration date: N.A. Began: June 1, 1982.
Channel capacity: 36. Channels available but not in use: 20.
Basic Service
Subscribers: 376.
Programming (received off-air): WDEF-TV (C), WDSI-TV (F), WRCB-TV (N), WTCI (P), WTVC (A) Chattanooga; WATE-TV (A), WBIR-TV (N), WVLT-TV (C) Knoxville.
Programming (via satellite): WGN-TV (W) Chicago; CNN; ESPN; Fox Family Channel; Nashville Network; TBS Superstation; USA Network.
Fee: $20.00 installation; $12.00 monthly.
Pay Service 1
Pay Units: 180.
Programming (via satellite): HBO.
Fee: $8.00 monthly.
Miles of plant: 18.0 (coaxial). Homes passed: 400.
Manager: C. K. Allen. Chief technician: Faron Jackson.
Ownership: Rapid Communications Partners LP (MSO). Purchased from Telephone & Data Systems Inc., February 1, 1999.

NORRIS—Comcast Cablevision of the South, Box 1169, Hwy. 27S, Harriman, TN 37748. Phone: 423-637-5411. County: Anderson. ICA: TN0156.
TV Market Ranking: 71. Franchise award date: N.A. Franchise expiration date: N.A. Began: N.A.
Channel capacity: N.A. Channels available but not in use: N.A.
Basic Service
Subscribers: 7,003.
Programming (received off-air): WEMT (F) Greeneville; WFEM-LP (I) Heiskell; WATE-TV (A), WBIR-TV (N), WKOP-TV (P), WTNZ (F), WVLT-TV (C) Knoxville.
Programming (via satellite): WGN-TV (W) Chicago; A & E; American Movie Classics; C-SPAN; C-SPAN 2; CNN; Comedy Central; Discovery Channel; ESPN; Fox Family Channel; Headline News; Home Shopping Network; Kaleidoscope; Learning Channel; Lifetime; Nashville Network; Nickelodeon; Odyssey; Sci-Fi Channel; TBS Superstation; The Weather Channel; Turner Network TV; USA Network; VH1; ValueVision.
Current originations: Local news.
Fee: $32.05 installation; $18.95 monthly.
Pay Service 1
Pay Units: N.A.
Programming (via satellite): Cinemax; HBO; Showtime.
Fee: $9.00 monthly (Cinemax or HBO).
Manager: Roger Rule. Chief technician: Don Alford.
Ownership: Comcast Cable Communications Inc. (MSO).

OAK RIDGE—Tennessee Cablevision Inc., Box 5928, 120 Randolph Rd., Oak Ridge, TN 37830. Phone: 423-482-4444. Fax: 423-482-6553. Counties: Anderson, Morgan & Roane. Also serves Anderson County (portions), Claxton, Clinton, Oliver Springs, Roane County, South Clinton. ICA: TN0012.
TV Market Ranking: 71 (Anderson County, Claxton, Clinton, Oak Ridge, Oliver Springs, portions of Roane County, South Clinton); Below 100 (portions of Roane County). Franchise award date: N.A. Franchise expiration date: N.A. Began: November 4, 1965.
Channel capacity: 42 (not 2-way capable). Channels available but not in use: 3.
Basic Service
Subscribers: 19,547.
Programming (received off-air): WBXX-TV (W) Crossville; WPXK (X) Jellico; WATE-TV (A), WBIR-TV (N), WTNZ (F), WVLT-TV (C) Knoxville; WSJK (P) Sneedville; allband FM.
Programming (via satellite): WGN-TV (W) Chicago; A & E; American Movie Classics; Animal Planet; BET; C-SPAN; C-SPAN 2; CNBC; CNN; Country Music TV; Discovery Channel; ESPN; ESPN 2; Fox Family Channel; Fox Sports Net South; Goodlife TV Network; Headline News; History Channel; Home & Garden Television; Home Shopping Network; Learning Channel; MSNBC; MTV; Nashville Network; Nickelodeon; QVC; Sci-Fi Channel; TBS Superstation; TV Guide Channel; The Weather Channel; Turner Classic Movies; Turner Network TV; USA Network; VH1.
Current originations: Automated time-weather; educational access; local news.
Fee: $20.00 installation; $28.00 monthly.
Pay Service 1
Pay Units: N.A.
Programming (via satellite): Bravo.
Fee: $3.50 monthly.
Pay Service 2
Pay Units: 1,751.
Programming (via satellite): Disney Channel.
Fee: $7.00 monthly.
Pay Service 3
Pay Units: 429.
Programming (via satellite): The New Encore.
Fee: $6.50 monthly.
Pay Service 4
Pay Units: 2,268.
Programming (via satellite): HBO.
Fee: $10.00 monthly.
Pay Service 5
Pay Units: 3,427.
Programming (via satellite): Showtime.
Fee: $7.00 monthly.
Pay-Per-View
Addressable homes: 1,500.
Video Seat.
Local advertising: Yes. Available in satellite distributed programming. Rates: $15.00/Spot. Regional interconnect: Cabletime.
Equipment: RCA headend; RCA & Scientific-Atlanta amplifiers; Hitachi cameras; JVC & RCA VTRs; Video Data Systems character generator; Harris satellite antenna.
Miles of plant: 526.0 (coaxial). Homes passed: 25,593.
Manager: Daniel Childs. Chief technician: Danny Slack.
City fee: 3% of gross.
Ownership: Alexcom Ltd. Partnership (MSO).

PARIS—Paris Cablevision, Box 220, 508 E. Washington St., Paris, TN 38242. Phone: 901-642-7028. Fax: 901-642-5512. County: Henry. Also serves Henry County (portions). ICA: TN0030.
TV Market Ranking: Outside TV Markets. Franchise award date: N.A. Franchise expiration date: March 1, 2003. Began: May 1, 1969.
Channel capacity: 42 (not 2-way capable). Channels available but not in use: None.
Basic Service
Subscribers: 7,000.
Programming (received off-air): WBBJ-TV (A) Jackson; WLJT (P) Lexington; WQTV-LP (I) Murray; WKRN-TV (A), WSMV (N), WTVF (C), WZTV (F) Nashville; WPSD-TV (N) Paducah.
Programming (via satellite): WGN-TV (W) Chicago; C-SPAN; Home Shopping Network; TBS Superstation.
Current originations: Public access.
Fee: $41.58 installation (aerial), $65.39 (underground); $10.00 monthly.
Expanded Basic Service
Subscribers: N.A.
Programming (via satellite): A & E; American Movie Classics; BET; CNN; Comedy Central; Country Music TV; Discovery Channel; Disney Channel; E! Entertainment TV; ESPN; Fox Family Channel; Fox Sports Net South; Headline News; History Channel; Home & Garden Television; Lifetime; MTV; Nashville Network; Nick at Nite; Nickelodeon; Odyssey; The Weather Channel; Turner Network TV; USA Network; VH1.
Fee: $15.95 monthly.
Pay Service 1
Pay Units: 2,631.
Programming (via satellite): Cinemax; HBO (multiplexed); Showtime; The Movie Channel.
Fee: $7.95 monthly (TMC), $10.95 monthly (Cinemax, HBO or Showtime).
Pay Service 2
Pay Units: 140.
Programming (via satellite): DMX.
Fee: $8.95 monthly.
Pay-Per-View
Special events.
Fee: Varies.
Local advertising: Yes. Available in satellite distributed programming. Rates: $10.00/30 Seconds. Local sales manager: Kit Umbach. Regional interconnect: Intermedia Television Advertising.
Equipment: CAS headend; Anaconda amplifiers; Superior cable; Comtech satellite antenna.
Miles of plant: 185.0 (coaxial); None (fiber optic). Homes passed: 9,200. Total homes in franchised area: 9,200. Homes passed includes figures for Kentucky Lake, TN.
Plant manager: Duane Lear. Customer service manager: Dana Owens.
Ownership: Rifkin & Associates Inc. (MSO). Sale pends to InterMedia Partners.

PARSONS—InterMedia Partners, Box 250, 24 Circle Dr., McKenzie, TN 38201. Phone: 901-352-2273. Fax: 901-352-3164. Web site: http://www.intermediamtn.com. County: Decatur. Also serves Decatur County, Decaturville. ICA: TN0084.
TV Market Ranking: Below 100 (portions of Decatur County); Outside TV Markets (portions of Decatur County, Decaturville, Parsons). Franchise award date: May 3, 1965. Franchise expiration date: May 3, 2005. Began: September 1, 1967.
Channel capacity: 50 (not 2-way capable). Channels available but not in use: 9.
Basic Service
Subscribers: 1,353.
Programming (received off-air): WBBJ-TV (A), WMTU (U) Jackson; WLJT (P) Lexington; WDCN (P), WKRN-TV (A), WSMV (N), WTVF (C), WZTV (F) Nashville; allband FM.

Programming (via satellite): WGN-TV (W) Chicago; C-SPAN; Fox Family Channel; Learning Channel.
Fee: $12.03 monthly.

Expanded Basic Service
Subscribers: 1,159.
Programming (via satellite): A & E; American Movie Classics; BET; CNBC; CNN; Country Music TV; Discovery Channel; Disney Channel; ESPN; ESPN 2; FX; Headline News; History Channel; Home Shopping Network; Lifetime; MTV; Nashville Network; Nickelodeon; QVC; TBS Superstation; The Weather Channel; Trinity Bcstg. Network; Turner Network TV; USA Network; VH1.
Fee: $16.27 monthly.

Pay Service 1
Pay Units: 255.
Programming (via satellite): Cinemax; HBO; Showtime; The New Encore.
Fee: $11.95 monthly.

Pay-Per-View
Special events.

Equipment: Phasecom headend; Jerrold amplifiers; Superior cable; Eagle & Jerrold set top converters; Scientific-Atlanta satellite antenna; Scientific-Atlanta satellite receivers.
Miles of plant: 63.9 (coaxial); None (fiber optic). Homes passed: 2,400.
Manager: Robert L. Pace. Chief technician: Benny Jackson.
City fee: 2% of gross.
Ownership: InterMedia Partners (MSO). See Cable System Ownership.

PIKEVILLE—Bledsoe Telephone Co-op/CATV, Box 609, Cumberland Ave., Pikeville, TN 37367. Phone: 423-447-2121. Fax: 423-447-2498. County: Bledsoe. Also serves Bledsoe County (central portion). ICA: TN0158.
TV Market Ranking: 78 (portions of Bledsoe County); Below 100 (portions of Bledsoe County, Pikeville). Franchise award date: N.A. Franchise expiration date: January 1, 2000. Began: January 1, 1983.
Channel capacity: 22 (not 2-way capable). Channels available but not in use: None.

Basic Service
Subscribers: 2,084.
Programming (received off-air): WDEF-TV (C), WDSI-TV (F), WRCB-TV (N), WTCI (P), WTVC (A) Chattanooga; allband FM.
Programming (via satellite): WGN-TV (W) Chicago; A & E; CNN; Country Music TV; Discovery Channel; ESPN; Fox Sports Net South; Headline News; Home Shopping Network; Learning Channel; Nashville Network; TBS Superstation; The Weather Channel; Trinity Bcstg. Network; Turner Network TV; USA Network.
Current originations: Automated time-weather.
Fee: $40.00 installation; $16.00 monthly.

Pay Service 1
Pay Units: 256.
Programming (via satellite): The Movie Channel.
Fee: $10.00 installation; $10.50 monthly.

Equipment: Scientific-Atlanta headend; C-COR amplifiers; Comm/Scope cable; Beston character generator; Oak & Scientific-Atlanta set top converters; Eagle traps; Scientific-Atlanta satellite antenna; Scientific-Atlanta satellite receivers.
Miles of plant: 235.0 (coaxial). Homes passed: 3,766. Total homes in franchised area: 8,057.
Manager: Greg Anderson. Chief technician: Edward Harmon.
City fee: 3% of gross.
Ownership: Bledsoe Telephone Co. (MSO).

PINEY FLATS—Hickory Hill Cablevision, Box 860, 5571 Hwy. 11 E, Piney Flats, TN 37686. Phone: 423-538-8659. Fax: 423-538-6661. Counties: Carter & Sullivan. Also serves Bluff City, Carter County (portions), Hickory Hill, Kingsport, Rock Springs, Sullivan County (portions), Watauga. ICA: TN0026.
TV Market Ranking: Below 100. Franchise award date: N.A. Franchise expiration date: N.A. Began: February 1, 1975.
Channel capacity: 41. Channels available but not in use: 6.

Basic Service
Subscribers: 8,300.
Programming (received off-air): WCYB-TV (N) Bristol-Kingsport; WEMT (F) Greeneville; WJHL-TV (C) Johnson City; WAPK-LP (U), WKPT-TV (A) Kingsport; WSJK (P) Sneedville.
Programming (via satellite): WGN-TV (W) Chicago; WPIX (W) New York; A & E; C-SPAN; CNN; Country Music TV; Discovery Channel; ESPN; Fox Family Channel; Headline News; Home Shopping Network; Lifetime; Nickelodeon; TBS Superstation; Trinity Bcstg. Network; Turner Network TV; USA Network; ValueVision.
Fee: $29.95 installation; $12.95 monthly.

Expanded Basic Service
Subscribers: N.A.
Programming (via satellite): American Movie Classics; MTV; Nashville Network; Sci-Fi Channel; VH1.
Fee: $7.00 monthly.

Pay Service 1
Pay Units: N.A.
Programming (via satellite): Cinemax; Disney Channel; HBO; Showtime.
Fee: $10.00 installation; $8.00 monthly (Cinemax, Disney, or HBO).

Miles of plant: 257.0 (coaxial). Homes passed: 10,285. Total homes in franchised area: 50,000.
Manager: Earl Burchett. Chief technician: Kenny Smith.
Ownership: Rifkin & Associates Inc. (MSO). See Cable System Ownership.

PLEASANT HILL—Mid South Cable TV Inc., Box 910, 538 Cedar St., McKenzie, TN 38201. Phones: 901-352-2980; 800-541-4208. Fax: 901-352-3533. County: Cumberland. Also serves Crab Orchard, Crossville, Cumberland County (central portion). ICA: TN0159.
TV Market Ranking: Below 100. Franchise award date: N.A. Franchise expiration date: N.A. Began: July 1, 1988.
Channel capacity: 36 (not 2-way capable). Channels available but not in use: None.

Basic Service
Subscribers: 2,600.
Programming (received off-air): WDEF-TV (C), WRCB-TV (N), WTVC (A) Chattanooga; WCTE (P) Cookeville; WATE-TV (A), WBIR-TV (N), WTNZ (F), WVLT-TV (C) Knoxville; WTVF (C) Nashville.
Programming (via satellite): WGN-TV (W) Chicago; A & E; C-SPAN; CNBC; CNN; Comedy Central; Country Music TV; Discovery Channel; ESPN; Fox Family Channel; Headline News; Lifetime; MTV; Nashville Network; Nickelodeon; QVC; TBS Superstation; The Weather Channel; Travel Channel; Turner Network TV; USA Network; VH1.
Current originations: Automated time-weather; educational access.
Planned originations: Local news; local sports.
Fee: $40.00 installation; $19.95 monthly.

Pay Service 1
Pay Units: N.A.
Programming (via satellite): Cinemax; Disney Channel; HBO.
Fee: $8.00 monthly (Disney), $10.50 monthly (Cinemax or HBO).

Equipment: Jerrold & Scientific-Atlanta headend; Jerrold amplifiers; Times Fiber cable; Jerrold set top converters; Pico addressable traps; Jerrold & Scientific-Atlanta satellite receivers.
Miles of plant: 163.0 (coaxial).
Manager: Jerry Iles.
Ownership: Mid South Cable TV Inc. (MSO).

PORTLAND—InterMedia Partners, Box 250, 307 Circle Dr., McKenzie, TN 38201. Phone: 901-352-2273. Fax: 901-352-3164. Web site: http://www.intermediamtn.com. County: Sumner. Also serves Sumner County (portions). ICA: TN0080.
TV Market Ranking: 30 (Portland, portions of Sumner County); Below 100 (portions of Sumner County). Franchise award date: N.A. Franchise expiration date: July 1, 2003. Began: October 15, 1981.
Channel capacity: N.A. Channels available but not in use: N.A.

Basic Service
Subscribers: 1,659.
Programming (received off-air): WKYU-TV (P) Bowling Green; WPGD (I) Hendersonville; WDCN (P), WKRN-TV (A), WNAB (W), WSMV (N), WTVF (C), WUXP (U), WZTV (F) Nashville.
Fee: $60.00 installation; $10.00 monthly.

Digital Basic Service
Subscribers: N.A.
Programming (via satellite): BBC America; BET on Jazz; CNN/SI; DMX; Discovery Civilization Channel; Discovery Health Channel; Discovery Home & Leisure Channel; Discovery Kids Channel; Discovery People; Discovery Science Channel; Discovery Wings Channel; ESPN Classic Sports; ESPNews; Fox Sports World; Game Show Network; Golf Channel; Goodlife TV Network; Independent Film Channel; International Channel; Kaleidoscope; Lifetime; MuchMusic Network; Outdoor Channel; Outdoor Life Network; Ovation; Romance Classics; Speedvision; The Barker; The Inspirational Network; Turner Classic Movies; Weatherscan by the Weather Channel; ZDTV.
Fee: N.A.

Expanded Basic Service
Subscribers: 1,618.
Programming (via satellite): WGN-TV (W) Chicago; A & E; C-SPAN; CNBC; CNN; Country Music TV; Discovery Channel; Disney Channel; ESPN; ESPN 2; FX; Fox Family Channel; Fox News Channel; Headline News; Nashville Network; Nick at Nite; Nickelodeon; QVC; TBS Superstation; The Weather Channel; Turner Network TV; USA Network.
Fee: $60.00 installation; $6.65 monthly.

Pay Service 1
Pay Units: 352.
Programming (via satellite): The New Encore.
Fee: $1.50 monthly.

Pay Service 2
Pay Units: 396.
Programming (via satellite): HBO.
Fee: $9.95 monthly.

Pay Service 3
Pay Units: 260.
Programming (via satellite): Showtime.
Fee: $9.95 monthly.

Digital Pay Service 1
Pay Units: N.A.
Programming (via satellite): BET Movies/Starz!; Cinemax (multiplexed); Encore Action; Encore Love Stories; Encore Mystery; Encore True Stories & Drama; Encore Westerns; Flix (multiplexed); HBO; HBO Comedy; HBO Family; HBO Plus; HBO Signature; HBO Zone; Showtime (multiplexed); Starz!; Starz! Theater; Sundance Channel (multiplexed); The Movie Channel (multiplexed); The New Encore.
Fee: N.A.

Local advertising: Yes.
Equipment: Scientific-Atlanta headend; Magnavox amplifiers; Comm/Scope cable; Oak set top converters; Magnavox traps; Scientific-Atlanta satellite antenna; Scientific-Atlanta satellite receivers.
Miles of plant: 149.0 (coaxial). Homes passed: 2,621.
Manager: Robert Pace. Chief technician: Benny Jackson.
City fee: 3% of gross.
Ownership: InterMedia Partners (MSO). See Cable System Ownership.

PULASKI—Cablevision Communications, Box 1039, 2008 S. Main St., Columbia, TN 38401. Phone: 931-388-3550. Fax: 931-381-4446. Counties: Giles & Lincoln. Also serves Fayetteville, Giles County (portions), Lincoln County (unincorporated areas). ICA: TN0018.
TV Market Ranking: 96 (Fayetteville, portions of Giles County, portions of Lincoln County); Outside TV Markets (portions of Giles County, portions of Lincoln County, Pulaski). Franchise award date: N.A. Franchise expiration date: N.A. Began: February 1, 1963.
Channel capacity: 60. Channels available but not in use: 20.

Basic Service
Subscribers: 4,000.
Programming (received off-air): WAAY-TV (A), WAFF (N), WHNT-TV (C), WZDX (F) Huntsville-Decatur; WDCN (P), WKRN-TV (A), WSMV (N), WTVF (C), WZTV (F) Nashville; 14 FMs.
Programming (via satellite): A & E; American Movie Classics; BET; C-SPAN; CNBC; CNN; Comedy Central; Country Music TV; Court TV; Discovery Channel; ESPN; Fox Family Channel; Fox Sports Net South; Headline News; Home Shopping Network; Learning Channel; Lifetime; MTV; Nashville Network; Nickelodeon; Odyssey; TBS Superstation; The Weather Channel; Turner Network TV; USA Network; VH1.
Current originations: Local news.
Fee: $10.00 installation; $14.95 monthly; $7.50 additional installation.

Pay Service 1
Pay Units: 398.
Programming (via satellite): Cinemax.
Fee: $7.95 monthly.

Pay Service 2
Pay Units: 470.
Programming (via satellite): Disney Channel.
Fee: $6.95 monthly.

Pay Service 3
Pay Units: 2,429.
Programming (via satellite): HBO.
Fee: $7.95 monthly.

Pay Service 4
Pay Units: 667.
Programming (via satellite): Showtime.
Fee: $7.95 monthly.

Local advertising: Yes. Regional interconnect: Intermedia Television Advertising.
Equipment: Jerrold headend; Jerrold amplifiers; Times Fiber cable; Andrew satellite antenna; Hughes satellite receivers.
Miles of plant: 183.0 (coaxial). Additional miles planned: 7.0 (coaxial). Homes passed: 14,361. Total homes in franchised area: 15,056.
Manager: Chris Karn. Chief technician: Gary Powell. Marketing director: Claudia Lamb.

City fee: 3% of gross.
Ownership: Small Town Cable Corp. (MSO). Purchased from Charter Communications Inc., January 1, 1999.

RED BOILING SPRINGS—InterMedia Partners, Box 250, 307 Circle Dr., McKenzie, TN 38201. Phone: 901-352-2273. Fax: 901-352-3164. Web site: http://intermediamtn.com. County: Macon. ICA: TN0114.
TV Market Ranking: Below 100. Franchise award date: N.A. Franchise expiration date: N.A. Began: June 1, 1982.
Channel capacity: 39 (not 2-way capable). Channels available but not in use: 13.
Basic Service
Subscribers: 323.
Programming (received off-air): WCTE (P) Cookeville; WDCN (P), WKRN-TV (A), WSMV (N), WTVF (C), WUXP (U), WZTV (F) Nashville.
Programming (via satellite): C-SPAN; Headline News.
Fee: $60.00 installation; $10.00 monthly; $10.00 additional installation.
Digital Basic Service
Subscribers: N.A.
Programming (via satellite): BBC America; BET on Jazz; CNN/SI; DMX; Discovery Civilization Channel; Discovery Health Channel; Discovery Home & Leisure Channel; Discovery Kids Channel; Discovery People; Discovery Science Channel; Discovery Wings Channel; ESPN Classic Sports; ESPNews; Fox Sports World; Game Show Network; Golf Channel; Goodlife TV Network; Independent Film Channel; International Channel; Kaleidoscope; Lifetime; MuchMusic Network; Outdoor Channel; Outdoor Life Network; Ovation; Romance Classics; Speedvision; The Barker; The Inspirational Network; Turner Classic Movies; Weatherscan by the Weather Channel; ZDTV.
Fee: N.A.
Expanded Basic Service
Subscribers: 279.
Programming (via satellite): WGN-TV (W) Chicago; A & E; CNN; Country Music TV; Discovery Channel; ESPN; ESPN 2; Fox Family Channel; Headline News; Learning Channel; Lifetime; Nashville Network; Nick at Nite; Nickelodeon; TBS Superstation; Turner Classic Movies; Turner Network TV; USA Network.
Fee: $60.00 installation; $6.65 monthly.
Pay Service 1
Pay Units: 43.
Programming (via satellite): HBO.
Fee: $10.00 installation; $9.95 monthly.
Pay Service 2
Pay Units: 19.
Programming (via satellite): Showtime.
Fee: $9.95 monthly.
Pay Service 3
Pay Units: 48.
Programming (via satellite): The New Encore.
Fee: $1.50 monthly.
Digital Pay Service 1
Pay Units: N.A.
Programming (via satellite): BET Movies/Starz!; Cinemax (multiplexed); Encore Action; Encore Love Stories; Encore Mystery; Encore True Stories & Drama; Encore Westerns; Flix (multiplexed); HBO; HBO Comedy; HBO Family; HBO Plus; HBO Signature; HBO Zone; Showtime (multiplexed); Starz!; Starz! Theater; Sundance Channel (multiplexed); The Movie Channel (multiplexed); The New Encore.
Fee: N.A.
Equipment: Scientific-Atlanta headend; Scientific-Atlanta amplifiers; Oak set top converters; Scientific-Atlanta satellite antenna; Scientific-Atlanta satellite receivers.
Miles of plant: 15.0 (coaxial). Homes passed: 447.
Manager: Robert Pace. Chief technician: Benny Jackson.
Ownership: InterMedia Partners (MSO). See Cable System Ownership.

RIPLEY—Enstar Cable TV, 115 Southwest, Sikeston, MO 63801. Phone: 573-472-0244. Fax: 573-472-1559. County: Lauderdale. Also serves Gates, Halls, Henning, Lauderdale County (unincorporated areas). ICA: TN0160.
TV Market Ranking: Outside TV Markets. Franchise award date: N.A. Franchise expiration date: N.A. Began: June 1, 1982.
Channel capacity: 35 (not 2-way capable). Channels available but not in use: None.
Basic Service
Subscribers: 3,181.
Programming (received off-air): WBBJ-TV (A) Jackson; WHBQ-TV (F), WKNO (P), WLMT (U), WMC-TV (N), WPTY-TV (A), WREG-TV (C) Memphis.
Programming (via satellite): A & E; American Movie Classics; C-SPAN; Discovery Channel; ESPN; Fox Family Channel; Fox Sports Net South; Home & Garden Television; Lifetime; MTV; Nashville Network; QVC; The Weather Channel.
Current originations: Public access.
Fee: $10.00 installation; $20.58 monthly.
Expanded Basic Service
Subscribers: 3,153.
Programming (via satellite): Country Music TV; Nickelodeon; USA Network.
Fee: $1.44 monthly.
Expanded Basic Service 2
Subscribers: 3,086.
Programming (via satellite): WGN-TV (W) Chicago; CNN; Disney Channel; Headline News; TBS Superstation; Turner Network TV.
Fee: $8.00 monthly.
Pay Service 1
Pay Units: 535.
Programming (via satellite): Cinemax.
Fee: $10.95 monthly.
Pay Service 2
Pay Units: 822.
Programming (via satellite): HBO.
Fee: $11.95 monthly.
Pay Service 3
Pay Units: 371.
Programming (via satellite): Showtime.
Fee: $10.95 monthly.
Pay Service 4
Pay Units: 193.
Programming (via satellite): The Movie Channel.
Fee: $10.95 monthly.
Local advertising: Planned.
Equipment: Catel, Jerrold & Scientific-Atlanta headend; Scientific-Atlanta & Winegard amplifiers; Comm/Scope cable; Jerrold character generator; Jerrold & Scientific-Atlanta set top converters; Eagle, Intercept & PPC traps; Gardiner & Scientific-Atlanta satellite antenna; Electrohome, Gardiner & Microdyne satellite receivers.
Miles of plant: 201.0 (coaxial). Homes passed: 6,759.
Manager: Roger Wayland. Chief technician: Kevin Goetz.
Franchise fee: 5% of gross.
Ownership: Falcon Communications LP (MSO), joint venture formed September 30, 1998. See Cable System Ownership.

ROCKWOOD—Comcast Cablevision of the South, Box 1169, Hwy. 27S, Harriman, TN 37748. Phone: 423-637-5411. Counties: Cumberland & Roane. Also serves Cumberland County (portions). ICA: TN0163.
TV Market Ranking: Below 100. Franchise award date: N.A. Franchise expiration date: N.A. Began: N.A.
Channel capacity: N.A. Channels available but not in use: N.A.
Basic Service
Subscribers: 2,929.
Programming (received off-air): WDEF-TV (C), WTVC (A) Chattanooga; WATE-TV (A), WBIR-TV (N), WKOP-TV (P), WTNZ (F), WVLT-TV (C) Knoxville.
Programming (via satellite): WGN-TV (W) Chicago; A & E; American Movie Classics; C-SPAN; C-SPAN 2; CNN; Comedy Central; Country Music TV; Discovery Channel; ESPN; Fox Family Channel; Headline News; Home Shopping Network; Kaleidoscope; Learning Channel; Lifetime; MTV; Nashville Network; Nickelodeon; Odyssey; Sci-Fi Channel; TBS Superstation; The Weather Channel; Turner Network TV; USA Network; VH1; ValueVision.
Current originations: Local news.
Fee: $32.00 installation; $18.95 monthly.
Pay Service 1
Pay Units: N.A.
Programming (via satellite): Cinemax; HBO; Showtime.
Fee: $9.00 monthly (each).
Manager: Roger Rule. Chief technician: Don Alford.
Ownership: Comcast Cable Communications Inc. (MSO).

ROGERSVILLE—Small Town Cable, 225 Highland Villa, Nashville, TN 37211. Phone: 877-368-2110. County: Hawkins. Also serves Hawkins County (central portion), Surgoinsville. ICA: TN0087.
TV Market Ranking: Below 100. Franchise award date: N.A. Franchise expiration date: December 1, 2005. Began: December 1, 1988.
Channel capacity: 32. Channels available but not in use: None.
Basic Service
Subscribers: 1,173; Commercial subscribers: 2.
Programming (received off-air): WCYB-TV (N) Bristol-Kingsport; WLOS (A) Greenville-Spartanburg-Asheville; WJHL-TV (C) Johnson City; WKPT-TV (A) Kingsport; WBIR-TV (N) Knoxville; WSJK (P) Sneedville.
Programming (via satellite): WGN-TV (W) Chicago; A & E; CNN; Comedy Central; Country Music TV; Discovery Channel; ESPN; Fox Family Channel; Headline News; Lifetime; MTV; Nashville Network; QVC; TBS Superstation; The Weather Channel; Turner Network TV; USA Network.
Fee: $30.00 installation; $27.50 monthly.
Pay Service 1
Pay Units: 39.
Programming (via satellite): Disney Channel.
Fee: $30.00 installation; $7.50 monthly.
Pay Service 2
Pay Units: 118.
Programming (via satellite): HBO.
Fee: $30.00 installation; $9.95 monthly.
Pay Service 3
Pay Units: 84.
Programming (via satellite): Showtime.
Fee: $30.00 installation; $9.95 monthly.
Miles of plant: 78.0 (coaxial). Homes passed: 1,692.
Ownership: Small Town Cable Corp. (MSO). Purchased from Galaxy Cablevision, January 1, 1999.

SAVANNAH—InterMedia Partners, Box 250, 24 Circle Dr., McKenzie, TN 38201. Phone: 901-352-2273. Fax: 901-352-3164. Web site: http://www.intermediamtn.com. County: Hardin. Also serves Crump, Hardin County, Milledgeville, Saltillo. ICA: TN0041.
TV Market Ranking: Below 100 (portions of Hardin County); Outside TV Markets (Crump, portions of Hardin County, Milledgeville, Saltillo, Savannah). Franchise award date: September 3, 1965. Franchise expiration date: March 5, 2000. Began: June 1, 1965.
Channel capacity: 42 (not 2-way capable). Channels available but not in use: None.
Basic Service
Subscribers: 5,179.
Programming (received off-air): W18BL (I) Adamsville; WBBJ-TV (A), WMTU (U) Jackson; WLJT (P) Lexington; WMC-TV (N), WREG-TV (C) Memphis; WSMV (N), WTVF (C) Nashville.
Programming (via satellite): WGN-TV (W) Chicago; C-SPAN; FoxNet.
Current originations: Automated time-weather.
Fee: $11.70 monthly.
Expanded Basic Service
Subscribers: 4,632.
Programming (via satellite): A & E; American Movie Classics; BET; CNBC; CNN; Comedy Central; Country Music TV; Discovery Channel; Disney Channel; ESPN; ESPN 2; Fox Family Channel; Fox News Channel; Fox Sports Net South; Headline News; Learning Channel; Lifetime; MTV; Nashville Network; Nickelodeon; QVC; TBS Superstation; The Weather Channel; Turner Classic Movies; Turner Network TV; USA Network.
Fee: $15.22 monthly.
Pay Service 1
Pay Units: 1,926.
Programming (via satellite): Cinemax; HBO; Showtime; The New Encore.
Fee: $11.95 monthly.
Equipment: Scientific-Atlanta headend; Jerrold amplifiers; Jerrold addressable set top converters; Microdyne satellite antenna; Jerrold, Scientific-Atlanta & Standard Components satellite receivers.
Miles of plant: 183.0 (coaxial); None (fiber optic). Additional miles planned: 30.0 (coaxial). Homes passed: 7,342. Total homes in franchised area: 7,342.
Manager: Robert L. Pace. Chief technician: Benny Jackson.
City fee: 4% of gross.
Ownership: InterMedia Partners (MSO). See Cable System Ownership.

SCOTTS HILL—Pat's Cable TV, Box 555, Linden, TN 37096. Phone: 931-589-2696. Counties: Decatur & Henderson. ICA: TN0166.
TV Market Ranking: Below 100. Franchise award date: N.A. Franchise expiration date: N.A. Began: January 1, 1982.

Channel capacity: 12. Channels available but not in use: N.A.

Basic Service

Subscribers: N.A.

Programming (received off-air): WBBJ-TV (A) Jackson; WDCN (P), WKRN-TV (A), WSMV (N), WTVF (C), WZTV (F) Nashville.

Programming (via satellite): WGN-TV (W) Chicago; CNN; ESPN; Nashville Network; TBS Superstation; Turner Network TV.

Fee: $14.50 monthly.

Pay Service 1

Pay Units: N.A.

Programming (via satellite): HBO.

Fee: $9.00 monthly.

Manager: Dorothy Patterson. Chief technician: Bert Patterson.

Ownership: Pat's Inc. (MSO).

SELMER—Tennessee Cablevision Inc., Grove Center, Oak Ridge, TN 37830. Phone: 423-482-4444. Fax: 423-482-6553. County: McNairy. Also serves Adamsville, Bethel Springs, McNairy, McNairy County (portions). ICA: TN0060.

TV Market Ranking: Below 100 (Adamsville, Bethel Springs, McNairy, portions of McNairy County, Selmer); Outside TV Markets (portions of McNairy County). Franchise award date: June 1, 1965. Franchise expiration date: N.A. Began: June 1, 1965.

Channel capacity: 38 (2-way capable). Channels available but not in use: N.A.

Basic Service

Subscribers: 2,603; Commercial subscribers: 4.

Programming (received off-air): WBBJ-TV (A), WMTU (U) Jackson; WLJT (P) Lexington; WHBQ-TV (F), WKNO (P), WMC-TV (N), WPTY-TV (A), WREG-TV (C) Memphis; allband FM.

Programming (via satellite): WGN-TV (W) Chicago; A & E; BET; CNN; Country Music TV; Discovery Channel; ESPN; Fox Family Channel; Home Shopping Network; Lifetime; MTV; Nashville Network; Nickelodeon; QVC; TBS Superstation; The Weather Channel; Turner Network TV; USA Network.

Current originations: Automated time-weather.

Fee: $50.00 installation; $18.00 monthly; $2.00 converter.

Commercial fee: $2.00 monthly.

Pay Service 1

Pay Units: 322.

Programming (via satellite): Cinemax.

Fee: $40.00 installation; $9.95 monthly.

Pay Service 2

Pay Units: 230.

Programming (via satellite): Disney Channel.

Fee: $40.00 installation; $9.95 monthly.

Pay Service 3

Pay Units: 600.

Programming (via satellite): HBO.

Fee: $40.00 installation; $9.95 monthly.

Pay Service 4

Pay Units: 210.

Programming (via satellite): Showtime.

Fee: $40.00 installation; $9.95 monthly.

Local advertising: Planned.

Equipment: Gardiner & Jerrold headend; Jerrold amplifiers; Belden cable; Gardiner satellite antenna.

Miles of plant: 110.0 (coaxial). Homes passed: 2,700.

Manager: Jerry W. Creasy. Chief technician: Van Phelps. Marketing director: Judy Phelps.

City fee: 3% of gross.

Ownership: Time Warner Cable (MSO).

SEYMOUR—InterMedia, 725 Louisville Rd., Alcoa, TN 37701-1846. Phone: 423-984-1400. Fax: 423-983-0383. County: Sevier. Also serves Sevier County. ICA: TN0168.

TV Market Ranking: 71 (portions of Sevier County, Seymour); Outside TV Markets (portions of Sevier County). Franchise award date: N.A. Franchise expiration date: May 1, 2005. Began: December 1, 1982.

Channel capacity: 42. Channels available but not in use: 6.

Basic Service

Subscribers: 3,476.

Programming (received off-air): WATE-TV (A), WBIR-TV (N), WKOP-TV (P), WVLT-TV (C) Knoxville; WSJK (P) Sneedville.

Programming (via satellite): WGN-TV (W) Chicago; Headline News; Nickelodeon; QVC; TBS Superstation; The Weather Channel; Trinity Bcstg. Network.

Fee: $19.95 installation; $9.37 monthly.

Expanded Basic Service

Subscribers: N.A.

Programming (via satellite): A & E; American Movie Classics; CNBC; CNN; Country Music TV; Discovery Channel; ESPN; Fox Family Channel; Fox Sports Net South; Lifetime; MTV; Nashville Network; Turner Network TV; USA Network.

Fee: $8.04 monthly.

Pay Service 1

Pay Units: 886.

Programming (via satellite): Cinemax; Disney Channel; HBO; Showtime; The Movie Channel.

Fee: $10.00 installation; $10.95 monthly (each).

Miles of plant & homes passed included with Alcoa, TN.

Office manager: Paul Maynard. Technical operations manager: Mark Haley. Chief engineer: Dale Taylor. Business manager: Cathy Dunford.

Ownership: InterMedia Partners (MSO). See Cable System Ownership.

SHELBYVILLE—Cablevision of Shelbyville, 209 N. Thompson St., Shelbyville, TN 37160-4048. Phone: 931-684-8382. Fax: 931-684-0054. County: Bedford. Also serves Bell Buckle, Wartrace. ICA: TN0034.

TV Market Ranking: Below 100. Franchise award date: N.A. Franchise expiration date: N.A. Began: March 1, 1972.

Channel capacity: 37 (2-way capable). Channels available but not in use: N.A.

Basic Service

Subscribers: 6,000.

Programming (received off-air): WHNT-TV (C) Huntsville-Decatur; WDCN (P), WKRN-TV (A), WSMV (N), WTVF (C), WZTV (F) Nashville.

Programming (via satellite): A & E; BET; C-SPAN; Country Music TV; Fox Family Channel; QVC; The Weather Channel.

Current originations: Automated time-weather; public access.

Fee: $49.95 installation; $9.94 monthly; $24.95 additional installation.

Expanded Basic Service

Subscribers: 5,666.

Programming (via satellite): WGN-TV (W) Chicago; American Movie Classics; CNBC; CNN; Comedy Central; Discovery Channel; ESPN; Fox Sports Net South; Headline News; Lifetime; MTV; Nashville Network; Nickelodeon; TBS Superstation; Turner Network TV; USA Network; VH1.

Fee: $10.65 monthly.

Pay Service 1

Pay Units: 962.

Programming (via satellite): HBO.

Fee: $17.54 installation; $10.95 monthly.

Pay Service 2

Pay Units: 436.

Programming (via satellite): Cinemax.

Fee: $17.54 installation; $10.95 monthly.

Pay Service 3

Pay Units: 238.

Programming (via satellite): Disney Channel.

Fee: $17.54 installation; $10.95 monthly.

Pay Service 4

Pay Units: 436.

Programming (via satellite): Showtime.

Fee: $17.54 installation; $10.95 monthly.

Pay Service 5

Pay Units: N.A.

Programming (via satellite): The New Encore.

Fee: $1.75 monthly.

Pay-Per-View

Special events.

Fee: Varies.

Local advertising: Yes. Available in satellite distributed & character-generated programming. Rates: $20.00/Minute; $10.00/30 Seconds. Local sales manager: Doug Roberts. Regional interconnect: Intermedia Television Advertising.

Equipment: Scientific-Atlanta headend; Scientific-Atlanta amplifiers; Comm/Scope cable; Texscan/MSI character generator; Panasonic & Scientific-Atlanta set top converters; Eagle traps; Anixter & Scientific-Atlanta satellite antenna; Scientific-Atlanta satellite receivers; ChannelMatic & Spot Matic commercial insert.

Miles of plant: 162.1 (coaxial). Homes passed: 7,796.

Manager: Earl Hines. Chief technician: Rex Ferguson.

City fee: 3%-5% of gross.

Ownership: Rifkin & Associates Inc. (MSO). See Cable System Ownership.

SIMMERLY CREEK—FrontierVision, 12089 Hwy. 421 N, Zionville, NC 28698. Phone: 704-297-4090. Counties: Carter & Unicoi. Also serves Hampton, Roan Mountain. ICA: TN0105.

TV Market Ranking: Below 100. Franchise award date: N.A. Franchise expiration date: N.A. Began: June 1, 1990.

Channel capacity: 21. Channels available but not in use: N.A.

Basic Service

Subscribers: N.A.

Programming (received off-air): WCYB-TV (N) Bristol-Kingsport; WEMT (F) Greeneville; WJHL-TV (C) Johnson City; WKPT-TV (A) Kingsport; WSJK (P) Sneedville.

Programming (via satellite): WGN-TV (W) Chicago; CNN; Country Music TV; ESPN; Fox Family Channel; MTV; Nashville Network; Nickelodeon; TBS Superstation; USA Network.

Fee: $25.00 installation; $14.00 monthly.

Pay Service 1

Pay Units: N.A.

Programming (via satellite): Disney Channel; HBO.

Fee: $8.50 monthly (Disney), $9.95 monthly (HBO).

Miles of plant: 32.0 (coaxial). Homes passed: 620.

Manager: Bob Blevins. Chief technician: Steve Blackburn.

Ownership: FrontierVision Partners LP (MSO). See Cable System Ownership.

SMITHVILLE—Central Tennessee Cablevision, 406 Public Square, Smithville, TN 37166. Phones: 615-597-8481; 800-883-6786. County: DeKalb. Also serves DeKalb County, Dowelltown. ICA: TN0076.

TV Market Ranking: Below 100. Franchise award date: N.A. Franchise expiration date: N.A. Began: May 15, 1980.

Channel capacity: 39 (not 2-way capable). Channels available but not in use: 9.

Basic Service

Subscribers: 2,467.

Programming (received off-air): WCTE (P) Cookeville; WDCN (P), WKRN-TV (A), WSMV (N), WTVF (C), WZTV (F) Nashville.

Fee: $60.00 installation; $10.00 monthly.

Expanded Basic Service

Subscribers: 2,024.

Programming (via satellite): WGN-TV (W) Chicago; American Movie Classics; C-SPAN; CNBC; CNN; Country Music TV; Discovery Channel; ESPN; Fox Family Channel; Nashville Network; Nickelodeon; TBS Superstation; The Weather Channel; Turner Network TV; USA Network.

Fee: $60.00 installation; $6.65 monthly.

Pay Service 1

Pay Units: 101.

Programming (via satellite): Disney Channel.

Fee: $9.95 monthly.

Pay Service 2

Pay Units: 236.

Programming (via satellite): The New Encore.

Fee: $1.50 monthly.

Pay Service 3

Pay Units: 351.

Programming (via satellite): HBO.

Fee: $9.95 monthly.

Pay Service 4

Pay Units: 193.

Programming (via satellite): Showtime.

Fee: $9.95 monthly.

Local advertising: Yes.

Equipment: Scientific-Atlanta headend; Magnavox & RCA amplifiers; Comm/Scope cable; Oak set top converters; Scientific-Atlanta satellite antenna; Scientific-Atlanta satellite receivers.

Miles of plant: 120.0 (coaxial). Additional miles planned: 3.0 (coaxial). Homes passed: 2,787.

Manager: Kathy Harris. Chief technician: Raymond Strait.

Ownership: InterMedia Partners (MSO). See Cable System Ownership.

SMYRNA—Tennessee Valley CableVision, 6940 Moores Lane, Brentwood, TN 37027-2908. Phone: 615-244-5900. Fax: 615-377-3683. County: Rutherford. Also serves La Vergne, Rutherford County. ICA: TN0169.

TV Market Ranking: 30 (La Vergne, portions of Rutherford County, Smyrna); Below 100 (portions of Rutherford County). Franchise award date: N.A. Franchise expiration date: January 1, 2007. Began: October 1, 1980.

Channel capacity: 39 (2-way capable; operating 2-way). Channels available but not in use: 4.

Basic Service

Subscribers: 9,355.

Programming (received off-air): WPGD (I) Hendersonville; WHTN (I) Murfreesboro; WDCN (P), WKRN-TV (A), WSMV (N), WTVF (C), WUXP (U), WZTV (F) Nashville.

Programming (via satellite): Headline News; Learning Channel; QVC.

Fee: $27.91 installation; $8.49 monthly; $10.00 additional installation.

Commercial fee: $29.95 monthly.

Expanded Basic Service

Subscribers: 9,178.

Programming (via satellite): WGN-TV (W) Chicago; A & E; American Movie Classics; CNN; Country Music TV; Discovery Channel; ESPN; Fox Family Channel; Fox Sports

Net South; Lifetime; MTV; Nashville Network; Nickelodeon; TBS Superstation; The Weather Channel; Turner Network TV; USA Network; VH1.
Fee: $12.41 monthly.
Pay Service 1
Pay Units: 8,483.
Programming (via satellite): Cinemax; Disney Channel; HBO; Showtime; The Movie Channel.
Fee: $6.95 monthly (Disney), $9.95 monthly (Cinemax, HBO, Showtime or TMC).
Local advertising: Yes. Available in locally originated & taped programming. Regional interconnect: Intermedia Television Advertising.
Program Guide: TV Host.
Equipment: Scientific-Atlanta headend; Scientific-Atlanta amplifiers; Comm/Scope cable; Microdyne satellite antenna.
Miles of plant: 235.0 (coaxial). Homes passed: 15,293.
Manager: Dennis Marmon. Chief technician: Chris Jones. Marketing director: Sandra Staggs.
Ownership: InterMedia Partners (MSO). See Cable System Ownership.

SNEEDVILLE—Charter Communications Inc., 2491 Old Hwy. 25 E, Morristown, TN 37816. Phone: 423-586-8700. Fax: 423-586-9065. Web site: http://www.chartercom.com. County: Hancock. ICA: TN0113.
TV Market Ranking: Below 100. Franchise award date: N.A. Franchise expiration date: October 14, 2001. Began: January 1, 1966.
Channel capacity: 40 (not 2-way capable). Channels available but not in use: 21.
Basic Service
Subscribers: 438.
Programming (received off-air): WEMT (F) Greeneville; WATE-TV (A), WBIR-TV (N), WVLT-TV (C) Knoxville; WSJK (P) Sneedville.
Programming (via satellite): WGN-TV (W) Chicago; A & E; CNBC; CNN; Country Music TV; Discovery Channel; Disney Channel; ESPN; ESPN 2; Fox Family Channel; Headline News; Home & Garden Television; Learning Channel; Nashville Network; Nickelodeon; QVC; TBS Superstation; TV Food Network; The Weather Channel; Trinity Bcstg. Network; Turner Network TV; USA Network.
Current originations: Public access.
Fee: $40.00 installation; $14.95 monthly; $2.00 converter.
Pay Service 1
Pay Units: N.A.
Programming (via satellite): Cinemax; HBO.
Fee: N.A.
Pay-Per-View
Hot Choice; Viewer's Choice 1 & 2; special events.
Fee: Varies.
Local advertising: No.
Program Guide: CableView.
Equipment: Cadco & Scientific-Atlanta headend; Magnavox amplifiers; Comm/Scope cable; Scientific-Atlanta set top converters; Scientific-Atlanta satellite antenna; Electrohome satellite receivers.
Miles of plant: 12.0 (coaxial). Homes passed: 500. Total homes in franchised area: 500.
Manager: Jim Steet. Technical manager: Wes Hudson. Chief technician: Kelly Moore. Marketing director: Janie Beck.
City fee: 5% of basic.
Ownership: Charter Communications Inc. (MSO). Purchased from Marcus Cable, April 1, 1999.

SOMERVILLE—Time Warner Communications, Box 610, 12935 S. Main St., Somerville, TN 38068. Phone: 901-259-2225. County: Fayette. ICA: TN0094.
TV Market Ranking: Outside TV Markets. Franchise award date: May 1, 1981. Franchise expiration date: N.A. Began: September 1, 1981.
Channel capacity: 35 (not 2-way capable). Channels available but not in use: 2.
Basic Service
Subscribers: N.A.
Programming (received off-air): WHBQ-TV (F), WKNO (P), WLMT (U), WMC-TV (N), WPTY-TV (A), WREG-TV (C) Memphis.
Programming (via satellite): WGN-TV (W) Chicago; A & E; American Movie Classics; BET; C-SPAN; CNN; Country Music TV; Discovery Channel; ESPN; Fox Family Channel; Headline News; Home Shopping Network; Lifetime; MTV; Nashville Network; Nickelodeon; QVC; TBS Superstation; The Weather Channel; Turner Network TV; USA Network.
Fee: $25.00 installation; $14.95 monthly.
Pay Service 1
Pay Units: N.A.
Programming (via satellite): Cinemax; Disney Channel; HBO; Showtime.
Fee: $7.00 monthly (Disney), $9.00 monthly (Cinemax, HBO or Showtime).
Miles of plant: 29.1 (coaxial). Additional miles planned: 5.7 (coaxial). Homes passed: 1,127. Total homes in franchised area: 1,375.
Manager: Bob Moss. Chief technician: Art Brown.
City fee: 3% of gross.
Ownership: Time Warner Cable (MSO).

SPRING CITY—Spring City Cable TV Inc., Box 729, Spring City, TN 37381. Phone: 423-365-7288. County: Rhea. Also serves Rhea County. ICA: TN0086.
TV Market Ranking: 78 (portions of Rhea County); Below 100 (portions of Rhea County, Spring City). Franchise award date: N.A. Franchise expiration date: N.A. Began: October 1, 1982.
Channel capacity: 40 (2-way capable; operating 2-way). Channels available but not in use: 21.
Basic Service
Subscribers: 2,000.
Programming (received off-air): WDEF-TV (C), WDSI-TV (F), WTCI (P), WTVC (A) Chattanooga; WBIR-TV (N), WVLT-TV (C) Knoxville.
Programming (via satellite): WGN-TV (W) Chicago; CNN; Discovery Channel; ESPN; MTV; Nashville Network; Nickelodeon; TBS Superstation; Turner Classic Movies; USA Network.
Fee: $20.00 installation; $14.95 monthly.
Pay Service 1
Pay Units: N.A.
Programming (via satellite): Cinemax; HBO.
Fee: $10.00 installation; $9.45 monthly (each).
Equipment: Scientific-Atlanta headend; Magnavox amplifiers; Comm/Scope cable; Oak & Hamlin set top converters; Eagle traps; Scientific-Atlanta satellite antenna; Scientific-Atlanta satellite receivers.
Miles of plant: 32.0 (coaxial). Additional miles planned: 2.0 (coaxial).
Manager: Walter Hooper. Chief technician: John Beasley.
City fee: 3% of gross.
Ownership: Spring City Cable TV Inc.

SUMMERTOWN—Small Town Cable, 225 Highland Villa, Nashville, TN 37211. Phone: 877-368-2110. County: Lawrence. Also serves Ethridge, Lawrence County (unincorporated areas). ICA: TN0171.
TV Market Ranking: Outside TV Markets. Franchise award date: July 18, 1988. Franchise expiration date: N.A. Began: N.A.
Channel capacity: 22. Channels available but not in use: None.
Basic Service
Subscribers: 204.
Programming (received off-air): WZDX (F) Huntsville-Decatur; WDCN (P), WKRN-TV (A), WSMV (N), WTVF (C), WUXP (U), WZTV (F) Nashville.
Programming (via satellite): C-SPAN; TBS Superstation.
Current originations: Religious access; local news.
Fee: $40.00 installation; $10.95 monthly.
Expanded Basic Service
Subscribers: N.A.
Programming (via satellite): CNN; Discovery Channel; ESPN; ESPN 2; Fox Family Channel; History Channel; MTV; Nashville Network; Nickelodeon; The Weather Channel; USA Network.
Fee: $13.00 monthly.
Pay Service 1
Pay Units: 16.
Programming (via satellite): Disney Channel.
Fee: $8.45 monthly.
Pay Service 2
Pay Units: 35.
Programming (via satellite): Showtime.
Fee: $11.45 monthly.
Miles of plant: 25.0 (coaxial); None (fiber optic). Homes passed: 779.
Manager: Tom Salters. Chief technician: Doc Collins. Program director: Sheri Smith.
Ownership: Small Town Cable Corp. (MSO). Purchased from Charter Communications Inc., January 1, 1999.

TELLICO PLAINS—Rapid Cable, 1106 Knoxville Hwy., Wartburg, TN 37887. Phone: 800-228-8836. Fax: 423-346-7451. County: Monroe. ICA: TN0173.
TV Market Ranking: Below 100. Franchise award date: N.A. Franchise expiration date: N.A. Began: March 1, 1983.
Channel capacity: 36. Channels available but not in use: N.A.
Basic Service
Subscribers: 821.
Programming (received off-air): WATE-TV (A), WBIR-TV (N), WKOP-TV (P), WVLT-TV (C) Knoxville; WSJK (P) Sneedville.
Programming (via satellite): WGN-TV (W) Chicago; CNN; Discovery Channel; ESPN; Fox Family Channel; Nashville Network; TBS Superstation; Turner Network TV; USA Network.
Fee: $20.00 installation; $12.00 monthly.
Pay Service 1
Pay Units: 328.
Programming (via satellite): HBO.
Fee: $8.00 monthly.
Miles of plant: 23.0 (coaxial).
Manager: C. K. Allen. Chief technician: Faron Jackson.
Ownership: Rapid Communications Partners LP (MSO). Purchased from Telephone & Data Systems Inc., February 1, 1999.

TENNESSEE RIDGE—Peoples CATV Co., Box 310, Rte. 1, Erin, TN 37061. Phone: 931-289-4222. Fax: 931-289-4220. Counties: Houston & Stewart. Also serves Erin. ICA: TN0083.
TV Market Ranking: Outside TV Markets. Franchise award date: March 1, 1983. Franchise expiration date: January 1, 2003. Began: March 1, 1984.
Channel capacity: 36 (2-way capable). Channels available but not in use: 14.
Basic Service
Subscribers: 1,556.
Programming (received off-air): WDCN (P), WKRN-TV (A), WSMV (N), WTVF (C), WUXP (U), WZTV (F) Nashville.
Programming (via satellite): CNN; ESPN; Fox Family Channel; TBS Superstation; USA Network.
Current originations: Automated time-weather.
Fee: $25.00 installation; $10.95 monthly.
Expanded Basic Service
Subscribers: 686.
Programming (via satellite): WGN-TV (W) Chicago; Country Music TV; Discovery Channel; Nashville Network; Nickelodeon; The Weather Channel; Turner Network TV; VH1.
Fee: $7.95 monthly.
Pay Service 1
Pay Units: 270.
Programming (via satellite): Cinemax.
Fee: $25.00 installation; $7.75 monthly.
Pay Service 2
Pay Units: 57.
Programming (via satellite): Disney Channel.
Fee: $25.00 installation; $7.50 monthly.
Pay Service 3
Pay Units: 201.
Programming (via satellite): HBO.
Fee: $25.00 installation; $10.15 monthly.
Local advertising: No.
Equipment: Scientific-Atlanta headend; Scientific-Atlanta amplifiers; Times Fiber & Comm/Scope cable; Scientific-Atlanta set top converters; Pico traps; Scientific-Atlanta satellite antenna; Scientific-Atlanta satellite receivers.
Miles of plant: 108.0 (coaxial); None (fiber optic). Additional miles planned: 12.0 (coaxial). Total homes in franchised area: 3,400.
Manager: James H. Coakley. Chief technician: Steve Hall. Program director: Fay Lair. Marketing director: Bill Baggett.
Ownership: Peoples Telephone Co. Inc. (Tennessee) (MSO).

TIPTONVILLE—CableVision Communications, Box 218, Poplar Bluff, MO 63902. Phones: 573-686-0900; 573-686-6387. Fax: 573-686-3891. Counties: Lake & Obion. Also serves Hornbeak, Lake County, Ridgely, Samburg, Wynnburg. ICA: TN0059.
TV Market Ranking: Outside TV Markets. Franchise award date: February 9, 1978. Franchise expiration date: February 9, 1998. Began: July 1, 1979.
Channel capacity: 36 (not 2-way capable). Channels available but not in use: 8.
Basic Service
Subscribers: 2,455.
Programming (received off-air): KBSI (F), KFVS-TV (C) Cape Girardeau; WBBJ-TV (A) Jackson; WLJT (P) Lexington; WHBQ-TV (F), WMC-TV (N), WPTY-TV (A) Memphis; WPSD-TV (N) Paducah.
Programming (via satellite): WGN-TV (W) Chicago; CNN; Country Music TV; Discovery Channel; ESPN; Fox Family Channel; MTV; Nashville Network; Nickelodeon; TBS Superstation; The Inspirational Network; The Weather Channel; USA Network.
Current originations: Automated time-weather; public access; religious access; local news.
Fee: $35.00 installation; $13.95 monthly.
Pay Service 1
Pay Units: 1,190.
Programming (via satellite): Cinemax; Disney Channel; HBO.
Fee: $7.00 monthly (Disney), $10.00 monthly (Cinemax or HBO).
Local advertising: Yes (insert only). Available in satellite distributed & locally originated programming. Rates: $25.00/Week. Local sales manager: Jan Bell.
Equipment: Jerrold, Tocom & Triple Crown headend; Triple Crown amplifiers; Comm/Scope

cable; Jerrold set top converters; Triple Crown satellite antenna; Triple Crown satellite receivers.
Miles of plant: 52.0 (coaxial). Homes passed: 2,725.
Manager: Janet Norris.
Franchise fee: 3% of gross.
Ownership: Rifkin & Associates Inc. (MSO). Purchased from Triax Telecommunications Co. LLC, July 1, 1998. See Cable System Ownership.

TRENTON—Trenton TV Cable Co., Box 345, Hwy. 45, Trenton, TN 38382. Phone: 901-855-2808. Fax: 901-855-9512. County: Gibson. ICA: TN0071.
TV Market Ranking: Outside TV Markets. Franchise award date: N.A. Franchise expiration date: January 1, 1998. Began: May 1, 1968.
Channel capacity: 60. Channels available but not in use: 18.
Basic Service
Subscribers: 2,164.
Programming (received off-air): KFVS-TV (C) Cape Girardeau; WBBJ-TV (A), WMTU (U) Jackson; WLJT (P) Lexington; WHBQ-TV (F), WKNO (P), WMC-TV (N), WPTY-TV (A), WREG-TV (C) Memphis; WPSD-TV (N) Paducah.
Fee: $15.00 installation; $11.94 monthly.
Expanded Basic Service
Subscribers: 1,994.
Programming (via satellite): WGN-TV (W) Chicago; A & E; BET; C-SPAN; CNN; CNNfn; Country Music TV; Discovery Channel; ESPN; ESPN 2; Fox Family Channel; Fox Sports Net South; Headline News; Home & Garden Television; Home Shopping Network; Lifetime; Nashville Network; Sci-Fi Channel; TBS Superstation; The Weather Channel; Trinity Bcstg. Network; Turner Classic Movies; Turner Network TV; USA Network; VH1.
Fee: $22.74 monthly.
Pay Service 1
Pay Units: N.A.
Programming (via satellite): Cinemax; Disney Channel; HBO; Showtime.
Fee: $8.00 monthly (Disney), $11.14 monthly (Cinemax, HBO or Showtime).
Local advertising: Yes.
Equipment: Jerrold & Scientific-Atlanta headend; Jerrold & Scientific-Atlanta amplifiers; Times Fiber cable; Scientific-Atlanta satellite antenna.
Miles of plant: 50.0 (coaxial); None (fiber optic). Homes passed: 2,400. Total homes in franchised area: 2,400.
Manager: Harold Nowell. Chief technician: Stephen Nowell.
City fee: 2% of gross.
Ownership: Harold Nowell.

TULLAHOMA—Tullahoma Cablevision, 215 Industrial Blvd., Tullahoma, TN 37388. Phone: 931-455-2672. Fax: 931-455-5392. Counties: Coffee, Franklin & Moore. Also serves Coffee County (portions), Franklin County (portions), Moore County (portions). ICA: TN0032.
TV Market Ranking: 96 (portions of Franklin County); Below 100 (portions of Coffee County, portions of Moore County, Tullahoma); Outside TV Markets (portions of Coffee County, portions of Franklin County, portions of Moore County). Franchise award date: N.A. Franchise expiration date: May 1, 2002. Began: May 1, 1969.
Channel capacity: 38 (not 2-way capable). Channels available but not in use: 1.
Basic Service
Subscribers: 7,807.
Programming (received off-air): WHTN (I) Murfreesboro; WDCN (P), WKRN-TV (A), WSMV (N), WTVF (C), WUXP (U), WZTV (F) Nashville; 2 FMs.
Programming (via satellite): WGN-TV (W) Chicago; C-SPAN; Home Shopping Network; Learning Channel; TBS Superstation.
Current originations: Automated time-weather; public access; local news.
Fee: $37.50 installation; $10.00 monthly; $18.75 additional installation.
Expanded Basic Service
Subscribers: 7,120.
Programming (via satellite): A & E; American Movie Classics; BET; CNBC; CNN; Comedy Central; Country Music TV; Discovery Channel; ESPN; Fox Family Channel; Fox Sports Net South; Headline News; Lifetime; MTV; Nashville Network; Nickelodeon; The Weather Channel; Turner Network TV; USA Network; VH1.
Fee: $15.50 monthly.
Pay Service 1
Pay Units: 596.
Programming (via satellite): Cinemax.
Fee: $20.00 installation; $10.66 monthly.
Pay Service 2
Pay Units: 856.
Programming (via satellite): Disney Channel.
Fee: $20.00 installation; $7.72 monthly.
Pay Service 3
Pay Units: 116.
Programming (via satellite): DMX.
Fee: $8.69 monthly.
Pay Service 4
Pay Units: 1,494.
Programming (via satellite): HBO.
Fee: $10.66 monthly.
Pay Service 5
Pay Units: 864.
Programming (via satellite): Showtime.
Fee: $6.78 monthly.
Local advertising: Yes. Regional interconnect: Intermedia Television Advertising.
Equipment: CAS headend; Anaconda amplifiers; RF Systems satellite antenna.
Miles of plant: 220.0 (coaxial); None (fiber optic). Homes passed: 9,700. Total homes in franchised area: 9,700.
Manager: Terrell Mayton. Chief technician: Brian Langham. Program director: Suzette McCrorey. Marketing director: Sandra Staggs. Customer service manager: Stella O'Neal.
Ownership: Rifkin & Associates Inc. (MSO). See Cable System Ownership.

TURTLETOWN—Haywood Cable, Box 778, 1070 Jonathan Creek Rd., Waynesville, NC 28786. Phone: 704-926-2288. Fax: 704-926-2835. County: Polk. ICA: TN0065.
TV Market Ranking: Below 100. Franchise award date: N.A. Franchise expiration date: N.A. Began: August 13, 1990.
Channel capacity: 54 (not 2-way capable). Channels available but not in use: 20.
Basic Service
Subscribers: 1,300.
Programming (received off-air): WHNS (F,U), WSPA-TV (C), WYFF (N) Greenville-Spartanburg-Asheville.
Programming (via satellite): WGN-TV (W) Chicago; A & E; C-SPAN; C-SPAN 2; CNBC; CNN; Country Music TV; Discovery Channel; ESPN; Fox Family Channel; Headline News; Home Shopping Network; Learning Channel; Lifetime; MTV; Nashville Network; Nickelodeon; QVC; TBS Superstation; The Weather Channel; Turner Network TV; USA Network; VH1.
Fee: $25.00 installation; $20.95 monthly; $3.00 converter.
Pay Service 1
Pay Units: N.A.
Programming (via satellite): Cinemax; HBO.
Fee: $10.95 monthly (each).
Local advertising: Yes. Available in character-generated programming.
Equipment: Scientific-Atlanta headend; Scientific-Atlanta amplifiers; Times Fiber cable; Scientific-Atlanta & Standard Communications satellite receivers.
Miles of plant: 106.0 (coaxial). Additional miles planned: 5.0 (coaxial). Homes passed: 2,500.
Manager: C. L. Watson. Chief technician: Kelly West. Marketing director: K. Owens.
Franchise fee: 5% of gross.
Ownership: Carolina Country Cable (MSO).

VONORE—Rapid Cable, 1106 Knoxville Hwy., Wartburg, TN 37887. Phone: 800-228-8836. Fax: 423-346-7451. County: Monroe. ICA: TN0174.
TV Market Ranking: 71. Franchise award date: N.A. Franchise expiration date: N.A. Began: September 1, 1984.
Channel capacity: 36. Channels available but not in use: 22.
Basic Service
Subscribers: 145.
Programming (received off-air): WATE-TV (A), WBIR-TV (N), WTNZ (F), WVLT-TV (C) Knoxville; WSJK (P) Sneedville.
Fee: $20.00 installation; $12.00 monthly.
Pay Service 1
Pay Units: 83.
Programming (via satellite): HBO.
Fee: $8.00 monthly.
Miles of plant: 12.0 (coaxial).
Manager: C. K. Allen. Chief technician: Faron Jackson.
Ownership: Rapid Communications Partners LP (MSO). Purchased from Telephone & Data Systems Inc., February 1, 1999.

WALDEN CREEK—Comcast Cablevision of the South, 1725 Wears Valley Rd., Sevierville, TN 37862-8516. Phone: 615-428-0396. Web site: http://www.comcast.com. Counties: Blount, Cocke, Jefferson, Knox & Sevier. Also serves Blount County (portions), Cobbly Nob, Cosby, Jefferson County (portions), Knox County (portions), Newport, Pigeon Forge, Sevierville, Townsend, Wear Valley. ICA: TN0031.
TV Market Ranking: 71 (Blount County, Cobbly Nob, Jefferson County, Knox County, Pigeon Forge, Sevierville, Townsend, Walden Creek, Wear Valley); Below 100 (Cosby, Newport). Franchise award date: N.A. Franchise expiration date: N.A. Began: April 1, 1977.
Channel capacity: 31. Channels available but not in use: N.A.
Basic Service
Subscribers: 1,361.
Programming (received off-air): WATE-TV (A), WBIR-TV (N), WTNZ (F), WVLT-TV (C) Knoxville; WSJK (P) Sneedville.
Programming (via satellite): WGN-TV (W) Chicago; A & E; American Movie Classics; C-SPAN; CNN; Country Music TV; Discovery Channel; ESPN; Fox Family Channel; Headline News; Home Shopping Network; Lifetime; MTV; Nashville Network; Nickelodeon; TBS Superstation; The Weather Channel; Trinity Bcstg. Network; Turner Network TV; USA Network; VH1.
Fee: $29.95 installation; $12.95 monthly.
Pay Service 1
Pay Units: N.A.
Programming (via satellite): Cinemax; Disney Channel; HBO; Showtime; The Movie Channel.
Fee: $10.00 installation; $8.00 monthly (Cinemax, Disney or HBO).
Miles of plant: 230.0 (coaxial). Homes passed: 7,906.
Manager: Karen Kastens.
Ownership: Comcast Cable Communications Inc. (MSO).

WARTBURG—Communicomm Cable, Box 465, 1106 Hwy. 62, Wartburg, TN 37887. Phone: 615-346-6674. Counties: Fentress, Morgan & Scott. Also serves Burrville, Coalfield, Deer Lodge, Huntsville, Jamestown (Fentress County), Lancing, Morgan County, Oakdale, Oneida, Petros, Sunbright. ICA: TN0019.
TV Market Ranking: 71 (portions of Morgan County, Oakdale, Petros); Below 100 (Burrville, Coalfield, Deer Lodge, Huntsville, Jamestown, Lancing, portions of Morgan County, Oneida, Sunbright, Wartburg). Franchise award date: N.A. Franchise expiration date: N.A. Began: June 1, 1982.
Channel capacity: 52 (2-way capable; operating 2-way). Channels available but not in use: 12.
Basic Service
Subscribers: 8,000.
Programming (received off-air): WDEF-TV (C) Chattanooga; WCTE (P) Cookeville; WATE-TV (A), WBIR-TV (N), WTNZ (F), WVLT-TV (C) Knoxville.
Programming (via satellite): WGN-TV (W) Chicago; A & E; American Movie Classics; C-SPAN; C-SPAN 2; CNBC; CNN; Country Music TV; Discovery Channel; ESPN; Fox Family Channel; Headline News; Home Shopping Network; Lifetime; MTV; Nashville Network; Nickelodeon; QVC; TBS Superstation; Travel Channel; Turner Network TV; USA Network; VH1.
Fee: $50.00 installation; $21.95 monthly; $10.00 additional installation.
Pay Service 1
Pay Units: 450.
Programming (via satellite): Disney Channel.
Fee: $25.00 installation; $8.95 monthly.
Pay Service 2
Pay Units: 900.
Programming (via satellite): Cinemax.
Fee: $25.00 installation; $9.95 monthly.
Pay Service 3
Pay Units: 1,700.
Programming (via satellite): HBO.
Fee: $25.00 installation; $10.95 monthly.
Local advertising: Yes. Available in satellite distributed & character-generated programming. Rates: $5.00/30 Seconds.
Equipment: Scientific-Atlanta headend; Scientific-Atlanta amplifiers; Comm/Scope cable; Scientific-Atlanta satellite antenna; Scientific-Atlanta satellite receivers.
Miles of plant: 600.0 (coaxial). Homes passed: 14,250. Total homes in franchised area: 20,000.
Manager: Mike Adams. Chief technician: Faron Jackson.
City fee: 3% of gross.
Ownership: James Cable Partners (MSO).

WAVERLY—InterMedia Cable, Box 260, Jackson, MS 39205-0260. Phone: 601-355-1522. County: Humphreys. Also serves Humphreys County (portions). ICA: TN0075.
TV Market Ranking: Outside TV Markets. Franchise award date: August 28, 1978. Franchise expiration date: September 12, 2008. Began: January 1, 1979.
Channel capacity: 35 (not 2-way capable). Channels available but not in use: 5.
Basic Service
Subscribers: 1,737; Commercial subscribers: 5.
Programming (received off-air): WBBJ-TV (A) Jackson; WDCN (P), WKRN-TV (A), WSMV (N), WTVF (C), WZTV (F) Nashville.

Programming (via satellite): WGN-TV (W) Chicago; A & E; C-SPAN; CNN; Country Music TV; Discovery Channel; ESPN; Fox Family Channel; Lifetime; MTV; Nashville Network; Nickelodeon; QVC; TBS Superstation; The Movie Channel; The Weather Channel; Trinity Bcstg. Network; Turner Network TV; USA Network.
Current originations: Public access; educational access; government access.
Fee: $25.00 installation; $11.00 monthly.
Pay Service 1
Pay Units: 506.
Programming (via satellite): HBO.
Fee: $10.00 installation; $10.00 monthly.
Pay Service 2
Pay Units: 112.
Programming (via satellite): Disney Channel.
Fee: $10.00 installation; $9.95 monthly.
Equipment: Scientific-Atlanta headend; Scientific-Atlanta amplifiers; Cerro & Comm/Scope cable; Eagle traps; Scientific-Atlanta satellite antenna; Scientific-Atlanta satellite receivers.
Miles of plant: 33.0 (coaxial). Additional miles planned: 4.0 (coaxial). Homes passed: 1,954.
Manager: Keith Walker. Chief technician: Richard Meredith. Marketing director: Starr Latimer.
City fee: 5% of gross.
Ownership: InterMedia Partners (MSO). See Cable System Ownership.

WAYNESBORO—InterMedia Partners, Box 250, 24 Circle Dr., McKenzie, TN 38201. Phone: 901-352-2273. Fax: 901-352-3164. Web site: http://www.intermediamtn.com. County: Wayne. Also serves Collinwood, Wayne County (portions). ICA: TN0093.
TV Market Ranking: Below 100 (Collinwood, portions of Wayne County, Waynesboro); Outside TV Markets (portions of Wayne County). Franchise award date: N.A. Franchise expiration date: July 1, 2002. Began: April 1, 1965.
Channel capacity: 42 (not 2-way capable). Channels available but not in use: None.
Basic Service
Subscribers: 1,707.
Programming (received off-air): WOWL-TV (N) Florence; WHNT-TV (C) Huntsville-Decatur; WBBJ-TV (A) Jackson; WDCN (P), WKRN-TV (A), WSMV (N), WTVF (C), WZTV (F) Nashville; allband FM.
Programming (via satellite): WGN-TV (W) Chicago; C-SPAN; Fox Family Channel; Learning Channel.
Current originations: Automated time-weather.
Fee: $11.81 monthly.
Expanded Basic Service
Subscribers: 1,530.
Programming (via satellite): A & E; American Movie Classics; Animal Planet; BET; CNBC; CNN; Country Music TV; Discovery Channel; Disney Channel; ESPN; ESPN 2; FX; Fox Sports Net South; Headline News; History Channel; Home & Garden Television; Home Shopping Network; Lifetime; MTV; Nashville Network; Nickelodeon; QVC; TBS Superstation; The Weather Channel; Turner Classic Movies; Turner Network TV; USA Network; VH1.
Fee: $17.28 monthly.
Pay Service 1
Pay Units: 506.
Programming (via satellite): Cinemax; HBO; Showtime; The New Encore.
Fee: $11.95 monthly.
Local advertising: Yes.
Equipment: Scientific-Atlanta headend; Jerrold amplifiers; Regal set top converters; Anixter-Mark satellite antenna; Scientific-Atlanta satellite receivers.
Miles of plant: 77.1 (coaxial); 13.0 (fiber optic). Additional miles planned: 1.0 (coaxial). Homes passed: 2,762.
Manager: Robert L. Pace. Chief technician: Benny Jackson.
City fee: 5% of gross.
Ownership: InterMedia Partners (MSO). See Cable System Ownership.

WESTMORELAND—InterMedia Partners, Box 250, 307 Circle Dr., McKenzie, TN 38201. Phone: 901-352-2273. Fax: 901-352-3164. Web site: http://www.intermediamtn.com. Counties: Macon & Sumner. Also serves Siloam. ICA: TN0104.
TV Market Ranking: Below 100. Franchise award date: N.A. Franchise expiration date: N.A. Began: April 1, 1983.
Channel capacity: N.A. Channels available but not in use: N.A.
Basic Service
Subscribers: 590.
Programming (received off-air): WKYU-TV (P) Bowling Green; WPGD (I) Hendersonville; WHTN (I) Murfreesboro; WDCN (P), WKRN-TV (A), WNAB (W), WSMV (N), WTVF (C), WUXP (U), WZTV (F) Nashville.
Programming (via satellite): C-SPAN.
Fee: $60.00 installation; $10.00 monthly; $15.00 additional installation.
Digital Basic Service
Subscribers: N.A.
Programming (via satellite): BBC America; BET on Jazz; CNN/SI; DMX; Discovery Civilization Channel; Discovery Health Channel; Discovery Home & Leisure Channel; Discovery Kids Channel; Discovery People; Discovery Science Channel; Discovery Wings Channel; ESPN Classic Sports; ESPNews; Fox Sports World; Game Show Network; Golf Channel; Goodlife TV Network; Independent Film Channel; International Channel; Kaleidoscope; Lifetime; MuchMusic Network; Outdoor Channel; Outdoor Life Network; Ovation; Romance Classics; Speedvision; The Barker; The Inspirational Network; Turner Classic Movies; Weatherscan by the Weather Channel; ZDTV.
Fee: N.A.
Expanded Basic Service
Subscribers: 425.
Programming (via satellite): WGN-TV (W) Chicago; A & E; CNN; Country Music TV; Discovery Channel; Disney Channel; ESPN; ESPN 2; Fox Family Channel; Headline News; History Channel; Lifetime; MTV; Nashville Network; Nick at Nite; Nickelodeon; TBS Superstation; Turner Classic Movies; Turner Network TV; USA Network.
Fee: N.A.
Pay Service 1
Pay Units: 57.
Programming (via satellite): Cinemax.
Fee: $10.00 installation; $9.95 monthly.
Pay Service 2
Pay Units: 98.
Programming (via satellite): The New Encore.
Fee: $1.50 monthly.
Pay Service 3
Pay Units: 105.
Programming (via satellite): HBO.
Fee: $10.00 installation; $9.95 monthly.
Digital Pay Service 1
Pay Units: N.A.
Programming (via satellite): BET Movies/Starz!; Cinemax (multiplexed); Encore Action; Encore Love Stories; Encore Mystery; Encore True Stories & Drama; Encore Westerns; Flix (multiplexed); HBO; HBO Comedy; HBO Family; HBO Plus; HBO Signature; HBO Zone; Showtime (multiplexed); Starz!; Starz! Theater; Sundance Channel (multiplexed); The Movie Channel (multiplexed); The New Encore.
Fee: N.A.
Local advertising: Yes.
Equipment: Scientific-Atlanta headend; Scientific-Atlanta amplifiers; Comm/Scope cable.
Miles of plant: 22.2 (coaxial). Homes passed: 687.
Manager: Robert Pace. Chief technician: Benny Jackson.
Ownership: InterMedia Partners (MSO). See Cable System Ownership.

WESTPOINT—InterMedia Partners, Box 250, 24 Circle Dr., McKenzie, TN 38201. Phone: 901-352-2273. Fax: 901-352-3164. Web site: http://www.intermediamtn.com. County: Lawrence. ICA: TN0124.
TV Market Ranking: Below 100. Franchise award date: January 1, 1973. Franchise expiration date: June 1, 2006. Began: N.A.
Channel capacity: 42 (not 2-way capable). Channels available but not in use: N.A.
Basic Service
Subscribers: 53.
Programming (received off-air): WOWL-TV (N) Florence; WAAY-TV (A), WAFF (N), WHNT-TV (C), WZDX (F) Huntsville-Decatur; WDCN (P), WKRN-TV (A), WSMV (N), WTVF (C) Nashville.
Current originations: Automated time-weather.
Fee: N.A.
Expanded Basic Service
Subscribers: 48.
Programming (via satellite): American Movie Classics; CNN; Country Music TV; Discovery Channel; ESPN; Nashville Network; TBS Superstation; Turner Network TV.
Fee: N.A.
Pay Service 1
Pay Units: 10.
Programming (via satellite): HBO.
Fee: N.A.
Equipment: Broadband & Jerrold amplifiers; Scientific-Atlanta satellite receivers.
Miles of plant: 3.0 (coaxial); None (fiber optic). Homes passed: 109.
Manager: Robert L. Pace. Chief technician: Benny Jackson.
City fee: none.
Ownership: InterMedia Partners (MSO). See Cable System Ownership.

WHITE HOUSE—TMC of Green River, Box 1434, White House, TN 37188. Phone: 615-672-9666. Fax: 615-672-0616. Counties: Robertson & Sumner. Also serves Cross Plains, Millersville, Mitchellville, New Deal, Orlinda, Robertson County, Sumner County. ICA: TN0050.
TV Market Ranking: 30 (Cross Plains, Millersville, Mitchellville, New Deal, Orlinda, Robertson County, portions of Sumner County, White House); Below 100 (portions of Sumner County). Franchise award date: May 5, 1981. Franchise expiration date: N.A. Began: April 1, 1982.
Channel capacity: 116 (not 2-way capable). Channels available but not in use: 7.
Basic Service
Subscribers: 3,760.
Programming (received off-air): WPGD (I) Hendersonville; WDCN (P), WKRN-TV (A), WSMV (N), WTVF (C), WUXP (U), WZTV (F) Nashville.
Programming (via satellite): WGN-TV (W) Chicago; QVC; TBS Superstation; The Inspirational Network.
Current originations: Automated time-weather; public access; educational access; government access; local news.
Fee: $35.00 installation (aerial), $50.00 (underground); $15.00 monthly.
Expanded Basic Service
Subscribers: 3,608.
Programming (via satellite): A & E; CNN; Country Music TV; Discovery Channel; ESPN; Fox Family Channel; Lifetime; MTV; Nashville Network; Nickelodeon; Turner Network TV; USA Network.
Fee: $16.95 monthly.
Pay Service 1
Pay Units: 433.
Programming (via satellite): Cinemax.
Fee: $25.00 installation; $9.50 monthly.
Pay Service 2
Pay Units: 319.
Programming (via satellite): Disney Channel.
Fee: $25.00 installation; $9.50 monthly.
Pay Service 3
Pay Units: 643.
Programming (via satellite): HBO.
Fee: $25.00 installation; $10.00 monthly.
Pay Service 4
Pay Units: 336.
Programming (via satellite): The Movie Channel.
Fee: $25.00 installation; $9.50 monthly.
Local advertising: Yes. Available in character-generated programming. Regional interconnect: Cable Advertising Sales.
Equipment: Scientific-Atlanta headend; Jerrold amplifiers; CCS Hatfield cable; Scientific-Atlanta, Pioneer & RCA set top converters; Eagle & Pico traps; Microdyne satellite antenna; Microdyne satellite receivers.
Miles of plant: 156.0 (coaxial); 12.0 (fiber optic). Homes passed: 5,770.
Manager: Jennifer L. Motsinger. Chief technician: Ken Scott. Marketing director: Bill L. Benner.
City fee: 3% of gross.
Ownership: Tele-Media Corp. (MSO).

WHITESBURG—FrontierVision, Box 1747, Greeneville, TN 37744. Phone: 423-639-4321. Fax: 423-639-0145. Counties: Hamblen & Hawkins. Also serves Bulls Gap, Hamblen County, Hawkins County, Russellville. ICA: TN0079.
TV Market Ranking: 71 (portions of Hamblen County); Below 100 (Bulls Gap, portions of Hamblen County, Hawkins County, Russellville, Whitesburg). Franchise award date: February 25, 1983. Franchise expiration date: February 25, 1998. Began: May 1, 1983.
Channel capacity: 36 (not 2-way capable). Channels available but not in use: None.
Basic Service
Subscribers: 1,166.
Programming (received off-air): WCYB-TV (N) Bristol-Kingsport; WEMT (F) Greeneville; WATE-TV (A), WBIR-TV (N) Knoxville; WSJK (P) Sneedville.
Programming (via satellite): WGN-TV (W) Chicago; CNN; ESPN; Fox Family Channel; Lifetime; MTV; Nashville Network; Nickelodeon; TBS Superstation; The Weather Channel; USA Network.
Fee: $25.00 installation; $11.75 monthly; $20.00 additional installation.
Pay Service 1
Pay Units: 524.
Programming (via satellite): Cinemax; Disney Channel; HBO; The Movie Channel.
Fee: $8.00 monthly (each).
Local advertising: No.
Equipment: Triple Crown headend; Jerrold amplifiers.
Miles of plant: 64.5 (coaxial). Homes passed: 1,748.
Manager: Sue S. Wilson. Chief technician: Rick Short. Marketing director: Traci Williams.

City fee: 3% of gross.
Ownership: FrontierVision Partners LP (MSO). See Cable System Ownership.

WHITEVILLE—Time Warner Communications, Box 610, 12935 S. Main St., Somerville, TN 38068. Phone: 901-259-2225. County: Hardeman. ICA: TN0175.
TV Market Ranking: Below 100. Franchise award date: N.A. Franchise expiration date: N.A. Began: N.A.
Channel capacity: 35. Channels available but not in use: 2.
Basic Service
Subscribers: 260.
Programming (received off-air): WHBQ-TV (F), WKNO (P), WLMT (U), WMC-TV (N), WPTY-TV (A), WREG-TV (C) Memphis.
Programming (via satellite): WGN-TV (W) Chicago; A & E; American Movie Classics; BET; C-SPAN; CNN; Country Music TV; Court TV; Discovery Channel; ESPN; Fox Family Channel; Headline News; Home Shopping Network; Lifetime; MTV; Nashville Network; Nickelodeon; QVC; TBS Superstation; The Weather Channel; Turner Network TV; USA Network.
Fee: $39.00 installation; $19.05 monthly; $0.50 converter.
Pay Service 1
Pay Units: N.A.
Programming (via satellite): Cinemax; Disney Channel; HBO; Showtime.
Fee: $7.00 monthly (Disney), $9.95 monthly (Cinemax, HBO or Showtime).
Manager: Bob Moss. Chief technician: Art Brown.
Ownership: Time Warner Cable (MSO).

WINCHESTER—InterMedia Partners, Box 250, 307 Circle Dr., McKenzie, TN 38201. Phone: 901-352-2273. Fax: 901-352-3164. Web site: http://www.intermediamtn.com. County: Franklin. Also serves Cowan, Decherd, Estill Springs, Franklin County. ICA: TN0045.
TV Market Ranking: 78 (portions of Franklin County); 96 (portions of Franklin County); Outside TV Markets (Cowan, Decherd, Estill Springs, portions of Franklin County, Winchester). Franchise award date: January 1, 1971. Franchise expiration date: N.A. Began: August 10, 1967.
Channel capacity: N.A. Channels available but not in use: N.A.
Basic Service
Subscribers: 5,871.
Programming (received off-air): WNPX (X) Cookeville; WUPN-TV (U) Greensboro-High Point; WPGD (I) Hendersonville; WAFF (N) Huntsville-Decatur; WJFB (I) Lebanon; WHTN (I) Murfreesboro; WDCN (P), WKRN-TV (A), WNAB (W), WSMV (N), WTVF (C), WZTV (F) Nashville.
Programming (via satellite): WGN-TV (W) Chicago; C-SPAN; TBS Superstation.
Current originations: Public access; educational access; government access; leased access.
Fee: $35.00 installation; $13.95 monthly; $1.00 converter.
Digital Basic Service
Subscribers: N.A.
Programming (via satellite): BBC America; BET on Jazz; CNN/SI; DMX; Discovery Civilization Channel; Discovery Health Channel; Discovery Home & Leisure Channel; Discovery Kids Channel; Discovery People; Discovery Science Channel; Discovery Wings Channel; ESPN Classic Sports; ESPNews; Fox Sports World; Game Show Network; Golf Channel; Goodlife TV Network; Independent Film Channel; International Channel; Kaleidoscope; Lifetime; MuchMusic Network; Outdoor Channel; Outdoor Life Network; Ovation; Romance Classics; Speedvision; The Barker; The Inspirational Network; Turner Classic Movies; Weatherscan by the Weather Channel; ZDTV.
Fee: N.A.
Expanded Basic Service
Subscribers: 5,688.
Programming (via satellite): A & E; American Movie Classics; Animal Planet; BET; Bravo; C-SPAN 2; CNBC; CNN; Country Music TV; Discovery Channel; E! Entertainment TV; ESPN; ESPN 2; FX; fXM: Movies from Fox; Fox Family Channel; Fox News Channel; Fox Sports Net South; Headline News; History Channel; Home & Garden Television; Home Shopping Network; Learning Channel; Lifetime; MSNBC; MTV; Nashville Network; Nick at Nite's TV Land; Nickelodeon; Odyssey; QVC; Sci-Fi Channel; TV Guide Channel; TV Guide Sneak Prevue; The Weather Channel; Turner Network TV; USA Network; Univision; VH1.
Fee: N.A.
Pay Service 1
Pay Units: 274.
Programming (via satellite): Showtime.
Fee: $25.00 installation; $9.50 monthly.
Pay Service 2
Pay Units: 353.
Programming (via satellite): Cinemax.
Fee: $25.00 installation; $9.50 monthly.
Pay Service 3
Pay Units: 571.
Programming (via satellite): HBO.
Fee: $25.00 installation; $9.50 monthly.
Digital Pay Service 1
Pay Units: N.A.
Programming (via satellite): BET Movies/Starz!; Cinemax (multiplexed); Encore Action; Encore Love Stories; Encore Mystery; Encore True Stories & Drama; Encore Westerns; Flix (multiplexed); HBO; HBO Comedy; HBO Family; HBO Plus; HBO Signature; HBO Zone; Showtime (multiplexed); Starz!; Starz! Theater; Sundance Channel (multiplexed); The Movie Channel (multiplexed); The New Encore.
Fee: N.A.
Local advertising: Yes (locally produced & insert). Available in satellite distributed & character-generated programming. Rates: $6.50/30 Seconds. Local sales manager: Doug Roberts. Regional interconnect: Intermedia Television Advertising.
Equipment: Jerrold & Scientific-Atlanta headend; Jerrold & Magnavox amplifiers; Comm/Scope cable; JVC cameras; RCA character generator; Jerrold set top converters; Eagle traps; Scientific-Atlanta satellite antenna; Scientific-Atlanta satellite receivers; ChannelMatic commercial insert.
Miles of plant: 122.0 (coaxial). Additional miles planned: 5.0 (coaxial).
Manager: Robert Pace. Chief technician: Benny Jackson.
Franchise fee: 1% of gross.
Ownership: InterMedia Partners (MSO). See Cable System Ownership.

WOODBURY—Central Tennessee Cablevision, 301 W. Main St., Woodbury, TN 37190. Phone: 615-263-8572. County: Cannon. Also serves Bradyville, Cannon County. ICA: TN0101.
TV Market Ranking: Below 100. Franchise award date: N.A. Franchise expiration date: October 2, 1999. Began: November 1, 1981.
Channel capacity: 39. Channels available but not in use: 13.
Basic Service
Subscribers: 907.
Programming (received off-air): WDCN (P), WKRN-TV (A), WSMV (N), WTVF (C), WZTV (F) Nashville.
Current originations: Automated time-weather.
Fee: $60.00 installation; $10.00 monthly.
Expanded Basic Service
Subscribers: 758.
Programming (via satellite): WGN-TV (W) Chicago; CNBC; CNN; Discovery Channel; ESPN; Fox Family Channel; Headline News; Lifetime; MTV; Nashville Network; Nickelodeon; TBS Superstation; Turner Network TV; USA Network.
Fee: $60.00 installation; $6.65 monthly.
Pay Service 1
Pay Units: 58.
Programming (via satellite): Cinemax.
Fee: $9.95 monthly.
Pay Service 2
Pay Units: 45.
Programming (via satellite): Disney Channel.
Fee: $9.95 monthly.
Pay Service 3
Pay Units: 93.
Programming (via satellite): The New Encore.
Fee: $1.50 monthly.
Pay Service 4
Pay Units: 121.
Programming (via satellite): HBO.
Fee: $9.95 monthly.
Pay Service 5
Pay Units: 32.
Programming (via satellite): Showtime.
Fee: $9.95 monthly.
Local advertising: Yes. Regional interconnect: Intermedia Television Advertising.
Equipment: Scientific-Atlanta headend; Scientific-Atlanta amplifiers; Comm/Scope cable.
Miles of plant: 59.5 (coaxial). Homes passed: 1,149.
Manager: Kathy Harris. Chief technician: Raymond Strait.
City fee: 3% of gross.
Ownership: InterMedia Partners (MSO). See Cable System Ownership.

TEXAS

Total Systems: **791**
Total Communities Served: **1,716**
Franchises Not Yet Operating: **0**
Applications Pending: **0**
Communities with Applications: **0**
Number of Basic Subscribers: **3,574,093**
Number of Expanded Basic Subscribers: **2,465,619**
Number of Pay Units: **1,744,547**

Top 100 Markets Represented: Dallas-Fort Worth (12); Houston (15); San Antonio (45); Texarkana, TX-Shreveport, LA (58); Beaumont-Port Arthur (88); Amarillo (95).

For a list of all cable communities included in this section, see the Cable Community Index located in the back of this volume.
For explanation of terms used in cable system listings, see p. D-9.

ABERNATHY—Classic Cable, Box 429, 605 N.W. 3rd St., Plainville, KS 67663-0429. Phones: 785-434-7620; 800-999-8876. Fax: 785-434-2614. County: Hale. ICA: TX0388.
TV Market Ranking: Below 100. Franchise award date: August 14, 1978. Franchise expiration date: N.A. Began: November 1, 1979.
Channel capacity: 61 (2-way capable). Channels available but not in use: N.A.
Basic Service
Subscribers: 436.
Programming (received off-air): KAMC (A), KCBD-TV (N), KJTV (F), KLBK-TV (C), KPTB (I), KTXT-TV (P) Lubbock.
Programming (via translator): KVDA (O) San Antonio.
Programming (via satellite): WGN-TV (W) Chicago; KTVD (U) Denver; A & E; American Movie Classics; CNN; Country Music TV; Discovery Channel; Disney Channel; E! Entertainment TV; ESPN; Fox Family Channel; Fox News Channel; Fox Sports Net Southwest; Goodlife TV Network; Headline News; History Channel; Learning Channel; Lifetime; Nashville Network; Nick at Nite's TV Land; Nickelodeon; QVC; TBS Superstation; The Weather Channel; Turner Network TV; USA Network; Univision.
Current originations: Automated timeweather; religious access.
Fee: $35.00 installation; $28.95 monthly.
Pay Service 1
Pay Units: 104.
Programming (via satellite): HBO.
Fee: $9.95 monthly.
Pay Service 2
Pay Units: 37.
Programming (via satellite): Showtime.
Fee: $9.95 monthly.
Local advertising: No.
Equipment: Comtech satellite antenna.
Miles of plant: 14.6 (coaxial). Homes passed: 987.
Manager: Bill Flowers. Chief technician: Chris Christenson. Marketing director: Jennifer Hauschild.
City fee: 3% of gross.
Ownership: Classic Cable (MSO).

ABILENE—TCA Cable TV of Abilene, 1441 Woodard St., Abilene, TX 79605. Phone: 915-698-1510. Fax: 915-698-0319. Web site: http://www.tca-cable.com. County: Taylor. Also serves Dyess AFB, Taylor County (northern portion), Tye. ICA: TX0019.
TV Market Ranking: Below 100. Franchise award date: January 1, 1964. Franchise expiration date: March 19, 1997. Began: April 1, 1965.
Channel capacity: 39 (not 2-way capable). Channels available but not in use: None.
Basic Service
Subscribers: 32,144.
Programming (received off-air): KRBC-TV (N), KTAB-TV (C), KTXS-TV (A) Abilene-Sweetwater; KIDY (F) San Angelo; allband FM.
Programming (via microwave): KERA-TV (P), KTVT (C) Dallas-Fort Worth.
Programming (via satellite): C-SPAN; FX; Lifetime; QVC; TBS Superstation; TV Guide Channel; The Weather Channel; Univision.
Current originations: Automated timeweather; educational access; automated emergency alert.
Fee: $26.42 installation; $21.82 monthly.
Commercial fee: $4.95 monthly.
Expanded Basic Service
Subscribers: 25,175.
Programming (via satellite): A & E; American Movie Classics; BET; C-SPAN 2; CNBC; CNN; Country Music TV; Discovery Channel; E! Entertainment TV; ESPN; Fox Family Channel; Fox Sports Net Southwest; Headline News; MTV; Nashville Network; Nickelodeon; Turner Network TV; USA Network.
Fee: $10.91 monthly.
Pay Service 1
Pay Units: 2,671.
Programming (via satellite): Cinemax.
Fee: $2.00 installation; $11.38 monthly.
Pay Service 2
Pay Units: 1,556.
Programming (via satellite): Disney Channel.
Fee: $2.00 installation; $11.38 monthly.
Pay Service 3
Pay Units: 9,368.
Programming (via satellite): The New Encore.
Fee: $8.81 installation; $1.75 monthly.
Pay Service 4
Pay Units: 3,986.
Programming (via satellite): HBO.
Fee: $2.00 installation; $11.38 monthly.
Pay Service 5
Pay Units: 1,273.
Programming (via satellite): Showtime.
Fee: $2.00 installation; $11.38 monthly.
Pay Service 6
Pay Units: 6,290.
Programming (via satellite): Starz!
Fee: $8.81 installation; $4.75 monthly.
Pay-Per-View
Addressable homes: 10,497.
Action Pay-Per-View.
Fee: $3.99.
Local advertising: Yes. Available in satellite distributed programming. Rates: $15.00/Minute; $10.00/30 Seconds. Local sales manager: Terri Bennett.
Equipment: Jerrold, RCA & Scientific-Atlanta headend; Magnavox amplifiers; Comm/Scope & Times Fiber cable; Panasonic VTRs; Compuvid character generator; Jerrold set top converters; Jerrold addressable set top converters; Andrew, Anixter-Mark & Scientific-Atlanta satellite antenna; Microdyne & Standard Communications satellite receivers; Texscan commercial insert.
Miles of plant: 462.6 (coaxial). Homes passed: 48,558. Total homes in franchised area: 50,298.
Manager: Ruben Reveles. Chief technician: Alvin Ritz.
City fee: 5% of gross.
Ownership: TCA Cable TV Inc. (MSO); AT&T Broadband & Internet Services (MSO). See Cable System Ownership.

ACKERLY—National Cable Inc., Suite 106-A, 5151 Reed Rd., Columbus, OH 43220. Phones: 614-442-5890; 800-582-0504. Fax: 614-457-2567. Counties: Dawson & Martin. ICA: TX0681.
TV Market Ranking: Outside TV Markets. Franchise award date: June 3, 1989. Franchise expiration date: June 3, 2009. Began: June 6, 1990.
Channel capacity: 36 (not 2-way capable). Channels available but not in use: 19.
Basic Service
Subscribers: 55.
Programming (received off-air): KWAB-TV (N) Big Spring; KMID (A), KPEJ (F) Odessa-Midland.
Programming (via satellite): WGN-TV (W) Chicago; KMGH-TV (A), KRMA-TV (P) Denver; A & E; American Movie Classics; CNN; Country Music TV; Discovery Channel; ESPN; Fox Family Channel; GalaVision; Nashville Network; Showtime; TBS Superstation; Turner Network TV; USA Network.
Fee: $30.00 installation; $28.00 monthly; $3.00 converter.
Equipment: Nexus headend; Magnavox amplifiers; Times Fiber cable; Oak set top converters; Nexus satellite receivers.
Miles of plant: 3.8 (coaxial). Additional miles planned: 3.8 (coaxial). Homes passed: 109. Total homes in franchised area: 124.
Manager: Mansell Nelson. Chief technician: Ron Enas. Marketing director: Dave Beasley.
Ownership: National Cable (MSO).

ADKINS—Friendship Cable of Texas Inc., Box 9090, Tyler, TX 75711-9090. Phone: 903-581-2121. Fax: 903-581-2185. County: Bexar. ICA: TX0346.
TV Market Ranking: 45. Franchise award date: N.A. Franchise expiration date: N.A. Began: October 1, 1989.
Channel capacity: 54. Channels available but not in use: N.A.
Basic Service
Subscribers: 198.
Programming (received off-air): KRRT (W) Kerrville-San Antonio; KABB (F), KENS-TV (C), KHCE (P), KLRN (P), KMOL-TV (N), KSAT-TV (A), KVDA (O), KWEX-TV (S) San Antonio.
Programming (via satellite): CNN; Country Music TV; Discovery Channel; Disney Channel; ESPN; GalaVision; Headline News; MTV; Nashville Network; Nickelodeon; TBS Superstation; Turner Network TV; USA Network.
Fee: $30.00 installation; $27.20 monthly.
Pay Service 1
Pay Units: 5.
Programming (via satellite): Cinemax.
Fee: $10.95 monthly.
Pay Service 2
Pay Units: 16.
Programming (via satellite): HBO.
Fee: $10.99 monthly.
Pay Service 3
Pay Units: 40.
Programming (via satellite): Showtime.
Fee: $5.95 monthly.
Miles of plant: 46.0 (coaxial). Homes passed: 1,099.
Manager: Wanda Pyburn. Chief technician: David Burrell.
Ownership: Buford Television Inc. (MSO). See Cable System Ownership.

ADRIAN—High Plains Cablevision Inc., Box 310, 124 S. Main St., Lockney, TX 79241. Phone: 806-652-3328. Fax: 806-652-3139. County: Oldham. ICA: TX0706.
TV Market Ranking: Outside TV Markets. Franchise award date: N.A. Franchise expiration date: N.A. Began: N.A.
Channel capacity: N.A. Channels available but not in use: N.A.
Basic Service
Subscribers: 42.
Programming (received off-air): KAMR-TV (N), KCIT (F,U), KFDA-TV (C), KVII-TV (A) Amarillo.
Programming (via satellite): Turner Network TV.
Fee: N.A.
Manager: Jim Doucette. Chief technician: Jim Odle.
Ownership: High Plains Cablevision Inc. (MSO).

ALBA—Friendship Cable of Texas Inc., Box 9090, Tyler, TX 75711-9090. Phone: 903-581-2121. Fax: 903-581-2185. County: Wood. Also serves Wood County (portions). ICA: TX0603.
TV Market Ranking: Below 100. Franchise award date: N.A. Franchise expiration date: N.A. Began: August 1, 1989.
Channel capacity: 36. Channels available but not in use: N.A.
Basic Service
Subscribers: 100.
Programming (received off-air): KERA-TV (P) Dallas-Fort Worth; KETK-TV (N) Jacksonville; KFXK (F) Longview; KLTV (A) Tyler-Longview.
Programming (via satellite): WBBM-TV (C), WGN-TV (W) Chicago; A & E; Animal Planet; CNN; Country Music TV; Discovery Channel; ESPN; Fox Sports Net; Home Shopping Network; Lifetime; Nashville Network; Nickelodeon; Outdoor Life Network; TBS Superstation; The Weather Channel; Trinity Bcstg. Network; Turner Classic Movies; Turner Network TV; USA Network.
Fee: $30.00 installation; $32.40 monthly.
Pay Service 1
Pay Units: 10.
Programming (via satellite): Cinemax.
Fee: $10.95 monthly.

Pay Service 2
Pay Units: 6.
Programming (via satellite): HBO.
Fee: $10.95 monthly.
Pay Service 3
Pay Units: 5.
Programming (via satellite): Showtime.
Fee: $5.95 monthly.
Local advertising: No.
Miles of plant: 8.2 (coaxial). Homes passed: 239.
Manager: Marianne Bogy. Chief technician: Sonny Myers.
Ownership: Buford Television Inc. (MSO). See Cable System Ownership.

ALBANY—Friendship Cable of Texas Inc., Box 9090, Tyler, TX 75711-9090. Phone: 903-581-2121. Fax: 903-581-2185. County: Shackelford. ICA: TX0337.
TV Market Ranking: Below 100. Franchise award date: N.A. Franchise expiration date: N.A. Began: January 1, 1960.
Channel capacity: 30 (not 2-way capable). Channels available but not in use: N.A.
Basic Service
Subscribers: 791.
Programming (received off-air): KRBC-TV (N), KTAB-TV (C), KTXS-TV (A) Abilene-Sweetwater; 8 FMs.
Programming (via microwave): KERA-TV (P), KTVT (C), WFAA-TV (A) Dallas-Fort Worth.
Programming (via satellite): Discovery Channel; QVC; TBS Superstation; The Weather Channel; Trinity Bcstg. Network.
Current originations: Automated time-weather.
Fee: $30.00 installation; $11.86 monthly.
Expanded Basic Service
Subscribers: 680.
Programming (via satellite): American Movie Classics; Animal Planet; CNBC; CNN; Cartoon Network; Disney Channel; ESPN; FX; Fox Family Channel; Fox News Channel; Headline News; Home & Garden Television; Learning Channel; Lifetime; MTV; Nashville Network; Turner Network TV; USA Network.
Fee: $30.00 installation; $16.29 monthly.
Pay Service 1
Pay Units: 236.
Programming (via satellite): The New Encore.
Fee: $1.75 monthly.
Pay Service 2
Pay Units: 128.
Programming (via satellite): HBO.
Fee: $13.65 monthly.
Pay Service 3
Pay Units: 156.
Programming (via satellite): Starz!
Fee: $6.75 monthly.
Equipment: Entron & Jerrold headend; Jerrold amplifiers; Andrew satellite antenna.
Miles of plant: 26.0 (coaxial). Homes passed: 1,110. Total homes in franchised area: 1,110.
Manager: Larry Bryant. Chief technician: Joe Stewart.
City fee: $50.00 annually.
Ownership: Buford Television Inc. (MSO). See Cable System Ownership.

ALGOA—Star Cable Co., Drawer 1570, Brazoria, TX 77422. Phones: 409-798-9121; 800-395-2775. Fax: 409-798-4409. County: Galveston. ICA: TX0335.
TV Market Ranking: 15. Franchise award date: N.A. Franchise expiration date: N.A. Began: N.A.
Channel capacity: 36. Channels available but not in use: 1.
Basic Service
Subscribers: 341.
Programming (received off-air): KHSH-TV (H) Alvin; KVVV (I) Baytown; KLTJ (E) Galveston; KETH (E), KHOU-TV (C), KHTV (W), KPRC-TV (N), KRIV (F), KTRK-TV (A), KTXH (U), KUHT (P) Houston; KNWS-TV (I) Katy; KXLN-TV (S) Rosenberg.
Programming (via satellite): A & E; C-SPAN; CNN; Country Music TV; Discovery Channel; ESPN; Fox Family Channel; Fox Sports Net Southwest; Headline News; Lifetime; Nashville Network; Nickelodeon; QVC; TBS Superstation; The Inspirational Network; The Weather Channel; Turner Network TV; USA Network.
Fee: $31.34 monthly; $2.15 converter.
Pay Service 1
Pay Units: 51.
Programming (via satellite): Cinemax.
Fee: $10.95 monthly.
Pay Service 2
Pay Units: 55.
Programming (via satellite): Disney Channel.
Fee: $7.95 monthly.
Pay Service 3
Pay Units: 108.
Programming (via satellite): HBO.
Fee: $10.95 monthly.
Pay Service 4
Pay Units: 83.
Programming (via satellite): Showtime; The Movie Channel.
Fee: $12.95 monthly.
Miles of plant: 53.0 (coaxial). Homes passed: 1,116.
Manager: Mike Burns. Chief technician: Mayla Zubeck. Marketing director: Ella Wilmore.
Ownership: Star Cable Associates (MSO).

ALICE—Valley Cable TV Inc., 2921 S. Expressway 83, Harlingen, TX 78550-7615. Phone: 956-541-6782. Fax: 956-412-0959. Counties: Duval & Jim Wells. Also serves San Diego. ICA: TX0102.
TV Market Ranking: Outside TV Markets. Franchise award date: N.A. Franchise expiration date: N.A. Began: March 1, 1971.
Channel capacity: 39. Channels available but not in use: N.A.
Basic Service
Subscribers: 5,512.
Programming (received off-air): KEDT (P), KIII (A), KORO (S), KRIS-TV (N), KZTV (C) Corpus Christi.
Programming (via satellite): WGN-TV (W) Chicago; A & E; C-SPAN; CNN; Fox Family Channel; Headline News; Lifetime; MTV; Nashville Network; Nick at Nite; Nickelodeon; QVC; TBS Superstation; Telemundo; The Weather Channel; Trinity Bcstg. Network; Univision.
Current originations: Educational access.
Fee: $60.00 installation; $8.34 monthly.
Expanded Basic Service
Subscribers: 5,141.
Programming (via satellite): CNBC; Discovery Channel; ESPN; Fox Sports Net Southwest; GalaVision; Turner Network TV; USA Network.
Fee: $12.07 monthly.
Pay Service 1
Pay Units: 1,193.
Programming (via satellite): Cinemax.
Fee: $10.95 monthly.
Pay Service 2
Pay Units: 512.
Programming (via satellite): Disney Channel.
Fee: $10.95 monthly.
Pay Service 3
Pay Units: 1,892.
Programming (via satellite): HBO.
Fee: $10.95 monthly.
Local advertising: Yes. Regional interconnect: Cabletime.
Miles of plant: 130.0 (coaxial). Homes passed: 6,563. Total homes in franchised area: 6,563.
Manager: Juan Herrera. Chief technician: Al Velasquez.
Ownership: AT&T Broadband & Internet Services (MSO). Purchased from Tele-Communications Inc., March 9, 1999.

ALLEN—TCI Cablevision of Texas Inc., Box 64, Allen, TX 75002-3425. Phone: 214-727-5723. County: Collin. ICA: TX0100.
TV Market Ranking: 12. Franchise award date: N.A. Franchise expiration date: N.A. Began: December 1, 1980.
Channel capacity: 36. Channels available but not in use: None.
Basic Service
Subscribers: 5,867.
Programming (received off-air): KDAF (W), KDFI-TV (I), KDFW (F), KERA-TV (P), KTVT (C), KTXA (U), KXAS-TV (N), KXTX-TV (I), WFAA-TV (A) Dallas-Fort Worth.
Programming (via satellite): WGN-TV (W) Chicago; CNBC; CNN; Discovery Channel; Fox Family Channel; Headline News; Lifetime; MTV; Nashville Network; Nickelodeon; QVC; TBS Superstation; The Weather Channel.
Current originations: Public access; educational access; government access.
Fee: $60.00 installation; $17.95 monthly.
Expanded Basic Service
Subscribers: 3,970.
Programming (via satellite): American Movie Classics; ESPN; Fox Sports Net Southwest; Turner Network TV; USA Network.
Fee: $2.91 monthly.
Pay Service 1
Pay Units: 151.
Programming (via satellite): Cinemax.
Fee: $11.25 monthly.
Pay Service 2
Pay Units: 380.
Programming (via satellite): Disney Channel.
Fee: $11.25 monthly.
Pay Service 3
Pay Units: 1,495.
Programming (via satellite): The New Encore.
Fee: N.A.
Pay Service 4
Pay Units: 1,519.
Programming (via satellite): HBO.
Fee: $11.25 monthly.
Pay Service 5
Pay Units: 838.
Programming (via satellite): Showtime.
Fee: $11.25 monthly.
Pay Service 6
Pay Units: 78.
Programming (via satellite): The Movie Channel.
Fee: $11.25 monthly.
Miles of plant: 90.7 (coaxial). Homes passed: 6,671. Total homes in franchised area: 8,700.
Manager: Joann Holtzclaw. Chief technician: Mike Crain.
Ownership: AT&T Broadband & Internet Services (MSO). Purchased from Tele-Communications Inc., March 9, 1999.

ALLENDALE—Friendship Cable of Texas Inc., Box 9090, Tyler, TX 75711-9090. Phone: 903-581-2121. Fax: 903-581-2185. County: Montgomery. ICA: TX0707.
TV Market Ranking: 15. Franchise award date: N.A. Franchise expiration date: N.A. Began: N.A.
Channel capacity: 36 (not 2-way capable). Channels available but not in use: 9.
Basic Service
Subscribers: 144.
Programming (received off-air): KETH (E), KHOU-TV (C), KRIV (F), KTRK-TV (A), KTXH (U) Houston.
Programming (via satellite): KCNC-TV (C) Denver; Disney Channel; TBS Superstation; Turner Classic Movies.
Fee: $34.54 monthly.
Pay Service 1
Pay Units: 90.
Programming (via satellite): Showtime.
Fee: $5.95 monthly.
Miles of plant: 15.7 (coaxial). Homes passed: 328.
Manager: Wanda Pyburn. Chief technician: David Burrell.
Ownership: Buford Television Inc. (MSO). See Cable System Ownership.

ALPINE—Sul Ross State U., Box C-107, Alpine, TX 79832. Phone: 915-837-8011. County: Brewster. ICA: TX0708.
TV Market Ranking: Outside TV Markets. Franchise award date: N.A. Franchise expiration date: N.A. Began: N.A.
Channel capacity: N.A. Channels available but not in use: N.A.
Basic Service
Subscribers: 343.
Programming (via satellite): KCNC-TV (C), KMGH-TV (A), KRMA-TV (P), KUSA-TV (N) Denver; TBS Superstation.
Fee: N.A.
Miles of plant: 4.0 (coaxial). Homes passed: 375. Total homes in franchised area: 375.
Ownership: Sul Ross State University.

ALTO—Friendship Cable of Texas Inc., Box 9090, Tyler, TX 75711-9090. Phone: 903-581-2121. Fax: 903-581-2185. County: Cherokee. ICA: TX0435.
TV Market Ranking: Below 100. Franchise award date: N.A. Franchise expiration date: N.A. Began: June 1, 1983.
Channel capacity: 54. Channels available but not in use: N.A.
Basic Service
Subscribers: 333.
Programming (received off-air): KETK-TV (N) Jacksonville; KTRE (A) Lufkin; KSLA-TV (C), KTAL-TV (N) Shreveport-Texarkana; KLTV (A) Tyler-Longview.
Programming (via satellite): WGN-TV (W) Chicago; TBS Superstation.
Fee: $30.00 installation; $30.50 monthly.
Pay Service 1
Pay Units: 10.
Programming (via satellite): Cinemax.
Fee: $7.00 monthly.
Pay Service 2
Pay Units: 24.
Programming (via satellite): HBO.
Fee: $12.00 monthly.
Pay Service 3
Pay Units: 51.
Programming (via satellite): Showtime.
Fee: $7.00 monthly.
Miles of plant: 14.0 (coaxial). Homes passed: 514.
Manager: Marianne Bogy. Chief technician: Henry Harris.
City fee: 3% of gross.
Ownership: Buford Television Inc. (MSO). See Cable System Ownership.

ALTON—Time Warner Communications, 2921 S. Expressway 83, Harlingen, TX 78550-7615. Phone: 956-541-6782. Fax: 956-412-0959. County: Hidalgo. Also serves Mission, Palmhurst, Palmview. ICA: TX0066.

TV Market Ranking: Below 100. Franchise award date: N.A. Franchise expiration date: N.A. Began: N.A.

Channel capacity: 39. Channels available but not in use: N.A.

Basic Service

Subscribers: 5,375.

Programming (received off-air): KVEO (N) Brownsville; KGBT-TV (C), KLUJ (E), KMBH (P) Harlingen; KRGV-TV (A) Weslaco; XHAB-TV Matamoros.

Programming (via satellite): WGN-TV (W) Chicago; A & E; C-SPAN; CNN; Fox Family Channel; Headline News; Lifetime; MTV; Nashville Network; Nick at Nite; Nickelodeon; QVC; TBS Superstation; Telemundo; The Weather Channel.

Current originations: Educational access.

Fee: $60.00 installation; $10.58 monthly.

Expanded Basic Service

Subscribers: N.A.

Programming (via satellite): CNBC; Discovery Channel; ESPN; Fox Sports Net Southwest; Turner Network TV; USA Network; Univision.

Fee: $12.31 monthly.

Pay Service 1

Pay Units: 855.

Programming (via satellite): Cinemax.

Fee: $10.95 monthly.

Pay Service 2

Pay Units: 464.

Programming (via satellite): Disney Channel.

Fee: $10.95 monthly.

Pay Service 3

Pay Units: 1,402.

Programming (via satellite): HBO.

Fee: $10.95 monthly.

Pay Service 4

Pay Units: N.A.

Programming (via satellite): The New Encore.

Fee: N.A.

Miles of plant: 162.8 (coaxial). Homes passed: 10,490. Total homes in franchised area: 10,490.

Manager: Juan Herrera. Chief technician: Al Velasquez.

Ownership: Time Warner Cable (MSO); AT&T Broadband & Internet Services (MSO).

ALUM CREEK—Pine Forest Cablevision, Box 1039, Bastrop, TX 78602. Phone: 512-237-3595. Fax: 512-237-4299. County: Bastrop. ICA: TX0615.

TV Market Ranking: Outside TV Markets. Franchise award date: N.A. Franchise expiration date: N.A. Began: May 1, 1992.

Channel capacity: 54 (not 2-way capable). Channels available but not in use: 18.

Basic Service

Subscribers: 273; Commercial subscribers: 1.

Programming (received off-air): KEYE-TV (C), KLRU (P), KNVA (W), KTBC (F), KVUE-TV (A), KXAN-TV (N) Austin.

Programming (via satellite): A & E; American Movie Classics; CNN; Comedy Central; Country Music TV; Discovery Channel; E! Entertainment TV; ESPN; FX; Fox News Channel; History Channel; Learning Channel; Lifetime; MTV; Nashville Network; Nick at Nite; Nick at Nite's TV Land; QVC; Sci-Fi Channel; TBS Superstation; Travel Channel; Trinity Bcstg. Network; Turner Network TV; USA Network.

Fee: $35.00 installation; $19.95 monthly.

Commercial fee: $50.00 monthly.

Pay Service 1

Pay Units: N.A.

Programming (via satellite): Cinemax; HBO.

Fee: $7.95 monthly (Cinemax), $10.95 monthly (HBO).

Equipment: Magnavox & Scientific-Atlanta amplifiers; Times Fiber cable; Drake & Scientific-Atlanta satellite receivers.

Miles of plant: 32.0 (coaxial); 14.0 (fiber optic). Additional miles planned: 12.0 (coaxial). Homes passed: 200. Total homes in franchised area: 650.

Manager: Jeff Sullivan. Customer service manager: Marie Sullivan.

Ownership: Sullivan Communications (MSO).

ALVARADO—Charter Communications Inc., 5227 FM 813, Waxahachie, TX 75165. Phones: 972-938-9288; 800-477-0887. Fax: 972-923-0039. Counties: Ellis, Hill & Johnson. Also serves Grandview, Itasca, Keene, Maypearl, Venus. ICA: TX0270.

TV Market Ranking: 12 (Alvarado, Grandview, Keene, Maypearl, Venus); Outside TV Markets (Itasca). Franchise award date: N.A. Franchise expiration date: N.A. Began: March 1, 1982.

Channel capacity: 52. Channels available but not in use: N.A.

Basic Service

Subscribers: 1,316.

Programming (received off-air): KPXD (X) Arlington; KDAF (W), KDFI-TV (I), KDFW (F), KDTX-TV (T), KERA-TV (P), KFWD (O), KTVT (C), KTXA (U), KXAS-TV (N), KXTX-TV (I), WFAA-TV (A) Dallas-Fort Worth; KMPX (I) Decatur; KDTN (P) Denton; KUVN (S) Garland; KHSX-TV (H) Irving.

Programming (via satellite): WGN-TV (W) Chicago; C-SPAN; Cartoon Network; Learning Channel; TBS Superstation; TV Guide Channel; Univision.

Current originations: Public access; educational access.

Fee: $42.00 installation; $13.00 monthly.

Expanded Basic Service

Subscribers: N.A.

Programming (via satellite): A & E; American Movie Classics; BET; Bravo; CNN; Country Music TV; Discovery Channel; Disney Channel; E! Entertainment TV; ESPN; Fox Family Channel; Fox Sports Net Southwest; Headline News; Lifetime; MTV; Nashville Network; Nick at Nite's TV Land; Nickelodeon; QVC; Sci-Fi Channel; The Weather Channel; Turner Network TV; USA Network; Univision.

Fee: $15.89 monthly.

Pay Service 1

Pay Units: N.A.

Programming (via satellite): Cinemax; HBO; Showtime; The Movie Channel.

Fee: $10.95 monthly (Cinemax, Showtime or TMC), $12.95 monthly (HBO).

Pay-Per-View

Viewer's Choice.

Miles of plant: 36.0 (coaxial). Homes passed: 1,530.

Manager: Mary Scearce. Chief technician: Ken Stevens.

Ownership: Charter Communications Inc. (MSO). Purchased from Marcus Cable, April 1, 1999.

AMARILLO—TCA Cable TV of Amarillo, 5800 W. 45th Dr., Amarillo, TX 79109. Phone: 806-358-4801. Fax: 806-354-7419. Web site: http://www.tca-cable.com. County: Potter. Also serves Rolling Hills. ICA: TX0014.

TV Market Ranking: 95. Franchise award date: July 1, 1980. Franchise expiration date: July 1, 2000. Began: January 1, 1970.

Channel capacity: 78 (2-way capable; operating 2-way). Channels available but not in use: 3.

Basic Service

Subscribers: 46,778.

Programming (received off-air): KACV-TV (P), KAMR-TV (N), KCIT (F,U), KFDA-TV (C), KVII-TV (A) Amarillo; 10 FMs.

Programming (via satellite): WGN-TV (W) Chicago; Country Music TV; EWTN; Home Shopping Network; Learning Channel; QVC; TBS Superstation; The Weather Channel; Univision.

Current originations: Automated time-weather; educational access; automated emergency alert.

Fee: $35.00 installation; $9.22 monthly.

Expanded Basic Service

Subscribers: 30,541.

Programming (via satellite): A & E; C-SPAN; C-SPAN 2; CNN; Discovery Channel; ESPN; Fox Family Channel; Nashville Network; Nickelodeon; Trinity Bcstg. Network.

Fee: $7.51 monthly.

Expanded Basic Service 2

Subscribers: N.A.

Programming (via satellite): American Movie Classics; BET; CNBC; Fox Sports Net; Headline News; Lifetime; MTV; Odyssey; Sci-Fi Channel; TV Guide Channel; TV Guide Sneak Prevue; Turner Network TV; USA Network; VH1.

Fee: $7.51 monthly.

Expanded Basic Service 3

Subscribers: 500.

Programming (via satellite): Cartoon Network; Comedy Central; Court TV; ESPN 2; History Channel; Home & Garden Television; Outdoor Channel; The New Encore; Turner Classic Movies.

Fee: $5.34 monthly.

Pay Service 1

Pay Units: 5,645.

Programming (via satellite): Cinemax (multiplexed).

Fee: N.A.

Pay Service 2

Pay Units: 309.

Programming (via satellite): DMX.

Fee: N.A.

Pay Service 3

Pay Units: 7,596.

Programming (via satellite): The New Encore.

Fee: N.A.

Pay Service 4

Pay Units: 6,609.

Programming (via satellite): HBO (multiplexed).

Fee: N.A.

Pay Service 5

Pay Units: 5,277.

Programming (via satellite): The Movie Channel.

Fee: N.A.

Pay Service 6

Pay Units: 5,307.

Programming (via satellite): Showtime (multiplexed).

Fee: N.A.

Pay Service 7

Pay Units: 7,596.

Programming (via satellite): Starz!

Fee: N.A.

Pay-Per-View

Addressable homes: 33,644.

Viewer's Choice; movies.

Local advertising: Yes. Available in satellite distributed & character-generated programming. Rates: $16.00/30 Seconds. Local sales manager: Cindy Carver. Regional interconnect: Cabletime.

Program Guide: CableView.

Equipment: RCA & Scientific-Atlanta headend; C-COR amplifiers; Comm/Scope cable; Sony cameras; Sony VTRs; Texscan character generator; Jerrold set top converters; Jerrold addressable set top converters; Scientific-Atlanta satellite antenna; Scientific-Atlanta satellite receivers.

Miles of plant: 750.0 (coaxial); 100.0 (fiber optic). Additional miles planned: 15.0 (coaxial). Homes passed: 70,000. Total homes in franchised area: 70,000.

Manager: Larson Lloyd. Chief technician: Charlie Johnson. Marketing director: Alisa Mathies.

City fee: 5% of gross.

Ownership: TCA Cable TV Inc. (MSO); AT&T Broadband & Internet Services (MSO). See Cable System Ownership.

ANAHUAC—Friendship Cable of Texas Inc., Box 9090, Tyler, TX 75711-9090. Phone: 903-581-2121. Fax: 903-581-2185. County: Chambers. Also serves Hankamer. ICA: TX0376.

TV Market Ranking: 88 (Hankamer); Below 100 (Anahuac). Franchise award date: May 16, 1983. Franchise expiration date: May 16, 1998. Began: June 1, 1984.

Channel capacity: 36 (not 2-way capable). Channels available but not in use: None.

Basic Service

Subscribers: 531.

Programming (received off-air): KHSH-TV (H) Alvin; KHOU-TV (C), KHTV (W), KPRC-TV (N), KRIV (F), KTRK-TV (A), KUHT (P) Houston.

Programming (via satellite): WGN-TV (W) Chicago; BET; CNN; Disney Channel; ESPN; Fox Family Channel; Home Shopping Network; MTV; Nashville Network; Nickelodeon; TBS Superstation; The Weather Channel; USA Network.

Current originations: Automated time-weather.

Fee: $30.00 installation; $33.79 monthly.

Pay Service 1

Pay Units: 48.

Programming (via satellite): HBO.

Fee: $10.50 monthly.

Pay Service 2

Pay Units: 75.

Programming (via satellite): Showtime.

Fee: $10.50 monthly.

Pay Service 3

Pay Units: 5.

Programming (via satellite): The Movie Channel.

Fee: $10.50 monthly.

Local advertising: No.

Equipment: Scientific-Atlanta headend; Scientific-Atlanta amplifiers; Scientific-Atlanta cable; Scientific-Atlanta set top converters; Scientific-Atlanta satellite antenna; Scientific-Atlanta satellite receivers.

Miles of plant: 44.5 (coaxial). Homes passed: 1,320.

Manager: Wanda Pyburn. Chief technician: Mike Deal.

City fee: 3% of gross.

Ownership: Buford Television Inc. (MSO). See Cable System Ownership.

ANDERSON—National Cable Inc., Suite 106-A, 5151 Reed Rd., Columbus, OH 43220. Phones: 614-442-5890; 800-582-0504. Fax: 614-457-2567. County: Grimes. ICA: TX0666.

TV Market Ranking: Below 100. Franchise award date: N.A. Franchise expiration date: N.A. Began: N.A.

Channel capacity: 36. Channels available but not in use: 13.

Basic Service

Subscribers: 23.

Programming (received off-air): KBTX-TV (C) Bryan; KHTV (W), KPRC-TV (N), KTRK-TV (A), KUHT (P) Houston.

Programming (via satellite): WGN-TV (W) Chicago; A & E; American Movie Classics; CNN; Country Music TV; Discovery Channel; ESPN; Fox Family Channel; Nashville Network; Showtime; TBS Superstation; Turner Network TV; USA Network.

Fee: $28.00 monthly.

Miles of plant: 3.2 (coaxial). Homes passed: 147.

Manager: Paul Scott. Chief technician: Rob Spiller. Marketing director: Josh Thackery.

Ownership: National Cable (MSO).

ANDREWS—TCA Cable TV of Andrews, 412 W. Broadway, Andrews, TX 79714. Phones: 915-523-9174; 800-235-4233. Fax: 915-523-3325. Web site: http://www.tca-cable.com. County: Andrews. Also serves Andrews County. ICA: TX0141.

TV Market Ranking: Below 100. Franchise award date: N.A. Franchise expiration date: November 1, 1998. Began: March 1, 1972.

Channel capacity: 42 (2-way capable; operating 2-way partially). Channels available but not in use: None.

Basic Service

Subscribers: 172; Commercial subscribers: 187.

Programming (received off-air): KMID (A), KOCV-TV (P), KOSA-TV (C), KPEJ (F), KWES-TV (N) Odessa-Midland.

Programming (via satellite): WGN-TV (W) Chicago; TBS Superstation.

Fee: $38.00 installation; $6.22 monthly; $3.85 converter.

Expanded Basic Service

Subscribers: N.A.

Programming (via satellite): A & E; American Movie Classics; C-SPAN; CNBC; CNN; Country Music TV; Discovery Channel; Disney Channel; ESPN; ESPN 2; FX; Fox Family Channel; Fox Sports Net Southwest; Headline News; Learning Channel; Lifetime; MTV; Nashville Network; Nickelodeon; QVC; TV Guide Channel; The Inspirational Network; The Weather Channel; Trinity Bcstg. Network; Turner Network TV; USA Network; Univision; VH1.

Fee: $38.00 installation; $24.93 monthly.

Pay Service 1

Pay Units: 285.

Programming (via satellite): Cinemax.

Fee: $9.95 monthly.

Pay Service 2

Pay Units: 344.

Programming (via satellite): HBO.

Fee: $13.00 monthly.

Pay Service 3

Pay Units: 176.

Programming (via satellite): The Movie Channel.

Fee: $9.95 monthly.

Pay Service 4

Pay Units: 235.

Programming (via satellite): Showtime.

Fee: $9.95 monthly.

Pay-Per-View

Addressable homes: 975.

Viewer's Choice.

Fee: Varies.

Pay-per-view manager: Julie Harding.

Local advertising: Yes. Available in satellite distributed & character-generated programming. Rates: $40.00/Minute; $20.00/30 Seconds. Local sales manager: Jay Speegle.

Equipment: Scientific-Atlanta headend; Magnavox amplifiers; Comm/Scope & Times Fiber cable; Texscan character generator; Scientific-Atlanta set top converters; Tocom addressable set top converters; Eagle traps; Scientific-Atlanta satellite antenna; Scientific-Atlanta satellite receivers.

Miles of plant: 95.2 (coaxial); None (fiber optic). Homes passed: 3,974.

Manager: Archie Kountz. Chief technician: Harold Vilas. Marketing director: Diane Bower.

City fee: 3% of gross.

Ownership: TCA Cable TV Inc. (MSO); AT&T Broadband & Internet Services (MSO). See Cable System Ownership.

ANGLETON—CMA Cablevision, 139 E. Myrtle, Angleton, TX 77515. Phone: 409-849-5728. Fax: 409-849-2955. County: Brazoria. Also serves Bailey's Prairie, Danbury. ICA: TX0091.

TV Market Ranking: 15 (Danbury); Below 100 (Angleton, Bailey's Prairie). Franchise award date: December 1, 1979. Franchise expiration date: N.A. Began: April 18, 1979.

Channel capacity: 36 (2-way capable; operating 2-way). Channels available but not in use: None.

Basic Service

Subscribers: 3,824; Commercial subscribers: 6.

Programming (received off-air): KHOU-TV (C), KHTV (W), KPRC-TV (N), KRIV (F), KTRK-TV (A), KTXH (U), KUHT (P) Houston; KXLN-TV (S) Rosenberg.

Programming (via satellite): WGN-TV (W) Chicago; TBS Superstation.

Fee: $49.95 installation; $14.95 monthly.

Expanded Basic Service

Subscribers: 3,811.

Programming (via satellite): American Movie Classics; BET; C-SPAN; CNN; Country Music TV; Discovery Channel; ESPN; Fox Family Channel; Headline News; Lifetime; MTV; Nashville Network; Nickelodeon; The Weather Channel; Turner Network TV; USA Network.

Fee: $49.95 installation; $12.70 monthly.

Pay Service 1

Pay Units: 216.

Programming (via satellite): Cinemax.

Fee: $11.00 monthly.

Pay Service 2

Pay Units: 219.

Programming (via satellite): Disney Channel.

Fee: $7.95 monthly.

Pay Service 3

Pay Units: 1,074.

Programming (via satellite): HBO.

Fee: $11.00 monthly.

Pay Service 4

Pay Units: 88.

Programming (via satellite): The Movie Channel.

Fee: $11.00 monthly.

Pay Service 5

Pay Units: 390.

Programming (via satellite): Showtime.

Fee: N.A.

Pay-Per-View

Addressable homes: 1,238.

Local advertising: Yes. Available in taped & automated programming. Regional interconnect: Cabletime.

Program Guide: TV Blue Print.

Equipment: Scientific-Atlanta headend; C-COR & Scientific-Atlanta amplifiers; Comm/Scope cable; Sony cameras; Video Data Systems character generator; Scientific-Atlanta set top converters; Scientific-Atlanta addressable set top converters; Scientific-Atlanta satellite antenna; Scientific-Atlanta satellite receivers.

Miles of plant: 165.0 (coaxial). Additional miles planned: 9.0 (coaxial). Homes passed: 8,071. Total homes in franchised area: 8,071.

Manager: Glenn Parker. Chief technician: Will Murphey. Marketing director: Todd Felker.

City fee: 3% of gross.

Ownership: Cable Management Assoc. (MSO). Purchased from Charter Communications Inc., April 1, 1999.

ANNA—Friendship Cable of Texas Inc., Box 9090, Tyler, TX 75711-9090. Phone: 903-581-2121. Fax: 903-581-2185. County: Collin. Also serves Melissa. ICA: TX0709.

TV Market Ranking: 12. Franchise award date: N.A. Franchise expiration date: N.A. Began: N.A.

Channel capacity: 54. Channels available but not in use: N.A.

Basic Service

Subscribers: 440.

Programming (received off-air): KPXD (X) Arlington; KDFW (F), KERA-TV (P), KTVT (C), KXAS-TV (N), KXTX-TV (I), WFAA-TV (A) Dallas-Fort Worth.

Programming (via satellite): WGN-TV (W) Chicago; Disney Channel; TBS Superstation.

Fee: $30.00 installation; $32.60 monthly.

Pay Service 1

Pay Units: 38.

Programming (via satellite): HBO.

Fee: $12.00 monthly.

Pay Service 2

Pay Units: 26.

Programming (via satellite): The Movie Channel.

Fee: $9.00 monthly.

Pay Service 3

Pay Units: 88.

Programming (via satellite): Showtime.

Fee: $7.00 monthly.

Miles of plant: 30.7 (coaxial). Homes passed: 569.

Manager: Rodney Fletcher. Chief technician: Bo Jaubert.

Ownership: Buford Television Inc. (MSO). See Cable System Ownership.

ANSON—Friendship Cable of Texas Inc., Box 9090, Tyler, TX 75711-9090. Phone: 915-581-2121. Fax: 915-581-2185. County: Jones. Also serves Jones County (portions). ICA: TX0323.

TV Market Ranking: Below 100. Franchise award date: July 1, 1962. Franchise expiration date: July 1, 2007. Began: August 1, 1968.

Channel capacity: 33. Channels available but not in use: N.A.

Basic Service

Subscribers: 745.

Programming (received off-air): KRBC-TV (N), KTAB-TV (C), KTXS-TV (A) Abilene-Sweetwater; 4 FMs.

Programming (via satellite): BET; C-SPAN; Lifetime; QVC; TBS Superstation; The Weather Channel; Univision.

Current originations: Automated time-weather; religious access; automated emergency alert.

Fee: $30.00 installation; $13.42 monthly.

Expanded Basic Service

Subscribers: 640.

Programming (via satellite): A & E; American Movie Classics; Animal Planet; CNN; Cartoon Network; Country Music TV; Discovery Channel; ESPN; FX; Fox Family Channel; Fox News Channel; Fox Sports Net Southwest; Home & Garden Television; Learning Channel; MTV; Nashville Network; Nickelodeon; Turner Network TV; USA Network.

Fee: $30.00 installation; $14.96 monthly.

Pay Service 1

Pay Units: 72.

Programming (via satellite): Cinemax.

Fee: $12.50 monthly.

Pay Service 2

Pay Units: 39.

Programming (via satellite): Disney Channel.

Fee: $12.50 monthly.

Pay Service 3

Pay Units: 170.

Programming (via satellite): The New Encore.

Fee: $1.71 monthly.

Pay Service 4

Pay Units: 84.

Programming (via satellite): HBO.

Fee: $13.00 monthly.

Pay Service 5

Pay Units: 111.

Programming (via satellite): Starz!

Fee: $6.75 monthly.

Equipment: Jerrold & RCA headend; Jerrold amplifiers; Comm/Scope & Times Fiber cable; Compuvid character generator; Jerrold set top converters; Arcom & Eagle traps; Anixter-Mark & Scientific-Atlanta satellite antenna; Scientific-Atlanta satellite receivers.

Miles of plant: 25.0 (coaxial). Homes passed: 1,205.

Manager: Larry Bryant. Chief technician: Joe Stewart.

City fee: 2% of gross.

Ownership: Buford Television Inc. (MSO). See Cable System Ownership.

ANTON—Classic Cable, Box 429, 605 N.W. 3rd St., Plainville, KS 67663-0429. Phones: 785-434-7620; 800-999-8876. Fax: 785-434-2614. County: Hockley. ICA: TX0506.

TV Market Ranking: Below 100. Franchise award date: July 21, 1982. Franchise expiration date: July 2, 1997. Began: October 15, 1982.

Channel capacity: 41 (2-way capable). Channels available but not in use: N.A.

Basic Service

Subscribers: 147.

Programming (received off-air): KAMC (A), KCBD-TV (N), KJTV (F), KLBK-TV (C), KPTB (I), KTXT-TV (P) Lubbock.

Programming (via translator): KVDA (O) San Antonio.

Programming (via satellite): WGN-TV (W) Chicago; KTVD (U) Denver; American Movie Classics; CNN; Cartoon Network; Country Music TV; Discovery Channel; Disney Channel; ESPN; Fox Family Channel; Headline News; History Channel; Home Shopping Network; Learning Channel; Nashville Network; Nickelodeon; Sci-Fi Channel; TBS Superstation; The Weather Channel; Trinity Bcstg. Network; Turner Network TV; USA Network; Univision.

Current originations: Automated time-weather; public access; local news.

Fee: $35.00 installation; $28.95 monthly.

Pay Service 1

Pay Units: N.A.

Programming (via satellite): Cinemax.

Fee: $9.95 monthly.

Pay Service 2

Pay Units: 28.

Programming (via satellite): HBO.

Fee: $9.95 monthly.

Local advertising: No.

Miles of plant: 8.1 (coaxial). Homes passed: 454.

Manager: Bill Flowers. Chief technician: Chris Christenson. Marketing director: Jennifer Hauschild.
City fee: 3% of gross.
Ownership: Classic Cable (MSO).

APPLEHEAD—Horseshoe Bay-Applehead Cablevision, Box 8859, Horseshoe Bay, TX 78654. Phone: 830-598-6525. County: Llano. ICA: TX0704.
TV Market Ranking: Below 100. Franchise award date: N.A. Franchise expiration date: N.A. Began: July 1, 1990.
Channel capacity: 15. Channels available but not in use: 5.
Basic Service
Subscribers: N.A.
Programming (received off-air): KEYE-TV (C), KLRU (P), KTBC (F), KVUE-TV (A), KXAN-TV (N) Austin.
Programming (via satellite): ESPN; Headline News; TBS Superstation; USA Network.
Fee: Free installation; $30.00 monthly.
Miles of plant: 3.0 (coaxial). Homes passed: 11.
Ownership: Horseshoe Bay-Applehead Cablevision.

AQUA VISTA—Classic Cable, Box 429, 605 N.W. 3rd St., Plainville, KS 67663-0429. Phones: 785-434-7620; 800-999-8876. Fax: 785-434-2614. County: Kerr. ICA: TX0912.
TV Market Ranking: Below 100. Franchise award date: N.A. Franchise expiration date: N.A. Began: N.A.
Channel capacity: 22 (2-way capable). Channels available but not in use: N.A.
Basic Service
Subscribers: 99.
Programming (received off-air): KRRT (W) Kerrville-San Antonio; KABB (F), KENS-TV (C), KMOL-TV (N), KSAT-TV (A) San Antonio.
Programming (via satellite): KRMA-TV (P) Denver; A & E; C-SPAN; CNN; Discovery Channel; Disney Channel; ESPN; Fox Family Channel; Fox Sports Net Southwest; History Channel; Learning Channel; Nashville Network; TBS Superstation; The Weather Channel; Trinity Bcstg. Network; Turner Network TV; USA Network.
Fee: $35.00 installation; $27.95 monthly.
Pay Service 1
Pay Units: 16.
Programming (via satellite): HBO.
Fee: $10.95 monthly.
Pay Service 2
Pay Units: 7.
Programming (via satellite): Showtime.
Fee: $9.95 monthly.
Miles of plant: 6.0 (coaxial). Homes passed: 120.
Manager: Bill Flowers. Chief technician: Walt VanLue. Marketing director: Jennifer Hauschild.
Ownership: Classic Cable (MSO).

ARANSAS PASS—Cable One, 316 S. Commercial, Aransas Pass, TX 78336. Phone: 512-758-7621. Fax: 512-758-7096. Counties: Aransas, Nueces & San Patricio. Also serves City by the Sea, Gregory, Ingleside, Ingleside on the Bay, Palm Harbor, Taft. ICA: TX0097.
TV Market Ranking: Below 100. Franchise award date: April 27, 1979. Franchise expiration date: April 1, 2009. Began: June 1, 1981.
Channel capacity: 38 (not 2-way capable). Channels available but not in use: N.A.
Basic Service
Subscribers: 5,302; Commercial subscribers: 31.
Programming (received off-air): KEDT (P), KIII (A), KORO (S), KRIS-TV (N), KZTV (C) Corpus Christi.
Programming (via satellite): C-SPAN 2; Country Music TV; Home Shopping Network; TBS Superstation; Telemundo; Univision.
Current originations: Automated time-weather; public access; educational access; government access; leased access; automated emergency alert.
Fee: $16.04 installation; $6.09 monthly; $1.68 converter; $12.50 additional installation.
Commercial fee: $6.00 monthly.
Expanded Basic Service
Subscribers: 4,808.
Programming (via satellite): A & E; American Movie Classics; C-SPAN; CNN; Discovery Channel; ESPN; Fox Family Channel; Fox Sports Net Southwest; Headline News; Learning Channel; Lifetime; MTV; Nashville Network; Nick at Nite; Nickelodeon; Sci-Fi Channel; The Inspirational Network; The Weather Channel; Turner Network TV; USA Network.
Fee: $16.62 monthly.
Pay Service 1
Pay Units: 500.
Programming (via satellite): Cinemax.
Fee: $20.00 installation; $10.50 monthly.
Pay Service 2
Pay Units: 235.
Programming (via satellite): Disney Channel.
Fee: $20.00 installation; $8.95 monthly.
Pay Service 3
Pay Units: 1,304.
Programming (via satellite): HBO.
Fee: $20.00 installation; $11.00 monthly.
Pay Service 4
Pay Units: 214.
Programming (via satellite): The Movie Channel.
Fee: $20.00 installation; $10.50 monthly.
Pay Service 5
Pay Units: 222.
Programming (via satellite): Showtime.
Fee: $20.00 installation; $10.50 monthly.
Pay-Per-View
Addressable homes: 741.
Hot Choice; Viewer's Choice; special events.
Fee: Varies.
Local advertising: Yes. Available in satellite distributed programming. Rates: $12.00/30 Seconds. Local sales manager: Michel Crow.
Program Guide: TV Blue Print.
Equipment: RCA & Scientific-Atlanta headend; Century III & Scientific-Atlanta amplifiers; Comm/Scope cable; Sony VTRs; MSI & Nexus character generator; Hamlin, Jerrold & Pioneer set top converters; Jerrold addressable set top converters; Eagle & Vitek traps; Hughes, Scientific-Atlanta & Prodelin satellite antenna; Hughes, M/A-Com & Scientific-Atlanta satellite receivers; M/A-Com commercial insert.
Miles of plant: 160.0 (coaxial); 160.0 (fiber optic). Additional miles planned: 10.0 (coaxial). Homes passed: 7,450. Total homes in franchised area: 7,900.
Manager: David King. Chief technician: Martin Schooley.
City fee: 5% of gross.
Ownership: Cable One Inc. (MSO).

ARCHER CITY—Vista Cablevision, 3225 Maurine St., Wichita Falls, TX 76305. Phones: 940-855-5700; 940-855-9020. Fax: 940-855-0465. County: Archer. ICA: TX0710.
TV Market Ranking: Below 100. Franchise award date: January 1, 1980. Franchise expiration date: N.A. Began: January 1, 1980.
Channel capacity: 36. Channels available but not in use: N.A.
Basic Service
Subscribers: 479.
Programming (received off-air): KERA-TV (P) Dallas-Fort Worth; KAUZ-TV (C), KFDX-TV (N), KJTL (F,U), KSWO-TV (A) Wichita Falls-Lawton.
Programming (via satellite): C-SPAN; QVC; Trinity Bcstg. Network.
Current originations: Religious access; local sports.
Fee: $50.00 installation; $9.95 monthly.
Expanded Basic Service
Subscribers: N.A.
Programming (via satellite): WGN-TV (W) Chicago; A & E; American Movie Classics; CNN; Discovery Channel; ESPN; Fox Family Channel; Goodlife TV Network; Headline News; Lifetime; Nashville Network; Nickelodeon; TBS Superstation; The Weather Channel; Turner Network TV; USA Network.
Fee: N.A.
Pay Service 1
Pay Units: N.A.
Programming (via satellite): Cinemax; Disney Channel; HBO; Showtime.
Fee: $12.55 monthly (each).
Manager: Rick Orr. Chief technician: Milt Slavin.
City fee: 3% of gross.
Ownership: Time Warner Cable (MSO).

ARCOLA—Star Cable, Drawer 1570, Brazoria, TX 77422. Phones: 409-798-9121; 800-395-2775. Fax: 409-798-4409. Counties: Brazoria & Fort Bend. Also serves Iowa Colony. ICA: TX0243.
TV Market Ranking: 15. Franchise award date: N.A. Franchise expiration date: N.A. Began: N.A.
Channel capacity: 36 (not 2-way capable). Channels available but not in use: None.
Basic Service
Subscribers: 274.
Programming (received off-air): KHSH-TV (H) Alvin; KLTJ (E) Galveston; KETH (E), KHOU-TV (C), KHTV (W), KPRC-TV (N), KRIV (F), KTRK-TV (A), KTXH (U), KUHT (P) Houston; KNWS-TV (I) Katy; KXLN-TV (S) Rosenberg.
Programming (via satellite): A & E; BET; C-SPAN; CNN; Country Music TV; Discovery Channel; ESPN; Fox Family Channel; Fox Sports Net Southwest; Headline News; Lifetime; MTV; Nashville Network; Nickelodeon; QVC; TBS Superstation; The Weather Channel; Turner Network TV; USA Network.
Fee: $31.34 monthly; $2.15 converter.
Pay Service 1
Pay Units: 48.
Programming (via satellite): Cinemax.
Fee: $10.95 monthly.
Pay Service 2
Pay Units: 50.
Programming (via satellite): Disney Channel.
Fee: $7.95 monthly.
Pay Service 3
Pay Units: 99.
Programming (via satellite): HBO.
Fee: $10.95 monthly.
Pay Service 4
Pay Units: 91.
Programming (via satellite): Showtime.
Fee: $12.95 monthly.
Miles of plant: 43.3 (coaxial); None (fiber optic). Homes passed: 1,771. Total homes in franchised area: 1,771.
Manager: Mike Burns. Chief technician: Mayla Zubeck.
Ownership: Star Cable Associates (MSO).

ARGYLE—SouthTel Communications LP, Suite 202, 2444 Solomons Island Rd., Annapolis, MD 21401. Phone: 410-266-9393. County: Denton. Also serves Bartonville (portions). ICA: TX0533.
TV Market Ranking: 12. Franchise award date: N.A. Franchise expiration date: N.A. Began: February 1, 1983.
Channel capacity: 52. Channels available but not in use: N.A.
Basic Service
Subscribers: 269.
Programming (received off-air): KDAF (W), KDFI-TV (I), KDFW (F), KERA-TV (P), KTVT (C), KTXA (U), KXAS-TV (N), KXTX-TV (I), WFAA-TV (A) Dallas-Fort Worth; KDTN (P) Denton.
Programming (via satellite): WGN-TV (W) Chicago; A & E; C-SPAN; CNBC; CNN; Country Music TV; Discovery Channel; ESPN; ESPN 2; Fox Family Channel; Headline News; History Channel; Home & Garden Television; Home Shopping Network; Learning Channel; Lifetime; MuchMoreMusic; Nashville Network; Nickelodeon; Pax Net; QVC; TBS Superstation; The Weather Channel; Turner Classic Movies; Turner Network TV; USA Network.
Fee: $25.00 installation; $21.95 monthly.
Pay Service 1
Pay Units: N.A.
Programming (via satellite): HBO; Showtime; The Movie Channel.
Fee: N.A.
Miles of plant: 26.0 (coaxial); None (fiber optic). Homes passed: 374.
Manager: Roy E. Hayes. Chief technician: Roy E. Hayes.
Ownership: Bay Cable Inc. (MSO).

ARLINGTON—TCI of Arlington Inc., 2421 Matlock Rd., Arlington, TX 76015-1696. Phone: 817-265-7766. Fax: 817-548-7420. County: Tarrant. Also serves Dalworthington Gardens, Pantego. ICA: TX0011.
TV Market Ranking: 12. Franchise award date: N.A. Franchise expiration date: N.A. Began: August 1, 1981.
Channel capacity: 77 (not 2-way capable). Channels available but not in use: None.
Basic Service
Subscribers: 58,500.
Programming (received off-air): KPXD (X) Arlington; KDAF (W), KDFI-TV (I), KDFW (F), KDTX-TV (T), KERA-TV (P), KFWD (O), KTVT (C), KTXA (U), KXAS-TV (N), KXTX-TV (I), WFAA-TV (A) Dallas-Fort Worth; KMPX (I) Decatur; KDTN (P) Denton; KUVN (S) Garland; KHSX-TV (H) Irving.

Programming (via satellite): Discovery Channel; E! Entertainment TV; EWTN; Odyssey; TBS Superstation.
Current originations: Public access; educational access; government access; religious access; local news.
Fee: $44.95 installation; $10.17 monthly; $1.50 converter.

Expanded Basic Service
Subscribers: N.A.
Programming (via satellite): Animal Planet; BET; C-SPAN; C-SPAN 2; CNN; Cartoon Network; Country Music TV; ESPN; ESPN 2; FX; Fox Family Channel; Fox News Channel; Headline News; History Channel; Home & Garden Television; Learning Channel; Nashville Network; Nickelodeon; QVC; TV Guide Channel; TV Guide Sneak Prevue; The Weather Channel; USA Network; VH1.
Fee: $15.00 installation; $8.03 monthly.

Expanded Basic Service 2
Subscribers: N.A.
Programming (via satellite): A & E; American Movie Classics; Bravo; CNBC; Comedy Central; Court TV; Fox Sports Net Southwest; Lifetime; MTV; Sci-Fi Channel; Turner Network TV.
Fee: $4.94 monthly.

Pay Service 1
Pay Units: N.A.
Programming (via satellite): Cinemax (multiplexed); Disney Channel; HBO (multiplexed); Showtime (multiplexed); Starz!; The Movie Channel; The New Encore.
Fee: $10.00 installation; $1.75 monthly (Encore), $6.75 monthly (Starz), $10.00 monthly (Cinemax, Disney, HBO, Showtime or TMC).

Pay-Per-View
Addressable homes: 53,500.
Action Pay-Per-View; Playboy TV; Viewer's Choice.

Local advertising: Yes. Available in satellite distributed programming. Rates: $80.00/Minute; $40.00/30 Seconds. Local sales manager: Gary Hill.
Program Guide: On Cable.
Equipment: Jerrold headend; Magnavox amplifiers; Comm/Scope cable; Zenith addressable set top converters; Scientific-Atlanta satellite antenna.
Miles of plant: 1156.0 (coaxial); 200.0 (fiber optic). Homes passed: 118,000. Total homes in franchised area: 119,000.
Manager: Vince Thomas. Chief technician: Lawrence Dehmel. Marketing director: Steve Schuh.
City fee: 3% of gross.
Ownership: AT&T Broadband & Internet Services (MSO). Purchased from Tele-Communications Inc., March 9, 1999.

ARP—Friendship Cable of Texas Inc., Box 9090, Tyler, TX 75711-9090. Phone: 903-581-2121. Fax: 903-581-2185. Counties: Rusk & Smith. Also serves New London, Overton, Troup, Turnertown. ICA: TX0374.
TV Market Ranking: Below 100. Franchise award date: N.A. Franchise expiration date: N.A. Began: February 1, 1981.
Channel capacity: 36. Channels available but not in use: None.

Basic Service
Subscribers: 1,855.
Programming (received off-air): KLTS-TV (P), KSLA-TV (C), KTAL-TV (N), KTBS-TV (A) Shreveport-Texarkana; KLTV (A) Tyler-Longview.
Programming (via satellite): WGN-TV (W) Chicago; CNN; ESPN; Fox Family Channel; TBS Superstation.
Planned originations: Automated time-weather.
Fee: $30.00 installation; $29.80 monthly.

Pay Service 1
Pay Units: 95.
Programming (via satellite): Cinemax.
Fee: $7.00 monthly.

Pay Service 2
Pay Units: 200.
Programming (via satellite): HBO.
Fee: $12.00 monthly.

Pay Service 3
Pay Units: 345.
Programming (via satellite): Showtime.
Fee: $7.00 monthly.

Pay Service 4
Pay Units: 84.
Programming (via satellite): The Movie Channel.
Fee: $9.00 monthly.

Miles of plant: 78.0 (coaxial). Homes passed: 2,590.
Manager: Marianne Bogy. Chief technician: Henry Harris.
City fee: 3% of gross.
Ownership: Buford Television Inc. (MSO). See Cable System Ownership.

ARROWHEAD ADDITION—National Cable Inc., Suite 106-A, 5151 Reed Rd., Columbus, OH 43220. Phones: 614-442-5890; 800-582-0504. Fax: 614-457-2567. Counties: Jim Wells & Live Oak. Also serves Orange Grove (portions). ICA: TX0545.
TV Market Ranking: Outside TV Markets. Franchise award date: N.A. Franchise expiration date: N.A. Began: N.A.
Channel capacity: 36. Channels available but not in use: N.A.

Basic Service
Subscribers: 24.
Programming (received off-air): KEDT (P), KIII (A), KORO (S), KRIS-TV (N), KZTV (C) Corpus Christi; KABB (F) San Antonio.
Programming (via satellite): A & E; American Movie Classics; CNN; Country Music TV; Discovery Channel; ESPN; Fox Family Channel; GalaVision; Nashville Network; Showtime; TBS Superstation; Turner Network TV; USA Network.
Fee: $28.00 monthly.

Miles of plant: 13.9 (coaxial). Homes passed: 225.
Manager: Paul Scott. Chief technician: Rob Spiller. Marketing director: Josh Thackery.
Ownership: National Cable (MSO).

ASHERTON—Time Warner Communications, Box 1208, 690 Ford St., Eagle Pass, TX 78852-4546. Phones: 512-374-3617; 800-527-6221. County: Dimmit. Also serves Dimmit County (southern portion). ICA: TX0536.
TV Market Ranking: Outside TV Markets. Franchise award date: N.A. Franchise expiration date: N.A. Began: February 1, 1980.
Channel capacity: 22. Channels available but not in use: 8.

Basic Service
Subscribers: 369.
Programming (received off-air): KGNS-TV (N,A), KLDO-TV (O), KVTV (C) Laredo.
Programming (via satellite): WGN-TV (W) Chicago; WABC-TV (A) New York; CNN; ESPN; GalaVision; MTV; TBS Superstation; USA Network; Univision.
Fee: $60.00 installation; $16.65 monthly.

Pay Service 1
Pay Units: 54.
Programming (via satellite): HBO.
Fee: $11.00 monthly.

Pay Service 2
Pay Units: 62.
Programming (via satellite): Showtime.
Fee: $6.00 monthly.

Miles of plant: 17.0 (coaxial). Homes passed: 370.
Manager: Jimmy Gutierrez. Chief technician: Polo Vielma.
Ownership: Time Warner Cable (MSO); AT&T Broadband & Internet Services (MSO).

ASPERMONT—Cablecomm, 320 W. Main St., Brownfield, TX 79316. Phones: 806-637-2313; 800-638-8457. County: Stonewall. ICA: TX0461.
TV Market Ranking: Outside TV Markets. Franchise award date: July 1, 1980. Franchise expiration date: N.A. Began: March 15, 1981.
Channel capacity: 40 (not 2-way capable). Channels available but not in use: 23.

Basic Service
Subscribers: 342; Commercial subscribers: 2.
Programming (received off-air): KRBC-TV (N), KTAB-TV (C), KTXS-TV (A) Abilene-Sweetwater; allband FM.
Programming (via satellite): WGN-TV (W) Chicago; Discovery Channel; Fox Family Channel; QVC; TBS Superstation.
Fee: $64.50 installation; $10.91 monthly; $2.20 converter.

Expanded Basic Service
Subscribers: 336.
Programming (via satellite): CNN; Country Music TV; ESPN; Goodlife TV Network; Nashville Network; Turner Network TV; USA Network.
Fee: $20.00 installation; $9.55 monthly.

Pay Service 1
Pay Units: 94.
Programming (via satellite): HBO.
Fee: $20.00 installation; $10.50 monthly.

Pay Service 2
Pay Units: 67.
Programming (via satellite): The Movie Channel.
Fee: $20.00 installation; $10.50 monthly.

Local advertising: No.
Program Guide: Premium Channels.
Equipment: Scientific-Atlanta headend; Scientific-Atlanta amplifiers; Comm/Scope cable; Standard Components set top converters; Eagle & Pico traps; Scientific-Atlanta & M/A-Com addressable traps; Weatherscan satellite antenna; Automation Techniques & Scientific-Atlanta satellite receivers.
Miles of plant: 12.0 (coaxial). Homes passed: 591.
Manager: Rex Thackerson. Chief technician: Gary Strickland. Marketing director: Bill Forgey.
City fee: 3% of gross.
Ownership: Time Warner Cable (MSO); Fanch Communications Inc. (MSO). See Cable System Ownership.

ATASCOSA—Friendship Cable of Texas Inc., Box 9090, Tyler, TX 75711-9090. Phone: 903-581-2121. Fax: 903-581-2185. County: Bexar. ICA: TX0309.
TV Market Ranking: 45. Franchise award date: N.A. Franchise expiration date: N.A. Began: September 1, 1989.
Channel capacity: 54. Channels available but not in use: 32.

Basic Service
Subscribers: 453.
Programming (received off-air): KRRT (W) Kerrville-San Antonio; KABB (F), KENS-TV (C), KHCE (P), KLRN (P), KMOL-TV (N), KSAT-TV (A), KVDA (O), KWEX-TV (S) San Antonio.
Programming (via satellite): CNN; Country Music TV; Discovery Channel; Disney Channel; ESPN; GalaVision; Headline News; MTV; Nashville Network; Nickelodeon; TBS Superstation; Turner Network TV; USA Network.
Fee: $30.00 installation; $27.20 monthly.

Pay Service 1
Pay Units: 15.
Programming (via satellite): Cinemax.
Fee: $10.95 monthly.

Pay Service 2
Pay Units: 96.
Programming (via satellite): HBO.
Fee: $10.95 monthly.

Pay Service 3
Pay Units: 41.
Programming (via satellite): Showtime.
Fee: $5.95 monthly.

Miles of plant: 61.0 (coaxial). Homes passed: 1,338.
Manager: Wanda Pyburn. Chief technician: David Burrell.
Ownership: Buford Television Inc. (MSO). See Cable System Ownership.

ATHENS—TCA Cable TV, 518 E. Corsicana, Athens, TX 75751. Phone: 903-675-5917. Web site: http://www.tca-cable.com. County: Henderson. Also serves Henderson County. ICA: TX0711.
TV Market Ranking: Below 100 (Athens, portions of Henderson County); Outside TV Markets (portions of Henderson County). Franchise award date: N.A. Franchise expiration date: N.A. Began: October 15, 1968.
Channel capacity: 29. Channels available but not in use: N.A.

Basic Service
Subscribers: 3,779.
Programming (received off-air): KDFW (F), KERA-TV (P), KTVT (C), KXAS-TV (N), KXTX-TV (I), WFAA-TV (A) Dallas-Fort Worth; KLTV (A) Tyler-Longview; KWTX-TV (C) Waco-Temple; allband FM.
Programming (via satellite): CNN; ESPN; TBS Superstation; The Weather Channel.
Current originations: Automated time-weather.
Fee: $35.00 installation; $8.69 monthly.

Expanded Basic Service
Subscribers: 3,449.
Programming (via satellite): Turner Network TV.
Fee: N.A.

Pay Service 1
Pay Units: N.A.
Programming (via satellite): Fox Family Channel; Nickelodeon; Showtime; USA Network.
Fee: $35.00 installation; $9.00 monthly (each).

Equipment: CAS headend; CAS amplifiers; Phelps-Dodge cable; Scientific-Atlanta satellite antenna.
Miles of plant: 91.8 (coaxial).
Manager: Nathan Geick. Chief technician: Ronnie Babcock.
City fee: 3% of gross.
Ownership: TCA Cable TV Inc. (MSO); AT&T Broadband & Internet Services (MSO). See Cable System Ownership.

ATLANTA—Falcon Cable TV, 108 W. Houston, Marshall, TX 75670. Phone: 903-938-8337. County: Cass. Also serves Cass County (portions), Queen City. ICA: TX0188.
TV Market Ranking: 58 (Atlanta, portions of Cass County, Queen City); Below 100 (portions of Cass County); Outside TV Markets (portions of Cass County). Franchise award date: September 1, 1978. Franchise expiration date: N.A. Began: April 1, 1980.

Channel capacity: 38 (not 2-way capable). Channels available but not in use: None.
Basic Service
Subscribers: 1,296.
Programming (received off-air): KFXK (F) Longview; KLTS-TV (P), KMSS-TV (F), KSHV (U,W), KSLA-TV (C), KTAL-TV (N), KTBS-TV (A) Shreveport-Texarkana; KLTV (A) Tyler-Longview; allband FM.
Programming (via satellite): A & E; American Movie Classics; BET; C-SPAN; CNN; Comedy Central; Country Music TV; Discovery Channel; ESPN; Fox Family Channel; Fox Sports Net Southwest; Headline News; Lifetime; MTV; Nashville Network; Nickelodeon; QVC; TV Guide Channel; Turner Network TV; VH1.
Current originations: Leased access.
Fee: $63.00 installation; $25.79 monthly; $3.15 converter; $6.95 additional installation.
Expanded Basic Service
Subscribers: 1,213.
Programming (via satellite): WGN-TV (W) Chicago; Disney Channel; TBS Superstation; The Weather Channel; USA Network.
Fee: $5.77 monthly.
Pay Service 1
Pay Units: 128.
Programming (via satellite): Cinemax.
Fee: $15.00 installation; $11.95 monthly.
Pay Service 2
Pay Units: 189.
Programming (via satellite): HBO.
Fee: $11.95 monthly.
Pay Service 3
Pay Units: 105.
Programming (via satellite): Showtime.
Fee: $11.95 monthly.
Pay Service 4
Pay Units: 67.
Programming (via satellite): The Movie Channel.
Fee: $11.95 monthly.
Pay-Per-View
Movies.
Fee: $3.95.
Equipment: Scientific-Atlanta headend; GTE Sylvania amplifiers; Times Fiber & Perimeter 3 cable; Gardiner satellite antenna; Gardiner satellite receivers.
Miles of plant: 74.0 (coaxial). Homes passed: 4,079.
Manager: George Doss. Chief technician: Robert Hurd.
Franchise fee: 3% of gross.
Ownership: Falcon Communications LP (MSO), joint venture formed September 30, 1998. See Cable System Ownership.

AUSTIN—Time Warner Cable, 12012 N. Mo-Pac Expwy., Austin, TX 78758. Phone: 512-485-6100. Fax: 512-485-6105. Web site: http://www.timewarneraustin.com. Counties: Travis & Williamson. Also serves Cedar Park, Circle C, Rollingwood, San Leanna, Sunset Valley, Westlake Hills. ICA: TX0005.
TV Market Ranking: Below 100. Franchise award date: December 1, 1963. Franchise expiration date: August 1, 2011. Began: September 1, 1963.
Channel capacity: 58 (2-way capable; not operating 2-way). Channels available but not in use: None.
Basic Service
Subscribers: 212,000.
Programming (received off-air): KEYE-TV (C), KLRU (P), KNVA (W), KTBC (F), KVUE-TV (A), KXAN-TV (N) Austin; K13VC (I) Austin, Cedar Park; allband FM.
Programming (via satellite): C-SPAN; Learning Channel; TV Guide Channel.
Current originations: Automated time-weather; public access; educational access; government access; religious access; leased access; automated emergency alert; local news.
Fee: $28.21 installation; $8.58 monthly; $3.07 converter; $12.70 additional installation.
Digital Basic Service
Subscribers: N.A.
Programming (via satellite): BET on Jazz; CNNfn; Cinemax; Discovery Kids Channel; Discovery People; Discovery Science Channel; Discovery Wings Channel; Disney Channel; Game Show Network; HBO; HBO Comedy; HBO Family; HBO Plus; HBO Signature; HBO Zone; Outdoor Channel; Ovation; Playboy TV; Showtime; Showtime Extreme; Speedvision; Spice; Spice2; Sundance Channel; The Health Network; The Movie Channel.
Fee: N.A.
Expanded Basic Service
Subscribers: 194,000.
Programming (via satellite): WGN-TV (W) Chicago; A & E; Animal Planet; BET; Bravo; C-SPAN 2; CNBC; CNN; CNN/SI; Cartoon Network; Comedy Central; Country Music TV; Court TV; E! Entertainment TV; ESPN; Fox Family Channel; Fox News Channel; Fox Sports Net Southwest; Headline News; Home & Garden Television; Home Shopping Network; Lifetime; MSNBC; MTV; Nashville Network; Nick at Nite's TV Land; Nickelodeon; Odyssey; Pax Net; QVC; TBS Superstation; TV Food Network; TV Guide Sneak Prevue; Telemundo; The Weather Channel; Travel Channel; Trinity Bcstg. Network; Turner Network TV; USA Network; Univision; VH1.
Fee: $26.90 installation; $28.21 monthly.
Expanded Basic Service 2
Subscribers: 62,000.
Programming (via satellite): American Movie Classics; Discovery Channel; ESPN 2; Golf Channel; History Channel; Independent Film Channel; Sci-Fi Channel; The New Encore; Turner Classic Movies.
Fee: $28.21 installation; $6.70 monthly.
Pay Service 1
Pay Units: 116,000.
Programming (via satellite): Cinemax (multiplexed); Disney Channel; HBO (multiplexed).
Fee: $8.95 monthly (Disney), $10.95 monthly (Cinemax or HBO).
Pay-Per-View
Addressable homes: 93,000.
Action PPV delivered digitally; Hot Choice delivered digitally; Playboy TV delivered digitally; Viewer's Choice Digital.
Local advertising: Yes. Available in satellite distributed programming. Local sales manager: Jim Norton.
Equipment: Jerrold & Scientific-Atlanta headend; Scientific-Atlanta amplifiers; Comm/Scope cable; Panasonic cameras; Panasonic VTRs; Amiga & Texscan character generator; Scientific-Atlanta set top converters; Scientific-Atlanta addressable set top converters; Arcom & Pico traps; Scientific-Atlanta & Superior satellite antenna; Drake, Scientific-Atlanta & Standard Communications satellite receivers; ChannelMatic commercial insert.
Miles of plant: 2788.0 (coaxial); 65.0 (fiber optic). Homes passed: 318,000. Total homes in franchised area: 318,000.
Manager: Bill Carey. Chief technician: Matt Stanek. Program director: George Warmingham. Marketing director: Michelle Golden.
City fee: 5% of gross.
Ownership: Time Warner Cable (MSO); Advance/Newhouse Partnership (MSO).

AVINGER—Friendship Cable of Texas Inc., Box 9090, Tyler, TX 75711-9090. Phone: 903-581-2121. Fax: 903-581-2185. County: Cass. Also serves Cass County (portions). ICA: TX0597.
TV Market Ranking: Below 100 (Avinger, portions of Cass County); Outside TV Markets (portions of Cass County). Franchise award date: N.A. Franchise expiration date: N.A. Began: N.A.
Channel capacity: 37. Channels available but not in use: 9.
Basic Service
Subscribers: 94.
Programming (received off-air): KETK-TV (N) Jacksonville; KFXK (F) Longview; KLTS-TV (P), KSLA-TV (C) Shreveport-Texarkana; KLTV (A) Tyler-Longview.
Programming (via satellite): WGN-TV (W) Chicago; CNN; Country Music TV; Discovery Channel; ESPN; Fox Family Channel; Lifetime; Nashville Network; Nickelodeon; TBS Superstation; Turner Classic Movies; Turner Network TV; USA Network.
Fee: $33.55 monthly.
Pay Service 1
Pay Units: 29.
Programming (via satellite): Cinemax.
Fee: $10.95 monthly.
Pay Service 2
Pay Units: 23.
Programming (via satellite): HBO.
Fee: $10.95 monthly.
Local advertising: No.
Miles of plant: 8.0 (coaxial). Homes passed: 249.
Manager: Marianne Bogy. Chief technician: Sonny Myers.
Ownership: Buford Television Inc. (MSO). See Cable System Ownership.

AZLE—North Texas Cablecomm, Suite 6A, 328 W. Main St., Azle, TX 76020. Phone: 817-444-5606. Counties: Parker & Tarrant. Also serves Lake Country Estates, Lakeside, Parker County, Tarrant County. ICA: TX0712.
TV Market Ranking: 12 (Azle, Lake Country Estates, Lakeside, portions of Parker County, Tarrant County); Outside TV Markets (portions of Parker County). Franchise award date: N.A. Franchise expiration date: October 1, 1999. Began: December 1, 1984.
Channel capacity: 61 (2-way capable; operating 2-way). Channels available but not in use: 7.
Basic Service
Subscribers: 4,500.
Programming (received off-air): KPXD (X) Arlington; KDAF (W), KDFI-TV (I), KDFW (F), KDTX-TV (T), KERA-TV (P), KTVT (C), KXAS-TV (N), KXTX-TV (I), WFAA-TV (A) Dallas-Fort Worth.
Programming (via satellite): WGN-TV (W) Chicago; A & E; C-SPAN; CNBC; CNN; Country Music TV; Discovery Channel; ESPN; Fox Family Channel; Fox Sports Net Southwest; Headline News; Lifetime; MTV; Nashville Network; Nickelodeon; TBS Superstation; The Weather Channel; Turner Network TV; USA Network; VH1.
Fee: $29.95 installation; $24.50 monthly.
Pay Service 1
Pay Units: N.A.
Programming (via satellite): Disney Channel; HBO; Showtime.
Fee: $10.14 monthly (each).
Miles of plant: 47.7 (coaxial); 35.0 (fiber optic). Homes passed: 7,800. Total homes in franchised area: 7,800.
Manager: Richard Steward. Chief technician: Georgie Moreland.
City fee: 5% of gross.
Ownership: Fanch Communications Inc. (MSO). See Cable System Ownership.

AZTEC—Friendship Cable of Texas Inc., Box 9090, Tyler, TX 75711-9090. Phone: 903-581-2121. Fax: 903-581-2185. County: Bexar. ICA: TX0492.
TV Market Ranking: 45. Franchise award date: N.A. Franchise expiration date: N.A. Began: August 1, 1989.
Channel capacity: 54. Channels available but not in use: N.A.
Basic Service
Subscribers: 66.
Programming (received off-air): KRRT (W) Kerrville-San Antonio; KABB (F), KENS-TV (C), KHCE (P), KLRN (P), KMOL-TV (N), KSAT-TV (A), KWEX-TV (S) San Antonio.
Programming (via satellite): CNN; Country Music TV; Disney Channel; ESPN; Headline News; Nashville Network; TBS Superstation; Turner Network TV; USA Network.
Fee: $30.00 installation; $27.20 monthly.
Pay Service 1
Pay Units: 13.
Programming (via satellite): HBO.
Fee: $10.95 monthly.
Pay Service 2
Pay Units: 9.
Programming (via satellite): Showtime.
Fee: $5.95 monthly.
Miles of plant: 15.0 (coaxial). Homes passed: 560.
Manager: Wanda Pyburn. Chief technician: David Burrell.
Ownership: Buford Television Inc. (MSO). See Cable System Ownership.

BAILEY—Torrence Cablevision, Box 1167, Ridgeland, MS 39158. Phones: 601-981-6900; 800-977-8849. County: Fannin. ICA: TX0713.
TV Market Ranking: Below 100. Franchise award date: N.A. Franchise expiration date: N.A. Began: N.A.
Channel capacity: 36. Channels available but not in use: 21.
Basic Service
Subscribers: 18.
Programming (received off-air): KDFW (F), KERA-TV (P), KTVT (C), KXAS-TV (N), KXTX-TV (I), WFAA-TV (A) Dallas-Fort Worth.
Programming (via satellite): A & E; American Movie Classics; CNN; Country Music TV; Discovery Channel; Fox Family Channel; Nashville Network; Showtime; TBS Superstation; Turner Network TV; USA Network.
Fee: $28.00 monthly.
Miles of plant: 3.3 (coaxial). Homes passed: 89.
Ownership: Torrence Cable Inc. (MSO).

BAIRD—Brownwood TV Cable Service Inc., Box 1149, 310 Carnegie Blvd., Brownwood, TX 76801. Phone: 915-646-3576. Fax: 915-643-2846. County: Callahan. Also serves Clyde. ICA: TX0212.
TV Market Ranking: Below 100. Franchise award date: July 9, 1969. Franchise expiration date: March 12, 1999. Began: October 1, 1969.
Channel capacity: 30 (not 2-way capable). Channels available but not in use: 11.
Basic Service
Subscribers: 1,394.
Programming (received off-air): KRBC-TV (N), KTAB-TV (C), KTXS-TV (A) Abilene-Sweetwater; KERA-TV (P) Dallas-Fort Worth.
Programming (via satellite): WGN-TV (W) Chicago; ESPN; Fox Family Channel; Headline News; Nickelodeon; TBS Superstation.

Fee: $37.50 installation; $8.85 monthly; $2.50 converter; $23.75 additional installation.

Expanded Basic Service

Subscribers: N.A.

Programming (via satellite): CNBC; CNN; Lifetime; Nashville Network; QVC; The Weather Channel; Trinity Bcstg. Network; Turner Network TV.

Fee: $11.05 monthly.

Pay Service 1

Pay Units: N.A.

Programming (via satellite): Disney Channel; HBO.

Fee: $11.45 monthly (each).

Local advertising: No.

Equipment: Jerrold & Scientific-Atlanta headend; Magnavox amplifiers; Comm/Scope cable; Scientific-Atlanta set top converters; Scientific-Atlanta satellite antenna; Automation Techniques satellite receivers.

Miles of plant: 40.9 (coaxial). Homes passed: 2,154.

Manager: Karen McMillan. Chief technician: Paul Mathison.

City fee: 3% of gross.

Ownership: Brownwood TV Cable Service Inc. (MSO).

BALLINGER—TCA Cable TV, 28 W. Concho Ave., San Angelo, TX 76903. Phone: 915-655-8911. Fax: 915-658-6876.

Web site: http://www.tca-cable.com.

County: Runnels. ICA: TX0964.

TV Market Ranking: Below 100. Franchise award date: N.A. Franchise expiration date: January 1, 2003. Began: N.A.

Channel capacity: 36 (2-way capable). Channels available but not in use: 3.

Basic Service

Subscribers: 1,081; Commercial subscribers: 2.

Programming (received off-air): KRBC-TV (N), KTAB-TV (C), KTXS-TV (A) Abilene-Sweetwater; KERA-TV (P), WFAA-TV (A) Dallas-Fort Worth; KIDY (F), KLST (C) San Angelo.

Programming (via satellite): TBS Superstation.

Current originations: Public access.

Fee: $38.00 installation; $11.10 monthly; $0.25 converter.

Expanded Basic Service

Subscribers: 1,026.

Programming (via satellite): American Movie Classics; C-SPAN; CNN; Discovery Channel; Disney Channel; ESPN; Fox Family Channel; Fox Sports Net Southwest; Great American Country; Headline News; Learning Channel; Lifetime; MTV; Nashville Network; Nickelodeon; QVC; The Weather Channel; Turner Network TV; USA Network; Univision.

Fee: $38.00 installation; $24.50 monthly.

Pay Service 1

Pay Units: 238.

Programming (via satellite): HBO.

Fee: $13.00 monthly.

Pay Service 2

Pay Units: 149.

Programming (via satellite): HBO; Showtime.

Fee: $15.45 monthly.

Local advertising: Yes. Available in satellite distributed programming. Rates: $40.00/Minute; $20.00/30 Seconds. Local sales manager: Jay Speegle.

Equipment: Scientific-Atlanta headend; Jerrold amplifiers; Times Fiber & Comm/Scope cable; Scientific-Atlanta set top converters; Eagle traps; Andrew & Scientific-Atlanta satellite antenna; Scientific-Atlanta satellite receivers.

Miles of plant: 32.8 (coaxial); None (fiber optic). Homes passed: 1,256.

Manager: Archie Kountz. Chief engineer: Robert Amo. Marketing director: Mike Johnson. Customer service manager: Naomi Gonzales.

Ownership: TCA Cable TV Inc. (MSO); AT&T Broadband & Internet Services (MSO). See Cable System Ownership.

BALMORHEA—Balmorhea TV Cable, Box 1377, Alpine, TX 79831. Phone: 915-837-2300. Fax: 915-837-5423. E-mail: mtnzone@overland.net. County: Reeves. ICA: TX0714.

TV Market Ranking: Outside TV Markets. Franchise award date: N.A. Franchise expiration date: N.A. Began: January 1, 1967.

Channel capacity: 36 (not 2-way capable). Channels available but not in use: N.A.

Basic Service

Subscribers: 125.

Programming (received off-air): KMID (A), KOSA-TV (C), KPEJ (F), KWES-TV (N) Odessa-Midland; allband FM.

Programming (via satellite): WGN-TV (W) Chicago; KMGH-TV (A), KRMA-TV (P) Denver; CNN; Country Music TV; Discovery Channel; ESPN; Fox Family Channel; GalaVision; Home Shopping Network; Learning Channel; Nashville Network; Nickelodeon; TBS Superstation; The Weather Channel; Turner Classic Movies; Turner Network TV; Univision.

Fee: $35.00 installation; $26.45 monthly.

Pay Service 1

Pay Units: 34.

Programming (via satellite): HBO.

Fee: $10.00 installation; $6.96 monthly.

Pay Service 2

Pay Units: 20.

Programming (via satellite): Showtime.

Fee: $10.00 installation; $6.96 monthly.

Equipment: Blonder-Tongue & Scientific-Atlanta headend; Scientific-Atlanta amplifiers; Coral cable; RCA set top converters.

Miles of plant: 5.0 (coaxial); None (fiber optic). Additional miles planned: 1.0 (coaxial).

Manager: Steve Neu. Office manager: Lawrence Neu.

City fee: 2% of gross.

Ownership: Mountain Zone TV Systems (MSO).

BANDERA—Time Warner Communications, 900 Sidney Baker, Kerrville, TX 78028. Phones: 830-257-4700; 800-824-6807. Fax: 830-257-6776. County: Bandera. ICA: TX0445.

TV Market Ranking: Below 100. Franchise award date: N.A. Franchise expiration date: N.A. Began: November 1, 1982.

Channel capacity: 35. Channels available but not in use: 6.

Basic Service

Subscribers: 476.

Programming (received off-air): KRRT (W) Kerrville-San Antonio; KABB (F), KENS-TV (C), KLRN (P), KMOL-TV (N), KSAT-TV (A), KVDA (O), KWEX-TV (S) San Antonio.

Programming (via satellite): C-SPAN; C-SPAN 2; Country Music TV; Discovery Channel; TBS Superstation; The Weather Channel; Trinity Bcstg. Network.

Current originations: Local news.

Fee: $44.95 installation; $12.44 monthly; $12.50 additional installation.

Expanded Basic Service

Subscribers: N.A.

Programming (via satellite): A & E; American Movie Classics; Animal Planet; CNBC; CNN; Cartoon Network; Court TV; Disney Channel; ESPN; FX; Fox News Channel; Fox Sports Net Southwest; Headline News; History Channel; Home & Garden Television; Learning Channel; Lifetime; MSNBC; Nashville Network; Nickelodeon; QVC; Turner Network TV; USA Network.

Fee: $13.55 monthly.

Pay Service 1

Pay Units: 56.

Programming (via satellite): HBO.

Fee: $12.45 monthly.

Pay Service 2

Pay Units: 38.

Programming (via satellite): The Movie Channel.

Fee: $9.95 monthly.

Pay Service 3

Pay Units: 63.

Programming (via satellite): Showtime.

Fee: $9.95 monthly.

Pay Service 4

Pay Units: N.A.

Programming (via satellite): Starz!; The New Encore.

Fee: $1.75 monthly (Encore), $6.75 monthly (Starz).

Miles of plant: 11.0 (coaxial). Homes passed: 650. Total homes in franchised area: 650.

Manager: Linda Allerkamp. Chief technician: Jay Burton.

Ownership: Time Warner Cable (MSO). Purchased from AT&T Broadband & Internet Services, June 1, 1999.

BARSTOW—Classic Cable, Box 429, 605 N.W. 3rd St., Plainville, KS 67663-0429. Phones: 785-434-7620; 800-999-8876. Fax: 785-434-2614. County: Ward. ICA: TX0616.

TV Market Ranking: Below 100. Franchise award date: February 19, 1987. Franchise expiration date: February 18, 2007. Began: January 1, 1987.

Channel capacity: 61 (2-way capable). Channels available but not in use: N.A.

Basic Service

Subscribers: 99.

Programming (received off-air): KMLM (I), KOSA-TV (C), KPEJ (F) Odessa-Midland.

Programming (via satellite): WGN-TV (W) Chicago; KMGH-TV (A), KRMA-TV (P) Denver; CNN; Discovery Channel; ESPN; Fox Family Channel; GalaVision; Headline News; Home Shopping Network; Nashville Network; TBS Superstation; Telemundo; The Weather Channel; Turner Classic Movies; USA Network; Univision.

Fee: $35.00 installation; $27.95 monthly.

Pay Service 1

Pay Units: 21.

Programming (via satellite): HBO.

Fee: $11.60 monthly.

Pay Service 2

Pay Units: 3.

Programming (via satellite): Showtime.

Fee: $9.95 monthly.

Equipment: Scientific-Atlanta amplifiers; Comm/Scope & Belden cable; Scientific-Atlanta set top converters; Eagle traps; Comtech satellite antenna; Scientific-Atlanta & Pico satellite receivers.

Miles of plant: 6.0 (coaxial). Homes passed: 220.

Manager: Bill Flowers. Chief technician: Ben Hernandez. Marketing director: Jennifer Hauschild.

Ownership: Classic Cable (MSO).

BARTLETT—Time Warner Cable, 12012 N. Mo Pac Expressway, Austin, TX 78758-2904. Phone: 512-485-6100. Fax: 512-485-6105. Web site: http://timewarneraustin.com. Counties: Bell & Williamson. Also serves Granger, Holland. ICA: TX0287.

TV Market Ranking: Below 100. Franchise award date: September 28, 1994. Franchise expiration date: October 21, 2011. Began: May 1, 1982.

Channel capacity: 61 (not 2-way capable). Channels available but not in use: 16.

Basic Service

Subscribers: 750.

Programming (received off-air): KEYE-TV (C), KLRU (P), KNVA (W), KTBC (F), KVUE-TV (A), KXAN-TV (N) Austin; KNCT (P) Belton; KCEN-TV (N), KWTX-TV (C), KXXV (A) Waco-Temple.

Programming (via satellite): WGN-TV (W) Chicago; A & E; American Movie Classics; Animal Planet; C-SPAN; CNBC; CNN; Cartoon Network; Country Music TV; Discovery Channel; E! Entertainment TV; ESPN; ESPN 2; Fox Family Channel; GalaVision; Headline News; History Channel; Home & Garden Television; Learning Channel; Lifetime; MSNBC; MTV; Nashville Network; Nick at Nite; Nickelodeon; Pax Net; QVC; TBS Superstation; The Weather Channel; Travel Channel; Turner Classic Movies; Turner Network TV; USA Network.

Fee: $28.21 installation; $26.75 monthly; $24.75 additional installation.

Pay Service 1

Pay Units: N.A.

Programming (via satellite): Cinemax; HBO; Showtime.

Fee: $7.00 monthly (Cinemax or Showtime), $12.00 monthly (HBO).

Miles of plant: 51.5 (coaxial); None (fiber optic). Homes passed: 1,824.

Manager: Bill Carey. Chief technician: Matt Stanek. Program director: George Warmingham. Marketing director: Michelle Golden.

City fee: 5% of gross.

Ownership: Time Warner Cable (MSO); Advance/Newhouse Partnership (MSO).

BASTROP—Time Warner Communications, 1112 Main St., Bastrop, TX 78731. Phone: 512-321-6864. Fax: 512-303-6459. County: Bastrop. ICA: TX0297.

TV Market Ranking: Below 100. Franchise award date: N.A. Franchise expiration date: N.A. Began: March 1, 1980.

Channel capacity: 35. Channels available but not in use: N.A.

Basic Service

Subscribers: 1,425; Commercial subscribers: 11.

Programming (received off-air): KEYE-TV (C), KLRU (P), KTBC (F), KVUE-TV (A), KXAN-TV (N) Austin; KENS-TV (C), KMOL-TV (N), KSAT-TV (A) San Antonio.

Programming (via satellite): WGN-TV (W) Chicago; CNN; Fox Family Channel; Nickelodeon; TBS Superstation.

Fee: $40.00 installation; $18.67 monthly.

Pay Service 1

Pay Units: N.A.

Programming (via satellite): HBO.

Fee: $10.30 monthly.

Local advertising: Yes. Regional interconnect: Cabletime.

Equipment: Scientific-Atlanta headend; C-COR amplifiers; Comm/Scope cable; Standard Components set top converters; Scientific-Atlanta satellite antenna.

Miles of plant: 29.1 (coaxial).

Lead technician: Pete Cantu. Office assistant: Carmen Pearson.

Ownership: Time Warner Cable (MSO); Advance/Newhouse Partnership (MSO).

BATESVILLE—Falcon Cable TV, 1244 Encino Dr., Pleasanton, TX 78064. Phone: 830-569-

5509. Fax: 830-569-4828. County: Zavala. ICA: TX0886.
TV Market Ranking: Below 100. Franchise award date: N.A. Franchise expiration date: N.A. Began: N.A.
Channel capacity: 37. Channels available but not in use: 20.
Basic Service
Subscribers: 186.
Programming (received off-air): KRRT (W) Kerrville-San Antonio; KABB (F), KENS-TV (C), KLRN (P), KMOL-TV (N), KSAT-TV (A) San Antonio.
Programming (via satellite): WGN-TV (W) Chicago; ESPN; GalaVision; QVC; Univision.
Fee: $17.42 monthly.
Expanded Basic Service
Subscribers: 184.
Programming (via satellite): Fox Family Channel; Nashville Network; Sci-Fi Channel; TBS Superstation.
Fee: $3.93 monthly.
Pay Service 1
Pay Units: 18.
Programming (via satellite): Cinemax.
Fee: $10.95 monthly.
Pay Service 2
Pay Units: 46.
Programming (via satellite): HBO.
Fee: $11.95 monthly.
Miles of plant: 7.0 (coaxial). Homes passed: 313.
Manager: Lorna Gentry. Chief technician: Santos Guajardo.
Ownership: Falcon Communications LP (MSO), joint venture formed September 30, 1998. See Cable System Ownership.

BAY CITY—Northland Cable TV, 2404 Golden Ave., Bay City, TX 77414. Phone: 409-245-5511. Fax: 409-245-8256. County: Matagorda. Also serves Markham, Matagorda County, Van Vleck. ICA: TX0104.
TV Market Ranking: Outside TV Markets. Franchise award date: N.A. Franchise expiration date: March 10, 2003. Began: February 1, 1972.
Channel capacity: 43 (not 2-way capable). Channels available but not in use: None.
Basic Service
Subscribers: 5,425; Commercial subscribers: 127.
Programming (received off-air): KHOU-TV (C), KHTV (W), KPRC-TV (N), KRIV (F), KTRK-TV (A), KTXH (U), KUHT (P) Houston; KXLN-TV (S) Rosenberg; KAVU-TV (A) Victoria.
Programming (via satellite): WGN-TV (W) Chicago; C-SPAN; TBS Superstation; Univision.
Current originations: Automated time-weather; automated emergency alert.
Fee: $50.00 installation; $15.00 monthly; $2.00 converter.
Expanded Basic Service
Subscribers: 5,250.
Programming (via satellite): A & E; BET; CNN; Country Music TV; Discovery Channel; ESPN; Fox Family Channel; Fox Sports Net Southwest; Headline News; Home Shopping Network; Learning Channel; Lifetime; Nashville Network; Nick at Nite; Nickelodeon; QVC; TV Guide Channel; The Weather Channel; Trinity Bcstg. Network; USA Network.
Fee: $15.00 installation; $25.50 monthly.
Expanded Basic Service 2
Subscribers: 2,350.
Programming (via satellite): American Movie Classics; Cartoon Network; The New Encore; Turner Classic Movies; Turner Network TV.
Fee: $7.95 monthly.
Pay Service 1
Pay Units: 180.
Programming (via satellite): Cinemax.
Fee: $15.00 installation; $8.50 monthly.
Pay Service 2
Pay Units: 85.
Programming (via satellite): Disney Channel.
Fee: $15.00 installation; $7.50 monthly.
Pay Service 3
Pay Units: 1,350.
Programming (via satellite): HBO.
Fee: $15.00 installation; $10.50 monthly.
Pay Service 4
Pay Units: 125.
Programming (via satellite): Showtime.
Fee: $15.00 installation; $8.95 monthly.
Pay-Per-View
Addressable homes: 800.
Viewer's Choice.
Local advertising: Yes. Available in satellite distributed & automated programming. Regional interconnect: Cabletime.
Program Guide: Premium Channels.
Equipment: RCA, Scientific-Atlanta & Standard Electronics headend; RCA & Scientific-Atlanta amplifiers; Comm/Scope cable; Texscan/MSI character generator; RCA & Scientific-Atlanta set top converters; Scientific-Atlanta addressable set top converters; Arcom & Eagle traps; Prodelin, AFC & Scientific-Atlanta satellite antenna.
Miles of plant: 136.0 (coaxial); None (fiber optic). Homes passed: 6,400. Total homes in franchised area: 6,400.
Manager: Ken Knight. Chief technician: Dennis McCulloch. Marketing director: Pam Vallely.
City fee: 3% of basic gross; 1% of pay service net.
Ownership: Northland Communications Corp. (MSO).

BEACH CITY—Friendship Cable of Texas Inc., Box 9090, Tyler, TX 75711-9090. Phone: 903-581-2121. Fax: 903-581-2185. County: Chambers. Also serves Cove. ICA: TX0373.
TV Market Ranking: 15. Franchise award date: N.A. Franchise expiration date: N.A. Began: N.A.
Channel capacity: 36 (not 2-way capable). Channels available but not in use: None.
Basic Service
Subscribers: 508.
Programming (received off-air): KHOU-TV (C), KHTV (W), KPRC-TV (N), KRIV (F), KTRK-TV (A), KTXH (U), KUHT (P) Houston.
Programming (via satellite): WGN-TV (W) Chicago; A & E; C-SPAN; CNN; Country Music TV; Discovery Channel; Disney Channel; ESPN; Fox Family Channel; Fox Sports Net Southwest; Headline News; Lifetime; Nashville Network; Nickelodeon; QVC; TBS Superstation; The Inspirational Network; The Weather Channel; Turner Network TV; USA Network.
Fee: $33.75 monthly.
Pay Service 1
Pay Units: 23.
Programming (via satellite): Cinemax.
Fee: $10.95 monthly.
Pay Service 2
Pay Units: 48.
Programming (via satellite): HBO.
Fee: $10.95 monthly.
Pay Service 3
Pay Units: 61.
Programming (via satellite): Showtime.
Fee: $5.95 monthly.
Local advertising: Yes.
Miles of plant: 41.6 (coaxial). Homes passed: 1,000.
Manager: Wanda Pyburn. Chief technician: Mike Deal.
Ownership: Buford Television Inc. (MSO). See Cable System Ownership.

BEAUMONT—Time Warner Communications, 1460 Calder Ave., Beaumont, TX 77701-1746. Phone: 409-727-1515. Fax: 409-839-4215. County: Jefferson. ICA: TX0022.
TV Market Ranking: 88. Franchise award date: June 1, 1973. Franchise expiration date: April 1, 2009. Began: June 1, 1973.
Channel capacity: 61 (not 2-way capable). Channels available but not in use: None.
Basic Service
Subscribers: 28,253.
Programming (received off-air): KBMT (A), KBTV-TV (N), KFDM-TV (C), KITU (E) Beaumont-Port Arthur; KTXH (U), KUHT (P) Houston; KVHP (F) Lake Charles; KTCI-TV (P) Minneapolis-St. Paul; 17 FMs.
Programming (via satellite): C-SPAN; Discovery Channel; QVC; TBS Superstation; TV Guide Sneak Prevue.
Current originations: Automated time-weather; educational access; government access; leased access.
Fee: $44.95 installation; $9.92 monthly; $1.50 converter.
Expanded Basic Service
Subscribers: 27,123.
Programming (via satellite): A & E; American Movie Classics; Animal Planet; BET; CNBC; CNN; Court TV; ESPN; EWTN; FX; Fox Family Channel; Fox News Channel; Fox Sports Net Southwest; GalaVision; Headline News; Home & Garden Television; Home Shopping Network; Learning Channel; Lifetime; MSNBC; MTV; Nashville Network; Nickelodeon; Odyssey; TV Food Network; The Health Network; The New Encore; The Weather Channel; Travel Channel; Turner Network TV; USA Network.
Fee: $44.95 installation; $15.48 monthly.
Expanded Basic Service 2
Subscribers: N.A.
Programming (via satellite): Cartoon Network; Country Music TV; ESPN 2; Sci-Fi Channel.
Fee: N.A.
Pay Service 1
Pay Units: 2,228.
Programming (via satellite): Cinemax.
Fee: $12.45 monthly.
Pay Service 2
Pay Units: 1,152.
Programming (via satellite): Disney Channel.
Fee: $11.88 monthly.
Pay Service 3
Pay Units: 12,020.
Programming (via satellite): The New Encore.
Fee: $1.75 monthly.
Pay Service 4
Pay Units: 4,274.
Programming (via satellite): HBO.
Fee: $13.09 monthly.
Pay Service 5
Pay Units: 3,732.
Programming (via satellite): Showtime.
Fee: $13.09 monthly.
Pay Service 6
Pay Units: 2,044.
Programming (via satellite): The Movie Channel.
Fee: $13.09 monthly.
Pay Service 7
Pay Units: 6,217.
Programming (via satellite): Starz!
Fee: $6.75 monthly.
Pay Service 8
Pay Units: 332.
Programming (via satellite): DMX.
Fee: $9.47 monthly.
Pay Service 9
Pay Units: 249.
Programming: N.A.
Fee: $12.95 monthly.
Pay-Per-View
Addressable homes: 8,266.
Action Pay-Per-View; Playboy TV; Spice; Viewer's Choice.
Fee: $3.95 (Action Pay-Per-View); $3.99 (Spice); $7.95 (Playboy TV).
Pay-per-view manager: Mike Dolce.
Local advertising: Yes. Local sales manager: Joe Walker.
Program Guide: The Cable Guide.
Equipment: Scientific-Atlanta headend; Scientific-Atlanta amplifiers; Comm/Scope cable; Scientific-Atlanta satellite antenna; Scientific-Atlanta satellite receivers; Texscan/MSI commercial insert.
Miles of plant: 667.0 (coaxial). Homes passed: 50,935. Total homes in franchised area: 50,935.
Manager: Mike McKee. Customer service manager: Mary Lund.
City fee: 5% of gross.
Ownership: AT&T Broadband & Internet Services (MSO); Time Warner Cable (MSO); Advance/Newhouse Partnership (MSO).

BEAUMONT COLONY—Friendship Cable of Texas Inc., Box 9090, Tyler, TX 75711-9090. Phone: 903-581-2121. Fax: 903-581-2185. County: Hardin. ICA: TX0564.
TV Market Ranking: 88. Franchise award date: N.A. Franchise expiration date: N.A. Began: N.A.
Channel capacity: 36 (not 2-way capable). Channels available but not in use: 6.
Basic Service
Subscribers: 226.
Programming (received off-air): KBMT (A), KBTV-TV (N), KFDM-TV (C) Beaumont-Port Arthur; KVHP (F) Lake Charles.
Programming (via satellite): WGN-TV (W) Chicago; A & E; C-SPAN; CNN; Country Music TV; Discovery Channel; ESPN; Fox Family Channel; Fox Sports Net Southwest; Headline News; Lifetime; Nashville Network; Nickelodeon; QVC; TBS Superstation; The Inspirational Network; The Weather Channel; Turner Network TV; USA Network.
Fee: $34.95 monthly.
Pay Service 1
Pay Units: 26.
Programming (via satellite): Cinemax.
Fee: $10.95 monthly.
Pay Service 2
Pay Units: 15.
Programming (via satellite): HBO.
Fee: $10.95 monthly.
Pay Service 3
Pay Units: 22.
Programming (via satellite): Showtime.
Fee: $5.95 monthly.
Local advertising: Yes.
Miles of plant: 20.4 (coaxial). Homes passed: 408.
Manager: Wanda Pyburn. Chief technician: Mike Deal.
Ownership: Buford Television Inc. (MSO). See Cable System Ownership.

BEDFORD—TCI TKR of the Metroplex Inc., 934 E. Centerville Rd., Garland, TX 75041. Phone: 214-840-2388. County: Tarrant. Also serves Colleyville, Euless. ICA: TX0028.

TV Market Ranking: 12. Franchise award date: N.A. Franchise expiration date: N.A. Began: January 1, 1980.
Channel capacity: 70 (2-way capable; operating 2-way partially). Channels available but not in use: N.A.

Basic Service
Subscribers: 21,160.
Programming (received off-air): KDAF (W), KDFI-TV (I), KDFW (F), KERA-TV (P), KTVT (C), KTXA (U), KXAS-TV (N), KXTX-TV (I), WFAA-TV (A) Dallas-Fort Worth; KDTN (P) Denton; KUVN (S) Garland; KHSX-TV (H) Irving.
Programming (via satellite): WGN-TV (W) Chicago; A & E; C-SPAN; CNBC; CNN; Comedy Central; Country Music TV; Discovery Channel; Fox Family Channel; Headline News; Lifetime; MTV; Nashville Network; Nickelodeon; TBS Superstation; The Weather Channel; VH1.
Current originations: Automated time-weather; public access; educational access; government access; automated emergency alert; local news; local sports.
Fee: $60.00 installation; $10.52 monthly; $3.00 converter; $25.00 additional installation.

Expanded Basic Service
Subscribers: 20,492.
Programming (via satellite): American Movie Classics; ESPN; Fox Sports Net Southwest; Turner Network TV; USA Network.
Fee: $11.18 monthly.

Pay Service 1
Pay Units: N.A.
Programming (via satellite): Disney Channel; HBO; Showtime; The Movie Channel.
Fee: $25.00 installation; $10.25 monthly (Disney), $11.25 monthly (Showtime or TMC), $12.20 monthly (HBO).

Local advertising: Yes. Available in locally originated, character-generated, taped & automated programming. Local sales manager: Debra Friday.
Program Guide: The Cable Guide.
Miles of plant: 425.8 (coaxial). Homes passed: 39,278. Total homes in franchised area: 39,473.
Manager: Steve Crawford.
Ownership: AT&T Broadband & Internet Services (MSO). Purchased from Tele-Communications Inc., March 9, 1999.

BEDIAS—Mission Cable, 920 Whitmore Dr., Rockwall, TX 75087. Phones: 214-771-5014; 800-783-5708. Fax: 214-722-6218. County: Grimes. ICA: TX0669.
TV Market Ranking: Below 100. Franchise award date: July 15, 1989. Franchise expiration date: N.A. Began: N.A.
Channel capacity: 21. Channels available but not in use: 10.

Basic Service
Subscribers: 65.
Programming (received off-air): KBTX-TV (C) Bryan; KAMU-TV (P) College Station; KPRC-TV (N) Houston; KXXV (A) Waco-Temple.
Programming (via satellite): WGN-TV (W) Chicago; CNN; Discovery Channel; Fox Family Channel; Nashville Network; TBS Superstation.
Fee: $25.00 installation; $19.95 monthly.

Pay Service 1
Pay Units: 15.
Programming (via satellite): Disney Channel.
Fee: $9.00 monthly.

Pay Service 2
Pay Units: 17.
Programming (via satellite): Showtime.
Fee: $9.00 monthly.

Program Guide: TV Host.
Equipment: Blonder-Tongue headend; Magnavox amplifiers; Comm/Scope cable; Fisher traps; Weatherscan satellite antenna; Automation Techniques & DX Engineering satellite receivers.
Miles of plant: 3.0 (coaxial). Homes passed: 127. Total homes in franchised area: 127.
Manager: Jim Stafford. Chief technician: Jacky Oliver. Marketing & program director: Bruce Berkinshaw.
Ownership: Fanch Communications Inc. (MSO), Time Warner Cable (MSO). See Cable System Ownership.

BEEVILLE—Communications Services Inc., Box 28, Beeville, TX 78102. Phone: 512-358-3542. County: Bee. Also serves Chase Field Naval Air Station. ICA: TX0113.
TV Market Ranking: Outside TV Markets. Franchise award date: N.A. Franchise expiration date: N.A. Began: November 5, 1964.
Channel capacity: 39. Channels available but not in use: N.A.

Basic Service
Subscribers: 4,711.
Programming (received off-air): KEDT (P), KIII (A), KORO (S), KRIS-TV (N), KZTV (C) Corpus Christi; KENS-TV (C), KSAT-TV (A) San Antonio; allband FM.
Programming (via satellite): C-SPAN; CNBC; CNN; Discovery Channel; Fox Family Channel; FoxNet; Headline News; Knowledge TV; MTV; Nashville Network; Nick at Nite; Nickelodeon; QVC; TBS Superstation; The Weather Channel.
Current originations: Local news.
Fee: $33.17 installation; $11.18 monthly; $2.00 converter; $16.58 additional installation.

Expanded Basic Service
Subscribers: 4,066.
Programming (via satellite): American Movie Classics; Court TV; ESPN; Fox Sports Net Southwest; Turner Network TV; USA Network.
Fee: $10.00 installation; $9.94 monthly.

Pay Service 1
Pay Units: 188.
Programming (via satellite): Cinemax.
Fee: N.A.

Pay Service 2
Pay Units: 209.
Programming (via satellite): Disney Channel.
Fee: N.A.

Pay Service 3
Pay Units: 1,725.
Programming (via satellite): The New Encore.
Fee: N.A.

Pay Service 4
Pay Units: 760.
Programming (via satellite): HBO.
Fee: N.A.

Pay Service 5
Pay Units: 653.
Programming (via satellite): Showtime.
Fee: N.A.

Local advertising: No.
Program Guide: The Cable Guide.
Equipment: Jerrold headend; Jerrold amplifiers; Times Fiber cable; Jerrold set top converters; Eagle traps; Microdyne & Scientific-Atlanta satellite antenna; Scientific-Atlanta satellite receivers.
Miles of plant: 90.2 (coaxial). Homes passed: 6,044. Total homes in franchised area: 6,953.
Manager: John Salinas.
Ownership: AT&T Broadband & Internet Services (MSO). Purchased from Tele-Communications Inc., March 9, 1999.

BELLEVUE—Classic Cable, Box 429, 605 N.W. 3rd St., Plainville, KS 67663-0429. Phones: 785-434-7620; 800-999-8876. Fax: 785-434-2614. County: Clay. ICA: TX0716.
TV Market Ranking: Below 100. Franchise award date: N.A. Franchise expiration date: N.A. Began: October 1, 1988.
Channel capacity: 31 (2-way capable). Channels available but not in use: N.A.

Basic Service
Subscribers: 23.
Programming (received off-air): KDAF (W), KDFI-TV (I), KDFW (F), KERA-TV (P), KTVT (C), KTXA (U), KXAS-TV (N), KXTX-TV (I), WFAA-TV (A) Dallas-Fort Worth; KXII (C) Sherman; KAUZ-TV (C), KFDX-TV (N), KJTL (F,U), KSWO-TV (A) Wichita Falls-Lawton.
Programming (via satellite): WGN-TV (W) Chicago; CNN; ESPN; Nashville Network; TBS Superstation.
Fee: $35.00 installation; $27.95 monthly.

Pay Service 1
Pay Units: 1.
Programming (via satellite): Cinemax.
Fee: $9.95 monthly.

Pay Service 2
Pay Units: N.A.
Programming (via satellite): HBO.
Fee: $9.95 monthly.

Local advertising: Yes. Available in character-generated programming. Rates: $5.00/Day.
Equipment: Nexus headend; Scientific-Atlanta amplifiers; Comm/Scope cable; Jerrold set top converters; Pico traps.
Miles of plant: 4.0 (coaxial). Homes passed: 146.
Manager: Dave Walker. Chief technician: Roger Campbell. Marketing director: Jennifer Hauschild.
City fee: 3% of gross.
Ownership: Classic Cable (MSO).

BELLVILLE—CMA Cablevision, Box 133, La Grange, TX 78945. Phones: 409-968-6476; 800-272-0038. Fax: 409-968-5368. Counties: Austin & Waller. Also serves Hempstead, Sealy. ICA: TX0292.
TV Market Ranking: Below 100. Franchise award date: January 1, 1980. Franchise expiration date: January 1, 2004. Began: June 1, 1981.
Channel capacity: 35 (not 2-way capable). Channels available but not in use: 1.

Basic Service
Subscribers: 2,111.
Programming (received off-air): KTBC (F), KXAN-TV (N) Austin; KHOU-TV (C), KPRC-TV (N), KRIV (F), KTRK-TV (A), KUHT (P) Houston; allband FM.
Programming (via satellite): ESPN; Fox Family Channel; Nickelodeon; TBS Superstation; USA Network.
Fee: $35.00 installation; $15.95 monthly.

Pay Service 1
Pay Units: 136.
Programming (via satellite): Cinemax.
Fee: $11.50 monthly.

Pay Service 2
Pay Units: 142.
Programming (via satellite): Disney Channel.
Fee: $8.45 monthly.

Pay Service 3
Pay Units: 250.
Programming (via satellite): HBO.
Fee: $11.50 monthly.

Pay Service 4
Pay Units: 102.
Programming (via satellite): Showtime.
Fee: N.A.

Local advertising: Yes. Regional interconnect: Cabletime.
Equipment: Scientific-Atlanta headend; C-COR & Tocom amplifiers; Comm/Scope cable; Video Data Systems character generator; Standard Components set top converters; Scientific-Atlanta satellite antenna.
Miles of plant: 99.0 (coaxial); None (fiber optic).
Manager: Jerry L. Smith. Chief technician: Grady Daniels.
City fee: 3% of gross.
Ownership: Cable Management Assoc. (MSO).

BEN BOLT—National Cable Inc., Suite 106-A, 5151 Reed Rd., Columbus, OH 43220. Phones: 614-442-5890; 800-582-0504. Fax: 614-457-2567. County: Jim Wells. Also serves Alice (unincorporated areas). ICA: TX0717.
TV Market Ranking: Outside TV Markets. Franchise award date: N.A. Franchise expiration date: N.A. Began: N.A.
Channel capacity: 36. Channels available but not in use: 21.

Basic Service
Subscribers: 25.
Programming (received off-air): KEDT (P), KIII (A), KORO (S), KRIS-TV (N), KZTV (C) Corpus Christi.
Programming (via satellite): WGN-TV (W) Chicago; A & E; American Movie Classics; CNN; Country Music TV; Discovery Channel; ESPN; Fox Family Channel; Showtime; TBS Superstation; Turner Network TV; USA Network.
Fee: $28.00 monthly.

Miles of plant: 2.5 (coaxial). Homes passed: 101.
Manager: Paul Scott. Chief technician: Rob Spiller. Marketing director: Josh Thackery.
Ownership: National Cable (MSO).

BEN WHEELER—Friendship Cable of Texas Inc., Box 9090, Tyler, TX 75711-9090. Phone: 903-581-2121. Fax: 903-581-2185. Counties: Henderson & Van Zandt. Also serves Brownsboro, Calendar Lake, Colfax, Edom, Henderson County (portions), Murchison, Van, Van Zandt County (portions). ICA: TX0487.
TV Market Ranking: Below 100. Franchise award date: January 1, 1989. Franchise expiration date: January 1, 2009. Began: July 11, 1989.
Channel capacity: 36 (not 2-way capable). Channels available but not in use: 4.

Basic Service
Subscribers: 1,453.
Programming (received off-air): KDFW (F), KERA-TV (P), KTVT (C), KXAS-TV (N) Dallas-Fort Worth; KLTV (A) Tyler-Longview.

Programming (via satellite): WGN-TV (W) Chicago; A & E; CNN; Discovery Channel; ESPN; Fox Family Channel; Nashville Network; Nickelodeon; TBS Superstation; Turner Classic Movies; USA Network.
Fee: $30.00 installation; $32.70 monthly.
Pay Service 1
Pay Units: 79.
Programming (via satellite): Cinemax.
Fee: $10.95 monthly.
Pay Service 2
Pay Units: 73.
Programming (via satellite): Flix.
Fee: $1.95 monthly.
Pay Service 3
Pay Units: 81.
Programming (via satellite): HBO.
Fee: $12.00 monthly.
Pay Service 4
Pay Units: 146.
Programming (via satellite): Showtime.
Fee: $10.95 monthly.
Local advertising: Yes.
Miles of plant: 112.7 (coaxial). Homes passed: 2,350.
Manager: Marianne Bogy. Chief technician: Sonny Myers.
Ownership: Buford Television Inc. (MSO). See Cable System Ownership.

BENAVIDES—TCI Cablevision of Texas Inc., 208 W. Viggie St., Hebbronville, TX 78361-3048. Phone: 512-527-3267. County: Duval. Also serves Duval County (portions). ICA: TX0477.
TV Market Ranking: Outside TV Markets. Franchise award date: N.A. Franchise expiration date: N.A. Began: April 1, 1982.
Channel capacity: 35. Channels available but not in use: 13.
Basic Service
Subscribers: 488.
Programming (received off-air): KEDT (P), KIII (A), KRIS-TV (N), KZTV (C) Corpus Christi.
Programming (via satellite): WGN-TV (W) Chicago; CNN; Discovery Channel; ESPN; GalaVision; MTV; Nashville Network; Nickelodeon; TBS Superstation; The Weather Channel; Trinity Bcstg. Network; Turner Network TV; USA Network; Univision.
Current originations: Local news.
Fee: $60.00 installation; $21.32 monthly.
Pay Service 1
Pay Units: 34.
Programming (via satellite): Disney Channel.
Fee: N.A.
Pay Service 2
Pay Units: 152.
Programming (via satellite): HBO.
Fee: $15.00 installation; $11.00 monthly.
Pay Service 3
Pay Units: 127.
Programming (via satellite): Showtime.
Fee: $15.00 installation; $6.00 monthly.
Equipment: Gardiner satellite antenna; Gardiner satellite receivers.
Miles of plant: 16.0 (coaxial). Homes passed: 521. Total homes in franchised area: 647.
Manager: Juve Morante.
Ownership: AT&T Broadband & Internet Services (MSO). Purchased from Tele-Communications Inc., March 9, 1999.

BENJAMIN—Jayroc Cablevision, Box 6575, Abilene, TX 79608. Phone: 915-691-5787. County: Knox. ICA: TX0718.
TV Market Ranking: Outside TV Markets. Franchise award date: N.A. Franchise expiration date: N.A. Began: N.A.
Channel capacity: N.A. Channels available but not in use: N.A.
Basic Service
Subscribers: N.A.
Programming (received off-air): KJTL (F,U), KSWO-TV (A) Wichita Falls-Lawton.
Programming (via satellite): WGN-TV (W) Chicago; KCNC-TV (C), KMGH-TV (A) Denver; TBS Superstation.
Fee: N.A.
Ownership: Jayroc Inc. (MSO).

BENTSEN GROVE—Rapid Cable, Box 6310, 310 Walnut Extension, Branson, MO 65615. Phones: 417-334-7897; 800-972-0962. Fax: 417-334-7899. Counties: Hidalgo & Hildago County. Also serves Hidalgo County (portions). ICA: TX0235.
TV Market Ranking: Below 100. Franchise award date: N.A. Franchise expiration date: N.A. Began: June 1, 1989.
Channel capacity: 52 (not 2-way capable). Channels available but not in use: 33.
Basic Service
Subscribers: 154.
Programming (received off-air): KVEO (N) Brownsville; KGBT-TV (C), KMBH (P) Harlingen; KRGV-TV (A) Weslaco; XHAB-TV Matamoros; XHRIO (O) Matamoros-Brownsville.
Programming (via satellite): WGN-TV (W) Chicago; C-SPAN; CNN; Country Music TV; Discovery Channel; ESPN; Fox Family Channel; Fox News Channel; GalaVision; Lifetime; Nashville Network; Nickelodeon; TBS Superstation; The Weather Channel; Trinity Bcstg. Network; Turner Network TV; Univision.
Fee: $29.95 installation; $21.95 monthly; $2.95 converter.
Pay Service 1
Pay Units: 32.
Programming (via satellite): Cinemax.
Fee: $9.00 monthly.
Pay Service 2
Pay Units: 38.
Programming (via satellite): HBO.
Fee: $10.00 monthly.
Miles of plant: 25.0 (coaxial); 25.0 (fiber optic). Homes passed: 2,226.
Manager: Belinda Murphy. Chief engineer: Steve Rice. Marketing director: Bill Fischer.
Ownership: Rapid Communications Partners LP (MSO).

BERCLAIR—Torrence Cablevision, Box 1167, Ridgeland, MS 39158. Phones: 601-981-6900; 800-977-8849. County: Goliad. ICA: TX0694.
TV Market Ranking: Below 100. Franchise award date: N.A. Franchise expiration date: N.A. Began: February 15, 1990.
Channel capacity: 36 (not 2-way capable). Channels available but not in use: N.A.
Basic Service
Subscribers: 26.
Programming (received off-air): KIII (A), KRIS-TV (N) Corpus Christi; KVTV (C) Laredo; KABB (F), KLRN (P) San Antonio.
Programming (via satellite): WGN-TV (W) Chicago; A & E; American Movie Classics; CNN; Country Music TV; Discovery Channel; ESPN; Fox Family Channel; Nashville Network; Showtime; TBS Superstation; Turner Network TV; USA Network; Univision.
Current originations: Automated time-weather.
Fee: $28.00 monthly.
Equipment: Nexus headend; Magnavox amplifiers; Times Fiber cable; Oak set top converters; Nexus satellite receivers.
Miles of plant: 3.3 (coaxial). Homes passed: 94.
Ownership: Torrence Cable Inc. (MSO).

BERRYVILLE—Northland Cable TV, Box 538, Flint, TX 75762. Phones: 903-894-8200; 903-876-4554. Fax: 903-894-8204. Counties: Anderson & Henderson. Also serves Frankston. ICA: TX0368.
TV Market Ranking: Below 100. Franchise award date: June 7, 1982. Franchise expiration date: June 7, 1997. Began: June 1, 1983.
Channel capacity: 36 (2-way capable). Channels available but not in use: 5.
Basic Service
Subscribers: 570.
Programming (received off-air): KETK-TV (N) Jacksonville; KFXK (F) Longview; KLTV (A) Tyler-Longview.
Programming (via microwave): KDFW (F), KERA-TV (P), KTVT (C), KXTX-TV (I), WFAA-TV (A) Dallas-Fort Worth.
Programming (via satellite): WGN-TV (W) Chicago; A & E; CNN; Country Music TV; Discovery Channel; ESPN; Fox Family Channel; Fox Sports Net Southwest; Headline News; Learning Channel; Nashville Network; QVC; TBS Superstation; USA Network.
Current originations: Automated time-weather; local sports.
Fee: $49.95 installation (aerial), $64.95 (underground); $20.75 monthly; $3.00 converter.
Pay Service 1
Pay Units: 33.
Programming (via satellite): Disney Channel.
Fee: $24.95 installation; $7.00 monthly.
Pay Service 2
Pay Units: 63.
Programming (via satellite): HBO.
Fee: $24.95 installation; $10.50 monthly.
Pay Service 3
Pay Units: 52.
Programming (via satellite): Showtime.
Fee: $24.95 installation; $7.95 monthly.
Local advertising: Yes. Available in satellite distributed, locally originated, character-generated, taped & automated programming. Rates: $16.00/Minute; $8.00/30 Seconds. Local sales manager: Lynda Tracy.
Program Guide: Premium Channels.
Equipment: Hughes, M/A-Com & Scientific-Atlanta headend; Magnavox amplifiers; Comm/Scope cable; Texscan character generator; Hamlin, Jerrold & Scientific-Atlanta set top converters; Arcom, Eagle & Pico traps; AFC satellite antenna; Harris & DX Antenna satellite receivers; ChannelMatic commercial insert.
Miles of plant: 20.0 (coaxial). Homes passed: 950.
Manager: Jim Wiggins. Chief technician: Jim Bob Sanders. Marketing director: Charlotte Griffin.
City fee: 3% of gross.
Ownership: Northland Communications Corp. (MSO).

BERTRAM—Time Warner Cable, 12012 N. Mo Pac Expressway, Austin, TX 78758-2904. Phones: 512-485-6100; 800-418-8848. Fax: 512-485-6105.
Web site: http://timewarneraustin.com.
County: Burnet. ICA: TX0519.
TV Market Ranking: Below 100. Franchise award date: September 13, 1994. Franchise expiration date: September 13, 2009. Began: N.A.
Channel capacity: 52 (not 2-way capable). Channels available but not in use: 17.
Basic Service
Subscribers: 240.
Programming (received off-air): KEYE-TV (C), KLRU (P), KNVA (W), KTBC (F), KVUE-TV (A), KXAN-TV (N) Austin; KCEN-TV (N), KXXV (A) Waco-Temple.
Programming (via satellite): WGN-TV (W) Chicago; American Movie Classics; Animal Planet; CNN; Comedy Central; Country Music TV; Discovery Channel; ESPN; ESPN 2; Fox Family Channel; GalaVision; Headline News; Home & Garden Television; Learning Channel; Lifetime; MSNBC; Nashville Network; Nick at Nite; Nickelodeon; Pax Net; TBS Superstation; The Weather Channel; Turner Classic Movies; Turner Network TV; USA Network.
Fee: $28.21 installation; $25.70 monthly; $1.15 converter; $12.11 additional installation.
Pay Service 1
Pay Units: N.A.
Programming (via satellite): Cinemax; HBO; Showtime.
Fee: $7.00 monthly (Cinemax or Showtime), $12.00 monthly (HBO).
Miles of plant: 9.9 (coaxial); None (fiber optic). Homes passed: 409.
Manager: Bill Carey. Chief technician: Matt Stanek. Program director: George Warmingham. Marketing director: Michelle Golden.
Ownership: Time Warner Cable (MSO).

BIG LAKE—Western Community TV Cable, Box 2040, San Angelo, TX 76902. Phone: 915-834-3406. Fax: 915-655-1185. County: Reagan. ICA: TX0720.
TV Market Ranking: Outside TV Markets. Franchise award date: N.A. Franchise expiration date: N.A. Began: June 1, 1958.
Channel capacity: 22. Channels available but not in use: 1.
Basic Service
Subscribers: 1,065.
Programming (received off-air): KMID (A), KOSA-TV (C), KPEJ (F), KWES-TV (N) Odessa-Midland; KLST (C) San Angelo; 12 FMs.
Programming (via satellite): WGN-TV (W) Chicago; CNN; ESPN; Fox Family Channel; Odyssey; QVC; TBS Superstation; Univision.
Planned programming (via satellite): Nashville Network; Turner Network TV.
Fee: $20.00 installation; $9.00 monthly.
Pay Service 1
Pay Units: 495.
Programming (via satellite): Disney Channel.
Fee: $10.00 monthly.
Pay Service 2
Pay Units: 696.
Programming (via satellite): HBO.
Fee: $11.00 monthly.
Equipment: Ameco headend; Blonder-Tongue amplifiers; AFC satellite antenna.
Miles of plant: 16.1 (coaxial).
Manager: Daniel Anderson. Chief technician: Phil Pool.
Ownership: Wilbur L. Anderson (MSO).

BIG SPRING—TCA Cable TV, 2006 Birdwell, Big Spring, TX 79720. Phone: 915-267-3821. Fax: 915-264-0779.
Web site: http://www.tca-cable.com.
County: Howard. Also serves Coahoma, Howard County. ICA: TX0063.
TV Market Ranking: Below 100. Franchise award date: January 1, 1961. Franchise expiration date: N.A. Began: September 1, 1961.
Channel capacity: 35 (not 2-way capable). Channels available but not in use: N.A.
Basic Service
Subscribers: 8,665.
Programming (received off-air): KWAB-TV (N) Big Spring; KMID (A), KOSA-TV (C) Odessa-Midland; allband FM.

Programming (via microwave): KERA-TV (P), WFAA-TV (A) Dallas-Fort Worth.
Programming (via satellite): CNN; Country Music TV; ESPN; Fox Family Channel; TBS Superstation; The Weather Channel; Univision.
Fee: $42.59 installation; $12.14 monthly.

Expanded Basic Service
Subscribers: 7,473.
Programming (via satellite): Headline News; Lifetime; MTV; Nashville Network; Nickelodeon; USA Network.
Fee: $11.12 monthly.

Pay Service 1
Pay Units: N.A.
Programming (via satellite): Disney Channel; Showtime; The Movie Channel.
Fee: $35.00 installation; $9.88 monthly (each).

Local advertising: Yes. Regional interconnect: Cabletime.
Equipment: Scientific-Atlanta headend; C-COR amplifiers; Scientific-Atlanta satellite antenna.
Miles of plant: 188.6 (coaxial). Homes passed: 12,500.
Manager: Archie Kountz. Chief technician: Vern Bloodworth.
City fee: 3% of gross.
Ownership: TCA Cable TV Inc. (MSO); AT&T Broadband & Internet Services (MSO). See Cable System Ownership.

BIG WELLS—Falcon Cable TV, 1244 Encino Dr., Pleasanton, TX 78064. Phone: 830-569-5509. Fax: 830-569-4828. County: Dimmit. ICA: TX0887.
TV Market Ranking: Outside TV Markets. Franchise award date: N.A. Franchise expiration date: N.A. Began: N.A.
Channel capacity: 37. Channels available but not in use: 20.

Basic Service
Subscribers: 152.
Programming (received off-air): KRRT (W) Kerrville-San Antonio; KABB (F), KENS-TV (C), KLRN (P), KMOL-TV (N), KSAT-TV (A) San Antonio.
Programming (via satellite): WGN-TV (W) Chicago; ESPN; GalaVision; QVC; Univision.
Fee: $17.48 monthly.

Expanded Basic Service
Subscribers: 150.
Programming (via satellite): Fox Family Channel; Nashville Network; Sci-Fi Channel; TBS Superstation.
Fee: $6.00 installation; $4.05 monthly.

Pay Service 1
Pay Units: 9.
Programming (via satellite): Cinemax.
Fee: $10.95 monthly.

Pay Service 2
Pay Units: 28.
Programming (via satellite): HBO.
Fee: $11.95 monthly.

Miles of plant: 7.0 (coaxial). Homes passed: 313.
Manager: Lorna Gentry. Chief technician: Santos Guajardo.
Ownership: Falcon Communications LP (MSO), joint venture formed September 30, 1998. See Cable System Ownership.

BIRCH CREEK—BRDC Cablevision, Box 240, Giddings, TX 78942. Phone: 409-542-3151. Fax: 409-542-1187. County: Washington. ICA: TX0885.
TV Market Ranking: Below 100. Franchise award date: N.A. Franchise expiration date: N.A. Began: N.A.
Channel capacity: 36 (not 2-way capable). Channels available but not in use: 16.

Basic Service
Subscribers: 149.
Programming (received off-air): KLRU (P), KVUE-TV (A), KXAN-TV (N) Austin; KBTX-TV (C) Bryan; KHTV (W), KRIV (F), KTXH (U) Houston.
Programming (via satellite): WGN-TV (W) Chicago; CNN; Discovery Channel; Disney Channel; ESPN; Fox Family Channel; Fox Sports Net; Nashville Network; TBS Superstation; Turner Network TV; USA Network.
Fee: $25.00 installation; $21.95 monthly.

Pay Service 1
Pay Units: N.A.
Programming (via satellite): Cinemax; HBO; Showtime.
Fee: $9.95 monthly (each).

Miles of plant: 12.1 (coaxial); None (fiber optic). Homes passed: 350. Total homes in franchised area: 376.
Manager: David W. Peterson.
Ownership: Bluebonnet Rural Development Corp. (MSO).

BISHOP—TCI Cablevision of Texas, 4060 S. Padre Island Dr., Corpus Christi, TX 78411-4477. Phone: 512-857-5000. County: Nueces. ICA: TX0332.
TV Market Ranking: Below 100. Franchise award date: N.A. Franchise expiration date: N.A. Began: May 1, 1982.
Channel capacity: 35. Channels available but not in use: 10.

Basic Service
Subscribers: 682.
Programming (received off-air): KEDT (P), KIII (A), KORO (S), KRIS-TV (N), KZTV (C) Corpus Christi.
Programming (via satellite): WGN-TV (W) Chicago; American Movie Classics; CNBC; CNN; Discovery Channel; ESPN; Fox Family Channel; FoxNet; GalaVision; Headline News; Lifetime; Nashville Network; QVC; TBS Superstation; The Weather Channel; Turner Network TV.
Planned originations: Automated time-weather; automated emergency alert.
Fee: $35.63 installation; $10.35 monthly; $17.81 additional installation.

Pay Service 1
Pay Units: 157.
Programming (via satellite): Cinemax.
Fee: $8.00 monthly.

Pay Service 2
Pay Units: 92.
Programming (via satellite): Disney Channel.
Fee: N.A.

Pay Service 3
Pay Units: 251.
Programming (via satellite): The New Encore.
Fee: N.A.

Pay Service 4
Pay Units: 275.
Programming (via satellite): HBO.
Fee: $8.00 monthly.

Equipment: Scientific-Atlanta headend; Scientific-Atlanta amplifiers; Comm/Scope cable; Anixter-Mark satellite antenna; Scientific-Atlanta satellite receivers.
Miles of plant: 19.5 (coaxial). Homes passed: 1,127. Total homes in franchised area: 1,150.
Manager: Dennis Moore. Chief technician: Mando Blancas. Marketing director: Jerri Coppedge.
City fee: 3% of gross.
Ownership: AT&T Broadband & Internet Services (MSO). Purchased from Tele-Communications Inc., March 9, 1999.

BLACKWELL—Big Country Cablevision, Box 3528, Hwy. 87 N, San Angelo, TX 76902. Phones: 915-655-4657; 800-256-9032. Counties: Coke & Nolan. ICA: TX0472.
TV Market Ranking: Below 100. Franchise award date: N.A. Franchise expiration date: N.A. Began: December 1, 1987.
Channel capacity: 21. Channels available but not in use: 7.

Basic Service
Subscribers: 210.
Programming (received off-air): KRBC-TV (N), KTAB-TV (C), KTXS-TV (A) Abilene-Sweetwater; KIDY (F), KLST (C) San Angelo.
Programming (via satellite): WGN-TV (W) Chicago; CNN; Country Music TV; Discovery Channel; ESPN; Nashville Network; TBS Superstation; Turner Classic Movies; Turner Network TV.
Fee: $35.00 installation; $16.00 monthly.

Pay Service 1
Pay Units: 61.
Programming (via satellite): HBO.
Fee: $10.50 monthly.

Miles of plant: 18.0 (coaxial). Homes passed: 535.
Manager: Kenny White.
Ownership: Cable Management Assoc. (MSO).

BLANKET—Cab-Tel Corp., Suite 106-A, 5151 Reed Rd., Columbus, OH 43220. Phone: 614-442-5890. Fax: 614-457-2567. County: Brown. ICA: TX0643.
TV Market Ranking: Outside TV Markets. Franchise award date: February 5, 1988. Franchise expiration date: February 5, 2003. Began: August 1, 1988.
Channel capacity: 22 (2-way capable). Channels available but not in use: 5.

Basic Service
Subscribers: 114.
Programming (received off-air): KIDZ-LP (F) Abilene; KRBC-TV (N), KTAB-TV (C), KTXS-TV (A) Abilene-Sweetwater.
Programming (via satellite): WGN-TV (W) Chicago; A & E; CNN; Country Music TV; Discovery Channel; ESPN; Fox Family Channel; Lifetime; Nashville Network; QVC; TBS Superstation; The Weather Channel; Trinity Bcstg. Network; Turner Network TV; USA Network.
Fee: $29.95 installation; $21.95 monthly; $2.95 converter.

Pay Service 1
Pay Units: 18.
Programming (via satellite): HBO.
Fee: $10.00 monthly.

Pay Service 2
Pay Units: N.A.
Programming (via satellite): Cinemax; Disney Channel.
Fee: $7.00 monthly (Disney), $9.00 monthly (Cinemax).

Local advertising: No.
Miles of plant: 4.0 (coaxial). Homes passed: 198.
Manager: Bill Mayes. Systems/operations manager: Steve Miller.
Ownership: Rapid Communications Partners LP (MSO).

BLESSING—Mid Coast Cable TV Inc., Box 1269, 505 N. Machnic, El Campo, TX 77437. Phone: 409-543-6858. County: Matagorda. Also serves Matagorda County (portions). ICA: TX0490.
TV Market Ranking: Outside TV Markets. Franchise award date: November 1, 1982. Franchise expiration date: January 1, 1998. Began: August 24, 1983.
Channel capacity: 30. Channels available but not in use: 6.

Basic Service
Subscribers: 299.
Programming (received off-air): KHSH-TV (H) Alvin; KHOU-TV (C), KHTV (W), KPRC-TV (N), KTRK-TV (A), KTXH (U), KUHT (P) Houston; KXLN-TV (S) Rosenberg; allband FM.
Programming (via satellite): CNN; Country Music TV; Discovery Channel; ESPN; Fox Family Channel; Fox Sports Net Southwest; Nashville Network; Nickelodeon; Sci-Fi Channel; TBS Superstation; The Weather Channel; Turner Network TV; USA Network.
Fee: $25.00 installation; $19.00 monthly; $12.50 additional installation.

Pay Service 1
Pay Units: 33.
Programming (via satellite): Cinemax.
Fee: $10.00 installation; $10.50 monthly.

Pay Service 2
Pay Units: 47.
Programming (via satellite): HBO.
Fee: $10.00 installation; $11.50 monthly.

Equipment: Blonder-Tongue, M/A-Com & Triple Crown headend; Superior amplifiers; Comm/Scope cable; Jerrold, Scientific-Atlanta & Tocom set top converters; Arcom traps; Fort Worth Tower, Scientific-Atlanta satellite antenna; Jerrold satellite receivers.
Miles of plant: 11.0 (coaxial). Additional miles planned: 1.0 (coaxial). Homes passed: 475. Total homes in franchised area: 900.
Manager: Jake Landrum. Chief technician: Dickie Isaacs.
City fee: None.
Ownership: Mid Coast Cable TV Inc. (MSO).

BLOOMINGTON—Classic Cable, Box 429, 605 N.W. 3rd St., Plainville, KS 67663-0429. Phones: 785-434-7620; 800-999-8876. Fax: 785-434-2614. County: Victoria. ICA: TX0469.
TV Market Ranking: Below 100. Franchise award date: N.A. Franchise expiration date: N.A. Began: March 1, 1976.
Channel capacity: 41 (2-way capable). Channels available but not in use: N.A.

Basic Service
Subscribers: 377.
Programming (received off-air): KEDT (P), KZTV (C) Corpus Christi; KENS-TV (C), KMOL-TV (N), KSAT-TV (A) San Antonio; KVCT (F) Victoria; allband FM.
Programming (via satellite): WGN-TV (W) Chicago; A & E; Animal Planet; BET; CNN; Discovery Channel; Disney Channel; ESPN; Fox Family Channel; Fox News Channel; Headline News; Home Shopping Network; Learning Channel; Nashville Network; Nick at Nite's TV Land; Nickelodeon; Sci-Fi Channel; TBS Superstation; Telemundo; The Weather Channel; Trinity Bcstg. Network; Turner Classic Movies; Turner Network TV; USA Network; Univision.
Current originations: Automated time-weather.
Fee: $35.00 installation; $27.95 monthly; $15.00 additional installation.

Pay Service 1
Pay Units: 91.
Programming (via satellite): HBO.
Fee: $25.00 installation; $10.95 monthly.

Pay Service 2
Pay Units: 55.
Programming (via satellite): Showtime.
Fee: $9.95 monthly.

Local advertising: No.
Miles of plant: 15.0 (coaxial). Homes passed: 500.
Manager: Bill Flowers. Chief technician: Walt VanLue. Marketing director: Jennifer Hauschild.
Ownership: Classic Cable (MSO).

BLUE RIDGE—Torrence Cablevision, Box 1167, Ridgeland, MS 39158. Phones: 601-981-6900; 800-977-8849. County: Collin. ICA: TX0607.
TV Market Ranking: Below 100. Franchise award date: N.A. Franchise expiration date: N.A. Began: July 1, 1989.
Channel capacity: 35. Channels available but not in use: 6.
Basic Service
Subscribers: 82.
Programming (received off-air): KDAF (W), KDFW (F), KERA-TV (P), KTVT (C), KXAS-TV (N), WFAA-TV (A) Dallas-Fort Worth.
Programming (via satellite): WGN-TV (W) Chicago; A & E; BET; C-SPAN; CNN; Country Music TV; Discovery Channel; ESPN; Fox Family Channel; Fox Sports Net Southwest; Headline News; Home Shopping Network; Lifetime; Nashville Network; Nickelodeon; TBS Superstation; The Inspirational Network; Turner Network TV; USA Network; Univision; VH1.
Fee: $21.00 monthly.
Pay Service 1
Pay Units: 19.
Programming (via satellite): Cinemax.
Fee: $10.95 monthly.
Pay Service 2
Pay Units: 9.
Programming (via satellite): Disney Channel.
Fee: $10.95 monthly.
Pay Service 3
Pay Units: 23.
Programming (via satellite): HBO.
Fee: $10.95 monthly.
Local advertising: Yes.
Miles of plant: 5.4 (coaxial). Homes passed: 237.
Ownership: Torrence Cable Inc. (MSO).

BLUFF DALE—Torrence Cablevision, Box 1167, Ridgeland, MS 39158. Phones: 601-981-6900; 800-977-8849. County: Erath. ICA: TX0693.
TV Market Ranking: Outside TV Markets. Franchise award date: N.A. Franchise expiration date: N.A. Began: N.A.
Channel capacity: 36. Channels available but not in use: 21.
Basic Service
Subscribers: 24.
Programming (received off-air): KDAF (W), KDFW (F), KERA-TV (P), KTVT (C), KXAS-TV (N), KXTX-TV (I), WFAA-TV (A) Dallas-Fort Worth.
Programming (via satellite): A & E; American Movie Classics; CNN; Country Music TV; Discovery Channel; ESPN; Fox Family Channel; Nashville Network; Showtime; TBS Superstation; USA Network.
Fee: $28.00 monthly.
Miles of plant: 2.4 (coaxial). Homes passed: 91.
Ownership: Torrence Cable Inc. (MSO).

BOERNE—Guadalupe Valley Communication Systems Inc., 1221 S. Main St., Boerne, TX 78006. Phone: 830-885-7606. Fax: 830-249-8107. Counties: Bexar & Kendall. Also serves Bexar County, Kendall County. ICA: TX0315.
TV Market Ranking: 45 (Bexar County, Boerne, portions of Kendall County); Below 100 (portions of Kendall County); Outside TV Markets (portions of Kendall County). Franchise award date: January 1, 1980. Franchise expiration date: N.A. Began: August 1, 1981.
Channel capacity: 35 (not 2-way capable). Channels available but not in use: None.
Basic Service
Subscribers: 4,153.
Programming (received off-air): KRRT (W) Kerrville-San Antonio; KABB (F), KENS-TV (C), KLRN (P), KMOL-TV (N), KSAT-TV (A), KVDA (O), KWEX-TV (S) San Antonio.
Programming (via satellite): WGN-TV (W) Chicago; A & E; American Movie Classics; C-SPAN; CNBC; CNN; Country Music TV; Discovery Channel; ESPN; Fox Family Channel; Fox Sports Net Southwest; Headline News; Learning Channel; Lifetime; MTV; Nashville Network; Nick at Nite; Nickelodeon; QVC; TBS Superstation; The Weather Channel; Turner Network TV; USA Network.
Fee: $25.00 installation; $16.50 monthly; $1.50 converter.
Pay Service 1
Pay Units: 754.
Programming (via satellite): HBO.
Fee: $12.00 monthly.
Pay Service 2
Pay Units: 462.
Programming (via satellite): The Movie Channel.
Fee: $9.95 monthly.
Pay Service 3
Pay Units: 737.
Programming (via satellite): Showtime.
Fee: $9.95 monthly.
Local advertising: Yes. Available in character-generated programming. Rates: $0.60/30 Seconds. Local sales manager: Jan Alexander.
Equipment: Scientific-Atlanta headend; Texscan amplifiers; Scientific-Atlanta set top converters; Microdyne satellite antenna; Microdyne satellite receivers.
Miles of plant: 80.0 (coaxial); 12.0 (fiber optic).
Manager: Tom See. Chief technician: Scott Maytum. Marketing director & customer service manager: Jan Alexander.
Ownership: Guadalupe Valley Communications Systems Inc. (MSO).

BOLING—Star Cable, Drawer 1570, Brazoria, TX 77422. Phones: 409-798-9121; 800-395-2775. Fax: 409-798-4409. County: Wharton. ICA: TX0485.
TV Market Ranking: Below 100. Franchise award date: N.A. Franchise expiration date: N.A. Began: N.A.
Channel capacity: 35 (not 2-way capable). Channels available but not in use: 12.
Basic Service
Subscribers: 151; Commercial subscribers: 18.
Programming (received off-air): KHOU-TV (C), KHTV (W), KPRC-TV (N), KRIV (F), KTRK-TV (A), KTXH (U), KUHT (P) Houston; KXLN-TV (S) Rosenberg.
Programming (via satellite): WGN-TV (W) Chicago; CNN; ESPN; Fox Family Channel; Fox Sports Net Southwest; Nashville Network; Nickelodeon; TBS Superstation; The Weather Channel; Turner Network TV; USA Network.
Fee: $29.95 monthly; $2.15 converter.
Pay Service 1
Pay Units: 25.
Programming (via satellite): Cinemax.
Fee: $10.95 monthly.
Pay Service 2
Pay Units: 29.
Programming (via satellite): Disney Channel.
Fee: $7.95 monthly.
Pay Service 3
Pay Units: 57.
Programming (via satellite): HBO.
Fee: $10.95 monthly.
Pay Service 4
Pay Units: 42.
Programming (via satellite): The Movie Channel.
Fee: $6.95 monthly.
Miles of plant: 11.5 (coaxial); None (fiber optic). Homes passed: 489.
Manager: Mike Burns. Chief technician: Mayla Zubeck.
Ownership: Star Cable Associates (MSO).

BONHAM—Cable One, 524 N. Main, Bonham, TX 75418. Phone: 903-583-2131. Fax: 903-583-2088. E-mail: cableone@netexas.net. County: Fannin. Also serves Fannin County. ICA: TX0169.
TV Market Ranking: Below 100. Franchise award date: N.A. Franchise expiration date: January 12, 2001. Began: February 1, 1958.
Channel capacity: 26 (not 2-way capable). Channels available but not in use: None.
Basic Service
Subscribers: 3,565.
Programming (received off-air): KTEN (A,N,F) Ada; KDAF (W), KDFI-TV (I), KDFW (F), KERA-TV (P), KTVT (C), KTXA (U), KXAS-TV (N), KXTX-TV (I), WFAA-TV (A) Dallas-Fort Worth; KUVN (S) Garland; KTAQ (I) Greenville; KXII (C) Sherman; 6 FMs.
Programming (via satellite): TBS Superstation; TV Guide Channel.
Fee: $11.72 installation; $12.15 monthly; $0.95 converter.
Expanded Basic Service
Subscribers: 3,031.
Programming (via satellite): A & E; American Movie Classics; BET; C-SPAN; CNBC; CNN; Cartoon Network; Country Music TV; Discovery Channel; Disney Channel; ESPN; ESPN 2; FX; Fox Family Channel; Fox Sports Net Southwest; Headline News; History Channel; Home Shopping Network; Learning Channel; Lifetime; MTV; Nashville Network; Nickelodeon; Sci-Fi Channel; The Inspirational Network; The Weather Channel; Trinity Bcstg. Network; Turner Network TV; USA Network; VH1.
Fee: $11.72 installation; $16.82 monthly.
Pay Service 1
Pay Units: 275.
Programming (via satellite): Cinemax (multiplexed).
Fee: $5.95 installation; $13.95 monthly.
Pay Service 2
Pay Units: 585.
Programming (via satellite): HBO (multiplexed).
Fee: $5.95 installation; $13.95 monthly.
Pay Service 3
Pay Units: 118.
Programming (via satellite): Showtime.
Fee: $5.95 installation; $10.95 monthly.
Pay Service 4
Pay Units: N.A.
Programming (via satellite): The Movie Channel.
Fee: $10.95 monthly.
Pay-Per-View
Addressable homes: 1,580.
Viewer's Choice.
Fee: $2.99.
Local advertising: Yes. Available in locally originated programming. Rates: $3.00/Spot.
Equipment: Scientific-Atlanta headend; Scientific-Atlanta & GTE Sylvania amplifiers; Comm/Scope cable; MSI character generator; Zenith set top converters; Zenith addressable set top converters; Hughes & M/A-Com satellite antenna; Scientific-Atlanta satellite receivers; Sony commercial insert.
Miles of plant: 89.0 (coaxial); 19.0 (fiber optic). Homes passed: 3,670. Total homes in franchised area: 3,770.
Manager: Rod Ralls.
City fee: 3% of gross.
Ownership: Cable One Inc. (MSO).

BOOKER—Classic Cable, Box 429, 605 N.W. 3rd St., Plainville, KS 67663-0429. Phones: 785-434-7620; 800-999-8876. Fax: 785-434-2614. County: Lipscomb. ICA: TX0456.
TV Market Ranking: Outside TV Markets. Franchise award date: N.A. Franchise expiration date: N.A. Began: September 1, 1955.
Channel capacity: 41 (2-way capable). Channels available but not in use: N.A.
Basic Service
Subscribers: 340; Commercial subscribers: 48.
Programming (received off-air): Allband FM.
Programming (via microwave): KACV-TV (P), KAMR-TV (N), KCIT (F,U), KFDA-TV (C), KVII-TV (A) Amarillo.
Programming (via satellite): WGN-TV (W) Chicago; A & E; American Movie Classics; Animal Planet; CNN; Country Music TV; Discovery Channel; Disney Channel; E! Entertainment TV; ESPN; Fox Family Channel; Headline News; History Channel; Learning Channel; Lifetime; Nashville Network; Nick at Nite's TV Land; Nickelodeon; QVC; Sci-Fi Channel; TBS Superstation; Telemundo; The Weather Channel; Turner Network TV; USA Network.
Fee: $35.00 installation; $27.95 monthly.
Pay Service 1
Pay Units: 101.
Programming (via satellite): HBO.
Fee: $9.95 monthly.
Equipment: Scientific-Atlanta headend; Magnavox amplifiers; Times Fiber cable; Tandy character generator; Scientific-Atlanta set top converters; Scientific-Atlanta satellite receivers.
Miles of plant: 12.0 (coaxial). Homes passed: 515.
Manager: Bill Flowers. Chief technician: Rick Rattan. Marketing director: Jennifer Hauschild.
City fee: 1% of gross.
Ownership: Classic Cable (MSO).

BORGER—Charter Communications Inc., Box 5044, 201 E. 10th St., Borger, TX 79007. Phone: 806-273-3744. Fax: 806-273-5258. County: Hutchinson. Also serves Fritch, Phillips, Stinnett. ICA: TX0068.
TV Market Ranking: 95 (Fritch); Outside TV Markets (Borger, Phillips, Stinnett). Franchise award date: N.A. Franchise expiration date: N.A. Began: February 1, 1978.
Channel capacity: 44. Channels available but not in use: N.A.
Basic Service
Subscribers: 5,068.
Programming (received off-air): KACV-TV (P), KAMR-TV (N), KCIT (F,U), KFDA-TV (C), KVII-TV (A) Amarillo; 7 FMs.
Programming (via satellite): WGN-TV (W) Chicago; C-SPAN; Home Shopping Network; QVC; TBS Superstation.
Fee: $11.50 monthly.
Expanded Basic Service
Subscribers: N.A.
Programming (via satellite): American Movie Classics; BET; C-SPAN 2; CNBC; CNN; Country Music TV; Discovery Channel; E! Entertainment TV; ESPN; Fox Family Channel; Fox Sports Net Southwest; Headline News; Lifetime; MTV; Nashville Network;

Nickelodeon; The Weather Channel; Trinity Bcstg. Network; Turner Network TV; Univision.
Fee: $35.00 installation; $19.50 monthly.
Pay Service 1
Pay Units: N.A.
Programming (via satellite): Cinemax; Disney Channel; HBO; The Movie Channel.
Fee: $15.00 installation; $8.50 monthly (Disney), $9.95 monthly (Cinemax), $10.95 monthly (TMC), $11.75 monthly (HBO).
Local advertising: Yes.
Equipment: Scientific-Atlanta headend; GTE Sylvania amplifiers; Comm/Scope cable; Oak set top converters; Scientific-Atlanta satellite antenna.
Miles of plant: 166.0 (coaxial). Homes passed: 10,361. Total homes in franchised area: 11,085.
Manager: Wayne Susee. Chief technician: Randy Loucks.
City fee: 3% of gross.
Ownership: Charter Communications Inc. (MSO). Purchased from Marcus Cable, April 1, 1999.

BOWIE—Southwest Cablevision, Box 869, 2804-B FM 51 S, Decatur, TX 76234. Phone: 817-627-3099. Fax: 817-627-8303. County: Montague. ICA: TX0191.
TV Market Ranking: Outside TV Markets. Franchise award date: October 1, 1984. Franchise expiration date: October 1, 1999. Began: October 1, 1969.
Channel capacity: N.A. Channels available but not in use: N.A.
Basic Service
Subscribers: 1,869; Commercial subscribers: 58.
Programming (received off-air): KDFI-TV (I), KDFW (F), KERA-TV (P), KTVT (C), KTXA (U), KXAS-TV (N), KXTX-TV (I) Dallas-Fort Worth; KMPX (I) Decatur; KUVN (S) Garland; KAUZ-TV (C), KFDX-TV (N), KJTL (F,U), KSWO-TV (A) Wichita Falls-Lawton; 2 FMs.
Current originations: Automated time-weather; religious access.
Fee: $55.00 installation; $19.90 monthly.
Expanded Basic Service
Subscribers: 1,749.
Programming (via satellite): A & E; American Movie Classics; BET; C-SPAN; C-SPAN 2; CNBC; CNN; Cartoon Network; Comedy Central; Country Music TV; Discovery Channel; ESPN; ESPN 2; EWTN; Fox Family Channel; Fox Sports Net Southwest; Good-life TV Network; Headline News; Learning Channel; Lifetime; MTV; Nashville Network; Nickelodeon; Odyssey; QVC; Sci-Fi Channel; The Weather Channel; Travel Channel; Trinity Bcstg. Network; Turner Network TV; USA Network; Univision; VH1.
Fee: $20.00 installation; $3.60 monthly.
Expanded Basic Service 2
Subscribers: 1,740.
Programming (via satellite): WGN-TV (W) Chicago; TBS Superstation.
Fee: N.A.
Pay Service 1
Pay Units: 429.
Programming (via satellite): Cinemax; Disney Channel; HBO.
Fee: $20.00 installation; $9.95 monthly (each).
Local advertising: Yes. Available in character-generated & taped programming.
Equipment: Tocom headend; Tocom amplifiers.
Miles of plant: 42.0 (coaxial). Additional miles planned: 6.0 (coaxial). Homes passed: 2,600.
Manager: Danny Neumann. Chief technician: Harley Hill. Marketing director: Kathy Shull.
City fee: 3% of gross.
Ownership: James Cable Partners (MSO).

BOYD—South Tel, Suite 202, 2444 Solomons Island Rd., Annapolis, MD 21401. Phones: 410-266-9393; 800-535-0450. County: Wise. Also serves Aurora, Newark, Rhome. ICA: TX0279.
TV Market Ranking: 12. Franchise award date: N.A. Franchise expiration date: N.A. Began: November 1, 1982.
Channel capacity: 35 (2-way capable). Channels available but not in use: N.A.
Basic Service
Subscribers: 286.
Programming (received off-air): KPXD (X) Arlington; KDAF (W), KDFI-TV (I), KDFW (F), KERA-TV (P), KTVT (C), KTXA (U), KXAS-TV (N), KXTX-TV (I), WFAA-TV (A) Dallas-Fort Worth.
Programming (via satellite): WGN-TV (W) Chicago; A & E; CNN; Country Music TV; Discovery Channel; ESPN; ESPN 2; Fox Family Channel; Headline News; History Channel; Home Shopping Network; Learning Channel; Lifetime; MTV; Nashville Network; Nickelodeon; QVC; TBS Superstation; The Weather Channel; Turner Network TV; USA Network.
Fee: $35.00 installation; $12.50 monthly; $2.00 converter; $25.00 additional installation.
Pay Service 1
Pay Units: N.A.
Programming (via satellite): Cinemax; Disney Channel; HBO.
Fee: $10.00 installation; $8.00 monthly (each).
Local advertising: Yes (locally produced). Available in character-generated programming. Rates: $30.00/Month; $7.00/Week.
Equipment: Cadco, Gardiner & Scientific-Atlanta headend; Magnavox amplifiers; Comm/Scope cable; BEI character generator; Pioneer set top converters; Drake & Prodelin satellite antenna; Gardiner satellite receivers.
Miles of plant: 37.0 (coaxial). Homes passed: 1,400.
Manager: George Moreland. Chief technician: Dan Cluster.
Ownership: Bay Cable Inc. (MSO).

BRACKETTVILLE—Falcon Cable TV, 1244 Encino Dr., Pleasanton, TX 78064. Phones: 830-569-5509; 800-292-4502. Fax: 830-569-4828. County: Kinney. Also serves Fort Clark Springs. ICA: TX0356.
TV Market Ranking: Below 100. Franchise award date: N.A. Franchise expiration date: N.A. Began: May 1, 1961.
Channel capacity: 25. Channels available but not in use: None.
Basic Service
Subscribers: 895.
Programming (received off-air): KVAW (O) Eagle Pass; 2 FMs.
Programming (via microwave): KENS-TV (C), KLRN (P), KMOL-TV (N), KSAT-TV (A) San Antonio.
Programming (via satellite): WGN-TV (W) Chicago; Bravo; CNN; ESPN; Fox Family Channel; FoxNet; Lifetime; Nashville Network; QVC; Sci-Fi Channel; TBS Superstation; Univision.
Fee: $35.00 installation; $17.10 monthly.
Expanded Basic Service
Subscribers: 881.
Programming (via satellite): Country Music TV; Discovery Channel; Disney Channel; Home Shopping Network; Nickelodeon.
Fee: $3.42 monthly.
Pay Service 1
Pay Units: 40.
Programming (via satellite): Cinemax.
Fee: $10.95 monthly.
Pay Service 2
Pay Units: 83.
Programming (via satellite): HBO.
Fee: $11.95 monthly.
Pay Service 3
Pay Units: 57.
Programming (via satellite): The Movie Channel.
Fee: $10.95 monthly.
Equipment: Catel & Microdyne headend; C-COR amplifiers; Comm/Scope cable; Eagle traps; R. H. Tyler satellite antenna; Microdyne satellite receivers.
Miles of plant: 38.0 (coaxial). Homes passed: 1,185.
Manager: Lorna Gentry. Chief technician: Santos Guajardo.
Franchise fee: 2% of gross.
Ownership: Falcon Communications LP (MSO), joint venture formed September 30, 1998. See Cable System Ownership.

BRADY—Classic Cable, Box 429, 605 N.W. 3rd St., Plainville, KS 67663-0429. Phones: 785-434-7620; 800-999-8876. Fax: 785-434-2614. County: McCulloch. ICA: TX0180.
TV Market Ranking: Outside TV Markets. Franchise award date: N.A. Franchise expiration date: N.A. Began: September 1, 1965.
Channel capacity: 41 (2-way capable). Channels available but not in use: N.A.
Basic Service
Subscribers: 1,768.
Programming (received off-air): KTXS-TV (A) Abilene-Sweetwater; KXAM-TV (N) Llano; KIDY (F) San Angelo; 4 FMs.
Programming (via microwave): KRBC-TV (N) Abilene-Sweetwater; KLST (C) San Angelo.
Programming (via satellite): WGN-TV (W) Chicago; KRMA-TV (P) Denver; A & E; BET; C-SPAN; CNBC; CNN; Cartoon Network; Country Music TV; Discovery Channel; Disney Channel; ESPN; Fox Family Channel; Fox News Channel; Fox Sports Net Southwest; Headline News; Learning Channel; Lifetime; Nashville Network; Nick at Nite's TV Land; Nickelodeon; QVC; TBS Superstation; The Weather Channel; Trinity Bcstg. Network; Turner Classic Movies; Turner Network TV; USA Network; Univision.
Current originations: Automated time-weather; public access; educational access; automated emergency alert.
Fee: $35.00 installation; $27.95 monthly.
Pay Service 1
Pay Units: 215.
Programming (via satellite): HBO.
Fee: $35.00 installation; $10.95 monthly.
Pay Service 2
Pay Units: 211.
Programming (via satellite): Showtime.
Fee: $9.95 monthly.
Pay Service 3
Pay Units: 199.
Programming (via satellite): The Movie Channel.
Fee: $5.95 monthly.
Equipment: Jerrold headend; Vikoa amplifiers; Cerro cable; Andrew satellite antenna.
Miles of plant: 46.0 (coaxial). Homes passed: 2,932.
Manager: Bill Flowers. Chief technician: Walt VanLue. Marketing director: Jennifer Hauschild.
City fee: 2% of gross.
Ownership: Classic Cable (MSO).

BRAZORIA—Star Cable, Drawer 1570, Brazoria, TX 77422. Phones: 409-798-9121; 800-395-2775. Fax: 409-798-4409. County: Brazoria. Also serves Brazoria County, Jones Creek. ICA: TX0128.
TV Market Ranking: 15 (portions of Brazoria County); Below 100 (Brazoria, portions of Brazoria County, Jones Creek). Franchise award date: N.A. Franchise expiration date: N.A. Began: October 1, 1982.
Channel capacity: 40 (not 2-way capable). Channels available but not in use: None.
Basic Service
Subscribers: 2,894; Commercial subscribers: 7.
Programming (received off-air): KHSH-TV (H) Alvin; KVVV (I) Baytown; KTMD (O) Galveston; KETH (E), KHOU-TV (C), KHTV (W), KPRC-TV (N), KRIV (F), KTRK-TV (A), KTXH (U), KUHT (P), KZJL (I) Houston; KNWS-TV (I) Katy; KXLN-TV (S) Rosenberg.
Programming (via satellite): WGN-TV (W) Chicago; TBS Superstation.
Fee: $15.00 installation; $13.37 monthly; $2.15 converter.
Expanded Basic Service
Subscribers: 2,783.
Programming (via satellite): American Movie Classics; BET; CNBC; CNN; Country Music TV; Discovery Channel; ESPN; Fox Family Channel; Fox Sports Net Southwest; Lifetime; MTV; Nashville Network; Nickelodeon; QVC; The Weather Channel; Turner Network TV; USA Network; VH1.
Fee: $18.12 monthly.
Pay Service 1
Pay Units: 230.
Programming (via satellite): Cinemax.
Fee: $10.95 monthly.
Pay Service 2
Pay Units: 363.
Programming (via satellite): Disney Channel.
Fee: $7.95 monthly.
Pay Service 3
Pay Units: 623.
Programming (via satellite): HBO.
Fee: $10.95 monthly.
Pay Service 4
Pay Units: 488.
Programming (via satellite): Showtime; The Movie Channel.
Fee: $12.95 monthly.
Local advertising: Yes (locally produced & insert). Local sales manager: Nancy Gachman. Regional interconnect: Cabletime.
Miles of plant: 153.7 (coaxial); None (fiber optic). Homes passed: 5,119. Total homes in franchised area: 5,119.
Manager: Mike Burns. Chief technician: Mayla Zubeck.
City fee: 3% of gross.
Ownership: Star Cable Associates (MSO).

BRECKENRIDGE—Friendship Cable of Texas Inc., Box 9090, Tyler, TX 75711-9090. Phone: 903-581-2121. Fax: 903-581-2185. County: Stephens. ICA: TX0184.
TV Market Ranking: Outside TV Markets. Franchise award date: N.A. Franchise expiration date: N.A. Began: January 1, 1952.
Channel capacity: 38. Channels available but not in use: N.A.
Basic Service
Subscribers: 2,681.
Programming (received off-air): KRBC-TV (N), KTAB-TV (C), KTXS-TV (A) Abilene-Sweetwater; allband FM.
Programming (via microwave): KERA-TV (P), KTVT (C), KXTX-TV (I), WFAA-TV (A) Dallas-Fort Worth.

Programming (via satellite): Animal Planet; C-SPAN; Discovery Channel; FX; Odyssey; QVC; TBS Superstation; The Weather Channel; Trinity Bcstg. Network.
Current originations: Automated time-weather.
Fee: $30.00 installation; $12.86 monthly.
Expanded Basic Service
Subscribers: 2,233.
Programming (via satellite): A & E; American Movie Classics; CNBC; CNN; Cartoon Network; ESPN; Fox Family Channel; Fox News Channel; Fox Sports Net Southwest; Home & Garden Television; Knowledge TV; Learning Channel; Lifetime; Nashville Network; Nickelodeon; Turner Network TV; USA Network; Univision.
Fee: $30.00 installation; $18.58 monthly.
Pay Service 1
Pay Units: 165.
Programming (via satellite): Cinemax.
Fee: $13.02 monthly.
Pay Service 2
Pay Units: 600.
Programming (via satellite): The New Encore.
Fee: $1.75 monthly.
Pay Service 3
Pay Units: 159.
Programming (via satellite): HBO.
Fee: $14.01 monthly.
Pay Service 4
Pay Units: 142.
Programming (via satellite): Showtime.
Fee: $14.01 monthly.
Pay Service 5
Pay Units: 351.
Programming (via satellite): Starz!
Fee: $6.75 monthly.
Program Guide: The Cable Guide.
Equipment: Jerrold headend; Tocom & Scientific-Atlanta amplifiers; CCS Hatfield cable; Sony cameras; Sony VTRs; Tocom set top converters; Prodelin satellite antenna; Scientific-Atlanta satellite receivers.
Miles of plant: 104.5 (coaxial). Total homes in franchised area: 3,576.
Manager: Larry Bryant. Chief technician: Joe Stewart.
City fee: 3% of gross.
Ownership: Buford Television Inc. (MSO). See Cable System Ownership.

BREMOND—Galaxy Cablevision, 307 N. 5th St., Leesville, LA 71496. Phone: 318-238-1361. County: Robertson. ICA: TX0723.
TV Market Ranking: Below 100. Franchise award date: N.A. Franchise expiration date: June 19, 2000. Began: N.A.
Channel capacity: 25. Channels available but not in use: None.
Basic Service
Subscribers: 231.
Programming (received off-air): KVUE-TV (A), KXAN-TV (N) Austin; KNCT (P) Belton; KCEN-TV (N), KWTX-TV (C) Waco-Temple.
Programming (via satellite): TBS Superstation.
Fee: $22.75 monthly.
Homes passed: 634.
Manager: Eulin Guidry. Technical manager: Randy Berry.
Ownership: Galaxy Cablevision (MSO).

BRENHAM—Northland Cable TV, 221 E. Main, Brenham, TX 77833. Phone: 409-836-6901. Fax: 409-836-1736. County: Washington. Also serves Washington County (portions). ICA: TX0124.
TV Market Ranking: Below 100. Franchise award date: September 1, 1964. Franchise expiration date: September 1, 2004. Began: September 1, 1971.
Channel capacity: 35 (2-way capable; operating 2-way). Channels available but not in use: None.
Basic Service
Subscribers: 4,018; Commercial subscribers: 708.
Programming (received off-air): KVUE-TV (A) Austin; KBTX-TV (C) Bryan; KAMU-TV (P) College Station; KHOU-TV (C), KHTV (W), KPRC-TV (N), KRIV (F), KTRK-TV (A), KTXH (U), KUHT (P) Houston; allband FM.
Programming (via satellite): TBS Superstation; TV Guide Channel.
Current originations: Automated time-weather; religious access; local news.
Fee: $50.00 installation; $10.25 monthly. Commercial fee: $5.08 monthly.
Expanded Basic Service
Subscribers: 3,911.
Programming (via satellite): A & E; BET; C-SPAN; CNN; Country Music TV; Discovery Channel; ESPN; Fox Family Channel; Headline News; Home Shopping Network; Lifetime; Nashville Network; Nick at Nite; Nickelodeon; USA Network.
Fee: $50.00 installation; $11.00 monthly.
Expanded Basic Service 2
Subscribers: 653.
Programming (via satellite): Fox Sports Net Southwest; MTV; Turner Network TV.
Fee: $35.00 installation; $7.00 monthly.
Pay Service 1
Pay Units: 189.
Programming (via satellite): Cinemax.
Fee: $10.00 installation; $7.50 monthly.
Pay Service 2
Pay Units: 103.
Programming (via satellite): Disney Channel.
Fee: $10.00 installation; $7.50 monthly.
Pay Service 3
Pay Units: 804.
Programming (via satellite): HBO.
Fee: $25.00 installation; $9.95 monthly.
Pay Service 4
Pay Units: 79.
Programming (via satellite): The Movie Channel.
Fee: $10.00 installation; $8.95 monthly.
Pay Service 5
Pay Units: 85.
Programming (via satellite): Showtime.
Fee: $10.00 installation; $8.95 monthly.
Local advertising: Yes (locally produced). Available in satellite distributed, locally originated, character-generated, taped & automated programming. Rates: $7.00/Minute; $3.50/30 Seconds. Local sales manager: Barbara Jacobs.
Equipment: Scientific-Atlanta & Standard Electronics headend; C-COR amplifiers; Comm/Scope cable; JVC & Sony cameras; Sony VTRs; Texscan character generator; Scientific-Atlanta set top converters; Eagle traps; Prodelin & Scientific-Atlanta satellite antenna; Standard Electronics & Scientific-Atlanta satellite receivers; ChannelMatic commercial insert.
Miles of plant: 99.0 (coaxial). Additional miles planned: 2.0 (coaxial). Homes passed: 5,040.
Manager: Dan Bayless. Chief technician: Ken Holle. Program director: Prentice Mearns. Marketing director: Barbara England.
City fee: 3% of gross.
Ownership: Northland Communications Corp. (MSO).

BRIDGE CITY—Warner Cable, Box 1960, 875 North St., Vidor, TX 77670-1960. Phones: 409-769-8161; 800-828-8380. County: Orange. ICA: TX0145.
TV Market Ranking: 88. Franchise award date: July 25, 1977. Franchise expiration date: April 5, 2009. Began: July 25, 1977.
Channel capacity: 81 (not 2-way capable). Channels available but not in use: 29.
Basic Service
Subscribers: 2,806; Commercial subscribers: 1.
Programming (received off-air): KBMT (A), KBTV-TV (N), KFDM-TV (C), KITU (E) Beaumont-Port Arthur; KLTL-TV (P), KVHP (F) Lake Charles.
Programming (via satellite): WGN-TV (W) Chicago; C-SPAN; Country Music TV; Fox Family Channel; MTV; Nashville Network; Nickelodeon; QVC; TBS Superstation; The Weather Channel; VH1.
Current originations: Automated time-weather; educational access; religious access; leased access; automated emergency alert.
Fee: $27.20 installation; $9.28 monthly; $1.65 converter.
Expanded Basic Service
Subscribers: 2,655.
Programming (via satellite): A & E; American Movie Classics; Animal Planet; CNBC; CNN; Cartoon Network; Court TV; Discovery Channel; Disney Channel; E! Entertainment TV; ESPN; ESPN 2; Fox Sports Net Southwest; Headline News; History Channel; Home & Garden Television; Learning Channel; Lifetime; Nick at Nite's TV Land; Odyssey; Sci-Fi Channel; TV Food Network; Travel Channel; Turner Classic Movies; Turner Network TV; USA Network; WB 100+ Station Group.
Fee: $20.00 installation; $25.05 monthly.
Pay Service 1
Pay Units: 184.
Programming (via satellite): Cinemax.
Fee: $20.00 installation; $11.45 monthly.
Pay Service 2
Pay Units: 548.
Programming (via satellite): HBO.
Fee: $20.00 installation; $11.45 monthly.
Pay Service 3
Pay Units: 306.
Programming (via satellite): Showtime.
Fee: $20.00 installation; $11.45 monthly.
Pay Service 4
Pay Units: 64.
Programming (via satellite): Starz!
Fee: $20.00 installation; $7.95 monthly.
Local advertising: Yes. Available in satellite distributed, taped & automated programming. Rates: $5.00/Day.
Program Guide: Premium Channels.
Equipment: Scientific-Atlanta headend; Magnavox amplifiers; Comm/Scope cable; Atari character generator; Hamlin & Jerrold set top converters; Eagle & Pico traps; Scientific-Atlanta satellite antenna; Scientific-Atlanta satellite receivers.
Miles of plant: 80.0 (coaxial); None (fiber optic). Homes passed: 4,203.
Manager: Jim Dwyer. Marketing director: Bill Forgey.
City fee: 5% of gross.
Ownership: Time Warner Cable (MSO); Fanch Communications Inc. (MSO). See Cable System Ownership.

BRONTE—West Texas Cablevision, Box 3528, Hwy. 87 N, San Angelo, TX 76902. Phone: 915-655-4657. County: Coke. ICA: TX0725.
TV Market Ranking: Below 100. Franchise award date: N.A. Franchise expiration date: N.A. Began: N.A.
Channel capacity: 21. Channels available but not in use: N.A.
Basic Service
Subscribers: 309.
Programming (received off-air): KRBC-TV (N), KTXS-TV (A) Abilene-Sweetwater; KIDY (F), KLST (C) San Angelo.
Programming (via satellite): WGN-TV (W) Chicago; ESPN; Fox Family Channel; Nashville Network; TBS Superstation.
Fee: $35.00 installation; $20.40 monthly.
Pay Service 1
Pay Units: N.A.
Programming (via satellite): Cinemax; Disney Channel; HBO.
Fee: $7.95 monthly (Disney), $9.95 monthly (Cinemax or HBO).
Miles of plant: 19.0 (coaxial).
Manager: Kenny White.
Ownership: Cable Management Assoc. (MSO).

BROOKELAND—Friendship Cable of Texas Inc., Box 9090, Tyler, TX 75711-9090. Phone: 903-581-2121. Fax: 903-581-2185. Counties: Jasper, Newton & Sabine. Also serves Browndell, Jasper County (portions), Newton County (portions). ICA: TX0513.
TV Market Ranking: Outside TV Markets. Franchise award date: N.A. Franchise expiration date: N.A. Began: N.A.
Channel capacity: 36 (not 2-way capable). Channels available but not in use: 9.
Basic Service
Subscribers: 197.
Programming (received off-air): KBTV-TV (N), KFDM-TV (C) Beaumont-Port Arthur; KTRE (A) Lufkin.
Programming (via satellite): WGN-TV (W) Chicago; A & E; CNN; Country Music TV; Discovery Channel; ESPN; Fox Family Channel; Headline News; Nashville Network; TBS Superstation; USA Network.
Fee: $33.50 monthly.
Pay Service 1
Pay Units: 12.
Programming (via satellite): Cinemax.
Fee: $10.95 monthly.
Pay Service 2
Pay Units: 13.
Programming (via satellite): HBO.
Fee: $10.95 monthly.
Pay Service 3
Pay Units: 8.
Programming (via satellite): Showtime.
Fee: $5.95 monthly.
Local advertising: Yes.
Miles of plant: 18.3 (coaxial). Homes passed: 481.
Manager: Wanda Pyburn. Chief technician: Mike Deal.
Ownership: Buford Television Inc. (MSO). See Cable System Ownership.

BROOKSHIRE—Northland Cable, 221 E. Main St., Brenham, TX 77833. Phone: 409-836-6939. Fax: 409-836-1736. County: Waller. ICA: TX0353.

TV Market Ranking: 15. Franchise award date: N.A. Franchise expiration date: N.A. Began: N.A.

Channel capacity: 35. Channels available but not in use: 14.

Basic Service

Subscribers: N.A.

Programming (received off-air): KHOU-TV (C), KHTV (W), KPRC-TV (N), KRIV (F), KTRK-TV (A), KTXH (U), KUHT (P) Houston; 15 FMs.

Programming (via satellite): WGN-TV (W) Chicago; CNN; Country Music TV; ESPN; Fox Family Channel; MTV; Nickelodeon; TBS Superstation; USA Network; Univision.

Fee: $25.00 installation; $9.95 monthly.

Pay Service 1

Pay Units: N.A.

Programming (via satellite): Cinemax; HBO; Showtime.

Fee: $7.95 monthly (Cinemax or Showtime), $9.95 monthly (HBO).

Miles of plant: 250.0 (coaxial).

Manager: Doug Eisle.

Ownership: Northland Communications Corp. (MSO).

BROWNFIELD—Cablecomm, 320 W. Main St., Brownfield, TX 79316. Phones: 806-637-2313; 800-638-8457. County: Terry. Also serves Terry County. ICA: TX0151.

TV Market Ranking: Below 100 (Brownfield, portions of Terry County); Outside TV Markets (portions of Terry County). Franchise award date: April 5, 1979. Franchise expiration date: April 5, 1999. Began: April 5, 1989.

Channel capacity: 36 (not 2-way capable). Channels available but not in use: 3.

Basic Service

Subscribers: 2,378; Commercial subscribers: 10.

Programming (received off-air): KAMC (A), KCBD-TV (N), KJTV (F), KLBK-TV (C), KTXT-TV (P) Lubbock.

Programming (via satellite): WGN-TV (W) Chicago; C-SPAN; Home Shopping Network; TBS Superstation.

Current originations: Automated time-weather; automated emergency alert.

Fee: $27.90 installation; $9.68 monthly; $1.60 converter.

Expanded Basic Service

Subscribers: 2,317.

Programming (via satellite): American Movie Classics; CNN; Discovery Channel; Disney Channel; ESPN; Fox Family Channel; Fox Sports Net Southwest; Headline News; Knowledge TV; Lifetime; MTV; Nashville Network; Nickelodeon; The Weather Channel; Trinity Bcstg. Network; Turner Network TV; USA Network; Univision.

Fee: $20.00 installation; $14.53 monthly.

Pay Service 1

Pay Units: 225.

Programming (via satellite): Cinemax.

Fee: $15.00 installation; $9.00 monthly.

Pay Service 2

Pay Units: 324.

Programming (via satellite): HBO.

Fee: $15.00 installation; $9.00 monthly.

Pay Service 3

Pay Units: 210.

Programming (via satellite): Showtime.

Fee: $15.00 installation; $9.00 monthly.

Local advertising: Yes. Available in character-generated programming. Rates: $3.00/Day. Regional interconnect: Cabletime.

Program Guide: Premium Channels.

Equipment: Scientific-Atlanta headend; Texscan amplifiers; Comm/Scope cable; Texscan character generator; Scientific-Atlanta & Pioneer set top converters; Eagle & Pico traps; Scientific-Atlanta satellite antenna; Scientific-Atlanta, M/A-Com & Automation Techniques satellite receivers.

Miles of plant: 54.0 (coaxial). Homes passed: 3,816.

Manager: Rex Thackerson. Chief technician: Gary Strickland. Marketing director: Bill J. Forgey.

City fee: 2% of gross.

Ownership: Fanch Communications Inc. (MSO); Time Warner Cable (MSO). See Cable System Ownership.

BROWNSVILLE—Time Warner Communications, 2921 S. Expressway 83, Harlingen, TX 78550-7615. Phone: 956-541-6782. Fax: 956-412-0959. County: Cameron. Also serves Cameron County (portions), Olmito, Rancho Viejo, Rio Del Sol. ICA: TX0726.

TV Market Ranking: Below 100. Franchise award date: N.A. Franchise expiration date: N.A. Began: N.A.

Channel capacity: 39. Channels available but not in use: N.A.

Basic Service

Subscribers: 31,640.

Programming (received off-air): KVEO (N) Brownsville; KGBT-TV (C), KLUJ (E), KMBH (P) Harlingen; KRGV-TV (A) Weslaco; XHAB-TV Matamoros; XHRIO (O) Matamoros-Brownsville.

Programming (via satellite): WGN-TV (W) Chicago; A & E; C-SPAN; CNN; Fox Family Channel; Headline News; Lifetime; MTV; Nashville Network; Nick at Nite; Nickelodeon; QVC; TBS Superstation; The Weather Channel.

Current originations: Automated time-weather; educational access; local news.

Fee: $60.00 installation; $10.93 monthly.

Expanded Basic Service

Subscribers: 30,402.

Programming (via satellite): CNBC; Discovery Channel; ESPN; Fox Sports Net Southwest; Turner Network TV; USA Network; Univision.

Fee: $13.28 monthly.

Pay Service 1

Pay Units: 4,341.

Programming (via satellite): Cinemax.

Fee: $10.95 monthly.

Pay Service 2

Pay Units: 2,253.

Programming (via satellite): Disney Channel.

Fee: $10.95 monthly.

Pay Service 3

Pay Units: 6,701.

Programming (via satellite): HBO.

Fee: $10.95 monthly.

Pay Service 4

Pay Units: N.A.

Programming (via satellite): The New Encore.

Fee: N.A.

Local advertising: Yes. Regional interconnect: Cabletime.

Miles of plant: 417.5 (coaxial).

Manager: Juan Herrera. Chief technician: Al Velasquez.

Ownership: AT&T Broadband & Internet Services (MSO); Time Warner Cable (MSO); Advance/Newhouse Partnership (MSO).

BROWNWOOD—Brownwood TV Cable Service Inc., Box 1149, 310 Carnegie Blvd., Brownwood, TX 76801. Phone: 915-646-3576. Fax: 915-643-2846. County: Brown. Also serves Bangs, Early. ICA: TX0059.

TV Market Ranking: Outside TV Markets. Franchise award date: February 1, 1957. Franchise expiration date: N.A. Began: September 1, 1957.

Channel capacity: 35 (not 2-way capable). Channels available but not in use: 3.

Basic Service

Subscribers: 8,813.

Programming (received off-air): KRBC-TV (N), KTAB-TV (C), KTXS-TV (A) Abilene-Sweetwater; KIDY (F), KLST (C) San Angelo; 5 FMs.

Programming (via microwave): KDFW (F), KERA-TV (P), KTVT (C), WFAA-TV (A) Dallas-Fort Worth.

Programming (via satellite): QVC; TBS Superstation.

Current originations: Automated time-weather; local news.

Fee: $37.50 installation; $8.85 monthly; $2.50 converter; $23.50 additional installation.

Expanded Basic Service

Subscribers: N.A.

Programming (via satellite): American Movie Classics; BET; CNBC; CNN; Country Music TV; Discovery Channel; ESPN; Fox Family Channel; Headline News; Lifetime; Nashville Network; Nickelodeon; The Weather Channel; Trinity Bcstg. Network; Turner Network TV; USA Network; Univision.

Fee: $11.05 monthly.

Pay Service 1

Pay Units: N.A.

Programming (via satellite): Cinemax; Disney Channel; HBO; Showtime.

Fee: $11.45 monthly (each).

Local advertising: Yes (locally produced & insert). Available in satellite distributed & locally originated programming. Rates: $30.00/Minute; $17.00/30 Seconds.

Program Guide: Premium Channels.

Equipment: Scientific-Atlanta & Jerrold headend; GTE Sylvania & Magnavox amplifiers; Comm/Scope cable; Jerrold & Magnavox set top converters; Eagle traps; Scientific-Atlanta satellite antenna; Automation Techniques satellite receivers.

Miles of plant: 197.0 (coaxial); None (fiber optic). Homes passed: 14,000.

Manager: Karen McMillan. Chief technician: Paul Mathison.

City fee: 2% of gross.

Ownership: Brownwood TV Cable Service Inc. (MSO).

BRUNI—TCI Cablevision of Texas Inc., 208 W. Viggie St., Hebbronville, TX 78361-3048. Phone: 512-527-3267. County: Webb. ICA: TX0680.

TV Market Ranking: Outside TV Markets. Franchise award date: N.A. Franchise expiration date: N.A. Began: N.A.

Channel capacity: 24. Channels available but not in use: 10.

Basic Service

Subscribers: 132.

Programming (received off-air): KGNS-TV (N,A), KLDO-TV (O), KVTV (C) Laredo.

Programming (via satellite): WGN-TV (W) Chicago; WABC-TV (A) New York; ESPN; GalaVision; MTV; Nashville Network; TBS Superstation; USA Network; Univision.

Fee: $60.00 installation; $16.78 monthly.

Pay Service 1

Pay Units: 53.

Programming (via satellite): HBO.

Fee: $11.00 monthly.

Pay Service 2

Pay Units: 44.

Programming (via satellite): Showtime.

Fee: $6.00 monthly.

Miles of plant: 3.7 (coaxial). Total homes in franchised area: 148.

Manager: Juve Morante.

Ownership: AT&T Broadband & Internet Services (MSO). Purchased from Tele-Communications Inc., March 9, 1999.

BRYAN—TCA Cable TV, 4114 E. 29th St., Bryan, TX 77802-4398. Phone: 409-846-2229. Fax: 409-268-0139. County: Brazos. Also serves Brazos County (unincorporated areas), College Station. ICA: TX0020.

TV Market Ranking: Below 100. Franchise award date: July 1, 1953. Franchise expiration date: N.A. Began: January 1, 1954.

Channel capacity: 80 (2-way capable). Channels available but not in use: 20.

Basic Service

Subscribers: 33,000.

Programming (received off-air): KBTX-TV (C) Bryan; KAMU-TV (P) College Station; KHOU-TV (C), KHTV (W), KPRC-TV (N), KTRK-TV (A), KUHT (P) Houston; KCEN-TV (N), KXXV (A) Waco-Temple; 21 FMs.

Programming (via satellite): WGN-TV (W) Chicago; A & E; BET; C-SPAN; CNN; Country Music TV; Discovery Channel; ESPN; Fox Family Channel; Headline News; Lifetime; MTV; Nashville Network; Nickelodeon; Odyssey; TBS Superstation; The Weather Channel; Trinity Bcstg. Network; Turner Network TV; Univision.

Current originations: Automated time-weather; public access; educational access; government access; local news.

Fee: $35.00 installation; $22.16 monthly.

Pay Service 1

Pay Units: N.A.

Programming (via satellite): Cinemax; Disney Channel; HBO; Showtime.

Fee: $9.00 monthly (Disney), $10.00 monthly (HBO or TMC).

Local advertising: Yes (insert only). Available in satellite distributed programming. Local sales manager: Mark Mullinex. Regional interconnect: Cabletime.

Equipment: Scientific-Atlanta headend; Scientific-Atlanta & C-COR amplifiers; Comm/Scope, Times Fiber & Trilogy cable; MSI character generator; Jerrold set top converters; Tocom addressable set top converters; Eagle traps; Scientific-Atlanta satellite antenna; Scientific-Atlanta satellite receivers.

Miles of plant: 500.0 (coaxial); 50.0 (fiber optic). Homes passed: 49,000. Total homes in franchised area: 50,000.

Manager: Randy Rogers. Chief technician: Patrick Clarke. Marketing director: Jacqueline Rapacki.

City fee: 2% of gross.

Ownership: TCA Cable TV Inc. (MSO). See Cable System Ownership.

BUCHANAN DAM—Northland Cable, Box 366, 1101 Mission Hill Dr., Marble Falls, TX 78654-1906. Phone: 830-693-7500. Fax: 830-693-6056. Counties: Burnet & Llano. Also serves Inks Lake, Long Mountain Estates, West Lake Buchanan. ICA: TX0800.

TV Market Ranking: Below 100. Franchise award date: N.A. Franchise expiration date: N.A. Began: N.A.

Channel capacity: 30 (2-way capable; not operating 2-way). Channels available but not in use: None.

Basic Service

Subscribers: 900.

Programming (received off-air): KEYE-TV (C), KLRU (P), KNVA (W), KTBC (F), KVUE-TV (A) Austin; KXAM-TV (N) Llano.

Programming (via satellite): WGN-TV (W) Chicago; A & E; American Movie Classics; C-SPAN; CNN; Cartoon Network; Discovery Channel; ESPN; Fox Family Channel; Fox Sports Net Southwest; Great American Country; Headline News; History Channel; Learning Channel; Lifetime; Nashville Network; QVC; TBS Superstation; The Weather Channel; Trinity Bcstg. Network; Turner Classic Movies; Turner Network TV; USA Network.
Fee: $50.00 installation; $27.45 monthly.

Pay Service 1
Pay Units: 43.
Programming (via satellite): Disney Channel.
Fee: $8.00 monthly.

Pay Service 2
Pay Units: 84.
Programming (via satellite): HBO.
Fee: $11.95 monthly.

Pay Service 3
Pay Units: 47.
Programming (via satellite): Showtime.
Fee: $11.50 monthly.

Equipment: Scientific-Atlanta amplifiers.
Miles of plant: 6.4 (coaxial).
Manager: Rich Beatty. Chief technician: David Simpson. Marketing director: Debbie Jones.
Ownership: Northland Communications Corp. (MSO).

BUCKHOLTS—National Cable Inc., Suite 106-A, 5151 Reed Rd., Columbus, OH 43220. Phones: 614-442-5890; 800-582-0504. Fax: 614-457-2567. County: Milam. ICA: TX0903.
TV Market Ranking: Below 100. Franchise award date: N.A. Franchise expiration date: N.A. Began: N.A.
Channel capacity: N.A. Channels available but not in use: N.A.

Basic Service
Subscribers: 24.
Programming (received off-air): KEYE-TV (C), KTBC (F) Austin; KCEN-TV (N), KCTF (P), KWKT (F), KWTX-TV (C) Waco-Temple.
Programming (via satellite): WGN-TV (W) Chicago; A & E; American Movie Classics; CNN; Country Music TV; Discovery Channel; ESPN; Fox Family Channel; Showtime; TBS Superstation; Turner Network TV; USA Network.
Fee: $28.00 monthly.

Miles of plant: None (fiber optic). Homes passed: 172.
Manager: Paul Scott. Chief technician: Rob Spiller. Marketing director: Josh Thackery.
Ownership: National Cable (MSO).

BUFFALO—Northland Cable, Box 282, 114 W. Main St., Madisonville, TX 77864. Phone: 409-348-3173. Fax: 409-348-6092. County: Leon. ICA: TX0426.
TV Market Ranking: Outside TV Markets. Franchise award date: June 2, 1975. Franchise expiration date: October 2, 2004. Began: December 1, 1975.
Channel capacity: 36 (not 2-way capable). Channels available but not in use: None.

Basic Service
Subscribers: 552; Commercial subscribers: 4.
Programming (received off-air): KDFW (F), KERA-TV (P), KTVT (C), KXAS-TV (N), KXTX-TV (I), WFAA-TV (A) Dallas-Fort Worth; KCEN-TV (N), KWKT (F), KWTX-TV (C) Waco-Temple.
Programming (via satellite): American Movie Classics; ESPN; Fox Family Channel; TBS Superstation.
Current originations: Automated time-weather.
Fee: $49.95 installation; $26.40 monthly.

Pay Service 1
Pay Units: 50.
Programming (via satellite): Disney Channel.
Fee: $7.95 monthly.

Pay Service 2
Pay Units: 85.
Programming (via satellite): HBO.
Fee: $11.00 monthly.

Pay Service 3
Pay Units: 46.
Programming (via satellite): Showtime.
Fee: $11.00 monthly.

Local advertising: No.
Equipment: Scientific-Atlanta headend; Magnavox amplifiers; Comm/Scope cable; Sony cameras; Scientific-Atlanta set top converters; Scientific-Atlanta satellite antenna; Scientific-Atlanta satellite receivers.
Miles of plant: 17.0 (coaxial). Homes passed: 700. Total homes in franchised area: 700.
Manager: Mike Taylor. Chief technician: Allan Fautheree.
City fee: 3% of gross.
Ownership: Northland Communications Corp. (MSO).

BUFFALO GAP—Big Country Cablevision Inc., Box 549, 102 Oak St., Merkel, TX 79536. Phones: 915-928-4750; 800-588-4750. Fax: 915-928-3452. County: Taylor. ICA: TX0729.
TV Market Ranking: Below 100. Franchise award date: January 1, 1982. Franchise expiration date: N.A. Began: N.A.
Channel capacity: 21. Channels available but not in use: 1.

Basic Service
Subscribers: 140.
Programming (received off-air): KRBC-TV (N), KTAB-TV (C), KTXS-TV (A) Abilene-Sweetwater.
Programming (via satellite): WGN-TV (W) Chicago; CNN; Country Music TV; Discovery Channel; ESPN; Fox Family Channel; Lifetime; MTV; Nashville Network; Nickelodeon; TBS Superstation; The Weather Channel; Turner Network TV; USA Network.
Fee: $38.35 installation; $20.05 monthly.

Pay Service 1
Pay Units: N.A.
Programming (via satellite): HBO; Showtime.
Fee: $10.00 installation.

Miles of plant: 6.0 (coaxial); None (fiber optic).
Manager: Mark Reaves. Marketing director: J. Ketchum.
Ownership: Cable Management Assoc. (MSO).

BUFFALO SPRINGS LAKE—Classic Cable, Box 429, 605 N.W. 3rd St., Plainville, KS 67663-0429. Phones: 785-434-7620; 800-999-8876. Fax: 785-434-2614. County: Lubbock. ICA: TX0574.
TV Market Ranking: Below 100. Franchise award date: N.A. Franchise expiration date: January 9, 2018. Began: August 1, 1982.
Channel capacity: 41 (2-way capable). Channels available but not in use: N.A.

Basic Service
Subscribers: 87.
Programming (received off-air): KAMC (A), KCBD-TV (N), KJTV (F), KLBK-TV (C), KPTB (I), KTXT-TV (P) Lubbock.
Programming (via satellite): WGN-TV (W) Chicago; CNN; Country Music TV; Discovery Channel; Disney Channel; ESPN; Fox Family Channel; Headline News; History Channel; Home Shopping Network; MTV; Nashville Network; Nickelodeon; TBS Superstation; Trinity Bcstg. Network; Turner Classic Movies; Turner Network TV; USA Network.
Fee: $35.00 installation; $27.95 monthly.

Pay Service 1
Pay Units: 9.
Programming (via satellite): Cinemax.
Fee: $9.95 monthly.

Pay Service 2
Pay Units: 12.
Programming (via satellite): HBO.
Fee: $9.95 monthly.

Pay Service 3
Pay Units: N.A.
Programming (via satellite): Showtime.
Fee: $9.95 monthly.

Miles of plant: 6.5 (coaxial). Homes passed: 283.
Manager: Bill Flowers. Chief technician: Chris Christenson. Marketing director: Jennifer Hauschild.
City fee: 5% of gross.
Ownership: Classic Cable (MSO).

BURKBURNETT—Friendship Cable of Texas Inc., Box 9090, Tyler, TX 75711-9090. Phone: 903-581-2121. Fax: 903-581-2185. County: Wichita. ICA: TX0154.
TV Market Ranking: Below 100. Franchise award date: N.A. Franchise expiration date: N.A. Began: January 1, 1980.
Channel capacity: 37. Channels available but not in use: N.A.

Basic Service
Subscribers: 2,141.
Programming (received off-air): KAUZ-TV (C), KFDX-TV (N), KJTL (F,U), KSWO-TV (A) Wichita Falls-Lawton; 2 FMs.
Programming (via translator): KERA-TV (P) Dallas-Fort Worth.
Programming (via satellite): C-SPAN; Discovery Channel; FX; Lifetime; Odyssey; QVC; TBS Superstation; The Weather Channel.
Current originations: Automated time-weather; educational access.
Fee: $30.00 installation; $11.98 monthly.

Expanded Basic Service
Subscribers: 1,997.
Programming (via satellite): American Movie Classics; Animal Planet; CNBC; CNN; Cartoon Network; Court TV; ESPN; Fox Family Channel; Fox News Channel; Fox Sports Net Southwest; Headline News; Home & Garden Television; Learning Channel; MTV; Nashville Network; Nickelodeon; Turner Network TV; USA Network.
Fee: $30.00 installation; $14.68 monthly.

Pay Service 1
Pay Units: 293.
Programming (via satellite): Cinemax.
Fee: $12.84 monthly.

Pay Service 2
Pay Units: 811.
Programming (via satellite): The New Encore.
Fee: $1.75 monthly.

Pay Service 3
Pay Units: 404.
Programming (via satellite): HBO.
Fee: $13.83 monthly.

Pay Service 4
Pay Units: 498.
Programming (via satellite): Starz!
Fee: $6.75 monthly.

Program Guide: The Cable Guide.
Equipment: Tocom headend; Theta-Com amplifiers; Times Fiber cable; Video Data Systems character generator; Standard Components set top converters; Fort Worth Tower satellite antenna.
Miles of plant: 65.0 (coaxial). Homes passed: 3,795. Total homes in franchised area: 3,795.
Manager: Larry Bryant. Chief technician: Ron Johnson.
City fee: 3% of gross.
Ownership: Buford Television Inc. (MSO). See Cable System Ownership.

BURLESON—Mallard Cablevision, 100-D El Chico Trail, Willow Park, TX 76087. Phones: 817-441-8073; 800-669-2288. Fax: 817-441-6464. Counties: Johnson & Tarrant. Also serves Alvarado, Briaroaks, Homesteads, Rendon, Tarrant County (portions). ICA: TX0103.
TV Market Ranking: 12. Franchise award date: N.A. Franchise expiration date: N.A. Began: October 1, 1986.
Channel capacity: 36. Channels available but not in use: 6.

Basic Service
Subscribers: 1,321.
Programming (received off-air): KDAF (W), KDFI-TV (I), KDFW (F), KERA-TV (P), KTVT (C), KTXA (U), KXAS-TV (N), KXTX-TV (I), WFAA-TV (A) Dallas-Fort Worth.
Programming (via satellite): WGN-TV (W) Chicago; CNBC; CNN; Discovery Channel; ESPN; Headline News; Home Shopping Network; MTV; Nashville Network; Nickelodeon; TBS Superstation; The Weather Channel; Turner Network TV; USA Network.
Fee: $20.00 installation; $21.50 monthly; $2.00 converter.

Pay Service 1
Pay Units: 161.
Programming (via satellite): Cinemax.
Fee: $11.95 monthly.

Pay Service 2
Pay Units: 120.
Programming (via satellite): Disney Channel.
Fee: $9.95 monthly.

Pay Service 3
Pay Units: 392.
Programming (via satellite): HBO.
Fee: $11.95 monthly.

Pay Service 4
Pay Units: 248.
Programming (via satellite): Showtime.
Fee: $9.95 monthly.

Local advertising: Yes.
Equipment: Catel headend; Scientific-Atlanta amplifiers; Comm/Scope cable; Eagle & Pico traps.
Miles of plant: 300.0 (coaxial). Homes passed: 6,500. Total homes in franchised area: 6,500.
Manager: Doug Grassmann.
Ownership: Mallard Cablevision (MSO). Purchased from Cambridge Communications, May 1, 1999.

BURNET—Northland Cable TV, Box 366, 1101 Mission Hill Dr., Marble Falls, TX 78654-1906. Phone: 830-693-7500. Fax: 830-693-6056. County: Burnet. ICA: TX0296.
TV Market Ranking: Below 100. Franchise award date: N.A. Franchise expiration date: October 1, 1999. Began: April 1, 1964.
Channel capacity: 62 (2-way capable). Channels available but not in use: N.A.

Basic Service
Subscribers: 1,125.
Programming (received off-air): KEYE-TV (C), KLRU (P), KNVA (W), KTBC (F), KVUE-TV (A) Austin; KXAM-TV (N) Llano; allband FM.
Programming (via satellite): WGN-TV (W) Chicago; A & E; C-SPAN; CNN; Discovery Channel; ESPN; Fox Family Channel; Fox Sports Net Southwest; Great American Country; Headline News; Learning Channel; Nashville Network; QVC; TBS Superstation; TV Guide Channel; The Weather Channel; Trinity Bcstg. Network; Turner Network TV; USA Network; Univision.
Current originations: Automated time-weather.

Fee: $50.00 installation; $26.15 monthly.

Expanded Basic Service

Subscribers: 294.

Programming (via satellite): American Movie Classics; CNNfn; Cartoon Network; ESPN 2; History Channel; Lifetime; Nickelodeon; Turner Classic Movies.

Fee: $8.50 monthly.

Pay Service 1

Pay Units: 107.

Programming (via satellite): Cinemax.

Fee: $8.50 monthly.

Pay Service 2

Pay Units: 64.

Programming (via satellite): Disney Channel.

Fee: $8.00 monthly.

Pay Service 3

Pay Units: 85.

Programming (via satellite): HBO.

Fee: $11.95 monthly.

Pay Service 4

Pay Units: 45.

Programming (via satellite): The Movie Channel.

Fee: $8.00 monthly.

Local advertising: Yes. Available in satellite distributed & character-generated programming. Local sales manager: Rod McGhehee.

Equipment: Scientific-Atlanta & Cadco headend; Scientific-Atlanta amplifiers; Times Fiber cable; RCA & Scientific-Atlanta set top converters; Eagle traps; Scientific-Atlanta satellite antenna; Scientific-Atlanta satellite receivers; ChannelMatic commercial insert.

Miles of plant: 40.0 (coaxial); None (fiber optic). Additional miles planned: 1.0 (coaxial). Homes passed: 1,750.

Manager: Rich Beatty. Chief technician: David Simpson. Marketing director: Debbie Jones.

City fee: 3% of gross.

Ownership: Northland Communications Corp. (MSO).

BURTON—BRDC Cablevision, Box 240, Giddings, TX 78942. Phone: 409-542-3151. Fax: 409-542-1187. County: Washington. ICA: TX0409.

TV Market Ranking: Below 100. Franchise award date: October 11, 1989. Franchise expiration date: October 11, 2009. Began: August 1, 1990.

Channel capacity: 36 (not 2-way capable). Channels available but not in use: 16.

Basic Service

Subscribers: 83.

Programming (received off-air): KBTX-TV (C) Bryan; KHOU-TV (C), KHTV (W), KPRC-TV (N), KRIV (F), KTRK-TV (A), KTXH (U), KUHT (P) Houston.

Programming (via satellite): WGN-TV (W) Chicago; CNN; Discovery Channel; Disney Channel; ESPN; Fox Family Channel; Fox Sports Net South; Nashville Network; Sci-Fi Channel; TBS Superstation; Turner Network TV; USA Network.

Fee: $25.00 installation; $21.95 monthly; $1.00 converter.

Pay Service 1

Pay Units: N.A.

Programming (via satellite): Cinemax; HBO.

Fee: $9.95 monthly (each).

Pay Service 2

Pay Units: 14.

Programming (via satellite): Showtime.

Fee: $9.95 monthly.

Equipment: C-COR amplifiers; Comm/Scope cable; Jerrold & Hamlin set top converters; Pico traps; ChannelMaster satellite antenna; Standard Communications satellite receivers.

Miles of plant: 5.0 (coaxial); None (fiber optic). Homes passed: 175. Total homes in franchised area: 193.

Manager: David W. Peterson.

City fee: 5% of gross.

Ownership: Bluebonnet Rural Development Corp. (MSO).

BYERS—Byers-Petrolia Cable TV, Box 271, Byers, TX 76357. Phone: 817-529-6123. Fax: 817-529-6125. County: Clay. Also serves Petrolia. ICA: TX0448.

TV Market Ranking: Below 100. Franchise award date: January 1, 1983. Franchise expiration date: January 1, 1998. Began: April 1, 1984.

Channel capacity: 30 (not 2-way capable). Channels available but not in use: 17.

Basic Service

Subscribers: 400.

Programming (received off-air): KAUZ-TV (C), KFDX-TV (N), KJTL (F,U), KSWO-TV (A) Wichita Falls-Lawton.

Programming (via satellite): WGN-TV (W) Chicago; CNN; ESPN; Fox Family Channel; TBS Superstation; USA Network.

Fee: $21.45 installation; $14.95 monthly.

Pay Service 1

Pay Units: N.A.

Programming (via satellite): Cinemax; HBO.

Fee: $7.00 monthly (Cinemax), $9.00 monthly (HBO).

Equipment: Scientific-Atlanta headend; Scientific-Atlanta amplifiers; Scientific-Atlanta cable; Pico traps; Scientific-Atlanta & Anixter-Mark satellite antenna; Scientific-Atlanta satellite receivers.

Miles of plant: 15.5 (coaxial); None (fiber optic). Homes passed: 640. Total homes in franchised area: 650.

Manager: Dana Terrell. Chief technician: Weldon Craig.

City fee: 4% of basic gross.

Ownership: Byers-Petrolia Cable TV Co. Inc.

CACTUS—High Plains Cablevision Inc., Box 310, 124 S. Main St., Lockney, TX 79241. Phone: 806-652-3328. Fax: 806-652-3139. County: Moore. Also serves Etter. ICA: TX0730.

TV Market Ranking: Outside TV Markets. Franchise award date: N.A. Franchise expiration date: N.A. Began: N.A.

Channel capacity: 28. Channels available but not in use: 6.

Basic Service

Subscribers: 239.

Programming (received off-air): KAMR-TV (N), KCIT (F,U), KFDA-TV (C), KVII-TV (A) Amarillo.

Programming (via satellite): TBS Superstation; Turner Network TV.

Fee: $25.00 installation; $29.96 monthly.

Pay Service 1

Pay Units: N.A.

Programming (via satellite): Cinemax; Showtime.

Fee: $7.00 monthly (each).

Manager: Jim Doucette. Chief technician: Jim Odle.

Ownership: High Plains Cablevision Inc. (MSO).

CADDO PEAK—Friendship Cable of Texas Inc., Box 9090, Tyler, TX 75711-9090. Phone: 903-581-2121. Fax: 903-581-2185. Counties: Johnson & Tarrant. Also serves Joshua. ICA: TX0259.

TV Market Ranking: 12. Franchise award date: N.A. Franchise expiration date: N.A. Began: N.A.

Channel capacity: 36. Channels available but not in use: 5.

Basic Service

Subscribers: 457.

Programming (received off-air): KDAF (W), KDFI-TV (I), KDFW (F), KERA-TV (P), KTVT (C), KTXA (U), KXAS-TV (N), KXTX-TV (I), WFAA-TV (A) Dallas-Fort Worth.

Programming (via satellite): WGN-TV (W) Chicago; A & E; CNN; Country Music TV; Discovery Channel; Disney Channel; ESPN; Fox Family Channel; Fox Sports Net Southwest; Goodlife TV Network; Headline News; Home Shopping Network; Lifetime; Nashville Network; Nickelodeon; TBS Superstation; Turner Network TV; USA Network.

Fee: $37.72 monthly.

Pay Service 1

Pay Units: 15.

Programming (via satellite): Cinemax.

Fee: $10.95 monthly.

Pay Service 2

Pay Units: 50.

Programming (via satellite): HBO.

Fee: $10.95 monthly.

Pay Service 3

Pay Units: 69.

Programming (via satellite): Showtime.

Fee: $5.95 monthly.

Local advertising: Yes.

Miles of plant: 69.0 (coaxial). Homes passed: 1,629.

Manager: Rodney Fletcher. Chief technician: Steven Williams.

Ownership: Buford Television Inc. (MSO). See Cable System Ownership.

CALDWELL—Classic Cable, Box 429, 605 N.W. 3rd St., Plainville, KS 67663-0429. Phones: 785-434-7620; 800-999-8876. Fax: 785-434-2614. County: Burleson. ICA: TX0206.

TV Market Ranking: Below 100. Franchise award date: October 13, 1970. Franchise expiration date: N.A. Began: October 1, 1971.

Channel capacity: 61 (2-way capable). Channels available but not in use: N.A.

Basic Service

Subscribers: 1,129.

Programming (received off-air): KTBC (F), KVUE-TV (A), KXAN-TV (N) Austin; KBTX-TV (C), KYLE (W) Bryan; KAMU-TV (P) College Station; KHTV (W), KTXH (U) Houston; KCEN-TV (N), KWKT (F) Waco-Temple; allband FM.

Programming (via satellite): WGN-TV (W) Chicago; A & E; CNN; Cartoon Network; Country Music TV; Discovery Channel; Disney Channel; ESPN; Fox Family Channel; Fox News Channel; Fox Sports Net Southwest; Headline News; History Channel; Home & Garden Television; Learning Channel; Lifetime; Nashville Network; Nick at Nite's TV Land; Nickelodeon; QVC; TBS Superstation; The Weather Channel; Trinity Bcstg. Network; Turner Network TV; USA Network; Univision.

Fee: $35.00 installation; $29.95 monthly.

Pay Service 1

Pay Units: 170.

Programming (via satellite): HBO.

Fee: $10.95 monthly.

Pay Service 2

Pay Units: 122.

Programming (via satellite): Showtime.

Fee: $9.95 monthly.

Pay Service 3

Pay Units: 128.

Programming (via satellite): The Movie Channel.

Fee: $5.95 monthly.

Equipment: Scientific-Atlanta headend; Scientific-Atlanta amplifiers; Comm/Scope cable; Scientific-Atlanta set top converters; Pico traps; Fort Worth Tower & Scientific-Atlanta satellite antenna; M/A-Com & Scientific-Atlanta satellite receivers.

Miles of plant: 32.0 (coaxial). Homes passed: 1,523.

Manager: Bill Flowers. Chief technician: Walt VanLue. Marketing director: Jennifer Hauschild.

Ownership: Classic Cable (MSO).

CALVERT—Galaxy Cablevision, 307 N. 5th St., Leesville, LA 71496. Phone: 318-238-1361. County: Robertson. ICA: TX0731.

TV Market Ranking: Below 100. Franchise award date: N.A. Franchise expiration date: November 30, 2011. Began: N.A.

Channel capacity: 32. Channels available but not in use: 5.

Basic Service

Subscribers: 306.

Programming (received off-air): KTBC (F), KVUE-TV (A) Austin; KNCT (P) Belton; KBTX-TV (C) Bryan; KAMU-TV (P) College Station; KTVT (C) Dallas-Fort Worth; KCEN-TV (N), KWTX-TV (C) Waco-Temple.

Programming (via satellite): Turner Classic Movies; Turner Network TV.

Fee: $23.00 monthly.

Homes passed: 886.

Manager: Eulin Guidry. Technical manager: Randy Berry.

Ownership: Galaxy Cablevision (MSO).

CAMERON—Galaxy Cablevision, 307 N. 5th St., Leesville, LA 71496. Phone: 318-238-1361. County: Milam. Also serves Milam County (portions). ICA: TX0160.

TV Market Ranking: Below 100 (Cameron); Outside TV Markets (Milam County). Franchise award date: N.A. Franchise expiration date: December 6, 2001. Began: January 1, 1973.

Channel capacity: 40. Channels available but not in use: None.

Basic Service

Subscribers: 1,468.

Programming (received off-air): KTBC (F), KVUE-TV (A), KXAN-TV (N) Austin; KNCT (P) Belton; KBTX-TV (C) Bryan; KLRN (P) San Antonio; KCEN-TV (N), KWTX-TV (C) Waco-Temple; allband FM.

Programming (via satellite): WGN-TV (W) Chicago; ESPN; Fox Family Channel; TBS Superstation; Turner Classic Movies; USA Network.

Current originations: Automated timeweather.

Fee: $30.00 installation; $22.60 monthly.

Pay Service 1

Pay Units: N.A.

Programming (via satellite): HBO; Showtime.

Fee: $12.00 monthly (each).

Equipment: CAS headend; CAS amplifiers; Systems Wire cable; AFC satellite antenna.

Miles of plant: 62.6 (coaxial). Homes passed: 2,824.

Manager: Eulin Guidry. Technical manager: Randy Berry.

City fee: 3% of gross.

Ownership: Galaxy Cablevision (MSO).

CAMP WOOD—Classic Cable, Box 429, 605 N.W. 3rd St., Plainville, KS 67663-0429. Phones: 785-434-7620; 800-999-8876. Fax: 785-434-2614. County: Real. ICA: TX0559.

TV Market Ranking: Below 100. Franchise award date: N.A. Franchise expiration date: July 23, 2003. Began: July 23, 1988.

Channel capacity: 36 (2-way capable). Channels available but not in use: N.A.

Basic Service

Subscribers: 183.

Programming (via translator): KENS-TV (C), KMOL-TV (N), KSAT-TV (A) San Antonio.
Programming (via satellite): WGN-TV (W) Chicago; KCNC-TV (C), KMGH-TV (A), KRMA-TV (P), KUSA-TV (N) Denver; Animal Planet; CNN; Country Music TV; Discovery Channel; Disney Channel; ESPN; Fox Family Channel; Fox News Channel; FoxNet; Headline News; Learning Channel; Nashville Network; QVC; TBS Superstation; The Weather Channel; Trinity Bcstg. Network; Turner Classic Movies; Turner Network TV; USA Network; Univision.
Fee: $35.00 installation; $27.95 monthly; $2.00 converter; $22.00 additional installation.
Commercial fee: $3.50 monthly.

Pay Service 1
Pay Units: 12.
Programming (via satellite): Showtime.
Fee: $9.95 monthly.

Pay Service 2
Pay Units: 40.
Programming (via satellite): HBO.
Fee: $10.95 monthly.

Miles of plant: 6.2 (coaxial). Homes passed: 405.
Manager: Bill Flowers. Chief technician: Walt VanLue. Marketing director: Jennifer Hauschild.
Camp Wood fee: 3% of gross.
Ownership: Classic Cable (MSO).

CAMPBELL—Torrence Cablevision, Box 1167, Ridgeland, MS 39158. Phones: 601-981-6900; 800-977-8849. County: Hunt. ICA: TX0581.
TV Market Ranking: Below 100. Franchise award date: N.A. Franchise expiration date: N.A. Began: June 1, 1989.
Channel capacity: 35. Channels available but not in use: 6.

Basic Service
Subscribers: 102.
Programming (received off-air): KDAF (W), KDFW (F), KERA-TV (P), KTVT (C), KXAS-TV (N), WFAA-TV (A) Dallas-Fort Worth.
Programming (via satellite): WGN-TV (W) Chicago; A & E; American Movie Classics; BET; C-SPAN; CNN; Country Music TV; Discovery Channel; ESPN; Fox Family Channel; Fox Sports Net Southwest; Headline News; Home Shopping Network; Lifetime; Nashville Network; Nickelodeon; Showtime; TBS Superstation; The Inspirational Network; Turner Network TV; USA Network; Univision; VH1.
Fee: $21.00 monthly.

Pay Service 1
Pay Units: 23.
Programming (via satellite): Cinemax.
Fee: $10.95 monthly.

Pay Service 2
Pay Units: 7.
Programming (via satellite): Disney Channel.
Fee: $10.95 monthly.

Pay Service 3
Pay Units: 30.
Programming (via satellite): HBO.
Fee: $10.95 monthly.

Local advertising: Yes.
Miles of plant: 11.6 (coaxial). Homes passed: 277.
Ownership: Torrence Cable Inc. (MSO).

CAMPBELLTON—Torrence Cablevision, Box 1167, Ridgeland, MS 39158. Phones: 601-981-6900; 800-977-8849. County: Atascosa. ICA: TX0689.
TV Market Ranking: Outside TV Markets. Franchise award date: N.A. Franchise expiration date: N.A. Began: November 1, 1989.
Channel capacity: 36. Channels available but not in use: 21.

Basic Service
Subscribers: 22.
Programming (received off-air): KABB (F), KENS-TV (C), KLRN (P), KMOL-TV (N), KSAT-TV (A) San Antonio.
Programming (via satellite): WGN-TV (W) Chicago; A & E; American Movie Classics; CNN; Country Music TV; Discovery Channel; ESPN; Fox Family Channel; Nashville Network; Showtime; TBS Superstation; USA Network.
Fee: $28.00 monthly.

Miles of plant: 3.6 (coaxial). Homes passed: 104.
Ownership: Torrence Cable Inc. (MSO).

CAMPO ALTO—Torrence Cablevision, Box 1167, Ridgeland, MS 39158. Phones: 601-981-6900; 800-977-8849. County: Hidalgo. ICA: TX0732.
TV Market Ranking: Below 100. Franchise award date: N.A. Franchise expiration date: N.A. Began: N.A.
Channel capacity: 35. Channels available but not in use: N.A.

Basic Service
Subscribers: N.A.
Programming (received off-air): KVEO (N) Brownsville; KGBT-TV (C), KMBH (P) Harlingen; KRGV-TV (A) Weslaco.
Programming (via satellite): WGN-TV (W) Chicago; TBS Superstation.
Fee: $24.95 monthly.

Ownership: Torrence Cable Inc. (MSO).

CANADIAN—Classic Cable, Box 429, 605 N.W. 3rd St., Plainville, KS 67663-0429. Phones: 785-434-7620; 800-999-8876. Fax: 785-434-2614. County: Hemphill. ICA: TX0334.
TV Market Ranking: Outside TV Markets. Franchise award date: N.A. Franchise expiration date: June 30, 1999. Began: September 1, 1958.
Channel capacity: 41 (2-way capable; operating 2-way). Channels available but not in use: N.A.

Basic Service
Subscribers: 804; Commercial subscribers: 16.
Programming (received off-air): KCIT (F,U) Amarillo; KETA (P) Oklahoma City.
Programming (via microwave): KAMR-TV (N), KFDA-TV (C), KVII-TV (A) Amarillo.
Programming (via satellite): WGN-TV (W) Chicago; A & E; American Movie Classics; Animal Planet; C-SPAN; CNN; Country Music TV; Discovery Channel; Disney Channel; E! Entertainment TV; ESPN; Fox Family Channel; Fox News Channel; Fox Sports Net Southwest; Headline News; History Channel; Learning Channel; Lifetime; Nashville Network; Nick at Nite's TV Land; Nickelodeon; QVC; TBS Superstation; The Weather Channel; Trinity Bcstg. Network; Turner Network TV; USA Network; Univision.
Current originations: Public access; educational access; automated emergency alert.
Fee: $35.00 installation; $27.95 monthly; $2.00 converter.
Commercial fee: $24.50 monthly.

Pay Service 1
Pay Units: 26.
Programming (via satellite): Cinemax.
Fee: $9.95 monthly.

Pay Service 2
Pay Units: 75.
Programming (via satellite): HBO.
Fee: $10.95 monthly.

Pay Service 3
Pay Units: 71.
Programming (via satellite): Showtime.
Fee: $9.95 monthly.

Pay Service 4
Pay Units: 111.
Programming (via satellite): The Movie Channel.
Fee: $5.95 monthly.

Local advertising: No.
Equipment: Scientific-Atlanta & Standard Electronics headend; Magnavox amplifiers; Times Fiber cable; Standard Components set top converters; Jerrold addressable set top converters; Eagle & Pico traps; AFC & Scientific-Atlanta satellite antenna; Standard Components & Scientific-Atlanta satellite receivers.
Miles of plant: 23.0 (coaxial). Homes passed: 1,122.
Manager: Bill Flowers. Chief technician: Rick Rattan. Marketing director: Jennifer Hauschild.
City fee: 2% of gross.
Ownership: Classic Cable (MSO).

CANTON—East Texas Cable Co., Suite 103, 301 E. Hwy. 243, Canton, TX 75103. Phone: 903-567-2260. Fax: 903-567-4048. County: Van Zandt. ICA: TX0280.
TV Market Ranking: Below 100. Franchise award date: N.A. Franchise expiration date: N.A. Began: July 1, 1983.
Channel capacity: 35 (2-way capable). Channels available but not in use: None.

Basic Service
Subscribers: 1,370.
Programming (received off-air): KDAF (W), KDFI-TV (I), KDFW (F), KERA-TV (P), KTVT (C), KTXA (U), KXAS-TV (N), KXTX-TV (I), WFAA-TV (A) Dallas-Fort Worth; KETK-TV (N) Jacksonville; KLTV (A) Tyler-Longview.
Programming (via satellite): WGN-TV (W) Chicago; The Weather Channel.
Current originations: Automated time-weather; public access; local news.
Fee: $12.76 monthly.

Expanded Basic Service
Subscribers: N.A.
Programming (via satellite): A & E; CNN; Country Music TV; Discovery Channel; Headline News; History Channel; Lifetime; MTV; Nashville Network; TBS Superstation; Travel Channel; Turner Classic Movies; VH1.
Fee: $5.95 monthly.

Expanded Basic Service 2
Subscribers: N.A.
Programming (via satellite): American Movie Classics; Cartoon Network; ESPN; Fox Family Channel; Fox Sports Net Southwest; Home & Garden Television; Nick at Nite; Nickelodeon; Turner Network TV; USA Network.
Fee: $5.95 monthly.

Pay Service 1
Pay Units: N.A.
Programming (via satellite): Cinemax; Disney Channel; HBO; Showtime.
Fee: $7.95 monthly (Cinemax or Disney), $8.95 monthly (Showtime), $9.95 monthly (HBO).

Miles of plant: 54.0 (coaxial); None (fiber optic). Homes passed: 1,450. Total homes in franchised area: 1,678.
Manager: Jim Roby.
Ownership: Jim Roby.

CANYON—TCA Cable of Amarillo Inc., 1911-A 4th Ave., Canyon, TX 79015. Phone: 806-655-2114. County: Randall. ICA: TX0114.
TV Market Ranking: 95. Franchise award date: N.A. Franchise expiration date: N.A. Began: April 5, 1977.
Channel capacity: 30 (2-way capable; operating 2-way). Channels available but not in use: None.

Basic Service
Subscribers: 2,760.
Programming (received off-air): KACV-TV (P), KAMR-TV (N), KCIT (F,U), KFDA-TV (C), KVII-TV (A) Amarillo; allband FM.
Programming (via satellite): WGN-TV (W) Chicago; A & E; CNBC; CNN; Discovery Channel; ESPN; Lifetime; MTV; Nashville Network; Nickelodeon; TBS Superstation; The Weather Channel; Trinity Bcstg. Network; Turner Network TV; USA Network.
Current originations: Automated time-weather.
Planned originations: Public access; local news.
Fee: $35.00 installation; $10.00 monthly.

Pay Service 1
Pay Units: N.A.
Programming (via satellite): Disney Channel; HBO; Showtime; The Movie Channel.
Fee: $35.00 installation; $8.40 monthly (each).

Local advertising: Yes. Available in character-generated programming. Rates: $1.00/Day. Regional interconnect: Cabletime.
Miles of plant: 160.0 (coaxial).
Manager: Brady DeBord. Chief technician: Troy Grider. Marketing director: Vel Allen.
City fee: 3% of gross.
Ownership: TCA Cable TV Inc. (MSO). See Cable System Ownership.

CANYON LAKE—Guadalupe Valley Communication Systems Inc., 1221 S. Main St., Boerne, TX 78006. Phone: 830-885-7606. Fax: 830-249-8107. County: Comal. Also serves Comal County (portions). ICA: TX0199.
TV Market Ranking: 45 (portions of Comal County); Below 100 (Canyon Lake, portions of Comal County); Outside TV Markets (portions of Comal County). Franchise award date: N.A. Franchise expiration date: N.A. Began: January 1, 1983.
Channel capacity: 35 (not 2-way capable). Channels available but not in use: None.

Basic Service
Subscribers: 2,968.
Programming (received off-air): KRRT (W) Kerrville-San Antonio; KABB (F), KENS-TV (C), KLRN (P), KMOL-TV (N), KSAT-TV (A), KVDA (O), KWEX-TV (S) San Antonio.
Programming (via satellite): WGN-TV (W) Chicago; A & E; American Movie Classics; C-SPAN; CNBC; CNN; Discovery Channel; ESPN; Fox Family Channel; Fox Sports Net Southwest; Headline News; Learning Channel; Lifetime; MTV; Nashville Network; Nick at Nite; Nickelodeon; QVC; TBS Superstation; The Weather Channel; Turner Network TV.
Fee: $20.00 installation; $16.50 monthly; $1.50 converter.

Pay Service 1
Pay Units: 419.
Programming (via satellite): HBO.
Fee: $12.00 monthly.

Pay Service 2
Pay Units: 347.
Programming (via satellite): The Movie Channel.
Fee: $9.95 monthly.

Pay Service 3
Pay Units: 526.
Programming (via satellite): Showtime.
Fee: $9.95 monthly.

Local advertising: Yes. Available in character-generated programming. Rates: $0.60/30 Seconds. Local sales manager: Jan Alexander.

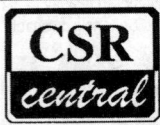

Equipment: Microdyne headend; Texscan amplifiers; Scientific-Atlanta set top converters; Scientific-Atlanta satellite antenna; Microdyne satellite receivers.
Miles of plant: 90.0 (coaxial).
Manager: Tom See. Chief technician: Scott Maytum. Marketing director & customer service manager: Jan Alexander.
Ownership: Guadalupe Valley Communications Systems Inc. (MSO).

CAPISALLO PARK—Torrence Cablevision, Box 1167, Ridgeland, MS 39158. Phones: 601-981-6900; 800-977-8849. County: Hidalgo. Also serves Heidelberg. ICA: TX0685.
TV Market Ranking: Below 100. Franchise award date: N.A. Franchise expiration date: N.A. Began: N.A.
Channel capacity: 36. Channels available but not in use: 18.
Basic Service
Subscribers: 9.
Programming (received off-air): KVEO (N) Brownsville; KGBT-TV (C), KMBH (P) Harlingen; KRGV-TV (A) Weslaco.
Programming (via satellite): WGN-TV (W) Chicago; A & E; American Movie Classics; CNN; Discovery Channel; ESPN; Fox Family Channel; GalaVision; Nashville Network; Showtime; TBS Superstation; Turner Network TV; USA Network.
Fee: $28.00 monthly.
Miles of plant: 3.4 (coaxial). Homes passed: 115.
Ownership: Torrence Cable Inc. (MSO).

CARLSBAD—Classic Cable, Box 429, 605 N.W. 3rd St., Plainville, KS 67663-0429. Phones: 785-434-7620; 800-999-8876. Fax: 785-434-2614. County: Tom Green. ICA: TX0733.
TV Market Ranking: Below 100. Franchise award date: N.A. Franchise expiration date: N.A. Began: N.A.
Channel capacity: 22 (2-way capable). Channels available but not in use: N.A.
Basic Service
Subscribers: 35.
Programming (received off-air): KTXS-TV (A) Abilene-Sweetwater; KACB-TV (N), KIDY (F), KLST (C) San Angelo.
Programming (via satellite): WGN-TV (W) Chicago; CNN; Country Music TV; ESPN; Fox Family Channel; History Channel; Learning Channel; Nashville Network; Nickelodeon; TBS Superstation; The Weather Channel; Trinity Bcstg. Network; Turner Classic Movies; Turner Network TV; USA Network.
Fee: $35.00 installation; $26.95 monthly.
Pay Service 1
Pay Units: 4.
Programming (via satellite): Cinemax.
Fee: $9.95 monthly.
Pay Service 2
Pay Units: 7.
Programming (via satellite): HBO.
Fee: $9.95 monthly.
Miles of plant: 12.0 (coaxial). Homes passed: 245.
Manager: Bill Flowers. Chief technician: Ben Hernandez. Marketing director: Jennifer Hauschild.
Ownership: Classic Cable (MSO).

CARMINE—BRDC Cablevision, Box 240, Giddings, TX 78942. Phone: 409-542-3151. Fax: 409-542-1187. County: Fayette. ICA: TX0653.
TV Market Ranking: Outside TV Markets. Franchise award date: N.A. Franchise expiration date: N.A. Began: December 20, 1990.
Channel capacity: 36. Channels available but not in use: 13.
Basic Service
Subscribers: 76.
Programming (received off-air): KEYE-TV (C), KLRU (P), KTBC (F), KVUE-TV (A), KXAN-TV (N) Austin.
Programming (via satellite): WGN-TV (W) Chicago; CNN; Country Music TV; Discovery Channel; Disney Channel; ESPN; Fox Family Channel; Fox Sports Net South; Life Network; Nashville Network; QVC; Sci-Fi Channel; TBS Superstation; Trinity Bcstg. Network; Turner Network TV; USA Network.
Fee: $25.00 installation; $19.95 monthly.
Pay Service 1
Pay Units: 20.
Programming (via satellite): HBO.
Fee: $9.95 monthly.
Pay Service 2
Pay Units: 13.
Programming (via satellite): Cinemax.
Fee: $9.95 monthly.
Pay Service 3
Pay Units: N.A.
Programming (via satellite): Showtime.
Fee: $9.95 monthly.
Miles of plant: 8.7 (coaxial).
Manager: David W. Peterson.
Ownership: Bluebonnet Rural Development Corp. (MSO).

CAROLINA COVE—World Wide Systems Inc., Box 2150, Hwy. 195, Trinity, TX 75862. Phone: 409-594-2405. County: Walker. Also serves Lake Livingston. ICA: TX0568.
TV Market Ranking: Below 100. Franchise award date: N.A. Franchise expiration date: N.A. Began: February 1, 1985.
Channel capacity: 12. Channels available but not in use: 1.
Basic Service
Subscribers: N.A.
Programming (received off-air): KBTX-TV (C) Bryan; KTRE (A) Lufkin.
Programming (via satellite): Discovery Channel; Fox Sports Net Southwest; Headline News.
Fee: N.A.
Pay Service 1
Pay Units: N.A.
Programming (via satellite): Cinemax; Disney Channel; HBO.
Fee: $6.00 monthly (Disney), $8.00 monthly (Cinemax or HBO).
Miles of plant: 8.0 (coaxial). Homes passed: 300.
Manager: Joe West.
Ownership: Joe West.

CARROLLTON—TCI TKR of the Metroplex Inc., 934 E. Centerville Rd., Garland, TX 75041. Phones: 972-840-2288; 972-840-2388. Counties: Dallas & Denton. Also serves Addison, Hebron. ICA: TX0035.
TV Market Ranking: 12. Franchise award date: N.A. Franchise expiration date: N.A. Began: January 1, 1979.
Channel capacity: 50 (2-way capable; operating 2-way partially). Channels available but not in use: N.A.
Basic Service
Subscribers: 18,101.
Programming (received off-air): KDAF (W), KDFI-TV (I), KDFW (F), KERA-TV (P), KTVT (C), KTXA (U), KXAS-TV (N), KXTX-TV (I), WFAA-TV (A) Dallas-Fort Worth; KDTN (P) Denton; KUVN (S) Garland; KHSX-TV (H) Irving.
Programming (via satellite): WGN-TV (W) Chicago; A & E; C-SPAN; CNBC; CNN; Discovery Channel; Fox Family Channel; Headline News; Home Shopping Network; Lifetime; MTV; Nashville Network; Nickelodeon; TBS Superstation; The Weather Channel; Trinity Bcstg. Network; Univision; VH1.
Current originations: Automated time-weather; public access; educational access; government access; automated emergency alert; local news; local sports.
Fee: $60.00 installation; $11.73 monthly; $3.00 converter; $25.00 additional installation.
Expanded Basic Service
Subscribers: 1,879.
Programming (via satellite): American Movie Classics; ESPN; Fox Sports Net Southwest; Turner Network TV; USA Network.
Fee: $10.30 monthly.
Pay Service 1
Pay Units: N.A.
Programming (via satellite): Disney Channel; HBO; Showtime; The Movie Channel.
Fee: $25.00 installation; $10.25 monthly (Disney, Showtime or TMC), $12.20 monthly (HBO).
Local advertising: Yes. Available in locally originated, character-generated, taped & automated programming. Local sales manager: Debra Friday.
Program Guide: The Cable Guide.
Miles of plant: 291.7 (coaxial). Homes passed: 29,900. Total homes in franchised area: 30,049.
Manager: Steve Crawford.
Ownership: AT&T Broadband & Internet Services (MSO). Purchased from Tele-Communications Inc., March 9, 1999.

CARROLLTON—Charter Communications Inc., 5227 FM 813, Waxahachie, TX 75165. Phones: 972-938-9288; 800-477-0887. Fax: 972-923-0039. Counties: Dallas & Denton. Also serves Addison, Westlake. ICA: TX0734.
TV Market Ranking: 12. Franchise award date: January 1, 1987. Franchise expiration date: N.A. Began: June 1, 1987.
Channel capacity: 55 (not 2-way capable). Channels available but not in use: 4.
Basic Service
Subscribers: 5,148.
Programming (received off-air): KDAF (W), KDFI-TV (I), KDFW (F), KDTX-TV (T), KERA-TV (P), KFWD (O), KTVT (C), KTXA (U), KXAS-TV (N), KXTX-TV (I), WFAA-TV (A) Dallas-Fort Worth; KMPX (I) Decatur; KDTN (P) Denton; KUVN (S) Garland; KHSX-TV (H) Irving.
Programming (via satellite): WGN-TV (W) Chicago; C-SPAN; TBS Superstation; TV Guide Channel.
Fee: $38.00 installation; $12.10 monthly; $9.95 additional installation.
Expanded Basic Service
Subscribers: N.A.
Programming (via satellite): A & E; American Movie Classics; BET; Bravo; CNBC; CNN; Comedy Central; Country Music TV; Discovery Channel; E! Entertainment TV; ESPN; Fox Family Channel; Fox Sports Net Southwest; Headline News; Lifetime; MTV; Nashville Network; Nickelodeon; QVC; The Weather Channel; Turner Network TV; USA Network; VH1.
Fee: $13.89 monthly.
Pay Service 1
Pay Units: N.A.
Programming (via satellite): Cinemax; Disney Channel; HBO; Showtime; The Movie Channel.
Fee: $9.75 monthly (TMC), $9.95 monthly (Disney), $10.75 monthly (Showtime), $10.95 monthly (Cinemax).
Local advertising: Yes.
Miles of plant: 27.0 (coaxial).
Manager: Mary Searce. Chief technician: Ken Stevens. Marketing director: Dale Dring.
City fee: 4% of net.
Ownership: Charter Communications Inc. (MSO). Purchased from Marcus Cable, April 1, 1999.

CARTHAGE—Falcon Cable TV, 108 W. Houston, Marshall, TX 75670. Phone: 903-938-8335. County: Panola. ICA: TX0193.
TV Market Ranking: Below 100. Franchise award date: January 1, 1972. Franchise expiration date: March 27, 2009. Began: April 1, 1973.
Channel capacity: 62. Channels available but not in use: 4.
Basic Service
Subscribers: 2,067.
Programming (received off-air): KETK-TV (N) Jacksonville; KFXK (F) Longview; KLTS-TV (P), KMSS-TV (F), KSHV (U,W), KSLA-TV (C), KTAL-TV (N), KTBS-TV (A) Shreveport-Texarkana; KLTV (A) Tyler-Longview; allband FM.
Programming (via satellite): WGN-TV (W) Chicago; A & E; BET; C-SPAN; CNBC; E! Entertainment TV; ESPN 2; FX; Fox Family Channel; Home Shopping Network; Lifetime; MTV; Nickelodeon; QVC; Sci-Fi Channel; TBS Superstation; TV Guide Sneak Prevue; The Weather Channel; Trinity Bcstg. Network.
Current originations: Public access; educational access; government access; local access.
Fee: $63.00 installation; $23.58 monthly; $2.61 converter.
Expanded Basic Service
Subscribers: 1,895.
Programming (via satellite): CNN; ESPN; Fox Sports Net Southwest; Headline News; Nashville Network; TV Food Network; USA Network.
Fee: $6.66 monthly.
Expanded Basic Service 2
Subscribers: 687.
Programming (via satellite): American Movie Classics; Country Music TV; Discovery Channel; Disney Channel; Home & Garden Television; Turner Network TV.
Fee: $8.75 monthly.
Expanded Basic Service 3
Subscribers: 206.
Programming (via satellite): Cartoon Network; fXM: Movies from Fox; History Channel; Outdoor Life Network; The Health Network.
Fee: $7.50 monthly.
Pay Service 1
Pay Units: 195.
Programming (via satellite): Cinemax.
Fee: $25.00 installation; $11.95 monthly.
Pay Service 2
Pay Units: 294.
Programming (via satellite): HBO.

Fee: $25.00 installation; $11.95 monthly.

Pay Service 3

Pay Units: 170.

Programming (via satellite): Showtime.

Fee: $11.95 monthly.

Pay Service 4

Pay Units: 103.

Programming (via satellite): The Movie Channel.

Fee: $25.00 installation; $11.95 monthly.

Pay Service 5

Pay Units: 103.

Programming (via satellite): The New Encore.

Fee: $5.95 monthly.

Pay-Per-View

Action Pay-Per-View; Spice; Viewer's Choice; movies.

Fee: $3.95 (movies).

Equipment: Scientific-Atlanta, Telemet & To-com headend; Theta-Com amplifiers; Sony cameras; Panasonic VTRs; BEI character generator; Vitek traps; Gardiner satellite antenna; Gardiner satellite receivers.

Miles of plant: 86.0 (coaxial).

Manager: George Doss. Chief technician: Robert Hurd.

Franchise fee: 2% of gross.

Ownership: Falcon Communications LP (MSO), joint venture formed September 30, 1998. See Cable System Ownership.

CASTROVILLE—Falcon Cable TV, 1244 Encino Dr., Pleasanton, TX 78064. Phone: 830-569-5509. Fax: 830-569-4828. County: Medina. ICA: TX0427.

TV Market Ranking: 45. Franchise award date: N.A. Franchise expiration date: N.A. Began: September 1, 1982.

Channel capacity: 37 (not 2-way capable). Channels available but not in use: 1.

Basic Service

Subscribers: 564.

Programming (received off-air): KRRT (W) Kerrville-San Antonio; KABB (F), KENS-TV (C), KLRN (P), KMOL-TV (N), KSAT-TV (A), KVDA (O), KWEX-TV (S) San Antonio.

Programming (via satellite): Bravo; C-SPAN; Country Music TV; E! Entertainment TV; ESPN; Fox Family Channel; Headline News; Home Shopping Network; Learning Channel; Lifetime; Nashville Network; QVC; Sci-Fi Channel; The Weather Channel; Travel Channel.

Current originations: Automated time-weather.

Fee: $15.00 installation; $22.61 monthly; $10.00 additional installation.

Expanded Basic Service

Subscribers: 554.

Programming (via satellite): American Movie Classics; Discovery Channel; USA Network.

Fee: $2.00 monthly.

Expanded Basic Service 2

Subscribers: 547.

Programming (via satellite): WGN-TV (W) Chicago; CNN; Disney Channel; TBS Superstation; Turner Network TV.

Fee: $6.75 monthly.

Pay Service 1

Pay Units: 32.

Programming (via satellite): Cinemax.

Fee: $10.95 monthly.

Pay Service 2

Pay Units: 65.

Programming (via satellite): HBO.

Fee: $11.95 monthly.

Pay Service 3

Pay Units: 57.

Programming (via satellite): Showtime.

Fee: $10.95 monthly.

Pay Service 4

Pay Units: 26.

Programming (via satellite): The Movie Channel.

Fee: $10.95 monthly.

Local advertising: Yes. Available in character-generated programming. Regional interconnect: Cabletime.

Equipment: Microdyne & Scientific-Atlanta headend; Magnavox amplifiers; Jerrold cable; GTE Sylvania set top converters; Eagle traps; Fort Worth Tower & Scientific-Atlanta satellite antenna; Automation Techniques, M/A-Com & Microdyne satellite receivers.

Miles of plant: 14.0 (coaxial). Homes passed: 595.

Manager: Lorna Gentry. Chief technician: Santos Guajardo.

Franchise fee: 3% of gross.

Ownership: Falcon Communications LP (MSO), joint venture formed September 30, 1998. See Cable System Ownership.

CEDAR CREEK—Torrence Cablevision, Box 1167, Ridgeland, MS 39158. Phones: 601-981-6900; 800-977-8849. County: Bastrop. ICA: TX0901.

TV Market Ranking: Below 100. Franchise award date: N.A. Franchise expiration date: N.A. Began: N.A.

Channel capacity: N.A. Channels available but not in use: N.A.

Basic Service

Subscribers: 540.

Programming (received off-air): KEYE-TV (C), KTBC (F), KXAN-TV (N) Austin; KLRN (P), KMOL-TV (N), KSAT-TV (A) San Antonio.

Programming (via satellite): WGN-TV (W) Chicago; A & E; American Movie Classics; CNN; Country Music TV; Discovery Channel; ESPN; Fox Family Channel; Showtime; TBS Superstation; Turner Network TV; USA Network.

Fee: $23.00 monthly.

Homes passed: 1,902.

Ownership: Torrence Cable Inc. (MSO).

CEDAR CREEK LAKE—Torrence Cablevision, Box 1167, Ridgeland, MS 39158. Phones: 601-981-6900; 800-977-8849. County: Kaufman. ICA: TX0736.

TV Market Ranking:. Franchise award date: N.A. Franchise expiration date: N.A. Began: N.A.

Channel capacity: 36. Channels available but not in use: 21.

Basic Service

Subscribers: 56.

Programming (received off-air): KDFW (F), KERA-TV (P), KTVT (C), KXAS-TV (N), WFAA-TV (A) Dallas-Fort Worth.

Programming (via satellite): A & E; American Movie Classics; CNN; Country Music TV; Discovery Channel; ESPN; Fox Family Channel; Nashville Network; Showtime; TBS Superstation; Turner Network TV; USA Network.

Fee: $22.00 monthly.

Miles of plant: 5.5 (coaxial). Homes passed: 180.

Ownership: Torrence Cable Inc. (MSO).

CEDAR SPRINGS—Friendship Cable of Texas Inc., Box 9090, Tyler, TX 75711-9090. Phone: 903-581-2121. Fax: 903-581-2185. County: Upshur. ICA: TX0628.

TV Market Ranking: Below 100. Franchise award date: N.A. Franchise expiration date: N.A. Began: January 1, 1989.

Channel capacity: 36. Channels available but not in use: 10.

Basic Service

Subscribers: 101.

Programming (received off-air): KETK-TV (N) Jacksonville; KFXK (F) Longview; KLTS-TV (P), KSLA-TV (C) Shreveport-Texarkana; KLTV (A) Tyler-Longview.

Programming (via satellite): WGN-TV (W) Chicago; CNN; Country Music TV; Discovery Channel; ESPN; Fox Family Channel; Lifetime; Nashville Network; Nickelodeon; TBS Superstation; USA Network.

Fee: $32.50 monthly.

Pay Service 1

Pay Units: 24.

Programming (via satellite): Cinemax.

Fee: $10.95 monthly.

Pay Service 2

Pay Units: 22.

Programming (via satellite): HBO.

Fee: $10.95 monthly.

Local advertising: Yes.

Miles of plant: 8.5 (coaxial). Homes passed: 208.

Manager: Marianne Bogy. Chief technician: Sonny Myers.

Ownership: Buford Television Inc. (MSO). See Cable System Ownership.

CENTER—Friendship Cable of Texas Inc., Box 9090, Tyler, TX 75711-9090. Phone: 903-581-2121. Fax: 903-581-2185. County: Shelby. ICA: TX0192.

TV Market Ranking: Below 100. Franchise award date: N.A. Franchise expiration date: N.A. Began: July 1, 1970.

Channel capacity: 80. Channels available but not in use: N.A.

Basic Service

Subscribers: 1,843.

Programming (received off-air): KTRE (A) Lufkin; KLTS-TV (P), KSLA-TV (C), KTAL-TV (N), KTBS-TV (A) Shreveport-Texarkana; KLTV (A) Tyler-Longview; allband FM.

Programming (via satellite): WGN-TV (W) Chicago; A & E; BET; C-SPAN; CNN; Cartoon Network; Discovery Channel; ESPN; FX; Fox Family Channel; Fox Sports Net; Great American Country; Headline News; Home & Garden Television; Home Shopping Network; Learning Channel; Lifetime; MuchMusic Network; Nashville Network; Nickelodeon; Outdoor Life Network; TBS Superstation; The Weather Channel; Trinity Bcstg. Network; Turner Classic Movies; Turner Network TV; USA Network; Univision.

Current originations: Automated time-weather; local news.

Fee: $30.00 installation; $26.95 monthly.

Pay Service 1

Pay Units: 410.

Programming (via satellite): HBO.

Fee: $10.00 monthly.

Pay Service 2

Pay Units: 228.

Programming (via satellite): Cinemax.

Fee: $10.00 monthly.

Pay Service 3

Pay Units: 149.

Programming (via satellite): The Movie Channel.

Fee: $10.00 monthly.

Pay Service 4

Pay Units: 240.

Programming (via satellite): Showtime.

Fee: $5.95 monthly.

Local advertising: Yes. Rates: $50.00/Month.

Equipment: Tocom headend; Vikoa amplifiers; Systems Wire cable; Fort Worth Tower satellite antenna.

Miles of plant: 65.0 (coaxial). Homes passed: 2,600.

Manager: Marianne Bogy. Chief technician: Henry Harris.

City fee: 2% of gross.

Ownership: Buford Television Inc. (MSO). See Cable System Ownership.

CENTER POINT—Classic Cable, Box 429, 605 N.W. 3rd St., Plainville, KS 67663-0429. Phones: 785-434-7620; 800-999-8876. Fax: 785-434-2614. Counties: Kerr & Panola. Also serves Woods. ICA: TX0913.

TV Market Ranking: Below 100 (Center Point); Outside TV Markets (Woods). Franchise award date: N.A. Franchise expiration date: N.A. Began: N.A.

Channel capacity: 61 (2-way capable). Channels available but not in use: N.A.

Basic Service

Subscribers: 504.

Programming (received off-air): KRRT (W) Kerrville-San Antonio; KABB (F), KENS-TV (C), KMOL-TV (N), KSAT-TV (A) San Antonio.

Programming (via satellite): WGN-TV (W) Chicago; KRMA-TV (P) Denver; A & E; Animal Planet; CNBC; CNN; Country Music TV; Discovery Channel; Disney Channel; ESPN; Fox Family Channel; Fox News Channel; Fox Sports Net Southwest; Headline News; History Channel; Learning Channel; Nashville Network; Nick at Nite's TV Land; Nickelodeon; QVC; TBS Superstation; Telemundo; The Weather Channel; Trinity Bcstg. Network; Turner Classic Movies; Turner Network TV; USA Network.

Fee: $35.00 installation; $27.95 monthly.

Pay Service 1

Pay Units: 24.

Programming (via satellite): Cinemax.

Fee: $9.95 monthly.

Pay Service 2

Pay Units: 87.

Programming (via satellite): HBO.

Fee: $10.95 monthly.

Pay Service 3

Pay Units: 41.

Programming (via satellite): Showtime.

Fee: $9.95 monthly.

Pay Service 4

Pay Units: 42.

Programming (via satellite): The Movie Channel.

Fee: $5.95 monthly.

Miles of plant: 17.9 (coaxial). Homes passed: 640.

Manager: Bill Flowers. Chief technician: Walt VanLue. Marketing director: Jennifer Hauschild.

Ownership: Classic Cable (MSO).

CENTERVILLE—Mission Cable, 920 Whitmore Dr., Rockwall, TX 75087. Phone: 800-783-5708. Fax: 214-722-6218. County: Leon. ICA: TX0463.

TV Market Ranking: Outside TV Markets. Franchise award date: July 15, 1989. Franchise expiration date: N.A. Began: February 1, 1982.

Channel capacity: 21 (not 2-way capable). Channels available but not in use: None.

Basic Service

Subscribers: 340; Commercial subscribers: 61.

Programming (received off-air): KBTX-TV (C) Bryan; KAMU-TV (P) College Station; KCEN-TV (N), KXXV (A) Waco-Temple.

Programming (via satellite): WGN-TV (W) Chicago; CNN; Discovery Channel; ESPN; Fox Family Channel; Fox Sports Net Southwest; Nashville Network; TBS Superstation; Turner Network TV; USA Network.

Current originations: Automated time-weather; public access; educational access; government access; leased access; automated emergency alert; local news; local sports.
Fee: $40.00 installation; $19.95 monthly.

Pay Service 1
Pay Units: 32.
Programming (via satellite): Disney Channel.
Fee: $9.00 monthly.

Pay Service 2
Pay Units: 42.
Programming (via satellite): HBO.
Fee: $9.00 monthly.

Pay Service 3
Pay Units: 48.
Programming (via satellite): Showtime.
Fee: $9.00 monthly.

Equipment: Blonder-Tongue, DX Engineering & Tru-Spec headend; Comm/Scope amplifiers; Weatherscan satellite antenna; Automation Techniques & Uniden satellite receivers.
Miles of plant: 9.7 (coaxial). Homes passed: 453. Total homes in franchised area: 581.
Manager: Jim Stafford. Chief technician: Jacky Oliver. Marketing & program director: Bruce Berkinshaw.
City fee: 3% of basic & pay revenues.
Ownership: Fanch Communications Inc. (MSO); Time Warner Cable (MSO). See Cable System Ownership.

CENTRAL—Friendship Cable of Texas Inc., Box 9090, Tyler, TX 75711-9090. Phone: 903-581-2121. Fax: 903-581-2185. County: Angelina. Also serves Clawson, Redland. ICA: TX0339.
TV Market Ranking: Below 100. Franchise award date: N.A. Franchise expiration date: N.A. Began: N.A.
Channel capacity: 36. Channels available but not in use: 3.

Basic Service
Subscribers: 816.
Programming (received off-air): KETK-TV (N) Jacksonville; KTRE (A) Lufkin; KSLA-TV (C) Shreveport-Texarkana.
Programming (via satellite): WGN-TV (W) Chicago; A & E; American Movie Classics; BET; CNN; Country Music TV; Discovery Channel; Disney Channel; ESPN; Fox Family Channel; Fox Sports Net Southwest; Headline News; Home Shopping Network; Lifetime; Nashville Network; Nickelodeon; TBS Superstation; The Weather Channel; Turner Network TV; USA Network.
Fee: $33.85 monthly.

Pay Service 1
Pay Units: 38.
Programming (via satellite): Cinemax.
Fee: $10.95 monthly.

Pay Service 2
Pay Units: 37.
Programming (via satellite): HBO.
Fee: $10.95 monthly.

Pay Service 3
Pay Units: 126.
Programming (via satellite): Showtime.
Fee: $5.95 monthly.

Local advertising: No.
Miles of plant: 78.9 (coaxial). Homes passed: 1,741. Total homes in franchised area: 1,741.
Manager: Marianne Bogy. Chief technician: Henry Harris.
Ownership: Buford Television Inc. (MSO). See Cable System Ownership.

CHANDLER—Northland Cable TV, Box 538, Flint, TX 75762. Phones: 903-566-8757; 903-894-8200. Fax: 903-894-8204. County: Henderson. ICA: TX0452.
TV Market Ranking: Below 100. Franchise award date: September 28, 1981. Franchise expiration date: June 26, 1999. Began: February 15, 1982.
Channel capacity: 36 (2-way capable). Channels available but not in use: 5.

Basic Service
Subscribers: 600.
Programming (received off-air): KETK-TV (N) Jacksonville; KFXK (F) Longview; KLTV (A) Tyler-Longview.
Programming (via microwave): KDFW (F), KERA-TV (P), KTVT (C), KXTX-TV (I), WFAA-TV (A) Dallas-Fort Worth.
Programming (via satellite): WGN-TV (W) Chicago; A & E; CNN; Country Music TV; Discovery Channel; ESPN; Fox Family Channel; Fox Sports Net Southwest; Headline News; Learning Channel; Nashville Network; QVC; TBS Superstation; USA Network.
Current originations: Automated time-weather; local sports.
Fee: $49.95 installation; $20.75 monthly; $3.00 converter.

Pay Service 1
Pay Units: 28.
Programming (via satellite): Disney Channel.
Fee: $24.95 installation; $7.00 monthly.

Pay Service 2
Pay Units: 46.
Programming (via satellite): HBO.
Fee: $24.95 installation; $10.50 monthly.

Pay Service 3
Pay Units: 28.
Programming (via satellite): Showtime.
Fee: $24.95 installation; $7.95 monthly.

Local advertising: Yes. Available in satellite distributed, locally originated, character-generated, taped & automated programming. Rates: $16.00/Minute; $8.00/30 Seconds. Local sales manager: Lynda Tracy.
Program Guide: Premium Channels.
Equipment: Hughes, M/A-Com & Scientific-Atlanta headend; Magnavox & Texscan amplifiers; Comm/Scope & Trilogy cable; Texscan character generator; Hamlin, Jerrold & Scientific-Atlanta set top converters; Arcom, Eagle & Pico traps; Harris satellite antenna; Harris satellite receivers; ChannelMatic & Sony commercial insert.
Miles of plant: 18.0 (coaxial).
Manager: Jim Wiggins. Chief technician: Jim Bob Sanders. Marketing director: Charlotte Griffin.
City fee: 5% of gross.
Ownership: Northland Communications Corp. (MSO).

CHANNING—High Plains Cablevision Inc., Box 310, 124 S. Main St., Lockney, TX 79241. Phone: 806-652-3328. Fax: 806-652-3139. County: Hartley. ICA: TX0737.
TV Market Ranking: Outside TV Markets. Franchise award date: N.A. Franchise expiration date: N.A. Began: N.A.
Channel capacity: N.A. Channels available but not in use: N.A.

Basic Service
Subscribers: 59.
Programming (received off-air): KAMR-TV (N), KCIT (F,U), KFDA-TV (C), KVII-TV (A) Amarillo.
Programming (via satellite): Turner Network TV.
Fee: N.A.

Manager: Jim Doucette. Chief technician: Jim Odle.
Ownership: High Plains Cablevision Inc. (MSO).

CHAPPELL HILL—BRDC Cablevision, Box 240, Giddings, TX 78942. Phone: 409-542-3151. Fax: 409-542-1187. County: Washington. Also serves Bluebonnet Hills. ICA: TX0888.
TV Market Ranking: Below 100. Franchise award date: N.A. Franchise expiration date: N.A. Began: N.A.
Channel capacity: 36 (not 2-way capable). Channels available but not in use: 17.

Basic Service
Subscribers: 100.
Programming (received off-air): KHOU-TV (C), KHTV (W), KPRC-TV (N), KRIV (F), KTRK-TV (A), KTXH (U), KUHT (P) Houston.
Programming (via satellite): WGN-TV (W) Chicago; CNN; Discovery Channel; Disney Channel; ESPN; Fox Family Channel; Fox Sports Net Southwest; Nashville Network; Sci-Fi Channel; TBS Superstation; Turner Network TV; USA Network.
Fee: $25.00 installation; $21.95 monthly.

Pay Service 1
Pay Units: N.A.
Programming (via satellite): Cinemax; HBO.
Fee: $9.95 monthly (each).

Pay Service 2
Pay Units: 31.
Programming (via satellite): Showtime.
Fee: $9.95 monthly.

Miles of plant: 14.4 (coaxial); None (fiber optic). Homes passed: 250. Total homes in franchised area: 359.
Manager: David W. Peterson.
Ownership: Bluebonnet Rural Development Corp. (MSO).

CHARLOTTE—Time Warner Communications, 207 E. Colorado St., Pearsall, TX 78061-3234. Phone: 800-527-6221. County: Atascosa. Also serves Atascosa County. ICA: TX0508.
TV Market Ranking: 45 (portions of Atascosa County); Outside TV Markets (portions of Atascosa County, Charlotte). Franchise award date: N.A. Franchise expiration date: N.A. Began: September 1, 1982.
Channel capacity: 26. Channels available but not in use: N.A.

Basic Service
Subscribers: 190.
Programming (received off-air): KRRT (W) Kerrville-San Antonio; KABB (F), KENS-TV (C), KLRN (P), KMOL-TV (N), KSAT-TV (A), KVDA (O), KWEX-TV (S) San Antonio.
Programming (via satellite): WGN-TV (W) Chicago; CNN; ESPN; Fox Family Channel; Fox Sports Net Southwest; GalaVision; Headline News; Nashville Network; Nickelodeon; TBS Superstation; The Weather Channel; USA Network.
Fee: $30.00 installation; $19.18 monthly; $30.00 additional installation.

Pay Service 1
Pay Units: 42.
Programming (via satellite): HBO.
Fee: $9.00 monthly.

Pay Service 2
Pay Units: 37.
Programming (via satellite): Showtime.
Fee: $9.00 monthly.

Pay Service 3
Pay Units: 15.
Programming (via satellite): The Movie Channel.
Fee: N.A.

Miles of plant: 10.0 (coaxial). Homes passed: 439. Total homes in franchised area: 488.
Manager: Marcos Reyes.
Ownership: Time Warner Cable (MSO); AT&T Broadband & Internet Services (MSO).

CHEEK—Friendship Cable of Texas Inc., Box 9090, Tyler, TX 75711-9090. Phone: 903-581-2121. Fax: 903-581-2185. County: Jefferson. ICA: TX0576.
TV Market Ranking: 88. Franchise award date: N.A. Franchise expiration date: N.A. Began: N.A.
Channel capacity: 36 (not 2-way capable). Channels available but not in use: 9.

Basic Service
Subscribers: 133.
Programming (received off-air): KBMT (A), KBTV-TV (N), KFDM-TV (C) Beaumont-Port Arthur; KVHP (F) Lake Charles.
Programming (via satellite): WGN-TV (W) Chicago; BET; CNN; Country Music TV; Discovery Channel; ESPN; Fox Family Channel; Fox Sports Net Southwest; Headline News; Lifetime; Nashville Network; Nickelodeon; QVC; TBS Superstation; The Inspirational Network; The Weather Channel; Turner Network TV; USA Network.
Fee: $34.20 monthly.

Pay Service 1
Pay Units: 7.
Programming (via satellite): Cinemax.
Fee: $10.95 monthly.

Pay Service 2
Pay Units: 20.
Programming (via satellite): HBO.
Fee: $10.95 monthly.

Pay Service 3
Pay Units: 16.
Programming (via satellite): Showtime.
Fee: $5.95 monthly.

Local advertising: Yes.
Miles of plant: 7.4 (coaxial). Homes passed: 284.
Manager: Wanda Pyburn. Chief technician: Mike Deal.
Ownership: Buford Television Inc. (MSO). See Cable System Ownership.

CHESTER—Friendship Cable of Texas Inc., Box 9090, Tyler, TX 75711-9090. Phone: 903-581-2121. Fax: 903-581-2185. County: Tyler. ICA: TX0671.
TV Market Ranking: Below 100. Franchise award date: August 24, 1989. Franchise expiration date: August 24, 2014. Began: August 24, 1989.
Channel capacity: 36. Channels available but not in use: N.A.

Basic Service
Subscribers: 75.
Programming (received off-air): KBTV-TV (N), KFDM-TV (C) Beaumont-Port Arthur; KTRE (A) Lufkin.
Programming (via satellite): WGN-TV (W) Chicago; A & E; CNN; Country Music TV; Discovery Channel; ESPN; Fox Family Channel; Lifetime; Nashville Network; Nickelodeon; Sci-Fi Channel; TBS Superstation; Trinity Bcstg. Network; Turner Network TV; USA Network.
Fee: $30.00 installation; $26.80 monthly.

Pay Service 1
Pay Units: 22.
Programming (via satellite): HBO.
Fee: $10.00 monthly.

Pay Service 2
Pay Units: 18.
Programming (via satellite): Showtime.
Fee: $5.95 monthly.

Miles of plant: 7.7 (coaxial). Homes passed: 136.
Manager: Wanda Pyburn. Chief technician: Mike Deal.
Franchise fee: 3% of gross.
Ownership: Buford Television Inc. (MSO). See Cable System Ownership.

CHILDRESS—Classic Cable, Box 598, 241 Commerce, Childress, TX 79201. Phone: 940-937-8202. Fax: 940-937-2708. County: Childress. Also serves Childress County. ICA: TX0195.

TV Market Ranking: Outside TV Markets. Franchise award date: June 30, 1991. Franchise expiration date: June 26, 2006. Began: November 1, 1956.

Channel capacity: 35 (not 2-way capable). Channels available but not in use: None.

Basic Service

Subscribers: 1,750.

Programming (received off-air): KWET (P) Cheyenne.

Programming (via microwave): KAMR-TV (N), KFDA-TV (C), KVII-TV (A) Amarillo.

Programming (via satellite): WGN-TV (W) Chicago; A & E; American Movie Classics; C-SPAN; CNN; Cartoon Network; Country Music TV; Discovery Channel; Disney Channel; ESPN; Fox Family Channel; Fox Sports Net Southwest; History Channel; Home Shopping Network; Learning Channel; Lifetime; MTV; Nashville Network; Nickelodeon; Odyssey; Sci-Fi Channel; TBS Superstation; The Inspirational Network; The Weather Channel; Turner Classic Movies; Turner Network TV; USA Network; Univision.

Current originations: Automated time-weather; automated emergency alert.

Fee: $30.00 installation; $26.07 monthly; $0.36 converter.

Pay Service 1

Pay Units: 127.

Programming (via satellite): Cinemax.

Fee: $11.65 monthly.

Pay Service 2

Pay Units: 194.

Programming (via satellite): HBO.

Fee: $11.65 monthly.

Equipment: Scientific-Atlanta headend; GTE Sylvania amplifiers; Anaconda cable; Scientific-Atlanta satellite antenna.

Miles of plant: 42.0 (coaxial). Homes passed: 2,466. Total homes in franchised area: 2,466.

Office manager: Mary Love.

City fee: 3% of gross.

Ownership: Classic Cable (MSO). Purchased from Cable One Inc., July 29, 1998.

CHILLICOTHE—Classic Cable, Box 429, 605 N.W. 3rd St., Plainville, KS 67663-0429. Phones: 785-434-7620; 800-999-8876. Fax: 785-434-2614. County: Hardeman. ICA: TX0530.

TV Market Ranking: Outside TV Markets. Franchise award date: N.A. Franchise expiration date: October 10, 2006. Began: January 1, 1983.

Channel capacity: 41 (2-way capable). Channels available but not in use: N.A.

Basic Service

Subscribers: 249; Commercial subscribers: 32.

Programming (received off-air): KAUZ-TV (C), KFDX-TV (N), KJTL (F,U), KSWO-TV (A) Wichita Falls-Lawton.

Programming (via satellite): WGN-TV (W) Chicago; American Movie Classics; Animal Planet; CNN; Country Music TV; Discovery Channel; Disney Channel; E! Entertainment TV; ESPN; Fox Family Channel; Fox Sports Net Southwest; History Channel; Lifetime; Nashville Network; Nick at Nite's TV Land; QVC; TBS Superstation; The Weather Channel; Trinity Bcstg. Network; Turner Network TV; USA Network; Univision.

Current originations: Automated time-weather.

Fee: $35.00 installation; $27.95 monthly.

Pay Service 1

Pay Units: 35.

Programming (via satellite): Cinemax.

Fee: $9.95 monthly.

Pay Service 2

Pay Units: 45.

Programming (via satellite): HBO.

Fee: $9.95 monthly.

Local advertising: No.

Miles of plant: 6.7 (coaxial). Homes passed: 461.

Manager: Bill Flowers. Chief technician: Rick Rattan. Marketing director: Jennifer Hauschild.

City fee: 2% of gross.

Ownership: Classic Cable (MSO). Purchased from Fanch Communications Inc.

CHILTON—Galaxy Cablevision, 307 N. 5th St., Leesville, LA 71496. Phone: 318-238-1361. County: Falls. ICA: TX0598.

TV Market Ranking: Below 100. Franchise award date: N.A. Franchise expiration date: N.A. Began: July 1, 1984.

Channel capacity: 21. Channels available but not in use: None.

Basic Service

Subscribers: 88.

Programming (received off-air): KVUE-TV (A) Austin; KNCT (P) Belton; KCEN-TV (N), KWTX-TV (C) Waco-Temple.

Programming (via satellite): TBS Superstation.

Fee: $30.00 installation; $22.75 monthly.

Pay Service 1

Pay Units: N.A.

Programming (via satellite): Cinemax; HBO; Showtime.

Fee: $12.00 monthly (each).

Miles of plant: 6.2 (coaxial). Homes passed: 313.

Manager: Eulin Guidry. Technical manager: Randy Berry.

Ownership: Galaxy Cablevision (MSO).

CHINA—Timberlake Cablevision Inc., Box 2024, 660 W. Barkley St., Sour Lake, TX 77659. Phone: 409-287-3014. Fax: 409-287-3695. County: Jefferson. ICA: TX0738.

TV Market Ranking: 88. Franchise award date: N.A. Franchise expiration date: N.A. Began: N.A.

Channel capacity: N.A. Channels available but not in use: N.A.

Basic Service

Subscribers: 481.

Programming (received off-air): KBMT (A), KBTV-TV (N), KFDM-TV (C) Beaumont-Port Arthur; KHOU-TV (C), KHTV (W), KPRC-TV (N), KRIV (F), KTRK-TV (A), KTXH (U), KUHT (P) Houston.

Programming (via satellite): CNN; Nickelodeon.

Fee: $25.00 installation; $15.95 monthly.

Pay Service 1

Pay Units: N.A.

Programming (via satellite): HBO; Showtime; The Movie Channel.

Fee: $10.00 monthly (each).

Manager: Eldon Israel.

Ownership: Cable Management Assoc. (MSO).

CHRISTOVAL—Classic Cable, Box 429, 605 N.W. 3rd St., Plainville, KS 67663-0429. Phones: 785-434-7620; 800-999-8876. Fax: 785-434-2614. County: Tom Green. ICA: TX0589.

TV Market Ranking: Below 100. Franchise award date: N.A. Franchise expiration date: N.A. Began: January 1, 1981.

Channel capacity: 36 (2-way capable). Channels available but not in use: N.A.

Basic Service

Subscribers: 137.

Programming (received off-air): KTXS-TV (A) Abilene-Sweetwater; KACB-TV (N), KIDY (F), KLST (C) San Angelo.

Programming (via microwave): KRMA-TV (P) Denver.

Programming (via satellite): WGN-TV (W) Chicago; A & E; CNN; Cartoon Network; Country Music TV; Discovery Channel; Disney Channel; ESPN; Fox Family Channel; Headline News; Home & Garden Television; Learning Channel; Nashville Network; Nick at Nite's TV Land; Nickelodeon; Sci-Fi Channel; TBS Superstation; The Weather Channel; Turner Classic Movies; Turner Network TV; USA Network; Univision.

Fee: $35.00 installation; $27.95 monthly.

Pay Service 1

Pay Units: 19.

Programming (via satellite): HBO.

Fee: $10.95 monthly.

Pay Service 2

Pay Units: 17.

Programming (via satellite): Showtime.

Fee: $9.95 monthly.

Equipment: Scientific-Atlanta satellite antenna; Scientific-Atlanta satellite receivers.

Miles of plant: 8.5 (coaxial). Homes passed: 255.

Manager: Bill Flowers. Chief technician: Ben Hernandez. Marketing director: Jennifer Hauschild.

Ownership: Classic Cable (MSO).

CLARENDON—Classic Cable, Box 429, 605 N.W. 3rd St., Plainville, KS 67663-0429. Phones: 785-434-7620; 800-999-8876. Fax: 785-434-2614. County: Donley. ICA: TX0398.

TV Market Ranking: Outside TV Markets. Franchise award date: N.A. Franchise expiration date: N.A. Began: June 15, 1962.

Channel capacity: 41 (2-way capable). Channels available but not in use: N.A.

Basic Service

Subscribers: 606; Commercial subscribers: 297.

Programming (received off-air): KACV-TV (P), KAMR-TV (N), KCIT (F,U), KFDA-TV (C), KVII-TV (A) Amarillo; allband FM.

Programming (via satellite): WGN-TV (W) Chicago; American Movie Classics; Animal Planet; C-SPAN; CNN; Country Music TV; Discovery Channel; Disney Channel; E! Entertainment TV; ESPN; Fox Family Channel; Fox News Channel; Fox Sports Net Southwest; Headline News; History Channel; Home & Garden Television; Learning Channel; Lifetime; Nashville Network; Nick at Nite's TV Land; Nickelodeon; QVC; Sci-Fi Channel; TBS Superstation; The Weather Channel; Turner Network TV; USA Network.

Current originations: Automated time-weather; public access; religious access.

Fee: $35.00 installation; $28.95 monthly.

Pay Service 1

Pay Units: 59.

Programming (via satellite): HBO.

Fee: $20.00 installation; $10.95 monthly.

Pay Service 2

Pay Units: 26.

Programming (via satellite): Showtime.

Fee: $9.95 monthly.

Pay Service 3

Pay Units: 30.

Programming (via satellite): The Movie Channel.

Fee: $5.95 monthly.

Local advertising: Yes. Available in character-generated programming. Rates: $50.00/Month; $15.00/Week; $3.00/Day.

Equipment: Jerrold headend; Jerrold amplifiers; U.S. Tower satellite antenna.

Miles of plant: 23.5 (coaxial). Homes passed: 812.

Manager: Bill Flowers. Chief technician: Rick Rattan. Marketing director: Jennifer Hauschild.

City fee: 2% of gross.

Ownership: Classic Cable (MSO).

CLARKSVILLE—Friendship Cable of Texas Inc., Box 9090, Tyler, TX 75711-9090. Phone: 903-581-2121. Fax: 903-581-2185. Counties: Lamar, Red River & Titus. Also serves Annona, Avery, Blossom, Bogata, Deport, Detroit, Reno, Talco. ICA: TX0200.

TV Market Ranking: Outside TV Markets. Franchise award date: N.A. Franchise expiration date: N.A. Began: March 1, 1963.

Channel capacity: 21. Channels available but not in use: N.A.

Basic Service

Subscribers: 3,472.

Programming (received off-air): KMSS-TV (F), KTAL-TV (N), KTBS-TV (A) Shreveport-Texarkana; allband FM.

Programming (via microwave): KDFW (F), KERA-TV (P), KTVT (C), KXAS-TV (N), WFAA-TV (A) Dallas-Fort Worth.

Programming (via satellite): BET; CNN; Country Music TV; Discovery Channel; ESPN; Fox Family Channel; Nashville Network; TBS Superstation; The Weather Channel; Turner Network TV.

Current originations: Automated time-weather.

Fee: $30.00 installation; $28.25 monthly.

Pay Service 1

Pay Units: 226.

Programming (via satellite): Cinemax.

Fee: $11.00 monthly.

Pay Service 2

Pay Units: 632.

Programming (via satellite): HBO.

Fee: $11.00 monthly.

Pay Service 3

Pay Units: 342.

Programming (via satellite): Showtime.

Fee: $5.95 monthly.

Pay Service 4

Pay Units: 182.

Programming (via satellite): The Movie Channel.

Fee: $10.95 monthly.

Local advertising: Yes. Rates: $270.00/Year.

Equipment: Ameco headend; Ameco amplifiers; Scientific-Atlanta satellite antenna.

Miles of plant: 126.1 (coaxial). Homes passed: 6,299.

Manager: Marianne Bogy. Chief technician: Sonny Myers.

Ownership: Buford Television Inc. (MSO). See Cable System Ownership.

CLAUDE—Classic Cable, Box 429, 605 N.W. 3rd St., Plainville, KS 67663-0429. Phones: 785-434-7620; 800-999-8876. Fax: 785-434-2614. County: Armstrong. ICA: TX0516.

TV Market Ranking: 95. Franchise award date: N.A. Franchise expiration date: N.A. Began: February 1, 1981.

Channel capacity: 36 (2-way capable). Channels available but not in use: N.A.

Basic Service

Subscribers: 258; Commercial subscribers: 21.

Programming (received off-air): KACV-TV (P), KAMR-TV (N), KCIT (F,U), KFDA-TV (C), KVII-TV (A) Amarillo.

Programming (via satellite): WGN-TV (W) Chicago; CNN; Cartoon Network; Country Music TV; Discovery Channel; Disney Channel; E! Entertainment TV; ESPN; Fox Family Channel; Fox Sports Net Southwest; Good-

life TV Network; Learning Channel; Nashville Network; Nick at Nite's TV Land; QVC; Sci-Fi Channel; TBS Superstation; The Weather Channel; Turner Network TV; USA Network.
Fee: $35.00 installation; $27.95 monthly.
Pay Service 1
Pay Units: 38.
Programming (via satellite): HBO.
Fee: $20.00 installation; $10.95 monthly.
Pay Service 2
Pay Units: 16.
Programming (via satellite): Showtime.
Fee: $20.00 installation; $9.95 monthly.
Miles of plant: 9.5 (coaxial). Homes passed: 411.
Manager: Bill Flowers. Chief technician: Rick Rattan. Marketing director: Jennifer Hauschild.
Ownership: Classic Cable (MSO).

CLEBURNE—Charter Communications Inc., 219 N. Ridgeway, Cleburne, TX 76031. Phone: 817-558-2165. Fax: 817-558-9931. County: Johnson. ICA: TX0088.
TV Market Ranking: 12. Franchise award date: August 1, 1979. Franchise expiration date: N.A. Began: January 1, 1980.
Channel capacity: 35 (not 2-way capable). Channels available but not in use: None.
Basic Service
Subscribers: 3,972.
Programming (received off-air): KDAF (W), KDFI-TV (I), KDFW (F), KERA-TV (P), KTVT (C), KTXA (U), KXAS-TV (N), KXTX-TV (I), WFAA-TV (A) Dallas-Fort Worth; KUVN (S) Garland; 22 FMs.
Programming (via satellite): WGN-TV (W) Chicago; American Movie Classics; C-SPAN; CNBC; CNN; Discovery Channel; ESPN; Headline News; Lifetime; MTV; Nashville Network; Nickelodeon; QVC; TBS Superstation; The Weather Channel; Turner Network TV; USA Network.
Current originations: Automated time-weather; public access; government access.
Fee: $45.00 installation; $12.86 monthly; $15.95 additional installation.
Pay Service 1
Pay Units: N.A.
Programming (via satellite): Cinemax; Disney Channel; Fox Sports Net Southwest; HBO; Showtime; The Movie Channel.
Fee: $7.95 monthly (Cinemax or Disney), $9.95 monthly (HBO, Fox Sports, Showtime or TMC).
Local advertising: Yes (insert only). Available in satellite distributed programming. Rates: $25.00/30 Seconds. Local sales manager: Tom Soulsby.
Program Guide: The Cable Connection.
Equipment: Phasecom headend; GTE Sylvania amplifiers; Comm/Scope cable; Panasonic cameras; Sony VTRs; Video Data Systems character generator; Jerrold & Hamlin set top converters; Eagle traps; Scientific-Atlanta satellite antenna; Scientific-Atlanta satellite receivers.
Miles of plant: 121.0 (coaxial). Additional miles planned: 0.5 (coaxial). Homes passed: 8,303.
Manager: Geary Stills. Chief technician: Feral Mosley. Program director: Cathy Sykes. Marketing director: Bruce Williams.
City fee: 4% of gross.
Ownership: Charter Communications Inc. (MSO). Purchased from Marcus Cable, April 1, 1999.

CLEVELAND—Crown Cable, 1108 N. Washington, Cleveland, TX 77327. Phone: 281-592-4057. Fax: 281-592-2940. County: Liberty. ICA: TX0170.
TV Market Ranking: Below 100. Franchise award date: May 10, 1977. Franchise expiration date: May 10, 2007. Began: November 1, 1978.
Channel capacity: 42 (not 2-way capable). Channels available but not in use: 5.
Basic Service
Subscribers: 2,108; Commercial subscribers: 6.
Programming (received off-air): KBMT (A), KBTV-TV (N) Beaumont-Port Arthur; KBTX-TV (C) Bryan; KHOU-TV (C), KHTV (W), KPRC-TV (N), KRIV (F), KTRK-TV (A), KUHT (P) Houston.
Programming (via satellite): A & E; American Movie Classics; BET; C-SPAN; CNBC; CNN; Country Music TV; Discovery Channel; ESPN; Fox Family Channel; Headline News; Lifetime; MTV; Nashville Network; Nickelodeon; QVC; TBS Superstation; The Inspirational Network; The Weather Channel; Turner Network TV; USA Network; VH1.
Fee: $49.95 installation; $41.85 monthly.
Pay Service 1
Pay Units: 156.
Programming (via satellite): Cinemax.
Fee: $11.50 monthly.
Pay Service 2
Pay Units: 119.
Programming (via satellite): Disney Channel.
Fee: $7.95 monthly.
Pay Service 3
Pay Units: 284.
Programming (via satellite): HBO.
Fee: $11.50 monthly.
Pay Service 4
Pay Units: 183.
Programming (via satellite): Showtime.
Fee: $11.50 monthly.
Pay-Per-View
Addressable homes: 786.
Local advertising: Yes. Available in character-generated programming. Regional interconnect: BCS Cable Advertising Inc.
Program Guide: Premium Channels.
Equipment: Scientific-Atlanta headend; Scientific-Atlanta amplifiers; Comm/Scope cable; Amiga character generator; Scientific-Atlanta set top converters; Scientific-Atlanta traps; Scientific-Atlanta satellite antenna; Scientific-Atlanta satellite receivers.
Miles of plant: 84.0 (coaxial). Homes passed: 3,000. Total homes in franchised area: 3,200.
Manager: Steve Boatman. Marketing director: Todd Felker.
City fee: 5% of gross.
Ownership: Charter Communications Inc. (MSO).

CLIFTON—Friendship Cable of Texas Inc., Box 9090, Tyler, TX 75711-9090. Phone: 903-581-2121. Fax: 903-581-2185. County: Bosque. ICA: TX0288.
TV Market Ranking: Below 100. Franchise award date: N.A. Franchise expiration date: N.A. Began: February 1, 1982.
Channel capacity: 35. Channels available but not in use: 5.
Basic Service
Subscribers: 814.
Programming (received off-air): KDFW (F), KERA-TV (P), KTVT (C), KXAS-TV (N), KXTX-TV (I), WFAA-TV (A) Dallas-Fort Worth; KCEN-TV (N), KWKT (F), KWTX-TV (C), KXXV (A) Waco-Temple.
Programming (via satellite): Discovery Channel; QVC; TBS Superstation.
Fee: $30.00 installation; $12.44 monthly.
Expanded Basic Service
Subscribers: 713.
Programming (via satellite): American Movie Classics; Animal Planet; C-SPAN; CNBC; CNN; Cartoon Network; ESPN; FX; Fox Family Channel; Fox News Channel; Fox Sports Net Southwest; Headline News; Home & Garden Television; Learning Channel; Lifetime; Nashville Network; Nickelodeon; The Weather Channel; Turner Network TV; USA Network.
Fee: $30.00 installation; $15.70 monthly.
Pay Service 1
Pay Units: 91.
Programming (via satellite): Cinemax.
Fee: $12.90 monthly.
Pay Service 2
Pay Units: 170.
Programming (via satellite): The New Encore.
Fee: $1.75 monthly.
Pay Service 3
Pay Units: 121.
Programming (via satellite): HBO.
Fee: $12.90 monthly.
Pay Service 4
Pay Units: 121.
Programming (via satellite): Starz!
Fee: $6.75 monthly.
Equipment: Scientific-Atlanta satellite antenna; Scientific-Atlanta satellite receivers.
Miles of plant: 24.0 (coaxial). Homes passed: 1,410. Total homes in franchised area: 1,410.
Manager: Larry Bryant. Chief technician: Joe Stewart.
Ownership: Buford Television Inc. (MSO). See Cable System Ownership.

COLEMAN—North Texas Cablecomm, 112 S. Concho St., Coleman, TX 76834. Phone: 915-625-2923.
Web site: http://www.cablecomm.com.
County: Coleman. ICA: TX0178.
TV Market Ranking: Outside TV Markets. Franchise award date: August 1, 1958. Franchise expiration date: September 14, 2004. Began: April 1, 1959.
Channel capacity: 36 (not 2-way capable). Channels available but not in use: 2.
Basic Service
Subscribers: 1,910; Commercial subscribers: 12.
Programming (received off-air): KIDZ-LP (F) Abilene; KRBC-TV (N), KTAB-TV (C), KTXS-TV (A) Abilene-Sweetwater; KDFW (F) Dallas-Fort Worth; KIDY (F), KLST (C) San Angelo.
Programming (via microwave): KERA-TV (P), WFAA-TV (A) Dallas-Fort Worth.
Programming (via satellite): Country Music TV; Home Shopping Network; TBS Superstation.
Current originations: Automated time-weather; educational access; government access; religious access; leased access; local news; local sports.
Fee: $35.95 installation (aerial), $49.95 (underground); $12.95 monthly; $1.60 converter; $20.00 additional installation.
Expanded Basic Service
Subscribers: 1,780.
Programming (via satellite): A & E; American Movie Classics; Animal Planet; C-SPAN; CNN; Discovery Channel; Disney Channel; ESPN; ESPN 2; Fox Family Channel; Fox News Channel; Fox Sports Net Southwest; Headline News; Lifetime; MTV; Nashville Network; Nick at Nite's TV Land; Nickelodeon; Outdoor Channel; The Weather Channel; Trinity Bcstg. Network; Turner Network TV; USA Network; Univision.
Fee: $20.00 installation; $16.00 monthly.
Pay Service 1
Pay Units: 150.
Programming (via satellite): Cinemax.
Fee: $20.00 installation; $9.95 monthly.
Pay Service 2
Pay Units: 184.
Programming (via satellite): HBO.
Fee: $20.00 installation; $9.95 monthly.
Pay Service 3
Pay Units: 125.
Programming (via satellite): Showtime.
Fee: $20.00 installation; $9.95 monthly.
Local advertising: Yes. Available in locally originated programming. Rates: $7.50/30 Seconds. Local sales manager: Don Harmes.
Program Guide: Premium Channels.
Equipment: Jerrold headend; Texscan amplifiers; CCS Hatfield & Comm/Scope cable; JVC cameras; JVC, Sony & RCA VTRs; Scientific-Atlanta set top converters; Eagle & Intercept traps; Scientific-Atlanta satellite antenna; Scientific-Atlanta & Automation Techniques satellite receivers.
Miles of plant: 63.0 (coaxial). Homes passed: 2,990.
Manager: Rex Thackerson. Chief technician: Duwayne Hunter. Marketing director: Bill Forgey.
City fee: 2% of gross.
Ownership: Fanch Communications Inc. (MSO); Time Warner Cable (MSO). See Cable System Ownership.

COLETO CREEK—National Cable Inc., Suite 106-A, 5151 Reed Rd., Columbus, OH 43220. Phones: 614-442-5890; 800-582-0504. Fax: 614-457-2567. Counties: Goliad & Victoria. ICA: TX0626.
TV Market Ranking: Below 100. Franchise award date: N.A. Franchise expiration date: N.A. Began: N.A.
Channel capacity: N.A. Channels available but not in use: N.A.
Basic Service
Subscribers: 75.
Programming (received off-air): KZTV (C) Corpus Christi; KLRN (P) San Antonio; KAVU-TV (A), KVCT (F) Victoria.
Programming (via satellite): A & E; American Movie Classics; CNN; Country Music TV; Discovery Channel; ESPN; Fox Family Channel; Nashville Network; QVC; Showtime; TBS Superstation; Turner Network TV; USA Network.
Fee: $22.00 monthly.
Pay Service 1
Pay Units: 52.
Programming (via satellite): Fox Sports Net Southwest; HBO.
Fee: $10.50 monthly (each).
Miles of plant: 5.0 (coaxial). Homes passed: 211.
Manager: Paul Scott. Chief technician: Rob Spiller. Marketing director: Josh Thackery.
Ownership: National Cable (MSO).

COLLINSVILLE—North Texas Communications Co., Drawer 587, 205 N. Walnut St., Muenster, TX 76252. Phone: 940-736-2255. Fax: 940-759-5557. County: Grayson. ICA: TX0970.
TV Market Ranking: Below 100. Franchise award date: N.A. Franchise expiration date: N.A. Began: N.A.
Channel capacity: N.A. Channels available but not in use: N.A.
Basic Service
Subscribers: 164.
Programming (received off-air): KTEN (A,N,F) Ada; KPXD (X) Arlington; KDAF (W), KDFI-TV (I), KDFW (F), KDTX-TV (T), KERA-TV (P), KFWD (O), KTVT (C), KTXA (U), KXAS-TV (N), KXTX-TV (I), WFAA-TV (A) Dallas-Fort Worth; KMPX (I) Decatur; KDTN (P) Denton; KUVN (S) Garland; KHSX-TV (H) Irving; KXII (C) Sherman.

Programming (via satellite): WGN-TV (W) Chicago; A & E; C-SPAN; CNBC; CNN; Country Music TV; Discovery Channel; Disney Channel; ESPN; Fox Family Channel; Fox Sports Net Southwest; Golf Channel; Headline News; History Channel; Home & Garden Television; Learning Channel; Lifetime; Nashville Network; Nickelodeon; QVC; TBS Superstation; The Weather Channel; Turner Classic Movies; Turner Network TV; USA Network.
Fee: $26.95 monthly.
Pay Service 1
Pay Units: 28.
Programming (via satellite): Cinemax.
Fee: $10.00 monthly.
Pay Service 2
Pay Units: 41.
Programming (via satellite): HBO.
Fee: $10.00 monthly.
Miles of plant: 15.0 (coaxial). Homes passed: 267.
Manager: Alvin M. Fuhrman. CATV Supervisor: Joe Yosten. Program director: Gene Fuhrman. Marketing director: Joey Anderson.
Ownership: North Texas Communications Co. (MSO).

COLMESNEIL—Friendship Cable of Texas Inc., Box 9090, Tyler, TX 75711-9090. Phone: 903-581-2121. Fax: 903-581-2185. County: Tyler. Also serves Doucette. ICA: TX0475.
TV Market Ranking: Below 100. Franchise award date: N.A. Franchise expiration date: N.A. Began: N.A.
Channel capacity: 36 (not 2-way capable). Channels available but not in use: 8.
Basic Service
Subscribers: 252.
Programming (received off-air): KBTV-TV (N), KFDM-TV (C) Beaumont-Port Arthur; KTRE (A) Lufkin.
Programming (via satellite): WGN-TV (W) Chicago; A & E; CNN; Country Music TV; Discovery Channel; ESPN; Fox Family Channel; Headline News; Nashville Network; TBS Superstation; Turner Network TV; USA Network.
Fee: $33.67 monthly.
Pay Service 1
Pay Units: 19.
Programming (via satellite): Cinemax.
Fee: $10.95 monthly.
Pay Service 2
Pay Units: 16.
Programming (via satellite): HBO.
Fee: $10.95 monthly.
Pay Service 3
Pay Units: 18.
Programming (via satellite): Showtime.
Fee: $5.95 monthly.
Local advertising: Yes.
Miles of plant: 22.4 (coaxial). Homes passed: 538.
Manager: Wanda Pyburn. Chief technician: Mike Deal.
Ownership: Buford Television Inc. (MSO). See Cable System Ownership.

COLORADO CITY—Cablecomm, Box 685, 1325 Westpoint, Colorado City, TX 79512. Phones: 915-728-3600; 800-874-6190. County: Mitchell. Also serves Lake Colorado City, Mitchell County. ICA: TX0172.
TV Market Ranking: Below 100. Franchise award date: March 31, 1977. Franchise expiration date: March 31, 2007. Began: April 1, 1962.
Channel capacity: 36 (not 2-way capable). Channels available but not in use: 2.
Basic Service
Subscribers: 2,110; Commercial subscribers: 9.
Programming (received off-air): KRBC-TV (N), KTAB-TV (C), KTXS-TV (A) Abilene-Sweetwater; KWAB-TV (N) Big Spring; KJTV (F) Lubbock; KLST (C) San Angelo; 8 FMs.
Programming (via microwave): KERA-TV (P), KTVT (C), WFAA-TV (A) Dallas-Fort Worth.
Programming (via satellite): WGN-TV (W) Chicago; TBS Superstation.
Current originations: Automated time-weather; public access; local news.
Fee: $27.90 installation; $9.26 monthly; $1.60 converter.
Expanded Basic Service
Subscribers: 1,896.
Programming (via satellite): American Movie Classics; C-SPAN; CNN; Discovery Channel; Disney Channel; ESPN; Fox Family Channel; Fox Sports Net Southwest; Headline News; Home Shopping Network; Knowledge TV; MTV; Nashville Network; Nickelodeon; The Weather Channel; Trinity Bcstg. Network; Turner Network TV; USA Network; Univision.
Fee: $20.00 installation; $14.69 monthly.
Pay Service 1
Pay Units: 153.
Programming (via satellite): Cinemax.
Fee: $20.00 installation; $9.00 monthly.
Pay Service 2
Pay Units: 221.
Programming (via satellite): HBO.
Fee: $20.00 installation; $9.00 monthly.
Pay Service 3
Pay Units: 173.
Programming (via satellite): Showtime.
Fee: $20.00 installation; $9.00 monthly.
Local advertising: Yes. Available in character-generated programming. Rates: $2.00/Day. Regional interconnect: Cabletime.
Program Guide: Premium Channels.
Equipment: Jerrold headend; GTE Sylvania amplifiers; CCS Hatfield & Comm/Scope cable; Texscan character generator; Scientific-Atlanta set top converters; Eagle & Intercept traps; Scientific-Atlanta satellite antenna; Automation Techniques & Scientific-Atlanta satellite receivers.
Miles of plant: 63.0 (coaxial). Homes passed: 3,192.
Manager: Rex Thackerson. Chief technician: Gary Redwine. Marketing director: Cynthia Odlozil.
City fee: 3% of gross.
Ownership: Fanch Communications Inc. (MSO); Time Warner Cable (MSO). See Cable System Ownership.

COLUMBUS—Time Warner Communications, Box 640, Columbus, TX 78934-2216. Phone: 409-732-2211. County: Colorado. ICA: TX0257.
TV Market Ranking: Outside TV Markets. Franchise award date: N.A. Franchise expiration date: N.A. Began: June 1, 1974.
Channel capacity: 26. Channels available but not in use: 1.
Basic Service
Subscribers: 1,148.
Programming (received off-air): KTBC (F) Austin; KHOU-TV (C), KHTV (W), KPRC-TV (N), KRIV (F), KTRK-TV (A), KTXH (U), KUHT (P) Houston; 1 FM.
Programming (via satellite): CNBC; CNN; Cartoon Network; Discovery Channel; Fox Family Channel; Nashville Network; TBS Superstation; The Weather Channel.
Fee: $60.00 installation; $16.95 monthly.
Expanded Basic Service
Subscribers: 931.

Programming (via satellite): American Movie Classics; ESPN; Fox Sports Net Southwest; Turner Network TV; USA Network.
Fee: $3.00 monthly.
Pay Service 1
Pay Units: 39.
Programming (via satellite): Disney Channel.
Fee: N.A.
Pay Service 2
Pay Units: 398.
Programming (via satellite): The New Encore.
Fee: N.A.
Pay Service 3
Pay Units: 170.
Programming (via satellite): HBO.
Fee: N.A.
Pay Service 4
Pay Units: 96.
Programming (via satellite): Showtime.
Fee: N.A.
Pay Service 5
Pay Units: 32.
Programming (via satellite): The Movie Channel.
Fee: N.A.
Local advertising: No. Regional interconnect: Cabletime.
Program Guide: The Cable Guide.
Equipment: Jerrold & Scientific-Atlanta headend; Jerrold amplifiers; Times Fiber cable; Jerrold set top converters; Eagle traps; Scientific-Atlanta satellite antenna.
Miles of plant: 33.9 (coaxial). Homes passed: 1,657. Total homes in franchised area: 1,696.
Manager: Domingo Puente.
City fee: 3% of gross.
Ownership: AT&T Broadband & Internet Services (MSO); Time Warner Cable (MSO); Advance/Newhouse Partnership (MSO).

COMANCHE—Falcon Cable TV, 108 W. Houston, Marshall, TX 75670. Phone: 903-938-8335. County: Comanche. ICA: TX0227.
TV Market Ranking: Outside TV Markets. Franchise award date: N.A. Franchise expiration date: N.A. Began: September 1, 1958.
Channel capacity: 32. Channels available but not in use: 1.
Basic Service
Subscribers: 1,441.
Programming (received off-air): KRBC-TV (N), KTAB-TV (C) Abilene-Sweetwater; KDFW (F) Dallas-Fort Worth; allband FM.
Programming (via microwave): KDAF (W), KDFW (F), KERA-TV (P), KXAS-TV (N), WFAA-TV (A) Dallas-Fort Worth.
Programming (via satellite): American Movie Classics; Bravo; Country Music TV; E! Entertainment TV; ESPN; Fox Family Channel; Learning Channel; Lifetime; Nickelodeon; QVC; Sci-Fi Channel; Trinity Bcstg. Network; USA Network.
Current originations: Public access; educational access; government access.
Fee: $63.00 installation; $22.54 monthly; $3.15 converter.
Expanded Basic Service
Subscribers: 1,166.
Programming (via satellite): WGN-TV (W) Chicago; CNN; Disney Channel; Headline News; Nashville Network; TBS Superstation; The Weather Channel; Turner Network TV.
Fee: $9.50 monthly.
Pay Service 1
Pay Units: 90.
Programming (via satellite): Cinemax.
Fee: $15.00 installation; $11.95 monthly.
Pay Service 2
Pay Units: 124.
Programming (via satellite): HBO.
Fee: $15.00 installation; $11.95 monthly.
Pay Service 3
Pay Units: 34.
Programming (via satellite): Showtime.
Fee: $11.95 monthly.
Local advertising: Yes. Rates: $1.00/Day.
Equipment: Scientific-Atlanta headend; Ameco amplifiers; Times Fiber cable.
Miles of plant: 50.0 (coaxial). Homes passed: 2,000.
Manager: George Doss. Chief technician: Robert Hurd.
Franchise fee: 3% of gross.
Ownership: Falcon Communications LP (MSO), joint venture formed September 30, 1998. See Cable System Ownership.

COMBINE—Charter Communications Inc., 5227 FM 813, Waxahachie, TX 75165. Phones: 972-938-9288; 800-477-0887. Fax: 972-923-0039. Counties: Dallas & Kaufman. ICA: TX0917.
TV Market Ranking: 12. Franchise award date: N.A. Franchise expiration date: N.A. Began: N.A.
Channel capacity: N.A. Channels available but not in use: N.A.
Basic Service
Subscribers: 192.
Programming (received off-air): KDAF (W), KDFI-TV (I), KDFW (F), KDTX-TV (T), KERA-TV (P), KTVT (C), KTXA (U), KXAS-TV (N), KXTX-TV (I), WFAA-TV (A) Dallas-Fort Worth; KDTN (P) Denton; KHSX-TV (H) Irving.
Programming (via satellite): WGN-TV (W) Chicago; C-SPAN; CNN; Country Music TV; Discovery Channel; ESPN; Fox Family Channel; Fox Sports Net Southwest; Headline News; MTV; Nashville Network; Nickelodeon; TBS Superstation; The Weather Channel; VH1.
Fee: $26.00 installation; $20.51 monthly.
Pay Service 1
Pay Units: N.A.
Programming (via satellite): Disney Channel; HBO; Showtime; The Movie Channel.
Fee: $5.95 monthly (Showtime or TMC), $8.95 monthly (Disney) $9.95 monthly (HBO).
Manager: Mary Scearce. Chief technician: Ken Stevens.
Ownership: Charter Communications Inc. (MSO). Purchased from Marcus Cable, April 1, 1999.

COMFORT—Classic Cable, Box 429, 605 N.W. 3rd St., Plainville, KS 67663-0429. Phones: 785-434-7620; 800-999-8876. Fax: 785-434-2614. County: Kendall. ICA: TX0400.
TV Market Ranking: Below 100. Franchise award date: N.A. Franchise expiration date: N.A. Began: January 1, 1983.

Channel capacity: 61 (2-way capable). Channels available but not in use: N.A.

Basic Service

Subscribers: 57.

Programming (received off-air): KRRT (W) Kerrville-San Antonio; KABB (F), KENS-TV (C), KMOL-TV (N), KSAT-TV (A) San Antonio.

Programming (via satellite): WGN-TV (W) Chicago; KRMA-TV (P) Denver; A & E; Animal Planet; C-SPAN; CNN; Country Music TV; Discovery Channel; Disney Channel; ESPN; Fox Family Channel; Fox News Channel; Fox Sports Net Southwest; Headline News; History Channel; Home Shopping Network; Nashville Network; Nick at Nite's TV Land; Nickelodeon; TBS Superstation; Telemundo; The Weather Channel; Trinity Bcstg. Network; Turner Classic Movies; Turner Network TV; USA Network; Univision.

Current originations: Automated time-weather.

Planned originations: Public access; educational access; government access; local news.

Fee: $35.00 installation; $23.95 monthly.

Pay Service 1

Pay Units: 8.

Programming (via satellite): HBO.

Fee: $10.95 monthly.

Pay Service 2

Pay Units: 19.

Programming (via satellite): Showtime.

Fee: $9.95 monthly.

Pay Service 3

Pay Units: 16.

Programming (via satellite): The Movie Channel.

Fee: $5.95 monthly.

Miles of plant: 19.8 (coaxial). Homes passed: 500. Total homes in franchised area: 800.

Manager: Bill Flowers. Chief technician: Walt VanLue. Marketing director: Jennifer Hauschild.

Ownership: Classic Cable (MSO).

COMMERCE—Paragon Cable, 1111 Main St., Commerce, TX 75428. Phone: 903-886-6144. Fax: 903-886-4024. Counties: Delta, Fannin & Hunt. Also serves Cooper, Honey Grove. ICA: TX0099.

TV Market Ranking: Below 100 (Commerce); Outside TV Markets (Cooper, Honey Grove). Franchise award date: N.A. Franchise expiration date: April 3, 1999. Began: April 1, 1963.

Channel capacity: 35 (not 2-way capable). Channels available but not in use: 1.

Basic Service

Subscribers: 3,995.

Programming (received off-air): KPXD (X) Arlington; KDAF (W), KDFI-TV (I), KDFW (F), KERA-TV (P), KTVT (C), KTXA (U), KXAS-TV (N), KXTX-TV (I), WFAA-TV (A) Dallas-Fort Worth; KTAQ (I) Greenville; KXII (C) Sherman; KLTV (A) Tyler-Longview; allband FM.

Current originations: Public access.

Fee: $17.39 installation; $7.02 monthly; $2.00 converter; $24.95 additional installation.

Expanded Basic Service

Subscribers: N.A.

Programming (via satellite): WGN-TV (W) Chicago; A & E; Animal Planet; BET; C-SPAN; C-SPAN 2; CNBC; CNN; Discovery Channel; ESPN; Fox Family Channel; Fox News Channel; Headline News; History Channel; Lifetime; MSNBC; MTV; Nashville Network; Nickelodeon; QVC; TBS Superstation; The Weather Channel; Trinity Bcstg. Network; Turner Classic Movies; Turner Network TV; USA Network; VH1.

Fee: $13.51 installation; $28.25 monthly.

Pay Service 1

Pay Units: N.A.

Programming (via satellite): Disney Channel; HBO; Showtime.

Fee: $24.95 installation; $7.00 monthly (Disney), $10.95 monthly (HBO or Showtime).

Local advertising: Yes (locally produced & insert). Available in character-generated programming. Rates: $75.00/Month. Local sales manager: Dr. Haskins.

Program Guide: The Cable Guide.

Equipment: Jerrold & Scientific-Atlanta headend; Jerrold amplifiers; Cerro & Times Fiber cable; Sony VTRs; Shintron character generator; Jerrold & Panasonic set top converters; Pico traps; Andrew satellite antenna; Hughes, Scientific-Atlanta & Standard Communications satellite receivers.

Miles of plant: 79.0 (coaxial). Homes passed: 6,683. Total homes in franchised area: 6,703.

Manager: Leroy Pardue. Chief technician: Rodney Harding.

City fee: 3% of gross.

Ownership: AT&T Broadband & Internet Services (MSO); Time Warner Cable (MSO); Advance/Newhouse Partnership (MSO).

CONROE—Conroe Cable TV, 3027 S.E. Loop 323, Tyler, TX 75701. Phone: 903-595-4321. County: Montgomery. Also serves Montgomery County, Panorama Village. Plans service to Willis. ICA: TX0741.

TV Market Ranking: 15 (portions of Montgomery County); Below 100 (Conroe, portions of Montgomery County, Panorama Village). Franchise award date: N.A. Franchise expiration date: N.A. Began: September 1, 1969.

Channel capacity: 39. Channels available but not in use: N.A.

Basic Service

Subscribers: 11,322.

Programming (received off-air): KBTX-TV (C) Bryan; KHOU-TV (C), KHTV (W), KPRC-TV (N), KRIV (F), KTRK-TV (A), KUHT (P) Houston; 1 FM.

Programming (via satellite): Cartoon Network.

Planned programming (via satellite): Fox Family Channel; TBS Superstation; Univision.

Current originations: Automated time-weather; local news.

Fee: $35.00 installation; $10.00 monthly.

Pay Service 1

Pay Units: N.A.

Programming (via satellite): HBO.

Fee: $35.00 installation; $9.95 monthly.

Local advertising: Yes. Rates: $50.00/Minute. Regional interconnect: Woodlands Communications Network.

Equipment: Jerrold headend; Anaconda amplifiers; Anaconda & Superior cable; Scientific-Atlanta satellite antenna.

Miles of plant: 169.0 (coaxial).

Manager: Nathan Geick.

City fee: 4% of gross.

Ownership: TCA Cable TV Inc. (MSO). See Cable System Ownership.

CONROE WEST—Lakewood Cablevision, 12504 Walden Rd., Montgomery, TX 77356. Phone: 409-582-4855. County: Montgomery. Also serves Montgomery (unincorporated areas). ICA: TX0742.

TV Market Ranking: Below 100. Franchise award date: N.A. Franchise expiration date: N.A. Began: N.A.

Channel capacity: 36. Channels available but not in use: 13.

Basic Service

Subscribers: 267.

Programming (received off-air): KHOU-TV (C), KHTV (W), KRIV (F), KTRK-TV (A), KUHT (P) Houston; KXLN-TV (S) Rosenberg.

Programming (via satellite): KCNC-TV (C) Denver; A & E; American Movie Classics; CNN; Country Music TV; Discovery Channel; ESPN; Fox Family Channel; Nashville Network; Showtime; TBS Superstation; Turner Network TV; USA Network.

Fee: $28.00 monthly.

Miles of plant: 30.0 (coaxial). Homes passed: 691.

Office manager: Timmie Adams. Manager: Charlie Garland.

Ownership: Moffat Communications Ltd. (MSO).

COOLIDGE—Northland Cable, 515 W. Tyler, Mexia, TX 76667. Phone: 254-562-2872. Fax: 254-562-6454. County: Limestone. ICA: TX0569.

TV Market Ranking: Below 100. Franchise award date: August 3, 1989. Franchise expiration date: August 2, 2004. Began: June 30, 1982.

Channel capacity: 35 (2-way capable; operating 2-way). Channels available but not in use: N.A.

Basic Service

Subscribers: 190.

Programming (received off-air): KDAF (W), KDFI-TV (I), KDFW (F), KERA-TV (P), KTVT (C), KTXA (U), KXAS-TV (N), KXTX-TV (I), WFAA-TV (A) Dallas-Fort Worth; KCEN-TV (N), KWKT (F), KWTX-TV (C), KXXV (A) Waco-Temple.

Programming (via satellite): BET; CNN; Country Music TV; Discovery Channel; ESPN; Fox Family Channel; Fox Sports Net Southwest; Nashville Network; TBS Superstation; Trinity Bcstg. Network; Turner Network TV; Univision.

Fee: $55.00 installation; $25.25 monthly; $30.00 additional installation.

Pay Service 1

Pay Units: 27.

Programming (via satellite): Cinemax.

Fee: $10.00 monthly.

Pay Service 2

Pay Units: 33.

Programming (via satellite): HBO.

Fee: $10.00 monthly.

Local advertising: No.

Equipment: RCA headend; Theta-Com amplifiers; Times Fiber cable; Pico traps; Microwave Assoc. satellite antenna; Microwave Assoc. satellite receivers.

Miles of plant: 6.0 (coaxial); None (fiber optic). Homes passed: 300. Total homes in franchised area: 325.

Manager: Jimmie Cullins.

City fee: 2% of gross.

Ownership: Northland Communications Corp. (MSO).

COPPELL—Paragon Cable, 2951 Kinwest Pkwy., Irving, TX 75063. Phone: 972-221-6531. Fax: 972-221-7070. County: Dallas. ICA: TX0121.

TV Market Ranking: 12. Franchise award date: March 1, 1981. Franchise expiration date: October 28, 2008. Began: March 13, 1981.

Channel capacity: 69 (not 2-way capable). Channels available but not in use: 47.

Basic Service

Subscribers: 7,711.

Programming (received off-air): KPXD (X) Arlington; KDAF (W), KDFI-TV (I), KDFW (F), KDTX-TV (T), KERA-TV (P), KFWD (O), KTVT (C), KTXA (U), KXAS-TV (N), KXTX-TV (I), WFAA-TV (A) Dallas-Fort Worth; KMPX (I) Decatur; KDTN (P) Denton; KUVN (S) Garland; KHSX-TV (H) Irving; KLDT (I) Lake Dallas.

Programming (via satellite): Bravo; Home Shopping Network; TV Guide Channel; TV Guide Sneak Prevue.

Current originations: Automated time-weather; public access; educational access; government access; religious access; local sports.

Fee: $26.90 installation; $9.42 monthly; $2.76 converter; $27.46 additional installation.

Expanded Basic Service

Subscribers: 6,742.

Programming (via satellite): A & E; American Movie Classics; Animal Planet; BET; Bravo; C-SPAN; C-SPAN 2; CNBC; Cartoon Network; Comedy Central; Country Music TV; Court TV; Discovery Channel; E! Entertainment TV; ESPN; ESPN 2; Fox Family Channel; Fox Sports Net Southwest; Headline News; History Channel; Home & Garden Television; Learning Channel; Lifetime; MOVIEplex; MSNBC; MTV; Nashville Network; Nick at Nite; Nickelodeon; QVC; The Weather Channel; Travel Channel; Turner Network TV; USA Network; VH1; ValueVision.

Fee: $22.88 monthly.

A la Carte 1

Subscribers: N.A.

Programming (via satellite): WGN-TV (W) Chicago; TBS Superstation.

Fee: N.A.

Pay Service 1

Pay Units: 313.

Programming (via satellite): Cinemax.

Fee: $12.50 monthly.

Pay Service 2

Pay Units: 341.

Programming (via satellite): Disney Channel.

Fee: $9.40 monthly.

Pay Service 3

Pay Units: 777.

Programming (via satellite): HBO.

Fee: $12.50 monthly.

Pay Service 4

Pay Units: 155.

Programming (via satellite): The Movie Channel.

Fee: $12.50 monthly.

Pay Service 5

Pay Units: 300.

Programming (via satellite): Showtime.

Fee: $12.50 monthly.

Pay-Per-View

Hot Choice; Viewer's Choice.

Local advertising: Yes. Available in character-generated programming. Rates: $30.00/Minute; $16.00-500.00/30 Seconds. Local sales manager: Christine Pierret.

Program Guide: The Cable Guide.

Equipment: Cadco headend; Scientific-Atlanta amplifiers; Comm/Scope cable; Panasonic set top converters; Zenith addressable set top converters.

Miles of plant: 114.6 (coaxial); 7.2 (fiber optic). Homes passed: 11,347.

Manager: Walter Nesbit. Chief technician: Bob Macioch. Program director: Philip Haley. Marketing director: Jim Fellhauer.

City fee: 5% of gross.

Ownership: AT&T Broadband & Internet Services (MSO); Time Warner Cable (MSO); Advance/Newhouse Partnership (MSO).

CORPUS CHRISTI—TCI Cablevision of Texas Inc., Box 6607, Corpus Christi, TX 78466-

6607. Phone: 512-857-5000. County: Nueces. Also serves Agua Dulce, Corpus Christi Naval Air Station, Driscoll, Nueces County, Robstown. ICA: TX0010.

TV Market Ranking: Below 100. Franchise award date: N.A. Franchise expiration date: N.A. Began: February 1, 1972.

Channel capacity: 55. Channels available but not in use: N.A.

Basic Service

Subscribers: 48,387.

Programming (received off-air): K47DF (F), K68DJ (I), KEDT (P), KIII (A), KORO (S), KRIS-TV (N), KTMV-LP (U), KZTV (C) Corpus Christi; 14 FMs.

Programming (via satellite): WGN-TV (W) Chicago; BET; C-SPAN 2; CNBC; Discovery Channel; QVC; TV Guide Sneak Prevue; The Weather Channel.

Current originations: Automated time-weather; public access; educational access; government access; religious access.

Fee: $4.95 installation; $11.28 monthly; $1.09 converter; $17.29 additional installation.

Digital Basic Service

Subscribers: N.A.

Programming (via satellite): BBC America; Box Classic; Box Pulse; Discovery Civilization Channel; (analog); Discovery Home & Leisure Channel; Discovery Kids Channel; Discovery People; Discovery Science Channel; Discovery Wings Channel; ESPN 2; ESPN Classic Sports; ESPNews; Fox Sports World; Game Show Network; Golf Channel; History Channel; Home & Garden Television; Independent Film Channel; MuchMusic Network; Outdoor Life Network; Romance Classics; Sci-Fi Channel; Speedvision; The Barker; Turner Classic Movies.

Fee: $11.71 monthly.

Expanded Basic Service

Subscribers: 46,921.

Programming (via satellite): A & E; Animal Planet; C-SPAN; CNN; Cartoon Network; Comedy Central; Country Music TV; Court TV; Disney Channel; E! Entertainment TV; ESPN; FX; Fox Family Channel; Fox News Channel; Fox Sports Net Southwest; GalaVision; Gems Television; Headline News; History Channel; Home Shopping Network; Knowledge TV; Learning Channel; Lifetime; MSNBC; MTV; Nashville Network; Nickelodeon; TBS Superstation; TV Food Network; Turner Network TV; USA Network.

Fee: $11.53 installation; $19.00 monthly.

Pay Service 1

Pay Units: 4,448.

Programming (via satellite): Cinemax.

Fee: $12.23 monthly.

Pay Service 2

Pay Units: 5,419.

Programming (via satellite): Starz!

Fee: $6.75 monthly.

Pay Service 3

Pay Units: 20,093.

Programming (via satellite): The New Encore.

Fee: $1.75 monthly.

Pay Service 4

Pay Units: 21,683.

Programming (via satellite): HBO.

Fee: $12.73 monthly.

Pay Service 5

Pay Units: 12,640.

Programming (via satellite): Showtime.

Fee: $10.36 monthly.

Pay Service 6

Pay Units: N.A.

Programming (via satellite): DMX.

Fee: $11.53 installation; $9.95 monthly.

Digital Pay Service 1

Pay Units: N.A.

Programming (via satellite): Encore Love Stories; Encore Mystery; Encore Westerns; HBO Plus; HBO Signature; Starz! Theater; The Movie Channel.

Fee: N.A.

Pay-Per-View

Addressable homes: 1,367.

Viewer's Choice.

Local advertising: Yes.

Program Guide: The Cable Guide.

Equipment: Jerrold headend; Anaconda amplifiers; Anaconda cable; Comtech & Scientific-Atlanta satellite antenna; Microdyne satellite receivers.

Miles of plant: 1118.0 (coaxial). Homes passed: 87,857. Total homes in franchised area: 87,873.

Manager: Randy Grimes. Chief technician: Mando Blancas. Marketing director: Jerri Coppedge.

City fee: 4% of gross.

Ownership: AT&T Broadband & Internet Services (MSO). Purchased from Tele-Communications Inc., March 9, 1999.

CORRIGAN—TCA Cable, 1415 S. First St., Lufkin, TX 75901. Phone: 409-639-1116. Fax: 409-634-6889. Counties: Angelina & Polk. Also serves Angelina County, Burke, Diboll, Fuller Springs, Lufkin, Polk County (portions). ICA: TX0051.

TV Market Ranking: Below 100 (Angelina County, Burke, Corrigan, Diboll, Fuller Springs, Lufkin, portions of Polk County); Outside TV Markets (portions of Polk County). Franchise award date: June 17, 1958. Franchise expiration date: October 4, 2003. Began: February 27, 1960.

Channel capacity: 60 (not 2-way capable). Channels available but not in use: 16.

Basic Service

Subscribers: 12,733.

Programming (received off-air): KFDM-TV (C) Beaumont-Port Arthur; KRIV (F) Houston; KTRE (A) Lufkin; KLSB-TV (N) Nacogdoches; 7 FMs.

Programming (via microwave): KHOU-TV (C), KHTV (W), KPRC-TV (N), KTRK-TV (A), KUHT (P) Houston.

Programming (via satellite): WGN-TV (W) Chicago; BET; C-SPAN; CNN; Cartoon Network; Court TV; Discovery Channel; Disney Channel; ESPN; ESPN 2; Fox Family Channel; Fox Sports Net South; Home Shopping Network; MTV; Nashville Network; Nickelodeon; Odyssey; Sci-Fi Channel; TBS Superstation; Turner Classic Movies; Turner Network TV; USA Network; Univision.

Current originations: Automated time-weather; educational access; automated emergency alert.

Fee: $24.22 installation; $27.16 monthly; $15.00 additional installation.

Pay Service 1

Pay Units: 1,126.

Programming (via satellite): Cinemax.

Fee: $13.95 monthly.

Pay Service 2

Pay Units: 621.

Programming (via satellite): Showtime.

Fee: $10.95 monthly.

Pay Service 3

Pay Units: 2,014.

Programming (via satellite): HBO.

Fee: $13.95 monthly.

Pay-Per-View

Addressable homes: 8,534.

Hot Choice; Viewer's Choice.

Interactive Services

Home shopping.

Local advertising: Yes. Available in satellite distributed, locally originated & taped programming. Local sales manager: John Baldwin. Regional interconnect: Woodlands Communications Network.

Program Guide: Premium Channels.

Equipment: Scientific-Atlanta headend; Scientific-Atlanta amplifiers; Comm/Scope cable; Sony cameras; Telemation & Sony VTRs; Zenith set top converters; Zenith addressable set top converters; Hughes & Scientific-Atlanta satellite antenna; Scientific-Atlanta satellite receivers; Sony commercial insert.

Miles of plant: 374.0 (coaxial). Homes passed: 18,472. Total homes in franchised area: 18,472.

Manager: Glenn Parker. Chief technician: Jerry Teer. Marketing director: Mike Evans.

City fee: 5% of gross.

Ownership: TCA Cable Partners (MSO). Purchased from Cable One Inc., June 15, 1998.

CORSICANA—Northland Cable TV, 605 W. 7th Ave., Corsicana, TX 75110. Phone: 903-872-3131. Fax: 903-872-6623. County: Navarro. ICA: TX0082.

TV Market Ranking: Outside TV Markets. Franchise award date: N.A. Franchise expiration date: January 1, 2006. Began: May 1, 1971.

Channel capacity: N.A. Channels available but not in use: N.A.

Basic Service

Subscribers: 5,700.

Programming (received off-air): KDAF (W), KDFI-TV (I), KDFW (F), KERA-TV (P), KTVT (C), KTXA (U), KXAS-TV (N), KXTX-TV (I), WFAA-TV (A) Dallas-Fort Worth; KDTN (P) Denton; KHSX-TV (H) Irving; KWTX-TV (C), KXXV (A) Waco-Temple; 16 FMs.

Programming (via satellite): WGN-TV (W) Chicago; Headline News; TBS Superstation; TV Guide Channel.

Current originations: Automated time-weather; local news.

Fee: $19.95 installation; $14.11 monthly.

Expanded Basic Service

Subscribers: N.A.

Programming (via satellite): A & E; BET; C-SPAN; C-SPAN 2; CNBC; CNN; Country Music TV; Discovery Channel; E! Entertainment TV; ESPN; Fox Family Channel; Fox Sports Net Southwest; History Channel; Lifetime; MTV; Nashville Network; Nickelodeon; QVC; Telemundo; The Weather Channel; Trinity Bcstg. Network; Turner Network TV; USA Network; Univision.

Fee: $9.69 monthly.

Pay Service 1

Pay Units: N.A.

Programming (via satellite): Cinemax; Disney Channel; HBO; Showtime; The New Encore.

Fee: $10.00 installation; $4.28 monthly (Encore), $9.08 monthly (Disney), $9.95 monthly (Cinemax), $11.13 monthly (Showtime).

Local advertising: Yes. Rates: $27.50/Minute (4 spots).

Equipment: Scientific-Atlanta headend; Theta-Com amplifiers; Times Fiber cable; Sony cameras; Sony VTRs; Sony character generator; Scientific-Atlanta satellite antenna.

Miles of plant: 130.0 (coaxial). Additional miles planned: 10.0 (coaxial). Homes passed: 8,977.

Manager: Richard C. Parker. Chief technician: Bobby Brady.

City fee: 3% of gross.

Ownership: Northland Communications Corp.

COTULLA—Time Warner Communications, 207 E. Colorado St., Pearsall, TX 78061-3234. Phone: 800-527-6221. County: La Salle. Also serves La Salle County (portions). ICA: TX0266.

TV Market Ranking: Outside TV Markets. Franchise award date: N.A. Franchise expiration date: N.A. Began: September 15, 1966.

Channel capacity: 35. Channels available but not in use: 1.

Basic Service

Subscribers: 1,130.

Programming (received off-air): KRRT (W) Kerrville-San Antonio; KGNS-TV (N,A), KLDO-TV (O), KVTV (C) Laredo; allband FM.

Programming (via microwave): KENS-TV (C), KLRN (P), KMOL-TV (N), KSAT-TV (A), KWEX-TV (S) San Antonio.

Programming (via satellite): C-SPAN; C-SPAN 2; CNN; Country Music TV; Discovery Channel; ESPN; EWTN; Fox Family Channel; Fox Sports Net Southwest; GalaVision; Headline News; Home Shopping Network; Lifetime; MTV; Nashville Network; Nickelodeon; Odyssey; TBS Superstation; The Weather Channel; Turner Network TV; USA Network.

Current originations: Automated time-weather.

Fee: $30.00 installation; $19.22 monthly; $30.00 additional installation.

Pay Service 1

Pay Units: 83.

Programming (via satellite): Disney Channel.

Fee: $7.00 monthly.

Pay Service 2

Pay Units: 350.

Programming (via satellite): HBO.

Fee: $9.00 monthly.

Pay Service 3

Pay Units: 52.

Programming (via satellite): The Movie Channel.

Fee: N.A.

Equipment: Jerrold headend; Jerrold amplifiers; Comm/Scope cable.

Miles of plant: 17.0 (coaxial). Homes passed: 1,550. Total homes in franchised area: 1,715.

Manager: Marcos Reyes.

Ownership: Time Warner Cable (MSO); AT&T Broadband & Internet Services (MSO).

COUNTRY CLUB SHORES—Torrence Cablevision, Box 1167, Ridgeland, MS 39158. Phones: 601-981-6900; 800-977-8849. County: Kaufman. Also serves Kemp (unincorporated areas). ICA: TX0743.

TV Market Ranking: 12 (Country Club Shores); Below 100 (Kemp). Franchise award date: N.A. Franchise expiration date: N.A. Began: N.A.

Channel capacity: 36. Channels available but not in use: 21.

Basic Service

Subscribers: 48.

Programming (received off-air): KDFW (F), KERA-TV (P), KTVT (C), KXAS-TV (N), WFAA-TV (A) Dallas-Fort Worth.

Programming (via satellite): A & E; American Movie Classics; CNN; Country Music TV; Discovery Channel; ESPN; Fox Family Channel; Nashville Network; Showtime; TBS Superstation; Turner Network TV; USA Network.

Fee: $28.00 monthly.

Miles of plant: 8.3 (coaxial). Homes passed: 217.

Ownership: Torrence Cable Inc. (MSO).

COUNTRY HAVEN—Classic Cable, Box 429, 605 N.W. 3rd St., Plainville, KS 67663-0429. Phones: 785-434-7620; 800-999-8876. Fax: 785-434-2614. County: Lubbock. ICA: TX0961.

TV Market Ranking: Below 100. Franchise award date: N.A. Franchise expiration date: N.A. Began: N.A.
Channel capacity: N.A. Channels available but not in use: N.A.

Basic Service

Subscribers: 27.
Programming (received off-air): KAMC (A), KCBD-TV (N), KJTV (F), KLBK-TV (C), KTXT-TV (P) Lubbock.
Programming (via satellite): WGN-TV (W) Chicago; A & E; American Movie Classics; CNN; Country Music TV; Discovery Channel; Disney Channel; ESPN; ESPN 2; Fox Family Channel; Headline News; History Channel; Home Shopping Network; Nashville Network; TBS Superstation; Telemundo; The Weather Channel; Turner Network TV; USA Network; Univision.
Fee: $35.00 installation; $27.95 monthly.

Pay Service 1

Pay Units: 3.
Programming (via satellite): HBO.
Fee: $10.95 monthly.

Pay Service 2

Pay Units: 2.
Programming (via satellite): Showtime.
Fee: $9.95 monthly.

Miles of plant: 14.0 (coaxial). Homes passed: 274.
Manager: Bill Flowers. Chief technician: Chris Christenson. Marketing director: Jennifer Hauschild.
Ownership: Classic Cable (MSO).

CRANDALL—Charter Communications Inc., 5227 FM 813, Waxahachie, TX 75165. Phones: 972-938-9288; 800-477-0887. Fax: 972-923-0039. County: Kaufman. ICA: TX0554.
TV Market Ranking: 12. Franchise award date: N.A. Franchise expiration date: N.A. Began: July 1, 1982.
Channel capacity: 52. Channels available but not in use: N.A.

Basic Service

Subscribers: 303.
Programming (received off-air): KDAF (W), KDFI-TV (I), KDFW (F), KERA-TV (P), KTVT (C), KTXA (U), KXAS-TV (N), KXTX-TV (I), WFAA-TV (A) Dallas-Fort Worth; KMPX (I) Decatur; KDTN (P) Denton; KHSX-TV (H) Irving.
Programming (via satellite): WGN-TV (W) Chicago; TBS Superstation.
Current originations: Public access.
Fee: $26.00 installation; $8.45 monthly.

Expanded Basic Service

Subscribers: N.A.
Programming (via satellite): A & E; CNN; Country Music TV; Discovery Channel; ESPN; Fox Family Channel; Headline News; Home Shopping Network; Lifetime; MTV; Nashville Network; Nickelodeon; The Weather Channel; Turner Network TV; USA Network.
Fee: $13.11 monthly.

Pay Service 1

Pay Units: N.A.
Programming (via satellite): HBO; Showtime; The Movie Channel.
Fee: $7.00 monthly (Showtime), $10.00 monthly (TMC), $12.00 monthly (HBO).

Miles of plant: 8.7 (coaxial). Homes passed: 337.
Manager: Mary Scearce. Chief technician: Ken Stevens.
Ownership: Charter Communications Inc. (MSO). Purchased from Marcus Cable, April 1, 1999.

CRANE—Classic Cable, Box 429, 605 N.W. 3rd St., Plainville, KS 67663-0429. Phones: 785-434-7620; 800-999-8876. Fax: 785-434-2614. County: Crane. Also serves Crane County (unincorporated areas). ICA: TX0228.
TV Market Ranking: Below 100. Franchise award date: April 30, 1987. Franchise expiration date: N.A. Began: April 1, 1978.
Channel capacity: 41 (2-way capable). Channels available but not in use: N.A.

Basic Service

Subscribers: 1,038.
Programming (received off-air): KMID (A), KMLM (I), KOCV-TV (P), KOSA-TV (C), KPEJ (F), KWES-TV (N) Odessa-Midland; allband FM.
Programming (via satellite): WGN-TV (W) Chicago; A & E; C-SPAN; CNN; Country Music TV; Discovery Channel; Disney Channel; ESPN; Fox Family Channel; Fox Sports Net Southwest; GalaVision; Goodlife TV Network; Headline News; Learning Channel; Lifetime; Nashville Network; Nick at Nite's TV Land; Nickelodeon; QVC; TBS Superstation; The Weather Channel; Turner Network TV; USA Network; Univision.
Current originations: Automated time-weather; educational access.
Fee: $35.00 installation; $27.50 monthly.

Pay Service 1

Pay Units: 211.
Programming (via satellite): HBO.
Fee: $10.95 monthly.

Pay Service 2

Pay Units: 93.
Programming (via satellite): Showtime.
Fee: $9.95 monthly.

Pay Service 3

Pay Units: 92.
Programming (via satellite): The Movie Channel.
Fee: $5.95 monthly.

Equipment: Scientific-Atlanta headend; Theta-Com amplifiers; Times Fiber & Belden cable; Hamlin set top converters; Eagle traps; Scientific-Atlanta satellite antenna; Scientific-Atlanta satellite receivers.
Miles of plant: 28.4 (coaxial). Homes passed: 1,974.
Manager: Bill Flowers. Chief technician: Ben Hernandez. Marketing director: Jennifer Hauschild.
City fee: 3% of gross.
Ownership: Classic Cable (MSO).

CRANFILLS GAP—National Cable Inc., Suite 106-A, 5151 Reed Rd., Columbus, OH 43220. Phones: 614-442-5890; 800-582-0504. Fax: 614-457-2567. County: Bosque. ICA: TX0904.
TV Market Ranking: Below 100. Franchise award date: N.A. Franchise expiration date: N.A. Began: N.A.
Channel capacity: N.A. Channels available but not in use: N.A.

Basic Service

Subscribers: 28.
Programming (received off-air): KAMU-TV (P) College Station; KDFW (F), WFAA-TV (A) Dallas-Fort Worth; KCEN-TV (N), KWTX-TV (C) Waco-Temple.
Programming (via satellite): WGN-TV (W) Chicago; A & E; American Movie Classics; CNN; Country Music TV; Discovery Channel; ESPN; Fox Family Channel; Showtime; TBS Superstation; Turner Network TV; USA Network.
Fee: $28.00 monthly.

Homes passed: 156.
Manager: Paul Scott. Chief technician: Rob Spiller. Marketing director: Josh Thackery.
Ownership: National Cable (MSO).

CRAWFORD—Galaxy Cablevision, 307 N. 5th St., Leesville, LA 71496. Phone: 318-238-1361. County: McLennan. ICA: TX0584.
TV Market Ranking: Below 100. Franchise award date: N.A. Franchise expiration date: N.A. Began: January 1, 1984.
Channel capacity: 25. Channels available but not in use: None.

Basic Service

Subscribers: 119.
Programming (received off-air): KNCT (P) Belton; WFAA-TV (A) Dallas-Fort Worth; KCEN-TV (N), KWTX-TV (C) Waco-Temple.
Programming (via satellite): WGN-TV (W) Chicago; TBS Superstation.
Fee: $30.00 installation; $22.75 monthly.

Pay Service 1

Pay Units: N.A.
Programming (via satellite): Cinemax; HBO; Showtime.
Fee: $12.00 monthly (each).

Miles of plant: 8.1 (coaxial). Homes passed: 305.
Manager: Eulin Guidry. Technical manager: Randy Berry.
Ownership: Galaxy Cablevision (MSO).

CRESSON—Torrence Cablevision, Box 1167, Ridgeland, MS 39158. Phones: 601-981-6900; 800-977-8849. County: Hood. ICA: TX0745.
TV Market Ranking: 12. Franchise award date: N.A. Franchise expiration date: N.A. Began: N.A.
Channel capacity: 36. Channels available but not in use: 21.

Basic Service

Subscribers: 7.
Programming (received off-air): KDFW (F), KERA-TV (P), KTVT (C), KXAS-TV (N), KXTX-TV (I), WFAA-TV (A) Dallas-Fort Worth.
Programming (via satellite): WGN-TV (W) Chicago; A & E; American Movie Classics; CNN; Country Music TV; Discovery Channel; ESPN; Fox Family Channel; Showtime; TBS Superstation; Turner Network TV; USA Network.
Fee: $28.00 monthly.

Miles of plant: 1.6 (coaxial). Homes passed: 67.
Ownership: Torrence Cable Inc. (MSO).

CROCKETT—Northland Cable TV LP, Box 1228, 1202 E. Houston, Crockett, TX 75835. Phone: 409-544-2031. Fax: 409-544-9660. County: Houston. ICA: TX0159.
TV Market Ranking: Outside TV Markets. Franchise award date: N.A. Franchise expiration date: June 1, 1999. Began: August 1, 1963.
Channel capacity: 54 (2-way capable; not operating 2-way). Channels available but not in use: 8.

Basic Service

Subscribers: 2,306.
Programming (received off-air): KBTX-TV (C) Bryan; K16BY (I) Crockett; KRIV (F) Houston; KETK-TV (N) Jacksonville; KTRE (A) Lufkin; KLSB-TV (N) Nacogdoches; 5 FMs.
Programming (via microwave): KHOU-TV (C), KHTV (W), KTRK-TV (A), KUHT (P) Houston.
Programming (via satellite): WGN-TV (W) Chicago; C-SPAN; Cartoon Network; TV Guide Channel.
Current originations: Automated time-weather.
Fee: $50.00 installation; $25.00 monthly.

Expanded Basic Service

Subscribers: 2,280.
Programming (via satellite): A & E; American Movie Classics; BET; CNBC; CNN; Discovery Channel; ESPN; Fox Family Channel; Fox News Channel; Fox Sports Net Southwest; Great American Country; Headline News; Home Shopping Network; Nashville Network; QVC; TBS Superstation; The Weather Channel; Travel Channel; Turner Network TV; USA Network; Univision.
Fee: $26.50 monthly.

Expanded Basic Service 2

Subscribers: N.A.
Programming (via satellite): Cartoon Network; ESPN 2; fXM: Movies from Fox; History Channel; Home & Garden Television; Lifetime; Nickelodeon; Sci-Fi Channel; Turner Classic Movies.
Fee: N.A.

Pay Service 1

Pay Units: 190.
Programming (via satellite): The New Encore.
Fee: $2.95 monthly.

Pay Service 2

Pay Units: 200.
Programming (via satellite): HBO.
Fee: $11.75 monthly.

Pay Service 3

Pay Units: 190.
Programming (via satellite): Starz!
Fee: $7.95 monthly.

Pay Service 4

Pay Units: 140.
Programming (via satellite): The Movie Channel.
Fee: $11.25 monthly.

Local advertising: Yes. Available in locally originated programming. Rates: $2.25/30 Seconds. Local sales manager: Linda Tracy.
Equipment: Scientific-Atlanta & Harris headend; Scientific-Atlanta amplifiers; Times Fiber cable; Scientific-Atlanta set top converters; Eagle & Arcom traps; Scientific-Atlanta satellite antenna; Scientific-Atlanta satellite receivers.
Miles of plant: 67.0 (coaxial). Additional miles planned: 2.0 (coaxial). Homes passed: 3,541. Total homes in franchised area: 3,541.
Manager: Brent Richey.
City fee: 2% of gross.
Ownership: Northland Communications Corp. (MSO).

CROSBYTON—Classic Cable, Box 429, 605 N.W. 3rd St., Plainville, KS 67663-0429. Phones: 785-434-7620; 800-999-8876. Fax: 785-434-2614. County: Crosby. ICA: TX0384.
TV Market Ranking: Below 100. Franchise award date: October 1, 1978. Franchise expiration date: October 1, 2003. Began: October 1, 1978.
Channel capacity: 61 (2-way capable). Channels available but not in use: N.A.

Basic Service

Subscribers: 474; Commercial subscribers: 45.
Programming (received off-air): KAMC (A), KCBD-TV (N), KJTV (F), KLBK-TV (C), KPTB (I), KTXT-TV (P) Lubbock; allband FM.
Programming (via satellite): WGN-TV (W) Chicago; KTVD (U) Denver; American Movie Classics; CNN; Cartoon Network; Country Music TV; Discovery Channel; Disney Channel; E! Entertainment TV; ESPN; Fox Family Channel; Fox News Channel; Fox Sports Net Southwest; Headline News; History Channel; Learning Channel; Lifetime; Nashville Network; Nick at Nite's TV Land; Nickelodeon; QVC; TBS Superstation; The Weather Channel; Trinity Bcstg. Network; Turner Network TV; USA Network; Univision.
Current originations: Automated time-weather.
Fee: $35.00 installation; $28.95 monthly.

Pay Service 1
Pay Units: 39.
Programming (via satellite): Cinemax.
Fee: $9.95 monthly.
Pay Service 2
Pay Units: 75.
Programming (via satellite): HBO.
Fee: $9.95 monthly.
Local advertising: No.
Equipment: Tocom headend; Tocom amplifiers; Texscan VTRs; U.S. Tower satellite antenna.
Miles of plant: 12.0 (coaxial). Homes passed: 869.
Manager: Bill Flowers. Chief technician: Chris Christenson. Marketing director: Jennifer Hauschild.
City fee: 3% of gross.
Ownership: Classic Cable (MSO).

CROWELL—Classic Cable, Box 429, 605 N.W. 3rd St., Plainville, KS 67663-0429. Phones: 785-434-7620; 800-999-8876. Fax: 785-434-2614. County: Foard. ICA: TX0509.
TV Market Ranking: Outside TV Markets. Franchise award date: N.A. Franchise expiration date: N.A. Began: January 1, 1977.
Channel capacity: 61 (2-way capable). Channels available but not in use: N.A.
Basic Service
Subscribers: 365; Commercial subscribers: 40.
Programming (received off-air): KVII-TV (A) Amarillo; KAUZ-TV (C), KFDX-TV (N), KJTL (F,U), KSWO-TV (A) Wichita Falls-Lawton; 1 FM.
Programming (via satellite): WGN-TV (W) Chicago; A & E; American Movie Classics; Animal Planet; CNN; Cartoon Network; Country Music TV; Discovery Channel; Disney Channel; E! Entertainment TV; ESPN; Fox Family Channel; Fox Sports Net Southwest; Headline News; History Channel; Learning Channel; Lifetime; Nashville Network; Nick at Nite's TV Land; QVC; Sci-Fi Channel; TBS Superstation; The Weather Channel; Trinity Bcstg. Network; Turner Network TV; USA Network; Univision.
Current originations: Automated time-weather.
Fee: $35.00 installation; $28.95 monthly.
Pay Service 1
Pay Units: 35.
Programming (via satellite): Cinemax.
Fee: $9.95 monthly.
Pay Service 2
Pay Units: 52.
Programming (via satellite): HBO.
Fee: $9.95 monthly.
Local advertising: No.
Equipment: Broadband amplifiers; Comm/Scope cable; Microdyne satellite antenna.
Miles of plant: 11.3 (coaxial). Homes passed: 595.
Manager: Bill Flowers. Chief technician: Rick Rattan. Marketing director: Jennifer Hauschild.
City fee: 3% of gross.
Ownership: Classic Cable (MSO).

CRYSTAL BEACH—Star Cable, Drawer 1570, Brazoria, TX 77422. Phones: 409-798-9121; 800-395-2775. Fax: 409-798-4409. County: Galveston. Also serves High Island, Port Bolivar. ICA: TX0132.
TV Market Ranking: 88 (High Island); Below 100 (Crystal Beach); Outside TV Markets (Port Bolivar). Franchise award date: N.A. Franchise expiration date: N.A. Began: February 1, 1983.
Channel capacity: 36 (not 2-way capable). Channels available but not in use: None.
Basic Service
Subscribers: 1,958; Commercial subscribers: 138.
Programming (received off-air): KHSH-TV (H) Alvin; KVVV (I) Baytown; KLTJ (E) Galveston; KETH (E), KHOU-TV (C), KHTV (W), KPRC-TV (N), KRIV (F), KTRK-TV (A), KTXH (U), KUHT (P) Houston; KNWS-TV (I) Katy.
Programming (via satellite): WGN-TV (W) Chicago; TBS Superstation; Turner Classic Movies.
Fee: $15.39 monthly; $2.15 converter.
Expanded Basic Service
Subscribers: 1,893.
Programming (via satellite): CNBC; CNN; Country Music TV; Discovery Channel; ESPN; Fox Family Channel; Fox Sports Net Southwest; Headline News; Lifetime; MTV; Nashville Network; Nickelodeon; The Weather Channel; Trinity Bcstg. Network; Turner Network TV; USA Network.
Fee: $16.25 monthly.
Pay Service 1
Pay Units: 141.
Programming (via satellite): Cinemax.
Fee: $10.95 monthly.
Pay Service 2
Pay Units: 149.
Programming (via satellite): Disney Channel.
Fee: $7.95 monthly.
Pay Service 3
Pay Units: 311.
Programming (via satellite): HBO.
Fee: $10.95 monthly.
Pay Service 4
Pay Units: 232.
Programming (via satellite): Showtime.
Fee: $12.95 monthly.
Miles of plant: 104.4 (coaxial); None (fiber optic). Homes passed: 4,959. Total homes in franchised area: 4,959.
Manager: Mike Burns. Chief technician: Mayla Zubeck.
City fee: 3% of gross.
Ownership: Star Cable Associates (MSO).

CRYSTAL CITY—Time Warner Communications, Box 1208, 690 Ford St., Eagle Pass, TX 78852-4546. Phone: 512-374-3617. Counties: Dimmit & Zavala. Also serves Carrizo Springs, Dimmit County, Zavala County. ICA: TX0147.
TV Market Ranking: Below 100 (portions of Dimmit County, portions of Zavala County); Outside TV Markets (Carrizo Springs, Crystal City, portions of Dimmit County, portions of Zavala County). Franchise award date: N.A. Franchise expiration date: N.A. Began: September 1, 1968.
Channel capacity: 38. Channels available but not in use: N.A.
Basic Service
Subscribers: 3,808.
Programming (received off-air): KGNS-TV (N,A) Laredo; allband FM.
Programming (via microwave): KENS-TV (C), KLRN (P), KMOL-TV (N), KSAT-TV (A), KWEX-TV (S) San Antonio.
Programming (via satellite): WGN-TV (W) Chicago; C-SPAN; CNN; Discovery Channel; ESPN; EWTN; GalaVision; Headline News; Lifetime; MTV; Nashville Network; Nickelodeon; Odyssey; TBS Superstation; The Weather Channel; Turner Network TV; USA Network; VH1.
Current originations: Automated time-weather.
Fee: $60.00 installation; $19.26 monthly; $2.00 converter.
Pay Service 1
Pay Units: 119.
Programming (via satellite): Disney Channel.
Fee: $7.00 monthly.
Pay Service 2
Pay Units: 653.
Programming (via satellite): HBO.
Fee: $15.00 installation; $11.00 monthly.
Pay Service 3
Pay Units: 594.
Programming (via satellite): Showtime.
Fee: $6.00 monthly.
Equipment: Ameco & Collins headend; Ameco & RCA amplifiers; Ameco cable.
Miles of plant: 89.0 (coaxial). Homes passed: 4,104.
Manager: Jimmy Gutierrez. Chief technician: Polo Vielma.
City fee: 2% of gross.
Ownership: AT&T Broadband & Internet Services (MSO); Time Warner Cable (MSO); Advance/Newhouse Partnership (MSO).

CUERO—Time Warner Communications, 1102 N. Esplanade, Cuero, TX 77954-3606. Phone: 512-275-5781. Fax: 512-275-9284. County: DeWitt. Also serves DeWitt County. ICA: TX0202.
TV Market Ranking: Below 100 (Cuero, portions of DeWitt County); Outside TV Markets (portions of DeWitt County). Franchise award date: N.A. Franchise expiration date: N.A. Began: September 1, 1974.
Channel capacity: 35. Channels available but not in use: 1.
Basic Service
Subscribers: 2,208.
Programming (received off-air): KRRT (W) Kerrville-San Antonio; KENS-TV (C), KLRN (P), KMOL-TV (N), KSAT-TV (A), KVDA (O) San Antonio; KAVU-TV (A) Victoria; 5 FMs.
Programming (via satellite): WGN-TV (W) Chicago; BET; C-SPAN; CNN; Discovery Channel; ESPN; EWTN; Fox Sports Net Southwest; Headline News; Home Shopping Network; Lifetime; MTV; Nashville Network; Nickelodeon; TBS Superstation; The Weather Channel; Trinity Bcstg. Network; Turner Network TV; USA Network; Univision.
Current originations: Automated time-weather; government access.
Fee: $25.00 installation; $17.80 monthly.
Pay Service 1
Pay Units: 147.
Programming (via satellite): Disney Channel.
Fee: $7.00 monthly.
Pay Service 2
Pay Units: 526.
Programming (via satellite): HBO.
Fee: $15.00 installation; $9.00 monthly.
Pay Service 3
Pay Units: 57.
Programming (via satellite): The Movie Channel.
Fee: $9.00 monthly.
Pay Service 4
Pay Units: 160.
Programming (via satellite): Showtime.
Fee: $9.00 monthly.
Equipment: Jerrold headend; RCA amplifiers; Comm/Scope cable; MSI character generator; AFC & Comtech satellite antenna; Avantek satellite receivers.
Miles of plant: 60.0 (coaxial). Homes passed: 2,375. Total homes in franchised area: 2,500.
Manager: Dennis Moore.
City fee: 2% of gross.
Ownership: AT&T Broadband & Internet Services (MSO); Time Warner Cable (MSO); Advance/Newhouse Partnership (MSO).

CUMBY—Friendship Cable of Texas Inc., Box 9090, Tyler, TX 75711-9090. Phone: 903-581-2121. Fax: 903-561-2185. County: Hopkins. ICA: TX0567.
TV Market Ranking: Outside TV Markets. Franchise award date: N.A. Franchise expiration date: N.A. Began: July 1, 1985.
Channel capacity: 54. Channels available but not in use: N.A.
Basic Service
Subscribers: 137.
Programming (received off-air): KDFW (F), KERA-TV (P), WFAA-TV (A) Dallas-Fort Worth.
Programming (via satellite): TBS Superstation.
Fee: $30.00 installation; $31.25 monthly.
Pay Service 1
Pay Units: 11.
Programming (via satellite): Cinemax.
Fee: $7.00 monthly.
Pay Service 2
Pay Units: 3.
Programming (via satellite): HBO.
Fee: $12.00 monthly.
Pay Service 3
Pay Units: 10.
Programming (via satellite): Showtime.
Fee: $5.95 monthly.
Miles of plant: 6.2 (coaxial). Homes passed: 302.
Manager: Rodney Fletcher. Chief technician: Bo Jaubert.
Ownership: Buford Television Inc. (MSO). See Cable System Ownership.

CUSHING—Friendship Cable of Texas Inc., Box 9090, Tyler, TX 75711-9090. Phone: 903-581-2121. Fax: 903-561-2185. County: Nacogdoches. ICA: TX0604.
TV Market Ranking: Below 100. Franchise award date: N.A. Franchise expiration date: N.A. Began: February 1, 1984.
Channel capacity: 37. Channels available but not in use: 6.
Basic Service
Subscribers: 224.
Programming (received off-air): KTRE (A) Lufkin; KSLA-TV (C), KTAL-TV (N), KTBS-TV (A) Shreveport-Texarkana; KLTV (A) Tyler-Longview.
Programming (via satellite): WGN-TV (W) Chicago; TBS Superstation.
Fee: $30.00 installation; $30.99 monthly.
Pay Service 1
Pay Units: 15.
Programming (via satellite): Cinemax.
Fee: $7.00 monthly.
Pay Service 2
Pay Units: 4.
Programming (via satellite): HBO.
Fee: $12.00 monthly.
Pay Service 3
Pay Units: 26.
Programming (via satellite): Showtime.
Fee: $5.95 monthly.
Miles of plant: 7.0 (coaxial). Homes passed: 263.
Manager: Marianne Bogy. Chief technician: Henry Harris.
Ownership: Buford Television Inc. (MSO). See Cable System Ownership.

CUT AND SHOOT—Northland Cable, Box 839, 1144 Antique Lane, New Caney, TX 77357. Phone: 713-689-2048. Fax: 713-689-7643. Counties: Harris & Montgomery. Also serves Harris County (portions). ICA: TX0746.
TV Market Ranking: 15 (Harris County); Below 100 (Cut And Shoot). Franchise award date: N.A. Franchise expiration date: N.A. Began: July 1, 1987.
Channel capacity: N.A. Channels available but not in use: N.A.

Basic Service
Subscribers: N.A.
Programming (received off-air): KHSH-TV (H) Alvin; KTMD (O) Galveston; KETH (E), KHOU-TV (C), KHTV (W), KPRC-TV (N), KRIV (F), KTRK-TV (A), KTXH (U), KUHT (P) Houston.
Programming (via satellite): WGN-TV (W) Chicago; A & E; CNN; Country Music TV; Discovery Channel; ESPN; Fox Family Channel; Fox Sports Net Southwest; Headline News; Lifetime; Nashville Network; Nickelodeon; TBS Superstation; The Weather Channel; USA Network.
Fee: $17.95 monthly.
Pay Service 1
Pay Units: N.A.
Programming (via satellite): Disney Channel; HBO; Showtime.
Fee: $7.95 monthly (each).
Ownership: Northland Communications Corp. (MSO).

CYPRESS—Friendship Cable of Texas Inc., Box 9090, Tyler, TX 75711-9090. Phone: 903-581-2121. Fax: 903-581-2185. Counties: Harris & Montgomery. Also serves Rose Hill. ICA: TX0284.
TV Market Ranking: 15. Franchise award date: N.A. Franchise expiration date: N.A. Began: N.A.
Channel capacity: 42 (not 2-way capable). Channels available but not in use: 1.
Basic Service
Subscribers: 550.
Programming (received off-air): KHOU-TV (C), KHTV (W), KPRC-TV (N), KRIV (F), KTRK-TV (A), KTXH (U), KUHT (P) Houston.
Programming (via satellite): A & E; C-SPAN; CNN; Country Music TV; Discovery Channel; Disney Channel; ESPN; Fox Family Channel; Headline News; Lifetime; Nashville Network; Nickelodeon; QVC; TBS Superstation; The Inspirational Network; USA Network.
Fee: $34.45 monthly.
Pay Service 1
Pay Units: 33.
Programming (via satellite): Cinemax.
Fee: $10.95 monthly.
Pay Service 2
Pay Units: 58.
Programming (via satellite): HBO.
Fee: $10.95 monthly.
Pay Service 3
Pay Units: 61.
Programming (via satellite): Showtime.
Fee: $5.95 monthly.
Local advertising: Yes.
Miles of plant: 79.1 (coaxial). Homes passed: 1,622.
Manager: Wanda Pyburn. Chief technician: David Burrell. Marketing director: Dianne Huffstickler.
Ownership: Buford Television Inc. (MSO). See Cable System Ownership.

DAINGERFIELD—Star Cable Assoc., Box 626, 200 Scurry St., Daingerfield, TX 75638. Phone: 903-645-7353. Fax: 903-645-3298. Counties: Cass & Morris. Also serves Cason, Hughes Springs, Lone Star, Morris County. ICA: TX0152.
TV Market Ranking: Below 100 (Daingerfield, Hughes Springs, Lone Star, portions of Morris County); Outside TV Markets (Cason, portions of Morris County). Franchise award date: N.A. Franchise expiration date: N.A. Began: July 31, 1979.
Channel capacity: 62. Channels available but not in use: 20.
Basic Service
Subscribers: 2,739; Commercial subscribers: 173.
Programming (received off-air): KETK-TV (N) Jacksonville; K54CB (I) Mount Pleasant; KMSS-TV (F), KSHV (U,W), KSLA-TV (C), KTAL-TV (N), KTBS-TV (A) Shreveport-Texarkana; KLTV (A) Tyler-Longview.
Programming (via microwave): KERA-TV (P), WFAA-TV (A) Dallas-Fort Worth.
Programming (via satellite): WGN-TV (W) Chicago; TBS Superstation.
Fee: $19.95 installation; $12.00 monthly; $1.50 converter.
Expanded Basic Service
Subscribers: 2,592.
Programming (via satellite): A & E; American Movie Classics; BET; CNN; Country Music TV; Discovery Channel; ESPN; Fox Family Channel; Fox News Channel; Fox Sports Net Southwest; Headline News; Home Shopping Network; Lifetime; MTV; Nashville Network; Nick at Nite's TV Land; Nickelodeon; QVC; Sci-Fi Channel; The Weather Channel; Trinity Bcstg. Network; Turner Network TV; USA Network.
Fee: $17.90 monthly.
Pay Service 1
Pay Units: 252.
Programming (via satellite): Cinemax.
Fee: $7.95 monthly.
Pay Service 2
Pay Units: 247.
Programming (via satellite): Disney Channel.
Fee: $7.95 monthly.
Pay Service 3
Pay Units: 448.
Programming (via satellite): HBO.
Fee: $10.95 monthly.
Pay Service 4
Pay Units: 401.
Programming (via satellite): Showtime; The Movie Channel.
Fee: $12.95 monthly (each).
Local advertising: Yes. Regional interconnect: Cabletime.
Miles of plant: 110.0 (coaxial). Homes passed: 3,929.
Manager: Mike Burns.
City fee: 2% of gross.
Ownership: Star Cable Associates (MSO).

DALHART—TCA Cable TV of Dalhart, 317 E. 7th St., Dalhart, TX 79022. Phone: 806-249-4820. Web site: http://www.tca-cable.com. County: Dallam. Also serves Dallam County. ICA: TX0182.
TV Market Ranking: Outside TV Markets. Franchise award date: N.A. Franchise expiration date: N.A. Began: August 1, 1962.
Channel capacity: 23. Channels available but not in use: N.A.
Basic Service
Subscribers: 2,302.
Programming (received off-air): KACV-TV (P), KAMR-TV (N), KCIT (F,U), KFDA-TV (C), KVII-TV (A) Amarillo; 6 FMs.
Programming (via satellite): CNN; Discovery Channel; ESPN; Fox Family Channel; Lifetime; MTV; Nashville Network; Odyssey; TBS Superstation; The Weather Channel; Turner Network TV; USA Network.
Current originations: Automated time-weather.
Fee: $35.00 installation; $7.82 monthly.
Pay Service 1
Pay Units: N.A.
Programming (via satellite): Disney Channel; HBO; Showtime; The Movie Channel.
Fee: $10.00 monthly (each).
Equipment: Andrew satellite antenna.
Miles of plant: 60.0 (coaxial). Homes passed: 2,898.
Manager: Charles Hembree. Chief technician: Mark Harris.
City fee: 2% of gross.
Ownership: TCA Cable TV Inc. (MSO); AT&T Broadband & Internet Services (MSO). See Cable System Ownership.

DALLAS—TCI Cablevision of Dallas Inc., 1565 Chenault St., Dallas, TX 75228-5499. Phone: 214-328-5000. Fax: 214-320-7336. County: Dallas. ICA: TX0003.
TV Market Ranking: 12. Franchise award date: April 4, 1981. Franchise expiration date: N.A. Began: January 1, 1982.
Channel capacity: 100 (2-way capable; operating 2-way). Channels available but not in use: 15.
Basic Service
Subscribers: 157,000.
Programming (received off-air): KDAF (W), KDFI-TV (I), KDFW (F), KDTX-TV (T), KERA-TV (P), KFWD (O), KTVT (C), KTXA (U), KXAS-TV (N), KXTX-TV (I), WFAA-TV (A) Dallas-Fort Worth; KDTN (P) Denton; KUVN (S) Garland; KHSX-TV (H) Irving; 22 FMs.
Programming (via satellite): WGN-TV (W) Chicago; A & E; BET; C-SPAN; C-SPAN 2; CNBC; CNN; Cartoon Network; Comedy Central; Country Music TV; Discovery Channel; EWTN; Fox Family Channel; GalaVision; Goodlife TV Network; Headline News; Home Shopping Network; Kaleidoscope; Knowledge TV; Lifetime; MTV; Nashville Network; Nick at Nite; Nickelodeon; Odyssey; QVC; TBS Superstation; The Box; The Weather Channel; VH1.
Current originations: Automated time-weather; public access; educational access; government access; religious access; leased access; library access; automated emergency alert.
Fee: $60.00 installation; $13.15 monthly; $1.90 converter.
Expanded Basic Service
Subscribers: 116,901.
Programming (via satellite): American Movie Classics; ESPN; Fox Sports Net Southwest; Turner Network TV; USA Network.
Fee: $12.68 monthly.
Pay Service 1
Pay Units: 18,090.
Programming (via satellite): Cinemax.
Fee: $11.12 monthly.
Pay Service 2
Pay Units: 11,570.
Programming (via satellite): Disney Channel.
Fee: N.A.
Pay Service 3
Pay Units: 51,255.
Programming (via satellite): The New Encore.
Fee: N.A.
Pay Service 4
Pay Units: 49,211.
Programming (via satellite): HBO.
Fee: $11.12 monthly.
Pay Service 5
Pay Units: 21,456.
Programming (via satellite): Showtime.
Fee: $11.12 monthly.
Pay Service 6
Pay Units: 10,660.
Programming (via satellite): The Movie Channel.
Fee: $11.12 monthly.
Pay Service 7
Pay Units: N.A.
Programming (via satellite): DMX.
Fee: N.A.
Pay-Per-View
Addressable homes: 101,352.
Hot Choice; Viewer's Choice.
Interactive Services
Burglar alarm; fire alarm; police surveillance; medical alert; polling; home shopping; database; games.
Equipment: Pioneer-QUBE.
Fee: $19.95 installation; $12.95 monthly.
Local advertising: Yes. Available in satellite distributed programming. Rates: $250.00/Hour; $125.00/30 Minutes; $45.00-$65.00/Spot.
Program Guide: The Cable Guide.
Equipment: Scientific-Atlanta headend; C-COR amplifiers; Comm/Scope cable; Ikegami cameras; Sony VTRs; Video Data Systems character generator; Pioneer set top converters; Eagle traps; AFC, Scientific-Atlanta & Harris satellite antenna; Scientific-Atlanta satellite receivers.
Miles of plant: 3877.0 (coaxial); 38.0 (fiber optic). Homes passed: 410,172. Total homes in franchised area: 512,713.
Manager: Clem Madox.
City fee: 5% of gross.
Ownership: AT&T Broadband & Internet Services (MSO). Purchased from Tele-Communications Inc., March 9, 1999.

DARROUZETT—Classic Cable, Box 429, 605 N.W. 3rd St., Plainville, KS 67663-0429. Phones: 785-434-7620; 800-999-8876. Fax: 785-434-2614. County: Lipscomb. ICA: TX0662.
TV Market Ranking: Outside TV Markets. Franchise award date: August 14, 1981. Franchise expiration date: N.A. Began: November 1, 1981.
Channel capacity: 36 (2-way capable). Channels available but not in use: N.A.
Basic Service
Subscribers: 94.
Programming (received off-air): KACV-TV (P), KAMR-TV (N), KCIT (F,U), KFDA-TV (C), KVII-TV (A) Amarillo.
Programming (via satellite): WGN-TV (W) Chicago; CNN; Discovery Channel; Disney Channel; ESPN; Fox Family Channel; Home & Garden Television; Learning Channel; Nashville Network; Nick at Nite's TV Land; Sci-Fi Channel; TBS Superstation; The Weather Channel; Turner Network TV; USA Network.
Current originations: Automated time-weather.
Fee: $35.00 installation; $27.95 monthly.
Pay Service 1
Pay Units: 8.
Programming (via satellite): HBO.
Fee: $20.00 installation; $10.95 monthly.

Pay Service 2
Pay Units: 21.
Programming (via satellite): Showtime.
Fee: $9.95 monthly.
Miles of plant: 4.0 (coaxial). Homes passed: 201.
Manager: Bill Flowers. Chief technician: Rick Rattan. Marketing director: Jennifer Hauschild.
City fee: 2% of gross.
Ownership: Classic Cable (MSO).

DE KALB—TCA Cable TV, 609 E. North Front St., New Boston, TX 75570-3005. Phone: 903-628-5569. Web site: http://www.tca-cable.com. County: Bowie. Also serves Bowie County. ICA: TX0324.
TV Market Ranking: 58 (portions of Bowie County, De Kalb); Outside TV Markets (portions of Bowie County). Franchise award date: N.A. Franchise expiration date: N.A. Began: March 1, 1980.
Channel capacity: 35. Channels available but not in use: 7.
Basic Service
Subscribers: 699.
Programming (received off-air): KLTS-TV (P), KMSS-TV (F), KSLA-TV (C), KTAL-TV (N), KTBS-TV (A) Shreveport-Texarkana.
Programming (via microwave): WFAA-TV (A) Dallas-Fort Worth.
Programming (via satellite): WGN-TV (W) Chicago; CNBC; CNN; Discovery Channel; ESPN; Fox Family Channel; Lifetime; MTV; Nashville Network; Nickelodeon; Odyssey; QVC; TBS Superstation; The Inspirational Network; The Weather Channel; Turner Network TV; USA Network.
Fee: $34.13 installation; $10.65 monthly.
Pay Service 1
Pay Units: 33.
Programming (via satellite): Disney Channel.
Fee: $10.00 monthly.
Pay Service 2
Pay Units: 219.
Programming (via satellite): The New Encore.
Fee: N.A.
Pay Service 3
Pay Units: 133.
Programming (via satellite): HBO.
Fee: $11.95 monthly.
Pay Service 4
Pay Units: 66.
Programming (via satellite): Showtime.
Fee: $11.95 monthly.
Miles of plant: 20.8 (coaxial). Homes passed: 1,156. Total homes in franchised area: 2,217.
Manager: Ron Eubanks.
Ownership: TCA Cable TV Inc. (MSO); AT&T Broadband & Internet Services (MSO). See Cable System Ownership.

DE LEON—Friendship Cable of Texas Inc., Box 9090, Tyler, TX 75711-9090. Phone: 903-581-2121. Fax: 903-581-2185. County: Comanche. ICA: TX0310.
TV Market Ranking: Outside TV Markets. Franchise award date: N.A. Franchise expiration date: N.A. Began: February 1, 1962.
Channel capacity: 35. Channels available but not in use: 4.
Basic Service
Subscribers: 897.
Programming (received off-air): KRBC-TV (N), KTAB-TV (C) Abilene-Sweetwater; allband FM.
Programming (via microwave): KDFW (F), KERA-TV (P), KTVT (C), KXAS-TV (N), WFAA-TV (A) Dallas-Fort Worth.
Programming (via satellite): C-SPAN; Discovery Channel; QVC; TBS Superstation; The Weather Channel.
Current originations: Automated time-weather; public access.
Fee: $30.00 installation; $12.36 monthly.
Expanded Basic Service
Subscribers: 794.
Programming (via satellite): American Movie Classics; Animal Planet; CNBC; CNN; Cartoon Network; ESPN; FX; Fox Family Channel; Fox News Channel; Fox Sports Net Southwest; Headline News; Home & Garden Television; Learning Channel; Lifetime; Nashville Network; Odyssey; Turner Network TV; USA Network; Univision.
Fee: $30.00 installation; $16.20 monthly.
Pay Service 1
Pay Units: 75.
Programming (via satellite): Cinemax.
Fee: $12.90 monthly.
Pay Service 2
Pay Units: 260.
Programming (via satellite): The New Encore.
Fee: $1.75 monthly.
Pay Service 3
Pay Units: 87.
Programming (via satellite): HBO.
Fee: $12.90 monthly.
Pay Service 4
Pay Units: 139.
Programming (via satellite): Starz!
Fee: $6.75 monthly.
Program Guide: The Cable Guide.
Equipment: Jerrold headend; Jerrold amplifiers; composite cable; Hughes satellite antenna.
Miles of plant: 28.0 (coaxial). Homes passed: 1,223. Total homes in franchised area: 1,223.
Manager: Larry Bryant. Chief technician: Joe Stewart.
City fee: 2% of gross.
Ownership: Buford Television Inc. (MSO). See Cable System Ownership.

DE SOTO—TCI TKR of the Metroplex Inc., 934 E. Centerville Rd., Garland, TX 75041. Phone: 214-840-2388. County: Dallas. Also serves Cedar Hill. ICA: TX0053.
TV Market Ranking: 12. Franchise award date: N.A. Franchise expiration date: N.A. Began: February 1, 1979.
Channel capacity: 40 (2-way capable; operating 2-way partially). Channels available but not in use: None.
Basic Service
Subscribers: 6,715.
Programming (received off-air): KDAF (W), KDFI-TV (I), KDFW (F), KDTX-TV (T), KERA-TV (P), KTVT (C), KTXA (U), KXAS-TV (N), KXTX-TV (I), WFAA-TV (A) Dallas-Fort Worth; KUVN (S) Garland; KHSX-TV (H) Irving.
Programming (via satellite): WGN-TV (W) Chicago; A & E; C-SPAN; CNBC; CNN; Discovery Channel; Fox Family Channel; Headline News; Home Shopping Network; Lifetime; MTV; Nashville Network; Nickelodeon; TBS Superstation; The Weather Channel; Trinity Bcstg. Network; Univision; VH1.
Current originations: Automated time-weather; public access; educational access; government access; automated emergency alert; local news; local sports.
Fee: $60.00 installation; $19.45 monthly; $2.00 converter; $25.00 additional installation.
Expanded Basic Service
Subscribers: 5,184.
Programming (via satellite): American Movie Classics; ESPN; Fox Sports Net Southwest; Turner Network TV; USA Network.
Fee: $3.50 monthly.
Pay Service 1
Pay Units: N.A.
Programming (via satellite): Disney Channel; HBO; Showtime; The Movie Channel.
Fee: $25.00 installation; $10.25 monthly (Disney), $11.25 monthly (Showtime or TMC), $12.20 monthly (HBO).
Local advertising: Yes. Available in locally originated, character-generated, taped & automated programming. Local sales manager: Debra Friday.
Equipment: Scientific-Atlanta satellite antenna.
Miles of plant: 258.5 (coaxial). Homes passed: 16,225. Total homes in franchised area: 16,306.
Manager: Steve Crawford.
Ownership: AT&T Broadband & Internet Services (MSO). Purchased from Tele-Communications Inc., March 9, 1999.

DECATUR—Southwest Cablevision, Box 869, 2804-B FM 51 S, Decatur, TX 76234. Phone: 817-627-3099. Fax: 817-627-8303. County: Wise. Also serves Alvord, Bridgeport, Chico, Lake Bridgeport, Runaway Bay. ICA: TX0168.
TV Market Ranking: Outside TV Markets. Franchise award date: September 1, 1979. Franchise expiration date: N.A. Began: June 1, 1980.
Channel capacity: 60 (not 2-way capable). Channels available but not in use: 10.
Basic Service
Subscribers: 2,715; Commercial subscribers: 24.
Programming (received off-air): KDAF (W), KDFI-TV (I), KDFW (F), KERA-TV (P), KTVT (C), KTXA (U), KXAS-TV (N), KXTX-TV (I), WFAA-TV (A) Dallas-Fort Worth; KMPX (I) Decatur; KDTN (P) Denton; KUVN (S) Garland; KHSX-TV (H) Irving; KAUZ-TV (C) Wichita Falls-Lawton.
Current originations: Automated time-weather; religious access; local sports.
Fee: $55.00 installation; $19.90 monthly; $2.45 converter; $20.00 additional installation.
Expanded Basic Service
Subscribers: 2,604.
Programming (via satellite): A & E; American Movie Classics; BET; C-SPAN; C-SPAN 2; CNBC; CNN; Comedy Central; Country Music TV; Discovery Channel; ESPN; EWTN; Fox Family Channel; Fox Sports Net Southwest; Headline News; Learning Channel; Lifetime; MTV; Nashville Network; Nickelodeon; Odyssey; QVC; The Weather Channel; Trinity Bcstg. Network; Turner Network TV; USA Network; Univision; VH1.
Fee: $20.00 installation; $3.60 monthly.
Expanded Basic Service 2
Subscribers: 2,604.
Programming (via satellite): WGN-TV (W) Chicago; Cartoon Network; ESPN 2; Goodlife TV Network; Sci-Fi Channel; TBS Superstation; TV Guide Channel; Travel Channel.
Fee: N.A.
Pay Service 1
Pay Units: 918.
Programming (via satellite): Cinemax; Disney Channel; HBO.
Fee: $20.00 installation; $9.95 monthly (each).
Local advertising: Yes. Available in character-generated & taped programming. Regional interconnect: Cabletime.
Program Guide: The Cable Guide.
Equipment: Scientific-Atlanta headend; Scientific-Atlanta amplifiers; Comm/Scope & Times Fiber cable; Panasonic cameras; Panasonic VTRs; MSI character generator; Oak & Hamlin set top converters; Eagle traps; Scientific-Atlanta satellite antenna; Scientific-Atlanta satellite receivers.
Miles of plant: 77.0 (coaxial). Homes passed: 3,333.
Manager: Danny Neumann. Chief technician: Harley Hill. Marketing director: Kathy Shull.
City fee: 3% of gross.
Ownership: James Cable Partners (MSO).

DEL RIO—Time Warner Communications, 312 Pecan St., Del Rio, TX 78840-5100. Phone: 830-775-3567. County: Val Verde. Also serves Laughlin AFB. ICA: TX0056.
TV Market Ranking: Below 100. Franchise award date: N.A. Franchise expiration date: N.A. Began: September 1, 1955.
Channel capacity: 53. Channels available but not in use: N.A.
Basic Service
Subscribers: 10,730.
Programming (received off-air): 3 FMs.
Programming (via microwave): KENS-TV (C), KLRN (P), KMOL-TV (N), KSAT-TV (A), KWEX-TV (S) San Antonio.
Programming (via satellite): WGN-TV (W) Chicago; C-SPAN; ESPN; Fox Family Channel; TBS Superstation; USA Network; Univision.
Fee: $30.57 installation; $18.14 monthly; $15.28 additional installation.
Pay Service 1
Pay Units: N.A.
Programming (via satellite): GalaVision.
Fee: $11.95 monthly.
Local advertising: Yes. Regional interconnect: Cabletime.
Program Guide: The Cable Guide.
Miles of plant: 190.0 (coaxial). Additional miles planned: 1.0 (coaxial). Homes passed: 15,621.
Manager: Glenn Scallorn. Chief technician: Jack Howley.
City fee: 2% of gross.
Ownership: AT&T Broadband & Internet Services (MSO); Time Warner Cable (MSO); Advance/Newhouse Partnership (MSO).

DENTON—Charter Communications Inc., 205 Industrial St., Denton, TX 76201. Phone: 817-566-2901. Fax: 817-380-1189. County: Denton. Also serves Corinth, Hickory Creek, Lake Dallas. ICA: TX0040.
TV Market Ranking: 12. Franchise award date: January 20, 1979. Franchise expiration date: December 6, 2003. Began: November 1, 1979.
Channel capacity: 60 (2-way capable; operating 2-way partially). Channels available but not in use: 5.
Basic Service
Subscribers: 16,852.
Programming (received off-air): KDAF (W), KDFI-TV (I), KDFW (F), KERA-TV (P), KTVT (C), KTXA (U), KXAS-TV (N), KXTX-TV (I), WFAA-TV (A) Dallas-Fort Worth; KDTN (P) Denton; KUVN (S) Garland; 1 FM.
Programming (via satellite): WGN-TV (W) Chicago; C-SPAN; CNBC; CNN; Discovery Channel; ESPN; Fox Family Channel; Headline News; QVC; TBS Superstation; The Weather Channel; Turner Network TV; USA Network; Univision.
Current originations: Automated time-weather; public access; educational access; automated emergency alert; local news; local sports.
Planned originations: Government access.
Fee: $40.00 installation; $15.95 monthly; $10.00 additional installation.
Expanded Basic Service
Subscribers: 5,568.

Programming (via satellite): A & E; American Movie Classics; BET; Bravo; Country Music TV; Lifetime; MTV; Nashville Network; Nickelodeon.
Fee: $10.00 installation; $3.95 monthly.

Pay Service 1
Pay Units: 9,558.
Programming (via satellite): Cinemax; Disney Channel; HBO; Showtime.
Fee: $10.00 installation; $7.35 monthly (Disney), $10.15 monthly (Cinemax or Showtime), $11.15 monthly (HBO).

Pay Service 2
Pay Units: 1,007.
Programming (via satellite): Fox Sports Net Southwest.
Fee: $10.00 installation; $4.95 monthly.

Local advertising: Yes. Available in satellite distributed & locally originated programming. Rates: $9.00/Minute; $5.00/30 Seconds. Local sales manager: Tim Crouch.
Program Guide: The Cable Connection.
Equipment: Scientific-Atlanta headend; Magnavox & RCA amplifiers; Comm/Scope cable; JVC cameras; JVC VTRs; Video Data Systems character generator; Oak set top converters; Tocom addressable set top converters; Andrew satellite antenna; Scientific-Atlanta satellite receivers.
Miles of plant: 330.0 (coaxial). Additional miles planned: 10.0 (coaxial). Homes passed: 26,668. Total homes in franchised area: 26,800.
Manager: John Enlow. Chief technician: Mark Gearhart. Program director: Tim Crouch. Marketing director: Beverly Gambell.
City fee: 5% of gross.
Ownership: Charter Communications Inc. (MSO). Purchased from Marcus Cable, April 1, 1999.

DEVINE—Falcon Cable TV, 1244 Encino Dr., Pleasanton, TX 78064. Phone: 830-569-5509. Fax: 830-569-4828. Counties: Atascosa & Medina. Also serves Lytle, Medina County, Natalia. ICA: TX0747.
TV Market Ranking: 45 (Devine, Lytle, portions of Medina County, Natalia); Below 100 (portions of Medina County). Franchise award date: N.A. Franchise expiration date: N.A. Began: November 1, 1981.
Channel capacity: 37. Channels available but not in use: 1.

Basic Service
Subscribers: 1,264.
Programming (received off-air): KRRT (W) Kerrville-San Antonio; KABB (F), KENS-TV (C), KLRN (P), KMOL-TV (N), KSAT-TV (A), KVDA (O), KWEX-TV (S) San Antonio.
Programming (via satellite): Bravo; C-SPAN; Country Music TV; E! Entertainment TV; ESPN; Fox Family Channel; Headline News; Home Shopping Network; Learning Channel; Lifetime; Nashville Network; QVC; Sci-Fi Channel; The Weather Channel; Travel Channel.
Current originations: Automated time-weather.
Fee: $15.00 installation; $22.78 monthly; $10.00 additional installation.

Expanded Basic Service
Subscribers: 1,246.
Programming (via satellite): American Movie Classics; Discovery Channel; USA Network.
Fee: $1.64 monthly.

Expanded Basic Service 2
Subscribers: 1,201.
Programming (via satellite): WGN-TV (W) Chicago; CNN; Disney Channel; TBS Superstation; Turner Network TV.
Fee: $6.75 monthly.

Pay Service 1
Pay Units: 107.
Programming (via satellite): Cinemax.
Fee: $10.95 monthly.

Pay Service 2
Pay Units: 131.
Programming (via satellite): HBO.
Fee: $11.95 monthly.

Pay Service 3
Pay Units: 104.
Programming (via satellite): Showtime.
Fee: $10.95 monthly.

Pay Service 4
Pay Units: 48.
Programming (via satellite): The Movie Channel.
Fee: $10.95 monthly.

Local advertising: Yes. Available in character-generated programming. Regional interconnect: Cabletime.
Program Guide: Premium Channels.
Equipment: Microdyne & Scientific-Atlanta headend; Magnavox amplifiers; Jerrold cable; SpectraView character generator; GTE Sylvania set top converters; Eagle & Pico traps; Fort Worth Tower & Scientific-Atlanta satellite antenna; M/A-Com & Microdyne satellite receivers.
Miles of plant: 92.0 (coaxial). Homes passed: 2,786.
Manager: Lorna Gentry. Chief technician: Santos Guajardo.
Franchise fee: 3% of gross.
Ownership: Falcon Communications LP (MSO), joint venture formed September 30, 1998. See Cable System Ownership.

DIANA—Friendship Cable of Texas Inc., Box 9090, Tyler, TX 75711-9090. Phone: 903-581-2121. Fax: 903-581-2185. County: Upshur. ICA: TX0566.
TV Market Ranking: Below 100. Franchise award date: January 1, 1989. Franchise expiration date: January 1, 2009. Began: June 26, 1989.
Channel capacity: 36. Channels available but not in use: 7.

Basic Service
Subscribers: 297.
Programming (received off-air): KERA-TV (P) Dallas-Fort Worth; KETK-TV (N) Jacksonville; KFXK (F) Longview; KSLA-TV (C) Shreveport-Texarkana; KLTV (A) Tyler-Longview.
Programming (via satellite): WGN-TV (W) Chicago; CNN; Country Music TV; Discovery Channel; ESPN; Fox Family Channel; Lifetime; Nashville Network; Nickelodeon; TBS Superstation; Turner Classic Movies; USA Network.
Fee: $30.00 installation; $32.64 monthly.

Pay Service 1
Pay Units: 24.
Programming (via satellite): Cinemax.
Fee: $10.95 monthly.

Pay Service 2
Pay Units: 22.
Programming (via satellite): HBO.
Fee: $10.95 monthly.

Pay Service 3
Pay Units: 38.
Programming (via satellite): Showtime.
Fee: $5.95 monthly.

Local advertising: Yes.
Miles of plant: 28.6 (coaxial). Homes passed: 533.
Manager: Marianne Bogy. Chief technician: Sonny Myers.
Ownership: Buford Television Inc. (MSO). See Cable System Ownership.

DICKENS—Classic Cable, Box 429, 605 N.W. 3rd St., Plainville, KS 67663-0429. Phones: 785-434-7620; 800-999-8876. Fax: 785-434-2614. County: Dickens. ICA: TX0748.
TV Market Ranking: Outside TV Markets. Franchise award date: October 20, 1983. Franchise expiration date: October 20, 2008. Began: N.A.
Channel capacity: 41 (2-way capable). Channels available but not in use: N.A.

Basic Service
Subscribers: 69; Commercial subscribers: 17.
Programming (received off-air): KAMC (A), KCBD-TV (N), KJTV (F), KLBK-TV (C) Lubbock.
Programming (via satellite): WGN-TV (W) Chicago; CNN; Country Music TV; Discovery Channel; Disney Channel; ESPN; Fox Family Channel; Headline News; History Channel; Home Shopping Network; Nashville Network; TBS Superstation; The Weather Channel; Trinity Bcstg. Network; Turner Network TV; USA Network.
Fee: $35.00 installation; $27.95 monthly.

Pay Service 1
Pay Units: 8.
Programming (via satellite): Cinemax.
Fee: $9.95 monthly.

Pay Service 2
Pay Units: 10.
Programming (via satellite): HBO.
Fee: $9.95 monthly.

Program Guide: The Cable Guide.
Miles of plant: 9.2 (coaxial). Homes passed: 173.
Manager: Bill Flowers. Chief technician: Chris Christenson. Marketing director: Jennifer Hauschild.
City fee: 1% of gross.
Ownership: Classic Cable (MSO).

DILLEY—Time Warner Communications, 207 E. Colorado St., Pearsall, TX 78061-3234. Phone: 800-527-6221. County: Frio. Also serves Frio County. ICA: TX0344.
TV Market Ranking: 45 (portions of Frio County); Outside TV Markets (Dilley, portions of Frio County). Franchise award date: N.A. Franchise expiration date: N.A. Began: March 16, 1976.
Channel capacity: 35. Channels available but not in use: 3.

Basic Service
Subscribers: 830.
Programming (received off-air): KRRT (W) Kerrville-San Antonio; KENS-TV (C), KLRN (P), KMOL-TV (N), KSAT-TV (A) San Antonio; allband FM.
Programming (via satellite): WGN-TV (W) Chicago; C-SPAN; CNN; Country Music TV; Discovery Channel; ESPN; EWTN; Fox Family Channel; Fox Sports Net Southwest; GalaVision; Headline News; Home Shopping Network; Lifetime; MTV; Nashville Network; Nickelodeon; TBS Superstation; The Weather Channel; Trinity Bcstg. Network; Turner Network TV; USA Network; Univision; VH1.
Planned originations: Automated time-weather.
Fee: $30.00 installation; $19.34 monthly; $30.00 additional installation.

Pay Service 1
Pay Units: 56.
Programming (via satellite): Disney Channel.
Fee: $7.00 monthly.

Pay Service 2
Pay Units: 180.
Programming (via satellite): HBO.
Fee: $9.00 monthly.

Pay Service 3
Pay Units: 105.
Programming (via satellite): Showtime.
Fee: $9.00 monthly.

Equipment: Tocom headend; Tocom amplifiers; Superior cable; Ampex cameras.
Miles of plant: 11.0 (coaxial). Homes passed: 1,075. Total homes in franchised area: 1,192.
Manager: Marcos Reyes.
City fee: 3% of gross.
Ownership: Time Warner Cable (MSO); AT&T Broadband & Internet Services (MSO). Purchased from Tele-Communications Inc., December 31, 1998.

DIME BOX—BRDC Cablevision, Box 240, Giddings, TX 78942. Phone: 409-542-3151. Fax: 409-542-1187. County: Lee. ICA: TX0601.
TV Market Ranking: Below 100. Franchise award date: N.A. Franchise expiration date: N.A. Began: October 31, 1990.
Channel capacity: 36. Channels available but not in use: 12.

Basic Service
Subscribers: 129.
Programming (received off-air): KLRU (P), KTBC (F), KVUE-TV (A), KXAN-TV (N) Austin; KBTX-TV (C) Bryan.
Programming (via satellite): WGN-TV (W) Chicago; American Movie Classics; CNN; Discovery Channel; Disney Channel; ESPN; Fox Family Channel; Fox Sports Net Southwest; Learning Channel; Nashville Network; QVC; Sci-Fi Channel; TBS Superstation; Trinity Bcstg. Network; Turner Network TV; USA Network.
Fee: $25.00 installation; $21.95 monthly.

Pay Service 1
Pay Units: 6.
Programming (via satellite): Cinemax.
Fee: $9.95 monthly.

Pay Service 2
Pay Units: 22.
Programming (via satellite): HBO.
Fee: $9.95 monthly.

Pay Service 3
Pay Units: N.A.
Programming (via satellite): Showtime.
Fee: $9.95 monthly.

Miles of plant: 13.9 (coaxial).
Manager: David W. Peterson.
Ownership: Bluebonnet Rural Development Corp. (MSO).

DIMMITT—Classic Cable, Box 429, 605 N.W. 3rd St., Plainville, KS 67663-0429. Phones: 785-434-7620; 800-999-8876. Fax: 785-434-2614. County: Castro. ICA: TX0255.
TV Market Ranking: Outside TV Markets. Franchise award date: N.A. Franchise expiration date: October 4, 2005. Began: February 1, 1964.
Channel capacity: 36 (2-way capable). Channels available but not in use: N.A.

Basic Service
Subscribers: 1,254.
Programming (received off-air): KACV-TV (P), KAMR-TV (N), KCIT (F,U), KFDA-TV (C), KVII-TV (A) Amarillo; KJTV (F), KLBK-TV (C) Lubbock; allband FM.
Programming (via satellite): WGN-TV (W) Chicago; A & E; Animal Planet; C-SPAN; CNN; Country Music TV; Discovery Channel; Disney Channel; E! Entertainment TV; ESPN; Fox Family Channel; Fox News Channel; Fox Sports Net Southwest; Headline News; History Channel; Home Shopping Network; Nashville Network; Nick at Nite's TV Land; Nickelodeon; TBS Superstation; Telemundo; The Weather Channel; Turner Classic Movies; Turner Network TV; USA Network; Univision.

Current originations: Automated time-weather.
Fee: $35.00 installation; $28.95 monthly.
Pay Service 1
Pay Units: 162.
Programming (via satellite): HBO.
Fee: $15.00 installation; $10.95 monthly.
Pay Service 2
Pay Units: 98.
Programming (via satellite): Showtime.
Fee: $15.00 installation; $9.95 monthly.
Pay Service 3
Pay Units: 110.
Programming (via satellite): The Movie Channel.
Fee: $5.95 monthly.
Equipment: Jerrold, Scientific-Atlanta & Standard Communications headend; Jerrold & Texscan amplifiers; Comm/Scope, CCS Hatfield & Jerrold cable; Compuvid character generator; Jerrold & Panasonic set top converters; Eagle traps; Prodelin satellite antenna; M/A-Com & Scientific-Atlanta satellite receivers.
Miles of plant: 25.0 (coaxial). Homes passed: 1,680. Total homes in franchised area: 1,698.
Manager: Bill Flowers. Chief technician: Chris Christenson. Marketing director: Jennifer Hauschild.
City fee: 2% of gross.
Ownership: Classic Cable (MSO).

DIXIE—Northland Cable TV, Box 538, Flint, TX 75762. Phones: 903-566-8757; 903-894-8200. Fax: 903-894-8204. County: Smith. Also serves Smith County (unincorporated areas). ICA: TX0911.
TV Market Ranking: Below 100. Franchise award date: N.A. Franchise expiration date: N.A. Began: N.A.
Channel capacity: 21 (2-way capable). Channels available but not in use: 1.
Basic Service
Subscribers: 120.
Programming (received off-air): KDFW (F), KERA-TV (P), KXTX-TV (I), WFAA-TV (A) Dallas-Fort Worth; KETK-TV (N) Jacksonville; KFXK (F) Longview; KLTV (A) Tyler-Longview.
Programming (via satellite): WGN-TV (W) Chicago; A & E; CNN; Country Music TV; Discovery Channel; ESPN; Fox Family Channel; Goodlife TV Network; Headline News; Learning Channel; Nashville Network; TBS Superstation; USA Network.
Fee: $60.00 installation; $20.75 monthly.
Pay Service 1
Pay Units: 20.
Programming (via satellite): Showtime.
Fee: N.A.
Local advertising: No.
Equipment: Scientific-Atlanta headend; Jerrold amplifiers; Comm/Scope cable; Jerrold set top converters; Eagle traps; Harris satellite antenna; DX Engineering satellite receivers.
Miles of plant: 8.5 (coaxial). Homes passed: 200. Total homes in franchised area: 200.
Manager: Jim Wiggins. Chief technician: Jim Bob Sanders. Marketing director: Charlotte Griffin.
Ownership: Northland Communications Corp. (MSO).

DODD CITY—Torrence Cablevision, Box 1167, Ridgeland, MS 39158. Phones: 601-981-6900; 800-977-8849. County: Fannin. Also serves Windom. ICA: TX0902.
TV Market Ranking: Below 100. Franchise award date: N.A. Franchise expiration date: N.A. Began: N.A.
Channel capacity: N.A. Channels available but not in use: N.A.
Basic Service
Subscribers: 137.
Programming (received off-air): KDFW (F), KERA-TV (P), KTVT (C), KXAS-TV (N), WFAA-TV (A) Dallas-Fort Worth.
Programming (via satellite): WGN-TV (W) Chicago; A & E; American Movie Classics; CNN; Country Music TV; Discovery Channel; ESPN; Fox Family Channel; Showtime; TBS Superstation; Turner Network TV; USA Network.
Fee: $21.00 monthly.
Homes passed: 319.
Ownership: Torrence Cable Inc. (MSO).

DUBLIN—Northland Cable TV, Box 70, 975 N. Lillian St., Stephenville, TX 76401. Phone: 254-968-4189. Fax: 254-968-8350. County: Erath. ICA: TX0749.
TV Market Ranking: Outside TV Markets. Franchise award date: N.A. Franchise expiration date: N.A. Began: N.A.
Channel capacity: 54 (not 2-way capable). Channels available but not in use: 22.
Basic Service
Subscribers: 1,014.
Programming (received off-air): KDAF (W), KDFI-TV (I), KDFW (F), KTVT (C), KTXA (U), KXAS-TV (N), KXTX-TV (I), WFAA-TV (A) Dallas-Fort Worth; KWTX-TV (C), KXXV (A) Waco-Temple.
Programming (via satellite): WTVS (P) Detroit.
Current originations: Public access.
Fee: $54.13 installation; $17.00 monthly.
Expanded Basic Service
Subscribers: N.A.
Programming (via satellite): A & E; American Movie Classics; C-SPAN; CNN; Cartoon Network; Discovery Channel; ESPN; Fox Family Channel; Fox Sports Net Southwest; Great American Country; Headline News; Home Shopping Network; Learning Channel; Nashville Network; QVC; TBS Superstation; The Weather Channel; Trinity Bcstg. Network; Turner Network TV; USA Network; Univision.
Fee: $28.01 monthly.
Pay Service 1
Pay Units: 26.
Programming (via satellite): HBO.
Fee: $12.39 monthly.
Pay Service 2
Pay Units: 104.
Programming (via satellite): The Movie Channel.
Fee: $11.26 monthly.
Pay Service 3
Pay Units: N.A.
Programming (via satellite): Showtime.
Fee: $11.26 monthly.
Equipment: Scientific-Atlanta headend; Scientific-Atlanta amplifiers; Times Fiber cable; Viacom character generator; Scientific-Atlanta set top converters; Arcom traps; Scientific-Atlanta satellite antenna; Scientific-Atlanta & Standard Electronics satellite receivers.
Manager: Carroll Lee. Chief technician: Greg Perry.
Ownership: Northland Communications Corp. (MSO).

DUMAS—Charter Communications Inc., Box 420, 211 E. 7th St., Dumas, TX 79029. Phone: 806-935-6487. County: Moore. Also serves Sunray. ICA: TX0137.
TV Market Ranking: Outside TV Markets. Franchise award date: N.A. Franchise expiration date: N.A. Began: July 1, 1967.
Channel capacity: 35 (not 2-way capable). Channels available but not in use: None.
Basic Service
Subscribers: 3,750.
Programming (received off-air): KACV-TV (P), KAMR-TV (N), KCIT (F,U), KFDA-TV (C), KVII-TV (A) Amarillo; allband FM.
Programming (via satellite): WGN-TV (W) Chicago; American Movie Classics; C-SPAN; C-SPAN 2; CNN; Country Music TV; Discovery Channel; ESPN; Fox Family Channel; Fox Sports Net Southwest; Headline News; Home Shopping Network; Lifetime; MTV; Nashville Network; Nickelodeon; QVC; TBS Superstation; The Weather Channel; Trinity Bcstg. Network; Turner Network TV; USA Network; Univision; VH1.
Current originations: Automated time-weather; religious access.
Fee: $35.00 installation; $19.14 monthly; $20.00 additional installation.
Pay Service 1
Pay Units: N.A.
Programming (via satellite): Cinemax; Disney Channel; HBO; The Movie Channel.
Fee: $9.33 monthly (Disney), $9.81 monthly (Cinemax), $12.28 monthly (TMC), $12.39 monthly (HBO).
Pay-Per-View
Special events.
Fee: Varies.
Local advertising: Yes. Available in satellite distributed programming.
Equipment: Scientific-Atlanta headend; Jerrold amplifiers; Times Fiber cable; Pioneer & Oak set top converters; Eagle traps; Scientific-Atlanta satellite antenna; Microdyne, Scientific-Atlanta & Standard Communications satellite receivers.
Miles of plant: 49.0 (coaxial). Homes passed: 4,588. Total homes in franchised area: 5,109.
Manager: Wayne Susee.
City fee: 2% of gross.
Ownership: Charter Communications Inc. (MSO). Purchased from Marcus Cable, April 1, 1999.

DUNCANVILLE—Charter Communications Inc., 206 E. Center St., Duncanville, TX 75116-4851. Phone: 214-296-2283. Fax: 214-296-5677. County: Dallas. ICA: TX0080.
TV Market Ranking: 12. Franchise award date: June 8, 1979. Franchise expiration date: October 19, 1999. Began: April 6, 1980.
Channel capacity: 78 (2-way capable; operating 2-way). Channels available but not in use: None.
Basic Service
Subscribers: 5,350.
Programming (received off-air): KDAF (W), KDFI-TV (I), KDFW (F), KDTX-TV (T), KERA-TV (P), KFWD (O), KTVT (C), KTXA (U), KXAS-TV (N), KXTX-TV (I), WFAA-TV (A) Dallas-Fort Worth; KMPX (I) Decatur; KDTN (P) Denton; KUVN (S) Garland; 23 FMs.
Programming (via satellite): WGN-TV (W) Chicago; C-SPAN; TBS Superstation.
Current originations: Automated time-weather; public access; educational access; government access; automated emergency alert.
Fee: $40.00 installation; $9.77 monthly.
Expanded Basic Service
Subscribers: 5,339.
Programming (via satellite): A & E; C-SPAN 2; CNBC; CNN; Discovery Channel; ESPN; Fox Family Channel; Fox Sports Net Southwest; Headline News; Lifetime; MTV; Nashville Network; Nickelodeon; QVC; The Weather Channel; Turner Network TV; USA Network; VH1.
Fee: $2.00 installation; $11.75 monthly.
Pay Service 1
Pay Units: N.A.
Programming (via satellite): Cinemax; Disney Channel; HBO; Showtime; The Movie Channel.
Fee: $15.00 installation; $8.50 monthly (Disney), $9.25 monthly (Cinemax), $10.25 monthly (TMC), $10.50 monthly (Showtime) $10.85 monthly (HBO).
Local advertising: Yes (locally produced & insert). Available in satellite distributed programming. Local sales manager: Tom Soulsby.
Program Guide: The Cable Guide.
Equipment: Scientific-Atlanta headend; GTE Sylvania amplifiers; Comm/Scope cable; Sony cameras; Sony VTRs; Video Data Systems character generator; Oak & Zenith set top converters; Zenith addressable set top converters; Eagle & Pico traps; Scientific-Atlanta satellite antenna; Microdyne, Scientific-Atlanta & Standard Communications satellite receivers; ChannelMatic & Sony commercial insert.
Miles of plant: 142.0 (coaxial); 15.0 (fiber optic). Homes passed: 13,333.
Manager: Dusty Matthews. Chief technician: Tom Ford. Program director: Todd Noyes. Marketing director: Pam Laney.
City fee: 5% of gross.
Ownership: Charter Communications Inc. (MSO). Purchased from Marcus Cable, April 1, 1999.

EAGLE LAKE—Time Warner Communications, Box 640, Columbus, TX 78934-2216. Phone: 409-732-2211. County: Colorado. ICA: TX0278.
TV Market Ranking: Below 100. Franchise award date: N.A. Franchise expiration date: N.A. Began: August 1, 1975.
Channel capacity: 29. Channels available but not in use: N.A.
Basic Service
Subscribers: 792.
Programming (received off-air): KTBC (F), KXAN-TV (N) Austin; KHOU-TV (C), KHTV (W), KPRC-TV (N), KRIV (F), KTRK-TV (A), KTXH (U), KUHT (P) Houston; allband FM.
Programming (via satellite): CNBC; CNN; Fox Family Channel; Nashville Network; TBS Superstation; The Weather Channel; Univision.
Current originations: Automated time-weather.
Fee: $32.36 installation; $9.70 monthly.
Commercial fee: $10.45 monthly.
Expanded Basic Service
Subscribers: 712.
Programming (via satellite): American Movie Classics; ESPN; Fox Sports Net Southwest; Turner Network TV; USA Network.
Fee: $10.23 monthly.
Pay Service 1
Pay Units: 50.
Programming (via satellite): Disney Channel.
Fee: N.A.
Pay Service 2
Pay Units: 293.
Programming (via satellite): The New Encore.
Fee: N.A.
Pay Service 3
Pay Units: 130.
Programming (via satellite): HBO.
Fee: N.A.
Pay Service 4
Pay Units: 79.
Programming (via satellite): Showtime.
Fee: N.A.
Local advertising: No.
Equipment: Jerrold & Scientific-Atlanta headend; Jerrold amplifiers; Times Fiber cable; Eagle traps; Scientific-Atlanta satellite antenna.

Miles of plant: 31.0 (coaxial). Homes passed: 1,404. Total homes in franchised area: 1,404.
Manager: Domingo Puente.
City fee: 3% of gross.
Ownership: Time Warner Cable (MSO); AT&T Broadband & Internet Services (MSO).

EAGLE PASS—Time Warner Communications, Box 1208, 690 Ford St., Eagle Pass, TX 78853. Phones: 512-773-5376; 800-527-6221. County: Maverick. Also serves Maverick County. ICA: TX0067.
TV Market Ranking: Below 100. Franchise award date: N.A. Franchise expiration date: N.A. Began: September 1, 1959.
Channel capacity: 38. Channels available but not in use: N.A.
Basic Service
Subscribers: 8,117.
Programming (received off-air): KVAW (O) Eagle Pass; XEW-TV, XHDF-TV Mexico City; 4 FMs.
Programming (via microwave): KENS-TV (C), KLRN (P), KMOL-TV (N), KSAT-TV (A), KWEX-TV (S) San Antonio.
Programming (via satellite): WGN-TV (W) Chicago; C-SPAN; CNN; Discovery Channel; ESPN; EWTN; GalaVision; Headline News; Learning Channel; Lifetime; MTV; Nashville Network; Nickelodeon; TBS Superstation; The Weather Channel; Turner Network TV; USA Network; VH1.
Current originations: Educational access; government access.
Fee: $60.00 installation; $18.16 monthly; $2.00 converter.
Pay Service 1
Pay Units: 478.
Programming (via satellite): Disney Channel.
Fee: $7.00 monthly.
Pay Service 2
Pay Units: 1,628.
Programming (via satellite): HBO.
Fee: $11.23 monthly.
Pay Service 3
Pay Units: 930.
Programming (via satellite): Showtime.
Fee: $11.23 monthly.
Pay Service 4
Pay Units: 68.
Programming (via satellite): The Movie Channel.
Fee: $15.00 installation; $11.23 monthly.
Local advertising: Yes. Regional interconnect: Cabletime.
Equipment: Jerrold headend; Jerrold amplifiers; Times Fiber cable; Scientific-Atlanta satellite antenna.
Miles of plant: 159.0 (coaxial). Homes passed: 10,420.
Manager: Jimmy Gutierrez. Chief technician: Polo Vielma.
City fee: 2% of gross.
Ownership: AT&T Broadband & Internet Services (MSO); Time Warner Cable (MSO); Advance/Newhouse Partnership (MSO).

EAST MOUNTAIN—Gilmer Cable Co., Box 1600, 111 Marshall, Gilmer, TX 75644. Phone: 903-843-5597. Fax: 903-843-2045. County: Upshur. Also serves Glenwood, Glenwood Acres. Plans service to West Mountain. ICA: TX0750.
TV Market Ranking: Below 100. Franchise award date: November 14, 1988. Franchise expiration date: November 14, 2003. Began: November 1, 1990.
Channel capacity: 42 (2-way capable; operating 2-way). Channels available but not in use: 6.
Basic Service
Subscribers: 240.
Programming (via microwave): KDFW (F), KERA-TV (P), KTVT (C), KXAS-TV (N) Dallas-Fort Worth.
Programming (via satellite): American Movie Classics; CNN; ESPN.
Fee: N.A.
Expanded Basic Service
Subscribers: 212.
Programming (via satellite): A & E; Fox Family Channel; Fox Sports Net Southwest; MTV; Nickelodeon; USA Network.
Fee: N.A.
Pay Service 1
Pay Units: 14.
Programming (via satellite): Disney Channel.
Fee: $10.00 installation; $5.95 monthly.
Pay Service 2
Pay Units: 63.
Programming (via satellite): HBO.
Fee: $10.00 installation; $8.95 monthly.
Pay Service 3
Pay Units: 44.
Programming (via satellite): Showtime.
Fee: $10.00 installation; $6.95 monthly.
Local advertising: Yes. Available in character-generated programming. Regional interconnect: Cabletime.
Equipment: C-COR amplifiers; Comm/Scope cable; Eagle traps; Scientific-Atlanta satellite receivers.
Miles of plant: 10.0 (coaxial).
Manager: David P. Mooney. Chief technician: Ed Lefevere. Marketing director: Robbie Mooney.
City fee: 4% of basic.
Ownership: David P. Mooney (MSO).

EASTLAND—Friendship Cable of Texas Inc., Box 9090, Tyler, TX 75711-9090. Phone: 903-581-2121. Fax: 903-581-2185. County: Eastland. Also serves Cisco, Eastland County, Ranger. ICA: TX0131.
TV Market Ranking: Outside TV Markets. Franchise award date: N.A. Franchise expiration date: N.A. Began: August 1, 1958.
Channel capacity: 37. Channels available but not in use: N.A.
Basic Service
Subscribers: 3,321.
Programming (received off-air): KRBC-TV (N), KTAB-TV (C), KTXS-TV (A) Abilene-Sweetwater; allband FM.
Programming (via microwave): KERA-TV (P), KTVT (C), WFAA-TV (A) Dallas-Fort Worth.
Programming (via satellite): CNBC; Discovery Channel; FX; Learning Channel; Odyssey; QVC; TBS Superstation; The Weather Channel; Univision.
Current originations: Automated time-weather; public access.
Fee: $30.00 installation; $13.05 monthly.
Expanded Basic Service
Subscribers: 2,870.
Programming (via satellite): American Movie Classics; Animal Planet; C-SPAN; CNN; Cartoon Network; Country Music TV; ESPN; Fox Family Channel; Fox News Channel; Headline News; Home & Garden Television; Lifetime; MTV; Nashville Network; Nickelodeon; Turner Network TV; USA Network.
Fee: $30.00 installation; $15.47 monthly.
Pay Service 1
Pay Units: 223.
Programming (via satellite): Cinemax.
Fee: $12.90 monthly.
Pay Service 2
Pay Units: 911.
Programming (via satellite): The New Encore.
Fee: $1.75 monthly.
Pay Service 3
Pay Units: 426.
Programming (via satellite): HBO.
Fee: $12.90 monthly.
Pay Service 4
Pay Units: 171.
Programming (via satellite): Showtime.
Fee: $12.90 monthly.
Pay Service 5
Pay Units: 563.
Programming (via satellite): Starz!
Fee: $6.75 monthly.
Program Guide: The Cable Guide.
Equipment: Jerrold headend; Jerrold amplifiers; Scientific-Atlanta satellite antenna; Scientific-Atlanta satellite receivers.
Miles of plant: 124.0 (coaxial). Homes passed: 4,824. Total homes in franchised area: 4,824.
Manager: Larry Bryant. Chief technician: Joe Stewart.
City fee: 3% of gross.
Ownership: Buford Television Inc. (MSO). See Cable System Ownership.

ECTOR—Friendship Cable of Texas Inc., Box 9090, Tyler, TX 75711-9090. Phone: 903-581-2121. Fax: 903-581-2185. County: Fannin. ICA: TX0585.
TV Market Ranking: Below 100. Franchise award date: N.A. Franchise expiration date: N.A. Began: April 1, 1985.
Channel capacity: 54. Channels available but not in use: N.A.
Basic Service
Subscribers: 136.
Programming (received off-air): KPXD (X) Arlington; KDFW (F), KERA-TV (P), KTVT (C), KXAS-TV (N), WFAA-TV (A) Dallas-Fort Worth; KXII (C) Sherman.
Programming (via satellite): TBS Superstation.
Fee: $30.00 installation; $29.25 monthly.
Pay Service 1
Pay Units: 5.
Programming (via satellite): Cinemax.
Fee: $7.00 monthly.
Pay Service 2
Pay Units: 1.
Programming (via satellite): HBO.
Fee: $12.00 monthly.
Pay Service 3
Pay Units: 20.
Programming (via satellite): Showtime.
Fee: $3.20 monthly.
Miles of plant: 9.6 (coaxial). Homes passed: 278.
Manager: Rodney Fletcher. Chief technician: Bo Jaubert.
Ownership: Buford Television Inc. (MSO). See Cable System Ownership.

ECTOR COUNTY—US Cable of West Texas, Box 255, 7800 W. University Blvd., Odessa, TX 79764-8573. Phone: 915-498-8366. Fax: 915-381-8246. County: Ector. ICA: TX0115.
TV Market Ranking: Below 100. Franchise award date: N.A. Franchise expiration date: N.A. Began: July 1, 1981.
Channel capacity: 60 (not 2-way capable). Channels available but not in use: N.A.
Basic Service
Subscribers: 1,950.
Programming (received off-air): KMID (A), KMLM (I), KOCV-TV (P), KOSA-TV (C), KPEJ (F), KWES-TV (N) Odessa-Midland.
Programming (via satellite): WGN-TV (W) Chicago; A & E; American Movie Classics; Animal Planet; C-SPAN; CNN; Cartoon Network; Discovery Channel; Disney Channel; ESPN; Fox Family Channel; Fox Sports Net Southwest; Headline News; History Channel; Home Shopping Network 2; Learning Channel; Lifetime; MTV; Nickelodeon; Outdoor Channel; Sci-Fi Channel; TBS Superstation; Telemundo; The New Encore; The Weather Channel; Turner Network TV; USA Network; Univision.
Fee: N.A.
Pay Service 1
Pay Units: 1,035.
Programming (via satellite): HBO; Showtime; The Movie Channel.
Fee: $10.95 monthly (each).
Local advertising: No.
Equipment: R. H. Tyler satellite antenna.
Miles of plant: 140.0 (coaxial); None (fiber optic). Homes passed: 4,882.
Manager: Daryl Koedyker. Chief technician: David Harris. Marketing director: Candy Boyer. Customer service manager: Kenny Harris.
County fee: None.
Ownership: US Cable Corp. (MSO).

EDCOUCH—Time Warner Communications, 2921 S. Expwy. 83, Harlingen, TX 78550-7615. Phone: 956-541-6782. Fax: 956-412-0959. County: Hidalgo. Also serves Elsa, Hidalgo County, La Villa. ICA: TX0185.
TV Market Ranking: Below 100. Franchise award date: N.A. Franchise expiration date: N.A. Began: January 1, 1975.
Channel capacity: 38. Channels available but not in use: N.A.
Basic Service
Subscribers: 1,528.
Programming (received off-air): KVEO (N) Brownsville; KGBT-TV (C), KLUJ (E), KMBH (P) Harlingen; KRGV-TV (A) Weslaco; XHAB-TV Matamoros; XHRIO (O) Matamoros-Brownsville.
Programming (via satellite): WGN-TV (W) Chicago; A & E; C-SPAN; CNN; Fox Family Channel; Headline News; Lifetime; MTV; Nashville Network; Nickelodeon; QVC; TBS Superstation; The Weather Channel.
Fee: $60.00 installation; $10.93 monthly.
Expanded Basic Service
Subscribers: 1,516.
Programming (via satellite): CNBC; Discovery Channel; ESPN; Fox Sports Net Southwest; Turner Network TV; USA Network; Univision.
Fee: $11.86 monthly.
Pay Service 1
Pay Units: 122.
Programming (via satellite): Cinemax.
Fee: N.A.
Pay Service 2
Pay Units: 56.
Programming (via satellite): Disney Channel.
Fee: N.A.
Pay Service 3
Pay Units: 238.
Programming (via satellite): HBO.
Fee: N.A.
Miles of plant: 38.7 (coaxial). Homes passed: 2,813. Total homes in franchised area: 2,813.
Manager: Juan Herrera. Chief technician: Al Velasquez.
Ownership: Time Warner Cable (MSO); AT&T Broadband & Internet Services (MSO).

EDEN—Classic Cable, Box 429, 605 N.W. 3rd St., Plainville, KS 67663-0429. Phones: 785-434-7620; 800-999-8876. Fax: 785-434-2614. County: Concho. ICA: TX0434.
TV Market Ranking: Outside TV Markets. Franchise award date: N.A. Franchise expiration date: October 26, 1997. Began: January 1, 1973.

Channel capacity: 41 (2-way capable). Channels available but not in use: N.A.

Basic Service

Subscribers: 417.

Programming (received off-air): KRBC-TV (N), KTXS-TV (A) Abilene-Sweetwater; KIDY (F), KLST (C) San Angelo; 2 FMs.

Programming (via satellite): WGN-TV (W) Chicago; KRMA-TV (P) Denver; A & E; Animal Planet; CNN; Cartoon Network; Country Music TV; Discovery Channel; Disney Channel; ESPN; Fox Family Channel; Fox News Channel; Fox Sports Net Southwest; Headline News; Learning Channel; Lifetime; Nashville Network; Nick at Nite's TV Land; Nickelodeon; QVC; TBS Superstation; The Weather Channel; Trinity Bcstg. Network; Turner Classic Movies; Turner Network TV; USA Network; Univision.

Current originations: Local news.

Fee: $35.00 installation; $28.95 monthly.

Pay Service 1

Pay Units: 40.

Programming (via satellite): HBO.

Fee: $35.00 installation; $10.95 monthly.

Pay Service 2

Pay Units: 56.

Programming (via satellite): Showtime.

Fee: $9.95 monthly.

Pay Service 3

Pay Units: 48.

Programming (via satellite): The Movie Channel.

Fee: $5.95 monthly.

Equipment: Jerrold headend; Vikoa amplifiers; Vikoa cable; Scientific-Atlanta satellite antenna.

Miles of plant: 15.0 (coaxial). Homes passed: 687.

Manager: Bill Flowers. Chief technician: Walt VanLue. Marketing director: Jennifer Hauschild.

City fee: 2% of gross.

Ownership: Classic Cable (MSO).

EDNA—CableVision Ltd., Box 977, 813 Vanderbilt Rd., Edna, TX 77957. Phone: 512-782-2993. Fax: 512-782-0572. County: Jackson. ICA: TX0207.

TV Market Ranking: Below 100. Franchise award date: N.A. Franchise expiration date: N.A. Began: January 1, 1959.

Channel capacity: N.A. Channels available but not in use: N.A.

Basic Service

Subscribers: N.A.

Programming (received off-air): KHOU-TV (C), KHTV (W), KPRC-TV (N), KRIV (F), KTRK-TV (A), KTXH (U), KUHT (P) Houston; KAVU-TV (A), KVCT (F) Victoria; allband FM.

Programming (via satellite): WGN-TV (W) Chicago; A & E; American Movie Classics; CNN; Country Music TV; Discovery Channel; ESPN; ESPN 2; Fox Family Channel; Fox Sports Net Southwest; Lifetime; Nashville Network; Nickelodeon; QVC; TBS Superstation; Turner Network TV; USA Network; Univision.

Fee: $10.00 installation; $8.25 monthly.

Pay Service 1

Pay Units: N.A.

Programming (via satellite): Disney Channel; HBO; Showtime.

Fee: $10.00 installation; $9.00 monthly (HBO).

Equipment: Scientific-Atlanta headend; Jerrold amplifiers; Comm/Scope cable; Tocom set top converters; Gardiner satellite antenna; Microdyne satellite receivers.

Miles of plant: 34.7 (coaxial). Additional miles planned: 5.0 (coaxial). Homes passed: 2,250.

Manager: Jake Landrum. Chief technician: Ken Zeber.

City fee: 3% of gross.

Ownership: Cable-Vision Ltd. (MSO).

EGAN—Friendship Cable of Texas Inc., Box 9090, Tyler, TX 75711-9090. Phone: 903-581-2121. Fax: 903-581-2185. County: Johnson. ICA: TX0366.

TV Market Ranking: 12. Franchise award date: N.A. Franchise expiration date: N.A. Began: N.A.

Channel capacity: 36. Channels available but not in use: 8.

Basic Service

Subscribers: 259.

Programming (received off-air): KPXD (X) Arlington; KDAF (W), KDFI-TV (I), KDFW (F), KERA-TV (P), KTVT (C), KTXA (U), KXAS-TV (N), KXTX-TV (I), WFAA-TV (A) Dallas-Fort Worth.

Programming (via satellite): WGN-TV (W) Chicago; A & E; American Movie Classics; CNN; Country Music TV; Discovery Channel; Disney Channel; ESPN; Fox Family Channel; Fox Sports Net Southwest; Goodlife TV Network; Lifetime; Nashville Network; Nickelodeon; TBS Superstation; Trinity Bcstg. Network; Turner Network TV; USA Network; Univision.

Fee: $30.00 monthly.

Pay Service 1

Pay Units: 11.

Programming (via satellite): Cinemax.

Fee: $10.95 monthly.

Pay Service 2

Pay Units: 21.

Programming (via satellite): HBO.

Fee: $10.95 monthly.

Pay Service 3

Pay Units: 34.

Programming (via satellite): Showtime.

Fee: $5.95 monthly.

Local advertising: Yes.

Miles of plant: 49.1 (coaxial). Homes passed: 959.

Manager: Rodney Fletcher. Chief technician: Steven Williams.

Ownership: Buford Television Inc. (MSO). See Cable System Ownership.

EL CAMPO—Mid Coast Cable TV, Box 1269, 505 N. Machnic, El Campo, TX 77437. Phone: 409-543-6858. County: Wharton. ICA: TX0133.

TV Market Ranking: Below 100. Franchise award date: N.A. Franchise expiration date: May 1, 2004. Began: March 15, 1973.

Channel capacity: 40 (2-way capable; operating 2-way). Channels available but not in use: None.

Basic Service

Subscribers: 3,698.

Programming (received off-air): KHOU-TV (C), KHTV (W), KPRC-TV (N), KRIV (F), KTRK-TV (A), KTXH (U), KUHT (P) Houston; KAVU-TV (A) Victoria; allband FM.

Programming (via satellite): WGN-TV (W) Chicago; C-SPAN; TBS Superstation.

Current originations: Automated time-weather; government access; automated emergency alert.

Fee: $25.00 installation; $7.10 monthly; $2.00 converter.

Expanded Basic Service

Subscribers: 3,613.

Programming (via satellite): A & E; American Movie Classics; CNBC; CNN; Country Music TV; ESPN; Fox Family Channel; Fox Sports Net Southwest; Headline News; Learning Channel; Lifetime; MTV; Nashville Network; Nickelodeon; Odyssey; QVC; The Weather Channel; Turner Network TV; USA Network; Univision.

Fee: $25.00 installation; $12.85 monthly.

Pay Service 1

Pay Units: 150.

Programming (via satellite): Cinemax.

Fee: $9.00 monthly.

Pay Service 2

Pay Units: 96.

Programming (via satellite): Disney Channel.

Fee: $9.00 monthly.

Pay Service 3

Pay Units: 403.

Programming (via satellite): HBO.

Fee: $9.00 monthly.

Pay Service 4

Pay Units: 123.

Programming (via satellite): The Movie Channel.

Fee: $9.00 monthly.

Pay Service 5

Pay Units: 146.

Programming (via satellite): Showtime.

Fee: $9.00 monthly.

Local advertising: Yes. Available in satellite distributed programming. Regional interconnect: Cabletime.

Program Guide: Cabletime.

Equipment: Scientific-Atlanta headend; Scientific-Atlanta amplifiers; Comm/Scope cable; MSI character generator; Prodelin & Scientific-Atlanta satellite antenna; Scientific-Atlanta satellite receivers.

Miles of plant: 78.0 (coaxial). Homes passed: 4,700.

Manager: Jake Landrum. Chief technician: Dickie Isaacs.

City fee: 4% of basic.

Ownership: Mid Coast Cable TV Inc. (MSO).

EL PASO—Time Warner Communications, 7010 Airport Rd., El Paso, TX 79906-4943. Phone: 915-772-1123. E-mail: twc@elp.rr.com. Counties: El Paso, TX; Dona Ana, NM. Also serves Anthony, Del Cerro Estates, Dona Ana County (portions), La Mesa, Mesquite, San Miguel, Santa Teresa, Sunland Park, Sunland Park II, Vado, NM; Anthony, Biggs Airfield, Canutillo, Clint, El Paso County, Fabens, Fort Bliss, Horizon City, Moon City, Socorro, TX. ICA: TX0009.

TV Market Ranking: Below 100. Franchise award date: January 1, 1968. Franchise expiration date: March 1, 2007. Began: February 1, 1972.

Channel capacity: 80 (2-way capable; operating 2-way). Channels available but not in use: 1.

Basic Service

Subscribers: 118,000; Commercial subscribers: 617.

Programming (received off-air): KCOS (P), KDBC-TV (C), KFOX-TV (F), KINT-TV (S), KKWB (W), KSCE (E), KTSM-TV (N), KVIA-TV (A) El Paso; KMAZ (T), KRWG-TV (P) Las Cruces; XEPM-TV, XHIJ-TV (O) El Paso-Juarez; 16 FMs.

Programming (via microwave): KTLA (W) Los Angeles.

Programming (via satellite): KTLA (W) Los Angeles; TBS Superstation.

Current originations: Public access; educational access; government access; automated emergency alert.

Fee: $29.84 installation; $7.20 monthly; $2.76 converter; $15.60 additional installation.

Commercial fee: $29.95 monthly.

Expanded Basic Service

Subscribers: 115,000.

Programming (via satellite): A & E; Animal Planet; BET; Bravo; C-SPAN; C-SPAN 2; CNBC; CNN; CNN/SI; Cartoon Network; Comedy Central; Country Music TV; Court TV; Discovery Channel; E! Entertainment TV; ESPN; ESPN 2; EWTN; Fox Family Channel; Fox News Channel; Fox Sports Net Southwest; GalaVision; Gems Television; Headline News; Home & Garden Television; Learning Channel; Lifetime; MSNBC; MTV; Nashville Network; Nickelodeon; QVC; The Weather Channel; Travel Channel; Turner Classic Movies; Turner Network TV; USA Network; VH1; ValueVision.

Fee: $29.84 installation; $21.56 monthly.

Expanded Basic Service 2

Subscribers: N.A.

Programming (via satellite): Flix; History Channel; Independent Film Channel; MOVIEplex; Sci-Fi Channel.

Fee: $1.95 monthly.

Pay Service 1

Pay Units: 8,451.

Programming (via satellite): Cinemax (multiplexed).

Fee: $12.50 monthly.

Pay Service 2

Pay Units: N.A.

Programming (via satellite): Disney Channel.

Fee: $8.35 monthly.

Pay Service 3

Pay Units: 16,402.

Programming (via satellite): HBO (multiplexed).

Fee: $12.50 monthly.

Pay Service 4

Pay Units: 7,044.

Programming (via satellite): Showtime (multiplexed).

Fee: $12.50 monthly.

Pay Service 5

Pay Units: 2,696.

Programming (via satellite): The Movie Channel (multiplexed).

Fee: $12.50 monthly.

Pay-Per-View

Addressable homes: 42,390.

Spice; Viewer's Choice.

Fee: $3.95 (Viewer's Choice); $6.95 (Spice).

Pay-per-view manager: Rosa Celis.

Local advertising: Yes. Available in locally originated programming. Rates: $400.00/Minute; $200.00/30 Seconds. Local sales manager: Scott Farley.

Program Guide: The Cable Guide.

Equipment: Scientific-Atlanta & General Instrument headend; C-COR amplifiers; Comm/Scope cable; Hitachi cameras; Sony VTRs; 3M character generator; Jerrold & Panasonic set top converters; General Instrument addressable set top converters; Toshiba modems; Sprucer computer servers; Pico traps;

Simulsat, Hughes & Scientific-Atlanta satellite antenna; Scientific-Atlanta satellite receivers; ChannelMatic commercial insert.
Miles of plant: 2004.0 (coaxial); 412.0 (fiber optic). Homes passed: 220,000. Total homes in franchised area: 220,000.
Manager: John Neal. Chief technician: Ramon Diaz. Program director: Bob Cordell. Customer service manager: Elizabeth Gil.
City fee: 5% of gross.
Ownership: AT&T Broadband & Internet Services (MSO); Time Warner Cable (MSO); Advance/Newhouse Partnership (MSO).

ELDORADO—Classic Cable, Box 429, 605 N.W. 3rd St., Plainville, KS 67663-0429. Phones: 785-434-7620; 800-999-8876. Fax: 785-434-2614. County: Schleicher. ICA: TX0342.
TV Market Ranking: Outside TV Markets. Franchise award date: N.A. Franchise expiration date: N.A. Began: September 1, 1960.
Channel capacity: 41 (2-way capable). Channels available but not in use: N.A.
Basic Service
Subscribers: 527.
Programming (received off-air): KTXS-TV (A) Abilene-Sweetwater; KACB-TV (N), KIDY (F), KLST (C) San Angelo; allband FM.
Programming (via satellite): WGN-TV (W) Chicago; KRMA-TV (P) Denver; A & E; Animal Planet; C-SPAN; C-SPAN 2; CNN; Country Music TV; Discovery Channel; Disney Channel; ESPN; Fox Family Channel; Fox News Channel; Fox Sports Net Southwest; GalaVision; Headline News; Learning Channel; Lifetime; Nashville Network; Nick at Nite's TV Land; Nickelodeon; QVC; TBS Superstation; The Weather Channel; Turner Classic Movies; Turner Network TV; USA Network; Univision.
Current originations: Local news.
Fee: $35.00 installation; $28.95 monthly.
Pay Service 1
Pay Units: 55.
Programming (via satellite): HBO.
Fee: $35.00 installation; $10.95 monthly.
Pay Service 2
Pay Units: 64.
Programming (via satellite): Showtime.
Fee: $9.95 monthly.
Pay Service 3
Pay Units: 56.
Programming (via satellite): The Movie Channel.
Fee: $5.95 monthly.
Equipment: RCA headend; RCA amplifiers; Comm/Scope cable; Telemation cameras; Andrew satellite antenna.
Miles of plant: 20.0 (coaxial). Homes passed: 1,092.
Manager: Bill Flowers. Chief technician: Ben Hernandez. Marketing director: Jennifer Hauschild.
City fee: 2% of gross.
Ownership: Classic Cable (MSO).

ELECTRA—Friendship Cable of Texas Inc., Box 9090, Tyler, TX 75711-9090. Phone: 903-581-2121. Fax: 903-581-2185. County: Wichita. ICA: TX0285.
TV Market Ranking: Below 100. Franchise award date: N.A. Franchise expiration date: N.A. Began: April 1, 1978.
Channel capacity: 35. Channels available but not in use: 7.
Basic Service
Subscribers: 471.
Programming (received off-air): KAUZ-TV (C), KFDX-TV (N), KJTL (F,U), KSWO-TV (A) Wichita Falls-Lawton; allband FM.
Programming (via translator): KERA-TV (P) Dallas-Fort Worth.
Programming (via satellite): Court TV; Discovery Channel; Knowledge TV; QVC; TBS Superstation; The Weather Channel.
Current originations: Automated time-weather; local news.
Fee: $30.00 installation; $12.77 monthly.
Expanded Basic Service
Subscribers: 453.
Programming (via satellite): American Movie Classics; Animal Planet; C-SPAN; CNBC; CNN; Cartoon Network; ESPN; FX; Fox Family Channel; Fox News Channel; Headline News; Home & Garden Television; Learning Channel; Lifetime; MTV; Nashville Network; Turner Network TV; USA Network; Univision.
Fee: $30.00 installation; $17.91 monthly.
Pay Service 1
Pay Units: 31.
Programming (via satellite): Cinemax.
Fee: $13.59 monthly.
Pay Service 2
Pay Units: 192.
Programming (via satellite): The New Encore.
Fee: $1.75 monthly.
Pay Service 3
Pay Units: 93.
Programming (via satellite): HBO.
Fee: $13.59 monthly.
Pay Service 4
Pay Units: 94.
Programming (via satellite): Starz!
Fee: $6.75 monthly.
Equipment: Tocom headend; Tocom amplifiers; Times Fiber cable; Tocom set top converters; Comtech & RF Systems satellite antenna.
Miles of plant: 22.0 (coaxial). Homes passed: 1,208. Total homes in franchised area: 1,397.
Manager: Larry Bryant. Chief technician: Ron Johnson.
City fee: 3% of gross.
Ownership: Buford Television Inc. (MSO). See Cable System Ownership.

ELGIN—Time Warner, 1905 N. Mays St., Round Rock, TX 78664-2127. Phone: 512-485-5555. Fax: 512-485-6109. County: Bastrop. ICA: TX0249.
TV Market Ranking: Below 100. Franchise award date: May 18, 1993. Franchise expiration date: July 19, 2009. Began: April 1, 1980.
Channel capacity: 35. Channels available but not in use: 11.
Basic Service
Subscribers: 348.
Programming (received off-air): KEYE-TV (C), KLRU (P), KNVA (W), KTBC (F), KVUE-TV (A), KXAN-TV (N) Austin; allband FM.
Programming (via satellite): A & E; American Movie Classics; BET; C-SPAN; Country Music TV; Discovery Channel; Fox Family Channel; Fox Sports Net Southwest; Headline News; Lifetime; Nashville Network; Nick at Nite; Nickelodeon; The Weather Channel; Turner Network TV; Univision.
Current originations: Automated time-weather.
Fee: $28.21 installation; $16.75 monthly; $25.96 additional installation.
Expanded Basic Service
Subscribers: N.A.
Programming (via satellite): WGN-TV (W) Chicago; Animal Planet; CNN; Cartoon Network; Comedy Central; Court TV; ESPN; ESPN 2; Golf Channel; History Channel; Home & Garden Television; Learning Channel; MSNBC; MTV; Pax Net; TBS Superstation; Travel Channel; Turner Classic Movies; USA Network.
Fee: $29.32 monthly.
Pay Service 1
Pay Units: N.A.
Programming (via satellite): Cinemax; Disney Channel; HBO; Showtime.
Fee: $4.95 monthly (Disney Channel); $10.95 monthly (Cinemax, HBO or Showtime).
Local advertising: Yes (insert only). Regional interconnect: Cabletime.
Equipment: Jerrold headend; Jerrold amplifiers; Comm/Scope cable; Video Data Systems character generator; Jerrold & Standard Components set top converters; Harris & Scientific-Atlanta satellite antenna; Microdyne & Scientific-Atlanta satellite receivers.
Miles of plant: 48.0 (coaxial). Additional miles planned: 1.6 (coaxial). Homes passed: 1,858.
Manager: Larry Converse. Office manager: Robin Seaton. Chief technician: Pete Cantu. Marketing director: Colleen O'Shields.
City fee: 3% of gross.
Ownership: Time Warner Cable (MSO).

ELLINGER—National Cable Inc., Suite 106-A, 5151 Reed Rd., Columbus, OH 43220. Phones: 614-442-5890; 800-582-0504. Fax: 614-457-2567. County: Fayette. ICA: TX0751.
TV Market Ranking: Outside TV Markets. Franchise award date: N.A. Franchise expiration date: N.A. Began: N.A.
Channel capacity: 36. Channels available but not in use: 21.
Basic Service
Subscribers: 36.
Programming (received off-air): KEYE-TV (C), KLRU (P), KTBC (F), KVUE-TV (A) Austin; KTXH (U) Houston; KAVU-TV (A) Victoria.
Programming (via satellite): A & E; American Movie Classics; CNN; Country Music TV; Discovery Channel; ESPN; Fox Family Channel; Nashville Network; Showtime; TBS Superstation; Turner Network TV; USA Network.
Fee: $28.00 monthly.
Miles of plant: 4.4 (coaxial). Homes passed: 183.
Manager: Paul Scott. Chief technician: Rob Spiller. Marketing director: Josh Thackery.
Ownership: National Cable (MSO).

ELMO—Friendship Cable of Texas Inc., Box 9090, Tyler, TX 75711-9090. Phone: 903-581-2121. Fax: 903-581-2185. County: Kaufman. Also serves Sleepy Hollow. ICA: TX0489.
TV Market Ranking: 12. Franchise award date: N.A. Franchise expiration date: N.A. Began: N.A.
Channel capacity: 36. Channels available but not in use: 18.
Basic Service
Subscribers: 145.
Programming (received off-air): KPXD (X) Arlington; KDFW (F), KERA-TV (P), KXAS-TV (N), WFAA-TV (A) Dallas-Fort Worth.
Programming (via satellite): WGN-TV (W) Chicago; CNN; Country Music TV; Discovery Channel; Disney Channel; ESPN; Fox Family Channel; Headline News; Nashville Network; TBS Superstation; USA Network.
Fee: $33.45 monthly.
Pay Service 1
Pay Units: 48.
Programming (via satellite): Cinemax.
Fee: $10.95 monthly.
Pay Service 2
Pay Units: 42.
Programming (via satellite): HBO.
Fee: $10.95 monthly.
Local advertising: Yes.
Miles of plant: 24.0 (coaxial). Homes passed: 477.
Manager: Rodney Fletcher. Chief technician: Steven Williams.
Ownership: Buford Television Inc. (MSO). See Cable System Ownership.

EMORY—Cablecomm, 920 Whitmore Dr., Rockwall, TX 75087. Phone: 972-771-0202. Fax: 972-722-6218. Counties: Hunt & Rains. Also serves Kings Court RV Park, Point, Rains County. ICA: TX0375.
TV Market Ranking: Outside TV Markets. Franchise award date: December 1, 1980. Franchise expiration date: January 1, 2000. Began: N.A.
Channel capacity: 60 (2-way capable; operating 2-way). Channels available but not in use: 40.
Basic Service
Subscribers: 305; Commercial subscribers: 26.
Programming (received off-air): KPXD (X) Arlington; KDAF (W), KDFI-TV (I), KDFW (F), KERA-TV (P), KTVT (C), KTXA (U), KXAS-TV (N), KXTX-TV (I), WFAA-TV (A) Dallas-Fort Worth; KFXK (F) Longview; KLTV (A) Tyler-Longview; 2 FMs.
Programming (via satellite): WGN-TV (W) Chicago; CNN; ESPN; Fox Family Channel; Headline News; MTV; Nashville Network; TBS Superstation; Turner Network TV.
Current originations: Automated time-weather; public access; educational access; government access; religious access; library access; automated emergency alert; local sports.
Fee: $40.00 installation; $20.95 monthly; $25.00 additional installation.
Commercial fee: $18.00 monthly.
Pay Service 1
Pay Units: N.A.
Programming (via satellite): Disney Channel; HBO; Showtime.
Fee: $25.00 installation; $9.00 monthly (each).
Local advertising: Yes (locally produced & insert). Available in character-generated programming. Rates: $10.00/Week. Local sales manager: G. A. Reeves.
Program Guide: CableView.
Equipment: Jerrold headend; Jerrold amplifiers; Comm/Scope cable; Sony cameras; Sony VTRs; Beston character generator; Jerrold set top converters; RMS traps; Comm/Scope, Hughes & Miralite satellite antenna; Comm/Scope satellite receivers.
Miles of plant: 26.0 (coaxial). Additional miles planned: 5.0 (coaxial). Homes passed: 900. Total homes in franchised area: 2,000.
Manager: Rhonda Jordon. Chief technician: Lynn Anderson.
City fee: 2% of basic fees.
Ownership: Fanch Communications Inc. (MSO); Time Warner Cable (MSO). See Cable System Ownership.

ENCINAL—Time Warner Communications, 207 E. Colorado St., Pearsall, TX 78061-3234. Phone: 800-527-6221. County: La Salle. Also serves La Salle County (southern portion). ICA: TX0565.
TV Market Ranking: Outside TV Markets. Franchise award date: N.A. Franchise expiration date: N.A. Began: July 1, 1983.
Channel capacity: 24. Channels available but not in use: N.A.
Basic Service
Subscribers: 171.

Programming (received off-air): KGNS-TV (N,A), KLDO-TV (O), KVTV (C) Laredo; XEW-TV Mexico City.
Programming (via satellite): WGN-TV (W) Chicago; WABC-TV (A) New York; CNN; Discovery Channel; ESPN; Fox Family Channel; GalaVision; Headline News; Lifetime; Nashville Network; Nickelodeon; TBS Superstation; The Weather Channel; USA Network; Univision.
Fee: $25.00 installation; $19.32 monthly; $25.00 additional installation.

Pay Service 1
Pay Units: 62.
Programming (via satellite): HBO.
Fee: $9.00 monthly.

Miles of plant: 6.2 (coaxial). Homes passed: 308.
Manager: Marcos Reyes.
Ownership: Time Warner Cable (MSO); AT&T Broadband & Internet Services (MSO).

ENNIS—Cablecomm, 305 S. Dallas, Ennis, TX 75119. Phone: 214-875-8601. County: Ellis. Also serves Alma, Garrett. ICA: TX0123.
TV Market Ranking: 12. Franchise award date: February 10, 1989. Franchise expiration date: February 10, 2004. Began: March 1, 1980.
Channel capacity: 60 (not 2-way capable). Channels available but not in use: 16.

Basic Service
Subscribers: 2,015; Commercial subscribers: 4.
Programming (received off-air): KDAF (W), KDFI-TV (I), KDFW (F), KDTX-TV (T), KERA-TV (P), KFWD (O), KTVT (C), KTXA (U), KXAS-TV (N), KXTX-TV (I), WFAA-TV (A) Dallas-Fort Worth; KMPX (I) Decatur; KDTN (P) Denton; KUVN (S) Garland; KHSX-TV (H) Irving.
Current originations: Automated time-weather; religious access; leased access; automated emergency alert.
Fee: $32.80 installation; $10.82 monthly; $1.65 converter.

Expanded Basic Service
Subscribers: 1,958.
Programming (via satellite): WGN-TV (W) Chicago; A & E; American Movie Classics; BET; C-SPAN; CNBC; CNN; Discovery Channel; Disney Channel; ESPN; Fox Family Channel; Fox Sports Net Southwest; Headline News; Lifetime; MTV; Nashville Network; Nickelodeon; QVC; TBS Superstation; The Weather Channel; Turner Network TV; USA Network.
Fee: $20.00 installation; $14.00 monthly.

Pay Service 1
Pay Units: 109.
Programming (via satellite): Cinemax.
Fee: $10.00 installation; $11.45 monthly.

Pay Service 2
Pay Units: 320.
Programming (via satellite): HBO.
Fee: $10.00 installation; $11.45 monthly.

Pay Service 3
Pay Units: 144.
Programming (via satellite): The Movie Channel.
Fee: $10.00 installation; $11.45 monthly.

Pay Service 4
Pay Units: 195.
Programming (via satellite): Showtime.
Fee: $10.00 installation; $11.45 monthly.

Local advertising: Yes. Available in satellite distributed, taped & automated programming. Rates: $2.50/Day. Local sales manager: Daryl Campbell. Regional interconnect: Cabletime.
Program Guide: Premium Channels.
Equipment: Scientific-Atlanta headend; C-COR amplifiers; Comm/Scope cable; Atari character generator; Scientific-Atlanta set top converters; Scientific-Atlanta satellite antenna; Scientific-Atlanta satellite receivers.
Miles of plant: 100.0 (coaxial). Homes passed: 5,337.
Manager: Rex Thackerson. Chief technician: Scott Donley. Marketing director: Bill Forgey.
City fee: 3% of gross (Alma & Garrett); 5% of gross (Ennis).
Ownership: Fanch Communications Inc. (MSO); Time Warner Cable (MSO). See Cable System Ownership.

EUSTACE—Torrence Cablevision, Box 1167, Ridgeland, MS 39158. Phones: 601-981-6900; 800-977-8849. County: Henderson. Also serves Henderson County (portions). ICA: TX0547.
TV Market Ranking: Outside TV Markets. Franchise award date: N.A. Franchise expiration date: N.A. Began: N.A.
Channel capacity: 35. Channels available but not in use: 18.

Basic Service
Subscribers: 57.
Programming (received off-air): KDFW (F), KERA-TV (P), KXAS-TV (N) Dallas-Fort Worth; KLTV (A) Tyler-Longview.
Programming (via satellite): WGN-TV (W) Chicago; A & E; American Movie Classics; CNN; Country Music TV; Discovery Channel; ESPN; Fox Family Channel; Headline News; Nashville Network; Showtime; TBS Superstation; Turner Network TV; USA Network.
Fee: $24.00 monthly.

Pay Service 1
Pay Units: 10.
Programming (via satellite): Cinemax.
Fee: $10.95 monthly.

Pay Service 2
Pay Units: 29.
Programming (via satellite): HBO.
Fee: $10.95 monthly.

Local advertising: Yes.
Miles of plant: 11.0 (coaxial). Homes passed: 352.
Ownership: Torrence Cable Inc. (MSO).

EVANT—Post Cablevision of Texas Ltd., Drawer 829, 1108 Parker St., Goldthwaite, TX 76844. Phone: 915-648-3041. County: Coryell. ICA: TX0631.
TV Market Ranking: Below 100. Franchise award date: N.A. Franchise expiration date: N.A. Began: April 1, 1982.
Channel capacity: 21. Channels available but not in use: None.

Basic Service
Subscribers: N.A.
Programming (received off-air): KNCT (P) Belton; KCEN-TV (N), KWKT (F), KWTX-TV (C) Waco-Temple.
Programming (via translator): KERA-TV (P), KTVT (C), WFAA-TV (A) Dallas-Fort Worth.
Programming (via satellite): WGN-TV (W) Chicago; CNN; Country Music TV; Discovery Channel; ESPN; Fox Family Channel; Home Shopping Network; Nashville Network; Nickelodeon; TBS Superstation; The Weather Channel; USA Network.
Fee: $25.00 installation; $20.78 monthly.

Pay Service 1
Pay Units: N.A.
Programming (via satellite): Disney Channel; HBO.
Fee: $7.54 monthly (Disney), $10.78 monthly (HBO).

Miles of plant: 5.6 (coaxial). Homes passed: 206.
Manager: Denise Casbeer. Chief technician: Joe Dean.
Ownership: Fanch Communications Inc. (MSO). See Cable System Ownership.

FAIRFIELD—Northland Cable TV, 515 W. Tyler, Mexia, TX 76667. Phone: 254-562-2872. Fax: 254-562-6454. County: Freestone. Also serves Teague. ICA: TX0150.
TV Market Ranking: Outside TV Markets. Franchise award date: February 1, 1965. Franchise expiration date: June 1, 1999. Began: November 1, 1968.
Channel capacity: 42 (2-way capable; operating 2-way). Channels available but not in use: 7.

Basic Service
Subscribers: 2,108.
Programming (received off-air): KDAF (W), KDFI-TV (I), KDFW (F), KERA-TV (P), KTVT (C), KTXA (U), KXAS-TV (N), KXTX-TV (I), WFAA-TV (A) Dallas-Fort Worth; KCEN-TV (N), KWKT (F), KWTX-TV (C), KXXV (A) Waco-Temple; allband FM.
Programming (via satellite): A & E; American Movie Classics; BET; C-SPAN; CNN; CNNfn; Cartoon Network; Country Music TV; Discovery Channel; ESPN; ESPN 2; Fox Family Channel; Fox News Channel; Fox Sports Net Southwest; Headline News; Learning Channel; Nashville Network; Nickelodeon; QVC; Sci-Fi Channel; TBS Superstation; TV Guide Channel; The Weather Channel; Trinity Bcstg. Network; Turner Classic Movies; Turner Network TV; Univision.
Current originations: Automated time-weather.
Fee: $55.00 installation; $25.25 monthly.

Pay Service 1
Pay Units: 97.
Programming (via satellite): Starz!; The New Encore.
Fee: $35.00 installation; $10.00 monthly.

Pay Service 2
Pay Units: 202.
Programming (via satellite): Showtime.
Fee: $35.00 installation; $10.00 monthly.

Pay Service 3
Pay Units: 237.
Programming (via satellite): HBO.
Fee: $35.00 installation; $10.50 monthly.

Pay Service 4
Pay Units: 141.
Programming (via satellite): The Movie Channel.
Fee: $35.00 installation; $10.00 monthly.

Local advertising: Yes. Available in satellite distributed & character-generated programming. Rates: $8.32/Minute; $4.16/30 Seconds. Local sales manager: Cathy Lane.
Program Guide: Premium Channels.
Equipment: Harris & Scientific-Atlanta headend; Scientific-Atlanta amplifiers; Times Fiber cable; Texscan character generator; Scientific-Atlanta set top converters; Eagle & Arcom traps; Scientific-Atlanta satellite antenna; Scientific-Atlanta satellite receivers.
Miles of plant: 92.0 (coaxial); None (fiber optic). Homes passed: 3,835. Total homes in franchised area: 3,835.
Manager: Jimmie Cullins.
City fee: 3% of gross.
Ownership: Northland Communications Corp. (MSO).

FALFURRIAS—Valley Cable TV Inc., 2921 S. Expressway 83, Harlingen, TX 78550-7615. Phone: 956-541-6782. Fax: 956-412-0959. County: Brooks. ICA: TX0269.
TV Market Ranking: Outside TV Markets. Franchise award date: N.A. Franchise expiration date: N.A. Began: N.A.
Channel capacity: 35. Channels available but not in use: 5.

Basic Service
Subscribers: 1,318.
Programming (received off-air): KEDT (P), KIII (A), KRIS-TV (N), KZTV (C) Corpus Christi; K07TS (I) Falfurrias.
Programming (via satellite): WGN-TV (W) Chicago; A & E; C-SPAN; CNN; Fox Family Channel; Headline News; Lifetime; MTV; Nashville Network; Nickelodeon; QVC; TBS Superstation; Telemundo; The Weather Channel; Trinity Bcstg. Network; Univision.
Fee: $60.00 installation; $10.05 monthly.

Expanded Basic Service
Subscribers: 1,250.
Programming (via satellite): CNBC; Discovery Channel; ESPN; Fox Sports Net Southwest; GalaVision; Turner Network TV; USA Network.
Fee: $11.19 monthly.

Pay Service 1
Pay Units: 211.
Programming (via satellite): Cinemax.
Fee: $10.95 monthly.

Pay Service 2
Pay Units: 61.
Programming (via satellite): Disney Channel.
Fee: $10.95 monthly.

Pay Service 3
Pay Units: 318.
Programming (via satellite): HBO.
Fee: $10.95 monthly.

Miles of plant: 38.7 (coaxial). Homes passed: 1,541. Total homes in franchised area: 1,541.
Manager: Juan Herrera. Chief technician: Al Velasquez.
Ownership: AT&T Broadband & Internet Services (MSO). Purchased from Tele-Communications Inc., March 9, 1999.

FANNETT—Friendship Cable of Texas Inc., Box 9090, Tyler, TX 75711-9090. Phone: 903-581-2121. Fax: 903-581-2185. County: Jefferson. Also serves Hamshire, Hillebrandt, Labelle. ICA: TX0319.
TV Market Ranking: 88. Franchise award date: N.A. Franchise expiration date: N.A. Began: September 1, 1989.
Channel capacity: 36 (not 2-way capable). Channels available but not in use: None.

Basic Service
Subscribers: 1,184.
Programming (received off-air): KBMT (A), KBTV-TV (N), KFDM-TV (C), KITU (E) Beaumont-Port Arthur.
Programming (via satellite): WGN-TV (W) Chicago; A & E; C-SPAN; CNN; Country Music TV; Discovery Channel; Disney Channel; E! Entertainment TV; ESPN; Fox Family Channel; Fox Sports Net Southwest; Headline News; Lifetime; Nashville Network; Nickelodeon; Odyssey; QVC; Sci-Fi Channel; TBS Superstation; The Weather Channel; Turner Network TV; USA Network.
Fee: $34.45 monthly.

Pay Service 1
Pay Units: 64.
Programming (via satellite): Cinemax.
Fee: $10.50 monthly.

Pay Service 2
Pay Units: 81.
Programming (via satellite): HBO.
Fee: $10.50 monthly.

Pay Service 3
Pay Units: 127.
Programming (via satellite): Showtime.
Fee: $5.95 monthly.

Local advertising: No.
Miles of plant: 81.0 (coaxial). Homes passed: 2,109.
Manager: Wanda Pyburn. Chief technician: Mike Deal.

Ownership: Buford Television Inc. (MSO). See Cable System Ownership.

FARMERS BRANCH—TCI Cablevision of Dallas Inc., 1565 Chenault St., Dallas, TX 75228-5499. Phone: 214-328-5000. Fax: 214-320-7336. County: Dallas. ICA: TX0077.

TV Market Ranking: 12. Franchise award date: N.A. Franchise expiration date: N.A. Began: N.A.

Channel capacity: 52. Channels available but not in use: N.A.

Basic Service

Subscribers: 4,365.

Programming (received off-air): KDAF (W), KDFI-TV (I), KDFW (F), KDTX-TV (T), KERA-TV (P), KFWD (O), KTVT (C), KTXA (U), KXAS-TV (N), KXTX-TV (I), WFAA-TV (A) Dallas-Fort Worth; KDTN (P) Denton; KUVN (S) Garland; KHSX-TV (H) Irving.

Programming (via satellite): WGN-TV (W) Chicago; A & E; C-SPAN; CNBC; CNN; Comedy Central; Discovery Channel; Electronic Program Guide; Fox Family Channel; Headline News; Lifetime; MTV; Nashville Network; Nickelodeon; Odyssey; TBS Superstation; The Weather Channel; VH1.

Current originations: Public access; educational access; government access; religious access.

Fee: $60.00 installation; $19.05 monthly; $1.90 converter.

Expanded Basic Service

Subscribers: 4,218.

Programming (via satellite): American Movie Classics; ESPN; Fox Sports Net Southwest; Turner Network TV; USA Network.

Fee: $3.70 monthly.

Pay Service 1

Pay Units: 3.

Programming (via satellite): Cinemax.

Fee: $9.45 monthly.

Pay Service 2

Pay Units: N.A.

Programming (via satellite): DMX.

Fee: N.A.

Pay Service 3

Pay Units: 456.

Programming (via satellite): Disney Channel.

Fee: N.A.

Pay Service 4

Pay Units: 1,525.

Programming (via satellite): The New Encore.

Fee: N.A.

Pay Service 5

Pay Units: 1,777.

Programming (via satellite): HBO.

Fee: $11.12 monthly.

Pay Service 6

Pay Units: 717.

Programming (via satellite): The Movie Channel.

Fee: $11.12 monthly.

Pay Service 7

Pay Units: 845.

Programming (via satellite): Showtime.

Fee: $11.12 monthly.

Local advertising: Yes.

Program Guide: The Cable Guide.

Miles of plant: 121.0 (coaxial). Homes passed: 9,260. Total homes in franchised area: 9,747.

Manager: Clem Madox.

Ownership: AT&T Broadband & Internet Services (MSO). Purchased from Tele-Communications Inc., March 9, 1999.

FAYSVILLE—Torrence Cablevision, Box 1167, Ridgeland, MS 39158. Phones: 601-981-6900; 800-977-8849. County: Hidalgo. ICA: TX0687.

TV Market Ranking: Below 100. Franchise award date: N.A. Franchise expiration date: N.A. Began: N.A.

Channel capacity: 36. Channels available but not in use: 18.

Basic Service

Subscribers: 19.

Programming (received off-air): KVEO (N) Brownsville; KGBT-TV (C), KLUJ (E) Harlingen; KRGV-TV (A) Weslaco.

Programming (via satellite): WGN-TV (W) Chicago; A & E; American Movie Classics; CNN; Country Music TV; Discovery Channel; ESPN; Fox Family Channel; GalaVision; Nashville Network; Showtime; TBS Superstation; Turner Network TV; USA Network.

Fee: $28.00 monthly.

Miles of plant: 3.0 (coaxial). Homes passed: 83.

Ownership: Torrence Cable Inc. (MSO).

FENTRESS—National Cable Inc., Suite 106-A, 5151 Reed Rd., Columbus, OH 43220. Phones: 614-442-5890; 800-582-0504. Fax: 614-457-2567. County: Caldwell. Also serves Prairie Lea. ICA: TX0611.

TV Market Ranking: Below 100. Franchise award date: N.A. Franchise expiration date: N.A. Began: June 25, 1990.

Channel capacity: 36 (not 2-way capable). Channels available but not in use: N.A.

Basic Service

Subscribers: 56.

Programming (received off-air): KEYE-TV (C), KLRU (P), KVUE-TV (A) Austin; KENS-TV (C), KMOL-TV (N), KWEX-TV (S) San Antonio.

Programming (via satellite): WGN-TV (W) Chicago; A & E; American Movie Classics; CNN; Country Music TV; Discovery Channel; ESPN; Fox Family Channel; GalaVision; Nashville Network; Showtime; TBS Superstation; Turner Network TV; USA Network.

Current originations: Automated time-weather; public access; educational access; automated emergency alert; local sports.

Fee: $30.00 installation; $28.00 monthly; $3.00 converter.

Equipment: Nexus headend; Magnavox amplifiers; Times Fiber cable; Nexus satellite receivers.

Miles of plant: 8.6 (coaxial). Homes passed: 97.

Manager: Paul Scott. Chief technician: Rob Spiller. Marketing director: Josh Thackery.

Ownership: National Cable (MSO).

FLAT—National Cable Inc., Suite 106-A, 5151 Reed Rd., Columbus, OH 43220. Phones: 614-442-5890; 800-582-0504. Fax: 614-457-2567. County: Coryell. ICA: TX0699.

TV Market Ranking: Below 100. Franchise award date: N.A. Franchise expiration date: N.A. Began: October 1, 1989.

Channel capacity: 36 (not 2-way capable). Channels available but not in use: 21.

Basic Service

Subscribers: 34.

Programming (received off-air): KNCT (P) Belton; KCEN-TV (N), KWKT (F), KWTX-TV (C), KXXV (A) Waco-Temple.

Programming (via satellite): WGN-TV (W) Chicago; A & E; American Movie Classics; CNN; Country Music TV; Discovery Channel; ESPN; Fox Family Channel; Nashville Network; Showtime; TBS Superstation; Turner Network TV; USA Network.

Current originations: Automated time-weather; public access; educational access; government access; leased access; automated emergency alert.

Fee: $28.00 monthly.

Equipment: Nexus headend; Magnavox amplifiers; Times Fiber cable; Oak set top converters; Nexus satellite receivers.

Miles of plant: 2.3 (coaxial). Homes passed: 82.

Manager: Paul Scott. Chief technician: Rob Spiller. Marketing director: Josh Thackery.

Ownership: National Cable (MSO).

FLATONIA—Classic Cable, Box 429, 605 N.W. 3rd St., Plainville, KS 67663-0429. Phones: 785-434-7620; 800-999-8876. Fax: 785-434-2614. County: Fayette. ICA: TX0755.

TV Market Ranking: Outside TV Markets. Franchise award date: December 14, 1982. Franchise expiration date: December 14, 2002. Began: April 1, 1983.

Channel capacity: 36 (2-way capable). Channels available but not in use: N.A.

Basic Service

Subscribers: 375.

Programming (received off-air): KBVO-LP (U), KLRU (P), KTBC (F), KVUE-TV (A), KXAN-TV (N) Austin; KRIV (F), KTXH (U) Houston; KENS-TV (C), KMOL-TV (N), KSAT-TV (A) San Antonio.

Programming (via satellite): WGN-TV (W) Chicago; A & E; CNN; Cartoon Network; Country Music TV; Discovery Channel; Disney Channel; ESPN; Fox Family Channel; Fox Sports Net Southwest; Headline News; Learning Channel; Nashville Network; Nick at Nite's TV Land; Nickelodeon; TBS Superstation; The Weather Channel; Trinity Bcstg. Network; Turner Classic Movies; Turner Network TV; USA Network; Univision.

Fee: $35.00 installation; $26.95 monthly; $15.00 additional installation.

Pay Service 1

Pay Units: 92.

Programming (via satellite): HBO.

Fee: $10.00 installation; $10.95 monthly.

Pay Service 2

Pay Units: 25.

Programming (via satellite): Showtime.

Fee: $9.95 monthly.

Local advertising: No.

Equipment: RCA amplifiers; Pioneer set top converters; Eagle & Drop Shop traps; Scientific-Atlanta satellite receivers.

Miles of plant: 6.0 (coaxial). Homes passed: 529.

Manager: Bill Flowers. Chief technician: Walt VanLue. Marketing director: Jennifer Hauschild.

City fee: 3% of gross.

Ownership: Classic Cable (MSO).

FLINT—Northland Cable TV, Box 538, Flint, TX 75762. Phones: 903-894-8200; 903-566-8757. Fax: 903-894-8204. Counties: Cherokee & Smith. Also serves Bullard, Gresham, Noonday. ICA: TX0189.

TV Market Ranking: Below 100. Franchise award date: January 3, 1983. Franchise expiration date: September 10, 2000. Began: May 1, 1983.

Channel capacity: 36 (2-way capable). Channels available but not in use: 2.

Basic Service

Subscribers: 2,151.

Programming (received off-air): KDAF (W), KDFI-TV (I), KERA-TV (P), KTVT (C), KXTX-TV (I), WFAA-TV (A) Dallas-Fort Worth; KETK-TV (N) Jacksonville; KFXK (F) Longview; K20DL (I) Tyler; KLTV (A) Tyler-Longview.

Programming (via satellite): WGN-TV (W) Chicago; TBS Superstation.

Current originations: Automated time-weather; local sports.

Fee: $15.00 monthly; $3.00 converter.

Expanded Basic Service

Subscribers: 2,138.

Programming (via satellite): A & E; C-SPAN; CNN; Country Music TV; Discovery Channel; ESPN; ESPN 2; Fox Family Channel; Fox News Channel; Headline News; Home & Garden Television; Learning Channel; Lifetime; Nashville Network; Nickelodeon; QVC; TV Guide Channel; The Weather Channel; Travel Channel; Turner Classic Movies; Turner Network TV; USA Network.

Fee: $49.95 installation; $25.75 monthly.

Expanded Basic Service 2

Subscribers: 713.

Programming (via satellite): CNBC; Cartoon Network; ESPN 2; Fox Sports Net Southwest; Lifetime; Nickelodeon; Turner Classic Movies.

Fee: $7.95 monthly.

Pay Service 1

Pay Units: 128.

Programming (via satellite): Cinemax.

Fee: $24.95 installation; $12.00 monthly.

Pay Service 2

Pay Units: 184.

Programming (via satellite): Disney Channel.

Fee: $24.95 installation; $12.00 monthly.

Pay Service 3

Pay Units: 282.

Programming (via satellite): HBO.

Fee: $24.95 installation; $12.00 monthly.

Pay Service 4

Pay Units: 178.

Programming (via satellite): Showtime.

Fee: $24.95 installation; $12.00 monthly.

Local advertising: Yes (locally produced). Available in satellite distributed, locally originated, character-generated, taped & automated programming. Rates: $10.00/Minute; $5.00/30 Seconds. Local sales manager: Lynda Tracy.

Program Guide: Premium Channels.

Equipment: Hughes, M/A-Com & Scientific-Atlanta headend; Magnavox & Texscan amplifiers; Comm/Scope & Trilogy cable; Texscan character generator; Hamlin, Jerrold & Scientific-Atlanta set top converters; Arcom, Eagle & Pico traps; AFC & Comtech satellite antenna; Harris satellite receivers; Channel-Matic commercial insert.

Miles of plant: 121.0 (coaxial). Additional miles planned: 1.0 (coaxial). Homes passed: 2,712. Total homes in franchised area: 2,712.

Manager: Jim Wiggins. Chief technician: Jim Bob Sanders. Marketing director: Charlotte Griffin.

Franchise fee: 5% of gross.

Ownership: Northland Communications Corp. (MSO).

FLORENCE—Time Warner Cable, 12012 N. Mo Pac Expressway, Austin, TX 78758-2904. Phone: 512-485-6100. Fax: 512-485-6105. Web site: http://www.timewarneraustin.com. County: Williamson. ICA: TX0539.

TV Market Ranking: Below 100. Franchise award date: September 6, 1994. Franchise expiration date: N.A. Began: July 1, 1983.

Channel capacity: 53 (not 2-way capable). Channels available but not in use: 15.

Basic Service

Subscribers: 220.

Programming (received off-air): KEYE-TV (C), KLRU (P), KNVA (W), KTBC (F), KVUE-TV (A), KXAN-TV (N) Austin; KNCT (P) Belton; KCEN-TV (N), KWTX-TV (C), KXXV (A) Waco-Temple.

Programming (via satellite): WGN-TV (W) Chicago; A & E; Animal Planet; CNN; Comedy Central; Country Music TV; Discovery Channel; ESPN; ESPN 2; Fox Family Channel; GalaVision; Headline News; History Channel; Home & Garden Television; Learning Channel; Lifetime; MSNBC; Nashville Network; Nick at Nite; Nickelodeon; Pax Net; TBS Superstation; The Weather Channel; Turner Classic Movies; Turner Network TV; USA Network.
Fee: $28.21 installation; $23.95 monthly; $1.15 converter.
Pay Service 1
Pay Units: N.A.
Programming (via satellite): Cinemax; HBO; Showtime.
Fee: $7.00 monthly (Cinemax or Showtime), $12.00 monthly (HBO).
Miles of plant: 8.1 (coaxial). Homes passed: 364.
Manager: Bill Carey. Chief technician: Matt Stanek. Program director: George Warmingham. Marketing director: Michelle Golden.
Ownership: Time Warner Cable (MSO); Advance/Newhouse Partnership (MSO).

FLORESVILLE—CabTel Corp., Suite 106A, 5151 Reed Rd., Columbus, OH 43220. Phones: 614-442-5890; 800-582-0504. Fax: 614-457-2567. County: Wilson. Also serves Poth. ICA: TX0236.
TV Market Ranking: 45 (Floresville); Outside TV Markets (Poth). Franchise award date: April 1, 1981. Franchise expiration date: N.A. Began: April 1, 1981.
Channel capacity: 35. Channels available but not in use: 8.
Basic Service
Subscribers: N.A.
Programming (received off-air): KRRT (W) Kerrville-San Antonio; KENS-TV (C), KLRN (P), KMOL-TV (N), KSAT-TV (A), KWEX-TV (S) San Antonio.
Programming (via satellite): WGN-TV (W) Chicago; CNN; Discovery Channel; ESPN; Fox Family Channel; GalaVision; Lifetime; Nashville Network; Nickelodeon; TBS Superstation; USA Network; VH1.
Fee: $13.00 monthly.
Pay Service 1
Pay Units: N.A.
Programming (via satellite): Disney Channel; HBO; The Movie Channel.
Fee: $7.50 monthly (each).
Miles of plant: 53.0 (coaxial). Homes passed: 1,850.
Manager: Barbara Mills. Chief technician: Richard Grahn.
Ownership: National Cable (MSO). Purchased from Hillsboro Cable TV LP.

FLOWER MOUND—Communications Services Inc., 3357 Long Prairie Rd., Flower Mound, TX 75028-2701. Phones: 214-539-9299; 214-727-5724. County: Denton. Also serves Double Oak, Highland Village. ICA: TX0107.
TV Market Ranking: 12. Franchise award date: N.A. Franchise expiration date: N.A. Began: August 1, 1980.
Channel capacity: 41 (not 2-way capable). Channels available but not in use: N.A.
Basic Service
Subscribers: 8,953.
Programming (received off-air): KDAF (W), KDFI-TV (I), KDFW (F), KDTX-TV (T), KERA-TV (P), KFWD (O), KTVT (C), KTXA (U), KXAS-TV (N), KXTX-TV (I), WFAA-TV (A) Dallas-Fort Worth; KMPX (I) Decatur; KDTN (P) Denton; KUVN (S) Garland; KHSX-TV (H) Irving.
Programming (via satellite): WGN-TV (W) Chicago; A & E; CNBC; CNN; Discovery Channel; Fox Family Channel; Headline News; MTV; Nashville Network; Nickelodeon; Odyssey; TBS Superstation; The New Encore; The Weather Channel.
Current originations: Government access.
Fee: $60.00 installation; $11.71 monthly; $0.64 converter; $60.00 additional installation.
Expanded Basic Service
Subscribers: 8,734.
Programming (via satellite): American Movie Classics; ESPN; Fox Sports Net Southwest; Turner Network TV; USA Network.
Fee: $8.90 monthly.
Pay Service 1
Pay Units: 456.
Programming (via satellite): Cinemax.
Fee: $12.70 monthly.
Pay Service 2
Pay Units: 665.
Programming (via satellite): Disney Channel.
Fee: $12.70 monthly.
Pay Service 3
Pay Units: 1,411.
Programming (via satellite): HBO.
Fee: $12.70 monthly.
Pay Service 4
Pay Units: 269.
Programming (via satellite): The Movie Channel.
Fee: $12.70 monthly.
Pay Service 5
Pay Units: 640.
Programming (via satellite): Showtime.
Fee: $12.70 monthly.
Local advertising: No.
Program Guide: The Cable Guide.
Equipment: Scientific-Atlanta headend; Scientific-Atlanta amplifiers; Comm/Scope cable; Oak set top converters; Scientific-Atlanta satellite antenna; Scientific-Atlanta satellite receivers.
Miles of plant: 209.5 (coaxial).
Manager: Larry Bryant. Chief technician: Dave Cope.
Ownership: AT&T Broadband & Internet Services (MSO). Purchased from Tele-Communications Inc., March 9, 1999.

FLOYDADA—TCA Cable TV, 119 E. Kentucky, Floydada, TX 79235. Phone: 806-983-2911. Web site: http://www.tca-cable.com. County: Floyd. ICA: TX0237.
TV Market Ranking: Outside TV Markets. Franchise award date: N.A. Franchise expiration date: N.A. Began: January 1, 1979.
Channel capacity: 25. Channels available but not in use: N.A.
Basic Service
Subscribers: 1,220.
Programming (received off-air): KAMC (A), KCBD-TV (N), KLBK-TV (C), KTXT-TV (P) Lubbock.
Programming (via satellite): WGN-TV (W) Chicago; Cartoon Network; Fox Family Channel; TBS Superstation; The Inspirational Network.
Fee: $35.00 installation; $10.00 monthly.
Pay Service 1
Pay Units: N.A.
Programming (via satellite): Showtime.
Fee: $35.00 installation; $9.95 monthly.
Equipment: Scientific-Atlanta headend; Prodelin & Scientific-Atlanta satellite antenna; Microdyne satellite receivers.
Miles of plant: 21.0 (coaxial). Homes passed: 1,840.
Manager: Pete Strom.
City fee: 2%-3% of gross.
Ownership: TCA Cable TV Inc. (MSO); AT&T Broadband & Internet Services (MSO). See Cable System Ownership.

FOLLETT—Classic Cable, Box 429, 605 N.W. 3rd St., Plainville, KS 67663-0429. Phones: 785-434-7620; 800-999-8876. Fax: 785-434-2614. County: Lipscomb. ICA: TX0610.
TV Market Ranking: Outside TV Markets. Franchise award date: January 1, 1981. Franchise expiration date: N.A. Began: April 1, 1982.
Channel capacity: 36 (2-way capable). Channels available but not in use: N.A.
Basic Service
Subscribers: 121.
Programming (received off-air): KAMR-TV (N), KCIT (F,U), KFDA-TV (C), KVII-TV (A) Amarillo; KWET (P) Cheyenne.
Programming (via satellite): WGN-TV (W) Chicago; CNN; Discovery Channel; Disney Channel; ESPN; Fox Family Channel; Fox Sports Net Southwest; History Channel; Learning Channel; Nashville Network; Nick at Nite's TV Land; Sci-Fi Channel; TBS Superstation; The Weather Channel; Trinity Bcstg. Network; Turner Network TV; USA Network.
Fee: $35.00 installation; $27.95 monthly.
Pay Service 1
Pay Units: 15.
Programming (via satellite): HBO.
Fee: $10.95 monthly.
Pay Service 2
Pay Units: 7.
Programming (via satellite): Showtime.
Fee: $9.95 monthly.
Miles of plant: 7.0 (coaxial). Homes passed: 235.
Manager: Bill Flowers. Chief technician: Rick Rattan. Marketing director: Jennifer Hauschild.
Ownership: Classic Cable (MSO).

FORSAN—Torrence Cablevision, Box 1167, Ridgeland, MS 39158. Phones: 601-981-6900; 800-977-8849. County: Howard. ICA: TX0695.
TV Market Ranking: Below 100. Franchise award date: N.A. Franchise expiration date: N.A. Began: N.A.
Channel capacity: 36. Channels available but not in use: 19.
Basic Service
Subscribers: 54.
Programming (received off-air): KWAB-TV (N) Big Spring; KMID (A), KOCV-TV (P), KOSA-TV (C), KPEJ (F) Odessa-Midland.
Programming (via satellite): WGN-TV (W) Chicago; A & E; American Movie Classics; CNN; Country Music TV; Discovery Channel; ESPN; Fox Family Channel; GalaVision; Nashville Network; Showtime; TBS Superstation; Turner Network TV; USA Network.
Fee: $28.00 monthly.
Miles of plant: 3.2 (coaxial). Homes passed: 82.
Ownership: Torrence Cable Inc. (MSO).

FORT DAVIS—Fort Davis TV Cable, Box 1377, Alpine, TX 79831. Phone: 915-837-2300. Fax: 915-837-5423. E-mail: mtnzone@overland.net. County: Jeff Davis. ICA: TX0531.
TV Market Ranking: Outside TV Markets. Franchise award date: September 10, 1965. Franchise expiration date: N.A. Began: December 1, 1965.
Channel capacity: 36 (not 2-way capable). Channels available but not in use: N.A.
Basic Service
Subscribers: 290.
Programming (received off-air): KMID (A), KOSA-TV (C), KWES-TV (N) Odessa-Midland; allband FM.
Programming (via satellite): WGN-TV (W) Chicago; KMGH-TV (A), KRMA-TV (P) Denver; A & E; CNN; Country Music TV; Discovery Channel; ESPN; Fox Family Channel; FoxNet; GalaVision; Home Shopping Network; Learning Channel; Nashville Network; Nickelodeon; TBS Superstation; The Weather Channel; Trinity Bcstg. Network; Turner Classic Movies; Turner Network TV; Univision.
Fee: $35.00 installation; $26.57 monthly; $35.00 additional installation.
Pay Service 1
Pay Units: 65.
Programming (via satellite): HBO.
Fee: $10.00 installation; $7.00 monthly.
Pay Service 2
Pay Units: 32.
Programming (via satellite): Showtime.
Fee: $10.00 installation; $7.00 monthly.
Equipment: Blonder-Tongue & Scientific-Atlanta headend; C-COR, Jerrold & Scientific-Atlanta amplifiers; Comm/Scope cable; RCA set top converters.
Miles of plant: 19.0 (coaxial); None (fiber optic). Homes passed: 375. Total homes in franchised area: 400.
Manager: Steve Neu. Office manager: Lawrence Neu.
City fee: None.
Ownership: Mountain Zone TV Systems (MSO).

FORT HOOD—Time Warner Cable, Box 7852, Waco, TX 76714. Phone: 254-532-5341. Fax: 254-399-2025. County: Bell. ICA: TX0757.
TV Market Ranking: Below 100. Franchise award date: December 1, 1980. Franchise expiration date: N.A. Began: December 31, 1980.
Channel capacity: 36 (not 2-way capable). Channels available but not in use: None.
Basic Service
Subscribers: 7,682; Commercial subscribers: 11.
Programming (received off-air): KVUE-TV (A), KXAN-TV (N) Austin; KNCT (P) Belton; KCEN-TV (N), KWTX-TV (C), KXXV (A) Waco-Temple.
Programming (via satellite): WGN-TV (W) Chicago; C-SPAN; Fox Sports Net Southwest; TBS Superstation.
Current originations: Government access; automated emergency alert.
Fee: $39.95 installation; $14.95 monthly.
Expanded Basic Service
Subscribers: 7,510.
Programming (via satellite): American Movie Classics; BET; CNN; Comedy Central; Discovery Channel; ESPN; Fox Family Channel; Headline News; Lifetime; MTV; Nashville Network; Nickelodeon; TV Guide Channel; The Weather Channel; USA Network; Univision; VH1.
Fee: $39.95 installation; $5.50 monthly.
Pay Service 1
Pay Units: 1,400.
Programming (via satellite): Cinemax.
Fee: $9.75 monthly.
Pay Service 2
Pay Units: 763.
Programming (via satellite): Disney Channel.
Fee: $7.95 monthly.
Pay Service 3
Pay Units: 71.
Programming (via satellite): DMX.
Fee: $12.95 monthly.
Pay Service 4
Pay Units: 3,369.

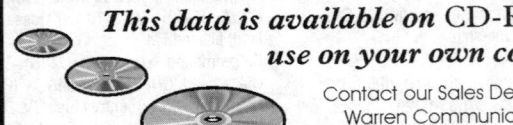

Programming (via satellite): HBO.
Fee: $9.75 monthly.

Pay Service 5
Pay Units: 705.
Programming (via satellite): The Movie Channel.
Fee: $9.75 monthly.

Pay Service 6
Pay Units: 1,340.
Programming (via satellite): Showtime.
Fee: $9.75 monthly.

Pay-Per-View
Addressable homes: 7,682.

Local advertising: Yes. Available in satellite distributed programming. Local sales manager: B. Kilpatrick. Regional interconnect: Cabletime.
Program Guide: Cabletime.
Equipment: Scientific-Atlanta headend; Texscan amplifiers; Comm/Scope cable; Amiga character generator; Scientific-Atlanta addressable set top converters; Scientific-Atlanta satellite receivers.
Miles of plant: 91.0 (coaxial). Homes passed: 12,389.
Manager: Mike Fanning. Chief technician: Billy Johnson.
City fee: 5% of gross.
Ownership: Time Warner Cable (MSO); Advance/Newhouse Partnership (MSO). Purchased from Charter Communications Inc.

FORT WORTH—Charter Communications Inc., 4800 Bluemound Rd., Fort Worth, TX 76106. Phone: 817-509-6272. Counties: Denton, Johnson & Tarrant. Also serves Benbrook, Blue Mound, Burleson, Crowley, Edgecliff Village, Everman, Forest Hill, Haltom City, Hurst, Keller, Kennedale, Lake Worth, North Richland Hills, Richland Hills, Saginaw, Southlake, Watauga, Westover Hills, White Settlement. ICA: TX0008.
TV Market Ranking: 12. Franchise award date: March 1, 1980. Franchise expiration date: March 1, 2006. Began: January 1, 1982.
Channel capacity: 61 (2-way capable; operating 2-way). Channels available but not in use: 5.

Basic Service
Subscribers: 100,428; Commercial subscribers: 200.
Programming (received off-air): KDAF (W), KDFI-TV (I), KDFW (F), KDTX-TV (T), KFWD (O), KTVT (C), KTXA (U), KXAS-TV (N), KXTX-TV (I), WFAA-TV (A) Dallas-Fort Worth; KDTN (P) Denton; KUVN (S) Garland; KHSX-TV (H) Irving.
Programming (via satellite): WGN-TV (W) Chicago; TBS Superstation.
Current originations: Automated time-weather; public access; educational access; government access; religious access; leased access; automated emergency alert.
Fee: $30.00 installation; $3.95 monthly; $15.00 additional installation.
Commercial fee: $29.95 monthly.

Expanded Basic Service
Subscribers: N.A.
Programming (via satellite): A & E; American Movie Classics; CNBC; CNN; Discovery Channel; ESPN; Goodlife TV Network; Headline News; Lifetime; MTV; Nashville Network; Nickelodeon; The Weather Channel; Turner Network TV; USA Network; Univision; VH1.
Fee: $25.00 installation; $13.72 monthly.

Pay Service 1
Pay Units: N.A.
Programming (via satellite): Bravo; Cinemax; Disney Channel; Fox Sports Net Southwest; HBO; Playboy TV; Showtime; The Movie Channel.
Fee: $7.95 monthly (Cinemax or Disney), $8.95 monthly (Bravo or Playboy), $9.95 monthly (Fox Sports, HBO, Showtime or TMC).

Local advertising: Yes (locally produced). Available in satellite distributed & locally originated programming. Rates: $25.00/30 Seconds. Local sales manager: Wes Hart.
Program Guide: The Cable Connection.
Equipment: Scientific-Atlanta headend; Magnavox amplifiers; Comm/Scope & General cable; Ikegami cameras; Panasonic & Sony VTRs; Quanta, 3M & Video Data Systems character generator; Tocom addressable set top converters; Scientific-Atlanta satellite antenna; Scientific-Atlanta satellite receivers; ChannelMatic commercial insert.
Miles of plant: 3156.0 (coaxial). Homes passed: 220,756.
Manager: Alan Collins. Chief technician: Farrell Moseley. Program director: Cathy Sikes. Marketing director: Bob Crowell.
City fee: 5% of gross.
Ownership: Charter Communications Inc. (MSO). Purchased from Marcus Cable, April 1, 1999.

FRANKLIN—Galaxy Cablevision, 307 N. 5th St., Leesville, LA 71496. Phone: 318-238-1361. County: Robertson. ICA: TX0758.
TV Market Ranking: Below 100. Franchise award date: N.A. Franchise expiration date: September 17, 2000. Began: N.A.
Channel capacity: 28. Channels available but not in use: None.

Basic Service
Subscribers: 443.
Programming (received off-air): KTBC (F), KVUE-TV (A) Austin; KNCT (P) Belton; KBTX-TV (C) Bryan; KAMU-TV (P) College Station; KTVT (C) Dallas-Fort Worth; KCEN-TV (N), KWTX-TV (C) Waco-Temple.
Programming (via satellite): Turner Network TV.
Fee: $23.00 monthly.

Homes passed: 795.
Manager: Eulin Guidry. Technical manager: Randy Berry.
Ownership: Galaxy Cablevision (MSO).

FREDERICKSBURG—Time Warner Communications, 711 N. Llano, Fredericksburg, TX 78624. Phone: 830-997-4646. Fax: 830-997-6996. County: Gillespie. Also serves Gillespie County. ICA: TX0149.
TV Market Ranking: Below 100. Franchise award date: N.A. Franchise expiration date: N.A. Began: January 1, 1968.
Channel capacity: 39. Channels available but not in use: N.A.

Basic Service
Subscribers: 3,720.
Programming (received off-air): KEYE-TV (C), KLRU (P), KTBC (F), KVUE-TV (A), KXAN-TV (N) Austin; KENS-TV (C), KMOL-TV (N), KSAT-TV (A) San Antonio; 1 FM.
Programming (via satellite): A & E; C-SPAN; Country Music TV; DMX; Discovery Channel; FX; TBS Superstation; The Weather Channel; Trinity Bcstg. Network; Univision.
Current originations: Automated time-weather; local news.
Fee: $24.95 installation; $14.47 monthly; $3.50 converter; $10.00 additional installation.

Digital Basic Service
Subscribers: N.A.
Programming (via satellite): BBC America; Bravo; Discovery Home & Leisure Channel; Discovery Kids Channel; Discovery People; Discovery Science Channel; ESPN Classic Sports; ESPNews; Fox Sports World; Game Show Network; History Channel; Home & Garden Television; Independent Film Channel; MuchMusic Network; Outdoor Life Network; Romance Classics; Sci-Fi Channel; The Barker; Turner Classic Movies.
Fee: $10.00 monthly.

Expanded Basic Service
Subscribers: 3,266.
Programming (via satellite): CNBC; CNN; Cartoon Network; Disney Channel; ESPN; Fox Family Channel; Fox News Channel; Fox Sports Net Southwest; Headline News; Lifetime; MTV; Nashville Network; Nickelodeon; Turner Network TV; USA Network; VH1.
Fee: $24.95 installation; $12.37 monthly.

Pay Service 1
Pay Units: N.A.
Programming (via satellite): Starz!; The New Encore.
Fee: $3.98 monthly (each).

Pay Service 2
Pay Units: 273.
Programming (via satellite): HBO.
Fee: $13.00 monthly.

Pay Service 3
Pay Units: 232.
Programming (via satellite): Showtime.
Fee: $13.00 monthly.

Digital Pay Service 1
Pay Units: N.A.
Programming (via satellite): DMX; Encore Love Stories; Encore Mystery; Encore Westerns; HBO Plus; HBO Signature; Showtime (multiplexed); Starz! (multiplexed); The Movie Channel.
Fee: $10.00 monthly (TMC), $39.99 monthly (Encore Love Stories, Mystery & Westerns, HBO, Showtime & Starz).

Pay-Per-View
Spice delivered digitally; movies delivered digitally.
Fee: $2.99.

Local advertising: Yes.
Equipment: Tocom headend; CAS & Tocom amplifiers; U.S. Tower satellite antenna.
Miles of plant: 127.0 (coaxial). Homes passed: 3,900. Total homes in franchised area: 4,100.
Manager: John Kyle. Office manager: Wanda Riley. Chief technician: Rick Brodrick.
City fee: 2% of gross.
Ownership: Time Warner Cable (MSO). Purchased from AT&T Broadband & Internet Services, June 1, 1999.

FREER—TCI Cablevision of Texas Inc., 208 W. Viggie St., Hebbronville, TX 78361-3048. Phone: 512-527-3267. County: Duval. Also serves Duval County (northern portion). ICA: TX0225.
TV Market Ranking: Outside TV Markets. Franchise award date: N.A. Franchise expiration date: N.A. Began: January 1, 1968.
Channel capacity: 35. Channels available but not in use: 2.

Basic Service
Subscribers: 999.
Programming (received off-air): KEDT (P), KIII (A), KRIS-TV (N), KZTV (C) Corpus Christi; KGNS-TV (N,A), KLDO-TV (O) Laredo; KENS-TV (C), KSAT-TV (A) San Antonio.
Programming (via satellite): C-SPAN; CNN; Country Music TV; Discovery Channel; ESPN; GalaVision; Headline News; Home Shopping Network; Lifetime; MTV; Nashville Network; Nickelodeon; Odyssey; TBS Superstation; The Weather Channel; Trinity Bcstg. Network; Turner Network TV; USA Network; Univision; VH1.
Current originations: Automated time-weather.
Fee: $60.00 installation; $19.71 monthly.

Pay Service 1
Pay Units: 79.
Programming (via satellite): Disney Channel.
Fee: $7.00 monthly.

Pay Service 2
Pay Units: 343.
Programming (via satellite): HBO.
Fee: $11.00 monthly.

Pay Service 3
Pay Units: 39.
Programming (via satellite): The Movie Channel.
Fee: $9.00 monthly.

Pay Service 4
Pay Units: 128.
Programming (via satellite): Showtime.
Fee: $6.00 monthly.

Equipment: AFC satellite antenna.
Miles of plant: 18.1 (coaxial). Homes passed: 1,980.
Manager: Juve Morante.
City fee: 2% of gross.
Ownership: AT&T Broadband & Internet Services (MSO). Purchased from Tele-Communications Inc., March 9, 1999.

FRIONA—Classic Cable, Box 429, 605 N. W. 3rd St., Plainville, KS 67663-0429. Phones: 785-434-7620; 800-999-8876. Fax: 785-434-2614. County: Parmer. Also serves Bovina. ICA: TX0277.
TV Market Ranking: Below 100. Franchise award date: July 11, 1983. Franchise expiration date: July 11, 1998. Began: January 1, 1959.
Channel capacity: 41 (2-way capable). Channels available but not in use: N.A.

Basic Service
Subscribers: 950; Commercial subscribers: 95.
Programming (received off-air): KACV-TV (P), KAMR-TV (N), KCIT (F,U), KFDA-TV (C), KVII-TV (A) Amarillo; KPTB (I) Lubbock; allband FM.
Programming (via translator): KVDA (O) San Antonio.
Programming (via satellite): WGN-TV (W) Chicago; A & E; American Movie Classics; Animal Planet; C-SPAN; CNN; Cartoon Network; Comedy Central; Country Music TV; Discovery Channel; Disney Channel; E! Entertainment TV; ESPN; ESPN 2; Fox Family Channel; Fox News Channel; Fox Sports Net Southwest; GalaVision; Goodlife TV Network; Headline News; History Channel; Home & Garden Television; Home Shopping Network; Learning Channel; Lifetime; Nashville Network; Nick at Nite's TV Land;

Nickelodeon; QVC; Sci-Fi Channel; TBS Superstation; The Weather Channel; Travel Channel; Turner Network TV; USA Network; Univision; VH1.
Current originations: Automated time-weather; local sports.
Fee: $35.00 installation; $25.95 monthly; $1.50 converter.
Pay Service 1
Pay Units: 143.
Programming (via satellite): HBO.
Fee: $25.00 installation; $9.95 monthly.
Pay Service 2
Pay Units: 87.
Programming (via satellite): Showtime.
Fee: $9.95 monthly.
Pay Service 3
Pay Units: 82.
Programming (via satellite): The Movie Channel.
Fee: $9.95 monthly.
Local advertising: Yes. Available in locally originated programming. Rates: $15.00/Month.
Equipment: Jerrold headend; Jerrold amplifiers; Vikoa & Times Fiber cable; Texscan character generator; Jerrold set top converters; AFC satellite antenna; Hughes & Comtech satellite receivers.
Miles of plant: 30.2 (coaxial). Homes passed: 1,933.
Manager: Bill Flowers. Chief technician: Chris Christenson. Marketing director: Jennifer Hauschild.
City fee: 3% of gross.
Ownership: Classic Cable (MSO).

FROST—Charter Communications Inc., 5227 FM 813, Waxahachie, TX 75165. Phones: 972-938-9288; 800-477-0887. Fax: 972-923-0039. County: Navarro. Also serves Blooming Grove. ICA: TX0424.
TV Market Ranking: Outside TV Markets. Franchise award date: N.A. Franchise expiration date: N.A. Began: November 1, 1983.
Channel capacity: 52. Channels available but not in use: N.A.
Basic Service
Subscribers: 236.
Programming (received off-air): KDAF (W), KDFI-TV (I), KDFW (F), KDTX-TV (T), KERA-TV (P), KTVT (C), KTXA (U), KXAS-TV (N), KXTX-TV (I), WFAA-TV (A) Dallas-Fort Worth; KDTN (P) Denton; KHSX-TV (H) Irving; KWTX-TV (C) Waco-Temple.
Programming (via satellite): WGN-TV (W) Chicago; TBS Superstation.
Fee: $26.00 installation; $8.45 monthly.
Expanded Basic Service
Subscribers: N.A.
Programming (via satellite): CNN; Country Music TV; Discovery Channel; ESPN; Fox Family Channel; Headline News; Home Shopping Network; Lifetime; MTV; Nashville Network; Nickelodeon; The Weather Channel; Turner Network TV; USA Network.
Fee: $11.11 monthly.
Pay Service 1
Pay Units: N.A.
Programming (via satellite): Cinemax; HBO; Showtime.
Fee: $7.00 monthly (Showtime), $9.00 monthly (Cinemax), $11.00 monthly (HBO).
Miles of plant: 19.8 (coaxial). Homes passed: 719.
Manager: Mary Scearce. Chief technician: Ken Stevens.
Ownership: Charter Communications Inc. (MSO). Purchased from Marcus Cable, April 1, 1999.

FRUITVALE—Friendship Cable of Texas Inc., Box 9090, Tyler, TX 75711-9090. Phone: 903-581-2121. Fax: 903-581-2185. County: Van Zandt. ICA: TX0580.
TV Market Ranking: Below 100. Franchise award date: December 11, 1988. Franchise expiration date: December 11, 2008. Began: March 1, 1990.
Channel capacity: 36. Channels available but not in use: 7.
Basic Service
Subscribers: 103.
Programming (received off-air): KPXD (X) Arlington; KDFW (F), KERA-TV (P), KXAS-TV (N) Dallas-Fort Worth; KLTV (A) Tyler-Longview.
Programming (via satellite): WGN-TV (W) Chicago; A & E; CNN; Country Music TV; Discovery Channel; ESPN; Fox Family Channel; Nashville Network; TBS Superstation; USA Network.
Fee: $30.00 installation; $33.35 monthly.
Pay Service 1
Pay Units: 26.
Programming (via satellite): Cinemax.
Fee: $10.95 monthly.
Pay Service 2
Pay Units: 28.
Programming (via satellite): HBO.
Fee: $10.95 monthly.
Local advertising: Yes.
Miles of plant: 14.2 (coaxial). Homes passed: 279.
Manager: Marianne Bogy. Chief technician: Sonny Myers.
Ownership: Buford Television Inc. (MSO). See Cable System Ownership.

GAINESVILLE—TCA Cable TV, 104 N. Morris, Gainesville, TX 76240. Phone: 940-665-3241. Web site: http://www.tca-cable.com. County: Cooke. Also serves Cooke County, Oak Ridge. ICA: TX0117.
TV Market Ranking: Below 100 (portions of Cooke County, Gainesville); Outside TV Markets (portions of Cooke County, Oak Ridge). Franchise award date: N.A. Franchise expiration date: N.A. Began: March 2, 1967.
Channel capacity: 41. Channels available but not in use: N.A.
Basic Service
Subscribers: 5,014.
Programming (received off-air): KTEN (A,N,F) Ada; KDFW (F), KERA-TV (P), KTVT (C), KTXA (U), KXAS-TV (N), KXTX-TV (I), WFAA-TV (A) Dallas-Fort Worth; KXII (C) Sherman; KAUZ-TV (C) Wichita Falls-Lawton.
Programming (via satellite): A & E; BET; C-SPAN; CNBC; CNN; Discovery Channel; Fox Family Channel; FoxNet; Headline News; Lifetime; MTV; Nashville Network; Nickelodeon; QVC; TBS Superstation; The Weather Channel.
Current originations: Automated time-weather; public access; leased access; automated emergency alert.
Fee: $38.97 installation; $9.40 monthly; $2.00 converter; $19.49 additional installation.
Expanded Basic Service
Subscribers: 4,608.
Programming (via satellite): American Movie Classics; Country Music TV; ESPN; Fox Sports Net Southwest; Turner Network TV; USA Network.
Fee: $11.68 monthly.
Pay Service 1
Pay Units: 139.
Programming (via satellite): Cinemax.
Fee: N.A.
Pay Service 2
Pay Units: 341.
Programming (via satellite): Disney Channel.
Fee: N.A.
Pay Service 3
Pay Units: 2,067.
Programming (via satellite): The New Encore.
Fee: N.A.
Pay Service 4
Pay Units: 1,343.
Programming (via satellite): HBO.
Fee: N.A.
Pay Service 5
Pay Units: 379.
Programming (via satellite): Showtime.
Fee: N.A.
Local advertising: Yes. Available in satellite distributed programming. Regional interconnect: Cabletime.
Program Guide: The Cable Guide.
Equipment: Scientific-Atlanta headend; Jerrold amplifiers; Comm/Scope & Times Fiber cable; MSI & Video Data Systems character generator; Jerrold set top converters; Eagle traps; Andrew satellite antenna; Scientific-Atlanta satellite receivers.
Miles of plant: 121.1 (coaxial). Homes passed: 5,905. Total homes in franchised area: 6,071.
Manager: Ricky Allen. Chief technician: Gary Hinkle.
City fee: 3% of gross.
Ownership: TCA Cable TV Inc. (MSO); AT&T Broadband & Internet Services (MSO). See Cable System Ownership.

GANADO—Cablevision Ltd., Box 977, 813 Vanderbilt Rd., Edna, TX 77957. Phone: 512-782-2993. Fax: 512-782-0572. County: Jackson. ICA: TX0428.
TV Market Ranking: Below 100. Franchise award date: N.A. Franchise expiration date: N.A. Began: January 1, 1961.
Channel capacity: N.A. Channels available but not in use: N.A.
Basic Service
Subscribers: N.A.
Programming (received off-air): KHOU-TV (C), KHTV (W), KPRC-TV (N), KRIV (F), KTRK-TV (A), KTXH (U), KUHT (P) Houston; KAVU-TV (A), KVCT (F) Victoria; allband FM.
Programming (via satellite): WGN-TV (W) Chicago; A & E; American Movie Classics; CNN; Discovery Channel; ESPN; ESPN 2; Fox Family Channel; Fox Sports Net Southwest; Lifetime; Nashville Network; Nickelodeon; QVC; TBS Superstation; Turner Network TV; Univision.
Fee: $10.00 installation; $8.25 monthly.
Pay Service 1
Pay Units: N.A.
Programming (via satellite): Disney Channel; Showtime.
Fee: N.A.
Equipment: Tocom & Scientific-Atlanta headend; Jerrold amplifiers; Comm/Scope cable; Tocom set top converters; Prodelin satellite antenna; Microdyne satellite receivers.
Miles of plant: 15.0 (coaxial). Homes passed: 700. Total homes in franchised area: 700.
Manager: Jake Landrum. Chief technician: Ken Zeber.
City fee: 2% of gross.
Ownership: Cable-Vision Ltd. (MSO).

GARDEN CITY—Torrence Cablevision, Box 1167, Ridgeland, MS 39158. Phones: 601-981-6900; 800-977-8849. County: Glasscock. ICA: TX0760.
TV Market Ranking: Below 100. Franchise award date: N.A. Franchise expiration date: N.A. Began: April 6, 1990.
Channel capacity: 36 (not 2-way capable). Channels available but not in use: 19.
Basic Service
Subscribers: 64.
Programming (received off-air): KWAB-TV (N) Big Spring; KMID (A), KOSA-TV (C), KPEJ (F) Odessa-Midland.
Programming (via satellite): WGN-TV (W) Chicago; KRMA-TV (P) Denver; A & E; American Movie Classics; CNN; Country Music TV; Discovery Channel; ESPN; Fox Family Channel; GalaVision; Nashville Network; Showtime; TBS Superstation; Turner Network TV; USA Network.
Current originations: Automated time-weather; automated emergency alert.
Fee: $30.00 installation; $28.00 monthly; $3.00 converter.
Equipment: Nexus headend; Magnavox amplifiers; Times Fiber cable; Oak set top converters; Nexus satellite receivers.
Miles of plant: 4.3 (coaxial). Additional miles planned: 4.3 (coaxial). Homes passed: 107. Total homes in franchised area: 115.
Ownership: Torrence Cable Inc. (MSO).

GARDEN RIDGE—Time Warner Cable, Box 1008, San Marcos, TX 78666-1008. Phones: 512-353-3456; 800-881-9190. Fax: 512-396-4664. County: Comal. Also serves Comal County, Northcliffe. ICA: TX0263.
TV Market Ranking: 45 (portions of Comal County, Garden Ridge, Northcliffe); Outside TV Markets (portions of Comal County). Franchise award date: N.A. Franchise expiration date: N.A. Began: June 1, 1984.
Channel capacity: 62 (not 2-way capable). Channels available but not in use: 20.
Basic Service
Subscribers: 1,345.
Programming (received off-air): KEYE-TV (C) Austin; KRRT (W) Kerrville-San Antonio; KABB (F), KENS-TV (C), KLRN (P), KMOL-TV (N), KSAT-TV (A), KVDA (O), KWEX-TV (S) San Antonio.
Programming (via satellite): C-SPAN; C-SPAN 2; Country Music TV; Discovery Channel; Fox News Channel; Learning Channel; MTV; QVC; TBS Superstation; The Weather Channel; Trinity Bcstg. Network.
Fee: $18.75 installation; $11.47 monthly.
Expanded Basic Service
Subscribers: 1,062.
Programming (via satellite): A & E; American Movie Classics; Animal Planet; CNBC; CNN; Cartoon Network; ESPN; Encore Movie Networks; FX; Fox Family Channel; Fox Sports Net Southwest; Headline News; Home & Garden Television; Lifetime; MTV; Nashville Network; Nickelodeon; Turner Network TV; USA Network; VH1.
Fee: $11.02 monthly.
Pay Service 1
Pay Units: 103.
Programming (via satellite): Disney Channel.
Fee: $13.00 monthly.
Pay Service 2
Pay Units: N.A.
Programming (via satellite): Starz!; The New Encore.
Fee: $1.75 monthly (Encore), $6.75 monthly (Starz).
Pay Service 3
Pay Units: 488.
Programming (via satellite): HBO.
Fee: $13.00 monthly.
Pay Service 4
Pay Units: 391.
Programming (via satellite): The Movie Channel.
Fee: $13.00 monthly.
Pay Service 5
Pay Units: 117.

Programming (via satellite): Showtime.
Fee: $13.00 monthly.
Pay-Per-View
Addressable homes: 116.
Viewer's Choice.
Miles of plant: 52.2 (coaxial). Homes passed: 858. Total homes in franchised area: 1,940.
Manager: Dennis Moore. Office manager: Wanda Riley. Technical supervisor: Bruce Buchanan. Chief technician: Greg Krueger.
Ownership: Time Warner Cable (MSO). Purchased from AT&T Broadband & Internet Services, June 1, 1999.

GARDENDALE—Classic Cable, Box 429, 605 N.W. 3rd St., Plainville, KS 67663-0429. Phones: 785-434-7620; 800-999-8876. Fax: 785-434-2614. County: Ector. ICA: TX0575.
TV Market Ranking: Below 100. Franchise award date: N.A. Franchise expiration date: N.A. Began: N.A.
Channel capacity: 36 (2-way capable). Channels available but not in use: N.A.
Basic Service
Subscribers: 23.
Programming (received off-air): KMID (A), KMLM (I), KOCV-TV (P), KOSA-TV (C), KPEJ (F), KWES-TV (N) Odessa-Midland.
Programming (via satellite): WGN-TV (W) Chicago; CNN; Discovery Channel; Disney Channel; ESPN; Fox Family Channel; Home Shopping Network; Nashville Network; Nick at Nite's TV Land; Nickelodeon; TBS Superstation; The Weather Channel; Turner Classic Movies; Turner Network TV; USA Network.
Fee: $35.00 installation; $27.95 monthly.
Pay Service 1
Pay Units: N.A.
Programming (via satellite): HBO; Showtime.
Fee: $9.95 monthly (each).
Miles of plant: 15.2 (coaxial). Homes passed: 285.
Manager: Bill Flowers. Chief technician: Ben Hernandez. Marketing director: Jennifer Hauschild.
Ownership: Classic Cable (MSO).

GARFIELD—Mission Cable, 920 Whitmore Dr., Rockwall, TX 75087. Phone: 800-783-5708. Fax: 214-722-6218. Counties: Bastrop & Travis. Also serves Meadow Lake Heights, Stony Point, Swiss Alpine Village. ICA: TX0303.
TV Market Ranking: Below 100. Franchise award date: July 3, 1986. Franchise expiration date: July 3, 2006. Began: May 1, 1988.
Channel capacity: 36. Channels available but not in use: N.A.
Basic Service
Subscribers: 418.
Programming (received off-air): KEYE-TV (C), KLRU (P), KTBC (F), KVUE-TV (A), KXAN-TV (N) Austin.
Programming (via satellite): WGN-TV (W) Chicago; A & E; BET; C-SPAN; CNN; Discovery Channel; ESPN; Fox Family Channel; GalaVision; MTV; Nashville Network; Nickelodeon; TBS Superstation; The Weather Channel; USA Network; Univision.
Fee: $30.00 installation; $16.95 monthly.
Pay Service 1
Pay Units: 92.
Programming (via satellite): Cinemax.
Fee: $9.00 monthly.
Pay Service 2
Pay Units: 22.
Programming (via satellite): Disney Channel.
Fee: $9.00 monthly.
Pay Service 3
Pay Units: 135.
Programming (via satellite): HBO.
Fee: $9.00 monthly.
Program Guide: TV Host.
Miles of plant: 32.0 (coaxial). Homes passed: 914.
Manager: Jim Stafford. Chief technician: Jacky Oliver. Marketing & program director: Bruce Berkinshaw.
Ownership: Fanch Communications Inc. (MSO); Time Warner Cable (MSO). See Cable System Ownership.

GARLAND—TCI Cablevision of the Metroplex Inc., 934 E. Centerville Rd., Garland, TX 75041. Phone: 214-840-2388. Fax: 214-271-4535. Counties: Dallas & Rockwall. Also serves Dallas County, Rowlett, Sunnyvale. ICA: TX0013.
TV Market Ranking: 12. Franchise award date: N.A. Franchise expiration date: N.A. Began: October 1, 1979.
Channel capacity: 51 (2-way capable; operating 2-way). Channels available but not in use: N.A.
Basic Service
Subscribers: 39,219.
Programming (received off-air): KDAF (W), KDFI-TV (I), KDFW (F), KDTX-TV (T), KERA-TV (P), KTVT (C), KTXA (U), KXAS-TV (N), KXTX-TV (I), WFAA-TV (A) Dallas-Fort Worth; KDTN (P) Denton; KUVN (S) Garland; KHSX-TV (H) Irving; allband FM.
Programming (via satellite): WGN-TV (W) Chicago; A & E; BET; C-SPAN; CNBC; CNN; CNN International; Cartoon Network; Comedy Central; Discovery Channel; Fox Family Channel; Headline News; Home Shopping Network; Lifetime; MTV; Nashville Network; Nickelodeon; TBS Superstation; The Weather Channel; Turner Classic Movies; VH1.
Current originations: Automated time-weather; public access; educational access; government access; automated emergency alert; local news; local sports.
Fee: $60.00 installation; $11.35 monthly; $3.00 converter.
Expanded Basic Service
Subscribers: 37,292.
Programming (via satellite): American Movie Classics; ESPN; Fox Sports Net Southwest; Turner Network TV; USA Network.
Fee: $10.32 monthly.
Pay Service 1
Pay Units: N.A.
Programming (via satellite): Disney Channel; HBO; Showtime; The Movie Channel.
Fee: $25.00 installation; $10.25 monthly (Disney), $11.25 monthly (Showtime or TMC), $12.20 monthly (HBO).
Local advertising: Yes. Available in locally originated, character-generated, taped & automated programming. Local sales manager: Debra Friday.
Program Guide: The Cable Guide.
Equipment: Phasecom & Scientific-Atlanta headend; GTE Sylvania amplifiers; Comm/Scope & Times Fiber cable; Hitachi cameras; Panasonic VTRs; GTE Sylvania set top converters; Scientific-Atlanta satellite antenna.
Miles of plant: 1552.6 (coaxial). Homes passed: 73,631. Total homes in franchised area: 144,132.
Manager: Theresa Kirk-Fowler.
City fee: 3% of gross.
Ownership: AT&T Broadband & Internet Services (MSO). Purchased from Tele-Communications Inc., March 9, 1999.

GARRISON—Friendship Cable of Texas Inc., Box 9090, Tyler, TX 75711-9090. Phone: 903-581-2121. Fax: 903-581-2185. County: Nacogdoches. ICA: TX0528.
TV Market Ranking: Below 100. Franchise award date: N.A. Franchise expiration date: September 1, 1997. Began: October 1, 1983.
Channel capacity: 54. Channels available but not in use: N.A.
Basic Service
Subscribers: 303.
Programming (received off-air): KTRE (A) Lufkin; KLTS-TV (P), KSLA-TV (C), KTAL-TV (N), KTBS-TV (A) Shreveport-Texarkana.
Programming (via satellite): WGN-TV (W) Chicago; TBS Superstation.
Fee: $30.00 installation; $31.50 monthly.
Pay Service 1
Pay Units: 25.
Programming (via satellite): Cinemax.
Fee: $7.00 monthly.
Pay Service 2
Pay Units: 10.
Programming (via satellite): HBO.
Fee: $12.00 monthly.
Pay Service 3
Pay Units: 40.
Programming (via satellite): Showtime.
Fee: $7.00 monthly.
Miles of plant: 12.0 (coaxial). Homes passed: 379.
Manager: Marianne Bogy. Chief technician: Henry Harris.
City fee: 3% of gross.
Ownership: Buford Television Inc. (MSO). See Cable System Ownership.

GARWOOD—National Cable Inc., Suite 106-A, 5151 Reed Rd., Columbus, OH 43220. Phones: 614-442-5890; 800-582-0504. Fax: 614-457-2567. County: Colorado. Also serves Nada. ICA: TX0573.
TV Market Ranking: Below 100. Franchise award date: N.A. Franchise expiration date: N.A. Began: N.A.
Channel capacity: 35. Channels available but not in use: 8.
Basic Service
Subscribers: 80.
Programming (received off-air): KHOU-TV (C), KHTV (W), KPRC-TV (N), KRIV (F), KTRK-TV (A), KTXH (U), KUHT (P) Houston.
Programming (via satellite): WGN-TV (W) Chicago; A & E; American Movie Classics; C-SPAN; CNN; Country Music TV; Discovery Channel; ESPN; Fox Family Channel; Fox Sports Net Southwest; Headline News; Lifetime; Nashville Network; Nickelodeon; QVC; Showtime; TBS Superstation; The Inspirational Network; The Weather Channel; Turner Network TV; USA Network.
Fee: $21.00 monthly.
Pay Service 1
Pay Units: 6.
Programming (via satellite): Cinemax.
Fee: $10.95 monthly.
Pay Service 2
Pay Units: 9.
Programming (via satellite): Disney Channel.
Fee: $10.95 monthly.
Local advertising: Yes.
Miles of plant: 12.6 (coaxial). Homes passed: 314.
Manager: Paul Scott. Chief technician: Rob Spiller. Marketing director: Josh Thackery.
Ownership: National Cable (MSO).

GARY—Friendship Cable of Texas Inc., Box 9090, Tyler, TX 75711-9090. Phone: 903-581-2121. Fax: 903-581-2185. County: Panola. Also serves Lake Murvaul. ICA: TX0399.
TV Market Ranking: Below 100. Franchise award date: December 1, 1989. Franchise expiration date: December 1, 2004. Began: February 1, 1990.
Channel capacity: 36. Channels available but not in use: 9.
Basic Service
Subscribers: 257.
Programming (received off-air): KMSS-TV (F), KSLA-TV (C), KTAL-TV (N), KTBS-TV (A) Shreveport-Texarkana.
Programming (via satellite): WGN-TV (W) Chicago; CNN; Country Music TV; Discovery Channel; ESPN; Fox Family Channel; Headline News; Nashville Network; TBS Superstation; Turner Network TV; USA Network.
Fee: $30.00 installation; $33.85 monthly.
Pay Service 1
Pay Units: 11.
Programming (via satellite): Cinemax.
Fee: $10.95 monthly.
Pay Service 2
Pay Units: 11.
Programming (via satellite): HBO.
Fee: $10.95 monthly.
Pay Service 3
Pay Units: 23.
Programming (via satellite): Showtime.
Fee: $5.95 monthly.
Local advertising: Yes.
Miles of plant: 38.7 (coaxial). Homes passed: 801.
Manager: Marianne Bogy. Chief technician: Henry Harris.
Ownership: Buford Television Inc. (MSO). See Cable System Ownership.

GATESVILLE—Gatesville Cable TV, Box 739, 2536 E. Main St., Gatesville, TX 76528. Phone: 817-865-5315. County: Coryell. Also serves Fort Gates. ICA: TX0167.
TV Market Ranking: Below 100. Franchise award date: N.A. Franchise expiration date: N.A. Began: January 1, 1952.
Channel capacity: 12. Channels available but not in use: N.A.
Basic Service
Subscribers: N.A.
Programming (received off-air): KTBC (F) Austin; KNCT (P) Belton; KDFW (F), KERA-TV (P), KTVT (C), KXTX-TV (I), WFAA-TV (A) Dallas-Fort Worth; KCEN-TV (N), KWTX-TV (C) Waco-Temple; 4 FMs.
Programming (via satellite): Fox Family Channel; TBS Superstation.
Current originations: Automated time-weather.
Fee: $10.00 installation; $9.00 monthly.
Pay Service 1
Pay Units: N.A.
Programming (via satellite): Showtime.
Fee: $10.00 monthly.
Local advertising: Yes. Regional interconnect: Cabletime.
Equipment: Jerrold headend; CAS amplifiers; composite cable; Comtech satellite antenna.
Miles of plant: 65.7 (coaxial). Homes passed: 3,380.
Manager: Gail Ussery.
City fee: 2% of gross.
Ownership: TCA Cable TV Inc. (MSO). See Cable System Ownership.

GAUSE—National Cable Inc., Suite 106-A, 5151 Reed Rd., Columbus, OH 43220. Phones: 614-442-5890; 800-582-0504. Fax: 614-457-2567. County: Milam. ICA: TX0660.
TV Market Ranking: Below 100. Franchise award date: N.A. Franchise expiration date: N.A. Began: N.A.
Channel capacity: 36. Channels available but not in use: 21.

Basic Service
Subscribers: 37.
Programming (received off-air): KBTX-TV (C) Bryan; KAMU-TV (P) College Station; KCEN-TV (N), KWKT (F), KXXV (A) Waco-Temple.
Programming (via satellite): WGN-TV (W) Chicago; A & E; American Movie Classics; CNN; Country Music TV; Discovery Channel; ESPN; Fox Family Channel; Nashville Network; Showtime; TBS Superstation; Turner Network TV; USA Network.
Fee: $28.00 monthly.
Miles of plant: 6.2 (coaxial). Homes passed: 162.
Manager: Paul Scott. Chief technician: Rob Spiller. Marketing director: Josh Thackery.
Ownership: National Cable (MSO).

GEORGE WEST—TCI Cablevision of Texas, 4060 S. Padre Island Dr., Corpus Christi, TX 78411-4477. Phone: 512-857-5000. County: Live Oak. ICA: TX0343.
TV Market Ranking: Outside TV Markets. Franchise award date: N.A. Franchise expiration date: N.A. Began: December 1, 1981.
Channel capacity: 30. Channels available but not in use: 9.
Basic Service
Subscribers: 568.
Programming (received off-air): KEDT (P), KRIS-TV (N), KZTV (C) Corpus Christi; KSAT-TV (A) San Antonio.
Programming (via satellite): American Movie Classics; C-SPAN; CNBC; CNN; Cartoon Network; Discovery Channel; ESPN; Fox Family Channel; FoxNet; Headline News; Lifetime; Nashville Network; TBS Superstation; Turner Network TV; USA Network; Univision.
Fee: $37.70 installation; $10.16 monthly; $18.85 additional installation.
Pay Service 1
Pay Units: 243.
Programming (via satellite): The New Encore.
Fee: N.A.
Pay Service 2
Pay Units: 155.
Programming (via satellite): Showtime.
Fee: N.A.
Miles of plant: 21.0 (coaxial). Homes passed: 1,084. Total homes in franchised area: 1,300.
Manager: Dennis Moore. Chief technician: Mando Blancas. Marketing director: Jerri Coppedge.
Ownership: AT&T Broadband & Internet Services (MSO). Purchased from Tele-Communications Inc., March 9, 1999.

GEORGETOWN—Williamson County Cablevision, Box 1999, 111 N. College, Georgetown, TX 78627. Phones: 512-869-1505; 512-930-3085. Fax: 512-869-2962. County: Williamson. ICA: TX0081.
TV Market Ranking: Below 100. Franchise award date: January 1, 1972. Franchise expiration date: February 11, 2003. Began: January 1, 1972.
Channel capacity: 80 (2-way capable; operating 2-way). Channels available but not in use: 2.
Basic Service
Subscribers: 11,000; Commercial subscribers: 1,000.
Programming (received off-air): KEYE-TV (C), KLRU (P), KNVA (W), KTBC (F), KVUE-TV (A), KXAN-TV (N) Austin; K13VC (I) Austin, Cedar Park.
Programming (via satellite): WGN-TV (W) Chicago; C-SPAN.
Current originations: Automated time-weather; public access; educational access.
Fee: $35.00 installation; $5.99 monthly; $1.50 converter; $25.00 additional installation.
Expanded Basic Service
Subscribers: N.A.
Programming (via satellite): Animal Planet; C-SPAN 2; FX; Fox News Channel; Goodlife TV Network; Home & Garden Television; Knowledge TV; MSNBC; Outdoor Life Network; QVC; TV Food Network; The Health Network; The Weather Channel; Toon Disney; Travel Channel.
Fee: $12.49 monthly.
Expanded Basic Service 2
Subscribers: N.A.
Programming (via satellite): A & E; American Movie Classics; BET; CNBC; CNN; Country Music TV; Court TV; Discovery Channel; Disney Channel; E! Entertainment TV; ESPN; ESPN 2; ESPN Classic Sports; ESPNews; Fox Family Channel; Fox Sports Net Southwest; Headline News; Learning Channel; Lifetime; MTV; Nashville Network; Nick at Nite's TV Land; Nickelodeon; Sci-Fi Channel; TBS Superstation; Trinity Bcstg. Network; Turner Network TV; USA Network; Univision; VH1.
Fee: $27.99 monthly.
A la Carte 1
Subscribers: N.A.
Programming (via satellite): Cartoon Network; Comedy Central; Golf Channel; History Channel; MOVIEplex; Speedvision; Sundance Channel; Turner Classic Movies.
Fee: $4.99 monthly (package); $1.25 monthly (each).
Pay Service 1
Pay Units: 566.
Programming (via satellite): Cinemax (multiplexed).
Fee: $20.00 installation; $9.99 monthly.
Pay Service 2
Pay Units: N.A.
Programming (via satellite): Starz!; The New Encore.
Fee: $9.99 monthly (Encore & Starz).
Pay Service 3
Pay Units: 1,122.
Programming (via satellite): HBO (multiplexed).
Fee: $11.49 monthly.
Pay Service 4
Pay Units: 1,173.
Programming (via satellite): Showtime.
Fee: $8.99 monthly.
Pay-Per-View
Addressable homes: 3,000.
Viewer's Choice.
Local advertising: Yes. Available in locally originated & character-generated programming. Regional interconnect: Cabletime.
Equipment: Scientific-Atlanta headend; C-COR amplifiers; Comm/Scope cable; Scientific-Atlanta set top converters; Arcom, Eagle & PPC traps; Scientific-Atlanta & U.S. Tower satellite antenna; Microdyne, Scientific-Atlanta & Standard Communications satellite receivers.
Miles of plant: 227.9 (coaxial); 29.3 (fiber optic). Additional miles planned: 15.0 (coaxial). Homes passed: 13,862.
Manager: Dale Hoffman. Chief technician & marketing director: Wesley Houghteling.
City fee: 5% of basic gross & pay net.
Ownership: M. K. McDaniel (MSO); John Muraglia (MSO); E. D. Hoffman (MSO). Sale pends to TCA Cable TV Inc.

GILMER—Gilmer Cable TV Co., Box 1600, 111 Marshall, Gilmer, TX 75644. Phone: 903-843-5597. Fax: 903-843-2045. County: Upshur. ICA: TX0229.
TV Market Ranking: Below 100. Franchise award date: January 1, 1979. Franchise expiration date: October 27, 2007. Began: March 2, 1981.
Channel capacity: 35. Channels available but not in use: 11.
Basic Service
Subscribers: 1,600.
Programming (received off-air): KETK-TV (N) Jacksonville; KFXK (F) Longview; KLTS-TV (P), KMSS-TV (F), KSLA-TV (C), KTAL-TV (N), KTBS-TV (A) Shreveport-Texarkana; KLTV (A) Tyler-Longview; allband FM.
Programming (via microwave): KDFW (F), KERA-TV (P), KTVT (C), KXAS-TV (N) Dallas-Fort Worth.
Programming (via satellite): CNN.
Current originations: Automated time-weather.
Fee: $29.50 installation; $14.45 monthly; $2.00 converter; $16.85 additional installation.
Expanded Basic Service
Subscribers: N.A.
Programming (via satellite): A & E; ESPN; Fox Family Channel; Fox Sports Net Southwest; MTV; Nickelodeon; USA Network.
Fee: $10.00 installation; $7.50 monthly.
Pay Service 1
Pay Units: N.A.
Programming (via satellite): Disney Channel; HBO; Showtime.
Fee: $20.00 installation; $5.95 monthly (Disney), $6.95 monthly (Showtime), $8.95 monthly (HBO).
Local advertising: Yes. Available in satellite distributed & character-generated programming. Regional interconnect: Cabletime.
Equipment: Scientific-Atlanta headend; C-COR amplifiers; Comm/Scope cable; MSI character generator; Hamlin & Scientific-Atlanta set top converters; Eagle & Intercept traps; Harris satellite antenna; Harris & Scientific-Atlanta satellite receivers.
Miles of plant: 37.2 (coaxial). Additional miles planned: 2.0 (coaxial). Homes passed: 1,906. Total homes in franchised area: 1,961.
Manager: David P. Mooney. Chief technician: Ed Lefevere. Marketing director: Robbie Mooney.
City fee: 4% of gross.
Ownership: David P. Mooney (MSO).

GLADEWATER—TCA Cable TV, 507 N.E. Loop 485, Gladewater, TX 75647. Phones: 903-753-5932; 903-845-4036. Web site: http://www.tca-cable.com. County: Gregg. Also serves Clarksville City, Liberty City, Union Grove, Warren City, White Oak. ICA: TX0558.
TV Market Ranking: Below 100. Franchise award date: N.A. Franchise expiration date: April 22, 2008. Began: March 1, 1974.
Channel capacity: 26. Channels available but not in use: 2.
Basic Service
Subscribers: 4,199.
Programming (received off-air): KSLA-TV (C), KTAL-TV (N), KTBS-TV (A) Shreveport-Texarkana; KLTV (A) Tyler-Longview.
Planned programming (received off-air): KLTS-TV (P) Shreveport-Texarkana.
Programming (via satellite): CNN; Discovery Channel; ESPN; Fox Family Channel; Lifetime; MTV; Nashville Network; Nickelodeon; TBS Superstation; The Weather Channel; USA Network.
Current originations: Automated time-weather.
Fee: $35.00 installation; $8.58 monthly.
Pay Service 1
Pay Units: N.A.
Programming (via satellite): Disney Channel; HBO; Showtime; The Movie Channel.
Fee: $35.00 installation; $9.75 monthly.
Local advertising: Yes. Regional interconnect: Cabletime.
Equipment: Jerrold headend; C-COR amplifiers; Comm/Scope cable; Andrew & Scientific-Atlanta satellite antenna.
Miles of plant: 130.1 (coaxial). Homes passed: 6,600.
Manager: Chris Downing. Chief technician: Tim Moran.
City fee: 2% of gross.
Ownership: TCA Cable TV Inc. (MSO); AT&T Broadband & Internet Services (MSO). See Cable System Ownership.

GLEN ROSE—Glen Rose Cablevision, 4958 N. 35th St., Arlington, VA 22207. County: Somervell. ICA: TX0362.
TV Market Ranking: 12. Franchise award date: September 1, 1981. Franchise expiration date: N.A. Began: N.A.
Channel capacity: 25. Channels available but not in use: 3.
Basic Service
Subscribers: 592.
Programming (received off-air): KDFW (F), KERA-TV (P), KTVT (C), KXAS-TV (N), KXTX-TV (I), WFAA-TV (A) Dallas-Fort Worth; allband FM.
Programming (via satellite): C-SPAN; CNN; ESPN; Fox Family Channel; Nashville Network; TBS Superstation; USA Network.
Fee: $15.00 installation; $10.00 monthly.
Pay Service 1
Pay Units: 259.
Programming (via satellite): Showtime.
Fee: $15.00 installation; $10.95 monthly.
Equipment: Scientific-Atlanta headend; GTE Sylvania amplifiers; Times Fiber cable; MSI character generator; Oak set top converters; Eagle traps; Scientific-Atlanta satellite antenna; Scientific-Atlanta satellite receivers.
Miles of plant: 25.0 (coaxial). Homes passed: 1,000.
Manager: H. K. Alexander.
Ownership: South Shore Cable TV Inc. (MSO).

GOAT CREEK—Classic Cable, Box 429, 605 N.W. 3rd St., Plainville, KS 67663-0429. Phones: 785-434-7620; 800-999-8876. Fax: 785-434-2614. County: Kerr. ICA: TX0914.
TV Market Ranking: Below 100. Franchise award date: N.A. Franchise expiration date: N.A. Began: N.A.
Channel capacity: 35. Channels available but not in use: 23.
Basic Service
Subscribers: N.A.
Programming (received off-air): KRRT (W) Kerrville-San Antonio; KENS-TV (C), KMOL-TV (N), KSAT-TV (A) San Antonio.
Programming (via satellite): CNN; Discovery Channel; ESPN; Fox Family Channel; Nashville Network; TBS Superstation.
Fee: $17.95 monthly.
Pay Service 1
Pay Units: N.A.
Programming (via satellite): HBO.
Fee: $10.00 monthly.
Manager: Mark Livingston.
Ownership: Classic Cable (MSO).

GODLEY—Charter Communications Inc., 5227 FM 813, Waxahachie, TX 75165. Phones: 972-938-9288; 800-477-0887. Fax: 972-923-0039. County: Johnson. ICA: TX0562.
TV Market Ranking: 12. Franchise award date: June 10, 1982. Franchise expiration date: N.A. Began: May 1, 1985.

Channel capacity: 52. Channels available but not in use: N.A.

Basic Service

Subscribers: 103.

Programming (received off-air): KDAF (W), KDFI-TV (I), KDFW (F), KERA-TV (P), KTVT (C), KTXA (U), KXAS-TV (N), KXTX-TV (I), WFAA-TV (A) Dallas-Fort Worth; KDTN (P) Denton; KHSX-TV (H) Irving.

Programming (via satellite): WGN-TV (W) Chicago; TBS Superstation.

Fee: $26.00 installation; $8.45 monthly.

Expanded Basic Service

Subscribers: N.A.

Programming (via satellite): CNN; Country Music TV; Discovery Channel; ESPN; Fox Family Channel; Headline News; Lifetime; MTV; Nashville Network; Nickelodeon; The Weather Channel; Turner Network TV; USA Network.

Fee: $13.11 monthly.

Pay Service 1

Pay Units: N.A.

Programming (via satellite): Cinemax; HBO; Showtime.

Fee: $7.00 monthly (Showtime), $9.00 monthly (Cinemax), $11.00 monthly (HBO).

Local advertising: Yes.

Miles of plant: 10.0 (coaxial). Homes passed: 315.

Manager: Mary Scearce. Chief technician: Ken Stevens. Marketing director: Sherry Walden.

City fee: 3% of gross.

Ownership: Charter Communications Inc. (MSO). Purchased from Marcus Cable, April 1, 1999.

GOLDEN—Friendship Cable of Texas Inc., Box 9090, Tyler, TX 75711-9090. Phone: 903-581-2121. Fax: 903-581-2185. County: Wood. ICA: TX0538.

TV Market Ranking: Below 100. Franchise award date: January 1, 1989. Franchise expiration date: January 1, 2009. Began: August 1, 1989.

Channel capacity: 36 (not 2-way capable). Channels available but not in use: 7.

Basic Service

Subscribers: 166.

Programming (received off-air): KERA-TV (P) Dallas-Fort Worth; KETK-TV (N) Jacksonville; KFXK (F) Longview; KLTV (A) Tyler-Longview.

Programming (via satellite): WBBM-TV (C), WGN-TV (W) Chicago; CNN; Country Music TV; Discovery Channel; ESPN; Fox Family Channel; Lifetime; Nashville Network; Nickelodeon; TBS Superstation; USA Network.

Current originations: Automated time-weather; government access.

Fee: $30.00 installation; $32.50 monthly.

Pay Service 1

Pay Units: 19.

Programming (via satellite): Cinemax.

Fee: $10.95 monthly.

Pay Service 2

Pay Units: 16.

Programming (via satellite): HBO.

Fee: $10.95 monthly.

Pay Service 3

Pay Units: 20.

Programming (via satellite): Showtime.

Fee: $5.95 monthly.

Local advertising: Yes.

Miles of plant: 16.6 (coaxial). Homes passed: 365.

Manager: Marianne Bogy. Chief technician: Sonny Myers.

Ownership: Buford Television Inc. (MSO). See Cable System Ownership.

GOLDSMITH—Classic Cable, Box 429, 605 N.W. 3rd St., Plainville, KS 67663-0429. Phones: 785-434-7620; 800-999-8876. Fax: 785-434-2614. County: Ector. ICA: TX0670.

TV Market Ranking: Below 100. Franchise award date: January 1, 1982. Franchise expiration date: January 1, 1998. Began: January 1, 1983.

Channel capacity: 22 (2-way capable). Channels available but not in use: N.A.

Basic Service

Subscribers: 20.

Programming (received off-air): KMID (A), KMLM (I), KOCV-TV (P), KOSA-TV (C), KPEJ (F), KWES-TV (N) Odessa-Midland.

Programming (via satellite): WGN-TV (W) Chicago; CNN; Discovery Channel; ESPN; Fox Family Channel; Headline News; Home Shopping Network; Nashville Network; Sci-Fi Channel; TBS Superstation; Turner Classic Movies; Turner Network TV; USA Network.

Fee: $35.00 installation; $27.95 monthly.

Pay Service 1

Pay Units: 3.

Programming (via satellite): HBO.

Fee: $8.00 installation; $9.95 monthly.

Pay Service 2

Pay Units: 2.

Programming (via satellite): Showtime.

Fee: $9.95 monthly.

Local advertising: No.

Equipment: Harris & Triple Crown headend; Triple Crown amplifiers; Comm/Scope cable; Eagle traps; U.S. Tower satellite antenna; Harris satellite receivers.

Miles of plant: 5.0 (coaxial). Homes passed: 139.

Manager: Bill Flowers. Chief technician: Ben Hernandez. Marketing director: Jennifer Hauschild.

City fee: 3% of basic gross.

Ownership: Classic Cable (MSO).

GOLDTHWAITE—Post Cablevision of Texas Ltd., Drawer 829, 1108 Parker St., Goldthwaite, TX 76844. Phone: 915-648-3041. County: Mills. ICA: TX0761.

TV Market Ranking: Outside TV Markets. Franchise award date: N.A. Franchise expiration date: N.A. Began: January 1, 1958.

Channel capacity: 27. Channels available but not in use: 2.

Basic Service

Subscribers: 1,564.

Programming (received off-air): KRBC-TV (N) Abilene-Sweetwater; KNCT (P) Belton; KCEN-TV (N), KWKT (F), KWTX-TV (C), KXXV (A) Waco-Temple; allband FM.

Programming (via microwave): KDFW (F), KTVT (C), WFAA-TV (A) Dallas-Fort Worth.

Programming (via satellite): WGN-TV (W) Chicago; CNN; Country Music TV; Discovery Channel; ESPN; Fox Family Channel; Home Shopping Network; Nashville Network; TBS Superstation; The Weather Channel; Univision.

Current originations: Automated time-weather.

Fee: $25.00 installation; $20.32 monthly.

Pay Service 1

Pay Units: N.A.

Programming (via satellite): Disney Channel; HBO.

Fee: $7.51 monthly (Disney), $9.65 monthly (HBO.

Equipment: Tocom headend; Tocom amplifiers; Comm/Scope cable.

Miles of plant: 26.0 (coaxial).

Manager: Denise Casbeer. Chief technician: Joe Dean.

City fee: 2% of gross.

Ownership: Fanch Communications Inc. (MSO). See Cable System Ownership.

GOLIAD—Falcon Cable TV, 1244 Encino Dr., Pleasanton, TX 78064. Phone: 830-569-5509. Fax: 830-569-4828. County: Goliad. ICA: TX0395.

TV Market Ranking: Below 100. Franchise award date: N.A. Franchise expiration date: N.A. Began: April 1, 1969.

Channel capacity: 42. Channels available but not in use: 6.

Basic Service

Subscribers: 643.

Programming (received off-air): KZTV (C) Corpus Christi; KRRT (W) Kerrville-San Antonio; KABB (F), KENS-TV (C), KLRN (P), KMOL-TV (N), KSAT-TV (A) San Antonio; KAVU-TV (A), KVCT (F) Victoria; allband FM.

Programming (via satellite): Bravo; CNN; Country Music TV; E! Entertainment TV; ESPN; Fox Family Channel; Headline News; Home Shopping Network; Learning Channel; Nickelodeon; QVC; Sci-Fi Channel; Travel Channel; USA Network; Univision.

Current originations: Automated time-weather; local news.

Fee: $15.00 installation; $23.24 monthly; $10.00 additional installation.

Expanded Basic Service

Subscribers: 618.

Programming (via satellite): A & E; American Movie Classics; Nashville Network.

Fee: $2.69 monthly.

Expanded Basic Service 2

Subscribers: 610.

Programming (via satellite): Discovery Channel; Disney Channel; History Channel; TBS Superstation; Turner Network TV.

Fee: $6.75 monthly.

Pay Service 1

Pay Units: 64.

Programming (via satellite): HBO.

Fee: $11.95 monthly.

Pay Service 2

Pay Units: 65.

Programming (via satellite): Showtime.

Fee: $10.95 monthly.

Pay Service 3

Pay Units: 33.

Programming (via satellite): The Movie Channel.

Fee: $10.95 monthly.

Local advertising: Yes. Regional interconnect: Cabletime.

Equipment: Jerrold headend; Magnavox amplifiers; Comm/Scope & Times Fiber cable; Jerrold set top converters; Eagle & Pico traps; Scientific-Atlanta satellite antenna; Scientific-Atlanta satellite receivers.

Miles of plant: 22.0 (coaxial). Homes passed: 952.

Manager: Lorna Gentry. Chief technician: Santos Guajardo.

Franchise fee: 3% of gross.

Ownership: Falcon Communications LP (MSO), joint venture formed September 30, 1998. See Cable System Ownership.

GOLINDA—National Cable Inc., Suite 106-A, 5151 Reed Rd., Columbus, OH 43220. Phones: 614-442-5890; 800-582-0504. Fax: 614-457-2567. Counties: Falls & McLennan. Also serves Lorena. ICA: TX0905.

TV Market Ranking: Below 100. Franchise award date: N.A. Franchise expiration date: N.A. Began: N.A.

Channel capacity: N.A. Channels available but not in use: N.A.

Basic Service

Subscribers: 29.

Programming (received off-air): KDFW (F) Dallas-Fort Worth; KCEN-TV (N), KCTF (P), KWKT (F), KWTX-TV (C), KXXV (A) Waco-Temple.

Programming (via satellite): WGN-TV (W) Chicago; A & E; American Movie Classics; CNN; Country Music TV; Discovery Channel; ESPN; Fox Family Channel; Showtime; TBS Superstation; Turner Network TV; USA Network.

Fee: $28.00 monthly.

Homes passed: 149.

Manager: Paul Scott. Chief technician: Rob Spiller. Marketing director: Josh Thackery.

Ownership: National Cable (MSO).

GONZALES—Time Warner Communications, 941 St. Joseph, Gonzales, TX 78629. Phone: 830-672-6722. County: Gonzales. ICA: TX0209.

TV Market Ranking: Outside TV Markets. Franchise award date: N.A. Franchise expiration date: N.A. Began: November 15, 1973.

Channel capacity: 54. Channels available but not in use: N.A.

Basic Service

Subscribers: 2,110.

Programming (received off-air): KEYE-TV (C), KLRU (P), KTBC (F) Austin; KENS-TV (C), KMOL-TV (N), KSAT-TV (A), KWEX-TV (S) San Antonio; allband FM.

Programming (via satellite): CNBC; CNN; Discovery Channel; Fox Family Channel; Nashville Network; Nickelodeon; QVC; TBS Superstation.

Fee: $36.66 installation; $8.43 monthly; $18.33 additional installation.

Expanded Basic Service

Subscribers: 1,912.

Programming (via satellite): American Movie Classics; ESPN; Fox Sports Net Southwest; Turner Network TV; USA Network.

Fee: $10.75 monthly.

Pay Service 1

Pay Units: 94.

Programming (via satellite): Disney Channel.

Fee: N.A.

Pay Service 2

Pay Units: 655.

Programming (via satellite): The New Encore.

Fee: N.A.

Pay Service 3

Pay Units: 325.

Programming (via satellite): Showtime.

Fee: N.A.

Local advertising: Planned.

Program Guide: The Cable Guide.

Equipment: Jerrold headend; Jerrold amplifiers; Times Fiber cable; Jerrold set top converters; Eagle traps; Scientific-Atlanta satellite antenna.

Miles of plant: 46.1 (coaxial). Homes passed: 2,204. Total homes in franchised area: 2,272.

Manager: Jim Gutierrez.

City fee: 3% of gross.

Ownership: AT&T Broadband & Internet Services (MSO); Time Warner Cable (MSO); Advance/Newhouse Partnership (MSO).

GOODRICH—Star Cable, Drawer 1570, Brazoria, TX 77422. Phones: 409-798-9121; 800-395-2775. Fax: 409-798-4409. County: Polk. ICA: TX0174.

TV Market Ranking: Outside TV Markets. Franchise award date: N.A. Franchise expiration date: N.A. Began: N.A.

Channel capacity: 52 (not 2-way capable). Channels available but not in use: 11.

Basic Service

Subscribers: 1,532; Commercial subscribers: 101.

Programming (received off-air): KBTX-TV (C) Bryan; KPXB (X) Conroe; KHOU-TV (C), KHTV (W), KPRC-TV (N), KRIV (F), KTRK-TV (A), KTXH (U), KUHT (P) Houston; KCTL-LP (I), KETX-LP (I) Livingston; KTRE (A) Lufkin.
Programming (via satellite): CNN; Fox Family Channel; TBS Superstation.
Fee: $13.90 monthly; $2.15 converter.

Expanded Basic Service
Subscribers: 1,512.
Programming (via satellite): WGN-TV (W) Chicago; A & E; American Movie Classics; BET; CNBC; Country Music TV; Discovery Channel; ESPN; Fox News Channel; Fox Sports Net Southwest; History Channel; Home & Garden Television; MTV; Nashville Network; Nickelodeon; QVC; Sci-Fi Channel; The Weather Channel; Turner Network TV; USA Network.
Fee: $17.74 monthly.

Pay Service 1
Pay Units: 87.
Programming (via satellite): Cinemax.
Fee: $10.95 monthly.

Pay Service 2
Pay Units: 144.
Programming (via satellite): Disney Channel.
Fee: $7.95 monthly.

Pay Service 3
Pay Units: 164.
Programming (via satellite): HBO.
Fee: $10.95 monthly.

Pay Service 4
Pay Units: 191.
Programming (via satellite): Showtime; The Movie Channel.
Fee: $12.95 monthly.

Miles of plant: 135.0 (coaxial). Homes passed: 3,037.
Manager: Mike Burns. Chief technician: Mayla Zubeck.
Ownership: Star Cable Associates (MSO).

GORDON—Mallard Cablevision, 100-D El Chico Trail, Willow Park, TX 76087. Phones: 817-441-8073; 800-669-2288. Fax: 817-441-6464. County: Palo Pinto. ICA: TX0593.
TV Market Ranking: Outside TV Markets. Franchise award date: N.A. Franchise expiration date: N.A. Began: October 1, 1985.
Channel capacity: 27 (not 2-way capable). Channels available but not in use: 7.

Basic Service
Subscribers: 129.
Programming (received off-air): KDFW (F), KERA-TV (P), KTVT (C), KTXA (U), KXAS-TV (N), KXTX-TV (I), WFAA-TV (A) Dallas-Fort Worth.
Programming (via satellite): WGN-TV (W) Chicago; A & E; Animal Planet; CNN; Country Music TV; Discovery Channel; ESPN; Fox Family Channel; Nashville Network; Sci-Fi Channel; TBS Superstation; USA Network.
Current originations: Automated time-weather; government access.
Fee: $30.00 installation; $16.80 monthly; $2.00 converter.

Pay Service 1
Pay Units: 17.
Programming (via satellite): Cinemax.
Fee: $10.00 installation; $10.00 monthly.

Pay Service 2
Pay Units: 30.
Programming (via satellite): HBO.
Fee: $10.00 installation; $11.00 monthly.

Local advertising: No.
Equipment: Texscan amplifiers; Comm/Scope cable; Scientific-Atlanta satellite antenna.
Miles of plant: 5.2 (coaxial). Homes passed: 180.
Manager: Doug Grassmann.
Ownership: Mallard Cablevision (MSO). Purchased from Cambridge Communications, May 1, 1999.

GOREE—Goree Cablevision, Box 6575, Abilene, TX 79608. Phone: 915-691-5787. County: Knox. ICA: TX0762.
TV Market Ranking: Outside TV Markets. Franchise award date: N.A. Franchise expiration date: N.A. Began: N.A.
Channel capacity: N.A. Channels available but not in use: None.

Basic Service
Subscribers: 75.
Programming (received off-air): KTXS-TV (A) Abilene-Sweetwater; KCBD-TV (N), KLBK-TV (C) Lubbock.
Programming (via satellite): WGN-TV (W) Chicago; ESPN; Fox Family Channel; Nickelodeon; TBS Superstation; Turner Network TV.
Fee: N.A.

Manager: D. H. Pope.
Ownership: Jayroc Inc. (MSO).

GORMAN—Friendship Cable of Texas Inc., Box 9090, Tyler, TX 75711-9090. Phone: 903-581-2121. Fax: 903-581-2185. County: Eastland. ICA: TX0464.
TV Market Ranking: Outside TV Markets. Franchise award date: N.A. Franchise expiration date: N.A. Began: October 1, 1968.
Channel capacity: 35. Channels available but not in use: 8.

Basic Service
Subscribers: 436.
Programming (received off-air): KRBC-TV (N), KTAB-TV (C) Abilene-Sweetwater; KXTX-TV (I) Dallas-Fort Worth; allband FM.
Programming (via microwave): KDFW (F), KERA-TV (P), KTVT (C), KXAS-TV (N), WFAA-TV (A) Dallas-Fort Worth.
Programming (via satellite): Discovery Channel; FX; QVC; TBS Superstation; The Weather Channel.
Current originations: Automated emergency alert.
Fee: $30.00 installation; $12.36 monthly.

Expanded Basic Service
Subscribers: 383.
Programming (via satellite): American Movie Classics; Animal Planet; CNBC; CNN; Cartoon Network; ESPN; Fox Family Channel; Fox News Channel; Fox Sports Net Southwest; Headline News; Home & Garden Television; Knowledge TV; Learning Channel; Nashville Network; Turner Network TV; USA Network; Univision.
Fee: $30.00 installation; $16.20 monthly.

Pay Service 1
Pay Units: 56.
Programming (via satellite): Cinemax.
Fee: $12.90 monthly.

Pay Service 2
Pay Units: 249.
Programming (via satellite): The New Encore.
Fee: $1.75 monthly.

Pay Service 3
Pay Units: 64.
Programming (via satellite): HBO.
Fee: $12.90 monthly.

Pay Service 4
Pay Units: 159.
Programming (via satellite): Starz!
Fee: $6.75 monthly.

Equipment: CAS headend; CAS amplifiers; CAS cable.
Miles of plant: 16.0 (coaxial). Homes passed: 579. Total homes in franchised area: 579.

Manager: Larry Bryant. Chief technician: Joe Stewart.
Ownership: Buford Television Inc. (MSO). See Cable System Ownership.

GRAHAM—Paragon Cable, Box 958, 616 Oak St., Graham, TX 76450. Phone: 817-549-3737. Fax: 817-549-7220. County: Young. Also serves Young County. ICA: TX0142.
TV Market Ranking: Outside TV Markets. Franchise award date: May 15, 1952. Franchise expiration date: November 1, 1999. Began: June 1, 1952.
Channel capacity: 61 (not 2-way capable). Channels available but not in use: 27.

Basic Service
Subscribers: 3,364; Commercial subscribers: 237.
Programming (received off-air): KAUZ-TV (C), KFDX-TV (N), KSWO-TV (A) Wichita Falls-Lawton; 18 FMs.
Programming (via microwave): KDFW (F), KERA-TV (P), KTVT (C), KXAS-TV (N), KXTX-TV (I), WFAA-TV (A) Dallas-Fort Worth.
Programming (via satellite): A & E; American Movie Classics; C-SPAN; CNN; Country Music TV; Discovery Channel; ESPN; Fox Family Channel; Learning Channel; Lifetime; MTV; Nashville Network; Nick at Nite; Nickelodeon; TBS Superstation; The Weather Channel; Trinity Bcstg. Network; Turner Network TV; USA Network.
Current originations: Automated time-weather; public access; religious access; automated emergency alert.
Fee: $39.95 installation; $19.70 monthly.
Commercial fee: $4.50 monthly.

Pay Service 1
Pay Units: 221.
Programming (via satellite): Disney Channel.
Fee: $7.00 monthly.

Pay Service 2
Pay Units: 320.
Programming (via satellite): HBO.
Fee: $11.45 monthly.

Pay Service 3
Pay Units: 184.
Programming (via satellite): Showtime.
Fee: $11.45 monthly.

Local advertising: Yes. Available in character-generated programming. Regional interconnect: Cabletime.
Program Guide: The Cable Guide.
Equipment: Jerrold & Scientific-Atlanta headend; Jerrold amplifiers; M/A-Com cable; Texscan character generator; Jerrold & Panasonic set top converters; Eagle traps; Andrew & Hughes satellite antenna; Scientific-Atlanta satellite receivers.
Miles of plant: 62.0 (coaxial). Homes passed: 4,985. Total homes in franchised area: 4,985.
Manager: LeRoy Pardue. Chief technician: Rodney Harding.
City fee: 3% of gross.
Ownership: AT&T Broadband & Internet Services (MSO); Time Warner Cable (MSO); Advance/Newhouse Partnership (MSO).

GRANADA HILLS—Time Warner Cable, 12012 N. Mo Pac Expwy., Austin, TX 78758-2904. Phone: 512-485-6100. Fax: 512-485-6105. Web site: http://www.timewarneraustin.com. Counties: Bastrop, Hays, Travis & Williamson. Also serves Buda, Cedar Valley, Dripping Springs, Hays, Hutto, Lago Vista, Round Rock, Smithville, Taylor. ICA: TX0763.
TV Market Ranking: Below 100 (Buda, Cedar Valley, Dripping Springs, Granada Hills, Hays, Hutto, Lago Vista, Round Rock, Taylor); Outside TV Markets (Smithville). Franchise award date: January 1, 1996. Franchise expiration date: November 15, 2000. Began: July 1, 1983.
Channel capacity: 140 (2-way capable; operating 2-way). Channels available but not in use: 40.

Basic Service
Subscribers: 4,700.
Programming (received off-air): KEYE-TV (C), KLRU (P), KNVA (W), KTBC (F), KVUE-TV (A), KXAN-TV (N) Austin; K13VC (I) Austin, Cedar Park.
Programming (via satellite): C-SPAN; Knowledge TV; Learning Channel; Pax Net; TV Guide Channel.
Current originations: Automated time-weather; local news.
Fee: $28.21 installation; $7.25 monthly; $3.07 converter; $12.11 additional installation.

Digital Basic Service
Subscribers: N.A.
Programming (via satellite): BET on Jazz; CNNfn; Cinemax; Discovery Kids Channel; Discovery People; Discovery Science Channel; Discovery Wings Channel; Disney Channel; Game Show Network; HBO; HBO Comedy; HBO Family; HBO Plus; HBO Signature; HBO Zone; Outdoor Channel; Ovation; Playboy TV; Showtime; Showtime Extreme; Speedvision; Sundance Channel; The Health Network; The Movie Channel.
Fee: N.A.

Expanded Basic Service
Subscribers: N.A.
Programming (via satellite): WGN-TV (W) Chicago; A & E; American Movie Classics; Animal Planet; BET; Bravo; C-SPAN 2; CNBC; CNN; CNN/SI; Cartoon Network; Comedy Central; Country Music TV; Court TV; Discovery Channel; E! Entertainment TV; ESPN; ESPN 2; Fox Family Channel; Fox News Channel; Fox Sports Net Southwest; Headline News; Home & Garden Television; Home Shopping Network; Lifetime; MSNBC; MTV; Nashville Network; Nick at Nite's TV Land; Nickelodeon; Odyssey; QVC; TBS Superstation; TV Food Network; TV Guide Sneak Prevue; Telemundo; The Weather Channel; Travel Channel; Trinity Bcstg. Network; Turner Network TV; USA Network; Univision; VH1.
Fee: $22.49 monthly.

Expanded Basic Service 2
Subscribers: N.A.
Programming (via satellite): Golf Channel; History Channel; Independent Film Channel; Sci-Fi Channel; The New Encore; Turner Classic Movies.
Fee: $3.95 monthly.

Pay Service 1
Pay Units: N.A.

Programming (via satellite): Cinemax (multiplexed); Disney Channel; HBO (multiplexed); Playboy TV; Showtime.
Fee: $8.95 monthly Disney, 10.95 monthly (Cinemax, HBO or Showtime) $13.95 monthly (Playboy).

Pay-Per-View
Action PPV delivered digitally; Hot Choice delivered digitally; Spice delivered digitally; Viewer's Choice Digital; Viewer's Choice Digital.
Fee: $3.95-$4.95.

Miles of plant: 49.6 (coaxial).
Manager: Bill Carey. Chief technician: Matt Stanek. Program director: George Warmingham. Marketing director: Michelle Golden.
Ownership: Time Warner Cable (MSO); Advance/Newhouse Partnership (MSO).

GRANBURY—North Texas Cablecomm, Box 909, Granbury, TX 76048. Phone: 817-573-6872. Counties: Hood & Somervell. Also serves Glen Rose, Hood County, Somervell, Tolar. ICA: TX0764.
TV Market Ranking: 12 (Granbury, portions of Hood County); Outside TV Markets (Glen Rose, portions of Hood County, Somervell, Tolar). Franchise award date: N.A. Franchise expiration date: N.A. Began: January 1, 1979.
Channel capacity: 35 (2-way capable; operating 2-way). Channels available but not in use: 14.

Basic Service
Subscribers: N.A.
Programming (received off-air): KDFI-TV (I), KDFW (F), KERA-TV (P), KTVT (C), KTXA (U), KXAS-TV (N), KXTX-TV (I), WFAA-TV (A) Dallas-Fort Worth; KWTX-TV (C) Waco-Temple.
Programming (via satellite): WGN-TV (W) Chicago; A & E; CNN; ESPN; Fox Family Channel; MTV; Nashville Network; Nickelodeon; TBS Superstation; USA Network.
Planned programming (via satellite): The Weather Channel.
Planned originations: Public access.
Fee: $29.95 installation; $19.95 monthly.

Pay Service 1
Pay Units: N.A.
Programming (via satellite): Disney Channel; Showtime; The Movie Channel.
Fee: $20.00 installation; $9.95 monthly (each).

Local advertising: Yes. Available in satellite distributed & locally originated programming.
Miles of plant: 130.0 (coaxial).
Manager: Russ Hamby.
City fee: 3% of gross.
Ownership: Fanch Communications Inc. (MSO). See Cable System Ownership.

GRAND PRAIRIE—TCI Cablevision of the Metroplex Inc., 934 E. Centerville Rd., Garland, TX 75041. Phone: 214-840-2388. Fax: 214-264-2456. Counties: Dallas, Ellis & Tarrant. Also serves Cockrell Hill. ICA: TX0030.
TV Market Ranking: 12. Franchise award date: N.A. Franchise expiration date: N.A. Began: June 30, 1979.
Channel capacity: 39 (2-way capable; operating 2-way partially). Channels available but not in use: None.

Basic Service
Subscribers: 14,284.
Programming (received off-air): KDAF (W), KDFI-TV (I), KDFW (F), KERA-TV (P), KTVT (C), KTXA (U), KXAS-TV (N), KXTX-TV (I), WFAA-TV (A) Dallas-Fort Worth; KDTN (P) Denton; KUVN (S) Garland; KHSX-TV (H) Irving; allband FM.
Programming (via satellite): WGN-TV (W) Chicago; A & E; BET; C-SPAN; CNBC; CNN; Comedy Central; Discovery Channel; Fox Family Channel; Lifetime; MTV; Nashville Network; Nickelodeon; TBS Superstation; The Weather Channel; VH1.
Current originations: Automated time-weather; public access; educational access; government access; automated emergency alert; local news; local sports.
Fee: $60.00 installation; $19.45 monthly; $2.00 converter; $25.00 additional installation.

Expanded Basic Service
Subscribers: 12,007.
Programming (via satellite): American Movie Classics; ESPN; Fox Sports Net Southwest; Turner Network TV; USA Network.
Fee: $3.50 monthly.

Pay Service 1
Pay Units: N.A.
Programming (via satellite): Disney Channel; HBO; Showtime; The Movie Channel.
Fee: $25.00 installation; $10.25 monthly (Disney), $11.25 monthly (Showtime or TMC), $12.20 monthly (HBO).

Local advertising: Yes. Available in locally originated, character-generated, taped & automated programming. Local sales manager: Debra Friday.
Equipment: GTE Sylvania headend; GTE Sylvania amplifiers; GTE Sylvania cable; Sony cameras; Sony VTRs; GTE Sylvania character generator; GTE Sylvania set top converters; Scientific-Atlanta satellite antenna.
Miles of plant: 399.7 (coaxial). Homes passed: 36,748. Total homes in franchised area: 36,931.
Manager: Steve Crawford.
City fee: 3% of gross.
Ownership: AT&T Broadband & Internet Services (MSO). Purchased from Tele-Communications Inc., March 9, 1999.

GRANDFALLS—Classic Cable, Box 429, 605 N.W. 3rd St., Plainville, KS 67663-0429. Phones: 785-434-7620; 800-999-8876. Fax: 785-434-2614. County: Ward. ICA: TX0765.
TV Market Ranking: Below 100. Franchise award date: N.A. Franchise expiration date: N.A. Began: July 1, 1982.
Channel capacity: 36 (2-way capable). Channels available but not in use: N.A.

Basic Service
Subscribers: 60.
Programming (received off-air): KMID (A), KMLM (I), KOSA-TV (C), KPEJ (F), KWES-TV (N) Odessa-Midland.
Programming (via satellite): WGN-TV (W) Chicago; Animal Planet; CNN; Disney Channel; ESPN; Fox Family Channel; Home Shopping Network; Nashville Network; TBS Superstation; The Weather Channel; Turner Classic Movies; Turner Network TV; Univision.
Current originations: Automated time-weather.
Fee: $35.00 installation; $27.95 monthly.

Pay Service 1
Pay Units: 26.
Programming (via satellite): HBO.
Fee: $9.95 monthly.

Pay Service 2
Pay Units: 6.
Programming (via satellite): Showtime.
Fee: $9.95 monthly.

Miles of plant: 6.0 (coaxial). Homes passed: 233.
Manager: Bill Flowers. Chief technician: Ben Hernandez. Program director: Glen Chase. Marketing director: Jennifer Hauschild.
City fee: 2% of gross monthly receipts.
Ownership: Classic Cable (MSO).

GRAPE CREEK—West Texas Cablevision Inc., Box 3528, Hwy. 87 N, San Angelo, TX 76902. Phone: 915-655-4657. County: Tom Green. Also serves San Angelo. ICA: TX0326.
TV Market Ranking: Below 100. Franchise award date: October 1, 1980. Franchise expiration date: N.A. Began: July 1, 1982.
Channel capacity: 21. Channels available but not in use: None.

Basic Service
Subscribers: 775.
Programming (received off-air): KRBC-TV (N), KTXS-TV (A) Abilene-Sweetwater; KIDY (F), KLST (C) San Angelo.
Programming (via satellite): WGN-TV (W) Chicago; CNN; ESPN; Fox Family Channel; Nashville Network; TBS Superstation; USA Network.
Fee: $15.00 installation; $20.40 monthly.

Pay Service 1
Pay Units: N.A.
Programming (via satellite): Cinemax; Disney Channel; HBO.
Fee: $10.50 monthly (each).

Miles of plant: 45.0 (coaxial); None (fiber optic). Homes passed: 1,203.
Manager: Kenny White. Marketing director: Jane Ketcham.
Ownership: Cable Management Assoc. (MSO).

GRAPELAND—Friendship Cable of Texas Inc., Box 9090, Tyler, TX 75711-9090. Phone: 903-581-2121. Fax: 903-581-2185. County: Houston. Also serves Latexo. ICA: TX0382.
TV Market Ranking: Below 100. Franchise award date: N.A. Franchise expiration date: April 18, 1999. Began: April 1, 1974.
Channel capacity: 22. Channels available but not in use: N.A.

Basic Service
Subscribers: 651.
Programming (received off-air): K16BY (I) Crockett; KTVT (C) Dallas-Fort Worth; KFXK (F) Longview; KTRE (A) Lufkin; KLTV (A) Tyler-Longview; allband FM.
Programming (via microwave): KXAS-TV (N), WFAA-TV (A) Dallas-Fort Worth.
Programming (via satellite): WGN-TV (W) Chicago; CNN; Discovery Channel; ESPN; Nashville Network; Nickelodeon; TBS Superstation; Turner Network TV; USA Network.
Current originations: Automated time-weather.
Fee: $30.00 installation; $26.65 monthly.

Pay Service 1
Pay Units: 43.
Programming (via satellite): Showtime.
Fee: $11.00 monthly.

Pay Service 2
Pay Units: 11.
Programming (via satellite): Cinemax.
Fee: $10.95 monthly.

Pay Service 3
Pay Units: 26.
Programming (via satellite): HBO.
Fee: $10.95 monthly.

Equipment: Tocom & Dorate headend; Tocom amplifiers; Times Fiber cable; Eagle traps; Weatherscan satellite antenna; Microdyne & DX Communications satellite receivers.
Miles of plant: 34.5 (coaxial). Homes passed: 1,175.
Manager: Wanda Pyburn. Chief technician: David Burrell.
City fee: 2% of gross after 10 years.
Ownership: Buford Television Inc. (MSO). See Cable System Ownership.

GRAPEVINE—Paragon Cable, 2951 Kinwest Pkwy., Irving, TX 75063. Phone: 972-221-6531. Fax: 972-221-7070. County: Tarrant. ICA: TX0071.
TV Market Ranking: 12. Franchise award date: January 20, 1981. Franchise expiration date: July 31, 2009. Began: August 20, 1981.
Channel capacity: 69 (not 2-way capable). Channels available but not in use: 47.

Basic Service
Subscribers: 10,092.
Programming (received off-air): KPXD (X) Arlington; KDAF (W), KDFI-TV (I), KDFW (F), KDTX-TV (T), KERA-TV (P), KFWD (O), KTVT (C), KTXA (U), KXAS-TV (N), KXTX-TV (I), WFAA-TV (A) Dallas-Fort Worth; KMPX (I) Decatur; KDTN (P) Denton; KUVN (S) Garland; KHSX-TV (H) Irving; KLDT (I) Lake Dallas; 21 FMs.
Programming (via satellite): Home Shopping Network; TV Guide Channel.
Current originations: Automated time-weather; public access; educational access; government access; religious access; library access; automated emergency alert; local news; local sports.
Fee: $26.90 installation; $9.06 monthly; $2.76 converter.

Expanded Basic Service
Subscribers: 9,430.
Programming (via satellite): A & E; American Movie Classics; Animal Planet; BET; Bravo; C-SPAN; C-SPAN 2; CNBC; CNN; Cartoon Network; Comedy Central; Country Music TV; Court TV; Discovery Channel; E! Entertainment TV; ESPN; ESPN 2; Fox Family Channel; Fox Sports Net Southwest; Headline News; History Channel; Home & Garden Television; Learning Channel; Lifetime; MOVIEplex; MSNBC; MTV; Nashville Network; Nick at Nite; Nickelodeon; QVC; The Weather Channel; Travel Channel; Turner Network TV; USA Network; VH1; ValueVision.
Fee: $20.18 monthly.

Pay Service 1
Pay Units: 505.
Programming (via satellite): Cinemax.
Fee: $12.50 monthly.

Pay Service 2
Pay Units: 368.
Programming (via satellite): Disney Channel.
Fee: $9.40 monthly.

Pay Service 3
Pay Units: 1,116.
Programming (via satellite): HBO.
Fee: $12.50 monthly.

Pay Service 4
Pay Units: 251.
Programming (via satellite): The Movie Channel.
Fee: $12.50 monthly.

Pay Service 5
Pay Units: 492.
Programming (via satellite): Showtime.
Fee: $12.50 monthly.

Pay-Per-View
Hot Choice; Viewer's Choice.

Local advertising: Yes. Available in satellite distributed & locally originated programming. Rates: $16.00-$500.00/30 Seconds. Local sales manager: Christine Pierret.
Program Guide: The Cable Guide.
Equipment: Scientific-Atlanta headend; Scientific-Atlanta amplifiers; Comm/Scope cable; C-COR & AT&T fiber optic cable; Zenith addressable set top converters; Eagle & Gamco traps; Andrew & Scientific-Atlanta satellite antenna; Standard Communications satellite receivers.
Miles of plant: 199.9 (coaxial); 3.8 (fiber optic). Homes passed: 15,825.

Manager: Walter Nesbit. Chief technician: Bob Macioch. Program director: Philip Haley. Marketing director: Jim Fellhauer.
City fee: 5% of gross.
Ownership: AT&T Broadband & Internet Services (MSO); Time Warner Cable (MSO); Advance/Newhouse Partnership (MSO).

GREEN ACRES/ZION HILL—National Cable Inc., Suite 106-A, 5151 Reed Rd., Columbus, OH 43220. Phones: 614-442-5890; 800-582-0504. Fax: 614-457-2567. County: Parker. Also serves Weatherford (unincorporated areas). ICA: TX0766.
TV Market Ranking: 12. Franchise award date: N.A. Franchise expiration date: N.A. Began: N.A.
Channel capacity: 36. Channels available but not in use: 21.
Basic Service
Subscribers: 42.
Programming (received off-air): KDAF (W), KDFI-TV (I), KDFW (F), KERA-TV (P), KXAS-TV (N), WFAA-TV (A) Dallas-Fort Worth.
Programming (via satellite): WGN-TV (W) Chicago; A & E; American Movie Classics; CNN; Country Music TV; Discovery Channel; ESPN; Fox Family Channel; Showtime; TBS Superstation; Turner Network TV; USA Network.
Fee: $28.00 monthly.
Miles of plant: 10.2 (coaxial). Homes passed: 225.
Manager: Paul Scott. Chief technician: Rob Spiller. Marketing director: Josh Thackery.
Ownership: National Cable (MSO).

GREENVILLE—Time Warner Cable, Box 1195, 4520 Stonewall, Greenville, TX 75403. Phone: 903-455-0012. Fax: 903-455-9743. County: Hunt. ICA: TX0078.
TV Market Ranking: Below 100. Franchise award date: November 1, 1966. Franchise expiration date: N.A. Began: June 1, 1967.
Channel capacity: 54 (2-way capable; operating 2-way). Channels available but not in use: 3.
Basic Service
Subscribers: 7,589.
Programming (received off-air): KDAF (W), KDFI-TV (I), KDFW (F), KDTX-TV (T), KERA-TV (P), KTVT (C), KTXA (U), KXAS-TV (N), KXTX-TV (I), WFAA-TV (A) Dallas-Fort Worth; KDTN (P) Denton; KTAQ (I) Greenville; KHSX-TV (H) Irving.
Programming (via satellite): WGN-TV (W) Chicago; TBS Superstation.
Current originations: Automated time-weather.
Fee: $8.03 monthly.
Expanded Basic Service
Subscribers: N.A.
Programming (via satellite): A & E; BET; C-SPAN; C-SPAN 2; CNBC; CNN; Cartoon Network; Country Music TV; Discovery Channel; ESPN; Fox Family Channel; Headline News; History Channel; Home Shopping Network; Learning Channel; Lifetime; MTV; Nashville Network; Nickelodeon; Odyssey; QVC; The Health Network; The Weather Channel; Turner Network TV; USA Network; Univision; VH1.
Fee: $15.86 monthly.
Pay Service 1
Pay Units: 993.
Programming (via satellite): Cinemax.
Fee: $25.00 installation; $8.95 monthly.
Pay Service 2
Pay Units: 306.
Programming (via satellite): Disney Channel.
Fee: $25.00 installation; $8.95 monthly.
Pay Service 3
Pay Units: 1,279.
Programming (via satellite): HBO.
Fee: $25.00 installation; $8.95 monthly.
Pay Service 4
Pay Units: 266.
Programming (via satellite): Fox Sports Net Southwest.
Fee: $25.00 installation; $5.95 monthly.
Pay Service 5
Pay Units: 561.
Programming (via satellite): Showtime.
Fee: $25.00 installation; $8.95 monthly.
Pay-Per-View
Addressable homes: 1,500.
Hot Choice; Viewer's Choice.
Fee: $3.95.
Local advertising: Yes. Available in satellite distributed programming. Rates: $40.00-$85.00/Month.
Equipment: Scientific-Atlanta headend; Scientific-Atlanta amplifiers; Comm/Scope cable; JVC & Vikoa cameras; Sony VTRs; MSI character generator; Jerrold & Scientific-Atlanta set top converters; Pico traps; Scientific-Atlanta satellite antenna; Scientific-Atlanta satellite receivers.
Miles of plant: 147.1 (coaxial). Homes passed: 8,573.
Manager: Ray Little. Chief technician: Don Bowman.
City fee: 2% of gross.
Ownership: AT&T Broadband & Internet Services (MSO); Time Warner Cable (MSO); Advance/Newhouse Partnership (MSO).

GROOM—Classic Cable, Box 429, 605 N.W. 3rd St., Plainville, KS 67663-0429. Phones: 785-434-7620; 800-999-8876. Fax: 785-434-2614. County: Carson. ICA: TX0458.
TV Market Ranking: Outside TV Markets. Franchise award date: January 1, 1982. Franchise expiration date: N.A. Began: May 1, 1982.
Channel capacity: 41 (2-way capable). Channels available but not in use: N.A.
Basic Service
Subscribers: 145; Commercial subscribers: 12.
Programming (received off-air): KACV-TV (P), KAMR-TV (N), KCIT (F,U), KFDA-TV (C), KVII-TV (A) Amarillo; 1 FM.
Programming (via satellite): WGN-TV (W) Chicago; CNN; Discovery Channel; Disney Channel; ESPN; Fox Family Channel; Fox Sports Net Southwest; History Channel; Learning Channel; Nashville Network; Nick at Nite's TV Land; TBS Superstation; The Weather Channel; Turner Network TV; USA Network.
Current originations: Automated time-weather.
Fee: $35.00 installation; $27.95 monthly; $10.00 additional installation.
Pay Service 1
Pay Units: 33.
Programming (via satellite): HBO.
Fee: $20.00 installation; $10.95 monthly.
Pay Service 2
Pay Units: 10.
Programming (via satellite): Showtime.
Fee: $9.95 monthly.
Local advertising: No.
Equipment: Scientific-Atlanta headend; GTE Sylvania amplifiers; Comm/Scope cable; Cable Text character generator; Eagle traps; Scientific-Atlanta satellite antenna; Scientific-Atlanta satellite receivers.
Miles of plant: 5.9 (coaxial). Homes passed: 283.
Manager: Bill Flowers. Chief technician: Rick Rattan. Marketing director: Jennifer Hauschild.
City fee: 3% of gross.
Ownership: Classic Cable (MSO).

GROVETON—Friendship Cable of Texas Inc., Box 9090, Tyler, TX 75711-9090. Phone: 903-581-2121. Fax: 903-581-2185. County: Trinity. ICA: TX0486.
TV Market Ranking: Below 100. Franchise award date: N.A. Franchise expiration date: N.A. Began: October 1, 1988.
Channel capacity: 54. Channels available but not in use: N.A.
Basic Service
Subscribers: 254.
Programming (received off-air): KBTX-TV (C) Bryan; K16BY (I) Crockett; KHOU-TV (C), KHTV (W), KPRC-TV (N), KRIV (F), KTRK-TV (A), KTXH (U), KUHT (P) Houston; KETK-TV (N) Jacksonville; KTRE (A) Lufkin.
Programming (via satellite): BET; CNN; Discovery Channel; ESPN; Headline News; Nashville Network; Trinity Bcstg. Network; Turner Classic Movies; Turner Network TV.
Fee: $30.00 installation; $26.95 monthly.
Pay Service 1
Pay Units: 5.
Programming (via satellite): Cinemax.
Fee: $10.95 monthly.
Pay Service 2
Pay Units: 19.
Programming (via satellite): HBO.
Fee: $9.00 monthly.
Pay Service 3
Pay Units: 13.
Programming (via satellite): Showtime.
Fee: $5.95 monthly.
Miles of plant: 12.0 (coaxial). Homes passed: 481.
Manager: Wanda Pyburn. Chief technician: David Burrell.
Ownership: Buford Television Inc. (MSO). See Cable System Ownership.

GRUVER—Gruver Cablevision Inc., Box 827, 308 Main St., Gruver, TX 79040-0827. Phone: 806-733-5295. County: Hansford. ICA: TX0768.
TV Market Ranking: Outside TV Markets. Franchise award date: N.A. Franchise expiration date: N.A. Began: N.A.
Channel capacity: 12. Channels available but not in use: N.A.
Basic Service
Subscribers: 446.
Programming (received off-air): KAMR-TV (N), KFDA-TV (C), KVII-TV (A) Amarillo.
Programming (via satellite): WGN-TV (W) Chicago; CNN; ESPN; Headline News; Nashville Network; TBS Superstation.
Fee: $10.00 installation; $11.50 monthly.
Pay Service 1
Pay Units: N.A.
Programming (via satellite): Disney Channel; Showtime.
Fee: $10.00 installation; $9.00 monthly (Disney), $10.00 monthly (Showtime).
Manager: Pat Morley.
Ownership: Gruver Cablevision Inc. (MSO).

GUN BARREL CITY—Northland Cable TV, Box 289, 326 W. Main, Mabank, TX 75147. Phone: 903-887-0240. Fax: 903-887-7395. Counties: Henderson & Kaufman. Also serves Enchanted Oaks, Mabank, Payne Springs, Seven Points, Tool. ICA: TX0084.
TV Market Ranking: Outside TV Markets. Franchise award date: April 9, 1980. Franchise expiration date: November 1, 2008. Began: September 1, 1981.
Channel capacity: 36 (not 2-way capable). Channels available but not in use: 6.
Basic Service
Subscribers: 3,100.
Programming (received off-air): KPXD (X) Arlington; KDAF (W), KDFI-TV (I), KDFW (F), KERA-TV (P), KTVT (C), KXAS-TV (N), KXTX-TV (I), WFAA-TV (A) Dallas-Fort Worth; KLTV (A) Tyler-Longview.
Programming (via satellite): WGN-TV (W) Chicago; A & E; CNN; Country Music TV; ESPN; Fox Family Channel; Headline News; Home Shopping Network; Learning Channel; TBS Superstation; The Weather Channel; Trinity Bcstg. Network; USA Network.
Current originations: Public access.
Fee: $40.00 installation; $24.95 monthly; $20.00 additional installation.
Expanded Basic Service
Subscribers: N.A.
Programming (via satellite): American Movie Classics; Cartoon Network; fXM: Movies from Fox; Nickelodeon; Turner Classic Movies; USA Network.
Fee: $5.50 monthly.
Pay Service 1
Pay Units: 194.
Programming (via satellite): Disney Channel.
Fee: $30.00 installation; $7.50 monthly.
Pay Service 2
Pay Units: 1,029.
Programming (via satellite): HBO.
Fee: $30.00 installation; $11.00 monthly.
Pay Service 3
Pay Units: 125.
Programming (via satellite): Cinemax.
Fee: $30.00 installation; $11.00 monthly.
Local advertising: Yes. Available in locally originated, character-generated & taped programming. Rates: $50.00/Month. Local sales manager: Linda Webb.
Program Guide: Premium Channels.
Equipment: Blonder-Tongue & Scientific-Atlanta headend; Magnavox & Scientific-Atlanta amplifiers; Comm/Scope cable; Texscan character generator; Scientific-Atlanta set top converters; Arcom traps; Scientific-Atlanta & Antenna Technology satellite antenna; Scientific-Atlanta satellite receivers.
Miles of plant: 149.0 (coaxial); 15.0 (fiber optic). Homes passed: 8,665. Total homes in franchised area: 8,665.
Manager: Wayne Helmig. Chief technician: Randy Spence.
City fee: 4% of gross.
Ownership: Northland Communications Corp. (MSO).

GUSTINE—Cable Ventures Ltd., Suite 106-A, 5151 Reed Rd., Columbus, OH 43220. Phone: 614-442-5890. Fax: 614-457-2567. County: Comanche. ICA: TX0605.
TV Market Ranking: Outside TV Markets. Franchise award date: N.A. Franchise expiration date: N.A. Began: August 1, 1988.
Channel capacity: 35 (2-way capable). Channels available but not in use: 14.
Basic Service
Subscribers: 94.
Programming (received off-air): KTAB-TV (C) Abilene-Sweetwater; KERA-TV (P), KXAS-TV (N), WFAA-TV (A) Dallas-Fort Worth; KCEN-TV (N), KWKT (F), KWTX-TV (C), KXXV (A) Waco-Temple.
Programming (via satellite): WGN-TV (W) Chicago; A & E; CNN; Discovery Channel; ESPN; Fox Family Channel; Fox News Channel; Lifetime; Nashville Network; TBS Superstation; The Weather Channel; Trinity Bcstg. Network; USA Network.

Fee: $40.00 installation; $20.95 monthly; $2.95 converter.

Pay Service 1

Pay Units: 12.

Programming (via satellite): Cinemax; Disney Channel.

Fee: $7.00 monthly (Disney), $9.00 monthly (Cinemax).

Local advertising: No.

Miles of plant: 6.0 (coaxial). Homes passed: 227.

Manager: Bill Mays. Systems/operations manager: Steve Miller.

Ownership: Cable Ventures Ltd. (MSO).

GUTHRIE—6666 Supply House, Box 177, Guthrie, TX 79236. Phone: 806-596-4459. County: King. ICA: TX0703.

TV Market Ranking: Outside TV Markets. Franchise award date: N.A. Franchise expiration date: N.A. Began: October 15, 1965.

Channel capacity: 6. Channels available but not in use: N.A.

Basic Service

Subscribers: 54.

Programming (received off-air): 5 FMs.

Programming (via translator): KRBC-TV (N), KTXS-TV (A) Abilene-Sweetwater; KFDX-TV (N), KSWO-TV (A) Wichita Falls-Lawton.

Fee: $7.00 monthly.

Equipment: Vikoa headend; Benco & Jerrold amplifiers; CAS & Vikoa cable.

Miles of plant: 3.0 (coaxial). Homes passed: 55.

City fee: None.

Ownership: Larry Fitzgerald.

GUY—Star Cable, Drawer 1570, Brazoria, TX 77422. Phones: 409-798-9121; 800-395-2775. Fax: 409-798-4409. Counties: Brazoria & Fort Bend. Also serves Damon. ICA: TX0439.

TV Market Ranking: Below 100. Franchise award date: N.A. Franchise expiration date: N.A. Began: N.A.

Channel capacity: 52 (not 2-way capable). Channels available but not in use: 25.

Basic Service

Subscribers: 153.

Programming (received off-air): KLTJ (E) Galveston; KETH (E), KHOU-TV (C), KHTV (W), KPRC-TV (N), KRIV (F), KTRK-TV (A), KTXH (U), KUHT (P) Houston; KNWS-TV (I) Katy.

Programming (via satellite): CNN; Discovery Channel; ESPN; Fox Family Channel; Fox Sports Net Southwest; MTV; Nashville Network; Nickelodeon; QVC; TBS Superstation; The Weather Channel; Turner Network TV; USA Network.

Fee: $30.99 monthly; $2.15 converter.

Pay Service 1

Pay Units: 31.

Programming (via satellite): Cinemax.

Fee: $10.95 monthly.

Pay Service 2

Pay Units: 29.

Programming (via satellite): Disney Channel.

Fee: $7.95 monthly.

Pay Service 3

Pay Units: 44.

Programming (via satellite): HBO.

Fee: $10.95 monthly.

Pay Service 4

Pay Units: 32.

Programming (via satellite): Showtime.

Fee: $12.95 monthly.

Miles of plant: 30.3 (coaxial); None (fiber optic). Homes passed: 672.

Manager: Mike Burns. Chief technician: Mayla Zubeck.

Ownership: Star Cable Associates (MSO).

HALE CENTER—Classic Cable, Box 429, 605 N.W. 3rd St., Plainville, KS 67663-0429. Phones: 785-434-7620; 800-999-8876. Fax: 785-434-2614. County: Hale. ICA: TX0402.

TV Market Ranking: Below 100. Franchise award date: August 7, 1978. Franchise expiration date: N.A. Began: August 1, 1981.

Channel capacity: 61 (2-way capable). Channels available but not in use: N.A.

Basic Service

Subscribers: 410.

Programming (received off-air): KAMC (A), KCBD-TV (N), KJTV (F), KLBK-TV (C), KTXT-TV (P), KUPT-LP (U) Lubbock; KVDA (O) San Antonio.

Programming (via satellite): WGN-TV (W) Chicago; A & E; American Movie Classics; CNN; Cartoon Network; Country Music TV; Discovery Channel; Disney Channel; E! Entertainment TV; ESPN; Fox Family Channel; Fox Sports Net Southwest; Goodlife TV Network; Headline News; History Channel; Home & Garden Television; Learning Channel; Lifetime; Nashville Network; Nick at Nite's TV Land; Nickelodeon; QVC; Sci-Fi Channel; TBS Superstation; The Weather Channel; Trinity Bcstg. Network; Turner Network TV; USA Network; Univision.

Current originations: Automated time-weather.

Fee: $35.00 installation; $28.95 monthly.

Pay Service 1

Pay Units: 68.

Programming (via satellite): HBO.

Fee: $10.95 monthly.

Pay Service 2

Pay Units: 38.

Programming (via satellite): Showtime.

Fee: $9.95 monthly.

Pay Service 3

Pay Units: 21.

Programming (via satellite): The Movie Channel.

Fee: $5.95 monthly.

Local advertising: No.

Miles of plant: 14.4 (coaxial). Homes passed: 827.

Manager: Bill Flowers. Chief technician: Chris Christenson. Marketing director: Jennifer Hauschild.

Hale Center fee: 4% of gross.

Ownership: Classic Cable (MSO).

HALLSVILLE—Falcon Cable TV, 108 W. Houston, Marshall, TX 75670. Phone: 903-938-8337. County: Harrison. ICA: TX0421.

TV Market Ranking: Below 100. Franchise award date: January 1, 1981. Franchise expiration date: N.A. Began: December 31, 1981.

Channel capacity: 37 (2-way capable). Channels available but not in use: None.

Basic Service

Subscribers: 689.

Programming (received off-air): KETK-TV (N) Jacksonville; KLTS-TV (P), KMSS-TV (F), KSHV (U,W), KSLA-TV (C), KTAL-TV (N), KTBS-TV (A) Shreveport-Texarkana; KLTV (A) Tyler-Longview.

Programming (via satellite): American Movie Classics; Bravo; C-SPAN; CNBC; CNN; Country Music TV; E! Entertainment TV; ESPN; Fox Family Channel; Headline News; Home Shopping Network; Lifetime; MTV; Nashville Network; Nickelodeon; QVC.

Fee: $63.00 installation; $22.66 monthly; $3.15 converter.

Expanded Basic Service

Subscribers: 607.

Programming (via satellite): Discovery Channel; Sci-Fi Channel; TV Food Network; The Weather Channel; USA Network.

Fee: $5.12 monthly.

Expanded Basic Service 2

Subscribers: 511.

Programming (via satellite): WGN-TV (W) Chicago; Disney Channel; TBS Superstation; Turner Network TV.

Fee: $7.50 monthly.

Pay Service 1

Pay Units: 81.

Programming (via satellite): Cinemax.

Fee: $25.00 installation; $11.95 monthly.

Pay Service 2

Pay Units: 142.

Programming (via satellite): HBO.

Fee: $11.95 monthly.

Pay Service 3

Pay Units: 42.

Programming (via satellite): Showtime.

Fee: $11.95 monthly.

Equipment: Gardiner headend; C-COR amplifiers; Perimeter 3 & Times Fiber cable; Hamlin set top converters; Eagle & Vitek traps; Gardiner satellite antenna; Gardiner satellite receivers.

Miles of plant: 17.0 (coaxial). Homes passed: 946.

Manager: George Doss. Chief technician: Robert Hurd.

Franchise fee: 3% of gross.

Ownership: Falcon Communications LP (MSO), joint venture formed September 30, 1998. See Cable System Ownership.

HAMILTON—Hamilton TV Cable Co., 111 N. Rice, Hamilton, TX 76531. Phone: 940-386-3418. County: Hamilton. ICA: TX0267.

TV Market Ranking: Outside TV Markets. Franchise award date: January 1, 1963. Franchise expiration date: April 1, 2007. Began: June 1, 1963.

Channel capacity: 21 (not 2-way capable). Channels available but not in use: 3.

Basic Service

Subscribers: 1,125.

Programming (received off-air): KDFW (F), KERA-TV (P), KTVT (C), KXAS-TV (N), WFAA-TV (A) Dallas-Fort Worth; KCEN-TV (N), KWKT (F), KWTX-TV (C), KXXV (A) Waco-Temple; allband FM.

Programming (via satellite): WGN-TV (W) Chicago; American Movie Classics; CNN; Discovery Channel; ESPN; Fox Family Channel; Nashville Network; TBS Superstation; Turner Network TV.

Current originations: Automated emergency alert.

Fee: $17.00 installation; $15.50 monthly; $1.00 converter.

Pay Service 1

Pay Units: 205.

Programming (via satellite): HBO.

Fee: $17.00 installation; $9.00 monthly.

Local advertising: No.

Equipment: Blonder-Tongue & Drake headend; Coral amplifiers; Comm/Scope cable; Jerrold set top converters; Eagle traps; Prodelin satellite antenna; Drake satellite receivers.

Miles of plant: 22.0 (coaxial); None (fiber optic). Homes passed: 1,549. Total homes in franchised area: 1,549.

Manager: Richard C. Jones.

City fee: 2% of gross.

Ownership: Wilbur L. Anderson Northland Cable (MSO); Richard C. Jones.

HAMLIN—Friendship Cable of Texas Inc., Box 9090, Tyler, TX 75711-9090. Phone: 903-581-2121. Fax: 903-581-2185. County: Jones. Also serves Jones County (portions). ICA: TX0294.

TV Market Ranking: Below 100. Franchise award date: June 16, 1966. Franchise expiration date: June 16, 2004. Began: August 1, 1968.

Channel capacity: 33 (not 2-way capable). Channels available but not in use: N.A.

Basic Service

Subscribers: 758.

Programming (received off-air): KRBC-TV (N), KTAB-TV (C), KTXS-TV (A) Abilene-Sweetwater; 4 FMs.

Programming (via satellite): BET; C-SPAN; Lifetime; QVC; TBS Superstation; The Weather Channel; Univision.

Current originations: Automated time-weather; religious access.

Fee: $30.00 installation (aerial), $45.00 (underground); $13.19 monthly.

Expanded Basic Service

Subscribers: 618.

Programming (via satellite): A & E; American Movie Classics; Animal Planet; CNN; Cartoon Network; Country Music TV; Discovery Channel; ESPN; FX; Fox Family Channel; Fox News Channel; Fox Sports Net Southwest; Home & Garden Television; Learning Channel; MTV; Nashville Network; Nickelodeon; Turner Network TV; USA Network.

Fee: $30.00 installation; $14.75 monthly.

Pay Service 1

Pay Units: 83.

Programming (via satellite): Cinemax.

Fee: $12.50 monthly.

Pay Service 2

Pay Units: 34.

Programming (via satellite): Disney Channel.

Fee: $12.50 monthly.

Pay Service 3

Pay Units: 186.

Programming (via satellite): The New Encore.

Fee: $1.71 monthly.

Pay Service 4

Pay Units: 99.

Programming (via satellite): HBO.

Fee: $13.00 monthly.

Pay Service 5

Pay Units: 113.

Programming (via satellite): Starz!

Fee: $6.75 monthly.

Equipment: Jerrold headend; Jerrold amplifiers; BEI character generator; Jerrold & GTE Sylvania set top converters; Arcom & Eagle traps; Anixter-Mark & Scientific-Atlanta satellite antenna; Scientific-Atlanta & Standard Communications satellite receivers.

Miles of plant: 22.0 (coaxial). Homes passed: 1,363.

Manager: Lary Bryant. Chief technician: Joe Stewart.

City fee: 2% of gross.

Ownership: Buford Television Inc. (MSO). See Cable System Ownership.

HAPPY—Classic Cable, Box 429, 605 N.W. 3rd St., Plainville, KS 67663-0429. Phones: 785-434-7620; 800-999-8876. Fax: 785-434-2614. Counties: Randall & Swisher. ICA: TX0583.

TV Market Ranking: Outside TV Markets. Franchise award date: N.A. Franchise expiration date: June 20, 2003. Began: January 1, 1987.

Channel capacity: 36 (2-way capable). Channels available but not in use: N.A.

Basic Service

Subscribers: 126.

Programming (received off-air): KACV-TV (P), KAMR-TV (N), KCIT (F,U), KFDA-TV (C), KVII-TV (A) Amarillo.
Programming (via satellite): WGN-TV (W) Chicago; A & E; CNN; Country Music TV; Discovery Channel; Disney Channel; ESPN; Fox Family Channel; History Channel; Home Shopping Network; Learning Channel; Nashville Network; Nick at Nite's TV Land; Nickelodeon; TBS Superstation; The Weather Channel; Turner Classic Movies; Turner Network TV; USA Network.
Fee: $35.00 installation; $27.95 monthly.
Pay Service 1
Pay Units: 25.
Programming (via satellite): HBO.
Fee: $10.95 monthly.
Pay Service 2
Pay Units: 9.
Programming (via satellite): Showtime.
Fee: $9.95 monthly.
Equipment: Blonder-Tongue & Scientific-Atlanta headend; Scientific-Atlanta amplifiers; Comm/Scope & Scientific-Atlanta cable; Scientific-Atlanta satellite receivers.
Miles of plant: 6.0 (coaxial). Homes passed: 273.
Manager: Bill Flowers. Chief technician: Chris Christenson. Marketing director: Jennifer Hauschild.
Ownership: Classic Cable (MSO).

HARBOR POINT—Torrence Cablevision, Box 1167, Ridgeland, MS 39158. Phones: 601-981-6900; 800-977-8849. County: Henderson. ICA: TX0769.
TV Market Ranking: Outside TV Markets. Franchise award date: N.A. Franchise expiration date: N.A. Began: N.A.
Channel capacity: 36. Channels available but not in use: 21.
Basic Service
Subscribers: 46.
Programming (received off-air): KDFW (F), KERA-TV (P), KTVT (C), KXAS-TV (N), WFAA-TV (A) Dallas-Fort Worth.
Programming (via satellite): WGN-TV (W) Chicago; A & E; American Movie Classics; CNN; Country Music TV; Discovery Channel; ESPN; Fox Family Channel; Nashville Network; Showtime; TBS Superstation; Turner Network TV; USA Network.
Fee: $28.00 monthly.
Miles of plant: 11.6 (coaxial). Homes passed: 214.
Ownership: Torrence Cable Inc. (MSO).

HARLINGEN—Time Warner Communications, Box 2327, 2921 S. Expwy. 83, Harlingen, TX 78551. Phone: 956-425-7880. Fax: 956-412-0959. County: Cameron. Also serves Cameron County (western portion), Combes, La Feria, Palm Valley, Primera, Rio Hondo, San Benito, Santa Rosa. ICA: TX0036.
TV Market Ranking: Below 100. Franchise award date: March 1, 1968. Franchise expiration date: N.A. Began: December 8, 1968.
Channel capacity: 35. Channels available but not in use: 3.
Basic Service
Subscribers: 24,340.
Programming (received off-air): KVEO (N) Brownsville; KGBT-TV (C), KMBH (P) Harlingen; KRGV-TV (A) Weslaco; XHAB-TV Matamoros; allband FM.
Programming (via satellite): C-SPAN; Discovery Channel; FX; Fox News Channel; Nashville Network; QVC; TBS Superstation; Trinity Bcstg. Network; Univision.
Current originations: Automated time-weather; public access; government access.
Fee: $22.95 installation; $14.00 monthly.
Digital Basic Service
Subscribers: N.A.
Programming (received off-air): KVEO (N) Brownsville.
Programming (via satellite): BBC America; Bravo; Discovery Home & Leisure Channel; Discovery Kids Channel; Discovery People; Discovery Science Channel; ESPN Classic Sports; ESPNews; Fox Sports World; Game Show Network; History Channel; Home & Garden Television; Independent Film Channel; MuchMusic Network; Outdoor Life Network; Romance Classics; Sci-Fi Channel; TV Guide Channel; Turner Classic Movies.
Fee: $39.99 monthly.
Expanded Basic Service
Subscribers: 23,668.
Programming (via satellite): A & E; American Movie Classics; CNN; CNNfn; Disney Channel; ESPN; EWTN; Fox Family Channel; Fox Sports Net Southwest; Gems Television; Headline News; Learning Channel; Lifetime; MTV; Nickelodeon; The Weather Channel; Turner Network TV; USA Network.
Fee: $25.00 installation; $29.00 monthly.
Expanded Basic Service
Subscribers: N.A.
Programming (via satellite): Box Exitos; Box Tejano; CBS TeleNoticias; CNN en Espanol; Canal 9; CineLatino; Discovery en Espanol; Fox Sports World Espanol.
Fee: $6.99 monthly.
Pay Service 1
Pay Units: 2,962.
Programming (via satellite): Cinemax.
Fee: $15.00 installation; $12.45 monthly.
Pay Service 2
Pay Units: 4,557.
Programming (via satellite): HBO.
Fee: $15.00 installation; $12.90 monthly.
Pay Service 3
Pay Units: N.A.
Programming (via satellite): DMX; Showtime; Starz!; The New Encore.
Fee: $1.75 monthly (Encore), $6.75 monthly (Starz), $9.45 monthly (Showtime).
Digital Pay Service 1
Pay Units: N.A.
Programming (via satellite): DMX; Encore Love Stories; Encore Mystery; Encore Westerns; HBO (multiplexed); Showtime (multiplexed); Starz! (multiplexed); The Movie Channel.
Fee: $7.00 monthly (Showtime 2), $10.00 monthly (HBO or TMC).
Pay-Per-View
Spice delivered digitally; movies delivered digitally.
Local advertising: Yes. Available in satellite distributed & character-generated programming. Rates: $20.00/Minute; $10.00/30 Seconds. Regional interconnect: Cabletime.
Equipment: Scientific-Atlanta headend; Scientific-Atlanta amplifiers; Times Fiber cable; U.S. Tower satellite antenna; Microdyne satellite receivers.
Miles of plant: 384.4 (coaxial); None (fiber optic). Homes passed: 29,442. Total homes in franchised area: 29,442.
Manager: Juan Herrera.
City fee: 3% of gross.
Ownership: AT&T Broadband & Internet Services (MSO); Time Warner Cable (MSO); Advance/Newhouse Partnership (MSO).

HARPER—Cableview Co., Box 67, Harper, TX 78631. Phone: 830-864-4660. County: Gillespie. ICA: TX0622.
TV Market Ranking: Below 100. Franchise award date: N.A. Franchise expiration date: N.A. Began: February 1, 1972.
Channel capacity: 25 (not 2-way capable). Channels available but not in use: 5.
Basic Service
Subscribers: 200.
Programming (received off-air): KRRT (W) Kerrville-San Antonio; KXAM-TV (N) Llano; KENS-TV (C), KMOL-TV (N), KSAT-TV (A) San Antonio.
Programming (via satellite): A & E; CNN; Country Music TV; Discovery Channel; ESPN; Fox Family Channel; Nashville Network; TBS Superstation; Turner Network TV; USA Network.
Fee: $25.00 installation; $24.00 monthly.
Pay Service 1
Pay Units: 45.
Programming (via satellite): HBO.
Fee: $10.00 installation; $7.00 monthly.
Equipment: M/A-Com headend; Tocom amplifiers; Comm/Scope cable; Microwave Filter traps.
Miles of plant: 11.0 (coaxial). Homes passed: 215. Total homes in franchised area: 250.
Manager: Mitchel Harper.
City fee fee: 5% of gross.
Ownership: Mitchell Harper.

HARRIS COUNTY (northern portion)—Scott Cable Communications Inc., Suite 122, 27326 Robinson Rd., Conroe, TX 77385-8930. Phone: 713-367-8900. County: Harris. ICA: TX0213.
TV Market Ranking: 15. Franchise award date: N.A. Franchise expiration date: N.A. Began: September 1, 1981.
Channel capacity: N.A. Channels available but not in use: N.A.
Basic Service
Subscribers: N.A.
Programming (received off-air): KHOU-TV (C), KHTV (W), KPRC-TV (N), KRIV (F), KTRK-TV (A), KUHT (P) Houston.
Programming (via satellite): WGN-TV (W) Chicago; CNN; ESPN; Lifetime; MTV; TBS Superstation; USA Network.
Fee: $25.00 installation; $9.00 monthly.
Pay Service 1
Pay Units: N.A.
Programming (via satellite): Cinemax; HBO; The Movie Channel.
Fee: $9.00 monthly (Cinemax or TMC), $10.00 monthly (HBO).
Equipment: Gardiner satellite antenna; Gardiner satellite receivers.
Miles of plant: 8.1 (coaxial). Homes passed: 2,126.
Ownership: American Cable Entertainment (MSO).

HART—Classic Cable, Box 429, 605 N.W. 3rd St., Plainville, KS 67663-0429. Phones: 785-434-7620; 800-998-8876. Fax: 785-434-2614. County: Castro. ICA: TX0534.
TV Market Ranking: Outside TV Markets. Franchise award date: N.A. Franchise expiration date: October 1, 2001. Began: April 1, 1982.
Channel capacity: 36 (2-way capable). Channels available but not in use: N.A.
Basic Service
Subscribers: 285.
Programming (received off-air): KACV-TV (P), KAMR-TV (N), KCIT (F,U), KFDA-TV (C), KVII-TV (A) Amarillo; KAMC (A), KCBD-TV (N), KJTV (F) Lubbock; allband FM.
Programming (via satellite): WGN-TV (W) Chicago; A & E; CNN; Country Music TV; Discovery Channel; Disney Channel; ESPN; Fox Family Channel; History Channel; Learning Channel; Nashville Network; Nick at Nite's TV Land; Nickelodeon; TBS Superstation; Telemundo; The Weather Channel; Trinity Bcstg. Network; Turner Network TV; USA Network; Univision.
Current originations: Automated time-weather.
Fee: $35.00 installation; $27.95 monthly.
Pay Service 1
Pay Units: 81.
Programming (via satellite): HBO.
Fee: $15.00 installation; $10.95 monthly.
Pay Service 2
Pay Units: 28.
Programming (via satellite): Showtime.
Fee: $15.00 installation; $9.95 monthly.
Equipment: Avantek, Jerrold & Scientific-Atlanta headend; Texscan amplifiers; Comm/Scope cable; Compuvid character generator; Jerrold & Panasonic set top converters; Eagle traps; Scientific-Atlanta satellite antenna; Scientific-Atlanta satellite receivers.
Miles of plant: 7.7 (coaxial). Homes passed: 373. Total homes in franchised area: 385.
Manager: Bill Flowers. Chief technician: Chris Christenson. Marketing director: Jennifer Hauschild.
City fee: 2% of gross.
Ownership: Classic Cable (MSO).

HASKELL—Harmon Cable Communications, Box 1146, 127 E. McHarg, Stamford, TX 79553. Phone: 915-773-3391. Fax: 915-773-2753. County: Haskell. Also serves Rule. ICA: TX0321.
TV Market Ranking: Outside TV Markets. Franchise award date: N.A. Franchise expiration date: N.A. Began: January 1, 1962.
Channel capacity: 30. Channels available but not in use: N.A.
Basic Service
Subscribers: 1,059.
Programming (received off-air): KIDZ-LP (F) Abilene; KRBC-TV (N), KTAB-TV (C), KTXS-TV (A) Abilene-Sweetwater; 2 FMs.
Programming (via satellite): WGN-TV (W) Chicago; C-SPAN; Fox Family Channel; QVC; TBS Superstation.
Current originations: Automated time-weather.
Fee: $30.00 installation; $9.30 monthly.
Expanded Basic Service
Subscribers: N.A.
Programming (via satellite): A & E; American Movie Classics; Animal Planet; CNN; Comedy Central; Country Music TV; Discovery Channel; Disney Channel; E! Entertainment TV; ESPN; ESPN 2; Fox Sports Net Southwest; Headline News; History Channel; Home & Garden Television; Home Shopping Network; Learning Channel; Lifetime; MSNBC; MTV; Nashville Network; Nick at Nite's TV Land; Nickelodeon; Sci-Fi Channel; The Weather Channel; Trinity Bcstg. Network; Turner Classic Movies; Turner Network TV; USA Network; Univision.
Fee: $16.75 monthly.
Pay Service 1
Pay Units: N.A.
Programming (via satellite): Cinemax; HBO; Showtime; The New Encore.
Fee: $35.00 installation; $3.95 monthly (The New Encore), $9.95 monthly (Cinemax, HBO or Showtime).
Local advertising: No.
Equipment: Jerrold headend; Texscan amplifiers; Comm/Scope cable; Scientific-Atlanta & Jerrold set top converters; Arcom, Eagle & Pico traps; AFC & Scientific-Atlanta satellite antenna; Scientific-Atlanta & Harris satellite receivers.
Miles of plant: 21.0 (coaxial). Homes passed: 1,186. Total homes in franchised area: 1,800.
Manager: L. R. Cagle.
City fee: 2% of basic.

Ownership: Fanch Communications Inc. (MSO); Time Warner Cable (MSO). Purchased from Harmon Cable Communications, June 21, 1999.

HASSE—Cable Ventures Ltd., Suite 106-A, 5151 Reed Rd., Columbus, OH 43220. Phone: 614-442-5890. Fax: 614-457-2567. County: Comanche. ICA: TX0550.
TV Market Ranking: Outside TV Markets. Franchise award date: N.A. Franchise expiration date: N.A. Began: August 1, 1988.
Channel capacity: 52 (2-way capable). Channels available but not in use: 34.
Basic Service
Subscribers: 77.
Programming (received off-air): KRBC-TV (N), KTAB-TV (C) Abilene-Sweetwater; KXAS-TV (N), WFAA-TV (A) Dallas-Fort Worth; KWKT (F), KWTX-TV (C), KXXV (A) Waco-Temple.
Programming (via satellite): WGN-TV (W) Chicago; A & E; C-SPAN; CNN; Discovery Channel; ESPN; Fox Family Channel; Fox News Channel; Golf Channel; Lifetime; Nashville Network; Nickelodeon; TBS Superstation; The Weather Channel; Trinity Bcstg. Network.
Fee: $29.95 installation; $20.95 monthly.
Pay Service 1
Pay Units: 11.
Programming (via satellite): HBO.
Fee: $10.00 monthly.
Pay Service 2
Pay Units: N.A.
Programming (via satellite): Cinemax; Disney Channel.
Fee: $7.00 monthly (Disney), $9.00 monthly (Cinemax).
Miles of plant: 17.6 (coaxial). Homes passed: 348.
Systems/operations manager: Steve Miller.
Ownership: Cable Ventures Ltd. (MSO).

HAWKINS—Friendship Cable of Texas Inc., Box 9090, Tyler, TX 75711-9090. Phone: 903-581-2121. Fax: 903-581-2185. Counties: Gregg, Smith, Upshur & Wood. Also serves Big Sandy, Gladewater, Owentown, Winona, Wood County (portions). ICA: TX0289.
TV Market Ranking: Below 100. Franchise award date: N.A. Franchise expiration date: April 1, 2007. Began: February 1, 1983.
Channel capacity: 54. Channels available but not in use: N.A.
Basic Service
Subscribers: 1,234.
Programming (received off-air): KDFW (F), KERA-TV (P), KTVT (C), KXAS-TV (N), WFAA-TV (A) Dallas-Fort Worth; KFXK (F) Longview; KLTV (A) Tyler-Longview.
Programming (via satellite): ESPN; Fox Family Channel; TBS Superstation.
Current originations: Public access.
Fee: $30.00 installation; $32.20 monthly.
Pay Service 1
Pay Units: 61.
Programming (via satellite): Cinemax.
Fee: $7.00 monthly.
Pay Service 2
Pay Units: 109.
Programming (via satellite): Flix.
Fee: $1.95 monthly.
Pay Service 3
Pay Units: 87.
Programming (via satellite): HBO.
Fee: $12.00 monthly.
Pay Service 4
Pay Units: 140.
Programming (via satellite): Showtime.
Fee: $7.00 monthly.
Miles of plant: 89.0 (coaxial). Homes passed: 2,156.
Manager: Marianne Bogy. Chief technician: Sonny Myers.
City fee: 2.5% of gross.
Ownership: Buford Television Inc. (MSO). See Cable System Ownership.

HAWLEY—Jayroc Cablevision, Box 6575, Abilene, TX 79608. Phone: 915-691-5787. Fax: 915-676-2882. County: Jones. ICA: TX0974.
TV Market Ranking: Below 100. Franchise award date: N.A. Franchise expiration date: N.A. Began: N.A.
Channel capacity: N.A. Channels available but not in use: N.A.
Basic Service
Subscribers: N.A.
Programming (received off-air): KRBC-TV (N), KTAB-TV (C), KTXS-TV (A) Abilene-Sweetwater.
Programming (via satellite): WGN-TV (W) Chicago; American Movie Classics; Animal Planet; CNN; Cartoon Network; Country Music TV; Discovery Channel; Disney Channel; ESPN; Fox Family Channel; Fox Sports Net Southwest; FoxNet; Goodlife TV Network; Learning Channel; Nashville Network; Nick at Nite's TV Land; Nickelodeon; QVC; Sci-Fi Channel; TBS Superstation; The Weather Channel; Travel Channel; Turner Classic Movies; Turner Network TV; USA Network.
Fee: N.A.
Pay Service 1
Pay Units: N.A.
Programming (via satellite): Cinemax; HBO; Showtime.
Fee: N.A.
Manager: Dorton Canon.
Ownership: Jayroc Inc. (MSO).

HEARNE—TCA Cable TV Inc., 209 W. 4th St., Hearne, TX 77859. Phone: 409-279-5201. County: Robertson. ICA: TX0231.
TV Market Ranking: Below 100. Franchise award date: November 1, 1968. Franchise expiration date: October 31, 2004. Began: November 1, 1968.
Channel capacity: 36 (2-way capable). Channels available but not in use: 2.
Basic Service
Subscribers: 1,590.
Programming (received off-air): KEYE-TV (C), KTBC (F), KVUE-TV (A) Austin; KBTX-TV (C) Bryan; KAMU-TV (P) College Station; KCEN-TV (N), KWKT (F), KXXV (A) Waco-Temple; allband FM.
Programming (via microwave): KHTV (W), KTRK-TV (A), KTXH (U) Houston.
Programming (via satellite): WGN-TV (W) Chicago; BET; C-SPAN; CNN; Country Music TV; Discovery Channel; ESPN; Fox Family Channel; Fox Sports Net Southwest; Goodlife TV Network; Headline News; Nashville Network; Nickelodeon; QVC; TBS Superstation; The Weather Channel; Trinity Bcstg. Network; Turner Network TV; USA Network; Univision.
Current originations: Automated time-weather; local news; local sports.
Fee: $33.70 installation; $19.35 monthly; $12.50 additional installation.
Pay Service 1
Pay Units: 480.
Programming (via satellite): HBO.
Fee: $11.00 monthly.
Pay Service 2
Pay Units: 240.
Programming (via satellite): Cinemax.
Fee: $10.00 monthly.
Pay Service 3
Pay Units: 155.
Programming (via satellite): Disney Channel.
Fee: $6.95 monthly.
Local advertising: Yes. Available in character-generated & automated programming. Regional interconnect: Cabletime.
Equipment: Jerrold headend; C-COR amplifiers; Comm/Scope cable; Video Data Systems character generator; Arcom traps; Scientific-Atlanta satellite antenna; Scientific-Atlanta satellite receivers.
Miles of plant: 30.0 (coaxial). Homes passed: 1,830. Total homes in franchised area: 1,900.
Manager: Randy Rodgers. Chief technician: Jim Davis. Marketing director: Jennie Kipp.
City fee: 2% of gross.
Ownership: TCA Cable TV Inc. (MSO). See Cable System Ownership.

HEBBRONVILLE—TCI Cablevision of Texas Inc., 208 W. Viggie St., Hebbronville, TX 78361-3048. Phone: 512-527-3267. County: Jim Hogg. ICA: TX0260.
TV Market Ranking: Outside TV Markets. Franchise award date: N.A. Franchise expiration date: N.A. Began: January 1, 1968.
Channel capacity: 37. Channels available but not in use: N.A.
Basic Service
Subscribers: 1,496.
Programming (received off-air): KEDT (P) Corpus Christi; KGNS-TV (N,A), KLDO-TV (O) Laredo.
Programming (via microwave): KIII (A), KZTV (C) Corpus Christi; KGNS-TV (N,A) Laredo.
Programming (via satellite): C-SPAN; CNN; Country Music TV; Discovery Channel; ESPN; EWTN; GalaVision; Headline News; Home Shopping Network; Lifetime; MTV; Nashville Network; Nickelodeon; Odyssey; TBS Superstation; The Weather Channel; Trinity Bcstg. Network; Turner Network TV; USA Network; Univision; VH1.
Fee: $60.00 installation; $19.92 monthly.
Pay Service 1
Pay Units: 74.
Programming (via satellite): Disney Channel.
Fee: $7.00 monthly.
Pay Service 2
Pay Units: 433.
Programming (via satellite): HBO.
Fee: $11.00 monthly.
Pay Service 3
Pay Units: 24.
Programming (via satellite): The Movie Channel.
Fee: $9.00 monthly.
Pay Service 4
Pay Units: 258.
Programming (via satellite): Showtime.
Fee: $6.00 monthly.
Equipment: AFC satellite antenna.
Miles of plant: 26.4 (coaxial). Homes passed: 1,629. Total homes in franchised area: 1,845.
Manager: Juve Morante.
City fee: 2% of gross.
Ownership: AT&T Broadband & Internet Services (MSO). Purchased from Tele-Communications Inc., March 9, 1999.

HEDLEY—Classic Cable, Box 429, 605 N.W. 3rd St., Plainville, KS 67663-0429. Phones: 785-434-7620; 800-999-8876. Fax: 785-434-2614. County: Donley. ICA: TX0772.
TV Market Ranking: Outside TV Markets. Franchise award date: N.A. Franchise expiration date: N.A. Began: N.A.
Channel capacity: 36 (2-way capable). Channels available but not in use: N.A.
Basic Service
Subscribers: 82.
Programming (received off-air): KACV-TV (P), KAMR-TV (N), KCIT (F,U), KFDA-TV (C), KVII-TV (A) Amarillo.
Programming (via satellite): WGN-TV (W) Chicago; CNN; Country Music TV; Discovery Channel; Disney Channel; ESPN; Fox Family Channel; Goodlife TV Network; Headline News; Learning Channel; Nashville Network; Nick at Nite's TV Land; TBS Superstation; The Weather Channel; Turner Network TV; USA Network.
Fee: $35.00 installation; $27.95 monthly.
Pay Service 1
Pay Units: 9.
Programming (via satellite): HBO.
Fee: $10.95 monthly.
Pay Service 2
Pay Units: 6.
Programming (via satellite): Showtime.
Fee: $9.95 monthly.
Miles of plant: 3.0 (coaxial). Homes passed: 179.
Manager: Bill Flowers. Chief technician: Rick Rattan. Marketing director: Jennifer Hauschild.
Ownership: Classic Cable (MSO).

HEIGHTS—Star Cable Co., Drawer 1570, Brazoria, TX 77422. Phones: 409-798-9121; 800-395-2775. Fax: 409-798-4409. County: Brazoria. Also serves Alvin, Manvel, Pearland. ICA: TX0143.
TV Market Ranking: 15. Franchise award date: N.A. Franchise expiration date: N.A. Began: N.A.
Channel capacity: 36 (not 2-way capable). Channels available but not in use: None.
Basic Service
Subscribers: 942.
Programming (received off-air): KHSH-TV (H) Alvin; KLTJ (E), KTMD (O) Galveston; KETH (E), KHOU-TV (C), KHTV (W), KPRC-TV (N), KRIV (F), KTRK-TV (A), KTXH (U), KUHT (P) Houston; KNWS-TV (I) Katy; KXLN-TV (S) Rosenberg.
Programming (via satellite): WGN-TV (W) Chicago; A & E; American Movie Classics; C-SPAN; CNN; Country Music TV; Discovery Channel; ESPN; Fox Family Channel; Fox Sports Net Southwest; Headline News; Lifetime; Nashville Network; Nickelodeon; TBS Superstation; The Weather Channel; Turner Network TV; USA Network; VH1.
Fee: $31.34 monthly; $2.15 converter.
Pay Service 1
Pay Units: 146.
Programming (via satellite): Cinemax.
Fee: $10.95 monthly.
Pay Service 2
Pay Units: 165.

Programming (via satellite): Disney Channel.
Fee: $7.95 monthly.
Pay Service 3
Pay Units: 329.
Programming (via satellite): HBO.
Fee: $10.95 monthly.
Pay Service 4
Pay Units: 261.
Programming (via satellite): Showtime.
Fee: $12.95 monthly.
Miles of plant: 148.0 (coaxial); None (fiber optic). Homes passed: 4,363. Total homes in franchised area: 4,363.
Manager: Mike Burns. Chief technician: Mayla Zubeck.
Ownership: Star Cable Associates (MSO).

HEMPHILL—Star Cable, 595 San Antonio Ave., Many, LA 71449. Phone: 318-256-2097. Fax: 318-256-9536. County: Sabine. ICA: TX0450.
TV Market Ranking: Outside TV Markets. Franchise award date: January 1, 1974. Franchise expiration date: January 1, 1997. Began: August 1, 1974.
Channel capacity: 12. Channels available but not in use: N.A.
Basic Service
Subscribers: N.A.
Programming (received off-air): KALB-TV (N) Alexandria; KBMT (A), KBTV-TV (N), KFDM-TV (C) Beaumont-Port Arthur; KPLC-TV (N) Lake Charles; KTRE (A) Lufkin; KSLA-TV (C), KTBS-TV (A) Shreveport-Texarkana; allband FM.
Planned programming (received off-air): KTAL-TV (N) Shreveport-Texarkana.
Fee: $5.00 installation; $7.45 monthly.
Pay Service 1
Pay Units: N.A.
Programming (via satellite): Showtime.
Fee: $19.95 installation; $7.95 monthly.
Equipment: Blonder-Tongue headend; Coral & SKL amplifiers; Coral & SKL cable.
Miles of plant: 8.0 (coaxial). Homes passed: 612.
City fee: 2% of gross.
Ownership: Star Cable Associates (MSO). Purchased from Illini Cablevision Inc., February 1, 1999.

HEMPSTEAD—CMA Cablevision, Box 133, La Grange, TX 78945. Phones: 409-968-6476; 800-272-0038. Fax: 409-968-5368. County: Waller. ICA: TX0305.
TV Market Ranking: Outside TV Markets. Franchise award date: N.A. Franchise expiration date: June 23, 2009. Began: May 1, 1982.
Channel capacity: 35 (not 2-way capable). Channels available but not in use: None.
Basic Service
Subscribers: 455.
Programming (received off-air): KHSH-TV (H) Alvin; KLTJ (E), KTMD (O) Galveston; KETH (E), KHOU-TV (C), KHTV (W), KPRC-TV (N), KRIV (F), KTRK-TV (A), KUHT (P) Houston; KXLN-TV (S) Rosenberg; allband FM.
Programming (via satellite): C-SPAN.
Fee: $15.95 monthly.
Expanded Basic Service
Subscribers: 432.
Programming (via satellite): A & E; American Movie Classics; BET; CNN; Country Music TV; Discovery Channel; ESPN; Fox Family Channel; Fox Sports Net Southwest; MTV; Nashville Network; Nickelodeon; TBS Superstation; The Weather Channel; Turner Network TV; USA Network.
Fee: $15.57 monthly.
Pay Service 1
Pay Units: 8.
Programming (via satellite): Cinemax.
Fee: $11.50 monthly.
Pay Service 2
Pay Units: 6.
Programming (via satellite): Disney Channel.
Fee: $8.45 monthly.
Pay Service 3
Pay Units: 66.
Programming (via satellite): HBO.
Fee: $11.50 monthly.
Pay Service 4
Pay Units: 10.
Programming (via satellite): Showtime.
Fee: $11.50 monthly.
Equipment: Scientific-Atlanta headend; Tocom amplifiers; Comm/Scope cable; Video Data Systems character generator; Standard Components set top converters.
Miles of plant: 31.0 (coaxial); None (fiber optic). Homes passed: 1,542. Total homes in franchised area: 1,542.
Manager: Jerry Smith. Chief technician: Grady Daniels.
City fee: 3% of gross.
Ownership: Cable Management Assoc. (MSO). Purchased from Charter Communications Inc., April 1, 1999.

HENDERSON—TCA Cable TV, 109 N. High St., Henderson, TX 75652. Phone: 903-657-3333. Fax: 903-657-7977.
Web site: http://www.tca-cable.com.
County: Rusk. Also serves Rusk County. ICA: TX0140.
TV Market Ranking: Below 100. Franchise award date: January 1, 1968. Franchise expiration date: N.A. Began: September 5, 1968.
Channel capacity: 35. Channels available but not in use: 3.
Basic Service
Subscribers: 4,376.
Programming (received off-air): KFXK (F) Longview; KTRE (A) Lufkin; KLTS-TV (P), KSLA-TV (C), KTAL-TV (N), KTBS-TV (A) Shreveport-Texarkana; KLTV (A) Tyler-Longview; 6 FMs.
Programming (via microwave): KERA-TV (P), KTVT (C), KXTX-TV (I) Dallas-Fort Worth.
Programming (via satellite): BET; C-SPAN; CNN; ESPN; Home Shopping Network; TBS Superstation; The Weather Channel; Univision.
Current originations: Automated time-weather.
Fee: $35.00 installation; $8.01 monthly.
Expanded Basic Service
Subscribers: N.A.
Programming (via satellite): CNBC; Discovery Channel; Fox Family Channel; Headline News; Lifetime; MTV; Nashville Network; Nickelodeon; USA Network.
Fee: $4.95 monthly.
Pay Service 1
Pay Units: N.A.
Programming (via satellite): Cinemax; Disney Channel; HBO; Showtime.
Fee: $35.00 installation; $9.79 monthly (each).
Local advertising: Yes. Regional interconnect: Cabletime.
Equipment: Scientific-Atlanta satellite antenna.
Miles of plant: 98.2 (coaxial). Additional miles planned: 2.0 (coaxial). Homes passed: 4,500.
Manager: Ronnie Powell. Chief technician: James McCain.
Ownership: TCA Cable TV Inc. (MSO); AT&T Broadband & Internet Services (MSO). See Cable System Ownership.

HENRIETTA—Friendship Cable of Texas Inc., Box 9090, Tyler, TX 75711-9090. Phone: 903-581-2121. Fax: 903-581-2185. County: Clay. ICA: TX0314.
TV Market Ranking: Below 100. Franchise award date: N.A. Franchise expiration date: N.A. Began: September 1, 1978.
Channel capacity: 35. Channels available but not in use: 6.
Basic Service
Subscribers: 669.
Programming (received off-air): KAUZ-TV (C), KFDX-TV (N), KJTL (F,U), KSWO-TV (A) Wichita Falls-Lawton; allband FM.
Programming (via translator): KERA-TV (P) Dallas-Fort Worth.
Programming (via satellite): Discovery Channel; Knowledge TV; Odyssey; QVC; TBS Superstation; The Weather Channel.
Current originations: Automated time-weather.
Fee: $30.00 installation; $11.32 monthly.
Expanded Basic Service
Subscribers: 610.
Programming (via satellite): American Movie Classics; Animal Planet; C-SPAN; CNBC; CNN; Cartoon Network; Court TV; Disney Channel; ESPN; FX; Fox Family Channel; Fox News Channel; Headline News; Home & Garden Television; Learning Channel; Lifetime; MTV; Nashville Network; Turner Network TV; USA Network.
Fee: $30.00 installation; $15.89 monthly.
Pay Service 1
Pay Units: 37.
Programming (via satellite): Cinemax.
Fee: $13.59 monthly.
Pay Service 2
Pay Units: 249.
Programming (via satellite): The New Encore.
Fee: $1.75 monthly.
Pay Service 3
Pay Units: 115.
Programming (via satellite): HBO.
Fee: $13.59 monthly.
Pay Service 4
Pay Units: 135.
Programming (via satellite): Starz!
Fee: $6.75 monthly.
Local advertising: No.
Equipment: Tocom headend; Tocom amplifiers; Arcom traps; Fort Worth Tower satellite antenna.
Miles of plant: 24.0 (coaxial). Homes passed: 1,205. Total homes in franchised area: 1,205.
Manager: Larry Bryant. Chief technician: Ron Johnson.
City fee: 3% of gross.
Ownership: Buford Television Inc. (MSO). See Cable System Ownership.

HEREFORD—Hereford Cablevision Co., Box 1656, 119 E. 4th, Hereford, TX 79045. Phone: 806-364-3912. Fax: 806-364-7147. County: Deaf Smith. ICA: TX0125.
TV Market Ranking: Outside TV Markets. Franchise award date: March 1, 1972. Franchise expiration date: November 1, 2006. Began: June 14, 1973.
Channel capacity: 54 (not 2-way capable). Channels available but not in use: 10.
Basic Service
Subscribers: 4,191.
Programming (received off-air): KACV-TV (P), KCIT (F,U), KFDA-TV (C), KVII-TV (A) Amarillo; allband FM.
Programming (via satellite): WGN-TV (W) Chicago; A & E; Animal Planet; C-SPAN; C-SPAN 2; CNBC; CNN; Country Music TV; Discovery Channel; Disney Channel; ESPN; ESPN 2; EWTN; Fox Family Channel; Fox Sports Net Southwest; GalaVision; Headline News; History Channel; Home & Garden Television; Learning Channel; Lifetime; MSNBC; MTV; Nashville Network; Nickelodeon; Odyssey; QVC; Sci-Fi Channel; TBS Superstation; The Weather Channel; Toon Disney; Trinity Bcstg. Network; Turner Classic Movies; Turner Network TV; USA Network; Univision; VH1; WB 100+ Station Group.
Current originations: Automated time-weather.
Fee: $18.11 installation; $27.95 monthly; $1.05 converter.
Pay Service 1
Pay Units: 184.
Programming (via satellite): Cinemax.
Fee: $10.00 installation; $9.65 monthly.
Pay Service 2
Pay Units: 605.
Programming (via satellite): HBO.
Fee: $10.00 installation; $9.65 monthly.
Pay Service 3
Pay Units: 184.
Programming (via satellite): Showtime.
Fee: $10.00 installation; $8.55 monthly.
Local advertising: Yes.
Equipment: Standard Communications headend; Scientific-Atlanta amplifiers; Scientific-Atlanta cable; Texscan character generator; Scientific-Atlanta set top converters; Eagle traps; Prodelin & Scientific-Atlanta satellite antenna.
Miles of plant: 61.0 (coaxial); None (fiber optic). Homes passed: 5,000. Total homes in franchised area: 5,000.
Manager Lloyd Ames.
City fee: 3% of gross.
Ownership: Hereford Cable TV Inc.; Southwestern Cable Investments Corp.

HICO—Northland Cable TV, Box 70, 975 N. Lillian St., Stephenville, TX 76401. Phone: 254-968-4189. Fax: 254-968-8350. County: Hamilton. ICA: TX0774.
TV Market Ranking: Outside TV Markets. Franchise award date: N.A. Franchise expiration date: June 1, 1999. Began: March 1, 1969.
Channel capacity: 29 (not 2-way capable). Channels available but not in use: N.A.
Basic Service
Subscribers: 390.
Programming (received off-air): KDAF (W), KDFI-TV (I), KDFW (F), KERA-TV (P), KTVT (C), KTXA (U), KXAS-TV (N), KXTX-TV (I), WFAA-TV (A) Dallas-Fort Worth; KWTX-TV (C), KXXV (A) Waco-Temple; allband FM.
Programming (via satellite): C-SPAN; CNN; Country Music TV; Discovery Channel; ESPN; Fox Family Channel; Headline News; Home Shopping Network; Nashville Network; The Weather Channel; Trinity Bcstg. Network; Turner Network TV; USA Network.
Current originations: Automated time-weather.
Fee: $50.00 installation; $17.25 monthly.
Pay Service 1
Pay Units: 75.
Programming (via satellite): The Movie Channel.
Fee: $15.00 installation; $10.45 monthly.
Equipment: Scientific-Atlanta headend; Jerrold amplifiers; Times Fiber cable; Scientific-Atlanta set top converters; Eagle traps; Scientific-Atlanta satellite antenna; Scientific-Atlanta satellite receivers.
Miles of plant: 11.2 (coaxial). Additional miles planned: 1.0 (coaxial).
Manager: Carroll Lee. Chief technician: Greg Perry.
City fee: 2% of gross.
Ownership: Northland Communications Corp. (MSO).

HIDALGO—Time Warner Communications, 2921 S. Expwy. 83, Harlingen, TX 78550-7615. Phone: 956-541-6782. Fax: 956-412-0959. County: Hidalgo. Also serves Las Milpas. ICA: TX0244.

TV Market Ranking: Below 100. Franchise award date: N.A. Franchise expiration date: N.A. Began: N.A.

Channel capacity: 35. Channels available but not in use: 6.

Basic Service

Subscribers: 566.

Programming (received off-air): KVEO (N) Brownsville; KGBT-TV (C), KLUJ (E), KMBH (P) Harlingen; KRGV-TV (A) Weslaco; XHAB-TV Matamoros; XHRIO (O) Matamoros-Brownsville.

Programming (via satellite): WGN-TV (W) Chicago; A & E; C-SPAN; CNN; Fox Family Channel; Headline News; Lifetime; MTV; Nashville Network; Nickelodeon; QVC; TBS Superstation; The Weather Channel.

Fee: $60.00 installation; $11.06 monthly.

Expanded Basic Service

Subscribers: 556.

Programming (via satellite): CNBC; Discovery Channel; ESPN; Fox Sports Net Southwest; Turner Network TV; USA Network; Univision.

Fee: $12.31 monthly.

Pay Service 1

Pay Units: 62.

Programming (via satellite): Cinemax.

Fee: $10.95 monthly.

Pay Service 2

Pay Units: 33.

Programming (via satellite): Disney Channel.

Fee: $10.95 monthly.

Pay Service 3

Pay Units: 116.

Programming (via satellite): HBO.

Fee: $10.95 monthly.

Pay Service 4

Pay Units: N.A.

Programming (via satellite): The New Encore.

Fee: N.A.

Miles of plant: 52.3 (coaxial). Homes passed: 1,761. Total homes in franchised area: 1,761.

Manager: Juan Herrera. Chief technician: Al Velasquez.

Ownership: Time Warner Cable (MSO); AT&T Broadband & Internet Services (MSO).

HIGGINS—Classic Cable, Box 429, 605 N.W. 3rd St., Plainville, KS 67663-0429. Phones: 785-434-7620; 800-999-8876. Fax: 785-434-2614. County: Lipscomb. ICA: TX0590.

TV Market Ranking: Outside TV Markets. Franchise award date: January 1, 1980. Franchise expiration date: N.A. Began: September 1, 1981.

Channel capacity: 36 (2-way capable). Channels available but not in use: N.A.

Basic Service

Subscribers: 128; Commercial subscribers: 14.

Programming (received off-air): KAMR-TV (N), KCIT (F,U), KFDA-TV (C), KVII-TV (A) Amarillo; KWET (P) Cheyenne.

Programming (via satellite): WGN-TV (W) Chicago; A & E; CNN; Country Music TV; Discovery Channel; Disney Channel; ESPN; Fox Family Channel; History Channel; Home & Garden Television; Learning Channel; Nashville Network; Nick at Nite's TV Land; Sci-Fi Channel; TBS Superstation; The Weather Channel; Turner Network TV; USA Network.

Fee: $35.00 installation; $27.95 monthly.

Pay Service 1

Pay Units: 12.

Programming (via satellite): HBO.

Fee: $10.95 monthly.

Pay Service 2

Pay Units: 18.

Programming (via satellite): Showtime.

Fee: $9.95 monthly.

Equipment: Microdyne satellite antenna; Microdyne satellite receivers.

Miles of plant: 6.9 (coaxial). Homes passed: 219.

Manager: Bill Flowers. Chief technician: Rick Rattan. Marketing director: Jennifer Hauschild.

Ownership: Classic Cable (MSO).

HIGHLAND RANGE—Highland Cable, 28 West Concho Ave., San Angelo, TX 76903. Phone: 915-655-8911. Fax: 915-658-6876. County: Tom Green. ICA: TX0676.

TV Market Ranking: Below 100. Franchise award date: N.A. Franchise expiration date: N.A. Began: N.A.

Channel capacity: 52 (2-way capable). Channels available but not in use: 25.

Basic Service

Subscribers: 100.

Programming (received off-air): KRBC-TV (N), KTXS-TV (A) Abilene-Sweetwater; KACB-TV (N), KIDY (F), KLST (C) San Angelo.

Programming (via satellite): KRMA-TV (P) Denver; A & E; CNN; Discovery Channel; Fox Family Channel; Nashville Network; Nickelodeon; QVC; TBS Superstation; The Weather Channel; Turner Network TV; USA Network; VH1.

Fee: $50.00 installation; $21.20 monthly.

Pay Service 1

Pay Units: N.A.

Programming (via satellite): Cinemax; Disney Channel; HBO.

Fee: $9.00 monthly (each).

Miles of plant: 5.0 (coaxial). Homes passed: 130.

Manager: Archie Kountz. Chief technician: Bob Amo.

Ownership: Highland Cable.

HILLSBORO—Northland Cable, 515 W. Tyler, Mexia, TX 76667. Phone: 254-562-2872. Fax: 254-562-6454. County: Hill. ICA: TX0175.

TV Market Ranking: Below 100. Franchise award date: June 19, 1990. Franchise expiration date: December 20, 2003. Began: December 1, 1979.

Channel capacity: 52 (not 2-way capable). Channels available but not in use: 1.

Basic Service

Subscribers: 1,390.

Programming (received off-air): KDFW (F), KERA-TV (P), KTVT (C), KXAS-TV (N), WFAA-TV (A) Dallas-Fort Worth; KCEN-TV (N), KWTX-TV (C) Waco-Temple.

Programming (via satellite): WGN-TV (W) Chicago; Fox Family Channel; TBS Superstation.

Fee: $55.00 installation; $23.95 monthly.

Pay Service 1

Pay Units: N.A.

Programming (via satellite): Cinemax; Showtime.

Fee: $10.00 monthly (each).

Equipment: Scientific-Atlanta & Gardiner headend; Magnavox amplifiers; Scientific-Atlanta, Pioneer & Oak set top converters; Eagle traps; AFC satellite antenna.

Miles of plant: 47.7 (coaxial); None (fiber optic). Homes passed: 3,006. Total homes in franchised area: 3,246.

Manager: Jimmie Cullins.

Ownership: Northland Communications Corp. (MSO).

HOLIDAY LAKES—Star Cable, Drawer 1570, Brazoria, TX 77422. Phones: 409-798-9121; 800-395-2775. Fax: 409-798-4409. County: Brazoria. ICA: TX0514.

TV Market Ranking: Below 100. Franchise award date: N.A. Franchise expiration date: November 1, 1998. Began: August 1, 1986.

Channel capacity: 62 (not 2-way capable). Channels available but not in use: 33.

Basic Service

Subscribers: 80.

Programming (received off-air): KHSH-TV (H) Alvin; KVVV (I) Baytown; KETH (E), KHOU-TV (C), KHTV (W), KPRC-TV (N), KRIV (F), KTRK-TV (A), KTXH (U), KUHT (P) Houston.

Programming (via satellite): WGN-TV (W) Chicago; American Movie Classics; CNN; Country Music TV; Discovery Channel; ESPN; Fox Family Channel; Fox Sports Net Southwest; Lifetime; Nashville Network; Nickelodeon; TBS Superstation; The Weather Channel; Turner Network TV; USA Network; Univision.

Planned programming (via satellite): A & E.

Fee: $31.34 monthly; $2.15 converter.

Pay Service 1

Pay Units: 15.

Programming (via satellite): Cinemax.

Fee: $10.95 monthly.

Pay Service 2

Pay Units: 23.

Programming (via satellite): HBO.

Fee: $10.95 monthly.

Pay Service 3

Pay Units: 13.

Programming (via satellite): The Movie Channel.

Fee: $6.95 monthly.

Miles of plant: 9.9 (coaxial); None (fiber optic). Homes passed: 420. Total homes in franchised area: 420.

Manager: Mike Burns. Chief technician: Mayla Zubeck.

City fee: 3% of gross.

Ownership: Star Cable Associates (MSO).

HOLLIDAY—Vista Cablevision, 3225 Maurine St., Wichita Falls, TX 76305. Phone: 940-855-5700. Fax: 940-855-0465. County: Archer. ICA: TX0422.

TV Market Ranking: Below 100. Franchise award date: N.A. Franchise expiration date: N.A. Began: July 1, 1982.

Channel capacity: 60. Channels available but not in use: N.A.

Basic Service

Subscribers: 358.

Programming (received off-air): KERA-TV (P) Dallas-Fort Worth; KAUZ-TV (C), KFDX-TV (N), KJTL (F,U), KSWO-TV (A) Wichita Falls-Lawton.

Programming (via satellite): WGN-TV (W) Chicago; CNN; ESPN; Fox Family Channel; Lifetime; MTV; Nashville Network; Nickelodeon; The Weather Channel; USA Network.

Fee: $50.00 installation; $9.95 monthly; $2.00 converter.

Pay Service 1

Pay Units: N.A.

Programming (via satellite): HBO; Showtime; The Movie Channel.

Fee: $10.00 installation; $12.55 monthly (each).

Local advertising: No.

Equipment: Scientific-Atlanta headend; Magnavox amplifiers; Comm/Scope cable; Eagle traps; Scientific-Atlanta satellite receivers.

Miles of plant: 17.5 (coaxial). Homes passed: 732.

Manager: Rick Orr. Chief technician: Milt Slavin.

City fee: 3% of gross.

Ownership: Time Warner Cable (MSO).

HOMER—Friendship Cable of Texas Inc., Box 9090, Tyler, TX 75711-9090. Phone: 903-581-2121. Fax: 903-581-2185. Counties: Angelina & Burleson. Also serves Bald Hill, Little Flock. ICA: TX0300.

TV Market Ranking: Below 100. Franchise award date: N.A. Franchise expiration date: N.A. Began: N.A.

Channel capacity: 36. Channels available but not in use: 4.

Basic Service

Subscribers: 681.

Programming (received off-air): KETK-TV (N) Jacksonville; KTRE (A) Lufkin; KSLA-TV (C) Shreveport-Texarkana.

Programming (via satellite): WXIA-TV (N) Atlanta; WGN-TV (W) Chicago; KMGH-TV (A) Denver; American Movie Classics; BET; CNN; Country Music TV; Discovery Channel; ESPN; Fox Family Channel; Fox Sports Net Southwest; Headline News; Home Shopping Network; Lifetime; Nashville Network; Nickelodeon; TBS Superstation; USA Network.

Fee: $33.39 monthly.

Pay Service 1

Pay Units: 29.

Programming (via satellite): Cinemax.

Fee: $10.95 monthly.

Pay Service 2

Pay Units: 27.

Programming (via satellite): HBO.

Fee: $10.95 monthly.

Pay Service 3

Pay Units: 92.

Programming (via satellite): Showtime.

Fee: $5.95 monthly.

Local advertising: Yes.

Miles of plant: 74.2 (coaxial). Homes passed: 1,468.

Manager: Marianne Bogy. Chief technician: Henry Harris.

Ownership: Buford Television Inc. (MSO). See Cable System Ownership.

HONDO—Falcon Cable TV, 1244 Encino Dr., Pleasanton, TX 78064. Phone: 830-569-5509. Fax: 830-569-4828. County: Medina. ICA: TX0218.

TV Market Ranking: 45. Franchise award date: January 1, 1980. Franchise expiration date: N.A. Began: January 1, 1981.

Channel capacity: 33 (not 2-way capable). Channels available but not in use: None.

Basic Service

Subscribers: 1,206.

Programming (received off-air): KRRT (W) Kerrville-San Antonio; KABB (F), KENS-TV (C), KLRN (P), KMOL-TV (N), KSAT-TV (A), KWEX-TV (S) San Antonio.

Programming (via satellite): A & E; American Movie Classics; C-SPAN; CNN; ESPN; Fox Family Channel; GalaVision; Headline News; Lifetime; MTV; QVC; TBS Superstation.

Fee: $22.50 installation; $20.73 monthly; $2.50 converter; $12.50 additional installation.

Expanded Basic Service

Subscribers: 1,180.

Programming (via satellite): Country Music TV; Nickelodeon; USA Network.

Fee: $1.78 monthly.

Expanded Basic Service 2

Subscribers: 1,164.

Programming (via satellite): WGN-TV (W) Chicago; Discovery Channel; Disney Channel; Nashville Network; Turner Network TV.

Fee: $7.30 monthly.

Pay Service 1

Pay Units: 81.

Programming (via satellite): Cinemax.

Fee: $10.95 monthly.

Pay Service 2

Pay Units: 285.

Programming (via satellite): HBO.

Fee: $11.95 monthly.

Pay Service 3

Pay Units: 119.

Programming (via satellite): Showtime.

Fee: $10.95 monthly.

Pay Service 4

Pay Units: 54.

Programming (via satellite): The Movie Channel.

Fee: $10.95 monthly.

Local advertising: Yes. Available in character-generated programming. Regional interconnect: Cabletime.

Program Guide: Premium Channels.

Equipment: Scientific-Atlanta amplifiers; Comm/Scope cable; Scientific-Atlanta set top converters; Pico traps; Scientific-Atlanta satellite antenna; Microdyne satellite receivers.

Miles of plant: 31.0 (coaxial). Homes passed: 1,375.

Manager: Lorna Gentry. Chief technician: Santos Guajardo.

Franchise fee: 2% of gross.

Ownership: Falcon Communications LP (MSO), joint venture formed September 30, 1998. See Cable System Ownership.

HONEY GROVE—TCA Cable TV, 25 S.E. 19th St., Paris, TX 75460-6101. Phone: 903-785-0086. Fax: 903-784-7099. Web site: http://www.tca-cable.com. County: Fannin. ICA: TX0776.

TV Market Ranking: Outside TV Markets. Franchise award date: N.A. Franchise expiration date: N.A. Began: N.A.

Channel capacity: 25. Channels available but not in use: N.A.

Basic Service

Subscribers: 655.

Programming (received off-air): KTEN (A,N,F) Ada; KDAF (W), KDFI-TV (I), KDFW (F), KERA-TV (P), KTVT (C), KTXA (U), KXAS-TV (N), KXTX-TV (I), WFAA-TV (A) Dallas-Fort Worth; KXII (C) Sherman.

Programming (via satellite): WGN-TV (W) Chicago; A & E; American Movie Classics; BET; C-SPAN; CNN; Discovery Channel; Disney Channel; ESPN; Fox Family Channel; Headline News; Learning Channel; Lifetime; Nashville Network; Nickelodeon; Odyssey; Pax Net; TBS Superstation; The Weather Channel; Turner Network TV; USA Network.

Fee: $35.00 installation; $20.69 monthly.

Pay Service 1

Pay Units: N.A.

Programming (via satellite): Cinemax; HBO; Showtime.

Fee: $8.00 monthly (Cinemax), $9.95 monthly (Showtime), $10.95 monthly (HBO), $19.95 monthly (Cinemax, HBO & Showtime).

Manager: Tim Masters. Chief technician: Bob Holmon.

Ownership: TCA Cable TV Inc. (MSO); AT&T Broadband & Internet Services (MSO). See Cable System Ownership.

HOOKS—TCA Cable TV, 609 E. North Front St., New Boston, TX 75570-3005. Phone: 903-628-5569. Web site: http://www.tca-cable.com. County: Bowie. Also serves Bowie County, Red River Army Depot. ICA: TX0272.

TV Market Ranking: 58 (portions of Bowie County, Hooks, Red River Army Depot); Outside TV Markets (portions of Bowie County). Franchise award date: N.A. Franchise expiration date: N.A. Began: February 1, 1980.

Channel capacity: 34. Channels available but not in use: 3.

Basic Service

Subscribers: 1,122.

Programming (received off-air): KLTS-TV (P), KMSS-TV (F), KSLA-TV (C), KTAL-TV (N), KTBS-TV (A) Shreveport-Texarkana.

Programming (via microwave): WFAA-TV (A) Dallas-Fort Worth.

Programming (via satellite): WGN-TV (W) Chicago; American Movie Classics; CNBC; CNN; Comedy Central; Discovery Channel; ESPN; Fox Family Channel; Fox Sports Net Southwest; Lifetime; MTV; Nashville Network; Nickelodeon; Odyssey; QVC; TBS Superstation; The Weather Channel; Trinity Bcstg. Network; Turner Network TV; USA Network.

Fee: $34.02 installation; $10.05 monthly.

Pay Service 1

Pay Units: 82.

Programming (via satellite): Disney Channel.

Fee: N.A.

Pay Service 2

Pay Units: 390.

Programming (via satellite): The New Encore.

Fee: N.A.

Pay Service 3

Pay Units: 209.

Programming (via satellite): HBO.

Fee: N.A.

Pay Service 4

Pay Units: 135.

Programming (via satellite): Showtime.

Fee: N.A.

Miles of plant: 35.7 (coaxial). Homes passed: 1,525. Total homes in franchised area: 4,000.

Manager: Ron Eubanks.

Ownership: TCA Cable TV Inc. (MSO); AT&T Broadband & Internet Services (MSO). See Cable System Ownership.

HORSESHOE BAY—Northland Cable TV, Box 366, 1101 Mission Hill Dr., Marble Falls, TX 78654-1906. Phone: 830-598-6525. Fax: 830-693-6056. Counties: Burnet & Llano. Also serves Cottonwood Shores, Oak Ridge. ICA: TX0250.

TV Market Ranking: Below 100. Franchise award date: N.A. Franchise expiration date: January 1, 1998. Began: October 15, 1982.

Channel capacity: 35 (2-way capable; not operating 2-way). Channels available but not in use: 12.

Basic Service

Subscribers: 76.

Programming (received off-air): KEYE-TV (C), KLRU (P), KNVA (W), KTBC (F), KVUE-TV (A) Austin; KXAM-TV (N) Llano; allband FM.

Programming (via satellite): WGN-TV (W) Chicago; C-SPAN; Headline News; QVC; TBS Superstation; TV Guide Sneak Prevue.

Current originations: Automated time-weather.

Fee: $60.00 installation; $19.50 monthly.

Expanded Basic Service

Subscribers: N.A.

Programming (via satellite): A & E; American Movie Classics; CNBC; CNN; Cartoon Network; Discovery Channel; ESPN; Fox Family Channel; Fox Sports Net Southwest; History Channel; Learning Channel; Nashville Network; The Weather Channel; Trinity Bcstg. Network; Turner Network TV; USA Network.

Fee: $50.00 installation; $27.95 monthly.

Expanded Basic Service 2

Subscribers: N.A.

Programming (via satellite): American Movie Classics; CNBC; Cartoon Network; Nickelodeon; Turner Classic Movies; Turner Network TV.

Fee: $8.50 monthly.

Pay Service 1

Pay Units: 20.

Programming (via satellite): Cinemax.

Fee: $8.95 monthly.

Pay Service 2

Pay Units: 58.

Programming (via satellite): Starz!; The New Encore.

Fee: $11.50 monthly.

Pay Service 3

Pay Units: 276.

Programming (via satellite): HBO.

Fee: $11.95 monthly.

Pay Service 4

Pay Units: 120.

Programming (via satellite): Showtime.

Fee: $11.50 monthly.

Local advertising: Yes. Available in satellite distributed & character-generated programming. Local sales manager: Pat Tims.

Equipment: Scientific-Atlanta headend; Scientific-Atlanta amplifiers; Comm/Scope & Times Fiber cable; Texscan character generator; Scientific-Atlanta, Oak & NSC set top converters; Eagle, Arcom & Pico traps; Scientific-Atlanta satellite antenna; Scientific-Atlanta satellite receivers; ChannelMatic & Standard Communications commercial insert.

Miles of plant: 35.0 (coaxial); None (fiber optic). Additional miles planned: 5.0 (coaxial). Homes passed: 1,700. Total homes in franchised area: 2,778.

Manager: Rich Beatty. Chief technician: David Simpson. Marketing director: Debbie Jones.

Franchise fee: 3% of gross.

Ownership: Northland Communications Corp. (MSO).

HOUSTON—Phonoscope Ltd., 6013 Westline Dr., Houston, TX 77036. Phone: 713-272-4600. Fax: 713-271-7709. Counties: Fort Bend, Harris & Montgomery. Also serves Fort Bend County (portions), Montgomery County (portions). ICA: TX0777.

TV Market Ranking: 15 (portions of Fort Bend County, Houston, portions of Montgomery County); Below 100 (portions of Fort Bend County, portions of Montgomery County). Franchise award date: September 1, 1986. Franchise expiration date: N.A. Began: January 1, 1987.

Channel capacity: 72. Channels available but not in use: 12.

Basic Service

Subscribers: 16,829.

Programming (received off-air): KHSH-TV (H) Alvin; KVVV (I) Baytown; KPXB (X) Conroe; KLTJ (E), KTMD (O) Galveston; KETH (E), KHOU-TV (C), KHTV (W), KPRC-TV (N), KRIV (F), KTRK-TV (A), KTXH (U), KUHT (P) Houston; KNWS-TV (I) Katy; KXLN-TV (S) Rosenberg.

Programming (via satellite): WGN-TV (W) Chicago; A & E; BET; C-SPAN; C-SPAN 2; CNBC; CNN; Cartoon Network; Comedy Central; Country Music TV; Discovery Channel; Disney Channel; E! Entertainment TV; ESPN; ESPN 2; Fox Family Channel; Fox Sports Net Southwest; Headline News; International Channel; Learning Channel; Lifetime; MTV; NASA TV; Nashville Network; Nickelodeon; Odyssey; QVC; Sci-Fi Channel; TBS Superstation; TV Guide Channel; The Weather Channel; Turner Network TV; USA Network; VH1.

Current originations: Public access; educational access; government access; leased access; automated emergency alert; local news.

Fee: $25.00 installation; $18.95 monthly.

Pay Service 1

Pay Units: N.A.

Programming (via satellite): Cinemax; HBO; Playboy TV; Showtime; The Movie Channel.

Fee: $8.00 monthly (Playboy), $9.00 monthly (Cinemax), $11.50 monthly (Showtime or TMC), $12.50 monthly (HBO).

Pay-Per-View

Special events.

Fee: Varies.

Local advertising: Yes. Available in satellite distributed, locally originated, character-generated, taped & automated programming. Rates: $40.00/Minute; $20.00/30 Seconds. Local sales manager: Don Newton.

Program Guide: TV Host.

Equipment: C-COR & Magnavox amplifiers; Siecor cable; Amiga character generator; Pioneer set top converters; Philips satellite antenna; Arvis commercial insert.

Miles of plant: 350.0 (fiber optic).

Manager: Rhonda Druke. Chief technician: Ted Viens.

Franchise fee: 3% of gross.

Ownership: Phonoscope Ltd.

HOUSTON—Warner Cable Communications, 8400 W. Tidwell, Houston, TX 77040. Phones: 713-462-1900; 713-462-9000. Fax: 713-895-2635. Web site: http://www.twchouston.com. Counties: Brazoria, Chambers, Fort Bend, Galveston, Harris, Montgomery & Waller. Also serves Alvin, Arbor Vineyard, Ashford Park, Autumn Run, Bacliff, Bammel Oaks, Barker's Landing, Barrett Station, Bayou Vista, Baytown, Bear Creek Farms, Bellaire, Bermuda Beach, Blue Bell, Brazoria County, Briar Creek, Briar Hills, Broken Bayou, Brook Hollow West, Brookside Village, Bunker Hill, Burger Estates, Chambers County (western portion), Channelview, Chimney Hill, Clear Lake Shores, Clute, Colonies, Concord Colony, Copperfield, Cornerstone Village North, Cottonwood, Crosby, Cypress Trails, Deer Park, Deerfield Village, Dickinson, Easton Common Village, Ed-Lou, El Lago, Enclave at Pavillion, Fleetwood, Fleetwood Oaks, Forest Bend, Fort Bend County, Freeport, Frick Road Park, Friendswood, Galena Park, Galveston, Galveston County, Granada, Harris County, Hearthstone, Hearthstone Green, Heatherglen, Hedwig, Heritage Park, Highlands, Hillcrest Village, Hillshire, Hitchcock, Humble, Hunter Creek, Jacinto City, Jamaica Beach, Jamestown Colony, Jersey Village, Katy, Keegans Glen, Kemah, Klienbrook, La Marque, La Porte, Lake Jackson, Langham Colony, League City, Magnolia, Maple Leaf Gardens, Memorial Thicket, Mills Walk, Mission Bend, Missouri City, Modot Village, Montgomery County, Morgans Point, Nassau Bay, Needville, North Cliffe Manor, North Pines Ranchetts, Northwest Green, Northwest Park, Oakland Village, Omega Bay, Paddock, Pasadena, Pearland, Piney Point, Pinedale, Pirate Beach, Pirate Cove, Reid Estates, Richmond, Richwood, Rolling Fork, Rosenberg, Santa Fe, Seabrook, Sepco Park, Settlers Village, Shenandoah (unincorporated areas), Shoreacres, Sommerall, South Creek, South Houston, Spring Valley, Spring Valley Creek, Stafford, Stone Creek, Stonehenge, Suffolk Chase, Sugar

Land, Sundown, Tallowood, Tanner Road, Taylor Lake Village, Texas City, The Meadows, The Woodlands, Thornhill Apartments, Tiki Island, Tomball, Turtle Lake, Waller County, Webster, Wedgewood, West Hollow, West Hollow Villa, West Trails, West University Place, White Oak Manor, Willow Point, Windfern, Windfern Manor, Windfern Meadow, Woodfern, Woodfern Manor, Woodgate, Yorkshire. ICA: TX0001.

TV Market Ranking: 15 (Alvin, Arbor Vineyard, Ashford Park, Autumn Run, Bacliff, Bammel Oaks, Barker's Landing, Barrett Station, Bayou Vista, Baytown, Bear Creek Farms, Bellaire, Blue Bell, portions of Brazoria County, Briar Creek, Briar Hills, Broken Bayou, Brook Hollow West, Brookside Village, Bunker Hill, Burger Estates, Chambers County, Channelview, Chimney Hill, Clear Lake Shores, Colonies, Concord Colony, Copperfield, Cornerstone Village North, Cottonwood, Crosby, Cypress Trails, Deer Park, Deerfield Village, Dickinson, Easton Common Village, Ed-Lou, El Lago, Enclave at Pavillion, Fleetwood, Fleetwood Oaks, Forest Bend, portions of Fort Bend County, Frick Road Park, Friendswood, Galena Park, portions of Galveston County, Granada, Harris County, Hearthstone, Hearthstone Green, Heatherglen, Hedwig, Heritage Park, Highlands, Hillcrest Village, Hillshire, Hitchcock, Houston, Humble, Hunter Creek, Jacinto City, Jamestown Colony, Jersey Village, Katy, Keegans Glen, Kemah, Klienbrook, La Marque, La Porte, Langham Colony, League City, Magnolia, Maple Leaf Gardens, Memorial Thicket, Mills Walk, Mission Bend, Missouri City, Modot Village, portions of Montgomery County, Morgans Point, Nassau Bay, North Cliffe Manor, North Pines Ranchetts, Northwest Green, Northwest Park, Oakland Village, Omega Bay, Paddock, Pasadena, Pearland, Piney Point, Pinedale, Reid Estates, Richmond, Rolling Fork, Rosenberg, Santa Fe, Seabrook, Sepco Park, Settlers Village, Shenandoah, Shoreacres, Sommerall, South Creek, South Houston, Spring Valley, Spring Valley Creek, Stafford, Stone Creek, Stonehenge, Suffolk Chase, Sugar Land, Sundown, Tallowood, Taylor Lake Village, The Meadows, The Woodlands, Thornhill Apartments, Tomball, Turtle Lake, portions of Waller County, Webster, Wedgewood, West Hollow, West Hollow Villa, West Trails, West University Place, White Oak Manor, Willow Point, Windfern, Windfern Manor, Windfern Meadow, Woodfern, Woodfern Manor, Woodgate, Yorkshire); Below 100 (Bermuda Beach, portions of Brazoria County, Clute, portions of Fort Bend County, Freeport, Galveston, portions of Galveston County, Jamaica Beach, Lake Jackson, portions of Montgomery County, Needville, Pirate Beach, Pirate Cove, Richwood, Texas City, Tiki Island, portions of Waller County). Franchise award date:

Channel capacity: 45 (2-way capable; operating 2-way). Channels available but not in use: 1.

Basic Service

Subscribers: 642,502.

Programming (received off-air): KHSH-TV (H) Alvin; KPXB (X) Conroe; KLTJ (E), KTMD (O) Galveston; KETH (E), KHOU-TV (C), KHTV (W), KPRC-TV (N), KRIV (F), KTRK-TV (A), KTXH (U), KUHT (P), KZJL (I) Houston; KNWS-TV (I) Katy; KXLN-TV (S) Rosenberg; 4 FMs.

Programming (via satellite): CNN International; TV Guide Channel; ValueVision.

Current originations: Automated time-weather; public access; educational access; government access; leased access; automated emergency alert.

Fee: $29.84 installation; $11.00 monthly; $2.76 converter.

Expanded Basic Service

Subscribers: 526,208.

Programming (via satellite): WGN-TV (W) Chicago; A & E; Animal Planet; BET; C-SPAN; C-SPAN 2; CNBC; CNN; Cartoon Network; Comedy Central; Country Music TV; Court TV; Discovery Channel; E! Entertainment TV; ESPN; ESPN 2; Fox Family Channel; GalaVision; Gems Television; Headline News; History Channel; Home & Garden Television; International Channel; Learning Channel; Lifetime; MSNBC; MTV; Nashville Network; Nickelodeon; Odyssey; QVC; Sci-Fi Channel; TBS Superstation; The Weather Channel; Travel Channel; Turner Network TV; USA Network; VH1.

Fee: $26.90 installation; $20.71 monthly.

Expanded Basic Service 2

Subscribers: N.A.

Programming (via satellite): American Movie Classics; Bravo; Fox Sports Net Southwest; Golf Channel; The New Encore; Turner Classic Movies.

Fee: $2.77 monthly.

Pay Service 1

Pay Units: 79,857.

Programming (via satellite): Cinemax.

Fee: $4.95 installation; $12.48 monthly.

Pay Service 2

Pay Units: 167,687.

Programming (via satellite): HBO (multiplexed).

Fee: $4.95 installation; $12.48 monthly.

Pay Service 3

Pay Units: 31,971.

Programming (via satellite): The Movie Channel.

Fee: $4.95 installation; $12.48 monthly.

Pay Service 4

Pay Units: 98,964.

Programming (via satellite): Showtime (multiplexed).

Fee: $12.48 monthly.

Pay Service 5

Pay Units: N.A.

Programming (via satellite): Disney Channel; Starz!; Sundance Channel.

Fee: $4.95 installation; $3.95 monthly (Sundance), $9.96 monthly (Disney), $12.48 monthly (Starz).

Pay-Per-View

Playboy TV; movies.

Local advertising: Yes. Available in satellite distributed programming. Local sales manager: Ray Purser.

Program Guide: Cable Monthly.

Equipment: Scientific-Atlanta headend; Jerrold amplifiers; Comm/Scope cable; Sony cameras; Panasonic VTRs; BEI character generator; Pioneer set top converters; Gardiner satellite antenna; Scientific-Atlanta satellite receivers.

Miles of plant: 13892.0 (coaxial). Homes passed: 1,343,177. Total homes in franchised area: 1,343,177.

President: Ronald McMillan. Chief technician: Allen Hudz. V.P., Marketing: Bradley Greenwald.

Ownership: AT&T Broadband & Internet Services (MSO); Time Warner Cable (MSO); Advance/Newhouse Partnership (MSO).

HOWARDWICK—Classic Cable, Box 429, 605 N.W. 3rd St., Plainville, KS 67663-0429. Phones: 785-434-7620; 800-999-8876. Fax: 785-434-2614. County: Donley. ICA: TX0602.

TV Market Ranking: Outside TV Markets. Franchise award date: N.A. Franchise expiration date: October 1, 2002. Began: January 1, 1978.

Channel capacity: 36 (2-way capable). Channels available but not in use: N.A.

Basic Service

Subscribers: 89; Commercial subscribers: 7.

Programming (received off-air): KACV-TV (P), KAMR-TV (N), KCIT (F,U), KFDA-TV (C), KVII-TV (A) Amarillo.

Programming (via satellite): WGN-TV (W) Chicago; American Movie Classics; CNN; Country Music TV; Discovery Channel; Disney Channel; ESPN; Fox Family Channel; Learning Channel; Lifetime; Nashville Network; Nick at Nite's TV Land; TBS Superstation; The Weather Channel; Trinity Bcstg. Network; Turner Network TV.

Current originations: Automated time-weather.

Fee: $35.00 installation; $27.95 monthly.

Pay Service 1

Pay Units: 9.

Programming (via satellite): HBO.

Fee: $9.95 monthly.

Equipment: Magnavox amplifiers; Comm/Scope cable.

Miles of plant: 7.0 (coaxial). Homes passed: 247.

Manager: Bill Flowers. Chief technician: Rick Rattan. Marketing director: Jennifer Hauschild.

City fee: 2% of gross.

Ownership: Classic Cable (MSO).

HUBBARD—Charter Communications Inc., 5227 FM 813, Waxahachie, TX 75165. Phones: 972-938-9288; 800-477-0887. Fax: 972-923-0039. Counties: Hill & Navarro. Also serves Dawson. ICA: TX0393.

TV Market Ranking: Below 100. Franchise award date: N.A. Franchise expiration date: N.A. Began: July 1, 1983.

Channel capacity: 52. Channels available but not in use: N.A.

Basic Service

Subscribers: 357.

Programming (received off-air): KDAF (W), KDFI-TV (I), KDFW (F), KDTX-TV (T), KERA-TV (P), KTVT (C), KTXA (U), KXAS-TV (N), KXTX-TV (I), WFAA-TV (A) Dallas-Fort Worth; KDTN (P) Denton; KHSX-TV (H) Irving; KWTX-TV (C) Waco-Temple.

Programming (via satellite): WGN-TV (W) Chicago; TBS Superstation.

Fee: $26.00 installation; $8.45 monthly.

Expanded Basic Service

Subscribers: N.A.

Programming (via satellite): CNN; Country Music TV; Discovery Channel; ESPN; Fox Family Channel; Headline News; Home Shopping Network; Lifetime; MTV; Nashville Network; Nickelodeon; The Weather Channel; Turner Network TV; USA Network.

Fee: $13.11 monthly.

Pay Service 1

Pay Units: N.A.

Programming (via satellite): Cinemax; HBO; Showtime.

Fee: $7.00 monthly (Showtime), $9.00 monthly (Cinemax), $12.00 monthly (HBO).

Miles of plant: 21.7 (coaxial). Homes passed: 842.

Manager: Mary Scearce. Chief technician: Ken Stevens.

Ownership: Charter Communications Inc. (MSO). Purchased from Marcus Cable, April 1, 1999.

HUDSON—TCA Cable, 1415 S. First St., Lufkin, TX 75901. Phone: 409-639-1116. Fax: 409-634-6889. County: Angelina. ICA: TX0357.

TV Market Ranking: Below 100. Franchise award date: N.A. Franchise expiration date: N.A. Began: December 1, 1982.

Channel capacity: 41 (2-way capable). Channels available but not in use: N.A.

Basic Service

Subscribers: 814.

Programming (received off-air): KFXK (F) Longview; KTRE (A) Lufkin; KLSB-TV (N) Nacogdoches.

Programming (via satellite): WGN-TV (W) Chicago; KCNC-TV (C), KRMA-TV (P) Denver; A & E; CNN; Discovery Channel; Disney Channel; ESPN; Fox Family Channel; Fox News Channel; Fox Sports Net Southwest; FoxNet; Great American Country; Headline News; History Channel; Learning Channel; Nashville Network; Nick at Nite's TV Land; Nickelodeon; QVC; Sci-Fi Channel; TBS Superstation; The Weather Channel; Trinity Bcstg. Network; Turner Classic Movies; Turner Network TV; USA Network.

Current originations: Local news.

Fee: $35.00 installation; $28.95 monthly.

Pay Service 1

Pay Units: 111.

Programming (via satellite): HBO.

Fee: $35.00 installation; $10.95 monthly.

Pay Service 2

Pay Units: 181.

Programming (via satellite): Showtime.

Fee: $9.95 monthly.

Pay Service 3

Pay Units: 142.

Programming (via satellite): The Movie Channel.

Fee: $9.95 monthly.

Equipment: Blonder-Tongue headend; Scientific-Atlanta amplifiers; Comm/Scope cable; Eagle traps.

Miles of plant: 35.0 (coaxial). Homes passed: 1,200. Total homes in franchised area: 1,200.

Manager: Glenn Parker. Chief technician: Jerry Teer.

City fee: 3% of gross.

Ownership: TCA Cable Partners (MSO). Purchased from Classic Cable, December 31, 1998.

HUFFMAN—Northland Cable, Box 839, 1144 Antique Lane, New Caney, TX 77357. Phone: 713-689-2048. Fax: 713-689-7643. County: Harris. Also serves Indian Shores. ICA: TX0778.

TV Market Ranking: 15. Franchise award date: N.A. Franchise expiration date: N.A. Began: July 1, 1987.

Channel capacity: N.A. Channels available but not in use: N.A.

Basic Service

Subscribers: N.A.

Programming (received off-air): KHSH-TV (H) Alvin; KBTX-TV (C) Bryan; KTMD (O) Galveston; KHOU-TV (C), KHTV (W), KPRC-TV (N), KRIV (F), KTRK-TV (A), KTXH (U), KUHT (P) Houston.

Programming (via satellite): WGN-TV (W) Chicago; A & E; CNN; Country Music TV; Discovery Channel; ESPN; Fox Family Channel; Fox Sports Net Southwest; Headline News; Lifetime; Nashville Network; Nickelodeon; TBS Superstation; The Weather Channel; USA Network.

Fee: $17.95 monthly.

Pay Service 1

Pay Units: N.A.

Programming (via satellite): Disney Channel; HBO; Showtime.

Fee: $7.95 monthly (each).

Manager: Chuck Nichols.

Ownership: Northland Communications Corp. (MSO).

HULL—Friendship Cable of Texas Inc., Box 9090, Tyler, TX 75711-9090. Phone: 903-581-2121. Fax: 903-581-2185. County: Liberty. Also serves Batson, Daisetta, Hardin. ICA: TX0299.
TV Market Ranking: 88. Franchise award date: N.A. Franchise expiration date: N.A. Began: N.A.
Channel capacity: 36 (not 2-way capable). Channels available but not in use: None.
Basic Service
Subscribers: 889.
Programming (received off-air): KBMT (A), KBTV-TV (N), KFDM-TV (C) Beaumont-Port Arthur; KHOU-TV (C), KHTV (W), KPRC-TV (N), KRIV (F), KTRK-TV (A), KTXH (U), KUHT (P) Houston.
Programming (via satellite): A & E; C-SPAN; CNN; Country Music TV; Discovery Channel; Disney Channel; ESPN; Fox Family Channel; Fox Sports Net Southwest; Headline News; Lifetime; Nashville Network; Nickelodeon; QVC; TBS Superstation; The Inspirational Network; The Weather Channel; Turner Network TV; USA Network; VH1.
Fee: $33.81 monthly.
Pay Service 1
Pay Units: 39.
Programming (via satellite): Cinemax.
Fee: $10.95 monthly.
Pay Service 2
Pay Units: 72.
Programming (via satellite): HBO.
Fee: $10.95 monthly.
Pay Service 3
Pay Units: 93.
Programming (via satellite): Showtime.
Fee: $10.95 monthly.
Local advertising: Yes.
Miles of plant: 85.4 (coaxial). Homes passed: 1,680.
Manager: Wanda Pyburn. Chief technician: Mike Deal.
Ownership: Buford Television Inc. (MSO). See Cable System Ownership.

HUNTINGTON—Communicom, Box 640, 2504 Westwood Rd., Westlake, LA 70669. Phone: 318-436-5538. Fax: 318-433-0405. County: Angelina. ICA: TX0417.
TV Market Ranking: Below 100. Franchise award date: N.A. Franchise expiration date: N.A. Began: N.A.
Channel capacity: 27 (not 2-way capable). Channels available but not in use: 10.
Basic Service
Subscribers: 481.
Programming (received off-air): KETK-TV (N) Jacksonville; KTRE (A) Lufkin.
Programming (via satellite): WGN-TV (W) Chicago; WJBK (F) Detroit; CNN; Discovery Channel; ESPN; Fox Family Channel; Nashville Network; TBS Superstation; Turner Network TV; USA Network.
Fee: $11.00 monthly; $2.95 converter.
Pay Service 1
Pay Units: N.A.
Programming (via satellite): Disney Channel; Showtime.
Fee: $9.95 monthly (each).
Miles of plant: 17.0 (coaxial). Homes passed: 739. Total homes in franchised area: 900.
Manager: Brian Sparks. Chief technician: Carson Fasske.
City fee: 3% of gross.
Ownership: James Cable Partners (MSO).

HUNTSVILLE—TCA/Huntsville Cable TV, Box 1260, 1620 Normal Park, Huntsville, TX 77340. Phone: 409-295-5733. Fax: 409-295-5851. County: Walker. Also serves Elkins Lake, Walker County. ICA: TX0094.
TV Market Ranking: Below 100 (Elkins Lake, Huntsville, portions of Walker County); Outside TV Markets (portions of Walker County). Franchise award date: N.A. Franchise expiration date: N.A. Began: August 9, 1962.
Channel capacity: 38. Channels available but not in use: None.
Basic Service
Subscribers: 6,571.
Programming (received off-air): KBTX-TV (C) Bryan; KPXB (X) Conroe; KHOU-TV (C), KHTV (W), KPRC-TV (N), KRIV (F), KTRK-TV (A), KTXH (U), KUHT (P) Houston; KTRE (A) Lufkin; allband FM.
Programming (via satellite): A & E; C-SPAN; CNBC; CNN; Country Music TV; E! Entertainment TV; ESPN; EWTN; Fox Family Channel; Headline News; Home Shopping Network; Lifetime; Nashville Network; TBS Superstation; The Weather Channel.
Current originations: Automated time-weather; public access; educational access; local news.
Fee: $37.13 installation; $15.19 monthly; $2.00 converter.
Expanded Basic Service
Subscribers: 5,028.
Programming (via satellite): BET; Discovery Channel; MTV; Nick at Nite; Nickelodeon; Turner Network TV; USA Network; VH1.
Fee: $3.81 installation; $5.62 monthly.
Pay Service 1
Pay Units: 1,732.
Programming (via satellite): HBO.
Fee: $10.00 monthly.
Pay Service 2
Pay Units: 1,324.
Programming (via satellite): Cinemax.
Fee: $8.00 monthly.
Pay Service 3
Pay Units: 386.
Programming (via satellite): Disney Channel.
Fee: $8.00 monthly.
Pay Service 4
Pay Units: 1,295.
Programming (via satellite): Showtime.
Fee: $7.00 monthly.
Pay Service 5
Pay Units: 584.
Programming (via satellite): Fox Sports Net Southwest.
Fee: $8.00 monthly.
Pay-Per-View
Addressable homes: 5,028.
Viewer's Choice; special events.
Local advertising: Yes. Available in satellite distributed programming. Rates: $6.00/Minute. Local sales manager: Sue Ellisor. Regional interconnect: Woodlands Communications Network.
Equipment: Times Fiber & C-COR cable; Scientific-Atlanta addressable set top converters; Scientific-Atlanta satellite antenna.
Miles of plant: 175.0 (coaxial). Homes passed: 9,300. Total homes in franchised area: 10,845.
Manager: Johnnie D. Blalack. Chief technician: Mark Schmidt.
City fee: 4% of gross.
Ownership: TCA Cable TV Inc. (MSO). See Cable System Ownership.

IDALOU—Classic Cable, Box 429, 605 N.W. 3rd St., Plainville, KS 67663-0429. Phones: 785-434-7620; 800-999-8876. Fax: 785-434-2614. County: Lubbock. ICA: TX0406.
TV Market Ranking: Below 100. Franchise award date: December 13, 1988. Franchise expiration date: N.A. Began: May 1, 1980.
Channel capacity: 61 (2-way capable). Channels available but not in use: N.A.

Basic Service
Subscribers: 361.
Programming (received off-air): KAMC (A), KCBD-TV (N), KJTV (F), KLBK-TV (C), KPTB (I), KTXT-TV (P), KUPT-LP (U) Lubbock.
Programming (via translator): KVDA (O) San Antonio.
Programming (via satellite): WGN-TV (W) Chicago; American Movie Classics; CNN; Cartoon Network; Country Music TV; Discovery Channel; Disney Channel; E! Entertainment TV; ESPN; Fox Family Channel; Fox News Channel; Fox Sports Net Southwest; Headline News; History Channel; Home & Garden Television; Learning Channel; Lifetime; Nashville Network; Nick at Nite's TV Land; Nickelodeon; QVC; TBS Superstation; The Weather Channel; Travel Channel; Trinity Bcstg. Network; Turner Network TV; USA Network; Univision.
Current originations: Automated time-weather; local news.
Fee: $35.00 installation; $27.95 monthly.
Pay Service 1
Pay Units: 40.
Programming (via satellite): Cinemax.
Fee: $9.95 monthly.
Pay Service 2
Pay Units: 79.
Programming (via satellite): HBO.
Fee: $9.95 monthly.
Miles of plant: 10.6 (coaxial). Homes passed: 796.
Manager: Bill Flowers. Chief technician: Chris Christenson. Marketing director: Jennifer Hauschild.
City fee: 3% of gross.
Ownership: Classic Cable (MSO).

IMPERIAL—Classic Cable, Box 429, 605 N.W. 3rd St., Plainville, KS 67663-0429. Phones: 785-434-7620; 800-999-8876. Fax: 785-434-2614. County: Pecos. ICA: TX0968.
TV Market Ranking: Below 100. Franchise award date: N.A. Franchise expiration date: N.A. Began: N.A.
Channel capacity: 22 (2-way capable). Channels available but not in use: N.A.
Basic Service
Subscribers: 33.
Programming (received off-air): KMID (A), KMLM (I), KOSA-TV (C), KPEJ (F), KWES-TV (N) Odessa-Midland.
Programming (via satellite): WGN-TV (W) Chicago; American Movie Classics; CNBC; ESPN; Fox Family Channel; Home Shopping Network; Nashville Network; Trinity Bcstg. Network; Turner Classic Movies; Turner Network TV; Univision.
Fee: $35.00 installation; $26.95 monthly.
Pay Service 1
Pay Units: 8.
Programming (via satellite): HBO.
Fee: $9.95 monthly.
Miles of plant: 5.0 (coaxial). Homes passed: 155.
Manager: Bill Flowers. Chief technician: Ben Hernandez. Marketing director: Jennifer Hauschild.
Ownership: Classic Cable (MSO).

INDIAN LAKE/LAKE THUNDERBIRD—BRDC Cablevision, Box 240, Giddings, TX 78942. Phone: 409-542-3151. Fax: 409-542-1187. County: Bastrop. ICA: TX0951.
TV Market Ranking: Below 100. Franchise award date: N.A. Franchise expiration date: N.A. Began: N.A.
Channel capacity: 36. Channels available but not in use: 13.
Basic Service
Subscribers: 171.
Programming (received off-air): KEYE-TV (C), KLRU (P), KNVA (W), KTBC (F), KVUE-TV (A), KXAN-TV (N) Austin.
Programming (via satellite): WGN-TV (W) Chicago; CNN; Country Music TV; Discovery Channel; Disney Channel; ESPN; Fox Family Channel; Fox Sports Net Southwest; Learning Channel; Nashville Network; QVC; Sci-Fi Channel; TBS Superstation; Trinity Bcstg. Network; Turner Network TV; USA Network.
Fee: $25.00 installation; $19.95 monthly.
Pay Service 1
Pay Units: 46.
Programming (via satellite): HBO.
Fee: $9.95 monthly.
Pay Service 2
Pay Units: 37.
Programming (via satellite): Cinemax.
Fee: $9.95 monthly.
Pay Service 3
Pay Units: N.A.
Programming (via satellite): Showtime.
Fee: $9.95 monthly.
Miles of plant: 11.0 (coaxial).
Manager: David W. Peterson.
Ownership: Bluebonnet Rural Development Corp. (MSO).

INDIAN SPRINGS—Star Cable, Drawer 1570, Brazoria, TX 77422. Phones: 409-798-9121; 800-395-2775. Fax: 409-798-4409. County: Polk. ICA: TX0385.
TV Market Ranking: Outside TV Markets. Franchise award date: N.A. Franchise expiration date: N.A. Began: N.A.
Channel capacity: 52 (not 2-way capable). Channels available but not in use: 20.
Basic Service
Subscribers: 306.
Programming (received off-air): KBTX-TV (C) Bryan; KPXB (X) Conroe; KHOU-TV (C), KHTV (W), KPRC-TV (N), KRIV (F), KTRK-TV (A), KTXH (U), KUHT (P) Houston; KCTL-LP (I), KETX-LP (I) Livingston; KTRE (A) Lufkin.
Programming (via satellite): A & E; American Movie Classics; CNN; Country Music TV; Discovery Channel; ESPN; Fox Family Channel; Fox News Channel; Fox Sports Net Southwest; MTV; Nashville Network; Nickelodeon; TBS Superstation; The Weather Channel; Turner Network TV; USA Network.
Fee: $31.34 monthly; $2.15 converter.
Pay Service 1
Pay Units: 16.
Programming (via satellite): Cinemax.
Fee: $10.95 monthly.
Pay Service 2
Pay Units: 34.

Programming (via satellite): Disney Channel.
Fee: $7.95 monthly.
Pay Service 3
Pay Units: 41.
Programming (via satellite): HBO.
Fee: $10.95 monthly.
Pay Service 4
Pay Units: 30.
Programming (via satellite): Showtime.
Fee: $12.95 monthly.
Miles of plant: 44.8 (coaxial); None (fiber optic). Homes passed: 897. Total homes in franchised area: 897.
Manager: Mike Burns. Chief technician: Mayla Zubeck.
Ownership: Star Cable Associates (MSO).

INGRAM—Classic Cable, Box 429, 605 N.W. 3rd St., Plainville, KS 67663-0429. Phones: 785-434-7620; 800-999-8876. Fax: 785-434-2614. County: Kerr. Also serves Hunt. ICA: TX0232.
TV Market Ranking: Below 100. Franchise award date: N.A. Franchise expiration date: January 1, 1998. Began: November 1, 1966.
Channel capacity: 41 (2-way capable). Channels available but not in use: N.A.
Basic Service
Subscribers: 2,128.
Programming (received off-air): KRRT (W) Kerrville-San Antonio; KABB (F), KENS-TV (C), KLRN (P), KMOL-TV (N), KSAT-TV (A) San Antonio; allband FM.
Programming (via satellite): WGN-TV (W) Chicago; A & E; American Movie Classics; Animal Planet; C-SPAN; CNBC; CNN; Country Music TV; Discovery Channel; Disney Channel; ESPN; Fox Family Channel; Fox News Channel; Fox Sports Net Southwest; Headline News; History Channel; Learning Channel; Lifetime; MTV; Nashville Network; Nick at Nite's TV Land; Nickelodeon; QVC; TBS Superstation; The Weather Channel; Travel Channel; Trinity Bcstg. Network; Turner Network TV; USA Network.
Current originations: Automated time-weather; educational access.
Fee: $35.00 installation; $27.95 monthly.
Pay Service 1
Pay Units: 74.
Programming (via satellite): Cinemax.
Fee: $9.95 monthly.
Pay Service 2
Pay Units: 206.
Programming (via satellite): HBO.
Fee: $10.95 monthly.
Pay Service 3
Pay Units: 150.
Programming (via satellite): Showtime.
Fee: $9.95 monthly.
Pay Service 4
Pay Units: 290.
Programming (via satellite): The Movie Channel.
Fee: $5.95 monthly.
Miles of plant: 112.0 (coaxial). Homes passed: 2,274.
Manager: Bill Flowers. Chief technician: Walt VanLue. Marketing director: Jennifer Hauschild.
City fee: None.
Ownership: Classic Cable (MSO).

IOLA—National Cable Inc., Suite 106-A, 5151 Reed Rd., Columbus, OH 43220. Phones: 614-442-5890; 800-582-0504. Fax: 614-457-2567. County: Grimes. ICA: TX0677.
TV Market Ranking: Below 100. Franchise award date: N.A. Franchise expiration date: N.A. Began: N.A.
Channel capacity: 36. Channels available but not in use: 21.
Basic Service
Subscribers: 41.
Programming (received off-air): KBTX-TV (C) Bryan; KHTV (W), KUHT (P) Houston; KAVU-TV (A) Victoria; KCEN-TV (N) Waco-Temple.
Programming (via satellite): WGN-TV (W) Chicago; A & E; American Movie Classics; CNN; Country Music TV; Discovery Channel; ESPN; Fox Family Channel; Showtime; TBS Superstation; Turner Network TV; USA Network.
Fee: $28.00 monthly.
Miles of plant: 3.7 (coaxial). Homes passed: 129.
Manager: Paul Scott. Chief technician: Rob Spiller. Marketing director: Josh Thackery.
Ownership: National Cable (MSO).

IOWA PARK—Friendship Cable of Texas Inc., Box 9090, Tyler, TX 75711-9090. Phone: 903-581-2121. Fax: 903-581-2185. County: Wichita. ICA: TX0211.
TV Market Ranking: Below 100. Franchise award date: N.A. Franchise expiration date: N.A. Began: March 1, 1979.
Channel capacity: 35. Channels available but not in use: 5.
Basic Service
Subscribers: 1,070.
Programming (received off-air): KAUZ-TV (C), KFDX-TV (N), KJTL (F,U), KSWO-TV (A) Wichita Falls-Lawton; allband FM.
Programming (via translator): KERA-TV (P) Dallas-Fort Worth.
Programming (via satellite): Court TV; Discovery Channel; Knowledge TV; Odyssey; QVC; TBS Superstation.
Current originations: Automated time-weather.
Fee: $30.00 installation; $12.09 monthly.
Expanded Basic Service
Subscribers: 1,027.
Programming (via satellite): American Movie Classics; Animal Planet; C-SPAN; CNBC; CNN; Cartoon Network; Country Music TV; Disney Channel; ESPN; FX; Fox Family Channel; Fox News Channel; Headline News; Home & Garden Television; Learning Channel; MTV; Nashville Network; Nickelodeon; The Weather Channel; Turner Network TV; USA Network.
Fee: $30.00 installation; $15.05 monthly.
Pay Service 1
Pay Units: 75.
Programming (via satellite): Cinemax.
Fee: $13.83 monthly.
Pay Service 2
Pay Units: 460.
Programming (via satellite): The New Encore.
Fee: $1.75 monthly.
Pay Service 3
Pay Units: 235.
Programming (via satellite): HBO.
Fee: $13.83 monthly.
Pay Service 4
Pay Units: 264.
Programming (via satellite): Starz!
Fee: $6.75 monthly.
Equipment: Tocom headend; Tocom amplifiers; Times Fiber cable; Tocom set top converters; Fort Worth Tower satellite antenna.
Miles of plant: 37.0 (coaxial). Homes passed: 2,198. Total homes in franchised area: 2,198.
Manager: Larry Bryant. Chief technician: Ron Johnson.
City fee: 3% of gross.
Ownership: Buford Television Inc. (MSO). See Cable System Ownership.

IRVING—Paragon Cable, 2951 Kinwest Pkwy., Irving, TX 75063. Phone: 972-221-6531. Fax: 972-221-7070. County: Dallas. Also serves Las Colinas. ICA: TX0016.
TV Market Ranking: 12. Franchise award date: April 1, 1981. Franchise expiration date: July 1, 2013. Began: October 1, 1981.
Channel capacity: N.A. Channels available but not in use: 47.
Basic Service
Subscribers: 41,141.
Programming (received off-air): KPXD (X) Arlington; KDAF (W), KDFI-TV (I), KDFW (F), KDTX-TV (T), KERA-TV (P), KFWD (O), KTVT (C), KTXA (U), KXAS-TV (N), KXTX-TV (I), WFAA-TV (A) Dallas-Fort Worth; KMPX (I) Decatur; KUVN (S) Garland; KLDT (I) Lake Dallas.
Programming (via satellite): TV Guide Channel; TV Guide Sneak Prevue.
Current originations: Automated time-weather; public access; educational access; government access; religious access; local sports.
Fee: $26.90 installation; $8.85 monthly; $2.76 converter; $27.46 additional installation.
Expanded Basic Service
Subscribers: 31,734.
Programming (via satellite): A & E; American Movie Classics; Animal Planet; BET; Bravo; C-SPAN; C-SPAN 2; CNBC; CNN; Cartoon Network; Comedy Central; Country Music TV; Court TV; Discovery Channel; E! Entertainment TV; ESPN; ESPN 2; Fox Family Channel; Fox Sports Net Southwest; Headline News; History Channel; Home & Garden Television; Home Shopping Network; Learning Channel; Lifetime; MOVIEplex; MSNBC; MTV; Nashville Network; Nick at Nite; Nickelodeon; QVC; The Weather Channel; Travel Channel; Turner Network TV; USA Network; VH1; ValueVision.
Fee: $26.90 installation; $19.82 monthly.
Pay Service 1
Pay Units: 2,622.
Programming (via satellite): Cinemax.
Fee: $12.50 monthly.
Pay Service 2
Pay Units: 4,075.
Programming (via satellite): Disney Channel.
Fee: $9.40 monthly.
Pay Service 3
Pay Units: 9,489.
Programming (via satellite): HBO.
Fee: $12.50 monthly.
Pay Service 4
Pay Units: 1,237.
Programming (via satellite): The Movie Channel.
Fee: $12.50 monthly.
Pay Service 5
Pay Units: 5,525.
Programming (via satellite): Showtime.
Fee: $12.50 monthly.
Pay-Per-View
Hot Choice; Viewer's Choice.
Fee: $3.95.
Local advertising: Yes. Available in satellite distributed & locally originated programming. Rates: $30.00/Minute; $16.00-$500.00/30 Seconds. Local sales manager: Christine Pierret.
Program Guide: The Cable Guide.
Equipment: Scientific-Atlanta amplifiers; Panasonic set top converters; Zenith addressable set top converters.
Miles of plant: 566.2 (coaxial); 28.3 (fiber optic). Homes passed: 77,004.
Manager: Walter Nesbit. Chief technician: Bob Macioch. Program director: Philip Haley. Marketing director: Jim Fellhauer.
City fee: 5% of gross.
Ownership: AT&T Broadband & Internet Services (MSO); Time Warner Cable (MSO); Advance/Newhouse Partnership (MSO).

JACKSBORO—Southwest Cablevision, Box 869, 2804-B FM 51 S, Decatur, TX 76234. Phone: 817-627-3099. Fax: 817-627-8303. Counties: Jack & Palo Pinto. Also serves Bryson, Graford, Possum Kingdom Lake. ICA: TX0781.
TV Market Ranking: Outside TV Markets. Franchise award date: March 1, 1977. Franchise expiration date: March 1, 2007. Began: June 14, 1977.
Channel capacity: 60 (not 2-way capable). Channels available but not in use: 8.
Basic Service
Subscribers: 2,910.
Programming (received off-air): KDFI-TV (I), KDFW (F), KERA-TV (P), KTVT (C), KTXA (U), KXAS-TV (N), KXTX-TV (I), WFAA-TV (A) Dallas-Fort Worth; KAUZ-TV (C), KFDX-TV (N), KJTL (F,U) Wichita Falls-Lawton; allband FM.
Current originations: Automated time-weather; religious access.
Fee: $55.00 installation; $20.90 monthly; $2.45 converter; $15.00 additional installation.
Expanded Basic Service
Subscribers: 2,692.
Programming (via satellite): A & E; American Movie Classics; BET; C-SPAN; C-SPAN 2; CNBC; CNN; Cartoon Network; Comedy Central; Country Music TV; Discovery Channel; ESPN; EWTN; Fox Family Channel; Fox Sports Net Southwest; Goodlife TV Network; Headline News; Learning Channel; Lifetime; MTV; Nashville Network; Nickelodeon; Odyssey; QVC; Sci-Fi Channel; TV Guide Channel; The Weather Channel; Travel Channel; Trinity Bcstg. Network; Turner Network TV; USA Network; Univision; VH1.
Fee: $55.00 installation; $4.40 monthly.
Expanded Basic Service 2
Subscribers: 2,691.
Programming (via satellite): WGN-TV (W) Chicago; TBS Superstation.
Fee: N.A.
Pay Service 1
Pay Units: 722.
Programming (via satellite): Cinemax; Disney Channel; HBO.
Fee: $20.00 installation; $8.95 monthly (Disney), $9.95 monthly (Cinemax), $11.95 monthly (HBO).
Local advertising: Yes. Available in character-generated & taped programming. Rates: On request. Local sales manager: Kathy Shull. Regional interconnect: Cabletime.
Equipment: Scientific-Atlanta headend; Scientific-Atlanta amplifiers; Comm/Scope & Times Fiber cable; Panasonic cameras; Magnavox VTRs; MSI character generator; Oak set top converters; Eagle traps; Scientific-Atlanta satellite antenna; Scientific-Atlanta satellite receivers.
Miles of plant: 33.3 (coaxial).
Manager: Danny Neumann. Chief technician: Harley Hill. Marketing director: Kathy Shull.
City fee: 3% of gross.
Ownership: James Cable Partners (MSO).

JACKSON'S LANDING—Northland Cable TV, Box 538, Flint, TX 75762. Phone: 903-894-8200. Fax: 903-894-8204. County: Henderson. ICA: TX0274.

TV Market Ranking: Below 100. Franchise award date: N.A. Franchise expiration date: N.A. Began: N.A.
Channel capacity: 36 (2-way capable). Channels available but not in use: 5.
Basic Service
Subscribers: 628.
Programming (received off-air): KETK-TV (N) Jacksonville; KFXK (F) Longview; KLTV (A) Tyler-Longview.
Programming (via microwave): KDFW (F), KERA-TV (P), KTVT (C), KXTX-TV (I), WFAA-TV (A) Dallas-Fort Worth.
Programming (via satellite): WGN-TV (W) Chicago; A & E; CNN; Country Music TV; Discovery Channel; ESPN; Fox Family Channel; Fox Sports Net Southwest; Headline News; Learning Channel; Nashville Network; QVC; TBS Superstation; USA Network.
Current originations: Automated time-weather; local sports.
Fee: $21.75 monthly.
Pay Service 1
Pay Units: 28.
Programming (via satellite): Disney Channel.
Fee: $7.00 monthly.
Pay Service 2
Pay Units: 68.
Programming (via satellite): HBO.
Fee: $10.50 monthly.
Pay Service 3
Pay Units: 67.
Programming (via satellite): Showtime.
Fee: $7.95 monthly.
Local advertising: Yes. Available in satellite distributed, locally originated, character-generated, taped & automated programming. Rates: $16.00/Minute; $8.00/30 Seconds. Local sales manager: Patricia Wallace.
Program Guide: Premium Channels.
Equipment: Hughes, M/A-Com & Scientific-Atlanta headend; Magnavox amplifiers; Comm/Scope cable; Texscan character generator; Scientific-Atlanta, Hamlin & Oak set top converters; Arcom & Eagle traps; Scientific-Atlanta satellite antenna; Scientific-Atlanta satellite receivers; ChannelMatic & Sony commercial insert.
Miles of plant: 15.0 (coaxial). Homes passed: 1,500. Total homes in franchised area: 1,500.
Manager: Jim Wiggins. Chief technician: Jim Bob Sanders. Marketing director: Charlotte Griffin.
Ownership: Northland Communications Corp. (MSO).

JACKSONVILLE—TCA Cable TV, 316 S. Main St., Jacksonville, TX 75766. Phone: 903-586-8122. Fax: 903-586-1752. County: Cherokee. Also serves Cherokee County. ICA: TX0110.
TV Market Ranking: Below 100. Franchise award date: January 1, 1969. Franchise expiration date: February 14, 1999. Began: July 3, 1953.
Channel capacity: 62 (2-way capable; operating 2-way). Channels available but not in use: N.A.
Basic Service
Subscribers: 4,220.
Programming (received off-air): KDFW (F), KERA-TV (P), KTVT (C), KXAS-TV (N), KXTX-TV (I), WFAA-TV (A) Dallas-Fort Worth; KETK-TV (N) Jacksonville; KFXK (F) Longview; KLTV (A) Tyler-Longview; 6 FMs.
Programming (via satellite): WGN-TV (W) Chicago; A & E; BET; C-SPAN; C-SPAN 2; CNBC; CNN; Comedy Central; Discovery Channel; E! Entertainment TV; ESPN; Fox Headline News; Lifetime; MTV; Nashville Family Channel; Fox Sports Net Southwest; Network; Nickelodeon; Odyssey; QVC; TBS Superstation; The Weather Channel; Turner Network TV; USA Network; Univision; VH1.
Current originations: Automated time-weather.
Fee: $49.95 installation; $9.61 monthly; $25.00 additional installation.
Pay Service 1
Pay Units: N.A.
Programming (via satellite): American Movie Classics; Cinemax; Disney Channel; HBO; Playboy TV; Showtime; The Movie Channel.
Fee: $10.95 monthly (each).
Local advertising: Yes. Available in satellite distributed programming. Rates: $75.00/Hour; $45.00/30 Minutes; $10.00/Minute; $6.00/30 Seconds.
Equipment: Jerrold & Scientific-Atlanta headend; Magnavox amplifiers; Times Fiber cable; Jerrold set top converters; Jerrold addressable set top converters; Anixter-Mark & Scientific-Atlanta satellite antenna; Anixter-Mark, Scientific-Atlanta & Standard Communications satellite receivers.
Miles of plant: 96.4 (coaxial). Homes passed: 6,114. Total homes in franchised area: 6,114.
Manager: Ronnie Powell. Chief technician: Brad Casey.
City fee: 3% of gross.
Ownership: TCA Cable TV Inc. (MSO); AT&T Broadband & Internet Services (MSO). See Cable System Ownership.

JARRELL—Williamson County Cablevision Co., Box 1999, 111 N. College St., Georgetown, TX 78627. Phones: 512-869-1505; 512-930-3085. Fax: 512-869-2962. County: Williamson. ICA: TX0972.
TV Market Ranking: Below 100. Franchise award date: N.A. Franchise expiration date: N.A. Began: N.A.
Channel capacity: N.A. Channels available but not in use: N.A.
Basic Service
Subscribers: 152.
Programming (received off-air): KEYE-TV (C), KLRU (P), KNVA (W), KTBC (F), KVUE-TV (A), KXAN-TV (N) Austin; K13VC (I) Austin, Cedar Park.
Programming (via satellite): WGN-TV (W) Chicago; Animal Planet; C-SPAN; C-SPAN 2; FX; Fox News Channel; Goodlife TV Network; Home & Garden Television; Knowledge TV; MSNBC; Outdoor Life Network; QVC; TV Food Network; TV Guide Channel; The Health Network; The Weather Channel; Toon Disney; Travel Channel.
Current originations: Public access; educational access.
Fee: $12.49 monthly; $1.50 converter.
Expanded Basic Service
Subscribers: N.A.
Programming (via satellite): A & E; American Movie Classics; BET; CNBC; CNN; Country Music TV; Court TV; Discovery Channel; Disney Channel; E! Entertainment TV; ESPN; ESPN 2; ESPN Classic Sports; ESPNews; Fox Family Channel; Fox Sports Net Southwest; Headline News; Learning Channel; Lifetime; MTV; Nashville Network; Nick at Nite's TV Land; Nickelodeon; Sci-Fi Channel; TBS Superstation; Trinity Bcstg. Network; Turner Network TV; USA Network; Univision; VH1.
Fee: $15.50 monthly.
A la Carte 1
Subscribers: N.A.
Programming (via satellite): Cartoon Network; Comedy Central; Golf Channel; History Channel; MOVIEplex; Speedvision; Sundance Channel; Turner Classic Movies.
Fee: $4.99 monthly (package), $1.25 monthly (each).
Pay Service 1
Pay Units: N.A.
Programming (via satellite): Cinemax (multiplexed); HBO (multiplexed); Showtime; Starz!; The New Encore.
Fee: $8.99 monthly (Showtime), $9.99 monthly (Cinemax or Encore & Starz), $11.49 monthly (HBO).
Pay-Per-View
Viewer's Choice.
Manager: Dale E. Hoffman. Chief technician & marketing director: Wesley Houghteling.
Ownership: M. K. McDaniel (MSO); John Muraglia (MSO); E. D. Hoffman (MSO). Sale pends to TCA Cable TV Inc.

JASPER—Tri-City Cablevision, 122 N. Austin, Jasper, TX 75951. Phone: 409-384-6862. Fax: 409-384-7817. County: Jasper. ICA: TX0157.
TV Market Ranking: Outside TV Markets. Franchise award date: November 14, 1977. Franchise expiration date: November 7, 1997. Began: August 1, 1967.
Channel capacity: 42 (not 2-way capable). Channels available but not in use: 5.
Basic Service
Subscribers: 2,846; Commercial subscribers: 16.
Programming (received off-air): KBMT (A), KBTV-TV (N), KFDM-TV (C) Beaumont-Port Arthur; KPLC-TV (N) Lake Charles; KTRE (A) Lufkin; allband FM.
Programming (via microwave): KHTV (W), KTRK-TV (A), KUHT (P) Houston.
Programming (via satellite): TBS Superstation.
Current originations: Automated time-weather; local news.
Fee: $49.95 installation; $14.95 monthly.
Expanded Basic Service
Subscribers: 2,833.
Programming (via satellite): A & E; American Movie Classics; BET; C-SPAN; CNBC; CNN; Country Music TV; Discovery Channel; ESPN; Fox Family Channel; Headline News; Lifetime; MTV; Nickelodeon; The Inspirational Network; The Weather Channel; Turner Network TV; USA Network.
Fee: $49.95 installation; $10.95 monthly.
Pay Service 1
Pay Units: 263.
Programming (via satellite): Cinemax.
Fee: $15.00 installation; $10.45 monthly.
Pay Service 2
Pay Units: 115.
Programming (via satellite): Disney Channel.
Fee: $7.95 monthly.
Pay Service 3
Pay Units: 476.
Programming (via satellite): HBO.
Fee: $10.45 monthly.
Pay Service 4
Pay Units: 333.
Programming (via satellite): Showtime.
Fee: $10.45 monthly.
Pay-Per-View
Addressable homes: 2,006.
Viewer's Choice.
Local advertising: Yes. Available in satellite distributed programming. Regional interconnect: Cabletime.
Program Guide: Premium Channels.
Equipment: Scientific-Atlanta headend; Scientific-Atlanta amplifiers; Comm/Scope cable; Sony VTRs; Quanta character generator; Scientific-Atlanta set top converters; Scientific-Atlanta addressable set top converters; Scientific-Atlanta satellite antenna; Scientific-Atlanta satellite receivers.
Miles of plant: 100.0 (coaxial). Additional miles planned: 20.0 (coaxial). Homes passed: 3,900. Total homes in franchised area: 3,900.
Manager: Burl Corkran. Chief technician: Bryce Beatty. Chief technician: Burl Corkran. Marketing director: Jane Ketcham.
City fee: 5%.
Ownership: Charter Communications Inc. (MSO).

JAYTON—Jayroc Cablevision, Box 6575, Abilene, TX 79608. Phone: 915-691-5787. County: Kent. ICA: TX0557.
TV Market Ranking: Outside TV Markets. Franchise award date: N.A. Franchise expiration date: N.A. Began: July 1, 1982.
Channel capacity: 21. Channels available but not in use: N.A.
Basic Service
Subscribers: N.A.
Programming (received off-air): KTXS-TV (A) Abilene-Sweetwater; KCBD-TV (N), KLBK-TV (C) Lubbock.
Programming (via satellite): WGN-TV (W) Chicago; ESPN; Fox Family Channel; Nickelodeon; TBS Superstation.
Fee: N.A.
Pay Service 1
Pay Units: N.A.
Programming (via satellite): Cinemax; HBO.
Fee: N.A.
Homes passed: 330.
Manager: D. H. Pope.
Ownership: Jayroc Inc. (MSO).

JEFFERSON—Falcon Cable TV, 108 W. Houston, Marshall, TX 75670. Phone: 903-938-8335. County: Marion. Also serves Marion County. ICA: TX0370.
TV Market Ranking: 58 (portions of Marion County); Below 100 (Jefferson, portions of Marion County); Outside TV Markets (portions of Marion County). Franchise award date: January 1, 1981. Franchise expiration date: N.A. Began: April 1, 1983.
Channel capacity: 42 (2-way capable). Channels available but not in use: 4.
Basic Service
Subscribers: 590.
Programming (received off-air): KETK-TV (N) Jacksonville; KFXK (F) Longview; KLTS-TV (P), KMSS-TV (F), KSHV (U,W), KSLA-TV (C), KTAL-TV (N), KTBS-TV (A) Shreveport-Texarkana; KLTV (A) Tyler-Longview.
Programming (via satellite): American Movie Classics; BET; Bravo; CNBC; CNN; Country Music TV; ESPN; Fox Family Channel; Fox Sports Net Southwest; Headline News; Home Shopping Network; Lifetime; MTV; Nashville Network; Nickelodeon; QVC; Trinity Bcstg. Network.
Fee: $63.00 installation; $23.85 monthly; $3.15 converter.
Expanded Basic Service
Subscribers: 489.
Programming (via satellite): Discovery Channel; Sci-Fi Channel; The Weather Channel; USA Network.
Fee: $3.92 monthly.
Expanded Basic Service 2
Subscribers: 393.
Programming (via satellite): WGN-TV (W) Chicago; C-SPAN; Disney Channel; TBS Superstation; Turner Network TV.
Fee: $7.50 monthly.
Pay Service 1
Pay Units: 103.
Programming (via satellite): Cinemax.
Fee: $15.00 installation; $11.95 monthly.
Pay Service 2
Pay Units: 173.
Programming (via satellite): HBO.
Fee: $11.95 monthly.

Pay Service 3
Pay Units: 35.
Programming (via satellite): Showtime.
Fee: $11.95 monthly.
Local advertising: No. Regional interconnect: Cabletime.
Equipment: Phasecom headend; C-COR amplifiers; Times Fiber cable; Hamlin set top converters; Eagle & Vitek traps; M/A-Com satellite antenna; M/A-Com satellite receivers.
Miles of plant: 26.0 (coaxial). Homes passed: 2,267.
Manager: George Doss. Chief technician: Marty Bowen.
Franchise fee: 3% of gross.
Ownership: Falcon Communications LP (MSO), joint venture formed September 30, 1998. See Cable System Ownership.

JEWETT—Northland Cable, 515 W. Tyler, Mexia, TX 76667. Phone: 254-562-2872. Fax: 254-562-6454. County: Leon. ICA: TX0541.
TV Market Ranking: Outside TV Markets. Franchise award date: May 19, 1980. Franchise expiration date: May 29, 2001. Began: August 1, 1981.
Channel capacity: 30 (2-way capable; operating 2-way). Channels available but not in use: N.A.
Basic Service
Subscribers: 237.
Programming (received off-air): KBTX-TV (C) Bryan; WFAA-TV (A) Dallas-Fort Worth; KRMA-TV (P) Denver; KETK-TV (N) Jacksonville; KCEN-TV (N), KWKT (F), KWTX-TV (C), KXXV (A) Waco-Temple.
Programming (via satellite): WGN-TV (W) Chicago; CNN; Country Music TV; Discovery Channel; ESPN; Fox Family Channel; Fox Sports Net Southwest; Headline News; Lifetime; Nashville Network; QVC; TBS Superstation; Trinity Bcstg. Network; Turner Network TV; USA Network.
Fee: $55.00 installation; $25.25 monthly.
Pay Service 1
Pay Units: 9.
Programming (via satellite): Disney Channel.
Fee: $10.00 monthly.
Pay Service 2
Pay Units: 57.
Programming (via satellite): HBO.
Fee: $10.00 monthly.
Equipment: Scientific-Atlanta headend; Scientific-Atlanta amplifiers; Pico traps; Prodelin satellite antenna; Microdyne satellite receivers.
Miles of plant: 28.0 (coaxial). Homes passed: 363. Total homes in franchised area: 390.
Manager: Jimmie Cullins.
City fee: 2% of gross.
Ownership: Northland Communications Corp. (MSO).

JOAQUIN—Mansfield Cablevision, Box 1050, Mansfield, LA 71052. Phone: 318-872-3268. Fax: 318-872-2520. County: Shelby. ICA: TX0783.
TV Market Ranking: 58. Franchise award date: N.A. Franchise expiration date: N.A. Began: N.A.
Channel capacity: N.A. Channels available but not in use: N.A.
Basic Service
Subscribers: 238.
Programming (received off-air): KLTS-TV (P), KSLA-TV (C), KTAL-TV (N), KTBS-TV (A) Shreveport-Texarkana.
Programming (via satellite): WGN-TV (W) Chicago; CNN; ESPN; Fox Family Channel; TBS Superstation; USA Network.
Fee: $20.00 installation; $13.45 monthly.
Pay Service 1
Pay Units: N.A.
Programming (via satellite): Disney Channel; HBO; Showtime.
Fee: $10.95 monthly (each).
Manager: Craig Perkins. Chief technician: Don Custer. Advertising manager: Kim Kent. Office manager: Carolyn Goldman.
Ownership: Cable Management Assoc. (MSO).

JOHNSON CITY—Post Cablevision of Texas Ltd., Drawer 829, 1108 Parker St., Goldthwaite, TX 76844. Phone: 915-648-3041. County: Blanco. ICA: TX0560.
TV Market Ranking: Below 100. Franchise award date: N.A. Franchise expiration date: November 1, 2002. Began: July 1, 1984.
Channel capacity: 24. Channels available but not in use: None.
Basic Service
Subscribers: N.A.
Programming (received off-air): KEYE-TV (C), KLRU (P), KTBC (F), KVUE-TV (A), KXAN-TV (N) Austin.
Programming (via satellite): WGN-TV (W) Chicago; C-SPAN; CNN; Country Music TV; Discovery Channel; ESPN; Fox Family Channel; Home Shopping Network; MTV; Nashville Network; Nickelodeon; TBS Superstation; Turner Network TV; USA Network; Univision.
Fee: $25.00 installation; $21.60 monthly.
Pay Service 1
Pay Units: N.A.
Programming (via satellite): Disney Channel; HBO; The Movie Channel.
Fee: $7.58 monthly (Disney), $9.74 monthly (HBO or TMC).
Miles of plant: 8.1 (coaxial). Homes passed: 325.
Manager: Denise Casbeer. Chief technician: Joe Dean.
Ownership: Fanch Communications Inc. (MSO). See Cable System Ownership.

JOSEPHINE—Friendship Cable of Texas Inc., Box 9090, Tyler, TX 75711-9090. Phone: 903-581-2121. Fax: 903-581-2185. County: Collin. Also serves Collin County (portions), Copeville, Lavon, Nevada. ICA: TX0784.
TV Market Ranking: Below 100. Franchise award date: N.A. Franchise expiration date: N.A. Began: April 5, 1989.
Channel capacity: 36 (not 2-way capable). Channels available but not in use: N.A.
Basic Service
Subscribers: 395.
Programming (received off-air): KDAF (W), KDFW (F), KERA-TV (P), KTVT (C), KTXA (U), KXAS-TV (N), KXTX-TV (I), WFAA-TV (A) Dallas-Fort Worth.
Programming (via satellite): WGN-TV (W) Chicago; A & E; BET; C-SPAN; CNN; Country Music TV; Discovery Channel; Disney Channel; ESPN; ESPN 2; Fox Sports Net Southwest; Headline News; Lifetime; Nashville Network; Nickelodeon; TBS Superstation; The Inspirational Network; The Weather Channel; Turner Classic Movies; Turner Network TV; USA Network; VH1.
Fee: $30.00 installation; $32.20 monthly.
Pay Service 1
Pay Units: 33.
Programming (via satellite): Cinemax.
Fee: $10.00 monthly.
Pay Service 2
Pay Units: 38.
Programming (via satellite): HBO.
Fee: $10.00 monthly.
Pay Service 3
Pay Units: 64.
Programming (via satellite): Showtime.
Fee: $5.95 monthly.
Local advertising: Yes. Available in character-generated & taped programming.
Equipment: Jerrold & Starline amplifiers; Comm/Scope cable; Hamlin, Scientific-Atlanta & Jerrold set top converters; Pico & Northeast Filter traps; Scientific-Atlanta & Cadco satellite receivers.
Miles of plant: 62.9 (coaxial). Homes passed: 872.
Manager: Rodney Fletcher. Chief technician: Steven Willims.
Ownership: Buford Television Inc. (MSO). See Cable System Ownership.

JOSHUA—North Texas Cablevision, Box 909, Granbury, TX 76048. Phone: 817-573-6872. County: Johnson. Also serves Burleson City, Johnson County (portions). ICA: TX0785.
TV Market Ranking: 12. Franchise award date: N.A. Franchise expiration date: April 1, 1998. Began: February 1, 1984.
Channel capacity: N.A. Channels available but not in use: N.A.
Basic Service
Subscribers: 1,192.
Programming (received off-air): KDFW (F), KERA-TV (P), KTVT (C), KXAS-TV (N), KXTX-TV (I), WFAA-TV (A) Dallas-Fort Worth.
Programming (via satellite): Turner Classic Movies.
Fee: $31.50 installation; $20.99 monthly.
Miles of plant: 19.2 (coaxial).
Manager: Russ Hamby.
City fee: 5% of gross.
Ownership: Fanch Communications Inc. (MSO). See Cable System Ownership.

JUNCTION—Classic Cable, Box 429, 605 N.W. 3rd St., Plainville, KS 67663-0429. Phones: 785-434-7620; 800-999-8876. Fax: 785-434-2614. County: Kimble. ICA: TX0320.
TV Market Ranking: Outside TV Markets. Franchise award date: N.A. Franchise expiration date: N.A. Began: June 1, 1957.
Channel capacity: 41 (2-way capable). Channels available but not in use: N.A.
Basic Service
Subscribers: 902.
Programming (received off-air): KTXS-TV (A) Abilene-Sweetwater; KXAN-TV (N) Austin; KIDY (F), KLST (C) San Angelo; 4 FMs.
Programming (via microwave): WFAA-TV (A) Dallas-Fort Worth; KXAM-TV (N) Llano.
Programming (via satellite): WGN-TV (W) Chicago; KRMA-TV (P) Denver; A & E; Animal Planet; CNN; Country Music TV; Discovery Channel; Disney Channel; ESPN; Fox Family Channel; Fox News Channel; Fox Sports Net Southwest; Headline News; History Channel; Learning Channel; Lifetime; Nashville Network; Nick at Nite's TV Land; Nickelodeon; QVC; TBS Superstation; Telemundo; The Weather Channel; Trinity Bcstg. Network; Turner Network TV; USA Network; Univision.
Fee: $35.00 installation; $28.95 monthly.
Pay Service 1
Pay Units: 91.
Programming (via satellite): HBO.
Fee: $10.00 installation; $10.95 monthly.
Pay Service 2
Pay Units: 130.
Programming (via satellite): Showtime.
Fee: $9.95 monthly.
Pay Service 3
Pay Units: 100.
Programming (via satellite): The Movie Channel.
Fee: $5.95 monthly.
Local advertising: No.
Equipment: Jerrold headend; Jerrold amplifiers; Eagle traps; Andrew satellite antenna.
Miles of plant: 27.0 (coaxial). Homes passed: 1,179.
Manager: Bill Flowers. Chief technician: Walt VanLue. Marketing director: Jennifer Hauschild.
City fee: 2% of gross.
Ownership: Classic Cable (MSO).

KATY (southern portion)—Friendship Cable of Texas Inc., Box 9090, Tyler, TX 75711-9090. Phone: 903-581-2121. Fax: 903-581-2185. County: Fort Bend. Also serves Fort Bend County (portions). ICA: TX0786.
TV Market Ranking: 15 (portions of Fort Bend County, Katy); Below 100 (portions of Fort Bend County). Franchise award date: N.A. Franchise expiration date: N.A. Began: N.A.
Channel capacity: 36 (not 2-way capable). Channels available but not in use: 2.
Basic Service
Subscribers: 190.
Programming (received off-air): KHOU-TV (C), KHTV (W), KPRC-TV (N), KRIV (F), KTRK-TV (A), KTXH (U), KUHT (P) Houston.
Programming (via satellite): A & E; C-SPAN; CNN; Country Music TV; Discovery Channel; Disney Channel; ESPN; Fox Family Channel; Fox Sports Net Southwest; Headline News; Lifetime; Nashville Network; Nickelodeon; QVC; TBS Superstation; The Inspirational Network; The Weather Channel; Turner Network TV; USA Network.
Fee: $34.70 monthly.
Pay Service 1
Pay Units: 15.
Programming (via satellite): Cinemax.
Fee: $10.95 monthly.
Pay Service 2
Pay Units: 22.
Programming (via satellite): HBO.
Fee: $10.95 monthly.
Pay Service 3
Pay Units: 12.
Programming (via satellite): Showtime.
Fee: $5.95 monthly.
Local advertising: Yes.
Miles of plant: 18.6 (coaxial). Homes passed: 313.
Manager: Wanda Pyburn. Chief technician: David Burrell.
Ownership: Buford Television Inc. (MSO). See Cable System Ownership.

KAUFMAN—Northland Cable, Box 538, Flint, TX 75762. Phones: 903-894-8200; 903-566-8757. Fax: 903-894-8204. County: Kaufman. ICA: TX0262.
TV Market Ranking: 12. Franchise award date: N.A. Franchise expiration date: N.A. Began: March 23, 1981.
Channel capacity: 35 (not 2-way capable). Channels available but not in use: 9.
Basic Service
Subscribers: 1,443.
Programming (received off-air): KDFW (F), KERA-TV (P), KTVT (C), KXAS-TV (N), KXTX-TV (I), WFAA-TV (A) Dallas-Fort Worth; KLTV (A) Tyler-Longview.
Programming (via satellite): WGN-TV (W) Chicago; CNN; ESPN; Headline News; Nickelodeon; TBS Superstation; The Inspirational Network; Turner Classic Movies; USA Network.
Fee: $24.95 installation; $10.60 monthly.
Pay Service 1
Pay Units: N.A.
Programming (via satellite): Disney Channel; HBO; Showtime.

Fee: $24.95 installation; $10.00 monthly (each).
Local advertising: Yes.
Equipment: Scientific-Atlanta headend; Theta-Com amplifiers; Comm/Scope cable; Hamlin & Jerrold set top converters; Arcom traps.
Miles of plant: 31.0 (coaxial). Homes passed: 1,600. Total homes in franchised area: 1,600.
Manager: Jim Wiggins. Chief technician: Jim Bob Sanders. Marketing director: Charlotte Griffin.
City fee: 3% of gross.
Ownership: Northland Communications Corp. (MSO).

KEMPNER—National Cable Inc., Suite 106-A, 5151 Reed Rd., Columbus, OH 43220. Phones: 614-442-5890; 800-582-0504. Fax: 614-457-2567. Counties: Coryell & Lampasas. Also serves Copperas Cove (unincorporated areas). ICA: TX0674.
TV Market Ranking: Below 100. Franchise award date: N.A. Franchise expiration date: N.A. Began: N.A.
Channel capacity: 36. Channels available but not in use: 21.
Basic Service
Subscribers: 167.
Programming (received off-air): KNCT (P) Belton; KCEN-TV (N), KWKT (F), KWTX-TV (C), KXXV (A) Waco-Temple.
Programming (via satellite): WGN-TV (W) Chicago; A & E; American Movie Classics; CNN; Country Music TV; Discovery Channel; ESPN; Fox Family Channel; Showtime; TBS Superstation; Turner Network TV; USA Network.
Fee: $28.00 monthly.
Miles of plant: 5.1 (coaxial). Homes passed: 403.
Manager: Paul Scott. Chief technician: Rob Spiller. Marketing director: Josh Thackery.
Ownership: National Cable (MSO).

KENEDY—Classic Cable, Box 429, 605 N.W. 3rd St., Plainville, KS 67663-0429. Phones: 785-434-7620; 800-999-8876. Fax: 785-434-2614. County: Karnes. Also serves Karnes City. ICA: TX0281.
TV Market Ranking: Outside TV Markets. Franchise award date: N.A. Franchise expiration date: N.A. Began: July 1, 1977.
Channel capacity: 41 (2-way capable). Channels available but not in use: N.A.
Basic Service
Subscribers: 1,426.
Programming (received off-air): KRRT (W) Kerrville-San Antonio; KABB (F), KENS-TV (C), KLRN (P), KMOL-TV (N), KSAT-TV (A), KVDA (O), KWEX-TV (S) San Antonio; 1 FM.
Programming (via satellite): WGN-TV (W) Chicago; A & E; Animal Planet; CNN; Country Music TV; Discovery Channel; Disney Channel; ESPN; EWTN; Fox Family Channel; Fox News Channel; Fox Sports Net Southwest; Headline News; Learning Channel; Nashville Network; Nick at Nite's TV Land; Nickelodeon; QVC; TBS Superstation; The Weather Channel; Trinity Bcstg. Network; Turner Classic Movies; Turner Network TV; USA Network.
Current originations: Automated time-weather; local news.
Fee: $35.00 installation; $28.95 monthly; $15.00 additional installation.
Pay Service 1
Pay Units: 171.
Programming (via satellite): HBO.
Fee: $25.00 installation; $10.95 monthly.
Pay Service 2
Pay Units: 178.
Programming (via satellite): Showtime.
Fee: $9.95 monthly.
Pay Service 3
Pay Units: 150.
Programming (via satellite): The Movie Channel.
Fee: $5.95 monthly.
Equipment: Blonder-Tongue & RCA headend; GTE Sylvania & RMS amplifiers; Comm/Scope cable; RMS satellite antenna.
Miles of plant: 65.0 (coaxial). Homes passed: 2,412.
Manager: Bill Flowers. Chief technician: Walt VanLue. Marketing director: Jennifer Hauschild.
City fee: 3% of gross.
Ownership: Classic Cable (MSO).

KENEFICK—Friendship Cable of Texas Inc., Box 9090, Tyler, TX 75711-9090. Phone: 903-581-2121. Fax: 903-581-2185. County: Liberty. Also serves Liberty County (portions). ICA: TX0438.
TV Market Ranking: 11 (Liberty County); Below 100 (Kenefick). Franchise award date: N.A. Franchise expiration date: N.A. Began: N.A.
Channel capacity: 36 (not 2-way capable). Channels available but not in use: 3.
Basic Service
Subscribers: 698.
Programming (received off-air): KHOU-TV (C), KHTV (W), KPRC-TV (N), KRIV (F), KTRK-TV (A), KTXH (U), KUHT (P) Houston.
Programming (via satellite): WGN-TV (W) Chicago; American Movie Classics; CNN; Country Music TV; Discovery Channel; Disney Channel; ESPN; Fox Family Channel; Fox Sports Net Southwest; Lifetime; Nashville Network; Nickelodeon; QVC; TBS Superstation; The Weather Channel; Turner Network TV; USA Network.
Fee: $34.02 monthly.
Pay Service 1
Pay Units: 21.
Programming (via satellite): Cinemax.
Fee: $10.50 monthly.
Pay Service 2
Pay Units: 56.
Programming (via satellite): HBO.
Fee: $10.50 monthly.
Pay Service 3
Pay Units: 58.
Programming (via satellite): Showtime.
Fee: $6.95 monthly.
Miles of plant: 43.7 (coaxial). Homes passed: 890.
Manager: Wanda Pyburn. Chief technician: David Burrell.
Ownership: Buford Television Inc. (MSO). See Cable System Ownership.

KENNEDALE—Charter Communications Inc., Box 2666, Fort Worth, TX 76113. Phone: 817-737-4731. Fax: 817-738-7472. County: Tarrant. ICA: TX0958.
TV Market Ranking: 12. Franchise award date: N.A. Franchise expiration date: N.A. Began: N.A.
Channel capacity: N.A. Channels available but not in use: N.A.
Basic Service
Subscribers: N.A.
Programming (received off-air): KPXD (X) Arlington; KDAF (W), KDFI-TV (I), KDFW (F), KDTX-TV (T), KERA-TV (P), KFWD (O), KTVT (C), KTXA (U), KXAS-TV (N), KXTX-TV (I), WFAA-TV (A) Dallas-Fort Worth; KMPX (I) Decatur; KDTN (P) Denton; KUVN (S) Garland.
Programming (via satellite): WGN-TV (W) Chicago; Bravo; C-SPAN; C-SPAN 2; Home Shopping Network; QVC; TBS Superstation; The Weather Channel.
Current originations: Automated time-weather; educational access; leased access.
Fee: $42.72 installation; $11.28 monthly.
Expanded Basic Service
Subscribers: N.A.
Programming (via satellite): A & E; American Movie Classics; BET; CNBC; CNN; Cartoon Network; Country Music TV; Discovery Channel; Disney Channel; E! Entertainment TV; ESPN; EWTN; FX; Fox Family Channel; Fox Sports Net Southwest; Headline News; History Channel; Learning Channel; Lifetime; MSNBC; MTV; Nashville Network; Nickelodeon; Odyssey; TV Food Network; TV Guide Channel; Turner Network TV; USA Network; VH1.
Fee: $42.72 installation; $14.32 monthly.
Pay Service 1
Pay Units: N.A.
Programming (via satellite): Cinemax; HBO (multiplexed); Showtime; The Movie Channel.
Fee: $9.15 monthly (Cinemax), $10.45 monthly (TMC), $11.05 monthly (Showtime), $12.05 monthly (HBO).
Pay-Per-View
Hot Choice; Playboy TV.
Ownership: Charter Communications Inc. (MSO). Purchased from Marcus Cable, April 1, 1999.

KERENS—Northland Cable TV, 605 W. 7th Ave., Corsicana, TX 75110. Phone: 903-872-3131. Fax: 903-872-6623. County: Navarro. ICA: TX0443.
TV Market Ranking: Outside TV Markets. Franchise award date: June 3, 1980. Franchise expiration date: N.A. Began: N.A.
Channel capacity: 29. Channels available but not in use: 4.
Basic Service
Subscribers: 264.
Programming (received off-air): KDFW (F), KERA-TV (P), KTVT (C), KTXA (U), KXAS-TV (N), KXTX-TV (I), WFAA-TV (A) Dallas-Fort Worth; KLTV (A) Tyler-Longview.
Programming (via satellite): WGN-TV (W) Chicago; A & E; CNN; Country Music TV; Discovery Channel; ESPN; Fox Family Channel; Fox Sports Net Southwest; Home Shopping Network; Nashville Network; TBS Superstation; USA Network.
Fee: $40.00 installation; $21.25 monthly.
Pay Service 1
Pay Units: 70.
Programming (via satellite): Disney Channel; HBO; The Movie Channel.
Fee: $30.00 installation; $7.50 monthly (Disney), $8.50 monthly (TMC), $10.25 monthly (HBO).
Homes passed: 658. Total homes in franchised area: 658.
Manager: Wayne Helmig.
Franchise fee: 4% of gross.
Ownership: Northland Communications Corp. (MSO).

KERMIT—Classic Cable, Box 429, 605 N.W. 3rd St., Plainville, KS 67663-0429. Phones: 785-434-7620; 800-999-8876. Fax: 785-434-2614. County: Winkler. Also serves Winkler County (portions). ICA: TX0161.
TV Market Ranking: Below 100 (portions of Winkler County); Outside TV Markets (portions of Winkler County). Franchise award date: March 26, 1991. Franchise expiration date: March 25, 2001. Began: August 1, 1972.
Channel capacity: 70 (2-way capable). Channels available but not in use: N.A.
Basic Service
Subscribers: 1,766.
Programming (received off-air): KMID (A), KMLM (I), KOSA-TV (C), KPEJ (F), KWES-TV (N) Odessa-Midland.
Programming (via satellite): WGN-TV (W) Chicago; KRMA-TV (P) Denver; A & E; CNN; Country Music TV; Discovery Channel; Disney Channel; ESPN; Fox Family Channel; Fox Sports Net Southwest; GalaVision; Headline News; Learning Channel; Lifetime; Nashville Network; Nick at Nite's TV Land; Nickelodeon; QVC; TBS Superstation; TV Guide Channel; Telemundo; The Weather Channel; Turner Classic Movies; Turner Network TV; USA Network; Univision.
Current originations: Automated time-weather; local news.
Fee: $35.00 installation; $29.95 monthly.
Pay Service 1
Pay Units: 83.
Programming (via satellite): Showtime.
Fee: $15.00 installation; $9.95 monthly.
Pay Service 2
Pay Units: 96.
Programming (via satellite): The Movie Channel.
Fee: $15.00 installation; $5.95 monthly.
Pay Service 3
Pay Units: 323.
Programming (via satellite): HBO.
Fee: $15.00 installation; $10.95 monthly.
Pay Service 4
Pay Units: N.A.
Programming (via satellite): Starz!; The New Encore.
Fee: $6.95 monthly.
Local advertising: Yes. Regional interconnect: Cabletime.
Equipment: Scientific-Atlanta headend; Theta-Com amplifiers; Times Fiber & Belden cable; Hamlin set top converters; Eagle traps; Scientific-Atlanta satellite antenna; Scientific-Atlanta satellite receivers.
Miles of plant: 33.0 (coaxial). Homes passed: 3,528. Total homes in franchised area: 3,528.
Manager: Bill Flowers. Chief technician: Walt VanLue. Marketing director: Jennifer Hauschild.
City fee: 2% of gross ($1,000 minimum).
Ownership: Classic Cable (MSO).

KERRVILLE—Time Warner Communications, 900 Sidney Baker St., Kerrville, TX 78028-3397. Phone: 210-257-4700. County: Kerr. Also serves Kerr County. ICA: TX0061.
TV Market Ranking: Below 100. Franchise award date: N.A. Franchise expiration date: May 1, 2003. Began: January 1, 1957.
Channel capacity: 65. Channels available but not in use: 2.
Basic Service
Subscribers: 8,401.
Programming (received off-air): KRRT (W) Kerrville-San Antonio; KENS-TV (C), KLRN (P), KMOL-TV (N), KSAT-TV (A) San Antonio; allband FM.
Programming (via satellite): A & E; C-SPAN; C-SPAN 2; CNBC; CNN; Country Music TV; Discovery Channel; Fox Family Channel; Lifetime; MTV; Nickelodeon; Odyssey; QVC; The Weather Channel; Travel Channel; USA Network; Univision; VH1.
Current originations: Automated time-weather.
Fee: $40.00 installation; $9.98 monthly; $20.00 additional installation.
Expanded Basic Service
Subscribers: N.A.
Programming (via satellite): WGN-TV (W) Chicago; American Movie Classics; ESPN; Nashville Network; TBS Superstation; Turner Network TV.

Fee: N.A.
Pay Service 1
Pay Units: N.A.
Programming (via satellite): Disney Channel; Fox Sports Net Southwest; HBO; Showtime; The Movie Channel.
Fee: $15.00 installation; $7.95 monthly (Fox Sports), $10.70 monthly (Disney, Showtime or TMC), $12.45 monthly (HBO).
Pay-Per-View
Addressable homes: 2,101.
Local advertising: Yes. Rates: $Varies. Local sales manager: Kim Parker.
Program Guide: The Cable Guide.
Equipment: RCA headend; Theta-Com amplifiers; Systems Wire cable; Harris satellite antenna.
Homes passed: 12,933.
Manager: Russell Hughes. Chief technician: Jay Burton.
City fee: 5% of gross.
Ownership: AT&T Broadband & Internet Services (MSO); Time Warner Cable (MSO); Advance/Newhouse Partnership (MSO).

KILGORE—Kilgore Cable TV Co., Box 150, 333 Houston St., Kilgore, TX 75662. Phone: 903-984-8584. Fax: 903-983-1172. County: Gregg. ICA: TX0130.
TV Market Ranking: Below 100. Franchise award date: March 8, 1977. Franchise expiration date: N.A. Began: February 9, 1978.
Channel capacity: 36 (2-way capable; operating 2-way). Channels available but not in use: None.
Basic Service
Subscribers: 4,000.
Programming (received off-air): KFXK (F) Longview; KSLA-TV (C), KTAL-TV (N), KTBS-TV (A) Shreveport-Texarkana; KLTV (A) Tyler-Longview; allband FM.
Programming (via microwave): KDFW (F), KERA-TV (P), KTVT (C), KXAS-TV (N) Dallas-Fort Worth.
Programming (via satellite): C-SPAN; CNN; Cartoon Network; ESPN; Fox Family Channel; Headline News; Nickelodeon; Sci-Fi Channel; TBS Superstation; Turner Classic Movies.
Current originations: Local news.
Fee: $25.00 installation; $13.95 monthly.
Expanded Basic Service
Subscribers: 2,949.
Programming (via satellite): A & E; American Movie Classics; CNBC; Country Music TV; Discovery Channel; Home Shopping Network; Lifetime; Nashville Network; The Weather Channel; Trinity Bcstg. Network; Turner Network TV; USA Network; VH1.
Fee: $25.00 installation; $4.95 monthly.
Pay Service 1
Pay Units: 531.
Programming (via satellite): Cinemax.
Fee: $9.95 monthly.
Pay Service 2
Pay Units: 370.
Programming (via satellite): Disney Channel.
Fee: $7.50 monthly.
Pay Service 3
Pay Units: 962.
Programming (via satellite): HBO.
Fee: $11.25 monthly.
Local advertising: No.
Equipment: Jerrold headend; AEL amplifiers; Times Fiber cable; Harris satellite antenna.
Miles of plant: 96.6 (coaxial). Additional miles planned: 25.0 (fiber optic). Homes passed: 5,075. Total homes in franchised area: 5,075.
Manager: Bo Balch. Chief technician: Michael Miears.
City fee: 2% of basic.
Ownership: WEHCO Video Inc. (MSO); TCA Cable Partners (MSO).

KILGORE—Friendship Cable of Texas Inc., Box 9090, Tyler, TX 75711-9090. Phone: 903-581-2121. Fax: 903-581-2185. County: Gregg. ICA: TX0505.
TV Market Ranking: Below 100. Franchise award date: N.A. Franchise expiration date: N.A. Began: N.A.
Channel capacity: 36. Channels available but not in use: 6.
Basic Service
Subscribers: 299.
Programming (received off-air): KETK-TV (N) Jacksonville; KLTS-TV (P), KSLA-TV (C) Shreveport-Texarkana; KLTV (A) Tyler-Longview.
Programming (via satellite): WGN-TV (W) Chicago; CNN; Country Music TV; Discovery Channel; ESPN; Fox Family Channel; Nashville Network; TBS Superstation; Turner Network TV; USA Network.
Fee: $34.98 monthly.
Pay Service 1
Pay Units: 19.
Programming (via satellite): Cinemax.
Fee: $10.95 monthly.
Pay Service 2
Pay Units: 28.
Programming (via satellite): HBO.
Fee: $10.95 monthly.
Pay Service 3
Pay Units: 28.
Programming (via satellite): Showtime.
Fee: $5.95 monthly.
Local advertising: Yes.
Miles of plant: 19.9 (coaxial). Homes passed: 496.
Manager: Marianne Bogy. Chief technician: Henry Harris.
Ownership: Buford Television Inc. (MSO). See Cable System Ownership.

KILLEEN—Time Warner Cable, Box 579, 309 N. College St., Killeen, TX 76541. Phone: 817-634-3145. Fax: 817-634-3231. Counties: Bell & Coryell. Also serves Bell County, Copperas Cove, Harker Heights, Nolanville. ICA: TX0023.
TV Market Ranking: Below 100. Franchise award date: N.A. Franchise expiration date: N.A. Began: January 1, 1965.
Channel capacity: 36 (2-way capable; operating 2-way). Channels available but not in use: N.A.
Basic Service
Subscribers: 39,318.
Programming (received off-air): KEYE-TV (C), KTBC (F), KXAN-TV (N) Austin; KNCT (P) Belton; KCEN-TV (N), KWKT (F), KWTX-TV (C), KXXV (A) Waco-Temple; allband FM.
Programming (via microwave): KTVT (C), WFAA-TV (A) Dallas-Fort Worth.
Programming (via satellite): A & E; BET; C-SPAN; CNBC; CNN; Cartoon Network; Country Music TV; Discovery Channel; ESPN; Fox Family Channel; Headline News; Lifetime; MTV; Nashville Network; Nickelodeon; Odyssey; QVC; TBS Superstation; The Inspirational Network; The Weather Channel; Turner Network TV; USA Network; Univision; VH1.
Current originations: Automated time-weather.
Fee: $23.90 monthly.
Pay Service 1
Pay Units: 7,556.
Programming (via satellite): Cinemax.
Fee: $9.95 monthly.
Pay Service 2
Pay Units: 2,461.
Programming (via satellite): Disney Channel.
Fee: $9.95 monthly.
Pay Service 3
Pay Units: 8,948.
Programming (via satellite): HBO.
Fee: $9.95 monthly.
Pay Service 4
Pay Units: 582.
Programming (via satellite): Fox Sports Net Southwest.
Fee: $5.95 monthly.
Pay Service 5
Pay Units: 1,780.
Programming (via satellite): The Movie Channel.
Fee: $9.95 monthly.
Pay Service 6
Pay Units: 3,264.
Programming (via satellite): Showtime.
Fee: $9.95 monthly.
Local advertising: Yes (locally produced). Local sales manager: Joe Webb. Regional interconnect: Waco-Temple-Killeen Interconnect.
Equipment: Scientific-Atlanta headend; GTE Sylvania & Scientific-Atlanta amplifiers; Comm/Scope cable; System Concepts character generator; Scientific-Atlanta set top converters; Scientific-Atlanta satellite antenna; Scientific-Atlanta satellite receivers.
Miles of plant: 554.0 (coaxial). Homes passed: 44,793.
Manager: Chuck Davis. Chief technician: Drayton Loertcher.
City fee: 3% of gross.
Ownership: Time Warner Cable (MSO); Advance/Newhouse Partnership (MSO).

KINGSLAND—Northland Cable TV, Box 366, 1101 Mission Hill Dr., Marble Falls, TX 78654-1906. Phone: 830-693-7500. Fax: 830-693-6056. Counties: Burnet & Llano. Also serves Burnet County, Granite Shoals, Lake L. B. Johnson, Llano County (portions), Sunrise Beach. ICA: TX0126.
TV Market Ranking: Below 100. Franchise award date: N.A. Franchise expiration date: N.A. Began: January 1, 1971.
Channel capacity: 36 (2-way capable). Channels available but not in use: 2.
Basic Service
Subscribers: 111.
Programming (received off-air): KEYE-TV (C), KLRU (P), KNVA (W), KTBC (F), KVUE-TV (A) Austin; KXAM-TV (N) Llano.
Programming (via satellite): WGN-TV (W) Chicago; C-SPAN; Headline News; QVC; TBS Superstation; TV Guide Sneak Prevue.
Planned originations: Automated time-weather; local news.
Fee: $16.75 monthly.
Expanded Basic Service
Subscribers: N.A.
Programming (via satellite): A & E; CNN; Discovery Channel; ESPN; Fox Family Channel; Fox Sports Net Southwest; Great American Country; History Channel; Learning Channel; Nashville Network; The Weather Channel; Trinity Bcstg. Network; USA Network.
Fee: $27.15 monthly.
Expanded Basic Service 2
Subscribers: N.A.
Programming (via satellite): American Movie Classics; CNBC; Cartoon Network; Nickelodeon; Turner Classic Movies; Turner Network TV.
Fee: $8.50 monthly.
Pay Service 1
Pay Units: 177.
Programming (via satellite): Cinemax.
Fee: $8.95 monthly.
Pay Service 2
Pay Units: 251.
Programming (via satellite): HBO.
Fee: $11.95 monthly.
Pay Service 3
Pay Units: 28.
Programming (via satellite): Starz!; The New Encore.
Fee: $11.50 monthly.
Pay Service 4
Pay Units: 19.
Programming (via satellite): Showtime.
Fee: $11.50 monthly.
Local advertising: Yes. Available in satellite distributed programming. Local sales manager: Pat Tims.
Equipment: Scientific-Atlanta headend; Scientific-Atlanta amplifiers; Comm/Scope, Times Fiber & Systems Wire cable; Eagle traps; Mark V & U.S. Tower satellite antenna; Standard Communications, Scientific-Atlanta & Wegener satellite receivers; ChannelMatic & Sony commercial insert.
Miles of plant: 106.0 (coaxial); None (fiber optic). Homes passed: 5,000.
Manager: Rich Beatty. Chief technician: David Simpson. Marketing director: Debbie Jones.
Ownership: Northland Communications Corp. (MSO).

KINGSVILLE—CMA Cablevision, 415 S. 6th St., Kingsville, TX 78363. Phone: 512-595-5726. Fax: 512-592-8825. Counties: Kleberg & Nueces. Also serves Agua Dulce, Driscoll. ICA: TX0926.
TV Market Ranking: Below 100. Franchise award date: October 1, 1980. Franchise expiration date: N.A. Began: October 1, 1980.
Channel capacity: 38 (2-way capable; operating 2-way). Channels available but not in use: None.
Basic Service
Subscribers: 5,504; Commercial subscribers: 2.
Programming (received off-air): KEDT (P), KIII (A), KORO (S), KRIS-TV (N), KZTV (C) Corpus Christi.
Programming (via satellite): WGN-TV (W) Chicago; EWTN; Learning Channel; QVC; TBS Superstation.
Current originations: Local news.
Fee: $49.95 installation; $14.95 monthly.
Expanded Basic Service
Subscribers: 5,167.
Programming (via satellite): A & E; American Movie Classics; BET; C-SPAN; CNN; Discovery Channel; ESPN; Fox Family Channel; GalaVision; Headline News; Lifetime; MTV; Nashville Network; Nickelodeon; Trinity Bcstg. Network; Turner Network TV; USA Network; Univision.

Fee: $49.95 installation; $11.95 monthly.

Pay Service 1

Pay Units: 321.

Programming (via satellite): Cinemax.

Fee: $15.00 installation; $10.45 monthly.

Pay Service 2

Pay Units: 262.

Programming (via satellite): Disney Channel.

Fee: $15.00 installation; $7.95 monthly.

Pay Service 3

Pay Units: 1,487.

Programming (via satellite): HBO.

Fee: $15.00 installation; $11.00 monthly.

Pay Service 4

Pay Units: 118.

Programming (via satellite): The Movie Channel.

Fee: $15.00 installation; $11.00 monthly.

Pay Service 5

Pay Units: 491.

Programming (via satellite): Showtime.

Fee: $15.00 installation; $11.00 monthly.

Pay-Per-View

Addressable homes: 2,223.

Local advertising: Yes. Available in locally originated, character-generated & taped programming. Regional interconnect: Cabletime.

Program Guide: Premium Channels.

Equipment: Scientific-Atlanta headend; C-COR amplifiers; Comm/Scope cable; Atari character generator; Scientific-Atlanta set top converters; Scientific-Atlanta satellite antenna; Scientific-Atlanta satellite receivers.

Miles of plant: 110.0 (coaxial). Total homes in franchised area: 11,661.

Manager: Kenneth Herrington. Chief technician: James Hughes Sr. Marketing director: Jim Gutierrez. Customer service director: Rosemary Garcia.

Ownership: Cable Management Assoc. (MSO). Purchased from Charter Communications Inc., April 1, 1999.

KINGWOOD—Kingwood Cablevision Inc., 4103 W. Lake Houston Pkwy., Kingwood, TX 77339. Phone: 713-360-7500. Fax: 713-360-1320. Counties: Harris & Montgomery. Also serves Forest Cove, Porter. ICA: TX0052.

TV Market Ranking: 15. Franchise award date: January 1, 1972. Franchise expiration date: N.A. Began: September 1, 1974.

Channel capacity: 36 (2-way capable; operating 2-way). Channels available but not in use: None.

Basic Service

Subscribers: 14,956.

Programming (received off-air): KHOU-TV (C), KHTV (W), KPRC-TV (N), KRIV (F), KTRK-TV (A), KTXH (U), KUHT (P) Houston; 14 FMs.

Programming (via satellite): WGN-TV (W) Chicago; A & E; C-SPAN; CNBC; CNN; Discovery Channel; ESPN; Fox Family Channel; Fox Sports Net Southwest; Headline News; Home Shopping Network; Lifetime; MTV; Nashville Network; Nickelodeon; Odyssey; TBS Superstation; TV Guide Channel; The Weather Channel; Turner Classic Movies; Turner Network TV; USA Network; VH1.

Current originations: Leased access.

Planned originations: Automated emergency alert.

Fee: $32.50 installation; $20.95 monthly; $3.00 converter; $10.00 additional installation.

Pay Service 1

Pay Units: 468.

Programming (via satellite): Cinemax.

Fee: $9.95 monthly.

Pay Service 2

Pay Units: 946.

Programming (via satellite): Disney Channel.

Fee: $9.95 monthly.

Pay Service 3

Pay Units: 4,940.

Programming (via satellite): HBO.

Fee: $11.00 monthly.

Pay Service 4

Pay Units: 457.

Programming (via satellite): The Movie Channel.

Fee: $9.95 monthly.

Pay Service 5

Pay Units: 530.

Programming (via satellite): Showtime.

Fee: $9.95 monthly.

Pay-Per-View

Addressable homes: 3,771.

Special events.

Interactive Services

Subscribers: 3,913.

Burglar alarm; medical alert.

Equipment: Tocom.

Fee: $195.00 installation; $19.95 monthly.

Local advertising: Yes. Available in satellite distributed, locally originated & character-generated programming. Rates: $500.00/Month.

Equipment: Scientific-Atlanta headend; GTE Sylvania amplifiers; Comm/Scope cable; Amiga character generator; Tocom set top converters; Tocom addressable set top converters; Eagle & Pico traps; Mark V & Scientific-Atlanta satellite antenna; Scientific-Atlanta satellite receivers; ChannelMatic commercial insert.

Miles of plant: 227.0 (coaxial); 4.4 (fiber optic). Homes passed: 17,322. Total homes in franchised area: 17,322.

Manager: Charles P. Garland. Chief technician: Terry Bagley. Marketing director: Anne Whitehouse.

Franchise fee: 4% of basic gross.

Ownership: Moffat Communications Ltd. (MSO).

KIRBYVILLE—Communicom, Box 640, 2504 Westwood Rd., Westlake, LA 70669. Phone: 318-436-5538. Counties: Jasper & Newton. Also serves Newton. ICA: TX0345.

TV Market Ranking: Outside TV Markets. Franchise award date: March 24, 1981. Franchise expiration date: N.A. Began: October 1, 1979.

Channel capacity: N.A. Channels available but not in use: N.A.

Basic Service

Subscribers: N.A.

Programming (received off-air): KALB-TV (N) Alexandria; KBMT (A), KBTV-TV (N), KFDM-TV (C) Beaumont-Port Arthur; KLTL-TV (P), KPLC-TV (N) Lake Charles.

Programming (via satellite): WGN-TV (W) Chicago; ESPN; Fox Family Channel; Nashville Network; TBS Superstation; USA Network.

Fee: $15.00 installation; $11.00 monthly.

Pay Service 1

Pay Units: N.A.

Programming (via satellite): Disney Channel; Showtime.

Fee: $9.95 monthly (each).

Miles of plant: 27.3 (coaxial). Homes passed: 1,070.

Manager: Brian Sparks.

Ownership: James Cable Partners (MSO).

KNIPPA—Torrence Cablevision, Box 1167, Ridgeland, MS 39158. Phones: 601-981-6900; 800-977-8849. County: Uvalde. ICA: TX0629.

TV Market Ranking: Below 100. Franchise award date: N.A. Franchise expiration date: N.A. Began: February 15, 1990.

Channel capacity: 36 (not 2-way capable). Channels available but not in use: 21.

Basic Service

Subscribers: 78.

Programming (received off-air): KRRT (W) Kerrville-San Antonio; KLRN (P), KSAT-TV (A) San Antonio.

Programming (via satellite): WGN-TV (W) Chicago; KCNC-TV (C), KMGH-TV (A) Denver; A & E; American Movie Classics; CNN; Country Music TV; Discovery Channel; ESPN; Fox Family Channel; Showtime; TBS Superstation; Turner Network TV; USA Network.

Fee: $28.00 monthly.

Equipment: Nexus headend; Magnavox amplifiers; Times Fiber cable; Oak set top converters; Nexus satellite receivers.

Miles of plant: 6.6 (coaxial). Homes passed: 165.

Ownership: Torrence Cable Inc. (MSO).

KNOX CITY—Classic Cable, Box 429, 605 N.W. 3rd St., Plainville, KS 67663-0429. Phones: 785-434-7620; 800-999-8876. Fax: 785-434-2614. Counties: Haskell & Knox. Also serves O'Brien. ICA: TX0429.

TV Market Ranking: Outside TV Markets. Franchise award date: N.A. Franchise expiration date: January 1, 2007. Began: December 1, 1957.

Channel capacity: 41 (2-way capable). Channels available but not in use: N.A.

Basic Service

Subscribers: 539; Commercial subscribers: 90.

Programming (received off-air): KRBC-TV (N), KTAB-TV (C), KTXS-TV (A) Abilene-Sweetwater; KJTL (F,U) Wichita Falls-Lawton; 1 FM.

Programming (via satellite): WGN-TV (W) Chicago; A & E; American Movie Classics; Animal Planet; C-SPAN; CNN; Cartoon Network; Country Music TV; Discovery Channel; Disney Channel; E! Entertainment TV; ESPN; Fox Family Channel; Fox News Channel; Fox Sports Net Southwest; Goodlife TV Network; Headline News; History Channel; Learning Channel; Lifetime; Nashville Network; Nick at Nite's TV Land; Nickelodeon; QVC; TBS Superstation; The Weather Channel; Travel Channel; Trinity Bcstg. Network; Turner Network TV; USA Network; Univision.

Current originations: Automated timeweather; local news.

Fee: $35.00 installation; $26.95 monthly.

Pay Service 1

Pay Units: 151.

Programming (via satellite): HBO.

Fee: $9.95 monthly.

Pay Service 2

Pay Units: 71.

Programming (via satellite): Showtime.

Fee: $9.95 monthly.

Local advertising: No.

Equipment: Jerrold headend; Jerrold amplifiers.

Miles of plant: 25.2 (coaxial). Homes passed: 846.

Manager: Bill Flowers. Chief technician: Rick Rattan. Marketing director: Jennifer Hauschild.

Ownership: Classic Cable (MSO).

KOSSE—Mission Cable, 920 Whitmore Dr., Rockwall, TX 75087. Phone: 800-783-5708. Fax: 214-722-6218. County: Limestone. ICA: TX0577.

TV Market Ranking: Below 100. Franchise award date: November 3, 1987. Franchise expiration date: N.A. Began: N.A.

Channel capacity: 21 (not 2-way capable). Channels available but not in use: N.A.

Basic Service

Subscribers: 81; Commercial subscribers: 6.

Programming (received off-air): KCEN-TV (N), KWKT (F), KWTX-TV (C), KXXV (A) Waco-Temple.

Programming (via satellite): WGN-TV (W) Chicago; CNN; Discovery Channel; ESPN; Fox Family Channel; Nashville Network; TBS Superstation; Turner Network TV.

Fee: $25.00 installation; $19.95 monthly.

Pay Service 1

Pay Units: 21.

Programming (via satellite): Disney Channel.

Fee: $9.00 monthly.

Pay Service 2

Pay Units: 38.

Programming (via satellite): HBO.

Fee: $9.00 monthly.

Program Guide: TV Host.

Equipment: Blonder-Tongue headend; Magnavox amplifiers; Comm/Scope cable; Northeast Filter traps; Weatherscan satellite antenna; DX Antenna satellite receivers.

Miles of plant: 8.0 (coaxial). Homes passed: 284.

Manager: Jim Stafford. Chief technician: Jacky Oliver. Marketing & program director: Bruce Berkinshaw.

Ownership: Fanch Communications Inc. (MSO). See Cable System Ownership.

KOUNTZE—Time Warner Cable, Box 1960, 875 North St., Vidor, TX 77670-1960. Phones: 409-769-8161; 800-828-8380. County: Hardin. ICA: TX0386.

TV Market Ranking: 88. Franchise award date: July 2, 1980. Franchise expiration date: N.A. Began: October 1, 1982.

Channel capacity: 36 (not 2-way capable). Channels available but not in use: 2.

Basic Service

Subscribers: 424; Commercial subscribers: 1.

Programming (received off-air): KBMT (A), KBTV-TV (N), KFDM-TV (C), KITU (E) Beaumont-Port Arthur; KVHP (F) Lake Charles.

Programming (via satellite): WGN-TV (W) Chicago; CNBC; Discovery Channel; QVC; TBS Superstation.

Fee: $30.30 installation; $12.57 monthly; $1.75 converter.

Expanded Basic Service

Subscribers: 407.

Programming (via satellite): A & E; American Movie Classics; BET; CNN; Country Music TV; Disney Channel; ESPN; Fox Family Channel; Fox Sports Net Southwest; Lifetime; MTV; Nashville Network; Nickelodeon; Turner Network TV; USA Network.

Fee: $20.00 installation; $17.99 monthly.

Pay Service 1

Pay Units: 85.

Programming (via satellite): HBO.

Fee: $20.00 installation; $11.45 monthly.

Pay Service 2

Pay Units: 48.

Programming (via satellite): Showtime.

Fee: $20.00 installation; $11.45 monthly.

Local advertising: No.

Program Guide: Premium Channels.

Equipment: Scientific-Atlanta headend; Magnavox amplifiers; Comm/Scope cable; Scientific-Atlanta & Jerrold set top converters; Pico & Eagle traps; Scientific-Atlanta satellite antenna; Scientific-Atlanta satellite receivers.

Miles of plant: 26.0 (coaxial); None (fiber optic). Homes passed: 871.

Manager: Jim Dwyer. Marketing director: Bill Forgey.

City fee: 5% of basic.
Ownership: Time Warner Cable (MSO); Fanch Communications Inc. (MSO). See Cable System Ownership.

KRESS—Classic Cable, Box 429, 605 N.W. 3rd St., Plainville, KS 67663-0429. Phones: 785-434-7620; 800-999-8876. Fax: 785-434-2614. County: Swisher. ICA: TX0588.
TV Market Ranking: Outside TV Markets. Franchise award date: December 5, 1988. Franchise expiration date: December 5, 2003. Began: May 1, 1987.
Channel capacity: 41 (2-way capable). Channels available but not in use: N.A.
Basic Service
Subscribers: 159; Commercial subscribers: 27.
Programming (received off-air): KACV-TV (P), KAMR-TV (N), KFDA-TV (C), KVII-TV (A) Amarillo; KAMC (A), KCBD-TV (N), KJTV (F), KLBK-TV (C) Lubbock.
Programming (via satellite): WGN-TV (W) Chicago; CNN; Country Music TV; Discovery Channel; Disney Channel; ESPN; Fox Family Channel; Home Shopping Network; Learning Channel; Nashville Network; Sci-Fi Channel; TBS Superstation; The Weather Channel; Trinity Bcstg. Network; Turner Classic Movies; Turner Network TV; USA Network; Univision.
Fee: $35.00 installation; $27.95 monthly.
Pay Service 1
Pay Units: 17.
Programming (via satellite): Cinemax.
Fee: $9.95 monthly.
Pay Service 2
Pay Units: 33.
Programming (via satellite): HBO.
Fee: $9.95 monthly.
Local advertising: No.
Miles of plant: 5.9 (coaxial). Homes passed: 262.
Manager: Bill Flowers. Chief technician: Chris Christenson. Marketing director: Jennifer Hauschild.
Ownership: Classic Cable (MSO).

KRUM—Friendship Cable of Texas Inc., Box 9090, Tyler, TX 75711-9090. Phone: 903-581-2121. Fax: 903-581-2185. County: Denton. ICA: TX0517.
TV Market Ranking: 12. Franchise award date: N.A. Franchise expiration date: N.A. Began: August 1, 1984.
Channel capacity: 54. Channels available but not in use: N.A.
Basic Service
Subscribers: 303.
Programming (received off-air): KPXD (X) Arlington; KDFW (F), KERA-TV (P), KTVT (C), KTXA (U), KXAS-TV (N), KXTX-TV (I), WFAA-TV (A) Dallas-Fort Worth.
Programming (via satellite): WGN-TV (W) Chicago; Disney Channel; TBS Superstation.
Fee: $30.00 installation; $32.55 monthly.
Pay Service 1
Pay Units: 14.
Programming (via satellite): HBO.
Fee: $12.00 monthly.
Pay Service 2
Pay Units: 12.
Programming (via satellite): The Movie Channel.
Fee: $9.00 monthly.
Pay Service 3
Pay Units: 37.
Programming (via satellite): Showtime.
Fee: $7.00 monthly.
Miles of plant: 9.9 (coaxial). Homes passed: 415.
Manager: Rodney Fletcher. Chief technician: Bo Jaubert.
Ownership: Buford Television Inc. (MSO). See Cable System Ownership.

KYLE—Time Warner Entertainment/Advance-Newhouse, 12012 N. MoPac Expwy., Austin, TX 75758. Phone: 512-485-5555. Fax: 512-485-6109. County: Hays. Also serves Hays County, Mountain City. ICA: TX0268.
TV Market Ranking: Below 100. Franchise award date: August 2, 1994. Franchise expiration date: October 26, 2007. Began: January 1, 1982.
Channel capacity: 35. Channels available but not in use: None.
Basic Service
Subscribers: 1,001.
Programming (received off-air): KEYE-TV (C), KLRU (P), KNVA (W), KTBC (F), KVUE-TV (A), KXAN-TV (N) Austin; KENS-TV (C) San Antonio.
Programming (via satellite): American Movie Classics; CNBC; Country Music TV; Headline News; Lifetime; Odyssey; Pax Net; The Weather Channel; Trinity Bcstg. Network; VH1.
Fee: $28.21 installation; $9.50 monthly; $25.96 additional installation.
Expanded Basic Service
Subscribers: N.A.
Programming (via satellite): A & E; Animal Planet; C-SPAN; CNN; Cartoon Network; Discovery Channel; ESPN; ESPN 2; Fox Family Channel; Fox Sports Net Southwest; Golf Channel; History Channel; Home & Garden Television; Learning Channel; MSNBC; MTV; Nashville Network; Nickelodeon; TBS Superstation; Travel Channel; Turner Classic Movies; Turner Network TV; USA Network; Univision.
Fee: N.A.
Pay Service 1
Pay Units: 82.
Programming (via satellite): Disney Channel.
Fee: $8.95 monthly.
Pay Service 2
Pay Units: 218.
Programming (via satellite): HBO.
Fee: $11.40 monthly.
Pay Service 3
Pay Units: 126.
Programming (via satellite): Showtime.
Fee: $8.95 monthly.
Pay Service 4
Pay Units: 12.
Programming (via satellite): The Movie Channel.
Fee: $8.95 monthly.
Pay Service 5
Pay Units: N.A.
Programming (via satellite): The New Encore.
Fee: $1.75 monthly.
Miles of plant: 39.0 (coaxial). Homes passed: 1,430. Total homes in franchised area: 1,430.
Manager: Bill Carey.
Ownership: Time Warner Cable (MSO); Advance/Newhouse Partnership (MSO).

LA COSTE—TCI Cablevision of Texas, 207 E. Colorado St., Pearsall, TX 78061-3234. Phone: 800-527-6221. Fax: 210-396-4664. County: Medina. Also serves Medina County. ICA: TX0787.
TV Market Ranking: 45 (La Coste, portions of Medina County); Below 100 (portions of Medina County); Outside TV Markets (portions of Medina County). Franchise award date: N.A. Franchise expiration date: N.A. Began: March 1, 1984.
Channel capacity: 26. Channels available but not in use: N.A.
Basic Service
Subscribers: 166.
Programming (received off-air): KRRT (W) Kerrville-San Antonio; KABB (F), KENS-TV (C), KLRN (P), KMOL-TV (N), KSAT-TV (A), KWEX-TV (S) San Antonio.
Programming (via satellite): WGN-TV (W) Chicago; CNN; ESPN; Headline News; Lifetime; Nashville Network; Nickelodeon; TBS Superstation; The Weather Channel; USA Network.
Fee: $30.00 installation; $19.16 monthly; $30.00 additional installation.
Pay Service 1
Pay Units: 43.
Programming (via satellite): HBO.
Fee: $9.00 monthly.
Pay Service 2
Pay Units: 19.
Programming (via satellite): The Movie Channel.
Fee: $9.00 monthly.
Pay Service 3
Pay Units: 31.
Programming (via satellite): Showtime.
Fee: $9.00 monthly.
Miles of plant: 8.1 (coaxial). Total homes in franchised area: 362.
Manager: Marcos Reyes.
Ownership: AT&T Broadband & Internet Services (MSO). Purchased from Tele-Communications Inc., March 9, 1999.

LA GRANGE—CMA Cablevision, Box 133, 840 E. Travis, La Grange, TX 78945. Phones: 409-968-6476; 800-272-0038. Fax: 409-968-5368. Counties: Colorado, Fayette, Lavaca & Lee. Also serves Giddings, Hallettsville, Schulenburg, Weimar. ICA: TX0073.
TV Market Ranking: Outside TV Markets. Franchise award date: January 11, 1978. Franchise expiration date: January 11, 2003. Began: December 1, 1962.
Channel capacity: 35 (not 2-way capable). Channels available but not in use: 1.
Basic Service
Subscribers: 6,355.
Programming (received off-air): KEYE-TV (C), KLRU (P), KNVA (W), KTBC (F), KVUE-TV (A), KXAN-TV (N) Austin; KHOU-TV (C), KPRC-TV (N), KTRK-TV (A), KTXH (U) Houston; KXLN-TV (S) Rosenberg; KSAT-TV (A) San Antonio; allband FM.
Programming (via satellite): WGN-TV (W) Chicago; C-SPAN; Home Shopping Network; TBS Superstation.
Planned originations: Local news; local sports.
Fee: $35.00 installation; $12.25 monthly; $1.31 converter; $15.00 additional installation.
Expanded Basic Service
Subscribers: 5,310.
Programming (via satellite): A & E; American Movie Classics; BET; CNN; Country Music TV; Discovery Channel; E! Entertainment TV; ESPN; Fox Family Channel; Fox Sports Net Southwest; History Channel; Lifetime; Nashville Network; Nick at Nite's TV Land; Nickelodeon; Odyssey; The Weather Channel; Turner Network TV; USA Network; VH1.
Fee: $16.87 monthly.
Pay Service 1
Pay Units: 282.
Programming (via satellite): Cinemax.
Fee: $15.00 installation; $10.45 monthly.
Pay Service 2
Pay Units: 400.
Programming (via satellite): Disney Channel.
Fee: $15.00 installation; $10.45 monthly.
Pay Service 3
Pay Units: 1,068.
Programming (via satellite): HBO.
Fee: $15.00 installation; $10.45 monthly.
Pay Service 4
Pay Units: 660.
Programming (via satellite): Showtime.
Fee: $15.00 installation; $10.45 monthly.
Local advertising: Yes (locally produced & insert). Available in satellite distributed, locally originated & character-generated programming. Rates: On request. Regional interconnect: Cabletime.
Program Guide: Premium Channels.
Equipment: Cadco, Electrohome & M/A-Com headend; Jerrold amplifiers; Comm/Scope & Times Fiber cable; Texscan character generator; Hamlin, Oak & Pioneer set top converters; Arcom, Eagle & Intercept traps; M/A-Com & Scientific-Atlanta satellite antenna; Electrohome, Scientific-Atlanta & Standard Communications satellite receivers.
Miles of plant: 170.0 (coaxial); 56.0 (fiber optic). Homes passed: 9,820. Total homes in franchised area: 9,820. Headend: ISS. Set Top Converter: RCA. Traps: Pico (87), Vitek (82). Satellite receiver: Macom.
Manager: Jerry L. Smith. Chief technician: Grady Daniels.
State fee: 3% of gross.
Ownership: Cable Management Assoc. (MSO). Purchased from Charter Communications Inc., April 1, 1999.

LA GRULLA—Time Warner Communications, 208 W. Viggie St., Hebbronville, TX 78361-3048. Phone: 512-527-3267. County: Starr. Also serves Garciasville, Santa Cruz. ICA: TX0788.
TV Market Ranking: Below 100. Franchise award date: N.A. Franchise expiration date: August 1, 1998. Began: May 15, 1984.
Channel capacity: 31. Channels available but not in use: N.A.
Basic Service
Subscribers: 1,989.
Programming (received off-air): KVEO (N) Brownsville; KGBT-TV (C), KMBH (P) Harlingen; KNVO (S) McAllen; KRGV-TV (A) Weslaco.
Programming (via satellite): American Movie Classics; CNN; Country Music TV; Discovery Channel; ESPN; EWTN; Fox Family Channel; FoxNet; GalaVision; Lifetime; Nickelodeon; TBS Superstation; Telemundo; Turner Network TV; USA Network; Univision.
Fee: $25.00 installation; $19.09 monthly; $7.50 additional installation.
Pay Service 1
Pay Units: N.A.
Programming (via satellite): Cinemax; HBO.
Fee: $9.75 monthly (HBO).
Miles of plant: 68.2 (coaxial).
Manager: Juve Morante.
City fee: 3% of gross.
Ownership: Time Warner Cable (MSO); AT&T Broadband & Internet Services (MSO).

LA PRYOR—Falcon Cable TV, 1244 Encino Dr., Pleasanton, TX 78064. Phone: 830-569-5509. Fax: 830-569-4828. County: Zavala. ICA: TX0789.
TV Market Ranking: Below 100. Franchise award date: N.A. Franchise expiration date: N.A. Began: N.A.
Channel capacity: 37. Channels available but not in use: 19.

Basic Service
Subscribers: 316.
Programming (received off-air): KRRT (W) Kerrville-San Antonio; KABB (F), KENS-TV (C), KLRN (P), KMOL-TV (N), KSAT-TV (A) San Antonio.
Programming (via satellite): Country Music TV; ESPN; Fox Family Channel; GalaVision; QVC; Sci-Fi Channel; Univision.
Fee: $17.72 monthly.
Expanded Basic Service
Subscribers: 308.
Programming (via satellite): WGN-TV (W) Chicago; Nashville Network; TBS Superstation.
Fee: $3.41 monthly.
Pay Service 1
Pay Units: 27.
Programming (via satellite): Cinemax.
Fee: $10.95 monthly.
Pay Service 2
Pay Units: 97.
Programming (via satellite): HBO.
Fee: $11.95 monthly.
Miles of plant: 13.0 (coaxial). Homes passed: 456.
Manager: Lorna Gentry. Chief technician: Santos Guajardo.
Ownership: Falcon Communications LP (MSO), joint venture formed September 30, 1998. See Cable System Ownership.

LAKE ARROWHEAD—Vista Cablevision, 3225 Maurine St., Wichita Falls, TX 76305. Phone: 940-855-5700. Fax: 940-855-0465. County: Clay. ICA: TX0923.
TV Market Ranking: Below 100. Franchise award date: N.A. Franchise expiration date: N.A. Began: N.A.
Channel capacity: N.A. Channels available but not in use: N.A.
Basic Service
Subscribers: 209.
Programming (received off-air): KERA-TV (P) Dallas-Fort Worth; KAUZ-TV (C), KFDX-TV (N), KJTL (F,U), KSWO-TV (A) Wichita Falls-Lawton.
Programming (via satellite): C-SPAN; QVC; Trinity Bcstg. Network.
Current originations: Local sports.
Fee: $50.00 installation; $9.95 monthly; $30.00 additional installation.
Expanded Basic Service
Subscribers: 207.
Programming (via satellite): WGN-TV (W) Chicago; A & E; American Movie Classics; CNN; Discovery Channel; ESPN; Fox Family Channel; Headline News; Learning Channel; Lifetime; MTV; Nashville Network; Nickelodeon; TBS Superstation; The Weather Channel; Turner Network TV; USA Network.
Fee: $11.52 monthly.
Pay Service 1
Pay Units: N.A.
Programming (via satellite): Cinemax; Disney Channel; HBO; Showtime.
Fee: N.A.
Manager: Rick Orr. Chief technician: Milt Slavin.
Ownership: Time Warner Cable (MSO).

LAKE BROWNWOOD—National Cable Inc., Suite 106-A, 5151 Reed Rd., Columbus, OH 43220. Phone: 614-442-5890. Fax: 614-457-2567. County: Brown. ICA: TX0419.
TV Market Ranking: Outside TV Markets. Franchise award date: N.A. Franchise expiration date: N.A. Began: April 27, 1981.
Channel capacity: 23 (2-way capable). Channels available but not in use: 2.
Basic Service
Subscribers: 552.
Programming (received off-air): KIDZ-LP (F) Abilene; KRBC-TV (N), KTAB-TV (C), KTXS-TV (A) Abilene-Sweetwater.
Programming (via satellite): WGN-TV (W) Chicago; A & E; CNN; Discovery Channel; ESPN; Fox Family Channel; Fox News Channel; Lifetime; Nashville Network; TBS Superstation; The Weather Channel; Trinity Bcstg. Network; Turner Classic Movies; Turner Network TV; USA Network.
Current originations: Automated time-weather.
Fee: $40.00 installation; $21.95 monthly; $2.95 converter.
Pay Service 1
Pay Units: 67.
Programming (via satellite): Cinemax.
Fee: $25.00 installation; $9.00 monthly.
Pay Service 2
Pay Units: 40.
Programming (via satellite): Disney Channel.
Fee: $7.00 monthly.
Pay Service 3
Pay Units: 98.
Programming (via satellite): HBO.
Fee: $25.00 installation; $10.00 monthly.
Local advertising: No.
Equipment: Catel headend; Blonder-Tongue amplifiers; Times Fiber cable; BEI character generator; Pico traps; Weatherscan satellite antenna; Comtech satellite receivers.
Miles of plant: 20.0 (coaxial). Homes passed: 830.
Manager: Bill Mays. Systems/operations manager: Steve Miller.
City fee: None.
Ownership: Cable Ventures Ltd. (MSO).

LAKE CHEROKEE—Friendship Cable of Texas Inc., Box 9090, Tyler, TX 75711-9090. Phone: 903-581-2121. Fax: 903-581-2185. Counties: Gregg, Panola & Rusk. Also serves Beckville, Elderville, Lakeport, Tatum. ICA: TX0795.
TV Market Ranking: Below 100. Franchise award date: N.A. Franchise expiration date: N.A. Began: October 1, 1984.
Channel capacity: 54. Channels available but not in use: N.A.
Basic Service
Subscribers: 2,271.
Programming (received off-air): KFXK (F) Longview; KLTS-TV (P), KSLA-TV (C), KTAL-TV (N), KTBS-TV (A) Shreveport-Texarkana; KLTV (A) Tyler-Longview.
Programming (via satellite): WGN-TV (W) Chicago; TBS Superstation.
Fee: $30.00 installation; $30.00 monthly.
Pay Service 1
Pay Units: 181.
Programming (via satellite): Cinemax.
Fee: $7.00 monthly.
Pay Service 2
Pay Units: 341.
Programming (via satellite): HBO.
Fee: $12.00 monthly.
Pay Service 3
Pay Units: 112.
Programming (via satellite): The Movie Channel.
Fee: $9.00 monthly.
Pay Service 4
Pay Units: 437.
Programming (via satellite): Showtime.
Fee: $7.00 monthly.
Pay Service 5
Pay Units: 627.
Programming (via satellite): Flix.
Fee: $1.95 monthly.
Local advertising: Yes. Regional interconnect: Cabletime.
Miles of plant: 104.0 (coaxial). Homes passed: 3,239.
Manager: Marianne Bogy. Chief technician: Francis Richard.
Ownership: Buford Television Inc. (MSO). See Cable System Ownership.

LAKE KIOWA—North Texas Communications Co., Drawer 587, 205 N. Walnut St., Muenster, TX 76252. Phone: 940-736-2255. Fax: 940-759-5557. Counties: Cooke & Denton. Also serves Cooke County (portions), Denton County (portions). ICA: TX0792.
TV Market Ranking: Below 100. Franchise award date: N.A. Franchise expiration date: N.A. Began: N.A.
Channel capacity: 60 (not 2-way capable). Channels available but not in use: 14.
Basic Service
Subscribers: 569.
Programming (received off-air): KTEN (A,N,F) Ada; KPXD (X) Arlington; KDAF (W), KDFI-TV (I), KDFW (F), KDTX-TV (T), KERA-TV (P), KFWD (O), KTVT (C), KTXA (U), KXAS-TV (N), KXTX-TV (I), WFAA-TV (A) Dallas-Fort Worth; KMPX (I) Decatur; KDTN (P) Denton; KUVN (S) Garland; KHSX-TV (H) Irving; KXII (C) Sherman.
Programming (via satellite): WGN-TV (W) Chicago; A & E; C-SPAN; CNBC; CNN; Country Music TV; Discovery Channel; Disney Channel; ESPN; Fox Family Channel; Fox Sports Net Southwest; Golf Channel; Headline News; History Channel; Home & Garden Television; Learning Channel; Lifetime; Nashville Network; Nickelodeon; QVC; TBS Superstation; The Weather Channel; Turner Classic Movies; Turner Network TV; USA Network.
Fee: $26.20 monthly.
Pay Service 1
Pay Units: 66.
Programming (via satellite): Cinemax.
Fee: $10.00 monthly.
Pay Service 2
Pay Units: 103.
Programming (via satellite): HBO.
Fee: $10.00 monthly.
Miles of plant: 42.0 (coaxial); 8.0 (fiber optic). Homes passed: 801. Total homes in franchised area: 801.
Manager: Alvin M. Fuhrman. CATV Supervisor: Joseph R. Yosten. Program director: Gene Fuhrman. Marketing director: Joey Anderson.
Ownership: North Texas Communications Co. (MSO).

LAKE PALESTINE—Northland Cable TV, Box 538, Flint, TX 75762. Phones: 903-894-8200; 903-566-8757. Fax: 903-894-8204. County: Smith. Also serves Big Eddy, Emerald Bay, Noonday. ICA: TX0220.
TV Market Ranking: Below 100. Franchise award date: November 17, 1982. Franchise expiration date: November 17, 1997. Began: April 1, 1983.
Channel capacity: 36 (2-way capable). Channels available but not in use: 2.
Basic Service
Subscribers: 1,460.
Programming (received off-air): KETK-TV (N) Jacksonville; KFXK (F) Longview; KLTV (A) Tyler-Longview.
Programming (via microwave): KDFW (F), KERA-TV (P), KTVT (C), KXTX-TV (I), WFAA-TV (A) Dallas-Fort Worth.
Current originations: Automated time-weather; local sports.
Fee: $60.00 installation; $11.00 monthly; $3.00 converter.
Expanded Basic Service
Subscribers: 1,450.
Programming (via satellite): WGN-TV (W) Chicago; A & E; CNN; Country Music TV; Discovery Channel; ESPN; Fox Family Channel; Goodlife TV Network; Headline News; Learning Channel; Nashville Network; QVC; TBS Superstation; Travel Channel; USA Network.
Fee: $49.95 installation; $21.75 monthly.
Expanded Basic Service 2
Subscribers: 364.
Programming (via satellite): CNBC; Cartoon Network; Fox Sports Net Southwest; MTV.
Fee: $24.95 installation; $5.35 monthly.
Pay Service 1
Pay Units: 101.
Programming (via satellite): Cinemax.
Fee: $24.95 installation; $7.50 monthly.
Pay Service 2
Pay Units: 56.
Programming (via satellite): Disney Channel.
Fee: $24.95 installation; $7.00 monthly.
Pay Service 3
Pay Units: 155.
Programming (via satellite): HBO.
Fee: $24.95 installation; $10.50 monthly.
Pay Service 4
Pay Units: 104.
Programming (via satellite): Showtime.
Fee: $24.95 installation; $7.95 monthly.
Local advertising: Yes (locally produced). Available in satellite distributed, locally originated, character-generated, taped & automated programming. Rates: $10.00/Minute; $5.00/30 Seconds. Local sales manager: Lynda Tracy.
Program Guide: Premium Channels.
Equipment: Hughes, M/A-Com & Scientific-Atlanta headend; Magnavox & Texscan amplifiers; Comm/Scope cable; JVC cameras; Texscan character generator; Jerrold, Hamlin & Scientific-Atlanta set top converters; Arcom, Eagle & Pico traps; Harris, Scientific-Atlanta & Comtech satellite antenna; Scientific-Atlanta satellite receivers; ChannelMatic commercial insert.
Miles of plant: 109.0 (coaxial). Homes passed: 2,000. Total homes in franchised area: 2,000.
Manager: Jim Wiggins. Chief technician: Jim Bob Sanders. Marketing director: Charlotte Griffin.
Franchise fee: 5% of gross (Emerald Bay).
Ownership: Northland Communications Corp. (MSO).

LAKE THUNDERBIRD ESTATES—BRDC Cablevision, Box 240, Giddings, TX 78942. Phone: 409-542-3151. Fax: 409-542-1187. County: Bastrop. ICA: TX0794.
TV Market Ranking: Below 100. Franchise award date: N.A. Franchise expiration date: N.A. Began: N.A.
Channel capacity: N.A. Channels available but not in use: N.A.
Basic Service
Subscribers: 889.
Programming (received off-air): KEYE-TV (C), KLRU (P), KTBC (F), KVUE-TV (A), KXAN-TV (N) Austin.
Programming (via satellite): WGN-TV (W) Chicago; TBS Superstation.
Fee: N.A.
Manager: David W. Peterson.
Ownership: Bluebonnet Rural Development Corp. (MSO).

LAKEHILLS—TCI Cablevision of Texas, 108 W. Hefferman St., Beeville, TX 78102-4603. Phone: 512-358-3542. Fax: 512-358-3544. County: Bandera. ICA: TX0521.

TV Market Ranking: Below 100. Franchise award date: N.A. Franchise expiration date: N.A. Began: May 1, 1984.
Channel capacity: 17. Channels available but not in use: N.A.

Basic Service

Subscribers: 234.
Programming (received off-air): KRRT (W) Kerrville-San Antonio; KENS-TV (C), KLRN (P), KMOL-TV (N), KSAT-TV (A), KWEX-TV (S) San Antonio.
Programming (via satellite): CNN; ESPN; Nickelodeon; TBS Superstation.
Fee: $25.00 installation; $17.03 monthly; $10.00 additional installation.

Pay Service 1

Pay Units: 77.
Programming (via satellite): HBO.
Fee: $9.00 monthly.

Pay Service 2

Pay Units: 66.
Programming (via satellite): Showtime.
Fee: $9.00 monthly.

Miles of plant: 26.0 (coaxial). Homes passed: 400. Total homes in franchised area: 450.
Office supervisor: Denise Longolia. Technical supervisor: John Salinas.
Ownership: AT&T Broadband & Internet Services (MSO). Purchased from Tele-Communications Inc., March 9, 1999.

LAKEWAY—Cablevision of Lake Travis, 620 S, 919 Ranch Rd., Austin, TX 78734. Phone: 512-263-9194. Fax: 512-263-3445. County: Travis. Also serves Briarcliff, Jonestown, Lake Travis. ICA: TX0135.
TV Market Ranking: Below 100. Franchise award date: N.A. Franchise expiration date: N.A. Began: December 1, 1968.
Channel capacity: 50 (2-way capable; operating 2-way). Channels available but not in use: 3.

Basic Service

Subscribers: 5,200.
Programming (received off-air): KEYE-TV (C), KLRU (P), KTBC (F), KVUE-TV (A), KXAN-TV (N) Austin; KENS-TV (C), KSAT-TV (A) San Antonio; allband FM.
Programming (via satellite): WGN-TV (W) Chicago; C-SPAN; CNBC; Fox Family Channel; Headline News; Lifetime; MTV; Nickelodeon; TBS Superstation; The Inspirational Network; The Weather Channel.
Current originations: Automated time-weather; public access.
Fee: $18.45 installation; $9.31 monthly; $24.60 additional installation.

Pay Service 1

Pay Units: N.A.
Programming (via satellite): Cinemax; HBO.
Fee: $15.00 installation; $8.00 monthly (each).

Local advertising: Yes. Regional interconnect: Cabletime.
Program Guide: The Cable Guide.
Equipment: Scientific-Atlanta headend; Scientific-Atlanta amplifiers; Systems Wire cable; MSI character generator; Scientific-Atlanta & Hamlin set top converters; Pico traps; Scientific-Atlanta satellite antenna; Scientific-Atlanta satellite receivers.
Miles of plant: 350.0 (coaxial); 20.0 (fiber optic). Homes passed: 15,000. Total homes in franchised area: 25,000.
Manager: K. L. King. Chief technician: J. E. Pickle.
City fee: 2% of gross.
Ownership: J. R. King Enterprises Inc.

LAMESA—Northland Cable TV, 1012 S. First St., Lamesa, TX 79331. Phone: 806-872-8561. Fax: 806-872-8825. County: Dawson. Also serves Dawson County (unincorporated areas). ICA: TX0148.
TV Market Ranking: Below 100 (portions of Dawson County); Outside TV Markets (portions of Dawson County, Lamesa). Franchise award date: January 1, 1966. Franchise expiration date: N.A. Began: April 1, 1966.
Channel capacity: 54 (not 2-way capable). Channels available but not in use: None.

Basic Service

Subscribers: 3,247.
Programming (received off-air): KAMC (A), KCBD-TV (N), KJTV (F), KLBK-TV (C), KTXT-TV (P), KUPT-LP (U) Lubbock; KMID (A), KMLM (I), KPEJ (F) Odessa-Midland; allband FM.
Programming (via satellite): WGN-TV (W) Chicago; A & E; C-SPAN; CNN; Country Music TV; Discovery Channel; ESPN; FX; Fox Family Channel; Fox Sports Net; Headline News; Home Shopping Network; Learning Channel; Nashville Network; TBS Superstation; TV Guide Channel; Telemundo; The Weather Channel; Travel Channel; USA Network; Univision.
Current originations: Religious access; automated emergency alert.
Fee: $50.00 installation; $27.05 monthly.

Expanded Basic Service

Subscribers: 3,076.
Programming (via satellite): American Movie Classics; Cartoon Network; ESPN 2; History Channel; Lifetime; Nickelodeon; Turner Classic Movies; Turner Network TV.
Fee: $37.00 installation; $9.69 monthly.

Pay Service 1

Pay Units: 349.
Programming (via satellite): Cinemax.
Fee: $30.00 installation; $8.66 monthly.

Pay Service 2

Pay Units: 257.
Programming (via satellite): Disney Channel.
Fee: $30.00 installation; $8.12 monthly.

Pay Service 3

Pay Units: 448.
Programming (via satellite): HBO.
Fee: $30.00 installation; $11.91 monthly.

Local advertising: No. Local sales manager: Beverly Kinnison. Regional interconnect: Cabletime.
Equipment: Scientific-Atlanta headend; Scientific-Atlanta amplifiers; Times Fiber cable; Scientific-Atlanta set top converters; Eagle traps; Scientific-Atlanta satellite antenna; Scientific-Atlanta & Standard Electronics satellite receivers.
Miles of plant: 57.0 (coaxial); None (fiber optic). Additional miles planned: 3.0 (coaxial). Homes passed: 4,100. Total homes in franchised area: 4,100.
Manager: Mickey Flanagan.
City fee: 2% of gross.
Ownership: Northland Communications Corp. (MSO).

LAMPASAS—Classic Cable, Box 71, 403 E. 3rd St., Lampasas, TX 76550. Phone: 512-556-6112. Fax: 512-556-8244.
E-mail: cgillit@classic-cable.com.
County: Lampasas. Also serves Lampasas County. ICA: TX0183.
TV Market Ranking: Below 100 (portions of Lampasas County); Outside TV Markets (Lampasas, portions of Lampasas County). Franchise award date: March 29, 1962. Franchise expiration date: March 10, 2002. Began: January 1, 1964.
Channel capacity: 53 (not 2-way capable). Channels available but not in use: None.

Basic Service

Subscribers: 2,309; Commercial subscribers: 18.
Programming (received off-air): KTBC (F), KVUE-TV (A) Austin; KNCT (P) Belton; KDFW (F), WFAA-TV (A) Dallas-Fort Worth; KAKW (U,W) Killeen; KCEN-TV (N), KWKT (F), KWTX-TV (C), KXXV (A) Waco-Temple.
Programming (via satellite): WGN-TV (W) Chicago; A & E; C-SPAN; C-SPAN 2; CNN; Cartoon Network; Country Music TV; Discovery Channel; Disney Channel; E! Entertainment TV; ESPN; Fox Family Channel; Fox Sports Net Southwest; Headline News; History Channel; Home & Garden Television; Learning Channel; Lifetime; MSNBC; MTV; Nashville Network; Nickelodeon; QVC; Sci-Fi Channel; TBS Superstation; TV Guide Channel; The Inspirational Network; The Weather Channel; Turner Classic Movies; Turner Network TV; USA Network; Univision.
Current originations: Automated time-weather; leased access; automated emergency alert.
Fee: $35.00 installation; $29.75 monthly; $1.02 converter; $15.37 additional installation.
Commercial fee: $12.00 monthly.

Pay Service 1

Pay Units: 320.
Programming (via satellite): Cinemax (multiplexed).
Fee: $15.70 installation; $15.95 monthly.

Pay Service 2

Pay Units: 321.
Programming (via satellite): HBO (multiplexed).
Fee: $15.70 installation; $15.95 monthly.

Pay Service 3

Pay Units: 108.
Programming (via satellite): Showtime (multiplexed).
Fee: $15.70 installation; $12.95 monthly.

Pay Service 4

Pay Units: 108.
Programming (via satellite): The Movie Channel (multiplexed).
Fee: $15.70 installation; $12.95 monthly.

Pay-Per-View

Addressable homes: 613.
Hot Choice; Viewer's Choice.
Fee: $2.99-$5.95.
Pay-per-view manager: Carl Gillit.

Local advertising: Yes (insert only). Available in satellite distributed programming. Regional interconnect: Cabletime.
Equipment: Scientific-Atlanta headend; GTE Sylvania & Scientific-Atlanta amplifiers; Comm/Scope cable; Comm/Scope fiber optic cable; Texscan character generator; Oak & Jerrold set top converters; Oak & Jerrold addressable set top converters; PPC traps; Hughes, M/A-Com & Scientific-Atlanta satellite antenna; Scientific-Atlanta & General Instrument satellite receivers; Sony commercial insert.
Miles of plant: 52.0 (coaxial); 3.0 (fiber optic). Homes passed: 2,852. Satellite Antenna(s): Vertex.
Manager: Carl Gillit. Customer service manager: Barbara Hamrick.
City fee: 5% of basic gross.
Ownership: Classic Cable (MSO). Purchased from Cable One Inc., June 1, 1998.

LANCASTER—TCI TKR of the Metroplex Inc., 934 E. Centerville Rd., Garland, TX 75041. Phone: 214-840-2388. County: Dallas. Also serves Hutchins. ICA: TX0092.
TV Market Ranking: 12. Franchise award date: N.A. Franchise expiration date: N.A. Began: January 1, 1980.
Channel capacity: 40. Channels available but not in use: None.

Basic Service

Subscribers: 2,529.
Programming (received off-air): KDAF (W), KDFI-TV (I), KDFW (F), KERA-TV (P), KTVT (C), KTXA (U), KXAS-TV (N), KXTX-TV (I), WFAA-TV (A) Dallas-Fort Worth; KDTN (P) Denton; KUVN (S) Garland; KHSX-TV (H) Irving.
Programming (via satellite): WGN-TV (W) Chicago; A & E; C-SPAN; CNBC; CNN; Comedy Central; Discovery Channel; Fox Family Channel; Headline News; Lifetime; MTV; Nashville Network; Nickelodeon; TBS Superstation; The Weather Channel; VH1.
Current originations: Automated time-weather; public access; educational access; government access; automated emergency alert; local news; local sports.
Fee: $60.00 installation; $19.45 monthly; $2.00 converter; $25.00 additional installation.

Expanded Basic Service

Subscribers: 2,182.
Programming (via satellite): American Movie Classics; ESPN; Fox Sports Net Southwest; Turner Network TV; USA Network.
Fee: $3.50 monthly.

Pay Service 1

Pay Units: N.A.
Programming (via satellite): Disney Channel; HBO; Showtime; The Movie Channel.
Fee: $25.00 installation; $10.25 monthly (Disney), $11.24 monthly (Showtime or TMC), $12.20 monthly (HBO).

Local advertising: Yes.
Equipment: Scientific-Atlanta satellite antenna.
Miles of plant: 120.8 (coaxial). Homes passed: 8,066. Total homes in franchised area: 8,106.
Manager: Steve Crawford.
Ownership: AT&T Broadband & Internet Services (MSO). Purchased from Tele-Communications Inc., March 9, 1999.

LANEVILLE—Friendship Cable of Texas Inc., Box 9090, Tyler, TX 75711-9090. Phone: 903-581-2121. Fax: 903-581-2185. County: Rusk. ICA: TX0796.
TV Market Ranking: Below 100. Franchise award date: N.A. Franchise expiration date: N.A. Began: N.A.
Channel capacity: 30. Channels available but not in use: N.A.

Basic Service

Subscribers: 74.
Programming (received off-air): KMSS-TV (F), KSLA-TV (C), KTAL-TV (N) Shreveport-Texarkana; KLTV (A) Tyler-Longview.
Programming (via satellite): WGN-TV (W) Chicago; TBS Superstation.
Fee: $30.50 monthly.

Pay Service 1

Pay Units: 15.
Programming (via satellite): Showtime.
Fee: $5.95 monthly.

Pay Service 2

Pay Units: 9.
Programming (via satellite): Cinemax.
Fee: $7.00 monthly.

Miles of plant: 4.0 (coaxial). Homes passed: 130.
Manager: Marianne Bogy. Chief technician: Henry Harris.
Ownership: Buford Television Inc. (MSO). See Cable System Ownership.

LANSING—Friendship Cable of Texas Inc., Box 9090, Tyler, TX 75711-9090. Phone: 903-

581-2121. Fax: 903-581-2185. County: Harrison. ICA: TX0336.
TV Market Ranking: Below 100. Franchise award date: N.A. Franchise expiration date: N.A. Began: N.A.
Channel capacity: 36. Channels available but not in use: 4.
Basic Service
Subscribers: 748.
Programming (received off-air): KETK-TV (N) Jacksonville; KFXK (F) Longview; KLTS-TV (P), KSLA-TV (C) Shreveport-Texarkana; KLTV (A) Tyler-Longview.
Programming (via satellite): WGN-TV (W) Chicago; A & E; CNN; Country Music TV; Discovery Channel; ESPN; Fox Family Channel; Fox Sports Net Southwest; Goodlife TV Network; Home Shopping Network; Nashville Network; TBS Superstation; Turner Network TV; USA Network.
Fee: $34.95 monthly.
Pay Service 1
Pay Units: 36.
Programming (via satellite): Cinemax.
Fee: $10.95 monthly.
Pay Service 2
Pay Units: 73.
Programming (via satellite): HBO.
Fee: $10.95 monthly.
Pay Service 3
Pay Units: 93.
Programming (via satellite): Showtime.
Fee: $5.95 monthly.
Local advertising: Yes.
Miles of plant: 47.9 (coaxial). Homes passed: 1,116.
Manager: Marianne Bogy. Chief technician: Sonny Myers.
Ownership: Buford Television Inc. (MSO). See Cable System Ownership.

LAREDO—Paragon Cable, 1313 W. Calton Rd., Laredo, TX 78041. Phone: 956-721-0600. Fax: 956-721-0612. County: Webb. Also serves Rio Bravo, Webb County. ICA: TX0029.
TV Market Ranking: Below 100 (Laredo, Rio Bravo, portions of Webb County); Outside TV Markets (portions of Webb County). Franchise award date: N.A. Franchise expiration date: December 31, 2003. Began: November 1, 1961.
Channel capacity: 79 (2-way capable; operating 2-way). Channels available but not in use: 10.
Basic Service
Subscribers: 27,502; Commercial subscribers: 480.
Programming (received off-air): KGNS-TV (N,A), KLDO-TV (O), KVTV (C) Laredo; KENS-TV (C), KLRN (P), KMOL-TV (N), KSAT-TV (A) San Antonio.
Programming (via microwave): KENS-TV (C), KLRN (P), KMOL-TV (N), KSAT-TV (A) San Antonio.
Programming (via satellite): C-SPAN; EWTN; Telemundo; Univision.
Current originations: Automated time-weather; public access; educational access; government access; religious access; leased access; automated emergency alert.
Fee: $35.00 installation; $5.19 monthly; $3.01 converter; $25.00 additional installation.
Expanded Basic Service
Subscribers: 23,538.
Programming (received off-air): XEFE-TV, XHBR Laredo-Nuevo Laredo.
Programming (via satellite): A & E; American Movie Classics; Animal Planet; CNBC; CNN; Cartoon Network; Comedy Central; Country Music TV; Discovery Channel; Disney Channel; E! Entertainment TV; ESPN; ESPN 2; Fox Family Channel; Fox News Channel; Fox Sports Net Southwest; GalaVision; Gems Television; Headline News; Learning Channel; Lifetime; MSNBC; MTV; Nashville Network; Nickelodeon; QVC; Sci-Fi Channel; TV Food Network; TV Guide Channel; The New Encore; The Weather Channel; Turner Network TV; USA Network; VH1.
Fee: $23.00 installation; $22.35 monthly.
Expanded Basic Service 2
Subscribers: 26,450.
Programming (via satellite): CNN/SI; Court TV; ESPN Classic Sports; History Channel; Knowledge TV; MTV Latin America; Nick at Nite's TV Land; TBS Superstation; Turner Classic Movies.
Fee: $0.50 monthly.
Pay Service 1
Pay Units: N.A.
Programming (via satellite): Cinemax (multiplexed); HBO en Espanol.
Fee: $9.95 monthly (each).
Pay Service 2
Pay Units: 13,500.
Programming (via satellite): HBO (multiplexed).
Fee: $13.95 installation; $9.95 monthly.
Pay Service 3
Pay Units: 3,850.
Programming (via satellite): The Movie Channel.
Fee: $13.95 installation; $9.95 monthly.
Pay Service 4
Pay Units: 3,450.
Programming (via satellite): Showtime.
Fee: $13.95 installation; $9.95 monthly.
Pay-Per-View
Addressable homes: 12,746.
Hot Choice; Spice; Viewer's Choice; movies.
Fee: $3.95-$4.95.
Local advertising: Yes. Available in satellite distributed & character-generated programming. Rates: $140.00/30 Seconds. Local sales manager: John Speer.
Equipment: Jerrold & Scientific-Atlanta headend; C-COR amplifiers; Comm/Scope cable; Siecor fiber optic cable; Sony VTRs; Texscan character generator; C-COR & Hamlin set top converters; Jerrold addressable set top converters; Arcom traps; Scientific-Atlanta satellite antenna; Jerrold satellite receivers.
Miles of plant: 528.0 (coaxial); 110.0 (fiber optic). Homes passed: 47,000.
Manager: Esteban Ventura. Chief engineer: Robert Rodriguez. Marketing director: Lisa Rogerio. Customer service manager: San Juanita Rodriguez.
City fee: 5% of gross.
Ownership: Time Warner Cable (MSO); AT&T Broadband & Internet Services (MSO).

LAS GALLINAS—Friendship Cable of Texas Inc., Box 9090, Tyler, TX 75711-9090. Phone: 903-581-2121. Fax: 903-581-2185. County: Bexar. ICA: TX0239.
TV Market Ranking: 45. Franchise award date: N.A. Franchise expiration date: N.A. Began: January 1, 1989.
Channel capacity: 54. Channels available but not in use: N.A.
Basic Service
Subscribers: 458.
Programming (received off-air): KRRT (W) Kerrville-San Antonio; KABB (F), KENS-TV (C), KHCE (P), KLRN (P), KMOL-TV (N), KSAT-TV (A), KVDA (O), KWEX-TV (S) San Antonio.
Programming (via satellite): CNN; Country Music TV; Discovery Channel; Disney Channel; ESPN; GalaVision; Headline News; MTV; Nashville Network; Nickelodeon; TBS Superstation; Turner Network TV; USA Network.
Fee: $30.00 installation; $27.20 monthly.
Pay Service 1
Pay Units: 15.
Programming (via satellite): Cinemax.
Fee: $10.95 monthly.
Pay Service 2
Pay Units: 75.
Programming (via satellite): Showtime.
Fee: $10.95 monthly.
Pay Service 3
Pay Units: 40.
Programming (via satellite): HBO.
Fee: $10.95 monthly.
Miles of plant: 70.0 (coaxial). Homes passed: 2,138.
Manager: Wanda Pyburn. Chief technician: David Burrell.
Ownership: Buford Television Inc. (MSO). See Cable System Ownership.

LASARA—Torrence Cablevision, Box 1167, Ridgeland, MS 39158. Phones: 601-981-6900; 800-977-8849. County: Willacy. ICA: TX0621.
TV Market Ranking: Below 100. Franchise award date: N.A. Franchise expiration date: N.A. Began: N.A.
Channel capacity: 36. Channels available but not in use: 18.
Basic Service
Subscribers: 19.
Programming (received off-air): KVEO (N) Brownsville; KGBT-TV (C), KLUJ (E) Harlingen; KRGV-TV (A) Weslaco.
Programming (via satellite): WGN-TV (W) Chicago; A & E; American Movie Classics; CNN; Country Music TV; Discovery Channel; ESPN; Fox Family Channel; Showtime; TBS Superstation; Turner Network TV; USA Network.
Fee: $28.00 monthly.
Miles of plant: 4.2 (coaxial). Homes passed: 217.
Ownership: Torrence Cable Inc. (MSO).

LAVERNIA—Comfort Cable Co., Box 507, 523 8th St., Comfort, TX 78013. Phone: 830-995-2813. Fax: 830-995-2245. County: Wilson. ICA: TX0441.
TV Market Ranking: 45. Franchise award date: November 5, 1985. Franchise expiration date: November 5, 2001. Began: March 1, 1986.
Channel capacity: 36. Channels available but not in use: 24.
Basic Service
Subscribers: 119.
Programming (received off-air): KENS-TV (C), KLRN (P), KMOL-TV (N), KSAT-TV (A), KWEX-TV (S) San Antonio.
Programming (via satellite): ESPN; Fox Family Channel; Headline News; Nashville Network; Nickelodeon; TBS Superstation; The Movie Channel.
Fee: $21.95 monthly.
Miles of plant: 23.0 (coaxial). Homes passed: 660.
Manager: David Petty. Chief technician: Ronald W. Petty. Marketing director: Eddie K. Petty.
Ownership: Petty General Construction Co. Inc. (MSO).

LAWN—Big Country Cablevision, Box 549, 102 Oak St., Merkel, TX 79536. Phones: 915-928-4750; 800-588-4750. Fax: 915-928-3452. County: Taylor. ICA: TX0649.
TV Market Ranking: Below 100. Franchise award date: N.A. Franchise expiration date: N.A. Began: September 1, 1990.
Channel capacity: 26. Channels available but not in use: 14.
Basic Service
Subscribers: 81.
Programming (received off-air): KRBC-TV (N), KTAB-TV (C), KTXS-TV (A) Abilene-Sweetwater.
Programming (via satellite): WGN-TV (W) Chicago; CNN; ESPN; Nashville Network; TBS Superstation; Trinity Bcstg. Network; USA Network.
Fee: $38.35 installation; $16.75 monthly.
Pay Service 1
Pay Units: 19.
Programming (via satellite): Cinemax.
Fee: $11.00 monthly.
Pay Service 2
Pay Units: 21.
Programming (via satellite): HBO.
Fee: $11.50 monthly.
Miles of plant: 5.0 (coaxial). Homes passed: 186.
Manager: Mark Reaves. Marketing director: J. Ketchum.
Ownership: Cable Management Assoc. (MSO).

LEANDER—Cablevision of Leander, Box 1999, 111 N. College, Georgetown, TX 78627. Phones: 512-930-3085; 512-869-1505. Fax: 512-869-2962. County: Williamson. ICA: TX0251.
TV Market Ranking: Below 100. Franchise award date: January 1, 1980. Franchise expiration date: January 1, 2007. Began: December 1, 1981.
Channel capacity: 78 (2-way capable). Channels available but not in use: 7.
Basic Service
Subscribers: 3,000.
Programming (received off-air): KEYE-TV (C), KLRU (P), KNVA (W), KTBC (F), KVUE-TV (A), KXAN-TV (N) Austin; K13VC (I) Austin, Cedar Park.
Programming (via satellite): WGN-TV (W) Chicago; Animal Planet; C-SPAN; C-SPAN 2; FX; Fox News Channel; Goodlife TV Network; Home & Garden Television; Knowledge TV; MSNBC; Outdoor Life Network; QVC; TV Food Network; TV Guide Channel; The Health Network; The Weather Channel; Toon Disney; Travel Channel.
Current originations: Automated time-weather; public access; educational access.
Fee: $35.00 installation; $27.99 monthly; $1.50 converter.
Expanded Basic Service
Subscribers: N.A.
Programming (via satellite): A & E; American Movie Classics; BET; CNBC; CNN; Country Music TV; Court TV; Discovery Channel; Dis-

ney Channel; E! Entertainment TV; ESPN; ESPN 2; ESPN Classic Sports; ESPNews; Fox Family Channel; Fox Sports Net Southwest; Headline News; Learning Channel; Lifetime; MTV; Nashville Network; Nick at Nite's TV Land; Nickelodeon; Sci-Fi Channel; TBS Superstation; Trinity Bcstg. Network; Turner Network TV; USA Network; Univision; VH1.
Fee: $15.50 monthly.

A la Carte 1
Subscribers: N.A.
Programming (via satellite): Cartoon Network; Comedy Central; Golf Channel; History Channel; MOVIEplex; Speedvision; Sundance Channel; Turner Classic Movies.
Fee: $4.99 monthly (package); $1.25 monthly (each).

Pay Service 1
Pay Units: 238.
Programming (via satellite): Cinemax (multiplexed).
Fee: $15.00 installation; $9.99 monthly.

Pay Service 2
Pay Units: N.A.
Programming (via satellite): Starz!; The New Encore.
Fee: $15.00 installation; $9.99 monthly (Encore & Starz).

Pay Service 3
Pay Units: 454.
Programming (via satellite): HBO (multiplexed).
Fee: $15.00 installation; $11.49 monthly.

Pay Service 4
Pay Units: 438.
Programming (via satellite): Showtime.
Fee: $15.00 installation; $8.99 monthly.

Pay-Per-View
Addressable homes: 500.
Viewer's Choice.

Local advertising: Yes.
Program Guide: Cabletime.
Equipment: Microdyne & Scientific-Atlanta headend; C-COR amplifiers; Comm/Scope cable; Scientific-Atlanta set top converters; Arcom & Eagle traps; U.S. Tower & Scientific-Atlanta satellite antenna; Microdyne & Scientific-Atlanta satellite receivers.
Miles of plant: 60.1 (coaxial); 9.0 (fiber optic). Homes passed: 4,311.
Manager: Dale Hoffman. Chief technician & marketing director: Wesley Houghteling.
City fee: 3% of basic gross.
Ownership: M. K. McDaniel (MSO); John Muraglia (MSO); E. D. Hoffman (MSO). See Cable System Ownership.

LEFORS—Classic Cable, Box 429, 605 N.W. 3rd St., Plainville, KS 67663-0429. Phones: 785-434-7620; 800-999-8876. Fax: 785-434-2614. County: Gray. ICA: TX0563.
TV Market Ranking: Outside TV Markets. Franchise award date: December 12, 1967. Franchise expiration date: N.A. Began: July 1, 1968.
Channel capacity: 41 (2-way capable). Channels available but not in use: N.A.

Basic Service
Subscribers: 207.
Programming (received off-air): KAMR-TV (N), KCIT (F,U), KFDA-TV (C), KVII-TV (A) Amarillo; KWET (P) Cheyenne; 1 FM.
Programming (via satellite): WGN-TV (W) Chicago; A & E; C-SPAN; CNN; Court TV; Discovery Channel; Disney Channel; E! Entertainment TV; ESPN; ESPN 2; Fox Family Channel; Headline News; History Channel; Learning Channel; Nashville Network; Nick at Nite's TV Land; Sci-Fi Channel; TBS Superstation; The Weather Channel; Trinity Bcstg. Network; Turner Network TV; USA Network.
Current originations: Automated time-weather.
Fee: $35.00 installation; $27.95 monthly.

Pay Service 1
Pay Units: 41.
Programming (via satellite): HBO.
Fee: $10.95 monthly.

Pay Service 2
Pay Units: 15.
Programming (via satellite): Showtime.
Fee: $9.95 monthly.

Local advertising: No.
Equipment: Microwave Assoc. headend; Ameco amplifiers; Ameco cable; Cable Text character generator; Eagle traps; Comtech satellite antenna; Microwave Assoc. satellite receivers.
Miles of plant: 6.6 (coaxial). Homes passed: 307. Total homes in franchised area: 590.
Manager: Bill Flowers. Chief technician: Rick Rattan. Marketing director: Jennifer Hauschild.
City fee: 3% of gross.
Ownership: Classic Cable (MSO).

LEON SPRINGS—TCI Cablevision of Central Texas, 108 W. Hefferman St., Beeville, TX 78102-4603. Phone: 512-358-3542. Fax: 512-358-3544. County: Bexar. ICA: TX0430.
TV Market Ranking: 45. Franchise award date: N.A. Franchise expiration date: N.A. Began: January 1, 1985.
Channel capacity: 35. Channels available but not in use: 6.

Basic Service
Subscribers: 630.
Programming (received off-air): KRRT (W) Kerrville-San Antonio; KABB (F), KENS-TV (C), KLRN (P), KMOL-TV (N), KSAT-TV (A), KWEX-TV (S) San Antonio.
Programming (via satellite): WGN-TV (W) Chicago; C-SPAN; C-SPAN 2; CNN; Cartoon Network; Country Music TV; Discovery Channel; ESPN; Fox Sports Net Southwest; Headline News; Lifetime; MTV; Nashville Network; Nickelodeon; TBS Superstation; The Weather Channel; Trinity Bcstg. Network; Turner Network TV; USA Network.
Fee: $25.00 installation; $17.80 monthly.

Pay Service 1
Pay Units: 124.
Programming (via satellite): Disney Channel.
Fee: N.A.

Pay Service 2
Pay Units: 134.
Programming (via satellite): HBO.
Fee: N.A.

Pay Service 3
Pay Units: 191.
Programming (via satellite): Showtime.
Fee: N.A.

Miles of plant: 76.0 (coaxial). Homes passed: 700. Total homes in franchised area: 700.
Office supervisor: Denise Longolia. Technical supervisor: John Salinas.
Ownership: AT&T Broadband & Internet Services (MSO). Purchased from Tele-Communications Inc., March 9, 1999.

LEONA—Mission Cable, 920 Whitmore Dr., Rockwall, TX 75087. Phone: 800-783-5708. Fax: 214-722-6218. County: Leon. ICA: TX0702.
TV Market Ranking: Outside TV Markets. Franchise award date: July 15, 1989. Franchise expiration date: N.A. Began: N.A.
Channel capacity: 21 (not 2-way capable). Channels available but not in use: None.

Basic Service
Subscribers: 32.
Programming (received off-air): KBTX-TV (C) Bryan; KCEN-TV (N), KWTX-TV (C), KXXV (A) Waco-Temple.
Programming (via satellite): WGN-TV (W) Chicago; Discovery Channel; ESPN; Fox Family Channel; Nashville Network; Turner Network TV.
Fee: $25.00 installation; $19.95 monthly.

Pay Service 1
Pay Units: 6.
Programming (via satellite): Disney Channel.
Fee: $9.00 monthly.

Pay Service 2
Pay Units: 7.
Programming (via satellite): Showtime.
Fee: $9.00 monthly.

Program Guide: TV Host.
Equipment: Blonder-Tongue headend; Magnavox amplifiers; Comm/Scope cable; Northeast Filter traps; Weatherscan satellite antenna; Uniden satellite receivers.
Miles of plant: 3.0 (coaxial). Homes passed: 73. Total homes in franchised area: 73.
Manager: Jim Stafford. Chief technician: Jacky Oliver. Marketing & program director: Bruce Berkinshaw.
City fee: 3% of basic & premium.
Ownership: Fanch Communications Inc. (MSO); Time Warner Cable (MSO). See Cable System Ownership.

LEONARD—Friendship Cable of Texas Inc., Box 9090, Tyler, TX 75711-9090. Phone: 903-581-2121. Fax: 903-581-2185. Counties: Fannin & Hunt. Also serves Celeste. ICA: TX0367.
TV Market Ranking: Below 100. Franchise award date: N.A. Franchise expiration date: N.A. Began: October 1, 1982.
Channel capacity: 54. Channels available but not in use: N.A.

Basic Service
Subscribers: 619.
Programming (received off-air): KDAF (W), KDFW (F), KERA-TV (P), KTVT (C), KXAS-TV (N), KXTX-TV (I), WFAA-TV (A) Dallas-Fort Worth; 13 FMs.
Programming (via satellite): WGN-TV (W) Chicago; Disney Channel; TBS Superstation.
Fee: $30.00 installation; $32.60 monthly.

Pay Service 1
Pay Units: 36.
Programming (via satellite): HBO.
Fee: $12.00 monthly.

Pay Service 2
Pay Units: 28.
Programming (via satellite): The Movie Channel.
Fee: $9.00 monthly.

Pay Service 3
Pay Units: 93.
Programming (via satellite): Showtime.
Fee: $7.00 monthly.

Miles of plant: 35.3 (coaxial). Homes passed: 1,723.
Manager: Rodney Fletcher. Chief technician: Bo Jaubert.
Ownership: Buford Television Inc. (MSO). See Cable System Ownership.

LEVELLAND—CableComm, 711 Ave. G, Levelland, TX 79336. Phone: 806-894-4996. County: Hockley. Also serves Hockley County. ICA: TX0112.
TV Market Ranking: Below 100 (portions of Hockley County, Levelland); Outside TV Markets (portions of Hockley County). Franchise award date: January 1, 1966. Franchise expiration date: September 21, 1999. Began: January 1, 1966.
Channel capacity: 36 (not 2-way capable). Channels available but not in use: 3.

Basic Service
Subscribers: 3,635; Commercial subscribers: 6.
Programming (received off-air): KTVT (C) Dallas-Fort Worth; KAMC (A), KCBD-TV (N), KJTV (F), KLBK-TV (C), KTXT-TV (P) Lubbock.
Programming (via satellite): WGN-TV (W) Chicago; C-SPAN; Home Shopping Network; TBS Superstation.
Current originations: Automated emergency alert.
Fee: $28.00 installation; $14.56 monthly; $1.60 converter.

Expanded Basic Service
Subscribers: 3,547.
Programming (via satellite): American Movie Classics; CNN; Discovery Channel; Disney Channel; ESPN; Fox Family Channel; Fox Sports Net Southwest; Headline News; Knowledge TV; Lifetime; MTV; Nashville Network; Nickelodeon; The Weather Channel; Trinity Bcstg. Network; Turner Network TV; USA Network; Univision.
Fee: $20.00 installation; $4.85 monthly.

Pay Service 1
Pay Units: 389.
Programming (via satellite): Cinemax.
Fee: $20.00 installation; $9.00 monthly.

Pay Service 2
Pay Units: 555.
Programming (via satellite): HBO.
Fee: $20.00 installation; $9.00 monthly.

Pay Service 3
Pay Units: 395.
Programming (via satellite): Showtime.
Fee: $20.00 installation; $9.00 monthly.

Local advertising: Yes. Available in character-generated programming. Rates: $3.00/Day.
Program Guide: Premium Channels.
Equipment: Scientific-Atlanta headend; Texscan amplifiers; Comm/Scope cable; Texscan character generator; Scientific-Atlanta set top converters; Intercept & Eagle traps; Scientific-Atlanta satellite antenna; Scientific-Atlanta satellite receivers.
Miles of plant: 76.0 (coaxial). Homes passed: 6,068.
Manager: Rex Thackerson. Chief technician: Monty Hodge. Marketing director: Bill Forgey.
City fee: 3% of gross.
Ownership: Fanch Communications Inc. (MSO); Time Warner Cable (MSO). See Cable System Ownership.

LEWISVILLE—Paragon Cable, 2951 Kinwest Pkwy., Irving, TX 75063. Phone: 972-221-6531. Fax: 972-221-7070. County: Denton. ICA: TX0057.
TV Market Ranking: 12. Franchise award date: May 17, 1982. Franchise expiration date: October 8, 2012. Began: February 1, 1983.
Channel capacity: 69 (not 2-way capable). Channels available but not in use: 47.

Basic Service
Subscribers: 16,619.
Programming (received off-air): KPXD (X) Arlington; KDAF (W), KDFI-TV (I), KDFW (F), KDTX-TV (T), KERA-TV (P), KFWD (O), KTVT (C), KTXA (U), KXAS-TV (N), KXTX-TV (I), WFAA-TV (A) Dallas-Fort Worth; KMPX (I) Decatur; KDTN (P) Denton; KUVN (S) Garland; KHSX-TV (H) Irving; KLDT (I) Lake Dallas.
Programming (via satellite): Bravo; Home Shopping Network; TV Guide Channel; TV Guide Sneak Prevue.

Current originations: Automated time-weather; public access; educational access; government access; religious access; library access; automated emergency alert; local news; local sports.
Fee: $26.90 installation; $8.95 monthly; $2.76 converter; $27.46 additional installation.

Expanded Basic Service
Subscribers: 13,390.
Programming (via satellite): A & E; American Movie Classics; Animal Planet; BET; Bravo; C-SPAN; C-SPAN 2; CNBC; Cartoon Network; Comedy Central; Country Music TV; Court TV; Discovery Channel; E! Entertainment TV; ESPN; ESPN 2; Fox Family Channel; Fox Sports Net Southwest; History Channel; Home & Garden Television; Learning Channel; Lifetime; MSNBC; MTV; Nashville Network; Nick at Nite; Nickelodeon; QVC; The Health Network; The Weather Channel; Travel Channel; Turner Network TV; USA Network; VH1; ValueVision; Weatherscan by the Weather Channel.
Fee: $26.90 installation; $20.89 monthly.

A la Carte 1
Subscribers: N.A.
Programming (via satellite): WGN-TV (W) Chicago; TBS Superstation.
Fee: N.A.

Pay Service 1
Pay Units: 1,417.
Programming (via satellite): Cinemax.
Fee: $12.50 monthly.

Pay Service 2
Pay Units: 512.
Programming (via satellite): Disney Channel.
Fee: $9.40 monthly.

Pay Service 3
Pay Units: 2,444.
Programming (via satellite): HBO.
Fee: $12.50 monthly.

Pay Service 4
Pay Units: 434.
Programming (via satellite): The Movie Channel.
Fee: $12.50 monthly.

Pay Service 5
Pay Units: 844.
Programming (via satellite): Showtime.
Fee: $12.50 monthly.

Pay-Per-View
Hot Choice; Viewer's Choice.
Fee: $3.95.

Local advertising: Yes. Available in satellite distributed & locally originated programming. Rates: $30.00/Minute; $16.00 - $500.00/30 seconds. Local sales manager: Christine Pierret.
Program Guide: The Cable Guide.
Equipment: Scientific-Atlanta headend; Texscan amplifiers; General & Times Fiber cable; Amiga character generator; Zenith & Panasonic set top converters; Zenith addressable set top converters; Harris satellite antenna; Scientific-Atlanta satellite receivers.
Miles of plant: 224.8 (coaxial); 5.3 (fiber optic). Homes passed: 26,933.
Manager: Walter Nesbit. Chief technician: Bob Macioch. Program director: Philip Haley. Marketing director: Jim Fellhauer.
City fee: 5% of gross.
Ownership: Time Warner Cable (MSO); AT&T Broadband & Internet Services (MSO).

LEXINGTON—Cable-Vision Ltd., Box 757, Gatesville, TX 76528. Phone: 817-865-7520. County: Lee. ICA: TX0522.
TV Market Ranking: Outside TV Markets. Franchise award date: January 1, 1983. Franchise expiration date: January 1, 1998. Began: January 1, 1983.
Channel capacity: 32. Channels available but not in use: 15.

Basic Service
Subscribers: N.A.
Programming (received off-air): KTBC (F), KXAN-TV (N) Austin; KBTX-TV (C) Bryan; KAMU-TV (P) College Station; KCEN-TV (N) Waco-Temple.
Programming (via satellite): CNN.
Fee: $10.00 installation; $9.00 monthly.

Pay Service 1
Pay Units: N.A.
Programming (via satellite): The Movie Channel.
Fee: $10.00 monthly.

Local advertising: No.
Equipment: Jerrold amplifiers; Comm/Scope cable; Scientific-Atlanta satellite receivers.
Miles of plant: 8.7 (coaxial). Additional miles planned: 2.0 (coaxial). Homes passed: 400. Total homes in franchised area: 450.
Chief technician: Harold Smith.
City fee: 3% of gross.
Ownership: Cable-Vision Ltd. (MSO).

LIBERTY—Time Warner Communications, 1460 Calder Ave., Beaumont, TX 77701-1746. Phone: 409-727-1515. Fax: 409-839-4215. County: Liberty. Also serves Dayton. ICA: TX0129.
TV Market Ranking: 15 (Dayton); Below 100 (Liberty). Franchise award date: N.A. Franchise expiration date: May 8, 1998. Began: January 1, 1968.
Channel capacity: 38 (not 2-way capable). Channels available but not in use: N.A.

Basic Service
Subscribers: 3,051.
Programming (received off-air): KHSH-TV (H) Alvin; KVVV (I) Baytown; KFDM-TV (C) Beaumont-Port Arthur; KPXB (X) Conroe; KETH (E), KHOU-TV (C), KHTV (W), KPRC-TV (N), KRIV (F), KTRK-TV (A), KTXH (U), KUHT (P) Houston.
Programming (via satellite): C-SPAN; Discovery Channel; TBS Superstation.
Current originations: Educational access.
Fee: $39.41 installation; $9.24 monthly; $0.56 converter; $19.70 additional installation.

Expanded Basic Service
Subscribers: 2,563.
Programming (via satellite): A & E; American Movie Classics; BET; CNBC; CNN; ESPN; FX; Fox Family Channel; Fox News Channel; Fox Sports Net Southwest; Headline News; MTV; Nashville Network; Nickelodeon; The Weather Channel; Turner Network TV; USA Network.
Fee: $1.50 monthly.

Pay Service 1
Pay Units: 226.
Programming (via satellite): Cinemax.
Fee: $13.20 monthly.

Pay Service 2
Pay Units: 257.
Programming (via satellite): Disney Channel.
Fee: N.A.

Pay Service 3
Pay Units: 1,339.
Programming (via satellite): The New Encore.
Fee: N.A.

Pay Service 4
Pay Units: 390.
Programming (via satellite): HBO.
Fee: $13.20 monthly.

Pay Service 5
Pay Units: 227.
Programming (via satellite): The Movie Channel.
Fee: $25.00 installation; $13.20 monthly.

Pay Service 6
Pay Units: 447.
Programming (via satellite): Showtime.
Fee: $13.20 monthly.

Pay Service 7
Pay Units: N.A.
Programming (via satellite): Starz!
Fee: N.A.

Pay-Per-View
Addressable homes: 117.

Local advertising: No.
Equipment: Scientific-Atlanta headend; GTE Sylvania amplifiers; Comm/Scope & Phelps-Dodge cable; Scientific-Atlanta satellite antenna; Scientific-Atlanta satellite receivers.
Miles of plant: 87.1 (coaxial). Homes passed: 4,995. Total homes in franchised area: 7,641.
Manager: Mike McKee. Customer service manager: Mary Lund.
City fee: 3% of gross.
Ownership: AT&T Broadband & Internet Services (MSO); Time Warner Cable (MSO); Advance/Newhouse Partnership (MSO).

LIBERTY HILL—Time Warner Cable, 12012 N. Mo Pac Expressway, Austin, TX 78758-2904. Phone: 512-485-6100. Fax: 512-485-6105. Web site: http://www.timewarneraustin.com. County: Williamson. ICA: TX0582.
TV Market Ranking: Below 100. Franchise award date: N.A. Franchise expiration date: N.A. Began: January 1, 1984.
Channel capacity: 54 (not 2-way capable). Channels available but not in use: 21.

Basic Service
Subscribers: 170.
Programming (received off-air): KEYE-TV (C), KLRU (P), KNVA (W), KTBC (F), KVUE-TV (A), KXAN-TV (N) Austin.
Programming (via satellite): WGN-TV (W) Chicago; A & E; Animal Planet; CNN; Comedy Central; Country Music TV; Discovery Channel; ESPN; ESPN 2; Fox Family Channel; GalaVision; Headline News; History Channel; Home & Garden Television; Learning Channel; Lifetime; MSNBC; Nashville Network; Nick at Nite; Nickelodeon; Pax Net; TBS Superstation; The Weather Channel; Turner Classic Movies; Turner Network TV; USA Network.
Fee: $28.21 installation; $24.40 monthly; $1.15 converter; $12.11 additional installation.

Pay Service 1
Pay Units: N.A.
Programming (via satellite): HBO; Showtime.
Fee: $7.00 monthly (Showtime), $12.00 monthly (HBO).

Miles of plant: 8.1 (coaxial). Homes passed: 276.
Manager: Bill Carey. Chief technician: Matt Stanek. Program director: George Warmingham. Marketing director: Michelle Golden.
Ownership: Time Warner Cable (MSO); Advance/Newhouse Partnership (MSO).

LINDEN—Star Cable, Box 626, 200 Scurry St., Daingerfield, TX 75638. Phone: 903-645-7353. County: Cass. Plans service to Queen City. ICA: TX0381.
TV Market Ranking: 58. Franchise award date: N.A. Franchise expiration date: N.A. Began: September 1, 1982.
Channel capacity: 42. Channels available but not in use: 11.

Basic Service
Subscribers: 536; Commercial subscribers: 111.
Programming (received off-air): KETK-TV (N) Jacksonville; KLTS-TV (P), KMSS-TV (F), KSHV (U,W), KSLA-TV (C), KTAL-TV (N), KTBS-TV (A) Shreveport-Texarkana; KLTV (A) Tyler-Longview.
Programming (via satellite): WGN-TV (W) Chicago; TBS Superstation.
Fee: $19.95 installation; $12.00 monthly; $1.50 converter.

Expanded Basic Service
Subscribers: 513.
Programming (via satellite): A & E; American Movie Classics; CNN; Country Music TV; Discovery Channel; ESPN; Fox Family Channel; Fox Sports Net Southwest; Lifetime; Nashville Network; Nick at Nite's TV Land; Nickelodeon; The Weather Channel; Trinity Bcstg. Network; Turner Network TV; USA Network.
Fee: $17.75 monthly.

Pay Service 1
Pay Units: 53.
Programming (via satellite): Disney Channel.
Fee: $7.95 monthly.

Pay Service 2
Pay Units: 105.
Programming (via satellite): HBO.
Fee: $10.95 monthly.

Pay Service 3
Pay Units: 90.
Programming (via satellite): Showtime; The Movie Channel.
Fee: $12.95 monthly (each).

Miles of plant: 19.0 (coaxial). Homes passed: 877.
Manager: Mike Burns.
City fee: 2% of gross.
Ownership: Star Cable Associates (MSO).

LITTLE RIVER-ACADEMY—Centrovision Inc., Box 3157, Temple, TX 76501. Phone: 817-773-1163. County: Bell. ICA: TX0499.
TV Market Ranking: Below 100. Franchise award date: N.A. Franchise expiration date: N.A. Began: August 1, 1982.
Channel capacity: N.A. Channels available but not in use: N.A.

Basic Service
Subscribers: N.A.
Programming (received off-air): KLRU (P), KTBC (F), KVUE-TV (A), KXAN-TV (N) Austin; KNCT (P) Belton; KCEN-TV (N), KWTX-TV (C) Waco-Temple.
Programming (via satellite): WGN-TV (W) Chicago; TBS Superstation.
Fee: N.A.

Miles of plant: 9.0 (coaxial). Homes passed: 450.
Manager: Alton Shepard.
Ownership: Centrovision Inc. (MSO).

LITTLEFIELD—Cablecomm, 425 Phelps Ave., Littlefield, TX 79339. Phone: 806-385-4522. County: Lamb. ICA: TX0186.
TV Market Ranking: Below 100. Franchise award date: N.A. Franchise expiration date: June 9, 2003. Began: December 1, 1974.
Channel capacity: 36 (not 2-way capable). Channels available but not in use: 5.

Basic Service
Subscribers: 1,580; Commercial subscribers: 7.
Programming (received off-air): KAMC (A), KCBD-TV (N), KJTV (F), KLBK-TV (C), KTXT-TV (P) Lubbock.
Programming (via satellite): WGN-TV (W) Chicago; C-SPAN; Home Shopping Network; TBS Superstation.

Current originations: Automated time-weather; public access; automated emergency alert; local news.
Fee: $27.90 installation; $14.35 monthly; $1.60 converter.

Expanded Basic Service
Subscribers: 1,543.
Programming (via satellite): American Movie Classics; CNN; Discovery Channel; Disney Channel; ESPN; Fox Family Channel; Fox Sports Net Southwest; Headline News; Knowledge TV; MTV; Nashville Network; Nickelodeon; The Weather Channel; Trinity Bcstg. Network; Turner Network TV; USA Network; Univision.
Fee: $20.00 installation; $5.07 monthly.

Pay Service 1
Pay Units: 129.
Programming (via satellite): Cinemax.
Fee: $20.00 installation; $9.00 monthly.

Pay Service 2
Pay Units: 180.
Programming (via satellite): HBO.
Fee: $20.00 installation; $9.00 monthly.

Pay Service 3
Pay Units: 112.
Programming (via satellite): Showtime.
Fee: $20.00 installation; $9.00 monthly.

Local advertising: Yes. Available in character-generated programming. Rates: $3.00/Day.
Program Guide: Premium Channels.
Equipment: Jerrold & Scientific-Atlanta headend; Theta-Com & Texscan amplifiers; Comm/Scope cable; BEI character generator; Scientific-Atlanta set top converters; Eagle traps; Scientific-Atlanta satellite antenna; Automation Techniques & Scientific-Atlanta satellite receivers.
Miles of plant: 33.0 (coaxial). Homes passed: 2,768.
Manager: Rex Thackerson. Chief technician: Rick Elmore. Marketing director: Bill Forgey.
City fee: 3% of gross.
Ownership: Fanch Communications Inc. (MSO); Time Warner Cable (MSO). See Cable System Ownership.

LIVERPOOL—Star Cable, Drawer 1570, Brazoria, TX 77422. Phones: 409-798-9121; 800-395-2775. Fax: 409-798-4409. County: Brazoria. ICA: TX0333.
TV Market Ranking: 15. Franchise award date: N.A. Franchise expiration date: N.A. Began: October 1, 1989.
Channel capacity: 62 (not 2-way capable). Channels available but not in use: 18.

Basic Service
Subscribers: 512; Commercial subscribers: 4.
Programming (received off-air): KHSH-TV (H) Alvin; KVVV (I) Baytown; KPXB (X) Conroe; KLTJ (E), KTMD (O) Galveston; KETH (E), KHOU-TV (C), KHTV (W), KPRC-TV (N), KRIV (F), KTRK-TV (A), KTXH (U), KUHT (P) Houston; KNWS-TV (I) Katy.
Programming (via satellite): WGN-TV (W) Chicago; A & E; American Movie Classics; CNN; Country Music TV; Discovery Channel; ESPN; Fox Family Channel; Fox Sports Net Southwest; Headline News; History Channel; Lifetime; MTV; Nashville Network; Nickelodeon; QVC; Sci-Fi Channel; TBS Superstation; The Weather Channel; Turner Network TV; USA Network; VH1.
Fee: $31.64 monthly; $2.15 converter.

Pay Service 1
Pay Units: 70.
Programming (via satellite): Cinemax.
Fee: $10.95 monthly.

Pay Service 2
Pay Units: 93.
Programming (via satellite): Disney Channel.
Fee: $7.95 monthly.

Pay Service 3
Pay Units: 129.
Programming (via satellite): HBO.
Fee: $10.95 monthly.

Pay Service 4
Pay Units: 131.
Programming (via satellite): Showtime.
Fee: $12.95 monthly.

Miles of plant: 54.6 (coaxial); None (fiber optic). Homes passed: 1,126. Total homes in franchised area: 1,126.
Manager: Mike Burns. Chief technician: Mayla Zubeck.
Ownership: Star Cable Associates (MSO).

LIVINGSTON—Cable One, 101 S. Washington, Livingston, TX 77351. Phone: 409-327-4512. County: Polk. Also serves Polk County (portions). ICA: TX0208.
TV Market Ranking: Outside TV Markets. Franchise award date: January 1, 1958. Franchise expiration date: April 8, 2001. Began: April 26, 1963.
Channel capacity: 36 (not 2-way capable). Channels available but not in use: None.

Basic Service
Subscribers: 1,892.
Programming (received off-air): KFDM-TV (C) Beaumont-Port Arthur; KRIV (F), KTXH (U) Houston; KCTL-LP (I), KETX-LP (I) Livingston; KTRE (A) Lufkin; KLSB-TV (N) Nacogdoches; 15 FMs.
Programming (via microwave): KHOU-TV (C), KHTV (W), KPRC-TV (N), KTRK-TV (A), KUHT (P) Houston.
Programming (via satellite): WGN-TV (W) Chicago; WPIX (W) New York; BET; C-SPAN; CNN; Discovery Channel; ESPN; Fox Sports Net Southwest; Home Shopping Network; MTV; Nashville Network; Nickelodeon; TBS Superstation; USA Network; Univision.
Current originations: Automated time-weather; public access; educational access.
Fee: $37.95 installation; $17.80 monthly; $10.00 additional installation.

Pay Service 1
Pay Units: 147.
Programming (via satellite): Cinemax.
Fee: $9.95 monthly.

Pay Service 2
Pay Units: 101.
Programming (via satellite): Disney Channel.
Fee: $7.95 monthly.

Pay Service 3
Pay Units: 161.
Programming (via satellite): HBO.
Fee: $10.50 monthly.

Pay Service 4
Pay Units: 78.
Programming (via satellite): Showtime.
Fee: N.A.

Pay-Per-View
Addressable homes: 1,411.
Viewer's Choice.
Fee: $3.95.

Local advertising: Yes. Available in satellite distributed programming. Local sales manager: Harland Moidel.
Program Guide: Premium Channels.
Equipment: Scientific-Atlanta headend; GTE Sylvania & Scientific-Atlanta amplifiers; Comm/Scope cable; Oak addressable set top converters; AFC satellite antenna; Scientific-Atlanta satellite receivers.
Miles of plant: 50.0 (coaxial). Homes passed: 2,250. Total homes in franchised area: 2,250.
Manager: Glen Parker. Chief technician: Jerry Teer. Marketing director: Mike Evans.
City fee: 5% of gross.
Ownership: Cable One Inc. (MSO).

LOCKHART—Time Warner Entertainment/Advance-Newhouse, 12012 N. MoPac Expwy., Austin, TX 78758. Phone: 512-485-6100. Fax: 512-485-6105. County: Caldwell. ICA: TX0163.
TV Market Ranking: Below 100. Franchise award date: August 16, 1994. Franchise expiration date: October 26, 2007. Began: September 1, 1974.
Channel capacity: 35. Channels available but not in use: 2.

Basic Service
Subscribers: 218.
Programming (received off-air): KEYE-TV (C), KLRU (P), KNVA (W), KTBC (F), KVUE-TV (A), KXAN-TV (N) Austin; KENS-TV (C) San Antonio; allband FM.
Programming (via satellite): C-SPAN; Knowledge TV; Pax Net; QVC; Univision.
Current originations: Automated time-weather; public access; educational access; government access.
Fee: $28.21 installation; $8.50 monthly; $25.96 additional installation.

Expanded Basic Service
Subscribers: N.A.
Programming (via satellite): WGN-TV (W) Chicago; A & E; American Movie Classics; Animal Planet; BET; CNBC; CNN; Cartoon Network; Comedy Central; Country Music TV; Court TV; Discovery Channel; ESPN; ESPN 2; FX; Fox Family Channel; Fox Sports Net Southwest; Headline News; History Channel; Home & Garden Television; Learning Channel; Lifetime; MSNBC; MTV; Nashville Network; Nick at Nite's TV Land; Nickelodeon; TBS Superstation; Telemundo; The Weather Channel; Travel Channel; Turner Classic Movies; Turner Network TV; USA Network.
Fee: $29.84 monthly.

Pay Service 1
Pay Units: N.A.
Programming (via satellite): Cinemax.
Fee: $10.95 monthly.

Pay Service 2
Pay Units: 90.
Programming (via satellite): Disney Channel.
Fee: N.A.

Pay Service 3
Pay Units: 250.
Programming (via satellite): HBO.
Fee: $10.95 monthly.

Pay Service 4
Pay Units: 81.
Programming (via satellite): The Movie Channel.
Fee: $10.00 installation; $11.50 monthly.

Pay Service 5
Pay Units: 202.
Programming (via satellite): Showtime.
Fee: $10.00 installation; $10.95 monthly.

Pay Service 6
Pay Units: 778.
Programming (via satellite): The New Encore.
Fee: $1.75 monthly.

Local advertising: Yes. Regional interconnect: Cabletime.
Program Guide: Premium Channels.
Equipment: Jerrold headend; Jerrold amplifiers; Times Fiber cable; Jerrold set top converters; Eagle traps; Andrew & M/A-Com satellite antenna.
Miles of plant: 59.0 (coaxial). Homes passed: 3,500.
Manager: Bill Carey. Chief technician: Matt Stanek. Program director: George Warmingham. Marketing director: Michelle Golden.
City fee: 4% of gross.
Ownership: Time Warner Cable (MSO); Advance/Newhouse Partnership (MSO).

LOCKNEY—Classic Cable, Box 429, 605 N.W. 3rd St., Plainville, KS 67663-0429. Phones: 785-434-7620; 800-999-8876. Fax: 785-434-2614. County: Floyd. ICA: TX0414.
TV Market Ranking: Outside TV Markets. Franchise award date: December 10, 1980. Franchise expiration date: N.A. Began: May 15, 1981.
Channel capacity: 41 (2-way capable). Channels available but not in use: N.A.

Basic Service
Subscribers: 453; Commercial subscribers: 61.
Programming (received off-air): KVII-TV (A) Amarillo; KAMC (A), KCBD-TV (N), KJTV (F), KLBK-TV (C), KTXT-TV (P) Lubbock.
Programming (via satellite): WGN-TV (W) Chicago; A & E; American Movie Classics; CNN; Cartoon Network; Country Music TV; Discovery Channel; Disney Channel; E! Entertainment TV; ESPN; Fox Family Channel; Headline News; History Channel; Learning Channel; Lifetime; Nashville Network; Nick at Nite's TV Land; Nickelodeon; QVC; Sci-Fi Channel; TBS Superstation; The Weather Channel; Turner Network TV; USA Network; Univision.
Fee: $35.00 installation; $27.95 monthly.

Pay Service 1
Pay Units: 35.
Programming (via satellite): Cinemax.
Fee: $9.95 monthly.

Pay Service 2
Pay Units: 86.
Programming (via satellite): HBO.
Fee: $9.95 monthly.

Equipment: Scientific-Atlanta satellite antenna; Microdyne satellite receivers.
Miles of plant: 12.0 (coaxial). Homes passed: 778.
Manager: Bill Flowers. Chief technician: Chris Christenson. Marketing director: Jennifer Hauschild.
Ownership: Classic Cable (MSO).

LOLITA—Koch Cable TV, Box 120, La Ward, TX 77970. Phone: 512-872-2362. County: Jackson. Also serves Vanderbilt. ICA: TX0637.
TV Market Ranking: Below 100. Franchise award date: N.A. Franchise expiration date: N.A. Began: October 1, 1979.
Channel capacity: 36. Channels available but not in use: 15.

Basic Service
Subscribers: 298.
Programming (received off-air): KHOU-TV (C), KHTV (W), KPRC-TV (N), KTRK-TV (A), KTXH (U), KUHT (P) Houston; KAVU-TV (A) Victoria.
Programming (via satellite): CNN; Discovery Channel; ESPN; Fox Family Channel; Nashville Network; Odyssey; TBS Superstation; The Weather Channel; Turner Network TV; USA Network.
Fee: $30.00 installation; $14.00 monthly.

Pay Service 1
Pay Units: 25.
Programming (via satellite): Disney Channel.
Fee: $7.50 monthly.

Pay Service 2
Pay Units: 130.
Programming (via satellite): HBO.
Fee: $10.50 monthly.

Miles of plant: 6.5 (coaxial). Homes passed: 350.
Manager: William R. Koch.
Ownership: Lolita Cable TV Inc.

LOMETA—Post Cablevision of Texas Ltd., Drawer 829, 1108 Parker St., Goldthwaite, TX 76844. Phone: 915-648-3041. County: Lampasas. ICA: TX0599.
TV Market Ranking: Below 100. Franchise award date: N.A. Franchise expiration date: N.A. Began: December 1, 1971.
Channel capacity: 25. Channels available but not in use: 3.
Basic Service
Subscribers: N.A.
Programming (received off-air): KEYE-TV (C), KVUE-TV (A) Austin; KNCT (P) Belton; KCEN-TV (N), KWKT (F), KWTX-TV (C) Waco-Temple; allband FM.
Programming (via satellite): CNN; Country Music TV; ESPN; Fox Family Channel; Home Shopping Network; Nashville Network; TBS Superstation; USA Network; Univision.
Fee: $25.00 installation; $18.14 monthly.
Pay Service 1
Pay Units: N.A.
Programming (via satellite): Disney Channel; HBO.
Fee: $7.58 monthly (Disney), $10.83 monthly (HBO).
Equipment: Blonder-Tongue headend; Ameco amplifiers; Times Fiber cable.
Miles of plant: 9.0 (coaxial). Homes passed: 245.
Manager: Denise Casbeer. Chief technician: Jerry Stembridge.
City fee: None.
Ownership: Fanch Communications Inc. (MSO). See Cable System Ownership.

LONGVIEW—Longview Cable Television, Box 4399, 711 N. High St., Longview, TX 75606. Phone: 903-758-9991. Fax: 903-758-3083. County: Gregg. ICA: TX0033.
TV Market Ranking: Below 100. Franchise award date: June 1, 1965. Franchise expiration date: August 26, 1998. Began: August 1, 1972.
Channel capacity: 55. Channels available but not in use: None.
Basic Service
Subscribers: 24,930.
Programming (received off-air): KDFW (F), KERA-TV (P), KTVT (C), KXAS-TV (N) Dallas-Fort Worth; KETK-TV (N) Jacksonville; KFXK (F) Longview; KMSS-TV (F), KSLA-TV (C), KTAL-TV (N), KTBS-TV (A) Shreveport-Texarkana; KLTV (A) Tyler-Longview.
Programming (via satellite): WGN-TV (W) Chicago; C-SPAN; C-SPAN 2; TBS Superstation.
Current originations: Public access; educational access; government access; automated emergency alert.
Fee: $29.31 installation; $8.50 monthly; $3.65 converter.
Expanded Basic Service
Subscribers: 24,089.
Programming (via satellite): CNN; ESPN; ESPN 2; EWTN; Fox Family Channel; History Channel; Nick at Nite; Nickelodeon; Trinity Bcstg. Network; Turner Network TV.
Fee: $14.65 installation; $4.66 monthly.
Expanded Basic Service 2
Subscribers: 20,068.
Programming (via satellite): A & E; American Movie Classics; BET; CNBC; Cartoon Network; Country Music TV; Discovery Channel; Headline News; Home Shopping Network; Learning Channel; Lifetime; Nashville Network; Odyssey; Sci-Fi Channel; The Weather Channel; Turner Classic Movies; USA Network; Univision; VH1.
Fee: $14.65 installation; $10.78 monthly.
Pay Service 1
Pay Units: 2,537.
Programming (via satellite): Cinemax.
Fee: $9.95 monthly.
Pay Service 2
Pay Units: 2,357.
Programming (via satellite): Disney Channel.
Fee: $7.50 monthly.
Pay Service 3
Pay Units: 6,326.
Programming (via satellite): HBO.
Fee: $14.65 installation; $11.25 monthly.
Pay Service 4
Pay Units: 463.
Programming (via satellite): Showtime.
Fee: $10.95 monthly.
Pay-Per-View
Addressable homes: 1,632.
Viewer's Choice.
Local advertising: Yes (locally produced). Available in satellite distributed, character-generated, taped & automated programming. Rates: $15.00/Minute; $9.00/30 Seconds. Local sales manager: Dawn Benoit. Regional interconnect: Cabletime.
Equipment: Scientific-Atlanta & Jerrold headend; Texscan amplifiers; Comm/Scope & Times Fiber cable; AT&T fiber optic cable; Texscan & MSI character generator; Zenith addressable set top converters; Pico & Arcom traps; Scientific-Atlanta satellite antenna; General Instrument satellite receivers; Falcone International commercial insert.
Miles of plant: 561.0 (coaxial); 32.0 (fiber optic). Additional miles planned: 50.0 (coaxial); 200.0 (fiber optic). Homes passed: 33,101.
Manager: Robert E. Durham. Chief technician: Neilan Davis. Customer service manager: Maria Fuller.
City fee: 5% of gross.
Ownership: WEHCO Video Inc. (MSO).

LOOP—Torrence Cablevision, Box 1167, Ridgeland, MS 39158. Phones: 601-981-6900; 800-977-8849. County: Gaines. ICA: TX0686.
TV Market Ranking: Outside TV Markets. Franchise award date: N.A. Franchise expiration date: N.A. Began: May 25, 1990.
Channel capacity: 36 (not 2-way capable). Channels available but not in use: 20.
Basic Service
Subscribers: 51.
Programming (received off-air): KAMC (A), KCBD-TV (N), KJTV (F), KLBK-TV (C) Lubbock.
Programming (via translator): KXTX-TV (I) Dallas-Fort Worth.
Programming (via satellite): WGN-TV (W) Chicago; A & E; American Movie Classics; CNN; Country Music TV; Discovery Channel; ESPN; Fox Family Channel; Showtime; TBS Superstation; Turner Network TV; USA Network.
Fee: $28.00 monthly.
Equipment: Nexus headend; Magnavox amplifiers; Times Fiber cable; Oak set top converters; Nexus satellite receivers.
Miles of plant: 4.6 (coaxial). Homes passed: 114. Total homes in franchised area: 114.
Ownership: Torrence Cable Inc. (MSO).

LORAINE—Cablecomm, Box 685, 1325 Westpoint, Colorado City, TX 79512. Phones: 915-728-3600; 800-874-6190. County: Mitchell. ICA: TX0529.
TV Market Ranking: Below 100. Franchise award date: N.A. Franchise expiration date: April 14, 2013. Began: April 14, 1988.
Channel capacity: 36 (not 2-way capable). Channels available but not in use: 11.
Basic Service
Subscribers: 236; Commercial subscribers: 1.
Programming (received off-air): KRBC-TV (N), KTAB-TV (C), KTXS-TV (A) Abilene-Sweetwater; KWAB-TV (N) Big Spring; KIDY (F), KLST (C) San Angelo.
Programming (via satellite): WGN-TV (W) Chicago; C-SPAN; TBS Superstation.
Fee: $29.50 installation; $12.10 monthly; $1.60 converter.
Expanded Basic Service
Subscribers: 235.
Programming (via satellite): CNN; Discovery Channel; Disney Channel; ESPN; Fox Family Channel; Fox Sports Net Southwest; Headline News; Nashville Network; Trinity Bcstg. Network; Turner Network TV; USA Network; Univision.
Fee: $20.00 installation; $1.00 monthly.
Pay Service 1
Pay Units: 13.
Programming (via satellite): Cinemax.
Fee: $20.00 installation; $9.00 monthly.
Pay Service 2
Pay Units: 18.
Programming (via satellite): HBO.
Fee: $20.00 installation; $9.00 monthly.
Local advertising: No.
Program Guide: Premium Channels.
Equipment: Scientific-Atlanta & Tocom headend; GTE Sylvania amplifiers; Comm/Scope cable; Tandy character generator; Scientific-Atlanta set top converters; Intercept & Eagle traps; Scientific-Atlanta satellite antenna; Scientific-Atlanta & Microdyne satellite receivers.
Miles of plant: 7.0 (coaxial). Homes passed: 384.
Manager: Rex Thackerson. Chief technician: Gary Redwine. Marketing director: Cynthia Odlozil.
City fee: 2% of gross.
Ownership: Fanch Communications Inc. (MSO); Time Warner Cable (MSO). See Cable System Ownership.

LORENA—Galaxy Cablevision, 307 N. 5th St., Leesville, LA 71496. Phone: 318-238-1361. Counties: Falls & McLennan. Also serves Bruceville-Eddy, McLennan County. ICA: TX0801.
TV Market Ranking: Below 100. Franchise award date: N.A. Franchise expiration date: N.A. Began: June 1, 1983.
Channel capacity: 29. Channels available but not in use: None.
Basic Service
Subscribers: 680.
Programming (received off-air): KNCT (P) Belton; WFAA-TV (A) Dallas-Fort Worth; KCEN-TV (N), KWTX-TV (C) Waco-Temple.
Programming (via satellite): WGN-TV (W) Chicago; TBS Superstation; Turner Network TV.
Fee: $30.00 installation; $23.50 monthly.
Pay Service 1
Pay Units: N.A.
Programming (via satellite): Cinemax; HBO; Showtime.
Fee: $12.00 monthly (each).
Miles of plant: 19.8 (coaxial). Homes passed: 927.
Manager: Eulin Guidry. Technical manager: Randy Berry.
Ownership: Galaxy Cablevision (MSO).

LORENZO—Classic Cable, Box 429, 605 N.W. 3rd St., Plainville, KS 67663-0429. Phones: 785-434-7620; 800-999-8876. Fax: 785-434-2614. County: Crosby. ICA: TX0484.
TV Market Ranking: Below 100. Franchise award date: March 9, 1981. Franchise expiration date: N.A. Began: December 1, 1981.
Channel capacity: 41 (2-way capable). Channels available but not in use: N.A.
Basic Service
Subscribers: 104.
Programming (received off-air): KAMC (A), KCBD-TV (N), KJTV (F), KLBK-TV (C), KTXT-TV (P), KUPT-LP (U) Lubbock.
Programming (via satellite): WGN-TV (W) Chicago; American Movie Classics; CNN; Cartoon Network; Discovery Channel; Disney Channel; ESPN; Fox Family Channel; Headline News; History Channel; Nashville Network; Nick at Nite's TV Land; QVC; TBS Superstation; Telemundo; The Weather Channel; Trinity Bcstg. Network; Turner Network TV; USA Network.
Fee: $35.00 installation; $27.95 monthly.
Pay Service 1
Pay Units: 10.
Programming (via satellite): Cinemax.
Fee: $9.95 monthly.
Pay Service 2
Pay Units: 21.
Programming (via satellite): HBO.
Fee: $9.95 monthly.
Equipment: Fort Worth Tower & Scientific-Atlanta satellite antenna; Microdyne satellite receivers.
Miles of plant: 8.4 (coaxial). Homes passed: 509.
Manager: Bill Flowers. Chief technician: Chris Christenson. Marketing director: Jennifer Hauschild.
City fee: 3% of gross.
Ownership: Classic Cable (MSO).

LOS FRESNOS—Time Warner Communications, 2921 S. Expwy. 83, Harlingen, TX 78550-7615. Phone: 956-541-6782. Fax: 956-412-0959. County: Cameron. Also serves Cameron County, Indian Lake. ICA: TX0264.
TV Market Ranking: Below 100. Franchise award date: N.A. Franchise expiration date: N.A. Began: March 1, 1980.
Channel capacity: 35. Channels available but not in use: 6.
Basic Service
Subscribers: 1,107.
Programming (received off-air): KVEO (N) Brownsville; KGBT-TV (C), KLUJ (E), KMBH (P) Harlingen; KRGV-TV (A) Weslaco; XHAB-TV Matamoros; XHRIO (O) Matamoros-Brownsville.
Programming (via satellite): WGN-TV (W) Chicago; A & E; C-SPAN; CNN; Fox Family Channel; Headline News; Lifetime; MTV; Nashville Network; Nickelodeon; QVC; TBS Superstation; The Weather Channel.
Fee: $60.00 installation; $19.64 monthly.
Expanded Basic Service
Subscribers: 1,097.
Programming (via satellite): CNBC; Discovery Channel; ESPN; Fox Sports Net Southwest; Turner Network TV; USA Network; Univision.
Fee: $1.75 monthly.
Pay Service 1
Pay Units: 123.
Programming (via satellite): Cinemax.
Fee: N.A.
Pay Service 2
Pay Units: 75.
Programming (via satellite): Disney Channel.
Fee: N.A.

Pay Service 3
Pay Units: 207.
Programming (via satellite): HBO.
Fee: N.A.
Pay Service 4
Pay Units: N.A.
Programming (via satellite): The New Encore.
Fee: N.A.
Miles of plant: 25.1 (coaxial). Homes passed: 1,585. Total homes in franchised area: 1,585.
Manager: Juan Herrera. Chief technician: Al Velasquez.
Ownership: Time Warner Cable (MSO); AT&T Broadband & Internet Services (MSO).

LOST PINES—Friendship Cable of Texas Inc., Box 9090, Tyler, TX 75711-9090. Phone: 903-581-2121. Fax: 903-581-2185. County: Bastrop. ICA: TX0950.
TV Market Ranking: Below 100. Franchise award date: N.A. Franchise expiration date: N.A. Began: N.A.
Channel capacity: 54. Channels available but not in use: N.A.
Basic Service
Subscribers: 989.
Programming (received off-air): KEYE-TV (C), KLRU (P), KTBC (F), KVUE-TV (A), KXAN-TV (N) Austin.
Programming (via satellite): WGN-TV (W) Chicago; A & E; BET; CNN; Country Music TV; Discovery Channel; E! Entertainment TV; ESPN; Fox Family Channel; Headline News; Lifetime; Nashville Network; Nickelodeon; Sci-Fi Channel; TBS Superstation; The Weather Channel; Trinity Bcstg. Network; Turner Network TV; USA Network; Univision.
Fee: $30.00 installation; $28.74 monthly.
Pay Service 1
Pay Units: 84.
Programming (via satellite): Cinemax.
Fee: $10.95 monthly.
Pay Service 2
Pay Units: 142.
Programming (via satellite): HBO.
Fee: $10.95 monthly.
Pay Service 3
Pay Units: 50.
Programming (via satellite): Showtime.
Fee: $10.95 monthly.
Miles of plant: 84.0 (coaxial). Homes passed: 1,870.
Manager: Wanda Pyburn. Chief technician: David Burrell.
Ownership: Buford Television Inc. (MSO). See Cable System Ownership.

LOTT—Galaxy Cablevision, 307 N. 5th St., Leesville, LA 71496. Phone: 318-238-1361. County: Falls. ICA: TX0515.
TV Market Ranking: Below 100. Franchise award date: N.A. Franchise expiration date: June 27, 2007. Began: May 1, 1984.
Channel capacity: 27. Channels available but not in use: None.
Basic Service
Subscribers: 180.
Programming (received off-air): KVUE-TV (A) Austin; KNCT (P) Belton; KCEN-TV (N), KWTX-TV (C) Waco-Temple.
Programming (via satellite): WGN-TV (W) Chicago; TBS Superstation.
Fee: $30.00 installation; $23.75 monthly.
Pay Service 1
Pay Units: N.A.
Programming (via satellite): Cinemax; HBO; Showtime.
Fee: $9.00 monthly (each).
Miles of plant: 8.7 (coaxial). Homes passed: 378.
Manager: Eulin Guidry. Technical manager: Randy Berry.
Ownership: Galaxy Cablevision (MSO).

LOUISE—Mid Coast Cable TV, Box 1269, 505 N. Machnic, El Campo, TX 77437. Phone: 409-543-6858. County: Wharton. ICA: TX0579.
TV Market Ranking: Below 100. Franchise award date: N.A. Franchise expiration date: N.A. Began: March 1, 1982.
Channel capacity: 27 (not 2-way capable). Channels available but not in use: 1.
Basic Service
Subscribers: 247.
Programming (received off-air): KHOU-TV (C), KHTV (W), KPRC-TV (N), KRIV (F), KTRK-TV (A), KTXH (U), KUHT (P) Houston; KAVU-TV (A) Victoria.
Programming (via satellite): WGN-TV (W) Chicago; CNN; Discovery Channel; ESPN; Fox Family Channel; Lifetime; Nashville Network; TBS Superstation; The Weather Channel; USA Network.
Fee: $25.00 installation; $15.05 monthly.
Expanded Basic Service
Subscribers: 202.
Programming (via satellite): American Movie Classics; C-SPAN; Country Music TV; Fox Sports Net Southwest; Learning Channel; Nickelodeon; Odyssey; Univision.
Fee: $10.00 installation; $4.03 monthly.
Pay Service 1
Pay Units: 96.
Programming (via satellite): HBO.
Fee: $12.00 monthly.
Local advertising: No.
Miles of plant: 8.0 (coaxial). Homes passed: 280.
Manager: Jake Landrum. Chief technician: Dickie Isaacs.
Ownership: Mid Coast Cable TV Inc. (MSO).

LOVELADY—Friendship Cable of Texas Inc., Box 9090, Tyler, TX 75711-9090. Phone: 903-581-2121. Fax: 903-581-2185. County: Houston. ICA: TX0956.
TV Market Ranking: Outside TV Markets. Franchise award date: N.A. Franchise expiration date: N.A. Began: N.A.
Channel capacity: 54. Channels available but not in use: N.A.
Basic Service
Subscribers: 175.
Programming (received off-air): KBTX-TV (C) Bryan; K16BY (I) Crockett; KETK-TV (N) Jacksonville; KFXK (F) Longview; KTRE (A) Lufkin.
Programming (via satellite): WGN-TV (W) Chicago; A & E; American Movie Classics; C-SPAN; CNBC; CNN; Discovery Channel; ESPN; History Channel; Nashville Network; Nickelodeon; TBS Superstation; Trinity Bcstg. Network; Turner Network TV; USA Network.
Fee: $30.00 installation; $28.70 monthly.
Pay Service 1
Pay Units: 16.
Programming (via satellite): Showtime.
Fee: $5.95 monthly.
Pay Service 2
Pay Units: 2.
Programming (via satellite): Cinemax.
Fee: $10.95 monthly.
Pay Service 3
Pay Units: 4.
Programming (via satellite): HBO.
Fee: $10.95 monthly.
Miles of plant: 12.1 (coaxial). Homes passed: 320.
Manager: Wanda Pyburn. Chief technician: David Burrell.
Ownership: Buford Television Inc. (MSO). See Cable System Ownership.

LOWRY CROSSING—Friendship Cable of Texas Inc., Box 9090, Tyler, TX 75711-9090. Phone: 903-581-2121. Fax: 903-581-2185. County: Collin. Also serves New Hope. ICA: TX0256.
TV Market Ranking: 12. Franchise award date: N.A. Franchise expiration date: N.A. Began: N.A.
Channel capacity: 54. Channels available but not in use: 1.
Basic Service
Subscribers: 925.
Programming (received off-air): KDAF (W), KDFI-TV (I), KDFW (F), KERA-TV (P), KTVT (C), KTXA (U), KXAS-TV (N), KXTX-TV (I), WFAA-TV (A) Dallas-Fort Worth; KDTN (P) Denton; KHSX-TV (H) Irving.
Programming (via satellite): WGN-TV (W) Chicago; CNN; Discovery Channel; Disney Channel; ESPN; Fox Family Channel; Headline News; Lifetime; MTV; Nashville Network; Nickelodeon; TBS Superstation; The Weather Channel; Turner Network TV.
Fee: $30.00 installation; $32.55 monthly.
Pay Service 1
Pay Units: 133.
Programming (via satellite): HBO.
Fee: $12.00 monthly.
Pay Service 2
Pay Units: 82.
Programming (via satellite): The Movie Channel.
Fee: $9.00 monthly.
Pay Service 3
Pay Units: 268.
Programming (via satellite): Showtime.
Fee: $7.00 monthly.
Pay Service 4
Pay Units: 345.
Programming (via satellite): Flix.
Fee: $1.95 monthly.
Pay Service 5
Pay Units: 67.
Programming (via satellite): Cinemax.
Fee: $11.00 monthly.
Miles of plant: 84.4 (coaxial). Homes passed: 1,663.
Manager: Rodney Fletcher. Chief technician: Bo Jaubert.
Ownership: Buford Television Inc. (MSO). See Cable System Ownership.

LUBBOCK—Classic Cable, Box 429, 605 N.W. 3rd St., Plainville, KS 67663-0429. Phones: 785-434-7620; 800-999-8876. Fax: 785-434-2614. Counties: Hockley, Lubbock & Terry. Also serves Friendship, Meadow, New Deal, Ropesville, Shallowater (unincorporated areas), Smyer. ICA: TX0802.
TV Market Ranking: Below 100. Franchise award date: N.A. Franchise expiration date: N.A. Began: N.A.
Channel capacity: 41 (2-way capable). Channels available but not in use: N.A.
Basic Service
Subscribers: 1,065.
Programming (received off-air): KAMC (A), KCBD-TV (N), KJTV (F), KLBK-TV (C), KTXT-TV (P) Lubbock.
Programming (via satellite): WGN-TV (W) Chicago; A & E; American Movie Classics; CNN; Country Music TV; Discovery Channel; ESPN; Fox Family Channel; Showtime; TBS Superstation; Turner Network TV; USA Network.
Fee: $35.00 installation; $27.95 monthly.
Pay Service 1
Pay Units: 102.
Programming (via satellite): Cinemax.
Fee: $10.10 monthly.
Pay Service 2
Pay Units: 205.
Programming (via satellite): HBO.
Fee: $10.10 monthly.
Pay Service 3
Pay Units: 63.
Programming (via satellite): Showtime.
Fee: $10.10 monthly.
Miles of plant: 71.0 (coaxial). Homes passed: 2,830.
Manager: Bill Flowers. Chief technician: Chris Christenson. Marketing director: Jennifer Hauschild.
Ownership: Classic Cable (MSO).

LUBBOCK—Cox Communications, 6710 Hartford Ave., Lubbock, TX 79413. Phones: 806-793-2222; 806-793-7381. Fax: 806-793-7818. County: Lubbock. ICA: TX0012.
TV Market Ranking: Below 100. Franchise award date: February 25, 1965. Franchise expiration date: March 1, 1999. Began: March 1, 1965.
Channel capacity: 52 (not 2-way capable). Channels available but not in use: N.A.
Basic Service
Subscribers: 45,627.
Programming (received off-air): KAMC (A), KCBD-TV (N), KGLR-LP (I), KJTV (F), KLBK-TV (C), KPTB (I), KTXT-TV (P), KUPT-LP (U) Lubbock; KBZO-LP (I) Woodrow; 10 FMs.
Programming (via satellite): WGN-TV (W) Chicago; A & E; American Movie Classics; BET; C-SPAN; C-SPAN 2; CNBC; CNN; Cartoon Network; Comedy Central; Country Music TV; Discovery Channel; E! Entertainment TV; ESPN; ESPN 2; FX; Fox Family Channel; Fox Sports Net Southwest; Headline News; History Channel; Home & Garden Television; Learning Channel; Lifetime; MSNBC; MTV; Music Choice; Nashville Network; Nick at Nite's TV Land; Nickelodeon; Odyssey; Outdoor Life Network; QVC; Sci-Fi Channel; TBS Superstation; TV Guide Channel; Telemundo; The Weather Channel; Trinity Bcstg. Network; Turner Network TV; USA Network; Univision; VH1.
Current originations: Public access.
Fee: $42.04 installation; $11.86 monthly.
Pay Service 1
Pay Units: 44,927.
Programming (via satellite): Cinemax (multiplexed); Flix; HBO (multiplexed); Showtime; The Movie Channel.
Fee: $2.95 monthly (Flix), $11.00 monthly (Cinemax, HBO, Showtime or TMC).
Pay-Per-View
Addressable homes: 30,380.
Hot Choice; Viewer's Choice; special events.
Fee: $3.95.

Local advertising: Yes. Available in satellite distributed, locally originated, character-generated, taped & automated programming. Rates: $60.00/Minute; $30.00/30 Seconds. Local sales manager: Bill Ferrell.
Program Guide: The Cable Guide.
Equipment: Scientific-Atlanta headend; Scientific-Atlanta & Theta-Com amplifiers; Comm/Scope cable; Texscan character generator; Jerrold addressable set top converters; Scientific-Atlanta satellite antenna; Scientific-Atlanta satellite receivers; ChannelMatic commercial insert.
Miles of plant: 668.0 (coaxial); 135.0 (fiber optic). Additional miles planned: 11.0 (coaxial). Homes passed: 84,909. Total homes in franchised area: 87,403.
Manager: Randy Wink. Chief technician: John Linton. Marketing director: Wayde Klein.
City fee: 3% of gross.
Ownership: Cox Communications Inc. (MSO).

LUBBOCK COUNTY (southeastern portion)—Classic Cable, Box 429, 605 N.W. 3rd St., Plainville, KS 67663-0429. Phones: 785-434-7620; 800-999-8876. Fax: 785-434-2614. County: Lubbock. ICA: TX0348.
TV Market Ranking: Below 100. Franchise award date: N.A. Franchise expiration date: N.A. Began: January 1, 1992.
Channel capacity: 36 (2-way capable). Channels available but not in use: N.A.
Basic Service
Subscribers: 191.
Programming (received off-air): KAMC (A), KCBD-TV (N), KJTV (F), KLBK-TV (C), KTXT-TV (P), KUPT-LP (U) Lubbock; KOMI-LP (I) Woodward.
Programming (via satellite): WGN-TV (W) Chicago; A & E; BET; C-SPAN; CNN; Country Music TV; Discovery Channel; Disney Channel; ESPN; Fox Family Channel; Fox News Channel; Fox Sports Net Southwest; Headline News; Learning Channel; Lifetime; Nashville Network; Nickelodeon; QVC; TBS Superstation; Telemundo; The Weather Channel; Trinity Bcstg. Network; Turner Classic Movies; Turner Network TV; USA Network; Univision.
Fee: $35.00 installation; $26.95 monthly.
Pay Service 1
Pay Units: 48.
Programming (via satellite): HBO.
Fee: $10.95 monthly.
Pay Service 2
Pay Units: 46.
Programming (via satellite): Showtime.
Fee: $9.95 monthly.
Pay Service 3
Pay Units: 55.
Programming (via satellite): The Movie Channel.
Fee: $5.95 monthly.
Miles of plant: 38.0 (coaxial). Homes passed: 1,052.
Manager: Bill Flowers. Chief technician: Chris Christenson. Marketing director: Jennifer Hauschild.
Ownership: Classic Cable (MSO).

LUCAS—Friendship Cable of Texas Inc., Box 9090, Tyler, TX 75711-9090. Phone: 903-581-2121. Fax: 903-581-2185. County: Collin. Also serves Fairview, Forest Grove. ICA: TX0329.
TV Market Ranking: 12 (Fairview, Lucas); Below 100 (Forest Grove). Franchise award date: N.A. Franchise expiration date: N.A. Began: January 1, 1983.
Channel capacity: 54. Channels available but not in use: N.A.
Basic Service
Subscribers: 886.
Programming (received off-air): KDAF (W), KDFW (F), KERA-TV (P), KTVT (C), KTXA (U), KXAS-TV (N), KXTX-TV (I), WFAA-TV (A) Dallas-Fort Worth.
Programming (via satellite): WGN-TV (W) Chicago; CNN; Disney Channel; ESPN; TBS Superstation.
Fee: $30.00 installation; $31.75 monthly.
Pay Service 1
Pay Units: 130.
Programming (via satellite): HBO.
Fee: $12.00 monthly.
Pay Service 2
Pay Units: 68.
Programming (via satellite): The Movie Channel.
Fee: $9.00 monthly.
Pay Service 3
Pay Units: 172.
Programming (via satellite): Showtime.
Fee: $7.00 monthly.
Pay Service 4
Pay Units: 254.
Programming (via satellite): Flix.
Fee: $1.95 monthly.
Pay Service 5
Pay Units: 62.
Programming (via satellite): Cinemax.
Fee: $11.00 monthly.
Miles of plant: 83.4 (coaxial). Homes passed: 1,523.
Manager: Rodney Fletcher. Chief technician: Bo Jaubert.
Ownership: Buford Television Inc. (MSO). See Cable System Ownership.

LUEDERS—Jayroc Cablevision, Box 6575, Abilene, TX 79608. Phone: 915-691-5787. County: Jones. ICA: TX0803.
TV Market Ranking: Below 100. Franchise award date: N.A. Franchise expiration date: N.A. Began: N.A.
Channel capacity: N.A. Channels available but not in use: N.A.
Basic Service
Subscribers: N.A.
Programming (received off-air): KRBC-TV (N), KTAB-TV (C), KTXS-TV (A) Abilene-Sweetwater.
Programming (via satellite): WGN-TV (W) Chicago.
Fee: N.A.
Ownership: Jayroc Inc. (MSO).

LULING—Time Warner Cable, 12012 N. Mo Pac Expressway, Austin, TX 78758-2904. Phone: 512-485-6100. Fax: 512-485-6105. Web site: http://www.timewarneraustin.com. County: Caldwell. ICA: TX0221.
TV Market Ranking: Outside TV Markets. Franchise award date: October 22, 1992. Franchise expiration date: March 2, 2001. Began: N.A.
Channel capacity: N.A. Channels available but not in use: 2.
Basic Service
Subscribers: 1,550; Commercial subscribers: 13.
Programming (received off-air): KEYE-TV (C), KLRU (P), KNVA (W), KTBC (F), KVUE-TV (A), KXAN-TV (N) Austin; KRRT (W) Kerrville-San Antonio; KENS-TV (C), KLRN (P), KVDA (O) San Antonio.
Programming (via satellite): WGN-TV (W) Chicago; A & E; American Movie Classics; CNN; Country Music TV; Discovery Channel; ESPN; Fox Family Channel; Fox Sports Net Southwest; Headline News; Nashville Network; Nick at Nite; Nickelodeon; Pax Net; QVC; TBS Superstation; The Weather Channel; Trinity Bcstg. Network; Turner Network TV; USA Network; Univision; VH1.
Current originations: Automated time-weather.
Fee: $28.21 installation; $20.90 monthly; $1.15 converter; $12.11 additional installation.
Pay Service 1
Pay Units: 200.
Programming (via satellite): Cinemax.
Fee: $15.00 installation; $10.95 monthly.
Pay Service 2
Pay Units: 60.
Programming (via satellite): Disney Channel.
Fee: $15.00 installation; $8.00 monthly.
Pay Service 3
Pay Units: 480.
Programming (via satellite): HBO.
Fee: $15.00 installation; $10.95 monthly.
Pay Service 4
Pay Units: N.A.
Programming (via satellite): Showtime.
Fee: $15.00 installation; $10.95 monthly.
Local advertising: Yes. Available in locally originated & character-generated programming.
Equipment: Scientific-Atlanta headend; C-COR amplifiers; Comm/Scope cable; Video Data Systems character generator; Scientific-Atlanta & ChannelMaster satellite antenna; Scientific-Atlanta satellite receivers.
Miles of plant: 33.6 (coaxial). Homes passed: 2,010. Total homes in franchised area: 2,010.
Manager: Bill Carey. Chief technician: Matt Stanek. Program director: George Warmingham. Marketing director: Michelle Golden.
City fee: 3% of gross.
Ownership: Time Warner Cable (MSO); Advance/Newhouse Partnership (MSO).

LYONS—Classic Cable, Box 429, 605 N.W. 3rd St., Plainville, KS 67663-0429. Phones: 785-434-7620; 800-999-8876. Fax: 785-434-2614. County: Burleson. Also serves Somerville. ICA: TX0331.
TV Market Ranking: Below 100. Franchise award date: November 20, 1985. Franchise expiration date: N.A. Began: February 1, 1986.
Channel capacity: 41 (2-way capable). Channels available but not in use: N.A.
Basic Service
Subscribers: 527.
Programming (received off-air): KTBC (F), KVUE-TV (A), KXAN-TV (N) Austin; KBTX-TV (C) Bryan; KAMU-TV (P) College Station; KWKT (F) Waco-Temple.
Programming (via microwave): KHOU-TV (C), KHTV (W), KTXH (U) Houston.
Programming (via satellite): WGN-TV (W) Chicago; A & E; American Movie Classics; BET; CNN; Cartoon Network; Country Music TV; Discovery Channel; Disney Channel; ESPN; Fox Family Channel; Fox Sports Net Southwest; History Channel; Home & Garden Television; Learning Channel; MTV; Nashville Network; Nickelodeon; QVC; TBS Superstation; The Weather Channel; Trinity Bcstg. Network; Turner Network TV; USA Network; Univision.
Current originations: Public access.
Fee: $35.00 installation; $26.95 monthly.
Pay Service 1
Pay Units: 72.
Programming (via satellite): HBO.
Fee: $10.95 monthly.
Pay Service 2
Pay Units: 58.
Programming (via satellite): Showtime.
Fee: $9.95 monthly.
Pay Service 3
Pay Units: 63.
Programming (via satellite): The Movie Channel.
Fee: $5.95 monthly.
Local advertising: No.
Equipment: Scientific-Atlanta amplifiers; Comm/Scope cable; Scientific-Atlanta set top converters; Pico traps; Scientific-Atlanta satellite antenna; M/A-Com & Scientific-Atlanta satellite receivers.
Miles of plant: 15.0 (coaxial). Homes passed: 847.
Manager: Bill Flowers. Chief technician: Walt VanLue. Marketing director: Jennifer Hauschild.
City fee: 3% of gross.
Ownership: Classic Cable (MSO).

MADISONVILLE—Northland Cable, Box 282, 114 W. Main St., Madisonville, TX 77864. Phone: 409-348-3173. Fax: 409-348-6092. County: Madison. Also serves Madison County. ICA: TX0242.
TV Market Ranking: Below 100 (portions of Madison County, Madisonville); Outside TV Markets (portions of Madison County). Franchise award date: N.A. Franchise expiration date: N.A. Began: August 1, 1955.
Channel capacity: 40. Channels available but not in use: 4.
Basic Service
Subscribers: 1,264; Commercial subscribers: 6.
Programming (received off-air): KBTX-TV (C) Bryan; KAMU-TV (P) College Station; KHOU-TV (C), KHTV (W), KRIV (F), KTRK-TV (A) Houston; KCEN-TV (N) Waco-Temple; allband FM.
Programming (via satellite): American Movie Classics; Fox Family Channel; TBS Superstation.
Current originations: Automated time-weather; religious access.
Fee: $49.95 installation; $26.90 monthly.
Pay Service 1
Pay Units: 192.
Programming (via satellite): Cinemax.
Fee: $10.70 monthly.
Pay Service 2
Pay Units: 103.
Programming (via satellite): Disney Channel.
Fee: $7.95 monthly.
Pay Service 3
Pay Units: 295.
Programming (via satellite): HBO.
Fee: $10.70 monthly.
Pay Service 4
Pay Units: 115.
Programming (via satellite): Showtime.
Fee: $10.70 monthly.
Local advertising: Yes. Available in character-generated programming. Rates: $50.00/Month or $15.00/Page. Regional interconnect: Cabletime.
Equipment: Scientific-Atlanta headend; Scientific-Atlanta amplifiers; Comm/Scope cable; Microgen & Quanta character generator; Scientific-Atlanta set top converters; Scientific-Atlanta satellite antenna; Scientific-Atlanta satellite receivers.
Miles of plant: 49.0 (coaxial). Homes passed: 1,800.
Manager: Mike Taylor. Chief technician: Allan Fautheree. Marketing director: Todd Felker.
City fee: 2% of gross.
Ownership: Northland Communications Corp. (MSO).

MAGNOLIA—Friendship Cable of Texas, Box 9090, Tyler, TX 75711-9090. Phone: 903-581-2121. Fax: 903-581-2185. Counties: Har-

ris & Montgomery. Also serves Hockley, Pinehurst, Tomball. ICA: TX0301.
TV Market Ranking: 15. Franchise award date: N.A. Franchise expiration date: N.A. Began: N.A.
Channel capacity: 36 (not 2-way capable). Channels available but not in use: 1.
Basic Service
Subscribers: 724.
Programming (received off-air): KHOU-TV (C), KHTV (W), KPRC-TV (N), KRIV (F), KTRK-TV (A), KTXH (U), KUHT (P) Houston.
Programming (via satellite): A & E; C-SPAN; CNN; Country Music TV; Discovery Channel; Disney Channel; ESPN; Fox Family Channel; Fox Sports Net Southwest; Headline News; Lifetime; Nashville Network; Nickelodeon; QVC; TBS Superstation; The Inspirational Network; The Weather Channel; Turner Network TV; USA Network.
Fee: $34.95 monthly.
Pay Service 1
Pay Units: 25.
Programming (via satellite): Cinemax.
Fee: $10.95 monthly.
Pay Service 2
Pay Units: 61.
Programming (via satellite): HBO.
Fee: $10.95 monthly.
Pay Service 3
Pay Units: 125.
Programming (via satellite): Showtime.
Fee: $5.95 monthly.
Local advertising: Yes. Regional interconnect: Woodlands Communications Network.
Miles of plant: 85.0 (coaxial). Homes passed: 1,523.
Manager: Wanda Pyburn. Chief technician: David Burrell.
Ownership: Buford Television Inc. (MSO). See Cable System Ownership.

MALAKOFF—Northland Cable TV, Box 289, 326 W. Main, Gun Barrel City, TX 75147. Phone: 903-887-0240. County: Henderson. Also serves Caney City, Log Cabin Estates, Star Harbor, Trinidad. ICA: TX0806.
TV Market Ranking: Outside TV Markets. Franchise award date: February 11, 1980. Franchise expiration date: February 5, 2005. Began: N.A.
Channel capacity: 29 (not 2-way capable). Channels available but not in use: None.
Basic Service
Subscribers: 950.
Programming (received off-air): KPXD (X) Arlington; KDAF (W), KDFI-TV (I), KDFW (F), KERA-TV (P), KTVT (C), KTXA (U), KXAS-TV (N), KXTX-TV (I), WFAA-TV (A) Dallas-Fort Worth; KLTV (A) Tyler-Longview.
Programming (via satellite): ESPN; Nashville Network; TBS Superstation.
Fee: $40.00 installation; $25.50 monthly.
Expanded Basic Service
Subscribers: N.A.
Programming (via satellite): WGN-TV (W) Chicago; A & E; CNN; Cartoon Network; Country Music TV; Discovery Channel; Fox Family Channel; Fox Sports Net Southwest; Headline News; Home Shopping Network; Lifetime; Nickelodeon; The Weather Channel; USA Network.
Fee: N.A.
Pay Service 1
Pay Units: N.A.
Programming (via satellite): Disney Channel; HBO; The Movie Channel.
Fee: $30.00 installation; $7.50 monthly (Disney), $8.50 monthly (TMC), $11.00 monthly (HBO).

Miles of plant: 58.0 (coaxial); None (fiber optic).
Manager: Wayne Helmig.
Franchise fee: 4% of gross.
Ownership: Northland Communications Corp. (MSO).

MALONE—Torrence Cable Inc., Box 1167, Ridgeland, MS 39158. Phones: 601-981-6900; 800-977-8849. County: Hill. Also serves Penelope. ICA: TX0591.
TV Market Ranking: Below 100. Franchise award date: N.A. Franchise expiration date: N.A. Began: N.A.
Channel capacity: 35. Channels available but not in use: 18.
Basic Service
Subscribers: 64.
Programming (received off-air): KDFW (F), KERA-TV (P), KXAS-TV (N), WFAA-TV (A) Dallas-Fort Worth.
Programming (via satellite): WGN-TV (W) Chicago; A & E; American Movie Classics; CNN; Country Music TV; Discovery Channel; ESPN; Fox Family Channel; Showtime; TBS Superstation; Turner Network TV; USA Network.
Fee: $24.00 monthly.
Pay Service 1
Pay Units: 25.
Programming (via satellite): Cinemax.
Fee: $10.95 monthly.
Pay Service 2
Pay Units: 23.
Programming (via satellite): HBO.
Fee: $10.95 monthly.
Local advertising: Yes.
Miles of plant: 11.0 (coaxial). Homes passed: 254.
Ownership: Torrence Cable Inc. (MSO).

MANOR—Mission Cable, 920 Whitmore Dr., Rockwall, TX 75087. Phones: 214-783-5708; 800-783-5708. Fax: 214-722-6218. County: Travis. ICA: TX0470.
TV Market Ranking: Below 100. Franchise award date: October 3, 1983. Franchise expiration date: October 3, 1998. Began: July 1, 1984.
Channel capacity: 36 (not 2-way capable). Channels available but not in use: 12.
Basic Service
Subscribers: 129; Commercial subscribers: 20.
Programming (received off-air): KEYE-TV (C), KLRU (P), KTBC (F), KVUE-TV (A), KXAN-TV (N) Austin.
Programming (via satellite): WGN-TV (W) Chicago; A & E; BET; C-SPAN; CNN; Discovery Channel; ESPN; Fox Family Channel; GalaVision; MTV; Nashville Network; Nickelodeon; TBS Superstation; The Weather Channel; USA Network; Univision.
Fee: $30.00 installation; $16.95 monthly.
Pay Service 1
Pay Units: 33.
Programming (via satellite): Cinemax.
Fee: $9.00 monthly.
Pay Service 2
Pay Units: 8.
Programming (via satellite): Disney Channel.
Fee: $9.00 monthly.
Pay Service 3
Pay Units: 54.
Programming (via satellite): HBO.
Fee: $9.00 monthly.
Miles of plant: 6.0 (coaxial). Additional miles planned: 80.0 (coaxial). Homes passed: 354. Total homes in franchised area: 540.

Manager: Jim Stafford. Chief technician: Jacky Oliver. Marketing & program director: Bruce Berkinshaw.
Franchise fee: 4% of gross.
Ownership: Fanch Communications Inc. (MSO); Time Warner Cable (MSO). See Cable System Ownership.

MANSFIELD—Charter Communications Inc., No. 109, 208 E. Broad St., Mansfield, TX 76063-5533. Phones: 817-509-6272; 817-509-2225. Fax: 817-740-9578. County: Tarrant. ICA: TX0086.
TV Market Ranking: 12. Franchise award date: N.A. Franchise expiration date: N.A. Began: June 6, 1980.
Channel capacity: 35. Channels available but not in use: N.A.
Basic Service
Subscribers: N.A.
Programming (received off-air): KPXD (X) Arlington; KDAF (W), KDFI-TV (I), KDFW (F), KERA-TV (P), KFWD (O), KTVT (C), KTXA (U), KXAS-TV (N), KXTX-TV (I), WFAA-TV (A) Dallas-Fort Worth; KMPX (I) Decatur; KDTN (P) Denton; KUVN (S) Garland; allband FM.
Programming (via satellite): WGN-TV (W) Chicago; C-SPAN; Home Shopping Network; QVC; Trinity Bcstg. Network.
Current originations: Automated time-weather; public access; educational access; government access; leased access; automated emergency alert; local news.
Fee: $25.00 installation; $10.61 monthly; $10.00 additional installation.
Expanded Basic Service
Subscribers: N.A.
Programming (via satellite): A & E; American Movie Classics; BET; Bravo; C-SPAN 2; CNBC; CNN; Cartoon Network; Country Music TV; Discovery Channel; Disney Channel; E! Entertainment TV; ESPN; EWTN; FX; Fox Family Channel; Fox Sports Net Southwest; Headline News; History Channel; Home & Garden Television; Learning Channel; Lifetime; MSNBC; MTV; Nashville Network; Nickelodeon; Odyssey; TBS Superstation; TV Food Network; The Weather Channel; Turner Network TV; USA Network; VH1.
Fee: $14.45 monthly.
Pay Service 1
Pay Units: N.A.
Programming (via satellite): Cinemax; HBO (multiplexed); Showtime; The Movie Channel.
Fee: $15.00 installation; $11.05 monthly (Cinemax, Showtime or TMC), $12.95 monthly (HBO).
Pay-Per-View
Hot Choice; Playboy TV; Viewer's Choice.
Fee: $3.95.
Local advertising: No.
Equipment: RCA & Scientific-Atlanta headend; C-COR amplifiers; Comm/Scope cable; Video Data Systems character generator; Oak set top converters; Scientific-Atlanta satellite antenna; Scientific-Atlanta satellite receivers.
Miles of plant: 141.1 (coaxial). Homes passed: 8,550.
Manager: Dave Warehimen. System engineer: Robert Wilson.
City fee: 4% of gross.
Ownership: Charter Communications Inc. (MSO). Purchased from Marcus Cable, April 1, 1999.

MARATHON—Marathon TV Cable, Box 1377, Alpine, TX 79831. Phone: 915-837-2300. Fax: 915-837-5423. E-mail: mtnzone@overland.net. County: Brewster. ICA: TX0613.

TV Market Ranking: Outside TV Markets. Franchise award date: N.A. Franchise expiration date: N.A. Began: October 1, 1968.
Channel capacity: 36 (not 2-way capable). Channels available but not in use: 3.
Basic Service
Subscribers: 140.
Programming (received off-air): KOSA-TV (C), KPEJ (F), KWES-TV (N) Odessa-Midland; allband FM.
Programming (via translator): KMID (A) Odessa-Midland.
Programming (via satellite): WGN-TV (W) Chicago; KMGH-TV (A), KRMA-TV (P) Denver; A & E; CNN; Country Music TV; Discovery Channel; ESPN; Fox Family Channel; GalaVision; Home Shopping Network; Learning Channel; Nashville Network; Nickelodeon; TBS Superstation; The Weather Channel; Turner Classic Movies; Turner Network TV; Univision.
Fee: $35.00 installation; $24.00 monthly.
Pay Service 1
Pay Units: 48.
Programming (via satellite): HBO.
Fee: $10.00 installation; $8.95 monthly.
Pay Service 2
Pay Units: 23.
Programming (via satellite): Showtime.
Fee: $10.00 installation; $7.95 monthly.
Equipment: Blonder-Tongue & Scientific-Atlanta headend; Jerrold & Scientific-Atlanta amplifiers; Times Fiber cable; RCA set top converters.
Miles of plant: 8.0 (coaxial). Homes passed: 225. Total homes in franchised area: 250.
Manager: Steve Neu.
Ownership: Mountain Zone TV Systems (MSO).

MARBLE FALLS—Northland Cable TV, Box 366, 1101 Mission Hill Dr., Marble Falls, TX 78654-1906. Phone: 830-693-7500. Fax: 830-693-6056. County: Burnet. Also serves Meadowlakes. ICA: TX0807.
TV Market Ranking: Below 100. Franchise award date: N.A. Franchise expiration date: N.A. Began: N.A.
Channel capacity: 35 (2-way capable). Channels available but not in use: 2.
Basic Service
Subscribers: 47.
Programming (received off-air): KEYE-TV (C), KLRU (P), KNVA (W), KTBC (F), KVUE-TV (A) Austin; KXAM-TV (N) Llano.
Programming (via satellite): WGN-TV (W) Chicago; C-SPAN; Headline News; QVC; TBS Superstation; TV Guide Sneak Prevue.
Fee: $15.75 monthly.
Expanded Basic Service
Subscribers: N.A.
Programming (via satellite): A & E; CNN; Discovery Channel; ESPN; Fox Family Channel; Fox Sports Net Southwest; Great American Country; History Channel; Learning Channel; Nashville Network; The Weather Channel; Trinity Bcstg. Network; USA Network.
Fee: $26.15 monthly.
Expanded Basic Service 2
Subscribers: N.A.
Programming (via satellite): American Movie Classics; CNBC; Cartoon Network; Nickelodeon; Turner Classic Movies; Turner Network TV.
Fee: $8.50 monthly.
Pay Service 1
Pay Units: N.A.
Programming (via satellite): Cinemax; HBO; Starz!; The New Encore.
Fee: $8.95 monthly (Cinemax), $11.50 monthly (Showtime, or Starz! & Encore), $11.95 monthly (HBO).

Miles of plant: 32.0 (coaxial). Homes passed: 2,325.
Manager: Rich Beatty. Chief technician: David Simpson. Marketing director: Debbie Jones.
Ownership: Northland Communications Corp. (MSO).

MARFA—Marfa TV Cable Co. Inc., Box 1377, Albine, TX 79831. Phone: 915-837-2300. E-mail: mtnzone@overland.net. County: Presidio. ICA: TX0360.
TV Market Ranking: Outside TV Markets. Franchise award date: February 18, 1957. Franchise expiration date: June 1, 2000. Began: September 1, 1958.
Channel capacity: 36 (not 2-way capable). Channels available but not in use: None.
Basic Service
Subscribers: 800.
Programming (received off-air): Allband FM.
Programming (via translator): KCOS (P), KVIA-TV (A) El Paso; KOSA-TV (C), KWES-TV (N) Odessa-Midland.
Programming (via satellite): WGN-TV (W) Chicago; CNN; ESPN; Nickelodeon; TBS Superstation; Univision.
Fee: $15.00 installation; $12.00 monthly; $15.00 additional installation.
Pay Service 1
Pay Units: N.A.
Programming (via satellite): HBO.
Fee: $9.00 monthly.
Local advertising: No.
Equipment: Scientific-Atlanta headend; Tocom amplifiers; Comm/Scope cable; Eagle traps; Scientific-Atlanta satellite antenna; Scientific-Atlanta satellite receivers.
Miles of plant: 16.0 (coaxial). Homes passed: 1,012. Total homes in franchised area: 1,012.
Manager: Steve Neu. Office manager: Lawrence Neu.
City fee: $200 annually.
Ownership: Mountain Zone TV Systems (MSO). Purchased from Marfa TV Cable Co. Inc.

MARLIN—Northland Cable, 151 Coleman St., Marlin, TX 76661-2812. Phone: 254-883-3171. Fax: 254-883-2911. County: Falls. ICA: TX0203.
TV Market Ranking: Below 100. Franchise award date: January 1, 1964. Franchise expiration date: December 31, 2011. Began: March 1, 1965.
Channel capacity: 42. Channels available but not in use: 6.
Basic Service
Subscribers: 1,553.
Programming (received off-air): KTVT (C), KXTX-TV (I), WFAA-TV (A) Dallas-Fort Worth; KCEN-TV (N), KCTF (P), KWKT (F), KWTX-TV (C), KXXV (A) Waco-Temple.
Programming (via satellite): C-SPAN; QVC; The Inspirational Network.
Current originations: Automated time-weather.
Fee: $35.00 installation; $8.60 monthly.
Expanded Basic Service
Subscribers: 1,550.
Programming (via satellite): A & E; American Movie Classics; BET; CNBC; CNN; Country Music TV; Discovery Channel; ESPN; Fox Family Channel; Headline News; Lifetime; MTV; Nickelodeon; TBS Superstation; The Weather Channel; Turner Network TV; USA Network; Univision.
Fee: $35.00 installation; $14.34 monthly.
Pay Service 1
Pay Units: 87.
Programming (via satellite): Cinemax.
Fee: N.A.
Pay Service 2
Pay Units: 57.
Programming (via satellite): Disney Channel.
Fee: N.A.
Pay Service 3
Pay Units: 191.
Programming (via satellite): HBO.
Fee: N.A.
Pay Service 4
Pay Units: 134.
Programming (via satellite): Showtime.
Fee: N.A.
Local advertising: Yes. Regional interconnect: Cabletime.
Equipment: Scientific-Atlanta headend; Magnavox amplifiers; Times Fiber cable; Texscan character generator; Scientific-Atlanta set top converters; Scientific-Atlanta satellite receivers.
Miles of plant: 41.0 (coaxial). Homes passed: 2,800. Total homes in franchised area: 2,800.
Manager: Jim Cullins. Chief technician: Randy Dobson. Marketing director: Todd Felker.
City fee: 5% of gross.
Ownership: Northland Communications Corp. (MSO).

MARSHALL—Falcon Cable TV, 108 W. Houston, Marshall, TX 75670. Phone: 903-938-8335. County: Harrison. Also serves Harrison County (portions). ICA: TX0083.
TV Market Ranking: 58 (portions of Harrison County, Marshall); Below 100 (portions of Harrison County). Franchise award date: November 15, 1965. Franchise expiration date: July 22, 2002. Began: February 1, 1974.
Channel capacity: 61 (2-way capable; operating 2-way). Channels available but not in use: None.
Basic Service
Subscribers: 4,650; Commercial subscribers: 8.
Programming (received off-air): KETK-TV (N) Jacksonville; KLTS-TV (P), KMSS-TV (F), KSHV (U,W), KSLA-TV (C), KTAL-TV (N), KTBS-TV (A) Shreveport-Texarkana; allband FM.
Programming (via microwave): KERA-TV (P) Dallas-Fort Worth.
Programming (via satellite): A & E; American Movie Classics; BET; C-SPAN; CNBC; Comedy Central; Country Music TV; E! Entertainment TV; ESPN 2; FX; Fox Family Channel; Headline News; Home Shopping Network; Lifetime; MTV; Nickelodeon; QVC; Sci-Fi Channel; TV Guide Channel; TV Guide Sneak Prevue; The Inspirational Network; The Weather Channel; Trinity Bcstg. Network; VH1.
Current originations: Automated time-weather.
Fee: $63.00 installation; $25.17 monthly.
Expanded Basic Service
Subscribers: 4,308.
Programming (via satellite): CNN; ESPN; Nashville Network; TV Food Network; USA Network.
Fee: $6.10 monthly.
Expanded Basic Service 2
Subscribers: 2,163.
Programming (via satellite): Discovery Channel; Disney Channel; Fox Sports Net Southwest; Home & Garden Television; TBS Superstation; Turner Network TV.
Fee: $8.75 monthly.
Expanded Basic Service 3
Subscribers: 712.
Programming (via satellite): Cartoon Network; fXM: Movies from Fox; History Channel; Outdoor Life Network; The Health Network.
Fee: $7.50 monthly.
Pay Service 1
Pay Units: 592.
Programming (via satellite): Cinemax.
Fee: $25.00 installation; $11.95 monthly.
Pay Service 2
Pay Units: 903.
Programming (via satellite): HBO.
Fee: $11.95 monthly.
Pay Service 3
Pay Units: 266.
Programming (via satellite): The Movie Channel.
Fee: $11.95 monthly.
Pay Service 4
Pay Units: 452.
Programming (via satellite): Showtime.
Fee: $11.95 monthly.
Pay Service 5
Pay Units: N.A.
Programming (via satellite): The New Encore.
Fee: $5.95 monthly.
Pay-Per-View
Action Pay-Per-View; Spice; Viewer's Choice.
Local advertising: Yes (locally produced & insert). Available in character-generated programming. Local sales manager: John Beard. Regional interconnect: Cabletime.
Equipment: Scientific-Atlanta headend; C-COR amplifiers; Comm/Scope cable; Sony VTRs; Hamlin set top converters; Eagle & Vitek traps; Scientific-Atlanta satellite antenna; Scientific-Atlanta satellite receivers.
Miles of plant: 231.0 (coaxial). Homes passed: 11,899.
Manager: George Doss. Chief technician: Robert Hurd.
Franchise fee: 5% of gross.
Ownership: Falcon Communications LP (MSO), joint venture formed September 30, 1998. See Cable System Ownership.

MART—Friendship Cable of Texas Inc., Box 9090, Tyler, TX 75711-9090. Phone: 903-581-2121. Fax: 903-581-2185. County: McLennan. ICA: TX0359.
TV Market Ranking: Below 100. Franchise award date: N.A. Franchise expiration date: N.A. Began: January 1, 1983.
Channel capacity: 35. Channels available but not in use: 5.
Basic Service
Subscribers: 591.
Programming (received off-air): KDFW (F), KERA-TV (P), KTVT (C), KXAS-TV (N), KXTX-TV (I), WFAA-TV (A) Dallas-Fort Worth; KCEN-TV (N), KWKT (F), KWTX-TV (C), KXXV (A) Waco-Temple.
Programming (via satellite): Discovery Channel; Learning Channel; TBS Superstation.
Fee: $30.00 installation; $12.42 monthly.
Expanded Basic Service
Subscribers: 519.
Programming (via satellite): American Movie Classics; Animal Planet; C-SPAN; CNBC; CNN; Cartoon Network; Disney Channel; ESPN; FX; Fox Family Channel; Fox News Channel; Headline News; Home & Garden Television; Lifetime; Nashville Network; Nickelodeon; QVC; The Weather Channel; Turner Network TV; USA Network.
Fee: $30.00 installation; $15.41 monthly.
Pay Service 1
Pay Units: 108.
Programming (via satellite): Cinemax.
Fee: $12.90 monthly.
Pay Service 2
Pay Units: 173.
Programming (via satellite): The New Encore.
Fee: $1.75 monthly.
Pay Service 3
Pay Units: 133.
Programming (via satellite): HBO.
Fee: $12.90 monthly.
Pay Service 4
Pay Units: 122.
Programming (via satellite): Starz!
Fee: $6.75 monthly.
Program Guide: The Cable Guide.
Miles of plant: 16.0 (coaxial). Homes passed: 1,019. Total homes in franchised area: 1,019.
Manager: Larry Bryant. Chief technician: Joe Stewart.
Ownership: Buford Television Inc. (MSO). See Cable System Ownership.

MASON—Classic Cable, Box 429, 605 N.W. 3rd St., Plainville, KS 67663-0429. Phones: 785-434-7620; 800-999-8876. Fax: 785-434-2614. County: Mason. Also serves Mason County. ICA: TX0363.
TV Market Ranking: Below 100 (Mason, portions of Mason County); Outside TV Markets (portions of Mason County). Franchise award date: N.A. Franchise expiration date: N.A. Began: January 1, 1967.
Channel capacity: 78 (2-way capable). Channels available but not in use: N.A.
Basic Service
Subscribers: 723; Commercial subscribers: 21.
Programming (received off-air): KEYE-TV (C), KLRU (P), KTBC (F), KVUE-TV (A), KXAN-TV (N) Austin; KLST (C) San Angelo; 8 FMs.
Programming (via satellite): A & E; CNN; Country Music TV; Discovery Channel; ESPN; FX; Fox Family Channel; Fox News Channel; Fox Sports Net Southwest; Home & Garden Television; Home Shopping Network; Nashville Network; Nick at Nite's TV Land; TBS Superstation; The Weather Channel; Trinity Bcstg. Network; Turner Network TV; USA Network; Univision.
Current originations: Automated time-weather; local news.
Fee: $35.00 installation; $29.95 monthly.
Pay Service 1
Pay Units: 43.
Programming (via satellite): Disney Channel.
Fee: $10.95 monthly.
Pay Service 2
Pay Units: 64.
Programming (via satellite): HBO.
Fee: $10.63 monthly.
Pay Service 3
Pay Units: 30.
Programming (via satellite): Cinemax.
Fee: $10.63 monthly.
Pay Service 4
Pay Units: N.A.
Programming (via satellite): Starz!; The New Encore.
Fee: $6.95 monthly.
Equipment: Blonder-Tongue headend; Tocom amplifiers; Superior & Times Fiber cable; Vitek traps; Prodelin satellite antenna; Microwave Assoc. & Microdyne satellite receivers.
Miles of plant: 24.0 (coaxial). Homes passed: 1,051.
Manager: Bill Flowers. Chief technician: Walt VanLue. Program director: David McDonald. Marketing director: Jennifer Hauschild.
City fee: 3% of gross.
Ownership: Classic Cable (MSO).

MATADOR—Classic Cable, Box 429, 605 N.W. 3rd St., Plainville, KS 67663-0429. Phones: 785-434-7620; 800-999-8876. Fax: 785-434-2614. County: Motley. ICA: TX0500.

TV Market Ranking: Outside TV Markets. Franchise award date: N.A. Franchise expiration date: November 1, 2007. Began: November 1, 1957.
Channel capacity: 61 (2-way capable). Channels available but not in use: N.A.

Basic Service

Subscribers: 259; Commercial subscribers: 19.
Programming (received off-air): KAMC (A), KCBD-TV (N), KJTV (F), KLBK-TV (C) Lubbock.
Programming (via satellite): WGN-TV (W) Chicago; KRMA-TV (P) Denver; American Movie Classics; Animal Planet; CNN; Cartoon Network; Country Music TV; Discovery Channel; Disney Channel; E! Entertainment TV; ESPN; Fox Family Channel; Fox Sports Net Southwest; Goodlife TV Network; Headline News; History Channel; Learning Channel; Lifetime; Nashville Network; Nick at Nite's TV Land; QVC; TBS Superstation; The Weather Channel; Trinity Bcstg. Network; Turner Network TV; USA Network; Univision.
Fee: $35.00 installation; $27.95 monthly.

Pay Service 1

Pay Units: 29.
Programming (via satellite): Cinemax.
Fee: $9.95 monthly.

Pay Service 2

Pay Units: 29.
Programming (via satellite): HBO.
Fee: $9.95 monthly.

Local advertising: No. Regional interconnect: Northern Ohio Interconnect.
Equipment: Jerrold headend; Jerrold & Vikoa amplifiers; Phelps-Dodge & Vikoa cable.
Miles of plant: 11.0 (coaxial). Homes passed: 394.
Manager: Bill Flowers. Chief technician: Rick Rattan. Marketing director: Jennifer Hauschild.
City fee: 2% of gross.
Ownership: Classic Cable (MSO).

MATAGORDA—Northland Cable TV, 2404 Golden Ave., Bay City, TX 77414. Phone: 409-245-5511. Fax: 409-245-8256. County: Matagorda. ICA: TX0418.
TV Market Ranking: Outside TV Markets. Franchise award date: N.A. Franchise expiration date: N.A. Began: August 1, 1984.
Channel capacity: 28 (not 2-way capable). Channels available but not in use: 6.

Basic Service

Subscribers: 175.
Programming (received off-air): KLTJ (E) Galveston; KHOU-TV (C), KHTV (W), KPRC-TV (N), KRIV (F), KTRK-TV (A), KTXH (U), KUHT (P) Houston; KAVU-TV (A) Victoria.
Programming (via satellite): American Movie Classics; C-SPAN; CNN; Discovery Channel; ESPN; Fox Family Channel; Nashville Network; TBS Superstation; The Weather Channel; Turner Network TV.
Fee: $50.00 installation; $26.00 monthly; $2.00 converter.

Pay Service 1

Pay Units: 30.
Programming (via satellite): Cinemax.
Fee: $8.50 monthly.

Pay Service 2

Pay Units: 30.
Programming (via satellite): HBO.
Fee: $10.50 monthly.

Local advertising: No.
Equipment: Jerrold & RCA amplifiers; Comm/Scope cable; RCA set top converters; Arcom & Eagle traps; Anixter & Scientific-Atlanta satellite antenna.
Miles of plant: 14.0 (coaxial). Homes passed: 736.
Manager: Ken Knight. Chief technician: Dennis McCulloch. Marketing director: Pam Valley.
Ownership: Northland Communications Corp. (MSO).

MATHIS—TCI Cablevision of Texas, 4060 S. Padre Island Dr., Corpus Christi, TX 78411-4477. Phone: 512-857-5000. County: San Patricio. Also serves Lake City, Lakeside. ICA: TX0216.
TV Market Ranking: Below 100. Franchise award date: N.A. Franchise expiration date: N.A. Began: February 14, 1982.
Channel capacity: 35. Channels available but not in use: 10.

Basic Service

Subscribers: 1,142.
Programming (received off-air): KEDT (P), KIII (A), KORO (S), KRIS-TV (N), KZTV (C) Corpus Christi.
Programming (via satellite): WGN-TV (W) Chicago; American Movie Classics; CNBC; CNN; Discovery Channel; ESPN; Fox Family Channel; FoxNet; GalaVision; Headline News; Lifetime; Nashville Network; QVC; TBS Superstation; The Weather Channel; Turner Network TV.
Current originations: Automated time-weather; automated emergency alert.
Fee: $37.56 installation; $10.51 monthly; $18.78 additional installation.

Pay Service 1

Pay Units: 155.
Programming (via satellite): Cinemax.
Fee: $8.00 monthly.

Pay Service 2

Pay Units: 92.
Programming (via satellite): Disney Channel.
Fee: $8.00 monthly.

Pay Service 3

Pay Units: 309.
Programming (via satellite): The New Encore.
Fee: N.A.

Pay Service 4

Pay Units: 292.
Programming (via satellite): HBO.
Fee: $8.00 monthly.

Local advertising: No.
Equipment: Scientific-Atlanta headend; Scientific-Atlanta amplifiers; Comm/Scope cable; Anixter-Mark satellite antenna; Scientific-Atlanta satellite receivers.
Miles of plant: 69.1 (coaxial). Homes passed: 2,084.
Manager: Dennis Moore. Chief technician: Mando Blancas. Marketing director: Jerri Coppedge.
City fee: 3% of gross.
Ownership: AT&T Broadband & Internet Services (MSO). Purchased from Tele-Communications Inc., March 9, 1999.

MAUD—TCA Cable TV, 609 E. North Front St., New Boston, TX 75570-3005. Phone: 903-628-5569. Web site: http://www.tca-cable.com. County: Bowie. Also serves Bowie County. ICA: TX0482.
TV Market Ranking: 58 (portions of Bowie County, Maud); Outside TV Markets (portions of Bowie County). Franchise award date: N.A. Franchise expiration date: January 1, 2001. Began: August 1, 1981.
Channel capacity: 35. Channels available but not in use: 8.

Basic Service

Subscribers: 352.
Programming (received off-air): KLTS-TV (P), KMSS-TV (F), KSLA-TV (C), KTAL-TV (N), KTBS-TV (A) Shreveport-Texarkana.
Programming (via satellite): WGN-TV (W) Chicago; CNBC; CNN; Comedy Central; Discovery Channel; Fox Family Channel; Lifetime; MTV; Nashville Network; Nickelodeon; QVC; TBS Superstation; The Weather Channel.
Fee: $33.72 installation; $9.81 monthly.

Expanded Basic Service

Subscribers: 343.
Programming (via satellite): American Movie Classics; ESPN; Fox Sports Net Southwest; Turner Network TV; USA Network.
Fee: $11.10 monthly.

Pay Service 1

Pay Units: 25.
Programming (via satellite): Disney Channel.
Fee: N.A.

Pay Service 2

Pay Units: 105.
Programming (via satellite): The New Encore.
Fee: N.A.

Pay Service 3

Pay Units: 78.
Programming (via satellite): HBO.
Fee: $10.00 monthly.

Pay Service 4

Pay Units: 52.
Programming (via satellite): Showtime.
Fee: N.A.

Equipment: Scientific-Atlanta headend; Scientific-Atlanta amplifiers; Scientific-Atlanta cable; Harris satellite receivers.
Miles of plant: 10.7 (coaxial). Homes passed: 502. Total homes in franchised area: 1,059.
Manager: Ron Eubanks.
City fee: 2% of gross.
Ownership: TCA Cable TV Inc. (MSO); AT&T Broadband & Internet Services (MSO). See Cable System Ownership.

MAURICEVILLE—Friendship Cable of Texas Inc., Box 9090, Tyler, TX 75711-9090. Phones: 903-581-2121; 800-888-7538. Fax: 903-581-2185. Counties: Jasper, Newton & Orange. Also serves Deweyville, Evadale, Hampton, North Vidor, Orangefield. ICA: TX0808.
TV Market Ranking: 88 (Deweyville, Hampton, Mauriceville, North Vidor, Orangefield); Outside TV Markets (Evadale). Franchise award date: N.A. Franchise expiration date: N.A. Began: N.A.
Channel capacity: 43. Channels available but not in use: 3.

Basic Service

Subscribers: 3,363.
Programming (received off-air): KBMT (A), KBTV-TV (N), KFDM-TV (C) Beaumont-Port Arthur; KLTL-TV (P), KVHP (F) Lake Charles; KFXK (F) Longview.
Programming (via satellite): WGN-TV (W) Chicago; CNN; Discovery Channel; Disney Channel; ESPN; Fox Family Channel; Home Shopping Network; MTV; Nashville Network; TBS Superstation; The Weather Channel; USA Network.
Fee: $32.66 monthly.

Pay Service 1

Pay Units: 317.
Programming (via satellite): Cinemax.
Fee: $10.95 monthly.

Pay Service 2

Pay Units: 472.
Programming (via satellite): HBO.
Fee: $10.95 monthly.

Pay Service 3

Pay Units: 541.
Programming (via satellite): Showtime.
Fee: $5.95 monthly.

Pay Service 4

Pay Units: 301.
Programming (via satellite): Starz!
Fee: $8.95 monthly.

Miles of plant: 227.0 (coaxial). Homes passed: 6,615.
Manager: Wanda Pyburn. Chief technician: Mike Deal.
Ownership: Buford Television Inc. (MSO). See Cable System Ownership.

MAXWELL—Torrence Cablevision, Box 1167, Ridgeland, MS 39158. Phones: 601-981-6900; 800-977-8849. County: Caldwell. ICA: TX0809.
TV Market Ranking: Below 100. Franchise award date: N.A. Franchise expiration date: N.A. Began: N.A.
Channel capacity: 36. Channels available but not in use: 21.

Basic Service

Subscribers: 28.
Programming (received off-air): KEYE-TV (C), KLRU (P), KTBC (F), KVUE-TV (A), KXAN-TV (N) Austin; KVDA (O) San Antonio.
Programming (via satellite): WGN-TV (W) Chicago; A & E; American Movie Classics; CNN; Country Music TV; Discovery Channel; ESPN; Fox Family Channel; Showtime; TBS Superstation; Turner Network TV; USA Network.
Fee: $28.00 monthly.

Miles of plant: 2.7 (coaxial). Homes passed: 127.
Ownership: Torrence Cable Inc. (MSO).

MAY—Cable Ventures Inc., Suite 106-A, 5151 Reed Rd., Columbus, OH 43220. Phone: 614-442-5890. Fax: 614-457-2567. County: Brown. ICA: TX0683.
TV Market Ranking: Outside TV Markets. Franchise award date: N.A. Franchise expiration date: N.A. Began: January 1, 1989.
Channel capacity: 23 (2-way capable). Channels available but not in use: 7.

Basic Service

Subscribers: 53.
Programming (received off-air): KIDZ-LP (F) Abilene; KRBC-TV (N), KTAB-TV (C), KTXS-TV (A) Abilene-Sweetwater.
Programming (via satellite): WGN-TV (W) Chicago; CNN; Discovery Channel; ESPN; Fox Family Channel; Lifetime; Nashville Network; QVC; TBS Superstation; The Weather Channel; USA Network.
Fee: $40.00 installation; $29.95 monthly.

Pay Service 1

Pay Units: 6.
Programming (via satellite): HBO.
Fee: $10.00 monthly.

Pay Service 2

Pay Units: N.A.
Programming (via satellite): Cinemax; Disney Channel.
Fee: $7.00 monthly (Disney), $9.00 monthly (Cinemax).

Local advertising: No.
Miles of plant: 3.0 (coaxial). Homes passed: 148.
Manager: Bill Mayes. System/operations manager: Steve Miller.
Ownership: Cable Ventures Ltd. (MSO).

McKINNEY—TCI Cablevision of Texas Inc., Box 64, Allen, TX 75002-3425. Phone: 214-727-5723. County: Collin. ICA: TX0087.
TV Market Ranking: 12. Franchise award date: N.A. Franchise expiration date: N.A. Began: July 8, 1988.
Channel capacity: 36. Channels available but not in use: None.

Basic Service
Subscribers: 4,396.
Programming (received off-air): KDAF (W), KDFI-TV (I), KDFW (F), KERA-TV (P), KTVT (C), KTXA (U), KXAS-TV (N), KXTX-TV (I), WFAA-TV (A) Dallas-Fort Worth; KDTN (P) Denton; 2 FMs.
Programming (via satellite): WGN-TV (W) Chicago; CNBC; CNN; Cartoon Network; Discovery Channel; Fox Family Channel; Headline News; Lifetime; MTV; Nashville Network; Nickelodeon; Odyssey; QVC; TBS Superstation; The Weather Channel; Turner Classic Movies.
Current originations: Public access; educational access; government access.
Fee: $60.00 installation; $17.95 monthly.
Expanded Basic Service
Subscribers: 2,850.
Programming (via satellite): American Movie Classics; ESPN; Fox Sports Net Southwest; Turner Network TV; USA Network.
Fee: $2.91 monthly.
Pay Service 1
Pay Units: 131.
Programming (via satellite): Cinemax.
Fee: N.A.
Pay Service 2
Pay Units: 227.
Programming (via satellite): Disney Channel.
Fee: N.A.
Pay Service 3
Pay Units: 1,052.
Programming (via satellite): The New Encore.
Fee: N.A.
Pay Service 4
Pay Units: 1,263.
Programming (via satellite): HBO.
Fee: N.A.
Pay Service 5
Pay Units: 66.
Programming (via satellite): The Movie Channel.
Fee: N.A.
Pay Service 6
Pay Units: 691.
Programming (via satellite): Showtime.
Fee: N.A.
Miles of plant: 129.6 (coaxial). Homes passed: 8,402. Total homes in franchised area: 16,750.
Manager: Joann Holtzclaw. Chief technician: Mike Crain.
Ownership: AT&T Broadband & Internet Services (MSO). Purchased from Tele-Communications Inc., March 9, 1999.

McLEAN—Charter Communications Inc., Box 2373, 1423 N. Hobart, Pampa, TX 79065. Phone: 806-665-2381. County: Gray. ICA: TX0488.
TV Market Ranking: Outside TV Markets. Franchise award date: N.A. Franchise expiration date: N.A. Began: January 1, 1966.
Channel capacity: 21. Channels available but not in use: N.A.
Basic Service
Subscribers: 337.
Programming (received off-air): KACV-TV (P), KAMR-TV (N), KCIT (F,U), KFDA-TV (C), KVII-TV (A) Amarillo; allband FM.
Programming (via microwave): TBS Superstation; WGN-TV (W) Chicago.
Programming (via satellite): CNN; ESPN; Nickelodeon; The Weather Channel.
Current originations: Automated time-weather; automated emergency alert.
Fee: $35.00 installation; $15.95 monthly.
Pay Service 1
Pay Units: N.A.
Programming (via satellite): HBO.
Fee: $15.00 installation; $11.75 monthly.
Equipment: Scientific-Atlanta headend; Texscan amplifiers.
Miles of plant: 8.1 (coaxial). Homes passed: 480.
Manager: John Mason. Chief technician: Jim Hampton.
City fee: 2% of gross.
Ownership: Charter Communications Inc. (MSO). Purchased from Marcus Cable, April 1, 1999.

MEDINA—Advanced Cable, 5940 Zangs Dr., San Antonio, TX 78238. Phone: 210-521-1500. Fax: 210-681-6239. County: Bandera. ICA: TX0684.
TV Market Ranking: 45. Franchise award date: N.A. Franchise expiration date: N.A. Began: February 2, 1990.
Channel capacity: 36 (not 2-way capable). Channels available but not in use: 21.
Basic Service
Subscribers: 52.
Programming (received off-air): KRRT (W) Kerrville-San Antonio; KENS-TV (C), KLRN (P), KMOL-TV (N), KSAT-TV (A) San Antonio.
Programming (via satellite): WGN-TV (W) Chicago; A & E; American Movie Classics; CNN; Country Music TV; Discovery Channel; ESPN; Fox Family Channel; Showtime; TBS Superstation; Turner Network TV; USA Network.
Fee: $28.00 monthly.
Equipment: Nexus headend; Magnavox amplifiers; Times Fiber cable; Oak set top converters; Nexus satellite receivers.
Miles of plant: 3.2 (coaxial). Homes passed: 116.
Manager: Paul Scott. Chief technician: Rob Spiller. Marketing director: Josh Thackery.
Ownership: Advanced Cable Technologies.

MEMPHIS—Classic Cable, Box 427, 118 S. 5th, Memphis, TX 79245. Phone: 806-259-2436. Fax: 806-259-3471. County: Hall. Also serves Hall County (portions). ICA: TX0302.
TV Market Ranking: Outside TV Markets. Franchise award date: N.A. Franchise expiration date: N.A. Began: July 1, 1958.
Channel capacity: 29 (not 2-way capable). Channels available but not in use: N.A.
Basic Service
Subscribers: 812; Commercial subscribers: 22.
Programming (received off-air): 2 FMs.
Programming (via microwave): KAMR-TV (N), KFDA-TV (C), KVII-TV (A) Amarillo; KETA (P) Oklahoma City.
Programming (via satellite): WGN-TV (W) Chicago; C-SPAN; Country Music TV; Discovery Channel; Disney Channel; ESPN; Fox Family Channel; Home Shopping Network; Lifetime; MTV; Nashville Network; Nickelodeon; TBS Superstation; The Inspirational Network; The Weather Channel; Turner Classic Movies; Turner Network TV; USA Network; Univision.
Fee: $20.00 installation; $28.25 monthly; $20.00 additional installation.
Pay Service 1
Pay Units: 45.
Programming (via satellite): Cinemax.
Fee: $20.00 installation; $11.65 monthly.
Pay Service 2
Pay Units: 71.
Programming (via satellite): HBO.
Fee: $11.65 monthly.
Local advertising: Yes.
Equipment: Scientific-Atlanta & DX Engineering headend; GTE Sylvania amplifiers; Anaconda cable; Oak set top converters; Scientific-Atlanta satellite antenna; Scientific-Atlanta satellite receivers.
Miles of plant: 23.0 (coaxial). Homes passed: 1,275.
District manager: Mark Hanlin. Chief technician: Rick Rattan.
City fee: 3% of gross.
Ownership: Classic Cable (MSO). Purchased from Cable One Inc., July 29, 1998.

MENARD—Classic Cable, Box 429, 605 N.W. 3rd St., Plainville, KS 67663-0429. Phones: 785-434-7620; 800-999-8876. Fax: 785-434-2614. County: Menard. ICA: TX0392.
TV Market Ranking: Outside TV Markets. Franchise award date: N.A. Franchise expiration date: N.A. Began: November 1, 1958.
Channel capacity: 41 (2-way capable). Channels available but not in use: N.A.
Basic Service
Subscribers: 540.
Programming (received off-air): KTXS-TV (A) Abilene-Sweetwater; KIDY (F), KLST (C) San Angelo; 5 FMs.
Programming (via microwave): KRBC-TV (N) Abilene-Sweetwater; KDTX-TV (T) Dallas-Fort Worth.
Programming (via satellite): WGN-TV (W) Chicago; KRMA-TV (P) Denver; A & E; Animal Planet; CNN; Country Music TV; Discovery Channel; Disney Channel; ESPN; Fox Family Channel; Fox News Channel; Fox Sports Net Southwest; Headline News; Learning Channel; Lifetime; Nashville Network; Nick at Nite's TV Land; Nickelodeon; QVC; TBS Superstation; Telemundo; The Weather Channel; Trinity Bcstg. Network; Turner Classic Movies; Turner Network TV; USA Network; Univision.
Current originations: Local news.
Fee: $35.00 installation; $28.95 monthly.
Pay Service 1
Pay Units: 46.
Programming (via satellite): HBO.
Fee: $10.95 monthly.
Pay Service 2
Pay Units: 71.
Programming (via satellite): Showtime.
Fee: $9.95 monthly.
Pay Service 3
Pay Units: 62.
Programming (via satellite): The Movie Channel.
Fee: $5.95 monthly.
Equipment: Hughes, Jerrold & Scientific-Atlanta headend; Vikoa amplifiers; Eagle traps; Andrew satellite antenna.
Miles of plant: 20.0 (coaxial). Homes passed: 844.
Manager: Bill Flowers. Chief technician: Walt VanLue. Marketing director: Jennifer Hauschild.
City fee: 2% of gross.
Ownership: Classic Cable (MSO).

MERIDIAN—Mission Cable, 920 Whitmore Dr., Rockwall, TX 75087. Phone: 800-783-5708. Fax: 214-722-6218. County: Bosque. ICA: TX0446.
TV Market Ranking: Outside TV Markets. Franchise award date: July 15, 1989. Franchise expiration date: N.A. Began: January 15, 1982.
Channel capacity: 35 (not 2-way capable). Channels available but not in use: N.A.
Basic Service
Subscribers: 284; Commercial subscribers: 59.
Programming (received off-air): KDFW (F), KERA-TV (P), KTVT (C), KXAS-TV (N), KXTX-TV (I), WFAA-TV (A) Dallas-Fort Worth; KCEN-TV (N), KWKT (F), KWTX-TV (C), KXXV (A) Waco-Temple.
Programming (via satellite): WGN-TV (W) Chicago; CNN; Country Music TV; Discovery Channel; ESPN; Fox Family Channel; Fox Sports Net Southwest; GalaVision; Nashville Network; TBS Superstation; Turner Network TV; USA Network.
Fee: $25.00 installation; $20.95 monthly; $10.00 additional installation.
Pay Service 1
Pay Units: 50.
Programming (via satellite): Cinemax.
Fee: $25.00 installation; $9.00 monthly.
Pay Service 2
Pay Units: 32.
Programming (via satellite): Disney Channel.
Fee: $25.00 installation; $9.00 monthly.
Pay Service 3
Pay Units: 52.
Programming (via satellite): HBO.
Fee: $25.00 installation; $9.00 monthly.
Local advertising: No.
Program Guide: TV Host.
Equipment: Scientific-Atlanta headend; Scientific-Atlanta amplifiers; Comm/Scope cable; Scientific-Atlanta set top converters; Pico traps; Scientific-Atlanta satellite antenna; Scientific-Atlanta satellite receivers.
Miles of plant: 11.0 (coaxial). Homes passed: 606.
Manager: Jim Stafford. Chief technician: Jacky Oliver. Marketing & program director: Bruce Berkinshaw.
City fee: 3% of basic & premium.
Ownership: Fanch Communications Inc. (MSO); Time Warner Cable (MSO). See Cable System Ownership.

MERKEL—Big Country Cablevision Inc., Box 549, 102 Oak St., Merkel, TX 79536. Phones: 915-928-4750; 800-588-4750. Fax: 915-928-3452. County: Taylor. ICA: TX0355.
TV Market Ranking: Below 100. Franchise award date: September 20, 1971. Franchise expiration date: N.A. Began: July 1, 1972.
Channel capacity: 21. Channels available but not in use: None.
Basic Service
Subscribers: 690.
Programming (received off-air): KRBC-TV (N), KTAB-TV (C), KTXS-TV (A) Abilene-Sweetwater; allband FM.
Programming (via satellite): WGN-TV (W) Chicago; A & E; CNN; Country Music TV; Discovery Channel; ESPN; Fox Family Channel; Lifetime; MTV; Nashville Network; Nickelodeon; TBS Superstation; The Weather Channel; Turner Network TV; USA Network; Univision.

Current originations: Automated time-weather.
Fee: $38.35 installation; $20.65 monthly.
Pay Service 1
Pay Units: N.A.
Programming (via satellite): Disney Channel; HBO; Showtime.
Fee: $10.00 installation.
Local advertising: No.
Equipment: Scientific-Atlanta headend; Jerrold amplifiers; Comm/Scope cable; Intercept traps; Microdyne satellite receivers.
Miles of plant: 18.0 (coaxial). Additional miles planned: 3.0 (coaxial). Homes passed: 1,040. Total homes in franchised area: 1,170.
Manager: Mark Reaves. Marketing director: J. Ketchum.
City fee: 2% of gross.
Ownership: Cable Management Assoc. (MSO).

MERTZON—Classic Cable, Box 429, 605 N.W. 3rd St., Plainville, KS 67663-0429. Phones: 785-434-7620; 800-999-8876. Fax: 785-434-2614. County: Irion. Also serves Sherwood. ICA: TX0810.
TV Market Ranking: Below 100. Franchise award date: N.A. Franchise expiration date: N.A. Began: June 1, 1981.
Channel capacity: 41 (2-way capable). Channels available but not in use: N.A.
Basic Service
Subscribers: 688.
Programming (received off-air): KTXS-TV (A) Abilene-Sweetwater; KACB-TV (N), KIDY (F), KLST (C) San Angelo.
Programming (via satellite): A & E; American Movie Classics; Animal Planet; CNN; Country Music TV; Discovery Channel; Disney Channel; E! Entertainment TV; ESPN; Fox Family Channel; Fox Sports Net Southwest; Headline News; Learning Channel; Lifetime; Nashville Network; Nick at Nite's TV Land; QVC; Sci-Fi Channel; TBS Superstation; The Weather Channel; Travel Channel; Turner Network TV; USA Network; Univision.
Current originations: Local news.
Fee: $35.00 installation; $27.95 monthly.
Pay Service 1
Pay Units: 67.
Programming (via satellite): HBO.
Fee: $9.95 monthly.
Pay Service 2
Pay Units: 31.
Programming (via satellite): Showtime.
Fee: $9.95 monthly.
Miles of plant: 20.0 (coaxial).
Manager: Bill Flowers. Chief technician: Ben Hernandez. Marketing director: Jennifer Hauschild.
Ownership: Classic Cable (MSO).

MESQUITE—TCI Cablevision of Dallas Inc., 1565 Chenault St., Dallas, TX 75228-5499. Phone: 214-328-5000. Fax: 214-320-7336. County: Dallas. ICA: TX0032.
TV Market Ranking: 12. Franchise award date: N.A. Franchise expiration date: N.A. Began: June 1, 1981.
Channel capacity: 92. Channels available but not in use: 13.
Basic Service
Subscribers: 15,324.
Programming (received off-air): KDAF (W), KDFI-TV (I), KDFW (F), KDTX-TV (T), KERA-TV (P), KFWD (O), KTVT (C), KTXA (U), KXAS-TV (N), KXTX-TV (I), WFAA-TV (A) Dallas-Fort Worth; KDTN (P) Denton; KUVN (S) Garland; KHSX-TV (H) Irving.
Programming (via satellite): WGN-TV (W) Chicago; A & E; BET; C-SPAN; C-SPAN 2; CNBC; CNN; Comedy Central; Country Music TV; Discovery Channel; EWTN; Electronic Program Guide; Fox Family Channel; GalaVision; Goodlife TV Network; Headline News; Home Shopping Network; Knowledge TV; Lifetime; MTV; Nashville Network; News Plus; Nickelodeon; Odyssey; QVC; TBS Superstation; The Box; The Weather Channel; VH1.
Current originations: Automated time-weather; public access; educational access; government access; religious access; leased access; local news.
Fee: $60.00 installation; $19.05 monthly; $1.90 converter.
Expanded Basic Service
Subscribers: 13,583.
Programming (via satellite): American Movie Classics; ESPN; Fox Sports Net Southwest; Turner Network TV; USA Network.
Fee: $3.70 monthly.
Pay Service 1
Pay Units: 1,510.
Programming (via satellite): Cinemax.
Fee: $11.12 monthly.
Pay Service 2
Pay Units: 1,463.
Programming (via satellite): Disney Channel.
Fee: N.A.
Pay Service 3
Pay Units: 5,619.
Programming (via satellite): The New Encore.
Fee: N.A.
Pay Service 4
Pay Units: 4,578.
Programming (via satellite): HBO.
Fee: $11.12 monthly.
Pay Service 5
Pay Units: 765.
Programming (via satellite): The Movie Channel.
Fee: $11.12 monthly.
Pay Service 6
Pay Units: 2,040.
Programming (via satellite): Showtime.
Fee: $11.12 monthly.
Pay Service 7
Pay Units: N.A.
Programming (via satellite): DMX.
Fee: N.A.
Miles of plant: 374.0 (coaxial). Homes passed: 34,372. Total homes in franchised area: 38,191.
Manager: Clem Madox.
Ownership: AT&T Broadband & Internet Services (MSO). Purchased from Tele-Communications Inc., March 9, 1999.

MEXIA—Northland Cable TV, 515 W. Tyler, Mexia, TX 76667. Phone: 254-562-2872. Fax: 254-562-6454. County: Limestone. Also serves Forest Glade, Groesbeck, Lake Mexia, Point Enterprise, Shiloh, Tehuacana. ICA: TX0166.
TV Market Ranking: Below 100 (Groesbeck); Outside TV Markets (Forest Glade, Lake Mexia, Point Enterprise, Shiloh, Tehuacana). Franchise award date: April 15, 1965. Franchise expiration date: December 14, 2008. Began: December 7, 1966.
Channel capacity: 52 (2-way capable; operating 2-way). Channels available but not in use: 2.
Basic Service
Subscribers: 4,123.
Programming (received off-air): KDAF (W), KDFI-TV (I), KDFW (F), KERA-TV (P), KTVT (C), KXAS-TV (N), KXTX-TV (I), WFAA-TV (A) Dallas-Fort Worth; KAKW (U,W) Killeen; KCEN-TV (N), KWKT (F), KWTX-TV (C), KXXV (A) Waco-Temple; allband FM.
Programming (via satellite): A & E; American Movie Classics; BET; CNBC; CNN; Cartoon Network; Country Music TV; Discovery Channel; ESPN; ESPN 2; FX; fXM: Movies from Fox; Fox Family Channel; Fox News Channel; Fox Sports Net Southwest; Headline News; History Channel; Home & Garden Television; Home Shopping Network; Learning Channel; Lifetime; Nashville Network; Nickelodeon; QVC; Sci-Fi Channel; TBS Superstation; TV Guide Channel; The Weather Channel; Travel Channel; Trinity Bcstg. Network; Turner Classic Movies; Turner Network TV; USA Network; Univision; VH1.
Current originations: Automated time-weather; local news.
Fee: $50.00 installation; $25.25 monthly; $30.00 additional installation.
Pay Service 1
Pay Units: 177.
Programming (via satellite): Starz!; The New Encore.
Fee: $35.00 installation; $10.00 monthly.
Pay Service 2
Pay Units: 280.
Programming (via satellite): Showtime.
Fee: $35.00 installation; $10.00 monthly.
Pay Service 3
Pay Units: 543.
Programming (via satellite): HBO.
Fee: $35.00 installation; $10.50 monthly.
Pay Service 4
Pay Units: 180.
Programming (via satellite): The Movie Channel.
Fee: $35.00 installation; $10.00 monthly.
Local advertising: Yes. Available in character-generated & taped programming. Rates: $8.32/Minute; $4.16/30 Seconds. Local sales manager: Cathey Lane.
Program Guide: Premium Channels.
Equipment: Scientific-Atlanta, Harris & Standard Communications headend; Scientific-Atlanta amplifiers; Times Fiber cable; SpectraView character generator; Scientific-Atlanta set top converters; Eagle & Pico traps; Scientific-Atlanta satellite antenna; Scientific-Atlanta satellite receivers.
Miles of plant: 115.0 (coaxial); 19.0 (fiber optic). Homes passed: 6,800. Total homes in franchised area: 6,800.
Manager: Jimmie Cullins.
City fee: 3% of gross.
Ownership: Northland Communications Corp. (MSO).

MIAMI—High Plains Cablevision, Box 618, Lockney, TX 79241. Phone: 800-749-0184. County: Roberts. ICA: TX0459.
TV Market Ranking: Outside TV Markets. Franchise award date: N.A. Franchise expiration date: N.A. Began: February 1, 1982.
Channel capacity: 12. Channels available but not in use: N.A.
Basic Service
Subscribers: 225.
Programming (received off-air): KAMR-TV (N), KFDA-TV (C), KVII-TV (A) Amarillo; KWET (P) Cheyenne.
Programming (via satellite): WGN-TV (W) Chicago; C-SPAN; TBS Superstation.
Current originations: Automated time-weather.
Fee: $35.00 installation; $9.00 monthly.
Pay Service 1
Pay Units: N.A.
Programming (via satellite): The Movie Channel.
Fee: $11.00 monthly.
Miles of plant: 6.8 (coaxial). Homes passed: 590.
Manager: Roger Campbell.
City fee: 3% of gross.
Ownership: Multichannel TV Inc.

MIDLAND—Cox Cable, 2530 S. Midkiff, Midland, TX 79701. Phones: 915-694-7721; 915-694-6481. Fax: 915-694-3267. County: Midland. Also serves Midland County (portions). ICA: TX0024.
TV Market Ranking: Below 100. Franchise award date: N.A. Franchise expiration date: N.A. Began: October 19, 1968.
Channel capacity: 54. Channels available but not in use: 5.
Basic Service
Subscribers: 30,376.
Programming (received off-air): KMID (A), KMLM (I), KOCV-TV (P), KOSA-TV (C), KPEJ (F), KWES-TV (N) Odessa-Midland; 9 FMs.
Programming (via microwave): KDFW (F), KERA-TV (P), KTVT (C), KXTX-TV (I), WFAA-TV (A) Dallas-Fort Worth.
Programming (via satellite): WGN-TV (W) Chicago; C-SPAN; C-SPAN 2; CNBC; EWTN; Fox Family Channel; Home Shopping Network; QVC; TBS Superstation; The Weather Channel; Trinity Bcstg. Network; Univision.
Current originations: Automated time-weather.
Fee: $28.62 installation; $11.04 monthly.
Expanded Basic Service
Subscribers: 28,857.
Programming (via satellite): A & E; BET; Bravo; CNN; Comedy Central; Country Music TV; ESPN; Fox Sports Net Southwest; Headline News; Lifetime; MTV; Nickelodeon; TV Guide Channel; USA Network; Univision; VH1.
Fee: $15.00 installation; $9.82 monthly.
Pay Service 1
Pay Units: 16,872.
Programming (via satellite): Cinemax; Disney Channel; HBO; Showtime; The Movie Channel.
Fee: $15.00 installation; $7.95 monthly (Disney), $8.95 monthly (Cinemax), $9.95 monthly (Showtime), $10.95 monthly (TMC), $11.95 monthly (HBO).
Pay-Per-View
Addressable homes: 13,000.
Hot Choice; Viewer's Choice.
Local advertising: Yes. Regional interconnect: Cabletime.
Program Guide: The Cable Guide.
Equipment: Scientific-Atlanta headend; Theta-Com amplifiers; Plastoid cable; Andrew & Scientific-Atlanta satellite antenna; Scientific-Atlanta satellite receivers.
Miles of plant: 515.0 (coaxial); 18.0 (fiber optic). Additional miles planned: 294.0 (fiber optic). Homes passed: 44,467.
Manager: Randy Wink. Chief technician: Mike Simons. Marketing director: Glenn Green.
City fee: 5% of gross.
Ownership: Cox Communications Inc. (MSO).

MIDWAY—Mission Cable, 920 Whitmore Dr., Rockwall, TX 75087. Phone: 800-783-5708. Fax: 214-722-6218. County: Madison. ICA: TX0675.
TV Market Ranking: Outside TV Markets. Franchise award date: N.A. Franchise expiration date: N.A. Began: N.A.
Channel capacity: 21. Channels available but not in use: 10.
Basic Service
Subscribers: 87.
Programming (received off-air): KBTX-TV (C) Bryan; KTXH (U) Houston; KETK-TV (N) Jacksonville; KTRE (A) Lufkin.

Programming (via satellite): WGN-TV (W) Chicago; CNN; Discovery Channel; ESPN; Nashville Network; TBS Superstation; Turner Network TV.

Fee: $25.00 installation; $20.95 monthly.

Pay Service 1

Pay Units: 12.

Programming (via satellite): Disney Channel.

Fee: $9.00 monthly.

Pay Service 2

Pay Units: 26.

Programming (via satellite): Showtime.

Fee: $9.00 monthly.

Equipment: Blonder-Tongue headend; Magnavox amplifiers; Comm/Scope cable; Northeast Filter traps; Weatherscan satellite antenna; Automation Techniques satellite receivers.

Miles of plant: 4.0 (coaxial). Homes passed: 133. Total homes in franchised area: 171.

Chief technician: Barry Greer. Marketing & program director: Bruce Berkinshaw.

City fee: 3% of gross.

Ownership: Fanch Communications Inc. (MSO); Time Warner Cable (MSO). See Cable System Ownership.

MILES—TCA Cable TV, 28 W. Concho Ave., San Angelo, TX 76903. Phone: 915-655-8911. Fax: 915-658-6876.

Web site: http://www.tca-cable.com.

County: Runnels. ICA: TX0963.

TV Market Ranking: 7,30. Franchise award date: N.A. Franchise expiration date: April 1, 2007. Began: N.A.

Channel capacity: 36 (not 2-way capable). Channels available but not in use: 5.

Basic Service

Subscribers: 163.

Programming (received off-air): KTXS-TV (A) Abilene-Sweetwater; KERA-TV (P), WFAA-TV (A) Dallas-Fort Worth; KACB-TV (N), KIDY (F), KLST (C) San Angelo.

Programming (via satellite): TBS Superstation.

Fee: $38.00 installation; $13.50 monthly; $0.25 converter.

Expanded Basic Service

Subscribers: 157.

Programming (via satellite): American Movie Classics; C-SPAN; CNN; Comedy Central; Discovery Channel; ESPN; Fox Family Channel; Fox Sports Net Southwest; Headline News; Learning Channel; Lifetime; MTV; Nashville Network; Nickelodeon; Odyssey; QVC; Sci-Fi Channel; The Weather Channel; Turner Network TV; USA Network; Univision.

Fee: $38.00 installation; $24.50 monthly.

Pay Service 1

Pay Units: 27.

Programming (via satellite): HBO.

Fee: $13.00 monthly.

Equipment: Scientific-Atlanta headend; Jerrold amplifiers; Times Fiber cable; Texscan character generator; Scientific-Atlanta set top converters; Eagle traps; Scientific-Atlanta satellite antenna; Scientific-Atlanta satellite receivers.

Miles of plant: 9.3 (coaxial). Homes passed: 277.

Manager: Archie Kountz. Chief technician: Robert Hurd. Customer service manager: Naomi Gonzales. Marketing director: Mike Johnson.

Ownership: TCA Cable TV Inc. (MSO); AT&T Broadband & Internet Services (MSO). See Cable System Ownership.

MILLSAP—Mallard Cablevision, 100-D El Chico Trail, Willow Park, TX 76087. Phones: 817-441-8073; 800-669-2288. Fax: 817-441-6464. County: Parker. ICA: TX0523.

TV Market Ranking: Outside TV Markets. Franchise award date: N.A. Franchise expiration date: N.A. Began: December 1, 1981.

Channel capacity: 27. Channels available but not in use: 12.

Basic Service

Subscribers: 228.

Programming (received off-air): KDFW (F), KERA-TV (P), KTVT (C), KTXA (U), KXAS-TV (N), KXTX-TV (I), WFAA-TV (A) Dallas-Fort Worth.

Programming (via satellite): WGN-TV (W) Chicago; A & E; Fox Family Channel; FoxNet; Nashville Network; Sci-Fi Channel; TBS Superstation.

Fee: $30.00 installation; $16.80 monthly.

Pay Service 1

Pay Units: 60.

Programming (via satellite): Cinemax.

Fee: $10.00 monthly.

Pay Service 2

Pay Units: 76.

Programming (via satellite): HBO.

Fee: $11.00 monthly.

Miles of plant: 14.0 (coaxial). Homes passed: 395.

Manager: Doug Grassmann. V.P., operations: Steve Sizemore.

Ownership: Mallard Cablevision (MSO). Purchased from Cambridge Communications, May 1, 1999.

MINEOLA—TCA Cable TV, 403 W. Broad, Mineola, TX 75773. Phone: 903-569-2651. Fax: 903-569-2662.

Web site: http://www.tca-cable.com.

Counties: Franklin, Smith, Van Zandt & Wood. Also serves Franklin County, Grand Saline, Lindale, Quitman, Smith County, Van Zandt County, Winnsboro, Wood County. ICA: TX0812.

TV Market Ranking: Below 100 (Grand Saline, Lindale, Mineola, Quitman, portions of Smith County, portions of Van Zandt County, portions of Wood County); Outside TV Markets (Franklin County, portions of Smith County, portions of Van Zandt County, Winnsboro, portions of Wood County). Franchise award date: N.A. Franchise expiration date: N.A. Began: January 1, 1963.

Channel capacity: 31. Channels available but not in use: N.A.

Basic Service

Subscribers: N.A.

Programming (received off-air): KDFW (F), KERA-TV (P), KTVT (C), KXAS-TV (N), KXTX-TV (I), WFAA-TV (A) Dallas-Fort Worth; KETK-TV (N) Jacksonville; KFXK (F) Longview; KSLA-TV (C), KTAL-TV (N) Shreveport-Texarkana; KLTV (A) Tyler-Longview; allband FM.

Programming (via satellite): WGN-TV (W) Chicago; CNN; ESPN; Headline News; QVC; TBS Superstation; The Weather Channel.

Current originations: Automated time-weather.

Fee: $35.00 installation; $14.95 monthly.

Expanded Basic Service

Subscribers: N.A.

Programming (via satellite): Country Music TV; Discovery Channel; Fox Family Channel; Lifetime; Nashville Network; Nickelodeon; The Inspirational Network; The New Encore; Turner Network TV; USA Network.

Fee: $10.00 installation; $15.95 monthly.

Pay Service 1

Pay Units: N.A.

Programming (via satellite): Disney Channel; Fox Sports Net Southwest; HBO; The Movie Channel.

Fee: $35.00 installation; $9.00 monthly (each).

Equipment: Entron headend; Entron amplifiers; Scientific-Atlanta satellite antenna.

Miles of plant: 195.9 (coaxial).

Manager: Clyde Bowling. Chief technician: Glen Lovette.

Ownership: TCA Cable TV Inc. (MSO); AT&T Broadband & Internet Services (MSO). See Cable System Ownership.

MINERAL WELLS—TCA Cable TV, Box 577, Mineral Wells, TX 76067-0609. Phone: 940-328-1281. Web site: http://www.tca-cable.com. County: Palo Pinto. Also serves Palo Pinto County. ICA: TX0106.

TV Market Ranking: Below 100 (Palo Pinto County); Outside TV Markets (Mineral Wells). Franchise award date: N.A. Franchise expiration date: N.A. Began: June 1, 1951.

Channel capacity: 42 (not 2-way capable). Channels available but not in use: N.A.

Basic Service

Subscribers: 5,209.

Programming (received off-air): KDFW (F), KERA-TV (P), KTVT (C), KTXA (U), KXAS-TV (N), KXTX-TV (I), WFAA-TV (A) Dallas-Fort Worth; 13 FMs.

Programming (via satellite): C-SPAN; CNBC; CNN; Discovery Channel; Fox Family Channel; FoxNet; Headline News; Knowledge TV; Lifetime; MTV; Nashville Network; Nickelodeon; Odyssey; QVC; TBS Superstation; The Weather Channel; Univision.

Current originations: Automated time-weather; public access; automated emergency alert.

Fee: $38.24 installation; $9.85 monthly; $2.00 converter.

Expanded Basic Service

Subscribers: 4,849.

Programming (via satellite): American Movie Classics; ESPN; Fox Sports Net Southwest; Turner Network TV; USA Network.

Fee: $13.28 monthly.

Pay Service 1

Pay Units: 421.

Programming (via satellite): Cinemax.

Fee: $10.00 installation; $12.65 monthly.

Pay Service 2

Pay Units: 243.

Programming (via satellite): Disney Channel.

Fee: $10.95 monthly.

Pay Service 3

Pay Units: 2,323.

Programming (via satellite): The New Encore.

Fee: N.A.

Pay Service 4

Pay Units: 991.

Programming (via satellite): HBO.

Fee: $10.00 installation; $12.65 monthly.

Pay Service 5

Pay Units: 311.

Programming (via satellite): Showtime.

Fee: $10.00 installation; $12.65 monthly.

Pay-Per-View

Addressable homes: 400.

Local advertising: Yes (locally produced). Available in character-generated programming. Rates: $2.00/Day.

Program Guide: The Cable Guide.

Equipment: Jerrold & Scientific-Atlanta headend; GTE Sylvania & Scientific-Atlanta amplifiers; Times Fiber cable; Texscan/MSI character generator; Jerrold & Scientific-Atlanta set top converters; Jerrold addressable set top converters; Pico & Arcom traps; Scientific-Atlanta & Anixter satellite antenna; Scientific-Atlanta satellite receivers.

Miles of plant: 119.8 (coaxial). Homes passed: 6,270. Total homes in franchised area: 6,498.

Manager: Raymond Greenwood. Chief technician: Scott Wilber.

City fee: 2% of basic gross.

Ownership: TCA Cable TV Inc. (MSO); AT&T Broadband & Internet Services (MSO). See Cable System Ownership.

MONAHANS—Classic Cable, Box 429, 605 N. W. 3rd St., Plainville, KS 67633-0429. Phones: 785-434-7620; 800-999-8876. Fax: 785-434-2614. County: Ward. Also serves Thorntonville, Ward County. ICA: TX0134.

TV Market Ranking: Below 100 (Monahans, Thorntonville, portions of Ward County); Outside TV Markets (portions of Ward County). Franchise award date: July 24, 1990. Franchise expiration date: July 23, 2000. Began: December 1, 1972.

Channel capacity: 52 (2-way capable). Channels available but not in use: N.A.

Basic Service

Subscribers: 2,524.

Programming (received off-air): KMID (A), KMLM (I), KOCV-TV (P), KOSA-TV (C), KPEJ (F), KWES-TV (N) Odessa-Midland; 6 FMs.

Programming (via satellite): WGN-TV (W) Chicago; A & E; American Movie Classics; Animal Planet; BET; C-SPAN; CNBC; CNN; Comedy Central; Country Music TV; Discovery Channel; Disney Channel; ESPN; Fox Family Channel; Fox News Channel; Fox Sports Net Southwest; GalaVision; Goodlife TV Network; Headline News; History Channel; Home & Garden Television; Learning Channel; Lifetime; Nashville Network; Nick at Nite's TV Land; Nickelodeon; QVC; Sci-Fi Channel; TBS Superstation; TV Guide Channel; Telemundo; The Health Network; The Weather Channel; Turner Network TV; USA Network; Univision.

Current originations: Automated time-weather; educational access.

Fee: $35.00 installation; $27.95 monthly.

Pay Service 1

Pay Units: 179.

Programming (via satellite): Cinemax.

Fee: $15.00 installation; $9.95 monthly.

Pay Service 2

Pay Units: 211.

Programming (via satellite): The Movie Channel.

Fee: $5.95 monthly.

Pay Service 3

Pay Units: 526.

Programming (via satellite): HBO.

Fee: $10.95 monthly.

Pay Service 4

Pay Units: 160.

Programming (via satellite): Showtime.

Fee: $9.95 monthly.

Local advertising: Yes. Available in character-generated programming. Regional interconnect: Cabletime.

Equipment: Scientific-Atlanta headend; Texscan amplifiers; Comm/Scope & Belden cable; Eagle traps; Scientific-Atlanta satellite antenna; Scientific-Atlanta satellite receivers.

Miles of plant: 68.0 (coaxial). Homes passed: 4,682. Total homes in franchised area: 4,770.

Manager: Bill Flowers. Chief technician: Ben Hernandez. Marketing director: Jennifer Hauschild.

City fee: 2% of gross ($1,000 minimum).

Ownership: Classic Cable (MSO).

MONT BELVIEU—Star Cable, Drawer 1570, Brazoria, TX 77422. Phones: 409-798-9121; 800-395-2775. Fax: 409-798-4409. Counties: Chambers, Harris & Liberty. Also serves Baytown, Chambers County (western portion), Harris County (southeastern portion), Liberty

County (southeastern portion), Old River-Winfree. ICA: TX0156.
TV Market Ranking: 15 (Baytown, portions of Chambers County, Harris County, Liberty County, Mont Belvieu, Old River-Winfree); 88 (portions of Chambers County). Franchise award date: N.A. Franchise expiration date: N.A. Began: N.A.
Channel capacity: 62 (not 2-way capable). Channels available but not in use: 10.
Basic Service
Subscribers: 3,223; Commercial subscribers: 12.
Programming (received off-air): KHSH-TV (H) Alvin; KVVV (I) Baytown; KPXB (X) Conroe; KLTJ (E), KTMD (O) Galveston; KETH (E), KHOU-TV (C), KHTV (W), KPRC-TV (N), KRIV (F), KTRK-TV (A), KTXH (U), KUHT (P) Houston; KNWS-TV (I) Katy; KXLN-TV (S) Rosenberg.
Programming (via satellite): WGN-TV (W) Chicago; TBS Superstation.
Fee: $13.90 monthly; $2.15 converter.
Expanded Basic Service
Subscribers: 3,141.
Programming (via satellite): A & E; BET; C-SPAN; CNBC; CNN; Cartoon Network; Country Music TV; Discovery Channel; ESPN; ESPN 2; FX; Fox Family Channel; Fox News Channel; Fox Sports Net Southwest; Headline News; Learning Channel; Lifetime; MTV; Nashville Network; Nick at Nite's TV Land; Nickelodeon; QVC; Sci-Fi Channel; The Weather Channel; Turner Classic Movies; Turner Network TV; USA Network; VH1.
Fee: $17.74 monthly.
Pay Service 1
Pay Units: 340.
Programming (via satellite): Cinemax.
Fee: $12.00 monthly.
Pay Service 2
Pay Units: 381.
Programming (via satellite): Disney Channel.
Fee: $7.95 monthly.
Pay Service 3
Pay Units: 788.
Programming (via satellite): HBO.
Fee: $12.00 monthly.
Pay Service 4
Pay Units: 814.
Programming (via satellite): Showtime; The Movie Channel.
Fee: $12.95 monthly.
Miles of plant: 138.9 (coaxial); None (fiber optic). Homes passed: 3,932. Total homes in franchised area: 3,932.
Manager: Mike Burns. Chief technician: Mayla Zubeck.
Ownership: Star Cable Associates (MSO).

MONTAGUE—Classic Cable, Box 429, 605 N.W. 3rd St., Plainville, KS 67663-0429. Phones: 785-434-7620; 800-999-8876. Fax: 785-434-2614. County: Montague. ICA: TX0700.
TV Market Ranking: Outside TV Markets. Franchise award date: N.A. Franchise expiration date: N.A. Began: October 1, 1988.
Channel capacity: 31 (2-way capable). Channels available but not in use: N.A.
Basic Service
Subscribers: 34.
Programming (received off-air): KDFI-TV (I), KDFW (F), KERA-TV (P), KTVT (C), KTXA (U), KXAS-TV (N), KXTX-TV (I), WFAA-TV (A) Dallas-Fort Worth; KXII (C) Sherman; KAUZ-TV (C), KFDX-TV (N), KJTL (F,U), KSWO-TV (A) Wichita Falls-Lawton.
Programming (via satellite): WGN-TV (W) Chicago; CNN; Discovery Channel; Disney Channel; ESPN; Nashville Network; TBS Superstation; Turner Network TV.
Fee: $35.00 installation; $26.95 monthly.
Pay Service 1
Pay Units: 5.
Programming (via satellite): Cinemax.
Fee: $9.95 monthly.
Pay Service 2
Pay Units: 7.
Programming (via satellite): HBO.
Fee: $9.95 monthly.
Local advertising: Yes. Available in character-generated programming. Rates: $5.00/Day.
Equipment: Nexus headend; Scientific-Atlanta amplifiers; Comm/Scope cable; Pico traps; Drake satellite receivers.
Miles of plant: 4.0 (coaxial). Homes passed: 119.
Manager: Dave Walker. Chief technician: Roger Campbell. Marketing director: Jennifer Hauschild.
Ownership: Classic Cable (MSO).

MONTE ALTO—Torrence Cablevision, Box 1167, Ridgeland, MS 39158. Phones: 601-981-6900; 800-977-8849. County: Hidalgo. Also serves Edcouch (unincorporated areas). ICA: TX0813.
TV Market Ranking: Below 100. Franchise award date: N.A. Franchise expiration date: N.A. Began: N.A.
Channel capacity: 36. Channels available but not in use: 18.
Basic Service
Subscribers: 14.
Programming (received off-air): KVEO (N) Brownsville; KORO (S) Corpus Christi; KGBT-TV (C), KMBH (P) Harlingen; KRGV-TV (A) Weslaco.
Programming (via satellite): WGN-TV (W) Chicago; A & E; American Movie Classics; CNN; Country Music TV; Discovery Channel; ESPN; Fox Family Channel; Showtime; TBS Superstation; Turner Network TV; USA Network.
Fee: $28.00 monthly.
Miles of plant: 7.4 (coaxial). Homes passed: 364.
Ownership: Torrence Cable Inc. (MSO).

MONTGOMERY—Intermedia Cable, 660 Mainstream Drive, Nashville, TN 37208. Phone: 615-244-5990. County: Montgomery. ICA: TX0916.
TV Market Ranking: Below 100. Franchise award date: N.A. Franchise expiration date: N.A. Began: N.A.
Channel capacity: N.A. Channels available but not in use: N.A.
Basic Service
Subscribers: N.A.
Programming (received off-air): KHSH-TV (H) Alvin; KETH (E), KHOU-TV (C), KHTV (W), KPRC-TV (N), KRIV (F), KTRK-TV (A), KTXH (U), KUHT (P) Houston.
Programming (via satellite): C-SPAN; CNBC; CNN; Country Music TV; Discovery Channel; Fox Family Channel; Headline News; Lifetime; MTV; Nashville Network; Nickelodeon; The Weather Channel; VH1.
Fee: N.A.
Expanded Basic Service
Subscribers: N.A.
Programming (via satellite): WGN-TV (W) Chicago; A & E; E! Entertainment TV; ESPN; Fox Sports Net Southwest; TBS Superstation; Turner Network TV; USA Network.
Fee: N.A.
Pay Service 1
Pay Units: N.A.
Programming (via satellite): Disney Channel; HBO; Showtime.
Fee: N.A.
Manager: Meade Collard. Chief technician: Paul Neagle.
Ownership: Northland Communications Corp. (MSO).

MOODY—Centrovision Inc., Box 3157, Temple, TX 76501. Phone: 817-773-1163. County: McLennan. ICA: TX0501.
TV Market Ranking: Below 100. Franchise award date: N.A. Franchise expiration date: N.A. Began: April 1, 1981.
Channel capacity: N.A. Channels available but not in use: N.A.
Basic Service
Subscribers: N.A.
Programming (received off-air): KTBC (F), KVUE-TV (A) Austin; KNCT (P) Belton; KERA-TV (P), KTVT (C), KXTX-TV (I), WFAA-TV (A) Dallas-Fort Worth; KCEN-TV (N), KWTX-TV (C) Waco-Temple.
Programming (via satellite): WGN-TV (W) Chicago; TBS Superstation.
Fee: N.A.
Miles of plant: 10.0 (coaxial). Homes passed: 450.
Manager: Alton Shepard.
Ownership: Centrovision Inc. (MSO).

MORAN—Double D Cable, Box 6845, Abilene, TX 79608. Phone: 915-691-5787. Fax: 915-676-2882. County: Shackelford. ICA: TX0975.
TV Market Ranking: Below 100. Franchise award date: N.A. Franchise expiration date: N.A. Began: N.A.
Channel capacity: N.A. Channels available but not in use: N.A.
Basic Service
Subscribers: N.A.
Programming (received off-air): KRBC-TV (N), KTAB-TV (C), KTXS-TV (A) Abilene-Sweetwater.
Programming (via satellite): WGN-TV (W) Chicago; American Movie Classics; Animal Planet; CNN; Country Music TV; Discovery Channel; ESPN; Fox Family Channel; Fox Sports Net Southwest; Goodlife TV Network; Nashville Network; Nick at Nite's TV Land; QVC; TBS Superstation; Turner Classic Movies; Turner Network TV; USA Network.
Fee: N.A.
Pay Service 1
Pay Units: N.A.
Programming (via satellite): Cinemax; HBO.
Fee: N.A.
Manager: Dorton Canon.
Ownership: Jayroc Inc. (MSO).

MORGAN'S POINT RESORT—Centrovision Inc., Box 3157, Temple, TX 76501. Phone: 817-773-1163. County: Bell. ICA: TX0814.
TV Market Ranking: Below 100. Franchise award date: N.A. Franchise expiration date: N.A. Began: N.A.
Channel capacity: N.A. Channels available but not in use: N.A.
Basic Service
Subscribers: N.A.
Programming (received off-air): KLRU (P), KTBC (F), KVUE-TV (A), KXAN-TV (N) Austin; KNCT (P) Belton; KCEN-TV (N), KWTX-TV (C) Waco-Temple.
Programming (via satellite): WGN-TV (W) Chicago; TBS Superstation.
Fee: N.A.
Manager: Alton Shepard.
Ownership: Centrovision Inc. (MSO).

MORTON—Cablecomm, 711 Ave. G, Levelland, TX 79336. Phones: 806-894-4996; 800-248-1024. County: Cochran. ICA: TX0364.
TV Market Ranking: Outside TV Markets. Franchise award date: N.A. Franchise expiration date: N.A. Began: May 1, 1974.
Channel capacity: 35. Channels available but not in use: 11.
Basic Service
Subscribers: 595; Commercial subscribers: 2.
Programming (received off-air): KAMC (A), KCBD-TV (N), KJTV (F), KLBK-TV (C), KTXT-TV (P) Lubbock.
Programming (via satellite): WGN-TV (W) Chicago; C-SPAN; Home Shopping Network; TBS Superstation.
Current originations: Automated time-weather.
Fee: $37.40 installation; $11.57 monthly; $1.75 converter.
Expanded Basic Service
Subscribers: 585.
Programming (via satellite): CNN; Discovery Channel; Disney Channel; ESPN; Fox Family Channel; Fox Sports Net Southwest; Nashville Network; Trinity Bcstg. Network; Turner Network TV; USA Network; Univision.
Fee: $20.00 installation; $11.57 monthly.
Pay Service 1
Pay Units: N.A.
Programming (via satellite): Disney Channel; HBO.
Fee: $15.00 installation; $8.50 monthly (each).
Local advertising: No.
Equipment: Scientific-Atlanta headend; Vikoa amplifiers; Vitek cable; BEI character generator; Scientific-Atlanta satellite antenna; M/A-Com & Scientific-Atlanta satellite receivers.
Miles of plant: 14.0 (coaxial). Homes passed: 1,053.
Manager: Rex Thackerson. Chief technician: Monty Hodge. Marketing director: Bill Forgey.
City fee: 2% of gross.
Ownership: Fanch Communications Inc. (MSO); Time Warner Cable (MSO). See Cable System Ownership.

MOSS BLUFF—Friendship Cable of Texas Inc., Box 9090, Tyler, TX 75711-9090. Phone: 903-581-2121. Fax: 903-581-2185. County: Liberty. Also serves Liberty County (portions). ICA: TX0474.
TV Market Ranking: Below 100. Franchise award date: N.A. Franchise expiration date: N.A. Began: N.A.
Channel capacity: 36 (not 2-way capable). Channels available but not in use: 4.
Basic Service
Subscribers: 224.
Programming (received off-air): KHOU-TV (C), KHTV (W), KPRC-TV (N), KRIV (F), KTRK-TV (A), KTXH (U), KUHT (P) Houston.
Programming (via satellite): WGN-TV (W) Chicago; A & E; C-SPAN; CNN; Country Music TV; Discovery Channel; ESPN; Fox Family Channel; Fox Sports Net Southwest; Headline News; Lifetime; Nashville Network; Nickelodeon; QVC; TBS Superstation; The Inspirational Network; The Weather Channel; Turner Network TV; USA Network.
Fee: $34.95 monthly.
Pay Service 1
Pay Units: 32.
Programming (via satellite): Showtime.
Fee: $5.95 monthly.
Pay Service 2
Pay Units: 21.
Programming (via satellite): HBO.
Fee: $10.95 monthly.

Pay Service 3
Pay Units: 4.
Programming (via satellite): Cinemax.
Fee: $10.95 monthly.
Local advertising: Yes.
Miles of plant: 25.1 (coaxial). Homes passed: 592.
Manager: Wanda Pyburn. Chief technician: Mike Deal.
Ownership: Buford Television Inc. (MSO). See Cable System Ownership.

MOULTON—National Cable, Suite 106-A, 5151 Reed Rd., Columbus, OH 43220. Phones: 614-442-5890; 800-582-0504. Fax: 614-457-2567. County: Lavaca. ICA: TX0497.
TV Market Ranking: Outside TV Markets. Franchise award date: N.A. Franchise expiration date: July 1, 1997. Began: July 1, 1983.
Channel capacity: 52. Channels available but not in use: N.A.
Basic Service
Subscribers: 143.
Programming (received off-air): KEYE-TV (C), KTBC (F), KVUE-TV (A), KXAN-TV (N) Austin; KABB (F), KENS-TV (C), KLRN (P), KMOL-TV (N), KSAT-TV (A) San Antonio.
Programming (via satellite): WGN-TV (W) Chicago; CNN; Country Music TV; Discovery Channel; ESPN; Fox Family Channel; MTV; Nashville Network; Nickelodeon; TBS Superstation; Turner Network TV; USA Network.
Fee: $25.00 installation; $24.00 monthly.
Pay Service 1
Pay Units: N.A.
Programming (via satellite): HBO; Showtime.
Fee: N.A.
Miles of plant: 13.0 (coaxial).
Manager: Roy E. Hayes. System/operations manager: Steve Miller.
City fee: 3% of gross.
Ownership: National Cable (MSO). Purchased from Bay Cable Inc., May 31, 1999.

MOUND—National Cable Inc., Suite 106-A, 5151 Reed Rd., Columbus, OH 43220. Phones: 614-442-5890; 800-582-0504. Fax: 614-457-2567. County: Coryell. ICA: TX0701.
TV Market Ranking: Below 100. Franchise award date: N.A. Franchise expiration date: N.A. Began: N.A.
Channel capacity: 36. Channels available but not in use: 21.
Basic Service
Subscribers: 27.
Programming (received off-air): KNCT (P) Belton; KCEN-TV (N), KWKT (F), KWTX-TV (C), KXXV (A) Waco-Temple.
Programming (via satellite): WGN-TV (W) Chicago; A & E; American Movie Classics; CNN; Country Music TV; Discovery Channel; ESPN; Fox Family Channel; Showtime; TBS Superstation; Turner Network TV; USA Network.
Fee: $28.00 monthly.
Miles of plant: 2.6 (coaxial). Homes passed: 70.
Manager: Paul Scott. Chief technician: Rob Spiller. Marketing director: Josh Thackery.
Ownership: National Cable (MSO).

MOUNT ENTERPRISE—Friendship Cable of Texas Inc., Box 9090, Tyler, TX 75711. Phone: 903-581-2121. Fax: 903-581-2185. County: Rusk. ICA: TX0973.
TV Market Ranking: Below 100. Franchise award date: N.A. Franchise expiration date: N.A. Began: N.A.
Channel capacity: N.A. Channels available but not in use: N.A.
Basic Service
Subscribers: 84.
Programming (received off-air): KTRE (A) Lufkin; KLTS-TV (P), KMSS-TV (F), KSLA-TV (C), KTAL-TV (N) Shreveport-Texarkana.
Programming (via satellite): WGN-TV (W) Chicago; A & E; CNN; Country Music TV; Discovery Channel; Disney Channel; ESPN; Fox Family Channel; Headline News; Learning Channel; Lifetime; Nashville Network; Nickelodeon; QVC; TBS Superstation; The Weather Channel; Trinity Bcstg. Network; Turner Classic Movies; Turner Network TV; USA Network.
Fee: $24.53 installation; $30.00 monthly.
Pay Service 1
Pay Units: 5.
Programming (via satellite): HBO.
Fee: $12.95 monthly.
Pay Service 2
Pay Units: 10.
Programming (via satellite): Showtime.
Fee: $5.95 monthly.
Miles of plant: 15.0 (coaxial). Homes passed: 789.
Manager: Marianne Bogy. Chief technician: Henry Harris.
Ownership: Buford Television Inc. (MSO). See Cable System Ownership.

MOUNT PLEASANT—TCA Cable TV, 919 W. First St., Mount Pleasant, TX 75455-4301. Phone: 903-572-6107. Fax: 903-572-5669. Web site: http://www.tca-cable.com. County: Titus. Also serves Titus County (portions). ICA: TX0089.
TV Market Ranking: Outside TV Markets. Franchise award date: N.A. Franchise expiration date: N.A. Began: October 1, 1968.
Channel capacity: 38. Channels available but not in use: N.A.
Basic Service
Subscribers: 3,929.
Programming (received off-air): K54CB (I) Mount Pleasant; KSLA-TV (C), KTAL-TV (N), KTBS-TV (A) Shreveport-Texarkana; KLTV (A) Tyler-Longview; 9 FMs.
Programming (via microwave): KDFW (F), KERA-TV (P), KXAS-TV (N), WFAA-TV (A) Dallas-Fort Worth.
Programming (via satellite): A & E; BET; C-SPAN; CNN; Fox Family Channel; FoxNet; Headline News; Lifetime; MTV; Nashville Network; Nickelodeon; QVC; TBS Superstation; The Weather Channel.
Current originations: Automated time-weather.
Fee: $36.74 installation; $10.57 monthly; $2.00 converter; $18.37 additional installation.
Expanded Basic Service
Subscribers: 3,470.
Programming (via satellite): American Movie Classics; ESPN; Fox Sports Net Southwest; Turner Network TV; USA Network.
Fee: $11.15 monthly.
Pay Service 1
Pay Units: 177.
Programming (via satellite): Cinemax.
Fee: $25.00 installation; $11.00 monthly.
Pay Service 2
Pay Units: 259.
Programming (via satellite): Disney Channel.
Fee: $25.00 installation; $11.00 monthly.
Pay Service 3
Pay Units: 1,118.
Programming (via satellite): The New Encore.
Fee: N.A.
Pay Service 4
Pay Units: 985.
Programming (via satellite): HBO.
Fee: $25.00 installation; $11.00 monthly.
Pay Service 5
Pay Units: 96.
Programming (via satellite): The Movie Channel.
Fee: $25.00 installation; $11.00 monthly.
Pay Service 6
Pay Units: 337.
Programming (via satellite): Showtime.
Fee: $25.00 installation; $11.00 monthly.
Local advertising: Planned.
Program Guide: The Cable Guide.
Equipment: Scientific-Atlanta headend; Broadband amplifiers; Times Fiber & Comm/Scope cable; Jerrold set top converters; Eagle traps; Scientific-Atlanta satellite antenna; Scientific-Atlanta satellite receivers.
Miles of plant: 88.9 (coaxial). Homes passed: 8,218. Total homes in franchised area: 23,152.
Manager: Ron Eubanks.
City fee: 3% of gross.
Ownership: TCA Cable TV Inc. (MSO); AT&T Broadband & Internet Services (MSO). See Cable System Ownership.

MOUNT VERNON—TCA Cable TV, 919 W. First St., Mount Pleasant, TX 75455-4301. Phone: 903-572-6107. Fax: 903-572-5669. Web site: http://www.tca-cable.com. County: Franklin. Also serves Franklin County (portions). ICA: TX0311.
TV Market Ranking: Outside TV Markets. Franchise award date: N.A. Franchise expiration date: N.A. Began: August 1, 1968.
Channel capacity: 35. Channels available but not in use: 1.
Basic Service
Subscribers: 792.
Programming (received off-air): KSLA-TV (C), KTAL-TV (N), KTBS-TV (A) Shreveport-Texarkana; KLTV (A) Tyler-Longview.
Programming (via microwave): KDFW (F), KERA-TV (P), KTVT (C), KXAS-TV (N), WFAA-TV (A) Dallas-Fort Worth.
Programming (via satellite): A & E; BET; C-SPAN; CNN; Fox Family Channel; FoxNet; Headline News; Lifetime; MTV; Nashville Network; Nickelodeon; QVC; TBS Superstation; The Weather Channel.
Current originations: Automated time-weather.
Fee: $36.78 installation; $10.23 monthly.
Expanded Basic Service
Subscribers: 691.
Programming (via satellite): American Movie Classics; ESPN; Fox Sports Net Southwest; Turner Network TV; USA Network.
Fee: $11.63 monthly.
Pay Service 1
Pay Units: 41.
Programming (via satellite): Cinemax.
Fee: $25.00 installation; $11.00 monthly.
Pay Service 2
Pay Units: 42.
Programming (via satellite): Disney Channel.
Fee: $25.00 installation; $11.00 monthly.
Pay Service 3
Pay Units: 197.
Programming (via satellite): The New Encore.
Fee: N.A.
Pay Service 4
Pay Units: 147.
Programming (via satellite): HBO.
Fee: $25.00 installation; $11.00 monthly.
Pay Service 5
Pay Units: 12.
Programming (via satellite): The Movie Channel.
Fee: $25.00 installation; $11.00 monthly.
Pay Service 6
Pay Units: 45.
Programming (via satellite): Showtime.
Fee: $25.00 installation; $11.00 monthly.
Local advertising: No.
Equipment: Scientific-Atlanta headend; Jerrold amplifiers; Times Fiber cable; Scientific-Atlanta satellite receivers.
Miles of plant: 19.2 (coaxial). Homes passed: 1,215. Total homes in franchised area: 4,451.
Manager: Ron Eubanks.
City fee: 3% of gross.
Ownership: TCA Cable TV Inc. (MSO); AT&T Broadband & Internet Services (MSO). See Cable System Ownership.

MUENSTER—North Texas Communications Co., Drawer 587, 205 N. Walnut St., Muenster, TX 76252. Phone: 940-736-2255. Fax: 940-759-5557. County: Cooke. Also serves Lindsay. ICA: TX0447.
TV Market Ranking: Below 100 (Lindsay); Outside TV Markets (Muenster). Franchise award date: January 1, 1967. Franchise expiration date: March 1, 2012. Began: February 1, 1968.
Channel capacity: 60 (not 2-way capable). Channels available but not in use: 33.
Basic Service
Subscribers: 625.
Programming (received off-air): KTEN (A,N,F) Ada; KPXD (X) Arlington; KDAF (W), KDFI-TV (I), KDFW (F), KDTX-TV (T), KERA-TV (P), KFWD (O), KTVT (C), KTXA (U), KXAS-TV (N), KXTX-TV (I), WFAA-TV (A) Dallas-Fort Worth; KMPX (I) Decatur; KHSX-TV (H) Irving; KXII (C) Sherman; allband FM.
Current originations: Automated time-weather; religious access; automated emergency alert.
Fee: $22.50 installation; $13.95 monthly; $1.58 converter; $35.00 additional installation.
Expanded Basic Service
Subscribers: 528.
Programming (via satellite): WGN-TV (W) Chicago; A & E; C-SPAN; CNBC; CNN; Country Music TV; Discovery Channel; Disney Channel; ESPN; EWTN; Fox Family Channel; Fox Sports Net Southwest; Headline News; History Channel; Home & Garden Television; Home Shopping Network; Learning Channel; Lifetime; Nashville Network; Nickelodeon; TBS Superstation; The Weather Channel; Turner Classic Movies; Turner Network TV; USA Network.
Fee: $6.55 monthly.
Pay Service 1
Pay Units: 60.
Programming (via satellite): Cinemax.
Fee: $15.00 installation; $10.00 monthly.
Pay Service 2
Pay Units: 107.
Programming (via satellite): HBO.
Fee: $15.00 installation; $10.00 monthly.
Local advertising: Yes. Local sales manager: Bernice Bartel.
Equipment: Scientific-Atlanta headend; Scientific-Atlanta amplifiers; Times Fiber cable; Texscan character generator; Scientific-Atlanta set top converters; Scientific-Atlanta addressable set top converters; Vitek traps; Scientific-Atlanta satellite antenna; Microwave Assoc. & Scientific-Atlanta satellite receivers.
Miles of plant: 18.2 (coaxial). Homes passed: 650. Total homes in franchised area: 660.
Manager: Alvin M. Fuhrman. CATV supervisor: Joe Yosten. Program director: Gene Fuhrman. Marketing director: Joey Anderson.
City fee: 4% of gross.
Ownership: North Texas Communications Co. (MSO).

For a list of all cable communities included in this section, see the **Cable Community Index** located in the back of this volume.

MULESHOE—Classic Cable, Box 429, 605 N.W. 3rd St., Plainville, KS 67663-0429. Phones: 785-434-7620; 800-999-8876. Fax: 785-434-2614. Counties: Bailey & Lamb. Also serves Amherst, Earth, Sudan. ICA: TX0164.
TV Market Ranking: Below 100 (Earth, Muleshoe, Sudan); Outside TV Markets (Amherst). Franchise award date: January 1, 1959. Franchise expiration date: February 14, 1999. Began: February 1, 1959.
Channel capacity: 36 (2-way capable; operating 2-way partially). Channels available but not in use: N.A.
Basic Service
Subscribers: 2,162; Commercial subscribers: 117.
Programming (received off-air): KVII-TV (A) Amarillo; KAMC (A), KCBD-TV (N), KJTV (F), KLBK-TV (C), KPTB (I) Lubbock; KENW (P) Portales; allband FM.
Programming (via translator): KVDA (O) San Antonio.
Programming (via satellite): WGN-TV (W) Chicago; A & E; American Movie Classics; Animal Planet; C-SPAN; CNN; Cartoon Network; Comedy Central; Country Music TV; Discovery Channel; Disney Channel; E! Entertainment TV; ESPN; Fox Family Channel; Fox Sports Net Southwest; Goodlife TV Network; Headline News; History Channel; Home Shopping Network; Learning Channel; Lifetime; Nashville Network; Nick at Nite's TV Land; Nickelodeon; QVC; TBS Superstation; The Weather Channel; Trinity Bcstg. Network; Turner Network TV; USA Network; Univision.
Current originations: Automated timeweather; local news.
Fee: $35.00 installation; $28.95 monthly; $3.00 converter.
Pay Service 1
Pay Units: 223.
Programming (via satellite): HBO.
Fee: $20.00 installation; $10.95 monthly.
Pay Service 2
Pay Units: 131.
Programming (via satellite): Showtime.
Fee: $9.95 monthly.
Pay Service 3
Pay Units: 126.
Programming (via satellite): The Movie Channel.
Fee: $5.95 monthly.
Local advertising: No.
Equipment: Jerrold headend; Jerrold amplifiers; Comm/Scope & Times Fiber cable; Pioneer settop converters; Pioneer addressable set top converters; Eagle traps; Comtech, Hughes & Microdyne satellite antenna; Comtech, Hughes & Microdyne satellite receivers.
Miles of plant: 81.4 (coaxial). Homes passed: 3,116. Satellite Antenna: Scientific-Atlanta. Satellite Receiver: Standard.
Manager: Bill Flowers. Chief technician: Chris Christenson. Marketing director: Jennifer Hauschild.
City fee: 3% of gross.
Ownership: Classic Cable (MSO). Purchased from Fanch Communications Inc.

MUNDAY—Harmon Cable Communications, Box 1146, 127 E. McHarg, Stamford, TX 79553. Phone: 915-773-3391. Fax: 915-773-2753. County: Knox. ICA: TX0415.
TV Market Ranking: Outside TV Markets. Franchise award date: N.A. Franchise expiration date: N.A. Began: January 1, 1963.
Channel capacity: 30. Channels available but not in use: 10.
Basic Service
Subscribers: 564.
Programming (received off-air): KRBC-TV (N), KTAB-TV (C), KTXS-TV (A) Abilene-Sweetwater; KAUZ-TV (C), KFDX-TV (N), KJTL (F,U), KSWO-TV (A) Wichita Falls-Lawton; allband FM.
Programming (via satellite): WGN-TV (W) Chicago; TBS Superstation.
Current originations: Automated timeweather.
Fee: $35.00 installation; $9.50 monthly.
Expanded Basic Service
Subscribers: N.A.
Programming (via satellite): Animal Planet; C-SPAN; CNN; Comedy Central; Country Music TV; Discovery Channel; Disney Channel; E! Entertainment TV; ESPN; ESPN 2; Fox Family Channel; Fox Sports Net Southwest; History Channel; Home & Garden Television; Learning Channel; Lifetime; MSNBC; Nashville Network; Nick at Nite's TV Land; Nickelodeon; QVC; Sci-Fi Channel; The Weather Channel; Trinity Bcstg. Network; Turner Classic Movies; Turner Network TV; USA Network; Univision; VH1.
Fee: $15.75 monthly.
Pay Service 1
Pay Units: N.A.
Programming (via satellite): Cinemax; HBO; Showtime.
Fee: $30.00 installation; $9.95 monthly (each).
Equipment: Texscan amplifiers; Comm/Scope cable; Jerrold & Scientific-Atlanta set top converters; Arcom, Eagle & Pico traps; Scientific-Atlanta satellite antenna; Harris & Scientific-Atlanta satellite receivers.
Miles of plant: 6.8 (coaxial). Homes passed: 750. Total homes in franchised area: 750.
Manager: L. R. Cagle.
City fee: 2% of basic.
Ownership: Fanch Communications Inc. (MSO); Time Warner Cable (MSO). Purchased from Harmon Cable Communications, June 21, 1999.

MUSTANG RIDGE—Mission Cable, 920 Whitmore Dr., Rockwall, TX 75087. Phone: 800-783-5708. Fax: 214-722-6218. County: Travis. Also serves Creedmoor. ICA: TX0467.
TV Market Ranking: Below 100. Franchise award date: November 1, 1988. Franchise expiration date: N.A. Began: N.A.
Channel capacity: N.A. Channels available but not in use: N.A.
Basic Service
Subscribers: 159.
Programming (received off-air): KEYE-TV (C), KLRU (P), KTBC (F), KVUE-TV (A), KXAN-TV (N) Austin.
Programming (via satellite): WGN-TV (W) Chicago; A & E; BET; C-SPAN; CNN; Discovery Channel; ESPN; Fox Family Channel; GalaVision; Nashville Network; Nickelodeon; TBS Superstation; The Weather Channel; USA Network; Univision; VH1.
Fee: $30.00 installation; $16.95 monthly.
Pay Service 1
Pay Units: 37.
Programming (via satellite): Cinemax.
Fee: $9.00 monthly.
Pay Service 2
Pay Units: 14.
Programming (via satellite): Disney Channel.
Fee: $9.00 monthly.
Pay Service 3
Pay Units: 55.
Programming (via satellite): HBO.
Fee: $9.00 monthly.
Program Guide: TV Host.
Miles of plant: 46.0 (coaxial). Homes passed: 563.
Manager: Jim Stafford. Chief technician: Jacky Oliver. Marketing & program director: Bruce Berkinshaw.
Franchise fee: 4% of gross.
Ownership: Fanch Communications Inc. (MSO); Time Warner Cable (MSO). See Cable System Ownership.

MYRTLE SPRINGS—Friendship Cable of Texas Inc., Box 9090, Tyler, TX 75711-9090. Phone: 903-581-2121. Fax: 903-581-2185. County: Van Zandt. ICA: TX0625.
TV Market Ranking: Below 100. Franchise award date: January 1, 1989. Franchise expiration date: January 1, 2009. Began: August 1, 1989.
Channel capacity: 36 (not 2-way capable). Channels available but not in use: 11.
Basic Service
Subscribers: 44.
Programming (received off-air): KPXD (X) Arlington; KDFW (F), KERA-TV (P), KXAS-TV (N) Dallas-Fort Worth; KLTV (A) Tyler-Longview.
Programming (via satellite): WGN-TV (W) Chicago; CNN; Country Music TV; Discovery Channel; ESPN; Fox Family Channel; Lifetime; Nashville Network; Nickelodeon; TBS Superstation; USA Network.
Fee: $30.00 installation; $32.45 monthly.
Pay Service 1
Pay Units: 18.
Programming (via satellite): Cinemax.
Fee: $10.95 monthly.
Pay Service 2
Pay Units: 20.
Programming (via satellite): HBO.
Fee: $10.95 monthly.
Local advertising: Yes.
Miles of plant: 8.6 (coaxial). Homes passed: 212.
Manager: Marianne Bogy. Chief technician: Sonny Myers.
Ownership: Buford Television Inc. (MSO). See Cable System Ownership.

NACOGDOCHES—Nacogdoches Cable TV, 409 N. Fredonia St., Nacogdoches, TX 75961. Phone: 409-564-6353. County: Nacogdoches. Also serves Nacogdoches County. ICA: TX0065.
TV Market Ranking: Below 100. Franchise award date: N.A. Franchise expiration date: N.A. Began: September 1, 1960.
Channel capacity: N.A. Channels available but not in use: N.A.
Basic Service
Subscribers: 10,576.
Programming (received off-air): KPRC-TV (N) Houston; KTRE (A) Lufkin; KSLA-TV (C), KTBS-TV (A) Shreveport-Texarkana; KLTV (A) Tyler-Longview; 6 FMs.
Programming (via microwave): KERA-TV (P), KTVT (C), KXTX-TV (I), WFAA-TV (A) Dallas-Fort Worth; KTAL-TV (N) Shreveport-Texarkana.
Programming (via satellite): CNN; ESPN.
Current originations: Automated timeweather; educational access.
Fee: $35.00 installation; $10.00 monthly.
Pay Service 1
Pay Units: N.A.
Programming (via satellite): Fox Sports Net Southwest; Showtime.
Fee: $10.00 monthly (Showtime).
Local advertising: Yes. Regional interconnect: Woodlands Communications Network.
Equipment: Scientific-Atlanta headend; C-COR amplifiers; Phelps-Dodge cable; Scientific-Atlanta satellite antenna.
Miles of plant: 201.5 (coaxial). Homes passed: 11,000.
Manager: Brad Haile.
City fee: 2% of gross.
Ownership: TCA Cable TV Inc. (MSO). See Cable System Ownership.

NAPLES—Star Cable Co., Box 626, 200 Scurry St., Daingerfield, TX 75638. Phone: 903-645-7353. County: Morris. Also serves Omaha. ICA: TX0295.
TV Market Ranking: Outside TV Markets. Franchise award date: N.A. Franchise expiration date: N.A. Began: N.A.
Channel capacity: 42. Channels available but not in use: 7.
Basic Service
Subscribers: 750; Commercial subscribers: 51.
Programming (received off-air): K54CB (I) Mount Pleasant; KMSS-TV (F), KSHV (U,W), KSLA-TV (C), KTAL-TV (N), KTBS-TV (A) Shreveport-Texarkana.
Programming (via microwave): KERA-TV (P), WFAA-TV (A) Dallas-Fort Worth.
Programming (via satellite): WGN-TV (W) Chicago; TBS Superstation.
Fee: $13.95 monthly; $1.50 converter.
Expanded Basic Service
Subscribers: 701.
Programming (via satellite): A & E; BET; CNN; Country Music TV; Discovery Channel; ESPN; Fox Family Channel; Fox Sports Net Southwest; Lifetime; MTV; Nashville Network; Nick at Nite's TV Land; Nickelodeon; Sci-Fi Channel; The Weather Channel; Trinity Bcstg. Network; Turner Network TV; USA Network.
Fee: $9.00 monthly.
Pay Service 1
Pay Units: 57.
Programming (via satellite): Cinemax.
Fee: $7.95 monthly.
Pay Service 2
Pay Units: 59.
Programming (via satellite): Disney Channel.
Fee: $7.95 monthly.
Pay Service 3
Pay Units: 121.
Programming (via satellite): HBO.
Fee: $10.95 monthly.
Pay Service 4
Pay Units: 78.
Programming (via satellite): Showtime; The Movie Channel.
Fee: $12.95 monthly.
Miles of plant: 33.0 (coaxial). Homes passed: 1,341.
Manager: Mike Burns.
Ownership: Star Cable Associates (MSO).

NAVASOTA—Northland Cable TV, 221 E. Main, Brenham, TX 77833. Phone: 409-836-6901. Fax: 409-836-1736. County: Grimes. ICA: TX0210.

TV Market Ranking: Below 100. Franchise award date: January 10, 1966. Franchise expiration date: January 1, 1999. Began: June 1, 1967.

Channel capacity: 41 (2-way capable; operating 2-way). Channels available but not in use: 13.

Basic Service

Subscribers: 1,774; Commercial subscribers: 209.

Programming (received off-air): KBTX-TV (C) Bryan; KAMU-TV (P) College Station; KHOU-TV (C), KHTV (W), KPRC-TV (N), KRIV (F), KTRK-TV (A), KTXH (U), KUHT (P) Houston; allband FM.

Programming (via satellite): Home Shopping Network; Univision.

Current originations: Automated time-weather.

Fee: $50.00 installation; $21.25 monthly; $20.00 additional installation.

Commercial fee: $4.25 monthly.

Expanded Basic Service

Subscribers: 1,731.

Programming (via satellite): WGN-TV (W) Chicago; BET; CNN; Discovery Channel; ESPN; Fox Family Channel; Headline News; Learning Channel; Nashville Network; TBS Superstation; TV Guide Channel; Travel Channel.

Fee: $50.00 installation; $10.25 monthly.

Pay Service 1

Pay Units: 123.

Programming (via satellite): Cinemax.

Fee: $35.00 installation; $11.50 monthly.

Pay Service 2

Pay Units: 152.

Programming (via satellite): HBO.

Fee: $35.00 installation; $13.50 monthly.

Pay Service 3

Pay Units: 118.

Programming (via satellite): The Movie Channel.

Fee: $35.00 installation; $12.00 monthly.

Local advertising: Yes. Available in satellite distributed, locally originated, character-generated, taped & automated programming. Rates: $35.00/Month; $10.00/Week; $7.00/Minute; $3.50/30 Seconds. Local sales manager: Barbara Jacobs.

Equipment: Scientific-Atlanta & Standard Electronics headend; Scientific-Atlanta amplifiers; Comm/Scope cable; Texscan character generator; Scientific-Atlanta set top converters; Eagle traps; M/A-Com & Scientific-Atlanta satellite antenna; Scientific-Atlanta & Standard Electronics satellite receivers; Texscan commercial insert.

Miles of plant: 39.0 (coaxial). Additional miles planned: 2.0 (coaxial). Homes passed: 2,200. Total homes in franchised area: 2,400.

Manager: Dan Bayless. Chief technician: Ken Holle. Program director: Prentice Mearns. Marketing director: Barbara England.

City fee: 3% of gross.

Ownership: Northland Communications Corp. (MSO).

NAZARETH—High Plains Cablevision Inc., Box 310, 124 S. Main St., Lockney, TX 79241. Phone: 806-652-3328. Fax: 806-652-3139. County: Castro. ICA: TX0817.

TV Market Ranking: Outside TV Markets. Franchise award date: N.A. Franchise expiration date: N.A. Began: N.A.

Channel capacity: N.A. Channels available but not in use: N.A.

Basic Service

Subscribers: 88.

Programming (received off-air): KAMR-TV (N), KCIT (F,U), KFDA-TV (C), KVII-TV (A) Amarillo.

Programming (via satellite): Turner Network TV.

Fee: N.A.

Manager: Jim Doucette.

Ownership: High Plains Cablevision Inc. (MSO).

NEW BOSTON—TCA Cable TV, 609 E. North Front St., New Boston, TX 75570-3005. Phone: 903-628-5569.

Web site: http://www.tca-cable.com.

County: Bowie. Also serves Bowie County (northern portion). ICA: TX0204.

TV Market Ranking: 58. Franchise award date: N.A. Franchise expiration date: N.A. Began: January 1, 1979.

Channel capacity: 35. Channels available but not in use: 5.

Basic Service

Subscribers: 1,796.

Programming (received off-air): KMSS-TV (F), KSLA-TV (C), KTAL-TV (N), KTBS-TV (A) Shreveport-Texarkana.

Programming (via microwave): KDFW (F), KERA-TV (P), WFAA-TV (A) Dallas-Fort Worth.

Programming (via satellite): WGN-TV (W) Chicago; CNBC; CNN; Discovery Channel; Fox Family Channel; Lifetime; MTV; Nashville Network; Nickelodeon; QVC; TBS Superstation; The Weather Channel; Trinity Bcstg. Network.

Fee: $33.96 installation; $10.23 monthly.

Expanded Basic Service

Subscribers: 1,694.

Programming (via satellite): American Movie Classics; Court TV; ESPN; Fox Sports Net Southwest; Turner Network TV; USA Network.

Fee: $10.68 monthly.

Pay Service 1

Pay Units: 137.

Programming (via satellite): Disney Channel.

Fee: $10.00 monthly.

Pay Service 2

Pay Units: 377.

Programming (via satellite): HBO.

Fee: $11.95 monthly.

Pay Service 3

Pay Units: 217.

Programming (via satellite): Showtime.

Fee: $11.95 monthly.

Pay Service 4

Pay Units: 655.

Programming (via satellite): The New Encore.

Fee: N.A.

Local advertising: Yes. Regional interconnect: Cabletime.

Program Guide: The Cable Guide.

Equipment: Scientific-Atlanta headend; GTE Sylvania amplifiers; Comm/Scope cable; MSI character generator; Scientific-Atlanta satellite antenna.

Miles of plant: 34.1 (coaxial). Homes passed: 2,323. Total homes in franchised area: 4,951.

Manager: Ron Eubanks.

Ownership: TCA Cable TV Inc. (MSO); AT&T Broadband & Internet Services (MSO). See Cable System Ownership.

NEW BRAUNFELS—Time Warner Cable, Box 1008, San Marcos, TX 78666-1008. Phones: 512-353-3456; 800-881-9190. Fax: 512-396-4664. Counties: Comal & Guadalupe. Also serves Comal County (portions), Guadalupe County (portions). ICA: TX0054.

TV Market Ranking: 45 (portions of Comal County, portions of Guadalupe County, New Braunfels); Outside TV Markets (portions of Comal County, portions of Guadalupe County). Franchise award date: N.A. Franchise expiration date: N.A. Began: July 1, 1979.

Channel capacity: 40 (not 2-way capable). Channels available but not in use: None.

Basic Service

Subscribers: 13,535.

Programming (received off-air): KRRT (W) Kerrville-San Antonio; KABB (F), KENS-TV (C), KLRN (P), KMOL-TV (N), KSAT-TV (A), KVDA (O), KWEX-TV (S) San Antonio; 16 FMs.

Programming (via satellite): A & E; C-SPAN; Discovery Channel; QVC; TBS Superstation; The Weather Channel.

Fee: $24.95 installation; $10.98 monthly; $3.30 converter.

Expanded Basic Service

Subscribers: 11,239.

Programming (via satellite): American Movie Classics; Animal Planet; CNBC; CNN; Cartoon Network; Country Music TV; Disney Channel; ESPN; EWTN; Encore Movie Networks; FX; Fox Family Channel; Fox News Channel; Fox Sports Net Southwest; Headline News; Knowledge TV; MTV; Nashville Network; Nickelodeon; Odyssey; The Health Network; Turner Network TV; USA Network.

Fee: $15.55 monthly.

Pay Service 1

Pay Units: 337.

Programming (via satellite): Cinemax.

Fee: $12.20 monthly.

Pay Service 2

Pay Units: 1,107.

Programming (via satellite): HBO.

Fee: $10.00 installation; $13.00 monthly.

Pay Service 3

Pay Units: 1,686.

Programming (via satellite): Showtime.

Fee: $10.00 installation; $11.95 monthly.

Pay Service 4

Pay Units: 4,336.

Programming (via satellite): The New Encore.

Fee: $1.75 monthly.

Pay Service 5

Pay Units: N.A.

Programming (via satellite): Starz!

Fee: $6.75 monthly.

Pay-Per-View

Addressable homes: 1,737.

Action Pay-Per-View; Viewer's Choice.

Local advertising: Yes (locally produced & insert). Available in satellite distributed programming.

Program Guide: The Cable Guide.

Equipment: Jerrold headend; C-COR amplifiers; Times Fiber cable; Sony VTRs; Video Data Systems character generator; Jerrold set top converters; Eagle traps; Scientific-Atlanta satellite antenna; Falcone International commercial insert.

Miles of plant: 480.0 (coaxial); None (fiber optic). Homes passed: 16,725. Total homes in franchised area: 16,725.

Manager: Dennis Moore. Office manager: Wanda Riley. Technical supervisor: Bruce Buchanan. Chief technician: Greg Krueger.

City fee: 3% of gross.

Ownership: Time Warner Cable (MSO). Purchased from AT&T Broadband & Internet Services, June 1, 1999.

NEW CANEY—Northland Cable TV, Box 839, 1144 Antique Lane, New Caney, TX 77357. Phone: 713-689-2048. Fax: 713-689-7643. County: Montgomery. Also serves Grangerland, Patton Village, Porter Heights, Roman Forest, Splendora, Woodbranch (village). ICA: TX0105.

TV Market Ranking: 15 (New Caney, Patton Village, Porter Heights, Roman Forest, Splendora, Woodbranch); Below 100 (Grangerland). Franchise award date: N.A. Franchise expiration date: N.A. Began: October 22, 1981.

Channel capacity: 35 (not 2-way capable). Channels available but not in use: None.

Basic Service

Subscribers: 4,000; Commercial subscribers: 140.

Programming (received off-air): KPXB (X) Conroe; KHOU-TV (C), KHTV (W), KPRC-TV (N), KRIV (F), KTRK-TV (A), KTXH (U), KUHT (P) Houston; allband FM.

Programming (via satellite): WGN-TV (W) Chicago; Home Shopping Network; TBS Superstation.

Current originations: Automated time-weather.

Fee: $50.00 installation; $21.25 monthly; $20.00 additional installation.

Commercial fee: $11.25 monthly.

Expanded Basic Service

Subscribers: 3,686.

Programming (via satellite): A & E; C-SPAN; CNBC; CNN; Discovery Channel; ESPN; Fox Family Channel; Fox Sports Net Southwest; Headline News; MTV; Nashville Network; Nick at Nite; Nickelodeon; QVC; The Weather Channel; Trinity Bcstg. Network.

Fee: $50.00 installation; $12.25 monthly.

Expanded Basic Service 2

Subscribers: 2,202.

Programming (via satellite): Country Music TV; ESPN 2; Lifetime; Turner Network TV; USA Network.

Fee: $35.00 installation; $6.00 monthly.

Pay Service 1

Pay Units: 566.

Programming (via satellite): Cinemax.

Fee: $35.00 installation; $7.50 monthly.

Pay Service 2

Pay Units: 730.

Programming (via satellite): HBO.

Fee: $35.00 installation; $11.50 monthly.

Pay Service 3

Pay Units: 368.

Programming (via satellite): Showtime.

Fee: $35.00 installation; $10.00 monthly.

Pay Service 4

Pay Units: 367.

Programming (via satellite): The Movie Channel.

Fee: $35.00 installation; $11.50 monthly.

Local advertising: Yes. Available in satellite distributed & character-generated programming. Rates: $35.00/Month; $10.00/Week; $7.00/Minute; $3.50/30 Seconds.

Program Guide: Premium Channels.

Equipment: Scientific-Atlanta headend; Texscan amplifiers; Comm/Scope cable; Texscan character generator; Scientific-Atlanta set top converters; Eagle traps; Scientific-Atlanta satellite antenna; ChannelMaster commercial insert.

Miles of plant: 250.0 (coaxial). Additional miles planned: 20.0 (fiber optic). Homes passed: 7,200.

Manager: Richard Gammon. Chief technician: Antonio Cardona. Program director: Prentice Mearns. Marketing director: Hope Beck.

City fee: 3% of gross.

Ownership: Northland Communications Corp. (MSO).

NEW CHAPEL HILL—Northland Cable TV, Box 538, Flint, TX 75762. Phones: 903-894-8200; 903-566-8757. Fax: 903-894-8204.

County: Smith. Also serves Lake Tyler, Smith County (unincorporated areas). ICA: TX0222.
TV Market Ranking: Below 100. Franchise award date: December 1, 1983. Franchise expiration date: June 6, 2006. Began: March 15, 1984.
Channel capacity: 36 (2-way capable). Channels available but not in use: N.A.
Basic Service
Subscribers: 2,643.
Programming (received off-air): KETK-TV (N) Jacksonville; KFXK (F) Longview; KLTV (A) Tyler-Longview.
Programming (via microwave): KDFW (F), KERA-TV (P), KTVT (C), KXTX-TV (I), WFAA-TV (A) Dallas-Fort Worth.
Current originations: Automated time-weather; local sports.
Fee: $60.00 installation; $11.00 monthly; $3.00 converter.
Expanded Basic Service
Subscribers: 1,320.
Programming (via satellite): WGN-TV (W) Chicago; A & E; CNN; Country Music TV; Discovery Channel; ESPN; Fox Family Channel; Goodlife TV Network; Headline News; Learning Channel; Nashville Network; QVC; TBS Superstation; Travel Channel; USA Network.
Fee: $49.95 installation; $21.75 monthly.
Expanded Basic Service 2
Subscribers: 369.
Programming (via satellite): CNBC; Cartoon Network; Fox Sports Net Southwest; MTV.
Fee: $24.95 installation; $5.35 monthly.
Pay Service 1
Pay Units: 96.
Programming (via satellite): Cinemax.
Fee: $24.95 installation; $7.50 monthly.
Pay Service 2
Pay Units: 104.
Programming (via satellite): Disney Channel.
Fee: $24.95 installation; $7.00 monthly.
Pay Service 3
Pay Units: 133.
Programming (via satellite): HBO.
Fee: $24.95 installation; $10.50 monthly.
Pay Service 4
Pay Units: 91.
Programming (via satellite): Showtime.
Fee: $24.95 installation; $7.95 monthly.
Local advertising: Yes (locally produced). Available in satellite distributed, locally originated, character-generated, taped & automated programming. Rates: $10.00/Minute; $5.00/30 Seconds. Local sales manager: Lynda Tracy.
Program Guide: Premium Channels.
Equipment: Hughes, M/A-Com & Scientific-Atlanta headend; Magnavox & Texscan amplifiers; Comm/Scope & Trilogy cable; Texscan character generator; Hamlin, Jerrold & Scientific-Atlanta set top converters; Arcom, Eagle & Pico traps; AFC & Comtech satellite antenna; DX Engineering satellite receivers; ChannelMatic commercial insert.
Miles of plant: 92.3 (coaxial).
Manager: Jim Wiggins. Chief technician: Jim Bob Sanders. Program director: John Hawkins. Marketing director: Charlotte Griffin.
City fee: 5% of gross.
Ownership: Northland Communications Corp. (MSO).

NEW SUMMERFIELD—Friendship Cable of Texas Inc., Box 9090, Tyler, TX 75711-9090. Phone: 903-581-2121. Fax: 903-581-2185. County: Cherokee. ICA: TX0818.
TV Market Ranking: Below 100. Franchise award date: N.A. Franchise expiration date: N.A. Began: N.A.
Channel capacity: 30. Channels available but not in use: N.A.
Basic Service
Subscribers: 92.
Programming (received off-air): KETK-TV (N) Jacksonville; KLTV (A) Tyler-Longview.
Programming (via satellite): TBS Superstation.
Fee: $26.95 monthly.
Pay Service 1
Pay Units: 58.
Programming (via satellite): Showtime.
Fee: $7.00 monthly.
Miles of plant: 4.0 (coaxial). Homes passed: 145.
Manager: Marianne Bogy. Chief technician: Henry Harris.
Ownership: Buford Television Inc. (MSO). See Cable System Ownership.

NEW ULM—National Cable Inc., Suite 106-A, 5151 Reed Rd., Columbus, OH 43220. Phones: 614-442-5890; 800-582-0504. Fax: 614-457-2567. County: Austin. ICA: TX0819.
TV Market Ranking: Outside TV Markets. Franchise award date: N.A. Franchise expiration date: N.A. Began: N.A.
Channel capacity: 36. Channels available but not in use: 21.
Basic Service
Subscribers: 22.
Programming (received off-air): KETH (E), KHOU-TV (C), KRIV (F), KTRK-TV (A), KTXH (U) Houston.
Programming (via satellite): WGN-TV (W) Chicago; KCNC-TV (C) Denver; A & E; American Movie Classics; CNN; Country Music TV; Discovery Channel; ESPN; Fox Family Channel; Showtime; TBS Superstation; Turner Network TV; USA Network.
Fee: $4.00 installation; $28.00 monthly.
Miles of plant: 6.6 (coaxial). Homes passed: 97.
Manager: Paul Scott. Chief technician: Rob Spiller. Marketing director: Josh Thackery.
Ownership: National Cable (MSO).

NIXON—Classic Cable, Box 429, 605 N.W. 3rd St., Plainville, KS 67663-0429. Phones: 785-434-7620; 800-999-8876. Fax: 785-434-2614. County: Gonzales. ICA: TX0431.
TV Market Ranking: Outside TV Markets. Franchise award date: June 9, 1981. Franchise expiration date: June 9, 2001. Began: December 1, 1981.
Channel capacity: 36 (2-way capable; operating 2-way). Channels available but not in use: N.A.
Basic Service
Subscribers: 331.
Programming (received off-air): KRRT (W) Kerrville-San Antonio; KABB (F), KENS-TV (C), KLRN (P), KMOL-TV (N), KSAT-TV (A), KVDA (O), KWEX-TV (S) San Antonio.
Programming (via satellite): WGN-TV (W) Chicago; A & E; Animal Planet; CNN; Country Music TV; Discovery Channel; Disney Channel; ESPN; Fox Family Channel; Fox News Channel; Fox Sports Net Southwest; Headline News; Home Shopping Network; Learning Channel; Nashville Network; Nickelodeon; TBS Superstation; The Weather Channel; Trinity Bcstg. Network; Turner Classic Movies; Turner Network TV; USA Network.
Fee: $35.00 installation; $26.95 monthly.
Pay Service 1
Pay Units: 92.
Programming (via satellite): HBO.
Fee: $10.00 installation; $10.95 monthly.
Pay Service 2
Pay Units: 28.
Programming (via satellite): Showtime.
Fee: $9.95 monthly.
Local advertising: No.
Equipment: Scientific-Atlanta headend; C-COR amplifiers; Trilogy cable; Jerrold set top converters; Pico traps; Scientific-Atlanta satellite receivers.
Miles of plant: 6.5 (coaxial). Homes passed: 724.
Manager: Bill Flowers. Chief technician: Walt VanLue. Marketing director: Jennifer Hauschild.
City fee: 3% of gross.
Ownership: Classic Cable (MSO).

NOCONA—Friendship Cable, 6380 Copeland Rd., Tyler, TX 75703. Phone: 903-561-5533. County: Montague. ICA: TX0282.
TV Market Ranking: Outside TV Markets. Franchise award date: N.A. Franchise expiration date: N.A. Began: December 25, 1971.
Channel capacity: 35. Channels available but not in use: 11.
Basic Service
Subscribers: 1,170.
Programming (received off-air): KERA-TV (P), KXAS-TV (N), WFAA-TV (A) Dallas-Fort Worth; KXII (C) Sherman; KAUZ-TV (C), KFDX-TV (N), KJTL (F,U), KSWO-TV (A) Wichita Falls-Lawton.
Programming (via satellite): CNBC; CNN; Discovery Channel; ESPN; MTV; Nashville Network; TBS Superstation; The Weather Channel; Turner Network TV; USA Network.
Current originations: Automated time-weather; local sports.
Fee: $33.30 installation; $9.79 monthly; $16.65 additional installation.
Pay Service 1
Pay Units: 67.
Programming (via satellite): Disney Channel.
Fee: N.A.
Pay Service 2
Pay Units: 77.
Programming (via satellite): Showtime.
Fee: N.A.
Pay Service 3
Pay Units: 126.
Programming (via satellite): The Movie Channel.
Fee: N.A.
Pay Service 4
Pay Units: 379.
Programming (via satellite): The New Encore.
Fee: N.A.
Miles of plant: 25.0 (coaxial). Homes passed: 1,400. Total homes in franchised area: 1,500.
Manager: Steve Lowe. Chief technician: Scott Wilber.
City fee: 2% of gross.
Ownership: Buford Television Inc. (MSO). Purchased from Tele-Communications Inc., May 1, 1998. See Cable System Ownership.

NOME—Friendship Cable of Texas Inc., Box 9090, Tyler, TX 75711-9090. Phone: 903-581-2121. Fax: 903-581-2185. County: Jefferson. ICA: TX0644.
TV Market Ranking: 88. Franchise award date: N.A. Franchise expiration date: N.A. Began: N.A.
Channel capacity: 36 (not 2-way capable). Channels available but not in use: 3.
Basic Service
Subscribers: 116.
Programming (received off-air): KBMT (A), KBTV-TV (N), KFDM-TV (C) Beaumont-Port Arthur; KHOU-TV (C), KHTV (W), KPRC-TV (N), KRIV (F), KTRK-TV (A), KTXH (U), KUHT (P) Houston.
Programming (via satellite): A & E; CNN; Country Music TV; Discovery Channel; Disney Channel; ESPN; Fox Family Channel; Fox Sports Net Southwest; Headline News; Lifetime; Nashville Network; Nickelodeon; TBS Superstation; The Inspirational Network; The Weather Channel; Turner Classic Movies; Turner Network TV; USA Network; VH1.
Fee: $34.00 monthly.
Pay Service 1
Pay Units: 30.
Programming (via satellite): HBO.
Fee: $10.95 monthly.
Pay Service 2
Pay Units: 24.
Programming (via satellite): Cinemax.
Fee: $10.95 monthly.
Miles of plant: 6.6 (coaxial). Homes passed: 198.
Manager: Wanda Pyburn. Chief technician: Mike Deal.
Ownership: Buford Television Inc. (MSO). See Cable System Ownership.

NORDHEIM—National Cable Inc., Suite 106-A, 5151 Reed Rd., Columbus, OH 43220. Phones: 614-442-5890; 800-582-0504. Fax: 614-457-2567. County: DeWitt. ICA: TX0661.
TV Market Ranking: Below 100. Franchise award date: N.A. Franchise expiration date: N.A. Began: N.A.
Channel capacity: 36. Channels available but not in use: 21.
Basic Service
Subscribers: 40.
Programming (received off-air): KABB (F), KENS-TV (C), KLRN (P), KMOL-TV (N), KSAT-TV (A) San Antonio.
Programming (via satellite): WGN-TV (W) Chicago; A & E; American Movie Classics; CNN; Country Music TV; Discovery Channel; ESPN; Fox Family Channel; Showtime; TBS Superstation; Turner Network TV; USA Network.
Fee: $28.00 monthly.
Miles of plant: 6.9 (coaxial). Homes passed: 138.
Manager: Paul Scott. Chief technician: Rob Spiller. Marketing director: Josh Thackery.
Ownership: National Cable (MSO).

NORMANGEE—Mission Cable, 920 Whitmore Dr., Rockwall, TX 75087. Phone: 800-783-5708. Fax: 214-722-6218. Counties: Leon & Madison. ICA: TX0494.
TV Market Ranking: Below 100. Franchise award date: February 19, 1987. Franchise expiration date: N.A. Began: N.A.
Channel capacity: 21. Channels available but not in use: N.A.
Basic Service
Subscribers: 143.
Programming (received off-air): KBTX-TV (C) Bryan; KAMU-TV (P) College Station; KCEN-TV (N), KWKT (F), KWTX-TV (C), KXXV (A) Waco-Temple.
Programming (via satellite): WGN-TV (W) Chicago; CNN; Discovery Channel; ESPN; Fox Family Channel; Nashville Network; TBS Superstation; Turner Network TV; USA Network.
Fee: $25.00 installation; $20.95 monthly.
Pay Service 1
Pay Units: 18.
Programming (via satellite): Disney Channel.
Fee: $9.00 monthly.

Pay Service 2
Pay Units: 30.
Programming (via satellite): Showtime.
Fee: $9.00 monthly.
Equipment: Blonder-Tongue headend; Magnavox amplifiers; Comm/Scope cable; Northeast Filter traps; Weatherscan satellite antenna; Automation Techniques satellite receivers.
Miles of plant: 4.1 (coaxial). Homes passed: 463. Total homes in franchised area: 463.
Manager: Don Blair. Chief technician: Barry Greer. Marketing & program director: Bruce Berkinshaw.
City fee: 3% of basic & premium.
Ownership: Fanch Communications Inc. (MSO); Time Warner Cable (MSO). See Cable System Ownership.

NORTH SILSBEE—Friendship Cable of Texas, Box 9090, Tyler, TX 75711-9090. Phone: 903-581-2121. Fax: 903-581-2185. County: Hardin. ICA: TX0380.
TV Market Ranking: 88. Franchise award date: N.A. Franchise expiration date: N.A. Began: N.A.
Channel capacity: 36 (not 2-way capable). Channels available but not in use: 3.
Basic Service
Subscribers: 584.
Programming (received off-air): KBMT (A), KBTV-TV (N), KFDM-TV (C) Beaumont-Port Arthur; KVHP (F) Lake Charles.
Programming (via satellite): WGN-TV (W) Chicago; A & E; C-SPAN; CNN; Country Music TV; Discovery Channel; Disney Channel; ESPN; Fox Family Channel; Fox Sports Net Southwest; Headline News; Lifetime; Nashville Network; Nickelodeon; QVC; TBS Superstation; The Inspirational Network; The Weather Channel; Turner Network TV; USA Network; VH1.
Fee: $34.75 monthly.
Pay Service 1
Pay Units: 28.
Programming (via satellite): Cinemax.
Fee: $10.95 monthly.
Pay Service 2
Pay Units: 34.
Programming (via satellite): HBO.
Fee: $10.95 monthly.
Pay Service 3
Pay Units: 59.
Programming (via satellite): Showtime.
Fee: $10.95 monthly.
Local advertising: Yes.
Miles of plant: 62.2 (coaxial). Homes passed: 1,176.
Manager: Wanda Pyburn. Chief technician: Mike Deal.
Franchise fee: None.
Ownership: Buford Television Inc. (MSO). See Cable System Ownership.

NORTH ZULCH—Mission Cable, 920 Whitmore Dr., Rockwall, TX 75087. Phone: 800-783-5708. Fax: 214-722-6218. County: Madison. ICA: TX0678.
TV Market Ranking: Below 100. Franchise award date: July 15, 1989. Franchise expiration date: N.A. Began: N.A.
Channel capacity: 21 (not 2-way capable). Channels available but not in use: 9.
Basic Service
Subscribers: 60.
Programming (received off-air): KBTX-TV (C) Bryan; KAMU-TV (P) College Station; KCEN-TV (N) Waco-Temple.
Programming (via satellite): WGN-TV (W) Chicago; CNN; Discovery Channel; ESPN; Fox Family Channel; Nashville Network; TBS Superstation.
Fee: $25.00 installation; $20.95 monthly.
Pay Service 1
Pay Units: N.A.
Programming (via satellite): Disney Channel; Showtime.
Fee: $9.00 monthly (each).
Equipment: Blonder-Tongue headend; Magnavox amplifiers; Comm/Scope cable; Northeast Filter traps; Weatherscan satellite antenna; Automation Techniques satellite receivers.
Miles of plant: 4.0 (coaxial). Homes passed: 119.
Manager: Jim Stafford. Chief technician: Jacky Oliver. Marketing & program director: Bruce Berkinshaw.
Ownership: Fanch Communications Inc. (MSO); Time Warner Cable (MSO). See Cable System Ownership.

NORTHEAST HAYS—Time Warner Cable, 12012 N. Mo Pac Expressway, Austin, TX 78758-2904. Phone: 512-485-6100. Fax: 512-485-6105.
Web site: http://www.timewarneraustin.com.
County: Hays. ICA: TX0347.
TV Market Ranking: Below 100. Franchise award date: N.A. Franchise expiration date: N.A. Began: N.A.
Channel capacity: 78 (2-way capable; operating 2-way). Channels available but not in use: 33.
Basic Service
Subscribers: 930.
Programming (received off-air): KEYE-TV (C), KLRU (P), KNVA (W), KTBC (F), KVUE-TV (A), KXAN-TV (N) Austin; KENS-TV (C) San Antonio.
Programming (via satellite): C-SPAN; Country Music TV; Lifetime; Odyssey; Pax Net; The Weather Channel; VH1.
Current originations: Local news.
Fee: $28.21 installation; $9.50 monthly.
Expanded Basic Service
Subscribers: 264.
Programming (via satellite): A & E; American Movie Classics; Animal Planet; CNN; Cartoon Network; Discovery Channel; ESPN; ESPN 2; Fox Family Channel; Fox Sports Net Southwest; Golf Channel; Headline News; History Channel; Home & Garden Television; Learning Channel; MSNBC; MTV; Nashville Network; Nick at Nite; Nickelodeon; TBS Superstation; Travel Channel; Turner Classic Movies; Turner Network TV; USA Network; Univision.
Fee: $15.62 monthly.
Pay Service 1
Pay Units: N.A.
Programming (via satellite): Disney Channel; HBO; Showtime; The Movie Channel; The New Encore.
Fee: $1.75 monthly (Encore), $8.95 monthly (Disney, Showtime or TMC), $11.40 monthly (HBO).
Pay-Per-View
Addressable homes: 60.
Miles of plant: 48.0 (coaxial). Homes passed: 1,057. Total homes in franchised area: 1,165.
Manager: Bill Carey. Chief technician: Matt Stanek. Program director: George Warmingham. Marketing director: Michelle Golden.
Ownership: Time Warner Cable (MSO); Advance/Newhouse Partnership (MSO).

NURSERY—National Cable Inc., Suite 106-A, 5151 Reed Rd., Columbus, OH 43220. Phones: 614-442-5890; 800-582-0504. Fax: 614-457-2567. County: Victoria. ICA: TX0555.
TV Market Ranking: Below 100. Franchise award date: N.A. Franchise expiration date: N.A. Began: N.A.
Channel capacity: 35. Channels available but not in use: 8.
Basic Service
Subscribers: 130.
Programming (received off-air): KENS-TV (C) San Antonio; KAVU-TV (A), KVCT (F) Victoria.
Programming (via satellite): WGN-TV (W) Chicago; KCNC-TV (C), KMGH-TV (A), KUSA-TV (N) Denver; A & E; American Movie Classics; CNN; Country Music TV; Discovery Channel; ESPN; Fox Family Channel; Showtime; TBS Superstation; The Weather Channel; Turner Network TV; USA Network.
Fee: $21.00 monthly.
Pay Service 1
Pay Units: 23.
Programming (via satellite): Disney Channel.
Fee: $10.95 monthly.
Pay Service 2
Pay Units: 54.
Programming (via satellite): HBO.
Fee: $10.95 monthly.
Miles of plant: 18.1 (coaxial). Homes passed: 360.
Manager: Paul Scott. Chief technician: Rob Spiller. Marketing director: Josh Thackery.
Ownership: National Cable (MSO).

O'DONNELL—Cablecomm, 320 W. Main St., Brownfield, TX 79316. Phones: 806-637-2313; 800-638-8457. County: Lynn. ICA: TX0496.
TV Market Ranking: Outside TV Markets. Franchise award date: July 1, 1980. Franchise expiration date: July 1, 2005. Began: March 9, 1976.
Channel capacity: 35 (not 2-way capable). Channels available but not in use: 16.
Basic Service
Subscribers: 259.
Programming (received off-air): KAMC (A), KCBD-TV (N), KJTV (F), KLBK-TV (C), KTXT-TV (P) Lubbock.
Programming (via satellite): WGN-TV (W) Chicago; Cartoon Network; Discovery Channel; Fox Family Channel; QVC; TBS Superstation.
Fee: $11.50 monthly.
Expanded Basic Service
Subscribers: 256.
Programming (via satellite): CNN; Country Music TV; ESPN; Goodlife TV Network; Nashville Network; Turner Network TV; USA Network; Univision.
Fee: $9.21 monthly.
Pay Service 1
Pay Units: 94.
Programming (via satellite): HBO.
Fee: $20.00 installation; $10.50 monthly.
Local advertising: No.
Program Guide: Premium Channels.
Equipment: Blonder-Tongue & Strato Vision headend; Scientific-Atlanta amplifiers; Comm/Scope cable; Scientific-Atlanta set top converters; Pico & Eagle traps; Scientific-Atlanta satellite antenna; Scientific-Atlanta satellite receivers.
Miles of plant: 13.0 (coaxial). Homes passed: 465.
Manager: Rex Thackerson. Chief technician: Gary Strickland. Marketing director: Bill Forgey.
City fee: 2% of gross.
Ownership: Fanch Communications Inc. (MSO); Time Warner Cable (MSO). See Cable System Ownership.

OAK GROVE—Northland Cable, Box 538, Flint, TX 75762. Phones: 903-894-8200; 903-566-8757. Fax: 903-894-8204. County: Kaufman. ICA: TX0820.
TV Market Ranking: 12. Franchise award date: N.A. Franchise expiration date: N.A. Began: N.A.
Channel capacity: N.A. Channels available but not in use: N.A.
Basic Service
Subscribers: 111.
Programming (received off-air): KDAF (W), KDFI-TV (I), KERA-TV (P), KTVT (C), KTXA (U), KXAS-TV (N), WFAA-TV (A) Dallas-Fort Worth; KCEN-TV (N), KWKT (F), KWTX-TV (C), KXXV (A) Waco-Temple.
Programming (via satellite): WGN-TV (W) Chicago; CNN; Country Music TV; ESPN; Fox Family Channel; GalaVision; MTV; Nashville Network; Nickelodeon; TBS Superstation; Trinity Bcstg. Network; VH1.
Fee: $24.95 installation; $12.95 monthly.
Pay Service 1
Pay Units: 8.
Programming (via satellite): Disney Channel.
Fee: $10.00 monthly.
Pay Service 2
Pay Units: 51.
Programming (via satellite): HBO.
Fee: $11.00 monthly.
Pay Service 3
Pay Units: 20.
Programming (via satellite): Showtime.
Fee: $11.00 monthly.
Manager: Jim Wiggins. Chief technician: Jim Bob Sanders. Marketing director: Charlotte Griffin.
Ownership: Northland Communications Corp. (MSO).

OAKWOOD—Mission Cable, 920 Whitmore Dr., Rockwall, TX 75087. Phone: 800-783-5708. Fax: 214-722-6214. County: Leon. ICA: TX0526.
TV Market Ranking: Outside TV Markets. Franchise award date: July 15, 1989. Franchise expiration date: N.A. Began: N.A.
Channel capacity: 21. Channels available but not in use: None.
Basic Service
Subscribers: 163.
Programming (received off-air): KERA-TV (P), KTVT (C) Dallas-Fort Worth; KETK-TV (N) Jacksonville; KFXK (F) Longview; KLTV (A) Tyler-Longview; KWTX-TV (C) Waco-Temple.
Programming (via satellite): WGN-TV (W) Chicago; CNN; Discovery Channel; Fox Family Channel; Nashville Network; TBS Superstation.
Fee: $25.00 installation; $20.95 monthly.
Pay Service 1
Pay Units: 16.
Programming (via satellite): Disney Channel.
Fee: $9.00 monthly.
Pay Service 2
Pay Units: 36.
Programming (via satellite): Showtime.
Fee: $9.00 monthly.
Local advertising: No.
Equipment: Blonder-Tongue headend; Magnavox amplifiers; Comm/Scope cable; Northeast Filter traps; Weatherscan satellite antenna; Automation Techniques satellite receivers.
Miles of plant: 6.0 (coaxial). Homes passed: 255. Total homes in franchised area: 397.
Manager: Jim Stafford. Chief technician: Jacky Oliver. Marketing & program director: Bruce Berkinshaw.
City fee: 3% of basic & premium.
Ownership: Fanch Communications Inc. (MSO); Time Warner Cable (MSO). See Cable System Ownership.

ODESSA—Cable One, Box 33, 315 W. 8th St., Odessa, TX 79761. Phone: 915-334-7217. Fax: 915-334-7216. County: Ector. Also serves Ector County, Mission Dorado. ICA: TX0025.
TV Market Ranking: Below 100. Franchise award date: November 10, 1970. Franchise expiration date: May 10, 2002. Began: December 10, 1968.
Channel capacity: 61 (2-way capable; operating 2-way). Channels available but not in use: N.A.
Basic Service
Subscribers: 27,600; Commercial subscribers: 22.
Programming (received off-air): KMID (A), KMLM (I), KOCV-TV (P), KOSA-TV (C), KPEJ (F), KWES-TV (N) Odessa-Midland.
Programming (via satellite): A & E; American Movie Classics; BET; C-SPAN; C-SPAN 2; CNBC; CNN; Cartoon Network; Comedy Central; Country Music TV; Discovery Channel; Disney Channel; E! Entertainment TV; ESPN; ESPN 2; Fox Family Channel; Fox Sports Net Southwest; Goodlife TV Network; Headline News; History Channel; Home & Garden Television; Home Shopping Network; Learning Channel; Lifetime; MSNBC; MTV; Nashville Network; Nickelodeon; Odyssey; QVC; Sci-Fi Channel; TBS Superstation; TV Guide Channel; Telemundo; The Weather Channel; Travel Channel; Turner Network TV; USA Network; Univision; VH1.
Current originations: Educational access; government access; automated emergency alert.
Fee: $40.17 installation; $28.90 monthly.
Pay Service 1
Pay Units: 1,998.
Programming (via satellite): Cinemax (multiplexed).
Fee: $10.00 installation; $13.95 monthly.
Pay Service 2
Pay Units: 8,202.
Programming (via satellite): HBO (multiplexed).
Fee: $10.00 installation; $13.95 monthly.
Pay Service 3
Pay Units: 1,080.
Programming (via satellite): The Movie Channel.
Fee: $10.00 installation; $10.95 monthly.
Pay Service 4
Pay Units: 3,136.
Programming (via satellite): Showtime (multiplexed).
Fee: $10.00 installation; $10.95 monthly.
Pay Service 5
Pay Units: 161.
Programming (via satellite): DMX.
Fee: $9.50 monthly.
Pay-Per-View
Addressable homes: 7,900.
Hot Choice; Viewer's Choice.
Fee: $2.99.
Local advertising: Yes. Available in satellite distributed programming. Rates: $10.00/30 Seconds. Local sales manager: Lance Leasure. Regional interconnect: Cabletime.
Program Guide: Preview Guide.
Equipment: Scientific-Atlanta headend; Century III & Scientific-Atlanta amplifiers; Comm/Scope cable; Panasonic & Sony VTRs; Texscan & MSI character generator; Pioneer & Standard Components set top converters; Jerrold addressable set top converters; Eagle & Pico traps; Simulsat satellite antenna; Scientific-Atlanta satellite receivers; Sony commercial insert.
Miles of plant: 450.0 (coaxial); 16.0 (fiber optic). Additional miles planned: 2.0 (coaxial). Homes passed: 38,585. Total homes in franchised area: 40,365.
Manager: Dennis Edwards. Chief technician: Larry Tate. Marketing director: Terri Hale.
City fee: 3% of gross.
Ownership: Cable One Inc. (MSO).

ODESSA (western portion)—US Cable of West Texas, Box 255, 7800 W. University, Odessa, TX 79764. Phone: 915-498-8366. Fax: 915-381-8246. County: Ector. ICA: TX0824.
TV Market Ranking: Below 100. Franchise award date: N.A. Franchise expiration date: N.A. Began: October 1, 1981.
Channel capacity: 36 (not 2-way capable). Channels available but not in use: 1.
Basic Service
Subscribers: 2,373.
Programming (received off-air): KMID (A), KMLM (I), KOCV-TV (P), KOSA-TV (C), KPEJ (F), KWES-TV (N) Odessa-Midland.
Programming (via satellite): WGN-TV (W) Chicago; A & E; American Movie Classics; C-SPAN; CNN; Country Music TV; Discovery Channel; ESPN; Fox Family Channel; Fox Sports Net Southwest; Headline News; Home Shopping Network; Home Shopping Network 2; Learning Channel; Lifetime; MTV; Nashville Network; Nickelodeon; TBS Superstation; Telemundo; The Inspirational Network; The Weather Channel; Turner Network TV; USA Network; Univision.
Fee: $10.32 monthly.
Pay Service 1
Pay Units: N.A.
Programming (via satellite): Disney Channel; HBO; Showtime; The Movie Channel.
Fee: $7.95 monthly (Disney), $10.95 monthly (HBO, Showtime or TMC).
Pay-Per-View
Addressable homes: 2,300.
Local advertising: Yes. Available in locally originated programming. Rates: $40.00/Month; $2.50/Day.
Miles of plant: 140.0 (coaxial); None (fiber optic).
Manager: Daryl Koedyker. Chief technician: David Harris. Marketing director: Candy Boyer. Customer service manager: Kenny Harris.
Ownership: US Cable Corp. (MSO).

OGLESBY—Torrence Cablevision, Box 1167, Ridgeland, MS 39158. Phones: 601-981-6900; 800-977-8849. County: Coryell. ICA: TX0654.
TV Market Ranking: Below 100. Franchise award date: N.A. Franchise expiration date: N.A. Began: N.A.
Channel capacity: 36. Channels available but not in use: 21.
Basic Service
Subscribers: 68.
Programming (received off-air): KNCT (P) Belton; KCEN-TV (N), KWKT (F), KWTX-TV (C), KXXV (A) Waco-Temple.
Programming (via satellite): WGN-TV (W) Chicago; A & E; American Movie Classics; CNN; Discovery Channel; ESPN; Fox Family Channel; Showtime; TBS Superstation; Turner Network TV; USA Network.
Fee: $28.00 monthly.
Miles of plant: 3.5 (coaxial). Homes passed: 175.
Ownership: Torrence Cable Inc. (MSO).

OILTON—TCI Cablevision of Texas Inc., 208 W. Viggie St., Hebbronville, TX 78361-3048. Phone: 512-527-3267. County: Webb. Also serves Mirando City. ICA: TX0825.
TV Market Ranking: Below 100. Franchise award date: N.A. Franchise expiration date: N.A. Began: June 1, 1984.
Channel capacity: 21. Channels available but not in use: 6.
Basic Service
Subscribers: 180.
Programming (received off-air): KGNS-TV (N,A), KLDO-TV (O), KVTV (C) Laredo.
Programming (via satellite): WGN-TV (W) Chicago; WABC-TV (A) New York; CNN; Country Music TV; ESPN; GalaVision; Nickelodeon; TBS Superstation; USA Network; Univision.
Fee: $60.00 installation; $16.78 monthly.
Pay Service 1
Pay Units: 79.
Programming (via satellite): HBO.
Fee: $11.00 monthly.
Pay Service 2
Pay Units: 59.
Programming (via satellite): Showtime.
Fee: $6.00 monthly.
Miles of plant: 9.1 (coaxial). Total homes in franchised area: 189.
Manager: Juve Morante.
Ownership: AT&T Broadband & Internet Services (MSO). Purchased from Tele-Communications Inc., March 9, 1999.

OKLAHOMA—Friendship Cable of Texas Inc., Box 9090, Tyler, TX 75711-9090. Phones: 903-581-2121; 800-888-7538. Fax: 903-581-2185. Counties: Hardin, Harris & Montgomery. Also serves Lakewood. ICA: TX0308.
TV Market Ranking: 15. Franchise award date: N.A. Franchise expiration date: N.A. Began: N.A.
Channel capacity: 42 (not 2-way capable). Channels available but not in use: 2.
Basic Service
Subscribers: 1,133.
Programming (received off-air): KHOU-TV (C), KHTV (W), KPRC-TV (N), KRIV (F), KTRK-TV (A), KTXH (U), KUHT (P) Houston.
Programming (via satellite): WGN-TV (W) Chicago; A & E; C-SPAN; CNN; Country Music TV; Discovery Channel; Disney Channel; ESPN; Fox Family Channel; Fox Sports Net Southwest; Headline News; Lifetime; Nashville Network; Nickelodeon; QVC; TBS Superstation; The Inspirational Network; The Weather Channel; Turner Network TV; USA Network; VH1.
Fee: $34.95 monthly.
Pay Service 1
Pay Units: 52.
Programming (via satellite): Cinemax.
Fee: $10.95 monthly.
Pay Service 2
Pay Units: 92.
Programming (via satellite): HBO.
Fee: $10.95 monthly.
Pay Service 3
Pay Units: 123.
Programming (via satellite): Showtime.
Fee: $10.95 monthly.
Miles of plant: 97.9 (coaxial). Homes passed: 1,765.
Manager: Wanda Pyburn. Chief technician: David Burrell.
Ownership: Buford Television Inc. (MSO). See Cable System Ownership.

OLNEY—Friendship Cable of Texas Inc., Box 9090, Tyler, TX 75711-9090. Phone: 903-581-2121. Fax: 903-581-2185. County: Young. Also serves Young County (portions). ICA: TX0215.
TV Market Ranking: Outside TV Markets. Franchise award date: N.A. Franchise expiration date: N.A. Began: October 1, 1971.
Channel capacity: 36. Channels available but not in use: N.A.
Basic Service
Subscribers: 1,207.
Programming (received off-air): KAUZ-TV (C), KFDX-TV (N), KJTL (F,U), KSWO-TV (A) Wichita Falls-Lawton; allband FM.
Programming (via translator): KERA-TV (P), KTVT (C), KXAS-TV (N), WFAA-TV (A) Dallas-Fort Worth.
Programming (via satellite): C-SPAN; Discovery Channel; Learning Channel; Odyssey; QVC; TBS Superstation; The Weather Channel.
Current originations: Public access.
Fee: $30.00 installation; $13.19 monthly.
Expanded Basic Service
Subscribers: 1,006.
Programming (via satellite): American Movie Classics; Animal Planet; CNBC; CNN; Cartoon Network; Court TV; Disney Channel; ESPN; FX; Fox Family Channel; Fox News Channel; Headline News; Home & Garden Television; Lifetime; MTV; Nashville Network; Turner Network TV; USA Network; Univision.
Fee: $30.00 installation; $17.61 monthly.
Pay Service 1
Pay Units: 87.
Programming (via satellite): Cinemax.
Fee: $12.84 monthly.
Pay Service 2
Pay Units: 284.
Programming (via satellite): The New Encore.
Fee: $1.75 monthly.
Pay Service 3
Pay Units: 128.
Programming (via satellite): HBO.
Fee: $13.83 monthly.
Pay Service 4
Pay Units: 53.
Programming (via satellite): Showtime.
Fee: $13.83 monthly.
Pay Service 5
Pay Units: 198.
Programming (via satellite): Starz!
Fee: $6.75 monthly.
Local advertising: Planned.
Program Guide: The Cable Guide.
Equipment: CAS & Scientific-Atlanta headend; CAS amplifiers; Comm/Scope cable; Prodelin satellite antenna; Scientific-Atlanta satellite receivers.
Miles of plant: 31.0 (coaxial). Homes passed: 2,085. Total homes in franchised area: 2,085.
Manager: Larry Bryant. Chief technician: Ron Johnson.
City fee: 3% of gross.
Ownership: Buford Television Inc. (MSO). See Cable System Ownership.

OLTON—Classic Cable, Box 429, 605 N.W. 3rd St., Plainville, KS 67663-0429. Phones: 785-434-7620; 800-999-8876. Fax: 785-434-2614. County: Lamb. ICA: TX0387.
TV Market Ranking: Outside TV Markets. Franchise award date: December 4, 1978. Franchise expiration date: N.A. Began: July 1, 1981.
Channel capacity: 41 (2-way capable). Channels available but not in use: N.A.
Basic Service
Subscribers: 393; Commercial subscribers: 11.
Programming (received off-air): KAMC (A), KCBD-TV (N), KJTV (F), KLBK-TV (C), KPTB (I), KTXT-TV (P), KUPT-LP (U) Lubbock.
Programming (via translator): KVDA (O) San Antonio.
Programming (via satellite): WGN-TV (W) Chicago; A & E; American Movie Classics; Animal Planet; CNN; Cartoon Network; Country Music TV; Discovery Channel; Disney

Channel; ESPN; Fox Family Channel; Fox News Channel; Fox Sports Net Southwest; Goodlife TV Network; History Channel; Home Team Sports; Learning Channel; Lifetime; Nashville Network; Nick at Nite's TV Land; Nickelodeon; QVC; Sci-Fi Channel; TBS Superstation; The Weather Channel; Trinity Bcstg. Network; Turner Network TV; USA Network; Univision.
Current originations: Automated time-weather.
Fee: $35.00 installation; $27.95 monthly; $3.00 converter.
Pay Service 1
Pay Units: 57.
Programming (via satellite): HBO.
Fee: $35.00 installation; $10.95 monthly.
Pay Service 2
Pay Units: 32.
Programming (via satellite): Showtime.
Fee: $9.95 monthly.
Pay Service 3
Pay Units: 33.
Programming (via satellite): The Movie Channel.
Fee: $5.95 monthly.
Local advertising: No.
Miles of plant: 19.6 (coaxial). Homes passed: 767.
Manager: Bill Flowers. Chief technician: Chris Christenson. Marketing director: Jennifer Hauschild.
City fee: 3% of gross.
Ownership: Classic Cable (MSO).

ORANGE—Time Warner Communications, 1460 Calder Ave., Beaumont, TX 77701-1746. Phone: 409-727-1515. Fax: 409-839-4215. County: Orange. Also serves Pinehurst, West Orange. ICA: TX0058.
TV Market Ranking: 88. Franchise award date: N.A. Franchise expiration date: March 28, 2010. Began: January 1, 1968.
Channel capacity: 38 (not 2-way capable). Channels available but not in use: N.A.
Basic Service
Subscribers: 8,112.
Programming (received off-air): KBMT (A), KBTV-TV (N), KFDM-TV (C), KITU (E) Beaumont-Port Arthur; KVHP (F) Lake Charles; allband FM.
Programming (via microwave): KTXH (U), KUHT (P) Houston.
Programming (via satellite): C-SPAN; CNBC; Discovery Channel; Nashville Network; Odyssey; QVC; TBS Superstation; Travel Channel.
Current originations: Government access.
Fee: $40.47 installation; $9.55 monthly; $0.49 converter; $20.24 additional installation.
Expanded Basic Service
Subscribers: 7,811.
Programming (via satellite): A & E; American Movie Classics; Animal Planet; BET; CNN; Cartoon Network; ESPN; FX; Fox Family Channel; Fox News Channel; Fox Sports Net Southwest; Headline News; Nickelodeon; The Weather Channel; Turner Network TV; USA Network.
Fee: $1.50 monthly.
Pay Service 1
Pay Units: 619.
Programming (via satellite): Cinemax.
Fee: $20.00 installation; $13.20 monthly.
Pay Service 2
Pay Units: 697.
Programming (via satellite): Disney Channel.
Fee: $20.00 installation; $11.95 monthly.
Pay Service 3
Pay Units: 1,205.
Programming (via satellite): HBO.
Fee: $25.00 installation; $13.20 monthly.
Pay Service 4
Pay Units: 1,204.
Programming (via satellite): Showtime.
Fee: $25.00 installation; $13.20 monthly.
Pay Service 5
Pay Units: 684.
Programming (via satellite): The Movie Channel.
Fee: $20.00 installation; $13.20 monthly.
Pay Service 6
Pay Units: 3,862.
Programming (via satellite): The New Encore.
Fee: N.A.
Pay Service 7
Pay Units: N.A.
Programming (via satellite): Starz!
Fee: N.A.
Pay-Per-View
Addressable homes: 1,402.
Viewer's Choice.
Local advertising: Yes (locally produced & insert). Available in satellite distributed programming.
Equipment: Jerrold & Scientific-Atlanta headend; Scientific-Atlanta & GTE Sylvania amplifiers; Comm/Scope & Phelps-Dodge cable; Scientific-Atlanta satellite antenna; Scientific-Atlanta satellite receivers.
Miles of plant: 187.9 (coaxial). Homes passed: 14,127. Total homes in franchised area: 14,127.
Manager: Mike McKee. Customer service manager: Mary Lund.
City fee: 5% of gross.
Ownership: AT&T Broadband & Internet Services (MSO); Time Warner Cable (MSO); Advance/Newhouse Partnership (MSO).

ORANGE GROVE—TCI Cablevision of Texas, 4060 S. Padre Island Dr., Corpus Christi, TX 78411-4477. Phone: 512-857-5000. County: Jim Wells. ICA: TX0510.
TV Market Ranking: Below 100. Franchise award date: N.A. Franchise expiration date: N.A. Began: August 1, 1984.
Channel capacity: 30. Channels available but not in use: 18.
Basic Service
Subscribers: 215.
Programming (received off-air): KEDT (P), KIII (A), KORO (S), KRIS-TV (N), KZTV (C) Corpus Christi.
Programming (via satellite): CNN; Discovery Channel; ESPN; Fox Family Channel; Nashville Network; TBS Superstation.
Fee: $37.25 installation; $10.69 monthly; $18.62 additional installation.
Pay Service 1
Pay Units: 83.
Programming (via satellite): Showtime.
Fee: N.A.
Pay Service 2
Pay Units: 2.
Programming (via satellite): The New Encore.
Fee: N.A.
Miles of plant: 6.9 (coaxial). Homes passed: 427. Total homes in franchised area: 500.
Manager: Dennis Moore. Chief technician: Mando Blancas. Marketing director: Jerri Coppedge.
City fee: 3% of gross.
Ownership: AT&T Broadband & Internet Services (MSO). Purchased from Tele-Communications Inc., March 9, 1999.

ORE CITY—Star Cable, Box 626, 200 Scurry St., Daingerfield, TX 75638. Phones: 903-645-7353; 800-327-2288. County: Upshur. ICA: TX0542.
TV Market Ranking: Below 100. Franchise award date: N.A. Franchise expiration date: N.A. Began: N.A.
Channel capacity: 62. Channels available but not in use: 30.
Basic Service
Subscribers: 397.
Programming (received off-air): KETK-TV (N) Jacksonville; KLTS-TV (P), KMSS-TV (F), KSHV (U,W), KSLA-TV (C), KTAL-TV (N), KTBS-TV (A) Shreveport-Texarkana; KLTV (A) Tyler-Longview.
Programming (via satellite): WGN-TV (W) Chicago; TBS Superstation.
Fee: $13.30 monthly; $1.50 converter.
Expanded Basic Service
Subscribers: 386.
Programming (via satellite): A & E; American Movie Classics; CNN; Country Music TV; Discovery Channel; ESPN; Fox Family Channel; Fox Sports Net Southwest; Lifetime; Nashville Network; Nick at Nite's TV Land; Nickelodeon; Sci-Fi Channel; The Weather Channel; Trinity Bcstg. Network; Turner Network TV; USA Network.
Fee: $16.45 monthly.
Pay Service 1
Pay Units: 40.
Programming (via satellite): Disney Channel.
Fee: $7.95 monthly.
Pay Service 2
Pay Units: 83.
Programming (via satellite): HBO.
Fee: $10.95 monthly.
Pay Service 3
Pay Units: 101.
Programming (via satellite): Showtime; The Movie Channel.
Fee: $12.95 monthly.
Miles of plant: 21.0 (coaxial). Homes passed: 686.
Manager: Jon Brown. Chief technician: Rory Dawkins.
Ownership: Star Cable Associates (MSO).

OYSTER CREEK—Star Cable, Drawer 1570, Brazoria, TX 77422. Phones: 409-798-9121; 800-395-2775. Fax: 409-798-4409. County: Brazoria. Also serves Freeport, Surfside Beach, Turtle Cove. ICA: TX0283.
TV Market Ranking: Below 100. Franchise award date: N.A. Franchise expiration date: N.A. Began: N.A.
Channel capacity: 42 (not 2-way capable). Channels available but not in use: 5.
Basic Service
Subscribers: 548; Commercial subscribers: 274.
Programming (received off-air): KHSH-TV (H) Alvin; KVVV (I) Baytown; KLTJ (E), KTMD (O) Galveston; KETH (E), KHOU-TV (C), KHTV (W), KPRC-TV (N), KRIV (F), KTRK-TV (A), KTXH (U), KUHT (P) Houston; KXLN-TV (S) Rosenberg.
Programming (via satellite): WGN-TV (W) Chicago; TBS Superstation.
Fee: $15.09 monthly; $2.15 converter.
Expanded Basic Service
Subscribers: 523.
Programming (via satellite): CNN; Country Music TV; Discovery Channel; ESPN; Fox Family Channel; Fox Sports Net Southwest; Headline News; History Channel; Home & Garden Television; Lifetime; MTV; Nashville Network; Nickelodeon; QVC; The Weather Channel; Turner Network TV; USA Network.
Fee: $16.55 monthly.
Pay Service 1
Pay Units: 82.
Programming (via satellite): Disney Channel.
Fee: $7.95 monthly.
Pay Service 2
Pay Units: 188.
Programming (via satellite): HBO.
Fee: $10.95 monthly.
Pay Service 3
Pay Units: 163.
Programming (via satellite): Showtime; The Movie Channel.
Fee: $12.95 monthly.
Miles of plant: 34.5 (coaxial); None (fiber optic). Homes passed: 1,400. Total homes in franchised area: 1,400.
Manager: Mike Burns. Chief technician: Mayla Zubeck.
Ownership: Star Cable Associates (MSO).

OZONA—Circle Bar Cable TV Inc., Box 777, 1002 Ave. E, Ozona, TX 76943. Phone: 915-392-3323. County: Crockett. ICA: TX0252.
TV Market Ranking: Outside TV Markets. Franchise award date: N.A. Franchise expiration date: January 1, 2014. Began: February 9, 1955.
Channel capacity: 33 (not 2-way capable). Channels available but not in use: None.
Basic Service
Subscribers: 1,381.
Programming (received off-air): KACB-TV (N), KLST (C) San Angelo; 9 FMs.
Programming (via microwave): KMID (A), KPEJ (F) Odessa-Midland.
Programming (via satellite): WGN-TV (W) Chicago; KRMA-TV (P) Denver; A & E; CNN; Discovery Channel; Disney Channel; ESPN; Fox Family Channel; History Channel; Learning Channel; Lifetime; Nashville Network; Nickelodeon; Prime TV; TBS Superstation; Telemundo; The Weather Channel; Trinity Bcstg. Network; Turner Classic Movies; Turner Network TV; Univision; VH1.
Fee: $30.00 installation; $22.95 monthly.
Pay Service 1
Pay Units: N.A.
Programming (via satellite): Cinemax; HBO; Showtime; The Movie Channel.
Fee: $10.00 installation; $10.00 monthly (each).
Equipment: RCA headend; Scientific-Atlanta amplifiers; Times Fiber cable; Tocom set top converters; Andrew & Scientific-Atlanta satellite antenna; Hughes & Scientific-Atlanta satellite receivers.
Miles of plant: 50.0 (coaxial); None (fiber optic). Homes passed: 1,700. Total homes in franchised area: 1,700.
Manager: Bill Haynes.
City fee: None.
Ownership: UNEV Communications Inc. (MSO).

PADUCAH—Classic Cable, Box 429, 605 N.W. 3rd St., Plainville, KS 67663-0429. Phones: 785-434-7620; 800-999-8876. Fax: 785-434-2614. Counties: Cottle & Haskell. Also serves Rochester. ICA: TX0405.

TV Market Ranking: Outside TV Markets. Franchise award date: N.A. Franchise expiration date: N.A. Began: August 1, 1954.

Channel capacity: 40 (2-way capable). Channels available but not in use: N.A.

Basic Service

Subscribers: 593; Commercial subscribers: 75.

Programming (received off-air): KJTV (F) Lubbock; allband FM.

Programming (via microwave): KACV-TV (P), KAMR-TV (N), KCIT (F,U), KFDA-TV (C), KVII-TV (A) Amarillo.

Planned programming (via microwave): KTVT (C) Dallas-Fort Worth.

Programming (via satellite): WGN-TV (W) Chicago; A & E; American Movie Classics; Animal Planet; CNN; Cartoon Network; Country Music TV; Discovery Channel; Disney Channel; E! Entertainment TV; ESPN; Fox Family Channel; Fox News Channel; Fox Sports Net Southwest; Goodlife TV Network; Headline News; History Channel; Learning Channel; Lifetime; Nashville Network; Nick at Nite's TV Land; QVC; Sci-Fi Channel; TBS Superstation; The Weather Channel; Travel Channel; Trinity Bcstg. Network; Turner Network TV; USA Network; Univision.

Current originations: Automated time-weather; local news.

Fee: $35.00 installation; $29.95 monthly.

Pay Service 1

Pay Units: 52.

Programming (via satellite): Cinemax.

Fee: $9.95 monthly.

Pay Service 2

Pay Units: 90.

Programming (via satellite): HBO.

Fee: $9.95 monthly.

Pay Service 3

Pay Units: 26.

Programming (via satellite): Showtime.

Fee: $9.95 monthly.

Equipment: Ameco & Jerrold headend; CAS & Vikoa amplifiers; Comm/Scope & Times Fiber cable; Fort Worth Tower satellite antenna.

Miles of plant: 16.0 (coaxial). Homes passed: 923.

Manager: Bill Flowers. Chief technician: Rick Rattan. Marketing director: Jennifer Hauschild.

City fee: 2% of gross.

Ownership: Classic Cable (MSO).

PALACIOS—Falcon Cable TV, 822 Market St., Portland, TX 78374. Phone: 512-643-8588. Fax: 512-643-3641. County: Matagorda. ICA: TX0223.

TV Market Ranking: Outside TV Markets. Franchise award date: N.A. Franchise expiration date: N.A. Began: August 1, 1962.

Channel capacity: 62. Channels available but not in use: 22.

Basic Service

Subscribers: 1,044.

Programming (received off-air): KHOU-TV (C), KHTV (W), KPRC-TV (N), KRIV (F), KTRK-TV (A), KTXH (U), KUHT (P) Houston; KAVU-TV (A) Victoria; allband FM.

Programming (via satellite): Bravo; C-SPAN; Country Music TV; Disney Channel; E! Entertainment TV; ESPN; ESPN 2; FX; Fox Family Channel; GalaVision; Headline News; Home Shopping Network; Lifetime; Nashville Network; QVC; Sci-Fi Channel; Trinity Bcstg. Network; Univision.

Fee: $15.00 installation; $21.10 monthly; $2.00 converter; $7.50 additional installation.

Expanded Basic Service

Subscribers: 922.

Programming (via satellite): Comedy Central; Discovery Channel; TV Food Network; The Weather Channel; VH1.

Fee: $3.92 monthly.

Expanded Basic Service 2

Subscribers: 882.

Programming (via satellite): WGN-TV (W) Chicago; Fox Sports Net Southwest; History Channel; TBS Superstation; Turner Network TV.

Fee: $5.95 monthly.

Pay Service 1

Pay Units: 50.

Programming (via satellite): Cinemax.

Fee: $9.95 monthly.

Pay Service 2

Pay Units: 96.

Programming (via satellite): HBO.

Fee: $10.00 monthly.

Pay Service 3

Pay Units: 10.

Programming (via satellite): The Movie Channel.

Fee: $9.95 monthly.

Pay Service 4

Pay Units: 17.

Programming (via satellite): Showtime.

Fee: $9.95 monthly.

Local advertising: Yes. Regional interconnect: Cabletime.

Equipment: RCA headend; Jerrold amplifiers; Comm/Scope cable; AFC satellite antenna.

Miles of plant: 30.0 (coaxial). Homes passed: 3,200.

Office manager: Jenny Brumley. Chief technician: Mike Kelsch.

Franchise fee: 4% of gross.

Ownership: Falcon Communications LP (MSO), joint venture formed September 30, 1998. See Cable System Ownership.

PALESTINE—Paragon Cable, 418 Old Elkhart Rd., Palestine, TX 75801. Phone: 903-729-0133. Fax: 903-723-1019. County: Anderson. Also serves Anderson County, Elkhart. ICA: TX0070.

TV Market Ranking: Below 100 (portions of Anderson County, Elkhart, Palestine); Outside TV Markets (portions of Anderson County). Franchise award date: N.A. Franchise expiration date: April 8, 2000. Began: January 1, 1955.

Channel capacity: 52 (not 2-way capable). Channels available but not in use: 18.

Basic Service

Subscribers: 7,616.

Programming (received off-air): KPXD (X) Arlington; KETK-TV (N) Jacksonville; KFXK (F) Longview; KLTV (A) Tyler-Longview; 18 FMs.

Programming (via microwave): KDFW (F), KERA-TV (P), KXAS-TV (N), WFAA-TV (A) Dallas-Fort Worth.

Programming (via satellite): Fox Family Channel; Headline News; QVC; TBS Superstation.

Current originations: Automated time-weather; public access; government access; religious access; automated emergency alert; local sports.

Fee: $24.95 installation; $9.50 monthly; $15.00 additional installation.

Expanded Basic Service

Subscribers: N.A.

Programming (via microwave): KXTX-TV (I) Dallas-Fort Worth.

Programming (via satellite): WGN-TV (W) Chicago; A & E; BET; C-SPAN; CNN; Country Music TV; ESPN; Learning Channel; Lifetime; MTV; Nashville Network; Nickelodeon; The Inspirational Network; The Weather Channel.

Fee: $5.00 installation; $3.50 monthly.

Pay Service 1

Pay Units: N.A.

Programming (via satellite): Cinemax; Disney Channel; HBO; Showtime; The Movie Channel.

Fee: $19.95 installation; $7.00 monthly (Disney), $11.45 monthly (Cinemax, HBO TMC or Showtime).

Local advertising: Yes. Available in locally originated programming. Rates: $6.00/30 Seconds. Regional interconnect: Cabletime.

Program Guide: The Cable Guide.

Equipment: Scientific-Atlanta headend; Jerrold amplifiers; Comm/Scope cable; Sony cameras; Sony VTRs; Video Data Systems character generator; Jerrold & DX Engineering set top converters; Keystone traps; Andrew satellite antenna; Scientific-Atlanta satellite receivers.

Miles of plant: 187.0 (coaxial). Homes passed: 10,247. Total homes in franchised area: 10,554.

Manager: Ron Gardner. Chief technician: Rodney Harding.

City fee: 5% of gross.

Ownership: AT&T Broadband & Internet Services (MSO); Time Warner Cable (MSO); Advance/Newhouse Partnership (MSO).

PALO PINTO—Mallard Cablevision, 100-D El Chico Trail, Willow Park, TX 76087. Phones: 817-441-8073; 800-669-2288. Fax: 817-441-6464. County: Palo Pinto. ICA: TX0639.

TV Market Ranking: Outside TV Markets. Franchise award date: N.A. Franchise expiration date: N.A. Began: June 1, 1979.

Channel capacity: 27 (not 2-way capable). Channels available but not in use: 12.

Basic Service

Subscribers: 94.

Programming (received off-air): KDFW (F), KERA-TV (P), KTVT (C), KTXA (U), KXAS-TV (N), KXTX-TV (I), WFAA-TV (A) Dallas-Fort Worth; allband FM.

Programming (via satellite): WGN-TV (W) Chicago; A & E; ESPN; Fox Family Channel; Fox Sports Net Southwest; Nashville Network; Sci-Fi Channel; TBS Superstation.

Fee: $30.00 installation; $16.80 monthly.

Pay Service 1

Pay Units: 18.

Programming (via satellite): HBO.

Fee: $10.00 installation; $10.50 monthly.

Local advertising: No.

Equipment: Delta-Benco-Cascade headend; Texscan amplifiers; Comm/Scope cable; Pico traps.

Miles of plant: 5.0 (coaxial). Homes passed: 145.

Manager: Doug Grassmann.

Ownership: Mallard Cablevision (MSO). Purchased from Cambridge Communications, May 1, 1999.

PAMPA—Charter Communications Inc., Box 2373, 1423 N. Hobart, Pampa, TX 79065. Phone: 806-665-2381. Counties: Carson & Gray. Also serves Panhandle, White Deer. ICA: TX0064.

TV Market Ranking: 95 (Panhandle, White Deer); Outside TV Markets (Pampa). Franchise award date: N.A. Franchise expiration date: N.A. Began: February 17, 1967.

Channel capacity: 21. Channels available but not in use: None.

Basic Service

Subscribers: N.A.

Programming (received off-air): KACV-TV (P), KAMR-TV (N), KCIT (F,U), KFDA-TV (C), KVII-TV (A) Amarillo; allband FM.

Programming (via satellite): WGN-TV (W) Chicago; C-SPAN; C-SPAN 2; CNBC; CNN; ESPN; Fox Sports Net Southwest; Nickelodeon; QVC; TBS Superstation; The Weather Channel; Turner Network TV.

Current originations: Automated time-weather; automated emergency alert.

Fee: $25.00 installation; $13.00 monthly.

Pay Service 1

Pay Units: N.A.

Programming (via satellite): Cinemax; Disney Channel; HBO; The Movie Channel.

Fee: $8.50 monthly (Disney), $9.95 monthly (Cinemax), $10.95 monthly (TMC), $11.75 monthly (HBO).

Equipment: Scientific-Atlanta headend; GTE Sylvania amplifiers; Oak set top converters; Scientific-Atlanta satellite antenna.

Miles of plant: 115.4 (coaxial). Homes passed: 11,871.

Manager: John Mason. Chief technician: Jim Hampton.

City fee: 5% of gross.

Ownership: Charter Communications Inc. (MSO). Purchased from Marcus Cable, April 1, 1999.

PARADISE—Torrence Cablevision, Box 1167, Ridgeland, MS 39158. Phones: 601-981-6900; 800-977-8849. County: Wise. ICA: TX0679.

TV Market Ranking: 12. Franchise award date: N.A. Franchise expiration date: N.A. Began: N.A.

Channel capacity: 36. Channels available but not in use: 21.

Basic Service

Subscribers: 27.

Programming (received off-air): KDFW (F), KERA-TV (P), KTVT (C), KXAS-TV (N), KXTX-TV (I), WFAA-TV (A) Dallas-Fort Worth.

Programming (via satellite): WGN-TV (W) Chicago; A & E; American Movie Classics; CNN; Country Music TV; Discovery Channel; ESPN; Fox Family Channel; Showtime; TBS Superstation; Turner Network TV; USA Network.

Fee: $28.00 monthly.

Miles of plant: 3.8 (coaxial). Homes passed: 127.

Ownership: Torrence Cable Inc. (MSO).

PARIS—TCA Cable TV, 25 S.E. 19th St., Paris, TX 75460-6101. Phone: 903-785-0086. Fax: 903-784-7099.

Web site: http://www.tca-cable.com.

County: Lamar. Also serves Lamar County (unincorporated areas), Reno (Lamar County). ICA: TX0060.

TV Market Ranking: Outside TV Markets. Franchise award date: June 11, 1984. Franchise expiration date: June 11, 2009. Began: April 1, 1956.

Channel capacity: 30 (2-way capable; operating 2-way). Channels available but not in use: None.

Basic Service

Subscribers: 11,300.

Programming (received off-air): KTEN (A,N,F) Ada; KXII (C) Sherman; 14 FMs.

Programming (via microwave): KDFW (F), KERA-TV (P), KTVT (C), KXAS-TV (N), WFAA-TV (A) Dallas-Fort Worth.

Programming (via satellite): WGN-TV (W) Chicago; Home Shopping Network; TBS Superstation.

Current originations: Automated time-weather; educational access; government access; religious access; leased access; automated emergency alert.
Fee: $31.41 installation; $17.13 monthly; $2.00 converter.
Expanded Basic Service
Subscribers: 10,202.
Programming (via satellite): BET; CNN; Discovery Channel; ESPN; Fox Family Channel; Fox Sports Net Southwest; Goodlife TV Network; Lifetime; Nashville Network; Nick at Nite; Nickelodeon; Odyssey; Sci-Fi Channel; The Weather Channel; Trinity Bcstg. Network; Turner Network TV; USA Network.
Fee: $4.19 installation; $10.65 monthly.
Pay Service 1
Pay Units: 1,726.
Programming (via satellite): Cinemax.
Fee: $4.19 installation; $8.00 monthly.
Pay Service 2
Pay Units: 800.
Programming (via satellite): Disney Channel.
Fee: $4.19 installation; $8.00 monthly.
Pay Service 3
Pay Units: 3,590.
Programming (via satellite): HBO.
Fee: $4.19 installation; $10.00 monthly.
Local advertising: Yes (locally produced). Available in satellite distributed & character-generated programming. Local sales manager: Steve Golden. Regional interconnect: Cabletime.
Program Guide: Premium Channels.
Equipment: Scientific-Atlanta headend; C-COR amplifiers; Comm/Scope cable; Texscan character generator; Jerrold set top converters; Eagle traps; Scientific-Atlanta satellite antenna; Scientific-Atlanta satellite receivers.
Miles of plant: 239.0 (coaxial). Additional miles planned: 5.0 (coaxial). Homes passed: 14,750. Total homes in franchised area: 14,750.
Manager: Tim Masters. Chief technician: Bob Holmon.
City fee: 2% of gross.
Ownership: TCA Cable TV Inc. (MSO); AT&T Broadband & Internet Services (MSO). See Cable System Ownership.

PARKWAY VILLAGE—Warner Cable, Box 1960, 875 North St., Vidor, TX 77670-1960. Phones: 409-769-8161; 800-828-8380. County: Jefferson. ICA: TX0668.
TV Market Ranking: 88. Franchise award date: July 30, 1982. Franchise expiration date: N.A. Began: August 1, 1983.
Channel capacity: 36 (not 2-way capable). Channels available but not in use: 14.
Basic Service
Subscribers: 29.
Programming (received off-air): KBMT (A), KFDM-TV (C), KITU (E) Beaumont-Port Arthur; KVHP (F) Lake Charles.
Programming (via satellite): WGN-TV (W) Chicago; C-SPAN; QVC; TBS Superstation.
Fee: $29.30 installation; $12.57 monthly; $1.75 converter.
Expanded Basic Service
Subscribers: N.A.
Programming (via satellite): A & E; American Movie Classics; BET; CNN; Cartoon Network; Country Music TV; Discovery Channel; Disney Channel; ESPN; Fox Family Channel; Headline News; Learning Channel; Lifetime; MTV; Nashville Network; Nickelodeon; Prime Sports Radio; The Weather Channel; Turner Classic Movies; Turner Network TV; USA Network; VH1.
Fee: $20.00 installation; $17.99 monthly.
Pay Service 1
Pay Units: 14.
Programming (via satellite): HBO.
Fee: $20.00 installation; $11.45 monthly.
Pay Service 2
Pay Units: 13.
Programming (via satellite): Showtime.
Fee: $20.00 installation; $11.45 monthly.
Local advertising: No.
Program Guide: Premium Channels.
Equipment: Scientific-Atlanta headend; Magnavox amplifiers; Comm/Scope cable; Scientific-Atlanta & Jerrold set top converters; Pico & Eagle traps; Scientific-Atlanta satellite antenna; Scientific-Atlanta satellite receivers.
Miles of plant: 2.0 (coaxial). Homes passed: 140. Total homes in franchised area: 140.
Manager: Jim Dwyer. Marketing director: Bill Forgey.
Franchise fee: 2.5% of gross.
Ownership: Time Warner Cable (MSO); Fanch Communications Inc. (MSO). See Cable System Ownership.

PEARSALL—Time Warner Communications, 625 N. Oak St., Pearsall, TX 78061. Phones: 830-334-4231; 800-527-6221. Fax: 830-334-2647. County: Frio. Also serves Frio County. ICA: TX0196.
TV Market Ranking: 45 (portions of Frio County); Outside TV Markets (portions of Frio County, Pearsall). Franchise award date: N.A. Franchise expiration date: N.A. Began: May 1, 1975.
Channel capacity: 38 (2-way capable; operating 2-way). Channels available but not in use: N.A.
Basic Service
Subscribers: 2,116.
Programming (received off-air): KRRT (W) Kerrville-San Antonio; KABB (F), KENS-TV (C), KLRN (P), KMOL-TV (N), KSAT-TV (A), KVDA (O), KWEX-TV (S) San Antonio.
Programming (via satellite): Animal Planet; C-SPAN; CNN; Cartoon Network; Country Music TV; Discovery Channel; ESPN; EWTN; FX; Fox Family Channel; Fox News Channel; Fox Sports Net Southwest; GalaVision; Headline News; Home Shopping Network; Learning Channel; Lifetime; MOVIEplex; MTV; Nashville Network; Nickelodeon; TBS Superstation; The Weather Channel; Trinity Bcstg. Network; Turner Network TV; USA Network.
Current originations: Public access; local news.
Fee: $24.95 installation; $22.46 monthly; $30.00 additional installation.
Pay Service 1
Pay Units: 161.
Programming (via satellite): Disney Channel.
Fee: $15.00 installation; $10.45 monthly.
Pay Service 2
Pay Units: 439.
Programming (via satellite): HBO.
Fee: $15.00 installation; $12.90 monthly.
Pay Service 3
Pay Units: 310.
Programming (via satellite): Showtime.
Fee: $15.00 installation; $12.90 monthly.
Pay Service 4
Pay Units: N.A.
Programming (via satellite): Starz!; The New Encore.
Fee: $1.75 monthly (Encore), $6.75 monthly (Starz).
Local advertising: Yes.
Equipment: Jerrold, Microdyne & Scientific-Atlanta headend; RCA amplifiers; Comm/Scope cable; RCA cameras; RCA VTRs; Hamlin set top converters; AFC satellite antenna.
Homes passed: 2,461. Total homes in franchised area: 3,084.
Manager: Marcos Reyes.
City fee: 3% of gross.
Ownership: AT&T Broadband & Internet Services (MSO); Time Warner Cable (MSO); Advance/Newhouse Partnership (MSO). Purchased from Tele-Communications Inc., December 31, 1998.

PECAN GAP—Torrence Cablevision, Box 1167, Ridgeland, MS 39158. Phones: 601-981-6900; 800-977-8849. County: Delta. ICA: TX0831.
TV Market Ranking: Outside TV Markets. Franchise award date: N.A. Franchise expiration date: N.A. Began: N.A.
Channel capacity: 36. Channels available but not in use: 21.
Basic Service
Subscribers: 36.
Programming (received off-air): KDAF (W), KDFW (F), KERA-TV (P), KXAS-TV (N), WFAA-TV (A) Dallas-Fort Worth.
Programming (via satellite): WGN-TV (W) Chicago; A & E; American Movie Classics; CNN; Country Music TV; Discovery Channel; ESPN; Fox Family Channel; Showtime; TBS Superstation; Turner Network TV; USA Network.
Fee: $28.00 monthly.
Miles of plant: 2.8 (coaxial). Homes passed: 112.
Ownership: Torrence Cable Inc. (MSO).

PECOS—Classic Cable, Box 587, 1504 N. Main St., Monahans, TX 79756. Phone: 915-943-4335. County: Reeves. Also serves Reeves County (portions). ICA: TX0138.
TV Market Ranking: Outside TV Markets. Franchise award date: July 12, 1979. Franchise expiration date: July 11, 1999. Began: March 17, 1955.
Channel capacity: 61 (2-way capable). Channels available but not in use: N.A.
Basic Service
Subscribers: 2,980.
Programming (received off-air): KMLM (I), KOSA-TV (C) Odessa-Midland; allband FM.
Programming (via microwave): KMID (A), KPEJ (F), KWES-TV (N) Odessa-Midland.
Programming (via satellite): WGN-TV (W) Chicago; KTLA (W) Los Angeles; A & E; American Movie Classics; C-SPAN; CNBC; CNN; Country Music TV; Discovery Channel; ESPN; EWTN; Electronic Program Guide Jr.; Fox Family Channel; GalaVision; Goodlife TV Network; Headline News; Learning Channel; Lifetime; MTV; Nashville Network; Nickelodeon; Odyssey; QVC; TBS Superstation; Telemundo; The Weather Channel; Turner Network TV; USA Network; Univision; VH1.
Current originations: Automated time-weather.
Fee: $35.00 installation; $27.95 monthly.
Pay Service 1
Pay Units: 173.
Programming (via satellite): Cinemax.
Fee: $9.95 monthly.
Pay Service 2
Pay Units: 414.
Programming (via satellite): HBO.
Fee: $10.95 monthly.
Pay Service 3
Pay Units: 92.
Programming (via satellite): Showtime.
Fee: $9.95 monthly.
Pay Service 4
Pay Units: 189.
Programming (via satellite): The Movie Channel.
Fee: $5.95 monthly.
Local advertising: Yes. Regional interconnect: Cabletime.
Equipment: Scientific-Atlanta amplifiers; Cerro & Times Fiber cable; Scientific-Atlanta set top converters; Eagle traps; Scientific-Atlanta satellite antenna; Scientific-Atlanta satellite receivers.
Miles of plant: 64.0 (coaxial). Homes passed: 4,586. Total homes in franchised area: 4,635.
Manager: Bill Flowers. Chief technician: Ben Hernandez. Marketing director: Jennifer Hauschild.
City fee: 2% of gross.
Ownership: Classic Cable (MSO).

PELICAN BAY—SouthTel Communications LP, Suite 202, 2444 Solomons Island Rd., Annapolis, MD 21401. Phone: 410-266-9393. County: Tarrant. Also serves Briar. ICA: TX0832.
TV Market Ranking: 12. Franchise award date: N.A. Franchise expiration date: N.A. Began: July 1, 1984.
Channel capacity: 54. Channels available but not in use: N.A.
Basic Service
Subscribers: 331.
Programming (received off-air): KDAF (W), KDFI-TV (I), KDFW (F), KERA-TV (P), KTVT (C), KTXA (U), KXAS-TV (N), KXTX-TV (I), WFAA-TV (A) Dallas-Fort Worth.
Programming (via satellite): WGN-TV (W) Chicago; CNN; Country Music TV; Discovery Channel; ESPN; Fox Family Channel; Headline News; Home Shopping Network; Learning Channel; MuchMoreMusic; Nashville Network; Nickelodeon; QVC; TBS Superstation; The Weather Channel; Turner Network TV; USA Network.
Fee: $25.00 installation; $25.55 monthly.
Pay Service 1
Pay Units: N.A.
Programming (via satellite): Disney Channel; HBO; Showtime.
Fee: N.A.
Miles of plant: 11.2 (coaxial).
Manager: Roy E. Hays.
Ownership: Bay Cable Inc. (MSO). Purchased from Brookridge Cable Special Purpose Partnership, June 1, 1998.

PERRIN—Mallard Cablevision, 100-D El Chico Trail, Willow Park, TX 76087. Phones: 817-441-8073; 800-669-2288. Fax: 817-441-6464. County: Jack. ICA: TX0640.
TV Market Ranking: Outside TV Markets. Franchise award date: N.A. Franchise expiration date: N.A. Began: December 1, 1984.
Channel capacity: 27. Channels available but not in use: 12.
Basic Service
Subscribers: 97.
Programming (received off-air): KDFW (F), KERA-TV (P), KTVT (C), KTXA (U), KXAS-TV (N), KXTX-TV (I), WFAA-TV (A) Dallas-Fort Worth.
Programming (via satellite): WGN-TV (W) Chicago; A & E; ESPN; Fox Family Channel; Fox Sports Net Southwest; Nashville Network; Sci-Fi Channel; TBS Superstation.
Fee: $30.00 installation; $16.80 monthly; $20.00 additional installation.
Pay Service 1
Pay Units: 20.
Programming (via satellite): Cinemax.
Fee: $10.00 installation; $9.95 monthly.
Pay Service 2
Pay Units: 23.
Programming (via satellite): HBO.
Fee: $10.50 monthly.
Equipment: Blonder-Tongue headend; Anaconda amplifiers; Comm/Scope cable; Pico traps.

Miles of plant: 5.0 (coaxial). Homes passed: 136.
Manager: Doug Grassmann.
Ownership: Mallard Cablevision (MSO). Purchased from Cambridge Communications, May 1, 1999.

PERRYTON—TCA Cable of Perryton, Box 949, 217 S. Ash St., Perryton, TX 79070. Phone: 806-435-3231. Fax: 806-435-7887. Web site: http://www.tca-cable.com. County: Ochiltree. ICA: TX0165.
TV Market Ranking: Outside TV Markets. Franchise award date: July 17, 1957. Franchise expiration date: N.A. Began: January 1, 1957.
Channel capacity: 42 (not 2-way capable). Channels available but not in use: N.A.
Basic Service
Subscribers: 2,608; Commercial subscribers: 20.
Programming (received off-air): KAMR-TV (N), KCIT (F,U), KFDA-TV (C), KVII-TV (A) Amarillo; KETA (P) Oklahoma City; 5 FMs.
Programming (via satellite): C-SPAN; C-SPAN 2; Discovery Channel; FX; Fox News Channel; Great American Country; Lifetime; Odyssey; Pax Net; QVC; TBS Superstation; The Weather Channel; Univision; VH1; WB 100+ Station Group.
Fee: $38.00 installation; $12.92 monthly; $2.25 converter; $25.00 additional installation.
Expanded Basic Service
Subscribers: 2,193.
Programming (via satellite): American Movie Classics; Animal Planet; CNBC; CNN; Cartoon Network; Disney Channel; ESPN; Fox Family Channel; Fox Sports Net Southwest; Learning Channel; MOVIEplex; MTV; Nashville Network; Nickelodeon; Turner Network TV; USA Network.
Fee: $15.05 monthly.
Pay Service 1
Pay Units: N.A.
Programming (via satellite): Cinemax; HBO; Showtime; Starz!; The New Encore.
Fee: $1.75 monthly (Encore); $6.75 monthly (Starz); $12.95 monthly (Cinemax); $13.40 monthly (HBO or Showtime Showtime).
Pay-Per-View
Viewer's Choice; movies.
Local advertising: Yes (insert only). Available in satellite distributed, taped & automated programming.
Equipment: Jerrold & Scientific-Atlanta headend; Jerrold amplifiers; Comm/Scope cable; Jerrold set top converters; Jerrold & Starcom addressable set top converters; Andrew & Scientific-Atlanta satellite antenna; Standard Communications satellite receivers.
Miles of plant: 43.0 (coaxial); None (fiber optic). Homes passed: 3,387. Total homes in franchised area: 3,387.
Manager: Jim Hall. Chief technician: Mike Wennberg.
City fee: 2% of gross.
Ownership: TCA Cable TV Inc. (MSO); AT&T Broadband & Internet Services (MSO). See Cable System Ownership.

PETERSBURG—Classic Cable, Box 429, 605 N.W. 3rd St., Plainville, KS 67663-0429. Phones: 785-434-7620; 800-999-8876. Fax: 785-434-2614. County: Hale. ICA: TX0483.
TV Market Ranking: Below 100. Franchise award date: April 12, 1982. Franchise expiration date: N.A. Began: May 1, 1982.
Channel capacity: 22 (2-way capable; operating 2-way). Channels available but not in use: N.A.
Basic Service
Subscribers: 137.
Programming (received off-air): KAMC (A), KCBD-TV (N), KJTV (F), KLBK-TV (C), KPTB (I), KTXT-TV (P) Lubbock.
Programming (via satellite): WGN-TV (W) Chicago; American Movie Classics; Animal Planet; CNN; Discovery Channel; Disney Channel; ESPN; Fox Family Channel; Headline News; History Channel; Learning Channel; Lifetime; Nashville Network; QVC; TBS Superstation; The Weather Channel; Travel Channel; Trinity Bcstg. Network; Turner Network TV; USA Network; Univision.
Fee: $35.00 installation; $26.95 monthly.
Pay Service 1
Pay Units: 9.
Programming (via satellite): Cinemax.
Fee: $9.95 monthly.
Pay Service 2
Pay Units: 34.
Programming (via satellite): HBO.
Fee: $9.95 monthly.
Local advertising: No.
Equipment: Weatherscan satellite antenna; Microdyne satellite receivers.
Miles of plant: 7.2 (coaxial). Homes passed: 487.
Manager: Bill Flowers. Chief technician: Chris Christenson. Marketing director: Jennifer Hauschild.
Ownership: Classic Cable (MSO).

PETTUS—Torrence Cablevision, Box 1167, Ridgeland, MS 39158. Phones: 601-981-6900; 800-977-8849. County: Bee. ICA: TX0561.
TV Market Ranking: Outside TV Markets. Franchise award date: N.A. Franchise expiration date: N.A. Began: N.A.
Channel capacity: 36. Channels available but not in use: 21.
Basic Service
Subscribers: 68.
Programming (received off-air): KABB (F), KENS-TV (C), KLRN (P), KMOL-TV (N), KSAT-TV (A) San Antonio.
Programming (via satellite): WGN-TV (W) Chicago; A & E; American Movie Classics; CNN; Country Music TV; Discovery Channel; ESPN; Fox Family Channel; Showtime; TBS Superstation; Turner Network TV; USA Network; Univision.
Fee: $28.00 monthly.
Miles of plant: 7.6 (coaxial). Homes passed: 250.
Ownership: Torrence Cable Inc. (MSO).

PFLUGERVILLE—Cablevision of Pflugerville Inc., Box 1999, 111 N. College St., Georgetown, TX 78627. Phones: 512-869-1505; 512-930-3085. Fax: 512-869-2962. County: Travis. ICA: TX0127.
TV Market Ranking: Below 100. Franchise award date: N.A. Franchise expiration date: January 17, 2015. Began: January 18, 1980.
Channel capacity: 78 (2-way capable; operating 2-way). Channels available but not in use: None.
Basic Service
Subscribers: 10,000.
Programming (received off-air): KEYE-TV (C), KLRU (P), KNVA (W), KTBC (F), KVUE-TV (A), KXAN-TV (N) Austin; K13VC (I) Austin, Cedar Park.
Programming (via satellite): WGN-TV (W) Chicago; Animal Planet; C-SPAN; C-SPAN 2; FX; Fox News Channel; Goodlife TV Network; Home & Garden Television; Knowledge TV; MSNBC; Outdoor Life Network; QVC; TV Food Network; TV Guide Channel; The Health Network; The Weather Channel; Toon Disney; Travel Channel.
Current originations: Automated time-weather; public access; educational access.
Fee: $20.00 installation; $27.99 monthly; $1.50 converter.
Expanded Basic Service
Subscribers: 9,000.
Programming (via satellite): A & E; American Movie Classics; BET; CNBC; CNN; Country Music TV; Court TV; Discovery Channel; Disney Channel; E! Entertainment TV; ESPN; ESPN 2; ESPN Classic Sports; ESPNews; Fox Family Channel; Fox Sports Net Southwest; Headline News; Learning Channel; Lifetime; MTV; Nashville Network; Nick at Nite's TV Land; Nickelodeon; Sci-Fi Channel; TBS Superstation; Trinity Bcstg. Network; Turner Network TV; USA Network; Univision; VH1.
Fee: $27.99 monthly.
A la Carte 1
Subscribers: N.A.
Programming (via satellite): Cartoon Network; Comedy Central; Golf Channel; History Channel; MOVIEplex; Speedvision; Sundance Channel; Turner Classic Movies.
Fee: $4.99 monthly (package); $1.25 monthly (each).
Pay Service 1
Pay Units: 581.
Programming (via satellite): Cinemax (multiplexed).
Fee: $9.99 monthly.
Pay Service 2
Pay Units: N.A.
Programming (via satellite): Starz!; The New Encore.
Fee: $9.99 monthly (Encore & Starz).
Pay Service 3
Pay Units: 1,523.
Programming (via satellite): HBO (multiplexed).
Fee: $11.99 monthly.
Pay Service 4
Pay Units: 1,172.
Programming (via satellite): Showtime.
Fee: $8.99 monthly.
Pay-Per-View
Addressable homes: 4,000.
Viewer's Choice 1 & 2.
Local advertising: Yes.
Equipment: Scientific-Atlanta headend; C-COR amplifiers; Comm/Scope & Times Fiber cable; Scientific-Atlanta set top converters; Arcom, Eagle & PPC traps; Pico addressable traps; Scientific-Atlanta & U.S. Tower satellite antenna; Microdyne & Standard Communications satellite receivers.
Miles of plant: 190.1 (coaxial); 18.4 (fiber optic). Additional miles planned: 20.0 (coaxial). Homes passed: 12,211.
Manager: Dale Hoffman. Chief technician & marketing director: Wesley Houghteling.
City fee: 3% of basic gross.
Ownership: M. K. McDaniel (MSO); John Muraglia (MSO); E. D. Hoffman (MSO); Connie Hartin III. See Cable System Ownership.

PHARR—Time Warner Communications, Box 2327, 2921 S. Expwy. 83, Harlingen, TX 78551. Phone: 956-425-7880. Fax: 956-412-0959. County: Hidalgo. Also serves Alamo, Edinburg, Lopezville, McAllen, San Juan (Hidalgo County). ICA: TX0017.
TV Market Ranking: Below 100. Franchise award date: N.A. Franchise expiration date: N.A. Began: January 1, 1966.
Channel capacity: 35. Channels available but not in use: 3.
Basic Service
Subscribers: 49,456.
Programming (received off-air): KVEO (N) Brownsville; KGBT-TV (C), KLUJ (E), KMBH (P) Harlingen; KRGV-TV (A) Weslaco; XHAB-TV Matamoros.
Programming (via satellite): C-SPAN; Discovery Channel; FX; Fox News Channel; QVC; TBS Superstation; Trinity Bcstg. Network; Univision.
Current originations: Educational access; government access.
Fee: $22.95 installation; $14.00 monthly.
Digital Basic Service
Subscribers: N.A.
Programming (via satellite): BBC America; Bravo; Discovery Home & Leisure Channel; Discovery Kids Channel; Discovery People; Discovery Science Channel; ESPN Classic Sports; ESPNews; Fox Sports World; Game Show Network; History Channel; Home & Garden Television; Independent Film Channel; MuchMusic Network; Outdoor Life Network; Romance Classics; Sci-Fi Channel; TV Guide Channel; Turner Classic Movies.
Fee: $25.00 installation; $39.99 monthly.
Expanded Basic Service
Subscribers: 46,676.
Programming (via satellite): A & E; American Movie Classics; CNN; CNNfn; Disney Channel; ESPN; EWTN; Fox Family Channel; Fox Sports Net Southwest; Gems Television; Headline News; Learning Channel; Lifetime; MTV; Nashville Network; Nickelodeon; The Weather Channel; Turner Network TV; USA Network.
Fee: $25.00 installation; $29.00 monthly.
Expanded Basic Service 2
Subscribers: N.A.
Programming (via satellite): Box Exitos; Box Tejano; CBS TeleNoticias; CNN en Espanol; Canal 9; CineLatino; Discovery en Espanol; Fox Sports World Espanol.
Fee: $6.99 monthly.
Pay Service 1
Pay Units: 5,950.
Programming (via satellite): Cinemax.
Fee: $12.45 monthly.
Pay Service 2
Pay Units: N.A.
Programming (via satellite): DMX; Showtime; Starz!; The New Encore.
Fee: $1.75 monthly (Encore), $6.75 monthly (Starz), $9.45 monthly (Showtime).
Pay Service 3
Pay Units: 10,173.
Programming (via satellite): HBO.
Fee: $12.90 monthly.
Digital Pay Service 1
Pay Units: N.A.
Programming (via satellite): DMX; Encore Love Stories; Encore Mystery; Encore Westerns; HBO Plus; HBO Signature; Showtime (multiplexed); Starz! (multiplexed); The Movie Channel.
Fee: $7.00 monthly (Showtime), $10.00 monthly (HBO or TMC).
Pay-Per-View
Spice delivered digitally; movies delivered digitally.
Local advertising: Yes. Regional interconnect: Cabletime.
Miles of plant: 619.9 (coaxial). Homes passed: 53,591. Total homes in franchised area: 53,597.
Manager: Juan Herrera.
Ownership: AT&T Broadband & Internet Services (MSO); Time Warner Cable (MSO); Advance/Newhouse Partnership (MSO).

PILOT POINT—Friendship Cable of Texas Inc., Box 9090, Tyler, TX 75711-9090. Phone: 903-581-2121. Fax: 903-581-2185. Counties: Collin, Denton & Grayson. Also serves Aubrey, Celina, Gunter, Krugerville, Lakewood Village, Little Elm, Oak Point, Prosper, Sanger, Tioga. ICA: TX0286.

TV Market Ranking: 12 (Celina, Little Elm, Oak Point, Prosper); Below 100 (Aubrey, Gunter, Krugerville, Lakewood Village, Pilot Point, Sanger, Tioga). Franchise award date: N.A. Franchise expiration date: N.A. Began: June 1, 1982.

Channel capacity: 54. Channels available but not in use: N.A.

Basic Service

Subscribers: 3,279.

Programming (received off-air): KPXD (X) Arlington; KDAF (W), KDFI-TV (I), KDFW (F), KERA-TV (P), KTVT (C), KTXA (U), KXAS-TV (N), KXTX-TV (I), WFAA-TV (A) Dallas-Fort Worth.

Programming (via satellite): CNN; Disney Channel; ESPN; Fox Family Channel; Headline News; Nickelodeon; Turner Classic Movies; USA Network.

Fee: $30.00 installation; $31.10 monthly.

Pay Service 1

Pay Units: 369.

Programming (via satellite): Cinemax.

Fee: $7.00 monthly.

Pay Service 2

Pay Units: 400.

Programming (via satellite): HBO.

Fee: $12.00 monthly.

Pay Service 3

Pay Units: 285.

Programming (via satellite): The Movie Channel.

Fee: $9.00 monthly.

Pay Service 4

Pay Units: 491.

Programming (via satellite): Showtime.

Fee: $7.00 monthly.

Pay Service 5

Pay Units: 654.

Programming (via satellite): Flix.

Fee: $1.95 monthly.

Local advertising: Yes. Regional interconnect: Cabletime.

Miles of plant: 157.5 (coaxial). Homes passed: 5,228.

Manager: Rodney Fletcher. Chief technician: Bo Jaubert.

Ownership: Buford Television Inc. (MSO). See Cable System Ownership.

PINELAND—Star Cable, 595 San Antonio Ave., Many, LA 71449. Phone: 318-256-2097. Fax: 318-256-9536. County: Sabine. ICA: TX0524.

TV Market Ranking: Outside TV Markets. Franchise award date: N.A. Franchise expiration date: N.A. Began: February 1, 1975.

Channel capacity: 12. Channels available but not in use: 4.

Basic Service

Subscribers: N.A.

Programming (received off-air): KALB-TV (N) Alexandria; KBMT (A), KBTV-TV (N), KFDM-TV (C) Beaumont-Port Arthur; KPLC-TV (N) Lake Charles; KTRE (A) Lufkin; KSLA-TV (C), KTBS-TV (A) Shreveport-Texarkana; allband FM.

Planned programming (received off-air): KTAL-TV (N) Shreveport-Texarkana.

Fee: $5.00 installation; $6.45 monthly.

Equipment: Blonder-Tongue headend; Coral & SKL amplifiers; Coral & SKL cable.

Miles of plant: 6.0 (coaxial). Homes passed: 400.

City fee: 2% of gross.

Ownership: Star Cable Associates (MSO). Purchased from Illini Cablevision Inc., February 1, 1999.

PITTSBURG—TCA Cable TV, 919 W. First St., Mount Pleasant, TX 75455-4301. Phone: 903-572-6107. Fax: 903-572-5669. Web site: http://www.tca-cable.com. County: Camp. Also serves Camp County (portions). ICA: TX0219.

TV Market Ranking: Below 100 (portions of Camp County, Pittsburg); Outside TV Markets (portions of Camp County). Franchise award date: N.A. Franchise expiration date: N.A. Began: November 1, 1969.

Channel capacity: 36. Channels available but not in use: N.A.

Basic Service

Subscribers: 1,388.

Programming (received off-air): K54CB (I) Mount Pleasant; KMSS-TV (F), KSLA-TV (C), KTAL-TV (N), KTBS-TV (A) Shreveport-Texarkana; KLTV (A) Tyler-Longview.

Programming (via microwave): KDFW (F), KERA-TV (P), KTVT (C), KXAS-TV (N), WFAA-TV (A) Dallas-Fort Worth.

Programming (via satellite): A & E; BET; C-SPAN; CNN; Fox Family Channel; Headline News; Lifetime; MTV; Nashville Network; Nickelodeon; QVC; TBS Superstation; The Weather Channel.

Fee: $31.86 installation; $10.08 monthly.

Commercial fee: $29.95 monthly.

Expanded Basic Service

Subscribers: 1,277.

Programming (via satellite): American Movie Classics; ESPN; Fox Sports Net Southwest; Turner Network TV; USA Network.

Fee: $10.97 monthly.

Pay Service 1

Pay Units: 57.

Programming (via satellite): Cinemax.

Fee: $25.00 installation; $11.00 monthly.

Pay Service 2

Pay Units: 62.

Programming (via satellite): Disney Channel.

Fee: $25.00 installation; $11.00 monthly.

Pay Service 3

Pay Units: 301.

Programming (via satellite): HBO.

Fee: $25.00 installation; $11.00 monthly.

Pay Service 4

Pay Units: 23.

Programming (via satellite): The Movie Channel.

Fee: $25.00 installation; $11.00 monthly.

Pay Service 5

Pay Units: 74.

Programming (via satellite): Showtime.

Fee: $25.00 installation; $11.00 monthly.

Pay Service 6

Pay Units: 364.

Programming (via satellite): The New Encore.

Fee: N.A.

Local advertising: Yes. Regional interconnect: Cabletime.

Equipment: Scientific-Atlanta headend; Jerrold amplifiers; Times Fiber cable; Scientific-Atlanta satellite antenna; Scientific-Atlanta satellite receivers.

Miles of plant: 33.2 (coaxial). Homes passed: 2,016. Total homes in franchised area: 11,218.

Manager: Ron Eubanks.

City fee: 3% of gross.

Ownership: TCA Cable TV Inc. (MSO); AT&T Broadband & Internet Services (MSO). See Cable System Ownership.

PLACEDO—Torrence Cablevision, Box 1167, Ridgeland, MS 39158. Phones: 601-981-6900; 800-977-8849. County: Victoria. ICA: TX0641.

TV Market Ranking: Below 100. Franchise award date: N.A. Franchise expiration date: N.A. Began: N.A.

Channel capacity: 35. Channels available but not in use: 14.

Basic Service

Subscribers: 45.

Programming (received off-air): KAVU-TV (A), KVCT (F) Victoria.

Programming (via satellite): WGN-TV (W) Chicago; KCNC-TV (C), KMGH-TV (A), KUSA-TV (N) Denver; A & E; American Movie Classics; CNN; Country Music TV; Discovery Channel; ESPN; Fox Family Channel; Showtime; TBS Superstation; The Weather Channel; Turner Network TV; USA Network.

Fee: $21.00 monthly.

Pay Service 1

Pay Units: 6.

Programming (via satellite): Disney Channel.

Fee: $10.95 monthly.

Pay Service 2

Pay Units: 33.

Programming (via satellite): HBO.

Fee: $10.95 monthly.

Miles of plant: 5.8 (coaxial). Homes passed: 209.

Ownership: Torrence Cable Inc. (MSO).

PLAINS—Classic Cable, Box 429, 605 N.W. 3rd St., Plainville, KS 67663-0429. Phones: 785-434-7620; 800-999-8876. Fax: 785-434-2614. County: Yoakum. ICA: TX0457.

TV Market Ranking: Below 100. Franchise award date: September 1, 1988. Franchise expiration date: August 31, 2003. Began: July 1, 1979.

Channel capacity: 36 (2-way capable; operating 2-way). Channels available but not in use: N.A.

Basic Service

Subscribers: 319.

Programming (received off-air): KAMC (A), KCBD-TV (N), KJTV (F), KLBK-TV (C) Lubbock; KENW (P) Portales.

Programming (via satellite): WGN-TV (W) Chicago; CNN; Cartoon Network; Country Music TV; Discovery Channel; Disney Channel; ESPN; Fox Family Channel; Home Shopping Network; Learning Channel; Lifetime; Nashville Network; Nick at Nite's TV Land; Nickelodeon; TBS Superstation; The Weather Channel; Trinity Bcstg. Network; Turner Classic Movies; Turner Network TV; USA Network; Univision.

Fee: $35.00 installation; $27.95 monthly.

Pay Service 1

Pay Units: 17.

Programming (via satellite): Showtime.

Fee: $9.95 monthly.

Pay Service 2

Pay Units: 43.

Programming (via satellite): HBO.

Fee: $11.95 monthly.

Equipment: Cascade amplifiers; Times Fiber cable; Scientific-Atlanta set top converters; Eagle traps; Fort Worth Tower satellite antenna; Scientific-Atlanta satellite receivers.

Miles of plant: 12.0 (coaxial). Homes passed: 591.

Manager: Bill Flowers. Chief technician: Chris Christenson. Marketing director: Jennifer Hauschild.

Ownership: Classic Cable (MSO).

PLAINVIEW—TCA Cable TV, Box 428, 2301 W. 5th St., Plainview, TX 79072. Phone: 806-293-2551. Fax: 806-293-1152. Web site: http://www.tca-cable.com. County: Hale. Also serves Hale County. ICA: TX0076.

TV Market Ranking: Below 100 (portions of Hale County); Outside TV Markets (portions of Hale County, Plainview). Franchise award date: N.A. Franchise expiration date: N.A. Began: March 15, 1965.

Channel capacity: 33. Channels available but not in use: N.A.

Basic Service

Subscribers: 6,850.

Programming (received off-air): KAMR-TV (N), KVII-TV (A) Amarillo; KAMC (A), KCBD-TV (N), KJTV (F), KLBK-TV (C), KTXT-TV (P) Lubbock; allband FM.

Programming (via satellite): CNN; Fox Family Channel; TBS Superstation; Univision.

Current originations: Automated time-weather.

Fee: $36.05 installation; $10.00 monthly.

Pay Service 1

Pay Units: N.A.

Programming (via satellite): Disney Channel; ESPN; MTV; Nashville Network; Nickelodeon; Showtime; The Movie Channel; USA Network.

Fee: $35.00 installation.

Local advertising: Yes. Regional interconnect: Cabletime.

Equipment: Scientific-Atlanta headend; GTE Sylvania amplifiers; Comm/Scope cable; Video Data Systems character generator; Tocom addressable set top converters; Scientific-Atlanta satellite antenna; Scientific-Atlanta satellite receivers.

Miles of plant: 103.5 (coaxial). Homes passed: 9,500.

Manager: Pete Strom. Chief technician: Roger Jones.

City fee: 3% of gross.

Ownership: TCA Cable TV Inc. (MSO); AT&T Broadband & Internet Services (MSO). See Cable System Ownership.

PLANO—TCI of Plano Inc., 1414 Summit Ave., Plano, TX 75074. Phone: 972-578-7573. Fax: 972-423-2248. Counties: Collin & Dallas. Also serves Murphy, Parker, Richardson. ICA: TX0833.

TV Market Ranking: 12. Franchise award date: N.A. Franchise expiration date: August 1, 1998. Began: September 19, 1984.

Channel capacity: 110 (2-way capable; operating 2-way). Channels available but not in use: N.A.

Basic Service

Subscribers: 66,250.

Programming (received off-air): KDAF (W), KDFI-TV (I), KDFW (F), KERA-TV (P), KTVT (C), KTXA (U), KXAS-TV (N), KXTX-TV (I), WFAA-TV (A) Dallas-Fort Worth; KHSX-TV (H) Irving.

Programming (via satellite): WGN-TV (W) Chicago; A & E; BET; C-SPAN; C-SPAN 2; CNBC; CNN; Country Music TV; ESPN; EWTN; Fox Family Channel; Headline News; Learning Channel; Lifetime; MTV; Nashville Network; National Jewish TV; News Plus; Nickelodeon; Odyssey; TBS Superstation; The Inspirational Network; The Weather Channel; Travel Channel; Trinity Bcstg. Network; USA Network; Univision; VH1.

Current originations: Public access; educational access; government access.

Fee: $17.53 installation; $11.19 monthly.

Expanded Basic Service

Subscribers: 60,107.

Programming (via satellite): Disney Channel.

Fee: $18.33 monthly.

Pay Service 1

Pay Units: N.A.

Programming (via satellite): Cinemax; HBO; Showtime; Starz!; The Movie Channel; The New Encore.

Fee: $10.00 installation; $1.75 monthly (Encore), $6.75 monthly (Starz), $10.00 monthly (Cinemax, HBO, Showtime or TMC).

Local advertising: Yes. Available in satellite distributed programming. Local sales manager: Clay Dover.

Program Guide: The Cable Guide.

Equipment: Scientific-Atlanta headend; Jerrold amplifiers; Comm/Scope cable; Sony VTRs; Video Data Systems character generator; Jerrold & Magnavox set top converters; Zenith addressable set top converters; Scientific-Atlanta satellite antenna; Scientific-Atlanta satellite receivers.

Miles of plant: 1260.1 (coaxial); 66.3 (fiber optic). Homes passed: 96,547.

Manager: Vince Thomae. Chief technician: Don Sargent. Program director: Jenni Ladd. Marketing director: Cathy Putman.

City fee: 5% of gross.

Ownership: AT&T Broadband & Internet Services (MSO). Purchased from Tele-Communications Inc., March 9, 1999.

PLEAK—Star Cable, Drawer 1570, Brazoria, TX 77422. Phones: 409-798-9121; 800-395-2775. Fax: 409-798-4409. Counties: Fort Bend & Wharton. Also serves Beasley, Hungerford, Kendleton. ICA: TX0265.

TV Market Ranking: Below 100. Franchise award date: N.A. Franchise expiration date: N.A. Began: August 1, 1989.

Channel capacity: 52 (not 2-way capable). Channels available but not in use: 12.

Basic Service

Subscribers: 543.

Programming (received off-air): KVVV (I) Baytown; KLTJ (E), KTMD (O) Galveston; KETH (E), KHOU-TV (C), KHTV (W), KPRC-TV (N), KRIV (F), KTRK-TV (A), KTXH (U), KUHT (P) Houston; KNWS-TV (I) Katy; KXLN-TV (S) Rosenberg.

Programming (via satellite): WGN-TV (W) Chicago; A & E; American Movie Classics; BET; CNN; Country Music TV; Discovery Channel; ESPN; Fox Family Channel; Fox Sports Net Southwest; Lifetime; MTV; Nashville Network; Nickelodeon; QVC; TBS Superstation; The Weather Channel; Turner Network TV; USA Network; VH1.

Fee: $31.34 monthly; $2.15 converter.

Pay Service 1

Pay Units: 71.

Programming (via satellite): Cinemax.

Fee: $10.95 monthly.

Pay Service 2

Pay Units: 76.

Programming (via satellite): Disney Channel.

Fee: $7.95 monthly.

Pay Service 3

Pay Units: 146.

Programming (via satellite): HBO.

Fee: $10.95 monthly.

Pay Service 4

Pay Units: 169.

Programming (via satellite): Showtime; The Movie Channel.

Fee: $12.95 monthly.

Miles of plant: 84.6 (coaxial); None (fiber optic). Homes passed: 1,585. Total homes in franchised area: 1,585.

Manager: Mike Burns. Chief technician: Mayla Zubeck.

Ownership: Star Cable Associates (MSO).

PLEASANT VALLEY—Rapid Cable, Box 6310, 310 Walnut Extension, Branson, MO 65615. Phones: 417-334-7897; 800-972-0962. Fax: 417-334-7899. E-mail: rcpcable@aol.com. County: Wichita. Also serves Iowa Park. ICA: TX0466.

TV Market Ranking: Below 100. Franchise award date: N.A. Franchise expiration date: N.A. Began: October 1, 1989.

Channel capacity: 52 (2-way capable; not operating 2-way). Channels available but not in use: 21.

Basic Service

Subscribers: 137.

Programming (received off-air): KERA-TV (P) Dallas-Fort Worth; KJBO-LP (U) Wichita Falls; KAUZ-TV (C), KFDX-TV (N), KJTL (F,U), KSWO-TV (A) Wichita Falls-Lawton.

Programming (via satellite): WGN-TV (W) Chicago; C-SPAN; CNBC; CNN; Comedy Central; Country Music TV; Discovery Channel; ESPN; Fox Family Channel; Headline News; Learning Channel; Lifetime; MTV; Nashville Network; Nickelodeon; Odyssey; QVC; TBS Superstation; The Weather Channel; Trinity Bcstg. Network; Turner Network TV; USA Network.

Fee: $40.00 installation; $29.95 monthly; $2.95 converter.

Pay Service 1

Pay Units: 15.

Programming (via satellite): Cinemax.

Fee: $9.00 monthly.

Pay Service 2

Pay Units: 11.

Programming (via satellite): Disney Channel.

Fee: $7.00 monthly.

Pay Service 3

Pay Units: 34.

Programming (via satellite): HBO.

Fee: $10.00 monthly.

Pay Service 4

Pay Units: N.A.

Programming (via satellite): Showtime; The Movie Channel.

Fee: $10.00 (Showtime), $10.95 monthly (TMC).

Local advertising: No.

Miles of plant: 33.0 (coaxial). Homes passed: 565.

Manager: Belinda Murphy. Chief engineer: Steve Rice. Program director: Beth Semptimphelter. Marketing director: Bill Fischer.

Ownership: Rapid Communications Partners LP (MSO).

PLEASANTON—Falcon Cable TV, 1244 Encino Dr., Pleasanton, TX 78064. Phone: 830-569-5509. Fax: 830-569-4828. County: Atascosa. ICA: TX0194.

TV Market Ranking: 45. Franchise award date: October 2, 1979. Franchise expiration date: N.A. Began: October 31, 1980.

Channel capacity: 35 (not 2-way capable). Channels available but not in use: None.

Basic Service

Subscribers: 1,355.

Programming (received off-air): KRRT (W) Kerrville-San Antonio; KABB (F), KENS-TV (C), KLRN (P), KMOL-TV (N), KSAT-TV (A), KWEX-TV (S) San Antonio; 15 FMs.

Programming (via satellite): A & E; American Movie Classics; C-SPAN; CNBC; Country Music TV; ESPN; Fox Family Channel; GalaVision; Headline News; Lifetime; Nashville Network; Nickelodeon; QVC; Sci-Fi Channel.

Current originations: Automated time-weather.

Fee: $20.00 installation; $22.23 monthly; $2.50 converter; $12.50 additional installation.

Expanded Basic Service

Subscribers: 1,319.

Programming (via satellite): Discovery Channel; MTV; USA Network.

Fee: $1.91 monthly.

Expanded Basic Service 2

Subscribers: 1,286.

Programming (via satellite): WGN-TV (W) Chicago; CNN; Disney Channel; TBS Superstation; Turner Network TV.

Fee: $7.75 monthly.

Pay Service 1

Pay Units: 61.

Programming (via satellite): Cinemax.

Fee: $10.95 monthly.

Pay Service 2

Pay Units: 225.

Programming (via satellite): HBO.

Fee: $11.95 monthly.

Pay Service 3

Pay Units: 114.

Programming (via satellite): The Movie Channel.

Fee: $10.95 monthly.

Pay Service 4

Pay Units: 219.

Programming (via satellite): Showtime.

Fee: $10.95 monthly.

Local advertising: Yes. Available in character-generated programming. Regional interconnect: Cabletime.

Program Guide: Premium Channels.

Equipment: Jerrold amplifiers; Comm/Scope cable; SpectraView character generator; Jerrold & Pioneer set top converters; Pico traps; Scientific-Atlanta satellite antenna; Gardiner satellite receivers.

Miles of plant: 56.0 (coaxial). Homes passed: 2,138.

Manager: Lorna Gentry. Chief technician: Santos Guajardo.

Franchise fee: 4% of gross.

Ownership: Falcon Communications LP (MSO), joint venture formed September 30, 1998. See Cable System Ownership.

PLUM GROVE—Friendship Cable of Texas Inc., Box 9090, Tyler, TX 75711-9090. Phone: 903-581-2121. Fax: 903-581-2185. County: Liberty. Also serves Liberty County (portions). ICA: TX0437.

TV Market Ranking: 11 (Liberty County); Below 100 (Plum Grove). Franchise award date: N.A. Franchise expiration date: N.A. Began: N.A.

Channel capacity: 36 (not 2-way capable). Channels available but not in use: 1.

Basic Service

Subscribers: 275.

Programming (received off-air): KHOU-TV (C), KHTV (W), KPRC-TV (N), KRIV (F), KTRK-TV (A), KTXH (U), KUHT (P) Houston.

Programming (via satellite): A & E; C-SPAN; CNN; Country Music TV; Discovery Channel; ESPN; Fox Family Channel; Fox Sports Net Southwest; Headline News; Lifetime; Nashville Network; Nickelodeon; QVC; TBS Superstation; The Inspirational Network; Turner Network TV; USA Network.

Fee: $33.70 monthly.

Pay Service 1

Pay Units: 17.

Programming (via satellite): Cinemax.

Fee: $10.95 monthly.

Pay Service 2

Pay Units: 38.

Programming (via satellite): Showtime.

Fee: $5.95 monthly.

Pay Service 3

Pay Units: 21.

Programming (via satellite): HBO.

Fee: $10.95 monthly.

Miles of plant: 26.6 (coaxial). Homes passed: 678.

Manager: Wanda Pyburn. Chief technician: David Burrell.

Ownership: Buford Television Inc. (MSO). See Cable System Ownership.

PONDER—SouthTel Communications LP, Suite 202, 2444 Solomons Island Rd., Annapolis, MD 21401. Phone: 410-266-9393. County: Denton. Also serves Justin. ICA: TX0512.

TV Market Ranking: 12. Franchise award date: N.A. Franchise expiration date: N.A. Began: July 1, 1983.

Channel capacity: 52. Channels available but not in use: N.A.

Basic Service

Subscribers: 104.

Programming (received off-air): KDAF (W), KDFI-TV (I), KDFW (F), KERA-TV (P), KTVT (C), KTXA (U), KXAS-TV (N), KXTX-TV (I), WFAA-TV (A) Dallas-Fort Worth.

Programming (via satellite): WGN-TV (W) Chicago; Animal Planet; CNN; Country Music TV; ESPN; Fox Family Channel; Learning Channel; Lifetime; MuchMoreMusic; Nickelodeon; QVC; TBS Superstation; Turner Network TV; USA Network.

Fee: $25.00 installation; $25.33 monthly.

Pay Service 1

Pay Units: N.A.

Programming (via satellite): HBO; Showtime; The Movie Channel.

Fee: N.A.

Miles of plant: 19.8 (coaxial).

Manager: Roy E. Hayes.

Ownership: Bay Cable Inc. (MSO). Purchased from Brookridge Cable Special Purpose Partnership, June 1, 1998.

PORT ARANSAS—Falcon Cable TV, 822 Market St., Portland, TX 78374. Phone: 512-643-8588. Fax: 512-643-3641. County: Nueces. ICA: TX0835.

TV Market Ranking: Below 100. Franchise award date: N.A. Franchise expiration date: N.A. Began: January 1, 1980.

Channel capacity: 62 (2-way capable; operating 2-way). Channels available but not in use: 23.

Basic Service

Subscribers: 787.

Programming (received off-air): K47DF (F), KEDT (P), KIII (A), KORO (S), KRIS-TV (N), KZTV (C) Corpus Christi; 6 FMs.

Programming (via satellite): A & E; C-SPAN; CNN; Country Music TV; Disney Channel; E! Entertainment TV; ESPN; FX; Fox Family Channel; Fox Sports Net Southwest; Headline News; Home Shopping Network; Lifetime; Nashville Network; Nickelodeon; QVC; Sci-Fi Channel; Trinity Bcstg. Network; USA Network.

Current originations: Public access; educational access; government access.

Fee: $22.50 installation; $17.81 monthly; $2.00 converter; $7.50 additional installation.

Expanded Basic Service
Subscribers: 687.
Programming (via satellite): Discovery Channel; MTV; The Weather Channel.
Fee: $2.91 monthly.

Expanded Basic Service 2
Subscribers: 677.
Programming (via satellite): WGN-TV (W) Chicago; TBS Superstation; Turner Network TV.
Fee: $4.95 monthly.

Pay Service 1
Pay Units: 58.
Programming (via satellite): Cinemax.
Fee: $9.95 monthly.

Pay Service 2
Pay Units: 107.
Programming (via satellite): HBO.
Fee: $9.95 monthly.

Pay Service 3
Pay Units: 60.
Programming (via satellite): The Movie Channel.
Fee: $9.75 monthly.

Pay Service 4
Pay Units: 86.
Programming (via satellite): Showtime.
Fee: $9.75 monthly.

Pay Service 5
Pay Units: N.A.
Programming (via satellite): The New Encore.
Fee: N.A.

Local advertising: Yes. Available in locally originated programming. Regional interconnect: Cabletime.
Equipment: Jerrold headend; Jerrold amplifiers; Comm/Scope cable; Video Data Systems character generator; Jerrold & Standard Components set top converters; Gardiner satellite antenna.
Miles of plant: 44.0 (coaxial). Homes passed: 1,400.
Office manager: Jenny Brumley. Chief technician: Mike Kelsch.
Franchise fee: 3% of gross.
Ownership: Falcon Communications LP (MSO), joint venture formed September 30, 1998. See Cable System Ownership.

PORT ARANSAS—Falcon Telecable, 822 Market St., Portland, TX 78374. Phone: 512-643-8588. Fax: 512-643-3641. County: Aransas. ICA: TX0937.
TV Market Ranking: Below 100. Franchise award date: N.A. Franchise expiration date: N.A. Began: N.A.
Channel capacity: 40. Channels available but not in use: None.

Basic Service
Subscribers: 246.
Programming (received off-air): K47DF (F), KEDT (P), KIII (A), KRIS-TV (N), KZTV (C) Corpus Christi.
Programming (via satellite): A & E; C-SPAN; CNBC; Comedy Central; Country Music TV; Disney Channel; ESPN; Fox Family Channel; Headline News; Home Shopping Network; Learning Channel; Lifetime; Nashville Network; Nickelodeon; QVC; Sci-Fi Channel; Travel Channel; Univision; VH1.
Current originations: Public access; educational access; government access.
Fee: $17.16 monthly.

Expanded Basic Service
Subscribers: 211.
Programming (via satellite): Fox Sports Net Southwest; MTV; The Weather Channel; USA Network.
Fee: $4.26 monthly.

Expanded Basic Service 2
Subscribers: 209.
Programming (via satellite): WGN-TV (W) Chicago; CNN; Discovery Channel; ESPN 2; TBS Superstation; Turner Network TV.
Fee: $6.95 monthly.

Pay Service 1
Pay Units: 11.
Programming (via satellite): Cinemax.
Fee: $9.95 monthly.

Pay Service 2
Pay Units: 12.
Programming (via satellite): HBO.
Fee: $12.95 monthly.

Pay Service 3
Pay Units: 13.
Programming (via satellite): Showtime.
Fee: $9.95 monthly.

Pay Service 4
Pay Units: 12.
Programming (via satellite): The Movie Channel.
Fee: $9.95 monthly.

Pay-Per-View
Playboy TV.

Office manager: Jenny Brumley. Chief technician: Mike Kelsch.
Ownership: Falcon Communications LP (MSO), joint venture formed September 30, 1998. See Cable System Ownership.

PORT ARTHUR—Time Warner Communications, 5330 Twin City Hwy., Port Arthur, TX 77627. Phone: 409-727-1515. Fax: 409-962-3424. County: Jefferson. Also serves Beauxart Gardens, Central Gardens, Groves, Nederland, Port Acres, Port Neches, Sabine Pass. ICA: TX0018.
TV Market Ranking: 88. Franchise award date: N.A. Franchise expiration date: N.A. Began: February 5, 1972.
Channel capacity: 77 (not 2-way capable). Channels available but not in use: 16.

Basic Service
Subscribers: 28,824.
Programming (received off-air): KBMT (A), KBTV-TV (N), KFDM-TV (C) Beaumont-Port Arthur; KVHP (F) Lake Charles; 13 FMs.
Programming (via microwave): KTXH (U), KUHT (P) Houston.
Programming (via satellite): C-SPAN; CNBC; Discovery Channel; Nashville Network; Odyssey; QVC; TBS Superstation.
Current originations: Educational access; government access; leased access.
Fee: $44.95 installation; $10.15 monthly; $1.50 converter.

Expanded Basic Service
Subscribers: 27,633.
Programming (via satellite): A & E; American Movie Classics; Animal Planet; BET; CNN; Cartoon Network; ESPN; FX; Fox Family Channel; Fox News Channel; Fox Sports Net Southwest; Headline News; Nickelodeon; The Weather Channel; Travel Channel; Turner Network TV; USA Network.
Fee: $44.95 installation; $12.99 monthly.

Pay Service 1
Pay Units: 3,768.
Programming (via satellite): Cinemax.
Fee: $20.00 installation; $12.45 monthly.

Pay Service 2
Pay Units: 1,228.
Programming (via satellite): Disney Channel.
Fee: $20.00 installation; $11.88 monthly.

Pay Service 3
Pay Units: 3,768.
Programming (via satellite): HBO.
Fee: $25.00 installation; $13.09 monthly.

Pay Service 4
Pay Units: 4,037.
Programming (via satellite): Showtime.
Fee: $25.00 installation; $13.09 monthly.

Pay Service 5
Pay Units: 2,356.
Programming (via satellite): The Movie Channel.
Fee: $20.00 installation; $13.09 monthly.

Pay Service 6
Pay Units: 13,757.
Programming (via satellite): The New Encore.
Fee: $1.75 monthly.

Pay Service 7
Pay Units: 305.
Programming (via satellite): DMX.
Fee: $9.47 monthly.

Pay Service 8
Pay Units: 5,794.
Programming (via satellite): Starz!
Fee: $6.75 monthly.

Pay-Per-View
Addressable homes: 6,742.
Viewer's Choice.

Local advertising: Yes (locally produced & insert). Available in locally originated programming. Local sales manager: Joe Walker.
Equipment: Scientific-Atlanta headend; Jerrold & Scientific-Atlanta amplifiers; Comm/Scope cable; Scientific-Atlanta satellite antenna; Scientific-Atlanta satellite receivers.
Miles of plant: 550.0 (coaxial); 50.0 (fiber optic). Homes passed: 50,213. Total homes in franchised area: 50,213.
Manager: Mike McKee. Customer service manager: Mary Lema.
City fee: 5% of gross.
Ownership: AT&T Broadband & Internet Services (MSO); Time Warner Cable (MSO); Advance/Newhouse Partnership (MSO).

PORT ISABEL—Time Warner Communications, Box 2327, 2921 S. Expwy. 83, Harlingen, TX 78551. Phone: 956-425-7880. Fax: 956-412-0959. County: Cameron. Also serves Cameron, Laguna Heights, Laguna Vista. ICA: TX0197.
TV Market Ranking: Below 100. Franchise award date: N.A. Franchise expiration date: N.A. Began: February 1, 1979.
Channel capacity: 35. Channels available but not in use: 6.

Basic Service
Subscribers: 3,510.
Programming (received off-air): KVEO (N) Brownsville; KGBT-TV (C), KMBH (P) Harlingen; KRGV-TV (A) Weslaco; XHAB-TV Matamoros.
Programming (via satellite): C-SPAN; Discovery Channel; FX; Fox News Channel; Nashville Network; QVC; TBS Superstation; Trinity Bcstg. Network; Univision.
Fee: $22.95 installation; $14.00 monthly.

Digital Basic Service
Subscribers: N.A.
Programming (via satellite): BBC America; Bravo; Discovery Home & Leisure Channel; Discovery Kids Channel; Discovery People; Discovery Science Channel; ESPN Classic Sports; ESPNews; Fox Sports World; Game Show Network; History Channel; Home & Garden Television; Independent Film Channel; MuchMusic Network; Outdoor Life Network; Romance Classics; Sci-Fi Channel; TV Guide Channel; Turner Classic Movies.
Fee: N.A.

Expanded Basic Service
Subscribers: 3,122.
Programming (via satellite): WGN-TV (W) Chicago; A & E; American Movie Classics; Animal Planet; CNN; CNNfn; Disney Channel; ESPN; EWTN; Fox Family Channel; Fox Sports Net Southwest; Gems Television; Headline News; History Channel; Learning Channel; Lifetime; MTV; Nashville Network; Nickelodeon; TV Guide Channel; The Weather Channel; Turner Network TV; USA Network.
Fee: $25.00 installation; $29.00 monthly.

Expanded Basic Service 2
Subscribers: N.A.
Programming (via satellite): Box Exitos; Box Tejano; CBS TeleNoticias; CNN en Espanol; Canal 9; CineLatino; Discovery en Espanol; Fox Sports World Espanol.
Fee: $6.99 monthly.

Pay Service 1
Pay Units: 354.
Programming (via satellite): Cinemax.
Fee: $12.45 monthly.

Pay Service 2
Pay Units: N.A.
Programming (via satellite): DMX; Showtime; Starz!; The New Encore.
Fee: $1.75 monthly (Encore), 6.75 monthly (Starz!), $9.45 monthly (Showtime).

Pay Service 3
Pay Units: 576.
Programming (via satellite): HBO.
Fee: $12.90 monthly.

Digital Pay Service 1
Pay Units: N.A.
Programming (via satellite): DMX; Encore Love Stories; Encore Mystery; Encore Westerns; HBO Plus; HBO Signature; Showtime (multiplexed); Starz! (multiplexed); The Movie Channel.
Fee: $7.00 monthly (Showtime), $10.00 monthly (HBO or TMC).

Pay-Per-View
Spice delivered digitally; movies delivered digitally.

Miles of plant: 34.3 (coaxial).
Manager: Juan Herrera.
Ownership: Time Warner Cable (MSO); AT&T Broadband & Internet Services (MSO).

PORT LAVACA—Cable One, 501 N. Virginia St., Port Lavaca, TX 77979. Phone: 361-552-9621. Fax: 361-552-7074. County: Calhoun. Also serves Calhoun County, Point Comfort. ICA: TX0146.
TV Market Ranking: Below 100. Franchise award date: January 1, 1958. Franchise expiration date: March 4, 2002. Began: July 1, 1958.
Channel capacity: 61 (not 2-way capable). Channels available but not in use: 26.

Basic Service
Subscribers: 4,494.
Programming (received off-air): KEDT (P) Corpus Christi; KAVU-TV (A), KVCT (F) Victoria; 12 FMs.
Programming (via microwave): KHOU-TV (C), KHTV (W), KPRC-TV (N), KTRK-TV (A) Houston.
Programming (via satellite): ESPN; Fox Family Channel; GalaVision; Nickelodeon; TBS Superstation; Univision.
Current originations: Automated time-weather; educational access.
Fee: $44.73 installation (aerial), $75.00 (underground); $13.95 monthly; $10.00 additional installation.

Pay Service 1
Pay Units: 617.
Programming (via satellite): Cinemax; Disney Channel; Fox Sports Net Southwest; HBO; Showtime; The Movie Channel.
Fee: $6.95 monthly (Disney or Fox Sports), $10.50 monthly (Cinemax, HBO, Showtime or TMC).

Pay-Per-View
Viewer's Choice.

Fee: $3.95.
Local advertising: Planned.
Equipment: RCA & Scientific-Atlanta headend; Scientific-Atlanta amplifiers; Scientific-Atlanta cable; MSI character generator; Oak set top converters; Andrew satellite antenna; Hughes & Scientific-Atlanta satellite receivers.
Miles of plant: 76.1 (coaxial).
Manager: David King.
City fee: 5% of gross.
Ownership: Cable One Inc. (MSO).

PORT O'CONNOR—TCI Cablevision of Texas, 4060 S. Padre Island Dr., Corpus Christi, TX 78411-4477. Phone: 512-857-5000. County: Calhoun. ICA: TX0369.
TV Market Ranking: Outside TV Markets. Franchise award date: N.A. Franchise expiration date: N.A. Began: December 1, 1972.
Channel capacity: 30. Channels available but not in use: 9.
Basic Service
Subscribers: 676.
Programming (received off-air): KHOU-TV (C), KTRK-TV (A), KTXH (U), KUHT (P) Houston; KAVU-TV (A) Victoria; allband FM.
Programming (via satellite): WGN-TV (W) Chicago; American Movie Classics; CNBC; CNN; Discovery Channel; ESPN; FoxNet; Headline News; Lifetime; Nashville Network; TBS Superstation; The Weather Channel; Turner Network TV; USA Network.
Fee: $60.00 installation; $10.29 monthly; $60.00 additional installation.
Pay Service 1
Pay Units: 152.
Programming (via satellite): Showtime.
Fee: $10.00 monthly.
Pay Service 2
Pay Units: 193.
Programming (via satellite): The New Encore.
Fee: N.A.
Miles of plant: 21.6 (coaxial). Homes passed: 950. Total homes in franchised area: 1,000.
Manager: Dennis Moore. Chief technician: Mando Blancas. Marketing director: Jerri Coppedge.
Ownership: AT&T Broadband & Internet Services (MSO). Purchased from Tele-Communications Inc., March 9, 1999.

PORTER—Friendship Cable of Texas Inc., Box 9090, Tyler, TX 75711-9090. Phone: 903-581-2121. Fax: 903-581-2185. County: Montgomery. ICA: TX0312.
TV Market Ranking: 15. Franchise award date: N.A. Franchise expiration date: N.A. Began: N.A.
Channel capacity: 36 (not 2-way capable). Channels available but not in use: 2.
Basic Service
Subscribers: 714.
Programming (received off-air): KETH (E), KHOU-TV (C), KHTV (W), KPRC-TV (N), KRIV (F), KTRK-TV (A), KTXH (U) Houston.
Programming (via satellite): CNN; Discovery Channel; ESPN; Fox Family Channel; Nashville Network; Showtime; TBS Superstation; USA Network.
Fee: $34.95 monthly.
Pay Service 1
Pay Units: 20.
Programming (via satellite): Cinemax.
Fee: $10.95 monthly.
Pay Service 2
Pay Units: 28.
Programming (via satellite): HBO.
Fee: $10.95 monthly.
Pay Service 3
Pay Units: 219.
Programming (via satellite): Showtime.
Fee: $5.95 monthly.
Miles of plant: 48.5 (coaxial). Homes passed: 1,406.
Manager: Wanda Pyburn. Chief technician: David Burrell.
Ownership: Buford Television Inc. (MSO). See Cable System Ownership.

PORTLAND—Falcon Cable TV, 822 Market St., Portland, TX 78374. Phone: 512-643-8588. Fax: 512-643-3641. County: San Patricio. ICA: TX0136.
TV Market Ranking: Below 100. Franchise award date: February 17, 1981. Franchise expiration date: N.A. Began: February 18, 1982.
Channel capacity: 54 (2-way capable; operating 2-way). Channels available but not in use: 7.
Basic Service
Subscribers: 2,324.
Programming (received off-air): K47DF (F), KEDT (P), KIII (A), KORO (S), KRIS-TV (N), KZTV (C) Corpus Christi; 6 FMs.
Programming (via satellite): A & E; American Movie Classics; C-SPAN; CNBC; CNN; Comedy Central; Country Music TV; Disney Channel; E! Entertainment TV; ESPN; ESPN 2; FX; Fox Family Channel; Fox Sports Net Southwest; GalaVision; Headline News; Home Shopping Network; Learning Channel; Lifetime; MTV; Nickelodeon; QVC; Sci-Fi Channel; The Weather Channel; Trinity Bcstg. Network; USA Network.
Current originations: Automated time-weather; public access; educational access; government access.
Fee: $15.00 installation; $19.62 monthly; $2.50 additional installation.
Expanded Basic Service
Subscribers: 2,007.
Programming (via satellite): Discovery Channel; Nashville Network; TBS Superstation; Turner Network TV.
Fee: $5.00 monthly.
Expanded Basic Service 2
Subscribers: 329.
Programming (via satellite): Cartoon Network; fXM: Movies from Fox; History Channel; Outdoor Life Network.
Fee: $5.00 monthly.
Pay Service 1
Pay Units: 205.
Programming (via satellite): Cinemax.
Fee: $25.00 installation; $9.95 monthly.
Pay Service 2
Pay Units: 510.
Programming (via satellite): HBO.
Fee: $25.00 installation; $10.75 monthly.
Pay Service 3
Pay Units: 146.
Programming (via satellite): The Movie Channel.
Fee: $25.00 installation; $9.95 monthly.
Pay Service 4
Pay Units: 269.
Programming (via satellite): Showtime.
Fee: $9.75 monthly.
Pay Service 5
Pay Units: N.A.
Programming (via satellite): Playboy TV; The New Encore.
Fee: N.A.
Local advertising: Yes. Available in character-generated programming. Local sales manager: Bill Helmbold. Regional interconnect: Cabletime.
Equipment: RCA headend; RCA amplifiers; Comm/Scope cable; Ikegami cameras; JVC VTRs; Jerrold set top converters; Eagle traps; Scientific-Atlanta satellite antenna; Scientific-Atlanta satellite receivers.
Miles of plant: 52.0 (coaxial). Homes passed: 4,500. Total homes in franchised area: 4,596.
Office manager: Jenny Brumley. Chief technician: Mike Kelsch.
Franchise fee: 3% of gross.
Ownership: Falcon Communications LP (MSO), joint venture formed September 30, 1998. See Cable System Ownership.

POST—Classic Cable, Box 429, 605 N.W. 3rd St., Plainville, KS 67663-0429. Phones: 785-434-7620; 800-999-8876. Fax: 785-434-2614. County: Garza. ICA: TX0241.
TV Market Ranking: Outside TV Markets. Franchise award date: August 3, 1964. Franchise expiration date: August 3, 1998. Began: November 10, 1968.
Channel capacity: 41 (2-way capable; operating 2-way). Channels available but not in use: N.A.
Basic Service
Subscribers: 925; Commercial subscribers: 103.
Programming (received off-air): KAMC (A), KCBD-TV (N), KJTV (F), KLBK-TV (C), KPTB (I), KTXT-TV (P) Lubbock; allband FM.
Programming (via translator): KVDA (O) San Antonio.
Programming (via satellite): WGN-TV (W) Chicago; A & E; American Movie Classics; Animal Planet; CNN; Cartoon Network; Country Music TV; Discovery Channel; Disney Channel; E! Entertainment TV; ESPN; Fox Family Channel; Fox News Channel; Fox Sports Net Southwest; Goodlife TV Network; History Channel; Learning Channel; Lifetime; Nashville Network; Nick at Nite's TV Land; Nickelodeon; QVC; Sci-Fi Channel; TBS Superstation; The Weather Channel; Turner Network TV; USA Network; Univision.
Current originations: Automated time-weather; religious access.
Fee: $35.00 installation; $27.95 monthly.
Pay Service 1
Pay Units: 79.
Programming (via satellite): Cinemax.
Fee: $9.95 monthly.
Pay Service 2
Pay Units: 62.
Programming (via satellite): Showtime.
Fee: $9.95 monthly.
Pay Service 3
Pay Units: 171.
Programming (via satellite): HBO.
Fee: $9.95 monthly.
Local advertising: Yes. Rates: $10.00/Month.
Program Guide: The Cable Guide.
Equipment: Jerrold headend; Jerrold amplifiers; Coral & Vikoa cable.
Miles of plant: 22.9 (coaxial). Homes passed: 1,464. Total homes in franchised area: 1,809.
Manager: Bill Flowers. Chief technician: Chris Christenson. Marketing director: Jennifer Hauschild.
City fee: 2% of gross.
Ownership: Classic Cable (MSO).

POTEET—Time Warner Communications, 207 E. Colorado St., Pearsall, TX 78061-3234. Phone: 800-527-6221. Fax: 512-396-4664. County: Atascosa. Also serves Atascosa County, Jourdanton. ICA: TX0238.
TV Market Ranking: 45 (portions of Atascosa County, Jourdanton, Poteet); Outside TV Markets (portions of Atascosa County). Franchise award date: N.A. Franchise expiration date: N.A. Began: April 12, 1982.
Channel capacity: 35. Channels available but not in use: None.
Basic Service
Subscribers: 921.
Programming (received off-air): KRRT (W) Kerrville-San Antonio; KABB (F), KENS-TV (C), KLRN (P), KMOL-TV (N), KSAT-TV (A), KVDA (O), KWEX-TV (S) San Antonio.
Programming (via satellite): WGN-TV (W) Chicago; C-SPAN; C-SPAN 2; CNN; Country Music TV; Discovery Channel; ESPN; EWTN; Fox Family Channel; Fox Sports Net Southwest; GalaVision; Headline News; Lifetime; MTV; Nashville Network; Nickelodeon; TBS Superstation; The Weather Channel; Trinity Bcstg. Network; Turner Network TV; USA Network.
Current originations: Local news.
Fee: $30.00 installation; $19.29 monthly; $30.00 additional installation.
Pay Service 1
Pay Units: 100.
Programming (via satellite): The Movie Channel.
Fee: N.A.
Pay Service 2
Pay Units: 78.
Programming (via satellite): Disney Channel.
Fee: $7.00 monthly.
Pay Service 3
Pay Units: 188.
Programming (via satellite): HBO.
Fee: $9.00 monthly.
Pay Service 4
Pay Units: 172.
Programming (via satellite): Showtime.
Fee: $9.00 monthly.
Equipment: Blonder-Tongue, Catel & Gardiner headend; Theta-Com amplifiers; Comm/Scope cable; Scientific-Atlanta set top converters; Weatherscan satellite antenna.
Miles of plant: 32.9 (coaxial). Homes passed: 1,839. Total homes in franchised area: 2,360.
Manager: Marcos Reyes.
Ownership: Time Warner Cable (MSO); AT&T Broadband & Internet Services (MSO).

POTOSI—Jayroc Cablevision, Box 6575, Abilene, TX 79608. Phone: 915-691-5787. County: Taylor. ICA: TX0837.
TV Market Ranking: Below 100. Franchise award date: N.A. Franchise expiration date: N.A. Began: N.A.
Channel capacity: N.A. Channels available but not in use: N.A.
Basic Service
Subscribers: N.A.
Programming (received off-air): KRBC-TV (N), KTAB-TV (C), KTXS-TV (A) Abilene-Sweetwater.
Programming (via satellite): WGN-TV (W) Chicago.
Fee: N.A.
Ownership: Jayroc Inc. (MSO).

POTTSBORO—Friendship Cable of Texas Inc., Box 9090, Tyler, TX 75711-9090. Phone: 903-581-2121. Fax: 903-581-2185. County: Grayson. ICA: TX0502.
TV Market Ranking: Below 100. Franchise award date: N.A. Franchise expiration date: N.A. Began: June 1, 1983.
Channel capacity: 42. Channels available but not in use: N.A.
Basic Service
Subscribers: 265.
Programming (received off-air): KTEN (A,N,F) Ada; KDAF (W), KDFI-TV (I), KERA-TV (P), KTVT (C), KTXA (U), KXAS-TV (N), KXTX-TV (I), WFAA-TV (A) Dallas-Fort Worth; KXII (C) Sherman.

Programming (via satellite): WGN-TV (W) Chicago; CNN; Country Music TV; Discovery Channel; Disney Channel; ESPN; Fox Family Channel; MTV; Nashville Network; Nickelodeon; TBS Superstation.
Fee: $30.00 installation; $30.85 monthly.
Pay Service 1
Pay Units: 6.
Programming (via satellite): HBO.
Fee: $12.00 monthly.
Pay Service 2
Pay Units: 11.
Programming (via satellite): The Movie Channel.
Fee: $9.00 monthly.
Pay Service 3
Pay Units: 23.
Programming (via satellite): Showtime.
Fee: $3.25 monthly.
Miles of plant: 9.2 (coaxial). Homes passed: 450.
Manager: Rodney Fletcher. Chief technician: Bo Jaubert.
Ownership: Buford Television Inc. (MSO). See Cable System Ownership.

POWDERLY—Friendship Cable of Texas Inc., Box 9090, Tyler, TX 75711-9090. Phone: 903-581-2121. Fax: 903-581-2185. County: Lamar. ICA: TX0361.
TV Market Ranking: Outside TV Markets. Franchise award date: N.A. Franchise expiration date: N.A. Began: October 1, 1988.
Channel capacity: 54. Channels available but not in use: N.A.
Basic Service
Subscribers: 551.
Programming (received off-air): KTEN (A,N,F) Ada; KXII (C) Sherman; KOED-TV (P) Tulsa.
Programming (via satellite): WGN-TV (W) Chicago; A & E; CNN; Cartoon Network; Country Music TV; Discovery Channel; Disney Channel; ESPN; Headline News; Nashville Network; TBS Superstation; Trinity Bcstg. Network; Turner Classic Movies; Turner Network TV; USA Network.
Fee: $30.00 installation; $30.59 monthly.
Pay Service 1
Pay Units: 11.
Programming (via satellite): Cinemax.
Fee: $11.00 monthly.
Pay Service 2
Pay Units: 57.
Programming (via satellite): HBO.
Fee: $11.00 monthly.
Pay Service 3
Pay Units: 44.
Programming (via satellite): Showtime.
Fee: $5.95 monthly.
Miles of plant: 51.2 (coaxial). Homes passed: 1,366.
Manager: Marianne Bogy. Chief technician: Sonny Myers.
Ownership: Buford Television Inc. (MSO). See Cable System Ownership.

PREMONT—Heritage Cablevision of Texas Inc., 208 W. Viggie St., Hebbronville, TX 78361-3048. Phone: 512-527-3267. County: Jim Wells. ICA: TX0352.
TV Market Ranking: Outside TV Markets. Franchise award date: N.A. Franchise expiration date: N.A. Began: April 1, 1982.
Channel capacity: 35. Channels available but not in use: 6.
Basic Service
Subscribers: 610.
Programming (received off-air): KEDT (P), KIII (A), KRIS-TV (N), KZTV (C) Corpus Christi.
Programming (via satellite): WGN-TV (W) Chicago; A & E; C-SPAN; CNN; Fox Family Channel; Headline News; Lifetime; MTV; Nashville Network; Nickelodeon; QVC; TBS Superstation; Telemundo; The Weather Channel; Trinity Bcstg. Network; Univision.
Fee: $60.00 installation; $9.75 monthly.
Expanded Basic Service
Subscribers: 567.
Programming (via satellite): CNBC; Discovery Channel; ESPN; Fox Sports Net Southwest; GalaVision; Turner Network TV; USA Network.
Fee: $12.00 monthly.
Pay Service 1
Pay Units: 106.
Programming (via satellite): Cinemax.
Fee: $10.95 monthly.
Pay Service 2
Pay Units: 42.
Programming (via satellite): Disney Channel.
Fee: $10.95 monthly.
Pay Service 3
Pay Units: 157.
Programming (via satellite): HBO.
Fee: $10.95 monthly.
Miles of plant: 18.7 (coaxial). Homes passed: 1,045. Total homes in franchised area: 1,045.
Manager: Juve Morante.
Ownership: AT&T Broadband & Internet Services (MSO). Purchased from Tele-Communications Inc., March 9, 1999.

PRESIDIO—Presidio TV Cable, Box 1377, Alpine, TX 79831. Phone: 915-837-2300. E-mail: mtnzone@overland.net. County: Presidio. ICA: TX0432.
TV Market Ranking: Outside TV Markets. Franchise award date: April 2, 1982. Franchise expiration date: April 2, 2007. Began: May 1, 1973.
Channel capacity: 36 (not 2-way capable). Channels available but not in use: 3.
Basic Service
Subscribers: 430.
Programming (received off-air): KVIA-TV (A) El Paso; KOSA-TV (C), KWES-TV (N) Odessa-Midland; allband FM.
Programming (via satellite): WGN-TV (W) Chicago; KMGH-TV (A), KRMA-TV (P) Denver; CNN; Cartoon Network; Country Music TV; Discovery Channel; ESPN; FoxNet; GalaVision; Home Shopping Network; Learning Channel; MTV; Nashville Network; Nickelodeon; TBS Superstation; Telemundo; The Weather Channel; Turner Classic Movies; Turner Network TV; USA Network; Univision.
Fee: $35.00 installation; $26.56 monthly; $35.00 additional installation.
Pay Service 1
Pay Units: N.A.
Programming (via satellite): HBO; Showtime.
Fee: $10.00 installation; $6.00 monthly each.
Equipment: Blonder-Tongue & Scientific-Atlanta headend; C-COR & Scientific-Atlanta amplifiers; Times Fiber cable; RCA set top converters.
Miles of plant: 25.0 (coaxial). Homes passed: 700. Total homes in franchised area: 800.
Manager: Steve Neu.
City fee: 2% of gross.
Ownership: Mountain Zone TV Systems (MSO).

PRESTON PENINSULA—Mission Cable, 920 Whitmore Dr., Rockwall, TX 75087. Phone: 800-783-5708. Fax: 214-722-6218. County: Grayson. ICA: TX0838.
TV Market Ranking: Below 100. Franchise award date: January 17, 1989. Franchise expiration date: N.A. Began: August 1, 1983.
Channel capacity: 35 (not 2-way capable). Channels available but not in use: N.A.
Basic Service
Subscribers: 1,070; Commercial subscribers: 198.
Programming (received off-air): KTEN (A,N,F) Ada; KDAF (W), KDFI-TV (I), KDFW (F), KERA-TV (P), KTVT (C), KTXA (U), KXAS-TV (N), WFAA-TV (A) Dallas-Fort Worth; KXII (C) Sherman.
Programming (via satellite): WGN-TV (W) Chicago; CNN; Discovery Channel; E! Entertainment TV; ESPN; Fox Family Channel; Fox Sports Net Southwest; Headline News; Nashville Network; Nickelodeon; QVC; TBS Superstation; The Inspirational Network; The Weather Channel; Travel Channel; Trinity Bcstg. Network; Turner Network TV; USA Network.
Fee: $25.00 installation; $19.95 monthly.
Pay Service 1
Pay Units: 112.
Programming (via satellite): Cinemax.
Fee: $9.00 monthly.
Pay Service 2
Pay Units: 46.
Programming (via satellite): Disney Channel.
Fee: $9.00 monthly.
Pay Service 3
Pay Units: 327.
Programming (via satellite): HBO.
Fee: $9.00 monthly.
Pay Service 4
Pay Units: 101.
Programming (via satellite): Showtime.
Fee: $9.00 monthly.
Miles of plant: 25.0 (coaxial). Homes passed: 2,331.
Manager: Jim Stafford. Chief technician: Jacky Oliver. Marketing & program director: Bruce Berkinshaw.
Ownership: Fanch Communications Inc. (MSO); Time Warner Cable (MSO). See Cable System Ownership.

PRICE—Friendship Cable of Texas Inc., Box 9090, Tyler, TX 75711-9090. Phone: 903-581-2121. Fax: 903-581-2185. County: Rusk. ICA: TX0648.
TV Market Ranking: Outside TV Markets. Franchise award date: N.A. Franchise expiration date: N.A. Began: January 1, 1989.
Channel capacity: 36. Channels available but not in use: 11.
Basic Service
Subscribers: 91.
Programming (received off-air): KETK-TV (N) Jacksonville; KFXK (F) Longview; KLTV (A) Tyler-Longview.
Programming (via satellite): WBBM-TV (C), WGN-TV (W) Chicago; CNN; Country Music TV; Discovery Channel; ESPN; Fox Family Channel; Lifetime; Nashville Network; Nickelodeon; TBS Superstation; Turner Classic Movies; USA Network.
Fee: $32.33 monthly.
Pay Service 1
Pay Units: 25.
Programming (via satellite): Cinemax.
Fee: $10.95 monthly.
Pay Service 2
Pay Units: 16.
Programming (via satellite): HBO.
Fee: $10.95 monthly.
Local advertising: Yes.
Miles of plant: 5.8 (coaxial). Homes passed: 191. Total homes in franchised area: 191.
Manager: Marianne Bogy. Chief technician: Henry Harris.
Ownership: Buford Television Inc. (MSO). See Cable System Ownership.

PROGRESO—Rapid Cable, Box 6310, 310 Walnut Extension, Branson, MO 65616. Phones: 417-334-7897; 800-972-0962. Fax: 417-334-7899. County: Hidalgo. ICA: TX0630.
TV Market Ranking: Below 100. Franchise award date: N.A. Franchise expiration date: N.A. Began: June 1, 1989.
Channel capacity: 52. Channels available but not in use: 28.
Basic Service
Subscribers: 22.
Programming (received off-air): KVEO (N) Brownsville; KGBT-TV (C), KMBH (P) Harlingen; KRGV-TV (A) Weslaco; XHAB-TV Matamoros; XHRIO (O) Matamoros-Brownsville.
Programming (via satellite): WGN-TV (W) Chicago; CNN; Country Music TV; Discovery Channel; ESPN; EWTN; Fox Family Channel; GalaVision; Lifetime; Nashville Network; Nickelodeon; TBS Superstation; The Weather Channel; Turner Network TV; Univision.
Fee: $29.95 installation; $21.95 monthly.
Pay Service 1
Pay Units: 8.
Programming (via satellite): Disney Channel.
Fee: $9.95 monthly.
Pay Service 2
Pay Units: 13.
Programming (via satellite): HBO.
Fee: $10.95 monthly.
Pay Service 3
Pay Units: N.A.
Programming (via satellite): Cinemax; Showtime; The Movie Channel.
Fee: $9.00 monthly (Cinemax), $10.00 monthly (Showtime), $10.95 monthly (TMC).
Miles of plant: 5.1 (coaxial). Homes passed: 207.
Manager: Belinda Murphy. Chief engineer: Steve Rice. Program director: Beth Semptimphelter. Marketing director: Bill Fischer.
Ownership: Rapid Communications Partners LP (MSO).

QUANAH—Classic Cable, Box 429, 605 N.W. 3rd St., Plainville, KS 67663-0429. Phones: 785-434-7620; 800-999-8876. Fax: 785-434-2614. County: Hardeman. ICA: TX0839.
TV Market Ranking: Outside TV Markets. Franchise award date: N.A. Franchise expiration date: N.A. Began: April 1, 1963.
Channel capacity: 41 (2-way capable; operating 2-way). Channels available but not in use: N.A.
Basic Service
Subscribers: 1,088; Commercial subscribers: 35.
Programming (received off-air): KAMR-TV (N), KFDA-TV (C) Amarillo; KWET (P) Cheyenne; KAUZ-TV (C), KFDX-TV (N), KJTL (F,U), KSWO-TV (A) Wichita Falls-Lawton.
Programming (via satellite): WGN-TV (W) Chicago; A & E; American Movie Classics; Animal Planet; C-SPAN; CNN; Country Music TV; Discovery Channel; Disney Channel; E! Entertainment TV; ESPN; Fox Family Channel; Fox Sports Net Southwest; Goodlife TV Network; Headline News; Learning Channel; Lifetime; Nashville Network; Nick at Nite's TV Land; Nickelodeon; Odyssey; QVC; Sci-Fi Channel; TBS Superstation; The Weather Channel; Turner Network TV; USA Network; Univision.
Current originations: Religious access; automated emergency alert.
Fee: $35.00 installation; $29.95 monthly; $0.98 converter.
Commercial fee: $23.10 monthly.
Pay Service 1
Pay Units: 81.

Programming (via satellite): The Movie Channel.
Fee: $5.95 monthly.
Pay Service 2
Pay Units: 64.
Programming (via satellite): Showtime.
Fee: $9.95 monthly.
Pay Service 3
Pay Units: 113.
Programming (via satellite): HBO.
Fee: $10.95 monthly.
Local advertising: No.
Equipment: Standard Components, Scientific-Atlanta & Blonder-Tongue headend; Magnavox amplifiers; Comm/Scope & Times Fiber cable; Atari character generator; Standard Components set top converters; Scientific-Atlanta addressable set top converters; Eagle & Pico traps; AFC & Scientific-Atlanta satellite antenna; Standard Components & Scientific-Atlanta satellite receivers.
Miles of plant: 33.0 (coaxial). Homes passed: 1,634.
Manager: Bill Flowers. Chief technician: Rick Rattan. Marketing director: Jennifer Hauschild.
City fee: 2% of gross.
Ownership: Classic Cable (MSO).

QUEMADO—Time Warner Communications, Box 1208, 690 Ford St., Eagle Pass, TX 78853. Phone: 800-527-6221. County: Maverick. ICA: TX0570.
TV Market Ranking: Below 100. Franchise award date: N.A. Franchise expiration date: N.A. Began: N.A.
Channel capacity: 12. Channels available but not in use: None.
Basic Service
Subscribers: 210.
Programming (via microwave): KENS-TV (C), KLRN (P), KMOL-TV (N), KSAT-TV (A), KWEX-TV (S) San Antonio; XEW-TV Mexico City.
Programming (via satellite): WGN-TV (W) Chicago; CNN; ESPN; Nashville Network; TBS Superstation.
Fee: $60.00 installation; $15.00 monthly.
Pay Service 1
Pay Units: 58.
Programming (via satellite): HBO.
Fee: N.A.
Miles of plant: 27.0 (coaxial). Homes passed: 300.
Manager: Jimmy Gutierrez. Chief technician: Polo Vielma.
Ownership: Time Warner Cable (MSO); AT&T Broadband & Internet Services (MSO).

QUINLAN—Friendship Cable of Texas Inc., Box 9090, Tyler, TX 75711-9090. Phone: 903-581-2121. Fax: 903-581-2185. Counties: Hunt, Montgomery, Rains & Van Zandt. Also serves Brinwood Shores, Caddo Mills, Cash, East Tawakoni, Hunt County (portions), Lake Tawakoni, Lone Oak, Oak Terrace, Panarama Estates, Rains County (portions), Rolling Oaks, South Tawakoni, West Tawakoni. ICA: TX0793.
TV Market Ranking: 12 (Caddo Mills, portions of Hunt County); Below 100 (Cash, Hunt County, Lake Tawakoni, Quinlan, Rains County, Rolling Oaks); Outside TV Markets (Brinwood Shores, East Tawakoni, Lone Oak, Oak Terrace, Panarama Estates, South Tawakoni, West Tawakoni). Franchise award date: N.A. Franchise expiration date: January 1, 2000. Began: October 1, 1982.
Channel capacity: 54. Channels available but not in use: 10.
Basic Service
Subscribers: 3,229.
Programming (received off-air): KDAF (W), KDFW (F), KERA-TV (P), KTVT (C), KTXA (U), KXAS-TV (N), KXTX-TV (I), WFAA-TV (A) Dallas-Fort Worth.
Programming (via satellite): WGN-TV (W) Chicago; CNN; Disney Channel; ESPN; Fox Family Channel; Nickelodeon; TBS Superstation; USA Network.
Current originations: Public access.
Fee: $30.00 installation; $31.10 monthly.
Pay Service 1
Pay Units: 396.
Programming (via satellite): Cinemax.
Fee: $7.00 monthly.
Pay Service 2
Pay Units: 437.
Programming (via satellite): HBO.
Fee: $12.00 monthly.
Pay Service 3
Pay Units: 572.
Programming (via satellite): Showtime.
Fee: $7.00 monthly.
Pay Service 4
Pay Units: 333.
Programming (via satellite): The Movie Channel.
Fee: $9.00 monthly.
Pay Service 5
Pay Units: 734.
Programming (via satellite): Flix.
Fee: $1.95 monthly.
Local advertising: Yes. Regional interconnect: Cabletime.
Miles of plant: 201.0 (coaxial). Homes passed: 6,454.
Manager: Rodney Fletcher. Chief technician: Bo Jaubert.
Ownership: Buford Television Inc. (MSO). See Cable System Ownership.

QUITAQUE—Classic Cable, Box 429, 605 N.W. 3rd St., Plainville, KS 67663-0429. Phones: 785-434-7620; 800-999-8876. Fax: 785-434-2614. County: Briscoe. ICA: TX0840.
TV Market Ranking: Outside TV Markets. Franchise award date: January 4, 1988. Franchise expiration date: January 4, 2013. Began: N.A.
Channel capacity: 41 (2-way capable; operating 2-way). Channels available but not in use: N.A.
Basic Service
Subscribers: 85.
Programming (received off-air): KACV-TV (P), KAMR-TV (N), KFDA-TV (C), KVII-TV (A) Amarillo; KJTV (F) Lubbock.
Programming (via satellite): WGN-TV (W) Chicago; CNN; Country Music TV; Discovery Channel; Disney Channel; ESPN; Fox Family Channel; Fox News Channel; Fox Sports Net Southwest; Home Shopping Network; Learning Channel; Nashville Network; QVC; TBS Superstation; The Weather Channel; Turner Network TV; USA Network.
Fee: $35.00 installation; $27.95 monthly.
Pay Service 1
Pay Units: 6.
Programming (via satellite): Cinemax.
Fee: $9.95 monthly.
Pay Service 2
Pay Units: 12.
Programming (via satellite): HBO.
Fee: $9.95 monthly.
Miles of plant: 8.2 (coaxial). Homes passed: 254.
Manager: Bill Flowers. Chief technician: Chris Christenson. Marketing director: Jennifer Hauschild.
City fee: 2% of gross subscriber revenue.
Ownership: Classic Cable (MSO).

RALLS—Classic Cable, Box 429, 605 N.W. 3rd St., Plainville, KS 67663-0429. Phones: 785-434-7620; 800-999-8876. Fax: 785-434-2614. County: Crosby. ICA: TX0377.
TV Market Ranking: Below 100. Franchise award date: October 14, 1977. Franchise expiration date: October 14, 2002. Began: October 1, 1978.
Channel capacity: 61 (2-way capable; operating 2-way). Channels available but not in use: N.A.
Basic Service
Subscribers: 373.
Programming (received off-air): KAMC (A), KCBD-TV (N), KJTV (F), KLBK-TV (C), KPTB (I), KTXT-TV (P), KUPT-LP (U) Lubbock.
Programming (via translator): KVDA (O) San Antonio.
Programming (via satellite): WGN-TV (W) Chicago; American Movie Classics; CNN; Country Music TV; Discovery Channel; Disney Channel; E! Entertainment TV; ESPN; Fox Family Channel; Fox Sports Net Southwest; History Channel; Learning Channel; Lifetime; Nashville Network; Nick at Nite's TV Land; Nickelodeon; QVC; Sci-Fi Channel; TBS Superstation; The Weather Channel; Trinity Bcstg. Network; Turner Network TV; USA Network; Univision.
Current originations: Local news.
Fee: $35.00 installation; $29.95 monthly.
Pay Service 1
Pay Units: 28.
Programming (via satellite): Cinemax.
Fee: $9.95 monthly.
Pay Service 2
Pay Units: 63.
Programming (via satellite): HBO.
Fee: $9.95 monthly.
Local advertising: No.
Miles of plant: 13.1 (coaxial). Homes passed: 833.
Manager: Bill Flowers. Chief technician: Chris Christenson. Marketing director: Jennifer Hauschild.
City fee: 3% of gross.
Ownership: Classic Cable (MSO).

RANDOLPH—Torrence Cablevision, Box 1167, Ridgeland, MS 39158. Phones: 601-981-6900; 800-977-8849. County: Fannin. ICA: TX0690.
TV Market Ranking: Below 100. Franchise award date: N.A. Franchise expiration date: N.A. Began: N.A.
Channel capacity: 36. Channels available but not in use: 21.
Basic Service
Subscribers: 12.
Programming (received off-air): KDAF (W), KDFW (F), KERA-TV (P), KXAS-TV (N), WFAA-TV (A) Dallas-Fort Worth.
Programming (via satellite): WGN-TV (W) Chicago; A & E; American Movie Classics; CNN; Country Music TV; Discovery Channel; Fox Family Channel; Showtime; TBS Superstation; Turner Network TV; USA Network.
Fee: $28.00 monthly.
Miles of plant: 3.8 (coaxial). Homes passed: 86.
Ownership: Torrence Cable Inc. (MSO).

RAYMONDVILLE—Time Warner Communications, 2921 S. Expwy. 83, Harlingen, TX 78550-7615. Phone: 956-541-6782. Fax: 956-412-0959. County: Willacy. Also serves Lyford, Willacy County. ICA: TX0173.
TV Market Ranking: Below 100. Franchise award date: N.A. Franchise expiration date: N.A. Began: November 1, 1968.
Channel capacity: 38. Channels available but not in use: N.A.
Basic Service
Subscribers: 1,252.
Programming (received off-air): KVEO (N) Brownsville; KGBT-TV (C), KLUJ (E), KMBH (P) Harlingen; KRGV-TV (A) Weslaco; XHAB-TV Matamoros; XHRIO (O) Matamoros-Brownsville.
Programming (via satellite): WGN-TV (W) Chicago; A & E; C-SPAN; CNN; Fox Family Channel; Headline News; Lifetime; MTV; Nashville Network; Nickelodeon; QVC; TBS Superstation; The Weather Channel.
Fee: $60.00 installation; $10.93 monthly.
Expanded Basic Service
Subscribers: N.A.
Programming (via satellite): CNBC; Discovery Channel; ESPN; Fox Sports Net Southwest; Turner Network TV; USA Network; Univision.
Fee: $1.75 monthly.
Pay Service 1
Pay Units: 217.
Programming (via satellite): Cinemax.
Fee: N.A.
Pay Service 2
Pay Units: 107.
Programming (via satellite): Disney Channel.
Fee: N.A.
Pay Service 3
Pay Units: 418.
Programming (via satellite): HBO.
Fee: N.A.
Pay Service 4
Pay Units: N.A.
Programming (via satellite): The New Encore.
Fee: N.A.
Miles of plant: 46.3 (coaxial). Homes passed: 3,078. Total homes in franchised area: 3,078.
Manager: Juan Herrera. Chief technician: Al Velasquez.
Ownership: Time Warner Cable (MSO); AT&T Broadband & Internet Services (MSO).

RAYWOOD—Friendship Cable of Texas Inc., Box 9090, Tyler, TX 75711-9090. Phone: 903-581-2121. Fax: 903-581-2185. County: Liberty. Also serves Ames, Devers. ICA: TX0340.
TV Market Ranking: Below 100. Franchise award date: N.A. Franchise expiration date: N.A. Began: N.A.
Channel capacity: 36 (not 2-way capable). Channels available but not in use: None.
Basic Service
Subscribers: 480.
Programming (received off-air): KBMT (A), KBTV-TV (N), KFDM-TV (C) Beaumont-Port Arthur; KHOU-TV (C), KHTV (W), KPRC-TV (N), KRIV (F), KTRK-TV (A), KTXH (U), KUHT (P) Houston.
Programming (via satellite): A & E; BET; C-SPAN; CNN; Country Music TV; Discovery Channel; Disney Channel; ESPN; Fox Family Channel; Fox Sports Net Southwest; Headline News; Home Shopping Network; Lifetime; Nashville Network; Nickelodeon; TBS Superstation; The Inspirational Network; The Weather Channel; Turner Network TV; USA Network; VH1.
Fee: $33.90 monthly.
Pay Service 1
Pay Units: 33.
Programming (via satellite): Cinemax.
Fee: $10.95 monthly.
Pay Service 2
Pay Units: 43.
Programming (via satellite): HBO.
Fee: $10.95 monthly.
Pay Service 3
Pay Units: 42.
Programming (via satellite): Showtime.

Fee: $5.95 monthly.
Local advertising: Yes.
Miles of plant: 45.3 (coaxial). Homes passed: 1,102.
Manager: Wanda Pyburn. Chief technician: Mike Deal.
Ownership: Buford Television Inc. (MSO). See Cable System Ownership.

REALITOS—National Cable Inc., Suite 106-A, 5151 Reed Rd., Columbus, OH 43220. Phones: 614-442-5890; 800-582-0504. Fax: 614-457-2567. County: Duval. ICA: TX0841.
TV Market Ranking: Outside TV Markets. Franchise award date: N.A. Franchise expiration date: N.A. Began: N.A.
Channel capacity: 36. Channels available but not in use: 21.
Basic Service
Subscribers: 29.
Programming (received off-air): KEDT (P), KORO (S), KZTV (C) Corpus Christi; KGNS-TV (N,A), KLDO-TV (O) Laredo.
Programming (via satellite): WGN-TV (W) Chicago; A & E; American Movie Classics; CNN; Country Music TV; Discovery Channel; ESPN; Fox Family Channel; Showtime; TBS Superstation; Turner Network TV; USA Network.
Fee: $28.00 monthly.
Miles of plant: 2.9 (coaxial). Homes passed: 90.
Manager: Paul Scott. Chief technician: Rob Spiller. Marketing director: Josh Thackery.
Ownership: National Cable (MSO).

RED ACKERS—Northland Cable TV, Box 538, Flint, TX 75762. Phones: 903-566-5787; 903-894-8200. Fax: 903-894-8204. County: Henderson. ICA: TX0407.
TV Market Ranking: Below 100. Franchise award date: N.A. Franchise expiration date: N.A. Began: November 1, 1983.
Channel capacity: 36 (2-way capable). Channels available but not in use: 5.
Basic Service
Subscribers: 633.
Programming (received off-air): KETK-TV (N) Jacksonville; KFXK (F) Longview; KLTV (A) Tyler-Longview.
Programming (via microwave): KDFW (F), KERA-TV (P), KTVT (C), KXTX-TV (I), WFAA-TV (A) Dallas-Fort Worth.
Programming (via satellite): WGN-TV (W) Chicago; A & E; CNN; Country Music TV; Discovery Channel; ESPN; Fox Family Channel; Fox Sports Net Southwest; Headline News; Learning Channel; Nashville Network; QVC; TBS Superstation; USA Network.
Current originations: Automated time-weather; local sports.
Fee: $49.95 installation; $20.75 monthly; $3.00 converter.
Pay Service 1
Pay Units: 57.
Programming (via satellite): Showtime.
Fee: $24.95 installation; $7.95 monthly.
Pay Service 2
Pay Units: 23.
Programming (via satellite): Disney Channel.
Fee: $24.95 installation; $7.00 monthly.
Pay Service 3
Pay Units: 62.
Programming (via satellite): HBO.
Fee: $24.95 installation; $10.50 monthly.
Local advertising: Yes. Available in satellite distributed, locally originated, character-generated, taped & automated programming. Rates: $8.00/Minute; $4.00/30 Seconds. Local sales manager: Lynda Tracy.
Program Guide: Premium Channels.
Equipment: M/A-Com & Scientific-Atlanta headend; Magnavox amplifiers; Comm/Scope cable; Texscan character generator; Hamlin, Jerrold & Scientific-Atlanta set top converters; Arcom, Eagle & Pico traps; Scientific-Atlanta satellite antenna; Scientific-Atlanta satellite receivers; ChannelMatic & Sony commercial insert.
Miles of plant: 26.5 (coaxial). Homes passed: 780.
Manager: Jim Wiggins. Chief technician: Jim Bob Sanders. Marketing director: Charlotte Griffin.
Ownership: Northland Communications Corp. (MSO).

REDWATER—Friendship Cable of Arkansas Inc., Box 9090, Tyler, TX 75711-9090. Phone: 903-581-2121. Fax: 903-581-2185. County: Bowie. Also serves Buchanan, Leary. ICA: TX0436.
TV Market Ranking: 58. Franchise award date: N.A. Franchise expiration date: N.A. Began: May 1, 1989.
Channel capacity: 54. Channels available but not in use: N.A.
Basic Service
Subscribers: 1,195.
Programming (received off-air): KLTS-TV (P), KMSS-TV (F), KSHV (U,W), KSLA-TV (C), KTAL-TV (N), KTBS-TV (A) Shreveport-Texarkana.
Programming (via satellite): WGN-TV (W) Chicago; A & E; CNN; Country Music TV; Discovery Channel; Disney Channel; ESPN; Headline News; History Channel; Lifetime; Nashville Network; Nickelodeon; TBS Superstation; The Weather Channel; Trinity Bcstg. Network; USA Network.
Fee: $30.00 installation; $28.95 monthly.
Pay Service 1
Pay Units: 184.
Programming (via satellite): HBO.
Fee: $10.00 monthly.
Pay Service 2
Pay Units: 17.
Programming (via satellite): Cinemax.
Fee: $10.95 monthly.
Pay Service 3
Pay Units: 67.
Programming (via satellite): Showtime.
Fee: $5.95 monthly.
Miles of plant: 93.0 (coaxial). Homes passed: 2,895.
Manager: Arl Cope.
Ownership: Buford Television Inc. (MSO). See Cable System Ownership.

REFUGIO—TCI Cablevision of Texas, 4060 S. Padre Island Dr., Corpus Christi, TX 78411-4477. Phone: 512-857-5000. County: Refugio. Also serves Woodsboro. ICA: TX0214.
TV Market Ranking: Below 100 (Woodsboro); Outside TV Markets (Refugio). Franchise award date: N.A. Franchise expiration date: N.A. Began: February 1, 1981.
Channel capacity: 35. Channels available but not in use: 8.
Basic Service
Subscribers: 1,538.
Programming (received off-air): KEDT (P), KIII (A), KORO (S), KRIS-TV (N), KZTV (C) Corpus Christi.
Programming (via satellite): WGN-TV (W) Chicago; BET; C-SPAN; CNBC; CNN; Discovery Channel; Fox Family Channel; Fox-Net; Headline News; Lifetime; Nashville Network; TBS Superstation; The Weather Channel.
Fee: $37.49 installation; $10.45 monthly; $18.74 additional installation.

Expanded Basic Service
Subscribers: 1,421.
Programming (via satellite): American Movie Classics; ESPN; Fox Sports Net Southwest; Turner Network TV; USA Network.
Fee: $10.55 monthly.
Pay Service 1
Pay Units: 524.
Programming (via satellite): The New Encore.
Fee: N.A.
Pay Service 2
Pay Units: 145.
Programming (via satellite): Disney Channel.
Fee: $10.95 monthly.
Pay Service 3
Pay Units: 495.
Programming (via satellite): HBO.
Fee: $10.95 monthly.
Pay Service 4
Pay Units: 348.
Programming (via satellite): Showtime.
Fee: $10.95 monthly.
Equipment: Scientific-Atlanta satellite antenna.
Miles of plant: 59.7 (coaxial). Homes passed: 2,122. Total homes in franchised area: 2,122.
Manager: Dennis Moore. Chief technician: Mando Blancas. Marketing director: Jerri Coppedge.
Ownership: AT&T Broadband & Internet Services (MSO). Purchased from Tele-Communications Inc., March 9, 1999.

REKLAW—Friendship Cable of Texas Inc., Box 9090, Tyler, TX 75711-9090. Phone: 903-581-2121. Fax: 903-581-2185. County: Cherokee. ICA: TX0698.
TV Market Ranking: Below 100. Franchise award date: N.A. Franchise expiration date: N.A. Began: N.A.
Channel capacity: 37. Channels available but not in use: 18.
Basic Service
Subscribers: 43.
Programming (received off-air): KETK-TV (N) Jacksonville; KFXK (F) Longview; KTRE (A) Lufkin.
Programming (via satellite): WGN-TV (W) Chicago; KRMA-TV (P) Denver; A & E; CNN; Discovery Channel; ESPN; Fox Family Channel; Nashville Network; Showtime; TBS Superstation; USA Network.
Fee: $32.45 monthly.
Pay Service 1
Pay Units: 24.
Programming (via satellite): Showtime.
Fee: $5.95 monthly.
Miles of plant: 2.4 (coaxial). Homes passed: 83.
Manager: Marianne Bogy. Chief technician: Francis Richard.
Ownership: Buford Television Inc. (MSO). See Cable System Ownership.

RENO (Parker County)—Friendship Cable of Texas Inc., Box 9090, Tyler, TX 75711-9090. Phone: 903-581-2121. Fax: 903-581-2185. County: Parker. Also serves Parker County (portions). ICA: TX0261.
TV Market Ranking: 12. Franchise award date: N.A. Franchise expiration date: N.A. Began: N.A.
Channel capacity: 36. Channels available but not in use: 8.
Basic Service
Subscribers: 440.
Programming (received off-air): KPXD (X) Arlington; KDAF (W), KDFI-TV (I), KDFW (F), KERA-TV (P), KTVT (C), KTXA (U), KXAS-TV (N), KXTX-TV (I), WFAA-TV (A) Dallas-Fort Worth.
Programming (via satellite): WGN-TV (W) Chicago; A & E; CNN; Country Music TV; Discovery Channel; Disney Channel; ESPN; Fox Family Channel; Fox Sports Net Southwest; Goodlife TV Network; Headline News; Home Shopping Network; Nashville Network; Nickelodeon; TBS Superstation; Turner Network TV; USA Network.
Fee: $31.10 monthly.
Pay Service 1
Pay Units: 26.
Programming (via satellite): Cinemax.
Fee: $10.95 monthly.
Pay Service 2
Pay Units: 31.
Programming (via satellite): HBO.
Fee: $10.95 monthly.
Pay Service 3
Pay Units: 84.
Programming (via satellite): Showtime.
Fee: $5.95 monthly.
Local advertising: Yes.
Miles of plant: 9.2 (coaxial). Homes passed: 450.
Manager: Rodney Fletcher. Chief technician: Steven Williams.
Ownership: Buford Television Inc. (MSO). See Cable System Ownership.

RICARDO—Ricardo Cable TV, Box 997, Riviera, TX 78379. Phone: 512-296-3232. Fax: 512-296-3125. County: Kleberg. Also serves Kingsville (unincorporated areas). ICA: TX0664.
TV Market Ranking: Outside TV Markets. Franchise award date: N.A. Franchise expiration date: N.A. Began: N.A.
Channel capacity: 36. Channels available but not in use: 21.
Basic Service
Subscribers: 43.
Programming (received off-air): KEDT (P), KIII (A), KORO (S), KRIS-TV (N), KZTV (C) Corpus Christi.
Programming (via satellite): WGN-TV (W) Chicago; A & E; American Movie Classics; CNN; Country Music TV; Discovery Channel; ESPN; Fox Family Channel; Showtime; TBS Superstation; Turner Network TV; USA Network.
Fee: $28.00 monthly.
Miles of plant: 7.0 (coaxial). Homes passed: 151.
Manager: Bill Colston Jr. Chief technician: Leslie Colston.
Ownership: Riviera Telephone Co. (MSO).

RICE—Northland Cable, Box 550, Corsicana, TX 75151. Phone: 903-872-3131. Fax: 903-872-6623. Counties: Ellis & Navarro. ICA: TX0843.

TV Market Ranking: Outside TV Markets. Franchise award date: February 20, 1989. Franchise expiration date: February 20, 2004. Began: N.A.
Channel capacity: 52 (not 2-way capable). Channels available but not in use: N.A.

Basic Service
Subscribers: 130.
Programming (received off-air): KDAF (W), KDFW (F), KERA-TV (P), KTVT (C), KTXA (U), KXAS-TV (N), KXTX-TV (I), WFAA-TV (A) Dallas-Fort Worth; KWTX-TV (C) Waco-Temple.
Programming (via satellite): CNN; Discovery Channel; ESPN; Fox Family Channel; MTV; Nashville Network; Nickelodeon; TBS Superstation; USA Network.
Fee: $55.00 installation; $23.95 monthly.

Pay Service 1
Pay Units: 54.
Programming (via satellite): HBO.
Fee: $10.50 monthly.

Pay Service 2
Pay Units: 41.
Programming (via satellite): Showtime.
Fee: $10.00 monthly.
Miles of plant: 12.0 (coaxial); None (fiber optic).
Business manager: Mike Taylor.
Ownership: Northland Communications Corp. (MSO).

RICHARDS—Torrence Cablevision, Box 1167, Ridgeland, MS 39158. Phones: 601-981-6900; 800-977-8849. County: Grimes. ICA: TX0906.
TV Market Ranking: Below 100. Franchise award date: N.A. Franchise expiration date: N.A. Began: N.A.
Channel capacity: N.A. Channels available but not in use: N.A.

Basic Service
Subscribers: 21.
Programming (received off-air): KHOU-TV (C), KPRC-TV (N), KTRK-TV (A), KUHT (P) Houston.
Programming (via satellite): WGN-TV (W) Chicago; A & E; American Movie Classics; CNN; Country Music TV; Discovery Channel; ESPN; Fox Family Channel; Showtime; TBS Superstation; Turner Network TV; USA Network.
Fee: $28.00 monthly.
Homes passed: 136.
Ownership: Torrence Cable Inc. (MSO).

RICHLAND SPRINGS—Post Cablevision of Texas Ltd., Drawer 829, 1108 Parker St., Goldthwaite, TX 76844. Phone: 915-648-3041. County: San Saba. ICA: TX0632.
TV Market Ranking: Outside TV Markets. Franchise award date: N.A. Franchise expiration date: N.A. Began: October 1, 1983.
Channel capacity: 20. Channels available but not in use: None.

Basic Service
Subscribers: N.A.
Programming (received off-air): KRBC-TV (N) Abilene-Sweetwater; KNCT (P) Belton; KLST (C) San Angelo; KCEN-TV (N), KWTX-TV (C), KXXV (A) Waco-Temple.
Programming (via satellite): WGN-TV (W) Chicago; CNN; Country Music TV; Discovery Channel; ESPN; Fox Family Channel; Home Shopping Network; Nashville Network; TBS Superstation; Turner Network TV; USA Network.
Fee: N.A.

Pay Service 1
Pay Units: N.A.
Programming (via satellite): HBO.
Fee: $10.68 monthly.
Miles of plant: 6.2 (coaxial). Homes passed: 206.
Manager: Denise Casbeer. Chief technician: Jerry Stembridge.
Ownership: Fanch Communications Inc. (MSO). See Cable System Ownership.

RIESEL—Cabletex Systems Inc., Box 547, Riesel, TX 76682. Phone: 254-896-2818. Fax: 254-896-2118. County: McLennan. ICA: TX0556.
TV Market Ranking: Below 100. Franchise award date: N.A. Franchise expiration date: N.A. Began: April 1, 1988.
Channel capacity: 36. Channels available but not in use: N.A.

Basic Service
Subscribers: N.A.
Programming (received off-air): KDAF (W), KERA-TV (P), KTVT (C), KXTX-TV (I), WFAA-TV (A) Dallas-Fort Worth; KCEN-TV (N), KWKT (F), KWTX-TV (C), KXXV (A) Waco-Temple.
Programming (via satellite): WGN-TV (W) Chicago; CNN; Country Music TV; Discovery Channel; ESPN; Home Shopping Network; MTV; Nashville Network; Nickelodeon; TBS Superstation; Turner Network TV.
Fee: $15.00 installation; $13.95 monthly.

Pay Service 1
Pay Units: N.A.
Programming (via satellite): Cinemax; Disney Channel; HBO; Showtime; The Movie Channel.
Fee: $8.75 monthly (each).
Miles of plant: 9.5 (coaxial). Homes passed: 337.
Manager: George Merilian. Chief technician: Rick Pick.
Ownership: Cabletex Systems Inc.

RIO GRANDE CITY—Time Warner Communications, 2921 S. Expwy. 83, Harlingen, TX 78550-7615. Phone: 956-541-6782. Fax: 956-412-0959. County: Starr. ICA: TX0181.
TV Market Ranking: Below 100. Franchise award date: N.A. Franchise expiration date: N.A. Began: July 1, 1968.
Channel capacity: 38. Channels available but not in use: N.A.

Basic Service
Subscribers: 2,335.
Programming (received off-air): KVEO (N) Brownsville; KGBT-TV (C), KMBH (P) Harlingen; KRGV-TV (A) Weslaco.
Programming (via satellite): WGN-TV (W) Chicago; A & E; C-SPAN; CNN; Fox Family Channel; GalaVision; Headline News; Lifetime; MTV; Nashville Network; Nickelodeon; QVC; TBS Superstation; Telemundo; The Weather Channel; Trinity Bcstg. Network.
Fee: $60.00 installation; $21.72 monthly; $0.45 converter.

Expanded Basic Service
Subscribers: 2,133.
Programming (via satellite): CNBC; Discovery Channel; ESPN; Fox Sports Net Southwest; Turner Network TV; USA Network; Univision.
Fee: $1.95 monthly.

Pay Service 1
Pay Units: 265.
Programming (via satellite): Cinemax.
Fee: N.A.

Pay Service 2
Pay Units: 146.
Programming (via satellite): Disney Channel.
Fee: N.A.

Pay Service 3
Pay Units: 556.
Programming (via satellite): HBO.
Fee: N.A.
Local advertising: Yes. Regional interconnect: Cabletime.
Miles of plant: 38.8 (coaxial). Homes passed: 2,903. Total homes in franchised area: 2,903.
Manager: Juan Herrera. Chief technician: Al Velasquez.
Ownership: AT&T Broadband & Internet Services (MSO); Time Warner Cable (MSO); Advance/Newhouse Partnership (MSO).

RIO VISTA—National Cable Inc., Suite 106-A, 5151 Reed Rd., Columbus, OH 43220. Phones: 614-442-5890; 800-582-0504. Fax: 614-457-2567. County: Johnson. ICA: TX0535.
TV Market Ranking: 12. Franchise award date: N.A. Franchise expiration date: N.A. Began: N.A.
Channel capacity: 35. Channels available but not in use: 19.

Basic Service
Subscribers: 31.
Programming (received off-air): KDFW (F), KERA-TV (P), KXAS-TV (N), WFAA-TV (A) Dallas-Fort Worth.
Programming (via satellite): WGN-TV (W) Chicago; A & E; American Movie Classics; CNN; Country Music TV; Discovery Channel; ESPN; Fox Family Channel; Showtime; TBS Superstation; Turner Network TV; USA Network.
Fee: $24.00 monthly.

Pay Service 1
Pay Units: 29.
Programming (via satellite): Cinemax.
Fee: $10.95 monthly.

Pay Service 2
Pay Units: 31.
Programming (via satellite): HBO.
Fee: $10.95 monthly.
Local advertising: Yes.
Miles of plant: 15.0 (coaxial). Homes passed: 373.
Manager: Paul Scott. Chief technician: Rob Spiller. Marketing director: Josh Thackery.
Ownership: National Cable (MSO).

RISING STAR—Brownwood TV Cable Service Inc., Box 1149, 310 Carnegie Blvd., Brownwood, TX 76801. Phone: 915-646-3576. Fax: 915-643-2846. County: Eastland. Also serves Cross Plains. ICA: TX0354.
TV Market Ranking: Outside TV Markets. Franchise award date: N.A. Franchise expiration date: June 10, 2002. Began: April 1, 1974.
Channel capacity: N.A. Channels available but not in use: N.A.

Basic Service
Subscribers: 608.
Programming (received off-air): KRBC-TV (N), KTAB-TV (C) Abilene-Sweetwater; KDFW (F), KERA-TV (P), WFAA-TV (A) Dallas-Fort Worth; allband FM.
Programming (via microwave): KTVT (C) Dallas-Fort Worth.
Programming (via satellite): WGN-TV (W) Chicago; ESPN; Fox Family Channel; Nashville Network; TBS Superstation.
Fee: $37.50 installation; $8.85 monthly.

Expanded Basic Service
Subscribers: N.A.
Programming (via satellite): Trinity Bcstg. Network; Turner Network TV.
Fee: $11.05 monthly.

Pay Service 1
Pay Units: N.A.
Programming (via satellite): HBO.
Fee: $11.45 monthly.
Miles of plant: 6.0 (coaxial). Additional miles planned: 1.0 (coaxial). Homes passed: 1,043.
Manager: Karen McMillan. Chief technician: Paul Mathison.
City fee: 2% of gross.
Ownership: Brownwood TV Cable Service Inc. (MSO).

RIVER OAKS (Tarrant County)—Mallard Cablevision, 100-D El Chico Trail, Willow Park, TX 76087. Phones: 817-441-8073; 800-669-2288. Fax: 817-441-6464. County: Tarrant. Also serves Carswell AFB, Sansom Park, Westworth Village. ICA: TX0884.
TV Market Ranking: 12. Franchise award date: N.A. Franchise expiration date: N.A. Began: May 1, 1982.
Channel capacity: 60. Channels available but not in use: 17.

Basic Service
Subscribers: 2,400.
Programming (received off-air): KDAF (W), KDFI-TV (I), KDFW (F), KERA-TV (P), KTVT (C), KTXA (U), KXAS-TV (N), KXTX-TV (I), WFAA-TV (A) Dallas-Fort Worth; KMPX (I) Decatur; KDTN (P) Denton.
Programming (via satellite): WGN-TV (W) Chicago; A & E; American Movie Classics; Animal Planet; BET; CNN; Cartoon Network; Country Music TV; Discovery Channel; Disney Channel; ESPN; FX; Fox Family Channel; Fox News Channel; Fox Sports Net Southwest; Headline News; History Channel; Home & Garden Television; Home Shopping Network; Learning Channel; Lifetime; MTV; Nashville Network; Nickelodeon; TBS Superstation; Telemundo; The Weather Channel; Trinity Bcstg. Network; Turner Network TV; USA Network; Univision.
Current originations: Automated timeweather.
Fee: $29.95 monthly.

Pay Service 1
Pay Units: 337.
Programming (via satellite): Cinemax.
Fee: $11.95 monthly.

Pay Service 2
Pay Units: 482.
Programming (via satellite): HBO.
Fee: $11.95 monthly.
Miles of plant: 80.0 (coaxial). Homes passed: 4,675.
Manager: Doug Grassmann.
Ownership: Mallard Cablevision (MSO). Purchased from Cambridge Communications, May 1, 1999.

RIVERSIDE—Friendship Cable of Texas Inc., Box 9090, Tyler, TX 75711-9090. Phone: 903-581-2121. Fax: 903-581-2185. County: Walker. ICA: TX0527.
TV Market Ranking: Outside TV Markets. Franchise award date: N.A. Franchise expiration date: N.A. Began: January 1, 1990.
Channel capacity: 54. Channels available but not in use: N.A.

Basic Service
Subscribers: 193.
Programming (received off-air): KBTX-TV (C) Bryan; KRIV (F) Houston; KETK-TV (N) Jacksonville; KTRE (A) Lufkin.
Programming (via satellite): WGN-TV (W) Chicago; KTLA (W) Los Angeles; CNN; Discovery Channel; Disney Channel; ESPN; Nashville Network; Nickelodeon; TBS Superstation; Turner Network TV; USA Network.
Fee: $30.00 installation; $26.65 monthly.

Pay Service 1
Pay Units: 6.
Programming (via satellite): Cinemax.
Fee: $10.95 monthly.

Pay Service 2
Pay Units: 8.
Programming (via satellite): HBO.

Fee: $10.95 monthly.
Pay Service 3
Pay Units: 30.
Programming (via satellite): Showtime.
Fee: $10.95 monthly.
Miles of plant: 16.0 (coaxial). Homes passed: 422.
Manager: Wanda Pyburn. Chief technician: David Burrell.
Ownership: Buford Television Inc. (MSO). See Cable System Ownership.

RIVIERA—Riviera Cable TV, Box 997, Riviera, TX 78379. Phone: 512-296-3125. County: Kleberg. ICA: TX0657.
TV Market Ranking: Outside TV Markets. Franchise award date: N.A. Franchise expiration date: N.A. Began: N.A.
Channel capacity: 36. Channels available but not in use: 21.
Basic Service
Subscribers: 45.
Programming (received off-air): KEDT (P), KIII (A), KORO (S), KRIS-TV (N), KZTV (C) Corpus Christi.
Programming (via satellite): WGN-TV (W) Chicago; A & E; American Movie Classics; CNN; Country Music TV; Discovery Channel; ESPN; Fox Family Channel; Showtime; TBS Superstation; Turner Network TV; USA Network.
Fee: $28.00 monthly.
Miles of plant: 4.0 (coaxial). Homes passed: 167.
Manager: Bill Colston Jr. Chief technician: Leslie Colston.
Ownership: Riviera Telephone Co. (MSO).

ROARING SPRINGS—Classic Cable, Box 429, 605 N.W. 3rd St., Plainville, KS 67663-0429. Phones: 785-434-7620; 800-999-8876. Fax: 785-434-2614. County: Motley. ICA: TX0960.
TV Market Ranking: Outside TV Markets. Franchise award date: N.A. Franchise expiration date: N.A. Began: N.A.
Channel capacity: 61 (2-way capable; operating 2-way). Channels available but not in use: N.A.
Basic Service
Subscribers: 80.
Programming (received off-air): KAMC (A), KCBD-TV (N), KJTV (F), KLBK-TV (C) Lubbock.
Programming (via satellite): WGN-TV (W) Chicago; CNN; Country Music TV; Discovery Channel; Disney Channel; ESPN; Fox Family Channel; Fox Sports Net Southwest; Headline News; Learning Channel; Nashville Network; TBS Superstation; The Weather Channel; Trinity Bcstg. Network; Turner Network TV; USA Network.
Fee: $35.00 installation; $27.95 monthly.
Pay Service 1
Pay Units: 14.
Programming (via satellite): Cinemax.
Fee: $9.95 monthly.
Pay Service 2
Pay Units: 14.
Programming (via satellite): HBO.
Fee: $9.95 monthly.
Miles of plant: 4.7 (coaxial). Homes passed: 141.
Manager: Bill Flowers. Chief technician: Rick Rattan. Marketing director: Jennifer Hauschild.
Ownership: Classic Cable (MSO).

ROBERT LEE—West Texas Cablevision, Box 3528, Hwy. 87 N, San Angelo, TX 76902. Phone: 915-655-4657. Counties: Coke & Tom Green. Also serves Tom Green County. ICA: TX0327.
TV Market Ranking: Below 100. Franchise award date: February 23, 1979. Franchise expiration date: N.A. Began: August 1, 1980.
Channel capacity: 21. Channels available but not in use: None.
Basic Service
Subscribers: 432.
Programming (received off-air): KRBC-TV (N), KTXS-TV (A) Abilene-Sweetwater; KIDY (F), KLST (C) San Angelo; allband FM.
Programming (via satellite): WGN-TV (W) Chicago; ESPN; Fox Family Channel; Nashville Network; TBS Superstation.
Fee: $35.00 installation; $20.40 monthly.
Pay Service 1
Pay Units: N.A.
Programming (via satellite): Cinemax; Disney Channel; HBO.
Fee: $7.95 monthly (Disney), $9.95 monthly (Cinemax or HBO).
Equipment: Microdyne & Phasecom headend; Theta-Com amplifiers; Panasonic cable; Microdyne satellite antenna.
Miles of plant: 22.0 (coaxial); None (fiber optic). Homes passed: 648.
Manager: Kenny White. Marketing director: Jane Ketcham.
City fee: 2% of gross.
Ownership: Cable Management Assoc. (MSO).

ROBY—Classic Cable, Box 429, 605 N.W. 3rd St., Plainville, KS 67663-0429. Phones: 785-434-7620; 800-999-8876. Fax: 785-434-2614. County: Fisher. ICA: TX0844.
TV Market Ranking: Below 100. Franchise award date: December 6, 1988. Franchise expiration date: December 6, 2013. Began: N.A.
Channel capacity: 22 (2-way capable; operating 2-way). Channels available but not in use: N.A.
Basic Service
Subscribers: 185; Commercial subscribers: 14.
Programming (received off-air): KRBC-TV (N), KTAB-TV (C), KTXS-TV (A) Abilene-Sweetwater; KIDY (F) San Angelo.
Programming (via satellite): WGN-TV (W) Chicago; CNN; Country Music TV; Discovery Channel; Disney Channel; ESPN; Fox Family Channel; Fox Sports Net Southwest; Learning Channel; Nashville Network; Nick at Nite's TV Land; QVC; TBS Superstation; The Weather Channel; Turner Classic Movies; Turner Network TV; USA Network; Univision.
Current originations: Local news.
Fee: $35.00 installation; $26.95 monthly.
Pay Service 1
Pay Units: 16.
Programming (via satellite): Showtime.
Fee: $9.95 monthly.
Pay Service 2
Pay Units: 46.
Programming (via satellite): HBO.
Fee: $9.95 monthly.
Miles of plant: 8.1 (coaxial). Homes passed: 469.
Manager: Bill Flowers. Chief technician: Rick Rattan. Marketing director: Jennifer Hauschild.
City fee: 1% of gross.
Ownership: Classic Cable (MSO).

ROCHESTER—Rochester Cablevision, Box 6575, Abilene, TX 79608. Phone: 915-691-5787. County: Haskell. ICA: TX0845.
TV Market Ranking: Outside TV Markets. Franchise award date: N.A. Franchise expiration date: N.A. Began: N.A.
Channel capacity: N.A. Channels available but not in use: N.A.
Basic Service
Subscribers: N.A.
Programming (received off-air): KRBC-TV (N), KTAB-TV (C), KTXS-TV (A) Abilene-Sweetwater.
Programming (via satellite): WGN-TV (W) Chicago; ESPN; Fox Family Channel; TBS Superstation; USA Network.
Fee: N.A.
Pay Service 1
Pay Units: N.A.
Programming (via satellite): Cinemax; HBO.
Fee: N.A.
Manager: D. H. Pope.
Ownership: Jayroc Inc. (MSO).

ROCK SPRINGS—Classic Cable, Box 429, 605 N.W. 3rd St., Plainville, KS 67663-0429. Phones: 785-434-7620; 800-999-8876. Fax: 785-434-2614. County: Edwards. ICA: TX0480.
TV Market Ranking: Outside TV Markets. Franchise award date: March 13, 1989. Franchise expiration date: March 13, 2004. Began: August 1, 1960.
Channel capacity: 22 (2-way capable; operating 2-way). Channels available but not in use: N.A.
Basic Service
Subscribers: 252.
Programming (received off-air): KRRT (W) Kerrville-San Antonio; KOCB (W) Oklahoma City; KENS-TV (C), KMOL-TV (N), KSAT-TV (A) San Antonio; allband FM.
Programming (via satellite): WGN-TV (W) Chicago; A & E; CNN; Discovery Channel; Disney Channel; ESPN; Fox Family Channel; FoxNet; Nashville Network; Nick at Nite's TV Land; TBS Superstation; The Weather Channel; Trinity Bcstg. Network; Turner Network TV; USA Network; Univision.
Current originations: Automated timeweather.
Fee: $35.00 installation; $27.95 monthly; $2.00 converter; $22.00 additional installation.
Commercial fee: $3.50 monthly.
Pay Service 1
Pay Units: 12.
Programming (via satellite): Showtime.
Fee: $9.95 monthly.
Pay Service 2
Pay Units: 64.
Programming (via satellite): HBO.
Fee: $11.95 monthly.
Equipment: Jerrold headend; Jerrold amplifiers; Sony VTRs; Eagle traps; U.S. Tower satellite antenna.
Miles of plant: 15.5 (coaxial). Homes passed: 570.
Manager: Bill Flowers. Chief technician: Walt VanLue. Marketing director: Jennifer Hauschild.
City fee: 3% of gross.
Ownership: Classic Cable (MSO). Purchased from Rocksprings-Canyon TV Co. Inc.

ROCKDALE—Classic Cable, Box 429, 605 N.W. 3rd St., Plainville, KS 67663-0429. Phones: 785-434-7620; 800-999-8876. Fax: 785-434-2614. County: Milam. ICA: TX0158.
TV Market Ranking: Below 100. Franchise award date: June 8, 1971. Franchise expiration date: N.A. Began: August 1, 1972.
Channel capacity: 58 (2-way capable; operating 2-way). Channels available but not in use: N.A.
Basic Service
Subscribers: 1,875.
Programming (received off-air): KEYE-TV (C), KLRU (P), KTBC (F), KVUE-TV (A), KXAN-TV (N) Austin; KCEN-TV (N), KWKT (F), KWTX-TV (C) Waco-Temple; allband FM.
Programming (via satellite): WGN-TV (W) Chicago; A & E; BET; C-SPAN; CNN; Cartoon Network; Country Music TV; Discovery Channel; Disney Channel; ESPN; Fox Family Channel; Fox News Channel; Fox Sports Net Southwest; Headline News; Learning Channel; Lifetime; Nashville Network; Nick at Nite's TV Land; Nickelodeon; QVC; Sci-Fi Channel; TBS Superstation; The Health Network; The Weather Channel; Trinity Bcstg. Network; Turner Classic Movies; Turner Network TV; USA Network; Univision.
Current originations: Automated timeweather.
Fee: $35.00 installation; $27.95 monthly.
Pay Service 1
Pay Units: 218.
Programming (via satellite): The Movie Channel.
Fee: $5.95 monthly.
Pay Service 2
Pay Units: N.A.
Programming (via satellite): Cinemax.
Fee: $9.95 monthly.
Pay Service 3
Pay Units: 215.
Programming (via satellite): Showtime.
Fee: $9.95 monthly.
Pay Service 4
Pay Units: 212.
Programming (via satellite): HBO.
Fee: $9.95 monthly.
Local advertising: Yes. Regional interconnect: Cabletime.
Equipment: Magnavox amplifiers; Comm/Scope cable; Scientific-Atlanta set top converters; Scientific-Atlanta & U.S. Tower satellite antenna; M/A-Com & Scientific-Atlanta satellite receivers.
Miles of plant: 49.0 (coaxial). Homes passed: 3,000.
Manager: Bill Flowers. Chief technician: Walt VanLue. Marketing director: Jennifer Hauschild.
City fee: 3% of gross.
Ownership: Classic Cable (MSO).

ROCKPORT—Falcon Cable TV, 822 Market St., Portland, TX 78374. Phone: 512-643-8588. Fax: 512-643-3641. County: Aransas. Also serves Fulton, Holiday Beach. ICA: TX0116.
TV Market Ranking: Below 100 (Fulton, Rockport); Outside TV Markets (Holiday Beach). Franchise award date: N.A. Franchise expiration date: N.A. Began: December 1, 1979.
Channel capacity: 44 (not 2-way capable). Channels available but not in use: None.
Basic Service
Subscribers: 4,436; Commercial subscribers: 700.
Programming (received off-air): K47DF (F), KEDT (P), KIII (A), KRIS-TV (N), KZTV (C) Corpus Christi; 5 FMs.
Programming (via satellite): A & E; C-SPAN; CNBC; Comedy Central; Country Music TV; Disney Channel; ESPN; Fox Family Channel; Headline News; Home Shopping Network; Learning Channel; Lifetime; Nashville Network; Nickelodeon; QVC; Sci-Fi Channel; Travel Channel; Univision; VH1.
Fee: $25.00 installation (aerial), $35.00 (underground); $17.94 monthly; $25.00 additional installation.
Expanded Basic Service
Subscribers: 3,308.
Programming (via satellite): American Movie Classics; ESPN Classic Sports; Fox Sports Net Southwest; MTV; TV Food Network; TV Guide Channel; The Weather Channel; USA Network.

Fee: $4.57 monthly.

Expanded Basic Service 2

Subscribers: 3,351.

Programming (via satellite): WGN-TV (W) Chicago; CNN; Discovery Channel; ESPN 2; TBS Superstation; Turner Network TV.

Fee: $6.95 monthly.

Pay Service 1

Pay Units: 354.

Programming (via satellite): Cinemax.

Fee: $9.95 monthly.

Pay Service 2

Pay Units: 598.

Programming (via satellite): HBO.

Fee: $12.95 monthly.

Pay Service 3

Pay Units: 249.

Programming (via satellite): The Movie Channel.

Fee: $9.95 monthly.

Pay Service 4

Pay Units: 377.

Programming (via satellite): Showtime.

Fee: $9.95 monthly.

Pay Service 5

Pay Units: N.A.

Programming (via satellite): Playboy TV.

Fee: N.A.

Local advertising: Yes. Available in automated programming. Regional interconnect: Cabletime.

Equipment: Scientific-Atlanta headend; C-COR & Delta-Benco-Cascade amplifiers; Cerro & Scientific-Atlanta cable; JVC VTRs; Oak set top converters; Microdyne, Scientific-Atlanta & U.S. Tower satellite antenna; Comtech, Microdyne & Scientific-Atlanta satellite receivers.

Miles of plant: 181.0 (coaxial). Homes passed: 7,000. Total homes in franchised area: 7,000.

Office manager: Jenny Brumley. Chief technician: Mike Kelsch.

Franchise fee: 2% of gross.

Ownership: Falcon Communications LP (MSO), joint venture formed September 30, 1998. See Cable System Ownership.

ROCKWALL—Mission Cable, 920 Whitmore Dr., Rockwall, TX 75087. Phone: 800-783-5708. Fax: 214-722-6218. County: Rockwall. ICA: TX0155.

TV Market Ranking: 12. Franchise award date: January 17, 1989. Franchise expiration date: N.A. Began: January 1, 1983.

Channel capacity: 61 (not 2-way capable). Channels available but not in use: None.

Basic Service

Subscribers: 2,595.

Programming (received off-air): KDAF (W), KDFI-TV (I), KDFW (F), KDTX-TV (T), KERA-TV (P), KTVT (C), KTXA (U), KXAS-TV (N), KXTX-TV (I), WFAA-TV (A) Dallas-Fort Worth; KDTN (P) Denton.

Programming (via satellite): WGN-TV (W) Chicago; A & E; American Movie Classics; C-SPAN; C-SPAN 2; CNBC; CNN; Cartoon Network; Country Music TV; Discovery Channel; E! Entertainment TV; Fox Family Channel; Fox Sports Net Southwest; Good-life TV Network; Headline News; Home Shopping Network; Home Shopping Network 2; Lifetime; MTV; Nashville Network; Nickelodeon; QVC; TBS Superstation; The Inspirational Network; The Weather Channel; Travel Channel; Turner Network TV; USA Network; VH1.

Current originations: Public access; educational access; government access; leased access; library access; local news.

Fee: $40.00 installation; $19.95 monthly.

Pay Service 1

Pay Units: 172.

Programming (via satellite): Cinemax.

Fee: $9.00 monthly.

Pay Service 2

Pay Units: 167.

Programming (via satellite): Disney Channel.

Fee: $9.00 monthly.

Pay Service 3

Pay Units: 573.

Programming (via satellite): HBO.

Fee: $9.00 monthly.

Pay Service 4

Pay Units: 125.

Programming (via satellite): The Movie Channel.

Fee: $9.00 monthly.

Pay Service 5

Pay Units: 223.

Programming (via satellite): Showtime.

Fee: $9.00 monthly.

Local advertising: Yes. Available in taped programming.

Program Guide: TV Host.

Equipment: Scientific-Atlanta headend; Scientific-Atlanta amplifiers; Times Fiber cable; Oak set top converters; Scientific-Atlanta satellite antenna; Scientific-Atlanta satellite receivers.

Miles of plant: 64.0 (coaxial). Homes passed: 3,722.

Manager: Don Blair. Chief technician: Bill Thomison. Marketing & program director: Bruce Berkinshaw.

City fee: 3% of gross.

Ownership: Fanch Communications Inc. (MSO); Time Warner Cable (MSO). See Cable System Ownership.

ROCKWELL—TCA Cable of Amarillo, 5800 W. 45th Dr., Amarillo, TX 79109. Phone: 806-358-4801. Fax: 806-354-7419. County: Randall. Also serves Lake Tanglewood. ICA: TX0847.

TV Market Ranking: 95. Franchise award date: N.A. Franchise expiration date: N.A. Began: N.A.

Channel capacity: 25 (2-way capable; operating 2-way). Channels available but not in use: None.

Basic Service

Subscribers: 1,099.

Programming (received off-air): KACV-TV (P), KAMR-TV (N), KCIT (F,U), KFDA-TV (C), KVII-TV (A) Amarillo.

Programming (via satellite): WGN-TV (W) Chicago; A & E; CNN; Discovery Channel; ESPN; Lifetime; Nashville Network; Nickelodeon; TBS Superstation; Trinity Bcstg. Network; Turner Network TV; USA Network.

Fee: $35.00 installation; $16.25 monthly.

Pay Service 1

Pay Units: N.A.

Programming (via satellite): Disney Channel; HBO; Showtime; The Movie Channel.

Fee: $35.00 installation; $10.00 monthly (each).

Miles of plant: 70.0 (coaxial); None (fiber optic). Homes passed: 2,200. Total homes in franchised area: 2,250.

Manager: Larson Lloyd. Chief technician: Charlie Johnson. Marketing director: Alisa Mathies.

Ownership: TCA Cable TV Inc. (MSO); AT&T Broadband & Internet Services (MSO). See Cable System Ownership.

ROGERS—Centrovision Inc., Box 3157, Temple, TX 76501. Phone: 817-773-1163. County: Bell. ICA: TX0548.

TV Market Ranking: Below 100. Franchise award date: N.A. Franchise expiration date: N.A. Began: June 1, 1983.

Channel capacity: N.A. Channels available but not in use: N.A.

Basic Service

Subscribers: N.A.

Programming (received off-air): KLRU (P), KTBC (F), KVUE-TV (A), KXAN-TV (N) Austin; KNCT (P) Belton; KCEN-TV (N), KWTX-TV (C) Waco-Temple.

Programming (via satellite): WGN-TV (W) Chicago; TBS Superstation.

Fee: N.A.

Homes passed: 350.

Manager: Alton Shepard.

Ownership: Centrovision Inc. (MSO).

ROMA—Time Warner Communications, Box 928, 703 Grant St., Roma, TX 78584. Phone: 210-849-1523. County: Starr. Also serves Escobares, Garceno, Los Barreras, Los Morenos, Rosita, Starr County. ICA: TX0118.

TV Market Ranking: Below 100. Franchise award date: N.A. Franchise expiration date: N.A. Began: February 16, 1976.

Channel capacity: 37. Channels available but not in use: N.A.

Basic Service

Subscribers: 3,630.

Programming (received off-air): KVEO (N) Brownsville; KGBT-TV (C), KMBH (P) Harlingen; KNVO (S) McAllen; KRGV-TV (A) Weslaco; 11 FMs.

Programming (via satellite): A & E; American Movie Classics; C-SPAN; CNN; Country Music TV; Discovery Channel; ESPN; EWTN; Fox Family Channel; FoxNet; GalaVision; Lifetime; Nashville Network; Nickelodeon; QVC; TBS Superstation; Telemundo; Trinity Bcstg. Network; Turner Network TV; USA Network; Univision.

Current originations: Local news.

Fee: $19.95 installation; $19.16 monthly; $7.50 additional installation.

Pay Service 1

Pay Units: N.A.

Programming (via satellite): Cinemax; Disney Channel; HBO; Showtime.

Fee: $12.90 monthly (each).

Local advertising: Yes. Regional interconnect: Cabletime.

Equipment: Jerrold headend; AEL amplifiers; Times Fiber cable.

Miles of plant: 117.2 (coaxial). Additional miles planned: 6.0 (coaxial). Homes passed: 5,799.

Manager: Juve Morante.

City fee: 3% of gross.

Ownership: AT&T Broadband & Internet Services (MSO); Time Warner Cable (MSO); Advance/Newhouse Partnership (MSO).

ROSCOE—Big Country Cablevision Inc., Box 549, 102 Oak St., Merkel, TX 79536. Phones: 915-928-4750; 800-588-4750. Fax: 915-928-3452. County: Nolan. ICA: TX0471.

TV Market Ranking: Below 100. Franchise award date: November 20, 1968. Franchise expiration date: November 20, 2008. Began: August 1, 1971.

Channel capacity: 21. Channels available but not in use: None.

Basic Service

Subscribers: 410.

Programming (received off-air): KRBC-TV (N), KTAB-TV (C), KTXS-TV (A) Abilene-Sweetwater; allband FM.

Programming (via satellite): WGN-TV (W) Chicago; A & E; CNN; Country Music TV; Discovery Channel; ESPN; Fox Family Channel; Lifetime; MTV; Nashville Network; Nickelodeon; TBS Superstation; The Weather Channel; Turner Network TV; USA Network; Univision.

Current originations: Automated time-weather.

Fee: $38.35 installation; $20.26 monthly.

Pay Service 1

Pay Units: N.A.

Programming (via satellite): HBO.

Planned programming (via satellite): Cinemax.

Fee: $7.50 installation; $8.50 monthly.

Equipment: Scientific-Atlanta headend; Jerrold amplifiers; Comm/Scope cable; Intercept traps; Weatherscan satellite antenna; Microdyne satellite receivers.

Miles of plant: 13.0 (coaxial). Additional miles planned: 2.0 (coaxial). Homes passed: 540.

Manager: Mark Reaves. Marketing director: J. Ketchum.

City fee: 2% of gross.

Ownership: Cable Management Assoc. (MSO).

ROSE CITY—Friendship Cable of Texas, Box 9090, Tyler, TX 75711-9090. Phone: 903-581-2121. Fax: 903-581-2185. County: Orange. ICA: TX0606.

TV Market Ranking: 88. Franchise award date: N.A. Franchise expiration date: N.A. Began: September 1, 1984.

Channel capacity: 36 (not 2-way capable). Channels available but not in use: 13.

Basic Service

Subscribers: 70.

Programming (received off-air): KBMT (A), KBTV-TV (N), KFDM-TV (C) Beaumont-Port Arthur.

Programming (via satellite): WGN-TV (W) Chicago; CNN; ESPN; Fox Family Channel; MTV; Nashville Network; Nickelodeon; TBS Superstation; USA Network.

Fee: $30.65 monthly.

Pay Service 1

Pay Units: 6.

Programming (via satellite): HBO.

Fee: $10.50 monthly.

Pay Service 2

Pay Units: 6.

Programming (via satellite): Showtime.

Fee: $6.95 monthly.

Pay Service 3

Pay Units: 2.

Programming (via satellite): Cinemax.

Fee: $10.50 monthly.

Miles of plant: 7.8 (coaxial). Homes passed: 242.

Manager: Wanda Pyburn. Chief technician: Mike Deal.

City fee: 3% of gross.

Ownership: Buford Television Inc. (MSO). See Cable System Ownership.

ROSEBUD—Rosebud Cable TV, Box 268, Groesbeck, TX 76642. Phone: 817-729-2221. County: Falls. ICA: TX0389.

TV Market Ranking: Below 100. Franchise award date: N.A. Franchise expiration date: N.A. Began: January 1, 1966.

Channel capacity: 54 (2-way capable; operating 2-way). Channels available but not in use: 25.

Basic Service

Subscribers: 340.

Programming (received off-air): KEYE-TV (C), KLRU (P), KTBC (F) Austin; KNCT (P) Belton; KCEN-TV (N), KWTX-TV (C) Waco-Temple; allband FM.

Programming (via satellite): WGN-TV (W) Chicago; BET; CNBC; CNN; Country Music TV; Discovery Channel; ESPN; Fox Family Channel; Nashville Network; TBS Superstation; Turner Network TV.

Fee: $30.00 installation; $18.00 monthly; $3.00 converter; $15.00 additional installation.

Pay Service 1
Pay Units: N.A.
Programming (via satellite): Cinemax; Disney Channel; HBO; The Movie Channel.
Fee: $15.00 installation; $10.95 monthly (HBO).
Local advertising: No.
Equipment: Scientific-Atlanta headend; Scientific-Atlanta amplifiers; Times Fiber cable; Scientific-Atlanta set top converters; Scientific-Atlanta & M/A-Com satellite antenna; Scientific-Atlanta & M/A-Com satellite receivers.
Miles of plant: 12.0 (coaxial). Homes passed: 850.
Manager: Danny Spurlock.
City fee: 3% of gross.
Ownership: Danny Spurlock.

ROTAN—Friendship Cable of Texas Inc., Box 9090, Tyler, TX 75711-9090. Phone: 903-581-2121. Fax: 903-581-2185. County: Fisher. ICA: TX0365.
TV Market Ranking: Below 100. Franchise award date: January 1, 1966. Franchise expiration date: January 1, 2009. Began: August 1, 1968.
Channel capacity: 33 (not 2-way capable). Channels available but not in use: N.A.
Basic Service
Subscribers: 553.
Programming (received off-air): KRBC-TV (N), KTAB-TV (C), KTXS-TV (A) Abilene-Sweetwater; 4 FMs.
Programming (via satellite): BET; C-SPAN; Lifetime; QVC; TBS Superstation; The Weather Channel; Univision.
Current originations: Automated time-weather.
Fee: $30.00 installation; $13.42 monthly.
Commercial fee: $15.95 monthly.
Expanded Basic Service
Subscribers: 435.
Programming (via satellite): A & E; American Movie Classics; Animal Planet; CNN; Cartoon Network; Country Music TV; Discovery Channel; ESPN; FX; Fox Family Channel; Fox News Channel; Fox Sports Net Southwest; Home & Garden Television; Learning Channel; MTV; Nashville Network; Nickelodeon; Turner Network TV; USA Network.
Fee: $30.00 installation; $17.10 monthly.
Pay Service 1
Pay Units: 59.
Programming (via satellite): Cinemax.
Fee: $12.50 monthly.
Pay Service 2
Pay Units: 122.
Programming (via satellite): The New Encore.
Fee: $1.71 monthly.
Pay Service 3
Pay Units: 75.
Programming (via satellite): HBO.
Fee: $13.00 monthly.
Pay Service 4
Pay Units: 83.
Programming (via satellite): Starz!
Fee: $6.75 monthly.
Pay Service 5
Pay Units: 18.
Programming (via satellite): Disney Channel.
Fee: $12.50 monthly.
Equipment: Jerrold headend; Magnavox amplifiers; Times Fiber cable; Compuvid character generator; Jerrold set top converters; Arcom & Eagle traps; Anixter-Mark & Scientific-Atlanta satellite antenna; Scientific-Atlanta & Standard Communications satellite receivers.
Miles of plant: 15.0 (coaxial). Homes passed: 926. Total homes in franchised area: 960.
Manager: Larry Bryant. Chief technician: Joe Stewart.
City fee: 2% of gross.
Ownership: Buford Television Inc. (MSO). See Cable System Ownership.

ROXTON—TCA Cable, Box 130489, Tyler, TX 75713-0489. Phone: 903-595-3701. Fax: 903-595-1929. County: Lamar. ICA: TX0595.
TV Market Ranking: Outside TV Markets. Franchise award date: N.A. Franchise expiration date: N.A. Began: January 1, 1970.
Channel capacity: 12. Channels available but not in use: N.A.
Basic Service
Subscribers: N.A.
Programming (received off-air): KDFW (F), KERA-TV (P), KTVT (C), WFAA-TV (A) Dallas-Fort Worth; KXII (C) Sherman.
Fee: $20.00 installation.
Miles of plant: 9.0 (coaxial). Homes passed: 250.
Manager: Fred Nichol.
Ownership: TCA Cable TV Inc. See Cable System Ownership.

ROYSE CITY—Friendship Cable Ltd., Box 9090, Tyler, TX 75711-9090. Phone: 903-581-2121. Fax: 903-581-2185. County: Rockwall. Also serves Fate, Mobile City, Rockwall County (portions). ICA: TX0325.
TV Market Ranking: 12. Franchise award date: N.A. Franchise expiration date: N.A. Began: January 1, 1987.
Channel capacity: 41. Channels available but not in use: None.
Basic Service
Subscribers: 988.
Programming (received off-air): KDAF (W), KDFW (F), KERA-TV (P), KTVT (C), KTXA (U), KXAS-TV (N), KXTX-TV (I), WFAA-TV (A) Dallas-Fort Worth.
Programming (via satellite): WGN-TV (W) Chicago; A & E; American Movie Classics; CNN; Country Music TV; Discovery Channel; E! Entertainment TV; ESPN; ESPN 2; Fox Sports Net Southwest; Headline News; Lifetime; MTV; Nashville Network; Nickelodeon; QVC; Sci-Fi Channel; TBS Superstation; The Inspirational Network; The Weather Channel; Turner Network TV; USA Network; Univision.
Fee: $30.00 installation; $30.90 monthly.
Pay Service 1
Pay Units: 64.
Programming (via satellite): Cinemax.
Fee: $8.95 monthly.
Pay Service 2
Pay Units: 94.
Programming (via satellite): HBO.
Fee: $9.95 monthly.
Pay Service 3
Pay Units: 120.
Programming (via satellite): Showtime.
Fee: $5.95 monthly.
Local advertising: Yes. Available in locally originated, character-generated & taped programming.
Equipment: Comm/Scope headend; Magnavox amplifiers; Texscan character generator; Hamlin & Jerrold set top converters; Pico & Northeast Filter traps; Scientific-Atlanta & Comtech satellite antenna; Scientific-Atlanta satellite receivers.
Miles of plant: 63.6 (coaxial). Homes passed: 1,651.
Manager: Rodney Fletcher. Chief technician: Steven Williams.
Ownership: Buford Television Inc. (MSO). See Cable System Ownership.

RUNGE—Classic Cable, Box 429, 605 N.W. 3rd St., Plainville, KS 67663-0429. Phones: 785-434-7620; 800-999-8876. Fax: 785-434-2614. County: Karnes. ICA: TX0959.
TV Market Ranking: Outside TV Markets. Franchise award date: N.A. Franchise expiration date: N.A. Began: N.A.
Channel capacity: 41 (2-way capable; operating 2-way). Channels available but not in use: N.A.
Basic Service
Subscribers: 134.
Programming (received off-air): KRRT (W) Kerrville-San Antonio; KABB (F), KENS-TV (C), KLRN (P), KMOL-TV (N), KSAT-TV (A), KVDA (O), KWEX-TV (S) San Antonio.
Programming (via satellite): WGN-TV (W) Chicago; A & E; American Movie Classics; BET; CNN; Country Music TV; Discovery Channel; Disney Channel; ESPN; Learning Channel; Nashville Network; Nick at Nite's TV Land; Nickelodeon; QVC; TBS Superstation; The Weather Channel; Trinity Bcstg. Network; Turner Classic Movies; Turner Network TV; USA Network.
Current originations: Public access.
Fee: $35.00 installation; $27.95 monthly.
Pay Service 1
Pay Units: 20.
Programming (via satellite): Showtime.
Fee: $9.95 monthly.
Pay Service 2
Pay Units: 26.
Programming (via satellite): HBO.
Fee: $10.95 monthly.
Miles of plant: 6.9 (coaxial). Homes passed: 450.
Manager: Bill Flowers. Chief technician: Walt VanLue. Marketing director: Jennifer Hauschild.
Ownership: Classic Cable (MSO).

RUSK—Friendship Cable of Texas Inc., Box 9090, Tyler, TX 75711-9090. Phone: 903-581-2121. Fax: 903-581-2185. County: Cherokee. Also serves Cherokee County. ICA: TX0253.
TV Market Ranking: Below 100. Franchise award date: N.A. Franchise expiration date: N.A. Began: January 1, 1963.
Channel capacity: 54. Channels available but not in use: N.A.
Basic Service
Subscribers: 1,235.
Programming (received off-air): KETK-TV (N) Jacksonville; KFXK (F) Longview; KSLA-TV (C) Shreveport-Texarkana; KLTV (A) Tyler-Longview.
Programming (via microwave): KDFW (F), KERA-TV (P), KTVT (C), KXAS-TV (N), WFAA-TV (A) Dallas-Fort Worth.
Programming (via satellite): A & E; C-SPAN; CNN; Country Music TV; Discovery Channel; ESPN; Fox Family Channel; Fox Sports Net Southwest; Headline News; Lifetime; MTV; Nashville Network; Nickelodeon; TBS Superstation; The Weather Channel; Turner Network TV.
Fee: $30.00 installation; $30.00 monthly.
Pay Service 1
Pay Units: 106.
Programming (via satellite): Cinemax.
Fee: $7.00 monthly.
Pay Service 2
Pay Units: 111.
Programming (via satellite): HBO.
Fee: $12.00 monthly.
Pay Service 3
Pay Units: 89.
Programming (via satellite): The Movie Channel.
Fee: $9.00 monthly.
Pay Service 4
Pay Units: 212.
Programming (via satellite): Showtime.
Fee: $7.00 monthly.
Pay Service 5
Pay Units: 247.
Programming (via satellite): Flix.
Fee: $1.95 monthly.
Equipment: Scientific-Atlanta headend; Tocom amplifiers; Times Fiber cable; Eagle traps; Scientific-Atlanta satellite antenna; Scientific-Atlanta satellite receivers.
Miles of plant: 35.0 (coaxial). Homes passed: 1,912.
Manager: Marianne Bogy. Chief technician: Henry Harris.
City fee: 2% of gross.
Ownership: Buford Television Inc. (MSO). See Cable System Ownership.

SABINAL—Falcon Cable TV, 1244 Encino Dr., Pleasanton, TX 78064. Phone: 830-569-5509. Fax: 830-569-4828. County: Uvalde. ICA: TX0442.
TV Market Ranking: Below 100. Franchise award date: January 1, 1969. Franchise expiration date: N.A. Began: October 1, 1971.
Channel capacity: 37 (not 2-way capable). Channels available but not in use: 8.
Basic Service
Subscribers: 332.
Programming (received off-air): KRRT (W) Kerrville-San Antonio; KABB (F), KENS-TV (C), KLRN (P), KMOL-TV (N), KSAT-TV (A), KWEX-TV (S) San Antonio.
Programming (via satellite): American Movie Classics; Bravo; C-SPAN; CNN; Country Music TV; ESPN; Fox Family Channel; GalaVision; Headline News; Learning Channel; Nashville Network; QVC; Sci-Fi Channel; Travel Channel.
Fee: $22.50 installation; $22.55 monthly; $2.50 converter; $12.50 additional installation.
Expanded Basic Service
Subscribers: 325.
Programming (via satellite): Discovery Channel; Nickelodeon; USA Network.
Fee: $2.72 monthly.
Expanded Basic Service 2
Subscribers: 318.
Programming (via satellite): WGN-TV (W) Chicago; TBS Superstation; Turner Network TV.
Fee: $3.95 monthly.
Pay Service 1
Pay Units: 25.
Programming (via satellite): Cinemax.
Fee: $10.95 monthly.
Pay Service 2
Pay Units: 61.
Programming (via satellite): HBO.
Fee: $11.95 monthly.
Local advertising: No.
Program Guide: Premium Channels.
Equipment: Jerrold amplifiers; Comm/Scope cable; Pioneer set top converters; Pico traps; Scientific-Atlanta satellite antenna; DX Antenna satellite receivers.
Miles of plant: 13.0 (coaxial). Homes passed: 522.
Manager: Lorna Gentry. Chief technician: Santos Guajardo.
Franchise fee: 2% of gross.
Ownership: Falcon Communications LP (MSO), joint venture formed September 30, 1998. See Cable System Ownership.

SALADO—Centrovision Inc., Box 3157, Temple, TX 76501. Phone: 817-773-1163. County: Bell. ICA: TX0504.

TV Market Ranking: Below 100. Franchise award date: N.A. Franchise expiration date: N.A. Began: February 1, 1982.
Channel capacity: N.A. Channels available but not in use: N.A.

Basic Service
Subscribers: N.A.
Programming (received off-air): KLRU (P), KTBC (F), KVUE-TV (A), KXAN-TV (N) Austin; KNCT (P) Belton; KCEN-TV (N), KWTX-TV (C) Waco-Temple.
Programming (via satellite): WGN-TV (W) Chicago; TBS Superstation.
Fee: N.A.
Miles of plant: 12.0 (coaxial). Homes passed: 450.
Manager: Alton Shepard.
Ownership: Centrovision Inc. (MSO).

SAN ANGELO—TCA of San Angelo, 28 W. Concho, San Angelo, TX 76903. Phone: 915-655-8911. Fax: 915-658-6876. Web site: http://www.tca-cable.com. County: Tom Green. Also serves Goodfellow AFB, Harvest Acres. ICA: TX0021.
TV Market Ranking: Below 100. Franchise award date: October 1, 1957. Franchise expiration date: November 1, 1998. Began: October 1, 1958.
Channel capacity: 61 (2-way capable; operating 2-way). Channels available but not in use: 2.

Basic Service
Subscribers: 25,000; Commercial subscribers: 10,000.
Programming (received off-air): KTXS-TV (A) Abilene-Sweetwater; KERA-TV (P), WFAA-TV (A) Dallas-Fort Worth; KACB-TV (N), KIDY (F), KLST (C) San Angelo.
Programming (via satellite): FX; TBS Superstation.
Current originations: Automated time-weather.
Fee: $38.00 installation; $4.88 monthly; $3.36 converter.

Expanded Basic Service
Subscribers: N.A.
Programming (via satellite): A & E; American Movie Classics; BET; C-SPAN; CNBC; CNN; Cartoon Network; Comedy Central; Court TV; Discovery Channel; Disney Channel; E! Entertainment TV; ESPN; ESPN 2; Fox Family Channel; Fox Sports Net Southwest; GalaVision; Great American Country; Headline News; History Channel; Learning Channel; Lifetime; MTV; Nashville Network; Nick at Nite's TV Land; Nickelodeon; QVC; Sci-Fi Channel; TV Guide Channel; TV Guide Sneak Prevue; The Inspirational Network; The Weather Channel; Trinity Bcstg. Network; Turner Classic Movies; Turner Network TV; USA Network; Univision; VH1.
Fee: $38.00 installation; $26.98 monthly.

Pay Service 1
Pay Units: N.A.
Programming (via satellite): Cinemax; Starz!; The New Encore.
Fee: $10.00 monthly.

Pay Service 2
Pay Units: 2,505.
Programming (via satellite): HBO.
Fee: $10.95 monthly.

Pay Service 3
Pay Units: 139.
Programming (via satellite): Flix; Showtime; Starz!; The Movie Channel; The New Encore.
Fee: $13.50 monthly.

Pay Service 4
Pay Units: 751.
Programming (via satellite): DMX.
Fee: $8.95 monthly.

Pay-Per-View
Addressable homes: 5,961.
Viewer's Choice 1 & 2; Viewer's Choice 5.
Fee: $3.95.
Pay-per-view manager: Julie Harding.
Local advertising: Yes (locally produced & insert). Available in satellite distributed programming. Rates: $40.00/Minute; $20.00/30 Seconds. Local sales manager: Jay Speegle. Regional interconnect: Cabletime.
Equipment: Scientific-Atlanta headend; Scientific-Atlanta amplifiers; Comm/Scope cable; General & AT&T fiber optic cable; Texscan character generator; Scientific-Atlanta set top converters; Jerrold addressable set top converters; Eagle traps; Scientific-Atlanta satellite antenna; Scientific-Atlanta satellite receivers.
Miles of plant: 445.0 (coaxial); 30.0 (fiber optic). Homes passed: 42,825.
Controller: George Clark. Manager: Archie Kountz. Technical operations manager: Robert E. Amo. Marketing manager: Mike Johnson. Customer service manager: Naomi Gonzales.
City fee: 2% of gross.
Ownership: TCA Cable TV Inc. (MSO); AT&T Broadband & Internet Services (MSO). See Cable System Ownership.

SAN ANTONIO—Paragon Cable, Suite 200, 84 N.E. Loop 410, San Antonio, TX 78216. Phone: 210-352-4600. Fax: 210-342-6845. Counties: Bexar, Blanco, Comal & Guadalupe. Also serves Alamo Heights, Army Residence Community, Balcones Heights, Bexar County, Blanco, Brooks AFB, Castle Hills, China Grove, Cibolo, Cibolo Creek, Comal County, Converse, Elmendorf, Fort Sam Houston, Geronimo, Grey Forest, Guadalupe County, Helotes, Hill Country Village, Hollywood Park, Kelly AFB, Kirby, Lackland AFB, Leon Valley, Live Oak, Marion, Olmos Park, Randolph AFB, Scenic Oaks, Schertz, Selma, Shavano Park, Terrell Hills, Timberwood Park, Universal City, Windcrest. ICA: TX0002.
TV Market Ranking: 45 (Alamo Heights, Army Residence Community, Balcones Heights, Bexar County, Brooks AFB, Castle Hills, China Grove, Cibolo, Cibolo Creek, portions of Comal County, Converse, Elmendorf, Fort Sam Houston, Geronimo, Grey Forest, portions of Guadalupe County, Helotes, Hill Country Village, Hollywood Park, Kelly AFB, Kirby, Lackland AFB, Leon Valley, Live Oak, Marion, Olmos Park, Randolph AFB, San Antonio, Scenic Oaks, Schertz, Selma, Shavano Park, Terrell Hills, Timberwood Park, Universal City, Windcrest); Below 100 (Blanco); Outside TV Markets (portions of Comal County, portions of Guadalupe County). Franchise award date: September 1, 1978. Franchise expiration date: November 5, 2003. Began: September 1, 1979.
Channel capacity: 44 (2-way capable; operating 2-way). Channels available but not in use: N.A.

Basic Service
Subscribers: 300,715; Commercial subscribers: 22,320.
Programming (received off-air): KRRT (W) Kerrville-San Antonio; KABB (F), KENS-TV (C), KHCE (P), KLRN (P), KMOL-TV (N), KSAT-TV (A), KVDA (O), KWEX-TV (S) San Antonio; 28 FMs.
Programming (via satellite): WGN-TV (W) Chicago; Fox Family Channel; GalaVision; Headline News; Nickelodeon; TBS Superstation; TV Guide Channel; Univision.
Current originations: Public access; educational access; government access; religious access; leased access; local news.
Fee: $26.90 installation; $22.21 monthly; $0.17 converter; $10.00 additional installation.

Expanded Basic Service
Subscribers: 220,323.
Programming (via satellite): A & E; American Movie Classics; Animal Planet; BET; C-SPAN; C-SPAN 2; CNBC; CNN; CNN en Espanol; Cartoon Network; Comedy Central; Country Music TV; Court TV; Discovery Channel; E! Entertainment TV; ESPN; ESPN 2; Fox News Channel; Fox Sports Net Southwest; Home & Garden Television; Home Shopping Network; Kaleidoscope; Learning Channel; Lifetime; MSNBC; MTV; Nashville Network; Nick at Nite's TV Land; Odyssey; QVC; Romance Classics; Sci-Fi Channel; TV Food Network; The Weather Channel; Travel Channel; Turner Network TV; USA Network; VH1.
Fee: $25.00 installation; $22.21 monthly.

Expanded Basic Service 2
Subscribers: N.A.
Programming (via satellite): Bravo; CNN/SI; Flix; Golf Channel; History Channel.
Fee: $3.75 monthly.

Pay Service 1
Pay Units: 21,858.
Programming (via satellite): Disney Channel.
Fee: $10.00 installation; $6.00 monthly.

Pay Service 2
Pay Units: 89,763.
Programming (via satellite): HBO (multiplexed).
Fee: $10.00 installation; $12.50 monthly.

Pay Service 3
Pay Units: 33,189.
Programming (via satellite): The Movie Channel.
Fee: $10.00 installation; $8.00 monthly.

Pay Service 4
Pay Units: 54,615.
Programming (via satellite): Showtime (multiplexed).
Fee: $12.00 monthly.

Pay Service 5
Pay Units: N.A.
Programming (via satellite): Cinemax.
Fee: $8.00 monthly.

Pay-Per-View
Addressable homes: 84,169.
Movies; special events.
Fee: $2.26.

Interactive Services
Subscribers: 84,169.
Polling.
Local advertising: Yes. Available in satellite distributed & locally originated programming. Rates: $5000.00/Minute; $2500.00/30 Seconds. Local sales manager: Phil Johnson.
Program Guide: The Cable Guide.
Equipment: Scientific-Atlanta headend; Scientific-Atlanta amplifiers; Comm/Scope cable; Ikegami cameras; Sony VTRs; Amiga character generator; Zenith addressable set top converters; Arcom traps; Anixter-Mark satellite antenna; Scientific-Atlanta satellite receivers.
Miles of plant: 4491.0 (coaxial); 291.0 (fiber optic). Homes passed: 1,201,093.
Manager: Navarra R. Williams. Chief technician: Bill Prestridge. Program director: T. J. Connolly. Marketing director: Anne Carlson.
City fee: 5% of gross.
Ownership: Time Warner Cable (MSO).

SAN AUGUSTINE—Friendship Cable of Texas Inc., Box 9090, Tyler, TX 75711-9090. Phone: 903-581-2121. Fax: 903-581-2185. County: San Augustine. ICA: TX0317.
TV Market Ranking: Below 100. Franchise award date: N.A. Franchise expiration date: N.A. Began: August 1, 1970.
Channel capacity: 80. Channels available but not in use: N.A.

Basic Service
Subscribers: 782.
Programming (received off-air): KTRE (A) Lufkin; KSLA-TV (C), KTAL-TV (N), KTBS-TV (A) Shreveport-Texarkana; allband FM.
Planned programming (received off-air): KLTS-TV (P) Shreveport-Texarkana.
Programming (via satellite): WGN-TV (W) Chicago; A & E; BET; C-SPAN; CNN; Cartoon Network; Discovery Channel; ESPN; FX; Fox Sports Net; Great American Country; Headline News; Home & Garden Television; Home Shopping Network; Learning Channel; Lifetime; MuchMusic Network; Nashville Network; Nickelodeon; Outdoor Life Network; TBS Superstation; The Weather Channel; Trinity Bcstg. Network; Turner Classic Movies; Turner Network TV; USA Network; Univision.
Current originations: Automated time-weather.
Fee: $30.00 installation; $28.70 monthly.

Pay Service 1
Pay Units: 98.
Programming (via satellite): Cinemax.
Fee: $10.00 monthly.

Pay Service 2
Pay Units: 183.
Programming (via satellite): HBO.
Fee: $10.00 monthly.

Pay Service 3
Pay Units: 107.
Programming (via satellite): Showtime.
Fee: $5.95 monthly.

Pay Service 4
Pay Units: 62.
Programming (via satellite): The Movie Channel.
Fee: $10.00 monthly.
Local advertising: Yes. Rates: $50.00/Month.
Equipment: Tocom headend; Vikoa amplifiers; Systems Wire cable; Fort Worth Tower satellite antenna.
Miles of plant: 40.0 (coaxial). Homes passed: 1,200.
Manager: Marianne Bogey. Chief technician: Henry Harris.
City fee: 2% of gross.
Ownership: Buford Television Inc. (MSO). See Cable System Ownership.

SAN CARLOS—Rapid Cable, Box 6310, 310 Walnut Extension, Branson, MO 65616. Phones: 417-334-7897; 800-972-0962. Fax: 417-334-7899. E-mail: rcpcable@aol.com. Counties: Hidalgo & Jim Wells. Also serves Edinburg, La Blanca, Orange Grove. ICA: TX0624.

TV Market Ranking: Below 100. Franchise award date: N.A. Franchise expiration date: N.A. Began: N.A.
Channel capacity: 32. Channels available but not in use: 6.
Basic Service
Subscribers: 37.
Programming (received off-air): KVEO (N) Brownsville; KGBT-TV (C), KLUJ (E), KMBH (P) Harlingen; KRGV-TV (A) Weslaco; XHRIO (O) Matamoros-Brownsville; XEW-TV Mexico City.
Programming (via translator): KWKT (F) Waco-Temple.
Programming (via satellite): WGN-TV (W) Chicago; CNN; Country Music TV; Discovery Channel; ESPN; EWTN; Fox Family Channel; GalaVision; Headline News; MTV Latin America; Nashville Network; TBS Superstation; USA Network; Univision.
Fee: $29.95 monthly; $2.95 converter.
Pay Service 1
Pay Units: N.A.
Programming (via satellite): Cinemax; Showtime; The Movie Channel.
Fee: $9.00 monthly (Cinemax), $10.00 monthly (Showtime), $10.95 monthly (TMC).
Pay Service 2
Pay Units: 22.
Programming (via satellite): HBO.
Fee: $10.00 monthly.
Pay Service 3
Pay Units: 17.
Programming (via satellite): Disney Channel.
Fee: $7.00 monthly.
Local advertising: No.
Miles of plant: 17.4 (coaxial). Homes passed: 756.
Manager: Belinda Murphy. Chief engineer: Steve Rice. Marketing director: Bill Fischer. Program director: Beth Semptimphelter.
Ownership: Rapid Communications Partners LP (MSO).

SAN LEON—Star Cable, Drawer 1570, Brazoria, TX 77422. Phones: 409-798-9121; 800-395-2775. Fax: 409-798-4409. County: Galveston. ICA: TX0240.
TV Market Ranking: 15. Franchise award date: N.A. Franchise expiration date: N.A. Began: December 10, 1987.
Channel capacity: 42 (not 2-way capable). Channels available but not in use: 6.
Basic Service
Subscribers: 626; Commercial subscribers: 37.
Programming (received off-air): KHSH-TV (H) Alvin; KVVV (I) Baytown; KPXB (X) Conroe; KLTJ (E) Galveston; KETH (E), KHOU-TV (C), KHTV (W), KPRC-TV (N), KRIV (F), KTRK-TV (A), KTXH (U), KUHT (P) Houston; KNWS-TV (I) Katy.
Programming (via satellite): WGN-TV (W) Chicago; CNBC; CNN; Discovery Channel; ESPN; Fox Family Channel; Fox Sports Net Southwest; Lifetime; MTV; Nashville Network; Nickelodeon; QVC; Sci-Fi Channel; TBS Superstation; The Weather Channel; Turner Network TV; USA Network; VH1.
Current originations: Public access.
Fee: $25.00 installation; $31.64 monthly; $2.15 converter.
Pay Service 1
Pay Units: 76.
Programming (via satellite): Disney Channel.
Fee: $7.95 monthly.
Pay Service 2
Pay Units: 201.
Programming (via satellite): HBO.
Fee: $10.95 monthly.
Pay Service 3
Pay Units: 190.
Programming (via satellite): Showtime; The Movie Channel.
Fee: $12.95 monthly.
Miles of plant: 36.0 (coaxial); None (fiber optic). Homes passed: 1,815. Total homes in franchised area: 1,815.
Manager: Mike Burns. Chief technician: Mayla Zubeck.
Ownership: Star Cable Associates (MSO).

SAN MARCOS—Time Warner Communications, Box 1008, San Marcos, TX 78666-1008. Phones: 512-353-3456; 800-881-9190. Fax: 512-396-4664. Counties: Caldwell & Hays. Also serves Martindale. ICA: TX0849.
TV Market Ranking: Below 100. Franchise award date: N.A. Franchise expiration date: N.A. Began: November 1, 1973.
Channel capacity: 78 (2-way capable; operating 2-way). Channels available but not in use: 24.
Basic Service
Subscribers: 12,026.
Programming (received off-air): KEYE-TV (C), KLRU (P), KNVA (W), KTBC (F), KVUE-TV (A), KXAN-TV (N) Austin; KENS-TV (C), KMOL-TV (N), KSAT-TV (A) San Antonio; 14 FMs.
Programming (via satellite): BET; C-SPAN; CNBC; Odyssey; The Weather Channel; Trinity Bcstg. Network.
Current originations: Educational access; local news.
Fee: $60.00 installation; $10.46 monthly.
Expanded Basic Service
Subscribers: 7,889.
Programming (via satellite): A & E; C-SPAN 2; CNN; Country Music TV; Discovery Channel; E! Entertainment TV; ESPN; FX; Fox Family Channel; Fox Sports Net Southwest; FoxNet; Gems Television; Headline News; Intro TV; Learning Channel; Lifetime; MSNBC; MTV; Nashville Network; Nickelodeon; QVC; TBS Superstation; Turner Network TV; USA Network; Univision; VH1.
Fee: $10.39 monthly.
Pay Service 1
Pay Units: 479.
Programming (via satellite): Disney Channel.
Fee: $13.00 monthly.
Pay Service 2
Pay Units: 3,218.
Programming (via satellite): HBO.
Fee: $13.00 monthly.
Pay Service 3
Pay Units: 55.
Programming (via satellite): The Movie Channel.
Fee: $13.00 monthly.
Pay Service 4
Pay Units: 1,534.
Programming (via satellite): Showtime.
Fee: $13.00 monthly.
Pay Service 5
Pay Units: N.A.
Programming (via satellite): Starz!; The New Encore.
Fee: N.A.
Pay-Per-View
Addressable homes: 11,517.
Action Pay-Per-View; Playboy TV; Spice; Viewer's Choice.
Local advertising: Yes. Local sales manager: David Roberts.
Equipment: Scientific-Atlanta headend; Theta-Com amplifiers; Comm/Scope cable; Jerrold addressable set top converters; Hughes & Scientific-Atlanta satellite antenna.
Miles of plant: 264.4 (coaxial); 90.0 (fiber optic). Homes passed: 18,462. Total homes in franchised area: 19,797.
Manager: Dennis Moore. Office manager: Wanda Riley. Technical supervisor: Bruce Buchanan.
City fee: 4% of gross.
Ownership: Time Warner Cable (MSO). Purchased from AT&T Broadband & Internet Services, June 1, 1999.

SAN PATRICIO—TCI Cablevision of Texas, 4060 S. Padre Island Dr., Corpus Christi, TX 78411-4477. Phone: 512-857-5000. County: San Patricio. Also serves Odem. ICA: TX0473.
TV Market Ranking: Below 100. Franchise award date: N.A. Franchise expiration date: March 1, 2013. Began: March 1, 1982.
Channel capacity: 35. Channels available but not in use: 10.
Basic Service
Subscribers: 235.
Programming (received off-air): KEDT (P), KIII (A), KORO (S), KRIS-TV (N), KZTV (C) Corpus Christi.
Programming (via satellite): WGN-TV (W) Chicago; American Movie Classics; CNBC; CNN; Discovery Channel; ESPN; Fox Family Channel; FoxNet; GalaVision; Headline News; Lifetime; Nashville Network; QVC; TBS Superstation; The Weather Channel; Turner Network TV.
Fee: $60.00 installation; $17.99 monthly.
Pay Service 1
Pay Units: 51.
Programming (via satellite): Cinemax.
Fee: $8.00 monthly.
Pay Service 2
Pay Units: 24.
Programming (via satellite): Disney Channel.
Fee: N.A.
Pay Service 3
Pay Units: 92.
Programming (via satellite): HBO.
Fee: $8.00 monthly.
Pay Service 4
Pay Units: 72.
Programming (via satellite): The New Encore.
Fee: N.A.
Equipment: Scientific-Atlanta headend; Scientific-Atlanta amplifiers; Comm/Scope cable; Anixter-Mark satellite antenna; Microdyne satellite receivers.
Miles of plant: 11.4 (coaxial). Homes passed: 535. Total homes in franchised area: 800.
Manager: Dennis Moore. Chief technician: Mando Blancas. Marketing director: Jerri Coppedge.
City fee: 3% of gross.
Ownership: AT&T Broadband & Internet Services (MSO). Purchased from Tele-Communications Inc., March 9, 1999.

SAN SABA—Classic Cable, Box 429, 605 N.W. 3rd St., Plainville, KS 67663-0429. Phones: 785-434-7620; 800-999-8876. Fax: 785-434-2614. County: San Saba. ICA: TX0291.
TV Market Ranking: Below 100. Franchise award date: N.A. Franchise expiration date: N.A. Began: August 1, 1957.
Channel capacity: 41 (2-way capable; operating 2-way). Channels available but not in use: N.A.
Basic Service
Subscribers: 782.
Programming (received off-air): KXAN-TV (N) Austin; KNCT (P) Belton; KCEN-TV (N), KWKT (F), KWTX-TV (C), KXXV (A) Waco-Temple; 4 FMs.
Programming (via satellite): WGN-TV (W) Chicago; A & E; Animal Planet; CNN; Country Music TV; Discovery Channel; Disney Channel; ESPN; Fox Family Channel; Fox News Channel; Fox Sports Net Southwest; Headline News; History Channel; Learning Channel; Lifetime; Nashville Network; Nick at Nite's TV Land; Nickelodeon; QVC; TBS Superstation; The Weather Channel; Trinity Bcstg. Network; Turner Network TV; USA Network; Univision.
Current originations: Automated time-weather.
Fee: $35.00 installation; $29.95 monthly.
Pay Service 1
Pay Units: 94.
Programming (via satellite): The Movie Channel.
Fee: $5.95 monthly.
Pay Service 2
Pay Units: 99.
Programming (via satellite): Showtime.
Fee: $9.95 monthly.
Pay Service 3
Pay Units: 65.
Programming (via satellite): HBO.
Fee: $10.95 monthly.
Equipment: Tocom headend; Tocom amplifiers; Comm/Scope cable; Fort Worth Tower satellite antenna.
Miles of plant: 36.0 (coaxial). Homes passed: 1,354.
Manager: Bill Flowers. Chief technician: Walt VanLue. Marketing director: Jennifer Hauschild.
City fee: 2% of gross.
Ownership: Classic Cable (MSO).

SAN YGNACIO—TCI Cablevision of Texas Inc., 208 W. Viggie St., Hebbronville, TX 78361-3048. Phone: 512-527-3267. County: Zapata. ICA: TX0647.
TV Market Ranking: Below 100. Franchise award date: N.A. Franchise expiration date: N.A. Began: February 1, 1980.
Channel capacity: 21. Channels available but not in use: 8.
Basic Service
Subscribers: 185.
Programming (received off-air): KGNS-TV (N,A), KLDO-TV (O), KVTV (C) Laredo; XEW-TV Mexico City.
Programming (via satellite): WGN-TV (W) Chicago; WABC-TV (A) New York; CNN; ESPN; GalaVision; Nashville Network; TBS Superstation; Univision.
Fee: $60.00 installation; $15.00 monthly.
Pay Service 1
Pay Units: 60.
Programming (via satellite): HBO.
Fee: $20.00 installation; $11.00 monthly.
Miles of plant: 8.2 (coaxial). Homes passed: 193. Total homes in franchised area: 218.
Manager: Juve Morante.
Ownership: AT&T Broadband & Internet Services (MSO). Purchased from Tele-Communications Inc., March 9, 1999.

SANDIA—National Cable Inc., Suite 106-A, 5151 Reed Rd., Columbus, OH 43220. Phones: 614-442-5890; 800-582-0504. Fax: 614-457-2567. County: Jim Wells. ICA: TX0667.
TV Market Ranking: Below 100. Franchise award date: N.A. Franchise expiration date: N.A. Began: N.A.
Channel capacity: 36. Channels available but not in use: 21.
Basic Service
Subscribers: 83.
Programming (received off-air): KEDT (P), KIII (A), KORO (S), KRIS-TV (N), KZTV (C) Corpus Christi.

Programming (via satellite): WGN-TV (W) Chicago; A & E; American Movie Classics; CNN; Country Music TV; Discovery Channel; ESPN; Fox Family Channel; Showtime; TBS Superstation; Turner Network TV; USA Network.
Fee: $28.00 monthly.
Miles of plant: 4.2 (coaxial). Homes passed: 132.
Manager: Paul Scott. Chief technician: Rob Spiller. Marketing director: Josh Thackery.
Ownership: National Cable (MSO).

SANTA ANNA—Brownwood TV Cable Service Inc., Box 1149, 310 Carnegie Blvd., Brownwood, TX 76801. Phone: 915-646-3576. Fax: 915-643-2846. County: Coleman. ICA: TX0425.
TV Market Ranking: Outside TV Markets. Franchise award date: February 9, 1965. Franchise expiration date: April 10, 2001. Began: July 1, 1965.
Channel capacity: 30 (not 2-way capable). Channels available but not in use: 19.
Basic Service
Subscribers: 282.
Programming (received off-air): KRBC-TV (N), KTAB-TV (C), KTXS-TV (A) Abilene-Sweetwater.
Programming (via microwave): KDFW (F), KERA-TV (P), KTVT (C), WFAA-TV (A) Dallas-Fort Worth.
Programming (via satellite): ESPN; Fox Family Channel; Nashville Network; TBS Superstation.
Fee: $37.50 installation; $8.85 monthly; $23.75 additional installation.
Pay Service 1
Pay Units: N.A.
Programming (via satellite): HBO.
Fee: N.A.
Local advertising: No.
Equipment: Scientific-Atlanta headend; Magnavox amplifiers; Times Fiber cable; Eagle traps.
Miles of plant: 11.8 (coaxial). Homes passed: 712.
Manager: Karen McMillan. Chief technician: Paul Mathison.
City fee: 5% of gross.
Ownership: Brownwood TV Cable Service Inc. (MSO).

SANTA FE—Star Cable, Drawer 1570, Brazoria, TX 77422. Phones: 409-798-9121; 800-395-2775. Fax: 409-798-4409. County: Galveston. ICA: TX0411.
TV Market Ranking: 15. Franchise award date: N.A. Franchise expiration date: N.A. Began: N.A.
Channel capacity: 62 (not 2-way capable). Channels available but not in use: 28.
Basic Service
Subscribers: 329.
Programming (received off-air): KHSH-TV (H) Alvin; KLTJ (E), KTMD (O) Galveston; KETH (E), KHOU-TV (C), KHTV (W), KPRC-TV (N), KRIV (F), KTRK-TV (A), KTXH (U), KUHT (P) Houston; KNWS-TV (I) Katy; KXLN-TV (S) Rosenberg.
Programming (via satellite): WGN-TV (W) Chicago; A & E; American Movie Classics; CNN; Country Music TV; Discovery Channel; ESPN; Fox Family Channel; Fox Sports Net Southwest; Headline News; Learning Channel; Nashville Network; QVC; TBS Superstation; The Weather Channel; Turner Network TV; USA Network.
Fee: $31.34 monthly; $2.15 converter.
Pay Service 1
Pay Units: 75.
Programming (via satellite): HBO.
Fee: $10.95 monthly.
Pay Service 2
Pay Units: 282.
Programming (via satellite): Showtime.
Fee: $4.15 monthly.
Miles of plant: 35.2 (coaxial); None (fiber optic). Homes passed: 753. Total homes in franchised area: 753.
Manager: Mike Burns. Chief technician: Mayla Zubeck.
Ownership: Star Cable Associates (MSO).

SANTA MARIA/BLUETOWN—Torrence Cablevision, Box 1167, Ridgeland, MS 39158. Phones: 601-981-6900; 800-977-8849. County: Cameron. ICA: TX0552.
TV Market Ranking: Below 100. Franchise award date: N.A. Franchise expiration date: N.A. Began: N.A.
Channel capacity: 36. Channels available but not in use: 21.
Basic Service
Subscribers: 11.
Programming (received off-air): KVEO (N) Brownsville; KGBT-TV (C), KMBH (P) Harlingen; KRGV-TV (A) Weslaco.
Programming (via satellite): WGN-TV (W) Chicago; A & E; American Movie Classics; CNN; Discovery Channel; ESPN; Fox Family Channel; Showtime; TBS Superstation; Turner Network TV; USA Network.
Fee: $28.00 monthly.
Miles of plant: 7.2 (coaxial). Homes passed: 266.
Ownership: Torrence Cable Inc. (MSO).

SANTO—Mallard Cablevision, 100-D El Chico Trail, Willow Park, TX 76087. Phones: 817-441-8073; 800-669-2288. Fax: 817-441-6464. County: Palo Pinto. ICA: TX0665.
TV Market Ranking: Outside TV Markets. Franchise award date: N.A. Franchise expiration date: N.A. Began: August 1, 1985.
Channel capacity: 27. Channels available but not in use: 12.
Basic Service
Subscribers: 78.
Programming (received off-air): KDFW (F), KERA-TV (P), KTVT (C), KTXA (U), KXAS-TV (N), KXTX-TV (I), WFAA-TV (A) Dallas-Fort Worth.
Programming (via satellite): WGN-TV (W) Chicago; A & E; ESPN; Fox Family Channel; Fox Sports Net Southwest; Nashville Network; Sci-Fi Channel; TBS Superstation.
Fee: $30.00 installation; $16.80 monthly.
Pay Service 1
Pay Units: 19.
Programming (via satellite): Cinemax.
Fee: $10.00 installation; $9.95 monthly.
Pay Service 2
Pay Units: 22.
Programming (via satellite): HBO.
Fee: $10.00 installation; $10.50 monthly.
Equipment: Cadco headend; Anaconda amplifiers; Pico traps; Scientific-Atlanta satellite antenna; GLR satellite receivers.
Miles of plant: 5.0 (coaxial). Homes passed: 150.
Manager: Doug Grassmann.
Ownership: Mallard Cablevision (MSO). Purchased from Cambridge Communications, May 1, 1999.

SARGENT—Star Cable, Drawer 1570, Brazoria, TX 77422. Phones: 409-798-9121; 800-395-2775. Fax: 409-798-4409. County: Matagorda. ICA: TX0248.
TV Market Ranking: Outside TV Markets. Franchise award date: N.A. Franchise expiration date: N.A. Began: September 1, 1989.
Channel capacity: 52 (not 2-way capable). Channels available but not in use: 23.
Basic Service
Subscribers: 388.
Programming (received off-air): KHSH-TV (H) Alvin; KVVV (I) Baytown; KETH (E), KHOU-TV (C), KHTV (W), KPRC-TV (N), KRIV (F), KTRK-TV (A), KTXH (U), KUHT (P), KZJL (I) Houston.
Programming (via satellite): WGN-TV (W) Chicago; American Movie Classics; CNN; Country Music TV; Discovery Channel; ESPN; Fox Family Channel; Fox Sports Net Southwest; Lifetime; Nashville Network; Nickelodeon; TBS Superstation; The Weather Channel; Turner Network TV; USA Network.
Fee: $31.34 monthly; $2.15 converter.
Pay Service 1
Pay Units: 44.
Programming (via satellite): Cinemax.
Fee: $10.95 monthly.
Pay Service 2
Pay Units: 71.
Programming (via satellite): HBO.
Fee: $10.95 monthly.
Pay Service 3
Pay Units: 57.
Programming (via satellite): Showtime.
Fee: $12.95 monthly.
Miles of plant: 49.9 (coaxial); None (fiber optic). Homes passed: 1,733. Total homes in franchised area: 1,733.
Manager: Mike Burns. Chief technician: Mayla Zubeck.
Ownership: Star Cable Associates (MSO).

SEADRIFT—TCI Cablevision of Texas, 4060 S. Padre Island Dr., Corpus Christi, TX 78411-4477. Phone: 512-857-5000. County: Calhoun. ICA: TX0433.
TV Market Ranking: Below 100. Franchise award date: N.A. Franchise expiration date: March 1, 1999. Began: December 1, 1981.
Channel capacity: 30. Channels available but not in use: 10.
Basic Service
Subscribers: 374.
Programming (received off-air): KEDT (P), KIII (A), KRIS-TV (N), KZTV (C) Corpus Christi; KAVU-TV (A) Victoria.
Programming (via satellite): WGN-TV (W) Chicago; CNBC; CNN; Discovery Channel; ESPN; Fox Family Channel; FoxNet; Lifetime; Nashville Network; TBS Superstation; The Weather Channel; Turner Network TV; USA Network.
Fee: $60.00 installation; $10.02 monthly; $60.00 additional installation.
Pay Service 1
Pay Units: 105.
Programming (via satellite): Showtime.
Fee: $10.00 monthly.
Pay Service 2
Pay Units: 189.
Programming (via satellite): The New Encore.
Fee: N.A.
Miles of plant: 9.2 (coaxial). Homes passed: 690. Total homes in franchised area: 700.
Manager: Dennis Moore. Chief technician: Mando Blancas. Marketing director: Jerri Coppedge.
City fee: None.
Ownership: AT&T Broadband & Internet Services (MSO). Purchased from Tele-Communications Inc., March 9, 1999.

SEBASTIAN—Rapid Cable, Box 6310, 310 Walnut Extension, Branson, MO 65615. Phones: 417-334-7897; 800-972-0962. Fax: 417-334-7899. E-mail: rcpcable@aol.com. County: Willacy. ICA: TX0481.
TV Market Ranking: Below 100. Franchise award date: N.A. Franchise expiration date: N.A. Began: June 1, 1989.
Channel capacity: 52 (2-way capable; not operating 2-way). Channels available but not in use: 28.
Basic Service
Subscribers: 49.
Programming (received off-air): KVEO (N) Brownsville; KGBT-TV (C), KMBH (P) Harlingen; KRGV-TV (A) Weslaco; XHAB-TV Matamoros; XHRIO (O) Matamoros-Brownsville; XEW-TV Mexico City.
Programming (via translator): KWKT (F) Waco-Temple.
Programming (via satellite): WGN-TV (W) Chicago; CNN; Country Music TV; Discovery Channel; ESPN; EWTN; Fox Family Channel; GalaVision; Lifetime; Nashville Network; Nickelodeon; TBS Superstation; The Weather Channel; Turner Network TV; Univision.
Fee: $40.00 installation; $29.95 monthly; $2.95 converter.
Pay Service 1
Pay Units: 14.
Programming (via satellite): Disney Channel.
Fee: $7.00 monthly.
Pay Service 2
Pay Units: 24.
Programming (via satellite): HBO.
Fee: $10.00 monthly.
Pay Service 3
Pay Units: N.A.
Programming (via satellite): Cinemax; Showtime; The Movie Channel.
Fee: $9.00 monthly (Cinemax), $10.00 monthly (Showtime), $10.95 monthly (TMC).
Local advertising: No.
Miles of plant: 6.2 (coaxial). Homes passed: 504.
Manager: Belinda Murphy. Chief engineer: Steve Rice. Program director: Beth Semptimphelter. Marketing director: Bill Fischer.
Ownership: Rapid Communications Partners LP (MSO).

SEGUIN—Communications Services Inc., 1239 E. College St., Seguin, TX 78155-3995. Phone: 830-379-1505. County: Guadalupe. Also serves Guadalupe County (portions). ICA: TX0090.
TV Market Ranking: Outside TV Markets. Franchise award date: N.A. Franchise expiration date: N.A. Began: July 1, 1979.
Channel capacity: 40. Channels available but not in use: N.A.
Basic Service
Subscribers: 7,159.
Programming (received off-air): KRRT (W) Kerrville-San Antonio; KABB (F), KENS-TV (C), KLRN (P), KMOL-TV (N), KSAT-TV (A), KWEX-TV (S) San Antonio; allband FM.
Programming (via satellite): WGN-TV (W) Chicago; A & E; C-SPAN; CNBC; CNN; Discovery Channel; Fox Family Channel; Headline News; Knowledge TV; Lifetime; MTV; Nashville Network; Nickelodeon; Odyssey; QVC; TBS Superstation; The Weather Channel.
Fee: $38.84 installation; $9.24 monthly; $1.07 converter; $19.42 additional installation.
Expanded Basic Service
Subscribers: 6,202.
Programming (via satellite): American Movie Classics; ESPN; Fox Sports Net Southwest; Turner Network TV; USA Network.
Fee: $11.07 monthly.
Pay Service 1
Pay Units: 263.

Programming (via satellite): Cinemax.
Fee: N.A.
Pay Service 2
Pay Units: 295.
Programming (via satellite): Disney Channel.
Fee: $10.00 installation; $11.50 monthly.
Pay Service 3
Pay Units: 722.
Programming (via satellite): HBO.
Fee: $10.00 installation; $11.50 monthly.
Pay Service 4
Pay Units: 1,099.
Programming (via satellite): Showtime.
Fee: $10.00 installation; $11.50 monthly.
Pay Service 5
Pay Units: 2,847.
Programming (via satellite): The New Encore.
Fee: N.A.
Local advertising: Yes (locally produced & insert). Available in satellite distributed programming.
Program Guide: The Cable Guide.
Equipment: Jerrold headend; C-COR amplifiers; Times Fiber cable; Sony VTRs; Video Data Systems character generator; Jerrold set top converters; Eagle traps; Scientific-Atlanta satellite antenna.
Miles of plant: 195.0 (coaxial). Homes passed: 8,159. Total homes in franchised area: 10,233.
Manager: Dennis Moore.
City fee: 3% of gross.
Ownership: AT&T Broadband & Internet Services (MSO). Purchased from Tele-Communications Inc., March 9, 1999.

SEMINOLE—US Cable of West Texas, 611 W. Ave. A, Seminole, TX 79360. Phone: 915-758-9221. Fax: 915-758-3379. E-mail: uscable@wtaccess.com. Counties: Brewster, Culberson, Gaines, Pecos, Terrell, Upton & Val Verde, TX; Chaves, NM. Also serves Dexter, Hagerman, NM; Alpine, Brewster County, Comstock, Denver City, Fort Stockton, Iraan, Lajitas, McCamey, Rankin, Sanderson, Seagraves, Van Horn, TX. ICA: TX0074.
TV Market Ranking: Below 100 (Comstock, Dexter, Hagerman); Outside TV Markets (Alpine, Brewster County, Denver City, Fort Stockton, Iraan, Lajitas, McCamey, Rankin, Sanderson, Seagraves, Seminole, Van Horn). Franchise award date: N.A. Franchise expiration date: January 1, 2002. Began: July 1, 1953.
Channel capacity: 60 (2-way capable; operating 2-way partially). Channels available but not in use: 9.
Basic Service
Subscribers: 1,856.
Programming (received off-air): KDBC-TV (C), KTSM-TV (N), KVIA-TV (A) El Paso; KAMC (A), KCBD-TV (N), KJTV (F), KLBK-TV (C) Lubbock; KMID (A), KOCV-TV (P), KOSA-TV (C), KPEJ (F), KWES-TV (N) Odessa-Midland; KENW (P) Portales; 1 FM.
Programming (via satellite): Telemundo; The Inspirational Network.
Current originations: Community channel.
Fee: $35.28 installation; $11.19 monthly; $0.86 converter.
Expanded Basic Service
Subscribers: 1,666.
Programming (via satellite): C-SPAN; CNN; Country Music TV; Disney Channel; E! Entertainment TV; ESPN; Fox Family Channel; Headline News; History Channel; Home & Garden Television; Knowledge TV; Learning Channel; MTV; Nashville Network; Nickelodeon; Sci-Fi Channel; TV Guide Channel; The Weather Channel; Turner Network TV; USA Network; Univision; VH1.
Fee: $15.69 monthly.
Expanded Basic Service 2
Subscribers: 1,744.
Programming (via satellite): WGN-TV (W) Chicago; American Movie Classics; Discovery Channel; TBS Superstation.
Fee: $2.25 monthly.
Pay Service 1
Pay Units: 116.
Programming (via satellite): Cinemax.
Fee: $10.95 monthly.
Pay Service 2
Pay Units: 259.
Programming (via satellite): HBO.
Fee: $10.95 monthly.
Pay Service 3
Pay Units: 52.
Programming (via satellite): The Movie Channel.
Fee: $10.95 monthly.
Pay Service 4
Pay Units: 144.
Programming (via satellite): Showtime.
Fee: $10.95 monthly.
Pay Service 5
Pay Units: 35.
Programming (via satellite): Golf Channel.
Fee: $6.95 monthly.
Pay-Per-View
Viewer's Choice.
Fee: Varies.
Pay-per-view manager: Candy Boyer.
Local advertising: Yes. Available in satellite distributed programming. Local sales manager: Bill Bartlett.
Equipment: Jerrold headend; Jerrold amplifiers; Times Fiber cable; U.S. Tower satellite antenna.
Miles of plant: 491.5 (coaxial); None (fiber optic). Homes passed: 21,906. Total homes in franchised area: 21,906.
Manager: Kenny Harris. Regional manager: Daryl Koedyker. Chief technician: Jess Webb. Marketing director: Candy Boyer.
City fee: 2% of gross.
Ownership: US Cable Corp. (MSO).

SEVEN POINTS—Torrence Cablevision, Box 1167, Ridgeland, MS 39158. Phones: 601-981-6900; 800-977-8849. County: Henderson. ICA: TX0423.
TV Market Ranking: Below 100. Franchise award date: N.A. Franchise expiration date: N.A. Began: N.A.
Channel capacity: 36. Channels available but not in use: N.A.
Basic Service
Subscribers: 142.
Programming (received off-air): KDAF (W), KDFW (F), KERA-TV (P), KTXA (U), KXTX-TV (I), WFAA-TV (A) Dallas-Fort Worth; KETK-TV (N) Jacksonville.
Programming (via satellite): WGN-TV (W) Chicago; A & E; American Movie Classics; CNN; Country Music TV; Discovery Channel; ESPN; Fox Family Channel; Showtime; TBS Superstation; Turner Network TV; USA Network.
Fee: $28.00 monthly.
Miles of plant: 22.4 (coaxial). Homes passed: 688.
Ownership: Torrence Cable Inc. (MSO).

SEYMOUR—Friendship Cable of Texas Inc., Box 9090, Tyler, TX 75711-9090. Phone: 903-581-2121. Fax: 903-581-2185. County: Baylor. ICA: TX0254.
TV Market Ranking: Outside TV Markets. Franchise award date: N.A. Franchise expiration date: N.A. Began: February 1, 1977.
Channel capacity: 35. Channels available but not in use: 5.
Basic Service
Subscribers: 1,152.
Programming (received off-air): KAUZ-TV (C), KFDX-TV (N), KJTL (F,U), KSWO-TV (A) Wichita Falls-Lawton; allband FM.
Programming (via satellite): C-SPAN; Discovery Channel; Learning Channel; Lifetime; Odyssey; QVC; TBS Superstation; The Weather Channel; Univision.
Current originations: Automated time-weather.
Fee: $30.00 installation; $13.03 monthly.
Expanded Basic Service
Subscribers: 955.
Programming (via satellite): American Movie Classics; Animal Planet; CNN; Cartoon Network; Disney Channel; ESPN; FX; Fox Family Channel; Fox News Channel; Headline News; Home & Garden Television; MTV; Nashville Network; Nickelodeon; Turner Network TV; USA Network.
Fee: $30.00 installation; $18.32 monthly.
Pay Service 1
Pay Units: 47.
Programming (via satellite): Cinemax.
Fee: $12.84 monthly.
Pay Service 2
Pay Units: 332.
Programming (via satellite): The New Encore.
Fee: $1.75 monthly.
Pay Service 3
Pay Units: 140.
Programming (via satellite): HBO.
Fee: $13.83 monthly.
Pay Service 4
Pay Units: 188.
Programming (via satellite): Starz!
Fee: $6.75 monthly.
Program Guide: The Cable Guide.
Equipment: Tocom headend; Tocom amplifiers; Tocom cable; Comtech & RF Systems satellite antenna.
Miles of plant: 29.0 (coaxial). Homes passed: 1,700. Total homes in franchised area: 1,700.
Manager: Larry Bryant. Chief technician: Ron Johnson.
City fee: 3% of gross.
Ownership: Buford Television Inc. (MSO). See Cable System Ownership.

SHAMROCK—Classic Cable, Box 429, 605 N.W. 3rd St., Plainville, KS 67663-0429. Phones: 785-434-7620; 800-999-8876. Fax: 785-434-2614. County: Wheeler. ICA: TX0318.
TV Market Ranking: Below 100. Franchise award date: N.A. Franchise expiration date: N.A. Began: August 1, 1957.
Channel capacity: 58 (2-way capable; operating 2-way). Channels available but not in use: N.A.
Basic Service
Subscribers: 898; Commercial subscribers: 390.
Programming (received off-air): KWET (P) Cheyenne.
Programming (via microwave): KAMR-TV (N), KCIT (F,U), KFDA-TV (C), KVII-TV (A) Amarillo; KETA (P) Oklahoma City.
Programming (via satellite): WGN-TV (W) Chicago; American Movie Classics; Animal Planet; CNN; Cartoon Network; Country Music TV; Court TV; Discovery Channel; Disney Channel; E! Entertainment TV; ESPN; Fox Family Channel; Fox News Channel; Fox Sports Net Southwest; Goodlife TV Network; Headline News; History Channel; Home & Garden Television; Learning Channel; Lifetime; Nashville Network; Nick at Nite's TV Land; Nickelodeon; QVC; Sci-Fi Channel; TBS Superstation; The Inspirational Network; The Weather Channel; Turner Network TV; USA Network; Univision.
Current originations: Automated time-weather; public access.
Fee: $35.00 installation; $29.95 monthly.
Pay Service 1
Pay Units: 45.
Programming (via satellite): The Movie Channel.
Fee: $5.95 monthly.
Pay Service 2
Pay Units: 41.
Programming (via satellite): Cinemax.
Fee: $9.95 monthly.
Pay Service 3
Pay Units: 46.
Programming (via satellite): Showtime.
Fee: $9.95 monthly.
Pay Service 4
Pay Units: 87.
Programming (via satellite): HBO.
Fee: $10.95 monthly.
Local advertising: Yes. Available in character-generated programming. Rates: $1.50/Minute; $3.00/Page.
Equipment: Jerrold headend; Jerrold amplifiers; Times Fiber cable; Fort Worth Tower satellite antenna.
Miles of plant: 25.0 (coaxial). Homes passed: 1,313.
Manager: Bill Flowers. Chief technician: Rick Rattan. Marketing director: Jennifer Hauschild.
City fee: 2% of gross.
Ownership: Classic Cable (MSO).

SHEFFIELD—Sheffield TV Cable, Box 420182, Del Rio, TX 78842. Phone: 830-775-3567. County: Pecos. ICA: TX0691.
TV Market Ranking: Outside TV Markets. Franchise award date: N.A. Franchise expiration date: N.A. Began: December 1, 1963.
Channel capacity: 8. Channels available but not in use: N.A.
Basic Service
Subscribers: 65.
Programming (received off-air): KMID (A), KOSA-TV (C), KWES-TV (N) Odessa-Midland.
Programming (via satellite): WGN-TV (W) Chicago; CNN; ESPN; TBS Superstation; Univision.
Fee: N.A.
Miles of plant: 3.0 (coaxial). Homes passed: 100.
Manager: Rahe Slover.
Ownership: Rahe Slover.

SHEPHERD—Lakewood Cablevision, 12504 Walden Rd., Montgomery, TX 77356. Phone: 409-582-4855. Counties: Polk & San Jacinto. Also serves Coldspring, Memorial Point, Onalaska, Point Blank. ICA: TX0851.
TV Market Ranking: Outside TV Markets. Franchise award date: N.A. Franchise expiration date: N.A. Began: January 31, 1972.
Channel capacity: 35 (not 2-way capable). Channels available but not in use: N.A.
Basic Service
Subscribers: 4,625.
Programming (received off-air): KHOU-TV (C), KHTV (W), KPRC-TV (N), KRIV (F), KTRK-TV (A), KTXH (U), KUHT (P) Houston; KETK-TV (N) Jacksonville; KCTL-LP (I) Livingston; KTRE (A) Lufkin; 9 FMs.
Programming (via satellite): WGN-TV (W) Chicago; A & E; C-SPAN; CNN; Country Music TV; Discovery Channel; ESPN; Fox Family Channel; Fox Sports Net Southwest; Headline News; Home Shopping Network; Lifetime; MTV; Nashville Network; Nickelodeon;

TBS Superstation; TV Guide Channel; The Weather Channel; Trinity Bcstg. Network; Turner Network TV; USA Network.
Fee: $52.00 installation; $22.95 monthly.

Pay Service 1
Pay Units: 270.
Programming (via satellite): Cinemax.
Fee: $9.95 monthly.

Pay Service 2
Pay Units: 283.
Programming (via satellite): Disney Channel.
Fee: $9.95 monthly.

Pay Service 3
Pay Units: 639.
Programming (via satellite): HBO.
Fee: $12.00 monthly.

Pay Service 4
Pay Units: 601.
Programming (via satellite): The Movie Channel.
Fee: $9.95 monthly.

Pay Service 5
Pay Units: 524.
Programming (via satellite): Showtime.
Fee: $9.95 monthly.

Pay-Per-View
Addressable homes: 3,556.
Special events.

Local advertising: Yes. Available in character-generated & taped programming.
Program Guide: CableView.
Equipment: DX Engineering & Scientific-Atlanta headend; Scientific-Atlanta amplifiers; Tocom addressable set top converters.
Miles of plant: 200.0 (coaxial); 12.0 (fiber optic). Additional miles planned: 25.0 (coaxial); 30.5 (fiber optic).
Office manager: Timmie Adams. Manager: Charlie Garland.
Ownership: Moffat Communications Ltd. (MSO).

SHERIDAN—National Cable Inc., Suite 106-A, 5151 Reed Rd., Columbus, OH 43220. Phones: 614-442-5890; 800-582-0504. Fax: 614-457-2567. County: Colorado. ICA: TX0645.
TV Market Ranking: Below 100. Franchise award date: N.A. Franchise expiration date: N.A. Began: N.A.
Channel capacity: 35. Channels available but not in use: 11.

Basic Service
Subscribers: 63.
Programming (received off-air): KHOU-TV (C), KPRC-TV (N), KTRK-TV (A), KUHT (P) Houston.
Programming (via satellite): WGN-TV (W) Chicago; A & E; American Movie Classics; C-SPAN; CNN; Country Music TV; Discovery Channel; ESPN; Fox Family Channel; Showtime; TBS Superstation; Turner Network TV; USA Network.
Fee: $21.00 monthly.

Pay Service 1
Pay Units: 7.
Programming (via satellite): Disney Channel.
Fee: $10.95 monthly.

Pay Service 2
Pay Units: 6.
Programming (via satellite): Showtime.
Fee: $10.95 monthly.

Miles of plant: 9.8 (coaxial). Homes passed: 195.
Manager: Paul Scott. Chief technician: Rob Spiller. Marketing director: Josh Thackery.
Ownership: National Cable (MSO).

SHERMAN—Cable One, Box 1223, 3720 Texoma Pkwy., Sherman, TX 75090. Phone: 903-893-6548. Fax: 903-868-2754. County: Grayson. Also serves Denison, Grayson County (northern portion), Knollwood. ICA: TX0042.
TV Market Ranking: Below 100. Franchise award date: March 7, 1966. Franchise expiration date: August 13, 2000. Began: August 1, 1957.
Channel capacity: 78 (2-way capable; operating 2-way partially). Channels available but not in use: None.

Basic Service
Subscribers: 20,454.
Programming (received off-air): KTEN (A,N,F) Ada; KDAF (W), KDFI-TV (I), KDFW (F), KERA-TV (P), KTVT (C), KXAS-TV (N), KXTX-TV (I), WFAA-TV (A) Dallas-Fort Worth; KTAQ (I) Greenville; KXII (C) Sherman.
Programming (via satellite): WGN-TV (W) Chicago; A & E; American Movie Classics; BET; Bravo; C-SPAN; C-SPAN 2; CNBC; CNN; Cartoon Network; Comedy Central; Country Music TV; Discovery Channel; Disney Channel; ESPN; ESPN 2; EWTN; FX; Fox Family Channel; Fox Sports Net Southwest; Headline News; History Channel; Learning Channel; Lifetime; MSNBC; MTV; Nashville Network; Nick at Nite; Nick at Nite's TV Land; Nickelodeon; Odyssey; QVC; Sci-Fi Channel; TBS Superstation; TV Guide Channel; The Inspirational Network; The Weather Channel; Trinity Bcstg. Network; Turner Network TV; USA Network; Univision; VH1.
Current originations: Automated time-weather; public access; educational access; government access; leased access; local sports.
Fee: $40.21 installation; $32.45 monthly; $0.46 converter; $11.74 additional installation.

Pay Service 1
Pay Units: 5,213.
Programming (via satellite): Cinemax (multiplexed).
Fee: $13.95 monthly.

Pay Service 2
Pay Units: 5,674.
Programming (via satellite): HBO (multiplexed).
Fee: $13.95 monthly.

Pay Service 3
Pay Units: 2,208.
Programming (via satellite): The Movie Channel.
Fee: $10.95 monthly.

Pay Service 4
Pay Units: 2,215.
Programming (via satellite): Showtime (multiplexed).
Fee: $10.95 monthly.

Pay Service 5
Pay Units: 184.
Programming (via satellite): DMX.
Fee: $8.95 monthly.

Pay-Per-View
Addressable homes: 12,000.
Hot Choice; Viewer's Choice.
Fee: $2.99 (Hot Choice); $2.99 (Viewer's Choice).

Local advertising: Yes (locally produced). Available in satellite distributed & locally originated programming. Rates: $24.00/Minute; $12.00/30 Seconds. Local sales manager: Brian Bertrand.
Equipment: Scientific-Atlanta headend; Scientific-Atlanta amplifiers; Comm/Scope & Scientific-Atlanta cable; Sony cameras; Sony VTRs; Video Data Systems character generator; Scientific-Atlanta & Standard Components set top converters; Zenith addressable set top converters; Scientific-Atlanta & Andrew satellite antenna; Scientific-Atlanta satellite receivers; Sony & ChannelMatic commercial insert.
Miles of plant: 401.0 (coaxial); 46.0 (fiber optic). Homes passed: 27,500. Total homes in franchised area: 28,800.
Manager: Claude H. Edwards. Chief technician: Cecil Miller. Program director: Darla Hutcherson. Marketing director: Donna Perry. Customer service manager: Pam Roberts.
City fee: 5% of gross.
Ownership: Cable One Inc. (MSO).

SHERWOOD SHORES—Friendship Cable of Texas Inc., Box 9090, Tyler, TX 75711-9090. Phone: 903-581-2121. Fax: 903-581-2185. County: Grayson. Also serves Gordonville. ICA: TX0413.
TV Market Ranking: Below 100. Franchise award date: N.A. Franchise expiration date: N.A. Began: N.A.
Channel capacity: 36. Channels available but not in use: N.A.

Basic Service
Subscribers: 257.
Programming (received off-air): KDFW (F), KTVT (C), KTXA (U), KXAS-TV (N), WFAA-TV (A) Dallas-Fort Worth.
Programming (via satellite): WGN-TV (W) Chicago; Disney Channel; TBS Superstation; Turner Classic Movies.
Fee: $30.00 installation; $30.35 monthly.

Pay Service 1
Pay Units: 5.
Programming (via satellite): HBO.
Fee: $12.00 monthly.

Pay Service 2
Pay Units: 25.
Programming (via satellite): Showtime.
Fee: $3.95 monthly.

Pay Service 3
Pay Units: 5.
Programming (via satellite): The Movie Channel.
Fee: $9.00 monthly.

Miles of plant: 20.0 (coaxial). Homes passed: 750.
Manager: Rodney Fletcher. Chief technician: Bo Jaubert.
Ownership: Buford Television Inc. (MSO). See Cable System Ownership.

SHINER—Falcon Cable TV, 1244 Encino Dr., Pleasanton, TX 78064. Phone: 830-569-5509. Fax: 830-569-4828. County: Lavaca. ICA: TX0383.
TV Market Ranking: Outside TV Markets. Franchise award date: January 1, 1974. Franchise expiration date: N.A. Began: January 23, 1975.
Channel capacity: 62 (not 2-way capable). Channels available but not in use: 26.

Basic Service
Subscribers: 701.
Programming (received off-air): KTBC (F) Austin; KABB (F), KENS-TV (C), KLRN (P), KMOL-TV (N), KSAT-TV (A) San Antonio; KAVU-TV (A), KVCT (F) Victoria; allband FM.
Programming (via satellite): A & E; Bravo; CNN; Country Music TV; E! Entertainment TV; ESPN; EWTN; Fox Family Channel; Headline News; Home Shopping Network; Learning Channel; Nashville Network; Nickelodeon; QVC; Travel Channel; USA Network.
Current originations: Public access; educational access; government access.
Fee: $15.00 installation; $20.33 monthly; $10.00 additional installation.

Expanded Basic Service
Subscribers: 664.
Programming (via satellite): American Movie Classics; Discovery Channel; Sci-Fi Channel.
Fee: $2.34 monthly.

Expanded Basic Service 2
Subscribers: 633.
Programming (via satellite): WGN-TV (W) Chicago; BET; Disney Channel; TBS Superstation; Turner Network TV.
Fee: $6.75 monthly.

Pay Service 1
Pay Units: 53.
Programming (via satellite): HBO.
Fee: $19.95 installation; $11.95 monthly.

Pay Service 2
Pay Units: 51.
Programming (via satellite): Showtime.
Fee: $10.95 monthly.

Pay Service 3
Pay Units: 20.
Programming (via satellite): The Movie Channel.
Fee: $10.95 monthly.

Local advertising: Yes. Regional interconnect: Cabletime.
Program Guide: Premium Channels.
Equipment: Jerrold amplifiers; Times Fiber cable; Jerrold set top converters; Eagle traps; Scientific-Atlanta satellite antenna; M/A-Com satellite receivers.
Miles of plant: 30.0 (coaxial). Homes passed: 946.
Manager: Lorna Gentry. Chief technician: Santos Guajardo.
Franchise fee: 5% of gross.
Ownership: Falcon Communications LP (MSO), joint venture formed September 30, 1998. See Cable System Ownership.

SIERRA BLANCA—Sierra Cable TV, Drawer F, Hwy. 80, Sierra Blanca, TX 79851. Phone: 915-369-2341. County: Hudspeth. ICA: TX0853.
TV Market Ranking: Outside TV Markets. Franchise award date: N.A. Franchise expiration date: N.A. Began: January 1, 1985.
Channel capacity: 13. Channels available but not in use: N.A.

Basic Service
Subscribers: 135.
Programming (received off-air): KCOS (P), KDBC-TV (C), KFOX-TV (F), KTSM-TV (N), KVIA-TV (A) El Paso; XEJ-TV El Paso-Juarez.
Programming (via satellite): CNN; Fox Family Channel; Nashville Network; TBS Superstation.
Fee: N.A.

Pay Service 1
Pay Units: N.A.
Programming (via satellite): HBO.
Fee: N.A.

Manager: H. A. Virdell Jr.
Ownership: H. A. Virdell Jr.

SILSBEE—Cable Texas Inc., Box 186, Silsbee, TX 77656. Phone: 409-385-5953. Fax: 409-385-2473. Counties: Hardin & Jasper. Also serves Buna, Lumberton. ICA: TX0079.
TV Market Ranking: 88. Franchise award date: January 1, 1968. Franchise expiration date: N.A. Began: January 1, 1968.
Channel capacity: 36 (not 2-way capable). Channels available but not in use: 2.

Basic Service
Subscribers: 2,919.
Programming (received off-air): KBMT (A), KBTV-TV (N), KFDM-TV (C), KITU (E) Beaumont-Port Arthur; KVHP (F) Lake Charles.
Programming (via satellite): WGN-TV (W) Chicago; KRMA-TV (P) Denver; A & E; C-SPAN; CNN; Cartoon Network; Fox Family Channel; Headline News; Home Shopping

Network; Learning Channel; Lifetime; MTV; Nashville Network; Nickelodeon; Sci-Fi Channel; TBS Superstation; The Weather Channel; Turner Classic Movies.

Current originations: Automated time-weather; local sports.

Fee: $30.00 installation; $17.00 monthly; $3.00 converter; $30.00 additional installation.

Pay Service 1

Pay Units: N.A.

Programming (via satellite): Cinemax; Disney Channel; HBO; Showtime.

Fee: $15.00 installation; $8.00 monthly (Cinemax, Disney or Showtime), $10.00 monthly (HBO).

Local advertising: Yes. Available in locally originated & character-generated programming. Rates: $90.00/Minute; $50.00/30 Seconds. Local sales manager: Leslie Nieland.

Program Guide: The Cable Guide.

Equipment: Scientific-Atlanta headend; GTE Sylvania amplifiers; Comm/Scope cable; Texscan character generator; Scientific-Atlanta set top converters; Intercept & Vitek traps; Scientific-Atlanta satellite antenna; Scientific-Atlanta satellite receivers.

Miles of plant: 167.0 (coaxial). Additional miles planned: 10.0 (coaxial). Homes passed: 9,100. Total homes in franchised area: 12,000.

Manager: Scott Nieland. Chief technician: Rodney Stage.

City fee: 3% of gross.

Ownership: The Hilliard Group (MSO).

SILVERTON—Classic Cable, Box 429, 605 N.W. 3rd St., Plainville, KS 67663-0429. Phones: 785-434-7620; 800-999-8876. Fax: 785-434-2614. County: Briscoe. ICA: TX0525.

TV Market Ranking: Outside TV Markets. Franchise award date: April 8, 1986. Franchise expiration date: N.A. Began: August 1, 1969.

Channel capacity: 41 (2-way capable; operating 2-way). Channels available but not in use: N.A.

Basic Service

Subscribers: 195.

Programming (received off-air): KACV-TV (P), KAMR-TV (N), KFDA-TV (C), KVII-TV (A) Amarillo; KCBD-TV (N), KJTV (F), KLBK-TV (C) Lubbock; 1 FM.

Programming (via satellite): WGN-TV (W) Chicago; American Movie Classics; CNN; Country Music TV; Discovery Channel; Disney Channel; ESPN; Fox Family Channel; Fox News Channel; Fox Sports Net Southwest; Goodlife TV Network; Headline News; Lifetime; Nashville Network; QVC; TBS Superstation; The Inspirational Network; The Weather Channel; Travel Channel; Trinity Bcstg. Network; Turner Network TV; USA Network; Univision.

Current originations: Automated time-weather.

Fee: $35.00 installation; $28.95 monthly.

Pay Service 1

Pay Units: 18.

Programming (via satellite): Cinemax.

Fee: $9.95 monthly.

Pay Service 2

Pay Units: 26.

Programming (via satellite): HBO.

Fee: $9.95 monthly.

Local advertising: No.

Equipment: Benco & Jerrold headend; Jerrold amplifiers; Ameco cable; Fort Worth Tower satellite antenna.

Miles of plant: 8.1 (coaxial). Homes passed: 375.

Manager: Bill Flowers. Chief technician: Chris Christenson. Marketing director: Jennifer Hauschild.

City fee: 2% of gross.

Ownership: Classic Cable (MSO).

SINTON—Falcon Cable TV, 822 Market St., Portland, TX 78374. Phone: 512-643-8588. Fax: 512-643-3641. County: San Patricio. ICA: TX0224.

TV Market Ranking: Below 100. Franchise award date: N.A. Franchise expiration date: N.A. Began: January 5, 1981.

Channel capacity: 37. Channels available but not in use: None.

Basic Service

Subscribers: 1,028.

Programming (received off-air): K47DF (F), KEDT (P), KIII (A), KORO (S), KRIS-TV (N), KZTV (C) Corpus Christi; 12 FMs.

Programming (via satellite): C-SPAN; CNN; Country Music TV; Discovery Channel; Disney Channel; E! Entertainment TV; ESPN; Fox Family Channel; GalaVision; Headline News; Home Shopping Network; Lifetime; MTV; Nashville Network; Nickelodeon; QVC; Sci-Fi Channel; The Weather Channel; Travel Channel; Trinity Bcstg. Network; USA Network.

Current originations: Public access; educational access; government access.

Fee: $20.00 installation; $20.89 monthly; $2.00 converter; $2.50 additional installation.

Expanded Basic Service

Subscribers: 698.

Programming (via satellite): WGN-TV (W) Chicago; TBS Superstation; Turner Network TV.

Fee: $4.30 monthly.

Pay Service 1

Pay Units: 87.

Programming (via satellite): Cinemax.

Fee: $9.95 monthly.

Pay Service 2

Pay Units: 198.

Programming (via satellite): HBO.

Fee: $22.50 installation; $10.75 monthly.

Pay Service 3

Pay Units: 84.

Programming (via satellite): The Movie Channel.

Fee: $22.50 installation; $9.75 monthly.

Pay Service 4

Pay Units: 291.

Programming (via satellite): Showtime.

Fee: $9.75 monthly.

Pay Service 5

Pay Units: N.A.

Programming (via satellite): The New Encore.

Fee: N.A.

Local advertising: Yes. Regional interconnect: Cabletime.

Equipment: Jerrold headend; Jerrold amplifiers; Comm/Scope cable; Video Data Systems & Magnavox character generator; Jerrold set top converters; Gardiner satellite antenna.

Miles of plant: 38.0 (coaxial). Homes passed: 1,262. Total homes in franchised area: 2,000.

Office manager: Jenny Brumley. Chief technician: Mike Kelsch.

Franchise fee: 3% of gross.

Ownership: Falcon Communications LP (MSO), joint venture formed September 30, 1998. See Cable System Ownership.

SKELLYTOWN—Classic Cable, Box 429, 605 N.W. 3rd St., Plainville, KS 67663-0429. Phones: 785-434-7620; 800-999-8876. Fax: 785-434-2614. County: Carson. ICA: TX0586.

TV Market Ranking: Outside TV Markets. Franchise award date: January 1, 1982. Franchise expiration date: N.A. Began: May 1, 1982.

Channel capacity: 36 (2-way capable; operating 2-way). Channels available but not in use: N.A.

Basic Service

Subscribers: 108.

Programming (received off-air): KACV-TV (P), KAMR-TV (N), KCIT (F,U), KFDA-TV (C), KVII-TV (A) Amarillo; 1 FM.

Programming (via satellite): WGN-TV (W) Chicago; CNN; Cartoon Network; Discovery Channel; Disney Channel; ESPN; Fox Family Channel; Fox Sports Net Southwest; History Channel; Learning Channel; Nashville Network; Nick at Nite's TV Land; QVC; Sci-Fi Channel; TBS Superstation; The Weather Channel; Trinity Bcstg. Network; Turner Network TV.

Current originations: Automated time-weather; local news.

Fee: $35.00 installation; $27.95 monthly; $10.00 additional installation.

Pay Service 1

Pay Units: 8.

Programming (via satellite): Showtime.

Fee: $9.95 monthly.

Pay Service 2

Pay Units: 8.

Programming (via satellite): HBO.

Fee: $10.95 monthly.

Local advertising: No.

Equipment: Scientific-Atlanta headend; GTE Sylvania amplifiers; Comm/Scope cable; Cable Text character generator; Jerrold set top converters; Eagle traps; Scientific-Atlanta satellite antenna; Scientific-Atlanta satellite receivers.

Miles of plant: 6.3 (coaxial). Homes passed: 258. Total homes in franchised area: 263.

Manager: Bill Flowers. Chief technician: Rick Rattan. Marketing director: Jennifer Hauschild.

City fee: 3% of gross.

Ownership: Classic Cable (MSO).

SLATON—Cablecomm, 129 S. 9th St., Slaton, TX 79364. Phone: 806-828-4336. County: Lubbock. ICA: TX0201.

TV Market Ranking: Below 100. Franchise award date: June 10, 1986. Franchise expiration date: June 10, 2001. Began: January 15, 1979.

Channel capacity: 36 (not 2-way capable). Channels available but not in use: 5.

Basic Service

Subscribers: 1,115; Commercial subscribers: 1.

Programming (received off-air): KAMC (A), KCBD-TV (N), KJTV (F), KLBK-TV (C), KTXT-TV (P) Lubbock.

Programming (via satellite): WGN-TV (W) Chicago; C-SPAN; Home Shopping Network; TBS Superstation; Univision.

Fee: $27.90 installation; $13.60 monthly; $1.55 converter.

Expanded Basic Service

Subscribers: 1,087.

Programming (via satellite): American Movie Classics; CNN; Discovery Channel; Disney Channel; ESPN; Fox Family Channel; Fox Sports Net Southwest; Headline News; Knowledge TV; MTV; Nashville Network; Nickelodeon; The Weather Channel; Turner Network TV; USA Network.

Fee: $20.00 installation; $3.40 monthly.

Pay Service 1

Pay Units: 139.

Programming (via satellite): Cinemax.

Fee: $20.00 installation; $9.00 monthly.

Pay Service 2

Pay Units: 220.

Programming (via satellite): HBO.

Fee: $20.00 installation; $9.00 monthly.

Pay Service 3

Pay Units: 97.

Programming (via satellite): Showtime.

Fee: $20.00 installation; $9.00 monthly.

Local advertising: Yes. Available in character-generated programming. Rates: $3.00/Day.

Program Guide: Premium Channels.

Equipment: Scientific-Atlanta headend; Texscan amplifiers; Comm/Scope cable; BEI character generator; Scientific-Atlanta set top converters; Pico traps; Scientific-Atlanta satellite antenna; Microdyne & Automation Techniques satellite receivers.

Miles of plant: 31.0 (coaxial). Homes passed: 2,388.

Manager: Rex Thackerson. Chief technician: Randy Trammel. Marketing director: Bruce Berkinshaw.

City fee: 2% of gross.

Ownership: Fanch Communications Inc. (MSO); Time Warner Cable (MSO). See Cable System Ownership.

SMILEY—National Cable Inc., Suite 106-A, 5151 Reed Rd., Columbus, OH 43220. Phones: 614-442-5890; 800-582-0504. Fax: 614-457-2567. County: Gonzales. ICA: TX0652.

TV Market Ranking: Outside TV Markets. Franchise award date: N.A. Franchise expiration date: N.A. Began: November 1, 1989.

Channel capacity: 36 (not 2-way capable). Channels available but not in use: 21.

Basic Service

Subscribers: 43.

Programming (received off-air): KRRT (W) Kerrville-San Antonio; KABB (F), KENS-TV (C), KLRN (P), KMOL-TV (N), KSAT-TV (A) San Antonio.

Programming (via satellite): WGN-TV (W) Chicago; A & E; American Movie Classics; CNN; Country Music TV; Discovery Channel; ESPN; Fox Family Channel; Showtime; TBS Superstation; Turner Network TV; USA Network.

Fee: $28.00 monthly.

Equipment: Nexus headend; Magnavox amplifiers; Times Fiber cable; Oak set top converters; Nexus satellite receivers.

Miles of plant: 5.5 (coaxial). Homes passed: 185.

Manager: Paul Scott. Chief technician: Rob Spiller. Marketing director: Josh Thackery.

Ownership: National Cable (MSO).

SNOOK—National Cable Inc., Suite 106-A, 5151 Reed Rd., Columbus, OH 43220. Phones: 614-442-5890; 800-582-0504. Fax: 614-457-2567. County: Burleson. ICA: TX0854.

TV Market Ranking: Below 100. Franchise award date: N.A. Franchise expiration date: N.A. Began: N.A.
Channel capacity: 36. Channels available but not in use: 21.
Basic Service
Subscribers: 65.
Programming (received off-air): KBTX-TV (C) Bryan; KAMU-TV (P) College Station; KTRK-TV (A) Houston; KCEN-TV (N) Waco-Temple.
Programming (via satellite): WGN-TV (W) Chicago; A & E; American Movie Classics; BET; CNN; Country Music TV; Discovery Channel; ESPN; Fox Family Channel; Showtime; TBS Superstation; Turner Network TV; USA Network.
Fee: $29.00 monthly.
Miles of plant: 11.0 (coaxial). Homes passed: 259.
Manager: Paul Scott. Chief technician: Rob Spiller. Marketing director: Josh Thackery.
Ownership: National Cable (MSO).

SNYDER—TCA Cable TV, Box 366, 2211 Ave. R, Snyder, TX 79549. Phone: 915-573-3536. Fax: 915-573-6360.
Web site: http://www.tca-cable.com.
County: Scurry. Also serves Hermleigh, Scurry County. ICA: TX0120.
TV Market Ranking: Below 100. Franchise award date: N.A. Franchise expiration date: December 1, 2000. Began: December 1, 1958.
Channel capacity: 30 (not 2-way capable). Channels available but not in use: N.A.
Basic Service
Subscribers: 4,699.
Programming (received off-air): KRBC-TV (N), KTAB-TV (C), KTXS-TV (A) Abilene-Sweetwater; KERA-TV (P), WFAA-TV (A) Dallas-Fort Worth; KCBD-TV (N), KLBK-TV (C), KUPT-LP (U) Lubbock; KPCB (I) Snyder; allband FM.
Programming (via microwave): KERA-TV (P) Dallas-Fort Worth.
Programming (via satellite): TBS Superstation.
Current originations: Automated time-weather.
Fee: $40.00 installation; $7.03 monthly.
Expanded Basic Service
Subscribers: 4,580.
Programming (received off-air): KJTV (F) Lubbock.
Programming (via satellite): A & E; American Movie Classics; C-SPAN; CNN; Country Music TV; Discovery Channel; Disney Channel; ESPN; Fox Family Channel; Fox Sports Net Southwest; Headline News; Nashville Network; Nick at Nite's TV Land; Nickelodeon; QVC; The Weather Channel; Turner Network TV; USA Network; Univision.
Fee: $13.52 monthly.
Pay Service 1
Pay Units: 1,986.
Programming (via satellite): Cinemax; HBO.
Fee: $40.00 installation; $10.50 monthly (each).
Local advertising: Yes. Regional interconnect: Cabletime.
Equipment: CAS headend; Kaiser amplifiers; Ameco cable; Andrew satellite antenna.
Miles of plant: 108.0 (coaxial); None (fiber optic). Homes passed: 5,620.
Manager: Victor Means. Chief technician: Peter Pena.
City fee: 3% of gross.
Ownership: TCA Cable TV Inc. (MSO); AT&T Broadband & Internet Services (MSO). See Cable System Ownership.

SOMERSET—TCI Cablevision of Texas Inc., 207 E. Colorado St., Pearsall, TX 78061-3234. Phone: 800-527-6221. Counties: Atascosa & Bexar. Also serves Atascosa County, Bexar County (unincorporated areas), Primrose, Shallimar, Twin Valley. ICA: TX0290.
TV Market Ranking: 45 (portions of Atascosa County, Bexar County, Primrose, Shallimar, Somerset, Twin Valley); Outside TV Markets (portions of Atascosa County). Franchise award date: N.A. Franchise expiration date: N.A. Began: September 1, 1983.
Channel capacity: 35. Channels available but not in use: 1.
Basic Service
Subscribers: 438.
Programming (received off-air): KRRT (W) Kerrville-San Antonio; KABB (F), KENS-TV (C), KLRN (P), KMOL-TV (N), KSAT-TV (A), KVDA (O), KWEX-TV (S) San Antonio.
Programming (via satellite): WGN-TV (W) Chicago; C-SPAN; C-SPAN 2; CNN; Country Music TV; Discovery Channel; ESPN; EWTN; Fox Family Channel; Fox Sports Net Southwest; GalaVision; Headline News; Lifetime; MTV; Nashville Network; Nickelodeon; TBS Superstation; The Weather Channel; Trinity Bcstg. Network; Turner Network TV; USA Network.
Fee: $30.00 installation; $19.32 monthly; $30.00 additional installation.
Pay Service 1
Pay Units: 68.
Programming (via satellite): The Movie Channel.
Fee: N.A.
Pay Service 2
Pay Units: 41.
Programming (via satellite): Disney Channel.
Fee: $7.00 monthly.
Pay Service 3
Pay Units: 144.
Programming (via satellite): HBO.
Fee: $9.00 monthly.
Pay Service 4
Pay Units: 120.
Programming (via satellite): Showtime.
Fee: $9.00 monthly.
Miles of plant: 36.0 (coaxial). Homes passed: 1,377.
Manager: Marcos Reyes.
Ownership: AT&T Broadband & Internet Services (MSO). Purchased from Tele-Communications Inc., March 9, 1999.

SONORA—Classic Cable, Box 429, 605 N.W. 3rd St., Plainville, KS 67663-0429. Phones: 785-434-7620; 800-999-8876. Fax: 785-434-2614. County: Sutton. ICA: TX0245.
TV Market Ranking: Outside TV Markets. Franchise award date: N.A. Franchise expiration date: N.A. Began: April 1, 1955.
Channel capacity: 61 (2-way capable; operating 2-way). Channels available but not in use: N.A.
Basic Service
Subscribers: 1,085.
Programming (received off-air): KTXS-TV (A) Abilene-Sweetwater; KACB-TV (N), KIDY (F), KLST (C) San Angelo; 4 FMs.
Programming (via translator): KVDA (O) San Antonio.
Programming (via satellite): WGN-TV (W) Chicago; KRMA-TV (P) Denver; A & E; Animal Planet; C-SPAN; CNN; Country Music TV; Discovery Channel; Disney Channel; ESPN; Fox Family Channel; Fox News Channel; Fox Sports Net Southwest; Headline News; History Channel; Learning Channel; Lifetime; Nashville Network; Nick at Nite's TV Land; Nickelodeon; QVC; TBS Superstation; The Weather Channel; Trinity Bcstg. Network; Turner Classic Movies; Turner Network TV; USA Network; Univision.
Current originations: Automated time-weather.
Fee: $35.00 installation; $29.95 monthly.
Pay Service 1
Pay Units: 131.
Programming (via satellite): The Movie Channel.
Fee: $5.95 monthly.
Pay Service 2
Pay Units: 131.
Programming (via satellite): Showtime.
Fee: $9.95 monthly.
Pay Service 3
Pay Units: 167.
Programming (via satellite): HBO.
Fee: $10.95 monthly.
Equipment: RCA headend; Jerrold & RCA amplifiers; Comm/Scope cable; Jerrold set top converters; Eagle traps; Andrew satellite antenna.
Miles of plant: 36.0 (coaxial). Homes passed: 1,758.
Manager: Bill Flowers. Chief technician: Ben Hernandez. Marketing director: Jennifer Hauschild.
City fee: 2% of gross.
Ownership: Classic Cable (MSO).

SOUR LAKE—Timberlake Cablevision Inc., Box 2024, 660 W. Barkley St., Sour Lake, TX 77659. Phone: 409-287-3014. Fax: 409-287-3695. Counties: Hardin & Jefferson. Also serves Beaumont (portions), Bevil Oaks. ICA: TX0162.
TV Market Ranking: 88. Franchise award date: February 1, 1983. Franchise expiration date: February 1, 1998. Began: N.A.
Channel capacity: 25. Channels available but not in use: N.A.
Basic Service
Subscribers: 2,595.
Programming (received off-air): KBMT (A), KBTV-TV (N), KFDM-TV (C) Beaumont-Port Arthur; KHOU-TV (C), KHTV (W), KPRC-TV (N), KRIV (F), KTRK-TV (A), KTXH (U), KUHT (P) Houston.
Programming (via satellite): CNN; Nickelodeon; Turner Classic Movies.
Fee: $25.00 installation; $15.95 monthly.
Pay Service 1
Pay Units: N.A.
Programming (via satellite): HBO; Showtime; The Movie Channel.
Fee: $10.00 monthly (each).
Local advertising: No.
Miles of plant: 120.0 (coaxial). Homes passed: 3,500. Total homes in franchised area: 4,000.
Manager: Eldon Isrel.
Ownership: Cable Management Assoc. (MSO).

SOUTH PADRE ISLAND—Time Warner Communications, 2921 S. Expwy. 83, Harlingen, TX 78550-7615. Phone: 956-541-6782. Fax: 956-412-0959. County: Cameron. ICA: TX0855.
TV Market Ranking: Below 100. Franchise award date: N.A. Franchise expiration date: N.A. Began: April 1, 1979.
Channel capacity: 35. Channels available but not in use: 6.
Basic Service
Subscribers: 5,304.
Programming (received off-air): KVEO (N) Brownsville; KGBT-TV (C), KLUJ (E), KMBH (P) Harlingen; KRGV-TV (A) Weslaco; XHAB-TV Matamoros; XHRIO (O) Matamoros-Brownsville.
Programming (via satellite): WGN-TV (W) Chicago; A & E; C-SPAN; CNN; Fox Family Channel; Headline News; Lifetime; MTV; Nashville Network; Nickelodeon; QVC; TBS Superstation; The Weather Channel.
Fee: $60.00 installation; $19.64 monthly.
Expanded Basic Service
Subscribers: 1,188.
Programming (via satellite): CNBC; Discovery Channel; ESPN; Fox Sports Net Southwest; Turner Network TV; USA Network; Univision.
Fee: $1.75 monthly.
Pay Service 1
Pay Units: 168.
Programming (via satellite): Cinemax.
Fee: $10.95 monthly.
Pay Service 2
Pay Units: 61.
Programming (via satellite): Disney Channel.
Fee: $10.95 monthly.
Pay Service 3
Pay Units: 308.
Programming (via satellite): HBO.
Fee: $10.95 monthly.
Pay Service 4
Pay Units: N.A.
Programming (via satellite): The New Encore.
Fee: N.A.
Miles of plant: 26.0 (coaxial).
Manager: Juan Herrera. Chief technician: Al Velasquez.
Ownership: Time Warner Cable (MSO); AT&T Broadband & Internet Services (MSO). Purchased from Tele-Communications Inc., December 31, 1998.

SOUTH SHORES—Cable Ventures, Suite 106-A, 5151 Reed Rd., Columbus, OH 43220. Phone: 614-442-5890. Fax: 614-457-2567. County: Brown. ICA: TX0966.
TV Market Ranking: Outside TV Markets. Franchise award date: N.A. Franchise expiration date: N.A. Began: N.A.
Channel capacity: 23 (2-way capable). Channels available but not in use: 2.
Basic Service
Subscribers: 93.
Programming (received off-air): KIDZ-LP (F) Abilene; KRBC-TV (N), KTAB-TV (C), KTXS-TV (A) Abilene-Sweetwater.
Programming (via satellite): WGN-TV (W) Chicago; A & E; CNN; Discovery Channel; ESPN; Fox Family Channel; Fox News Channel; Lifetime; Nashville Network; TBS Superstation; The Weather Channel; Trinity Bcstg. Network; Turner Network TV; USA Network.
Fee: $29.95 installation; $21.95 monthly.
Pay Service 1
Pay Units: 14.
Programming (via satellite): Cinemax.
Fee: $9.00 monthly.
Pay Service 2
Pay Units: 6.
Programming (via satellite): Disney Channel.
Fee: $7.00 monthly.
Pay Service 3
Pay Units: 20.
Programming (via satellite): HBO.
Fee: $10.00 monthly.
Miles of plant: 5.0 (coaxial). Homes passed: 108.
Manager: Bill Mayes. System/operations manager: Steve Miller.
Ownership: Cable Ventures Ltd. (MSO). Purchased from Rapid Communications Partners LP, June 1, 1998.

SOUTH SILSBEE—Friendship Cable of Texas Inc., Box 9090, Tyler, TX 75711-9090. Phone:

903-581-2121. Fax: 903-581-2185. County: Hardin. ICA: TX0614.
TV Market Ranking: 88. Franchise award date: N.A. Franchise expiration date: N.A. Began: N.A.
Channel capacity: 36 (not 2-way capable). Channels available but not in use: 5.
Basic Service
Subscribers: 101.
Programming (received off-air): KBMT (A), KBTV-TV (N), KFDM-TV (C) Beaumont-Port Arthur; KVHP (F) Lake Charles.
Programming (via satellite): WGN-TV (W) Chicago; A & E; C-SPAN; CNN; Country Music TV; Discovery Channel; Disney Channel; ESPN; Fox Family Channel; Fox Sports Net Southwest; Headline News; Lifetime; Nashville Network; Nickelodeon; QVC; TBS Superstation; The Inspirational Network; The Weather Channel; Turner Network TV; USA Network; VH1.
Fee: $34.65 monthly.
Pay Service 1
Pay Units: 5.
Programming (via satellite): Cinemax.
Fee: $10.95 monthly.
Pay Service 2
Pay Units: 6.
Programming (via satellite): HBO.
Fee: $10.95 monthly.
Pay Service 3
Pay Units: 9.
Programming (via satellite): Showtime.
Fee: $5.95 monthly.
Local advertising: Yes.
Miles of plant: 10.7 (coaxial). Homes passed: 225.
Manager: Wanda Pyburn. Chief technician: Mike Deal.
Ownership: Buford Television Inc. (MSO). See Cable System Ownership.

SOUTH WEATHERFORD—Charter Communications Inc., 4528 W. Vickery St., Fort Worth, TX 76107. Phone: 817-737-4731. Fax: 817-738-7472. County: Parker. ICA: TX0455.
TV Market Ranking: 12. Franchise award date: N.A. Franchise expiration date: N.A. Began: November 1, 1989.
Channel capacity: 36. Channels available but not in use: 8.
Basic Service
Subscribers: N.A.
Programming (received off-air): KDAF (W), KDFI-TV (I), KDFW (F), KDTX-TV (T), KERA-TV (P), KTVT (C), KTXA (U), KXAS-TV (N), KXTX-TV (I), WFAA-TV (A) Dallas-Fort Worth; KDTN (P) Denton; KHSX-TV (H) Irving.
Programming (via satellite): WGN-TV (W) Chicago; A & E; C-SPAN; CNN; Comedy Central; Country Music TV; Discovery Channel; ESPN; Home Shopping Network; MTV; TBS Superstation; The Inspirational Network; The Weather Channel.
Fee: $99.95 installation; $19.95 monthly.
Pay Service 1
Pay Units: N.A.
Programming (via satellite): Disney Channel; HBO.
Fee: $9.95 monthly (each).
Miles of plant: 25.0 (coaxial). Homes passed: 600.
Ownership: Charter Communications Inc. (MSO). Purchased from Marcus Cable, April 1, 1999.

SPEARMAN—Classic Cable, Box 429, 605 N.W. 3rd St., Plainville, KS 67663-0429. Phones: 785-434-7620; 800-999-8876. Fax: 785-434-2614. County: Hansford. ICA: TX0298.
TV Market Ranking: Outside TV Markets. Franchise award date: December 8, 1985. Franchise expiration date: N.A. Began: September 1, 1960.
Channel capacity: 61 (2-way capable; operating 2-way). Channels available but not in use: N.A.
Basic Service
Subscribers: 1,028; Commercial subscribers: 99.
Programming (received off-air): KAMR-TV (N), KCIT (F,U), KFDA-TV (C), KVII-TV (A) Amarillo; 17 FMs.
Programming (via translator): KETA (P) Oklahoma City.
Programming (via satellite): WGN-TV (W) Chicago; A & E; American Movie Classics; Animal Planet; CNN; Country Music TV; Court TV; Discovery Channel; Disney Channel; E! Entertainment TV; ESPN; Fox Family Channel; Fox News Channel; Fox Sports Net Southwest; Headline News; Learning Channel; Lifetime; Nashville Network; Nick at Nite's TV Land; QVC; Sci-Fi Channel; TBS Superstation; The Inspirational Network; The Weather Channel; Travel Channel; Trinity Bcstg. Network; Turner Network TV; USA Network; Univision.
Current originations: Automated timeweather; leased access; local news.
Fee: $35.00 installation; $29.95 monthly; $15.00 additional installation.
Pay Service 1
Pay Units: 66.
Programming (via satellite): The Movie Channel.
Fee: $5.95 monthly.
Pay Service 2
Pay Units: 27.
Programming (via satellite): Cinemax.
Fee: $9.95 monthly.
Pay Service 3
Pay Units: 65.
Programming (via satellite): Showtime.
Fee: $9.95 monthly.
Pay Service 4
Pay Units: 107.
Programming (via satellite): HBO.
Fee: $10.95 monthly.
Local advertising: Yes. Available in locally originated & character-generated programming. Rates: $40.00/Month; $10.00/Week; $2.00/Day.
Equipment: Jerrold headend; Jerrold amplifiers; Times Fiber & Jerrold cable; Beston character generator; Jerrold set top converters; Microdyne satellite receivers.
Miles of plant: 20.0 (coaxial). Homes passed: 1,124. Total homes in franchised area: 1,300.
Manager: Bill Flowers. Chief technician: Rick Rattan. Marketing director: Jennifer Hauschild.
City fee: 2% of gross.
Ownership: Classic Cable (MSO).

SPICEWOOD BEACH—Post Cablevision of Texas Ltd., Drawer 829, 1108 Parker St., Goldthwaite, TX 76844. Phone: 915-648-3041. County: Burnet. ICA: TX0633.
TV Market Ranking: Below 100. Franchise award date: N.A. Franchise expiration date: January 1, 2004. Began: December 1, 1984.
Channel capacity: 22. Channels available but not in use: 1.
Basic Service
Subscribers: N.A.
Programming (received off-air): KEYE-TV (C), KLRU (P), KTBC (F), KVUE-TV (A), KXAN-TV (N) Austin.
Programming (via satellite): WGN-TV (W) Chicago; A & E; CNN; Country Music TV; Discovery Channel; ESPN; Fox Family Channel; Nashville Network; Nickelodeon; QVC; TBS Superstation; USA Network.
Fee: $25.00 installation; $17.88 monthly.
Pay Service 1
Pay Units: N.A.
Programming (via satellite): Disney Channel; HBO.
Fee: $7.44 monthly (Disney), $10.63 monthly (HBO).
Equipment: Triple Crown headend; Times Fiber cable; M/A-Com satellite antenna; Anderson satellite receivers.
Miles of plant: 3.7 (coaxial). Homes passed: 206. Total homes in franchised area: 206.
Manager: Denise Casbeer. Chief technician: Jerry Stembridge.
City fee: 2% of gross.
Ownership: Fanch Communications Inc. (MSO). See Cable System Ownership.

SPLENDORA—Friendship Cable of Texas Inc., Box 9090, Tyler, TX 75711-9090. Phone: 903-581-2121. Fax: 903-581-2185. Counties: Liberty & Montgomery. Also serves Firetower Road. ICA: TX0372.
TV Market Ranking: 15. Franchise award date: N.A. Franchise expiration date: N.A. Began: N.A.
Channel capacity: 36. Channels available but not in use: 1.
Basic Service
Subscribers: 1,002.
Programming (received off-air): KHOU-TV (C), KHTV (W), KPRC-TV (N), KRIV (F), KTRK-TV (A), KTXH (U), KUHT (P) Houston.
Programming (via satellite): A & E; C-SPAN; CNN; Country Music TV; Discovery Channel; Disney Channel; ESPN; Fox Family Channel; Fox Sports Net Southwest; Headline News; Lifetime; Nashville Network; Nickelodeon; QVC; TBS Superstation; The Inspirational Network; The Weather Channel; Turner Network TV; USA Network.
Fee: $34.95 monthly.
Pay Service 1
Pay Units: 51.
Programming (via satellite): Cinemax.
Fee: $10.95 monthly.
Pay Service 2
Pay Units: 69.
Programming (via satellite): HBO.
Fee: $10.95 monthly.
Pay Service 3
Pay Units: 149.
Programming (via satellite): Showtime.
Fee: $5.95 monthly.
Local advertising: Yes.
Miles of plant: 99.9 (coaxial). Homes passed: 2,130.
Manager: Wanda Pyburn. Chief technician: David Burrell.
Ownership: Buford Television Inc. (MSO). See Cable System Ownership.

SPRING—Cablevision Communications, Suite 122, 27326 Robinson Rd., Conroe, TX 77385-8930. Phone: 713-367-8900. Counties: Harris & Montgomery. Also serves Fox Run, Gleneagles, Oak Ridge North, Rayford Forest, Shenandoah, Spring Forest, Spring Hills, Spring Oaks, Timber Ridge, Vicksburg, Woodloch. ICA: TX0044.
TV Market Ranking: 15. Franchise award date: N.A. Franchise expiration date: N.A. Began: January 1, 1979.
Channel capacity: 55 (2-way capable; operating 2-way). Channels available but not in use: N.A.
Basic Service
Subscribers: 13,657; Commercial subscribers: 526.
Programming (received off-air): KHSH-TV (H) Alvin; KPXB (X) Conroe; KTMD (O) Galveston; KETH (E), KHOU-TV (C), KHTV (W), KPRC-TV (N), KRIV (F), KTRK-TV (A), KTXH (U), KUHT (P), KZJL (I) Houston; KNWS-TV (I) Katy; KXLN-TV (S) Rosenberg.
Programming (via satellite): WGN-TV (W) Chicago; Fox Family Channel; TBS Superstation.
Fee: $28.00 installation; $13.25 monthly; $3.65 converter.
Commercial fee: $28.90 monthly.
Expanded Basic Service
Subscribers: 13,257.
Programming (via satellite): A & E; American Movie Classics; BET; C-SPAN; CNBC; CNN; Cartoon Network; Country Music TV; Discovery Channel; Disney Channel; E! Entertainment TV; ESPN; ESPN 2; FX; Fox Sports Net Southwest; Headline News; History Channel; Learning Channel; Lifetime; MTV; Nashville Network; Nick at Nite's TV Land; Nickelodeon; QVC; The Weather Channel; Turner Network TV; USA Network.
Fee: $20.97 installation; $15.65 monthly.
Pay Service 1
Pay Units: 2,783.
Programming (via satellite): HBO (multiplexed).
Fee: $8.00 monthly.
Pay Service 2
Pay Units: 1,547.
Programming (via satellite): The Movie Channel.
Fee: $8.00 monthly.
Pay Service 3
Pay Units: 2,034.
Programming (via satellite): Showtime.
Fee: $8.00 monthly.
Pay Service 4
Pay Units: 478.
Programming (via satellite): Cinemax.
Fee: $8.00 monthly.
Pay-Per-View
Addressable homes: 4,200.
Spice.
Fee: $3.95.
Local advertising: Yes. Available in satellite distributed programming.
Equipment: Scientific-Atlanta headend; Magnavox amplifiers; Times Fiber cable; MSI character generator; Standard Electronics set top converters; Jerrold addressable set top converters; Eagle traps; Scientific-Atlanta satellite antenna; Scientific-Atlanta satellite receivers.
Miles of plant: 415.0 (coaxial). Homes passed: 29,980.
City fee: 3% of gross.
Ownership: Rifkin & Associates Inc. (MSO). Purchased from American Cable Entertainment, February 1, 1999.

SPRINGTOWN—Southwest Cablevision, Box 869, 2804-B FM 51 S, Decatur, TX 76234. Phone: 817-627-3099. Fax: 817-627-8303. County: Parker. ICA: TX0390.
TV Market Ranking: 12. Franchise award date: September 1, 1983. Franchise expiration date: N.A. Began: September 1, 1983.
Channel capacity: 38 (not 2-way capable). Channels available but not in use: N.A.
Basic Service
Subscribers: 319.
Programming (received off-air): KDAF (W), KDFI-TV (I), KDFW (F), KDTX-TV (T), KERA-TV (P), KTVT (C), KTXA (U), KXAS-TV (N), KXTX-TV (I), WFAA-TV (A) Dallas-Fort Worth; KDTN (P) Denton.
Fee: $55.00 installation; $20.95 monthly; $2.45 converter.
Expanded Basic Service
Subscribers: 313.
Programming (via satellite): WGN-TV (W) Chicago; A & E; American Movie Classics;

C-SPAN; CNBC; CNN; Country Music TV; Discovery Channel; ESPN; Fox Family Channel; Fox Sports Net Southwest; Goodlife TV Network; Headline News; MTV; Nashville Network; Nickelodeon; QVC; TBS Superstation; The Weather Channel; Turner Network TV; USA Network.
Fee: N.A.

Pay Service 1
Pay Units: 188.
Programming (via satellite): Cinemax; Disney Channel; HBO.
Fee: $20.00 installation; $8.95 monthly (Disney), $9.95 monthly (Cinemax), $11.95 monthly (HBO).

Local advertising: No.
Miles of plant: 43.9 (coaxial). Homes passed: 850.
Manager: Danny Neumann. Chief technician: Harley Hill. Marketing director: Kathy Shull.
City fee: 4% of gross.
Ownership: James Cable Partners (MSO).

SPUR—Classic Cable, Box 429, 605 N.W. 3rd St., Plainville, KS 67663-0429. Phones: 785-434-7620; 800-999-8876. Fax: 785-434-2614. County: Dickens. ICA: TX0358.
TV Market Ranking: Outside TV Markets. Franchise award date: February 2, 1965. Franchise expiration date: August 1, 1997. Began: December 6, 1965.
Channel capacity: 41 (2-way capable; operating 2-way). Channels available but not in use: N.A.

Basic Service
Subscribers: 421; Commercial subscribers: 17.
Programming (received off-air): KAMC (A), KCBD-TV (N), KJTV (F), KLBK-TV (C), KTXT-TV (P) Lubbock; 1 FM.
Programming (via satellite): WGN-TV (W) Chicago; American Movie Classics; Animal Planet; CNN; Cartoon Network; Country Music TV; Discovery Channel; Disney Channel; E! Entertainment TV; ESPN; Fox Family Channel; Fox News Channel; Fox Sports Net Southwest; Headline News; History Channel; Learning Channel; Lifetime; Nashville Network; Nick at Nite's TV Land; Nickelodeon; QVC; Sci-Fi Channel; TBS Superstation; The Weather Channel; Trinity Bcstg. Network; Turner Network TV; USA Network; Univision.
Current originations: Automated time-weather.
Fee: $35.00 installation; $28.95 monthly.

Pay Service 1
Pay Units: 34.
Programming (via satellite): Cinemax.
Fee: $9.95 monthly.

Pay Service 2
Pay Units: 55.
Programming (via satellite): HBO.
Fee: $9.95 monthly.

Local advertising: Yes. Rates: $2.00/Day.
Equipment: Scientific-Atlanta & Tocom headend; Tocom amplifiers; Vikoa cable; Sony cameras; Comtech satellite antenna.
Miles of plant: 13.7 (coaxial). Homes passed: 758. Total homes in franchised area: 1,025.
Manager: Bill Flowers. Chief technician: Chris Christenson. Marketing director: Jennifer Hauschild.
City fee: 2% of gross.
Ownership: Classic Cable (MSO).

ST. FRANCIS VILLAGE—Torrence Cablevision, Box 1167, Ridgeland, MS 39158. Phones: 601-981-6900; 800-977-8849. County: Tarrant. ICA: TX0544.
TV Market Ranking: 12. Franchise award date: N.A. Franchise expiration date: N.A. Began: N.A.
Channel capacity: 35. Channels available but not in use: 17.

Basic Service
Subscribers: 98.
Programming (received off-air): KDFW (F), KERA-TV (P), KXAS-TV (N), WFAA-TV (A) Dallas-Fort Worth.
Programming (via satellite): WGN-TV (W) Chicago; A & E; American Movie Classics; CNN; Country Music TV; Discovery Channel; ESPN; EWTN; Fox Family Channel; Showtime; TBS Superstation; USA Network.
Fee: $19.00 monthly.

Pay Service 1
Pay Units: 4.
Programming (via satellite): Cinemax.
Fee: $10.95 monthly.

Pay Service 2
Pay Units: 3.
Programming (via satellite): HBO.
Fee: $10.95 monthly.

Local advertising: No.
Homes passed: 357.
Ownership: Torrence Cable Inc. (MSO).

ST. JO—Classic Cable, Box 429, 605 N.W. 3rd St., Plainville, KS 67663-0429. Phones: 785-434-7620; 800-999-8876. Fax: 785-434-2614. County: Montague. ICA: TX0571.
TV Market Ranking: Outside TV Markets. Franchise award date: N.A. Franchise expiration date: N.A. Began: July 1, 1984.
Channel capacity: 36 (2-way capable; operating 2-way). Channels available but not in use: N.A.

Basic Service
Subscribers: 184.
Programming (received off-air): KDAF (W), KDFI-TV (I), KDFW (F), KERA-TV (P), KTVT (C), KTXA (U), KXAS-TV (N), KXTX-TV (I), WFAA-TV (A) Dallas-Fort Worth; KXII (C) Sherman; KAUZ-TV (C), KFDX-TV (N), KJTL (F,U), KSWO-TV (A) Wichita Falls-Lawton.
Programming (via satellite): CNN; Country Music TV; Discovery Channel; Disney Channel; E! Entertainment TV; ESPN; Fox Family Channel; Fox Sports Net Southwest; Home & Garden Television; Nashville Network; Nick at Nite's TV Land; Outdoor Channel; QVC; Sci-Fi Channel; TBS Superstation; The Weather Channel; Turner Classic Movies; Turner Network TV.
Current originations: Local news.
Fee: $35.00 installation; $27.95 monthly.

Pay Service 1
Pay Units: 19.
Programming (via satellite): Cinemax.
Fee: $9.95 monthly.

Pay Service 2
Pay Units: 26.
Programming (via satellite): HBO.
Fee: $9.95 monthly.

Local advertising: Yes. Available in character-generated programming. Rates: $5.00/Day.
Equipment: Cadco & ISS headend; Scientific-Atlanta amplifiers; Comm/Scope cable; Drake satellite receivers.
Miles of plant: 10.0 (coaxial). Homes passed: 321.
Manager: Dave Walker. Chief technician: Roger Campbell. Marketing director: Jennifer Hauschild.
City fee: 3% of gross.
Ownership: Classic Cable (MSO).

STAMFORD—Harmon Cable Communications, Box 1146, 127 E. McHarg, Stamford, TX 79553. Phone: 915-773-3391. Fax: 915-773-2753. County: Jones. ICA: TX0247.
TV Market Ranking: Below 100. Franchise award date: N.A. Franchise expiration date: N.A. Began: April 1, 1961.
Channel capacity: 36 (not 2-way capable). Channels available but not in use: 10.

Basic Service
Subscribers: 1,127.
Programming (received off-air): KIDZ-LP (F) Abilene; KRBC-TV (N), KTAB-TV (C), KTXS-TV (A) Abilene-Sweetwater.
Programming (via satellite): WGN-TV (W) Chicago; C-SPAN; Fox Family Channel; QVC; TBS Superstation.
Current originations: Automated time-weather.
Fee: $35.00 installation; $9.30 monthly.

Expanded Basic Service
Subscribers: N.A.
Programming (via satellite): A & E; American Movie Classics; Animal Planet; CNN; Comedy Central; Country Music TV; Discovery Channel; Disney Channel; E! Entertainment TV; ESPN; ESPN 2; Fox Sports Net Southwest; Headline News; History Channel; Home & Garden Television; Home Shopping Network; Learning Channel; Lifetime; MSNBC; MTV; Nashville Network; Nick at Nite's TV Land; Nickelodeon; Sci-Fi Channel; The Weather Channel; Trinity Bcstg. Network; Turner Classic Movies; Turner Network TV; USA Network; Univision.
Fee: $16.75 monthly.

Pay Service 1
Pay Units: N.A.
Programming (via satellite): Cinemax; HBO; Showtime; The New Encore.
Fee: $35.00 installation; $3.95 monthly (The New Encore), $9.95 monthly (Cinemax, HBO or Showtime).

Equipment: Jerrold headend; Texscan amplifiers; Jerrold cable; Jerrold & Scientific-Atlanta set top converters; Arcom & Eagle traps; AFC satellite antenna; Harris & Scientific-Atlanta satellite receivers.
Miles of plant: 20.0 (coaxial). Homes passed: 1,747. Total homes in franchised area: 2,000.
Manager: L. R. Cagle.
City fee: 2% of basic.
Ownership: Fanch Communications Inc. (MSO); Time Warner Cable (MSO). Purchased from Harmon Cable Communications, June 21, 1999.

STANTON—Cablecomm, Box 685, 1325 Westpoint, Colorado City, TX 79512. Phones: 915-728-3600; 800-874-6190. County: Martin. ICA: TX0350.
TV Market Ranking: Below 100. Franchise award date: March 7, 1978. Franchise expiration date: N.A. Began: December 15, 1978.
Channel capacity: 36 (not 2-way capable). Channels available but not in use: 6.

Basic Service
Subscribers: 657; Commercial subscribers: 2.
Programming (received off-air): KWAB-TV (N) Big Spring; KMID (A), KMLM (I), KOCV-TV (P), KOSA-TV (C), KPEJ (F), KWES-TV (N) Odessa-Midland.
Programming (via satellite): WGN-TV (W) Chicago; Home Shopping Network; TBS Superstation.
Fee: $42.10 installation; $13.60 monthly; $1.85 converter.

Expanded Basic Service
Subscribers: 653.
Programming (via satellite): American Movie Classics; C-SPAN; CNN; Discovery Channel; Disney Channel; ESPN; Fox Family Channel; Fox Sports Net Southwest; Nashville Network; Nickelodeon; Odyssey; The Weather Channel; Turner Network TV; USA Network; Univision.
Fee: $20.00 installation; $3.40 monthly.

Pay Service 1
Pay Units: 64.
Programming (via satellite): Cinemax.
Fee: $20.00 installation; $9.00 monthly.

Pay Service 2
Pay Units: 115.
Programming (via satellite): HBO.
Fee: $20.00 installation; $9.00 monthly.

Local advertising: Yes.
Program Guide: Premium Channels.
Equipment: Tocom & Scientific-Atlanta headend; GTE Sylvania amplifiers; CCS Hatfield cable; Texscan character generator; Scientific-Atlanta set top converters; Eagle & Intercept traps; Scientific-Atlanta satellite antenna; Automation Techniques & Microdyne satellite receivers.
Miles of plant: 18.0 (coaxial). Homes passed: 1,046. Total homes in franchised area: 1,046.
Manager: Rex Thackerson. Chief technician: Gary Redwine. Marketing director: Cynthia Odlozil.
City fee: 3% of gross.
Ownership: Fanch Communications Inc. (MSO); Time Warner Cable (MSO). See Cable System Ownership.

STEPHENVILLE—Northland Cable TV, Box 70, 975 N. Lillian St., Stephenville, TX 76401. Phone: 254-968-4189. Fax: 254-968-8350. County: Erath. ICA: TX0098.
TV Market Ranking: Outside TV Markets. Franchise award date: N.A. Franchise expiration date: September 1, 1998. Began: July 15, 1967.
Channel capacity: 53 (not 2-way capable). Channels available but not in use: N.A.

Basic Service
Subscribers: 4,806.
Programming (received off-air): KDAF (W), KDFI-TV (I), KDFW (F), KERA-TV (P), KTVT (C), KTXA (U), KXAS-TV (N), KXTX-TV (I), WFAA-TV (A) Dallas-Fort Worth; KWTX-TV (C) Waco-Temple; allband FM.
Programming (via satellite): C-SPAN; QVC; TBS Superstation.
Current originations: Automated time-weather; automated emergency alert.
Fee: $34.95 installation; $17.32 monthly.
Commercial fee: $5.32 monthly.

Expanded Basic Service
Subscribers: N.A.
Programming (via satellite): A & E; CNN; Discovery Channel; ESPN; Fox Family Channel; Fox News Channel; Great American Country; Headline News; Nashville Network; TV Guide Channel; The Weather Channel; Trinity Bcstg. Network; Turner Network TV; USA Network; Univision.
Fee: $28.31 monthly.

Expanded Basic Service 2
Subscribers: N.A.
Programming (via satellite): American Movie Classics; CNNfn; Cartoon Network; ESPN 2; Fox Sports Net Southwest; History Channel; Home & Garden Television; Lifetime; MTV; Nickelodeon; Travel Channel; Turner Classic Movies.
Fee: $10.77 monthly.

Pay Service 1
Pay Units: 360.
Programming (via satellite): Cinemax.
Fee: $10.38 monthly.

Pay Service 2
Pay Units: 100.
Programming (via satellite): Disney Channel.

Fee: $8.12 monthly.

Pay Service 3

Pay Units: 445.

Programming (via satellite): HBO.

Fee: $12.45 monthly.

Pay Service 4

Pay Units: 420.

Programming (via satellite): The Movie Channel.

Fee: $11.31 monthly.

Pay Service 5

Pay Units: 40.

Programming (via satellite): Showtime.

Fee: $11.31 monthly.

Pay Service 6

Pay Units: N.A.

Programming (via satellite): Starz!; The New Encore.

Fee: $4.85 monthly (each).

Local advertising: Yes. Available in character-generated programming. Rates: $25.00/Week. Local sales manager: Debra Hoover.

Equipment: Scientific-Atlanta headend; Scientific-Atlanta amplifiers; Times Fiber cable; Scientific-Atlanta set top converters; Eagle traps; Scientific-Atlanta satellite antenna; Scientific-Atlanta & Standard Communications satellite receivers.

Miles of plant: 80.0 (coaxial). Homes passed: 7,200. Total homes in franchised area: 7,600.

Manager: Carroll Lee. Chief technician: Greg Perry.

City fee: 3% of gross.

Ownership: Northland Communications Corp. (MSO).

STERLING CITY—Classic Cable, Box 429, 605 N.W. 3rd St., Plainville, KS 67663-0429. Phones: 785-434-7620; 800-999-8876. Fax: 785-434-2614. County: Sterling. ICA: TX0856.

TV Market Ranking: Outside TV Markets. Franchise award date: N.A. Franchise expiration date: N.A. Began: N.A.

Channel capacity: 22 (2-way capable; operating 2-way). Channels available but not in use: N.A.

Basic Service

Subscribers: 280.

Programming (received off-air): KTXS-TV (A) Abilene-Sweetwater; KACB-TV (N), KIDY (F), KLST (C) San Angelo.

Programming (via satellite): American Movie Classics; Animal Planet; CNN; Cartoon Network; Country Music TV; Discovery Channel; Disney Channel; E! Entertainment TV; ESPN; Fox Family Channel; Fox Sports Net Southwest; Headline News; Learning Channel; Lifetime; Nashville Network; Nick at Nite's TV Land; QVC; Sci-Fi Channel; TBS Superstation; The Weather Channel; Trinity Bcstg. Network; Turner Network TV; USA Network; Univision.

Fee: $35.00 installation; $26.95 monthly.

Pay Service 1

Pay Units: 19.

Programming (via satellite): Showtime.

Fee: $9.95 monthly.

Pay Service 2

Pay Units: 83.

Programming (via satellite): HBO.

Fee: $9.95 monthly.

Miles of plant: 200.0 (coaxial). Homes passed: 419.

Manager: Bill Flowers. Chief technician: Ben Hernandez. Marketing director: Jennifer Hauschild.

Ownership: Classic Cable (MSO).

STOCKDALE—TCI Cablevision of Texas Inc., 1239 E. College St., Seguin, TX 78155-3995. Phone: 830-379-1505. Fax: 512-396-4664. County: Wilson. Also serves Wilson County. ICA: TX0600.

TV Market Ranking: 45 (Stockdale, portions of Wilson County); Outside TV Markets (portions of Wilson County). Franchise award date: N.A. Franchise expiration date: N.A. Began: December 1, 1982.

Channel capacity: 54 (not 2-way capable). Channels available but not in use: 25.

Basic Service

Subscribers: 218.

Programming (received off-air): KRRT (W) Kerrville-San Antonio; KABB (F), KENS-TV (C), KLRN (P), KMOL-TV (N), KSAT-TV (A), KWEX-TV (S) San Antonio.

Programming (via satellite): WGN-TV (W) Chicago; CNN; Discovery Channel; ESPN; Headline News; Lifetime; Nashville Network; Nickelodeon; TBS Superstation; Turner Network TV; USA Network.

Fee: $10.60 monthly.

Pay Service 1

Pay Units: 28.

Programming (via satellite): HBO.

Fee: $11.00 monthly.

Pay Service 2

Pay Units: 18.

Programming (via satellite): The Movie Channel.

Fee: $9.00 monthly.

Pay Service 3

Pay Units: 32.

Programming (via satellite): Showtime.

Fee: $6.00 monthly.

Pay Service 4

Pay Units: 19.

Programming (via satellite): Disney Channel.

Fee: N.A.

Pay-Per-View

Addressable homes: 1.

Miles of plant: 10.0 (coaxial); None (fiber optic). Homes passed: 243.

Manager: Dennis Moore. Chief technician: Greg Krueger. Marketing director: Vicki Triplett.

Ownership: AT&T Broadband & Internet Services (MSO). Purchased from Tele-Communications Inc., March 9, 1999.

STONEBRIDGE RANCH—TCI Cablevision of Texas Inc., Box 64, Allen, TX 75002-3425. Phone: 214-727-5723. County: Collin. ICA: TX0857.

TV Market Ranking: 12. Franchise award date: N.A. Franchise expiration date: N.A. Began: July 8, 1988.

Channel capacity: 62. Channels available but not in use: 22.

Basic Service

Subscribers: 1,123.

Programming (received off-air): KDAF (W), KDFI-TV (I), KDFW (F), KERA-TV (P), KTVT (C), KTXA (U), KXAS-TV (N), KXTX-TV (I), WFAA-TV (A) Dallas-Fort Worth; KDTN (P) Denton.

Programming (via satellite): WGN-TV (W) Chicago; A & E; C-SPAN; CNBC; CNN; Cartoon Network; Comedy Central; Discovery Channel; Fox Family Channel; Headline News; Lifetime; MTV; Nashville Network; Nickelodeon; Odyssey; QVC; TBS Superstation; The Weather Channel; Turner Classic Movies; Univision; VH1.

Current originations: Public access; educational access; government access.

Fee: $60.00 installation; $17.95 monthly.

Expanded Basic Service

Subscribers: 540.

Programming (via satellite): American Movie Classics; ESPN; Fox Sports Net Southwest; Turner Network TV; USA Network.

Fee: $2.91 monthly.

Pay Service 1

Pay Units: 50.

Programming (via satellite): Cinemax.

Fee: N.A.

Pay Service 2

Pay Units: 60.

Programming (via satellite): Disney Channel.

Fee: N.A.

Pay Service 3

Pay Units: 132.

Programming (via satellite): The New Encore.

Fee: N.A.

Pay Service 4

Pay Units: 165.

Programming (via satellite): HBO.

Fee: N.A.

Pay Service 5

Pay Units: 79.

Programming (via satellite): Showtime.

Fee: N.A.

Pay Service 6

Pay Units: 8.

Programming (via satellite): The Movie Channel.

Fee: N.A.

Miles of plant: 20.0 (coaxial).

Manager: Joann Holtzclaw. Chief technician: Mike Crain.

Ownership: AT&T Broadband & Internet Services (MSO). Purchased from Tele-Communications Inc., March 9, 1999.

STRATFORD—Classic Cable, Box 429, 605 N.W. 3rd St., Plainville, KS 67663-0429. Phones: 785-434-7620; 800-999-8876. Fax: 785-434-2614. County: Sherman. ICA: TX0404.

TV Market Ranking: Outside TV Markets. Franchise award date: N.A. Franchise expiration date: December 16, 2001. Began: April 1, 1963.

Channel capacity: 41 (2-way capable; operating 2-way). Channels available but not in use: N.A.

Basic Service

Subscribers: 623; Commercial subscribers: 8.

Programming (received off-air): KAMR-TV (N), KCIT (F,U), KFDA-TV (C), KVII-TV (A) Amarillo; KETA (P) Oklahoma City.

Programming (via satellite): WGN-TV (W) Chicago; A & E; American Movie Classics; Animal Planet; C-SPAN; CNN; Country Music TV; Discovery Channel; Disney Channel; ESPN; Fox Family Channel; Fox News Channel; Headline News; History Channel; Learning Channel; Lifetime; Nashville Network; Nick at Nite's TV Land; Nickelodeon; Odyssey; QVC; Sci-Fi Channel; TBS Superstation; The Weather Channel; Turner Network TV; USA Network; Univision.

Current originations: Educational access; automated emergency alert.

Fee: $35.00 installation; $28.95 monthly; $2.00 converter.

Commercial fee: $24.50 monthly.

Pay Service 1

Pay Units: 51.

Programming (via satellite): The Movie Channel.

Fee: $5.95 monthly.

Pay Service 2

Pay Units: 55.

Programming (via satellite): Showtime.

Fee: $9.95 monthly.

Pay Service 3

Pay Units: 63.

Programming (via satellite): HBO.

Fee: $10.95 monthly.

Equipment: DX Communications headend; Magnavox amplifiers; Times Fiber cable; Standard Components set top converters; Hamlin addressable set top converters; Eagle & Pico traps; AFC & Scientific-Atlanta satellite antenna; DX Communications satellite receivers.

Miles of plant: 19.0 (coaxial). Homes passed: 835.

Manager: Bill Flowers. Chief technician: Rick Rattan. Marketing director: Jennifer Hauschild.

City fee: 2% of gross.

Ownership: Classic Cable (MSO).

STRAWN—Strawn TV Cable Inc., Box 48, Strawn, TX 76475. Phones: 254-672-5296; 254-672-5653. E-mail: talley@ourtown.com. County: Palo Pinto. ICA: TX0596.

TV Market Ranking: Outside TV Markets. Franchise award date: November 10, 1973. Franchise expiration date: June 11, 1998. Began: November 10, 1973.

Channel capacity: 20. Channels available but not in use: None.

Basic Service

Subscribers: 190.

Programming (received off-air): KRBC-TV (N), KTXS-TV (A) Abilene-Sweetwater; KDAF (W), KDFI-TV (I), KDFW (F), KERA-TV (P), KTVT (C), KTXA (U), KXAS-TV (N), KXTX-TV (I), WFAA-TV (A) Dallas-Fort Worth; allband FM.

Programming (via satellite): Discovery Channel; ESPN; Fox Sports Net Southwest; MTV; Nashville Network; Nickelodeon; TBS Superstation.

Fee: $20.00 installation; $15.00 monthly.

Pay Service 1

Pay Units: 21.

Programming (via satellite): Cinemax.

Fee: $5.00 monthly.

Pay Service 2

Pay Units: 22.

Programming (via satellite): HBO.

Fee: $10.00 monthly.

Equipment: Tocom headend; Tocom amplifiers; Tocom cable.

Miles of plant: 10.5 (coaxial); None (fiber optic). Homes passed: 250. Total homes in franchised area: 250.

Manager: Buddy Talley.

City fee: None.

Ownership: Albert A. Talley; J. D. Harrison.

SULLIVAN CITY—Time Warner Communications, 2921 S. Expwy. 83, Harlingen, TX 78550-7615. Phone: 956-541-6782. Fax: 956-412-0959. County: Hidalgo. Also serves La Joya, Penitas. ICA: TX0328.

TV Market Ranking: Below 100. Franchise award date: N.A. Franchise expiration date: N.A. Began: July 1, 1985.

Channel capacity: 35. Channels available but not in use: 5.

Basic Service

Subscribers: 816.

Programming (received off-air): KVEO (N) Brownsville; KGBT-TV (C), KLUJ (E), KMBH (P) Harlingen; KRGV-TV (A) Weslaco; XHAB-TV Matamoros.

Programming (via satellite): WGN-TV (W) Chicago; A & E; C-SPAN; CNN; Fox Family Channel; Headline News; Lifetime; MTV; Nashville Network; Nickelodeon; QVC; TBS Superstation; Telemundo; The Weather Channel.

Current originations: Educational access; local news.

Fee: $60.00 installation; $19.64 monthly.

Expanded Basic Service

Subscribers: 802.

Programming (via satellite): CNBC; Discovery Channel; ESPN; Fox Sports Net South-

west; Turner Network TV; USA Network; Univision.
Fee: $1.75 monthly.
Pay Service 1
Pay Units: 81.
Programming (via satellite): Cinemax.
Fee: $10.95 monthly.
Pay Service 2
Pay Units: 31.
Programming (via satellite): Disney Channel.
Fee: $10.95 monthly.
Pay Service 3
Pay Units: 151.
Programming (via satellite): HBO.
Fee: $10.95 monthly.
Pay Service 4
Pay Units: N.A.
Programming (via satellite): The New Encore.
Fee: N.A.
Miles of plant: 34.7 (coaxial). Homes passed: 1,150. Total homes in franchised area: 1,150.
Manager: Juan Herrera. Chief technician: Al Velasquez.
Ownership: Time Warner Cable (MSO); AT&T Broadband & Internet Services (MSO). Purchased from Tele-Communications Inc. (50%), December 31, 1998.

SULPHUR SPRINGS—TCA Cable TV, 220 Linda Dr., Sulphur Springs, TX 75482-4355. Phone: 903-885-3757.
Web site: http://www.tca-cable.com.
County: Hopkins. Also serves Hopkins County. ICA: TX0859.
TV Market Ranking: Outside TV Markets. Franchise award date: N.A. Franchise expiration date: N.A. Began: June 1, 1954.
Channel capacity: 35. Channels available but not in use: N.A.
Basic Service
Subscribers: 5,956.
Programming (received off-air): KDFW (F), KERA-TV (P), KTVT (C), KXAS-TV (N), KXTX-TV (I), WFAA-TV (A) Dallas-Fort Worth; KSLA-TV (C), KTAL-TV (N), KTBS-TV (A) Shreveport-Texarkana; KLTV (A) Tyler-Longview; allband FM.
Planned programming (via satellite): News Plus; TBS Superstation.
Current originations: Automated time-weather; local news.
Fee: $35.00 installation; $10.00 monthly.
Pay Service 1
Pay Units: N.A.
Programming (via satellite): Showtime.
Fee: $25.00 installation; $9.75 monthly.
Local advertising: Yes. Rates: $6.25/Minute; $3.75/30 Seconds. Regional interconnect: Cabletime.
Equipment: C-COR headend; C-COR amplifiers; Scientific-Atlanta satellite antenna.
Miles of plant: 65.4 (coaxial).
Manager: Joe Suggs.
Ownership: TCA Cable TV Inc. (MSO); AT&T Broadband & Internet Services (MSO). See Cable System Ownership.

SUNDOWN—Classic Cable, Box 429, 605 N.W. 3rd St., Plainville, KS 67663-0429. Phones: 785-434-7620; 800-999-8876. Fax: 785-434-2614. County: Hockley. ICA: TX0410.
TV Market Ranking: Below 100. Franchise award date: June 21, 1988. Franchise expiration date: June 21, 2003. Began: January 1, 1979.
Channel capacity: 22 (2-way capable; operating 2-way). Channels available but not in use: N.A.
Basic Service
Subscribers: 268.
Programming (received off-air): KAMC (A), KCBD-TV (N), KJTV (F), KLBK-TV (C), KTXT-TV (P), KUPT-LP (U) Lubbock.
Programming (via satellite): WGN-TV (W) Chicago; CNN; Country Music TV; Discovery Channel; ESPN; Fox Family Channel; Home Shopping Network; Learning Channel; Lifetime; Nashville Network; Nickelodeon; TBS Superstation; The Weather Channel; Turner Network TV; USA Network; Univision.
Current originations: Educational access; local news.
Fee: $35.00 installation; $25.95 monthly.
Pay Service 1
Pay Units: 37.
Programming (via satellite): Cinemax.
Fee: $10.74 monthly.
Pay Service 2
Pay Units: 53.
Programming (via satellite): HBO.
Fee: $11.72 monthly.
Equipment: GTE Sylvania amplifiers; Times Fiber & Belden cable; Scientific-Atlanta set top converters; Eagle traps; Fort Worth Tower satellite antenna; Scientific-Atlanta satellite receivers.
Miles of plant: 8.1 (coaxial). Homes passed: 764.
Manager: Bill Flowers. Chief technician: Chris Christenson. Marketing director: Jennifer Hauschild.
Ownership: Classic Cable (MSO).

SWEENY—Falcon Cable TV, 822 Market St., Portland, TX 78374. Phone: 512-643-8588. Fax: 512-643-3641. County: Brazoria. ICA: TX0246.
TV Market Ranking: Below 100. Franchise award date: N.A. Franchise expiration date: N.A. Began: May 1, 1980.
Channel capacity: 37 (not 2-way capable). Channels available but not in use: 1.
Basic Service
Subscribers: 1,006.
Programming (received off-air): KHOU-TV (C), KHTV (W), KPRC-TV (N), KRIV (F), KTRK-TV (A), KTXH (U), KUHT (P) Houston; KXLN-TV (S) Rosenberg; allband FM.
Programming (via satellite): A & E; Bravo; C-SPAN; CNN; Country Music TV; E! Entertainment TV; ESPN; Fox Family Channel; Fox Sports Net Southwest; Headline News; Home Shopping Network; Lifetime; Nashville Network; Nickelodeon; QVC; Sci-Fi Channel; Travel Channel.
Fee: $30.00 installation; $17.89 monthly.
Expanded Basic Service
Subscribers: 976.
Programming (via satellite): Discovery Channel; The Weather Channel; USA Network.
Fee: $2.26 monthly.
Expanded Basic Service 2
Subscribers: 966.
Programming (via satellite): Disney Channel; TBS Superstation; Turner Network TV.
Fee: $4.45 monthly.
Pay Service 1
Pay Units: 71.
Programming (via satellite): Cinemax.
Fee: $10.95 monthly.
Pay Service 2
Pay Units: 167.
Programming (via satellite): HBO.
Fee: $11.95 monthly.
Pay Service 3
Pay Units: 52.
Programming (via satellite): The Movie Channel.
Fee: $10.95 monthly.
Pay Service 4
Pay Units: 121.
Programming (via satellite): Showtime.
Fee: $10.95 monthly.
Local advertising: Yes. Available in character-generated programming. Regional interconnect: Cabletime.
Equipment: RCA headend; RCA amplifiers; Comm/Scope cable; Tocom & Scientific-Atlanta set top converters; Harris & Prodelin satellite antenna; Harris & Scientific-Atlanta satellite receivers.
Miles of plant: 28.0 (coaxial). Homes passed: 1,868.
Office manager: Jenny Brumley. Chief technician: Mike Kelsch.
Franchise fee: 5% of gross.
Ownership: Falcon Communications LP (MSO), joint venture formed September 30, 1998. See Cable System Ownership.

SWEETWATER—TCA Cable TV, Box 688, 1118 E. Broadway, Sweetwater, TX 79556. Phone: 915-236-6375. Fax: 915-235-3164. Web site: http://www.tca-cable.com. County: Nolan. Also serves Nolan County (northern portion). ICA: TX0108.
TV Market Ranking: Below 100. Franchise award date: April 24, 1962. Franchise expiration date: April 21, 2010. Began: July 1, 1966.
Channel capacity: 42 (2-way capable; operating 2-way). Channels available but not in use: N.A.
Basic Service
Subscribers: 4,111.
Programming (received off-air): KRBC-TV (N), KTAB-TV (C), KTXS-TV (A) Abilene-Sweetwater; KERA-TV (P), KTVT (C), WFAA-TV (A) Dallas-Fort Worth.
Programming (via satellite): American Movie Classics; BET; C-SPAN; C-SPAN 2; Discovery Channel; FX; Headline News; QVC; TBS Superstation; The Weather Channel; Trinity Bcstg. Network; Univision.
Current originations: Automated time-weather.
Fee: $33.66 installation (aerial), $45.00 (underground); $18.03 monthly; $3.00 converter; $16.83 additional installation.
Expanded Basic Service
Subscribers: N.A.
Programming (via satellite): A & E; CNBC; CNN; Comedy Central; Country Music TV; E! Entertainment TV; ESPN; Fox Family Channel; Fox Sports Net Southwest; Goodlife TV Network; Lifetime; MTV; Nashville Network; Nickelodeon; Turner Network TV; USA Network.
Fee: $12.59 monthly.
Pay Service 1
Pay Units: 316.
Programming (via satellite): Cinemax.
Fee: $10.00 installation; $10.95 monthly.
Pay Service 2
Pay Units: 98.
Programming (via satellite): Disney Channel.
Fee: $10.00 installation; $10.95 monthly.
Pay Service 3
Pay Units: 411.
Programming (via satellite): HBO.
Fee: $10.95 monthly.
Pay Service 4
Pay Units: 130.
Programming (via satellite): Showtime.
Fee: $10.95 monthly.
Pay Service 5
Pay Units: N.A.
Programming (via satellite): The New Encore.
Fee: $1.75 monthly.
Local advertising: Yes. Available in character-generated, taped & automated programming.
Equipment: Jerrold headend; Jerrold amplifiers; Times Fiber cable; Compuvid character generator; Jerrold & GTE Sylvania set top converters; Jerrold addressable set top converters; Eagle, Northeast Filter & Pico traps; Andrew & Anixter satellite antenna; Microdyne & Standard Communications satellite receivers; ADS commercial insert.
Miles of plant: 86.7 (coaxial). Homes passed: 6,226. Total homes in franchised area: 6,226.
Manager: Victor Means. Chief technician: Bill Neely.
City fee: 3% of gross.
Ownership: TCA Cable TV Inc. (MSO); AT&T Broadband & Internet Services (MSO). Purchased from Tele-Communications Inc., February 2, 1998. See Cable System Ownership.

TAHOKA—Cablecomm, 320 W. Main St., Brownfield, TX 79316. Phones: 806-637-2313; 800-638-8457. County: Lynn. ICA: TX0322.
TV Market Ranking: Below 100. Franchise award date: April 9, 1979. Franchise expiration date: November 1, 2005. Began: April 9, 1979.
Channel capacity: 35 (not 2-way capable). Channels available but not in use: 8.
Basic Service
Subscribers: 604; Commercial subscribers: 2.
Programming (received off-air): KAMC (A), KCBD-TV (N), KJTV (F), KLBK-TV (C), KTXT-TV (P) Lubbock.
Programming (via satellite): WGN-TV (W) Chicago; Cartoon Network; Discovery Channel; Fox Family Channel; QVC; TBS Superstation.
Current originations: Automated emergency alert.
Fee: $31.10 installation; $10.98 monthly; $1.65 converter.
Expanded Basic Service
Subscribers: 600.
Programming (via satellite): CNN; ESPN; Fox Sports Net Southwest; Goodlife TV Network; Lifetime; MTV; Nashville Network; Nickelodeon; The Weather Channel; Trinity Bcstg. Network; Turner Network TV; USA Network; Univision.
Fee: $20.00 installation; $9.98 monthly.
Pay Service 1
Pay Units: 19.
Programming (via satellite): Disney Channel.
Fee: $20.00 installation; $11.50 monthly.
Pay Service 2
Pay Units: 160.

Programming (via satellite): HBO.
Fee: $20.00 installation; $11.50 monthly.
Pay Service 3
Pay Units: 29.
Programming (via satellite): The Movie Channel.
Fee: $20.00 installation; $11.50 monthly.
Local advertising: Yes. Available in character-generated programming.
Program Guide: Premium Channels.
Equipment: Scientific-Atlanta headend; Scientific-Atlanta amplifiers; Comm/Scope cable; Scientific-Atlanta set top converters; Pico & Eagle traps; Scientific-Atlanta & Hughes satellite antenna; Microdyne & Scientific-Atlanta satellite receivers.
Miles of plant: 19.0 (coaxial). Homes passed: 1,201.
Manager: Rex Thackerson. Chief technician: Gary Strickland. Marketing director: Bill Forgey.
City fee: 5% of gross.
Ownership: Fanch Communications Inc. (MSO); Time Warner Cable (MSO). See Cable System Ownership.

TAYLOR—Cablevision of Taylor, 1905 N. Mays St., Round Rock, TX 78664-2127. Phone: 512-485-5555. County: Williamson. ICA: TX0139.
TV Market Ranking: Below 100. Franchise award date: October 24, 1967. Franchise expiration date: N.A. Began: April 1, 1968.
Channel capacity: 36. Channels available but not in use: 11.
Basic Service
Subscribers: 2,999.
Programming (received off-air): KEYE-TV (C), KLRU (P), KTBC (F), KVUE-TV (A), KXAN-TV (N) Austin; KCEN-TV (N), KWTX-TV (C) Waco-Temple; 1 FM.
Programming (via satellite): CNN; Country Music TV; Discovery Channel; ESPN; Fox Family Channel; Headline News; Learning Channel; Lifetime; MTV; Nashville Network; Nickelodeon; TBS Superstation; The Weather Channel; Turner Network TV; USA Network; Univision.
Fee: $40.00 installation; $16.20 monthly; $2.00 converter; $15.00 additional installation.
Pay Service 1
Pay Units: N.A.
Programming (via satellite): Cinemax; Disney Channel; Fox Sports Net Southwest; HBO.
Fee: $5.00 monthly (Fox Sports), $6.75 monthly (Cinemax) $7.75 monthly (HBO), $7.95 monthly (Disney).
Pay-Per-View
Special events.
Local advertising: Yes (insert only). Available in locally originated programming. Local sales manager: Larry Converse. Regional interconnect: Cabletime.
Equipment: Jerrold & Scientific-Atlanta headend; Jerrold amplifiers; Times Fiber cable; Hamlin set top converters; Scientific-Atlanta addressable set top converters; Eagle traps; Harris satellite antenna; Microdyne & Scientific-Atlanta satellite receivers.
Miles of plant: 75.0 (coaxial). Homes passed: 4,580. Total homes in franchised area: 4,600.
Manager: Todd Bowen. Chief technician: William Memmer. Marketing & program director: Arnold Rivas.
City fee: 3% of gross.
Ownership: Time Warner Cable (MSO).

TEMPLE—Time Warner Cable, Box 928, 15 N. 33rd St., Temple, TX 76501. Phone: 817-778-4201. Fax: 817-771-1199. County: Bell. Also serves Belton. ICA: TX0038.
TV Market Ranking: Below 100. Franchise award date: N.A. Franchise expiration date: N.A. Began: August 10, 1965.
Channel capacity: 36 (2-way capable; operating 2-way). Channels available but not in use: N.A.
Basic Service
Subscribers: 16,514.
Programming (received off-air): KEYE-TV (C), KTBC (F), KXAN-TV (N) Austin; KNCT (P) Belton; KCEN-TV (N), KWKT (F), KWTX-TV (C), KXXV (A) Waco-Temple; 9 FMs.
Programming (via microwave): KTVT (C), WFAA-TV (A) Dallas-Fort Worth.
Current originations: Automated time-weather; leased access.
Fee: $4.95 monthly; $3.50 converter.
Expanded Basic Service
Subscribers: 16,434.
Programming (via satellite): A & E; BET; C-SPAN; CNBC; CNN; Country Music TV; ESPN; Fox Family Channel; Headline News; Lifetime; MTV; Nashville Network; Nickelodeon; Odyssey; QVC; TBS Superstation; The Inspirational Network; The Weather Channel; Turner Classic Movies; Turner Network TV; USA Network; Univision; VH1.
Fee: $32.50 installation; $18.95 monthly.
Pay Service 1
Pay Units: 2,213.
Programming (via satellite): Cinemax.
Fee: $25.00 installation; $9.95 monthly.
Pay Service 2
Pay Units: 1,039.
Programming (via satellite): Disney Channel.
Fee: $25.00 installation; $9.95 monthly.
Pay Service 3
Pay Units: 2,515.
Programming (via satellite): HBO.
Fee: $25.00 installation; $9.95 monthly.
Pay Service 4
Pay Units: 563.
Programming (via satellite): Fox Sports Net Southwest.
Fee: $25.00 installation; $5.95 monthly.
Pay Service 5
Pay Units: 578.
Programming (via satellite): The Movie Channel.
Fee: $25.00 installation; $9.95 monthly.
Pay Service 6
Pay Units: 1,038.
Programming (via satellite): Showtime.
Fee: $25.00 installation; $9.95 monthly.
Pay-Per-View
Viewer's Choice.
Local advertising: Yes (locally produced). Available in satellite distributed programming. Local sales manager: Joe Webb. Regional interconnect: Waco-Temple-Killeen Interconnect.
Equipment: Scientific-Atlanta headend; GTE Sylvania amplifiers; Comm/Scope cable; System Concepts character generator; Scientific-Atlanta set top converters; Scientific-Atlanta addressable set top converters; Scientific-Atlanta satellite antenna; Scientific-Atlanta satellite receivers.
Miles of plant: 324.0 (coaxial). Homes passed: 27,466.
Manager: Don Wright. Chief technician: Wes Ramos. Marketing director: Danny Daniel.
City fee: 5% of gross.
Ownership: Time Warner Cable (MSO); Advance/Newhouse Partnership (MSO).

TEMPLE—Centrovision Inc., Box 3157, Temple, TX 76501. Phone: 817-773-1163. County: Bell. ICA: TX0861.
TV Market Ranking: Below 100. Franchise award date: N.A. Franchise expiration date: N.A. Began: N.A.
Channel capacity: N.A. Channels available but not in use: N.A.
Basic Service
Subscribers: 444.
Programming (received off-air): KEYE-TV (C), KLRU (P), KTBC (F), KVUE-TV (A), KXAN-TV (N) Austin; KNCT (P) Belton; KTVT (C) Dallas-Fort Worth; KCEN-TV (N), KWTX-TV (C), KXXV (A) Waco-Temple.
Programming (via satellite): WGN-TV (W) Chicago; Headline News; TBS Superstation.
Fee: N.A.
Manager: Alton Shepard.
Ownership: Centrovision Inc. (MSO).

TENAHA—Friendship Cable of Texas Inc., Box 9090, Tyler, TX 75711-9090. Phone: 903-581-2121. Fax: 903-561-2185. County: Shelby. ICA: TX0507.
TV Market Ranking: Below 100. Franchise award date: N.A. Franchise expiration date: N.A. Began: May 1, 1984.
Channel capacity: 54. Channels available but not in use: N.A.
Basic Service
Subscribers: 243.
Programming (received off-air): KETK-TV (N) Jacksonville; KTRE (A) Lufkin; KLTS-TV (P), KSLA-TV (C), KTAL-TV (N), KTBS-TV (A) Shreveport-Texarkana.
Programming (via satellite): WGN-TV (W) Chicago; BET; CNN; Discovery Channel; ESPN; Fox Family Channel; Nashville Network; Nickelodeon; TBS Superstation; USA Network.
Fee: $30.00 installation; $30.95 monthly.
Pay Service 1
Pay Units: 22.
Programming (via satellite): Cinemax.
Fee: $7.00 monthly.
Pay Service 2
Pay Units: 11.
Programming (via satellite): HBO.
Fee: $12.00 monthly.
Pay Service 3
Pay Units: 28.
Programming (via satellite): Showtime.
Fee: $7.00 monthly.
Miles of plant: 14.0 (coaxial). Homes passed: 440.
Manager: Marianne Bogy. Chief technician: Henry Harris.
Ownership: Buford Television Inc. (MSO). See Cable System Ownership.

TERRELL—Friendship Cable Ltd., Box 9090, Tyler, TX 75711-9090. Phone: 903-581-2121. Fax: 903-581-2185. Counties: Dallas, Kaufman & Rockwall. Also serves Balch Springs, Dallas County (portions), Forney, Happy Country Homes, Heath, Kaufman County, McClendon-Chisolm, Oak Ridge, Seagoville. ICA: TX0920.
TV Market Ranking: 12 (Balch Springs, Dallas County, Forney, Happy Country Homes, Heath, portions of Kaufman County, McClendon-Chisolm, Oak Ridge, Seagoville, Terrell); Outside TV Markets (portions of Kaufman County). Franchise award date: N.A. Franchise expiration date: N.A. Began: N.A.
Channel capacity: 42. Channels available but not in use: N.A.
Basic Service
Subscribers: 9,063.
Programming (received off-air): KDFW (F), KERA-TV (P), KTVT (C), KXAS-TV (N), KXTX-TV (I), WFAA-TV (A) Dallas-Fort Worth.
Programming (via satellite): WGN-TV (W) Chicago; A & E; American Movie Classics; BET; C-SPAN; CNN; Country Music TV; Discovery Channel; Disney Channel; ESPN; Fox Family Channel; Fox Sports Net Southwest; Headline News; Lifetime; MTV; Nashville Network; Nickelodeon; TBS Superstation; The Weather Channel; Turner Network TV; USA Network.
Fee: $32.20 monthly.
Pay Service 1
Pay Units: 1,483.
Programming (via satellite): Cinemax.
Fee: $11.00 monthly.
Pay Service 2
Pay Units: 2,008.
Programming (via satellite): HBO.
Fee: $11.00 monthly.
Pay Service 3
Pay Units: 2,395.
Programming (via satellite): Showtime.
Fee: $11.00 monthly.
Pay Service 4
Pay Units: 1,223.
Programming (via satellite): The Movie Channel.
Fee: $10.95 monthly.
Pay-Per-View
Addressable homes: 139.
Viewer's Choice.
Local advertising: Yes.
Miles of plant: 353.5 (coaxial). Homes passed: 18,991.
Manager: Rodney Fletcher. Chief technician: Steven Williams.
Ownership: Buford Television Inc. (MSO). See Cable System Ownership.

TEXARKANA—Cable One, 221 Texas Blvd., Texarkana, TX 75501. Phone: 903-794-3426. Fax: 903-792-3919. Counties: Bowie, TX; Miller, AR. Also serves Texarkana, AR; Bowie County, Nash, Wake Village, TX. ICA: TX0031.
TV Market Ranking: 58. Franchise award date: June 1, 1973. Franchise expiration date: February 22, 2002. Began: April 1, 1974.
Channel capacity: 60 (not 2-way capable). Channels available but not in use: None.
Basic Service
Subscribers: 22,879; Commercial subscribers: 3,586.
Programming (received off-air): KETG (P) Arkadelphia; KLFI-LP (I), KMSS-TV (F), KSHV (U,W), KSLA-TV (C), KTAL-TV (N), KTBS-TV (A) Shreveport-Texarkana.
Programming (via microwave): KATV (A) Little Rock.
Programming (via satellite): WGN-TV (W) Chicago; BET; C-SPAN; EWTN; Electronic Program Guide; QVC; TBS Superstation; TV Guide Sneak Prevue; VH1.
Current originations: Automated time-weather; public access; automated emergency alert; local news.
Fee: $20.67 installation; $10.97 monthly; $2.50 converter.
Expanded Basic Service
Subscribers: 21,984.
Programming (via satellite): A & E; American Movie Classics; CNBC; CNN; Comedy Central; Country Music TV; Discovery Channel; Disney Channel; ESPN; ESPN Classic Sports; FX; Fox Family Channel; Fox Sports Net Southwest; Golf Channel; Headline News; Learning Channel; Lifetime; MSNBC; MTV; Nashville Network; Nickelodeon; Sci-Fi Channel; TV Food Network; The Weather Channel; Turner Network TV; USA Network.
Fee: $13.78 monthly.
Expanded Basic Service 2
Subscribers: N.A.
Programming (via satellite): Cartoon Network; Court TV; History Channel; Turner Classic Movies.

Fee: $1.95 monthly.

A la Carte 1

Subscribers: N.A.

Programming (via satellite): Music Choice.

Fee: N.A.

Pay Service 1

Pay Units: 12,000.

Programming (via satellite): Cinemax (multiplexed); Flix; HBO (multiplexed); Showtime (multiplexed); The Movie Channel.

Fee: $8.95 monthly (TMC), $9.95 monthly (Cinemax), $10.95 monthly (Showtime), $11.95 monthly (HBO).

Pay-Per-View

Addressable homes: 8,978.

Action Pay-Per-View; Hot Choice; Spice; Viewer's Choice.

Fee: $2.95-$3.95.

Local advertising: Yes. Available in character-generated & automated programming. Rates: $30.00/Minute; $15.00/30 Seconds.

Equipment: Scientific-Atlanta headend; Magnavox amplifiers; Comm/Scope cable; Sony VTRs; BEI & Video Data Systems character generator; Jerrold addressable set top converters; Harris & Scientific-Atlanta satellite antenna.

Miles of plant: 510.1 (coaxial); 42.0 (fiber optic). Additional miles planned: 23.0 (coaxial). Homes passed: 34,451.

Manager: Jay Butler. Chief technician: John Lanier. Program director: Terri Karam. Marketing director: Sandra Glover.

City fee: 5% of gross.

Ownership: Cable One Inc. (MSO).

TEXHOMA—Texhoma Cable TV, Box 7, Canadian, TX 79014. Phone: 405-423-7583. Counties: Sherman, TX; Texas, OK. Also serves Texhoma, OK. ICA: TX0476.

TV Market Ranking: Outside TV Markets. Franchise award date: N.A. Franchise expiration date: N.A. Began: January 1, 1983.

Channel capacity: 30. Channels available but not in use: N.A.

Basic Service

Subscribers: N.A.

Programming (received off-air): KAMR-TV (N), KFDA-TV (C), KVII-TV (A) Amarillo; KWET (P) Cheyenne.

Programming (via satellite): WGN-TV (W) Chicago; ESPN; Fox Family Channel; Nashville Network; TBS Superstation.

Current originations: Automated time-weather.

Fee: N.A.

Pay Service 1

Pay Units: N.A.

Programming (via satellite): Cinemax; HBO.

Fee: N.A.

Miles of plant: 13.5 (coaxial). Homes passed: 523.

Manager: Lee Tucker.

Ownership: Bob Tips.

TEXLINE—Fanch Communications, Box 563, 501 S. First, Clayton, NM 88415. Phone: 505-374-9312. County: Dallam. ICA: TX0642.

TV Market Ranking: Outside TV Markets. Franchise award date: N.A. Franchise expiration date: N.A. Began: August 1, 1977.

Channel capacity: 12. Channels available but not in use: N.A.

Basic Service

Subscribers: 178; Commercial subscribers: 56.

Programming (received off-air): KAMR-TV (N), KFDA-TV (C), KVII-TV (A) Amarillo.

Programming (via satellite): TBS Superstation; Turner Classic Movies.

Fee: $25.00 installation; $18.85 monthly.

Miles of plant: 7.5 (coaxial). Homes passed: 200.

Manager: Jean Hinds.

Ownership: Fanch Communications Inc. (MSO). See Cable System Ownership.

THE COLONY—TCI Cablevision of Texas Inc., 5200 Hwy. 423, The Colony, TX 75056-2252. Phone: 800-824-0290. Counties: Collin & Denton. Also serves Eastvale, Frisco. ICA: TX0085.

TV Market Ranking: 12. Franchise award date: N.A. Franchise expiration date: N.A. Began: July 1, 1981.

Channel capacity: 41. Channels available but not in use: N.A.

Basic Service

Subscribers: 3,736.

Programming (received off-air): KDAF (W), KDFI-TV (I), KDFW (F), KERA-TV (P), KTVT (C), KTXA (U), KXAS-TV (N), KXTX-TV (I), WFAA-TV (A) Dallas-Fort Worth.

Programming (via satellite): WGN-TV (W) Chicago; A & E; CNBC; CNN; Discovery Channel; Fox Family Channel; Headline News; Lifetime; MTV; Nashville Network; Nickelodeon; Odyssey; TBS Superstation; The Weather Channel.

Current originations: Automated time-weather; government access; local news.

Fee: $60.00 installation; $10.13 monthly; $60.00 additional installation.

Expanded Basic Service

Subscribers: 3,592.

Programming (via satellite): American Movie Classics; ESPN; Fox Sports Net Southwest; Turner Network TV; USA Network.

Fee: $9.50 monthly.

Pay Service 1

Pay Units: 496.

Programming (via satellite): Cinemax.

Fee: $5.00 installation; $8.50 monthly.

Pay Service 2

Pay Units: 516.

Programming (via satellite): Disney Channel.

Fee: $5.00 installation; $8.50 monthly.

Pay Service 3

Pay Units: 1,827.

Programming (via satellite): The New Encore.

Fee: N.A.

Pay Service 4

Pay Units: 1,413.

Programming (via satellite): HBO.

Fee: $5.00 installation; $8.50 monthly.

Pay Service 5

Pay Units: 258.

Programming (via satellite): The Movie Channel.

Fee: $5.00 installation; $10.00 monthly.

Pay Service 6

Pay Units: 692.

Programming (via satellite): Showtime.

Fee: $5.00 installation; $8.50 monthly.

Local advertising: Yes (locally produced & insert). Available in satellite distributed programming.

Program Guide: The Cable Guide.

Equipment: Jerrold headend; Theta-Com amplifiers; Times Fiber cable; Video Data Systems character generator; Jerrold addressable set top converters; Microdyne satellite antenna; Microdyne satellite receivers.

Miles of plant: 92.4 (coaxial). Homes passed: 8,587. Total homes in franchised area: 9,311.

Manager: Larry Bryant. Chief technician: David Cope.

City fee: 5% of gross.

Ownership: AT&T Broadband & Internet Services (MSO). Purchased from Tele-Communications Inc., March 9, 1999.

THE WOODS—Classic Cable, Box 429, 605 N.W. 3rd St., Plainville, KS 67663-0429. Phones: 785-434-7620; 800-999-8876. Fax: 785-434-2614. County: Kerr. ICA: TX0915.

TV Market Ranking: Below 100. Franchise award date: N.A. Franchise expiration date: N.A. Began: N.A.

Channel capacity: 35. Channels available but not in use: 23.

Basic Service

Subscribers: N.A.

Programming (received off-air): KRRT (W) Kerrville-San Antonio; KENS-TV (C), KLRN (P), KMOL-TV (N), KSAT-TV (A) San Antonio.

Programming (via satellite): CNN; Discovery Channel; ESPN; Fox Family Channel; Nashville Network; TBS Superstation.

Fee: $17.95 monthly.

Pay Service 1

Pay Units: N.A.

Programming (via satellite): HBO.

Fee: $10.00 monthly.

Manager: Mark Livingston.

Ownership: Classic Cable (MSO).

THORNDALE—Time Warner Cable, 12012 N. Mo Pac Expressway, Austin, TX 78758-2904. Phone: 512-485-6100. Fax: 512-485-6105. Web site: http://www.timewarneraustin.com. Counties: Milam & Williamson. Also serves Thrall. ICA: TX0391.

TV Market Ranking: Below 100. Franchise award date: September 14, 1994. Franchise expiration date: December 5, 2009. Began: October 1, 1982.

Channel capacity: 60 (not 2-way capable). Channels available but not in use: 21.

Basic Service

Subscribers: 450.

Programming (received off-air): KEYE-TV (C), KLRU (P), KNVA (W), KTBC (F), KVUE-TV (A), KXAN-TV (N) Austin; KCEN-TV (N), KWTX-TV (C), KXXV (A) Waco-Temple.

Programming (via satellite): WGN-TV (W) Chicago; A & E; American Movie Classics; Animal Planet; C-SPAN; CNN; Country Music TV; Discovery Channel; ESPN; ESPN 2; Fox Family Channel; GalaVision; Headline News; History Channel; Home & Garden Television; Learning Channel; Lifetime; MSNBC; MTV; Nashville Network; Nick at Nite; Nickelodeon; Pax Net; TBS Superstation; The Weather Channel; Turner Classic Movies; Turner Network TV; USA Network.

Fee: $28.21 installation; $26.20 monthly; $1.15 converter; $12.11 additional installation.

Pay Service 1

Pay Units: N.A.

Programming (via satellite): HBO; Showtime; The Movie Channel.

Fee: $7.00 monthly (Showtime), $9.00 monthly (TMC), $12.00 monthly (HBO).

Miles of plant: 19.8 (coaxial). Homes passed: 845.

Manager: Bill Carey. Chief technician: Matt Stanek. Program director: George Warmingham. Marketing director: Michelle Golden.

City fee: 3% of gross.

Ownership: Time Warner Cable (MSO); Advance/Newhouse Partnership (MSO).

THORNTON—Thornton Cable TV, Box 131689, Tyler, TX 75713. Phones: 903-581-7047; 800-256-9032. County: Limestone. ICA: TX0592.

TV Market Ranking: Below 100. Franchise award date: N.A. Franchise expiration date: N.A. Began: January 1, 1990.

Channel capacity: 30. Channels available but not in use: 16.

Basic Service

Subscribers: 124.

Programming (received off-air): KCEN-TV (N), KWKT (F), KWTX-TV (C), KXXV (A) Waco-Temple.

Programming (via satellite): WGN-TV (W) Chicago; A & E; Cartoon Network; Country Music TV; Discovery Channel; ESPN; Nashville Network; TBS Superstation; Trinity Bcstg. Network; Turner Network TV; USA Network.

Fee: $25.00 installation; $15.00 monthly.

Pay Service 1

Pay Units: 20.

Programming (via satellite): Cinemax.

Fee: $9.00 monthly.

Pay Service 2

Pay Units: 32.

Programming (via satellite): HBO.

Fee: $9.00 monthly.

Miles of plant: 7.0 (coaxial). Homes passed: 254.

Manager: Nanelle Houston. Chief technician: Greg Houston.

Ownership: Progressive Cable Communications Inc. (MSO).

THREE RIVERS—Falcon Cable TV, 1244 Encino Dr., Pleasanton, TX 78064. Phone: 830-569-5509. Fax: 830-569-4828. County: Live Oak. ICA: TX0401.

TV Market Ranking: Outside TV Markets. Franchise award date: January 1, 1978. Franchise expiration date: N.A. Began: October 1, 1978.

Channel capacity: 23 (not 2-way capable). Channels available but not in use: None.

Basic Service

Subscribers: 510.

Programming (received off-air): KEDT (P), KIII (A), KRIS-TV (N), KZTV (C) Corpus Christi; KRRT (W) Kerrville-San Antonio; KABB (F), KENS-TV (C), KMOL-TV (N), KSAT-TV (A), KWEX-TV (S) San Antonio; allband FM.

Programming (via satellite): ESPN; Fox Family Channel; TBS Superstation; Turner Network TV.

Fee: $15.00 installation; $18.61 monthly; $10.00 additional installation.

Expanded Basic Service

Subscribers: 504.

Programming (via satellite): CNN; Country Music TV; Discovery Channel; Disney Channel; Home Shopping Network; Nashville Network.

Fee: $5.98 monthly.

Pay Service 1

Pay Units: 27.

Programming (via satellite): Cinemax.

Fee: $10.95 monthly.

Pay Service 2

Pay Units: 70.

Programming (via satellite): HBO.

Fee: $11.95 monthly.

Pay Service 3

Pay Units: 84.

Programming (via satellite): Showtime.

Fee: $10.95 monthly.

Local advertising: No.

Equipment: Jerrold headend; Jerrold amplifiers; Times Fiber cable; Eagle & Pico traps; Scientific-Atlanta satellite antenna; M/A-Com & Scientific-Atlanta satellite receivers.

Miles of plant: 15.0 (coaxial). Homes passed: 892.

Manager: Lorna Gentry. Chief technician: Santos Guajardo.

Franchise fee: 3% of gross.

Ownership: Falcon Communications LP (MSO), joint venture formed September 30, 1998. See Cable System Ownership.

THROCKMORTON—Friendship Cable, Box 139400, Tyler, TX 75713. Phone: 800-999-6845. Counties: Throckmorton & Young. Also serves Lake Graham, Newcastle. ICA: TX0511.
TV Market Ranking: Outside TV Markets. Franchise award date: N.A. Franchise expiration date: N.A. Began: January 1, 1982.
Channel capacity: N.A. Channels available but not in use: N.A.
Basic Service
Subscribers: N.A.
Programming (received off-air): KRBC-TV (N) Abilene-Sweetwater; KAUZ-TV (C), KFDX-TV (N), KSWO-TV (A) Wichita Falls-Lawton; 2 FMs.
Programming (via satellite): WGN-TV (W) Chicago; CNN; ESPN; Fox Family Channel; TBS Superstation.
Current originations: Automated time-weather.
Fee: $10.00 installation; $11.00 monthly.
Pay Service 1
Pay Units: N.A.
Programming (via satellite): Disney Channel; HBO; Nashville Network; Nickelodeon; Showtime; The Movie Channel.
Fee: $3.00 monthly (Nashville or Nickelodeon), $10.00 monthly (Showtime or TMC), $12.00 monthly (Disney or HBO).
Local advertising: Yes. Rates: $2.50/Day.
Miles of plant: 14.3 (coaxial).
Manager: Bill Tyler.
City fee: 3% basic gross.
Ownership: TGN Cable.

THUNDERBIRD BAY—Cable Ventures Ltd., Suite 106-A, 5151 Reed Rd., Columbus, OH 43220. Phone: 614-442-5890. Fax: 614-457-2567. County: Brown. Also serves Kirkland Docks. ICA: TX0408.
TV Market Ranking: Outside TV Markets. Franchise award date: N.A. Franchise expiration date: N.A. Began: May 1, 1989.
Channel capacity: 53 (2-way capable). Channels available but not in use: 38.
Basic Service
Subscribers: 168.
Programming (received off-air): KIDZ-LP (F) Abilene; KRBC-TV (N), KTAB-TV (C), KTXS-TV (A) Abilene-Sweetwater.
Programming (via satellite): WGN-TV (W) Chicago; KTLA (W) Los Angeles; Animal Planet; CNN; Discovery Channel; ESPN; Fox Family Channel; Lifetime; Nashville Network; Nickelodeon; TBS Superstation; Turner Network TV.
Fee: $40.00 installation; $29.95 monthly; $2.95 converter.
Pay Service 1
Pay Units: 2.
Programming (via satellite): Cinemax.
Fee: $9.00 monthly.
Pay Service 2
Pay Units: 31.
Programming (via satellite): HBO.
Fee: $10.00 monthly.
Pay Service 3
Pay Units: 2.
Programming (via satellite): Disney Channel.
Fee: $7.00 monthly.
Local advertising: No.
Miles of plant: 18.0 (coaxial). Homes passed: 775.
Manager: Bill Mayes. System/operations manager: Steve Miller.
Ownership: Cable Ventures Ltd. (MSO).

TILDEN—Falcon Cable TV, 1244 Encino Dr., Pleasanton, TX 78064. Phone: 830-569-5509. Fax: 830-569-4828. County: McMullen. ICA: TX0663.
TV Market Ranking: Outside TV Markets. Franchise award date: N.A. Franchise expiration date: N.A. Began: January 1, 1989.
Channel capacity: 37. Channels available but not in use: 19.
Basic Service
Subscribers: 58.
Programming (received off-air): KABB (F), KENS-TV (C), KLRN (P), KMOL-TV (N), KSAT-TV (A), KVDA (O) San Antonio.
Programming (via satellite): WGN-TV (W) Chicago; CNN; Country Music TV; ESPN; Fox Family Channel; GalaVision; QVC.
Fee: $15.00 installation; $20.35 monthly.
Expanded Basic Service
Subscribers: 57.
Programming (via satellite): Discovery Channel; Nashville Network; Sci-Fi Channel; TBS Superstation.
Fee: $4.63 monthly.
Pay Service 1
Pay Units: 30.
Programming (via satellite): HBO.
Fee: $15.00 installation; $11.95 monthly.
Miles of plant: 3.0 (coaxial). Homes passed: 97.
Manager: Lorna Gentry. Chief technician: Santos Guajardo.
Ownership: Falcon Communications LP (MSO), joint venture formed September 30, 1998. See Cable System Ownership.

TIMPSON—Friendship Cable of Texas Inc., Box 9090, Tyler, TX 75711-9090. Phone: 903-581-2121. Fax: 903-581-2185. County: Shelby. ICA: TX0572.
TV Market Ranking: Below 100. Franchise award date: N.A. Franchise expiration date: October 1, 1997. Began: January 1, 1985.
Channel capacity: 54. Channels available but not in use: N.A.
Basic Service
Subscribers: 311.
Programming (received off-air): KTRE (A) Lufkin; KLTS-TV (P), KSLA-TV (C), KTAL-TV (N), KTBS-TV (A) Shreveport-Texarkana.
Programming (via satellite): WGN-TV (W) Chicago; Animal Planet; BET; CNN; Country Music TV; Discovery Channel; E! Entertainment TV; ESPN; Fox Sports Net; Headline News; Home Shopping Network; Lifetime; Nashville Network; Nickelodeon; Outdoor Life Network; TBS Superstation; The Weather Channel; Trinity Bcstg. Network; Turner Classic Movies; Turner Network TV; USA Network.
Fee: $30.00 installation; $31.65 monthly.
Pay Service 1
Pay Units: 23.
Programming (via satellite): Cinemax.
Fee: $7.00 monthly.
Pay Service 2
Pay Units: 18.
Programming (via satellite): HBO.
Fee: $12.00 monthly.
Pay Service 3
Pay Units: 32.
Programming (via satellite): Showtime.
Fee: $7.00 monthly.
Miles of plant: 7.0 (coaxial). Homes passed: 489.
Manager: Marianne Bogey. Chief technician: Henry Harris.
City fee: 3% of gross.
Ownership: Buford Television Inc. (MSO). See Cable System Ownership.

TOLEDO VILLAGE—Friendship Cable of Texas Inc., Box 9090, Tyler, TX 75711-9090. Phone: 903-581-2121. Fax: 903-581-2185. Counties: Newton & Sabine. Also serves Burkeville. ICA: TX0864.
TV Market Ranking: Outside TV Markets. Franchise award date: N.A. Franchise expiration date: N.A. Began: November 1, 1989.
Channel capacity: 36. Channels available but not in use: N.A.
Basic Service
Subscribers: 192.
Programming (received off-air): KLAX-TV (A) Alexandria; KLFY-TV (C) Lafayette; KLTL-TV (P), KPLC-TV (N) Lake Charles.
Programming (via satellite): WXIA-TV (N) Atlanta; WGN-TV (W) Chicago; WABC-TV (A) New York; WRAL-TV (C) Raleigh-Durham; A & E; American Movie Classics; C-SPAN; C-SPAN 2; CNBC; CNN; Country Music TV; Discovery Channel; ESPN; Fox Family Channel; History Channel; Learning Channel; Nashville Network; QVC; TBS Superstation; The Weather Channel; Turner Network TV; USA Network.
Fee: $30.00 installation; $29.95 monthly.
Pay Service 1
Pay Units: 15.
Programming (via satellite): HBO.
Fee: $10.50 monthly.
Pay Service 2
Pay Units: 24.
Programming (via satellite): Showtime.
Fee: $5.95 monthly.
Miles of plant: 13.0 (coaxial). Homes passed: 480.
Manager: Wanda Pyburn. Chief technician: Mike Deal.
Ownership: Buford Television Inc. (MSO). See Cable System Ownership.

TRENT—Jayroc Cablevision, Box 6575, Abilene, TX 79608. Phone: 915-691-5787. Fax: 915-676-2882. County: Taylor. ICA: TX0976.
TV Market Ranking: Below 100. Franchise award date: N.A. Franchise expiration date: N.A. Began: N.A.
Channel capacity: N.A. Channels available but not in use: N.A.
Basic Service
Subscribers: N.A.
Programming (received off-air): KRBC-TV (N), KTAB-TV (C), KTXS-TV (A) Abilene-Sweetwater.
Programming (via satellite): WGN-TV (W) Chicago; American Movie Classics; Animal Planet; CNN; Cartoon Network; Country Music TV; Discovery Channel; ESPN; Fox Family Channel; Fox Sports Net Southwest; Good-life TV Network; Nashville Network; Nick at Nite's TV Land; Outdoor Life Network; QVC; Sci-Fi Channel; TBS Superstation; Turner Classic Movies; Turner Network TV; USA Network.
Fee: N.A.
Pay Service 1
Pay Units: N.A.
Programming (via satellite): Cinemax; HBO.
Fee: N.A.
Manager: Dorton Canon.
Ownership: Jayroc Inc. (MSO).

TRENTON—Northland Cable TV, Box 10, Whitewright, TX 75491. Phone: 903-364-5322. County: Fannin. ICA: TX0866.
TV Market Ranking: Below 100. Franchise award date: January 7, 1982. Franchise expiration date: N.A. Began: N.A.
Channel capacity: 31. Channels available but not in use: 19.
Basic Service
Subscribers: 75.
Programming (received off-air): KDFW (F), KERA-TV (P), KTVT (C), KXAS-TV (N), WFAA-TV (A) Dallas-Fort Worth; KXII (C) Sherman.
Programming (via satellite): ESPN; Fox Family Channel; Nashville Network; TBS Superstation.
Fee: $50.00 installation; $21.50 monthly.
Pay Service 1
Pay Units: N.A.
Programming (via satellite): Disney Channel; The Movie Channel.
Fee: $35.00 installation; $7.00 monthly (Disney), $8.50 monthly (TMC).
Manager: Allan Layman.
Ownership: Northland Communications Corp. (MSO).

TRINITY—Friendship Cable of Texas Inc., Box 9090, Tyler, TX 75711-9090. Phones: 903-581-2121; 800-283-8688. Fax: 903-581-2185. County: Trinity. ICA: TX0205.
TV Market Ranking: Outside TV Markets. Franchise award date: January 1, 1971. Franchise expiration date: N.A. Began: N.A.
Channel capacity: 54 (not 2-way capable). Channels available but not in use: N.A.
Basic Service
Subscribers: 1,518.
Programming (received off-air): KBTX-TV (C) Bryan; K16BY (I) Crockett; KHOU-TV (C), KHTV (W), KPRC-TV (N), KRIV (F), KTRK-TV (A), KTXH (U), KUHT (P) Houston; KETK-TV (N) Jacksonville; KTRE (A) Lufkin; allband FM.
Programming (via satellite): CNN; Discovery Channel; ESPN; Fox Family Channel; Headline News; Nashville Network; TBS Superstation; Turner Network TV.
Planned originations: Automated time-weather.
Fee: $30.00 installation; $29.45 monthly.
Commercial fee: $3.00 monthly.
Pay Service 1
Pay Units: 127.
Programming (via satellite): Showtime.
Fee: $5.95 monthly.
Pay Service 2
Pay Units: 152.
Programming (via satellite): HBO.
Fee: $10.00 monthly.
Pay Service 3
Pay Units: 28.
Programming (via satellite): Cinemax.
Fee: $10.00 monthly.
Local advertising: No.
Equipment: Cadco headend; CAS amplifiers; Essex cable; Texscan character generator; Panasonic set top converters; Eagle traps; Gardiner satellite antenna; Gardiner satellite receivers.
Miles of plant: 69.0 (coaxial). Homes passed: 2,637.
Manager: Wanda Pyburn. Chief technician: David Burrell.
City fee: 5% of gross.
Ownership: Buford Television Inc. (MSO). See Cable System Ownership.

TROPHY CLUB—Charter Communications Inc., 5227 FM 813, Waxahachie, TX 75165. Phones: 972-938-9288; 800-477-0887. Fax: 972-923-0039. Counties: Denton & Tarrant. Also serves Haslet, Marshall Creek, Roanoke, Southlake. ICA: TX0919.
TV Market Ranking: 12. Franchise award date: N.A. Franchise expiration date: N.A. Began: N.A.
Channel capacity: N.A. Channels available but not in use: N.A.
Basic Service
Subscribers: 3,730.
Programming (received off-air): KDAF (W), KDFI-TV (I), KDFW (F), KDTX-TV (T), KERA-TV (P), KFWD (O), KTVT (C), KTXA (U), KXAS-TV (N), KXTX-TV (I), WFAA-TV (A)

Dallas-Fort Worth; KMPX (I) Decatur; KDTN (P) Denton; KUVN (S) Garland; KHSX-TV (H) Irving.
Programming (via satellite): WGN-TV (W) Chicago; C-SPAN; TBS Superstation; TV Guide Channel.
Fee: $38.00 installation; $12.78 monthly.

Expanded Basic Service
Subscribers: N.A.
Programming (via satellite): A & E; American Movie Classics; BET; Bravo; CNBC; CNN; Comedy Central; Country Music TV; Discovery Channel; E! Entertainment TV; ESPN; Fox Family Channel; Fox Sports Net Southwest; Headline News; Lifetime; MTV; Nashville Network; Nickelodeon; QVC; The Weather Channel; Turner Network TV; USA Network; VH1.
Fee: $14.00 monthly.

Pay Service 1
Pay Units: N.A.
Programming (via satellite): Cinemax; Disney Channel; HBO; Showtime; The Movie Channel.
Fee: $9.75 monthly (TMC), $9.95 monthly (Disney), $10.75 monthly (Showtime), $10.95 monthly (Cinemax), $11.95 monthly (HBO).

Pay-Per-View
Movies.
Local advertising: Yes. Regional interconnect: Cabletime.
Manager: Mary Scearce. Chief technician: Ken Stevens.
Ownership: Charter Communications Inc. (MSO). Purchased from Marcus Cable, April 1, 1999.

TROY—Centrovision Inc., Box 3157, Temple, TX 76501. Phone: 817-773-1163. County: Bell. ICA: TX0532.
TV Market Ranking: Below 100. Franchise award date: N.A. Franchise expiration date: N.A. Began: October 1, 1981.
Channel capacity: N.A. Channels available but not in use: N.A.

Basic Service
Subscribers: N.A.
Programming (received off-air): KTBC (F), KVUE-TV (A), KXAN-TV (N) Austin; KNCT (P) Belton; KTVT (C), KXTX-TV (I), WFAA-TV (A) Dallas-Fort Worth.
Programming (via satellite): WGN-TV (W) Chicago; TBS Superstation.
Fee: N.A.
Miles of plant: 8.0 (coaxial). Homes passed: 375.
Manager: Alton Shepard.
Ownership: Centrovision Inc. (MSO).

TRUMBULL—Time Warner Cable, Suite One, 300 First Stamford Place, Stamford, CT 06902-6372. Phone: 203-328-0600. Fax: 203-328-0690. County: Ellis. ICA: TX0351.
TV Market Ranking: 12. Franchise award date: N.A. Franchise expiration date: N.A. Began: March 1, 1982.
Channel capacity: 52. Channels available but not in use: N.A.

Basic Service
Subscribers: N.A.
Programming (received off-air): KDAF (W), KDFW (F), KERA-TV (P), KTVT (C), KTXA (U), KXAS-TV (N), KXTX-TV (I), WFAA-TV (A) Dallas-Fort Worth.
Programming (via satellite): WGN-TV (W) Chicago; A & E; BET; CNN; Country Music TV; Discovery Channel; ESPN; Fox Family Channel; Lifetime; MTV; Nashville Network; Nickelodeon; TBS Superstation; The Weather Channel; Travel Channel; Turner Network TV.
Fee: N.A.

Pay Service 1
Pay Units: N.A.
Programming (via satellite): Cinemax; Disney Channel; Fox Sports Net Southwest; HBO; Showtime.
Fee: $5.00 monthly (Fox Sports), $7.00 monthly (Disney or Showtime), $9.00 monthly (Cinemax), $10.00 monthly (HBO).
Miles of plant: 37.2 (coaxial). Homes passed: 1,046.
Manager: David Bach. Chief technician: Fred Rhoads.
Ownership: Time Warner Cable (MSO).

TULETA—National Cable Inc., Suite 106-A, 5151 Reed Rd., Columbus, OH 43220. Phones: 614-442-5890; 800-582-0504. Fax: 614-457-2567. County: Bee. ICA: TX0907.
TV Market Ranking: Below 100. Franchise award date: N.A. Franchise expiration date: N.A. Began: N.A.
Channel capacity: N.A. Channels available but not in use: N.A.

Basic Service
Subscribers: 30.
Programming (received off-air): KEDT (P), KIII (A), KZTV (C) Corpus Christi; KABB (F), KENS-TV (C), KMOL-TV (N), KSAT-TV (A) San Antonio.
Programming (via satellite): WGN-TV (W) Chicago; A & E; American Movie Classics; CNN; Country Music TV; Discovery Channel; ESPN; Fox Family Channel; Showtime; TBS Superstation; Turner Network TV; USA Network.
Fee: $28.00 monthly.
Homes passed: 112.
Manager: Paul Scott. Chief technician: Rob Spiller. Marketing director: Josh Thackery.
Ownership: National Cable (MSO).

TULIA—Classic Cable, Box 429, 605 N.W. 3rd St., Plainville, KS 67663-0429. Phones: 785-434-7620; 800-999-8876. Fax: 785-434-2614. County: Swisher. ICA: TX0226.
TV Market Ranking: Outside TV Markets. Franchise award date: June 17, 1980. Franchise expiration date: June 17, 2000. Began: January 10, 1965.
Channel capacity: 61 (2-way capable; operating 2-way). Channels available but not in use: N.A.

Basic Service
Subscribers: 1,325; Commercial subscribers: 54.
Programming (received off-air): KACV-TV (P), KAMR-TV (N), KCIT (F,U), KFDA-TV (C), KVII-TV (A) Amarillo; KLBK-TV (C) Lubbock; allband FM.
Programming (via satellite): WGN-TV (W) Chicago; A & E; Animal Planet; CNN; Comedy Central; Country Music TV; Discovery Channel; Disney Channel; E! Entertainment TV; ESPN; ESPN 2; Fox Family Channel; Fox News Channel; Fox Sports Net Southwest; Goodlife TV Network; Headline News; History Channel; Learning Channel; Lifetime; Nashville Network; Nick at Nite's TV Land; Nickelodeon; QVC; Sci-Fi Channel; TBS Superstation; The Health Network; The Inspirational Network; The Weather Channel; Trinity Bcstg. Network; Turner Classic Movies; Turner Network TV; USA Network; Univision.
Current originations: Automated time-weather; educational access; local news.
Fee: $35.00 installation; $29.95 monthly.

Pay Service 1
Pay Units: 77.
Programming (via satellite): The Movie Channel.
Fee: $5.95 monthly.

Pay Service 2
Pay Units: 82.
Programming (via satellite): Showtime.
Fee: $9.95 monthly.

Pay Service 3
Pay Units: 169.
Programming (via satellite): HBO.
Fee: $10.95 monthly.
Local advertising: Yes. Available in locally originated programming.
Equipment: Jerrold headend; Ameco amplifiers; Vikoa cable; Concord & Sony cameras; Fort Worth Tower satellite antenna.
Miles of plant: 30.3 (coaxial). Homes passed: 1,858. Total homes in franchised area: 2,100.
Manager: Bill Flowers. Chief technician: Chris Christenson. Marketing director: Jennifer Hauschild.
City fee: 2% of gross.
Ownership: Classic Cable (MSO).

TURKEY—High Plains Cablevision Inc., Box 310, 124 S. Main St., Lockney, TX 79241. Phone: 806-652-3328. Fax: 806-652-3139. County: Hall. ICA: TX0900.
TV Market Ranking: Outside TV Markets. Franchise award date: N.A. Franchise expiration date: N.A. Began: August 1, 1991.
Channel capacity: 36. Channels available but not in use: N.A.

Basic Service
Subscribers: 141.
Programming (received off-air): KAMR-TV (N), KFDA-TV (C), KVII-TV (A) Amarillo; KJTV (F) Lubbock.
Programming (via satellite): WGN-TV (W) Chicago; CNN; Discovery Channel; ESPN; Fox Family Channel; Nashville Network; TBS Superstation; Turner Network TV.
Fee: $25.00 installation; $19.79 monthly.

Pay Service 1
Pay Units: 8.
Programming (via satellite): Disney Channel.
Fee: $7.95 monthly.

Pay Service 2
Pay Units: 70.
Programming (via satellite): Showtime; The Movie Channel.
Fee: $10.95 monthly.
Miles of plant: 4.5 (coaxial); None (fiber optic). Homes passed: 300.
Manager: Jim Doucette. Chief technician: Jim Odle.
Ownership: High Plains Cablevision Inc. (MSO).

TUSCOLA—Big Country Cablevision Inc., Box 549, 102 Oak St., Merkel, TX 79536. Phones: 915-928-4750; 800-588-4750. Fax: 915-928-3452. County: Taylor. ICA: TX0176.
TV Market Ranking: Below 100. Franchise award date: February 15, 1983. Franchise expiration date: February 15, 2008. Began: December 30, 1983.
Channel capacity: 21. Channels available but not in use: 1.

Basic Service
Subscribers: 142.
Programming (received off-air): KRBC-TV (N), KTAB-TV (C), KTXS-TV (A) Abilene-Sweetwater.
Programming (via satellite): Fox Family Channel.
Fee: $10.50 installation; $14.90 monthly.

Expanded Basic Service
Subscribers: N.A.
Programming (via satellite): CNN; ESPN; Nashville Network; TBS Superstation; The Weather Channel; USA Network.
Fee: N.A.

Pay Service 1
Pay Units: N.A.
Programming (via satellite): HBO; Showtime.
Fee: $20.00 installation.
Local advertising: No.
Equipment: Scientific-Atlanta headend; C-COR amplifiers; Comm/Scope cable; Intercept traps; Weatherscan satellite antenna; Scientific-Atlanta satellite receivers.
Miles of plant: 60.0 (coaxial). Additional miles planned: 5.0 (coaxial). Homes passed: 3,000. Total homes in franchised area: 3,500.
Manager: Mark Reaves. Marketing director: J. Ketchum.
City fee: 5% of gross.
Ownership: Cable Management Assoc. (MSO).

TYLER—TCA Cable TV, 322 N. Glenwood Blvd., Tyler, TX 75702. Phone: 972-647-5730. Fax: 903-593-6189. County: Smith. Also serves Smith County, Whitehouse. ICA: TX0027.
TV Market Ranking: Below 100. Franchise award date: January 1, 1970. Franchise expiration date: May 1, 2003. Began: March 1, 1951.
Channel capacity: 63 (2-way capable; operating 2-way). Channels available but not in use: N.A.

Basic Service
Subscribers: 29,753.
Programming (received off-air): KDFW (F), KERA-TV (P), KTVT (C), KXAS-TV (N), KXTX-TV (I), WFAA-TV (A) Dallas-Fort Worth; KETK-TV (N) Jacksonville; KFXK (F) Longview; KLTV (A) Tyler-Longview; 18 FMs.
Programming (via satellite): WGN-TV (W) Chicago; A & E; BET; C-SPAN; C-SPAN 2; Discovery Channel; E! Entertainment TV; Headline News; Lifetime; MTV; Odyssey; QVC; TBS Superstation; TV Guide Channel; The Weather Channel; Univision.
Current originations: Automated time-weather; educational access; religious access; automated emergency alert.
Fee: $31.19 installation; $9.35 monthly; $15.59 additional installation.

Expanded Basic Service
Subscribers: 28,200.
Programming (via satellite): CNBC; CNN; Comedy Central; ESPN; Fox Family Channel; Fox Sports Net Southwest; Nashville Network; Nickelodeon; Turner Network TV; USA Network; VH1.
Fee: $14.26 monthly.

Pay Service 1
Pay Units: 3,935.
Programming (via satellite): American Movie Classics.
Fee: N.A.

Pay Service 2
Pay Units: 2,442.
Programming (via satellite): Cinemax.
Fee: $5.00 installation; $11.40 monthly.

Pay Service 3
Pay Units: 2,769.
Programming (via satellite): Disney Channel.
Fee: $5.00 installation; $11.40 monthly.

Pay Service 4
Pay Units: 1,927.
Programming (via satellite): The New Encore.
Fee: N.A.

Pay Service 5
Pay Units: 6,014.
Programming (via satellite): HBO.
Fee: $5.00 installation; $11.40 monthly.

Pay Service 6
Pay Units: 411.
Programming (via satellite): Playboy TV.
Fee: $5.00 installation; $11.40 monthly.

Pay Service 7
Pay Units: 3,353.
Programming (via satellite): Showtime.
Fee: $5.00 installation; $11.40 monthly.
Pay-Per-View
Addressable homes: 10,948.
Spice.
Fee: $4.95.
Interactive Services
Subscribers: 3,509.
Local advertising: Yes (insert only). Available in satellite distributed programming. Rates: $15.00/30 Seconds.
Program Guide: The Cable Guide.
Equipment: Jerrold & Scientific-Atlanta headend; Magnavox amplifiers; Times Fiber cable; Jerrold set top converters; Jerrold addressable set top converters; Scientific-Atlanta satellite antenna; Scientific-Atlanta satellite receivers.
Miles of plant: 651.9 (coaxial). Homes passed: 42,941. Total homes in franchised area: 42,941.
Manager: Vince Thomas.
City fee: 5% of gross.
Ownership: TCA Cable TV Inc. (MSO); AT&T Broadband & Internet Services (MSO). See Cable System Ownership.

UNIVERSITY PARK—Charter Communications Inc., 4528 Cole, Dallas, TX 75205. Phone: 214-522-8086. Fax: 214-522-8164. County: Dallas. Also serves Highland Park. ICA: TX0062.
TV Market Ranking: 12. Franchise award date: April 1, 1979. Franchise expiration date: N.A. Began: January 1, 1980.
Channel capacity: 77 (not 2-way capable). Channels available but not in use: None.
Basic Service
Subscribers: 7,868; Commercial subscribers: 53.
Programming (received off-air): KDAF (W), KDFI-TV (I), KDFW (F), KDTX-TV (T), KERA-TV (P), KFWD (O), KTVT (C), KTXA (U), KXAS-TV (N), KXTX-TV (I), WFAA-TV (A) Dallas-Fort Worth; KMPX (I) Decatur; KDTN (P) Denton; KUVN (S) Garland; KHSX-TV (H) Irving; 23 FMs.
Programming (via satellite): WGN-TV (W) Chicago; A & E; American Movie Classics; Bravo; C-SPAN; C-SPAN 2; CNBC; CNN; Comedy Central; Country Music TV; Discovery Channel; E! Entertainment TV; ESPN; ESPN 2; FX; Fox Family Channel; Fox Sports Net Southwest; Headline News; Learning Channel; Lifetime; MSNBC; MTV; Nashville Network; Nickelodeon; Odyssey; TBS Superstation; TV Food Network; The Weather Channel; Travel Channel; Turner Network TV; USA Network; VH1; Z Music Television.
Current originations: Automated time-weather; public access; educational access; government access; automated emergency alert.
Fee: $40.00 installation; $23.81 monthly; $25.00 additional installation.
Commercial fee: $5.00 monthly.
Pay Service 1
Pay Units: 988.
Programming (via satellite): Cinemax.
Fee: $2.00 installation; $9.45 monthly.
Pay Service 2
Pay Units: 1,491.
Programming (via satellite): Disney Channel.
Fee: $2.00 installation; $9.50 monthly.
Pay Service 3
Pay Units: 2,674.
Programming (via satellite): HBO.
Fee: $2.00 installation; $12.05 monthly.
Pay Service 4
Pay Units: 1,416.
Programming (via satellite): The Movie Channel.
Fee: $2.00 installation; $10.80 monthly.
Pay Service 5
Pay Units: 699.
Programming (via satellite): Showtime.
Fee: $2.00 installation; $11.75 monthly.
Pay-Per-View
Addressable homes: 3,274.
Special events.
Fee: Varies.
Interactive Services
Burglar alarm.
Local advertising: Yes (locally produced & insert). Available in satellite distributed & character-generated programming. Rates: $7.50/Minute; $5.00/30 Seconds.
Program Guide: The Cable Guide.
Equipment: Scientific-Atlanta & M/A-Com headend; Magnavox amplifiers; Comm/Scope cable; Sony VTRs; Video Data Systems character generator; Jerrold addressable set top converters; Eagle traps; AFC & Antenna Technology satellite antenna; Scientific-Atlanta, M/A-Com & Microdyne satellite receivers; ChannelMatic & Sony commercial insert.
Miles of plant: 119.7 (coaxial); 17.0 (fiber optic). Homes passed: 12,695.
Manager: Dusty Matthews. Chief technician: Clarence Brooks. Marketing director: Scott Justice.
City fee: 5% of gross.
Ownership: Charter Communications Inc. (MSO). Purchased from Marcus Cable, April 1, 1999.

UVALDE—Time Warner Communications, 340 N. Getty St., Uvalde, TX 78802. Phones: 210-278-2525; 800-827-5090. Fax: 210-278-2726. County: Uvalde. Also serves Uvalde County (portions). ICA: TX0095.
TV Market Ranking: Below 100. Franchise award date: N.A. Franchise expiration date: N.A. Began: June 25, 1955.
Channel capacity: 44 (2-way capable; operating 2-way). Channels available but not in use: None.
Basic Service
Subscribers: 5,170.
Programming (received off-air): KRRT (W) Kerrville-San Antonio; KABB (F), KENS-TV (C), KLRN (P), KMOL-TV (N), KSAT-TV (A) San Antonio; allband FM.
Programming (via satellite): C-SPAN; C-SPAN 2; EWTN; FX; Lifetime; QVC; TV Guide Channel; The Weather Channel.
Current originations: Public access; government access; leased access.
Fee: $33.89 installation; $14.60 monthly; $0.92 converter; $18.82 additional installation.
Expanded Basic Service
Subscribers: 5,056.
Programming (via satellite): WGN-TV (W) Chicago; CNN; Country Music TV; Discovery Channel; ESPN; Fox Family Channel; Fox Sports Net Southwest; Headline News; Intro TV; Knowledge TV; MTV; Nashville Network; Nick at Nite; Nickelodeon; TBS Superstation; Turner Network TV; USA Network; Univision; VH1.
Fee: $16.95 installation; $10.07 monthly.
Pay Service 1
Pay Units: 669.
Programming (via satellite): HBO.
Fee: $20.00 installation; $13.40 monthly.
Pay Service 2
Pay Units: 235.
Programming (via satellite): Showtime.
Fee: $20.00 installation; $13.00 monthly.
Pay Service 3
Pay Units: 102.

Programming (via satellite): The Movie Channel.
Fee: $20.00 installation; $13.00 monthly.
Pay Service 4
Pay Units: 35.
Programming (via satellite): DMX.
Fee: $9.95 monthly.
Pay Service 5
Pay Units: 1,159.
Programming (via satellite): The New Encore.
Fee: $1.75 monthly.
Pay Service 6
Pay Units: 545.
Programming (via satellite): Starz!
Fee: $4.75 monthly.
Pay-Per-View
Addressable homes: 572.
Action Pay-Per-View.
Local advertising: Yes. Regional interconnect: Cabletime.
Program Guide: The Cable Guide.
Equipment: Telemet headend; Scientific-Atlanta amplifiers; Comm/Scope cable; Regal set top converters; Jerrold addressable set top converters; Eagle traps; Comtech satellite antenna; Scientific-Atlanta satellite receivers.
Miles of plant: 103.5 (coaxial). Homes passed: 7,425.
Manager: Ted Luce. Chief technician: Rick Boone. Marketing director: Jerri Coppedge. Customer service manager: Olga Castillion.
City fee: 5% of gross.
Ownership: AT&T Broadband & Internet Services (MSO); Time Warner Cable (MSO); Advance/Newhouse Partnership (MSO).

VALENTINE—Valentine TV Cable, Box 1377, Alpine, TX 79831. Phone: 915-837-2300. Fax: 915-837-5423. E-mail: mtnzone@overland.net. County: Jeff Davis. ICA: TX0692.
TV Market Ranking: Outside TV Markets. Franchise award date: February 22, 1980. Franchise expiration date: January 1, 2016. Began: July 1, 1983.
Channel capacity: 36 (not 2-way capable). Channels available but not in use: N.A.
Basic Service
Subscribers: 38.
Programming (received off-air): KOSA-TV (C), KWES-TV (N) Odessa-Midland; allband FM.
Programming (via satellite): KMGH-TV (A), KRMA-TV (P) Denver; CNN; Discovery Channel; ESPN; Fox Family Channel; FoxNet; GalaVision; Learning Channel; Nashville Network; Nickelodeon; TBS Superstation; Turner Network TV; Univision.
Fee: $35.00 installation; $24.00 monthly; $35.00 additional installation.
Pay Service 1
Pay Units: N.A.
Programming (via satellite): HBO.
Fee: $10.00 installation; $8.95 monthly.
Equipment: Blonder-Tongue & Scientific-Atlanta headend; C-COR amplifiers; Times Fiber cable; DX Engineering satellite receivers.
Miles of plant: 3.0 (coaxial). Homes passed: 100. Total homes in franchised area: 125.
Manager: Steve Neu.
Ownership: Mountain Zone TV Systems (MSO).

VALLEY MILLS—Mission Cable, 920 Whitmore Dr., Rockwall, TX 75087. Phone: 800-783-5708. Fax: 214-722-6218. County: Bosque. ICA: TX0444.
TV Market Ranking: Below 100. Franchise award date: July 15, 1989. Franchise expiration date: June 1, 1998. Began: December 28, 1983.
Channel capacity: 35 (not 2-way capable). Channels available but not in use: N.A.
Basic Service
Subscribers: 330; Commercial subscribers: 33.
Programming (received off-air): KDFW (F), KERA-TV (P), KTVT (C), KXAS-TV (N), KXTX-TV (I), WFAA-TV (A) Dallas-Fort Worth; KCEN-TV (N), KWKT (F), KWTX-TV (C) Waco-Temple.
Programming (via satellite): WGN-TV (W) Chicago; CNN; Cartoon Network; Country Music TV; Discovery Channel; ESPN; Fox Family Channel; Fox Sports Net Southwest; Home Shopping Network; Nashville Network; Nickelodeon; TBS Superstation; Turner Network TV; USA Network.
Fee: $40.00 installation; $20.95 monthly.
Pay Service 1
Pay Units: 76.
Programming (via satellite): Cinemax.
Fee: $25.00 installation; $9.00 monthly.
Pay Service 2
Pay Units: 43.
Programming (via satellite): Disney Channel.
Fee: $25.00 installation; $9.00 monthly.
Pay Service 3
Pay Units: 37.
Programming (via satellite): HBO.
Fee: $9.00 monthly.
Equipment: Scientific-Atlanta headend; Scientific-Atlanta amplifiers; Comm/Scope cable; Scientific-Atlanta set top converters; Pico traps; Scientific-Atlanta satellite antenna; Scientific-Atlanta satellite receivers.
Miles of plant: 8.9 (coaxial). Homes passed: 414. Total homes in franchised area: 655.
Manager: Jim Stafford. Chief technician: Jacky Oliver. Marketing & program director: Bruce Berkinshaw.
City fee: 3% of gross.
Ownership: Fanch Communications Inc. (MSO). See Cable System Ownership.

VALLEY VIEW—North Texas Communications Co., Drawer 587, 205 N. Walnut St., Muenster, TX 76252. Phone: 940-736-2255. Fax: 940-759-5557. County: Cooke. ICA: TX0468.
TV Market Ranking: Below 100. Franchise award date: January 1, 1984. Franchise expiration date: January 1, 2000. Began: November 15, 1984.
Channel capacity: 40 (not 2-way capable). Channels available but not in use: 6.
Basic Service
Subscribers: 355.
Programming (received off-air): KTEN (A,N,F) Ada; KPXD (X) Arlington; KDAF (W), KDFI-TV (I), KDFW (F), KDTX-TV (T), KERA-TV (P), KFWD (O), KTVT (C), KTXA (U), KXAS-TV (N), KXTX-TV (I), WFAA-TV (A) Dallas-Fort Worth; KMPX (I) Decatur; KUVN (S)

Garland; KHSX-TV (H) Irving; KXII (C) Sherman; allband FM.
Current originations: Automated time-weather; religious access.
Fee: $22.50 installation; $13.95 monthly; $2.50 converter; $35.00 additional installation.
Expanded Basic Service
Subscribers: 321.
Programming (via satellite): WGN-TV (W) Chicago; A & E; C-SPAN; CNBC; CNN; Country Music TV; Discovery Channel; Disney Channel; ESPN; EWTN; Fox Family Channel; Fox Sports Net Southwest; Headline News; History Channel; Home & Garden Television; Home Shopping Network; Learning Channel; Lifetime; Nashville Network; Nickelodeon; TBS Superstation; The Weather Channel; Turner Classic Movies; Turner Network TV; USA Network.
Fee: N.A.
Pay Service 1
Pay Units: 38.
Programming (via satellite): Cinemax.
Fee: $15.00 installation; $10.00 monthly.
Pay Service 2
Pay Units: 55.
Programming (via satellite): HBO.
Fee: $15.00 installation; $10.00 monthly.
Pay-Per-View
Addressable homes: 138.
Local advertising: Yes (locally produced). Available in character-generated programming. Local sales manager: Bernice Bartel.
Equipment: Scientific-Atlanta headend; Scientific-Atlanta amplifiers; Scientific-Atlanta cable; Texscan character generator; Scientific-Atlanta set top converters; Scientific-Atlanta addressable set top converters; Vitek traps; Scientific-Atlanta satellite antenna; Microwave Assoc. & Scientific-Atlanta satellite receivers.
Miles of plant: 26.0 (coaxial); 7.0 (fiber optic). Homes passed: 560. Total homes in franchised area: 560.
Manager: Alvin M. Fuhrman. CATV Supervisor: Joe Yosten. Program director: Gene Fuhrman. Marketing director: Joey Anderson.
City fee: 3% of gross.
Ownership: North Texas Communications Co. (MSO).

VEGA—Gruver Cablevision Inc., Box 827, 308 Main St., Gruver, TX 79040-0827. Phone: 806-733-5295. County: Oldham. ICA: TX0868.
TV Market Ranking: 95. Franchise award date: N.A. Franchise expiration date: N.A. Began: N.A.
Channel capacity: 12. Channels available but not in use: N.A.
Basic Service
Subscribers: 255.
Programming (received off-air): KACV-TV (P), KAMR-TV (N), KCIT (F,U), KFDA-TV (C), KVII-TV (A) Amarillo.
Programming (via satellite): WGN-TV (W) Chicago; CNN; ESPN; Headline News; TBS Superstation.
Fee: $10.00 installation; $15.00 monthly.
Pay Service 1
Pay Units: N.A.
Programming (via satellite): Disney Channel; Showtime.
Fee: $10.00 installation; $9.00 monthly (Disney), $10.00 monthly (Showtime).
Manager: Pat Morley.
Ownership: Gruver Cablevision Inc. (MSO).

VERNON—Friendship Cable of Texas Inc., Box 9090, Tyler, TX 75711-9090. Phone: 903-581-2121. Fax: 903-581-2185. County: Wilbarger. ICA: TX0119.
TV Market Ranking: Outside TV Markets. Franchise award date: N.A. Franchise expiration date: June 1, 2001. Began: November 1, 1976.
Channel capacity: 37. Channels available but not in use: N.A.
Basic Service
Subscribers: 3,293.
Programming (received off-air): KAUZ-TV (C), KFDX-TV (N), KJTL (F,U), KSWO-TV (A) Wichita Falls-Lawton; allband FM.
Programming (via translator): KWET (P) Cheyenne.
Programming (via satellite): C-SPAN; CNBC; Court TV; Discovery Channel; FX; Fox Family Channel; Odyssey; TBS Superstation; The Weather Channel.
Current originations: Automated time-weather; educational access.
Fee: $30.00 installation; $12.57 monthly.
Expanded Basic Service
Subscribers: 2,934.
Programming (via satellite): American Movie Classics; Animal Planet; BET; CNN; Cartoon Network; Disney Channel; ESPN; Fox News Channel; Headline News; Home & Garden Television; Learning Channel; Lifetime; MTV; Nashville Network; Nickelodeon; Turner Network TV; USA Network; Univision.
Fee: $30.00 installation; $15.86 monthly.
Pay Service 1
Pay Units: 410.
Programming (via satellite): Cinemax.
Fee: $12.62 monthly.
Pay Service 2
Pay Units: 1,041.
Programming (via satellite): The New Encore.
Fee: $1.75 monthly.
Pay Service 3
Pay Units: 541.
Programming (via satellite): HBO.
Fee: $13.59 monthly.
Pay Service 4
Pay Units: 622.
Programming (via satellite): Starz!
Fee: $6.75 monthly.
Program Guide: The Cable Guide.
Equipment: Tocom headend; Tocom amplifiers; CCS Hatfield cable; Comtech & RF Systems satellite antenna.
Miles of plant: 81.0 (coaxial). Homes passed: 5,783. Total homes in franchised area: 5,783.
Manager: Larry Bryant. Chief technician: Ron Johnson.
City fee: 3% of gross.
Ownership: Buford Television Inc. (MSO). See Cable System Ownership.

VICTORIA—TCA Cable TV, 105 Industrial Dr., Victoria, TX 77901. Phone: 512-573-6301. Fax: 512-573-1205. County: Victoria. Also serves Victoria County (unincorporated areas). ICA: TX0043.
TV Market Ranking: Below 100. Franchise award date: January 1, 1955. Franchise expiration date: N.A. Began: January 12, 1954.
Channel capacity: 35. Channels available but not in use: 1.
Basic Service
Subscribers: 19,893; Commercial subscribers: 2,279.
Programming (received off-air): KAVU-TV (A), KVCT (F) Victoria; 21 FMs.
Programming (via microwave): KHTV (W), KPRC-TV (N), KUHT (P) Houston; KENS-TV (C), KLRN (P), KMOL-TV (N), KSAT-TV (A) San Antonio.
Programming (via satellite): C-SPAN; CNN; CNNfn; Discovery Channel; ESPN; EWTN; Fox Family Channel; Goodlife TV Network; Headline News; Lifetime; MTV; Nashville Network; Nickelodeon; Odyssey; QVC; TBS Superstation; TV Guide Channel; The Weather Channel; USA Network; Univision; VH1.
Planned originations: Automated emergency alert.
Fee: $35.00 installation; $7.94 monthly; $25.00 additional installation.
Commercial fee: $2.63 monthly.
Pay Service 1
Pay Units: N.A.
Programming (via satellite): Cinemax; Disney Channel; Fox Sports Net Southwest; HBO; Showtime.
Fee: $35.00 installation; $7.00 monthly (Disney), $10.00 monthly (Cinemax, Fox Sports, HBO or Showtime).
Local advertising: Yes (locally produced & insert). Available in satellite distributed programming. Local sales manager: W. R. Kostrzewski. Regional interconnect: Cabletime.
Program Guide: Premium Channels.
Equipment: Jerrold & Scientific-Atlanta headend; Jerrold amplifiers; Scientific-Atlanta & Comm/Scope cable; Jerrold set top converters; Jerrold addressable set top converters; Eagle traps; Scientific-Atlanta satellite antenna; Scientific-Atlanta satellite receivers.
Miles of plant: 350.4 (coaxial). Additional miles planned: 7.0 (coaxial). Homes passed: 24,911. Total homes in franchised area: 25,409.
Manager: Ray Griffith. Chief technician: James Farrow.
City fee: 2% of gross.
Ownership: TCA Cable TV Inc. (MSO). See Cable System Ownership.

VIDOR—Warner Cable, Box 1960, 875 North St., Vidor, TX 77670-1960. Phones: 409-769-8161; 800-828-8380. County: Orange. Also serves Pine Forest. ICA: TX0093.
TV Market Ranking: 88. Franchise award date: December 13, 1979. Franchise expiration date: N.A. Began: June 1, 1979.
Channel capacity: 81 (not 2-way capable). Channels available but not in use: 29.
Basic Service
Subscribers: 4,997; Commercial subscribers: 3.
Programming (received off-air): KBMT (A), KBTV-TV (N), KFDM-TV (C), KITU (E) Beaumont-Port Arthur; KLTL-TV (P), KVHP (F) Lake Charles.
Programming (via satellite): C-SPAN; TBS Superstation.
Current originations: Automated time-weather; automated emergency alert.
Fee: $27.20 installation; $9.28 monthly; $1.70 converter.
Expanded Basic Service
Subscribers: 2,505.
Programming (via satellite): WGN-TV (W) Chicago; A & E; American Movie Classics; Animal Planet; CNBC; CNN; Cartoon Network; Country Music TV; Court TV; Discovery Channel; Disney Channel; E! Entertainment TV; ESPN; ESPN 2; Fox Family Channel; Fox Sports Net Southwest; Headline News; History Channel; Home & Garden Television; Learning Channel; Lifetime; MOVIEplex; MTV; Nashville Network; Nick at Nite's TV Land; Nickelodeon; Odyssey; QVC; Sci-Fi Channel; The Health Network; The Weather Channel; Travel Channel; Turner Classic Movies; Turner Network TV; USA Network; VH1.
Fee: $20.00 installation; $25.05 monthly.
Pay Service 1
Pay Units: 426.
Programming (via satellite): Cinemax.
Fee: $20.00 installation; $11.45 monthly.
Pay Service 2
Pay Units: 1,058.
Programming (via satellite): HBO.
Fee: $20.00 installation; $11.45 monthly.
Pay Service 3
Pay Units: 591.
Programming (via satellite): Showtime.
Fee: $20.00 installation; $11.45 monthly.
Pay Service 4
Pay Units: 48.
Programming (via satellite): Starz!
Fee: $7.95 monthly.
Local advertising: Yes. Available in character-generated & taped programming. Rates: $5.00/Day.
Program Guide: Premium Channels.
Equipment: Scientific-Atlanta headend; Magnavox amplifiers; Comm/Scope cable; Atari character generator; Scientific-Atlanta & Jerrold set top converters; Pico & Eagle traps; Scientific-Atlanta satellite antenna; Scientific-Atlanta satellite receivers.
Miles of plant: 220.0 (coaxial). Homes passed: 7,766.
Manager: Jim Dwyer. Marketing director: Bill Forgey.
City fee: 3% of basic.
Ownership: Fanch Communications Inc. (MSO); Time Warner Cable (MSO). See Cable System Ownership.

VIDOR (southern portion)—Friendship Cable of Texas, Box 9090, Tyler, TX 75711-9090. Phone: 903-581-2121. Fax: 903-581-2185. County: Orange. ICA: TX0551.
TV Market Ranking: 88. Franchise award date: N.A. Franchise expiration date: N.A. Began: October 1, 1984.
Channel capacity: 36 (not 2-way capable). Channels available but not in use: 12.
Basic Service
Subscribers: 153.
Programming (received off-air): KBMT (A), KBTV-TV (N), KFDM-TV (C) Beaumont-Port Arthur.
Programming (via satellite): WGN-TV (W) Chicago; CNN; ESPN; Fox Family Channel; MTV; Nashville Network; Nickelodeon; TBS Superstation; USA Network.
Fee: $33.75 monthly.
Pay Service 1
Pay Units: 12.
Programming (via satellite): HBO.
Fee: $10.50 monthly.
Pay Service 2
Pay Units: 25.
Programming (via satellite): Showtime.
Fee: $6.95 monthly.
Pay Service 3
Pay Units: 1.
Programming (via satellite): Cinemax.
Fee: $10.50 monthly.
Miles of plant: 10.9 (coaxial). Homes passed: 322.
Manager: Wanda Pyburn. Chief technician: Mike Deal.
City fee: 3% of gross.
Ownership: Buford Television Inc. (MSO). See Cable System Ownership.

WACO—Time Warner Cable, Box 7852, 215 Factory Dr., Waco, TX 76710-6959. Phone: 817-776-1141. Fax: 817-776-2651. County: McLennan. Also serves Bellmead, Beverly Hills, Lacy-Lakeview, McGregor, McLennan County (portions), Northcrest, Robinson, Woodway. ICA: TX0015.
TV Market Ranking: Below 100. Franchise award date: N.A. Franchise expiration date: June 1, 2007. Began: October 1, 1965.
Channel capacity: 75 (not 2-way capable). Channels available but not in use: None.

Basic Service

Subscribers: 45,300.

Programming (received off-air): KNCT (P) Belton; KXTX-TV (I) Dallas-Fort Worth; KCEN-TV (N), KCTF (P), KWKT (F), KWTX-TV (C), KXXV (A) Waco-Temple.

Programming (via microwave): KERA-TV (P), KTVT (C), WFAA-TV (A) Dallas-Fort Worth.

Programming (via satellite): A & E; BET; C-SPAN; CNBC; CNN; ESPN; Fox Family Channel; Headline News; Lifetime; MTV; Nashville Network; Nickelodeon; Odyssey; TBS Superstation; The Weather Channel; Turner Network TV; USA Network; Univision; VH1.

Fee: $23.16 installation; $6.35 monthly; $1.95 converter.

Pay Service 1

Pay Units: 5,492.

Programming (via satellite): Cinemax.

Fee: $9.50 monthly.

Pay Service 2

Pay Units: 2,569.

Programming (via satellite): Disney Channel.

Fee: $9.50 monthly.

Pay Service 3

Pay Units: 10,106.

Programming (via satellite): HBO (multiplexed).

Fee: $9.50 monthly.

Pay Service 4

Pay Units: 1,155.

Programming (via satellite): The Movie Channel.

Fee: $9.50 monthly.

Pay Service 5

Pay Units: 3,558.

Programming (via satellite): Showtime (multiplexed).

Fee: $9.50 monthly.

Pay Service 6

Pay Units: 769.

Programming (via satellite): DMX.

Fee: $8.95 monthly.

Pay Service 7

Pay Units: 6,693.

Programming (via satellite): The New Encore (multiplexed).

Fee: $4.95 monthly.

Pay-Per-View

Addressable homes: 17,000.

Hot Choice; Viewer's Choice.

Fee: $4.95.

Local advertising: Yes. Available in locally originated programming. Rates: $200.00/Minute; $100.00/30 Seconds. Local sales manager: Ron Brush. Regional interconnect: Waco-Temple-Killeen Interconnect.

Equipment: Scientific-Atlanta headend; Scientific-Atlanta amplifiers; Comm/Scope cable; Sony VTRs; Scientific-Atlanta set top converters; Scientific-Atlanta addressable set top converters; Scientific-Atlanta satellite antenna; Scientific-Atlanta satellite receivers.

Miles of plant: 884.0 (coaxial). Homes passed: 70,566.

Manager: John Mankin. Chief technician: Billy Johnson. Marketing director: Bill Hughes.

City fee: 5% of gross.

Ownership: Time Warner Cable (MSO); Advance/Newhouse Partnership (MSO).

WAELDER—National Cable, Suite 106-A, 5151 Reed Rd., Columbus, OH 43220. Phones: 614-442-5890; 800-582-0504. Fax: 614-457-2567. County: Gonzales. ICA: TX0518.

TV Market Ranking: Outside TV Markets. Franchise award date: N.A. Franchise expiration date: N.A. Began: October 1, 1983.

Channel capacity: 52. Channels available but not in use: N.A.

Basic Service

Subscribers: 41.

Programming (received off-air): KEYE-TV (C) Austin; KABB (F), KENS-TV (C), KLRN (P), KMOL-TV (N), KSAT-TV (A), KVDA (O) San Antonio.

Programming (via satellite): WGN-TV (W) Chicago; CNN; Country Music TV; Discovery Channel; ESPN; Fox Family Channel; Learning Channel; MTV; MuchMoreMusic; Nickelodeon; QVC; TBS Superstation; Turner Network TV.

Fee: $25.00 installation; $25.83 monthly.

Pay Service 1

Pay Units: N.A.

Programming (via satellite): Cinemax; HBO.

Fee: N.A.

Miles of plant: 9.9 (coaxial).

Manager: Roy E. Hayes. System/operations manager: Steve Miller.

Ownership: National Cable (MSO). Purchased from Bay Cable Inc., May 31, 1999.

WALDEN—Lakewood Cablevision, 12504 Walden Rd., Montgomery, TX 77356. Phone: 409-582-4855. Fax: 409-582-4392. County: Montgomery. Also serves April Sound Subdivision, Clearwater Cove, Lake Conroe East, Montgomery, Montgomery County, Tri-Lake Estates. ICA: TX0869.

TV Market Ranking: 15 (portions of Montgomery County); Below 100 (April Sound Subdivision, Clearwater Cove, Lake Conroe East, Montgomery, portions of Montgomery County, Tri-Lake Estates, Walden). Franchise award date: N.A. Franchise expiration date: N.A. Began: September 1, 1984.

Channel capacity: 36 (not 2-way capable). Channels available but not in use: None.

Basic Service

Subscribers: 4,135.

Programming (received off-air): KBTX-TV (C) Bryan; KHOU-TV (C), KHTV (W), KPRC-TV (N), KRIV (F), KTRK-TV (A), KTXH (U), KUHT (P) Houston.

Programming (via satellite): WGN-TV (W) Chicago; Fox Sports Net Southwest; TBS Superstation.

Fee: $52.50 installation; $22.95 monthly.

Pay Service 1

Pay Units: 280.

Programming (via satellite): Cinemax.

Fee: $9.95 monthly.

Pay Service 2

Pay Units: 405.

Programming (via satellite): Disney Channel.

Fee: $9.95 monthly.

Pay Service 3

Pay Units: 954.

Programming (via satellite): HBO.

Fee: $12.00 monthly.

Pay Service 4

Pay Units: 796.

Programming (via satellite): The Movie Channel.

Fee: $9.95 monthly.

Pay Service 5

Pay Units: 746.

Programming (via satellite): Showtime.

Fee: $9.95 monthly.

Equipment: DX Engineering & Scientific-Atlanta headend; Scientific-Atlanta amplifiers; Comm/Scope cable; Tocom addressable set top converters.

Office manager: Timmie Adams. Manager: Charlie Garland.

City fee: 5% of gross.

Ownership: Moffat Communications Ltd. (MSO).

WALLER—Northland Cable, 221 E. Main St., Brenham, TX 77833. Phone: 409-836-6939. Fax: 409-836-1736. County: Waller. Also serves Prairie View. ICA: TX0304.

TV Market Ranking: Below 100. Franchise award date: N.A. Franchise expiration date: N.A. Began: July 1, 1983.

Channel capacity: 52. Channels available but not in use: N.A.

Basic Service

Subscribers: N.A.

Programming (received off-air): KHOU-TV (C), KHTV (W), KPRC-TV (N), KRIV (F), KTRK-TV (A), KTXH (U), KUHT (P) Houston.

Programming (via satellite): WGN-TV (W) Chicago; A & E; BET; C-SPAN; CNN; Cartoon Network; Country Music TV; Discovery Channel; ESPN; Fox Family Channel; Fox Sports Net Southwest; Headline News; Home Shopping Network; MTV; Nashville Network; Nickelodeon; TBS Superstation; The Weather Channel; Turner Classic Movies; Turner Network TV; USA Network.

Fee: $25.00 installation; $9.95 monthly.

Pay Service 1

Pay Units: N.A.

Programming (via satellite): Cinemax; HBO; Showtime.

Fee: $9.00 monthly (each).

Miles of plant: 44.0 (coaxial). Homes passed: 1,266.

Manager: Doug Eisle.

Ownership: Northland Communications Corp. (MSO).

WALLIS—Star Cable, Drawer 1570, Brazoria, TX 77422. Phones: 409-798-9121; 800-395-2775. Fax: 409-798-4409. Counties: Austin, Fort Bend & Wharton. Also serves East Bernard, Orchard. ICA: TX0275.

TV Market Ranking: Below 100. Franchise award date: N.A. Franchise expiration date: N.A. Began: September 15, 1989.

Channel capacity: 36 (not 2-way capable). Channels available but not in use: 3.

Basic Service

Subscribers: 549.

Programming (received off-air): KVVV (I) Baytown; KETH (E), KHOU-TV (C), KHTV (W), KPRC-TV (N), KRIV (F), KTRK-TV (A), KTXH (U), KUHT (P), KZJL (I) Houston; KNWS-TV (I) Katy; KXLN-TV (S) Rosenberg.

Programming (via satellite): WGN-TV (W) Chicago; American Movie Classics; CNN; Discovery Channel; ESPN; Fox Family Channel; Fox Sports Net Southwest; Headline News; MTV; Nashville Network; Nickelodeon; Sci-Fi Channel; TBS Superstation; The Weather Channel; Turner Network TV; USA Network.

Fee: $31.34 monthly; $2.15 converter.

Pay Service 1

Pay Units: 64.

Programming (via satellite): Cinemax.

Fee: $10.95 monthly.

Pay Service 2

Pay Units: 85.

Programming (via satellite): Disney Channel.

Fee: $7.95 monthly.

Pay Service 3

Pay Units: 105.

Programming (via satellite): HBO.

Fee: $10.95 monthly.

Pay Service 4

Pay Units: 124.

Programming (via satellite): Showtime; The Movie Channel.

Fee: $12.95 monthly.

Miles of plant: 47.7 (coaxial); None (fiber optic). Homes passed: 1,457. Total homes in franchised area: 1,457.

Manager: Mike Burns. Chief technician: Mayla Zubeck.

Ownership: Star Cable Associates (MSO).

WALNUT SPRINGS—National Cable Inc., Suite 106-A, 5151 Reed Rd., Columbus, OH 43220. Phones: 614-442-5890; 800-582-0504. Fax: 614-457-2567. County: Bosque. ICA: TX0871.

TV Market Ranking: Outside TV Markets. Franchise award date: N.A. Franchise expiration date: N.A. Began: N.A.

Channel capacity: 36. Channels available but not in use: 21.

Basic Service

Subscribers: 41.

Programming (received off-air): KDFW (F), KERA-TV (P), KTVT (C), KXAS-TV (N), KXTX-TV (I), WFAA-TV (A) Dallas-Fort Worth.

Programming (via satellite): WGN-TV (W) Chicago; A & E; American Movie Classics; CNN; Country Music TV; Discovery Channel; ESPN; Fox Family Channel; Showtime; TBS Superstation; Turner Network TV; USA Network.

Fee: $28.00 monthly.

Miles of plant: 8.7 (coaxial). Homes passed: 324.

Manager: Paul Scott. Chief technician: Rob Spiller. Marketing director: Josh Thackery.

Ownership: National Cable (MSO).

WATERWOOD—Northland Cable, Box 1228, 1202 E. Houston, Crockett, TX 74835. Phone: 409-544-2031. County: San Jacinto. Also serves San Jacinto County (portions). ICA: TX0872.

TV Market Ranking: Below 100 (portions of San Jacinto County, Waterwood); Outside TV Markets (portions of San Jacinto County). Franchise award date: N.A. Franchise expiration date: N.A. Began: January 1, 1976.

Channel capacity: 36 (not 2-way capable). Channels available but not in use: N.A.

Basic Service

Subscribers: 388; Commercial subscribers: 3.

Programming (received off-air): KBTX-TV (C) Bryan; KHTV (W), KPRC-TV (N), KRIV (F), KTRK-TV (A), KTXH (U), KUHT (P) Houston; KTRE (A) Lufkin.

Programming (via satellite): WGN-TV (W) Chicago; A & E; American Movie Classics; CNN; Country Music TV; Discovery Channel; ESPN; Fox Sports Net; Lifetime; Nashville Network; TBS Superstation; The Weather Channel; Turner Network TV; USA Network.

Current originations: Automated time-weather; public access; educational access.

Fee: $50.00 installation; $23.95 monthly.

Pay Service 1

Pay Units: 81.

Programming (via satellite): HBO.

Fee: $11.00 monthly.

Pay Service 2

Pay Units: 57.

Programming (via satellite): The Movie Channel.

Fee: $9.00 monthly.

Local advertising: Yes.

Miles of plant: 26.0 (coaxial).

Manager: Ken Schuett. Chief technician: Jimmie Hutchison.

Ownership: Northland Communications Corp. (MSO).

WAXAHACHIE—Charter Communications Inc., 5227 FM 813, Waxahachie, TX 75165. Phones: 972-938-9288; 800-477-0887. Fax: 972-923-0039. Counties: Dallas, Ellis & Hamilton. Also serves Carlton, Ellis County, Ferris, Glenn Heights, Italy, Midlothian, Milford, Oak Leaf, Ovilla, Palmer, Pecan Hill, Red Oak, Rockett. ICA: TX0122.

TV Market Ranking: 12 (Ellis County, Ferris, Glenn Heights, Midlothian, Oak Leaf, Ovilla,

Palmer, Pecan Hill, Red Oak, Rockett, Waxahachie); Outside TV Markets (Carlton, Italy, Milford). Franchise award date: N.A. Franchise expiration date: N.A. Began: February 1, 1982.

Channel capacity: 54. Channels available but not in use: N.A.

Basic Service

Subscribers: 5,072.

Programming (received off-air): KPXD (X) Arlington; KDAF (W), KDFI-TV (I), KDFW (F), KDTX-TV (T), KERA-TV (P), KFWD (O), KTVT (C), KTXA (U), KXAS-TV (N), KXTX-TV (I), WFAA-TV (A) Dallas-Fort Worth; KMPX (I) Decatur; KDTN (P) Denton; KUVN (S) Garland; KHSX-TV (H) Irving.

Programming (via satellite): WGN-TV (W) Chicago; C-SPAN; Cartoon Network; Learning Channel; TBS Superstation; TV Guide Channel; The Barker; Univision.

Current originations: Public access; educational access.

Fee: $42.00 installation; $13.00 monthly.

Expanded Basic Service

Subscribers: N.A.

Programming (via satellite): A & E; American Movie Classics; BET; Bravo; CNN; Country Music TV; Discovery Channel; Disney Channel; E! Entertainment TV; ESPN; Fox Family Channel; Fox Sports Net Southwest; Headline News; Lifetime; MTV; Nashville Network; Nick at Nite's TV Land; Nickelodeon; QVC; Sci-Fi Channel; The Weather Channel; Turner Network TV; USA Network.

Fee: $15.89 monthly.

Pay Service 1

Pay Units: N.A.

Programming (via satellite): Cinemax; HBO; Showtime; The Movie Channel.

Fee: $10.95 monthly (Cinemax, Showtime or TMC), $12.95 monthly (HBO).

Pay-Per-View

Addressable homes: 2,878.

Action Pay-Per-View; Viewer's Choice.

Local advertising: Yes. Regional interconnect: Cabletime.

Equipment: Tocom addressable set top converters.

Miles of plant: 108.0 (coaxial). Total homes in franchised area: 15,240.

Manager: Mary Scearce. Chief technician: Ken Stevens. Marketing director: Carol Blake.

Ownership: Charter Communications Inc. (MSO). Purchased from Marcus Cable, April 1, 1999.

WEATHERFORD—Charter Communications Inc., 104 Tower St., Weatherford, TX 76086. Phone: 817-596-0800. Fax: 817-598-0721. County: Parker. ICA: TX0111.

TV Market Ranking: 12. Franchise award date: N.A. Franchise expiration date: N.A. Began: January 1, 1980.

Channel capacity: 44 (2-way capable; operating 2-way). Channels available but not in use: N.A.

Basic Service

Subscribers: 3,302.

Programming (received off-air): KDAF (W), KDFI-TV (I), KDFW (F), KERA-TV (P), KTVT (C), KTXA (U), KXAS-TV (N), KXTX-TV (I), WFAA-TV (A) Dallas-Fort Worth.

Programming (via satellite): WGN-TV (W) Chicago; C-SPAN; CNBC; CNN; ESPN; Headline News; Lifetime; MTV; Nashville Network; Nickelodeon; QVC; TBS Superstation; The Inspirational Network; The Weather Channel; USA Network; Univision.

Current originations: Automated time-weather; public access; government access.

Fee: $45.00 installation; $10.45 monthly; $2.50 converter; $15.95 additional installation.

Pay Service 1

Pay Units: N.A.

Programming (via satellite): Cinemax; Disney Channel; HBO; Showtime.

Fee: $7.95 monthly (Cinemax or Disney), $9.95 monthly (HBO or Showtime).

Local advertising: Yes (insert only). Available in satellite distributed & locally originated programming. Rates: $25.00/30 Seconds. Local sales manager: Pam Pollastrini.

Equipment: Phasecom & Scientific-Atlanta headend; Magnavox amplifiers; Comm/Scope cable; Sony VTRs; Video Data Systems character generator; Hamlin, Jerrold & Oak set top converters; Eagle traps; Scientific-Atlanta satellite antenna; Scientific-Atlanta satellite receivers; Falcone International commercial insert.

Miles of plant: 68.5 (coaxial). Homes passed: 6,065.

Manager: Vickie Count. Chief technician: Jim Denote. Marketing director: Scott Justice.

City fee: 3% of gross.

Ownership: Charter Communications Inc. (MSO). Purchased from Marcus Cable, April 1, 1999.

WEINERT—Weinert Cablevision, Box 6575, Abilene, TX 79608. Phone: 915-691-5787. County: Haskell. ICA: TX0873.

TV Market Ranking: Outside TV Markets. Franchise award date: N.A. Franchise expiration date: N.A. Began: N.A.

Channel capacity: N.A. Channels available but not in use: N.A.

Basic Service

Subscribers: N.A.

Programming (received off-air): KTXS-TV (A) Abilene-Sweetwater; KCBD-TV (N), KLBK-TV (C) Lubbock.

Programming (via satellite): WGN-TV (W) Chicago; ESPN; Fox Family Channel; Nickelodeon; TBS Superstation; Turner Network TV.

Fee: N.A.

Manager: D. H. Pope.

Ownership: Jayroc Inc. (MSO).

WELCH—Torrence Cablevision, Box 1167, Ridgeland, MS 39158. Phones: 601-981-6900; 800-977-8849. County: Dawson. ICA: TX0910.

TV Market Ranking: Outside TV Markets. Franchise award date: N.A. Franchise expiration date: N.A. Began: N.A.

Channel capacity: N.A. Channels available but not in use: N.A.

Basic Service

Subscribers: 38.

Programming (received off-air): KAMC (A), KCBD-TV (N), KJTV (F), KLBK-TV (C), KTXT-TV (P) Lubbock; KMID (A), KPEJ (F) Odessa-Midland.

Programming (via satellite): WGN-TV (W) Chicago; A & E; American Movie Classics; CNN; Country Music TV; Discovery Channel; ESPN; Fox Family Channel; Showtime; TBS Superstation; Turner Network TV; USA Network.

Fee: $28.00 monthly.

Homes passed: 85.

Ownership: Torrence Cable Inc. (MSO).

WELLINGTON—Classic Cable, Box 192, 908 West Ave., Wellington, TX 79095. Phone: 806-447-2061. Fax: 806-447-2471. County: Collingsworth. Also serves Collingsworth County. ICA: TX0313.

TV Market Ranking: Below 100 (portions of Collingsworth County); Outside TV Markets (portions of Collingsworth County, Wellington). Franchise award date: May 2, 1955. Franchise expiration date: November 2, 2002. Began: May 1, 1955.

Channel capacity: 40 (not 2-way capable). Channels available but not in use: 6.

Basic Service

Subscribers: 850; Commercial subscribers: 9.

Programming (received off-air): KCIT (F,U) Amarillo; 3 FMs.

Programming (via microwave): KAMR-TV (N), KFDA-TV (C), KVII-TV (A) Amarillo.

Programming (via satellite): C-SPAN; CNN; Country Music TV; Discovery Channel; Disney Channel; ESPN; Fox Family Channel; Headline News; Home Shopping Network; Lifetime; MTV; Nashville Network; Nickelodeon; Odyssey; The Weather Channel; Turner Classic Movies; Turner Network TV; USA Network; Univision.

Current originations: Automated time-weather; public access.

Fee: $20.00 installation; $10.01 monthly; $20.00 additional installation.

Pay Service 1

Pay Units: 200.

Programming (via satellite): Cinemax; HBO.

Fee: $20.00 installation; $12.00 monthly (each).

Local advertising: No.

Program Guide: Premium Channels.

Equipment: Jerrold & Scientific-Atlanta headend; GTE Sylvania amplifiers; Anaconda cable; Jerrold & Oak set top converters; Eagle & Pico traps; Scientific-Atlanta satellite antenna; Scientific-Atlanta satellite receivers.

Miles of plant: 21.0 (coaxial); None (fiber optic). Homes passed: 1,210.

Manager: Genarah Manuel. Chief technician: Tim Cummings.

City fee: 3% of gross.

Ownership: Classic Cable (MSO). Purchased from Cable One Inc., July 29, 1998.

WELLMAN—Torrence Cablevision, Box 1167, Ridgeland, MS 39158. Phones: 601-981-6900; 800-977-8849. County: Terry. ICA: TX0874.

TV Market Ranking: Outside TV Markets. Franchise award date: N.A. Franchise expiration date: N.A. Began: N.A.

Channel capacity: 36. Channels available but not in use: 20.

Basic Service

Subscribers: 44.

Programming (received off-air): KXTX-TV (I) Dallas-Fort Worth; KAMC (A), KCBD-TV (N), KJTV (F), KLBK-TV (C), KTXT-TV (P) Lubbock.

Programming (via satellite): WGN-TV (W) Chicago; A & E; American Movie Classics; CNN; Country Music TV; Discovery Channel; ESPN; Fox Family Channel; Showtime; TBS Superstation; Turner Network TV; USA Network.

Fee: $28.00 monthly.

Miles of plant: 2.4 (coaxial). Homes passed: 82.

Ownership: Torrence Cable Inc. (MSO).

WELLS—Friendship Cable of Texas Inc., Box 9090, Tyler, TX 75711-9090. Phone: 903-581-2121. Fax: 903-581-2185. County: Cherokee. ICA: TX0546.

TV Market Ranking: Below 100. Franchise award date: N.A. Franchise expiration date: N.A. Began: October 12, 1983.

Channel capacity: 54. Channels available but not in use: N.A.

Basic Service

Subscribers: 146.

Programming (received off-air): KTRE (A) Lufkin; KSLA-TV (C), KTAL-TV (N) Shreveport-Texarkana; KLTV (A) Tyler-Longview.

Programming (via satellite): WGN-TV (W) Chicago; A & E; Animal Planet; BET; C-SPAN; CNN; Country Music TV; Discovery Channel; ESPN; Fox Sports Net; Headline News; Home Shopping Network; Lifetime; Nashville Network; Nickelodeon; Outdoor Life Network; TBS Superstation; The Weather Channel; Trinity Bcstg. Network; Turner Classic Movies; Turner Network TV; USA Network; VH1.

Fee: $30.00 installation; $31.00 monthly.

Pay Service 1

Pay Units: 14.

Programming (via satellite): Cinemax.

Fee: $7.00 monthly.

Pay Service 2

Pay Units: 10.

Programming (via satellite): HBO.

Fee: $12.00 monthly.

Pay Service 3

Pay Units: 18.

Programming (via satellite): Showtime.

Fee: $7.00 monthly.

Miles of plant: 9.0 (coaxial). Homes passed: 354.

Manager: Marianne Bogey. Chief technician: Henry Harris.

Ownership: Buford Television Inc. (MSO). See Cable System Ownership.

WESLACO—Time Warner Communications, Box 2327, 2921 S. Expwy. 83, Harlingen, TX 78551. Phone: 956-425-7880. Fax: 956-412-0959. County: Hidalgo. Also serves Donna, Hidalgo County, Mercedes. ICA: TX0048.

TV Market Ranking: Below 100 (Donna, portions of Hidalgo County, Mercedes, Weslaco); Outside TV Markets (portions of Hidalgo County). Franchise award date: N.A. Franchise expiration date: N.A. Began: October 1, 1967.

Channel capacity: 35. Channels available but not in use: 5.

Basic Service

Subscribers: 8,682.

Programming (received off-air): KVEO (N) Brownsville; KGBT-TV (C), KLUJ (E), KMBH (P) Harlingen; KRGV-TV (A) Weslaco; XHAB-TV Matamoros.

Programming (via satellite): C-SPAN; Discovery Channel; FX; Fox News Channel; Nashville Network; QVC; TBS Superstation; Univision.

Current originations: Educational access; government access.

Fee: $22.95 installation; $14.00 monthly.

Expanded Basic Service

Subscribers: 8,432.

Programming (via satellite): A & E; American Movie Classics; Animal Planet; CNN; CNNfn; Disney Channel; ESPN; EWTN; Fox Family Channel; Fox Sports Net Southwest; Gems Television; Headline News; Learning Channel; Lifetime; MTV; Nickelodeon; TV Guide Channel; The Weather Channel; Turner Network TV; USA Network.

Fee: $25.00 installation; $29.00 monthly.

Pay Service 1

Pay Units: 1,113.

Programming (via satellite): Cinemax.

Fee: $12.45 monthly.

Pay Service 2

Pay Units: 1,733.

Programming (via satellite): HBO.

Fee: $12.90 monthly.

Pay Service 3

Pay Units: N.A.

Programming (via satellite): DMX; Showtime; Starz!; The New Encore.
Fee: $1.75 monthly (Encore), $6.75 monthly (Starz), $9.45 monthly (Showtime).
Pay-Per-View
Movies.
Miles of plant: 216.3 (coaxial). Homes passed: 19,499. Total homes in franchised area: 19,504.
Manager: Juan Herrera.
Ownership: Time Warner Cable (MSO); AT&T Broadband & Internet Services (MSO).

WEST—Friendship Cable of Texas Inc., Box 9090, Tyler, TX 75711-9090. Phone: 903-581-2121. Fax: 903-581-2188. County: McLennan. ICA: TX0371.
TV Market Ranking: Below 100. Franchise award date: N.A. Franchise expiration date: N.A. Began: May 1, 1982.
Channel capacity: 35. Channels available but not in use: 5.
Basic Service
Subscribers: 516.
Programming (received off-air): KDFW (F), KERA-TV (P), KTVT (C), KXAS-TV (N), KXTX-TV (I), WFAA-TV (A) Dallas-Fort Worth; KCEN-TV (N), KWKT (F), KWTX-TV (C), KXXV (A) Waco-Temple.
Programming (via satellite): Discovery Channel; Learning Channel; TBS Superstation.
Fee: $30.00 installation; $12.62 monthly.
Expanded Basic Service
Subscribers: 480.
Programming (via satellite): American Movie Classics; Animal Planet; C-SPAN; CNBC; CNN; Cartoon Network; Disney Channel; ESPN; FX; Fox Family Channel; Fox News Channel; Headline News; Home & Garden Television; Lifetime; Nashville Network; Nickelodeon; QVC; The Weather Channel; Turner Network TV; USA Network.
Fee: $30.00 installation; $15.40 monthly.
Pay Service 1
Pay Units: 68.
Programming (via satellite): Cinemax.
Fee: $12.90 monthly.
Pay Service 2
Pay Units: 95.
Programming (via satellite): The New Encore.
Fee: $1.75 monthly.
Pay Service 3
Pay Units: 81.
Programming (via satellite): HBO.
Fee: $12.90 monthly.
Pay Service 4
Pay Units: 47.
Programming (via satellite): Starz!
Fee: $6.75 monthly.
Equipment: Scientific-Atlanta satellite antenna; Scientific-Atlanta satellite receivers.
Miles of plant: 19.0 (coaxial). Homes passed: 935. Total homes in franchised area: 935.
Manager: Larry Bryant. Chief technician: Joe Stewart.
City fee: None.
Ownership: Buford Television Inc. (MSO). See Cable System Ownership.

WEST ALPINE—US Cable, 108 S. Lackey, Alpine, TX 79830. Phone: 915-837-3637. Fax: 915-837-2759. County: Brewster. ICA: TX0875.
TV Market Ranking: Outside TV Markets. Franchise award date: July 5, 1985. Franchise expiration date: N.A. Began: July 1, 1985.
Channel capacity: 36 (not 2-way capable). Channels available but not in use: None.
Basic Service
Subscribers: 88.
Programming (received off-air): KOSA-TV (C), KWES-TV (N) Odessa-Midland; allband FM.
Programming (via satellite): WGN-TV (W) Chicago; KRMA-TV (P), KUSA-TV (N) Denver; CNN; Discovery Channel; ESPN; Fox Family Channel; MTV; Nashville Network; TBS Superstation; Turner Network TV; Univision.
Fee: $35.00 installation; $26.39 monthly; $0.86 converter.
Pay Service 1
Pay Units: N.A.
Programming (via satellite): Cinemax; HBO; Showtime.
Fee: $10.95 monthly (each).
Pay-Per-View
Special events.
Fee: Varies.
Equipment: Blonder-Tongue & Scientific-Atlanta headend; Scientific-Atlanta amplifiers; Times Fiber cable; RCA set top converters.
Miles of plant: 2.0 (coaxial). Total homes in franchised area: 90.
Manager: Daryl Koedyker. Chief technician: Ramon Barragin.
City fee: 2% of gross.
Ownership: US Cable Corp. (MSO).

WEST COLUMBIA—Falcon Cable TV, 822 Market St., Portland, TX 78374. Phone: 512-643-8588. Fax: 512-643-3641. County: Brazoria. Also serves Columbia Lakes. ICA: TX0233.
TV Market Ranking: Below 100. Franchise award date: N.A. Franchise expiration date: N.A. Began: January 1, 1973.
Channel capacity: 37. Channels available but not in use: 1.
Basic Service
Subscribers: 1,213.
Programming (received off-air): KHOU-TV (C), KHTV (W), KPRC-TV (N), KRIV (F), KTRK-TV (A), KTXH (U), KUHT (P) Houston; KXLN-TV (S) Rosenberg; allband FM.
Programming (via satellite): A & E; Bravo; C-SPAN; CNN; Country Music TV; E! Entertainment TV; ESPN; Fox Sports Net Southwest; Headline News; Home Shopping Network; Nashville Network; Nickelodeon; QVC; Sci-Fi Channel; The Inspirational Network; Travel Channel.
Fee: $30.00 installation; $17.79 monthly; $15.00 additional installation.
Expanded Basic Service
Subscribers: 1,179.
Programming (via satellite): Discovery Channel; TV Food Network; The Weather Channel; USA Network.
Fee: $1.88 monthly.
Expanded Basic Service 2
Subscribers: 1,153.
Programming (via satellite): Disney Channel; TBS Superstation; Turner Network TV.
Fee: $4.45 monthly.
Pay Service 1
Pay Units: 151.
Programming (via satellite): Cinemax.
Fee: $10.00 installation; $10.95 monthly.
Pay Service 2
Pay Units: 405.
Programming (via satellite): HBO.
Fee: $11.95 monthly.
Pay Service 3
Pay Units: 105.
Programming (via satellite): The Movie Channel.
Fee: $10.95 monthly.
Pay Service 4
Pay Units: 136.
Programming (via satellite): Showtime.
Fee: $10.95 monthly.
Local advertising: Yes (locally produced). Available in character-generated programming. Rates: $0.10/Minute. Local sales manager: Brenda Landrum. Regional interconnect: Cabletime.
Program Guide: Premium Channels.
Equipment: Tocom headend; Scientific-Atlanta amplifiers; Comm/Scope cable; Scientific-Atlanta satellite antenna; Scientific-Atlanta satellite receivers.
Miles of plant: 57.0 (coaxial). Homes passed: 2,231.
Office manager: Jenny Brumley. Chief technician: Mike Kelsch.
Franchise fee: 3% of gross.
Ownership: Falcon Communications LP (MSO), joint venture formed September 30, 1998. See Cable System Ownership.

WEST ODESSA—US Cable of West Texas, 611 W. Ave. A, Seminole, TX 79360. Phone: 915-758-9221. Fax: 915-758-3379. E-mail: uscable@wtaccess.com. County: Ector. ICA: TX0969.
TV Market Ranking: Below 100. Franchise award date: N.A. Franchise expiration date: N.A. Began: N.A.
Channel capacity: 60 (not 2-way capable). Channels available but not in use: 10.
Basic Service
Subscribers: 2,034.
Programming (received off-air): KMID (A), KMLM (I), KOCV-TV (P), KOSA-TV (C), KPEJ (F), KWES-TV (N) Odessa-Midland.
Programming (via satellite): CNN; Country Music TV; Disney Channel; ESPN; Fox Sports Net Southwest; Home Shopping Network 2; Nashville Network; Nickelodeon; TV Guide Channel; Telemundo; The Weather Channel; Turner Network TV; USA Network.
Fee: $35.28 installation; $16.00 monthly; $0.86 converter.
Expanded Basic Service
Subscribers: 1,760.
Programming (via satellite): A & E; Animal Planet; C-SPAN; Cartoon Network; Encore Movie Networks; Fox Family Channel; Headline News; History Channel; Learning Channel; Lifetime; MTV; Outdoor Channel; Sci-Fi Channel; Univision.
Fee: $11.46 monthly.
A la Carte 1
Subscribers: 1,850.
Programming (via satellite): WGN-TV (W) Chicago; American Movie Classics; Discovery Channel; TBS Superstation.
Fee: $2.25 each.
Pay Service 1
Pay Units: 485.
Programming (via satellite): HBO.
Fee: $10.95 monthly.
Pay Service 2
Pay Units: 197.
Programming (via satellite): The Movie Channel.
Fee: $10.95 monthly.
Pay Service 3
Pay Units: 286.
Programming (via satellite): Showtime.
Fee: $10.95 monthly.
Pay Service 4
Pay Units: 67.
Programming (via satellite): Spice.
Fee: $10.95 monthly.
Pay-per-view manager: Candy Boyer.
Miles of plant: 169.0 (coaxial). Homes passed: 4,882.
Manager: Kenny Harris. Regional manager: Daryl Koedyker. Chief technician: Jess Webb.
Ownership: US Cable Corp. (MSO).

WESTBROOK—Torrence Cablevision, Box 1167, Ridgeland, MS 39158. Phones: 601-981-6900; 800-977-8849. County: Mitchell. ICA: TX0877.
TV Market Ranking: Below 100. Franchise award date: N.A. Franchise expiration date: N.A. Began: N.A.
Channel capacity: 36. Channels available but not in use: 21.
Basic Service
Subscribers: 45.
Programming (received off-air): KTXS-TV (A) Abilene-Sweetwater; KWAB-TV (N) Big Spring.
Programming (via satellite): WGN-TV (W) Chicago; KMGH-TV (A), KRMA-TV (P) Denver; A & E; American Movie Classics; CNN; Country Music TV; Discovery Channel; ESPN; Fox Family Channel; Showtime; TBS Superstation; Turner Network TV; USA Network.
Fee: $28.00 monthly.
Miles of plant: 4.3 (coaxial). Homes passed: 115.
Ownership: Torrence Cable Inc. (MSO).

WESTHOFF—National Cable Inc., Suite 106-A, 5151 Reed Rd., Columbus, OH 43220. Phones: 614-442-5890; 800-582-0504. Fax: 614-457-2567. County: DeWitt. ICA: TX0909.
TV Market Ranking: Outside TV Markets. Franchise award date: N.A. Franchise expiration date: N.A. Began: N.A.
Channel capacity: N.A. Channels available but not in use: N.A.
Basic Service
Subscribers: 37.
Programming (received off-air): KABB (F), KENS-TV (C), KLRN (P), KMOL-TV (N), KSAT-TV (A) San Antonio.
Programming (via satellite): WGN-TV (W) Chicago; A & E; American Movie Classics; CNN; Country Music TV; Discovery Channel; ESPN; Fox Family Channel; Showtime; TBS Superstation; Turner Network TV; USA Network.
Fee: $28.00 monthly.
Homes passed: 88.
Manager: Paul Scott. Chief technician: Rob Spiller. Marketing director: Josh Thackery.
Ownership: National Cable (MSO).

WESTMINSTER—Torrence Cablevision, Box 1167, Ridgeland, MS 39158. Phones: 601-981-6900; 800-977-8849. County: Collin. ICA: TX0634.
TV Market Ranking: Below 100. Franchise award date: N.A. Franchise expiration date: N.A. Began: N.A.
Channel capacity: 36. Channels available but not in use: 21.
Basic Service
Subscribers: 43.
Programming (received off-air): KDFW (F), KERA-TV (P), KTVT (C), KXAS-TV (N), KXTX-TV (I), WFAA-TV (A) Dallas-Fort Worth.
Programming (via satellite): WGN-TV (W) Chicago; A & E; American Movie Classics; CNN; Country Music TV; Discovery Channel; ESPN; Fox Family Channel; Showtime; TBS Superstation; Turner Network TV; USA Network.
Fee: $28.00 monthly.
Miles of plant: 8.3 (coaxial). Homes passed: 205.
Ownership: Torrence Cable Inc. (MSO).

WHARTON—Falcon Cable TV, 822 Market St., Portland, TX 78374. Phone: 512-643-8588. Fax: 512-643-3641. County: Wharton. ICA: TX0171.

TV Market Ranking: Below 100. Franchise award date: N.A. Franchise expiration date: April 21, 2002. Began: November 1, 1973.
Channel capacity: 37. Channels available but not in use: None.
Basic Service
Subscribers: 2,245.
Programming (received off-air): KHOU-TV (C), KHTV (W), KPRC-TV (N), KRIV (F), KTRK-TV (A), KTXH (U), KUHT (P) Houston; KXLN-TV (S) Rosenberg; KAVU-TV (A) Victoria; allband FM.
Programming (via satellite): A & E; American Movie Classics; BET; C-SPAN; CNN; Country Music TV; ESPN; Fox Family Channel; Fox Sports Net Southwest; Headline News; Home Shopping Network; Lifetime; MTV; Nashville Network; Nickelodeon; QVC; USA Network.
Current originations: Automated time-weather; public access; automated emergency alert.
Fee: $30.00 installation; $18.34 monthly; $2.00 converter; $7.50 additional installation.
Expanded Basic Service
Subscribers: 2,149.
Programming (via satellite): Discovery Channel; Sci-Fi Channel; The Weather Channel.
Fee: $1.94 monthly.
Expanded Basic Service 2
Subscribers: 2,127.
Programming (via satellite): Disney Channel; TBS Superstation; Turner Network TV.
Fee: $4.45 monthly.
Pay Service 1
Pay Units: 162.
Programming (via satellite): Cinemax.
Fee: $10.00 installation; $10.95 monthly.
Pay Service 2
Pay Units: 283.
Programming (via satellite): HBO.
Fee: $10.00 installation; $11.95 monthly.
Pay Service 3
Pay Units: 164.
Programming (via satellite): Showtime.
Fee: $10.95 monthly.
Pay Service 4
Pay Units: 125.
Programming (via satellite): The Movie Channel.
Fee: $10.00 installation; $10.95 monthly.
Local advertising: Yes (locally produced). Available in character-generated programming. Rates: $75.00/Month; $25.00/Week; $5.00/Day. Local sales manager: Wayne R. Helmig. Regional interconnect: Cabletime.
Equipment: Jerrold headend; RCA amplifiers; Comm/Scope cable; Texscan/MSI character generator; Scientific-Atlanta set top converters; Eagle traps; Prodelin satellite antenna; Cerro satellite receivers.
Miles of plant: 77.0 (coaxial). Homes passed: 4,060.
Office manager: Jenny Brumley. Chief technician: Mike Kelsch.
Franchise fee: 3% of gross.
Ownership: Falcon Communications LP (MSO), joint venture formed September 30, 1998. See Cable System Ownership.

WHEELER—Wheeler TV System Inc., Box 380, S. Hwy. 83, Wheeler, TX 79096. Phone: 806-826-3026. Fax: 806-826-3313. County: Wheeler. ICA: TX0460.
TV Market Ranking: Below 100. Franchise award date: N.A. Franchise expiration date: N.A. Began: March 1, 1958.
Channel capacity: 4. Channels available but not in use: N.A.
Basic Service
Subscribers: 440.
Programming (via microwave): KAMR-TV (N), KFDA-TV (C), KVII-TV (A) Amarillo.
Current originations: Automated time-weather.
Fee: $10.00 installation; $20.00 monthly.
Miles of plant: 11.0 (coaxial). Homes passed: 545.
Manager: Robert Ware. Chief technician: Franke Coates.
City fee: 2% of gross.
Ownership: Wheeler TV System Inc.

WHITEFACE—Classic Cable, Box 429, 605 N.W. 3rd St., Plainville, KS 67663-0429. Phones: 785-434-7620; 800-999-8876. Fax: 785-434-2614. County: Cochran. ICA: TX0879.
TV Market Ranking: Outside TV Markets. Franchise award date: August 4, 1988. Franchise expiration date: N.A. Began: September 1, 1988.
Channel capacity: 22 (2-way capable; operating 2-way). Channels available but not in use: N.A.
Basic Service
Subscribers: 77.
Programming (received off-air): KAMC (A), KCBD-TV (N), KJTV (F), KLBK-TV (C), KTXT-TV (P) Lubbock.
Programming (via satellite): WGN-TV (W) Chicago; CNN; Discovery Channel; Disney Channel; ESPN; Fox Family Channel; Headline News; History Channel; Home Shopping Network; Nashville Network; Nick at Nite's TV Land; TBS Superstation; The Weather Channel; Trinity Bcstg. Network; Turner Classic Movies; Turner Network TV; USA Network; Univision.
Fee: $35.00 installation; $25.95 monthly.
Pay Service 1
Pay Units: 8.
Programming (via satellite): Cinemax.
Fee: $9.95 monthly.
Pay Service 2
Pay Units: 12.
Programming (via satellite): HBO.
Fee: $9.95 monthly.
Local advertising: No.
Miles of plant: 4.5 (coaxial). Homes passed: 224.
Manager: Bill Flowers. Chief technician: Chris Christenson. Marketing director: Jennifer Hauschild.
City fee: 2% of gross.
Ownership: Classic Cable (MSO).

WHITESBORO—TCA Cable TV, 104 N. Morris, Gainesville, TX 76240. Phone: 940-665-3241. Web site: http://www.tca-cable.com. County: Grayson. Also serves Sadler. ICA: TX0271.
TV Market Ranking: Below 100. Franchise award date: N.A. Franchise expiration date: N.A. Began: July 1, 1967.
Channel capacity: 36. Channels available but not in use: N.A.
Basic Service
Subscribers: 1,121.
Programming (received off-air): KDAF (W), KDFI-TV (I), KDFW (F), KERA-TV (P), KTVT (C), KTXA (U), KXAS-TV (N), KXTX-TV (I), WFAA-TV (A) Dallas-Fort Worth; KXII (C) Sherman; KAUZ-TV (C) Wichita Falls-Lawton.
Programming (via satellite): CNBC; CNN; Discovery Channel; Fox Family Channel; Headline News; Knowledge TV; Nashville Network; Nickelodeon; QVC; TBS Superstation; The Weather Channel.
Current originations: Automated time-weather.
Fee: $39.60 installation; $10.08 monthly; $19.80 additional installation.
Commercial fee: $10.95 monthly.
Expanded Basic Service
Subscribers: 1,024.
Programming (via satellite): American Movie Classics; Court TV; ESPN; Fox Sports Net Southwest; Turner Network TV; USA Network.
Fee: $11.63 monthly.
Pay Service 1
Pay Units: 55.
Programming (via satellite): Disney Channel.
Fee: $7.50 installation; $10.95 monthly.
Pay Service 2
Pay Units: 337.
Programming (via satellite): The New Encore.
Fee: N.A.
Pay Service 3
Pay Units: 110.
Programming (via satellite): HBO.
Fee: $7.50 installation; $10.95 monthly.
Pay Service 4
Pay Units: 53.
Programming (via satellite): Showtime.
Fee: $7.50 installation; $10.95 monthly.
Local advertising: Yes (insert only). Available in satellite distributed programming.
Program Guide: Premium Channels.
Equipment: Scientific-Atlanta headend; Jerrold amplifiers; Times Fiber cable; Fort Worth Tower satellite antenna.
Miles of plant: 26.7 (coaxial). Homes passed: 1,530. Total homes in franchised area: 2,975.
Manager: Ricky Allen. Chief technician: Gary Hinkle.
City fee: 4% of gross.
Ownership: TCA Cable TV Inc. (MSO); AT&T Broadband & Internet Services (MSO). See Cable System Ownership.

WHITEWRIGHT—Cable One, Box 1223, Sherman, TX 75091. Phone: 903-364-5322. Counties: Fannin & Grayson. Also serves Bells, Howe, Savoy, Tom Bean, Van Alstyne. ICA: TX0153.
TV Market Ranking: Below 100. Franchise award date: December 4, 1978. Franchise expiration date: July 9, 2001. Began: April 1, 1982.
Channel capacity: 35 (not 2-way capable). Channels available but not in use: 5.
Basic Service
Subscribers: 1,883.
Programming (received off-air): KDAF (W), KDFI-TV (I), KDFW (F), KERA-TV (P), KTVT (C), KTXA (U), KXAS-TV (N), KXTX-TV (I), WFAA-TV (A) Dallas-Fort Worth; KXII (C) Sherman; allband FM.
Programming (via satellite): A & E; C-SPAN; CNN; Country Music TV; Discovery Channel; ESPN; Fox Family Channel; Headline News; Home Shopping Network; Nashville Network; TBS Superstation; The Weather Channel; USA Network.
Current originations: Automated time-weather.
Fee: $50.00 installation; $21.25 monthly; $3.00 converter; $15.00 additional installation.
Pay Service 1
Pay Units: 99.
Programming (via satellite): Cinemax.
Fee: $29.95 installation; $8.00 monthly.
Pay Service 2
Pay Units: 163.
Programming (via satellite): Disney Channel.
Fee: $35.00 installation; $7.00 monthly.
Pay Service 3
Pay Units: 134.
Programming (via satellite): HBO.
Fee: $35.00 installation; $10.25 monthly.
Pay Service 4
Pay Units: 595.
Programming (via satellite): Fox Sports Net Southwest.
Fee: $35.00 installation; $9.75 monthly.
Pay Service 5
Pay Units: 169.
Programming (via satellite): The Movie Channel.
Fee: $35.00 installation; $8.50 monthly.
Pay Service 6
Pay Units: 131.
Programming (via satellite): Showtime.
Fee: $35.00 installation; $9.50 monthly.
Local advertising: Yes. Available in character-generated programming. Rates: $45.00/Month; $15.00/Week. Local sales manager: Pat Alexander.
Program Guide: Premium Channels.
Equipment: Scientific-Atlanta headend; C-COR amplifiers; Times Fiber cable; Texscan character generator; Scientific-Atlanta set top converters; Eagle & Pico traps; Scientific-Atlanta satellite antenna; Harris, Microdyne & Scientific-Atlanta satellite receivers.
Miles of plant: 77.0 (coaxial). Homes passed: 3,800. Total homes in franchised area: 4,100.
Manager: Claude Edwards. Chief engineer: Cecil Miller. Marketing director & program director: Allan Layman.
City fee: 3% of gross.
Ownership: Cable One Inc. (MSO). Purchased from Northland Communications Corp., May 1, 1999.

WHITNEY—Charter Communications Inc., 5227 FM 813, Waxahachie, TX 75165. Phones: 972-938-9288; 800-477-0887. Fax: 972-923-0039. County: Hill. Also serves Lake Whitney. ICA: TX0403.
TV Market Ranking: Below 100. Franchise award date: N.A. Franchise expiration date: N.A. Began: October 1, 1982.
Channel capacity: 52. Channels available but not in use: N.A.
Basic Service
Subscribers: 972.
Programming (received off-air): KDAF (W), KDFI-TV (I), KDFW (F), KDTX-TV (T), KERA-TV (P), KTVT (C), KTXA (U), KXAS-TV (N), KXTX-TV (I), WFAA-TV (A) Dallas-Fort Worth; KHSX-TV (H) Irving; KWTX-TV (C) Waco-Temple.
Programming (via satellite): WGN-TV (W) Chicago; TBS Superstation.

Fee: $26.00 installation; $8.45 monthly; $15.00 additional installation.

Expanded Basic Service

Subscribers: N.A.

Programming (via satellite): American Movie Classics; CNN; Country Music TV; Discovery Channel; ESPN; Fox Family Channel; Fox Sports Net Southwest; Lifetime; MTV; Nashville Network; Nickelodeon; The Weather Channel; Turner Network TV; USA Network.

Fee: $11.41 monthly.

Pay Service 1

Pay Units: N.A.

Programming (via satellite): Cinemax; Disney Channel; HBO; Showtime.

Fee: $7.00 monthly (Showtime), $8.95 monthly (Disney), $9.00 monthly (Cinemax), $12.00 monthly (HBO).

Miles of plant: 18.0 (coaxial).

Manager: Mary Scearce. Chief technician: Ken Stevens.

Ownership: Charter Communications Inc. (MSO). Purchased from Marcus Cable, April 1, 1999.

WICHITA FALLS—Vista Cablevision Inc., 3225 Maurine St., Wichita Falls, TX 76305. Phone: 940-855-5700. Fax: 940-855-0465. Counties: Archer & Wichita. Also serves Lakeside City, Sheppard AFB, Wichita County (unincorporated areas). ICA: TX0026.

TV Market Ranking: Below 100. Franchise award date: N.A. Franchise expiration date: N.A. Began: November 1, 1979.

Channel capacity: 38 (not 2-way capable). Channels available but not in use: None.

Basic Service

Subscribers: 24,689; Commercial subscribers: 31.

Programming (received off-air): KAUZ-TV (C), KFDX-TV (N), KJTL (F,U), KSWO-TV (A) Wichita Falls-Lawton; 24 FMs.

Programming (via microwave): KERA-TV (P) Dallas-Fort Worth.

Programming (via satellite): C-SPAN; C-SPAN 2; CNBC; E! Entertainment TV; QVC.

Current originations: Public access; educational access; government access; leased access; automated emergency alert; local sports.

Fee: $50.00 installation; $10.10 monthly.

Expanded Basic Service

Subscribers: 23,881.

Programming (via satellite): WGN-TV (W) Chicago; A & E; American Movie Classics; BET; CNN; Discovery Channel; ESPN; Fox Family Channel; Headline News; Lifetime; MTV; Nashville Network; Nickelodeon; Odyssey; TBS Superstation; The Weather Channel; Travel Channel; Turner Network TV; USA Network; Univision.

Fee: $50.00 installation; $11.52 monthly.

Pay Service 1

Pay Units: N.A.

Programming (via satellite): Cinemax; Disney Channel; HBO; Showtime.

Fee: $12.55 monthly (each).

Local advertising: Yes (locally produced & insert). Available in satellite distributed, locally originated & character-generated programming. Rates: $40.00/Minute; $20.00/30 Seconds. Local sales manager: Ralph Dunkelberg III.

Equipment: Scientific-Atlanta headend; Magnavox amplifiers; Comm/Scope cable; Sony cameras; Sony VTRs; Compuvid & Laird character generator; Hamlin & Jerrold set top converters; Eagle traps; Microdyne satellite antenna.

Miles of plant: 500.0 (coaxial); None (fiber optic). Homes passed: 43,100.

Manager: Rick Orr. Chief technician: Milt Slavin.

City fee: 5% of gross.

Ownership: Time Warner Cable (MSO); Advance/Newhouse Partnership (MSO).

WICKETT—Classic Cable, Box 429, 605 N.W. 3rd St., Plainville, KS 67663-0429. Phones: 785-434-7620; 800-999-8876. Fax: 785-434-2614. County: Ward. ICA: TX0880.

TV Market Ranking: Below 100. Franchise award date: October 14, 1982. Franchise expiration date: October 14, 1997. Began: N.A.

Channel capacity: 36 (2-way capable; operating 2-way). Channels available but not in use: N.A.

Basic Service

Subscribers: 98.

Programming (received off-air): KMID (A), KMLM (I), KOSA-TV (C), KPEJ (F), KWES-TV (N) Odessa-Midland.

Programming (via satellite): WGN-TV (W) Chicago; CNN; Country Music TV; Discovery Channel; Disney Channel; ESPN; Fox Family Channel; History Channel; Home Shopping Network; Learning Channel; Nashville Network; TBS Superstation; The Weather Channel; Turner Network TV; USA Network; Univision.

Fee: $35.00 installation; $27.95 monthly.

Pay Service 1

Pay Units: 6.

Programming (via satellite): Showtime.

Fee: $9.95 monthly.

Pay Service 2

Pay Units: 32.

Programming (via satellite): HBO.

Fee: $9.95 monthly.

Miles of plant: 7.0 (coaxial). Homes passed: 231.

Manager: Bill Flowers. Chief technician: Ben Hernandez. Marketing director: Jennifer Hauschild.

City fee: 2% of gross subscriber revenue.

Ownership: Classic Cable (MSO).

WILDWOOD RESORT CITY—Friendship Cable of Texas Inc., Box 9090, Tyler, TX 75711-9090. Phone: 903-581-2121. Fax: 903-581-2185. Counties: Hardin & Tyler. ICA: TX0537.

TV Market Ranking: 88. Franchise award date: N.A. Franchise expiration date: N.A. Began: N.A.

Channel capacity: 36 (not 2-way capable). Channels available but not in use: 5.

Basic Service

Subscribers: 343.

Programming (received off-air): KBMT (A), KBTV-TV (N), KFDM-TV (C) Beaumont-Port Arthur; KVHP (F) Lake Charles.

Programming (via satellite): WGN-TV (W) Chicago; A & E; CNN; Country Music TV; Discovery Channel; ESPN; Fox Family Channel; Fox Sports Net Southwest; Headline News; Lifetime; Nashville Network; Nickelodeon; TBS Superstation; The Inspirational Network; The Weather Channel; Turner Classic Movies; Turner Network TV; USA Network.

Fee: $32.51 monthly.

Pay Service 1

Pay Units: 10.

Programming (via satellite): Cinemax.

Fee: $10.95 monthly.

Pay Service 2

Pay Units: 9.

Programming (via satellite): Disney Channel.

Fee: $10.95 monthly.

Pay Service 3

Pay Units: 33.

Programming (via satellite): HBO.

Fee: $10.95 monthly.

Pay Service 4

Pay Units: 22.

Programming (via satellite): Showtime.

Fee: $5.95 monthly.

Miles of plant: 21.0 (coaxial). Homes passed: 386.

Manager: Wanda Pyburn. Chief technician: Mike Deal.

Ownership: Buford Television Inc. (MSO). See Cable System Ownership.

WILLOW PARK—Mallard Cablevision, 100-D El Chico Trail, Willow Park, TX 76087. Phones: 817-441-8073; 800-669-2288. Fax: 817-441-6464. Counties: Palo Pinto & Parker. Also serves Aledo, Annetta, Annetta North, Annetta South, Hudson Oaks, Olson Green Acres, Parker County. ICA: TX0177.

TV Market Ranking: 12 (Aledo, Annetta, Annetta North, Annetta South, Hudson Oaks, portions of Parker County, Willow Park); Outside TV Markets (Olson Green Acres, portions of Parker County). Franchise award date: December 1, 1981. Franchise expiration date: December 1, 2001. Began: December 1, 1982.

Channel capacity: 40 (2-way capable; operating 2-way). Channels available but not in use: 6.

Basic Service

Subscribers: 1,002.

Programming (received off-air): KDAF (W), KDFI-TV (I), KDFW (F), KDTX-TV (T), KERA-TV (P), KTVT (C), KTXA (U), KXAS-TV (N), KXTX-TV (I), WFAA-TV (A) Dallas-Fort Worth; KMPX (I) Decatur; KDTN (P) Denton; KINT-TV (S) El Paso.

Programming (via satellite): WGN-TV (W) Chicago; A & E; CNBC; CNN; Discovery Channel; ESPN; FX; Fox Family Channel; Fox News Channel; Fox Sports Net Southwest; Headline News; Home Shopping Network; Lifetime; MTV; Nashville Network; Nickelodeon; TBS Superstation; The Inspirational Network; The Weather Channel; Turner Network TV; USA Network.

Current originations: Automated timeweather; government access.

Fee: $30.00 installation; $29.95 monthly; $2.00 converter.

Pay Service 1

Pay Units: 79.

Programming (via satellite): Cinemax.

Fee: $10.00 installation; $11.95 monthly.

Pay Service 2

Pay Units: 89.

Programming (via satellite): Disney Channel.

Fee: $10.00 installation; $9.95 monthly.

Pay Service 3

Pay Units: 292.

Programming (via satellite): HBO.

Fee: $10.00 installation; $11.95 monthly.

Local advertising: No.

Equipment: Catel & Microdyne headend; Scientific-Atlanta amplifiers; Comm/Scope cable; Panasonic cameras; Sony VTRs; Eagle & Pico traps; Fort Worth Tower satellite antenna.

Miles of plant: 290.0 (coaxial); 90.0 (fiber optic). Homes passed: 2,302.

Manager: Doug Grassmann.

City fee: 4% of gross.

Ownership: Mallard Cablevision (MSO). Purchased from Cambridge Communications, May 1, 1999.

WILLS POINT—Mission Cablevision, 920 Whitmore Dr., Rockwall, TX 75087. Phone: 800-783-5708. Fax: 214-722-6218. County: Van Zandt. Also serves Edgewood. ICA: TX0338.

TV Market Ranking: Below 100 (Wills Point); Outside TV Markets (Edgewood). Franchise award date: N.A. Franchise expiration date: June 1, 1999. Began: February 1, 1983.

Channel capacity: 35 (2-way capable; operating 2-way). Channels available but not in use: 6.

Basic Service

Subscribers: 907.

Programming (received off-air): KDAF (W), KDFI-TV (I), KDFW (F), KERA-TV (P), KTVT (C), KTXA (U), KXTX-TV (I), WFAA-TV (A) Dallas-Fort Worth; KLTV (A) Tyler-Longview.

Programming (via satellite): WGN-TV (W) Chicago; C-SPAN; CNN; ESPN; Fox Family Channel; MTV; Nashville Network; Nickelodeon; TBS Superstation; USA Network.

Fee: $25.00 installation; $20.95 monthly; $15.00 additional installation.

Pay Service 1

Pay Units: N.A.

Programming (via satellite): Cinemax; Disney Channel; HBO; Showtime; The Movie Channel.

Fee: $15.00 installation; $9.00 monthly (each).

Local advertising: Yes (locally produced). Rates: $5.00/Day.

Equipment: Scientific-Atlanta headend; Scientific-Atlanta amplifiers; Comm/Scope cable; Panasonic cameras; Panasonic VTRs; Scientific-Atlanta set top converters; Scientific-Atlanta addressable set top converters; Eagle traps; Fort Worth Tower satellite antenna; Microdyne satellite receivers.

Miles of plant: 40.0 (coaxial). Additional miles planned: 17.0 (coaxial). Homes passed: 1,110.

Manager: Rhonda Jordon. Chief technician: Lynn Anderson.

City fee: 3% of gross.

Ownership: Fanch Communications Inc. (MSO); Time Warner Cable (MSO). See Cable System Ownership.

WILMER—Metro Cable, Suite 100, 3617 Kim Dr., Irving, TX 75061. Phone: 972-986-0243. County: Dallas. ICA: TX0307.

TV Market Ranking: 12. Franchise award date: N.A. Franchise expiration date: October 1, 1997. Began: January 1, 1985.

Channel capacity: 36. Channels available but not in use: 9.

Basic Service

Subscribers: N.A.

Programming (received off-air): KDAF (W), KDFI-TV (I), KDFW (F), KDTX-TV (T), KTVT (C), KTXA (U), KXAS-TV (N), KXTX-TV (I), WFAA-TV (A) Dallas-Fort Worth.

Programming (via satellite): WGN-TV (W) Chicago; A & E; C-SPAN; CNN; ESPN; GalaVision; Goodlife TV Network; Home Shopping Network; Lifetime; MTV; Nashville Network; Nickelodeon; TBS Superstation; The Weather Channel; Univision.

Fee: $12.00 monthly.

Pay Service 1

Pay Units: N.A.

Programming (via satellite): Cinemax; Disney Channel; HBO.

Fee: $7.50 monthly (each).

Equipment: Magnavox & Phasecom headend; Scientific-Atlanta cable; Video Data Systems character generator; Hughes satellite antenna; DX Communications satellite receivers.

Miles of plant: 12.0 (coaxial). Homes passed: 1,250. Total homes in franchised area: 1,250.
Manager: David Gorman. Chief technician: Ron Palluth.
Ownership: Future Communications Inc.

WILSON—Cablecomm, 320 W. Main St., Brownfield, TX 79316. Phones: 806-637-2313; 800-638-8457. County: Lynn. ICA: TX0650.
TV Market Ranking: Below 100. Franchise award date: September 20, 1982. Franchise expiration date: September 20, 2007. Began: January 1, 1983.
Channel capacity: 40 (not 2-way capable). Channels available but not in use: 29.
Basic Service
Subscribers: 37.
Programming (received off-air): KAMC (A), KCBD-TV (N), KJTV (F), KLBK-TV (C), KTXT-TV (P) Lubbock.
Programming (via satellite): WGN-TV (W) Chicago; ESPN; Fox Family Channel; Nashville Network; TBS Superstation.
Fee: $32.30 installation; $16.95 monthly; $2.00 converter.
Pay Service 1
Pay Units: 37.
Programming (via satellite): HBO.
Fee: $7.55 monthly.
Local advertising: No.
Program Guide: Premium Channels.
Equipment: Blonder-Tongue, Scientific-Atlanta & Tocom headend; Scientific-Atlanta amplifiers; Comm/Scope cable; Standard Components & Scientific-Atlanta set top converters; Pico & Eagle traps; Vidare satellite antenna; Hughes & Automation Techniques satellite receivers.
Miles of plant: 4.0 (coaxial). Homes passed: 186.
Manager: Rex Thackerson. Chief technician: Gary Strickland. Marketing director: Bill Forgey.
City fee: 2% of gross.
Ownership: Fanch Communications Inc. (MSO); Time Warner Cable (MSO). See Cable System Ownership.

WIMBERLEY—Time Warner, 12012 N. Mo Pac Expressway, Austin, TX 78758. Phone: 512-485-6100. Fax: 512-485-6105. County: Hays. ICA: TX0217.
TV Market Ranking: Below 100. Franchise award date: N.A. Franchise expiration date: N.A. Began: November 1, 1982.
Channel capacity: 35. Channels available but not in use: None.
Basic Service
Subscribers: 707.
Programming (received off-air): KEYE-TV (C), KLRU (P), KNVA (W), KTBC (F), KVUE-TV (A), KXAN-TV (N) Austin; KENS-TV (C) San Antonio.
Programming (via satellite): C-SPAN; C-SPAN 2; CNBC; Country Music TV; Lifetime; Odyssey; Pax Net; The Weather Channel; Trinity Bcstg. Network; Univision.
Current originations: Local news.
Fee: $28.21 installation; $9.50 monthly; $25.96 additional installation.
Expanded Basic Service
Subscribers: N.A.
Programming (via satellite): A & E; American Movie Classics; Animal Planet; CNN; Cartoon Network; Discovery Channel; ESPN; ESPN 2; Fox Family Channel; Fox Sports Net Southwest; Golf Channel; Headline News; History Channel; Home & Garden Television; Learning Channel; MSNBC; MTV; Nashville Network; Nick at Nite; Nickelodeon; TBS Superstation; Travel Channel; Turner Classic Movies; Turner Network TV; USA Network; VH1.
Fee: $25.12 monthly.
Pay Service 1
Pay Units: 93.
Programming (via satellite): Disney Channel.
Fee: $8.95 monthly.
Pay Service 2
Pay Units: N.A.
Programming (via satellite): The New Encore.
Fee: N.A.
Pay Service 3
Pay Units: 536.
Programming (via satellite): HBO.
Fee: $11.40 monthly.
Pay Service 4
Pay Units: 23.
Programming (via satellite): The Movie Channel.
Fee: $8.95 monthly.
Pay Service 5
Pay Units: 167.
Programming (via satellite): Showtime.
Fee: $8.95 monthly.
Local advertising: Yes. Regional interconnect: Cabletime.
Miles of plant: 53.0 (coaxial). Homes passed: 2,061.
Chief technician: Matt Stanek. Program director: George Warmingham. Marketing director: Michelle Golden.
Ownership: Time Warner Cable (MSO).

WINK—Classic Cable, Box 429, 605 N.W. 3rd St., Plainville, KS 67663-0429. Phones: 785-434-7620; 800-999-8876. Fax: 785-434-2614. County: Winkler. ICA: TX0478.
TV Market Ranking: Below 100. Franchise award date: November 3, 1981. Franchise expiration date: November 3, 2001. Began: April 3, 1984.
Channel capacity: 52 (2-way capable; operating 2-way). Channels available but not in use: N.A.
Basic Service
Subscribers: 256.
Programming (received off-air): KMLM (I), KOSA-TV (C), KPEJ (F), KWES-TV (N) Odessa-Midland.
Programming (via microwave): KMID (A) Odessa-Midland.
Programming (via satellite): WGN-TV (W) Chicago; KRMA-TV (P) Denver; A & E; Animal Planet; C-SPAN; CNN; Cartoon Network; Country Music TV; Discovery Channel; ESPN; Fox Family Channel; Fox Sports Net Southwest; Headline News; History Channel; Home Shopping Network; Learning Channel; Lifetime; Nashville Network; Nick at Nite's TV Land; Nickelodeon; TBS Superstation; The Weather Channel; Turner Classic Movies; Turner Network TV; USA Network; Univision.
Current originations: Educational access.
Fee: $35.00 installation; $27.95 monthly.
Pay Service 1
Pay Units: 25.
Programming (via satellite): Disney Channel.
Fee: $8.95 monthly.
Pay Service 2
Pay Units: 55.
Programming (via satellite): Cinemax.
Fee: $10.95 monthly.
Pay Service 3
Pay Units: 65.
Programming (via satellite): HBO.
Fee: $11.95 monthly.
Local advertising: No.
Equipment: Scientific-Atlanta headend; Texscan amplifiers; Times Fiber & Belden cable; Scientific-Atlanta set top converters; Eagle traps; Anixter-Mark & Scientific-Atlanta satellite antenna.
Miles of plant: 11.2 (coaxial). Homes passed: 518. Total homes in franchised area: 614.
Manager: Bill Flowers. Chief technician: Ben Hernandez. Marketing director: Jennifer Hauschild.
City fee: 2% of gross ($100 minimum).
Ownership: Classic Cable (MSO).

WINNIE—Warner Cable, Box 1960, 875 North St., Vidor, TX 77670-1960. Phones: 409-769-8161; 800-828-8380. Counties: Chambers & Jefferson. Also serves Hamshire. ICA: TX0258.
TV Market Ranking: 88. Franchise award date: N.A. Franchise expiration date: N.A. Began: February 1, 1983.
Channel capacity: 36 (not 2-way capable). Channels available but not in use: 4.
Basic Service
Subscribers: 995; Commercial subscribers: 1.
Programming (received off-air): KHSH-TV (H) Alvin; KBMT (A), KBTV-TV (N), KFDM-TV (C) Beaumont-Port Arthur; KHOU-TV (C), KHTV (W), KPRC-TV (N), KRIV (F), KTXH (U), KUHT (P) Houston.
Fee: $30.00 installation; $10.58 monthly; $1.75 converter.
Expanded Basic Service
Subscribers: 857.
Programming (via satellite): WGN-TV (W) Chicago; BET; CNN; Cartoon Network; Country Music TV; Discovery Channel; Disney Channel; ESPN; Fox Family Channel; Fox Sports Net Southwest; Lifetime; MTV; Nashville Network; Nickelodeon; QVC; TBS Superstation; The Weather Channel; Turner Classic Movies; Turner Network TV; USA Network.
Fee: $20.00 installation; $17.90 monthly.
Pay Service 1
Pay Units: 225.
Programming (via satellite): HBO.
Fee: $20.00 installation; $11.45 monthly.
Pay Service 2
Pay Units: 117.
Programming (via satellite): Showtime.
Fee: $20.00 installation; $11.45 monthly.
Local advertising: No.
Program Guide: Premium Channels.
Equipment: Scientific-Atlanta headend; Magnavox amplifiers; Comm/Scope cable; Scientific-Atlanta & Jerrold set top converters; Pico & Eagle traps; Scientific-Atlanta & Harris satellite antenna; Scientific-Atlanta satellite receivers.
Miles of plant: 42.0 (coaxial); None (fiber optic). Homes passed: 1,650.
Manager: Jim Dwyer. Marketing director: Bill Forgey.
Franchise fee: None.
Ownership: Time Warner Cable (MSO); Fanch Communications Inc. (MSO). See Cable System Ownership.

WINTERS—TCA Cable TV, 28 W. Concho Ave., San Angelo, TX 76903. Phone: 915-655-8911. Fax: 915-658-6876. Web site: http://www.tca-cable.com. County: Runnels. ICA: TX0965.
TV Market Ranking: 7,30. Franchise award date: N.A. Franchise expiration date: July 1, 2002. Began: N.A.
Channel capacity: 36 (not 2-way capable). Channels available but not in use: 4.
Basic Service
Subscribers: 578; Commercial subscribers: 1.
Programming (received off-air): KRBC-TV (N), KTAB-TV (C), KTXS-TV (A) Abilene-Sweetwater; KERA-TV (P), WFAA-TV (A) Dallas-Fort Worth; KIDY (F), KLST (C) San Angelo.
Programming (via satellite): TBS Superstation.
Fee: $38.00 installation; $10.90 monthly; $0.25 converter.
Expanded Basic Service
Subscribers: 554.
Programming (via satellite): American Movie Classics; C-SPAN; CNN; Discovery Channel; ESPN; Fox Family Channel; Fox Sports Net Southwest; Great American Country; Headline News; Learning Channel; Lifetime; MTV; Nashville Network; Nickelodeon; Odyssey; QVC; The Weather Channel; Turner Network TV; USA Network; Univision.
Fee: $38.00 installation; $24.50 monthly.
Pay Service 1
Pay Units: 90.
Programming (via satellite): Disney Channel; HBO.
Fee: $15.45 monthly.
Pay Service 2
Pay Units: 145.
Programming (via satellite): HBO.
Fee: $13.00 monthly.
Pay Service 3
Pay Units: 91.
Programming (via satellite): HBO; Showtime.
Fee: $15.45 monthly.
Pay Service 4
Pay Units: N.A.
Programming (via satellite): Disney Channel; Showtime.
Fee: $14.45 monthly.
Equipment: Scientific-Atlanta headend; Jerrold amplifiers; Times Fiber & Comm/Scope cable; Scientific-Atlanta set top converters; Eagle traps; Scientific-Atlanta satellite antenna; Scientific-Atlanta satellite receivers.
Miles of plant: 19.0 (coaxial). Homes passed: 792.
Manager: Archie Kountz. Chief engineer: Robert Ano. Customer service manager: Naomi Gonzales. Marketing director: Mike Johnson.
Ownership: TCA Cable TV Inc. (MSO); AT&T Broadband & Internet Services (MSO). See Cable System Ownership.

WODEN—Friendship Cable of Texas Inc., Box 9090, Tyler, TX 75711-9090. Phone: 903-581-2121. Fax: 903-581-2185. County: Nacogdoches. Also serves Nacogdoches County (portions). ICA: TX0553.
TV Market Ranking: Below 100. Franchise award date: N.A. Franchise expiration date: N.A. Began: N.A.
Channel capacity: 36. Channels available but not in use: 7.
Basic Service
Subscribers: 213.
Programming (received off-air): KETK-TV (N) Jacksonville; KTRE (A) Lufkin; KSLA-TV (C) Shreveport-Texarkana.
Programming (via satellite): WXIA-TV (N) Atlanta; WBBM-TV (C), WGN-TV (W) Chicago; CNN; Country Music TV; Discovery Channel; ESPN; Fox Family Channel; Headline News; Lifetime; Nashville Network; Nickelodeon; TBS Superstation; Turner Classic Movies; USA Network.

Fee: $34.35 monthly.
Pay Service 1
Pay Units: 14.
Programming (via satellite): Cinemax.
Fee: $10.95 monthly.
Pay Service 2
Pay Units: 15.
Programming (via satellite): HBO.
Fee: $10.95 monthly.
Pay Service 3
Pay Units: 19.
Programming (via satellite): Showtime.
Fee: $5.95 monthly.
Local advertising: Yes.
Miles of plant: 18.2 (coaxial). Homes passed: 415.
Manager: Marianne Bogy. Chief technician: Henry Harris.
Ownership: Buford Television Inc. (MSO). See Cable System Ownership.

WOLFE CITY—Friendship Cable of Texas Inc., Box 9090, Tyler, TX 75711-9090. Phones: 903-581-2121; 903-561-4411. Fax: 903-561-4031. Counties: Fannin & Hunt. Also serves Ladonia. ICA: TX0449.
TV Market Ranking: Outside TV Markets. Franchise award date: N.A. Franchise expiration date: N.A. Began: August 1, 1982.
Channel capacity: 52. Channels available but not in use: N.A.
Basic Service
Subscribers: 581.
Programming (received off-air): KDFW (F), KERA-TV (P), KTVT (C), KXAS-TV (N), KXTX-TV (I), WFAA-TV (A) Dallas-Fort Worth.
Programming (via satellite): WGN-TV (W) Chicago; CNN; Disney Channel; ESPN; Fox Family Channel; Nickelodeon; TBS Superstation; The Weather Channel; Turner Classic Movies; USA Network.
Current originations: Public access.
Fee: $30.00 installation; $31.55 monthly.
Pay Service 1
Pay Units: 38.
Programming (via satellite): HBO.
Fee: $12.00 monthly.
Pay Service 2
Pay Units: 85.
Programming (via satellite): Showtime.
Fee: $7.00 monthly.
Pay Service 3
Pay Units: 27.
Programming (via satellite): The Movie Channel.
Fee: $9.00 monthly.
Miles of plant: 31.0 (coaxial). Homes passed: 1,002.
Manager: Rodney Fletcher. Chief technician: Bo Jaubert.
Ownership: Buford Television Inc. (MSO). See Cable System Ownership.

WOODROW—Classic Cable, Box 429, 605 N.W. 3rd St., Plainville, KS 67663-0429. Phones: 785-434-7620; 800-999-8876. Fax: 785-434-2614. County: Lubbock. Also serves Lubbock County (portions). ICA: TX0330.
TV Market Ranking: Below 100. Franchise award date: October 24, 1985. Franchise expiration date: October 24, 2000. Began: January 1, 1985.
Channel capacity: 41 (2-way capable; operating 2-way). Channels available but not in use: N.A.
Basic Service
Subscribers: 162.
Programming (received off-air): KAMC (A), KCBD-TV (N), KJTV (F), KLBK-TV (C), KTXT-TV (P), KUPT-LP (U) Lubbock.
Programming (via translator): KVDA (O) San Antonio.
Programming (via satellite): WGN-TV (W) Chicago; A & E; American Movie Classics; CNN; Cartoon Network; Discovery Channel; Disney Channel; E! Entertainment TV; ESPN; Fox Family Channel; Goodlife TV Network; Headline News; Learning Channel; Lifetime; Nashville Network; Nick at Nite's TV Land; Nickelodeon; QVC; Sci-Fi Channel; TBS Superstation; The Weather Channel; Travel Channel; Turner Network TV; USA Network; Univision; VH1.
Fee: $35.00 installation; $27.95 monthly.
Pay Service 1
Pay Units: 25.
Programming (via satellite): Cinemax.
Fee: $9.95 monthly.
Pay Service 2
Pay Units: 18.
Programming (via satellite): Showtime.
Fee: $9.95 monthly.
Pay Service 3
Pay Units: 45.
Programming (via satellite): HBO.
Fee: $9.95 monthly.
Local advertising: No.
Miles of plant: 19.4 (coaxial). Homes passed: 1,137.
Manager: Bill Flowers. Chief technician: Chris Christenson. Marketing director: Jennifer Hauschild.
City fee: 3% of gross.
Ownership: Classic Cable (MSO).

WOODVILLE—Friendship Cable of Texas Inc., Box 9090, Tyler, TX 75711-9090. Phone: 903-581-2121. Fax: 903-581-2185. Counties: Fannin & Tyler. Also serves Hillister, Ivanhoe Estates, Spurger, Warren. ICA: TX0882.
TV Market Ranking: Outside TV Markets. Franchise award date: April 1, 1977. Franchise expiration date: March 1, 2000. Began: April 1, 1977.
Channel capacity: 54 (not 2-way capable). Channels available but not in use: N.A.
Basic Service
Subscribers: 1,075.
Programming (received off-air): KBMT (A), KBTV-TV (N), KFDM-TV (C) Beaumont-Port Arthur; KHOU-TV (C), KRIV (F), KTXH (U) Houston; KTRE (A) Lufkin; 11 FMs.
Programming (via microwave): KHTV (W), KTRK-TV (A), KUHT (P) Houston.
Programming (via satellite): WGN-TV (W) Chicago; A & E; CNN; Comedy Central; Country Music TV; Discovery Channel; ESPN; Fox Sports Net Southwest; Headline News; Home Shopping Network; MTV; Nashville Network; Nickelodeon; Odyssey; Sci-Fi Channel; TBS Superstation; The Weather Channel; Turner Network TV; USA Network; VH1.
Fee: $30.00 installation; $32.65 monthly.
Pay Service 1
Pay Units: 39.
Programming (via satellite): Cinemax.
Fee: $11.00 monthly.
Pay Service 2
Pay Units: 81.
Programming (via satellite): HBO.
Fee: $11.00 monthly.
Pay Service 3
Pay Units: 47.
Programming (via satellite): Showtime.
Fee: $5.95 monthly.
Local advertising: No.
Equipment: Scientific-Atlanta headend; Jerrold amplifiers; Comm/Scope cable; Scientific-Atlanta set top converters; Scientific-Atlanta satellite antenna; Scientific-Atlanta satellite receivers.
Miles of plant: 113.2 (coaxial). Homes passed: 2,817.
Manager: Wanda Pyburn. Chief technician: Mike Deal.
City fee: 3% of basic.
Ownership: Buford Television Inc. (MSO). See Cable System Ownership.

WORTHAM—Northland Cable, 515 W. Tyler, Mexia, TX 76667. Phone: 254-562-2872. Fax: 254-562-6454. County: Freestone. ICA: TX0549.
TV Market Ranking: Outside TV Markets. Franchise award date: January 1, 1988. Franchise expiration date: August 1, 2001. Began: January 1, 1988.
Channel capacity: 35 (2-way capable; operating 2-way). Channels available but not in use: 12.
Basic Service
Subscribers: 277.
Programming (received off-air): KDAF (W), KDFI-TV (I), KDFW (F), KERA-TV (P), KTVT (C), KTXA (U), KXAS-TV (N), KXTX-TV (I), WFAA-TV (A) Dallas-Fort Worth; KCEN-TV (N), KWKT (F), KWTX-TV (C), KXXV (A) Waco-Temple.
Programming (via satellite): WGN-TV (W) Chicago; American Movie Classics; BET; CNN; Country Music TV; Discovery Channel; ESPN; Fox Family Channel; Fox Sports Net Southwest; Headline News; Nashville Network; TBS Superstation; Turner Network TV.
Current originations: Automated time-weather.
Fee: $55.00 installation; $25.25 monthly.
Pay Service 1
Pay Units: 22.
Programming (via satellite): Disney Channel.
Fee: N.A.
Pay Service 2
Pay Units: 30.
Programming (via satellite): Showtime.
Fee: N.A.
Equipment: Scientific-Atlanta headend; Scientific-Atlanta amplifiers; Times Fiber cable; Pico traps; Prodelin satellite antenna; Microdyne satellite receivers.
Miles of plant: 10.0 (coaxial); None (fiber optic). Homes passed: 350. Total homes in franchised area: 360.
Manager: Jimmie Cullins.
Ownership: Northland Communications Corp. (MSO).

WYLIE—TCI Cablevision of Texas Inc., Box 64, Allen, TX 75002-3425. Phone: 214-727-5723. Counties: Collin & Dallas. Also serves Farmersville, Princeton, Sachse, St. Paul. ICA: TX0109.
TV Market Ranking: 12. Franchise award date: N.A. Franchise expiration date: N.A. Began: March 1, 1980.
Channel capacity: 36. Channels available but not in use: 5.
Basic Service
Subscribers: 2,874.
Programming (received off-air): KDAF (W), KDFI-TV (I), KDFW (F), KERA-TV (P), KTVT (C), KTXA (U), KXAS-TV (N), KXTX-TV (I), WFAA-TV (A) Dallas-Fort Worth.
Programming (via satellite): WGN-TV (W) Chicago; CNBC; CNN; Discovery Channel; Fox Family Channel; Lifetime; MTV; Nashville Network; QVC; TBS Superstation; The Weather Channel.
Fee: $60.00 installation; $17.35 monthly.
Expanded Basic Service
Subscribers: 2,642.
Programming (via satellite): American Movie Classics; ESPN; Fox Sports Net Southwest; Turner Network TV; USA Network.
Fee: $2.91 monthly.
Pay Service 1
Pay Units: 106.
Programming (via satellite): Cinemax.
Fee: $15.00 installation; $10.00 monthly.
Pay Service 2
Pay Units: 184.
Programming (via satellite): Disney Channel.
Fee: $15.00 installation; $10.00 monthly.
Pay Service 3
Pay Units: 857.
Programming (via satellite): The New Encore.
Fee: N.A.
Pay Service 4
Pay Units: 1,132.
Programming (via satellite): HBO.
Fee: $15.00 installation; $10.00 monthly.
Pay Service 5
Pay Units: 53.
Programming (via satellite): The Movie Channel.
Fee: $15.00 installation; $10.00 monthly.
Pay Service 6
Pay Units: 656.
Programming (via satellite): Showtime.
Fee: $15.00 installation; $10.00 monthly.
Local advertising: Yes (locally produced & insert). Available in satellite distributed programming.
Equipment: Jerrold headend; Jerrold amplifiers; Times Fiber cable; MSI character generator; Jerrold set top converters; Pico traps; Microdyne satellite antenna; Microdyne satellite receivers; Falcone International commercial insert.
Miles of plant: 133.1 (coaxial). Homes passed: 6,116. Total homes in franchised area: 11,410.
Manager: Joann Holtzclaw. Chief technician: Mike Crain.
City fee: 3% of gross.
Ownership: AT&T Broadband & Internet Services (MSO). Purchased from Tele-Communications Inc., March 9, 1999.

YOAKUM—Time Warner Communications, 410 W. Grand Ave., Yoakum, TX 77995-2618. Phone: 512-293-5293. County: Lavaca. ICA: TX0883.
TV Market Ranking: Below 100. Franchise award date: N.A. Franchise expiration date: N.A. Began: March 1, 1972.
Channel capacity: 52. Channels available but not in use: 21.
Basic Service
Subscribers: 1,690.
Programming (received off-air): KEYE-TV (C), KLRU (P), KTBC (F) Austin; KHOU-TV (C) Houston; KENS-TV (C), KMOL-TV (N), KSAT-TV (A), KVDA (O) San Antonio; KAVU-TV (A) Victoria; allband FM.
Programming (via satellite): CNN; Discovery Channel; Fox Family Channel; Headline News; Knowledge TV; Nashville Network; Nickelodeon; Odyssey; QVC; TBS Superstation; The Weather Channel.
Current originations: Local news.
Fee: $60.00 installation; $17.95 monthly.
Commercial fee: $10.95 monthly.
Expanded Basic Service
Subscribers: 1,475.
Programming (via satellite): American Movie Classics; Court TV; ESPN; Fox Sports Net

Southwest; Turner Network TV; USA Network.
Fee: $2.50 monthly.

Pay Service 1
Pay Units: 77.
Programming (via satellite): Disney Channel.
Fee: $10.00 installation; $11.50 monthly.

Pay Service 2
Pay Units: 646.
Programming (via satellite): The New Encore.
Fee: N.A.

Pay Service 3
Pay Units: 213.
Programming (via satellite): HBO.
Fee: N.A.

Pay Service 4
Pay Units: 200.
Programming (via satellite): Showtime.
Fee: $10.00 installation; $11.50 monthly.

Program Guide: The Cable Guide.
Equipment: Scientific-Atlanta headend; Jerrold amplifiers; Times Fiber cable; MSI character generator; Jerrold set top converters; Eagle traps; Scientific-Atlanta satellite antenna.
Miles of plant: 48.6 (coaxial). Total homes in franchised area: 2,169.
Manager: Carol Martin. Chief technician: Bill Black.
City fee: 5% of gross.
Ownership: AT&T Broadband & Internet Services (MSO); Time Warner Cable (MSO); Advance/Newhouse Partnership (MSO).

YORKTOWN—Classic Cable, Box 429, 605 N.W. 3rd St., Plainville, KS 67663-0429. Phones: 785-434-7620; 800-999-8876. Fax: 785-434-2614. County: DeWitt. ICA: TX0349.
TV Market Ranking: Below 100. Franchise award date: N.A. Franchise expiration date: N.A. Began: November 14, 1978.
Channel capacity: 41 (2-way capable; operating 2-way). Channels available but not in use: N.A.

Basic Service
Subscribers: 625.
Programming (received off-air): KUPT-LP (U) Lubbock; KABB (F), KENS-TV (C), KLRN (P), KMOL-TV (N), KSAT-TV (A), KVDA (O) San Antonio; KAVU-TV (A), KVCT (F) Victoria; 1 FM.
Programming (via satellite): WGN-TV (W) Chicago; A & E; Animal Planet; CNN; Country Music TV; Discovery Channel; Disney Channel; ESPN; Fox Family Channel; Fox News Channel; Fox Sports Net Southwest; Headline News; Learning Channel; Nashville Network; Nick at Nite's TV Land; Nickelodeon; QVC; TBS Superstation; The Weather Channel; Trinity Bcstg. Network; Turner Classic Movies; Turner Network TV; USA Network; Univision.
Current originations: Automated time-weather; local news.
Fee: $35.00 installation; $27.95 monthly.

Pay Service 1
Pay Units: 65.
Programming (via satellite): The Movie Channel.
Fee: $5.95 monthly.

Pay Service 2
Pay Units: 66.
Programming (via satellite): Showtime.
Fee: $9.95 monthly.

Pay Service 3
Pay Units: 70.
Programming (via satellite): HBO.
Fee: $10.95 monthly.

Equipment: Tocom headend; Blonder-Tongue & Jerrold amplifiers; CCS Hatfield cable.
Miles of plant: 18.0 (coaxial). Homes passed: 1,000. Total homes in franchised area: 1,050.
Manager: Bill Flowers. Chief technician: Walt VanLue. Marketing director: Jennifer Hauschild.
City fee: 3% of gross.
Ownership: Classic Cable (MSO).

ZAPATA—TCI Cablevision of Texas Inc., 208 W. Viggie St., Hebbronville, TX 78361-3048. Phone: 512-527-3267. County: Zapata. ICA: TX0198.
TV Market Ranking: Outside TV Markets. Franchise award date: N.A. Franchise expiration date: N.A. Began: September 1, 1973.
Channel capacity: 38. Channels available but not in use: N.A.

Basic Service
Subscribers: 2,375.
Programming (received off-air): KGNS-TV (N,A), KLDO-TV (O), KVTV (C) Laredo; XHDF-TV Mexico City; XHAW-TV Monterrey; allband FM.
Programming (via microwave): KIII (A), KRIS-TV (N), KZTV (C) Corpus Christi.
Programming (via satellite): WGN-TV (W) Chicago; C-SPAN; CNN; Country Music TV; Discovery Channel; ESPN; EWTN; GalaVision; Headline News; Home Shopping Network; Lifetime; MTV; Nashville Network; Nickelodeon; TBS Superstation; The Weather Channel; Trinity Bcstg. Network; Turner Network TV; USA Network; Univision; VH1.
Current originations: Public access; local news.
Fee: $60.00 installation; $19.57 monthly.

Pay Service 1
Pay Units: 172.
Programming (via satellite): Disney Channel.
Fee: $15.00 installation; $7.00 monthly.

Pay Service 2
Pay Units: 521.
Programming (via satellite): HBO.
Fee: $15.00 installation; $11.00 monthly.

Pay Service 3
Pay Units: 31.
Programming (via satellite): The Movie Channel.
Fee: $15.00 installation; $9.00 monthly.

Pay Service 4
Pay Units: 258.
Programming (via satellite): Showtime.
Fee: $15.00 installation; $6.00 monthly.

Equipment: AFC satellite antenna.
Miles of plant: 57.7 (coaxial). Homes passed: 2,439. Total homes in franchised area: 4,688.
Manager: Juve Morante.
City fee: 2% of gross.
Ownership: AT&T Broadband & Internet Services (MSO). Purchased from Tele-Communications Inc., March 9, 1999.

ZAVALLA—Friendship Cable of Texas Inc., Box 9090, Tyler, TX 75711-9090. Phone: 903-581-2121. Fax: 903-581-2185. County: Angelina. Also serves Angelina County (portions). ICA: TX0379.
TV Market Ranking: Below 100. Franchise award date: N.A. Franchise expiration date: N.A. Began: N.A.
Channel capacity: 36 (not 2-way capable). Channels available but not in use: 7.

Basic Service
Subscribers: 391.
Programming (received off-air): KBTV-TV (N), KFDM-TV (C) Beaumont-Port Arthur; KTRE (A) Lufkin.
Programming (via satellite): WXIA-TV (N) Atlanta; WBBM-TV (C), WGN-TV (W) Chicago; A & E; CNN; Country Music TV; Discovery Channel; Disney Channel; ESPN; Fox Family Channel; Headline News; Home Shopping Network; Nashville Network; Nickelodeon; TBS Superstation; USA Network.
Fee: $33.15 monthly.

Pay Service 1
Pay Units: 20.
Programming (via satellite): Cinemax.
Fee: $10.95 monthly.

Pay Service 2
Pay Units: 21.
Programming (via satellite): HBO.
Fee: $10.95 monthly.

Pay Service 3
Pay Units: 37.
Programming (via satellite): Showtime.
Fee: $5.95 monthly.

Local advertising: Yes.
Miles of plant: 40.1 (coaxial). Homes passed: 887.
Manager: Wanda Pyburn. Chief technician: Mike Deal.
Ownership: Buford Television Inc. (MSO). See Cable System Ownership.

UTAH

Total Systems: **79**
Total Communities Served: **233**
Franchises Not Yet Operating: **0**
Applications Pending: **0**

Communities with Applications: **0**
Number of Basic Subscribers: **266,636**
Number of Expanded Basic Subscribers: **170,632**
Number of Pay Units: **210,932**

Top 100 Markets Represented: Salt Lake City (48).

For a list of all cable communities included in this section, see the Cable Community Index located in the back of this volume.
For explanation of terms used in cable system listings, see p. D-9.

BEAR RIVER CITY—AT&T Cable Services, 5152 South 1500 West, Riverdale, UT 84405. Phone: 800-486-9829. County: Box Elder. Also serves Corinne, Honeyville. ICA: UT0039.

TV Market Ranking: Below 100. Franchise award date: January 7, 1987. Franchise expiration date: January 7, 2002. Began: February 15, 1988.

Channel capacity: 36 (not 2-way capable). Channels available but not in use: 9.

Basic Service

Subscribers: 411.

Programming (received off-air): KUWB (W) Ogden; KBYU-TV (P) Provo; KSL-TV (N), KSTU (F), KTVX (A), KUED (P), KUTV (C) Salt Lake City.

Programming (via satellite): WGN-TV (W) Chicago; A & E; CNN; Discovery Channel; ESPN; Fox Family Channel; Fox Sports Net; Learning Channel; Nashville Network; Nickelodeon; TBS Superstation; Turner Network TV; USA Network; VH1.

Fee: $36.42 installation; $22.95 monthly.

Pay Service 1

Pay Units: 54.

Programming (via satellite): Cinemax.

Fee: $12.20 monthly.

Pay Service 2

Pay Units: 79.

Programming (via satellite): Disney Channel.

Fee: $10.95 monthly.

Pay Service 3

Pay Units: 67.

Programming (via satellite): HBO.

Fee: $13.15 monthly.

Local advertising: No.

Program Guide: The Cable Guide.

Equipment: Pico headend; Magnavox amplifiers; Times Fiber cable; Pioneer & Jerrold set top converters; Pico traps; Comtech satellite antenna; Pico satellite receivers.

Miles of plant: 27.6 (coaxial). Homes passed: 762. Total homes in franchised area: 762.

Regional manager: Alan Hintze. Chief technician: Craig Davis. Marketing manager: Ron Williams. Office manager: Lorraine Nelson.

City fee: 5% of gross.

Ownership: AT&T Broadband & Internet Services (MSO). Purchased from Insight Communications Co., November 2, 1998.

BEAVER—Blackstone Cable LLC, 1104 W. Ironwood Dr., Coeur d'Alene, ID 83814-2605. Phone: 208-664-3370. Fax: 208-664-5888. County: Beaver. ICA: UT0035.

TV Market Ranking: Outside TV Markets. Franchise award date: N.A. Franchise expiration date: December 31, 2006. Began: January 20, 1982.

Channel capacity: 19 (not 2-way capable). Channels available but not in use: 4.

Basic Service

Subscribers: 476.

Programming (via translator): KBYU-TV (P) Provo; KJZZ-TV (U), KSL-TV (N), KSTU (F), KTVX (A), KUED (P), KUTV (C) Salt Lake City.

Programming (via satellite): WGN-TV (W) Chicago; American Movie Classics; CNN; Cartoon Network; Discovery Channel; Disney Channel; ESPN; Fox Family Channel; Fox News Channel; Nashville Network; TBS Superstation; The Inspirational Network; Turner Classic Movies; Turner Network TV; USA Network.

Current originations: Automated time-weather.

Fee: $43.50 installation; $21.00 monthly; $21.50 additional installation.

Pay Service 1

Pay Units: 86.

Programming (via satellite): HBO.

Fee: $10.95 monthly.

Equipment: Microwave Assoc. headend; Blonder-Tongue amplifiers; Times Fiber cable; Sony cameras; Sony VTRs; Metrodata character generator; Pioneer set top converters; Prodelin satellite antenna.

Miles of plant: 20.5 (coaxial); None (fiber optic). Homes passed: 830.

Manager: Ted Hughett.

City fee: 5% of basic.

Ownership: Blackstone Cable LLC (MSO).

BLANDING—Peak Cablevision, 1750 S. Hwy. 10, Price, UT 84501. Phone: 435-637-6813. Fax: 435-637-9755. County: San Juan. ICA: UT0032.

TV Market Ranking: Outside TV Markets. Franchise award date: N.A. Franchise expiration date: N.A. Began: November 1, 1981.

Channel capacity: 23. Channels available but not in use: N.A.

Basic Service

Subscribers: 453.

Programming (via translator): KBYU-TV (P) Provo; KSL-TV (N), KSTU (F), KTVX (A), KUED (P), KUTV (C) Salt Lake City.

Programming (via satellite): WGN-TV (W) Chicago; A & E; CNN; Country Music TV; Discovery Channel; ESPN; Fox Family Channel; Fox Sports Net; Nashville Network; TBS Superstation; Turner Network TV; USA Network.

Current originations: Public access.

Fee: $25.00 installation; $17.59 monthly.

Pay Service 1

Pay Units: 110.

Programming (via satellite): Disney Channel.

Fee: $9.00 monthly.

Pay Service 2

Pay Units: 128.

Programming (via satellite): HBO.

Fee: $11.00 monthly.

Pay Service 3

Pay Units: 79.

Programming (via satellite): The Movie Channel.

Fee: $10.00 monthly.

Equipment: Pico & Comtech headend; Magnavox & Ameco amplifiers; Times Fiber cable; MSI character generator; Jerrold set top converters; Pico traps; Comtech satellite antenna; Comtech & Pico satellite receivers.

Miles of plant: 11.0 (coaxial). Homes passed: 924.

Manager: Shane Baggs. Chief technician: Jon C. Almon.

City fee: 3% of gross.

Ownership: Peak Cablevision LLC (MSO). See Cable System Ownership.

BRIAN HEAD—Blackstone Cable LLC, 1104 W. Ironwood Dr., Coeur d'Alene, ID 83814-2605. Phone: 208-664-3370. Fax: 208-664-5888. County: Iron. ICA: UT0069.

TV Market Ranking: Below 100. Franchise award date: N.A. Franchise expiration date: March 1, 2006. Began: January 1, 1981.

Channel capacity: 19 (not 2-way capable). Channels available but not in use: 2.

Basic Service

Subscribers: 577.

Programming (via translator): KJZZ-TV (U), KSL-TV (N), KSTU (F), KTVX (A), KUED (P), KUTV (C) Salt Lake City.

Programming (via satellite): WGN-TV (W) Chicago; CNN; Country Music TV; Discovery Channel; Disney Channel; ESPN; Fox Family Channel; Nashville Network; TBS Superstation; The Weather Channel; Turner Network TV; VH1.

Current originations: Local news.

Fee: $43.50 installation; $21.00 monthly; $21.50 additional installation.

Pay Service 1

Pay Units: 47.

Programming (via satellite): HBO.

Fee: $10.95 monthly.

Miles of plant: 5.5 (coaxial); None (fiber optic). Homes passed: 1,115.

Manager: Ted Hughett.

City fee: 5% of basic.

Ownership: Blackstone Cable LLC (MSO).

BRIGHAM CITY—AT&T Cable Services, 5152 South 1500 West, Ogden, UT 84405. Phone: 800-486-9829. Fax: 801-723-8548. County: Box Elder. Also serves Box Elder County (unincorporated areas), Perry. ICA: UT0013.

TV Market Ranking: Below 100. Franchise award date: January 23, 1975. Franchise expiration date: January 23, 2005. Began: December 1, 1978.

Channel capacity: 36 (not 2-way capable). Channels available but not in use: None.

Basic Service

Subscribers: 4,700; Commercial subscribers: 619.

Programming (received off-air): KUWB (W) Ogden; KBYU-TV (P) Provo; KJZZ-TV (U), KSL-TV (N), KSTU (F), KTVX (A), KUED (P), KUTV (C) Salt Lake City.

Programming (via satellite): WGN-TV (W) Chicago; A & E; American Movie Classics; C-SPAN; CNN; Country Music TV; Discovery Channel; E! Entertainment TV; ESPN; Fox Family Channel; Fox Sports Net; Headline News; Home Shopping Network; Lifetime; MSNBC; MTV; Nashville Network; Nick at Nite; Nickelodeon; Odyssey; Sci-Fi Channel; TBS Superstation; The Weather Channel; Turner Network TV; USA Network; VH1.

Fee: $54.00 installation; $25.95 monthly.

Pay Service 1

Pay Units: 190.

Programming (via satellite): Cinemax.

Fee: $15.25 installation; $10.95 monthly.

Pay Service 2

Pay Units: 514.

Programming (via satellite): Disney Channel.

Fee: $15.25 installation; $10.95 monthly.

Pay Service 3

Pay Units: 818.

Programming (via satellite): HBO.

Fee: $15.25 installation; $10.95 monthly.

Pay Service 4

Pay Units: 254.

Programming (via satellite): Showtime.

Fee: $15.25 installation; $10.95 monthly.

Pay Service 5

Pay Units: 59.

Programming (via satellite): The Movie Channel.

Fee: $15.25 installation; $10.95 monthly.

Local advertising: No.

Equipment: Jerrold & Cadco headend; Scientific-Atlanta & Jerrold amplifiers; Times Fiber & Comm/Scope cable; Atari character generator; Panasonic & Hamlin set top converters; Intercept & Pico traps; Scientific-Atlanta, Prodelin & Hughes satellite antenna; Standard Components & Scientific-Atlanta satellite receivers.

Miles of plant: 67.0 (coaxial). Homes passed: 4,604. Total homes in franchised area: 4,604.

Regional director: Dick Freedman. Chief engineer: Bob Hillard.

City fee: 5% of gross.

Ownership: AT&T Broadband & Internet Services (MSO). Tele-Communications Inc. purchased from Insight Communications Co., October 30, 1998.

CASTLE DALE—Peak Cablevision, 1750 S. Hwy. 10, Price, UT 84501. Phone: 435-637-6813. Fax: 435-637-9755. County: Emery. Also serves Emery County, Huntington, Orangeville. ICA: UT0017.

TV Market Ranking: Outside TV Markets. Franchise award date: N.A. Franchise expiration date: N.A. Began: August 1, 1981.

Channel capacity: 28. Channels available but not in use: N.A.

Basic Service

Subscribers: 841.

Programming (via translator): KBYU-TV (P) Provo; KSL-TV (N), KSTU (F), KTVX (A), KUED (P), KUTV (C) Salt Lake City.

Programming (via satellite): WGN-TV (W) Chicago; CNBC; CNN; Lifetime; Nashville Network; Nickelodeon; QVC; TBS Superstation.

Fee: $60.00 installation; $19.06 monthly; $40.00 additional installation.

Expanded Basic Service

Subscribers: 796.

Programming (via satellite): American Movie Classics; ESPN; Fox Sports Net; Turner Network TV; USA Network.
Fee: $1.89 monthly.

Pay Service 1
Pay Units: 176.
Programming (via satellite): Cinemax.
Fee: $13.15 monthly.

Pay Service 2
Pay Units: 220.
Programming (via satellite): Disney Channel.
Fee: $9.00 monthly.

Pay Service 3
Pay Units: 302.
Programming (via satellite): HBO.
Fee: $10.00 monthly.

Pay Service 4
Pay Units: 470.
Programming (via satellite): The New Encore.
Fee: N.A.

Equipment: Scientific-Atlanta satellite antenna; Scientific-Atlanta satellite receivers.
Miles of plant: 49.2 (coaxial). Homes passed: 2,389. Total homes in franchised area: 2,490.
Manager: Shane Baggs.
Ownership: Peak Cablevision LLC (MSO). See Cable System Ownership.

CEDAR CITY—Peak Cablevision, 1750 S. Hwy. 10, Price, UT 84501. Phone: 435-586-7655. Fax: 435-637-9755. County: Iron. ICA: UT0015.
TV Market Ranking: Below 100. Franchise award date: September 18, 1975. Franchise expiration date: August 22, 2005. Began: December 10, 1979.
Channel capacity: 36 (not 2-way capable). Channels available but not in use: 5.

Basic Service
Subscribers: 4,172.
Programming (received off-air): KCSG (I) Cedar City; allband FM.
Programming (via translator): KBYU-TV (P) Provo; KSL-TV (N), KSTU (F), KTVX (A), KUED (P), KUTV (C) Salt Lake City.
Programming (via satellite): WGN-TV (W) Chicago; KCNC-TV (C), KMGH-TV (A), KUSA-TV (N) Denver; American Movie Classics; CNN; Discovery Channel; ESPN; Fox Family Channel; Fox Sports Net; Home Shopping Network; MTV; Nashville Network; Nickelodeon; TBS Superstation; The Weather Channel; Turner Network TV; USA Network.
Current originations: Automated time-weather; local news.
Fee: $39.95 installation; $20.95 monthly; $15.00 additional installation.

Pay Service 1
Pay Units: 148.
Programming (via satellite): Cinemax.
Fee: $15.00 installation; $10.95 monthly.

Pay Service 2
Pay Units: 286.
Programming (via satellite): Disney Channel.
Fee: $10.95 monthly.

Pay Service 3
Pay Units: 561.
Programming (via satellite): HBO.
Fee: $10.95 monthly.

Pay Service 4
Pay Units: 193.
Programming (via satellite): Showtime.
Fee: $10.95 monthly.

Local advertising: Yes. Available in locally originated & taped programming. Local sales manager: Steve Web. Regional interconnect: Northwest Cable Advertising.
Equipment: Jerrold, RCA & Scientific-Atlanta headend; Jerrold amplifiers; Comm/Scope cable; Oak & Hamlin set top converters; Intercept & Arcom traps; Scientific-Atlanta, M/A-Com & Microdyne satellite antenna; Hughes & Scientific-Atlanta satellite receivers.
Miles of plant: 78.0 (coaxial); None (fiber optic). Additional miles planned: 3.0 (coaxial). Homes passed: 8,000.
Manager: Shane Baggs. Chief technician: Randy Humphrey.
City fee: 4% of gross.
Ownership: AT&T Broadband & Internet Services (MSO). Tele-Communications Inc. purchased from Insight Communications Co., November 1, 1998.

CENTRAL—Blackstone Cable LLC, 1104 W. Ironwood Dr., Coeur d'Alene, ID 83814-2605. Phone: 208-664-3370. Fax: 208-664-5888. County: Sevier. ICA: UT0070.
TV Market Ranking: Outside TV Markets. Franchise award date: N.A. Franchise expiration date: September 17, 2005. Began: N.A.
Channel capacity: N.A. Channels available but not in use: N.A.

Basic Service
Subscribers: 409.
Programming (via translator): KULC (P) Ogden; KBYU-TV (P) Provo; KJZZ-TV (U), KSL-TV (N), KSTU (F), KTVX (A), KUED (P), KUTV (C) Salt Lake City.
Programming (via satellite): WGN-TV (W) Chicago; A & E; America's Voice; American Movie Classics; Animal Planet; CNN; Cartoon Network; Country Music TV; Discovery Channel; Disney Channel; E! Entertainment TV; ESPN; Fox Family Channel; Fox Sports Net; Headline News; History Channel; Home Shopping Network; Lifetime; Nashville Network; Nick at Nite's TV Land; Nickelodeon; Outdoor Channel; QVC; Sci-Fi Channel; TBS Superstation; The Health Network; The Inspirational Network; Trinity Bcstg. Network; Turner Classic Movies; Turner Network TV; USA Network.
Fee: $43.50 installation; $21.00 monthly; $21.50 additional installation.

Pay Service 1
Pay Units: 82.
Programming (via satellite): HBO.
Fee: $10.95 monthly.

Pay Service 2
Pay Units: 23.
Programming (via satellite): Cinemax.
Fee: $10.95 monthly.

Manager: Rick Swanger.
Ownership: Blackstone Cable LLC (MSO). Purchased from Southern Utah Cable Vision.

CLEVELAND—B & L Communications, Box 970, Andalusia, AL 36420. Phones: 205-222-6110; 800-782-7486. County: Emery. Also serves Elmo. ICA: UT0055.
TV Market Ranking: Outside TV Markets. Franchise award date: N.A. Franchise expiration date: N.A. Began: July 1, 1990.
Channel capacity: 32. Channels available but not in use: 8.

Basic Service
Subscribers: 201.
Programming (received off-air): KBYU-TV (P) Provo; KJZZ-TV (U), KSL-TV (N), KSTU (F), KTVX (A), KUED (P), KUTV (C) Salt Lake City.
Programming (via satellite): WGN-TV (W) Chicago; American Movie Classics; C-SPAN; CNN; Discovery Channel; ESPN; Home Shopping Network; Learning Channel; Nashville Network; TBS Superstation; USA Network.
Fee: $35.00 installation; $18.25 monthly.

Pay Service 1
Pay Units: 40.
Programming (via satellite): Cinemax.
Fee: $10.00 monthly.

Pay Service 2
Pay Units: 40.
Programming (via satellite): Disney Channel.
Fee: $8.00 monthly.

Pay Service 3
Pay Units: 41.
Programming (via satellite): HBO.
Fee: $11.00 monthly.

Local advertising: No.
Miles of plant: 6.0 (coaxial); None (fiber optic). Homes passed: 300. Total homes in franchised area: 300.
Manager: Allen Sharp.
Ownership: B & L Communications (MSO).

COALVILLE—TCI Cablevision of Utah Inc., No. 105, 1777 Sun Peak Dr., Park City, UT 84098. Phone: 801-649-4020. County: Summit. Also serves Hoytsville, Summit County (portions). ICA: UT0049.
TV Market Ranking: 48. Franchise award date: N.A. Franchise expiration date: November 1, 1998. Began: January 1, 1984.
Channel capacity: 25. Channels available but not in use: N.A.

Basic Service
Subscribers: 300.
Programming (received off-air): KSL-TV (N), KSTU (F), KTVX (A), KUED (P), KUTV (C) Salt Lake City.
Programming (via satellite): WGN-TV (W) Chicago; CNBC; CNN; Discovery Channel; Lifetime; Nashville Network; Odyssey; TBS Superstation.
Current originations: Automated time-weather.
Fee: $60.00 installation; $19.68 monthly; $40.00 additional installation.

Expanded Basic Service
Subscribers: 227.
Programming (via satellite): American Movie Classics; ESPN; Fox Sports Net; Turner Network TV; USA Network.
Fee: $1.89 monthly.

Pay Service 1
Pay Units: 65.
Programming (via satellite): Disney Channel.
Fee: $10.00 installation; $10.00 monthly.

Pay Service 2
Pay Units: 73.
Programming (via satellite): HBO.
Fee: $10.00 installation; $11.00 monthly.

Pay Service 3
Pay Units: 110.
Programming (via satellite): The New Encore.
Fee: N.A.

Equipment: MSI character generator.
Miles of plant: 11.5 (coaxial). Homes passed: 585. Total homes in franchised area: 654.
Manager: Kent Pearce.
Ownership: AT&T Broadband & Internet Services (MSO). Purchased from Tele-Communications Inc., March 9, 1999.

DELTA—Peak Cablevision, 1750 S. Hwy. 10, Price, UT 84501. Phone: 435-586-7655. Fax: 435-637-9755. County: Millard. ICA: UT0024.
TV Market Ranking: Outside TV Markets. Franchise award date: September 9, 1981. Franchise expiration date: February 1, 2001. Began: June 1, 1983.
Channel capacity: 40 (not 2-way capable). Channels available but not in use: 13.

Basic Service
Subscribers: 300.
Programming (via translator): KBYU-TV (P) Provo; KSL-TV (N), KSTU (F), KTVX (A), KUED (P), KUTV (C) Salt Lake City.
Programming (via satellite): WGN-TV (W) Chicago; American Movie Classics; CNN; Country Music TV; Discovery Channel; ESPN; Fox Family Channel; Headline News; Home Shopping Network; MTV; Nashville Network; Odyssey; TBS Superstation; Turner Network TV; USA Network.
Fee: $39.95 installation; $21.95 monthly; $3.95 converter; $15.00 additional installation.

Pay Service 1
Pay Units: 35.
Programming (via satellite): Cinemax.
Fee: $15.00 installation; $10.95 monthly.

Pay Service 2
Pay Units: 78.
Programming (via satellite): Disney Channel.
Fee: $15.00 installation; $10.95 monthly.

Pay Service 3
Pay Units: 70.
Programming (via satellite): HBO.
Fee: $15.00 installation; $10.95 monthly.

Pay Service 4
Pay Units: 49.
Programming (via satellite): Showtime.
Fee: $15.00 installation; $10.95 monthly.

Pay Service 5
Pay Units: 32.
Programming (via satellite): The Movie Channel.
Fee: $15.00 installation; $10.95 monthly.

Local advertising: No.
Equipment: Scientific-Atlanta, RCA & Cadco headend; GTE Sylvania amplifiers; Comm/Scope cable; Oak & Hamlin set top converters; Arcom & Intercept traps; M/A-Com, Harris & Scientific-Atlanta satellite antenna; Scientific-Atlanta & Hughes satellite receivers.
Miles of plant: 25.0 (coaxial). Homes passed: 900. Total homes in franchised area: 1,441.
Manager: Shane Baggs. Chief technician: Randy Humphrey.
City fee: 4% of gross.
Ownership: AT&T Broadband & Internet Services (MSO). Tele-Communications Inc. purchased from Insight Communications Co., November 1, 1998.

DUCHESNE—Peak Cablevision, 1750 S. Hwy. 10, Price, UT 84501. Phone: 435-637-6813. Fax: 435-637-9755. County: Duchesne. ICA: UT0052.
TV Market Ranking: Outside TV Markets. Franchise award date: N.A. Franchise expiration date: N.A. Began: October 1, 1981.
Channel capacity: 35. Channels available but not in use: 13.

Basic Service
Subscribers: 197.
Programming (via translator): KBYU-TV (P) Provo; KSL-TV (N), KSTU (F), KTVX (A), KUED (P), KUTV (C) Salt Lake City.
Programming (via satellite): WGN-TV (W) Chicago; CNN; Lifetime; Nashville Network; Nickelodeon; QVC; TBS Superstation.
Fee: $60.00 installation; $19.82 monthly; $40.00 additional installation.

Expanded Basic Service
Subscribers: 160.
Programming (via satellite): American Movie Classics; ESPN; Fox Sports Net; Turner Network TV; USA Network.
Fee: $1.89 monthly.

Pay Service 1
Pay Units: 51.
Programming (via satellite): Disney Channel.
Fee: $11.00 monthly.

Pay Service 2
Pay Units: 63.
Programming (via satellite): HBO.
Fee: $11.00 monthly.
Pay Service 3
Pay Units: 33.
Programming (via satellite): Showtime.
Fee: $11.00 monthly.
Pay Service 4
Pay Units: 78.
Programming (via satellite): The New Encore.
Fee: N.A.
Miles of plant: 18.0 (coaxial). Homes passed: 501. Total homes in franchised area: 530.
Manager: Shane Baggs.
City fee: 3% of gross.
Ownership: Peak Cablevision LLC (MSO). See Cable System Ownership.

DUGWAY—Dugway Cable TV Corp., Box 157, Dugway, UT 84022. Phones: 801-522-2606; 801-831-4404. County: Tooele. ICA: UT0046.
TV Market Ranking: Outside TV Markets. Franchise award date: N.A. Franchise expiration date: N.A. Began: October 15, 1980.
Channel capacity: 40. Channels available but not in use: N.A.
Basic Service
Subscribers: 450.
Programming (received off-air): KBYU-TV (P) Provo; KSL-TV (N), KSTU (F), KTVX (A), KUED (P), KUTV (C) Salt Lake City.
Programming (via microwave): KTVU (F) Oakland-San Francisco.
Programming (via satellite): WGN-TV (W) Chicago; ESPN; TBS Superstation; Turner Classic Movies.
Fee: $11.00 monthly.
Pay Service 1
Pay Units: N.A.
Programming (via satellite): HBO.
Fee: $8.00 monthly.
Equipment: Scientific-Atlanta headend; Theta-Com amplifiers; Comm/Scope cable; Scientific-Atlanta satellite antenna.
Miles of plant: 10.0 (coaxial). Homes passed: 600.
City fee: 3% of gross.
Ownership: Keith Antcliff (MSO).

EAST CARBON—Peak Cablevision, 1750 S. Hwy. 10, Price, UT 84501. Phone: 435-637-6813. Fax: 435-637-9755. County: Carbon. Also serves Sunnyside. ICA: UT0050.
TV Market Ranking: Outside TV Markets. Franchise award date: N.A. Franchise expiration date: N.A. Began: November 1, 1980.
Channel capacity: 35. Channels available but not in use: 13.
Basic Service
Subscribers: 445.
Programming (via translator): KSL-TV (N), KSTU (F), KTVX (A), KUED (P), KUTV (C) Salt Lake City.
Programming (via satellite): WGN-TV (W) Chicago; CNN; Fox Family Channel; Lifetime; Nashville Network; Nickelodeon; QVC; TBS Superstation.
Fee: $60.00 installation; $19.40 monthly; $40.00 additional installation.
Expanded Basic Service
Subscribers: 420.
Programming (via satellite): American Movie Classics; ESPN; Fox Sports Net; Turner Network TV; USA Network.
Fee: $1.89 monthly.
Pay Service 1
Pay Units: 77.
Programming (via satellite): Disney Channel.
Fee: N.A.
Pay Service 2
Pay Units: 128.
Programming (via satellite): HBO.
Fee: N.A.
Pay Service 3
Pay Units: 104.
Programming (via satellite): Showtime.
Fee: N.A.
Pay Service 4
Pay Units: 264.
Programming (via satellite): The New Encore.
Fee: N.A.
Miles of plant: 8.9 (coaxial). Homes passed: 507. Total homes in franchised area: 765.
Manager: Shane Baggs.
Ownership: Peak Cablevision LLC (MSO). See Cable System Ownership.

ENOCH—Blackstone Cable LLC, 1104 W. Ironwood Dr., Coeur d'Alene, ID 83814-2605. Phone: 208-664-3370. Fax: 208-664-5888. County: Iron. ICA: UT0071.
TV Market Ranking: Below 100. Franchise award date: March 1, 1988. Franchise expiration date: March 2, 2003. Began: September 15, 1988.
Channel capacity: 36 (not 2-way capable). Channels available but not in use: 15.
Basic Service
Subscribers: 321.
Programming (via translator): KBYU-TV (P) Provo; KJZZ-TV (U), KSL-TV (N), KSTU (F), KTVX (A), KUED (P), KUTV (C) Salt Lake City.
Programming (via satellite): WGN-TV (W) Chicago; CNN; Cartoon Network; Discovery Channel; Disney Channel; ESPN; Fox Family Channel; Nashville Network; TBS Superstation; The Inspirational Network; The Sports Network; Turner Classic Movies; Turner Network TV; USA Network.
Current originations: Local news.
Fee: $43.50 installation; $22.50 monthly; $21.50 additional installation.
Pay Service 1
Pay Units: 13.
Programming (via satellite): Cinemax.
Fee: $10.95 monthly.
Pay Service 2
Pay Units: 45.
Programming (via satellite): HBO.
Fee: $10.95 monthly.
Miles of plant: 16.5 (coaxial); None (fiber optic). Homes passed: 526.
Manager: Ted Hughett.
City fee: 3% of gross.
Ownership: Blackstone Cable LLC (MSO).

ENTERPRISE—Blackstone Cable LLC, 1104 W. Ironwood Dr., Coeur d'Alene, ID 83814-2605. Phone: 208-664-3370. Fax: 208-664-5888. County: Washington. ICA: UT0056.
TV Market Ranking: Outside TV Markets. Franchise award date: November 13, 1986. Franchise expiration date: November 13, 2001. Began: September 21, 1987.
Channel capacity: 36. Channels available but not in use: N.A.
Basic Service
Subscribers: 279.
Programming (via translator): KBYU-TV (P) Provo; KJZZ-TV (U), KSL-TV (N), KSTU (F), KTVX (A), KUED (P), KUTV (C) Salt Lake City.
Programming (via satellite): WGN-TV (W) Chicago; C-SPAN; CNN; Discovery Channel; ESPN; Headline News; Nashville Network; Nickelodeon; QVC; Sci-Fi Channel; TBS Superstation; Turner Network TV.
Fee: $43.50 installation; $21.00 monthly; $32.50 additional installation.
Expanded Basic Service
Subscribers: 261.
Programming (received off-air): KULC (P) Ogden.
Programming (via satellite): KTLA (W) Los Angeles; American Movie Classics; Country Music TV; Disney Channel; E! Entertainment TV; ESPN 2; Fox Family Channel; Fox Sports Net; History Channel; Learning Channel; Nick at Nite's TV Land; Outdoor Channel; The Weather Channel; Turner Classic Movies; VH1.
Fee: N.A.
Pay Service 1
Pay Units: 19.
Programming (via satellite): HBO.
Fee: $21.50 installation; $10.95 monthly.
Pay Service 2
Pay Units: 19.
Programming (via satellite): Showtime.
Fee: $21.50 installation; $10.95 monthly.
Miles of plant: 6.0 (coaxial). Homes passed: 300. Total homes in franchised area: 375.
Manager: Ted Hughett.
Ownership: Blackstone Cable LLC (MSO). Purchased from Enterprise Cable TV, December 1, 1998.

EPHRAIM—Peak Cablevision, 1750 S. Hwy. 10, Price, UT 84501. Phone: 435-637-6813. Fax: 435-637-9755. County: Sanpete. Also serves Manti. ICA: UT0022.
TV Market Ranking: Outside TV Markets. Franchise award date: N.A. Franchise expiration date: N.A. Began: February 1, 1982.
Channel capacity: 27 (2-way capable; operating 2-way). Channels available but not in use: N.A.
Basic Service
Subscribers: 777.
Programming (via translator): KBYU-TV (P) Provo; KSL-TV (N), KSTU (F), KTVX (A), KUED (P), KUTV (C) Salt Lake City.
Programming (via satellite): WGN-TV (W) Chicago; CNBC; CNN; Lifetime; Nashville Network; Nickelodeon; QVC; TBS Superstation.
Fee: $60.00 installation; $19.19 monthly; $40.00 additional installation.
Expanded Basic Service
Subscribers: 716.
Programming (via satellite): American Movie Classics; ESPN; Fox Sports Net; Turner Network TV; USA Network.
Fee: $1.89 monthly.
Pay Service 1
Pay Units: 85.
Programming (via satellite): Cinemax.
Fee: $8.00 monthly.
Pay Service 2
Pay Units: 132.
Programming (via satellite): Disney Channel.
Fee: $9.00 monthly.
Pay Service 3
Pay Units: 181.
Programming (via satellite): HBO.
Fee: $10.00 monthly.
Pay Service 4
Pay Units: 323.
Programming (via satellite): The New Encore.
Fee: N.A.
Equipment: Scientific-Atlanta headend; Magnavox amplifiers; Times Fiber cable; Magnavox traps; Scientific-Atlanta satellite antenna; Scientific-Atlanta satellite receivers.
Miles of plant: 21.0 (coaxial). Homes passed: 1,521. Total homes in franchised area: 1,551.
Manager: Shane Baggs.
City fee: 3% of gross.
Ownership: Peak Cablevision LLC (MSO). See Cable System Ownership.

ESCALANTE—B & L Cable, Box 580, Orangeville, UT 84537. Phones: 435-748-2345; 800-782-7486. Fax: 435-748-5746. County: Garfield. ICA: UT0083.
TV Market Ranking: Outside TV Markets. Franchise award date: May 1, 1992. Franchise expiration date: May 1, 2007. Began: October 1, 1992.
Channel capacity: 32 (not 2-way capable). Channels available but not in use: 13.
Basic Service
Subscribers: 130.
Programming (received off-air): KBYU-TV (P) Provo; KJZZ-TV (U), KSL-TV (N), KSTU (F), KTVX (A), KUED (P), KUTV (C) Salt Lake City.
Programming (via satellite): WGN-TV (W) Chicago; A & E; CNN; Cartoon Network; Discovery Channel; ESPN; ESPN 2; Fox Family Channel; Goodlife TV Network; Nashville Network; TBS Superstation; Turner Classic Movies; Turner Network TV; USA Network; ValueVision.
Fee: $35.00 installation; $16.95 monthly.
Pay Service 1
Pay Units: 35.
Programming (via satellite): Cinemax.
Fee: $10.00 monthly.
Pay Service 2
Pay Units: 32.
Programming (via satellite): Disney Channel.
Fee: $8.00 monthly.
Pay Service 3
Pay Units: 43.
Programming (via satellite): HBO.
Fee: $11.00 monthly.
Miles of plant: 6.0 (coaxial). Homes passed: 175. Total homes in franchised area: 300.
Operations manager: Maurice Rabren. Chief technician: Chris Alexander.
Ownership: B & L Communications (MSO).

EUREKA—Blackstone Cable LLC, 1104 W. Ironwood Dr., Coeur d'Alene, ID 83814-2605. Phone: 208-664-3370. Fax: 208-664-5888. County: Juab. ICA: UT0057.
TV Market Ranking: Below 100. Franchise award date: N.A. Franchise expiration date: July 13, 2002. Began: February 1, 1982.
Channel capacity: 19 (not 2-way capable). Channels available but not in use: 2.
Basic Service
Subscribers: 132.
Programming (received off-air): KBYU-TV (P) Provo; KSL-TV (N), KSTU (F), KTVX (A), KUED (P), KUTV (C) Salt Lake City.
Programming (via satellite): WGN-TV (W) Chicago; CNN; Country Music TV; Discovery Channel; Disney Channel; ESPN; Fox Family Channel; Nashville Network; TBS Superstation; Turner Classic Movies; Turner Network TV.
Current originations: Local news.
Fee: $43.50 installation; $21.00 monthly; $21.50 additional installation.
Pay Service 1
Pay Units: 21.
Programming (via satellite): HBO.
Fee: $10.95 monthly.
Miles of plant: 5.3 (coaxial); None (fiber optic). Homes passed: 301. Total homes in franchised area: 301.
Manager: Ted Hughett.
City fee: 3% of basic.
Ownership: Blackstone Cable LLC (MSO). See Cable System Ownership.

FARMINGTON—AT&T Cable Services, 5152 South 1500 West, Riverdale, UT 84405. Phone: 801-444-4824. County: Davis. Also serves Al's Apple Acre Mobile Home Park, Bountiful, Centerville, Clearfield, Clinton, Davis County, East Layton, Elite Mobile Home Park, Fruit

Heights, Hill AFB, Kaysville, Layton, North Salt Lake, Somerset Condominiums, Sunset, West Bountiful, Woods Cross. ICA: UT0004.
TV Market Ranking: 48. Franchise award date: N.A. Franchise expiration date: N.A. Began: May 1, 1981.
Channel capacity: 38. Channels available but not in use: N.A.
Basic Service
Subscribers: 24,405.
Programming (received off-air): KUWB (W) Ogden; KBYU-TV (P) Provo; KSL-TV (N), KSTU (F), KTVX (A), KUED (P), KUTV (C) Salt Lake City.
Programming (via satellite): WGN-TV (W) Chicago; A & E; C-SPAN; CNBC; CNN; Discovery Channel; Fox Family Channel; Headline News; Lifetime; MTV; Nashville Network; Nickelodeon; Odyssey; QVC; TBS Superstation; The Weather Channel.
Current originations: Educational access.
Fee: $60.00 installation; $9.10 monthly; $40.00 additional installation.
Expanded Basic Service
Subscribers: 23,326.
Programming (via satellite): American Movie Classics; ESPN; Fox Sports Net; Turner Network TV; USA Network.
Fee: $12.53 monthly.
Pay Service 1
Pay Units: 2,586.
Programming (via satellite): Disney Channel.
Fee: $11.95 monthly.
Pay Service 2
Pay Units: 7,188.
Programming (via satellite): HBO.
Fee: $11.95 monthly.
Pay Service 3
Pay Units: 1,306.
Programming (via satellite): The Movie Channel.
Fee: N.A.
Pay Service 4
Pay Units: 3,934.
Programming (via satellite): Showtime.
Fee: $11.95 monthly.
Pay Service 5
Pay Units: 11,131.
Programming (via satellite): The New Encore.
Fee: N.A.
Program Guide: The Cable Guide.
Equipment: Scientific-Atlanta headend; Scientific-Atlanta amplifiers; Times Fiber cable; Scientific-Atlanta & Hughes satellite antenna.
Miles of plant: 687.3 (coaxial). Homes passed: 47,674. Total homes in franchised area: 60,371.
Regional director: Dick Freedman. Chief enginner: Bob Hillard.
City fee: 3% of gross.
Ownership: AT&T Broadband & Internet Services (MSO). Purchased from Tele-Communications Inc., March 9, 1999.

FERRON—Peak Cablevision, 1750 S. Hwy. 10, Price, UT 84501. Phone: 435-637-6813. Fax: 435-637-9755. County: Emery. ICA: UT0054.
TV Market Ranking: Outside TV Markets. Franchise award date: N.A. Franchise expiration date: N.A. Began: August 1, 1982.
Channel capacity: 27 (2-way capable; operating 2-way). Channels available but not in use: N.A.
Basic Service
Subscribers: 289.
Programming (via translator): KBYU-TV (P) Provo; KSL-TV (N), KSTU (F), KTVX (A), KUED (P), KUTV (C) Salt Lake City.
Programming (via satellite): WGN-TV (W) Chicago; CNN; Lifetime; Nashville Network; Nickelodeon; QVC; TBS Superstation.
Fee: $60.00 installation; $19.46 monthly; $40.00 additional installation.
Expanded Basic Service
Subscribers: 282.
Programming (via satellite): American Movie Classics; ESPN; Fox Sports Net; Turner Network TV; USA Network.
Fee: $1.89 monthly.
Pay Service 1
Pay Units: 52.
Programming (via satellite): Cinemax.
Fee: $8.00 monthly.
Pay Service 2
Pay Units: 82.
Programming (via satellite): Disney Channel.
Fee: N.A.
Pay Service 3
Pay Units: 94.
Programming (via satellite): HBO.
Fee: $10.00 monthly.
Pay Service 4
Pay Units: 153.
Programming (via satellite): The New Encore.
Fee: N.A.
Equipment: Scientific-Atlanta headend; Magnavox amplifiers; Times Fiber cable; Eagle, Pico & Intercept traps; Scientific-Atlanta satellite antenna; Scientific-Atlanta satellite receivers.
Miles of plant: 14.8 (coaxial). Homes passed: 475. Total homes in franchised area: 490.
Manager: Shane Baggs.
City fee: 3% of gross.
Ownership: Peak Cablevision LLC (MSO). See Cable System Ownership.

FIELDING—AT&T Cable Services, 5152 South 1500 West, Riverdale, UT 84405. Phone: 800-486-9829. County: Box Elder. Also serves Plymouth. Plans service to Riverside. ICA: UT0051.
TV Market Ranking: Outside TV Markets. Franchise award date: February 24, 1987. Franchise expiration date: February 24, 2002. Began: May 17, 1988.
Channel capacity: 36 (not 2-way capable). Channels available but not in use: 7.
Basic Service
Subscribers: 264.
Programming (received off-air): KUWB (W) Ogden; KBYU-TV (P) Provo; KJZZ-TV (U), KSL-TV (N), KSTU (F), KTVX (A), KUED (P), KUTV (C) Salt Lake City.
Programming (via satellite): WGN-TV (W) Chicago; A & E; CNN; Discovery Channel; ESPN; Fox Family Channel; Fox Sports Net; MSNBC; Nashville Network; Nickelodeon; QVC; TBS Superstation; Turner Network TV; USA Network; VH1.
Current originations: Public access.
Fee: $36.42 installation; $22.95 monthly.
Pay Service 1
Pay Units: 30.
Programming (via satellite): Cinemax.
Fee: $12.20 monthly.
Pay Service 2
Pay Units: 47.
Programming (via satellite): Disney Channel.
Fee: $10.95 monthly.
Pay Service 3
Pay Units: 60.
Programming (via satellite): HBO.
Fee: $13.15 monthly.
Pay Service 4
Pay Units: N.A.
Programming (via satellite): Starz!; The New Encore.
Fee: $1.75 monthly (Encore), $4.75 monthly (Starz).
Local advertising: No.
Equipment: Pico headend; Magnavox amplifiers; Times Fiber cable; Pioneer & Jerrold set top converters; Pico traps; Comtech satellite antenna; Pico satellite receivers.
Miles of plant: 22.9 (coaxial). Homes passed: 505.
Regional manager: Alan Hintze. Chief technician: Craig Davis. Marketing manager: Ron Williams. Office manager: Lorraine Nelson.
Franchise fee: 3% of gross.
Ownership: AT&T Broadband & Internet Services (MSO). Purchased from Insight Communications Co., November 2, 1998.

FILLMORE—Peak Cablevision, 1750 S. Hwy. 10, Price, UT 84501. Phone: 435-637-6813. Fax: 435-637-9755. County: Millard. ICA: UT0036.
TV Market Ranking: Outside TV Markets. Franchise award date: N.A. Franchise expiration date: December 31, 1999. Began: March 1, 1985.
Channel capacity: 35. Channels available but not in use: 5.
Basic Service
Subscribers: 397; Commercial subscribers: 9.
Programming (via translator): KJZZ-TV (U), KSL-TV (N), KSTU (F), KTVX (A), KUED (P), KUTV (C) Salt Lake City.
Programming (via satellite): WGN-TV (W) Chicago; A & E; American Movie Classics; CNN; Country Music TV; Discovery Channel; ESPN; Fox Family Channel; Fox Sports Net; History Channel; Lifetime; Nashville Network; Nickelodeon; Odyssey; QVC; Sci-Fi Channel; TBS Superstation; The Weather Channel; Turner Network TV; USA Network.
Fee: $25.00 installation; $21.78 monthly; $10.00 additional installation.
Pay Service 1
Pay Units: 41.
Programming (via satellite): Cinemax.
Fee: $12.20 monthly.
Pay Service 2
Pay Units: 79.
Programming (via satellite): Disney Channel.
Fee: $7.95 monthly.
Pay Service 3
Pay Units: 96.
Programming (via satellite): HBO.
Fee: $13.15 monthly.
Pay Service 4
Pay Units: 154.
Programming (via satellite): The New Encore.
Fee: $1.75 monthly.
Pay Service 5
Pay Units: N.A.
Programming (via satellite): Showtime; Starz!
Fee: $8.95 monthly (Showtime), $10.95 monthly (Starz).
Miles of plant: 10.0 (coaxial). Homes passed: 500. Total homes in franchised area: 810.
Manager: Ron Beaty. Chief technican: Bodie Peebles.
Ownership: Peak Cablevision LLC (MSO). See Cable System Ownership.

FRUIT HEIGHTS—AT&T Cable Services, 5152 South 1500 West, Riverdale, UT 84405. Phone: 800-486-9829. County: Davis. ICA: UT0038.
TV Market Ranking: 48. Franchise award date: August 15, 1989. Franchise expiration date: August 15, 2004. Began: March 1, 1990.
Channel capacity: 52 (2-way capable; operating 2-way). Channels available but not in use: 15.
Basic Service
Subscribers: 458; Commercial subscribers: 8.
Programming (received off-air): KUWB (W) Ogden; KBYU-TV (P) Provo; KSL-TV (N), KSTU (F), KTVX (A), KUED (P), KUTV (C) Salt Lake City.
Programming (via satellite): WGN-TV (W) Chicago; A & E; American Movie Classics; Animal Planet; C-SPAN; CNBC; CNN; Discovery Channel; ESPN; Fox Family Channel; Fox Sports Net; Headline News; Home Shopping Network; Lifetime; MSNBC; Nashville Network; Nickelodeon; Odyssey; TBS Superstation; The Weather Channel; Turner Network TV; USA Network; VH1.
Fee: $54.00 installation; $25.95 monthly.
Pay Service 1
Pay Units: 84.
Programming (via satellite): Disney Channel.
Fee: $15.25 installation; $10.95 monthly.
Pay Service 2
Pay Units: 87.
Programming (via satellite): HBO.
Fee: $15.25 installation; $10.95 monthly.
Pay Service 3
Pay Units: 32.
Programming (via satellite): Showtime.
Fee: $15.25 installation; $10.95 monthly.
Pay Service 4
Pay Units: 9.
Programming (via satellite): The Movie Channel.
Fee: $15.25 installation; $10.95 monthly.
Local advertising: No.
Equipment: Olson & Standard Components headend; Scientific-Atlanta amplifiers; Times Fiber cable; Atari character generator; Panasonic & Hamlin set top converters; Intercept traps; Standard Components satellite receivers.
Miles of plant: 11.0 (coaxial). Homes passed: 780. Total homes in franchised area: 780.
Regional manager: Alan Hintze. Chief technician: Craig Davis. Marketing manager: Ron Williams. Office manager: Lorraine Nelson.
City fee: 5% of gross.
Ownership: AT&T Broadband & Internet Services (MSO). Purchased from Insight Communications Co., November 2, 1998.

GLENWOOD—Blackstone Cable LLC, 1104 W. Ironwood Dr., Coeur d'Alene, ID 83814-2605. Phone: 208-664-3370. Fax: 208-664-5888. County: Sevier. ICA: UT0084.
TV Market Ranking: Outside TV Markets. Franchise award date: N.A. Franchise expiration date: N.A. Began: N.A.
Channel capacity: N.A. Channels available but not in use: N.A.
Basic Service
Subscribers: 98.

Programming (received off-air): KULC (P) Ogden; KBYU-TV (P) Provo; KJZZ-TV (U), KSL-TV (N), KSTU (F), KTVX (A), KUED (P), KUTV (C) Salt Lake City.
Programming (via satellite): WGN-TV (W) Chicago; Animal Planet; CNN; Discovery Channel; Disney Channel; E! Entertainment TV; ESPN; Fox Family Channel; Fox Sports Net; Knowledge TV; Nashville Network; Nick at Nite's TV Land; Nickelodeon; Outdoor Channel; QVC; TBS Superstation; The Health Network; The Inspirational Network; Turner Network TV; USA Network.
Current originations: Public access.
Fee: N.A.
Pay Service 1
Pay Units: 17.
Programming (via satellite): HBO.
Fee: N.A.
Manager: Ted Hughett.
Ownership: Blackstone Cable LLC (MSO).

GOSHEN—Blackstone Cable LLC, 1104 W. Ironwood Dr., Coeur d'Alene, ID 83814-2605. Phone: 208-664-3370. Fax: 208-664-5888. County: Utah. ICA: UT0063.
TV Market Ranking: Below 100. Franchise award date: N.A. Franchise expiration date: June 11, 2001. Began: June 1, 1982.
Channel capacity: 19 (not 2-way capable). Channels available but not in use: N.A.
Basic Service
Subscribers: 83.
Programming (received off-air): KBYU-TV (P) Provo; KSL-TV (N), KSTU (F), KTVX (A), KUED (P), KUTV (C) Salt Lake City.
Programming (via satellite): WGN-TV (W) Chicago; CNN; Country Music TV; Discovery Channel; Disney Channel; ESPN; Fox Family Channel; Nashville Network; TBS Superstation; Turner Classic Movies; Turner Network TV.
Current originations: Automated time-weather.
Fee: $43.50 installation; $21.00 monthly; $21.50 additional installation.
Pay Service 1
Pay Units: 16.
Programming (via satellite): HBO.
Fee: $10.95 monthly.
Miles of plant: 5.4 (coaxial); None (fiber optic). Homes passed: 215. Total homes in franchised area: 215.
Manager: Ted Hughett.
City fee: 3% of gross.
Ownership: Blackstone Cable LLC (MSO).

GRANTSVILLE—TCI Cablevision of Utah Inc., 22 W. Vine St., Tooele, UT 84074. Phone: 801-882-6604. County: Tooele. Also serves Tooele County. ICA: UT0026.
TV Market Ranking: 48 (Grantsville, portions of Tooele County); Outside TV Markets (portions of Tooele County). Franchise award date: N.A. Franchise expiration date: N.A. Began: March 1, 1985.
Channel capacity: 35. Channels available but not in use: 10.
Basic Service
Subscribers: 538.
Programming (received off-air): KSL-TV (N), KSTU (F), KTVX (A), KUED (P), KUTV (C) Salt Lake City.
Programming (via satellite): WGN-TV (W) Chicago; CNBC; CNN; Discovery Channel; Fox Family Channel; Lifetime; Nashville Network; Nickelodeon; QVC; TBS Superstation.
Fee: $60.00 installation; $20.21 monthly; $40.00 additional installation.
Expanded Basic Service
Subscribers: 371.
Programming (via satellite): American Movie Classics; ESPN; Fox Sports Net; Turner Network TV; USA Network.
Fee: $1.89 monthly.
Pay Service 1
Pay Units: 57.
Programming (via satellite): Disney Channel.
Fee: N.A.
Pay Service 2
Pay Units: 144.
Programming (via satellite): HBO.
Fee: N.A.
Pay Service 3
Pay Units: 83.
Programming (via satellite): Showtime.
Fee: N.A.
Pay Service 4
Pay Units: N.A.
Programming (via satellite): The New Encore.
Fee: N.A.
Miles of plant: 24.0 (coaxial). Homes passed: 1,300. Total homes in franchised area: 1,380.
Manager: Mike Oswald.
Ownership: AT&T Broadband & Internet Services (MSO). Purchased from Tele-Communications Inc., March 9, 1999.

GREEN RIVER—Falcon Telecable, 919 S. Main St., St. George, UT 84770. Phone: 435-628-3681. Counties: Emery & Grand. Also serves Emery County. ICA: UT0059.
TV Market Ranking: Outside TV Markets. Franchise award date: N.A. Franchise expiration date: N.A. Began: April 1, 1983.
Channel capacity: 37. Channels available but not in use: 7.
Basic Service
Subscribers: 238.
Programming (via translator): KBYU-TV (P) Provo; KJZZ-TV (U), KSL-TV (N), KSTU (F), KTVX (A), KUED (P), KUTV (C) Salt Lake City.
Programming (via satellite): Bravo; CNN; Country Music TV; E! Entertainment TV; ESPN; Fox Family Channel; Headline News; Learning Channel; MTV; Nashville Network; QVC; USA Network; Univision.
Fee: $19.95 installation; $14.33 monthly.
Expanded Basic Service
Subscribers: 224.
Programming (via satellite): Discovery Channel; Disney Channel; Lifetime; Nickelodeon; Sci-Fi Channel.
Fee: $3.88 monthly.
Expanded Basic Service 2
Subscribers: 230.
Programming (via satellite): WGN-TV (W) Chicago; TBS Superstation.
Fee: $2.15 monthly.
Pay Service 1
Pay Units: 34.
Programming (via satellite): Cinemax.
Fee: $10.50 monthly.
Pay Service 2
Pay Units: 64.
Programming (via satellite): HBO.
Fee: $10.50 monthly.
Miles of plant: 10.0 (coaxial). Homes passed: 292.
Manager: Richard Reniewicki. Chief technician: Robert Hannon.
Franchise fee: 3% of gross.
Ownership: Falcon Communications LP (MSO), joint venture formed September 30, 1998. See Cable System Ownership.

GUNNISON—Peak Cablevision, 1750 S. Hwy. 10, Price, UT 84501. Phone: 435-637-6813. Fax: 435-637-9755. County: Sanpete. Also serves Centerfield. ICA: UT0037.
TV Market Ranking: Outside TV Markets. Franchise award date: N.A. Franchise expiration date: January 1, 1999. Began: January 1, 1984.
Channel capacity: 25 (2-way capable; operating 2-way). Channels available but not in use: N.A.
Basic Service
Subscribers: 447.
Programming (via translator): KBYU-TV (P) Provo; KSL-TV (N), KSTU (F), KTVX (A), KUED (P), KUTV (C) Salt Lake City.
Programming (via satellite): WGN-TV (W) Chicago; CNN; Lifetime; Nashville Network; Nickelodeon; QVC; TBS Superstation.
Fee: $60.00 installation; $19.70 monthly; $40.00 additional installation.
Expanded Basic Service
Subscribers: 401.
Programming (via satellite): American Movie Classics; ESPN; Fox Sports Net; Turner Network TV; USA Network.
Fee: $1.89 monthly.
Pay Service 1
Pay Units: 86.
Programming (via satellite): Disney Channel.
Fee: $10.00 installation; $9.50 monthly.
Pay Service 2
Pay Units: 102.
Programming (via satellite): HBO.
Fee: $10.00 installation; $10.50 monthly.
Pay Service 3
Pay Units: 207.
Programming (via satellite): The New Encore.
Fee: N.A.
Equipment: Phasecom headend; Magnavox amplifiers; Scientific-Atlanta cable; Prodelin satellite antenna.
Miles of plant: 17.5 (coaxial). Homes passed: 800. Total homes in franchised area: 1,110.
Manager: Shane Baggs.
City fee: 3% of gross.
Ownership: Peak Cablevision LLC (MSO). See Cable System Ownership.

HEBER CITY—TCI Cablevision of Utah Inc., No. 105, 1777 Sun Peak Dr., Park City, UT 84098. Phone: 435-649-4020. County: Wasatch. Also serves Midway, Wasatch County. ICA: UT0018.
TV Market Ranking: 48 (Heber City, Midway, portions of Wasatch County); Below 100 (portions of Wasatch County); Outside TV Markets (portions of Wasatch County). Franchise award date: N.A. Franchise expiration date: N.A. Began: August 1, 1982.
Channel capacity: 37. Channels available but not in use: N.A.
Basic Service
Subscribers: 1,526.
Programming (received off-air): KBYU-TV (P) Provo; KSL-TV (N), KSTU (F), KTVX (A), KUED (P), KUTV (C) Salt Lake City.
Programming (via satellite): WGN-TV (W) Chicago; C-SPAN; CNBC; CNN; Discovery Channel; Fox Family Channel; Headline News; Lifetime; MTV; Nashville Network; Nickelodeon; Odyssey; QVC; TBS Superstation; The Weather Channel.
Current originations: Educational access.
Planned originations: Automated time-weather; public access.
Fee: $60.00 installation; $9.10 monthly; $40.00 additional installation.
Expanded Basic Service
Subscribers: 1,451.
Programming (via satellite): American Movie Classics; ESPN; Fox Sports Net; Turner Network TV; USA Network.
Fee: $11.20 monthly.
Pay Service 1
Pay Units: 104.
Programming (via satellite): Cinemax.
Fee: $10.00 monthly.
Pay Service 2
Pay Units: 184.
Programming (via satellite): Disney Channel.
Fee: $9.45 monthly.
Pay Service 3
Pay Units: 280.
Programming (via satellite): HBO.
Fee: $10.00 monthly.
Pay Service 4
Pay Units: 572.
Programming (via satellite): The New Encore.
Fee: N.A.
Equipment: Catel & Scientific-Atlanta headend; Scientific-Atlanta amplifiers; Comm/Scope cable; Sony VTRs; Compuvid character generator; Scientific-Atlanta set top converters; Eagle traps; Scientific-Atlanta satellite antenna; Standard Communications satellite receivers.
Miles of plant: 45.6 (coaxial). Homes passed: 2,183. Total homes in franchised area: 3,040.
Manager: Kent Pearce.
Ownership: AT&T Broadband & Internet Services (MSO). Purchased from Tele-Communications Inc., March 9, 1999.

HOOPER—AT&T Cable Services, 5152 South 1500 West, Riverdale, UT 84405. Phone: 800-486-9829. Counties: Davis & Weber. Also serves Clearfield, Clinton, Davis County (portions), Farr West, Layton, Ogden, Plain City, Pleasant View, Syracuse, Weber County (portions), West Haven, West Point. ICA: UT0008.
TV Market Ranking: 48 (Clearfield, Clinton, Davis County, Farr West, Hooper, Layton, Ogden, Syracuse, Weber County, West Haven, West Point); Below 100 (Plain City, Pleasant View). Franchise award date: N.A. Franchise expiration date: N.A. Began: December 30, 1987.
Channel capacity: 36 (not 2-way capable). Channels available but not in use: None.
Basic Service
Subscribers: 5,000.
Programming (received off-air): KUWB (W) Ogden; KBYU-TV (P) Provo; KSL-TV (N), KSTU (F), KTVX (A), KUED (P), KUTV (C) Salt Lake City.
Programming (via satellite): WGN-TV (W) Chicago; American Movie Classics; CNN; Country Music TV; Discovery Channel; E! Entertainment TV; ESPN; Fox Family Channel; Fox Sports Net; Headline News; Home Shopping Network; Lifetime; MSNBC; MTV; Nashville Network; Nickelodeon; Odyssey; Sci-Fi Channel; TBS Superstation; The Weather Channel; Turner Network TV; USA Network; VH1.
Fee: $54.00 installation; $25.95 monthly.
Pay Service 1
Pay Units: 285.
Programming (via satellite): Cinemax.
Fee: $15.25 installation; $10.95 monthly.
Pay Service 2
Pay Units: 719.
Programming (via satellite): Disney Channel.
Fee: $15.25 installation; $10.95 monthly.
Pay Service 3
Pay Units: 1,055.
Programming (via satellite): HBO.
Fee: $15.25 installation; $10.95 monthly.
Pay Service 4
Pay Units: 102.
Programming (via satellite): The Movie Channel.
Fee: $15.25 installation; $10.95 monthly.

Pay Service 5
Pay Units: 466.
Programming (via satellite): Showtime.
Fee: $15.25 installation; $10.95 monthly.
Local advertising: No.
Equipment: Cadco headend; Scientific-Atlanta amplifiers; Times Fiber cable; Atari character generator; Panasonic set top converters; Intercept traps; Prodelin satellite antenna; Standard Communications satellite receivers.
Miles of plant: 206.0 (coaxial). Homes passed: 8,311.
Regional manager: Alan Hintze. Chief technician: Craig Davis. Marketing manager: Ron Williams. Office manager: Lorraine Nelson.
Ownership: AT&T Broadband & Internet Services (MSO). Purchased from Insight Communications Co., November 2, 1998.

HUNTSVILLE—Colonial Cablevision, 3011 Joaquin Miller Rd., Oakland, CA 94602. Phone: 801-745-0745. Fax: 510-531-8858. County: Weber. Also serves Eden. ICA: UT0064.
TV Market Ranking: 48. Franchise award date: N.A. Franchise expiration date: N.A. Began: October 1, 1986.
Channel capacity: 42 (not 2-way capable). Channels available but not in use: 15.
Basic Service
Subscribers: 275.
Programming (received off-air): KULC (P) Ogden; KBYU-TV (P) Provo; KSL-TV (N), KSTU (F), KTVX (A), KUED (P), KUTV (C) Salt Lake City.
Programming (via satellite): WGN-TV (W) Chicago; TBS Superstation.
Fee: $25.00 installation; $18.95 monthly.
Expanded Basic Service
Subscribers: N.A.
Programming (via satellite): A & E; CNN; Country Music TV; Discovery Channel; ESPN; Fox Family Channel; Nashville Network; Sci-Fi Channel; Turner Network TV; USA Network.
Fee: N.A.
Pay Service 1
Pay Units: 20.
Programming (via satellite): Disney Channel.
Fee: $10.00 monthly.
Pay Service 2
Pay Units: 20.
Programming (via satellite): HBO.
Fee: N.A.
Pay Service 3
Pay Units: N.A.
Programming (via satellite): Cinemax.
Fee: N.A.
Miles of plant: 11.2 (coaxial).
Manager: Neal Schnog.
Ownership: Neal Schnog.

HURRICANE—Falcon Telecable, 919 S. Main St., St. George, UT 84770. Phone: 435-628-3681. County: Washington. Also serves La Verkin, Toquerville. ICA: UT0027.
TV Market Ranking: Below 100 (Toquerville); Outside TV Markets (Hurricane, La Verkin). Franchise award date: N.A. Franchise expiration date: N.A. Began: September 1, 1981.
Channel capacity: 42. Channels available but not in use: 3.
Basic Service
Subscribers: 1,675.
Programming (received off-air): KCSG (I) Cedar City; KVBC (N) Las Vegas.
Programming (via translator): KBYU-TV (P) Provo; KJZZ-TV (U), KSL-TV (N), KSTU (F), KTVX (A), KUED (P), KUTV (C) Salt Lake City.
Programming (via satellite): A & E; American Movie Classics; C-SPAN; CNBC; Comedy Central; Country Music TV; Discovery Channel; Disney Channel; E! Entertainment TV; ESPN; Fox Family Channel; Fox Sports Net; Headline News; Learning Channel; Lifetime; Nashville Network; Nickelodeon; QVC; The Inspirational Network; Travel Channel; USA Network; VH1.
Current originations: Public access; educational access; government access.
Fee: $35.00 installation; $20.14 monthly.
Expanded Basic Service
Subscribers: 1,598.
Programming (via satellite): WGN-TV (W) Chicago; CNN; TBS Superstation; Turner Network TV.
Fee: $4.40 monthly.
Pay Service 1
Pay Units: 305.
Programming (via satellite): HBO.
Fee: $10.45 monthly.
Pay Service 2
Pay Units: 232.
Programming (via satellite): Showtime.
Fee: $10.45 monthly.
Pay Service 3
Pay Units: 182.
Programming (via satellite): The Movie Channel.
Fee: $10.45 monthly.
Pay Service 4
Pay Units: 7.
Programming (via satellite): Cinemax.
Fee: N.A.
Miles of plant: 77.0 (coaxial). Homes passed: 2,727.
Manager: Richard Reniewicki. Chief technician: Robert Hannon.
Franchise fee: 1%-4% of gross.
Ownership: Falcon Communications LP (MSO), joint venture formed September 30, 1998. See Cable System Ownership.

IVINS—Enstar Cable TV, 919 S. Main St., St. George, UT 84770. Phone: 435-628-3681. County: Washington. ICA: UT0078.
TV Market Ranking: Outside TV Markets. Franchise award date: N.A. Franchise expiration date: N.A. Began: N.A.
Channel capacity: 43. Channels available but not in use: None.
Basic Service
Subscribers: 256.
Programming (received off-air): KCSG (I) Cedar City; KVBC (N) Las Vegas.
Programming (via translator): KBYU-TV (P) Provo; KJZZ-TV (U), KSL-TV (N), KSTU (F), KTVX (A), KUED (P), KUTV (C) Salt Lake City.
Programming (via satellite): A & E; C-SPAN; CNBC; Comedy Central; Country Music TV; E! Entertainment TV; ESPN; ESPN 2; FX; Fox Family Channel; Fox Sports Net; Learning Channel; Lifetime; MTV; Nickelodeon; QVC; Univision; VH1.
Fee: $17.55 monthly.
Expanded Basic Service
Subscribers: 240.
Programming (via satellite): American Movie Classics; Discovery Channel; Disney Channel; USA Network.
Fee: $1.31 monthly.
Expanded Basic Service 2
Subscribers: 226.
Programming (via satellite): WGN-TV (W) Chicago; CNN; Headline News; Nashville Network; TBS Superstation; Turner Network TV.
Fee: $5.75 monthly.
Pay Service 1
Pay Units: 17.
Programming (via satellite): Cinemax.
Fee: $10.50 monthly.
Pay Service 2
Pay Units: 17.
Programming (via satellite): Showtime.
Fee: $10.50 monthly.
Pay Service 3
Pay Units: 25.
Programming (via satellite): HBO.
Fee: $10.50 monthly.
Pay Service 4
Pay Units: 11.
Programming (via satellite): The Movie Channel.
Fee: $10.50 monthly.
Pay-Per-View
Special events.
Miles of plant: 19.0 (coaxial). Homes passed: 588.
Manager: Richard Reniewicki. Chief technician: Robert Hannon.
Franchise fee: 3% of gross.
Ownership: Falcon Communications LP (MSO), joint venture formed September 30, 1998. See Cable System Ownership.

KAMAS—All West Inc., Box 588, 50 West 100 North, Kamas, UT 84036. Phones: 801-783-4371; 801-783-4928. County: Summit. Also serves Francis, Marion, Oakley, Peoa. ICA: UT0053.
TV Market Ranking: 48. Franchise award date: N.A. Franchise expiration date: N.A. Began: November 1, 1983.
Channel capacity: 33 (not 2-way capable). Channels available but not in use: 1.
Basic Service
Subscribers: 716.
Programming (received off-air): KULC (P) Ogden; KBYU-TV (P) Provo; KJZZ-TV (U), KSL-TV (N), KSTU (F), KTVX (A), KUED (P), KUTV (C) Salt Lake City.
Programming (via satellite): WGN-TV (W) Chicago; A & E; American Movie Classics; CNN; ESPN; History Channel; Nashville Network; Nick at Nite; TBS Superstation; Turner Network TV; USA Network.
Fee: $50.00 installation; $17.95 monthly; $2.00 converter.
Expanded Basic Service
Subscribers: 353.
Programming (via satellite): Country Music TV; Discovery Channel; Disney Channel; Fox Family Channel; Fox Sports Net; Nickelodeon; Sci-Fi Channel; Travel Channel.
Fee: $8.00 monthly.
Pay Service 1
Pay Units: 99.
Programming (via satellite): HBO.
Fee: $10.00 monthly.
Pay Service 2
Pay Units: 46.
Programming (via satellite): Showtime.
Fee: $10.00 monthly.
Pay Service 3
Pay Units: 37.
Programming (via satellite): The Movie Channel.
Fee: $10.00 monthly.
Local advertising: Yes. Rates: $1.00/day.
Miles of plant: 26.0 (coaxial); 8.0 (fiber optic). Additional miles planned: 1.0 (coaxial). Homes passed: 1,000. Total homes in franchised area: 1,400.
Manager: D. Vernile Prince. Chief technician: Steve Taylor.
Ownership: All West/Utah Inc. (MSO).

KANAB—Peak Cablevision, 1750 S. Hwy. 10, Price, UT 84501. Phone: 435-637-6813. Fax: 435-637-9755. County: Kane. ICA: UT0033.
TV Market Ranking: Outside TV Markets. Franchise award date: N.A. Franchise expiration date: N.A. Began: February 1, 1982.
Channel capacity: 35. Channels available but not in use: 13.
Basic Service
Subscribers: 387.
Programming (via translator): KBYU-TV (P) Provo; KSL-TV (N), KSTU (F), KTVX (A), KUED (P), KUTV (C) Salt Lake City.
Programming (via satellite): WGN-TV (W) Chicago; CNN; Lifetime; Nickelodeon; QVC; TBS Superstation.
Fee: $60.00 installation; $19.61 monthly; $40.00 additional installation.
Expanded Basic Service
Subscribers: 312.
Programming (via satellite): American Movie Classics; ESPN; Fox Sports Net; Turner Network TV; USA Network.
Fee: $1.89 monthly.
Pay Service 1
Pay Units: 90.
Programming (via satellite): Disney Channel.
Fee: N.A.
Pay Service 2
Pay Units: 95.
Programming (via satellite): HBO.
Fee: $10.00 monthly.
Pay Service 3
Pay Units: 44.
Programming (via satellite): Showtime.
Fee: $10.00 monthly.
Pay Service 4
Pay Units: 132.
Programming (via satellite): The New Encore.
Fee: N.A.
Miles of plant: 18.0 (coaxial). Homes passed: 900. Total homes in franchised area: 900.
Manager: Shane Baggs.
Ownership: Peak Cablevision LLC (MSO). See Cable System Ownership.

KANARRAVILLE—Blackstone Cable LLC, 1104 W. Ironwood Dr., Coeur d'Alene, ID 83814-2605. Phone: 208-664-3370. Fax: 208-664-5888. County: Iron. ICA: UT0067.
TV Market Ranking: Below 100. Franchise award date: N.A. Franchise expiration date: N.A. Began: January 1, 1991.
Channel capacity: 36. Channels available but not in use: N.A.
Basic Service
Subscribers: 73.
Programming (via translator): KBYU-TV (P) Provo; KJZZ-TV (U), KSL-TV (N), KSTU (F), KTVX (A), KUED (P), KUTV (C) Salt Lake City.
Programming (via satellite): WGN-TV (W) Chicago; C-SPAN; CNN; Discovery Channel; ESPN; Nashville Network; Odyssey; QVC; TBS Superstation; Turner Network TV.
Fee: $43.50 installation; $21.00 monthly; $32.50 additional installation.
Expanded Basic Service
Subscribers: 48.
Programming (via satellite): Disney Channel; E! Entertainment TV; Fox Family Channel; Fox Sports Net; Learning Channel; Nick at Nite's TV Land; Turner Classic Movies.
Fee: N.A.
Pay Service 1
Pay Units: 6.
Programming (via satellite): Showtime.
Fee: $21.50 installation; $10.95 monthly.
Miles of plant: 5.0 (coaxial). Homes passed: 110.
Manager: Ted Hughett.

Ownership: Blackstone Cable LLC (MSO). Purchased from Enterprise Cable TV, December 1, 1998.

LEEDS—Falcon Cablevision, 919 S. Main St., St. George, UT 84770. Phone: 435-628-3681. Fax: 801-673-4225. County: Washington. Also serves Harrisburg Junction. ICA: UT0072.
TV Market Ranking: Below 100. Franchise award date: N.A. Franchise expiration date: N.A. Began: July 1, 1989.
Channel capacity: 37. Channels available but not in use: 20.
Basic Service
Subscribers: 66.
Programming (via translator): KVBC (N) Las Vegas; KBYU-TV (P) Provo; KSL-TV (N), KTVX (A), KUED (P), KUTV (C) Salt Lake City.
Programming (via satellite): WGN-TV (W) Chicago; CNN; Country Music TV; Discovery Channel; Disney Channel; ESPN; Fox Family Channel; Headline News; Sci-Fi Channel; TBS Superstation.
Fee: $35.00 installation; $18.51 monthly.
Pay Service 1
Pay Units: 8.
Programming (via satellite): Showtime.
Fee: $35.00 installation; $10.45 monthly.
Miles of plant: 13.0 (coaxial). Homes passed: 122.
Manager: Richard Reniewicki. Chief technician: Robert Hannon.
Franchise fee: 2% of gross.
Ownership: Falcon Communications LP (MSO), joint venture formed September 30, 1998. See Cable System Ownership.

LEWISTON—TCI Cablevision of Utah Inc., 1350 E. Miller Ave., Salt Lake City, UT 84106. Phone: 801-485-0500. Counties: Cache, UT; Franklin, ID. Also serves Franklin, Franklin County (portions), ID. ICA: UT0040.
TV Market Ranking: Outside TV Markets. Franchise award date: February 1, 1987. Franchise expiration date: February 1, 2002. Began: October 13, 1988.
Channel capacity: 34 (not 2-way capable). Channels available but not in use: 14.
Basic Service
Subscribers: 302.
Programming (received off-air): KIDK (C), KISU-TV (P) Idaho Falls-Pocatello; KBYU-TV (P) Provo; KSL-TV (N), KSTU (F), KTVX (A), KUTV (C) Salt Lake City.
Programming (via satellite): WGN-TV (W) Chicago; CNN; Discovery Channel; ESPN; Fox Family Channel; Nashville Network; Nickelodeon; TBS Superstation; USA Network; VH1.
Fee: $25.00 installation; $17.86 monthly.
Pay Service 1
Pay Units: 39.
Programming (via satellite): Cinemax.
Fee: $10.00 installation; $10.50 monthly.
Pay Service 2
Pay Units: 61.
Programming (via satellite): Disney Channel.
Fee: $10.00 installation; $9.50 monthly.
Pay Service 3
Pay Units: 51.
Programming (via satellite): HBO.
Fee: $10.00 installation; $11.50 monthly.
Local advertising: No.
Program Guide: TV Entertainment.
Equipment: Pico headend; Magnavox amplifiers; Times Fiber cable; Jerrold set top converters; Pico traps; Pico satellite receivers.
Miles of plant: 28.0 (coaxial). Homes passed: 746.
Manager: Kent Pearce. Chief technician: Mike Stockdale. Maintenance manager: Everett Priest. Office manager: Bill Rappley.
Franchise fee: 3% of gross (city) & basic (county).
Ownership: AT&T Broadband & Internet Services (MSO). Purchased from Tele-Communications Inc., March 9, 1999.

LOGAN—Charter Communications, Box 488, 1350 North 200 West, Logan, UT 84341. Phone: 435-752-9731. Fax: 435-753-6099. E-mail: charter@charter_utah.com. County: Cache. Also serves Cache County (unincorporated areas), Clarkston, Hyde Park, Hyrum, Mendon, Millville, Newton, Nibley, North Logan, Paradise, Providence, River Heights, Wellsville. ICA: UT0006.
TV Market Ranking: Below 100 (Hyrum, Logan, Mendon, Millville, Nibley, Paradise, Providence, River Heights, Wellsville); Outside TV Markets (Cache County, Clarkston, Hyde Park, Newton, North Logan). Franchise award date: December 22, 1970. Franchise expiration date: December 22, 2000. Began: January 7, 1971.
Channel capacity: 110 (2-way capable; operating 2-way). Channels available but not in use: 42.
Basic Service
Subscribers: 15,500.
Programming (received off-air): KULC (P), KUWB (W) Ogden; KBYU-TV (P) Provo; KJZZ-TV (U), KSL-TV (N), KSTU (F), KTVX (A), KUED (P), KUTV (C) Salt Lake City; allband FM.
Programming (via satellite): WGN-TV (W) Chicago; A & E; American Movie Classics; Animal Planet; C-SPAN; C-SPAN 2; CNBC; CNN; Cartoon Network; Comedy Central; Country Music TV; Discovery Channel; E! Entertainment TV; ESPN; ESPN 2; Fox Family Channel; Fox Sports Net; Golf Channel; Headline News; History Channel; Home & Garden Television; Learning Channel; Lifetime; MTV; Nashville Network; Nick at Nite's TV Land; Nickelodeon; Odyssey; Outdoor Life Network; QVC; Romance Classics; Sci-Fi Channel; TBS Superstation; TV Food Network; TV Guide Channel; The Weather Channel; Travel Channel; Turner Classic Movies; Turner Network TV; USA Network; Univision; VH1; ZDTV.
Planned programming (via satellite): Pax Net.
Current originations: Public access; educational access; government access; leased access; automated emergency alert; local sports.
Fee: $21.65 installation; $29.70 monthly.
Pay Service 1
Pay Units: 1,195.
Programming (via satellite): Cinemax (multiplexed).
Fee: $7.50 installation; $8.00 monthly.
Pay Service 2
Pay Units: 1,069.
Programming (via satellite): Disney Channel.
Fee: $7.50 installation; $8.00 monthly.
Pay Service 3
Pay Units: 536.
Programming (via satellite): Starz!; The New Encore.
Fee: $4.95 monthly.
Pay Service 4
Pay Units: 1,687.
Programming (via satellite): HBO (multiplexed).
Fee: $7.50 installation; $10.00 monthly.
Pay Service 5
Pay Units: 1,290.
Programming (via satellite): Showtime (multiplexed).
Fee: $9.00 monthly.
Pay Service 6
Pay Units: 578.
Programming (via satellite): The Movie Channel.
Fee: N.A.
Pay-Per-View
Addressable homes: 7,500.
Viewer's Choice.
Fee: $3.95.
Local advertising: Yes (locally produced). Available in satellite distributed, locally originated, character-generated, taped & automated programming. Rates: $15.00-$25.00/30 Minutes. Local sales manager: Bob Farley. Regional interconnect: Northwest Cable Advertising.
Program Guide: The Cable Guide.
Equipment: Ameco, Cadco & Jerrold headend; C-COR amplifiers; Capscan, CCS Hatfield & Hughes cable; Hitachi & Sony cameras; Fisher, Panasonic & Sony VTRs; MSI & Texscan character generator; General Instrument addressable set top converters; Pico traps; Scientific-Atlanta satellite antenna; Scientific-Atlanta, Microdyne & Uniden satellite receivers.
Miles of plant: 370.0 (coaxial); 2534.0 (fiber optic). Homes passed: 22,688. Total homes in franchised area: 23,250.
Manager: Randall Lee. Chief technician: Chester Redd. Marketing director: Ryan Morris.
City fee: 5% of gross.
Ownership: Charter Communications Inc. (MSO). Sale pends to AT&T Broadband & Internet Services.

LYMAN—Blackstone Cable LLC, 1104 W. Ironwood Dr., Coeur d'Alene, ID 83814-2605. Phone: 208-664-3370. Fax: 208-664-5888. County: Wayne. Also serves Bicknell, Loa. ICA: UT0073.
TV Market Ranking: Outside TV Markets. Franchise award date: N.A. Franchise expiration date: November 4, 2002. Began: N.A.
Channel capacity: N.A. Channels available but not in use: N.A.
Basic Service
Subscribers: 211.
Programming (via translator): KULC (P) Ogden; KBYU-TV (P) Provo; KJZZ (U), KSL-TV (N), KSTU (F), KTVX (A), KUED (P), KUTV (C) Salt Lake City.
Programming (via satellite): WGN-TV (W) Chicago; A & E; Animal Planet; CNN; Cartoon Network; Country Music TV; Discovery Channel; Disney Channel; E! Entertainment TV; ESPN; Fox Family Channel; Fox Sports Net; Headline News; Lifetime; Nashville Network; Nick at Nite's TV Land; Nickelodeon; Outdoor Channel; QVC; TBS Superstation; The Health Network; The Inspirational Network; Turner Classic Movies; Turner Network TV; USA Network.
Fee: $43.50 installation; $21.00 monthly; $21.50 additional installation.
Pay Service 1
Pay Units: 5.
Programming (via satellite): Cinemax.
Fee: $10.95 monthly.
Pay Service 2
Pay Units: 22.
Programming (via satellite): HBO.
Fee: $10.95 monthly.
Manager: Rick Swanger.
Ownership: Blackstone Cable LLC (MSO). Purchased from Southern Utah Cable Vision.

MANILA—Myvocom Inc., Box 127, Manila, UT 84046. Phone: 801-784-3175. County: Daggett. ICA: UT0058.
TV Market Ranking: Below 100. Franchise award date: November 1, 1987. Franchise expiration date: November 1, 2002. Began: May 15, 1988.
Channel capacity: 12. Channels available but not in use: 1.
Basic Service
Subscribers: N.A.
Programming (via translator): KSL-TV (N), KTVX (A), KUED (P), KUTV (C) Salt Lake City.
Programming (via satellite): CNN; Discovery Channel; ESPN; Nashville Network; TBS Superstation.
Fee: $25.00 installation; $14.95 monthly.
Pay Service 1
Pay Units: N.A.
Programming (via satellite): Disney Channel; HBO.
Fee: $5.00 monthly (Disney), $10.00 monthly (HBO).
Homes passed: 300.
Manager: Patrick Asbill.
Ownership: Myvocom.

MILFORD—Peak Cablevision, 1750 S. Hwy. 10, Price, UT 84501. Phone: 435-637-6813. Fax: 435-637-9755. County: Beaver. ICA: UT0074.
TV Market Ranking: Outside TV Markets. Franchise award date: N.A. Franchise expiration date: March 19, 2011. Began: March 1, 1983.
Channel capacity: 35 (not 2-way capable). Channels available but not in use: N.A.
Basic Service
Subscribers: 386.
Programming (via translator): KJZZ-TV (U), KSL-TV (N), KSTU (F), KTVX (A), KUED (P), KUTV (C) Salt Lake City.
Programming (via satellite): WGN-TV (W) Chicago; CNN; Country Music TV; Discovery Channel; ESPN; Fox Family Channel; Fox Sports Net; Lifetime; Nashville Network; Nickelodeon; QVC; TBS Superstation; The Weather Channel; Turner Network TV; USA Network.
Fee: $25.00 installation; $21.78 monthly.
Pay Service 1
Pay Units: 69.
Programming (via satellite): Disney Channel.
Fee: $7.95 monthly.
Pay Service 2
Pay Units: 116.
Programming (via satellite): HBO.
Fee: $13.15 monthly.
Pay Service 3
Pay Units: 75.
Programming (via satellite): Showtime.
Fee: $12.20 monthly.
Pay Service 4
Pay Units: 146.
Programming (via satellite): The New Encore.
Fee: $1.75 monthly.
Pay Service 5
Pay Units: N.A.
Programming (via satellite): Starz!
Fee: $10.95 monthly.
Miles of plant: 7.0 (coaxial); None (fiber optic). Homes passed: 394.
Manager: Ron Beaty. Chief technician: Bodie Peebles.
Franchise fee: 5% of gross.
Ownership: Peak Cablevision LLC (MSO). See Cable System Ownership.

MINERSVILLE—Peak Cablevision, 1750 S. Hwy. 10, Price, UT 84501. Phone: 435-637-6813. Fax: 435-637-9755. County: Beaver. ICA: UT0062.
TV Market Ranking: Outside TV Markets. Franchise award date: N.A. Franchise expiration date: January 10, 2004. Began: July 10, 1991.

Channel capacity: 35 (not 2-way capable). Channels available but not in use: 5.

Basic Service

Subscribers: 165.

Programming (via translator): KBYU-TV (P) Provo; KSL-TV (N), KSTU (F), KTVX (A), KUED (P), KUTV (C) Salt Lake City.

Programming (via satellite): WGN-TV (W) Chicago; A & E; American Movie Classics; CNN; Country Music TV; Discovery Channel; ESPN; Fox Family Channel; Fox Sports Net; Headline News; History Channel; Learning Channel; Lifetime; Nashville Network; Nickelodeon; QVC; Sci-Fi Channel; TBS Superstation; The Weather Channel; Turner Network TV; USA Network.

Fee: $25.00 installation; $21.15 monthly.

Pay Service 1

Pay Units: 7.

Programming (via satellite): Cinemax.

Fee: $12.20 monthly.

Pay Service 2

Pay Units: 13.

Programming (via satellite): Disney Channel.

Fee: $7.95 monthly.

Pay Service 3

Pay Units: 34.

Programming (via satellite): HBO.

Fee: $13.15 monthly.

Pay Service 4

Pay Units: N.A.

Programming (via satellite): Showtime; Starz!

Fee: $10.95 monthly (Starz), $11.00 monthly (Showtime).

Local advertising: No.

Miles of plant: 5.0 (coaxial). Homes passed: 228. Total homes in franchised area: 228.

Manager: Ron Beaty. Chief technician: Bodie Peebles. Marketing director: T. Homesley.

Franchise fee: 5% of gross.

Ownership: Peak Cablevision LLC (MSO). See Cable System Ownership.

MOAB—Peak Cablevision, 1750 S. Hwy. 10, Price, UT 84501. Phone: 435-637-6813. Fax: 435-637-9755. County: Grand. Also serves Grand County. ICA: UT0016.

TV Market Ranking: Below 100 (portions of Grand County); Outside TV Markets (portions of Grand County, Moab). Franchise award date: April 1, 1975. Franchise expiration date: N.A. Began: April 1, 1955.

Channel capacity: 35. Channels available but not in use: N.A.

Basic Service

Subscribers: 3,977.

Programming (received off-air): 7 FMs.

Programming (via microwave): KREX-TV (C,N) Grand Junction; KSL-TV (N), KTVX (A), KUED (P), KUTV (C) Salt Lake City.

Programming (via satellite): WGN-TV (W) Chicago; A & E; American Movie Classics; C-SPAN; C-SPAN 2; CNN; Country Music TV; Discovery Channel; ESPN; Fox Family Channel; Headline News; Lifetime; MTV; Nashville Network; Nickelodeon; QVC; TBS Superstation; Turner Network TV; USA Network.

Current originations: Automated time-weather; government access; local news.

Fee: $60.00 installation; $20.00 monthly; $40.00 additional installation.

Pay Service 1

Pay Units: 193.

Programming (via satellite): Cinemax.

Fee: $10.00 installation; $9.95 monthly.

Pay Service 2

Pay Units: 154.

Programming (via satellite): Disney Channel.

Fee: $10.00 installation; $9.95 monthly.

Pay Service 3

Pay Units: 221.

Programming (via satellite): HBO.

Fee: $10.00 installation; $9.95 monthly.

Pay Service 4

Pay Units: 116.

Programming (via satellite): Showtime.

Fee: $10.00 installation; $9.95 monthly.

Local advertising: Yes (locally produced & insert). Available in locally originated, character-generated & taped programming. Rates: $8.00/Minute; $4.00/30 Seconds. Local sales manager: Jim Corwin.

Equipment: RCA headend; Magnavox amplifiers; Times Fiber cable; RCA cameras; Sony VTRs; Texscan character generator; Jerrold set top converters; Andrew & Scientific-Atlanta satellite antenna; Standard Components satellite receivers.

Miles of plant: 85.0 (coaxial). Homes passed: 3,168. Total homes in franchised area: 3,168.

Manager: Shane Baggs.

City fee: 1.5% of gross.

Ownership: Peak Cablevision LLC (MSO). See Cable System Ownership.

MONA—Blackstone Cable LLC, 1104 W. Ironwood Dr., Coeur d'Alene, ID 83814-2605. Phone: 208-664-3370. Fax: 208-664-5888. County: Juab. ICA: UT0065.

TV Market Ranking: Below 100. Franchise award date: N.A. Franchise expiration date: October 8, 2001. Began: June 1, 1982.

Channel capacity: 19 (not 2-way capable). Channels available but not in use: 1.

Basic Service

Subscribers: 93.

Programming (received off-air): KBYU-TV (P) Provo; KJZZ-TV (U), KSL-TV (N), KSTU (F), KTVX (A), KUED (P), KUTV (C) Salt Lake City.

Programming (via satellite): WGN-TV (W) Chicago; CNN; Country Music TV; Discovery Channel; Disney Channel; ESPN; Fox Family Channel; Nashville Network; TBS Superstation; Turner Classic Movies; Turner Network TV.

Current originations: Automated time-weather; local news.

Fee: $43.50 installation; $21.00 monthly; $21.50 additional installation.

Pay Service 1

Pay Units: 11.

Programming (via satellite): HBO.

Fee: $10.95 monthly.

Miles of plant: 5.0 (coaxial); None (fiber optic). Homes passed: 185. Total homes in franchised area: 185.

Manager: Ted Hughett.

Franchise fee: 3% of basic.

Ownership: Blackstone Cable LLC (MSO).

MONROE—Blackstone Cable LLC, 1104 W. Ironwood Dr., Coeur d'Alene, ID 83814-2605. Phone: 208-664-3370. Fax: 208-664-5888. County: Sevier. ICA: UT0045.

TV Market Ranking: Outside TV Markets. Franchise award date: N.A. Franchise expiration date: October 27, 2002. Began: September 24, 1984.

Channel capacity: 19 (not 2-way capable). Channels available but not in use: None.

Basic Service

Subscribers: 346.

Programming (via microwave): KJZZ-TV (U) Salt Lake City.

Programming (via translator): KBYU-TV (P) Provo; KSL-TV (N), KSTU (F), KTVX (A), KUED (P), KUTV (C) Salt Lake City.

Programming (via satellite): WGN-TV (W) Chicago; American Movie Classics; CNN; Country Music TV; Discovery Channel; Disney Channel; ESPN; Fox Family Channel; Nashville Network; TBS Superstation; The Inspirational Network; Turner Classic Movies; Turner Network TV.

Current originations: Local news.

Fee: $43.50 installation; $21.00 monthly; $21.50 additional installation.

Pay Service 1

Pay Units: 11.

Programming (via satellite): Cinemax.

Fee: $10.95 monthly.

Pay Service 2

Pay Units: 37.

Programming (via satellite): HBO.

Fee: $10.95 monthly.

Equipment: Triple Crown headend; Triple Crown amplifiers; General cable; Paraclipse satellite antenna; Triple Crown satellite receivers.

Miles of plant: 13.0 (coaxial); None (fiber optic). Homes passed: 605. Total homes in franchised area: 645.

Manager: Ted Hughett.

City fee: 3% of basic.

Ownership: Blackstone Cable LLC (MSO).

MONTICELLO—Peak Cablevision, 1750 S. Hwy. 10, Price, UT 84501. Phone: 435-637-6813. Fax: 435-637-9755. County: San Juan. ICA: UT0044.

TV Market Ranking: Outside TV Markets. Franchise award date: N.A. Franchise expiration date: N.A. Began: August 20, 1980.

Channel capacity: 23. Channels available but not in use: N.A.

Basic Service

Subscribers: 381.

Programming (via translator): KBYU-TV (P) Provo; KSL-TV (N), KSTU (F), KTVX (A), KUED (P), KUTV (C) Salt Lake City.

Programming (via satellite): WGN-TV (W) Chicago; A & E; CNN; Country Music TV; Discovery Channel; ESPN; Fox Family Channel; Fox Sports Net; Nashville Network; TBS Superstation; Turner Network TV; USA Network.

Planned programming (via satellite): Nickelodeon.

Current originations: Public access.

Fee: $20.00 installation; $17.59 monthly.

Pay Service 1

Pay Units: 63.

Programming (via satellite): Disney Channel.

Fee: $10.00 installation; $10.50 monthly.

Pay Service 2

Pay Units: 100.

Programming (via satellite): HBO.

Fee: $10.00 installation; $11.45 monthly.

Pay Service 3

Pay Units: 64.

Programming (via satellite): The Movie Channel.

Fee: $10.00 installation; $10.50 monthly.

Program Guide: The Cable Guide.

Equipment: Pico & Comtech headend; Ameco & Magnavox amplifiers; Times Fiber cable; MSI character generator; Jerrold set top converters; Pico traps; Pico & Comtech satellite receivers.

Miles of plant: 9.0 (coaxial). Homes passed: 664.

Manager: Shane Baggs. Chief technician: Jon C. Almon.

City fee: 3% of gross.

Ownership: Peak Cablevision LLC (MSO). See Cable Systen Ownership.

MORGAN CITY—AT&T Cable Services, 5152 South 1500 West, Riverdale, UT 84405. Phone: 801-444-4824. County: Morgan. ICA: UT0048.

TV Market Ranking: 48. Franchise award date: N.A. Franchise expiration date: N.A. Began: April 1, 1982.

Channel capacity: 35. Channels available but not in use: 10.

Basic Service

Subscribers: 415.

Programming (received off-air): KBYU-TV (P) Provo; KSL-TV (N), KSTU (F), KTVX (A), KUED (P), KUTV (C) Salt Lake City.

Programming (via satellite): CNBC; CNN; Discovery Channel; Headline News; Lifetime; Nashville Network; Nickelodeon; QVC; TBS Superstation.

Current originations: Automated time-weather; public access; educational access; government access.

Fee: $60.00 installation; $19.96 monthly; $40.00 additional installation.

Expanded Basic Service

Subscribers: 353.

Programming (via satellite): American Movie Classics; ESPN; Fox Sports Net; Turner Network TV; USA Network.

Fee: $1.89 monthly.

Pay Service 1

Pay Units: 31.

Programming (via satellite): Cinemax.

Fee: $9.95 monthly.

Pay Service 2

Pay Units: 95.

Programming (via satellite): Disney Channel.

Fee: $9.45 monthly.

Pay Service 3

Pay Units: 108.

Programming (via satellite): HBO.

Fee: $9.95 monthly.

Pay Service 4

Pay Units: 195.

Programming (via satellite): The New Encore.

Fee: N.A.

Local advertising: Yes (locally produced). Available in satellite distributed & locally originated programming. Rates: $1.00/ Day (Personal); $300.00/ Day (Commercial). Local sales manager: Rebecca Bowlings.

Equipment: Gardiner & Scientific-Atlanta headend; Scientific-Atlanta amplifiers; Panasonic cameras; Panasonic VTRs; Compuvid character generator; Scientific-Atlanta set top converters; Eagle traps; Scientific-Atlanta & Strato Vision satellite antenna; Standard Communications satellite receivers.

Miles of plant: 11.6 (coaxial). Homes passed: 592. Total homes in franchised area: 643.

Regional director: Dick Freedman. Chief engineer: Bob Hillard.

City fee: 3% of gross.

Ownership: AT&T Broadband & Internet Services (MSO). Purchased from Tele-Communications Inc., March 9, 1999.

MORGAN COUNTY—TCI Cablevision of Utah Inc., 1350 E. Miller Ave., Salt Lake City, UT 84106. Phone: 801-485-0500. County: Morgan. ICA: UT0061.

TV Market Ranking: 48 (portions); Below 100 (portions). Franchise award date: N.A. Franchise expiration date: N.A. Began: November 1, 1984.

Channel capacity: 35. Channels available but not in use: 11.

Basic Service

Subscribers: 360.

Programming (received off-air): KBYU-TV (P) Provo; KSL-TV (N), KSTU (F), KTVX (A), KUED (P), KUTV (C) Salt Lake City.

Programming (via satellite): CNBC; CNN; Discovery Channel; Headline News; Lifetime; Nashville Network; Nickelodeon; QVC; TBS Superstation.

Fee: $60.00 installation; $19.96 monthly; $40.00 additional installation.

Expanded Basic Service
Subscribers: 182.
Programming (via satellite): American Movie Classics; ESPN; Fox Sports Net; Turner Network TV; USA Network.
Fee: $1.89 monthly.
Pay Service 1
Pay Units: 13.
Programming (via satellite): Cinemax.
Fee: N.A.
Pay Service 2
Pay Units: 37.
Programming (via satellite): Disney Channel.
Fee: N.A.
Pay Service 3
Pay Units: 55.
Programming (via satellite): HBO.
Fee: N.A.
Pay Service 4
Pay Units: 98.
Programming (via satellite): The New Encore.
Fee: N.A.
Miles of plant: 10.2 (coaxial).
Manager: Kent Pierce. Chief technician: Jeff Rosenquist.
Ownership: AT&T Broadband & Internet Services (MSO). Purchased from Tele-Communications Inc., March 9, 1999.

MORONI—Peak Cablevision, 1750 S. Hwy. 10, Price, UT 84501. Phone: 435-637-6813. Fax: 435-637-9755. County: Sanpete. Also serves Fountain Green. ICA: UT0042.
TV Market Ranking: Outside TV Markets. Franchise award date: N.A. Franchise expiration date: July 1, 1998. Began: June 1, 1983.
Channel capacity: 25. Channels available but not in use: N.A.
Basic Service
Subscribers: 379.
Programming (received off-air): KBYU-TV (P) Provo; KSL-TV (N), KSTU (F), KTVX (A), KUED (P), KUTV (C) Salt Lake City.
Programming (via satellite): WGN-TV (W) Chicago; CNN; Lifetime; Nashville Network; Nickelodeon; QVC; TBS Superstation.
Fee: $60.00 installation; $19.54 monthly; $40.00 additional installation.
Expanded Basic Service
Subscribers: 353.
Programming (via satellite): American Movie Classics; ESPN; Fox Sports Net; Turner Network TV; USA Network.
Fee: $1.89 monthly.
Pay Service 1
Pay Units: 33.
Programming (via satellite): Cinemax.
Fee: $8.00 monthly.
Pay Service 2
Pay Units: 72.
Programming (via satellite): Disney Channel.
Fee: $8.00 monthly.
Pay Service 3
Pay Units: 59.
Programming (via satellite): HBO.
Fee: N.A.
Pay Service 4
Pay Units: 140.
Programming (via satellite): The New Encore.
Fee: N.A.
Equipment: Cadco headend; Magnavox amplifiers; Times Fiber cable; Magnavox traps; Scientific-Atlanta satellite antenna.
Miles of plant: 21.1 (coaxial). Additional miles planned: 11.0 (coaxial). Homes passed: 688. Total homes in franchised area: 710.
Manager: Shane Baggs.
City fee: 3% of gross.
Ownership: Peak Cablevision LLC (MSO). See Cable System Ownership.

MOUNT PLEASANT—Peak Cablevision, 1750 S. Hwy. 10, Price, UT 84501. Phone: 435-637-6813. Fax: 435-637-9755. County: Sanpete. Also serves Fairview, Sanpete County, Spring City. ICA: UT0023.
TV Market Ranking: Outside TV Markets. Franchise award date: N.A. Franchise expiration date: N.A. Began: November 1, 1981.
Channel capacity: 26. Channels available but not in use: N.A.
Basic Service
Subscribers: 855.
Programming (via translator): KBYU-TV (P) Provo; KSL-TV (N), KSTU (F), KTVX (A), KUTV (C) Salt Lake City.
Programming (via satellite): WGN-TV (W) Chicago; CNBC; CNN; Lifetime; Nashville Network; Nickelodeon; TBS Superstation.
Fee: $60.00 installation; $19.10 monthly; $40.00 additional installation.
Expanded Basic Service
Subscribers: 785.
Programming (via satellite): American Movie Classics; ESPN; Fox Sports Net; QVC; Turner Network TV; USA Network.
Fee: $1.89 monthly.
Pay Service 1
Pay Units: 105.
Programming (via satellite): Cinemax.
Fee: $8.00 monthly.
Pay Service 2
Pay Units: 127.
Programming (via satellite): Disney Channel.
Fee: $8.00 monthly.
Pay Service 3
Pay Units: 192.
Programming (via satellite): HBO.
Fee: N.A.
Pay Service 4
Pay Units: 391.
Programming (via satellite): The New Encore.
Fee: N.A.
Equipment: Scientific-Atlanta headend; Magnavox amplifiers; Times Fiber cable; Scientific-Atlanta satellite antenna.
Miles of plant: 48.4 (coaxial). Homes passed: 1,516. Total homes in franchised area: 1,550.
Manager: Shane Baggs.
City fee: 3% of basic gross.
Ownership: Peak Cablevision LLC (MSO). See Cable System Ownership.

NEPHI—TCI Cablevision of Utah Inc., 1750 S. Hwy. 10, Price, UT 84501-4364. Phone: 801-637-6813. County: Juab. ICA: UT0028.
TV Market Ranking: Outside TV Markets. Franchise award date: N.A. Franchise expiration date: N.A. Began: January 1, 1981.
Channel capacity: 35. Channels available but not in use: 9.
Basic Service
Subscribers: 881.
Programming (received off-air): KBYU-TV (P) Provo; KSL-TV (N), KSTU (F), KTVX (A), KUED (P), KUTV (C) Salt Lake City.
Programming (via satellite): WGN-TV (W) Chicago; CNBC; CNN; Discovery Channel; Fox Family Channel; Lifetime; MTV; Nashville Network; Nickelodeon; QVC; TBS Superstation.
Fee: $60.00 installation; $19.76 monthly; $40.00 additional installation.
Expanded Basic Service
Subscribers: 735.
Programming (via satellite): American Movie Classics; ESPN; Fox Sports Net; Turner Network TV; USA Network.
Fee: $1.89 monthly.

Pay Service 1
Pay Units: 161.
Programming (via satellite): Disney Channel.
Fee: N.A.
Pay Service 2
Pay Units: 180.
Programming (via satellite): HBO.
Fee: $11.95 monthly.
Pay Service 3
Pay Units: 123.
Programming (via satellite): Showtime.
Fee: $11.95 monthly.
Pay Service 4
Pay Units: 347.
Programming (via satellite): The New Encore.
Fee: N.A.
Local advertising: Planned.
Equipment: Scientific-Atlanta headend; Jerrold amplifiers; Scientific-Atlanta satellite antenna; Scientific-Atlanta satellite receivers.
Miles of plant: 21.4 (coaxial). Homes passed: 1,200. Total homes in franchised area: 1,250.
Manager: Greg Palacios. Chief technician: Shane Baggs.
City fee: 3% of gross.
Ownership: AT&T Broadband & Internet Services (MSO). Purchased from Tele-Communications Inc., March 9, 1999.

NEW HARMONY—Blackstone Cable LLC, 1104 W. Ironwood Dr., Coeur d'Alene, ID 83814-2605. Phone: 208-664-3370. Fax: 208-664-5888. County: Washington. Also serves Washington County (unincorporated areas). ICA: UT0068.
TV Market Ranking: Below 100 (New Harmony, portions of Washington County); Outside TV Markets (portions of Washington County). Franchise award date: September 1, 1990. Franchise expiration date: September 1, 2005. Began: October 15, 1990.
Channel capacity: 36. Channels available but not in use: 22.
Basic Service
Subscribers: 47.
Programming (received off-air): KCSG (I) Cedar City.
Programming (via translator): KBYU-TV (P) Provo; KJZZ-TV (U), KSL-TV (N), KSTU (F), KTVX (A), KUED (P), KUTV (C) Salt Lake City.
Programming (via satellite): WGN-TV (W) Chicago; C-SPAN; CNN; Discovery Channel; ESPN; Nashville Network; QVC; TBS Superstation; Turner Network TV.
Fee: $43.50 installation; $21.00 monthly; $21.50 additional installation.
Expanded Basic Service
Subscribers: 42.
Programming (via satellite): Disney Channel; E! Entertainment TV; Fox Family Channel; Fox Sports Net; Learning Channel; Nick at Nite's TV Land; Turner Classic Movies.
Fee: N.A.
Pay Service 1
Pay Units: 4.
Programming (via satellite): Showtime.
Fee: $21.50 installation; $10.95 monthly.
Miles of plant: 3.0 (coaxial). Homes passed: 80.
Manager: Ted Hughett.
Ownership: Blackstone Cable LLC (MSO). Purchased from Enterprise Cable TV, December 1, 1998.

PANGUITCH—Blackstone Cable LLC, 1104 W. Ironwood Dr., Coeur d'Alene, ID 83814-2605. Phone: 208-664-3370. Fax: 208-664-5888. County: Garfield. ICA: UT0043.
TV Market Ranking: Outside TV Markets. Franchise award date: N.A. Franchise expiration date: December 31, 2011. Began: February 22, 1982.
Channel capacity: 36 (not 2-way capable). Channels available but not in use: 11.
Basic Service
Subscribers: 170.
Programming (via translator): KULC (P) Ogden; KBYU-TV (P) Provo; KJZZ-TV (U) KSL-TV (N), KSTU (F), KTVX (A), KUED (P), KUTV (C) Salt Lake City.
Programming (via satellite): WGN-TV (W) Chicago; American Movie Classics; CNN; Cartoon Network; Country Music TV; Discovery Channel; Disney Channel; ESPN; Fox Family Channel; Nashville Network; QVC; TBS Superstation; The Inspirational Network; The Sports Network; Turner Network TV; USA Network; VH1.
Current originations: Local news.
Fee: $43.50 installation; $21.00 monthly; $21.50 additional installation.
Pay Service 1
Pay Units: 30.
Programming (via satellite): HBO.
Fee: $10.95 monthly.
Equipment: Microwave Assoc. headend; Blonder-Tongue amplifiers; Times Fiber cable; Metrodata character generator; Prodelin satellite antenna.
Miles of plant: 11.0 (coaxial); None (fiber optic). Homes passed: 681.
Manager: Ted Hughett.
City fee: 3% of basic.
Ownership: Blackstone Cable LLC (MSO).

PARAGONAH—Blackstone Cable LLC, 1104 W. Ironwood Dr., Coeur d'Alene, ID 83814-2605. Phone: 208-664-3370. Fax: 208-664-5888. County: Iron. ICA: UT0085.
TV Market Ranking: Below 100. Franchise award date: N.A. Franchise expiration date: N.A. Began: N.A.
Channel capacity: N.A. Channels available but not in use: N.A.
Basic Service
Subscribers: 50.
Programming (received off-air): KULC (P), KUWB (W) Ogden; KBYU-TV (P) Provo; KJZZ-TV (U), KSL-TV (N), KSTU (F), KTVX (A), KUED (P), KUTV (C) Salt Lake City.
Programming (via satellite): WGN-TV (W) Chicago; C-SPAN; CNN; Discovery Channel; ESPN; Nashville Network; QVC; TBS Superstation; Turner Network TV.
Fee: N.A.
Expanded Basic Service
Subscribers: 48.
Programming (via satellite): Disney Channel; E! Entertainment TV; Fox Family Channel; Fox Sports Net; Learning Channel; Nick at Nite's TV Land; Turner Classic Movies.
Fee: N.A.

Pay Service 1
Pay Units: 9.
Programming (via satellite): HBO.
Fee: N.A.
Manager: Ted Hughett.
Ownership: Blackstone Cable LLC (MSO).

PARK CITY—TCI Cablevision of Utah Inc., No. 105, 1777 Sun Peak Dr., Park City, UT 84098. Phone: 435-649-4020. County: Summit. Also serves Jeremy Ranch, Summit County. ICA: UT0010.
TV Market Ranking: 48 (Jeremy Ranch, Park City, portions of Summit County); Outside TV Markets (portions of Summit County). Franchise award date: N.A. Franchise expiration date: N.A. Began: October 1, 1980.
Channel capacity: 35. Channels available but not in use: 7.
Basic Service
Subscribers: 3,431.
Programming (received off-air): K45AX (I) Park City; KSL-TV (N), KSTU (F), KTVX (A), KUED (P), KUTV (C) Salt Lake City.
Programming (via satellite): WGN-TV (W) Chicago; CNBC; CNN; Discovery Channel; Fox Family Channel; Headline News; Lifetime; Odyssey; QVC; TBS Superstation; The Weather Channel.
Current originations: Automated timeweather.
Fee: $60.00 installation; $10.00 monthly; $1.17 converter; $40.00 additional installation.
Expanded Basic Service
Subscribers: 3,250.
Programming (via satellite): American Movie Classics; ESPN; Fox Sports Net; MTV; Turner Network TV; USA Network.
Fee: $11.54 monthly.
Pay Service 1
Pay Units: 473.
Programming (via satellite): Disney Channel.
Fee: $29.00 installation; $10.00 monthly.
Pay Service 2
Pay Units: 907.
Programming (via satellite): HBO.
Fee: $29.00 installation; $10.00 monthly.
Pay Service 3
Pay Units: 617.
Programming (via satellite): Showtime.
Fee: $10.00 monthly.
Pay Service 4
Pay Units: 969.
Programming (via satellite): The New Encore.
Fee: N.A.
Local advertising: Yes. Regional interconnect: TCI Media Services-Salt Lake City, UT.
Program Guide: The Cable Guide.
Equipment: Gardiner headend; RCA amplifiers; Scientific-Atlanta satellite antenna; Scientific-Atlanta satellite receivers.
Miles of plant: 108.7 (coaxial). Homes passed: 5,883. Total homes in franchised area: 7,500.
Manager: Kent Pearce.
City fee: 3% of gross.
Ownership: AT&T Broadband & Internet Services (MSO). Purchased from Tele-Communications Inc., March 9, 1999.

PAROWAN—Blackstone Cable LLC, 1104 W. Ironwood Dr., Coeur d'Alene, ID 83814-2605. Phone: 208-664-3370. Fax: 208-664-5888. County: Iron. ICA: UT0034.
TV Market Ranking: Below 100. Franchise award date: N.A. Franchise expiration date: August 29, 2004. Began: December 8, 1981.
Channel capacity: 19 (not 2-way capable). Channels available but not in use: 1.
Basic Service
Subscribers: 512.
Programming (via translator): KBYU-TV (P) Provo; KSL-TV (N), KSTU (F), KTVX (A), KUED (P), KUTV (C) Salt Lake City.
Programming (via satellite): WGN-TV (W) Chicago; CNN; Cartoon Network; Discovery Channel; ESPN; Fox Family Channel; Nashville Network; TBS Superstation; Turner Network TV; USA Network.
Current originations: Automated timeweather; local news.
Fee: $43.50 installation; $21.00 monthly; $21.50 additional installation.
Expanded Basic Service
Subscribers: 493.
Programming (via translator): KJZZ-TV (U) Salt Lake City.
Programming (via satellite): American Movie Classics; Disney Channel; Fox News Channel; The Inspirational Network.
Fee: N.A.
Pay Service 1
Pay Units: 79.
Programming (via satellite): HBO.
Fee: $10.95 monthly.
Equipment: Microwave Assoc. headend; Blonder-Tongue amplifiers; Times Fiber cable; Metrodata character generator; Pioneer satellite antenna.
Miles of plant: 18.5 (coaxial); None (fiber optic). Homes passed: 990.
Manager: Ted Hughett.
City fee: 5% of gross.
Ownership: Blackstone Cable LLC (MSO).

PRICE—Peak Cablevision, 1750 S. Hwy. 10, Price, UT 84501. Phone: 435-637-6813. Fax: 435-637-9755. County: Carbon. Also serves Carbon County (portions), Helper, Wellington. ICA: UT0011.
TV Market Ranking: Outside TV Markets. Franchise award date: N.A. Franchise expiration date: N.A. Began: July 1, 1979.
Channel capacity: 34 (not 2-way capable). Channels available but not in use: N.A.
Basic Service
Subscribers: 4,595.
Programming (received off-air): 1 FM.
Programming (via translator): KBYU-TV (P) Provo; KSL-TV (N), KSTU (F), KTVX (A), KUED (P), KUTV (C) Salt Lake City.
Programming (via satellite): WGN-TV (W) Chicago; C-SPAN; CNN; Discovery Channel; Fox Family Channel; Headline News; Lifetime; MTV; Nashville Network; Nickelodeon; QVC; TBS Superstation; The Weather Channel.
Current originations: Automated timeweather.
Planned originations: Automated emergency alert.
Fee: $60.00 installation; $19.80 monthly; $1.02 converter; $40.00 additional installation.
Expanded Basic Service
Subscribers: 4,129.
Programming (via satellite): American Movie Classics; ESPN; Fox Sports Net; Turner Network TV; USA Network.
Fee: $1.89 monthly.
Pay Service 1
Pay Units: 411.
Programming (via satellite): Cinemax.
Fee: $10.00 installation; $10.95 monthly.
Pay Service 2
Pay Units: 586.
Programming (via satellite): Disney Channel.
Fee: $10.95 monthly.
Pay Service 3
Pay Units: 1,117.
Programming (via satellite): HBO.
Fee: $11.95 monthly.
Pay Service 4
Pay Units: 470.
Programming (via satellite): Showtime.
Fee: $11.95 monthly.
Pay Service 5
Pay Units: 2,230.
Programming (via satellite): The New Encore.
Fee: N.A.
Pay-Per-View
Addressable homes: 1,000.
Local advertising: Yes. Local sales manager: Paul Venturella.
Program Guide: The Cable Guide.
Equipment: Scientific-Atlanta & Jerrold headend; Scientific-Atlanta & C-COR amplifiers; Jerrold & Scientific-Atlanta set top converters; Scientific-Atlanta addressable set top converters; Pico traps; Scientific-Atlanta satellite antenna; Scientific-Atlanta satellite receivers.
Miles of plant: 133.2 (coaxial). Homes passed: 5,793. Total homes in franchised area: 6,170.
Manager: Shane Baggs.
City fee: 3% of gross.
Ownership: Peak Cablevision LLC (MSO). See Cable System Ownership.

PROVO—TCI Cablevision of Utah Inc., 1515 Riverside Ave., Provo, UT 84604. Phone: 801-377-8600. Fax: 801-377-6014. County: Utah. Also serves Spanish Fork, Utah County (portions). ICA: UT0005.
TV Market Ranking: 48 (portions of Utah County); Below 100 (Provo, Spanish Fork, portions of Utah County). Franchise award date: N.A. Franchise expiration date: N.A. Began: November 1, 1975.
Channel capacity: 80. Channels available but not in use: 20.
Basic Service
Subscribers: 26,434.
Programming (received off-air): KBYU-TV (P) Provo; KSL-TV (N), KSTU (F), KTVX (A), KUED (P), KUTV (C) Salt Lake City; allband FM.
Programming (via satellite): C-SPAN; CNN; Discovery Channel; Fox Family Channel; Headline News; Lifetime; MTV; Nashville Network; Nickelodeon; TBS Superstation; The Weather Channel.
Current originations: Automated timeweather; educational access.
Fee: $60.00 installation; $10.00 monthly.
Expanded Basic Service
Subscribers: 7,124.
Programming (via satellite): American Movie Classics; ESPN; Fox Sports Net; QVC; Turner Network TV; USA Network.
Fee: $1.86 monthly.
Pay Service 1
Pay Units: 1,070.
Programming (via satellite): Disney Channel.
Fee: N.A.
Pay Service 2
Pay Units: 1,344.
Programming (via satellite): HBO.
Fee: N.A.
Pay Service 3
Pay Units: 360.
Programming (via satellite): The Movie Channel.
Fee: N.A.
Pay Service 4
Pay Units: 388.
Programming (via satellite): Showtime.
Fee: N.A.
Pay Service 5
Pay Units: 3,895.
Programming (via satellite): The New Encore.
Fee: N.A.
Pay-Per-View
Addressable homes: 1,200.
Action Pay-Per-View.
Local advertising: Yes. Regional interconnect: TCI Media Services-Salt Lake City, UT.
Program Guide: The Cable Guide.
Equipment: Jerrold & Scientific-Atlanta headend; Jerrold amplifiers; Times Fiber cable; Jerrold addressable set top converters; Scientific-Atlanta satellite antenna.
Miles of plant: 264.4 (coaxial); 30.0 (fiber optic).
Manager: Paul Venturella. Chief technician: Steve King. Marketing director: Susan Hawks.
City fee: 2% of gross.
Ownership: AT&T Broadband & Internet Services (MSO). Purchased from Tele-Communications Inc., March 9, 1999.

RANDOLPH—All West Inc., Box 588, 50 West 100 North, Kamas, UT 84036. Phone: 801-783-4371. County: Rich. Also serves Woodruff. ICA: UT0066.
TV Market Ranking: Outside TV Markets. Franchise award date: N.A. Franchise expiration date: N.A. Began: June 1, 1982.
Channel capacity: 22 (not 2-way capable). Channels available but not in use: None.
Basic Service
Subscribers: 139.
Programming (received off-air): KSL-TV (N), KSTU (F), KTVX (A), KUED (P), KUTV (C) Salt Lake City.
Programming (via satellite): WGN-TV (W) Chicago; American Movie Classics; CNN; Discovery Channel; ESPN; Fox Family Channel; Fox Sports Net; Nashville Network; Nickelodeon; TBS Superstation; Turner Network TV; USA Network.
Fee: $50.00 installation; $14.00 monthly.
Pay Service 1
Pay Units: 33.
Programming (via satellite): Disney Channel.
Fee: $9.95 monthly.
Pay Service 2
Pay Units: 23.
Programming (via satellite): HBO.
Fee: $12.00 monthly.
Miles of plant: 11.3 (coaxial); 12.0 (fiber optic). Homes passed: 180. Total homes in franchised area: 225.
Manager: Vernile Prince. Chief technician: Doug Holden.
Ownership: All West/Utah Inc. (MSO).

RICHFIELD—Peak Cablevision, 1750 S. Hwy. 10, Price, UT 84501. Phone: 435-637-6813. Fax: 435-637-9755. County: Sevier. ICA: UT0020.
TV Market Ranking: Outside TV Markets. Franchise award date: N.A. Franchise expiration date: September 1, 1999. Began: December 1, 1980.
Channel capacity: 35. Channels available but not in use: 7.
Basic Service
Subscribers: 1,178.
Programming (via translator): KBYU-TV (P) Provo; KSL-TV (N), KSTU (F), KTVX (A), KUED (P), KUTV (C) Salt Lake City.
Programming (via satellite): WGN-TV (W) Chicago; C-SPAN; CNBC; CNN; Discovery Channel; Fox Family Channel; Headline News; Lifetime; MTV; Nashville Network; Nickelodeon; QVC; TBS Superstation.
Current originations: Automated timeweather; public access.
Fee: $60.00 installation; $19.97 monthly; $40.00 additional installation.

Expanded Basic Service
Subscribers: 985.
Programming (via satellite): American Movie Classics; ESPN; Fox Sports Net; Turner Network TV; USA Network.
Fee: $1.89 monthly.
Pay Service 1
Pay Units: 105.
Programming (via satellite): Cinemax.
Fee: $9.95 monthly.
Pay Service 2
Pay Units: 213.
Programming (via satellite): Disney Channel.
Fee: $9.45 monthly.
Pay Service 3
Pay Units: 253.
Programming (via satellite): HBO.
Fee: $9.95 monthly.
Pay Service 4
Pay Units: 516.
Programming (via satellite): The New Encore.
Fee: N.A.
Local advertising: Planned.
Equipment: Catel & Triple Crown headend; Magnavox amplifiers; General cable; Beston character generator; Scientific-Atlanta & Eagle set top converters; Scientific-Atlanta & Eagle traps; United Satellite Systems satellite antenna; Comtech satellite receivers.
Miles of plant: 31.0 (coaxial). Homes passed: 1,976. Total homes in franchised area: 2,000.
Manager: Shane Baggs.
City fee: 3% of gross.
Ownership: Peak Cablevision LLC (MSO). See Cable System Ownership.

RICHMOND—TCI Cablevision of Utah Inc., 25 West 1000 North, Smithfield, UT 84335. Phone: 801-563-3051. County: Cache. Also serves Cache County, Smithfield. ICA: UT0021.
TV Market Ranking: Below 100 (portions of Cache County); Outside TV Markets (portions of Cache County, Richmond, Smithfield). Franchise award date: N.A. Franchise expiration date: January 1, 2001. Began: October 1, 1982.
Channel capacity: 35. Channels available but not in use: 10.
Basic Service
Subscribers: 1,977.
Programming (via microwave): KBYU-TV (P) Provo; KSL-TV (N), KSTU (F), KTVX (A), KUED (P), KUTV (C) Salt Lake City.
Programming (via satellite): WGN-TV (W) Chicago; CNBC; CNN; Discovery Channel; Fox Family Channel; Lifetime; MTV; Nashville Network; Nickelodeon; Odyssey; QVC; TBS Superstation.
Fee: $60.00 installation; $21.20 monthly; $40.00 additional installation.
Expanded Basic Service
Subscribers: 1,468.
Programming (via satellite): American Movie Classics; ESPN; Fox Sports Net; Turner Network TV; USA Network.
Fee: $1.89 monthly.
Pay Service 1
Pay Units: 310.
Programming (via satellite): Disney Channel.
Fee: $10.95 monthly.
Pay Service 2
Pay Units: 305.
Programming (via satellite): HBO.
Fee: $11.95 monthly.
Pay Service 3
Pay Units: 173.
Programming (via satellite): Showtime.
Fee: $11.95 monthly.
Pay Service 4
Pay Units: 749.
Programming (via satellite): The New Encore.
Fee: N.A.
Program Guide: The Cable Guide.
Equipment: Scientific-Atlanta headend; Scientific-Atlanta amplifiers; Scientific-Atlanta satellite antenna; Scientific-Atlanta satellite receivers.
Miles of plant: 29.5 (coaxial).
Manager: Lynn Mason.
City fee: 3% of basic gross.
Ownership: AT&T Broadband & Internet Services (MSO). Purchased from Tele-Communications Inc., March 9, 1999.

RIVERDALE—AT&T Cable Services, 5152 South 1500 West, Riverdale, UT 84405. Phone: 801-444-4824. Fax: 801-392-4866. Counties: Davis & Weber. Also serves Harrisville, North Ogden, Ogden, Ogden Canyon, Ron Clair, Roy, South Ogden, South Weber, Uintah City, Washington Terrace, Weber County (portions), West Ogden. ICA: UT0075.
TV Market Ranking: 48 (Harrisville, Ogden, Ogden Canyon, Riverdale, Ron Clair, Roy, South Ogden, South Weber, Uintah City, Washington Terrace, portions of Weber County); Below 100 (North Ogden, portions of Weber County, West Ogden). Franchise award date: January 1, 1981. Franchise expiration date: N.A. Began: January 1, 1982.
Channel capacity: 35 (not 2-way capable). Channels available but not in use: 14.
Basic Service
Subscribers: 257.
Programming (received off-air): KBYU-TV (P) Provo; KSL-TV (N), KSTU (F), KTVX (A), KUED (P), KUTV (C) Salt Lake City.
Programming (via satellite): WGN-TV (W) Chicago; American Movie Classics; CNN; Discovery Channel; ESPN; Fox Family Channel; MTV; Nashville Network; Nickelodeon; Sci-Fi Channel; TBS Superstation; USA Network.
Fee: $25.00 installation; $9.00 monthly.
Pay Service 1
Pay Units: 46.
Programming (via satellite): The Movie Channel.
Fee: $19.95 installation; $10.95 monthly.
Pay Service 2
Pay Units: 69.
Programming (via satellite): Showtime.
Fee: $19.95 installation; $10.95 monthly.
Local advertising: No.
Equipment: Cadco headend; Scientific-Atlanta amplifiers; Times Fiber cable; Panasonic & Hamlin set top converters; Intercept traps; Prodelin satellite antenna; Standard Components & Harris satellite receivers.
Miles of plant: 6.0 (coaxial). Total homes in franchised area: 459.
Regional director: Dick Freedman. Chief engineer: Bob Hillard.
City fee: 3% of gross.
Ownership: AT&T Broadband & Internet Services (MSO). Purchased from Tele-Communications Inc., March 9, 1999.

ROCKVILLE—Falcon Telecable, 919 S. Main St., St. George, UT 84770. Phone: 435-628-3681. County: Washington. Also serves Springdale. ICA: UT0077.
TV Market Ranking: Below 100 (Springdale); Outside TV Markets (Rockville). Franchise award date: N.A. Franchise expiration date: N.A. Began: N.A.
Channel capacity: 54. Channels available but not in use: 33.
Basic Service
Subscribers: 103.
Programming (via translator): KBYU-TV (P) Provo; KSL-TV (N), KSTU (F), KTVX (A), KUED (P), KUTV (C) Salt Lake City.
Programming (via satellite): WGN-TV (W) Chicago; American Movie Classics; CNN; Country Music TV; Discovery Channel; Disney Channel; ESPN; Headline News; Lifetime; QVC; Sci-Fi Channel; TBS Superstation; Travel Channel.
Fee: $20.56 monthly.
Pay Service 1
Pay Units: 23.
Programming (via satellite): HBO.
Fee: $10.50 monthly.
Pay Service 2
Pay Units: 20.
Programming (via satellite): Showtime.
Fee: $10.50 monthly.
Pay Service 3
Pay Units: 1.
Programming (via satellite): The Movie Channel.
Fee: N.A.
Miles of plant: 13.0 (coaxial). Homes passed: 418.
Manager: Richard Reniewicki. Chief technician: Robert Hannon.
Franchise fee: 2% of gross.
Ownership: Falcon Communications LP (MSO), joint venture formed September 30, 1998. See Cable System Ownership.

ROOSEVELT—Peak Cablevision, 1750 S. Hwy. 10, Price, UT 84501. Phone: 435-637-6813. Fax: 435-637-9755. County: Duchesne. ICA: UT0030.
TV Market Ranking: Below 100. Franchise award date: N.A. Franchise expiration date: N.A. Began: August 1, 1981.
Channel capacity: 35. Channels available but not in use: 12.
Basic Service
Subscribers: 844.
Programming (via translator): KBYU-TV (P) Provo; KSL-TV (N), KSTU (F), KTVX (A), KUED (P), KUTV (C) Salt Lake City.
Programming (via satellite): WGN-TV (W) Chicago; CNBC; CNN; Lifetime; Nashville Network; Nickelodeon; QVC; TBS Superstation.
Fee: $60.00 installation; $19.34 monthly; $40.00 additional installation.
Expanded Basic Service
Subscribers: 786.
Programming (via satellite): American Movie Classics; ESPN; Fox Sports Net; Turner Network TV; USA Network.
Fee: $1.89 monthly.
Pay Service 1
Pay Units: 203.
Programming (via satellite): Disney Channel.
Fee: $10.95 monthly.
Pay Service 2
Pay Units: 282.
Programming (via satellite): HBO.
Fee: $11.00 monthly.
Pay Service 3
Pay Units: 191.
Programming (via satellite): Showtime.
Fee: $11.00 monthly.
Pay Service 4
Pay Units: 412.
Programming (via satellite): The New Encore.
Fee: N.A.
Miles of plant: 22.0 (coaxial). Homes passed: 1,153. Total homes in franchised area: 1,207.
Manager: Shane Baggs.
City fee: 3% of gross.
Ownership: Peak Cablevision LLC (MSO). See Cable System Ownership.

SALEM—TCI Cablevision of Utah Inc., 1515 North, River Side Ave., Provo, UT 84604. Phone: 801-377-8600. County: Utah. Also serves Elk Ridge, Payson, Spanish Fork City, Spring Lake, Utah County. ICA: UT0009.
TV Market Ranking: 48 (portions of Utah County); Below 100 (Elk Ridge, Payson, Salem, Spanish Fork City, Spring Lake, portions of Utah County). Franchise award date: N.A. Franchise expiration date: N.A. Began: November 1, 1980.
Channel capacity: 38. Channels available but not in use: N.A.
Basic Service
Subscribers: 4,044.
Programming (received off-air): KBYU-TV (P) Provo; KSL-TV (N), KSTU (F), KTVX (A), KUED (P), KUTV (C) Salt Lake City; 11 FMs.
Programming (via satellite): WGN-TV (W) Chicago; C-SPAN; CNBC; CNN; Discovery Channel; Fox Family Channel; Headline News; Lifetime; MTV; Nashville Network; Nickelodeon; QVC; TBS Superstation; The Weather Channel.
Fee: $60.00 installation; $9.46 monthly; $1.09 converter; $40.00 additional installation.
Expanded Basic Service
Subscribers: 3,968.
Programming (via satellite): American Movie Classics; ESPN; Fox Sports Net; Turner Network TV; USA Network.
Fee: $14.36 monthly.
Pay Service 1
Pay Units: 682.
Programming (via satellite): Disney Channel.
Fee: $9.00 monthly.
Pay Service 2
Pay Units: 804.
Programming (via satellite): HBO.
Fee: $9.00 monthly.
Pay Service 3
Pay Units: 470.
Programming (via satellite): Showtime.
Fee: $9.00 monthly.
Pay Service 4
Pay Units: 1,662.
Programming (via satellite): The New Encore.
Fee: N.A.
Pay Service 5
Pay Units: N.A.
Programming (via satellite): The Movie Channel.
Fee: $13.15 monthly.
Equipment: Jerrold & Scientific-Atlanta headend; Jerrold amplifiers; Scientific-Atlanta satellite receivers.
Miles of plant: 135.3 (coaxial). Homes passed: 6,578. Total homes in franchised area: 7,194.
Manager: Paul Venturella. Chief technician: Steve King.
City fee: 3% of gross.
Ownership: AT&T Broadband & Internet Services (MSO). Purchased from Tele-Communications Inc., March 9, 1999.

SALINA—Peak Cablevision, 1750 S. Hwy. 10, Price, UT 84501. Phone: 435-637-6813. Fax: 435-637-9755. County: Sevier. Also serves Aurora, Redmond, Sevier County. ICA: UT0029.
TV Market Ranking: Outside TV Markets. Franchise award date: N.A. Franchise expiration date: N.A. Began: May 1, 1982.
Channel capacity: 29. Channels available but not in use: N.A.
Basic Service
Subscribers: 719.

Programming (via translator): KBYU-TV (P) Provo; KSL-TV (N), KSTU (F), KTVX (A), KUED (P), KUTV (C) Salt Lake City.
Programming (via satellite): WGN-TV (W) Chicago; CNN; Discovery Channel; Fox Family Channel; Lifetime; Nashville Network; Nickelodeon; QVC; TBS Superstation.
Fee: $59.90 installation; $19.69 monthly; $31.95 additional installation.

Expanded Basic Service
Subscribers: 620.
Programming (via satellite): American Movie Classics; ESPN; Fox Sports Net; Turner Network TV; USA Network.
Fee: $1.89 monthly.

Pay Service 1
Pay Units: 77.
Programming (via satellite): Cinemax.
Fee: N.A.

Pay Service 2
Pay Units: 129.
Programming (via satellite): Disney Channel.
Fee: N.A.

Pay Service 3
Pay Units: 169.
Programming (via satellite): HBO.
Fee: N.A.

Pay Service 4
Pay Units: 297.
Programming (via satellite): The New Encore.
Fee: N.A.

Miles of plant: 43.7 (coaxial). Homes passed: 1,183. Total homes in franchised area: 1,265.
Manager: Shane Baggs.
Ownership: Peak Cablevision LLC (MSO). See Cable System Ownership.

SALT LAKE CITY—TCI Cablevision of Utah Inc., 1350 E. Miller Ave., Salt Lake City, UT 84106. Phone: 801-485-0500. Fax: 801-487-1887. County: Salt Lake. Also serves Bluffdale, Draper, Herriman, Midvale, Murray, Riverton, Salt Lake County, Sandy (eastern portion), South Jordan, South Salt Lake City. ICA: UT0001.
TV Market Ranking: 48. Franchise award date: January 1, 1966. Franchise expiration date: January 1, 2004. Began: March 1, 1970.
Channel capacity: N.A. Channels available but not in use: N.A.

Basic Service
Subscribers: 101,016.
Programming (received off-air): KULC (P) Ogden; KBYU-TV (P) Provo; KJZZ-TV (U), KSL-TV (N), KSTU (F), KTVX (A), KUED (P), KUTV (C) Salt Lake City.
Programming (via translator): KUWB (W) Ogden.
Programming (via satellite): FX; Lifetime; Odyssey; QVC; TV Guide Sneak Prevue.
Current originations: Educational access.
Fee: $60.00 installation; $9.31 monthly; $1.90 converter; $40.00 additional installation.

Expanded Basic Service
Subscribers: 100,100.
Programming (via satellite): WGN-TV (W) Chicago; A & E; American Movie Classics; C-SPAN; CNBC; CNN; Discovery Channel; Disney Channel; ESPN; Fox Family Channel; Fox Sports Net; Headline News; Intro TV; MTV; Nashville Network; Nickelodeon; TBS Superstation; The Weather Channel; Turner Network TV; USA Network.
Fee: $31.13 installation; $11.88 monthly.

Pay Service 1
Pay Units: 35,306.
Programming (via satellite): HBO.
Fee: $13.15 monthly.

Pay Service 2
Pay Units: 8,090.
Programming (via satellite): The Movie Channel.
Fee: $13.15 monthly.

Pay Service 3
Pay Units: 13,100.
Programming (via satellite): Showtime.
Fee: $13.15 monthly.

Pay Service 4
Pay Units: 997.
Programming (via satellite): Cinemax.
Fee: N.A.

Pay Service 5
Pay Units: 49,873.
Programming (via satellite): The New Encore.
Fee: $1.75 monthly.

Pay Service 6
Pay Units: 1.
Programming (via satellite): Xchange.
Fee: N.A.

Pay Service 7
Pay Units: N.A.
Programming (via satellite): DMX; TV-Japan.
Fee: $9.95 monthly (DMX).

Pay-Per-View
Addressable homes: 14,296.

Local advertising: Yes. Regional interconnect: Northwest Cable Advertising.
Program Guide: The Cable Guide.
Equipment: Jerrold headend; Jerrold amplifiers; Systems Wire cable; Scientific-Atlanta satellite antenna.
Miles of plant: 1200.0 (coaxial). Homes passed: 132,952. Total homes in franchised area: 235,482.
Manager: Kent Pearce. Chief technician: Everett Preece. Marketing director: Leslie White.
City fee: 5% of gross (Salt Lake City).
Ownership: AT&T Broadband & Internet Services (MSO). Purchased from Tele-Communications Inc., March 9, 1999.

SANDY—TCI Cablevision, 9075 South 700 West, Sandy, UT 84070. Phones: 801-566-0694; 801-561-9275. Fax: 801-255-2711. Counties: Salt Lake & Utah. Also serves Alpine, American Fork, Highland, Lehi, Lindon, Mapleton, Midvale (western portion), Orem, Pleasant Grove, Springville, Utah County (unincorporated areas), West Jordan. ICA: UT0002.
TV Market Ranking: 48 (Alpine, American Fork, Highland, Lehi, Lindon, Midvale, Orem, Pleasant Grove, Sandy, portions of Utah County, West Jordan); Below 100 (Mapleton, Springville, portions of Utah County). Franchise award date: May 25, 1977. Franchise expiration date: January 1, 2007. Began: August 22, 1980.
Channel capacity: 43 (not 2-way capable). Channels available but not in use: None.

Basic Service
Subscribers: 28,549.
Programming (received off-air): KULC (P) Ogden; KBYU-TV (P) Provo; KJZZ-TV (U), KSL-TV (N), KSTU (F), KTVX (A), KUED (P), KUTV (C) Salt Lake City.
Programming (via satellite): WGN-TV (W) Chicago; A & E; American Movie Classics; Animal Planet; C-SPAN; CNBC; CNN; Discovery Channel; E! Entertainment TV; ESPN; ESPN 2; Fox Family Channel; Fox Sports Net Rocky Mountain; Goodlife TV Network; Headline News; Home Shopping Network; Learning Channel; Lifetime; MSNBC; MTV; Nashville Network; Nickelodeon; QVC; Sci-Fi Channel; TBS Superstation; TV Guide Channel; The Weather Channel; Turner Network TV; USA Network; VH1.
Current originations: Public access; government access.
Fee: $40.74 installation; $21.38 monthly.

Pay Service 1
Pay Units: 2,578.
Programming (via satellite): Cinemax.
Fee: $15.00 installation; $9.95 monthly.

Pay Service 2
Pay Units: 3,748.
Programming (via satellite): Disney Channel.
Fee: $15.00 installation; $9.95 monthly.

Pay Service 3
Pay Units: 6,320.
Programming (via satellite): The New Encore.
Fee: $3.95 monthly.

Pay Service 4
Pay Units: 5,158.
Programming (via satellite): HBO.
Fee: $15.00 installation; $9.95 monthly.

Pay Service 5
Pay Units: 3,781.
Programming (via satellite): Showtime.
Fee: $9.95 monthly.

Pay-Per-View
Addressable homes: 10,974.
Viewer's Choice.

Local advertising: Yes. Available in taped programming. Rates: $60.00/30 Seconds. Local sales manager: Derek Mattson. Regional interconnect: TCI Media Services-Salt Lake City, UT.
Equipment: Jerrold & Scientific-Atlanta headend; Jerrold amplifiers; Times Fiber cable; Jerrold set top converters; Jerrold addressable set top converters; Pico traps; M/A-Com, Scientific-Atlanta & Vertex satellite antenna.
Miles of plant: 907.0 (coaxial). Additional miles planned: 14.0 (coaxial). Homes passed: 67,922. Total homes in franchised area: 70,985.
Manager: Lance Barns. Chief technician: Julius Airam. Marketing director: Chris Jeffers.
City fee: 5% of gross.
Ownership: AT&T Broadband & Internet Services (MSO). Tele-Communications Inc. purchased from Insight Communications Co., October 30, 1998.

SANTAQUIN—Blackstone Cable LLC, 1104 W. Ironwood Dr., Coeur d'Alene, ID 83814-2605. Phone: 208-664-3370. Fax: 208-664-5888. County: Utah. ICA: UT0041.
TV Market Ranking: Below 100. Franchise award date: N.A. Franchise expiration date: February 10, 2002. Began: September 1, 1981.
Channel capacity: 22 (not 2-way capable). Channels available but not in use: 5.

Basic Service
Subscribers: 652.
Programming (received off-air): KBYU-TV (P) Provo; KSL-TV (N), KSTU (F), KTVX (A), KUED (P), KUTV (C) Salt Lake City.
Programming (via satellite): WGN-TV (W) Chicago; CNN; Cartoon Network; Discovery Channel; ESPN; Nashville Network; QVC; TBS Superstation; Turner Network TV.
Current originations: Local news.
Fee: $43.50 installation; $21.00 monthly; $21.50 additional installation.

Expanded Basic Service
Subscribers: 599.
Programming (via translator): KJZZ-TV (U) Salt Lake City.
Programming (via satellite): Disney Channel; Fox Family Channel; Fox News Channel; Turner Classic Movies.
Fee: N.A.

Pay Service 1
Pay Units: 51.
Programming (via satellite): HBO.
Fee: $10.95 monthly.

Pay Service 2
Pay Units: 6.
Programming (via satellite): Cinemax.
Fee: $10.95 monthly.

Miles of plant: 15.7 (coaxial); None (fiber optic). Homes passed: 1,002.
Manager: Ted Hughett.
City fee: 3% of basic.
Ownership: Blackstone Cable LLC (MSO).

ST. GEORGE—Falcon Telecable, 919 S. Main St., St. George, UT 84770. Phone: 435-628-3681. County: Washington. Also serves Santa Clara, Washington. ICA: UT0007.
TV Market Ranking: Outside TV Markets. Franchise award date: October 1, 1977. Franchise expiration date: N.A. Began: December 15, 1978.
Channel capacity: 43 (2-way capable; operating 2-way partially). Channels available but not in use: None.

Basic Service
Subscribers: 4,900.
Programming (received off-air): KCSG (I) Cedar City.
Programming (via translator): KVBC (N) Las Vegas; KBYU-TV (P) Provo; KJZZ-TV (U), KSL-TV (N), KSTU (F), KTVX (A), KUED (P), KUTV (C) Salt Lake City.
Programming (via satellite): A & E; C-SPAN; CNBC; Comedy Central; Country Music TV; E! Entertainment TV; ESPN; ESPN 2; FX; Fox Family Channel; Fox Sports Net; Learning Channel; Lifetime; MTV; Nickelodeon; QVC; Univision; VH1.
Current originations: Automated time-weather; public access; educational access; government access; religious access.
Fee: $35.00 installation; $17.43 monthly.

Expanded Basic Service
Subscribers: 5,119.
Programming (via satellite): American Movie Classics; Discovery Channel; Disney Channel; USA Network.
Fee: $1.40 monthly.

Expanded Basic Service 2
Subscribers: 4,947.
Programming (via satellite): WGN-TV (W) Chicago; CNN; Headline News; Nashville Network; TBS Superstation; Turner Network TV.
Fee: $5.95 monthly.

Pay Service 1
Pay Units: 455.
Programming (via satellite): Cinemax.
Fee: $10.50 monthly.

Pay Service 2
Pay Units: 788.
Programming (via satellite): HBO.
Fee: $10.50 monthly.

Pay Service 3
Pay Units: 552.
Programming (via satellite): Showtime.
Fee: $10.50 monthly.

Pay Service 4
Pay Units: 365.
Programming (via satellite): The Movie Channel.
Fee: $10.50 monthly.

Pay-Per-View
Special events.

Local advertising: Yes (locally produced). Available in character-generated programming.
Equipment: Blonder-Tongue & Scientific-Atlanta headend; GTE Sylvania & Magnavox amplifiers; Times Fiber cable; Video Data Systems character generator; Jerrold set top converters; Scientific-Atlanta satellite antenna.
Miles of plant: 360.0 (coaxial). Homes passed: 22,496.
Manager: Richard Reniewicki. Chief technician: Robert Hannon.
Franchise fee: 2%-3% of gross.

Ownership: Falcon Communications LP (MSO), joint venture formed September 30, 1998. See Cable System Ownership.

STANSBURY PARK—TCI Cablevision of Utah Inc., 22 W. Vine St., Tooele, UT 84074. Phone: 801-882-6604. County: Tooele. ICA: UT0060.
TV Market Ranking: 48. Franchise award date: N.A. Franchise expiration date: N.A. Began: July 1, 1982.
Channel capacity: 31. Channels available but not in use: 7.
Basic Service
Subscribers: 306.
Programming (received off-air): KSL-TV (N), KSTU (F), KTVX (A), KUED (P), KUTV (C) Salt Lake City.
Programming (via satellite): WGN-TV (W) Chicago; CNBC; CNN; Discovery Channel; Fox Family Channel; Lifetime; Nashville Network; Nickelodeon; TBS Superstation.
Fee: $60.00 installation; $20.29 monthly; $40.00 additional installation.
Expanded Basic Service
Subscribers: 185.
Programming (via satellite): American Movie Classics; ESPN; Fox Sports Net; Turner Network TV; USA Network.
Fee: $1.89 monthly.
Pay Service 1
Pay Units: 26.
Programming (via satellite): Disney Channel.
Fee: N.A.
Pay Service 2
Pay Units: 77.
Programming (via satellite): HBO.
Fee: N.A.
Pay Service 3
Pay Units: 47.
Programming (via satellite): Showtime.
Fee: N.A.
Pay Service 4
Pay Units: N.A.
Programming (via satellite): TV-Japan; The New Encore.
Fee: N.A.
Miles of plant: 9.0 (coaxial).
Manager: Mike Oswald.
Ownership: AT&T Broadband & Internet Services (MSO). Purchased from Tele-Communications Inc., March 9, 1999.

TOOELE—TCI Cablevision of Utah Inc., 22 W. Vine St., Tooele, UT 84074. Phone: 435-882-6604. County: Tooele. Also serves Tooele Army Depot, Tooele County. ICA: UT0012.
TV Market Ranking: 48 (Tooele, Tooele Army Depot, portions of Tooele County); Below 100 (portions of Tooele County). Franchise award date: N.A. Franchise expiration date: N.A. Began: July 1, 1980.
Channel capacity: 29. Channels available but not in use: N.A.
Basic Service
Subscribers: 2,228.
Programming (received off-air): KBYU-TV (P) Provo; KSL-TV (N), KSTU (F), KTVX (A), KUED (P) Salt Lake City; allband FM.
Programming (via satellite): WGN-TV (W) Chicago; CNBC; CNN; Discovery Channel; Fox Family Channel; Lifetime; Nashville Network; Nickelodeon; Odyssey; QVC; TBS Superstation.
Current originations: Automated time-weather.
Fee: $60.00 installation; $20.13 monthly; $40.00 additional installation.
Expanded Basic Service
Subscribers: 1,775.
Programming (via satellite): American Movie Classics; ESPN; Fox Sports Net; Turner Network TV; USA Network.
Fee: $1.86 monthly.
Pay Service 1
Pay Units: 350.
Programming (via satellite): Disney Channel.
Fee: $12.00 installation; $11.95 monthly.
Pay Service 2
Pay Units: 965.
Programming (via satellite): HBO.
Fee: $12.00 installation; $11.95 monthly.
Pay Service 3
Pay Units: 348.
Programming (via satellite): Showtime.
Fee: $12.00 installation; $11.95 monthly.
Pay Service 4
Pay Units: N.A.
Programming (via satellite): The New Encore.
Fee: N.A.
Program Guide: The Cable Guide.
Equipment: Scientific-Atlanta headend; Jerrold amplifiers; Times Fiber cable; BEI character generator; Jerrold set top converters; Microdyne satellite antenna.
Miles of plant: 59.0 (coaxial). Homes passed: 5,350. Total homes in franchised area: 6,195.
Manager: Mike Oswald.
City fee: 4% of gross.
Ownership: AT&T Broadband & Internet Services (MSO). Purchased from Tele-Communications Inc., March 9, 1999.

TREMONTON—AT&T Cable Services, 5152 South 1500 West, Riverdale, UT 84405. Phone: 800-486-9829. County: Box Elder. Also serves Deweyville, Garland. ICA: UT0019.
TV Market Ranking: Below 100 (Deweyville, Tremonton); Outside TV Markets (Garland). Franchise award date: N.A. Franchise expiration date: N.A. Began: January 1, 1980.
Channel capacity: 36 (not 2-way capable). Channels available but not in use: None.
Basic Service
Subscribers: 1,459.
Programming (received off-air): KUWB (W) Ogden; KBYU-TV (P) Provo; KSL-TV (N), KSTU (F), KTVX (A), KUED (P), KUTV (C) Salt Lake City.
Programming (via satellite): WGN-TV (W) Chicago; American Movie Classics; CNN; Country Music TV; Discovery Channel; E! Entertainment TV; ESPN; Fox Family Channel; Fox Sports Net; Headline News; Home Shopping Network; Lifetime; MSNBC; MTV; Nashville Network; Nickelodeon; Odyssey; Sci-Fi Channel; TBS Superstation; The Weather Channel; Turner Network TV; USA Network.
Current originations: Automated time-weather.
Fee: $54.00 installation; $25.95 monthly.
Pay Service 1
Pay Units: 107.
Programming (via satellite): Cinemax.
Fee: $15.25 installation; $10.95 monthly.
Pay Service 2
Pay Units: 191.
Programming (via satellite): Disney Channel.
Fee: $15.25 installation; $10.95 monthly.
Pay Service 3
Pay Units: 285.
Programming (via satellite): HBO.
Fee: $15.25 installation; $10.95 monthly.
Pay Service 4
Pay Units: 19.
Programming (via satellite): The Movie Channel.
Fee: $15.25 installation; $10.95 monthly.
Pay Service 5
Pay Units: 63.
Programming (via satellite): Showtime.
Fee: $15.25 installation; $10.95 monthly.

Local advertising: No.
Equipment: Cadco & Olson headend; Scientific-Atlanta amplifiers; Times Fiber cable; Intercept traps; Scientific-Atlanta satellite antenna; Standard Components satellite receivers.
Miles of plant: 41.0 (coaxial). Homes passed: 2,104. Total homes in franchised area: 2,104.
Regional manager: Alan Hintze. Chief technician: Craig Davis. Marketing manager: Ron Williams. Office manager: Lorraine Nelson.
City fee: 3% of gross.
Ownership: AT&T Broadband & Internet Services (MSO). Purchased from Insight Communications Co., November 2, 1998.

VERNAL—Peak Cablevision, 1750 S. Hwy. 10, Price, UT 84501. Phone: 435-789-1723. Fax: 435-637-9755. County: Uintah. Also serves Naples. ICA: UT0014.
TV Market Ranking: Below 100. Franchise award date: July 5, 1978. Franchise expiration date: October 15, 2007. Began: October 1, 1956.
Channel capacity: 40 (not 2-way capable). Channels available but not in use: 9.
Basic Service
Subscribers: 3,593.
Programming (via translator): KBYU-TV (P) Provo; KJZZ-TV (U), KSL-TV (N), KSTU (F), KTVX (A), KUED (P), KUTV (C) Salt Lake City.
Programming (via satellite): WGN-TV (W) Chicago; KCNC-TV (C), KMGH-TV (A), KUSA-TV (N) Denver; American Movie Classics; CNN; Country Music TV; Discovery Channel; ESPN; Fox Family Channel; Fox Sports Net; Home Shopping Network; Lifetime; MTV; Nashville Network; Nickelodeon; Odyssey; TBS Superstation; The Weather Channel; Turner Network TV; USA Network.
Current originations: Automated time-weather; local news.
Fee: $38.75 installation; $21.45 monthly; $1.45 converter.
Pay Service 1
Pay Units: 198.
Programming (via satellite): Cinemax.
Fee: $15.90 installation; $10.95 monthly.
Pay Service 2
Pay Units: 360.
Programming (via satellite): Disney Channel.
Fee: $15.90 installation; $10.95 monthly.
Pay Service 3
Pay Units: 945.
Programming (via satellite): HBO.
Fee: $15.90 installation; $10.95 monthly.
Pay Service 4
Pay Units: 86.
Programming (via satellite): The Movie Channel.
Fee: $15.90 installation; $10.95 monthly.
Pay Service 5
Pay Units: 253.
Programming (via satellite): Showtime.
Fee: $15.90 installation; $10.95 monthly.
Local advertising: Yes.
Equipment: Scientific-Atlanta, RCA & Cadco headend; GTE Sylvania amplifiers; Comm/Scope cable; Oak & Hamlin set top converters; Intercept & Arcom traps; Andrew, M/A-Com & Scientific-Atlanta satellite antenna; Hughes & Scientific-Atlanta satellite receivers.
Miles of plant: 123.0 (coaxial). Homes passed: 5,500.
Manager: Shane Baggs. Chief technician: Paul Harvey.
City fee: 6% of gross.
Ownership: AT&T Broadband & Internet Services (MSO). Tele-Communications Inc. purchased from Insight Communications Co., February 1, 1999.

WENDOVER—TCI Cablevision of Utah Inc., 22 W. Vine St., Tooele, UT 84074. Phone: 801-882-6604. Counties: Tooele, UT; Elko, NV. Also serves West Wendover, NV. ICA: UT0025.
TV Market Ranking: Outside TV Markets. Franchise award date: N.A. Franchise expiration date: N.A. Began: March 1, 1982.
Channel capacity: 36 (2-way capable; operating 2-way). Channels available but not in use: N.A.
Basic Service
Subscribers: 1,025.
Programming (received off-air): KSL-TV (N), KTVX (A), KUED (P), KUTV (C) Salt Lake City.
Programming (via satellite): WGN-TV (W) Chicago; C-SPAN; CNBC; CNN; Discovery Channel; Fox Family Channel; FoxNet; Lifetime; MTV; Nashville Network; Nickelodeon; QVC; TBS Superstation; The Weather Channel; USA Network; Univision.
Fee: $25.00 installation; $21.59 monthly; $15.00 additional installation.
Expanded Basic Service
Subscribers: 944.
Programming (via satellite): American Movie Classics; ESPN; Fox Sports Net; GalaVision; Turner Network TV.
Fee: $1.89 monthly.
Pay Service 1
Pay Units: 286.
Programming (via satellite): Cinemax.
Fee: $10.00 monthly.
Pay Service 2
Pay Units: 168.
Programming (via satellite): Disney Channel.
Fee: N.A.
Pay Service 3
Pay Units: 451.
Programming (via satellite): HBO.
Fee: $10.00 monthly.
Pay Service 4
Pay Units: 225.
Programming (via satellite): The Movie Channel.
Fee: $10.00 monthly.
Pay Service 5
Pay Units: N.A.
Programming (via satellite): The New Encore.
Fee: N.A.
Local advertising: No.
Equipment: Standard Communications headend; Scientific-Atlanta amplifiers; Comm/Scope cable; Hamlin set top converters; Pico traps; Scientific-Atlanta satellite antenna; Standard Communications satellite receivers.
Miles of plant: 17.7 (coaxial). Homes passed: 1,416. Total homes in franchised area: 1,466.
Manager: Mike Oswald.
City fee: 3% of gross.
Ownership: AT&T Broadband & Internet Services (MSO). Purchased from Tele-Communications Inc., March 9, 1999.

WEST VALLEY CITY—TCI Cablevision of Utah Inc., 1350 E. Miller Ave., Salt Lake City, UT 84106. Phone: 801-485-0500. County: Salt Lake. Also serves Bennion, Kearns, Magna, Salt Lake County (portions), Taylorsville. ICA: UT0080.

TV Market Ranking: 48. Franchise award date: N.A. Franchise expiration date: N.A. Began: N.A.

Channel capacity: 36. Channels available but not in use: None.

Basic Service

Subscribers: 510.

Programming (received off-air): KULC (P) Ogden; KBYU-TV (P) Provo; KJZZ-TV (U), KSL-TV (N), KSTU (F), KTVX (A), KUED (P), KUTV (C) Salt Lake City.

Programming (via translator): KUWB (W) Ogden.

Programming (via satellite): C-SPAN; Lifetime; Odyssey; QVC; The Weather Channel.

Fee: $47.78 installation; $9.48 monthly.

Expanded Basic Service

Subscribers: N.A.

Programming (via satellite): WGN-TV (W) Chicago; A & E; American Movie Classics; CNBC; CNN; Discovery Channel; ESPN; Fox Family Channel; Fox Sports Net; Headline News; MTV; Nashville Network; Nickelodeon; TBS Superstation; Turner Network TV; USA Network.

Fee: $47.78 installation; $10.83 monthly.

Pay Service 1

Pay Units: N.A.

Programming (via satellite): Disney Channel; HBO; Showtime; The Movie Channel.

Fee: $10.95 monthly (Disney), $12.20 monthly (Showtime or TMC), $13.15 monthly (HBO).

Manager: Kent Pearce. Chief technician: Ellis Waddel.

Ownership: AT&T Broadband & Internet Services (MSO). Purchased from Tele-Communications Inc., March 9, 1999.

WILLARD—AT&T Cable Services, 5152 South 1500 West, Riverdale, UT 84405. Phone: 800-486-9829. County: Box Elder. ICA: UT0047.

TV Market Ranking: Below 100. Franchise award date: January 17, 1987. Franchise expiration date: January 17, 2002. Began: November 15, 1987.

Channel capacity: 36 (not 2-way capable). Channels available but not in use: 6.

Basic Service

Subscribers: 249.

Programming (received off-air): KUWB (W) Ogden; KBYU-TV (P) Provo; KSL-TV (N), KSTU (F), KTVX (A), KUED (P), KUTV (C) Salt Lake City.

Programming (via satellite): WGN-TV (W) Chicago; A & E; C-SPAN; CNN; Discovery Channel; ESPN; Fox Family Channel; Fox Sports Net; Home Shopping Network; Learning Channel; Lifetime; Nashville Network; Nickelodeon; QVC; TBS Superstation; Travel Channel; Turner Network TV; USA Network; VH1.

Fee: $36.42 installation; $22.95 monthly.

Pay Service 1

Pay Units: 19.

Programming (via satellite): Cinemax.

Fee: $12.20 monthly.

Pay Service 2

Pay Units: 28.

Programming (via satellite): Disney Channel.

Fee: $10.95 monthly.

Pay Service 3

Pay Units: 25.

Programming (via satellite): HBO.

Fee: $13.15 monthly.

Pay Service 4

Pay Units: N.A.

Programming (via satellite): Showtime.

Fee: $12.20 monthly.

Local advertising: No.

Program Guide: The Cable Guide.

Equipment: Pico headend; Magnavox amplifiers; Times Fiber cable; Pioneer & Jerrold set top converters; Pico traps; Comtech satellite antenna; Pico satellite receivers.

Miles of plant: 11.0 (coaxial). Homes passed: 600. Total homes in franchised area: 729.

Regional manager: Alan Hintze. Chief technician: Craig Davis. Marketing manager: Ron Williams. Office manager: Lorraine Nelson.

City fee: 5% of basic.

Ownership: AT&T Broadband & Internet Services (MSO). Purchased from Insight Communications Co., November 2, 1998.

VERMONT

Total Systems: . . . 76
Total Communities Served: . . . 258
Franchises Not Yet Operating: . . . 34
Applications Pending: . . . 0
Communities with Applications: . . . 0
Number of Basic Subscribers: . . . 136,576
Number of Expanded Basic Subscribers: . . . 112,426
Number of Pay Units: . . . 35,025

Top 100 Markets Represented: Albany-Schenectady-Troy (34).

For a list of all cable communities included in this section, see the Cable Community Index located in the back of this volume.
For explanation of terms used in cable system listings, see p. D-9.

***ALBANY TWP.**—FrontierVision Partners LP, Suite P-200, 1777 S. Harrison St., Denver, CO 80210. Phone: 303-757-1588. Fax: 303-757-6105. County: Orleans. ICA: VT0031.
TV Market Ranking: Outside TV Markets. Franchise award date: N.A. Franchise expiration date: N.A. Scheduled to begin: N.A.
Channel capacity: N.A.
Ownership: FrontierVision Partners LP (MSO). See Cable System Ownership.

***ALBURG TWP.**—FrontierVision Partners LP, Suite P-200, 1777 S. Harrison St., Denver, CO 80210. Phone: 303-757-1588. Fax: 303-757-6105. County: Grand Isle. ICA: VT0032.
TV Market Ranking: Below 100. Franchise award date: N.A. Franchise expiration date: N.A. Scheduled to begin: N.A.
Channel capacity: N.A.
Ownership: FrontierVision Partners LP (MSO). See Cable System Ownership.

***BAKERSFIELD TWP.**—FrontierVision Partners LP, Suite P-200, 1777 S. Harrison St., Denver, CO 80210. Phone: 303-757-1588. Fax: 303-757-6105. County: Franklin. ICA: VT0033.
TV Market Ranking: Below 100. Franchise award date: N.A. Franchise expiration date: N.A. Scheduled to begin: N.A.
Channel capacity: N.A.
Ownership: FrontierVision Partners LP (MSO). See Cable System Ownership.

***BARNARD TWP.**—FrontierVision Partners LP, Suite P-200, 1777 S. Harrison St., Denver, CO 80210. Phone: 303-757-1588. Fax: 303-757-6105. County: Windsor. ICA: VT0034.
TV Market Ranking: Below 100. Franchise award date: N.A. Franchise expiration date: N.A. Scheduled to begin: N.A.
Channel capacity: N.A.
Ownership: FrontierVision Partners LP (MSO). See Cable System Ownership.

***BARNET TWP.**—FrontierVision Partners LP, Suite P-200, 1777 S. Harrison St., Denver, CO 80210. Phone: 303-757-1588. Fax: 303-757-6105. County: Caledonia. ICA: VT0035.
TV Market Ranking: Outside TV Markets. Franchise award date: N.A. Franchise expiration date: N.A. Scheduled to begin: N.A.
Channel capacity: N.A.
Ownership: FrontierVision Partners LP (MSO). See Cable System Ownership.

BARRE—Helicon Cable Communications, Box 547, South Barre, VT 05670. Phone: 802-476-6693. Fax: 802-476-1104. Counties: Orange, Washington & Windsor. Also serves Barre (town), Berlin, Chelsea Twp., East Barre, Graniteville, Marshfield Twp., Orange, Orange (town), Plainfield Twp., South Royalton, Tunbridge Twp., Washington, Washington (town), Websterville, Williamstown. ICA: VT0005.
TV Market Ranking: Below 100 (Chelsea Twp., East Barre, Graniteville, Orange, South Royalton, Tunbridge Twp., Washington, Websterville, Williamstown); Outside TV Markets (Barre, Berlin, Marshfield Twp., Plainfield Twp.). Franchise award date: N.A. Franchise expiration date: April 1, 2003. Began: May 1, 1952.
Channel capacity: 65. Channels available but not in use: 1.

Basic Service
Subscribers: 6,502; Commercial subscribers: 104.
Programming (received off-air): WCAX-TV (C), WETK (P), WVNY (A) Burlington; WNNE (N) Hartford-Hanover; WPTZ (N) Plattsburgh; WMTW-TV (A) Portland-Poland Spring; CBMT Montreal; CHLT-TV Sherbrooke; 15 FMs.
Programming (via satellite): FoxNet; QVC.
Current originations: Automated time-weather.
Fee: $20.00 installation; $7.61 monthly.

Expanded Basic Service
Subscribers: 5,948.
Programming (via satellite): A & E; C-SPAN; CNBC; CNN; Cartoon Network; Comedy Central; Country Music TV; Court TV; Discovery Channel; ESPN; EWTN; Electronic Program Guide; FX; Fox Family Channel; Headline News; Home Shopping Network; Home Shopping Network 2; Learning Channel; Lifetime; MTV; Nashville Network; Nick at Nite; Nickelodeon; Sci-Fi Channel; Superaudio Cable Radio Service; TBS Superstation; TV Food Network; TV Guide Channel; The Weather Channel; Trinity Bcstg. Network; Turner Network TV; USA Network; VH1.
Fee: $20.00 installation; $18.42 monthly.

Pay Service 1
Pay Units: 148.
Programming (via satellite): Cinemax.
Fee: $10.40 monthly.

Pay Service 2
Pay Units: 449.
Programming (via satellite): Disney Channel.
Fee: $10.40 monthly.

Pay Service 3
Pay Units: 841.
Programming (via satellite): HBO.
Fee: $11.95 monthly.

Pay Service 4
Pay Units: 739.
Programming (via satellite): The Movie Channel.
Fee: $10.40 monthly.

Pay Service 5
Pay Units: 741.
Programming (via satellite): Showtime.
Fee: $10.40 monthly.

Pay Service 6
Pay Units: 201.
Programming (via satellite): New England Sports Network.
Fee: $6.95 monthly.

Pay-Per-View
Addressable homes: 1,586.
Action Pay-Per-View; Hot Choice; Spice; Viewer's Choice.
Fee: $3.75-$5.95.
Pay-per-view manager: Neyda Conklin.
Local advertising: Yes. Available in satellite distributed programming. Local sales manager: David Baum. Regional interconnect: Cable AdNet-New England.
Program Guide: CableView.
Equipment: Jerrold & Scientific-Atlanta headend; Philips & Magnavox amplifiers; Comm/Scope cable; Jerrold set top converters; Jerrold addressable set top converters; Eagle traps; Anixter-Mark & Harris satellite antenna; Comtech & Scientific-Atlanta satellite receivers.
Miles of plant: 170.9 (coaxial); 17.0 (fiber optic). Additional miles planned: 20.0 (fiber optic). Homes passed: 9,538.
Manager: William Jenson. Chief technician: Mike Parker. Marketing & program director: David Baum.
State fee: 0.005% of gross.
Ownership: Helicon Corp. (MSO). See Cable System Ownership.

BELLOWS FALLS—Adelphia Cable, 106 Kimball Ave., South Burlington, VT 05403. Phones: 802-658-3050; 800-442-2335. Fax: 802-658-5488. Counties: Windham, VT; Cheshire, NH. Also serves North Walpole, NH; North Westminster, Rockingham, VT. ICA: VT0015.
TV Market Ranking: Below 100 (North Walpole, Rockingham); Outside TV Markets (Bellows Falls, North Westminster). Franchise award date: N.A. Franchise expiration date: N.A. Began: October 1, 1953.
Channel capacity: 60 (2-way capable; operating 2-way). Channels available but not in use: 20.

Basic Service
Subscribers: 1,776; Commercial subscribers: 3.
Programming (received off-air): WCDC (A) Adams; WBZ-TV (C), WCVB-TV (A), WHDH-TV (N), WSBK-TV (U) Boston; WNDS (I) Derry; WNNE (N) Hartford-Hanover; WEKW-TV (P) Keene; WMUR-TV (A,F) Manchester; WGBY-TV (P) Springfield; WVTA (P) Windsor; allband FM.
Programming (via translator): WCAX-TV (C) Burlington.
Programming (via satellite): FoxNet; TBS Superstation; TV Guide Channel.
Current originations: Public access; educational access; government access.
Fee: $50.48 installation (aerial), $56.40 (underground); $8.71 monthly; $0.57 converter; $16.44 additional installation.

Expanded Basic Service
Subscribers: 1,767.
Programming (via satellite): A & E; American Movie Classics; Animal Planet; C-SPAN; CNBC; CNN; Discovery Channel; E! Entertainment TV; ESPN; Fox Family Channel; Fox Sports Net New England; Headline News; Knowledge TV; Learning Channel; Lifetime; MTV; Nashville Network; Nickelodeon; QVC; The Weather Channel; Travel Channel; Turner Network TV; USA Network; VH1.
Fee: $42.00 installation; $19.28 monthly.

A la Carte 1
Subscribers: N.A.
Programming (via satellite): Cartoon Network; Comedy Central; ESPN 2; History Channel; Sci-Fi Channel; The New Encore.
Fee: $5.95 monthly (package); $1.95 monthly (each).

Pay Service 1
Pay Units: N.A.
Programming (via satellite): Cinemax (multiplexed); Disney Channel; HBO (multiplexed); New England Sports Network; Showtime; The Movie Channel.
Fee: $9.95 monthly (each).

Pay-Per-View
Addressable homes: 924.
Hot Choice; Spice; Viewer's Choice 1 & 2.
Equipment: Scientific-Atlanta headend; C-COR amplifiers; Times Fiber cable; Pioneer set top converters; Pioneer addressable set top converters; Scientific-Atlanta satellite antenna; Omni & Standard Communications satellite receivers; Sony commercial insert.
Miles of plant: 34.0 (coaxial). Homes passed: 2,445. Total homes in franchised area: 2,640.
Manager: Terry Gould. Chief technician: David Andrews.
Ownership: Adelphia Communications Corp. (MSO).

BENNINGTON—Better TV Inc. of Bennington, 107 McKinley St., Bennington, VT 05201. Phone: 802-447-1534. Fax: 802-442-2063. Counties: Bennington, VT; Rensselaer, NY. Also serves Hoosick, Hoosick Falls, North Hoosick, NY; North Bennington, Old Bennington, Pownal, Shaftsbury, Woodford, VT. ICA: VT0004.
TV Market Ranking: 34. Franchise award date: October 1, 1961. Franchise expiration date: October 1, 1999. Began: April 1, 1962.
Channel capacity: 40 (2-way capable; not operating 2-way). Channels available but not in use: None.

Basic Service
Subscribers: 9,799.
Programming (received off-air): WMHT (P), WNYT (N), WRGB (C), WTEN (A), WXXA-TV (F) Albany-Schenectady; WSBK-TV (U) Boston; WCAX-TV (C) Burlington; WPIX (W) New York; allband FM.
Programming (via satellite): The Weather Channel.
Current originations: Automated time-weather; public access; educational access; government access; religious access; local news.
Fee: $34.00 installation; $6.32 monthly.

Expanded Basic Service
Subscribers: 8,750.
Programming (via satellite): A & E; C-SPAN; CNBC; CNN; Discovery Channel; ESPN; ESPN 2; EWTN; Fox Family Channel; Home Shopping Network; Learning Channel; Lifetime; Nickelodeon; Odyssey; QVC; Turner Network TV; USA Network.
Fee: $34.00 installation; $27.01 monthly.

Expanded Basic Service 2
Subscribers: 7,398.
Programming (via satellite): Fox Sports Net New England; MTV; Nashville Network; New England Sports Network; VH1.
Fee: $33.00 installation; $25.00 monthly.

Pay Service 1
Pay Units: 653.
Programming (via satellite): Cinemax.
Fee: $25.00 installation; $11.50 monthly.
Pay Service 2
Pay Units: 437.
Programming (via satellite): Disney Channel.
Fee: $25.00 installation; $8.95 monthly.
Pay Service 3
Pay Units: 1,771.
Programming (via satellite): HBO.
Fee: $25.00 installation; $11.50 monthly.
Pay Service 4
Pay Units: 194.
Programming (via satellite): The Movie Channel.
Fee: $25.00 installation; $11.50 monthly.
Pay Service 5
Pay Units: 310.
Programming (via satellite): Showtime.
Fee: $25.00 installation; $11.50 monthly.
Pay-Per-View
Addressable homes: 3,229.
Local advertising: Yes. Available in automated programming. Local sales manager: Joe Brown. Regional interconnect: Cable AdNet-New England.
Equipment: Scientific-Atlanta headend; Texscan amplifiers; Comm/Scope cable; GE & Jerrold cameras; Texscan character generator; Scientific-Atlanta set top converters; Scientific-Atlanta addressable set top converters; Pico traps; Scientific-Atlanta satellite antenna; Scientific-Atlanta satellite receivers.
Miles of plant: 258.5 (coaxial); 68.5 (fiber optic). Additional miles planned: 10.0 (coaxial); 7.0 (fiber optic). Homes passed: 13,091.
Manager: Judith Hill. Chief technician: Ernest Thompson. Marketing & program director: Kevin Dempsey.
State fee: 0.005% of gross.
Ownership: Adelphia Communications Corp. (MSO).

***BLOOMFIELD TWP.**—FrontierVision Partners LP, Suite P-200, 1777 S. Harrison St., Denver, CO 80210. Phone: 303-757-1588. Fax: 303-757-6105. County: Essex. ICA: VT0038.
TV Market Ranking: Outside TV Markets. Franchise award date: N.A. Franchise expiration date: N.A. Scheduled to begin: N.A.
Channel capacity: N.A.
Ownership: FrontierVision Partners LP (MSO). See Cable System Ownership.

BRADFORD—Helicon Cablevision, Box 350, Danville, VT 05828-0350. Phones: 802-748-8917; 800-214-0737. County: Orange. ICA: VT0021.
TV Market Ranking: Below 100. Franchise award date: N.A. Franchise expiration date: N.A. Began: January 1, 1977.
Channel capacity: 12 (not 2-way capable). Channels available but not in use: 3.
Basic Service
Subscribers: 488.
Programming (received off-air): WBZ-TV (C), WCVB-TV (A) Boston; WCAX-TV (C), WVNY (A) Burlington; WNNE (N) Hartford-Hanover; WMUR-TV (A,F) Manchester; WCSH (N) Portland; WMTW-TV (A) Portland-Poland Spring; WVTA (P) Windsor.
Fee: $25.00 installation; $12.54 monthly; $10.00 additional installation.
Pay Service 1
Pay Units: 64.
Programming (via satellite): HBO.
Fee: $9.95 monthly.
Equipment: Jerrold headend; Jerrold amplifiers; TeleWire cable.
Miles of plant: 6.0 (coaxial). Additional miles planned: 3.0 (coaxial). Homes passed: 560. Total homes in franchised area: 560.
Manager: Paul Saminski.
State fee: 0.005% of gross.
Ownership: Helicon Corp. (MSO). See Cable System Ownership.

BRAINTREE—Adelphia Communications Corp., Box 68, Grange Rd., Montpelier, VT 05602. Phone: 802-223-2852. Fax: 802-223-8941. County: Orange. Also serves Randolph. ICA: VT0039.
TV Market Ranking: Below 100. Franchise award date: N.A. Franchise expiration date: N.A. Began: N.A.
Channel capacity: 40. Channels available but not in use: 1.
Basic Service
Subscribers: 840.
Programming (received off-air): WBZ-TV (C) Boston; WCAX-TV (C), WVNY (A) Burlington; WNNE (N) Hartford-Hanover; WPTZ (N) Plattsburgh; WMTW-TV (A) Portland-Poland Spring; WVTA (P) Windsor.
Programming (via satellite): C-SPAN; Learning Channel; TBS Superstation.
Fee: $33.00 installation; $8.95 monthly.
Expanded Basic Service
Subscribers: N.A.
Programming (via satellite): A & E; American Movie Classics; CNN; Discovery Channel; ESPN; Fox Family Channel; Fox Sports Net New England; Headline News; Home Shopping Network; Lifetime; MTV; Nashville Network; New England Sports Network; Nickelodeon; QVC; The Inspirational Network; The Weather Channel; Turner Network TV; USA Network.
Fee: $17.00 monthly.
Pay Service 1
Pay Units: N.A.
Programming (via satellite): Cinemax; Disney Channel; HBO; Showtime; The Movie Channel.
Fee: $10.00 monthly (each).
Local advertising: Yes. Available in automated programming.
Equipment: Scientific-Atlanta headend; Texscan amplifiers; Comm/Scope cable; Texscan character generator; Scientific-Atlanta set top converters; Scientific-Atlanta addressable set top converters; Eagle traps; Andrew, M/A-Com & Scientific-Atlanta satellite antenna; Scientific-Atlanta satellite receivers.
Miles of plant: 27.0 (coaxial). Additional miles planned: 6.0 (coaxial).
Manager: Byron Hill. Chief technician: Al Sutphen.
Ownership: Adelphia Communications Corp. (MSO).

BRATTLEBORO—Adelphia Cable, 106 Kimball Ave., South Burlington, VT 05403. Phones: 802-658-3050; 800-442-2335. Fax: 802-658-5488. Counties: Windham, VT; Cheshire, NH. Also serves Chesterfield, West Chesterfield, NH. ICA: VT0010.
TV Market Ranking: Below 100. Franchise award date: N.A. Franchise expiration date: N.A. Began: January 1, 1954.
Channel capacity: 52. Channels available but not in use: None.
Basic Service
Subscribers: 4,221; Commercial subscribers: 28.
Programming (received off-air): WCDC (A) Adams; WBZ-TV (C), WCVB-TV (A), WHDH-TV (N), WSBK-TV (U) Boston; WNDS (I) Derry; WNNE (N) Hartford-Hanover; WEKW-TV (P) Keene; WMUR-TV (A,F) Manchester; WGBY-TV (P) Springfield; WVTA (P) Windsor; allband FM.
Programming (via translator): WCAX-TV (C) Burlington.
Programming (via satellite): FoxNet; TBS Superstation; TV Guide Channel.
Current originations: Public access; educational access; government access.
Fee: $50.48 installation (aerial), $56.40 (underground); $8.71 monthly; $0.57 converter; $16.44 additional installation.
Expanded Basic Service
Subscribers: N.A.
Programming (via satellite): A & E; American Movie Classics; Animal Planet; C-SPAN; CNBC; CNN; Discovery Channel; E! Entertainment TV; ESPN; Fox Family Channel; Fox Sports Net New England; Headline News; Knowledge TV; Learning Channel; Lifetime; MTV; Nashville Network; Nickelodeon; QVC; The Weather Channel; Travel Channel; Turner Network TV; USA Network; VH1.
Fee: $19.28 monthly.
A la Carte 1
Subscribers: N.A.
Programming (via satellite): Cartoon Network; Comedy Central; ESPN 2; History Channel; Sci-Fi Channel; The New Encore.
Fee: $5.95 monthly (package); $1.95 monthly (each).
Pay Service 1
Pay Units: 3,546.
Programming (via satellite): Disney Channel; HBO (multiplexed); New England Sports Network; Showtime; The Movie Channel.
Fee: $9.95 monthly (each).
Pay Service 2
Pay Units: N.A.
Programming (via satellite): Cinemax (multiplexed).
Fee: $9.95 monthly.
Pay-Per-View
Hot Choice; Spice; Viewer's Choice 1 & 2.
Equipment: Scientific-Atlanta headend; Magnavox amplifiers; Comm/Scope cable; Scientific-Atlanta satellite antenna.
Miles of plant: 72.0 (coaxial). Homes passed: 5,285. Total homes in franchised area: 5,400.
Manager: Terry Gould. Chief technician: Gary Winslow.
State fee: 0.005% of gross.
Ownership: Adelphia Communications Corp. (MSO).

BURLINGTON—Adelphia Cable, 106 Kimball Ave., South Burlington, VT 05403. Phone: 802-658-3050. Fax: 802-658-5488. Counties: Addison & Chittenden. Also serves Colchester (portions), East Middlebury, Essex, Essex Junction, South Burlington, St. George (town), Williston, Winooski. ICA: VT0001.
TV Market Ranking: Below 100. Franchise award date: January 1, 1952. Franchise expiration date: N.A. Began: May 1, 1952.
Channel capacity: 52 (2-way capable; operating 2-way). Channels available but not in use: None.
Basic Service
Subscribers: 27,000.
Programming (received off-air): WCAX-TV (C), WETK (P), WFFF-TV (F), WVNY (A) Burlington; WCFE-TV (P), WPTZ (N) Plattsburgh; CBFT, CBMT, CFCF-TV Montreal; 26 FMs.
Programming (via satellite): Learning Channel; TBS Superstation.
Current originations: Public access; educational access; government access; leased access.
Fee: $52.00 installation; $9.17 monthly; $39.00 additional installation.
Expanded Basic Service
Subscribers: 12,000.
Programming (via satellite): A & E; C-SPAN; CNBC; CNN; Discovery Channel; ESPN; EWTN; Fox Family Channel; FoxNet; Goodlife TV Network; Headline News; Home Shopping Network; Lifetime; Nashville Network; Nickelodeon; The Inspirational Network; The Weather Channel; Turner Network TV.
Fee: $12.88 monthly.
Expanded Basic Service 2
Subscribers: 15,067.
Programming (via satellite): American Movie Classics; Bravo; Fox Sports Net New England; MTV; New England Sports Network; USA Network; VH1.
Fee: $4.15 monthly.
Pay Service 1
Pay Units: N.A.
Programming (via satellite): Cinemax; Disney Channel; HBO; Showtime; The Movie Channel.
Fee: $10.00 monthly (each).
Pay-Per-View
Addressable homes: 27,000.
Local advertising: Yes. Available in satellite distributed, locally originated, character-generated, taped & automated programming. Local sales manager: P. Hughes. Regional interconnect: Cable AdNet-New England.
Equipment: Scientific-Atlanta headend; Scientific-Atlanta amplifiers; Comm/Scope cable; Sony VTRs; Texscan character generator; Scientific-Atlanta & GTE Sylvania set top converters; Scientific-Atlanta addressable set top converters; ChannelMaster, M/A-Com & Scientific-Atlanta satellite antenna; Scientific-Atlanta satellite receivers.
Miles of plant: 425.0 (coaxial); 40.0 (fiber optic). Homes passed: 37,000. Total homes in franchised area: 65,000.
Manager: Marlene Booska. Chief technician: John Rivolta. Program director: Lori Murphy. Marketing director: R. Scott Bill.
State fee: 0.005% of gross.
Ownership: Adelphia Communications Corp. (MSO).

***CABOT TWP.**—FrontierVision Partners LP, Suite P-200, 1777 S. Harrison St., Denver, CO 80210. Phone: 303-757-1588. Fax: 303-757-6105. County: Washington. ICA: VT0090.
TV Market Ranking: Outside TV Markets. Franchise award date: N.A. Franchise expiration date: N.A. Scheduled to begin: N.A.
Channel capacity: N.A.
Ownership: FrontierVision Partners LP (MSO). See Cable System Ownership.

***CHARLESTON TWP.**—FrontierVision Partners LP, Suite P-200, 1777 S. Harrison St., Denver, CO 80210. Phone: 303-757-1588. Fax: 303-757-6105. County: Orleans. ICA: VT0043.
TV Market Ranking: Outside TV Markets. Franchise award date: N.A. Franchise expiration date: N.A. Scheduled to begin: N.A.
Channel capacity: N.A.
Ownership: FrontierVision Partners LP (MSO). See Cable System Ownership.

CHELSEA—Helicon Cablevision, Box 350, Danville, VT 05828-0350. Phones: 802-748-8917; 800-214-0737. County: Orange. ICA: VT0027.
TV Market Ranking: Below 100. Franchise award date: N.A. Franchise expiration date: N.A. Began: February 1, 1981.
Channel capacity: 12. Channels available but not in use: 3.
Basic Service
Subscribers: 171.
Programming (received off-air): WRGB (C) Albany-Schenectady; WCAX-TV (C), WETK (P), WVNY (A) Burlington; WNNE (N) Hart-

ford-Hanover; WMTW-TV (A) Portland-Poland Spring; CBNT St. John's.
Fee: $25.00 installation; $7.00 monthly; $10.00 additional installation.
Miles of plant: 3.7 (coaxial). Homes passed: 215.
Manager: Paul Saminski.
State fee: 0.005% of gross.
Ownership: Helicon Corp. (MSO). See Cable System Ownership.

***COVENTRY TWP.**—FrontierVision Partners LP, Suite P-200, 1777 S. Harrison St., Denver, CO 80210. Phone: 303-757-1588. Fax: 303-757-6105. County: Orleans. ICA: VT0044.
TV Market Ranking: Outside TV Markets. Franchise award date: N.A. Franchise expiration date: N.A. Scheduled to begin: N.A.
Channel capacity: N.A.
Ownership: FrontierVision Partners LP (MSO). See Cable System Ownership.

EAST CORINTH—Olsen TV, Box 1134, East Corinth, VT 05040. Phone: 802-439-5780. County: Orange. ICA: VT0030.
TV Market Ranking: Below 100. Franchise award date: N.A. Franchise expiration date: N.A. Began: March 1, 1971.
Channel capacity: 8. Channels available but not in use: 3.
Basic Service
Subscribers: 29.
Programming (received off-air): WCAX-TV (C), WETK (P), WVNY (A) Burlington; WPTZ (N) Plattsburgh; WMTW-TV (A) Portland-Poland Spring; allband FM.
Fee: $20.00 installation; $6.18 monthly.
Equipment: Blonder-Tongue headend; Blonder-Tongue amplifiers; Evans cable.
Miles of plant: 2.0 (coaxial). Homes passed: 48. Total homes in franchised area: 51.
Manager: Roy Olsen.
State fee: 0.005% of gross.
Ownership: Roy Olsen.

***EAST MONTPELIER TWP.**—FrontierVision Partners LP, Suite P-200, 1777 S. Harrison St., Denver, CO 80210. Phone: 303-757-1588. Fax: 303-757-6105. County: Washington. ICA: VT0045.
TV Market Ranking: Outside TV Markets. Franchise award date: N.A. Franchise expiration date: N.A. Scheduled to begin: N.A.
Channel capacity: N.A.
Ownership: FrontierVision Partners LP (MSO). See Cable System Ownership.

ENOSBURG FALLS—North Country Cablevision Inc., Box 576, 271 Main St., Enosburg Falls, VT 05450. Phone: 802-933-8843. Fax: 802-933-8843. County: Franklin. Also serves Berkshire, Enosburg, Richford. ICA: VT0024.
TV Market Ranking: Outside TV Markets. Franchise award date: N.A. Franchise expiration date: N.A. Began: August 1, 1981.
Channel capacity: 40 (2-way capable; operating 2-way). Channels available but not in use: 4.
Basic Service
Subscribers: 862.
Programming (received off-air): WCAX-TV (C), WETK (P), WFFF-TV (F), WVNY (A) Burlington; WCFE-TV (P), WPTZ (N) Plattsburgh; CBMT, CFCF-TV, CFTM-TV Montreal.
Programming (via translator): WMTW-TV (A) Portland-Poland Spring.
Programming (via satellite): Discovery Channel; Disney Channel; EWTN; Fox Family Channel; FoxNet; Nashville Network; QVC; TBS Superstation; USA Network.
Current originations: Educational access; local news.
Fee: $25.00 installation; $15.50 monthly.
Expanded Basic Service
Subscribers: 360.
Programming (received off-air): WWBI-LP (U) Plattsburgh.
Programming (via satellite): WGN-TV (W) Chicago; A & E; C-SPAN; CNN; ESPN; Learning Channel; Lifetime; New England Sports Network; Sci-Fi Channel; The New Encore; Turner Classic Movies.
Fee: $11.75 monthly.
Pay Service 1
Pay Units: 85.
Programming (via satellite): Cinemax.
Fee: $11.75 monthly.
Pay Service 2
Pay Units: 149.
Programming (via satellite): HBO.
Fee: $11.75 monthly.
Equipment: Jerrold & DX Communications headend; Jerrold amplifiers; Times Fiber & Trilogy cable; Siecor fiber optic cable; Eagle traps; Microdyne satellite antenna; DX Communications satellite receivers.
Miles of plant: 39.0 (coaxial); 11.0 (fiber optic). Additional miles planned: 12.0 (coaxial); 15.0 (fiber optic). Homes passed: 1,500. Total homes in franchised area: 2,000.
Manager: Gary Fiske.
State fee: 0.005% of gross.
Ownership: Gary Fiske.

FAIR HAVEN—Adelphia Communications Corp., Box 520, 539 Charlestown Rd., Springfield, VT 05156. Phones: 802-885-4529; 800-356-2966. Fax: 802-885-8590. County: Rutland. Also serves Bomoseen, Castleton, Castleton Corners, East Poultney, Hydeville, Poultney. ICA: VT0012.
TV Market Ranking: Outside TV Markets. Franchise award date: N.A. Franchise expiration date: N.A. Began: May 1, 1973.
Channel capacity: 27 (not 2-way capable). Channels available but not in use: None.
Basic Service
Subscribers: 3,868.
Programming (received off-air): WNYT (N), WRGB (C), WTEN (A), WXXA-TV (F) Albany-Schenectady; WCAX-TV (C) Burlington; WPTZ (N) Plattsburgh; WVER (P) Rutland; allband FM.
Programming (via satellite): WGN-TV (W) Chicago; A & E; C-SPAN; CNN; ESPN; Fox Family Channel; Headline News; Home Shopping Network; Lifetime; MTV; Nashville Network; Nickelodeon; TBS Superstation; The Weather Channel; USA Network.
Fee: $91.34 installation; $19.32 monthly; $0.95 converter; $11.89 additional installation.
Pay Service 1
Pay Units: N.A.
Programming (via satellite): Cinemax; Disney Channel; HBO.
Fee: $9.95 monthly (Disney), $10.95 monthly (Cinemax), $11.95 monthly (HBO).
Equipment: Blonder-Tongue headend; Texscan amplifiers; Plastoid & Times Fiber cable; Gardiner satellite antenna.
Miles of plant: 61.2 (coaxial). Total homes in franchised area: 5,084.
Manager: Robert Snowdon. Chief technician: Henry Hryckiewicz. Marketing director: Cathy Brusseau.
State fee: 0.005% of gross.
Ownership: Adelphia Communications Corp. (MSO).

***FAIRFAX TWP.**—FrontierVision Partners LP, Suite P-200, 1777 S. Harrison St., Denver, CO 80210. Phone: 303-757-1588. Fax: 303-757-6105. County: Franklin. ICA: VT0046.
TV Market Ranking: Below 100. Franchise award date: N.A. Franchise expiration date: N.A. Scheduled to begin: N.A.
Channel capacity: N.A.
Ownership: FrontierVision Partners LP (MSO). See Cable System Ownership.

***FAIRLEE TWP.**—FrontierVision Partners LP, Suite P-200, 1777 S. Harrison St., Denver, CO 80210. Phone: 303-757-1588. Fax: 303-757-6105. County: Orange. ICA: VT0047.
TV Market Ranking: Below 100. Franchise award date: N.A. Franchise expiration date: N.A. Scheduled to begin: N.A.
Channel capacity: N.A.
Ownership: FrontierVision Partners LP (MSO). See Cable System Ownership.

***FLETCHER TWP.**—FrontierVision Partners LP, Suite P-200, 1777 S. Harrison St., Denver, CO 80210. Phone: 303-757-1588. Fax: 303-757-6105. County: Franklin. ICA: VT0048.
TV Market Ranking: Below 100. Franchise award date: N.A. Franchise expiration date: N.A. Scheduled to begin: N.A.
Channel capacity: N.A.
Ownership: FrontierVision Partners LP (MSO). See Cable System Ownership.

GRAFTON—Adelphia Cable, Box 520, 539 Charlestown Rd., Springfield, VT 05156. Phones: 802-885-4529; 800-347-5002. Fax: 802-885-8590. County: Windham. Also serves Athens, Cambridgeport, Saxtons River. ICA: VT0072.
TV Market Ranking: Outside TV Markets. Franchise award date: N.A. Franchise expiration date: N.A. Began: August 1, 1953.
Channel capacity: 23. Channels available but not in use: None.
Basic Service
Subscribers: 358.
Programming (received off-air): WBZ-TV (C), WCVB-TV (A), WGBH-TV (P), WHDH-TV (N) Boston; WCAX-TV (C) Burlington; WLVI-TV (W) Cambridge-Boston; WNNE (N) Hartford-Hanover; WMUR-TV (A,F) Manchester; WVTA (P) Windsor; allband FM.
Programming (via satellite): Nashville Network; TBS Superstation.
Current originations: Public access.
Fee: $45.00 installation; $15.93 monthly; $0.89 converter.
Expanded Basic Service
Subscribers: 275.
Programming (via satellite): A & E; CNN; ESPN; Fox Family Channel; Headline News; USA Network.
Fee: $13.76 monthly.
Pay Service 1
Pay Units: 24.
Programming (via satellite): Cinemax.
Fee: $25.00 installation; $10.95 monthly.
Pay Service 2
Pay Units: 18.
Programming (via satellite): Disney Channel.
Fee: $9.95 monthly.
Pay Service 3
Pay Units: 40.
Programming (via satellite): HBO.
Fee: $11.95 monthly.
Pay Service 4
Pay Units: 16.
Programming (via satellite): New England Sports Network.
Fee: $9.95 monthly.
Local advertising: Yes.
Equipment: Jerrold headend; Jerrold & GTE Sylvania amplifiers; Times Fiber cable; Eagle traps; M/A-Com satellite antenna; M/A-Com satellite receivers.
Miles of plant: 14.0 (coaxial). Additional miles planned: 1.0 (coaxial).
Manager: Robert Snowdon. Chief technician: Henry Hryckiewicz.
State fee: 0.005% of gross.
Ownership: Adelphia Communications Corp. (MSO).

***GRAND ISLE TWP.**—FrontierVision Parners LP, Suite P-200, 1777 S. Harrison St., Denver, CO 80210. Phone: 303-757-1588. Fax: 303-757-6105. County: Grand Isle. ICA: VT0049.
TV Market Ranking: Below 100. Franchise award date: N.A. Franchise expiration date: N.A. Scheduled to begin: N.A.
Channel capacity: N.A.
Ownership: FrontierVision Partners LP (MSO). See Cable System Ownership.

***GUILFORD TWP.**—FrontierVision Partners LP, Suite P-200, 1777 S. Harrison St., Denver, CO 80210. Phone: 303-757-1588. Fax: 303-757-6105. County: Windham. ICA: VT0050.
TV Market Ranking: Below 100. Franchise award date: N.A. Franchise expiration date: N.A. Scheduled to begin: N.A.
Channel capacity: N.A.
Ownership: FrontierVision Partners LP (MSO). See Cable System Ownership.

HARDWICK—FrontierVision, Box 760, Lebanon, NH 03766-1076. Phone: 603-448-6280. Fax: 603-448-2809. County: Caledonia. Also serves East Hardwick. ICA: VT0052.
TV Market Ranking: Outside TV Markets. Franchise award date: N.A. Franchise expiration date: N.A. Began: December 1, 1969.
Channel capacity: 28 (not 2-way capable). Channels available but not in use: None.
Basic Service
Subscribers: 532.
Programming (received off-air): WCAX-TV (C), WETK (P), WVNY (A) Burlington; WPTZ (N) Plattsburgh; WMTW-TV (A) Portland-Poland Spring; CBMT, CFCF-TV Montreal; allband FM.
Programming (via satellite): WGN-TV (W) Chicago; CNN; FoxNet; MTV; Nashville Network; TBS Superstation; Turner Network TV.
Fee: $9.44 monthly.
Expanded Basic Service
Subscribers: 463.
Programming (via satellite): American Movie Classics; Court TV; ESPN; Nickelodeon; USA Network.
Fee: $8.50 monthly.
Pay Service 1
Pay Units: 45.
Programming (via satellite): Cinemax.
Fee: $27.50 installation; $9.95 monthly.
Pay Service 2
Pay Units: 132.
Programming (via satellite): The New Encore.
Fee: N.A.
Pay Service 3
Pay Units: 72.
Programming (via satellite): HBO.
Fee: $27.50 installation; $10.95 monthly.
Pay Service 4
Pay Units: 52.
Programming (via satellite): Starz!
Fee: N.A.
Equipment: Blonder-Tongue headend; Texscan amplifiers; Plastoid cable.
Miles of plant: 12.5 (coaxial). Homes passed: 733.
Manager: Keith Froleiks. Chief technician: Rodney King.
State fee: 0.005% of gross.
Ownership: FrontierVision Partners LP (MSO). See Cable System Ownership.

***HARTLAND TWP.**—FrontierVision Partners LP, Suite P-200, 1777 S. Harrison St., Denver, CO 80210. Phone: 303-757-1588. Fax: 303-757-6105. County: Windsor. ICA: VT0053.
TV Market Ranking: Below 100. Franchise award date: N.A. Franchise expiration date: N.A. Scheduled to begin: N.A.
Channel capacity: N.A.
Ownership: FrontierVision Partners LP (MSO). See Cable System Ownership.

***IRASBURG TWP.**—FrontierVision Partners LP, Suite P-200, 1777 S. Harrison St., Denver, CO 80210. Phone: 303-757-1588. Fax: 303-757-6105. County: Orleans. ICA: VT0054.
TV Market Ranking: Outside TV Markets. Franchise award date: N.A. Franchise expiration date: N.A. Scheduled to begin: N.A.
Channel capacity: N.A.
Ownership: FrontierVision Partners LP (MSO). See Cable System Ownership.

JACKSONVILLE—Area Telecable, 100 N. Commercial Plaza, West Dover, VT 05356. Phone: 802-464-5200. Fax: 802-464-0075. County: Windham. ICA: VT0088.
TV Market Ranking: Outside TV Markets. Franchise award date: N.A. Franchise expiration date: N.A. Began: N.A.
Channel capacity: 45. Channels available but not in use: N.A.
Basic Service
Subscribers: 53.
Programming (received off-air): WBZ-TV (C), WCVB-TV (A), WFXT (F), WGBH-TV (P), WHDH-TV (N), WSBK-TV (U) Boston; WFSB (C) Hartford; WNNE (N) Hartford-Hanover; WMUR-TV (A,F) Manchester; WVTA (P) Windsor; WUNI (S) Worcester.
Fee: $37.50 installation; $11.00 monthly.
Local advertising: Yes. Local sales manager: Jeff Kozlowski.
Miles of plant: 3.5 (coaxial); None (fiber optic).
Manager: Jeff Kozlowski. Chief technician: Ernie Scialabba.
Ownership: Gateway Cablevision Corp. (MSO).

***JAMAICA TWP.**—FrontierVision Partners LP, Suite P-200, 1777 S. Harrison St., Denver, CO 80210. Phone: 303-757-1588. Fax: 303-757-6105. County: Windham. ICA: VT0055.
TV Market Ranking: Below 100 (portions); Outside TV
Channel capacity: N.A.
Ownership: FrontierVision Partners LP (MSO). See Cable System Ownership.

JEFFERSONVILLE—Jeffersonville Cable TV Corp., Box 453, Stowe, VT 05672. Phones: 802-644-5016; 800-696-9282. County: Lamoille. Also serves Cambridge, Cambridge (town), Cambridge Junction. ICA: VT0056.
TV Market Ranking: Below 100. Franchise award date: N.A. Franchise expiration date: N.A. Began: July 1, 1988.
Channel capacity: 12. Channels available but not in use: 2.
Basic Service
Subscribers: 160.
Programming (received off-air): WCAX-TV (C), WVNY (A) Burlington; WCFE-TV (P), WPTZ (N) Plattsburgh; CBMT, CFCF-TV Montreal.
Programming (via satellite): ESPN; Headline News; TBS Superstation.
Fee: $35.00 installation; $12.00 monthly.
Pay Service 1
Pay Units: N.A.
Programming (via satellite): HBO.
Fee: $11.00 monthly.
Manager: Rick Rothammer.
Ownership: Richard Landy (MSO).

KILLINGTON—Adelphia Communications Corp., Box 520, 539 Charlestown Rd., Springfield, VT 05156. Phones: 802-885-4529; 800-356-2966. Fax: 802-885-8590. Counties: Rutland & Windsor. Also serves Mendon (portions), Sherburne (town), West Bridgewater. ICA: VT0089.
TV Market Ranking: Below 100. Franchise award date: N.A. Franchise expiration date: N.A. Began: N.A.
Channel capacity: 42. Channels available but not in use: None.
Basic Service
Subscribers: 3,164.
Programming (received off-air): WCAX-TV (C) Burlington; WNNE (N) Hartford-Hanover; WVTA (P) Windsor.
Programming (via microwave): WBZ-TV (C), WHDH-TV (N), WSBK-TV (U) Boston; WENH (P) Durham; WMUR-TV (A,F) Manchester.
Programming (via satellite): A & E; C-SPAN; CNBC; CNN; Country Music TV; Discovery Channel; E! Entertainment TV; ESPN; Fox Family Channel; Fox Sports Net New England; FoxNet; Headline News; Home Shopping Network 2; Learning Channel; Lifetime; MTV; Nashville Network; Nickelodeon; QVC; Sci-Fi Channel; TBS Superstation; The Weather Channel; Travel Channel; Turner Classic Movies; Turner Network TV; USA Network; VH1.
Current originations: Public access.
Fee: $35.00 installation; $22.08 monthly; $1.01 converter; $13.64 additional installation.
Pay Service 1
Pay Units: N.A.
Programming (via satellite): Cinemax; Disney Channel; HBO; New England Sports Network.
Fee: $9.95 monthly (Disney or NESN), $10.95 monthly (Cinemax), $11.95 monthly (HBO).
Ownership: Adelphia Communications Corp. (MSO).

***LONDONDERRY TWP.**—FrontierVision Partners LP, Suite P-200, 1777 S. Harrison St., Denver, CO 80210. Phone: 303-757-1588. Fax: 303-757-6105. County: Windham. ICA: VT0057.
TV Market Ranking: Outside TV Markets. Franchise award date: N.A. Franchise expiration date: N.A. Scheduled to begin: N.A.
Channel capacity: N.A.
Ownership: FrontierVision Partners LP (MSO). See Cable System Ownership.

***LUNENBURG TWP.**—FrontierVision Partners LP, Suite P-200, 1777 S. Harrison St., Denver, CO 80210. Phone: 303-757-1588. Fax: 303-757-6105. County: Essex. ICA: VT0058.
TV Market Ranking: Outside TV Markets. Franchise award date: N.A. Franchise expiration date: N.A. Scheduled to begin: N.A.
Channel capacity: N.A.
Ownership: FrontierVision Partners LP (MSO). See Cable System Ownership.

MANCHESTER—Adelphia Communications Corp., 107 McKinley St., Bennington, VT 05201-2029. Phones: 802-447-1534; 800-347-5002. Fax: 802-442-2063.
Web site: http://www.adelphia.net.
Counties: Bennington & Windham. Also serves Arlington, Birch Hill, Bondville, Dorset, East Arlington, East Dorset, Peru Twp., Sandgate, South Dorset, Stratton, Stratton Mountain, Sunderland, West Arlington (portions), Winhall. ICA: VT0008.
TV Market Ranking: Below 100 (Arlington, Birch Hill, Stratton, Stratton Mountain, Sunderland, West Arlington); Outside TV Markets (Bondville, Dorset, East Arlington, East Dorset, Manchester, Peru Twp., Sandgate, South Dorset, Winhall). Franchise award date: N.A. Franchise expiration date: N.A. Began: November 1, 1960.
Channel capacity: 30 (2-way capable). Channels available but not in use: None.
Basic Service
Subscribers: 4,442.
Programming (received off-air): WMHT (P), WNYT (N), WRGB (C), WTEN (A) Albany-Schenectady; WVTA (P) Windsor; allband FM.
Programming (via translator): WCAX-TV (C) Burlington.
Programming (via satellite): WPIX (W) New York; C-SPAN; Fox Sports Net New England; FoxNet; TBS Superstation.
Current originations: Automated time-weather; public access; educational access; government access; automated emergency alert; local news.
Fee: $45.00 installation; $11.25 monthly; $3.25 converter; $12.99 additional installation.
Expanded Basic Service
Subscribers: 4,095.
Programming (via satellite): A & E; Animal Planet; CNN; ESPN; Fox Sports Net New England; Headline News; Home Shopping Network; Lifetime; MTV; Nashville Network; Nickelodeon; The Weather Channel; USA Network.
Fee: $15.81 monthly.
Pay Service 1
Pay Units: 183.
Programming (via satellite): Cinemax.
Fee: $10.95 monthly.
Pay Service 2
Pay Units: 130.
Programming (via satellite): Disney Channel.
Fee: $9.95 monthly.
Pay Service 3
Pay Units: 696.
Programming (via satellite): HBO.
Fee: $12.95 monthly.
Pay Service 4
Pay Units: 87.
Programming (via satellite): New England Sports Network.
Fee: $9.95 monthly.
Pay-Per-View
Addressable homes: 1,133.
Local advertising: Yes. Regional interconnect: Galaxy Broadcasting.
Equipment: Blonder-Tongue headend; GTE Sylvania amplifiers; Plastoid & Times Fiber cable; Harris satellite antenna.
Miles of plant: 170.9 (coaxial); 207.0 (fiber optic). Homes passed: 6,981. Total homes in franchised area: 8,134.
Manager: Judith Hill. Chief technician: Ernie Thompson.
City fee: None.
Ownership: Adelphia Communications Corp. (MSO).

MIDDLEBURY—Mountain Cable Co., 106 Kimball Ave., South Burlington, VT 05403. Phone: 800-347-5002. County: Addison. Also serves Weybridge (portions). ICA: VT0059.
TV Market Ranking: Below 100. Franchise award date: N.A. Franchise expiration date: N.A. Began: N.A.
Channel capacity: 54. Channels available but not in use: 4.
Basic Service
Subscribers: 2,099.
Programming (received off-air): WNYT (N), WRGB (C), WTEN (A) Albany-Schenectady; WCAX-TV (C), WETK (P), WFFF-TV (F), WVNY (A) Burlington; WCFE-TV (P), WPTZ (N) Plattsburgh; CBMT, CFCF-TV Montreal.
Programming (via satellite): WGN-TV (W) Chicago; Learning Channel; TBS Superstation; Turner Network TV.
Current originations: Public access; leased access.
Fee: $25.00 installation; $8.95 monthly.
Expanded Basic Service
Subscribers: 1,176.
Programming (via satellite): A & E; C-SPAN; CNBC; CNN; Discovery Channel; ESPN; EWTN; Fox Family Channel; FoxNet; Goodlife TV Network; Headline News; Home Shopping Network; Lifetime; Nashville Network; Nickelodeon; The Inspirational Network; The Weather Channel.
Fee: $11,75 monthly.
Expanded Basic Service 2
Subscribers: 716.
Programming (via satellite): American Movie Classics; Bravo; Fox Sports Net New England; MTV; New England Sports Network; USA Network; VH1.
Fee: $7.30 monthly.
Pay Service 1
Pay Units: N.A.
Programming (via satellite): Cinemax; Disney Channel; HBO; Showtime; The Movie Channel.
Fee: $10.00 monthly (each).
Local advertising: No. Regional interconnect: Cable AdNet-New England.
Equipment: Scientific-Atlanta headend; Scientific-Atlanta & Texscan amplifiers; Comm/Scope cable; Texscan character generator; Scientific-Atlanta & Texscan set top converters; Scientific-Atlanta addressable set top converters; ChannelMaster, M/A-Com & Scientific-Atlanta satellite antenna; Scientific-Atlanta satellite receivers.
Miles of plant: 48.9 (coaxial).
Manager: Tom McLaughlin. Chief technician: John Rivolta.
Ownership: Adelphia Communications Corp. (MSO).

***MIDDLETOWN SPRINGS TWP.**—FrontierVision Partners LP, Suite P-200, 1777 S. Harrison St., Denver, CO 80210. Phone: 303-757-1588. Fax: 303-757-6105. County: Rutland. ICA: VT0060.
TV Market Ranking: Outside TV Markets. Franchise award date: N.A. Franchise expiration date: N.A. Scheduled to begin: N.A.
Channel capacity: N.A.

Ownership: FrontierVision Partners LP (MSO). See Cable System Ownership.

MILTON—Adelphia Cable, Box 808, 72 W. Milton Rd., Milton, VT 05468. Phones: 802-893-1551; 800-356-1777. Fax: 802-893-7310. Counties: Chittenden & Franklin. Also serves Colchester, Georgia. ICA: VT0006.

TV Market Ranking: Below 100. Franchise award date: N.A. Franchise expiration date: N.A. Began: October 1, 1983.

Channel capacity: 40. Channels available but not in use: 5.

Basic Service

Subscribers: 7,325.

Programming (received off-air): WCAX-TV (C), WETK (P), WFFF-TV (F), WVNY (A) Burlington; WCFE-TV (P), WPTZ (N), WWBI-LP (U) Plattsburgh; CBMT, CFCF-TV Montreal.

Programming (via satellite): Cartoon Network; FoxNet; Headline News; Learning Channel; TBS Superstation.

Current originations: Local news.

Fee: $10.45 monthly.

Expanded Basic Service

Subscribers: 6,475.

Programming (via satellite): A & E; Animal Planet; C-SPAN; CNN; Discovery Channel; ESPN; ESPN 2; EWTN; Fox Family Channel; Fox News Channel; Home Shopping Network; Lifetime; MTV; Nashville Network; Nickelodeon; Sci-Fi Channel; TV Guide Channel; The Weather Channel; Turner Network TV; USA Network; VH1.

Fee: $6.00 monthly.

A la Carte 1

Subscribers: N.A.

Programming (via satellite): WSBK-TV (U) Boston; WGN-TV (W) Chicago; WPIX (W) New York; New England Sports Network.

Fee: N.A.

Pay Service 1

Pay Units: N.A.

Programming (via satellite): Cinemax; Disney Channel; HBO; Showtime.

Fee: $11.00 monthly (each).

Pay-Per-View

Addressable homes: 3,900.

Special events.

Equipment: Scientific-Atlanta addressable set top converters.

Miles of plant: 250.0 (coaxial). Homes passed: 7,500.

Manager: Marlene Booska. Chief technician: Wayne Deslaurier.

Ownership: Adelphia Communications Corp. (MSO). Purchased from Lake Champlain Cable TV Corp., January 15, 1999.

MONTPELIER—Adelphia Cable Communications, Box 68, Grange Rd., Montpelier, VT 05602. Phones: 802-223-2852; 800-347-5002. Fax: 802-223-8941. Counties: Orange, Washington & Windsor. Also serves Berlin, Bethel, Duxbury, Duxbury Twp., Middlesex, Moretown, Moretown Twp., Randolph, Waterbury.

TV Market Ranking: Below 100 (Bethel, Duxbury, Duxbury Twp., Middlesex, Moretown, Moretown Twp., Randolph, Waterbury); Outside TV Markets (Berlin, Montpelier). Franchise award date: January 1, 1952. Franchise expiration date: N.A. Began: November 1, 1952.

Channel capacity: 43 (2-way capable; operating 2-way). Channels available but not in use: None.

Basic Service

Subscribers: 7,572.

Programming (received off-air): WCAX-TV (C), WETK (P), WFFF-TV (F), WVNY (A) Burlington; WNNE (N) Hartford-Hanover; WPTZ (N) Plattsburgh; CBMT Montreal.

Programming (via satellite): C-SPAN; Learning Channel; TBS Superstation; TV Guide Channel.

Current originations: Public access; educational access; government access; leased access.

Fee: $40.00 installation; $10.85 monthly.

Expanded Basic Service

Subscribers: 6,318.

Programming (via satellite): A & E; American Movie Classics; CNBC; CNN; Discovery Channel; ESPN; EWTN; FX; Fox Family Channel; Fox Sports Net New England; FoxNet; Headline News; Home Shopping Network; Lifetime; MTV; Nashville Network; New England Sports Network; Nickelodeon; QVC; The Inspirational Network; The Weather Channel; Turner Network TV; USA Network.

Fee: $15.00 installation; $17.90 monthly.

Pay Service 1

Pay Units: 457.

Programming (via satellite): Cinemax.

Fee: $10.00 installation; $11.50 monthly.

Pay Service 2

Pay Units: 383.

Programming (via satellite): Disney Channel.

Fee: $8.95 monthly.

Pay Service 3

Pay Units: 940.

Programming (via satellite): HBO.

Fee: $11.50 monthly.

Pay Service 4

Pay Units: 582.

Programming (via satellite): Showtime.

Fee: $11.50 monthly.

Pay Service 5

Pay Units: 442.

Programming (via satellite): The Movie Channel.

Fee: $11.50 monthly.

Pay-Per-View

Addressable homes: 3,541.

Movies; special events.

Fee: $3.95.

Local advertising: Yes. Available in automated programming. Regional interconnect: Media Partners.

Equipment: Scientific-Atlanta headend; Scientific-Atlanta amplifiers; Comm/Scope cable; Sony VTRs; Texscan character generator; Scientific-Atlanta set top converters; Scientific-Atlanta addressable set top converters; Eagle traps; Scientific-Atlanta & M/A-Com satellite antenna; Scientific-Atlanta & M/A-Com satellite receivers.

Miles of plant: 308.3 (coaxial); 36.0 (fiber optic). Homes passed: 12,539.

Manager: Kenric Kite. Chief technician: Douglas Pierce. Program director: Thomas Cheney.

State fee: 0.005% of gross.

Ownership: Adelphia Communications Corp. (MSO).

MORRISVILLE—FrontierVision, Box 760, Lebanon, NH 03766-1076. Phone: 603-448-6280. Fax: 603-448-2809. County: Lamoille. Also serves Hyde Park, Johnson, Morristown, North Hyde Park. ICA: VT0062.

TV Market Ranking: Below 100. Franchise award date: N.A. Franchise expiration date: N.A. Began: January 1, 1979.

Channel capacity: 28. Channels available but not in use: None.

Basic Service

Subscribers: 1,477.

Programming (received off-air): WCAX-TV (C), WETK (P), WVNY (A) Burlington; WNNE (N) Hartford-Hanover; WMTW-TV (A) Portland-Poland Spring; CBMT, CFCF-TV Montreal; allband FM.

Programming (via satellite): WGN-TV (W) Chicago; CNN; FoxNet; MTV; Nashville Network; TBS Superstation; Turner Network TV.

Fee: $9.37 monthly.

Expanded Basic Service

Subscribers: 1,246.

Programming (via satellite): American Movie Classics; Court TV; ESPN; Nickelodeon; USA Network.

Fee: $8.44 monthly.

Pay Service 1

Pay Units: 129.

Programming (via satellite): Cinemax.

Fee: $9.95 monthly.

Pay Service 2

Pay Units: 345.

Programming (via satellite): The New Encore.

Fee: N.A.

Pay Service 3

Pay Units: 179.

Programming (via satellite): HBO.

Fee: $10.95 monthly.

Pay Service 4

Pay Units: 150.

Programming (via satellite): Starz!

Fee: N.A.

Equipment: Texscan amplifiers; Harris satellite antenna.

Miles of plant: 35.7 (coaxial). Homes passed: 1,968.

Manager: Keith Froleiks. Chief technician: Rodney King.

Ownership: FrontierVision Partners LP (MSO). See Cable System Ownership.

MOUNT ASCUTNEY—Adelphia Cable, Box 520, 539 Charlestown Rd., Springfield, VT 05156. Phones: 802-885-4529; 800-356-2966. Fax: 802-885-8590. County: Windsor. Also serves Bridgewater, Cavendish, Chester, Chester Depot (village), Ludlow, Perkinsville, Plymouth, Proctorsville, Springfield, Sunrise, Taftsville, Tyson, Windsor, Woodstock. ICA: VT0002.

TV Market Ranking: Below 100. Franchise award date: N.A. Franchise expiration date: N.A. Began: May 1, 1953.

Channel capacity: 42 (not 2-way capable). Channels available but not in use: 1.

Basic Service

Subscribers: 11,099.

Programming (received off-air): WCAX-TV (C), WFFF-TV (F) Burlington; WENH (P) Durham; WNNE (N) Hartford-Hanover; WMUR-TV (A,F) Manchester; WVTA (P) Windsor; allband FM.

Programming (via microwave): WBZ-TV (C), WCVB-TV (A), WHDH-TV (N), WSBK-TV (U) Boston.

Programming (via satellite): FoxNet; TBS Superstation.

Current originations: Public access.

Fee: $45.00 installation; $9.26 monthly; $0.89 converter.

Expanded Basic Service

Subscribers: 10,107.

Programming (via satellite): A & E; C-SPAN; CNBC; CNN; Country Music TV; Discovery Channel; E! Entertainment TV; ESPN; Fox Family Channel; Fox Sports Net New England; Headline News; Home Shopping Network; Learning Channel; Lifetime; MTV; Nashville Network; Nickelodeon; QVC; Sci-Fi Channel; The Weather Channel; Turner Classic Movies; Turner Network TV; USA Network; VH1.

Fee: $19.60 monthly.

Pay Service 1

Pay Units: 727.

Programming (via satellite): Cinemax.

Fee: $9.95 monthly.

Pay Service 2

Pay Units: 293.

Programming (via satellite): Disney Channel.

Fee: $9.95 monthly.

Pay Service 3

Pay Units: 1,049.

Programming (via satellite): HBO.

Fee: $11.95 monthly.

Pay Service 4

Pay Units: 284.

Programming (via satellite): New England Sports Network.

Fee: $9.95 monthly.

Pay-Per-View

Viewer's Choice 1 & 2.

Local advertising: Yes. Regional interconnect: Galaxy Broadcasting.

Equipment: Delta-Benco-Cascade headend; Delta-Benco-Cascade & Magnavox amplifiers; Times Fiber cable; Magnavox set top converters; Scientific-Atlanta satellite antenna.

Miles of plant: 768.8 (coaxial). Additional miles planned: 62.1 (coaxial).

Manager: Terry Gould. Chief technician: David Gunzinger. Marketing director: Jody Gintof.

State fee: 0.005% of gross.

Ownership: Adelphia Communications Corp. (MSO).

NEWFANE—Southern Vermont Cable Co., Box 166, Bondville, VT 05340. Phone: 800-544-5931. County: Windham. Also serves Newfane Hill, South Newfane, Williamsville. ICA: VT0023.

TV Market Ranking: Below 100. Franchise award date: N.A. Franchise expiration date: October 1, 1998. Began: September 1, 1968.

Channel capacity: 60 (not 2-way capable). Channels available but not in use: 4.

Basic Service

Subscribers: 412.

Programming (received off-air): WBZ-TV (C), WCVB-TV (A), WFXT (F), WHDH-TV (N) Boston; WMUR-TV (A,F) Manchester; WMTW-TV (A) Portland-Poland Spring; WVTA (P) Windsor; allband FM.

Programming (via translator): WCAX-TV (C) Burlington.

Programming (via satellite): WSBK-TV (U) Boston; WGN-TV (W) Chicago; A & E; C-SPAN; CNN; Discovery Channel; E! Entertainment TV; ESPN; Fox Family Channel; Headline News; History Channel; Learning Channel; Nashville Network; New England Sports Network; Nickelodeon; QVC; TBS Superstation; The Weather Channel; Turner Classic Movies; Turner Network TV; USA Network.

Fee: $37.50 installation; $19.95 monthly; $17.50 additional installation.

Expanded Basic Service

Subscribers: 142.

Programming (via satellite): American Movie Classics; Cartoon Network; Comedy Central; Disney Channel; ESPN 2; Home & Garden Television; Outdoor Channel; Sci-Fi Channel; VH1.

Fee: $5.95 monthly.

Pay Service 1

Pay Units: 54.

Programming (via satellite): HBO.

Fee: $27.50 installation; $9.95 monthly.

Local advertising: No.

Equipment: Cadco & ISS headend; Magnavox & Texscan amplifiers; Belden, Times Fiber & Trilogy cable; Vitek traps; Scientific-Atlanta satellite antenna; ISS & Harris satellite receivers.

Miles of plant: 15.0 (coaxial); None (fiber optic). Additional miles planned: 3.0 (coaxial). Homes passed: 450.

Manager: Ernest Scialabba.

State fee: 0.005% of gross.

Ownership: Southern Vermont Cable Co. (MSO).

NEWPORT—Adelphia Cable, 1125 E. Main St., Newport, VT 05855-1810. Phone: 802-334-2614. Fax: 802-334-7391. Counties: Essex & Orleans. Also serves Barton, Beebe Plain, Derby Center, Derby Line, Glover, Island Pond, Newport Center, Orleans. Plans service to North Troy. ICA: VT0013.

TV Market Ranking: Outside TV Markets. Franchise award date: October 1, 1962. Franchise expiration date: N.A. Began: October 1, 1962.

Channel capacity: 61 (not 2-way capable). Channels available but not in use: N.A.

Basic Service

Subscribers: 3,050.

Programming (received off-air): WCAX-TV (C), WETK (P), WVNY (A) Burlington; WPTZ (N) Plattsburgh; WMTW-TV (A) Portland-Poland Spring; CBMT, CFCF-TV Montreal; CHLT-TV Sherbrooke; allband FM.

Programming (via satellite): WSBK-TV (U) Boston; WGN-TV (W) Chicago; C-SPAN; CNN; Country Music TV; ESPN; EWTN; FoxNet; Home Shopping Network; Learning Channel; Nashville Network; New England Sports Network; TBS Superstation; TV Guide Channel; TV Guide Sneak Prevue; Trinity Bcstg. Network; Z Music Television.

Current originations: Automated time-weather; public access; educational access; government access.

Fee: $9.95 installation; $8.45 monthly.

Expanded Basic Service

Subscribers: 600.

Programming (via satellite): A & E; American Movie Classics; Cartoon Network; Comedy Central; Discovery Channel; ESPN 2; Fox Family Channel; Fox Sports Net New England; Headline News; Lifetime; MTV; Nick at Nite; Nickelodeon; Sci-Fi Channel; Storyvision Network; The Weather Channel; Turner Network TV; USA Network; VH1.

Fee: $12.50 monthly.

Pay Service 1

Pay Units: N.A.

Programming (via satellite): Cinemax (multiplexed); Disney Channel; HBO (multiplexed); Showtime (multiplexed); The Movie Channel.

Fee: $2.77 monthly (Disney), $8.95 monthly (Cinemax, HBO, Showtime or TMC).

Pay-Per-View

Addressable homes: 1,600.

Viewer's Choice.

Local advertising: Yes. Available in satellite distributed programming.

Equipment: Jerrold headend; Jerrold amplifiers; Trilogy cable; AT&T & Alcoa fiber optic cable; Jerrold addressable set top converters; PPC traps; Anixter-Mark satellite antenna; Standard Agile Omni satellite receivers.

Miles of plant: 90.0 (coaxial); 60.0 (fiber optic). Additional miles planned: 60.0 (coaxial); 40.0 (fiber optic). Homes passed: 5,000. Total homes in franchised area: 10,000.

Manager: David Ames. Chief technician: Roy Langdon.

State fee: 0.005% of gross.

Ownership: Adelphia Communications Corp. (MSO).

***NEWPORT TWP.**—FrontierVision Partners LP, Suite P-200, 1777 S. Harrison St., Denver, CO 80210. Phone: 303-757-1588. Fax: 303-757-6105. County: Orleans. ICA: VT0063.

TV Market Ranking: Outside TV Markets. Franchise award date: N.A. Franchise expiration date: N.A. Scheduled to begin: N.A.

Channel capacity: N.A.

Ownership: FrontierVision Partners LP (MSO). See Cable System Ownership.

NORTHFIELD (village)—Trans-Video Inc., Village Common, Northfield, VT 05663. Phone: 802-485-3811. Fax: 802-485-8450. County: Washington. Also serves Northfield (town), Riverton. ICA: VT0018.

TV Market Ranking: Below 100 (Riverton); Outside TV Markets (town of Northfield, village of Northfield). Franchise award date: N.A. Franchise expiration date: N.A. Began: December 21, 1951.

Channel capacity: 78 (2-way capable; operating 2-way). Channels available but not in use: 28.

Basic Service

Subscribers: 1,650.

Programming (received off-air): WCAX-TV (C), WETK (P), WVNY (A) Burlington; WPTZ (N) Plattsburgh; CFCF-TV Montreal; allband FM.

Programming (via satellite): Animal Planet; FoxNet; Home & Garden Television; Home Shopping Network; Learning Channel; TBS Superstation.

Current originations: Local news.

Fee: $15.00 installation; $15.65 monthly; $3.15 converter.

Expanded Basic Service

Subscribers: 1,100.

Programming (via satellite): WSBK-TV (U) Boston; WPIX (W) New York; A & E; American Movie Classics; C-SPAN; CNBC; CNN; Cartoon Network; Comedy Central; Country Music TV; Court TV; Discovery Channel; E! Entertainment TV; ESPN 2; ESPN Classic Sports; Fox Family Channel; History Channel; Lifetime; MTV; Nashville Network; Nickelodeon; QVC; Sci-Fi Channel; TV Food Network; TV Guide Channel; The Weather Channel; Turner Classic Movies; Turner Network TV; USA Network; VH1.

Fee: $15.00 installation; $19.04 monthly.

Pay Service 1

Pay Units: 60.

Programming (via satellite): Cinemax.

Fee: $11.25 monthly.

Pay Service 2

Pay Units: 20.

Programming (via satellite): Disney Channel.

Fee: $10.25 monthly.

Pay Service 3

Pay Units: 100.

Programming (via satellite): HBO.

Fee: $11.25 monthly.

Pay Service 4

Pay Units: 35.

Programming (via satellite): New England Sports Network.

Fee: $9.50 monthly.

Pay-Per-View

Viewer's Choice; movies; special events.

Local advertising: Yes (locally produced). Local sales manager: George Goodrich.

Equipment: Jerrold headend; Jerrold amplifiers; Times Fiber cable; Texscan character generator; Scientific-Atlanta set top converters; Eagle & Intercept traps; Scientific-Atlanta satellite antenna; Scientific-Atlanta satellite receivers.

Miles of plant: 40.0 (coaxial); 6.0 (fiber optic). Homes passed: 1,900. Total homes in franchised area: 2,200.

Manager: George L. Goodrich Jr.

State fee: 0.005% of gross.

Ownership: Trans-Video Inc.

***ORWELL TWP.**—FrontierVision Partners LP, Suite P-200, 1777 S. Harrison St., Denver, CO 80210. Phone: 303-757-1588. Fax: 303-757-6105. County: Addison. ICA: VT0064.

TV Market Ranking: Outside TV Markets. Franchise award date: N.A. Franchise expiration date: N.A. Scheduled to begin: N.A.

Channel capacity: N.A.

Ownership: FrontierVision Partners LP (MSO). See Cable System Ownership.

PAWLET—Adelphia Communications Corp., Box 520, 539 Charlestown Rd., Springfield, VT 05156. Phones: 802-885-4529; 800-356-2966. Fax: 802-885-8590. County: Rutland. Also serves West Pawlet. ICA: VT0028.

TV Market Ranking: Outside TV Markets. Franchise award date: N.A. Franchise expiration date: N.A. Began: September 1, 1966.

Channel capacity: 60 (not 2-way capable). Channels available but not in use: 48.

Basic Service

Subscribers: 255.

Programming (received off-air): WNYT (N), WRGB (C), WTEN (A) Albany-Schenectady; WCAX-TV (C) Burlington; WPTZ (N) Plattsburgh; WVER (P) Rutland.

Programming (via satellite): CNN; ESPN; Fox Family Channel; USA Network.

Current originations: Public access.

Fee: $105.81 installation; $15.00 monthly; $13.78 additional installation.

Pay Service 1

Pay Units: 54.

Programming (via satellite): HBO.

Fee: $25.00 installation; $11.95 monthly.

Miles of plant: 5.0 (coaxial).

Manager: Robert Snowdon. Chief technician: Henry Hryckiewicz.

Ownership: Adelphia Communications Corp. (MSO).

***PEACHAM TWP.**—FrontierVision Partners LP, Suite P-200, 1777 S. Harrison St., Denver, CO 80210. Phone: 303-757-1588. Fax: 303-757-6105. County: Caledonia. ICA: VT0065.

TV Market Ranking: Outside TV Markets. Franchise award date: N.A. Franchise expiration date: N.A. Scheduled to begin: N.A.

Channel capacity: N.A.

Ownership: FrontierVision Partners LP (MSO). See Cable System Ownership.

PITTSFORD—Adelphia Communications Corp., Box 520, 539 Charlestown Rd., Springfield, VT 05156. Phones: 802-885-4529; 800-356-2966. Fax: 802-885-8590. County: Rutland. Also serves Chittenden, Pittsford (village). ICA: VT0066.

TV Market Ranking: Below 100 (Chittenden); Outside TV Markets (Pittsford). Franchise award date: N.A. Franchise expiration date: N.A. Began: December 1, 1971.

Channel capacity: 26. Channels available but not in use: None.

Basic Service

Subscribers: 1,015.

Programming (received off-air): WNYT (N), WRGB (C), WTEN (A), WXXA-TV (F) Albany-Schenectady; WCAX-TV (C), WVNY (A) Burlington; WPTZ (N) Plattsburgh; WVER (P) Rutland; allband FM.

Programming (via satellite): TBS Superstation.

Fee: $100.40 installation; $9.62 monthly; $0.99 converter; $13.07 additional installation.

Expanded Basic Service

Subscribers: N.A.

Programming (via satellite): A & E; C-SPAN; CNN; ESPN; Fox Family Channel; Headline News; Home Shopping Network; Lifetime; MTV; Nashville Network; Nickelodeon; USA Network.

Fee: $10.50 monthly.

Pay Service 1

Pay Units: N.A.

Programming (via satellite): Cinemax; Disney Channel; HBO.

Fee: $9.95 monthly (Disney), $10.95 monthly (Cinemax), $11.95 monthly (HBO).

Equipment: Blonder-Tongue headend; Texscan amplifiers; Gardiner satellite antenna.

Miles of plant: 10.0 (coaxial).

Manager: Robert Snowdon. Chief technician: Henry Hryckiewicz.

State fee: 0.005% of gross.

Ownership: Adelphia Communications Corp. (MSO).

PUTNEY—Southern Vermont Cable Co., Box 166, Bondville, VT 05340. Phone: 800-544-5931. County: Windham. ICA: VT0067.

TV Market Ranking: Below 100. Franchise award date: October 1, 1988. Franchise expiration date: N.A. Began: January 1, 1978.

Channel capacity: 60 (not 2-way capable). Channels available but not in use: 15.

Basic Service

Subscribers: 429.

Programming (received off-air): WBZ-TV (C), WCVB-TV (A), WHDH-TV (N) Boston; WNNE (N) Hartford-Hanover; WEKW-TV (P) Keene; WMUR-TV (A,F) Manchester; WVTA (P) Windsor; allband FM.

Programming (via satellite): WSBK-TV (U) Boston; WGN-TV (W) Chicago; KTLA (W) Los Angeles; A & E; CNBC; CNN; Discovery Channel; E! Entertainment TV; ESPN; Headline News; History Channel; Lifetime; Nashville Network; New England Sports Network; Nickelodeon; QVC; TBS Superstation; The Weather Channel; Turner Classic Movies; Turner Network TV; USA Network.

Fee: $37.50 installation; $19.95 monthly.

Expanded Basic Service

Subscribers: 174.

Programming (via satellite): American Movie Classics; Cartoon Network; Comedy Central; Disney Channel; Home & Garden Television; Learning Channel; Outdoor Channel; Sci-Fi Channel; Travel Channel.

Fee: $5.95 monthly.

Pay Service 1

Pay Units: 59.

Programming (via satellite): HBO.

Fee: $27.50 installation; $9.95 monthly.

Local advertising: Planned.

Equipment: Blonder-Tongue, ISS & Cadco headend; Theta-Com amplifiers; Times Fiber & Trilogy cable.

Miles of plant: 15.0 (coaxial); None (fiber optic). Additional miles planned: 2.0 (coaxial). Homes passed: 540.

Manager: Ernest Scialabba.

State fee: 0.005% of gross.

Ownership: Southern Vermont Cable Co. (MSO).

READING—Adelphia Communications Corp., Box 520, 539 Charlestown Rd., Springfield, VT 05156. Phones: 802-885-4529; 800-347-5002. Fax: 802-885-8590. County: Windsor. ICA: VT0029.

TV Market Ranking: Below 100. Franchise award date: N.A. Franchise expiration date: N.A. Began: June 1, 1954.

Channel capacity: 60. Channels available but not in use: 48.

Basic Service

Subscribers: 37.

Programming (received off-air): WCAX-TV (C) Burlington; WNNE (N) Hartford-Hanover; WMTW-TV (A) Portland-Poland Spring; WVTA (P) Windsor.

Programming (via satellite): A & E; CNN; ESPN; Fox Family Channel; TBS Superstation; USA Network.

Current originations: Public access.

Fee: $45.00 installation; $19.65 monthly.

Pay Service 1

Pay Units: 3.

Programming (via satellite): HBO.

Fee: $11.95 monthly.
Equipment: ChannelMaster headend; Jerrold amplifiers; Vikoa cable.
Miles of plant: 2.0 (coaxial). Homes passed: 66.
Manager: Terry Gould. Chief technician: David Gunzinger. Marketing director: Kevin Dempsey.
State fee: 0.005% of gross.
Ownership: Adelphia Communications Corp. (MSO).

RICHMOND—Adelphia Cable, Box 808, 72 W. Milton Rd., Milton, VT 05468. Phones: 802-893-1551; 800-356-1777. Fax: 802-893-7310. County: Chittenden. Also serves Jericho, Underhill (town). ICA: VT0068.
TV Market Ranking: Below 100. Franchise award date: N.A. Franchise expiration date: N.A. Began: December 1, 1985.
Channel capacity: 40 (not 2-way capable). Channels available but not in use: 5.
Basic Service
Subscribers: 1,800.
Programming (received off-air): WCAX-TV (C), WETK (P), WFFF-TV (F), WVNY (A) Burlington; WCFE-TV (P), WPTZ (N) Plattsburgh; CFCF-TV Montreal.
Programming (via satellite): Discovery Channel; Headline News; TBS Superstation; The Weather Channel.
Current originations: Local news.
Fee: $29.95 installation; $10.45 monthly.
Expanded Basic Service
Subscribers: N.A.
Programming (via satellite): A & E; C-SPAN; CNN; ESPN; Fox Family Channel; Home Shopping Network; Lifetime; MTV; Nashville Network; Nickelodeon; Turner Network TV; USA Network; VH1.
Fee: $6.00 monthly.
Expanded Basic Service 2
Subscribers: N.A.
Programming (via satellite): WPIX (W) New York; New England Sports Network.
Fee: N.A.
Pay Service 1
Pay Units: 753.
Programming (via satellite): Cinemax; Disney Channel; HBO; Showtime.
Fee: $11.00 monthly (each).
Pay-Per-View
Addressable homes: 1,200.
Special events.
Manager: Marlene Booska. Chief technician: Wayne Deslaurier.
State fee: 0.005% of gross.
Ownership: Adelphia Communications Corp. (MSO). Purchased from Lake Champlain Cable TV Corp., January 15, 1999.

ROCHESTER—Mountain Cable Co., Box 68, Grange Rd., Montpelier, VT 05602. Phone: 800-347-5002. Fax: 802-223-8941. County: Windsor. ICA: VT0069.
TV Market Ranking: Below 100. Franchise award date: N.A. Franchise expiration date: N.A. Began: N.A.
Channel capacity: 14. Channels available but not in use: N.A.
Basic Service
Subscribers: 183.
Programming (received off-air): WCAX-TV (C), WETK (P), WVNY (A) Burlington; WPTZ (N) Plattsburgh.
Programming (via satellite): Learning Channel.
Fee: $33.00 installation; $8.95 monthly.
Expanded Basic Service
Subscribers: N.A.
Programming (via satellite): CNN; ESPN; Nashville Network; TBS Superstation; Turner Network TV; USA Network.
Fee: $8.05 monthly.
Pay Service 1
Pay Units: N.A.
Programming (via satellite): HBO.
Fee: $10.00 monthly.
Local advertising: No.
Equipment: Scientific-Atlanta headend; Texscan amplifiers; Comm/Scope cable; Texscan character generator; Oak set top converters; Eagle traps; Scientific-Atlanta satellite antenna; Scientific-Atlanta satellite receivers.
Miles of plant: 6.0 (coaxial).
Manager: Byron Hill. Chief technician: Al Sutphen.
Ownership: Adelphia Communications Corp. (MSO).

***RUPERT TWP.**—FrontierVision Partners LP, Suite P-200, 1777 S. Harrison St., Denver, CO 80210. Phone: 303-757-1588. Fax: 303-757-6105. County: Bennington. ICA: VT0070.
TV Market Ranking: Outside TV Markets. Franchise award date: N.A. Franchise expiration date: N.A. Scheduled to begin: N.A.
Channel capacity: N.A.
Ownership: FrontierVision Partners LP (MSO). See Cable System Ownership.

RUTLAND—Adelphia Cable, 106 Kimball Ave., South Burlington, VT 05403. Phones: 802-773-2755; 800-649-2755. Fax: 802-775-1133. County: Rutland. Also serves Brandon Twp., Clarendon Twp., Danby, Forest Dale, Mendon Twp., Mount Tabor, Proctor Twp., Rutland (city), Rutland Twp., Wallingford Twp., West Rutland Twp. ICA: VT0003.
TV Market Ranking: Below 100 (portions of Brandon Twp., Clarendon Twp., Mendon Twp., portions of Proctor Twp., Rutland, Rutland Twp., Wallingford Twp., portions of West Rutland Twp.); Outside TV Markets (portions of Brandon Twp., Danby, Forest Dale, Mount Tabor, portions of Proctor Twp., portions of West Rutland Twp.). Franchise award date: June 1, 1959. Franchise expiration date: January 1, 1999. Began: November 1, 1959.
Channel capacity: 35 (not 2-way capable). Channels available but not in use: None.
Basic Service
Subscribers: 10,625.
Programming (received off-air): WMHT (P), WRGB (C), WTEN (A) Albany-Schenectady; WCAX-TV (C), WFFF-TV (F), WVNY (A) Burlington; WNNE (N) Hartford-Hanover; WPTZ (N) Plattsburgh; WVER (P) Rutland; 20 FMs.
Programming (via satellite): C-SPAN; Discovery Channel; Learning Channel.
Current originations: Automated time-weather; public access; educational access; government access; leased access; library access.
Fee: $52.00 installation; $21.55 monthly; $2.92 converter; $39.00 additional installation.
Expanded Basic Service
Subscribers: 10,465.
Programming (via satellite): CNBC; CNN; ESPN; FX; Fox Family Channel; Headline News; Home Shopping Network; Lifetime; Nashville Network; Nickelodeon; The Weather Channel; Turner Network TV; VH1.
Fee: $12.33 monthly.
Expanded Basic Service 2
Subscribers: 6,000.
Programming (via satellite): American Movie Classics; MTV; USA Network.
Fee: $4.09 monthly.
Pay Service 1
Pay Units: 900.
Programming (via satellite): Disney Channel.
Fee: $9.45 monthly.
Pay Service 2
Pay Units: 2,000.
Programming (via satellite): HBO.
Fee: $11.50 monthly.
Pay Service 3
Pay Units: 700.
Programming (via satellite): The Movie Channel.
Fee: $11.50 monthly.
Pay Service 4
Pay Units: 1,000.
Programming (via satellite): Showtime.
Fee: $11.50 monthly.
Pay-Per-View
Addressable homes: 7,000.
Special events.
Fee: Varies.
Local advertising: Yes. Available in locally originated, character-generated & taped programming. Regional interconnect: Cable AdNet-New England.
Program Guide: The Entertainer.
Equipment: Scientific-Atlanta headend; Jerrold amplifiers; Comm/Scope cable; Sony VTRs; Texscan character generator; Scientific-Atlanta set top converters; Scientific-Atlanta addressable set top converters; Eagle traps; Scientific-Atlanta satellite antenna; Scientific-Atlanta satellite receivers.
Miles of plant: 280.0 (coaxial); 30.0 (fiber optic). Homes passed: 16,000. Total homes in franchised area: 16,500.
Manager: Henry Poplaski. Chief technician: Norman Lozier. Program director: Michael Valentine. Marketing director: R. Scott Bill. Customer service manager: Eileen Franzoni.
State fee: 0.005% of gross.
Ownership: Adelphia Communications Corp. (MSO).

***RYEGATE TWP.**—FrontierVision Partners LP, Suite P-200, 1777 S. Harrison St., Denver, CO 80210. Phone: 303-757-1588. Fax: 303-757-6105. County: Caledonia. ICA: VT0071.
TV Market Ranking: Outside TV Markets. Franchise award date: N.A. Franchise expiration date: N.A. Scheduled to begin: N.A.
Channel capacity: N.A.
Ownership: FrontierVision Partners LP (MSO). See Cable System Ownership.

SHELBURNE—Adelphia Cable, Suite 4, 4281 Shelburne, Shelburne, VT 05482. Phone: 802-985-3308. Fax: 802-985-2872. Counties: Addison & Chittenden. Also serves Bristol, Bristol Village, Charlotte, Ferrisburg, Huntington Twp., Starksboro Twp., Vergennes. ICA: VT0011.
TV Market Ranking: Below 100. Franchise award date: August 9, 1984. Franchise expiration date: December 31, 2014. Began: July 1, 1985.
Channel capacity: 41 (2-way capable; operating 2-way). Channels available but not in use: None.
Basic Service
Subscribers: 3,936.
Programming (received off-air): WCAX-TV (C), WETK (P), WFFF-TV (F), WVNY (A) Burlington; WCFE-TV (P), WPTZ (N) Plattsburgh; CBMT, CFCF-TV Montreal.
Programming (via satellite): A & E; C-SPAN; CNBC; CNN; Discovery Channel; Fox Family Channel; Headline News; Learning Channel; Lifetime; MTV; Nashville Network; Nickelodeon; TBS Superstation; The Weather Channel; USA Network; VH1.
Fee: $39.95 installation; $14.95 monthly; $2.00 converter.
Pay Service 1
Pay Units: N.A.
Programming (via satellite): Cinemax; Disney Channel; HBO; New England Sports Network; Showtime.
Fee: $7.95 monthly (each).
Pay-Per-View
Addressable homes: 1,600.
Equipment: Scientific-Atlanta headend; C-COR amplifiers; Times Fiber cable; Scientific-Atlanta set top converters; Scientific-Atlanta addressable set top converters; Scientific-Atlanta satellite antenna; Scientific-Atlanta satellite receivers.
Miles of plant: 63.2 (coaxial). Additional miles planned: 37.0 (coaxial). Homes passed: 4,870. Total homes in franchised area: 5,000.
Manager: Sharon Armell. Chief technician: Steve Schuyler. Marketing director: Steve Schouten.
Ownership: Adelphia Communications Corp. (MSO). Purchased from Small Cities Cable TV Corp.

ST. ALBANS (city)—FrontierVision, 24 Catherine St., St. Albans, VT 05478-2249. Phone: 802-524-2139. Fax: 802-524-7525. County: Franklin. Also serves St. Albans Twp., Swanton (village), Swanton Twp. ICA: VT0007.
TV Market Ranking: Below 100. Franchise award date: N.A. Franchise expiration date: N.A. Began: May 1, 1970.
Channel capacity: 37. Channels available but not in use: None.
Basic Service
Subscribers: 5,116.
Programming (received off-air): WCAX-TV (C), WETK (P), WFFF-TV (F), WVNY (A) Burlington; WCFE-TV (P), WPTZ (N) Plattsburgh; CBFT, CBMT, CFCF-TV Montreal; 14 FMs.
Programming (via satellite): C-SPAN; CNN; Comedy Central; Discovery Channel; Fox Family Channel; FoxNet; Lifetime; MTV; Nickelodeon; QVC; TBS Superstation; The Weather Channel; VH1.
Current originations: Automated time-weather.
Fee: $60.00 installation; $9.56 monthly; $2.00 converter.
Expanded Basic Service
Subscribers: 4,730.
Programming (via satellite): American Movie Classics; CNBC; Disney Channel; ESPN; Nashville Network; Turner Network TV; USA Network.
Fee: $9.69 monthly.
Pay Service 1
Pay Units: 363.
Programming (via satellite): Cinemax.
Fee: $19.95 installation; $12.95 monthly.
Pay Service 2
Pay Units: 1,309.
Programming (via satellite): The New Encore.
Fee: N.A.
Pay Service 3
Pay Units: 862.
Programming (via satellite): HBO.
Fee: $12.95 monthly.
Pay Service 4
Pay Units: 252.
Programming (via satellite): New England Sports Network.
Fee: N.A.
Pay Service 5
Pay Units: 313.
Programming (via satellite): Showtime.
Fee: $12.95 monthly.
Pay Service 6
Pay Units: 813.
Programming (via satellite): Starz!
Fee: N.A.

Pay-Per-View
Addressable homes: 117.
Program Guide: The Cable Guide.
Equipment: Jerrold headend; Jerrold amplifiers; Times Fiber cable; Sony cameras; Sony VTRs; AFC satellite antenna.
Miles of plant: 93.3 (coaxial). Homes passed: 7,625. Total homes in franchised area: 8,163.
Manager: Keith Froleiks. Chief technician: Rodney King.
State fee: 0.005% of gross.
Ownership: FrontierVision Partners LP (MSO). See Cable System Ownership.

ST. JOHNSBURY—Helicon Cable Communications, Box 350, Danville, VT 05828-0350. Phone: 802-748-8917. Fax: 802-748-9397. Counties: Caledonia, Essex & Orange, VT; Grafton, NH. Also serves Bath, Haverhill, North Haverhill, Piermont, Pike, Woodsville, NH; Barnet, Bradford Twp., Burke, Burke Hollow, Concord, Danville (town), East Burke, East Ryegate, East St. Johnsbury, Groton, Kirby, Lyndon, Lyndon Center, Lyndon Corners, Lyndonville, McIndoes, Mountain Lakes, Newbury, North Danville, Passumpsic, Peacham, Ryegate, Sheffield, South Ryegate, St. Johnsbury Center, Sutton, Waterford, Wells River, West Burke, Wheelock, VT. ICA: VT0009.
TV Market Ranking: Below 100 (Bradford Twp., Newbury, North Haverhill, Piermont, Pike, Woodsville); Outside TV Markets (Barnet, Bath, Burke, Burke Hollow, Concord, Danville, East Burke, East Ryegate, East St. Johnsbury, Groton, Haverhill, Kirby, Lyndon, Lyndon Center, Lyndon Corners, Lyndonville, McIndoes, Mountain Lakes, North Danville, Passumpsic, Peacham, Ryegate, Sheffield, South Ryegate, St. Johnsbury, St. Johnsbury Center, Sutton, Waterford, Wells River, West Burke, Wheelock). Franchise award date: January 1, 1954. Franchise expiration date: N.A. Began: March 1, 1954.
Channel capacity: 72. Channels available but not in use: 27.
Basic Service
Subscribers: 7,383; Commercial subscribers: 298.
Programming (received off-air): WCAX-TV (C), WFFF-TV (F), WVNY (A) Burlington; WNNE (N) Hartford-Hanover; WLED-TV (P) Littleton; WMTW-TV (A) Portland-Poland Spring; WVTB (P) St. Johnsbury; CBMT Montreal; allband FM.
Programming (via microwave): WBZ-TV (C) Boston.
Programming (via satellite): FoxNet; QVC; TV Guide Channel.
Current originations: Automated time-weather; public access; government access.
Fee: $20.00 installation; $7.10 monthly; $18.00 additional installation.
Expanded Basic Service
Subscribers: 6,677.
Programming (received off-air): CHLT-TV Sherbrooke.
Programming (via satellite): A & E; C-SPAN; CNBC; CNN; Country Music TV; Discovery Channel; ESPN; Fox Family Channel; Fox Sports Net New England; Headline News; Home Shopping Network; MTV; Nashville Network; Nick at Nite; Nickelodeon; Sci-Fi Channel; The Weather Channel; Trinity Bcstg. Network; Turner Network TV; USA Network; VH1.
Fee: $20.00 installation; $23.74 monthly.
A la Carte 1
Subscribers: N.A.
Programming (via satellite): WSBK-TV (U) Boston; TBS Superstation.
Fee: $2.00 monthly (package); $1.50 monthly (each).
Pay Service 1
Pay Units: 113.
Programming (via satellite): Cinemax.
Fee: $10.40 monthly.
Pay Service 2
Pay Units: 513.
Programming (via satellite): Disney Channel.
Fee: $10.40 monthly.
Pay Service 3
Pay Units: 1,480.
Programming (via satellite): HBO.
Fee: $11.95 monthly.
Pay Service 4
Pay Units: 935.
Programming (via satellite): The Movie Channel.
Fee: $10.40 monthly.
Pay Service 5
Pay Units: 957.
Programming (via satellite): Showtime.
Fee: $10.40 monthly.
Pay Service 6
Pay Units: 479.
Programming (via satellite): New England Sports Network.
Fee: $4.50 monthly.
Pay-Per-View
Addressable homes: 2,367.
Action Pay-Per-View.
Fee: $3.75-$4.50.
Local advertising: Yes. Available in satellite distributed programming. Rates: $75.00/Minute; $50.00/30 Seconds. Local sales manager: David Baum. Regional interconnect: Cable AdNet-New England.
Program Guide: CableView.
Equipment: Jerrold & Scientific-Atlanta headend; Philips amplifiers; General cable; MSI character generator; Jerrold set top converters; Anixter-Mark & Scientific-Atlanta satellite antenna; Scientific-Atlanta satellite receivers.
Miles of plant: 368.0 (coaxial); 60.0 (fiber optic). Homes passed: 12,132.
Manager: Harold Berman. Chief technician: Michael Parker. Marketing & program director: David Baum.
State fee: 0.005% of gross.
Ownership: Helicon Corp. (MSO). See Cable System Ownership.

***STAMFORD TWP.**—FrontierVision Partners LP, Suite P-200, 1777 S. Harrison St., Denver, CO 80210. Phone: 303-757-1588. Fax: 303-757-6105. County: Bennington. ICA: VT0073.
TV Market Ranking: 34. Franchise award date: N.A. Franchise expiration date: N.A. Scheduled to begin: N.A.
Channel capacity: N.A.
Ownership: FrontierVision Partners LP (MSO). See Cable System Ownership.

STOWE—Stowe Cablevision, Box 453, Stowe, VT 05672. Phone: 802-253-9282. County: Lamoille. ICA: VT0074.
TV Market Ranking: Below 100. Franchise award date: N.A. Franchise expiration date: N.A. Began: January 1, 1985.
Channel capacity: 13. Channels available but not in use: N.A.
Basic Service
Subscribers: N.A.
Programming (received off-air): WRGB (C) Albany-Schenectady; WCAX-TV (C), WETK (P), WFFF-TV (F), WVNY (A) Burlington; WPTZ (N) Plattsburgh; CBMT, CFCF-TV Montreal.
Programming (via satellite): ESPN; TBS Superstation; USA Network.
Current originations: Public access.
Fee: $25.00 installation; $11.55 monthly.
Pay Service 1
Pay Units: N.A.
Programming (via satellite): HBO.
Fee: $11.00 monthly.
Equipment: Scientific-Atlanta headend; Magnavox amplifiers; Scientific-Atlanta cable; Pico traps; Anixter-Mark satellite antenna; Anixter-Mark satellite receivers.
Miles of plant: 20.0 (coaxial).
Manager: Sandy Godin. Chief technician: Rick Rothammer.
Ownership: Richard Landy (MSO).

***THETFORD TWP.**—FrontierVision Partners LP, Suite P-200, 1777 S. Harrison St., Denver, CO 80210. Phone: 303-757-1588. Fax: 303-757-6105. County: Orange. ICA: VT0075.
TV Market Ranking: Below 100. Franchise award date: N.A. Franchise expiration date: N.A. Scheduled to begin: N.A.
Channel capacity: N.A.
Ownership: FrontierVision Partners LP (MSO). See Cable System Ownership.

***TOWNSHEND TWP.**—FrontierVision Partners LP, Suite P-200, 1777 S. Harrison St., Denver, CO 80210. Phone: 303-757-1588. Fax: 303-757-6105. County: Windham. ICA: VT0076.
TV Market Ranking: Outside TV Markets. Franchise award date: N.A. Franchise expiration date: N.A. Scheduled to begin: N.A.
Channel capacity: N.A.
Ownership: FrontierVision Partners LP (MSO). See Cable System Ownership.

***TROY TWP.**—FrontierVision Partners LP, Suite P-200, 1777 S. Harrison St., Denver, CO 80210. Phone: 303-757-1588. Fax: 303-757-6105. County: Orleans. ICA: VT0077.
TV Market Ranking: Outside TV Markets. Franchise award date: N.A. Franchise expiration date: N.A. Scheduled to begin: N.A.
Channel capacity: N.A.
Ownership: FrontierVision Partners LP (MSO). See Cable System Ownership.

WAITSFIELD—Waitsfield Cable Co., Box 9, Waitsfield, VT 05673. Phone: 802-496-5800. Fax: 802-496-5811. County: Washington. Also serves Fayston, Moretown, Warren, Washington County (portions). ICA: VT0014.
TV Market Ranking: Below 100 (Fayston, Moretown, Waitsfield, Warren, portions of Washington County); Outside TV Markets (portions of Washington County). Franchise award date: N.A. Franchise expiration date: N.A. Began: October 1, 1982.
Channel capacity: 30. Channels available but not in use: N.A.
Basic Service
Subscribers: 3,268.
Programming (received off-air): WCAX-TV (C), WETK (P), WFFF-TV (F), WVNY (A) Burlington; WPTZ (N) Plattsburgh; WMTW-TV (A) Portland-Poland Spring; 2 FMs.
Programming (via satellite): A & E; CNN; ESPN; Nickelodeon; TBS Superstation; The Weather Channel; USA Network.
Fee: $25.00 installation; $11.50 monthly.
Pay Service 1
Pay Units: 960.
Programming (via satellite): Cinemax.
Fee: $10.95 monthly.
Pay Service 2
Pay Units: 1,308.
Programming (via satellite): HBO.
Fee: $10.95 monthly.
Pay Service 3
Pay Units: 480.
Programming (via satellite): Showtime.
Fee: $10.95 monthly.
Program Guide: The Cable Guide.
Miles of plant: 288.3 (coaxial). Total homes in franchised area: 3,350.
Manager: John Simms. Chief technicians: Jim Roupp & Don Whittman.
Ownership: Waitsfield-Fayston Telephone Co.

***WARDSBORO TWP.**—FrontierVision Partners LP, Suite P-200, 1777 S. Harrison St., Denver, CO 80210. Phone: 303-757-1588. Fax: 303-757-6105. County: Windham. ICA: VT0078.
TV Market Ranking: Below 100. Franchise award date: N.A. Franchise expiration date: N.A. Scheduled to begin: N.A.
Channel capacity: N.A.
Ownership: FrontierVision Partners LP (MSO). See Cable System Ownership.

WEST DOVER—Area Telecable, 100 N. Commercial Plaza, West Dover, VT 05356. Phone: 802-464-5200. Fax: 802-464-0075. County: Windham. ICA: VT0016.
TV Market Ranking: Below 100. Franchise award date: N.A. Franchise expiration date: N.A. Began: January 1, 1982.
Channel capacity: 24 (not 2-way capable). Channels available but not in use: 3.
Basic Service
Subscribers: 1,603.
Programming (received off-air): WRGB (C) Albany-Schenectady; WFXT (F), WHDH-TV (N), WSBK-TV (U) Boston; WLVI-TV (W) Cambridge-Boston; WNNE (N) Hartford-Hanover; WMUR-TV (A,F) Manchester; WVTA (P) Windsor.
Programming (via satellite): WGN-TV (W) Chicago; WPIX (W), WWOR-TV (U) New York; A & E; American Movie Classics; Animal Planet; C-SPAN; CNBC; CNN; Discovery Channel; E! Entertainment TV; ESPN; ESPN 2; FX; Fox Family Channel; Fox News Channel; Game Show Network; Golf Channel; Home Shopping Network; Lifetime; MTV; Nashville Network; Nickelodeon; TBS Superstation; TV Guide Channel; The Weather Channel; Trinity Bcstg. Network; Turner Network TV; USA Network.
Current originations: Automated time-weather; local news.
Fee: $37.50 installation; $18.07 monthly; $2.00 converter.
Pay Service 1
Pay Units: N.A.
Programming (via satellite): HBO; Showtime.
Fee: $8.00 monthly (Showtime).
Local advertising: Yes (locally produced). Available in satellite distributed programming. Local sales manager: Jeff Kozlowski.
Miles of plant: 45.0 (coaxial). Homes passed: 2,150. Total homes in franchised area: 2,300.
Manager: Jeff Kozlowski. Chief technician: Ernie Scialabba.

Franchise fee: 0.5%.
Ownership: Gateway Cablevision Corp. (MSO).

***WESTFORD TWP.**—FrontierVision Partners LP, Suite P-200, 1777 S. Harrison St., Denver, CO 80210. Phone: 303-757-1588. Fax: 303-757-6105. County: Chittenden. ICA: VT0081.
TV Market Ranking: Below 100. Franchise award date: N.A. Franchise expiration date: N.A. Scheduled to begin: N.A.
Channel capacity: N.A.
Ownership: FrontierVision Partners LP (MSO). See Cable System Ownership.

***WESTMINSTER TWP.**—FrontierVision Partners LP, Suite P-200, 1777 S. Harrison St., Denver, CO 80210. Phone: 303-757-1588. Fax: 303-757-6105. County: Windham. ICA: VT0082.
TV Market Ranking: Outside TV Markets. Franchise award date: N.A. Franchise expiration date: N.A. Scheduled to begin: N.A.
Channel capacity: N.A.
Ownership: FrontierVision Partners LP (MSO). See Cable System Ownership.

WESTON—Adelphia Communications Corp., Box 520, 539 Charlestown Rd., Springfield, VT 05156. Phones: 802-885-4529; 800-356-2966. Fax: 802-885-8590. Counties: Windham & Windsor. Also serves Londonderry Twp., South Londonderry. ICA: VT0083.
TV Market Ranking: Below 100 (Weston); Outside TV Markets (Londonderry Twp., South Londonderry). Franchise award date: N.A. Franchise expiration date: N.A. Began: September 14, 1962.
Channel capacity: 60. Channels available but not in use: 32.
Basic Service
Subscribers: 506.
Programming (received off-air): WBZ-TV (C), WCVB-TV (A), WGBH-TV (P), WHDH-TV (N) Boston; WCAX-TV (C) Burlington; WENH (P) Durham; WNNE (N) Hartford-Hanover; WMUR-TV (A,F) Manchester; WVTA (P) Windsor; allband FM.
Programming (via satellite): TBS Superstation.
Fee: $45.00 installation; $11.75 monthly; $0.89 converter.
Expanded Basic Service
Subscribers: 377.
Programming (via satellite): A & E; C-SPAN; CNBC; CNN; Discovery Channel; ESPN; Fox Family Channel; Headline News; Home Shopping Network; Nashville Network; Sci-Fi Channel; Turner Network TV; USA Network.
Fee: $16.41 monthly.
Pay Service 1
Pay Units: 50.
Programming (via satellite): HBO.
Fee: $11.95 monthly.
Pay Service 2
Pay Units: 29.
Programming (via satellite): Cinemax.
Fee: $10.95 monthly.
Pay Service 3
Pay Units: 12.
Programming (via satellite): Disney Channel.
Fee: $9.95 monthly.
Pay Service 4
Pay Units: 11.
Programming (via satellite): New England Sports Network.
Fee: $9.95 monthly.
Equipment: Blonder-Tongue headend; GTE Sylvania amplifiers; Times Fiber cable; M/A-Com satellite antenna.
Miles of plant: 5.0 (coaxial). Additional miles planned: 2.0 (coaxial).
Manager: Terry Gould. Chief technician: David Gunzinger. Marketing director: Kevin Dempsey.
State fee: 0.005% of gross.
Ownership: Adelphia Communications Corp. (MSO).

WHITINGHAM—Area Telecable, 100 N. Commercial Plaza, West Dover, VT 05356. Phone: 802-464-5200. Fax: 802-464-0075. County: Windham. ICA: VT0087.
TV Market Ranking: Outside TV Markets. Franchise award date: N.A. Franchise expiration date: N.A. Began: N.A.
Channel capacity: 45 (2-way capable; not operating 2-way). Channels available but not in use: N.A.
Basic Service
Subscribers: 20.
Programming (received off-air): WCDC (A) Adams; WNYT (N), WRGB (C) Albany-Schenectady; WNNE (N) Hartford-Hanover; WGGB-TV (A) Springfield; WVTA (P) Windsor; WUNI (S) Worcester.
Fee: $37.50 installation; $11.00 monthly.
Local advertising: Yes. Local sales manager: Jeff Kozlowski.
Miles of plant: 2.0 (coaxial); None (fiber optic). Homes passed: 85.
Manager: Jeff Kozlowski. Chief technician: Ernie Scialabba.
Ownership: Gateway Cablevision Corp. (MSO).

WILLIAMSTOWN (portions)—North Valley Cable Systems Inc., Box 303, Waterbury, VT 05676. Phone: 802-244-7748. County: Orange. ICA: VT0084.
TV Market Ranking: Below 100. Franchise award date: N.A. Franchise expiration date: N.A. Began: February 1, 1981.
Channel capacity: 12. Channels available but not in use: 6.
Basic Service
Subscribers: 18.
Programming (received off-air): WCAX-TV (C), WVNY (A) Burlington; WPTZ (N) Plattsburgh; WMTW-TV (A) Portland-Poland Spring.
Programming (via satellite): E! Entertainment TV.
Fee: $29.00 installation; $7.35 monthly.
Equipment: Pico headend; Theta-Com amplifiers; Times Fiber cable.
Miles of plant: 2.0 (coaxial).
Manager: M. P. Siegel.
Ownership: North Valley Cable Systems Inc.

WILMINGTON—Duncan Cable TV Service, Box 685, Wilmington, VT 05363. Phone: 802-464-2233. Fax: 802-464-2233. County: Windham. ICA: VT0017.
TV Market Ranking: Below 100. Franchise award date: N.A. Franchise expiration date: N.A. Began: January 1, 1966.
Channel capacity: 40 (2-way capable; operating 2-way). Channels available but not in use: None.
Basic Service
Subscribers: 1,000.
Programming (received off-air): WTEN (A) Albany-Schenectady; WNNE (N) Hartford-Hanover; WVTA (P) Windsor; allband FM.
Programming (via microwave): WBZ-TV (C), WCVB-TV (A), WFXT (F), WGBH-TV (P), WHDH-TV (N) Boston; WLVI-TV (W) Cambridge-Boston.
Programming (via satellite): WSBK-TV (U) Boston; A & E; American Movie Classics; CNBC; CNN; Court TV; Discovery Channel; ESPN; Home & Garden Television; Learning Channel; Lifetime; Nashville Network; Nickelodeon; QVC; Sci-Fi Channel; TBS Superstation; Turner Network TV; VH1.
Current originations: Automated time-weather; public access; educational access; government access; automated emergency alert; local sports.
Fee: $47.50 installation; $22.19 monthly.
Pay Service 1
Pay Units: 190.
Programming (via satellite): HBO.
Fee: $9.95 monthly.
Pay Service 2
Pay Units: 75.
Programming (via satellite): Disney Channel.
Fee: $6.95 monthly.
Local advertising: Yes. Available in character-generated, taped & automated programming.
Equipment: Blonder-Tongue & Jerrold headend; Blonder-Tongue, GTE Sylvania & Texscan amplifiers; Comm/Scope & Times Fiber cable; Info/Soft character generator; Arcom & Intercept traps; Standard Communications satellite receivers.
Miles of plant: 52.0 (coaxial); 12.0 (fiber optic). Additional miles planned: 3.0 (coaxial). Homes passed: 2,100. Total homes in franchised area: 2,600.
Manager: Cliff Duncan.
Franchise fee: None.
Ownership: Clifford Duncan.

***WINDHAM TWP.**—FrontierVision Partners LP, Suite P-200, 1777 S. Harrison St., Denver, CO 80210. Phone: 303-757-1588. Fax: 303-757-6105. County: Windham. ICA: VT0085.
TV Market Ranking: Outside TV Markets. Franchise award date: N.A. Franchise expiration date: N.A. Scheduled to begin: N.A.
Channel capacity: N.A.
Ownership: FrontierVision Partners LP (MSO). See Cable System Ownership.

VIRGINIA

Total Systems: **156**
Total Communities Served: **609**
Franchises Not Yet Operating: **0**
Applications Pending: **0**
Communities with Applications: **0**
Number of Basic Subscribers: **1,837,172**
Number of Expanded Basic Subscribers: **647,710**
Number of Pay Units: **959,779**

Top 100 Markets Represented: Washington, DC (9); Norfolk-Newport News-Portsmouth-Hampton (44); Richmond-Petersburg (63); Roanoke-Lynchburg (70).

**For a list of all cable communities included in this section, see the Cable Community Index located in the back of this volume.
For explanation of terms used in cable system listings, see p. D-9.**

ACCOMAC—Falcon Cable TV, 216 Moore Ave., Suffolk, VA 23434. Phone: 888-874-6100. Counties: Accomack & Northampton. Also serves Accomack County, Bloxom, Cheriton, Eastville, Hallwood, Keller, Melfa, Northampton County (southern portion), Onancock, Onley, Parksley, Saxis, Wachapreague. ICA: VA0158.

TV Market Ranking: 44 (Cheriton, Eastville, portions of Northampton County); Below 100 (portions of Accomack County, Hallwood, portions of Northampton County, Saxis); Outside TV Markets (Accomac, portions of Accomack County, Bloxom, Keller, Melfa, Onancock, Onley, Parksley, Wachapreague). Franchise award date: N.A. Franchise expiration date: N.A. Began: June 5, 1970.

Channel capacity: 37. Channels available but not in use: None.

Basic Service

Subscribers: 5,203.

Programming (received off-air): WHRO-TV (P), WVEC-TV (A) Hampton-Norfolk; WAVY-TV (N), WTKR (C), WTVZ (W) Portsmouth-Norfolk; WBOC-TV (C), WMDT (A) Salisbury; 14 FMs.

Programming (via satellite): American Movie Classics; BET; Bravo; C-SPAN; Comedy Central; E! Entertainment TV; ESPN; Home Team Sports; Lifetime; MTV; QVC; Sci-Fi Channel; The Inspirational Network; Travel Channel; VH1.

Current originations: Public access; educational access; government access; community access.

Fee: $25.00 installation; $22.06 monthly.

Expanded Basic Service

Subscribers: 4,648.

Programming (via satellite): CNN; Nashville Network; Nickelodeon; USA Network.

Fee: $3.99 monthly.

Expanded Basic Service 2

Subscribers: 4,058.

Programming (via satellite): Discovery Channel; Disney Channel; History Channel; TBS Superstation; The Weather Channel; Turner Network TV.

Fee: $7.07 monthly.

Pay Service 1

Pay Units: 413.

Programming (via satellite): Cinemax.

Fee: $25.00 installation; $10.95 monthly.

Pay Service 2

Pay Units: 851.

Programming (via satellite): HBO.

Fee: $25.00 installation; $11.95 monthly.

Pay Service 3

Pay Units: 226.

Programming (via satellite): Showtime.

Fee: $10.95 monthly.

Pay Service 4

Pay Units: 169.

Programming (via satellite): The New Encore.

Fee: N.A.

Local advertising: Yes.

Equipment: Scientific-Atlanta headend; GTE Sylvania & Jerrold amplifiers; Times Fiber cable; Sony VTRs; Scientific-Atlanta character generator; Pioneer set top converters; Scientific-Atlanta satellite antenna.

Miles of plant: 288.0 (coaxial). Homes passed: 8,425.

Manager: Jack Edwards. Chief technician: Mahlon Fritz.

Franchise fee: 3%-5% of gross.

Ownership: Falcon Communications LP (MSO), joint venture formed September 30, 1998. See Cable System Ownership.

ALEXANDRIA—Jones Intercable, 617A S. Pickett St., Alexandria, VA 22304. Phones: 703-751-7710; 703-823-3000. Fax: 703-567-4444. Counties: Alexandria City & Arlington. Also serves Fort Myer Military Base. ICA: VA0009.

TV Market Ranking: 9. Franchise award date: July 26, 1979. Franchise expiration date: June 18, 2009. Began: November 6, 1980.

Channel capacity: 51 (2-way capable; operating 2-way). Channels available but not in use: None.

Basic Service

Subscribers: 38,400; Commercial subscribers: 2,718.

Programming (received off-air): WMPT (P) Annapolis; WTMW (H) Arlington; WNVC (E) Fairfax; WNVT (P) Goldvein; WPXW (X) Manassas; W48AW (I), WBDC-TV (W), WDCA (U), WETA-TV (P), WHUT-TV (P), WJLA-TV (A), WRC-TV (N), WTTG (F), WUSA (C) Washington; allband FM.

Programming (via microwave): NewsChannel 8.

Programming (via satellite): Knowledge TV; Sundance Channel; TBS Superstation; TV Guide Channel.

Current originations: Public access; educational access; government access; leased access; automated emergency alert; local news; local sports.

Fee: $26.74 installation; $10.42 monthly; $1.45 converter.

Commercial fee: $50.00 monthly.

Expanded Basic Service

Subscribers: N.A.

Programming (via satellite): A & E; American Movie Classics; BET; Bravo; C-SPAN; C-SPAN 2; CNBC; CNN; Comedy Central; Court TV; Discovery Channel; ESPN; Fox Family Channel; Headline News; Home Team Sports; Lifetime; MTV; Nashville Network; Nickelodeon; Odyssey; Product Information Network; TV Guide Sneak Prevue; The Weather Channel; Turner Network TV; USA Network; VH1.

Fee: $26.74 installation; $12.91 monthly.

Pay Service 1

Pay Units: 8,088.

Programming (via satellite): Cinemax.

Fee: $10.95 monthly.

Pay Service 2

Pay Units: 5,558.

Programming (via satellite): Disney Channel.

Fee: $7.95 monthly.

Pay Service 3

Pay Units: 12,528.

Programming (via satellite): HBO.

Fee: $10.95 monthly.

Pay Service 4

Pay Units: 4,556.

Programming (via satellite): Showtime.

Fee: $10.95 monthly.

Pay-Per-View

Addressable homes: 22,144.

Action Pay-Per-View; Spice.

Fee: $3.95.

Local advertising: Yes. Available in satellite distributed & automated programming. Rates: $50.00/Minute; $35.00/30 Seconds. Local sales manager: Pat Halty.

Program Guide: The Entertainer.

Equipment: Scientific-Atlanta headend; Jerrold amplifiers; Comm/Scope cable; Hitachi cameras; Sony VTRs; Video Data Systems character generator; Jerrold, Magnavox & Regency set top converters; Scientific-Atlanta addressable set top converters; Scientific-Atlanta satellite antenna; Scientific-Atlanta satellite receivers; ChannelMatic commercial insert.

Miles of plant: 274.0 (coaxial). Homes passed: 62,000. Total homes in franchised area: 62,000.

Manager: Marie Schuler. Chief technician: Tim Dezinney. Program director: Celetta Sanders. Marketing director: Frankie Edwards.

City fee: 3% of gross.

Ownership: Jones Intercable Inc. (MSO).

ALTAVISTA—Adelphia Cablevision, 560 Patton St., Danville, VA 24541-1310. Phone: 804-797-4135. Fax: 804-793-6920. County: Campbell. ICA: VA0068.

TV Market Ranking: 70. Franchise award date: October 9, 1979. Franchise expiration date: N.A. Began: August 22, 1980.

Channel capacity: 35 (not 2-way capable). Channels available but not in use: None.

Basic Service

Subscribers: Included with Danville, VA.

Programming (received off-air): WUPN-TV (U) Greensboro-High Point; WBRA-TV (P) Roanoke; WDBJ (C), WJPR (F), WSET-TV (A), WSLS-TV (N) Roanoke-Lynchburg.

Programming (via satellite): WGN-TV (W) Chicago; Home Shopping Network.

Current originations: Automated time-weather.

Fee: $50.00 installation (aerial), $59.95 (underground); $5.65 monthly; $1.80 converter; $10.00 additional installation.

Expanded Basic Service

Subscribers: N.A.

Programming (via satellite): A & E; American Movie Classics; BET; C-SPAN; CNBC; Country Music TV; ESPN; Fox Family Channel; Home Team Sports; Lifetime; MTV; Nashville Network; Nickelodeon; QVC; The Inspirational Network; The Weather Channel; Travel Channel; Turner Network TV; USA Network; VH1.

Fee: $16.23 monthly.

A la Carte 1

Subscribers: N.A.

Programming (via satellite): CNN; Discovery Channel; TBS Superstation.

Fee: $2.30 monthly (package); $1.25 monthly (each).

Pay Service 1

Pay Units: 97.

Programming (via satellite): Cinemax.

Fee: $10.00 monthly.

Pay Service 2

Pay Units: 53.

Programming (via satellite): Disney Channel.

Fee: $9.95 monthly.

Pay Service 3

Pay Units: 377.

Programming (via satellite): HBO.

Fee: $10.00 monthly.

Pay Service 4

Pay Units: 74.

Programming (via satellite): Showtime.

Fee: $11.95 monthly.

Local advertising: No.

Program Guide: TV Host.

Equipment: Scientific-Atlanta headend; GTE Sylvania & Texscan amplifiers; Times Fiber cable; Oak & Scientific-Atlanta set top converters; Eagle & Pico traps; Scientific-Atlanta & ChannelMaster satellite antenna; DX Antenna & Scientific-Atlanta satellite receivers.

Miles of plant: 80.0 (coaxial). Homes passed: 2,100.

Manager: Ted Crane. Chief technician: Michael Pruitt. Marketing director: Jerry Lesser.

City fee: 3% of gross.

Ownership: Time Warner Cable (MSO).

AMELIA COUNTY (portions)—FrontierVision, Suite P-200, 1777 S. Harrison St., Denver, CO 80210. Phone: 303-757-1588. Fax: 303-757-6105. County: Amelia. ICA: VA0084.

TV Market Ranking: 63 (portions of Amelia County); Outside TV Markets (portions of Amelia County). Franchise award date: December 12, 1988. Franchise expiration date: December 12, 1998. Began: February 1, 1989.

Channel capacity: 62 (not 2-way capable). Channels available but not in use: 25.

Basic Service

Subscribers: 694.

Programming (received off-air): WCVE-TV (P), WRIC-TV (A), WRLH-TV (F), WTVR-TV (C), WWBT (N) Richmond-Petersburg.

Programming (via satellite): WGN-TV (W) Chicago; BET; C-SPAN; CNBC; CNN; Country Music TV; Discovery Channel; ESPN; Fox Family Channel; Headline News; MTV; Nashville Network; Nickelodeon; QVC; The Weather Channel; Trinity Bcstg. Network; Turner Network TV; USA Network.

Fee: $40.00 installation; $14.95 monthly.

Expanded Basic Service

Subscribers: 687.

Programming (via satellite): Disney Channel.

Fee: N.A.

Pay Service 1

Pay Units: 114.

Programming (via satellite): HBO.

Fee: $10.95 monthly.

Pay Service 2

Pay Units: 162.

Programming (via satellite): Showtime.
Fee: $10.95 monthly.
Pay Service 2
Pay Units: 142.
Programming (via satellite): The Movie Channel.
Fee: N.A.
Local advertising: No.
Program Guide: CableView.
Equipment: Magnavox amplifiers; Times Fiber cable; Scientific-Atlanta & Zenith set top converters; Eagle & PPC traps; Comtech & Scientific-Atlanta satellite antenna; Scientific-Atlanta satellite receivers.
Miles of plant: 87.0 (coaxial). Homes passed: 1,488.
Manager: Dan Callahan. Chief technician: Gary Shoemaker.
County fee: 3% of gross.
Ownership: FrontierVision Partners LP (MSO). See Cable System Ownership.

AMHERST COUNTY (southern portion)—Adelphia Cable TV, 324 W. Main St., Charlottesville, VA 22903. Phone: 804-977-7845. Fax: 804-293-9263. County: Amherst. Also serves Amherst. ICA: VA0039.
TV Market Ranking: 70. Franchise award date: January 1, 1968. Franchise expiration date: July 21, 2001. Began: January 1, 1970.
Channel capacity: 34 (not 2-way capable). Channels available but not in use: None.
Basic Service
Subscribers: 4,623.
Programming (received off-air): WCVE-TV (P), WTVR-TV (C), WWBT (N) Richmond-Petersburg; WBRA-TV (P) Roanoke; WDBJ (C), WJPR (F), WSET-TV (A), WSLS-TV (N) Roanoke-Lynchburg; allband FM.
Programming (via satellite): WGN-TV (W) Chicago; QVC; TBS Superstation.
Fee: $50.00 installation; $22.95 monthly; $2.50 converter; $25.00 additional installation.
Expanded Basic Service
Subscribers: 4,564.
Programming (via satellite): A & E; BET; C-SPAN; CNN; Cartoon Network; Discovery Channel; Disney Channel; ESPN; Fox Family Channel; Headline News; Home Shopping Network; Home Team Sports; Lifetime; MTV; Nashville Network; Nickelodeon; The Weather Channel; Turner Network TV; USA Network.
Fee: N.A.
Pay Service 1
Pay Units: 531.
Programming (via satellite): Cinemax.
Fee: $11.50 monthly.
Pay Service 2
Pay Units: 723.
Programming (via satellite): HBO.
Fee: $11.50 monthly.
Pay Service 3
Pay Units: 256.
Programming (via satellite): Showtime.
Fee: $11.50 monthly.
Pay Service 4
Pay Units: 125.
Programming (via satellite): The Movie Channel.
Fee: $11.50 monthly.
Pay-Per-View
Addressable homes: 2,547.
Local advertising: No.
Equipment: Jerrold & Scientific-Atlanta headend; Scientific-Atlanta amplifiers; Comm/Scope cable; SpectraView character generator; Jerrold & Pioneer set top converters; Jerrold addressable set top converters; AFC, Scientific-Atlanta & Superior satellite antenna; Comtech & Scientific-Atlanta satellite receivers.
Miles of plant: 151.7 (coaxial). Homes passed: 7,141.
Manager: Dell Hanley.
City fee: 5% of gross.
Ownership: Adelphia Communications Corp. (MSO).

APPOMATTOX—Nesbe Cable TV, Box 10516, Lynchburg, VA 24506. Phone: 804-352-2554. County: Appomattox. Also serves Pamplin. ICA: VA0088.
TV Market Ranking: 70. Franchise award date: April 12, 1982. Franchise expiration date: N.A. Began: May 1, 1982.
Channel capacity: 18. Channels available but not in use: None.
Basic Service
Subscribers: 705.
Programming (received off-air): WCVE-TV (P) Richmond-Petersburg; WDBJ (C), WFXR-TV (F), WSET-TV (A), WSLS-TV (N) Roanoke-Lynchburg.
Programming (via satellite): WGN-TV (W) Chicago; CNN; ESPN; Fox Family Channel; TBS Superstation.
Fee: $38.50 installation; $16.00 monthly; $2.00 converter.
Expanded Basic Service
Subscribers: N.A.
Programming (via satellite): MTV; Nashville Network; Nickelodeon; The Weather Channel; USA Network.
Fee: $10.00 installation; $2.00 monthly.
Pay Service 1
Pay Units: N.A.
Programming (via satellite): HBO.
Fee: $10.50 monthly.
Equipment: Scientific-Atlanta headend; Scientific-Atlanta amplifiers; Scientific-Atlanta cable; Scientific-Atlanta satellite antenna; Scientific-Atlanta satellite receivers.
Miles of plant: 32.9 (coaxial). Homes passed: 1,113.
Manager: Frank Staley. Chief technician: Ricky Tomlin.
City fee: 5% of gross.
Ownership: Bahakel Communications Ltd. (MSO).

ARLINGTON—Cable TV Arlington, 2707 Wilson Blvd., Arlington, VA 22201. Phone: 703-841-7700. Fax: 703-524-6146.
Web site: http://www.ctva.com.
County: Arlington. ICA: VA0005.
TV Market Ranking: 9. Franchise award date: March 3, 1973. Franchise expiration date: June 30, 2013. Began: July 18, 1978.
Channel capacity: 63 (not 2-way capable). Channels available but not in use: None.
Basic Service
Subscribers: 59,578; Commercial subscribers: 302.
Programming (received off-air): WMPT (P) Annapolis; WTMW (H) Arlington; WNVC (E) Fairfax; WNVT (P) Goldvein; WPXW (X) Manassas; WBDC-TV (W), WDCA (U), WETA-TV (P), WHUT-TV (P), WJLA-TV (A), WRC-TV (N), WTTG (F), WUSA (C) Washington.
Programming (via microwave): NewsChannel 8.
Programming (via satellite): Animal Planet; C-SPAN; Electronic Program Guide; FX; Learning Channel; TBS Superstation.
Current originations: Public access; educational access; government access.
Fee: $23.96 installation; $14.77 monthly; $15.00 additional installation.
Commercial fee: $69.95 monthly.
Expanded Basic Service
Subscribers: N.A.
Programming (via satellite): A & E; American Movie Classics; BET; BET on Jazz; Bravo; C-SPAN 2; CNBC; CNN; Comedy Central; Court TV; Discovery Channel; Disney Channel; E! Entertainment TV; ESPN; ESPN 2; Fox Family Channel; Headline News; History Channel; Home Team Sports; Lifetime; MSNBC; MTV; Nashville Network; Nickelodeon; QVC; Sci-Fi Channel; Telemundo; The Weather Channel; Turner Classic Movies; Turner Network TV; USA Network; Univision; VH1.
Fee: $21.37 monthly.
Pay Service 1
Pay Units: 5,308.
Programming (via satellite): Cinemax.
Fee: $15.00 installation; $10.95 monthly.
Pay Service 2
Pay Units: 11,560.
Programming (via satellite): The Movie Channel.
Fee: $15.00 installation; $10.95 monthly.
Pay Service 3
Pay Units: 15,537.
Programming (via satellite): HBO.
Fee: $15.00 installation; $10.95 monthly.
Pay Service 4
Pay Units: 4,152.
Programming (via satellite): Showtime.
Fee: $15.00 installation; $10.95 monthly.
Pay-Per-View
Addressable homes: 11,613.
Spice; movies.
Fee: $6.99.
Local advertising: Yes. Available in satellite distributed programming. Local sales manager: Charlie Phillips.
Equipment: Scientific-Atlanta headend; Scientific-Atlanta amplifiers; Comm/Scope & Scientific-Atlanta cable; Sony cameras; Sony VTRs; MSI character generator; Jerrold & Pioneer set top converters; Jerrold addressable set top converters; Eagle traps; Scientific-Atlanta satellite antenna; Scientific-Atlanta satellite receivers; ChannelMatic commercial insert.
Miles of plant: 450.0 (coaxial); 5.0 (fiber optic). Additional miles planned: 5.0 (coaxial). Homes passed: 89,968. Total homes in franchised area: 89,968.
Manager: William Hysell. Chief technician: Frank Cruise. Marketing & program director: Don Murphy.
County fee: 4% of gross.
Ownership: Prime Cable (MSO). Purchased from SBC Media Ventures, July 1, 1998. See Cable System Ownership.

BASTIAN—Cooney Cable Assoc. Inc., 228 Park Ave., Worcester, MA 01609. Phone: 508-754-5865. Fax: 508-752-7342. County: Bland. Also serves Bland County. ICA: VA0124.
TV Market Ranking: Below 100. Franchise award date: N.A. Franchise expiration date: January 1, 2003. Began: January 1, 1983.
Channel capacity: 12. Channels available but not in use: None.
Basic Service
Subscribers: N.A.
Programming (received off-air): WVVA (N) Bluefield; WXII (N) Greensboro-High Point; WJHL-TV (C) Johnson City; WKPT-TV (A) Kingsport; WOAY-TV (A) Oak Hill-Beckley; WBRA-TV (P) Roanoke; WDBJ (C), WSET-TV (A), WSLS-TV (N) Roanoke-Lynchburg.
Fee: $25.00 installation; $10.00 monthly.
Expanded Basic Service
Subscribers: N.A.
Programming (via satellite): WGN-TV (W) Chicago; ESPN; TBS Superstation.
Fee: $25.00 installation; $10.00 monthly.
Pay Service 1
Pay Units: N.A.
Programming (via satellite): The Movie Channel.
Fee: $10.00 monthly.
Equipment: Blonder-Tongue headend; Kaiser amplifiers; M/A-Com cable; Vitek traps; Microdyne satellite receivers.
Miles of plant: 7.0 (coaxial). Additional miles planned: 3.0 (coaxial).
Ownership: Cooney Cable Assoc. Inc. (MSO).

BEDFORD—Cablevision Communications, Box 1212, Bedford, VA 24523. Phone: 540-586-5310. Fax: 540-586-1847. County: Bedford. Plans service to Bedford County. ICA: VA0048.
TV Market Ranking: 70. Franchise award date: N.A. Franchise expiration date: N.A. Began: June 1, 1981.
Channel capacity: 77 (2-way capable; not operating 2-way). Channels available but not in use: 40.
Basic Service
Subscribers: 2,143.
Programming (received off-air): WBRA-TV (P), WPXR (X) Roanoke; WDBJ (C), WJPR (F), WSET-TV (A), WSLS-TV (N) Roanoke-Lynchburg.
Programming (via satellite): WGN-TV (W) Chicago; C-SPAN; C-SPAN 2; TBS Superstation; USA Network.
Current originations: Local news.
Fee: $64.43 installation; $7.91 monthly; $15.00 additional installation.
Expanded Basic Service
Subscribers: N.A.
Programming (via satellite): A & E; American Movie Classics; BET; CNN; Comedy Central; Discovery Channel; ESPN; Fox Family Channel; Headline News; Learning Channel; Lifetime; MTV; Nashville Network; Nickelodeon; The Weather Channel; Turner Network TV.
Fee: $13.35 monthly.
Pay Service 1
Pay Units: 230.
Programming (via satellite): Cinemax.
Fee: $11.72 installation; $10.95 monthly.
Pay Service 2
Pay Units: 410.
Programming (via satellite): Disney Channel.
Fee: $11.72 installation; $8.95 monthly.
Pay Service 3
Pay Units: 657.
Programming (via satellite): HBO.
Fee: $11.72 installation; $10.95 monthly.
Pay Service 4
Pay Units: 363.
Programming (via satellite): Showtime.
Fee: $11.72 installation; $8.95 monthly.
Pay Service 5
Pay Units: 182.
Programming (via satellite): The Movie Channel.
Fee: $8.95 monthly.
Equipment: Scientific-Atlanta headend; Scientific-Atlanta amplifiers; Times Fiber cable; Scientific-Atlanta set top converters; Scientific-Atlanta satellite antenna; Scientific-Atlanta satellite receivers.
Miles of plant: 84.0 (coaxial); 26.0 (fiber optic). Homes passed: 4,351. Total homes in franchised area: 5,044.
Manager: Dave Burke. Chief technician: Tom Moyer.
City fee: 3% of gross.
Ownership: Rifkin & Associates Inc. (MSO). See Cable System Ownership.

BEDFORD COUNTY (southwestern portion)—Blue Ridge Cablecomm, Box 627, 5234 Lee Hwy., Troutville, VA 24175. Phone: 540-992-4144. Fax: 540-996-3102. County: Bedford. Also serves Smith Mountain Lake. ICA: VA0174.

TV Market Ranking: 70. Franchise award date: August 15, 1991. Franchise expiration date: August 14, 2001. Began: August 15, 1991.

Channel capacity: 35 (not 2-way capable). Channels available but not in use: 13.

Basic Service

Subscribers: 1,270; Commercial subscribers: 15.

Programming (received off-air): WBRA-TV (P), WPXR (X) Roanoke; WDBJ (C), WJPR (F), WSET-TV (A), WSLS-TV (N) Roanoke-Lynchburg.

Programming (via satellite): WGN-TV (W) Chicago; QVC; Sci-Fi Channel; TBS Superstation.

Fee: $24.95 installation (aerial), $34.95 (underground); $12.29 monthly; $1.25 converter.

Commercial fee: $9.57 monthly.

Expanded Basic Service

Subscribers: 1,200.

Programming (via satellite): A & E; American Movie Classics; C-SPAN; CNBC; CNN; Discovery Channel; ESPN; Fox Family Channel; Learning Channel; Lifetime; MTV; Nashville Network; Nickelodeon; The Weather Channel; Turner Network TV; USA Network.

Fee: $17.41 monthly.

Pay Service 1

Pay Units: 144.

Programming (via satellite): Cinemax.

Fee: $11.50 monthly.

Pay Service 2

Pay Units: 75.

Programming (via satellite): Disney Channel.

Fee: $8.95 monthly.

Pay Service 3

Pay Units: 201.

Programming (via satellite): HBO.

Fee: $11.50 monthly.

Pay Service 4

Pay Units: 112.

Programming (via satellite): Showtime; The Movie Channel.

Fee: $11.50 monthly (each).

Local advertising: Yes.

Equipment: Blonder-Tongue & Jerrold headend; Texscan & Magnavox amplifiers; Hamlin, Scientific-Atlanta & Pioneer set top converters; Eagle, Regal & RMS traps; Prodelin satellite antenna; M/A-Com & Scientific-Atlanta satellite receivers.

Miles of plant: 79.0 (coaxial); 16.0 (fiber optic). Homes passed: 2,353.

System manager: John Banlew. Manager: Ron Carruth. Chief technician: John Kalafut. Marketing director: Ron Cassell.

Franchise fee: 3% of basic.

Ownership: Fanch Communications Inc. (MSO). See Cable System Ownership.

BELLE HAVEN—Falcon Cable TV, 216 Moore Ave., Suffolk, VA 23434. Phone: 804-539-2312. Counties: Accomack & Northampton. Also serves Exmore, Nassawodox, Northampton County, Painter. ICA: VA0046.

TV Market Ranking: 44 (portions of Northampton County); Below 100 (portions of Northampton County); Outside TV Markets (Belle Haven, Exmore, Nassawodox, portions of Northampton County, Painter). Franchise award date: N.A. Franchise expiration date: N.A. Began: September 28, 1981.

Channel capacity: 37. Channels available but not in use: None.

Basic Service

Subscribers: 1,576.

Programming (received off-air): WHRO-TV (P), WVEC-TV (A) Hampton-Norfolk; WAVY-TV (N), WTKR (C), WTVZ (W) Portsmouth-Norfolk; WBOC-TV (C), WMDT (A) Salisbury; 14 FMs.

Programming (via satellite): American Movie Classics; BET; Bravo; C-SPAN; Comedy Central; E! Entertainment TV; ESPN; Home Team Sports; Lifetime; MTV; QVC; Sci-Fi Channel; The Inspirational Network; Travel Channel; VH1.

Fee: $15.00 installation; $22.30 monthly.

Expanded Basic Service

Subscribers: 1,388.

Programming (via satellite): CNN; Nashville Network; Nickelodeon; USA Network.

Fee: $3.46 monthly.

Expanded Basic Service 2

Subscribers: 1,214.

Programming (via satellite): Discovery Channel; Disney Channel; History Channel; TBS Superstation; The Weather Channel; Turner Network TV.

Fee: $7.01 monthly.

Pay Service 1

Pay Units: 131.

Programming (via satellite): Cinemax.

Fee: $10.95 monthly.

Pay Service 2

Pay Units: 328.

Programming (via satellite): HBO.

Fee: $11.95 monthly.

Pay Service 3

Pay Units: 65.

Programming (via satellite): Showtime.

Fee: $10.95 monthly.

Pay Service 4

Pay Units: N.A.

Programming (via satellite): The New Encore.

Fee: N.A.

Miles of plant: 60.0 (coaxial). Homes passed: 2,201.

Manager: Jack Edwards. Chief technician: Mahlon Fritz.

Franchise fee: 3%-5% of gross.

Ownership: Falcon Communications LP (MSO), joint venture formed September 30, 1998. See Cable System Ownership.

BEN HUR—Century Virginia Corp., Box 1300, 838 Park Ave. NE, Norton, VA 24273. Phone: 540-523-3522. County: Lee. Also serves Lee County (portions), Poor Valley. ICA: VA0123.

TV Market Ranking: Below 100. Franchise award date: N.A. Franchise expiration date: N.A. Began: January 1, 1984.

Channel capacity: N.A. Channels available but not in use: N.A.

Basic Service

Subscribers: N.A.

Programming (received off-air): WCYB-TV (N) Bristol-Kingsport; WJHL-TV (C) Johnson City; WKPT-TV (A) Kingsport; WBIR-TV (N) Knoxville; WSJK (P) Sneedville.

Programming (via satellite): WGN-TV (W) Chicago.

Fee: N.A.

Miles of plant: 15.0 (coaxial).

Manager: John Taylor.

Ownership: Century Communications Corp. (MSO). See Cable System Ownership.

BIRCHLEAF—Cooney Cable Assoc. of Bastian LP, Box 69, Delbarton, WV 25670. Phones: 304-426-4609; 800-682-9455. Fax: 304-426-6726. County: Dickenson. Also serves Haysi (unincorporated areas). ICA: VA0184.

TV Market Ranking: Outside TV Markets. Franchise award date: N.A. Franchise expiration date: N.A. Began: N.A.

Channel capacity: N.A. Channels available but not in use: N.A.

Basic Service

Subscribers: 357.

Programming (received off-air): WCYB-TV (N) Bristol-Kingsport; WEMT (F) Greeneville; WLFG (I) Grundy; WJHL-TV (C) Johnson City; WKPT-TV (A) Kingsport; WSBN-TV (P) Norton.

Programming (via satellite): WGN-TV (W) Chicago; American Movie Classics; C-SPAN; CNN; Country Music TV; Discovery Channel; E! Entertainment TV; ESPN; ESPN 2; Fox Family Channel; Headline News; History Channel; Home Team Sports; Learning Channel; Lifetime; Nashville Network; Nickelodeon; Outdoor Channel; QVC; Sci-Fi Channel; TBS Superstation; The Weather Channel; Travel Channel; Trinity Bcstg. Network; Turner Network TV; USA Network.

Fee: N.A.

Pay Service 1

Pay Units: 21.

Programming (via satellite): Disney Channel.

Fee: N.A.

Pay Service 2

Pay Units: 14.

Programming (via satellite): HBO.

Fee: N.A.

Pay Service 3

Pay Units: 18.

Programming (via satellite): Showtime.

Fee: N.A.

Pay Service 4

Pay Units: 24.

Programming (via satellite): The Movie Channel.

Fee: N.A.

Homes passed: 475.

Manager: John B. Cooney. Chief technician: Greg Goad.

Ownership: Cooney Cable Assoc. Inc. (MSO).

BISHOP—Bishop TV Club Inc., Box 99, Bishop, VA 24604. Phone: 540-988-5907. County: Tazewell. Also serves Crocketts Cove. ICA: VA0118.

TV Market Ranking: Below 100. Franchise award date: May 1, 1982. Franchise expiration date: N.A. Began: May 1, 1982.

Channel capacity: 12 (not 2-way capable). Channels available but not in use: N.A.

Basic Service

Subscribers: 170.

Programming (received off-air): WVVA (N) Bluefield; WCYB-TV (N) Bristol-Kingsport; WCHS-TV (A), WOWK-TV (C), WVAH-TV (F,U) Charleston-Huntington; WSWP-TV (P) Grandview; WOAY-TV (A) Oak Hill-Beckley.

Programming (via satellite): ESPN; FX; Fox Family Channel; Nashville Network; TBS Superstation.

Fee: $10.00 monthly.

Pay Service 1

Pay Units: 55.

Programming (via satellite): HBO.

Fee: $10.00 installation; $6.00 monthly.

Miles of plant: 5.0 (coaxial). Homes passed: 211. Total homes in franchised area: 211.

Manager: H. L. Bowling Jr.

Ownership: Bishop TV Club Inc.

BLACKSBURG—Adelphia Cable, 1401 S. Main St., Blacksburg, VA 24060. Phone: 540-552-3341. Fax: 540-552-2416. County: Montgomery. Also serves Alleghany Springs, Christiansburg, Elliston, Lafayette, Montgomery County, Shawsville. ICA: VA0020.

TV Market Ranking: 70. Franchise award date: December 1, 1964. Franchise expiration date: December 1, 2009. Began: July 1, 1970.

Channel capacity: 62 (2-way capable; operating 2-way). Channels available but not in use: 6.

Basic Service

Subscribers: 13,205.

Programming (received off-air): WDRL-TV (U) Danville; WBRA-TV (P), WPXR (X) Roanoke; WDBJ (C), WFXR-TV (F), WSET-TV (A), WSLS-TV (N) Roanoke-Lynchburg; allband FM.

Programming (via satellite): WGN-TV (W) Chicago; C-SPAN; Home Shopping Network; QVC; TBS Superstation.

Current originations: Automated time-weather; public access.

Fee: $31.45 installation; $9.79 monthly; $29.92 additional installation.

Expanded Basic Service

Subscribers: 12,188.

Programming (via satellite): A & E; American Movie Classics; BET; Bravo; CNBC; CNN; Comedy Central; Country Music TV; Discovery Channel; ESPN; ESPN 2; FX; Fox Family Channel; Headline News; History Channel; Home Team Sports; International Channel; Learning Channel; Lifetime; MTV; Nashville Network; Nickelodeon; Sci-Fi Channel; TV Guide Sneak Prevue; The Weather Channel; Travel Channel; Turner Classic Movies; Turner Network TV; USA Network; VH1.

Fee: $31.12 monthly.

Pay Service 1

Pay Units: 632.

Programming (via satellite): Cinemax.

Fee: $10.50 monthly.

Pay Service 2

Pay Units: 390.

Programming (via satellite): Disney Channel.

Fee: $8.25 monthly.

Pay Service 3

Pay Units: 2,626.

Programming (via satellite): HBO (multiplexed).

Fee: $10.50 monthly.

Pay Service 4

Pay Units: 500.

Programming (via satellite): Showtime.

Fee: $10.50 monthly.

Pay Service 5

Pay Units: 435.

Programming (via satellite): The Movie Channel.

Fee: N.A.

Pay Service 6

Pay Units: N.A.

Programming (via satellite): Independent Film Channel.

Fee: $8.25 monthly.

Pay-Per-View

Addressable homes: 3,407.

Action Pay-Per-View; Playboy TV; Spice; Viewer's Choice 5 & 9.

Local advertising: No.

Equipment: Scientific-Atlanta headend; Magnavox amplifiers; Comm/Scope cable; BEI character generator; Pioneer addressable set top converters; Scientific-Atlanta satellite antenna; Scientific-Atlanta satellite receivers.

Miles of plant: 335.0 (coaxial). Homes passed: 18,411. Total homes in franchised area: 19,968.

Manager: Lon Carruth. Chief technician: Chip Schrader.

City fee: 5% of gross.

Ownership: Adelphia Communications Corp. (MSO).

BLACKSTONE—Nesbe Cable TV, Box 10516, Lynchburg, VA 24506. Phone: 804-821-7110. County: Nottoway. ICA: VA0081.

TV Market Ranking: 63. Franchise award date: March 1, 1982. Franchise expiration date: N.A. Began: April 1, 1982.
Channel capacity: 20. Channels available but not in use: None.

Basic Service
Subscribers: 791.
Programming (received off-air): WVIR-TV (N) Charlottesville; WGNT (U) Portsmouth-Norfolk; WCVE-TV (P), WRIC-TV (A), WRLH-TV (F), WTVR-TV (C), WWBT (N) Richmond-Petersburg.
Programming (via satellite): WGN-TV (W) Chicago; CNN; ESPN; Nashville Network; TBS Superstation.
Fee: $38.50 installation; $16.00 monthly.

Pay Service 1
Pay Units: N.A.
Programming (via satellite): Disney Channel; HBO.
Fee: $7.50 monthly (Disney), $10.50 monthly (HBO).

Equipment: Scientific-Atlanta headend; Theta-Com amplifiers; Comm/Scope cable; Pico traps; Scientific-Atlanta satellite antenna; Scientific-Atlanta satellite receivers.
Miles of plant: 25.0 (coaxial). Homes passed: 1,500.
Manager: Frank Staley. Chief technician: Ricky Tomlin.
City fee: 5% of gross.
Ownership: Bahakel Communications Ltd. (MSO).

BOWLING GREEN—Tri-State Cablecomm, Box 789, 112 N. Main St., Bowling Green, VA 22427. Phones: 804-633-9511; 800-489-7070. Fax: 804-633-7329. County: Caroline. Also serves Caroline County. ICA: VA0093.
TV Market Ranking: 63 (Bowling Green, portions of Caroline County); Below 100 (portions of Caroline County). Franchise award date: February 3, 1972. Franchise expiration date: September 3, 2007. Began: January 1, 1973.
Channel capacity: 35 (not 2-way capable). Channels available but not in use: 3.

Basic Service
Subscribers: 961; Commercial subscribers: 6.
Programming (received off-air): WUPV (U) Ashland; WCVE-TV (P), WCVW (P), WRIC-TV (A), WRLH-TV (F), WTVR-TV (C), WWBT (N) Richmond-Petersburg; WDCA (U), WUSA (C) Washington; allband FM.
Programming (via satellite): WGN-TV (W) Chicago; QVC; TBS Superstation.
Current originations: Public access.
Fee: $35.64 installation; $20.10 monthly; $0.75 converter.
Commercial fee: $14.40 monthly.

Expanded Basic Service
Subscribers: 917.
Programming (via satellite): A & E; Animal Planet; BET; CNN; Discovery Channel; ESPN; ESPN 2; Fox Family Channel; Home Team Sports; Learning Channel; Lifetime; MTV; Nashville Network; Nickelodeon; Sci-Fi Channel; The Weather Channel; Turner Network TV; USA Network.
Fee: $13.95 monthly.

Pay Service 1
Pay Units: 32.
Programming (via satellite): Cinemax.
Fee: $11.50 monthly.

Pay Service 2
Pay Units: 116.
Programming (via satellite): Disney Channel.
Fee: $8.95 monthly.

Pay Service 3
Pay Units: 75.
Programming (via satellite): HBO.
Fee: $11.50 monthly.

Local advertising: Planned.
Equipment: Blonder-Tongue headend; Magnavox amplifiers; Times Fiber cable; Scientific-Atlanta set top converters; Eagle traps; AFC satellite antenna; M/A-Com satellite receivers.
Miles of plant: 49.0 (coaxial). Homes passed: 1,415. Total homes in franchised area: 3,502.
Manager: Thomas A. Olsen. Chief technician: Alfred Trigger. Marketing director: Trish Lindsey.
City fee: 4% of gross plus $500.00 annually.
Ownership: Fanch Communications Inc. (MSO); Time Warner Cable (MSO). See Cable System Ownership.

BRISTOL—FrontierVision, Suite P-200, 1777 S. Harrison St., Denver, CO 80210. Phone: 303-757-1588. Fax: 303-757-6105. Counties: Washington, VA; Sullivan, TN. Also serves Sullivan County (northern portion), TN; Abingdon (portions), Burson Place, VA. ICA: VA0071.
TV Market Ranking: Below 100. Franchise award date: N.A. Franchise expiration date: N.A. Began: N.A.
Channel capacity: 42 (not 2-way capable). Channels available but not in use: 12.

Basic Service
Subscribers: 1,515.
Programming (received off-air): WCYB-TV (N) Bristol-Kingsport; WEMT (F) Greeneville; WJHL-TV (C) Johnson City; WKPT-TV (A) Kingsport; WSBN-TV (P) Norton; WSJK (P) Sneedville.
Programming (via satellite): WGN-TV (W) Chicago; A & E; C-SPAN; CNBC; CNN; Country Music TV; Discovery Channel; ESPN; Fox Family Channel; Headline News; Home Shopping Network; Lifetime; MTV; Nashville Network; Nickelodeon; TBS Superstation; The Inspirational Network; Turner Network TV; USA Network; VH1.
Current originations: Public access; government access.
Fee: $40.00 installation; $17.95 monthly; $3.00 converter.

Pay Service 1
Pay Units: 202.
Programming (via satellite): Cinemax.
Fee: $15.00 installation; $10.95 monthly.

Pay Service 2
Pay Units: 221.
Programming (via satellite): HBO.
Fee: $10.95 monthly.

Equipment: Magnavox amplifiers; Comm/Scope cable; Scientific-Atlanta set top converters; Eagle & PPC traps; Scientific-Atlanta satellite antenna; Microdyne satellite receivers.
Miles of plant: 68.0 (coaxial). Homes passed: 1,864. Total homes in franchised area: 1,864.
President & chief executive officer: James Vaugh. Vice president: David Heyrend. Executive vice president: John Koo.
Ownership: FrontierVision Partners LP (MSO). See Cable System Ownership.

BROOKNEAL—Adelphia Cable, 560 Patton St., Danville, VA 24541-1310. Phones: 804-797-4135; 800-223-2734. Fax: 804-793-6920. County: Campbell. ICA: VA0125.
TV Market Ranking: 70. Franchise award date: May 17, 1983. Franchise expiration date: May 17, 2003. Began: N.A.
Channel capacity: 35 (not 2-way capable). Channels available but not in use: 1.

Basic Service
Subscribers: Included with Danville, VA.
Programming (received off-air): WBRA-TV (P) Roanoke; WDBJ (C), WJPR (F), WSET-TV (A), WSLS-TV (N) Roanoke-Lynchburg.
Programming (via satellite): WGN-TV (W) Chicago; BET; QVC.
Fee: $50.00 installation (aerial), $59.95 (underground); $5.55 monthly; $1.80 converter; $10.00 additional installation.

Expanded Basic Service
Subscribers: N.A.
Programming (via satellite): A & E; American Movie Classics; CNBC; Comedy Central; Country Music TV; ESPN; Fox Family Channel; Headline News; Home Team Sports; Lifetime; MTV; Nashville Network; Nickelodeon; The Inspirational Network; The Weather Channel; Travel Channel; Turner Network TV; USA Network; VH1.
Fee: $16.05 monthly.

A la Carte 1
Subscribers: N.A.
Programming (via satellite): CNN; Discovery Channel; TBS Superstation.
Fee: $2.30 monthly (package); $1.25 monthly (each).

Pay Service 1
Pay Units: 75.
Programming (via satellite): Cinemax.
Fee: $10.00 monthly.

Pay Service 2
Pay Units: 29.
Programming (via satellite): Disney Channel.
Fee: $9.95 monthly.

Pay Service 3
Pay Units: 199.
Programming (via satellite): HBO.
Fee: $10.00 monthly.

Pay Service 4
Pay Units: 61.
Programming (via satellite): Showtime.
Fee: $11.95 monthly.

Local advertising: No.
Program Guide: TV Host.
Equipment: Scientific-Atlanta headend; GTE Sylvania amplifiers; Times Fiber cable; Oak & Scientific-Atlanta set top converters; Eagle & Pico traps; ChannelMaster & Scientific-Atlanta satellite antenna; DX Antenna & Scientific-Atlanta satellite receivers.
Miles of plant: 14.0 (coaxial). Homes passed: 551.
Manager: Ted Crane. Chief technician: Michael Pruitt. Marketing director: Jerry Lesser.
Franchise fee: 3%.
Ownership: Adelphia Communications Corp. (MSO).

BROSVILLE—Chatmoss Cablevision, 12349 Martinsville Hwy., Danville, VA 24541. Phone: 804-685-1521. Fax: 804-685-1803. E-mail: chatmoss@ns.gamewood.net. County: Pittsylvania. Also serves Bachelor's Hall, Cascade, Dry Fork, Tunstall (Pittsylvania County), Vandola, Whitmell. ICA: VA0075.
TV Market Ranking: Below 100 (Bachelor's Hall, Brosville, Dry Fork, Tunstall, Whitmell); Outside TV Markets (Cascade, Vandola). Franchise award date: February 6, 1989. Franchise expiration date: February 6, 2004. Began: July 1, 1989.
Channel capacity: 61 (2-way capable; operating 2-way partially). Channels available but not in use: 8.

Basic Service
Subscribers: 1,666.
Programming (received off-air): WDRL-TV (U) Danville; WFMY-TV (C), WGHP (F), WXII (N) Greensboro-High Point; WSSV-LP (I) Martinsville; WXIV-LP (I) Reidsville; WBRA-TV (P), WPXR (X) Roanoke; WDBJ (C), WFXR-TV (F), WSET-TV (A), WSLS-TV (N) Roanoke-Lynchburg; WVFT (I) Rock Hill; WUNL-TV (P), WXLV-TV (A) Winston-Salem; 24 FMs.
Programming (via satellite): WGN-TV (W) Chicago; A & E; American Movie Classics; BET; C-SPAN; CNBC; CNN; Cartoon Network; Comedy Central; Country Music TV; Discovery Channel; ESPN; ESPN 2; Electronic Program Guide; Fox Family Channel; Goodlife TV Network; Headline News; Home Shopping Network; Home Team Sports; Learning Channel; Lifetime; MTV; Nashville Network; Nick at Nite; Nickelodeon; QVC; Sci-Fi Channel; TBS Superstation; The Weather Channel; Trinity Bcstg. Network; Turner Network TV; USA Network; VH1.
Current originations: Public access; automated emergency alert; local news.
Fee: Free installation; $21.00 monthly; $2.50 converter.

Pay Service 1
Pay Units: 161.
Programming (via satellite): Cinemax.
Fee: $8.95 monthly.

Pay Service 2
Pay Units: 148.
Programming (via satellite): Disney Channel.
Fee: $7.95 monthly.

Pay Service 3
Pay Units: 344.
Programming (via satellite): HBO.
Fee: $9.95 monthly.

Pay Service 4
Pay Units: 122.
Programming (via satellite): Showtime.
Fee: $8.95 monthly.

Pay-Per-View
Addressable homes: 1,425.

Local advertising: No.
Equipment: Philips amplifiers; Comm/Scope cable; Comm/Scope fiber optic cable; Jerrold set top converters; Jerrold addressable set top converters; Arcom traps; Scientific-Atlanta satellite antenna; Scientific-Atlanta satellite receivers.
Miles of plant: 130.0 (coaxial); 20.0 (fiber optic). Homes passed: 2,200. Total homes in franchised area: 2,400.
Manager: Charles F. Lewis. Chief technician: Frankie Betterton. Customer service manager: Ida S. Lewis.
Franchise fee: 5% of gross.
Ownership: John P. Shoemaker Jr.

BUCHANAN—Buchanan CableVision, Box 1212, Bedford, VA 24523-2033. Phones: 540-586-5310; 800-564-8079. Fax: 540-586-1847. County: Botetourt. ICA: VA0126.
TV Market Ranking: 70. Franchise award date: N.A. Franchise expiration date: N.A. Began: N.A.
Channel capacity: 37 (not 2-way capable). Channels available but not in use: 17.

Basic Service
Subscribers: 383.
Programming (received off-air): WBRA-TV (P), WPXR (X) Roanoke; WDBJ (C), WFXR-TV (F), WSET-TV (A), WSLS-TV (N) Roanoke-Lynchburg.
Programming (via satellite): WGN-TV (W) Chicago; American Movie Classics; CNN; Country Music TV; Discovery Channel; ESPN; Fox Family Channel; Nashville Network; TBS Superstation; Turner Network TV; USA Network.
Fee: $66.43 installation; $17.71 monthly.

Pay Service 1
Pay Units: N.A.
Programming (via satellite): HBO; Showtime.
Fee: $10.95 monthly (Showtime), $11.95 monthly (HBO).

Miles of plant: 14.1 (coaxial). Homes passed: 562. Total homes in franchised area: 562.
Manager: Dave Burke. Chief technician: Tom Moyer. Marketing director: Hal Schlenger.

Ownership: Rifkin & Associates Inc. (MSO). See Cable System Ownership.

BUENA VISTA—Adelphia Cable Communications, 2154 Sycamore Ave., Buena Vista, VA 24416. Phone: 800-835-4949. Fax: 540-261-7616. County: Rockbridge. Also serves Rockbridge County. ICA: VA0127.

TV Market Ranking: 70 (Buena Vista, portions of Rockbridge County); Outside TV Markets (portions of Rockbridge County). Franchise award date: N.A. Franchise expiration date: N.A. Began: December 1, 1968.

Channel capacity: 54 (not 2-way capable). Channels available but not in use: 25.

Basic Service

Subscribers: Included with Lexington, VA.

Programming (received off-air): WBRA-TV (P), WPXR (X) Roanoke; WDBJ (C), WJPR (F), WSET-TV (A), WSLS-TV (N) Roanoke-Lynchburg; WVPT (P) Staunton.

Programming (via satellite): C-SPAN; CNBC; TBS Superstation.

Current originations: Public access.

Fee: $33.00 installation; $24.95 monthly.

Expanded Basic Service

Subscribers: N.A.

Programming (via satellite): A & E; American Movie Classics; CNN; Country Music TV; Discovery Channel; ESPN; FX; Fox Family Channel; Headline News; Home Team Sports; Lifetime; MSNBC; MTV; Nashville Network; Nickelodeon; The Weather Channel; Turner Network TV; USA Network.

Fee: N.A.

Pay Service 1

Pay Units: 329.

Programming (via satellite): Cinemax.

Fee: $25.00 installation; $11.00 monthly.

Pay Service 2

Pay Units: 132.

Programming (via satellite): Disney Channel.

Fee: $25.00 installation; $8.50 monthly.

Pay Service 3

Pay Units: 719.

Programming (via satellite): HBO.

Fee: $25.00 installation; $11.00 monthly.

Pay Service 4

Pay Units: N.A.

Programming (via satellite): Showtime.

Fee: N.A.

Local advertising: No.

Equipment: Scientific-Atlanta headend; Jerrold & Magnavox amplifiers; Comm/Scope cable; Microtek character generator; Scientific-Atlanta set top converters; Eagle & Gamco traps; Microdyne, Prodelin & Scientific-Atlanta satellite antenna; Scientific-Atlanta satellite receivers.

Miles of plant & homes passed included with Lexington, VA.

Manager: Gary N. Judy. Chief technician: Joe Clements.

City fee: 5% of gross.

Ownership: Adelphia Communications Corp. (MSO).

CALLAGHAN—Callaghan Cable TV, Box 247, HC37, Lewisburg, WV 24901. Phone: 304-645-1397. County: Alleghany. Also serves Johnson Creek. ICA: VA0120.

TV Market Ranking: Below 100. Franchise award date: N.A. Franchise expiration date: N.A. Began: July 1, 1974.

Channel capacity: 12. Channels available but not in use: N.A.

Basic Service

Subscribers: 602.

Programming (received off-air): WVVA (N) Bluefield; WSWP-TV (P) Grandview; WDBJ (C), WSET-TV (A), WSLS-TV (N) Roanoke-Lynchburg.

Programming (via satellite): CNN; Headline News; TBS Superstation; Turner Network TV.

Fee: $50.00 installation; $6.70 monthly.

Miles of plant: 5.0 (coaxial).

Manager: Chip James.

Ownership: Clearview Cable TV Inc. (MSO).

CHARLES CITY COUNTY (portions)—FrontierVision, Suite P-200, 1777 S. Harrison St., Denver, CO 80210. Phone: 303-757-1588. Fax: 303-757-6105. County: Charles City. ICA: VA0078.

TV Market Ranking: 63. Franchise award date: November 28, 1988. Franchise expiration date: November 28, 2003. Began: November 1, 1989.

Channel capacity: 62 (not 2-way capable). Channels available but not in use: 18.

Basic Service

Subscribers: 1,154.

Programming (received off-air): WVEC-TV (A) Hampton-Norfolk; WAVY-TV (N), WTKR (C) Portsmouth-Norfolk; WCVE-TV (P), WRIC-TV (A), WRLH-TV (F), WTVR-TV (C), WWBT (N) Richmond-Petersburg.

Programming (via satellite): A & E; BET; C-SPAN; C-SPAN 2; CNBC; CNN; Country Music TV; Discovery Channel; Disney Channel; ESPN; Fox Family Channel; Headline News; Learning Channel; Lifetime; MTV; Nashville Network; Nickelodeon; QVC; TBS Superstation; The Weather Channel; USA Network; VH1.

Current originations: Automated time-weather.

Fee: $40.00 installation; $16.95 monthly; $2.00 converter.

Pay Service 1

Pay Units: 399.

Programming (via satellite): HBO.

Fee: $10.95 monthly.

Pay Service 2

Pay Units: 379.

Programming (via satellite): Showtime.

Fee: $10.95 monthly.

Pay Service 3

Pay Units: 61.

Programming (via satellite): Cinemax.

Fee: N.A.

Pay Service 4

Pay Units: 373.

Programming (via satellite): The Movie Channel.

Fee: N.A.

Local advertising: No.

Program Guide: CableView.

Equipment: Magnavox amplifiers; Times Fiber & Trilogy cable; Scientific-Atlanta & Zenith set top converters; Eagle & PPC traps; Comtech satellite antenna; Scientific-Atlanta satellite receivers.

Miles of plant: 130.0 (coaxial). Homes passed: 1,938.

President & chief executive officer: James Vaugh. Vice president: David Heyrend. Executive vice president: John Koo.

County fee: 3% of gross.

Ownership: FrontierVision Partners LP (MSO). See Cable System Ownership.

CHARLOTTESVILLE—Multi-Channel TV Cable Co., 324 W. Main St., Charlottesville, VA 22901. Phone: 800-835-4949. Fax: 804-293-9263. County: Albemarle. Also serves Albemarle County, Lake Monticello. ICA: VA0131.

TV Market Ranking: Below 100. Franchise award date: January 1, 1963. Franchise expiration date: N.A. Began: February 1, 1963.

Channel capacity: 59 (not 2-way capable). Channels available but not in use: None.

Basic Service

Subscribers: 25,325.

Programming (received off-air): WVIR-TV (N) Charlottesville; WHSV-TV (A,F) Harrisonburg; WCVE-TV (P), WRIC-TV (A), WTVR-TV (C), WWBT (N) Richmond-Petersburg; WVPT (P) Staunton; WDCA (U), WTTG (F), WUSA (C) Washington.

Programming (via satellite): BET; C-SPAN; CNBC; ESPN; Fox Family Channel; Home Shopping Network; TBS Superstation.

Current originations: Public access; government access; leased access.

Fee: $50.00 installation; $30.95 monthly; $15.00 additional installation.

Expanded Basic Service

Subscribers: 14,000.

Programming (via satellite): A & E; CNN; Country Music TV; Discovery Channel; Headline News; Home Team Sports; MTV; Music Choice; Nashville Network; Nickelodeon; The Weather Channel; Turner Network TV; USA Network; VH1.

Fee: $15.00 installation; $6.50 monthly.

Pay Service 1

Pay Units: 3,000.

Programming (via satellite): Cinemax.

Fee: $5.00 installation; $9.95 monthly.

Pay Service 2

Pay Units: 1,300.

Programming (via satellite): Disney Channel.

Fee: $5.00 installation; $7.95 monthly.

Pay Service 3

Pay Units: 4,800.

Programming (via satellite): HBO.

Fee: $5.00 installation; $9.95 monthly.

Pay Service 4

Pay Units: 1,800.

Programming (via satellite): The Movie Channel.

Fee: $5.00 installation; $9.95 monthly.

Pay Service 5

Pay Units: 1,000.

Programming (via satellite): Showtime.

Fee: $5.00 installation; $9.95 monthly.

Pay-Per-View

Addressable homes: 8,500.

Special events.

Local advertising: No.

Program Guide: The Cable Guide.

Equipment: Scientific-Atlanta headend; C-COR, Magnavox & GTE Sylvania amplifiers; Comm/Scope cable; Texscan character generator; Jerrold & Scientific-Atlanta set top converters; Jerrold & Scientific-Atlanta addressable set top converters; PPC traps; Microdyne, RCA & Scientific-Atlanta satellite antenna; Microdyne & Scientific-Atlanta satellite receivers; ChannelMatic commercial insert.

Miles of plant: 526.0 (coaxial); 130.0 (fiber optic). Additional miles planned: 37.0 (coaxial).

Manager: Dell Hanley. Chief technician: Gary Bennett.

Ownership: Adelphia Communications Corp. (MSO).

CHASE CITY—Tele-Media Co. of Southern Virginia, 329 E. 5th St., Chase City, VA 23924. Phone: 804-372-5455. Fax: 804-372-5411. County: Mecklenburg. Also serves Boydton, Mecklenburg County (portions). ICA: VA0095.

TV Market Ranking: Outside TV Markets. Franchise award date: N.A. Franchise expiration date: March 9, 2002. Began: December 1, 1970.

Channel capacity: 64 (not 2-way capable). Channels available but not in use: 25.

Basic Service

Subscribers: 1,096; Commercial subscribers: 14.

Programming (received off-air): WRAL-TV (C), WRDC (U), WTVD (A) Raleigh-Durham; WCVE-TV (P), WRLH-TV (F), WWBT (N) Richmond-Petersburg; WUNP-TV (P) Roanoke Rapids; WSET-TV (A) Roanoke-Lynchburg; WRAY-TV (I) Wilson.

Programming (via satellite): WGN-TV (W) Chicago; QVC; TBS Superstation.

Current originations: Automated time-weather.

Fee: $44.00 installation; $15.10 monthly; $0.75 converter.

Expanded Basic Service

Subscribers: 996.

Programming (via satellite): A & E; American Movie Classics; BET; CNN; Discovery Channel; Disney Channel; ESPN; ESPN 2; Fox Family Channel; Headline News; Home & Garden Television; Home Shopping Network; Learning Channel; MTV; Nashville Network; Nick at Nite's TV Land; Nickelodeon; Speedvision; The Weather Channel; Turner Network TV; USA Network.

Fee: $13.05 monthly.

Pay Service 1

Pay Units: 295.

Programming (via satellite): HBO.

Fee: $10.50 monthly.

Pay Service 2

Pay Units: 535.

Programming (via satellite): Showtime; The Movie Channel.

Fee: $11.95 monthly.

Equipment: Blonder-Tongue headend; Blonder-Tongue amplifiers; Comm/Scope cable; Scientific-Atlanta & Pioneer set top converters; Eagle traps.

Miles of plant: 45.0 (coaxial); None (fiber optic). Homes passed: 1,905.

Manager: Robert Loveridge. Chief technician: Tim Ellington.

City fee: 3% of gross to $100,000; 4% thereafter.

Ownership: Tele-Media Corp. (MSO).

CHESAPEAKE—Rapid Cable, Box 6310, 310 Walnut Extension, Branson, MO 65615-6310. Phones: 417-334-7897; 800-972-0962. Fax: 417-334-7899. E-mail: rcpcable@aol.com. County: Chesapeake City. ICA: VA0183.

TV Market Ranking: 44. Franchise award date: September 15, 1982. Franchise expiration date: N.A. Began: N.A.

Channel capacity: 36 (2-way capable; not operating 2-way). Channels available but not in use: 9.

Basic Service

Subscribers: 107.

Programming (received off-air): WHRO-TV (P), WVEC-TV (A) Hampton-Norfolk; WAVY-TV

(N), WGNT (U), WTKR (C), WTVZ (W) Portsmouth-Norfolk.
Programming (via satellite): WGN-TV (W) Chicago; BET; C-SPAN; CNN; Country Music TV; Discovery Channel; ESPN; Fox Family Channel; Home Team Sports; Lifetime; MTV; Nashville Network; Nickelodeon; TBS Superstation; Turner Network TV; USA Network.
Current originations: Government access.
Fee: $29.95 installation; $21.95 monthly; $2.95 converter.

Pay Service 1
Pay Units: 20.
Programming (via satellite): Cinemax.
Fee: $9.00 monthly.

Pay Service 2
Pay Units: 15.
Programming (via satellite): Disney Channel.
Fee: $7.00 monthly.

Pay Service 3
Pay Units: 26.
Programming (via satellite): HBO.
Fee: $10.00 monthly.

Miles of plant: 3.0 (coaxial). Homes passed: 300.
Manager: Belinda Murphy. Chief engineer: Steve Rice. Program director: Beth Semptimphelter. Marketing director: Bill Fischer.
Ownership: Rapid Communications Partners LP (MSO).

CHESTERFIELD COUNTY—Comcast Cablevision of Chesterfield Inc., 6510 Ironbridge Rd., Richmond, VA 23234-5206. Phone: 804-743-1171. Fax: 804-743-1613. County: Chesterfield. ICA: VA0132.
TV Market Ranking: 63. Franchise award date: July 1, 1979. Franchise expiration date: N.A. Began: June 1, 1980.
Channel capacity: 41 (2-way capable; operating 2-way). Channels available but not in use: N.A.

Basic Service
Subscribers: 65,983; Commercial subscribers: 515.
Programming (received off-air): WCVE-TV (P), WCVW (P), WRIC-TV (A), WRLH-TV (F), WTVR-TV (C), WWBT (N) Richmond-Petersburg; 19 FMs.
Programming (via satellite): WGN-TV (W) Chicago; A & E; BET; C-SPAN; C-SPAN 2; CNBC; CNN; Cartoon Network; Discovery Channel; ESPN; Fox Family Channel; Goodlife TV Network; Headline News; Home Shopping Network; Home Team Sports; Lifetime; MTV; Music Choice; Nashville Network; Nickelodeon; TBS Superstation; TV Guide Channel; The Weather Channel; Travel Channel; Turner Network TV; USA Network; VH1.
Current originations: Public access; educational access; leased access; local news.
Fee: $59.06 installation; $23.04 monthly; $1.03 converter.
Commercial fee: $10.00 monthly.

Pay Service 1
Pay Units: N.A.
Programming (via satellite): Disney Channel; HBO; Showtime; The Movie Channel.
Fee: $40.00 installation; $10.00 monthly (Disney, Showtime or TMC), $11.00 monthly (HBO).

Pay-Per-View
Addressable homes: 7,100.

Local advertising: Yes. Available in satellite distributed, locally originated, character-generated, taped & automated programming. Local sales manager: Barry Coffman.
Program Guide: CableView.
Equipment: Scientific-Atlanta headend; Jerrold amplifiers; Times Fiber cable; Hitachi & Sony cameras; Panasonic & Sony VTRs; Shintron character generator; Jerrold set top converters; Scientific-Atlanta satellite antenna; Scientific-Atlanta satellite receivers.
Miles of plant: 1500.0 (coaxial).
Manager: Kirby Brooks. Chief technician: Abe Jennings. Marketing director: Erin Ratliff.
Ownership: Comcast Cable Communications Inc. (MSO).

CHINCOTEAGUE—Falcon Cable TV, 216 Moore Ave., Suffolk, VA 23434. Phone: 804-539-2312. County: Accomack. ICA: VA0065.
TV Market Ranking: Below 100. Franchise award date: March 1, 1964. Franchise expiration date: April 1, 1999. Began: March 15, 1965.
Channel capacity: 54. Channels available but not in use: 13.

Basic Service
Subscribers: 2,352.
Programming (received off-air): WVEC-TV (A) Hampton-Norfolk; WAVY-TV (N), WTKR (C) Portsmouth-Norfolk; WBOC-TV (C), WCPB (P), WMDT (A) Salisbury; WTTG (F) Washington; allband FM.
Programming (via satellite): CNN; Comedy Central; Country Music TV; ESPN 2; FX; Fox Family Channel; Home Shopping Network; Lifetime; MTV; Nashville Network; Nickelodeon; QVC; Sci-Fi Channel; TBS Superstation; The Inspirational Network; Travel Channel; VH1.
Fee: $15.00 installation; $17.53 monthly.

Expanded Basic Service
Subscribers: 1,751.
Programming (via satellite): A & E; ESPN; Home Team Sports; The Weather Channel; Turner Network TV.
Current originations: Public access; educational access; government access.
Fee: $7.96 monthly.

Expanded Basic Service 2
Subscribers: 1,066.
Programming (via satellite): American Movie Classics; Discovery Channel; Disney Channel; Headline News; History Channel; USA Network.
Fee: $6.46 monthly.

Pay Service 1
Pay Units: 68.
Programming (via satellite): Cinemax.
Fee: $20.00 installation; $10.95 monthly.

Pay Service 2
Pay Units: 274.
Programming (via satellite): HBO.
Fee: $20.00 installation; $11.95 monthly.

Pay Service 3
Pay Units: 45.
Programming (via satellite): Showtime.
Fee: $20.00 installation; $10.95 monthly.

Pay Service 4
Pay Units: 39.
Programming (via satellite): The Movie Channel.
Fee: $10.95 monthly.

Equipment: Blonder-Tongue, Jerrold & Scientific-Atlanta headend; Jerrold amplifiers; Vikoa cable; Scientific-Atlanta satellite antenna; Scientific-Atlanta satellite receivers.
Miles of plant: 55.0 (coaxial). Homes passed: 3,860.
Manager: Jack Edwards. Chief technician: Mahlon Fritz.
Franchise fee: 2% of gross.
Ownership: Falcon Communications LP (MSO), joint venture formed September 30, 1998. See Cable System Ownership.

CLARKSVILLE—Tri-State Cablecomm, 329 E. 5th St., Chase City, VA 23924. Phone: 804-372-5455. Fax: 804-372-5411. County: Mecklenburg. Also serves Mecklenburg County (portions). ICA: VA0101.
TV Market Ranking: Outside TV Markets. Franchise award date: June 12, 1979. Franchise expiration date: N.A. Began: February 20, 1981.
Channel capacity: 35 (not 2-way capable). Channels available but not in use: 12.

Basic Service
Subscribers: 683; Commercial subscribers: 18.
Programming (received off-air): WUNC-TV (P) Chapel Hill; WNCN (N) Goldsboro; WLFL (U), WRAL-TV (C), WRDC (U), WTVD (A) Raleigh-Durham; WSET-TV (A), WSLS-TV (N) Roanoke-Lynchburg; 21 FMs.
Programming (via satellite): WGN-TV (W) Chicago; QVC; TBS Superstation.
Fee: $38.54 installation; $12.62 monthly; $0.75 converter.

Expanded Basic Service
Subscribers: 642.
Programming (via satellite): A & E; CNN; Comedy Central; Discovery Channel; ESPN; Lifetime; MTV; Nashville Network; Nickelodeon; Turner Network TV; USA Network.
Fee: $12.62 monthly.

Pay Service 1
Pay Units: 263.
Programming (via satellite): HBO.
Fee: $20.00 installation; $11.50 monthly.

Equipment: Blonder-Tongue headend; Scientific-Atlanta amplifiers; Times Fiber cable; Scientific-Atlanta & Pioneer set top converters; Eagle traps; Scientific-Atlanta satellite antenna; Scientific-Atlanta satellite receivers.
Miles of plant: 30.0 (coaxial). Homes passed: 1,166. Total homes in franchised area: 1,236.
Manager: Susan T. Morse. Chief technician: Tim Ellington.
City fee: 3% of gross.
Ownership: Fanch Communications Inc. (MSO); Time Warner Cable (MSO). See Cable System Ownership.

CLINTWOOD—Century Mountain Corp., Box 1300, 838 Park Ave. NE, Norton, VA 24273. Phone: 540-523-3522. County: Dickenson. Also serves Clinchco, Dickenson County. ICA: VA0057.
TV Market Ranking: Below 100. Franchise award date: N.A. Franchise expiration date: January 1, 2003. Began: June 1, 1964.
Channel capacity: 24. Channels available but not in use: N.A.

Basic Service
Subscribers: 2,456.
Programming (received off-air): WCYB-TV (N) Bristol-Kingsport; WJHL-TV (C) Johnson City; WKPT-TV (A) Kingsport; WSBN-TV (P) Norton; allband FM.
Programming (via satellite): CNN; ESPN; Fox Family Channel; MTV; Nashville Network; TBS Superstation.
Fee: $25.00 installation; $18.30 monthly; $10.00 additional installation.

Pay Service 1
Pay Units: N.A.
Programming (via satellite): HBO.
Fee: $20.00 installation; $8.95 monthly.

Local advertising: No. Regional interconnect: Cabletime.
Equipment: Blonder-Tongue headend; AEL, Ameco & Jerrold amplifiers; Comm/Scope cable; Jerrold set top converters.
Miles of plant: 91.0 (coaxial). Homes passed: 3,250.
Manager: John Taylor. Chief technician: Gregory Davis. Marketing director: Barry L. Simmons.
City fee: $100.00 annually.
Ownership: Century Communications Corp. (MSO). See Cable System Ownership.

COEBURN—Century Communications Corp., Box 1300, Norton, VA 24230. Phone: 540-679-3361. County: Wise. Also serves Banner, Bondtown, Crab Orchard, Maytown, Riverview, Wise County. ICA: VA0122.
TV Market Ranking: Below 100. Franchise award date: N.A. Franchise expiration date: N.A. Began: January 1, 1974.
Channel capacity: 40. Channels available but not in use: 28.

Basic Service
Subscribers: 1,667.
Programming (received off-air): WSAZ-TV (N) Charleston-Huntington; WLOS (A), WYFF (N) Greenville-Spartanburg-Asheville; WJHL-TV (C) Johnson City; WKPT-TV (A) Kingsport; WSBN-TV (P) Norton; WSJK (P) Sneedville; allband FM.
Programming (via satellite): ESPN; TBS Superstation.
Fee: $25.00 installation; $10.00 monthly.

Pay Service 1
Pay Units: 530.
Programming (via satellite): The Movie Channel.
Fee: $15.00 installation; $6.95 monthly.

Manager: Charles Himelrick. Chief technician: Stanley Baskiewicz. Marketing & program director: John E. Finley.
Ownership: Century Communications Corp. (MSO). See Cable System Ownership.

COLONIAL BEACH—Tri-State Cablecomm, 233 Colonial Ave., Colonial Beach, VA 22443. Phone: 804-224-7101. Fax: 804-224-9616. County: Westmoreland. Also serves Curley's Trailer Park, Potomac Shores, Westmoreland County (unincorporated areas), Westmoreland Shores. ICA: VA0063.
TV Market Ranking: Outside TV Markets. Franchise award date: April 13, 1980. Franchise expiration date: April 8, 2008. Began: November 1, 1980.
Channel capacity: 35 (not 2-way capable). Channels available but not in use: 7.

Basic Service
Subscribers: 1,661.
Programming (received off-air): WTMW (H) Arlington; WNVT (P) Goldvein; WDCA (U), WETA-TV (P), WJLA-TV (A), WRC-TV (N), WTTG (F), WUSA (C) Washington; allband FM.
Programming (via satellite): WGN-TV (W) Chicago; QVC; TBS Superstation.
Current originations: Government access.
Fee: $32.07 installation (aerial), $36.45 (underground); $11.34 monthly; $0.75 converter.

Expanded Basic Service
Subscribers: 1,618.
Programming (via satellite): C-SPAN; CNN; Discovery Channel; ESPN; Fox Family Channel; Home Team Sports; Lifetime; MTV; Nashville Network; Nickelodeon; The Weather Channel; Turner Network TV; USA Network.
Fee: $12.28 monthly.

Pay Service 1
Pay Units: 130.
Programming (via satellite): Disney Channel.
Fee: $8.95 monthly.

Pay Service 2
Pay Units: 498.
Programming (via satellite): HBO.
Fee: $11.50 monthly.

Pay Service 3
Pay Units: 218.
Programming (via satellite): The Movie Channel.

Fee: $11.50 monthly.
Equipment: Scientific-Atlanta headend; Scientific-Atlanta amplifiers; Times Fiber cable; Oak, Scientific-Atlanta & Pioneer set top converters; Eagle traps; Scientific-Atlanta satellite antenna; Microdyne satellite receivers.
Miles of plant: 41.0 (coaxial). Additional miles planned: 10.0 (coaxial). Homes passed: 2,633. Total homes in franchised area: 4,725.
Manager: Thomas A. Olsen. Chief technician: Tim Trigger. Marketing director: James R. Guthrie.
City fee: 5% of gross.
Ownership: Fanch Communications Inc. (MSO); Time Warner Cable (MSO). See Cable System Ownership.

COVINGTON—CFW Cable of Virginia Inc., Box 312, Covington, VA 24426. Phone: 540-962-1184. Fax: 540-965-7070. County: Alleghany. Also serves Alleghany County, Clifton Forge, Iron Gate. ICA: VA0036.
TV Market Ranking: 70 (portions of Alleghany County); Below 100 (Clifton Forge, Covington); Outside TV Markets (portions of Alleghany County, Iron Gate). Franchise award date: July 10, 1962. Franchise expiration date: February 10, 2005. Began: December 19, 1963.
Channel capacity: 77 (2-way capable). Channels available but not in use: 39.
Basic Service
Subscribers: 7,000.
Programming (received off-air): WBRA-TV (P), WPXR (X) Roanoke; WDBJ (C), WFXR-TV (F), WJPR (F), WSET-TV (A), WSLS-TV (N) Roanoke-Lynchburg; 1 FM.
Programming (via satellite): WGN-TV (W) Chicago; A & E; American Movie Classics; Animal Planet; BET; C-SPAN; C-SPAN 2; CNN; Cartoon Network; Discovery Channel; ESPN; ESPN 2; Fox Family Channel; Headline News; History Channel; Home & Garden Television; Home Shopping Network; Home Team Sports; Learning Channel; Lifetime; MTV; Nashville Network; Nickelodeon; QVC; TBS Superstation; TV Guide Channel; The Inspirational Network; The Weather Channel; Travel Channel; Turner Network TV; USA Network; VH1.
Current originations: Automated time-weather; public access; automated emergency alert.
Fee: $25.00 installation; $22.60 monthly; $2.16 converter.
A la Carte 1
Subscribers: N.A.
Programming (via satellite): Country Music TV; Sci-Fi Channel.
Fee: $1.00 monthly (each).
Pay Service 1
Pay Units: 497.
Programming (via satellite): Cinemax (multiplexed).
Fee: $2.00 installation; $9.95 monthly.
Pay Service 2
Pay Units: 564.
Programming (via satellite): HBO (multiplexed).
Fee: $2.00 installation; $11.95 monthly.
Pay Service 3
Pay Units: 201.
Programming (via satellite): Showtime.
Fee: $2.00 installation; $11.95 monthly.
Pay Service 4
Pay Units: 195.
Programming (via satellite): Disney Channel.
Fee: $2.00 installation; $8.50 monthly.
Pay-Per-View
Addressable homes: 1,278.
Viewer's Choice; special events.
Fee: Varies.
Local advertising: Yes (insert only). Available in character-generated programming. Rates: $50.00/Month.
Equipment: Scientific-Atlanta headend; Jerrold amplifiers; Comm/Scope, Times Fiber & Belden cable; Texscan character generator; Regal set top converters; Jerrold addressable set top converters; Scientific-Atlanta satellite antenna; Agile satellite receivers.
Miles of plant: 132.7 (coaxial). Additional miles planned: 20.0 (coaxial); 30.0 (fiber optic). Homes passed: 7,747. Total homes in franchised area: 9,870.
Manager: Kathryn B. Skeens. Chief technician: Monty L. Crawford. Office manager: Debra Hancock.
City fee: 3% of gross.
Ownership: CFW Communications (MSO).

CRAIGSVILLE—Multi-Channel TV Cable Co. of Virginia, 2815 N. Augusta St., Staunton, VA 24401. Phone: 800-835-4949. Fax: 540-886-7948. County: Augusta. Also serves Augusta Springs. ICA: VA0133.
TV Market Ranking: Outside TV Markets. Franchise award date: N.A. Franchise expiration date: N.A. Began: N.A.
Channel capacity: 60 (not 2-way capable). Channels available but not in use: 34.
Basic Service
Subscribers: 429.
Programming (received off-air): WHSV-TV (A,F) Harrisonburg; WTVR-TV (C) Richmond-Petersburg; WDBJ (C), WSET-TV (A), WSLS-TV (N) Roanoke-Lynchburg; WVPT (P) Staunton.
Programming (via satellite): TBS Superstation.
Fee: $33.00 installation; $8.25 monthly.
Expanded Basic Service
Subscribers: 415.
Programming (via satellite): C-SPAN; C-SPAN 2; CNN; Country Music TV; Discovery Channel; Disney Channel; ESPN; Fox Family Channel; Headline News; Learning Channel; MTV; Nashville Network; Nickelodeon; Odyssey; QVC; The Weather Channel; Turner Network TV; USA Network.
Fee: N.A.
Pay Service 1
Pay Units: 96.
Programming (via satellite): Cinemax.
Fee: $11.50 monthly.
Pay Service 2
Pay Units: 93.
Programming (via satellite): HBO.
Fee: $11.50 monthly.
Local advertising: No.
Equipment: Scientific-Atlanta headend; Magnavox amplifiers; Comm/Scope cable; Scientific-Atlanta set top converters; Eagle & Pico traps; Scientific-Atlanta satellite antenna; Microdyne satellite receivers.
Miles of plant: 17.3 (coaxial); None (fiber optic). Homes passed: 750.
Manager: Dell Hanley. Chief technician: Ron Herron. Program director: John Adduchi. Marketing director: David Owens.
Ownership: Adelphia Communications Corp. (MSO).

CRAWFORD MANOR—Tel-Con Systems, Box 217, Verona, VA 24482. Phone: 540-248-3400. Fax: 540-248-3488. County: Augusta. ICA: VA0119.
TV Market Ranking: Below 100. Franchise award date: N.A. Franchise expiration date: N.A. Began: August 1, 1982.
Channel capacity: 21 (not 2-way capable). Channels available but not in use: 4.
Basic Service
Subscribers: 140.
Programming (received off-air): WVIR-TV (N) Charlottesville; WHSV-TV (A,F) Harrisonburg; WWBT (N) Richmond-Petersburg; WVPT (P) Staunton; WDCA (U), WJLA-TV (A), WTTG (F), WUSA (C) Washington.
Programming (via satellite): A & E; CNN; ESPN; Fox Family Channel; Nashville Network; TBS Superstation; USA Network.
Fee: $30.00 installation; $14.95 monthly.
Pay Service 1
Pay Units: 19.
Programming (via satellite): Disney Channel.
Fee: $7.00 monthly.
Pay Service 2
Pay Units: 28.
Programming (via satellite): Showtime.
Fee: $9.00 monthly.
Equipment: Jerrold amplifiers; Comm/Scope cable.
Miles of plant: 4.5 (coaxial). Homes passed: 175.
Manager: M. Fitzgerald.
Ownership: Davi Communications Inc.

CREWE—Nesbe Cable TV, Box 10516, Lynchburg, VA 24506. Phone: 804-821-7110. County: Nottoway. ICA: VA0099.
TV Market Ranking: Outside TV Markets. Franchise award date: March 8, 1982. Franchise expiration date: N.A. Began: March 1, 1983.
Channel capacity: 20. Channels available but not in use: None.
Basic Service
Subscribers: 529.
Programming (received off-air): WVIR-TV (N) Charlottesville; WCVE-TV (P), WRIC-TV (A), WRLH-TV (F), WTVR-TV (C), WWBT (N) Richmond-Petersburg.
Programming (via satellite): WGN-TV (W) Chicago; CNN; ESPN; Fox Family Channel; TBS Superstation.
Fee: $38.50 installation; $16.00 monthly.
Pay Service 1
Pay Units: N.A.
Programming (via satellite): HBO.
Fee: $10.00 monthly.
Equipment: Scientific-Atlanta headend; Scientific-Atlanta amplifiers; Scientific-Atlanta cable; Drop Shop traps; Pico & Scientific-Atlanta satellite antenna; Microdyne & Scientific-Atlanta satellite receivers.
Miles of plant: 22.0 (coaxial). Homes passed: 900.
Manager: Frank Staley. Chief technician: Ricky Tomlin.
City fee: 5% of gross.
Ownership: Bahakel Communications Ltd. (MSO).

CROZET—Multi-Channel TV Cable Co. of Virginia, 324 W. Main St., Charlottesville, VA 22901. Phone: 800-835-4949. Fax: 804-293-9263. County: Albemarle. Also serves Albemarle County. ICA: VA0097.
TV Market Ranking: Below 100. Franchise award date: N.A. Franchise expiration date: N.A. Began: September 1, 1979.
Channel capacity: 26 (not 2-way capable). Channels available but not in use: 4.
Basic Service
Subscribers: 803.
Programming (received off-air): WVIR-TV (N) Charlottesville; WCVE-TV (P), WRIC-TV (A), WTVR-TV (C), WWBT (N) Richmond-Petersburg.
Programming (via satellite): WGN-TV (W) Chicago; CNN; Discovery Channel; ESPN; Fox Family Channel; Lifetime; MTV; Nashville Network; Nickelodeon; QVC; TBS Superstation; The Weather Channel; Turner Network TV; USA Network.
Current originations: Automated time-weather.
Fee: $50.00 installation; $19.95 monthly.
Pay Service 1
Pay Units: N.A.
Programming (via satellite): Disney Channel; HBO; Showtime.
Fee: $7.00 monthly (Disney), $10.00 monthly (HBO or Showtime).
Local advertising: No.
Equipment: Blonder-Tongue & M/A-Com headend; C-COR, Magnavox & Scientific-Atlanta amplifiers; Comm/Scope cable; Jerrold & Scientific-Atlanta set top converters; PPC traps; Microdyne, RCA & Scientific-Atlanta satellite antenna; Microdyne & Scientific-Atlanta satellite receivers.
Miles of plant: 23.0 (coaxial). Homes passed: 973.
Manager: Dell Hanley. Chief technician: Gary Bennett.
Ownership: Adelphia Communications Corp. (MSO).

CULPEPER—TCI of Virginia Inc., 301 E. Culpeper St., Culpeper, VA 22701-3039. Phone: 540-825-2920. Fax: 540-829-6678. County: Culpeper. Also serves Culpeper County. ICA: VA0047.
TV Market Ranking: Below 100 (Culpeper, portions of Culpeper County); Outside TV Markets (portions of Culpeper County). Franchise award date: N.A. Franchise expiration date: January 1, 1999. Began: December 1, 1970.
Channel capacity: 110 (2-way capable; operating 2-way). Channels available but not in use: 59.
Note: Subscribers, pay units & miles of plant include figures for Orange, VA.
Basic Service
Subscribers: 5,813.
Programming (received off-air): WVIR-TV (N) Charlottesville; WNVT (P) Goldvein; WPXW (X) Manassas; WTVR-TV (C) Richmond-Petersburg; WDCA (U), WETA-TV (P), WJLA-TV (A), WRC-TV (N), WTTG (F), WUSA (C) Washington; 10 FMs.
Programming (via satellite): BET; C-SPAN; C-SPAN 2; CNBC; CNN; Comedy Central; Discovery Channel; Fox Family Channel; Headline News; Lifetime; MTV; Nashville Network; Nickelodeon; QVC; TBS Superstation; The Weather Channel; VH1.
Current originations: Automated time-weather.
Fee: $22.87 installation (aerial), $45.74 (underground); $8.05 monthly; $3.95 converter; $20.00 additional installation.
Expanded Basic Service
Subscribers: 5,385.
Programming (via satellite): A & E; American Movie Classics; Country Music TV; E! Entertainment TV; ESPN; FX; Fox Sports Net; Home Shopping Network; Home Team Sports; Intro TV; Knowledge TV; Learning Channel; Odyssey; TV Food Network; The Inspirational Network; Turner Network TV; USA Network.
Fee: $12.21 monthly.
Pay Service 1
Pay Units: 834.
Programming (via satellite): Cinemax.
Fee: $11.95 monthly.
Pay Service 2
Pay Units: 573.
Programming (via satellite): Disney Channel.
Fee: $11.95 monthly.
Pay Service 3
Pay Units: 2,009.
Programming (via satellite): The New Encore.
Fee: $1.00 monthly.

Pay Service 4
Pay Units: 1,733.
Programming (via satellite): HBO.
Fee: $12.80 monthly.
Pay Service 5
Pay Units: 519.
Programming (via satellite): Showtime.
Fee: $11.95 monthly.
Pay Service 6
Pay Units: 89.
Programming (via satellite): DMX.
Fee: $9.95 monthly.
Pay Service 7
Pay Units: 919.
Programming (via satellite): Starz!
Fee: $4.75 monthly.
Local advertising: Yes. Local sales manager: Jeff Petagna.
Program Guide: The Cable Guide.
Equipment: Scientific-Atlanta headend; Jerrold amplifiers; Comm/Scope & Times Fiber cable; AT&T & Comm/Scope fiber optic cable; MSI character generator; Scientific-Atlanta set top converters; Jerrold addressable set top converters; Eagle traps; Scientific-Atlanta satellite antenna; Scientific-Atlanta satellite receivers.
Miles of plant: 110.0 (coaxial); 20.0 (fiber optic).
Manager: Chuck Horner. Chief technician: Frank Kish.
Franchise fee: 3% -5% of gross.
Ownership: AT&T Broadband & Internet Services (MSO). Purchased from Tele-Communications Inc., March 9, 1999.

CULPEPER COUNTY—GS Communications Inc., Box 398, 442 W. Patrick St., Frederick, MD 21705. Phone: 301-662-6822. Fax: 301-662-1307. County: Culpeper. ICA: VA0182.
TV Market Ranking: Below 100. Franchise award date: N.A. Franchise expiration date: N.A. Began: January 1, 1994.
Channel capacity: 90 (2-way capable; operating 2-way). Channels available but not in use: 20.
Basic Service
Subscribers: 1,913.
Programming (received off-air): WTMW (H) Arlington; WHTJ (P), WVIR-TV (N) Charlottesville; WNVC (E) Fairfax; WPXW (X) Manassas; WBDC-TV (W), WDCA (U), WETA-TV (P), WJLA-TV (A), WRC-TV (N), WTTG (F), WUSA (C) Washington.
Programming (via satellite): WGN-TV (W) Chicago; C-SPAN; C-SPAN 2; QVC; TBS Superstation; TV Guide Channel.
Fee: $13.65 monthly.
Expanded Basic Service
Subscribers: 1,770.
Programming (via satellite): A & E; American Movie Classics; BET; CNBC; CNN; Cartoon Network; Comedy Central; Discovery Channel; E! Entertainment TV; ESPN; ESPN 2; EWTN; Fox Family Channel; FoxNet; Great American Country; Headline News; History Channel; Home & Garden Television; Home Team Sports; Learning Channel; Lifetime; MTV; Nashville Network; Nick at Nite; Nickelodeon; Sci-Fi Channel; TV Food Network; The Weather Channel; Trinity Bcstg. Network; Turner Network TV; USA Network; VH1.
Fee: $15.30 monthly.
Pay Service 1
Pay Units: 705.
Programming (via satellite): Cinemax; Disney Channel; HBO; Showtime.
Fee: $8.95 monthly (Cinemax, Disney or Showtime); $10.95 monthly (HBO).
Pay-Per-View
Addressable homes: 540.
Sports Pay-Per-View; special events.
Miles of plant: 150.0 (coaxial); 40.0 (fiber optic). Homes passed: 3,000. Total homes in franchised area: 3,000.
Manager: Rich Angerman. Operations manager: John Gregury. Chief technician: Brian Bemis. Marketing director: Scott Shealer.
Ownership: Great Southern Printing & Manufacturing Co. (MSO).

DAMASCUS—CableVision, 105 N. Main St., Lebanon, VA 24266. Phones: 540-889-0669; 800-654-7619. Fax: 540-889-3382. County: Washington. Also serves Hollyfield, Ketron's Corner, Roetown, Washington County. ICA: VA0134.
TV Market Ranking: Below 100. Franchise award date: N.A. Franchise expiration date: N.A. Began: July 1, 1977.
Channel capacity: 36 (not 2-way capable). Channels available but not in use: N.A.
Basic Service
Subscribers: 823.
Programming (received off-air): WCYB-TV (N) Bristol-Kingsport; WEMT (F) Greeneville; WJHL-TV (C) Johnson City; WKPT-TV (A) Kingsport; WSBN-TV (P) Norton; WDBJ (C) Roanoke-Lynchburg; WSJK (P) Sneedville; allband FM.
Programming (via satellite): WGN-TV (W) Chicago; TBS Superstation.
Fee: $45.98 installation; $9.95 monthly.
Expanded Basic Service
Subscribers: N.A.
Programming (via satellite): C-SPAN; CNN; Country Music TV; Discovery Channel; ESPN; Fox Family Channel; Headline News; Lifetime; MTV; Nashville Network; Nickelodeon; QVC; Turner Network TV; USA Network.
Fee: $13.30 monthly.
Pay Service 1
Pay Units: 85.
Programming (via satellite): Disney Channel; HBO; Showtime.
Fee: $8.95 monthly (Disney or Showtime), $10.45 monthly (HBO).
Local advertising: Yes. Rates: $10.00/Week; $5.00/3 Days; $2.00/Day.
Equipment: Standard Communications headend; Jerrold amplifiers; Comm/Scope cable.
Miles of plant: 32.0 (coaxial).
Manager: Dave Burke. Plant manager: Daryl Boyd. Customer service manager: Nickie Ketron.
City fee: 3% of gross.
Ownership: Rifkin & Associates Inc. (MSO). See Cable System Ownership.

DANVILLE—Adelphia Cable, 560 Patton St., Danville, VA 24541-1310. Phone: 804-797-4135. Fax: 804-793-6920. Counties: Pittsylvania, VA; Caswell, NC. Also serves Caswell County (portions), Yanceyville, NC; Chatham, Glenwood, Pittsylvania County, Ringgold, Westover Hills, VA. ICA: VA0012.
TV Market Ranking: 47 (portions of Caswell County); 70 (portions of Pittsylvania County); 73 (portions of Caswell County, Yanceyville); Below 100 (portions of Caswell County, Chatham, Danville, Glenwood, portions of Pittsylvania County, Ringgold, Westover Hills). Franchise award date: March 3, 1987. Franchise expiration date: March 3, 2002. Began: January 1, 1969.
Channel capacity: 60. Channels available but not in use: 9.
Basic Service
Subscribers: 26,328; Commercial subscribers: 31. Includes figures for Altavista, Brookneal & Hurt, VA.
Programming (received off-air): WUNC-TV (P) Chapel Hill; WDRL-TV (U) Danville; WFMY-TV (C), WXII (N) Greensboro-High Point; W14AU (I) Reidsville; WBRA-TV (P) Roanoke; WDBJ (C), WFXR-TV (F), WSET-TV (A), WSLS-TV (N) Roanoke-Lynchburg; allband FM.
Programming (via satellite): A & E; American Movie Classics; BET; C-SPAN; C-SPAN 2; CNBC; E! Entertainment TV; ESPN; ESPN 2; FX; Fox Family Channel; Golf Channel; Goodlife TV Network; Headline News; Home Shopping Network; Home Team Sports; Lifetime; MSNBC; MTV; Nashville Network; Nickelodeon; QVC; Sci-Fi Channel; TV Food Network; TV Guide Channel; The Inspirational Network; The Weather Channel; Turner Network TV; USA Network; VH1.
Current originations: Public access; educational access; government access; local news.
Fee: $50.00 installation (aerial), $59.95 (underground); $7.90 monthly; $1.80 converter.
Expanded Basic Service
Subscribers: 22,960.
Programming (via satellite): WGN-TV (W) Chicago; CNN; Cartoon Network; Discovery Channel; TBS Superstation.
Fee: $18.18 monthly.
Pay Service 1
Pay Units: 2,083.
Programming (via satellite): Cinemax.
Fee: $10.00 monthly.
Pay Service 2
Pay Units: 1,714.
Programming (via satellite): Disney Channel.
Fee: $9.95 monthly.
Pay Service 3
Pay Units: 829.
Programming (via satellite): The New Encore.
Fee: $3.95 monthly.
Pay Service 4
Pay Units: 7,799.
Programming (via satellite): HBO.
Fee: $11.95 monthly.
Pay Service 5
Pay Units: 1,056.
Programming (via satellite): Showtime.
Fee: $11.95 monthly.
Local advertising: Yes. Available in satellite distributed, locally originated, character-generated, taped & automated programming. Rates: $36.00/Minute; $18.00/30 Seconds.
Program Guide: TV Host.
Equipment: Scientific-Atlanta headend; C-COR & Jerrold amplifiers; Comm/Scope & Times Fiber cable; JVC cameras; Sony VTRs; Oak & Scientific-Atlanta set top converters; Eagle & Pico traps; ChannelMaster, RCA & Scientific-Atlanta satellite antenna; DX Antenna, Jerrold & Scientific-Atlanta satellite receivers.
Miles of plant: 623.0 (coaxial). Homes passed: 32,575. Total homes in franchised area: 35,698.
Manager: Ted Crane. Chief technician: Michael Pruitt. Marketing director: Jerry Lesser.
City fee: 5% of gross.
Ownership: Adelphia Communications Corp. (MSO).

DILLWYN—FrontierVision, Suite P-200, 1777 S. Harrison St., Denver, CO 80210. Phone: 303-757-1588. Fax: 303-757-6105. County: Buckingham. Also serves Buckingham County (portions). ICA: VA0076.
TV Market Ranking: 70 (portions of Buckingham County); Below 100 (portions of Buckingham County); Outside TV Markets (portions of Buckingham County, Dillwyn). Franchise award date: December 12, 1988. Franchise expiration date: December 12, 1998. Began: March 22, 1990.
Channel capacity: 54 (not 2-way capable). Channels available but not in use: 16.
Basic Service
Subscribers: 912.
Programming (received off-air): WVIR-TV (N) Charlottesville; WCVE-TV (P), WRIC-TV (A), WRLH-TV (F), WTVR-TV (C), WWBT (N) Richmond-Petersburg; WSET-TV (A) Roanoke-Lynchburg.
Programming (via satellite): BET; C-SPAN; CNBC; CNN; Country Music TV; Discovery Channel; Disney Channel; ESPN; Headline News; Lifetime; Nashville Network; Nickelodeon; QVC; TBS Superstation; The Weather Channel; Trinity Bcstg. Network; USA Network; VH1.
Fee: $40.00 installation; $14.95 monthly; $2.00 converter.
Pay Service 1
Pay Units: 139.
Programming (via satellite): HBO.
Fee: $15.00 installation; $10.95 monthly.
Pay Service 2
Pay Units: 251.
Programming (via satellite): Showtime.
Fee: $15.00 installation; $10.95 monthly.
Pay Service 3
Pay Units: 231.
Programming (via satellite): The Movie Channel.
Fee: N.A.
Local advertising: No.
Program Guide: CableView.
Equipment: Magnavox amplifiers; Times Fiber cable; Scientific-Atlanta & Zenith set top converters; Eagle & PPC traps; Comtech satellite antenna; Scientific-Atlanta satellite receivers.
Miles of plant: 107.0 (coaxial). Homes passed: 2,120.
Manager: Dan Callahan. Chief technician: Gary Shoemaker.
Franchise fee: 5% of gross.
Ownership: FrontierVision Partners LP (MSO). See Cable System Ownership.

DINWIDDIE—Adelphia Cable, 25225-D Harwell Dr., Petersburg, VA 23805. Phones: 804-861-6387; 800-835-4949. Fax: 804-733-7064. County: Dinwiddie. ICA: VA0186.
TV Market Ranking: 63. Franchise award date: N.A. Franchise expiration date: N.A. Began: N.A.
Channel capacity: N.A. Channels available but not in use: N.A.
Basic Service
Subscribers: 2,496.
Programming (received off-air): WUPV (U) Ashland; WCVE-TV (P), WCVW (P), WRIC-TV (A), WRLH-TV (F), WTVR-TV (C), WWBT (N) Richmond-Petersburg.
Programming (via satellite): WGN-TV (W) Chicago; A & E; Animal Planet; BET; C-SPAN; CNBC; CNN; Cartoon Network; Discovery Channel; ESPN 2; FX; Fox Family Channel; Home Shopping Network; Learning Channel; MSNBC; Nashville Network; Nickelodeon; Trinity Bcstg. Network; Turner Classic Movies; Turner Network TV.
Fee: N.A.
Expanded Basic Service
Subscribers: N.A.
Programming (via satellite): Country Music TV; Disney Channel; ESPN; Lifetime; MTV; TBS Superstation; USA Network.
Fee: N.A.
Pay Service 1
Pay Units: N.A.
Programming (via satellite): Cinemax; HBO.
Fee: N.A.

Homes passed: 3,912.
Manager: Luke Matthews. Plant manager: William Smith. Chief technician: Oliver Thornton. Office manager: Debra Cage.
Ownership: Adelphia Communications Corp. (MSO).

DRAKES BRANCH—Cable Comm, Box 465, Rte. 644, Farmville, VA 23901. Phone: 804-392-8144. Fax: 804-392-5262. County: Charlotte. Also serves Charlotte County (portions). ICA: VA0172.
TV Market Ranking: Outside TV Markets. Franchise award date: February 5, 1990. Franchise expiration date: February 5, 2005. Began: February 5, 1990.
Channel capacity: 35. Channels available but not in use: 6.
Basic Service
Subscribers: 149.
Programming (received off-air): WCVE-TV (P), WRLH-TV (F) Richmond-Petersburg; WDBJ (C), WSET-TV (A), WSLS-TV (N) Roanoke-Lynchburg.
Programming (via satellite): WGN-TV (W) Chicago; C-SPAN; QVC; TBS Superstation.
Current originations: Government access.
Fee: $24.95 installation; $18.09 monthly; $0.75 converter.
Expanded Basic Service
Subscribers: 139.
Programming (via satellite): A & E; American Movie Classics; Animal Planet; BET; CNN; Cartoon Network; Country Music TV; Discovery Channel; ESPN; ESPN 2; Fox Family Channel; Learning Channel; Lifetime; Nashville Network; Nickelodeon; The Weather Channel; Turner Network TV; USA Network; VH1.
Fee: $13.66 monthly.
Pay Service 1
Pay Units: 16.
Programming (via satellite): Cinemax.
Fee: $11.50 monthly.
Pay Service 2
Pay Units: 17.
Programming (via satellite): HBO.
Fee: $11.50 monthly.
Local advertising: No.
Equipment: Blonder-Tongue headend; Jerrold & Magnavox amplifiers; Comm/Scope & Times Fiber cable; Scientific-Atlanta set top converters; Eagle traps.
Miles of plant: 15.0 (coaxial); None (fiber optic). Homes passed: 341. Total homes in franchised area: 500.
Manager: Susan T. Morse. Operations director: Thomas A. Olsen. Chief technician: Steve Fore. Marketing director: Trish Lindsey.
Franchise fee: 3% of gross.
Ownership: Fanch Communications Inc. (MSO); Time Warner Cable (MSO). See Cable System Ownership.

DUFFIELD—Century Cable TV, Box 1300, 838 Park Ave. NE, Norton, VA 24273. Phone: 540-523-3522. Counties: Lee & Scott. Also serves Clinchport (portions), Jasper (portions), Nickelsville. ICA: VA0092.
TV Market Ranking: Below 100 (Clinchport, Duffield, Nickelsville); Outside TV Markets (Jasper). Franchise award date: N.A. Franchise expiration date: N.A. Began: January 1, 1974.
Channel capacity: 24. Channels available but not in use: N.A.
Basic Service
Subscribers: 728.
Programming (received off-air): WCYB-TV (N) Bristol-Kingsport; WJHL-TV (C) Johnson City; WKPT-TV (A) Kingsport; WSJK (P) Sneedville.
Programming (via satellite): WGN-TV (W) Chicago; TBS Superstation.
Fee: $19.19 monthly.
Miles of plant: 38.5 (coaxial). Homes passed: 1,062.
Manager: Robert G. Parsons.
Ownership: Century Communications Corp. (MSO). See Cable System Ownership.

EDINBURG—Shenandoah Cable TV Co., Box 459, Edinburg, VA 22824. Phone: 540-984-4140. Fax: 540-984-4920. County: Shenandoah. Also serves Shenandoah County. ICA: VA0136.
TV Market Ranking: Below 100 (Edinburg, portions of Shenandoah County); Outside TV Markets (portions of Shenandoah County). Franchise award date: N.A. Franchise expiration date: N.A. Began: September 1, 1981.
Channel capacity: 25. Channels available but not in use: N.A.
Basic Service
Subscribers: 2,700.
Programming (received off-air): WWPB (P) Hagerstown; WHSV-TV (A,F) Harrisonburg; WWPX (I) Martinsburg; WVPT (P) Staunton; WDCA (U), WJLA-TV (A), WRC-TV (N), WTTG (F), WUSA (C) Washington; WAZT-LP (I) Woodstock.
Programming (via satellite): WGN-TV (W) Chicago; A & E; American Movie Classics; Animal Planet; BET; C-SPAN; C-SPAN 2; CNBC; CNN; Cartoon Network; Country Music TV; Discovery Channel; Disney Channel; ESPN; ESPN 2; EWTN; Fox Family Channel; Headline News; History Channel; Home & Garden Television; Home Shopping Network; Home Team Sports; Learning Channel; Lifetime; MSNBC; Nashville Network; Nick at Nite's TV Land; Nickelodeon; Outdoor Channel; QVC; Romance Classics; Sci-Fi Channel; TBS Superstation; TV Guide Channel; The Weather Channel; Travel Channel; Trinity Bcstg. Network; Turner Classic Movies; Turner Network TV; USA Network; VH1.
Current originations: Automated time-weather.
Fee: $20.00-$30.00 installation; $29.95 monthly.
Pay Service 1
Pay Units: N.A.
Programming (via satellite): The Movie Channel.
Fee: $10.00 monthly.
Equipment: Scientific-Atlanta headend; GTE Sylvania amplifiers; Comm/Scope cable; Microdyne satellite antenna; Microdyne satellite receivers.
Miles of plant: 44.0 (coaxial). Additional miles planned: 16.0 (coaxial).
President: Christopher French. Chief technician: Tommy Keeler. Vice president, operations: David Ferguson.
City fee: 3% of gross.
Ownership: Shenandoah Telecommunications Inc.

EMPORIA—SVHH Cable Acquisition LP, Box 710, 1711 Seymour Dr., South Boston, VA 24592. Phone: 800-835-4949. County: Greensville. Also serves Greensville County. ICA: VA0053.
TV Market Ranking: 63 (portions of Greensville County); Below 100 (Emporia); Outside TV Markets (portions of Greensville County). Franchise award date: N.A. Franchise expiration date: November 16, 2006. Began: June 1, 1968.
Channel capacity: 80 (not 2-way capable). Channels available but not in use: None.
Basic Service
Subscribers: 2,776; Commercial subscribers: 12.
Programming (received off-air): WVEC-TV (A) Hampton-Norfolk; WAVY-TV (N), WGNT (U), WTKR (C) Portsmouth-Norfolk; WCVE-TV (P), WRIC-TV (A), WRLH-TV (F), WTVR-TV (C), WWBT (N) Richmond-Petersburg; allband FM.
Programming (via satellite): WGN-TV (W) Chicago; TBS Superstation.
Current originations: Government access.
Fee: $28.95 monthly; $39.00 additional installation.
Expanded Basic Service
Subscribers: N.A.
Programming (via satellite): A & E; American Movie Classics; BET; C-SPAN; C-SPAN 2; CNBC; CNN; Cartoon Network; Country Music TV; Discovery Channel; ESPN; ESPN 2; FX; Fox Family Channel; Headline News; History Channel; Home Shopping Network; Home Team Sports; Learning Channel; Lifetime; MTV; Nashville Network; Nickelodeon; Product Information Network; QVC; TV Guide Channel; The Weather Channel; Travel Channel; Turner Network TV; USA Network; VH1.
Fee: N.A.
Pay Service 1
Pay Units: 531.
Programming (via satellite): Cinemax.
Fee: $11.50 monthly.
Pay Service 2
Pay Units: 98.
Programming (via satellite): Disney Channel.
Fee: $8.95 monthly.
Pay Service 3
Pay Units: 893.
Programming (via satellite): HBO.
Fee: $11.50 monthly.
Pay Service 4
Pay Units: 295.
Programming (via satellite): The Movie Channel.
Fee: $11.50 monthly.
Local advertising: Yes. Local sales manager: Gwen Howell.
Equipment: Scientific-Atlanta headend; C-COR amplifiers; Comm/Scope cable; Oak, Pioneer & Jerrold set top converters; Intercept, Pico & Eagle traps; Scientific-Atlanta & Superior satellite antenna; Scientific-Atlanta satellite receivers.
Miles of plant: 62.0 (coaxial); 24.0 (fiber optic). Homes passed: 4,186.
Manager: Luke Matthews. Plant manager: William Smith. Marketing director: Chuck Balestri. Customer service manager: Debra Cage.
City fee: 3% of gross.
Ownership: Adelphia Communications Corp. (MSO).

EWING—Tele-Media Co. of Cumberland Gap, Box 1037, Pineville, KY 40977. Phone: 606-337-5569. County: Lee. Also serves Rose Hill. ICA: VA0137.
TV Market Ranking: Below 100. Franchise award date: May 6, 1976. Franchise expiration date: May 6, 2001. Began: March 1, 1976.
Channel capacity: 25. Channels available but not in use: 3.
Basic Service
Subscribers: 910.
Programming (received off-air): WCYB-TV (N) Bristol-Kingsport; WJHL-TV (C) Johnson City; WKPT-TV (A) Kingsport; WATE-TV (A), WBIR-TV (N), WVLT-TV (C) Knoxville; WSBN-TV (P) Norton; WSJK (P) Sneedville.
Programming (via satellite): WGN-TV (W) Chicago; Fox Family Channel; QVC.
Current originations: Automated time-weather; public access; educational access; government access; local news.
Fee: $41.75 installation (aerial), $60.50 (underground); $13.25 monthly; $2.45 converter.
Expanded Basic Service
Subscribers: 889.
Programming (via satellite): CNN; Country Music TV; Discovery Channel; ESPN; Nashville Network; TBS Superstation; USA Network.
Fee: $7.70 monthly.
Pay Service 1
Pay Units: 116.
Programming (via satellite): Disney Channel.
Fee: $25.00 installation; $8.00 monthly.
Pay Service 2
Pay Units: 64.
Programming (via satellite): HBO.
Fee: $25.00 installation; $10.00 monthly.
Pay Service 3
Pay Units: 102.
Programming (via satellite): Showtime.
Fee: $25.00 installation; $9.95 monthly.
Local advertising: No.
Equipment: C-COR headend; C-COR amplifiers; Comm/Scope cable; Scientific-Atlanta set top converters; DX Engineering satellite receivers.
Miles of plant: 45.9 (coaxial). Homes passed: 1,156. Total homes in franchised area: 2,500.
Manager: David L. Richardson. Chief technician: Jim Thompson. Marketing director: Bill Benner.
City fee: 3% of gross ($50 minimum).
Ownership: Tele-Media Corp. (MSO).

FAIRFAX COUNTY—Media General Cable of Fairfax Inc., Box 10800, 14650 Old Lee Rd., Chantilly, VA 20151-0800. Phone: 703-378-8400. Fax: 703-378-3840.
E-mail: mediageneralcable@prodigy.com.
Counties: Arlington & Fairfax. Also serves Alexandria (portions), Annandale, Burke, Centreville, Chantilly, Clifton, Fairfax, Fairfax Station, Falls Church, Great Falls, Herndon, Lorton, McLean, Oakton, Springfield, Vienna. ICA: VA0001.
TV Market Ranking: 9. Franchise award date: September 1, 1982. Franchise expiration date: N.A. Began: August 1, 1983.
Channel capacity: 120 (2-way capable). Channels available but not in use: None.
Basic Service
Subscribers: 237,000.
Programming (received off-air): WMPT (P) Annapolis; WTMW (H) Arlington; WNVC (E) Fairfax; WNVT (P) Goldvein; WPXW (X) Manassas; WBDC-TV (W), WDCA (U), WETA-TV (P), WHUT-TV (P), WJLA-TV (A), WRC-TV (N), WTTG (F), WUSA (C) Washington; 29 FMs.
Programming (via microwave): NewsChannel 8.
Programming (via satellite): WGN-TV (W) Chicago; C-SPAN; C-SPAN 2; C-SPAN Extra; E! Entertainment TV; NASA TV; Nick at Nite's TV Land; TBS Superstation; TV Guide Channel; Univision.
Current originations: Automated time-weather; public access; educational access; government access; leased access; local news; local sports.
Fee: $33.05 installation; $12.28 monthly; $1.95 converter; $34.44 additional installation.
Expanded Basic Service
Subscribers: 200,851.
Programming (via satellite): A & E; American Movie Classics; Animal Planet; Arabic Channel; BET; Bravo; CNBC; CNN; CNN International; CNNfn; Cartoon Network; Comedy Central; Court TV; Discovery Channel;

ESPN; ESPN 2; EWTN; Fox Family Channel; Goodlife TV Network; Headline News; History Channel; Home & Garden Television; Home Shopping Network; Independent Film Channel; International Channel; Kaleidoscope; Learning Channel; Lifetime; MSNBC; MTV; Nashville Network; Nickelodeon; Odyssey; Outdoor Life Network; Ovation; QVC; Romance Classics; Sci-Fi Channel; Speedvision; Telemundo; The Box-Country; The Health Network; The Weather Channel; Travel Channel; Trinity Bcstg. Network; Turner Classic Movies; Turner Network TV; USA Network; VH1.
Fee: $34.20 monthly.

A la Carte 1
Subscribers: N.A.
Programming (via satellite): ESPNews; Golf Channel; Home Team Sports.
Fee: $10.95 monthly (package).

Pay Service 1
Pay Units: 37,218.
Programming (via satellite): Cinemax (multiplexed).
Fee: $11.99 monthly.

Pay Service 2
Pay Units: 24,439.
Programming (via satellite): Disney Channel.
Fee: $10.99 monthly.

Pay Service 3
Pay Units: 66,674.
Programming (via satellite): HBO (multiplexed).
Fee: $12.99 monthly.

Pay Service 4
Pay Units: 17,056.
Programming (via satellite): The Movie Channel.
Fee: $11.99 monthly.

Pay Service 5
Pay Units: 32,087.
Programming (via satellite): Showtime (multiplexed).
Fee: $11.99 monthly.

Pay Service 6
Pay Units: 14,836.
Programming (via satellite): Home Team Sports.
Fee: $10.99 monthly.

Pay-Per-View
Addressable homes: 220,000.
Hot Choice; Playboy TV; Spice; special events.
Fee: Varies.
Pay-per-view manager: Ted Hodgins.

Local advertising: Yes. Available in satellite distributed, locally originated & character-generated programming. Local sales manager: Jim Hughes. Regional interconnect: Mega Advertising.
Program Guide: Cable Edition.
Equipment: Phasecom headend; Jerrold amplifiers; Comm/Scope, M/A-Com & Times Fiber cable; Hitachi & Ikegami cameras; Sony VTRs; MSI, Quanta & Texscan character generator; Jerrold & Zenith set top converters; Zenith addressable set top converters; Andrew satellite antenna; Scientific-Atlanta satellite receivers.
Miles of plant: 4200.0 (coaxial); 8.0 (fiber optic). Homes passed: 324,797. Total homes in franchised area: 324,797.
President & chief executive officer: Tom Waldrop. Program director: Janet Kohler Dueweke. Senior vice president, marketing & programming: Don Mathison.
County fee: 5% of gross.
Ownership: Media General Inc. (MSO). See Cable System Ownership.

FARMVILLE—Cable Comm, Box 465, Rte. 644, Farmville, VA 23901. Phone: 804-392-8144. Fax: 804-392-5262. Counties: Cumberland & Prince Edward. Also serves Cumberland County (southwestern portion), Hampden Sydney, Prince Edward County (northwestern portion). ICA: VA0050.
TV Market Ranking: Outside TV Markets. Franchise award date: January 10, 1991. Franchise expiration date: January 10, 2006. Began: November 11, 1979.
Channel capacity: 35 (not 2-way capable). Channels available but not in use: 4.

Basic Service
Subscribers: 2,075; Commercial subscribers: 463.
Programming (received off-air): WCVE-TV (P), WCVW (P), WRIC-TV (A), WRLH-TV (F), WTVR-TV (C), WWBT (N) Richmond-Petersburg; WSET-TV (A) Roanoke-Lynchburg; allband FM.
Programming (via satellite): WGN-TV (W) Chicago; C-SPAN; Odyssey; QVC; TBS Superstation.
Current originations: Automated time-weather.
Fee: $24.95 installation; $15.55 monthly; $0.75 converter.
Commercial fee: $11.35 monthly.

Expanded Basic Service
Subscribers: 1,897.
Programming (via satellite): A & E; Animal Planet; BET; CNN; Cartoon Network; Comedy Central; Country Music TV; Discovery Channel; ESPN; ESPN 2; Fox Family Channel; Fox News Channel; Headline News; History Channel; Home & Garden Television; Home Team Sports; Lifetime; MTV; Nashville Network; Nickelodeon; Pax Net; The Weather Channel; Travel Channel; Turner Network TV; USA Network; VH1.
Fee: $14.95 monthly.

Pay Service 1
Pay Units: 94.
Programming (via satellite): Disney Channel.
Fee: $14.95 installation; $8.95 monthly.

Pay Service 2
Pay Units: 397.
Programming (via satellite): HBO.
Fee: $14.95 installation; $11.50 monthly.

Pay Service 3
Pay Units: 90.
Programming (via satellite): Showtime.
Fee: $14.95 installation; $11.50 monthly.

Local advertising: Yes (locally produced). Rates: $3.00-$5.00/Day.
Equipment: Scientific-Atlanta headend; C-COR amplifiers; Times Fiber cable; Oak, Scientific-Atlanta & Pioneer set top converters; Eagle traps; Scientific-Atlanta satellite antenna; Gardiner satellite receivers.
Miles of plant: 73.0 (coaxial); None (fiber optic). Homes passed: 3,161.
Manager: Susan T. Morse. Chief technician: Steve Fore. Marketing director: Trish Lindsey.
City fee: 3% of gross.
Ownership: Fanch Communications Inc. (MSO); Time Warner Cable (MSO). See Cable System Ownership.

FLOYD—Time Warner Cable, Box 950, 651 S. Main St., Dobson, NC 27017. Phone: 910-386-4461. Fax: 910-386-9691. Counties: Carroll & Floyd. Also serves Floyd County, Sulphur Springs. ICA: VA0104.
TV Market Ranking: 70 (Floyd, portions of Floyd County); Outside TV Markets (portions of Floyd County, Sulphur Springs). Franchise award date: August 1, 1983. Franchise expiration date: August 1, 1998. Began: December 1, 1986.
Channel capacity: 52 (not 2-way capable). Channels available but not in use: 27.

Basic Service
Subscribers: 387; Commercial subscribers: 8.
Programming (received off-air): WBRA-TV (P) Roanoke; WDBJ (C), WFXR-TV (F), WSET-TV (A), WSLS-TV (N) Roanoke-Lynchburg.
Programming (via satellite): WGN-TV (W) Chicago; QVC; TBS Superstation.
Current originations: Local advertising.
Fee: $31.00 installation (aerial), $50.00 (underground); $9.75 monthly.

Expanded Basic Service
Subscribers: N.A.
Programming (via satellite): A & E; CNN; Country Music TV; Discovery Channel; ESPN; Fox Family Channel; MTV; Nashville Network; Nickelodeon; Turner Network TV; USA Network.
Fee: $16.92 monthly.

Pay Service 1
Pay Units: 29.
Programming (via satellite): Cinemax.
Fee: $10.95 monthly.

Pay Service 2
Pay Units: 22.
Programming (via satellite): Disney Channel.
Fee: $8.00 monthly.

Pay Service 3
Pay Units: 67.
Programming (via satellite): HBO.
Fee: $10.95 monthly.

Pay Service 4
Pay Units: 15.
Programming (via satellite): Showtime.
Fee: $10.95 monthly.

Miles of plant: 19.0 (coaxial). Homes passed: 669.
Manager: Gary Carpenter. Chief technician: Ken Ross.
County fee: $500 annually.
Ownership: Time Warner Cable (MSO).

FORT BELVOIR ARMY BASE—Jones Communications, 4391 Dale Blvd., Woodbridge, VA 22193. Phone: 703-730-2225. Fax: 703-670-5479. County: Fairfax. ICA: VA0055.
TV Market Ranking: 9. Franchise award date: December 1, 1980. Franchise expiration date: N.A. Began: June 1, 1981.
Channel capacity: 64 (2-way capable; not operating 2-way). Channels available but not in use: None.

Basic Service
Subscribers: 2,384.
Programming (received off-air): WMPT (P) Annapolis; WTMW (H) Arlington; WNVC (E) Fairfax; WNVT (P) Goldvein; WPXW (X) Manassas; WBDC-TV (W), WDCA (U), WETA-TV (P), WHUT-TV (P), WJLA-TV (A), WRC-TV (N), WTTG (F), WUSA (C) Washington.
Programming (via microwave): NewsChannel 8.
Programming (via satellite): WGN-TV (W) Chicago; A & E; American Movie Classics; BET; C-SPAN; C-SPAN 2; CNBC; CNN; Cartoon Network; Comedy Central; Discovery Channel; E! Entertainment TV; ESPN; ESPN 2; FMX Cable FM System; FX; fXM: Movies from Fox; Fox Family Channel; Great American Country; Headline News; History Channel; Home & Garden Television; Home Team Sports; Knowledge TV; Learning Channel; Lifetime; MTV; Nashville Network; Nickelodeon; Odyssey; QVC; Sci-Fi Channel; TBS Superstation; TV Guide Channel; The Weather Channel; Turner Classic Movies; Turner Network TV; USA Network; Univision; VH1.
Fee: $29.95 installation; $23.37 monthly.

Pay Service 1
Pay Units: N.A.
Programming (via satellite): Cinemax; Disney Channel; HBO; Showtime; The Movie Channel; The New Encore.
Fee: $3.95 monthly (Encore), $9.99 monthly (Cinemax, Disney, HBO, Showtime or TMC).

Pay-Per-View
Addressable homes: 1,000.
Spice.

Equipment: Scientific-Atlanta headend; Scientific-Atlanta amplifiers; Scientific-Atlanta set top converters; Scientific-Atlanta addressable set top converters; Scientific-Atlanta satellite antenna; Scientific-Atlanta satellite receivers.
Miles of plant: 40.0 (coaxial); None (fiber optic).
Manager: Troy Fitzhugh. Chief technician: Ray Ness. Marketing director: Mike Draughon. Customer service manager: Betty Lewis.
Ownership: Jones Intercable Inc. (MSO).

FORT CHISWELL—Time Warner Cable, Box 950, 651 S. Main St., Dobson, NC 27017. Phone: 910-386-4461. Counties: Carroll & Wythe. Also serves Austinville, Carroll County (portions), Ivanhoe, Max Meadows. ICA: VA0066.
TV Market Ranking: Below 100 (Austinville, portions of Carroll County, Fort Chiswell, Ivanhoe); Outside TV Markets (portions of Carroll County). Franchise award date: N.A. Franchise expiration date: June 1, 1999. Began: January 1, 1985.
Channel capacity: 35. Channels available but not in use: 2.

Basic Service
Subscribers: 1,938; Commercial subscribers: 250.
Programming (received off-air): WBRA-TV (P), WPXR (X) Roanoke; WDBJ (C), WSLS-TV (N) Roanoke-Lynchburg; WVFT (I) Rock Hill.
Programming (via satellite): WGN-TV (W) Chicago; WABC-TV (A) New York; TBS Superstation.
Fee: $31.00 installation (aerial), $50.00 (underground); $10.00 monthly.

Expanded Basic Service
Subscribers: 1,848.
Programming (via satellite): C-SPAN; CNN; Comedy Central; Country Music TV; Discovery Channel; ESPN; ESPN 2; Fox Family Channel; Headline News; MTV; Nashville Network; QVC; The Weather Channel; Turner Network TV; USA Network.
Fee: $20.42 monthly.

Pay Service 1
Pay Units: 161.

Programming (via satellite): Cinemax.
Fee: $10.95 monthly.
Pay Service 2
Pay Units: 89.
Programming (via satellite): Disney Channel.
Fee: $8.00 monthly.
Pay Service 3
Pay Units: 312.
Programming (via satellite): HBO.
Fee: $10.95 monthly.
Pay Service 4
Pay Units: 94.
Programming (via satellite): Showtime.
Fee: $10.95 monthly.
Pay Service 5
Pay Units: 89.
Programming (via satellite): The Movie Channel.
Fee: $8.00 monthly.
Miles of plant: 135.0 (coaxial). Homes passed: 2,318.
Manager: Mary Stone. Chief technician: Jay Murphy.
Ownership: Time Warner Cable (MSO).

FRANKLIN—Falcon Cable TV, Box 994, 408 Franklin St., Franklin, VA 23851. Phone: 757-569-9122. Fax: 757-569-8621. Counties: Isle of Wight, Southampton & Sussex. Also serves Boykins, Branchville, Carrollton, Courtland, Isle of Wight County, Ivor, Newsoms, Rushmere, Smithfield, Southampton County, Sussex County, Wakefield, Waverly, Windsor. ICA: VA0023.
TV Market Ranking: 44 (Carrollton, Franklin, Isle of Wight County, Ivor, Rushmere, Smithfield, portions of Southampton County, portions of Sussex County, Wakefield, Waverly, Windsor); 63 (Ivor, portions of Southampton County, portions of Sussex County, Wakefield, Waverly); Outside TV Markets (Boykins, Branchville, Courtland, Newsoms, portions of Southampton County). Franchise award date: February 9, 1982. Franchise expiration date: N.A. Began: June 15, 1982.
Channel capacity: 35 (not 2-way capable). Channels available but not in use: 1.
Basic Service
Subscribers: 8,200.
Programming (received off-air): WHRO-TV (P), WVEC-TV (A) Hampton-Norfolk; WAVY-TV (N), WGNT (U), WTKR (C), WTVZ (W) Portsmouth-Norfolk; allband FM.
Programming (via satellite): WGN-TV (W) Chicago; C-SPAN; Home Shopping Network; TBS Superstation.
Fee: $39.95 installation; $8.00 monthly; $15.00 additional installation.
Expanded Basic Service
Subscribers: 8,200.
Programming (via satellite): A & E; American Movie Classics; BET; CNBC; CNN; Discovery Channel; E! Entertainment TV; ESPN; Headline News; Home Team Sports; Lifetime; MTV; Nashville Network; Nick at Nite; Nickelodeon; The Weather Channel; Turner Network TV; USA Network.
Fee: $10.00 installation; $9.95 monthly.
Pay Service 1
Pay Units: 428.
Programming (via satellite): Disney Channel.
Fee: $9.95 monthly.
Pay Service 2
Pay Units: 3,214.
Programming (via satellite): HBO.
Fee: $9.95 monthly.
Pay Service 3
Pay Units: 354.
Programming (via satellite): The Movie Channel.
Fee: $9.95 monthly.
Pay Service 4
Pay Units: 593.
Programming (via satellite): Showtime.
Fee: $9.95 monthly.
Local advertising: Yes. Available in taped programming.
Equipment: Cadco, M/A-Com & Standard Components headend; GTE Sylvania & Jerrold amplifiers; Comm/Scope cable; Sony VTRs; Hamlin set top converters; Arcom traps; M/A-Com, Drake & Standard Components satellite antenna; Anixter-Mark satellite receivers.
Miles of plant: 404.0 (coaxial). Additional miles planned: 5.0 (coaxial). Homes passed: 14,360.
Manager: Sharon C. Stallings. Chief technician: Michael Hochman.
City fee: 3% of gross.
Ownership: Falcon Communications LP (MSO). See Cable System Ownership.

FRANKLIN COUNTY—CableVision Communications, Box 7, Redwood, VA 24146. Phone: 540-489-1300. Fax: 540-489-6250. Counties: Bedford, Franklin & Pittsylvania. Also serves Boones Mill, Ferrum, Gladehill, Moneta, Penhook, Pittsylvania County (northwestern portion), Redwood, Rocky Mount, Scruggs, Union Hall, Wirtz. ICA: VA0033.
TV Market Ranking: 70 (Boones Mill, Ferrum, Franklin County, Gladehill, Moneta, Penhook, portions of Pittsylvania County, Redwood, Rocky Mount, Scruggs, Union Hall, Wirtz); Below 100 (portions of Pittsylvania County); Outside TV Markets (portions of Pittsylvania County). Franchise award date: January 1, 1987. Franchise expiration date: January 1, 2002. Began: November 1, 1988.
Channel capacity: 60 (not 2-way capable). Channels available but not in use: 8.
Basic Service
Subscribers: 6,366.
Programming (received off-air): WBRA-TV (P), WPXR (X) Roanoke; WDBJ (C), WJPR (F), WSET-TV (A), WSLS-TV (N) Roanoke-Lynchburg.
Programming (via satellite): WGN-TV (W) Chicago; A & E; American Movie Classics; BET; C-SPAN; CNBC; CNN; Comedy Central; Country Music TV; Discovery Channel; E! Entertainment TV; ESPN; ESPN 2; Fox Family Channel; Headline News; History Channel; Home & Garden Television; Home Shopping Network; Home Team Sports; Learning Channel; Lifetime; MTV; Nashville Network; Nickelodeon; QVC; Sci-Fi Channel; TBS Superstation; TV Guide Channel; The Health Network; The Weather Channel; Turner Classic Movies; Turner Network TV; USA Network; VH1.
Current originations: Public access; educational access; local news; local sports.
Fee: $20.00 installation; $26.90 monthly.
Pay Service 1
Pay Units: 4,500.
Programming (via satellite): Cinemax; Disney Channel; HBO.
Fee: $10.00 installation; $7.00 monthly (Disney), $9.00 monthly (Cinemax), $9.50 monthly (HBO).
Pay Service 2
Pay Units: N.A.
Programming (via satellite): Showtime; The Movie Channel.
Fee: N.A.
Local advertising: Yes. Available in locally originated & taped programming.
Equipment: Scientific-Atlanta headend; Magnavox amplifiers; Trilogy cable; Pioneer set top converters; Arcom traps; Scientific-Atlanta satellite antenna; Scientific-Atlanta satellite receivers.
Miles of plant: 374.0 (coaxial); None (fiber optic). Additional miles planned: 20.0 (coaxial); 36.0 (fiber optic). Homes passed: 11,500. Total homes in franchised area: 16,000.
Manager: David Burke. Chief technician: Tom Moyer.
County fee: 3% of basic.
Ownership: Rifkin & Associates Inc. (MSO). See Cable System Ownership.

FREDERICKSBURG—Media General Cable of Fredericksburg Inc., Box 117, 1310 Belman Rd., Fredericksburg, VA 22404. Phone: 540-373-6343. Fax: 540-371-2391. Counties: Spotsylvania & Stafford. Also serves Spotsylvania, Spotsylvania County, Stafford, Stafford County. ICA: VA0019.
TV Market Ranking: Below 100. Franchise award date: August 1, 1964. Franchise expiration date: March 1, 2004. Began: August 15, 1964.
Channel capacity: 60 (2-way capable; operating 2-way). Channels available but not in use: 4.
Basic Service
Subscribers: 15,359; Commercial subscribers: 205.
Programming (received off-air): WNVC (E) Fairfax; WNVT (P) Goldvein; WPXW (X) Manassas; WCVE-TV (P), WRIC-TV (A), WTVR-TV (C), WWBT (N) Richmond-Petersburg; WDCA (U), WETA-TV (P), WHUT-TV (P), WJLA-TV (A), WRC-TV (N), WTTG (F), WUSA (C) Washington; 24 FMs.
Programming (via satellite): C-SPAN; EWTN; TBS Superstation; TV Guide Channel.
Current originations: Automated time-weather; public access; educational access; government access; leased access; automated emergency alert.
Fee: $44.55 installation; $11.25 monthly; $2.00 converter; $30.00 additional installation.
Expanded Basic Service
Subscribers: 14,309.
Programming (via satellite): A & E; American Movie Classics; BET; CNBC; CNN; Discovery Channel; E! Entertainment TV; ESPN; Fox Family Channel; Headline News; Home Shopping Network; Learning Channel; Lifetime; MTV; Nashville Network; Nickelodeon; The Weather Channel; Turner Network TV; USA Network; VH1.
Fee: $21.00 monthly.
Pay Service 1
Pay Units: 1,291.
Programming (via satellite): Cinemax.
Fee: $3.50 installation; $11.00 monthly.
Pay Service 2
Pay Units: 1,105.
Programming (via satellite): Disney Channel.
Fee: $3.50 installation; $9.00 monthly.
Pay Service 3
Pay Units: 2,713.
Programming (via satellite): HBO.
Fee: $3.50 installation; $11.00 monthly.
Pay Service 4
Pay Units: 764.
Programming (via satellite): Showtime.
Fee: $3.50 installation; $11.00 monthly.
Pay Service 5
Pay Units: 679.
Programming (via satellite): The Movie Channel.
Fee: $3.50 installation; $11.00 monthly.
Pay Service 6
Pay Units: 7,066.
Programming (via satellite): Home Team Sports.
Fee: $4.95 monthly.
Pay-Per-View
Addressable homes: 9,480.
Action Pay-Per-View; Viewer's Choice.
Fee: Varies.
Local advertising: Yes. Available in satellite distributed & locally originated programming. Rates: $11.50/30 Seconds. Local sales manager: Tom Baugh.
Program Guide: CableView.
Equipment: Jerrold headend; Jerrold amplifiers; Comm/Scope cable; Texscan character generator; Jerrold set top converters; Jerrold addressable set top converters; Pico traps; Scientific-Atlanta satellite antenna; Scientific-Atlanta satellite receivers.
Miles of plant: 303.8 (coaxial); 9.0 (fiber optic). Additional miles planned: 9.0 (coaxial). Homes passed: 19,789. Total homes in franchised area: 20,000.
Manager: Donald W. Craig. Chief technician: Matthew Hartwig.
City fee: 3%-5% of gross.
Ownership: Media General Inc. (MSO). See Cable System Ownership.

FRONT ROYAL—Central Virginia Cable Inc., Box 522, 15 N. Royal Ave., Front Royal, VA 22630-2611. Phones: 540-635-5338; 800-835-4949. Counties: Rappahannock & Warren. Also serves Bentonville, Castleton, Chester Gap, Huntly, Riverton, Warren County, Washington. ICA: VA0139.
TV Market Ranking: Below 100 (Castleton, Huntly); Outside TV Markets (Bentonville, Chester Gap, Front Royal, Riverton, Warren County, Washington). Franchise award date: N.A. Franchise expiration date: N.A. Began: February 19, 1964.
Channel capacity: 43. Channels available but not in use: N.A.
Basic Service
Subscribers: 8,529.
Programming (received off-air): WBFF (F), WJZ-TV (C) Baltimore; WHAG-TV (N) Hagerstown; WHSV-TV (A,F) Harrisonburg; WTVR-TV (C) Richmond-Petersburg; WVPT (P) Staunton; WDCA (U), WETA-TV (P), WJLA-TV (A), WRC-TV (N), WTTG (F), WUSA (C) Washington.
Programming (via satellite): TBS Superstation; TV Guide Channel.
Current originations: Automated time-weather; public access; educational access; government access; local news.
Fee: $33.00 installation; $10.00 monthly.
Expanded Basic Service
Subscribers: 8,375.
Programming (via satellite): A & E; American Movie Classics; BET; CNBC; CNN; Country Music TV; Discovery Channel; ESPN; Fox Family Channel; Home Shopping Network; Home Team Sports; Lifetime; MTV; Nashville Network; Nickelodeon; The Weather Channel; Turner Network TV; USA Network.
Fee: $25.00 installation; $12.45 monthly.
Pay Service 1
Pay Units: N.A.
Programming (via satellite): Cinemax; Disney Channel; HBO; Showtime; The Movie Channel.
Fee: $10.00 installation; $9.50 monthly (Disney), $11.50 monthly (Cinemax, HBO, Showtime or TMC).
Local advertising: Yes. Available in taped programming.
Equipment: GE, Magnavox & Scientific-Atlanta headend; Magnavox amplifiers; Comm/Scope cable; Pioneer & Scientific-Atlanta set top converters; Scientific-Atlanta addressable set top converters; Eagle, PPC & Pico traps; M/A-Com & Scientific-Atlanta satellite antenna; Scientific-Atlanta & Standard Components satellite receivers.
Miles of plant: 250.0 (coaxial). Additional miles planned: 30.0 (coaxial).

Manager: Richard Burke. Chief technician: Ken Skiles.
City fee: 3% of gross.
Ownership: Adelphia Communications Corp. (MSO).

GALAX—Southwest Virginia Cable, 112 Washington St., Galax, VA 24333. Phone: 800-835-4949. Fax: 540-236-4714. Counties: Carroll & Grayson. Also serves Carroll County (portions), Fries, Grayson County (portions), Hillsville, Oldtown, Woodlawn. ICA: VA0140.
TV Market Ranking: Outside TV Markets. Franchise award date: N.A. Franchise expiration date: N.A. Began: November 1, 1966.
Channel capacity: 36 (2-way capable; operating 2-way). Channels available but not in use: 1.
Basic Service
Subscribers: 6,225.
Programming (received off-air): WCCB (F) Charlotte; WFMY-TV (C), WGHP (F), WXII (N) Greensboro-High Point; WBRA-TV (P) Roanoke; WDBJ (C), WSLS-TV (N) Roanoke-Lynchburg.
Programming (via satellite): CNBC; CNN; Country Music TV; Discovery Channel; ESPN; Fox Family Channel; Headline News; Home Team Sports; Lifetime; MTV; Nashville Network; Nickelodeon; QVC; TBS Superstation; TV Guide Channel; The Weather Channel; Turner Network TV; USA Network; VH1.
Current originations: Automated time-weather.
Fee: $40.00 installation; $23.45 monthly; $2.52 converter; $25.00 additional installation.
Pay Service 1
Pay Units: N.A.
Programming (via satellite): Cinemax; Disney Channel; HBO; Showtime; The Movie Channel.
Fee: $7.95 monthly (Disney), $9.95 monthly (Cinemax, HBO, Showtime or TMC).
Pay-Per-View
Addressable homes: 1,500.
Special events.
Fee: Varies.
Local advertising: No.
Program Guide: The Cable Guide.
Equipment: Jerrold & Scientific-Atlanta headend; Jerrold amplifiers; Comm/Scope & Trilogy cable; Scientific-Atlanta set top converters; Scientific-Atlanta addressable set top converters; Eagle traps; Microdyne & Scientific-Atlanta satellite antenna; Standard Components satellite receivers.
Miles of plant: 236.0 (coaxial); 12.0 (fiber optic). Homes passed: 7,437.
Manager: Hilda Sexton. Chief technician: Rick Carrel.
City fee: 3% of gross.
Ownership: Adelphia Communications Corp. (MSO).

GLADE SPRING—Comcast Cablevision of the South, Box 38, 12191 Maple St., Glade Spring, VA 24340. Phone: 540-429-5149. Fax: 540-429-5400. Counties: Smyth & Washington. Also serves Abingdon, Chilhowie, Saltville, Seven Mile Ford, Smyth County, Sugar Grove, Washington County. ICA: VA0032.
TV Market Ranking: Below 100. Franchise award date: May 17, 1979. Franchise expiration date: N.A. Began: January 1, 1980.
Channel capacity: 36 (not 2-way capable). Channels available but not in use: None.
Basic Service
Subscribers: 12,786.
Programming (received off-air): WCYB-TV (N) Bristol-Kingsport; WJHL-TV (C) Johnson City; WKPT-TV (A) Kingsport; WMSY-TV (P) Marion; WDBJ (C), WSLS-TV (N) Roanoke-Lynchburg.
Programming (via satellite): CNN; ESPN; Fox Family Channel; Headline News; Lifetime; Nashville Network; Nickelodeon; TBS Superstation.
Current originations: Automated time-weather.
Fee: $30.75 installation; $20.64 monthly; $19.25 additional installation.
Pay Service 1
Pay Units: N.A.
Programming (via satellite): Cinemax; Disney Channel; HBO; Showtime; The Movie Channel.
Fee: $7.95 monthly (Showtime), $9.95 monthly (Cinemax, Disney, HBO or TMC).
Pay-Per-View
Addressable homes: 1,570.
Equipment: Jerrold headend; Jerrold amplifiers; Times Fiber cable; MSI character generator; AFC satellite antenna.
Miles of plant: 453.3 (coaxial); 40.8 (fiber optic). Homes passed: 15,849.
Manager: Don Kersey. Chief technician: Jack Clayman. Marketing director: Alice Mathews.
City fee: 3% of gross.
Ownership: Comcast Cable Communications Inc. (MSO).

GLASGOW—SVHH Cable Acquisition LP, Box 1097, 5 W. Nelson St., Lexington, VA 24450-2033. Phones: 540-464-5893; 800-835-4949. Fax: 540-464-6301. County: Rockbridge. Also serves Rockbridge County. ICA: VA0103.
TV Market Ranking: 70 (Glasgow, portions of Rockbridge County); Outside TV Markets (portions of Rockbridge County). Franchise award date: July 1, 1975. Franchise expiration date: N.A. Began: January 1, 1973.
Channel capacity: 36 (not 2-way capable). Channels available but not in use: 14.
Basic Service
Subscribers: 750.
Programming (received off-air): WDBJ (C), WSET-TV (A), WSLS-TV (N) Roanoke-Lynchburg; WVPT (P) Staunton; allband FM.
Programming (via satellite): WGN-TV (W) Chicago; CNN; ESPN; Fox Family Channel; Home Shopping Network; Nashville Network; Nickelodeon; QVC; TBS Superstation; Turner Network TV; USA Network.
Fee: $33.00 installation; $22.90 monthly; $20.00 additional installation.
Pay Service 1
Pay Units: 117.
Programming (via satellite): HBO.
Fee: $25.00 installation; $10.95 monthly.
Pay Service 2
Pay Units: 47.
Programming (via satellite): The Movie Channel.
Fee: $25.00 installation; $10.95 monthly.
Local advertising: No.
Program Guide: Premium Channels.
Equipment: Blonder-Tongue, Scientific-Atlanta & Tocom headend; Delta-Benco-Cascade & Scientific-Atlanta amplifiers; Comm/Scope cable; Pioneer & Oak set top converters; Pico traps; Comtech & Scientific-Atlanta satellite receivers.
Miles of plant: 33.0 (coaxial); None (fiber optic). Homes passed: 985. Total homes in franchised area: 1,183.
Manager: Gary Judy. Chief technician: Joe Clements. Marketing director: Stan Howell.
City fee: None.
Ownership: Adelphia Communications Corp. (MSO).

GLOUCESTER COUNTY—Gloucester Cablevision, Box 857, Rte. 616, Summerville Plantation, Gloucester, VA 23061. Phone: 804-693-3535. Fax: 804-693-2885.
E-mail: dap1stcomm@aol.com. County: Gloucester. ICA: VA0031.
TV Market Ranking: 44 (portions of Gloucester County); Outside TV Markets (portions of Gloucester County). Franchise award date: July 15, 1980. Franchise expiration date: July 15, 2005. Began: June 1, 1981.
Channel capacity: 61 (2-way capable; operating 2-way). Channels available but not in use: 6.
Basic Service
Subscribers: 8,681; Commercial subscribers: 89.
Programming (received off-air): WHRO-TV (P), WVEC-TV (A) Hampton-Norfolk; WAVY-TV (N), WGNT (U), WTKR (C), WTVZ (W) Portsmouth-Norfolk; WRIC-TV (A), WTVR-TV (C) Richmond-Petersburg; WVBT (F) Virginia Beach.
Programming (via satellite): WGN-TV (W) Chicago; A & E; American Movie Classics; BET; Bravo; C-SPAN; C-SPAN 2; CNBC; CNN; Cartoon Network; Country Music TV; Court TV; Discovery Channel; Disney Channel; ESPN; ESPN 2; FX; Fox Family Channel; Headline News; History Channel; Home & Garden Television; Home Team Sports; Knowledge TV; Learning Channel; Lifetime; MTV; Nashville Network; Nick at Nite; Nickelodeon; Odyssey; Outdoor Channel; QVC; Sci-Fi Channel; TBS Superstation; TV Food Network; TV Guide Channel; The Weather Channel; Travel Channel; Turner Network TV; USA Network; VH1.
Current originations: Automated time-weather; public access; religious access; leased access; local news.
Fee: $50.00 installation; $26.45 monthly; $14.75 additional installation.
Pay Service 1
Pay Units: 666.
Programming (via satellite): Cinemax.
Fee: $14.75 installation; $9.95 monthly.
Pay Service 2
Pay Units: 30.
Programming (via satellite): DMX.
Fee: $9.95 monthly.
Pay Service 3
Pay Units: 2,039.
Programming (via satellite): HBO (multiplexed).
Fee: $14.75 installation; $9.95 monthly.
Pay Service 4
Pay Units: 379.
Programming (via satellite): Showtime.
Fee: $14.75 installation; $9.95 monthly.
Pay Service 5
Pay Units: 673.
Programming (via satellite): The Movie Channel.
Fee: $14.75 installation; $9.95 monthly.
Pay-Per-View
Addressable homes: 4,500.
Hot Choice; Viewer's Choice.
Fee: Varies.
Local advertising: Yes (locally produced). Available in locally originated, character-generated & taped programming. Rates: $160.00/30 Seconds. Local sales manager: Kevin Hornsby.
Equipment: Microdyne, Scientific-Atlanta & ISS headend; Texscan amplifiers; Scala character generator; Standard Components, Scientific-Atlanta & Hamlin set top converters; Intercept traps; Intercept addressable traps; M/A-Com & Scientific-Atlanta satellite antenna; Microdyne & ISS satellite receivers; Falcone International commercial insert.
Miles of plant: 353.0 (coaxial); 85.0 (fiber optic). Homes passed: 11,310. Total homes in franchised area: 12,500.
Manager: William T. Newborg. Chief technician: James Foust. Customer service manager: Barbara Theis.
City fee: 3% of gross.
Ownership: 1st Commonwealth Communications Inc. (MSO). See Cable System Ownership.

GORDONSVILLE—FrontierVision, Suite P-200, 1777 S. Harrison St., Denver, CO 80210. Phone: 303-757-1588. Fax: 303-757-6105. County: Orange. Also serves Orange County (portions). ICA: VA0102.
TV Market Ranking: Below 100. Franchise award date: November 6, 1980. Franchise expiration date: N.A. Began: March 1, 1982.
Channel capacity: N.A. Channels available but not in use: N.A.
Basic Service
Subscribers: 462.
Programming (received off-air): WVIR-TV (N) Charlottesville; WCVE-TV (P), WRIC-TV (A), WRLH-TV (F), WTVR-TV (C), WWBT (N) Richmond-Petersburg.
Programming (via satellite): A & E; BET; CNN; Discovery Channel; ESPN; Fox Family Channel; Headline News; MTV; Nashville Network; Nickelodeon; TBS Superstation; USA Network.
Fee: $40.00 installation; $17.95 monthly; $2.00 converter.
Pay Service 1
Pay Units: 80.
Programming (via satellite): HBO.
Fee: $15.00 installation; $10.95 monthly.
Pay Service 2
Pay Units: 93.
Programming (via satellite): Showtime.
Fee: N.A.
Pay Service 3
Pay Units: 88.
Programming (via satellite): The Movie Channel.
Fee: N.A.
Equipment: GTE Sylvania amplifiers; Scientific-Atlanta & GTE Sylvania set top converters; Eagle & PPC traps; ChannelMaster & Microdyne satellite antenna; Microdyne satellite receivers.
Miles of plant: 19.5 (coaxial). Homes passed: 778.
President & chief executive officer: James Vaugh. Vice president: David Heyrend. Executive vice president: John Koo.
City & County fee: 3% of basic.
Ownership: FrontierVision Partners LP (MSO). See Cable System Ownership.

GOSHEN—Hillside CATV Inc., 181 Golfview Dr., Advance, NC 27006. Phone: 336-998-5182. Fax: 336-998-8888. County: Rockbridge. ICA: VA0165.
TV Market Ranking: Outside TV Markets. Franchise award date: October 1, 1990. Franchise expiration date: January 1, 2006. Began: December 1, 1990.
Channel capacity: 36 (2-way capable; not operating 2-way). Channels available but not in use: 18.
Basic Service
Subscribers: 185.
Programming (received off-air): WDBJ (C), WFXR-TV (F), WSET-TV (A), WSLS-TV (N) Roanoke-Lynchburg; WVPT (P) Staunton.
Programming (via satellite): WGN-TV (W) Chicago; CNN; Country Music TV; Discovery Channel; ESPN; Fox Family Channel; Nashville Network; Nickelodeon; TBS Superstation; USA Network; VH1.
Fee: $35.00 installation; $17.50 monthly.
Pay Service 1
Pay Units: 40.

Programming (via satellite): HBO.
Fee: $10.00 monthly.
Pay Service 2
Pay Units: 24.
Programming (via satellite): Showtime.
Fee: $10.00 monthly.
Miles of plant: 8.0 (coaxial); None (fiber optic). Homes passed: 235.
Manager: John Lyda. Chief technician: T. Rocky Orrell. Customer service manager: James Hicks.
Ownership: Hillside CATV Inc.

GREENE COUNTY—FrontierVision, Box 1747, Greenville, TN 37744. Phone: 800-753-0778. Fax: 423-639-0145. County: Greene. ICA: VA0082.
TV Market Ranking: Below 100. Franchise award date: May 7, 1983. Franchise expiration date: May 7, 1998. Began: June 22, 1984.
Channel capacity: 42. Channels available but not in use: 3.
Basic Service
Subscribers: 1,800.
Programming (received off-air): WVIR-TV (N) Charlottesville; WHSV-TV (A,F) Harrisonburg; WTVR-TV (C) Richmond-Petersburg; WVPT (P) Staunton; WDCA (U) Washington; allband FM.
Programming (via satellite): A & E; Disney Channel; ESPN; Fox Family Channel; Nashville Network; Nickelodeon; TBS Superstation.
Fee: $15.00 installation; $13.75 monthly.
Pay Service 1
Pay Units: 192.
Programming (via satellite): HBO.
Fee: $10.00 monthly.
Pay Service 2
Pay Units: 228.
Programming (via satellite): Showtime.
Fee: N.A.
Pay Service 3
Pay Units: 219.
Programming (via satellite): The Movie Channel.
Fee: N.A.
Pay Service 4
Pay Units: 92.
Programming (via satellite): Starz!
Fee: N.A.
Pay Service 5
Pay Units: 89.
Programming (via satellite): The New Encore.
Fee: N.A.
Equipment: Scientific-Atlanta headend; Broadband & Jerrold amplifiers; Capscan & Comm/Scope cable; Scientific-Atlanta satellite antenna; Scientific-Atlanta satellite receivers.
Miles of plant: 88.0 (coaxial). Additional miles planned: 40.0 (coaxial). Homes passed: 2,623.
Manager: Dan Callahan. Chief technician: Gary Shoemaker.
Ownership: Greene Communications Inc.-Virginia.

GRUNDY—Adelphia Cable Communications, 306 Suffolk Ave., Richlands, VA 24641. Phone: 800-385-4949. Fax: 540-863-9358. County: Buchanan. Also serves Big Rock, Brushy, Deel, Deskins, Harman, Hurley, Leemaster, Maxie, Roseann, Slate Creek, Stacy, Vansant, Wolford. ICA: VA0044.
TV Market Ranking: Below 100. Franchise award date: N.A. Franchise expiration date: N.A. Began: N.A.
Channel capacity: 35 (not 2-way capable). Channels available but not in use: None.
Basic Service
Subscribers: 4,370.
Programming (received off-air): WVVA (N) Bluefield; WCYB-TV (N) Bristol-Kingsport; W07DA (I), WLFG (I) Grundy; WJHL-TV (C) Johnson City; WKPT-TV (A) Kingsport; WVSX (I) Lewisburg; WSBN-TV (P) Norton; WOAY-TV (A) Oak Hill-Beckley; WDBJ (C) Roanoke-Lynchburg.
Programming (via satellite): FoxNet; TBS Superstation.
Fee: $46.00 installation (aerial), $60.00 (underground); $11.50 monthly; $3.25 converter; $23.00 additional installation.
Expanded Basic Service
Subscribers: 4,099.
Programming (via satellite): A & E; American Movie Classics; CNBC; CNN; Country Music TV; Discovery Channel; Disney Channel; ESPN; Fox Family Channel; Headline News; Home Team Sports; Lifetime; MTV; Nashville Network; Nickelodeon; QVC; TV Guide Channel; The Weather Channel; Turner Network TV; USA Network; VH1.
Fee: $19.50 monthly.
Pay Service 1
Pay Units: 296.
Programming (via satellite): Cinemax.
Fee: $11.50 monthly.
Pay Service 2
Pay Units: 329.
Programming (via satellite): HBO.
Fee: $11.50 monthly.
Pay Service 3
Pay Units: 139.
Programming (via satellite): Showtime.
Fee: $11.50 monthly.
Pay Service 4
Pay Units: 93.
Programming (via satellite): The Movie Channel.
Fee: $11.50 monthly.
Pay-Per-View
Addressable homes: 1,141.
Movies; special events.
Fee: Varies.
Local advertising: Yes. Available in taped programming.
Equipment: Scientific-Atlanta headend; Magnavox amplifiers; Comm/Scope, Times Fiber & Trilogy cable; Jerrold & Scientific-Atlanta set top converters; Jerrold & Scientific-Atlanta addressable set top converters; Andrew, RCA & Scientific-Atlanta satellite antenna; Electrohome, Hughes & Omni satellite receivers; ChannelMatic commercial insert.
Miles of plant: 204.0 (coaxial); None (fiber optic). Homes passed: 6,341. Total homes in franchised area: 8,765.
Manager: Ralph E. Bowman. Chief technician: Danny Nelson. Program director: Jeff Abbas. Marketing director: Dave Owens.
Ownership: Adelphia Communications Corp. (MSO).

HAMPTON—Cox Communications, 1323 W. Pembroke Ave., Hampton, VA 23661. Phones: 757-722-2851; 800-874-6390. Fax: 757-728-0515. County: Hampton City. Also serves Fort Monroe, Langley AFB. ICA: VA0008.
TV Market Ranking: 44. Franchise award date: N.A. Franchise expiration date: N.A. Began: October 1, 1966.
Channel capacity: 36 (not 2-way capable). Channels available but not in use: N.A.
Basic Service
Subscribers: 37,092; Commercial subscribers: 14.
Programming (received off-air): WHRO-TV (P), WVEC-TV (A) Hampton-Norfolk; WAVY-TV (N), WGNT (U), WTKR (C), WTVZ (W) Portsmouth-Norfolk.
Programming (via satellite): A & E; BET; C-SPAN; CNBC; CNN; Cartoon Network; Discovery Channel; ESPN; Fox Family Channel; Headline News; Home Shopping Network; Home Team Sports; Lifetime; MTV; Nashville Network; Nickelodeon; QVC; TBS Superstation; The Inspirational Network; The Weather Channel; Turner Network TV; USA Network; VH1.
Current originations: Automated time-weather; educational access.
Fee: $48.00 installation; $8.16 monthly; $1.00 converter.
Pay Service 1
Pay Units: 5,491.
Programming (via satellite): Cinemax.
Fee: $11.59 monthly.
Pay Service 2
Pay Units: 3,407.
Programming (via satellite): Disney Channel.
Fee: $9.65 monthly.
Pay Service 3
Pay Units: 12,435.
Programming (via satellite): HBO.
Fee: $11.59 monthly.
Pay Service 4
Pay Units: 5,604.
Programming (via satellite): The Movie Channel.
Fee: $11.59 monthly.
Pay Service 5
Pay Units: 5,385.
Programming (via satellite): Showtime.
Fee: $11.59 monthly.
Pay-Per-View
Addressable homes: 13,500.
Local advertising: Yes. Regional interconnect: Tidewater Cable Interconnect.
Program Guide: TV Host.
Equipment: Jerrold headend; C-COR amplifiers; Comm/Scope cable; Sony VTRs; Jerrold set top converters; Pioneer addressable set top converters; Scientific-Atlanta satellite antenna; Scientific-Atlanta satellite receivers.
Miles of plant: 665.0 (coaxial); 670.2 (fiber optic). Homes passed: 61,688. Total homes in franchised area: 63,339.
Manager: William T. Day. Chief technician: Ron Horchler. Program director: Glen Chalmers. Marketing director: Gregg D. Paolo.
Ownership: Cox Communications Inc. (MSO).

HAMPTON ROADS—Cox Cable Hampton Roads Inc., 225 Clearfield Ave., Virginia Beach, VA 23462. Phone: 757-224-4269. Fax: 757-671-1501. Counties: Chesapeake City, Norfolk City, Portsmouth City & Virginia Beach City, VA; Currituck, NC. Also serves Currituck County (northern portion), NC; Chesapeake, Fort Story, Norfolk, Norfolk Naval Base/Southside Hampton Roads, Portsmouth, U.S. Coast Guard 5th District, U.S. Coast Guard Support Center, Virginia Beach, VA. ICA: VA0002.
TV Market Ranking: 44. Franchise award date: N.A. Franchise expiration date: N.A. Began: January 16, 1978.
Channel capacity: 50 (2-way capable). Channels available but not in use: None.
Basic Service
Subscribers: 391,706; Commercial subscribers: 1,275.
Programming (received off-air): WHRO-TV (P), WVEC-TV (A) Hampton-Norfolk; WAVY-TV (N), WGNT (U), WPXV (X), WTKR (C), WTVZ (W) Portsmouth-Norfolk.
Programming (via satellite): WSBK-TV (U) Boston; WGN-TV (W) Chicago; A & E; American Movie Classics; BET; Bravo; C-SPAN; CNBC; CNN; Cartoon Network; Comedy Central; Discovery Channel; E! Entertainment TV; ESPN; Fox Family Channel; Headline News; Home Team Sports; Learning Channel; Lifetime; MTV; Music Choice; Nashville Network; Nickelodeon; Odyssey; QVC; TBS Superstation; TV Guide Channel; The Health Network; The Weather Channel; Travel Channel; Turner Classic Movies; Turner Network TV; USA Network; VH1.
Current originations: Public access; educational access; government access; religious access; leased access; automated emergency alert; local news.
Fee: $40.00 installation; $20.75 monthly; $10.00 additional installation.
Commercial fee: $5.50 monthly.
Pay Service 1
Pay Units: 167,271.
Programming (via satellite): Cinemax; Disney Channel; HBO; Showtime; The New Encore.
Fee: $15.00 installation; $5.95-$10.95 monthly (each).
Pay-Per-View
Addressable homes: 73,828.
Hot Choice; Viewer's Choice; special events.
Fee: $3.95-$5.95.
Local advertising: Yes (locally produced). Available in satellite distributed & locally originated programming. Rates: $575.00/Hour; $325.00/30 Minutes; $140-$190.00/Minute; $70.00-$95.00/30 Seconds. Local sales manager: Eric Zitron. Regional interconnect: Tidewater Cable Interconnect.
Program Guide: The Cable Guide.
Equipment: Hughes, Scientific-Atlanta & Theta-Com headend; Scientific-Atlanta amplifiers; Comm/Scope cable; Ikegami & Hitachi cameras; Sony VTRs; Texscan, MSI & Chyron character generator; Scientific-Atlanta set top converters; Jerrold addressable set top converters; Eagle traps; Scientific-Atlanta satellite antenna; Scientific-Atlanta satellite receivers; ChannelMatic & Texscan commercial insert.
Miles of plant: 3326.0 (coaxial); 150.0 (fiber optic). Homes passed: N.A.
Manager: Franklin R. Bowers. Chief technician: Dana G. Coltrin. Program director: Irv Hill. Marketing director: Larry G. Michel.
City fee: 3%-5% of gross.
Ownership: Cox Communications Inc. (MSO).

HARRISONBURG—Adelphia Cable, 160-B N. Mason St., Harrisonburg, VA 22802. Phone: 540-434-9979. Fax: 540-434-3920. County: Rockingham. Also serves Bridgewater, Broadway, Dayton, Mount Crawford, Rawley Springs, Rockingham County, Timberville. ICA: VA0016.
TV Market Ranking: Below 100. Franchise award date: January 1, 1952. Franchise expiration date: July 13, 2002. Began: August 1, 1952.
Channel capacity: 60 (not 2-way capable). Channels available but not in use: 2.
Basic Service
Subscribers: 16,454.
Programming (received off-air): WVIR-TV (N) Charlottesville; WHSV-TV (A,F) Harrisonburg; WRIC-TV (A), WTVR-TV (C), WWBT (N) Richmond-Petersburg; WVPT (P) Staunton; WDCA (U), WRC-TV (N), WTTG (F), WUSA (C) Washington; WAZT-LP (I) Woodstock; allband FM.
Programming (via satellite): TBS Superstation; TV Guide Channel.
Fee: $45.43 installation (aerial), $75.72 (underground); $10.48 monthly; $1.87 converter.
Expanded Basic Service
Subscribers: 15,306.
Programming (via satellite): A & E; American Movie Classics; BET; C-SPAN; C-SPAN 2; CNN; Country Music TV; Discovery Channel; E! Entertainment TV; ESPN; Fox Family Channel; Headline News; History Channel; Home & Garden Television; Home Team Sports; Learning Channel; Lifetime; MTV; Nashville Network; Nickelodeon; Odyssey; QVC; The Weather Channel; Turner Classic

Movies; Turner Network TV; USA Network; VH1.
Fee: $37.80 installation; $18.70 monthly.

A la Carte 1
Subscribers: N.A.
Programming (via satellite): Cartoon Network; ESPN 2; Sci-Fi Channel; The New Encore.
Fee: $2.95 monthly (package); $.80-$1.50 monthly (each).

Pay Service 1
Pay Units: 6,422.
Programming (via satellite): Cinemax (multiplexed); Disney Channel; HBO (multiplexed); Music Choice; Showtime (multiplexed); The Movie Channel.
Fee: $10.00 installation; $6.95 monthly (Music Choice), $11.50 monthly (Cinemax, Disney, HBO, Showtime or TMC).

Pay-Per-View
Addressable homes: 6,834.
Action Pay-Per-View; Hot Choice; Spice; Viewer's Choice.

Local advertising: No.
Equipment: Jerrold & Scientific-Atlanta headend; C-COR & Jerrold amplifiers; Comm/Scope cable; Texscan character generator; Jerrold set top converters; Pioneer addressable set top converters; Scientific-Atlanta satellite antenna; Scientific-Atlanta satellite receivers.
Miles of plant: 344.0 (coaxial); 15.0 (fiber optic). Homes passed: 21,430. Total homes in franchised area: 28,300.
Manager: Debbie Reed. Chief technician: Phillip Bennett. Business manager: Sue Grandstaff.
City fee: Varies.
Ownership: Adelphia Communications Corp. (MSO).

HAYSI—K & V Cable TV Co., Drawer M, Haysi, VA 24256. Phone: 540-865-4253. Fax: 540-865-9832. County: Dickenson. Also serves Dickenson County (portions). ICA: VA0116.
TV Market Ranking: Below 100. Franchise award date: January 4, 1983. Franchise expiration date: January 4, 1998. Began: January 1, 1983.
Channel capacity: 14 (not 2-way capable). Channels available but not in use: None.

Basic Service
Subscribers: 200; Commercial subscribers: 15.
Programming (received off-air): WCYB-TV (N) Bristol-Kingsport; WEMT (F) Greeneville; WJHL-TV (C) Johnson City; WKPT-TV (A) Kingsport; WSBN-TV (P) Norton.
Programming (via satellite): WGN-TV (W) Chicago; CNN; ESPN; Fox Family Channel; Nashville Network; TBS Superstation; USA Network.
Fee: $10.00 monthly.
Commercial fee: $10.00 monthly.

Pay Service 1
Pay Units: 18.
Programming (via satellite): HBO.
Fee: $10.00 monthly.

Local advertising: No.
Equipment: DX Engineering & Jerrold headend; Blonder-Tongue amplifiers; Gamco traps; Dark Star & Scientific-Atlanta satellite antenna; DX Engineering, Jerrold & Scientific-Atlanta satellite receivers.
Miles of plant: 20.0 (coaxial). Homes passed: 300.
Manager: Gerene R. Fleming. Chief technician: Dennis H. Fleming.
City fee: 1% of gross.
Ownership: Dennis Fleming.

HEATHSVILLE—FrontierVision, Suite P-200, 1777 S. Harrison St., Denver, CO 80210. Phone: 303-757-1588. Fax: 303-757-6105. County: Northumberland. ICA: VA0051.
TV Market Ranking: Outside TV Markets. Franchise award date: March 10, 1988. Franchise expiration date: March 10, 2003. Began: December 1, 1988.
Channel capacity: 41 (not 2-way capable). Channels available but not in use: 9.

Basic Service
Subscribers: 1,972.
Programming (received off-air): WHRO-TV (P), WVEC-TV (A) Hampton-Norfolk; WAVY-TV (N), WGNT (U), WTKR (C) Portsmouth-Norfolk; WCVW (P), WRIC-TV (A), WRLH-TV (F), WTVR-TV (C) Richmond-Petersburg.
Programming (via satellite): A & E; C-SPAN; CNN; Country Music TV; Discovery Channel; ESPN; Fox Family Channel; Headline News; Home Shopping Network; Home Team Sports; Lifetime; MTV; Nashville Network; Nickelodeon; Odyssey; TBS Superstation; The Weather Channel; VH1.
Fee: $40.00 installation; $17.95 monthly; $2.00 converter.

Pay Service 1
Pay Units: 253.
Programming (via satellite): Disney Channel.
Fee: $15.00 installation; $8.95 monthly.

Pay Service 2
Pay Units: 645.
Programming (via satellite): HBO.
Fee: $15.00 installation; $9.95 monthly.

Pay Service 3
Pay Units: 514.
Programming (via satellite): Showtime.
Fee: $15.00 installation; $9.95 monthly.

Equipment: Magnavox amplifiers; Scientific-Atlanta set top converters; Eagle & PPC traps; Scientific-Atlanta & Prodelin satellite antenna; Regency, Scientific-Atlanta & Zenith satellite receivers.
Miles of plant: 203.0 (coaxial). Homes passed: 3,822. Total homes in franchised area: 3,822.
President & chief executive officer: James Vaugh. Vice president, engineering: David Heyrend. Executive vice president: John Koo.
County fee: 3% of gross.
Ownership: FrontierVision Partners LP (MSO). See Cable System Ownership.

HENRICO COUNTY—MediaOne, 5401 Staples Hill Rd., Richmond, VA 23228. Phone: 804-915-5400. Fax: 804-915-5426. Counties: Goochland, Hanover & Henrico. Also serves Ashland, Goochland County, Goochland Court House, Hanover County (portions). ICA: VA0003.
TV Market Ranking: 63 (Ashland, portions of Goochland County, Goochland Court House, Hanover County, Henrico County); Below 100 (portions of Goochland County). Franchise award date: June 1, 1977. Franchise expiration date: November 13, 2005. Began: March 26, 1979.
Channel capacity: 78 (2-way capable). Channels available but not in use: None.

Basic Service
Subscribers: 94,301; Commercial subscribers: 397.
Programming (received off-air): WUPV (U) Ashland; WCVE-TV (P), WCVW (P), WRIC-TV (A), WRLH-TV (F), WTVR-TV (C), WWBT (N) Richmond-Petersburg.
Programming (via satellite): A & E; American Movie Classics; BET; C-SPAN; CNBC; CNN; Discovery Channel; ESPN; Fox Family Channel; Headline News; Home Shopping Network; Lifetime; MTV; Nashville Network; Nickelodeon; QVC; TV Guide Channel; The Weather Channel; Turner Network TV; USA Network; VH1.
Current originations: Automated time-weather; public access; educational access; government access; religious access; leased access; local news; local sports.
Fee: $26.73 installation; $33.86 monthly.

Expanded Basic Service
Subscribers: N.A.
Programming (via satellite): Animal Planet; Bravo; C-SPAN 2; CNBC; Cartoon Network; Comedy Central; Court TV; E! Entertainment TV; ESPN Classic Sports; FX; Fox News Channel; Golf Channel; Home & Garden Television; Home Team Sports; Learning Channel; MSNBC; MuchMusic Network; Nick at Nite's TV Land; Outdoor Life Network; QVC; Speedvision; TV Food Network; TV Guide Sneak Prevue.
Fee: N.A.

Pay Service 1
Pay Units: 60,288.
Programming (via satellite): Cinemax (multiplexed); Disney Channel; HBO (multiplexed).
Fee: $18.00 installation; $9.95 monthly (each).

Pay-Per-View
Addressable homes: 12,088.

Local advertising: Yes. Available in satellite distributed, locally originated, character-generated, taped & automated programming. Rates: $70.00/Minute; $35.00/30 Seconds. Local sales manager: M. Zoller.
Equipment: Scientific-Atlanta headend; Magnavox amplifiers; Comm/Scope cable; Sony cameras; Sony VTRs; Metrodata character generator; Pioneer, RCA & Scientific-Atlanta set top converters; Arco & Eagle traps; M/A-Com & Scientific-Atlanta satellite antenna; Microdyne, Scientific-Atlanta & ISS satellite receivers; TV Watch commercial insert.
Miles of plant: 2017.5 (coaxial). Homes passed: 124,572. Total homes in franchised area: 152,000.
Manager: David R. Lee. Chief technician: Russ Pomfrey. Marketing director: Sarwar Affar.
City fee: 5% of gross.
Ownership: MediaOne Group (MSO). See Cable System Ownership.

HOPEWELL—Tele-Media Co. of Hopewell/Prince George, 2200 River Rd., Prince George, VA 23875. Phone: 804-862-3232. County: Prince George. Also serves Prince George County. ICA: VA0022.
TV Market Ranking: 63. Franchise award date: February 28, 1977. Franchise expiration date: February 28, 2002. Began: September 15, 1977.
Channel capacity: 35 (not 2-way capable). Channels available but not in use: None.

Basic Service
Subscribers: 9,827; Commercial subscribers: 179.
Programming (received off-air): WUPV (U) Ashland; WCVE-TV (P), WCVW (P), WRIC-TV (A), WRLH-TV (F), WTVR-TV (C), WWBT (N) Richmond-Petersburg; allband FM.
Programming (via satellite): WGN-TV (W) Chicago; C-SPAN; QVC; TBS Superstation; TV Guide Channel; Trinity Bcstg. Network.
Current originations: Automated time-weather; public access.
Fee: $36.87 installation; $12.70 monthly; $0.90 converter.
Commercial fee: $12.69 monthly.

Expanded Basic Service
Subscribers: 9,555.
Programming (via satellite): A & E; BET; CNN; Discovery Channel; ESPN; Headline News; Home Team Sports; Lifetime; MTV; Nashville Network; Nickelodeon; Sci-Fi Channel; The Weather Channel; Turner Network TV; USA Network; VH1.
Fee: $13.55 monthly.

Pay Service 1
Pay Units: 718.
Programming (via satellite): Cinemax.
Fee: $20.00 installation; $11.50 monthly.

Pay Service 2
Pay Units: 640.
Programming (via satellite): Disney Channel.
Fee: $20.00 installation; $8.95 monthly.

Pay Service 3
Pay Units: 1,536.
Programming (via satellite): HBO.
Fee: $20.00 installation; $11.50 monthly.

Pay Service 4
Pay Units: 2,223.
Programming (via satellite): Showtime.
Fee: $20.00 installation; $11.50 monthly.

Pay Service 5
Pay Units: 1,928.
Programming (via satellite): The Movie Channel.
Fee: $11.50 monthly.

Pay-Per-View
Special events.
Fee: Varies.

Local advertising: Yes (locally produced & insert). Rates: $15.00/Minute; $10.00/30 Seconds.
Equipment: Jerrold headend; GTE Sylvania amplifiers; Times Fiber & Comm/Scope cable; Blonder-Tongue character generator; Scientific-Atlanta & Pioneer set top converters; Scientific-Atlanta satellite antenna; Microdyne satellite receivers.
Miles of plant: 239.0 (coaxial). Homes passed: 13,768. Total homes in franchised area: 15,365.
Manager: Thomas A. Olsen. Chief technician: John Hockenberry. Marketing director: Jim Guthrie.
City fee: 5% of gross.
Ownership: Tele-Media Corp. (MSO).

HOT SPRINGS—Bath CATV Inc., 228 Park Ave., Worcester, MA 01609. Phone: 508-754-5865. Fax: 508-752-7342. County: Bath. Also serves Bacova, Bath County, Warm Springs. ICA: VA0096.
TV Market Ranking: Outside TV Markets. Franchise award date: N.A. Franchise expiration date: N.A. Began: April 23, 1969.
Channel capacity: 40 (not 2-way capable). Channels available but not in use: 3.

Basic Service
Subscribers: 931.
Programming (received off-air): WVVA (N) Bluefield; WBRA-TV (P), WPXR (X) Roanoke; WDBJ (C), WFXR-TV (F), WSET-TV (A), WSLS-TV (N) Roanoke-Lynchburg; allband FM.
Programming (via satellite): WGN-TV (W) Chicago; A & E; American Movie Classics; C-SPAN; CNN; Discovery Channel; ESPN; ESPN 2; Fox Family Channel; Headline News; History Channel; Home Team Sports; Learning Channel; Lifetime; Nashville Network; Nickelodeon; QVC; TBS Superstation; The Weather Channel; Trinity Bcstg. Network; Turner Network TV; USA Network.
Current originations: Automated time-weather.
Fee: $50.00 installation; $24.95 monthly; $10.00 additional installation.

Pay Service 1
Pay Units: 45.
Programming (via satellite): Disney Channel.
Fee: $15.00 installation; $7.95 monthly.

Pay Service 2
Pay Units: 82.
Programming (via satellite): HBO.
Fee: $15.00 installation; $11.95 monthly.

Pay Service 3
Pay Units: 57.

Programming (via satellite): Flix; Showtime; The Movie Channel.
Fee: $11.95 monthly.
Local advertising: No.
Equipment: Jerrold headend; Jerrold amplifiers; Times Fiber cable; GTE Sylvania cameras; Oak set top converters; Jerrold addressable set top converters; RMS traps; Scientific-Atlanta satellite antenna; Scientific-Atlanta satellite receivers.
Miles of plant: 30.0 (coaxial). Homes passed: 1,000. Total homes in franchised area: 1,000.
Manager: John B. Cooney. Chief technician: Tim Siron.
Ownership: Cooney Cable Assoc. Inc. (MSO).

HURT—Adelphia Cable, 560 Patton St., Danville, VA 24541-1310. Phone: 804-797-4135. Fax: 804-793-6920. County: Pittsylvania. Also serves Gretna. ICA: VA0087.
TV Market Ranking: 70. Franchise award date: July 19, 1982. Franchise expiration date: July 19, 2002. Began: January 1, 1980.
Channel capacity: 35 (not 2-way capable). Channels available but not in use: None.
Basic Service
Subscribers: Included with Danville, VA.
Programming (received off-air): WUPN-TV (U) Greensboro-High Point; WBRA-TV (P) Roanoke; WDBJ (C), WJPR (F), WSET-TV (A), WSLS-TV (N) Roanoke-Lynchburg.
Programming (via satellite): WGN-TV (W) Chicago; Home Shopping Network.
Fee: $50.00 installation (aerial), $59.95 (underground); $5.65 monthly; $1.80 converter; $10.00 additional installation.
Expanded Basic Service
Subscribers: 1,489.
Programming (via satellite): A & E; American Movie Classics; BET; C-SPAN; CNBC; Country Music TV; ESPN; Fox Family Channel; Home Team Sports; Lifetime; MTV; Nashville Network; Nickelodeon; QVC; The Inspirational Network; The Weather Channel; Travel Channel; Turner Network TV; USA Network; VH1.
Fee: $16.23 monthly.
A la Carte 1
Subscribers: N.A.
Programming (via satellite): CNN; Discovery Channel; TBS Superstation.
Fee: $2.30 monthly (package); $1.25 monthly (each).
Pay Service 1
Pay Units: 158.
Programming (via satellite): Cinemax.
Fee: $10.00 monthly.
Pay Service 2
Pay Units: 71.
Programming (via satellite): Disney Channel.
Fee: $9.95 monthly.
Pay Service 3
Pay Units: 634.
Programming (via satellite): HBO.
Fee: $10.00 monthly.
Pay Service 4
Pay Units: 160.
Programming (via satellite): Showtime.
Fee: $11.95 monthly.
Local advertising: No.
Program Guide: TV Host.
Equipment: Scientific-Atlanta headend; GTE Sylvania & Texscan amplifiers; Comm/Scope & Times Fiber cable; Oak & Scientific-Atlanta set top converters; Arcom, Eagle & Pico traps; ChannelMaster & Scientific-Atlanta satellite antenna; DX Antenna & Scientific-Atlanta satellite receivers.
Miles of plant: 27.9 (coaxial). Homes passed: 3,625.
Manager: Ted Crane. Chief technician: Michael Pruitt. Marketing director: Jerry Lesser.
Ownership: Time Warner Cable (MSO).

INDEPENDENCE—Southwest Virginia Cable, 112 Washington St., Galax, VA 24333. Phone: 800-835-4949. Fax: 540-236-4714. County: Grayson. Also serves Grayson County. ICA: VA0142.
TV Market Ranking: Outside TV Markets. Franchise award date: N.A. Franchise expiration date: N.A. Began: January 1, 1975.
Channel capacity: 30 (not 2-way capable). Channels available but not in use: 4.
Basic Service
Subscribers: 479.
Programming (received off-air): WFMY-TV (C), WGHP (F), WXII (N) Greensboro-High Point; WBRA-TV (P) Roanoke; WDBJ (C), WSLS-TV (N) Roanoke-Lynchburg; WXLV-TV (A) Winston-Salem; allband.
Programming (via satellite): CNBC; CNN; Discovery Channel; ESPN; Fox Family Channel; Headline News; Home Team Sports; Lifetime; MTV; Nashville Network; Nickelodeon; QVC; TBS Superstation; USA Network; VH1.
Fee: $40.00 installation; $21.34 monthly; $25.00 additional installation.
Pay Service 1
Pay Units: 79.
Programming (via satellite): HBO.
Fee: $20.00 installation; $9.95 monthly.
Local advertising: No.
Equipment: Jerrold & Scientific-Atlanta headend; Jerrold amplifiers; Comm/Scope cable; Scientific-Atlanta set top converters; Scientific-Atlanta addressable set top converters; Eagle traps; Microdyne & Scientific-Atlanta satellite antenna; Standard Components satellite receivers.
Miles of plant: 16.5 (coaxial); None (fiber optic). Homes passed: 583.
Manager: Hilda Sexton. Chief technician: Rick Carrel.
City fee: 3% of gross.
Ownership: Adelphia Communications Corp. (MSO).

JAMES CITY COUNTY—Cox Communications, 112 New Quarter Dr., Williamsburg, VA 23188. Phone: 757-229-7622. Fax: 757-229-0432. County: James City. ICA: VA0027.
TV Market Ranking: 44 (James City County); 63 (James City County). Franchise award date: June 1, 1981. Franchise expiration date: June 1, 2005. Began: March 1, 1982.
Channel capacity: 52 (2-way capable). Channels available but not in use: N.A.
Basic Service
Subscribers: 14,236; Commercial subscribers: 117.
Programming (received off-air): WHRO-TV (P), WVEC-TV (A) Hampton-Norfolk; WAVY-TV (N), WGNT (U), WTKR (C), WTVZ (W) Portsmouth-Norfolk; WCVE-TV (P), WRIC-TV (A), WRLH-TV (F), WTVR-TV (C), WWBT (N) Richmond-Petersburg; 28 FMs.
Programming (via satellite): WGN-TV (W) Chicago; A & E; American Movie Classics; BET; C-SPAN; C-SPAN 2; CNBC; CNN; Discovery Channel; ESPN; Fox Family Channel; Headline News; Home Shopping Network; Home Team Sports; Lifetime; MTV; Music Choice; Nashville Network; Nickelodeon; QVC; TBS Superstation; TV Guide Channel; The Inspirational Network; The Weather Channel; Turner Network TV; USA Network; VH1.
Current originations: Public access; educational access; government access; religious access; leased access.
Fee: $15.00 installation; $16.50 monthly; $7.50 additional installation.
Pay Service 1
Pay Units: 8,538.

Programming (via satellite): Cinemax; Disney Channel; HBO; Showtime.
Fee: $10.00 installation; $8.95 monthly (Disney), $9.95 monthly (Cinemax, HBO or Showtime).
Pay-Per-View
Special events.
Fee: Varies.
Local advertising: Yes. Available in satellite distributed programming. Regional interconnect: Tidewater Cable Interconnect.
Equipment: Phasecom & Scientific-Atlanta headend; Magnavox amplifiers; Comm/Scope cable; Sony cameras; Sony VTRs; MSI character generator; Pioneer set top converters; Eagle traps; Anixter-Pruzan & Scientific-Atlanta satellite antenna; Catel, Microdyne & Scientific-Atlanta satellite receivers; Texscan, MSI & Sony commercial insert.
Miles of plant: 429.0 (coaxial); 27.0 (fiber optic). Homes passed: 15,248.
Manager: Frank Bowers. Marketing director: Ken Dye.
County fee: 3% of gross.
Ownership: Cox Communications Inc. (MSO).

JARRATT—CWA Cable, Box 1048, Littleton, NC 27850. Phone: 919-586-7156. Fax: 919-586-6997. Counties: Greensville & Sussex. ICA: VA0114.
TV Market Ranking: 63. Franchise award date: November 1, 1989. Franchise expiration date: January 1, 2005. Began: July 1, 1990.
Channel capacity: 35. Channels available but not in use: 18.
Basic Service
Subscribers: 360.
Programming (received off-air): WRAL-TV (C) Raleigh-Durham; WRIC-TV (A), WTVR-TV (C), WWBT (N) Richmond-Petersburg.
Programming (via satellite): WGN-TV (W) Chicago; BET; C-SPAN; CNN; Discovery Channel; ESPN; Fox Family Channel; MTV; Nashville Network; Nickelodeon; QVC; TBS Superstation; The Weather Channel; Turner Network TV; USA Network.
Current originations: Educational access; religious access.
Fee: $35.00 installation (aerial), $70.00 (underground); $17.50 monthly.
Pay Service 1
Pay Units: 39.
Programming (via satellite): Cinemax.
Fee: $10.00 monthly.
Pay Service 2
Pay Units: 49.
Programming (via satellite): HBO.
Fee: $10.00 monthly.
Equipment: Jerrold amplifiers; Oak set top converters; Uniden satellite antenna; Drake satellite receivers.
Miles of plant: 40.0 (coaxial); 24.0 (fiber optic). Homes passed: 400. Total homes in franchised area: 450.
Manager: C. Winston Ashworth Jr. Marketing & program director: Cathy I. Ashworth.
County fee: 5% of gross.
Ownership: Charles Wins Ashworth II (MSO).

JONESVILLE—CC & S Cable TV, Box 301, Rte. 2, Jonesville, VA 24263. Phone: 540-346-1288. County: Lee. ICA: VA0115.
TV Market Ranking: Below 100. Franchise award date: N.A. Franchise expiration date: N.A. Began: March 15, 1972.
Channel capacity: 8. Channels available but not in use: None.
Basic Service
Subscribers: N.A.
Programming (received off-air): WCYB-TV (N) Bristol-Kingsport; WLOS (A) Greenville-Spartanburg-Asheville; WJHL-TV (C) Johnson City; WKPT-TV (A) Kingsport; WATE-TV (A), WBIR-TV (N) Knoxville; WSBN-TV (P) Norton; WSJK (P) Sneedville; allband FM.
Fee: $10.00 installation; $5.00 monthly.
Equipment: Blonder-Tongue headend; Ameco amplifiers; Essex cable.
Miles of plant: 10.0 (coaxial). Additional miles planned: 3.0 (coaxial). Homes passed: 350. Total homes in franchised area: 400.
Manager: Claude A. Pennington.
City fee: 2% of gross.
Ownership: Claude A. Pennington.

KEEN MOUNTAIN—Southwest Virginia Cable, 306 Suffolk Ave., Richlands, VA 24641. Phone: 800-835-4949. Fax: 540-964-2505. Counties: Buchanan & Tazewell. Also serves Garden Creek, Janey, Mavisdale, Mount Heron, Oakwood, Pilgrims Knob, Whitewood. ICA: VA0083.
TV Market Ranking: Below 100. Franchise award date: N.A. Franchise expiration date: N.A. Began: N.A.
Channel capacity: 35 (not 2-way capable). Channels available but not in use: None.
Basic Service
Subscribers: 967.
Programming (received off-air): WVVA (N) Bluefield; WCYB-TV (N) Bristol-Kingsport; W07DA (I), WLFG (I) Grundy; WJHL-TV (C) Johnson City; WKPT-TV (A) Kingsport; WVSX (I) Lewisburg; WSBN-TV (P) Norton; WOAY-TV (A) Oak Hill-Beckley; WDBJ (C) Roanoke-Lynchburg.
Programming (via satellite): FoxNet; TBS Superstation.
Fee: $46.00 installation (aerial), $60.00 (underground); $11.40 monthly; $3.25 converter; $23.00 additional installation.
Expanded Basic Service
Subscribers: 903.
Programming (via satellite): A & E; American Movie Classics; CNBC; CNN; Country Music TV; Discovery Channel; Disney Channel; ESPN; Fox Family Channel; Headline News; Home Team Sports; Lifetime; MTV; Nashville Network; Nickelodeon; QVC; TV Guide Channel; The Weather Channel; Turner Network TV; USA Network; VH1.
Fee: $19.60 monthly.
Pay Service 1
Pay Units: 69.
Programming (via satellite): Cinemax.
Fee: $11.50 monthly.
Pay Service 2
Pay Units: 84.
Programming (via satellite): HBO.
Fee: $11.50 monthly.
Pay Service 3
Pay Units: 45.
Programming (via satellite): Showtime.
Fee: $11.50 monthly.

Pay Service 4
Pay Units: 28.
Programming (via satellite): The Movie Channel.
Fee: $11.50 monthly.
Pay-Per-View
Addressable homes: 318.
Movies; special events.
Fee: Varies.
Local advertising: Yes. Available in taped programming.
Equipment: Scientific-Atlanta headend; Magnavox amplifiers; Comm/Scope, Times Fiber & Trilogy cable; Jerrold & Scientific-Atlanta set top converters; Jerrold & Scientific-Atlanta addressable set top converters; Andrew, RCA & Scientific-Atlanta satellite antenna; Electrohome, Hughes & Omni satellite receivers; ChannelMatic commercial insert.
Miles of plant: 68.0 (coaxial); None (fiber optic). Homes passed: 1,515.
Manager: Ralph E. Bowman. Chief technician: Danny Nelson. Program director: Jeff Abbas. Marketing director: Dave Owens.
Ownership: Adelphia Communications Corp. (MSO).

KENBRIDGE—Cable Comm, Box 465, Rte. 644, Farmville, VA 23901. Phone: 804-392-8144. Fax: 804-392-5262. County: Lunenburg. Also serves Lunenburg County (portions). ICA: VA0110.
TV Market Ranking: Outside TV Markets. Franchise award date: October 15, 1991. Franchise expiration date: October 15, 1998. Began: December 1, 1980.
Channel capacity: 30 (not 2-way capable). Channels available but not in use: 4.
Basic Service
Subscribers: 288; Commercial subscribers: 8.
Programming (received off-air): WCVE-TV (P), WCVW (P), WRIC-TV (A), WRLH-TV (F), WTVR-TV (C), WWBT (N) Richmond-Petersburg; allband FM.
Programming (via satellite): WGN-TV (W) Chicago; Fox Family Channel; Lifetime; QVC; TBS Superstation.
Fee: $24.95 installation; $18.94 monthly; $0.75 converter.
Commercial fee: $13.76 monthly.
Expanded Basic Service
Subscribers: 265.
Programming (via satellite): A & E; American Movie Classics; CNN; Discovery Channel; ESPN; ESPN 2; MTV; Nashville Network; Nickelodeon; Turner Network TV; USA Network.
Fee: $12.79 monthly.
Pay Service 1
Pay Units: 55.
Programming (via satellite): HBO.
Fee: $11.95 monthly.
Pay Service 2
Pay Units: 2.
Programming (via satellite): Showtime.
Fee: $11.95 monthly.
Equipment: Scientific-Atlanta headend; AEL amplifiers; Times Fiber cable; Scientific-Atlanta set top converters; Eagle traps; Scientific-Atlanta satellite antenna.
Miles of plant: 10.0 (coaxial); None (fiber optic). Homes passed: 686. Total homes in franchised area: 851.
Manager: Susan T. Morse. Chief technician: Steve Fore. Marketing director: Trish Lindsey.
City fee: 3% of basic.
Ownership: Fanch Communications Inc. (MSO); Time Warner Cable (MSO). See Cable System Ownership.

KEYSVILLE—Cable Comm, Box 465, Rte. 644, Farmville, VA 23901. Phone: 804-392-8144. Fax: 804-392-5262. County: Charlotte. Also serves Charlotte County (eastern portion), Charlotte Court House, Phenix. ICA: VA0143.
TV Market Ranking: 70 (Phenix); Outside TV Markets (Charlotte County, Charlotte Court House, Keysville). Franchise award date: March 1, 1982. Franchise expiration date: N.A. Began: October 1, 1985.
Channel capacity: 35 (not 2-way capable). Channels available but not in use: 6.
Basic Service
Subscribers: 482; Commercial subscribers: 11.
Programming (received off-air): WCVE-TV (P), WRLH-TV (F) Richmond-Petersburg; WDBJ (C), WSET-TV (A), WSLS-TV (N) Roanoke-Lynchburg.
Programming (via satellite): WGN-TV (W) Chicago; C-SPAN; QVC; TBS Superstation.
Current originations: Government access.
Fee: $24.95 installation; $18.09 monthly; $0.75 converter.
Commercial fee: $13.41 monthly.
Expanded Basic Service
Subscribers: 441.
Programming (via satellite): A & E; American Movie Classics; Animal Planet; BET; CNN; Cartoon Network; Country Music TV; Discovery Channel; ESPN; ESPN 2; Fox Family Channel; Learning Channel; Lifetime; Nashville Network; Nickelodeon; The Weather Channel; Turner Network TV; USA Network; VH1.
Fee: $13.66 monthly.
Pay Service 1
Pay Units: 42.
Programming (via satellite): Cinemax.
Fee: $11.50 monthly.
Pay Service 2
Pay Units: 69.
Programming (via satellite): HBO.
Fee: $11.50 monthly.
Equipment: Blonder-Tongue headend; Magnavox, Jerrold & C-COR amplifiers; Times Fiber & Comm/Scope cable; Scientific-Atlanta set top converters; Eagle traps.
Miles of plant: 42.0 (coaxial); None (fiber optic). Homes passed: 1,006. Total homes in franchised area: 2,062.
Manager: Susan T. Morse. Chief technician: Steve Fore. Marketing director: Trish Lindsey.
Franchise fee: 3% of gross.
Ownership: Fanch Communications Inc. (MSO); Time Warner Cable (MSO). See Cable System Ownership.

KING GEORGE—Western Shore Cable, Box 159, Hollywood, MD 20636. Phone: 800-427-0705. Fax: 703-775-5313. Counties: Caroline & King George. Also serves Bowling Green, Caroline County (unincorporated areas), Dahlgren, Port Royal. ICA: VA0058.
TV Market Ranking: 63 (Bowling Green, portions of Caroline County); Below 100 (portions of Caroline County, Dahlgren); Outside TV Markets (portions of Caroline County, King George, Port Royal). Franchise award date: March 6, 1986. Franchise expiration date: March 6, 2001. Began: December 8, 1987.
Channel capacity: 54. Channels available but not in use: 12.
Basic Service
Subscribers: 3,000.
Programming (received off-air): WTMW (H) Arlington; WNVC (E) Fairfax; WNVT (P) Goldvein; WPXW (X) Manassas; WTVR-TV (C), WWBT (N) Richmond-Petersburg; WBDC-TV (W), WDCA (U), WETA-TV (P), WJLA-TV (A), WRC-TV (N), WTTG (F), WUSA (C) Washington.
Programming (via satellite): QVC; TBS Superstation.
Current originations: Public access.
Fee: $30.00 installation; $8.00 monthly.
Expanded Basic Service
Subscribers: 2,850.
Programming (via satellite): A & E; BET; C-SPAN; CNBC; CNN; Country Music TV; Discovery Channel; ESPN; Fox Family Channel; Headline News; Home Team Sports; Learning Channel; Lifetime; MTV; Nashville Network; Nickelodeon; Sci-Fi Channel; The Weather Channel; Turner Network TV; USA Network; VH1.
Fee: $16.00 monthly.
Pay Service 1
Pay Units: N.A.
Programming (via satellite): Cinemax; Disney Channel; HBO; Showtime.
Fee: $8.95 monthly (Disney), $10.95 monthly (Cinemax, HBO or Showtime).
Miles of plant: 140.0 (coaxial). Additional miles planned: 20.0 (coaxial). Homes passed: 4,500.
Ownership: Billy R. Jones (MSO).

KING WILLIAM (portions)—OnePoint Communications, Box 22, Ladysmith, VA 22501. Phone: 804-448-0166. Fax: 804-448-9347. County: King William. Also serves Aylett, Central Garage. ICA: VA0166.
TV Market Ranking: 63. Franchise award date: January 1, 1988. Franchise expiration date: January 1, 2003. Began: January 1, 1988.
Channel capacity: N.A. Channels available but not in use: N.A.
Basic Service
Subscribers: 870.
Programming (received off-air): WUPV (U) Ashland; WCVE-TV (P), WCVW (P), WRIC-TV (A), WRLH-TV (F), WTVR-TV (C), WWBT (N) Richmond-Petersburg.
Programming (via satellite): CNN; The Weather Channel.
Fee: $40.00 installation (aerial), $65.00 (underground); $16.95 monthly.
Expanded Basic Service
Subscribers: 690.
Programming (via satellite): A & E; American Movie Classics; BET; C-SPAN; Country Music TV; Court TV; Discovery Channel; ESPN; Fox Family Channel; Headline News; Learning Channel; Lifetime; MTV; Nashville Network; Nickelodeon; Sci-Fi Channel; TBS Superstation; Turner Network TV; USA Network; VH1.
Fee: $8.00 monthly.
Pay Service 1
Pay Units: 1,038.
Programming (via satellite): Disney Channel; Flix; HBO; Showtime; The Movie Channel.
Fee: $4.95 monthly (Flix), $10.95 monthly (HBO, Disney, Showtime or TMC).
Miles of plant: 27.0 (coaxial).
Manager: Carol Lewis. Chief technician: Dick McKinney.
Ownership: OnePoint Communications (MSO).

LACEY SPRING—FrontierVision, Suite P-200, 1777 S. Harrison St., Denver, CO 80210. Phone: 303-757-1588. Fax: 303-757-6105. County: Rockingham. ICA: VA0144.
TV Market Ranking: Below 100. Franchise award date: April 13, 1988. Franchise expiration date: N.A. Began: September 1, 1990.
Channel capacity: 40. Channels available but not in use: 3.
Basic Service
Subscribers: 126.
Programming (received off-air): WVIR-TV (N) Charlottesville; WHSV-TV (A,F) Harrisonburg; WVPT (P) Staunton; WTTG (F), WUSA (C) Washington; WAZT-LP (I) Woodstock.
Programming (via satellite): WGN-TV (W) Chicago; A & E; American Movie Classics; C-SPAN; CNBC; CNN; Country Music TV; Discovery Channel; Disney Channel; ESPN; Fox Family Channel; Headline News; Home Shopping Network; Home Team Sports; Learning Channel; Lifetime; MTV; Nashville Network; Nickelodeon; Odyssey; QVC; Sci-Fi Channel; TBS Superstation; The Weather Channel; Trinity Bcstg. Network; Turner Network TV; USA Network; VH1.
Fee: $47.50 installation; $19.95 monthly; $1.50 converter; $25.00 additional installation.
Pay Service 1
Pay Units: 39.
Programming (via satellite): HBO.
Fee: $9.00 monthly.
Pay Service 2
Pay Units: 28.
Programming (via satellite): Showtime.
Fee: $9.00 monthly.
Miles of plant: 10.0 (coaxial). Homes passed: 203.
Manager: Dan Callahan. Chief technician: Gary Shoemaker.
Ownership: FrontierVision Partners LP (MSO). See Cable System Ownership.

LAKE GASTON—CWA Cable, Box 1048, Littleton, NC 27850. Phones: 919-586-7156; 800-448-0490. Fax: 919-586-6997. Counties: Brunswick & Mecklenburg. Also serves Bracey, Brunswick County (portions), Mecklenburg County (portions). ICA: VA0170.
TV Market Ranking: Outside TV Markets. Franchise award date: N.A. Franchise expiration date: N.A. Began: July 30, 1993.
Channel capacity: 40. Channels available but not in use: 20.
Basic Service
Subscribers: 360.
Programming (received off-air): WLFL (U), WRAL-TV (C), WRDC (U), WTVD (A) Raleigh-Durham; WRIC-TV (A) Richmond-Petersburg; WUNP-TV (P) Roanoke Rapids.
Programming (via satellite): WGN-TV (W) Chicago; A & E; C-SPAN; C-SPAN 2; CNN; Discovery Channel; ESPN; Fox Family Channel; MTV; Nashville Network; Nickelodeon; QVC; TBS Superstation; The Weather Channel; Travel Channel; Turner Network TV; USA Network.
Fee: $35.00 installation (aerial), $70.00 (underground); $17.50 monthly.
Pay Service 1
Pay Units: 58.
Programming (via satellite): HBO.
Fee: $10.00 monthly.
Miles of plant: 30.0 (coaxial).
Manager: C. Winston Ashworth Jr. Marketing & program director: Cathy I. Ashworth.
Ownership: Charles Wins Ashworth II (MSO).

LAKE HOLSTON—FrontierVision, Suite P-200, 1777 S. Harrison St., Denver, CO 80210. Phone: 303-757-1588. Fax: 303-757-6105. Counties: Washington, VA; Sullivan, TN. Also serves Sullivan County (northern portion), TN. ICA: VA0108.
TV Market Ranking: Below 100. Franchise award date: July 9, 1984. Franchise expiration date: July 9, 1999. Began: April 1, 1989.
Channel capacity: 42 (not 2-way capable). Channels available but not in use: 20.
Basic Service
Subscribers: 293.
Programming (received off-air): WCYB-TV (N) Bristol-Kingsport; WEMT (F) Greeneville;

WJHL-TV (C) Johnson City; WKPT-TV (A) Kingsport; WSJK (P) Sneedville.
Programming (via satellite): WGN-TV (W) Chicago; C-SPAN; CNN; Discovery Channel; ESPN; Fox Family Channel; Headline News; Home Shopping Network; Lifetime; MTV; Nashville Network; Nickelodeon; TBS Superstation; VH1.
Fee: $17.95 monthly.

Pay Service 1
Pay Units: 54.
Programming (via satellite): Cinemax.
Fee: $15.00 installation; $10.00 monthly.

Pay Service 2
Pay Units: 41.
Programming (via satellite): HBO.
Fee: $15.00 installation; $10.95 monthly.

Local advertising: No.
Program Guide: CableView.
Equipment: Magnavox amplifiers; Comm/Scope cable; Scientific-Atlanta set top converters; Eagle & PPC traps; Prodelin satellite antenna; Microdyne satellite receivers.
Miles of plant: 28.0 (coaxial). Homes passed: 615. Total homes in franchised area: 615.
President & chief exececutive officer: James Vaugh. Vice president, engineering: David Heyrend. Executive vice president: John Koo.
County fee: 3% of gross.
Ownership: FrontierVision Partners LP (MSO). See Cable System Ownership.

LANCASTER COUNTY—Northern Neck Cablevision, Box 1147, Rte. 227, Cook's Corner, Saluda, VA 23149. Phone: 804-435-2828. Fax: 804-435-1569. E-mail: pattgibbs@aol.com. Counties: Lancaster & Northumberland. Also serves Irvington (town), Kilmarnock (town), Northumberland County, White Stone (town). ICA: VA0146.
TV Market Ranking: Outside TV Markets. Franchise award date: January 1, 1982. Franchise expiration date: October 1, 2001. Began: June 1, 1982.
Channel capacity: 61 (2-way capable; operating 2-way). Channels available but not in use: None.

Basic Service
Subscribers: 1,821; Commercial subscribers: 218.
Programming (received off-air): WHRO-TV (P), WVEC-TV (A) Hampton-Norfolk; WAVY-TV (N), WGNT (U), WTKR (C), WTVZ (W) Portsmouth-Norfolk; WCVE-TV (P), WRIC-TV (A), WRLH-TV (F), WTVR-TV (C), WWBT (N) Richmond-Petersburg.
Programming (via satellite): WGN-TV (W) Chicago; A & E; American Movie Classics; BET; Bravo; C-SPAN; C-SPAN 2; CNBC; CNN; Cartoon Network; Country Music TV; Court TV; Discovery Channel; Disney Channel; ESPN; ESPN 2; Fox Family Channel; Fox News Channel; Golf Channel; Headline News; History Channel; Home & Garden Television; Home Team Sports; Learning Channel; Lifetime; MTV; Nashville Network; Nick at Nite's TV Land; Nickelodeon; Outdoor Channel; QVC; Sci-Fi Channel; TBS Superstation; TV Food Network; TV Guide Channel; The Health Network; The Weather Channel; Turner Network TV; USA Network; VH1.
Current originations: Automated time-weather; public access; government access; religious access.
Fee: $50.00 installation; $26.45 monthly.

Expanded Basic Service
Subscribers: 469.
Programming (via satellite): Cartoon Network; ESPN 2; History Channel; Sci-Fi Channel; TV Food Network; Travel Channel; Turner Classic Movies.
Fee: $5.95 monthly.

Pay Service 1
Pay Units: 192.
Programming (via satellite): Cinemax.
Fee: $9.95 monthly.

Pay Service 2
Pay Units: 407.
Programming (via satellite): HBO (multiplexed).
Fee: $9.95 monthly.

Pay Service 3
Pay Units: 88.
Programming (via satellite): The Movie Channel.
Fee: $9.95 monthly.

Pay Service 4
Pay Units: 85.
Programming (via satellite): Showtime.
Fee: $9.95 monthly.

Pay Service 5
Pay Units: 10.
Programming (via satellite): DMX.
Fee: $9.95 monthly.

Pay-Per-View
Addressable homes: 1,950.
Hot Choice; Viewer's Choice.
Fee: $3.95.

Local advertising: Yes. Available in locally originated, character-generated & taped programming. Rates: $160.00/30 Seconds. Local sales manager: Jonelle Boyd.
Equipment: Cadco & Blonder-Tongue headend; Texscan amplifiers; Comm/Scope cable; Scala character generator; Standard Components, Scientific-Atlanta & Hamlin set top converters; Intercept traps; Intercept addressable traps; Microdyne & ChannelMaster satellite receivers; Falcone International commercial insert.
Miles of plant: 146.0 (coaxial); 13.0 (fiber optic). Homes passed: 3,385.
Manager: Patricia Gibbs. Chief technician: James Foust. Customer service manager: Jonelle Boyd.
County fee: 3% of basic gross.
Ownership: 1st Commonwealth Communications Inc. (MSO).

LAWRENCEVILLE—Cable Comm, Box 465, Rte. 644, Farmville, VA 23901. Phone: 804-392-8144. Fax: 804-392-5262. County: Brunswick. Also serves Brunswick County. ICA: VA0089.
TV Market Ranking: 63 (portions of Brunswick County); Outside TV Markets (portions of Brunswick County, Lawrenceville). Franchise award date: June 14, 1978. Franchise expiration date: December 14, 2008. Began: June 1, 1980.
Channel capacity: 35. Channels available but not in use: 14.

Basic Service
Subscribers: 707; Commercial subscribers: 11.
Programming (received off-air): WRAL-TV (C) Raleigh-Durham; WCVE-TV (P), WCVW (P), WRIC-TV (A), WRLH-TV (F), WTVR-TV (C), WWBT (N) Richmond-Petersburg; WNVN-LP (I) Roanoke Rapids; allband FM.
Programming (via satellite): Comedy Central; QVC; TBS Superstation.
Fee: $24.95 installation; $19.40 monthly; $0.75 converter.
Commercial fee: $13.57 monthly.

Expanded Basic Service
Subscribers: 628.
Programming (via satellite): A & E; BET; CNN; Discovery Channel; ESPN; ESPN 2; Lifetime; MTV; Nashville Network; Nickelodeon; The Weather Channel; Turner Network TV; USA Network.
Fee: $12.85 monthly.

Pay Service 1
Pay Units: 217.
Programming (via satellite): HBO.
Fee: $14.95 installation; $11.95 monthly.

Equipment: Scientific-Atlanta headend; Scientific-Atlanta amplifiers; Times Fiber cable; Scientific-Atlanta set top converters; Eagle traps; Scientific-Atlanta satellite antenna.
Miles of plant: 25.0 (coaxial); None (fiber optic). Additional miles planned: 3.0 (coaxial). Homes passed: 1,400. Total homes in franchised area: 1,677.
Manager: Susan T. Morse. Chief technician: Steve Fore. Marketing director: Trish Lindsey.
City fee: 3% of basic.
Ownership: Fanch Communications Inc. (MSO); Time Warner Cable (MSO). See Cable System Ownership.

LEBANON—CableVision, 105 N. Main St., Lebanon, VA 24266. Phones: 540-889-0669; 800-654-7619. Fax: 540-889-3382. County: Russell. Also serves Castlewood, Dante, Honaker, Russell County, St. Paul, Swords Creek. ICA: VA0035.
TV Market Ranking: Below 100. Franchise award date: N.A. Franchise expiration date: October 1, 2004. Began: October 1, 1964.
Channel capacity: 36 (not 2-way capable). Channels available but not in use: N.A.

Basic Service
Subscribers: 5,400.
Programming (received off-air): WCYB-TV (N) Bristol-Kingsport; WEMT (F) Greeneville; WLFG (I) Grundy; WJHL-TV (C) Johnson City; WKPT-TV (A) Kingsport; WSBN-TV (P) Norton; WDBJ (C) Roanoke-Lynchburg; WSJK (P) Sneedville; allband FM.
Programming (via satellite): WGN-TV (W) Chicago; QVC; TBS Superstation; The Weather Channel.
Current originations: Public access.
Fee: $53.64 installation; $9.25 monthly.

Expanded Basic Service
Subscribers: N.A.
Programming (via satellite): A & E; C-SPAN; CNN; Country Music TV; Discovery Channel; ESPN; ESPN 2; Fox Family Channel; Headline News; Home Team Sports; Learning Channel; Lifetime; MTV; Nashville Network; Nickelodeon; Trinity Bcstg. Network; Turner Network TV; USA Network; VH1.
Fee: $13.70 monthly.

Pay Service 1
Pay Units: 179.
Programming (via satellite): Cinemax.
Fee: $10.95 monthly.

Pay Service 2
Pay Units: 271.
Programming (via satellite): Disney Channel.
Fee: $8.95 monthly.

Pay Service 3
Pay Units: 699.
Programming (via satellite): HBO.
Fee: $10.95 monthly.

Pay Service 4
Pay Units: 70.
Programming (via satellite): Showtime.
Fee: $8.95 monthly.

Pay Service 5
Pay Units: 70.
Programming (via satellite): The Movie Channel.
Fee: $8.95 monthly.

Equipment: Jerrold & Standard Communications headend; Scientific-Atlanta satellite antenna.
Miles of plant: 175.0 (coaxial). Additional miles planned: 2.0 (coaxial). Homes passed: 8,095.
Manager: Dave Burke. Plant manager: Daryl Boyd. Customer service manager: Nickie Ketron.
City fee: 2% of gross.
Ownership: Rifkin & Associates Inc. (MSO). See Cable System Ownership.

LEBANON (portions)—Cooney Cable Assoc. of Bastian LP, Box 69, Delbarton, WV 25670. Phones: 304-426-4609; 800-682-9455. Fax: 304-426-6726. County: Russell. Also serves Castlewood, Cleveland, Hansonville, Spring City. ICA: VA0185.
TV Market Ranking: Below 100. Franchise award date: N.A. Franchise expiration date: N.A. Began: N.A.
Channel capacity: N.A. Channels available but not in use: N.A.

Basic Service
Subscribers: 990.
Programming (received off-air): WCYB-TV (N) Bristol-Kingsport; WEMT (F) Greeneville; WLFG (I) Grundy; WJHL-TV (C) Johnson City; WKPT-TV (A) Kingsport; WSBN-TV (P) Norton.
Programming (via satellite): WGN-TV (W) Chicago; American Movie Classics; C-SPAN; CNN; Discovery Channel; E! Entertainment TV; ESPN; ESPN 2; Fox Family Channel; Great American Country; Headline News; History Channel; Home Team Sports; Learning Channel; Lifetime; MTV; Nashville Network; Nickelodeon; Outdoor Life Network; QVC; TBS Superstation; The Weather Channel; Travel Channel; Trinity Bcstg. Network; Turner Network TV; USA Network; VH1.
Fee: N.A.

Pay Service 1
Pay Units: 65.
Programming (via satellite): Disney Channel.
Fee: N.A.

Pay Service 2
Pay Units: 154.
Programming (via satellite): HBO.
Fee: N.A.

Pay Service 3
Pay Units: 101.
Programming (via satellite): Showtime.
Fee: N.A.

Pay Service 4
Pay Units: 46.
Programming (via satellite): The Movie Channel.
Fee: N.A.

Homes passed: 1,604.
Manager: John B. Cooney. Chief technician: Greg Goad.
Ownership: Cooney Cable Assoc. Inc. (MSO).

LEXINGTON—Adelphia Cable Communications, Box 1097, 5 W. Nelson St., Lexington, VA 24450-2033. Phones: 540-464-5893; 800-835-4949. Fax: 540-464-6301. County: Rockbridge. Also serves Rockbridge County. ICA: VA0147.
TV Market Ranking: 70 (Lexington, portions of Rockbridge County); Outside TV Markets (portions of Rockbridge County). Franchise award date: N.A. Franchise expiration date: N.A. Began: July 1, 1975.
Channel capacity: 36 (2-way capable; not operating 2-way). Channels available but not in use: 5.
Note: Subscribers, miles of plant & homes passed include figures for Buena Vista, VA.

Basic Service
Subscribers: 5,700.
Programming (received off-air): WBRA-TV (P), WPXR (X) Roanoke; WDBJ (C), WJPR (F), WSET-TV (A), WSLS-TV (N) Roanoke-Lynchburg; WVPT (P) Staunton.
Programming (via satellite): C-SPAN; CNBC; TBS Superstation.
Fee: $33.00 installation; $24.95 monthly; $25.00 additional installation.

Expanded Basic Service
Subscribers: N.A.
Programming (via satellite): A & E; American Movie Classics; CNN; Country Music

TV; Discovery Channel; ESPN; FX; Fox Family Channel; Headline News; Home Team Sports; Lifetime; MSNBC; MTV; Nashville Network; Nickelodeon; The Weather Channel; Turner Network TV; USA Network.
Fee: N.A.

Pay Service 1
Pay Units: 381.
Programming (via satellite): Cinemax.
Fee: $25.00 installation; $11.00 monthly.

Pay Service 2
Pay Units: 153.
Programming (via satellite): Disney Channel.
Fee: $25.00 installation; $8.50 monthly.

Pay Service 3
Pay Units: 697.
Programming (via satellite): HBO.
Fee: $25.00 installation; $11.00 monthly.

Pay Service 4
Pay Units: N.A.
Programming (via satellite): Showtime.
Fee: N.A.

Local advertising: No.
Equipment: Scientific-Atlanta & Jerrold headend; Texscan amplifiers; Times Fiber & Comm/Scope cable; Microtek character generator; Hamlin & Jerrold set top converters; Gamco & Eagle traps; Microdyne, Prodelin & Scientific-Atlanta satellite antenna; Microdyne satellite receivers.
Miles of plant: 139.0 (coaxial); 15.0 (fiber optic). Homes passed: 7,558.
Manager: Gary N. Judy. Chief technician: Joe Clements.
City fee: 5% of gross.
Ownership: Adelphia Communications Corp. (MSO).

LOUDOUN COUNTY—Cablevision of Loudoun, 21545 Ridgetop Circle, Sterling, VA 20166. Phones: 703-404-0316; 703-430-8200. Fax: 703-404-8167. County: Loudoun. Also serves Hamilton, Leesburg, Lovettsville, Middleburg, Purcellville, Round Hill. ICA: VA0021.
TV Market Ranking: 9 (Leesburg, portions of Loudoun County); Below 100 (Hamilton, portions of Loudoun County, Lovettsville, Middleburg, Purcellville, Round Hill). Franchise award date: May 16, 1983. Franchise expiration date: May 15, 2005. Began: March 1, 1984.
Channel capacity: 85 (2-way capable). Channels available but not in use: None.

Basic Service
Subscribers: 34,000.
Programming (received off-air): WMPT (P) Annapolis; WNVC (E) Fairfax; WNVT (P) Goldvein; WPXW (X) Manassas; WBDC-TV (W), WDCA (U), WETA-TV (P), WHUT-TV (P), WJLA-TV (A), WRC-TV (N), WTTG (F), WUSA (C) Washington; 25 FMs.
Programming (via satellite): WGN-TV (W) Chicago; A & E; American Movie Classics; Animal Planet; BET; C-SPAN; C-SPAN 2; CNBC; CNN; Cartoon Network; Comedy Central; Country Music TV; Court TV; Discovery Channel; E! Entertainment TV; ESPN; Fox Family Channel; Headline News; Home Shopping Network; Learning Channel; Lifetime; MTV; Nashville Network; Nick at Nite's TV Land; Nickelodeon; Odyssey; QVC; Sci-Fi Channel; TBS Superstation; TV Guide Channel; The Weather Channel; Turner Network TV; USA Network; Univision; VH1.
Current originations: Automated time-weather; educational access; government access; religious access; leased access; automated emergency alert.
Fee: $29.95 installation; $33.26 monthly.

Pay Service 1
Pay Units: 2,750.
Programming (via satellite): Cinemax.
Fee: $14.95 monthly.

Pay Service 2
Pay Units: 2,750.
Programming (via satellite): Disney Channel.
Fee: $12.95 monthly.

Pay Service 3
Pay Units: 10,275.
Programming (via satellite): HBO.
Fee: $12.95 monthly.

Pay Service 4
Pay Units: 8,750.
Programming (via satellite): Home Team Sports.
Fee: $3.95 monthly.

Pay Service 5
Pay Units: 5,325.
Programming (via satellite): The Movie Channel.
Fee: $12.95 monthly.

Pay Service 6
Pay Units: 6,364.
Programming (via satellite): Showtime.
Fee: $12.95 monthly.

Pay Service 7
Pay Units: 8,150.
Programming (via satellite): Flix.
Fee: $1.95 monthly.

Pay Service 8
Pay Units: 8,000.
Programming (via satellite): Golf Channel.
Fee: $3.95 monthly.

Pay-Per-View
Addressable homes: 30,000.
Action Pay-Per-View; Playboy TV; Spice; Viewer's Choice.
Fee: $4.95.

Local advertising: Yes (locally produced). Available in satellite distributed & locally originated programming. Rates: $12.00/30 Seconds.
Program Guide: CableView.
Equipment: Jerrold headend; Jerrold amplifiers; Times Fiber cable; Sony VTRs; MSI character generator; Jerrold set top converters; General Instrument modems; Scientific-Atlanta satellite antenna; Scientific-Atlanta satellite receivers.
Miles of plant: 565.0 (coaxial); 95.0 (fiber optic). Additional miles planned: 30.0 (coaxial). Homes passed: 46,000. Total homes in franchised area: 51,000.
Manager: Noel Brown. Chief engineer: Paul Quackenbush. Marketing director: Amy Bobchek.
County fee: 5% of gross.
Ownership: Benchmark Communications (MSO).

LOUISA—Adelphia Cable Communications, 324 W. Main St., Charlottesville, VA 22903. Phone: 800-835-4949. Fax: 804-293-9263. County: Louisa. Also serves Lake Louisa, Louisa County, Mineral. Plans service to Louisa Twp. ICA: VA0090.
TV Market Ranking: 63 (portions of Louisa County); Below 100 (Lake Louisa, Louisa, portions of Louisa County, Mineral). Franchise award date: June 1, 1984. Franchise expiration date: N.A. Began: January 1, 1985.
Channel capacity: 40. Channels available but not in use: 19.

Basic Service
Subscribers: 449; Commercial subscribers: 9.
Programming (received off-air): WUPV (U) Ashland; WVIR-TV (N) Charlottesville; WCVE-TV (P), WRIC-TV (A), WRLH-TV (F), WTVR-TV (C), WWBT (N) Richmond-Petersburg.
Programming (via satellite): TBS Superstation.
Current originations: Public access; educational access; government access.
Fee: $75.00 installation; $20.50 monthly.
Commercial fee: $20.00 monthly.

Expanded Basic Service
Subscribers: N.A.
Programming (via satellite): A & E; C-SPAN; CNN; Discovery Channel; ESPN; Fox Family Channel; Headline News; MTV; Nashville Network; Nickelodeon; QVC; The Weather Channel; Turner Network TV.
Fee: N.A.

Pay Service 1
Pay Units: N.A.
Programming (via satellite): Disney Channel; HBO; Showtime.
Fee: $7.95 monthly (Disney), $9.95 monthly (Showtime), $10.00 monthly (HBO).

Pay-Per-View
Special events.

Local advertising: No.
Equipment: Scientific-Atlanta headend; Magnavox, Scientific-Atlanta & GTE Sylvania amplifiers; Comm/Scope cable; Texscan character generator; Jerrold & Scientific-Atlanta set top converters; Scientific-Atlanta addressable set top converters; PPC traps; Scientific-Atlanta satellite antenna; Scientific-Atlanta & Microdyne satellite receivers; ChannelMatic commercial insert.
Miles of plant: 58.0 (coaxial). Additional miles planned: 6.0 (coaxial). Homes passed: 1,103.
Manager: Dell Hanley. Chief technician: Gary Bennett. Marketing director: Pat Hogan.
City fee: 3% of gross.
Ownership: Adelphia Communications Corp. (MSO).

LURAY—Valley Cablevision Inc., 2815 N. Augusta St., Staunton, VA 24401. Phone: 800-835-4949. Fax: 540-886-7948. Counties: Augusta & Page, VA; Augusta, PA. Also serves Weyers Cave, PA; Mount Sidney, Page City, Stanley, VA. ICA: VA0042.
TV Market Ranking: Below 100. Franchise award date: N.A. Franchise expiration date: N.A. Began: October 15, 1965.
Channel capacity: 60 (not 2-way capable). Channels available but not in use: 17.

Basic Service
Subscribers: 6,019.
Programming (via satellite): A & E; American Movie Classics; CNBC; CNN; Comedy Central; Country Music TV; Discovery Channel; ESPN; EWTN; Fox Family Channel; Headline News; Home Shopping Network; Home Team Sports; Learning Channel; Lifetime; MTV; Nashville Network; Nickelodeon; QVC; The Inspirational Network; The Weather Channel; Travel Channel; Turner Classic Movies; Turner Network TV; USA Network; VH1.
Fee: $35.00 installation; $11.95 monthly; $2.00 converter.

Expanded Basic Service
Subscribers: 5,735.
Programming (via satellite): A & E; American Movie Classics; CNBC; CNN; Cartoon Network; Comedy Central; Country Music TV; Discovery Channel; Disney Channel; ESPN; ESPN 2; FX; Fox Family Channel; Headline News; Home & Garden Television; Home Shopping Network; Home Team Sports; Learning Channel; Lifetime; MSNBC; MTV; Nashville Network; Nick at Nite's TV Land; Nickelodeon; QVC; Sci-Fi Channel; TV Food Network; The Health Network; The Weather Channel; Travel Channel; Turner Classic Movies; Turner Network TV; USA Network; VH1.
Fee: N.A.

Pay Service 1
Pay Units: 612.
Programming (via satellite): Cinemax.
Fee: $11.50 monthly.

Pay Service 2
Pay Units: 779.
Programming (via satellite): HBO.
Fee: $11.50 monthly.

Pay Service 3
Pay Units: 265.
Programming (via satellite): Showtime.
Fee: $11.50 monthly.

Pay Service 4
Pay Units: 184.
Programming (via satellite): The Movie Channel.
Fee: $11.50 monthly.

Pay-Per-View
Addressable homes: 3,366.
Viewer's Choice 1 & 2.
Fee: $3.95.

Local advertising: No.
Equipment: Scientific-Atlanta headend; Scientific-Atlanta amplifiers; Comm/Scope cable; Scientific-Atlanta set top converters; Scientific-Atlanta addressable set top converters; Eagle & Pico traps; Microdyne satellite receivers.
Miles of plant: 255.2 (coaxial). Additional miles planned: 9.1 (coaxial). Homes passed: 6,850. Includes figures for Shenandoah, VA.
Manager: James V. Kitchen. Chief technician: Ron Herron.
City fee: 1% of gross.
Ownership: Adelphia Communications Corp. (MSO).

LYNCHBURG—Lynchburg Cablevision, 2820 Linkhome Dr., Lynchburg, VA 24503. Phone: 804-384-1000. Fax: 804-384-1199. Counties: Bedford & Campbell. Also serves Bedford County (portions), Campbell County. ICA: VA0013.
TV Market Ranking: 70. Franchise award date: January 1, 1972. Franchise expiration date: December 31, 2003. Began: June 1, 1977.
Channel capacity: 54 (2-way capable; operating 2-way). Channels available but not in use: N.A.

Basic Service
Subscribers: 21,631.
Programming (received off-air): WBRA-TV (P), WPXR (X) Roanoke; WDBJ (C), WJPR (F), WSET-TV (A), WSLS-TV (N) Roanoke-Lynchburg; WVPT (P) Staunton.
Programming (via satellite): WGN-TV (W) Chicago; A & E; American Movie Classics; BET; C-SPAN; CNBC; CNN; Comedy Central; Discovery Channel; ESPN; Fox Family Channel; Headline News; Lifetime; MTV; Nashville Network; Nickelodeon; QVC; TBS Superstation; The Weather Channel; Travel Channel; Turner Network TV; USA Network.
Current originations: Automated time-weather; public access; educational access; automated emergency alert; local news; local sports.
Fee: $39.76 installation; $29.82 monthly.

Pay Service 1
Pay Units: 2,640.
Programming (via satellite): Cinemax.
Fee: $10.95 monthly.

Pay Service 2
Pay Units: 1,193.
Programming (via satellite): Disney Channel.
Fee: $8.00 monthly.

Pay Service 3
Pay Units: 4,528.
Programming (via satellite): HBO.
Fee: $10.95 monthly.

Pay-Per-View
Addressable homes: 9,145.
Movies; special events.

Local advertising: Yes. Available in satellite distributed, locally originated & character-generated programming. Rates: $15.00/30 Seconds.
Local sales manager: Carroll Sluss.

Equipment: Scientific-Atlanta headend; Magnavox amplifiers; Comm/Scope cable; Sony cameras; Sony VTRs; BEI & System Concepts character generator; Hamlin set top converters; Scientific-Atlanta satellite antenna.
Miles of plant: 367.6 (coaxial); 355.0 (fiber optic). Homes passed: 29,000.
Manager: James Kitchen. Office manager: Robin Roarke.
City fee: 4% of gross.
Ownership: Adelphia Communications Corp. (MSO).

MADISON—GPA Cable, Box 943, Osprey, FL 34229. Phone: 941-924-8882. County: Madison. ICA: VA0106.
TV Market Ranking: Below 100. Franchise award date: January 1, 1989. Franchise expiration date: January 1, 2009. Began: September 1, 1989.
Channel capacity: 62 (2-way capable). Channels available but not in use: 20.
Basic Service
Subscribers: 969.
Programming (received off-air): WVIR-TV (N) Charlottesville; WRIC-TV (A), WRLH-TV (F), WTVR-TV (C), WWBT (N) Richmond-Petersburg; WDCA (U), WETA-TV (P), WJLA-TV (A), WTTG (F), WUSA (C) Washington.
Programming (via satellite): WGN-TV (W) Chicago; A & E; CNN; Cartoon Network; Country Music TV; Discovery Channel; ESPN; ESPN 2; Fox Family Channel; History Channel; Home Team Sports; MTV; Nashville Network; Nickelodeon; QVC; Sci-Fi Channel; Trinity Bcstg. Network; Turner Classic Movies; Turner Network TV; USA Network; VH1.
Fee: $40.00 installation; $21.95 monthly.
Pay Service 1
Pay Units: N.A.
Programming (via satellite): Disney Channel; HBO; Showtime.
Fee: $7.95 monthly (Disney), $8.95 monthly (Showtime), $9.95 monthly (HBO).
Miles of plant: 70.0 (coaxial). Homes passed: 1,500. Total homes in franchised area: 1,500.
Manager: George Pancner. Chief technician: John Pancner.
Ownership: GPA Cable (MSO).

MANASSAS—Jones Communications of Virginia Inc., 9540 Center St., Manassas, VA 22110. Phone: 703-670-0189. Fax: 703-257-6989. Counties: Fairfax & Prince William. Also serves Dale City, Dumfries, Fort Belvoir, Lake Ridge, Manassas Park, Montclair, Occoquan, Prince William County (portions), Quantico, Triangle, Westridge, Woodbridge. ICA: VA0148.
TV Market Ranking: 9. Franchise award date: N.A. Franchise expiration date: October 16, 2000. Began: January 7, 1986.
Channel capacity: 64 (2-way capable; operating 2-way). Channels available but not in use: None.
Basic Service
Subscribers: 27,986.
Programming (received off-air): WMPT (P) Annapolis; WNVC (E) Fairfax; WNVT (P) Goldvein; WPXW (X) Manassas; WDCA (U), WETA-TV (P), WHUT-TV (P), WJLA-TV (A), WRC-TV (N), WTTG (F), WUSA (C) Washington.
Programming (via satellite): WGN-TV (W) Chicago; A & E; American Movie Classics; BET; Bravo; C-SPAN; C-SPAN 2; CNBC; CNN; Cartoon Network; Comedy Central; Country Music TV; Court TV; Discovery Channel; E! Entertainment TV; ESPN; EWTN; Fox Family Channel; Headline News; Home Shopping Network; Knowledge TV; Learning Channel; Lifetime; MTV; Nashville Network; Nickelodeon; Sci-Fi Channel; TBS Superstation; TV Guide Channel; The Inspirational Network; The Weather Channel; Turner Network TV; USA Network; Univision; VH1.
Current originations: Public access; government access; library access; automated emergency alert; local news.
Fee: $25.00 installation; $26.53 monthly.
Pay Service 1
Pay Units: 2,050.
Programming (via satellite): The New Encore.
Fee: $2.95 monthly.
Pay Service 2
Pay Units: 2,100.
Programming (via satellite): Cinemax.
Fee: $10.95 monthly.
Pay Service 3
Pay Units: 2,740.
Programming (via satellite): Disney Channel.
Fee: $10.95 monthly.
Pay Service 4
Pay Units: 5,200.
Programming (via satellite): HBO.
Fee: $10.95 monthly.
Pay Service 5
Pay Units: 2,100.
Programming (via satellite): Home Team Sports.
Fee: $9.95 monthly.
Pay Service 6
Pay Units: 4,120.
Programming (via satellite): The Movie Channel.
Fee: $10.95 monthly.
Pay Service 7
Pay Units: 5,075.
Programming (via satellite): Showtime.
Fee: $10.95 monthly.
Pay-Per-View
Addressable homes: 27,986.
Action Pay-Per-View; Playboy TV; Viewer's Choice.
Fee: $4.95.
Local advertising: Yes. Available in satellite distributed programming. Rates: $12.00/30 Seconds.
Program Guide: CableView.
Miles of plant: 490.0 (coaxial); None (fiber optic). Homes passed: 38,000. Total homes in franchised area: 38,300.
Manager: Troy Fitzhugh. Chief technician: Ray Ness. Marketing director: Mike Draughon.
Ownership: Jones Intercable Inc. (MSO).

MARION—Adelphia Cable, 112 Washington St., Galax, VA 24333. Phone: 800-835-4949. County: Smyth. Also serves Atkins, Smyth County. ICA: VA0149.
TV Market Ranking: Below 100. Franchise award date: N.A. Franchise expiration date: N.A. Began: October 19, 1983.
Channel capacity: 36. Channels available but not in use: 8.
Basic Service
Subscribers: 3,874.
Programming (received off-air): WVVA (N) Bluefield; WCYB-TV (N) Bristol-Kingsport; WJHL-TV (C) Johnson City; WKPT-TV (A) Kingsport; WDBJ (C), WSLS-TV (N) Roanoke-Lynchburg.
Programming (via translator): WMSY-TV (P) Marion.
Programming (via satellite): CNBC; CNN; Country Music TV; Discovery Channel; ESPN; Fox Family Channel; Headline News; Home Team Sports; Lifetime; MTV; Nashville Network; Nickelodeon; QVC; TBS Superstation; TV Guide Channel; The Weather Channel; Turner Network TV; USA Network; VH1.
Fee: $50.00 installation; $22.95 monthly; $2.00 converter.
Pay Service 1
Pay Units: N.A.
Programming (via satellite): Cinemax; Disney Channel; HBO; Showtime; The Movie Channel.
Fee: $7.95 monthly (Disney), $8.95 monthly (Cinemax, HBO, Showtime or TMC).
Local advertising: Yes (locally produced & insert). Rates: $6.00/Minute; $4.00/30 Seconds.
Equipment: Jerrold & Scientific-Atlanta headend; Jerrold amplifiers; Comm/Scope cable; Scientific-Atlanta set top converters; Scientific-Atlanta addressable set top converters; Eagle traps; Scientific-Atlanta & Microdyne satellite antenna; Standard Communications satellite receivers.
Miles of plant: 108.0 (coaxial).
Manager: Hilda Sexton. Chief technician: Jerry Parks.
Ownership: Adelphia Communications Corp. (MSO).

MARTINSVILLE—Adelphia Cable Communications, 390 Commonwealth Blvd., Martinsville, VA 24112. Phone: 800-835-4949. Fax: 703-666-2577. County: Henry. Also serves Axton, Bassett, Collinsville, Fieldale, Henry County, Horse Pasture, Ridgeway, Stanleytown, Villa Heights. ICA: VA0150.
TV Market Ranking: 70 (Bassett, portions of Henry County); Below 100 (Axton, Collinsville, Fieldale, portions of Henry County, Horse Pasture, Martinsville, Ridgeway, Stanleytown, Villa Heights). Franchise award date: January 1, 1966. Franchise expiration date: April 28, 2010. Began: March 22, 1966.
Channel capacity: 54 (not 2-way capable). Channels available but not in use: None.
Basic Service
Subscribers: 21,172.
Programming (received off-air): WFMY-TV (C), WGHP (F), WUPN-TV (U), WXII (N) Greensboro-High Point; WBRA-TV (P) Roanoke; WDBJ (C), WSET-TV (A), WSLS-TV (N) Roanoke-Lynchburg; WXLV-TV (A) Winston-Salem; 12 FMs.
Programming (via microwave): WTTG (F) Washington.
Programming (via satellite): WGN-TV (W) Chicago; A & E; BET; C-SPAN; CNBC; CNN; Comedy Central; Country Music TV; Discovery Channel; ESPN; Fox Family Channel; Goodlife TV Network; Headline News; Home Team Sports; Lifetime; MTV; Nashville Network; Nickelodeon; QVC; TBS Superstation; The Inspirational Network; The Weather Channel; Turner Classic Movies; Turner Network TV; USA Network; VH1.
Current originations: Automated time-weather; public access; educational access; government access.
Fee: $33.00 installation; $35.31 monthly.
Pay Service 1
Pay Units: 2,021.
Programming (via satellite): Cinemax.
Fee: $15.00 installation; $11.50 monthly.
Pay Service 2
Pay Units: 811.
Programming (via satellite): Disney Channel.
Fee: $15.00 installation; $9.00 monthly.
Pay Service 3
Pay Units: 2,868.
Programming (via satellite): HBO.
Fee: $15.00 installation; $11.50 monthly.
Pay Service 4
Pay Units: 570.
Programming (via satellite): The Movie Channel.
Fee: $15.00 installation; $11.50 monthly.
Pay Service 5
Pay Units: 1,001.
Programming (via satellite): Showtime.
Fee: $15.00 installation; $11.50 monthly.
Pay-Per-View
Addressable homes: 11,552.
Local advertising: Yes. Available in satellite distributed, locally originated, character-generated, taped & automated programming.
Program Guide: TV Guide.
Equipment: RCA headend; Magnavox amplifiers; Comm/Scope cable; Texscan character generator; Scientific-Atlanta set top converters; Scientific-Atlanta addressable set top converters; Eagle traps; Scientific-Atlanta satellite antenna; Scientific-Atlanta satellite receivers.
Miles of plant: 600.0 (coaxial); 18.0 (fiber optic). Additional miles planned: 20.0 (coaxial). Homes passed: 30,600. Total homes in franchised area: 32,100.
Manager: Terry Nosse. Plant manager: Tony Bushnell.
City fee: 5% of gross.
Ownership: Adelphia Communications Corp. (MSO).

MATHEWS—FrontierVision, Suite P-200, 1777 S. Harrison St., Denver, CO 80210. Phone: 303-757-1588. Fax: 303-757-6105. County: Mathews. ICA: VA0056.
TV Market Ranking: 44. Franchise award date: March 22, 1988. Franchise expiration date: March 22, 2003. Began: December 1, 1988.
Channel capacity: 42 (not 2-way capable). Channels available but not in use: 1.
Basic Service
Subscribers: 1,961.
Programming (received off-air): WHRO-TV (P), WVEC-TV (A) Hampton-Norfolk; WAVY-TV (N), WGNT (U), WTKR (C), WTVZ (W) Portsmouth-Norfolk.
Programming (via satellite): A & E; BET; C-SPAN; C-SPAN 2; CNN; Country Music TV; Discovery Channel; ESPN; Fox Family Channel; Headline News; Home Shopping Network; Home Team Sports; Lifetime; MTV; Nashville Network; Nickelodeon; Odyssey; TBS Superstation; The Weather Channel; VH1.
Fee: $40.00 installation; $17.95 monthly.
Expanded Basic Service
Subscribers: 1,915.
Programming (via satellite): Disney Channel.
Fee: N.A.
Pay Service 1
Pay Units: 216.
Programming (via satellite): HBO.
Fee: $9.95 monthly.
Pay Service 2
Pay Units: 359.
Programming (via satellite): Showtime.
Fee: $9.95 monthly.
Pay Service 3
Pay Units: 44.
Programming (via satellite): Cinemax.
Fee: N.A.
Pay Service 4
Pay Units: 333.
Programming (via satellite): The Movie Channel.
Fee: N.A.
Local advertising: No.
Program Guide: CableView.
Equipment: Magnavox amplifiers; Comm/Scope & Times Fiber cable; Scientific-Atlanta set top converters; Eagle & PPC traps; Scientific-Atlanta, Comtech & Prodelin satellite antenna; Scientific-Atlanta satellite receivers.
Miles of plant: 192.7 (coaxial). Homes passed: 3,095.

Manager: Dan Callahan. Chief technician: Gary Shoemaker.
County fee: 5% of gross.
Ownership: FrontierVision Partners LP (MSO). See Cable System Ownership.

McKENNEY—Adelphia Cable Communications, 25225 Harwell Dr., Petersburg, VA 23803. Phone: 800-835-4949. Fax: 804-733-7242. County: Dinwiddie. Also serves Petersburg (unincorporated areas). ICA: VA0086.
TV Market Ranking: 63. Franchise award date: January 15, 1986. Franchise expiration date: January 15, 2001. Began: July 31, 1986.
Channel capacity: 36 (2-way capable; operating 2-way). Channels available but not in use: None.
Basic Service
Subscribers: 142.
Programming (received off-air): WCVE-TV (P), WCVW (P), WRIC-TV (A), WRLH-TV (F), WTVR-TV (C), WWBT (N) Richmond-Petersburg.
Programming (via satellite): A & E; BET; C-SPAN; CNBC; CNN; Cartoon Network; Discovery Channel; FX; Fox Family Channel; Home Shopping Network; Learning Channel; Nashville Network; Nickelodeon; Trinity Bcstg. Network; Turner Classic Movies; Turner Network TV.
Current originations: Educational access; government access; local news.
Fee: $39.00 installation (aerial), $60.00 (underground); $17.05 monthly; $29.00 additional installation.
Expanded Basic Service
Subscribers: N.A.
Programming (via satellite): WGN-TV (W) Chicago; Country Music TV; ESPN; Lifetime; MTV; TBS Superstation; USA Network.
Fee: $9.52 monthly.
Pay Service 1
Pay Units: N.A.
Programming (via satellite): Cinemax; Disney Channel; HBO.
Fee: $6.00 monthly (HBO), $8.00 monthly (Disney), $11.50 monthly (Cinemax).
Equipment: Cadco headend; Magnavox amplifiers; Trilogy cable; Pioneer set top converters; Eagle traps; Microdyne & Scientific-Atlanta satellite antenna.
Total homes in franchised area: 292.
Manager: Luke Matthews. Office manager: Debra Cage.
County fee: 5% of gross.
Ownership: Adelphia Communications Corp. (MSO).

MIDDLESEX COUNTY—Middlesex Cablevision, Box 1147, Rte. 227, Cook's Corner, Saluda, VA 23149. Phone: 804-758-5870. Fax: 804-693-2885. E-mail: pattgibbs@aol.com. County: Middlesex. Also serves Deltaville, Saluda, Urbanna. ICA: VA0085.
TV Market Ranking: Outside TV Markets. Franchise award date: March 1, 1983. Franchise expiration date: February 1, 2003. Began: April 2, 1984.
Channel capacity: 61 (2-way capable; operating 2-way). Channels available but not in use: None.
Basic Service
Subscribers: 2,791.
Programming (received off-air): WHRO-TV (P), WVEC-TV (A) Hampton-Norfolk; WAVY-TV (N), WGNT (U), WTKR (C), WTVZ (W) Portsmouth-Norfolk; WCVE-TV (P), WRIC-TV (A), WRLH-TV (F), WTVR-TV (C), WWBT (N) Richmond-Petersburg.
Programming (via satellite): WGN-TV (W) Chicago; A & E; American Movie Classics; BET; Bravo; C-SPAN; C-SPAN 2; CNBC; CNN; Country Music TV; Court TV; Discovery Channel; ESPN; Fox Family Channel; Headline News; Home & Garden Television; Home Team Sports; Learning Channel; Lifetime; MTV; Nashville Network; Nickelodeon; Outdoor Channel; QVC; TBS Superstation; TV Guide Channel; The Weather Channel; Turner Network TV; USA Network; VH1.
Fee: $50.00 installation; $26.45 monthly.
Expanded Basic Service
Subscribers: 821.
Programming (via satellite): Cartoon Network; ESPN 2; History Channel; Sci-Fi Channel; TV Food Network; Travel Channel; Turner Classic Movies.
Fee: $5.95 monthly.
Pay Service 1
Pay Units: 184.
Programming (via satellite): Cinemax.
Fee: $9.95 monthly.
Pay Service 2
Pay Units: 408.
Programming (via satellite): HBO.
Fee: $9.95 monthly.
Pay Service 3
Pay Units: 256.
Programming (via satellite): Disney Channel.
Fee: $8.95 monthly.
Pay Service 4
Pay Units: 102.
Programming (via satellite): The Movie Channel.
Fee: $9.95 monthly.
Pay Service 5
Pay Units: 65.
Programming (via satellite): Showtime.
Fee: $9.95 monthly.
Pay Service 6
Pay Units: 9.
Programming (via satellite): DMX.
Fee: $32.50 installation; $9.95 monthly.
Pay-Per-View
Addressable homes: 2,000.
Hot Choice; Viewer's Choice; special events.
Fee: Varies.
Equipment: Cadco headend; Texscan amplifiers; Scala character generator; Standard Components, Pioneer & Hamlin set top converters; Intercept traps; Anixter-Mark & Scientific-Atlanta satellite antenna; Drake & Standard Components satellite receivers.
Miles of plant: 170.0 (coaxial); 13.0 (fiber optic). Homes passed: 3,969.
Manager: Patricia Gibbs. Chief technician: James Foust. Customer service manager: Jonelle Boyd.
County fee: 3% of basic gross.
Ownership: 1st Commonwealth Communications Inc. (MSO).

MONTEREY—Highland Communications, Box 339, Monterey, VA 24465. Phone: 540-468-3390. Fax: 540-468-1989. County: Highland. Also serves Blue Grass, Highland County, Hightown. ICA: VA0113.
TV Market Ranking: Below 100 (portions of Highland County); Outside TV Markets (Blue Grass, portions of Highland County, Hightown, Monterey). Franchise award date: N.A. Franchise expiration date: N.A. Began: January 1, 1973.
Channel capacity: 11 (not 2-way capable). Channels available but not in use: N.A.
Basic Service
Subscribers: 347.
Programming (received off-air): WHSV-TV (A,F) Harrisonburg; WBRA-TV (P), WPXR (X) Roanoke; WDBJ (C), WSET-TV (A), WSLS-TV (N) Roanoke-Lynchburg; WVFT (I) Rock Hill; WVPT (P) Staunton.
Programming (via satellite): American Movie Classics; CNN; Country Music TV; Discovery Channel; ESPN; Fox Family Channel; Nashville Network; TBS Superstation; Turner Network TV; USA Network.
Fee: $150.00 installation; $19.85 monthly; $2.00 converter.
Pay Service 1
Pay Units: 76.
Programming (via satellite): HBO.
Fee: $10.00 monthly.
Pay Service 2
Pay Units: 12.
Programming (via satellite): Disney Channel.
Fee: $7.49 monthly.
Equipment: Blonder-Tongue & Microdyne headend; GTE Sylvania amplifiers; Times Fiber cable.
Miles of plant: 30.0 (coaxial). Homes passed: 460. Total homes in franchised area: 580.
Manager: Elmer E. Halterman.
City fee: 1.5% of gross.
Ownership: Highland Communications Cooperative Inc.

MONTROSS—FrontierVision, Suite P-200, 1777 S. Harrison St., Denver, CO 80210. Phone: 303-757-1588. Fax: 303-757-6105. County: Westmoreland. Also serves Westmoreland. ICA: VA0049.
TV Market Ranking: Below 100 (Westmoreland); Outside TV Markets (Montross). Franchise award date: April 21, 1988. Franchise expiration date: April 21, 2003. Began: December 1, 1988.
Channel capacity: 42 (not 2-way capable). Channels available but not in use: 1.
Basic Service
Subscribers: 2,535.
Programming (received off-air): WCVE-TV (P), WRIC-TV (A), WRLH-TV (F), WTVR-TV (C), WWBT (N) Richmond-Petersburg; WETA-TV (P), WJLA-TV (A), WRC-TV (N), WTTG (F), WUSA (C) Washington.
Programming (via satellite): A & E; C-SPAN; C-SPAN 2; CNN; Discovery Channel; ESPN; Fox Family Channel; Headline News; Home Shopping Network; Home Team Sports; Lifetime; MTV; Nashville Network; Nickelodeon; Odyssey; TBS Superstation; The Weather Channel; VH1.
Current originations: Automated time-weather.
Fee: $40.00 installation; $17.95 monthly.
Expanded Basic Service
Subscribers: 2,476.
Programming (via satellite): Disney Channel.
Fee: N.A.
Pay Service 1
Pay Units: 401.
Programming (via satellite): HBO.
Fee: $15.00 installation; $9.95 monthly.
Pay Service 2
Pay Units: 586.
Programming (via satellite): Showtime.
Fee: $15.00 installation; $9.95 monthly.
Pay Service 3
Pay Units: 493.
Programming (via satellite): The Movie Channel.
Fee: N.A.
Pay Service 4
Pay Units: 106.
Programming (via satellite): Cinemax.
Fee: N.A.
Pay Service 5
Pay Units: 115.
Programming (via satellite): Starz!
Fee: N.A.
Pay Service 6
Pay Units: 115.
Programming (via satellite): The New Encore.
Fee: N.A.
Local advertising: No.
Program Guide: CableView.
Equipment: Magnavox amplifiers; Comm/Scope & Times Fiber cable; Scientific-Atlanta set top converters; Eagle & PPC traps; Scientific-Atlanta & Prodelin satellite antenna; Scientific-Atlanta satellite receivers.
Miles of plant: 271.3 (coaxial). Homes passed: 4,053. Total homes in franchised area: 4,328.
President & chief executive officer: James Vaugh. Vice president, engineering: David Heyrend. Executive vice president: John Koo.
Franchise fee: 2% of gross.
Ownership: FrontierVision Partners LP (MSO). See Cable System Ownership.

MOUNT CLINTON—FrontierVision, Suite P-200, 1777 S. Harrison St., Denver, CO 80210. Phone: 303-757-1588. Fax: 303-757-6105. County: Rockingham. ICA: VA0153.
TV Market Ranking: Below 100. Franchise award date: April 13, 1988. Franchise expiration date: N.A. Began: September 1, 1989.
Channel capacity: 40. Channels available but not in use: 3.
Basic Service
Subscribers: 471.
Programming (received off-air): WVIR-TV (N) Charlottesville; WHSV-TV (A,F) Harrisonburg; WRLH-TV (F) Richmond-Petersburg; WVPT (P) Staunton; WTTG (F), WUSA (C) Washington.
Programming (via satellite): WGN-TV (W) Chicago; A & E; American Movie Classics; C-SPAN; CNBC; CNN; Country Music TV; Discovery Channel; Disney Channe; ESPN; Fox Family Channel; Headline News; Home Shopping Network; Home Team Sports; Learning Channel; Lifetime; MTV; Nashville Network; Nickelodeon; Odyssey; QVC; Sci-Fi Channel; TBS Superstation; The Weather Channel; Trinity Bcstg. Network; Turner Network TV; USA Network; VH1.
Fee: $47.50 installation; $19.95 monthly; $1.50 converter; $25.00 additional installation.
Pay Service 1
Pay Units: 83.
Programming (via satellite): HBO.
Fee: $9.00 monthly.
Pay Service 2
Pay Units: 63.
Programming (via satellite): Showtime.
Fee: $9.00 monthly.
Miles of plant: 45.0 (coaxial). Homes passed: 935.

Manager: Dan Callahan. Chief technician: Gary Shoemaker.
Ownership: FrontierVision Partners LP (MSO). See Cable System Ownership.

NEW KENT—New Kent Cablevision, Box 888, West Point, VA 23181. Phone: 804-843-3112. Fax: 804-843-3305. County: New Kent. Also serves Eltham, Lanexa, New Kent County (unincorporated areas), Providence Forge, Quinton. ICA: VA0156.
TV Market Ranking: 63. Franchise award date: January 1, 1987. Franchise expiration date: N.A. Began: July 15, 1989.
Channel capacity: 53. Channels available but not in use: 4.
Basic Service
Subscribers: 2,162.
Programming (received off-air): WUPV (U) Ashland; WPEN-LP (I) Hampton; WHRO-TV (P), WVEC-TV (A) Hampton-Norfolk; WAVY-TV (N), WGNT (U), WTKR (C), WTVZ (W) Portsmouth-Norfolk; WCVE-TV (P), WCVW (P), WRIC-TV (A), WRLH-TV (F), WTVR-TV (C), WWBT (N) Richmond-Petersburg.
Programming (via satellite): WGN-TV (W) Chicago; A & E; American Movie Classics; Animal Planet; BET; Bravo; C-SPAN; C-SPAN 2; CNBC; CNN; Cartoon Network; Comedy Central; Country Music TV; Discovery Channel; Disney Channel; ESPN; ESPN 2; FX; Fox Family Channel; Fox News Channel; Headline News; History Channel; Home Team Sports; Knowledge TV; Learning Channel; Lifetime; MSNBC; MTV; Nashville Network; Nickelodeon; QVC; Romance Classics; Sci-Fi Channel; Speedvision; TBS Superstation; TV Guide Channel; The Health Network; The Weather Channel; Toon Disney; Trinity Bcstg. Network; Turner Network TV; USA Network; VH1.
Current originations: Local news.
Fee: $50.00 installation (aerial), $33.00 (underground); $26.45 monthly; $3.00 converter.
Expanded Basic Service
Subscribers: N.A.
Programming (via satellite): Cinemax; Golf Channel; HBO Plus; Home & Garden Television; Nick at Nite's TV Land; Outdoor Channel; Turner Classic Movies.
Fee: $7.50 monthly.
Pay Service 1
Pay Units: 92.
Programming (via satellite): Cinemax.
Fee: $9.95 monthly.
Pay Service 2
Pay Units: N.A.
Programming (via satellite): DMX.
Fee: $9.95 monthly.
Pay Service 3
Pay Units: 443.
Programming (via satellite): HBO.
Fee: $9.95 monthly.
Pay Service 4
Pay Units: 60.
Programming (via satellite): The Movie Channel.
Fee: $9.95 monthly.
Pay Service 5
Pay Units: 20.
Programming (via satellite): Showtime.
Fee: $9.95 monthly.
Pay-Per-View
Hot Choice; Viewer's Choice.
Miles of plant: 160.0 (coaxial); None (fiber optic). Additional miles planned: 5.0 (coaxial). Homes passed: 2,500.
Manager: Mike Gilberti.
County fee: 3% of gross.
Ownership: 1st Commonwealth Communications Inc. (MSO). Sale pends to Cox Communications Inc.

NEW MARKET—FrontierVision, Suite P-200, 1777 S. Harrison St., Denver, CO 80210. Phone: 303-757-1588. Fax: 303-757-6105. County: Shenandoah. Also serves Mount Jackson. ICA: VA0079.
TV Market Ranking: Below 100. Franchise award date: August 20, 1973. Franchise expiration date: N.A. Began: N.A.
Channel capacity: 54 (not 2-way capable). Channels available but not in use: 26.
Basic Service
Subscribers: 1,227.
Programming (received off-air): WHSV-TV (A,F) Harrisonburg; WTVR-TV (C) Richmond-Petersburg; WVPT (P) Staunton; WDCA (U), WJLA-TV (A), WRC-TV (N), WTTG (F), WUSA (C) Washington.
Programming (via satellite): A & E; CNBC; CNN; Country Music TV; Discovery Channel; ESPN; Fox Family Channel; Home Team Sports; Lifetime; Nashville Network; Nickelodeon; QVC; TV Guide Channel; The Weather Channel; Turner Network TV; USA Network.
Current originations: Automated time-weather; public access; government access.
Fee: $40.00 installation; $16.50 monthly; $2.00 converter.
Pay Service 1
Pay Units: 46.
Programming (via satellite): Disney Channel.
Fee: $15.00 installation; $8.95 monthly.
Pay Service 2
Pay Units: 177.
Programming (via satellite): HBO.
Fee: $15.00 installation; $10.95 monthly.
Pay Service 3
Pay Units: 74.
Programming (via satellite): Showtime.
Fee: $15.00 installation; $10.95 monthly.
Local advertising: No.
Program Guide: CableView.
Equipment: Magnavox amplifiers; Trilogy & Times Fiber cable; Scientific-Atlanta & Zenith set top converters; Eagle & PPC traps; Comtech & Microdyne satellite antenna; Scientific-Atlanta satellite receivers.
Miles of plant: 37.0 (coaxial). Homes passed: 1,621.
President & chief executive officer: James Vaugh. Vice president, engineering: David Heyrend. Executive vice president: John Koo.
City fee: 3% of gross.
Ownership: FrontierVision Partners LP (MSO). See Cable System Ownership.

NEWCASTLE—Time Warner Cable, Box 950, 651 S. Main St., Dobson, NC 27017. Phone: 910-386-4461. Fax: 910-386-9691. County: Craig. Also serves Craig County (portions). ICA: VA0105.
TV Market Ranking: 70. Franchise award date: N.A. Franchise expiration date: N.A. Began: N.A.
Channel capacity: 52. Channels available but not in use: 27.
Basic Service
Subscribers: 594; Commercial subscribers: 13.
Programming (received off-air): WBRA-TV (P) Roanoke; WDBJ (C), WFXR-TV (F), WSET-TV (A), WSLS-TV (N) Roanoke-Lynchburg.
Programming (via satellite): WGN-TV (W) Chicago; QVC; TBS Superstation; The Weather Channel; Turner Network TV.
Fee: $31.00 installation (aerial), $50.00 (underground); $9.75 monthly.
Expanded Basic Service
Subscribers: 626.
Programming (via satellite): CNN; Country Music TV; Discovery Channel; ESPN; Fox Family Channel; MTV; Nashville Network; Nickelodeon; USA Network.
Fee: $16.92 monthly.
Pay Service 1
Pay Units: 65.
Programming (via satellite): Cinemax.
Fee: $10.95 monthly.
Pay Service 2
Pay Units: 46.
Programming (via satellite): Disney Channel.
Fee: $8.00 monthly.
Pay Service 3
Pay Units: 87.
Programming (via satellite): HBO.
Fee: $10.95 monthly.
Pay Service 4
Pay Units: 64.
Programming (via satellite): Showtime.
Fee: $10.95 monthly.
Miles of plant: 23.0 (coaxial). Homes passed: 657.
Manager: Mary Stone. Chief technician: Jay Murphy.
Ownership: Time Warner Cable (MSO).

NEWPORT NEWS—Cox Communications, 179 Louise Dr., Newport News, VA 23601. Phones: 757-595-6969; 757-595-4491. Fax: 757-595-2396. Counties: Newport News City & York. Also serves Fort Eustis Army Base, Yorktown Naval Weapons Station. ICA: VA0006.
TV Market Ranking: 44. Franchise award date: October 1, 1966. Franchise expiration date: N.A. Began: January 1, 1967.
Channel capacity: 62. Channels available but not in use: 2.
Basic Service
Subscribers: 46,367.
Programming (received off-air): W51BH (I) Gloucester; WHRO-TV (P), WVEC-TV (A) Hampton-Norfolk; WAVY-TV (N), WGNT (U), WPXV (X), WTKR (C), WTVZ (W) Portsmouth-Norfolk; WVBT (F) Virginia Beach.
Programming (via satellite): WGN-TV (W) Chicago; C-SPAN; C-SPAN 2; Odyssey; QVC; TBS Superstation; TV Guide Channel.
Current originations: Automated time-weather; educational access; government access; automated emergency alert; local news.
Planned originations: Public access.
Fee: $31.82 installation; $9.41 monthly.
Expanded Basic Service
Subscribers: 46,250.
Programming (via satellite): A & E; American Movie Classics; BET; CNBC; CNN; Country Music TV; Court TV; Discovery Channel; E! Entertainment TV; ESPN; FX; Fox Family Channel; Headline News; Home Team Sports; Knowledge TV; Learning Channel; Lifetime; MTV; Nashville Network; Nickelodeon; The Inspirational Network; The Weather Channel; Turner Network TV; USA Network; Univision; VH1.
Fee: $12.23 monthly.
Pay Service 1
Pay Units: 7,000.
Programming (via satellite): Cinemax.
Fee: $5.00 installation; $9.95 monthly.
Pay Service 2
Pay Units: 3,900.
Programming (via satellite): Disney Channel.
Fee: $5.00 installation; $9.95 monthly.
Pay Service 3
Pay Units: 23,000.
Programming (via satellite): HBO.
Fee: $5.00 installation; $9.95 monthly.
Pay Service 4
Pay Units: 4,000.
Programming (via satellite): Showtime.
Fee: $5.00 installation; $9.95 monthly.
Pay Service 5
Pay Units: 14,000.
Programming (via satellite): The New Encore.
Fee: $1.75 monthly.
Pay Service 6
Pay Units: 4,300.
Programming (via satellite): Starz!
Fee: $4.75 monthly.
Pay Service 7
Pay Units: 1,300.
Programming (via satellite): DMX.
Fee: $9.95 monthly.
Pay-Per-View
Addressable homes: 21,000.
Spice.
Local advertising: Yes. Available in satellite distributed, locally originated & automated programming. Rates: $100.00/Hour; $25.00/Minute; $15.00/30 Seconds. Regional interconnect: Tidewater Cable Interconnect.
Equipment: Scientific-Atlanta & Jerrold headend; GTE Sylvania & Jerrold amplifiers; Comm/Scope & Times Fiber cable; JVC cameras; Sony VTRs; Quanta & MSI character generator; Jerrold set top converters; Jerrold addressable set top converters; Eagle traps; Anixter-Pruzan & Scientific-Atlanta satellite antenna; Microdyne satellite receivers; ChannelMatic commercial insert.
Miles of plant: 750.0 (coaxial); 46.0 (fiber optic). Homes passed: 75,000. Total homes in franchised area: 75,000.
Manager: Katie Gunderson. Chief technician: Brian Schade.
City fee: 3% of gross.
Ownership: Cox Communications Inc. (MSO).

NORTON—Century Virginia Corp., Box 1300, 838 Park Ave. NE, Norton, VA 24273. Phone: 540-523-3522. Counties: Lee & Wise. Also serves Appalachia, Big Stone Gap, Bold Camp, Esserville, Indian Creek, Josephine, Keokee, Lee County, Stephens, Wise, Wise County. ICA: VA0157.
TV Market Ranking: Below 100 (Appalachia, Bold Camp, Indian Creek, Josephine, Keokee, portions of Lee County, Norton, Stephens, Wise, portions of Wise County); Outside TV Markets (Big Stone Gap, Esserville, portions of Lee County, portions of Wise County). Franchise award date: N.A. Franchise expiration date: N.A. Began: January 1, 1958.
Channel capacity: 36. Channels available but not in use: None.
Basic Service
Subscribers: 16,800.
Programming (received off-air): WCYB-TV (N) Bristol-Kingsport; WEMT (F) Greeneville; WJHL-TV (C) Johnson City; WKPT-TV (A) Kingsport; WATE-TV (A) Knoxville; WSBN-TV (P) Norton; WDBJ (C) Roanoke-Lynchburg; WSJK (P) Sneedville; allband FM.
Programming (via satellite): A & E; American Movie Classics; Comedy Central; Country Music TV; Discovery Channel; E! Entertainment TV; ESPN; Fox Family Channel; Headline News; Lifetime; Nashville Network; Nickelodeon; QVC; TBS Superstation; The Weather Channel; Turner Network TV; VH1.
Current originations: Automated time-weather; local news.
Fee: $30.00 installation; $15.95 monthly; $10.00 additional installation.
Expanded Basic Service
Subscribers: N.A.
Programming (via satellite): CNN; Home Team Sports; MTV; USA Network.
Fee: $20.00 installation; $4.95 monthly.
Pay Service 1
Pay Units: N.A.

Programming (via satellite): Cinemax; Disney Channel; HBO.
Fee: $20.00 installation; $9.00 monthly (Disney), $11.95 monthly (Cinemax or HBO).
Local advertising: No. Regional interconnect: Cabletime.
Equipment: Jerrold & Scientific-Atlanta headend; Jerrold amplifiers; Times Fiber cable; Oak set top converters.
Miles of plant: 483.0 (coaxial); 17.0 (fiber optic).
Manager: John Taylor. Chief technician: Gregory Davis. Marketing director: Barry L. Simmons.
Franchise fee: 3% of gross.
Ownership: Century Communications Corp. (MSO). See Cable System Ownership.

ORANGE—TCI of Virginia Inc., 301 E. Culpeper St., Culpeper, VA 22701-3039. Phone: 703-825-2920. County: Orange. Also serves Orange County. ICA: VA0073.
TV Market Ranking: Below 100. Franchise award date: N.A. Franchise expiration date: N.A. Began: December 1, 1970.
Channel capacity: 60 (2-way capable). Channels available but not in use: 27.
Basic Service
Subscribers: Included with Culpeper, VA.
Programming (received off-air): WVIR-TV (N) Charlottesville; WCVE-TV (P), WTVR-TV (C) Richmond-Petersburg; WDCA (U), WJLA-TV (A), WRC-TV (N), WTTG (F), WUSA (C) Washington; 10 FMs.
Programming (via satellite): BET; C-SPAN; C-SPAN 2; CNN; Comedy Central; Discovery Channel; Fox Family Channel; Headline News; Lifetime; MTV; Nashville Network; Nickelodeon; QVC; TBS Superstation; The Weather Channel; VH1.
Current originations: Automated time-weather.
Fee: $60.00 installation; $9.19 monthly.
Expanded Basic Service
Subscribers: Included with Culpeper, VA.
Programming (via satellite): American Movie Classics; ESPN; Home Team Sports; Turner Network TV; USA Network.
Fee: $12.01 monthly.
Pay Service 1
Pay Units: Included with Culpeper, VA.
Programming (via satellite): Cinemax; Disney Channel; HBO; Showtime; The New Encore.
Fee: N.A.
Equipment: Scientific-Atlanta headend; Kaiser amplifiers; Essex cable; Scientific-Atlanta satellite antenna; Scientific-Atlanta satellite receivers.
Miles of plant & homes passed included with Culpeper, VA.
Manager: Chuck Horner. Chief technician: Frank Kish. Program director: Al Gage. Marketing director: Brenda Dean.
City fee: 7% of gross.
Ownership: AT&T Broadband & Internet Services (MSO). Purchased from Tele-Communications Inc., March 9, 1999.

PEARISBURG—CableVision Communications, Box 2200, 68 5th St., Buckhannon, WV 26201. Phone: 304-472-4193. Fax: 304-472-0756. Counties: Giles, VA; Mercer & Monroe, WV. Also serves Giles County (portions), Lilly Heights, Narrows, Pembroke, VA; Glen Lyn, Lynn Side, Mercer County, Monroe County, Rich Creek, Ripplemead, WV. ICA: VA0043.
TV Market Ranking: 70 (portions of Giles County); Below 100 (portions of Giles County, Glen Lyn, Lilly Heights, Lynn Side, Mercer County, Monroe County, Narrows, Pearisburg, Pembroke, Rich Creek, Ripplemead). Franchise award date: N.A. Franchise expiration date: N.A. Began: December 1, 1970.
Channel capacity: 36. Channels available but not in use: 3.
Basic Service
Subscribers: 3,128.
Programming (received off-air): WVVA (N) Bluefield; WSWP-TV (P) Grandview; WOAY-TV (A) Oak Hill-Beckley; WBRA-TV (P) Roanoke; WDBJ (C), WFXR-TV (F), WSET-TV (A), WSLS-TV (N) Roanoke-Lynchburg.
Programming (via satellite): WGN-TV (W) Chicago; CNBC; Disney Channel; Fox Family Channel; Headline News; TBS Superstation.
Current originations: Automated time-weather.
Fee: $61.25 installation; $14.40 monthly; $1.24 converter.
Expanded Basic Service
Subscribers: 2,639.
Programming (via satellite): A & E; American Movie Classics; C-SPAN; CNN; Discovery Channel; ESPN; FX; Great American Country; Learning Channel; Lifetime; MTV; Nashville Network; Nickelodeon; QVC; Sci-Fi Channel; The Weather Channel; Trinity Bcstg. Network; Turner Network TV; USA Network.
Fee: $13.38 monthly.
Pay Service 1
Pay Units: 1,910.
Programming (via satellite): Cinemax; HBO; Showtime; The Movie Channel; The New Encore.
Fee: $3.99 monthly (Encore), $7.99 monthly (Cinemax) $11.99 monthly (HBO, Showtime, or TMC).
Equipment: Blonder-Tongue headend; GTE Sylvania amplifiers; Comm/Scope cable.
Miles of plant: 198.0 (coaxial). Homes passed: 5,288.
Manager: Willie Critchfield. Plant manager: Gary Lucas. Marketing director: Kenny Phillips.
City fee: 2.5% of gross.
Ownership: Rifkin & Associates Inc. (MSO). See Cable System Ownership.

PENNINGTON GAP—Century Virginia Corp., Box 1300, 838 Park Ave. NE, Norton, VA 24273. Phone: 540-523-3522. County: Lee. ICA: VA0091.
TV Market Ranking: Below 100. Franchise award date: N.A. Franchise expiration date: N.A. Began: October 1, 1955.
Channel capacity: 12. Channels available but not in use: None.
Basic Service
Subscribers: N.A.
Programming (received off-air): WCYB-TV (N) Bristol-Kingsport; WLOS (A) Greenville-Spartanburg-Asheville; WJHL-TV (C) Johnson City; WKPT-TV (A) Kingsport; WATE-TV (A), WBIR-TV (N), WVLT-TV (C) Knoxville; WSJK (P) Sneedville; allband FM.
Programming (via satellite): ESPN; Fox Family Channel; TBS Superstation.
Fee: $10.00 installation; $8.00 monthly.
Pay Service 1
Pay Units: N.A.
Programming (via satellite): HBO.
Fee: $25.00 installation; $11.95 monthly.
Local advertising: Yes. Regional interconnect: Cabletime.
Equipment: Jerrold headend; Jerrold amplifiers; Scientific-Atlanta satellite antenna; Scientific-Atlanta satellite receivers.
Miles of plant: 21.7 (coaxial). Homes passed: 1,100. Total homes in franchised area: 1,300.
Manager: John Taylor. Chief technician: Wayne Sizemore.
Ownership: Century Communications Corp. (MSO). See Cable System Ownership.

PETERSBURG—Tele-Media, Box 271, 351-57 Franklin St., Petersburg, VA 23804. Phone: 804-732-5522. Fax: 804-732-3590. Counties: Chesterfield, Dinwiddie & Prince George. Also serves Colonial Heights, Fort Lee, Prince George County (portions). ICA: VA0015.
TV Market Ranking: 63 (Colonial Heights, Fort Lee, Petersburg, portions of Prince George County); Outside TV Markets (portions of Prince George County). Franchise award date: January 1, 1968. Franchise expiration date: N.A. Began: October 14, 1968.
Channel capacity: 54 (not 2-way capable). Channels available but not in use: 3.
Basic Service
Subscribers: 17,511.
Programming (received off-air): WCVE-TV (P), WCVW (P), WRIC-TV (A), WRLH-TV (F), WTVR-TV (C), WWBT (N) Richmond-Petersburg.
Programming (via satellite): WGN-TV (W) Chicago; American Movie Classics; C-SPAN; C-SPAN 2; CNN; ESPN; Fox Family Channel; Home Team Sports; QVC; TBS Superstation; Turner Network TV.
Current originations: Public access.
Fee: $27.82 installation; $8.09 monthly.
Expanded Basic Service
Subscribers: 16,252.
Programming (via satellite): A & E; BET; CNBC; Country Music TV; Discovery Channel; Headline News; Learning Channel; Lifetime; MTV; Nashville Network; Nickelodeon; The Inspirational Network; The Weather Channel; Trinity Bcstg. Network; USA Network.
Fee: $20.00 installation; $15.61 monthly.
Pay Service 1
Pay Units: 2,705.
Programming (via satellite): Cinemax.
Fee: $2.00 installation; $9.15 monthly.
Pay Service 2
Pay Units: 971.
Programming (via satellite): Disney Channel.
Fee: $2.00 installation; $9.50 monthly.
Pay Service 3
Pay Units: 4,157.
Programming (via satellite): HBO.
Fee: $2.00 installation; $12.60 monthly.
Pay Service 4
Pay Units: 989.
Programming (via satellite): The Movie Channel.
Fee: $2.00 installation; $9.15 monthly.
Pay Service 5
Pay Units: 1,785.
Programming (via satellite): Showtime.
Fee: $2.00 installation; $12.25 monthly.
Pay-Per-View
Addressable homes: 9,800.
Playboy TV; Viewer's Choice.
Local advertising: Yes (insert only). Rates: $8.00/Minute. Local sales manager: Margaret Symes.
Equipment: Jerrold headend; Jerrold amplifiers; Comm/Scope cable; Oak addressable set top converters; Simulsat satellite antenna; Scientific-Atlanta satellite receivers.
Miles of plant: 255.0 (coaxial); 5.0 (fiber optic). Homes passed: 24,006. Total homes in franchised area: 25,000.
Manager: Joyce Johnson. Chief technician: Ed Land. Marketing director: Judy Queen.
City fee: 3% of gross.
Ownership: Tele-Media Corp. (MSO). Purchased from Marcus Cable, September 1, 1998.

POQUOSON—Cox Communications, 1323 W. Pembroke Ave., Hampton, VA 23661. Phones: 757-722-2851; 800-874-6390. Fax: 757-728-0515. County: York. ICA: VA0180.
TV Market Ranking: 44. Franchise award date: N.A. Franchise expiration date: N.A. Began: N.A.
Channel capacity: N.A. Channels available but not in use: N.A.
Basic Service
Subscribers: 3,244.
Programming (received off-air): WHRO-TV (P), WVEC-TV (A) Hampton-Norfolk; WAVY-TV (N), WGNT (U), WTKR (C), WTVZ (W) Portsmouth-Norfolk; WCVE-TV (P) Richmond-Petersburg.
Programming (via satellite): C-SPAN; TBS Superstation.
Current originations: Public access.
Fee: $29.00 installation; $7.78 monthly.
Expanded Basic Service
Subscribers: N.A.
Programming (via satellite): A & E; C-SPAN 2; CNBC; CNN; Discovery Channel; ESPN; Fox Family Channel; Home Team Sports; Lifetime; MTV; Nashville Network; Nickelodeon; QVC; The Inspirational Network; The Weather Channel; Turner Network TV; USA Network; VH1.
Fee: N.A.
A la Carte 1
Subscribers: N.A.
Programming (via satellite): WGN-TV (W) Chicago; Cartoon Network; ESPN 2; The New Encore.
Fee: N.A.
Pay Service 1
Pay Units: N.A.
Programming (via satellite): Cinemax; Disney Channel; HBO; Showtime; The Movie Channel.
Fee: N.A.
Pay-Per-View
Movies; special events.
Fee: Varies.
Ownership: Cox Communications Inc. (MSO).

POWHATAN—Benchmark Communications, Box 665, 2277 Academy Rd., Powhatan, VA 23139. Phone: 804-598-2900. County: Powhatan. Also serves Ballsville, Flat Rock, Jefferson, Macon, Powhatan County, Provost. ICA: VA0100.
TV Market Ranking: 63. Franchise award date: N.A. Franchise expiration date: N.A. Began: June 11, 1990.
Channel capacity: 62. Channels available but not in use: N.A.
Basic Service
Subscribers: 3,200.
Programming (received off-air): WCVE-TV (P), WCVW (P), WRIC-TV (A), WRLH-TV (F), WTVR-TV (C), WWBT (N) Richmond-Petersburg.
Programming (via satellite): WGN-TV (W) Chicago; CNN; MTV; TBS Superstation.
Fee: $5.00 monthly.
Expanded Basic Service
Subscribers: N.A.
Programming (via satellite): A & E; BET; C-SPAN; CNBC; Discovery Channel; ESPN; Fox Family Channel; Headline News; Learning Channel; Lifetime; Nashville Network; Nickelodeon; QVC; The Weather Channel; USA Network; VH1.
Fee: $17.95 monthly.
Pay Service 1
Pay Units: N.A.
Programming (via satellite): Cinemax; Disney Channel; HBO; Showtime.
Fee: $7.95 monthly (each).
Miles of plant: 35.0 (coaxial). Homes passed: 900.
Manager: Robin Reams.
Ownership: Benchmark Communications (MSO). Purchased from Billy R. Jones, July 2, 1999.

PULASKI—Adelphia Cable, 641 E. Main St., Pulaski, VA 24301. Phone: 800-835-4949. County: Pulaski. Also serves Dublin, Pulaski County. ICA: VA0159.

TV Market Ranking: Below 100 (Dublin, Pulaski, portions of Pulaski County); Outside TV Markets (portions of Pulaski County). Franchise award date: N.A. Franchise expiration date: N.A. Began: December 15, 1965.

Channel capacity: 36 (not 2-way capable). Channels available but not in use: 1.

Basic Service

Subscribers: 6,952.

Programming (received off-air): WVVA (N) Bluefield; WBRA-TV (P) Roanoke; WDBJ (C), WFXR-TV (F), WSET-TV (A), WSLS-TV (N) Roanoke-Lynchburg.

Programming (via satellite): A & E; CNBC; CNN; Comedy Central; Country Music TV; Discovery Channel; ESPN; ESPN 2; Fox Family Channel; Headline News; Home Team Sports; Lifetime; MTV; Nashville Network; Nickelodeon; QVC; TBS Superstation; TV Guide Channel; The Inspirational Network; The Weather Channel; Turner Network TV; USA Network; VH1.

Current originations: Public access.

Fee: $50.00 installation; $29.95 monthly; $2.00 converter.

Pay Service 1

Pay Units: N.A.

Programming (via satellite): Cinemax; Disney Channel; HBO; Playboy TV; Showtime.

Fee: $7.95 monthly (each).

Pay-Per-View

Addressable homes: 3,987.

Special events.

Local advertising: No.

Equipment: Jerrold & Scientific-Atlanta headend; Magnavox amplifiers; Comm/Scope cable; Scientific-Atlanta set top converters; Scientific-Atlanta addressable set top converters; Eagle traps; Scientific-Atlanta & Microdyne satellite antenna; Standard Communications satellite receivers.

Miles of plant: 180.0 (coaxial); 12.0 (fiber optic).

Manager: Ralph E. Bowman. Chief technician: Nick Cole.

City fee: 3% of gross.

Ownership: Adelphia Communications Corp. (MSO).

RADFORD—American Cable Entertainment, 613 2nd St., Radford, VA 24141. Phone: 540-639-3991. Fax: 540-731-4289. Counties: Montgomery & Pulaski. Also serves Christiansburg, Fairlawn, Montgomery County, Pulaski County (portions). ICA: VA0029.

TV Market Ranking: 70 (Christiansburg, Fairlawn, Montgomery County, Pulaski County, portions of Radford); Below 100 (Pulaski County); Outside TV Markets (Pulaski County). Franchise award date: N.A. Franchise expiration date: September 1, 1999. Began: January 1, 1970.

Channel capacity: 42 (2-way capable; operating 2-way). Channels available but not in use: None.

Basic Service

Subscribers: 11,386; Commercial subscribers: 2,661.

Programming (received off-air): WBRA-TV (P), WPXR (X) Roanoke; WDBJ (C), WFXR-TV (F), WSET-TV (A), WSLS-TV (N) Roanoke-Lynchburg; allband FM.

Programming (via satellite): WGN-TV (W) Chicago; QVC; TBS Superstation; TV Guide Channel.

Current originations: Educational access.

Fee: $29.95 installation; $7.83 monthly; $1.12 converter.

Expanded Basic Service

Subscribers: 10,844.

Programming (via satellite): A & E; BET; C-SPAN; CNBC; CNN; Comedy Central; Country Music TV; ESPN; Fox Family Channel; Headline News; Lifetime; MTV; Nashville Network; Nick at Nite; Nickelodeon; The Inspirational Network; The Weather Channel; Trinity Bcstg. Network; USA Network; VH1.

Fee: $29.95 installation; $17.61 monthly.

A la Carte 1

Subscribers: 9,343.

Programming (via satellite): American Movie Classics; Discovery Channel; Home Team Sports; Turner Network TV.

Fee: $16.50 installation; $3.05 monthly (package).

Pay Service 1

Pay Units: 717.

Programming (via satellite): Cinemax.

Fee: $7.00 monthly.

Pay Service 2

Pay Units: 589.

Programming (via satellite): Disney Channel.

Fee: $7.00 monthly.

Pay Service 3

Pay Units: 966.

Programming (via satellite): HBO.

Fee: $10.00 monthly.

Pay Service 4

Pay Units: 589.

Programming (via satellite): The Movie Channel.

Fee: $5.95 monthly.

Pay Service 5

Pay Units: 633.

Programming (via satellite): Showtime.

Fee: $7.00 monthly.

Pay Service 6

Pay Units: 121.

Programming (via satellite): Music Choice.

Fee: $9.95 monthly.

Pay Service 7

Pay Units: 317.

Programming (via satellite): The New Encore.

Fee: $1.95 monthly.

Pay-Per-View

Addressable homes: 2,541.

Special events.

Fee: $2.32.

Local advertising: Yes. Available in satellite distributed programming.

Equipment: Scientific-Atlanta headend; Magnavox amplifiers; Trilogy & Times Fiber cable; Panasonic, Jerrold & Standard Components set top converters; Tocom addressable traps; AFC & Scientific-Atlanta satellite antenna; Scientific-Atlanta satellite receivers.

Miles of plant: 299.6 (coaxial); 8.0 (fiber optic). Homes passed: 15,365.

Manager: Ervin Stauss. Chief technician: Kenneth Sawyers.

City fee: 5% of gross.

Ownership: American Cable Entertainment (MSO).

RESTON—Jones Intercable Inc., Box 2400, Reston, VA 22090. Phone: 703-716-9770. County: Fairfax. ICA: VA0017.

TV Market Ranking: 9. Franchise award date: N.A. Franchise expiration date: N.A. Began: January 1, 1970.

Channel capacity: 70. Channels available but not in use: N.A.

Basic Service

Subscribers: 14,642; Commercial subscribers: 13.

Programming (received off-air): WMPT (P) Annapolis; WBAL-TV (N), WMAR-TV (A) Baltimore; WNVC (E) Fairfax; WNVT (P) Goldvein; WPXW (X) Manassas; WBDC-TV (W), WDCA (U), WETA-TV (P), WHUT-TV (P), WJLA-TV (A), WRC-TV (N), WTTG (F), WUSA (C) Washington; allband FM.

Programming (via satellite): C-SPAN; C-SPAN 2; Learning Channel; TV Guide Channel.

Fee: $40.32 installation; $12.82 monthly.

Expanded Basic Service

Subscribers: 12,522.

Programming (via microwave): NewsChannel 8.

Programming (via satellite): A & E; American Movie Classics; BET; CNBC; CNN; Comedy Central; Country Music TV; Discovery Channel; E! Entertainment TV; ESPN; Fox Family Channel; Headline News; Home Shopping Network; Lifetime; MTV; Nashville Network; News Plus; Nickelodeon; Odyssey; QVC; TBS Superstation; The Weather Channel; Turner Network TV; USA Network; Univision; VH1.

Fee: $15.00 installation; $11.49 monthly.

Pay Service 1

Pay Units: 11,094.

Programming (via satellite): Bravo; Cinemax; Disney Channel; HBO; Home Team Sports; Showtime; The Movie Channel.

Fee: $25.00 installation; $4.95 monthly (HTS), $10.45 monthly (Bravo or Disney), $11.50 monthly (Cinemax, HBO, Showtime or TMC).

Pay-Per-View

Addressable homes: 1,581.

Action Pay-Per-View; Spice; Viewer's Choice.

Local advertising: Yes.

Equipment: Scientific-Atlanta headend; Theta-Com amplifiers; Comm/Scope cable; Sony VTRs; MSI character generator; Jerrold & Pioneer set top converters; Scientific-Atlanta satellite antenna; Scientific-Atlanta satellite receivers.

Miles of plant: 144.0 (coaxial). Homes passed: 18,834. Total homes in franchised area: 22,500.

Manager: Dave Cox. Chief technician: Tom Melson. Marketing director: Katrina Leary.

City fee: None.

Ownership: Jones Intercable Inc. (MSO).

RICHLANDS—Adelphia Cable Communications, 306 Suffolk Ave., Richlands, VA 24641. Phone: 800-835-4949. Fax: 703-963-9358. Counties: Buchanan & Tazewell. Also serves Cedar Bluff, Clay Pool Hill, Doran, Maple Gap, Paint Lick, Pounding Mill, Raven, Red Ash, Royal City, Seaboard, Steelsburg, Swords Creek, Tookland, Wardell, Whitten Valley. ICA: VA0041.

TV Market Ranking: Below 100 (Cedar Bluff, Paint Lick, Pounding Mill, Richlands, Seaboard, Wardell, Whitten Valley); Outside TV Markets (Clay Pool Hill, Doran, Maple Gap, Raven, Red Ash, Royal City, Steelsburg, Swords Creek, Tookland). Franchise award date: N.A. Franchise expiration date: N.A. Began: January 1, 1952.

Channel capacity: 35 (not 2-way capable). Channels available but not in use: None.

Basic Service

Subscribers: 5,221.

Programming (received off-air): WVVA (N) Bluefield; WCYB-TV (N) Bristol-Kingsport; W07DA (I), WLFG (I) Grundy; WJHL-TV (C) Johnson City; WKPT-TV (A) Kingsport; WVSX (I) Lewisburg; WSBN-TV (P) Norton; WOAY-TV (A) Oak Hill-Beckley; WDBJ (C) Roanoke-Lynchburg; allband FM.

Programming (via satellite): FoxNet; TBS Superstation.

Current originations: Automated time-weather; public access; educational access.

Fee: $46.00 installation (aerial), $60.00 (underground); $11.50 monthly; $3.25 converter; $23.00 additional installation.

Expanded Basic Service

Subscribers: 4,873.

Programming (via satellite): A & E; American Movie Classics; CNBC; CNN; Country Music TV; Discovery Channel; Disney Channel; ESPN; Fox Family Channel; Headline News; Home Team Sports; Lifetime; MTV; Nashville Network; Nickelodeon; QVC; TV Guide Channel; The Weather Channel; Turner Network TV; USA Network; VH1.

Fee: $19.50 monthly.

Pay Service 1

Pay Units: 478.

Programming (via satellite): Cinemax.

Fee: $11.50 monthly.

Pay Service 2

Pay Units: 550.

Programming (via satellite): HBO.

Fee: $11.50 monthly.

Pay Service 3

Pay Units: 245.

Programming (via satellite): Showtime.

Fee: $11.50 monthly.

Pay Service 4

Pay Units: 168.

Programming (via satellite): The Movie Channel.

Fee: $11.50 monthly.

Pay-Per-View

Addressable homes: 1,810.

Movies; special events.

Fee: Varies.

Local advertising: Yes (locally produced & insert). Available in locally originated & character-generated programming. Rates: $6.00/Minute; $4.00/30 Seconds.

Program Guide: The Cable Guide.

Equipment: Scientific-Atlanta headend; Magnavox amplifiers; Comm/Scope, Trilogy & Times Fiber cable; Sony VTRs; Jerrold & Scientific-Atlanta set top converters; Scientific-Atlanta & Jerrold addressable set top converters; Andrew, Scientific-Atlanta & RCA satellite antenna; Omni, Electrohome & Hughes satellite receivers; ChannelMatic commercial insert.

Miles of plant: 161.0 (coaxial); None (fiber optic). Homes passed: 7,368.

Manager: Ralph E. Bowman. Chief technician: Danny Nelson. Program director: Jeff Abbas. Marketing director: Dave Owens.

City fee: 3% of gross.

Ownership: Adelphia Communications Corp. (MSO).

RICHMOND—MediaOne, 918 North Blvd., Richmond, VA 23230-4687. Phone: 804-266-1900. Fax: 804-353-0285. County: Henrico. ICA: VA0004.

TV Market Ranking: 63. Franchise award date: January 1, 1978. Franchise expiration date: N.A. Began: June 25, 1980.

Channel capacity: 40 (2-way capable). Channels available but not in use: N.A.

Basic Service

Subscribers: 140,176.

Programming (received off-air): WUPV (U) Ashland; WCVE-TV (P), WCVW (P), WRIC-TV (A), WRLH-TV (F), WTVR-TV (C), WWBT (N) Richmond-Petersburg; allband FM.

Programming (via satellite): WGN-TV (W) Chicago; A & E; American Movie Classics; BET; C-SPAN; CNBC; CNN; Court TV; Discovery Channel; ESPN; Fox Family Channel; Headline News; Home Shopping Network; Home Team Sports; Lifetime; MTV; Music Choice; Nashville Network; Nickelodeon; TBS Superstation; The Weather Channel; Turner Network TV; USA Network; VH1.

Current originations: Automated time-weather; public access; educational access; government access; religious access; leased access; local news.

Fee: $30.00 installation; $19.50 monthly; $15.00 additional installation.
Commercial fee: $19.00 monthly.

Pay Service 1
Pay Units: 37,210.
Programming (via satellite): Cinemax; Disney Channel; HBO.
Fee: $15.00 installation; $9.95 monthly (each).

Pay-Per-View
Addressable homes: 1,705.
Hot Choice; Viewer's Choice.

Local advertising: Yes. Available in satellite distributed, locally originated & taped programming. Rates: $30.00/30 Seconds. Local sales manager: Matthew Zoller.
Equipment: Scientific-Atlanta headend; Magnavox & Scientific-Atlanta amplifiers; Comm/Scope cable; Sony cameras; Texscan character generator; Oak & Pioneer set top converters; Scientific-Atlanta satellite antenna; Microdyne satellite receivers; Arvis commercial insert.
Miles of plant: 731.0 (coaxial); None (fiber optic). Homes passed: 90,752.
Manager: David R. Lee. Chief technician: Laurence Loyd. Marketing director: Kenneth Dye.
City fee: 3% of gross.
Ownership: MediaOne Group (MSO). See Cable System Ownership.

RIVER OAKS—OnePoint Communications, Suite 114, 1200 Mercantile Lane, Largo, MD 20774. Phones: 301-618-4800; 877-288-8228. Counties: Fairfax & Prince William. Also serves Southridge. ICA: VA0178.
TV Market Ranking: 9. Franchise award date: N.A. Franchise expiration date: N.A. Began: N.A.
Channel capacity: N.A. Channels available but not in use: N.A.

Basic Service
Subscribers: 930.
Programming (received off-air): WMPT (P) Annapolis; WTMW (H) Arlington; WNVC (E) Fairfax; WNVT (P) Goldvein; WPXW (X) Manassas; WBDC-TV (W), WDCA (U), WETA-TV (P), WHUT-TV (P), WJLA-TV (A), WRC-TV (N), WTTG (F), WUSA (C) Washington.
Programming (via satellite): CNN; The Weather Channel.
Fee: $3.50 converter.

Expanded Basic Service
Subscribers: 456.
Programming (via satellite): WGN-TV (W) Chicago; A & E; American Movie Classics; BET; Bravo; C-SPAN; C-SPAN 2; CNBC; Cartoon Network; Comedy Central; Country Music TV; Court TV; Discovery Channel; E! Entertainment TV; ESPN; ESPN 2; Fox Family Channel; Headline News; Home Shopping Network; Home Team Sports; Learning Channel; Lifetime; MTV; Nashville Network; Nickelodeon; Sci-Fi Channel; TBS Superstation; Turner Network TV; USA Network; Univision; VH1.
Fee: $15.00 monthly.

Pay Service 1
Pay Units: 16.
Programming (via satellite): Cinemax.
Fee: $10.00 monthly.

Pay Service 2
Pay Units: 20.
Programming (via satellite): Disney Channel.
Fee: $10.00 monthly.

Pay Service 3
Pay Units: 63.
Programming (via satellite): Flix.
Fee: $10.00 monthly.

Pay Service 4
Pay Units: 85.
Programming (via satellite): HBO.
Fee: $10.00 monthly.

Pay Service 5
Pay Units: 108.
Programming (via satellite): The Movie Channel.
Fee: $10.00 monthly.

Pay Service 6
Pay Units: 126.
Programming (via satellite): Showtime.
Fee: $10.00 monthly.

Ownership: OnePoint Communications (MSO).

ROANOKE—Cox Communications, 5400 Fallowater Lane SW, Roanoke, VA 24014. Phone: 540-776-3848. Fax: 540-776-3847. Web site: http://www.virtualroanoke.com. County: Roanoke. Also serves Roanoke County, Vinton. ICA: VA0007.
TV Market Ranking: 70. Franchise award date: January 20, 1975. Franchise expiration date: May 30, 2003. Began: November 18, 1976.
Channel capacity: 78 (not 2-way capable). Channels available but not in use: 4.

Basic Service
Subscribers: 57,488.
Programming (received off-air): WDRL-TV (U) Danville; WBRA-TV (P), WPXR (X) Roanoke; WDBJ (C), WFXR-TV (F), WJPR (F), WSET-TV (A), WSLS-TV (N) Roanoke-Lynchburg; 8 FMs.
Programming (via satellite): WGN-TV (W) Chicago; C-SPAN; Knowledge TV; QVC; TBS Superstation; TV Guide Channel.
Current originations: Automated time-weather; public access; educational access; government access; religious access.
Fee: $18.99 installation; $9.25 monthly; $1.15 converter; $16.71 additional installation.

Expanded Basic Service
Subscribers: 54,068.
Programming (via satellite): A & E; American Movie Classics; BET; Bravo; CNBC; CNN; Comedy Central; Discovery Channel; Disney Channel; E! Entertainment TV; ESPN; FX; Fox Family Channel; Headline News; History Channel; Home & Garden Television; Home Shopping Network; Home Team Sports; Learning Channel; Lifetime; MSNBC; MTV; Nashville Network; Nick at Nite's TV Land; Nickelodeon; Odyssey; Outdoor Life Network; Product Information Network; Sci-Fi Channel; Speedvision; TV Guide Sneak Prevue; The Weather Channel; Turner Network TV; USA Network; VH1.
Fee: $18.99 installation; $28.10 monthly.

Expanded Basic Service 2
Subscribers: 12,534.
Programming (via satellite): Cartoon Network; Country Music TV; ESPN 2; Independent Film Channel; Turner Classic Movies.
Fee: $15.95 monthly.

Pay Service 1
Pay Units: 6,371.
Programming (via satellite): Cinemax.
Fee: $10.95 monthly.

Pay Service 2
Pay Units: 17,107.
Programming (via satellite): HBO (multiplexed).
Fee: $11.95 monthly.

Pay Service 3
Pay Units: 4,055.
Programming (via satellite): Showtime.
Fee: $10.95 monthly.

Pay Service 4
Pay Units: 1,654.
Programming (via satellite): The New Encore.
Fee: $2.95 monthly.

Pay Service 5
Pay Units: 1,119.
Programming (via satellite): Music Choice.
Fee: $4.95 monthly.

Pay-Per-View
Addressable homes: 22,000.
Movies; special events.
Fee: $3.95.

Local advertising: Yes. Available in satellite distributed & locally originated programming. Rates: $35.00/Minute; $17.50/30 Seconds. Local sales manager: Gary Greason.
Program Guide: The Cable Guide.
Equipment: Scientific-Atlanta headend; Century III & Scientific-Atlanta amplifiers; Comm/Scope & Times Fiber cable; Sony VTRs; Oak & Scientific-Atlanta set top converters; Tocom addressable set top converters; Eagle traps; Scientific-Atlanta satellite antenna; Scientific-Atlanta satellite receivers; ChannelMatic commercial insert.
Miles of plant: 1050.0 (coaxial); 159.0 (fiber optic). Homes passed: 92,000. Total homes in franchised area: 92,000.
Manager: Gary McCollum. Chief technician: George Buchan Jr. Marketing director: Bill Sledd.
City fee: 5% of gross.
Ownership: Cox Communications Inc. (MSO).

ROCKINGHAM—FrontierVision, Suite P-200, 1777 S. Harrison St., Denver, CO 80210. Phone: 303-757-1588. Fax: 303-757-6105. County: Rockingham. Also serves Lacy Spring, McGaheysville. ICA: VA0151.
TV Market Ranking: Below 100. Franchise award date: April 13, 1988. Franchise expiration date: N.A. Began: September 1, 1988.
Channel capacity: 40. Channels available but not in use: None.

Basic Service
Subscribers: 4,013.
Programming (received off-air): WVIR-TV (N) Charlottesville; WHSV-TV (A,F) Harrisonburg; WTVR-TV (C), WWBT (N) Richmond-Petersburg; WVPT (P) Staunton; WDCA (U), WTTG (F), WUSA (C) Washington.
Programming (via satellite): WGN-TV (W) Chicago; QVC; TBS Superstation.
Fee: $47.50 installation; $8.95 monthly; $1.50 converter.

Expanded Basic Service
Subscribers: N.A.
Programming (via satellite): A & E; American Movie Classics; C-SPAN; CNBC; CNN; Country Music TV; Discovery Channel; ESPN; Fox Family Channel; Headline News; Home Shopping Network; Home Team Sports; Learning Channel; MTV; Nashville Network; Nickelodeon; Odyssey; Sci-Fi Channel; The Weather Channel; Trinity Bcstg. Network; Turner Network TV; USA Network; VH1.
Fee: $9.95 monthly.

Pay Service 1
Pay Units: N.A.
Programming (via satellite): Cinemax; Disney Channel; HBO; Showtime; The Movie Channel.
Fee: $8.00 monthly (Disney), $9.00 monthly (Cinemax, HBO, Showtime or TMC).

Manager: Willie Critchfield. Chief technician: Bill Turner.
Ownership: FrontierVision Partners LP (MSO). See Cable System Ownership.

ROSEDALE—Cabletronix, Box 133, Cedar Bluff, VA 24609. Phone: 540-963-2245. County: Russell. Also serves Belfast Mills. ICA: VA0161.
TV Market Ranking: Below 100. Franchise award date: N.A. Franchise expiration date: N.A. Began: June 1, 1977.
Channel capacity: 28. Channels available but not in use: 12.

Basic Service
Subscribers: N.A.
Programming (received off-air): WVVA (N) Bluefield; WCYB-TV (N) Bristol-Kingsport; WOWK-TV (C) Charleston-Huntington; WJHL-TV (C) Johnson City; WKPT-TV (A) Kingsport.
Fee: N.A.

Miles of plant: 3.0 (coaxial).
Manager: Robert Waldron.
Ownership: Cabletronix (MSO); Vic Waldron (MSO).

RURAL RETREAT—Rural Retreat Cable TV Inc., Box 234A, Rte. 1, Rural Retreat, VA 24368. Phone: 540-686-5242. Fax: 540-686-5242. County: Wythe. ICA: VA0109.
TV Market Ranking: Below 100. Franchise award date: N.A. Franchise expiration date: N.A. Began: January 1, 1976.
Channel capacity: 35 (not 2-way capable). Channels available but not in use: 4.

Basic Service
Subscribers: 700.
Programming (received off-air): WVVA (N) Bluefield; WCYB-TV (N) Bristol-Kingsport; WXII (N) Greensboro-High Point; WLFG (I) Grundy; WJHL-TV (C) Johnson City; WKPT-TV (A) Kingsport; WBRA-TV (P), WPXR (X) Roanoke; WDBJ (C), WFXR-TV (F), WSLS-TV (N) Roanoke-Lynchburg.
Programming (via satellite): WGN-TV (W) Chicago; A & E; CNN; Cartoon Network; Country Music TV; Discovery Channel; ESPN; ESPN 2; Fox Family Channel; Learning Channel; MTV; NASA TV; Nashville Network; Nick at Nite's TV Land; Outdoor Channel; QVC; TBS Superstation; Turner Classic Movies; Turner Network TV.
Current originations: Public access; religious access.
Fee: $10.00 installation; $12.36 monthly.

Pay Service 1
Pay Units: 250.
Programming (via satellite): HBO.
Fee: $10.00 monthly.

Local advertising: Yes. Available in character-generated & taped programming.
Equipment: Blonder-Tongue headend; GTE Sylvania amplifiers; Times Fiber cable; Blonder-Tongue traps; Microdyne satellite receivers.
Miles of plant: 25.0 (coaxial); None (fiber optic). Homes passed: 750.
Manager: James P. Sage.
City fee: 3% of gross.
Ownership: James P. Sage.

RUTHER GLEN—OnePoint Communications, Suite 114, 1200 Mercantile Lane, Largo, MD 20774. Phone: 800-625-6646. County: Caroline. Also serves Lady Smith, Woodford. ICA: VA0130.
TV Market Ranking: 63 (Lady Smith, Ruther Glen); Below 100 (Woodford). Franchise award date: N.A. Franchise expiration date: N.A. Began: October 1, 1989.
Channel capacity: 61. Channels available but not in use: 21.

Basic Service
Subscribers: 1,779.
Programming (received off-air): WUPV (U) Ashland; WCVE-TV (P), WCVW (P), WRIC-TV (A), WRLH-TV (F), WTVR-TV (C), WWBT (N) Richmond-Petersburg.
Programming (via satellite): Learning Channel; QVC.

Fee: $60.00 installation (aerial), $94.50 (underground); $6.95 monthly; $4.25 converter; $22.50 additional installation.

Expanded Basic Service

Subscribers: N.A.

Programming (via satellite): A & E; American Movie Classics; BET; CNN; Cartoon Network; Country Music TV; Court TV; Discovery Channel; ESPN; Fox Family Channel; Headline News; Home Team Sports; Lifetime; MTV; Nashville Network; Nickelodeon; Sci-Fi Channel; TBS Superstation; The Weather Channel; Turner Classic Movies; Turner Network TV; USA Network; VH1.

Fee: $28.95 monthly.

Pay Service 1

Pay Units: N.A.

Programming (via satellite): Cinemax; Disney Channel; Flix; HBO; Showtime; The Movie Channel.

Fee: $4.95 monthly (Flix), $10.95 monthly (Disney), $11.95 monthly (Showtime or TMC), $13.95 monthly (Cinemax or HBO).

Pay-Per-View

Addressable homes: 1,500.

Special events.

Manager: Carol Lewis.

Ownership: OnePoint Communications (MSO).

SALEM—Adelphia Cable, Box 827, Salem, VA 24153. Phone: 540-389-9385. Fax: 540-389-4338. County: Roanoke. Also serves Roanoke County. ICA: VA0024.

TV Market Ranking: 70. Franchise award date: January 1, 1969. Franchise expiration date: October 1, 1999. Began: July 1, 1970.

Channel capacity: 82. Channels available but not in use: 10.

Basic Service

Subscribers: 12,996.

Programming (received off-air): WDRL-TV (U) Danville; WBRA-TV (P), WPXR (X) Roanoke; WDBJ (C), WFXR-TV (F), WSET-TV (A), WSLS-TV (N) Roanoke-Lynchburg; 3 FMs.

Programming (via satellite): WGN-TV (W) Chicago; C-SPAN; Home Shopping Network; Product Information Network; QVC; TBS Superstation; TV Guide Channel; TV Guide Sneak Prevue.

Current originations: Automated time-weather; public access.

Fee: $22.55 installation; $7.65 monthly.

Expanded Basic Service

Subscribers: 11,930.

Programming (via satellite): A & E; American Movie Classics; BET; Bravo; CNBC; CNN; Cartoon Network; Comedy Central; Country Music TV; Discovery Channel; E! Entertainment TV; ESPN; ESPN 2; FX; Fox Family Channel; Goodlife TV Network; Headline News; History Channel; Home Team Sports; Learning Channel; Lifetime; MTV; Nashville Network; Nickelodeon; Odyssey; QVC; Sci-Fi Channel; TV Guide Sneak Prevue; The Weather Channel; Travel Channel; Turner Network TV; USA Network; VH1.

Fee: $22.75 installation; $24.60 monthly.

Pay Service 1

Pay Units: 805.

Programming (via satellite): Cinemax.

Fee: $11.75 monthly.

Pay Service 2

Pay Units: 850.

Programming (via satellite): Disney Channel.

Fee: $15.00 installation; $8.25 monthly.

Pay Service 3

Pay Units: 3,858.

Programming (via satellite): HBO.

Fee: $15.00 installation; $11.75 monthly.

Pay Service 4

Pay Units: 574.

Programming (via satellite): Showtime.

Fee: $15.00 installation; $11.75 monthly.

Pay Service 5

Pay Units: 574.

Programming (via satellite): The Movie Channel.

Fee: N.A.

Pay Service 6

Pay Units: N.A.

Programming (via satellite): Starz!; The New Encore.

Fee: $4.95 monthly.

Pay-Per-View

Addressable homes: 4,850.

Spice; Viewer's Choice 4, 5 & 7.

Equipment: Scientific-Atlanta headend; Scientific-Atlanta amplifiers; Comm/Scope cable; BEI character generator; Regal set top converters; Pioneer addressable set top converters; Scientific-Atlanta satellite antenna.

Miles of plant: 287.0 (coaxial); 40.0 (fiber optic). Additional miles planned: 15.0 (coaxial). Homes passed: 15,000. Total homes in franchised area: 16,111.

Manager: Lon Carruth. Chief technician: John Van Lew. Marketing director: Stan Howell.

City fee: 5% of gross.

Ownership: Adelphia Communications Corp. (MSO).

SCOTTSVILLE—Community Cablevision, Box 395, Lovingston, VA 22949. Phone: 804-263-4805. Fax: 804-263-4821. Counties: Albemarle, Buckingham & Fluvanna. Also serves Albemarle County (portions), Buckingham County (portions), Fluvanna County (portions). ICA: VA0111.

TV Market Ranking: 63 (portions of Fluvanna County); 70 (portions of Albemarle County, portions of Buckingham County); Below 100 (portions of Albemarle County, portions of Buckingham County, Scottsville); Outside TV Markets (portions of Buckingham County, portions of Fluvanna County). Franchise award date: N.A. Franchise expiration date: N.A. Began: July 1, 1990.

Channel capacity: 35 (2-way capable; operating 2-way). Channels available but not in use: 15.

Basic Service

Subscribers: 46.

Programming (received off-air): WVIR-TV (N) Charlottesville; WCVE-TV (P), WRIC-TV (A), WRLH-TV (F), WTVR-TV (C), WWBT (N) Richmond-Petersburg.

Programming (via satellite): CNN; Cinemax; Discovery Channel; Disney Channel; ESPN; HBO; Nashville Network; Nickelodeon; Odyssey; TBS Superstation; Turner Network TV.

Fee: $50.00 installation; $29.50 monthly.

Miles of plant: None (fiber optic). Homes passed: 500.

Manager: Joe Lee McClellan. Chief technician: Terry Engelhardt.

Ownership: Nelson County Cablevision Corporation (MSO).

SHENANDOAH—Adelphia Cable Communications, 2815 N. Augusta St., Staunton, VA 24401. Phone: 800-835-4949. Fax: 540-886-7948. Counties: Page & Rockingham. Also serves Elkton, McGaheysville, Page County (portions), Rockingham County (portions). ICA: VA0060.

TV Market Ranking: Below 100 (Elkton, McGaheysville, portions of Page County, Rockingham County, Shenandoah); Outside TV Markets (portions of Page County). Franchise award date: N.A. Franchise expiration date: N.A. Began: June 1, 1977.

Channel capacity: 60 (not 2-way capable). Channels available but not in use: N.A.

Basic Service

Subscribers: 2,767.

Programming (received off-air): WVIR-TV (N) Charlottesville; WHSV-TV (A,F) Harrisonburg; WTVR-TV (C) Richmond-Petersburg; WVPT (P) Staunton; WDCA (U), WETA-TV (P), WJLA-TV (A), WRC-TV (N), WTTG (F), WUSA (C) Washington.

Programming (via satellite): C-SPAN; C-SPAN 2; TBS Superstation.

Fee: $50.00 installation; $21.95 monthly.

Expanded Basic Service

Subscribers: 2,645.

Programming (via satellite): A & E; American Movie Classics; CNBC; CNN; Cartoon Network; Comedy Central; Country Music TV; Discovery Channel; Disney Channel; ESPN; ESPN 2; FX; Fox Family Channel; Headline News; Home & Garden Television; Home Shopping Network; Home Team Sports; Learning Channel; Lifetime; MSNBC; MTV; Nashville Network; Nick at Nite's TV Land; Nickelodeon; QVC; Sci-Fi Channel; TV Food Network; The Health Network; The Inspirational Network; The Weather Channel; Travel Channel; Turner Classic Movies; Turner Network TV; USA Network; VH1.

Fee: N.A.

Pay Service 1

Pay Units: 265.

Programming (via satellite): Cinemax.

Fee: $11.50 monthly.

Pay Service 2

Pay Units: 347.

Programming (via satellite): HBO.

Fee: $11.50 monthly.

Pay Service 3

Pay Units: 159.

Programming (via satellite): Showtime.

Fee: $11.50 monthly.

Pay Service 4

Pay Units: 85.

Programming (via satellite): The Movie Channel.

Fee: $11.50 monthly.

Pay-Per-View

Addressable homes: 3,366.

Special events.

Equipment: Jerrold headend; Scientific-Atlanta amplifiers; Comm/Scope cable; Scientific-Atlanta set top converters; Scientific-Atlanta addressable set top converters; Eagle & Pico traps; Microdyne satellite receivers.

Homes passed: 3,000. Miles of plant: Included with Luray, VA.

Manager: Dell Hanley. Chief technician: Ron Herron.

City fee: 3% of gross.

Ownership: Adelphia Communications Corp. (MSO).

SOUTH BOSTON—Adelphia Cable Communications, Box 710, 1711 Seymour Dr., South Boston, VA 24592. Phone: 800-835-4949. Fax: 804-575-5760. County: Halifax. Also serves Halifax, Halifax County. ICA: VA0040.

TV Market Ranking: 70 (portions of Halifax County); Below 100 (Halifax, portions of Halifax County, South Boston); Outside TV Markets (portions of Halifax County). Franchise award date: July 12, 1968. Franchise expiration date: February 3, 2007. Began: September 1, 1976.

Channel capacity: 40 (not 2-way capable). Channels available but not in use: None.

Basic Service

Subscribers: 5,024; Commercial subscribers: 21.

Programming (received off-air): WUPN-TV (U) Greensboro-High Point; WRAL-TV (C), WTVD (A) Raleigh-Durham; WBRA-TV (P) Roanoke; WUNP-TV (P) Roanoke Rapids; WDBJ (C), WJPR (F), WSET-TV (A), WSLS-TV (N) Roanoke-Lynchburg.

Programming (via satellite): WGN-TV (W) Chicago; TBS Superstation.

Fee: $39.00 installation; $30.00 monthly; $3.25 converter.

Expanded Basic Service

Subscribers: N.A.

Programming (via satellite): A & E; BET; C-SPAN; CNN; Cartoon Network; Country Music TV; Discovery Channel; ESPN 2; FX; Fox Family Channel; Headline News; History Channel; Home Shopping Network; Learning Channel; MSNBC; Nashville Network; QVC; The Inspirational Network; The Weather Channel; Turner Network TV.

Fee: N.A.

Expanded Basic Service 2

Subscribers: N.A.

Programming (via satellite): ESPN; Lifetime; MTV; Nickelodeon; USA Network; VH1.

Fee: N.A.

Pay Service 1

Pay Units: 606.

Programming (via satellite): Cinemax.

Fee: $11.50 monthly.

Pay Service 2

Pay Units: 139.

Programming (via satellite): Disney Channel.

Fee: $8.95 monthly.

Pay Service 3

Pay Units: 828.

Programming (via satellite): HBO.

Fee: $11.50 monthly.

Pay Service 4

Pay Units: 206.

Programming (via satellite): The Movie Channel.

Fee: $11.50 monthly.

Pay Service 5

Pay Units: 212.

Programming (via satellite): Showtime.

Fee: $11.50 monthly.

Pay-Per-View

Addressable homes: 2,879.

Local advertising: Yes. Local sales manager: Gwen Howell.

Equipment: Cadco, Jerrold & Scientific-Atlanta headend; AEL amplifiers; Comm/Scope, Systems Wire & Times Fiber cable; Intercept set top converters; Jerrold addressable set top converters; Scientific-Atlanta satellite antenna; Scientific-Atlanta satellite receivers.

Miles of plant: 134.1 (coaxial); None (fiber optic). Homes passed: 7,684.

Manager: Luke Matthews. Plant manager: William Smith. Marketing director: Chuck Balestri. Customer service manager: Debra Cage.

City fee: 5% of gross.

Ownership: Adelphia Communications Corp. (MSO).

SOUTH HILL—SVHH Cable Acquisition LP, Box 710, 1711 Seymour Dr., South Boston, VA 24592. Phone: 800-835-4949. Fax: 804-575-5760. County: Mecklenburg. Also serves La Crosse, Mecklenburg County. ICA: VA0062.
TV Market Ranking: Outside TV Markets. Franchise award date: July 1, 1968. Franchise expiration date: N.A. Began: March 1, 1977.
Channel capacity: 31 (not 2-way capable). Channels available but not in use: None.
Basic Service
Subscribers: 2,074; Commercial subscribers: 8.
Programming (received off-air): WNCN (N) Goldsboro; WLFL (U), WRAL-TV (C), WRAZ (W), WRDC (U), WTVD (A) Raleigh-Durham; WCVE-TV (P), WRIC-TV (A), WRLH-TV (F), WTVR-TV (C), WWBT (N) Richmond-Petersburg; WUNP-TV (P) Roanoke Rapids; allband FM.
Programming (via satellite): WGN-TV (W) Chicago; A & E; CNN; Cartoon Network; Discovery Channel; Fox Family Channel; Home Shopping Network; Nashville Network; QVC; TBS Superstation; The Weather Channel; Turner Network TV.
Fee: $39.00 installation; $27.08 monthly; $3.25 converter; $29.00 additional installation.
Expanded Basic Service
Subscribers: N.A.
Programming (via satellite): ESPN; Lifetime; MTV; Nickelodeon; USA Network.
Fee: N.A.
Pay Service 1
Pay Units: 247.
Programming (via satellite): Cinemax.
Fee: $11.50 monthly.
Pay Service 2
Pay Units: 59.
Programming (via satellite): Disney Channel.
Fee: $8.95 monthly.
Pay Service 3
Pay Units: 332.
Programming (via satellite): HBO.
Fee: $11.50 monthly.
Pay Service 4
Pay Units: 84.
Programming (via satellite): The Movie Channel.
Fee: $11.50 monthly.
Pay-Per-View
Addressable homes: 698.
Local advertising: Yes. Local sales manager: Gwen Howell.
Program Guide: TV Entertainment.
Equipment: Cadco, Jerrold & Scientific-Atlanta headend; AEL & Scientific-Atlanta amplifiers; Comm/Scope cable; Pioneer & Oak set top converters; Jerrold addressable set top converters; Scientific-Atlanta satellite antenna; Scientific-Atlanta & Standard Communications satellite receivers.
Miles of plant: 47.9 (coaxial). Homes passed: 2,773.
Manager: Luke Matthews. Plant manager: William Smith. Marketing director: Chuck Balestri. Customer service manager: Debra Cage.
City fee: 3% of gross.
Ownership: Adelphia Communications Corp. (MSO).

SPEEDWELL—Cooney Cable Associates of Bastian LP, 228 Park Ave., Worcester, MA 01609. Phone: 508-754-5865. Fax: 508-752-7342. County: Wythe. Also serves Crockett, Rural Retreat (portions). ICA: VA0176.
TV Market Ranking: Below 100. Franchise award date: December 12, 1989. Franchise expiration date: December 11, 2004. Began: N.A.
Channel capacity: 45 (not 2-way capable). Channels available but not in use: 15.
Basic Service
Subscribers: 426.
Programming (received off-air): WVVA (N) Bluefield; WCYB-TV (N) Bristol-Kingsport; WJHL-TV (C) Johnson City; WKPT-TV (A) Kingsport; WMSY-TV (P) Marion; WDBJ (C), WFXR-TV (F), WSLS-TV (N) Roanoke-Lynchburg.
Programming (via satellite): WGN-TV (W) Chicago; C-SPAN; CNN; Country Music TV; Discovery Channel; E! Entertainment TV; ESPN; ESPN 2; Fox Family Channel; Headline News; History Channel; Learning Channel; Nashville Network; Nickelodeon; Outdoor Channel; QVC; TBS Superstation; The Weather Channel; Travel Channel; Trinity Bcstg. Network; Turner Classic Movies; Turner Network TV; USA Network.
Fee: $40.00 installation; $26.95 monthly; $1.95 converter.
Pay Service 1
Pay Units: 38.
Programming (via satellite): Disney Channel.
Fee: $7.95 monthly.
Pay Service 2
Pay Units: 39.
Programming (via satellite): HBO.
Fee: $11.95 monthly.
Pay Service 3
Pay Units: 16.
Programming (via satellite): Showtime; The Movie Channel.
Fee: $10.95 monthly (Showtime); $11.95 monthly (Showtime & TMC).
Miles of plant: 34.5 (coaxial); None (fiber optic). Homes passed: 527.
Manager: John B. Cooney. Customer service manager: Karen A. Perrone.
Ownership: Cooney Cable Assoc. Inc. (MSO).

SPOTSYLVANIA—Prestige Cable TV, Box 8086, 10841 Houser Dr., Fredericksburg, VA 22404. Phone: 540-898-6666. Fax: 540-898-5475. Counties: Orange, Spotsylvania & Stafford. Also serves Garrisonville, Lake of the Woods, Spotsylvania County (northern portion), Stafford County (northern portion). ICA: VA0018.
TV Market Ranking: 9 (portions of Stafford County); Below 100 (Garrisonville, Lake of the Woods, Spotsylvania, portions of Spotsylvania County, portions of Stafford County); Outside TV Markets (portions of Spotsylvania County). Franchise award date: N.A. Franchise expiration date: May 1, 1998. Began: May 1, 1982.
Channel capacity: 54. Channels available but not in use: 3.
Basic Service
Subscribers: 32,160.
Programming (received off-air): WPXW (X) Manassas; WCVE-TV (P), WRIC-TV (A), WTVR-TV (C), WWBT (N) Richmond-Petersburg; WDCA (U), WETA-TV (P), WJLA-TV (A), WRC-TV (N), WTTG (F), WUSA (C) Washington.
Programming (via satellite): C-SPAN; Cartoon Network; QVC; TV Guide Channel; TV Guide Sneak Prevue.
Current originations: Automated time-weather; government access; local news.
Fee: $47.54 installation; $10.17 monthly.
Expanded Basic Service
Subscribers: 27,440.
Programming (via satellite): A & E; American Movie Classics; BET; C-SPAN 2; CNBC; CNN; Country Music TV; Discovery Channel; ESPN; Fox Family Channel; Headline News; Home Team Sports; Lifetime; MTV; Nashville Network; Nickelodeon; The Weather Channel; Trinity Bcstg. Network; Turner Network TV; USA Network; VH1.
Fee: $11.78 monthly.
A la Carte 1
Subscribers: N.A.
Programming (via satellite): TBS Superstation.
Fee: $1.00 monthly.
Pay Service 1
Pay Units: 11,500.
Programming (via satellite): Cinemax; Disney Channel; HBO; Playboy TV; Showtime; The Movie Channel.
Fee: $9.95 monthly (Disney), $11.50 monthly (Cinemax, HBO, Showtime or TMC), $12.00 monthly (Playboy).
Pay-Per-View
Addressable homes: 10,680.
Action Pay-Per-View; Playboy TV; Viewer's Choice.
Fee: $3.25-$4.95.
Local advertising: Yes.
Program Guide: The Cable Guide.
Equipment: Scientific-Atlanta headend; Scientific-Atlanta amplifiers; Scientific-Atlanta cable; Scientific-Atlanta set top converters; Scientific-Atlanta addressable set top converters; Scientific-Atlanta satellite antenna; Scientific-Atlanta satellite receivers.
Miles of plant: 900.0 (coaxial). Homes passed: 35,000.
Manager: William R. Smith. Chief technician: Steve Haskins. Marketing director: Joe Keenan.
City fee: 3% of gross.
Ownership: Prestige Cable TV Inc. (MSO).

STANARDSVILLE—FrontierVision, Suite P-200, 1777 S. Harrison St., Denver, CO 80210. Phone: 303-757-1588. Fax: 303-757-6105. County: Greene. Also serves Ruckersville. ICA: VA0067.
TV Market Ranking: Below 100. Franchise award date: October 18, 1983. Franchise expiration date: October 18, 1998. Began: N.A.
Channel capacity: 42 (not 2-way capable). Channels available but not in use: 16.
Basic Service
Subscribers: 1,587.
Programming (received off-air): WVIR-TV (N) Charlottesville; WHSV-TV (A,F) Harrisonburg; WTVR-TV (C) Richmond-Petersburg; WVPT (P) Staunton; WDCA (U), WTTG (F) Washington.
Programming (via satellite): WGN-TV (W) Chicago; A & E; CNN; Comedy Central; Discovery Channel; ESPN; Fox Family Channel; Headline News; Home Team Sports; MTV; Nashville Network; Nickelodeon; TBS Superstation; Turner Network TV; VH1.
Fee: $40.00 installation; $21.50 monthly; $2.00 converter.
Pay Service 1
Pay Units: 109.
Programming (via satellite): Disney Channel.
Fee: $15.00 installation; $8.95 monthly.
Pay Service 2
Pay Units: 485.
Programming (via satellite): HBO.
Fee: $15.00 installation; $11.00 monthly.
Pay Service 3
Pay Units: 145.
Programming (via satellite): Showtime.
Fee: $11.00 monthly.
Local advertising: No.
Program Guide: CableView.
Equipment: Broadband amplifiers; Comm/Scope cable; Scientific-Atlanta set top converters; Eagle & PPC traps; Scientific-Atlanta & Comtech satellite antenna; Scientific-Atlanta satellite receivers.
Miles of plant: 81.0 (coaxial). Homes passed: 2,119.
President & chief executive officer: James Vaugh. Vice president, engineering: David Heyrend. Executive vice president: John Koo.
Franchise fee: 5% of gross.
Ownership: FrontierVision Partners LP (MSO). See Cable System Ownership.

STAUNTON—Multi-Channel TV Cable Co., 308 N. Central Ave., Staunton, VA 24401. Phones: 800-835-4949. Fax: 540-886-7948. Counties: Augusta & Rockingham, VA; Augusta, PA. Also serves Fishersville, Stuarts Draft, Waynesboro, PA; Augusta, Augusta County (portions), Churchville, Crimora, Greenville, Grottoes, Harriston, Mint Spring, New Hope, Rockingham City, Steels Tavern, Verona, VA. ICA: VA0026.
TV Market Ranking: Below 100 (Augusta, portions of Augusta County, Churchville, Crimora, Fishersville, Greenville, Grottoes, Harriston, Mint Spring, New Hope, Rockingham City, Staunton, Stuarts Draft, Verona, Waynesboro); Outside TV Markets (portions of Augusta County). Franchise award date: January 1, 1952. Franchise expiration date: N.A. Began: January 1, 1952.
Channel capacity: 55 (2-way capable). Channels available but not in use: N.A.
Basic Service
Subscribers: N.A.
Programming (received off-air): WVIR-TV (N) Charlottesville; WHSV-TV (A,F) Harrisonburg; WRIC-TV (A), WTVR-TV (C), WWBT (N) Richmond-Petersburg; WSET-TV (A), WSLS-TV (N) Roanoke-Lynchburg; WVPT (P) Staunton; WJLA-TV (A), WTTG (F), WUSA (C) Washington; allband FM.
Programming (via satellite): C-SPAN; C-SPAN 2; TBS Superstation.
Current originations: Educational access; automated emergency alert.
Fee: $33.00 installation; $10.00 monthly.
Expanded Basic Service
Subscribers: 23,723.
Programming (via satellite): A & E; American Movie Classics; BET; CNBC; CNN; Cartoon Network; Comedy Central; Country Music TV; Discovery Channel; ESPN; ESPN 2; FX; Fox Family Channel; Headline News; History Channel; Home Shopping Network; Home Team Sports; Learning Channel; Lifetime; MSNBC; MTV; Nashville Network; Nickelodeon; Odyssey; QVC; The Inspirational Network; The Weather Channel; Travel Channel; Turner Network TV; USA Network; VH1.
Fee: $33.00 installation; $13.40 monthly.
Pay Service 1
Pay Units: 2,433.
Programming (via satellite): Cinemax.
Fee: $20.00 installation; $11.50 monthly.
Pay Service 2
Pay Units: 622.
Programming (via satellite): Disney Channel.
Fee: $20.00 installation; $8.95 monthly.
Pay Service 3
Pay Units: 3,385.
Programming (via satellite): HBO.
Fee: $20.00 installation; $11.50 monthly.
Pay Service 4
Pay Units: 1,253.
Programming (via satellite): Showtime.
Fee: $20.00 installation; $11.50 monthly.
Pay Service 5
Pay Units: 731.
Programming (via satellite): The Movie Channel.
Fee: $20.00 installation; $11.50 monthly.
Pay-Per-View
Addressable homes: 5,255.

Special events.
Local advertising: Yes. Available in taped programming.
Program Guide: The Cable Guide.
Equipment: Scientific-Atlanta headend; Scientific-Atlanta amplifiers; Times Fiber cable; Texscan character generator; Scientific-Atlanta set top converters; Scientific-Atlanta addressable set top converters; Scientific-Atlanta traps; Scientific-Atlanta satellite antenna; Scientific-Atlanta satellite receivers; ChannelMatic commercial insert.
Miles of plant: 662.8 (coaxial); 10.0 (fiber optic). Additional miles planned: 4.2 (coaxial).
Manager: James V. Kitchen. Chief technician: Ron Herron. Marketing director: Chuck Balestri.
City fee: 3% of gross.
Ownership: Adelphia Communications Corp. (MSO).

STUART—FrontierVision, Suite P-200, 1777 S. Harrison St., Denver, CO 80210. Phone: 303-757-1588. Fax: 303-757-6105. County: Patrick. Also serves Patrick Springs. ICA: VA0069.
TV Market Ranking: Outside TV Markets. Franchise award date: April 16, 1983. Franchise expiration date: April 25, 1998. Began: April 16, 1983.
Channel capacity: 42 (not 2-way capable). Channels available but not in use: 2.
Basic Service
Subscribers: 1,264.
Programming (received off-air): WGPX (X) Burlington; WFMY-TV (C), WGHP (F), WLXI-TV (T) Greensboro-High Point; WBRA-TV (P) Roanoke; WDBJ (C), WSLS-TV (N) Roanoke-Lynchburg; WXLV-TV (A) Winston-Salem.
Programming (via satellite): QVC.
Current originations: Public access; educational access; government access.
Fee: $47.50 installation; $9.00 monthly; $1.86 converter; $10.00 additional installation.
Expanded Basic Service
Subscribers: 1,136.
Programming (via satellite): WGN-TV (W) Chicago; A & E; C-SPAN; CNN; Cartoon Network; Country Music TV; Discovery Channel; Disney Channel; ESPN; FX; Fox Family Channel; Headline News; Learning Channel; Lifetime; Nashville Network; Nickelodeon; Sci-Fi Channel; TBS Superstation; The Inspirational Network; The Weather Channel; Turner Network TV; USA Network; VH1.
Fee: $15.18 monthly.
Pay Service 1
Pay Units: 134.
Programming (via satellite): Cinemax.
Fee: $15.00 installation; $10.95 monthly.
Pay Service 2
Pay Units: 145.
Programming (via satellite): HBO.
Fee: $11.95 monthly.
Pay Service 3
Pay Units: 41.
Programming (via satellite): The Movie Channel.
Fee: $11.95 monthly.
Pay Service 4
Pay Units: 46.
Programming (via satellite): Showtime.
Fee: $11.95 monthly.
Local advertising: No.
Program Guide: CableView.
Equipment: Magnavox amplifiers; Comm/Scope & Times Fiber cable; Eagle & PPC traps; M/A-Com & Prodelin satellite antenna; Drake satellite receivers.
Miles of plant: 70.1 (coaxial). Homes passed: 2,196.
Manager: Dan Callahan. Chief technician: Gary Shoemaker.
Ownership: FrontierVision Partners LP (MSO). See Cable System Ownership.

SUFFOLK—Falcon Cable TV, 216 Moore Ave., Suffolk, VA 23434. Phone: 757-539-2312. County: Suffolk City. ICA: VA0025.
TV Market Ranking: 44. Franchise award date: February 1, 1984. Franchise expiration date: February 1, 2009. Began: October 24, 1984.
Channel capacity: 60 (2-way capable; operating 2-way). Channels available but not in use: 2.
Basic Service
Subscribers: 7,084.
Programming (received off-air): WHRO-TV (P), WVEC-TV (A) Hampton-Norfolk; WAVY-TV (N), WGNT (U), WPXV (X), WTKR (C), WTVZ (W) Portsmouth-Norfolk; WVBT (F) Virginia Beach.
Programming (via satellite): A & E; BET; C-SPAN; C-SPAN 2; CNBC; Comedy Central; Country Music TV; ESPN; ESPN 2; Goodlife TV Network; Home Team Sports; Learning Channel; Lifetime; MTV; Nashville Network; QVC; Sci-Fi Channel; TV Guide Channel; TV Guide Sneak Prevue; The Inspirational Network; Travel Channel; USA Network; VH1.
Current originations: Automated time-weather; public access; educational access; government access; automated emergency alert; local news.
Fee: $19.95 installation; $22.93 monthly.
Expanded Basic Service
Subscribers: 6,354.
Programming (via satellite): WGN-TV (W) Chicago; American Movie Classics; TBS Superstation.
Fee: $1.79 monthly.
Expanded Basic Service 2
Subscribers: 6,354.
Programming (via satellite): CNN; Discovery Channel; Disney Channel; Fox Family Channel; Headline News; Nickelodeon; The Weather Channel; Turner Network TV.
Fee: $7.24 monthly.
Pay Service 1
Pay Units: 1,353.
Programming (via satellite): Cinemax.
Fee: $10.95 monthly.
Pay Service 2
Pay Units: 2,480.
Programming (via satellite): HBO.
Fee: $19.95 installation; $11.95 monthly.
Pay Service 3
Pay Units: 516.
Programming (via satellite): The Movie Channel.
Fee: $19.95 installation; $10.95 monthly.
Pay Service 4
Pay Units: 1,039.
Programming (via satellite): Showtime.
Fee: $19.95 installation; $10.95 monthly.
Pay Service 5
Pay Units: N.A.
Programming (via satellite): Bravo; The New Encore.
Fee: N.A.
Pay-Per-View
Addressable homes: 5,422.
Action Pay-Per-View; Spice; Viewer's Choice.
Fee: $3.95.
Local advertising: Yes. Available in character-generated programming. Regional interconnect: Tidewater Cable Interconnect.
Miles of plant: 444.0 (coaxial). Homes passed: 18,145.
Manager: Jack Edwards. Chief technician: Mahlon Fritz.
Franchise fee: 3% of gross.
Ownership: Falcon Communications LP (MSO), joint venture formed September 30, 1998; Suffolk Cablevision Inc. See Cable System Ownership.

TANGIER ISLAND—Falcon Cable TV, 216 Moore Ave., Suffolk, VA 23434. Phone: 804-539-2312. County: Accomack. ICA: VA0117.
TV Market Ranking: Outside TV Markets. Franchise award date: N.A. Franchise expiration date: N.A. Began: June 1, 1973.
Channel capacity: 12. Channels available but not in use: None.
Basic Service
Subscribers: 127.
Programming (received off-air): WHRO-TV (P), WVEC-TV (A) Hampton-Norfolk; WAVY-TV (N), WGNT (U), WTKR (C), WTVZ (W) Portsmouth-Norfolk; WBOC-TV (C), WCPB (P) Salisbury.
Programming (via satellite): CNN; ESPN; TBS Superstation.
Fee: $19.50 installation; $17.41 monthly.
Pay Service 1
Pay Units: 8.
Programming (via satellite): HBO.
Fee: $11.95 monthly.
Equipment: Ameco headend; Jerrold amplifiers; Jerrold cable.
Miles of plant: 3.0 (coaxial). Homes passed: 213. Total homes in franchised area: 290.
Manager: Jack Edwards. Chief technician: Mahlon Fritz.
Ownership: Falcon Communications LP (MSO), joint venture formed September 30, 1998. See Cable System Ownership.

TAPPAHANNOCK—Tri-State Cablecomm, Box 789, 112 N. Main St., Bowling Green, VA 22427. Phones: 804-633-9511; 800-489-7070. Fax: 804-633-7329. County: Essex. Also serves Essex County (portions). ICA: VA0080.
TV Market Ranking: 63 (portions of Essex County); Below 100 (portions of Essex County, Tappahannock); Outside TV Markets (portions of Essex County). Franchise award date: February 1, 1972. Franchise expiration date: September 25, 2000. Began: March 1, 1972.
Channel capacity: 35 (not 2-way capable). Channels available but not in use: 3.
Basic Service
Subscribers: 1,074; Commercial subscribers: 36.
Programming (received off-air): WUPV (U) Ashland; WCVE-TV (P), WCVW (P), WRIC-TV (A), WRLH-TV (F), WTVR-TV (C), WWBT (N) Richmond-Petersburg; WETA-TV (P), WTTG (F) Washington; allband FM.
Programming (via satellite): WGN-TV (W) Chicago; Home Shopping Network; Pax Net; TBS Superstation.
Fee: $54.98 installation; $19.92 monthly; $0.75 converter.
Commercial fee: $14.12 monthly.
Expanded Basic Service
Subscribers: 976.
Programming (via satellite): A & E; BET; CNN; Discovery Channel; ESPN; ESPN 2; Fox Family Channel; Home Team Sports; Learning Channel; Lifetime; MTV; Nashville Network; Nickelodeon; Sci-Fi Channel; The Weather Channel; Turner Classic Movies; Turner Network TV; USA Network.
Fee: $13.95 monthly.
Pay Service 1
Pay Units: 43.
Programming (via satellite): Cinemax.
Fee: $11.50 monthly.
Pay Service 2
Pay Units: 61.
Programming (via satellite): Disney Channel.
Fee: $8.95 monthly.
Pay Service 3
Pay Units: 94.
Programming (via satellite): HBO.
Fee: $11.50 monthly.
Equipment: Blonder-Tongue headend; Magnavox amplifiers; Times Fiber & Comm/Scope cable; Scientific-Atlanta set top converters; Eagle traps; AFC & Harris satellite antenna; M/A-Com satellite receivers.
Miles of plant: 28.0 (coaxial). Additional miles planned: 2.0 (coaxial). Homes passed: 1,378. Total homes in franchised area: 1,578.
Manager: Thomas A. Olsen. Chief technician: Alfred Trigger. Marketing director: Trish Lindsey.
City fee: 4% of gross.
Ownership: Fanch Communications Inc. (MSO); Time Warner Cable (MSO). See Cable System Ownership.

TAZEWELL—Adelphia Cable Communications, 306 Suffolk Ave., Richlands, VA 24641. Phone: 800-835-4949. Fax: 703-963-9358. County: Tazewell. Also serves Adria, Bandy, Baptist Valley, Cliffield, Gratton, North Tazewell, Tiptop. ICA: VA0045.
TV Market Ranking: Below 100. Franchise award date: N.A. Franchise expiration date: N.A. Began: N.A.
Channel capacity: 36 (not 2-way capable). Channels available but not in use: None.
Basic Service
Subscribers: 3,945.
Programming (received off-air): WVVA (N) Bluefield; WCYB-TV (N) Bristol-Kingsport; W07DA (I), WLFG (I) Grundy; WJHL-TV (C) Johnson City; WKPT-TV (A) Kingsport; WVSX (I) Lewisburg; WSBN-TV (P) Norton; WOAY-TV (A) Oak Hill-Beckley; WDBJ (C) Roanoke-Lynchburg.
Programming (via satellite): FoxNet; TBS Superstation.
Current originations: Public access; educational access; government access; automated emergency alert.
Fee: $46.00 installation (aerial), $60.00 (underground); $11.50 monthly; $3.25 converter; $23.00 additional installation.
Expanded Basic Service
Subscribers: 3,708.
Programming (via satellite): A & E; American Movie Classics; CNBC; CNN; Country Music TV; Discovery Channel; Disney Channel; ESPN; Fox Family Channel; Headline News; Home Team Sports; Lifetime; MTV; Nashville Network; Nickelodeon; QVC; TV Guide Channel; The Weather Channel; Turner Network TV; USA Network; VH1.
Fee: $19.50 monthly.
Pay Service 1
Pay Units: 366.
Programming (via satellite): Cinemax.
Fee: $11.50 monthly.
Pay Service 2
Pay Units: 448.
Programming (via satellite): HBO.
Fee: $11.50 monthly.
Pay Service 3
Pay Units: 197.
Programming (via satellite): Showtime.
Fee: $11.50 monthly.
Pay Service 4
Pay Units: 157.
Programming (via satellite): The Movie Channel.
Fee: $11.50 monthly.
Pay-Per-View
Addressable homes: 1,416.
Movies; special events.
Fee: Varies.
Local advertising: Yes. Available in taped programming.

Equipment: Scientific-Atlanta headend; Magnavox amplifiers; Comm/Scope, Times Fiber & Trilogy cable; Jerrold & Scientific-Atlanta set top converters; Scientific-Atlanta & Jerrold addressable set top converters; Andrew, Scientific-Atlanta & RCA satellite antenna; Omni & Hughes satellite receivers; ChannelMatic commercial insert.
Miles of plant: 175.0 (coaxial); None (fiber optic). Homes passed: 5,575.
Manager: Ralph E. Bowman. Chief technician: Danny Nelson. Program director: Jeff Abbas. Marketing director: Dave Owens.
Ownership: Adelphia Communications Corp. (MSO).

TIMBERLAKE—Nesbe Cable TV, Box 10516, Lynchburg, VA 24506. Phone: 804-821-7110. Counties: Appomattox, Bedford & Campbell. Also serves Alta Vista, Bedford County (northern portion), Clarion, Concord, Evington, Forest, Goode, Rustburg. ICA: VA0128.
TV Market Ranking: 70. Franchise award date: N.A. Franchise expiration date: N.A. Began: December 1, 1984.
Channel capacity: 56. Channels available but not in use: 2.
Basic Service
Subscribers: 6,437.
Programming (received off-air): WBRA-TV (P) Roanoke; WDBJ (C), WSET-TV (A), WSLS-TV (N) Roanoke-Lynchburg.
Programming (via satellite): WGN-TV (W) Chicago; BET; C-SPAN; CNBC; CNN; ESPN; Fox Family Channel; Lifetime; MTV; Nashville Network; Nickelodeon; The Inspirational Network; The Weather Channel.
Planned originations: Public access; government access.
Fee: $38.50 installation; $19.50 monthly.
Pay Service 1
Pay Units: N.A.
Programming (via satellite): Cinemax; Disney Channel; HBO; The Movie Channel.
Fee: $7.50 monthly (Disney), $10.50 monthly (Cinemax, HBO or TMC).
Local advertising: Yes.
Equipment: Scientific-Atlanta headend; Scientific-Atlanta amplifiers; Scientific-Atlanta cable; Scientific-Atlanta satellite antenna; Scientific-Atlanta satellite receivers.
Miles of plant: 185.4 (coaxial). Additional miles planned: 55.0 (coaxial).
Manager: Frank Staley. Chief technician: Ricky Tomlin.
Ownership: Bahakel Communications Ltd. (MSO).

TROUTVILLE—Adelphia Cable, Box 627, 5324 Lee Hwy., Troutville, VA 24175. Phone: 540-992-4144. Fax: 540-966-3102. Counties: Bedford, Botetourt & Roanoke. Also serves Bedford, Blue Ridge, Chamblissburg, Cloverdale, Daleville, Fincastle, Goodview, Huddleston, Moneta, Montvale, Nace, Stewartsville, Thaxton, Vinton. ICA: VA0037.
TV Market Ranking: 70. Franchise award date: April 30, 1982. Franchise expiration date: August 17, 2020. Began: November 1, 1983.
Channel capacity: 35 (not 2-way capable). Channels available but not in use: N.A.
Basic Service
Subscribers: 7,269; Commercial subscribers: 75.
Programming (received off-air): WBRA-TV (P), WPXR (X) Roanoke; WDBJ (C), WFXR-TV (F), WSET-TV (A), WSLS-TV (N) Roanoke-Lynchburg.
Programming (via satellite): WGN-TV (W) Chicago; C-SPAN; QVC; Sci-Fi Channel; TBS Superstation.
Current originations: Government access.
Fee: $24.95 installation (aerial), $34.95 (underground); $12.29 monthly; $0.75 converter.
Expanded Basic Service
Subscribers: 6,802.
Programming (via satellite): A & E; All News Channel; American Movie Classics; CNBC; CNN; Discovery Channel; ESPN; Fox Family Channel; Headline News; Learning Channel; Lifetime; MTV; Nashville Network; Nick at Nite; Nickelodeon; The Weather Channel; Turner Network TV; USA Network.
Fee: $11.51 installation; $17.41 monthly.
Pay Service 1
Pay Units: 1,052.
Programming (via satellite): Cinemax.
Fee: $20.00 installation; $11.50 monthly.
Pay Service 2
Pay Units: 655.
Programming (via satellite): Disney Channel.
Fee: $20.00 installation; $8.95 monthly.
Pay Service 3
Pay Units: 1,564.
Programming (via satellite): HBO.
Fee: $20.00 installation; $11.50 monthly.
Pay Service 4
Pay Units: 750.
Programming (via satellite): Showtime; The Movie Channel.
Fee: $11.50 monthly (each).
Equipment: Blonder-Tongue & Scientific-Atlanta headend; Magnavox amplifiers; Comm/Scope & Times Fiber cable; Pioneer & Scientific-Atlanta set top converters; Eagle traps; Scientific-Atlanta satellite antenna; M/A-Com & Scientific-Atlanta satellite receivers.
Miles of plant: 356.0 (coaxial). Homes passed: 9,755. Total homes in franchised area: 9,971.
Manager: Lon Carruth. Chief technician: John Van Lew.
Franchise fee: 3% of gross.
Ownership: Adelphia Communications Corp. (MSO); Time Warner Cable (MSO). Purchased from Fanch Communications Inc., April 15, 1999.

VICTORIA—Tele-Media Co. of Southern Virginia, Box 465, Rte. 644, Farmville, VA 23901. Phone: 804-392-8144. Fax: 804-392-5262. County: Lunenburg. Also serves Lunenburg County (portions). ICA: VA0098.
TV Market Ranking: Outside TV Markets. Franchise award date: N.A. Franchise expiration date: March 9, 2003. Began: December 1, 1970.
Channel capacity: 64 (not 2-way capable). Channels available but not in use: 30.
Basic Service
Subscribers: 549.
Programming (received off-air): WCVE-TV (P), WCVW (P), WRIC-TV (A), WRLH-TV (F), WTVR-TV (C), WWBT (N) Richmond-Petersburg.
Programming (via satellite): WGN-TV (W) Chicago; C-SPAN; QVC; TBS Superstation.
Fee: $46.94 installation; $13.98 monthly; $0.75 converter.
Expanded Basic Service
Subscribers: 524.
Programming (via satellite): A & E; BET; CNN; Discovery Channel; ESPN; Fox Family Channel; Headline News; Learning Channel; Nashville Network; Nickelodeon; Turner Network TV; VH1.
Fee: $13.98 monthly.
Pay Service 1
Pay Units: 48.
Programming (via satellite): Disney Channel.
Fee: $8.95 monthly.
Pay Service 2
Pay Units: 117.
Programming (via satellite): HBO.
Fee: $10.50 monthly.
Pay Service 3
Pay Units: 118.
Programming (via satellite): Showtime.
Fee: $10.50 monthly.
Pay Service 4
Pay Units: 101.
Programming (via satellite): The Movie Channel.
Fee: $10.50 monthly.
Equipment: Blonder-Tongue headend; Magnavox amplifiers; Comm/Scope cable; Pioneer & Scientific-Atlanta set top converters; Eagle traps; Microdyne satellite receivers.
Miles of plant: 20.0 (coaxial); None (fiber optic). Homes passed: 1,009.
Manager: Susan T. Morse. Chief technician: Steve Fore. Operations director: Frank Vicente.
City fee: 3% of gross.
Ownership: Tele-Media Corp. (MSO).

WARRENTON—Prestige Cable, Box 490, Warrenton, VA 20188. Phone: 540-349-8000. Fax: 540-341-0042. Counties: Fauquier & Prince William. Also serves Bealton, Catlett, Gainesville, Marshall, Nokesville, Remington. ICA: VA0034.
TV Market Ranking: Below 100. Franchise award date: December 1, 1986. Franchise expiration date: January 1, 2006. Began: December 1, 1986.
Channel capacity: 54 (2-way capable; not operating 2-way). Channels available but not in use: 6.
Basic Service
Subscribers: 7,000.
Programming (received off-air): WNVC (E) Fairfax; WNVT (P) Goldvein; WPXW (X) Manassas; WBDC-TV (W), WDCA (U), WETA-TV (P), WJLA-TV (A), WRC-TV (N), WTTG (F), WUSA (C) Washington.
Programming (via satellite): Home Shopping Network; QVC; TBS Superstation; TV Guide Channel; TV Guide Sneak Prevue.
Fee: $45.00 installation; $9.09 monthly.
Expanded Basic Service
Subscribers: 6,800.
Programming (via satellite): A & E; American Movie Classics; BET; C-SPAN; C-SPAN 2; CNBC; CNN; Cartoon Network; Country Music TV; Discovery Channel; ESPN; ESPN 2; Fox Family Channel; Headline News; Home Team Sports; Learning Channel; Lifetime; MTV; Nashville Network; Nickelodeon; The Weather Channel; Trinity Bcstg. Network; Turner Network TV; USA Network; VH1.
Fee: $13.34 monthly.
Pay Service 1
Pay Units: 2,800.
Programming (via satellite): Cinemax; Disney Channel; HBO; Showtime; The Movie Channel.
Fee: $9.95 monthly (Disney), $11.50 monthly (Cinemax, HBO, Showtime or TMC).
Pay-Per-View
Addressable homes: 5,000.
Action Pay-Per-View; Playboy TV; Spice; Viewer's Choice.
Local advertising: No.
Equipment: Scientific-Atlanta headend; Scientific-Atlanta amplifiers; Scientific-Atlanta addressable set top converters; Scientific-Atlanta satellite receivers.
Miles of plant: 280.0 (coaxial); None (fiber optic). Additional miles planned: 10.0 (coaxial). Homes passed: 10,300. Total homes in franchised area: 10,500.
Manager: Lisa Cash. Chief technician: Steve Mayes. Marketing director: Janet Burton.
County fee: 5% of gross.
Ownership: Prestige Cable TV Inc. (MSO).

WARSAW—Tri-State Cablecomm, Box 789, 112 N. Main St., Bowling Green, VA 22427. Phones: 804-633-9511; 800-489-7070. Fax: 804-633-7329. County: Richmond. ICA: VA0094.
TV Market Ranking: Outside TV Markets. Franchise award date: April 1, 1984. Franchise expiration date: April 1, 2007. Began: February 13, 1986.
Channel capacity: 35 (not 2-way capable). Channels available but not in use: 3.
Basic Service
Subscribers: 909; Commercial subscribers: 16.
Programming (received off-air): WUPV (U) Ashland; WCVE-TV (P), WRIC-TV (A), WRLH-TV (F), WTVR-TV (C), WWBT (N) Richmond-Petersburg; WDCA (U), WTTG (F) Washington.
Programming (via satellite): WGN-TV (W) Chicago; C-SPAN; C-SPAN 2; QVC; TBS Superstation.
Fee: $59.56 installation; $19.01 monthly; $0.75 converter.
Commercial fee: $13.24 monthly.
Expanded Basic Service
Subscribers: 837.
Programming (via satellite): A & E; Animal Planet; BET; CNN; Discovery Channel; ESPN; ESPN 2; Fox Family Channel; Home Team Sports; Learning Channel; Lifetime; MTV; Nashville Network; Nickelodeon; Sci-Fi Channel; The Weather Channel; Turner Network TV; USA Network.
Fee: $13.95 monthly.
Pay Service 1
Pay Units: 50.
Programming (via satellite): Cinemax.
Fee: $11.50 monthly.
Pay Service 2
Pay Units: 87.
Programming (via satellite): Disney Channel.
Fee: $8.95 monthly.
Pay Service 3
Pay Units: 83.
Programming (via satellite): HBO.
Fee: $11.50 monthly.
Local advertising: No.
Equipment: Blonder-Tongue headend; Jerrold amplifiers; Times Fiber & Comm/Scope cable; Scientific-Atlanta set top converters; Eagle traps; Scientific-Atlanta satellite antenna; M/A-Com satellite receivers.
Miles of plant: 46.0 (coaxial). Homes passed: 1,265. Total homes in franchised area: 1,349.
Manager: Thomas A. Olsen. Chief technician: Alfred Trigger. Marketing director: Trish Lindsey.
City fee: 3% of basic.
Ownership: Fanch Communications Inc. (MSO); Time Warner Cable (MSO). See Cable System Ownership.

WEBER CITY—Scott County Telephone & Cable, Box 489, Gate City, VA 24251. Phone: 540-452-2201. Fax: 540-452-4313. Counties: Scott & Wise. Also serves Daniel Boone, Gate City, Hiltons, Nickelsville (portions), Sandy Ridge, Yuma. ICA: VA0054.
TV Market Ranking: Below 100. Franchise award date: March 15, 1965. Franchise expiration date: N.A. Began: May 5, 1965.
Channel capacity: 26. Channels available but not in use: 3.
Basic Service
Subscribers: N.A.
Programming (received off-air): WCYB-TV (N) Bristol-Kingsport; WBTV (C) Charlotte; WLOS (A), WYFF (N) Greenville-Spartanburg-Asheville; WJHL-TV (C) Johnson City; WKPT-TV (A) Kingsport; WATE-TV (A) Knoxville; WSBN-TV (P) Norton; WSJK (P) Sneedville; allband FM.

Programming (via satellite): WGN-TV (W) Chicago; WPIX (W) New York; A & E; CNN; ESPN; Fox Family Channel; MTV; Nashville Network; Nickelodeon; TBS Superstation; USA Network.
Current originations: Automated time-weather; educational access.
Fee: $35.00 installation; $11.00 monthly.
Pay Service 1
Pay Units: N.A.
Programming (via satellite): Disney Channel; HBO; Showtime; The Movie Channel.
Fee: $15.00 installation; $10.00 monthly (each).
Equipment: Scientific-Atlanta headend; Jerrold amplifiers; M/A-Com cable; Texscan character generator; Pioneer set top converters; Pico traps; Harris & Scientific-Atlanta satellite antenna; Harris & Scientific-Atlanta satellite receivers.
Miles of plant: 97.0 (coaxial). Additional miles planned: 20.0 (coaxial). Homes passed: 3,700. Total homes in franchised area: 6,000.
Manager: Bill Franklin. Chief technician: Bruce Ecker.
City fee: 3% of gross.
Ownership: Scott Telecom & Electronics Inc.

WEST POINT—West Point Cablevision, Box 888, West Point, VA 23181. Phone: 804-843-3112. Fax: 804-843-3305. Counties: King William & King and Queen. Also serves King and Queen County (unincorporated areas), Mattaponi, Shackelfords. ICA: VA0077.
TV Market Ranking: 63. Franchise award date: January 1, 1987. Franchise expiration date: June 1, 2011. Began: October 1, 1989.
Channel capacity: 61 (not 2-way capable). Channels available but not in use: 12.
Basic Service
Subscribers: 1,214.
Programming (received off-air): WUPV (U) Ashland; WPEN-LP (I) Hampton; WHRO-TV (P), WVEC-TV (A) Hampton-Norfolk; WAVY-TV (N), WGNT (U), WTKR (C), WTVZ (W) Portsmouth-Norfolk; WCVE-TV (P), WCVW (P), WRIC-TV (A), WRLH-TV (F), WTVR-TV (C), WWBT (N) Richmond-Petersburg.
Programming (via satellite): WGN-TV (W) Chicago; A & E; American Movie Classics; Animal Planet; BET; Bravo; C-SPAN; C-SPAN 2; CNBC; CNN; Cartoon Network; Comedy Central; Country Music TV; Discovery Channel; Disney Channel; ESPN; ESPN 2; FX; Fox Family Channel; Fox News Channel; Headline News; History Channel; Home Team Sports; Knowledge TV; Learning Channel; Lifetime; MSNBC; MTV; Nashville Network; Nickelodeon; QVC; Romance Classics; Sci-Fi Channel; Speedvision; TBS Superstation; TV Guide Channel; The Comedy Network; The Health Network; The Weather Channel; Toon Disney; Trinity Bcstg. Network; Turner Network TV; USA Network; VH1.
Current originations: Public access.
Fee: $50.00 installation (aerial), $33.00 (underground); $26.45 monthly; $3.00 converter.
Expanded Basic Service
Subscribers: N.A.
Programming (via satellite): Cinemax; Golf Channel; HBO Plus; Home & Garden Television; Nick at Nite's TV Land; Outdoor Channel; Turner Classic Movies.
Fee: $7.50 monthly.
Pay Service 1
Pay Units: 59.
Programming (via satellite): Cinemax.
Fee: $9.95 monthly.
Pay Service 2
Pay Units: N.A.
Programming (via satellite): DMX.
Fee: $9.95 monthly.
Pay Service 3
Pay Units: 205.
Programming (via satellite): HBO.
Fee: $9.95 monthly.
Pay Service 4
Pay Units: 9.
Programming (via satellite): Showtime.
Fee: $9.95 monthly.
Pay Service 5
Pay Units: 21.
Programming (via satellite): The Movie Channel.
Fee: $9.95 monthly.
Pay-Per-View
Hot Choice; Viewer's Choice.
Miles of plant: 48.5 (coaxial). Homes passed: 1,644.
Manager: Mike Gilberti. Chief technician: David Belcher.
City fee: 3% gross.
Ownership: 1st Commonwealth Communications Inc. (MSO). Sale pends to Cox Communications Inc.

WILLIAMSBURG—Cox Communications, 1323 W. Pembroke Ave., Hampton, VA 23661. Phones: 757-722-2851; 800-874-6390. Fax: 757-728-0515. County: James City. ICA: VA0177.
TV Market Ranking: 44. Franchise award date: N.A. Franchise expiration date: N.A. Began: N.A.
Channel capacity: N.A. Channels available but not in use: N.A.
Basic Service
Subscribers: 3,049.
Programming (received off-air): WHRO-TV (P), WVEC-TV (A) Hampton-Norfolk; WAVY-TV (N), WGNT (U), WTKR (C), WTVZ (W) Portsmouth-Norfolk; WCVE-TV (P), WRIC-TV (A), WTVR-TV (C), WWBT (N) Richmond-Petersburg.
Programming (via satellite): Cartoon Network.
Current originations: Local news.
Fee: $29.00 installation; $7.50 monthly.
Expanded Basic Service
Subscribers: N.A.
Programming (via satellite): A & E; C-SPAN; C-SPAN 2; CNBC; CNN; Discovery Channel; ESPN; Fox Family Channel; Headline News; Home Shopping Network; Home Team Sports; Learning Channel; MTV; Nickelodeon; QVC; TBS Superstation; The Weather Channel; Turner Network TV; USA Network; VH1.
Fee: N.A.
A la Carte 1
Subscribers: N.A.
Programming (via satellite): WGN-TV (W) Chicago; American Movie Classics; ESPN 2.
Fee: N.A.
Pay Service 1
Pay Units: N.A.
Programming (via satellite): Disney Channel; HBO; Showtime; The Movie Channel.
Fee: N.A.
Ownership: Cox Communications Inc. (MSO).

WINCHESTER—Adelphia Cable, 1039 N. Frederick Pike, Winchester, VA 22603-8672. Phone: 800-835-4949. Fax: 540-722-9223. Counties: Clarke & Frederick. Also serves Berryville, Boyce, Clarke County, Frederick County, Stephens City. ICA: VA0014.
TV Market Ranking: Below 100. Franchise award date: N.A. Franchise expiration date: January 1, 2010. Began: January 15, 1966.
Channel capacity: 59 (2-way capable; operating 2-way). Channels available but not in use: 1.
Basic Service
Subscribers: 23,350.
Programming (received off-air): WBFF (F), WJZ-TV (C), WMAR-TV (A) Baltimore; WHAG-TV (N), WJAL (W) Hagerstown; WHSV-TV (A,F) Harrisonburg; WBDC-TV (W), WDCA (U), WETA-TV (P), WJLA-TV (A), WUSA (C) Washington; allband FM.
Programming (via microwave): WBAL-TV (N) Baltimore; WRC-TV (N), WTTG (F) Washington.
Programming (via translator): WVPT (P) Staunton.
Programming (via satellite): C-SPAN; ESPN; TBS Superstation; TV Guide Channel.
Current originations: Automated time-weather; government access; religious access; local news; local sports.
Fee: $44.00 installation; $12.50 monthly; $1.05 converter.
Expanded Basic Service
Subscribers: 21,800.
Programming (via satellite): A & E; BET; CNBC; CNN; Comedy Central; Discovery Channel; Fox Family Channel; Headline News; Home Shopping Network; Learning Channel; Lifetime; MTV; Nashville Network; Nickelodeon; QVC; The Weather Channel; Turner Network TV; USA Network; VH1.
Fee: $44.00 installation; $19.31 monthly.
Pay Service 1
Pay Units: 4,305.
Programming (via satellite): Cinemax; Disney Channel; HBO.
Fee: $20.00 installation; $11.00 monthly (Cinemax, Disney or HBO).
Pay-Per-View
Addressable homes: 7,000.
Special events.
Local advertising: Yes. Available in taped programming. Rates: $100.00/Hour; $50.00/30 Minutes. Local sales manager: Sally Nelson.
Program Guide: The Cable Guide.
Equipment: Scientific-Atlanta headend; Magnavox amplifiers; Comm/Scope & Times cable; Sony cameras; Sony VTRs; Texscan character generator; Hamlin & Scientific-Atlanta set top converters; Scientific-Atlanta addressable set top converters; Eagle, PPC & Pico traps; Scientific-Atlanta addressable traps; RCA satellite antenna; Scientific-Atlanta satellite receivers; ChannelMatic commercial insert.
Miles of plant: 425.0 (coaxial); 150.0 (fiber optic). Additional miles planned: 100.0 (fiber optic). Homes passed: 28,000. Total homes in franchised area: 28,500.
Manager: Larry Whitehead. Chief technician: Jim Reed. Program director: Gene Rhodes. Marketing director: Chuck Balestri.
City fee: 5% of gross.
Ownership: Adelphia Communications Corp. (MSO).

WINTERGREEN—Nelson County Cablevision Corp., Box 395, Lovingston, VA 22949. Phone: 804-263-4805. Fax: 804-263-4821. Counties: Augusta & Nelson. Also serves Augusta County (portions), Nelson County (portions). ICA: VA0112.
TV Market Ranking: 70 (portions of Nelson County, Wintergreen); Below 100 (portions of Augusta County, portions of Nelson County); Outside TV Markets (portions of Augusta County). Franchise award date: N.A. Franchise expiration date: N.A. Began: October 1, 1967.
Channel capacity: 35 (2-way capable; operating 2-way). Channels available but not in use: 16.
Basic Service
Subscribers: 296.
Programming (received off-air): WCVE-TV (P), WRIC-TV (A), WTVR-TV (C), WWBT (N) Richmond-Petersburg; WDBJ (C), WJPR (F), WSET-TV (A), WSLS-TV (N) Roanoke-Lynchburg; allband FM.
Programming (via satellite): CNN; ESPN; Odyssey; TBS Superstation.
Planned originations: Automated time-weather.
Fee: $35.00 installation; $26.00 monthly.
Pay Service 1
Pay Units: 154.
Programming (via satellite): Cinemax; Disney Channel; HBO; Playboy TV; Showtime.
Fee: $4.95 monthly (Showtime), $5.00 monthly (Playboy), $7.00 monthly (Cinemax, Disney or HBO).
Local advertising: Yes.
Equipment: Entron headend; Ameco amplifiers; Cerro cable.
Miles of plant: 7.0 (coaxial); None (fiber optic). Additional miles planned: 35.0 (coaxial). Homes passed: 500. Total homes in franchised area: 4,000.
Manager: Joe Lee McClellan. Chief technician: Terry Englehardt.
Franchise fee: None.
Ownership: Nelson County Cablevision Corporation (MSO).

WISE—MCA Cable Inc., Box 978, 612 W. Main St., Wise, VA 24293. Phone: 540-328-5248. Fax: 540-328-3134. County: Wise. Also serves Coeburn, Wise County (portions). ICA: VA0168.
TV Market Ranking: Below 100. Franchise award date: August 1, 1991. Franchise expiration date: August 7, 2006. Began: May 24, 1992.
Channel capacity: 62 (2-way capable; operating 2-way). Channels available but not in use: 7.
Basic Service
Subscribers: 1,285.
Programming (received off-air): WCYB-TV (N) Bristol-Kingsport; WEMT (F) Greeneville; WLFG (I) Grundy; WYMT-TV (C) Hazard; WJHL-TV (C) Johnson City; WAPK-LP (U), WKPT-TV (A) Kingsport; WSBN-TV (P) Norton.
Programming (via satellite): WGN-TV (W) Chicago; WPIX (W) New York; A & E; American Movie Classics; C-SPAN; C-SPAN 2; CNBC; CNN; Cartoon Network; Comedy Central; Country Music TV; Court TV; Discovery Channel; Disney Channel; E! Entertainment TV; ESPN; ESPN 2; FX; Fox Family Channel; Goodlife TV Network; Headline News; Home & Garden Television; Home Team Sports; Learning Channel; Lifetime; MTV; Nashville Network; Nickelodeon; QVC; Sci-Fi Channel; TBS Superstation; The Weather Channel; Travel Channel; Trinity Bcstg. Network; Turner Classic Movies; Turner Network TV; USA Network; VH1.
Current originations: Public access; educational access; government access.
Fee: $25.00 installation; $21.20 monthly.
Pay Service 1
Pay Units: 128.
Programming (via satellite): Cinemax.
Fee: $7.95 monthly.
Pay Service 2
Pay Units: 12.
Programming (via satellite): Golf Channel.
Fee: $3.95 monthly.
Pay Service 3
Pay Units: 161.
Programming (via satellite): HBO.
Fee: $8.95 monthly.
Pay Service 4
Pay Units: 72.
Programming (via satellite): Showtime.
Fee: $6.95 monthly.
Pay Service 5
Pay Units: 54.

Programming (via satellite): The Movie Channel.
Fee: $6.95 monthly.
Equipment: Scientific-Atlanta & Olson headend; Jerrold amplifiers; Trilogy cable; Oak set top converters; Scientific-Atlanta & Olson satellite receivers.
Miles of plant: 76.0 (coaxial); None (fiber optic). Homes passed: 3,120.
Manager: Darrell Freddie Dean Jr. Chief technician: Jeff Dean. Office manager: Charlotte Carico.
Ownership: MCA Cable Inc.

WOODSTOCK—FrontierVision, Suite P-200, 1777 S. Harrison St., Denver, CO 80210. Phone: 303-757-1588. Fax: 303-757-6105. County: Shenandoah. Also serves Maurertown, Shenandoah County (portions), Strasburg, Toms Brook. ICA: VA0052.
TV Market Ranking: Below 100 (portions of Shenandoah County); Outside TV Markets (Maurertown, portions of Shenandoah County, Strasburg, Toms Brook, Woodstock). Franchise award date: N.A. Franchise expiration date: N.A. Began: April 1, 1971.
Channel capacity: 42. Channels available but not in use: 11.
Basic Service
Subscribers: 3,323.
Programming (received off-air): WBAL-TV (N) Baltimore; WHAG-TV (N) Hagerstown; WHSV-TV (A,F) Harrisonburg; WVPT (P) Staunton; WDCA (U), WJLA-TV (A), WRC-TV (N), WTTG (F), WUSA (C) Washington; WAZT-LP (I) Woodstock; allband FM.
Programming (via satellite): A & E; CNBC; CNN; Country Music TV; Discovery Channel; ESPN; Fox Family Channel; Home Shopping Network; Home Team Sports; Lifetime; Nashville Network; Nickelodeon; TV Guide Channel; The Weather Channel; Turner Network TV; USA Network.
Current originations: Automated time-weather; public access.
Fee: $40.00 installation; $16.50 monthly; $2.00 converter.
Pay Service 1
Pay Units: 171.
Programming (via satellite): Disney Channel.
Fee: $8.95 monthly.
Pay Service 2
Pay Units: 492.
Programming (via satellite): HBO.
Fee: $10.95 monthly.
Pay Service 3
Pay Units: 282.
Programming (via satellite): Showtime.
Fee: $10.95 monthly.
Local advertising: No.
Program Guide: CableView.
Equipment: Jerrold headend; Magnavox amplifiers; Times Fiber & Trilogy cable; Scientific-Atlanta & Zenith set top converters; Eagle & PPC traps; Microdyne & Comtech satellite antenna; Microdyne satellite receivers.
Miles of plant: 83.0 (coaxial). Homes passed: 3,816.
President & chief executive officer: James Vaugh. Vice president, engineering: David Heyrend. Executive vice president: John Koo.
City fee: 3% of gross.
Ownership: FrontierVision Partners LP (MSO). See Cable System Ownership.

WYTHEVILLE—Cablecomm, 565 E. Main St., Wytheville, VA 24382. Phone: 888-655-9629. County: Wythe. Also serves Wythe County. ICA: VA0061.
TV Market Ranking: Below 100. Franchise award date: N.A. Franchise expiration date: N.A. Began: December 1, 1969.
Channel capacity: 35. Channels available but not in use: N.A.
Basic Service
Subscribers: 3,251.
Programming (received off-air): WVVA (N) Bluefield; WKPT-TV (A) Kingsport; WBRA-TV (P) Roanoke; WDBJ (C), WSET-TV (A), WSLS-TV (N) Roanoke-Lynchburg; allband FM.
Programming (via satellite): C-SPAN; C-SPAN 2; Cartoon Network; Country Music TV; Discovery Channel; Fox Family Channel; QVC; TBS Superstation; The Weather Channel; Travel Channel; Trinity Bcstg. Network.
Fee: $44.95 installation; $13.88 monthly.
Expanded Basic Service
Subscribers: N.A.
Programming (via satellite): American Movie Classics; Animal Planet; CNN; Comedy Central; ESPN; ESPN 2; Encore Movie Networks; Fox News Channel; Headline News; Home & Garden Television; Learning Channel; Lifetime; MTV; Nashville Network; Nickelodeon; Turner Network TV; USA Network.
Fee: $14.31 monthly.
Pay Service 1
Pay Units: N.A.
Programming (via satellite): Cinemax; Disney Channel; HBO; Showtime; Starz!; The New Encore.
Fee: $12.95 installation; $1.95 monthly (Encore), $6.75 monthly (Starz), $12.00 monthly (Cinemax, Disney, HBO or Showtime).
Pay-Per-View
Special events.
Local advertising: No.
Equipment: Scientific-Atlanta headend; Jerrold amplifiers; Comm/Scope & Superior cable; Sony VTRs; Zenith addressable set top converters; Eagle traps; Scientific-Atlanta satellite antenna; Scientific-Atlanta satellite receivers.
Miles of plant: 62.1 (coaxial).
Manager: Brenda McNutt.
Ownership: Fanch Communications Inc. (MSO); Time Warner Cable (MSO). Purchased from Tele-Communications Inc., February 25, 1999. See Cable System Ownership.

YORKTOWN—Cox Communications, 225 Clearfield Ave, Virginia Beach, VA 23462. Phone: 757-224-1111. Fax: 804-898-7583. County: York. Also serves Grafton, York County (portions). ICA: VA0162.
TV Market Ranking: 44. Franchise award date: November 1, 1982. Franchise expiration date: November 1, 1997. Began: June 6, 1983.
Channel capacity: 60 (2-way capable; operating 2-way). Channels available but not in use: None.
Basic Service
Subscribers: 14,626; Commercial subscribers: 184.
Programming (received off-air): WHRO-TV (P), WVEC-TV (A) Hampton-Norfolk; WAVY-TV (N), WTKR (C), WTVZ (W) Portsmouth-Norfolk; WCVE-TV (P), WRIC-TV (A), WTVR-TV (C), WWBT (N) Richmond-Petersburg; allband FM.
Programming (via satellite): WGN-TV (W) Chicago; A & E; American Movie Classics; BET; C-SPAN; C-SPAN 2; CNBC; CNN; Discovery Channel; ESPN; Fox Family Channel; Headline News; Home Shopping Network; Home Team Sports; Lifetime; MTV; Nashville Network; Nickelodeon; QVC; TBS Superstation; TV Guide Channel; The Inspirational Network; The Weather Channel; Turner Network TV; USA Network; VH1.
Current originations: Public access; educational access; government access; religious access; leased access.
Fee: $15.00 installation; $16.50 monthly; $7.50 additional installation.
Pay Service 1
Pay Units: 9,388.
Programming (via satellite): Cinemax; Disney Channel; HBO; Showtime.
Fee: $10.00 installation; $8.75 monthly (HBO or Showtime), $8.95 monthly (Cinemax or Disney).
Pay-Per-View
Special events.
Fee: Varies.
Local advertising: Yes (insert only). Available in satellite distributed programming. Regional interconnect: Tidewater Cable Interconnect.
Equipment: Scientific-Atlanta headend; Magnavox amplifiers; Comm/Scope cable; Sony cameras; Sony VTRs; MSI character generator; Scientific-Atlanta set top converters; Eagle traps; Anixter-Mark & Scientific-Atlanta satellite antenna; Scientific-Atlanta satellite receivers; Texscan & Sony commercial insert.
Miles of plant: 371.0 (coaxial); 16.0 (fiber optic).
Manager: Paul K. Spacek. Chief technician: Mark Fout. Marketing director: Ken Dye.
Franchise fee: 3% of gross.
Ownership: MediaOne Group (MSO). See Cable System Ownership.

WASHINGTON

Total Systems: **182**
Total Communities Served: **532**
Franchises Not Yet Operating: **1**
Applications Pending: **0**
Communities with Applications: **0**
Number of Basic Subscribers: **1,264,767**
Number of Expanded Basic Subscribers: **856,214**
Number of Pay Units: **677,545**

Top 100 Markets Represented: Seattle-Tacoma (20); Portland (29); Spokane(76).

For a list of all cable communities included in this section, see the Cable Community Index located in the back of this volume.
For explanation of terms used in cable system listings, see p. D-9.

ABERDEEN—TCI Cablevision of Southwest Washington, Box 129, Olympia, WA 98507-0129. Phone: 360-357-3364. Fax: 360-532-5978. County: Grays Harbor. Also serves Central Park, Cosmopolis, Grays Harbor County, Hoquiam. ICA: WA0019.
TV Market Ranking: Outside TV Markets. Franchise award date: N.A. Franchise expiration date: N.A. Began: September 1, 1952.
Channel capacity: 42 (not 2-way capable). Channels available but not in use: N.A.
Basic Service
Subscribers: 11,971.
Programming (received off-air): KPTV (U) Portland; KCPQ (F) Seattle-Tacoma; 11 FMs.
Programming (via microwave): KOIN (C) Portland; KCTS-TV (P), KING-TV (N), KIRO-TV (C), KOMO-TV (A), KSTW (U), KTWB (W) Seattle-Tacoma.
Programming (via satellite): A & E; C-SPAN; CNN; Comedy Central; Discovery Channel; Lifetime; MTV; Nashville Network; Nickelodeon; Odyssey; QVC; TBS Superstation; VH1.
Current originations: Automated time-weather; public access; religious access.
Fee: $60.00 installation; $9.96 monthly; $0.58 converter; $40.00 additional installation.
Expanded Basic Service
Subscribers: 11,108.
Programming (via satellite): American Movie Classics; CNNfn; Court TV; ESPN; Fox Sports Net Northwest; Turner Network TV; USA Network.
Fee: $11.71 monthly.
Pay Service 1
Pay Units: 656.
Programming (via satellite): Cinemax.
Fee: $9.95 monthly.
Pay Service 2
Pay Units: 892.
Programming (via satellite): Disney Channel.
Fee: N.A.
Pay Service 3
Pay Units: 4,084.
Programming (via satellite): The New Encore.
Fee: N.A.
Pay Service 4
Pay Units: 1,687.
Programming (via satellite): HBO.
Fee: $9.95 monthly.
Pay Service 5
Pay Units: 1,150.
Programming (via satellite): Showtime.
Fee: $9.95 monthly.
Pay-Per-View
Movies.
Local advertising: Yes (locally produced). Available in satellite distributed programming. Local sales manager: Steve Lee.
Program Guide: The Cable Guide.
Equipment: Scientific-Atlanta headend; Magnavox amplifiers; Times Fiber & Trilogy cable; Sony VTRs; Jerrold set top converters; Jerrold addressable set top converters; Pico traps; Arcom & Eagle addressable traps; Scientific-Atlanta & Andrew satellite antenna; Scientific-Atlanta satellite receivers.
Miles of plant: 206.3 (coaxial). Homes passed: 13,954. Total homes in franchised area: 14,617.
Manager: Fred Comer. Chief technician: Wally Weidman. Marketing director: Carrie Prante.
City fee: 5% of gross.
Ownership: AT&T Broadband & Internet Services (MSO). Purchased from Tele-Communications Inc., March 9, 1999.

ALMIRA—Sun Country Cable, Box 127, 7 D St. SW, Quincy, WA 98848. Phone: 509-787-3543. Fax: 509-787-3884. County: Lincoln. ICA: WA0143.
TV Market Ranking: Outside TV Markets. Franchise award date: January 1, 1986. Franchise expiration date: January 1, 2001. Began: February 1, 1987.
Channel capacity: 35 (not 2-way capable). Channels available but not in use: 21.
Basic Service
Subscribers: 88.
Programming (received off-air): KAYU-TV (F), KSPS-TV (P) Spokane.
Programming (via microwave): KING-TV (N), KIRO-TV (C), KOMO-TV (A) Seattle-Tacoma.
Programming (via satellite): CNN; Discovery Channel; ESPN; Fox Family Channel; Lifetime; Nashville Network; TBS Superstation.
Fee: $39.95 installation; $22.20 monthly.
Pay Service 1
Pay Units: 5.
Programming (via satellite): Disney Channel.
Fee: $15.00 installation; $8.95 monthly.
Pay Service 2
Pay Units: 12.
Programming (via satellite): HBO.
Fee: $15.00 installation; $10.95 monthly.
Local advertising: No.
Equipment: Scientific-Atlanta & Triple Crown headend; Jerrold amplifiers; Panasonic & Tocom set top converters; Scientific-Atlanta satellite antenna; Triple Crown satellite receivers.
Miles of plant: 6.0 (coaxial).
Manager: Gary White. Technical manager: Arnie Hill. Office manager: Judy Vreeman.
Franchise fee: None.
Ownership: Sun Country Cable (MSO).

ANACORTES—TCI Cablevision of Washington Inc., 777 W. Horton Rd., Bellingham, WA 98226-7606. Phone: 360-384-1581. Counties: Island & Skagit. Also serves Baby Island, Bells Beach, Fox Spit, Island County, Skagit County (portions), Sunlight Beach, Whidbey Shores. ICA: WA0031.
TV Market Ranking: Below 100 (Anacortes, Baby Island, Bells Beach, Fox Spit, portions of Island County, portions of Skagit County, Sunlight Beach, Whidbey Shores); Outside TV Markets (portions of Island County, portions of Skagit County). Franchise award date: N.A. Franchise expiration date: N.A. Began: June 1, 1963.
Channel capacity: 32. Channels available but not in use: N.A.
Basic Service
Subscribers: 4,524.
Programming (received off-air): KVOS-TV (I) Bellingham; KCPQ (F), KCTS-TV (P), KING-TV (N), KIRO-TV (C), KOMO-TV (A), KSTW (U) Seattle-Tacoma; CBUT Vancouver; 20 FMs.
Programming (via satellite): CNBC; CNN; Discovery Channel; Fox Family Channel; Nashville Network; QVC; TBS Superstation; The Weather Channel.
Fee: $60.00 installation; $10.11 monthly; $0.59 converter; $40.00 additional installation.
Expanded Basic Service
Subscribers: 3,918.
Programming (via satellite): American Movie Classics; ESPN; Fox Sports Net Northwest; Turner Network TV; USA Network.
Fee: $11.03 monthly.
Pay Service 1
Pay Units: 321.
Programming (via satellite): Cinemax.
Fee: $20.00 installation; $12.70 monthly.
Pay Service 2
Pay Units: 353.
Programming (via satellite): Disney Channel.
Fee: N.A.
Pay Service 3
Pay Units: 1,405.
Programming (via satellite): The New Encore.
Fee: N.A.
Pay Service 4
Pay Units: 823.
Programming (via satellite): HBO.
Fee: $12.70 monthly.
Pay Service 5
Pay Units: 219.
Programming (via satellite): Showtime.
Fee: $12.70 monthly.
Local advertising: Yes (locally produced).
Program Guide: The Cable Guide.
Equipment: Jerrold headend; Jerrold amplifiers; Times Fiber cable; Scientific-Atlanta satellite antenna.
Miles of plant: 90.2 (coaxial). Homes passed: 5,145. Total homes in franchised area: 5,707.
Manager: Robert Huisman.
City fee: 7% of gross (utility tax).
Ownership: AT&T Broadband & Internet Services (MSO). Purchased from Tele-Communications Inc., March 9, 1999.

ANDERSON ISLAND—Millennium Digital Media, Suite 107, 3633 136th Place SE, Bellevue, WA 98006. Phones: 425-747-4600; 800-829-2225. Fax: 425-644-4621. Web site: http://www.millenniumdigital.com. County: Pierce. Also serves Herron Island, Key Peninsula. ICA: WA0157.
TV Market Ranking: 20. Franchise award date: January 1, 1989. Franchise expiration date: January 1, 2004. Began: September 1, 1989.
Channel capacity: 54. Channels available but not in use: N.A.
Basic Service
Subscribers: 850.
Programming (received off-air): KCPQ (F), KCTS-TV (P), KING-TV (N), KIRO-TV (C), KOMO-TV (A), KSTW (U), KTBW-TV (T), KTWB (W) Seattle-Tacoma; KBTC-TV (P) Tacoma.
Programming (via satellite): A & E; American Movie Classics; C-SPAN; CNBC; CNN; Discovery Channel; ESPN; Fox Family Channel; Fox Sports Net Northwest; Headline News; Lifetime; MTV; Nashville Network; Nickelodeon; Northwest Cable News; QVC; Sci-Fi Channel; TBS Superstation; Turner Network TV; USA Network; VH1.
Fee: $25.95 installation; $21.95 monthly; $2.00 converter.
Pay Service 1
Pay Units: 227.
Programming (via satellite): Cinemax.
Fee: $10.00 monthly.
Pay Service 2
Pay Units: 30.
Programming (via satellite): Disney Channel.
Fee: $8.95 monthly.
Pay Service 3
Pay Units: 80.
Programming (via satellite): HBO.
Fee: $10.00 monthly.
Pay Service 4
Pay Units: 80.
Programming (via satellite): Showtime.
Fee: $10.00 monthly.
Local advertising: Yes. Available in character-generated programming.
Miles of plant: 80.0 (coaxial).
Manager: Sheryll Curtis. Chief technician: Pat Carey.
Franchise fee: 5% of gross.
Ownership: Millennium Digital Media LLC (MSO). Purchased from Summit Communications Inc., April 7, 1999.

ARLINGTON—TCI Cablevision of Washington Inc., Suite B, 11515 State Ave., Marysville, WA 98271-7245. Phone: 360-659-1285. County: Snohomish. Also serves Snohomish County (northeastern portion). ICA: WA0021.
TV Market Ranking: 20 (portions of Snohomish County); Below 100 (Arlington, portions of Snohomish County); Outside TV Markets (portions of Snohomish County). Franchise award date: March 9, 1964. Franchise expiration date: N.A. Began: June 1, 1965.
Channel capacity: 54 (not 2-way capable). Channels available but not in use: 20.
Basic Service
Subscribers: 12,028.
Programming (received off-air): KVOS-TV (I) Bellingham; KCPQ (F), KCTS-TV (P), KING-TV (N), KIRO-TV (C), KOMO-TV (A),

KSTW (U), KTBW-TV (T), KTWB (W) Seattle-Tacoma; 17 FMs.
Programming (via satellite): A & E; C-SPAN; CNBC; CNN; Discovery Channel; Fox Family Channel; Headline News; Lifetime; MTV; Nashville Network; Nickelodeon; QVC; TBS Superstation; The Weather Channel.
Current originations: Automated time-weather; government access.
Fee: $60.00 installation; $9.79 monthly; $3.00 converter; $40.00 additional installation.

Expanded Basic Service
Subscribers: 10,188.
Programming (via satellite): American Movie Classics; ESPN; Fox Sports Net Northwest; Turner Network TV; USA Network.
Fee: $10.49 monthly.

Pay Service 1
Pay Units: 946.
Programming (via satellite): Disney Channel.
Fee: $15.00 installation; $11.95 monthly.

Pay Service 2
Pay Units: 3,177.
Programming (via satellite): The New Encore.
Fee: N.A.

Pay Service 3
Pay Units: 1,401.
Programming (via satellite): HBO.
Fee: $13.15 monthly.

Pay Service 4
Pay Units: 414.
Programming (via satellite): The Movie Channel.
Fee: $13.15 monthly.

Pay Service 5
Pay Units: 1,312.
Programming (via satellite): Showtime.
Fee: $13.15 monthly.

Local advertising: Yes (insert only). Available in satellite distributed programming.
Program Guide: The Cable Guide.
Equipment: Scientific-Atlanta headend; Jerrold & GTE Sylvania amplifiers; Comm/Scope cable; Pioneer VTRs; Texscan character generator; Scientific-Atlanta set top converters; Scientific-Atlanta addressable set top converters; Pico & Arcom traps; Scientific-Atlanta satellite antenna; M/A-Com satellite receivers.
Miles of plant: 171.1 (coaxial). Homes passed: 12,944. Total homes in franchised area: 13,942.
Manager: John Sheehan.
City fee: 5% of gross.
Ownership: AT&T Broadband & Internet Services (MSO). Purchased from Tele-Communications Inc., March 9, 1999.

AUBURN—TCI Cablevision Inc., 4020 Auburn Way N, Auburn, WA 98002. Phone: 253-288-7450. County: King. Also serves Algona, Black Diamond, Des Moines, Enumclaw, Federal Way, Kent, King County, Maple Valley, Normandy Park, Pacific, Renton, Seatac, Tukwila. ICA: WA0002.
TV Market Ranking: 20 (Algona, Auburn, Black Diamond, Des Moines, Enumclaw, Federal Way, Kent, portions of King County, Maple Valley, Normandy Park, Pacific, Renton, Seatac, Tukwila); Below 100 (portions of King County); Outside TV Markets (portions of King County). Franchise award date: N.A. Franchise expiration date: N.A. Began: December 1, 1951.
Channel capacity: 39 (not 2-way capable). Channels available but not in use: 1.

Basic Service
Subscribers: 137,426.
Programming (received off-air): KCPQ (F), KCTS-TV (P), KIRO-TV (C), KOMO-TV (A), KSTW (U), KTBW-TV (T), KTWB (W) Seattle-Tacoma; KBTC-TV (P) Tacoma; CBUT Vancouver; 23 FMs.
Programming (via microwave): KING-TV (N) Seattle-Tacoma.
Programming (via satellite): A & E; BET; C-SPAN; CNBC; CNN; Discovery Channel; Fox Family Channel; Headline News; Lifetime; MTV; Nashville Network; Nickelodeon; QVC; TBS Superstation; The Weather Channel; Univision.
Current originations: Automated time-weather; public access; educational access; government access; local news.
Fee: $60.00 installation; $20.16 monthly.

Expanded Basic Service
Subscribers: 122,339.
Programming (via satellite): American Movie Classics; ESPN; Fox Sports Net Northwest; Turner Network TV; USA Network.
Fee: $2.00 monthly.

Pay Service 1
Pay Units: 17,772.
Programming (via satellite): Cinemax.
Fee: $13.15 monthly.

Pay Service 2
Pay Units: 15,423.
Programming (via satellite): Disney Channel.
Fee: $11.95 monthly.

Pay Service 3
Pay Units: 59,194.
Programming (via satellite): The New Encore.
Fee: N.A.

Pay Service 4
Pay Units: 37,409.
Programming (via satellite): HBO.
Fee: $13.15 monthly.

Pay Service 5
Pay Units: 23,319.
Programming (via satellite): Showtime.
Fee: $13.15 monthly.

Pay Service 6
Pay Units: 2.
Programming (via satellite): Xchange.
Fee: N.A.

Pay-Per-View
Addressable homes: 59,603.

Local advertising: Yes. Available in satellite distributed programming.
Program Guide: The Cable Guide.
Equipment: Scientific-Atlanta headend; Jerrold amplifiers; Times Fiber cable; JVC cameras; Sony VTRs; Video Data Systems character generator; Jerrold set top converters; Jerrold addressable set top converters; Andrew satellite antenna; Scientific-Atlanta satellite receivers; Sony commercial insert.
Miles of plant: 2415.0 (coaxial). Homes passed: 349,711. Total homes in franchised area: 358,087.
Manager: Bill Bennett. Chief technician: Dave Jacobs. Marketing director: Lori Shelton.
City fee: 6% of gross. County fee: 5% of gross.
Ownership: AT&T Broadband & Internet Services (MSO). Purchased from Tele-Communications Inc., March 9, 1999.

BAINBRIDGE ISLAND—Northland Cable TV, 7686 N.E. High School Rd., Bainbridge Island, WA 98110. Phone: 206-842-6515. Fax: 206-842-1838. County: Kitsap. Also serves Indianola, Miller Bay Estates, Sandy Hook, Suquamish. ICA: WA0024.
TV Market Ranking: 20. Franchise award date: January 1, 1970. Franchise expiration date: January 1, 2020. Began: July 15, 1977.
Channel capacity: 44 (not 2-way capable). Channels available but not in use: None.

Basic Service
Subscribers: 5,300; Commercial subscribers: 249.
Programming (received off-air): KVOS-TV (I) Bellingham; KONG-TV (I) Everett; KCPQ (F), KCTS-TV (P), KING-TV (N), KIRO-TV (C), KOMO-TV (A), KSTW (U), KTBW-TV (T), KTWB (W) Seattle-Tacoma; KBTC-TV (P) Tacoma; allband FM.
Programming (via satellite): Headline News; QVC; TBS Superstation.
Current originations: Automated time-weather; educational access; government access; local news.
Fee: $55.00 installation (aerial), $150.00 (underground); $18.00 monthly; $20.00 converter.

Expanded Basic Service
Subscribers: 4,850.
Programming (via satellite): A & E; Bravo; C-SPAN; CNBC; CNN; Discovery Channel; ESPN; Fox Family Channel; Fox News Channel; Headline News; History Channel; Learning Channel; MTV; Nashville Network; Northwest Cable News; TV Guide Channel; The Weather Channel; Turner Network TV.
Fee: $55.00 installation; $26.95 monthly.

Expanded Basic Service 2
Subscribers: 3,359.
Programming (via satellite): American Movie Classics; Cartoon Network; ESPN 2; Fox Sports Net Northwest; Lifetime; Nickelodeon; Turner Classic Movies; USA Network.
Fee: $55.00 installation; $35.90 monthly.

Pay Service 1
Pay Units: 340.
Programming (via satellite): Disney Channel.
Fee: $40.00 installation; $7.95 monthly.

Pay Service 2
Pay Units: 893.
Programming (via satellite): HBO.
Fee: $40.00 installation; $11.50 monthly.

Pay Service 3
Pay Units: 435.
Programming (via satellite): Showtime.
Fee: $40.00 installation; $10.95 monthly.

Local advertising: Yes. Available in locally originated programming. Rates: $40.00/Month; $10.00/Week. Local sales manager: Andrew Weathers.
Equipment: Scientific-Atlanta headend; Magnavox & Texscan amplifiers; Comm/Scope & Times Fiber cable; Texscan character generator; Hamlin & NSC set top converters; PPC traps; Scientific-Atlanta satellite antenna; Scientific-Atlanta satellite receivers.
Miles of plant: 234.0 (coaxial); 15.0 (fiber optic). Homes passed: 8,745. Total homes in franchised area: 9,283.
Manager: Marit Saltrones. Chief technician: Mark Graves.
City fee: 5% of gross.
Ownership: Northland Communications Corp. (MSO).

BAYVIEW—Northland Cable TV, Box 1630, La Conner, WA 98257. Phone: 360-466-3317. Fax: 360-466-3560. Counties: Skagit & Whatcom. Also serves Burlington (rural areas), Conway, Whatcom County (southern portion). ICA: WA0149.
TV Market Ranking: Below 100. Franchise award date: N.A. Franchise expiration date: N.A. Began: November 1, 1989.
Channel capacity: 41 (not 2-way capable). Channels available but not in use: None.

Basic Service
Subscribers: 2,832.
Programming (received off-air): KVOS-TV (I) Bellingham; KCPQ (F), KCTS-TV (P), KING-TV (N), KIRO-TV (C), KOMO-TV (A), KSTW (U), KTWB (W) Seattle-Tacoma; CBUT, CKVU-TV Vancouver; CHEK-TV Victoria.
Programming (via satellite): WGN-TV (W) Chicago; QVC; TBS Superstation; Trinity Bcstg. Network.
Fee: $50.00 installation; $16.00 monthly.

Expanded Basic Service
Subscribers: 2,791.
Programming (via satellite): A & E; C-SPAN; CNN; Country Music TV; Discovery Channel; ESPN; Fox Family Channel; Headline News; Learning Channel; Lifetime; Nashville Network; Turner Network TV; USA Network; Univision.
Fee: $50.00 installation; $4.50 monthly.

Pay Service 1
Pay Units: 212.
Programming (via satellite): Disney Channel.
Fee: $9.95 monthly.

Pay Service 2
Pay Units: 203.
Programming (via satellite): Cinemax.
Fee: $9.95 monthly.

Pay Service 3
Pay Units: 316.
Programming (via satellite): HBO.
Fee: $9.95 monthly.

Pay Service 4
Pay Units: 143.
Programming (via satellite): Showtime.
Fee: $9.95 monthly.

Local advertising: Yes. Available in character-generated & taped programming. Rates: $3.00/30 Seconds. Local sales manager: Les Carney.
Equipment: Drake headend; GTE Sylvania amplifiers; Comm/Scope cable; Amiga character generator; Eagle traps.
Miles of plant: 175.0 (coaxial); None (fiber optic).
Manager: Jon Ulrich. Chief technician: Ed Knipper. Marketing director: Bede Wells.
Ownership: Northland Communications Corp. (MSO).

BELLINGHAM—TCI Cablevision of Washington Inc., 777 W. Horton Rd., Bellingham, WA 98226-7606. Phone: 360-384-1581. Fax: 360-647-8967. County: Whatcom. Also serves Samish Lake, Whatcom County. ICA: WA0011.
TV Market Ranking: Below 100 (Bellingham, Samish Lake, portions of Whatcom County); Outside TV Markets (portions of Whatcom County). Franchise award date: N.A. Franchise expiration date: N.A. Began: February 1, 1949.
Channel capacity: 38 (not 2-way capable). Channels available but not in use: N.A.

Basic Service
Subscribers: 21,655.
Programming (received off-air): KVOS-TV (I) Bellingham; KCPQ (F), KCTS-TV (P), KING-TV (N), KIRO-TV (C), KOMO-TV (A), KSTW (U) Seattle-Tacoma; CBUT, CHAN-TV Vancouver; CHEK-TV Victoria; 20 FMs.
Programming (via satellite): A & E; C-SPAN; CNBC; CNN; Discovery Channel; Fox Family Channel; Headline News; Lifetime; MTV; Nashville Network; Nickelodeon; Odyssey; QVC; TBS Superstation; The Weather Channel.
Current originations: Automated time-weather; educational access; government access; automated emergency alert; local news.
Fee: $60.00 installation; $10.18 monthly; $0.98 converter; $40.00 additional installation.

Expanded Basic Service
Subscribers: N.A.

Programming (via satellite): American Movie Classics; ESPN; Fox Sports Net Northwest; Turner Network TV; USA Network.
Fee: $9.54 monthly.

Pay Service 1
Pay Units: 1,887.
Programming (via satellite): Disney Channel.
Fee: N.A.

Pay Service 2
Pay Units: 6,830.
Programming (via satellite): The New Encore.
Fee: N.A.

Pay Service 3
Pay Units: 4,346.
Programming (via satellite): HBO.
Fee: $13.15 monthly.

Pay Service 4
Pay Units: 2,494.
Programming (via satellite): Showtime.
Fee: $13.15 monthly.

Local advertising: Yes (locally produced & insert). Available in satellite distributed, locally originated, character-generated & automated programming.
Program Guide: The Cable Guide.
Equipment: Jerrold & Scientific-Atlanta headend; GTE Sylvania amplifiers; Times Fiber cable; Sony cameras; Sony VTRs; Sony character generator; Hamlin, Jerrold & Scientific-Atlanta set top converters; Jerrold addressable set top converters; Scientific-Atlanta satellite antenna; Scientific-Atlanta satellite receivers.
Miles of plant: 371.7 (coaxial). Homes passed: 31,071. Total homes in franchised area: 31,473.
Manager: Dan Crocker.
City fee: 3% of gross.
Ownership: AT&T Broadband & Internet Services (MSO). Purchased from Tele-Communications Inc., March 9, 1999.

BENTON CITY—Columbia Basin Cable, Box 490, 611 6th St., Umatilla, OR 97882. Phones: 541-922-5759; 800-521-3916. Fax: 541-922-3758. County: Benton. Also serves Benton County, West Richland. ICA: WA0065.
TV Market Ranking: Below 100. Franchise award date: N.A. Franchise expiration date: N.A. Began: January 1, 1982.
Channel capacity: 60 (2-way capable; operating 2-way). Channels available but not in use: N.A.

Basic Service
Subscribers: 2,500.
Programming (received off-air): KEPR-TV (C), KNDU (N), KVEW (A) Pasco-Kennewick-Richland; KTNW (P) Richland.
Programming (via translator): KAYU-TV (F) Spokane.
Programming (via satellite): WGN-TV (W) Chicago; C-SPAN; QVC; TBS Superstation; TV Guide Channel; Trinity Bcstg. Network.
Current originations: Automated time-weather.
Fee: $35.00 installation; $17.95 monthly.

Expanded Basic Service
Subscribers: 2,101.
Programming (via satellite): A & E; American Movie Classics; Animal Planet; CNN; Comedy Central; Country Music TV; Discovery Channel; ESPN; ESPN 2; FX; fXM: Movies from Fox; Fox Family Channel; Fox News Channel; Fox Sports Net Northwest; Headline News; History Channel; Home & Garden Television; Home Shopping Network; Learning Channel; Lifetime; MTV; Nashville Network; Nickelodeon; Northwest Cable News; Sci-Fi Channel; The Weather Channel; Turner Classic Movies; Turner Network TV; USA Network; Univision; VH1.
Fee: $29.95 monthly.

Pay Service 1
Pay Units: 196.
Programming (via satellite): Disney Channel.
Fee: $9.95 monthly.

Pay Service 2
Pay Units: 613.
Programming (via satellite): HBO (multiplexed).
Fee: $10.95 monthly.

Pay Service 3
Pay Units: 390.
Programming (via satellite): Encore Movie Networks; Starz!; The New Encore.
Fee: $7.95 monthly.

Pay-Per-View
Planned.

Equipment: Blonder-Tongue headend; C-COR amplifiers; Times Fiber cable.
Miles of plant: 63.0 (coaxial); None (fiber optic). Homes passed: 2,988.
Manager: Kerry Stratton. Chief technician: Darrell Johnson. Marketing director & customer service manager: Charlotte Winkler.
City fee: 3% of gross.
Ownership: USA Media Group LLC (MSO). Purchased from Cambridge Communications, May 15, 1999.

BIG LAKE—Cedar Communications, Box 237, Lakewood, WA 98259. Phones: 360-652-0230; 360-336-2252. Fax: 360-652-1934. Counties: Skagit & Snohomish. Also serves Clear Lake, Lakewood. ICA: WA0085.
TV Market Ranking: Below 100. Franchise award date: N.A. Franchise expiration date: December 1, 2009. Began: January 1, 1964.
Channel capacity: 41 (2-way capable; operating 2-way partially). Channels available but not in use: N.A.

Basic Service
Subscribers: 4,200.
Programming (received off-air): KVOS-TV (I) Bellingham; KONG-TV (I) Everett; KCPQ (F), KCTS-TV (P), KING-TV (N), KIRO-TV (C), KOMO-TV (A), KSTW (U), KTWB (W) Seattle-Tacoma; CBUT Vancouver; allband FM.
Programming (via satellite): A & E; C-SPAN; CNN; CNNfn; Cartoon Network; Comedy Central; Discovery Channel; ESPN; ESPN 2; FX; fXM: Movies from Fox; Fox Family Channel; Fox Sports Net Northwest; Great American Country; Headline News; History Channel; Home & Garden Television; Learning Channel; Lifetime; MTV; Nashville Network; Nick at Nite; Nick at Nite's TV Land; Nickelodeon; Outdoor Channel; QVC; Sci-Fi Channel; TBS Superstation; TV Food Network; TV Guide Channel; The Health Network; The Weather Channel; Trinity Bcstg. Network; Turner Classic Movies; Turner Network TV; USA Network; VH1.
Current originations: Public access.
Fee: $19.95 installation (aerial), $39.95 (underground); $28.00 monthly.

Pay Service 1
Pay Units: N.A.
Programming (via satellite): Cinemax; Disney Channel; Flix; HBO (multiplexed); Showtime; The Movie Channel.
Fee: N.A.

Pay-Per-View
Addressable homes: 1,100.

Local advertising: Yes (locally produced). Available in satellite distributed programming.
Equipment: Scientific-Atlanta headend; Jerrold amplifiers; Times Fiber cable; Eagle traps; Scientific-Atlanta satellite antenna; Scientific-Atlanta satellite receivers.
Miles of plant: 200.0 (coaxial); 80.0 (fiber optic). Homes passed: 5,000.
Manager: Patrick Davis. Chief technician: Butch Thomas. Customer service manager: Carol Stamey.
Ownership: Davis Communications Inc. (MSO).

BLAINE—TCI Cablevision of Washington Inc., 777 W. Horton Rd., Bellingham, WA 98226-7606. Phone: 360-384-1581. Fax: 360-647-8967. County: Whatcom. Also serves Whatcom County. ICA: WA0036.
TV Market Ranking: Below 100 (Blaine, portions of Whatcom County); Outside TV Markets (portions of Whatcom County). Franchise award date: N.A. Franchise expiration date: N.A. Began: March 1, 1968.
Channel capacity: 31. Channels available but not in use: None.

Basic Service
Subscribers: 2,426.
Programming (received off-air): KVOS-TV (I) Bellingham; CBUT, CHAN-TV Vancouver; allband FM.
Programming (via microwave): KCPQ (F), KCTS-TV (P), KING-TV (N), KIRO-TV (C), KOMO-TV (A), KSTW (U) Seattle-Tacoma.
Programming (via satellite): C-SPAN; CNBC; CNN; Discovery Channel; Fox Family Channel; Headline News; Lifetime; Nashville Network; Nickelodeon; Odyssey; QVC; TBS Superstation; The Weather Channel.
Planned originations: Public access; religious access.
Fee: $60.00 installation; $18.60 monthly.

Expanded Basic Service
Subscribers: 2,021.
Programming (via satellite): American Movie Classics; ESPN; Fox Sports Net Northwest; Turner Network TV; USA Network.
Fee: $2.00 monthly.

Pay Service 1
Pay Units: 243.
Programming (via satellite): Disney Channel.
Fee: N.A.

Pay Service 2
Pay Units: 747.
Programming (via satellite): The New Encore.
Fee: N.A.

Pay Service 3
Pay Units: 455.
Programming (via satellite): HBO.
Fee: $35.00 installation; $13.15 monthly.

Pay Service 4
Pay Units: 197.
Programming (via satellite): Showtime.
Fee: $35.00 installation; $13.15 monthly.

Pay-Per-View
Special events.

Local advertising: No.
Equipment: Catel & Scientific-Atlanta headend; Magnavox amplifiers; Times Fiber cable; Hamlin set top converters; Jerrold addressable set top converters; Scientific-Atlanta satellite antenna; Antenna Technology & Simulsat satellite receivers.
Miles of plant: 116.9 (coaxial). Homes passed: 3,768. Total homes in franchised area: 4,134.
Manager: Dan Crocker. Chief technician: Ron Robertson.
City fee: 3% of gross.
Ownership: AT&T Broadband & Internet Services (MSO). Purchased from Tele-Communications Inc., March 9, 1999.

BREMERTON—TCI Cablevision of Washington Inc., 1225 Sylvan Way, Bremerton, WA 98310-3426. Phone: 360-377-8528. Fax: 360-377-7827. County: Kitsap. Also serves Kitsap County, Tracyton. ICA: WA0017.
TV Market Ranking: 20. Franchise award date: June 1, 1966. Franchise expiration date: N.A. Began: June 1, 1966.
Channel capacity: 39. Channels available but not in use: N.A.

Basic Service
Subscribers: 17,828.
Programming (received off-air): KCPQ (F), KCTS-TV (P), KING-TV (N), KIRO-TV (C), KOMO-TV (A), KSTW (U), KTBW-TV (T), KTWB (W) Seattle-Tacoma; KBTC-TV (P) Tacoma; CBUT Vancouver; 20 FMs.
Programming (via satellite): A & E; C-SPAN; CNBC; CNN; Discovery Channel; Fox Family Channel; Headline News; Lifetime; MTV; Nashville Network; Nickelodeon; QVC; TBS Superstation; The Weather Channel.
Current originations: Automated time-weather; public access; educational access; government access; automated emergency alert; local sports.
Fee: $60.00 installation; $9.69 monthly; $1.12 converter; $40.00 additional installation.

Expanded Basic Service
Subscribers: 13,846.
Programming (via satellite): American Movie Classics; ESPN; Fox Sports Net Northwest; Turner Network TV; USA Network.
Fee: $10.21 monthly.

Pay Service 1
Pay Units: 1,436.
Programming (via satellite): Cinemax.
Fee: $12.78 monthly.

Pay Service 2
Pay Units: 1,590.
Programming (via satellite): Disney Channel.
Fee: $10.95 monthly.

Pay Service 3
Pay Units: 6,344.
Programming (via satellite): The New Encore.
Fee: N.A.

Pay Service 4
Pay Units: 2,857.
Programming (via satellite): HBO.
Fee: $12.78 monthly.

Pay Service 5
Pay Units: 2,518.
Programming (via satellite): Showtime.
Fee: $12.78 monthly.

Local advertising: Yes (locally produced & insert). Available in automated programming.
Program Guide: The Cable Guide.
Equipment: Scientific-Atlanta headend; Jerrold amplifiers; Times Fiber cable; Jerrold set top converters; Scientific-Atlanta addressable set top converters; Scientific-Atlanta satellite antenna.
Miles of plant: 325.3 (coaxial). Total homes in franchised area: 28,995.
Manager: Jo Webster. Chief technician: Ken Effenberger.
City fee: 5% of gross.
Ownership: AT&T Broadband & Internet Services (MSO). Purchased from Tele-Communications Inc., March 9, 1999.

BREWSTER—Millennium Digital Media, Suite 107, 3633 136th Place SE, Bellevue, WA 98006. Phones: 425-747-4600; 800-829-2225. Fax: 425-644-4621.
Web site: http://www.millenniumdigital.com.
Counties: Douglas & Okanogan. Also serves Bridgeport, Bridgeport Bar, Pateros. ICA: WA0060.
TV Market Ranking: Outside TV Markets. Franchise award date: N.A. Franchise expiration date: N.A. Began: October 1, 1982.

Channel capacity: 35 (2-way capable; operating 2-way). Channels available but not in use: 13.

Basic Service

Subscribers: 1,117.

Programming (received off-air): KCTS-TV (P), KING-TV (N), KIRO-TV (C), KOMO-TV (A), KSTW (U) Seattle-Tacoma; KAYU-TV (F), KHQ-TV (N), KREM-TV (C), KXLY-TV (A) Spokane.

Programming (via microwave): TVW.

Programming (via satellite): WGN-TV (W) Chicago; A & E; American Movie Classics; CNN; Country Music TV; Discovery Channel; ESPN; Fox Family Channel; Fox Sports Net Northwest; Headline News; Learning Channel; Lifetime; Nashville Network; Nickelodeon; Northwest Cable News; QVC; Sci-Fi Channel; TBS Superstation; TV Guide Channel; Turner Classic Movies; Turner Network TV; USA Network; Univision.

Current originations: Public access; government access.

Fee: $25.00 installation; $26.95 monthly.

Pay Service 1

Pay Units: N.A.

Programming (via satellite): Disney Channel; HBO; Showtime.

Fee: $8.95 monthly (Disney), $14.95 monthly (HBO or Showtime).

Equipment: M/A-Com headend; GTE Sylvania amplifiers; Times Fiber cable; Video Data Systems character generator; Eagle traps; M/A-Com satellite antenna; M/A-Com satellite receivers.

Miles of plant: 45.7 (coaxial). Homes passed: 1,550. Total homes in franchised area: 1,550.

Manager: Steve Weed. Chief technician: Gene Fry.

Ownership: Millennium Digital Media LLC (MSO). Purchased from Summit Communications Inc., April 7, 1999.

BUCODA—Millennium Digital Media, Suite 107, 3633 136th Place SE, Bellevue, WA 98006. Phone: 206-747-4600. Web site: http://www.millenniumdigital.com. County: Thurston. ICA: WA0112.

TV Market Ranking: Outside TV Markets. Franchise award date: N.A. Franchise expiration date: January 1, 2007. Began: August 11, 1983.

Channel capacity: 35. Channels available but not in use: 17.

Basic Service

Subscribers: 153.

Programming (received off-air): KCPQ (F), KCTS-TV (P), KING-TV (N), KIRO-TV (C), KOMO-TV (A), KSTW (U), KTWB (W) Seattle-Tacoma.

Programming (via satellite): WGN-TV (W) Chicago; CNN; ESPN; Fox Family Channel; Nashville Network; QVC; TBS Superstation.

Current originations: Government access.

Fee: $25.00 installation; $19.45 monthly.

Pay Service 1

Pay Units: N.A.

Programming (via satellite): Showtime; The Movie Channel.

Fee: $20.00 installation; $12.95 monthly (each).

Equipment: Cadco headend; AEL amplifiers; Times Fiber cable; Video Data Systems character generator; Eagle traps; Prodelin satellite antenna; M/A-Com satellite receivers.

Miles of plant: 8.2 (coaxial). Homes passed: 280.

Manager: Steve Weed. Chief technician: Gene Fry.

City fee: 3% of gross.

Ownership: Millennium Digital Media LLC (MSO). Purchased from Summit Communications Inc., April 7, 1999.

BURLINGTON—TCI Cablevision of Washington Inc., 777 W. Horton Rd., Bellingham, WA 98226-7606. Phone: 360-384-1581. County: Skagit. Also serves Mount Vernon, Sedro Woolley, Skagit County. ICA: WA0018.

TV Market Ranking: Below 100 (Burlington, Mount Vernon, Sedro Woolley, portions of Skagit County); Outside TV Markets (portions of Skagit County). Franchise award date: N.A. Franchise expiration date: N.A. Began: July 1, 1952.

Channel capacity: 37. Channels available but not in use: N.A.

Basic Service

Subscribers: 12,991.

Programming (received off-air): KVOS-TV (I) Bellingham; KCPQ (F), KCTS-TV (P), KING-TV (N), KIRO-TV (C), KOMO-TV (A), KSTW (U) Seattle-Tacoma; CBUT, CHAN-TV Vancouver; allband FM.

Programming (via satellite): C-SPAN; C-SPAN 2; CNBC; CNN; Discovery Channel; Fox Family Channel; Headline News; Lifetime; MTV; Nashville Network; Odyssey; QVC; The Weather Channel.

Fee: $60.00 installation; $10.17 monthly; $0.57 converter; $40.00 additional installation.

Expanded Basic Service

Subscribers: 10,846.

Programming (via satellite): American Movie Classics; Court TV; ESPN; Fox Sports Net Northwest; Turner Network TV; USA Network.

Fee: $10.90 monthly.

Pay Service 1

Pay Units: 1,550.

Programming (via satellite): Cinemax.

Fee: $13.15 monthly.

Pay Service 2

Pay Units: 1,904.

Programming (via satellite): Disney Channel.

Fee: $20.00 installation; $9.00 monthly.

Pay Service 3

Pay Units: 3,886.

Programming (via satellite): The New Encore.

Fee: N.A.

Pay Service 4

Pay Units: 3,020.

Programming (via satellite): HBO.

Fee: $13.15 monthly.

Program Guide: The Cable Guide.

Equipment: Jerrold headend; GTE Sylvania & Jerrold amplifiers; Scientific-Atlanta satellite antenna.

Miles of plant: 222.9 (coaxial). Homes passed: 16,149. Total homes in franchised area: 16,158.

Manager: Robert Huisman. Chief technician: Craig Swenter.

City fee: 3% of gross.

Ownership: AT&T Broadband & Internet Services (MSO). Purchased from Tele-Communications Inc., March 9, 1999.

CAMANO ISLAND—Northland Cable, Box 1630, La Conner, WA 98257. Phone: 360-466-3317. Fax: 360-466-3560. Counties: Island & Snohomish. Also serves Snohomish County (northwestern portion), Stanwood. Plans service to Indian Beach, Lost Lake, Madrona Beach. ICA: WA0046.

TV Market Ranking: 20 (portions of Camano Island); Below 100 (portions of Camano Island, portions of Snohomish County, Stanwood); Outside TV Markets (portions of Snohomish County). Franchise award date: January 1, 1968. Franchise expiration date: January 1, 2006. Began: June 1, 1980.

Channel capacity: 41 (not 2-way capable). Channels available but not in use: 8.

Basic Service

Subscribers: 3,652.

Programming (received off-air): KVOS-TV (I) Bellingham; KCPQ (F), KCTS-TV (P), KING-TV (N), KIRO-TV (C), KOMO-TV (A), KSTW (U), KTWB (W) Seattle-Tacoma; CBUT Vancouver; allband FM.

Programming (via satellite): QVC; TV Guide Channel; Trinity Bcstg. Network.

Fee: $50.00 installation; $11.60 monthly; $3.00 converter.

Expanded Basic Service

Subscribers: 3,551.

Programming (via satellite): A & E; C-SPAN; CNBC; CNN; Discovery Channel; ESPN; Fox Family Channel; Headline News; Learning Channel; Lifetime; Nashville Network; TBS Superstation; Turner Network TV; USA Network.

Fee: $50.00 installation; $9.80 monthly.

Pay Service 1

Pay Units: 232.

Programming (via satellite): Cinemax.

Fee: $8.95 monthly.

Pay Service 2

Pay Units: 255.

Programming (via satellite): Disney Channel.

Fee: $8.95 monthly.

Pay Service 3

Pay Units: 423.

Programming (via satellite): HBO.

Fee: $25.00 installation; $10.95 monthly.

Pay Service 4

Pay Units: 40.

Programming (via satellite): Showtime.

Fee: N.A.

Local advertising: Yes. Available in character-generated & taped programming. Rates: $50.00/Minute; $3.00/30 Seconds. Local sales manager: Les Carney.

Equipment: Scientific-Atlanta headend; Magnavox amplifiers; Trilogy cable; Amiga character generator; Regal set top converters; PPC traps; Scientific-Atlanta satellite antenna; Scientific-Atlanta satellite receivers; ChannelMatic commercial insert.

Miles of plant: 134.0 (coaxial).

Manager: Jon Ulrich. Marketing director: Bede Wells.

County fee: 5% of gross.

Ownership: Northland Communications Corp. (MSO).

CARSON—Millennium Digital Media, Suite 107, 3633 136th Place SE, Bellevue, WA 98006. Phones: 425-747-4600; 800-829-2225. Fax: 425-644-4621.

Web site: http://www.millenniumdigital.com.

County: Skamania. Also serves Skamania, Stevenson. ICA: WA0061.

TV Market Ranking: Outside TV Markets. Franchise award date: N.A. Franchise expiration date: N.A. Began: January 1, 1953.

Channel capacity: 22. Channels available but not in use: 4.

Basic Service

Subscribers: 1,232.

Programming (received off-air): KATU (A), KGW (N), KOIN (C), KOPB-TV (P), KPTV (U) Portland; KPDX (F) Vancouver; allband FM.

Programming (via satellite): WGN-TV (W) Chicago; A & E; American Movie Classics; C-SPAN; CNN; Discovery Channel; ESPN; Fox Family Channel; Fox Sports Net Northwest; History Channel; Learning Channel; Lifetime; MuchMusic Network; Nashville Network; Nickelodeon; Northwest Cable News; QVC; TBS Superstation; Turner Classic Movies; Turner Network TV; USA Network.

Current originations: Automated time-weather; public access; educational access; government access.

Fee: $45.00 installation; $15.75 monthly.

Pay Service 1

Pay Units: N.A.

Programming (via satellite): Disney Channel; HBO; Showtime.

Fee: N.A.

Equipment: Jerrold headend; Jerrold amplifiers; Viking & Superior cable; Sony VTRs; MSI character generator; Scientific-Atlanta satellite antenna.

Miles of plant: 45.6 (coaxial). Homes passed: 1,520.

Manager: Steve Weed. Chief technician: Gene Fry.

City fee: 3% of gross.

Ownership: Millennium Digital Media LLC (MSO). Purchased from Summit Communications Inc., April 7, 1999.

CATHLAMET—Falcon Communications Ventures I, 1241 Duane St., Astoria, OR 97103. Phone: 503-325-6114. Fax: 503-325-7421. County: Wahkiakum. ICA: WA0145.

TV Market Ranking: Outside TV Markets. Franchise award date: N.A. Franchise expiration date: July 15, 2000. Began: September 1, 1967.

Channel capacity: 14. Channels available but not in use: None.

Basic Service

Subscribers: 507.

Programming (received off-air): KATU (A), KGW (N), KOIN (C), KOPB-TV (P), KPTV (U) Portland; KOMO-TV (A) Seattle-Tacoma; allband FM.

Programming (via satellite): CNN; ESPN; Fox Family Channel.

Fee: $40.00 installation; $13.71 monthly.

Expanded Basic Service

Subscribers: 482.

Programming (via satellite): Country Music TV; Disney Channel; TBS Superstation; USA Network.

Fee: $3.10 monthly.

Pay Service 1

Pay Units: 187.

Programming (via satellite): HBO.

Fee: $11.95 monthly.

Equipment: Blonder-Tongue & Jerrold headend; Vikoa amplifiers; Times Fiber & Vikoa cable; Eagle traps; Scientific-Atlanta addressable traps; M/A-Com satellite receivers.

Miles of plant: 31.0 (coaxial). Homes passed: 731.

Manager: Ray Romine. Chief technician: Bruce Johnson.

Ownership: Falcon Communications LP (MSO), joint venture formed September 30, 1998. See Cable System Ownership.

CENTRALIA-CHEHALIS—TCI Cablevision, Box 129, Olympia, WA 98507. Phones: 360-736-1166; 800-221-5232. Fax: 360-736-1160. Counties: Lewis & Thurston. Also serves Lewis County, Thurston County. ICA: WA0022.

TV Market Ranking: 20 (portions of Lewis County, portions of Thurston County); Outside TV Markets (Centralia-Chehalis, portions of Lewis County, portions of Thurston County). Franchise award date: N.A. Franchise expiration date: N.A. Began: October 1, 1965.

Channel capacity: 48 (not 2-way capable). Channels available but not in use: N.A.

Basic Service
Subscribers: 9,644.
Programming (received off-air): KCKA (P) Centralia; KATU (A), KGW (N), KOIN (C), KPTV (U) Portland; KCPQ (F), KCTS-TV (P), KING-TV (N), KIRO-TV (C), KOMO-TV (A), KSTW (U), KTWB (W) Seattle-Tacoma; all-band FM.
Programming (via satellite): C-SPAN; CNN; Discovery Channel; Fox Family Channel; Lifetime; MTV; Nashville Network; Nickelodeon; TBS Superstation.
Fee: $60.00 installation; $9.74 monthly; $1.00 converter; $40.00 additional installation.
Expanded Basic Service
Subscribers: 8,887.
Programming (via satellite): American Movie Classics; ESPN; Fox Sports Net Northwest; Turner Network TV; USA Network.
Fee: $10.24 monthly.
Pay Service 1
Pay Units: 725.
Programming (via satellite): Disney Channel.
Fee: $9.95 installation; $11.95 monthly.
Pay Service 2
Pay Units: 3,939.
Programming (via satellite): The New Encore.
Fee: N.A.
Pay Service 3
Pay Units: 1,064.
Programming (via satellite): HBO.
Fee: $9.95 installation; $11.95 monthly.
Pay Service 4
Pay Units: 747.
Programming (via satellite): Showtime.
Fee: $9.95 installation; $11.95 monthly.
Local advertising: Yes (locally produced & insert). Available in satellite distributed programming. Rates: $7.00-$20.00/30 Seconds.
Program Guide: The Cable Guide.
Equipment: Jerrold & Scientific-Atlanta headend; Jerrold & Theta-Com amplifiers; Comm/Scope & Times Fiber cable; Sony VTRs; Metrodata character generator; Jerrold set top converters; Jerrold addressable set top converters; Andrew satellite antenna; Microwave Assoc. satellite receivers.
Miles of plant: 205.2 (coaxial). Additional miles planned: 1.0 (coaxial). Homes passed: 12,818. Total homes in franchised area: 12,818.
Manager: Paul Renz.
City fee: 5% of gross.
Ownership: AT&T Broadband & Internet Services (MSO). Purchased from Tele-Communications Inc., March 9, 1999.

CHATTAROY—Phoenix Cable, 10 S. Franklin Turnpike, Ramsey, NJ 07446. Phone: 201-825-9090. Fax: 201-825-8794. Counties: Pend Oreille & Spokane. Also serves Diamond Lake. ICA: WA0181.
TV Market Ranking: 76. Franchise award date: November 1, 1989. Franchise expiration date: October 1, 2004. Began: July 1, 1990.
Channel capacity: 40. Channels available but not in use: 16.
Basic Service
Subscribers: 636.
Programming (received off-air): KAYU-TV (F), KHQ-TV (N), KREM-TV (C), KSPS-TV (P), KXLY-TV (A) Spokane.
Programming (via satellite): C-SPAN; CNN; Country Music TV; Discovery Channel; ESPN; Fox Family Channel; Fox Sports Net Northwest; Headline News; Home Shopping Network; Learning Channel; Nashville Network; Nickelodeon; Sci-Fi Channel; TBS Superstation; The Weather Channel; Turner Classic Movies; Turner Network TV; VH1.
Fee: $21.90 monthly.
Pay Service 1
Pay Units: 51.
Programming (via satellite): Disney Channel.
Fee: $6.95 monthly.
Pay Service 2
Pay Units: 126.
Programming (via satellite): The Movie Channel.
Fee: $6.95 monthly.
Pay Service 3
Pay Units: 174.
Programming (via satellite): Showtime.
Fee: $7.95 monthly.
Miles of plant: 67.0 (coaxial).
Manager: Charles Himelrick. Marketing & program director: Sean Feeney.
Franchise fee: 5% of gross.
Ownership: Phoenix Cable Inc. (MSO).

CHELAN—Millennium Digital Media, Box 967, Chelan, WA 98816. Phones: 509-682-3295; 800-829-2225. Fax: 509-682-3295. County: Chelan. Also serves Chelan Falls. ICA: WA0058.
TV Market Ranking: Below 100. Franchise award date: N.A. Franchise expiration date: January 1, 2005. Began: May 1, 1954.
Channel capacity: 36 (not 2-way capable). Channels available but not in use: 4.
Basic Service
Subscribers: 1,800.
Programming (received off-air): KING-TV (N), KIRO-TV (C), KOMO-TV (A), KSTW (U) Seattle-Tacoma; KAYU-TV (F), KHQ-TV (N), KREM-TV (C), KSPS-TV (P), KXLY-TV (A) Spokane; 8 FMs.
Programming (via microwave): TVW.
Programming (via satellite): A & E; American Movie Classics; C-SPAN; CNBC; CNN; Comedy Central; Discovery Channel; ESPN; Fox Family Channel; Fox Sports Net Northwest; Headline News; History Channel; Learning Channel; Lifetime; Nashville Network; Nickelodeon; Northwest Cable News; QVC; TBS Superstation; TV Guide Channel; Trinity Bcstg. Network; Turner Classic Movies; Turner Network TV; USA Network; Univision.
Current originations: Public access; educational access; government access; religious access.
Fee: $45.00 installation; $26.95 monthly.
Pay Service 1
Pay Units: N.A.
Programming (via satellite): Disney Channel; HBO; Showtime; The Movie Channel.
Fee: $8.95 monthly (Disney), $14.95 monthly (HBO, Showtime or TMC).
Local advertising: Yes. Available in character-generated programming.
Equipment: Jerrold headend; GTE Sylvania amplifiers; Times Fiber cable; Texscan character generator; Jerrold addressable set top converters; Eagle traps; Scientific-Atlanta satellite receivers.
Miles of plant: 50.0 (coaxial). Additional miles planned: 5.0 (coaxial).
Manager: Kerry Stratton. Chief technician: Lonnie Hubbard.
City fee: 3% of gross.
Ownership: Millennium Digital Media LLC (MSO). Purchased from Summit Communications Inc., April 7, 1999.

CHENEY—Cheney TV Cable, Box 117, Cheney, WA 99004. Phone: 509-235-5144. Fax: 509-235-5158. County: Spokane. ICA: WA0045.
TV Market Ranking: 76. Franchise award date: N.A. Franchise expiration date: N.A. Began: October 20, 1980.

Channel capacity: 52. Channels available but not in use: N.A.
Basic Service
Subscribers: 2,773.
Programming (received off-air): KWSU-TV (P) Pullman; KAYU-TV (F), KHQ-TV (N), KREM-TV (C), KSPS-TV (P), KXLY-TV (A) Spokane.
Programming (via satellite): WGN-TV (W) Chicago; CNN; Cartoon Network; ESPN; Fox Family Channel; MTV; TBS Superstation; Turner Classic Movies; USA Network.
Fee: $19.95 installation; $12.95 monthly.
Pay Service 1
Pay Units: N.A.
Programming (via satellite): Cinemax; HBO.
Fee: $10.45 monthly (each).
Miles of plant: 26.7 (coaxial).
Manager: Tom Davis. Chief technician: Tim Gainer.
Ownership: Davis Communications Inc. (MSO).

CHINOOK—Chinook Progressive Club TV, Box 15, Chinook, WA 98614. Phone: 206-777-8412. County: Pacific. ICA: WA0146.
TV Market Ranking: Outside TV Markets. Franchise award date: N.A. Franchise expiration date: January 1, 2010. Began: January 1, 1961.
Channel capacity: 12. Channels available but not in use: N.A.
Basic Service
Subscribers: 280.
Programming (received off-air): KATU (A), KGW (N), KOIN (C), KOPB-TV (P), KPTV (U) Portland.
Programming (via satellite): A & E; C-SPAN 2; CNN; Discovery Channel; ESPN; FX; Fox Family Channel; Learning Channel; Nashville Network; QVC; TBS Superstation; The Weather Channel; Travel Channel; Trinity Bcstg. Network; Turner Network TV; USA Network.
Current originations: Automated time-weather; public access; religious access.
Fee: $15.00 installation; $8.00 monthly; $15.00 additional installation.
Pay Service 1
Pay Units: 215.
Programming (via satellite): Showtime.
Fee: $7.00 monthly.
Local advertising: No.
Equipment: Entron & Jerrold headend; Entron, Vikoa & Times Fiber cable; Pico traps; Anixter-Mark satellite antenna.
Miles of plant: 7.0 (coaxial); None (fiber optic).
Manager: Trophy W. Hughes. Chief technician: Gary White.
City fee: None.
Ownership: Chinook Progressive Club TV.

CHINOOK PASS—Columbia Basin Cable TV, Box 490, 611 6th St., Umatilla, OR 97882. Phones: 541-922-5759; 800-521-3916. Fax: 541-922-3758. Counties: Kittitas West & Yakima. Also serves Cliffdell, Horseshoe Bend. ICA: WA0109.
TV Market Ranking: Below 100 (Cliffdell, Horseshoe Bend); Outside TV Markets (Chinook Pass). Franchise award date: N.A. Franchise expiration date: N.A. Began: November 1, 1980.

Channel capacity: 36. Channels available but not in use: 10.
Basic Service
Subscribers: 211.
Programming (received off-air): KAPP (A), KIMA-TV (C), KNDO (N), KYVE-TV (P) Yakima.
Programming (via satellite): WGN-TV (W) Chicago; A & E; American Movie Classics; Animal Planet; CNN; Country Music TV; Discovery Channel; Disney Channel; ESPN; ESPN 2; Fox Family Channel; Headline News; Nashville Network; Sci-Fi Channel; TBS Superstation; Trinity Bcstg. Network; Turner Network TV; USA Network; VH1.
Fee: $30.00 installation; $27.75 monthly.
Pay Service 1
Pay Units: 21.
Programming (via satellite): HBO.
Fee: $11.95 monthly.
Miles of plant: 17.0 (coaxial); None (fiber optic). Homes passed: 440.
Manager: Kerry Stratton. Chief technician: Darrell Johnson. Marketing director & customer service manager: Charlotte Winkler.
Ownership: USA Media Group LLC (MSO). Purchased from Cambridge Communications, May 15, 1999.

CLALLAM BAY—Northland Cable TV, 725 E. First St., Port Angeles, WA 98362. Phones: 360-452-8466; 800-244-7591. Fax: 360-457-5901. County: Clallam. Also serves Sekiu. ICA: WA0095.
TV Market Ranking: Outside TV Markets. Franchise award date: N.A. Franchise expiration date: May 1, 2012. Began: January 1, 1975.
Channel capacity: 42 (not 2-way capable). Channels available but not in use: 16.
Basic Service
Subscribers: 265; Commercial subscribers: 96.
Programming (received off-air): KCTS-TV (P), KING-TV (N), KIRO-TV (C), KOMO-TV (A) Seattle-Tacoma; CBUT, CHAN-TV Vancouver; CHEK-TV Victoria; 9 FMs.
Programming (via satellite): WGN-TV (W) Chicago; A & E; American Movie Classics; CNN; Country Music TV; Discovery Channel; ESPN; Fox Family Channel; FoxNet; Learning Channel; Lifetime; Nashville Network; Nickelodeon; QVC; TBS Superstation; Turner Network TV; USA Network.
Fee: $40.00 installation; $24.95 monthly; $10.00 additional installation.
Commercial fee: $4.50 monthly.
Pay Service 1
Pay Units: 60.
Programming (via satellite): Showtime.
Fee: $19.95 installation; $10.50 monthly.
Equipment: Ampex headend; Texscan amplifiers; Times Fiber cable; Pico traps; Hughes & Scientific-Atlanta satellite antenna; Standard Communications satellite receivers.
Miles of plant: 12.0 (coaxial). Homes passed: 410.
Manager: Daniel Withers. Chief technician: Michael Sturgeon. Program director: Dennis Bragg.
Franchise fee: 5% of gross.
Ownership: Northland Communications Corp. (MSO).

CLE ELUM—TCI Cablevision of Southwest Washington Inc., 4020 Auburn Way N, Auburn, WA 98002. Phone: 206-228-1101. Counties: Kittitas East & Kittitas West. Also serves Kittitas County, South Cle Elum. ICA: WA0068.
TV Market Ranking: Below 100 (Cle Elum, portions of Kittitas County, South Cle Elum); Outside TV Markets (portions of Kittitas County). Franchise award date: N.A. Franchise expiration date: March 1, 2001. Began: December 1, 1954.
Channel capacity: 36 (not 2-way capable). Channels available but not in use: N.A.
Basic Service
Subscribers: 990.
Programming (received off-air): Allband FM.
Programming (via microwave): KCPQ (F), KING-TV (N), KIRO-TV (C), KOMO-TV (A), KSTW (U) Seattle-Tacoma; KYVE-TV (P) Yakima.
Programming (via satellite): A & E; CNN; Comedy Central; Discovery Channel; Fox Family Channel; Headline News; Lifetime; MTV; Nashville Network; Nickelodeon; TBS Superstation; VH1.
Current originations: Automated time-weather; public access; government access; library access.
Fee: $60.00 installation; $9.81 monthly; $1.95 converter; $40.00 additional installation.
Commercial fee: $5.00 monthly.
Expanded Basic Service
Subscribers: 844.
Programming (via satellite): Court TV; ESPN; Fox Sports Net Northwest; Turner Network TV; USA Network.
Fee: $11.45 monthly.
Pay Service 1
Pay Units: 77.
Programming (via satellite): Disney Channel.
Fee: $19.95 installation; $8.50 monthly.
Pay Service 2
Pay Units: 364.
Programming (via satellite): The New Encore.
Fee: N.A.
Pay Service 3
Pay Units: 87.
Programming (via satellite): HBO.
Fee: $19.95 installation; $11.95 monthly.
Pay Service 4
Pay Units: 62.
Programming (via satellite): Showtime.
Fee: $19.95 installation; $11.95 monthly.
Local advertising: Yes (locally produced). Available in locally originated programming.
Equipment: Catel, Microwave Assoc. & Phasecom headend; Magnavox amplifiers; Times Fiber cable; Hamlin & Pioneer set top converters; Prodelin satellite antenna; Standard Communications satellite receivers.
Miles of plant: 22.9 (coaxial). Homes passed: 1,250. Total homes in franchised area: 1,575.
Manager: Keith Fischer. Chief technician: Dennis Moore.
City fee: 5% of basic gross.
Ownership: AT&T Broadband & Internet Services (MSO). Purchased from Tele-Communications Inc., March 9, 1999.

CLINTON—TCI Cablevision of Washington Inc., Suite B, 11515 State Ave., Marysville, WA 98271-7245. Phone: 360-659-1285. County: Island. Also serves Langley. ICA: WA0055.
TV Market Ranking: 20. Franchise award date: N.A. Franchise expiration date: N.A. Began: July 1, 1971.
Channel capacity: 21. Channels available but not in use: 7.
Basic Service
Subscribers: 1,362.
Programming (received off-air): KVOS-TV (I) Bellingham; KCPQ (F), KCTS-TV (P), KING-TV (N), KIRO-TV (C), KOMO-TV (A), KSTW (U), KTBW-TV (T), KTWB (W) Seattle-Tacoma; CBUT Vancouver.
Programming (via satellite): CNN; ESPN; TBS Superstation.
Fee: $60.00 installation; $10.66 monthly.
Pay Service 1
Pay Units: 192.
Programming (via satellite): Showtime.
Fee: $11.60 monthly.
Miles of plant: 31.1 (coaxial). Homes passed: 1,876. Total homes in franchised area: 2,240.
Manager: John Sheehan.
Ownership: AT&T Broadband & Internet Services (MSO). Purchased from Tele-Communications Inc., March 9, 1999.

CLYDE HILL—Telepro Communications, Suite 11, 13400 Northup Way, Bellevue, WA 98005-2026. Phone: 425-957-1657. Fax: 425-957-0119. County: King. ICA: WA0147.
TV Market Ranking: 20. Franchise award date: November 1, 1988. Franchise expiration date: N.A. Began: N.A.
Channel capacity: 49 (not 2-way capable). Channels available but not in use: N.A.
Basic Service
Subscribers: 3,300.
Programming (received off-air): KCPQ (F), KCTS-TV (P), KING-TV (N), KIRO-TV (C), KOMO-TV (A), KSTW (U), KTBW-TV (T), KTWB (W) Seattle-Tacoma; KBTC-TV (P) Tacoma; CBUT Vancouver.
Programming (via satellite): A & E; American Movie Classics; BET; Bravo; C-SPAN; CNBC; CNN; Cartoon Network; Discovery Channel; ESPN; ESPN 2; FX; Fox News Channel; Fox Sports Net Northwest; Headline News; History Channel; Home Shopping Network; Learning Channel; Lifetime; MTV; Nashville Network; Nickelodeon; Odyssey; QVC; Sci-Fi Channel; TBS Superstation; The Weather Channel; Travel Channel; Turner Network TV; USA Network; ValueVision.
Current originations: Public access; government access; local news.
Fee: $39.95 installation; $24.81 monthly; $5.00 converter; $30.00 additional installation.
Pay Service 1
Pay Units: 1,600.
Programming (via satellite): Disney Channel; HBO; Showtime; The Movie Channel.
Fee: $11.95 monthly (each).
Miles of plant: 25.0 (coaxial); None (fiber optic). Homes passed: 7,300. Total homes in franchised area: 8,200.
President: John Craig. Manager: Bill Glenn. Chief technician: Doug Moir. Program & marketing director: Tami Moir.
Ownership: Telepro Communications (MSO).

COLFAX—Colfax Highline Cable Co., Box 187, Colfax, WA 99111. Phone: 509-397-2211. Fax: 509-397-2274. County: Whitman. Also serves Steptoe. ICA: WA0075.
TV Market Ranking: Below 100. Franchise award date: N.A. Franchise expiration date: N.A. Began: December 1, 1953.
Channel capacity: 42 (not 2-way capable). Channels available but not in use: N.A.
Basic Service
Subscribers: 985.
Programming (received off-air): KLEW-TV (C) Lewiston; KUID-TV (P) Moscow; KWSU-TV (P) Pullman; KAYU-TV (F), KHQ-TV (N), KREM-TV (C), KSPS-TV (P), KXLY-TV (A) Spokane; allband FM.
Programming (via satellite): WGN-TV (W) Chicago; A & E; C-SPAN; CNN; Country Music TV; Discovery Channel; ESPN; EWTN; Fox Family Channel; Fox Sports Net Northwest; Headline News; Home Shopping Network; Home Shopping Network 2; Lifetime; MTV; Nashville Network; Nickelodeon; Sci-Fi Channel; TBS Superstation; Travel Channel; Turner Network TV; USA Network; VH1.
Current originations: Local news.
Fee: $20.00 installation; $18.00 monthly.
Pay Service 1
Pay Units: 95.
Programming (via satellite): Cinemax.
Fee: $7.00 monthly.
Pay Service 2
Pay Units: 80.
Programming (via satellite): Disney Channel.
Fee: $7.50 monthly.
Pay Service 3
Pay Units: 150.
Programming (via satellite): HBO.
Fee: $10.00 monthly.
Pay Service 4
Pay Units: 61.
Programming (via satellite): Showtime.
Fee: $7.95 monthly.
Pay Service 5
Pay Units: 49.
Programming (via satellite): The Movie Channel.
Fee: $10.00 monthly.
Equipment: Jerrold headend; Jerrold amplifiers.
Miles of plant: 25.0 (coaxial). Homes passed: 1,000.
Manager: Ken Julian.
City fee: None.
Ownership: Colfax Highline Cable Co.

COLVILLE—Falcon Telecable, 189 Buena Vista Dr., Colville, WA 99114. Phone: 509-684-3797. Fax: 509-684-6108. County: Stevens. Also serves Arden, Kettle Falls. ICA: WA0038.
TV Market Ranking: Outside TV Markets. Franchise award date: April 20, 1954. Franchise expiration date: N.A. Began: August 1, 1953.
Channel capacity: 40 (not 2-way capable). Channels available but not in use: None.
Basic Service
Subscribers: 2,547; Commercial subscribers: 135.
Programming (received off-air): KAYU-TV (F), KHQ-TV (N), KREM-TV (C), KSPS-TV (P), KXLY-TV (A) Spokane; allband FM.
Programming (via translator): CBUT Vancouver.
Programming (via satellite): A & E; Comedy Central; ESPN 2; Fox Sports Net Northwest; Home Shopping Network; MTV; Nickelodeon; QVC; TBS Superstation; Trinity Bcstg. Network; Turner Network TV; USA Network; VH1.
Current originations: Public access; educational access; government access.
Fee: $49.95 installation; $17.07 monthly; $15.00 additional installation.
Commercial fee: $4.00 monthly.
Expanded Basic Service
Subscribers: 2,346.
Programming (via satellite): CNN; Discovery Channel; ESPN; Headline News; Sci-Fi Channel.
Fee: $9.40 monthly.
Expanded Basic Service 2
Subscribers: 963.
Programming (via satellite): American Movie Classics; Country Music TV; Disney Channel; Fox Family Channel; Learning Channel; Nashville Network.
Fee: $7.50 monthly.
Expanded Basic Service 3
Subscribers: 461.
Programming (via satellite): Cartoon Network; E! Entertainment TV; History Channel; Home & Garden Television; The Weather Channel.
Fee: $6.00 monthly.
Pay Service 1
Pay Units: 328.
Programming (via satellite): HBO.
Fee: $25.95 installation; $11.95 monthly.
Pay Service 2
Pay Units: 148.
Programming (via satellite): The Movie Channel.
Fee: $25.95 installation; $10.95 monthly.
Pay Service 3
Pay Units: 251.
Programming (via satellite): Showtime.
Fee: $25.95 installation; $10.95 monthly.
Pay-Per-View
Special events.
Program Guide: CableView.
Equipment: Jerrold & Scientific-Atlanta headend; Jerrold & Scientific-Atlanta amplifiers; Comm/Scope cable; Texscan character generator; Scientific-Atlanta set top converters; Scientific-Atlanta addressable set top converters; Arcom, Eagle & Vitek traps; Fort Worth Tower & Scientific-Atlanta satellite antenna; Microdyne & Scientific-Atlanta satellite receivers.
Miles of plant: 71.0 (coaxial). Homes passed: 3,070.
Manager: Melvin Fox. Chief technician: Mark Sterkell. Marketing director: Debbie Gray.
City fee: 3% of gross.
Ownership: Falcon Communications LP (MSO), joint venture formed September 30, 1998. See Cable System Ownership.

CONCRETE—Millennium Digital Media, Suite 107, 3633 136th Place SE, Bellevue, WA 98006. Phones: 425-747-4600; 800-829-2225. Fax: 425-644-4621.
Web site: http://www.millenniumdigital.com.
County: Skagit. Also serves Hamilton, Lyman. ICA: WA0069.
TV Market Ranking: Below 100. Franchise award date: N.A. Franchise expiration date: N.A. Began: January 1, 1966.
Channel capacity: 35 (not 2-way capable). Channels available but not in use: 12.
Basic Service
Subscribers: 1,260.
Programming (received off-air): KVOS-TV (I) Bellingham; KCTS-TV (P), KING-TV (N), KIRO-TV (C), KOMO-TV (A) Seattle-Tacoma; 1 FM.
Programming (via satellite): WGN-TV (W) Chicago; A & E; American Movie Classics; Bravo; C-SPAN; CNN; Cartoon Network; Country Music TV; Discovery Channel; E! Entertainment TV; ESPN; FX; Fox Family Channel; Fox Sports Net Northwest; Fox-Net; Headline News; History Channel; Learning Channel; Lifetime; Nashville Network; Northwest Cable News; QVC; Sci-Fi Channel; TBS Superstation; TV Guide Channel; Turner Classic Movies; Turner Network TV; USA Network.
Fee: $45.00 installation; $26.95 monthly.
Pay Service 1
Pay Units: N.A.
Programming (via satellite): Disney Channel; HBO; Showtime.
Fee: $8.95 monthly (Disney), $14.95 monthly (HBO or Showtime).

Equipment: Jerrold headend; Cascade amplifiers; Anaconda cable.
Miles of plant: 47.8 (coaxial). Total homes in franchised area: 1,300.
Manager: Steve Weed. Chief technician: Gene Fry.
City fee: 2% of gross.
Ownership: Millennium Digital Media LLC (MSO). Purchased from Summit Communications Inc., April 7, 1999.

CONNELL—Community Cable Service, 729 S. Bernard St., Spokane, WA 99204. Phones: 509-624-4140; 800-572-0902. Fax: 509-624-7372. County: Franklin. ICA: WA0090.
TV Market Ranking: Below 100. Franchise award date: N.A. Franchise expiration date: N.A. Began: December 23, 1955.
Channel capacity: 64 (2-way capable; not operating 2-way). Channels available but not in use: None.
Basic Service
Subscribers: 647.
Programming (received off-air): KBWU-LP (I) Pasco; KEPR-TV (C), KNDU (N), KVEW (A) Pasco-Kennewick-Richland; KTNW (P) Richland; KHQ-TV (N), KSPS-TV (P) Spokane; 7 FMs.
Programming (via satellite): WGN-TV (W) Chicago; A & E; American Movie Classics; Bravo; C-SPAN; C-SPAN 2; CNBC; CNN; CNN International; Cartoon Network; Comedy Central; Country Music TV; Discovery Channel; E! Entertainment TV; ESPN; ESPN 2; ESPNews; EWTN; Fox Family Channel; Fox News Channel; Fox Sports Net Northwest; GalaVision; Goodlife TV Network; Headline News; History Channel; Home Shopping Network; Knowledge TV; Learning Channel; Lifetime; MTV; Nashville Network; Nick at Nite's TV Land; Nickelodeon; Odyssey; QVC; Sci-Fi Channel; TBS Superstation; TV Food Network; The Health Network; Travel Channel; Trinity Bcstg. Network; Turner Classic Movies; Turner Network TV; USA Network; Univision; VH1; Z Music Television.
Current originations: Automated time-weather.
Fee: $15.00 installation; $27.38 monthly.
Pay Service 1
Pay Units: 98.
Programming (via satellite): Cinemax.
Fee: $5.00 installation; $6.42 monthly.
Pay Service 2
Pay Units: 93.
Programming (via satellite): Disney Channel.
Fee: $5.00 installation; $5.34 monthly.
Pay Service 3
Pay Units: 118.
Programming (via satellite): HBO.
Fee: $5.00 installation; $9.65 monthly.
Pay Service 4
Pay Units: N.A.
Programming (via satellite): Showtime.
Fee: $5.00 installation; $8.09 monthly.
Equipment: Ameco, Nexus & Pico headend; Jerrold amplifiers; Trilogy cable.
Miles of plant: 9.0 (coaxial); None (fiber optic). Homes passed: 902. Total homes in franchised area: 920.
Manager: Martin Howser.
City fee: 6% of gross.
Ownership: Martin Howser (MSO).

COULEE CITY—Sun Country Cable, Box 127, 7 D St. SW, Quincy, WA 98848. Phone: 509-787-3543. Fax: 509-787-3884. County: Grant. ICA: WA0105.
TV Market Ranking: Outside TV Markets. Franchise award date: January 1, 1986. Franchise expiration date: January 1, 2001. Began: July 1, 1986.
Channel capacity: 35 (not 2-way capable). Channels available but not in use: 17.
Basic Service
Subscribers: 241.
Programming (via microwave): KING-TV (N), KIRO-TV (C), KOMO-TV (A) Seattle-Tacoma; KAYU-TV (F) Spokane.
Programming (via satellite): WGN-TV (W) Chicago; A & E; CNN; Cartoon Network; Discovery Channel; ESPN; Fox Family Channel; Lifetime; Nashville Network; TBS Superstation; Turner Network TV; USA Network.
Fee: $39.95 installation; $27.77 monthly.
Pay Service 1
Pay Units: 20.
Programming (via satellite): Disney Channel.
Fee: $15.00 installation; $8.95 monthly.
Pay Service 2
Pay Units: 33.
Programming (via satellite): HBO.
Fee: $15.00 installation; $10.95 monthly.
Local advertising: Yes. Available in character-generated programming. Rates: $1.00/Day.
Equipment: Triple Crown headend; Jerrold amplifiers; Atari character generator; Panasonic & Scientific-Atlanta set top converters; Scientific-Atlanta satellite antenna; Scientific-Atlanta & Triple Crown satellite receivers.
Miles of plant: 12.0 (coaxial). Homes passed: 360.
Manager: Gary White. Technical manager: Arnie Hill. Office manager: Judy Vreeman.
City fee: 2.5% of basic.
Ownership: Sun Country Cable (MSO).

COULEE DAM—TV Assn. of Coulee Dam, Box 67, Coulee Dam, WA 99116-0067. Phone: 509-633-2283. Counties: Douglas, Grant & Okanogan. Also serves Lone Pine. ICA: WA0092.
TV Market Ranking: Outside TV Markets. Franchise award date: N.A. Franchise expiration date: N.A. Began: September 1, 1954.
Channel capacity: 12 (not 2-way capable). Channels available but not in use: None.
Basic Service
Subscribers: 517.
Programming (received off-air): KAYU-TV (F), KHQ-TV (N), KREM-TV (C), KSPS-TV (P), KXLY-TV (A) Spokane; allband FM.
Programming (via satellite): CNN; Discovery Channel; ESPN; Nashville Network; TBS Superstation; Turner Network TV.
Fee: $20.00 installation; $7.50 monthly.
Pay Service 1
Pay Units: 225.
Programming (via satellite): HBO.
Fee: $7.00 monthly.
Local advertising: No.
Equipment: Composite headend; Jerrold amplifiers; Comm/Scope cable; Scientific-Atlanta & Drake satellite receivers.
Miles of plant: 8.0 (coaxial). Homes passed: 539. Total homes in franchised area: 539.
Manager: Jim Manning.
Ownership: TV Association of Coulee Dam.

COUPEVILLE—TCI Cablevision of Washington Inc., Suite B, 11515 State Ave., Marysville, WA 98271-7245. Phone: 360-659-1285. County: Island. Also serves Island County, Long Point, Madrona. ICA: WA0071.
TV Market Ranking: 20 (portions of Island County); Below 100 (Coupeville, portions of Island County, Long Point, Madrona). Franchise award date: N.A. Franchise expiration date: N.A. Began: March 1, 1972.
Channel capacity: 41. Channels available but not in use: N.A.
Basic Service
Subscribers: 736.
Programming (received off-air): KVOS-TV (I) Bellingham; KCPQ (F), KCTS-TV (P), KING-TV (N), KIRO-TV (C), KOMO-TV (A), KSTW (U), KTBW-TV (T), KTWB (W) Seattle-Tacoma; CBUT Vancouver; allband FM.
Programming (via satellite): C-SPAN; CNN; Discovery Channel; Fox Family Channel; Lifetime; Nashville Network; Nickelodeon; QVC; TBS Superstation; The Weather Channel.
Fee: $60.00 installation; $9.13 monthly; $40.00 additional installation.
Expanded Basic Service
Subscribers: 530.
Programming (via satellite): American Movie Classics; Court TV; ESPN; Fox Sports Net Northwest; Turner Network TV; USA Network.
Fee: $11.40 monthly.
Pay Service 1
Pay Units: 43.
Programming (via satellite): Disney Channel.
Fee: N.A.
Pay Service 2
Pay Units: 122.
Programming (via satellite): The New Encore.
Fee: N.A.
Pay Service 3
Pay Units: 62.
Programming (via satellite): HBO.
Fee: $12.66 monthly.
Pay Service 4
Pay Units: 46.
Programming (via satellite): Showtime.
Fee: $12.66 monthly.
Equipment: Scientific-Atlanta headend; Jerrold & Scientific-Atlanta amplifiers; Comm/Scope cable.
Miles of plant: 20.7 (coaxial). Homes passed: 1,044. Total homes in franchised area: 1,698.
Manager: John Sheehan.
City fee: 2% of gross plus 5% business tax.
Ownership: AT&T Broadband & Internet Services (MSO). Purchased from Tele-Communications Inc., March 9, 1999.

CRESTON—Cable Plus, Suite 120, 11400 S.E. 6th St., Bellevue, WA 98004. Phone: 425-462-2090. Fax: 425-462-2092. County: Lincoln. ICA: WA0150.
TV Market Ranking: Outside TV Markets. Franchise award date: October 6, 1989. Franchise expiration date: October 6, 2004. Began: May 1, 1989.
Channel capacity: 40. Channels available but not in use: N.A.
Basic Service
Subscribers: 75.
Programming (received off-air): KAYU-TV (F), KHQ-TV (N), KREM-TV (C), KSPS-TV (P), KXLY-TV (A) Spokane.
Programming (via satellite): A & E; Animal Planet; C-SPAN; CNN; CNN International; CNNfn; Country Music TV; Court TV; Discovery Channel; ESPN; ESPN 2; Fox Family Channel; Fox Sports Net Northwest; Goodlife TV Network; Headline News; History Channel; Home & Garden Television; Home Shopping Network; Learning Channel; Lifetime; Nashville Network; Nickelodeon; Odyssey; QVC; Sci-Fi Channel; TBS Superstation; The Weather Channel; Trinity Bcstg. Network; Turner Network TV; USA Network.
Fee: $35.00 installation; $21.95 monthly; $3.25 converter.
Pay Service 1
Pay Units: 7.
Programming (via satellite): Disney Channel.
Fee: $9.95 monthly.
Pay Service 2
Pay Units: 9.
Programming (via satellite): HBO.
Fee: $11.00 monthly.
Miles of plant: 8.0 (coaxial). Homes passed: 108.
Manager: Gary O'Malley. Chief technician: Dan Adams.
Ownership: Cable Plus (MSO).

DARRINGTON—Millennium Digital Media, Suite 107, 3633 136th Place SE, Bellevue, WA 98006. Phones: 425-747-4600; 800-829-2225. Fax: 425-644-4621.
Web site: http://www.millenniumdigital.com.
County: Snohomish. ICA: WA0078.
TV Market Ranking: Below 100. Franchise award date: N.A. Franchise expiration date: N.A. Began: January 1, 1960.
Channel capacity: 21. Channels available but not in use: N.A.
Basic Service
Subscribers: 664.
Programming (received off-air): KCTS-TV (P), KING-TV (N), KIRO-TV (C), KOMO-TV (A) Seattle-Tacoma; allband FM.
Programming (via satellite): A & E; American Movie Classics; Animal Planet; CNN; Discovery Channel; Disney Channel; E! Entertainment TV; ESPN; ESPN 2; Fox Family Channel; Fox Sports Net Northwest; FoxNet; Headline News; History Channel; Home & Garden Television; Learning Channel; Nashville Network; Nick at Nite's TV Land; Northwest Cable News; QVC; Sci-Fi Channel; TBS Superstation; TV Guide Channel; Turner Classic Movies; Turner Network TV; USA Network.
Fee: $45.00 installation; $27.95 monthly.
Pay Service 1
Pay Units: N.A.
Programming (via satellite): HBO; Showtime.
Fee: $14.95 monthly (each).
Equipment: Blonder-Tongue & Jerrold headend; Pathmaker amplifiers; Times Fiber cable; MSI character generator.
Miles of plant: 26.5 (coaxial). Homes passed: 810.
Manager: Steve Weed. Chief technician: Gene Fry.
City fee: 8% of gross.
Ownership: Millennium Digital Media LLC (MSO). Purchased from Summit Communications Inc., April 7, 1999.

DAVENPORT—Sun Country Cable, Box 127, 7 D St. SW, Quincy, WA 98848. Phones: 509-787-3543; 800-788-0120. Fax: 509-787-3884. County: Lincoln. ICA: WA0089.
TV Market Ranking: 76. Franchise award date: N.A. Franchise expiration date: N.A. Began: December 1, 1981.
Channel capacity: 35 (not 2-way capable). Channels available but not in use: 17.
Basic Service
Subscribers: 408.
Programming (received off-air): KAYU-TV (F), KHQ-TV (N), KREM-TV (C), KSPS-TV (P), KXLY-TV (A) Spokane.
Programming (via satellite): CNN; Cartoon Network; Discovery Channel; ESPN; Fox Family Channel; Lifetime; MTV; Nashville Network; Nickelodeon; TBS Superstation; The Weather Channel; USA Network.
Fee: $39.95 installation; $24.41 monthly.
Pay Service 1
Pay Units: 67.
Programming (via satellite): Disney Channel.
Fee: $15.00 installation; $8.95 monthly.

Pay Service 2
Pay Units: 182.
Programming (via satellite): HBO.
Fee: $15.00 installation; $9.95 monthly.
Equipment: Scientific-Atlanta headend; Scientific-Atlanta amplifiers; Times Fiber cable; Scientific-Atlanta satellite antenna; Scientific-Atlanta satellite receivers.
Miles of plant: 4.3 (coaxial). Homes passed: 620. Total homes in franchised area: 720.
Manager: Gary White. Technical manager: Arnie Hill. Office manager: Judy Vreeman.
City fee: 3% of gross.
Ownership: Sun Country Cable (MSO).

DAYTON—Touchet Valley TV Inc., Box 148, 204 E. Main St., Dayton, WA 99328. Phone: 509-382-2132. Fax: 509-382-4187. County: Columbia. ICA: WA0070.
TV Market Ranking: Outside TV Markets. Franchise award date: N.A. Franchise expiration date: N.A. Began: September 1, 1953.
Channel capacity: 12. Channels available but not in use: N.A.
Basic Service
Subscribers: N.A.
Programming (received off-air): KEPR-TV (C), KNDU (N) Pasco-Kennewick-Richland; KHQ-TV (N), KREM-TV (C), KSPS-TV (P), KXLY-TV (A) Spokane; allband FM.
Current originations: local news.
Fee: $15.00 installation; $11.50 monthly.
Pay Service 1
Pay Units: N.A.
Programming (via satellite): Disney Channel; Showtime.
Fee: $9.50 monthly (Disney), $15.00 monthly (Showtime).
Local advertising: Yes. Rates: $5.00/Minute; $1.00/Day.
Equipment: Jerrold headend; Ameco amplifiers; Viking cable.
Miles of plant: 25.0 (coaxial). Homes passed: 1,125.
Manager: David Klingenstein. Chief technician: Bob Truesdale.
Ownership: Ron Klingenstein.

DEER PARK—Sun Country Cable, Box 127, 7 D St. SW, Quincy, WA 98848. Phones: 509-787-3543; 800-788-0120. Fax: 509-787-3884. County: Spokane. ICA: WA0081.
TV Market Ranking: 76. Franchise award date: N.A. Franchise expiration date: May 1, 2005. Began: February 1, 1982.
Channel capacity: 35. Channels available but not in use: 17.
Basic Service
Subscribers: 442.
Programming (received off-air): KAYU-TV (F), KHQ-TV (N), KREM-TV (C), KSPS-TV (P), KXLY-TV (A) Spokane.
Programming (via satellite): CNN; Discovery Channel; ESPN; Fox Family Channel; Lifetime; Nashville Network; Nickelodeon; QVC; TBS Superstation; The Weather Channel; USA Network.
Fee: $39.95 installation; $24.59 monthly.
Pay Service 1
Pay Units: 58.
Programming (via satellite): Disney Channel.
Fee: $15.00 installation; $8.95 monthly.
Pay Service 2
Pay Units: 203.
Programming (via satellite): HBO.
Fee: $15.00 installation; $9.95 monthly.
Equipment: Scientific-Atlanta headend; Scientific-Atlanta amplifiers; Times Fiber cable; Panasonic & Scientific-Atlanta set top converters; Pico traps; Scientific-Atlanta satellite antenna; Scientific-Atlanta satellite receivers.
Miles of plant: 15.1 (coaxial). Additional miles planned: 0.5 (coaxial). Homes passed: 790.
Manager: Gary White. Technical manager: Arnie Hill. Chief technician: Dave Zigler. Marketing director: Nita McIntyre. Office manager: Judy Vreeman.
City fee: 3% of gross.
Ownership: Sun Country Cable (MSO).

DIAMOND LAKE—Phoenix Cable, 10 S. Franklin Turnpike, Ramsey, NJ 07446. Phone: 201-825-9090. Fax: 201-825-8794. County: Pend Oreille. ICA: WA0096.
TV Market Ranking: 76. Franchise award date: N.A. Franchise expiration date: N.A. Began: January 1, 1985.
Channel capacity: 31 (not 2-way capable). Channels available but not in use: None.
Basic Service
Subscribers: 200.
Programming (received off-air): KAYU-TV (F), KHQ-TV (N), KREM-TV (C), KSPS-TV (P), KXLY-TV (A) Spokane.
Programming (via satellite): Country Music TV; Fox Family Channel; Home Shopping Network; Learning Channel; TBS Superstation; VH1.
Planned originations: Automated time-weather.
Fee: $43.75 installation; $22.90 monthly.
Expanded Basic Service
Subscribers: 187.
Programming (via satellite): WGN-TV (W) Chicago; C-SPAN; CNN; Discovery Channel; ESPN; Headline News; Nashville Network; Nickelodeon; Turner Network TV; USA Network.
Fee: $25.00 installation; $4.95 monthly.
Pay Service 1
Pay Units: 11.
Programming (via satellite): Disney Channel.
Fee: $10.00 installation; $6.95 monthly.
Pay Service 2
Pay Units: 45.
Programming (via satellite): Showtime.
Fee: $10.00 installation; $7.95 monthly.
Pay Service 3
Pay Units: 29.
Programming (via satellite): The Movie Channel.
Fee: $10.00 installation; $6.95 monthly.
Equipment: Pico headend; Magnavox amplifiers; Times Fiber cable; Scientific-Atlanta set top converters; Pico traps; Anixter & Mark V satellite antenna; Drake & Scientific-Atlanta satellite receivers.
Miles of plant: 7.0 (coaxial). Homes passed: 500. Total homes in franchised area: 500.
Manager: Charles Himelrick. Chief technician: Richard Denney. Marketing & program director: Sean Feeney.
Ownership: Phoenix Cable Inc. (MSO).

DIXIE—TCI Cablevision of Yakima Inc., Box 1577, 126 W. Poplar St., Walla Walla, WA 99362-2847. Phone: 509-529-9500. Fax: 509-522-1719. County: Walla Walla. ICA: WA0139.
TV Market Ranking: Below 100. Franchise award date: N.A. Franchise expiration date: N.A. Began: January 1, 1964.
Channel capacity: 40. Channels available but not in use: None.
Basic Service
Subscribers: 78.
Programming (received off-air): KEPR-TV (C), KNDU (N), KVEW (A) Pasco-Kennewick-Richland.
Programming (via satellite): A & E; Discovery Channel; ESPN; Fox Family Channel; Headline News; Nashville Network; TBS Superstation; USA Network.
Fee: $39.15 installation; $9.85 monthly.
Pay Service 1
Pay Units: 25.
Programming (via satellite): Showtime.
Fee: $10.50 monthly.
Pay-Per-View
Addressable homes: 22.
Movies; special events.
Miles of plant: 3.0 (coaxial). Homes passed: 113.
Manager: Tim Klinefelter. Chief technician: Tim Ream. Program director: Dinah Morrison. Marketing director: Marlene Ashby.
Ownership: AT&T Broadband & Internet Services (MSO). Purchased from Tele-Communications Inc., March 9, 1999.

DUVALL—Millennium Digital Media, Suite 107, 3633 136th Place SE, Bellevue, WA 98006. Phones: 425-747-4600; 800-829-2225. Fax: 425-644-4621.
Web site: http://www.millenniumdigital.com.
County: King. Also serves Ames Lake, Carnation, Redmond, Sahalee, Snoqualmie Valley, Woodinville. ICA: WA0043.
TV Market Ranking: 20. Franchise award date: January 1, 1981. Franchise expiration date: N.A. Began: January 1, 1982.
Channel capacity: 35 (not 2-way capable). Channels available but not in use: 5.
Basic Service
Subscribers: 2,130.
Programming (received off-air): KONG-TV (I) Everett; KCPQ (F), KCTS-TV (P), KING-TV (N), KIRO-TV (C), KOMO-TV (A), KSTW (U), KTBW-TV (T), KTWB (W) Seattle-Tacoma.
Programming (via satellite): A & E; American Movie Classics; Animal Planet; C-SPAN; CNBC; CNN; Discovery Channel; ESPN; Fox Family Channel; Fox Sports Net Northwest; Headline News; History Channel; Home & Garden Television; Learning Channel; Lifetime; MTV; Nashville Network; Nickelodeon; Northwest Cable News; QVC; Sci-Fi Channel; TBS Superstation; Turner Network TV; USA Network; VH1.
Fee: $45.00 installation; $26.95 monthly.
Pay Service 1
Pay Units: N.A.
Programming (via satellite): Disney Channel; HBO; Showtime; The Movie Channel.
Fee: $8.95 monthly (Disney), $14.95 monthly (HBO, Showtime or TMC).
Local advertising: Yes. Available in character-generated programming.
Equipment: Triple Crown & Cadco headend; Pathmaker amplifiers; Times Fiber cable; Atari character generator; Prodelin satellite antenna; Triple Crown satellite receivers.
Miles of plant: 93.1 (coaxial). Homes passed: 2,900.
Manager: Steve Weed. Chief technician: Gene Fry.
Ownership: Millennium Digital Media LLC (MSO). Purchased from Summit Communications Inc., April 7, 1999.

EASTON—Cable Plus, Suite 120, 11400 S.E. 6th St., Bellevue, WA 98004. Phone: 425-462-2090. Fax: 425-462-2092. County: Kittitas West. Also serves Kittitas County (portions). ICA: WA0203.
TV Market Ranking: Outside TV Markets. Franchise award date: April 18, 1989. Franchise expiration date: April 18, 2014. Began: N.A.
Channel capacity: 56. Channels available but not in use: N.A.
Basic Service
Subscribers: 400.
Programming (received off-air): KCTS-TV (P), KING-TV (N), KIRO-TV (C), KOMO-TV (A), KSTW (U) Seattle-Tacoma.
Programming (via satellite): WGN-TV (W) Chicago; A & E; American Movie Classics; Animal Planet; CNBC; CNN; CNN International; CNNfn; Cartoon Network; Country Music TV; Discovery Channel; ESPN; ESPN 2; Fox Family Channel; Fox Sports Net Northwest; FoxNet; Golf Channel; Goodlife TV Network; Headline News; History Channel; Home Shopping Network; Learning Channel; Lifetime; MSNBC; MTV; Nashville Network; Nickelodeon; Northwest Cable News; QVC; TBS Superstation; The Weather Channel; Trinity Bcstg. Network; Turner Classic Movies; Turner Network TV; USA Network; VH1.
Fee: $35.00 installation; $23.95 monthly.
Pay Service 1
Pay Units: 11.
Programming (via satellite): Disney Channel.
Fee: $9.95 monthly.
Pay Service 2
Pay Units: 37.
Programming (via satellite): HBO.
Fee: $11.95 monthly.
Pay Service 3
Pay Units: 11.
Programming (via satellite): Showtime.
Fee: $10.95 monthly.
Miles of plant: 25.0 (coaxial). Homes passed: 522. Total homes in franchised area: 627.
Manager: Gary O'Malley. Chief technician: Dan Adams.
Ownership: Cable Plus (MSO).

EDMONDS—Chambers Cable of Edmonds, Suite 201, 190 W. Dayton St., Edmonds, WA 98020. Phone: 425-774-5146. Fax: 425-775-2299. Counties: King & Snohomish. Also serves Richmond Beach, Shoreline, Snohomish County (southwestern portion), Woodway. ICA: WA0012.
TV Market Ranking: 20 (Edmonds, Richmond Beach, Shoreline, portions of Snohomish County, Woodway); Below 100 (portions of Snohomish County). Franchise award date: N.A. Franchise expiration date: N.A. Began: January 1, 1966.
Channel capacity: 35 (not 2-way capable). Channels available but not in use: None.
Basic Service
Subscribers: 21,000.
Programming (received off-air): KVOS-TV (I) Bellingham; KCPQ (F), KCTS-TV (P), KING-TV (N), KIRO-TV (C), KOMO-TV (A), KSTW (U), KTBW-TV (T), KTWB (W) Seattle-Tacoma; KBTC-TV (P) Tacoma; CBUT Vancouver; 18 FMs.
Programming (via satellite): A & E; American Movie Classics; C-SPAN; CNN; Discovery Channel; ESPN; Fox Family Channel; Fox Sports Net Northwest; Headline News; Knowledge TV; MTV; Nashville Network; Nickelodeon; QVC; TBS Superstation; The Weather Channel; Turner Network TV; USA Network.
Current originations: Local sports.
Fee: $25.00 installation.
Pay Service 1
Pay Units: N.A.
Programming (via satellite): Disney Channel; HBO; Showtime; The Movie Channel.
Fee: $11.95 monthly (Disney), $13.95 monthly (HBO, Showtime or TMC).
Pay-Per-View
Special events.
Fee: Varies.

Local advertising: Yes. Available in satellite distributed programming. Local sales manager: Lonnie Baird.

Equipment: Scientific-Atlanta headend; GTE Sylvania amplifiers; Comm/Scope cable; Sony cameras; Sony VTRs; Quanta character generator; Jerrold set top converters; Eagle traps; M/A-Com satellite antenna; M/A-Com & Scientific-Atlanta satellite receivers.

Miles of plant: 330.0 (coaxial). Homes passed: 30,554.

Manager: Jack Gradwohl. Chief technician: Will Minyard. Marketing director: Kendra Thomlonson.

City fee: Varies.

Ownership: Chambers Communications Corp. (MSO).

ELLENSBURG—Falcon Cable TV, Box 674, 1105 E. 10th Ave., Ellensburg, WA 98926. Phones: 509-925-9210; 509-925-6106. Fax: 509-962-2034. Counties: Kittitas East & Kittitas West. Also serves Kittitas, Kittitas County. ICA: WA0023.

TV Market Ranking: Below 100 (Ellensburg, Kittitas, portions of Kittitas County); Outside TV Markets (portions of Kittitas County). Franchise award date: N.A. Franchise expiration date: January 1, 1999. Began: August 1, 1954.

Channel capacity: 35 (not 2-way capable). Channels available but not in use: None.

Basic Service

Subscribers: 7,683.

Programming (received off-air): KING-TV (N), KIRO-TV (C), KOMO-TV (A), KSTW (U) Seattle-Tacoma; KAPP (A), KCYU-LP (U), KIMA-TV (C), KNDO (N), KYVE-TV (P) Yakima; 3 FMs.

Programming (via satellite): A & E; C-SPAN; Headline News; Home Shopping Network; Learning Channel; Nickelodeon; Northwest Cable News; QVC; TBS Superstation; The Inspirational Network.

Current originations: Public access.

Fee: $46.95 installation; $14.36 monthly.

Expanded Basic Service

Subscribers: 7,073.

Programming (via satellite): CNN; Discovery Channel; ESPN; Fox Family Channel; Fox Sports Net Northwest; Lifetime; MTV; Nashville Network; Turner Network TV; USA Network; VH1.

Fee: $10.32 monthly.

Pay Service 1

Pay Units: 368.

Programming (via satellite): Cinemax.

Fee: $13.95 installation; $11.50 monthly.

Pay Service 2

Pay Units: 610.

Programming (via satellite): Starz!

Fee: $6.75 monthly.

Pay Service 3

Pay Units: 1,040.

Programming (via satellite): HBO.

Fee: $13.95 installation; $11.50 monthly.

Pay Service 4

Pay Units: 357.

Programming (via satellite): Showtime.

Fee: $13.95 installation; $11.50 monthly.

Pay Service 5

Pay Units: 225.

Programming (via satellite): The New Encore.

Fee: $1.75 monthly.

Local advertising: Yes. Local sales manager: Reed Larsen.

Equipment: Scientific-Atlanta headend; Century III & Jerrold amplifiers; Comm/Scope cable; Hamlin, Pioneer & Scientific-Atlanta set top converters; Eagle traps; Anixter-Mark & Scientific-Atlanta satellite antenna; Scientific-Atlanta satellite receivers.

Miles of plant: 135.0 (coaxial); None (fiber optic). Homes passed: 9,722.

Manager: Mary Owens. Chief technician: Ron Graaff. Office manager: Patti Whitman.

City fee: 5% of gross.

Ownership: Falcon Communications LP (MSO). Purchased from Tele-Communications Inc., September 30, 1998. See Cable System Ownership.

ELMER—TCI Cablevision of Washington Inc., Box 1480, Wenatchee, WA 98801. Phones: 509-663-5108; 800-851-0001. County: Okanogan. Also serves Elmer City. ICA: WA0128.

TV Market Ranking: Outside TV Markets. Franchise award date: N.A. Franchise expiration date: N.A. Began: October 1, 1956.

Channel capacity: 18. Channels available but not in use: 1.

Basic Service

Subscribers: 190.

Programming (received off-air): KAYU-TV (F), KHQ-TV (N), KREM-TV (C), KSPS-TV (P), KXLY-TV (A) Spokane; 10 FMs.

Programming (via satellite): CNN; Discovery Channel; Fox Family Channel; Lifetime; MTV; Nashville Network; Nickelodeon; TBS Superstation; The Weather Channel; USA Network.

Current originations: Public access.

Fee: $60.00 installation; $16.54 monthly.

Expanded Basic Service

Subscribers: 183.

Programming (via satellite): American Movie Classics; ESPN; Fox Sports Net Northwest; Turner Network TV.

Fee: $2.00 monthly.

Pay Service 1

Pay Units: 24.

Programming (via satellite): Disney Channel.

Fee: N.A.

Pay Service 2

Pay Units: 73.

Programming (via satellite): The New Encore.

Fee: N.A.

Pay Service 3

Pay Units: 78.

Programming (via satellite): HBO.

Fee: N.A.

Miles of plant: 12.7 (coaxial). Homes passed: 190. Total homes in franchised area: 266.

Manager: Bob Lam.

Ownership: AT&T Broadband & Internet Services (MSO). Purchased from Tele-Communications Inc., March 9, 1999.

ENTIAT—Millennium Digital Media, Suite 107, 3633 136th Place SE, Bellevue, WA 98006. Phones: 425-747-4600; 800-829-2225. Fax: 425-644-4621.

Web site: http://www.millenniumdigital.com.

County: Chelan. ICA: WA0116.

TV Market Ranking: Outside TV Markets. Franchise award date: N.A. Franchise expiration date: N.A. Began: February 1, 1983.

Channel capacity: 35 (2-way capable; operating 2-way). Channels available but not in use: 23.

Basic Service

Subscribers: 137.

Programming (received off-air): KOMO-TV (A) Seattle-Tacoma; KAYU-TV (F), KHQ-TV (N), KREM-TV (C), KSPS-TV (P), KXLY-TV (A) Spokane.

Programming (via microwave): TVW.

Programming (via satellite): WGN-TV (W) Chicago; A & E; American Movie Classics; CNN; Cartoon Network; Country Music TV; Discovery Channel; Disney Channel; E! Entertainment TV; ESPN; Fox Family Channel; Fox Sports Net Northwest; Headline News; History Channel; Learning Channel; Nashville Network; Northwest Cable News; QVC; TBS Superstation; TV Guide Channel; Turner Classic Movies; Turner Network TV; USA Network.

Current originations: Public access; government access.

Fee: $45.00 installation; $27.95 monthly; $20.00 additional installation.

Pay Service 1

Pay Units: N.A.

Programming (via satellite): HBO.

Fee: $14.95 monthly.

Equipment: M/A-Com headend; Pathmaker amplifiers; Times Fiber cable; Prodelin satellite antenna; M/A-Com satellite receivers.

Miles of plant: 8.5 (coaxial). Homes passed: 250.

Manager: Steve Weed. Chief technician: Gene Fry.

City fee: 1% of gross.

Ownership: Millennium Digital Media LLC (MSO). Purchased from Summit Communications Inc., April 7, 1999.

EPHRATA—Northland Cable TV, Box T, Moses Lake, WA 98837. Phone: 509-765-6151. County: Grant. Also serves Grant County, Soap Lake. ICA: WA0039.

TV Market Ranking: Below 100 (Ephrata, portions of Grant County); Outside TV Markets (portions of Grant County, Soap Lake). Franchise award date: N.A. Franchise expiration date: N.A. Began: January 1, 1953.

Channel capacity: 36 (2-way capable). Channels available but not in use: N.A.

Basic Service

Subscribers: 2,771.

Programming (received off-air): KAYU-TV (F), KHQ-TV (N), KREM-TV (C), KSPS-TV (P), KXLY-TV (A) Spokane; 14 FMs.

Programming (via microwave): KING-TV (N), KIRO-TV (C), KOMO-TV (A) Seattle-Tacoma; CHEK-TV Victoria.

Programming (via satellite): WGN-TV (W) Chicago; C-SPAN; C-SPAN 2; CNN; Discovery Channel; ESPN; Fox Family Channel; Headline News; Lifetime; MTV; Nashville Network; Nickelodeon; QVC; TBS Superstation; The Inspirational Network; The Weather Channel; Turner Network TV; USA Network.

Current originations: Automated timeweather.

Fee: $45.00 installation; $15.98 monthly; $2.20 converter; $10.00 additional installation.

Pay Service 1

Pay Units: Included with Moses Lake, WA.

Programming (via satellite): Cinemax; Disney Channel; HBO; Showtime; The Movie Channel.

Fee: $8.70 monthly (Disney), $9.15 monthly (Cinemax), $9.25 monthly (Showtime), $10.95 monthly (TMC), $12.30 monthly (HBO).

Local advertising: Yes. Available in character-generated programming. Regional interconnect: Cabletime.

Equipment: Scientific-Atlanta & RCA headend; Magnavox amplifiers; Comm/Scope cable; Video Data Systems character generator; Oak set top converters; Pico traps; Scientific-Atlanta & Microdyne satellite antenna; Scientific-Atlanta, Microdyne & Standard Communications satellite receivers.

Miles of plant: 44.8 (coaxial). Homes passed: 3,116. Total homes in franchised area: 3,200.

Manager: Dawn Hill. Chief technician: Kim Svetich.

City fee: 8% of gross.

Ownership: Northland Communications Corp. (MSO).

FAIRCHILD AFB—Fibervision Inc., Box 1320, Fairchild AFB, WA 99011. Phone: 800-628-6060. County: Spokane. Also serves Airway Heights. ICA: WA0153.

TV Market Ranking: 76. Franchise award date: N.A. Franchise expiration date: N.A. Began: September 1, 1981.

Channel capacity: 35. Channels available but not in use: N.A.

Basic Service

Subscribers: 2,200.

Programming (received off-air): KAYU-TV (F), KHQ-TV (N), KREM-TV (C), KSPS-TV (P), KXLY-TV (A) Spokane.

Programming (via satellite): WGN-TV (W) Chicago; CNN; ESPN; MTV; Nashville Network; TBS Superstation; USA Network.

Fee: $12.95 installation; $8.95 monthly.

Pay Service 1

Pay Units: N.A.

Programming (via satellite): Cinemax; Disney Channel; HBO.

Fee: $8.50 monthly (each).

Miles of plant: 77.0 (coaxial).

Manager: Keith Antcliff.

Ownership: The Hilliard Group (MSO).

FAIRFIELD—Northwest Cable LP, Box 618, Lockney, TX 79241-0618. Phone: 800-480-3766. Fax: 806-652-3139. County: Spokane. Also serves Rockford. ICA: WA0129.

TV Market Ranking: 76. Franchise award date: N.A. Franchise expiration date: N.A. Began: January 12, 1983.

Channel capacity: 24 (2-way capable; operating 2-way). Channels available but not in use: 12.

Basic Service

Subscribers: N.A.

Programming (received off-air): KWSU-TV (P) Pullman; KAYU-TV (F), KHQ-TV (N), KREM-TV (C), KSPS-TV (P), KXLY-TV (A) Spokane.

Programming (via satellite): ESPN; Fox Family Channel; Headline News; TBS Superstation; USA Network.

Planned originations: Government access.

Fee: $25.00 installation; $12.00 monthly.

Pay Service 1

Pay Units: N.A.

Programming (via satellite): HBO.

Fee: $10.00 monthly.

Equipment: Scientific-Atlanta headend; Magnavox amplifiers; Comm/Scope cable; Pico traps; Anixter-Mark satellite antenna; Scientific-Atlanta satellite receivers.

Miles of plant: 5.0 (coaxial). Homes passed: 190. Total homes in franchised area: 190.

Manager: Kenneth V. Mettler. Chief technician: Joseph R. Poire.

City fee: 3% of gross.

Ownership: Northwest Cable Ltd. Partnership (MSO).

FERNDALE—TCI Cablevision of Washington Inc., 777 W. Horton Rd., Bellingham, WA 98226-7606. Phone: 360-384-1581. Fax: 306-647-8967. County: Whatcom. Also serves Lummi Indian Reservation. ICA: WA0025.

TV Market Ranking: Below 100. Franchise award date: N.A. Franchise expiration date: N.A. Began: July 1, 1965.

Channel capacity: 38 (not 2-way capable). Channels available but not in use: N.A.

Basic Service

Subscribers: 9,019.

Programming (received off-air): KVOS-TV (I) Bellingham; CBUT, CHAN-TV Vancouver; allband FM.
Programming (via microwave): KCPQ (F), KCTS-TV (P), KING-TV (N), KIRO-TV (C), KOMO-TV (A), KSTW (U) Seattle-Tacoma.
Programming (via satellite): C-SPAN; CNBC; CNN; Discovery Channel; Fox Family Channel; Headline News; Lifetime; Nashville Network; Nickelodeon; Odyssey; QVC; TBS Superstation; The Weather Channel.
Fee: $60.00 installation; $10.33 monthly; $0.91 converter; $40.00 additional installation.

Expanded Basic Service
Subscribers: 4,562.
Programming (via satellite): American Movie Classics; ESPN; Fox Sports Net Northwest; Turner Network TV; USA Network.
Fee: $10.34 monthly.

Pay Service 1
Pay Units: 547.
Programming (via satellite): Disney Channel.
Fee: N.A.

Pay Service 2
Pay Units: 1,708.
Programming (via satellite): The New Encore.
Fee: N.A.

Pay Service 3
Pay Units: 952.
Programming (via satellite): HBO.
Fee: $35.00 installation; $13.15 monthly.

Pay Service 4
Pay Units: 416.
Programming (via satellite): Showtime.
Fee: $35.00 installation; $13.15 monthly.

Local advertising: Yes.
Program Guide: The Cable Guide.
Equipment: Scientific-Atlanta headend; Magnavox amplifiers; Times Fiber cable; Hamlin set top converters; Antenna Technology & Simulsat satellite antenna; Scientific-Atlanta satellite receivers.
Miles of plant: 152.6 (coaxial).
Manager: Dan Crocker.
City fee: 3% of gross.
Ownership: AT&T Broadband & Internet Services (MSO). Purchased from Tele-Communications Inc., March 9, 1999.

FORKS—Millennium Digital Media, Suite 107, 3633 136th Place SE, Bellevue, WA 98006. Phones: 425-747-4600; 800-829-2225. Fax: 425-644-4621.
Web site: http://www.millenniumdigital.com.
County: Clallam. Also serves Beaver, Clallam County (southeastern portion), Lake Creek. ICA: WA0048.
TV Market Ranking: Outside TV Markets. Franchise award date: N.A. Franchise expiration date: May 23, 2008. Began: December 30, 1965.
Channel capacity: 21. Channels available but not in use: 3.

Basic Service
Subscribers: 1,750.
Programming (received off-air): KVOS-TV (I) Bellingham; KCPQ (F), KCTS-TV (P), KING-TV (N), KIRO-TV (C), KOMO-TV (A), KSTW (U) Seattle-Tacoma; CBUT Vancouver; CHEK-TV Victoria; allband FM.
Programming (via satellite): WGN-TV (W) Chicago; A & E; American Movie Classics; CNN; Cartoon Network; Discovery Channel; Disney Channel; ESPN; Fox Family Channel; Fox Sports Net Northwest; History Channel; Learning Channel; Nashville Network; Northwest Cable News; QVC; TBS Superstation; TV Guide Channel; Telemundo; Turner Classic Movies; Turner Network TV; USA Network.
Current originations: Public access.
Fee: $45.00 installation; $29.95 monthly.

Pay Service 1
Pay Units: N.A.
Programming (via satellite): Cinemax; HBO; Showtime.
Fee: $14.95 monthly (each).

Local advertising: Yes. Rates: $40.00/Month; $15.00/Week. Local sales manager: Christi Baron.
Equipment: Catel, Jerrold & Scientific-Atlanta headend; Magnavox amplifiers; Phelps-Dodge cable; Scientific-Atlanta satellite antenna.
Miles of plant: 61.5 (coaxial). Homes passed: 2,300.
Manager: Steve Weed. Chief technician: Gene Fry.
City fee: None.
Ownership: Millennium Digital Media LLC (MSO). Purchased from Summit Communications Inc., April 7, 1999.

FREELAND—TCI Cablevision of Washington Inc., Suite B, 11515 State Ave., Marysville, WA 98271-7245. Phone: 360-659-1285. County: Island. Also serves Island County, Mutiny Bay. ICA: WA0053.
TV Market Ranking: 20 (Freeland, portions of Island County, Mutiny Bay); Below 100 (portions of Island County); Outside TV Markets (portions of Island County). Franchise award date: N.A. Franchise expiration date: January 1, 2003. Began: June 1, 1978.
Channel capacity: 62. Channels available but not in use: 32.

Basic Service
Subscribers: 916.
Programming (received off-air): KVOS-TV (I) Bellingham; KCPQ (F), KCTS-TV (P), KING-TV (N), KIRO-TV (C), KOMO-TV (A), KSTW (U), KTBW-TV (T), KTWB (W) Seattle-Tacoma; CBUT Vancouver; allband FM.
Programming (via satellite): C-SPAN; CNN; Discovery Channel; Fox Family Channel; Lifetime; Nashville Network; Nickelodeon; QVC; TBS Superstation; The Weather Channel.
Fee: $60.00 installation; $10.66 monthly.

Expanded Basic Service
Subscribers: 766.
Programming (via satellite): American Movie Classics; Court TV; ESPN; Fox Sports Net Northwest; Turner Network TV; USA Network.
Fee: $12.55 monthly.

Pay Service 1
Pay Units: 65.
Programming (via satellite): Disney Channel.
Fee: N.A.

Pay Service 2
Pay Units: 159.
Programming (via satellite): The New Encore.
Fee: N.A.

Pay Service 3
Pay Units: 118.
Programming (via satellite): HBO.
Fee: $12.66 monthly.

Pay Service 4
Pay Units: 91.
Programming (via satellite): Showtime.
Fee: $12.66 monthly.

Equipment: Blonder-Tongue headend; Jerrold amplifiers; Cerro & Times Fiber cable.
Miles of plant: 64.6 (coaxial). Homes passed: 1,931. Total homes in franchised area: 2,177.
Manager: John Sheehan.
County fee: 4% of gross.
Ownership: AT&T Broadband & Internet Services (MSO). Purchased from Tele-Communications Inc., March 9, 1999.

FRIDAY HARBOR—Century Communications, Box 549, 570 Guard St., Friday Harbor, WA 98250-8044. Phones: 360-378-4225; 800-626-6299. Fax: 360-378-6101. Web site: http://www.centurycomm.com. County: San Juan. Also serves San Juan County (portions). ICA: WA0084.
TV Market Ranking: Below 100. Franchise award date: N.A. Franchise expiration date: N.A. Began: December 15, 1974.
Channel capacity: 50 (2-way capable; operating 2-way). Channels available but not in use: None.

Basic Service
Subscribers: 1,261.
Programming (received off-air): KVOS-TV (I) Bellingham; KCPQ (F), KCTS-TV (P), KING-TV (N), KIRO-TV (C), KOMO-TV (A), KSTW (U), KTWB (W) Seattle-Tacoma; CBUT, CKVU-TV Vancouver; CHEK-TV Victoria; allband FM.
Programming (via satellite): C-SPAN; QVC; TBS Superstation; The Inspirational Network.
Fee: $30.75 installation; $16.98 monthly; $23.00 additional installation.

Expanded Basic Service
Subscribers: N.A.
Programming (via satellite): A & E; CNBC; CNN; Cartoon Network; Comedy Central; Country Music TV; Discovery Channel; Disney Channel; E! Entertainment TV; ESPN; ESPN 2; FX; Fox Family Channel; Fox News Channel; Fox Sports Net Northwest; Headline News; History Channel; Learning Channel; Lifetime; MTV; Nashville Network; Nick at Nite's TV Land; Nickelodeon; Northwest Cable News; Sci-Fi Channel; The Weather Channel; Turner Classic Movies; Turner Network TV; USA Network; VH1.
Fee: $28.35 monthly.

Pay Service 1
Pay Units: 63.
Programming (via satellite): The Movie Channel.
Fee: $10.95 monthly.

Pay Service 2
Pay Units: 136.
Programming (via satellite): HBO.
Fee: $10.00 installation; $10.95 monthly.

Pay Service 3
Pay Units: 96.
Programming (via satellite): Showtime.
Fee: $10.95 monthly.

Equipment: Scientific-Atlanta headend; Jerrold amplifiers; Times Fiber cable; Sony cameras; Sony VTRs; Video Data Systems character generator; Standard Components set top converters; Microwave Assoc. satellite antenna.
Miles of plant: 50.0 (coaxial); None (fiber optic). Homes passed: 1,447. Total homes in franchised area: 1,447.
Manager: Jim Elliot. Marketing director: Steve Delgado. Office manager: Randy Lindsey.
City fee: 3% of gross.
Ownership: Century Communications Corp. (MSO). See Cable System Ownership.

GARFIELD—Northwest Cable LP, Box 618, Lockney, TX 79241. Phone: 800-480-3766. Fax: 806-652-3139. County: Whitman. ICA: WA0117.
TV Market Ranking: Below 100. Franchise award date: N.A. Franchise expiration date: April 28, 1998. Began: January 16, 1984.
Channel capacity: 20. Channels available but not in use: 8.

Basic Service
Subscribers: 184.
Programming (received off-air): KWSU-TV (P) Pullman; KAYU-TV (F), KHQ-TV (N), KREM-TV (C), KSPS-TV (P), KXLY-TV (A) Spokane.
Programming (via satellite): ESPN; Fox Family Channel; Headline News; USA Network.
Fee: $25.00 installation; $12.00 monthly.

Pay Service 1
Pay Units: N.A.
Programming (via satellite): HBO.
Fee: $10.00 installation; $10.00 monthly.

Miles of plant: 5.0 (coaxial). Homes passed: 250.
Manager: Kenneth V. Mettler. Chief technician: Joseph R. Poire.
City fee: 3% of gross.
Ownership: Northwest Cable Ltd. Partnership (MSO).

GLENOMA—Millennium Digital Media, Suite 107, 3633 136th Place SE, Bellevue, WA 98006. Phones: 425-747-4600; 800-829-2225. Fax: 425-644-4621.
Web site: http://www.millenniumdigital.com.
County: Lewis. Also serves Randle. ICA: WA0208.
TV Market Ranking: Outside TV Markets. Franchise award date: N.A. Franchise expiration date: N.A. Began: N.A.
Channel capacity: N.A. Channels available but not in use: N.A.

Basic Service
Subscribers: N.A.
Programming (received off-air): KCTS-TV (P), KING-TV (N), KIRO-TV (C), KOMO-TV (A) Seattle-Tacoma.
Programming (via satellite): WGN-TV (W) Chicago; A & E; American Movie Classics; CNN; Discovery Channel; Disney Channel; E! Entertainment TV; ESPN; Fox Family Channel; Fox Sports Net Northwest; Fox-Net; Headline News; History Channel; Home & Garden Television; Learning Channel; Lifetime; Nashville Network; Nickelodeon; Northwest Cable News; QVC; Sci-Fi Channel; TBS Superstation; TV Guide Channel; Trinity Bcstg. Network; Turner Classic Movies; Turner Network TV; USA Network.
Current originations: Public access.
Fee: $29.95 monthly.

Pay Service 1
Pay Units: N.A.
Programming (via satellite): HBO; Showtime.
Fee: $14.95 monthly (each).

Manager: Steve Weed. Chief technician: Gene Fry.
Ownership: Millennium Digital Media LLC (MSO). Purchased from Summit Communications Inc., April 7, 1999.

GOLDENDALE—Columbia Basin Cable, Box 490, 611 6th St., Umatilla, OR 97882. Phones: 541-922-5759; 800-521-3916. Fax: 541-922-3758. County: Klickitat. ICA: WA0063.

TV Market Ranking: Outside TV Markets. Franchise award date: N.A. Franchise expiration date: N.A. Began: July 1, 1960.

Channel capacity: 45. Channels available but not in use: 6.

Basic Service

Subscribers: 1,235.

Programming (received off-air): KATU (A), KGW (N), KOIN (C), KOPB-TV (P), KPTV (U) Portland; KING-TV (N), KOMO-TV (A) Seattle-Tacoma; KPDX (F) Vancouver; allband FM.

Programming (via microwave): TVW.

Programming (via satellite): WGN-TV (W) Chicago; TBS Superstation; TV Guide Channel.

Fee: $35.00 installation; $17.95 monthly.

Expanded Basic Service

Subscribers: 1,109.

Programming (via satellite): A & E; Animal Planet; CNN; Comedy Central; Discovery Channel; ESPN; FX; fXM: Movies from Fox; Fox Family Channel; Fox News Channel; Fox Sports Net Northwest; Goodlife TV Network; Headline News; History Channel; Home & Garden Television; Home Shopping Network; Learning Channel; Nashville Network; Nickelodeon; QVC; The Weather Channel; Turner Classic Movies; Turner Network TV; USA Network; VH1.

Fee: $29.95 monthly.

Pay Service 1

Pay Units: 72.

Programming (via satellite): Disney Channel.

Fee: $9.95 monthly.

Pay Service 2

Pay Units: 263.

Programming (via satellite): HBO (multiplexed).

Fee: $10.95 monthly.

Pay Service 3

Pay Units: 176.

Programming (via satellite): Starz!; The New Encore (multiplexed).

Fee: $7.95 monthly.

Pay-Per-View

Planned.

Local advertising: Yes. Available in character-generated programming. Rates: $1.30/Day.

Equipment: Blonder-Tongue headend; Cascade & Vikoa amplifiers; Times Fiber cable; Scientific-Atlanta set top converters; Scientific-Atlanta & Standard Components satellite receivers.

Miles of plant: 87.0 (coaxial); None (fiber optic). Homes passed: 1,450. Total homes in franchised area: 1,500.

Manager: Kerry Stratton. Chief technician: Darrell Johnson. Marketing director: Charlotte Winkler. Customer service manager: Jane Allan.

City fee: 3% of gross.

Ownership: USA Media Group LLC (MSO). Purchased from Cambridge Communications, May 15, 1999.

GRAND COULEE—TCI Cablevision of Washington Inc., 1140 N. 94th St., Seattle, WA 98103-3306. Phone: 206-527-7545. Counties: Grant & Okanogan. Also serves Belvidere, Electric City, Koontzville. ICA: WA0154.

TV Market Ranking: Outside TV Markets. Franchise award date: N.A. Franchise expiration date: N.A. Began: August 1, 1980.

Channel capacity: 35. Channels available but not in use: 16.

Basic Service

Subscribers: 944.

Programming (received off-air): Allband FM.

Programming (via microwave): KAYU-TV (F), KHQ-TV (N), KREM-TV (C), KSPS-TV (P), KXLY-TV (A) Spokane.

Programming (via satellite): CNN; Discovery Channel; Fox Family Channel; Lifetime; MTV; Nashville Network; Nickelodeon; TBS Superstation; The Weather Channel.

Current originations: Automated time-weather; public access.

Fee: $60.00 installation; $10.25 monthly; $40.00 additional installation.

Expanded Basic Service

Subscribers: 678.

Programming (via satellite): American Movie Classics; ESPN; Fox Sports Net Northwest; Turner Network TV; USA Network.

Fee: $10.91 monthly.

Pay Service 1

Pay Units: 73.

Programming (via satellite): Disney Channel.

Fee: N.A.

Pay Service 2

Pay Units: 306.

Programming (via satellite): The New Encore.

Fee: N.A.

Pay Service 3

Pay Units: 284.

Programming (via satellite): HBO.

Fee: $13.15 monthly.

Equipment: Blonder-Tongue headend; Magnavox amplifiers; composite cable.

Miles of plant: 24.5 (coaxial). Total homes in franchised area: 1,094.

Manager: Bob Lam. Chief technician: Marty Adams.

City fee: None.

Ownership: AT&T Broadband & Internet Services (MSO). Purchased from Tele-Communications Inc., March 9, 1999.

GRANDVIEW—TCI Cablevision of Yakima Valley Inc., 1005 N. 16th Ave., Yakima, WA 98902-1351. Phone: 509-575-1690. Fax: 509-575-1754. County: Yakima. ICA: WA0047.

TV Market Ranking: Below 100. Franchise award date: N.A. Franchise expiration date: N.A. Began: March 1, 1979.

Channel capacity: 30. Channels available but not in use: N.A.

Basic Service

Subscribers: 1,529.

Programming (received off-air): KAPP (A), KIMA-TV (C), KNDO (N), KYVE-TV (P) Yakima.

Programming (via microwave): KSTW (U) Seattle-Tacoma.

Programming (via satellite): WGN-TV (W) Chicago; CNN; Discovery Channel; Fox Family Channel; GalaVision; Headline News; MTV; Nashville Network; Nickelodeon; TBS Superstation; Univision.

Fee: $60.00 installation; $19.00 monthly; $40.00 additional installation.

Expanded Basic Service

Subscribers: N.A.

Programming (via satellite): American Movie Classics; ESPN; Fox Sports Net Northwest; Turner Network TV; USA Network.

Fee: $2.00 monthly.

Pay Service 1

Pay Units: 39.

Programming (via satellite): Cinemax.

Fee: $12.05 monthly.

Pay Service 2

Pay Units: 67.

Programming (via satellite): Disney Channel.

Fee: N.A.

Pay Service 3

Pay Units: 424.

Programming (via satellite): The New Encore.

Fee: N.A.

Pay Service 4

Pay Units: 149.

Programming (via satellite): HBO.

Fee: $12.05 monthly.

Pay Service 5

Pay Units: 60.

Programming (via satellite): Showtime.

Fee: $12.05 monthly.

Miles of plant: 21.9 (coaxial). Homes passed: 2,391. Total homes in franchised area: 2,500.

Manager: Gary Bailey. Marketing director: Shelley Bjornson.

Ownership: AT&T Broadband & Internet Services (MSO). Purchased from Tele-Communications Inc., March 9, 1999.

GREENBANK—Cable Services, Box 855, Coupeville, WA 98239. Phone: 360-678-3712. County: Island. ICA: WA0189.

TV Market Ranking: 20. Franchise award date: N.A. Franchise expiration date: N.A. Began: June 2, 1993.

Channel capacity: 24. Channels available but not in use: None.

Basic Service

Subscribers: 57.

Programming (received off-air): KVOS-TV (I) Bellingham; KCPQ (F), KING-TV (N), KIRO-TV (C), KOMO-TV (A), KTWB (W) Seattle-Tacoma; CBUT Vancouver; CHEK-TV Victoria.

Programming (via satellite): A & E; CNBC; CNN; Discovery Channel; ESPN; Fox Family Channel; Headline News; Lifetime; Nashville Network; QVC; TBS Superstation; The Weather Channel; Turner Classic Movies.

Fee: $55.00 installation; $19.50 monthly.

Pay Service 1

Pay Units: 30.

Programming (via satellite): HBO.

Fee: $11.95 monthly.

Miles of plant: 4.0 (coaxial). Homes passed: 300.

Manager: Hershel Wayne Freeman. Office manager: Laurie Freeman.

Ownership: Hershel W. Freeman.

GUEMES ISLAND—Index Cable TV Inc., 1781 Old Hwy. 99 N, Burlington, WA 98233. Phone: 360-724-3802. Fax: 360-724-2006. County: Skagit. Also serves Skagit County (portions). ICA: WA0207.

TV Market Ranking: Outside TV Markets. Franchise award date: N.A. Franchise expiration date: N.A. Began: August 8, 1994.

Channel capacity: 36 (not 2-way capable). Channels available but not in use: N.A.

Basic Service

Subscribers: 177.

Programming (received off-air): KVOS-TV (I) Bellingham; KONG-TV (I) Everett; KCPQ (F), KCTS-TV (P), KING-TV (N), KIRO-TV (C), KOMO-TV (A), KSTW (U), KTWB (W) Seattle-Tacoma; CBUT, CKVU-TV Vancouver; CHEK-TV Victoria.

Programming (via satellite): WGN-TV (W) Chicago; A & E; C-SPAN; CNN; Discovery Channel; E! Entertainment TV; ESPN; Fox Family Channel; Fox Sports Net Northwest; Goodlife TV Network; Headline News; History Channel; Knowledge TV; Nashville Network; Northwest Cable News; TBS Superstation; Trinity Bcstg. Network; Turner Network TV; USA Network.

Fee: $39.95 installation; $23.00 monthly.

Pay Service 1

Pay Units: 10.

Programming (via satellite): HBO.

Fee: $9.95 monthly.

Miles of plant: 13.1 (coaxial); None (fiber optic). Homes passed: 220. Total homes in franchised area: 230.

Manager: Ed Varhaug.

Ownership: Index Cable TV Inc. (MSO).

HANSVILLE—North Star Cable Inc., Box 880, Kingston, WA 98346. Phone: 360-297-2295. County: Kitsap. ICA: WA0097.

TV Market Ranking: 20. Franchise award date: N.A. Franchise expiration date: N.A. Began: June 1, 1983.

Channel capacity: 40 (not 2-way capable). Channels available but not in use: 2.

Basic Service

Subscribers: 390.

Programming (received off-air): KONG-TV (I) Everett; KTBN-TV (T) Santa Ana; KCPQ (F), KCTS-TV (P), KING-TV (N), KIRO-TV (C), KOMO-TV (A), KSTW (U), KTWB (W) Seattle-Tacoma.

Fee: $40.00 installation; $27.50 monthly.

Expanded Basic Service

Subscribers: 387.

Programming (via satellite): A & E; American Movie Classics; Bloomberg Information TV; C-SPAN; CNN; Discovery Channel; Disney Channel; ESPN; Fox Family Channel; Fox Sports Net Northwest; Headline News; History Channel; Home & Garden Television; Learning Channel; Lifetime; Nashville Network; Nickelodeon; Northwest Cable News; Odyssey; QVC; Sci-Fi Channel; TBS Superstation; Turner Classic Movies; Turner Network TV; USA Network.

Fee: $40.00 installation; $30.00 monthly.

Pay Service 1

Pay Units: 46.

Programming (via satellite): HBO.

Fee: $11.75 monthly.

Miles of plant: 15.0 (coaxial); None (fiber optic). Homes passed: 748.

Manager: Bob Smiley.

Ownership: NorthStar Cable Inc. (MSO).

HARRINGTON—Northwest Cable LP, Box 618, Lockney, TX 79241-0618. Phone: 800-480-3766. Fax: 806-652-3139. County: Lincoln. ICA: WA0120.

TV Market Ranking: Outside TV Markets. Franchise award date: N.A. Franchise expiration date: N.A. Began: May 31, 1983.

Channel capacity: 24 (2-way capable; operating 2-way). Channels available but not in use: 12.

Basic Service

Subscribers: 148.

Programming (received off-air): KWSU-TV (P) Pullman; KAYU-TV (F), KHQ-TV (N), KREM-TV (C), KSPS-TV (P), KXLY-TV (A) Spokane.

Programming (via satellite): ESPN; Fox Family Channel; Headline News; USA Network.

Planned originations: Government access.

Fee: $25.00 installation; $12.00 monthly.

Pay Service 1

Pay Units: N.A.

Programming (via satellite): HBO.

Fee: $10.00 monthly.

Equipment: Scientific-Atlanta headend; Magnavox amplifiers; Comm/Scope cable; Pico traps; Anixter-Mark satellite antenna; Scientific-Atlanta satellite receivers.

Miles of plant: 5.0 (coaxial). Homes passed: 234. Total homes in franchised area: 234.

Manager: Kenneth V. Mettler. Chief technician: Joseph R. Poire.

City fee: 3% of gross.
Ownership: Northwest Cable Ltd. Partnership (MSO).

HOLLY—Falcon Video Communications, 4519 S.E. Mile Hill Dr., Port Orchard, WA 98366. Phone: 360-871-4043. County: Kitsap. ICA: WA0198.
TV Market Ranking: 20. Franchise award date: N.A. Franchise expiration date: N.A. Began: N.A.
Channel capacity: 7. Channels available but not in use: 1.
Basic Service
Subscribers: 43.
Programming (received off-air): KCPQ (F), KCTS-TV (P), KING-TV (N), KIRO-TV (C), KOMO-TV (A), KSTW (U) Seattle-Tacoma.
Fee: $17.95 monthly.
Miles of plant: 4.0 (coaxial); None (fiber optic). Homes passed: 76.
Chief technician: Richard Rumrill.
Ownership: Falcon Communications LP (MSO), joint venture formed September 30, 1998. See Cable System Ownership.

HOOD CANAL—Interstate Cable Inc., Box 2687, Salina, KS 67402-2687. Phones: 785-452-9409; 800-888-4788. Fax: 785-238-7190. County: Jefferson. Also serves Bridgehaven. ICA: WA0199.
TV Market Ranking: 20. Franchise award date: N.A. Franchise expiration date: N.A. Began: N.A.
Channel capacity: N.A. Channels available but not in use: N.A.
Basic Service
Subscribers: 84.
Programming (received off-air): KVOS-TV (I) Bellingham; KCPQ (F), KCTS-TV (P), KING-TV (N), KIRO-TV (C), KOMO-TV (A), KSTW (U), KTBW-TV (T), KTWB (W) Seattle-Tacoma; KBTC-TV (P) Tacoma.
Programming (via satellite): WGN-TV (W) Chicago; A & E; C-SPAN; CNBC; CNN; Comedy Central; Discovery Channel; ESPN; Fox Sports Net Northwest; Headline News; Home Shopping Network; Learning Channel; Lifetime; Nashville Network; QVC; TBS Superstation; Turner Network TV; USA Network.
Fee: $50.00 installation; $20.95 monthly.
Pay Service 1
Pay Units: N.A.
Programming (via satellite): Disney Channel; HBO; The New Encore.
Fee: $6.95 monthly (Encore), $7.95 monthly (Disney), $11.00 monthly (HBO).
Homes passed: 115.
Manager: Kenneth Trimble.
Ownership: Tristar Cable Inc. (MSO).

INDEX—Index Cable TV Inc., 1781 Old Hwy. 99 N, Burlington, WA 98233. Phone: 360-724-3802. Fax: 360-724-2006. County: Snohomish. Also serves Snohomish County. ICA: WA0193.
TV Market Ranking: Outside TV Markets. Franchise award date: July 6, 1988. Franchise expiration date: July 6, 2003. Began: January 1, 1989.
Channel capacity: 36 (not 2-way capable). Channels available but not in use: N.A.
Basic Service
Subscribers: 108.
Programming (received off-air): KCTS-TV (P), KING-TV (N), KIRO-TV (C), KOMO-TV (A) Seattle-Tacoma.
Programming (via satellite): WGN-TV (W) Chicago; A & E; C-SPAN; CNN; Discovery Channel; E! Entertainment TV; ESPN; Fox Family Channel; Fox Sports Net Northwest; FoxNet; Headline News; History Channel; Knowledge TV; Nashville Network; Sci-Fi Channel; TBS Superstation; Trinity Bcstg. Network; Turner Network TV; USA Network.
Fee: $39.95 installation; $21.50 monthly; $4.00 converter.
Pay Service 1
Pay Units: 24.
Programming (via satellite): HBO.
Fee: $10.95 monthly.
Miles of plant: 6.3 (coaxial); None (fiber optic). Homes passed: 200. Total homes in franchised area: 250.
Manager: Dan Collins.
Ownership: Index Cable TV Inc. (MSO).

IONE—Community Cable Service, 729 S. Bernard St., Spokane, WA 99204. Phones: 509-624-4140; 800-572-0902. Fax: 509-624-7372. County: Pend Oreille. ICA: WA0155.
TV Market Ranking: Outside TV Markets. Franchise award date: N.A. Franchise expiration date: N.A. Began: December 1, 1978.
Channel capacity: 62 (2-way capable; not operating 2-way). Channels available but not in use: N.A.
Basic Service
Subscribers: 222.
Programming (received off-air): KAYU-TV (F), KHQ-TV (N), KREM-TV (C), KSPS-TV (P), KXLY-TV (A) Spokane.
Programming (via satellite): WGN-TV (W) Chicago; A & E; American Movie Classics; Bravo; C-SPAN; C-SPAN 2; CNBC; CNN; CNN International; Cartoon Network; Comedy Central; Country Music TV; Discovery Channel; E! Entertainment TV; ESPN; ESPN 2; ESPNews; EWTN; Fox Family Channel; Fox News Channel; Fox Sports Net Northwest; Goodlife TV Network; Headline News; History Channel; Home & Garden Television; Home Shopping Network; Knowledge TV; Learning Channel; Lifetime; MTV; Nashville Network; Nick at Nite's TV Land; Nickelodeon; Odyssey; QVC; Sci-Fi Channel; TBS Superstation; TV Food Network; The Health Network; The Inspirational Network; Travel Channel; Trinity Bcstg. Network; Turner Classic Movies; Turner Network TV; USA Network; VH1; ValueVision; Z Music Television.
Current originations: Automated time-weather.
Fee: $15.00 installation; $25.60 monthly.
Pay Service 1
Pay Units: 57.
Programming (via satellite): HBO.
Fee: $5.00 installation; $9.11 monthly.
Pay Service 2
Pay Units: 48.
Programming (via satellite): Disney Channel.
Fee: $5.00 installation; $5.04 monthly.
Pay Service 3
Pay Units: 68.
Programming (via satellite): Cinemax.
Fee: $5.00 installation; $6.06 monthly.
Pay Service 4
Pay Units: N.A.
Programming (via satellite): Showtime.
Fee: $7.64 monthly.
Miles of plant: 49.0 (coaxial); None (fiber optic). Homes passed: 348.
Manager: Martin Howser.
Ownership: Martin Howser (MSO).

KAHLOTUS—Community Cable Service, 729 S. Bernard St., Spokane, WA 99204. Phones: 509-624-4140; 800-572-0902. Fax: 509-624-7372. County: Franklin. ICA: WA0140.
TV Market Ranking: Below 100. Franchise award date: N.A. Franchise expiration date: N.A. Began: January 1, 1955.
Channel capacity: N.A. Channels available but not in use: N.A.
Basic Service
Subscribers: 64.
Programming (received off-air): KBWU-LP (I) Pasco; KEPR-TV (C), KNDU (N) Pasco-Kennewick-Richland; KHQ-TV (N), KSPS-TV (P), KXLY-TV (A) Spokane; allband FM.
Programming (via satellite): WGN-TV (W) Chicago; A & E; American Movie Classics; Bravo; C-SPAN; C-SPAN 2; CNBC; CNN; CNN International; Cartoon Network; Comedy Central; Country Music TV; Discovery Channel; E! Entertainment TV; ESPN; ESPN 2; ESPNews; EWTN; Fox Family Channel; Fox News Channel; Fox Sports Net Northwest; GalaVision; Goodlife TV Network; Headline News; History Channel; Home & Garden Television; Home Shopping Network; Knowledge TV; Learning Channel; Lifetime; MTV; Nashville Network; Nick at Nite's TV Land; Nickelodeon; Odyssey; QVC; Sci-Fi Channel; TBS Superstation; TV Food Network; The Health Network; Travel Channel; Trinity Bcstg. Network; Turner Classic Movies; Turner Network TV; USA Network; Univision; VH1; ValueVision; Z Music Television.
Fee: $15.00 installation; $19.94 monthly.
Pay Service 1
Pay Units: 16.
Programming (via satellite): Disney Channel.
Fee: $5.00 installation; $5.24 monthly.
Pay Service 2
Pay Units: 25.
Programming (via satellite): HBO.
Fee: $5.00 installation; $9.47 monthly.
Pay Service 3
Pay Units: N.A.
Programming (via satellite): Cinemax; Showtime.
Fee: $6.30 monthly (Cinemax), $7.94 monthly (Showtime).
Equipment: Nexus & Pico headend; Jerrold amplifiers; Trilogy cable.
Miles of plant: 3.0 (coaxial); None (fiber optic). Homes passed: 139.
Manager: Martin Howser.
Franchise fee: 5% of gross.
Ownership: Martin Howser (MSO).

KALA POINT—Millennium Digital Media, Suite 107, 3633 136th Place SE, Bellevue, WA 98006. Phones: 425-747-4600; 800-829-2225. Fax: 425-644-4621.
Web site: http://www.millenniumdigital.com.
County: Kitsap. ICA: WA0156.
TV Market Ranking: 20. Franchise award date: N.A. Franchise expiration date: N.A. Began: July 1, 1991.
Channel capacity: 36. Channels available but not in use: 5.
Basic Service
Subscribers: 223.
Programming (received off-air): KVOS-TV (I) Bellingham; KCTS-TV (P), KING-TV (N), KIRO-TV (C), KOMO-TV (A), KSTW (U), KTBW-TV (T), KTWB (W) Seattle-Tacoma; CHAN-TV Vancouver; CHEK-TV Victoria.
Programming (via satellite): WGN-TV (W) Chicago; TBS Superstation.
Fee: N.A.
Homes passed: 320.
Manager: Steve Weed. Chief technician: Gene Fry.
Ownership: Millennium Digital Media LLC (MSO). Purchased from Summit Communications Inc., April 7, 1999.

KENNEWICK—Falcon Cable TV, 639 N. Kellogg St., Kennewick, WA 99336. Phone: 509-783-0123. Fax: 509-735-3795. Counties: Benton, Franklin & Walla Walla. Also serves Benton County, Burbank, Finley, Franklin County, Pasco, Richland. ICA: WA0008.
TV Market Ranking: Below 100 (Benton County, Burbank, Finley, portions of Franklin County, Kennewick, Pasco, Richland); Outside TV Markets (portions of Franklin County). Franchise award date: January 1, 1951. Franchise expiration date: N.A. Began: January 1, 1952.
Channel capacity: 55 (2-way capable; operating 2-way). Channels available but not in use: N.A.
Basic Service
Subscribers: 36,007.
Programming (received off-air): KBWU-LP (I) Pasco; KEPR-TV (C), KNDU (N), KVEW (A) Pasco-Kennewick-Richland; KTNW (P) Richland; 9 FMs.
Programming (via microwave): KCTS-TV (P), KSTW (U) Seattle-Tacoma.
Programming (via satellite): WGN-TV (W) Chicago; A & E; American Movie Classics; BET; C-SPAN; C-SPAN 2; CNBC; CNN; Comedy Central; Country Music TV; Discovery Channel; E! Entertainment TV; ESPN; Electronic Program Guide; Fox Family Channel; Fox Sports Net Northwest; Goodlife TV Network; Headline News; Home Shopping Network; Knowledge TV; Learning Channel; Lifetime; MTV; Nashville Network; Nickelodeon; QVC; TBS Superstation; The Weather Channel; Trinity Bcstg. Network; Turner Network TV; USA Network; Univision; VH1.
Current originations: Automated time-weather; public access; educational access; government access; religious access; leased access; local news; local sports.
Planned originations: Automated emergency alert.
Fee: $45.90 installation; $10.12 monthly; $0.64 converter; $22.95 additional installation.
Pay Service 1
Pay Units: 2,160.
Programming (via satellite): Cinemax.
Fee: $15.00 installation; $9.95 monthly.
Pay Service 2
Pay Units: 3,519.
Programming (via satellite): Disney Channel.
Fee: $15.00 installation; $9.95 monthly.
Pay Service 3
Pay Units: 10,309.
Programming (via satellite): HBO.
Fee: $15.00 installation; $9.95 monthly.
Pay Service 4
Pay Units: 3,595.
Programming (via satellite): Showtime.
Fee: $15.00 installation; $9.95 monthly.
Pay Service 5
Pay Units: N.A.
Programming (via satellite): The New Encore.
Fee: N.A.
Pay-Per-View
Addressable homes: 9,357.
Action Pay-Per-View.
Interactive Services
Home shopping.
Local advertising: Yes (locally produced). Available in satellite distributed, locally originated, character-generated, taped & automated programming. Rates: $60.00/Minute; $30.00/30 Seconds. Local sales manager: Lynn Bousquet.
Program Guide: Prevue Guide.
Equipment: RCA & Scientific-Atlanta headend; Century III & Scientific-Atlanta amplifiers;

Comm/Scope cable; Hitachi cameras; Sony VTRs; MSI character generator; Hamlin set top converters; Zenith addressable set top converters; Eagle traps; Anixter-Pruzan satellite antenna; Scientific-Atlanta satellite receivers.

Miles of plant: 660.7 (coaxial). Homes passed: 50,209. Total homes in franchised area: 50,407.

Manager: Ronald A. Asplund. Chief technician: Ron Root. Program director: Lloyd Swain.

City fee: 7% of gross.

Ownership: Falcon Communications LP (MSO). Purchased from Tele-Communications Inc., September 30, 1998. See Cable System Ownership.

KINGSTON—NorthStar Cable Inc., Box 880, Kingston, WA 98346. Phone: 360-297-2295. County: Kitsap. Also serves Gamblewood, Little Boston. ICA: WA0062.

TV Market Ranking: 20. Franchise award date: N.A. Franchise expiration date: N.A. Began: June 1, 1983.

Channel capacity: 40 (not 2-way capable). Channels available but not in use: None.

Basic Service

Subscribers: 1,106.

Programming (received off-air): KWPX (X) Bellevue; KONG-TV (I) Everett; KCPQ (F), KCTS-TV (P), KING-TV (N), KIRO-TV (C), KOMO-TV (A), KSTW (U), KTWB (W) Seattle-Tacoma.

Fee: $40.00 installation; $16.00 monthly.

Expanded Basic Service

Subscribers: 1,053.

Programming (via satellite): A & E; American Movie Classics; Bloomberg Information TV; C-SPAN; CNN; Discovery Channel; Disney Channel; ESPN; Fox Family Channel; Fox Sports Net Northwest; Headline News; History Channel; Home & Garden Television; Learning Channel; Lifetime; Nashville Network; Nickelodeon; Northwest Cable News; Odyssey; QVC; Sci-Fi Channel; TBS Superstation; Turner Classic Movies; Turner Network TV; USA Network.

Fee: $40.00 installation; $30.00 monthly.

Pay Service 1

Pay Units: 83.

Programming (via satellite): HBO.

Fee: $11.75 monthly.

Pay Service 2

Pay Units: 38.

Programming (via satellite): The Movie Channel.

Fee: $10.00 monthly.

Miles of plant: 20.0 (coaxial); None (fiber optic). Homes passed: 1,818.

Manager: Bob Smiley.

Ownership: NorthStar Cable Inc. (MSO).

LA CONNER—Northland Cable, Box 1630, La Conner, WA 98257. Phone: 360-466-3317. Fax: 360-466-3560. County: Skagit. Also serves Shelter Bay, Skagit County (unincorporated areas), Swinomish Indian Reservation. ICA: WA0158.

TV Market Ranking: Below 100. Franchise award date: N.A. Franchise expiration date: January 1, 1999. Began: November 1, 1976.

Channel capacity: 41 (not 2-way capable). Channels available but not in use: None.

Basic Service

Subscribers: 2,100.

Programming (received off-air): KVOS-TV (I) Bellingham; KCPQ (F), KCTS-TV (P), KING-TV (N), KIRO-TV (C), KOMO-TV (A), KSTW (U), KTWB (W) Seattle-Tacoma; CBUT Vancouver.

Programming (via satellite): QVC; TBS Superstation; TV Guide Channel; Trinity Bcstg. Network.

Fee: $50.00 installation; $10.80 monthly.

Expanded Basic Service

Subscribers: 2,028.

Programming (via satellite): A & E; C-SPAN; CNBC; CNN; Discovery Channel; ESPN; Fox Family Channel; Headline News; Learning Channel; Lifetime; MTV; Nashville Network; Turner Network TV.

Fee: $50.00 installation; $10.70 monthly.

Expanded Basic Service 2

Subscribers: 753.

Programming (via satellite): American Movie Classics; Cartoon Network; Fox Sports Net Northwest; Nickelodeon; Turner Classic Movies; USA Network.

Fee: $50.00 installation; $4.75 monthly.

Pay Service 1

Pay Units: 199.

Programming (via satellite): Cinemax.

Fee: $8.95 monthly.

Pay Service 2

Pay Units: 119.

Programming (via satellite): Disney Channel.

Fee: $8.95 monthly.

Pay Service 3

Pay Units: 290.

Programming (via satellite): HBO.

Fee: $19.95 installation; $11.50 monthly.

Local advertising: Yes. Available in character-generated programming. Rates: $50.00/Month; 3.00/30 Seconds. Local sales manager: Les Carney.

Equipment: Scientific-Atlanta headend; Texscan amplifiers; Amiga character generator; Regal set top converters; PPC traps; Scientific-Atlanta satellite antenna; Scientific-Atlanta satellite receivers; ChannelMatic commercial insert.

Miles of plant: 63.0 (coaxial); None (fiber optic).

Manager: Jon Ulrich. Chief technician: Ed Knipper. Marketing director: Bede Wells.

City fee: 3% of gross.

Ownership: Northland Communications Corp. (MSO).

LAKE BAY—Millennium Digital Media, Suite 107, 3633 136th Place SE, Bellevue, WA 98006. Phones: 425-747-4600; 800-829-2225. Fax: 425-644-4621.

Web site: http://www.millenniumdigital.com.

County: Pierce. ICA: WA0201.

TV Market Ranking: 12. Franchise award date: N.A. Franchise expiration date: N.A. Began: N.A.

Channel capacity: N.A. Channels available but not in use: N.A.

Basic Service

Subscribers: N.A.

Programming (received off-air): KONG-TV (I) Everett; KCPQ (F), KCTS-TV (P), KING-TV (N), KIRO-TV (C), KOMO-TV (A), KSTW (U), KTBW-TV (T), KTWB (W) Seattle-Tacoma; KBTC-TV (P) Tacoma.

Programming (via satellite): A & E; American Movie Classics; C-SPAN; CNN; Cartoon Network; Comedy Central; Discovery Channel; ESPN; Fox Family Channel; Fox Sports Net Northwest; Headline News; Lifetime; MTV; Nashville Network; Nickelodeon; Northwest Cable News; QVC; Sci-Fi Channel; TBS Superstation; TV Guide Channel; The Weather Channel; Turner Network TV; USA Network; VH1.

Fee: $49.95 installation; $25.95 monthly.

Pay Service 1

Pay Units: N.A.

Programming (via satellite): Cinemax; Disney Channel; HBO; Showtime.

Fee: $8.95 monthly (Disney), $10.00 monthly (Cinemax, HBO or Showtime).

Manager: Steve Weed. Chief technician: Gene Fry.

Ownership: Millennium Digital Media LLC (MSO). Purchased from Summit Communications Inc., April 7, 1999.

LAKE GOODWIN—Lake TV Cable, Box 237, Lakewood, WA 98259. Phone: 206-652-0230. Fax: 206-652-1934. County: Snohomish. Also serves Bryant, Seven Lakes. ICA: WA0159.

TV Market Ranking: Below 100. Franchise award date: N.A. Franchise expiration date: N.A. Began: July 1, 1982.

Channel capacity: 40 (2-way capable; operating 2-way). Channels available but not in use: 5.

Basic Service

Subscribers: 2,631.

Programming (received off-air): KVOS-TV (I) Bellingham; KCPQ (F), KCTS-TV (P), KING-TV (N), KIRO-TV (C), KOMO-TV (A), KSTW (U), KTBW-TV (T), KTWB (W) Seattle-Tacoma; CBUT Vancouver; allband FM.

Programming (via satellite): A & E; C-SPAN; CNN; CNNfn; Cartoon Network; Discovery Channel; ESPN; FX; Fox Family Channel; Fox Sports Net; Headline News; Lifetime; MTV; Nashville Network; Nickelodeon; QVC; TBS Superstation; Turner Classic Movies; Turner Network TV; USA Network; VH1.

Current originations: Automated time-weather.

Fee: $19.95 installation; $20.00 monthly.

Pay Service 1

Pay Units: N.A.

Programming (via satellite): Cinemax; Disney Channel; HBO.

Fee: $8.00 monthly (Disney), $9.00 monthly (Cinemax), $10.95 monthly (HBO).

Equipment: Scientific-Atlanta, Jerrold headend; GTE Sylvania amplifiers; Times Fiber cable; Eagle traps; Scientific-Atlanta satellite antenna; Scientific-Atlanta satellite receivers.

Miles of plant: 110.0 (coaxial); 15.0 (fiber optic).

Manager: Patrick Davis. Chief technician: Irv Pike.

Ownership: Davis Communications Inc. (MSO).

LEAVENWORTH—TCI Cablevision of Washington Inc., Box 1480, Wenatchee, WA 98801. Phone: 509-663-5108. County: Chelan. Also serves Chelan County, Dryden, Peshastin. ICA: WA0051.

TV Market Ranking: Below 100 (portions of Chelan County, Dryden, Leavenworth, Peshastin); Outside TV Markets (portions of Chelan County). Franchise award date: N.A. Franchise expiration date: N.A. Began: February 1, 1980.

Channel capacity: 35. Channels available but not in use: 7.

Basic Service

Subscribers: 1,794.

Programming (received off-air): KAYU-TV (F) Spokane; allband FM.

Programming (via microwave): KCTS-TV (P), KING-TV (N), KIRO-TV (C), KOMO-TV (A), KSTW (U) Seattle-Tacoma.

Programming (via satellite): A & E; CNN; Discovery Channel; Fox Family Channel; Headline News; Lifetime; MTV; Nashville Network; Nickelodeon; TBS Superstation; The Weather Channel.

Current originations: Automated time-weather; educational access.

Fee: $60.00 installation; $18.76 monthly; $15.00 additional installation.

Expanded Basic Service

Subscribers: 1,728.

Programming (via satellite): American Movie Classics; ESPN; Fox Sports Net Northwest; Turner Network TV; USA Network.

Fee: $2.00 monthly.

Pay Service 1

Pay Units: 155.

Programming (via satellite): Disney Channel.

Fee: $8.95 monthly.

Pay Service 2

Pay Units: 572.

Programming (via satellite): The New Encore.

Fee: N.A.

Pay Service 3

Pay Units: 114.

Programming (via satellite): HBO.

Fee: $10.95 monthly.

Pay Service 4

Pay Units: 257.

Programming (via satellite): Showtime.

Fee: $14.95 installation; $9.95 monthly.

Local advertising: Yes. Available in character-generated programming. Rates: $15.00/Week.

Equipment: Scientific-Atlanta headend; Magnavox amplifiers; Times Fiber cable; Scientific-Atlanta satellite antenna.

Miles of plant: 68.7 (coaxial). Homes passed: 2,053. Total homes in franchised area: 3,250.

Manager: Bob Lam.

City fee: 3% of gross.

Ownership: AT&T Broadband & Internet Services (MSO). Purchased from Tele-Communications Inc., March 9, 1999.

LIBERTY LAKE—Community Cable Service, 729 S. Bernard St., Spokane, WA 99204. Phones: 509-624-4140; 800-572-0902. Fax: 509-624-7372. County: Spokane. ICA: WA0123.

TV Market Ranking: 76. Franchise award date: N.A. Franchise expiration date: N.A. Began: N.A.

Channel capacity: 62 (2-way capable; not operating 2-way). Channels available but not in use: None.

Basic Service

Subscribers: 1,210.

Programming (received off-air): KWSU-TV (P) Pullman; KAYU-TV (F), KHQ-TV (N), KREM-TV (C), KSKN (U,W), KSPS-TV (P), KXLY-TV (A) Spokane.

Programming (via satellite): WGN-TV (W) Chicago; A & E; American Movie Classics; Bravo; C-SPAN; C-SPAN 2; CNBC; CNN; CNN International; Cartoon Network; Comedy Central; Country Music TV; Discovery Channel; E! Entertainment TV; ESPN; ESPN 2; ESPNews; EWTN; FX; Fox Family Channel; Fox News Channel; Fox Sports Net Northwest; Golf Channel; Goodlife TV Network; Headline News; History Channel; Home Shopping Network; Knowledge TV; Learning Channel; Lifetime; MTV; Nashville Network; Nickelodeon; Odyssey; QVC; Sci-Fi Channel; TBS Superstation; TV Food Network; The Health Network; The Weather Channel; Travel Channel; Trinity Bcstg. Network; Turner Classic Movies; Turner Network TV; USA Network; VH1; ValueVision; Z Music Television.

Fee: $20.00 installation; $27.36 monthly.

Pay Service 1

Pay Units: 152.

Programming (via satellite): Cinemax.

Fee: $5.00 installation; $6.36 monthly.

Pay Service 2

Pay Units: 89.

Programming (via satellite): Disney Channel.

Fee: $5.00 installation; $5.29 monthly.
Pay Service 3
Pay Units: 225.
Programming (via satellite): HBO.
Fee: $5.00 installation; $9.56 monthly.
Pay Service 4
Pay Units: N.A.
Programming (via satellite): Showtime.
Fee: $8.01 monthly.
Homes passed: 1,335.
Manager: Martin Howser.
Ownership: Martin Howser (MSO).

LIND—Community Cable Service, 729 S. Bernard St., Spokane, WA 99204. Phones: 509-624-4140; 800-572-0902. Fax: 509-624-7372. County: Adams. ICA: WA0115.
TV Market Ranking: Outside TV Markets. Franchise award date: N.A. Franchise expiration date: N.A. Began: December 1, 1953.
Channel capacity: 62 (2-way capable; not operating 2-way). Channels available but not in use: 3.
Basic Service
Subscribers: 223.
Programming (received off-air): KEPR-TV (C) Pasco-Kennewick-Richland; KWSU-TV (P) Pullman; KAYU-TV (F), KHQ-TV (N), KREM-TV (C), KSPS-TV (P), KXLY-TV (A) Spokane; 8 FMs.
Programming (via satellite): WGN-TV (W) Chicago; A & E; American Movie Classics; Bravo; C-SPAN; C-SPAN 2; CNBC; CNN; CNN International; Cartoon Network; Comedy Central; Country Music TV; Discovery Channel; E! Entertainment TV; ESPN; ESPN 2; ESPNews; EWTN; Fox Family Channel; Fox News Channel; Fox Sports Net Northwest; Goodlife TV Network; Headline News; History Channel; Home & Garden Television; Home Shopping Network; Knowledge TV; Learning Channel; Lifetime; MTV; Nashville Network; Nick at Nite's TV Land; Nickelodeon; Odyssey; QVC; Sci-Fi Channel; TBS Superstation; TV Food Network; The Health Network; The Inspirational Network; Travel Channel; Trinity Bcstg. Network; Turner Classic Movies; Turner Network TV; USA Network; VH1; ValueVision; Z Music Television.
Fee: $15.00 installation; $25.60 monthly.
Pay Service 1
Pay Units: 47.
Programming (via satellite): Cinemax.
Fee: $6.06 monthly.
Pay Service 2
Pay Units: 40.
Programming (via satellite): Disney Channel.
Fee: $5.04 monthly.
Pay Service 3
Pay Units: 58.
Programming (via satellite): HBO.
Fee: $9.11 monthly.
Pay Service 4
Pay Units: N.A.
Programming (via satellite): Showtime.
Fee: $7.64 monthly.
Equipment: Nexus & Pico headend; Jerrold amplifiers.
Miles of plant: 5.0 (coaxial). Additional miles planned: 1.0 (coaxial). Homes passed: 354.
Manager: Martin Howser.
Ownership: Martin Howser (MSO).

LONG BEACH—Falcon Community Ventures I, 1241 Duane St., Astoria, OR 97103. Phone: 503-325-6114. County: Pacific. Also serves Ilwaco, Nahcotta, Ocean Park, Pacific County, Seaview. ICA: WA0160.
TV Market Ranking: Outside TV Markets. Franchise award date: N.A. Franchise expiration date: N.A. Began: June 1, 1959.
Channel capacity: 22. Channels available but not in use: None.
Basic Service
Subscribers: 4,410.
Programming (received off-air): KATU (A), KGW (N), KOIN (C), KOPB-TV (P), KPTV (U) Portland; KING-TV (N), KOMO-TV (A) Seattle-Tacoma; KPDX (F) Vancouver; 13 FMs.
Programming (via satellite): Blazer Vision; Trinity Bcstg. Network.
Fee: $25.00 installation; $14.11 monthly.
Expanded Basic Service
Subscribers: 4,259.
Programming (via satellite): CNN; ESPN; TBS Superstation.
Fee: $3.16 monthly.
Expanded Basic Service 2
Subscribers: 938.
Programming (via satellite): Discovery Channel; Disney Channel; Goodlife TV Network; MTV; Nickelodeon; USA Network.
Fee: $5.20 monthly.
Pay Service 1
Pay Units: 150.
Programming (via satellite): Cinemax.
Fee: $10.00 installation; $10.95 monthly.
Pay Service 2
Pay Units: 275.
Programming (via satellite): HBO.
Fee: $10.00 installation; $11.95 monthly.
Pay Service 3
Pay Units: 249.
Programming (via satellite): Showtime.
Fee: $10.00 installation; $10.95 monthly.
Equipment: Microwave Assoc. & Scientific-Atlanta headend; Jerrold amplifiers; Comm/Scope cable; Sony VTRs; Video Data Systems character generator; Oak set top converters; Scientific-Atlanta satellite antenna; Scientific-Atlanta satellite receivers.
Miles of plant: 205.0 (coaxial). Homes passed: 6,164.
Manager: Ray Romine. Chief technician: Bruce Johnson.
Franchise fee: 2%-3% of gross.
Ownership: Falcon Communications LP (MSO), joint venture formed September 30, 1998. See Cable System Ownership.

LONGVIEW—Cowlitz Cablevision Inc., Box 998, 750 11th Ave., Longview, WA 98632. Phones: 360-577-2598; 800-626-6299. Fax: 360-577-1330. County: Cowlitz. Also serves Carrolls, Castle Rock, Cowlitz County, Kalama, Kelso, Rose Valley, Silver Lake, Toutle, Woodland. ICA: WA0013.
TV Market Ranking: 29 (portions of Cowlitz County, Kalama, Woodland); Below 100 (portions of Cowlitz County); Outside TV Markets (Carrolls, Castle Rock, portions of Cowlitz County, Kelso, Longview, Rose Valley, Silver Lake, Toutle). Franchise award date: N.A. Franchise expiration date: N.A. Began: August 1, 1965.
Channel capacity: 60 (not 2-way capable). Channels available but not in use: None.
Basic Service
Subscribers: 21,000.
Programming (received off-air): KATU (A), KGW (N), KOIN (C), KOPB-TV (P), KPTV (U) Portland; KCTS-TV (P), KOMO-TV (A), KSTW (U) Seattle-Tacoma; KPDX (F) Vancouver; 19 FMs.
Programming (via satellite): A & E; C-SPAN; CNBC; CNN; Discovery Channel; Disney Channel; E! Entertainment TV; ESPN; FX; Fox Sports Net Northwest; Headline News; Learning Channel; Lifetime; MSNBC; MTV; Nashville Network; Nick at Nite's TV Land; Nickelodeon; Northwest Cable News; Odyssey; QVC; Sci-Fi Channel; TBS Superstation; TV Guide Channel; The Weather Channel; Trinity Bcstg. Network; USA Network; Univision; VH1.
Current originations: Automated timeweather; public access; educational access; government access.
Fee: $25.59 installation; $29.17 monthly; $2.00 converter.
Expanded Basic Service
Subscribers: N.A.
Programming (via satellite): American Movie Classics; Animal Planet; Fox News Channel; Home & Garden Television; Outdoor Life Network; TBS Superstation; Turner Network TV.
Fee: $3.17 monthly.
Expanded Basic Service 2
Subscribers: N.A.
Programming (via satellite): Bravo; Comedy Central; ESPN 2; ESPN Classic Sports; Great American Country; History Channel; Romance Classics; Toon Disney.
Fee: $7.46 monthly.
Pay Service 1
Pay Units: N.A.
Programming (via satellite): Cinemax; HBO; Showtime.
Fee: $15.00 installation; $10.45 monthly (Cinemax), $12.45 monthly (Showtime), $14.95 monthly (HBO).
Pay-Per-View
Addressable homes: 4,100.
Viewer's Choice 1 & 2; movies; special events.
Fee: Varies.
Local advertising: Yes (locally produced & insert). Available in satellite distributed programming. Rates: $70.00/Minute; $35.00/30 Seconds.
Program Guide: TV Times.
Equipment: Scientific-Atlanta headend; Texscan amplifiers; Comm/Scope cable; Sony VTRs; Scientific-Atlanta set top converters; Scientific-Atlanta satellite antenna; Scientific-Atlanta satellite receivers; Seachange commercial insert.
Miles of plant: 487.0 (coaxial); 89.0 (fiber optic). Homes passed: 30,000. Total homes in franchised area: 35,000.
Manager: Jim Elliott. Chief technician: Cecil Williams. Marketing director: Steve Delgado.
City fee: 5% of gross.
Ownership: Century Communications Corp. (MSO). See Cable System Ownership.

LOOMIS—JKA Cable Systems Inc., Box 1273, Mount Vernon, WA 98273. Phones: 360-424-0426; 800-338-2521. Fax: 360-428-9063. County: Okanogan. ICA: WA0202.
TV Market Ranking: Outside TV Markets. Franchise award date: N.A. Franchise expiration date: N.A. Began: N.A.
Channel capacity: 12. Channels available but not in use: 8.
Basic Service
Subscribers: 40.
Programming (received off-air): KHQ-TV (N), KREM-TV (C), KSPS-TV (P), KXLY-TV (A) Spokane.
Fee: N.A.
Homes passed: 90.
Owner: Jerry Swatman.
Ownership: Jones Intercable Inc. (MSO).

LOON LAKE—Falcon Telecable, 189 Buena Vista Dr., Colville, WA 99114. Phone: 509-684-3797. Fax: 509-684-6108. County: Stevens. Also serves Chewelah, Deerlake. ICA: WA0161.
TV Market Ranking: 76 (Deerlake, Loon Lake); Outside TV Markets (Chewelah). Franchise award date: N.A. Franchise expiration date: N.A. Began: N.A.
Channel capacity: 36. Channels available but not in use: 5.
Basic Service
Subscribers: 1,062.
Programming (received off-air): KAYU-TV (F), KHQ-TV (N), KREM-TV (C), KSPS-TV (P), KXLY-TV (A) Spokane; allband FM.
Programming (via satellite): C-SPAN; Comedy Central; ESPN; Home Shopping Network; Learning Channel; MTV; Nickelodeon; Northwest Cable News; QVC; Sci-Fi Channel; TBS Superstation; Trinity Bcstg. Network; USA Network; VH1.
Fee: $49.95 installation; $21.41 monthly.
Expanded Basic Service
Subscribers: 1,033.
Programming (via satellite): A & E; CNN; Discovery Channel; Headline News.
Fee: $4.19 monthly.
Expanded Basic Service 2
Subscribers: 353.
Programming (via satellite): American Movie Classics; Country Music TV; Disney Channel; Fox Family Channel; Lifetime; Nashville Network.
Fee: $6.64 monthly.
Pay Service 1
Pay Units: 94.
Programming (via satellite): HBO.
Fee: $11.95 monthly.
Pay Service 2
Pay Units: 45.
Programming (via satellite): The Movie Channel.
Fee: $6.00 installation; $10.95 monthly.
Pay Service 3
Pay Units: 80.
Programming (via satellite): Showtime.
Fee: $10.95 monthly.
Pay-Per-View
Special events.
Local advertising: Yes.
Miles of plant: 48.0 (coaxial). Homes passed: 1,483.
Manager: Melvin Fox. Chief technician: Mark Sterkell.
Franchise fee: 3% of gross.
Ownership: Falcon Communications LP (MSO), joint venture formed September 30, 1998. See Cable System Ownership.

LUMMI INDIAN RESERVATION—San Juan Cable & Construction, 2568 McKenzie Rd., Bellingham, WA 98226-9204. Phone: 360-758-7879. County: Whatcom. ICA: WA0162.
TV Market Ranking: Below 100. Franchise award date: N.A. Franchise expiration date: N.A. Began: N.A.
Channel capacity: N.A. Channels available but not in use: N.A.
Basic Service
Subscribers: 217.
Programming (received off-air): KVOS-TV (I) Bellingham; KCPQ (F), KCTS-TV (P), KING-TV (N), KIRO-TV (C), KOMO-TV (A), KSTW (U) Seattle-Tacoma; CBUT, CHAN-TV, CKVU-TV Vancouver; CHEK-TV Victoria.
Fee: N.A.
Ownership: San Juan Cable & Construction.

LYLE—Cascade Cable Systems, Box 397, The Dalles, OR 97058. Phone: 541-298-4983. E-mail: jroth@gorge.net. County: Klickitat. ICA: WA0163.
TV Market Ranking: Outside TV Markets. Franchise award date: N.A. Franchise expiration date: N.A. Began: January 1, 1955.

Channel capacity: 22 (not 2-way capable). Channels available but not in use: 8.

Basic Service

Subscribers: 167.

Programming (received off-air): KATU (A), KGW (N), KOIN (C), KOPB-TV (P), KPTV (U) Portland; KPDX (F) Vancouver; allband FM.

Programming (via satellite): American Movie Classics; CNN; Discovery Channel; ESPN; Nashville Network; Northwest Cable News; TBS Superstation.

Fee: $25.00 installation; $15.00 monthly.

Pay Service 1

Pay Units: 31.

Programming (via satellite): The Movie Channel.

Fee: $10.00 installation; $10.00 monthly.

Equipment: Blonder-Tongue & Cadco headend; Cadco amplifiers; Comm/Scope cable; Pico traps; ADM satellite antenna; Drake & Standard Components satellite receivers.

Miles of plant: 5.0 (coaxial); None (fiber optic).

Manager: James F. Roth.

City fee: None.

Ownership: Cascade Cable Systems (MSO).

LYNDEN—TCI Cablevision of Washington Inc., 777 W. Horton Rd., Bellingham, WA 98226-7606. Phone: 360-384-1581. Fax: 360-647-8967. County: Whatcom. Also serves Everson, Nooksack, Whatcom County. ICA: WA0026.

TV Market Ranking: Below 100 (Everson, Lynden, Nooksack, portions of Whatcom County); Outside TV Markets (portions of Whatcom County). Franchise award date: N.A. Franchise expiration date: N.A. Began: January 1, 1967.

Channel capacity: 35 (not 2-way capable). Channels available but not in use: N.A.

Basic Service

Subscribers: 3,806.

Programming (received off-air): KVOS-TV (I) Bellingham; KSTW (U) Seattle-Tacoma; CBUT, CHAN-TV Vancouver; allband FM.

Programming (via microwave): KCPQ (F), KCTS-TV (P), KING-TV (N), KIRO-TV (C), KOMO-TV (A) Seattle-Tacoma.

Programming (via satellite): C-SPAN; CNBC; CNN; Discovery Channel; Fox Family Channel; Headline News; Lifetime; Nashville Network; Nickelodeon; Odyssey; QVC; TBS Superstation; The Weather Channel.

Fee: $60.00 installation; $10.25 monthly; $40.00 additional installation.

Expanded Basic Service

Subscribers: 3,183.

Programming (via satellite): American Movie Classics; ESPN; Fox Sports Net Northwest; Turner Network TV; USA Network.

Fee: $10.26 monthly.

Pay Service 1

Pay Units: 365.

Programming (via satellite): Disney Channel.

Fee: $35.00 installation; $10.95 monthly.

Pay Service 2

Pay Units: 890.

Programming (via satellite): The New Encore.

Fee: N.A.

Pay Service 3

Pay Units: 503.

Programming (via satellite): HBO.

Fee: $35.00 installation; $13.15 monthly.

Pay Service 4

Pay Units: 205.

Programming (via satellite): Showtime.

Fee: $35.00 installation; $13.15 monthly.

Pay-Per-View

Addressable homes: 260.

Movies; special events.

Local advertising: Yes.

Equipment: Scientific-Atlanta headend; Magnavox amplifiers; Times Fiber cable; Hamlin set top converters; Anixter-Mark & Scientific-Atlanta satellite antenna; M/A-Com & Scientific-Atlanta satellite receivers.

Miles of plant: 110.0 (coaxial). Homes passed: 6,278.

Manager: Dan Crocker.

City fee: 5% of gross.

Ownership: AT&T Broadband & Internet Services (MSO). Purchased from Tele-Communications Inc., March 9, 1999.

MALAGA—Sun Country Cable, Box 127, 7 D St. SW, Quincy, WA 98848. Phone: 509-787-3543. Fax: 509-787-3884. County: Chelan. ICA: WA0164.

TV Market Ranking: Below 100. Franchise award date: N.A. Franchise expiration date: N.A. Began: December 1, 1987.

Channel capacity: 32 (not 2-way capable). Channels available but not in use: 11.

Basic Service

Subscribers: 259.

Programming (received off-air): KCTS-TV (P), KING-TV (N), KIRO-TV (C), KOMO-TV (A), KSTW (U) Seattle-Tacoma; KAYU-TV (F) Spokane.

Programming (via satellite): WGN-TV (W) Chicago; A & E; CNN; Discovery Channel; ESPN; Fox Family Channel; Headline News; Lifetime; Nashville Network; TBS Superstation; Turner Network TV; USA Network.

Fee: $39.95 installation; $27.95 monthly.

Pay Service 1

Pay Units: 23.

Programming (via satellite): Disney Channel.

Fee: $15.00 installation; $8.95 monthly.

Pay Service 2

Pay Units: 44.

Programming (via satellite): HBO.

Fee: $15.00 installation; $10.95 monthly.

Equipment: Scientific-Atlanta & Triple Crown headend; Jerrold amplifiers; Panasonic & Scientific-Atlanta set top converters; Scientific-Atlanta & Triple Crown satellite receivers.

Miles of plant: 41.0 (coaxial).

Manager: Gary White. Technical manager: Arnie Hill. Office manager: Judy Vreeman.

City fee: 2.5% of basic.

Ownership: Sun Country Cable (MSO).

MALTBY—Cable Plus, Suite 120, 11400 S.E. 6th St., Bellevue, WA 98004. Phone: 425-462-2090. Fax: 425-462-2092. County: Snohomish. Also serves Snohomish County (southwestern portions). ICA: WA0205.

TV Market Ranking: 20. Franchise award date: August 22, 1990. Franchise expiration date: August 19, 2011. Began: November 18, 1987.

Channel capacity: 72. Channels available but not in use: 25.

Basic Service

Subscribers: 1,500.

Programming (received off-air): KONG-TV (I) Everett; KCPQ (F), KCTS-TV (P), KING-TV (N), KIRO-TV (C), KOMO-TV (A), KSTW (U), KTWB (W) Seattle-Tacoma.

Programming (via satellite): WGN-TV (W) Chicago; A & E; Animal Planet; C-SPAN; CNBC; CNN; CNN International; CNNfn; Cartoon Network; Country Music TV; Discovery Channel; ESPN; ESPN 2; ESPNews; Fox Family Channel; Fox News Channel; Fox Sports Net Northwest; Golf Channel; Headline News; History Channel; Home Shopping Network; Learning Channel; Lifetime; MTV; Nashville Network; Nickelodeon; Northwest Cable News; QVC; TBS Superstation; Trinity Bcstg. Network; Turner Classic Movies; Turner Network TV; USA Network; VH1.

Fee: $40.00 installation; $26.95 monthly.

Pay Service 1

Pay Units: 60.

Programming (via satellite): Cinemax.

Fee: $11.95 monthly.

Pay Service 2

Pay Units: 112.

Programming (via satellite): Disney Channel.

Fee: $9.95 monthly.

Pay Service 3

Pay Units: 121.

Programming (via satellite): HBO.

Fee: $11.00 monthly.

Pay Service 4

Pay Units: 45.

Programming (via satellite): The Movie Channel.

Fee: $11.00 monthly.

Pay Service 5

Pay Units: 133.

Programming (via satellite): Showtime.

Fee: $9.95 monthly.

Miles of plant: 110.0 (coaxial); 15.0 (fiber optic). Homes passed: 2,880. Total homes in franchised area: 3,000.

Manager: Gary O'Malley. Chief technician: Dan Adams.

Ownership: Cable Plus (MSO).

MANSFIELD—Sun Cable TV, Box 589, 300 Quetilquasoon 2, Manson, WA 98831. Phone: 509-687-3325. Fax: 509-687-3325. County: Douglas. ICA: WA0136.

TV Market Ranking: Outside TV Markets. Franchise award date: N.A. Franchise expiration date: N.A. Began: January 1, 1982.

Channel capacity: 40 (2-way capable). Channels available but not in use: 14.

Basic Service

Subscribers: 85.

Programming (received off-air): KREM-TV (C), KSPS-TV (P), KXLY-TV (A) Spokane.

Programming (via satellite): WGN-TV (W) Chicago; ESPN; Fox Family Channel; TBS Superstation; USA Network.

Fee: $45.00 installation; $16.50 monthly.

Pay Service 1

Pay Units: 39.

Programming (via satellite): HBO.

Fee: $10.95 monthly.

Miles of plant: 2.0 (coaxial); None (fiber optic). Homes passed: 120. Total homes in franchised area: 120.

Manager: Skip Gors.

City fee: 3% of gross.

Ownership: Sun Cable TV (MSO).

MANSON—Sun Cable TV, Box 589, 300 Quetilquasoon 2, Manson, WA 98831. Phone: 509-687-3325. Fax: 509-687-3325. County: Chelan. Also serves Upper South Shore. ICA: WA0165.

TV Market Ranking: Below 100 (Upper South Shore); Outside TV Markets (Manson). Franchise award date: N.A. Franchise expiration date: N.A. Began: January 1, 1984.

Channel capacity: 42 (2-way capable). Channels available but not in use: 6.

Basic Service

Subscribers: 850.

Programming (received off-air): KAYU-TV (F), KHQ-TV (N), KREM-TV (C), KSPS-TV (P), KXLY-TV (A) Spokane.

Programming (via satellite): WGN-TV (W) Chicago; CNN; Discovery Channel; TBS Superstation; Turner Network TV; USA Network.

Fee: $20.00 monthly.

Pay Service 1

Pay Units: 48.

Programming (via satellite): HBO.

Fee: $10.95 monthly.

Miles of plant: 35.0 (coaxial); None (fiber optic). Homes passed: 1,450.

Manager: Skip Gors.

Ownership: Sun Cable TV (MSO).

MAPLE FALLS—TCI Cablevision of Washington Inc., 777 W. Horton Rd., Bellingham, WA 98226-7606. Phone: 360-384-1581. County: Whatcom. Also serves Deming, Glen Mobile Home Park, Whatcom County (portions). ICA: WA0166.

TV Market Ranking: Below 100 (Deming, Glen Mobile Home Park, Maple Falls, portions of Whatcom County); Outside TV Markets (portions of Whatcom County). Franchise award date: N.A. Franchise expiration date: N.A. Began: December 1, 1989.

Channel capacity: N.A. Channels available but not in use: N.A.

Basic Service

Subscribers: 1,200.

Programming (received off-air): KVOS-TV (I) Bellingham; KCPQ (F), KCTS-TV (P), KING-TV (N), KIRO-TV (C), KOMO-TV (A) Seattle-Tacoma; CBUT, CHAN-TV Vancouver; CHEK-TV Victoria.

Programming (via satellite): WGN-TV (W) Chicago; CNN; Discovery Channel; ESPN; Fox Family Channel; Goodlife TV Network; Headline News; Learning Channel; Nashville Network; Nickelodeon; TBS Superstation; Turner Network TV; USA Network; VH1.

Fee: $20.00 installation.

Pay Service 1

Pay Units: N.A.

Programming (via satellite): Cinemax; Disney Channel; HBO.

Fee: $6.95 monthly (Disney), $7.95 monthly (Cinemax), $9.95 monthly (HBO).

Ownership: AT&T Broadband & Internet Services (MSO). Purchased from Tele-Communications Inc., March 9, 1999.

MARBLEMOUNT—Millennium Digital Media, Suite 107, 3633 136th Place SE, Bellevue, WA 98006. Phones: 425-747-4600; 800-8292225. Fax: 425-644-4621.

Web site: http://www.millenniumdigital.com.

County: Skagit. ICA: WA0194.

TV Market Ranking: Outside TV Markets. Franchise award date: N.A. Franchise expiration date: N.A. Began: N.A.

Channel capacity: 36. Channels available but not in use: 23.

Basic Service

Subscribers: 74.

Programming (received off-air): KCTS-TV (P), KING-TV (N), KIRO-TV (C), KOMO-TV (A) Seattle-Tacoma.
Programming (via satellite): WGN-TV (W) Chicago; A & E; C-SPAN; CNN; Country Music TV; Discovery Channel; ESPN; Fox Family Channel; FoxNet; Knowledge TV; MuchMusic Network; Nashville Network; Sci-Fi Channel; TBS Superstation; Trinity Bcstg. Network; Turner Network TV; USA Network.
Fee: $39.95 installation; $21.95 monthly.

Pay Service 1
Pay Units: N.A.
Programming (via satellite): HBO.
Fee: $9.95 monthly.

Miles of plant: 8.0 (coaxial). Homes passed: 110.
Manager: Steve Weed. Chief technician: Gene Fry.
Ownership: Millennium Digital Media LLC (MSO). Purchased from Summit Communications Inc., April 7, 1999.

MATTAWA—Sun Country Cable, Box 127, 7 D St. NW, Quincy, WA 98848. Phones: 509-787-3543; 800-788-0120. Fax: 509-787-3884. County: Grant. Also serves Desert Aire. ICA: WA0098.
TV Market Ranking: Outside TV Markets. Franchise award date: N.A. Franchise expiration date: N.A. Began: September 1, 1988.
Channel capacity: 35 (not 2-way capable). Channels available but not in use: 17.

Basic Service
Subscribers: 392.
Programming (received off-air): KEPR-TV (C), KNDU (N), KVEW (A) Pasco-Kennewick-Richland; KTNW (P) Richland; KAYU-TV (F) Spokane.
Programming (via satellite): WGN-TV (W) Chicago; A & E; American Movie Classics; CNN; Cartoon Network; Cartoon Network Tambien en Espanol; Comedy Central; Country Music TV; Discovery Channel; ESPN; ESPN 2; FX; Fox Family Channel; Fox Sports Net Northwest; Fox Sports World Espanol; GalaVision; History Channel; Home & Garden Television; Learning Channel; Lifetime; MTV Latin America; Nashville Network; Nick at Nite's TV Land; Northwest Cable News; Sci-Fi Channel; TBS Superstation; Telemundo; The Weather Channel; Trinity Bcstg. Network; Turner Network TV; Univision.
Fee: $39.95 installation; $35.17 monthly; $1.00 converter.

Pay Service 1
Pay Units: 26.
Programming (via satellite): Disney Channel.
Fee: $15.00 installation; $7.95 monthly.

Pay Service 2
Pay Units: 52.
Programming (via satellite): HBO.
Fee: $15.00 installation; $10.95 monthly.

Equipment: Triple Crown headend; Jerrold amplifiers; Standard Communications cable; Scientific-Atlanta set top converters; Scientific-Atlanta satellite antenna; Triple Crown satellite receivers.
Miles of plant: 40.0 (coaxial). Homes passed: 500. Total homes in franchised area: 550.
Technical manager: Arnie Hill. Office manager: Judy Vreeman.
City fee: 3%.
Ownership: Sun Country Cable (MSO).

MAXWELTON—Pioneer Cable Contractors, 23426 146th St. SE, Monroe, WA 98272. County: Island. Also serves Sandy Hook (Island County). ICA: WA0141.
TV Market Ranking: 20. Franchise award date: N.A. Franchise expiration date: N.A. Began: April 1, 1974.
Channel capacity: 29. Channels available but not in use: 2.

Basic Service
Subscribers: 450.
Programming (received off-air): KVOS-TV (I) Bellingham; KCPQ (F), KCTS-TV (P), KING-TV (N), KIRO-TV (C), KOMO-TV (A), KSTW (U), KTBW-TV (T), KTWB (W) Seattle-Tacoma; KBTC-TV (P) Tacoma; CBUT Vancouver.
Programming (via satellite): A & E; American Movie Classics; CNN; Discovery Channel; ESPN; Lifetime; Nashville Network; QVC; TBS Superstation; Travel Channel; Turner Network TV; USA Network.
Fee: $30.00 installation; $17.45 monthly.

Pay Service 1
Pay Units: N.A.
Programming (via satellite): Disney Channel; HBO; Showtime.
Fee: N.A.

Miles of plant: 2.1 (coaxial).
Manager: Connie Hooker.
Ownership: Network Cable Inc.

McCHORD AIR FORCE BASE—TCI of Tacoma Inc., 3119 Center St., Tacoma, WA 98409. Phone: 253-383-4311. County: Pierce. ICA: WA0050.
TV Market Ranking: 20. Franchise award date: N.A. Franchise expiration date: January 1, 2005. Began: June 1, 1978.
Channel capacity: 37 (not 2-way capable). Channels available but not in use: 1.

Basic Service
Subscribers: 1,189.
Programming (received off-air): KCPQ (F), KCTS-TV (P), KING-TV (N), KIRO-TV (C), KOMO-TV (A), KSTW (U), KTBW-TV (T), KTWB (W) Seattle-Tacoma; KBTC-TV (P) Tacoma; 8 FMs.
Programming (via satellite): A & E; BET; C-SPAN; CNBC; CNN; Discovery Channel; FX; Fox Family Channel; Headline News; Lifetime; MTV; Nashville Network; Nickelodeon; Northwest Cable News; QVC; TBS Superstation.
Current originations: Government access; leased access.
Fee: $44.95 installation; $23.83 monthly; $1.50 converter.

Expanded Basic Service
Subscribers: 1,141.
Programming (via satellite): American Movie Classics; ESPN; Fox Sports Net Northwest; Turner Network TV; USA Network.
Fee: $12.07 monthly.

Pay Service 1
Pay Units: 178.
Programming (via satellite): Cinemax.
Fee: $13.20 monthly.

Pay Service 2
Pay Units: 153.
Programming (via satellite): Disney Channel.
Fee: $12.45 monthly.

Pay Service 3
Pay Units: 511.
Programming (via satellite): The New Encore.
Fee: $1.75 monthly.

Pay Service 4
Pay Units: 340.
Programming (via satellite): HBO.
Fee: $14.15 monthly.

Pay Service 5
Pay Units: 151.
Programming (via satellite): Showtime.
Fee: $14.15 monthly.

Pay Service 6
Pay Units: 500.
Programming (via satellite): Starz!
Fee: $6.75 monthly.

Pay Service 7
Pay Units: 29.
Programming (via satellite): DMX.
Fee: $9.95 monthly.

Pay-Per-View
Addressable homes: 58.

Miles of plant: 32.5 (coaxial); None (fiber optic). Homes passed: 2,108. Total homes in franchised area: 2,452.
Manager: Barbara J. Wyatt. Customer service manager: Kathy Parhomski.
Ownership: AT&T Broadband & Internet Services (MSO). Purchased from Tele-Communications Inc., March 9, 1999.

MEDICAL LAKE—Cheney/Medical Lake TV Cable, Box 117, Cheney, WA 99004. Phone: 509-235-5144. County: Spokane. ICA: WA0066.
TV Market Ranking: 76. Franchise award date: N.A. Franchise expiration date: N.A. Began: October 3, 1981.
Channel capacity: 12. Channels available but not in use: None.

Basic Service
Subscribers: 920.
Programming (received off-air): KWSU-TV (P) Pullman; KHQ-TV (N), KREM-TV (C), KSPS-TV (P), KXLY-TV (A) Spokane.
Programming (via satellite): WGN-TV (W) Chicago; CNN; ESPN; TBS Superstation; Turner Classic Movies.
Fee: $19.95 installation; $8.50 monthly.

Pay Service 1
Pay Units: N.A.
Programming (via satellite): Cinemax; HBO.
Fee: $10.45 monthly (HBO).

Miles of plant: 21.7 (coaxial). Homes passed: 1,300.
Ownership: Davis Communications Inc. (MSO).

METALINE FALLS—Community Cable Service, 729 S. Bernard St., Spokane, WA 99204. Phones: 509-624-4140; 800-572-0902. Fax: 509-624-7372. County: Pend Oreille. Also serves Metaline. ICA: WA0113.
TV Market Ranking: Outside TV Markets. Franchise award date: N.A. Franchise expiration date: N.A. Began: July 1, 1958.
Channel capacity: 35 (2-way capable; not operating 2-way). Channels available but not in use: 11.

Basic Service
Subscribers: 213.
Programming (received off-air): KHQ-TV (N), KREM-TV (C), KSPS-TV (P), KXLY-TV (A) Spokane; allband FM.
Programming (via satellite): WGN-TV (W) Chicago; KMGH-TV (A), KUSA-TV (N) Denver; A & E; C-SPAN; CNBC; CNN; Cartoon Network; Comedy Central; Discovery Channel; E! Entertainment TV; ESPN; ESPN 2; Fox Family Channel; FoxNet; Goodlife TV Network; Headline News; History Channel; Learning Channel; Lifetime; Nashville Network; Nick at Nite's TV Land; Odyssey; Sci-Fi Channel; TBS Superstation; Turner Classic Movies; Turner Network TV; USA Network; ValueVision.
Fee: $15.00 installation; $19.88 monthly.

Pay Service 1
Pay Units: 55.
Programming (via satellite): Cinemax.
Fee: $5.95 monthly.

Pay Service 2
Pay Units: 37.
Programming (via satellite): Disney Channel.
Fee: $4.95 monthly.

Pay Service 3
Pay Units: 58.
Programming (via satellite): HBO.
Fee: $8.95 monthly.

Equipment: Nexus & Pico headend; Jerrold amplifiers; Trilogy cable.
Miles of plant: 8.0 (coaxial); None (fiber optic). Homes passed: 348.
Manager: Martin Howser.
City fee: None.
Ownership: Martin Howser (MSO).

MINERAL—TCI Cablevision of Southwest Washington Inc., Box 129, Olympia, WA 98507. Phones: 360-736-1166; 800-221-5232. Fax: 360-736-1160. County: Lewis. ICA: WA0132.
TV Market Ranking: Outside TV Markets. Franchise award date: N.A. Franchise expiration date: March 1, 2032. Began: June 1, 1984.
Channel capacity: 35 (not 2-way capable). Channels available but not in use: 11.

Basic Service
Subscribers: 118.
Programming (received off-air): KCPQ (F), KCTS-TV (P), KING-TV (N), KIRO-TV (C), KOMO-TV (A), KSTW (U) Seattle-Tacoma; allband FM.
Programming (via satellite): WGN-TV (W) Chicago; ESPN; Fox Family Channel; Nashville Network.
Fee: $60.00 installation; $18.20 monthly; $40.00 additional installation.

Pay Service 1
Pay Units: 62.
Programming (via satellite): HBO.
Fee: $9.95 installation; $10.95 monthly.

Equipment: Blonder-Tongue & Scientific-Atlanta headend; Magnavox amplifiers; Magnavox satellite antenna; Magnavox satellite receivers.
Miles of plant: 8.0 (coaxial). Homes passed: 169. Total homes in franchised area: 169.
Manager: Paul Renz.
City fee: None.
Ownership: AT&T Broadband & Internet Services (MSO). Purchased from Tele-Communications Inc., March 9, 1999.

MONTESANO—TCI Cablevision of Washington Inc., Box 129, 440 Yauger St., Olympia, WA 98507-0129. Phone: 360-357-3364. Fax: 360-532-5978. County: Grays Harbor. Also serves Elma, Grays Harbor County, McCleary. ICA: WA0032.
TV Market Ranking: Outside TV Markets. Franchise award date: N.A. Franchise expiration date: N.A. Began: January 1, 1954.
Channel capacity: 40. Channels available but not in use: N.A.

Basic Service
Subscribers: 5,166.
Programming (received off-air): KCKA (P) Centralia; allband FM.
Programming (via microwave): KPTV (U) Portland; KCPQ (F), KCTS-TV (P), KING-TV (N), KIRO-TV (C), KOMO-TV (A), KSTW (U), KTWB (W) Seattle-Tacoma.
Programming (via satellite): A & E; C-SPAN; CNN; Comedy Central; Discovery Channel; Fox Family Channel; Lifetime; MTV; Nashville Network; Nickelodeon; Odyssey; QVC; TBS Superstation; VH1.
Current originations: Automated time-weather.
Fee: $60.00 installation; $9.64 monthly; $0.63 converter; $40.00 additional installation.

Expanded Basic Service
Subscribers: 4,664.
Programming (via satellite): American Movie Classics; Court TV; ESPN; Fox Sports

Net Northwest; Turner Network TV; USA Network.
Fee: $11.03 monthly.

Pay Service 1
Pay Units: 422.
Programming (via satellite): Disney Channel.
Fee: N.A.

Pay Service 2
Pay Units: 2,008.
Programming (via satellite): The New Encore.
Fee: N.A.

Pay Service 3
Pay Units: 563.
Programming (via satellite): HBO.
Fee: N.A.

Pay Service 4
Pay Units: 172.
Programming (via satellite): The Movie Channel.
Fee: N.A.

Pay Service 5
Pay Units: 537.
Programming (via satellite): Showtime.
Fee: N.A.

Pay-Per-View
Movies.

Local advertising: Yes. Available in character-generated & taped programming.
Equipment: Microwave Assoc. & Scientific-Atlanta headend; Magnavox amplifiers; MSI character generator; Jerrold set top converters; Jerrold addressable set top converters; Arcom & Eagle addressable traps; Scientific-Atlanta satellite antenna.
Miles of plant: 132.6 (coaxial). Total homes in franchised area: 5,272.
Manager: Fred Comer. Chief technician: Wally Weidman. Marketing director: Carrie Prante.
City fee: 6% of gross (Elma & Montesano).
Ownership: AT&T Broadband & Internet Services (MSO). Purchased from Tele-Communications Inc., March 9, 1999.

MORTON—Mike's TV Inc., Box J, 201 Main St., Morton, WA 98356. Phone: 360-496-5635. Fax: 360-496-5635. County: Lewis. Also serves Lewis County. ICA: WA0082.
TV Market Ranking: Outside TV Markets. Franchise award date: January 1, 1968. Franchise expiration date: April 1, 2016. Began: January 1, 1950.
Channel capacity: 36 (not 2-way capable). Channels available but not in use: 4.

Basic Service
Subscribers: 647.
Programming (received off-air): KCPQ (F), KSTW (U) Seattle-Tacoma; allband FM.
Programming (via satellite): WGN-TV (W) Chicago; KCTS-TV (P), KING-TV (N), KIRO-TV (U), KOMO-TV (A) Seattle; CNN; Country Music TV; Discovery Channel; Fox Family Channel; Headline News; Home Shopping Network; Nashville Network; Nickelodeon; Northwest Cable News; TBS Superstation.
Current originations: Automated time-weather.
Fee: $25.00 installation; $24.70 monthly.

Expanded Basic Service
Subscribers: 615.
Programming (via satellite): Animal Planet; Comedy Central; E! Entertainment TV; ESPN; ESPN 2; Fox Sports Net Northwest; History Channel; Learning Channel; Outdoor Channel; Turner Classic Movies; Turner Network TV; USA Network.
Fee: $10.00 installation; $7.50 monthly.

Pay Service 1
Pay Units: 174.
Programming (via satellite): HBO.
Fee: $20.00 installation; $10.95 monthly.

Local advertising: Yes. Available in character-generated programming. Rates: $2.00/30 Seconds. Local sales manager: Esper Michael Fairhart.
Equipment: Blonder-Tongue headend; Magnavox amplifiers; Comm/Scope cable; BEI character generator; Eagle traps; Hughes satellite antenna; Scientific-Atlanta satellite receivers.
Miles of plant: 30.0 (coaxial); None (fiber optic). Homes passed: 780. Total homes in franchised area: 780.
Manager: Esper Michael Fairhart. Customer service manager: Sheryl K. Fairhart.
City fee: $100 annually.
Ownership: Mike's TV Inc.

MOSES LAKE—Northland Cable, Drawer T, 1305 Wheeler Rd., Moses Lake, WA 98837. Phone: 509-765-6151. Fax: 509-765-5132. County: Grant. Also serves Grant County, Larson AFB. ICA: WA0167.
TV Market Ranking: Below 100 (portions of Grant County); Outside TV Markets (portions of Grant County, Larson AFB, Moses Lake). Franchise award date: N.A. Franchise expiration date: December 31, 2001. Began: January 1, 1954.
Channel capacity: 40 (2-way capable). Channels available but not in use: 2.

Basic Service
Subscribers: 7,025.
Programming (received off-air): KING-TV (N), KIRO-TV (C), KOMO-TV (A), KSTW (U) Seattle-Tacoma; KAYU-TV (F), KHQ-TV (N), KREM-TV (C), KSPS-TV (P), KXLY-TV (A) Spokane; 2 FMs.
Programming (via satellite): WGN-TV (W) Chicago; C-SPAN; Fox Family Channel; QVC; TV Guide Channel; The Inspirational Network.
Current originations: Public access.
Fee: $45.00 installation; $10.00 monthly.

Expanded Basic Service
Subscribers: N.A.
Programming (via microwave): TVW.
Programming (via satellite): A & E; CNN; Country Music TV; Discovery Channel; ESPN; Fox News Channel; Fox Sports Net Northwest; Headline News; Home & Garden Television; Lifetime; MuchMusic Network; Nashville Network; Northwest Cable News; TBS Superstation; TV Food Network; The Weather Channel; Turner Network TV; USA Network; Univision.
Fee: N.A.

Expanded Basic Service 2
Subscribers: N.A.
Programming (via satellite): American Movie Classics; CNNfn; Cartoon Network; ESPN 2; fXM: Movies from Fox; Golf Channel; History Channel; Nickelodeon; Turner Classic Movies.
Fee: N.A.

Pay Service 1
Pay Units: 524.
Programming (via satellite): Cinemax.
Fee: $9.15 monthly.

Pay Service 2
Pay Units: 889.
Programming (via satellite): Disney Channel.
Fee: $8.70 monthly.

Pay Service 3
Pay Units: 1,473.
Programming (via satellite): HBO.
Fee: $12.30 monthly.

Pay Service 4
Pay Units: 499.
Programming (via satellite): The Movie Channel.
Fee: $10.95 monthly.

Pay Service 5
Pay Units: 606.
Programming (via satellite): Showtime.
Fee: $9.25 monthly.

Pay Service 6
Pay Units: N.A.
Programming (via satellite): Starz!; The New Encore.
Fee: N.A.

Pay-Per-View
Special events.

Local advertising: Yes. Available in locally originated & character-generated programming.
Program Guide: TV Host.
Equipment: RCA & Scientific-Atlanta headend; Magnavox amplifiers; Comm/Scope cable; Sony VTRs; MSI character generator; Oak set top converters; Pico traps; Scientific-Atlanta & AFC satellite antenna; Microdyne, Scientific-Atlanta & Standard Communications satellite receivers; ChannelMatic commercial insert.
Miles of plant: 125.2 (coaxial). Total homes in franchised area: 7,885.
Manager: Dawn Hill. Chief technician: Kim Svetich.
City fee: 8% of gross (utility tax).
Ownership: Northland Communications Corp. (MSO).

MOSSYROCK—TCI Cablevision of Southwest Washington Inc., Box 129, Olympia, WA 98507. Phones: 360-736-1166; 800-221-5232. Fax: 360-736-1160. County: Lewis. Also serves Lewis County, Mayfield Lake. ICA: WA0091.
TV Market Ranking: Outside TV Markets. Franchise award date: N.A. Franchise expiration date: March 1, 2032. Began: January 1, 1981.
Channel capacity: 23 (not 2-way capable). Channels available but not in use: N.A.

Basic Service
Subscribers: 424.
Programming (received off-air): KCKA (P) Centralia; KING-TV (N), KIRO-TV (C), KOMO-TV (A), KSTW (U) Seattle-Tacoma; allband FM.
Programming (via satellite): WGN-TV (W) Chicago; ESPN; Fox Family Channel; Nashville Network; TBS Superstation; USA Network.
Fee: $60.00 installation; $17.46 monthly; $40.00 additional installation.

Pay Service 1
Pay Units: 129.
Programming (via satellite): HBO.
Fee: $9.95 installation; $10.00 monthly.

Equipment: Blonder-Tongue, Jerrold & Scientific-Atlanta headend; Magnavox amplifiers; M/A-Com cable; Microwave Assoc. satellite antenna.
Miles of plant: 23.0 (coaxial). Homes passed: 561. Total homes in franchised area: 561.
Manager: Paul Renz.
City fee: 3% of gross (utility tax).
Ownership: AT&T Broadband & Internet Services (MSO). Purchased from Tele-Communications Inc., March 9, 1999.

NACHES—Columbia Basin Cable, Box 490, 611 6th St., Umatilla, OR 97882. Phones: 541-922-5759; 800-521-3916. Fax: 541-922-3758. County: Yakima. Also serves Cowiche, Gleed, Selah, Tieton, Yakima County (unincorporated areas). ICA: WA0059.
TV Market Ranking: Below 100. Franchise award date: N.A. Franchise expiration date: N.A. Began: January 1, 1984.
Channel capacity: 35. Channels available but not in use: 6.

Basic Service
Subscribers: 913.
Programming (received off-air): KTVT (C) Dallas-Fort Worth; KAPP (A), KIMA-TV (C), KNDO (N), KYVE-TV (P) Yakima.
Programming (via microwave): K53CY (F) Yakima.
Programming (via satellite): WGN-TV (W) Chicago; A & E; Animal Planet; C-SPAN; Discovery Channel; ESPN; FX; fXM: Movies from Fox; Fox Family Channel; Fox Sports Net Northwest; Goodlife TV Network; Headline News; History Channel; Lifetime; MTV; Nashville Network; Nickelodeon; QVC; TBS Superstation; Turner Network TV; USA Network; Univision; VH1.
Fee: $35.00 installation; $27.75 monthly.

Pay Service 1
Pay Units: 48.
Programming (via satellite): Disney Channel.
Fee: $9.95 monthly.

Pay Service 2
Pay Units: 150.
Programming (via satellite): HBO.
Fee: $10.95 monthly.

Pay Service 3
Pay Units: 57.
Programming (via satellite): Starz!
Fee: $7.95 monthly.

Miles of plant: 70.0 (coaxial); None (fiber optic). Homes passed: 1,850.
Manager: Kerry Stratton. Chief technician: Darrell Johnson. Marketing director & customer service manager: Charlotte Winkler.
Ownership: USA Media Group LLC (MSO). Purchased from Cambridge Communications, May 15, 1999.

NAPAVINE—Millennium Digital Media, Suite 107, 3633 136th Place SE, Bellevue, WA 98006. Phones: 425-747-4600; 800-829-2225. Fax: 425-644-4621.
Web site: http://www.millenniumdigital.com.
County: Lewis. ICA: WA0106.
TV Market Ranking: Outside TV Markets. Franchise award date: N.A. Franchise expiration date: January 1, 2008. Began: July 1, 1983.
Channel capacity: 35. Channels available but not in use: N.A.

Basic Service
Subscribers: 387.
Programming (received off-air): KCKA (P) Centralia; KCPQ (F), KCTS-TV (P), KING-TV (N), KIRO-TV (C), KOMO-TV (A), KSTW (U), KTWB (W) Seattle-Tacoma.
Programming (via microwave): TVW.
Programming (via satellite): WGN-TV (W) Chicago; American Movie Classics; Animal Planet; CNN; Cartoon Network; Discovery Channel; E! Entertainment TV; ESPN; FX; Fox Family Channel; Fox Sports Net Northwest; Headline News; History Channel; Home & Garden Television; Learning Channel; Nashville Network; Nickelodeon; Northwest Cable News; QVC; Sci-Fi Channel; TBS Superstation; Turner Classic Movies; Turner Network TV; USA Network.
Current originations: Public access; government access.
Fee: $45.00 installation; $27.95 monthly.

Pay Service 1
Pay Units: N.A.
Programming (via satellite): Disney Channel; HBO; Showtime.
Fee: $8.95 monthly (Disney), $14.95 monthly (HBO or Showtime).

Equipment: Cadco headend; Pathmaker amplifiers; Times Fiber cable; Video Data Systems character generator; Eagle traps; Prodelin satellite antenna; M/A-Com satellite receivers.
Miles of plant: 12.3 (coaxial).

Manager: Steve Weed. Chief technician: Gene Fry.
City fee: 3% of gross.
Ownership: Millennium Digital Media LLC (MSO). Purchased from Summit Communications Inc., April 7, 1999.

NASELLE—Falcon Community Ventures I, 1241 Duane St., Astoria, OR 97103. Phone: 503-325-6114. Fax: 503-325-7421. County: Pacific. ICA: WA0169.
TV Market Ranking: Outside TV Markets. Franchise award date: N.A. Franchise expiration date: N.A. Began: September 1, 1967.
Channel capacity: 14. Channels available but not in use: None.
Basic Service
Subscribers: 310.
Programming (received off-air): KATU (A), KGW (N), KOIN (C), KOPB-TV (P), KPTV (U) Portland; KCPQ (F) Seattle-Tacoma; allband FM.
Programming (via satellite): CNN; ESPN; Fox Family Channel.
Fee: $40.00 installation; $13.70 monthly.
Expanded Basic Service
Subscribers: 290.
Programming (via satellite): Disney Channel; Nashville Network; Sci-Fi Channel; TBS Superstation.
Fee: $4.57 monthly.
Pay Service 1
Pay Units: 112.
Programming (via satellite): HBO.
Fee: $11.95 monthly.
Equipment: Blonder-Tongue & Jerrold headend; Vikoa amplifiers; Times Fiber & Vikoa cable; Eagle traps; Scientific-Atlanta satellite antenna; M/A-Com satellite receivers.
Miles of plant: 18.0 (coaxial). Homes passed: 428.
Manager: Ray Romine. Chief technician: Bruce Johnson.
Ownership: Falcon Communications LP (MSO), joint venture formed September 30, 1998. See Cable System Ownership.

NESPELEM—JKA Cable Systems Inc., Box 1273, Mount Vernon, WA 98273. Phones: 360-424-0426; 800-338-2521. Fax: 360-428-9063. County: Okanogan. Also serves Colville Indian Agency. ICA: WA0170.
TV Market Ranking: Outside TV Markets. Franchise award date: N.A. Franchise expiration date: N.A. Began: August 1, 1962.
Channel capacity: 12 (not 2-way capable). Channels available but not in use: 2.
Basic Service
Subscribers: 230.
Programming (received off-air): KAYU-TV (F), KHQ-TV (N), KREM-TV (C), KSPS-TV (P), KXLY-TV (A) Spokane; allband FM.
Programming (via satellite): Discovery Channel; ESPN; Learning Channel; Sci-Fi Channel; Turner Network TV.
Fee: $60.00 installation; $7.72 monthly.
Pay Service 1
Pay Units: 2.
Programming (via satellite): The New Encore.
Fee: N.A.
Equipment: Blonder-Tongue headend; Scientific-Atlanta amplifiers.
Miles of plant: 11.1 (coaxial). Homes passed: 275. Total homes in franchised area: 587.
Owner: Jerry Swatman.
City fee: $12.00 annually.
Ownership: AT&T Broadband & Internet Services (MSO). Purchased from Tele-Communications Inc., March 9, 1999.

NEWPORT—Concept Cable, Box 810, 412 S. Union, Newport, WA 99156. Phone: 208-437-4544. Fax: 208-437-2740. Counties: Pend Oreille, WA; Bonner, ID. Also serves Bonner County (southern portion), Oldtown, Priest River, ID; Pend Oreille County, WA. ICA: WA0195.
TV Market Ranking: Outside TV Markets. Franchise award date: August 1, 1993. Franchise expiration date: July 31, 2003. Began: January 1, 1994.
Channel capacity: 78 (not 2-way capable). Channels available but not in use: 2.
Basic Service
Subscribers: 1,021.
Programming (received off-air): KUID-TV (P) Moscow; KAYU-TV (F), KHQ-TV (N), KREM-TV (C), KSKN (U,W), KSPS-TV (P), KXLY-TV (A) Spokane.
Programming (via satellite): C-SPAN; Fox News Channel; Northwest Cable News; TV Guide Channel.
Current originations: Educational access; government access.
Fee: $9.45 monthly; $0.40 converter.
Expanded Basic Service
Subscribers: 965.
Programming (via satellite): WGN-TV (W) Chicago; A & E; American Movie Classics; Animal Planet; CNBC; CNN; Cartoon Network; Comedy Central; Country Music TV; Court TV; Discovery Channel; E! Entertainment TV; ESPN; ESPN 2; ESPN Classic Sports; FX; fXM: Movies from Fox; Fox Family Channel; Fox Sports Net Northwest; Goodlife TV Network; Headline News; History Channel; Home & Garden Television; Knowledge TV; Learning Channel; Lifetime; MTV; MuchMusic Network; Nashville Network; Nick at Nite's TV Land; Nickelodeon; Odyssey; Outdoor Channel; QVC; Sci-Fi Channel; TBS Superstation; TV Food Network; The Health Network; The Weather Channel; Travel Channel; Trinity Bcstg. Network; Turner Classic Movies; Turner Network TV; USA Network; VH1; Z Music Television.
Fee: $9.95 monthly.
Pay Service 1
Pay Units: N.A.
Programming (via satellite): Cinemax (multiplexed); Disney Channel; HBO (multiplexed); MOVIEplex; Showtime (multiplexed); Starz!; The Movie Channel; The New Encore.
Fee: $2.95 monthly (Encore & Starz), $7.45 monthly (Disney), $7.95 monthly (TMC), $9.95 monthly (Cinemax, HBO or Showtime).
Pay-Per-View
Addressable homes: 600.
Miles of plant: 40.0 (coaxial); 10.0 (fiber optic). Homes passed: 1,800.
Manager: Keith Antcliff. Program & marketing director: Doris Dale.
Ownership: Keith Antcliff (MSO).

NORTH BONNEVILLE—North Bonneville Community Cable TV System, Box 7, North Bonneville, WA 98639. Phone: 509-427-8182. Fax: 509-427-7214. E-mail: cityofnb@saw.net. County: Skamania. ICA: WA0131.
TV Market Ranking: 29. Franchise award date: N.A. Franchise expiration date: N.A. Began: April 1, 1982.
Channel capacity: N.A. Channels available but not in use: N.A.
Basic Service
Subscribers: 185.
Programming (received off-air): KATU (A), KGW (N), KOIN (C), KOPB-TV (P), KPTV (U) Portland; KPDX (F) Vancouver; allband FM.
Programming (via satellite): WGN-TV (W) Chicago; CNN; Discovery Channel; Disney Channel; ESPN; Fox Family Channel; Nashville Network; Nickelodeon; Northwest Cable News; TBS Superstation; Turner Classic Movies; Turner Network TV.
Fee: $35.00 installation; $16.50 monthly.
Pay Service 1
Pay Units: 51.
Programming (via satellite): HBO.
Fee: $11.00 monthly.
Pay-Per-View
Special events.
Equipment: Scientific-Atlanta headend; Scientific-Atlanta amplifiers; Scientific-Atlanta cable; Scientific-Atlanta traps; Scientific-Atlanta satellite antenna; Scientific-Atlanta satellite receivers.
Miles of plant: 12.0 (coaxial). Homes passed: 208.
Manager: Ray Hays.
Ownership: North Bonneville Community Cable TV System.

NORTHPORT—Falcon Telecable, 189 Buena Vista Dr., Colville, WA 99114. Phone: 509-684-3797. Fax: 509-684-6108. County: Stevens. ICA: WA0172.
TV Market Ranking: Outside TV Markets. Franchise award date: N.A. Franchise expiration date: N.A. Began: N.A.
Channel capacity: 14. Channels available but not in use: None.
Basic Service
Subscribers: 88.
Programming (received off-air): KHQ-TV (N), KREM-TV (C), KSPS-TV (P), KXLY-TV (A) Spokane; CHAN-TV Vancouver.
Programming (via translator): CBUT Vancouver.
Programming (via satellite): CNN; ESPN; QVC.
Fee: $49.95 installation; $18.22 monthly.
Expanded Basic Service
Subscribers: 89.
Programming (via satellite): Country Music TV; Discovery Channel; Disney Channel; TBS Superstation.
Fee: $4.94 monthly.
Pay Service 1
Pay Units: 26.
Programming (via satellite): Showtime.
Fee: $10.95 monthly.
Local advertising: Yes.
Miles of plant: 3.0 (coaxial). Homes passed: 100.
Manager: Melvin Fox. Chief technician: Mark Sterkell.
Franchise fee: 2% of gross.
Ownership: Falcon Communications LP (MSO), joint venture formed September 30, 1998. See Cable System Ownership.

OAKESDALE—Northwest Cable LP, Box 618, Lockney, TX 79241. Phone: 800-480-3766. Fax: 806-652-3139. County: Whitman. ICA: WA0125.
TV Market Ranking: Below 100. Franchise award date: N.A. Franchise expiration date: N.A. Began: December 1, 1983.
Channel capacity: 24 (2-way capable; operating 2-way). Channels available but not in use: 12.
Basic Service
Subscribers: 106.
Programming (received off-air): KWSU-TV (P) Pullman; KAYU-TV (F), KHQ-TV (N), KREM-TV (C), KSPS-TV (P), KXLY-TV (A) Spokane.
Programming (via satellite): CNN; ESPN; Fox Family Channel; Headline News; Turner Classic Movies; USA Network.
Planned originations: Government access.
Fee: $25.00 installation; $12.00 monthly.
Pay Service 1
Pay Units: N.A.
Programming (via satellite): HBO.
Fee: $10.00 monthly.
Equipment: Scientific-Atlanta headend; Magnavox amplifiers; Comm/Scope cable; Pico traps; Anixter-Mark satellite antenna; Scientific-Atlanta satellite receivers.
Miles of plant: 6.0 (coaxial). Homes passed: 200. Total homes in franchised area: 200.
Manager: Kenneth V. Mettler. Chief technician: Joseph R. Poire.
City fee: 3% of gross.
Ownership: Northwest Cable Ltd. Partnership (MSO).

OCEAN SHORES—Coast Communications Co. Inc., Box 1569, Ocean Shores, WA 98569. Phone: 360-289-2252. Fax: 360-289-2750. County: Grays Harbor. Also serves Copalis Beach, Copalis Crossing, Grays Harbor County, Hogan's Corner, Ocean City, Pacific Beach. ICA: WA0042.
TV Market Ranking: Outside TV Markets. Franchise award date: August 17, 1967. Franchise expiration date: August 17, 2005. Began: February 1, 1968.
Channel capacity: 60 (not 2-way capable). Channels available but not in use: 3.
Basic Service
Subscribers: 2,311.
Programming (received off-air): 9 FMs.
Programming (via microwave): KCPQ (F), KCTS-TV (P), KING-TV (N), KIRO-TV (C), KOMO-TV (A), KSTW (U) Seattle-Tacoma.
Programming (via satellite): A & E; C-SPAN; CNBC; CNN; Court TV; Discovery Channel; ESPN; Fox Family Channel; Fox Sports Net Northwest; Headline News; History Channel; Home Shopping Network; Learning Channel; Lifetime; Nashville Network; Northwest Cable News; QVC; Sci-Fi Channel; TBS Superstation; The Weather Channel; Travel Channel; Trinity Bcstg. Network; Turner Classic Movies; Turner Network TV; USA Network.
Current originations: Automated time-weather; educational access.
Fee: $60.00 installation; $28.54 monthly; $2.95 converter; $10.00 additional installation.
Expanded Basic Service
Subscribers: N.A.
Programming (via satellite): Cartoon Network; MTV; Nickelodeon.
Fee: $5.95 monthly.
Pay Service 1
Pay Units: 150.
Programming (via satellite): Cinemax; Starz!; The New Encore.
Fee: $12.95 monthly (package).
Pay Service 2
Pay Units: 116.
Programming (via satellite): Disney Channel.
Fee: $8.95 monthly.
Pay Service 3
Pay Units: 321.
Programming (via satellite): HBO (multiplexed).
Fee: $12.95 monthly.
Pay Service 4
Pay Units: 109.
Programming (via satellite): DMX.
Fee: $8.95 monthly.
Pay Service 5
Pay Units: N.A.
Programming (via satellite): Showtime (multiplexed).
Fee: $12.95 monthly.

Pay-Per-View
Addressable homes: 320.
Spice.
Local advertising: Yes. Available in character-generated programming. Rates: $30.00/Month.
Equipment: Scientific-Atlanta headend; Jerrold & Magnavox amplifiers; Amphenol, Comm/Scope & Times Fiber cable; MSI & Texscan character generator; Jerrold, Magnavox & Hamlin set top converters; Pico & Eagle traps; Prodelin & Scientific-Atlanta satellite antenna; Scientific-Atlanta satellite receivers.
Miles of plant: 80.0 (coaxial). Homes passed: 3,000. Total homes in franchised area: 3,000.
Manager: Ron Thomasson.
City fee: 3% of gross.
Ownership: Edward Hewson (MSO).

ODESSA—Community Cable Service, 729 S. Bernard St., Spokane, WA 99204. Phones: 509-624-4140; 800-572-0902. Fax: 509-624-7372. County: Lincoln. ICA: WA0173.
TV Market Ranking: Outside TV Markets. Franchise award date: N.A. Franchise expiration date: N.A. Began: N.A.
Channel capacity: 62 (2-way capable; not operating 2-way). Channels available but not in use: 5.
Basic Service
Subscribers: 372.
Programming (received off-air): KAYU-TV (F), KHQ-TV (N), KREM-TV (C), KSPS-TV (P), KXLY-TV (A) Spokane.
Programming (via satellite): WGN-TV (W) Chicago; A & E; American Movie Classics; Bravo; C-SPAN; CNBC; CNN; CNN International; Cartoon Network; Comedy Central; Country Music TV; Discovery Channel; E! Entertainment TV; ESPN; ESPN 2; ESPNews; EWTN; Fox Family Channel; Fox News Channel; Fox Sports Net Northwest; Goodlife TV Network; Headline News; History Channel; Home & Garden Television; Home Shopping Network; Knowledge TV; Learning Channel; Lifetime; MTV; Nashville Network; Nick at Nite's TV Land; Nickelodeon; Odyssey; QVC; Sci-Fi Channel; TBS Superstation; TV Food Network; The Health Network; The Inspirational Network; Travel Channel; Trinity Bcstg. Network; Turner Classic Movies; Turner Network TV; USA Network; VH1; ValueVision; Z Music Television.
Current originations: Local news.
Fee: $15.00 installation; $26.86 monthly.
Pay Service 1
Pay Units: 74.
Programming (via satellite): Cinemax.
Fee: $5.00 installation; $6.36 monthly.
Pay Service 2
Pay Units: 56.
Programming (via satellite): Disney Channel.
Fee: $5.00 installation; $5.29 monthly.
Pay Service 3
Pay Units: 83.
Programming (via satellite): HBO.
Fee: $5.00 installation; $9.56 monthly.
Pay Service 4
Pay Units: N.A.
Programming (via satellite): Showtime.
Fee: $8.01 monthly.
Homes passed: 491.
Manager: Martin Howser.
Ownership: Martin Howser (MSO).

OLYMPIA—TCI Cablevision of Washington Inc., Box 129, 440 Yauger St., Olympia, WA 98507-0129. Phone: 360-357-3364. Counties: Pierce & Thurston. Also serves Lacey, Scott Lake, Steamboat Island, Summit Lake, Tenino, Thurston County (portions), Tumwater. ICA: WA0007.
TV Market Ranking: 20 (Lacey, Olympia, Scott Lake, Steamboat Island, Summit Lake, Tenino, portions of Thurston County, Tumwater); Outside TV Markets (portions of Thurston County). Franchise award date: N.A. Franchise expiration date: July 1, 2000. Began: February 1, 1966.
Channel capacity: 59. Channels available but not in use: N.A.
Basic Service
Subscribers: 41,775.
Programming (received off-air): KCKA (P) Centralia; KCPQ (F), KCTS-TV (P), KING-TV (N), KIRO-TV (C), KOMO-TV (A), KSTW (U), KTBW-TV (T), KTWB (W) Seattle-Tacoma; CBUT Vancouver; 20 FMs.
Programming (via satellite): A & E; C-SPAN; CNBC; CNN; Discovery Channel; Fox Family Channel; Headline News; Lifetime; MTV; Nashville Network; Nickelodeon; QVC; TBS Superstation.
Current originations: Automated time-weather; public access.
Fee: $60.00 installation; $9.77 monthly; $0.84 converter; $40.00 additional installation.
Expanded Basic Service
Subscribers: 34,463.
Programming (via satellite): American Movie Classics; ESPN; Fox Sports Net Northwest; Turner Network TV; USA Network.
Fee: $12.78 monthly.
Pay Service 1
Pay Units: 3,487.
Programming (via satellite): Cinemax.
Fee: $13.15 monthly.
Pay Service 2
Pay Units: 2,939.
Programming (via satellite): Disney Channel.
Fee: $10.95 monthly.
Pay Service 3
Pay Units: 11,560.
Programming (via satellite): The New Encore.
Fee: N.A.
Pay Service 4
Pay Units: 9,558.
Programming (via satellite): HBO.
Fee: $13.15 monthly.
Pay Service 5
Pay Units: 2,517.
Programming (via satellite): Showtime.
Fee: $13.15 monthly.
Local advertising: Yes.
Program Guide: The Cable Guide.
Equipment: Jerrold headend; Jerrold amplifiers; Essex, Systems Wire & Times Fiber cable; Scientific-Atlanta satellite antenna.
Miles of plant: 956.0 (coaxial). Homes passed: 55,941. Total homes in franchised area: 60,958.
Manager: Bill Lawson.
City fee: 4.5% of gross (Olympia).
Ownership: AT&T Broadband & Internet Services (MSO). Purchased from Tele-Communications Inc., March 9, 1999.

OMAK—TCI Cablevision of Okanogan Valley Inc., 1140 N. 94th St., Seattle, WA 98103-3306. Phone: 206-527-7545. Fax: 206-663-9072. County: Okanogan. Also serves Okanogan County (unincorporated areas). ICA: WA0044.
TV Market Ranking: Outside TV Markets. Franchise award date: January 1, 1953. Franchise expiration date: N.A. Began: August 1, 1953.
Channel capacity: 34 (not 2-way capable). Channels available but not in use: N.A.
Basic Service
Subscribers: 2,490.
Programming (received off-air): KAYU-TV (F) Spokane; 3 FMs.
Programming (via microwave): KSTW (U) Seattle-Tacoma; KHQ-TV (N), KREM-TV (C), KSPS-TV (P), KXLY-TV (A) Spokane; CHAN-TV Vancouver.
Programming (via satellite): A & E; CNN; Discovery Channel; Fox Family Channel; Lifetime; MTV; Nickelodeon; TBS Superstation; The Weather Channel.
Current originations: Public access.
Fee: $60.00 installation; $9.44 monthly; $2.95 converter; $40.00 additional installation.
Expanded Basic Service
Subscribers: 2,134.
Programming (via satellite): American Movie Classics; ESPN; Fox Sports Net Northwest; Nashville Network; USA Network.
Fee: $11.44 monthly.
Pay Service 1
Pay Units: 117.
Programming (via satellite): Cinemax.
Fee: $15.00 installation; $11.95 monthly.
Pay Service 2
Pay Units: 205.
Programming (via satellite): Disney Channel.
Fee: $15.00 installation; $8.50 monthly.
Pay Service 3
Pay Units: 818.
Programming (via satellite): The New Encore.
Fee: N.A.
Pay Service 4
Pay Units: 231.
Programming (via satellite): HBO.
Fee: $15.00 installation; $11.95 monthly.
Pay Service 5
Pay Units: 142.
Programming (via satellite): Showtime.
Fee: $15.00 installation; $11.95 monthly.
Local advertising: Yes (insert only). Available in locally originated & taped programming.
Program Guide: CableView.
Equipment: Catel, Scientific-Atlanta & M/A-Com headend; Broadband & Magnavox amplifiers; Comm/Scope & Times Fiber cable; Hamlin & Panasonic set top converters; Pico traps; Scientific-Atlanta satellite antenna; Scientific-Atlanta, M/A-Com & Standard Communications satellite receivers.
Miles of plant: 58.8 (coaxial). Homes passed: 2,679. Total homes in franchised area: 5,047.
Manager: Bob Lam. Chief technician: Marty Adams.
City fee: 10% of gross.
Ownership: AT&T Broadband & Internet Services (MSO). Purchased from Tele-Communications Inc., March 9, 1999.

ORCAS ISLAND—Sun Country Cable, Box 127, 7 D St. SW, Quincy, WA 98848. Phone: 509-787-3543. Fax: 509-787-3884. County: San Juan. ICA: WA0083.
TV Market Ranking: Below 100. Franchise award date: N.A. Franchise expiration date: N.A. Began: August 15, 1989.
Channel capacity: 54 (not 2-way capable). Channels available but not in use: 25.
Basic Service
Subscribers: 629.
Programming (received off-air): KVOS-TV (I) Bellingham; KCTS-TV (P), KING-TV (N), KIRO-TV (C), KOMO-TV (A), KSTW (U) Seattle-Tacoma; CBUT Vancouver; CHEK-TV Victoria.
Programming (via satellite): A & E; C-SPAN; CNBC; CNN; Discovery Channel; ESPN; Fox Family Channel; MTV; Nickelodeon; TBS Superstation; Turner Network TV; VH1.
Fee: $39.95 installation; $31.70 monthly.
Pay Service 1
Pay Units: 48.
Programming (via satellite): Disney Channel.
Fee: $15.00 installation; $7.95 monthly.
Pay Service 2
Pay Units: 98.
Programming (via satellite): HBO.
Fee: $15.00 installation; $9.95 monthly.
Pay Service 3
Pay Units: 61.
Programming (via satellite): Showtime.
Fee: $15.00 installation; $10.95 monthly.
Local advertising: Yes. Available in character-generated programming. Rates: $100.00/Day.
Equipment: Nexus headend; Jerrold amplifiers; Scientific-Atlanta set top converters; Scientific-Atlanta satellite antenna; Nexus satellite receivers.
Miles of plant: 26.0 (coaxial). Homes passed: 770.
Manager: Dan Adrian. Technical manager: Arnie Hill. Office manager: Judy Vreeman.
State fee: 5% of gross.
Ownership: Sun Country Cable (MSO).

OROVILLE—TCI Cablevision of Okanogan Valley Inc., 1140 N. 94th St., Seattle, WA 98103-3306. Phone: 206-527-7545. Fax: 206-663-9072. County: Okanogan. Also serves Okanogan County (unincorporated areas). ICA: WA0073.
TV Market Ranking: Outside TV Markets. Franchise award date: January 1, 1969. Franchise expiration date: August 7, 2009. Began: June 1, 1969.
Channel capacity: 29 (not 2-way capable). Channels available but not in use: 3.
Basic Service
Subscribers: 691.
Programming (received off-air): 3 FMs.
Programming (via microwave): KSTW (U) Seattle-Tacoma; KHQ-TV (N), KREM-TV (C), KSPS-TV (P), KXLY-TV (A) Spokane; CHAN-TV Vancouver.
Programming (via translator): KAYU-TV (F) Spokane.
Programming (via satellite): A & E; CNN; Discovery Channel; Fox Family Channel; Lifetime; MTV; Nickelodeon; TBS Superstation; The Weather Channel.
Current originations: Public access.
Fee: $60.00 installation; $19.16 monthly; $2.95 converter; $15.00 additional installation.
Expanded Basic Service
Subscribers: 669.
Programming (via satellite): American Movie Classics; ESPN; Fox Sports Net Northwest; Nashville Network; USA Network.
Fee: $1.75 monthly.
Pay Service 1
Pay Units: 21.
Programming (via satellite): Cinemax.
Fee: $15.00 installation; $11.95 monthly.
Pay Service 2
Pay Units: 43.
Programming (via satellite): Disney Channel.
Fee: $15.00 installation; $8.50 monthly.
Pay Service 3
Pay Units: 225.
Programming (via satellite): The New Encore.
Fee: N.A.
Pay Service 4
Pay Units: 39.
Programming (via satellite): HBO.
Fee: $15.00 installation; $11.95 monthly.

Pay Service 5
Pay Units: 29.
Programming (via satellite): Showtime.
Fee: $15.00 installation; $11.95 monthly.
Local advertising: Yes (insert only). Available in locally originated & taped programming.
Program Guide: CableView.
Equipment: Catel, M/A-Com & Scientific-Atlanta headend; Broadband & Magnavox amplifiers; Times Fiber & Comm/Scope cable; Hamlin & Panasonic set top converters; Pico traps; Prodelin satellite antenna; Microwave Assoc., Scientific-Atlanta & Standard Communications satellite receivers.
Miles of plant: 23.9 (coaxial). Homes passed: 1,032. Total homes in franchised area: 1,071.
Manager: Bob Lam. Chief technician: Marty Adams.
City fee: 5% of gross.
Ownership: AT&T Broadband & Internet Services (MSO). Purchased from Tele-Communications Inc., March 9, 1999.

OTHELLO—Northland Cable TV, Box T, Moses Lake, WA 98837. Phone: 509-765-6151. County: Adams. Also serves Adams County. ICA: WA0049.
TV Market Ranking: Outside TV Markets. Franchise award date: N.A. Franchise expiration date: September 13, 2001. Began: November 22, 1965.
Channel capacity: 36 (2-way capable). Channels available but not in use: N.A.
Basic Service
Subscribers: 1,977.
Programming (received off-air): KEPR-TV (C), KNDU (N), KVEW (A) Pasco-Kennewick-Richland; KING-TV (N), KIRO-TV (C) Seattle-Tacoma; KAYU-TV (F), KHQ-TV (N), KREM-TV (C), KSPS-TV (P), KXLY-TV (A) Spokane; 1 FM.
Programming (via satellite): WGN-TV (W) Chicago; C-SPAN; C-SPAN 2; CNN; Cartoon Network; Discovery Channel; ESPN; Fox Family Channel; Headline News; Nashville Network; Nickelodeon; QVC; TBS Superstation; The Inspirational Network; The Weather Channel; USA Network; Univision.
Fee: $45.00 installation; $16.77 monthly; $2.20 converter; $10.00 additional installation.
Pay Service 1
Pay Units: Included with Moses Lake, WA.
Programming (via satellite): Cinemax; Disney Channel; HBO; Showtime; The Movie Channel.
Fee: $8.70 monthly (Disney), $9.15 monthly (Cinemax), $9.25 monthly (Showtime), $10.95 monthly (TMC), $12.30 monthly (HBO).
Local advertising: Yes. Available in character-generated programming.
Program Guide: TV Host.
Equipment: RCA & Scientific-Atlanta headend; Magnavox amplifiers; Comm/Scope cable; Video Data Systems character generator; Oak set top converters; Pico traps; Scientific-Atlanta & AFC satellite antenna; Microdyne, Scientific-Atlanta & Standard Communications satellite receivers; ChannelMatic commercial insert.
Miles of plant: 34.6 (coaxial). Homes passed: 2,221. Total homes in franchised area: 2,221.
Manager: Dawn Hill. Chief technician: Kim Svetich.
City fee: 3% of basic.
Ownership: Northland Communications Corp. (MSO).

PACKWOOD—Millennium Digital Media, Suite 107, 3633 136th Place SE, Bellevue, WA 98006. Phones: 425-747-4600; 800-829-2225. Fax: 425-644-4621.
Web site: http://www.millenniumdigital.com.
County: Lewis. Also serves Randle, Silver Brook. ICA: WA0074.
TV Market Ranking: Outside TV Markets. Franchise award date: N.A. Franchise expiration date: April 1, 2032. Began: December 1, 1983.
Channel capacity: 35. Channels available but not in use: 19.
Basic Service
Subscribers: 619.
Programming (received off-air): KCTS-TV (P), KING-TV (N), KIRO-TV (C), KOMO-TV (A) Seattle-Tacoma.
Programming (via satellite): WGN-TV (W) Chicago; A & E; American Movie Classics; Animal Planet; CNN; Discovery Channel; Disney Channel; E! Entertainment TV; ESPN; Fox Family Channel; Fox Sports Net Northwest; FoxNet; Headline News; History Channel; Home & Garden Television; Learning Channel; Lifetime; Nashville Network; Nickelodeon; Northwest Cable News; QVC; Sci-Fi Channel; TBS Superstation; TV Guide Channel; Turner Classic Movies; Turner Network TV; USA Network.
Fee: $29.95 monthly.
Pay Service 1
Pay Units: N.A.
Programming (via satellite): HBO; Showtime.
Fee: $14.95 monthly (each).
Miles of plant: 28.4 (coaxial). Homes passed: 1,030.
Manager: Steve Weed. Chief technician: Gene Fry.
Ownership: Millennium Digital Media LLC (MSO). Purchased from Summit Communications Inc., April 7, 1999.

PE ELL—Millennium Digital Media, Suite 107, 3633 136th Place SE, Bellevue, WA 98006. Phones: 425-747-4600; 800-829-2225. Fax: 425-644-4600.
Web site: http://www.millenniumdigital.com.
County: Lewis. Also serves Doty, Dryad. ICA: WA0103.
TV Market Ranking: Outside TV Markets. Franchise award date: N.A. Franchise expiration date: January 1, 2007. Began: October 1, 1983.
Channel capacity: 35 (not 2-way capable). Channels available but not in use: N.A.
Basic Service
Subscribers: 322.
Programming (received off-air): KCKA (P) Centralia; KCPQ (F), KCTS-TV (P), KING-TV (N), KIRO-TV (C), KOMO-TV (A), KSTW (U), KTWB (W) Seattle-Tacoma.
Programming (via microwave): TVW.
Programming (via satellite): WGN-TV (W) Chicago; American Movie Classics; Animal Planet; CNN; Cartoon Network; Discovery Channel; ESPN; Fox Family Channel; Fox Sports Net Northwest; Headline News; History Channel; Home & Garden Television; Learning Channel; Nashville Network; Nickelodeon; Northwest Cable News; QVC; Sci-Fi Channel; TBS Superstation; Turner Classic Movies; Turner Network TV; USA Network.
Current originations: Educational access; government access.
Fee: $45.00 installation; $27.95 monthly.
Pay Service 1
Pay Units: N.A.
Programming (via satellite): Disney Channel; HBO; Showtime.
Fee: $8.95 monthly (Disney), $14.95 monthly (HBO or Showtime).
Local advertising: No.
Equipment: Cadco headend; Pathmaker amplifiers; Times Fiber cable; Video Data Systems character generator; Eagle traps; Prodelin satellite antenna; M/A-Com satellite receivers.
Miles of plant: 15.6 (coaxial). Homes passed: 410.
Manager: Steve Weed. Chief technician: Gene Fry.
City fee: None.
Ownership: Millennium Digital Media LLC (MSO). Purchased from Summit Communications Inc., April 7, 1999.

POINT ROBERTS—Delta CableVision, 5381 48th Ave., Delta, BC Canada, V4K 1W7. Phone: 604-940-3601. Fax: 604-946-5627. E-mail: admin@deltacable.com. County: Whatcom. ICA: WA0076.
TV Market Ranking: Below 100. Franchise award date: January 1, 1973. Franchise expiration date: January 1, 2018. Began: June 1, 1973.
Channel capacity: 78 (2-way capable; not operating 2-way). Channels available but not in use: 41.
Basic Service
Subscribers: 716.
Programming (received off-air): KVOS-TV (I) Bellingham; KCPQ (F), KCTS-TV (P), KING-TV (N), KIRO-TV (C), KOMO-TV (A), KSTW (U) Seattle-Tacoma; CBUFT, CBUT, CHAN-TV, CKVU-TV Vancouver; CHEK-TV Victoria; allband FM.
Programming (via satellite): WGN-TV (W) Chicago; A & E; C-SPAN; CNN; Discovery Channel; ESPN; Fox Family Channel; History Channel; Learning Channel; Nashville Network; Northwest Cable News; TBS Superstation; Turner Classic Movies; Turner Network TV; USA Network.
Current originations: Public access; educational access; local news; local sports.
Fee: $18.00 installation; $18.50 monthly; $5.00 converter; $18.00 additional installation.
Pay Service 1
Pay Units: 30.
Programming (via satellite): HBO.
Fee: $20.00 installation; $12.00 monthly.
Local advertising: Yes. Available in locally originated programming. Local sales manager: Henri Wendel.
Equipment: Jerrold & Scientific-Atlanta headend; C-COR amplifiers; Comm/Scope cable; Pirelli fiber optic cable; Amiga character generator; Jerrold set top converters; Andrew satellite antenna; Scientific-Atlanta satellite receivers.
Miles of plant: 30.0 (coaxial); 3.0 (fiber optic). Additional miles planned: 2.0 (coaxial); 2.0 (fiber optic). Homes passed: 1,050. Total homes in franchised area: 1,200.
Manager: John S. Thomas. Chief engineer: Gordon Duncan. Marketing director: Henri Wendel. Program director: Adnan Hussain. Customer service manager: Craig Johnson.
County fee: 4% of gross.
Ownership: Delta Cable Communications Ltd.

PORT ANGELES—Northland Cable TV, 725 E. First St., Port Angeles, WA 98362. Phone: 360-452-8466. Fax: 360-457-5901. County: Clallam. Also serves Clallam County (northwestern portion). ICA: WA0020.
TV Market Ranking: Outside TV Markets. Franchise award date: May 1, 1960. Franchise expiration date: September 23, 2003. Began: May 1, 1960.
Channel capacity: 42 (not 2-way capable). Channels available but not in use: 1.
Basic Service
Subscribers: 8,604; Commercial subscribers: 1,705.
Programming (received off-air): KVOS-TV (I) Bellingham; KCPQ (F), KCTS-TV (P), KING-TV (N), KIRO-TV (C), KOMO-TV (A), KSTW (U) Seattle-Tacoma; CBUT, CKVU-TV Vancouver; CHEK-TV Victoria.
Programming (via satellite): C-SPAN; Headline News; Learning Channel; QVC; TBS Superstation; TV Guide Channel.
Current originations: Automated time-weather; educational access; government access.
Fee: $50.00 installation; $16.50 monthly; $3.95 converter; $10.00 additional installation.
Commercial fee: $3.95 monthly.
Expanded Basic Service
Subscribers: 8,016.
Programming (via satellite): A & E; CNBC; CNN; Discovery Channel; ESPN; Fox Family Channel; Fox News Channel; Nashville Network; Turner Network TV.
Fee: $50.00 installation; $7.45 monthly.
Expanded Basic Service 2
Subscribers: 4,878.
Programming (via satellite): American Movie Classics; Cartoon Network; Country Music TV; Disney Channel; ESPN 2; Fox Sports Net Northwest; Lifetime; Nickelodeon; Travel Channel; Turner Classic Movies; USA Network.
Fee: $50.00 installation; $9.95 monthly.
Pay Service 1
Pay Units: 482.
Programming (via satellite): Cinemax.
Fee: $19.95 installation; $8.95 monthly.
Pay Service 2
Pay Units: 700.
Programming (via satellite): HBO.
Fee: $19.95 installation; $11.50 monthly.
Pay Service 3
Pay Units: 368.
Programming (via satellite): Showtime.
Fee: $19.95 installation; $10.50 monthly.
Pay Service 4
Pay Units: N.A.
Programming (via satellite): The Box.
Fee: N.A.
Local advertising: Yes. Available in satellite distributed, locally originated, character-generated, taped & automated programming. Rates: $10.00/30 Seconds. Local sales manager: Sheri Bryan.
Equipment: Jerrold headend; Texscan amplifiers; General & Times Fiber cable; Sony VTRs; Compuvid & Texscan character generator; Hamlin set top converters; Pico traps; Hughes & Standard Communications satellite antenna; Hughes & Scientific-Atlanta satellite receivers.

Miles of plant: 296.0 (coaxial). Additional miles planned: 5.0 (coaxial). Homes passed: 10,584. Total homes in franchised area: 15,000.
Manager: Daniel Withers. Chief technician: Michael Sturgeon. Program director: Dennis Bragg. Customer service manager: Rose Gosslin.
City fee: 4% of gross.
Ownership: Northland Communications Corp. (MSO).

PORT ORCHARD—Falcon Video Communications, 4519 S.E. Mile Hill Dr., Port Orchard, WA 98366. Phone: 360-871-4043. Fax: 360-871-5418. Counties: Kitsap & Mason. Also serves Allyn (portions), Bangor Submarine Base, Belfair, Bremerton, Jackson Park, Keyport, Keyport Naval Base, Kitsap Lake, Lake Symington, Lake Tahuya, Manchester, Mason County, North Shore, Olalla, Puget Sound Naval Shipyard, Seabeck, Silverdale, South Kitsap, Tahuya. ICA: WA0010.
TV Market Ranking: 20. Franchise award date: N.A. Franchise expiration date: N.A. Began: January 1, 1971.
Channel capacity: 42 (2-way capable; operating 2-way). Channels available but not in use: None.
Basic Service
Subscribers: 25,251.
Programming (received off-air): KVOS-TV (I) Bellingham; KCPQ (F), KCTS-TV (P), KING-TV (N), KIRO-TV (C), KOMO-TV (A), KSTW (U), KTBW-TV (T), KTWB (W) Seattle-Tacoma; allband FM.
Programming (via satellite): A & E; American Movie Classics; C-SPAN; CNBC; Comedy Central; E! Entertainment TV; Goodlife TV Network; Home Shopping Network; Lifetime; MTV; Nashville Network; Nickelodeon; QVC; Sci-Fi Channel; TBS Superstation; TV Guide Sneak Prevue; The Weather Channel; VH1.
Current originations: Public access; educational access; government access.
Fee: $45.00 installation; $18.96 monthly; $2.50 converter; $20.00 additional installation.
Expanded Basic Service
Subscribers: 23,078.
Programming (via satellite): CNN; Discovery Channel; Disney Channel; ESPN; Fox Family Channel; Fox Sports Net Northwest; Headline News; Turner Network TV; USA Network.
Fee: $8.73 monthly.
Pay Service 1
Pay Units: 2,153.
Programming (via satellite): Cinemax.
Fee: $20.00 installation; $10.95 monthly.
Pay Service 2
Pay Units: 3,392.
Programming (via satellite): HBO.
Fee: $20.00 installation; $11.95 monthly.
Pay Service 3
Pay Units: 3,173.
Programming (via satellite): Showtime.
Fee: $20.00 installation; $10.95 monthly.
Pay-Per-View
Addressable homes: 8,200.
Playboy TV.
Local advertising: Yes. Available in taped & automated programming.
Program Guide: TV Host.
Equipment: Scientific-Atlanta headend; Texscan amplifiers; Comm/Scope & Trilogy cable; Amiga character generator; Scientific-Atlanta set top converters; Scientific-Atlanta addressable set top converters; Scientific-Atlanta satellite antenna; Scientific-Atlanta satellite receivers.
Miles of plant: 992.0 (coaxial). Homes passed: 45,133.
Chief technician: Richard Rumrill. Marketing director: Keith Tyrrell.
City fee: 3%-5% of gross.
Ownership: Falcon Communications LP (MSO), joint venture formed September 30, 1998. See Cable System Ownership.

PORT TOWNSEND—Millennium Digital Media, Suite 107, 3633 136th Place SE, Bellevue, WA 98006. Phones: 425-747-4600; 800-829-2225. Fax: 425-644-4621. Web site: http://www.millenniumdigital.com. County: Jefferson. Also serves Brinnon, Port Hadlock, Port Ludlow, Quilcene. ICA: WA0027.
TV Market Ranking: 20 (Port Hadlock, Port Ludlow, Quilcene); Outside TV Markets (Brinnon, Port Townsend). Franchise award date: January 1, 1977. Franchise expiration date: N.A. Began: December 28, 1977.
Channel capacity: 35 (not 2-way capable). Channels available but not in use: 14.
Basic Service
Subscribers: 3,800.
Programming (received off-air): KVOS-TV (I) Bellingham; KCPQ (F), KCTS-TV (P), KING-TV (N), KIRO-TV (C), KOMO-TV (A), KSTW (U), KTBW-TV (T), KTWB (W) Seattle-Tacoma; CBUT, CKVU-TV Vancouver; CHEK-TV Victoria.
Programming (via microwave): TVW.
Programming (via satellite): A & E; American Movie Classics; Animal Planet; C-SPAN; CNBC; CNN; Cartoon Network; Discovery Channel; ESPN; ESPN 2; Fox Family Channel; Fox Sports Net Northwest; Headline News; History Channel; Home & Garden Television; Independent Film Channel; Learning Channel; Lifetime; Nashville Network; Nickelodeon; Northwest Cable News; QVC; Sci-Fi Channel; TBS Superstation; TV Guide Channel; Turner Classic Movies; Turner Network TV; USA Network.
Current originations: Government access.
Fee: $45.00 installation; $29.95 monthly.
Pay Service 1
Pay Units: N.A.
Programming (via satellite): Disney Channel; HBO; Showtime; The Movie Channel.
Fee: $8.95 monthly (Disney), $14.95 monthly (HBO, Showtime or TMC).
Equipment: Blonder-Tongue & Cadco headend; Pathmaker amplifiers; Times Fiber cable; Atari character generator; Cadco, Prodelin & Scientific-Atlanta satellite antenna; M/A-Com & Triple Crown satellite receivers.
Miles of plant: 173.3 (coaxial). Homes passed: 6,100.
Manager: Steve Weed. Chief technician: Gene Fry.
City fee: 3% of gross.
Ownership: Millennium Digital Media LLC (MSO). Purchased from Summit Communications Inc., April 7, 1999.

POULSBO—TCI Cablevision of Washington Inc., 1225 Sylvan Way, Bremerton, WA 98310-3426. Phone: 360-377-8528. County: Kitsap. Also serves Kitsap County (northern portion), Lofall. ICA: WA0041.
TV Market Ranking: 20. Franchise award date: N.A. Franchise expiration date: April 1, 2004. Began: January 1, 1964.
Channel capacity: 37. Channels available but not in use: 2.
Basic Service
Subscribers: 3,031.
Programming (received off-air): KVOS-TV (I) Bellingham; KCPQ (F), KCTS-TV (P), KING-TV (N), KIRO-TV (C), KOMO-TV (A), KSTW (U), KTBW-TV (T), KTWB (W) Seattle-Tacoma; KBTC-TV (P) Tacoma; allband FM.
Programming (via satellite): A & E; C-SPAN; CNBC; CNN; Discovery Channel; Fox Family Channel; Headline News; Lifetime; MTV; Nashville Network; Nickelodeon; QVC; TBS Superstation; The Weather Channel.
Fee: $60.00 installation; $18.72 monthly; $3.00 converter.
Expanded Basic Service
Subscribers: 2,703.
Programming (via satellite): American Movie Classics; ESPN; Fox Sports Net Northwest; Turner Network TV; USA Network.
Fee: $1.94 monthly.
Pay Service 1
Pay Units: 170.
Programming (via satellite): Cinemax.
Fee: N.A.
Pay Service 2
Pay Units: 235.
Programming (via satellite): Disney Channel.
Fee: N.A.
Pay Service 3
Pay Units: 945.
Programming (via satellite): The New Encore.
Fee: N.A.
Pay Service 4
Pay Units: 356.
Programming (via satellite): HBO.
Fee: N.A.
Pay Service 5
Pay Units: 296.
Programming (via satellite): Showtime.
Fee: N.A.
Local advertising: Planned. Available in satellite distributed, locally originated, character-generated & taped programming.
Equipment: Jerrold headend; Jerrold amplifiers; Times Fiber cable; Scientific-Atlanta satellite antenna.
Miles of plant: 62.5 (coaxial). Homes passed: 3,052. Total homes in franchised area: 5,085.
Manager: Patrick McDonald. Chief technician: Dennis Quinlan.
City fee: 3% of gross.
Ownership: AT&T Broadband & Internet Services (MSO). Purchased from Tele-Communications Inc., March 9, 1999.

PRESCOTT—TCI Cablevision of Yakima Inc., Box 1577, 126 W. Poplar St., Walla Walla, WA 99362-2847. Phone: 509-529-9500. Fax: 509-522-1719. County: Walla Walla. ICA: WA0133.
TV Market Ranking: Below 100. Franchise award date: N.A. Franchise expiration date: N.A. Began: January 1, 1964.
Channel capacity: 22. Channels available but not in use: 8.
Basic Service
Subscribers: 118.
Programming (received off-air): KEPR-TV (C), KNDU (N), KVEW (A) Pasco-Kennewick-Richland; KTNW (P) Richland; KAYU-TV (F) Spokane.
Programming (via satellite): Discovery Channel; ESPN; Fox Family Channel; Headline News; Nashville Network; TBS Superstation.
Fee: $39.15 installation; $11.97 monthly; $60.00 additional installation.
Pay Service 1
Pay Units: 25.
Programming (via satellite): The Movie Channel.
Fee: $10.50 monthly.
Miles of plant: 3.0 (coaxial). Homes passed: 201.
Manager: Tim Klinefelter. Chief technician: Tim Ream. Program director: Dinah Morrison. Marketing director: Marlene Ashby.
Ownership: AT&T Broadband & Internet Services (MSO). Purchased from Tele-Communications Inc., March 9, 1999.

PROSSER—Falcon Cable, 1005 N. 16th Ave., Yakima, WA 98902-1351. Phone: 509-575-1697. Counties: Benton & Yakima. Also serves Mapleton, Yakima County. ICA: WA0054.
TV Market Ranking: Below 100 (Mapleton, Prosser, portions of Yakima County); Outside TV Markets (portions of Yakima County). Franchise award date: January 1, 1973. Franchise expiration date: N.A. Began: July 14, 1973.
Channel capacity: 30. Channels available but not in use: N.A.
Basic Service
Subscribers: 1,326.
Programming (received off-air): KEPR-TV (C) Pasco-Kennewick-Richland; KAPP (A), KNDO (N), KYVE-TV (P) Yakima.
Programming (via microwave): KSTW (U) Seattle-Tacoma.
Programming (via satellite): WGN-TV (W) Chicago; CNN; Discovery Channel; Fox Family Channel; GalaVision; Headline News; MTV; Nashville Network; Nickelodeon; TBS Superstation; Univision.
Current originations: Automated time-weather.
Fee: $60.00 installation; $18.47 monthly; $40.00 additional installation.
Expanded Basic Service
Subscribers: N.A.
Programming (via satellite): American Movie Classics; ESPN; Fox Sports Net Northwest; Turner Network TV; USA Network.
Fee: $1.50 monthly.
Pay Service 1
Pay Units: 56.
Programming (via satellite): Cinemax.
Fee: $12.05 monthly.
Pay Service 2
Pay Units: 85.
Programming (via satellite): Disney Channel.
Fee: $9.20 monthly.
Pay Service 3
Pay Units: 387.
Programming (via satellite): The New Encore.
Fee: N.A.
Pay Service 4
Pay Units: 125.
Programming (via satellite): HBO.
Fee: $15.00 installation; $12.05 monthly.
Pay Service 5
Pay Units: 54.
Programming (via satellite): Showtime.
Fee: $12.05 monthly.
Local advertising: Yes (insert only).
Program Guide: CableView.
Equipment: Scientific-Atlanta & Catel headend; Magnavox amplifiers; Times Fiber cable; Sony cameras; Sony VTRs; Hamlin set top converters; Tocom addressable set top converters; Pico traps; Andrew satellite antenna; Scientific-Atlanta satellite receivers.
Miles of plant: 20.7 (coaxial). Homes passed: 1,879. Total homes in franchised area: 2,150.
Manager: Gary Bailey. Marketing director: Shelley Bjornson.
City fee: 3% of gross.
Ownership: Falcon Communications LP (MSO). Purchased from Tele-Communications Inc., October 1, 1998.

QUINCY—Sun Country Cable, Box 127, 7 D St. SW, Quincy, WA 98848. Phone: 509-787-3543. Fax: 509-787-3884. County: Grant. Also serves Crescent Bar, George. ICA: WA0057.

TV Market Ranking: Below 100. Franchise award date: N.A. Franchise expiration date: N.A. Began: August 1, 1978.

Channel capacity: 36. Channels available but not in use: None.

Basic Service

Subscribers: 1,290; Commercial subscribers: 115.

Programming (received off-air): KSTW (U) Seattle-Tacoma; 3 FMs.

Programming (via satellite): WGN-TV (W) Chicago; A & E; American Movie Classics; C-SPAN; CNN; Cartoon Network; Comedy Central; Discovery Channel; ESPN; Fox Family Channel; GalaVision; Headline News; Lifetime; MTV; Nashville Network; Nickelodeon; QVC; TBS Superstation; The Weather Channel; Turner Network TV; USA Network; Univision.

Current originations: Automated timeweather.

Fee: $39.95 installation; $29.52 monthly.

Pay Service 1

Pay Units: 159.

Programming (via satellite): Cinemax.

Fee: $15.00 installation; $8.95 monthly.

Pay Service 2

Pay Units: 101.

Programming (via satellite): Disney Channel.

Fee: $15.00 installation; $8.95 monthly.

Pay Service 3

Pay Units: 257.

Programming (via satellite): HBO.

Fee: $15.00 installation; $10.95 monthly.

Pay Service 4

Pay Units: 48.

Programming (via satellite): Showtime.

Fee: $15.00 installation; $10.95 monthly.

Local advertising: Yes. Available in character-generated programming. Rates: $1.00/Day.

Equipment: Scientific-Atlanta headend; Jerrold & Theta-Com amplifiers; Anixter-Pruzan cable; Atari character generator; Panasonic & Scientific-Atlanta set top converters; Andrew, Prodelin & Scientific-Atlanta satellite antenna; Hughes, Microdyne & Scientific-Atlanta satellite receivers.

Miles of plant: 38.0 (coaxial); 9.5 (fiber optic). Additional miles planned: 8.0 (coaxial). Homes passed: 1,800.

Manager: Gary White. Technical manager: Arnie Hill. Office manager: Judy Vreeman.

City fee: 4% of gross.

Ownership: Sun Country Cable (MSO).

RAYMOND—TCI Cablevision of Washington Inc., Box 129, 440 Yauger St., Olympia, WA 98507-0129. Phone: 360-357-3364. Fax: 360-532-5978. County: Pacific. Also serves Pacific County, South Bend. ICA: WA0040.

TV Market Ranking: Outside TV Markets. Franchise award date: N.A. Franchise expiration date: N.A. Began: July 1, 1951.

Channel capacity: 33. Channels available but not in use: N.A.

Basic Service

Subscribers: 2,538.

Programming (received off-air): KCKA (P) Centralia; KCPQ (F), KCTS-TV (P), KING-TV (N), KIRO-TV (C), KOMO-TV (A), KSTW (U) Seattle-Tacoma; allband FM.

Programming (via satellite): C-SPAN; CNBC; CNN; Discovery Channel; Fox Family Channel; Headline News; Lifetime; MTV; Nashville Network; Nickelodeon; QVC; TBS Superstation.

Fee: $60.00 installation; $8.90 monthly; $40.00 additional installation.

Expanded Basic Service

Subscribers: 2,509.

Programming (via satellite): American Movie Classics; ESPN; Fox Sports Net Northwest; Turner Network TV; USA Network.

Fee: $10.34 monthly.

Pay Service 1

Pay Units: 158.

Programming (via satellite): Cinemax.

Fee: $13.15 monthly.

Pay Service 2

Pay Units: 170.

Programming (via satellite): Disney Channel.

Fee: N.A.

Pay Service 3

Pay Units: 828.

Programming (via satellite): The New Encore.

Fee: N.A.

Pay Service 4

Pay Units: 445.

Programming (via satellite): HBO.

Fee: $13.15 monthly.

Pay Service 5

Pay Units: 145.

Programming (via satellite): Showtime.

Fee: $13.15 monthly.

Program Guide: The Cable Guide.

Equipment: Jerrold addressable set top converters; Arcom addressable traps; Scientific-Atlanta satellite antenna; Scientific-Atlanta satellite receivers.

Miles of plant: 61.0 (coaxial). Homes passed: 3,097. Total homes in franchised area: 3,097.

Manager: Fred Comer. Chief technician: Wally Weidman. Marketing director: Carrie Prante.

City fee: 3% of gross (utility tax).

Ownership: AT&T Broadband & Internet Services (MSO). Purchased from Tele-Communications Inc., March 9, 1999.

REARDAN—Northwest Cable LP, Box 618, Lockney, TX 79241-0618. Phone: 800-480-3766. Fax: 806-652-3139. County: Lincoln. ICA: WA0121.

TV Market Ranking: 76. Franchise award date: N.A. Franchise expiration date: N.A. Began: May 31, 1983.

Channel capacity: 24 (2-way capable; operating 2-way). Channels available but not in use: 12.

Basic Service

Subscribers: N.A.

Programming (received off-air): KAYU-TV (F), KHQ-TV (N), KREM-TV (C), KSKN (U,W), KSPS-TV (P), KXLY-TV (A) Spokane.

Programming (via satellite): ESPN; Fox Family Channel; Headline News; USA Network.

Planned originations: Government access.

Fee: $25.00 installation; $12.00 monthly.

Pay Service 1

Pay Units: N.A.

Programming (via satellite): HBO.

Fee: $10.00 monthly.

Equipment: Scientific-Atlanta headend; Magnavox amplifiers; Comm/Scope cable; Pico traps; Anixter-Mark satellite antenna; Scientific-Atlanta satellite receivers.

Miles of plant: 5.0 (coaxial). Homes passed: 225. Total homes in franchised area: 225.

Manager: Kenneth V. Mettler. Chief technician: Joseph R. Poire.

City fee: 3% of gross.

Ownership: Northwest Cable Ltd. Partnership (MSO).

REDMOND—TCI Cablevision Inc., 14870 N.E. 95th St., Redmond, WA 98052. Phone: 206-526-8400. County: King. Also serves Beaux Arts Village, Bellevue, Carnation, Fall City, Hunts Point, Issaquah, King County, Medina, Mercer Island, Mirrormont, Newcastle, Preston, Snoqualmie, Upper Preston, Yarrow Point. ICA: WA0034.

TV Market Ranking: 20 (Beaux Arts Village, Bellevue, Carnation, Fall City, Hunts Point, Issaquah, portions of King County, Medina, Mercer Island, Mirrormont, Newcastle, Preston, Redmond, Snoqualmie, Upper Preston, Yarrow Point); Below 100 (portions of King County); Outside TV Markets (portions of King County). Franchise award date: N.A. Franchise expiration date: N.A. Began: November 1, 1955.

Channel capacity: 55 (not 2-way capable). Channels available but not in use: N.A.

Basic Service

Subscribers: 10,326.

Programming (received off-air): KCPQ (F), KCTS-TV (P), KING-TV (N), KIRO-TV (C), KOMO-TV (A), KSTW (U), KTBW-TV (T), KTWB (W) Seattle-Tacoma; CBUT Vancouver; allband FM.

Programming (via satellite): CNN; Discovery Channel; Fox Family Channel; Headline News; Lifetime; MTV; Nashville Network; TBS Superstation.

Planned originations: Automated timeweather; educational access; leased access.

Fee: $60.00 installation; $9.56 monthly; $2.00 converter; $40.00 additional installation.

Commercial fee: $5.00 monthly.

Expanded Basic Service

Subscribers: 4,095.

Programming (via satellite): ESPN; Fox Sports Net Northwest; Nickelodeon; Turner Network TV; USA Network.

Fee: $9.56 monthly.

Pay Service 1

Pay Units: 362.

Programming (via satellite): Disney Channel.

Fee: $9.95 installation; $8.95 monthly.

Pay Service 2

Pay Units: 1,694.

Programming (via satellite): The New Encore.

Fee: N.A.

Pay Service 3

Pay Units: 517.

Programming (via satellite): HBO.

Fee: $9.95 installation; $12.07 monthly.

Pay Service 4

Pay Units: 279.

Programming (via satellite): Showtime.

Fee: $9.95 installation; $12.07 monthly.

Local advertising: Yes. Available in character-generated programming. Rates: $15.00/Week.

Program Guide: The Cable Guide.

Equipment: Scientific-Atlanta headend; Theta-Com & Magnavox amplifiers; Times Fiber & Comm/Scope cable; Atari character generator; Hamlin & Jerrold set top converters; Prodelin satellite antenna.

Miles of plant: 319.7 (coaxial). Additional miles planned: 3.0 (coaxial). Total homes in franchised area: N.A.

Manager: Keith Fischer. Chief technician: Dennis Moore.

City fee: 5% of gross.

Ownership: AT&T Broadband & Internet Services (MSO). Purchased from Tele-Communications Inc., March 9, 1999.

REPUBLIC—Television Assn. of Republic, Box 0555, 147-18 N. Clark, Republic, WA 99166-0555. Phone: 509-775-3822. County: Ferry. ICA: WA0177.

TV Market Ranking: Outside TV Markets. Franchise award date: December 1, 1953. Franchise expiration date: December 1, 2005. Began: December 1, 1953.

Channel capacity: 30 (not 2-way capable). Channels available but not in use: 10.

Basic Service

Subscribers: 574; Commercial subscribers: 12.

Programming (received off-air): KAYU-TV (F), KHQ-TV (N), KREM-TV (C), KSPS-TV (P), KXLY-TV (A) Spokane; allband FM.

Programming (via translator): CHAN-TV Vancouver.

Programming (via satellite): C-SPAN; CNN; Discovery Channel; ESPN; Fox Family Channel; Learning Channel; Nashville Network; Nick at Nite; Nickelodeon; TBS Superstation; Turner Classic Movies; Turner Network TV.

Fee: $40.00 installation; $19.00 monthly; $10.00 converter.

Pay Service 1

Pay Units: 139.

Programming (via satellite): Disney Channel.

Fee: $5.00 monthly.

Pay Service 2

Pay Units: 199.

Programming (via satellite): HBO.

Fee: $10.00 monthly.

Pay-Per-View

Addressable homes: 528.

Local advertising: No.

Equipment: Jerrold headend; Jerrold amplifiers; Scientific-Atlanta cable; Pico traps; Prodelin satellite antenna; Jerrold & Triple Crown satellite receivers.

Miles of plant: 25.0 (coaxial). Additional miles planned: 10.0 (coaxial). Homes passed: 800. Total homes in franchised area: 950.

Manager: Ken Coyle. Chief technician: Gus Nichols. Marketing director: Charles E. Yost.

Ownership: Television Assn. of Republic.

RITZVILLE—Community Cable Service, 729 S. Bernard St., Spokane, WA 99204. Phones: 509-624-4140; 800-572-0902. County: Adams. ICA: WA0178.

TV Market Ranking: Outside TV Markets. Franchise award date: N.A. Franchise expiration date: N.A. Began: June 1, 1981.

Channel capacity: 62 (2-way capable; not operating 2-way). Channels available but not in use: 2.

Basic Service

Subscribers: 638.

Programming (received off-air): KWSU-TV (P) Pullman; KAYU-TV (F), KHQ-TV (N), KREM-TV (C), KSPS-TV (P), KXLY-TV (A) Spokane.

Programming (via satellite): WGN-TV (W) Chicago; A & E; American Movie Classics; Bravo; C-SPAN; C-SPAN 2; CNBC; CNN; CNN International; Cartoon Network; Comedy Central; Country Music TV; Discovery Channel; E! Entertainment TV; ESPN; ESPN 2; ESPNews; EWTN; Fox Family Channel; Fox News Channel; Fox Sports Net Northwest; Goodlife TV Network; Headline News; History Channel; Home & Garden Television; Home Shopping Network; Knowledge TV; Learning Channel; Lifetime; MTV; Nashville Network; Nick at Nite's TV Land; Nickelodeon; Odyssey; QVC; Sci-Fi Channel; TBS Superstation; TV Food Network; The Health Network; Travel Channel; Trinity Bcstg. Network; Turner Classic Movies; Turner Network TV; USA Network; VH1; ValueVision; Z Music Television.

Current originations: Educational access; local news.

Fee: $15.00 installation; $25.16 monthly.

Pay Service 1
Pay Units: 123.
Programming (via satellite): Cinemax.
Fee: $5.00 installation; $6.42 monthly.
Pay Service 2
Pay Units: 80.
Programming (via satellite): Disney Channel.
Fee: $5.00 installation; $5.34 monthly.
Pay Service 3
Pay Units: 151.
Programming (via satellite): HBO.
Fee: $5.00 installation; $9.65 monthly.
Pay Service 4
Pay Units: N.A.
Programming (via satellite): Showtime.
Fee: $8.09 monthly.
Homes passed: 946.
Manager: Martin Howser.
Ownership: Martin Howser (MSO).

ROCHESTER—TCI Cablevision of Twin Cities Inc., Box 129, Olympia, WA 98507. Phones: 360-736-1166; 800-221-5232. Fax: 360-736-1160. Counties: Grays Harbor & Thurston. Also serves Grays Harbor, Oakville. ICA: WA0064.
TV Market Ranking: Outside TV Markets. Franchise award date: N.A. Franchise expiration date: November 1, 2002. Began: May 1, 1986.
Channel capacity: 33 (not 2-way capable). Channels available but not in use: N.A.
Basic Service
Subscribers: 1,330.
Programming (received off-air): KCKA (P) Centralia; KCPQ (F), KCTS-TV (P), KING-TV (N), KIRO-TV (C), KOMO-TV (A), KSTW (U), KTBW-TV (T) Seattle-Tacoma; allband FM.
Programming (via satellite): CNN; Discovery Channel; Nashville Network; TBS Superstation.
Current originations: Automated time-weather; local news.
Fee: $60.00 installation; $9.79 monthly; $40.00 additional installation.
Expanded Basic Service
Subscribers: 1,114.
Programming (via satellite): American Movie Classics; ESPN; Fox Sports Net Northwest; Turner Network TV; USA Network.
Fee: $9.33 monthly.
Pay Service 1
Pay Units: 624.
Programming (via satellite): The New Encore.
Fee: N.A.
Pay Service 2
Pay Units: 314.
Programming (via satellite): HBO.
Fee: $12.48 monthly.
Pay Service 3
Pay Units: 156.
Programming (via satellite): Showtime.
Fee: $12.48 monthly.
Equipment: Blonder-Tongue, Jerrold & Scientific-Atlanta headend; Jerrold amplifiers; Comm/Scope cable.
Miles of plant: 63.6 (coaxial). Homes passed: 1,357. Total homes in franchised area: 1,357.
Manager: Paul Renz.
City fee: 5% of gross.
Ownership: AT&T Broadband & Internet Services (MSO). Purchased from Tele-Communications Inc., March 9, 1999.

ROSALIA—Northwest Cable LP, Box 618, Lockney, TX 79241. Phone: 800-480-3766. Fax: 806-652-3139. County: Whitman. ICA: WA0122.
TV Market Ranking: 76. Franchise award date: N.A. Franchise expiration date: N.A. Began: February 28, 1983.
Channel capacity: 24 (2-way capable; operating 2-way). Channels available but not in use: 12.
Basic Service
Subscribers: N.A.
Programming (received off-air): KWSU-TV (P) Pullman; KAYU-TV (F), KHQ-TV (N), KREM-TV (C), KSKN (U,W), KSPS-TV (P), KXLY-TV (A) Spokane.
Programming (via satellite): ESPN; Fox Family Channel; Headline News; USA Network.
Planned originations: Government access.
Fee: $25.00 installation; $12.00 monthly.
Pay Service 1
Pay Units: N.A.
Programming (via satellite): HBO.
Fee: $10.00 monthly.
Equipment: Scientific-Atlanta headend; Magnavox amplifiers; Comm/Scope cable; Pico traps; Anixter-Mark satellite antenna; Scientific-Atlanta satellite receivers.
Miles of plant: 6.0 (coaxial). Homes passed: 220. Total homes in franchised area: 220.
Manager: Kenneth V. Mettler. Chief technician: Joseph R. Poire.
City fee: 3% of gross.
Ownership: Northwest Cable Ltd. Partnership (MSO).

ROSLYN—R & R Cable Co. Inc., Box 171, Roslyn, WA 98941-0171. Phone: 509-649-2212. Fax: 509-649-3300. County: Kittitas West. Also serves Lake Cle Elum, Ronald. ICA: WA0179.
TV Market Ranking: Below 100. Franchise award date: N.A. Franchise expiration date: N.A. Began: February 1, 1955.
Channel capacity: 28. Channels available but not in use: 14.
Basic Service
Subscribers: 791.
Programming (received off-air): KING-TV (N), KIRO-TV (C), KOMO-TV (A), KSTW (U) Seattle-Tacoma; allband FM.
Programming (via translator): KAPP (A), KNDO (N) Yakima.
Programming (via satellite): WGN-TV (W) Chicago; CNN; Fox Family Channel; Nickelodeon; TBS Superstation; USA Network.
Fee: $18.00 installation; $14.70 monthly.
Pay Service 1
Pay Units: N.A.
Programming (via satellite): The Movie Channel.
Fee: $10.80 monthly.
Equipment: Blonder-Tongue & Jerrold headend; Magnavox & Vikoa amplifiers; Cerro cable.
Miles of plant: 25.0 (coaxial). Total homes in franchised area: 1,500.
Manager: Douglas W. Weis. Chief technician: Dan Danubio.
City fee: 5% of gross.
Ownership: R & R Cable Co. Inc.

ROYAL CITY—Sun Country Cable, Box 127, 7 D St. SW, Quincy, WA 98848. Phone: 509-787-3543. Fax: 509-787-3884. County: Grant. ICA: WA0118.
TV Market Ranking: Outside TV Markets. Franchise award date: April 21, 1987. Franchise expiration date: April 21, 2002. Began: October 1, 1987.
Channel capacity: 35 (not 2-way capable). Channels available but not in use: 17.
Basic Service
Subscribers: 207.
Programming (via translator): KING-TV (N), KIRO-TV (C), KOMO-TV (A) Seattle-Tacoma.
Programming (via satellite): WGN-TV (W) Chicago; A & E; CNN; Cartoon Network; Discovery Channel; ESPN; Fox Family Channel; GalaVision; Lifetime; Nashville Network; TBS Superstation; Turner Network TV; USA Network; Univision.
Fee: $39.95 installation; $29.25 monthly.
Pay Service 1
Pay Units: 18.
Programming (via satellite): Disney Channel.
Fee: $15.00 installation; $8.95 monthly.
Pay Service 2
Pay Units: 47.
Programming (via satellite): HBO.
Fee: $15.00 installation; $10.95 monthly.
Equipment: Triple Crown headend; Jerrold amplifiers; Panasonic & Scientific-Atlanta set top converters; Scientific-Atlanta & Triple Crown satellite receivers.
Homes passed: 250.
Manager: Gary White. Technical manager: Arnie Hill. Office manager: Judy Vreeman.
Ownership: Sun Country Cable (MSO).

RUSTON—TCI of Tacoma Inc., 3119 Center St., Tacoma, WA 98409. Phone: 253-383-4311. Fax: 253-627-0433. County: Pierce. Also serves Tacoma. ICA: WA0006.
TV Market Ranking: 20. Franchise award date: N.A. Franchise expiration date: N.A. Began: August 1, 1971.
Channel capacity: 38 (2-way capable). Channels available but not in use: None.
Basic Service
Subscribers: 44,357.
Programming (received off-air): KCPQ (F), KCTS-TV (P), KING-TV (N), KIRO-TV (C), KOMO-TV (A), KSTW (U), KTBW-TV (T), KTWB (W) Seattle-Tacoma; KBTC-TV (P) Tacoma; 14 FMs.
Programming (via satellite): A & E; BET; C-SPAN; CNBC; CNN; Discovery Channel; FX; Fox Family Channel; Headline News; Lifetime; MTV; Nashville Network; Nickelodeon; Northwest Cable News; QVC; TBS Superstation.
Current originations: Government access; leased access.
Fee: $44.95 installation; $11.87 monthly; $1.50 converter.
Expanded Basic Service
Subscribers: 41,320.
Programming (via satellite): American Movie Classics; ESPN; Fox Sports Net Northwest; Turner Network TV; USA Network.
Fee: $12.07 monthly.
Pay Service 1
Pay Units: 6,204.
Programming (via satellite): Cinemax.
Fee: $10.25 installation; $13.20 monthly.
Pay Service 2
Pay Units: 4,088.
Programming (via satellite): Disney Channel.
Fee: $10.25 installation; $12.45 monthly.
Pay Service 3
Pay Units: 18,532.
Programming (via satellite): The New Encore.
Fee: $10.25 installation; $1.75 monthly.
Pay Service 4
Pay Units: 11,065.
Programming (via satellite): HBO.
Fee: $10.25 installation; $14.15 monthly.
Pay Service 5
Pay Units: 5,455.
Programming (via satellite): Showtime.
Fee: $10.25 installation; $14.15 monthly.
Pay Service 6
Pay Units: 16,349.
Programming (via satellite): Starz!
Fee: $6.75 monthly.
Pay Service 7
Pay Units: 909.
Programming (via satellite): DMX.
Fee: $9.95 monthly.
Local advertising: Yes (insert only). Available in satellite distributed, locally originated & character-generated programming. Regional interconnect: Northwest Cable Advertising.
Program Guide: The Cable Guide.
Equipment: Jerrold & Scientific-Atlanta headend; Jerrold amplifiers; Comm/Scope & Times Fiber cable; Sony VTRs; Metrodata & Texscan character generator; Jerrold, Oak & Scientific-Atlanta set top converters; Eagle & Pico traps; Andrew, Hughes & Scientific-Atlanta satellite antenna; Hughes & Scientific-Atlanta satellite receivers; ChannelMatic commercial insert.
Miles of plant: 630.3 (coaxial); None (fiber optic). Homes passed: 79,417. Total homes in franchised area: 82,645.
Manager: Barbara J. Wyatt. Chief technician: Ted Axtell. Customer service manager: Kathy Parhomski.
City fee: 8% of gross.
Ownership: AT&T Broadband & Internet Services (MSO). Purchased from Tele-Communications Inc., March 9, 1999.

RYDERWOOD—TCI Cablevision of Southwest Washington Inc., Box 129, Olympia, WA 98507. Phones: 360-736-1166; 800-221-5232. Fax: 360-736-1160. County: Cowlitz. ICA: WA0127.
TV Market Ranking: Outside TV Markets. Franchise award date: N.A. Franchise expiration date: N.A. Began: July 1, 1987.
Channel capacity: 21 (not 2-way capable). Channels available but not in use: N.A.
Basic Service
Subscribers: 208.
Programming (received off-air): KATU (A), KGW (N), KOIN (C), KOPB-TV (P), KPTV (U) Portland; KING-TV (N), KIRO-TV (C) Seattle-Tacoma; allband FM.
Programming (via satellite): CNN; ESPN; Fox Family Channel; TBS Superstation; Turner Network TV.
Fee: $60.00 installation; $18.49 monthly; $40.00 additional installation.
Pay Service 1
Pay Units: 14.
Programming (via satellite): Disney Channel.
Fee: $10.00 monthly.
Equipment: Blonder-Tongue & Jerrold headend; Magnavox & Vikoa amplifiers; Times Fiber & Vikoa cable.
Miles of plant: 3.5 (coaxial).
Manager: Paul Renz.
Ownership: AT&T Broadband & Internet Services (MSO). Purchased from Tele-Communications Inc., March 9, 1999.

SEATTLE (central district)—Millennium Digital Media, Suite 107, 3633 136th Place SE, Bellevue, WA 98006. Phones: 425-747-4600; 800-829-2225. Fax: 425-644-4621. Web site: http://www.millenniumdigital.com. County: King. ICA: WA0014.
TV Market Ranking: 20. Franchise award date: February 15, 1983. Franchise expiration date: February 1, 1998. Began: September 1, 1983.
Channel capacity: 54. Channels available but not in use: 7.
Basic Service
Subscribers: 11,896.
Programming (received off-air): KONG-TV (I) Everett; KCPQ (F), KCTS-TV (P), KING-TV (N), KIRO-TV (C), KOMO-TV (A), KSTW (U), KTBW-TV (T), KTWB (W) Seattle-Tacoma.
Programming (via microwave): TVW.
Programming (via satellite): A & E; American Movie Classics; BET; Bravo; C-SPAN;

CNBC; CNN; Chinese Television Network; Discovery Channel; ESPN; Fox Family Channel; Fox Sports Net Northwest; Headline News; International Channel; Lifetime; MTV; Nashville Network; Nickelodeon; Northwest Cable News; QVC; TBS Superstation; TV Guide Channel; The New Encore; The Weather Channel; Turner Network TV; USA Network; Univision; ValueVision; VH1.
Current originations: Public access; educational access; government access.
Fee: $35.00 installation; $26.95 monthly.

Pay Service 1
Pay Units: 3,522.
Programming (via satellite): Cinemax; Disney Channel; HBO; Showtime; The Movie Channel.
Fee: $20.00 installation; $4.95 monthly (Disney), $8.95 monthly (Cinemax or TMC), $10.95 monthly (HBO or Showtime).

Pay-Per-View
Addressable homes: 6,000.
Spice; Viewer's Choice 1 & 2; movies; special events.
Fee: $3.95 (movies); $5.95 (Spice).

Local advertising: Yes (locally produced & insert). Available in satellite distributed programming. Rates: On request. Local sales manager: Steven Weed.
Equipment: RCA headend; RCA amplifiers; Sony VTRs; Atari character generator; Jerrold set top converters; Jerrold addressable set top converters; Avantek satellite receivers.
Miles of plant: 126.5 (coaxial). Homes passed: 22,781. Total homes in franchised area: 28,000.
Manager: Steve Weed. Chief technician: Gene Fry.
Franchise fee: 10% of gross.
Ownership: Millennium Digital Media LLC (MSO). Purchased from Summit Communications Inc., April 7, 1999.

SEATTLE—TCI Cablevision Inc., 1140 N. 94th St., Seattle, WA 98103. Phone: 206-525-0332. Counties: Island, King & Snohomish. Also serves Bothell, Brier, Everett, Everett Naval Station, Gold Bar, Granite Falls, Island County, King County, Kirkland, Lake Forest Park, Lake Stevens, Lynnwood, Marysville, Mill Creek, Monroe, Mountlake Terrace, Mukilteo, Oak Harbor, Seattle, Snohomish, Snohomish County, Startup, Sultan, Whidbey Island Naval Air Station, Woodinville. ICA: WA0001.
TV Market Ranking: 20 (Bothell, Brier, Everett, Everett Naval Station, Gold Bar, Granite Falls, portions of Island County, portions of King County, Kirkland, Lake Forest Park, Lake Stevens, Lynnwood, Marysville, Mill Creek, Monroe, Mountlake Terrace, Mukilteo, Seattle, portions of Seattle, Snohomish, portions of Snohomish County, Startup, Sultan, Woodinville); Below 100 (portions of Island County, portions of King County, Oak Harbor, portions of Snohomish County, Whidbey Island Naval Air Station); Outside TV Markets (portions of Island County, portions of King County, portions of Snohomish County). Franchise award date: N.A. Franchise expiration date: N.A. Began: March 1, 1952.
Channel capacity: 37 (not 2-way capable). Channels available but not in use: None.

Basic Service
Subscribers: 283,460.
Programming (received off-air): KCPQ (F), KCTS-TV (P), KING-TV (N), KIRO-TV (C), KOMO-TV (A), KSTW (U), KTBW-TV (T), KTWB (W) Seattle-Tacoma; KBTC-TV (P) Tacoma; CBUT Vancouver; 28 FMs.
Programming (via satellite): C-SPAN 2; Home Shopping Network; TBS Superstation; TV Guide Channel.
Current originations: Public access.
Fee: $31.97 installation; $11.83 monthly; $1.00 converter.

Expanded Basic Service
Subscribers: 275,770.
Programming (via satellite): A & E; American Movie Classics; BET; C-SPAN; CNBC; CNN; Comedy Central; Court TV; Discovery Channel; ESPN; ESPN 2; FX; Fox Sports Net Northwest; Headline News; Learning Channel; Lifetime; MTV; Nashville Network; Nickelodeon; Odyssey; QVC; TV Guide Sneak Prevue; Turner Network TV; USA Network; VH1.
Fee: $11.13 monthly.

Expanded Basic Service 2
Subscribers: N.A.
Programming (via satellite): Bravo; Cartoon Network; fXM: Movies from Fox; Flix; History Channel; Sci-Fi Channel.
Fee: N.A.

Pay Service 1
Pay Units: 153,257.
Programming (via satellite): Cinemax; Disney Channel; HBO; Showtime; The Movie Channel.
Fee: $39.95 installation; $9.00 monthly (Disney or Showtime), $11.00 monthly (HBO or TMC).

Pay-Per-View
Addressable homes: 76,791.
Hot Choice; Viewer's Choice; movies; special events.
Fee: $4.95-$39.95.

Local advertising: Yes. Available in satellite distributed & locally originated programming. Local sales manager: Penny Taylor.
Program Guide: The Cable Guide.
Equipment: Scientific-Atlanta headend; Jerrold, Theta-Com & C-COR amplifiers; Cerro, Kaiser & Times Fiber cable; Hamlin, Oak & Texscan set top converters; Zenith addressable set top converters; Scientific-Atlanta & Antenna Technology satellite antenna; Scientific-Atlanta satellite receivers; Texscan/MSI commercial insert.
Miles of plant: 3239.0 (coaxial). Homes passed: 382,001. Total homes in franchised area: 392,000.
Manager: Bob Lam. Chief technician: Marty Adams.
City fee: 4% of gross.
Ownership: AT&T Broadband & Internet Services (MSO). Purchased from Tele-Communications Inc., March 9, 1999.

SEQUIM—Northland Cable TV, 725 E. First St., Port Angeles, WA 98362. Phone: 360-452-8466. Fax: 360-457-5901. County: Clallam. Also serves Clallam County (unincorporated areas). ICA: WA0029.
TV Market Ranking: Outside TV Markets. Franchise award date: May 1, 1967. Franchise expiration date: May 1, 2012. Began: September 1, 1971.
Channel capacity: 42 (not 2-way capable). Channels available but not in use: 1.

Basic Service
Subscribers: 4,960; Commercial subscribers: 210.
Programming (received off-air): KVOS-TV (I) Bellingham; KCPQ (F), KCTS-TV (P), KING-TV (N), KIRO-TV (C), KOMO-TV (A), KSTW (U) Seattle-Tacoma; CBUT, CKVU-TV Vancouver; CHEK-TV Victoria.
Programming (via satellite): C-SPAN; QVC; TBS Superstation; TV Guide Channel.
Current originations: Automated time-weather; educational access; government access; local sports.
Fee: $50.00 installation; $16.50 monthly; $3.00 converter; $10.00 additional installation.
Commercial fee: $3.95 monthly.

Expanded Basic Service
Subscribers: 4,637.
Programming (via satellite): A & E; CNBC; CNN; Discovery Channel; ESPN; Fox Family Channel; Headline News; MTV; Nashville Network; Turner Network TV.
Fee: $50.00 installation; $6.95 monthly.

Expanded Basic Service 2
Subscribers: 2,288.
Programming (via satellite): Cartoon Network; Disney Channel; Fox Sports Net Northwest; Goodlife TV Network; Lifetime; Travel Channel; USA Network.
Fee: $50.00 installation; $9.95 monthly.

Pay Service 1
Pay Units: 201.
Programming (via satellite): Cinemax.
Fee: $19.95 installation; $8.95 monthly.

Pay Service 2
Pay Units: 291.
Programming (via satellite): HBO.
Fee: $19.95 installation; $11.50 monthly.

Pay Service 3
Pay Units: 143.
Programming (via satellite): Showtime.
Fee: $19.95 installation; $10.50 monthly.

Pay Service 4
Pay Units: 31.
Programming (via satellite): The New Encore.
Fee: $6.95 monthly.

Local advertising: Yes. Available in satellite distributed, locally originated, character-generated, taped & automated programming. Rates: $10.00/30 Seconds. Local sales manager: Rich Kaake.
Equipment: Texscan amplifiers; Times Fiber cable; MSI & Texscan character generator; Hamlin set top converters; Pico traps; Hughes & Scientific-Atlanta satellite antenna; Standard Communications satellite receivers.
Miles of plant: 121.0 (coaxial); 19.0 (fiber optic). Additional miles planned: 12.0 (coaxial). Homes passed: 6,557.
Manager: Daniel Withers. Chief technician: Michael Sturgeon. Program director: Dennis Bragg. Customer service manager: Rose Gosslin.
City fee: 5% of gross.
Ownership: Northland Communications Corp. (MSO).

SHELTON—TCI Cablevision of Washington Inc., Box 129, 440 Yauger St., Olympia, WA 98507-0129. Phone: 360-357-3364. County: Mason. Also serves Mason County (southwestern portion). ICA: WA0030.
TV Market Ranking: 20 (portions of Mason County, Shelton); Outside TV Markets (portions of Mason County). Franchise award date: N.A. Franchise expiration date: N.A. Began: May 1, 1970.
Channel capacity: 37. Channels available but not in use: N.A.

Basic Service
Subscribers: 4,749.
Programming (received off-air): KCPQ (F), KCTS-TV (P), KING-TV (N), KIRO-TV (C), KOMO-TV (A), KSTW (U), KTWB (W) Seattle-Tacoma; allband FM.
Programming (via satellite): A & E; CNN; Comedy Central; Discovery Channel; Fox Family Channel; Lifetime; MTV; Nashville Network; Nickelodeon; TBS Superstation; VH1.
Fee: $27.57 monthly; $0.88 converter.

Expanded Basic Service
Subscribers: 4,216.
Programming (via satellite): American Movie Classics; Court TV; ESPN; FX; Fox Sports Net Northwest; MSNBC; QVC; Turner Network TV; USA Network.
Fee: $10.81 monthly.

Pay Service 1
Pay Units: 348.
Programming (via satellite): Disney Channel.
Fee: $11.15 monthly.

Pay Service 2
Pay Units: 1,833.
Programming (via satellite): The New Encore.
Fee: $1.75 monthly.

Pay Service 3
Pay Units: 959.
Programming (via satellite): HBO.
Fee: $13.05 monthly.

Pay Service 4
Pay Units: 132.
Programming (via satellite): Cinemax.
Fee: $12.45 monthly.

Pay Service 5
Pay Units: 289.
Programming (via satellite): Showtime.
Fee: $13.05 monthly.

Pay Service 6
Pay Units: N.A.
Programming (via satellite): Starz!
Fee: $4.75 monthly.

Pay-Per-View
Action Pay-Per-View; special events.

Local advertising: Yes (locally produced & insert). Available in character-generated programming. Local sales manager: Linda Boysen.
Program Guide: The Cable Guide.
Equipment: Scientific-Atlanta headend; Magnavox amplifiers; Comm/Scope & Times Fiber cable; Jerrold set top converters; Eagle traps; Scientific-Atlanta satellite antenna; Scientific-Atlanta satellite receivers.
Miles of plant: 109.5 (coaxial). Homes passed: 5,296. Total homes in franchised area: 5,398.
Manager: Anne McMillen.
City fee: 5% of gross.
Ownership: AT&T Broadband & Internet Services (MSO). Purchased from Tele-Communications Inc., March 9, 1999.

SKAMOKAWA—Wright Cablevision, Box 447, Cathlamet, WA 98612. Phone: 206-762-7840. County: Wahkiakum. ICA: WA0142.
TV Market Ranking: Outside TV Markets. Franchise award date: N.A. Franchise expiration date: N.A. Began: September 1, 1967.
Channel capacity: N.A. Channels available but not in use: N.A.

Basic Service
Subscribers: 47.
Programming (received off-air): KATU (A), KGW (N), KOIN (C), KPTV (U) Portland; KCTS-TV (P), KING-TV (N), KOMO-TV (A), KSTW (U) Seattle-Tacoma; allband FM.
Programming (via satellite): CNN.
Fee: $10.00 installation; $9.00 monthly.

Equipment: Blonder-Tongue & Jerrold headend; Vikoa amplifiers; Times Fiber & Vikoa cable.
Miles of plant: 4.0 (coaxial). Homes passed: 65. Total homes in franchised area: 95.
Manager: Don Wright.
Ownership: Wright Cablevision.

SKYKOMISH—Index Cable TV Inc., 1781 Old Hwy. 99 N, Burlington, WA 98233. Phone: 360-724-3802. Fax: 360-724-2006. County: King. Also serves Skykomish (town). ICA: WA0135.

TV Market Ranking: Outside TV Markets. Franchise award date: April 11, 1983. Franchise expiration date: April 11, 1998. Began: N.A.
Channel capacity: 36 (not 2-way capable). Channels available but not in use: N.A.
Basic Service
Subscribers: 98.
Programming (received off-air): KCTS-TV (P), KING-TV (N), KIRO-TV (C), KOMO-TV (A) Seattle-Tacoma.
Programming (via satellite): WGN-TV (W) Chicago; A & E; C-SPAN; CNN; Country Music TV; Discovery Channel; E! Entertainment TV; ESPN; Fox Family Channel; Fox Sports Net Northwest; FoxNet; Headline News; History Channel; Knowledge TV; Nashville Network; Sci-Fi Channel; TBS Superstation; Trinity Bcstg. Network; Turner Network TV; USA Network.
Fee: $39.95 installation; $21.50 monthly; $4.00 converter.
Pay Service 1
Pay Units: 31.
Programming (via satellite): HBO.
Fee: $9.95 monthly.
Miles of plant: 3.4 (coaxial); None (fiber optic). Homes passed: 150. Total homes in franchised area: 150.
Manager: Ed Varhaug.
Ownership: Index Cable TV Inc. (MSO).

SPANGLE—Northwest Cable LP, Box 618, Lockney, TX 79241. Phone: 800-480-3766. Fax: 806-652-3139. County: Spokane. ICA: WA0180.
TV Market Ranking: 76. Franchise award date: N.A. Franchise expiration date: N.A. Began: March 1, 1990.
Channel capacity: 16. Channels available but not in use: N.A.
Basic Service
Subscribers: 29.
Programming (received off-air): KWSU-TV (P) Pullman; KAYU-TV (F), KHQ-TV (N), KREM-TV (C), KSPS-TV (P), KXLY-TV (A) Spokane.
Programming (via satellite): WGN-TV (W) Chicago; A & E; CNN; Cartoon Network; Discovery Channel; ESPN; Nashville Network; TBS Superstation; Turner Network TV; USA Network.
Fee: $40.00 installation; $17.95 monthly.
Pay Service 1
Pay Units: N.A.
Programming (via satellite): HBO.
Fee: $10.00 installation; $8.00 monthly.
Manager: William Yusko. Chief technician: Dave Como.
Ownership: Northwest Cable Ltd. Partnership (MSO).

SPOKANE—AT&T Cable Services, Box Hay C-1, 1717 E. Buckeye, Spokane, WA 99207. Phones: 509-484-4900; 509-484-4931. Fax: 509-483-9261. County: Spokane. Also serves Millwood, Spokane County. ICA: WA0004.
TV Market Ranking: 76. Franchise award date: December 23, 1974. Franchise expiration date: July 2, 2005. Began: September 30, 1976.
Channel capacity: 78 (2-way capable; operating 2-way partially). Channels available but not in use: 4.
Basic Service
Subscribers: 93,405.
Programming (received off-air): KCDT (P) Coeur d'Alene; KAYU-TV (F), KHQ-TV (N), KREM-TV (C), KSKN (U,W), KSPS-TV (P), KXLY-TV (A) Spokane.
Programming (via satellite): WGN-TV (W) Chicago; TBS Superstation.
Fee: $11.34 installation; $6.63 monthly; $1.50 converter.
Digital Basic Service
Subscribers: N.A.
Programming (via satellite): BBC America; Box Classic; Box Pulse; Cartoon Network; Discovery Civilization Channel; Discovery Health Channel; Discovery Home & Leisure Channel; Discovery Kids Channel; Discovery People; Discovery Science Channel; Discovery Wings Channel; ESPN 2; ESPN Classic Sports; ESPNews; Fox Sports World; Game Show Network; Golf Channel; History Channel; Independent Film Channel; Much-Music Network; Romance Classics; The Barker; Turner Classic Movies.
Fee: $10.00 monthly.
Expanded Basic Service
Subscribers: 90,326.
Programming (received off-air): KIRO-TV (C) Seattle-Tacoma.
Programming (via satellite): A & E; American Movie Classics; Animal Planet; BET; Bravo; C-SPAN; CNBC; CNN; Comedy Central; Country Music TV; Discovery Channel; Disney Channel; E! Entertainment TV; ESPN; FX; Fox Family Channel; Fox News Channel; Fox Sports Net Northwest; Headline News; Home & Garden Television; Home Shopping Network; Learning Channel; Lifetime; MOVIEplex; MSNBC; MTV; NASA TV; Nashville Network; Nickelodeon; Northwest Cable News; Odyssey; Outdoor Life Network; Product Information Network; QVC; Sci-Fi Channel; Speedvision; TV Guide Channel; The Weather Channel; Travel Channel; Trinity Bcstg. Network; Turner Network TV; USA Network; VH1.
Fee: $21.81 monthly.
Expanded Basic Service 2
Subscribers: 18,479.
Programming (via satellite): Bravo; Cartoon Network; Court TV; ESPN 2; Golf Channel; History Channel; Turner Classic Movies.
Fee: $3.00 installation; $14.95 monthly.
A la Carte 1
Subscribers: N.A.
Programming (via satellite): The New Encore.
Fee: $1.00 monthly.
Pay Service 1
Pay Units: 10,437.
Programming (via satellite): Cinemax.
Fee: $3.00 installation; $9.60 monthly.
Pay Service 2
Pay Units: 18,676.
Programming (via satellite): HBO (multiplexed).
Fee: $3.00 installation; $9.60 monthly.
Pay Service 3
Pay Units: 5,006.
Programming (via satellite): The Movie Channel.
Fee: $3.00 installation; $9.60 monthly.
Pay Service 4
Pay Units: 9,296.
Programming (via satellite): Showtime.
Fee: $3.00 installation; $9.60 monthly.
Pay Service 5
Pay Units: 1,809.
Programming (via satellite): Music Choice.
Fee: $9.60 monthly.
Pay Service 6
Pay Units: N.A.
Programming (via satellite): Starz!
Fee: $6.75 monthly.
Digital Pay Service 1
Pay Units: N.A.
Programming (via satellite): Encore Love Stories; Encore Mystery; Encore Westerns; HBO Signature; Showtime (multiplexed); Starz! (multiplexed).

Fee: N.A.
Pay-Per-View
Addressable homes: 41,000.
Action Pay-Per-View; Hot Choice; Playboy TV; Spice delivered digitally; Viewer's Choice.
Interactive Services
Subscribers: 90,326.
Home shopping.
Local advertising: Yes (locally produced & insert). Available in satellite distributed, locally originated, taped & automated programming. Rates: $60.00/Minute; $30.00/30 Seconds. Local sales manager: Jeff Johnson.
Program Guide: The Cable Guide.
Equipment: Scientific-Atlanta headend; Scientific-Atlanta amplifiers; Comm/Scope cable; Ikegami & JVC cameras; Sony VTRs; Sony & Tektronix character generator; Jerrold & GTE Sylvania set top converters; Scientific-Atlanta addressable set top converters; Eagle traps; Scientific-Atlanta satellite antenna; Scientific-Atlanta satellite receivers; Channel-Matic, Spot Matic & Texscan commercial insert.
Miles of plant: 1528.0 (coaxial); 35.0 (fiber optic). Additional miles planned: 150.0 (coaxial). Homes passed: 131,071. Total homes in franchised area: 176,789.
Manager: Kenneth Watts. Chief technician: Matt Durand. Program & marketing director: Alison Ruckhaber.
City & County fee: 5% of gross.
Ownership: AT&T Broadband & Internet Services (MSO). Purchased from Tele-Communications Inc., March 9, 1999.

SPRAGUE—Northwest Cable LP, Box 618, Lockney, TX 79241. Phone: 800-480-3766. Fax: 806-652-3139. County: Lincoln. ICA: WA0130.
TV Market Ranking: Outside TV Markets. Franchise award date: N.A. Franchise expiration date: N.A. Began: June 9, 1983.
Channel capacity: 24 (2-way capable; operating 2-way). Channels available but not in use: 14.
Basic Service
Subscribers: N.A.
Programming (received off-air): KWSU-TV (P) Pullman; KAYU-TV (F), KHQ-TV (N), KREM-TV (C), KSPS-TV (P), KXLY-TV (A) Spokane.
Programming (via satellite): WGN-TV (W) Chicago; ESPN; Headline News.
Planned originations: Government access.
Fee: $25.00 installation; $10.00 monthly.
Pay Service 1
Pay Units: N.A.
Programming (via satellite): Cinemax.
Fee: $10.00 monthly.
Miles of plant: 5.0 (coaxial). Homes passed: 190. Total homes in franchised area: 190.
Manager: Kenneth V. Mettler. Chief technician: Joseph R. Poire.
City fee: 3% of gross.
Ownership: Northwest Cable Ltd. Partnership (MSO).

SPRINGDALE—Northwest Cable LP, Box 618, Lockney, TX 79241. Phone: 800-480-3766. Fax: 806-652-3139. County: Stevens. ICA: WA0182.
TV Market Ranking: 76. Franchise award date: August 1, 1988. Franchise expiration date: August 1, 2003. Began: July 1, 1989.
Channel capacity: N.A. Channels available but not in use: N.A.
Basic Service
Subscribers: 70.
Programming (received off-air): KWSU-TV (P) Pullman; KAYU-TV (F), KHQ-TV (N), KREM-TV (C), KSPS-TV (P), KXLY-TV (A) Spokane.
Programming (via satellite): WGN-TV (W) Chicago; CNN; ESPN; Nashville Network; TBS Superstation.
Fee: $20.75 monthly; $15.00 additional installation.
Pay Service 1
Pay Units: N.A.
Programming (via satellite): HBO.
Fee: $10.00 monthly.
Manager: William Yusko.
Ownership: Northwest Cable Ltd. Partnership (MSO).

ST. JOHN—St. John Cable Co. Inc., Box 268, St. John, WA 99171. Phone: 509-648-3322. Fax: 509-648-9900. County: Whitman. Also serves Endicott, Lacrosse. ICA: WA0119.
TV Market Ranking: Below 100. Franchise award date: N.A. Franchise expiration date: N.A. Began: January 1, 1983.
Channel capacity: N.A. Channels available but not in use: N.A.
Basic Service
Subscribers: 513.
Programming (received off-air): KUID-TV (P) Moscow; KWSU-TV (P) Pullman; KAYU-TV (F), KHQ-TV (N), KREM-TV (C), KSPS-TV (P), KXLY-TV (A) Spokane.
Programming (via satellite): WGN-TV (W) Chicago; CNN; ESPN; Lifetime; Nashville Network; TBS Superstation.
Planned originations: Local news.
Fee: $10.00 installation; $12.00 monthly.
Pay Service 1
Pay Units: N.A.
Programming (via satellite): Cinemax; Disney Channel; HBO.
Fee: $8.00 monthly (Cinemax or HBO), $10.00 monthly (Disney).
Miles of plant: 3.1 (coaxial).
Manager: Larry Dickerson.
Ownership: St. John Cable Co. Inc. (MSO).

STARBUCK—TCI Cablevision of Yakima Inc., Box 1577, 126 W. Poplar St., Walla Walla, WA 99362-2847. Phone: 509-529-9500. Fax: 509-522-1719. County: Columbia. ICA: WA0137.
TV Market Ranking: Below 100. Franchise award date: N.A. Franchise expiration date: N.A. Began: January 1, 1964.
Channel capacity: 22. Channels available but not in use: 8.
Basic Service
Subscribers: 70.
Programming (received off-air): KAYU-TV (F), KHQ-TV (N), KREM-TV (C), KSPS-TV (P), KXLY-TV (A) Spokane.
Programming (via satellite): Discovery Channel; ESPN; Fox Family Channel; Headline News; Nashville Network; TBS Superstation.

Fee: $39.15 installation; $12.03 monthly; $40.00 additional installation.
Pay Service 1
Pay Units: 14.
Programming (via satellite): Showtime.
Fee: $10.50 monthly.
Miles of plant: 3.0 (coaxial). Homes passed: 120. Total homes in franchised area: 120.
Manager: Tim Klinefelter. Chief technician: Tim Ream. Program director: Dinah Morrison. Marketing director: Marlene Ashby.
Ownership: AT&T Broadband & Internet Services (MSO). Purchased from Tele-Communications Inc., March 9, 1999.

SUDDEN VALLEY—TCI Cablevision of Washington Inc., 777 W. Horton Rd., Bellingham, WA 98226-7606. Phone: 360-384-1581. County: Whatcom. ICA: WA0067.
TV Market Ranking: Below 100. Franchise award date: N.A. Franchise expiration date: N.A. Began: April 1, 1974.
Channel capacity: 31. Channels available but not in use: 9.
Basic Service
Subscribers: 1,126.
Programming (received off-air): KVOS-TV (I) Bellingham; KONG-TV (I) Everett; KCPQ (F), KCTS-TV (P), KING-TV (N), KIRO-TV (C), KOMO-TV (A), KSTW (U) Seattle-Tacoma; CBUT, CHAN-TV Vancouver.
Programming (via satellite): A & E; CNN; Discovery Channel; ESPN; Fox Family Channel; Headline News; Nashville Network; TBS Superstation; USA Network.
Current originations: Local news.
Fee: $60.00 installation; $17.80 monthly.
Pay Service 1
Pay Units: 96.
Programming (via satellite): Disney Channel.
Fee: N.A.
Pay Service 2
Pay Units: 150.
Programming (via satellite): HBO.
Fee: N.A.
Pay Service 3
Pay Units: 93.
Programming (via satellite): Showtime.
Fee: N.A.
Pay Service 4
Pay Units: N.A.
Programming (via satellite): The New Encore.
Fee: N.A.
Miles of plant: 53.0 (coaxial). Homes passed: 1,279. Total homes in franchised area: 1,359.
Manager: Dan Crocker.
Ownership: AT&T Broadband & Internet Services (MSO). Purchased from Tele-Communications Inc., March 9, 1999.

SUMAS—City of Sumas TV Cable System, Box 9, 433 Cherry St., Sumas, WA 98295. Phone: 360-988-5711. Fax: 360-988-8855. County: Whatcom. ICA: WA0099.
TV Market Ranking: Below 100. Franchise award date: N.A. Franchise expiration date: N.A. Began: March 1, 1953.
Channel capacity: 12. Channels available but not in use: N.A.
Basic Service
Subscribers: 360.
Programming (received off-air): KVOS-TV (I) Bellingham; KONG-TV (I) Everett; KCPQ (F), KCTS-TV (P), KING-TV (N), KIRO-TV (C), KOMO-TV (A), KTWB (W) Seattle-Tacoma; CBUT, CKVU-TV Vancouver; CHEK-TV Victoria; 1 FM.
Programming (via satellite): A & E; C-SPAN; C-SPAN 2; CNN; Discovery Channel; ESPN; FX; Fox Sports Net Northwest; History Channel; Home & Garden Television; Knowledge TV; Learning Channel; Nashville Network; Nick at Nite's TV Land; Nickelodeon; Northwest Cable News; Odyssey; Outdoor Channel; QVC; TBS Superstation; Trinity Bcstg. Network; Turner Classic Movies; Turner Network TV.
Fee: $25.00 installation; $13.00 monthly.
Pay Service 1
Pay Units: 99.
Programming (via satellite): Showtime.
Fee: $15.00 installation; $8.00 monthly.
Local advertising: No.
Equipment: Blonder-Tongue headend; Blonder-Tongue amplifiers; Cerro cable.
Miles of plant: 8.0 (coaxial). Homes passed: 500.
Manager: Rod Fadden.
Ownership: City of Sumas TV Cable System.

SUNCREST—Optel, Suite 100, 1111 W. Mockingbird Lane, Dallas, TX 75247. Phone: 214-634-3800. County: Stevens. ICA: WA0086.
TV Market Ranking: 76. Franchise award date: June 1, 1984. Franchise expiration date: N.A. Began: November 5, 1985.
Channel capacity: 54. Channels available but not in use: 32.
Basic Service
Subscribers: 499.
Programming (received off-air): KAYU-TV (F), KHQ-TV (N), KREM-TV (C), KSPS-TV (P), KXLY-TV (A) Spokane.
Programming (via satellite): CNN; Discovery Channel; ESPN; Fox Family Channel; Headline News; MTV; Nashville Network; Nickelodeon; QVC; TBS Superstation; Turner Network TV; USA Network; VH1.
Current originations: Local news.
Fee: $15.00 installation; $17.00 monthly.
Pay Service 1
Pay Units: 59.
Programming (via satellite): Cinemax.
Fee: $10.00 installation; $10.00 monthly.
Pay Service 2
Pay Units: 35.
Programming (via satellite): Disney Channel.
Fee: $10.00 installation; $10.00 monthly.
Pay Service 3
Pay Units: 130.
Programming (via satellite): HBO.
Fee: $10.00 installation; $13.00 monthly.
Local advertising: No.
Equipment: Scientific-Atlanta headend; Scientific-Atlanta amplifiers; Scientific-Atlanta cable; Atari character generator; Scientific-Atlanta set top converters; Pico traps; Scientific-Atlanta satellite antenna; Scientific-Atlanta satellite receivers.
Miles of plant: 25.0 (coaxial). Additional miles planned: 4.0 (coaxial). Homes passed: 700. Total homes in franchised area: 700.
Manager: Norm Bonnett. Marketing director: Billie Van Eaton.
City fee: 3% of basic.
Ownership: Optel Cable (MSO).

SUNNYSIDE—Falcon Cable, 1005 N. 16th Ave., Yakima, WA 98902-1351. Phone: 509-575-1697. County: Yakima. Also serves Mabton, Yakima County (eastern portion). Plans service to Evergreen Mobile Home Park. ICA: WA0033.
TV Market Ranking: Below 100. Franchise award date: N.A. Franchise expiration date: December 1, 2003. Began: January 1, 1958.
Channel capacity: 30 (not 2-way capable). Channels available but not in use: N.A.
Basic Service
Subscribers: 2,870.
Programming (received off-air): KAYU-TV (F) Spokane; KAPP (A), KIMA-TV (C), KNDO (N), KYVE-TV (P) Yakima.
Programming (via microwave): KSTW (U) Seattle-Tacoma.
Programming (via satellite): WGN-TV (W) Chicago; CNN; Discovery Channel; Fox Family Channel; GalaVision; Headline News; MTV; Nashville Network; Nickelodeon; TBS Superstation; Univision.
Planned originations: Automated time-weather.
Fee: $60.00 installation; $18.20 monthly; $40.00 additional installation.
Expanded Basic Service
Subscribers: N.A.
Programming (via satellite): American Movie Classics; ESPN; Fox Sports Net Northwest; Turner Network TV; USA Network.
Fee: $1.50 monthly.
Pay Service 1
Pay Units: 98.
Programming (via satellite): Cinemax.
Fee: $15.00 installation; $12.05 monthly.
Pay Service 2
Pay Units: 125.
Programming (via satellite): Disney Channel.
Fee: $15.00 installation; $9.20 monthly.
Pay Service 3
Pay Units: 877.
Programming (via satellite): The New Encore.
Fee: N.A.
Pay Service 4
Pay Units: 360.
Programming (via satellite): HBO.
Fee: $15.00 installation; $12.05 monthly.
Pay Service 5
Pay Units: 130.
Programming (via satellite): Showtime.
Fee: $15.00 installation; $12.05 monthly.
Local advertising: Yes (insert only).
Program Guide: CableView.
Equipment: Catel & Scientific-Atlanta headend; Theta-Com amplifiers; Times Fiber cable; Hamlin set top converters; Pico traps; Scientific-Atlanta satellite antenna; Scientific-Atlanta satellite receivers.
Miles of plant: 65.8 (coaxial). Homes passed: 5,062. Total homes in franchised area: 5,200.
Manager: Gary Bailey. Marketing director: Shelley Bjornson.
City fee: 5% of gross.
Ownership: Falcon Communications LP (MSO). Purchased from Tele-Communications Inc., October 1, 1998.

TACOMA—TCI Cablevision Inc., 2316 S. State St., Tacoma, WA 98405. Phone: 253-597-7800. Fax: 253-272-4062. Counties: King, Kitsap, Pierce & Thurston. Also serves Bonney Lake, Buckley, Carbonado, Du Pont, Eatonville, Edgewood, Fife, Fircrest, Fort Lewis, Fox Island, Gig Harbor, Gig Harbor Peninsula, Graham, Lake Holliday, Lake Minterwood, Lake of the Woods, Lakebay, Lakewood Center, Madrona Point, McKenna, Milton, Orting, Park Place Mobile Home Park, Peninsula, Puyallup, Rainier, Roy, South Prairie, Spanaway, Steilacoom, Summit, Sumner, Thurston County, University Place, Wilkeson, Yelm. ICA: WA0003.
TV Market Ranking: 20 (Bonney Lake, Buckley, Carbonado, Du Pont, Eatonville, Edgewood, Fife, Fircrest, Fort Lewis, Fox Island, Gig Harbor, Gig Harbor Peninsula, Graham, Lake Holliday, Lake Minterwood, Lake of the Woods, Lakebay, Lakewood Center, Madrona Point, McKenna, Milton, Orting, Park Place Mobile Home Park, Peninsula, Puyallup, Rainier, Roy, South Prairie, Spanaway, Steilacoom, Summit, Sumner, Tacoma, portions of Thurston County, University Place, Wilkeson, Yelm); Outside TV Markets (portions of Thurston County). Franchise award date: N.A. Franchise expiration date: N.A. Began: January 1, 1967.
Channel capacity: 34. Channels available but not in use: None.
Basic Service
Subscribers: 149,350.
Programming (received off-air): KWPX (X) Bellevue; KONG-TV (I) Everett; KCPQ (F), KCTS-TV (P), KING-TV (N), KIRO-TV (C), KOMO-TV (A), KSTW (U), KTBW-TV (T), KTWB (W) Seattle-Tacoma; KBTC-TV (P) Tacoma; CBUT Vancouver; 24 FMs.
Programming (via satellite): C-SPAN 2; Court TV; Discovery Channel; Home Shopping Network; QVC; TBS Superstation; TV Guide Channel; TV Guide Sneak Prevue; Univision.
Current originations: Automated time-weather; public access; educational access; government access; leased access; local news.
Fee: N.A.
Digital Basic Service
Subscribers: N.A.
Programming (via satellite): BBC America; BET on Jazz; Box Classic; Box Edge; Box Pulse; Box Urban; Discovery Civilization Channel; Discovery Health Channel; Discovery Home & Leisure Channel; Discovery Kids Channel; Discovery People; Discovery Science Channel; Discovery Wings Channel; ESPN Classic Sports; ESPNews; Fox Sports World; Game Show Network; Golf Channel; History Channel International; Home & Garden Television; Independent Film Channel; Kaleidoscope; Lifetime Movie Network; MuchMusic Network; Outdoor Life Network; Ovation; Romance Classics; The Barker; The Biography Channel; Turner Classic Movies.
Fee: N.A.
Expanded Basic Service
Subscribers: N.A.
Programming (via satellite): A & E; American Movie Classics; Animal Planet; BET; Bravo; C-SPAN; CNBC; CNN; Cartoon Network; Comedy Central; Disney Channel; ESPN; ESPN 2; FX; fXM: Movies from Fox; Fox News Channel; Fox Sports Net Northwest; Headline News; History Channel; Learning Channel; Lifetime; MTV; Nashville Network; Nickelodeon; Northwest Cable News; Odyssey; Sci-Fi Channel; Shop at Home; Turner Network TV; USA Network; VH1.
Fee: N.A.
Pay Service 1
Pay Units: N.A.
Programming (via satellite): Cinemax; HBO (multiplexed); Showtime; Starz!; The Movie Channel; The New Encore.
Fee: $11.00 monthly (Showtime or TMC), $12.00 monthly (HBO).
Digital Pay Service 1
Pay Units: N.A.
Programming (via satellite): BET Movies/Starz!; DMX; Encore Love Stories; Encore Mystery; Encore Westerns; HBO Plus; HBO Signature; Showtime (multiplexed); Starz! Theater.
Fee: N.A.
Pay-Per-View
Addressable homes: 58,000.
Action PPV delivered digitally; Hot Choice; Hot Choice delivered digitally; Playboy TV; Spice; Spice delivered digitally; Viewer's Choice Digital; Viewer's Choice 1 & 2.
Local advertising: Yes. Rates: $50.00/Minute; $25.00/30 Seconds; $12.50/15 Seconds.

Equipment: Jerrold headend; Cascade, GTE Sylvania & Theta-Com amplifiers; Composite & Times Fiber cable; Sony VTRs; Jerrold & MSI character generator; Magnavox set top converters; Jerrold addressable set top converters; Scientific-Atlanta & Simulsat satellite antenna.
Miles of plant: 2580.0 (coaxial). Homes passed: 194,463. Total homes in franchised area: 200,000.
Manager: Eric Kronen. Chief technician: Jerry Rotondo. Marketing director: Colette Jelineo.
County fee: 3%-5% of gross.
Ownership: AT&T Broadband & Internet Services (MSO). Purchased from Tele-Communications Inc., March 9, 1999.

***TACOMA**—Tacoma City Light, 3628 S. 35th St., Tacoma, WA 98409. Phone: 800-752-6745. Fax: 253-502-8493. County: Pierce. ICA: WA0206.
TV Market Ranking: 20. Franchise award date: N.A. Franchise expiration date: N.A. Scheduled to begin: March 1, 1998.
Channel capacity: N.A.
Ownership: Tacoma City Light.

TEKOA—Community Cable Service, 729 S. Bernard St., Spokane, WA 99204. Phones: 509-624-4140; 800-572-0902. Fax: 509-624-7372. County: Whitman. ICA: WA0114.
TV Market Ranking: 76. Franchise award date: N.A. Franchise expiration date: N.A. Began: February 1, 1975.
Channel capacity: 62 (2-way capable; not operating 2-way). Channels available but not in use: 4.
Basic Service
Subscribers: 279.
Programming (received off-air): KWSU-TV (P) Pullman; KAYU-TV (F), KHQ-TV (N), KREM-TV (C), KSPS-TV (P), KXLY-TV (A) Spokane; allband FM.
Programming (via satellite): WGN-TV (W) Chicago; A & E; American Movie Classics; Bravo; C-SPAN; C-SPAN 2; CNBC; CNN; CNN International; Cartoon Network; Comedy Central; Country Music TV; Discovery Channel; E! Entertainment TV; ESPN; ESPN 2; ESPNews; EWTN; Fox Family Channel; Fox News Channel; Fox Sports Net Northwest; Headline News; History Channel; Home & Garden Television; Home Shopping Network; Knowledge TV; Learning Channel; Lifetime; MTV; Nashville Network; Nick at Nite's TV Land; Nickelodeon; Odyssey; QVC; Sci-Fi Channel; TBS Superstation; TV Food Network; The Health Network; The Inspirational Network; Travel Channel; Trinity Bcstg. Network; Turner Classic Movies; Turner Network TV; USA Network; VH1; ValueVision; Z Music Television.
Fee: $15.00 installation; $26.35 monthly.
Pay Service 1
Pay Units: 47.
Programming (via satellite): Cinemax.
Fee: $5.00 installation; $6.23 monthly.
Pay Service 2
Pay Units: 42.
Programming (via satellite): Disney Channel.
Fee: $5.00 installation; $5.18 monthly.
Pay Service 3
Pay Units: 70.
Programming (via satellite): HBO.
Fee: $5.00 installation; $9.38 monthly.
Pay Service 4
Pay Units: N.A.
Programming (via satellite): Showtime.
Fee: $7.86 monthly.
Miles of plant: 7.0 (coaxial); None (fiber optic). Homes passed: 441.
Manager: Martin Howser.
City fee: 3% of gross.
Ownership: Martin Howser (MSO).

THORP—Cable Plus, Suite 120, 11400 S.E. 6th St., Bellevue, WA 98004. Phone: 425-462-2090. Fax: 425-462-2092. County: Kittitas East. ICA: WA0204.
TV Market Ranking: Below 100. Franchise award date: October 6, 1989. Franchise expiration date: October 6, 2004. Began: N.A.
Channel capacity: 40. Channels available but not in use: N.A.
Basic Service
Subscribers: 50.
Programming (received off-air): KAPP (A), KIMA-TV (C), KNDO (N), KYVE-TV (P) Yakima.
Programming (via satellite): WGN-TV (W) Chicago; A & E; Animal Planet; C-SPAN; CNN; CNN International; CNNfn; Country Music TV; Discovery Channel; ESPN; ESPN 2; Fox Family Channel; Fox Sports Net Northwest; Headline News; History Channel; Home & Garden Television; Home Shopping Network; Learning Channel; Lifetime; Nashville Network; Nickelodeon; Northwest Cable News; QVC; Sci-Fi Channel; TBS Superstation; The Weather Channel; Trinity Bcstg. Network; Turner Network TV; USA Network.
Fee: $35.00 installation; $21.95 monthly.
Pay Service 1
Pay Units: 5.
Programming (via satellite): HBO.
Fee: $11.95 monthly.
Pay Service 2
Pay Units: 4.
Programming (via satellite): Showtime.
Fee: $10.95 monthly.
Pay Service 3
Pay Units: N.A.
Programming (via satellite): Disney Channel.
Fee: $9.95 monthly.
Miles of plant: 6.0 (coaxial). Homes passed: 77.
Manager: Gary O'Malley. Chief technician: Dan Adams.
Ownership: Cable Plus (MSO).

TOLEDO—RGA Cable TV, Box 331, Toledo, WA 98591. Phone: 360-864-4553. County: Lewis. ICA: WA0107.
TV Market Ranking: Outside TV Markets. Franchise award date: N.A. Franchise expiration date: N.A. Began: October 1, 1970.
Channel capacity: 25. Channels available but not in use: None.
Basic Service
Subscribers: 343.
Programming (received off-air): KATU (A), KGW (N), KOIN (C), KPTV (U) Portland; KCPQ (F), KCTS-TV (P), KING-TV (N), KIRO-TV (C), KOMO-TV (A), KSTW (U) Seattle-Tacoma; 1 FM.
Programming (via satellite): A & E; CNN; Country Music TV; ESPN; Fox Sports Net; Learning Channel; Nashville Network; Nick at Nite; QVC; TBS Superstation; Turner Network TV.
Current originations: Automated time-weather.
Fee: $30.00 installation; $25.00 monthly.
Pay Service 1
Pay Units: 48.
Programming (via satellite): The Movie Channel.
Fee: $20.00 installation; $12.00 monthly.
Equipment: Blonder-Tongue headend; Kaiser amplifiers; Times Fiber cable.
Miles of plant: 14.7 (coaxial). Homes passed: 427.
Manager: Glenn R. Ramsey. Chief technician: David Anderson.
City fee: 5% of gross.
Ownership: Glenn R. Ramsey.

TONASKET—TCI Cablevision of Okanogan Valley Inc., 45 Easy St., Wenatchee, WA 98801. Phone: 509-663-5108. Fax: 509-663-9072. County: Okanogan. Also serves Okanogan County (unincorporated areas). ICA: WA0079.
TV Market Ranking: Outside TV Markets. Franchise award date: January 1, 1953. Franchise expiration date: August 11, 2009. Began: January 1, 1954.
Channel capacity: 29 (not 2-way capable). Channels available but not in use: 3.
Basic Service
Subscribers: 607.
Programming (received off-air): KAYU-TV (F) Spokane; 3 FMs.
Programming (via microwave): KSTW (U) Seattle-Tacoma; KHQ-TV (N), KREM-TV (C), KSPS-TV (P), KXLY-TV (A) Spokane.
Programming (via satellite): C-SPAN; Discovery Channel; E! Entertainment TV; Northwest Cable News; Odyssey; QVC; TBS Superstation; The Weather Channel.
Current originations: Public access.
Fee: $25.32 installation; $13.68 monthly; $2.95 converter; $15.00 additional installation.
Expanded Basic Service
Subscribers: 583.
Programming (via satellite): A & E; American Movie Classics; Animal Planet; CNN; Cartoon Network; Disney Channel; ESPN; ESPN 2; FX; Fox Family Channel; Fox News Channel; Fox Sports Net Northwest; Learning Channel; Lifetime; MSNBC; MTV; Nashville Network; Nickelodeon; Turner Network TV; USA Network; Univision.
Fee: $25.32 installation; $18.04 monthly.
Pay Service 1
Pay Units: 28.
Programming (via satellite): Cinemax.
Fee: $15.00 installation; $13.40 monthly.
Pay Service 2
Pay Units: 27.
Programming (via satellite): Showtime.
Fee: $15.00 installation; $14.36 monthly.
Pay Service 3
Pay Units: N.A.
Programming (via satellite): Starz!; The New Encore.
Fee: $1.78 monthly (Encore), $6.85 monthly (Starz).
Pay Service 4
Pay Units: 36.
Programming (via satellite): HBO.
Fee: $15.00 installation; $14.36 monthly.
Local advertising: Yes (insert only). Available in locally originated & taped programming.
Program Guide: CableView.
Equipment: Catel, Microwave Assoc. & Scientific-Atlanta headend; Broadband & Magnavox amplifiers; Times Fiber & Comm/Scope cable; Hamlin set top converters; Pico traps; Prodelin satellite antenna; Microwave Assoc., Scientific-Atlanta & Standard Communications satellite receivers.
Miles of plant: 23.0 (coaxial). Homes passed: 801. Total homes in franchised area: 1,023.
Manager: Bob Lam.
City fee: 5% of gross.
Ownership: AT&T Broadband & Internet Services (MSO). Purchased from Tele-Communications Inc., March 9, 1999.

TOPPENISH—TCI Cablevision of Yakima Inc., 1005 N. 16th Ave., Yakima, WA 98902-1351. Phone: 509-575-1690. County: Yakima. Also serves Granger, Wapato, Zillah. ICA: WA0028.
TV Market Ranking: Below 100. Franchise award date: January 1, 1984. Franchise expiration date: September 1, 1998. Began: December 1, 1983.
Channel capacity: 39 (2-way capable; operating 2-way). Channels available but not in use: N.A.
Basic Service
Subscribers: 2,426.
Programming (received off-air): KAYU-TV (F) Spokane; KAPP (A), KIMA-TV (C), KNDO (N), KYVE-TV (P) Yakima.
Programming (via microwave): KSTW (U) Seattle-Tacoma.
Programming (via satellite): WGN-TV (W) Chicago; A & E; CNN; Discovery Channel; Electronic Program Guide; Fox Family Channel; GalaVision; Headline News; MTV; Nashville Network; Nickelodeon; TBS Superstation; The Weather Channel; Univision.
Current originations: Public access; educational access; government access; religious access; leased access.
Fee: $60.00 installation; $10.06 monthly; $40.00 additional installation.
Expanded Basic Service
Subscribers: N.A.
Programming (via satellite): American Movie Classics; ESPN; Fox Sports Net Northwest; Turner Network TV; USA Network.
Fee: $12.22 monthly.
Pay Service 1
Pay Units: 103.
Programming (via satellite): Cinemax.
Fee: $15.00 installation; $12.05 monthly.
Pay Service 2
Pay Units: 146.
Programming (via satellite): Disney Channel.
Fee: $15.00 installation; $8.95 monthly.
Pay Service 3
Pay Units: 928.
Programming (via satellite): The New Encore.
Fee: N.A.
Pay Service 4
Pay Units: 407.
Programming (via satellite): HBO.
Fee: $15.00 installation; $12.05 monthly.
Pay Service 5
Pay Units: 165.
Programming (via satellite): Showtime.
Fee: $15.00 installation; $12.05 monthly.
Local advertising: Yes (insert only).
Program Guide: CableView.
Equipment: Scientific-Atlanta headend; Times Fiber cable; Texscan character generator; Hamlin set top converters; Simulsat satellite antenna; Simulsat satellite receivers.
Miles of plant: 76.4 (coaxial). Homes passed: 5,583. Total homes in franchised area: 5,700.
Manager: Gary Bailey. Marketing director: Shelley Bjornson.
City fee: 5% of gross or utility tax maximum of 10%.
Ownership: AT&T Broadband & Internet Services (MSO). Purchased from Tele-Communications Inc., March 9, 1999.

TULALIP INDIAN RESERVATION—Tulalip Cablevision Co., 6326 33rd Ave. N, Tulalip, WA 98271. Phone: 360-651-3270. Fax: 360-651-3272. County: Snohomish. ICA: WA0184.
TV Market Ranking: 20. Franchise award date: January 1, 1988. Franchise expiration date: N.A. Began: N.A.
Channel capacity: 61 (not 2-way capable). Channels available but not in use: N.A.
Basic Service
Subscribers: 1,654.

Programming (received off-air): KVOS-TV (I) Bellingham; KONG-TV (I) Everett; KCPQ (F), KCTS-TV (P), KING-TV (N), KIRO-TV (C), KOMO-TV (A), KSTW (U), KTBW-TV (T), KTWB (W) Seattle-Tacoma.
Programming (via microwave): TVW.
Programming (via satellite): A & E; American Movie Classics; C-SPAN; C-SPAN 2; CNN; Cartoon Network; Discovery Channel; ESPN; ESPN 2; Fox Family Channel; Fox Sports Net Northwest; History Channel; Learning Channel; Lifetime; MTV; Nashville Network; Nickelodeon; Northwest Cable News; QVC; Sci-Fi Channel; TBS Superstation; TV Guide Channel; Turner Classic Movies; Turner Network TV; USA Network; VH1.
Current originations: Public access.
Fee: $78.00 installation; $25.00 monthly; $2.00 converter; $12.50 additional installation.

Pay Service 1
Pay Units: 120.
Programming (via satellite): Disney Channel.
Fee: $8.95 monthly.

Pay Service 2
Pay Units: 430.
Programming (via satellite): HBO.
Fee: $11.95 monthly.

Pay Service 3
Pay Units: 245.
Programming (via satellite): Showtime.
Fee: $10.95 monthly.

Local advertising: No.
Equipment: Standard Communications headend; Philips amplifiers; Comm/Scope cable; EIE set top converters; Eagle traps; Standard Communications satellite receivers.
Miles of plant: 100.0 (coaxial); None (fiber optic). Homes passed: 2,500.
Manager: Richard A. Brown. Chief engineer: Rick Dechenne. Marketing director & customer service manager: Judy Creswell.
Ownership: The Tulalip Tribe Inc.

TWISP—Millennium Digital Media, Suite 107, 3633 136th Place SE, Bellevue, WA 98006. Phones: 425-747-4600; 800-829-2225. Fax: 425-644-4621.
Web site: http://www.millenniumdigital.com.
County: Okanogan. Also serves Winthrop. ICA: WA0101.
TV Market Ranking: Outside TV Markets. Franchise award date: N.A. Franchise expiration date: January 1, 2007. Began: March 1, 1983.
Channel capacity: 35 (2-way capable; operating 2-way). Channels available but not in use: 23.

Basic Service
Subscribers: 144.
Programming (received off-air): KCTS-TV (P), KING-TV (N), KIRO-TV (C), KOMO-TV (A) Seattle-Tacoma.
Programming (via satellite): WGN-TV (W) Chicago; A & E; American Movie Classics; CNN; Comedy Central; Country Music TV; Discovery Channel; ESPN; Fox Family Channel; Fox Sports Net Northwest; FoxNet; Headline News; History Channel; Learning Channel; Nashville Network; Northwest Cable News; QVC; TBS Superstation; TV Guide Channel; Turner Classic Movies; Turner Network TV; USA Network.
Fee: $45.00 installation; $25.95 monthly.

Pay Service 1
Pay Units: N.A.
Programming (via satellite): Disney Channel; HBO; Showtime.
Fee: $8.95 monthly (Disney), $14.95 monthly (HBO or Showtime).

Equipment: GTE Sylvania amplifiers; Times Fiber cable; Video Data Systems character generator; Prodelin satellite antenna; M/A-Com satellite receivers.
Miles of plant: 8.7 (coaxial). Homes passed: 425. Total homes in franchised area: 425.
Manager: Steve Weed. Chief technician: Gene Fry.
City fee: 2% of gross.
Ownership: Millennium Digital Media LLC (MSO). Purchased from Summit Communications Inc., April 7, 1999.

UNION—Hood Canal Communications, Box 249, E. 300 Dalby Rd., Union, WA 98592-0249. Phone: 360-898-2481. Fax: 360-898-2244.
County: Mason. Also serves Agate, Hoodsport, Lake Cushman, Lower Hood Canal, Phillips Lake, Pickering, Shelton, Skokomish Valley, Timber Lakes. Plans service to Colony Surf, Lilliwaup Falls. ICA: WA0052.
TV Market Ranking: 20 (Hoodsport, Lower Hood Canal, Phillips Lake, Shelton, Skokomish Valley, Timber Lakes, Union); Outside TV Markets (Agate, Lake Cushman, Pickering). Franchise award date: N.A. Franchise expiration date: N.A. Began: N.A.
Channel capacity: 36 (2-way capable; operating 2-way). Channels available but not in use: N.A.

Basic Service
Subscribers: 2,100; Commercial subscribers: 226.
Programming (received off-air): KONG-TV (I) Everett; KCPQ (F), KCTS-TV (P), KING-TV (N), KIRO-TV (C), KOMO-TV (A), KSTW (U), KTWB (W) Seattle-Tacoma; KBTC-TV (P) Tacoma.
Programming (via microwave): TVW.
Programming (via satellite): A & E; American Movie Classics; C-SPAN; CNBC; CNN; Discovery Channel; ESPN; Fox Family Channel; Fox Sports Net Northwest; Headline News; History Channel; Home Shopping Network; Learning Channel; Lifetime; MTV; Nashville Network; Nick at Nite's TV Land; Nickelodeon; Northwest Cable News; TBS Superstation; Trinity Bcstg. Network; Turner Network TV; USA Network; VH1.
Current originations: Automated time-weather.
Fee: $19.95 monthly; $4.00 converter.
Commercial fee: $2.00 monthly.

Pay Service 1
Pay Units: 209.
Programming (via satellite): Cinemax.
Fee: $10.95 monthly.

Pay Service 2
Pay Units: 114.
Programming (via satellite): Disney Channel.
Fee: $8.95 monthly.

Pay Service 3
Pay Units: 341.
Programming (via satellite): HBO.
Fee: $10.95 monthly.

Local advertising: Yes. Available in character-generated programming. Rates: $7.50/Week. Local sales manager: Brandi Edinger.
Equipment: Drake headend; Texscan amplifiers; Comm/Scope cable; Dickel character generator; Hamlin & Pioneer set top converters; Pico traps.
Miles of plant: 70.0 (coaxial). Homes passed: N.A.
Manager: Rick Buechel. Chief technician: Les Stanley. Marketing director: Kellie Nielsen.
City fee: 3% of basic.
Ownership: Hood Canal Communications.

VADER—Millennium Digital Media, Suite 107, 3633 136th Place SE, Bellevue, WA 98006. Phones: 425-747-4600; 800-829-2225. Fax: 425-644-4621.
Web site: http://www.millenniumdigital.com.
County: Lewis. ICA: WA0126.
TV Market Ranking: Outside TV Markets. Franchise award date: N.A. Franchise expiration date: January 1, 2007. Began: August 1, 1983.
Channel capacity: 35. Channels available but not in use: N.A.

Basic Service
Subscribers: 140.
Programming (received off-air): KCKA (P) Centralia; KATU (A), KGW (N), KOIN (C), KOPB-TV (P), KPTV (U) Portland; KPDX (F) Vancouver.
Programming (via satellite): WGN-TV (W) Chicago; CNN; Fox Family Channel; Nashville Network; TBS Superstation.
Planned originations: Government access.
Fee: $45.00 installation; $17.80 monthly.

Pay Service 1
Pay Units: N.A.
Programming (via satellite): Showtime; The Movie Channel.
Fee: $20.00 installation; $12.95 monthly (each).

Equipment: Cadco headend; Pathmaker amplifiers; Times Fiber cable; Video Data Systems character generator; Eagle traps; Prodelin satellite antenna; M/A-Com satellite receivers.
Miles of plant: 5.7 (coaxial). Homes passed: 200.
Manager: Steve Weed. Chief technician: Gene Fry.
City fee: 5% of gross.
Ownership: Millennium Digital Media LLC (MSO). Purchased from Summit Communications Inc., April 7, 1999.

VANCOUVER—TCI of Southern Washington, 6916 N.E. 40th St., Vancouver, WA 98661. Phone: 360-892-6303. Fax: 360-892-8744.
Counties: Clark, WA; Multnomah, OR. Also serves Hayden Island, OR; Battle Ground, Camas, Clark County (unincorporated areas), Clark County (urban areas), La Center, Ridgefield, Washougal, WA. ICA: WA0005.
TV Market Ranking: 29. Franchise award date: November 26, 1981. Franchise expiration date: N.A. Began: October 1, 1982.
Channel capacity: 56 (not 2-way capable). Channels available but not in use: None.

Basic Service
Subscribers: 56,000.
Programming (received off-air): KATU (A), KGW (N), KNMT (T), KOIN (C), KOPB-TV (P), KPTV (U) Portland; KPXG (X), KWBP (W) Salem; KPDX (F) Vancouver.
Programming (via microwave): KCTS-TV (P) Seattle-Tacoma.
Programming (via satellite): WGN-TV (W) Chicago; C-SPAN; Discovery Channel; Learning Channel; TBS Superstation; TV Guide Channel; Univision.
Current originations: Public access; educational access; government access; religious access; leased access; automated emergency alert; local news; local sports.
Fee: $46.95 installation; $11.30 monthly; $1.60 converter.

Digital Basic Service
Subscribers: N.A.
Programming (via satellite): BBC America; Box Classic; Box Pulse; Bravo; Discovery Civilization Channel; Discovery Health Channel; Discovery Home & Leisure Channel; Discovery Kids Channel; Discovery People; Discovery Science Channel; Discovery Wings Channel; ESPN Classic Sports; ESPNews; Fox Sports World; Game Show Network; Golf Channel; History Channel; Independent Film Channel; MuchMusic Network; Outdoor Life Network; Romance Classics; Speedvision; The Barker; Turner Classic Movies.
Fee: $10.00 monthly; $3.25 converter.

Expanded Basic Service
Subscribers: 43,801.
Programming (via satellite): A & E; American Movie Classics; Animal Planet; BET; C-SPAN 2; CNBC; CNN; Cartoon Network; Comedy Central; Country Music TV; Disney Channel; E! Entertainment TV; ESPN; ESPN 2; FX; Fox Family Channel; Fox News Channel; Fox Sports Net Northwest; Great American Country; Headline News; History Channel; Home & Garden Television; Home Shopping Network; Lifetime; MSNBC; MTV; Nashville Network; Nickelodeon; Northwest Cable News; QVC; Sci-Fi Channel; The Weather Channel; Turner Network TV; USA Network; VH1.
Fee: $10.00 installation; $17.79 monthly.

Digital Expanded Basic Service
Subscribers: N.A.
Programming (via satellite): Box Exitos; Box Tejano; CBS TeleNoticias; Canal 9; CineLatino; Discovery en Espanol; Fox Sports World Espanol.
Fee: $6.99 monthly.

Pay Service 1
Pay Units: 2,963.
Programming (via satellite): Cinemax.
Fee: $10.95 monthly.

Pay Service 2
Pay Units: N.A.
Programming (via satellite): Starz!
Fee: $6.75 monthly.

Pay Service 3
Pay Units: 621.
Programming (via satellite): The New Encore.
Fee: $1.75 monthly.

Pay Service 4
Pay Units: 14,944.
Programming (via satellite): HBO.
Fee: $10.95 monthly.

Pay Service 5
Pay Units: 2,410.
Programming (via satellite): The Movie Channel.
Fee: $11.50 monthly.

Pay Service 6
Pay Units: 14,509.
Programming (via satellite): Showtime.
Fee: $10.95 monthly.

Digital Pay Service 1
Pay Units: N.A.
Programming (via satellite): Cinemax; DMX; Encore Love Stories; Encore Mystery; Encore Westerns; HBO Plus; HBO Signature; Showtime (multiplexed); Starz! Theater; The Movie Channel; The New Encore.
Fee: $9.95 monthly (DMX).

Pay-Per-View
Addressable homes: 35,000.
Spice delivered digitally.

Local advertising: Yes (locally produced). Available in satellite distributed & locally originated programming. Rates: $46.00/Minute; $23.00/30 Seconds. Local sales manager: Scott Carroll.
Equipment: General & Scientific-Atlanta headend; Texscan & Scientific-Atlanta amplifiers; M/A-Com & Trilogy cable; Hitachi cameras; Sony VTRs; Quanta & Texscan character generator; Pioneer addressable set top converters; Scientific-Atlanta satellite antenna; Scientific-Atlanta satellite receivers; ChannelMatic commercial insert.

Miles of plant: 1475.0 (coaxial). Additional miles planned: 60.0 (coaxial); 25.0 (fiber optic). Homes passed: 90,000.
Manager: Cal Broussard. Chief technician: Norrie Bush. Program director: Ken Lotka. Marketing director: Mike Williams.
City fee: 5% of gross.
Ownership: AT&T Broadband & Internet Services (MSO). Purchased from Tele-Communications Inc., March 9, 1999.

WAITSBURG—TCI Cablevision of Yakima Inc., Box 1577, 126 W. Poplar St., Walla Walla, WA 99362-2847. Phone: 509-529-9500. Fax: 509-522-1719. County: Walla Walla. ICA: WA0088.
TV Market Ranking: Below 100. Franchise award date: N.A. Franchise expiration date: N.A. Began: March 1, 1953.
Channel capacity: 40. Channels available but not in use: None.
Basic Service
Subscribers: 512.
Programming (received off-air): KEPR-TV (C) Pasco-Kennewick-Richland; KAYU-TV (F), KHQ-TV (N), KREM-TV (C), KSPS-TV (P), KXLY-TV (A) Spokane; allband FM.
Programming (via satellite): Discovery Channel; Fox Family Channel; Headline News; Nashville Network; TBS Superstation.
Current originations: Automated timeweather.
Fee: $36.17 installation; $9.72 monthly.
Expanded Basic Service
Subscribers: 464.
Programming (via satellite): A & E; American Movie Classics; ESPN; Turner Network TV; USA Network.
Fee: $11.10 monthly.
Pay Service 1
Pay Units: 113.
Programming (via satellite): Showtime.
Fee: $10.50 monthly.
Pay-Per-View
Addressable homes: 132.
Equipment: Jerrold headend; Jerrold amplifiers; Jerrold cable; Scientific-Atlanta satellite antenna.
Miles of plant: 13.0 (coaxial). Homes passed: 662.
Manager: Tim Klinefelter. Chief technician: Tim Ream. Program director: Dinah Morrison. Marketing director: Marlene Ashby.
City fee: None.
Ownership: AT&T Broadband & Internet Services (MSO). Purchased from Tele-Communications Inc., March 9, 1999.

WALLA WALLA—Falcon Cable TV, Box 1577, 126 W. Poplar St., Walla Walla, WA 99362-2847. Phone: 509-529-9500. Fax: 509-522-1719. County: Walla Walla. Also serves College Place, Walla Walla County. ICA: WA0016.
TV Market Ranking: Below 100. Franchise award date: N.A. Franchise expiration date: June 12, 2001. Began: October 1, 1953.
Channel capacity: 40 (2-way capable). Channels available but not in use: N.A.
Basic Service
Subscribers: 10,000.
Programming (received off-air): KEPR-TV (C), KNDU (N), KVEW (A) Pasco-Kennewick-Richland; KTNW (P) Richland; KAYU-TV (F) Spokane.
Programming (via microwave): KCTS-TV (P) Seattle-Tacoma; KHQ-TV (N), KREM-TV (C) Spokane.
Programming (via satellite): C-SPAN; Comedy Central; TBS Superstation; The Weather Channel.
Current originations: Automated timeweather; local news.
Fee: $37.44 installation; $9.85 monthly; $2.21 converter.
Expanded Basic Service
Subscribers: 9,100.
Programming (via satellite): A & E; American Movie Classics; CNN; Comedy Central; Discovery Channel; ESPN; FX; Fox Family Channel; Fox Sports Net Northwest; Headline News; Lifetime; MTV; Nashville Network; Nickelodeon; Turner Network TV; USA Network; Univision; VH1.
Fee: $11.85 monthly.
Pay Service 1
Pay Units: 601.
Programming (via satellite): Cinemax.
Fee: $11.70 monthly.
Pay Service 2
Pay Units: 733.
Programming (via satellite): Disney Channel.
Fee: $11.45 monthly.
Pay Service 3
Pay Units: 3,702.
Programming (via satellite): The New Encore.
Fee: $1.75 monthly.
Pay Service 4
Pay Units: 951.
Programming (via satellite): HBO.
Fee: $30.00 installation; $14.00 monthly.
Pay Service 5
Pay Units: 582.
Programming (via satellite): Showtime.
Fee: $30.00 installation; $14.00 monthly.
Pay Service 6
Pay Units: 3.
Programming (via satellite): Xchange.
Fee: N.A.
Pay-Per-View
Addressable homes: 3,300.
Local advertising: Yes (locally produced). Available in satellite distributed programming. Rates: $10.00/30 Seconds.
Program Guide: The Cable Guide.
Equipment: Jerrold headend; Jerrold amplifiers; Times Fiber cable; Sony VTRs; MSI, Jerrold & Texscan character generator; Tocom addressable set top converters; Andrew satellite antenna.
Miles of plant: 186.5 (coaxial); 24.0 (fiber optic). Homes passed: 15,099. Total homes in franchised area: 16,730.
Manager: Tim Klinefelter. Chief technician: Tim Ream. Program director: Dinah Morrison. Marketing director: Marlene Ashby.
City fee: 3% of gross.
Ownership: Falcon Communications LP (MSO). Purchased from Tele-Communications Inc., September 30, 1998. See Cable System Ownership.

WARDEN—Community Cable Service, 729 S. Bernard St., Spokane, WA 99204. Phones: 509-624-4140; 800-572-0902. Fax: 509-624-7372. County: Grant. ICA: WA0185.
TV Market Ranking: Outside TV Markets. Franchise award date: N.A. Franchise expiration date: N.A. Began: N.A.
Channel capacity: 62 (2-way capable; not operating 2-way). Channels available but not in use: 1.
Basic Service
Subscribers: 552.
Programming (received off-air): KEPR-TV (C), KNDU (N), KVEW (A) Pasco-Kennewick-Richland; KAYU-TV (F), KHQ-TV (N), KSPS-TV (P) Spokane.
Programming (via satellite): WGN-TV (W) Chicago; A & E; American Movie Classics; Bravo; C-SPAN; C-SPAN 2; CNBC; CNN; Cartoon Network; Comedy Central; Country Music TV; Discovery Channel; E! Entertainment TV; ESPN; ESPN 2; EWTN; Fox Family Channel; Fox Sports Net Northwest; Headline News; Home Shopping Network; Knowledge TV; Learning Channel; Lifetime; MTV; Nashville Network; Nickelodeon; Odyssey; QVC; Sci-Fi Channel; TBS Superstation; Trinity Bcstg. Network; Turner Network TV; USA Network; Univision; VH1.
Fee: $15.00 installation; $24.91 monthly.
Pay Service 1
Pay Units: 54.
Programming (via satellite): Disney Channel.
Fee: $5.00 installation; $5.47 monthly.
Pay Service 2
Pay Units: 92.
Programming (via satellite): HBO.
Fee: $5.00 installation; $10.59 monthly.
Pay Service 3
Pay Units: 125.
Programming (via satellite): Cinemax.
Fee: $5.00 installation; $6.70 monthly.
Homes passed: 719.
Manager: Martin Howser.
Ownership: Martin Howser (MSO).

WASHTUCNA—TCI Cablevision of Yakima Inc., Box 1577, 126 W. Poplar St., Walla Walla, WA 99362-2847. Phone: 509-529-9500. Fax: 509-522-1719. County: Adams. Also serves Washtucna (town). ICA: WA0134.
TV Market Ranking: Outside TV Markets. Franchise award date: N.A. Franchise expiration date: N.A. Began: February 1, 1954.
Channel capacity: 22. Channels available but not in use: 8.
Basic Service
Subscribers: 100.
Programming (received off-air): KAYU-TV (F), KHQ-TV (N), KREM-TV (C), KSPS-TV (P), KXLY-TV (A) Spokane.
Programming (via satellite): Discovery Channel; ESPN; Fox Family Channel; Headline News; Nashville Network; TBS Superstation.
Fee: $39.15 installation; $12.92 monthly.
Pay Service 1
Pay Units: 34.
Programming (via satellite): Showtime.
Fee: $10.50 monthly.
Equipment: Jerrold headend; Blonder-Tongue amplifiers; Belden cable.
Miles of plant: 4.0 (coaxial). Homes passed: 152. Total homes in franchised area: 152.
Manager: Tim Klinefelter. Chief technician: Tim Ream. Program director: Dinah Morrison. Marketing director: Marlene Ashby.
City fee: 2% of gross.
Ownership: AT&T Broadband & Internet Services (MSO). Purchased from Tele-Communications Inc., March 9, 1999.

WATERVILLE—Millennium Digital Media, Suite 107, 3633 136th Place SE, Bellevue, WA 98006. Phones: 425-747-4600; 800-829-2225. Fax: 425-644-4621.
Web site: http://www.millenniumdigital.com.
County: Douglas. ICA: WA0100.
TV Market Ranking: Below 100. Franchise award date: N.A. Franchise expiration date: N.A. Began: January 1, 1953.
Channel capacity: 30. Channels available but not in use: 10.
Basic Service
Subscribers: 328.
Programming (received off-air): KCTS-TV (P), KING-TV (N), KIRO-TV (C), KOMO-TV (A) Seattle-Tacoma; KAYU-TV (F), KHQ-TV (N), KREM-TV (C), KSPS-TV (P), KXLY-TV (A) Spokane; allband FM.
Programming (via microwave): TVW.
Programming (via satellite): WGN-TV (W) Chicago; A & E; American Movie Classics; Animal Planet; CNN; Discovery Channel; E! Entertainment TV; ESPN; Fox Family Channel; Fox Sports Net Northwest; Headline News; History Channel; Home & Garden Television; Learning Channel; Nashville Network; Nickelodeon; Northwest Cable News; QVC; Sci-Fi Channel; TBS Superstation; Turner Classic Movies; Turner Network TV; USA Network.
Current originations: Public access; government access.
Fee: $35.00 installation; $27.95 monthly.
Pay Service 1
Pay Units: N.A.
Programming (via satellite): Disney Channel; HBO.
Fee: $8.95 monthly (Disney), $14.95 monthly (HBO).
Equipment: Jerrold & SKL headend; Jerrold amplifiers; Times Fiber cable; Scientific-Atlanta satellite antenna; Scientific-Atlanta satellite receivers.
Miles of plant: 12.0 (coaxial). Homes passed: 450. Total homes in franchised area: 450.
Manager: Steve Weed. Chief technician: Gene Fry.
City fee: 3% of gross.
Ownership: Millennium Digital Media LLC (MSO). Purchased from Summit Communications Inc., April 7, 1999.

WENATCHEE—Falcon Cable TV, Box 1480, Wenatchee, WA 98801. Phone: 509-663-5108. Counties: Chelan & Douglas. Also serves Cashmere, Chelan County, Douglas County, East Wenatchee, Rock Island. ICA: WA0015.
TV Market Ranking: Below 100 (Cashmere, portions of Chelan County, portions of Douglas County, East Wenatchee, Rock Island, Wenatchee); Outside TV Markets (portions of Chelan County, portions of Douglas County). Franchise award date: January 1, 1953. Franchise expiration date: N.A. Began: August 1, 1953.
Channel capacity: 39 (2-way capable; operating 2-way). Channels available but not in use: N.A.
Basic Service
Subscribers: 19,643.
Programming (received off-air): 9 FMs.
Programming (via microwave): KCTS-TV (P), KING-TV (N), KIRO-TV (C), KOMO-TV (A), KSTW (U) Seattle-Tacoma.
Programming (via translator): KCPQ (F) Seattle-Tacoma; KAYU-TV (F), KHQ-TV (N), KREM-TV (C), KXLY-TV (A) Spokane.
Programming (via satellite): A & E; C-SPAN; CNBC; CNN; Discovery Channel; Fox Family Channel; Headline News; Lifetime; MTV; Nashville Network; Nickelodeon; Odyssey; QVC; TBS Superstation; The Weather Channel; Univision.
Current originations: Automated timeweather; educational access.
Fee: $60.00 installation; $8.93 monthly; $40.00 additional installation.
Expanded Basic Service
Subscribers: 15,509.
Programming (via satellite): American Movie Classics; ESPN; Fox Sports Net Northwest; Turner Network TV; USA Network.
Fee: $11.79 monthly.
Pay Service 1
Pay Units: 1,089.
Programming (via satellite): Cinemax.
Fee: $9.95 installation; $13.15 monthly.
Pay Service 2
Pay Units: 1,188.
Programming (via satellite): Disney Channel.
Fee: $10.95 monthly.

Pay Service 3
Pay Units: 5,750.
Programming (via satellite): The New Encore.
Fee: N.A.
Pay Service 4
Pay Units: 1,964.
Programming (via satellite): HBO.
Fee: $9.95 installation; $13.15 monthly.
Pay Service 5
Pay Units: 895.
Programming (via satellite): Showtime.
Fee: $9.95 installation; $13.15 monthly.
Local advertising: Yes.
Program Guide: The Cable Guide.
Equipment: Jerrold headend; Jerrold amplifiers; Times Fiber cable; Hitachi cameras; Sony VTRs; Video Data Systems & MSI character generator; Jerrold set top converters; Andrew satellite antenna; Hughes satellite receivers; ChannelMatic commercial insert.
Miles of plant: 302.2 (coaxial). Additional miles planned: 3.0 (coaxial). Total homes in franchised area: 22,675.
Manager: Bob Lam.
City fee: 3% of gross.
Ownership: Falcon Communications LP (MSO). Purchased from Tele-Communications Inc., September 30, 1998. See Cable System Ownership.

WESTPORT—TCI Cablevision of Southwest Washington Inc., 68 W. Wishkah, Aberdeen, WA 98520. Phone: 360-357-3364. Fax: 360-532-5978. Counties: Grays Harbor & Pacific. Also serves Grayland, Grays Harbor County, Pacific County, Tokeland. ICA: WA0037.
TV Market Ranking: Outside TV Markets. Franchise award date: N.A. Franchise expiration date: N.A. Began: April 1, 1961.
Channel capacity: 44 (not 2-way capable). Channels available but not in use: N.A.
Basic Service
Subscribers: 2,541.
Programming (received off-air): Allband FM.
Programming (via microwave): KCTS-TV (P), KING-TV (N), KIRO-TV (C), KOMO-TV (A), KSTW (U) Seattle-Tacoma.
Programming (via satellite): CNN; ESPN; Fox Family Channel; TBS Superstation; USA Network.
Current originations: Automated time-weather.
Fee: $60.00 installation; $16.45 monthly; $40.00 additional installation.
Pay Service 1
Pay Units: 286.
Programming (via satellite): Disney Channel.
Fee: $8.95 monthly.
Pay Service 2
Pay Units: 619.
Programming (via satellite): Showtime.
Fee: $10.03 monthly.
Pay-Per-View
Movies.
Equipment: Microwave Assoc. & Scientific-Atlanta headend; Jerrold amplifiers; General cable; Jerrold addressable set top converters; Arcom & Eagle addressable traps; Scientific-Atlanta satellite antenna; Scientific-Atlanta satellite receivers.
Miles of plant: 75.0 (coaxial). Homes passed: 3,514. Total homes in franchised area: 3,714.
Manager: Fred Comer. Chief technician: Wally Weidman. Marketing director: Carrie Prante.
City fee: 4% of gross.
Ownership: AT&T Broadband & Internet Services (MSO). Purchased from Tele-Communications Inc., March 9, 1999.

WHATCOM COUNTY (portions)—Cable Plus, Suite 120, 11400 S.E. 6th St., Bellevue, WA 98004. Phone: 425-462-2090. Fax: 425-462-2092. County: Whatcom. ICA: WA0080.
TV Market Ranking: Below 100. Franchise award date: January 1, 1992. Franchise expiration date: January 1, 2017. Began: October 1, 1992.
Channel capacity: 42 (2-way capable). Channels available but not in use: 7.
Basic Service
Subscribers: 1,100.
Programming (received off-air): KVOS-TV (I) Bellingham; KCPQ (F), KCTS-TV (P), KING-TV (N), KIRO-TV (C), KOMO-TV (A), KSTW (U) Seattle-Tacoma; CBUT, CHAN-TV, CKVU-TV Vancouver; CHEK-TV Victoria.
Programming (via satellite): WGN-TV (W) Chicago; A & E; American Movie Classics; C-SPAN; CNN; Discovery Channel; Disney Channel; ESPN; Fox Family Channel; Fox Sports Net Northwest; Headline News; History Channel; Learning Channel; Lifetime; MTV; Nashville Network; Nickelodeon; QVC; Sci-Fi Channel; TBS Superstation; TV Guide Channel; Turner Network TV; USA Network; VH1.
Fee: $30.00 installation; $24.92 monthly; $3.00 converter.
Pay Service 1
Pay Units: 135.
Programming (via satellite): HBO.
Fee: $8.95 monthly.
Pay Service 2
Pay Units: 79.
Programming (via satellite): Showtime.
Fee: $10.00 installation; $8.00 monthly.
Local advertising: No.
Equipment: Scientific-Atlanta headend; Philips amplifiers; Comm/Scope cable; Regal set top converters; Eagle traps; Paraclipse satellite antenna; Scientific-Atlanta satellite receivers.
Miles of plant: 70.0 (coaxial); 10.0 (fiber optic). Additional miles planned: 11.0 (coaxial). Homes passed: 1,500. Total homes in franchised area: 2,000.
Manager: Gary O'Malley. Chief technician: Dan Adams.
Franchise fee: 4% of gross.
Ownership: Cable Plus (MSO).

WHIDBEY ISLAND (b)—Millennium Digital Media, Suite 107, 3633 136th Place SE, Bellevue, WA 98006. Phones: 425-747-4600; 800-829-2225. Fax: 425-644-4621. Web site: http://www.millenniumdigital.com. County: Island. ICA: WA0186.
TV Market Ranking: 20. Franchise award date: January 1, 1990. Franchise expiration date: January 1, 2005. Began: February 1, 1991.
Channel capacity: 40. Channels available but not in use: 4.
Basic Service
Subscribers: 474.
Programming (received off-air): KVOS-TV (I) Bellingham; KCPQ (F), KCTS-TV (P), KING-TV (N), KIRO-TV (C), KOMO-TV (A), KSTW (U), KTBW-TV (T), KTWB (W) Seattle-Tacoma; CKVU-TV Vancouver; CHEK-TV Victoria.
Programming (via satellite): A & E; C-SPAN; CNN; Cartoon Network; Discovery Channel; ESPN; Headline News; Home Shopping Network; Learning Channel; Lifetime; MTV; Nashville Network; Nickelodeon; Sci-Fi Channel; TBS Superstation; The Inspirational Network; Turner Classic Movies; Turner Network TV; USA Network.
Fee: $50.00 installation; $22.45 monthly.
Pay Service 1
Pay Units: N.A.
Programming (via satellite): Cinemax; Disney Channel; HBO; Showtime.
Fee: $7.95 monthly (Disney), $11.00 monthly (Cinemax, HBO or Showtime).
Miles of plant: 30.0 (coaxial). Homes passed: 650.
Manager: Steve Weed. Chief technician: Gene Fry.
Ownership: Millennium Digital Media LLC (MSO). Purchased from Summit Communications Inc., April 7, 1999.

WHIDBEY ISLAND (c)—Millennium Digital Media, Suite 107, 3633 136th Place SE, Bellevue, WA 98006. Phones: 425-747-4600; 800-829-2225. Fax: 425-644-4621. Web site: http://www.millenniumdigital.com. County: Island. Also serves Coupeville, Greenbank. ICA: WA0200.
TV Market Ranking: 20. Franchise award date: N.A. Franchise expiration date: N.A. Began: N.A.
Channel capacity: 40. Channels available but not in use: 2.
Basic Service
Subscribers: 555.
Programming (received off-air): KVOS-TV (I) Bellingham; KCPQ (F), KCTS-TV (P), KING-TV (N), KIRO-TV (C), KOMO-TV (A), KSTW (U), KTBW-TV (T), KTWB (W) Seattle-Tacoma; CKVU-TV Vancouver; CHEK-TV Victoria.
Programming (via satellite): WGN-TV (W) Chicago; A & E; C-SPAN; C-SPAN 2; CNBC; CNN; Cartoon Network; Comedy Central; Discovery Channel; ESPN; ESPN 2; Headline News; Home Shopping Network; Learning Channel; Lifetime; MTV; Nashville Network; Nickelodeon; QVC; TBS Superstation; Turner Classic Movies; Turner Network TV; USA Network; VH1.
Fee: $50.00 installation; $23.45 monthly.
Pay Service 1
Pay Units: N.A.
Programming (via satellite): Cinemax; Disney Channel; HBO; Showtime; The New Encore.
Fee: $6.95 monthly (Encore), $7.95 monthly (Disney), $11.00 monthly (Cinemax, HBO or Showtime).
Miles of plant: 20.0 (coaxial). Homes passed: 950.
Manager: Steve Weed. Chief technician: Gene Fry.
Ownership: Millennium Digital Media LLC (MSO). Purchased from Summit Communications Inc., April 7, 1999.

WILBUR—Sun Country Cable, Box 127, 7 D St. SW, Quincy, WA 98848. Phones: 509-787-3543; 800-788-0120. Fax: 509-787-3884. County: Lincoln. ICA: WA0102.
TV Market Ranking: Outside TV Markets. Franchise award date: N.A. Franchise expiration date: N.A. Began: May 1, 1982.
Channel capacity: 35. Channels available but not in use: 17.
Basic Service
Subscribers: 336.
Programming (received off-air): KAYU-TV (F), KHQ-TV (N), KREM-TV (C), KSPS-TV (P), KXLY-TV (A) Spokane.
Programming (via satellite): A & E; CNN; Discovery Channel; ESPN; Fox Family Channel; Lifetime; Nashville Network; Nickelodeon; QVC; TBS Superstation; USA Network.
Fee: $39.95 installation; $24.30 monthly.
Pay Service 1
Pay Units: 32.
Programming (via satellite): Disney Channel.
Fee: $8.95 monthly.
Pay Service 2
Pay Units: 119.
Programming (via satellite): HBO.
Fee: $9.95 monthly.
Equipment: Scientific-Atlanta headend; Scientific-Atlanta amplifiers; Times Fiber cable; Scientific-Atlanta satellite antenna; Scientific-Atlanta satellite receivers.
Miles of plant: 10.2 (coaxial). Homes passed: 413. Total homes in franchised area: 450.
Manager: Gary White. Technical manager: Arnie Hill. Chief technician: Dave Zigler. Office manager: Judy Vreeman.
City fee: 3% of gross.
Ownership: Sun Country Cable (MSO).

WILSON CREEK—Sun Country Cable, Box 127, 7 D St. SW, Quincy, WA 98848. Phone: 509-787-3543. Fax: 509-787-3884. County: Grant. ICA: WA0187.
TV Market Ranking: Outside TV Markets. Franchise award date: N.A. Franchise expiration date: N.A. Began: December 1, 1987.
Channel capacity: 32. Channels available but not in use: 18.
Basic Service
Subscribers: 82.
Programming (received off-air): KAYU-TV (F), KHQ-TV (N), KREM-TV (C), KSPS-TV (P), KXLY-TV (A) Spokane.
Programming (via satellite): A & E; CNN; Discovery Channel; ESPN; Fox Family Channel; Nashville Network; TBS Superstation.
Fee: $39.95 installation; $19.20 monthly.
Pay Service 1
Pay Units: 9.
Programming (via satellite): Disney Channel.
Fee: $15.00 installation; $8.95 monthly.
Pay Service 2
Pay Units: 24.
Programming (via satellite): HBO.
Fee: $15.00 installation; $10.95 monthly.
Equipment: Triple Crown headend; Jerrold amplifiers; Panasonic set top converters; Scientific-Atlanta satellite antenna; Triple Crown satellite receivers.
Manager: Gary White. Technical manager: Arnie Hill. Office manager: Judy Vreeman.
Ownership: Sun Country Cable (MSO).

WINLOCK—TCI Cablevision of Twin Cities Inc., Box 129, Olympia, WA 98507. Phones: 360-736-1166; 800-221-5232. Fax: 360-736-1160. County: Lewis. ICA: WA0094.
TV Market Ranking: Outside TV Markets. Franchise award date: N.A. Franchise expiration date: N.A. Began: December 1, 1971.

Channel capacity: 23 (not 2-way capable). Channels available but not in use: N.A.

Basic Service

Subscribers: 359.

Programming (received off-air): KGW (N), KOIN (C), KPTV (U) Portland; KCPQ (F), KCTS-TV (P), KING-TV (N), KIRO-TV (C), KOMO-TV (A), KSTW (U) Seattle-Tacoma; allband FM.

Programming (via satellite): ESPN; Nashville Network.

Fee: $60.00 installation; $18.32 monthly; $40.00 additional installation.

Pay Service 1

Pay Units: 83.

Programming (via satellite): HBO.

Fee: $9.95 installation; $12.48 monthly.

Equipment: Catel, Jerrold & Scientific-Atlanta headend; Jerrold amplifiers; Cerro & Comm/Scope cable.

Miles of plant: 10.5 (coaxial). Homes passed: 519. Total homes in franchised area: 519.

Manager: Paul Renz.

City fee: 5% of gross.

Ownership: AT&T Broadband & Internet Services (MSO). Purchased from Tele-Communications Inc., March 9, 1999.

WISHRAM—Cascade Cable Systems, Box 397, The Dalles, OR 97058. Phone: 541-298-4983. E-mail: jroth@gorge.net. County: Klickitat. Also serves Wishram Heights. ICA: WA0188.

TV Market Ranking: Outside TV Markets. Franchise award date: N.A. Franchise expiration date: N.A. Began: September 1, 1954.

Channel capacity: 22 (not 2-way capable). Channels available but not in use: 8.

Basic Service

Subscribers: 133.

Programming (received off-air): KOAC-TV (P) Corvallis; KATU (A), KGW (N), KOIN (C), KPTV (U) Portland; KPDX (F) Vancouver; allband FM.

Programming (via satellite): KOMO-TV (A) Seattle; American Movie Classics; CNN; Discovery Channel; Disney Channel; ESPN; TBS Superstation.

Fee: $25.00 installation; $15.00 monthly.

Pay Service 1

Pay Units: 35.

Programming (via satellite): The Movie Channel.

Fee: $20.00 installation; $10.00 monthly.

Equipment: Blonder-Tongue & Cadco headend; Magnavox & Triple Crown amplifiers; Comm/Scope cable; Pico traps; ADM satellite antenna; Drake satellite receivers.

Miles of plant: 5.0 (coaxial); None (fiber optic).

Manager: James F. Roth.

Ownership: Cascade Cable Systems (MSO).

YACOLT—J & N Cable, 614 S. Columbus Ave., Goldendell, WA 98620. Phone: 509-773-5359. Fax: 509-773-7090. County: Clark. ICA: WA0110.

TV Market Ranking: 29. Franchise award date: November 1, 1988. Franchise expiration date: November 1, 2003. Began: July 1, 1989.

Channel capacity: 50 (not 2-way capable). Channels available but not in use: 30.

Basic Service

Subscribers: 197.

Programming (received off-air): KATU (A), KGW (N), KOIN (C), KOPB-TV (P), KPTV (U) Portland; KPDX (F) Vancouver.

Programming (via satellite): CNN; Cartoon Network; Comedy Central; Country Music TV; Court TV; Discovery Channel; ESPN; Home Shopping Network; Learning Channel; Nashville Network; Nickelodeon; Sci-Fi Channel; TBS Superstation; Turner Network TV; USA Network; VH1.

Fee: $39.95 installation; $15.95 monthly.

Pay Service 1

Pay Units: 30.

Programming (via satellite): The Movie Channel.

Fee: $10.95 monthly.

Pay Service 2

Pay Units: 30.

Programming (via satellite): Showtime.

Fee: $10.95 monthly.

Pay Service 3

Pay Units: 25.

Programming (via satellite): HBO.

Fee: $10.95 monthly.

Local advertising: No.

Equipment: Jerrold headend; Blonder-Tongue amplifiers; Belden cable; Eagle traps.

Miles of plant: 4.3 (coaxial). Homes passed: 300. Total homes in franchised area: 300.

Manager: Bob Olson. Chief technician: Keith Buckbee.

Franchise fee: 5% of gross.

Ownership: J & N Cable Co. (MSO). Purchased from Metroplex Communications Co.

YAKIMA—Falcon Cable TV, 1005 N. 16th Ave., Yakima, WA 98902-1351. Phone: 509-575-1697. County: Yakima. Also serves Moxee City, Selah, Union Gap, Wiley City, Yakima County, Yakima Indian Reservation. ICA: WA0009.

TV Market Ranking: Below 100 (Moxee City, Selah, Union Gap, Wiley City, Yakima, portions of Yakima County, portions of Yakima Indian Reservation); Outside TV Markets (portions of Yakima County, portions of Yakima Indian Reservation). Franchise award date: January 1, 1963. Franchise expiration date: September 1, 2002. Began: November 1, 1979.

Channel capacity: 38 (2-way capable). Channels available but not in use: N.A.

Basic Service

Subscribers: 23,840.

Programming (received off-air): KAPP (A), KIMA-TV (C), KNDO (N), KYVE-TV (P) Yakima.

Programming (via microwave): KSTW (U) Seattle-Tacoma.

Programming (via satellite): A & E; C-SPAN; CNBC; CNN; Discovery Channel; Electronic Program Guide; Fox Family Channel; GalaVision; Headline News; Knowledge TV; Lifetime; MTV; Nashville Network; Nickelodeon; TBS Superstation; The Weather Channel; Trinity Bcstg. Network; Univision.

Current originations: Public access; educational access; religious access; leased access.

Fee: $60.00 installation; $8.11 monthly; $0.63 converter; $40.00 additional installation.

Expanded Basic Service

Subscribers: 22,594.

Programming (via satellite): American Movie Classics; ESPN; Fox Sports Net Northwest; Turner Network TV; USA Network; VH1.

Fee: $10.79 monthly.

Pay Service 1

Pay Units: 1,384.

Programming (via satellite): Cinemax.

Fee: $15.00 installation; $12.05 monthly.

Pay Service 2

Pay Units: 1,946.

Programming (via satellite): Disney Channel.

Fee: $15.00 installation; $8.95 monthly.

Pay Service 3

Pay Units: 8,247.

Programming (via satellite): The New Encore.

Fee: N.A.

Pay Service 4

Pay Units: 3,465.

Programming (via satellite): HBO.

Fee: $15.00 installation; $12.05 monthly.

Pay Service 5

Pay Units: 2,637.

Programming (via satellite): Showtime.

Fee: $5.00 installation; $12.05 monthly.

Local advertising: Yes (insert only).

Program Guide: The Cable Guide.

Equipment: Catel & Scientific-Atlanta headend; Magnavox, RCA & Theta-Com amplifiers; Comm/Scope & Times Fiber cable; Hamlin & Panasonic set top converters; Pico traps; Scientific-Atlanta satellite antenna; Scientific-Atlanta satellite receivers.

Miles of plant: 419.6 (coaxial). Homes passed: 43,945. Total homes in franchised area: 47,524.

Manager: Gary Bailey. Marketing director: Shelley Bjornson.

City fee: 5% of gross.

Ownership: Falcon Communications LP (MSO). Purchased from Tele-Communications Inc., September 30, 1998. See Cable System Ownership.

WEST VIRGINIA

Total Systems: **224**
Total Communities Served: **1016**
Franchises Not Yet Operating: **0**
Applications Pending: **0**
Communities with Applications: **0**
Number of Basic Subscribers: **521,157**
Number of Expanded Basic Subscribers: **315,238**
Number of Pay Units: **186,781**

Top 100 Markets Represented: Pittsburgh (10); Charleston-Hungtingtion (36); Wheeling, WV-Steubenville, OH (90).

For a list of all cable communities included in this section, see the Cable Community Index located in the back of this volume.
For explanation of terms used in cable system listings, see p. D-9.

ALDERSON—Cablevision, 313 W. Main St., Oak Hill, WV 25901-2938. Phone: 800-585-9977. Counties: Greenbrier & Monroe. ICA: WV0091.
TV Market Ranking: Below 100. Franchise award date: N.A. Franchise expiration date: N.A. Began: January 1, 1968.
Channel capacity: N.A. Channels available but not in use: N.A.
Basic Service
Subscribers: 567.
Programming (received off-air): WVVA (N) Bluefield; WSWP-TV (P) Grandview; WOAY-TV (A) Oak Hill-Beckley; WDBJ (C), WFXR-TV (F), WSET-TV (A), WSLS-TV (N) Roanoke-Lynchburg; allband FM.
Programming (via satellite): WGN-TV (W) Chicago; TBS Superstation.
Fee: $25.00 installation; $10.50 monthly.
Expanded Basic Service
Subscribers: 554.
Programming (via satellite): C-SPAN; C-SPAN 2; CNN; Discovery Channel; ESPN; Fox Family Channel; Lifetime; MTV; Nashville Network; Nickelodeon; QVC; Trinity Bcstg. Network; Turner Network TV; USA Network; VH1.
Fee: N.A.
Pay Service 1
Pay Units: N.A.
Programming (via satellite): Cinemax; Disney Channel; HBO.
Fee: $20.00 installation; $11.00 monthly (each).
Equipment: Jerrold headend; Jerrold amplifiers; Superior cable.
Miles of plant: 25.0 (coaxial). Homes passed: 818.
Manager: Wayne Boone.
City fee: 2% of gross.
Ownership: Rifkin & Associates Inc. (MSO). See Cable System Ownership.

ALKOL—Capital Cablecomm, Box 368, Cabin Creek, WV 25035. Phone: 304-779-2854. Fax: 304-595-5248. Counties: Boone & Lincoln. Also serves Morrisville, Woodville. ICA: WV0240.
TV Market Ranking: 36. Franchise award date: N.A. Franchise expiration date: N.A. Began: N.A.
Channel capacity: 15 (not 2-way capable). Channels available but not in use: 1.
Basic Service
Subscribers: 270.
Programming (received off-air): WVVA (N) Bluefield; WCHS-TV (A), WOWK-TV (C), WSAZ-TV (N), WVAH-TV (F,U) Charleston-Huntington; WSWP-TV (P) Grandview; WOAY-TV (A) Oak Hill-Beckley.
Fee: $42.75 installation (aerial), $56.75 (underground); $9.50 monthly; $1.88 converter.
Expanded Basic Service
Subscribers: 265.
Programming (via satellite): ESPN; Fox Family Channel; Nashville Network; TBS Superstation.
Fee: $5.45 monthly.
Pay Service 1
Pay Units: 20.
Programming (via satellite): HBO.
Fee: $10.00 monthly.
Pay Service 2
Pay Units: 27.
Programming (via satellite): Cinemax.
Fee: $10.00 monthly.
Pay Service 3
Pay Units: 22.
Programming (via satellite): Disney Channel.
Fee: $8.00 monthly.
Miles of plant: 13.8 (coaxial); None (fiber optic). Homes passed: 456.
Manager: Robert L. Herrald. Chief technician: Allen Comer.
Ownership: Fanch Communications Inc. (MSO); Time Warner Cable (MSO). See Cable System Ownership.

ALUM BRIDGE—Basco Electronics Inc., 420 W. 2nd St., Weston, WV 26452. Phone: 304-269-7530. Fax: 304-269-6581. Counties: Gilmer & Lewis. Also serves Baldwin, Linn, Troy. ICA: WV0119.
TV Market Ranking: Below 100. Franchise award date: N.A. Franchise expiration date: N.A. Began: January 1, 1984.
Channel capacity: 35 (2-way capable; operating 2-way). Channels available but not in use: 17.
Basic Service
Subscribers: N.A.
Programming (received off-air): WCHS-TV (A) Charleston-Huntington; WBOY-TV (N), WDTV (C,A), WVFX (F) Clarksburg-Weston; WNPB-TV (P) Morgantown; allband FM.
Programming (via satellite): CNN; ESPN; Fox Family Channel; Learning Channel; MTV; Nashville Network; QVC; TBS Superstation; Turner Network TV; USA Network.
Fee: $50.00 installation; $17.90 monthly.
Pay Service 1
Pay Units: 80.
Programming (via satellite): HBO.
Fee: $10.00 installation; $10.38 monthly.
Pay Service 2
Pay Units: 20.
Programming (via satellite): Showtime.
Fee: $10.00 installation; $10.38 monthly.
Local advertising: No.
Equipment: Blonder-Tongue & Pico headend; Magnavox amplifiers; Comm/Scope cable; Jerrold set top converters; Pico traps; M/A-Com satellite antenna; Drake satellite receivers.
Miles of plant: 18.0 (coaxial). Additional miles planned: 10.0 (coaxial). Homes passed: 400.
Manager: Wilfred L. Sholes. Chief technician: Brian Queen. Marketing director: Sue M. Sholes.
Ownership: Basco Electronics Inc. (MSO).

ANSTED—Helicon Cablevision, Box A, 150 N. Pinch Rd., Pinch, WV 25156. Phones: 304-965-7026; 800-642-9163. Fax: 304-965-7768. County: Fayette. ICA: WV0245.
TV Market Ranking: 36. Franchise award date: N.A. Franchise expiration date: N.A. Began: N.A.
Channel capacity: N.A. Channels available but not in use: N.A.
Basic Service
Subscribers: 866.
Programming (received off-air): WVVA (N) Bluefield; WCHS-TV (A), WOWK-TV (C), WSAZ-TV (N), WVAH-TV (F,U) Charleston-Huntington; WSWP-TV (P) Grandview; WOAY-TV (A) Oak Hill-Beckley.
Programming (via satellite): A & E; C-SPAN; CNN; Cartoon Network; Country Music TV; Discovery Channel; ESPN; Fox Family Channel; Headline News; Lifetime; Nashville Network; QVC; The Weather Channel; Turner Network TV; USA Network.
Fee: $20.61 monthly; $1.50 converter.
A la Carte 1
Subscribers: N.A.
Programming (via satellite): WGN-TV (W) Chicago; American Movie Classics; TBS Superstation.
Fee: $4.20 monthly (package); $2.00 monthly (each).
Pay Service 1
Pay Units: N.A.
Programming (via satellite): Disney Channel; HBO; Showtime; The Movie Channel.
Fee: $8.95 monthly (Disney, Showtime or TMC).
Manager: Jack Wade.
Ownership: Helicon Corp. (MSO). See Cable System Ownership.

APPLE GROVE—FrontierVision, Suite P-200, 1777 S. Harrison St., Denver, CO 80210. Phone: 303-757-1588. Fax: 303-757-6105. Counties: Cabell & Mason. Also serves Cabell County (unincorporated areas), Glenwood, Green Bottom, Lesage, Mason City. ICA: WV0186.
TV Market Ranking: 36 (Apple Grove, Cabell County, Glenwood, Green Bottom, Lesage); Below 100 (Mason City). Franchise award date: N.A. Franchise expiration date: N.A. Began: January 1, 1988.
Channel capacity: 42. Channels available but not in use: 7.
Basic Service
Subscribers: 325.
Programming (received off-air): WKAS (P), WTSF (I) Ashland; WCHS-TV (A), WOWK-TV (C), WPBY-TV (P), WSAZ-TV (N), WVAH-TV (F,U) Charleston-Huntington.
Programming (via satellite): WGN-TV (W) Chicago; A & E; American Movie Classics; CNN; Discovery Channel; ESPN; Fox Family Channel; Headline News; Nashville Network; QVC; TBS Superstation; Travel Channel; Trinity Bcstg. Network; USA Network.
Fee: $29.95 installation; $21.95 monthly; $2.00 converter.
Expanded Basic Service
Subscribers: 304.
Programming (via satellite): Disney Channel.
Fee: N.A.
Pay Service 1
Pay Units: 13.
Programming (via satellite): HBO.
Fee: $29.95 installation; $8.95 monthly.
Pay Service 2
Pay Units: 30.
Programming (via satellite): Showtime.
Fee: $29.95 installation; $8.95 monthly.
Pay Service 3
Pay Units: 29.
Programming (via satellite): The Movie Channel.
Fee: N.A.
Miles of plant: 30.0 (coaxial). Homes passed: 631.
Manager: Steve Trippe. Chief technician: Bill Ricker.
Ownership: FrontierVision Partners LP (MSO). See Cable System Ownership.

ARNETTSVILLE—Century Huntington Co., Box 599, Dellslow, WV 26531. Phone: 304-292-6561. Counties: Marion & Monongalia. Also serves Bellview, Booth, Cassville, Core, Crown, Everettville, Fairmont, Greentown, Laurel Point, Maidsville, Marion County (portions), Montana Mines, National, Pleasant View (Monongalia County), Pursglove, Ridge Farms, Rivesville, Sanford. ICA: WV0046.
TV Market Ranking: Below 100. Franchise award date: N.A. Franchise expiration date: N.A. Began: December 1, 1969.
Channel capacity: 21 (not 2-way capable). Channels available but not in use: 1.
Basic Service
Subscribers: N.A.
Programming (received off-air): WBOY-TV (N), WDTV (C,A), WVFX (F) Clarksburg-Weston; WNPB-TV (P) Morgantown; KDKA-TV (C), WPGH-TV (F), WPXI (N), WTAE-TV (A) Pittsburgh; 18 FMs.
Programming (via satellite): ESPN; Fox Family Channel; Nickelodeon; TBS Superstation; Turner Network TV.
Fee: $30.00 installation; $9.95 monthly; $1.75 converter; $15.00 additional installation.
Expanded Basic Service
Subscribers: N.A.
Programming (received off-air): WCWB (W) Pittsburgh.
Programming (via satellite): MTV; Nashville Network; USA Network.
Fee: $15.00 installation; $4.95 monthly.
Pay Service 1
Pay Units: N.A.
Programming (via satellite): Disney Channel; HBO; Showtime; The Movie Channel.
Fee: $15.00 installation; $7.95 monthly (Disney), $11.95 monthly (HBO), $14.95 monthly (Showtime or TMC).
Local advertising: No.
Equipment: Jerrold, Blonder-Tongue & Catel headend; Jerrold & GTE Sylvania amplifiers; Comm/Scope cable; Hamlin & GTE Sylvania set top converters; Hamlin, Jerrold & GTE Sylvania addressable set top converters;

Arcom & Eagle traps; Microdyne satellite antenna; Microdyne satellite receivers.
Miles of plant: 85.0 (coaxial). Additional miles planned: 3.0 (coaxial). Homes passed: 2,500. Total homes in franchised area: 2,800.
Manager: Michael Ligouri. Chief technician: Ed Hinkle.
City fee: None.
Ownership: Century Communications Corp. (MSO). See Cable System Ownership.

AUBURN—CableVision Communications, Box 2200, 68 5th St., Buckhannon, WV 26201. Phone: 304-472-4193. Fax: 304-472-0756. County: Ritchie. ICA: WV0161.
TV Market Ranking: Below 100. Franchise award date: June 9, 1975. Franchise expiration date: N.A. Began: N.A.
Channel capacity: 12. Channels available but not in use: 4.
Basic Service
Subscribers: 13.
Programming (received off-air): WCHS-TV (A) Charleston-Huntington; WBOY-TV (N), WDTV (C,A) Clarksburg-Weston; WNPB-TV (P) Morgantown; WOAY-TV (A) Oak Hill-Beckley; WTAP-TV (N) Parkersburg-Marietta; WTRF-TV (C) Wheeling-Steubenville.
Fee: $61.25 installation; $11.27 monthly.
Equipment: Blonder-Tongue & Jerrold headend; Jerrold amplifiers.
Miles of plant: 2.0 (coaxial). Homes passed: 45. Total homes in franchised area: 45.
Manager: Willie Critchfield. Marketing director: Kenny Phillips.
Ownership: Rifkin & Associates Inc. (MSO). See Cable System Ownership.

AUGUSTA—CMA Cablevision Assoc. VII, 51 N. Main St., Keyser, WV 26726-3220. Phone: 304-788-2433. Fax: 304-788-6142. County: Hampshire. Also serves Hampshire County (portions), North River Mills, Shanks. ICA: WV0117.
TV Market Ranking: Below 100 (Augusta, portions of Hampshire County, North River Mills); Outside TV Markets (portions of Hampshire County, Shanks). Franchise award date: N.A. Franchise expiration date: N.A. Began: N.A.
Channel capacity: 21 (not 2-way capable). Channels available but not in use: 4.
Basic Service
Subscribers: 299.
Programming (received off-air): WHAG-TV (N) Hagerstown; WJLA-TV (A), WRC-TV (N), WTTG (F), WUSA (C) Washington; allband FM.
Programming (via translator): WNPB-TV (P) Morgantown.
Programming (via satellite): Fox Family Channel.
Current originations: Public access.
Fee: $59.95 installation; $5.15 monthly.
Expanded Basic Service
Subscribers: 299.
Programming (via satellite): WGN-TV (W) Chicago; Discovery Channel; ESPN; Headline News; Home Shopping Network; Nashville Network; QVC; TBS Superstation; USA Network.
Fee: $9.70 monthly.
Pay Service 1
Pay Units: 37.
Programming (via satellite): Cinemax.
Fee: $10.50 monthly.
Pay Service 2
Pay Units: 47.
Programming (via satellite): HBO.
Fee: $10.50 monthly.
Equipment: Blonder-Tongue & Cadco headend; Jerrold, Magnavox & Triple Crown amplifiers; Times Fiber cable; Scientific-Atlanta set top converters; ChannelMaster satellite antenna; Drake & Scientific-Atlanta satellite receivers.
Miles of plant: 27.0 (coaxial); None (fiber optic). Homes passed: 539.
Manager: Ronald Boyce. Chief technician: Fred Cavin. Program director: R. E. Steffan III. Marketing director: Kevin Munnell.
Ownership: Tele-Media Corp. (MSO).

BALLARD—Paxton Cable, Suite 280, 700 Ackerman Rd., Columbus, OH 43202. Phone: 614-263-6100. Fax: 614-263-7299. County: Monroe. Also serves Monroe County (unincorporated areas). ICA: WV0113.
TV Market Ranking: Below 100 (Ballard, portions of Monroe County); Outside TV Markets (portions of Monroe County). Franchise award date: N.A. Franchise expiration date: N.A. Began: February 1, 1988.
Channel capacity: 12. Channels available but not in use: None.
Basic Service
Subscribers: 360.
Programming (received off-air): WVVA (N) Bluefield; WSWP-TV (P) Grandview; WOAY-TV (A) Oak Hill-Beckley; WDBJ (C), WSLS-TV (N) Roanoke-Lynchburg.
Programming (via satellite): WGN-TV (W) Chicago; Discovery Channel; ESPN; Fox Family Channel; Headline News; TBS Superstation; USA Network.
Fee: $14.00 monthly.
Pay Service 1
Pay Units: N.A.
Programming (via satellite): HBO.
Fee: $12.00 monthly.
Miles of plant: 32.0 (coaxial). Homes passed: 450.
Manager: Chip James.
Ownership: Paxton Cable Television Inc. (MSO). Purchased from Clearview Cable TV Inc., September 3, 1998.

BANDYTOWN—Bradley's Inc., Box 41, Harton, WV 25208. Phones: 304-247-6231; 800-582-3546. County: Boone. Also serves Twilight. ICA: WV0167.
TV Market Ranking: 36. Franchise award date: N.A. Franchise expiration date: N.A. Began: January 1, 1979.
Channel capacity: 12. Channels available but not in use: N.A.
Basic Service
Subscribers: N.A.
Programming (received off-air): WVVA (N) Bluefield; WCHS-TV (A), WOWK-TV (C), WSAZ-TV (N), WVAH-TV (F,U) Charleston-Huntington; WSWP-TV (P) Grandview; WOAY-TV (A) Oak Hill-Beckley.
Programming (via satellite): ESPN; Fox Family Channel; Nashville Network; TBS Superstation.
Fee: N.A.
Pay Service 1
Pay Units: N.A.
Programming (via satellite): HBO.
Fee: N.A.
Miles of plant: 3.7 (coaxial).
Ownership: Bradley's Inc.

BECKLEY—Cablecomm, 115 Dye Dr., Beckley, WV 25801. Phone: 304-252-6358. Counties: Raleigh & Summers. Also serves Coal City, Eccles, Fairdale, Flat Top, Lester, Mabscott, Raleigh County (portions), Shady Spring, Summers County (unincorporated areas). ICA: WV0005.
TV Market Ranking: 36 (portions of Raleigh County); Below 100 (Beckley, Coal City, Eccles, Fairdale, Flat Top, Lester, Mabscott, portions of Raleigh County, Shady Spring, Summers County). Franchise award date: N.A. Franchise expiration date: N.A. Began: October 1, 1964.
Channel capacity: 45. Channels available but not in use: N.A.
Basic Service
Subscribers: 19,124.
Programming (received off-air): WVVA (N) Bluefield; WCHS-TV (A), WOWK-TV (C), WSAZ-TV (N), WVAH-TV (F,U) Charleston-Huntington; WSWP-TV (P) Grandview; WOAY-TV (A) Oak Hill-Beckley; allband FM.
Programming (via microwave): WDBJ (C) Roanoke-Lynchburg.
Programming (via satellite): C-SPAN; Fox Family Channel; TBS Superstation; The Inspirational Network; The Weather Channel.
Fee: $27.83 installation; $12.38 monthly.
Expanded Basic Service
Subscribers: N.A.
Programming (via satellite): BET; Country Music TV; ESPN; Headline News; Lifetime; MTV; Nashville Network; Nickelodeon; USA Network; VH1.
Fee: $15.00 installation; $9.53 monthly.
Pay Service 1
Pay Units: N.A.
Programming (via satellite): American Movie Classics; Bravo; Cinemax; Disney Channel; HBO; Showtime.
Fee: $15.00 installation; $10.95 monthly (each).
Local advertising: No.
Equipment: Scientific-Atlanta headend; Jerrold amplifiers; Comm/Scope cable; Sony cameras; Sony VTRs; MSI character generator; Jerrold & Pioneer set top converters; Zenith addressable set top converters; Eagle traps; Scientific-Atlanta satellite antenna; Scientific-Atlanta satellite receivers.
Miles of plant: 432.4 (coaxial). Additional miles planned: 21.0 (coaxial). Homes passed: 22,886.
Manager: Bill G. Cadle. Chief technician: Bill Noor.
City fee: 3% of gross.
Ownership: Fanch Communications Inc. (MSO); Time Warner Cable (MSO). Purchased from Tele-Communications Inc., February 25, 1999. See Cable System Ownership.

BEECH BOTTOM—Blue Devil Cable TV Inc., 116 S. 4th St., Toronto, OH 43964. Phone: 740-537-2214. Fax: 740-537-2802. County: Brooke. ICA: WV0114.
TV Market Ranking: 90. Franchise award date: N.A. Franchise expiration date: N.A. Began: January 1, 1952.
Channel capacity: 30. Channels available but not in use: 18.
Basic Service
Subscribers: 234.
Programming (received off-air): WNPB-TV (P) Morgantown; KDKA-TV (C), WCWB (W), WPGH-TV (F), WPXI (N), WQED (P), WTAE-TV (A) Pittsburgh; WTOV-TV (N) Steubenville-Wheeling; WTRF-TV (C) Wheeling-Steubenville; allband FM.
Programming (via satellite): CNN; ESPN; TBS Superstation; USA Network.
Fee: $15.00 installation; $9.75 monthly.
Pay Service 1
Pay Units: N.A.
Programming (via satellite): HBO.
Fee: $20.00 installation; $8.00 monthly.
Equipment: Blonder-Tongue headend; Jerrold amplifiers; Times Fiber cable; Eagle traps; Microdyne satellite antenna; Microdyne satellite receivers.
Miles of plant: 10.0 (coaxial). Homes passed: 450.
Manager: David Bates. Chief technician: Al Grimes.
City fee: $200 annually.
Ownership: Jefferson County Cable Inc. (MSO).

BEECH CREEK—Cooney Cable Assoc. of West Virginia, Box 69, Delbarton, WV 25670. Phone: 304-426-4609. County: Mingo. ICA: WV0140.
TV Market Ranking: Outside TV Markets. Franchise award date: N.A. Franchise expiration date: N.A. Began: June 1, 1978.
Channel capacity: N.A. Channels available but not in use: N.A.
Basic Service
Subscribers: 216.
Programming (received off-air): WVVA (N) Bluefield; WCHS-TV (A), WOWK-TV (C), WPBY-TV (P), WSAZ-TV (N), WVAH-TV (F,U) Charleston-Huntington; WKPI (P) Pikeville.
Programming (via satellite): WGN-TV (W) Chicago; ESPN; Fox Family Channel; TBS Superstation; Trinity Bcstg. Network; Turner Network TV.
Fee: $14.29 monthly.
Expanded Basic Service
Subscribers: 150.
Programming (via satellite): CNN; Country Music TV; Discovery Channel; Headline News; Nashville Network; Nickelodeon; QVC; USA Network.
Fee: $9.66 monthly.
Pay Service 1
Pay Units: 39.
Programming (via satellite): HBO.
Fee: $10.95 monthly.
Pay Service 2
Pay Units: 20.
Programming (via satellite): Showtime.
Fee: $9.95 monthly.
Miles of plant: 11.2 (coaxial); None (fiber optic).
Manager: John B. Cooney. Chief technician: Greg Goad.
Ownership: Cooney Cable Assoc. Inc. (MSO).

BELINGTON—Cablecomm, 315 First St., Parsons, WV 26287. Phone: 800-352-1030. County: Barbour. Also serves Barbour County, Junior. ICA: WV0077.
TV Market Ranking: Below 100. Franchise award date: N.A. Franchise expiration date: N.A. Began: June 1, 1956.
Channel capacity: 27 (2-way capable; operating 2-way partially). Channels available but not in use: N.A.
Basic Service
Subscribers: 1,006.
Programming (received off-air): WBOY-TV (N), WDTV (C,A), WVFX (F) Clarksburg-Weston; WNPB-TV (P) Morgantown; WTAE-TV (A) Pittsburgh; allband FM.
Programming (via satellite): C-SPAN; CNN; Discovery Channel; Fox Family Channel; FoxNet; Lifetime; MTV; Nashville Network; Nickelodeon; QVC; TBS Superstation; The Weather Channel; USA Network.
Current originations: Automated time-weather.
Fee: $59.95 installation; $18.07 monthly.
Expanded Basic Service
Subscribers: N.A.
Programming (via satellite): American Movie Classics; ESPN; Fox Sports Net Pittsburgh; Odyssey; Turner Network TV.
Fee: $1.85 monthly.
Pay Service 1
Pay Units: 245.
Programming (via satellite): HBO.
Fee: $13.15 monthly.

Pay Service 2
Pay Units: 135.
Programming (via satellite): Showtime.
Fee: $13.15 monthly.
Pay Service 3
Pay Units: 518.
Programming (via satellite): The New Encore.
Fee: N.A.
Local advertising: No.
Equipment: Jerrold headend; Jerrold amplifiers; Times Fiber cable; Jerrold set top converters; Microdyne satellite antenna; Microdyne satellite receivers.
Miles of plant: 25.0 (coaxial). Homes passed: 1,115. Total homes in franchised area: 1,267.
Manager: Sue Talbott.
Franchise fee: 3% of gross.
Ownership: Fanch Communications Inc. (MSO); Time Warner Cable (MSO). Purchased from Tele-Communications Inc., February 25, 1999. See Cable System Ownership.

BENS CREEK—CableVision Communications, Box 2200, 68 5th St., Buckhannon, WV 26201. Phone: 304-472-4193. Fax: 304-472-0756. County: Mingo. Also serves Mingo County (portions), Wharnecliffe. ICA: WV0135.
TV Market Ranking: Outside TV Markets. Franchise award date: December 12, 1985. Franchise expiration date: N.A. Began: N.A.
Channel capacity: 37 (not 2-way capable). Channels available but not in use: 24.
Basic Service
Subscribers: 206.
Programming (received off-air): WCHS-TV (A), WOWK-TV (C), WPBY-TV (P), WSAZ-TV (N) Charleston-Huntington; WVSX (I) Lewisburg.
Programming (via satellite): WGN-TV (W) Chicago; Fox Family Channel; Home Shopping Network; Lifetime; Nickelodeon; TBS Superstation.
Fee: $61.25 installation; $13.20 monthly; $0.73 converter.
Expanded Basic Service
Subscribers: N.A.
Programming (via satellite): A & E; American Movie Classics; C-SPAN; CNN; Discovery Channel; Disney Channel; ESPN; ESPN 2; Great American Country; Learning Channel; Nashville Network; Nick at Nite's TV Land; Sci-Fi Channel; Toon Disney; Trinity Bcstg. Network; Turner Network TV; USA Network.
Fee: $15.60 monthly.
Pay Service 1
Pay Units: 63.
Programming (via satellite): HBO.
Fee: $11.99 monthly.
Equipment: Blonder-Tongue, Olson & Standard Communications headend; C-COR amplifiers; Eagle traps; Scientific-Atlanta satellite antenna; Scientific-Atlanta satellite receivers.
Miles of plant: 11.0 (coaxial); None (fiber optic).
Manager: Paul Pecora. Plant manager: Garry Lucas. Marketing director: Kenny Phillips.
Ownership: Rifkin & Associates Inc. (MSO). See Cable System Ownership.

BERGOO—Cablecomm, 80 N. Market St., Webster Springs, WV 26288. Phone: 800-352-1030. County: Webster. ICA: WV0163.
TV Market Ranking: Outside TV Markets. Franchise award date: N.A. Franchise expiration date: N.A. Began: January 1, 1953.
Channel capacity: 12. Channels available but not in use: 4.
Basic Service
Subscribers: 37.
Programming (received off-air): WCHS-TV (A), WOWK-TV (C), WSAZ-TV (N), WVAH-TV (F,U) Charleston-Huntington; WBOY-TV (N), WDTV (C,A) Clarksburg-Weston; WSWP-TV (P) Grandview; WOAY-TV (A) Oak Hill-Beckley.
Fee: $59.95 installation; $7.50 monthly.
Miles of plant: 3.0 (coaxial). Homes passed: 43. Total homes in franchised area: 50.
Manager: Sue Talbott.
Ownership: Fanch Communications Inc. (MSO); Time Warner Cable (MSO). Purchased from Tele-Communications Inc., February 24, 1999. See Cable System Ownership.

BETHANY—Bocco Cable, Box 215, RR 2, Valley Grove, WV 26060. Phone: 304-336-7086. Fax: 304-336-7086. County: Brooke. Also serves Brooke County (portions). ICA: WV0152.
TV Market Ranking: 10,90. Franchise award date: N.A. Franchise expiration date: N.A. Began: March 1, 1991.
Channel capacity: 36 (2-way capable; operating 2-way). Channels available but not in use: N.A.
Basic Service
Subscribers: 79.
Programming (received off-air): WNPB-TV (P) Morgantown; KDKA-TV (C), WCWB (W), WPGH-TV (F), WQED (P), WQEX (P), WTAE-TV (A) Pittsburgh; WTOV-TV (N) Steubenville-Wheeling; WTRF-TV (C) Wheeling-Steubenville.
Programming (via satellite): WGN-TV (W) Chicago; A & E; C-SPAN; CNN; Discovery Channel; ESPN; ESPN 2; ESPNews; Fox Family Channel; Headline News; History Channel; MTV; Nashville Network; Nick at Nite; Nickelodeon; QVC; Sci-Fi Channel; TBS Superstation; The Weather Channel; Turner Classic Movies; Turner Network TV; USA Network.
Fee: $25.00 installation; $15.50 monthly.
Pay Service 1
Pay Units: 32.
Programming (via satellite): HBO.
Fee: $7.50 monthly.
Pay Service 2
Pay Units: 13.
Programming (via satellite): Showtime.
Fee: $5.00 monthly.
Miles of plant: 5.5 (coaxial); None (fiber optic). Homes passed: 125. Total homes in franchised area: 125.
Manager: Basil O. Ellis.
Ownership: Bocco Cable.

BEVERLY—CableVision Communications, Box 2200, 68 5th St., Buckhannon, WV 26201. Phone: 304-472-4193. Fax: 304-472-0756. County: Randolph. Also serves Crystal Springs, East Dailey, Elkins, Gilman, Huttonsville, Midland, Mill Creek, Valley Bend. ICA: WV0015.
TV Market Ranking: Below 100. Franchise award date: December 14, 1979. Franchise expiration date: N.A. Began: December 1, 1979.
Channel capacity: 59. Channels available but not in use: 3.
Basic Service
Subscribers: 7,201.
Programming (received off-air): WCHS-TV (A) Charleston-Huntington; WBOY-TV (N), WDTV (C,A), WVFX (F) Clarksburg-Weston; WNPB-TV (P) Morgantown; WPGH-TV (F), WPXI (N), WTAE-TV (A) Pittsburgh; WTRF-TV (C) Wheeling-Steubenville.
Programming (via satellite): C-SPAN; TBS Superstation.
Current originations: Public access.
Fee: $61.25 installation; $14.40 monthly; $2.27 converter.
Expanded Basic Service
Subscribers: 6,025.
Programming (via satellite): A & E; American Movie Classics; C-SPAN 2; CNBC; CNN; Cartoon Network; Discovery Channel; Disney Channel; E! Entertainment TV; ESPN; ESPN 2; FX; Fox Family Channel; Fox Sports Net Pittsburgh; Great American Country; Headline News; History Channel; Home & Garden Television; Home Shopping Network; Learning Channel; Lifetime; MTV; MuchMusic Network; Nashville Network; Nickelodeon; Outdoor Life Network; Sci-Fi Channel; TV Guide Channel; The Inspirational Network; The Weather Channel; Travel Channel; Trinity Bcstg. Network; Turner Network TV; USA Network; WB 100+ Station Group.
Fee: $16.19 monthly.
Pay Service 1
Pay Units: 2,742.
Programming (via satellite): Cinemax; HBO; Showtime; Starz!; The Movie Channel; The New Encore.
Fee: $17.50 installation; $3.99 monthly (Encore), $5.99 monthly (Encore & Starz), $7.95 monthly (Cinemax), $11.95 monthly (Showtime or TMC), $11.99 monthly (HBO).
Pay-Per-View
Addressable homes: 2,742.
Playboy TV; movies.
Local advertising: No. Regional interconnect: Cabletime.
Program Guide: CableView.
Equipment: Blonder-Tongue, DX Engineering & Scientific-Atlanta headend; C-COR & Jerrold amplifiers; Microdyne satellite antenna; Scientific-Atlanta satellite receivers.
Miles of plant: 210.0 (coaxial). Homes passed: 10,867.
Manager: Willie Critchfield. Marketing director: Kenny Phillips.
Ownership: Rifkin & Associates Inc. (MSO). See Cable System Ownership.

BIRCH RIVER—Paxton Cable, Suite 280, 700 Ackerman Rd., Columbus, OH 43202. Phone: 614-263-6100. Fax: 614-263-7299. Counties: Braxton, Clay & Nicholas. Also serves Clay County (unincorporated areas), Dille, Little Birch, Widen. ICA: WV0090.
TV Market Ranking: 36 (portions of Clay County); Below 100 (portions of Clay County, Little Birch); Outside TV Markets (Birch River, portions of Clay County, Dille, Widen). Franchise award date: N.A. Franchise expiration date: N.A. Began: July 1, 1968.
Channel capacity: 22. Channels available but not in use: 1.
Basic Service
Subscribers: 649.
Programming (received off-air): WCHS-TV (A), WOWK-TV (C), WSAZ-TV (N), WVAH-TV (F,U) Charleston-Huntington; WBOY-TV (N), WDTV (C,A) Clarksburg-Weston; WSWP-TV (P) Grandview; WOAY-TV (A) Oak Hill-Beckley.
Programming (via satellite): WGN-TV (W) Chicago; A & E; CNN; Discovery Channel; ESPN; Fox Family Channel; Nashville Network; TBS Superstation; Turner Network TV; USA Network.
Fee: $29.95 installation; $20.95 monthly; $2.00 converter.
Pay Service 1
Pay Units: 62.
Programming (via satellite): Disney Channel; HBO; Showtime.
Fee: $29.95 installation; $10.00 monthly (each).
Miles of plant: 39.0 (coaxial). Homes passed: 835.
Manager: Bob Houghton. Chief technician: Robert Cottrill Jr.
Ownership: Paxton Cable Television Inc. (MSO). Purchased from Bob Houghton, September 2, 1998.

BLUEFIELD—Comcast Communications, Box 1516, 1901 Leatherwood Lane, Bluefield, WV 24701. Phone: 304-325-0591. Fax: 304-325-7376. Counties: Mercer, WV; Bland & Tazewell, VA. Also serves Bland County (portions), Pocahontas, Rocky Gap, Tazewell County (portions), VA; Bluewell, Green Valley, Mercer County (portions), WV. ICA: WV0007.
TV Market Ranking: Below 100. Franchise award date: February 26, 1954. Franchise expiration date: January 1, 2002. Began: January 1, 1956.
Channel capacity: 37 (not 2-way capable). Channels available but not in use: None.
Basic Service
Subscribers: 15,588.
Programming (received off-air): WVVA (N) Bluefield; WSWP-TV (P) Grandview; WVSX (I) Lewisburg; WOAY-TV (A) Oak Hill-Beckley; WBRA-TV (P) Roanoke; WDBJ (C) Roanoke-Lynchburg.
Programming (via satellite): American Movie Classics; C-SPAN; CNN; Country Music TV; Discovery Channel; ESPN; ESPN 2; Fox Family Channel; Headline News; Home & Garden Television; Learning Channel; Lifetime; MTV; Nashville Network; Nickelodeon; QVC; TBS Superstation; TV Food Network; TV Guide Channel; The Inspirational Network; The Weather Channel; Turner Network TV; USA Network; VH1.
Current originations: Automated time-weather.
Planned originations: Local news.
Fee: $41.25 installation; $23.06 monthly; $25.25 additional installation.
Pay Service 1
Pay Units: 9,065.
Programming (via satellite): Cinemax; Disney Channel; HBO; Showtime.
Fee: $10.50 (Disney or Showtime), $12.50 monthly (Cinemax or HBO).
Pay-Per-View
Addressable homes: 5,500.
Viewer's Choice; movies; special events.
Equipment: Scientific-Atlanta headend; Scientific-Atlanta amplifiers; Comm/Scope cable; Scientific-Atlanta satellite antenna.
Miles of plant: 433.0 (coaxial); 33.0 (fiber optic). Homes passed: 19,219. Total homes in franchised area: 21,000.
Manager: Treva Taylor. Chief technician: Ken Taylor. Marketing director: Alice Matthews.
City fee: 5% of gross.
Ownership: Comcast Cable Communications Inc. (MSO).

BRANDYWINE—Brandywine Cablevision, Box 248, Brandywine, WV 26802-0248. Phones: 304-249-5610; 304-249-5185. County: Pendleton. Plans service to Sugar Grove. ICA: WV0168.
TV Market Ranking: Below 100. Franchise award date: N.A. Franchise expiration date: N.A. Began: N.A.
Channel capacity: N.A. Channels available but not in use: N.A.
Basic Service
Subscribers: 350.
Programming (received off-air): WHSV-TV (A,F) Harrisonburg; WJAC-TV (N) Johnstown-Altoona; WNPB-TV (P) Morgantown; WTVR-TV (C) Richmond-Petersburg; WDBJ (C), WSLS-TV (N) Roanoke-Lynchburg; WRC-TV (N), WTTG (F) Washington.
Programming (via satellite): Fox Family Channel; TBS Superstation.

Fee: $150.00 installation; $14.50 monthly.
Ownership: Brandywine Cablevision.

BROAD RUN—Basco Electronics Inc., 420 W. 2nd St., Weston, WV 26452. Phone: 304-269-7530. Fax: 304-269-6581. County: Harrison. ICA: WV0155.
TV Market Ranking: Below 100. Franchise award date: N.A. Franchise expiration date: N.A. Began: September 1, 1985.
Channel capacity: 35. Channels available but not in use: 18.
Basic Service
Subscribers: 87.
Programming (received off-air): WBOY-TV (N), WDTV (C,A) Clarksburg-Weston; WNPB-TV (P) Morgantown; WTAE-TV (A) Pittsburgh; allband FM.
Programming (via satellite): CNN; ESPN; Fox Family Channel; Learning Channel; MTV; Nashville Network; QVC; TBS Superstation; Turner Network TV; USA Network.
Fee: $50.00 installation; $17.90 monthly.
Pay Service 1
Pay Units: 12.
Programming (via satellite): Disney Channel.
Fee: $10.00 installation; $7.00 monthly.
Pay Service 2
Pay Units: 25.
Programming (via satellite): HBO.
Fee: $10.00 installation; $10.00 monthly.
Local advertising: No.
Equipment: Blonder-Tongue & Pico headend; Magnavox amplifiers; Comm/Scope cable; Jerrold set top converters; Pico traps; M/A-Com satellite antenna; Drake satellite receivers.
Miles of plant: 4.0 (coaxial). Homes passed: 100.
Manager: Wilfred L. Sholes. Chief technician: Brian Queen. Marketing director: Sue M. Sholes.
Ownership: Basco Electronics Inc. (MSO).

BROOKHAVEN—Century Huntington Co., Box 599, Dellslow, WV 26531. Phone: 304-292-6561. County: Monongalia. Also serves Monongalia County (portions), Richard. ICA: WV0170.
TV Market Ranking: 90 (portions of Monongalia County); Below 100 (Brookhaven, portions of Monongalia County, Richard). Franchise award date: N.A. Franchise expiration date: N.A. Began: June 1, 1965.
Channel capacity: 12. Channels available but not in use: 1.
Basic Service
Subscribers: N.A.
Programming (received off-air): WBOY-TV (N), WDTV (C,A) Clarksburg-Weston; WNPB-TV (P) Morgantown; KDKA-TV (C), WPGH-TV (F), WPXI (N), WQED (P), WTAE-TV (A) Pittsburgh; WTOV-TV (N) Steubenville-Wheeling; WTRF-TV (C) Wheeling-Steubenville; allband FM.
Planned programming (via satellite): Fox Family Channel; USA Network.
Current originations: Automated time-weather.
Fee: $6.95 installation; $5.50 monthly.
Equipment: Jerrold headend; Jerrold amplifiers; Times Fiber cable; Andrew satellite antenna.
Miles of plant: 28.5 (coaxial).
Manager: Michael Ligouri. Chief technician: Ed Hinkle.
City fee: None.
Ownership: Century Communications Corp. (MSO). See Cable System Ownership.

BRUNO—Cooney Cable Assoc., 228 Park Ave., Worcester, MA 01609. Phone: 508-754-5865. Fax: 508-752-7342. County: Logan. ICA: WV0171.
TV Market Ranking: Below 100. Franchise award date: October 1, 1991. Franchise expiration date: October 1, 2006. Began: N.A.
Channel capacity: 40 (not 2-way capable). Channels available but not in use: 6.
Basic Service
Subscribers: 379.
Programming (received off-air): WVVA (N) Bluefield; WCHS-TV (A), WOWK-TV (C), WSAZ-TV (N), WVAH-TV (F,U) Charleston-Huntington; WSWP-TV (P) Grandview.
Programming (via satellite): WGN-TV (W) Chicago; CNN; Country Music TV; ESPN; Fox Family Channel; MTV; Nashville Network; Nickelodeon; TBS Superstation; Turner Network TV; USA Network.
Fee: $48.18 installation; $27.45 monthly.
Pay Service 1
Pay Units: 58.
Programming (via satellite): HBO.
Fee: $25.00 installation; $11.95 monthly.
Pay Service 2
Pay Units: 35.
Programming (via satellite): Showtime.
Fee: $25.00 installation; $10.95 monthly.
Pay Service 3
Pay Units: 8.
Programming (via satellite): Showtime; The Movie Channel.
Fee: $11.95 monthly (Showtime & TMC).
Miles of plant: 15.0 (coaxial); None (fiber optic).
Manager: John Cooney. Chief technician: Ron Davis.
Ownership: Cooney Cable Assoc. Inc. (MSO).

BUCKHANNON—CableVision Communications, Box 2200, 68 5th St., Buckhannon, WV 26201. Phone: 304-472-4193. Fax: 304-472-0756. Counties: Lewis & Upshur. Also serves Adrian, Berlin, Deansville, French Creek, Hodgesville, Kesling Mill, Lewis County (northern portion), Lorentz, Reger, Rock Cave, Tennerton, Upshur County. ICA: WV0024.
TV Market Ranking: Below 100. Franchise award date: February 15, 1987. Franchise expiration date: N.A. Began: November 1, 1966.
Channel capacity: 50. Channels available but not in use: None.
Basic Service
Subscribers: 5,082.
Programming (received off-air): WCHS-TV (A) Charleston-Huntington; WBOY-TV (N), WDTV (C,A), WVFX (F) Clarksburg-Weston; WNPB-TV (P) Morgantown; KDKA-TV (C), WPGH-TV (F), WPXI (N), WTAE-TV (A) Pittsburgh; WTRF-TV (C) Wheeling-Steubenville; allband FM.
Programming (via satellite): WGN-TV (W) Chicago; CNN; Home Shopping Network; TBS Superstation; The Weather Channel; Trinity Bcstg. Network.
Fee: $61.25 installation; $15.98 monthly; $0.65 converter.
Expanded Basic Service
Subscribers: 4,338.
Programming (via satellite): A & E; American Movie Classics; C-SPAN; C-SPAN 2; CNBC; Cartoon Network; Comedy Central; Discovery Channel; Disney Channel; E! Entertainment TV; ESPN; ESPN 2; FX; Fox Family Channel; Fox Sports Net Pittsburgh; Great American Country; Headline News; History Channel; Home & Garden Television; Learning Channel; Lifetime; MTV; Nashville Network; Nickelodeon; Outdoor Channel; Sci-Fi Channel; Turner Network TV; USA Network; WB 100+ Station Group.
Fee: $12.88 monthly.
Pay Service 1
Pay Units: N.A.
Programming (via satellite): Cinemax; HBO; Showtime; Starz!; The Movie Channel; The New Encore.
Fee: $10.00 installation; $3.99 monthly (Encore), $5.99 monthly (Encore & Starz), $7.95 monthly (Cinemax), $11.95 monthly (Showtime or TMC), $11.99 monthly (HBO).
Local advertising: Yes. Rates: $4.00-$15.00/Spot. Regional interconnect: Cabletime.
Program Guide: The Cable Guide.
Equipment: M/A-Com & Hughes headend; Jerrold amplifiers; Jerrold set top converters; AFC satellite antenna; Microdyne satellite receivers.
Miles of plant: 157.0 (coaxial).
Manager: Willie Critchfield. Marketing director: Kenny Phillips.
City fee: 3% of gross.
Ownership: Rifkin & Associates Inc. (MSO). See Cable System Ownership.

BUD—Bud-Alpoca TV Cable Club Inc., Box 188, Bud, WV 24716. Phone: 304-294-5365. County: Wyoming. Also serves Alpoca. ICA: WV0138.
TV Market Ranking: Below 100. Franchise award date: N.A. Franchise expiration date: N.A. Began: July 1, 1983.
Channel capacity: N.A. Channels available but not in use: N.A.
Basic Service
Subscribers: 108.
Programming (received off-air): WVVA (N) Bluefield; WCHS-TV (A), WOWK-TV (C), WSAZ-TV (N) Charleston-Huntington; WSWP-TV (P) Grandview; WOAY-TV (A) Oak Hill-Beckley; WDBJ (C), WSLS-TV (N) Roanoke-Lynchburg.
Programming (via satellite): CNN; ESPN; Fox Family Channel; Nashville Network; TBS Superstation; Turner Network TV.
Fee: N.A.
Miles of plant: 6.0 (coaxial). Homes passed: 225.
Manager: Randy Hamilton.
Ownership: Bud-Alpoca TV Cable Club Inc.

BURNSVILLE—Helicon Cablevision, Box A, 150 N. Pinch Rd., Pinch, WV 25156. Phones: 304-965-7026; 800-642-9163. Fax: 304-965-7768. County: Braxton. ICA: WV0132.
TV Market Ranking: Below 100. Franchise award date: N.A. Franchise expiration date: N.A. Began: December 1, 1952.
Channel capacity: 40 (not 2-way capable). Channels available but not in use: 16.
Basic Service
Subscribers: 195.
Programming (received off-air): WCHS-TV (A), WVAH-TV (F,U) Charleston-Huntington; WBOY-TV (N), WDTV (C,A) Clarksburg-Weston; WNPB-TV (P) Morgantown; WOAY-TV (A) Oak Hill-Beckley.
Programming (via satellite): C-SPAN; Fox Family Channel; QVC; TBS Superstation.
Current originations: Automated time-weather.
Fee: $55.00 installation; $19.69 monthly; $20.00 additional installation.
Expanded Basic Service
Subscribers: N.A.
Programming (via satellite): A & E; American Movie Classics; CNN; Country Music TV; Discovery Channel; ESPN; Headline News; Lifetime; Nashville Network; Nickelodeon; Turner Network TV; USA Network.
Fee: N.A.
Pay Service 1
Pay Units: 13.
Programming (via satellite): HBO.
Fee: $20.00 installation; $8.50 monthly.
Pay Service 2
Pay Units: 9.
Programming (via satellite): The Movie Channel.
Fee: $20.00 installation; $8.50 monthly.
Local advertising: No.
Equipment: Jerrold headend; Jerrold amplifiers; Comm/Scope cable.
Miles of plant: 9.0 (coaxial). Homes passed: 343. Total homes in franchised area: 343.
Manager: Jack Wade. Chief technician: Ken Gabehardt. Marketing & program director: David Baum.
City fee: None.
Ownership: Helicon Corp. (MSO). See Cable System Ownership.

CAIRO—CableVision Communications, Box 2200, 68 5th St., Buckhannon, WV 26201. Phone: 304-472-4193. Fax: 304-472-0756. County: Ritchie. ICA: WV0137.
TV Market Ranking: Below 100. Franchise award date: August 18, 1967. Franchise expiration date: N.A. Began: August 1, 1967.
Channel capacity: 21. Channels available but not in use: None.
Basic Service
Subscribers: 134.
Programming (received off-air): WCHS-TV (A), WOWK-TV (C), WVAH-TV (F,U) Charleston-Huntington; WBOY-TV (N), WDTV (C,A) Clarksburg-Weston; WNPB-TV (P) Morgantown; WTAP-TV (N) Parkersburg-Marietta; WTRF-TV (C)Wheeling-Steubenville; allband FM.
Programming (via satellite): CNN; Discovery Channel; Disney Channel; ESPN; Nashville Network; TBS Superstation.
Fee: $61.25 installation; $14.18 monthly; $0.73 converter.
Pay Service 1
Pay Units: 5.
Programming (via satellite): HBO.
Fee: $11.99 monthly.
Equipment: Blonder-Tongue & Jerrold headend.
Miles of plant: 8.0 (coaxial). Additional miles planned: 1.3 (coaxial). Homes passed: 233.
Manager: Willie Critchfield. Chief technician: Bill Turner. Marketing director: Kenny Phillips.
City fee: 2% of gross.
Ownership: Rifkin & Associates Inc. (MSO). See Cable System Ownership.

CAMDEN ON GAULEY—Helicon Group Ltd., Box A, 150 N. Pinch Rd., Pinch, WV 25156. Phones: 304-965-7026; 800-642-9163. Fax: 304-965-7768. County: Webster. Also serves Webster County (portions). ICA: WV0230.

TV Market Ranking: Outside TV Markets. Franchise award date: N.A. Franchise expiration date: N.A. Began: January 1, 1970.
Channel capacity: 21. Channels available but not in use: 4.
Basic Service
Subscribers: 221.
Programming (received off-air): WCHS-TV (A), WSAZ-TV (N), WVAH-TV (F,U) Charleston-Huntington; WBOY-TV (N), WDTV (C,A) Clarksburg-Weston; WSWP-TV (P) Grandview; WOAY-TV (A) Oak Hill-Beckley.
Programming (via satellite): ESPN; Fox Family Channel; Nashville Network; TBS Superstation; Turner Network TV.
Fee: $17.91 monthly.
Expanded Basic Service
Subscribers: 223.
Programming (via satellite): CNN; Country Music TV; Discovery Channel; Headline News; USA Network.
Fee: $4.00 monthly.
Pay Service 1
Pay Units: 34.
Programming (via satellite): HBO.
Fee: $8.50 monthly.
Miles of plant: 10.5 (coaxial). Homes passed: 346.
Manager: Jack Wade. Chief technician: Ken Gabehardt. Marketing & program director: Dave Baum.
Ownership: Helicon Corp. (MSO). See Cable System Ownership.

CAMERON—CableVision Communications, Box 2200, 68 5th St., Buckhannon, WV 26201. Phone: 304-472-4193. Fax: 304-472-0756. County: Marshall. ICA: WV0085.
TV Market Ranking: 90. Franchise award date: N.A. Franchise expiration date: N.A. Began: January 1, 1950.
Channel capacity: 39 (not 2-way capable). Channels available but not in use: N.A.
Basic Service
Subscribers: 625; Commercial subscribers: 13.
Programming (received off-air): WOUC-TV (P) Cambridge; KDKA-TV (C), WCWB (W), WPGH-TV (F), WPXI (N), WTAE-TV (A) Pittsburgh; WTOV-TV (N) Steubenville-Wheeling; WTRF-TV (C) Wheeling-Steubenville; allband FM.
Programming (via satellite): Home Shopping Network; TBS Superstation; USA Network.
Current originations: Local access.
Fee: $61.25 installation; $9.54 monthly; $0.73 converter.
Expanded Basic Service
Subscribers: N.A.
Programming (via satellite): A & E; American Movie Classics; C-SPAN; CNN; Discovery Channel; Disney Channel; E! Entertainment TV; ESPN; ESPN 2; Fox Family Channel; Great American Country; Headline News; Home & Garden Television; Lifetime; MTV; MuchMusic Network; Nashville Network; Nickelodeon; Sci-Fi Channel; The Weather Channel; Trinity Bcstg. Network; Turner Network TV.
Fee: $17.83 monthly.
Pay Service 1
Pay Units: 294.
Programming (via satellite): Cinemax; HBO; Showtime; The Movie Channel.
Fee: $17.50 installation; $7.95 monthly (Cinemax), $11.95 monthly (Showtime or TMC), $11.99 monthly (HBO).
Equipment: Blonder-Tongue & Scientific-Atlanta headend; C-COR & Jerrold amplifiers; Capscan cable.
Miles of plant: 24.0 (coaxial). Homes passed: 990. Total homes in franchised area: 1,035.
Manager: Willie Critchfield. Marketing director: Kenny Phillips.
Ownership: Rifkin & Associates Inc. (MSO). See Cable System Ownership.

CANVAS—Econoco Inc., Box 147, Rte. 61, Kincaid, WV 25119. Phone: 304-469-2817. County: Nicholas. ICA: WV0172.
TV Market Ranking: Below 100. Franchise award date: N.A. Franchise expiration date: N.A. Began: January 1, 1982.
Channel capacity: 36 (not 2-way capable). Channels available but not in use: 19.
Basic Service
Subscribers: 275.
Programming (received off-air): WVVA (N) Bluefield; WCHS-TV (A), WOWK-TV (C), WSAZ-TV (N), WVAH-TV (F,U) Charleston-Huntington; WDTV (C,A) Clarksburg-Weston; WSWP-TV (P) Grandview; WOAY-TV (A) Oak Hill-Beckley.
Programming (via satellite): WGN-TV (W) Chicago; A & E; CNN; Discovery Channel; ESPN; Fox Family Channel; Nashville Network; TBS Superstation.
Fee: $25.00 installation; $20.72 monthly.
Pay Service 1
Pay Units: N.A.
Programming (via satellite): HBO.
Fee: $15.00 installation; $12.00 monthly.
Miles of plant: 24.0 (coaxial); None (fiber optic).
Manager: Sheila Bills. Chief technician: Eslie Bills.
Ownership: Econoco Inc. (MSO).

CAPON BRIDGE—Valley Cable, Box 78, Doylesburg, PA 17219. Phone: 717-349-7717. County: Hampshire. Also serves Hampshire County (portions). ICA: WV0123.
TV Market Ranking: Below 100. Franchise award date: January 1, 1974. Franchise expiration date: N.A. Began: June 28, 1974.
Channel capacity: 36 (not 2-way capable). Channels available but not in use: 7.
Basic Service
Subscribers: 268.
Programming (received off-air): WHAG-TV (N) Hagerstown; WHSV-TV (A,F) Harrisonburg; WDCA (U), WETA-TV (P), WJLA-TV (A), WRC-TV (N), WTTG (F), WUSA (C) Washington.
Programming (via satellite): C-SPAN; Discovery Channel; ESPN; Fox Family Channel; Nashville Network; TBS Superstation; Trinity Bcstg. Network; USA Network.
Current originations: Public access; religious access.
Fee: $40.00 installation; $15.25 monthly.
Expanded Basic Service
Subscribers: 99.
Programming (via satellite): A & E; Bravo; CNN; Country Music TV; Lifetime; Sci-Fi Channel; Turner Network TV.
Fee: $7.00 monthly.
Pay Service 1
Pay Units: 42.
Programming (via satellite): Disney Channel.
Fee: $6.59 monthly.
Pay Service 2
Pay Units: 45.
Programming (via satellite): Showtime.
Fee: $10.00 monthly.
Local advertising: Yes. Available in character-generated programming. Rates: $1.00/Day.
Equipment: Blonder-Tongue, Jerrold & M/A-Com headend; Jerrold amplifiers; Comm/Scope cable; Atari & Info/Soft character generator; Jerrold set top converters; PPC traps; Scientific-Atlanta satellite antenna; Drake satellite receivers.
Miles of plant: 26.7 (coaxial). Homes passed: 344. Total homes in franchised area: 600.
Manager: Barry L. Kepner.
City fee: 3% of gross.
Ownership: Valley Cable Systems (MSO).

CASS—Milestone Communications of New York LP, Suite 200, 1850 Woodmoor Dr., Monument, CO 80132. Phone: 719-488-2916. Fax: 719-488-3629. County: Pocahontas. ICA: WV0173.
TV Market Ranking: Outside TV Markets. Franchise award date: N.A. Franchise expiration date: May 15, 2005. Began: N.A.
Channel capacity: 22 (not 2-way capable). Channels available but not in use: 10.
Basic Service
Subscribers: 39.
Programming (received off-air): WDTV (C,A) Clarksburg-Weston; WDBJ (C), WSLS-TV (N) Roanoke-Lynchburg.
Programming (via satellite): WGN-TV (W) Chicago; CNN; ESPN; Fox Family Channel; Nashville Network; TBS Superstation; Turner Network TV; USA Network.
Fee: $50.00 installation (aerial), $60.00 (underground); $15.50 monthly; $10.00 additional installation.
Pay Service 1
Pay Units: 3.
Programming (via satellite): HBO.
Fee: $10.00 installation; $12.95 monthly.
Equipment: Standard Components & Scientific-Atlanta headend; Blonder-Tongue & Jerrold amplifiers.
Homes passed: 70.
Director of engineering: Randy Mock. Marketing director: Mike Drake.
Ownership: Milestone Communications LP (MSO).

CENTERVILLE—FrontierVision, Suite P-200, 1777 S. Harrison St., Denver, CO 80210. Phone: 303-757-1588. Fax: 303-757-6105. County: Wayne. Also serves Prichard, Wayne County (unincorporated areas). ICA: WV0107.
TV Market Ranking: 36 (Centerville, Prichard, portions of Wayne County); Outside TV Markets (portions of Wayne County). Franchise award date: N.A. Franchise expiration date: N.A. Began: January 1, 1988.
Channel capacity: 12. Channels available but not in use: None.
Basic Service
Subscribers: 380.
Programming (received off-air): WTSF (I) Ashland; WCHS-TV (A), WOWK-TV (C), WPBY-TV (P), WSAZ-TV (N), WVAH-TV (F,U) Charleston-Huntington.
Programming (via satellite): Country Music TV; ESPN; Fox Family Channel; Nashville Network; TBS Superstation.
Fee: $29.95 installation; $13.95 monthly; $2.00 converter.
Pay Service 1
Pay Units: 106.
Programming (via satellite): HBO.
Fee: $29.95 installation; $10.00 monthly.
Miles of plant: 13.0 (coaxial). Homes passed: 538.
Manager: Willie Critchfield. Chief technician: Bill Turner. Program director: Tamela Biggs.
Ownership: FrontierVision Partners LP (MSO). See Cable System Ownership.

CHARLES TOWN—GS Communications, 302 N. Mildred St., Ranson, WV 25438-1455. Phone: 304-725-9185. Fax: 304-725-0930. County: Jefferson. Also serves Bolivar, Harpers Ferry, Jefferson County, Kearneysville, Ranson, Rippon, Shannondale, Shenandoah Junction (unincorporated areas), Shepherdstown, Summit Point. ICA: WV0016.
TV Market Ranking: Below 100. Franchise award date: January 1, 1996. Franchise expiration date: N.A. Began: N.A.
Channel capacity: 71 (not 2-way capable). Channels available but not in use: 1.
Basic Service
Subscribers: 27,210.
Programming (received off-air): WJZ-TV (C), WMAR-TV (A) Baltimore; WHAG-TV (N), WJAL (W), WWPB (P) Hagerstown; WWPX (I) Martinsburg; WNPB-TV (P) Morgantown; WBDC-TV (W), WDCA (U), WETA-TV (P), WJLA-TV (A), WRC-TV (N), WTTG (F), WUSA (C) Washington.
Programming (via satellite): C-SPAN; C-SPAN 2; Home Shopping Network; QVC; TV Guide Channel; The Barker; The Weather Channel; Trinity Bcstg. Network; ValueVision.
Current originations: Public access; educational access; government access; local sports.
Fee: $37.00 installation; $11.00 monthly; $1.99 converter.
Expanded Basic Service
Subscribers: 25,878.
Programming (via satellite): A & E; American Movie Classics; BET; CNBC; CNN; Cartoon Network; Comedy Central; Discovery Channel; E! Entertainment TV; ESPN; ESPN 2; FX; Fox Family Channel; Great American Country; Headline News; History Channel; Home & Garden Television; Home Team Sports; Learning Channel; Lifetime; MSNBC; MTV; Nashville Network; Nick at Nite; Nickelodeon; Sci-Fi Channel; TBS Superstation; TV Food Network; Turner Network TV; USA Network; VH1.
Fee: $16.00 monthly.
Pay Service 1
Pay Units: 7,817.
Programming (via satellite): Cinemax; Disney Channel; HBO; Showtime; The Movie Channel.
Fee: $11.02 installation; $8.95 monthly (Disney), $10.95 monthly (Cinemax, HBO, Showtime or TMC).
Pay-Per-View
Addressable homes: 5,816.
Action Pay-Per-View; Hot Choice; Playboy TV; Spice; Viewer's Choice.
Fee: $3.99-$5.94.
Local advertising: Yes. Available in satellite distributed, locally originated, taped & automated programming. Local sales manager: Dave Whalends.
Program Guide: Teleguide.
Equipment: Hughes & Scientific-Atlanta headend; Magnavox amplifiers; Times Fiber & Comm/Scope cable; Compuvid character generator; Pioneer set top converters; Pioneer addressable set top converters; AFC & Scientific-Atlanta satellite antenna; Microdyne & Scientific-Atlanta satellite receivers.
Miles of plant: 879.0 (coaxial); 68.0 (fiber optic). Homes passed: 37,300. Subscribers, pay units, addressable homes, miles of plant & homes passed figures include Inwood & Martinsburg, WV.
Manager: Lawrence Willingham. Chief technician: John Nichols. Program director: Chris Haugh. Marketing director: Paul Espinosa.
City fee: 5% of gross.
Ownership: Great Southern Printing & Manufacturing Co. (MSO).

CHARLESTON—Capitol CableComm, Box 2673, 209 Broad St., Charleston, WV 25301. Phones: 304-345-8483; 888-345-8483. Fax: 304-357-6707.
E-mail: capitol@newwave.net.

County: Kanawha. Also serves Dunbar, Institute, Ruthdale, South Charleston. ICA: WV0001.
TV Market Ranking: 36. Franchise award date: N.A. Franchise expiration date: October 3, 2006. Began: January 1, 1966.
Channel capacity: 60. Channels available but not in use: 16.

Basic Service
Subscribers: 52,412; Commercial subscribers: 196.
Programming (received off-air): WCHS-TV (A), WOWK-TV (C), WPBY-TV (P), WSAZ-TV (N), WVAH-TV (F,U) Charleston-Huntington; WSWP-TV (P) Grandview.
Programming (via satellite): C-SPAN; C-SPAN 2; Home Shopping Network; Pax Net; QVC; TV Guide Channel; ValueVision.
Current originations: Public access; library access.
Fee: $30.00 installation; $8.18 monthly.

Expanded Basic Service
Subscribers: 30,623.
Programming (via satellite): A & E; American Movie Classics; Animal Planet; BET; Bravo; CNBC; CNN; Comedy Central; Country Music TV; Discovery Channel; E! Entertainment TV; ESPN; ESPN 2; Fox Family Channel; Fox News Channel; Headline News; Home & Garden Television; Learning Channel; Lifetime; MTV; Nashville Network; Nickelodeon; The Inspirational Network; The Weather Channel; Travel Channel; Trinity Bcstg. Network; Turner Network TV; USA Network; VH1.
Fee: $13.50 monthly.

Expanded Basic Service 2
Subscribers: N.A.
Programming (via satellite): WGN-TV (W) Chicago; Cartoon Network; Court TV; ESPN Classic Sports; Flix; Fox Sports Net Pittsburgh; Golf Channel; History Channel; Independent Film Channel; Sci-Fi Channel; TBS Superstation.
Fee: $5.00 monthly.

Pay Service 1
Pay Units: 5,436.
Programming (via satellite): Cinemax (multiplexed).
Fee: $15.00 installation; $10.95 monthly.

Pay Service 2
Pay Units: 4,357.
Programming (via satellite): Disney Channel.
Fee: $15.00 installation; $10.95 monthly.

Pay Service 3
Pay Units: 11,591.
Programming (via satellite): HBO (multiplexed).
Fee: $15.00 installation; $10.95 monthly.

Pay Service 4
Pay Units: 1,200.
Programming (via satellite): Showtime.
Fee: $15.00 installation; $10.95 monthly.

Pay Service 5
Pay Units: N.A.
Programming (via satellite): Music Choice; The Movie Channel.
Fee: $10.95 monthly (TMC).

Pay-Per-View
Action Pay-Per-View; Spice; Viewer's Choice 1-4.

Local advertising: Yes. Available in locally originated & taped programming. Local sales manager: Stan Gibbons.
Equipment: Ameco & RCA headend; Ameco & C-COR amplifiers; Ameco cable; Telemation cameras; Sony VTRs; Video Data Systems character generator; Scientific-Atlanta satellite antenna.
Miles of plant: 420.0 (coaxial). Homes passed: 43,444. Total homes in franchised area: 44,921.
Manager: Art Riley. Chief technician: Jack Wade. Marketing director: Michael Kelemen. Customer service manager: Kathleen Boggess.
Charleston fee: 5% of gross.
Ownership: Fanch Communications Inc. (MSO); Time Warner Cable (MSO). See Cable System Ownership.

CHATTAROY—Capital Cablecomm, Box 368, Cabin Creek, WV 25035. Phone: 304-779-2854. Fax: 304-595-5248. Counties: Mingo, WV; Pike, KY. Also serves Slater's Branch, Turkey Creek, KY; Borderland, WV. ICA: WV0072.
TV Market Ranking: Below 100. Franchise award date: N.A. Franchise expiration date: March 9, 2008. Began: September 1, 1956.
Channel capacity: 26 (not 2-way capable). Channels available but not in use: None.

Basic Service
Subscribers: 729.
Programming (received off-air): WCHS-TV (A), WOWK-TV (C), WPBY-TV (P), WSAZ-TV (N), WVAH-TV (F,U) Charleston-Huntington; WKPI (P) Pikeville; allband FM.
Programming (via satellite): WGN-TV (W) Chicago; Comedy Central; MTV; QVC; TBS Superstation; The Inspirational Network.
Current originations: Public access; educational access; government access.
Fee: $23.00 installation (aerial), $33.75 (underground); $11.15 monthly; $1.78 converter.

Expanded Basic Service
Subscribers: 717.
Programming (via satellite): CNN; Country Music TV; Discovery Channel; ESPN; Fox Family Channel; Lifetime; Nashville Network; Nickelodeon; The Weather Channel; USA Network.
Fee: $9.40 monthly.

Pay Service 1
Pay Units: 106.
Programming (via satellite): HBO.
Fee: $10.00 monthly.

Pay Service 2
Pay Units: 112.
Programming (via satellite): Cinemax.
Fee: $10.00 monthly.

Pay Service 3
Pay Units: 58.
Programming (via satellite): Disney Channel.
Fee: $8.00 monthly.

Equipment: Blonder-Tongue headend; Magnavox amplifiers; Comm/Scope cable; Comm/Scope & Jerrold set top converters; Scientific-Atlanta satellite antenna; M/A-Com satellite receivers.
Miles of plant: 15.2 (coaxial); None (fiber optic). Homes passed: 1,007.
Manager: Robert L. Herrald. Chief technician: Allen Comer. Marketing director: Bill Benner.
Franchise fee: 3% of gross.
Ownership: Fanch Communications Inc. (MSO); Time Warner Cable (MSO). See Cable System Ownership.

CHELYAN—Capital Cablecomm, Box 368, Cabin Creek, WV 25035. Phone: 304-779-2854. Fax: 304-595-5248. Counties: Boone, Fayette, Kanawha & Raleigh. Also serves Acme, Alta, Arnett, Ashford, Beasley Hollow, Belcher Road, Belle, Bloomingrose, Blunt, Boomer, Brownsville, Brush Creek, Cabin Creek, Campbells Creek, Camp Creek, Carbon, Cedar Grove, Charlton Heights, Chesapeake, Cinco, Clover Drive, Coal Fork, Columbia, Comfort, Coonskin Drive, Coopertown, Costa, Crown Hill, Dameron, Dawes, Decota, Deepwater, Diamond, Dry Branch Drive, Drybranch, Dupont City, Dutch Road, East Bank, Elk Forest, Elk Hills, Elk Two Mile, Elkridge, Eskdale, Fallsview, Fosterville, Gallagher, Gauley Bridge, Georges Creek, Giles, Glasgow, Glen Ferris, Handley, Hansford, Hernshaw, Holly, Holly Lawn, Hugheston, Hunter Road, Kanawha County, Kanawha Falls, Kayford, Kimberly, Knowlwood, Laing, Leewood, Lick Creek, London, MacDunn, Malden, Mammoth, Marmet, Masseyville, Meadowbrook, Miami, Montgomery, Montgomery Heights, Morris Drive, Morrisvale, Mount Carbon, Nabob, Nellis, Ohley, Paint Creek (portions), Paytona, Point Lick, Port Amherst, Posey, Powellton, Pratt, Prenter, Prenter Road, Quarrier, Quincy, Racine, Rand, Rensford, Ridgeview, Riverside, Ronda, Route Six, Rumble, Rutledge Road, Saxon, Seth, Sharon, Shrewsbury, Snow Hill, Spring Fork, Springfield, Stover, Tad, Union Addition, West Belle, Wevaco, Winifrede, Witcher. ICA: WV0006.
TV Market Ranking: 36 (Acme, Alta, Ashford, Beasley Hollow, Belcher Road, Belle, Bloomingrose, Blunt, Boomer, Brownsville, Brush Creek, Cabin Creek, Campbells Creek, Camp Creek, Carbon, Cedar Grove, Charlton Heights, Chelyan, Chesapeake, Cinco, Clover Drive, Coal Fork, Columbia, Comfort, Coonskin Drive, Coopertown, Costa, Crown Hill, Dawes, Decota, Deepwater, Diamond, Dry Branch Drive, Drybranch, Dupont City, Dutch Road, East Bank, Elk Forest, Elk Hills, Elk Two Mile, Elkridge, Eskdale, Fallsview, Fosterville, Gallagher, Gauley Bridge, Georges Creek, Giles, Glasgow, Glen Ferris, Handley, Hansford, Hernshaw, Holly, Holly Lawn, Hugheston, Hunter Road, Kanawha County, Kanawha Falls, Kayford, Kimberly, Knowlwood, Laing, Leewood, Lick Creek, London, MacDunn, Malden, Mammoth, Marmet, Meadowbrook, Miami, Montgomery, Montgomery Heights, Morris Drive, Morrisvale, Mount Carbon, Nabob, Nellis, Ohley, Paint Creek, Paytona, Point Lick, Port Amherst, Powellton, Pratt, Prenter, Prenter Road, Quarrier, Quincy, Racine, Rand, Rensford, Ridgeview, Riverside, Ronda, Route Six, Rumble, Rutledge Road, Seth, Sharon, Shrewsbury, Snow Hill, Spring Fork, Springfield, Tad, Union Addition, West Belle, Wevaco, Winifrede, Witcher); Below 100 (Arnett, Dameron, Masseyville, Posey, Saxon, Stover). Franchise award date: N.A. Franchise expiration date: N.A. Began: June 1, 1966.
Channel capacity: 52 (not 2-way capable). Channels available but not in use: 6.

Basic Service
Subscribers: 15,310.
Programming (received off-air): WCHS-TV (A), WOWK-TV (C), WPBY-TV (P), WSAZ-TV (N), WVAH-TV (F,U) Charleston-Huntington; WSWP-TV (P) Grandview; WOAY-TV (A) Oak Hill-Beckley.
Programming (via satellite): WGN-TV (W) Chicago; BET; Comedy Central; Learning Channel; MTV; QVC; TBS Superstation; The Inspirational Network.
Current originations: Automated time-weather; public access; educational access; government access; local news.
Fee: $35.50 installation (aerial), $48.75 (underground); $10.65 monthly; $0.93 converter.

Expanded Basic Service
Subscribers: 14,671.
Programming (via satellite): A & E; American Movie Classics; CNN; Country Music TV; Discovery Channel; ESPN; Fox Family Channel; Goodlife TV Network; Headline News; Home Shopping Network; Lifetime; Nashville Network; Nickelodeon; Sci-Fi Channel; The Weather Channel; Travel Channel; Turner Network TV; USA Network; VH1.
Fee: $13.75 monthly.

Pay Service 1
Pay Units: 561.
Programming (via satellite): Cinemax.
Fee: $25.00 installation; $10.00 monthly.

Pay Service 2
Pay Units: 421.
Programming (via satellite): Disney Channel.
Fee: $25.00 installation; $8.00 monthly.

Pay Service 3
Pay Units: 988.
Programming (via satellite): HBO.
Fee: $25.00 installation; $10.00 monthly.

Pay Service 4
Pay Units: 1,144.
Programming (via satellite): The Movie Channel.
Fee: $25.00 installation; $10.00 monthly.

Pay Service 5
Pay Units: 1,229.
Programming (via satellite): Showtime.
Fee: $25.00 installation; $10.00 monthly.

Pay-Per-View
Addressable homes: 850.
Movies; special events.

Local advertising: Yes. Rates: $5.00/Day.
Equipment: Jerrold headend; C-COR amplifiers; Trilogy cable; Scientific-Atlanta set top converters; Scientific-Atlanta & Microdyne satellite antenna; Scientific-Atlanta & M/A-Com satellite receivers.
Miles of plant: 411.7 (coaxial); 120.0 (fiber optic). Homes passed: 17,934.
Manager: Robert L. Herrald. Chief technician: Allen Comer. Marketing director: Bill Benner.
Ownership: Fanch Communications Inc. (MSO); Time Warner Cable (MSO). See Cable System Ownership.

CHESTER—TCI of West Virginia Inc., 16808 St. Clair Ave., East Liverpool, OH 43920-3095. Phone: 800-421-3145. Fax: 330-385-0322. County: Hancock. Also serves Hancock County (portions), Lawrenceville, Newell. ICA: WV0032.
TV Market Ranking: 10,90. Franchise award date: N.A. Franchise expiration date: N.A. Began: March 1, 1956.
Channel capacity: 41 (not 2-way capable). Channels available but not in use: N.A.

Basic Service
Subscribers: 2,303.
Programming (received off-air): WNPB-TV (P) Morgantown; KDKA-TV (C), WCWB (W), WPGH-TV (F), WPXI (N), WQED (P), WQEX (P), WTAE-TV (A) Pittsburgh; WTOV-TV (N) Steubenville-Wheeling; WTRF-TV (C) Wheeling-Steubenville; WFMJ-TV (N), WKBN-TV (C), WYTV (A,F) Youngstown.
Programming (via satellite): WGN-TV (W) Chicago; A & E; C-SPAN; CNN; Discovery Channel; Fox Family Channel; Headline News; Lifetime; MTV; Nashville Network; Nickelodeon; Odyssey; QVC; TBS Superstation; The Weather Channel.
Current originations: Automated time-weather.
Fee: $42.96 installation; $10.24 monthly; $20.00 additional installation.

Expanded Basic Service
Subscribers: 48.
Programming (via satellite): American Movie Classics; ESPN; Fox Sports Net Pittsburgh; Intro TV; Turner Network TV; USA Network.
Fee: $9.60 monthly.

Pay Service 1
Pay Units: 226.
Programming (via satellite): Cinemax.
Fee: $12.95 monthly.

Pay Service 2
Pay Units: 129.
Programming (via satellite): Disney Channel.

Fee: $12.95 monthly.
Pay Service 3
Pay Units: N.A.
Programming (via satellite): Starz!; The New Encore.
Fee: $1.75 monthly (Encore), $4.75 monthly (Starz).
Pay Service 4
Pay Units: 479.
Programming (via satellite): HBO.
Fee: $13.40 monthly.
Pay-Per-View
Addressable homes: 146.
Local advertising: No.
Equipment: Jerrold headend; Jerrold amplifiers; Jerrold addressable set top converters; AFC satellite antenna.
Miles of plant: 24.0 (coaxial); 5.0 (fiber optic). Homes passed: 3,009. Total homes in franchised area: 6,581.
Manager: Jim Underwood. Chief technician: Scott Boyd.
City fee: 3% of gross.
Ownership: AT&T Broadband & Internet Services (MSO). Purchased from Tele-Communications Inc., March 9, 1999.

CLARKSBURG—Century Huntington Co., Box 599, Dellslow, WV 26531. Phone: 304-292-6561. Fax: 304-624-4805. County: Harrison. ICA: WV0174.
TV Market Ranking: Below 100. Franchise award date: N.A. Franchise expiration date: N.A. Began: N.A.
Channel capacity: 24 (not 2-way capable). Channels available but not in use: N.A.
Basic Service
Subscribers: 101.
Programming (received off-air): WBOY-TV (N), WDTV (C,A), WVFX (F) Clarksburg-Weston; WNPB-TV (P) Morgantown.
Programming (via satellite): WGN-TV (W) Chicago; WABC-TV (A) New York; CNN; ESPN; MTV; Nashville Network; Nickelodeon; TBS Superstation; The Inspirational Network; USA Network.
Fee: $19.95 installation; $20.00 monthly; $0.29 converter.
Pay Service 1
Pay Units: N.A.
Programming (via satellite): HBO; Showtime.
Fee: $10.95 monthly (each).
Manager: Michael Ligouri. Chief technician: Ed Hinkle.
Ownership: Century Communications Corp. (MSO). See Cable System Ownership.

CLARKSBURG—Time Warner Cable, 507 Rosebud Plaza, Clarksburg, WV 26301. Phone: 304-623-6791. Fax: 304-624-4805. County: Harrison. Also serves Anmoore, Bridgeport, Harrison County (rural areas), Nutter Fort, Stonewood. ICA: WV0010.
TV Market Ranking: Below 100. Franchise award date: N.A. Franchise expiration date: N.A. Began: July 1, 1953.
Channel capacity: 33 (2-way capable; operating 2-way). Channels available but not in use: None.
Basic Service
Subscribers: 14,500.
Programming (received off-air): WBOY-TV (N), WDTV (C,A), WVFX (F) Clarksburg-Weston; WNPB-TV (P) Morgantown; KDKA-TV (C), WPXI (N), WTAE-TV (A) Pittsburgh.
Programming (via satellite): NASA TV; Pax Net; QVC; TV Guide Channel; TV Guide Sneak Prevue.
Current originations: Educational access; government access.
Fee: $38.47 installation; $31.07 monthly; $0.57 converter.
Expanded Basic Service
Subscribers: 9,500.
Programming (via satellite): A & E; American Movie Classics; Animal Planet; BET; C-SPAN; C-SPAN 2; CNBC; CNN; CNN/SI; Cartoon Network; Country Music TV; Court TV; Discovery Channel; E! Entertainment TV; ESPN; ESPN 2; EWTN; Fox Family Channel; Fox News Channel; Fox Sports Net Pittsburgh; Goodlife TV Network; Headline News; History Channel; Home & Garden Television; Home Shopping Network; Learning Channel; Lifetime; MSNBC; MTV; Nashville Network; Nickelodeon; Odyssey; TBS Superstation; TV Food Network; The Weather Channel; Travel Channel; Trinity Bcstg. Network; Turner Network TV; USA Network; VH1.
Fee: $22.20 monthly.
A la Carte 1
Subscribers: N.A.
Programming (via satellite): Bravo; ESPN Classic Sports; Flix; Golf Channel; Nick at Nite's TV Land; Sci-Fi Channel; Turner Classic Movies.
Fee: $6.95 monthly (package); $1.50 (each).
Pay Service 1
Pay Units: 716.
Programming (via satellite): Disney Channel.
Fee: $7.00 monthly.
Pay Service 2
Pay Units: 1,677.
Programming (via satellite): HBO (multiplexed).
Fee: $10.95 monthly.
Pay Service 3
Pay Units: 1,636.
Programming (via satellite): Showtime (multiplexed).
Fee: $10.95 monthly.
Pay Service 4
Pay Units: N.A.
Programming (via satellite): Cinemax (multiplexed).
Fee: $10.95 monthly.
Local advertising: Yes. Available in locally originated programming. Local sales manager: Ernest C. Gimmel.
Program Guide: TV Host.
Equipment: Jerrold headend; Jerrold amplifiers; Comm/Scope cable; Texscan character generator; Scientific-Atlanta set top converters; Craftsman & Eagle traps; Andrew satellite antenna; Hughes satellite receivers; Channel-Matic commercial insert.
Miles of plant: 233.0 (coaxial); None (fiber optic). Additional miles planned: 3.0 (coaxial). Homes passed: 16,751.
Manager: Ernest Gimmel. Chief technician: Steven Haney. Marketing director: Juanita Davis.
City fee: 3% of gross.
Ownership: Time Warner Cable (MSO).

CLARKSBURG—West Virginia Country Cable, Box 1696, 300 Chester Field Pkwy., Clarksburg, WV 26302-1696. Phones: 304-623-0150; 800-822-1206. County: Harrison. Also serves Crooked Run, Isaacs Creek, Katy Lick, Sardis. ICA: WV0175.
TV Market Ranking: Below 100. Franchise award date: N.A. Franchise expiration date: N.A. Began: January 1, 1983.
Channel capacity: 21. Channels available but not in use: 3.
Basic Service
Subscribers: 320.
Programming (received off-air): WBOY-TV (N), WDTV (C,A), WVFX (F) Clarksburg-Weston; WNPB-TV (P) Morgantown; WCWB (W), WTAE-TV (A) Pittsburgh; WTRF-TV (C) Wheeling-Steubenville.
Programming (via satellite): WGN-TV (W) Chicago; CNN; Discovery Channel; ESPN; Fox Family Channel; Nashville Network; TBS Superstation; Turner Network TV; USA Network.
Fee: $25.00 installation; $16.50 monthly.
Pay Service 1
Pay Units: N.A.
Programming (via satellite): Disney Channel; The Movie Channel.
Fee: $6.95 monthly (Disney), $11.00 monthly (TMC).
Miles of plant: 25.0 (coaxial).
Manager: Joe Nolan. Chief technician: Bill Martin.
Ownership: FinCom Corp. (MSO).

CLAY—Thompson Cablevision Co. Inc., Box 13309, Sissonville, WV 25360. Phone: 304-984-0025. County: Clay. ICA: WV0063.
TV Market Ranking: 36. Franchise award date: N.A. Franchise expiration date: N.A. Began: March 1, 1952.
Channel capacity: N.A. Channels available but not in use: N.A.
Basic Service
Subscribers: N.A.
Programming (received off-air): WCHS-TV (A), WOWK-TV (C), WSAZ-TV (N) Charleston-Huntington; WDTV (C,A) Clarksburg-Weston; WSWP-TV (P) Grandview; WOAY-TV (A) Oak Hill-Beckley; 5 FMs.
Fee: Free installation; $4.80 monthly.
Equipment: Jerrold headend; Jerrold amplifiers; Times Fiber cable.
Miles of plant: 34.1 (coaxial). Homes passed: 1,640.
Manager: Dale Thaxton.
City fee: None.
Ownership: Thompson Cablevision Co. Inc. (MSO).

COALTON—West Virginia Country Cable, Box 1696, 300 Chester Field Pkwy., Clarksburg, WV 26302-1696. Phones: 304-623-0150; 800-882-1206. County: Randolph. ICA: WV0176.
TV Market Ranking: Below 100. Franchise award date: N.A. Franchise expiration date: January 1, 2010. Began: January 1, 1990.
Channel capacity: 21. Channels available but not in use: 10.
Basic Service
Subscribers: 85.
Programming (received off-air): WBOY-TV (N), WDTV (C,A), WVFX (F) Clarksburg-Weston; WNPB-TV (P) Morgantown; WCWB (W), WTAE-TV (A) Pittsburgh; WTRF-TV (C) Wheeling-Steubenville.
Programming (via satellite): ESPN; Nashville Network; TBS Superstation; USA Network.
Fee: $25.00 installation; $13.25 monthly.
Miles of plant: 2.1 (coaxial).
Manager: Joe Nolan. Chief technician: Bill Martin.
Ownership: FinCom Corp. (MSO).

COLFAX—Century Huntington Co., Box 599, Dellslow, WV 26531. Phone: 304-292-6561. County: Marion. Also serves Marion County (portions), Pleasant Valley. ICA: WV0177.
TV Market Ranking: Below 100. Franchise award date: N.A. Franchise expiration date: N.A. Began: January 1, 1966.
Channel capacity: 36. Channels available but not in use: 8.
Basic Service
Subscribers: N.A.
Programming (received off-air): WBOY-TV (N), WDTV (C,A) Clarksburg-Weston; WNPB-TV (P) Morgantown; KDKA-TV (C), WPGH-TV (F), WPXI (N), WTAE-TV (A) Pittsburgh; WTOV-TV (N) Steubenville-Wheeling; WTRF-TV (C) Wheeling-Steubenville; allband FM.
Programming (via satellite): WGN-TV (W) Chicago; CNN; Country Music TV; ESPN; Home Shopping Network; Nashville Network; TBS Superstation; The Weather Channel; Turner Network TV.
Fee: $20.00 installation; $10.00 monthly.
Expanded Basic Service
Subscribers: N.A.
Programming (via satellite): MTV; USA Network.
Fee: $2.00 monthly.
Pay Service 1
Pay Units: N.A.
Programming (via satellite): Disney Channel; HBO; Playboy TV; Showtime.
Fee: $7.95 monthly (Playboy), $9.95 monthly (Disney, HBO or Showtime).
Equipment: Jerrold headend; Jerrold amplifiers; Jerrold cable.
Miles of plant & homes passed included with Whitehall, WV.
Manager: Michael Ligouri. Chief technician: Ed Hinkle.
City fee: None.
Ownership: Century Communications Corp. (MSO). See Cable System Ownership.

COLLIERS—Jefferson County Cable Inc., 116 S. 4th St., Toronto, OH 43964. Phone: 740-537-2214. Fax: 740-537-2802. County: Brooke. ICA: WV0146.
TV Market Ranking: 10,90. Franchise award date: N.A. Franchise expiration date: N.A. Began: February 1, 1972.
Channel capacity: 12. Channels available but not in use: N.A.
Basic Service
Subscribers: N.A.
Programming (received off-air): KDKA-TV (C), WCWB (W), WPGH-TV (F), WPXI (N), WQED (P), WQEX (P) Pittsburgh; WTOV-TV (N) Steubenville-Wheeling; WTRF-TV (C) Wheeling-Steubenville.
Planned programming (via translator): WNPB-TV (P) Morgantown.
Programming (via satellite): ESPN; TBS Superstation.
Fee: $25.00 installation; $9.00 monthly.
Pay Service 1
Pay Units: N.A.
Programming (via satellite): HBO.
Fee: $10.00 monthly.
Miles of plant: 4.0 (coaxial). Homes passed: 165.
Manager: David Bates.
City fee: None.
Ownership: Jefferson County Cable Inc. (MSO).

COTTAGEVILLE—Community Antenna Service, Box 282, Rte. 1, Washington, WV 26181. Phone: 304-863-8922. Fax: 304-863-6219. County: Jackson. Also serves Evans, Evergreen Hill, Millwood. ICA: WV0062.
TV Market Ranking: 36. Franchise award date: N.A. Franchise expiration date: N.A. Began: November 1, 1981.
Channel capacity: 36 (not 2-way capable). Channels available but not in use: 1.
Basic Service
Subscribers: 1,141.
Programming (received off-air): WCHS-TV (A), WOWK-TV (C), WPBY-TV (P), WSAZ-TV (N), WVAH-TV (F,U) Charleston-Huntington.
Programming (via satellite): WGN-TV (W) Chicago; CNN; CNNfn; ESPN; Fox Family Channel; Nashville Network; TBS Superstation; USA Network.
Fee: N.A.

Pay Service 1
Pay Units: N.A.
Programming (via satellite): Disney Channel; HBO.
Fee: N.A.
Miles of plant: 59.0 (coaxial); None (fiber optic). Homes passed: 1,685. Total homes in franchised area: 1,685.
Manager: Arthur R. Cooper.
Ownership: Arthur R. Cooper (MSO).

COWEN—Cablecomm, 80 N. Market St., Webster Springs, WV 26288. Phone: 800-352-1030. County: Webster. Also serves Upper Glade, Webster County (portions). ICA: WV0096.
TV Market Ranking: Below 100 (portions of Webster County); Outside TV Markets (Cowen, Upper Glade, portions of Webster County). Franchise award date: N.A. Franchise expiration date: N.A. Began: September 1, 1969.
Channel capacity: 28 (not 2-way capable). Channels available but not in use: 4.
Basic Service
Subscribers: 696.
Programming (received off-air): WCHS-TV (A) Charleston-Huntington; WBOY-TV (N), WDTV (C,A) Clarksburg-Weston; WSWP-TV (P) Grandview; allband FM.
Programming (via satellite): A & E; CNN; Discovery Channel; Fox Family Channel; FoxNet; Lifetime; MTV; Nashville Network; Nickelodeon; QVC; TBS Superstation; The Weather Channel.
Current originations: Automated time-weather.
Fee: $59.95 installation; $15.75 monthly.
Expanded Basic Service
Subscribers: 686.
Programming (via satellite): American Movie Classics; ESPN; Fox Sports Net Pittsburgh; Odyssey; Turner Network TV; USA Network.
Fee: $1.85 monthly.
Pay Service 1
Pay Units: 160.
Programming (via satellite): HBO.
Fee: $10.00 installation; $10.00 monthly.
Pay Service 2
Pay Units: 96.
Programming (via satellite): Showtime.
Fee: $10.00 monthly.
Pay Service 3
Pay Units: 359.
Programming (via satellite): The New Encore.
Fee: N.A.
Equipment: Blonder-Tongue headend; Jerrold amplifiers; Times Fiber cable; Jerrold set top converters; Microdyne satellite antenna; Microdyne satellite receivers.
Miles of plant: 32.8 (coaxial). Homes passed: 792. Total homes in franchised area: 851.
Manager: Sue Talbott.
City fee: 3% of gross.
Ownership: Fanch Communications Inc. (MSO); Time Warner Cable (MSO). Purchased from Tele-Communications Inc., February 24, 1999. See Cable System Ownership.

CRAIGSVILLE—Nesbe Cable, Box 388, Brown St., Craigsville, WV 26205. Phone: 304-742-3332. Fax: 304-742-3939. County: Nicholas. Also serves Cottle. ICA: WV0071.
TV Market Ranking: Outside TV Markets. Franchise award date: N.A. Franchise expiration date: N.A. Began: November 1, 1973.
Channel capacity: N.A. Channels available but not in use: N.A.
Basic Service
Subscribers: 1,035.
Programming (received off-air): WCHS-TV (A), WOWK-TV (C), WPBY-TV (P), WSAZ-TV (N) Charleston-Huntington; WBOY-TV (N), WDTV (C,A) Clarksburg-Weston; WSWP-TV (P) Grandview; WOAY-TV (A) Oak Hill-Beckley; allband FM.
Planned programming (via satellite): TBS Superstation.
Current originations: Automated time-weather.
Fee: $10.00 installation; $6.00 monthly.
Miles of plant: 22.0 (coaxial). Homes passed: 1,250.
Manager: Terry Ray.
Ownership: Bahakel Communications Ltd. (MSO).

CRAWLEY CREEK ROAD—Bowen Cablevision, Box 130, Wilkinson, WV 25653-0130. Phone: 304-752-3023. County: Logan. ICA: WV0236.
TV Market Ranking: 36. Franchise award date: N.A. Franchise expiration date: N.A. Began: N.A.
Channel capacity: N.A. Channels available but not in use: N.A.
Basic Service
Subscribers: N.A.
Programming (received off-air): WCHS-TV (A), WOWK-TV (C), WPBY-TV (P), WSAZ-TV (N), WVAH-TV (F,U) Charleston-Huntington.
Programming (via satellite): WGN-TV (W) Chicago; A & E; C-SPAN; CNN; Cartoon Network; Comedy Central; Country Music TV; Discovery Channel; ESPN; Fox Family Channel; Headline News; Lifetime; MTV; Nashville Network; Nickelodeon; QVC; Sci-Fi Channel; TBS Superstation; The Weather Channel; Trinity Bcstg. Network; Turner Network TV; USA Network; VH1.
Fee: N.A.
Pay Service 1
Pay Units: N.A.
Programming (via satellite): HBO.
Fee: N.A.
Manager: Gary Bowen.
Ownership: Bowen Cablevision Inc. (MSO).

CROSSROADS—Crossroads TV Cable, 511 Broadway Ave., Bridgeport, WV 26330-1201. Phone: 304-842-2421. County: Monongalia. ICA: WV0235.
TV Market Ranking: 90. Franchise award date: N.A. Franchise expiration date: N.A. Began: July 1, 1984.
Channel capacity: 40 (not 2-way capable). Channels available but not in use: 25.
Basic Service
Subscribers: 60.
Programming (received off-air): WBOY-TV (N), WDTV (C,A), WVFX (F) Clarksburg-Weston; WPCB-TV (I) Greensburg; KDKA-TV (C), WCWB (W), WPGH-TV (F), WPXI (N), WQED (P), WTAE-TV (A) Pittsburgh; WTOV-TV (N) Steubenville-Wheeling; WTRF-TV (C) Wheeling-Steubenville.
Programming (via satellite): Nashville Network.
Fee: $25.00 installation; $15.00 monthly.
Miles of plant: 12.0 (coaxial); None (fiber optic). Homes passed: 143.
Manager: Bill Flesher.
Ownership: Crossroads TV Cable Partnership.

CURTIN—Cablecomm, 80 N. Market St., Webster Springs, WV 26288-0747. Phone: 800-352-1030. County: Webster. ICA: WV0164.
TV Market Ranking: Outside TV Markets. Franchise award date: N.A. Franchise expiration date: N.A. Began: January 1, 1953.
Channel capacity: 12. Channels available but not in use: N.A.
Basic Service
Subscribers: 40.
Programming (received off-air): WCHS-TV (A), WSAZ-TV (N), WVAH-TV (F,U) Charleston-Huntington; WBOY-TV (N), WDTV (C,A) Clarksburg-Weston; WSWP-TV (P) Grandview; WOAY-TV (A) Oak Hill-Beckley.
Fee: $59.95 installation; $6.00 monthly.
Miles of plant: 1.8 (coaxial). Homes passed: 43. Total homes in franchised area: 50.
Manager: Sue Talbott.
Ownership: Fanch Communications Inc. (MSO); Time Warner Cable (MSO). Purchased from Tele-Communications Inc., February 24, 1999. See Cable System Ownership.

CYRUS—FrontierVision, Suite P-200, 1777 S. Harrison St., Denver, CO 80210. Phone: 303-757-1588. Fax: 303-757-6105. County: Wayne. ICA: WV0220.
TV Market Ranking: Below 100. Franchise award date: N.A. Franchise expiration date: N.A. Began: N.A.
Channel capacity: N.A. Channels available but not in use: N.A.
Basic Service
Subscribers: 134.
Programming (received off-air): WTSF (I) Ashland; WCHS-TV (A), WOWK-TV (C), WPBY-TV (P), WSAZ-TV (N), WVAH-TV (F,U) Charleston-Huntington.
Programming (via satellite): Country Music TV; ESPN; Fox Family Channel; Nashville Network; TBS Superstation.
Fee: $13.95 monthly.
Pay Service 1
Pay Units: 34.
Programming (via satellite): HBO.
Fee: N.A.
Miles of plant: 13.0 (coaxial). Homes passed: 148.
Manager: Willie Critchfield. Chief technician: Bill Turner.
Ownership: FrontierVision Partners LP (MSO). See Cable System Ownership.

DAVIS—Cablecomm, 315 First St., Parsons, WV 26287. Phone: 800-352-1030. County: Tucker. Also serves Canaan Valley (portions), Talheim Village, Thomas, Tucker County. ICA: WV0178.
TV Market Ranking: Below 100 (portions of Tucker County); Outside TV Markets (Canaan Valley, Davis, Talheim Village, Thomas, portions of Tucker County). Franchise award date: N.A. Franchise expiration date: N.A. Began: October 1, 1954.
Channel capacity: 38. Channels available but not in use: N.A.
Basic Service
Subscribers: 1,918.
Programming (received off-air): WBOY-TV (N), WDTV (C,A) Clarksburg-Weston; WNPB-TV (P) Morgantown; WTAE-TV (A) Pittsburgh; WTOV-TV (N) Steubenville-Wheeling; allband FM.
Programming (via satellite): WGN-TV (W) Chicago; CNBC; CNN; Cartoon Network; Discovery Channel; Fox Family Channel; FoxNet; Lifetime; MTV; Nashville Network; Nickelodeon; QVC; TBS Superstation; The Weather Channel.
Current originations: Automated time-weather.
Fee: $59.95 installation; $17.84 monthly.
Expanded Basic Service
Subscribers: 632.
Programming (via satellite): American Movie Classics; ESPN; Fox Sports Net Pittsburgh; Odyssey; Turner Network TV; USA Network.
Fee: $1.85 monthly.
Pay Service 1
Pay Units: 109.
Programming (via satellite): Cinemax.
Fee: $13.15 monthly.
Pay Service 2
Pay Units: 89.
Programming (via satellite): Disney Channel.
Fee: N.A.
Pay Service 3
Pay Units: 165.
Programming (via satellite): HBO.
Fee: $13.15 monthly.
Pay Service 4
Pay Units: 273.
Programming (via satellite): The New Encore.
Fee: N.A.
Local advertising: Yes.
Equipment: Jerrold headend; Jerrold amplifiers; Times Fiber cable.
Miles of plant: 12.3 (coaxial).
Chief technician: Charles Ketterman.
City fee: $25.00 annually.
Ownership: Fanch Communications Inc. (MSO); Time Warner Cable (MSO). Purchased from Tele-Communications Inc., February 25, 1999. See Cable System Ownership.

DAVY—Hurley Cablevision, Box 404, Panther, WV 24872. Phone: 304-938-5264. County: McDowell. Also serves Asco, Twin Branch. ICA: WV0122.
TV Market Ranking: Below 100. Franchise award date: N.A. Franchise expiration date: N.A. Began: January 1, 1982.
Channel capacity: 12 (2-way capable; operating 2-way). Channels available but not in use: None.
Basic Service
Subscribers: 326.
Programming (received off-air): WVVA (N) Bluefield; WCYB-TV (N) Bristol-Kingsport; WCHS-TV (A), WOWK-TV (C), WSAZ-TV (N),Charleston-Huntington; WSWP-TV (P) Grandview; WOAY-TV (A) Oak Hill-Beckley.
Programming (via satellite): WGN-TV (W) Chicago; ESPN; Fox Family Channel; Nashville Network; TBS Superstation; USA Network.
Fee: $20.00 installation; $17.95 monthly.
Pay Service 1
Pay Units: N.A.
Programming (via satellite): HBO.
Fee: $8.50 monthly.
Equipment: Blonder-Tongue headend; Cascade & Magnavox amplifiers; Times Fiber cable.
Miles of plant: 6.0 (coaxial). Homes passed: 350.
Manager: Thurman Hurley.
Ownership: Hurley Cablevision (MSO).

DELBARTON—Cooney Cable Assoc., 228 Park Ave., Worcester, MA 01609. Phone: 508-754-5865. Fax: 508-752-7342. County: Mingo. ICA: WV0087.
TV Market Ranking: Below 100. Franchise award date: January 1, 1951. Franchise expiration date: January 1, 2006. Began: January 1, 1951.
Channel capacity: 40 (not 2-way capable). Channels available but not in use: 5.
Basic Service
Subscribers: 654.
Programming (received off-air): WCHS-TV (A), WOWK-TV (C), WPBY-TV (P), WSAZ-TV (N), WVAH-TV (F,U) Charleston-Huntington; WYMT-TV (C) Hazard; WKPI (P) Pikeville.
Programming (via satellite): WGN-TV (W) Chicago; CNN; Country Music TV; Discovery Channel; Disney Channel; ESPN; Fox Family Channel; Lifetime; Nashville Network; Nickelodeon; QVC; TBS Superstation; Trinity Bcstg. Network; Turner Network TV; USA Network; VH1.
Fee: $48.18 installation; $27.45 monthly.
Pay Service 1
Pay Units: 91.
Programming (via satellite): HBO.
Fee: $25.00 installation; $11.95 monthly.
Pay Service 2
Pay Units: 44.
Programming (via satellite): Showtime.
Fee: $25.00 installation; $10.95 monthly.
Pay Service 3
Pay Units: 19.
Programming (via satellite): Showtime; The Movie Channel.
Fee: $11.95 monthly (Showtime & TMC).
Miles of plant: 19.0 (coaxial); None (fiber optic). Homes passed: 938.
Manager: John Cooney. Chief technician: Ron Davis.
Ownership: Cooney Cable Assoc. Inc. (MSO).

DIANA—West Virginia Country Cable, Box 1696, 300 Chester Field Pkwy., Clarksburg, WV 26302-1696. Phones: 304-623-0150; 800-882-1206. County: Webster. Also serves Grassy Creek, Jumbo, Webster County (unincorporated areas). ICA: WV0127.
TV Market Ranking: Below 100 (Diana, Grassy Creek, Jumbo, portions of Webster County); Outside TV Markets (portions of Webster County). Franchise award date: N.A. Franchise expiration date: N.A. Began: June 1, 1981.
Channel capacity: 21. Channels available but not in use: 9.
Basic Service
Subscribers: 200.
Programming (received off-air): WCHS-TV (A), WOWK-TV (C), WVAH-TV (F,U) Charleston-Huntington; WBOY-TV (N), WDTV (C,A) Clarksburg-Weston; WSWP-TV (P) Grandview; WOAY-TV (A) Oak Hill-Beckley.
Programming (via satellite): ESPN; Fox Family Channel; Nashville Network; USA Network.
Fee: $25.00 installation; $14.95 monthly.
Pay Service 1
Pay Units: N.A.
Programming (via satellite): HBO.
Fee: $11.00 monthly.
Miles of plant: 15.0 (coaxial). Homes passed: 305.
Manager: Joe Nolan. Chief technician: Bill Martin.
Ownership: FinCom Corp. (MSO).

DINGESS—CableVision Communications, Box 2200, 68 5th St., Buckhannon, WV 26201. Phone: 304-472-4193. Fax: 304-472-0756. Counties: Logan & Mingo. Also serves Breeden, Mingo County (unincorporated areas), Mudfork. ICA: WV0079.
TV Market Ranking: Outside TV Markets. Franchise award date: September 18, 1985. Franchise expiration date: N.A. Began: N.A.
Channel capacity: 37 (not 2-way capable). Channels available but not in use: 1.
Basic Service
Subscribers: 716.
Programming (received off-air): WCHS-TV (A), WOWK-TV (C), WPBY-TV (P), WSAZ-TV (N), WVAH-TV (F,U) Charleston-Huntington; WKPI (P) Pikeville.
Programming (via satellite): WGN-TV (W) Chicago; Animal Planet; C-SPAN; Home Shopping Network; TBS Superstation; Trinity Bcstg. Network.
Fee: $61.25 installation; $14.40 monthly; $1.24 converter.
Expanded Basic Service
Subscribers: N.A.
Programming (via satellite): A & E; American Movie Classics; CNN; Discovery Channel; Disney Channel; E! Entertainment TV; ESPN; Fox Family Channel; Great American Country; Headline News; Lifetime; MTV; Nashville Network; Nickelodeon; Sci-Fi Channel; The Weather Channel; Turner Network TV; USA Network; VH1.
Fee: $15.86 monthly.
Pay Service 1
Pay Units: 118.
Programming (via satellite): Cinemax.
Fee: $7.99 monthly.
Pay Service 2
Pay Units: 21.
Programming (via satellite): The New Encore.
Fee: $3.99 monthly.
Pay Service 3
Pay Units: 73.
Programming (via satellite): HBO.
Fee: $11.99 monthly.
Pay Service 4
Pay Units: 23.
Programming (via satellite): Showtime.
Fee: $11.99 monthly.
Pay Service 5
Pay Units: 20.
Programming (via satellite): The Movie Channel.
Fee: $11.99 monthly.
Equipment: Blonder-Tongue & Olson headend; C-COR amplifiers; Pico traps; Scientific-Atlanta satellite antenna; Scientific-Atlanta satellite receivers.
Miles of plant: 43.0 (coaxial); None (fiber optic). Homes passed: 1,070.
Manager: Willie Critchfield. Plant manager: Garry Lucasr. Marketing director: Kenny Phillips.
Ownership: Rifkin & Associates Inc. (MSO). See Cable System Ownership.

DIXIE—Capital Cablecomm, Box 368, Cabin Creek, WV 25035. Phone: 304-779-2854. Fax: 304-595-5248. Counties: Clay, Fayette, Kanawha & Nicholas. Also serves Belva, Bentree, Blue Creek. ICA: WV0111.
TV Market Ranking: 36. Franchise award date: N.A. Franchise expiration date: May 12, 2008. Began: April 1, 1970.
Channel capacity: 15 (not 2-way capable). Channels available but not in use: 1.
Basic Service
Subscribers: 372.
Programming (received off-air): WVVA (N) Bluefield; WCHS-TV (A), WOWK-TV (C), WSAZ-TV (N), WVAH-TV (F,U) Charleston-Huntington; WSWP-TV (P) Grandview; WOAY-TV (A) Oak Hill-Beckley.
Current originations: Public access; educational access; government access.
Fee: $35.25 installation (aerial), $49.00 (underground); $10.80 monthly; $1.84 converter.
Expanded Basic Service
Subscribers: 365.
Programming (via satellite): ESPN; Fox Family Channel; Nashville Network; TBS Superstation.
Fee: $6.70 monthly.
Pay Service 1
Pay Units: 24.
Programming (via satellite): Cinemax.
Fee: $25.00 installation; $10.00 monthly.
Pay Service 2
Pay Units: 16.
Programming (via satellite): Disney Channel.
Fee: $25.00 installation; $8.00 monthly.
Pay Service 3
Pay Units: 30.
Programming (via satellite): HBO.
Fee: $25.00 installation; $10.00 monthly.
Equipment: Blonder-Tongue headend; Jerrold & Magnavox amplifiers; Comm/Scope cable; Scientific-Atlanta set top converters; Harris satellite antenna; Microdyne & M/A-Com satellite receivers.
Miles of plant: 11.8 (coaxial); None (fiber optic). Homes passed: 606.
Manager: Robert L. Herrald. Chief technician: Allen Comer. Marketing director: Bill Benner.
Ownership: Fanch Communications Inc. (MSO); Time Warner Cable (MSO). See Cable System Ownership.

DORCAS—C T & R Cable, 29 Water St., Petersburg, WV 26847. Phone: 800-874-2930. County: Grant. Also serves Maysville. ICA: WV0224.
TV Market Ranking: Outside TV Markets. Franchise award date: N.A. Franchise expiration date: N.A. Began: May 15, 1991.
Channel capacity: 23 (not 2-way capable). Channels available but not in use: 11.
Basic Service
Subscribers: 390.
Programming (via translator): WHSV-TV (A,F) Harrisonburg; WJAC-TV (N) Johnstown-Altoona; WNPB-TV (P) Morgantown; WTTG (F), WUSA (C) Washington.
Programming (via satellite): WGN-TV (W) Chicago; CNN; Discovery Channel; ESPN; Fox Family Channel; Nashville Network; TBS Superstation; Turner Network TV.
Fee: $99.00 installation; $17.00 monthly.
Pay Service 1
Pay Units: 60.
Programming (via satellite): Showtime.
Fee: $9.00 monthly.
Miles of plant: 35.0 (coaxial).
Manager: Terry Hinkle. Chief technician: Matt Alt.
Ownership: C T & R Cable LLC (MSO).

DOROTHY—Helicon Cablevision, Box A, 150 N. Pinch Rd., Pinch, WV 25156. Phones: 304-965-7026; 800-642-9163. Fax: 304-965-7768. County: Raleigh. ICA: WV0246.
TV Market Ranking: 36. Franchise award date: N.A. Franchise expiration date: N.A. Began: N.A.
Channel capacity: N.A. Channels available but not in use: N.A.
Basic Service
Subscribers: 260.
Programming (received off-air): WCHS-TV (A), WOWK-TV (C), WSAZ-TV (N), WVAH-TV (F,U) Charleston-Huntington; WSWP-TV (P) Grandview; WOAY-TV (A) Oak Hill-Beckley.
Programming (via satellite): A & E; C-SPAN; CNN; Country Music TV; Discovery Channel; ESPN; Fox Family Channel; Headline News; Lifetime; Nashville Network; Nickelodeon; QVC; Turner Network TV; USA Network.
Fee: $19.61 monthly; $1.50 converter.
A la Carte 1
Subscribers: N.A.
Programming (via satellite): WGN-TV (W) Chicago; American Movie Classics; TBS Superstation.
Fee: $4.20 monthly (package); $2.00 monthly (each).
Pay Service 1
Pay Units: N.A.
Programming (via satellite): HBO; The Movie Channel.
Fee: $9.50 monthly (each).
Manager: Jack Wade.
Ownership: Helicon Corp. (MSO). See Cable System Ownership.

DUNLOW—Cablevision Communications, Box 2200, 68 5th St., Buckhannon, WV 26201. Phone: 304-472-4193. Fax: 304-472-0756. County: Wayne. Also serves Missouri Branch, Wayne County. ICA: WV0179.
TV Market Ranking: 36 (Dunlow, Missouri Branch, portions of Wayne County); Outside TV Markets (portions of Wayne County). Franchise award date: N.A. Franchise expiration date: N.A. Began: N.A.
Channel capacity: 37. Channels available but not in use: 22.
Basic Service
Subscribers: 137.
Programming (received off-air): WTSF (I) Ashland; WCHS-TV (A), WOWK-TV (C), WPBY-TV (P), WSAZ-TV (N), WVAH-TV (F,U) Charleston-Huntington.
Programming (via satellite): CNN; Discovery Channel; ESPN; Fox Family Channel; Nashville Network; TBS Superstation; Turner Network TV; USA Network.
Fee: $61.25 installation; $16.80 monthly; $1.24 converter.
Pay Service 1
Pay Units: 24.
Programming (via satellite): HBO.
Fee: $11.99 monthly.
Equipment: Blonder-Tongue & Philips headend; Philips amplifiers; Eagle traps; Scientific-Atlanta satellite antenna; Scientific-Atlanta satellite receivers.
Miles of plant: 13.0 (coaxial). Homes passed: 186.
Manager: Willie Critchfield. Plant manager: Garry Lucas. Marketing director: Kenny Phillips.
Ownership: Rifkin & Associates Inc. (MSO). See Cable System Ownership.

DURBIN—Milestone Communications of New York LP, Suite 200, 1850 Woodmoor Dr., Monument, CO 80132. Phone: 719-488-2916. Fax: 719-488-3629. County: Pocahontas. Also serves Arborvale, Bartow, Frank, Pinegrove. ICA: WV0180.
TV Market Ranking: Outside TV Markets. Franchise award date: N.A. Franchise expiration date: N.A. Began: N.A.
Channel capacity: 40 (not 2-way capable). Channels available but not in use: 13.
Basic Service
Subscribers: 234.
Programming (received off-air): WVVA (N) Bluefield; WBOY-TV (N), WDTV (C,A) Clarksburg-Weston; WKRN-TV (A) Nashville; WDBJ (C), WSLS-TV (N) Roanoke-Lynchburg.
Programming (via satellite): CNN; Country Music TV; Discovery Channel; Disney Channel; ESPN; ESPN 2; Fox Family Channel; FoxNet; Headline News; Nashville Network; Nickelodeon; Outdoor Channel; QVC; TBS Superstation; The Weather Channel; Trinity

Bcstg. Network; Turner Network TV; USA Network.
Current originations: Local news.
Fee: $50.00 installation (aerial), $60.00 (underground); $23.75 monthly; $10.00 additional installation.

Pay Service 1
Pay Units: 18.
Programming (via satellite): HBO.
Fee: $10.00 installation; $12.95 monthly.

Equipment: Standard Components & Scientific-Atlanta headend; Jerrold & Blonder-Tongue amplifiers.
Miles of plant: 21.0 (coaxial). Homes passed: 400.
Director of engineering: Randy Mock. Marketing director: Mark Drake.
Ownership: Milestone Communications LP (MSO).

EASTON—Century Huntington Co., Box 599, Dellslow, WV 26531. Phone: 304-292-6561. County: Monongalia. ICA: WV0181.
TV Market Ranking: Below 100. Franchise award date: N.A. Franchise expiration date: N.A. Began: N.A.
Channel capacity: N.A. Channels available but not in use: N.A.

Basic Service
Subscribers: N.A.
Programming (received off-air): WBOY-TV (N), WDTV (C,A), WVFX (F) Clarksburg-Weston; WNPB-TV (P) Morgantown; KDKA-TV (C), WCWB (W), WPGH-TV (F), WPXI (N), WQED (P), WTAE-TV (A) Pittsburgh.
Programming (via satellite): CNN; ESPN; Home Shopping Network; MTV; Nashville Network; Nickelodeon; TBS Superstation; The Weather Channel; VH1.
Fee: $19.95 installation; $11.00 monthly.

Expanded Basic Service
Subscribers: N.A.
Programming (via satellite): USA Network.
Fee: $1.00 monthly.

Pay Service 1
Pay Units: N.A.
Programming (via satellite): Disney Channel; HBO; Playboy TV; Showtime; The Movie Channel.
Fee: $7.95 monthly (Playboy), $9.95 monthly (Disney), $10.95 monthly (HBO, Showtime or TMC).

Manager: Michael Ligouri. Chief technician: Ed Hinkle.
Ownership: Century Communications Corp. (MSO). See Cable System Ownership.

ELIZABETH—Helicon Cablevision, Box A, 150 N. Pinch Rd., Pinch, WV 25156. Phones: 304-965-7026; 800-642-9163. Fax: 304-965-7768. County: Wirt. ICA: WV0115.
TV Market Ranking: Below 100. Franchise award date: N.A. Franchise expiration date: N.A. Began: June 15, 1968.
Channel capacity: 40 (not 2-way capable). Channels available but not in use: 15.

Basic Service
Subscribers: 363.
Programming (received off-air): WCHS-TV (A), WOWK-TV (C), WPBY-TV (P), WSAZ-TV (N), WVAH-TV (F,U) Charleston-Huntington; WBOY-TV (N), WDTV (C,A) Clarksburg-Weston; WTAP-TV (N) Parkersburg-Marietta; 1 FM.
Programming (via satellite): C-SPAN; QVC; TBS Superstation; The Weather Channel.
Current originations: Local news.
Fee: $55.00 installation; $19.16 monthly.

Expanded Basic Service
Subscribers: N.A.
Programming (via satellite): A & E; American Movie Classics; CNN; Country Music TV; Discovery Channel; ESPN; Fox Family Channel; Headline News; Lifetime; Nashville Network; Nickelodeon; Sci-Fi Channel; Turner Network TV; USA Network; VH1.
Fee: N.A.

Pay Service 1
Pay Units: 38.
Programming (via satellite): HBO.
Fee: $20.00 installation; $8.50 monthly.

Pay Service 2
Pay Units: 13.
Programming (via satellite): The Movie Channel.
Fee: $20.00 installation; $8.50 monthly.

Local advertising: No.
Equipment: Jerrold headend; Jerrold amplifiers; Comm/Scope cable; Pico traps; Microdyne satellite antenna; DX Engineering satellite receivers.
Miles of plant: 8.0 (coaxial). Homes passed: 627. Total homes in franchised area: 627.
Manager: Jack Wade. Chief technician: Ken Gabehardt. Marketing & program director: David Baum.
City fee: 2% of basic.
Ownership: Helicon Corp. (MSO). See Cable System Ownership.

ELKVIEW—Helicon Cablevision, Box A, 150 N. Pinch Rd., Pinch, WV 25156. Phones: 304-965-7026; 800-642-9163. Fax: 304-965-7768. County: Kanawha. Also serves Big Chimney, Blue Creek, Clendenin, Crede, Elk Hills, Falling Rock, Little Sandy, Milliken, Pinch, Youngs Bottom. ICA: WV0026.
TV Market Ranking: 36. Franchise award date: N.A. Franchise expiration date: N.A. Began: September 1, 1968.
Channel capacity: 65. Channels available but not in use: 13.

Basic Service
Subscribers: 4,135.
Programming (received off-air): WCHS-TV (A), WOWK-TV (C), WPBY-TV (P), WSAZ-TV (N), WVAH-TV (F,U) Charleston-Huntington; WSWP-TV (P) Grandview.
Programming (via satellite): WGN-TV (W) Chicago; A & E; American Movie Classics; C-SPAN; CNBC; CNN; Cartoon Network; Country Music TV; Discovery Channel; ESPN; Fox Family Channel; Headline News; Home Shopping Network; Lifetime; MTV; Nashville Network; Nickelodeon; QVC; Sci-Fi Channel; TBS Superstation; The Weather Channel; Trinity Bcstg. Network; Turner Network TV; USA Network; VH1.
Fee: $10.00 installation; $19.69 monthly; $15.00 additional installation.

Pay Service 1
Pay Units: 533.
Programming (via satellite): HBO.
Fee: $10.00 installation; $10.95 monthly.

Pay Service 2
Pay Units: 181.
Programming (via satellite): The Movie Channel.
Fee: $9.00 monthly.

Pay Service 3
Pay Units: 96.
Programming (via satellite): Disney Channel.
Fee: $9.00 monthly.

Pay Service 4
Pay Units: 133.
Programming (via satellite): Cinemax.
Fee: $9.00 monthly.

Pay Service 5
Pay Units: 133.
Programming (via satellite): Showtime.
Fee: $9.00 monthly.

Pay-Per-View
Addressable homes: 706.
Spice.

Equipment: Jerrold headend; Jerrold amplifiers; Comm/Scope cable; Jerrold set top converters; Jerrold addressable set top converters; Scientific-Atlanta satellite antenna.
Miles of plant: 108.5 (coaxial); 10.0 (fiber optic). Homes passed: 5,158.
Manager: Jack Wade. Chief technician: Ken Gabehardt. Marketing & program director: David Baum.
City fee: 3% of basic.
Ownership: Helicon Corp. (MSO). See Cable System Ownership.

ELLAMORE—Paxton Cable, Suite 280, 700 Ackerman Rd., Columbus, OH 43202. Phone: 614-263-6100. Fax: 614-263-7299. County: Randolph. Also serves Randolph County (unincorporated areas). ICA: WV0125.
TV Market Ranking: Below 100 (Ellamore, portions of Randolph County); Outside TV Markets (portions of Randolph County). Franchise award date: N.A. Franchise expiration date: N.A. Began: N.A.
Channel capacity: 12. Channels available but not in use: None.

Basic Service
Subscribers: 209.
Programming (received off-air): WCHS-TV (A) Charleston-Huntington; WBOY-TV (N), WDTV (C,A) Clarksburg-Weston; WNPB-TV (P) Morgantown; WTRF-TV (C) Wheeling-Steubenville.
Programming (via satellite): Discovery Channel; ESPN; Fox Family Channel; TBS Superstation; USA Network.
Fee: $14.00 monthly.

Pay Service 1
Pay Units: N.A.
Programming (via satellite): HBO.
Fee: $12.00 monthly.

Miles of plant: 30.0 (coaxial). Homes passed: 310.
Manager: Chip James.
Ownership: Paxton Cable Television Inc. (MSO). Purchased from Clearview Cable TV Inc., September 3, 1998.

ELLENBORO—Helicon Cablevision, Box A, 150 N. Pinch Rd., Pinch, WV 25156. Phones: 304-965-7026; 800-642-9163. Fax: 304-965-7768. County: Ritchie. ICA: WV0247.
TV Market Ranking: Below 100. Franchise award date: N.A. Franchise expiration date: N.A. Began: N.A.
Channel capacity: N.A. Channels available but not in use: N.A.

Basic Service
Subscribers: 258.
Programming (received off-air): WCHS-TV (A), WOWK-TV (C), WVAH-TV (F,U) Charleston-Huntington; WBOY-TV (N), WDTV (C,A), WVFX (F) Clarksburg-Weston; WNPB-TV (P) Morgantown; WTAP-TV (N) Parkersburg-Marietta; WTRF-TV (C) Wheeling-Steubenville.
Programming (via satellite): A & E; C-SPAN; CNN; Country Music TV; Discovery Channel; ESPN; Fox Family Channel; Headline News; Lifetime; Nashville Network; QVC; Turner Network TV; USA Network.
Fee: $20.91 monthly; $1.50 converter.

A la Carte 1
Subscribers: N.A.
Programming (via satellite): WGN-TV (W) Chicago; American Movie Classics; TBS Superstation.
Fee: $4.20 monthly (package); $2.00 monthly (each).

Pay Service 1
Pay Units: N.A.
Programming (via satellite): HBO.
Fee: $9.50 monthly.

Manager: Jack Wade.
Ownership: Helicon Corp. (MSO). See Cable System Ownership.

FAIRMONT—Time Warner Cable, 507 Rosebud Plaza, Clarksburg, WV 26301. Phone: 304-366-2880. Fax: 304-363-3524. County: Marion. Also serves Barrackville, Marion County (portions). ICA: WV0014.
TV Market Ranking: Below 100. Franchise award date: N.A. Franchise expiration date: N.A. Began: May 16, 1953.
Channel capacity: 78 (2-way capable; operating 2-way). Channels available but not in use: 2.

Basic Service
Subscribers: 10,500.
Programming (received off-air): WBOY-TV (N), WDTV (C,A), WVFX (F) Clarksburg-Weston; WNPB-TV (P) Morgantown; KDKA-TV (C), WPXI (N), WTAE-TV (A) Pittsburgh; allband FM.
Programming (via satellite): MTV; NASA TV; QVC; TBS Superstation; TV Guide Sneak Prevue.
Fee: $38.47 installation; $8.87 monthly; $3.33 converter.

Expanded Basic Service
Subscribers: N.A.
Programming (via satellite): A & E; American Movie Classics; Animal Planet; BET; Bravo; C-SPAN; C-SPAN 2; CNN; CNN/SI; Cartoon Network; Country Music TV; Court TV; Discovery Channel; E! Entertainment TV; ESPN; ESPN 2; ESPN Classic Sports; EWTN; Flix; Fox Family Channel; Fox News Channel; Fox Sports Net Pittsburgh; Golf Channel; Goodlife TV Network; Headline News; History Channel; Home & Garden Television; Home Shopping Network; Learning Channel; Lifetime; MSNBC; Nashville Network; Nick at Nite's TV Land; Nickelodeon; Odyssey; Sci-Fi Channel; TV Food Network; The Weather Channel; Turner Classic Movies; Turner Network TV; USA Network; VH1.
Fee: N.A.

Pay Service 1
Pay Units: 474.
Programming (via satellite): Disney Channel.
Fee: $7.00 monthly.

Pay Service 2
Pay Units: 1,535.
Programming (via satellite): HBO (multiplexed).
Fee: $10.95 monthly.

Pay Service 3
Pay Units: 1,484.
Programming (via satellite): Showtime (multiplexed).
Fee: $10.95 monthly.

Pay Service 4
Pay Units: N.A.
Programming (via satellite): Cinemax (multiplexed).
Fee: $10.95 monthly.

Pay-Per-View
Addressable homes: 10,000.

Local advertising: Yes. Available in locally originated programming. Local sales manager: Lenny Hannigan.
Program Guide: TV Host.
Equipment: Jerrold headend; Jerrold amplifiers; Vikoa cable; Hitachi cameras; Sony VTRs; 3M character generator; Scientific-Atlanta set top converters; Eagle traps; Scientific-Atlanta satellite antenna; Hughes satellite receivers; Falcone International commercial insert.
Miles of plant: 155.0 (coaxial); None (fiber optic). Homes passed: 11,071. Total homes in franchised area: 11,142.

Manager: Ernest Gimmel. Chief technician: Steven Haney. Marketing director: Juanita Davis.
City fee: 3% of gross.
Ownership: Time Warner Cable (MSO).

FANROCK—Wyoming Cablevision, Box 210, Rock View, WV 24880. Phone: 304-732-6114. Fax: 304-732-9370. County: Wyoming. Also serves Briar Creek, Indian Creek, Ramey. ICA: WV0182.
TV Market Ranking: Below 100. Franchise award date: N.A. Franchise expiration date: N.A. Began: January 1, 1989.
Channel capacity: 12. Channels available but not in use: 1.
Basic Service
Subscribers: 250.
Programming (received off-air): WVVA (N) Bluefield; WCHS-TV (A), WOWK-TV (C), WSAZ-TV (N) Charleston-Huntington; WSWP-TV (P) Grandview; WOAY-TV (A) Oak Hill-Beckley.
Programming (via satellite): Country Music TV; ESPN; Nashville Network; TBS Superstation.
Fee: $33.50 installation; $10.00 monthly.
Pay Service 1
Pay Units: N.A.
Programming (via satellite): HBO.
Fee: $10.00 monthly.
Manager: Frank Staley. Chief technician: Bill Keaton.
Ownership: Bahakel Communications Ltd. (MSO).

FARMINGTON—CableVision Communications, Box 2200, 68 5th St., Buckhannon, WV 26201. Phone: 304-472-4193. Fax: 304-472-0756. County: Marion. Also serves Idamay, Marion County (portions). ICA: WV0076.
TV Market Ranking: Below 100. Franchise award date: July 7, 1986. Franchise expiration date: July 7, 2006. Began: August 1, 1954.
Channel capacity: 36. Channels available but not in use: N.A.
Basic Service
Subscribers: 830.
Programming (received off-air): WBOY-TV (N), WDTV (C,A), WVFX (F) Clarksburg-Weston; WNPB-TV (P) Morgantown; KDKA-TV (C), WCWB (W), WPGH-TV (F), WPXI (N), WTAE-TV (A) Pittsburgh; WTOV-TV (N) Steubenville-Wheeling; WTRF-TV (C) Wheeling-Steubenville; allband FM.
Programming (via satellite): TBS Superstation.
Fee: $61.25 installation; $14.40 monthly; $1.24 converter.
Expanded Basic Service
Subscribers: 741.
Programming (via satellite): A & E; American Movie Classics; C-SPAN; CNN; Discovery Channel; Disney Channel; E! Entertainment TV; ESPN; Fox Family Channel; Great American Country; Home Shopping Network; Lifetime; MTV; Nashville Network; Nickelodeon; Sci-Fi Channel; The Weather Channel; Trinity Bcstg. Network; Turner Network TV; USA Network; VH1.
Fee: $16.33 monthly.
Pay Service 1
Pay Units: 388.
Programming (via satellite): Cinemax; HBO; Showtime; The Movie Channel.
Fee: $17.50 installation; $7.95 monthly (Cinemax), $11.95 (Showtime or TMC), $11.99 monthly (HBO).
Equipment: Jerrold headend; Jerrold amplifiers; Superior cable; Jerrold set top converters; AFC satellite antenna.
Miles of plant: 30.0 (coaxial). Additional miles planned: 5.0 (coaxial). Homes passed: 1,119.
Manager: Willie Critchfield. Marketing director: Kenny Phillips.
City fee: None.
Ownership: Rifkin & Associates Inc. (MSO). See Cable System Ownership.

FLAT ROCK—Coaxial Communications, 3770 E. Livingston Ave., Columbus, OH 43227. Phone: 614-236-1292. Fax: 614-238-7023. County: Mason. Also serves Mason County (unincorporated areas). ICA: WV0108.
TV Market Ranking: 36. Franchise award date: N.A. Franchise expiration date: N.A. Began: N.A.
Channel capacity: 17. Channels available but not in use: N.A.
Basic Service
Subscribers: 284.
Programming (received off-air): WCHS-TV (A), WOWK-TV (C), WPBY-TV (P), WSAZ-TV (N), WVAH-TV (F,U) Charleston-Huntington.
Programming (via satellite): WGN-TV (W) Chicago; CNN; Country Music TV; ESPN; Fox Family Channel; Nashville Network; TBS Superstation; USA Network.
Fee: $20.00 installation; $17.95 monthly.
Pay Service 1
Pay Units: 32.
Programming (via satellite): Disney Channel.
Fee: $10.00 monthly.
Pay Service 2
Pay Units: 75.
Programming (via satellite): HBO.
Fee: $10.00 monthly.
Local advertising: No.
Miles of plant: 18.0 (coaxial). Homes passed: 505.
Manager: Gregg Graff. Chief technician: Steve Crane.
Ownership: Coaxial Communications (MSO).

FLEMINGTON—CableVision Communications, Box 2200, 68 5th St., Buckhannon, WV 26201. Phone: 304-472-4193. Fax: 304-472-0756. Counties: Barbour, Harrison & Taylor. Also serves Brownton, Galloway, Lake Ridge, Rain Tree Acres, Rosemont, Simpson. ICA: WV0074.
TV Market Ranking: Below 100. Franchise award date: April 3, 1981. Franchise expiration date: N.A. Began: April 1, 1967.
Channel capacity: 29. Channels available but not in use: 1.
Basic Service
Subscribers: 835.
Programming (received off-air): WBOY-TV (N), WDTV (C,A), WVFX (F) Clarksburg-Weston; WNPB-TV (P) Morgantown; KDKA-TV (C), WPXI (N), WTAE-TV (A) Pittsburgh; allband FM.
Programming (via satellite): WGN-TV (W) Chicago; CNN; Disney Channel; ESPN; FoxNet; Nashville Network; TBS Superstation; Turner Network TV; USA Network.
Fee: $61.25 installation; $17.83 monthly; $1.24 converter.
A la Carte 1
Subscribers: N.A.
Programming (via satellite): American Movie Classics; Cartoon Network; Discovery Channel; Fox Family Channel; Home & Garden Television; Nickelodeon; QVC; The Weather Channel.
Fee: $6.00 monthly (package).
Pay Service 1
Pay Units: 146.
Programming (via satellite): HBO.
Fee: $17.50 installation; $11.99 monthly.
Pay Service 2
Pay Units: N.A.
Programming (via satellite): Cinemax; Showtime; The Movie Channel.
Fee: $7.95 monthly (Cinemax), $11.95 monthly (Showtime or TMC).
Equipment: Blonder-Tongue & Jerrold headend; Jerrold amplifiers.
Miles of plant: 30.0 (coaxial). Additional miles planned: 5.0 (coaxial). Homes passed: 1,150.
Manager: Willie Critchfield. Chief technician: Bill Turner. Marketing director: Kenny Phillips.
City fee: $150 annually.
Ownership: Rifkin & Associates Inc. (MSO). See Cable System Ownership.

FOLSOM—Jones TV Cable & Satellite Systems Inc., Box 8, Rte. 1, Folsom, WV 26348. Phone: 304-334-6504. Counties: Harrison & Wetzel. Also serves Wallace. ICA: WV0141.
TV Market Ranking: Below 100. Franchise award date: N.A. Franchise expiration date: N.A. Began: April 1, 1985.
Channel capacity: N.A. Channels available but not in use: N.A.
Basic Service
Subscribers: 200.
Programming (received off-air): WBOY-TV (N), WDTV (C,A), WVFX (F) Clarksburg-Weston; KDKA-TV (C), WTAE-TV (A) Pittsburgh; WTOV-TV (N) Steubenville-Wheeling; WTRF-TV (C) Wheeling-Steubenville.
Programming (via satellite): Headline News.
Fee: N.A.
Miles of plant: 8.7 (coaxial). Homes passed: 215.
Manager: Eugene Jones.
Ownership: Eugene Jones.

FORK RIDGE—TCI of West Virginia Inc., 215 1/2 N. Lafayette Ave., Moundsville, WV 26041. Phone: 800-352-1030. County: Marshall. Also serves Big Grave Creek, Lindsey Lane, Rodriquez Lane. ICA: WV0078.
TV Market Ranking: 90. Franchise award date: N.A. Franchise expiration date: N.A. Began: January 1, 1965.
Channel capacity: 20. Channels available but not in use: None.
Basic Service
Subscribers: N.A.
Programming (received off-air): WNPB-TV (P) Morgantown; KDKA-TV (C), WCWB (W), WPGH-TV (F), WPXI (N), WQED (P), WTAE-TV (A) Pittsburgh; WTOV-TV (N) Steubenville-Wheeling; WTRF-TV (C) Wheeling-Steubenville; allband FM.
Programming (via satellite): TBS Superstation.
Fee: Free installation; $8.00 monthly.
Pay Service 1
Pay Units: N.A.
Programming (via satellite): Cinemax; HBO.
Fee: $10.00 installation; $9.00 monthly (Cinemax), $10.00 monthly (HBO).
Equipment: Blonder-Tongue, Jerrold & Scientific-Atlanta headend; Blonder-Tongue & Jerrold amplifiers; Times Fiber cable; Scientific-Atlanta satellite antenna; Automation Techniques & Scientific-Atlanta satellite receivers.
Miles of plant: 19.8 (coaxial). Homes passed: 1,100. Total homes in franchised area: 1,300.
Manager: Dennis Snow. Chief technician: Dana Terry.
City fee: None.
Ownership: AT&T Broadband & Internet Services (MSO). Purchased from Tele-Communications Inc., March 9, 1999.

FRANKFORD—Clearview Cable TV Inc., Box 247 AA, Rte. 4, Lewisburg, WV 24901. Phone: 304-645-1397. County: Greenbrier. ICA: WV0098.
TV Market Ranking: Below 100. Franchise award date: N.A. Franchise expiration date: N.A. Began: N.A.
Channel capacity: 12. Channels available but not in use: None.
Basic Service
Subscribers: 515.
Programming (received off-air): WVVA (N) Bluefield; WSWP-TV (P) Grandview; WOAY-TV (A) Oak Hill-Beckley; WDBJ (C), WSLS-TV (N) Roanoke-Lynchburg.
Programming (via satellite): Discovery Channel; ESPN; Fox Family Channel; Headline News; Nashville Network; TBS Superstation; USA Network.
Fee: $15.00 monthly.
Pay Service 1
Pay Units: N.A.
Programming (via satellite): HBO.
Fee: $12.00 monthly.
Miles of plant: 45.0 (coaxial). Homes passed: 700.
Manager: Chip James.
Ownership: Clearview Cable TV Inc. (MSO).

FRANKLIN—CableVision Communications, Box 2200, 68 5th St., Buckhannon, WV 26201. Phone: 304-472-4193. Fax: 304-472-0756. County: Pendleton. Also serves Pendleton County. ICA: WV0095.
TV Market Ranking: Below 100 (Franklin, portions of Pendleton County); Outside TV Markets (portions of Pendleton County). Franchise award date: January 6, 1957. Franchise expiration date: N.A. Began: October 1, 1957.
Channel capacity: 29. Channels available but not in use: 3.
Basic Service
Subscribers: 732.
Programming (received off-air): WDTV (C,A) Clarksburg-Weston; WHSV-TV (A,F) Harrisonburg; WNPB-TV (P) Morgantown; WDBJ (C), WSLS-TV (N) Roanoke-Lynchburg; allband FM.
Programming (via satellite): CNN; Discovery Channel; Disney Channel; ESPN; Fox Family Channel; FoxNet; Great American Country; Nashville Network; Nickelodeon; QVC; TBS Superstation; The Weather Channel; Turner Network TV; USA Network.
Fee: $61.25 installation; $16.48 monthly; $13.84 additional installation.
A la Carte 1
Subscribers: N.A.
Programming (via satellite): WGN-TV (W) Chicago; Cartoon Network; ESPN 2; FX; Turner Classic Movies.
Fee: $3.99 monthly (package).
Pay Service 1
Pay Units: 150.
Programming (via satellite): HBO.
Fee: $11.99 monthly.
Pay Service 2
Pay Units: N.A.
Programming (via satellite): Cinemax; Showtime; The Movie Channel.
Fee: $7.95 monthly (Cinemax), $11.95 monthly (Showtime or TMC).
Equipment: Blonder-Tongue & Microdyne headend; Jerrold amplifiers; ChannelMaster & Microdyne satellite antenna; Microdyne satellite receivers.
Miles of plant: 30.0 (coaxial). Additional miles planned: 5.0 (coaxial). Homes passed: 815.
Manager: Willie Critchfield. Marketing director: Kenny Phillips.
City fee: None.
Ownership: Rifkin & Associates Inc. (MSO). See Cable System Ownership.

FRIENDLY—FrontierVision, Suite P-200, 1777 S. Harrison St., Denver, CO 80210. Phone:

For a list of all cable communities included in this section, see the **Cable Community Index** located in the back of this volume.

303-757-1588. Fax: 303-757-6105. County: Tyler. Also serves Sistersville. ICA: WV0133.
TV Market Ranking: Below 100. Franchise award date: N.A. Franchise expiration date: N.A. Began: January 1, 1970.
Channel capacity: 24 (not 2-way capable). Channels available but not in use: 5.
Basic Service
Subscribers: 157.
Programming (received off-air): WBOY-TV (N), WDTV (C,A) Clarksburg-Weston; WNPB-TV (P) Morgantown; WTAP-TV (N) Parkersburg-Marietta; WTOV-TV (N) Steubenville-Wheeling; allband FM.
Programming (via microwave): WJLA-TV (A) Washington.
Programming (via satellite): WGN-TV (W) Chicago; Fox Family Channel; Home Shopping Network.
Fee: $29.95 installation; $11.32 monthly; $0.73 converter.
Expanded Basic Service
Subscribers: 143.
Programming (via satellite): CNN; Discovery Channel; ESPN; Nashville Network; TBS Superstation.
Fee: $5.01 monthly.
Pay Service 1
Pay Units: 24.
Programming (via satellite): HBO.
Fee: $29.95 installation; $11.99 monthly.
Local advertising: Planned.
Equipment: Jerrold headend; Jerrold amplifiers; Jerrold cable; Scientific-Atlanta satellite receivers.
Miles of plant: 6.0 (coaxial). Homes passed: 255.
Manager: Steve Trippe. Chief technician: Bill Ricker.
City fee: None.
Ownership: FrontierVision Partners LP (MSO). See Cable System Ownership.

GANDEEVILLE—Econoco Inc., Box 147, Rte. 61, Kincaid, WV 25119. Phone: 304-469-2817. County: Roane. ICA: WV0183.
TV Market Ranking: 36. Franchise award date: N.A. Franchise expiration date: N.A. Began: October 1, 1987.
Channel capacity: 36 (not 2-way capable). Channels available but not in use: 19.
Basic Service
Subscribers: 181.
Programming (received off-air): WCHS-TV (A), WOWK-TV (C), WSAZ-TV (N), WVAH-TV (F,U) Charleston-Huntington; WBOY-TV (N), WDTV (C,A) Clarksburg-Weston; WSWP-TV (P) Grandview; WOAY-TV (A) Oak Hill-Beckley; WTAP-TV (N) Parkersburg-Marietta.
Programming (via satellite): WGN-TV (W) Chicago; A & E; CNN; ESPN; Fox Family Channel; Nashville Network; TBS Superstation.
Fee: $25.00 installation; $20.72 monthly.
Pay Service 1
Pay Units: N.A.
Programming (via satellite): HBO.
Fee: $15.00 installation; $12.00 monthly.
Miles of plant: 15.0 (coaxial).
Manager: Sheila Bills. Chief technician: Eslie Bills.
Ownership: Econoco Inc. (MSO).

GASSAWAY—Paxton Cable, Suite 280, 700 Ackerman Rd., Columbus, OH 43202. Phones: 614-263-6100; 614-263-7299. County: Braxton. Also serves Braxton County. ICA: WV0103.
TV Market Ranking: Below 100 (portions of Braxton County, Gassaway); Outside TV Markets (portions of Braxton County). Franchise award date: N.A. Franchise expiration date: N.A. Began: October 1, 1986.
Channel capacity: N.A. Channels available but not in use: N.A.
Basic Service
Subscribers: 555.
Programming (received off-air): WCHS-TV (A), WOWK-TV (C), WSAZ-TV (N), WVAH-TV (F,U) Charleston-Huntington; WBOY-TV (N), WDTV (C,A) Clarksburg-Weston; WSWP-TV (P) Grandview; WOAY-TV (A) Oak Hill-Beckley.
Programming (via satellite): TBS Superstation.
Fee: $6.51 monthly.
Miles of plant: 8.1 (coaxial). Homes passed: 625.
Manager: John Smith.
Ownership: Paxton Cable Television Inc. (MSO). Purchased from Ken Carder, February 1, 1999.

GASSAWAY—Cablecomm, 6 Garton Plaza, Weston, WV 26452-2129. Phones: 304-269-1111; 800-352-1030. County: Braxton. Also serves Braxton County, Flatwoods, Sutton. ICA: WV0061.
TV Market Ranking: Below 100 (portions of Braxton County, Flatwoods, Gassaway, Sutton); Outside TV Markets (portions of Braxton County). Franchise award date: N.A. Franchise expiration date: N.A. Began: January 1, 1954.
Channel capacity: 35. Channels available but not in use: 5.
Basic Service
Subscribers: 1,099.
Programming (received off-air): WCHS-TV (A), WOWK-TV (C), WSAZ-TV (N), WVAH-TV (F,U) Charleston-Huntington; WBOY-TV (N), WDTV (C,A) Clarksburg-Weston; WSWP-TV (P) Grandview; WNPB-TV (P) Morgantown; WOAY-TV (A) Oak Hill-Beckley; allband FM.
Programming (via satellite): CNBC; CNN; Discovery Channel; Fox Family Channel; Lifetime; MTV; Nashville Network; Nickelodeon; Odyssey; QVC; TBS Superstation; The Weather Channel.
Current originations: Automated time-weather.
Fee: $59.95 installation; $9.86 monthly.
Expanded Basic Service
Subscribers: 1,093.
Programming (via satellite): American Movie Classics; C-SPAN; ESPN; Fox Sports Net Pittsburgh; Turner Network TV; USA Network.
Fee: $9.93 monthly.
Pay Service 1
Pay Units: 181.
Programming (via satellite): Cinemax.
Fee: $13.15 monthly.
Pay Service 2
Pay Units: 111.
Programming (via satellite): Disney Channel.
Fee: N.A.
Pay Service 3
Pay Units: 216.
Programming (via satellite): HBO.
Fee: $13.15 monthly.
Pay Service 4
Pay Units: 391.
Programming (via satellite): The New Encore.
Fee: N.A.
Pay-Per-View
Special events.
Equipment: Jerrold headend; Jerrold amplifiers; Comm/Scope cable; Telemation cameras; Oak set top converters; Scientific-Atlanta satellite antenna.
Miles of plant: 44.7 (coaxial). Homes passed: 1,682.
Manager: John Smith. Chief technician: Dave Cottrell.
City fee: $900 annually.
Ownership: Fanch Communications Inc. (MSO); Time Warner Cable (MSO). Purchased from Tele-Communications Inc., February 25, 1999. See Cable System Ownership.

GILBERT—CableVision Communications, Box 2200, 68 5th St., Buckhannon, WV 26201. Phone: 304-472-4193. Fax: 304-472-0756. County: Mingo. Also serves Justice, Mingo County (portions). ICA: WV0075.
TV Market Ranking: Below 100 (Gilbert, Justice, portions of Mingo County); Outside TV Markets (Mingo County). Franchise award date: February 2, 1977. Franchise expiration date: N.A. Began: January 1, 1958.
Channel capacity: 43 (not 2-way capable). Channels available but not in use: 5.
Basic Service
Subscribers: 798.
Programming (received off-air): WCHS-TV (A), WOWK-TV (C), WPBY-TV (P), WSAZ-TV (N), WVAH-TV (F,U) Charleston-Huntington; allband FM.
Programming (via satellite): WGN-TV (W) Chicago; Animal Planet; Fox Family Channel; Home Shopping Network; TBS Superstation; Trinity Bcstg. Network.
Current originations: Local access.
Fee: $61.25 installation; $14.40 monthly; $1.24 converter.
Expanded Basic Service
Subscribers: N.A.
Programming (via satellite): American Movie Classics; C-SPAN; CNN; Discovery Channel; Disney Channel; E! Entertainment TV; ESPN; ESPN 2; Fox Sports Net; Great American Country; Headline News; Home Shopping Network; Learning Channel; Lifetime; MTV; Nashville Network; Nickelodeon; QVC; Sci-Fi Channel; The Weather Channel; Turner Network TV; USA Network; VH1.
Fee: $12.05 monthly.
Pay Service 1
Pay Units: 180.
Programming (via satellite): HBO.
Fee: $11.99 monthly.
Pay Service 2
Pay Units: N.A.
Programming (via satellite): Cinemax; Showtime; The Movie Channel.
Fee: $7.95 monthly (Cinemax), $11.99 monthly (Showtime or TMC).
Local advertising: Yes.
Equipment: Blonder-Tongue, Olson & Standard Communications headend; Ameco & Texscan amplifiers; Tocom set top converters; Eagle traps; Microdyne satellite antenna; Electrohome satellite receivers.
Miles of plant: 27.0 (coaxial); None (fiber optic). Homes passed: 1,122.
Manager: Willie Critchfield. Marketing director: Kenny Phillips.
City fee: None.
Ownership: Rifkin & Associates Inc. (MSO). See Cable System Ownership.

GLEN DALE—Marshall County Cable, Box 21300, Canton, OH 44701. Phone: 330-430-3517. Fax: 330-430-3511. Counties: Marshall & Ohio. Also serves Benwood, Cameron, Limestone, Moundsville, Sherard, Wheeling. ICA: WV0223.
TV Market Ranking: 90. Franchise award date: N.A. Franchise expiration date: N.A. Began: January 1, 1989.
Channel capacity: 36 (not 2-way capable). Channels available but not in use: 1.
Basic Service
Subscribers: 665.
Programming (received off-air): WPCB-TV (I) Greensburg; WNPB-TV (P) Morgantown; KDKA-TV (C), WCWB (W), WPGH-TV (F), WQED (P), WTAE-TV (A) Pittsburgh; WTOV-TV (N) Steubenville-Wheeling; WTRF-TV (C) Wheeling-Steubenville; WFMJ-TV (N) Youngstown.
Programming (via satellite): WGN-TV (W) Chicago; A & E; CNN; Country Music TV; Discovery Channel; ESPN; ESPN 2; Fox Family Channel; Fox Sports Net Pittsburgh; Headline News; Home Shopping Network; Learning Channel; Lifetime; MTV; Nashville Network; Nickelodeon; Sci-Fi Channel; TBS Superstation; The Weather Channel; Turner Network TV; USA Network; VH1.
Fee: $35.00 installation; $22.45 monthly.
Pay Service 1
Pay Units: 50.
Programming (via satellite): Cinemax.
Fee: $4.95 monthly.
Pay Service 2
Pay Units: 50.
Programming (via satellite): Disney Channel.
Fee: $9.00 monthly.
Pay Service 3
Pay Units: 100.
Programming (via satellite): HBO.
Fee: $11.00 monthly.
Miles of plant: 48.0 (coaxial); None (fiber optic). Homes passed: 820.
Manager: Dan Morgan.
Ownership: FinCom Corp. (MSO).

GLENHAYES—Kentucky/West Virginia Cable Inc., Box 216, Louisa, KY 41230. Phone: 603-638-3432. Counties: Wayne, WV; Lawrence, KY. Also serves Clifford, KY; Webb, WV. ICA: WV0139.
TV Market Ranking: 36. Franchise award date: N.A. Franchise expiration date: N.A. Began: N.A.
Channel capacity: 22 (not 2-way capable). Channels available but not in use: N.A.
Basic Service
Subscribers: 101.
Programming (received off-air): WCHS-TV (A), WOWK-TV (C), WPBY-TV (P), WSAZ-TV (N), WVAH-TV (F,U) Charleston-Huntington.
Programming (via satellite): WGN-TV (W) Chicago; CNN; Country Music TV; Discovery Channel; ESPN; Fox Family Channel; Nashville Network; QVC; Sci-Fi Channel; TBS Superstation; Trinity Bcstg. Network; Turner Network TV; USA Network.
Fee: $35.00 installation; $20.00 monthly.
Pay Service 1
Pay Units: 22.

Programming (via satellite): HBO.
Fee: $9.95 monthly.
Miles of plant: 14.0 (coaxial); None (fiber optic). Homes passed: 225.
Manager: Richard D. Wardell.
Ownership: Kentucky/West Virginia Cable Inc. (MSO).

GLENVILLE—Helicon Cablevision, Box A, 150 N. Pinch Rd., Pinch, WV 25156. Phones: 304-965-7026; 800-642-9163. Fax: 304-965-7768. County: Gilmer. ICA: WV0088.
TV Market Ranking: Below 100. Franchise award date: N.A. Franchise expiration date: October 12, 2001. Began: November 2, 1961.
Channel capacity: 40 (not 2-way capable). Channels available but not in use: 9.
Basic Service
Subscribers: 595.
Programming (received off-air): WCHS-TV (A), WSAZ-TV (N), WVAH-TV (F,U) Charleston-Huntington; WBOY-TV (N), WDTV (C,A), WVFX (F) Clarksburg-Weston; WNPB-TV (P) Morgantown.
Programming (via satellite): C-SPAN; Fox Family Channel; QVC; TBS Superstation; The Weather Channel.
Fee: $55.00 installation; $19.69 monthly.
Expanded Basic Service
Subscribers: N.A.
Programming (via satellite): A & E; American Movie Classics; CNBC; CNN; Country Music TV; Discovery Channel; ESPN; Headline News; Lifetime; MTV; Nashville Network; Nickelodeon; Turner Network TV; USA Network; VH1; ValueVision.
Fee: N.A.
Pay Service 1
Pay Units: 9.
Programming (via satellite): Cinemax.
Fee: $8.50 monthly.
Pay Service 2
Pay Units: 9.
Programming (via satellite): Disney Channel.
Fee: $8.50 monthly.
Pay Service 3
Pay Units: 43.
Programming (via satellite): HBO.
Fee: $8.50 monthly.
Pay Service 4
Pay Units: 20.
Programming (via satellite): The Movie Channel.
Fee: $8.50 monthly.
Equipment: Jerrold headend; Ameco & Jerrold amplifiers; Comm/Scope cable; Jerrold set top converters.
Miles of plant: 10.5 (coaxial). Homes passed: 1,079. Total homes in franchised area: 1,079.
Manager: Jack Wade. Chief technician: Ken Gabehardt. Marketing & program director: David Baum.
City fee: 3% of basic.
Ownership: Helicon Corp. (MSO). See Cable System Ownership.

GOLDTOWN—Econoco Inc., Box 147, Rte. 61, Kincaid, WV 25119. Phone: 304-469-2817. County: Jackson. Also serves Kenna. ICA: WV0184.
TV Market Ranking: 36. Franchise award date: N.A. Franchise expiration date: N.A. Began: June 1, 1989.
Channel capacity: 36 (not 2-way capable). Channels available but not in use: 19.
Basic Service
Subscribers: 317.
Programming (received off-air): WCHS-TV (A), WOWK-TV (C), WPBY-TV (P), WSAZ-TV (N), WVAH-TV (F,U) Charleston-Huntington; WOAY-TV (A) Oak Hill-Beckley.
Programming (via satellite): WGN-TV (W) Chicago; A & E; CNN; Country Music TV; Discovery Channel; ESPN; Fox Family Channel; Nashville Network; TBS Superstation; USA Network.
Fee: $25.00 installation; $20.72 monthly.
Pay Service 1
Pay Units: N.A.
Programming (via satellite): HBO.
Fee: $15.00 installation; $12.00 monthly.
Miles of plant: 25.0 (coaxial).
Manager: Sheila Bills. Chief technician: Eslie Bills.
Ownership: Econoco Inc. (MSO).

GRAFTON—Century Huntington Co., Box 599, Dellslow, WV 26531. Phone: 304-292-6561. Fax: 304-624-4805. County: Taylor. Also serves Parkview, Pruntytown, Taylor County (portions). ICA: WV0028.
TV Market Ranking: Below 100. Franchise award date: N.A. Franchise expiration date: N.A. Began: July 1, 1957.
Channel capacity: 20. Channels available but not in use: 7.
Basic Service
Subscribers: N.A.
Programming (received off-air): WBOY-TV (N), WDTV (C,A) Clarksburg-Weston; WJAC-TV (N) Johnstown-Altoona; WNPB-TV (P) Morgantown; KDKA-TV (C), WPGH-TV (F), WPXI (N), WQED (P), WTAE-TV (A) Pittsburgh; WTOV-TV (N) Steubenville-Wheeling; WTRF-TV (C) Wheeling-Steubenville; allband FM.
Current originations: Automated time-weather.
Fee: $6.95 installation; $7.50 monthly.
Equipment: Jerrold headend; Jerrold amplifiers; Times Fiber cable.
Miles of plant: 52.1 (coaxial). Homes passed: 5,098.
Manager: Michael Ligouri. Chief technician: Ed Hinkle.
City fee: $1.00 per subscriber annually.
Ownership: Century Communications Corp. (MSO). See Cable System Ownership.

GRANT TOWN—Helicon Cablevision, Box A, 150 N. Pinch Rd., Pinch, WV 25156. Phones: 304-965-7026; 800-642-9163. Fax: 304-965-7768. County: Marion. Also serves Baxter, Fairview. ICA: WV0083.
TV Market Ranking: Below 100. Franchise award date: N.A. Franchise expiration date: N.A. Began: January 1, 1968.
Channel capacity: 21. Channels available but not in use: None.
Basic Service
Subscribers: 925.
Programming (received off-air): WBOY-TV (N), WDTV (C,A) Clarksburg-Weston; WPCB-TV (I) Greensburg; WJAC-TV (N) Johnstown-Altoona; WNPB-TV (P) Morgantown; KDKA-TV (C), WCWB (W), WPGH-TV (F), WPXI (N), WTAE-TV (A) Pittsburgh; WTOV-TV (N) Steubenville-Wheeling; WTRF-TV (C) Wheeling-Steubenville; allband FM.
Programming (via satellite): CNN; Discovery Channel; ESPN; Headline News; MTV; QVC; TBS Superstation.
Fee: $55.00 installation; $16.25 monthly.
Pay Service 1
Pay Units: N.A.
Programming (via satellite): Cinemax; HBO.
Fee: $20.00 installation; $8.50 monthly (each).
Equipment: Jerrold amplifiers; AFC satellite antenna.
Miles of plant: 35.0 (coaxial). Homes passed: 1,479.
Manager: Craig Tomchek. Chief technician: Bruce Wishart. Marketing director: David Baum.
Ownership: Helicon Corp. (MSO). See Cable System Ownership.

GRANTSVILLE—Helicon Cablevision, Box A, 150 N. Pinch Rd., Pinch, WV 25156. Phones: 304-965-7026; 800-642-9163. Fax: 304-965-7768. County: Calhoun. ICA: WV0099.
TV Market Ranking: Below 100. Franchise award date: N.A. Franchise expiration date: N.A. Began: January 1, 1971.
Channel capacity: 40. Channels available but not in use: 14.
Basic Service
Subscribers: 495.
Programming (received off-air): WCHS-TV (A), WOWK-TV (C), WSAZ-TV (N), WVAH-TV (F,U) Charleston-Huntington; WBOY-TV (N), WDTV (C,A) Clarksburg-Weston; WSWP-TV (P) Grandview; WTAP-TV (N) Parkersburg-Marietta.
Programming (via satellite): C-SPAN; QVC; TBS Superstation; The Weather Channel.
Fee: $35.00 installation; $19.16 monthly.
Expanded Basic Service
Subscribers: N.A.
Programming (via satellite): A & E; American Movie Classics; CNN; Country Music TV; Discovery Channel; ESPN; Fox Family Channel; Headline News; Lifetime; Nashville Network; Turner Network TV; USA Network.
Fee: N.A.
Pay Service 1
Pay Units: 77.
Programming (via satellite): HBO.
Fee: $30.00 installation; $8.50 monthly.
Pay Service 2
Pay Units: 34.
Programming (via satellite): The Movie Channel.
Fee: $30.00 installation; $8.50 monthly.
Equipment: Jerrold headend; Jerrold amplifiers; Comm/Scope cable; Pico traps; Microdyne satellite antenna; Automation Techniques satellite receivers.
Miles of plant: 26.0 (coaxial). Homes passed: 787.
Manager: Jack Wade. Chief technician: Ken Gabehardt. Marketing & program director: David Baum.
City fee: 2% of basic.
Ownership: Helicon Corp. (MSO). See Cable System Ownership.

GRAYSVILLE—FrontierVision, Suite P-200, 1777 S. Harrison St., Denver, CO 80210. Phone: 303-757-1588. Fax: 303-757-6105. County: Marshall. Also serves Marshall County (unincorporated areas). ICA: WV0185.
TV Market Ranking: 90. Franchise award date: N.A. Franchise expiration date: N.A. Began: January 1, 1987.
Channel capacity: 24. Channels available but not in use: 8.
Basic Service
Subscribers: 68.
Programming (received off-air): WOUC-TV (P) Cambridge; WNPB-TV (P) Morgantown; KDKA-TV (C), WCWB (W), WPGH-TV (F), WPXI (N), WTAE-TV (A) Pittsburgh; WTOV-TV (N) Steubenville-Wheeling; WTRF-TV (C) Wheeling-Steubenville.
Programming (via satellite): Discovery Channel; ESPN; Nashville Network; TBS Superstation.
Fee: $29.95 installation; $15.20 monthly; $0.73 converter.
Pay Service 1
Pay Units: 16.
Programming (via satellite): HBO.
Fee: $11.99 monthly.
Miles of plant: 5.0 (coaxial). Homes passed: 123.
Manager: Steve Trippe. Chief technician: Bill Ricker.
Ownership: FrontierVision Partners LP (MSO). See Cable System Ownership.

GREENACRES—CableVision Communications, Box 2200, 68 5th St., Buckhannon, WV 26201. Phone: 304-472-4193. Fax: 304-472-0756. County: Wetzel. ICA: WV0166.
TV Market Ranking: 90. Franchise award date: N.A. Franchise expiration date: N.A. Began: N.A.
Channel capacity: 12. Channels available but not in use: 6.
Basic Service
Subscribers: 23.
Programming (received off-air): WBOY-TV (N), WDTV (C,A) Clarksburg-Weston; KDKA-TV (C), WTAE-TV (A) Pittsburgh; WTOV-TV (N) Steubenville-Wheeling; WTRF-TV (C) Wheeling-Steubenville.
Fee: $61.25 installation; $9.08 monthly.
Miles of plant: 2.0 (coaxial). Homes passed: 37.
Manager: Willie Critchfield. Marketing director: Kenny Phillips.
Ownership: Rifkin & Associates Inc. (MSO). See Cable System Ownership.

HAMLIN—Armstrong Cable Services, 311 Main St., Hamlin, WV 25523. Phone: 304-824-5114. Fax: 304-824-7711. County: Lincoln. Also serves Pleasant View (Lincoln County), West Hamlin. ICA: WV0047.
TV Market Ranking: 36. Franchise award date: December 2, 1968. Franchise expiration date: N.A.
Channel capacity: 36 (not 2-way capable). Channels available but not in use: 4.
Basic Service
Subscribers: 1,802.
Programming (received off-air): WTSF (I) Ashland; WLPX-TV (X) Charleston; WCHS-TV (A), WOWK-TV (C), WPBY-TV (P), WSAZ-TV (N), WVAH-TV (F,U) Charleston-Huntington.
Programming (via satellite): WGN-TV (W) Chicago; A & E; American Movie Classics; C-SPAN; CNBC; CNN; Cartoon Network; Country Music TV; Discovery Channel; ESPN; ESPN 2; Fox Family Channel; Fox Sports Net Pittsburgh; Headline News; Home Shopping Network; Lifetime; Nashville Network; Nickelodeon; TBS Superstation; The Weather Channel; Turner Network TV; USA Network; VH1.
Fee: $35.00 installation (aerial), $52.50 (underground); $24.05 monthly; $2.00 converter; $35.00 additional installation.
Pay Service 1
Pay Units: 191.
Programming (via satellite): Cinemax.
Fee: $9.95 installation; $9.95 monthly.
Pay Service 2
Pay Units: 276.
Programming (via satellite): HBO.
Fee: $9.95 installation; $11.95 monthly.
Pay Service 3
Pay Units: 121.
Programming (via satellite): Disney Channel.
Fee: $9.95 installation; $7.95 monthly.
Equipment: Scientific-Atlanta headend; Scientific-Atlanta amplifiers; Scientific-Atlanta set top converters; AFC satellite antenna.
Miles of plant: 70.0 (coaxial); None (fiber optic). Homes passed: 2,140. Total homes in franchised area: 2,850.

Manager: Todd L. Barrett. Chief technician: Russ Mutter. Marketing director: Jud D. Stewart.
Ownership: Armstrong Group of Companies (MSO).

HAMPDEN—Colane Cable TV Inc., Box 610, Omar, WV 25638. Phone: 304-946-2871. County: Mingo. ICA: WV0232.
TV Market Ranking: Below 100. Franchise award date: N.A. Franchise expiration date: N.A. Began: January 1, 1977.
Channel capacity: 34 (not 2-way capable). Channels available but not in use: N.A.
Basic Service
Subscribers: 172.
Programming (received off-air): WVVA (N) Bluefield; WCHS-TV (A), WOWK-TV (C), WPBY-TV (P), WSAZ-TV (N), WVAH-TV (F,U) Charleston-Huntington.
Programming (via satellite): WGN-TV (W) Chicago; Country Music TV; Discovery Channel; ESPN; Fox Family Channel; Nashville Network; USA Network.
Fee: $30.00 installation; $18.70 monthly.
Expanded Basic Service
Subscribers: 72.
Programming (via satellite): CNN; TBS Superstation.
Fee: $21.20 monthly.
Pay Service 1
Pay Units: 21.
Programming (via satellite): Showtime.
Fee: $10.50 monthly.
Miles of plant: 3.0 (coaxial); None (fiber optic). Homes passed: 220.
Manager: Gary Bowen.
Ownership: William Stark (MSO). Purchased from H & R Cable TV Inc.

HANOVER—Cooney Cable Assoc., 228 Park Ave., Worcester, MA 01609. Phone: 508-754-5865. Fax: 508-752-7342. County: Wyoming. Also serves Wyoming County. ICA: WV0070.
TV Market Ranking: Below 100 (portions of Wyoming County); Outside TV Markets (Hanover, portions of Wyoming County). Franchise award date: October 8, 1991. Franchise expiration date: October 8, 2006. Began: July 1, 1982.
Channel capacity: 36 (not 2-way capable). Channels available but not in use: 1.
Basic Service
Subscribers: 838.
Programming (received off-air): WVVA (N) Bluefield; WCHS-TV (A), WOWK-TV (C), WPBY-TV (P), WSAZ-TV (N), WVAH-TV (F,U) Charleston-Huntington; WSWP-TV (P) Grandview; WOAY-TV (A) Oak Hill-Beckley.
Programming (via satellite): WGN-TV (W) Chicago; CNN; Country Music TV; Discovery Channel; Disney Channel; ESPN; Fox Family Channel; Headline News; Lifetime; Nashville Network; Nickelodeon; TBS Superstation; Turner Network TV; USA Network.
Fee: $48.18 installation; $27.45 monthly.
Pay Service 1
Pay Units: 128.
Programming (via satellite): HBO.
Fee: $25.00 installation; $11.95 monthly.
Pay Service 2
Pay Units: 86.
Programming (via satellite): Showtime.
Fee: $25.00 installation; $10.95 monthly.
Miles of plant: 51.0 (coaxial); None (fiber optic). Homes passed: 1,258.
Manager: John Cooney. Chief technician: Ron Davis.
Ownership: Cooney Cable Assoc. Inc. (MSO).

HARMAN—Harman Cable Corp., Box 98, Main St., Harman, WV 26270. Phone: 304-227-4143. County: Randolph. ICA: WV0234.
TV Market Ranking: Outside TV Markets. Franchise award date: March 26, 1991. Franchise expiration date: January 1, 2007. Began: December 1, 1986.
Channel capacity: 12 (not 2-way capable). Channels available but not in use: 6.
Basic Service
Subscribers: 96.
Programming (received off-air): WBOY-TV (N), WDTV (C,A) Clarksburg-Weston.
Programming (via satellite): WGN-TV (W) Chicago; CNBC; Country Music TV; Discovery Channel; Fox Family Channel; Nashville Network; Odyssey; Primetime 24; TBS Superstation.
Fee: $20.00 installation; $15.90 monthly.
Local advertising: No.
Miles of plant: 3.0 (coaxial); None (fiber optic).
Manager: Klare Cooper.
Franchise fee: $50.00.
Ownership: Harman Cable Corp.

HARRISVILLE—Helicon Cablevision, Box A, 150 N. Pinch Rd., Pinch, WV 25156. Phones: 304-965-7026; 800-642-9163. Fax: 304-965-7768. County: Ritchie. ICA: WV0102.
TV Market Ranking: Below 100. Franchise award date: N.A. Franchise expiration date: April 1, 2018. Began: January 1, 1968.
Channel capacity: 40 (not 2-way capable). Channels available but not in use: 13.
Basic Service
Subscribers: 625.
Programming (received off-air): WCHS-TV (A), WOWK-TV (C), WVAH-TV (F,U) Charleston-Huntington; WBOY-TV (N), WDTV (C,A), WVFX (F) Clarksburg-Weston; WNPB-TV (P) Morgantown; WTAP-TV (N) Parkersburg-Marietta; WTRF-TV (C) Wheeling-Steubenville.
Programming (via satellite): C-SPAN; QVC; TBS Superstation.
Fee: N.A.
Expanded Basic Service
Subscribers: N.A.
Programming (via satellite): A & E; American Movie Classics; CNN; Country Music TV; Discovery Channel; ESPN; Fox Family Channel; Headline News; Lifetime; Nashville Network; The Weather Channel; Turner Network TV; USA Network.
Fee: $35.00 installation; $19.16 monthly.
Pay Service 1
Pay Units: 79.
Programming (via satellite): HBO.
Fee: $20.00 installation; $8.50 monthly.
Pay Service 2
Pay Units: 42.
Programming (via satellite): The Movie Channel.
Fee: $20.00 installation; $8.50 monthly.
Equipment: Jerrold amplifiers; Comm/Scope cable; Pico traps; Microdyne satellite antenna; DX Engineering satellite receivers.
Miles of plant: 16.2 (coaxial). Homes passed: 964.
Manager: Jack Wade. Chief technician: Ken Gabehardt. Marketing & program director: David Baum.
City fee: 2% of basic.
Ownership: Helicon Corp. (MSO). See Cable System Ownership.

HERNDON—Wyoming Cable TV Inc., Box 210, Rock View, WV 24880. Phone: 304-732-6114. Fax: 304-732-9370. County: Wyoming. Also serves Covel, Garwood. ICA: WV0187.
TV Market Ranking: Below 100. Franchise award date: N.A. Franchise expiration date: N.A. Began: March 1, 1981.
Channel capacity: 36 (not 2-way capable). Channels available but not in use: 17.
Basic Service
Subscribers: 150.
Programming (received off-air): WVVA (N) Bluefield; WCHS-TV (A), WOWK-TV (C), WSAZ-TV (N) Charleston-Huntington; WSWP-TV (P) Grandview; WOAY-TV (A) Oak Hill-Beckley; 12 FMs.
Programming (via satellite): WGN-TV (W) Chicago; CNN; Country Music TV; Discovery Channel; ESPN; Fox Family Channel; MTV; Nashville Network; Nickelodeon; QVC; TBS Superstation; The Weather Channel; Turner Network TV; USA Network.
Fee: $50.00 installation; $13.00 monthly.
Pay Service 1
Pay Units: 30.
Programming (via satellite): HBO.
Fee: $15.00 installation; $10.50 monthly.
Equipment: Blonder-Tongue & Scientific-Atlanta headend; Scientific-Atlanta amplifiers; CCS Hatfield & Comm/Scope cable; Intercept & Pico traps; Scientific-Atlanta satellite antenna; Microdyne satellite receivers.
Miles of plant: 8.0 (coaxial). Homes passed: 165. Total homes in franchised area: 170.
Manager: Frank Staley. Chief technician: Bill Keaton.
Ownership: Bahakel Communications Ltd. (MSO).

HINTON—Helicon Cablevision, Box A, 150 N. Pinch Rd., Pinch, WV 25156. Phones: 304-965-6104; 800-642-9163. Fax: 304-965-7768. County: Summers. Also serves Jumping Branch, Nimitz. ICA: WV0059.
TV Market Ranking: Below 100. Franchise award date: N.A. Franchise expiration date: N.A. Began: October 1, 1953.
Channel capacity: 40. Channels available but not in use: N.A.
Basic Service
Subscribers: 1,736.
Programming (received off-air): WVVA (N) Bluefield; WCHS-TV (A), WOWK-TV (C) Charleston-Huntington; WSWP-TV (P) Grandview; WOAY-TV (A) Oak Hill-Beckley; WDBJ (C), WSLS-TV (N) Roanoke-Lynchburg; allband FM.
Programming (via satellite): WGN-TV (W) Chicago; A & E; C-SPAN; CNBC; CNN; Country Music TV; Discovery Channel; ESPN; Fox Family Channel; Headline News; Home Shopping Network; Learning Channel; Lifetime; MTV; Nashville Network; Nickelodeon; QVC; Sci-Fi Channel; TBS Superstation; The Weather Channel; Trinity Bcstg. Network; Turner Network TV; USA Network.
Current originations: Automated time-weather; local news.
Fee: $55.00 installation; $19.16 monthly.
Pay Service 1
Pay Units: 127.
Programming (via satellite): The Movie Channel.
Fee: $8.50 monthly.
Pay Service 2
Pay Units: N.A.
Programming (via satellite): HBO; Showtime.
Fee: N.A.
Equipment: Jerrold headend; Jerrold amplifiers; Comm/Scope cable; RCA cameras; RCA VTRs; Jerrold set top converters; Microdyne satellite antenna; Microdyne satellite receivers.
Miles of plant: 38.4 (coaxial). Homes passed: 2,344.
Manager: Jack Wade. Chief technician: Ken Gabehardt. Marketing & program director: David Baum.
City fee: None.
Ownership: Helicon Corp. (MSO). See Cable System Ownership.

HOTCHKISS—Wyoming Cable TV Inc., Box 210, Rock View, WV 24880. Phone: 304-732-6114. Fax: 304-732-9370. County: Wyoming. ICA: WV0160.
TV Market Ranking: Below 100. Franchise award date: N.A. Franchise expiration date: N.A. Began: January 1, 1971.
Channel capacity: 12. Channels available but not in use: 6.
Basic Service
Subscribers: N.A.
Programming (received off-air): WVVA (N) Bluefield; WCHS-TV (A), WOWK-TV (C), WSAZ-TV (N) Charleston-Huntington; WSWP-TV (P) Grandview; WOAY-TV (A) Oak Hill-Beckley.
Fee: $35.70 installation; $7.35 monthly.
Equipment: Blonder-Tongue headend; CCS Hatfield cable.
Miles of plant: 2.0 (coaxial). Homes passed: 48.
Manager: Russell Belcher. Chief technician: Bill Keaton.
Ownership: Bahakel Communications Ltd. (MSO).

HUNTINGTON—Century Huntington Co., 51 W. 6th Ave., Huntington, WV 25701. Phone: 304-522-8226. Fax: 304-523-5493. Counties: Cabell & Wayne. Also serves Barboursville, East Pea Ridge, Guyan Estates, Lesage, Wayne County (northwestern portion), West Pea Ridge. ICA: WV0002.
TV Market Ranking: 36 (Barboursville, East Pea Ridge, Guyan Estates, Huntington, Lesage, portions of Wayne County, West Pea Ridge); Below 100 (portions of Wayne County). Franchise award date: N.A. Franchise expiration date: February 2, 2003. Began: N.A.
Channel capacity: 37 (not 2-way capable). Channels available but not in use: N.A.
Basic Service
Subscribers: 21,504.
Programming (received off-air): WKAS (P), WTSF (I) Ashland; WCHS-TV (A), WOWK-TV (C), WPBY-TV (P), WSAZ-TV (N), WVAH-TV (F,U) Charleston-Huntington; allband FM.
Programming (via satellite): WGN-TV (W) Chicago; C-SPAN; C-SPAN 2; Home Shopping Network; QVC; TBS Superstation.
Current originations: Automated time-weather.
Fee: $50.00 installation; $21.75 monthly; $1.38 converter.
Expanded Basic Service
Subscribers: 20,769.
Programming (via satellite): A & E; American Movie Classics; BET; CNBC; Country Music TV; Discovery Channel; Headline News; Lifetime; MTV; Nickelodeon; The Weather Channel; VH1.
Fee: $50.00 installation; $7.00 monthly.
Expanded Basic Service 2
Subscribers: 20,556.
Programming (via satellite): CNN; ESPN; Fox Family Channel; Nashville Network; Turner Network TV; USA Network.
Fee: $50.00 installation; $2.00 monthly.
Pay Service 1
Pay Units: 1,446.
Programming (via satellite): Cinemax.
Fee: $8.00 monthly.

Pay Service 2
Pay Units: 733.
Programming (via satellite): Disney Channel.
Fee: $8.00 monthly.
Pay Service 3
Pay Units: 2,495.
Programming (via satellite): HBO.
Fee: $10.00 monthly.
Pay Service 4
Pay Units: 959.
Programming (via satellite): Showtime.
Fee: $8.00 monthly.
Pay-Per-View
Addressable homes: 21,087.
Local advertising: Yes. Available in satellite distributed programming. Rates: $9.40/30 Seconds. Local sales manager: Joseph Feaganes.
Equipment: Scientific-Atlanta headend; Century III, Jerrold & Theta-Com amplifiers; Comm/Scope & Phelps-Dodge cable; Hughes & Scientific-Atlanta satellite antenna; Scientific-Atlanta & Standard Communications satellite receivers.
Miles of plant: 327.0 (coaxial). Homes passed: 40,500. Total homes in franchised area: 41,000.
Manager: Richard Fairbanks. Marketing director: Stacey D. Grounds.
City fee: 5% of gross.
Ownership: Century Communications Corp. (MSO). See Cable System Ownership.

HUTCHINSON—Century Huntington Co., Box 599, Dellslow, WV 26531. Phone: 304-292-6561. County: Marion. Also serves Marion County (portions), South Worthington, Swisher Hill. ICA: WV0094.
TV Market Ranking: Below 100. Franchise award date: N.A. Franchise expiration date: N.A. Began: November 1, 1968.
Channel capacity: N.A. Channels available but not in use: N.A.
Basic Service
Subscribers: N.A.
Programming (received off-air): WBOY-TV (N), WDTV (C,A) Clarksburg-Weston; WNPB-TV (P) Morgantown; KDKA-TV (C), WCWB (W), WTAE-TV (A) Pittsburgh; WTOV-TV (N) Steubenville-Wheeling; WTRF-TV (C) Wheeling-Steubenville.
Fee: N.A.
Homes passed: 800.
Manager: Michael Ligouri. Chief technician: Ed Hinkle.
Ownership: Century Communications Corp. (MSO). See Cable System Ownership.

IAEGER—TMC of KWV, Box 720, Iaeger, WV 24844. Phone: 304-938-2202. Fax: 304-938-5303. County: McDowell. Also serves Avondale, Beartown, Bradshaw, McDowell County (portions). ICA: WV0039.
TV Market Ranking: Below 100. Franchise award date: N.A. Franchise expiration date: January 9, 2004. Began: March 1, 1953.
Channel capacity: 26 (not 2-way capable). Channels available but not in use: None.
Basic Service
Subscribers: 2,354.
Programming (received off-air): WVVA (N) Bluefield; WCHS-TV (A), WOWK-TV (C), WVAH-TV (F,U) Charleston-Huntington; WSWP-TV (P) Grandview; WOAY-TV (A) Oak Hill-Beckley.
Programming (via satellite): WGN-TV (W) Chicago; CNBC; CNN; Country Music TV; Discovery Channel; ESPN; Fox Family Channel; Lifetime; MTV; Nashville Network; Nickelodeon; QVC; TBS Superstation; Turner Network TV; USA Network.
Current originations: Automated time-weather; public access; educational access; government access; local news.
Fee: $35.00 installation (aerial), $49.25 (underground); $21.55 monthly; $1.53 converter.
Pay Service 1
Pay Units: 272.
Programming (via satellite): Cinemax.
Fee: $25.00 installation; $9.50 monthly.
Pay Service 2
Pay Units: 295.
Programming (via satellite): HBO.
Fee: $25.00 installation; $10.00 monthly.
Pay Service 3
Pay Units: 194.
Programming (via satellite): Disney Channel.
Fee: $25.00 installation; $8.00 monthly.
Pay Service 4
Pay Units: 154.
Programming (via satellite): The Movie Channel.
Fee: $10.00 monthly.
Equipment: Scientific-Atlanta & Nexus headend; Jerrold amplifiers; Comm/Scope cable; Scientific-Atlanta set top converters.
Miles of plant: 83.5 (coaxial). Homes passed: 2,916. Total homes in franchised area: 3,698.
Manager: David Richardson. District manager: Robert Harold. Chief technician: Larry Lockhart. Marketing director: Bill Benner.
City fee: 3% of basic.
Ownership: Tele-Media Corp. (MSO).

INDEPENDENT MOUNTAIN—Capital Cablecomm, Box 368, Cabin Creek, WV 25035. Phone: 304-779-2854. Fax: 304-595-5248. County: Clay. ICA: WV0242.
TV Market Ranking: 36. Franchise award date: N.A. Franchise expiration date: N.A. Began: N.A.
Channel capacity: 15 (not 2-way capable). Channels available but not in use: 3.
Basic Service
Subscribers: 48.
Programming (received off-air): WVVA (N) Bluefield; WCHS-TV (A), WOWK-TV (C), WSAZ-TV (N), WVAH-TV (F,U) Charleston-Huntington; WDTV (C,A) Clarksburg-Weston; WSWP-TV (P) Grandview; WOAY-TV (A) Oak Hill-Beckley.
Fee: $40.00 installation (aerial), $54.00 (underground); $13.75 monthly.
Expanded Basic Service
Subscribers: 48.
Programming (via satellite): Fox Family Channel; Nashville Network; TBS Superstation.
Fee: $5.20 monthly.
Pay Service 1
Pay Units: 26.
Programming (via satellite): HBO.
Fee: $8.00 monthly.
Miles of plant: 4.0 (coaxial); None (fiber optic). Homes passed: 64.
Manager: Robert L. Herrald. Chief technician: Allen Comer.
Franchise fee: $0.25 per subscriber.
Ownership: Fanch Communications Inc. (MSO); Time Warner Cable (MSO). See Cable System Ownership.

INDORE—Capital Cablecomm, Box 368, Cabin Creek, WV 25035. Phone: 304-779-2854. Fax: 304-595-5248. County: Clay. Also serves Bickmore, Clay County (portions), Fola. ICA: WV0145.
TV Market Ranking: 36 (Bickmore, portions of Clay County, Fola, Indore); Below 100 (portions of Clay County); Outside TV Markets (portions of Clay County). Franchise award date: N.A. Franchise expiration date: July 5, 2006. Began: September 1, 1978.
Channel capacity: 15 (not 2-way capable). Channels available but not in use: 3.
Basic Service
Subscribers: 186.
Programming (received off-air): WVVA (N) Bluefield; WCHS-TV (A), WOWK-TV (C), WSAZ-TV (N), WVAH-TV (F,U) Charleston-Huntington; WDTV (C,A) Clarksburg-Weston; WSWP-TV (P) Grandview; WOAY-TV (A) Oak Hill-Beckley.
Current originations: Public access; educational access; government access.
Fee: $41.25 installation (aerial), $55.00 (underground); $13.25 monthly.
Expanded Basic Service
Subscribers: 183.
Programming (via satellite): Fox Family Channel; Nashville Network; TBS Superstation.
Fee: $5.60 monthly.
Pay Service 1
Pay Units: 88.
Programming (via satellite): HBO.
Fee: $8.00 monthly.
Equipment: Blonder-Tongue headend; Jerrold amplifiers; Comm/Scope cable; Eagle traps; M/A-Com satellite antenna; Microdyne satellite receivers.
Miles of plant: 13.5 (coaxial); None (fiber optic).
Manager: Robert L. Herrald. Chief technician: Allen Comer. Marketing director: Bill Benner.
Franchise fee: $0.25 per subscriber.
Ownership: Fanch Communications Inc. (MSO); Time Warner Cable (MSO). See Cable System Ownership.

INWOOD—GS Communications Inc. West Virginia Division, 302 N. Mildred St., Ranson, WV 25438-1455. Phone: 304-725-9185. Fax: 304-725-0930. County: Berkeley. Also serves Hedgesville. ICA: WV0021.
TV Market Ranking: Below 100. Franchise award date: February 1, 1985. Franchise expiration date: February 1, 2000. Began: February 1, 1985.
Channel capacity: 71 (not 2-way capable). Channels available but not in use: 1.
Basic Service
Subscribers: 27,210. Included with Charles Town, WV.
Programming (received off-air): WJZ-TV (C), WMAR-TV (A) Baltimore; WHAG-TV (N), WJAL (W), WWPB (P) Hagerstown; WWPX (I) Martinsburg; WNPB-TV (P) Morgantown; WBDC-TV (W), WDCA (U), WETA-TV (P), WJLA-TV (A), WRC-TV (N), WTTG (F), WUSA (C) Washington.
Programming (via satellite): C-SPAN; C-SPAN 2; Home Shopping Network; QVC; TV Guide Channel; The Barker; The Weather Channel; Trinity Bcstg. Network; ValueVision.
Current originations: Public access.
Fee: $37.00 installation; $11.00 monthly; $1.99 converter.
Expanded Basic Service
Subscribers: 25,878.
Programming (via satellite): A & E; American Movie Classics; BET; CNBC; CNN; Cartoon Network; Comedy Central; Discovery Channel; E! Entertainment TV; ESPN; ESPN 2; FX; Fox Family Channel; Great American Country; Headline News; History Channel; Home & Garden Television; Home Team Sports; Learning Channel; Lifetime; MSNBC; MTV; Nashville Network; Nick at Nite; Nickelodeon; Sci-Fi Channel; TV Food Network; Trinity Bcstg. Network; Turner Network TV; USA Network; VH1.
Fee: $32.65 installation; $16.00 monthly.
Pay Service 1
Pay Units: 7,817.
Programming (via satellite): Cinemax; Disney Channel; HBO; Showtime; The Movie Channel.
Fee: $11.02 installation; $8.95 monthly (Disney), $10.95 monthly (Cinemax, HBO, Showtime or TMC).
Pay-Per-View
Addressable homes: 5,816.
Action Pay-Per-View; Hot Choice; Playboy TV; Spice; Viewer's Choice.
Fee: $3.99 (Action Pay-Per-View; Hot Choice; Viewer's Choice), $4.95 (Spice), $5.94 (Playboy TV).
Pay-per-view manager: John McNeel.
Local advertising: Yes. Available in satellite distributed, locally originated & character-generated programming. Local sales manager: Dave Whalen.
Program Guide: Teleguide.
Equipment: ChannelMaster, Scientific-Atlanta & Standard Communications headend; Magnavox amplifiers; Scientific-Atlanta, Trilogy & Comm/Scope cable; Atari & Compuvid character generator; Pioneer set top converters; Tocom addressable set top converters; Eagle traps; Harris & Scientific-Atlanta satellite antenna; Jerrold, Standard Communications & Scientific-Atlanta satellite receivers; Channel-Matic commercial insert.
Miles of plant: 879.0 (coaxial); 68.0 (fiber optic). Homes passed: 37,300. Total homes in franchised area: 41,000. Included with Charles Town, WV.
Manager: Lawrence Willingham. Chief technican: John Nichols. Marketing director: Paul Espinosa. Customer service manager: Patty Ott.
Franchise fee: 5% of gross.
Ownership: Great Southern Printing & Manufacturing Co. (MSO).

IRELAND—Basco Electronics Inc., 420 W. 2nd St., Weston, WV 26452. Phone: 304-269-7530. Fax: 304-269-6581. County: Lewis. Also serves Crawford, Walkersville. ICA: WV0134.
TV Market Ranking: Below 100. Franchise award date: N.A. Franchise expiration date: N.A. Began: N.A.
Channel capacity: 35 (2-way capable). Channels available but not in use: 18.
Basic Service
Subscribers: 174.
Programming (received off-air): WCHS-TV (A) Charleston-Huntington; WBOY-TV (N), WDTV (C,A), WVFX (F) Clarksburg-Weston; WNPB-TV (P) Morgantown; allband FM.
Programming (via satellite): CNN; ESPN; Fox Family Channel; Learning Channel; MTV; Nashville Network; QVC; TBS Superstation; Turner Network TV; USA Network.
Fee: $50.00 installation; $15.00 monthly.
Pay Service 1
Pay Units: 40.
Programming (via satellite): HBO.
Fee: $10.00 installation; $10.00 monthly.
Pay Service 2
Pay Units: N.A.
Programming (via satellite): Disney Channel.
Fee: $10.00 installation; $7.00 monthly.
Local advertising: No.
Equipment: Blonder-Tongue & Pico headend; Jerrold amplifiers; Comm/Scope cable; Jerrold set top converters; Pico traps; M/A-Com satellite antenna; Drake satellite receivers.
Miles of plant: 8.0 (coaxial). Additional miles planned: 6.0 (coaxial). Homes passed: 250.
Manager: Wilfred L. Sholes. Chief technician: Brian Queen. Marketing director: Sue M. Sholes.
Ownership: Basco Electronics Inc. (MSO).

JENKINJONES—Obey's TV Cable, Box 181, Jenkinjones, WV 24848. Phone: 304-383-2245. County: McDowell. ICA: WV0226.
TV Market Ranking: Below 100. Franchise award date: January 1, 1995. Franchise expiration date: January 1, 2010. Began: June 1, 1966.
Channel capacity: 15 (not 2-way capable). Channels available but not in use: N.A.

Basic Service
Subscribers: 58.
Programming (received off-air): WVVA (N) Bluefield; WSWP-TV (P) Grandview; WVSX (I) Lewisburg; WOAY-TV (A) Oak Hill-Beckley; WDBJ (C) Roanoke-Lynchburg.
Programming (via satellite): WGN-TV (W) Chicago; America's Voice; Nashville Network; Nick at Nite's TV Land; Odyssey; TBS Superstation; Trinity Bcstg. Network.
Fee: $25.00 installation; $11.50 monthly.

Pay Service 1
Pay Units: 26.
Programming (via satellite): The Movie Channel.
Fee: $9.00 monthly.
Miles of plant: 2.0 (coaxial). Homes passed: 88. Total homes in franchised area: 88.
Manager: Clarence Obey.
Ownership: Clarence & Lois Obey.

JODIE—Capital Cablecomm, Box 368, Cabin Creek, WV 25035. Phone: 304-779-2854. Fax: 304-595-5248. Counties: Fayette & Nicholas. Also serves Beech Glen, Rich Creek, Swiss. ICA: WV0131.
TV Market Ranking: 36. Franchise award date: N.A. Franchise expiration date: N.A. Began: March 1, 1969.
Channel capacity: 15 (not 2-way capable). Channels available but not in use: None.

Basic Service
Subscribers: 217.
Programming (received off-air): WCHS-TV (A), WOWK-TV (C), WPBY-TV (P), WSAZ-TV (N), WVAH-TV (F,U) Charleston-Huntington; WDTV (C,A) Clarksburg-Weston; WSWP-TV (P) Grandview; WOAY-TV (A) Oak Hill-Beckley.
Current originations: Public access; educational access; government access.
Fee: $36.00 installation (aerial), $49.75 (underground); $11.00 monthly; $1.83 converter.

Expanded Basic Service
Subscribers: 211.
Programming (via satellite): ESPN; Fox Family Channel; Nashville Network; TBS Superstation.
Fee: $5.55 monthly.

Pay Service 1
Pay Units: 15.
Programming (via satellite): Cinemax.
Fee: $20.00 installation; $10.00 monthly.

Pay Service 2
Pay Units: 6.
Programming (via satellite): Disney Channel.
Fee: $20.00 installation; $8.00 monthly.

Pay Service 3
Pay Units: 19.
Programming (via satellite): HBO.
Fee: $20.00 installation; $10.00 monthly.
Equipment: Blonder-Tongue headend; Jerrold & Magnavox amplifiers; Comm/Scope cable; Scientific-Atlanta set top converters; Harris satellite antenna; Microdyne satellite receivers.
Miles of plant: 6.6 (coaxial); None (fiber optic). Homes passed: 327.
Manager: Robert L. Herrald. Chief technician: Allen Comer. Marketing director: Bill Benner.
City fee: None.
Ownership: Fanch Communications Inc. (MSO); Time Warner Cable (MSO). See Cable System Ownership.

JULIAN—Capital Cablecomm, Box 368, Cabin Creek, WV 25035. Phone: 304-779-2854. Fax: 304-595-5248. County: Boone. ICA: WV0243.
TV Market Ranking: 36. Franchise award date: N.A. Franchise expiration date: N.A. Began: N.A.
Channel capacity: 15 (not 2-way capable). Channels available but not in use: 4.

Basic Service
Subscribers: 112.
Programming (received off-air): WCHS-TV (A), WOWK-TV (C), WPBY-TV (P), WSAZ-TV (N), WVAH-TV (F,U) Charleston-Huntington; WOAY-TV (A) Oak Hill-Beckley.
Fee: $40.00 installation (aerial), $53.25 (underground); $9.50 monthly.

Expanded Basic Service
Subscribers: 112.
Programming (via satellite): ESPN; Fox Family Channel; Nashville Network; TBS Superstation.
Fee: $6.45 monthly.

Pay Service 1
Pay Units: 17.
Programming (via satellite): HBO.
Fee: $10.00 monthly.
Miles of plant: 3.5 (coaxial); None (fiber optic). Homes passed: 142.
Manager: Robert L. Herrald. Chief technician: Victor Canterbury.
Ownership: Fanch Communications Inc. (MSO); Time Warner Cable (MSO). See Cable System Ownership.

KERMIT—CableVision Communications, Box 2200, 68 5th St., Buckhannon, WV 26201. Phone: 304-472-4193. Fax: 304-472-0756. Counties: Logan, Mingo & Wayne, WV; Martin, KY. Also serves Hode, Laura, Lovely, Pilgrim, Warfield, Wolfcreek, KY; Calf Creek, Crum, East Kermit, Grey Eagle, Jennies Creek, Marrowbone, Steptown, Stonecoal, Three Forks, Tripp, WV. ICA: WV0038.
TV Market Ranking: Outside TV Markets. Franchise award date: November 1, 1985. Franchise expiration date: N.A. Began: N.A.
Channel capacity: 37 (not 2-way capable). Channels available but not in use: N.A.

Basic Service
Subscribers: 2,404.
Programming (received off-air): WTSF (I) Ashland; WCHS-TV (A), WOWK-TV (C), WPBY-TV (P), WSAZ-TV (N), WVAH-TV (F,U) Charleston-Huntington; WYMT-TV (C) Hazard; WKPI (P) Pikeville.
Programming (via satellite): WGN-TV (W) Chicago; TBS Superstation; Trinity Bcstg. Network.
Current originations: Public access.
Fee: $61.25 installation; $14.40 monthly; $1.24 converter.

Expanded Basic Service
Subscribers: 1,971.
Programming (via satellite): A & E; American Movie Classics; CNN; Discovery Channel; Disney Channel; E! Entertainment TV; ESPN; Fox Family Channel; Great American Country; Headline News; Home Shopping Network; Lifetime; MTV; Nashville Network; Nickelodeon; Outdoor Channel; Sci-Fi Channel; The Weather Channel; Turner Network TV; USA Network.
Fee: $17.10 monthly.

Pay Service 1
Pay Units: 1,069.
Programming (via satellite): Cinemax; HBO; Showtime; The Movie Channel; The New Encore.
Fee: $3.99 monthly (Encore), $7.99 monthly (Cinemax), $11.99 monthly (HBO, Showtime or TMC).
Equipment: Blonder-Tongue, Olson & M/A-Com headend; C-COR amplifiers; Eagle traps; Scientific-Atlanta satellite antenna; Scientific-Atlanta satellite receivers.
Miles of plant: 113.0 (coaxial). Homes passed: 3,247.
Manager: Willie Critchfield. Plant manager: Garry Lucas. Marketing director: Kenny Phillips.
Ownership: Rifkin & Associates Inc. (MSO). See Cable System Ownership.

KEYROCK—Holly TV Cable, Box 905, Pineville, WV 24874. Phone: 304-732-8626. County: Wyoming. Plans service to Glover. ICA: WV0143.
TV Market Ranking: Below 100. Franchise award date: N.A. Franchise expiration date: N.A. Began: November 1, 1980.
Channel capacity: N.A. Channels available but not in use: N.A.

Basic Service
Subscribers: N.A.
Programming (received off-air): WVVA (N) Bluefield; WCHS-TV (A), WOWK-TV (C), WSAZ-TV (N) Charleston-Huntington; WSWP-TV (P) Grandview; WJHL-TV (C) Johnson City; WOAY-TV (A) Oak Hill-Beckley; WDBJ (C) Roanoke-Lynchburg.
Programming (via satellite): ESPN; Nashville Network; TBS Superstation; The Inspirational Network.
Fee: $35.00 installation; $10.50 monthly.

Pay Service 1
Pay Units: N.A.
Programming (via satellite): Showtime.
Fee: $10.00 monthly.
Homes passed: 200.
Ownership: Roger Lamastus.

KEYSER—Tele-Media Co., 51 N. Main St., Keyser, WV 26726-3220. Phone: 304-788-2433. Fax: 304-788-6142. Counties: Mineral, WV; Allegany, MD. Also serves Allegany County (portions), Barton, Carlos, Frostburg, Klondike, Lonaconing, Luke, Midland, Midlothian, Morgantown, National, Westernport, Woodland, Zihlman, MD; Mineral County, Piedmont, WV. ICA: WV0020.
TV Market Ranking: Outside TV Markets. Franchise award date: October 1, 1965. Franchise expiration date: March 1, 2003. Began: April 1, 1952.
Channel capacity: 78 (2-way capable). Channels available but not in use: 22.

Basic Service
Subscribers: 12,377.
Programming (received off-air): WWPB (P) Hagerstown; KDKA-TV (C) Pittsburgh; allband FM.
Programming (via microwave): WJZ-TV (C) Baltimore; WHAG-TV (N) Hagerstown; WDCA (U), WJLA-TV (A), WTTG (F), WUSA (C) Washington.
Programming (via translator): WNPB-TV (P) Morgantown.
Programming (via satellite): WGN-TV (W) Chicago; TBS Superstation.
Current originations: Public access.
Fee: $59.95 installation; $8.95 monthly.

Expanded Basic Service
Subscribers: 11,400.
Programming (via satellite): A & E; American Movie Classics; BET; C-SPAN; CNN; Comedy Central; Country Music TV; Discovery Channel; Disney Channel; ESPN; ESPN 2; EWTN; Fox Family Channel; Goodlife TV Network; Headline News; Lifetime; MTV; Nashville Network; Nick at Nite's TV Land; Nickelodeon; QVC; The Weather Channel; Trinity Bcstg. Network; Turner Network TV; USA Network; VH1.
Fee: $18.95 monthly.

Pay Service 1
Pay Units: 941.
Programming (via satellite): Cinemax.
Fee: $15.00 installation; $10.50 monthly.

Pay Service 2
Pay Units: 1,181.
Programming (via satellite): HBO.
Fee: $15.00 installation; $10.50 monthly.

Pay Service 3
Pay Units: 841.
Programming (via satellite): Showtime.
Fee: $15.00 installation; $10.50 monthly.

Pay Service 4
Pay Units: 756.
Programming (via satellite): The Movie Channel.
Fee: $10.50 monthly.

Pay Service 5
Pay Units: 725.
Programming (via satellite): Flix.
Fee: $4.95 monthly.
Local advertising: Yes. Available in satellite distributed programming. Rates: $30.00/Month. Regional interconnect: Cabletime.
Program Guide: Premium Channels.
Equipment: Nexus headend; C-COR amplifiers; Comm/Scope cable; Scientific-Atlanta set top converters; Scientific-Atlanta satellite antenna; Microdyne satellite receivers.
Miles of plant: 267.0 (coaxial); 71.0 (fiber optic). Additional miles planned: 2.0 (coaxial). Homes passed: 14,542.
Manager: Ronald Boyce. Chief technician: Oscar Cavin. Marketing director: William Farley.
City fee: 3% of gross.
Ownership: Tele-Media Corp. (MSO).

KIMBALL—Comcast Cable, Box 1516, 1901 Leatherwood Lane, Bluefield, WV 24701. Phone: 304-325-0591. County: McDowell. Also serves Landraff, Vivian. ICA: WV0121.
TV Market Ranking: Below 100. Franchise award date: May 3, 1950. Franchise expiration date: N.A. Began: January 1, 1951.
Channel capacity: 21 (not 2-way capable). Channels available but not in use: 19.

Basic Service
Subscribers: 176.
Programming (received off-air): WVVA (N) Bluefield; WCHS-TV (A), WOWK-TV (C) Charleston-Huntington; WSWP-TV (P) Grandview; WJHL-TV (C) Johnson City; WOAY-TV (A) Oak Hill-Beckley.
Programming (via satellite): CNN; Country Music TV; Discovery Channel; ESPN; Fox Family Channel; Fox News Channel; Nashville Network; TBS Superstation; USA Network.

Fee: $25.00 installation; $13.95 monthly; $20.00 additional installation.

Pay Service 1

Pay Units: 104.

Programming (via satellite): HBO.

Fee: $20.00 installation; $12.50 monthly.

Miles of plant: 3.0 (coaxial). Homes passed: 328.

Manager: Treva Taylor. Chief technician: Ken Taylor.

City fee: 3% of gross.

Ownership: Comcast Cable Communications Inc. (MSO).

KINGWOOD—CableVision Communications, 107-1/2 B, Pleasant Ave., Kingwood, WV 26537. Phone: 304-329-1360. County: Preston. Also serves Albright, Arthurdale, Bretz, Corinth, Independence, Masontown, Newburg, Reedsville, Terra Alta. ICA: WV0189.

TV Market Ranking: Below 100 (Arthurdale, Bretz, Independence, Masontown, Newburg, Reedsville); Outside TV Markets (Albright, Corinth, Kingwood, Terra Alta). Franchise award date: N.A. Franchise expiration date: N.A. Began: June 1, 1967.

Channel capacity: N.A. Channels available but not in use: N.A.

Basic Service

Subscribers: 2,186.

Programming (received off-air): WBOY-TV (N), WDTV (C,A), WVFX (F) Clarksburg-Weston; WNPB-TV (P) Morgantown; KDKA-TV (C), WPGH-TV (F), WPXI (N), WTAE-TV (A) Pittsburgh; WTRF-TV (C) Wheeling-Steubenville; allband FM.

Programming (via satellite): WGN-TV (W) Chicago; C-SPAN; C-SPAN 2; TBS Superstation.

Fee: $29.95 installation; $10.95 monthly.

Expanded Basic Service

Subscribers: N.A.

Programming (via satellite): American Movie Classics; CNN; Comedy Central; Country Music TV; Discovery Channel; ESPN; Fox Family Channel; Headline News; Home Shopping Network; Learning Channel; Lifetime; MTV; Nashville Network; Nickelodeon; The Inspirational Network; The Weather Channel; Travel Channel; Turner Network TV; USA Network; VH1.

Fee: N.A.

Pay Service 1

Pay Units: N.A.

Programming (via satellite): Cinemax; Disney Channel; HBO; Showtime; The Movie Channel.

Fee: $7.50 installation; $10.95 monthly (Cinemax or Showtime), $11.95 monthly (HBO).

Equipment: Oak set top converters; RF Systems satellite antenna.

Miles of plant: 94.0 (coaxial).

Manager: Jack Clark. Chief technician: Jim Clark.

City fee: 3% of gross.

Ownership: Rifkin & Associates Inc. (MSO). See Cable System Ownership.

LEFT HAND—Econoco Inc., Box 147, Rte. 61, Kincaid, WV 25119. Phone: 304-469-2817. County: Roane. Also serves Amma, Newton. ICA: WV0190.

TV Market Ranking: 36. Franchise award date: N.A. Franchise expiration date: N.A. Began: October 1, 1989.

Channel capacity: 36 (not 2-way capable). Channels available but not in use: 19.

Basic Service

Subscribers: 459.

Programming (received off-air): WCHS-TV (A), WOWK-TV (C), WPBY-TV (P), WSAZ-TV (N), WVAH-TV (F,U) Charleston-Huntington; WBOY-TV (N), WDTV (C,A) Clarksburg-Weston; WSWP-TV (P) Grandview; WOAY-TV (A) Oak Hill-Beckley.

Programming (via satellite): WGN-TV (W) Chicago; A & E; CNN; ESPN; Fox Family Channel; Nashville Network; TBS Superstation.

Fee: $25.00 installation; $20.72 monthly.

Miles of plant: 58.0 (coaxial).

Manager: Sheila Bills. Chief technician: Eslie Bills.

Ownership: Econoco Inc. (MSO).

LEIVASY—Paxton Cable, Suite 280, 700 Ackerman Rd., Columbus, OH 43202. Phone: 614-263-6100. County: Nicholas. ICA: WV0156.

TV Market Ranking: Below 100. Franchise award date: N.A. Franchise expiration date: N.A. Began: April 1, 1981.

Channel capacity: 12. Channels available but not in use: N.A.

Basic Service

Subscribers: N.A.

Programming (received off-air): WCHS-TV (A), WOWK-TV (C), WSAZ-TV (N) Charleston-Huntington; WDTV (C,A) Clarksburg-Weston; WSWP-TV (P) Grandview; WOAY-TV (A) Oak Hill-Beckley.

Fee: N.A.

Miles of plant: 5.0 (coaxial). Homes passed: 100.

Manager: Cecil Eldridge. Director of operations: Lisa Collier.

Ownership: Paxton Cable Television Inc. (MSO).

LENORE—CableVision Communications, Box 2200, 68 5th St., Buckhannon, WV 26201. Phone: 304-472-4193. Fax: 304-472-0756. Counties: Mingo, WV; Martin, Morgan & Pike, KY. Also serves Caney, Elk Creek, Hatfield, Oppy, KY; Belo, Bias, Borderland, East Lovely, Laurel Creek, Maher, Millers Creek, Myrtle, Naugatuck, Nolan, Sheppardtown, Trace Creek, WV. ICA: WV0050.

TV Market Ranking: Below 100 (Bias, Borderland); Outside TV Markets (Belo, Caney, East Lovely, Elk Creek, Hatfield, Laurel Creek, Lenore, Maher, Millers Creek, Myrtle, Naugatuck, Nolan, Oppy, Sheppardtown, Trace Creek). Franchise award date: May 15, 1980. Franchise expiration date: N.A. Began: N.A.

Channel capacity: 37 (not 2-way capable). Channels available but not in use: N.A.

Basic Service

Subscribers: 1,709.

Programming (received off-air): WCHS-TV (A), WOWK-TV (C), WPBY-TV (P), WSAZ-TV (N), WVAH-TV (F,U) Charleston-Huntington; WYMT-TV (C) Hazard; WKPI (P) Pikeville.

Programming (via satellite): WGN-TV (W) Chicago; C-SPAN; TBS Superstation; The Inspirational Network; Trinity Bcstg. Network.

Fee: $61.25 installation; $14.40 monthly; $1.24 converter.

Expanded Basic Service

Subscribers: 1,437.

Programming (via satellite): A & E; American Movie Classics; CNN; Discovery Channel; Disney Channel; E! Entertainment TV; ESPN; Fox Family Channel; Great American Country; Home Shopping Network; Learning Channel; Lifetime; MuchMusic Network; Nashville Network; Nickelodeon; Sci-Fi Channel; The Weather Channel; Turner Network TV; USA Network; VH1.

Fee: $17.07 monthly.

Pay Service 1

Pay Units: 383.

Programming (via satellite): Cinemax.

Fee: $7.99 monthly.

Pay Service 2

Pay Units: 72.

Programming (via satellite): The New Encore.

Fee: $3.99 monthly.

Pay Service 3

Pay Units: 291.

Programming (via satellite): HBO.

Fee: $11.99 monthly.

Pay Service 4

Pay Units: 161.

Programming (via satellite): Showtime.

Fee: $11.99 monthly.

Pay Service 5

Pay Units: 125.

Programming (via satellite): The Movie Channel.

Fee: $11.99 monthly.

Equipment: Blonder-Tongue, Olson & Standard Communications headend; C-COR amplifiers; Eagle traps; Microdyne satellite antenna; Electrohome satellite receivers.

Miles of plant: 85.0 (coaxial). Homes passed: 2,391.

Manager: Willie Critchfield. Plant manager: Garry Lucas. Marketing director: Kenny Phillips.

County fee: 3% of gross.

Ownership: Rifkin & Associates Inc. (MSO). See Cable System Ownership.

LEWISBURG—Capital Cablecomm, 108 E. Washington St., Lewisburg, WV 24901. Phone: 304-645-1164. Fax: 304-645-2742. Counties: Greenbrier & Pocahontas. Also serves Caldwell, Fairlea, Greenbrier County (portions), Hillsboro, Pocahontas County (portions), Seebert. ICA: WV0033.

TV Market Ranking: Below 100 (Caldwell, Fairlea, Greenbrier County, Hillsboro, Lewisburg, portions of Pocahontas County, Seebert); Outside TV Markets (portions of Pocahontas County). Franchise award date: March 1, 1965. Franchise expiration date: November 21, 2004. Began: December 1, 1965.

Channel capacity: 40 (2-way capable; not operating 2-way). Channels available but not in use: None.

Basic Service

Subscribers: 3,154.

Programming (received off-air): WVVA (N) Bluefield; WCHS-TV (A) Charleston-Huntington; WSWP-TV (P) Grandview; WVSX (I) Lewisburg; WOAY-TV (A) Oak Hill-Beckley; WDBJ (C), WSLS-TV (N) Roanoke-Lynchburg; allband FM.

Programming (via satellite): WGN-TV (W) Chicago; BET; Learning Channel; MTV; QVC; TBS Superstation.

Current originations: Public access; government access.

Fee: $26.75 installation (aerial), $40.25 (underground); $13.00 monthly; $1.16 converter.

Expanded Basic Service

Subscribers: 2,967.

Programming (via satellite): A & E; American Movie Classics; Animal Planet; C-SPAN; CNN; Country Music TV; Discovery Channel; ESPN; ESPN 2; Fox Family Channel; Headline News; History Channel; Lifetime; Nashville Network; Nickelodeon; Sci-Fi Channel; The Weather Channel; Trinity Bcstg. Network; Turner Network TV; USA Network.

Fee: $12.50 monthly.

Pay Service 1

Pay Units: 212.

Programming (via satellite): Disney Channel.

Fee: $20.00 installation; $7.00 monthly.

Pay Service 2

Pay Units: 251.

Programming (via satellite): HBO.

Fee: $20.00 installation; $10.00 monthly.

Pay Service 3

Pay Units: 128.

Programming (via satellite): Cinemax.

Fee: $9.50 monthly.

Pay Service 4

Pay Units: 175.

Programming (via satellite): Showtime.

Fee: $10.00 monthly.

Local advertising: Yes. Available in satellite distributed & character-generated programming. Local sales manager: Ed Smith.

Equipment: Scientific-Atlanta & Sony headend; Magnavox & Jerrold amplifiers; Comm/Scope cable; Scientific-Atlanta set top converters; Eagle traps; Harris satellite antenna; Sony & Scientific-Atlanta satellite receivers.

Miles of plant: 85.0 (coaxial); None (fiber optic). Homes passed: 4,006.

Manager: James Morgan. Marketing director: Darlene Seamans.

Ownership: Fanch Communications Inc. (MSO); Time Warner Cable (MSO). See Cable System Ownership.

LITTLE OTTER—R & R Cable Co., Box 685, Sutton, WV 26601. Phone: 304-765-2527. Fax: 304-765-3125. County: Braxton. ICA: WV0227.

TV Market Ranking: Below 100. Franchise award date: N.A. Franchise expiration date: N.A. Began: February 15, 1979.

Channel capacity: 35 (not 2-way capable). Channels available but not in use: 7.

Basic Service

Subscribers: 100.

Programming (received off-air): WCHS-TV (A), WOWK-TV (C), WSAZ-TV (N), WVAH-TV (F,U) Charleston-Huntington; WBOY-TV (N), WDTV (C,A) Clarksburg-Weston; WSWP-TV (P) Grandview.

Programming (via satellite): C-SPAN; CNN; Discovery Channel; ESPN; Fox Family Channel; MTV; Nashville Network; Nickelodeon; TBS Superstation; Turner Network TV; USA Network.

Fee: $30.00 installation; $15.09 monthly.

Pay Service 1

Pay Units: 17.

Programming (via satellite): Disney Channel; Showtime.

Fee: N.A.

Miles of plant: 4.0 (coaxial). Homes passed: 110. Total homes in franchised area: 110.

Manager: Rodney E. Steorts.

Ownership: Rodney E. Steorts.

LITTLETON—CableVision Communications, Box 2200, 68 5th St., Buckhannon, WV 26201. Phone: 304-472-4193. Fax: 304-472-0756. County: Wetzel. Also serves Burton, Hundred. ICA: WV0106.

TV Market Ranking: 90. Franchise award date: July 6, 1986. Franchise expiration date: N.A. Began: October 1, 1970.

Channel capacity: 35. Channels available but not in use: N.A.

Basic Service

Subscribers: 376.

Programming (received off-air): WBOY-TV (N), WDTV (C,A) Clarksburg-Weston; WNPB-TV (P) Morgantown; KDKA-TV (C), WCWB (W), WPGH-TV (F), WPXI (N), WQED (P), WTAE-TV (A) Pittsburgh; WTOV-TV (N) Steubenville-Wheeling; WTRF-TV (C) Wheeling-Steubenville; allband FM.

Current originations: Public access.

Fee: $61.25 installation; $14.40 monthly; $1.24 converter.

Expanded Basic Service

Subscribers: 309.

Programming (via satellite): WGN-TV (W) Chicago; American Movie Classics; Animal Planet; CNN; Discovery Channel; Disney Channel; E! Entertainment TV; ESPN; ESPN 2; Fox Family Channel; Great American Country; Home Shopping Network; Lifetime; Nashville Network; Nickelodeon; Sci-Fi Channel; TBS Superstation; The Weather Channel; Trinity Bcstg. Network; Turner Network TV; USA Network.
Fee: $16.67 monthly.
Pay Service 1
Pay Units: 186.
Programming (via satellite): Cinemax; HBO; Showtime; The Movie Channel.
Fee: $10.00 installation; $7.95 monthly (Cinemax), $11.95 monthly (Showtime or TMC), $11.99 monthly (HBO).
Equipment: Blonder-Tongue, Olson & Standard Communications headend; C-COR amplifiers; Capscan cable.
Miles of plant: 17.0 (coaxial). Homes passed: 564.
Manager: Willie Critchfield. Chief technician: Bill Turner. Marketing director: Kenny Phillips.
Ownership: Rifkin & Associates Inc. (MSO). See Cable System Ownership.

LOGAN—Cablecomm, Box 1339, County Rte. 5, Mount Gay, WV 25637. Phone: 800-352-1030. Counties: Boone, Logan & Wyoming. Also serves Blair, Boone County, Chapmanville, Cyclone, Dingess Run, Logan County, Man, Mitchell Heights, Ottawa, Sharples-Clothier, West Logan, Wyoming County (portions), Yolyn. ICA: WV0017.
TV Market Ranking: 36 (portions of Boone County, Chapmanville, portions of Logan County, Ottawa, Sharples-Clothier); Below 100 (portions of Boone County, Cyclone, portions of Logan County, Man, portions of Wyoming County, Yolyn); Outside TV Markets (Blair, Dingess Run, Logan, portions of Logan County, Mitchell Heights, West Logan, portions of Wyoming County). Franchise award date: N.A. Franchise expiration date: N.A. Began: January 1, 1955.
Channel capacity: 40 (not 2-way capable). Channels available but not in use: N.A.
Basic Service
Subscribers: 10,455.
Programming (received off-air): WTSF (I) Ashland; WCHS-TV (A), WOWK-TV (C), WPBY-TV (P), WSAZ-TV (N), WVAH-TV (F,U) Charleston-Huntington.
Programming (via satellite): A & E; C-SPAN; CNBC; CNN; Comedy Central; Discovery Channel; Fox Family Channel; Headline News; Lifetime; MTV; Nashville Network; Nickelodeon; Odyssey; QVC; Superaudio Cable Radio Service; TBS Superstation; The Weather Channel; VH1.
Current originations: Automated time-weather; educational access; local news.
Fee: $30.75 installation; $10.26 monthly; $2.00 converter.
Expanded Basic Service
Subscribers: 9,783.
Programming (via satellite): American Movie Classics; C-SPAN 2; ESPN; Fox Sports Net Pittsburgh; Turner Network TV; USA Network.
Fee: $14.75 monthly.
Pay Service 1
Pay Units: 1,083.
Programming (via satellite): Cinemax.
Fee: $13.15 monthly.
Pay Service 2
Pay Units: 689.
Programming (via satellite): Disney Channel.
Fee: $11.95 monthly.
Pay Service 3
Pay Units: 1,906.
Programming (via satellite): HBO.
Fee: $13.15 monthly.
Pay Service 4
Pay Units: 627.
Programming (via satellite): Showtime.
Fee: $13.15 monthly.
Pay Service 5
Pay Units: 3,264.
Programming (via satellite): The New Encore.
Fee: N.A.
Pay-Per-View
Addressable homes: 1,640.
Local advertising: Yes.
Program Guide: The Cable Guide.
Equipment: Ameco headend; AEL amplifiers; Systems Wire cable; MSI character generator; Jerrold set top converters; Comtech satellite antenna.
Miles of plant: 252.0 (coaxial); 30.0 (fiber optic). Homes passed: 13,636.
Manager: Jerry Bennett. Chief technician: J. R. Vance.
Ownership: Fanch Communications Inc. (MSO); Time Warner Cable (MSO). Purchased from Tele-Communications Inc., February 25, 1999. See Cable System Ownership.

LOUDENDALE—Capital Cablecomm, Box 368, Cabin Creek, WV 25035. Phone: 304-779-2854. Fax: 304-595-5248. County: Kanawha. Also serves Cane Fork, Davis Creek. ICA: WV0097.
TV Market Ranking: 36. Franchise award date: N.A. Franchise expiration date: N.A. Began: January 1, 1974.
Channel capacity: 26 (not 2-way capable). Channels available but not in use: 1.
Basic Service
Subscribers: 609.
Programming (received off-air): WCHS-TV (A), WOWK-TV (C), WPBY-TV (P), WSAZ-TV (N), WVAH-TV (F,U) Charleston-Huntington; WSWP-TV (P) Grandview; WOAY-TV (A) Oak Hill-Beckley.
Programming (via satellite): WGN-TV (W) Chicago; Comedy Central; MTV; QVC; TBS Superstation.
Current originations: Public access; educational access; government access.
Fee: $36.50 installation (aerial), $50.25 (underground); $12.25 monthly; $1.83 converter.
Expanded Basic Service
Subscribers: 586.
Programming (via satellite): CNN; ESPN; Fox Family Channel; Headline News; Nashville Network; Nickelodeon; The Weather Channel; USA Network.
Fee: $8.45 monthly.
Pay Service 1
Pay Units: 36.
Programming (via satellite): Cinemax.
Fee: $25.00 installation; $10.00 monthly.
Pay Service 2
Pay Units: 29.
Programming (via satellite): Disney Channel.
Fee: $25.00 installation; $8.00 monthly.
Pay Service 3
Pay Units: 60.
Programming (via satellite): HBO.
Fee: $25.00 installation; $10.00 monthly.
Pay Service 4
Pay Units: 71.
Programming (via satellite): Showtime.
Fee: $25.00 installation; $10.00 monthly.
Pay Service 5
Pay Units: 67.
Programming (via satellite): The Movie Channel.
Fee: $25.00 installation; $10.00 monthly.
Equipment: Jerrold headend; Magnavox amplifiers; Comm/Scope cable; Scientific-Atlanta set top converters; Microdyne & Harris satellite antenna; Microdyne & Scientific-Atlanta satellite receivers.
Miles of plant: 18.4 (coaxial); None (fiber optic). Homes passed: 769.
Manager: Robert L. Herrald. Chief technician: Allen Comer. Marketing director: Bill Benner.
Franchise fee: None.
Ownership: Fanch Communications Inc. (MSO); Time Warner Cable (MSO). See Cable System Ownership.

LYBURN—Bowen Cablevision, Box 130, Wilkinson, WV 25653-0130. Phone: 304-752-3023. County: Logan. ICA: WV0237.
TV Market Ranking: Outside TV Markets. Franchise award date: N.A. Franchise expiration date: N.A. Began: N.A.
Channel capacity: N.A. Channels available but not in use: N.A.
Basic Service
Subscribers: N.A.
Programming (received off-air): WTSF (I) Ashland; WCHS-TV (A), WOWK-TV (C), WPBY-TV (P), WSAZ-TV (N), WVAH-TV (F,U) Charleston-Huntington.
Programming (via satellite): WGN-TV (W) Chicago; Country Music TV; ESPN; Fox Family Channel; Nashville Network; TBS Superstation; USA Network.
Fee: N.A.
Manager: Gary Bowen.
Ownership: Bowen Cablevision Inc. (MSO).

MADISON—CableVision Communications, Box 2200, 68 5th St., Buckhannon, WV 26201. Phone: 304-412-4193. Fax: 304-412-0756. County: Boone. Also serves Danville, Frontage Road, Quinland, Uneeda. ICA: WV0192.
TV Market Ranking: 36. Franchise award date: N.A. Franchise expiration date: N.A. Began: February 1, 1965.
Channel capacity: N.A. Channels available but not in use: N.A.
Basic Service
Subscribers: 1,689.
Programming (received off-air): WCHS-TV (A), WOWK-TV (C), WPBY-TV (P), WSAZ-TV (N), WVAH-TV (F,U) Charleston-Huntington; allband FM.
Programming (via satellite): WGN-TV (W) Chicago; C-SPAN; C-SPAN 2; QVC; TBS Superstation; ValueVision.
Fee: $25.00 installation.
Expanded Basic Service
Subscribers: N.A.
Programming (via satellite): A & E; CNN; Cartoon Network; Comedy Central; Country Music TV; ESPN; Fox Family Channel; Headline News; Learning Channel; Lifetime; MTV; Nashville Network; Nickelodeon; The Inspirational Network; The Weather Channel; Travel Channel; Trinity Bcstg. Network; Turner Network TV; USA Network; VH1.
Fee: N.A.
Pay Service 1
Pay Units: 98.
Programming (via satellite): Disney Channel.
Fee: $15.00 installation; $6.95 monthly.
Pay Service 2
Pay Units: 321.
Programming (via satellite): HBO.
Fee: $15.00 installation; $9.95 monthly.
Pay Service 3
Pay Units: 54.
Programming (via satellite): The Movie Channel.
Fee: $15.00 installation; $9.95 monthly.
Pay Service 4
Pay Units: 81.
Programming (via satellite): Showtime.
Fee: $15.00 installation; $9.95 monthly.
Equipment: Jerrold headend; Jerrold amplifiers; Times Fiber cable; Jerrold set top converters; Eagle traps; AFC satellite antenna; Scientific-Atlanta & Microdyne satellite receivers.
Miles of plant: 30.0 (coaxial).
Manager: Lester Errett. Chief technician: Danny Elias.
City fee: 3% of gross.
Ownership: Rifkin & Associates Inc. (MSO). See Cable System Ownership.

MANNINGTON—Mannington TV Inc., 206 Pleasant St., Mannington, WV 26582. Phone: 304-986-1650. County: Marion. Also serves Marion County, Rachel. ICA: WV0067.
TV Market Ranking: Below 100. Franchise award date: N.A. Franchise expiration date: N.A. Began: June 4, 1971.
Channel capacity: 12. Channels available but not in use: None.
Basic Service
Subscribers: 1,372.
Programming (received off-air): WBOY-TV (N), WDTV (C,A) Clarksburg-Weston; WNPB-TV (P) Morgantown; KDKA-TV (C), WPGH-TV (F), WPXI (N), WTAE-TV (A) Pittsburgh; WTOV-TV (N) Steubenville-Wheeling; WTRF-TV (C) Wheeling-Steubenville; allband FM.
Planned programming (received off-air): WQED (P) Pittsburgh.
Planned programming (via satellite): TBS Superstation.
Fee: $25.00 installation; $21.63 monthly.
Pay Service 1
Pay Units: 1,372.
Programming (via satellite): Disney Channel; HBO; Showtime.
Fee: $25.00 installation; $8.48 monthly (Disney Channel), $10.60 monthly (HBO or Showtime).
Equipment: Hughes, Jerrold & RCA headend; Jerrold amplifiers; Essex & Superior cable; Hughes satellite antenna.
Miles of plant: 47.1 (coaxial). Additional miles planned: 2.0 (coaxial). Homes passed: 1,400.
Manager: James A. Sturm.
City fee: 3% of gross.
Ownership: Mannington TV Inc.

MARLINTON—Milestone Communications of New York LP, Suite 200, 1850 Woodmoor Dr., Monument, CO 80132. Phone: 719-488-2916. Fax: 719-488-3629. County: Pocahontas. Also serves Buckeye, Campbelltown, Edray. ICA: WV0193.
TV Market Ranking: Below 100 (Buckeye, Campbelltown, Marlinton); Outside TV Markets (Edray). Franchise award date: N.A. Franchise expiration date: December 7, 2001. Began: May 15, 1954.
Channel capacity: 52 (not 2-way capable). Channels available but not in use: 14.
Basic Service
Subscribers: 871.
Programming (received off-air): WVVA (N) Bluefield; WSWP-TV (P) Grandview; WVSX (I) Lewisburg; WOAY-TV (A) Oak Hill-Beckley; WDBJ (C), WSET-TV (A), WSLS-TV (N) Roanoke-Lynchburg; allband FM.
Programming (via satellite): A & E; American Movie Classics; Animal Planet; CNN; Comedy Central; Country Music TV; Discovery Channel; ESPN; ESPN 2; Fox Family Channel; Fox News Channel; Headline

News; History Channel; Learning Channel; Lifetime; Nashville Network; Nick at Nite's TV Land; Nickelodeon; Outdoor Channel; QVC; Sci-Fi Channel; TBS Superstation; TV Guide Channel; The Weather Channel; Trinity Bcstg. Network; Turner Network TV; USA Network.
Fee: $50.00 installation (aerial), $60.00 (underground); $25.95 monthly; $3.00 converter; $10.00 additional installation.
Pay Service 1
Pay Units: 46.
Programming (via satellite): Disney Channel.
Fee: $10.00 installation; $7.95 monthly.
Pay Service 2
Pay Units: 60.
Programming (via satellite): HBO.
Fee: $10.00 installation; $12.95 monthly.
Pay Service 3
Pay Units: 52.
Programming (via satellite): Showtime; The Movie Channel.
Fee: $10.00 installation; $12.95 monthly.
Equipment: Standard Components & Scientific-Atlanta headend; Blonder-Tongue & Jerrold amplifiers.
Miles of plant: 51.0 (coaxial). Homes passed: 1,086.
Director of engineering: Randy Mock. Marketing director: Mike Drake.
City fee: None.
Ownership: Milestone Communications LP (MSO).

MARTINSBURG—GS Communications Inc. West Virginia Division, 302 N. Mildred St., Ranson, WV 25438-1455. Phone: 304-725-9185. Fax: 304-725-0930. County: Berkeley. Also serves Berkeley County (portions). ICA: WV0019.
TV Market Ranking: Below 100. Franchise award date: N.A. Franchise expiration date: January 1, 2001. Began: June 25, 1966.
Channel capacity: 71 (not 2-way capable). Channels available but not in use: 1.
Basic Service
Subscribers: Included with Charles Town, WV.
Programming (received off-air): WJZ-TV (C), WMAR-TV (A) Baltimore; WHAG-TV (N), WJAL (W), WWPB (P) Hagerstown; WWPX (I) Martinsburg; WNPB-TV (P) Morgantown; WBDC-TV (W), WDCA (U), WETA-TV (P), WJLA-TV (A), WRC-TV (N), WTTG (F), WUSA (C) Washington; 21 FMs.
Programming (via satellite): C-SPAN; C-SPAN 2; Home Shopping Network; QVC; TV Guide Channel; The Weather Channel; Trinity Bcstg. Network; ValueVision.
Current originations: Public access.
Fee: $37.00 installation; $11.00 monthly; $1.99 converter.
Expanded Basic Service
Subscribers: Included with Charles Town, WV.
Programming (via satellite): A & E; American Movie Classics; BET; CNBC; CNN; Cartoon Network; Comedy Central; Discovery Channel; E! Entertainment TV; ESPN; ESPN 2; FX; Fox Family Channel; Great American Country; Headline News; History Channel; Home & Garden Television; Home Team Sports; Learning Channel; Lifetime; MSNBC; MTV; Nashville Network; Nick at Nite; Nickelodeon; Sci-Fi Channel; TV Food Network; Trinity Bcstg. Network; Turner Network TV; USA Network; VH1.
Fee: $16.00 monthly.
Pay Service 1
Pay Units: Included with Charles Town, WV.
Programming (via satellite): Cinemax; Disney Channel; HBO; Showtime; The Movie Channel.
Fee: $11.02 installation; $8.95 monthly (Disney), $10.95 monthly (Cinemax, HBO or TMC).
Pay-Per-View
Addressable homes: 5,816.
Action Pay-Per-View; Hot Choice; Playboy TV; Spice; Viewer's Choice.
Fee: $3.99-$5.94.
Local advertising: Yes. Available in satellite distributed, locally originated & character-generated programming. Local sales manager: Dave Whalen.
Program Guide: Teleguide.
Equipment: Scientific-Atlanta headend; C-COR & Magnavox amplifiers; Comm/Scope cable; JVC cameras; JVC VTRs; Compuvid character generator; Jerrold & Pioneer set top converters; Vitek traps; Scientific-Atlanta satellite antenna; Scientific-Atlanta satellite receivers.
Miles of plant: 879.0 (coaxial); 68.0 (fiber optic). Homes passed: 37,300. Included with Charles Town, WV.
Manager: Lawrence Willingham. Office manager: Patricia A. Ott. Chief technician: John Nichols. Marketing director: Paul Espinosa.
Ownership: Great Southern Printing & Manufacturing Co. (MSO).

MATEWAN—CableVision Communications, Box 2200, 68 5th St., Buckhannon, WV 26201. Phone: 304-472-4193. Fax: 304-472-0756. County: Mingo. Also serves Blackberry City, North Matewan, Red Jacket. ICA: WV0073.
TV Market Ranking: Below 100. Franchise award date: June 6, 1966. Franchise expiration date: N.A. Began: N.A.
Channel capacity: 37. Channels available but not in use: 2.
Basic Service
Subscribers: 559.
Programming (received off-air): WCHS-TV (A), WOWK-TV (C), WPBY-TV (P), WSAZ-TV (N) Charleston-Huntington.
Programming (via satellite): WGN-TV (W) Chicago; Animal Planet; C-SPAN; Discovery Channel; FoxNet; Home Shopping Network; TBS Superstation; Trinity Bcstg. Network.
Fee: $61.25 installation; $14.40 monthly; $1.24 converter.
Expanded Basic Service
Subscribers: N.A.
Programming (via satellite): A & E; American Movie Classics; CNN; Disney Channel; ESPN; Fox Family Channel; Great American Country; Headline News; Learning Channel; Lifetime; MTV; Nashville Network; Nickelodeon; Sci-Fi Channel; The Weather Channel; Turner Network TV; USA Network; VH1.
Fee: $10.61 monthly.
Pay Service 1
Pay Units: 126.
Programming (via satellite): Cinemax.
Fee: $7.99 monthly.
Pay Service 2
Pay Units: 130.
Programming (via satellite): HBO.
Fee: $11.99 monthly.
Pay Service 3
Pay Units: 59.
Programming (via satellite): Showtime.
Fee: $11.99 monthly.
Pay Service 4
Pay Units: 34.
Programming (via satellite): The Movie Channel.
Fee: $11.99 monthly.
Equipment: Blonder-Tongue, Olson & Standard Communications headend; Jerrold amplifiers.
Miles of plant: 25.0 (coaxial); None (fiber optic). Homes passed: 1,159.
Manager: Willie Critchfield. Chief technician: Bill Turner. Marketing director: Kenny Phillips.
City fee: 2% of gross.
Ownership: Rifkin & Associates Inc. (MSO). See Cable System Ownership.

MAYSEL—Econoco Inc., Box 147, Rte. 61, Kincaid, WV 25119. Phone: 304-469-2817. County: Clay. Also serves Procious, Valley Fork, Wallback. ICA: WV0195.
TV Market Ranking: 36. Franchise award date: N.A. Franchise expiration date: N.A. Began: June 1, 1990.
Channel capacity: 36 (not 2-way capable). Channels available but not in use: 19.
Basic Service
Subscribers: 454.
Programming (received off-air): WCHS-TV (A), WOWK-TV (C), WPBY-TV (P), WSAZ-TV (N), WVAH-TV (F,U) Charleston-Huntington; WSWP-TV (P) Grandview; WOAY-TV (A) Oak Hill-Beckley.
Programming (via satellite): WGN-TV (W) Chicago; Country Music TV; Discovery Channel; ESPN; Fox Family Channel; Nashville Network; TBS Superstation.
Fee: $25.00 installation; $20.72 monthly.
Pay Service 1
Pay Units: N.A.
Programming (via satellite): Showtime.
Fee: $10.00 installation; $10.00 monthly.
Miles of plant: 38.0 (coaxial).
Manager: Sheila Bills. Chief technician: Eslie Bills.
Ownership: Econoco Inc. (MSO).

MEADOW BRIDGE—Bradley's Inc., Box 41, Wharton, WV 25208. Phone: 304-247-6231. Fax: 304-247-6255. County: Fayette. Also serves Danese, Layland, Maplewood. ICA: WV0089.
TV Market Ranking: Below 100. Franchise award date: February 23, 1981. Franchise expiration date: February 23, 2006. Began: November 1, 1981.
Channel capacity: 35 (not 2-way capable). Channels available but not in use: None.
Basic Service
Subscribers: 797.
Programming (received off-air): WVVA (N) Bluefield; WCHS-TV (A), WOWK-TV (C), WSAZ-TV (N), WVAH-TV (F,U) Charleston-Huntington; WSWP-TV (P) Grandview; WOAY-TV (A) Oak Hill-Beckley; WDBJ (C) Roanoke-Lynchburg.
Programming (via satellite): C-SPAN; QVC; TBS Superstation.
Current originations: Automated time-weather.
Fee: $40.56 installation; $10.22 monthly; $0.63 converter.
Expanded Basic Service
Subscribers: 34.
Programming (via satellite): WGN-TV (W) Chicago; CNN; Cartoon Network; Country Music TV; Discovery Channel; ESPN; Fox Family Channel; Fox Sports Net Pittsburgh; Home & Garden Television; Learning Channel; Lifetime; Nashville Network; Nickelodeon; Odyssey; The Inspirational Network; The Weather Channel; Turner Classic Movies; Turner Network TV; USA Network; VH1.
Fee: $5.00 installation; $14.38 monthly.
Pay Service 1
Pay Units: 41.
Programming (via satellite): Disney Channel.
Fee: $7.95 monthly.
Pay Service 2
Pay Units: 66.
Programming (via satellite): HBO.
Fee: $11.95 monthly.
Pay Service 3
Pay Units: 25.
Programming (via satellite): The Movie Channel.
Fee: $11.95 monthly.
Local advertising: No.
Equipment: Scientific-Atlanta headend; Texscan & Magnavox amplifiers; Texscan & Compuvid character generator; Scientific-Atlanta set top converters; Scientific-Atlanta addressable set top converters; Scientific-Atlanta satellite antenna; Scientific-Atlanta satellite receivers.
Miles of plant: 35.0 (coaxial). Additional miles planned: 7.0 (coaxial). Homes passed: 950. Total homes in franchised area: 1,000.
Manager: Robert Legg Jr. Chief technician: Chuck Bradley.
City fee: $100 annually.
Ownership: Bradley's Inc. (MSO).

MEADOWDALE—Westover TV Cable Co., Box 599, Dellslow, WV 26531. Phone: 304-292-6561. County: Marion. Also serves Marion County. ICA: WV0109.
TV Market Ranking: Below 100. Franchise award date: N.A. Franchise expiration date: N.A. Began: June 1, 1968.
Channel capacity: 12. Channels available but not in use: N.A.
Basic Service
Subscribers: N.A.
Programming (received off-air): WBOY-TV (N), WDTV (C,A) Clarksburg-Weston; WNPB-TV (P) Morgantown; KDKA-TV (C), WPGH-TV (F), WPXI (N), WQED (P), WTAE-TV (A) Pittsburgh; WTOV-TV (N) Steubenville-Wheeling; WTRF-TV (C) Wheeling-Steubenville; allband FM.
Planned programming (via satellite): Fox Family Channel.
Current originations: Automated time-weather.
Fee: $7.50 installation; $8.00 monthly.
Equipment: Jerrold headend; Jerrold amplifiers; Times Fiber cable; Andrew satellite antenna.
Miles of plant: 12.0 (coaxial). Homes passed: 500. Total homes in franchised area: 1,400.
Manager: Michael Ligouri. Chief technician: Ed Hinkle.
City fee: None.
Ownership: Century Communications Corp. (MSO). See Cable System Ownership.

MIDDLEBOURNE—Middlebourne TV Cable, Drawer 2, Jerusalem, OH 43747. Phone: 740-926-1742. County: Tyler. ICA: WV0105.
TV Market Ranking: Below 100. Franchise award date: N.A. Franchise expiration date: N.A. Began: November 1, 1967.
Channel capacity: 12. Channels available but not in use: 2.
Basic Service
Subscribers: 400.
Programming (received off-air): WBOY-TV (N), WDTV (C,A) Clarksburg-Weston; WNPB-TV (P) Morgantown; WTAP-TV (N) Parkersburg-Marietta; KDKA-TV (C), WPGH-TV (F), WPXI (N), WTAE-TV (A) Pittsburgh; WTOV-TV (N) Steubenville-Wheeling; WTRF-TV (C) Wheeling-Steubenville; allband FM.
Programming (via satellite): Cartoon Network; Turner Classic Movies.
Fee: $10.30 installation; $7.25 monthly.
Equipment: Blonder-Tongue headend; Coral & Jerrold amplifiers; Carro & Times Fiber cable.
Miles of plant: 13.0 (coaxial). Homes passed: 600.

Manager: Paul E. Richards.
City fee: $150 annually.
Ownership: Paul E. Richards (MSO).

MILTON—CableVision Communications, Box 2200, 68 5th St., Buckhannon, WV 26201. Phone: 304-472-4193. Fax: 304-472-0756. Counties: Cabell & Putnam. Also serves Barboursville, Cabell County, Culloden, Hurricane, Ona, Putnam County, Scott Depot. ICA: WV0012.
TV Market Ranking: 36. Franchise award date: December 1, 1975. Franchise expiration date: December 12, 1999. Began: March 1, 1976.
Channel capacity: 60. Channels available but not in use: N.A.
Basic Service
Subscribers: 11,117.
Programming (received off-air): WTSF (I) Ashland; WCHS-TV (A), WOWK-TV (C), WPBY-TV (P), WSAZ-TV (N), WVAH-TV (F,U) Charleston-Huntington.
Programming (via satellite): WGN-TV (W) Chicago; Home Shopping Network; TBS Superstation; TV Guide Channel; The Weather Channel.
Current originations: Local access.
Fee: $61.25 installation; $14.40 monthly; $1.24 converter.
Expanded Basic Service
Subscribers: N.A.
Programming (via satellite): A & E; American Movie Classics; C-SPAN; C-SPAN 2; CNBC; CNN; Cartoon Network; Comedy Central; Discovery Channel; E! Entertainment TV; ESPN; ESPN 2; FX; Fox Family Channel; Great American Country; Headline News; History Channel; Home & Garden Television; Knowledge TV; Learning Channel; Lifetime; MSNBC; MTV; Much-Music Network; Nashville Network; Nick at Nite's TV Land; Nickelodeon; Outdoor Channel; Prime Sports Radio; Sci-Fi Channel; TV Food Network; The Health Network; The Inspirational Network; Toon Disney; Travel Channel; Trinity Bcstg. Network; Turner Network TV; USA Network.
Fee: $17.32 monthly.
A la Carte 1
Subscribers: N.A.
Programming (via satellite): Turner Classic Movies.
Fee: $1.99 monthly.
Pay Service 1
Pay Units: 5,304.
Programming (via satellite): Cinemax; HBO (multiplexed); Playboy TV; Showtime; Starz!; The Movie Channel; The New Encore.
Fee: $10.00 installation; $4.99 monthly (Playboy), $5.99 (Encore & Starz), $7.99 monthly (Cinemax), $11.99 monthly (HBO, Showtime or TMC).
Local advertising: Yes. Available in locally originated programming. Rates: $4.00-$15.00/Spot.
Program Guide: The Cable Guide.
Equipment: Blonder-Tongue, Scientific-Atlanta & Standard Communications headend; Jerrold & Magnavox amplifiers; Magnavox set top converters; Andrew satellite antenna; Texscan commercial insert.
Miles of plant: 254.0 (coaxial). Homes passed: 12,330.
Manager: Willie Critchfield. Plant manager: Gary Lucas. Marketing director: Kenny Phillips.
City fee: $100 annually.
Ownership: Rifkin & Associates Inc. (MSO). See Cable System Ownership.

MONONGAH—Century Huntington Co., Box 599, Dellslow, WV 26531. Phone: 304-292-6561. County: Marion. Also serves Marion County. ICA: WV0055.
TV Market Ranking: Below 100. Franchise award date: N.A. Franchise expiration date: N.A. Began: January 1, 1954.
Channel capacity: 12. Channels available but not in use: 1.
Basic Service
Subscribers: N.A.
Programming (received off-air): WBOY-TV (N), WDTV (C,A) Clarksburg-Weston; WNPB-TV (P) Morgantown; KDKA-TV (C), WPGH-TV (F), WPXI (N), WQED (P), WTAE-TV (A) Pittsburgh; WTOV-TV (N) Steubenville-Wheeling; WTRF-TV (C) Wheeling-Steubenville; allband FM.
Current originations: Automated time-weather.
Fee: $7.50 installation; $7.50 monthly.
Equipment: Jerrold headend; Jerrold amplifiers; Times Fiber cable.
Miles of plant: 12.0 (coaxial). Homes passed: 1,950.
Manager: Micheal Ligouri. Chief technician: Ed Hinkle.
City fee: 0.5% of gross.
Ownership: Century Communications Corp. (MSO). See Cable System Ownership.

MOOREFIELD—Cable Equities, 741 N. Main St., Moorefield, WV 26836. Phone: 304-538-2361. Fax: 304-538-6175. County: Hardy. Also serves Durgon, Hardy County. ICA: WV0197.
TV Market Ranking: Below 100 (portions of Hardy County); Outside TV Markets (Durgon, portions of Hardy County, Moorefield). Franchise award date: N.A. Franchise expiration date: N.A. Began: July 1, 1969.
Channel capacity: N.A. Channels available but not in use: N.A.
Basic Service
Subscribers: 1,205.
Programming (received off-air): WHAG-TV (N), WWPB (P) Hagerstown; WHSV-TV (A,F) Harrisonburg; WJAC-TV (N) Johnstown-Altoona; WNPB-TV (P) Morgantown; WDCA (U), WTTG (F), WUSA (C) Washington; allband FM.
Programming (via satellite): C-SPAN; C-SPAN 2; TBS Superstation.
Fee: $29.95 installation; $11.00 monthly.
Expanded Basic Service
Subscribers: N.A.
Programming (via satellite): A & E; American Movie Classics; CNN; Comedy Central; Country Music TV; Discovery Channel; ESPN; Fox Family Channel; Headline News; MTV; Nashville Network; Nickelodeon; The Weather Channel; Turner Network TV; USA Network.
Fee: N.A.
Pay Service 1
Pay Units: N.A.
Programming (via satellite): Cinemax; Disney Channel; HBO; Showtime.
Fee: $15.00 installation; $11.95 monthly (HBO).
Equipment: Scientific-Atlanta & Jerrold headend; SKL amplifiers; Times Fiber cable; Comtech satellite antenna.
Miles of plant: 51.0 (coaxial).
Manager: Norman Barb. Chief technician: Doug Gent.
City fee: None.
Ownership: Rifkin & Associates Inc. (MSO). See Cable System Ownership.

MORGANTOWN—Century Huntington Co., Box 599, Dellslow, WV 26531. Phone: 304-292-6561. Counties: Monongalia & Preston. Also serves Granville, Monongalia County (portions), Osage, Preston County (portions), Rowlesburg, Star City. ICA: WV0198.
TV Market Ranking: 90 (portions of Monongalia County); Below 100 (Granville, portions of Monongalia County, Morgantown, Osage, portions of Preston County, Star City); Outside TV Markets (portions of Monongalia County, portions of Preston County, Rowlesburg). Franchise award date: N.A. Franchise expiration date: N.A. Began: July 1, 1953.
Channel capacity: 30. Channels available but not in use: 1.
Basic Service
Subscribers: 30,800.
Programming (received off-air): WBOY-TV (N), WDTV (C,A), WVFX (F) Clarksburg-Weston; WNPB-TV (P) Morgantown; KDKA-TV (C), WPGH-TV (F), WPXI (N), WQED (P), WTAE-TV (A) Pittsburgh; allband FM.
Programming (via satellite): A & E; American Movie Classics; C-SPAN; CNN; Country Music TV; ESPN; Fox Family Channel; Fox Sports Net Pittsburgh; Home Shopping Network; Lifetime; MTV; Nickelodeon; QVC; TBS Superstation; The Weather Channel; USA Network; VH1.
Current originations: Automated time-weather; public access.
Fee: $30.00 installation; $23.50 monthly.
Expanded Basic Service
Subscribers: 27,900.
Programming (via satellite): Discovery Channel; Nashville Network; Turner Network TV.
Fee: $2.25 monthly.
Pay Service 1
Pay Units: N.A.
Programming (via satellite): Cinemax; Disney Channel; HBO; Showtime.
Fee: $19.95 installation; $11.50 monthly (each).
Local advertising: No.
Equipment: Jerrold headend; Texscan amplifiers; Comm/Scope cable; Sony VTRs; Hamlin set top converters; Andrew & Anixter-Mark satellite antenna; Scientific-Atlanta satellite receivers.
Miles of plant: 204.0 (coaxial).
Manager: Michael Ligouri. Chief technician: Ed Hinkle.
City fee: 3% of gross.
Ownership: Century Communications Corp. (MSO). See Cable System Ownership.

MOUNDSVILLE—TCI of West Virginia Inc., 215 1/2 N. Lafayette Ave., Moundsville, WV 26041. Phone: 800-352-1030. County: Marshall. Also serves Glen Dale, Little Grave Creek, Marshall County, Middle Grave Creek, Washington Lands. ICA: WV0022.
TV Market Ranking: 90. Franchise award date: N.A. Franchise expiration date: N.A. Began: June 1, 1957.
Channel capacity: 54. Channels available but not in use: N.A.
Basic Service
Subscribers: 6,613.
Programming (received off-air): WNPB-TV (P) Morgantown; KDKA-TV (C), WPGH-TV (F), WPXI (N), WQED (P), WTAE-TV (A) Pittsburgh; WTOV-TV (N) Steubenville-Wheeling; WTRF-TV (C) Wheeling-Steubenville; allband FM.
Programming (via satellite): A & E; C-SPAN; C-SPAN 2; CNBC; CNN; Cartoon Network; Comedy Central; Discovery Channel; Fox Family Channel; Headline News; Lifetime; MTV; Nashville Network; Nickelodeon; Odyssey; QVC; TBS Superstation; The Weather Channel; VH1.
Fee: $59.95 installation; $18.37 monthly; $4.00 converter.
Expanded Basic Service
Subscribers: 6,404.
Programming (via satellite): American Movie Classics; ESPN; Fox Sports Net Pittsburgh; Turner Network TV; USA Network.
Fee: $1.85 monthly.
Pay Service 1
Pay Units: 501.
Programming (via satellite): Disney Channel.
Fee: $11.95 monthly.
Pay Service 2
Pay Units: 1,334.
Programming (via satellite): HBO.
Fee: $13.15 monthly.
Pay Service 3
Pay Units: 418.
Programming (via satellite): The Movie Channel.
Fee: $13.15 monthly.
Pay Service 4
Pay Units: 604.
Programming (via satellite): Showtime.
Fee: $13.15 monthly.
Pay Service 5
Pay Units: 2,598.
Programming (via satellite): The New Encore.
Fee: N.A.
Local advertising: Yes.
Equipment: Jerrold headend; Entron amplifiers; Viking cable; Metrodata character generator; Hughes satellite antenna.
Miles of plant: 100.7 (coaxial). Homes passed: 6,818. Total homes in franchised area: 18,736.
Manager: Dennis Snow.
City fee: 3% of gross.
Ownership: AT&T Broadband & Internet Services (MSO). Purchased from Tele-Communications Inc., March 9, 1999.

MOUNT LOOKOUT—Econoco Inc., Box 147, Rte. 61, Kincaid, WV 25119. Phone: 304-469-2817. Counties: Fayette & Nicholas. Also serves Mount Nebo, Nallen. ICA: WV0199.
TV Market Ranking: Below 100. Franchise award date: N.A. Franchise expiration date: N.A. Began: January 1, 1984.
Channel capacity: 36 (not 2-way capable). Channels available but not in use: 19.
Basic Service
Subscribers: 452.
Programming (received off-air): WCHS-TV (A), WOWK-TV (C), WSAZ-TV (N), WVAH-TV (F,U) Charleston-Huntington; WDTV (C,A) Clarksburg-Weston; WSWP-TV (P) Grandview; WOAY-TV (A) Oak Hill-Beckley.
Programming (via satellite): WGN-TV (W) Chicago; A & E; CNN; Discovery Channel; ESPN; Fox Family Channel; Nashville Network; TBS Superstation; USA Network.
Fee: $25.00 installation; $20.72 monthly.

Pay Service 1
Pay Units: N.A.
Programming (via satellite): HBO.
Fee: $10.00 installation; $12.00 monthly.
Miles of plant: 28.0 (coaxial).
Manager: Sheila Bills. Chief technician: Eslie Bills.
Ownership: Econoco Inc. (MSO).

MUD RIVER—Bowen Cablevision, Box 130, Wilkinson, WV 25653-0130. Phone: 304-752-3023. County: Boone. ICA: WV0238.
TV Market Ranking: 36. Franchise award date: N.A. Franchise expiration date: N.A. Began: N.A.
Channel capacity: N.A. Channels available but not in use: N.A.
Basic Service
Subscribers: N.A.
Programming (received off-air): WCHS-TV (A), WOWK-TV (C), WPBY-TV (P), WSAZ-TV (N), WVAH-TV (F,U) Charleston-Huntington.
Programming (via satellite): ESPN; Fox Family Channel; Nashville Network; USA Network.
Fee: N.A.
Manager: Gary Bowen.
Ownership: Bowen Cablevision Inc. (MSO).

MULLENS—Nesbe Cable, 216-A Howard Ave., Mullens, WV 25882. Phone: 304-294-6332. Fax: 304-294-4717. Counties: Raleigh & Wyoming. Also serves Alpoca (portion), Bud (portion), Corinne, Hotchkiss, Itmann, Maben, Otsego, Pierpoint, Slab Fork. ICA: WV0086.
TV Market Ranking: Below 100. Franchise award date: N.A. Franchise expiration date: N.A. Began: May 1, 1952.
Channel capacity: 64 (not 2-way capable). Channels available but not in use: None.
Basic Service
Subscribers: 1,400.
Programming (received off-air): WVVA (N) Bluefield; WCHS-TV (A), WOWK-TV (C) Charleston-Huntington; WSWP-TV (P) Grandview; WVSX (I) Lewisburg; WOAY-TV (A) Oak Hill-Beckley; WDBJ (C) Roanoke-Lynchburg; allband FM.
Programming (via satellite): C-SPAN; TBS Superstation; WB 100+ Station Group.
Fee: $35.00 installation; $12.95 monthly.
Expanded Basic Service
Subscribers: 1,311.
Programming (via satellite): A & E; American Movie Classics; CNN; Cartoon Network; Country Music TV; Discovery Channel; Disney Channel; ESPN; ESPN 2; Fox Family Channel; Fox Sports Net Pittsburgh; Golf Channel; Headline News; History Channel; Home & Garden Television; Home Shopping Network; Lifetime; MSNBC; MTV; Nashville Network; Nick at Nite's TV Land; Nickelodeon; Outdoor Channel; QVC; Sci-Fi Channel; The Health Network; The Inspirational Network; The Weather Channel; Trinity Bcstg. Network; Turner Classic Movies; Turner Network TV; USA Network; VH1; Wisdom Network.
Fee: $26.95 monthly.
Pay Service 1
Pay Units: N.A.
Programming (via satellite): Cinemax; HBO; The Movie Channel.
Fee: $10.50 monthly (each).
Equipment: Scientific-Atlanta headend; Scientific-Atlanta amplifiers; Trilogy & Comm/Scope cable; Scientific-Atlanta satellite receivers.
Miles of plant: 35.4 (coaxial); None (fiber optic). Homes passed: 1,620. Total homes in franchised area: 1,620.
Manager: Phil Halsey. Chief technician: Ron Campbell.
City fee: 5% of gross.
Ownership: Bahakel Communications Ltd. (MSO). Purchased from Mountaineer Cablevision Inc., May 1, 1999.

MURPHYTOWN—Community Antenna Service, Box 282, Rte. 1, Washington, WV 26181. Phone: 304-863-8922. Fax: 304-863-6219. County: Wood. Also serves Dallison, Davisville, Walker. ICA: WV0200.
TV Market Ranking: Below 100. Franchise award date: N.A. Franchise expiration date: N.A. Began: June 1, 1981.
Channel capacity: 36 (not 2-way capable). Channels available but not in use: 1.
Basic Service
Subscribers: 641.
Programming (received off-air): WOUB-TV (P) Athens; WCHS-TV (A), WOWK-TV (C), WPBY-TV (P), WSAZ-TV (N), WVAH-TV (F,U) Charleston-Huntington; WTAP-TV (N) Parkersburg-Marietta.
Fee: N.A.
Miles of plant: 40.0 (coaxial); None (fiber optic). Homes passed: 887. Total homes in franchised area: 887.
Manager: Arthur R. Cooper.
Ownership: Arthur R. Cooper (MSO).

NETTIE—Paxton Cable, Suite 280, 700 Ackerman Rd., Columbus, OH 43202. Phone: 614-263-6100. County: Nicholas. ICA: WV0120.
TV Market Ranking: Below 100. Franchise award date: N.A. Franchise expiration date: N.A. Began: April 1, 1981.
Channel capacity: 12. Channels available but not in use: N.A.
Basic Service
Subscribers: N.A.
Programming (received off-air): WCHS-TV (A), WOWK-TV (C), WSAZ-TV (N), WVAH-TV (F,U) Charleston-Huntington; WSWP-TV (P) Grandview; WOAY-TV (A) Oak Hill-Beckley.
Fee: N.A.
Pay Service 1
Pay Units: N.A.
Programming (via satellite): HBO.
Fee: N.A.
Miles of plant: 6.8 (coaxial). Homes passed: 400.
Manager: Cecil Eldridge. Director of operations: Lisa Collier.
Ownership: Paxton Cable Television Inc. (MSO). Purchased from Clear Vision CATV Systems.

NEW CUMBERLAND—TCI of West Virginia Inc., 16808 St. Clair Ave., East Liverpool, OH 43920-3095. Phone: 800-421-3145. Fax: 330-385-0322. County: Hancock. Also serves Hancock County (portions), New Manchester. ICA: WV0069.
TV Market Ranking: 10 (Hancock County, New Cumberland, New Manchester); 90 (Hancock County, New Cumberland, New Manchester). Franchise award date: N.A. Franchise expiration date: N.A. Began: June 1, 1970.
Channel capacity: 72 (not 2-way capable). Channels available but not in use: 32.
Basic Service
Subscribers: 1,172.
Programming (received off-air): WNPB-TV (P) Morgantown; KDKA-TV (C), WCWB (W), WPGH-TV (F), WPXI (N), WQED (P), WQEX (P), WTAE-TV (A) Pittsburgh; WTOV-TV (N) Steubenville-Wheeling; WTRF-TV (C) Wheeling-Steubenville; allband FM.
Programming (via satellite): C-SPAN; Odyssey; QVC; TBS Superstation.
Fee: $42.96 installation; $9.61 monthly.
Expanded Basic Service
Subscribers: N.A.
Programming (via satellite): A & E; American Movie Classics; CNBC; CNN; Discovery Channel; ESPN; FX; Fox Family Channel; Fox Sports Net Pittsburgh; Headline News; Intro TV; Lifetime; MTV; Nashville Network; Nickelodeon; The Weather Channel; Turner Network TV; USA Network.
Fee: $9.61 monthly.
Pay Service 1
Pay Units: 251.
Programming (via satellite): HBO.
Fee: $13.65 monthly.
Pay Service 2
Pay Units: 133.
Programming (via satellite): Showtime.
Fee: $13.65 monthly.
Pay Service 3
Pay Units: N.A.
Programming (via satellite): Disney Channel; Starz!; The New Encore.
Fee: $1.75 monthly (Encore), $4.75 monthly (Starz), $12.95 monthly (Disney).
Pay-Per-View
Addressable homes: 162.
Local advertising: No.
Equipment: Jerrold headend; Vikoa amplifiers; Vikoa cable; Scientific-Atlanta satellite antenna; Scientific-Atlanta satellite receivers.
Miles of plant: 34.3 (coaxial); 7.6 (fiber optic). Homes passed: 1,394. Total homes in franchised area: 1,470.
Manager: Jim Underwood. Chief technician: Scott Boyd.
City fee: None.
Ownership: AT&T Broadband & Internet Services (MSO). Purchased from Tele-Communications Inc., March 9, 1999.

NEW MARTINSVILLE—Cablecomm, 247 N. State Rte. 2, New Martinsville, WV 26155-2203. Phone: 800-352-1030. Counties: Tyler & Wetzel. Also serves Paden City, Proctor, Sistersville, Tyler County (portions), Wetzel County (portions). ICA: WV0025.
TV Market Ranking: 90 (New Martinsville, Proctor, portions of Wetzel County); Below 100 (Sistersville, portions of Tyler County, portions of Wetzel County); Outside TV Markets (Paden City, portions of Tyler County). Franchise award date: N.A. Franchise expiration date: N.A. Began: May 1, 1957.
Channel capacity: 27. Channels available but not in use: 1.
Basic Service
Subscribers: 5,152.
Programming (received off-air): WBOY-TV (N) Clarksburg-Weston; WNPB-TV (P) Morgantown; KDKA-TV (C), WPGH-TV (F), WTAE-TV (A) Pittsburgh; WTOV-TV (N) Steubenville-Wheeling; WTRF-TV (C) Wheeling-Steubenville; allband FM.
Programming (via satellite): A & E; CNN; Cartoon Network; Discovery Channel; Headline News; Lifetime; MTV; Nashville Network; Nickelodeon; QVC; TBS Superstation.
Current originations: Automated time-weather; local news.
Fee: $59.95 installation; $15.75 monthly; $20.00 additional installation.
Expanded Basic Service
Subscribers: 4,854.
Programming (via satellite): American Movie Classics; ESPN; Fox Sports Net Pittsburgh; Odyssey; Turner Network TV; USA Network.
Fee: $1.85 monthly.
Pay Service 1
Pay Units: 445.
Programming (via satellite): Cinemax.
Fee: $13.15 monthly.
Pay Service 2
Pay Units: 492.
Programming (via satellite): Disney Channel.
Fee: $11.95 monthly.
Pay Service 3
Pay Units: 1,834.
Programming (via satellite): The New Encore.
Fee: N.A.
Pay Service 4
Pay Units: 937.
Programming (via satellite): HBO.
Fee: $13.15 monthly.
Pay Service 5
Pay Units: 515.
Programming (via satellite): Showtime.
Fee: $13.15 monthly.
Local advertising: Yes. Rates: $65.00/Month/Spot. Local sales manager: Carman R. Harman.
Program Guide: The Cable Guide.
Equipment: Jerrold headend; AFC satellite antenna; Microdyne satellite receivers.
Miles of plant: 101.0 (coaxial). Homes passed: 5,676. Total homes in franchised area: 6,400.
Manager: Kenneth R. Heinlein.
Ownership: Fanch Communications Inc. (MSO); Time Warner Cable (MSO). Purchased from Tele-Communications Inc., February 25, 1999. See Cable System Ownership.

NITRO—Harmon Cable Communications, 78 Olde Main Plaza, St. Albans, WV 25177. Phone: 304-722-2933. Fax: 304-722-2203.
Web site: http://www.harmoncable.com.
Counties: Kanawha & Putnam. Also serves Cross Lanes, Poca, St. Albans. ICA: WV0009.
TV Market Ranking: 36. Franchise award date: N.A. Franchise expiration date: N.A. Began: February 1, 1966.
Channel capacity: 49 (not 2-way capable). Channels available but not in use: 3.
Basic Service
Subscribers: 13,935.
Programming (received off-air): WCHS-TV (A), WOWK-TV (C), WPBY-TV (P), WSAZ-TV (N), WVAH-TV (F,U) Charleston-Huntington; allband FM.
Programming (via satellite): WGN-TV (W) Chicago; C-SPAN; C-SPAN 2; Home Shopping Network; Pax Net; QVC; TBS Superstation; TV Guide Channel; Trinity Bcstg. Network; WB 100+ Station Group.
Current originations: Public access; educational access; government access; religious access; automated emergency alert; local news.
Fee: $40.00 installation; $8.26 monthly.
Expanded Basic Service
Subscribers: N.A.
Programming (via satellite): A & E; American Movie Classics; Animal Planet; BET; CNBC; CNN; Country Music TV; Discovery Channel; Disney Channel; E! Entertainment TV; ESPN; FX; Fox Family Channel; Fox Sports Net Pittsburgh; Headline News; Home & Garden Television; Learning Channel; Lifetime; MSNBC; MTV; Nashville Network; Nick at Nite's TV Land; Nickelodeon; Odyssey; Outdoor Channel; Sci-Fi Channel; The Weather Channel; Toon Disney; Turner Network TV; USA Network; VH1.
Fee: $10.00 installation; $17.50 monthly.
Expanded Basic Service 2
Subscribers: N.A.
Programming (via satellite): Cartoon Network; Comedy Central; ESPN 2; History Channel; Turner Classic Movies.
Fee: $2.95 monthly.
Pay Service 1
Pay Units: 1,743.
Programming (via satellite): Cinemax.

Fee: $9.00 monthly.

Pay Service 2

Pay Units: N.A.

Programming (via satellite): The New Encore.

Fee: $4.95 monthly.

Pay Service 3

Pay Units: 3,468.

Programming (via satellite): HBO (multiplexed).

Fee: $10.95 monthly.

Pay Service 4

Pay Units: 345.

Programming (via satellite): Showtime.

Fee: $10.95 monthly.

Pay-Per-View

Addressable homes: 2,883.

Movies; special events.

Fee: $3.95 (Movies); $19.95-$35.95 (special events).

Local advertising: Yes.

Equipment: Scientific-Atlanta headend; Scientific-Atlanta amplifiers; Trilogy cable; Scientific-Atlanta set top converters; Scientific-Atlanta addressable set top converters; Pico & Eagle traps; Scientific-Atlanta satellite receivers.

Miles of plant: 275.0 (coaxial). Homes passed: 18,712.

Manager: Joel Patten. Chief technician: Angelo Williams. Marketing director: Teresa McDonald.

Ownership: Fanch Communications Inc. (MSO); Time Warner Cable (MSO). Purchased from Harmon Cable Communications, June 21, 1999.

NORTHFORK—TMC of Northfork, Box 489, Northfork, WV 24868. Phone: 304-862-2571. Fax: 304-862-2559. County: McDowell. Also serves Algoma, Anawalt, Conkintown, Crumpler, Eckman, Elkhorn, Gilliam, Keystone, Kyle, Leckie, Maybeury, McDowell, Pageton, Powhatan, Rolfe, Skygusty, Switchback, Upland, Worth. ICA: WV0045.

TV Market Ranking: Below 100. Franchise award date: N.A. Franchise expiration date: September 13, 2002. Began: December 1, 1951.

Channel capacity: 15 (not 2-way capable). Channels available but not in use: None.

Basic Service

Subscribers: 1,529.

Programming (received off-air): WVVA (N) Bluefield; WCHS-TV (A), WOWK-TV (C) Charleston-Huntington; WSWP-TV (P) Grandview; WOAY-TV (A) Oak Hill-Beckley; allband FM.

Programming (via satellite): Fox Family Channel.

Current originations: Automated time-weather; public access; educational access; government access; local news.

Fee: $30.00 installation (aerial), $42.75 (underground); $10.45 monthly; $0.72 converter.

Expanded Basic Service

Subscribers: 1,415.

Programming (via satellite): CNN; ESPN; Nashville Network; TBS Superstation.

Fee: $7.34 monthly.

Pay Service 1

Pay Units: 212.

Programming (via satellite): Cinemax.

Fee: $20.00 installation; $8.00 monthly.

Pay Service 2

Pay Units: 165.

Programming (via satellite): Disney Channel.

Fee: $20.00 installation; $7.00 monthly.

Pay Service 3

Pay Units: 665.

Programming (via satellite): HBO.

Fee: $20.00 installation; $10.00 monthly.

Pay Service 4

Pay Units: 182.

Programming (via satellite): Showtime.

Fee: $20.00 installation; $7.00 monthly.

Local advertising: Yes. Available in character-generated programming.

Equipment: Blonder-Tongue headend; Coral & Jerrold amplifiers; Comm/Scope cable; Jerrold & Scientific-Atlanta set top converters; Eagle traps; Microdyne satellite antenna; M/A-Com & Microdyne satellite receivers.

Miles of plant: 65.0 (coaxial); None (fiber optic). Homes passed: 1,900.

Manager: Robert Harrald. Office manager: Virginia Steele. Chief technician: Michael Constantino. Marketing director: Bill Benner.

Ownership: Tele-Media Corp. (MSO).

OAK HILL—CableVision Communications, 313 W. Main St., Oak Hill, WV 25901. Phone: 304-465-0410. Fax: 304-465-8349. Counties: Fayette, Kanawha, Raleigh & Wyoming. Also serves Allen Junction, Amigo, Black Eagle, Brooklyn, Corrinne, Cunard, Fayetteville, Glen White, Helen, Lochgelly, Midway, Oak Ridge, Pea Ridge, Raleigh County (portions), Rhodell, Soak Creek, Sophia, Stephenson, Summerlee, Wyco, Wyoming County (portions). ICA: WV0023.

TV Market Ranking: 36 (Brooklyn, Cunard, Fayetteville, Oak Ridge, portions of Raleigh County); Below 100 (Allen Junction, Amigo, Black Eagle, Corrinne, Glen White, Helen, Lochgelly, Midway, portions of Oak Hill, Pea Ridge, portions of Raleigh County, Rhodell, Soak Creek, Sophia, Stephenson, Summerlee, Wyco, portions of Wyoming County); Outside TV Markets (portions of Wyoming County). Franchise award date: N.A. Franchise expiration date: N.A. Began: October 1, 1968.

Channel capacity: 35 (2-way capable). Channels available but not in use: 6.

Basic Service

Subscribers: 8,700.

Programming (received off-air): WVVA (N) Bluefield; WCHS-TV (A), WOWK-TV (C), WSAZ-TV (N), WVAH-TV (F,U) Charleston-Huntington; WSWP-TV (P) Grandview; WOAY-TV (A) Oak Hill-Beckley; 7 FMs.

Programming (via satellite): WGN-TV (W) Chicago; TBS Superstation.

Planned originations: Public access; educational access; government access; religious access; leased access; library access.

Fee: $70.13 installation; $9.50 monthly; $20.00 additional installation.

Expanded Basic Service

Subscribers: 6,638.

Programming (via satellite): American Movie Classics; BET; C-SPAN; C-SPAN 2; CNN; Comedy Central; Country Music TV; Discovery Channel; ESPN; Fox Family Channel; Home Shopping Network; Learning Channel; MTV; Nickelodeon; Turner Network TV; USA Network.

Fee: $70.13 installation; $14.85 monthly.

Pay Service 1

Pay Units: 542.

Programming (via satellite): Cinemax.

Fee: $12.75 installation; $8.95 monthly.

Pay Service 2

Pay Units: 923.

Programming (via satellite): Disney Channel.

Fee: $12.75 installation; $7.95 monthly.

Pay Service 3

Pay Units: 1,054.

Programming (via satellite): HBO.

Fee: $12.75 installation; $10.95 monthly.

Pay Service 4

Pay Units: 233.

Programming (via satellite): The Movie Channel.

Fee: $12.75 installation; $5.95 monthly.

Pay Service 5

Pay Units: 1,129.

Programming (via satellite): Showtime.

Fee: $12.75 installation; $8.95 monthly.

Pay-Per-View

Addressable homes: 8,700.

Special events.

Fee: Varies.

Local advertising: Yes. Available in locally originated programming. Rates: $8.00/Minute; $5.00/30 Seconds. Local sales manager: Bruce Rifkin.

Equipment: Jerrold, Scientific-Atlanta & ISS headend; Scientific-Atlanta amplifiers; Comm/Scope cable; Sony & JVC VTRs; Amiga character generator; Scientific-Atlanta set top converters; PPC traps; Scientific-Atlanta, Prodelin & Comtech satellite antenna; Standard Agile Omni satellite receivers.

Miles of plant: 204.1 (coaxial); None (fiber optic). Additional miles planned: 2.0 (coaxial). Homes passed: 10,900.

Manager: Keith Mains.

City and County fee: 3% of gross.

Ownership: Rifkin & Associates Inc. (MSO). See Cable System Ownership.

OAKVALE—Nesbe Cable, 216-A Howard Ave., Mullens, WV 25882. Phone: 304-294-6332. Fax: 304-294-4717. County: Mercer. Also serves Elgood, Hardy, Ingleside, Kellysville, Mercer County, Willowton. ICA: WV0201.

TV Market Ranking: Below 100. Franchise award date: N.A. Franchise expiration date: N.A. Began: N.A.

Channel capacity: 44 (not 2-way capable). Channels available but not in use: None.

Basic Service

Subscribers: 450.

Programming (received off-air): WVVA (N) Bluefield; WSWP-TV (P) Grandview; WOAY-TV (A) Oak Hill-Beckley; WBRA-TV (P) Roanoke; WDBJ (C), WFXR-TV (F), WSET-TV (A), WSLS-TV (N) Roanoke-Lynchburg.

Programming (via satellite): WGN-TV (W) Chicago; CNN; Cartoon Network; Country Music TV; Discovery Channel; ESPN; ESPN 2; Fox Family Channel; Golf Channel; Headline News; Home & Garden Television; Nashville Network; Nick at Nite's TV Land; QVC; Sci-Fi Channel; TBS Superstation; The Weather Channel; Trinity Bcstg. Network; Turner Classic Movies; Turner Network TV; USA Network.

Fee: $24.50 monthly.

Pay Service 1

Pay Units: N.A.

Programming (via satellite): Cinemax; Disney Channel; HBO.

Fee: $5.25 monthly (Disney), $11.13 monthly (Cinemax or HBO).

Miles of plant: 40.0 (coaxial); None (fiber optic). Homes passed: 560. Total homes in franchised area: 560.

Manager: Phil Halsey. Chief technician: Ron Campbell.

Ownership: Bahakel Communications Ltd. (MSO). Purchased from Mountaineer Cablevision Inc., May 1, 1999.

OCEANA—Wyoming TV Cable Co., Box 210, Rock View, WV 24880. Phone: 304-732-6114. Fax: 304-732-9370. County: Wyoming. Also serves Clear Fork, Cyclone, Huff Creek, Kopperston, Tower Fork. ICA: WV0049.

TV Market Ranking: Below 100. Franchise award date: N.A. Franchise expiration date: N.A. Began: January 1, 1976.

Channel capacity: 21. Channels available but not in use: N.A.

Basic Service

Subscribers: N.A.

Programming (received off-air): WVVA (N) Bluefield; WCHS-TV (A), WOWK-TV (C), WSAZ-TV (N) Charleston-Huntington; WSWP-TV (P) Grandview; WJHL-TV (C) Johnson City; WOAY-TV (A) Oak Hill-Beckley.

Programming (via satellite): WGN-TV (W) Chicago; CNN; ESPN; Fox Family Channel; Learning Channel; Lifetime; MTV; Nashville Network; Nickelodeon; TBS Superstation; The Inspirational Network; The Weather Channel; USA Network.

Fee: $11.00 monthly.

Pay Service 1

Pay Units: N.A.

Programming (via satellite): Disney Channel; HBO.

Fee: $21.00 installation; $10.50 monthly (each).

Local advertising: No.

Equipment: Blonder-Tongue, Microdyne & Scientific-Atlanta headend; Magnavox & Vikoa amplifiers; Comm/Scope cable; Jerrold set top converters; Intercept traps; Channel-Master & Scientific-Atlanta satellite antenna.

Miles of plant: 52.7 (coaxial). Homes passed: 2,394.

Manager: Ron Stewart. Chief technician: James Foster.

Ownership: Bahakel Communications Ltd. (MSO).

OMAR—Colane Cable TV Inc., Box 610, Omar, WV 25638. Phone: 304-946-2871. County: Logan. Also serves Barnabus, Cow Creek, Micco, Stirrat. ICA: WV0191.

TV Market Ranking: Below 100. Franchise award date: N.A. Franchise expiration date: N.A. Began: September 1, 1980.

Channel capacity: 20. Channels available but not in use: N.A.

Basic Service

Subscribers: N.A.

Programming (received off-air): WCHS-TV (A), WOWK-TV (C), WPBY-TV (P), WSAZ-TV (N), WVAH-TV (F,U) Charleston-Huntington; WSWP-TV (P) Grandview.

Programming (via satellite): American Movie Classics; Discovery Channel; ESPN; QVC; TBS Superstation; USA Network; VH1.

Fee: $20.00 installation; $12.50 monthly.

Pay Service 1

Pay Units: N.A.

Programming (via satellite): HBO.

Fee: $15.00 installation; $10.50 monthly.

Miles of plant: 22.9 (coaxial).

Ownership: William Stark (MSO).

PAGE—Helicon Cablevision, Box A, 150 N. Pinch Rd., Pinch, WV 25156. Phones: 304-965-7026; 800-642-9163. Fax: 304-965-7768. County: Fayette. ICA: WV0248.

TV Market Ranking: 36. Franchise award date: N.A. Franchise expiration date: N.A. Began: N.A.

Channel capacity: N.A. Channels available but not in use: N.A.

Basic Service

Subscribers: 420.

Programming (received off-air): WVVA (N) Bluefield; WCHS-TV (A), WOWK-TV (C), WSAZ-TV (N), WVAH-TV (F,U) Charleston-Huntington; WSWP-TV (P) Grandview; WOAY-TV (A) Oak Hill-Beckley.

Programming (via satellite): A & E; American Movie Classics; C-SPAN; CNN; Cartoon Network; Discovery Channel; ESPN; Fox Family Channel; Headline News; Lifetime; Nashville Network; Nickelodeon; QVC; The Weather Channel; Turner Network TV; USA Network.
Fee: $20.50 monthly; $1.50 converter.

A la Carte 1
Subscribers: N.A.
Programming (via satellite): WGN-TV (W) Chicago; Country Music TV; TBS Superstation.
Fee: $4.30 monthly; $2.00 monthly (each).

Pay Service 1
Pay Units: N.A.
Programming (via satellite): Disney Channel; HBO; Showtime; The Movie Channel.
Fee: $8.95 monthly (Disney, Showtime or TMC).

Ownership: Helicon Corp. (MSO). See Cable System Ownership.

PANTHER—CableVision Communications, Box 2200, 68 5th St., Buckhannon, WV 26201. Phone: 304-472-4193. Fax: 304-472-0756. Counties: McDowell & Mingo. Also serves Bull Creek, Isaban, Mohawk. ICA: WV0101.
TV Market Ranking: Below 100. Franchise award date: N.A. Franchise expiration date: N.A. Began: January 1, 1973.
Channel capacity: 12. Channels available but not in use: None.

Basic Service
Subscribers: 298.
Programming (received off-air): WVVA (N) Bluefield; WOWK-TV (C), WSAZ-TV (N) Charleston-Huntington; WOAY-TV (A) Oak Hill-Beckley.
Programming (via satellite): CNN; Discovery Channel; ESPN; Fox Family Channel; FoxNet; Nashville Network; TBS Superstation; USA Network.
Fee: $61.25 installation; $14.40 monthly; $1.24 converter.

Equipment: Blonder-Tongue & Philips headend; Tocom & Philips amplifiers.
Miles of plant: 25.0 (coaxial). Homes passed: 691.
Manager: Willie Critchfield. Plant manager: Garry Lucas. Marketing director: Kenny Phillips.
Ownership: Rifkin & Associates Inc. (MSO). See Cable System Ownership.

PANTHER—Hurley Cablevision, Box 404, Panther, WV 24872. Phone: 304-938-5264. County: McDowell. ICA: WV0233.
TV Market Ranking: Below 100. Franchise award date: N.A. Franchise expiration date: N.A. Began: N.A.
Channel capacity: N.A. Channels available but not in use: N.A.

Basic Service
Subscribers: 51.
Programming (received off-air): WVVA (N) Bluefield; WCHS-TV (A), WOWK-TV (C), WSAZ-TV (N), WVAH-TV (F,U) Charleston-Huntington; WSWP-TV (P) Grandview.
Programming (via satellite): Fox Family Channel; TBS Superstation.
Fee: $20.00 installation; $13.00 monthly.

Miles of plant: 2.5 (coaxial).
Manager: Thurman Hurley.
Ownership: Hurley Cablevision (MSO).

PARKERSBURG—Cablecomm, 1737 E. 7th St., Parkersburg, WV 26101-5007. Phone: 800-352-1030. Counties: Wood, WV; Washington, OH. Also serves Belpre, Washington County, OH; Lubeck, Mineralwells, North Hills, Vienna, Wood County, WV. ICA: WV0003.
TV Market Ranking: Below 100. Franchise award date: N.A. Franchise expiration date: N.A. Began: January 1, 1961.
Channel capacity: 62. Channels available but not in use: N.A.

Basic Service
Subscribers: 25,958.
Programming (received off-air): WOUB-TV (P) Athens; WCHS-TV (A), WOWK-TV (C), WPBY-TV (P), WVAH-TV (F,U) Charleston-Huntington; WTAP-TV (N) Parkersburg-Marietta; allband FM.
Programming (via microwave): WSAZ-TV (N) Charleston-Huntington; WBNS-TV (C), WSYX (A) Columbus.
Programming (via satellite): A & E; C-SPAN; CNBC; CNN; Cartoon Network; Discovery Channel; FX; Fox Family Channel; Headline News; Intro TV; Lifetime; MTV; Nashville Network; Nickelodeon; Odyssey; QVC; Super-audio Cable Radio Service; TBS Superstation; The Weather Channel.
Current originations: Automated time-weather; local news.
Fee: $59.95 installation; $10.42 monthly; $2.00 converter.

Expanded Basic Service
Subscribers: 24,059.
Programming (via satellite): American Movie Classics; Court TV; ESPN; Fox Sports Net Pittsburgh; Turner Network TV; USA Network.
Fee: $13.56 monthly.

Pay Service 1
Pay Units: 2,322.
Programming (via satellite): Cinemax.
Fee: $13.15 monthly.

Pay Service 2
Pay Units: 1,313.
Programming (via satellite): Disney Channel.
Fee: $11.95 monthly.

Pay Service 3
Pay Units: 9,479.
Programming (via satellite): The New Encore.
Fee: N.A.

Pay Service 4
Pay Units: 4,042.
Programming (via satellite): HBO.
Fee: $13.15 monthly.

Pay Service 5
Pay Units: 1,319.
Programming (via satellite): Showtime.
Fee: $13.15 monthly.

Pay Service 6
Pay Units: N.A.
Programming (via satellite): DMX.
Fee: N.A.

Local advertising: Yes. Rates: $14.00/Minute.
Program Guide: The Cable Guide.
Equipment: Jerrold headend; Jerrold amplifiers; General cable; AFC & Microdyne satellite antenna.
Miles of plant: 378.6 (coaxial). Homes passed: 30,101. Total homes in franchised area: 38,213.
Manager: Terry White. Chief technician: Jerry Buskirk.
City fee: None.
Ownership: Fanch Communications Inc. (MSO); Time Warner Cable (MSO). Purchased from Tele-Communications Inc., February 25, 1999. See Cable System Ownership.

PARSONS—TCI of West Virginia Inc., 315 First St., Parsons, WV 26287. County: Tucker. Also serves Hambleton, Hendricks, Porterwood, Tucker County. ICA: WV0203.
TV Market Ranking: Below 100 (portions of Tucker County); Outside TV Markets (Hambleton, Hendricks, Parsons, Porterwood, portions of Tucker County). Franchise award date: N.A. Franchise expiration date: N.A. Began: October 1, 1953.
Channel capacity: 21. Channels available but not in use: None.

Basic Service
Subscribers: 1,290.
Programming (received off-air): WBOY-TV (N), WDTV (C,A) Clarksburg-Weston; WNPB-TV (P) Morgantown; WTAE-TV (A) Pittsburgh; WTOV-TV (N) Steubenville-Wheeling; WTRF-TV (C) Wheeling-Steubenville; allband FM.
Programming (via satellite): WGN-TV (W) Chicago; American Movie Classics; CNN; Cartoon Network; Discovery Channel; ESPN; Fox Family Channel; Fox Sports Net Pittsburgh; Nashville Network; Nickelodeon; Odyssey; QVC; TBS Superstation; USA Network.
Current originations: Automated time-weather; religious access.
Fee: $59.95 installation; $16.60 monthly.

Pay Service 1
Pay Units: 101.
Programming (via satellite): Disney Channel.
Fee: $11.95 monthly.

Pay Service 2
Pay Units: 209.
Programming (via satellite): HBO.
Fee: $12.70 monthly.

Pay Service 3
Pay Units: 146.
Programming (via satellite): Showtime.
Fee: $12.20 monthly.

Program Guide: The Cable Guide.
Equipment: Jerrold headend; Jerrold amplifiers; Vikoa & Times Fiber cable; Microdyne satellite antenna; Microdyne satellite receivers.
Miles of plant: 27.8 (coaxial). Total homes in franchised area: 1,325.
Chief technician: Charles Ketterman.
City fee: 2% of gross.
Ownership: AT&T Broadband & Internet Services (MSO). Purchased from Tele-Communications Inc., March 9, 1999.

PAW PAW—Cablecomm, 201 S. Mechanic St., Cumberland, MD 21502-3037. Phone: 301-722-6540. Fax: 301-724-9348. County: Morgan. ICA: WV0130.
TV Market Ranking: Below 100. Franchise award date: N.A. Franchise expiration date: N.A. Began: December 20, 1968.
Channel capacity: 30 (2-way capable; not operating 2-way). Channels available but not in use: 2.

Basic Service
Subscribers: 219.
Programming (received off-air): WHAG-TV (N) Hagerstown; WNPB-TV (P) Morgantown; WJLA-TV (A), WTTG (F), WUSA (C) Washington; allband FM.
Programming (via satellite): Lifetime; Odyssey; QVC; The Weather Channel.
Fee: $47.65 installation; $9.84 monthly.

Expanded Basic Service
Subscribers: 210.
Programming (via satellite): American Movie Classics; CNN; Comedy Central; Discovery Channel; Disney Channel; ESPN; Home Team Sports; Nashville Network; Nickelodeon; TBS Superstation; Turner Network TV; USA Network; VH1.
Fee: $13.75 monthly.

Pay Service 1
Pay Units: 105.
Programming (via satellite): The New Encore.
Fee: $2.00 monthly.

Pay Service 2
Pay Units: 74.
Programming (via satellite): HBO.
Fee: $14.95 monthly.

Equipment: Jerrold headend; Magnavox amplifiers; ITT & Times Fiber cable.
Miles of plant: 7.0 (coaxial). Additional miles planned: 1.0 (coaxial). Homes passed: 269.
Chief technician: Jerry J. Fargione. Program director: Bob Hidey.
City fee: None.
Ownership: Fanch Communications Inc. (MSO); Time Warner Cable (MSO). Purchased from Tele-Communictions Inc., February 25, 1999. See Cable System Ownership.

PAX—Capital Cablecomm, Box 368, Cabin Creek, WV 25035. Phone: 304-779-2854. Fax: 304-595-5248. County: Fayette. ICA: WV0244.
TV Market Ranking: Below 100. Franchise award date: N.A. Franchise expiration date: N.A. Began: N.A.
Channel capacity: 15 (not 2-way capable). Channels available but not in use: 1.

Basic Service
Subscribers: 672.
Programming (received off-air): WVVA (N) Bluefield; WCHS-TV (A), WOWK-TV (C), WSAZ-TV (N), WVAH-TV (F,U) Charleston-Huntington; WSWP-TV (P) Grandview; WOAY-TV (A) Oak Hill-Beckley.
Fee: $41.00 installation (aerial), $54.75 (underground); $9.50 monthly; $1.87 converter.

Expanded Basic Service
Subscribers: 660.
Programming (via satellite): Discovery Channel; ESPN; Fox Family Channel; TBS Superstation.
Fee: $5.45 monthly.

Pay Service 1
Pay Units: 172.
Programming (via satellite): HBO.
Fee: $10.58 monthly.

Pay Service 2
Pay Units: 40.
Programming (via satellite): Cinemax.
Fee: $9.00 monthly.

Pay Service 3
Pay Units: 33.
Programming (via satellite): Disney Channel.
Fee: $7.00 monthly.

Miles of plant: 26.1 (coaxial); None (fiber optic). Homes passed: 935.
Manager: Robert L. Herrald. Chief technician: Victor Canterbury.
Ownership: Fanch Communications Inc. (MSO). See Cable System Ownership.

PENNSBORO—CableVision Communications, Box 2200, 68 5th St., Buckhannon, WV 26201. Phone: 304-472-4193. Fax: 304-472-0756. County: Ritchie. ICA: WV0092.
TV Market Ranking: Below 100. Franchise award date: December 11, 1965. Franchise expiration date: N.A. Began: October 1, 1966.
Channel capacity: 21. Channels available but not in use: None.

Basic Service
Subscribers: 539.
Programming (received off-air): WCHS-TV (A), WOWK-TV (C), WVAH-TV (F,U) Charleston-Huntington; WBOY-TV (N), WDTV (C,A), WVFX (F) Clarksburg-Weston; WNPB-TV (P) Morgantown; WTAP-TV (N) Parkersburg-Marietta; WTRF-TV (C) Wheeling-Steubenville.
Programming (via satellite): WGN-TV (W) Chicago; CNN; TBS Superstation.
Fee: $61.25 installation; $15.98 monthly; $1.24 converter.

Expanded Basic Service
Subscribers: 371.
Programming (via satellite): American Movie Classics; Discovery Channel; Disney Channel; ESPN; Fox Family Channel; Nashville Network; Nickelodeon; Turner Network TV.
Fee: $14.62 monthly.
Expanded Basic Service 2
Subscribers: N.A.
Programming (via satellite): A & E; C-SPAN; E! Entertainment TV; ESPN 2; Great American Country; Headline News; History Channel; Home Shopping Network; Learning Channel; Lifetime; Pax Net; The Weather Channel; Toon Disney.
Fee: N.A.
Pay Service 1
Pay Units: 139.
Programming (via satellite): HBO.
Fee: $10.00 installation; $11.99 monthly.
Pay Service 2
Pay Units: N.A.
Programming (via satellite): Cinemax; Showtime; The Movie Channel.
Fee: $7.95 monthly (Cinemax), $11.95 monthly (Showtime or TMC).
Equipment: Blonder-Tongue & Jerrold headend; Jerrold amplifiers.
Miles of plant: 23.0 (coaxial). Homes passed: 818.
Manager: Willie Critchfield. Marketing director: Kenny Phillips.
City fee: None.
Ownership: Rifkin & Associates Inc. (MSO). See Cable System Ownership.

PETERSBURG—CableVision Communications, Box 2200, 68 5th St., Buckhannon, WV 26201. Phone: 304-472-4193. Fax: 304-472-0756. County: Grant. Also serves Johnson Run, Meadow Ridge, North Fork. ICA: WV0064.
TV Market Ranking: Outside TV Markets. Franchise award date: N.A. Franchise expiration date: N.A. Began: July 1, 1958.
Channel capacity: 38. Channels available but not in use: 4.
Basic Service
Subscribers: 1,430.
Programming (received off-air): WHSV-TV (A,F) Harrisonburg; WJAC-TV (N), WWCP-TV (F) Johnstown-Altoona; WUSA (C) Washington; allband FM.
Programming (via satellite): WGN-TV (W) Chicago; C-SPAN; Home Shopping Network; TBS Superstation; Trinity Bcstg. Network.
Current originations: Local access.
Fee: $61.25 installation; $14.40 monthly; $1.24 converter.
Expanded Basic Service
Subscribers: N.A.
Programming (via satellite): A & E; American Movie Classics; CNN; Discovery Channel; Disney Channel; ESPN; ESPN 2; Fox Family Channel; Fox Sports Net Pittsburgh; Great American Country; Headline News; Lifetime; Nashville Network; Nickelodeon; QVC; Sci-Fi Channel; The Weather Channel; Turner Network TV; USA Network.
Fee: $14.26 monthly.
Pay Service 1
Pay Units: 774.
Programming (via satellite): HBO; Showtime; The New Encore.
Fee: $10.00 installation; $3.99 monthly (Encore), $11.95 monthly (Showtime), $11.99 monthly (HBO).
Pay Service 2
Pay Units: N.A.
Programming (via satellite): Cinemax; Starz!; The Movie Channel; The New Encore.
Fee: $5.99 monthly (Encore & Starz), $7.95 monthly (Cinemax),$11.95 monthly (TMC).
Equipment: Blonder-Tongue & DX Engineering headend; Jerrold amplifiers; Comm/Scope & Times Fiber cable; Scientific-Atlanta satellite antenna; Scientific-Atlanta satellite receivers.
Miles of plant: 35.0 (coaxial). Homes passed: 1,797.
Manager: Willie Critchfield. Chief technician: Bill Turner. Marketing director: Kenny Phillips.
City fee: 3% of gross.
Ownership: Rifkin & Associates Inc. (MSO). See Cable System Ownership.

PETERSTOWN—CableVision Communications, Box 2200, 68 5th St., Buckhannon, WV 26201. Phone: 304-472-4193. Fax: 304-472-0756. County: Monroe. ICA: WV0251.
TV Market Ranking: Below 100. Franchise award date: N.A. Franchise expiration date: N.A. Began: N.A.
Channel capacity: 37. Channels available but not in use: None.
Basic Service
Subscribers: 1,298.
Programming (received off-air): WVVA (N) Bluefield; WSWP-TV (P) Grandview; WVSX (I) Lewisburg; WOAY-TV (A) Oak Hill-Beckley; WBRA-TV (P), WPXR (X) Roanoke; WDBJ (C), WSET-TV (A), WSLS-TV (N) Roanoke-Lynchburg.
Programming (via satellite): WGN-TV (W) Chicago; TBS Superstation.
Fee: $61.25 installation; $14.40 monthly; $1.24 converter.
Expanded Basic Service
Subscribers: 1,092.
Programming (via satellite): A & E; American Movie Classics; C-SPAN; CNN; Discovery Channel; Disney Channel; ESPN; FX; Fox Family Channel; Great American Country; Learning Channel; Lifetime; MTV; Nashville Network; Nickelodeon; QVC; Sci-Fi Channel; The Weather Channel; Trinity Bcstg. Network; Turner Network TV; USA Network.
Fee: $14.85 monthly.
Pay Service 1
Pay Units: 376.
Programming (via satellite): Cinemax; HBO; Showtime; The Movie Channel; The New Encore.
Fee: $3.99 monthly (Encore); $7.99 monthly (Cinemax), $11.99 monthly (HBO, Showtime or TMC).
Ownership: Rifkin & Associates Inc. (MSO). Purchased from Triax Telecommunications Co. LLC, July 1, 1998. See Cable System Ownership.

PHILIPPI—Philippi Communications System, Box 460, 108 N. Main St., Philippi, WV 26416. Phone: 304-457-3700. Fax: 304-457-2703. County: Barbour. Also serves Barbour County (portions). ICA: WV0054.
TV Market Ranking: Below 100. Franchise award date: March 1, 1985. Franchise expiration date: March 1, 1999. Began: March 1, 1986.
Channel capacity: 46 (not 2-way capable). Channels available but not in use: None.
Basic Service
Subscribers: 1,312.
Programming (received off-air): WBOY-TV (N), WDTV (C,A), WVFX (F) Clarksburg-Weston; WNPB-TV (P) Morgantown; KDKA-TV (C), WCWB (W), WPXI (N), WTAE-TV (A) Pittsburgh.
Programming (via satellite): WGN-TV (W) Chicago; A & E; American Movie Classics; Animal Planet; C-SPAN; CNBC; CNN; CNN/SI; Country Music TV; Discovery Channel; Disney Channel; ESPN; ESPN 2; ESPNews; FX; Fox Family Channel; Fox Sports Net Pittsburgh; Headline News; History Channel; Learning Channel; Lifetime; MTV; Nashville Network; Nickelodeon; Odyssey; Outdoor Channel; Sci-Fi Channel; TBS Superstation; TV Guide Channel; The Weather Channel; Turner Network TV; USA Network; VH1; Z Music Television.
Current originations: Public access.
Fee: $25.00 installation; $23.29 monthly; $3.00 converter.
Pay Service 1
Pay Units: 197.
Programming (via satellite): HBO.
Fee: $5.00 installation; $10.00 monthly.
Pay Service 2
Pay Units: 89.
Programming (via satellite): Showtime.
Fee: $5.00 installation; $10.00 monthly.
Pay Service 3
Pay Units: 49.
Programming (via satellite): Cinemax.
Fee: $5.00 installation; $9.00 monthly.
Pay-Per-View
Addressable homes: 45.
Local advertising: Yes. Available in locally originated programming.
Equipment: Jerrold headend; Jerrold amplifiers; Comm/Scope cable; Jerrold set top converters; Jerrold addressable set top converters; Zenith modems; Zenith computer servers; Eagle traps; Comtech satellite antenna; Jerrold satellite receivers.
Miles of plant: 46.0 (coaxial). Homes passed: 2,000. Total homes in franchised area: 2,000.
Manager: Joseph Mattaliano. Chief technician: Carl Radcliff.
City fee: 5% of gross.
Ownership: Philippi Communications System.

PINE GROVE—CableVision Communications, Box 2200, 68 5th St., Buckhannon, WV 26201. Phone: 304-472-4193. Fax: 304-472-0756. County: Wetzel. Also serves Hastings, Jacksonburg, Reader, Wetzel County. ICA: WV0081.
TV Market Ranking: 90 (portions of Wetzel County); Below 100 (Hastings, Jacksonburg, Pine Grove, Reader, portions of Wetzel County). Franchise award date: N.A. Franchise expiration date: N.A. Began: January 1, 1954.
Channel capacity: 29. Channels available but not in use: 1.
Basic Service
Subscribers: 597.
Programming (received off-air): WBOY-TV (N), WDTV (C,A), WVFX (F) Clarksburg-Weston; WNPB-TV (P) Morgantown; WKRN-TV (A) Nashville; KDKA-TV (C), WTAE-TV (A) Pittsburgh; WTOV-TV (N) Steubenville-Wheeling; WTRF-TV (C) Wheeling-Steubenville; allband FM.
Programming (via satellite): WGN-TV (W) Chicago; CNN; Disney Channel; ESPN; Fox Family Channel; FoxNet; Nashville Network; TBS Superstation; Turner Network TV; USA Network.
Fee: $61.25 installation; $18.97 monthly; $1.24 converter.
A la Carte 1
Subscribers: N.A.
Programming (via satellite): A & E; Discovery Channel; ESPN 2; Lifetime; Nickelodeon; The Weather Channel.
Fee: $4.25 monthly (package).
Pay Service 1
Pay Units: 162.
Programming (via satellite): HBO.
Fee: $17.50 installation; $11.99 monthly.
Pay Service 2
Pay Units: N.A.
Programming (via satellite): Showtime.
Fee: $11.95 monthly.
Equipment: Blonder-Tongue & Jerrold headend; Jerrold amplifiers.
Miles of plant: 32.0 (coaxial). Homes passed: 1,059.
Manager: Willie Critchfield. Marketing director: Kenny Phillips.
City fee: 3% of gross.
Ownership: Rifkin & Associates Inc. (MSO). See Cable System Ownership.

PINEVILLE—Wyoming Cable TV Inc., Box 210, Rock View, WV 24880. Phone: 304-732-6114. Fax: 304-732-9370. County: Wyoming. Also serves Baileysville, Brenton, Cub Creek Junction, Jesse, Meeting House Branch, Mullensville, New Richmond, Rock View, Skinfork, Sun Hill, Turkey Creek. ICA: WV0204.
TV Market Ranking: Below 100. Franchise award date: October 1, 1952. Franchise expiration date: N.A. Began: October 1, 1952.
Channel capacity: 53 (not 2-way capable). Channels available but not in use: 24.
Basic Service
Subscribers: 5,200.
Programming (received off-air): WVVA (N) Bluefield; WCHS-TV (A), WOWK-TV (C) Charleston-Huntington; WSWP-TV (P) Grandview; WJHL-TV (C) Johnson City; WOAY-TV (A) Oak Hill-Beckley; 12 FMs.
Programming (via satellite): American Movie Classics; CNN; Country Music TV; Discovery Channel; ESPN; Fox Family Channel; Fox Sports Net Ohio; Fox Sports Net Pittsburgh; Headline News; Home Shopping Network; MTV; Nashville Network; Nickelodeon; TBS Superstation; The Inspirational Network; The Weather Channel; Turner Network TV; USA Network; VH1.
Planned originations: Public access.
Fee: $50.00 installation; $17.80 monthly; $30.00 additional installation.
Pay Service 1
Pay Units: 386.
Programming (via satellite): Disney Channel.
Fee: $30.00 installation; $5.75 monthly.
Pay Service 2
Pay Units: 794.
Programming (via satellite): HBO.
Fee: $30.00 installation; $10.50 monthly.
Pay Service 3
Pay Units: 114.
Programming (via satellite): The Movie Channel.
Fee: $30.00 installation; $10.50 monthly.
Pay Service 4
Pay Units: 376.
Programming (via satellite): Showtime.

Fee: $30.00 installation; $10.50 monthly.

Pay-Per-View

Addressable homes: 5,200.

Viewer's Choice.

Local advertising: Yes. Available in satellite distributed & character-generated programming.

Equipment: Scientific-Atlanta headend; Scientific-Atlanta amplifiers; Comm/Scope cable; Texscan character generator; Scientific-Atlanta set top converters; Scientific-Atlanta addressable set top converters; Scientific-Atlanta satellite antenna; Scientific-Atlanta satellite receivers; Sony commercial insert.

Miles of plant: 175.0 (coaxial). Homes passed: 5,900. Total homes in franchised area: 6,500.

Manager: Frank Staley. Chief technician: Bill Keaton. Marketing director: Rod Bono.

City fee: None.

Ownership: Bahakel Communications Ltd. (MSO).

PIPESTEM—Helicon Cablevision, Box A, 150 N. Pinch Rd., Pinch, WV 25156. Phones: 304-965-6104; 800-642-9163. Fax: 304-965-7768. Counties: Mingo & Summers. Also serves Lerona, Speedway. ICA: WV0118.

TV Market Ranking: Below 100. Franchise award date: N.A. Franchise expiration date: N.A. Began: N.A.

Channel capacity: 40. Channels available but not in use: N.A.

Basic Service

Subscribers: 314.

Programming (received off-air): WVVA (N) Bluefield; WVAH-TV (F,U) Charleston-Huntington; WSWP-TV (P) Grandview; WOAY-TV (A) Oak Hill-Beckley; WDBJ (C), WSLS-TV (N) Roanoke-Lynchburg.

Programming (via satellite): TBS Superstation.

Fee: $55.00 installation; $17.06 monthly.

Expanded Basic Service

Subscribers: N.A.

Programming (via satellite): A & E; C-SPAN; CNN; Country Music TV; Discovery Channel; ESPN; Fox Family Channel; Headline News; Lifetime; Nashville Network; Nickelodeon; QVC; Turner Network TV; USA Network.

Fee: N.A.

Pay Service 1

Pay Units: 100.

Programming (via satellite): HBO.

Fee: N.A.

Equipment: Jerrold amplifiers; Comm/Scope cable.

Miles of plant: 20.5 (coaxial). Homes passed: 380.

Manager: Jack Wade. Chief technician: Ken Gabehardt. Marketing & program director: David Baum.

Ownership: Helicon Corp. (MSO). See Cable System Ownership.

POCATALICO—Thompson Cable, Box 13309, Sissonville, WV 25360. Phone: 304-984-0025. County: Kanawha. Also serves Guthrie, Sissonville, Tyler Mountain. ICA: WV0036.

TV Market Ranking: 36. Franchise award date: N.A. Franchise expiration date: N.A. Began: January 1, 1982.

Channel capacity: N.A. Channels available but not in use: N.A.

Basic Service

Subscribers: N.A.

Programming (received off-air): WCHS-TV (A), WOWK-TV (C), WPBY-TV (P), WSAZ-TV (N), WVAH-TV (F,U) Charleston-Huntington.

Programming (via satellite): WGN-TV (W) Chicago; TBS Superstation.

Fee: N.A.

Miles of plant: 265.0 (coaxial). Homes passed: 3,725.

Ownership: Thompson Cablevision Co. Inc. (MSO).

POINT PLEASANT—Rifkin Communications Partners, Box 106, 1410 Jefferson Blvd., Point Pleasant, WV 25550. Phone: 304-675-3398. Fax: 304-675-2281. Counties: Fayette, Jackson, Mason, & Raleigh, WV; Gallia & Meigs, OH. Also serves Gallipolis, Gallipolis Ferry, Middleport, Pomeroy, Syracuse, OH; Bradley, Fayette County, Hartford, Henderson, Mason, Mount Alto, Mount Hope, New Haven, Ravenswood, Ripley, WV. ICA: WV0008.

TV Market Ranking: 36 (Gallipolis, Gallipolis Ferry, Point Pleasant); Below 100 (Bradley, Fayette County, Hartford, Henderson, Mason, Middleport, Mount Alto, Mount Hope, New Haven, Pomeroy, Ravenswood, Ripley, Syracuse). Franchise award date: N.A. Franchise expiration date: N.A. Began: April 1, 1965.

Channel capacity: 78 (not 2-way capable). Channels available but not in use: 40.

Basic Service

Subscribers: 12,600.

Programming (received off-air): WOUB-TV (P) Athens; WCHS-TV (A), WOWK-TV (C), WPBY-TV (P), WSAZ-TV (N), WVAH-TV (F,U) Charleston-Huntington; WBNS-TV (C), WSYX (A) Columbus; WTAP-TV (N) Parkersburg-Marietta; allband FM.

Programming (via satellite): WGN-TV (W) Chicago; C-SPAN; TBS Superstation.

Current originations: Public access; local news.

Fee: $39.95 installation; $9.25 monthly.

Expanded Basic Service

Subscribers: 12,100.

Programming (via satellite): A & E; CNBC; CNN; ESPN; Fox Family Channel; Headline News; Lifetime; MTV; Nashville Network; Nickelodeon; QVC; The Weather Channel; Turner Network TV; USA Network.

Fee: $13.70 monthly.

Pay Service 1

Pay Units: 559.

Programming (via satellite): Cinemax.

Fee: $9.95 monthly.

Pay Service 2

Pay Units: 854.

Programming (via satellite): Disney Channel.

Fee: $6.95 monthly.

Pay Service 3

Pay Units: 1,628.

Programming (via satellite): HBO.

Fee: $9.95 monthly.

Pay Service 4

Pay Units: 254.

Programming (via satellite): Showtime.

Fee: $9.95 monthly.

Equipment: Scientific-Atlanta headend; Jerrold amplifiers; Comm/Scope cable; Scientific-Atlanta set top converters; Andrew & Scientific-Atlanta satellite antenna.

Miles of plant: 460.0 (coaxial); 60.0 (fiber optic). Additional miles planned: 25.0 (coaxial). Homes passed: 19,136. Total homes in franchised area: 19,136.

Manager: Lester Errett. Chief technician: Daniel Elias. Program director: Randy Parsons. Marketing director: Hal Schlinger.

City fee: 5% of gross.

Ownership: Rifkin & Associates Inc. (MSO). See Cable System Ownership.

POND GAP—Capital Cablecomm, Box 368, Cabin Creek, WV 25035. Phone: 304-779-2854. Fax: 304-595-5248. County: Kanawha. Also serves Blakeley, Laurel Fork. ICA: WV0154.

TV Market Ranking: 36. Franchise award date: N.A. Franchise expiration date: N.A. Began: January 1, 1972.

Channel capacity: 15 (not 2-way capable). Channels available but not in use: 3.

Basic Service

Subscribers: 72.

Programming (received off-air): WVVA (N) Bluefield; WCHS-TV (A), WOWK-TV (C), WSAZ-TV (N), WVAH-TV (F,U) Charleston-Huntington; WDTV (C,A) Clarksburg-Weston; WSWP-TV (P) Grandview; WOAY-TV (A) Oak Hill-Beckley.

Current originations: Public access; educational access; government access.

Fee: $32.75 installation (aerial), $46.25 (underground); $13.90 monthly.

Expanded Basic Service

Subscribers: 70.

Programming (via satellite): Fox Family Channel; Nashville Network; TBS Superstation.

Fee: $5.30 monthly.

Pay Service 1

Pay Units: 33.

Programming (via satellite): HBO.

Fee: $20.00 installation; $8.00 monthly.

Equipment: Blonder-Tongue headend; Magnavox amplifiers; Comm/Scope cable; Eagle traps; M/A-Com satellite antenna; Microdyne satellite receivers.

Miles of plant: 4.4 (coaxial); None (fiber optic). Homes passed: 100.

Manager: Robert L. Herrald. Chief technician: Allen Comer. Marketing director: Bill Benner.

Ownership: Fanch Communications Inc. (MSO); Time Warner Cable (MSO). See Cable System Ownership.

PRICETOWN—CableVision Communications, Box 2200, 68 5th St., Buckhannon, WV 26201. Phone: 304-472-4193. Fax: 304-472-0756. County: Wetzel. ICA: WV0205.

TV Market Ranking: Below 100. Franchise award date: N.A. Franchise expiration date: N.A. Began: N.A.

Channel capacity: 42. Channels available but not in use: 35.

Basic Service

Subscribers: 6.

Programming (received off-air): WBOY-TV (N), WDTV (C,A) Clarksburg-Weston; WNPB-TV (P) Morgantown; KDKA-TV (C), WTAE-TV (A) Pittsburgh; WTOV-TV (N) Steubenville-Wheeling; WTRF-TV (C) Wheeling-Steubenville.

Fee: $61.25 installation; $9.08 monthly.

Miles of plant: 1.0 (coaxial). Homes passed: 21.

Manager: Willie Critchfield. Marketing director: Kenny Phillips.

Ownership: Rifkin & Associates Inc. (MSO). See Cable System Ownership.

PRINCETON—Cablecomm, Box 891, 819 Mercer St., Princeton, WV 24740. Phone: 304-425-8179. County: Mercer. Also serves Athens, Matoaka, Mercer County. ICA: WV0018.

TV Market Ranking: Below 100. Franchise award date: N.A. Franchise expiration date: N.A. Began: January 1, 1966.

Channel capacity: 44. Channels available but not in use: N.A.

Basic Service

Subscribers: 8,445.

Programming (received off-air): WVVA (N) Bluefield; WCHS-TV (A), WSAZ-TV (N) Charleston-Huntington; WSWP-TV (P) Grandview; WOAY-TV (A) Oak Hill-Beckley; WDBJ (C), WSLS-TV (N) Roanoke-Lynchburg; allband FM.

Programming (via satellite): Fox Family Channel; TBS Superstation; The Weather Channel.

Current originations: Automated time-weather.

Fee: $20.47 installation; $12.83 monthly.

Expanded Basic Service

Subscribers: N.A.

Programming (via satellite): A & E; C-SPAN; CNN; Country Music TV; Discovery Channel; ESPN; Headline News; MTV; Nashville Network; Nickelodeon; The Inspirational Network; USA Network; VH1.

Fee: $7.00 monthly.

Pay Service 1

Pay Units: N.A.

Programming (via satellite): Cinemax; Disney Channel; HBO; Showtime.

Fee: $15.00 installation; $10.95 monthly (each).

Local advertising: No.

Equipment: Jerrold headend; composite amplifiers; composite cable; Scientific-Atlanta satellite antenna.

Miles of plant: 132.7 (coaxial). Homes passed: 8,972.

Manager: Jack Hutchens. Chief technician: Kerry Ellison.

Ownership: Fanch Communications Inc. (MSO); Time Warner Cable (MSO). Purchased from Tele-Communications Inc., February 25, 1999. See Cable System Ownership.

PULLMAN—CableVision Communications, Box 2200, 68 5th St., Buckhannon, WV 26201. Phone: 304-472-4193. Fax: 304-472-0756. County: Ritchie. ICA: WV0159.

TV Market Ranking: Below 100. Franchise award date: December 2, 1980. Franchise expiration date: N.A. Began: N.A.

Channel capacity: 12. Channels available but not in use: 5.

Basic Service

Subscribers: 17.

Programming (received off-air): WCHS-TV (A), WOWK-TV (C) Charleston-Huntington; WBOY-TV (N), WDTV (C,A) Clarksburg-Weston; WNPB-TV (P) Morgantown; WTAP-TV (N) Parkersburg-Marietta; WTRF-TV (C) Wheeling-Steubenville.

Fee: $61.25 installation; $11.89 monthly.

Equipment: Blonder-Tongue & Jerrold headend; Jerrold amplifiers.

Miles of plant: 2.0 (coaxial). Homes passed: 62.

Manager: Willie Critchfield. Marketing director: Kenny Phillips.

Ownership: Rifkin & Associates Inc. (MSO). See Cable System Ownership.

RAGLAND—FrontierVision, Suite P-200, 1777 S. Harrison St., Denver, CO 80210. Phone: 303-757-1588. Fax: 303-757-6105. Counties: Mingo & Wayne, WV; Lawrence, Martin & Pike, KY. Also serves Lawrence County (portions), Martin County (portions), Pike County, KY; Mingo County (portions), Wayne County (portions), WV. ICA: WV0162.

TV Market Ranking: 36 (portions of Martin County, portions of Mingo County, portions of Wayne County); Below 100 (portions of Mingo County); Outside TV Markets (Lawrence County, portions of Martin County, portions of Mingo County, Pike County, Ragland, portions of Wayne County). Franchise award date: N.A. Franchise expiration date: N.A. Began: N.A.

Channel capacity: 6. Channels available but not in use: None.

Basic Service

Subscribers: 38.

Programming (received off-air): WCHS-TV (A), WOWK-TV (C), WPBY-TV (P), WSAZ-

TV (N), WVAH-TV (F,U) Charleston-Huntington.
Fee: $35.00 installation; $10.48 monthly.
Local advertising: No.
Equipment: Philips headend; Philips amplifiers; Pico traps; Scientific-Atlanta satellite antenna; Scientific-Atlanta & DX Engineering satellite receivers.
Miles of plant: 2.3 (coaxial). Homes passed: 45.
City fee: None.
Ownership: FrontierVision Partners LP (MSO). See Cable System Ownership.

RAVENCLIFF—Nesbe Cable, 216-A Howard Ave., Mullens, WV 25882. Phone: 304-294-6332. Fax: 304-294-4717. County: Wyoming. Also serves Glen Fork, Glen Rogers, McGraws, Sabine, Saulsville. ICA: WV0093.
TV Market Ranking: Below 100. Franchise award date: N.A. Franchise expiration date: N.A. Began: July 1, 1969.
Channel capacity: 64 (not 2-way capable). Channels available but not in use: None.
Basic Service
Subscribers: 550.
Programming (received off-air): WVVA (N) Bluefield; WCHS-TV (A), WOWK-TV (C), WSAZ-TV (N), WVAH-TV (F,U) Charleston-Huntington; WSWP-TV (P) Grandview; WOAY-TV (A) Oak Hill-Beckley.
Programming (via satellite): WGN-TV (W) Chicago; A & E; CNN; Cartoon Network; Country Music TV; Discovery Channel; ESPN; ESPN 2; Fox Family Channel; Golf Channel; Headline News; Home & Garden Television; MTV; Nashville Network; Nick at Nite's TV Land; Nickelodeon; QVC; Sci-Fi Channel; TBS Superstation; The Inspirational Network; The Weather Channel; Trinity Bcstg. Network; Turner Classic Movies; Turner Network TV; USA Network; VH1.
Fee: $37.00 installation; $22.95 monthly.
Pay Service 1
Pay Units: 23.
Programming (via satellite): Disney Channel.
Fee: $5.75 monthly.
Pay Service 2
Pay Units: 54.
Programming (via satellite): HBO.
Fee: $10.50 monthly.
Pay Service 3
Pay Units: 5.
Programming (via satellite): Showtime.
Fee: $10.50 monthly.
Pay Service 4
Pay Units: 13.
Programming (via satellite): The Movie Channel.
Fee: $10.50 monthly.
Equipment: ChannelMaster & Microdyne headend; Jerrold amplifiers; Comm/Scope cable; Arcom traps; ChannelMaster satellite antenna.
Miles of plant: 23.0 (coaxial); None (fiber optic). Homes passed: 600. Total homes in franchised area: 655.
Manager: Phil Halsey. Chief technician: Ron Campbell.
Ownership: Bahakel Communications Ltd. (MSO). Purchased from Mountaineer Cablevision Inc., May 1, 1999.

RED HOUSE—Century Communications, Box 100, Red House, WV 25168. Phones: 304-586-9675; 800-746-6818.
Web site:http://www.centurycomm.com.
Counties: Kanawha & Putnam. Also serves Bancroft, Buffalo, Eleanor, Elsinore, Hometown, Hurricane, Nitro (portions), Poca, Rock Branch, Scott Depot, St. Albans (portions), Teays Valley, Winfield. ICA: WV0027.
TV Market Ranking: 36. Franchise award date: N.A. Franchise expiration date: N.A. Began: February 15, 1977.
Channel capacity: 30. Channels available but not in use: N.A.
Basic Service
Subscribers: 4,600.
Programming (received off-air): WLPX-TV (X) Charleston; WCHS-TV (A), WOWK-TV (C), WPBY-TV (P), WSAZ-TV (N), WVAH-TV (F,U) Charleston-Huntington.
Programming (via satellite): WGN-TV (W) Chicago; A & E; American Movie Classics; C-SPAN; CNBC; Cartoon Network; Comedy Central; Country Music TV; Discovery Channel; E! Entertainment TV; ESPN; ESPN 2; FX; Fox Family Channel; Headline News; History Channel; Home Shopping Network; Learning Channel; Lifetime; MSNBC; MTV; Nashville Network; Nick at Nite's TV Land; Nickelodeon; QVC; Sci-Fi Channel; TBS Superstation; TV Guide Channel; The Inspirational Network; The Weather Channel; USA Network; VH1.
Fee: $10.00 installation; $13.95 monthly.
Expanded Basic Service
Subscribers: N.A.
Programming (via satellite): CNN; Disney Channel; Turner Network TV.
Fee: N.A.
Pay Service 1
Pay Units: 1,500.
Programming (via satellite): Cinemax; HBO (multiplexed).
Fee: $8.00 monthly (each).
Pay Service 2
Pay Units: N.A.
Programming (via satellite): Showtime.
Fee: N.A.
Equipment: Blonder-Tongue & Scientific-Atlanta headend; GTE Sylvania amplifiers; Comm/Scope & Times Fiber cable; Jerrold addressable set top converters; Eagle & GTE Sylvania traps; Andrew satellite antenna; Hughes, Microdyne & Scientific-Atlanta satellite receivers.
Miles of plant: 104.0 (coaxial). Additional miles planned: 2.0 (coaxial). Homes passed: 5,200. Total homes in franchised area: 5,600.
Manager: Richard Fairbank. Chief technician: Roy Blanchard.
City fee: 3% of gross.
Ownership: Century Communications Corp. (MSO). See Cable System Ownership.

RICHWOOD—CableVision Communications, Box 2200, 68 5th St., Buckhannon, WV 26201. Phone: 304-472-4193. Fax: 304-472-0756. County: Nicholas. Also serves Fenwick, Holcomb, La Frank, New Hope. ICA: WV0058.
TV Market Ranking: Below 100. Franchise award date: N.A. Franchise expiration date: N.A. Began: May 1, 1952.
Channel capacity: 37 (not 2-way capable). Channels available but not in use: None.
Basic Service
Subscribers: 1,372.
Programming (received off-air): WCHS-TV (A), WOWK-TV (C), WSAZ-TV (N), WVAH-TV (F,U) Charleston-Huntington; WBOY-TV (N) Clarksburg-Weston; WSWP-TV (P) Grandview; WOAY-TV (A) Oak Hill-Beckley; allband FM.
Programming (via satellite): WGN-TV (W) Chicago; Home Shopping Network; TBS Superstation; The Weather Channel.
Current originations: Local access.
Fee: $61.25 installation; $14.40 monthly; $1.24 converter.
Expanded Basic Service
Subscribers: N.A.
Programming (via satellite): A & E; American Movie Classics; C-SPAN; CNN; Discovery Channel; Disney Channel; E! Entertainment TV; ESPN; ESPN 2; FX; Fox Family Channel; Great American Country; History Channel; Lifetime; MTV; Nashville Network; Nickelodeon; Sci-Fi Channel; Trinity Bcstg. Network; Turner Network TV; USA Network.
Fee: $16.77 monthly.
Pay Service 1
Pay Units: 539.
Programming (via satellite): Cinemax; HBO; Showtime; The Movie Channel; The New Encore.
Fee: $17.50 installation; $3.99 monthly (Encore), $7.99 monthly (Cinemax), $11.99 monthly (HBO, Showtime or TMC).
Local advertising: No.
Equipment: Jerrold headend; Jerrold amplifiers; Capscan cable; Eagle traps; AFC satellite antenna; Microdyne satellite receivers.
Miles of plant: 32.0 (coaxial). Homes passed: 1,720.
Manager: Willie Critchfield. Chief technician: Bill Turner. Marketing director: Kenny Phillips.
City fee: 3% of gross.
Ownership: Rifkin & Associates Inc. (MSO). See Cable System Ownership.

RIG—C T & R Cable, 29 Water St., Petersburg, WV 26847. Phone: 304-257-4891. County: Hardy. ICA: WV0225.
TV Market Ranking: Outside TV Markets. Franchise award date: N.A. Franchise expiration date: N.A. Began: May 15, 1988.
Channel capacity: 23 (not 2-way capable). Channels available but not in use: 11.
Basic Service
Subscribers: 145.
Programming (via translator): WHSV-TV (A,F) Harrisonburg; WJAC-TV (N) Johnstown-Altoona; WNPB-TV (P) Morgantown; WTTG (F), WUSA (C) Washington.
Programming (via satellite): WGN-TV (W) Chicago; CNN; Discovery Channel; ESPN; Fox Family Channel; Nashville Network; TBS Superstation; Turner Network TV.
Fee: $99.00 installation; $16.00 monthly.
Pay Service 1
Pay Units: 50.
Programming (via satellite): Showtime.
Fee: $9.00 monthly.
Miles of plant: 8.0 (coaxial). Homes passed: 150.
Manager: Terry Hinkle. Chief technician: Matt Alt.
Ownership: C T & R Cable LLC (MSO).

ROBSON—Capital Cablecomm, Box 368, Cabin Creek, WV 25035. Phone: 304-779-2854. Fax: 304-595-5248. County: Fayette. Also serves Mulberry. ICA: WV0153.
TV Market Ranking: 36. Franchise award date: N.A. Franchise expiration date: N.A. Began: May 1, 1978.
Channel capacity: 15 (not 2-way capable). Channels available but not in use: 3.
Basic Service
Subscribers: 80.
Programming (received off-air): WVVA (N) Bluefield; WCHS-TV (A), WOWK-TV (C), WSAZ-TV (N), WVAH-TV (F,U) Charleston-Huntington; WDTV (C,A) Clarksburg-Weston; WSWP-TV (P) Grandview; WOAY-TV (A) Oak Hill-Beckley.
Current originations: Public access; educational access; government access.
Fee: $35.50 installation (aerial), $49.25 (underground); $13.40 monthly.
Expanded Basic Service
Subscribers: 79.
Programming (via satellite): Fox Family Channel; Nashville Network; TBS Superstation.
Fee: $5.80 monthly.
Pay Service 1
Pay Units: 49.
Programming (via satellite): HBO.
Fee: $10.00 installation; $8.00 monthly.
Equipment: Blonder-Tongue headend; Jerrold amplifiers; Comm/Scope cable; Eagle traps; Harris satellite antenna; M/A-Com & Microdyne satellite receivers.
Miles of plant: 5.3 (coaxial); None (fiber optic). Homes passed: 141.
Manager: Robert L. Herrald. Chief technician: Allen Comer. Marketing director: Bill Benner.
Ownership: Fanch Communications Inc. (MSO). See Cable System Ownership.

ROMNEY—TCI of West Virginia Inc., 201 S. Mechanic St., Cumberland, MD 21502-3037. Phone: 301-722-6540. County: Hampshire. Also serves Hampshire County. ICA: WV0065.
TV Market Ranking: Below 100 (portions of Hampshire County); Outside TV Markets (portions of Hampshire County, Romney). Franchise award date: N.A. Franchise expiration date: N.A. Began: October 1, 1958.
Channel capacity: 60 (not 2-way capable). Channels available but not in use: None.
Basic Service
Subscribers: N.A.
Programming (received off-air): WJZ-TV (C) Baltimore; WHAG-TV (N), WWPB (P) Hagerstown; WNPB-TV (P) Morgantown; WDCA (U), WJLA-TV (A), WTTG (F), WUSA (C) Washington; allband FM.
Programming (via satellite): C-SPAN; C-SPAN 2; Discovery Channel; FX; Home Shopping Network; Odyssey; QVC; TBS Superstation; The Weather Channel.
Current originations: Leased access.
Fee: $47.65 installation; $12.77 monthly.
Expanded Basic Service
Subscribers: N.A.
Programming (via satellite): A & E; American Movie Classics; BET; CNBC; CNN; Cartoon Network; Country Music TV; Disney Channel; E! Entertainment TV; ESPN; ESPN 2; EWTN; Encore Movie Networks; Fox Family Channel; Fox News Channel; Fox Sports Net; Headline News; Home & Garden Television; Home Team Sports; Learning Channel; Lifetime; MTV; Nashville Network; Nickelodeon; TV Food Network; Trinity Bcstg. Network; Turner Network TV; USA Network; VH1.
Fee: $18.75 monthly.
Pay Service 1
Pay Units: 517.
Programming (via satellite): The New Encore.
Fee: $2.17 monthly.
Pay Service 2
Pay Units: 289.
Programming (via satellite): HBO.
Fee: $16.63 monthly.
Pay Service 3
Pay Units: N.A.
Programming (via satellite): Cinemax; Showtime; Starz!
Fee: $7.51 monthly (Starz), $14.96 monthly (Cinemax), $16.63 monthly (Showtime).
Equipment: RCA & Scientific-Atlanta headend; Magnavox & SKL amplifiers; Times Fiber cable.
Miles of plant: 3.3 (coaxial).
Chief technician: Jerry Fargione.

Ownership: AT&T Broadband & Internet Services (MSO). Purchased from Tele-Communications Inc., March 9, 1999.

RONCEVERTE—Ronceverte TV Cable, Box 525, Ronceverte, WV 24970. Phone: 304-645-4036. Fax: 304-645-6158. County: Greenbrier. ICA: WV0208.
TV Market Ranking: Below 100. Franchise award date: February 1, 1991. Franchise expiration date: February 1, 2006. Began: N.A.
Channel capacity: 36 (not 2-way capable). Channels available but not in use: 07.
Basic Service
Subscribers: 1,010.
Programming (received off-air): WVVA (N) Bluefield; WSWP-TV (P) Grandview; WVSX (I) Lewisburg; WOAY-TV (A) Oak Hill-Beckley; WDBJ (C), WSLS-TV (N) Roanoke-Lynchburg; allband FM.
Programming (via satellite): WGN-TV (W) Chicago; A & E; CNN; Country Music TV; Discovery Channel; ESPN; ESPN 2; Fox Family Channel; Learning Channel; Lifetime; Nashville Network; Nickelodeon; Sci-Fi Channel; TBS Superstation; The Weather Channel; Trinity Bcstg. Network; Turner Classic Movies; Turner Network TV; USA Network; VH1.
Fee: $27.75 installation; $15.53 monthly.
Pay Service 1
Pay Units: 218.
Programming (via satellite): HBO.
Fee: $10.60 installation; $10.60 monthly.
Equipment: Jerrold, DX Engineering & Drake headend; Jerrold amplifiers; Times Fiber & Comm/Scope cable; Eagle traps.
Miles of plant: 36.0 (coaxial); None (fiber optic).
Manager: Gary W. Lemons.
City & county fee: 5% of gross.
Ownership: Ronceverte Television Corp.

RUPERT—Cablevision, 313 W. Main St., Oak Hill, WV 25901-2938. Phone: 800-585-9977. County: Greenbrier. Also serves Charmco, Crichton, Hines, Leslie, Marfrance, Orient Hill, Quinwood, Rainelle. ICA: WV0209.
TV Market Ranking: Below 100. Franchise award date: N.A. Franchise expiration date: N.A. Began: January 1, 1978.
Channel capacity: 30 (not 2-way capable). Channels available but not in use: 2.
Basic Service
Subscribers: 2,117.
Programming (received off-air): WVVA (N) Bluefield; WCHS-TV (A), WOWK-TV (C), WSAZ-TV (N), WVAH-TV (F,U) Charleston-Huntington; WSWP-TV (P) Grandview; WOAY-TV (A) Oak Hill-Beckley; WDBJ (C) Roanoke-Lynchburg; allband FM.
Programming (via satellite): WGN-TV (W) Chicago; TBS Superstation.
Fee: $15.00 installation.
Expanded Basic Service
Subscribers: N.A.
Programming (via satellite): A & E; C-SPAN; C-SPAN 2; CNN; Discovery Channel; ESPN; Fox Family Channel; Lifetime; MTV; Nashville Network; Nickelodeon; QVC; Trinity Bcstg. Network; Turner Network TV; USA Network; VH1.
Fee: N.A.
Pay Service 1
Pay Units: 105.
Programming (via satellite): Cinemax.
Fee: $9.95 monthly.
Pay Service 2
Pay Units: 62.
Programming (via satellite): Disney Channel.
Fee: $6.95 monthly.
Pay Service 3
Pay Units: 143.
Programming (via satellite): HBO.
Fee: $9.95 monthly.
Pay Service 4
Pay Units: N.A.
Programming (via satellite): The Movie Channel.
Fee: N.A.
Local advertising: Yes. Available in character-generated programming.
Equipment: Scientific-Atlanta headend; GTE Sylvania amplifiers; Comm/Scope cable; Hamlin set top converters; Scientific-Atlanta satellite antenna; Scientific-Atlanta satellite receivers.
Miles of plant: 47.0 (coaxial). Additional miles planned: 5.0 (coaxial).
Manager: Wayne Boone. Marketing director: Shelly Cline.
City fee: 3% of gross.
Ownership: Rifkin & Associates Inc. (MSO). See Cable System Ownership.

SALEM—CableVision Communications, Box 2200, 68 5th St., Buckhannon, WV 26201. Phone: 304-472-4193. Fax: 304-472-0756. County: Harrison. Also serves Bristol, Harrison County, Industrial, Lake Floyd. ICA: WV0066.
TV Market Ranking: Below 100. Franchise award date: N.A. Franchise expiration date: N.A. Began: July 20, 1962.
Channel capacity: 35. Channels available but not in use: None.
Basic Service
Subscribers: 1,461.
Programming (received off-air): WBOY-TV (N), WDTV (C,A), WVFX (F) Clarksburg-Weston; WNPB-TV (P) Morgantown; WKRN-TV (A) Nashville; WTOV-TV (N) Steubenville-Wheeling; WTRF-TV (C) Wheeling-Steubenville; allband FM.
Programming (via satellite): WGN-TV (W) Chicago; C-SPAN; FoxNet; TBS Superstation; The Weather Channel.
Fee: $61.25 installation; $14.40 monthly; $1.24 converter.
Expanded Basic Service
Subscribers: 856.
Programming (via satellite): A & E; American Movie Classics; CNN; Discovery Channel; Disney Channel; E! Entertainment TV; ESPN; ESPN 2; Fox Family Channel; Great American Country; History Channel; Home Shopping Network; Learning Channel; Lifetime; MTV; Nashville Network; Nickelodeon; Sci-Fi Channel; Trinity Bcstg. Network; Turner Network TV; USA Network.
Fee: $16.44 monthly.
Pay Service 1
Pay Units: 473.
Programming (via satellite): Cinemax; HBO.
Fee: $17.50 installation; $7.95 monthly (Cinemax), $11.99 monthly (HBO).
Pay Service 2
Pay Units: N.A.
Programming (via satellite): Showtime; The Movie Channel.
Fee: $11.95 monthly (each).
Local advertising: No.
Program Guide: CableView.
Equipment: Blonder-Tongue, DX Engineering & Jerrold headend; Jerrold amplifiers; AFC satellite antenna.
Miles of plant: 25.0 (coaxial). Homes passed: 1,461.
Manager: Willie Critchfield. Marketing director: Kenny Phillips.
City fee: None.
Ownership: Rifkin & Associates Inc. (MSO). See Cable System Ownership.

SALEM COLLEGE—Basco Electronics Inc., 420 W. 2nd St., Weston, WV 26452. Phone: 304-269-7530. Fax: 304-269-6581. County: Harrison. ICA: WV0110.
TV Market Ranking: Below 100. Franchise award date: N.A. Franchise expiration date: N.A. Began: September 1, 1984.
Channel capacity: 35 (2-way capable). Channels available but not in use: 23.
Basic Service
Subscribers: 370; Commercial subscribers: 21.
Programming (received off-air): WBOY-TV (N), WDTV (C,A) Clarksburg-Weston; WNPB-TV (P) Morgantown; WTAE-TV (A) Pittsburgh.
Programming (via satellite): CNN; ESPN; Fox Family Channel; Learning Channel; MTV; Nashville Network; TBS Superstation; USA Network. Current originations: Educational access.
Fee: $50.00 installation; $15.00 monthly.
Local advertising: No.
Equipment: Blonder-Tongue headend; Magnavox amplifiers; Comm/Scope cable; M/A-Com satellite antenna; Drake satellite receivers.
Miles of plant: 1.0 (coaxial). Homes passed: 500.
Manager: Wilfred L. Sholes. Chief technician: Brian Queen. Marketing director: Virginia M. Sholes.
Ownership: Basco Electronics Inc. (MSO).

SALT ROCK—FrontierVision, Suite P-200, 1777 S. Harrison St., Denver, CO 80210. Phone: 303-757-1588. Fax: 303-757-6105. County: Cabell. Also serves Barboursville, Cabell County (unincorporated areas). ICA: WV0084.
TV Market Ranking: 36. Franchise award date: N.A. Franchise expiration date: December 1, 1997. Began: January 1, 1988.
Channel capacity: 32. Channels available but not in use: None.
Basic Service
Subscribers: 780.
Programming (received off-air): WCHS-TV (A), WOWK-TV (C), WPBY-TV (P), WSAZ-TV (N), WVAH-TV (F,U) Charleston-Huntington.
Programming (via satellite): WGN-TV (W) Chicago; A & E; American Movie Classics; CNN; Country Music TV; Discovery Channel; ESPN; Fox Family Channel; Headline News; MTV; Nashville Network; Nickelodeon; QVC; TBS Superstation; Travel Channel; Turner Network TV; USA Network.
Fee: $29.95 installation; $21.95 monthly; $2.00 converter.
Expanded Basic Service
Subscribers: 678.
Programming (via satellite): Disney Channel.
Fee: N.A.
Pay Service 1
Pay Units: 65.
Programming (via satellite): HBO.
Fee: $9.95 monthly.
Pay Service 2
Pay Units: 52.
Programming (via satellite): Showtime.
Fee: $9.95 monthly.
Pay Service 3
Pay Units: 60.
Programming (via satellite): Cinemax.
Fee: N.A.
Pay Service 4
Pay Units: 48.
Programming (via satellite): The Movie Channel.
Fee: N.A.
Pay Service 5
Pay Units: 25.
Programming (via satellite): The New Encore.
Fee: N.A.
Miles of plant: 41.0 (coaxial). Homes passed: 1,023.
Manager: Steve Trippe. Chief technician: Bill Ricker.
Ownership: FrontierVision Partners LP (MSO). See Cable System Ownership.

SAND FORK—Cablecomm, 6 Garton Plaza, Weston, WV 26452-2129. Phone: 800-352-1030. County: Gilmer. ICA: WV0147.
TV Market Ranking: Below 100. Franchise award date: N.A. Franchise expiration date: N.A. Began: September 22, 1980.
Channel capacity: 20. Channels available but not in use: N.A.
Basic Service
Subscribers: 99.
Programming (received off-air): WCHS-TV (A), WOWK-TV (C), WSAZ-TV (N), WVAH-TV (F,U) Charleston-Huntington; WBOY-TV (N), WDTV (C,A) Clarksburg-Weston; WSWP-TV (P) Grandview; WOAY-TV (A) Oak Hill-Beckley.
Programming (via satellite): American Movie Classics; CNN; Discovery Channel; ESPN; Fox Family Channel; Lifetime; Nashville Network; TBS Superstation; Turner Network TV; USA Network.
Fee: $59.95 installation; $16.95 monthly.
Pay Service 1
Pay Units: 23.
Programming (via satellite): HBO.
Fee: $13.15 monthly.
Equipment: Blonder-Tongue headend.
Miles of plant: 4.0 (coaxial). Homes passed: 156. Total homes in franchised area: 312.
Manager: David Hashimoto. Chief technician: Dave Cottrell.
City fee: None.
Ownership: Fanch Communications Inc. (MSO); Time Warner Cable (MSO). Purchased from Tele-Communications Inc., February 25, 1999. See Cable System Ownership.

SARAH ANN—Tod's TV, Box 580, Omar, WV 25638. Phone: 304-946-2147. County: Logan. ICA: WV0148.
TV Market Ranking: Below 100. Franchise award date: N.A. Franchise expiration date: N.A. Began: September 1, 1981.
Channel capacity: 12. Channels available but not in use: 2.
Basic Service
Subscribers: N.A.
Programming (received off-air): WVVA (N) Bluefield; WCHS-TV (A), WPBY-TV (P), WSAZ-TV (N), WVAH-TV (F,U) Charleston-Huntington.
Programming (via satellite): Fox Family Channel; TBS Superstation.
Fee: N.A.
Pay Service 1
Pay Units: N.A.
Programming (via satellite): HBO.
Fee: N.A.
Miles of plant: 2.0 (coaxial). Homes passed: 138.
Manager: Charles Porter.
Ownership: Charles Porter.

SCARBRO—Helicon Cablevision, Box A, 150 N. Pinch Rd., Pinch, WV 25156. Phones: 304-965-7026; 800-642-9163. Fax: 304-965-7768. Counties: Fayette & Nicholas. Also serves Ames Heights, Beckwith, Drennen, Enon, Gilboa, Ingram Branch, Johnson Branch, Lansing, Lockwood, Mossy, North Page, Wriston. ICA: WV0031.

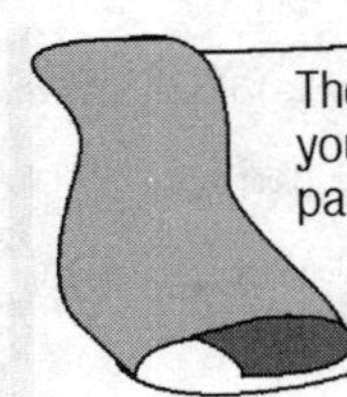

TV Market Ranking: 36. Franchise award date: N.A. Franchise expiration date: N.A. Began: January 1, 1952.
Channel capacity: 40 (not 2-way capable). Channels available but not in use: 16.

Basic Service
Subscribers: 996.
Programming (received off-air): WVVA (N) Bluefield; WCHS-TV (A), WOWK-TV (C), WVAH-TV (F,U) Charleston-Huntington; WSWP-TV (P) Grandview; WOAY-TV (A) Oak Hill-Beckley.
Programming (via satellite): C-SPAN; CNN; Cartoon Network; Discovery Channel; ESPN; Fox Family Channel; Headline News; Lifetime; Nashville Network; QVC; The Weather Channel; Turner Network TV; USA Network.
Fee: $20.69 monthly; $1.50 converter.

A la Carte 1
Subscribers: N.A.
Programming (via satellite): WGN-TV (W) Chicago; American Movie Classics; Country Music TV; TBS Superstation.
Fee: $4.30 monthly (package); $2.00 monthly (each).

Pay Service 1
Pay Units: 406.
Programming (via satellite): HBO.
Fee: $20.00 installation; $10.07 monthly.

Pay Service 2
Pay Units: 132.
Programming (via satellite): The Movie Channel.
Fee: $20.00 installation; $8.95 monthly.

Pay Service 3
Pay Units: N.A.
Programming (via satellite): Disney Channel; Showtime.
Fee: $8.95 monthly (each).

Equipment: Jerrold amplifiers; Comm/Scope cable; Jerrold set top converters; Pico traps; Scientific-Atlanta satellite antenna; DX Antenna satellite receivers.
Miles of plant: 116.0 (coaxial). Homes passed: 4,185.
Manager: Jack Wade. Chief technician: Ken Gabehardt. Marketing & program director: David Baum.
City fee: None.
Ownership: Helicon Corp. (MSO). See Cable System Ownership.

SHINNSTON—CableVision Communications, Box 2200, 68 5th St., Buckhannon, WV 26201. Phone: 304-472-4193. Fax: 304-472-0756. Counties: Harrison, Marion & Taylor. Also serves Adamsville, Allied, Bethlehem, Boothsville, Enterprise, Four States, Gypsy, Haywood, Hepzibah, Lumberport, Owings, Spelter, Taylor County (eastern portion), Worthington, Wyatt. ICA: WV0029.
TV Market Ranking: 90 (Bethlehem); Below 100 (Adamsville, Allied, Boothsville, Enterprise, Four States, Gypsy, Haywood, Hepzibah, Lumberport, Owings, Shinnston, Spelter, Taylor County, Worthington, Wyatt). Franchise award date: N.A. Franchise expiration date: February 28, 2004. Began: December 1, 1955.
Channel capacity: 36. Channels available but not in use: N.A.

Basic Service
Subscribers: 3,628.
Programming (received off-air): WBOY-TV (N), WDTV (C,A), WVFX (F) Clarksburg-Weston; WNPB-TV (P) Morgantown; KDKA-TV (C), WCWB (W), WPGH-TV (F), WPXI (N), WTAE-TV (A) Pittsburgh; WTRF-TV (C) Wheeling-Steubenville; allband FM.
Programming (via satellite): TBS Superstation.
Current originations: Local access.
Fee: $61.25 installation; $14.40 monthly; $1.24 converter.

Expanded Basic Service
Subscribers: 3,198.
Programming (via satellite): A & E; American Movie Classics; C-SPAN; CNN; Discovery Channel; Disney Channel; E! Entertainment TV; ESPN; ESPN 2; Fox Family Channel; Great American Country; History Channel; Home Shopping Network; Lifetime; MTV; Nashville Network; Nickelodeon; The Weather Channel; Trinity Bcstg. Network; Turner Network TV; USA Network.
Fee: $16.40 monthly.

Pay Service 1
Pay Units: 2,125.
Programming (via satellite): Cinemax; HBO; Showtime; The Movie Channel; The New Encore.
Fee: $17.50 installation; $3.99 monthly (Encore), $7.95 monthly (Cinemax), $11.95 monthly (Showtime or TMC), $11.99 monthly (HBO).

Local advertising: Yes. Rates: $4.00-$15.00/Spot.
Program Guide: CableView.
Equipment: Blonder-Tongue & DX Engineering headend; Jerrold amplifiers; Jerrold set top converters; Gardiner satellite antenna.
Miles of plant: 123.0 (coaxial). Homes passed: 4,622.
Manager: Willie Critchfield. Marketing director: Kenny Phillips.
City fee: $300 annually.
Ownership: Rifkin & Associates Inc. (MSO). See Cable System Ownership.

SIX MILE—Bowen Cablevision, Box 130, Wilkinson, WV 25653-0130. Phone: 304-752-3023. County: Boone. Also serves Greenview. ICA: WV0239.
TV Market Ranking: 36. Franchise award date: N.A. Franchise expiration date: N.A. Began: N.A.
Channel capacity: N.A. Channels available but not in use: N.A.

Basic Service
Subscribers: N.A.
Programming (received off-air): WCHS-TV (A), WOWK-TV (C), WPBY-TV (P), WSAZ-TV (N), WVAH-TV (F,U) Charleston-Huntington.
Programming (via satellite): WGN-TV (W) Chicago; A & E; C-SPAN; CNN; Cartoon Network; Comedy Central; Country Music TV; Discovery Channel; ESPN; Fox Family Channel; Headline News; Lifetime; MTV; Nashville Network; Nickelodeon; QVC; Sci-Fi Channel; TBS Superstation; The Weather Channel; Trinity Bcstg. Network; Turner Network TV; USA Network; VH1.
Fee: N.A.

Manager: Gary Bowen.
Ownership: Bowen Cablevision Inc. (MSO).

SMITHFIELD—CableVision Communications, Box 2200, 68 5th St., Buckhannon, WV 26201. Phone: 304-472-4193. Fax: 304-472-0756. County: Wetzel. ICA: WV0157.
TV Market Ranking: Below 100. Franchise award date: N.A. Franchise expiration date: N.A. Began: N.A.
Channel capacity: 42. Channels available but not in use: 28.

Basic Service
Subscribers: 62.
Programming (received off-air): WBOY-TV (N), WDTV (C,A), WVFX (F) Clarksburg-Weston; WNPB-TV (P) Morgantown; KDKA-TV (C), WPXI (N), WTAE-TV (A) Pittsburgh; WTOV-TV (N) Steubenville-Wheeling; WTRF-TV (C) Wheeling-Steubenville.
Programming (via satellite): CNN; ESPN; Fox Family Channel; Nashville Network; TBS Superstation; USA Network.
Fee: $61.25 installation; $18.00 monthly; $1.24 converter.

Pay Service 1
Pay Units: 14.
Programming (via satellite): HBO.
Fee: $11.99 monthly.

Miles of plant: 3.0 (coaxial). Homes passed: 90.
Manager: Willie Critchfield. Marketing director: Kenny Phillips.
Ownership: Rifkin & Associates Inc. (MSO). See Cable System Ownership.

SNOWSHOE—Coaxial Communications, 3770 E. Livingston Ave., Columbus, OH 43227. Phone: 614-236-1292. Fax: 614-238-7023. County: Pocahontas. Also serves Silvercreek, Slaty Fork. ICA: WV0212.
TV Market Ranking: Outside TV Markets. Franchise award date: N.A. Franchise expiration date: N.A. Began: December 1, 1982.
Channel capacity: 18 (not 2-way capable). Channels available but not in use: N.A.

Basic Service
Subscribers: 901.
Programming (received off-air): WCHS-TV (A), WVAH-TV (F,U) Charleston-Huntington; WFXR-TV (F), WSLS-TV (N) Roanoke-Lynchburg.
Programming (via satellite): WDIV (N), WJBK (F), WTVS (P), WXYZ-TV (A) Detroit; CNN; Discovery Channel; ESPN; Fox Family Channel; MTV; Nickelodeon; TBS Superstation; The Weather Channel.
Current originations: Automated time-weather.
Fee: $25.00 installation; $17.50 monthly.

Pay Service 1
Pay Units: 31.
Programming (via satellite): HBO.
Fee: $10.00 monthly.

Local advertising: No.
Equipment: Scientific-Atlanta headend; Texscan amplifiers; Times Fiber cable; Jerrold set top converters; Eagle traps; Harris, Microdyne & Scientific-Atlanta satellite antenna; ISS & Scientific-Atlanta satellite receivers.
Miles of plant: 17.0 (coaxial). Homes passed: 1,506.
Manager: Gregg Graff. Chief technician: Steve Crane. Program director: Tibbi Herlan.
Ownership: Coaxial Communications (MSO).

SPENCER—West Virginia Cablevision, Box A, 150 N. Pinch Rd., Pinch, WV 25156. Phones: 304-965-7026; 800-642-9163. Fax: 304-965-7768. County: Roane. ICA: WV0053.
TV Market Ranking: 36. Franchise award date: January 1, 1962. Franchise expiration date: N.A. Began: December 1, 1962.
Channel capacity: 40 (not 2-way capable). Channels available but not in use: N.A.

Basic Service
Subscribers: 1,262.
Programming (received off-air): WCHS-TV (A), WOWK-TV (C), WPBY-TV (P), WSAZ-TV (N), WVAH-TV (F,U) Charleston-Huntington; WTAP-TV (N) Parkersburg-Marietta.
Programming (via satellite): WGN-TV (W) Chicago; A & E; American Movie Classics; C-SPAN; C-SPAN 2; CNBC; CNN; Comedy Central; Country Music TV; Discovery Channel; ESPN; Fox Family Channel; Headline News; Home Shopping Network; Learning Channel; Lifetime; MTV; Nashville Network; Nickelodeon; QVC; Sci-Fi Channel; TBS Superstation; TV Food Network; The Weather Channel; Travel Channel; Trinity Bcstg. Network; Turner Network TV; USA Network; VH1; ValueVision.
Current originations: Educational access.
Fee: $55.00 installation; $19.69 monthly.

Pay Service 1
Pay Units: 43.
Programming (via satellite): Cinemax.
Fee: $9.00 monthly.

Pay Service 2
Pay Units: 23.
Programming (via satellite): Disney Channel.
Fee: $9.00 monthly.

Pay Service 3
Pay Units: 77.
Programming (via satellite): HBO.
Fee: $30.00 installation; $9.00 monthly.

Pay Service 4
Pay Units: N.A.
Programming (via satellite): Showtime.
Fee: N.A.

Pay Service 5
Pay Units: 37.
Programming (via satellite): The Movie Channel.
Fee: $30.00 installation; $9.00 monthly.

Local advertising: No.
Equipment: Jerrold headend; Jerrold amplifiers; Comm/Scope cable; Pico traps; Scientific-Atlanta satellite antenna; DX Antenna satellite receivers.
Miles of plant: 27.4 (coaxial). Homes passed: 2,116.
Manager: Jack Wade. Chief technician: Ken Gabehardt. Marketing & program director: David Baum.
City fee: 5% of basic.
Ownership: Helicon Corp. (MSO). See Cable System Ownership.

ST. MARYS—TCI of West Virginia Inc., 405 Cherry St., St. Mary's, WV 26170. Phone: 800-352-1030. County: Pleasants. Also serves Belmont, Pleasants County (portions). ICA: WV0057.
TV Market Ranking: Below 100. Franchise award date: N.A. Franchise expiration date: N.A. Began: August 1, 1959.
Channel capacity: 28. Channels available but not in use: N.A.

Basic Service
Subscribers: 1,532.
Programming (received off-air): WCHS-TV (A), WOWK-TV (C) Charleston-Huntington; WBOY-TV (N) Clarksburg-Weston; WNPB-TV (P) Morgantown; WTAP-TV (N) Parkersburg-Marietta; WTRF-TV (C) Wheeling-Steubenville; 14 FMs.
Programming (via satellite): WGN-TV (W) Chicago; CNN; Discovery Channel; Fox Fam-

ily Channel; FoxNet; Lifetime; MTV; Nashville Network; Nickelodeon; QVC; TBS Superstation.
Fee: $59.95 installation; $18.12 monthly.
Expanded Basic Service
Subscribers: 1,532.
Programming (via satellite): American Movie Classics; ESPN; Fox Sports Net Pittsburgh; Odyssey; Turner Network TV; USA Network.
Fee: $9.88 monthly.
Pay Service 1
Pay Units: 172.
Programming (via satellite): Cinemax.
Fee: $13.15 monthly.
Pay Service 2
Pay Units: 155.
Programming (via satellite): Disney Channel.
Fee: $11.95 monthly.
Pay Service 3
Pay Units: 258.
Programming (via satellite): HBO.
Fee: $13.15 monthly.
Equipment: Jerrold headend; Jerrold amplifiers; Times Fiber cable.
Miles of plant: 53.0 (coaxial). Homes passed: 1,750. Total homes in franchised area: 1,915.
Manager: Kenneth Heinlein.
City fee: None.
Ownership: AT&T Broadband & Internet Services (MSO). Purchased from Tele-Communications Inc., March 9, 1999.

SUMMERS COUNTY (portions)—Paxton Cable Television Inc., Suite 280, 700 Ackerman RD., Columbus, OH 43202. Phone: 614-263-6100. County: Summers. Also serves Hinton, Talcott. ICA: WV0222.
TV Market Ranking: Below 100. Franchise award date: N.A. Franchise expiration date: N.A. Began: N.A.
Channel capacity: 36. Channels available but not in use: 12.
Basic Service
Subscribers: 512.
Programming (received off-air): WVVA (N) Bluefield; WSWP-TV (P) Grandview; WVSX (I) Lewisburg; WOAY-TV (A) Oak Hill-Beckley; WDBJ (C), WSLS-TV (N) Roanoke-Lynchburg.
Programming (via satellite): WGN-TV (W) Chicago; American Movie Classics; C-SPAN; Cartoon Network; Discovery Channel; Disney Channel; ESPN 2; Fox News Channel; History Channel; Home & Garden Television; Learning Channel; Lifetime; MTV; Nickelodeon; Outdoor Channel; QVC; TBS Superstation; The Weather Channel; Trinity Bcstg. Network; USA Network; VH1.
Current originations: Educational access; government access; religious access.
Fee: $25.00 installation; $14.00 monthly.
Expanded Basic Service
Subscribers: 435.
Programming (via satellite): A & E; CNN; Country Music TV; ESPN; Fox Family Channel; Headline News; Nashville Network; Turner Network TV.
Fee: $25.00 installation; $5.95 monthly.
Pay Service 1
Pay Units: 59.
Programming (via satellite): HBO; Showtime.
Fee: $10.95 monthly (each).
Miles of plant: 33.0 (coaxial). Homes passed: 750.
Manager: Doug Rogers. Director of operations: LisaCollier.
Ownership: Paxton Cable Television Inc. (MSO). Purchased from Telehome Services Inc.

SUMMERSVILLE—Cablecomm, 6 Garton Plaza, Weston, WV 26452-2129. Phone: 800-352-1030. County: Nicholas. Also serves Nicholas County. ICA: WV0213.
TV Market Ranking: 36 (portions of Nicholas County); Below 100 (portions of Nicholas County, Summersville); Outside TV Markets (portions of Nicholas County). Franchise award date: N.A. Franchise expiration date: N.A. Began: August 1, 1960.
Channel capacity: 33. Channels available but not in use: N.A.
Basic Service
Subscribers: 1,471.
Programming (received off-air): WCHS-TV (A), WOWK-TV (C), WSAZ-TV (N), WVAH-TV (F,U) Charleston-Huntington; WDTV (C,A) Clarksburg-Weston; WSWP-TV (P) Grandview; WOAY-TV (A) Oak Hill-Beckley; allband FM.
Programming (via satellite): A & E; CNBC; CNN; Discovery Channel; Fox Family Channel; Lifetime; MTV; Nashville Network; Nickelodeon; Odyssey; QVC; TBS Superstation; The Weather Channel.
Current originations: Automated timeweather.
Fee: $59.95 installation; $17.28 monthly.
Expanded Basic Service
Subscribers: 1,348.
Programming (via satellite): American Movie Classics; C-SPAN; ESPN; Fox Sports Net Pittsburgh; Turner Network TV; USA Network.
Fee: $2.35 monthly.
Pay Service 1
Pay Units: 218.
Programming (via satellite): Cinemax.
Fee: $12.70 monthly.
Pay Service 2
Pay Units: 160.
Programming (via satellite): Disney Channel.
Fee: $11.95 monthly.
Pay Service 3
Pay Units: 499.
Programming (via satellite): The New Encore.
Fee: N.A.
Pay Service 4
Pay Units: 332.
Programming (via satellite): HBO.
Fee: $12.70 monthly.
Equipment: Jerrold headend; Jerrold amplifiers; Comm/Scope cable; Telemation cameras; Sony VTRs; Oak set top converters; Scientific-Atlanta satellite antenna.
Miles of plant: 32.1 (coaxial). Total homes in franchised area: 2,782.
Manager: David Hashimoto. Chief technician: Dave Cottrell.
City fee: $200 monthly.
Ownership: Fanch Communications Inc. (MSO); Time Warner Cable (MSO). Purchased from Tele-Communications Inc., February 25, 1999. See Cable System Ownership.

TANNER—Bob's TV Service, Box 389, Rte. 9, Birch River, WV 26610. Phone: 304-649-2447. Counties: Calhoun, Clay & Gilmer. Also serves Arnoldsburg, Kanawha Drive, Nebo. ICA: WV0149.
TV Market Ranking: Below 100 (Kanawha Drive, Tanner); Outside TV Markets (Arnoldsburg, Nebo). Franchise award date: N.A. Franchise expiration date: N.A. Began: August 1, 1983.
Channel capacity: 35. Channels available but not in use: N.A.
Basic Service
Subscribers: 91.
Programming (received off-air): WCHS-TV (A), WSAZ-TV (N), WVAH-TV (F,U) Charleston-Huntington; WBOY-TV (N), WDTV (C,A) Clarksburg-Weston; WSWP-TV (P) Grandview; WOAY-TV (A) Oak Hill-Beckley.
Programming (via satellite): CNN; Discovery Channel; ESPN; Nashville Network; TBS Superstation.
Fee: $150.00 installation; $17.00 monthly.
Pay Service 1
Pay Units: 12.
Programming (via satellite): HBO.
Fee: $11.00 monthly.
Miles of plant: 6.0 (coaxial). Homes passed: 133.
Manager: Bob Houghton.
Ownership: Bob Houghton (MSO).

TUNNELTON—Community Antenna Service, Box 282, Rte. 1, Washington, WV 26181. Phone: 304-863-8922. Fax: 304-863-6219. County: Preston. Also serves Denver, Fellowsville, Kingwood. ICA: WV0112.
TV Market Ranking: Below 100 (Denver, Fellowsville, Tunnelton); Outside TV Markets (Kingwood). Franchise award date: N.A. Franchise expiration date: N.A. Began: February 1, 1980.
Channel capacity: 36 (not 2-way capable). Channels available but not in use: 6.
Basic Service
Subscribers: 624.
Programming (received off-air): WBOY-TV (N), WDTV (C,A), WVFX (F) Clarksburg-Weston; WNPB-TV (P) Morgantown; KDKA-TV (C), WPGH-TV (F), WPXI (N), WTAE-TV (A) Pittsburgh.
Programming (via satellite): ESPN; Nashville Network; TBS Superstation; USA Network.
Fee: N.A.
Pay Service 1
Pay Units: N.A.
Programming (via satellite): HBO.
Fee: N.A.
Miles of plant: 37.0 (coaxial); None (fiber optic). Homes passed: 1,034. Total homes in franchised area: 1,034.
Manager: Arthur R. Cooper.
Ownership: Arthur R. Cooper (MSO).

TWELVE POLE—Green Tree Cable TV Inc., Box 85, Franklin Furnace, OH 45629. Phone: 614-354-9195. County: Mingo. ICA: WV0214.
TV Market Ranking: Outside TV Markets. Franchise award date: N.A. Franchise expiration date: N.A. Began: June 1, 1977.
Channel capacity: 5. Channels available but not in use: None.
Basic Service
Subscribers: N.A.
Programming (received off-air): WCHS-TV (A), WOWK-TV (C), WPBY-TV (P), WSAZ-TV (N), WVAH-TV (F,U) Charleston-Huntington.
Fee: N.A.
Manager: Donna Lycans. Chief technician: Aaron Lycans.
Ownership: Green Tree Cable TV Inc. (MSO).

UNION—Bradley's Inc., Box 41, Wharton, WV 25208. Phone: 304-247-6231. Fax: 304-247-6255. County: Monroe. ICA: WV0249.
TV Market Ranking: Below 100. Franchise award date: January 1, 1985. Franchise expiration date: January 1, 2000. Began: January 1, 1986.
Channel capacity: 36 (not 2-way capable). Channels available but not in use: 4.
Basic Service
Subscribers: 232.
Programming (received off-air): WVVA (N) Bluefield; WSWP-TV (P) Grandview; WOAY-TV (A) Oak Hill-Beckley; WBRA-TV (P) Roanoke; WDBJ (C), WSET-TV (A), WSLS-TV (N) Roanoke-Lynchburg; WVFT (I) Rock Hill.
Programming (via satellite): Discovery Channel; QVC; TBS Superstation.
Current originations: Automated timeweather.
Fee: $32.02 installation; $11.01 monthly.
Expanded Basic Service
Subscribers: 219.
Programming (via satellite): WGN-TV (W) Chicago; CNN; Cartoon Network; Country Music TV; ESPN; Fox Family Channel; Fox Sports Net Pittsburgh; Home & Garden Television; Nashville Network; Nickelodeon; Odyssey; The Inspirational Network; The Weather Channel; Turner Classic Movies; Turner Network TV; USA Network; VH1.
Fee: $12.41 monthly.
Pay Service 1
Pay Units: 20.
Programming (via satellite): Disney Channel.
Fee: N.A.
Pay Service 2
Pay Units: 36.
Programming (via satellite): HBO.
Fee: N.A.
Local advertising: No.
Miles of plant: 5.0 (coaxial); None (fiber optic). Homes passed: 325. Total homes in franchised area: 350.
Manager: Robert Legg Jr. Chief technician: Chuck Bradley.
Franchise fee: 3% of gross.
Ownership: Bradley's Inc. (MSO).

UPPER TRACT—CableVision Communications, Box 2200, 68 5th St., Buckhannon, WV 26201. Phone: 304-472-4193. Fax: 304-472-0756. County: Pendleton. ICA: WV0136.
TV Market Ranking: Outside TV Markets. Franchise award date: January 1, 1982. Franchise expiration date: N.A. Began: September 1, 1982.
Channel capacity: 12. Channels available but not in use: 6.
Basic Service
Subscribers: 180.
Programming (received off-air): WDTV (C,A) Clarksburg-Weston; WHAG-TV (N), WWPB (P) Hagerstown; WHSV-TV (A,F) Harrisonburg; WJAC-TV (N) Johnstown-Altoona; WNPB-TV (P) Morgantown; WTTG (F), WUSA (C) Washington.
Programming (via satellite): ESPN; Fox Family Channel; Nashville Network; TBS Superstation.
Fee: $61.25 installation; $13.39 monthly; $1.24 converter.
Pay Service 1
Pay Units: 2.
Programming (via satellite): HBO.
Fee: $11.99 monthly.
Equipment: Blonder-Tongue & DX Engineering headend; Jerrold amplifiers.
Miles of plant: 20.0 (coaxial). Homes passed: 250.
Manager: Willie Critchfield. Marketing director: Kenny Phillips.
City fee: None.
Ownership: Rifkin & Associates Inc. (MSO). See Cable System Ownership.

VARNEY—Cooney Cable Assoc., 228 Park Ave., Worcester, MA 01607. Phone: 508-754-5865. Fax: 508-752-7342. County: Mingo. ICA: WV0215.

TV Market Ranking: Below 100. Franchise award date: N.A. Franchise expiration date: N.A. Began: N.A.
Channel capacity: 40 (not 2-way capable). Channels available but not in use: 6.
Basic Service
Subscribers: 465.
Programming (received off-air): WVVA (N) Bluefield; WCHS-TV (A), WOWK-TV (C), WSAZ-TV (N), WVAH-TV (F,U) Charleston-Huntington; WSWP-TV (P) Grandview.
Programming (via satellite): WGN-TV (W) Chicago; CNN; Country Music TV; ESPN; Fox Family Channel; Nashville Network; Nickelodeon; TBS Superstation; Trinity Bcstg. Network; Turner Network TV; USA Network.
Fee: $48.18 installation; $27.45 monthly.
Pay Service 1
Pay Units: 57.
Programming (via satellite): HBO.
Fee: $25.00 installation; $11.95 monthly.
Pay Service 2
Pay Units: 35.
Programming (via satellite): Showtime.
Fee: $25.00 installation; $10.95 monthly.
Pay Service 3
Pay Units: 18.
Programming (via satellite): Showtime; The Movie Channel.
Fee: $11.95 monthly (Showtime or TMC).
Miles of plant: 15.0 (coaxial); None (fiber optic).
Manager: John Cooney. Chief technician: Ron Davis.
Ownership: Cooney Cable Assoc. Inc. (MSO).

VAUGHAN—Capital Cablecomm, Box 368, Cabin Creek, WV 25035. Phone: 304-779-2854. Fax: 304-595-5248. County: Nicholas. Also serves Twentymile. ICA: WV0158.
TV Market Ranking: 36. Franchise award date: N.A. Franchise expiration date: May 12, 2008. Began: June 1, 1980.
Channel capacity: 15 (not 2-way capable). Channels available but not in use: 6.
Basic Service
Subscribers: 74.
Programming (received off-air): WVVA (N) Bluefield; WCHS-TV (A), WOWK-TV (C), WPBY-TV (P), WSAZ-TV (N), WVAH-TV (F,U) Charleston-Huntington; WDTV (C,A) Clarksburg-Weston; WSWP-TV (P) Grandview; WOAY-TV (A) Oak Hill-Beckley.
Current originations: Public access; educational access; government access.
Fee: $32.00 installation (aerial), $45.00 (underground); $13.15 monthly.
Equipment: Blonder-Tongue headend; Jerrold & GTE Sylvania amplifiers; Comm/Scope cable.
Miles of plant: 4.8 (coaxial); None (fiber optic). Homes passed: 88.
Manager: Robert L. Herrald. Chief technician: Allen Comer. Marketing director: Bill Benner.
Ownership: Fanch Communications Inc. (MSO). See Cable System Ownership.

WAR—Thompson Cablevision Co., Box 13309, Sissonville, WV 25360. Phone: 304-984-0025. Counties: McDowell, WV; Tazewell, VA. Also serves Amonate, VA; Canebrake, Caretta, Cucumber, Hartwell, Newhall, Squire, Valls Creek, WV. ICA: WV0048.
TV Market Ranking: Below 100. Franchise award date: N.A. Franchise expiration date: April 1, 2007. Began: N.A.
Channel capacity: 31. Channels available but not in use: 4.
Basic Service
Subscribers: N.A.
Programming (received off-air): WCHS-TV (A), WOWK-TV (C), WPBY-TV (P), WSAZ-TV (N), WVAH-TV (F,U) Charleston-Huntington.
Programming (via satellite): WGN-TV (W) Chicago; TBS Superstation.
Fee: $18.45 monthly.
Pay Service 1
Pay Units: N.A.
Programming (via satellite): Disney Channel; HBO; Showtime.
Fee: N.A.
Miles of plant: 48.0 (coaxial). Homes passed: 2,483.
Manager: Anthony Cochran.
Ownership: Thompson Cablevision Co. Inc. (MSO).

WARDENSVILLE—Valley Cable, Box 78, Doylesburg, PA 17219. Phone: 717-349-7717. County: Hardy. Also serves Hardy County (portions). ICA: WV0124.
TV Market Ranking: Outside TV Markets. Franchise award date: N.A. Franchise expiration date: January 1, 2004. Began: October 9, 1974.
Channel capacity: 36 (not 2-way capable). Channels available but not in use: 7.
Basic Service
Subscribers: 300.
Programming (received off-air): WJAL (W) Hagerstown; WNPB-TV (P) Morgantown; WDCA (U), WETA-TV (P), WJLA-TV (A), WRC-TV (N), WTTG (F), WUSA (C) Washington; allband FM.
Programming (via satellite): A & E; Bravo; C-SPAN; CNN; Country Music TV; Discovery Channel; ESPN; Fox Family Channel; Lifetime; Nashville Network; Sci-Fi Channel; TBS Superstation; Trinity Bcstg. Network; Turner Network TV; USA Network.
Current originations: Automated time-weather.
Fee: $40.00 installation; $15.25 monthly.
Pay Service 1
Pay Units: 42.
Programming (via satellite): Showtime.
Fee: $10.00 monthly.
Local advertising: Yes. Available in character-generated programming.
Equipment: Blonder-Tongue headend; Jerrold amplifiers; Comm/Scope cable; Atari & Info/Soft character generator; Jerrold set top converters; Pico traps; Scientific-Atlanta satellite antenna; Drake satellite receivers.
Miles of plant: 10.9 (coaxial). Homes passed: 342. Total homes in franchised area: 375.
Manager: Barry L. Kepner.
City fee: 3% of gross.
Ownership: Valley Cable Systems (MSO).

WARWOOD—Centre TV Cable, 510 Warwood Ave., Wheeling, WV 26003. Phone: 304-277-2811. Counties: Brooke & Ohio. Also serves Power, RD No. 1 Trailer Courts, Short Creek. ICA: WV0043.
TV Market Ranking: 10,90.Franchise award date: N.A. Franchise expiration date: N.A. Began: January 1, 1950.
Channel capacity: 12. Channels available but not in use: N.A.
Basic Service
Subscribers: N.A.
Programming (received off-air): WNPB-TV (P) Morgantown; KDKA-TV (C), WPXI (N), WQED (P), WTAE-TV (A) Pittsburgh; WTOV-TV (N) Steubenville-Wheeling; WTRF-TV (C) Wheeling-Steubenville; WFMJ-TV (N), WYTV (A,F) Youngstown; allband FM.
Programming (via satellite): ESPN; TBS Superstation; USA Network.
Fee: $6.00 monthly.
Pay Service 1
Pay Units: N.A.
Programming (via satellite): HBO.
Fee: $25.00 installation; $9.00 monthly.
Equipment: AFC satellite antenna.
Miles of plant: 11.0 (coaxial). Homes passed: 2,776.
Manager: Kasmir Majewski.
Ownership: Kasmir Majewski (MSO).

WASHINGTON—Community Antenna Service, Box 282, Rte. 1, Washington, WV 26181. Phone: 304-863-8922. Fax: 304-863-6219. County: Wood. Also serves Belleville. ICA: WV0128.
TV Market Ranking: Below 100. Franchise award date: N.A. Franchise expiration date: N.A. Began: June 1, 1981.
Channel capacity: 36 (not 2-way capable). Channels available but not in use: 1.
Basic Service
Subscribers: 1,816.
Programming (received off-air): WOUB-TV (P) Athens; WCHS-TV (A), WOWK-TV (C), WPBY-TV (P), WSAZ-TV (N), WVAH-TV (F,U) Charleston-Huntington; WDTV (C,A) Clarksburg-Weston; WTAP-TV (N) Parkersburg-Marietta; WTRF-TV (C) Wheeling-Steubenville.
Programming (via satellite): CNNfn.
Fee: N.A.
Pay Service 1
Pay Units: N.A.
Programming (via satellite): HBO.
Fee: N.A.
Miles of plant: 73.0 (coaxial); None (fiber optic).
Manager: Arthur R. Cooper.
Ownership: Arthur R. Cooper (MSO).

WAYNE—CableVision Communications, Box 2200, 68 5th St., Buckhannon, WV 26201. Phone: 304-472-4193. Fax: 304-472-0756. Counties: Lincoln, Logan & Wayne. Also serves Atenville, Big Creek, Branchland, Chapmanville, Core Gap, Crabtree, East Lynn, Ferrellsburg, Fort Gay, Harts, Hubball, Kitchen, Lavalette, Midkiff, Ranger, Rockville, Sheridan. ICA: WV0035.
TV Market Ranking: 36. Franchise award date: October 10, 1982. Franchise expiration date: October 10, 2032. Began: N.A.
Channel capacity: 37. Channels available but not in use: None.
Basic Service
Subscribers: 3,522.
Programming (received off-air): WTSF (I) Ashland; WCHS-TV (A), WOWK-TV (C), WPBY-TV (P), WSAZ-TV (N), WVAH-TV (F,U) Charleston-Huntington.
Programming (via satellite): WGN-TV (W) Chicago; C-SPAN; Home Shopping Network; TBS Superstation; Trinity Bcstg. Network.
Current originations: Public access.
Fee: $61.25 installation; $14.40 monthly; $1.24 converter.
Expanded Basic Service
Subscribers: N.A.
Programming (via satellite): A & E; American Movie Classics; CNN; Discovery Channel; Disney Channel; E! Entertainment TV; ESPN; Fox Family Channel; Fox Sports Net Pittsburgh; Great American Country; Headline News; Learning Channel; Lifetime; MSNBC; MTV; Nashville Network; Nickelodeon; Outdoor Channel; The Weather Channel; Turner Network TV; USA Network.
Fee: $15.02 monthly.
Pay Service 1
Pay Units: 1,411.
Programming (via satellite): Cinemax; HBO; Showtime; The Movie Channel; The New Encore.
Fee: $17.50 installation; $3.99 monthly (Encore), $7.99 (Cinemax), $11.99 monthly (HBO, Showtime or TMC).
Equipment: Blonder-Tongue, Microdyne & Olson headend; C-COR amplifiers.
Miles of plant: 153.0 (coaxial). Homes passed: 3,789.
Manager: Willie Critchfield. Chief technician: Bill Turner. Marketing director: Kenny Phillips.
Ownership: Rifkin & Associates Inc. (MSO). See Cable System Ownership.

WEBSTER SPRINGS—Cablecomm, Box 747, 80 N. Main St., Webster Springs, WV 26288-0747. Phone: 800-352-1030. County: Webster. Also serves Webster County (central portion). ICA: WV0080.
TV Market Ranking: Below 100 (portions of Webster County); Outside TV Markets (portions of Webster County, Webster Springs). Franchise award date: N.A. Franchise expiration date: N.A. Began: January 1, 1953.
Channel capacity: 36 (not 2-way capable). Channels available but not in use: N.A.
Basic Service
Subscribers: 1,812.
Programming (received off-air): WCHS-TV (A) Charleston-Huntington; WBOY-TV (N), WDTV (C,A) Clarksburg-Weston; WSWP-TV (P) Grandview; WOAY-TV (A) Oak Hill-Beckley; allband FM.
Programming (via satellite): CNN; Cartoon Network; Discovery Channel; Fox Family Channel; FoxNet; Lifetime; MTV; Nashville Network; Nickelodeon; QVC; TBS Superstation; The Weather Channel.
Current originations: Automated time-weather; public access.
Fee: $59.95 installation; $18.83 monthly.
Expanded Basic Service
Subscribers: 894.
Programming (via satellite): American Movie Classics; ESPN; Fox Sports Net Pittsburgh; Odyssey; Turner Network TV; USA Network.
Fee: $1.85 monthly.
Pay Service 1
Pay Units: 79.
Programming (via satellite): Disney Channel.
Fee: $11.95 monthly.
Pay Service 2
Pay Units: 393.
Programming (via satellite): The New Encore.
Fee: N.A.
Pay Service 3
Pay Units: 153.
Programming (via satellite): HBO.
Fee: $13.15 monthly.
Pay Service 4
Pay Units: 96.
Programming (via satellite): Showtime.
Fee: $13.15 monthly.
Local advertising: No.
Program Guide: The Cable Guide.
Equipment: Blonder-Tongue headend; Jerrold amplifiers; Times Fiber cable; Jerrold set top converters; Microdyne satellite antenna; Microdyne satellite receivers.
Miles of plant: 25.0 (coaxial).
Manager: Sue Talbott.
City fee: 3% of gross.
Ownership: Fanch Communications Inc. (MSO); Time Warner Cable (MSO). Purchased from Tele-Communications Inc., February 25, 1999. See Cable System Ownership.

WEIRTON—TCI, 371 New York Blvd., Weirton, WV 26062. Phone: 304-748-5330. Fax: 304-748-1726. Counties: Brooke & Hancock. Also serves Brooke County, Hancock County. ICA: WV0013.

TV Market Ranking: 10,90. Franchise award date: N.A. Franchise expiration date: N.A. Began: November 1, 1952.

Channel capacity: 60 (not 2-way capable). Channels available but not in use: 7.

Basic Service

Subscribers: 9,066; Commercial subscribers: 176.

Programming (received off-air): WNEO (P) Alliance; WPCB-TV (I) Greensburg; KDKA-TV (C), WCWB (W), WPGH-TV (F), WPXI (N), WQED (P), WQEX (P), WTAE-TV (A) Pittsburgh; WTOV-TV (N) Steubenville-Wheeling; WTRF-TV (C) Wheeling-Steubenville.

Programming (via translator): WNPB-TV (P) Morgantown.

Programming (via satellite): A & E; American Movie Classics; BET; C-SPAN; CNN; Cartoon Network; Comedy Central; Discovery Channel; ESPN; FX; Fox Family Channel; Fox Sports Net Pittsburgh; Headline News; Lifetime; MSNBC; MTV; Nashville Network; Nick at Nite; Nickelodeon; Odyssey; QVC; TBS Superstation; TV Guide Channel; TV Guide Sneak Prevue; The Weather Channel; Turner Classic Movies; Turner Network TV; USA Network.

Current originations: Government access.

Fee: $27.81 installation; $13.95 monthly; $15.84 additional installation.

Pay Service 1

Pay Units: 389.

Programming (via satellite): Cinemax.

Fee: $9.95 monthly.

Pay Service 2

Pay Units: 606.

Programming (via satellite): Disney Channel.

Fee: $8.95 monthly.

Pay Service 3

Pay Units: 1,486.

Programming (via satellite): HBO.

Fee: $11.95 monthly.

Pay Service 4

Pay Units: 2,040.

Programming (via satellite): Showtime.

Fee: $10.95 monthly.

Pay Service 5

Pay Units: 217.

Programming (via satellite): The Movie Channel.

Fee: $9.95 monthly.

Pay-Per-View

Addressable homes: 190.

Local advertising: Yes.

Equipment: Scientific-Atlanta headend; C-COR amplifiers; Comm/Scope & Times Fiber cable; Sony cameras; Sony VTRs; Standard Components & Jerrold set top converters; Jerrold addressable set top converters; Anixter traps; Scientific-Atlanta satellite antenna.

Miles of plant: 101.0 (coaxial). Additional miles planned: 1.0 (coaxial). Homes passed: 11,381.

Manager: Linda Walker. Chief technician: Rob Mayer.

City fee: $100 annually.

Ownership: AT&T Broadband & Internet Services (MSO). Purchased from Tele-Communications Inc., March 9, 1999.

WELCH—Thompson Cablevision Co. Inc., Box 553, 99 Howard St., Welch, WV 24801. Phone: 304-436-4811. County: McDowell. Also serves Capels, Gary, Havaco, Hemphill, Maitland-Superior, North Welch. ICA: WV0042.

TV Market Ranking: Below 100. Franchise award date: N.A. Franchise expiration date: N.A. Began: July 1, 1951.

Channel capacity: 12. Channels available but not in use: 3.

Basic Service

Subscribers: 2,700.

Programming (received off-air): WVVA (N) Bluefield; WCHS-TV (A), WOWK-TV (C), WSAZ-TV (N) Charleston-Huntington; WSWP-TV (P) Grandview; WKPT-TV (A) Kingsport; WOAY-TV (A) Oak Hill-Beckley; WDBJ (C) Roanoke-Lynchburg; allband FM.

Planned programming (via satellite): ESPN; Fox Family Channel; Nickelodeon; TBS Superstation.

Current originations: Automated time-weather.

Fee: $15.00 installation; $13.95 monthly.

Pay Service 1

Pay Units: N.A.

Programming (via satellite): HBO.

Fee: $9.45 monthly.

Local advertising: Yes. Available in locally originated, character-generated & taped programming.

Equipment: Blonder-Tongue headend; Cascade amplifiers; Comm/Scope & Times Fiber cable; AFC satellite antenna.

Miles of plant: 57.0 (coaxial). Homes passed: 2,900.

Manager: Mark James. Office manager: Carla Roope. Chief technician: Ron Foster.

Ownership: Thompson Cablevision Co. Inc. (MSO).

WELLSBURG—TCI of West Virginia Inc., Box 2078, 2184 National Rd., Wheeling, WV 26003-5297. Phone: 800-352-1030. County: Brooke. Also serves Brooke County. ICA: WV0052.

TV Market Ranking: 10,90. Franchise award date: N.A. Franchise expiration date: N.A. Began: May 1, 1965.

Channel capacity: 31. Channels available but not in use: N.A.

Basic Service

Subscribers: 1,873.

Programming (received off-air): WNPB-TV (P) Morgantown; KDKA-TV (C), WCWB (W), WPGH-TV (F), WPXI (N), WQED (P), WTAE-TV (A) Pittsburgh; WTOV-TV (N) Steubenville-Wheeling; WTRF-TV (C) Wheeling-Steubenville; WYTV (A,F) Youngstown.

Programming (via satellite): A & E; CNN; Discovery Channel; Fox Family Channel; Lifetime; MTV; Nashville Network; Nickelodeon; QVC; TBS Superstation.

Fee: $59.95 installation; $9.55 monthly.

Expanded Basic Service

Subscribers: 1,861.

Programming (via satellite): American Movie Classics; C-SPAN; ESPN; Fox Sports Net Pittsburgh; Turner Network TV; USA Network.

Fee: $10.35 monthly.

Pay Service 1

Pay Units: 144.

Programming (via satellite): Disney Channel.

Fee: $11.95 monthly.

Pay Service 2

Pay Units: 736.

Programming (via satellite): The New Encore.

Fee: N.A.

Pay Service 3

Pay Units: 465.

Programming (via satellite): HBO.

Fee: $13.15 monthly.

Pay Service 4

Pay Units: 230.

Programming (via satellite): Showtime.

Fee: $13.15 monthly.

Equipment: Scientific-Atlanta satellite antenna; Scientific-Atlanta satellite receivers.

Miles of plant: 36.0 (coaxial). Homes passed: 2,196. Total homes in franchised area: 2,665.

Manager: Dennis Snow.

Ownership: AT&T Broadband & Internet Services (MSO). Purchased from Tele-Communications Inc., March 9, 1999.

WEST LIBERTY—Marshall County Cable, Box 1696, 300 Chester Field Pkwy., Clarksburg, WV 26302-1696. Phones: 304-623-0150; 800-882-1206. Counties: Brooke & Ohio. Also serves Ohio County (unincorporated areas), Triadelphia, Wheeling, Windsor Heights. ICA: WV0216.

TV Market Ranking: 90. Franchise award date: N.A. Franchise expiration date: N.A. Began: January 1, 1988.

Channel capacity: 36. Channels available but not in use: 9.

Basic Service

Subscribers: 340.

Programming (received off-air): WNPB-TV (P) Morgantown; KDKA-TV (C), WCWB (W), WPGH-TV (F), WQED (P), WTAE-TV (A) Pittsburgh; WTOV-TV (N) Steubenville-Wheeling; WTRF-TV (C) Wheeling-Steubenville.

Programming (via satellite): WGN-TV (W) Chicago; CNN; Discovery Channel; ESPN; Fox Family Channel; Fox Sports Net Pittsburgh; Headline News; Nashville Network; TBS Superstation; Turner Network TV; USA Network.

Current originations: Educational access.

Fee: $25.00 installation; $15.95 monthly.

Pay Service 1

Pay Units: N.A.

Programming (via satellite): Disney Channel; HBO.

Fee: $4.95 monthly (Disney), $11.00 monthly (HBO).

Miles of plant: 15.0 (coaxial).

Manager: Joe Nolan. Chief technician: Bill Martin.

Ownership: FinCom Corp. (MSO).

WEST MILFORD—CableVision Communications, Box 2200, 68 5th St., Buckhannon, WV 26201. Phone: 304-472-4193. Fax: 304-472-0756. County: Harrison. Also serves Goodhope, Lost Creek, Rider. ICA: WV0068.

TV Market Ranking: Below 100. Franchise award date: N.A. Franchise expiration date: N.A. Began: January 1, 1970.

Channel capacity: 30. Channels available but not in use: N.A.

Basic Service

Subscribers: 1,257.

Programming (received off-air): WBOY-TV (N), WDTV (C,A), WVFX (F) Clarksburg-Weston; WNPB-TV (P) Morgantown; WKRN-TV (A) Nashville; WTAE-TV (A) Pittsburgh; WTRF-TV (C) Wheeling-Steubenville; allband FM.

Programming (via satellite): WGN-TV (W) Chicago; CNN; Cartoon Network; Discovery Channel; Disney Channel; ESPN; ESPN 2; FX; Fox Family Channel; FoxNet; Great American Country; History Channel; Learning Channel; Lifetime; Nashville Network; Nickelodeon; TBS Superstation; The Weather Channel; Turner Network TV; USA Network.

Fee: $61.25 installation; $19.27 monthly; $1.24 converter.

A la Carte 1

Subscribers: N.A.

Programming (via satellite): The New Encore; Turner Classic Movies.

Fee: $5.99 monthly (package); 3.99 monthly (each).

Pay Service 1

Pay Units: 984.

Programming (via satellite): Cinemax; HBO (multiplexed); Showtime; The Movie Channel.

Fee: $17.50 installation; $7.95 monthly (Cinemax), $11.95 monthly (HBO, Showtime or TMC).

Equipment: Blonder-Tongue & Jerrold headend; Jerrold amplifiers.

Miles of plant: 33.0 (coaxial). Homes passed: 1,348.

Manager: Willie Critchfield. Marketing director: Kenny Phillips.

City fee: None.

Ownership: Rifkin & Associates Inc. (MSO). See Cable System Ownership.

WEST UNION—CableVision Communications, Box 2200, 68 5th St., Buckhannon, WV 26201. Phone: 304-472-4193. Fax: 304-472-0756. County: Doddridge. ICA: WV0104.

TV Market Ranking: Below 100. Franchise award date: N.A. Franchise expiration date: N.A. Began: January 1, 1966.

Channel capacity: 35. Channels available but not in use: 1.

Basic Service

Subscribers: 361.

Programming (received off-air): WCHS-TV (A) Charleston-Huntington; WBOY-TV (N), WDTV (C,A), WVFX (F) Clarksburg-Weston; WNPB-TV (P) Morgantown; WTAP-TV (N) Parkersburg-Marietta; WTAE-TV (A) Pittsburgh; WTOV-TV (N) Steubenville-Wheeling; WTRF-TV (C) Wheeling-Steubenville; allband FM.

Programming (via satellite): WGN-TV (W) Chicago; E! Entertainment TV; History Channel; Home Shopping Network; Learning Channel; Nick at Nite's TV Land; TBS Superstation; Trinity Bcstg. Network.

Fee: $61.25 installation; $15.98 monthly; $0.73 converter.

Expanded Basic Service

Subscribers: N.A.

Programming (via satellite): American Movie Classics; CNN; Discovery Channel; Disney Channel; ESPN; ESPN 2; Fox Family Channel; FoxNet; Great American Country; Lifetime; Nashville Network; Nickelodeon; Sci-Fi Channel; The Weather Channel; Turner Network TV; USA Network.

Fee: $14.62 monthly.

Pay Service 1

Pay Units: 22.

Programming (via satellite): HBO.

Fee: $17.50 installation; $11.99 monthly.

Pay Service 2

Pay Units: N.A.

Programming (via satellite): Cinemax.

Fee: $7.95 monthly.

Equipment: Blonder-Tongue & Jerrold headend; Jerrold amplifiers; Microdyne satellite antenna; Microdyne satellite receivers.

Miles of plant: 10.0 (coaxial). Homes passed: 608.

Manager: Willie Critchfield. Marketing director: Kenny Phillips.

City fee: None.

Ownership: Rifkin & Associates Inc. (MSO). See Cable System Ownership.

WESTON—Cablecomm, 6 Garton Plaza, Weston, WV 26452-2129. Phone: 800-352-1030. County: Lewis. Also serves Jane Lew, Lewis County. ICA: WV0034.

TV Market Ranking: Below 100. Franchise award date: N.A. Franchise expiration date: N.A. Began: January 1, 1954.

Channel capacity: 47. Channels available but not in use: N.A.

Basic Service

Subscribers: 3,742.

Programming (received off-air): WCHS-TV (A) Charleston-Huntington; WBOY-TV (N), WDTV (C,A), WVFX (F) Clarksburg-Weston; WNPB-TV (P) Morgantown; 20 FMs.
Programming (via microwave): WTAE-TV (A) Pittsburgh.
Programming (via satellite): CNN; Cartoon Network; Discovery Channel; Fox Family Channel; FoxNet; Lifetime; MTV; Nashville Network; Nickelodeon; QVC; TBS Superstation.
Current originations: Automated time-weather.
Fee: $59.95 installation; $9.75 monthly; $2.00 converter.

Expanded Basic Service
Subscribers: 3,613.
Programming (via satellite): American Movie Classics; ESPN; Fox Sports Net Pittsburgh; Turner Network TV; USA Network.
Fee: $11.78 monthly.

Pay Service 1
Pay Units: 504.
Programming (via satellite): Cinemax.
Fee: $13.15 monthly.

Pay Service 2
Pay Units: 300.
Programming (via satellite): Disney Channel.
Fee: $11.95 monthly.

Pay Service 3
Pay Units: 729.
Programming (via satellite): HBO.
Fee: $13.15 monthly.

Local advertising: Yes. Rates: $22.00/Day.
Program Guide: The Cable Guide.
Equipment: Jerrold headend; Jerrold amplifiers; Comm/Scope cable; Telemation cameras; Sony VTRs; Telemation character generator; Oak set top converters; Scientific-Atlanta satellite antenna.
Miles of plant: 108.8 (coaxial). Homes passed: 3,869. Total homes in franchised area: 11,607.
Manager: David Hashimoto. Chief technician: Dave Cottrell.
City fee: $250 annually.
Ownership: Fanch Communications Inc. (MSO); Time Warner Cable (MSO). Purchased from Tele-Communications Inc., February 25, 1999. See Cable System Ownership.

WESTOVER—Century Huntington Co., Box 599, Dellslow, WV 26531. Phone: 304-292-6561. County: Monongalia. Also serves Monongalia County. ICA: WV0056.
TV Market Ranking: 90 (portions of Monongalia County); Below 100 (portions of Monongalia County, Westover). Franchise award date: N.A. Franchise expiration date: N.A. Began: June 1, 1967.
Channel capacity: 12. Channels available but not in use: N.A.

Basic Service
Subscribers: 1,716.
Programming (received off-air): WBOY-TV (N), WDTV (C,A) Clarksburg-Weston; WNPB-TV (P) Morgantown; KDKA-TV (C), WPGH-TV (F), WPXI (N), WQED (P), WTAE-TV (A) Pittsburgh; WTOV-TV (N) Steubenville-Wheeling; WTRF-TV (C) Wheeling-Steubenville; allband FM.
Planned programming (via satellite): Fox Family Channel; USA Network.
Current originations: Automated time-weather.
Fee: $6.95 installation; $7.50 monthly.

Pay Service 1
Pay Units: N.A.
Planned programming (via microwave): HBO.
Fee: N.A.

Equipment: Jerrold headend; Jerrold amplifiers; Times Fiber cable.
Miles of plant: 25.0 (coaxial). Homes passed: 1,830.
Manager: Michael Ligouri. Chief technician: Ed Hinkle.
City fee: $0.50 per subscriber annually.
Ownership: Century Communications Corp. (MSO). See Cable System Ownership.

WHEELING—TCI of West Virginia Inc., Box 2078, 2184 National Rd., Wheeling, WV 26003-5297. Phone: 800-352-1030. Counties: Marshall & Ohio. Also serves Benwood, Bethlehem, Clearview, Marshall County, McMechen, Mozart, Ohio County, Shawnee Hills, Triadelphia, Valley Grove. ICA: WV0004.
TV Market Ranking: 90. Franchise award date: N.A. Franchise expiration date: N.A. Began: June 1, 1952.
Channel capacity: 61. Channels available but not in use: N.A.

Basic Service
Subscribers: 17,412.
Programming (received off-air): WNPB-TV (P) Morgantown; KDKA-TV (C), WCWB (W), WPGH-TV (F), WPXI (N), WQED (P), WTAE-TV (A) Pittsburgh; WTOV-TV (N) Steubenville-Wheeling; WTRF-TV (C) Wheeling-Steubenville; WYTV (A,F) Youngstown; 13 FMs.
Programming (via satellite): A & E; BET; C-SPAN; CNBC; CNN; Cartoon Network; Discovery Channel; Fox Family Channel; Headline News; Lifetime; MTV; Nashville Network; Nickelodeon; Odyssey; QVC; TBS Superstation; The Weather Channel.
Current originations: Automated time-weather; public access; government access; local news.
Fee: $59.95 installation; $9.00 monthly; $4.00 converter.

Expanded Basic Service
Subscribers: 17,062.
Programming (via satellite): American Movie Classics; Court TV; ESPN; Fox Sports Net Pittsburgh; Turner Network TV; USA Network.
Fee: $13.17 monthly.

Pay Service 1
Pay Units: 1,419.
Programming (via satellite): Disney Channel.
Fee: N.A.

Pay Service 2
Pay Units: 6,476.
Programming (via satellite): The New Encore.
Fee: N.A.

Pay Service 3
Pay Units: 3,728.
Programming (via satellite): HBO.
Fee: $13.15 monthly.

Pay Service 4
Pay Units: 2,870.
Programming (via satellite): Showtime.
Fee: $13.15 monthly.

Local advertising: Yes (locally produced & insert).
Program Guide: The Cable Guide.
Equipment: Jerrold headend; Jerrold & Magnavox amplifiers; Systems Wire cable; GTE Sylvania & Jerrold set top converters; Scientific-Atlanta satellite antenna.
Miles of plant: 264.3 (coaxial). Homes passed: 23,035. Total homes in franchised area: 46,382.
Manager: Dennis Snow.
Ownership: AT&T Broadband & Internet Services (MSO). Purchased from Tele-Communications Inc., March 9, 1999.

WHITE SULPHUR SPRINGS—Cablevision, 313 W. Main St., Oak Hill, WV 25901-2938. Phone: 800-585-9977. County: Greenbrier. ICA: WV0217.
TV Market Ranking: Below 100. Franchise award date: N.A. Franchise expiration date: N.A. Began: March 25, 1958.
Channel capacity: N.A. Channels available but not in use: N.A.

Basic Service
Subscribers: 1,468.
Programming (received off-air): WVVA (N) Bluefield; WSWP-TV (P) Grandview; WOAY-TV (A) Oak Hill-Beckley; WDBJ (C), WFXR-TV (F), WSET-TV (A), WSLS-TV (N) Roanoke-Lynchburg.
Programming (via satellite): WGN-TV (W) Chicago; TBS Superstation.
Fee: $10.00 installation; $18.95 monthly.

Expanded Basic Service
Subscribers: N.A.
Programming (via satellite): A & E; BET; C-SPAN; C-SPAN 2; CNN; Country Music TV; Discovery Channel; ESPN; Fox Family Channel; Headline News; Learning Channel; MTV; Nashville Network; Nickelodeon; QVC; Trinity Bcstg. Network; Turner Network TV; USA Network; VH1.
Fee: N.A.

Pay Service 1
Pay Units: 82.
Programming (via satellite): Cinemax.
Fee: $20.00 installation; $9.95 monthly.

Pay Service 2
Pay Units: 54.
Programming (via satellite): Disney Channel.
Fee: $6.95 monthly.

Pay Service 3
Pay Units: 133.
Programming (via satellite): HBO.
Fee: $9.95 monthly.

Pay Service 4
Pay Units: N.A.
Programming (via satellite): The Movie Channel.
Fee: N.A.

Equipment: Jerrold headend; Jerrold amplifiers; Comm/Scope cable.
Miles of plant: 32.9 (coaxial). Additional miles planned: 3.0 (coaxial).
Manager: Wayne Boone.
City fee: 3% of gross.
Ownership: Rifkin & Associates Inc. (MSO). See Cable System Ownership.

WHITEHALL—Century Huntington Co., Box 599, Dellslow, WV 26531. Phone: 304-292-6561. County: Marion. Also serves Marion County. ICA: WV0040.
TV Market Ranking: Below 100. Franchise award date: N.A. Franchise expiration date: N.A. Began: January 1, 1964.
Channel capacity: 36. Channels available but not in use: 8.

Basic Service
Subscribers: N.A.
Programming (received off-air): WBOY-TV (N), WDTV (C,A) Clarksburg-Weston; WNPB-TV (P) Morgantown; KDKA-TV (C), WPGH-TV (F), WPXI (N), WTAE-TV (A) Pittsburgh; WTOV-TV (N) Steubenville-Wheeling; WTRF-TV (C) Wheeling-Steubenville; allband FM.
Programming (via satellite): WGN-TV (W) Chicago; CNN; Country Music TV; ESPN; Home Shopping Network; Nashville Network; TBS Superstation; The Weather Channel; Turner Network TV.
Fee: $20.00 installation; $7.50 monthly.

Expanded Basic Service
Subscribers: N.A.
Programming (via satellite): MTV; USA Network.
Fee: $2.00 monthly.

Pay Service 1
Pay Units: N.A.
Programming (via satellite): Disney Channel; HBO; Playboy TV; Showtime.
Fee: $7.95 monthly (Playboy), $9.95 monthly (Disney, HBO or Showtime).

Equipment: Jerrold headend; Jerrold amplifiers; Jerrold cable.
Miles of plant: 89.0 (coaxial). Homes passed: 3,070. Miles of plant & homes passed include figures for Colfax, WV.
Manager: Michael Ligouri. Chief technician: Ed Hinkle.
City fee: None.
Ownership: Century Communications Corp. (MSO). See Cable System Ownership.

WHITESVILLE—Capital Cablecomm, Box 778, Whitesville, WV 25209. Phone: 304-854-1480. Fax: 304-595-5248. Counties: Boone & Raleigh. Also serves Boone County (portions), Branham Heights, Edwight, Eunice, Garrison, Janie, Keith, Leevale, Montcoal, Noama, Orgas, Pack Branch, Packsville, Pettus, Rock Creek, Seng Creek, Stickney, Sundial, Sylvester. ICA: WV0218.
TV Market Ranking: 36 (portions of Boone County, Branham Heights, Edwight, Eunice, Garrison, Janie, Keith, Leevale, Montcoal, Noama, Orgas, Pack Branch, Packsville, Pettus, Rock Creek, Seng Creek, Stickney, Sundial, Sylvester, Whitesville); Below 100 (portions of Boone County). Franchise award date: N.A. Franchise expiration date: March 23, 2003. Began: December 1, 1968.
Channel capacity: 52 (not 2-way capable). Channels available but not in use: 7.

Basic Service
Subscribers: 1,686.
Programming (received off-air): WCHS-TV (A), WOWK-TV (C), WPBY-TV (P), WSAZ-TV (N), WVAH-TV (F,U) Charleston-Huntington; WSWP-TV (P) Grandview; WOAY-TV (A) Oak Hill-Beckley; allband FM.
Programming (via satellite): WGN-TV (W) Chicago; BET; Comedy Central; Learning Channel; MTV; QVC; TBS Superstation; The Inspirational Network.
Current originations: Automated time-weather; public access; educational access; government access; local news.
Fee: $35.50 installation (aerial), $48.75 (underground); $10.35 monthly; $0.93 converter.

Expanded Basic Service
Subscribers: 1,649.

Programming (via satellite): A & E; American Movie Classics; CNN; Country Music TV; Discovery Channel; ESPN; Fox Family Channel; Goodlife TV Network; Headline News; Lifetime; Nashville Network; Nickelodeon; Sci-Fi Channel; The Weather Channel; Travel Channel; Turner Network TV; USA Network; VH1.
Fee: $13.35 monthly.

A la Carte 1
Subscribers: 25.
Programming (via satellite): Cartoon Network; Fox Sports Net Pittsburgh; Turner Classic Movies.
Fee: $3.95 monthly (package).

Pay Service 1
Pay Units: 121.
Programming (via satellite): Cinemax.
Fee: $25.00 installation; $10.00 monthly.

Pay Service 2
Pay Units: 54.
Programming (via satellite): Disney Channel.
Fee: $25.00 installation; $8.00 monthly.

Pay Service 3
Pay Units: 152.
Programming (via satellite): HBO.
Fee: $25.00 installation; $10.00 monthly.

Pay Service 4
Pay Units: 174.
Programming (via satellite): Showtime.
Fee: $25.00 installation; $10.00 monthly.

Pay Service 5
Pay Units: 169.
Programming (via satellite): The Movie Channel.
Fee: $25.00 installation; $10.00 monthly.

Local advertising: Yes. Available in character-generated programming.
Equipment: Catel headend; C-COR amplifiers; Trilogy cable; Scientific-Atlanta set top converters; Pico addressable traps; Scientific-Atlanta satellite antenna; M/A-Com satellite receivers.
Miles of plant: 46.3 (fiber optic). Homes passed: 2,145. Total homes in franchised area: 2,930.
Manager: Michael Kellerman. Chief technician: Steven Snodgrass. Marketing director: Bill Benner.
City fee: 5% of gross.
Ownership: Fanch Communications Inc. (MSO); Time Warner Cable (MSO). See Cable System Ownership.

WILEYVILLE—CableVision Communications, Box 2200, 68 5th St., Buckhannon, WV 26201. Phone: 304-472-4193. Fax: 304-472-0756. County: Wetzel. ICA: WV0165.
TV Market Ranking: 90. Franchise award date: N.A. Franchise expiration date: N.A. Began: N.A.
Channel capacity: 11. Channels available but not in use: 3.

Basic Service
Subscribers: 18.
Programming (received off-air): WBOY-TV (N), WDTV (C,A) Clarksburg-Weston; WNPB-TV (P) Morgantown; WTAP-TV (N) Parkersburg-Marietta; KDKA-TV (C), WTAE-TV (A) Pittsburgh; WTOV-TV (N) Steubenville-Wheeling; WTRF-TV (C) Wheeling-Steubenville.
Fee: $61.25 installation; $10.71 monthly.

Miles of plant: 3.0 (coaxial). Homes passed: 42.
Manager: Willie Critchfield. Marketing director: Kenny Phillips.
Ownership: Rifkin & Associates Inc. (MSO). See Cable System Ownership.

WILLIAMSON—CableVision Communications, Box 2200, 68 5th St., Buckhannon, WV 26201. Phone: 304-472-4193. Fax: 304-472-0756. Counties: Mingo, WV; Pike, KY. Also serves Aflex, Burnwell, Cantees, Fairview, Hardy, Huddy, New Camp, Pike County (unincorporated areas), Pond Creek, South Williamson, Stone, Turkey Creek, KY; Lobata, Merrimac, Rawl, Sprigg, Springtown, Vinson Street, WV. ICA: WV0030.
TV Market Ranking: Below 100. Franchise award date: June 25, 1971. Franchise expiration date: June 25, 2021. Began: N.A.
Channel capacity: 37 (not 2-way capable). Channels available but not in use: N.A.

Basic Service
Subscribers: 3,586.
Programming (received off-air): WCHS-TV (A), WOWK-TV (C), WPBY-TV (P), WSAZ-TV (N), WVAH-TV (F,U) Charleston-Huntington; WYMT-TV (C) Hazard; WKPI (P) Pikeville.
Programming (via satellite): WGN-TV (W) Chicago; TBS Superstation; The Weather Channel; Trinity Bcstg. Network.
Current originations: Educational access.
Fee: $61.25 installation; $14.40 monthly; $1.24 converter.

Expanded Basic Service
Subscribers: N.A.
Programming (via satellite): A & E; American Movie Classics; C-SPAN; CNN; Discovery Channel; Disney Channel; E! Entertainment TV; ESPN; FX; Fox Family Channel; Great American Country; Home Shopping Network; Learning Channel; Lifetime; MTV; Nashville Network; Nickelodeon; Outdoor Channel; Turner Network TV; USA Network.
Fee: $13.37 monthly.

Pay Service 1
Pay Units: 796.
Programming (via satellite): Cinemax.
Fee: $7.99 monthly.

Pay Service 2
Pay Units: 205.
Programming (via satellite): The New Encore.
Fee: $3.99 monthly.

Pay Service 3
Pay Units: 808.
Programming (via satellite): HBO.
Fee: $11.99 monthly.

Pay Service 4
Pay Units: 356.
Programming (via satellite): Showtime.
Fee: $11.99 monthly.

Pay Service 5
Pay Units: 274.
Programming (via satellite): The Movie Channel.
Fee: $11.99 monthly.

Local advertising: No. Regional interconnect: Cabletime.
Equipment: Blonder-Tongue, Olson & Standard Communications headend; C-COR amplifiers; Eagle traps; Microdyne satellite antenna; Electrohome satellite receivers.
Miles of plant: 89.0 (coaxial); None (fiber optic). Homes passed: 6,800.
Manager: Willie Critchfield. Chief technician: Garry Lucas. Marketing director: Kenny Phillips.
City fee: 1% of gross.
Ownership: Rifkin & Associates Inc. (MSO). See Cable System Ownership.

WINDSOR HEIGHTS—Centre TV Cable, 510 Warwood Ave., Wheeling, WV 26003. Phone: 304-277-2811. Counties: Brooke & Ohio. Also serves Beech Bottom, Warwood. ICA: WV0126.
TV Market Ranking: 10 (Beech Bottom, Windsor Heights); 90 (Beech Bottom, Warwood, Windsor Heights). Franchise award date: N.A. Franchise expiration date: N.A. Began: January 1, 1953.
Channel capacity: N.A. Channels available but not in use: N.A.

Basic Service
Subscribers: N.A.
Programming (received off-air): WNPB-TV (P) Morgantown; KDKA-TV (C), WCWB (W), WPGH-TV (F), WPXI (N), WQED (P), WTAE-TV (A) Pittsburgh; WTOV-TV (N) Steubenville-Wheeling; WTRF-TV (C) Wheeling-Steubenville; WKBN-TV (C) Youngstown.
Fee: N.A.

Miles of plant: 3.7 (coaxial). Homes passed: 310.
Manager: Kasmir Majewski.
Ownership: Kasmir Majewski (MSO).

WORTHINGTON—Century Huntington Co., Box 599, Dellslow, WV 26531. Phone: 304-292-6561. County: Marion. ICA: WV0151.
TV Market Ranking: Below 100. Franchise award date: N.A. Franchise expiration date: N.A. Began: May 1, 1953.
Channel capacity: 41. Channels available but not in use: 17.

Basic Service
Subscribers: N.A.
Programming (received off-air): WBOY-TV (N), WDTV (C,A) Clarksburg-Weston; WNPB-TV (P) Morgantown; KDKA-TV (C), WPGH-TV (F), WPXI (N), WTAE-TV (A) Pittsburgh; WTOV-TV (N) Steubenville-Wheeling; WTRF-TV (C) Wheeling-Steubenville; allband FM.
Fee: $3.00 monthly.

Equipment: Jerrold headend; Jerrold amplifiers.
Miles of plant: 4.0 (coaxial). Homes passed: 125.
Manager: Michael Ligouri. Chief technician: Ed Hinkle.
Ownership: Century Communications Corp. (MSO). See Cable System Ownership.

WYATT—West Virginia Country Cable, Box 1696, 300 Chester Field Pkwy., Clarksburg, WV 26302-1696. Phones: 304-623-0150; 800-882-1206. Counties: Harrison & Marion. Also serves Mannington (northwestern portion), Peora, Pine Bluff, Shinnston (portions). ICA: WV0219.
TV Market Ranking: Below 100. Franchise award date: N.A. Franchise expiration date: N.A. Began: October 1, 1983.
Channel capacity: N.A. Channels available but not in use: N.A.

Basic Service
Subscribers: 535.
Programming (received off-air): WBOY-TV (N), WDTV (C,A), WVFX (F) Clarksburg-Weston; WNPB-TV (P) Morgantown; WTAE-TV (A) Pittsburgh; WTRF-TV (C) Wheeling-Steubenville.
Programming (via satellite): WGN-TV (W) Chicago; CNN; ESPN; Headline News; Nashville Network; Nickelodeon; TBS Superstation; USA Network.
Fee: $25.00 installation; $12.50 monthly.

Pay Service 1
Pay Units: N.A.
Programming (via satellite): The Movie Channel.
Fee: $10.00 monthly.

Miles of plant: 11.0 (coaxial).
Manager: Duane Poling.
Ownership: FinCom Corp. (MSO).

WISCONSIN

Total Systems: **269**
Total Communities Served: **998**
Franchises Not Yet Operating: **1**
Applications Pending: **0**
Communities with Applications: **0**
Number of Basic Subscribers: **1,361,491**
Number of Expanded Basic Subscribers: **468,991**
Number of Pay Units: **376,988**

Top 100 Markets Represented: Minneapolis-St. Paul (13); Milwaukee (23); Green Bay (62); Duluth, MN-Superior, WI (89); Madison (93); Rockford-Freeport (97).

For a list of all cable communities included in this section, see the Cable Community Index located in the back of this volume.
For explanation of terms used in cable system listings, see p. D-9.

ADAMS—Charter Communications Inc., Box 1197, 55 W. Scott St., Fond du Lac, WI 54936-1197. Phones: 920-923-7196; 800-581-0081. Fax: 920-923-1235. County: Adams. Also serves Adams (town), Friendship, Preston. ICA: WI0099.

TV Market Ranking: Outside TV Markets. Franchise award date: N.A. Franchise expiration date: N.A. Began: July 31, 1981.

Channel capacity: 35 (2-way capable; operating 2-way). Channels available but not in use: 8.

Basic Service

Subscribers: 948.

Programming (received off-air): WEAU-TV (N) Eau Claire; WHA-TV (P), WISC-TV (C), WKOW-TV (A), WMSN-TV (F), WMTV (N) Madison; WAOW-TV (A), WSAW-TV (C) Wausau-Rhinelander.

Programming (via satellite): WGN-TV (W) Chicago; A & E; American Movie Classics; CNN; Discovery Channel; ESPN; ESPN 2; Fox Family Channel; Learning Channel; Lifetime; MTV; Nashville Network; Nickelodeon; QVC; TBS Superstation; Turner Network TV; USA Network.

Current originations: Automated time-weather; public access; government access; local news.

Fee: $34.95 installation; $12.43 monthly.

Pay Service 1

Pay Units: 189.

Programming (via satellite): Cinemax.

Fee: $14.95 installation; $12.50 monthly.

Pay Service 2

Pay Units: 149.

Programming (via satellite): Disney Channel.

Fee: $14.95 installation; $3.95 monthly.

Pay Service 3

Pay Units: 246.

Programming (via satellite): HBO.

Fee: $14.95 installation; $12.95 monthly.

Pay Service 4

Pay Units: 218.

Programming (via satellite): Showtime.

Fee: $14.95 installation; $12.50 monthly.

Local advertising: No.

Equipment: Scientific-Atlanta headend; Texscan amplifiers; Comm/Scope cable; Panasonic cameras; Panasonic VTRs; Texscan character generator; Scientific-Atlanta set top converters; Arcom & Eagle traps; Anixter-Pruzan & Scientific-Atlanta satellite antenna; Scientific-Atlanta & Microdyne satellite receivers.

Miles of plant: 30.0 (coaxial). Homes passed: 1,284.

Manager: Lisa Washa. Chief technician: Jeff Gerner.

City fee: 3% of gross.

Ownership: Charter Communications Inc. (MSO). Purchased from Marcus Cable, April 1, 1999.

ALBANY—Triax Cablevision, Box 110, 1504 2nd St. SE, Waseca, MN 56093. Phones: 507-835-5975; 800-332-0245. Fax: 507-835-4567. County: Green. Also serves Albany Twp. ICA: WI0152.

TV Market Ranking: 93,97. Franchise award date: N.A. Franchise expiration date: September 30, 2013. Began: February 1, 1984.

Channel capacity: 37 (not 2-way capable). Channels available but not in use: 1.

Basic Service

Subscribers: 330.

Programming (received off-air): WIFR (C) Freeport-Rockford; WHA-TV (P), WISC-TV (C), WKOW-TV (A), WMSN-TV (F), WMTV (N) Madison; WTVP (P) Peoria; WQRF-TV (F), WREX-TV (N) Rockford.

Programming (via satellite): WGN-TV (W) Chicago; TBS Superstation.

Current originations: Public access.

Fee: $45.00 installation; $12.50 monthly.

Expanded Basic Service

Subscribers: 317.

Programming (via satellite): A & E; American Movie Classics; Animal Planet; CNN; Country Music TV; Discovery Channel; ESPN; ESPN 2; Fox Family Channel; History Channel; Home Shopping Network; Learning Channel; Lifetime; MTV; Nashville Network; Nick at Nite's TV Land; Nickelodeon; Sci-Fi Channel; The Weather Channel; Trinity Bcstg. Network; Turner Network TV; USA Network.

Fee: $18.00 monthly.

Pay Service 1

Pay Units: 124.

Programming (via satellite): HBO; Showtime.

Fee: $25.00 installation; $11.99 monthly (each).

Equipment: Scientific-Atlanta headend; Scientific-Atlanta amplifiers; Scientific-Atlanta cable; Scientific-Atlanta set top converters; Vitek traps; Anixter satellite antenna; Scientific-Atlanta satellite receivers.

Miles of plant: 10.0 (coaxial). Homes passed: 471. Total homes in franchised area: 471.

Manager: Mike Nodgerson. Chief technician: Pat Alderman.

City fee: 3% of gross.

Ownership: Triax Telecommunications Co. LLC (MSO). See Cable System Ownership.

ALGOMA—Charter Communications Inc., Box 1197, 55 W. Scott St., Fon Du Lac, WI 54936-1197. Phones: 920-923-7196; 800-581-0081. Fax: 920-923-1235. County: Kewaunee. Also serves Pierce. ICA: WI0089.

TV Market Ranking: 62. Franchise award date: April 5, 1982. Franchise expiration date: N.A. Began: November 1, 1982.

Channel capacity: 35 (2-way capable; operating 2-way). Channels available but not in use: 2.

Basic Service

Subscribers: 2,000.

Programming (received off-air): WBAY-TV (A), WFRV-TV (C), WGBA (N), WLUK-TV (F), WPNE (P) Green Bay.

Programming (via satellite): WGN-TV (W) Chicago; A & E; American Movie Classics; C-SPAN; CNN; Cartoon Network; Comedy Central; Discovery Channel; ESPN; Fox Family Channel; Headline News; Lifetime; MTV; Nashville Network; Nick at Nite; Nickelodeon; QVC; TBS Superstation; The Inspirational Network; The Weather Channel; Turner Network TV; USA Network.

Current originations: Automated time-weather; public access.

Fee: $42.95 installation; $9.00 monthly.

Pay Service 1

Pay Units: 182.

Programming (via satellite): Cinemax.

Fee: $19.95 installation; $12.50 monthly.

Pay Service 2

Pay Units: 119.

Programming (via satellite): Disney Channel.

Fee: $19.95 installation; $9.35 monthly.

Pay Service 3

Pay Units: 244.

Programming (via satellite): HBO.

Fee: $19.95 installation; $12.95 monthly.

Pay Service 4

Pay Units: 244.

Programming (via satellite): Showtime.

Fee: $19.95 installation; $12.50 monthly.

Local advertising: Yes. Available in character-generated programming.

Equipment: Scientific-Atlanta headend; Scientific-Atlanta amplifiers; Comm/Scope cable; Video Data Systems character generator; Hamlin set top converters; Eagle traps; M/A-Com & Scientific-Atlanta satellite antenna; Microdyne satellite receivers.

Miles of plant: 20.0 (coaxial).

Manager: Lisa Washa. Chief technician: Jeff Gerner.

City fee: 3% of gross.

Ownership: Charter Communications Inc. (MSO). Purchased from Marcus Cable, April 1, 1999.

ALGOMA TWP.—Charter Communications Inc., 320 N. Wisconsin St., De Pere, WI 54115. Phone: 920-496-2040. Fax: 414-337-9251. County: Winnebago. Also serves Black Wolf, Nekimi, Omro (town), Winneconne (portions). ICA: WI0233.

TV Market Ranking: 62 (Algoma Twp., Winneconne); Below 100 (Black Wolf, Nekimi, Omro). Franchise award date: June 6, 1989. Franchise expiration date: June 6, 2004. Began: N.A.

Channel capacity: 42. Channels available but not in use: None.

Basic Service

Subscribers: 1,739.

Programming (received off-air): WACY (U) Appleton; WBAY-TV (A), WFRV-TV (C), WGBA (N), WLUK-TV (F), WPNE (P) Green Bay; WCGV-TV (I), WISN-TV (A), WMVS (P), WVTV (W) Milwaukee.

Programming (via satellite): WGN-TV (W) Chicago; TBS Superstation.

Current originations: Public access.

Fee: $56.73 installation; $7.01 monthly.

Expanded Basic Service

Subscribers: 1,978.

Programming (via satellite): A & E; American Movie Classics; C-SPAN; C-SPAN 2; CNBC; CNN; Discovery Channel; Disney Channel; ESPN; ESPN 2; EWTN; Fox Family Channel; Headline News; Home Shopping Network; Knowledge TV; Lifetime; MTV; Nashville Network; Nickelodeon; Odyssey; Sci-Fi Channel; The Weather Channel; Turner Network TV; USA Network; VH1.

Fee: $13.48 monthly.

Pay Service 1

Pay Units: 292.

Programming (via satellite): Cinemax.

Fee: $12.50 monthly.

Pay Service 2

Pay Units: 409.

Programming (via satellite): HBO.

Fee: $12.95 monthly.

Pay Service 3

Pay Units: 255.

Programming (via satellite): Showtime.

Fee: $12.50 monthly.

Equipment: Scientific-Atlanta headend; Comm/Scope cable; Panasonic set top converters; Eagle traps.

Miles of plant: 74.9 (coaxial). Homes passed: 3,114.

Ownership: Charter Communications Inc. (MSO). Purchased from Marcus Cable, April 1, 1999.

ALMA—US Cable, 128 W. Main St., Wabasha, MN 55981-1237. Phones: 651-565-4431; 800-642-5509. Fax: 651-565-2501. County: Buffalo. Also serves Buffalo, Cochrane. ICA: WI0234.

TV Market Ranking: Below 100. Franchise award date: N.A. Franchise expiration date: N.A. Began: January 1, 1960.

Channel capacity: 29 (not 2-way capable). Channels available but not in use: N.A.

Basic Service

Subscribers: 825.

Programming (received off-air): WEAU-TV (N) Eau Claire; WKBT (C), WXOW-TV (A) La Crosse; KARE (N), KMSP-TV (U), KSTP-TV (A), KTCA-TV (P), WCCO-TV (C) Minneapolis-St. Paul; KTTC (N) Rochester; allband FM.

Fee: $10.00 installation; $16.35 monthly.

Equipment: Blonder-Tongue & Scientific-Atlanta headend; C-COR amplifiers; Comm/Scope cable.

Miles of plant: 3.0 (coaxial).

Manager: Delmore Zirzow.

City fee: None.

Ownership: US Cable Corp. (MSO). Purchased from Fanch Communications Inc., April 30, 1999.

ALMOND—Cable Systems Management of Iowa Inc., 3600 Kennebec Dr., Eagan, MN 55122. Phone: 612-688-2623. Fax: 612-688-2624. County: Portage. ICA: WI0209.

TV Market Ranking: Outside TV Markets. Franchise award date: N.A. Franchise expiration date: N.A. Began: N.A.
Channel capacity: 40. Channels available but not in use: 19.
Basic Service
Subscribers: 81.
Programming (received off-air): WEAU-TV (N) Eau Claire; WAOW-TV (A), WHRM-TV (P), WSAW-TV (C) Wausau-Rhinelander.
Programming (via satellite): WGN-TV (W) Chicago; A & E; American Movie Classics; CNN; Country Music TV; Discovery Channel; ESPN; Fox Family Channel; Headline News; Nashville Network; Showtime; TBS Superstation; Trinity Bcstg. Network; Turner Network TV; USA Network.
Fee: $28.00 monthly.
Miles of plant: 4.2 (coaxial). Homes passed: 188.
Manager: Jeff Anderson.
Ownership: Cable Systems Management of Iowa Inc. (MSO).

AMERY—Amery Telephone Co., 116 N. Harriman Ave., Amery, WI 54001. Phone: 715-268-7101. Counties: Polk & St. Croix. Also serves Clayton (Polk County), Clear Lake, Deer Park, Polk County (portions). ICA: WI0080.
TV Market Ranking: 13 (portions of Polk County); Outside TV Markets (Amery, Clayton, Clear Lake, Deer Park, portions of Polk County). Franchise award date: N.A. Franchise expiration date: March 1, 1998. Began: September 1, 1984.
Channel capacity: 35. Channels available but not in use: 12.
Basic Service
Subscribers: 1,980.
Programming (received off-air): WEAU-TV (N), WQOW-TV (A) Eau Claire; WKBT (C) La Crosse; WHWC-TV (P) Menomonie; KARE (N), KMSP-TV (U), KSTP-TV (A), WCCO-TV (C) Minneapolis-St. Paul.
Programming (via satellite): WGN-TV (W) Chicago; A & E; CNN; Discovery Channel; ESPN; Lifetime; Nashville Network; Nickelodeon; TBS Superstation; USA Network.
Current originations: Public access.
Fee: $25.00 installation; $12.95 monthly.
Pay Service 1
Pay Units: 819.
Programming (via satellite): HBO; Showtime.
Fee: $7.95 monthly (Showtime), $8.95 monthly (HBO).
Miles of plant: 33.5 (coaxial). Homes passed: 2,000.
Manager: Michael Jensen.
Ownership: Northwest Community Communications Inc.

AMHERST (village)—Tomorrow Valley Cable TV Co., Box 279, 120 Mill St., Amherst, WI 54406. Phone: 715-824-5529. Fax: 715-824-2050. County: Portage. Also serves Amherst Junction, Amherst Twp. (western portion), Nelsonville. ICA: WI0144.
TV Market Ranking: Below 100. Franchise award date: N.A. Franchise expiration date: N.A. Began: November 1, 1984.
Channel capacity: 54. Channels available but not in use: 24.
Basic Service
Subscribers: 562.
Programming (received off-air): WACY (U) Appleton; WBAY-TV (A), WFRV-TV (C), WGBA (N), WLUK-TV (F) Green Bay; WAOW-TV (A), WHRM-TV (P), WSAW-TV (C) Wausau-Rhinelander; 9 FMs.
Programming (via satellite): WGN-TV (W) Chicago; A & E; American Movie Classics; CNN; Comedy Central; Discovery Channel; ESPN; ESPN 2; Fox Family Channel; Headline News; History Channel; Learning Channel; Nashville Network; Nickelodeon; TBS Superstation; The Weather Channel; Turner Network TV; USA Network.
Fee: $30.00 installation; $18.01 monthly; $2.00 converter; $10.00 additional installation.
Pay Service 1
Pay Units: N.A.
Programming (via satellite): Cinemax; HBO.
Fee: $7.50 installation; $9.95 monthly (each).
Miles of plant: 19.0 (coaxial). Homes passed: 666. Total homes in franchised area: 756.
Manager: Carl Bohman. Chief technician: Robert Lea.
Ownership: Amherst Telephone Co.

ANSON TWP.—S & K TV Systems, Box 127, 508 W. Miner Ave., Ladysmith, WI 54848. Phones: 715-532-7321; 800-924-7880. County: Chippewa. ICA: WI0235.
TV Market Ranking: Below 100. Franchise award date: January 1, 1989. Franchise expiration date: January 1, 1999. Began: September 1, 1989.
Channel capacity: 36. Channels available but not in use: 13.
Basic Service
Subscribers: 199.
Programming (received off-air): WEUX (F) Chippewa Falls; WEAU-TV (N), WQOW-TV (A) Eau Claire; WKBT (C) La Crosse; WHWC-TV (P) Menomonie.
Programming (via satellite): WGN-TV (W) Chicago; A & E; American Movie Classics; CNN; Discovery Channel; Disney Channel; ESPN; Fox Family Channel; Lifetime; Nashville Network; Nick at Nite's TV Land; Nickelodeon; TBS Superstation; The Weather Channel; Turner Network TV; USA Network; VH1.
Fee: $23.95 monthly.
Pay Service 1
Pay Units: N.A.
Programming (via satellite): HBO.
Fee: $9.95 monthly.
Manager: Randy Scott.
Ownership: S & K TV Systems (MSO).

ANTIGO—Charter Communications Inc., 2230 Neva Rd., Antigo, WI 54409-0296. Phone: 715-627-4817. Fax: 715-623-3628. County: Langlade. Also serves Antigo (town), Rolling, Rolling (town). ICA: WI0052.
TV Market Ranking: Below 100. Franchise award date: July 22, 1980. Franchise expiration date: N.A. Began: April 6, 1981.
Channel capacity: 35 (2-way capable; operating 2-way). Channels available but not in use: None.
Basic Service
Subscribers: 2,750.
Programming (received off-air): WBAY-TV (A), WFRV-TV (C), WGBA (N), WLUK-TV (F) Green Bay; WAOW-TV (A), WHRM-TV (P), WJFW-TV (N), WSAW-TV (C) Wausau-Rhinelander.
Programming (via satellite): WGN-TV (W) Chicago; A & E; American Movie Classics; C-SPAN; CNBC; CNN; Comedy Central; Discovery Channel; ESPN; Fox Family Channel; Headline News; Lifetime; Nashville Network; Nickelodeon; QVC; TBS Superstation; The Inspirational Network; The Weather Channel; Turner Network TV; USA Network; VH1.
Current originations: Automated time-weather; educational access; leased access.
Fee: $42.95 installation; $23.50 monthly.
Pay Service 1
Pay Units: 475.
Programming (via satellite): Cinemax.
Fee: $19.95 installation; $12.50 monthly.
Pay Service 2
Pay Units: 360.
Programming (via satellite): Disney Channel.
Fee: $19.95 installation; $9.35 monthly.
Pay Service 3
Pay Units: 575.
Programming (via satellite): HBO.
Fee: $10.00 installation; $12.95 monthly.
Pay Service 4
Pay Units: 555.
Programming (via satellite): Showtime.
Fee: $10.00 installation; $12.50 monthly.
Local advertising: Yes. Available in locally originated & character-generated programming.
Equipment: Scientific-Atlanta headend; Scientific-Atlanta amplifiers; Times Fiber cable; MSI & Texscan character generator; Hamlin set top converters; Eagle traps; Microdyne & M/A-Com satellite antenna; Microdyne satellite receivers.
Miles of plant: 55.0 (coaxial). Homes passed: 3,974.
Manager: Larry Kraklau. Chief technician: Bruce Wasleske. Marketing director: Susan Jirgl.
City fee: 3% of gross.
Ownership: Charter Communications Inc. (MSO). Purchased from Marcus Cable, April 1, 1999.

APPLETON—Time Warner Cable, Box 145, 1001 Kennedy Ave., Kimberly, WI 54136-0145. Phone: 920-496-2040. Fax: 920-831-9172. Counties: Brown, Calumet, Manitowoc, Marinette, Outagamie, Waushara & Winnebago. Also serves Allouez, Ashwaubenon, Bellevue, Buchanan (town), Center, Clayton (Winnebago County), Combined Locks, Dale, Darboy, De Pere, De Pere (town), Ellington, Freedom, Grand Chute (town), Green Bay, Greenville (town), Harrison (town), Hilbert (village), Hobart, Holland (town), Howard (village), Kaukauna, Kaukauna (town), Kimberly, Lawrence (town), Ledgeview (town), Little Chute, Little Suamico, Marinette, Medina, Menasha (town-northern portion), Neenah (town), Oneida, Oshkosh, Oshkosh (town), Pittsfield, Poy Sippi, Reedsville, Sherwood (village), St. Nazianz, Stockbridge (town), Stockbridge (village), Suamico, Valders, Vandenbroek, Vinland (town), Winchester (town), Woodville (town), Wrightstown. ICA: WI0006.
TV Market Ranking: 62 (Allouez, Appleton, Ashwaubenon, Bellevue, Buchanan, Center, Clayton, Combined Locks, Dale, Darboy, De Pere, Ellington, Freedom, Grand Chute, Green Bay, Greenville, Harrison, Hilbert, Hobart, Holland, Howard, Kaukauna, Kimberly, Lawrence, Ledgeview, Little Chute, Little Suamico, Medina, Menasha, Neenah, Oneida, Pittsfield, Reedsville, Sherwood, St. Nazianz, Stockbridge, Suamico, Valders, Vandenbroek, Woodville, Wrightstown); Below 100 (Oshkosh, Poy Sippi, Vinland, Winchester); Outside TV Markets (Marinette). Franchise award date: January 1, 1980. Franchise expiration date: January 1, 2008. Began: July 1, 1973.
Channel capacity: 80 (2-way capable; operating 2-way). Channels available but not in use: None.
Basic Service
Subscribers: 142,000.
Programming (received off-air): WACY (U) Appleton; WBAY-TV (A), WFRV-TV (C), WGBA (N), WLUK-TV (F), WPNE (P) Green Bay; WVTV (W) Milwaukee.
Programming (via satellite): EWTN; TV Guide Channel.
Current originations: Public access; educational access; government access; leased access.
Fee: N.A.
Expanded Basic Service
Subscribers: N.A.
Programming (via satellite): WGN-TV (W) Chicago; A & E; American Movie Classics; Animal Planet; Bravo; C-SPAN; C-SPAN 2; CNBC; CNN; CNN/SI; Cartoon Network; Comedy Central; Country Music TV; Court TV; Discovery Channel; E! Entertainment TV; ESPN; ESPN 2; FX; Fox Family Channel; Fox News Channel; Golf Channel; Headline News; History Channel; Learning Channel; Lifetime; MSNBC; MTV; Midwest Sports Channel; Nashville Network; Nickelodeon; QVC; Sci-Fi Channel; TBS Superstation; TV Food Network; TV Guide Sneak Prevue; The New Encore; The Weather Channel; Turner Classic Movies; Turner Network TV; USA Network; Univision; VH1; ValueVision.
Fee: N.A.
Pay Service 1
Pay Units: 48,000.
Programming (via satellite): Cinemax (multiplexed); Disney Channel; HBO (multiplexed); Showtime (multiplexed).
Fee: $11.25 monthly (each).
Pay-Per-View
Addressable homes: 54,000.
Spice; Viewer's Choice; movies.
Fee: Varies.
Local advertising: Yes (locally produced & insert). Available in satellite distributed programming.
Program Guide: Premium Channels.
Equipment: Scientific-Atlanta headend; Scientific-Atlanta amplifiers; Belden & Comm/Scope cable; Sony cameras; Sony VTRs; Knox character generator; Scientific-Atlanta addressable set top converters; Scientific-Atlanta satellite antenna; Scientific-Atlanta satellite receivers.
Miles of plant: 2700.0 (coaxial); 400.0 (fiber optic). Homes passed: 213,000.
Manager: Kathy Keating. Chief technician: Scott Ducott. Program director: Jim Last. Marketing director: Chris Doyle. Customer service manager: Audrey Niemann.
City fee: 4% of gross.
Ownership: Time Warner Cable (MSO).

ARENA—Spring Green CableComm, Box 609, 245 S. Winsted St., Spring Green, WI 53588-9431. Phone: 608-588-7454. Fax: 608-588-7067. County: Iowa. Also serves Arena (town). ICA: WI0236.
TV Market Ranking: 93. Franchise award date: N.A. Franchise expiration date: N.A. Began: November 1, 1985.
Channel capacity: 42 (not 2-way capable). Channels available but not in use: 14.
Basic Service
Subscribers: 110.
Programming (received off-air): WHA-TV (P), WISC-TV (C), WKOW-TV (A), WMTV (N) Madison.
Programming (via satellite): WGN-TV (W) Chicago; A & E; CNN; Discovery Channel; ESPN; Fox Family Channel; Headline News; Nashville Network; Nickelodeon; QVC; TBS Superstation; Turner Classic Movies; Turner Network TV; USA Network.
Fee: $49.95 installation; $29.85 monthly; $19.95 additional installation.
Pay Service 1
Pay Units: N.A.
Programming (via satellite): HBO.
Fee: $19.95 installation; $9.95 monthly.
Miles of plant: 7.8 (coaxial).

Manager: Kevin Mayne. Chief technician: Tad Peak. Customer service manager: Liz Reuter.
Ownership: Fanch Communications Inc. (MSO). See Cable System Ownership.

ARGYLE—Triax Cablevision, Box 110, 1504 2nd St. SE, Waseca, MN 56093. Phones: 507-835-5975; 800-332-0245. Fax: 507-835-4567. County: Lafayette. ICA: WI0175.
TV Market Ranking: Outside TV Markets. Franchise award date: N.A. Franchise expiration date: April 22, 2013. Began: March 1, 1985.
Channel capacity: 42 (not 2-way capable). Channels available but not in use: 10.
Basic Service
Subscribers: 218.
Programming (received off-air): WHA-TV (P), WISC-TV (C), WKOW-TV (A), WMSN-TV (F), WMTV (N) Madison.
Programming (via satellite): WGN-TV (W) Chicago; A & E; American Movie Classics; Animal Planet; CNN; Discovery Channel; ESPN; ESPN 2; Fox Family Channel; Headline News; History Channel; Home & Garden Television; Home Shopping Network; Learning Channel; Lifetime; MTV; Midwest Sports Channel; Nashville Network; Nick at Nite's TV Land; Nickelodeon; Sci-Fi Channel; TBS Superstation; The Weather Channel; Turner Network TV; USA Network.
Fee: $45.00 installation; $30.00 monthly.
Pay Service 1
Pay Units: 62.
Programming (via satellite): HBO; Showtime.
Fee: $11.99 monthly (each).
Local advertising: No.
Equipment: Scientific-Atlanta headend; Scientific-Atlanta amplifiers; Scientific-Atlanta cable; Scientific-Atlanta set top converters; Vitek traps; Scientific-Atlanta satellite antenna; Scientific-Atlanta satellite receivers.
Miles of plant: 6.0 (coaxial). Homes passed: 349.
Manager: Mike Nodgerson. Chief technician: Pat Alderman.
City fee: 3% of gross.
Ownership: Triax Telecommunications Co. LLC (MSO). See Cable System Ownership.

ASHLAND—Charter Communications Inc., Box 33, 307 E. Main St., Ashland, WI 54806. Phones: 715-682-2166; 800-262-2578. Fax: 715-234-5077. Counties: Ashland & Bayfield. Also serves Barksdale (town), Bayfield, Bayfield (town), Eileen (town), Washburn. ICA: WI0047.
TV Market Ranking: Outside TV Markets. Franchise award date: August 16, 1965. Franchise expiration date: N.A. Began: September 15, 1967.
Channel capacity: 34 (not 2-way capable). Channels available but not in use: None.
Basic Service
Subscribers: 4,495.
Programming (received off-air): KBJR-TV (N), KDLH (C), WDIO-TV (A,F), WDSE-TV (P) Duluth-Superior; WLEF-TV (P) Park Falls.
Programming (via satellite): WGN-TV (W) Chicago; C-SPAN; EWTN; FoxNet; QVC.
Fee: $42.95 installation; $11.00 monthly; $1.43 converter; $42.95 additional installation.
Expanded Basic Service
Subscribers: N.A.
Programming (via satellite): A & E; American Movie Classics; Animal Planet; Bravo; C-SPAN 2; CNBC; CNN; Comedy Central; Discovery Channel; Disney Channel; ESPN; ESPN 2; Fox Family Channel; Game Show Network; Headline News; Home & Garden Television; Lifetime; MSNBC; MTV; Midwest Sports Channel; Nashville Network; Nick at Nite's TV Land; Nickelodeon; TBS Superstation; The Weather Channel; Toon Disney; Turner Network TV; USA Network; VH1.
Fee: $42.95 installation; $21.95 monthly.
Expanded Basic Service 2
Subscribers: N.A.
Programming (via satellite): Cartoon Network; MOVIEplex; Outdoor Life Network; Speedvision; Starz!; The New Encore; Turner Classic Movies.
Fee: $6.95 monthly.
Pay Service 1
Pay Units: 562.
Programming (via satellite): Cinemax (multiplexed).
Fee: $19.95 installation; $12.95 monthly.
Pay Service 2
Pay Units: 679.
Programming (via satellite): HBO (multiplexed).
Fee: $19.95 installation; $12.95 monthly.
Pay Service 3
Pay Units: 748.
Programming (via satellite): Showtime; The Movie Channel.
Fee: $19.95 installation; $12.95 monthly.
Pay-Per-View
Movies; special events.
Local advertising: Yes. Available in locally originated programming. Rates: $30.00/Minute; $3.00/30 Seconds.
Equipment: Jerrold & Scientific-Atlanta headend; Jerrold amplifiers; Times Fiber cable; MSI character generator; Hamlin & Pioneer set top converters; Eagle traps; Scientific-Atlanta satellite antenna; Scientific-Atlanta satellite receivers.
Miles of plant: 75.0 (coaxial). Homes passed: 4,540. Total homes in franchised area: 5,075.
Manager: George Benjamin. Marketing director: Chris Finger.
City fee: 5% of gross.
Ownership: Charter Communications Inc. (MSO). Purchased from Marcus Cable, April 1, 1999.

AUBURNDALE—HLM Cable Corp., Box 620684, 2305-A Parview Rd., Middleton, WI 53562-2525. Phones: 608-831-7044; 800-451-5119. Fax: 608-836-5726. Counties: Marathon & Wood. Also serves Hewitt, Marshfield (portions). ICA: WI0166.
TV Market Ranking: Below 100. Franchise award date: N.A. Franchise expiration date: N.A. Began: N.A.
Channel capacity: 40 (not 2-way capable). Channels available but not in use: 12.
Basic Service
Subscribers: 353.
Programming (received off-air): WEAU-TV (N) Eau Claire; WAOW-TV (A), WHRM-TV (P), WSAW-TV (C) Wausau-Rhinelander.
Programming (via satellite): WGN-TV (W) Chicago; A & E; American Movie Classics; CNBC; CNN; Discovery Channel; ESPN; ESPN 2; Fox Family Channel; FoxNet; History Channel; Learning Channel; Lifetime; Nashville Network; Nick at Nite; Nick at Nite's TV Land; Nickelodeon; Sci-Fi Channel; TBS Superstation; The Weather Channel; Turner Network TV; USA Network; VH1.
Fee: $19.95 installation; $26.00 monthly; $1.50 converter.
Pay Service 1
Pay Units: 38.
Programming (via satellite): Disney Channel.
Fee: $14.95 installation; $6.95 monthly.
Pay Service 2
Pay Units: 90.
Programming (via satellite): Showtime.
Fee: $14.95 installation; $6.95 monthly.
Homes passed: 385.
Manager: Robert E. Ryan.
Ownership: H.L.M. Cable Co. (MSO).

AUGUSTA—KRM Cablevision Inc., Box 77, Mellen, WI 54546. Phone: 715-274-7631. County: Eau Claire. ICA: WI0141.
TV Market Ranking: Below 100. Franchise award date: March 1, 1976. Franchise expiration date: N.A. Began: September 1, 1978.
Channel capacity: 20 (not 2-way capable). Channels available but not in use: 4.
Basic Service
Subscribers: N.A.
Programming (received off-air): WEAU-TV (N), WQOW-TV (A) Eau Claire; WKBT (C), WLAX (F) La Crosse; WHWC-TV (P) Menomonie.
Programming (via satellite): WGN-TV (W) Chicago; CNN; Discovery Channel; ESPN; Fox Family Channel; Nashville Network; TBS Superstation; Turner Network TV; USA Network.
Fee: $35.00 installation; $14.00 monthly.
Pay Service 1
Pay Units: N.A.
Programming (via satellite): Disney Channel; The Movie Channel.
Fee: $8.00 monthly (Disney); $12.00 monthly (TMC).
Equipment: Scientific-Atlanta headend; Jerrold amplifiers; Prodelin satellite antenna.
Miles of plant: 16.0 (coaxial). Homes passed: 560. Total homes in franchised area: 560.
Manager: O. D. Miller. Chief technician: Keith Gehrett.
Franchise fee: $120 per year.
Ownership: KRM Cablevision (MSO).

AVOCA—Spring Green CableComm, Box 609, 245 S. Winsted St., Spring Green, WI 53588-9431. Phone: 608-588-7454. Fax: 608-588-7067. County: Iowa. ICA: WI0237.
TV Market Ranking: Outside TV Markets. Franchise award date: N.A. Franchise expiration date: N.A. Began: N.A.
Channel capacity: 36 (not 2-way capable). Channels available but not in use: 12.
Basic Service
Subscribers: 149.
Programming (received off-air): WHA-TV (P), WISC-TV (C), WKOW-TV (A), WMSN-TV (F), WMTV (N) Madison.
Programming (via satellite): WGN-TV (W) Chicago; A & E; CNN; Country Music TV; Discovery Channel; ESPN; Fox Family Channel; Headline News; Lifetime; Nashville Network; Nickelodeon; QVC; TBS Superstation; Turner Classic Movies; USA Network.
Fee: $49.95 installation; $29.85 monthly.
Pay Service 1
Pay Units: N.A.
Programming (via satellite): HBO.
Fee: $19.95 installation; $9.95 monthly.
Miles of plant: 3.8 (coaxial).
Manager: Kevin Mayne. Chief technician: Tad Peak. Customer service manager: Liz Reuter.
Ownership: Fanch Communications Inc. (MSO). See Cable System Ownership.

BAGLEY (village)—Dairyland Cable Systems Inc., 1140 Sextonville Rd., Richland Center, WI 53581. Phone: 608-647-6383. Fax: 608-647-7394. County: Grant. ICA: WI0238.
TV Market Ranking: Outside TV Markets. Franchise award date: N.A. Franchise expiration date: N.A. Began: July 1, 1989.
Channel capacity: 13. Channels available but not in use: N.A.
Basic Service
Subscribers: 80.
Programming (received off-air): KCRG-TV (A), KRIN (P), KWWL (N) Cedar Rapids-Waterloo; WKBT (C) La Crosse; WISC-TV (C) Madison.
Programming (via satellite): WGN-TV (W) Chicago; CNN; Discovery Channel; ESPN; Nashville Network; TBS Superstation; USA Network.
Fee: $25.00 installation; $14.95 monthly.
Pay Service 1
Pay Units: 11.
Programming (via satellite): The Movie Channel.
Fee: $10.50 monthly.
Manager: Jim Atkinson. Chief technician: Dale Davenport.
Ownership: Dairyland Cable Systems Inc. (MSO).

BALDWIN (village)—Baldwin Telecom Inc., 930 Maple St., Baldwin, WI 54002. Phone: 715-684-3346. Fax: 715-684-4747. County: St. Croix. Also serves Hammond (village), Woodville (village). ICA: WI0079.
TV Market Ranking: 13 (Hammond); Outside TV Markets (Baldwin, Woodville). Franchise award date: N.A. Franchise expiration date: N.A. Began: November 1, 1982.
Channel capacity: 40 (2-way capable; not operating 2-way). Channels available but not in use: 1.
Basic Service
Subscribers: 1,420.
Programming (received off-air): WEUX (F) Chippewa Falls; WEAU-TV (N), WQOW-TV (A) Eau Claire; WKBT (C) La Crosse; WHWC-TV (P) Menomonie; KARE (N), KLGT (W), KMSP-TV (U), KSTP-TV (A), KTCA-TV (P), KTCI-TV (P), KVBM-TV (H), WCCO-TV (C), WFTC (F) Minneapolis-St. Paul; KPXM (X) St. Cloud.
Programming (via satellite): WGN-TV (W) Chicago; A & E; CNN; Discovery Channel; ESPN; ESPN 2; EWTN; Fox Family Channel; History Channel; Learning Channel; Lifetime; Nashville Network; Nick at Nite's TV Land; Nickelodeon; QVC; Sci-Fi Channel; TBS Superstation; The Weather Channel; Turner Network TV; USA Network.
Current originations: Public access.
Fee: $25.95 installation; $16.50 monthly.
Pay Service 1
Pay Units: 312.
Programming (via satellite): Cinemax.
Fee: $15.00 installation; $6.30 monthly.
Pay Service 2
Pay Units: 339.
Programming (via satellite): HBO.
Fee: $15.00 installation; $8.40 monthly.
Pay Service 3
Pay Units: 59.
Programming (via satellite): Disney Channel.
Fee: $15.00 installation; $7.00 monthly.
Equipment: Scientific-Atlanta satellite antenna; Prodelin satellite receivers.
Miles of plant: 65.0 (coaxial); 11.0 (fiber optic). Homes passed: 2,232. Total homes in franchised area: 2,232.
Manager: Larry Knegendorf. Chief technician: Tim Kusilek.
City fee: 3% of gross.
Ownership: Baldwin TeleCom Inc. (MSO).

BANCROFT—Cable Systems Management of Iowa Inc., 3600 Kennebec Dr., Eagan, MN 55122. Phone: 612-688-2623. Fax: 612-688-2624. County: Portage. ICA: WI0215.
TV Market Ranking: Outside TV Markets. Franchise award date: N.A. Franchise expiration date: N.A. Began: N.A.

Channel capacity: 40. Channels available but not in use: 19.

Basic Service

Subscribers: 53.

Programming (received off-air): WEAU-TV (N) Eau Claire; WAOW-TV (A), WHRM-TV (P), WSAW-TV (C) Wausau-Rhinelander.

Programming (via satellite): WGN-TV (W) Chicago; A & E; American Movie Classics; Country Music TV; Discovery Channel; ESPN; Fox Family Channel; Headline News; Lifetime; Nashville Network; Showtime; TBS Superstation; Turner Network TV; USA Network.

Fee: $50.00 installation; $28.00 monthly.

Miles of plant: 4.4 (coaxial). Homes passed: 163.

Manager: Jeff Anderson.

Ownership: Cable Systems Management of Iowa Inc. (MSO).

BARABOO—Bresnan Communications Co., 413 Oak St., Baraboo, WI 53913-2497. Phones: 608-356-4836; 608-274-3822. Fax: 608-356-5404. Counties: Adams, Columbia & Sauk. Also serves Greenfield (Sauk County), Lake Delton, Reedsburg, West Baraboo, Wisconsin Dells. ICA: WI0042.

TV Market Ranking: 93 (Baraboo); Outside TV Markets (Greenfield, Lake Delton, Reedsburg, West Baraboo, Wisconsin Dells). Franchise award date: N.A. Franchise expiration date: N.A. Began: June 1, 1968.

Channel capacity: 77. Channels available but not in use: N.A.

Basic Service

Subscribers: 7,296.

Programming (received off-air): WGN-TV (W) Chicago; WHA-TV (P), WISC-TV (C), WKOW-TV (A), WMSN-TV (F), WMTV (N) Madison; allband FM.

Programming (via satellite): A & E; American Movie Classics; C-SPAN; CNN; Court TV; Discovery Channel; E! Entertainment TV; ESPN; ESPN 2; FX; Fox Family Channel; Headline News; History Channel; Learning Channel; Lifetime; MTV; Nashville Network; Nickelodeon; TBS Superstation; The Weather Channel; Turner Network TV; USA Network.

Current originations: Automated time-weather; government access; automated emergency alert.

Fee: $31.67 installation; $21.63 monthly; $2.85 converter.

Pay Service 1

Pay Units: 832.

Programming (via satellite): Cinemax.

Fee: $12.45 monthly.

Pay Service 2

Pay Units: 557.

Programming (via satellite): Disney Channel.

Fee: $12.45 monthly.

Pay Service 3

Pay Units: 3,058.

Programming (via satellite): The New Encore.

Fee: $1.75 monthly.

Pay Service 4

Pay Units: 2,453.

Programming (via satellite): HBO.

Fee: $12.90 monthly.

Pay Service 5

Pay Units: 106.

Programming (via satellite): DMX.

Fee: $9.95 monthly.

Pay Service 6

Pay Units: 1,436.

Programming (via satellite): Starz!

Fee: $3.95 monthly.

Pay-Per-View

Addressable homes: 1,431.

Local advertising: Yes. Rates: $15.00/15 Minutes. Local sales manager: Tim Root.

Program Guide: The Cable Guide.

Equipment: Jerrold headend; Jerrold amplifiers; Comm/Scope & Times Fiber cable.

Manager: Brian Shirk. Chief technician: Robert Beale. Customer service manager: Cindy Buzzell.

City fee: 1% of gross.

Ownership: Bresnan Communications Co. LP (MSO). Purchased from Tele-Communications Inc, February 2, 1999. See Cable System Ownership.

BARRON—Chibardun Telephone Cooperative, Box 164, 110 N. 2nd Ave., Dallas, WI 54733. Phone: 715-837-1011. Fax: 715-837-1196. County: Barron. ICA: WI0318.

TV Market Ranking: Outside TV Markets. Franchise award date: N.A. Franchise expiration date: N.A. Began: N.A.

Channel capacity: N.A. Channels available but not in use: N.A.

Basic Service

Subscribers: N.A.

Programming (received off-air): WEUX (F) Chippewa Falls; WEAU-TV (N), WQOW-TV (A) Eau Claire; WKBT (C) La Crosse; WHWC-TV (P) Menomonie; KARE (N), KLGT (W), KMSP-TV (U), KSTP-TV (A), KTCA-TV (P), WCCO-TV (C), WFTC (F) Minneapolis-St. Paul.

Fee: $12.95 monthly.

Expanded Basic Service

Subscribers: N.A.

Programming (via satellite): WGN-TV (W) Chicago; A & E; American Movie Classics; C-SPAN; C-SPAN 2; CNBC; CNN; CNN/SI; Comedy Central; Country Music TV; Court TV; Discovery Channel; E! Entertainment TV; ESPN; ESPN 2; Fox Family Channel; Headline News; Learning Channel; Lifetime; MTV; Nashville Network; Nick at Nite's TV Land; Nickelodeon; Outdoor Channel; QVC; Sci-Fi Channel; TBS Superstation; The Health Network; The Inspirational Network; The Weather Channel; Trinity Bcstg. Network; Turner Network TV; USA Network; VH1.

Fee: $19.95 monthly.

Expanded Basic Service 2

Subscribers: N.A.

Programming (via satellite): Animal Planet; Discovery People; Encore Movie Networks; Flix; Goodlife TV Network; Home & Garden Television; MSNBC; Outdoor Life Network; The New Encore; Z Music Television.

Fee: $5.95 monthly.

Expanded Basic Service 3

Subscribers: N.A.

Programming (via satellite): Cartoon Network; Game Show Network; History Channel; MuchMusic Network; Odyssey; Romance Classics; Speedvision; Travel Channel; Turner Classic Movies.

Fee: $5.95 monthly.

Pay Service 1

Pay Units: N.A.

Programming (via satellite): Cinemax (multiplexed); Disney Channel; HBO (multiplexed); Showtime (multiplexed); The Movie Channel.

Fee: $4.95 monthly (Disney), $8.95 monthly (Cinemax, TMC or Showtime), $9.00 monthly (HBO).

Manager: Rick Vergin. Chief technician: Doug Kurschner.

Ownership: Chibardun Cable TV Cooperative (MSO).

BAY CITY—Delta Cablevision I LP, 810 S. 2nd St., Alma, WI 54610-9756. Phone: 608-685-4545. County: Pierce. ICA: WI0239.

TV Market Ranking: Outside TV Markets. Franchise award date: N.A. Franchise expiration date: N.A. Began: March 1, 1989.

Channel capacity: 23. Channels available but not in use: N.A.

Basic Service

Subscribers: 122.

Programming (received off-air): WEAU-TV (N) Eau Claire; WKBT (C) La Crosse; KARE (N), KLGT (W), KMSP-TV (U), KSTP-TV (A), KTCA-TV (P), WCCO-TV (C), WFTC (F) Minneapolis-St. Paul.

Programming (via satellite): WGN-TV (W) Chicago; A & E; CNN; Discovery Channel; ESPN; Fox Family Channel; Headline News; Lifetime; Nashville Network; TBS Superstation; Turner Network TV; USA Network.

Fee: $25.00 installation; $17.00 monthly.

Pay Service 1

Pay Units: N.A.

Programming (via satellite): HBO; Showtime.

Fee: $25.00 installation; $9.95 monthly (each).

Manager: Delmore Zirzow. Chief technician: Jim Ireland.

Ownership: Fanch Communications Inc. (MSO). See Cable System Ownership.

BAYFIELD—Hadland Communications Inc., Box 1286, 265 Connies Lane, Bayfield, WI 54814. Phones: 715-779-5840; 715-779-5772. Fax: 715-779-5846.

E-mail: rhadland@win.bright.net.

County: Bayfield. ICA: WI0186.

TV Market Ranking: Outside TV Markets. Franchise award date: January 8, 1987. Franchise expiration date: June 30, 2002. Began: July 1, 1988.

Channel capacity: 56 (not 2-way capable). Channels available but not in use: 4.

Basic Service

Subscribers: 305.

Programming (received off-air): KBJR-TV (N), KDLH (C), WDIO-TV (A,F), WDSE-TV (P) Duluth-Superior; WLEF-TV (P) Park Falls; 15 FMs.

Programming (via satellite): WGN-TV (W) Chicago; A & E; American Movie Classics; Animal Planet; C-SPAN; C-SPAN 2; CNBC; CNN; Cartoon Network; Country Music TV; Discovery Channel; Disney Channel; ESPN; ESPN 2; FX; Fox Family Channel; Fox News Channel; Headline News; History Channel; Home & Garden Television; Learning Channel; Lifetime; MTV; Nashville Network; Nick at Nite's TV Land; Nickelodeon; Odyssey; Sci-Fi Channel; TBS Superstation; TV Guide Channel; The Health Network; The Weather Channel; Travel Channel; Turner Network TV; USA Network; VH1; ZDTV.

Current originations: Public access; local news.

Fee: $24.95 installation; $27.70 monthly.

Pay Service 1

Pay Units: 130.

Programming (via satellite): Cinemax (multiplexed).

Fee: $10.00 installation; $7.00 monthly.

Pay Service 2

Pay Units: 129.

Programming (via satellite): HBO (multiplexed).

Fee: $10.00 installation; $9.65 monthly.

Equipment: Scientific-Atlanta amplifiers; Times Fiber & Comm/Scope cable; Amiga character generator; Scientific-Atlanta set top converters; Eagle & Regal traps; Scientific-Atlanta satellite antenna; Scientific-Atlanta satellite receivers.

Miles of plant: 23.0 (coaxial); None (fiber optic). Homes passed: 402.

Manager: Robert Hadland.

Ownership: Hadland Communications Inc. Bob Hadland, principal.

BEAR CREEK—Northern Lakes Cable TV, Box 8, Bonduel, WI 54107. Phone: 715-758-2500. County: Outagamie. ICA: WI0240.

TV Market Ranking: 62. Franchise award date: N.A. Franchise expiration date: N.A. Began: May 1, 1990.

Channel capacity: 36. Channels available but not in use: 10.

Basic Service

Subscribers: 104.

Programming (received off-air): WACY (U) Appleton; WBAY-TV (A), WFRV-TV (C), WGBA (N), WLUK-TV (F), WPNE (P) Green Bay; WAOW-TV (A), WSAW-TV (C) Wausau-Rhinelander.

Programming (via satellite): WGN-TV (W) Chicago; A & E; CNN; Discovery Channel; ESPN; EWTN; Fox Family Channel; MTV; Nashville Network; Nickelodeon; TBS Superstation; Turner Classic Movies; USA Network.

Fee: $15.95 monthly.

Pay Service 1

Pay Units: N.A.

Programming (via satellite): Cinemax; HBO.

Fee: $9.95 monthly (each).

Manager: Robert Steichen.

Ownership: Northern Lakes Cable TV (MSO).

BELL CENTER—Richland Grant Telephone Co-op Inc., Box 67, 202 N. East St., Blue River, WI 53518. Phone: 608-537-2461. Fax: 608-537-2222. County: Crawford. ICA: WI0228.

TV Market Ranking: Outside TV Markets. Franchise award date: N.A. Franchise expiration date: N.A. Began: October 10, 1978.

Channel capacity: 40 (not 2-way capable). Channels available but not in use: 22.

Basic Service

Subscribers: 33.

Programming (received off-air): WEAU-TV (N) Eau Claire; WHLA-TV (P), WKBT (C), WLAX (F), WXOW-TV (A) La Crosse; 2 FMs.

Programming (via satellite): WGN-TV (W) Chicago; A & E; American Movie Classics; C-SPAN; C-SPAN 2; CNN; Cartoon Network; Comedy Central; Country Music TV; Discovery Channel; ESPN; Fox Family Channel; Goodlife TV Network; Headline News; History Channel; Home & Garden Television; Home Shopping Network; Knowledge TV; Learning Channel; Lifetime; MSNBC; Nashville Network; Nickelodeon; Odyssey; QVC; TBS Superstation; TV Guide Channel; The Weather Channel; Turner Network TV; USA Network; VH1.

Current originations: Local access.

Fee: $68.00 installation; $16.00 monthly.

Pay Service 1

Pay Units: 10.

Programming (via satellite): HBO.

Fee: $9.50 monthly.

Pay Service 2

Pay Units: N.A.

Programming (via satellite): Cinemax; Disney Channel; Showtime; The New Encore.

Fee: N.A.

Equipment: C-COR amplifiers; Comm/Scope cable.

Miles of plant: 7.0 (coaxial). Homes passed: 60. Total homes in franchised area: 75.

Manager: Dave Lull. Chief technician: Bob Brewer. Marketing director: Jamie Goldsmith.
Ownership: Richland Grant Telephone Co-op Inc.

BELLEVILLE—Belleville CATV Inc., 7713 Hillcrest Ave., Middleton, WI 53562. Phone: 608-233-5245. Fax: 608-836-1840. Counties: Dane & Green. ICA: WI0138.
TV Market Ranking: 93. Franchise award date: N.A. Franchise expiration date: July 1, 1998. Began: January 1, 1984.
Channel capacity: 35. Channels available but not in use: 15.
Basic Service
Subscribers: 607.
Programming (received off-air): WHA-TV (P), WISC-TV (C), WKOW-TV (A), WMSN-TV (F), WMTV (N) Madison.
Programming (via satellite): WGN-TV (W) Chicago; C-SPAN; CNN; ESPN; TBS Superstation.
Current originations: Educational access; local sports.
Planned originations: Government access.
Fee: $10.00 monthly.
Expanded Basic Service
Subscribers: 556.
Programming (via satellite): A & E; American Movie Classics; C-SPAN 2; CNN; Discovery Channel; Disney Channel; ESPN 2; Fox Family Channel; Headline News; History Channel; Learning Channel; Lifetime; MTV; Nashville Network; Nickelodeon; The Weather Channel; Turner Network TV; USA Network.
Fee: $10.95 monthly.
Pay Service 1
Pay Units: 195.
Programming (via satellite): HBO.
Fee: $9.95 monthly.
Equipment: Blonder-Tongue & Catel headend; Magnavox amplifiers; Comm/Scope cable; Pioneer set top converters; Intercept traps; Microdyne satellite antenna; M/A-Com satellite receivers.
Miles of plant: 15.0 (coaxial). Homes passed: 800. Total homes in franchised area: 800.
Manager: Richard C. Gall.
City fee: 3% of gross.
Ownership: Belleville CATV Inc.

BELOIT—Charter Communications Inc., Box 779, 1837 Park Ave., Beloit, WI 53511. Phone: 608-365-9555. Counties: Rock, WI; Winnebago, IL. Also serves Rockton (village), Rockton Twp., Roscoe Twp., South Beloit, IL; Beloit Twp., Turtle Twp., WI. ICA: WI0016.
TV Market Ranking: 93 (Turtle Twp.); 97 (Beloit, Beloit Twp., Rockton, Rockton Twp., Roscoe Twp., South Beloit). Franchise award date: June 21, 1965. Franchise expiration date: N.A. Began: November 1, 1968.
Channel capacity: 52 (not 2-way capable). Channels available but not in use: 12.
Basic Service
Subscribers: 20,438; Commercial subscribers: 79.
Programming (received off-air): WIFR (C) Freeport-Rockford; WHA-TV (P), WISC-TV (C), WKOW-TV (A), WMTV (N) Madison; WVTV (W) Milwaukee; WQRF-TV (F), WREX-TV (N) Rockford; 15 FMs.
Programming (via satellite): WGN-TV (W) Chicago; A & E; BET; C-SPAN; CNN; Cartoon Network; ESPN; EWTN; Fox Family Channel; Headline News; Lifetime; MTV; Nickelodeon; QVC; TBS Superstation; The Weather Channel; Travel Channel; Turner Network TV; USA Network.
Planned programming (via satellite): Discovery Channel; Nashville Network.
Current originations: Automated time-weather; public access; government access; automated emergency alert; local news.
Fee: $25.00 installation; $5.75 monthly; $2.00 converter; $10.00 additional installation.
Pay Service 1
Pay Units: 3,095.
Programming (via satellite): Cinemax.
Fee: $10.95 monthly.
Pay Service 2
Pay Units: 1,566.
Programming (via satellite): Disney Channel.
Fee: $7.95 monthly.
Pay Service 3
Pay Units: 5,660.
Programming (via satellite): HBO.
Fee: $10.95 monthly.
Local advertising: Yes (locally produced & insert). Available in satellite distributed & locally originated programming. Rates: $8.00/Minute; $4.00/30 Seconds. Local sales manager: Jerry Marion.
Equipment: Scientific-Atlanta headend; Scientific-Atlanta amplifiers; Trilogy cable; Hitachi & Sony cameras; Sony VTRs; NSC & Panasonic set top converters; Arcom traps; Scientific-Atlanta satellite antenna; Scientific-Atlanta & Standard Communications satellite receivers; Texscan commercial insert.
Miles of plant: 207.0 (coaxial). Homes passed: 21,300.
Manager: Mike Williams. Chief technician: Dennis Ritter. Marketing director: Dianne Carter.
City fee: 3% of gross.
Ownership: Charter Communications Inc. (MSO). Purchased from Marcus Cable, April 1, 1999.

BERLIN—Charter Communications Inc., Box 1197, 55 W. Scott St., Fond du Lac, WI 54936-1197. Phones: 920-923-7196; 800-581-0081. Fax: 920-923-1235. Counties: Green Lake & Waushara. Also serves Aurora (town), Berlin (town). ICA: WI0069.
TV Market Ranking: Below 100. Franchise award date: N.A. Franchise expiration date: N.A. Began: June 1, 1981.
Channel capacity: 35 (2-way capable; operating 2-way). Channels available but not in use: 1.
Basic Service
Subscribers: 1,695.
Programming (received off-air): WACY (U) Appleton; WBAY-TV (A), WFRV-TV (C), WGBA (N), WLUK-TV (F), WPNE (P) Green Bay; WISN-TV (A), WVTV (W) Milwaukee.
Programming (via satellite): WGN-TV (W) Chicago; A & E; American Movie Classics; C-SPAN; CNN; Comedy Central; Discovery Channel; ESPN; EWTN; Fox Family Channel; Headline News; Lifetime; MTV; Nashville Network; Nickelodeon; QVC; TBS Superstation; The Weather Channel; Turner Network TV; USA Network; VH1.
Current originations: Automated time-weather; educational access.
Fee: $34.95 installation; $9.97 monthly.
Pay Service 1
Pay Units: 277.
Programming (via satellite): Cinemax.
Fee: $14.95 installation; $12.50 monthly.
Pay Service 2
Pay Units: 169.
Programming (via satellite): Disney Channel.
Fee: $14.95 installation; $3.95 monthly.
Pay Service 3
Pay Units: 300.
Programming (via satellite): HBO.
Fee: $14.95 installation; $12.95 monthly.

Pay Service 4
Pay Units: 385.
Programming (via satellite): Showtime.
Fee: $14.95 installation; $12.50 monthly.
Local advertising: Yes. Available in character-generated programming.
Equipment: Scientific-Atlanta headend; Scientific-Atlanta amplifiers; Times Fiber cable; Texscan character generator; Scientific-Atlanta set top converters; Eagle traps; Scientific-Atlanta satellite antenna.
Miles of plant: 35.5 (coaxial). Homes passed: 2,315.
Manager: Lisa Washa. Chief technician: Jeff Gerner.
City fee: 3% of gross.
Ownership: Charter Communications Inc. (MSO). Purchased from Marcus Cable, April 1, 1999.

BLACK CREEK—Charter Communications Inc., Box 1818, 853 McIntosh St., Wausau, WI 54402-1818. Phones: 715-845-4223; 800-581-0081. Fax: 715-848-0081. County: Outagamie. Also serves Black Creek (town), Bovina, Shiocton. ICA: WI0123.
TV Market Ranking: 62. Franchise award date: N.A. Franchise expiration date: N.A. Began: June 1, 1983.
Channel capacity: 35. Channels available but not in use: N.A.
Basic Service
Subscribers: 458; Commercial subscribers: 1.
Programming (received off-air): WACY (U) Appleton; WBAY-TV (A), WFRV-TV (C), WGBA (N), WLUK-TV (F), WPNE (P) Green Bay.
Programming (via satellite): WGN-TV (W) Chicago; TBS Superstation.
Fee: $56.73 installation; $6.28 monthly.
Commercial fee: $30.00 monthly.
Expanded Basic Service
Subscribers: 450.
Programming (via satellite): A & E; CNN; Country Music TV; Discovery Channel; Disney Channel; ESPN; Fox Family Channel; Headline News; Lifetime; MTV; Nashville Network; Nickelodeon; Sci-Fi Channel; Turner Network TV; USA Network; VH1.
Fee: $14.36 monthly.
Pay Service 1
Pay Units: 143.
Programming (via satellite): Cinemax.
Fee: $12.50 monthly.
Pay Service 2
Pay Units: 195.
Programming (via satellite): HBO.
Fee: $12.95 monthly.
Local advertising: No.
Equipment: AEL & Winegard amplifiers; Standard Components, Scientific-Atlanta & Oak set top converters; Pico traps; Scientific-Atlanta satellite antenna; Scientific-Atlanta satellite receivers.
Miles of plant: 14.0 (coaxial). Homes passed: 750.
Manager: Scott Behn. Chief technician: Bruce Walsleske. Marketing director: Tim Schieffer.
City fee: 1% of gross.
Ownership: Charter Communications Inc. (MSO). Purchased from Marcus Cable, April 1, 1999.

BLACK RIVER FALLS—Charter Communications Inc., Box 279, 314 Main St., Onalaska, WI 54650. Phones: 608-783-5255; 800-658-9473. Fax: 608-783-7033. County: Jackson. Also serves Adams, Brockway. ICA: WI0082.
TV Market Ranking: Below 100 (Adams); Outside TV Markets (Black River Falls, Brockway). Franchise award date: January 1, 1974. Franchise expiration date: July 1, 2008. Began: January 1, 1975.
Channel capacity: 76 (not 2-way capable). Channels available but not in use: 45.
Basic Service
Subscribers: 1,492.
Programming (received off-air): WEAU-TV (N) Eau Claire; WHLA-TV (P), WKBT (C), WLAX (F), WXOW-TV (A) La Crosse.
Programming (via satellite): WGN-TV (W) Chicago; C-SPAN; C-SPAN 2; Home Shopping Network; QVC; TV Guide Channel.
Current originations: Local access.
Fee: $64.57 installation; $9.14 monthly.
Expanded Basic Service
Subscribers: 1,334.
Programming (via satellite): A & E; American Movie Classics; Animal Planet; CNBC; CNN; Cartoon Network; Comedy Central; Country Music TV; Court TV; Discovery Channel; Disney Channel; E! Entertainment TV; ESPN; ESPN 2; ESPN Classic Sports; ESPNews; FX; Fox Family Channel; Game Show Network; Golf Channel; Headline News; History Channel; Home & Garden Television; Learning Channel; Lifetime; MSNBC; MTV; Midwest Sports Channel; Nashville Network; Nick at Nite's TV Land; Nickelodeon; Outdoor Life Network; Sci-Fi Channel; Speedvision; TBS Superstation; The Barker; The Weather Channel; Toon Disney; Travel Channel; Turner Classic Movies; Turner Network TV; USA Network; VH1; WB 100+ Station Group.
Fee: $64.57 installation; $33.20 monthly.
Pay Service 1
Pay Units: 228.
Programming (via satellite): Cinemax (multiplexed).
Fee: $20.00 installation; $12.95 monthly.
Pay Service 2
Pay Units: 265.
Programming (via satellite): HBO (multiplexed).
Fee: $20.00 installation; $12.95 monthly.
Pay Service 3
Pay Units: 207.
Programming (via satellite): Showtime.
Fee: $20.00 installation; $12.95 monthly.
Pay Service 4
Pay Units: N.A.
Programming (via satellite): The Movie Channel.
Fee: $12.95 monthly.
Pay-Per-View
Addressable homes: 420.
Movies.
Local advertising: Yes. Local sales manager: Holly Hackner.
Equipment: Jerrold & Scientific-Atlanta headend; Scientific-Atlanta amplifiers; Systems Wire cable; Jerrold set top converters; KES & Farinon satellite antenna; Scientific-Atlanta satellite receivers.

Miles of plant: 47.0 (coaxial); 7.0 (fiber optic). Homes passed: 1,861. Total homes in franchised area: 1,861.
Manager: Shirley Hehn-Weibel. Chief technician: Tim Fischer.
City fee: 2.5% of gross.
Ownership: Charter Communications Inc. (MSO). Purchased from Marcus Cable, April 1, 1999.

BLANCHARDVILLE—Triax Cablevision, Box 334, 1102 N. 4th St., Chillicothe, IL 61523-0334. Phones: 309-274-4500; 800-874-2924. Fax: 309-274-3188. Counties: Iowa & Lafayette. ICA: WI0170.
TV Market Ranking: 93. Franchise award date: N.A. Franchise expiration date: April 21, 2014. Began: May 1, 1984.
Channel capacity: 37 (not 2-way capable). Channels available but not in use: 3.
Basic Service
Subscribers: 232.
Programming (received off-air): WHA-TV (P), WISC-TV (C), WKOW-TV (A), WMSN-TV (F), WMTV (N) Madison.
Programming (via satellite): WGN-TV (W) Chicago; A & E; American Movie Classics; Animal Planet; CNN; Country Music TV; Discovery Channel; Disney Channel; ESPN; ESPN 2; Fox Family Channel; History Channel; Home & Garden Television; Home Shopping Network; Learning Channel; Lifetime; MTV; Nashville Network; Nick at Nite's TV Land; Nickelodeon; TBS Superstation; The Inspirational Network; The Weather Channel; Trinity Bcstg. Network; Turner Network TV; USA Network.
Fee: $45.00 installation; $30.50 monthly.
Pay Service 1
Pay Units: 105.
Programming (via satellite): Cinemax; HBO; Showtime.
Fee: $7.95 monthly (Cinemax), $11.99 monthly (HBO or Showtime).
Equipment: Scientific-Atlanta headend; Scientific-Atlanta amplifiers; Scientific-Atlanta cable; Scientific-Atlanta set top converters; Vitek traps; Scientific-Atlanta satellite antenna; Scientific-Atlanta satellite receivers.
Miles of plant: 5.2 (coaxial). Homes passed: 384.
Manager: Mike Nodgerson. Chief technician: Pat Alderman.
Ownership: Triax Telecommunications Co. LLC (MSO). See Cable System Ownership.

BLOOMER—Charter Communications Inc., Box 539, 1725 S. Main St., Rice Lake, WI 54868 0539. Phones: 715-234-3821; 800-262-2578. Fax: 715-234-8537. County: Chippewa. ICA: WI0095.
TV Market Ranking: Below 100. Franchise award date: N.A. Franchise expiration date: March 20, 2012. Began: September 15, 1968.
Channel capacity: 35 (2-way capable; operating 2-way). Channels available but not in use: None.
Basic Service
Subscribers: 1,140.
Programming (received off-air): WEUX (F) Chippewa Falls; WEAU-TV (N), WQOW-TV (A) Eau Claire; WKBT (C) La Crosse; WHWC-TV (P) Menomonie; KMSP-TV (U), KTCA-TV (P), WCCO-TV (C) Minneapolis-St. Paul.
Programming (via satellite): WGN-TV (W) Chicago; A & E; American Movie Classics; C-SPAN; C-SPAN 2; CNBC; CNN; Comedy Central; Discovery Channel; Disney Channel; E! Entertainment TV; ESPN; Fox Family Channel; Headline News; Learning Channel; Lifetime; MTV; Nashville Network; Nickelodeon; QVC; TBS Superstation; The Weather Channel; Turner Network TV; USA Network; VH1.
Fee: $42.95 installation; $27.17 monthly.
Pay Service 1
Pay Units: 115.
Programming (via satellite): Cinemax.
Fee: $19.95 installation; $12.50 monthly.
Pay Service 2
Pay Units: 128.
Programming (via satellite): HBO.
Fee: $19.95 installation; $12.95 monthly.
Pay Service 3
Pay Units: 107.
Programming (via satellite): Showtime.
Fee: $19.95 installation; $12.50 monthly.
Local advertising: No. Local sales manager: Andy Jerome.
Equipment: Jerrold headend; Jerrold amplifiers; Times Fiber cable; Eagle traps; Scientific-Atlanta satellite antenna; Scientific-Atlanta satellite receivers.
Miles of plant: 19.2 (coaxial). Homes passed: 1,215.
Manager: Scott Binder. Chief technician: George Benjamin.
City fee: 2% of gross.
Ownership: Charter Communications Inc. (MSO). Purchased from Marcus Cable, April 1, 1999.

BLOOMINGDALE—Midwest Cable, Box 399, Sparta, WI 54656. Phone: 608-269-6247. County: Vernon. ICA: WI0232.
TV Market Ranking: Below 100. Franchise award date: N.A. Franchise expiration date: N.A. Began: January 1, 1970.
Channel capacity: 12. Channels available but not in use: 5.
Basic Service
Subscribers: 30.
Programming (received off-air): WEAU-TV (N) Eau Claire; WHLA-TV (P), WKBT (C), WLAX (F), WXOW-TV (A) La Crosse; KTTC (N) Rochester.
Fee: $20.00 installation; $7.00 monthly.
Pay Service 1
Pay Units: N.A.
Programming (via satellite): Cinemax.
Fee: $10.00 monthly.
Homes passed: 34.
Manager: Roger H. Alderman.
Ownership: Midwest Cable (MSO).

BLUE RIVER (village)—Dairyland Cable Systems Inc., 1140 Sextonville Rd., Richland Center, WI 53581. Phone: 608-647-6383. Fax: 608-647-7394. County: Grant. ICA: WI0242.
TV Market Ranking: Outside TV Markets. Franchise award date: N.A. Franchise expiration date: N.A. Began: November 1, 1989.
Channel capacity: 16. Channels available but not in use: N.A.
Basic Service
Subscribers: 112.
Programming (received off-air): WISC-TV (C), WKOW-TV (A), WMSN-TV (F), WMTV (N) Madison; WMVS (P) Milwaukee.
Programming (via satellite): WGN-TV (W) Chicago; CNN; Discovery Channel; ESPN; Nashville Network; Nickelodeon; TBS Superstation; USA Network; VH1.
Fee: $25.00 installation; $16.95 monthly.
Pay Service 1
Pay Units: 22.
Programming (via satellite): The Movie Channel.
Fee: $10.50 monthly.
Manager: Jim Atkinson. Chief technician: Dale Davenport.
Ownership: Dairyland Cable Systems Inc. (MSO).

BLUFFVIEW—HLM Cable Corp., Box 620684, 2305-A Parview Rd., Middleton, WI 53562-2525. Phones: 608-831-7044; 800-451-5119. Fax: 608-836-5726. County: Sauk. ICA: WI0212.
TV Market Ranking: Outside TV Markets. Franchise award date: N.A. Franchise expiration date: N.A. Began: May 1, 1989.
Channel capacity: 40 (not 2-way capable). Channels available but not in use: 19.
Basic Service
Subscribers: 112.
Programming (received off-air): WHA-TV (P), WISC-TV (C), WKOW-TV (A), WMSN-TV (F), WMTV (N) Madison.
Programming (via satellite): WGN-TV (W) Chicago; A & E; CNN; Comedy Central; ESPN; ESPN 2; Fox Family Channel; History Channel; Nashville Network; Sci-Fi Channel; TBS Superstation; The Weather Channel; Turner Network TV; USA Network.
Fee: $19.95 installation; $25.00 monthly; $1.50 converter.
Pay Service 1
Pay Units: 27.
Programming (via satellite): Showtime.
Fee: $14.95 installation; $6.95 monthly.
Homes passed: 172.
Ownership: H.L.M. Cable Co. (MSO).

BOAZ—Village of Boaz, 25433 Jackson St., Boaz, WI 53573. Phone: 608-536-3493. County: Richland. ICA: WI0229.
TV Market Ranking: Outside TV Markets. Franchise award date: N.A. Franchise expiration date: N.A. Began: N.A.
Channel capacity: 12. Channels available but not in use: N.A.
Basic Service
Subscribers: 63.
Programming (received off-air): WKBT (C) La Crosse; WHA-TV (P), WISC-TV (C), WKOW-TV (A), WMSN-TV (F), WMTV (N) Madison.
Programming (via satellite): ESPN; Nashville Network; TBS Superstation; Turner Network TV.
Fee: $8.00 monthly; $35.00 converter.
Pay Service 1
Pay Units: 23.
Programming (via satellite): HBO.
Fee: $8.00 monthly.
Equipment: Ameco & Jerrold headend; Ameco & Jerrold amplifiers; Essex cable.
Miles of plant: 3.0 (coaxial).
Village fee: None.
Ownership: Village of Boaz.

BONDUEL—Bonduel Cable TV, Box 8, Bonduel, WI 54107. Phone: 715-758-2500. County: Shawano. ICA: WI0163.
TV Market Ranking: 62. Franchise award date: May 1, 1981. Franchise expiration date: N.A. Began: February 1, 1983.
Channel capacity: 35. Channels available but not in use: 23.
Basic Service
Subscribers: 262.
Programming (received off-air): WBAY-TV (A), WFRV-TV (C), WGBA (N), WLUK-TV (F), WPNE (P) Green Bay.
Programming (via satellite): WGN-TV (W) Chicago; CNN; ESPN; Fox Family Channel; TBS Superstation; Turner Classic Movies; USA Network.
Fee: $15.00 installation; $8.10 monthly; $15.00 additional installation.
Pay Service 1
Pay Units: N.A.
Programming (via satellite): HBO.
Fee: N.A.
Equipment: Scientific-Atlanta headend; GTE Sylvania amplifiers; Times Fiber cable; Eagle traps; Scientific-Atlanta satellite antenna; Microdyne satellite receivers.
Miles of plant: 9.0 (coaxial). Homes passed: 400. Total homes in franchised area: 400.
Manager: Robert Steichen.
City fee: 3% of gross.
Ownership: Bonduel Cable TV.

BOULDER JUNCTION—Karban TV Systems Inc., 73A S. Stevens St., Rhinelander, WI 54501. Phone: 715-277-2339. County: Vilas. ICA: WI0243.
TV Market Ranking: Below 100. Franchise award date: N.A. Franchise expiration date: N.A. Began: August 1, 1990.
Channel capacity: 54 (not 2-way capable). Channels available but not in use: 29.
Basic Service
Subscribers: 164.
Programming (received off-air): WLEF-TV (P) Park Falls; WAOW-TV (A), WJFW-TV (N), WSAW-TV (C) Wausau-Rhinelander.
Programming (via satellite): WGN-TV (W) Chicago; A & E; CNN; Discovery Channel; ESPN; Fox Family Channel; Headline News; Lifetime; Nashville Network; Nickelodeon; TBS Superstation; Turner Network TV; USA Network.
Fee: $75.00 installation; $24.00 monthly.
Pay Service 1
Pay Units: 6.
Programming (via satellite): Disney Channel.
Fee: $9.00 monthly.
Pay Service 2
Pay Units: 17.
Programming (via satellite): HBO.
Fee: $10.00 monthly.
Miles of plant: 18.0 (coaxial). Homes passed: 200.
Manager: John Karban.
Ownership: Karban TV Systems Inc. (MSO).

BOYCEVILLE—Star Satellite TV & Cable, 410 E. Walnut St., Glenwood City, WI 54013. Phones: 715-643-2822; 715-643-2419. Fax: 715-643-5031. E-mail: starone@werewolf.net. County: Dunn. ICA: WI0313.
TV Market Ranking: Below 100. Franchise award date: January 1, 1988. Franchise expiration date: January 1, 2004. Began: January 1, 1988.
Channel capacity: N.A. Channels available but not in use: N.A.
Basic Service
Subscribers: 110.
Programming (received off-air): WEUX (F) Chippewa Falls; WEAU-TV (N), WQOW-TV (A) Eau Claire; WKBT (C) La Crosse; WHWC-TV (P) Menomonie; KARE (N), KLGT (W), KMSP-TV (U), KSTP-TV (A), KTCA-TV (P), WCCO-TV (C) Minneapolis-St. Paul.
Programming (via satellite): Country Music TV; Discovery Channel; Home Shopping Network; Nashville Network; Nick at Nite's TV Land; TBS Superstation; The Weather Channel.
Current originations: Automated time-weather; public access.
Fee: $10.00 installation; $17.00 monthly; $5.00 additional installation.
Expanded Basic Service
Subscribers: 110.
Programming (via satellite): WGN-TV (W) Chicago; A & E; American Movie Classics; CNN; Cartoon Network; Comedy Central; Disney Channel; Fox Family Channel; Game Show Network; Home & Garden Television; Learning Channel; Lifetime; MTV; Nick-

elodeon; Outdoor Channel; Sci-Fi Channel; TV Food Network; VH1.
Fee: $7.00 monthly.
Pay Service 1
Pay Units: 8.
Programming (via satellite): Cinemax.
Fee: $10.50 monthly.
Pay Service 2
Pay Units: 10.
Programming (via satellite): HBO.
Fee: $10.50 monthly.
Pay-Per-View
Addressable homes: 110.
Special events.
Fee: $2.99.
Pay-per-view manager: Steve Schmidt.
Local advertising: No. Available in locally originated programming. Rates: $15.00/month. Local sales manager: Steve Schmidt.
Equipment: Jerrold amplifiers; Comm/Scope cable; General Instrument set top converters; Microwave Filter traps; Unimesh satellite antenna; Drake & Uniden satellite receivers.
Miles of plant: 15.0 (coaxial); 3.0 (fiber optic). Homes passed: 425. Total homes in franchised area: 425.
Manager: Steve Schmidt.
Franchise fee: $.50 per sub.
Ownership: Star Satellite TV & Cable.

BOYD/CADOTT—Charter Communications Inc., Box 539, 1725 S. Main St., Rice Lake, WI 54868-0539. Phones: 715-234-3821; 800-262-2578. Fax: 715-234-8537. County: Chippewa. ICA: WI0131.
TV Market Ranking: Below 100. Franchise award date: N.A. Franchise expiration date: January 9, 2005. Began: N.A.
Channel capacity: 35 (not 2-way capable). Channels available but not in use: None.
Basic Service
Subscribers: 461.
Programming (received off-air): WEUX (F) Chippewa Falls; WEAU-TV (N), WQOW-TV (A) Eau Claire; WKBT (C) La Crosse; WHWC-TV (P) Menomonie; WSAW-TV (C) Wausau-Rhinelander.
Programming (via satellite): WGN-TV (W) Chicago; A & E; C-SPAN; CNBC; CNN; Discovery Channel; Disney Channel; E! Entertainment TV; ESPN; ESPN 2; Fox Family Channel; Headline News; Learning Channel; Lifetime; MTV; Nashville Network; Nickelodeon; QVC; TBS Superstation; The Weather Channel; Turner Network TV; USA Network.
Fee: $42.95 installation; $27.53 monthly.
Pay Service 1
Pay Units: 58.
Programming (via satellite): Cinemax.
Fee: $19.95 installation; $12.50 monthly.
Pay Service 2
Pay Units: 72.
Programming (via satellite): HBO.
Fee: $19.95 installation; $12.95 monthly.
Pay Service 3
Pay Units: 64.
Programming (via satellite): Showtime.
Fee: $19.95 installation; $12.50 monthly.
Miles of plant: 19.0 (coaxial). Homes passed: 657.
Manager: Scott Binder. Chief technician: George Benjamin.
Ownership: Charter Communications Inc. (MSO). Purchased from Marcus Cable, April 1, 1999.

BRANDON—Charter Communications Inc., Box 1197, 55 W. Scott St., Fond du Lac, WI 54936-1197. Phones: 920-923-7196; 800-581-0081. Fax: 920-923-1235. County: Fond du Lac. ICA: WI0187.
TV Market Ranking: Outside TV Markets. Franchise award date: N.A. Franchise expiration date: N.A. Began: February 1, 1982.
Channel capacity: 22 (not 2-way capable). Channels available but not in use: 5.
Basic Service
Subscribers: 201.
Programming (received off-air): WACY (U) Appleton; WBAY-TV (A), WFRV-TV (C), WGBA (N), WLUK-TV (F), WPNE (P) Green Bay; WISN-TV (A), WVTV (W) Milwaukee.
Programming (via satellite): WGN-TV (W) Chicago; A & E; American Movie Classics; C-SPAN; CNN; Comedy Central; Discovery Channel; ESPN; EWTN; Fox Family Channel; Headline News; Lifetime; MTV; Nashville Network; Nickelodeon; QVC; TBS Superstation; The Weather Channel; Turner Network TV; USA Network; VH1.
Fee: $34.95 installation; $8.75 monthly.
Pay Service 1
Pay Units: 27.
Programming (via satellite): Cinemax.
Fee: $12.15 installation; $12.50 monthly.
Pay Service 2
Pay Units: 29.
Programming (via satellite): HBO.
Fee: $12.15 installation; $12.95 monthly.
Pay Service 3
Pay Units: N.A.
Programming (via satellite): Disney Channel; Showtime.
Fee: $12.15 installation; $3.95 monthly (Disney), $12.95 monthly (Showtime).
Local advertising: No.
Equipment: Scientific-Atlanta headend; Microdyne satellite antenna.
Miles of plant: 3.0 (coaxial). Homes passed: 340.
Manager: Lisa Washa. Chief technician: Jeff Gerner.
City fee: 3% of gross.
Ownership: Charter Communications Inc. (MSO). Purchased from Marcus Cable, April 1, 1999.

BRIGGSVILLE—Cable Systems Management of Iowa Inc., 3600 Kennebec Dr., Eagan, MN 55122. Phone: 612-688-2623. Fax: 612-688-2624. County: Marquette. ICA: WI0216.
TV Market Ranking: Outside TV Markets. Franchise award date: N.A. Franchise expiration date: N.A. Began: N.A.
Channel capacity: 40. Channels available but not in use: 19.
Basic Service
Subscribers: 66.
Programming (received off-air): WHA-TV (P), WISC-TV (C), WKOW-TV (A), WMTV (N) Madison.
Programming (via satellite): WGN-TV (W) Chicago; A & E; American Movie Classics; CNN; Country Music TV; Discovery Channel; ESPN; Fox Family Channel; Headline News; Lifetime; Nashville Network; QVC; Showtime; TBS Superstation; Turner Network TV; USA Network.
Fee: $50.00 installation; $30.00 monthly.
Miles of plant: 4.2 (coaxial). Homes passed: 152.
Manager: Jeff Anderson.
Ownership: Cable Systems Management of Iowa Inc. (MSO).

BRILLION—Charter Communications Inc., Box 388, 3315 Lincoln Ave., Two Rivers, WI 54241-0308. Phone: 800-395-0995. Fax: 414-337-9251. County: Calumet. Also serves Potter. ICA: WI0098.
TV Market Ranking: 62. Franchise award date: July 14, 1980. Franchise expiration date: N.A. Began: May 11, 1981.
Channel capacity: 35 (not 2-way capable). Channels available but not in use: 4.
Basic Service
Subscribers: 805.
Programming (received off-air): WBAY-TV (A), WFRV-TV (C), WGBA (N), WLUK-TV (F), WPNE (P) Green Bay.
Programming (via satellite): WGN-TV (W) Chicago; A & E; American Movie Classics; C-SPAN; CNN; Discovery Channel; ESPN; Fox Family Channel; Headline News; Lifetime; MTV; Nashville Network; Nick at Nite; Nickelodeon; QVC; TBS Superstation; The Weather Channel; Turner Network TV; USA Network.
Current originations: Public access.
Fee: $42.95 installation; $12.75 monthly.
Pay Service 1
Pay Units: 135.
Programming (via satellite): Cinemax.
Fee: $19.95 installation; $12.50 monthly.
Pay Service 2
Pay Units: 100.
Programming (via satellite): Disney Channel.
Fee: $19.95 installation; $9.35 monthly.
Pay Service 3
Pay Units: 182.
Programming (via satellite): HBO.
Fee: $19.95 installation; $12.95 monthly.
Pay Service 4
Pay Units: 194.
Programming (via satellite): Showtime.
Fee: $19.95 installation; $12.50 monthly.
Local advertising: Yes. Available in character-generated programming.
Equipment: Scientific-Atlanta headend; Scientific-Atlanta amplifiers; Comm/Scope cable; Video Data Systems character generator; Hamlin set top converters; Eagle traps; M/A-Com & Scientific-Atlanta satellite antenna; Microdyne satellite receivers.
Miles of plant: 15.3 (coaxial). Homes passed: 1,195. Total homes in franchised area: 1,211.
Manager: Jim Ebenhoe. Chief technician: Duane Hendricks.
City fee: 3% of gross.
Ownership: Charter Communications Inc. (MSO). Purchased from Marcus Cable, April 1, 1999.

BRODHEAD—Charter Communications, Box 1127, 1348 Plainfield Ave., Janesville, WI 53547-1127. Phone: 608-754-3644. Fax: 608-754-8107. County: Green. Also serves Decatur. ICA: WI0094.
TV Market Ranking: 93. Franchise award date: N.A. Franchise expiration date: N.A. Began: N.A.
Channel capacity: 47 (not 2-way capable). Channels available but not in use: 6.
Basic Service
Subscribers: 891; Commercial subscribers: 86.
Programming (received off-air): WIFR (C) Freeport-Rockford; WHA-TV (P), WISC-TV (C), WKOW-TV (A), WMSN-TV (F), WMTV (N) Madison; WQRF-TV (F), WREX-TV (N), WTVO (A) Rockford.
Programming (via satellite): WGN-TV (W) Chicago; TBS Superstation; Turner Network TV.
Current originations: Automated time-weather; educational access; government access; local news.
Fee: $11.67 monthly.
Expanded Basic Service
Subscribers: N.A.
Programming (via satellite): A & E; American Movie Classics; Animal Planet; C-SPAN; CNBC; CNN; Discovery Channel; Disney Channel; E! Entertainment TV; ESPN; ESPN 2; ESPNews; Fox Family Channel; Headline News; Home & Garden Television; Lifetime; MTV; Nashville Network; Nickelodeon; Outdoor Life Network; QVC; Speedvision; The Weather Channel; Toon Disney; Turner Network TV; USA Network; VH1.
Fee: $29.95 monthly.
Pay Service 1
Pay Units: 184.
Programming (via satellite): Cinemax.
Fee: $12.95 monthly.
Pay Service 2
Pay Units: 217.
Programming (via satellite): HBO.
Fee: $12.95 monthly.
Pay Service 3
Pay Units: 159.
Programming (via satellite): Showtime.
Fee: $12.95 monthly.
Equipment: Scientific-Atlanta headend; Scientific-Atlanta amplifiers; Comm/Scope cable; Hamlin set top converters.
Miles of plant: 22.5 (coaxial). Homes passed: 1,720.
Manager: Marty Robinson. Chief technician: Tim Sanderson. Marketing director: Danette Knickmeier.
City fee: 3% of gross.
Ownership: Charter Communications Inc. (MSO). Purchased from Marcus Cable, April 1, 1999.

BROOKFIELD—Time Warner Cable, Box 3237, 1610 N. 2nd St., Milwaukee, WI 53201-3237. Phone: 414-271-9283. Fax: 414-224-6155. County: Waukesha. ICA: WI0028.
TV Market Ranking: 23. Franchise award date: N.A. Franchise expiration date: August 1, 1999. Began: January 1, 1985.
Channel capacity: 52. Channels available but not in use: 3.
Basic Service
Subscribers: 6,647.
Programming (received off-air): WCGV-TV (I), WDJT-TV (C), WISN-TV (A), WITI (F), WMVS (P), WMVT (P), WTMJ-TV (N), WVCY-TV (I), WVTV (W) Milwaukee.
Programming (via satellite): WGN-TV (W) Chicago; A & E; American Movie Classics; C-SPAN; C-SPAN 2; CNBC; CNN; Discovery Channel; ESPN; Fox Family Channel; Headline News; Learning Channel; Lifetime; MTV; Nashville Network; Nickelodeon; TBS Superstation; The Weather Channel; Turner Network TV; USA Network.
Current originations: Automated time-weather; public access; educational access; government access; leased access; local sports.
Fee: $75.00 installation; $9.45 monthly.
Pay Service 1
Pay Units: 211.
Programming (via satellite): Bravo.
Fee: $9.95 monthly.
Pay Service 2
Pay Units: 748.
Programming (via satellite): Cinemax.
Fee: $10.95 monthly.
Pay Service 3
Pay Units: 600.
Programming (via satellite): Disney Channel.
Fee: $8.95 monthly.
Pay Service 4
Pay Units: 1,647.
Programming (via satellite): HBO.
Fee: $10.95 monthly.
Pay Service 5
Pay Units: 751.
Programming (via satellite): The Movie Channel.
Fee: $9.95 monthly.
Pay Service 6
Pay Units: 181.

Programming (via satellite): Playboy TV.
Fee: $9.95 monthly.
Pay Service 7
Pay Units: 976.
Programming (via satellite): Showtime.
Fee: $9.95 monthly.
Local advertising: No.
Equipment: Scientific-Atlanta headend; Panasonic cameras; Sony & JVC VTRs; 3M & Texscan character generator; Scientific-Atlanta satellite antenna; Scientific-Atlanta satellite receivers.
Miles of plant: 227.0 (coaxial). Homes passed: 10,400. Total homes in franchised area: 10,400.
Manager: Chris Garven. Engineering director: Randy Gicatello.
Ownership: Time Warner Cable (MSO).

BROWNSVILLE—Dodge County Cablevision, Box 620684, 2305-A Parview Rd., Middleton, WI 53562-2525. Phones: 608-831-7044; 800-451-5119. Fax: 608-836-5726. Counties: Dodge & Fond du Lac. Also serves Farmersville, Kekoskee, Knowles, LeRoy, South Byron. ICA: WI0304.
TV Market Ranking: Below 100 (Kekoskee, Knowles, LeRoy, South Byron); Outside TV Markets (Brownsville, Farmersville). Franchise award date: N.A. Franchise expiration date: N.A. Began: December 1, 1987.
Channel capacity: 40 (not 2-way capable). Channels available but not in use: 12.
Basic Service
Subscribers: 372.
Programming (received off-air): WFRV-TV (C), WLUK-TV (F) Green Bay; WWRS-TV (I) Mayville; WCGV-TV (I), WISN-TV (A), WITI (F), WMVS (P), WTMJ-TV (N), WVTV (W) Milwaukee.
Programming (via satellite): WGN-TV (W) Chicago; A & E; American Movie Classics; CNN; Comedy Central; Discovery Channel; ESPN; ESPN 2; Fox Family Channel; History Channel; Learning Channel; Lifetime; Nashville Network; Nickelodeon; Sci-Fi Channel; TBS Superstation; The Weather Channel; Turner Network TV; USA Network.
Fee: $19.95 installation; $25.00 monthly; $1.50 converter.
Pay Service 1
Pay Units: 36.
Programming (via satellite): Disney Channel.
Fee: $14.95 installation; $6.95 monthly.
Pay Service 2
Pay Units: 80.
Programming (via satellite): Showtime.
Fee: $14.95 installation; $6.95 monthly.
Homes passed: 500. Total homes in franchised area: 500.
Manager: Robert E. Ryan. Marketing director: Carol E. Ferge.
Ownership: Dodge County Cablevision (MSO).

BURLINGTON—Time Warner Cable, 1403 Washington Rd., Kenosha, WI 53140. Phones: 414-656-8460; 800-933-4662. Fax: 414-656-8490. Counties: Racine & Walworth. Also serves Burlington (town), Dover (town), Elkhorn, La Grange, Lafayette, Lyons (town), Rochester, Rochester (village), Union Grove, Waterford, Yorkville. ICA: WI0023.
TV Market Ranking: 23 (Burlington, Dover, La Grange, Lafayette, Rochester, Union Grove, Waterford, Yorkville); 97 (Lyons); Below 100 (Elkhorn). Franchise award date: May 1, 1981. Franchise expiration date: N.A. Began: May 1, 1982.
Channel capacity: 35 (2-way capable; operating 2-way). Channels available but not in use: None.
Basic Service
Subscribers: 8,494.
Programming (received off-air): WGN-TV (W) Chicago; WPXE (X) Kenosha; WCGV-TV (I), WISN-TV (A), WITI (F), WMVS (P), WMVT (P), WTMJ-TV (N), WVCY-TV (I), WVTV (W) Milwaukee; WJJA (H) Racine.
Programming (via satellite): A & E; American Movie Classics; C-SPAN; CNN; Comedy Central; Discovery Channel; ESPN; Fox Family Channel; Headline News; Lifetime; MTV; Nashville Network; Nickelodeon; QVC; Sci-Fi Channel; TBS Superstation; The Weather Channel; Turner Network TV; USA Network; VH1.
Current originations: Automated time-weather; public access; educational access; government access; religious access; local news.
Fee: $42.95 installation; $23.95 monthly.
Pay Service 1
Pay Units: 1,707.
Programming (via satellite): Cinemax.
Fee: $25.00 installation; $12.50 monthly.
Pay Service 2
Pay Units: 1,263.
Programming (via satellite): Disney Channel.
Fee: $9.35 monthly.
Pay Service 3
Pay Units: 1,850.
Programming (via satellite): HBO.
Fee: $12.95 monthly.
Pay Service 4
Pay Units: 2,419.
Programming (via satellite): Showtime.
Fee: $12.50 monthly.
Local advertising: No.
Equipment: Scientific-Atlanta headend; Scientific-Atlanta amplifiers; Times Fiber cable; Scientific-Atlanta set top converters; Hughes & Scientific-Atlanta satellite antenna; Scientific-Atlanta satellite receivers; ChannelMatic commercial insert.
Miles of plant: 204.0 (coaxial). Homes passed: 13,057.
Manager: Rich Jennings. Chief technician: Robert Mould. Marketing director: Jane Larson. Customer service manager: Tori Miller.
City fee: 3% of gross.
Ownership: Time Warner Cable (MSO).

BUTTERNUT—KRM Cablevision, Box 77, Mellen, WI 54546. Phone: 715-274-7631. County: Ashland. ICA: WI0214.
TV Market Ranking: Outside TV Markets. Franchise award date: May 1, 1985. Franchise expiration date: N.A. Began: October 1, 1985.
Channel capacity: 20 (not 2-way capable). Channels available but not in use: 4.
Basic Service
Subscribers: N.A.
Programming (received off-air): WLEF-TV (P) Park Falls; WAOW-TV (A), WJFW-TV (N), WSAW-TV (C) Wausau-Rhinelander.
Programming (via satellite): WGN-TV (W) Chicago; CNN; Comedy Central; Discovery Channel; ESPN; Fox Family Channel; Nashville Network; TBS Superstation; Turner Network TV; USA Network.
Fee: $35.00 installation; $14.00 monthly; $15.00 additional installation.
Pay Service 1
Pay Units: N.A.
Programming (via satellite): Disney Channel; The Movie Channel.
Fee: $8.00 monthly (Disney); $12.00 monthly (TMC).
Equipment: Blonder-Tongue & Triple Crown headend; Jerrold amplifiers; Prodelin satellite antenna.
Miles of plant: 4.0 (coaxial). Homes passed: 164. Total homes in franchised area: 164.
Manager: O. D. Miller. Chief technician: Keith Gehrett.
City fee: None.
Ownership: KRM Cablevision (MSO).

CABLE—S & K TV Systems, Box 127, 503 W. Miner Ave., Ladysmith, WI 54848. Phones: 715-532-7321; 800-924-7880. County: Bayfield. ICA: WI0227.
TV Market Ranking: Outside TV Markets. Franchise award date: January 1, 1991. Franchise expiration date: January 1, 2001. Began: October 1, 1991.
Channel capacity: 36. Channels available but not in use: 18.
Basic Service
Subscribers: 95.
Programming (received off-air): KBJR-TV (N), KDLH (C), WDIO-TV (A,F), WDSE-TV (P) Duluth-Superior.
Programming (via satellite): WGN-TV (W) Chicago; A & E; American Movie Classics; CNN; Discovery Channel; ESPN; Fox Family Channel; Nashville Network; Nickelodeon; TBS Superstation; Turner Network TV; USA Network.
Fee: $30.00 installation; $24.95 monthly.
Pay Service 1
Pay Units: N.A.
Programming (via satellite): HBO.
Fee: $20.00 installation; $9.95 monthly.
Total homes in franchised area: 200.
Manager: Randy Scott.
Ownership: S & K TV Systems (MSO).

CASCO—Century Televideo, Box 126, 212 Church Ave., Casco, WI 54205-0126. Phone: 920-837-7474. Fax: 920-837-2330. Counties: Door & Kewaunee. Also serves Casco (town), Casco (village), Forestville (village), Luxemburg, Luxemburg (town). ICA: WI0115.
TV Market Ranking: 62. Franchise award date: February 1, 1983. Franchise expiration date: N.A. Began: February 1, 1983.
Channel capacity: 36 (2-way capable; operating 2-way). Channels available but not in use: 30.
Basic Service
Subscribers: 590.
Programming (received off-air): WACY (U) Appleton; WBAY-TV (A), WFRV-TV (C), WGBA (N), WLUK-TV (F), WPNE (P) Green Bay; allband FM.
Programming (via satellite): WGN-TV (W) Chicago; A & E; American Movie Classics; CNN; Discovery Channel; ESPN; EWTN; Fox Family Channel; Headline News; Lifetime; MTV; Nashville Network; Nick at Nite; Nickelodeon; QVC; TBS Superstation; Turner Network TV; USA Network; VH1.
Current originations: Educational access; local news.
Fee: $25.00 installation; $14.50 monthly; $1.00 converter.
Pay Service 1
Pay Units: 115.
Programming (via satellite): Cinemax.
Fee: $10.00 installation; $8.95 monthly.
Pay Service 2
Pay Units: 36.
Programming (via satellite): Disney Channel.
Fee: $10.00 installation; $7.95 monthly.
Pay Service 3
Pay Units: 181.
Programming (via satellite): HBO.
Fee: $10.00 installation; $9.95 monthly.
Local advertising: No (locally produced). Available in character-generated programming. Rates: $20.00/Week/Page.
Equipment: Scientific-Atlanta headend; Scientific-Atlanta amplifiers; Comm/Scope cable; Comtech & BEI character generator; Scientific-Atlanta set top converters; Arcom traps; KES & ChannelMaster satellite antenna; Scientific-Atlanta satellite receivers.
Miles of plant: 18.0 (coaxial). Homes passed: 800. Total homes in franchised area: 1,200.
Manager: Michael A. Gotstein. Chief technician: Matt Gunderson.
City fee: 3% of gross.
Ownership: Casco Telephone Co. (MSO).

CASSVILLE—Spring Green CableComm, Box 609, 245 S. Winsted St., Spring Green, WI 53588-9431. Phone: 608-588-7454. Fax: 608-588-7067. County: Grant. ICA: WI0125.
TV Market Ranking: Below 100. Franchise award date: June 1, 1980. Franchise expiration date: N.A. Began: June 1, 1967.
Channel capacity: 64 (2-way capable; not operating 2-way). Channels available but not in use: 17.
Basic Service
Subscribers: 481.
Programming (received off-air): KCRG-TV (A), KGAN (C), KWWL (N) Cedar Rapids-Waterloo; KFXB (F) Dubuque; WHA-TV (P), WISC-TV (C), WKOW-TV (A), WMSN-TV (F), WMTV (N) Madison.
Programming (via satellite): WGN-TV (W) Chicago; A & E; CNN; Discovery Channel; ESPN; ESPN 2; FX; Fox Family Channel; Headline News; Home Shopping Network; Nashville Network; Nickelodeon; TBS Superstation; The Weather Channel; Turner Classic Movies; Turner Network TV; USA Network.
Fee: $49.95 installation; $29.85 monthly.
Pay Service 1
Pay Units: N.A.
Programming (via satellite): Cinemax; Disney Channel; HBO.
Fee: $19.95 installation; $6.95 monthly (Disney), $9.95 monthly (Cinemax & HBO).
Miles of plant: 10.0 (coaxial); None (fiber optic). Homes passed: 705. Total homes in franchised area: 705.
Manager: Kevin Mayne. Chief technician: Tad Peak. Customer service manager: Liz Reuter.
Ownership: Fanch Communications Inc. (MSO). See Cable System Ownership.

CAZENOVIA—Community Antenna System Inc., 1010 Lake St., Hillsboro, WI 54634. Phone: 608-489-2321. Counties: Richland & Sauk. ICA: WI0222.
TV Market Ranking: Outside TV Markets. Franchise award date: January 1, 1970. Franchise expiration date: N.A. Began: January 1, 1971.
Channel capacity: 14 (not 2-way capable). Channels available but not in use: N.A.
Basic Service
Subscribers: 116.
Programming (received off-air): WKBT (C) La Crosse; WHA-TV (P), WISC-TV (C), WKOW-TV (A), WMSN-TV (F), WMTV (N) Madison.
Programming (via satellite): WGN-TV (W) Chicago; ESPN; Fox Family Channel; Nashville Network; TBS Superstation; Turner Network TV.
Fee: $50.00 installation; $15.02 monthly.
Pay Service 1
Pay Units: 30.
Programming (via satellite): Cinemax.
Fee: $6.95 monthly.
Local advertising: No.
Equipment: Jerrold headend.
Miles of plant: 2.0 (coaxial).

Manager: Randall Kubarski. Chief technician: Gregory Kubarski.
Ownership: Community Antenna System Inc. (MSO).

CEDARBURG—Time Warner Cable, Box 14924, 1138 S. 108th St., West Allis, WI 53214. Phone: 414-771-8400. Fax: 414-453-5405. County: Ozaukee. Also serves Grafton (town), Grafton (village). ICA: WI0031.
TV Market Ranking: 23. Franchise award date: February 1, 1981. Franchise expiration date: N.A. Began: December 1, 1981.
Channel capacity: 54 (2-way capable; operating 2-way). Channels available but not in use: 1.
Basic Service
Subscribers: 4,904; Commercial subscribers: 30.
Programming (received off-air): WCGV-TV (I), WDJT-TV (C), WISN-TV (A), WITI (F), WMVS (P), WMVT (P), WTMJ-TV (N), WVCY-TV (I), WVTV (W) Milwaukee.
Programming (via satellite): WGN-TV (W) Chicago; TBS Superstation.
Current originations: Automated time-weather; public access; educational access; government access; library access; automated emergency alert; local news; local sports.
Fee: $30.00 installation; $26.90 monthly.
Commercial fee: $30.00 monthly.
Expanded Basic Service
Subscribers: 4,870.
Programming (via satellite): A & E; American Movie Classics; Bravo; C-SPAN; CNBC; CNN; Cartoon Network; Comedy Central; Discovery Channel; Disney Channel; ESPN; ESPN 2; EWTN; Fox Family Channel; Headline News; Home Shopping Network; Knowledge TV; Learning Channel; Lifetime; MTV; Nashville Network; Nickelodeon; Sci-Fi Channel; Superaudio Cable Radio Service; TV Guide Channel; The Weather Channel; Turner Network TV; USA Network; VH1.
Fee: $21.60 monthly.
Pay Service 1
Pay Units: 631.
Programming (via satellite): Cinemax.
Fee: $2.00 installation; $10.95 monthly.
Pay Service 2
Pay Units: 1,100.
Programming (via satellite): HBO.
Fee: $2.00 installation; $10.95 monthly.
Pay Service 3
Pay Units: 683.
Programming (via satellite): Showtime.
Fee: $2.00 installation; $10.95 monthly.
Pay Service 4
Pay Units: 117.
Programming (via satellite): The Movie Channel.
Fee: $2.00 installation; $10.95 monthly.
Pay-Per-View
Addressable homes: 4,000.
Local advertising: Yes. Available in satellite distributed, locally originated, character-generated & taped programming. Rates: $22.00/Minute; $11.00/30 Seconds. Local sales manager: Ann Holtz.
Equipment: Scientific-Atlanta headend; Scientific-Atlanta amplifiers; Comm/Scope cable; Panasonic cameras; Panasonic VTRs; Compuvid character generator; Zenith set top converters; Zenith addressable set top converters; Eagle & Pico traps; Scientific-Atlanta satellite antenna; Scientific-Atlanta satellite receivers.
Miles of plant: 181.0 (coaxial). Homes passed: 9,008.
Manager: Joe Zuravle Jr. Chief technician: Denny Gorsuch. Program director: Ann Holtz. Marketing director: Mitch Miller.
City fee: 3% of gross (Cedarburg), 5% gross (Grafton).
Ownership: Time Warner Cable (MSO).

CHASEBURG—Triax Cablevision, Box 110, 1504 2nd St. SE, Waseca, MN 56093. Phones: 507-835-5975; 800-332-0245. Fax: 507-835-4567. County: Vernon. ICA: WI0219.
TV Market Ranking: Below 100. Franchise award date: May 3, 1977. Franchise expiration date: January 1, 2006. Began: February 1, 1969.
Channel capacity: 21 (not 2-way capable). Channels available but not in use: 5.
Basic Service
Subscribers: 115.
Programming (received off-air): WEAU-TV (N) Eau Claire; WHLA-TV (P), WKBT (C), WLAX (F), WXOW-TV (A) La Crosse.
Fee: $35.16 installation; $6.03 monthly; $1.58 converter.
Expanded Basic Service
Subscribers: 114.
Programming (via satellite): WGN-TV (W) Chicago; A & E; American Movie Classics; CNN; Discovery Channel; ESPN; Fox Family Channel; Nashville Network; Nickelodeon; TBS Superstation; Turner Network TV; USA Network.
Fee: $17.92 monthly.
Pay Service 1
Pay Units: 22.
Programming (via satellite): HBO.
Fee: $23.44 installation; $11.00 monthly.
Miles of plant: 1.7 (coaxial). Homes passed: 130.
Manager: Richard Giffen. Chief technician: Scott Walters.
Ownership: Triax Telecommunications Co. LLC (MSO). See Cable System Ownership.

CHILTON—Charter Communications Inc., Box 1197, 55 W. Scott St., Fon Du Lac, WI 54936-1197. Phones: 920-923-7196; 800-581-0081. Fax: 920-923-1235. County: Calumet. Also serves Charleston, Chilton (town). ICA: WI0102.
TV Market Ranking: 62. Franchise award date: October 21, 1980. Franchise expiration date: N.A. Began: June 1, 1990.
Channel capacity: 36. Channels available but not in use: 1.
Basic Service
Subscribers: 963.
Programming (received off-air): WACY (U) Appleton; WBAY-TV (A), WFRV-TV (C), WGBA (N), WLUK-TV (F), WPNE (P) Green Bay; WISN-TV (A), WITI (F), WTMJ-TV (N), WVTV (W) Milwaukee; 16 FMs.
Programming (via satellite): WGN-TV (W) Chicago; TBS Superstation.
Current originations: Automated time-weather; educational access; government access; automated emergency alert.
Fee: $56.73 installation; $6.22 monthly; $28.36 additional installation.
Expanded Basic Service
Subscribers: 956.
Programming (via satellite): American Movie Classics; C-SPAN; CNN; Discovery Channel; Disney Channel; ESPN; EWTN; Fox Family Channel; Knowledge TV; Lifetime; Nashville Network; Nickelodeon; Sci-Fi Channel; The Weather Channel; Turner Network TV; USA Network; VH1.
Fee: $13.69 monthly.
Pay Service 1
Pay Units: 142.
Programming (via satellite): Cinemax.
Fee: $12.50 monthly.
Pay Service 2
Pay Units: 261.
Programming (via satellite): HBO.
Fee: $12.95 monthly.
Pay Service 3
Pay Units: 149.
Programming (via satellite): Showtime.
Fee: $12.50 monthly.
Local advertising: Yes. Available in satellite distributed programming. Local sales manager: John Welton.
Equipment: Scientific-Atlanta headend; Scientific-Atlanta amplifiers; Times Fiber cable; Texscan character generator; Hamlin set top converters; Northeast Filter traps; Scientific-Atlanta satellite antenna; Scientific-Atlanta satellite receivers; ChannelMatic commercial insert.
Miles of plant: 18.6 (coaxial). Homes passed: 1,466.
Manager: Lisa Washa. Chief technician: Jeff Gerner.
Ownership: Charter Communications Inc. (MSO). Purchased from Marcus Cable, April 1, 1999.

CLINTONVILLE—Charter Communications Inc., 79 S. Main St., Clintonville, WI 54929. Phone: 800-395-0995. Fax: 414-337-3251. Counties: Shawano & Waupaca. Also serves Belle Plain, Caroline, Cloverleaf Lakes, Embarrass, Larrabee (town), Marion, Matteson (town). ICA: WI0073.
TV Market Ranking: 62 (Belle Plain, Embarrass); Below 100 (Caroline, Clintonville, Cloverleaf Lakes, Larrabee, Marion, Matteson). Franchise award date: N.A. Franchise expiration date: N.A. Began: December 1, 1980.
Channel capacity: 35 (2-way capable). Channels available but not in use: 3.
Basic Service
Subscribers: 2,026.
Programming (received off-air): WACY (U) Appleton; WBAY-TV (A), WFRV-TV (C), WGBA (N), WLUK-TV (F), WPNE (P) Green Bay; WAOW-TV (A), WSAW-TV (C) Wausau-Rhinelander.
Programming (via satellite): WGN-TV (W) Chicago; TBS Superstation.
Fee: $56.73 installation; $6.28 monthly.
Expanded Basic Service
Subscribers: 2,003.
Programming (via satellite): A & E; American Movie Classics; CNN; Country Music TV; Discovery Channel; Disney Channel; ESPN; Fox Family Channel; Headline News; Lifetime; MTV; Nashville Network; Nickelodeon; Odyssey; QVC; Sci-Fi Channel; The Weather Channel; Turner Network TV; USA Network; VH1.
Fee: $14.36 monthly.
Pay Service 1
Pay Units: 409.
Programming (via satellite): Cinemax.
Fee: $12.50 monthly.
Pay Service 2
Pay Units: 467.
Programming (via satellite): HBO.
Fee: $12.95 monthly.
Pay Service 3
Pay Units: 317.
Programming (via satellite): Showtime.
Fee: $12.50 monthly.
Local advertising: No.
Equipment: M/A-Com & Scientific-Atlanta headend; AEL & Winegard amplifiers; M/A-Com cable; Oak, Scientific-Atlanta & Standard Components set top converters; Intercept & Pico traps; Gardiner & Prodelin satellite antenna; Gardiner, Microdyne & Scientific-Atlanta satellite receivers.
Miles of plant: 39.0 (coaxial). Additional miles planned: 2.0 (coaxial). Total homes in franchised area: 4,325.
Manager: Jim Ebenhoe. Chief technician: Duane Hendricks.
City fee: 3% of basic.
Ownership: Charter Communications Inc. (MSO). Purchased from Marcus Cable, April 1, 1999.

COLEMAN—Charter Communications Inc., Box 1818, 853 McIntosh St., Wausau, WI 54402-1818. Phones: 715-845-4223; 800-581-0081. Fax: 715-848-0081. Counties: Marinette & Oconto. Also serves Gilliex, Pound. ICA: WI0173.
TV Market Ranking: 62 (Gilliex); Below 100 (Coleman, Pound). Franchise award date: February 1, 1982. Franchise expiration date: N.A. Began: December 31, 1982.
Channel capacity: 24. Channels available but not in use: N.A.
Basic Service
Subscribers: 311.
Programming (received off-air): WACY (U) Appleton; WBAY-TV (A), WFRV-TV (C), WGBA (N), WLUK-TV (F), WPNE (P) Green Bay.
Programming (via satellite): WGN-TV (W) Chicago; QVC; TBS Superstation.
Fee: $56.73 installation; $6.58 monthly.
Expanded Basic Service
Subscribers: 310.
Programming (via satellite): A & E; CNN; Country Music TV; Discovery Channel; Disney Channel; ESPN; Fox Family Channel; Headline News; Lifetime; Nashville Network; Nickelodeon; Sci-Fi Channel; The Weather Channel; Turner Network TV; USA Network; VH1.
Fee: $13.15 monthly.
Pay Service 1
Pay Units: 75.
Programming (via satellite): Cinemax.
Fee: $12.50 monthly.
Pay Service 2
Pay Units: 88.
Programming (via satellite): HBO.
Fee: $12.95 monthly.
Miles of plant: 9.3 (coaxial). Homes passed: 350.
Manager: Scott Behn. Chief technician: Bruce Wasleske. Marketing director: Tim Schnieffer.
Ownership: Charter Communications Inc. (MSO). Purchased from Marcus Cable, April 1, 1999.

COLFAX—Charter Communications Inc., Suite 1A, 394 Red Cedar St., Menomonie, WI 54751. Phone: 800-262-2578. Fax: 715-235-1439. County: Dunn. Also serves Colfax (village). ICA: WI0162.
TV Market Ranking: Below 100. Franchise award date: January 1, 1984. Franchise expiration date: August 1, 1998. Began: January 1, 1984.
Channel capacity: 30 (not 2-way capable). Channels available but not in use: 4.
Basic Service
Subscribers: 279.
Programming (received off-air): WEUX (F) Chippewa Falls; WEAU-TV (N), WQOW-TV (A) Eau Claire; WKBT (C) La Crosse; WHWC-TV (P) Menomonie; KARE (N), KMSP-TV (U), KSTP-TV (A), KTCA-TV (P), WCCO-TV (C) Minneapolis-St. Paul.
Programming (via satellite): WGN-TV (W) Chicago; TBS Superstation.
Fee: $42.95 installation; $14.68 monthly.
Expanded Basic Service
Subscribers: 263.
Programming (via satellite): A & E; CNN; Comedy Central; Discovery Channel; ESPN; ESPN 2; Fox Family Channel; Headline News;

Lifetime; MTV; Nashville Network; Nickelodeon; Turner Network TV; USA Network; VH1.
Fee: $42.95 installation; $13.45 monthly.

Pay Service 1
Pay Units: 54.
Programming (via satellite): Disney Channel.
Fee: $19.95 installation; $3.95 monthly.

Pay Service 2
Pay Units: 39.
Programming (via satellite): HBO.
Fee: $19.95 installation; $12.95 monthly.

Pay Service 3
Pay Units: 45.
Programming (via satellite): Showtime.
Fee: $19.95 installation; $12.50 monthly.

Pay Service 4
Pay Units: 21.
Programming (via satellite): Cinemax.
Fee: $12.50 monthly.

Local advertising: No.
Equipment: Triple Crown, Blonder-Tongue & Scientific-Atlanta headend; Triple Crown amplifiers; Scientific-Atlanta & Hamlin set top converters; Arcom & Eagle traps; AFC satellite antenna; AFC satellite receivers.
Miles of plant: 8.1 (coaxial). Homes passed: 477.
Manager: Karen Sanderson. Chief technician: Pat Anderson.
City fee: 3% of gross.
Ownership: Charter Communications Inc. (MSO). Purchased from Marcus Cable, April 1, 1999.

COLUMBUS—Bresnan Communications Inc., Suite 150, 5618 Odana Rd., Madison, WI 53719. Phone: 608-274-3822. Fax: 608-274-1436. Counties: Columbia & Dodge. Also serves Elba, Fall River. ICA: WI0078.
TV Market Ranking: 93. Franchise award date: N.A. Franchise expiration date: N.A. Began: November 1, 1981.
Channel capacity: 37. Channels available but not in use: N.A.

Basic Service
Subscribers: 1,391.
Programming (received off-air): WHA-TV (P), WISC-TV (C), WKOW-TV (A), WMSN-TV (F), WMTV (N) Madison; WMVS (P), WVTV (W) Milwaukee; 1 FM.
Programming (via satellite): WGN-TV (W) Chicago; C-SPAN; CNN; Discovery Channel; Fox Family Channel; Lifetime; MTV; Nashville Network; Nickelodeon; QVC; TBS Superstation.
Current originations: Automated time-weather; public access; educational access.
Fee: $60.00 installation; $10.00 monthly; $40.00 additional installation.

Expanded Basic Service
Subscribers: 1,258.
Programming (via satellite): A & E; American Movie Classics; Court TV; ESPN; Turner Network TV; USA Network.
Fee: $1.75 monthly.

Pay Service 1
Pay Units: 128.
Programming (via satellite): Cinemax.
Fee: $12.90 monthly.

Pay Service 2
Pay Units: 64.
Programming (via satellite): Disney Channel.
Fee: N.A.

Pay Service 3
Pay Units: 404.
Programming (via satellite): The New Encore.
Fee: N.A.

Pay Service 4
Pay Units: 241.
Programming (via satellite): HBO.
Fee: $12.90 monthly.

Equipment: Scientific-Atlanta satellite antenna; Scientific-Atlanta satellite receivers.
Miles of plant: 23.6 (coaxial). Homes passed: 1,764. Total homes in franchised area: 1,764.
Manager: Brian Shirk. Chief technician: Jerry Myers. Marketing director: Tim Roehl.
Ownership: Bresnan Communications Co. LP (MSO). Purchased from Tele-Communications Inc, February 2, 1999. See Cable System Ownership.

COON VALLEY—Triax Cablevision, Box 110, 1504 2nd St. SE, Waseca, MN 56093. Phones: 507-835-5975; 800-332-0245. Fax: 507-835-4567. County: Vernon. ICA: WI0171.
TV Market Ranking: Below 100. Franchise award date: May 7, 1968. Franchise expiration date: May 1, 1998. Began: February 1, 1969.
Channel capacity: 21 (not 2-way capable). Channels available but not in use: 1.

Basic Service
Subscribers: 294.
Programming (received off-air): WEAU-TV (N) Eau Claire; WHLA-TV (P), WKBT (C), WLAX (F), WXOW-TV (A) La Crosse; KTTC (N) Rochester; allband FM.
Fee: $35.16 installation; $7.60 monthly; $1.58 converter.

Expanded Basic Service
Subscribers: 268.
Programming (via satellite): WGN-TV (W) Chicago; A & E; CNN; Discovery Channel; ESPN; Fox Family Channel; Nashville Network; Nickelodeon; Sci-Fi Channel; TBS Superstation; Turner Network TV; USA Network; VH1.
Fee: $27.75 monthly.

Pay Service 1
Pay Units: 43.
Programming (via satellite): HBO.
Fee: $11.95 monthly.

Equipment: Blonder-Tongue headend; Vikoa amplifiers.
Miles of plant: 8.1 (coaxial). Homes passed: 360.
Manager: Richard Giffen. Chief technician: Scott Walters.
City fee: None.
Ownership: Triax Telecommunications Co. LLC (MSO). See Cable System Ownership.

CORNELL—Charter Communications Inc., Box 539, 1725 S. Main St., Rice Lake, WI 54868-0539. Phones: 715-234-3821; 800-262-2578. Fax: 715-234-8537. County: Chippewa. ICA: WI0150.
TV Market Ranking: Below 100. Franchise award date: N.A. Franchise expiration date: September 1, 2000. Began: December 15, 1970.
Channel capacity: 35 (not 2-way capable). Channels available but not in use: 1.

Basic Service
Subscribers: 453.
Programming (received off-air): WEUX (F) Chippewa Falls; WEAU-TV (N), WQOW-TV (A) Eau Claire; WKBT (C) La Crosse; WHWC-TV (P) Menomonie; KARE (N), KSTP-TV (A), WCCO-TV (C) Minneapolis-St. Paul.
Programming (via satellite): WGN-TV (W) Chicago; A & E; American Movie Classics; C-SPAN; C-SPAN 2; CNN; Comedy Central; Discovery Channel; E! Entertainment TV; ESPN; Fox Family Channel; FoxNet; Headline News; Learning Channel; Lifetime; MTV; Nashville Network; Nickelodeon; QVC; TBS Superstation; The Weather Channel; Turner Network TV; USA Network; VH1.
Fee: $42.95 installation; $27.30 monthly.

Pay Service 1
Pay Units: 60.
Programming (via satellite): Cinemax.
Fee: $19.95 installation; $12.50 monthly.

Pay Service 2
Pay Units: 82.
Programming (via satellite): HBO.
Fee: $19.95 installation; $12.95 monthly.

Pay Service 3
Pay Units: 86.
Programming (via satellite): Showtime.
Fee: $19.95 installation; $12.50 monthly.

Local advertising: No.
Equipment: Blonder-Tongue headend; Jerrold amplifiers; Times Fiber cable; Eagle traps; Scientific-Atlanta satellite antenna; Drake satellite receivers.
Miles of plant: 11.0 (coaxial). Homes passed: 478. Total homes in franchised area: 515.
Manager: Scott Binder. Chief technician: George Benjamin.
City fee: None.
Ownership: Charter Communications Inc. (MSO). Purchased from Marcus Cable, April 1, 1999.

DALLAS—Chibardun Cable TV Cooperative, Box 164, 110 N. 2nd Ave., Dallas, WI 54733. Phone: 715-837-1011. Fax: 715-837-1196. Counties: Barron & Dunn. Also serves Almena, Cameron, Hillsdale, Prairie Farm, Ridgeland, Sand Creek. ICA: WI0148.
TV Market Ranking: Below 100 (Almena, Dallas, Prairie Farm, Ridgeland, Sand Creek); Outside TV Markets (Cameron, Hillsdale). Franchise award date: N.A. Franchise expiration date: N.A. Began: March 1, 1980.
Channel capacity: 35. Channels available but not in use: N.A.

Basic Service
Subscribers: 2,082.
Programming (received off-air): WEUX (F) Chippewa Falls; WEAU-TV (N), WQOW-TV (A) Eau Claire; WKBT (C) La Crosse; WHWC-TV (P) Menomonie; KARE (N), KLGT (W), KMSP-TV (U), KSTP-TV (A), KTCA-TV (P), WCCO-TV (C), WFTC (F) Minneapolis-St. Paul.
Programming (via satellite): WGN-TV (W) Chicago; A & E; C-SPAN; CNN; Cartoon Network; Court TV; Discovery Channel; ESPN; Fox Family Channel; Headline News; Lifetime; MTV; Nashville Network; Nickelodeon; TBS Superstation; The Weather Channel; Turner Classic Movies; USA Network; VH1.
Fee: $15.00 installation; $14.95 monthly.

Pay Service 1
Pay Units: 160.
Programming (via satellite): Disney Channel.
Fee: $4.95 monthly.

Pay Service 2
Pay Units: 375.
Programming (via satellite): HBO.
Fee: $9.00 monthly.

Pay Service 3
Pay Units: 292.
Programming (via satellite): Showtime.
Fee: $8.95 monthly.

Pay Service 4
Pay Units: 320.
Programming (via satellite): The Movie Channel.
Fee: $8.95 monthly.

Miles of plant: 120.0 (coaxial); 50.0 (fiber optic). Homes passed: 2,616. Total homes in franchised area: 2,616.
Manager: Rick Vergin. Chief technician: Doug Kurschner.
Ownership: Chibardun Cable TV Cooperative (MSO).

DALTON—Cable Systems Management of Iowa Inc., 3600 Kennebec Dr., Eagan, MN 55122. Phone: 612-688-2623. Fax: 612-688-2624. County: Green Lake. ICA: WI0226.
TV Market Ranking: Outside TV Markets. Franchise award date: N.A. Franchise expiration date: N.A. Began: N.A.
Channel capacity: 40. Channels available but not in use: 19.

Basic Service
Subscribers: 42.
Programming (received off-air): WHA-TV (P), WISC-TV (C), WKOW-TV (A), WMTV (N) Madison.
Programming (via satellite): WGN-TV (W) Chicago; A & E; American Movie Classics; CNN; Country Music TV; Discovery Channel; ESPN; Fox Family Channel; Headline News; Lifetime; Nashville Network; Showtime; TBS Superstation; Turner Network TV; USA Network.
Fee: $30.00 monthly.

Miles of plant: 2.5 (coaxial). Homes passed: 101.
Manager: Jeff Anderson.
Ownership: Cable Systems Management of Iowa Inc. (MSO).

DANE—Charter Communications, Box 1127, 1348 Plainfield Ave., Janesville, WI 53547-1127. Phone: 608-754-3644. Fax: 608-754-8107. Counties: Columbia & Dane. Also serves Dane (town), Dane (village), Dekorra, Lodi, Lodi (town), Springfield, Vienna, Waunakee, West Point, Westport. ICA: WI0049.
TV Market Ranking: 93. Franchise award date: N.A. Franchise expiration date: N.A. Began: July 1, 1982.
Channel capacity: 40 (not 2-way capable). Channels available but not in use: None.

Basic Service
Subscribers: 4,301; Commercial subscribers: 58.
Programming (received off-air): WHPN-TV (U) Janesville; WHA-TV (P), WISC-TV (C), WKOW-TV (A), WMSN-TV (F), WMTV (N) Madison.
Programming (via satellite): WGN-TV (W) Chicago; C-SPAN.
Current originations: Automated time-weather; educational access; government access; local news; TVW - Television Wisconsin.
Fee: $42.95 installation; $29.95 monthly.

Expanded Basic Service
Subscribers: 4,027.

Programming (via satellite): A & E; American Movie Classics; Animal Planet; CNBC; CNN; Comedy Central; Discovery Channel; Disney Channel; ESPN; ESPN 2; ESPNews; Fox Family Channel; Headline News; History Channel; Learning Channel; Lifetime; MSNBC; MTV; Nashville Network; Nickelodeon; QVC; TBS Superstation; The Weather Channel; Turner Network TV; USA Network; VH1.
Fee: $29.95 monthly.

Pay Service 1
Pay Units: 539.
Programming (via satellite): Cinemax.
Fee: $12.95 monthly.

Pay Service 2
Pay Units: 733.
Programming (via satellite): HBO.
Fee: $12.95 monthly.

Pay Service 3
Pay Units: 467.
Programming (via satellite): Showtime.
Fee: $12.95 monthly.

Local advertising: Yes. Rates: $1.00/Minute. Local sales manager: Robert U'Ren.
Equipment: Scientific-Atlanta headend; Scientific-Atlanta & C-COR amplifiers; Times Fiber cable; Video Data Systems character generator; Eagle, Oak & Scientific-Atlanta set top converters; Eagle traps; Scientific-Atlanta & Prodelin satellite antenna; Scientific-Atlanta satellite receivers.
Miles of plant: 80.0 (coaxial). Homes passed: 6,702.
Manager: Marty Robinson. Chief technician: Tim Sanderson. Marketing director: Danette Knickmeier.
City fee: 3% of basic.
Ownership: Charter Communications Inc. (MSO). Purchased from Marcus Cable, April 1, 1999.

DARIEN—Walworth County Cablevision, Box 620684, 2305-A Parview Rd., Middleton, WI 53562-2525. Phones: 608-831-7044; 800-451-5119. Fax: 608-836-5726. County: Walworth. ICA: WI0246.
TV Market Ranking: 97. Franchise award date: N.A. Franchise expiration date: N.A. Began: December 1, 1988.
Channel capacity: 40 (not 2-way capable). Channels available but not in use: 8.

Basic Service
Subscribers: 288.
Programming (received off-air): WHPN-TV (U) Janesville; WPXE (X) Kenosha; WISC-TV (C), WKOW-TV (A), WMTV (N) Madison; WCGV-TV (I), WDJT-TV (C), WISN-TV (A), WITI (F), WMVS (P), WTMJ-TV (N), WVTV (W) Milwaukee.
Programming (via satellite): WGN-TV (W) Chicago; A & E; American Movie Classics; CNN; Comedy Central; Discovery Channel; ESPN; ESPN 2; Fox Family Channel; History Channel; Lifetime; Nashville Network; Nick at Nite; Nickelodeon; Sci-Fi Channel; TBS Superstation; The Weather Channel; Turner Network TV; USA Network; VH1.
Fee: $19.95 installation; $25.00 monthly; $1.50 converter.

Pay Service 1
Pay Units: 38.
Programming (via satellite): Disney Channel.
Fee: $14.95 installation; $6.95 monthly.

Pay Service 2
Pay Units: 75.
Programming (via satellite): Showtime.
Fee: $14.95 installation; $6.95 monthly.

Manager: Robert E. Ryan.
Ownership: H.L.M. Cable Co. (MSO).

DENMARK—Charter Communications Inc., 1623 Broadway Ave., Sheboygan, WI 53081-5700. Phone: 800-395-0995. Fax: 414-337-9251. County: Brown. ICA: WI0134.
TV Market Ranking: 62. Franchise award date: March 5, 1982. Franchise expiration date: March 5, 1997. Began: February 1, 1983.
Channel capacity: 35 (2-way capable; operating 2-way). Channels available but not in use: 6.

Basic Service
Subscribers: 359.
Programming (received off-air): WACY (U) Appleton; WBAY-TV (A), WFRV-TV (C), WGBA (N), WLUK-TV (F), WPNE (P) Green Bay.
Programming (via satellite): WGN-TV (W) Chicago; C-SPAN; CNN; Discovery Channel; ESPN; Fox Family Channel; Headline News; Lifetime; Nashville Network; Nick at Nite; Nickelodeon; QVC; TBS Superstation; The Inspirational Network; The Weather Channel; Turner Network TV; USA Network.
Fee: $42.95 installation; $13.02 monthly.

Pay Service 1
Pay Units: 76.
Programming (via satellite): Cinemax.
Fee: $19.95 installation; $12.50 monthly.

Pay Service 2
Pay Units: 63.
Programming (via satellite): Disney Channel.
Fee: $19.95 installation; $9.35 monthly.

Pay Service 3
Pay Units: 107.
Programming (via satellite): HBO.
Fee: $19.95 installation; $12.95 monthly.

Pay Service 4
Pay Units: 125.
Programming (via satellite): Showtime.
Fee: $19.95 installation; $12.50 monthly.

Local advertising: No.
Equipment: Scientific-Atlanta headend; Scientific-Atlanta amplifiers; Times Fiber cable; Video Data Systems character generator; Hamlin set top converters; Hamlin addressable set top converters; Eagle traps; Scientific-Atlanta & Microdyne satellite antenna; Scientific-Atlanta satellite receivers.
Miles of plant: 8.0 (coaxial). Homes passed: 629. Total homes in franchised area: 629.
Manager: Jim Ebenhoe. Chief technician: Duane Hendricks.
City fee: 3% of gross.
Ownership: Charter Communications Inc. (MSO). Purchased from Marcus Cable, April 1, 1999.

DICKEYVILLE—Spring Green CableComm, Box 609, 245 S. Winsted St., Spring Green, WI 53588-9431. Phone: 608-588-7454. Fax: 608-588-7067. County: Grant. Also serves Jamestown. ICA: WI0247.
TV Market Ranking: Below 100. Franchise award date: N.A. Franchise expiration date: N.A. Began: N.A.
Channel capacity: 64 (not 2-way capable). Channels available but not in use: 17.

Basic Service
Subscribers: 650.
Programming (received off-air): KCRG-TV (A), KGAN (C), KWWL (N) Cedar Rapids-Waterloo; KFXB (F) Dubuque; WHA-TV (P), WISC-TV (C), WKOW-TV (A), WMSN-TV (F), WMTV (N) Madison.
Programming (via satellite): WGN-TV (W) Chicago; A & E; C-SPAN; CNN; Discovery Channel; ESPN; ESPN 2; Fox Family Channel; Headline News; Home Shopping Network; Lifetime; Nashville Network; Nickelodeon; TBS Superstation; Turner Classic Movies; Turner Network TV; USA Network; VH1.
Fee: $49.95 installation; $29.85 monthly.

Pay Service 1
Pay Units: N.A.
Programming (via satellite): Cinemax; Disney Channel; HBO.
Fee: $19.95 installation; $6.95 monthly (Disney), $9.95 monthly (Cinemax or HBO).

Miles of plant: 19.3 (coaxial).
Manager: Kevin Mayne. Chief technician: Tad Peak. Customer service manager: Liz Reuter.
Ownership: Fanch Communications Inc. (MSO). See Cable System Ownership.

DODGEVILLE—Spring Green CableComm, Box 609, 245 S. Winsted St., Spring Green, WI 53588-9431. Phone: 608-588-7454. Fax: 608-588-7067. County: Iowa. Also serves Mineral Point. ICA: WI0067.
TV Market Ranking: Outside TV Markets. Franchise award date: March 1, 1979. Franchise expiration date: N.A. Began: May 1, 1980.
Channel capacity: 42 (2-way capable; operating 2-way). Channels available but not in use: N.A.

Basic Service
Subscribers: 1,738.
Programming (received off-air): KWWL (N) Cedar Rapids-Waterloo; KFXB (F) Dubuque; WHA-TV (P), WISC-TV (C), WKOW-TV (A), WMSN-TV (F), WMTV (N) Madison.
Programming (via satellite): WGN-TV (W) Chicago; A & E; C-SPAN; CNN; Discovery Channel; ESPN; ESPN 2; FX; Fox Family Channel; Headline News; Home Shopping Network; Learning Channel; Lifetime; Nashville Network; Nickelodeon; Sci-Fi Channel; TBS Superstation; The Weather Channel; Turner Classic Movies; Turner Network TV; USA Network; VH1.
Current originations: Educational access.
Fee: $49.95 installation; $29.85 monthly; $19.95 additional installation.

Pay Service 1
Pay Units: N.A.
Programming (via satellite): Cinemax; HBO.
Fee: $19.95 installation; $9.95 monthly (Cinemax or HBO).

Miles of plant: 27.9 (coaxial). Homes passed: 2,343.
Manager: Kevin Mayne. Chief technician: Tad Peak. Customer service manager: Liz Reuter.
City fee: 3% of gross.
Ownership: Fanch Communications Inc. (MSO). See Cable System Ownership.

DOWNSVILLE—S & K TV Systems, Box 127, 503 W. Miner Ave., Ladysmith, WI 54848. Phones: 715-532-7321; 800-924-7880. County: Dunn. ICA: WI0207.
TV Market Ranking: Below 100. Franchise award date: January 1, 1990. Franchise expiration date: January 1, 2000. Began: August 1, 1990.
Channel capacity: 36. Channels available but not in use: 16.

Basic Service
Subscribers: 135.
Programming (received off-air): WEUX (F) Chippewa Falls; WEAU-TV (N), WQOW-TV (A) Eau Claire; WKBT (C) La Crosse; WHWC-TV (P) Menomonie; KARE (N), KMSP-TV (U), KSTP-TV (A), WCCO-TV (C) Minneapolis-St. Paul.
Programming (via satellite): WGN-TV (W) Chicago; American Movie Classics; CNN; Discovery Channel; ESPN; Fox Family Channel; Nashville Network; TBS Superstation; Turner Network TV; USA Network.
Fee: $30.00 installation; $24.95 monthly.

Pay Service 1
Pay Units: N.A.
Programming (via satellite): HBO.
Fee: $20.00 installation; $9.95 monthly.

Homes passed: 195.
Manager: Randy Scott.
Ownership: S & K TV Systems (MSO).

DOYLESTOWN—Cable Systems Management of Iowa Inc., 3600 Kennebec Dr., Eagan, MN 55122. Phone: 612-688-2623. Fax: 612-688-2624. County: Columbia. ICA: WI0223.
TV Market Ranking: 93. Franchise award date: N.A. Franchise expiration date: N.A. Began: N.A.
Channel capacity: 40. Channels available but not in use: 19.

Basic Service
Subscribers: 35.
Programming (received off-air): WHA-TV (P), WISC-TV (C), WKOW-TV (A), WMTV (N) Madison.
Programming (via satellite): WGN-TV (W) Chicago; A & E; American Movie Classics; CNN; Country Music TV; Discovery Channel; ESPN; Fox Family Channel; Lifetime; Nashville Network; Showtime; TBS Superstation; Turner Network TV; USA Network.
Fee: $28.00 monthly.

Miles of plant: 4.1 (coaxial). Homes passed: 107.
Manager: Jeff Anderson.
Ownership: Cable Systems Management of Iowa Inc. (MSO).

DRESSER—Charter Communications Inc., Suite 1A, 394 Red Cedar St., Menomonie, WI 54751. Phone: 715-235-6837. Fax: 715-235-1439. County: Polk. Also serves Osceola, St. Croix Falls. ICA: WI0087.
TV Market Ranking: Outside TV Markets. Franchise award date: January 1, 1982. Franchise expiration date: N.A. Began: January 1, 1982.
Channel capacity: 36 (not 2-way capable). Channels available but not in use: 3.

Basic Service
Subscribers: 893.
Programming (received off-air): WEAU-TV (N) Eau Claire; WHWC-TV (P) Menomonie; KARE (N), KLGT (W), KMSP-TV (U), KSTP-TV (A), KTCA-TV (P), KVBM-TV (H), WCCO-TV (C), WFTC (F) Minneapolis-St. Paul; KPXM (X) St. Cloud.
Programming (via satellite): WGN-TV (W) Chicago; TBS Superstation.
Fee: $42.95 installation; $12.12 monthly.

Expanded Basic Service
Subscribers: 877.
Programming (via satellite): A & E; CNBC; CNN; Discovery Channel; ESPN; ESPN 2; Fox Family Channel; Headline News; Lifetime; MTV; Nashville Network; Nickelodeon; QVC; The Weather Channel; Turner Network TV; USA Network.
Fee: $42.95 installation; $15.13 monthly.

Pay Service 1
Pay Units: 131.
Programming (via satellite): Cinemax.
Fee: $19.95 installation; $12.50 monthly.

Pay Service 2
Pay Units: 269.
Programming (via satellite): Disney Channel.
Fee: $19.95 installation; $3.95 monthly.

Pay Service 3
Pay Units: 239.
Programming (via satellite): HBO.
Fee: $19.95 installation; $12.95 monthly.

Pay Service 4
Pay Units: 150.
Programming (via satellite): Showtime.
Fee: $19.95 installation; $12.50 monthly.

Local advertising: No.

Equipment: Scientific-Atlanta headend; Texscan amplifiers; Comm/Scope cable; Hamlin, Oak & Scientific-Atlanta set top converters; Arcom traps; Scientific-Atlanta satellite receivers.
Miles of plant: 48.3 (coaxial); 7.0 (fiber optic). Homes passed: 1,708.
Manager: Karen Sanderson. Chief technician: Pat Anderson.
City fee: 3% of gross.
Ownership: Charter Communications Inc. (MSO). Purchased from Marcus Cable, April 1, 1999.

DURAND—Durand Cable Co. Inc., 318 3rd Ave. W, Durand, WI 54736. Phone: 715-672-5966. Fax: 715-672-4344. Counties: Dunn & Pepin. Also serves Arkansaw, Eau Galle. ICA: WI0110.
TV Market Ranking: 13 (Eau Galle); Below 100 (Arkansaw, Durand). Franchise award date: January 1, 1968. Franchise expiration date: March 1, 2003. Began: September 1, 1968.
Channel capacity: 62 (2-way capable; operating 2-way). Channels available but not in use: 25.
Basic Service
Subscribers: 950.
Programming (received off-air): WEUX (F) Chippewa Falls; WEAU-TV (N), WQOW-TV (A) Eau Claire; WKBT (C) La Crosse; WHWC-TV (P) Menomonie; KARE (N), KMSP-TV (U), KSTP-TV (A), KTCA-TV (P), WCCO-TV (C), WFTC (F) Minneapolis-St. Paul; allband FM.
Programming (via satellite): WGN-TV (W) Chicago; A & E; American Movie Classics; CNN; Comedy Central; Country Music TV; Discovery Channel; ESPN; EWTN; Fox Family Channel; Home Shopping Network; Learning Channel; MTV; Nashville Network; Nickelodeon; TBS Superstation; The Weather Channel; Turner Network TV; USA Network; VH1.
Current originations: Automated time-weather.
Fee: $15.00 installation; $17.25 monthly; $10.00 additional installation.
Pay Service 1
Pay Units: 40.
Programming (via satellite): Disney Channel.
Fee: $10.00 installation; $8.00 monthly.
Pay Service 2
Pay Units: 150.
Programming (via satellite): HBO.
Fee: $10.00 installation; $9.00 monthly.
Local advertising: No.
Equipment: Scientific-Atlanta headend; Scientific-Atlanta amplifiers; Comm/Scope cable; Compuvid character generator; Scientific-Atlanta set top converters; Microdyne, Scientific-Atlanta & Standard Communications satellite receivers.
Miles of plant: 25.0 (coaxial); 4.0 (fiber optic). Additional miles planned: 2.0 (coaxial). Homes passed: 950. Total homes in franchised area: 1,100.
Manager: Jerry Levenske. Chief technician: John Kurtzhals.
City fee: $500 annually per subscriber.
Ownership: Durand Cable Co. Inc. (MSO).

EAGLE RIVER—Charter Communications Inc., Box 33, 307 E. Main St., Ashland, WI 54806. Phones: 715-682-2166; 800-262-2578. Fax: 715-234-5077. County: Vilas. Also serves Lincoln. ICA: WI0103.
TV Market Ranking: Below 100. Franchise award date: June 1, 1972. Franchise expiration date: January 21, 2002. Began: June 1, 1973.
Channel capacity: 45 (not 2-way capable). Channels available but not in use: 1.
Basic Service
Subscribers: 853.
Programming (received off-air): WLEF-TV (P) Park Falls; WAOW-TV (A), WJFW-TV (N), WSAW-TV (C) Wausau-Rhinelander.
Programming (via satellite): WGN-TV (W) Chicago; A & E; American Movie Classics; CNBC; CNN; Comedy Central; ESPN; Fox Family Channel; Lifetime; MTV; Nashville Network; Nickelodeon; QVC; TBS Superstation; The Weather Channel; Turner Network TV; USA Network; VH1.
Fee: $42.95 installation; $23.50 monthly.
Pay Service 1
Pay Units: 86.
Programming (via satellite): Cinemax.
Fee: $19.95 installation; $12.50 monthly.
Pay Service 2
Pay Units: 82.
Programming (via satellite): Disney Channel.
Fee: $19.95 installation; $9.35 monthly.
Pay Service 3
Pay Units: 110.
Programming (via satellite): HBO.
Fee: $19.95 installation; $12.95 monthly.
Pay Service 4
Pay Units: 143.
Programming (via satellite): Showtime.
Fee: $19.95 installation; $12.50 monthly.
Local advertising: Yes. Available in locally originated programming. Rates: $2.00/30 Seconds.
Equipment: Scientific-Atlanta headend; Jerrold & Superior amplifiers; Times Fiber cable; Hamlin & Jerrold set top converters; Eagle traps; Scientific-Atlanta satellite antenna; Scientific-Atlanta satellite receivers.
Miles of plant: 28.0 (coaxial). Homes passed: 1,908.
Manager: George Benjamin. Marketing director: Chris Finger.
Ownership: Charter Communications Inc. (MSO). Purchased from Marcus Cable, April 1, 1999.

EAU CLAIRE—Charter Communications Inc., 2207 Heimstead Rd., Eau Claire, WI 54703. Phone: 715-831-8940. Fax: 715-831-8950. Counties: Chippewa, Crawford, Dunn & Eau Claire. Also serves Altoona, Brunswick Twp., Chippewa Falls, Eagle Point, Elk Mound, Elk Mound (village), Hallie, Pleasant Valley, Seymour Twp., Tilden, Union, Washington, Wheaton. ICA: WI0011.
TV Market Ranking: Below 100. Franchise award date: N.A. Franchise expiration date: N.A. Began: January 1, 1961.
Channel capacity: 78 (2-way capable; operating 2-way). Channels available but not in use: N.A.
Basic Service
Subscribers: 28,816; Commercial subscribers: 49.
Programming (received off-air): WEAU-TV (N), WQOW-TV (A) Eau Claire; WKBT (C), WLAX (F) La Crosse; WHWC-TV (P) Menomonie; KTCA-TV (P), WCCO-TV (C) Minneapolis-St. Paul.
Programming (via satellite): WGN-TV (W) Chicago; C-SPAN; TBS Superstation; TV Guide Channel.
Current originations: Public access.
Fee: $40.00 installation; $17.45 monthly.
Expanded Basic Service
Subscribers: N.A.
Programming (via satellite): A & E; American Movie Classics; C-SPAN 2; CNBC; CNN; Discovery Channel; ESPN; EWTN; Fox Family Channel; Headline News; Home & Garden Television; Learning Channel; Lifetime; MTV; Nashville Network; Nickelodeon; QVC; The Health Network; The Weather Channel; Travel Channel; Trinity Bcstg. Network; Turner Network TV; USA Network; VH1; ValueVision.
Fee: N.A.
A la Carte 1
Subscribers: N.A.
Programming (via satellite): Comedy Central; Country Music TV; Court TV; E! Entertainment TV; ESPN 2; Flix; History Channel; Sci-Fi Channel.
Fee: N.A.
Pay Service 1
Pay Units: 8,200.
Programming (via satellite): Cinemax; Disney Channel; HBO; Showtime.
Fee: $15.00 installation; $8.95 monthly (Disney), $9.95 monthly (Cinemax, HBO or Showtime).
Pay-Per-View
Addressable homes: 14,000.
Action Pay-Per-View; Hot Choice; Spice; Viewer's Choice.
Local advertising: Yes.
Equipment: RCA headend; RCA amplifiers; Comm/Scope cable; MSI character generator; Scientific-Atlanta satellite antenna.
Miles of plant: 625.0 (coaxial); 110.0 (fiber optic). Homes passed: 39,000. Total homes in franchised area: 39,000.
Manager: Scott Binder. Technical operations manager: Tim Normand. Marketing director: Brad Elbers.
City fee: 3% of gross.
Ownership: Charter Communications Inc. (MSO). Purchased from Marcus Cable, April 1, 1999.

ELCHO (town)—Northern Lakes Cable TV, Box 8, Bonduel, WI 54107. Phone: 715-758-2500. County: Langlade. ICA: WI0203.
TV Market Ranking: Below 100. Franchise award date: May 1, 1990. Franchise expiration date: May 1, 2005. Began: July 1, 1990.
Channel capacity: 54. Channels available but not in use: N.A.
Basic Service
Subscribers: 115.
Programming (received off-air): WACY (U) Appleton; WBAY-TV (A), WFRV-TV (C), WGBA (N) Green Bay; WAOW-TV (A), WHRM-TV (P), WJFW-TV (N), WSAW-TV (C) Wausau-Rhinelander.
Programming (via satellite): WGN-TV (W) Chicago; A & E; CNN; Discovery Channel; ESPN; EWTN; Nashville Network; Nickelodeon; TBS Superstation; The Inspirational Network; Turner Classic Movies.
Fee: $30.00 installation; $15.95 monthly.
Pay Service 1
Pay Units: N.A.
Programming (via satellite): Cinemax.
Fee: $9.95 monthly.
Miles of plant: 9.0 (coaxial). Homes passed: 220.
Manager: Robert Steichen.
Ownership: Northern Lakes Cable TV (MSO).

ELLSWORTH—US Cable, 128 W. Main St., Wabasha, MN 55981-1237. Phones: 651-565-4431; 800-642-5509. Fax: 651-565-2501. County: Pierce. ICA: WI0248.
TV Market Ranking: 13. Franchise award date: N.A. Franchise expiration date: April 1, 2000. Began: February 1, 1986.
Channel capacity: N.A. Channels available but not in use: N.A.
Basic Service
Subscribers: N.A.
Programming (received off-air): WKBT (C) La Crosse; WHWC-TV (P) Menomonie; KARE (N), KMSP-TV (U), KSTP-TV (A), KTCI-TV (P), WCCO-TV (C) Minneapolis-St. Paul.
Programming (via satellite): WGN-TV (W) Chicago; C-SPAN; CNN; ESPN; Fox Family Channel; Lifetime; MTV; Nashville Network; Nickelodeon; TBS Superstation; The Weather Channel; USA Network; VH1.
Fee: $25.00 installation; $11.25 monthly.
Pay Service 1
Pay Units: N.A.
Programming (via satellite): Disney Channel; HBO; Showtime; The Movie Channel.
Fee: $9.00 monthly (each).
Miles of plant: 21.7 (coaxial).
Manager: Dennis Ender.
City fee: 3% of gross.
Ownership: US Cable Corp. (MSO). Purchased from Fanch Communications Inc., April 30, 1999.

ELMWOOD—DeMarce Cable TV Inc., Box 235, 116 S. Main St., Elmwood, WI 54740. Phone: 715-639-2121. Fax: 715-639-3026. County: Pierce. ICA: WI0249.
TV Market Ranking: Below 100. Franchise award date: January 1, 1962. Franchise expiration date: January 1, 2000. Began: January 1, 1962.
Channel capacity: 40 (not 2-way capable). Channels available but not in use: 4.
Basic Service
Subscribers: 975.
Programming (received off-air): WEAU-TV (N), WQOW-TV (A) Eau Claire; WKBT (C) La Crosse; WHWC-TV (P) Menomonie; KARE (N), KLGT (W), KMSP-TV (U), KTCA-TV (P), KVBM-TV (H), WCCO-TV (C), WFTC (F) Minneapolis-St. Paul.
Programming (via satellite): WGN-TV (W) Chicago; A & E; CNN; Country Music TV; Discovery Channel; ESPN; ESPN 2; Fox Family Channel; Fox News Channel; Headline News; History Channel; Learning Channel; Lifetime; MTV; Nickelodeon; Sci-Fi Channel; TBS Superstation; The Weather Channel; Turner Network TV; USA Network; VH1.
Current originations: Public access.
Fee: $18.91 monthly; $1.50 converter.
Pay Service 1
Pay Units: 105.
Programming (via satellite): HBO.
Fee: $10.00 monthly.
Local advertising: Yes. Available in locally originated programming. Rates: $2.00/Minute; $7.00/30 Seconds. Local sales manager: Mike DeMarce.
Equipment: Drake & Cadco headend; Philips amplifiers; Comm/Scope cable; Jerrold & Scientific-Atlanta set top converters; Eagle & Arcom traps; ChannelMaster satellite antenna; Drake, Blonder-Tongue & Jerrold satellite receivers.
Miles of plant: 44.0 (coaxial); None (fiber optic). Homes passed: 162. Total homes in franchised area: 1,140.
Manager: Mike DeMarce. Chief technician: Jeff DeMarce.
Ownership: DeMarce Cable TV (MSO).

ELROY—Community Antenna System Inc., 1010 Lake St., Hillsboro, WI 54634. Phone: 608-489-2321. County: Juneau. ICA: WI0132.
TV Market Ranking: Outside TV Markets. Franchise award date: January 1, 1963. Franchise expiration date: N.A. Began: October 1, 1963.
Channel capacity: 15 (not 2-way capable). Channels available but not in use: N.A.
Basic Service
Subscribers: 607.

Programming (received off-air): WEAU-TV (N) Eau Claire; WKBT (C) La Crosse; WHA-TV (P), WISC-TV (C), WKOW-TV (A), WMSN-TV (F), WMTV (N) Madison.
Programming (via satellite): WGN-TV (W) Chicago; ESPN; Fox Family Channel; Nashville Network; TBS Superstation; Turner Network TV.
Fee: $50.00 installation; $15.02 monthly.
Pay Service 1
Pay Units: 183.
Programming (via satellite): Cinemax.
Fee: $6.95 monthly.
Local advertising: No.
Equipment: Jerrold headend.
Miles of plant: 6.8 (coaxial). Homes passed: 656.
Manager: Randall Kubarski. Chief technician: Gregory Kubarski.
Ownership: Community Antenna System Inc. (MSO).

ENDEAVOR—Cable Systems Management of Iowa Inc., 3600 Kennebec Dr., Eagan, MN 55122. Phone: 612-688-2623. Fax: 612-688-2624. County: Marquette. ICA: WI0218.
TV Market Ranking: Outside TV Markets. Franchise award date: N.A. Franchise expiration date: N.A. Began: N.A.
Channel capacity: 40. Channels available but not in use: 19.
Basic Service
Subscribers: 74.
Programming (received off-air): WHA-TV (P), WISC-TV (C), WKOW-TV (A), WMTV (N) Madison.
Programming (via satellite): WGN-TV (W) Chicago; A & E; American Movie Classics; CNN; Country Music TV; Discovery Channel; ESPN; Fox Family Channel; Lifetime; Nashville Network; Showtime; TBS Superstation; Turner Network TV; USA Network.
Fee: $28.00 monthly.
Miles of plant: 3.4 (coaxial). Homes passed: 142.
Manager: Jeff Anderson.
Ownership: Cable Systems Management of Iowa Inc. (MSO).

FAIR WATER—Centurytel, Box 2, 121 Williams St., Randolph, WI 53956. Phone: 920-326-3151. Fax: 414-326-4127. County: Fond du Lac. ICA: WI0220.
TV Market Ranking: Outside TV Markets. Franchise award date: N.A. Franchise expiration date: N.A. Began: June 1, 1990.
Channel capacity: 36 (not 2-way capable). Channels available but not in use: 9.
Basic Service
Subscribers: 66.
Programming (received off-air): WBAY-TV (A), WFRV-TV (C), WGBA (N), WLUK-TV (F) Green Bay; WMVS (P), WVTV (W) Milwaukee.
Programming (via satellite): WGN-TV (W) Chicago; A & E; CNN; Comedy Central; Discovery Channel; ESPN; Fox Family Channel; Home Shopping Network; Learning Channel; Lifetime; MuchMusic Network; Nashville Network; Nickelodeon; Sci-Fi Channel; Turner Network TV; USA Network.
Fee: $15.95 monthly.
Pay Service 1
Pay Units: N.A.
Programming (via satellite): Cinemax; Disney Channel; HBO; Showtime.
Fee: $4.95 monthly (Disney), $9.95 monthly (Showtime), $12.00 monthly (HBO).
Manager: Gary G. Perleberg. Chief technician: Don Meinders. Marketing & program director: Jeffrey Beck.
Ownership: Pecoco Inc. (MSO).

FALL CREEK—KRM Cablevision Inc., Box 77, Mellen, WI 54546. Phone: 715-274-7631. County: Eau Claire. ICA: WI0160.
TV Market Ranking: Below 100. Franchise award date: January 1, 1973. Franchise expiration date: N.A. Began: December 1, 1975.
Channel capacity: 20 (not 2-way capable). Channels available but not in use: 2.
Basic Service
Subscribers: N.A.
Programming (received off-air): WEAU-TV (N), WQOW-TV (A) Eau Claire; WKBT (C), WLAX (F) La Crosse; WHWC-TV (P) Menomonie; KARE (N) Minneapolis-St. Paul.
Programming (via satellite): WGN-TV (W) Chicago; CNN; Comedy Central; Discovery Channel; ESPN; Fox Family Channel; Lifetime; Nashville Network; TBS Superstation; USA Network.
Fee: $35.00 installation; $14.00 monthly.
Pay Service 1
Pay Units: N.A.
Programming (via satellite): Disney Channel; Showtime.
Fee: $8.00 monthly (Disney); $11.00 monthly (Showtime).
Equipment: Scientific-Atlanta headend; Jerrold amplifiers; Comm/Scope cable; Wilson satellite antenna.
Miles of plant: 6.5 (coaxial). Homes passed: 415. Total homes in franchised area: 415.
Manager: O. D. Miller. Chief technician: Keith Gehrett.
City fee: None.
Ownership: KRM Cablevision (MSO).

FIFIELD—KRM Cablevision, Box 77, Mellen, WI 54546. Phone: 715-274-7631. County: Price. ICA: WI0250.
TV Market Ranking: Below 100. Franchise award date: N.A. Franchise expiration date: N.A. Began: N.A.
Channel capacity: N.A. Channels available but not in use: N.A.
Basic Service
Subscribers: N.A.
Programming (received off-air): WLEF-TV (P) Park Falls; WAOW-TV (A), WJFW-TV (N), WSAW-TV (C) Wausau-Rhinelander.
Programming (via satellite): WGN-TV (W) Chicago; CNN; Discovery Channel; ESPN; Fox Family Channel; Nashville Network; TBS Superstation; Turner Network TV; USA Network.
Fee: N.A.
Pay Service 1
Pay Units: N.A.
Programming (via satellite): Showtime.
Fee: N.A.
Chief technician: Keith Gehrett.
Ownership: KRM Cablevision (MSO).

FITCHBURG—Charter Communications Inc., 5555 Irish Lane, Madison, WI 53711-5897. Phone: 608-273-3883. Fax: 608-273-0288. County: Dane. Also serves Dunn (town), Goodland Park, Verona (town). ICA: WI0029.
TV Market Ranking: 93. Franchise award date: January 1, 1980. Franchise expiration date: January 1, 2000. Began: December 15, 1980.
Channel capacity: 54 (2-way capable; operating 2-way). Channels available but not in use: 14.
Basic Service
Subscribers: 4,580; Commercial subscribers: 8.
Programming (received off-air): WHA-TV (P), WISC-TV (C), WKOW-TV (A), WMSN-TV (F), WMTV (N) Madison; 25 FMs.
Programming (via satellite): WGN-TV (W) Chicago; A & E; American Movie Classics; BET; C-SPAN; CNBC; CNN; Cartoon Network; Discovery Channel; ESPN; Fox Family Channel; Fox Sports Net; Headline News; Home Shopping Network; Knowledge TV; Lifetime; MTV; Nashville Network; Nickelodeon; Odyssey; Sci-Fi Channel; TBS Superstation; TV Guide Channel; The Weather Channel; Turner Network TV; USA Network; VH1.
Current originations: Automated time-weather; public access; educational access; government access; automated emergency alert.
Fee: $50.00 installation; $25.20 monthly.
Commercial fee: $30.00 monthly.
Pay Service 1
Pay Units: 505.
Programming (via satellite): Cinemax.
Fee: $10.00 installation; $10.95 monthly.
Pay Service 2
Pay Units: 856.
Programming (via satellite): HBO.
Fee: $10.00 installation; $10.95 monthly.
Pay Service 3
Pay Units: 84.
Programming (via satellite): The Movie Channel.
Fee: $10.00 installation; $10.95 monthly.
Pay Service 4
Pay Units: 481.
Programming (via satellite): Showtime.
Fee: $10.00 installation; $10.95 monthly.
Pay-Per-View
Addressable homes: 4,580.
Local advertising: Yes. Available in satellite distributed programming.
Program Guide: The Channel Guide.
Equipment: Scientific-Atlanta headend; Jerrold amplifiers; Comm/Scope & Times Fiber cable; Sony cameras; Texscan character generator; Jerrold set top converters; Jerrold addressable set top converters; Scientific-Atlanta satellite antenna; Standard Communications satellite receivers.
Miles of plant: 150.0 (coaxial). Homes passed: 7,576.
Manager: Marty Robinson. Chief technician: Robert Mould. Marketing director: Mitch Miller.
City fee: 3% of gross.
Ownership: Charter Communications Inc. (MSO). Purchased from Marcus Cable, April 1, 1999.

FOND DU LAC—Charter Communications Inc., Box 1197, 55 W. Scott St., Fond du Lac, WI 54936-1197. Phones: 920-923-7196; 800-581-0081. Fax: 920-923-1235. Counties: Dodge & Fond du Lac. Also serves Ashford, Campbellsport, Eden (town), Eden (village), Eldorado, Empire, Fond du Lac (town), Friendship Twp., Lomira, Marshfield Twp., Mount Calvary, North Fond du Lac, St. Cloud, Taycheedah, Van Dyne. ICA: WI0018.
TV Market Ranking: Below 100. Franchise award date: N.A. Franchise expiration date: July 6, 2006. Began: November 1, 1979.
Channel capacity: 61. Channels available but not in use: 3.
Basic Service
Subscribers: 18,676; Commercial subscribers: 35.
Programming (received off-air): WACY (U) Appleton; WBAY-TV (A), WFRV-TV (C), WGBA (N), WLUK-TV (F), WPNE (P) Green Bay; WCGV-TV (I), WISN-TV (A), WITI (F), WMVS (P), WTMJ-TV (N), WVTV (W) Milwaukee.
Programming (via satellite): WGN-TV (W) Chicago; C-SPAN; Home Shopping Network; Knowledge TV; QVC; TBS Superstation; TV Guide Channel; ValueVision.
Current originations: Educational access; government access; local news; local sports.
Fee: $34.95 installation; $11.12 monthly; $2.00 converter.
Expanded Basic Service
Subscribers: 17,073.
Programming (via satellite): A & E; American Movie Classics; Bravo; CNBC; CNN; Cartoon Network; Comedy Central; Country Music TV; Court TV; Discovery Channel; E! Entertainment TV; ESPN; ESPN 2; EWTN; FX; Fox Family Channel; Headline News; Learning Channel; Lifetime; MTV; Nashville Network; Nickelodeon; Sci-Fi Channel; The Weather Channel; Travel Channel; Turner Network TV; USA Network; VH1.
Fee: $16.50 monthly.
Pay Service 1
Pay Units: 2,229.
Programming (via satellite): Cinemax.
Fee: $12.50 monthly.
Pay Service 2
Pay Units: 1,868.
Programming (via satellite): Disney Channel.
Fee: $3.95 monthly.
Pay Service 3
Pay Units: 1,428.
Programming (via satellite): HBO.
Fee: $12.95 monthly.
Pay Service 4
Pay Units: 2,402.
Programming (via satellite): Showtime.
Fee: $12.50 monthly.
Pay Service 5
Pay Units: 400.
Programming (via satellite): Music Choice.
Fee: $6.95 monthly.
Pay Service 6
Pay Units: 2,119.
Programming (via satellite): The New Encore.
Fee: $3.95 monthly.
Pay-Per-View
Special events.
Fee: Varies.
Local advertising: Yes (locally produced & insert). Available in satellite distributed, locally originated, taped & automated programming. Rates: $10.00/30 Seconds. Local sales manager: Susan Winn.
Equipment: Scientific-Atlanta headend; Scientific-Atlanta amplifiers; Comm/Scope cable; Sony & Panasonic cameras; Sony VTRs; Compuvid & Video Data Systems character generator; Scientific-Atlanta set top converters; Eagle & Vitek traps; Scientific-Atlanta satellite antenna; Sony commercial insert.
Miles of plant: 269.0 (coaxial); 60.0 (fiber optic). Homes passed: 24,259.
Manager: Lisa Washa. Chief technician: Jeff Gerner.
City fee: 5% of gross.
Ownership: Charter Communications Inc. (MSO). Purchased from Marcus Cable, April 1, 1999.

FORT MCCOY—Triax Cablevision, Box 110, 1504 2nd St. SE, Waseca, MN 56093. Phones: 507-835-5975; 800-332-0245. Fax: 507-835-4567. County: Monroe. ICA: WI0312.
TV Market Ranking: Below 100. Franchise award date: March 24, 1995. Franchise expiration date: August 30, 2009. Began: February 1, 1996.
Channel capacity: 78 (not 2-way capable). Channels available but not in use: 43.
Basic Service
Subscribers: 1,441.
Programming (received off-air): WEAU-TV (N) Eau Claire; WHLA-TV (P), WKBT (C), WLAX (F), WXOW-TV (A) La Crosse.
Programming (via satellite): WGN-TV (W) Chicago; A & E; BET; C-SPAN; C-SPAN 2; CNN; Comedy Central; Country Music TV;

Court TV; Discovery Channel; E! Entertainment TV; ESPN; ESPN 2; Fox Family Channel; Headline News; History Channel; Home Shopping Network; Learning Channel; MTV; Nashville Network; Odyssey; TBS Superstation; The Weather Channel; Turner Network TV; USA Network; VH1.
Current originations: Local news.
Fee: N.A.

Pay Service 1
Pay Units: N.A.
Programming (via satellite): Disney Channel; HBO.
Fee: N.A.

Miles of plant: 10.8 (coaxial); 11.6 (fiber optic). Homes passed: 1,475.
Manager: Richard Giffen. Chief technician: Scott Walters.
Ownership: Triax Telecommunications Co. LLC (MSO). See Cable System Ownership.

FOUNTAIN CITY—TCI of the Blufflands Inc., Box 408, 127 W. 4th St., Winona, MN 55987-0408. Phone: 507-452-6040. County: Buffalo. ICA: WI0178.
TV Market Ranking: Below 100. Franchise award date: January 1, 1963. Franchise expiration date: N.A. Began: January 1, 1963.
Channel capacity: 54 (2-way capable). Channels available but not in use: 29.

Basic Service
Subscribers: 316.
Programming (received off-air): WEAU-TV (N) Eau Claire; WHLA-TV (P), WKBT (C), WLAX (F), WXOW-TV (A) La Crosse; KTTC (N) Rochester.
Programming (via microwave): KSTP-TV (A), WCCO-TV (C) Minneapolis-St. Paul.
Fee: $10.50 monthly.

Expanded Basic Service
Subscribers: 277.
Programming (via satellite): American Movie Classics; C-SPAN; CNN; Discovery Channel; ESPN; FX; Fox Family Channel; Midwest Sports Channel; Nashville Network; TBS Superstation; Turner Network TV; USA Network.
Fee: $13.42 monthly.

Pay Service 1
Pay Units: 130.
Programming (via satellite): The New Encore.
Fee: $1.75 monthly.

Pay Service 2
Pay Units: 23.
Programming (via satellite): HBO.
Fee: $11.15 monthly.

Pay Service 3
Pay Units: 30.
Programming (via satellite): Showtime.
Fee: $11.15 monthly.

Pay Service 4
Pay Units: N.A.
Programming (via satellite): Starz!
Fee: $6.75 monthly.

Miles of plant: 5.9 (coaxial). Homes passed: 430.
Manager: Pat Ruda. Chief technician: Randy Gartner.
Ownership: AT&T Broadband & Internet Services (MSO). Purchased from Tele-Communications Inc., March 9, 1999.

FREMONT—Triax Cablevision, Box 334, 1102 N. 4th St., Chillicothe, IL 61523-0334. Phones: 309-274-4500; 800-874-2924. Fax: 309-274-3188. County: Waupaca. ICA: WI0172.
TV Market Ranking: Below 100. Franchise award date: N.A. Franchise expiration date: June 30, 1999. Began: March 1, 1985.
Channel capacity: 37 (not 2-way capable). Channels available but not in use: 10.

Basic Service
Subscribers: 136.
Programming (received off-air): WACY (U) Appleton; WBAY-TV (A), WFRV-TV (C), WGBA (N), WLUK-TV (F), WPNE (P) Green Bay; WSAW-TV (C) Wausau-Rhinelander.
Programming (via satellite): WGN-TV (W) Chicago; A & E; CNN; Country Music TV; Discovery Channel; ESPN; ESPN 2; Fox Family Channel; History Channel; Lifetime; Nashville Network; Nickelodeon; QVC; Sci-Fi Channel; TBS Superstation; The Weather Channel; Turner Network TV; USA Network.
Fee: $45.00 installation; $28.50 monthly.

Pay Service 1
Pay Units: 43.
Programming (via satellite): HBO; Showtime.
Fee: $11.99 monthly (each).

Miles of plant: 8.4 (coaxial). Homes passed: 378.
Manager: Mike Hodgerson. Chief technician: Pat Alderman.
Ownership: Triax Telecommunications Co. LLC (MSO). See Cable System Ownership.

GENOA CITY—TCI Cablevision of Wisconsin Inc., Box 927, Section B, Walworth, WI 53184-0927. Phone: 414-275-2197. Fax: 414-275-3786. Counties: Kenosha & Walworth, WI; McHenry, IL. Also serves Richmond, IL; Bloomfield (town), Pell Lake, Randall Twp., Twin Lakes, Wheatland, WI. ICA: WI0039.
TV Market Ranking: 23 (Wheatland); Below 100 (Bloomfield, Genoa City, Pell Lake, Randall Twp., Richmond, Twin Lakes). Franchise award date: N.A. Franchise expiration date: N.A. Began: June 1, 1982.
Channel capacity: 60 (not 2-way capable). Channels available but not in use: 5.

Basic Service
Subscribers: 3,664.
Programming (received off-air): WBBM-TV (C), WFLD (F), WGN-TV (W), WLS-TV (A), WMAQ-TV (N), WTTW (P) Chicago; WCGV-TV (I), WISN-TV (A), WITI (F), WMVS (P), WTMJ-TV (N) Milwaukee; allband FM.
Programming (via satellite): C-SPAN; CNN; Cartoon Network; Discovery Channel; Fox Family Channel; Headline News; MTV; Nashville Network; Nickelodeon; QVC; TBS Superstation.
Current originations: Automated time-weather; public access; automated emergency alert.
Fee: $28.59 installation; $9.80 monthly; $2.47 converter; $14.30 additional installation.

Expanded Basic Service
Subscribers: 3,384.
Programming (via satellite): American Movie Classics; CNBC; Court TV; ESPN; Lifetime; Turner Network TV; USA Network.
Fee: $12.14 monthly.

Pay Service 1
Pay Units: 215.
Programming (via satellite): Disney Channel.
Fee: N.A.

Pay Service 2
Pay Units: 1,270.
Programming (via satellite): The New Encore.
Fee: N.A.

Pay Service 3
Pay Units: 652.
Programming (via satellite): HBO.
Fee: N.A.

Pay Service 4
Pay Units: 199.
Programming (via satellite): The Movie Channel.
Fee: $10.00 installation.

Pay Service 5
Pay Units: 297.
Programming (via satellite): Showtime.
Fee: N.A.

Pay-Per-View
Addressable homes: 860.

Local advertising: Yes (locally produced). Available in locally originated programming. Rates: $1.00/Day. Local sales manager: Chris Fuller.
Equipment: Scientific-Atlanta & Microdyne headend; Vikoa & Magnavox amplifiers; Vikoa & Times Fiber cable; Texscan character generator; Pioneer & Eagle set top converters; Arcom, Eagle & Pico traps; Scientific-Atlanta & KES satellite antenna; Scientific-Atlanta & Microdyne satellite receivers.
Miles of plant: 133.9 (coaxial). Homes passed: 6,679.
Manager: Matt Forgas. Chief technician: Jeff Myers.
Ownership: AT&T Broadband & Internet Services (MSO). Purchased from Tele-Communications Inc., March 9, 1999.

GILLETT—Charter Communications Inc., Box 1818, 853 McIntosh St., Wausau, WI 54402-1818. Phones: 715-845-4223; 800-581-0081. Fax: 715-848-0081. Counties: Oconto & Shawano. Also serves Green Valley, Pulcifer. ICA: WI0181.
TV Market Ranking: 62 (Gillett); Below 100 (Green Valley, Pulcifer). Franchise award date: April 1, 1981. Franchise expiration date: N.A. Began: December 31, 1982.
Channel capacity: 24. Channels available but not in use: N.A.

Basic Service
Subscribers: 395.
Programming (received off-air): WACY (U) Appleton; WBAY-TV (A), WFRV-TV (C), WGBA (N), WLUK-TV (F), WPNE (P) Green Bay.
Programming (via satellite): WGN-TV (W) Chicago; TBS Superstation.
Fee: $56.73 installation; $6.58 monthly.

Expanded Basic Service
Subscribers: 392.
Programming (via satellite): A & E; CNN; Country Music TV; Discovery Channel; Disney Channel; ESPN; Fox Family Channel; Headline News; Lifetime; Nashville Network; Nickelodeon; Sci-Fi Channel; The Weather Channel; USA Network; VH1.
Fee: $13.17 monthly.

Pay Service 1
Pay Units: 89.
Programming (via satellite): Cinemax.
Fee: $12.50 monthly.

Pay Service 2
Pay Units: 105.
Programming (via satellite): HBO.
Fee: $12.95 monthly.

Miles of plant: 11.8 (coaxial). Homes passed: 804.
Manager: Scott Behn. Chief technician: Bruce Wasleske. Marketing director: Tim Schieffer.
Ownership: Charter Communications Inc. (MSO). Purchased from Marcus Cable, April 1, 1999.

GLENWOOD CITY—DeMarce TV & Cable Systems Inc., Box 235, 116 S. Main St., Elmwood, WI 54740. Phone: 715-639-2121. Fax: 715-639-3026. Counties: Dunn & St. Croix. Also serves Downing. ICA: WI0251.
TV Market Ranking: Outside TV Markets. Franchise award date: January 1, 1962. Franchise expiration date: January 1, 2005. Began: January 1, 1968.
Channel capacity: 40 (not 2-way capable). Channels available but not in use: 4.

Basic Service
Subscribers: 975.
Programming (received off-air): WEAU-TV (N), WQOW-TV (A) Eau Claire; WKBT (C) La Crosse; WHWC-TV (P) Menomonie; KARE (N), KLGT (W), KMSP-TV (U), KSTP-TV (A), KTCA-TV (P), KVBM-TV (H), WCCO-TV (C), WFTC (F) Minneapolis-St. Paul.
Programming (via satellite): WGN-TV (W) Chicago; A & E; American Movie Classics; CNN; Country Music TV; Discovery Channel; ESPN; ESPN 2; Fox Family Channel; Fox News Channel; Headline News; History Channel; Learning Channel; Lifetime; MTV; Nashville Network; Nickelodeon; QVC; Sci-Fi Channel; TBS Superstation; The Weather Channel; Turner Network TV; USA Network; VH1.
Current originations: Public access.
Fee: $18.91 monthly; $1.50 converter.

Pay Service 1
Pay Units: 105.
Programming (via satellite): HBO.
Fee: $10.00 monthly.

Local advertising: Yes. Rates: $2.00/Minute; $7.00/30 Seconds. Local sales manager: Mike DeMarce.
Equipment: Blonder-Tongue, Drake & Cadco headend; Philips amplifiers; Comm/Scope cable; Jerrold & Scientific-Atlanta set top converters; Eagle & Arcom traps; ChannelMaster satellite antenna; Drake, Blonder-Tongue & Jerrold satellite receivers.
Miles of plant: 44.0 (coaxial); None (fiber optic). Additional miles planned: 2.0 (coaxial). Homes passed: 162. Total homes in franchised area: 1,140.
Manager: Mike DeMarce. Chief technician: Jeff DeMarce.
Ownership: DeMarce Cable TV (MSO).

GLIDDEN—KRM Cablevision, Box 77, Mellen, WI 54546. Phone: 715-274-7631. County: Ashland. ICA: WI0191.
TV Market Ranking: Outside TV Markets. Franchise award date: April 1, 1980. Franchise expiration date: N.A. Began: April 1, 1985.
Channel capacity: 20 (not 2-way capable). Channels available but not in use: 4.

Basic Service
Subscribers: 165.
Programming (received off-air): KDLH (C), WDIO-TV (A,F) Duluth-Superior; WLEF-TV (P) Park Falls; WJFW-TV (N), WSAW-TV (C) Wausau-Rhinelander.
Programming (via satellite): WGN-TV (W) Chicago; CNN; Discovery Channel; ESPN; Fox Family Channel; Nashville Network; TBS Superstation; Turner Network TV; USA Network.
Fee: $35.00 installation; $14.00 monthly.

Pay Service 1
Pay Units: N.A.
Programming (via satellite): Disney Channel; The Movie Channel.
Fee: $10.00 installation; $8.00 monthly (Disney); $12.00 monthly (TMC).

Equipment: Blonder-Tongue & Triple Crown headend; Jerrold amplifiers.
Miles of plant: 5.0 (coaxial). Homes passed: 250. Total homes in franchised area: 250.
Manager: O. D. Miller. Chief technician: Keith Gehrett.
City fee: None.
Ownership: KRM Cablevision (MSO).

GOODMAN—Northern Lakes Cable TV, Box 8, Bonduel, WI 54107. Phone: 715-758-2500. County: Marinette. ICA: WI0206.

TV Market Ranking: Below 100. Franchise award date: N.A. Franchise expiration date: N.A. Began: September 1, 1988.
Channel capacity: 54 (not 2-way capable). Channels available but not in use: N.A.
Basic Service
Subscribers: 129.
Programming (received off-air): WACY (U) Appleton; WFRV-TV (C), WGBA (N), WLUK-TV (F), WPNE (P) Green Bay; WLUC-TV (N) Marquette; WAOW-TV (A), WJFW-TV (N), WSAW-TV (C) Wausau-Rhinelander.
Programming (via satellite): WGN-TV (W) Chicago; CNN; Discovery Channel; ESPN; Fox Family Channel; MTV; Nashville Network; Nickelodeon; TBS Superstation; Turner Classic Movies; USA Network.
Fee: $25.00 installation; $15.00 monthly.
Pay Service 1
Pay Units: N.A.
Programming (via satellite): Cinemax; HBO.
Fee: $9.95 monthly (each).
Equipment: Scientific-Atlanta headend; Scientific-Atlanta amplifiers; Times Fiber cable; Oak & Hamlin set top converters; Arcom traps; M/A-Com satellite antenna; Scientific-Atlanta satellite receivers.
Miles of plant: 4.5 (coaxial). Homes passed: 199. Total homes in franchised area: 199.
Manager: Robert Steichen.
Ownership: Northern Lakes Cable TV (MSO).

GRANTON—Cable Systems Management of Iowa Inc., 3600 Kennebec Dr., Eagan, MN 55122. Phone: 612-688-2623. Fax: 612-688-2624. County: Clark. ICA: WI0211.
TV Market Ranking: Outside TV Markets. Franchise award date: N.A. Franchise expiration date: N.A. Began: N.A.
Channel capacity: 40. Channels available but not in use: 19.
Basic Service
Subscribers: 50.
Programming (received off-air): WEAU-TV (N) Eau Claire; WAOW-TV (A), WHRM-TV (P), WSAW-TV (C) Wausau-Rhinelander.
Programming (via satellite): WGN-TV (W) Chicago; A & E; American Movie Classics; Country Music TV; Discovery Channel; ESPN; Fox Family Channel; Headline News; Lifetime; Nashville Network; Showtime; TBS Superstation; Turner Network TV; USA Network.
Fee: $50.00 installation; $30.00 monthly.
Miles of plant: 3.6 (coaxial). Homes passed: 182.
Manager: Jeff Anderson.
Ownership: Cable Systems Management of Iowa Inc. (MSO).

GRANTSBURG—Vision Communications, Box 355, 28 First Ave. W, Luck, WI 54853-0355. Phones: 715-472-2700; 715-472-2707. County: Burnett. ICA: WI0252.
TV Market Ranking: Outside TV Markets. Franchise award date: July 15, 1985. Franchise expiration date: N.A. Began: January 1, 1987.
Channel capacity: N.A. Channels available but not in use: N.A.
Basic Service
Subscribers: 245.
Programming (received off-air): WEAU-TV (N), WQOW-TV (A) Eau Claire; WHLA-TV (P), WKBT (C), WLAX (F), WXOW-TV (A) La Crosse; WHWC-TV (P) Menomonie; WITI (F), WTMJ-TV (N) Milwaukee; KSTP-TV (A), KTCI-TV (P), WCCO-TV (C), WFTC (F) Minneapolis-St. Paul.
Programming (via satellite): WGN-TV (W) Chicago; CNN; Discovery Channel; ESPN; Fox Family Channel; Headline News; Lifetime; MTV; Nashville Network; Nickelodeon; TBS Superstation; USA Network.
Fee: $45.00 installation; $18.95 monthly.
Pay Service 1
Pay Units: 14.
Programming (via satellite): Cinemax.
Fee: $8.00 monthly.
Pay Service 2
Pay Units: 21.
Programming (via satellite): Disney Channel.
Fee: $7.00 monthly.
Pay Service 3
Pay Units: 41.
Programming (via satellite): HBO.
Fee: $9.00 monthly.
Pay Service 4
Pay Units: 27.
Programming (via satellite): The Movie Channel.
Fee: $8.00 monthly.
Manager: John Klatt.
Ownership: Vision Communications LLC (MSO).

GREEN LAKE—Charter Communications Inc., Box 1197, 55 W. Scott St., Fond du Lac, WI 54936-1197. Phones: 920-923-7196; 800-581-0081. Fax: 920-923-1235. County: Green Lake. Also serves Brooklyn, Brooklyn (town), Green Lake County, Princeton, Princeton (town). ICA: WI0072.
TV Market Ranking: Below 100 (Brooklyn, town of Brooklyn, portions of Green Lake County, Princeton, town of Princeton); Outside TV Markets (portions of Green Lake County).
Channel capacity: 35 (2-way capable; operating 2-way). Channels available but not in use: 1.
Basic Service
Subscribers: 455.
Programming (received off-air): WACY (U) Appleton; WBAY-TV (A), WFRV-TV (C), WGBA (N), WLUK-TV (F), WPNE (P) Green Bay; WISN-TV (A), WVTV (W) Milwaukee.
Programming (via satellite): WGN-TV (W) Chicago; A & E; American Movie Classics; C-SPAN; CNN; Comedy Central; Discovery Channel; ESPN; EWTN; Fox Family Channel; Headline News; Lifetime; MTV; Nashville Network; Nickelodeon; QVC; TBS Superstation; The Weather Channel; Turner Network TV; USA Network; VH1.
Current originations: Automated time-weather; public access; local news.
Fee: $34.95 installation; $9.71 monthly.
Pay Service 1
Pay Units: 209.
Programming (via satellite): Cinemax.
Fee: $14.95 installation; $12.50 monthly.
Pay Service 2
Pay Units: 134.
Programming (via satellite): Disney Channel.
Fee: $14.95 installation; $3.95 monthly.
Pay Service 3
Pay Units: 224.
Programming (via satellite): HBO.
Fee: $14.95 installation; $12.95 monthly.
Pay Service 4
Pay Units: 310.
Programming (via satellite): Showtime.
Fee: $14.95 installation; $12.50 monthly.
Local advertising: Yes. Available in character-generated programming.
Equipment: Scientific-Atlanta headend; Scientific-Atlanta amplifiers; Times Fiber cable; Texscan character generator; Scientific-Atanta set top converters; Arcom & Eagle traps; Microdyne & Scientific-Atlanta satellite antenna; Scientific-Atlanta satellite receivers.
Miles of plant: 57.0 (coaxial). Homes passed: 1,977.
Manager: Lisa Washa. Chief technician: Jeff Gerner.
City fee: 3% of gross.
Ownership: Charter Communications Inc. (MSO). Purchased from Marcus Cable, April 1, 1999.

GREENFIELD (Milwaukee County)—Time Warner Cable, 5475 W. Abbott Ave., Greenfield, WI 53220-4900. Phone: 414-282-6300. Fax: 414-421-1206. County: Milwaukee. Also serves Bayside, Brown Deer, Cudahy, Fox Point, Franklin, Glendale, Greendale, Hales Corners, Oak Creek, River Hills, Shorewood, South Milwaukee, Whitefish Bay. ICA: WI0003.
TV Market Ranking: 23. Franchise award date: June 1, 1981. Franchise expiration date: N.A. Began: January 1, 1982.
Channel capacity: 108 (2-way capable; operating 2-way). Channels available but not in use: 33.
Basic Service
Subscribers: 56,466.
Programming (received off-air): WCIU-TV (I), WFLD (F), WTTW (P) Chicago; WHA-TV (P), WMTV (N) Madison; WCGV-TV (I), WISN-TV (A), WITI (F), WMVS (P), WTMJ-TV (N), WVCY-TV (I), WVTV (W) Milwaukee; 25 FMs.
Programming (via satellite): WGN-TV (W) Chicago; A & E; American Movie Classics; BET; C-SPAN; C-SPAN 2; CNBC; CNN; CNN/SI; Cartoon Network; Court TV; Discovery Channel; E! Entertainment TV; ESPN; Fox Family Channel; Headline News; Learning Channel; Lifetime; MTV; Nashville Network; National Jewish TV; Nickelodeon; QVC; TBS Superstation; The Weather Channel; Trinity Bcstg. Network; USA Network; VH1.
Current originations: Automated time-weather; educational access; government access; local news.
Fee: $25.00 installation; $24.53 monthly.
Pay Service 1
Pay Units: N.A.
Programming (via satellite): Bravo; Cinemax; Disney Channel; HBO; Playboy TV; Showtime; The Movie Channel.
Fee: $4.80 monthly (Bravo), $6.95 monthly (Disney), $9.75 monthly (Cinemax, HBO or Showtime), $10.00 monthly (Playboy or TMC).
Pay-Per-View
Addressable homes: 30,000.
Action Pay-Per-View; Playboy TV; Spice.
Fee: $4.95.
Equipment: Scientific-Atlanta headend; GTE Sylvania amplifiers; Comm/Scope cable; Hitachi cameras; Sony VTRs; Metrodata character generator; Zenith addressable set top converters; Scientific-Atlanta satellite antenna; Scientific-Atlanta satellite receivers.
Miles of plant: 799.0 (coaxial). Homes passed: 78,200. Total homes in franchised area: 78,200.
Manager: Irene Picard. Chief technician: Dennis Forer. Marketing director: Denise Stimac.
City fee: 3%-5% of gross.
Ownership: Time Warner Cable (MSO).

GREENLEAF—Wayside Telephone Co., 7235 County Rd. W, Greenleaf, WI 54126. Phone: 920-864-2105. Fax: 920-864-7506. County: Brown. ICA: WI0253.
TV Market Ranking: 62. Franchise award date: N.A. Franchise expiration date: N.A. Began: N.A.
Channel capacity: N.A. Channels available but not in use: N.A.
Basic Service
Subscribers: 130.
Programming (received off-air): WACY (U) Appleton; WBAY-TV (A), WFRV-TV (C), WGBA (N), WLUK-TV (F), WPNE (P) Green Bay.
Programming (via satellite): WGN-TV (W) Chicago; A & E; CNN; Discovery Channel; ESPN; Fox Family Channel; Lifetime; MTV; Nashville Network; Nickelodeon; TBS Superstation; Turner Network TV; USA Network; VH1.
Current originations: Automated time-weather.
Fee: $25.00 installation; $20.00 monthly.
Pay Service 1
Pay Units: N.A.
Programming (via satellite): Cinemax; Disney Channel; HBO.
Fee: $7.95 monthly (Disney), $8.95 monthly (Cinemax or HBO).
Manager: Mary Gotstein. Chief technician: Ron Kiekhaefer.
Ownership: Wayside Telephone Co.

GREENWOOD—KRM Cablevision, Box 77, Mellen, WI 54546. Phone: 715-274-7631. County: Clark. ICA: WI0159.
TV Market Ranking: Outside TV Markets. Franchise award date: N.A. Franchise expiration date: November 1, 1998. Began: May 1, 1984.
Channel capacity: 35 (2-way capable; operating 2-way). Channels available but not in use: 17.
Basic Service
Subscribers: 178.
Programming (received off-air): WEAU-TV (N) Eau Claire; WKBT (C), WLAX (F) La Crosse; WAOW-TV (A), WHRM-TV (P), WSAW-TV (C) Wausau-Rhinelander.
Programming (via satellite): WGN-TV (W) Chicago; CNN; Discovery Channel; ESPN; Fox Family Channel; Nashville Network; Nickelodeon; TBS Superstation; Turner Network TV; USA Network.
Current originations: Public access; educational access; government access.
Fee: $25.00 installation; $7.95 monthly.
Pay Service 1
Pay Units: N.A.
Programming (via satellite): Disney Channel; Showtime; The Movie Channel.
Fee: $8.95 monthly (Showtime or TMC).
Equipment: Scientific-Atlanta headend; Scientific-Atlanta amplifiers; Comm/Scope cable; Oak set top converters; Pico & Vitek traps; Scientific-Atlanta satellite antenna; Scientific-Atlanta satellite receivers.
Miles of plant: 10.0 (coaxial). Homes passed: 423. Total homes in franchised area: 423.
Manager: O. D. Miller. Chief technician: Keith Gehrett.
City fee: 3% of gross.
Ownership: KRM Cablevision (MSO).

GRESHAM—Charter Communications Inc., Box 1818, 853 McIntosh St., Wausau, WI 54402-1818. Phones: 715-845-4223; 800-581-0081. Fax: 715-848-0081. County: Shawano. ICA: WI0197.
TV Market Ranking: Below 100. Franchise award date: September 10, 1984. Franchise expiration date: September 10, 1999. Began: July 1, 1985.
Channel capacity: 35 (not 2-way capable). Channels available but not in use: N.A.
Basic Service
Subscribers: 146.
Programming (received off-air): WACY (U) Appleton; WBAY-TV (A), WFRV-TV (C), WGBA (N), WLUK-TV (F), WPNE (P) Green Bay.

Programming (via satellite): WGN-TV (W) Chicago; TBS Superstation.
Fee: $56.73 installation; $7.26 monthly; $28.36 additional installation.

Expanded Basic Service
Subscribers: 144.
Programming (via satellite): A & E; CNN; Country Music TV; Discovery Channel; Disney Channel; ESPN; Fox Family Channel; Lifetime; Nashville Network; Nickelodeon; Sci-Fi Channel; Turner Network TV; USA Network; VH1.
Fee: $12.71 monthly.

Pay Service 1
Pay Units: 47.
Programming (via satellite): Cinemax.
Fee: $12.50 monthly.

Pay Service 2
Pay Units: 64.
Programming (via satellite): HBO.
Fee: $12.50 monthly.

Equipment: Triple Crown headend; GTE Sylvania amplifiers; Times Fiber cable; Eagle traps; M/A-Com satellite antenna; Triple Crown satellite receivers.
Miles of plant: 4.5 (coaxial). Homes passed: 315.
Manager: Scott Behn. Chief technician: Bruce Wasleske. Marketing director: Tim Schniefer.
City fee: 3% of gross.
Ownership: Charter Communications Inc. (MSO). Purchased from Marcus Cable, April 1, 1999.

HAWKINS (village)—KRM Cablevision, Box 77, Mellen, WI 54546. Phone: 715-274-7631. County: Rusk. ICA: WI0254.
TV Market Ranking: Outside TV Markets. Franchise award date: N.A. Franchise expiration date: N.A. Began: N.A.
Channel capacity: N.A. Channels available but not in use: N.A.

Basic Service
Subscribers: N.A.
Programming (received off-air): WEAU-TV (N) Eau Claire; WLEF-TV (P) Park Falls; WAOW-TV (A), WSAW-TV (C) Wausau-Rhinelander.
Programming (via satellite): WGN-TV (W) Chicago; CNN; Comedy Central; Discovery Channel; ESPN; Nashville Network; TBS Superstation; Turner Network TV; USA Network.
Fee: N.A.

Pay Service 1
Pay Units: N.A.
Programming (via satellite): Disney Channel; The Movie Channel.
Fee: N.A.

Manager: O. D. Miller. Chief technician: Keith Gehrett.
Ownership: KRM Cablevision (MSO).

HAYWARD—Charter Communications Inc., Box 539, 1725 S. Main St., Rice Lake, WI 54868-0539. Phones: 715-234-3821; 800-262-2578. Fax: 715-234-8537. County: Sawyer. Also serves Hayward (town), Sand Lake, Stone Lake. ICA: WI0085.
TV Market Ranking: Outside TV Markets. Franchise award date: N.A. Franchise expiration date: April 11, 2001. Began: September 1, 1971.
Channel capacity: 35 (not 2-way capable). Channels available but not in use: None.

Basic Service
Subscribers: 1,245.
Programming (received off-air): KBJR-TV (N), KDLH (C), WDIO-TV (A,F), WDSE-TV (P) Duluth-Superior; WEAU-TV (N), WQOW-TV (A) Eau Claire; KMSP-TV (U) Minneapolis-St. Paul; WLEF-TV (P) Park Falls; WSAW-TV (C) Wausau-Rhinelander.
Programming (via satellite): WGN-TV (W) Chicago; A & E; American Movie Classics; C-SPAN; CNBC; CNN; Discovery Channel; Disney Channel; ESPN; Fox Family Channel; FoxNet; Headline News; Lifetime; MTV; Nashville Network; Nickelodeon; QVC; TBS Superstation; The Weather Channel; Turner Network TV; USA Network; VH1.
Current originations: Automated time-weather.
Fee: $42.95 installation; $26.06 monthly.

Pay Service 1
Pay Units: 189.
Programming (via satellite): Cinemax.
Fee: $19.95 installation; $12.50 monthly.

Pay Service 2
Pay Units: 205.
Programming (via satellite): HBO.
Fee: $19.95 installation; $12.95 monthly.

Pay Service 3
Pay Units: 235.
Programming (via satellite): Showtime.
Fee: $19.95 installation; $12.50 monthly.

Equipment: Jerrold headend; Jerrold amplifiers; Comm/Scope & Times Fiber cable; Sony cameras.
Miles of plant: 53.0 (coaxial). Homes passed: 1,505.
Manager: Scott Binder. Chief technician: George Benjamin.
City fee: 2% of gross.
Ownership: Charter Communications Inc. (MSO). Purchased from Marcus Cable, April 1, 1999.

HIGHLAND—Spring Green CableComm, Box 609, 245 S. Winsted St., Spring Green, WI 53588-9431. Phone: 608-588-7454. Fax: 608-588-7067. County: Iowa. ICA: WI0192.
TV Market Ranking: Outside TV Markets. Franchise award date: September 1, 1982. Franchise expiration date: April 1, 2001. Began: September 1, 1982.
Channel capacity: 40 (not 2-way capable). Channels available but not in use: 12.

Basic Service
Subscribers: 218.
Programming (received off-air): WHA-TV (P), WISC-TV (C), WKOW-TV (A), WMSN-TV (F), WMTV (N) Madison.
Programming (via satellite): WGN-TV (W) Chicago; A & E; CNN; Discovery Channel; ESPN; Fox Family Channel; Headline News; Nashville Network; Nickelodeon; TBS Superstation; Turner Classic Movies; Turner Network TV; USA Network.
Current originations: Public access.
Fee: $49.95 installation; $29.85 monthly.

Pay Service 1
Pay Units: N.A.
Programming (via satellite): Cinemax; HBO.
Fee: $19.95 installation; $9.95 monthly (each).

Equipment: Blonder-Tongue & Scientific-Atlanta headend; Jerrold amplifiers; Times Fiber cable; Intercept traps; Microdyne satellite receivers.
Miles of plant: 5.0 (coaxial). Homes passed: 250. Total homes in franchised area: 250.
Manager: Kevin Mayne. Chief technician: Tad Peak. Customer service manager: Liz Reuter.
Ownership: Fanch Communications Inc. (MSO). See Cable System Ownership.

HILLSBORO—Community Antenna System Inc., 1010 Lake St., Hillsboro, WI 54634. Phone: 608-489-2321. County: Vernon. ICA: WI0135.
TV Market Ranking: Outside TV Markets. Franchise award date: N.A. Franchise expiration date: N.A. Began: January 1, 1959.
Channel capacity: 15 (not 2-way capable). Channels available but not in use: N.A.

Basic Service
Subscribers: 634.
Programming (received off-air): WEAU-TV (N) Eau Claire; WKBT (C) La Crosse; WHA-TV (P), WISC-TV (C), WKOW-TV (A), WMSN-TV (F), WMTV (N) Madison.
Programming (via satellite): WGN-TV (W) Chicago; ESPN; Fox Family Channel; Nashville Network; TBS Superstation; Turner Network TV.
Fee: $50.00 installation; $15.02 monthly; $10.00 additional installation.

Pay Service 1
Pay Units: 145.
Programming (via satellite): Cinemax.
Fee: $6.95 monthly.

Equipment: Jerrold headend; Jerrold amplifiers; Plastoid & Times Fiber cable.
Miles of plant: 5.0 (coaxial).
Manager: Randall Kubarski. Chief technician: Gregory Kubarski.
City fee: None.
Ownership: Community Antenna System Inc. (MSO).

HOWARDS GROVE—Warner Cable, Box 224, Plymouth, WI 53073. Phone: 414-893-0542. Counties: Manitowoc & Sheboygan. Also serves Cleveland, Herman. ICA: WI0097.
TV Market Ranking: Outside TV Markets. Franchise award date: June 19, 1984. Franchise expiration date: June 19, 1999. Began: January 25, 1985.
Channel capacity: 35 (2-way capable; operating 2-way). Channels available but not in use: 10.

Basic Service
Subscribers: 1,022.
Programming (received off-air): WACY (U) Appleton; WBAY-TV (A), WFRV-TV (C), WGBA (N), WLUK-TV (F), WPNE (P) Green Bay; WMTV (N) Madison; WCGV-TV (I), WISN-TV (A), WITI (F), WMVS (P), WMVT (P), WTMJ-TV (N), WVTV (W) Milwaukee; allband FM.
Programming (via satellite): WGN-TV (W) Chicago; CNN; ESPN; Fox Family Channel; Headline News; Lifetime; MTV; Nashville Network; Nickelodeon; TBS Superstation; The Weather Channel; USA Network.
Current originations: Public access.
Planned originations: Automated emergency alert.
Fee: $40.00 installation; $9.51 monthly; $1.95 converter.

Pay Service 1
Pay Units: N.A.
Programming (via satellite): Cinemax; Disney Channel; HBO; Showtime.
Fee: $10.45 monthly (each).

Equipment: Scientific-Atlanta headend; Scientific-Atlanta amplifiers; Scientific-Atlanta cable; Video Data Systems character generator; Scientific-Atlanta set top converters; Pico & Arcom traps; Scientific-Atlanta satellite receivers.
Miles of plant: 150.0 (coaxial). Homes passed: 1,175. Total homes in franchised area: 1,175.
Manager: Norm Ruedinger. Marketing director: Mary Jane Daniels.
Ownership: Time Warner Cable (MSO).

HUDSON (town)—North American Communications Corp., Box 387, 901 Hwy. 212 E, Hector, MN 55342. Phones: 320-848-6781; 800-982-8038. Fax: 320-848-2478. County: St. Croix. ICA: WI0126.
TV Market Ranking: 13. Franchise award date: N.A. Franchise expiration date: N.A. Began: N.A.
Channel capacity: 60 (2-way capable; operating 2-way). Channels available but not in use: 19.

Basic Service
Subscribers: 729.
Programming (received off-air): WEUX (F) Chippewa Falls; WEAU-TV (N) Eau Claire; WHWC-TV (P) Menomonie; KARE (N), KLGT (W), KMSP-TV (U), KSTP-TV (A), KTCA-TV (P), KTCI-TV (P), WCCO-TV (C), WFTC (F) Minneapolis-St. Paul.
Programming (via satellite): WGN-TV (W) Chicago; A & E; American Movie Classics; C-SPAN; CNBC; CNN; Comedy Central; Discovery Channel; ESPN; ESPN 2; Fox Family Channel; History Channel; Learning Channel; Lifetime; MTV; Midwest Sports Channel; Nashville Network; Nick at Nite's TV Land; Nickelodeon; Odyssey; QVC; Sci-Fi Channel; TBS Superstation; The Weather Channel; Turner Network TV; USA Network; VH1.
Fee: $25.00 installation; $20.95 monthly.

Pay Service 1
Pay Units: 54.
Programming (via satellite): Cinemax.
Fee: $15.00 installation; $7.95 monthly.

Pay Service 2
Pay Units: 44.
Programming (via satellite): Disney Channel.
Fee: $15.00 installation; $6.95 monthly.

Pay Service 3
Pay Units: 77.
Programming (via satellite): HBO.
Fee: $15.00 installation; $9.95 monthly.

Pay Service 4
Pay Units: 57.
Programming (via satellite): Showtime.
Fee: $15.00 installation; $9.95 monthly.

Homes passed: 916.
Manager: George Honzay. Chief technician: Jason Janesich. Marketing director: Karla Huls.
Ownership: North American Communications Corp. (MSO).

HUSTISFORD—Charter Communications Inc., Rte. 2, County Hwy. J, Juneau, WI 53039. Phone: 920-349-3201. Fax: 920-349-3156. Counties: Dodge, Fond du Lac, Jefferson, Washington & Waukesha. Also serves Beaver Dam, Beaver Dam (town), Calamus Twp., Chester, Clyman, Concord, Emmet Twp., Fox Lake, Hartford, Hartford (town), Horicon, Hubbard Twp., Hustisford (village), Johnson Creek, Juneau, Lake Mills, Lake Mills (town), Lisbon, Mayville, Milford, Neosho, Oconomowoc, Polk, Portland, Portland (town), Slinger, Spacious Acres Trailer Court, Sullivan, Sussex, Theresa, Waterloo, Watertown, Waupun, Westford, Williamstown. ICA: WI0005.
TV Market Ranking: 23 (Concord, Hartford, Lisbon, Oconomowoc, Polk, Portland, Slinger, Sullivan, Sussex); 93 (Calamus Twp., Emmet Twp., Johnson Creek, Lake Mills, Milford, Waterloo, Watertown); Below 100 (Beaver Dam, Chester, Clyman, Fox Lake, Horicon, Hubbard Twp., Hustisford, Juneau, Mayville, Neosho, Portland, Spacious Acres Trailer Court, Theresa, Waupun, Westford, Williamstown); Outside TV Markets (Hustisford). Franchise award date: January 1, 1972. Franchise expiration date: N.A. Began: February 1, 1974.
Channel capacity: 54 (not 2-way capable). Channels available but not in use: 5.

Basic Service
Subscribers: 26,444; Commercial subscribers: 234.
Programming (received off-air): WHA-TV (P), WISC-TV (C), WKOW-TV (A), WMSN-

TV (F), WMTV (N) Madison; WISN-TV (A), WITI (F), WMVS (P), WTMJ-TV (N), WVTV (W) Milwaukee.

Programming (via satellite): WGN-TV (W) Chicago; C-SPAN; TBS Superstation; TV Guide Channel.

Current originations: Automated time-weather; public access; educational access; government access; religious access; leased access; library access; automated emergency alert; local news; local sports.

Fee: $45.00 installation; $25.20 monthly; $10.00 additional installation.

Commercial fee: $30.00 monthly.

Expanded Basic Service

Subscribers: 26,172.

Programming (via satellite): A & E; American Movie Classics; C-SPAN; CNBC; CNN; Cartoon Network; Comedy Central; Discovery Channel; Disney Channel; ESPN; EWTN; Fox Family Channel; Fox Sports Net; Headline News; Home Shopping Network; Knowledge TV; Lifetime; MTV; Nashville Network; Nickelodeon; Odyssey; Sci-Fi Channel; TBS Superstation; The Weather Channel; Turner Network TV; USA Network; Univision; VH1.

Fee: N.A.

Pay Service 1

Pay Units: 3,197.

Programming (via satellite): Cinemax.

Fee: $12.50 monthly.

Pay Service 2

Pay Units: 4,718.

Programming (via satellite): HBO.

Fee: $12.95 monthly.

Pay Service 3

Pay Units: 2,631.

Programming (via satellite): Showtime.

Fee: $12.50 monthly.

Pay Service 4

Pay Units: 402.

Programming (via satellite): The Movie Channel.

Fee: $12.50 monthly.

Pay Service 5

Pay Units: N.A.

Programming (via satellite): Disney Channel.

Fee: $3.95 monthly.

Pay-Per-View

Addressable homes: 17,000.

Local advertising: Yes. Available in satellite distributed, locally originated, character-generated & taped programming. Rates: $44.00/Minute; $22.00/30 Seconds. Local sales manager: Ann Holtz.

Program Guide: The Channel Guide.

Equipment: Scientific-Atlanta headend; Scientific-Atlanta amplifiers; Comm/Scope cable; Hitachi & Panasonic cameras; Panasonic, JVC & Sony VTRs; Texscan, Knox & Video Data Systems character generator; Oak & Hamlin set top converters; Zenith addressable set top converters; Pico & Eagle traps; Scientific-Atlanta satellite antenna; Scientific-Atlanta satellite receivers.

Miles of plant: 614.3 (coaxial). Additional miles planned: 25.9 (coaxial). Homes passed: 46,476.

Chief technician: Tom Gorsuch. Program director: Ann Holtz.

City fee: 5% of gross (varies).

Ownership: Charter Communications Inc. (MSO). Purchased from Marcus Cable, April 1, 1999.

INDEPENDENCE—Western Wisconsin Cable, 202 Whitehall Rd., Independence, WI 54747. Phone: 715-985-3004. Fax: 715-985-3261. Counties: Clark, Eau Claire, Jackson & Trempealeau. Also serves Alma Center, Arcadia, Blair, Eleva, Ettrick, Fairchild, Galesville, Hixton, Humbird, Lincoln Twp., Merillan, Northfield, Osseo, Pigeon, Pigeon Falls, Strum, Taylor, Trempealeau County, Whitehall. ICA: WI0032.

TV Market Ranking: Below 100 (Arcadia, Blair, Eleva, Ettrick, Fairchild, Galesville, Independence, Lincoln Twp., Osseo, Pigeon, Pigeon Falls, Strum, portions of Trempealeau County, Whitehall); Outside TV Markets (Alma Center, Hixton, Merillan, Northfield, Taylor, portions of Trempealeau County). Franchise award date: January 1, 1977. Franchise expiration date: June 1, 2007. Began: January 1, 1980.

Channel capacity: 44 (2-way capable; operating 2-way). Channels available but not in use: 9.

Basic Service

Subscribers: 6,628.

Programming (received off-air): WEAU-TV (N), WQOW-TV (A) Eau Claire; WHLA-TV (P), WKBT (C), WLAX (F), WXOW-TV (A) La Crosse; allband FM.

Programming (via satellite): WGN-TV (W) Chicago; C-SPAN; CNN; Comedy Central; Discovery Channel; ESPN; ESPN 2; Fox Family Channel; Headline News; Learning Channel; Lifetime; MTV; Nashville Network; Nickelodeon; Sci-Fi Channel; TBS Superstation; The Weather Channel; Turner Classic Movies; Turner Network TV; USA Network; VH1.

Current originations: Automated time-weather; public access; educational access; government access.

Fee: $25.00 installation; $21.00 monthly; $25.00 additional installation.

Pay Service 1

Pay Units: 620.

Programming (via satellite): Disney Channel.

Fee: $10.00 installation; $6.95 monthly.

Pay Service 2

Pay Units: 1,416.

Programming (via satellite): HBO.

Fee: $10.00 installation; $10.50 monthly.

Pay Service 3

Pay Units: 1,186.

Programming (via satellite): Cinemax.

Fee: $6.95 monthly.

Local advertising: Yes. Available in satellite distributed & locally originated programming. Rates: $4.00/30 Seconds; $60.00/Week. Local sales manager: Russ Manel.

Program Guide: TV Times.

Equipment: RCA & Scientific-Atlanta headend; AEL & Magnavox amplifiers; Times Fiber cable; Sony cameras; Sony VTRs; MSI character generator; Pioneer set top converters; Eagle traps; Scientific-Atlanta satellite antenna; Scientific-Atlanta satellite receivers; ChannelMatic commercial insert.

Miles of plant: 350.0 (coaxial); 66.0 (fiber optic). Homes passed: 7,500.

Manager: Mark Schroeder. Chief technician: Michael Flory. Program director: Russ Manch. Marketing director: Jane Holen.

City fee: None.

Ownership: Western Wisconsin Communications Cooperative.

IOLA—Triax Cablevision, Box 334, 1102 N. 4th St., Chillicothe, IL 61523-0334. Phones: 309-274-4500; 800-874-2924. Fax: 309-274-3188. County: Waupaca. Also serves Scandinavia. ICA: WI0118.

TV Market Ranking: Outside TV Markets. Franchise award date: N.A. Franchise expiration date: December 22, 2013. Began: December 23, 1998.

Channel capacity: 37 (not 2-way capable). Channels available but not in use: 3.

Basic Service

Subscribers: 429.

Programming (received off-air): WACY (U) Appleton; WBAY-TV (A), WFRV-TV (C), WGBA (N), WLUK-TV (F), WPNE (P) Green Bay; WAOW-TV (A), WSAW-TV (C) Wausau-Rhinelander.

Programming (via satellite): WGN-TV (W) Chicago; Animal Planet; Disney Channel; ESPN 2; Home Shopping Network; TBS Superstation; Trinity Bcstg. Network.

Fee: $45.00 installation; $13.50 monthly.

Expanded Basic Service

Subscribers: 405.

Programming (via satellite): A & E; American Movie Classics; CNN; Country Music TV; Discovery Channel; ESPN; Fox Family Channel; History Channel; Lifetime; MTV; Nashville Network; Nickelodeon; Sci-Fi Channel; The Weather Channel; Turner Network TV; USA Network.

Fee: $16.25 monthly.

Pay Service 1

Pay Units: 172.

Programming (via satellite): Cinemax; HBO; Showtime.

Fee: $25.00 installation; $7.95 monthly (Cinemax), $11.99 monthly (HBO or Showtime).

Equipment: Scientific-Atlanta headend; Scientific-Atlanta amplifiers; Scientific-Atlanta cable; Scientific-Atlanta set top converters; Vitek traps; Scientific-Atlanta satellite antenna; Scientific-Atlanta satellite receivers.

Miles of plant: 19.1 (coaxial). Homes passed: 800.

Manager: Mike Nodgerson. Chief technician: Pat Alderman.

City fee: 3% of gross.

Ownership: Triax Telecommunications Co. LLC (MSO). See Cable System Ownership.

IRON RIDGE—Warner Cable Communications, 5475 W. Abbott Ave., Greenfield, WI 53220-4900. Phone: 414-282-6300. Fax: 414-421-1206. County: Dodge. ICA: WI0255.

TV Market Ranking: Below 100. Franchise award date: N.A. Franchise expiration date: N.A. Began: N.A.

Channel capacity: 40. Channels available but not in use: N.A.

Basic Service

Subscribers: 210.

Programming (received off-air): WHA-TV (P), WISC-TV (C), WKOW-TV (A), WMSN-TV (F), WMTV (N) Madison; WCGV-TV (I), WDJT-TV (C), WISN-TV (A), WITI (F), WMVS (P), WMVT (P), WTMJ-TV (N), WVTV (W) Milwaukee.

Programming (via satellite): WGN-TV (W) Chicago; A & E; CNBC; CNN; Discovery Channel; ESPN; Fox Family Channel; Lifetime; MTV; Nashville Network; Nickelodeon; TBS Superstation; The Weather Channel; Turner Classic Movies; Turner Network TV; USA Network.

Planned programming (via satellite): Fox Sports Net.

Fee: $40.00 installation; $9.97 monthly.

Pay Service 1

Pay Units: N.A.

Programming (via satellite): Cinemax; Disney Channel; HBO.

Fee: $9.95 monthly (each).

Manager: Irene Picard. Chief technician: Rich Jaskowiak.

Ownership: Time Warner Cable (MSO). Sale pends to Charter Communications Inc.

IRONTON—Dairyland Cable Systems Inc., 1140 Sextonville Rd., Richland Center, WI 53581. Phone: 608-647-6383. Fax: 608-647-7394. County: Sauk. ICA: WI0256.

TV Market Ranking: Outside TV Markets. Franchise award date: N.A. Franchise expiration date: N.A. Began: December 1, 1988.

Channel capacity: 36. Channels available but not in use: N.A.

Basic Service

Subscribers: 68.

Programming (received off-air): WKBT (C) La Crosse; WISC-TV (C), WKOW-TV (A), WMSN-TV (F), WMTV (N) Madison.

Programming (via satellite): WGN-TV (W) Chicago; CNN; ESPN; Nashville Network; TBS Superstation; Turner Network TV; USA Network.

Fee: $25.00 installation; $14.95 monthly.

Pay Service 1

Pay Units: 9.

Programming (via satellite): HBO.

Fee: $10.50 monthly.

Manager: Jim Atkinson. Chief technician: Dale Davenport.

Ownership: Dairyland Cable Systems Inc. (MSO).

JANESVILLE—Charter Communications Inc., Box 1127, 1348 Plainfield Ave., Janesville, WI 53545-1127. Phone: 608-754-3644. Fax: 608-754-8107. Counties: Dane, Jefferson & Rock. Also serves Afton, Albion, Aztalan, Bradford, Clinton, Clinton (village), Edgerton, Evansville, Fort Atkinson, Fulton, Harmony, Indianford, Janesville (town), Jefferson, Koshkonong, Milton, Milton (town), Rock Twp., Sumner, Union Twp. ICA: WI0007.

TV Market Ranking: 93 (Afton, Albion, Aztalan, Bradford, Clinton, Edgerton, Evansville, Fort Atkinson, Harmony, Indianford, Janesville, Jefferson, Koshkonong, Milton, Rock Twp., Sumner, Union Twp.); 97 (Clinton, Fulton, Harmony, Janesville, Rock Twp.). Franchise award date: March 1, 1978. Franchise expiration date: June 1, 2003. Began: September 17, 1966.

Channel capacity: N.A. Channels available but not in use: N.A.

Basic Service

Subscribers: 22,746.

Programming (received off-air): WIFR (C) Freeport-Rockford; WHPN-TV (U) Janesville; WHA-TV (P), WISC-TV (C), WKOW-TV (A), WMSN-TV (F), WMTV (N) Madison; WVTV (W) Milwaukee; WQRF-TV (F), WREX-TV (N), WTVO (A) Rockford; 21 FMs.

Programming (via satellite): WGN-TV (W) Chicago; C-SPAN; C-SPAN 2; GRTV Network; Home Shopping Network; QVC; TV Guide Channel.

Current originations: Educational access; local news; local sports.

Fee: $27.49 installation; $8.78 monthly; $1.10 converter.

Expanded Basic Service

Subscribers: 21,513.

Programming (via satellite): A & E; American Movie Classics; Animal Planet; BET; Bravo; CNBC; CNN; Cartoon Network; Comedy Central; Country Music TV; Discovery Channel; Disney Channel; ESPN; ESPN 2; ESPN Classic Sports; ESPNews; EWTN; Fox Family Channel; Game Show Network; Headline News; History Channel; Home & Garden Television; Learning Channel; Lifetime; MSNBC; MTV; Midwest Sports Channel; Nashville Network; Nick at Nite's TV Land; Nickelodeon; Odyssey; Outdoor Life Network; Sci-Fi Channel; Speedvision; TBS Superstation; The Weather Channel; Toon Disney; Turner Classic Movies; Turner Network TV; USA Network; Univision; VH1.

Fee: $24.97 monthly.

Pay Service 1

Pay Units: 4,565.

Programming (via satellite): Cinemax.
Fee: $12.95 monthly.
Pay Service 2
Pay Units: 5,725.
Programming (via satellite): HBO (multiplexed).
Fee: $12.95 monthly.
Pay Service 3
Pay Units: 276.
Programming (via satellite): The Movie Channel.
Fee: $12.95 monthly.
Pay Service 4
Pay Units: 3,742.
Programming (via satellite): Showtime (multiplexed).
Fee: $12.95 monthly.
Pay Service 5
Pay Units: N.A.
Programming (via satellite): Starz!; The New Encore.
Fee: $12.95 monthly.
Pay-Per-View
Spice2; Viewer's Choice; Viewer's Choice 5; special events.
Fee: Varies.
Local advertising: Yes. Available in satellite distributed & locally originated programming. Local sales manager: Robert V. Penn.
Equipment: Scientific-Atlanta headend; Magnavox amplifiers; Times Fiber cable; Pioneer, Hamlin & Oak set top converters; Jerrold addressable set top converters; Scientific-Atlanta satellite antenna; Standard Components & Scientific-Atlanta satellite receivers; ChannelMatic commercial insert.
Miles of plant: 550.0 (coaxial). Homes passed: 49,103.
Manager: Marty Robinson. Chief technician: Tim Sanderson. Program director: Robert V. Penn. Marketing director: Danette Knickmeier.
Ownership: Charter Communications Inc. (MSO). Purchased from Time Warner Cable, April 1, 1999.

JUNCTION CITY—HLM Cable Corp., Box 620684, 2305-A Parview Rd., Middleton, WI 53562-0684. Phones: 608-831-7044; 800-451-5119. Fax: 608-836-5726. County: Portage. ICA: WI0257.
TV Market Ranking: Below 100. Franchise award date: N.A. Franchise expiration date: N.A. Began: N.A.
Channel capacity: 40 (not 2-way capable). Channels available but not in use: 12.
Basic Service
Subscribers: 103.
Programming (received off-air): WEAU-TV (N) Eau Claire; WAOW-TV (A), WHRM-TV (P), WJFW-TV (N), WSAW-TV (C) Wausau-Rhinelander.
Programming (via satellite): WGN-TV (W) Chicago; A & E; American Movie Classics; CNBC; CNN; Discovery Channel; ESPN; ESPN 2; Fox Family Channel; FoxNet; History Channel; Lifetime; Nashville Network; Nick at Nite; Nick at Nite's TV Land; Nickelodeon; Sci-Fi Channel; TBS Superstation; The Weather Channel; Turner Network TV; USA Network; VH1.
Fee: $19.95 installation; $25.00 monthly; $1.50 converter.
Pay Service 1
Pay Units: 13.
Programming (via satellite): Disney Channel.
Fee: $14.95 installation; $6.95 monthly.
Pay Service 2
Pay Units: 31.
Programming (via satellite): Showtime.
Fee: $14.95 installation; $6.95 monthly.
Manager: Robert E. Ryan.
Ownership: H.L.M. Cable Co. (MSO).

KELLNERSVILLE—Cable Systems Management of Iowa Inc., 3600 Kennebec Dr., Eagan, MN 55122. Phone: 612-688-2623. Fax: 612-688-2624. County: Manitowoc. ICA: WI0258.
TV Market Ranking: 62. Franchise award date: N.A. Franchise expiration date: N.A. Began: August 1, 1990.
Channel capacity: 40. Channels available but not in use: 20.
Basic Service
Subscribers: 55.
Programming (received off-air): WACY (U) Appleton; WBAY-TV (A), WFRV-TV (C), WLUK-TV (F), WPNE (P) Green Bay.
Programming (via satellite): WGN-TV (W) Chicago; A & E; American Movie Classics; CNN; Country Music TV; Discovery Channel; ESPN; Fox Family Channel; Home Shopping Network; Learning Channel; Nashville Network; Showtime; TBS Superstation; Turner Network TV; USA Network.
Fee: $50.00 installation; $30.00 monthly.
Miles of plant: 1.9 (coaxial). Homes passed: 121.
Manager: Jeff Anderson.
Ownership: Cable Systems Management of Iowa Inc. (MSO).

KENDALL—Community Antenna System Inc., 1010 Lake St., Hillsboro, WI 54634. Phone: 608-489-2321. County: Monroe. ICA: WI0201.
TV Market Ranking: Outside TV Markets. Franchise award date: January 1, 1961. Franchise expiration date: N.A. Began: January 1, 1963.
Channel capacity: 15 (not 2-way capable). Channels available but not in use: N.A.
Basic Service
Subscribers: 194.
Programming (received off-air): WEAU-TV (N) Eau Claire; WKBT (C) La Crosse; WHA-TV (P), WISC-TV (C), WKOW-TV (A), WMSN-TV (F), WMTV (N) Madison.
Programming (via satellite): WGN-TV (W) Chicago; ESPN; Fox Family Channel; Nashville Network; TBS Superstation; Turner Network TV.
Fee: $50.00 installation; $15.02 monthly.
Pay Service 1
Pay Units: 51.
Programming (via satellite): Cinemax.
Fee: $6.95 monthly.
Equipment: Jerrold headend.
Miles of plant: 4.0 (coaxial). Homes passed: 225. Total homes in franchised area: 225.
Manager: Randall Kubarski. Chief technician: Gregory Kubarski.
Ownership: Community Antenna System Inc. (MSO).

KENOSHA—Time Warner Cable, Southern Area Office, 1403 Washington Rd., Kenosha, WI 53140. Phone: 414-656-8460. Fax: 414-656-8490.
Web site: http://www.timewarnerwi.com.
Counties: Buffalo, Kenosha, Racine & Walworth. Also serves Bloomfield, Bristol, Burlington, Caledonia, Dover, Elmwood Park, Geneva, Lake Geneva, Linn, Lyons, Mount Pleasant, North Bay, Norway (town), Paddock Lake, Pleasant Prairie, Racine, Randall, Randall (town) (Racine County), Raymond (town), Rochester, Salem, Silver Lake, Somers, Spring Prairie, Sturtevant, Troy (town), Waterford (town), Wheatfield, Wheatland, Wind Point, Yorkville. ICA: WI0009.
TV Market Ranking: 23 (Bristol, Burlington, Caledonia, Elmwood Park, Kenosha, Mount Pleasant, North Bay, Norway, Paddock Lake, Pleasant Prairie, Racine, Raymond, Rochester, Salem, Silver Lake, Somers, Strurtevant, Troy, Waterford, Wheatfield, Wheatland, Wind Point, Yorkville); Below 100 (Bloomfield, Dover, Lake Geneva, Linn, Lyons, Randall, Spring Prairie). Franchise award date: July 5, 1983. Franchise expiration date: July 1, 1998. Began: June 1, 1984.
Channel capacity: 79 (not 2-way capable). Channels available but not in use: None.
Basic Service
Subscribers: 97,000.
Programming (received off-air): WBBM-TV (C), WFLD (F), WLS-TV (A), WMAQ-TV (N), WTTW (P) Chicago; WPXE (X) Kenosha; WCGV-TV (I), WDJT-TV (C), WISN-TV (A), WITI (F), WMVS (P), WMVT (P), WTMJ-TV (N), WVCY-TV (I), WVTV (W) Milwaukee; WJJA (H) Racine; allband FM.
Programming (via satellite): WGN-TV (W) Chicago; C-SPAN; C-SPAN 2; CNBC; CNN; Discovery Channel; E! Entertainment TV; ESPN; EWTN; Fox Family Channel; Midwest Sports Channel; Odyssey; QVC; TBS Superstation; TV Food Network; TV Guide Channel; The Weather Channel; Travel Channel; Univision.
Current originations: Automated time-weather; public access; educational access; government access; religious access; library access; automated emergency alert; local news; local sports.
Fee: $36.00 installation; $8.89 monthly; $0.82 converter; $15.95 additional installation.
Digital Basic Service
Subscribers: N.A.
Programming (via satellite): BBC America; Discovery Home & Leisure Channel; Discovery Kids Channel; Discovery People; Discovery Science Channel; Discovery Wings Channel; ESPN Classic Sports; ESPNews; Encore Love Stories; Encore Mystery; Encore Westerns; Fox Sports World Espanol; Game Show Network; Golf Channel; Home & Garden Television; Independent Film Channel; Outdoor Life Network; Romance Classics; Speedvision; Starz! Theater; Turner Classic Movies.
Fee: N.A.
Expanded Basic Service
Subscribers: 92,150.
Programming (via satellite): A & E; American Movie Classics; Animal Planet; BET; Bravo; Cartoon Network; Country Music TV; Court TV; ESPN 2; Encore Movie Networks; FX; Fox News Channel; Headline News; History Channel; Learning Channel; Lifetime; MTV; Nashville Network; Nickelodeon; Sci-Fi Channel; Turner Network TV; USA Network; VH1.
Fee: $17.15 monthly.
Pay Service 1
Pay Units: 22,000.
Programming (via satellite): Cinemax (multiplexed); Disney Channel; HBO (multiplexed); Showtime (multiplexed); Starz!; The Movie Channel; The New Encore.
Fee: $6.95 monthly (Disney), $10.95 monthly (Cinemax, HBO, Showtime or TMC).
Pay Service 2
Pay Units: N.A.
Programming (via satellite): DMX.
Fee: N.A.
Pay-Per-View
Addressable homes: 20,000.
Spice delivered digitally; movies; special events.
Fee: Varies.
Local advertising: Yes. Available in satellite distributed & locally originated programming. Local sales manager: Jim Wardrip.
Program Guide: Channel Guide.
Equipment: Scientific-Atlanta headend; C-COR amplifiers; Comm/Scope & Times Fiber cable; Prodelin cameras; Hamlin & Tocom set top converters; Tocom addressable set top converters; Scientific-Atlanta satellite antenna; Scientific-Atlanta satellite receivers.
Miles of plant: 680.0 (coaxial); 20.0 (fiber optic). Additional miles planned: 6.0 (coaxial). Homes passed: 142,000. Total homes in franchised area: 142,000.
Manager: Rich Jennings. Chief technician: Robert Mould. Production director: Jill Ianni. Marketing manager: Jane Larson. Customer service manager: Tori Miller.
City fee: 5% of gross (Kenosha & Somers).
Ownership: Time Warner Cable (MSO).

KEWAUNEE—Charter Communications Inc., 1623 Broadway Ave., Sheboygan, WI 53081-5700. Phone: 800-395-0995. Fax: 414-337-9251. County: Kewaunee. ICA: WI0111.
TV Market Ranking: 62. Franchise award date: July 14, 1980. Franchise expiration date: N.A. Began: June 5, 1981.
Channel capacity: 35 (2-way capable; operating 2-way). Channels available but not in use: 3.
Basic Service
Subscribers: 736.
Programming (received off-air): WBAY-TV (A), WFRV-TV (C), WGBA (N), WLUK-TV (F), WPNE (P) Green Bay.
Programming (via satellite): WGN-TV (W) Chicago; A & E; C-SPAN; CNN; Discovery Channel; ESPN; Fox Family Channel; Headline News; Lifetime; MTV; Nashville Network; Nick at Nite; Nickelodeon; QVC; TBS Superstation; The Inspirational Network; The Weather Channel; Turner Network TV; USA Network.
Current originations: Automated time-weather; public access; educational access; leased access.
Fee: $42.95 installation; $12.75 monthly; $19.95 additional installation.
Pay Service 1
Pay Units: 133.
Programming (via satellite): Cinemax.
Fee: $19.95 installation; $12.50 monthly.
Pay Service 2
Pay Units: 75.
Programming (via satellite): Disney Channel.
Fee: $19.95 installation; $9.35 monthly.
Pay Service 3
Pay Units: 158.
Programming (via satellite): HBO.
Fee: $19.95 installation; $12.95 monthly.
Pay Service 4
Pay Units: 172.
Programming (via satellite): Showtime.
Fee: $19.95 installation; $12.50 monthly.
Local advertising: No.
Equipment: Scientific-Atlanta headend; Scientific-Atlanta amplifiers; Comm/Scope cable; Video Data Systems character generator; Hamlin set top converters; Eagle traps; Scientific-Atlanta & Microdyne satellite antenna; Scientific-Atlanta satellite receivers.
Miles of plant: 17.0 (coaxial). Homes passed: 967.
Manager: Jim Ebenhoe. Chief technician: Duane Hendricks.
City fee: 3% of gross.
Ownership: Charter Communications Inc. (MSO). Purchased from Marcus Cable, April 1, 1999.

KINGSTON—Cable Systems Management of Iowa Inc., 3600 Kennebec Dr., Eagan, MN 55122. Phone: 612-688-2623. Fax: 612-688-2624. County: Green Lake. ICA: WI0213.

TV Market Ranking: Outside TV Markets. Franchise award date: N.A. Franchise expiration date: N.A. Began: N.A.
Channel capacity: 40. Channels available but not in use: 7.
Basic Service
Subscribers: 55.
Programming (received off-air): WHA-TV (P), WISC-TV (C), WKOW-TV (A), WMTV (N) Madison.
Programming (via satellite): WGN-TV (W) Chicago; A & E; American Movie Classics; CNN; Country Music TV; Discovery Channel; ESPN; Fox Family Channel; Headline News; Lifetime; Nashville Network; Showtime; TBS Superstation; Turner Network TV; USA Network.
Fee: $50.00 installation; $30.00 monthly.
Miles of plant: 3.2 (coaxial). Homes passed: 171.
Manager: Jeff Anderson.
Ownership: Cable Systems Management of Iowa Inc. (MSO).

KNAPP (village)—Baldwin Telecom Inc., 930 Maple St., Baldwin, WI 54002. Phone: 715-684-3346. Fax: 715-684-4747. County: Dunn. ICA: WI0259.
TV Market Ranking: Below 100. Franchise award date: October 28, 1988. Franchise expiration date: October 28, 2003. Began: July 1, 1989.
Channel capacity: 40 (2-way capable; not operating 2-way). Channels available but not in use: 11.
Basic Service
Subscribers: 130.
Programming (received off-air): WEUX (F) Chippewa Falls; WEAU-TV (N), WQOW-TV (A) Eau Claire; WKBT (C) La Crosse; WHWC-TV (P) Menomonie; KARE (N), KLGT (W), KMSP-TV (U), KSTP-TV (A), KTCA-TV (P), WCCO-TV (C), WFTC (F) Minneapolis-St. Paul.
Programming (via satellite): WGN-TV (W) Chicago; CNN; Discovery Channel; ESPN; Fox Family Channel; Learning Channel; Nashville Network; Nick at Nite's TV Land; Nickelodeon; QVC; TBS Superstation; The Weather Channel; Turner Network TV; USA Network.
Fee: $25.95 installation; $16.90 monthly.
Pay Service 1
Pay Units: 30.
Programming (via satellite): Cinemax.
Fee: $15.00 installation; $6.30 monthly.
Pay Service 2
Pay Units: 27.
Programming (via satellite): HBO.
Fee: $15.00 installation; $8.40 monthly.
Miles of plant: 6.0 (coaxial); None (fiber optic). Homes passed: 250. Total homes in franchised area: 250.
Manager: Larry Knegendorf. Chief technician: Tim Kusilek.
City fee: 3% of gross.
Ownership: Baldwin TeleCom Inc. (MSO).

LA CROSSE—Bresnan Communications Co., Box 758, 1022 S. 19th St., La Crosse, WI 54602. Phone: 608-784-9244. Fax: 608-784-8490. Counties: La Crosse, WI; Houston, MN. Also serves La Crescent, MN; Shelby, WI. ICA: WI0017.
TV Market Ranking: Below 100. Franchise award date: January 1, 1962. Franchise expiration date: N.A. Began: August 1, 1961.
Channel capacity: 78 (2-way capable; not operating 2-way). Channels available but not in use: 14.
Basic Service
Subscribers: 17,253.
Programming (received off-air): WEAU-TV (N) Eau Claire; WHLA-TV (P), WKBT (C), WLAX (F), WXOW-TV (A) La Crosse; 13 FMs.
Programming (via microwave): KAAL (A,F) Austin; KIMT (C) Mason City.
Programming (via satellite): WGN-TV (W) Chicago; C-SPAN; CNBC; CNN; Discovery Channel; EWTN; Fox Family Channel; Headline News; Lifetime; MTV; Nickelodeon; QVC; TBS Superstation; The Weather Channel; Travel Channel.
Current originations: Automated time-weather; public access; religious access.
Planned originations: Leased access.
Fee: $24.95 installation.
Expanded Basic Service
Subscribers: 15,271.
Programming (via satellite): A & E; American Movie Classics; ESPN; Nashville Network; Turner Network TV; USA Network.
Fee: $10.97 monthly.
Pay Service 1
Pay Units: 556.
Programming (via satellite): Cinemax.
Fee: $19.95 installation; $9.00 monthly.
Pay Service 2
Pay Units: 495.
Programming (via satellite): Disney Channel.
Fee: $6.95 monthly.
Pay Service 3
Pay Units: 6,485.
Programming (via satellite): The New Encore.
Fee: N.A.
Pay Service 4
Pay Units: 2,198.
Programming (via satellite): HBO.
Fee: $9.00 monthly.
Pay Service 5
Pay Units: 189.
Programming (via satellite): The Movie Channel.
Fee: $9.00 monthly.
Pay Service 6
Pay Units: 1,915.
Programming (via satellite): Showtime.
Fee: $9.00 monthly.
Pay-Per-View
Addressable homes: 4,500.
Local advertising: Yes (locally produced). Available in satellite distributed programming. Rates: $50.00/Minute; $25.00/30 Seconds.
Program Guide: The Cable Guide.
Equipment: Scientific-Atlanta headend; Jerrold amplifiers; Times Fiber cable; Hitachi cameras; Sony VTRs; Compuvid character generator; Jerrold set top converters; Intercept traps; AFC & Andrew satellite antenna; Scientific-Atlanta satellite receivers; Channel-Matic commercial insert.
Miles of plant: 196.0 (coaxial); 43.0 (fiber optic). Additional miles planned: 2.0 (coaxial). Homes passed: 23,258. Total homes in franchised area: 29,847.
Manager: Karen Troxell. Chief technician: Larry Ladwig. Marketing director: Scott Arenz.
City fee: 3% of basic gross.
Ownership: Bresnan Communications Co. LP (MSO). Purchased from Tele-Communications Inc, February 2, 1999. See Cable System Ownership.

LA VALLE—Spring Green CableComm, Box 609, 245 S. Winsted St., Spring Green, WI 53588-9431. Phone: 608-588-7454. Fax: 608-588-7067. County: Sauk. Also serves La Valle (town), Lake Redstone. ICA: WI0260.
TV Market Ranking: Outside TV Markets. Franchise award date: January 1, 1971. Franchise expiration date: August 1, 2001. Began: September 30, 1971.
Channel capacity: 40. Channels available but not in use: 12.
Basic Service
Subscribers: 370.
Programming (received off-air): WKBT (C) La Crosse; WHA-TV (P), WISC-TV (C), WKOW-TV (A), WMSN-TV (F), WMTV (N) Madison.
Programming (via satellite): WGN-TV (W) Chicago; A & E; CNN; Discovery Channel; ESPN; Fox Family Channel; Nashville Network; Nickelodeon; TBS Superstation; Turner Classic Movies; Turner Network TV; USA Network.
Fee: $49.95 installation; $29.85 monthly; $19.95 additional installation.
Pay Service 1
Pay Units: N.A.
Programming (via satellite): HBO.
Fee: $19.95 installation; $9.95 monthly.
Equipment: Scientific-Atlanta headend; Scientific-Atlanta amplifiers; M/A-Com cable; Pico traps; Harris satellite antenna; DX Communications satellite receivers.
Miles of plant: 28.0 (coaxial).
Manager: Kevin Mayne. Chief technician: Tad Peak. Customer service manager: Liz Reuter.
City fee: None.
Ownership: Fanch Communications Inc. (MSO). See Cable System Ownership.

LAC DU FLAMBEAU—Gauthier Cablevision, Box 399, Lac du Flambeau, WI 54538. Phone: 715-588-3580. County: Vilas. ICA: WI0182.
TV Market Ranking: Below 100. Franchise award date: N.A. Franchise expiration date: N.A. Began: January 3, 1984.
Channel capacity: 54 (2-way capable; operating 2-way). Channels available but not in use: N.A.
Basic Service
Subscribers: N.A.
Programming (received off-air): WLEF-TV (P) Park Falls; WAOW-TV (A), WJFW-TV (N), WSAW-TV (C) Wausau-Rhinelander; allband FM.
Programming (via satellite): WGN-TV (W) Chicago; CNN; ESPN; Lifetime; TBS Superstation; USA Network.
Fee: $45.00 installation; $10.00 monthly.
Pay Service 1
Pay Units: N.A.
Programming (via satellite): Cinemax; HBO.
Fee: $10.00 monthly (each).
Equipment: Triple Crown headend; Jerrold amplifiers; Times Fiber cable; KES & M/A-Com satellite antenna; Triple Crown satellite receivers.
Miles of plant: 14.0 (coaxial). Additional miles planned: 12.0 (coaxial). Homes passed: 300.
Manager: Charles Gauthier.
City fee: $1 per subscriber annually.
Ownership: Charles F. Gauthier.

LADYSMITH—Charter Communications Inc., Box 539, 1725 S. Main St., Rice Lake, WI 54868-0539. Phones: 715-234-3821; 800-262-2578. Fax: 715-234-8537. County: Rusk. Also serves Bruce, Flambeau, Grant, Tony (village). ICA: WI0081.
TV Market Ranking: Below 100 (Bruce); Outside TV Markets (Flambeau, Grant, Ladysmith). Franchise award date: N.A. Franchise expiration date: March 31, 1998. Began: June 1, 1967.
Channel capacity: 35 (not 2-way capable). Channels available but not in use: None.
Basic Service
Subscribers: 1,869.
Programming (received off-air): WEUX (F) Chippewa Falls; WEAU-TV (N), WQOW-TV (A) Eau Claire; WHWC-TV (P) Menomonie; WCCO-TV (C) Minneapolis-St. Paul; WSAW-TV (C) Wausau-Rhinelander.
Programming (via satellite): WGN-TV (W) Chicago; A & E; American Movie Classics; C-SPAN; C-SPAN 2; CNBC; CNN; Comedy Central; Country Music TV; Discovery Channel; Disney Channel; E! Entertainment TV; ESPN; Fox Family Channel; FoxNet; Headline News; Learning Channel; Lifetime; MTV; Nashville Network; Nickelodeon; QVC; TBS Superstation; The Weather Channel; Turner Network TV; USA Network; VH1.
Fee: $42.95 installation; $28.13 monthly.
Pay Service 1
Pay Units: 144.
Programming (via satellite): Cinemax.
Fee: $19.95 installation; $12.50 monthly.
Pay Service 2
Pay Units: 174.
Programming (via satellite): HBO.
Fee: $19.95 installation; $12.95 monthly.
Pay Service 3
Pay Units: 182.
Programming (via satellite): Showtime.
Fee: $19.95 installation; $12.50 monthly.
Local advertising: Yes. Local sales manager: Andy Jerome.
Equipment: Jerrold headend; Jerrold amplifiers; Times Fiber cable; Hamlin & Scientific-Atlanta set top converters; Eagle traps; Andrew & Scientific-Atlanta satellite antenna; Scientific-Atlanta satellite receivers.
Miles of plant: 26.0 (coaxial).
Manager: Scott Binder. Chief technician: George Benjamin.
City fee: None.
Ownership: Charter Communications Inc. (MSO). Purchased from Marcus Cable, April 1, 1999.

LAFAYETTE—Charter Communications Inc., Box 539, 1725 S. Main St., Rice Lake, WI 54868-0539. Phones: 715-234-3821; 800-262-2578. Fax: 715-234-8537. County: Chippewa. Also serves Lake Wissota. ICA: WI0091.
TV Market Ranking: Below 100. Franchise award date: N.A. Franchise expiration date: October 16, 2010. Began: January 1, 1979.
Channel capacity: 60 (not 2-way capable). Channels available but not in use: 25.
Basic Service
Subscribers: 1,064.
Programming (received off-air): WEUX (F) Chippewa Falls; WEAU-TV (N), WQOW-TV (A) Eau Claire; WKBT (C) La Crosse; WHWC-TV (P) Menomonie; WCCO-TV (C) Minneapolis-St. Paul.
Programming (via satellite): WGN-TV (W) Chicago; A & E; American Movie Classics; CNBC; CNN; Comedy Central; Discovery Channel; Disney Channel; E! Entertainment TV; ESPN; Fox Family Channel; FoxNet; Headline News; Learning Channel; Lifetime; MTV; Nashville Network; Nickelodeon; TBS Superstation; The Weather Channel; Turner Network TV; USA Network; VH1.
Fee: $42.95 installation; $23.50 monthly.
Pay Service 1
Pay Units: 134.
Programming (via satellite): Cinemax.
Fee: $19.95 installation; $12.50 monthly.
Pay Service 2
Pay Units: 150.
Programming (via satellite): HBO.
Fee: $12.95 monthly.
Pay Service 3
Pay Units: 168.
Programming (via satellite): Showtime.
Fee: $12.50 monthly.
Local advertising: No.

Equipment: Blonder-Tongue, Standard Communications & Triple Crown headend; Theta-Com & Triple Crown amplifiers; Comm/Scope cable; Hamlin & Scientific-Atlanta set top converters; AFC satellite antenna; AFC satellite receivers.
Miles of plant: 42.0 (coaxial). Homes passed: 1,391.
Manager: Scott Binder. Chief technician: George Benjamin.
Ownership: Charter Communications Inc. (MSO). Purchased from Marcus Cable, April 1, 1999.

LAKE HOLCOMBE—S & K TV Systems, Box 127, 503 W. Miner Ave., Ladysmith, WI 54848. Phones: 715-532-7321; 800-924-7880. County: Chippewa. ICA: WI0147.
TV Market Ranking: Outside TV Markets. Franchise award date: January 1, 1989. Franchise expiration date: January 1, 2004. Began: March 1, 1990.
Channel capacity: 36. Channels available but not in use: 15.
Basic Service
Subscribers: 360.
Programming (received off-air): WEUX (F) Chippewa Falls; WEAU-TV (N), WQOW-TV (A) Eau Claire; WKBT (C) La Crosse; WHWC-TV (P) Menomonie.
Programming (via satellite): WGN-TV (W) Chicago; A & E; American Movie Classics; CNN; Country Music TV; Discovery Channel; Disney Channel; ESPN; Fox Family Channel; Nashville Network; Nick at Nite's TV Land; TBS Superstation; The Weather Channel; Turner Network TV; USA Network.
Fee: $22.95 monthly.
Pay Service 1
Pay Units: N.A.
Programming (via satellite): Cinemax.
Fee: $6.95 monthly.
Homes passed: 500. Total homes in franchised area: 500.
Manager: Randy Scott.
Ownership: S & K TV Systems (MSO).

LAKE NEBAGAMON—Bresnan Communications Co., 302 E. Superior St., Duluth, MN 55802. Phone: 218-722-2815. Fax: 218-726-1008. County: Douglas. ICA: WI0133.
TV Market Ranking: 89. Franchise award date: August 1, 1989. Franchise expiration date: August 1, 2009. Began: June 1, 1990.
Channel capacity: 54 (2-way capable). Channels available but not in use: 31.
Basic Service
Subscribers: 225.
Programming (received off-air): KBJR-TV (N), KDLH (C), WDIO-TV (A,F), WDSE-TV (P) Duluth-Superior.
Programming (via satellite): WGN-TV (W) Chicago; A & E; American Movie Classics; C-SPAN; CNN; Court TV; Discovery Channel; ESPN; Fox Family Channel; Learning Channel; MTV; Nashville Network; Nick at Nite; Nickelodeon; TBS Superstation; Turner Network TV; USA Network.
Fee: $25.48 installation (aerial), $40.76 (underground); $15.89 monthly.
Pay Service 1
Pay Units: 44.
Programming (via satellite): HBO.
Fee: $11.00 monthly.
Pay Service 2
Pay Units: 41.
Programming (via satellite): Showtime.
Fee: $11.00 monthly.
Equipment: Scientific-Atlanta headend; Jerrold amplifiers; Comm/Scope & Times Fiber cable; Jerrold set top converters; Eagle & Pico traps; Prodelin satellite antenna.
Miles of plant: 26.0 (coaxial). Homes passed: 646. Total homes in franchised area: 650.
Manager: Michael J. McPhee. Chief technician: James Matuszewski. Marketing director: Steve Netzel.
Ownership: Bresnan Communications Co. LP (MSO). Purchased from Bresnan Communications Co, February 2, 1999. See Cable System Ownership.

LANCASTER—Spring Green CableComm, Box 609, 245 S. Winsted St., Spring Green, WI 53588-9431. Phone: 608-588-7454. Fax: 608-588-7067. County: Grant. ICA: WI0261.
TV Market Ranking: Below 100. Franchise award date: January 1, 1980. Franchise expiration date: N.A. Began: June 1, 1967.
Channel capacity: 64 (2-way capable; not operating 2-way). Channels available but not in use: 17.
Basic Service
Subscribers: 1,508.
Programming (received off-air): KCRG-TV (A), KGAN (C), KRIN (P), KWWL (N) Cedar Rapids-Waterloo; KFXB (F) Dubuque; WHA-TV (P), WISC-TV (C), WKOW-TV (A), WMTV (N) Madison.
Programming (via satellite): WGN-TV (W) Chicago; A & E; CNN; Discovery Channel; ESPN; ESPN 2; EWTN; FX; Fox Family Channel; Headline News; Home Shopping Network; Learning Channel; Lifetime; Nashville Network; Nickelodeon; Sci-Fi Channel; TBS Superstation; The Weather Channel; Turner Classic Movies; Turner Network TV; USA Network; VH1.
Current originations: Local news.
Fee: $49.95 installation; $29.85 monthly; $19.95 additional installation.
Pay Service 1
Pay Units: N.A.
Programming (via satellite): Cinemax; Disney Channel; HBO.
Fee: $19.95 installation; $6.95 monthly (Disney), $9.95 monthly (Cinemax or HBO).
Local advertising: Planned.
Equipment: Scientific-Atlanta headend; Magnavox amplifiers; Times Fiber fiber optic cable.
Miles of plant: 27.0 (coaxial).
Manager: Kevin Mayne. Chief technician: Tad Peak. Customer service manager: Liz Reuter.
City fee: 3% of basic gross.
Ownership: Fanch Communications Inc. (MSO). See Cable System Ownership.

LAND O'LAKES—Karban TV Systems Inc., 73A S. Stevens St., Rhinelander, WI 54501. Phone: 715-277-2339. County: Vilas. ICA: WI0262.
TV Market Ranking: Below 100. Franchise award date: N.A. Franchise expiration date: N.A. Began: July 1, 1989.
Channel capacity: 54. Channels available but not in use: 29.
Basic Service
Subscribers: 95.
Programming (received off-air): WLEF-TV (P) Park Falls; WAOW-TV (A), WJFW-TV (N), WSAW-TV (C) Wausau-Rhinelander.
Programming (via satellite): WGN-TV (W) Chicago; A & E; CNN; Discovery Channel; ESPN; Fox Family Channel; Headline News; Lifetime; Nashville Network; Nickelodeon; TBS Superstation; Turner Network TV; USA Network.
Fee: $75.00 installation; $24.00 monthly.
Pay Service 1
Pay Units: 3.
Programming (via satellite): Disney Channel.
Fee: $9.00 monthly.
Pay Service 2
Pay Units: 19.
Programming (via satellite): HBO.
Fee: $10.00 monthly.
Miles of plant: 8.0 (coaxial). Homes passed: 180.
Manager: John Karban.
Ownership: Karban TV Systems Inc. (MSO).

LAONA—Northern Lakes Cable TV, Box 8, Bonduel, WI 54107. Phone: 715-758-2500. County: Forest. ICA: WI0143.
TV Market Ranking: Outside TV Markets. Franchise award date: N.A. Franchise expiration date: N.A. Began: June 1, 1989.
Channel capacity: 54 (not 2-way capable). Channels available but not in use: N.A.
Basic Service
Subscribers: 320.
Programming (received off-air): WACY (U) Appleton; WBAY-TV (A), WFRV-TV (C), WGBA (N), WLUK-TV (F) Green Bay; WLUC-TV (N) Marquette; WAOW-TV (A), WHRM-TV (P), WJFW-TV (N), WSAW-TV (C) Wausau-Rhinelander.
Programming (via satellite): WGN-TV (W) Chicago; CNN; Discovery Channel; ESPN; Fox Family Channel; MTV; Nashville Network; Nickelodeon; TBS Superstation; Turner Classic Movies; USA Network.
Fee: $25.00 installation; $15.00 monthly.
Pay Service 1
Pay Units: N.A.
Programming (via satellite): Cinemax; HBO.
Fee: $9.95 monthly (each).
Equipment: Scientific-Atlanta headend; Scientific-Atlanta amplifiers; Comm/Scope cable; Oak & Hamlin set top converters; Arcom traps; Scientific-Atlanta satellite antenna; Scientific-Atlanta satellite receivers.
Miles of plant: 15.0 (coaxial). Homes passed: 550. Total homes in franchised area: 550.
Manager: Robert Steichen.
Ownership: Northern Lakes Cable TV (MSO).

LENA—Charter Communications Inc., Box 1197, 55 W. Scott St., Fon Du Lac, WI 54936-1197. Phones: 920-923-7196; 800-581-0081. Fax: 920-923-1235. County: Oconto. ICA: WI0204.
TV Market Ranking: 62. Franchise award date: March 1, 1983. Franchise expiration date: May 1, 1999. Began: May 1, 1984.
Channel capacity: 30. Channels available but not in use: N.A.
Basic Service
Subscribers: 147.
Programming (received off-air): WACY (U) Appleton; WBAY-TV (A), WFRV-TV (C), WGBA (N), WLUK-TV (F), WPNE (P) Green Bay.
Programming (via satellite): WGN-TV (W) Chicago; QVC; TBS Superstation.
Current originations: Public access.
Fee: $56.73 installation; $7.54 monthly.
Expanded Basic Service
Subscribers: 142.
Programming (via satellite): A & E; CNN; Discovery Channel; Disney Channel; ESPN; Fox Family Channel; Lifetime; MTV; Nashville Network; Nickelodeon; Sci-Fi Channel; Turner Network TV; USA Network.
Fee: $12.25 monthly.
Pay Service 1
Pay Units: 31.
Programming (via satellite): Cinemax.
Fee: $12.50 monthly.
Pay Service 2
Pay Units: 42.
Programming (via satellite): HBO.
Fee: $12.95 monthly.
Miles of plant: 3.7 (coaxial). Homes passed: 267.
Manager: Lisa Washa. Chief technician: Jeff Gerner.
Ownership: Charter Communications Inc. (MSO). Purchased from Marcus Cable, April 1, 1999.

LOGANVILLE (village)—Dairyland Cable Systems Inc., 1140 Sextonville Rd., Richland Center, WI 53581. Phone: 608-647-6383. Fax: 608-647-7394. County: Sauk. ICA: WI0263.
TV Market Ranking: Outside TV Markets. Franchise award date: N.A. Franchise expiration date: N.A. Began: September 1, 1989.
Channel capacity: 13. Channels available but not in use: N.A.
Basic Service
Subscribers: 89.
Programming (received off-air): WISC-TV (C), WKOW-TV (A), WMSN-TV (F), WMTV (N) Madison; WMVS (P) Milwaukee.
Programming (via satellite): WGN-TV (W) Chicago; CNN; ESPN; Nashville Network; Nickelodeon; TBS Superstation; Turner Network TV; USA Network.
Fee: $25.00 installation; $16.95 monthly.
Pay Service 1
Pay Units: 27.
Programming (via satellite): HBO.
Fee: $10.50 monthly.
Manager: Jim Atkinson. Chief technician: Dale Davenport.
Ownership: Dairyland Cable Systems Inc. (MSO).

LUCK—Vision Communications, Box 355, 28 First Ave. W, Luck, WI 54853-0355. Phone: 715-472-2700. Fax: 715-472-2707. County: Polk. Also serves Balsam Lake, Centuria, Frederic, Milltown. ICA: WI0104.
TV Market Ranking: Outside TV Markets. Franchise award date: July 15, 1985. Franchise expiration date: January 1, 2000. Began: December 1, 1985.
Channel capacity: 42 (2-way capable; operating 2-way). Channels available but not in use: 7.
Basic Service
Subscribers: 1,090.
Programming (received off-air): KDLH (C) Duluth-Superior; WEAU-TV (N), WQOW-TV (A) Eau Claire; WHWC-TV (P) Menomonie; KARE (N), KLGT (W), KMSP-TV (U), KSTP-TV (A), KTCA-TV (P), WCCO-TV (C), WFTC (F) Minneapolis-St. Paul.
Fee: $49.95 installation; $14.95 monthly.
Expanded Basic Service
Subscribers: N.A.
Programming (received off-air): KTCI-TV (P), KVBM-TV (H) Minneapolis-St. Paul; KPXM (X) St. Cloud.

Programming (via satellite): WGN-TV (W) Chicago; A & E; C-SPAN; CNN; Discovery Channel; ESPN; Fox Family Channel; Headline News; Home Shopping Network; Lifetime; MTV; Nashville Network; Nickelodeon; TBS Superstation; Turner Network TV; USA Network.
Fee: $6.55 monthly.

Pay Service 1
Pay Units: 300.
Programming (via satellite): Cinemax.
Fee: $9.00 monthly.

Pay Service 2
Pay Units: 157.
Programming (via satellite): Disney Channel.
Fee: $8.00 monthly.

Pay Service 3
Pay Units: 398.
Programming (via satellite): HBO.
Fee: $10.00 monthly.

Pay Service 4
Pay Units: 215.
Programming (via satellite): The Movie Channel.
Fee: $9.00 monthly.

Miles of plant: 57.0 (coaxial); 17.5 (fiber optic). Homes passed: 2,324.
Manager: John Klatt.
Ownership: Vision Communications LLC (MSO).

MADISON—Bresnan Communications Co., Suite 150, 5618 Odana Rd., Madison, WI 53719-1231. Phone: 608-274-3822. Fax: 608-274-1436. Counties: Columbia, Dane & Jefferson. Also serves Arlington, Berry, Blooming Grove, Burke, Cambridge, Christiana, Cross Plains (town), Cross Plains (village), De Forest, Deerfield, Deerfield Twp., Dunkirk, Dunn, Madison (town), Madison University, Maple Bluff, Marshall, McFarland (village), Medina (town), Middleton, Middleton (town), Monona, Oakland (town), Oregon (village), Oregon Twp., Pleasant Springs (town), Shorewood Hills, Stoughton, Sun Prairie, Sun Prairie Twp., University of Wisconsin, Westport (town), Windsor (town). ICA: WI0002.
TV Market Ranking: 93. Franchise award date: March 18, 1975. Franchise expiration date: N.A. Began: August 1, 1973.
Channel capacity: 36 (2-way capable; operating 2-way). Channels available but not in use: N.A.

Basic Service
Subscribers: 85,105.
Programming (received off-air): WHA-TV (P), WISC-TV (C), WKOW-TV (A), WMSN-TV (F), WMTV (N) Madison; 19 FMs.
Programming (via satellite): WGN-TV (W) Chicago; BET; C-SPAN; CNBC; CNN; Discovery Channel; Fox Family Channel; Headline News; Knowledge TV; MTV; Nashville Network; Nickelodeon; QVC; TBS Superstation; The Weather Channel.
Current originations: Automated time-weather; public access; educational access; government access.
Fee: $13.20 installation; $10.47 monthly; $2.26 converter.

Expanded Basic Service
Subscribers: 74,757.
Programming (via satellite): A & E; American Movie Classics; ESPN; Lifetime; Turner Network TV; USA Network.
Fee: $10.67 monthly.

Pay Service 1
Pay Units: 4,989.
Programming (via satellite): Cinemax.
Fee: $12.88 monthly.

Pay Service 2
Pay Units: 2,783.
Programming (via satellite): Disney Channel.
Fee: $12.88 monthly.

Pay Service 3
Pay Units: 27,607.
Programming (via satellite): The New Encore.
Fee: $1.75 monthly.

Pay Service 4
Pay Units: 20,914.
Programming (via satellite): HBO.
Fee: $13.78 monthly.

Pay Service 5
Pay Units: 5,755.
Programming (via satellite): Showtime.
Fee: $13.78 monthly.

Pay-Per-View
Addressable homes: 16,298.
Spice2.

Local advertising: Yes (locally produced). Available in satellite distributed programming. Local sales manager: Chris Eigenberger.
Program Guide: The Cable Guide.
Equipment: Jerrold headend; Jerrold amplifiers; Comm/Scope cable; Sony cameras; Sony VTRs; Texscan/MSI character generator; Pioneer addressable set top converters; Scientific-Atlanta satellite antenna; Scientific-Atlanta satellite receivers; ChannelMatic commercial insert.
Miles of plant: 1099.0 (coaxial). Homes passed: 129,603.
Manager: Brian Shirk. Chief technician: Jerry Myers. Marketing director: Tim Roehl.
City fee: 5% of gross.
Ownership: Bresnan Communications Co. LP (MSO). Purchased from Tele-Communications Inc, February 2, 1999. See Cable System Ownership.

MANAWA—Manawa Telecom Cable TV, Box 130, 131 2nd St., Manawa, WI 54949. Phone: 920-596-2700. Fax: 920-596-3775.
E-mail: manawa@netnet.net.
Web site: http://www.wolfnet.net.
County: Waupaca. Also serves Bear Lake, Little Wolf, Royalton Twp. ICA: WI0127.
TV Market Ranking: Below 100. Franchise award date: December 6, 1982. Franchise expiration date: November 1, 1997. Began: November 1, 1984.
Channel capacity: 36 (not 2-way capable). Channels available but not in use: 1.

Basic Service
Subscribers: 641.
Programming (received off-air): WACY (U) Appleton; WBAY-TV (A), WFRV-TV (C), WGBA (N), WLUK-TV (F), WPNE (P) Green Bay; WAOW-TV (A), WSAW-TV (C) Wausau-Rhinelander; allband FM.
Programming (via satellite): WGN-TV (W) Chicago; A & E; American Movie Classics; C-SPAN; CNBC; CNN; Discovery Channel; ESPN; ESPN 2; Fox Family Channel; Headline News; History Channel; Lifetime; MTV; Nashville Network; Nick at Nite; Nickelodeon; QVC; TBS Superstation; The Weather Channel; Turner Network TV; USA Network; VH1.
Current originations: Automated time-weather; public access; educational access; government access; automated emergency alert; local sports.
Fee: $20.00 installation; $19.45 monthly; $2.00 converter; $10.00 additional installation.

Pay Service 1
Pay Units: 82.
Programming (via satellite): Disney Channel.
Fee: $7.50 installation; $7.50 monthly.

Pay Service 2
Pay Units: 154.
Programming (via satellite): HBO.
Fee: $9.00 monthly.

Pay Service 3
Pay Units: 95.
Programming (via satellite): Showtime.
Fee: $9.25 monthly.

Local advertising: Yes (locally produced). Available in character-generated programming. Local sales manager: Karen Squires.
Program Guide: TV Blue Print.
Equipment: Jerrold headend; Scientific-Atlanta amplifiers; Comm/Scope cable; Panasonic cameras; Panasonic VTRs; Pioneer, Hamlin & Panasonic set top converters; Intercept & Eagle traps; Scientific-Atlanta satellite antenna; Scientific-Atlanta satellite receivers.
Miles of plant: 15.0 (coaxial); None (fiber optic). Homes passed: 766. Total homes in franchised area: 766.
Manager: Brian J. Squires. Chief technician: Thomas Squires.
City fee: 3% of basic gross.
Ownership: Manawa Telecom Inc.

MANITOWOC—Jones Intercable, 1614 Washington St., Manitowoc, WI 54220. Phone: 920-682-6511. Fax: 920-682-9505. County: Manitowoc. Also serves Cato, Manitowoc (town), Manitowoc Rapids, Newton (town), Whitelaw. ICA: WI0021.
TV Market Ranking: 62 (Cato, Manitowoc, Manitowoc Rapids, Whitelaw); Outside TV Markets (Newton). Franchise award date: November 3, 1980. Franchise expiration date: N.A. Began: December 15, 1981.
Channel capacity: 53 (2-way capable; not operating 2-way). Channels available but not in use: None.

Basic Service
Subscribers: 12,300; Commercial subscribers: 790.
Programming (received off-air): WACY (U) Appleton; WBAY-TV (A), WFRV-TV (C), WGBA (N), WLUK-TV (F), WPNE (P) Green Bay; WISN-TV (A) Milwaukee; WIWB (W) Suring; 22 FMs.
Programming (via satellite): WGN-TV (W) Chicago; C-SPAN; Discovery People; EWTN; Headline News; Home Shopping Network; Knowledge TV; Learning Channel; MSNBC; Product Information Network; TBS Superstation; TV Guide Channel; Trinity Bcstg. Network.
Current originations: Automated time-weather; public access; educational access; government access; library access; automated emergency alert; local news; local sports.
Fee: $35.00 installation; $13.25 monthly; $1.45 converter; $17.50 additional installation.

Expanded Basic Service
Subscribers: 11,900.
Programming (via satellite): A & E; American Movie Classics; CNBC; CNN; Comedy Central; Discovery Channel; Disney Channel; ESPN; ESPN 2; Fox Family Channel; Great American Country; History Channel; Lifetime; MTV; Midwest Sports Channel; Nashville Network; Nickelodeon; Sci-Fi Channel; The Weather Channel; Turner Network TV; USA Network; VH1.
Fee: $6.00 installation; $11.15 monthly.

Pay Service 1
Pay Units: 1,104.
Programming (via satellite): Cinemax.
Fee: $1.75 installation; $5.95 monthly.

Pay Service 2
Pay Units: 2,570.
Programming (via satellite): HBO.
Fee: $6.00 installation; $9.95 monthly.

Pay Service 3
Pay Units: 418.
Programming (via satellite): The Movie Channel.
Fee: $1.75 installation; $9.95 monthly.

Pay Service 4
Pay Units: 621.
Programming (via satellite): Showtime.
Fee: $6.00 installation; $9.95 monthly.

Pay-Per-View
Addressable homes: 3,900.
Special events.
Fee: Varies.

Local advertising: Yes. Available in satellite distributed programming. Rates: $13.00/30 Seconds. Local sales manager: Dean Schultz.
Program Guide: Jones Intercable Magazine.
Equipment: Scientific-Atlanta headend; Scientific-Atlanta amplifiers; Times Fiber & Comm/Scope cable; Compuvid character generator; Oak addressable set top converters; Scientific-Atlanta & Standard Communications traps; Scientific-Atlanta satellite antenna; Share Switcher & Logmatic commercial insert.
Miles of plant: 233.0 (coaxial); None (fiber optic). Homes passed: 18,900.
Manager: Jamie Lee. Chief technician: Keith Jolin. Program director: Kent Reeves.
City fee: 3% of gross.
Ownership: Jones Intercable Inc. (MSO).

MARINETTE—Time Warner Cable, Box 105, 3900 Hall Ave., Suite F, Marinette, WI 54143. Phone: 715-735-6667. Counties: Marinette, WI; Menominee, MI. Also serves Ingallston Twp., Menominee Twp., MI; Menominee (town), Peshtigo, Peshtigo (town), WI. ICA: WI0025.
TV Market Ranking: Below 100 (Ingallston Twp., Peshtigo); Outside TV Markets (Marinette, Menominee, Menominee Twp.). Franchise award date: August 9, 1966. Franchise expiration date: N.A. Began: March 1, 1970.
Channel capacity: 54 (not 2-way capable). Channels available but not in use: N.A.

Basic Service
Subscribers: 8,371; Commercial subscribers: 21.
Programming (received off-air): WACY (U) Appleton; WBAY-TV (A), WFRV-TV (C), WGBA (N), WLUK-TV (F), WPNE (P) Green Bay; WLUC-TV (N), WNMU-TV (P) Marquette; allband FM.
Programming (via satellite): C-SPAN; EWTN; QVC.
Current originations: Automated time-weather; public access; educational access; government access.
Fee: $30.00 installation; $8.11 monthly.

Expanded Basic Service
Subscribers: N.A.
Programming (received off-air): WGBA (N) Green Bay.
Programming (via microwave): WKBD-TV (U) Detroit.
Programming (via satellite): WGN-TV (W) Chicago; A & E; American Movie Classics; C-SPAN; CNBC; CNN; Comedy Central; Discovery Channel; E! Entertainment TV; ESPN; EWTN; Fox Family Channel; Headline News; Lifetime; MTV; Nashville Network; Nickelodeon; QVC; TBS Superstation; The Weather Channel; Turner Network TV; USA Network; VH1.
Fee: N.A.

Pay Service 1
Pay Units: 534.
Programming (via satellite): Cinemax.
Fee: $10.00 installation; $10.95 monthly.

Pay Service 2
Pay Units: 335.

Programming (via satellite): Disney Channel.
Fee: $9.95 monthly.

Pay Service 3
Pay Units: 1,032.
Programming (via satellite): HBO.
Fee: $10.95 monthly.

Pay Service 4
Pay Units: 276.
Programming (via satellite): The Movie Channel.
Fee: $10.95 monthly.

Pay Service 5
Pay Units: 571.
Programming (via satellite): Showtime.
Fee: $10.95 monthly.

Pay-Per-View
Viewer's Choice.

Local advertising: Yes. Available in satellite distributed programming.
Equipment: Scientific-Atlanta headend; C-COR amplifiers; Comm/Scope cable; Panasonic VTRs; Pioneer addressable set top converters; Scientific-Atlanta satellite antenna.
Miles of plant: 150.0 (coaxial). Additional miles planned: 2.0 (coaxial). Homes passed: 12,112. Total homes in franchised area: 12,852.
Chief technician: William J. Sebero. Marketing manager: Nancy Crabb.
Ownership: Time Warner Cable (MSO).

MARKESAN—Charter Communications Inc., Box 1197, 55 W. Scott St., Fond du Lac, WI 54936-1197. Phones: 920-923-7196; 800-581-0081. Fax: 920-923-1235. County: Green Lake. ICA: WI0137.
TV Market Ranking: Below 100. Franchise award date: April 4, 1977. Franchise expiration date: April 4, 2002. Began: December 29, 1977.
Channel capacity: 35 (not 2-way capable). Channels available but not in use: 3.

Basic Service
Subscribers: 476.
Programming (received off-air): WBAY-TV (A), WFRV-TV (C), WLUK-TV (F) Green Bay; WHA-TV (P), WISC-TV (C), WMTV (N) Madison; WISN-TV (A), WVTV (W) Milwaukee.
Programming (via satellite): WGN-TV (W) Chicago; A & E; American Movie Classics; CNBC; CNN; Comedy Central; Discovery Channel; ESPN; ESPN 2; EWTN; Fox Family Channel; Headline News; Learning Channel; Lifetime; MTV; Nashville Network; Nickelodeon; QVC; TBS Superstation; Turner Network TV; USA Network; VH1.
Fee: $34.95 installation; $10.38 monthly.

Pay Service 1
Pay Units: 69.
Programming (via satellite): Cinemax.
Fee: $14.95 installation; $12.50 monthly.

Pay Service 2
Pay Units: 62.
Programming (via satellite): Disney Channel.
Fee: $14.95 installation; $3.95 monthly.

Pay Service 3
Pay Units: 93.
Programming (via satellite): HBO.
Fee: $14.95 installation; $12.95 monthly.

Pay Service 4
Pay Units: 110.
Programming (via satellite): Showtime.
Fee: $14.95 installation; $12.50 monthly.

Equipment: Jerrold & Scientific-Atlanta headend; Scientific-Atlanta amplifiers; Times Fiber cable; Beston character generator; Scientific-Atlanta set top converters; Arcom & Eagle traps; Microdyne & Scientific-Atlanta satellite antenna; Scientific-Atlanta satellite receivers.
Miles of plant: 7.9 (coaxial). Homes passed: 608.
Manager: Lisa Washa. Chief technician: Jeff Gerner.
City fee: 3% of gross.
Ownership: Charter Communications Inc. (MSO). Purchased from Marcus Cable, April 1, 1999.

MARQUETTE—Cable Systems Management of Iowa Inc., 3600 Kennebec Dr., Eagan, MN 55122. Phone: 612-688-2623. Fax: 612-688-2624. County: Green Lake. ICA: WI0198.
TV Market Ranking: Outside TV Markets. Franchise award date: N.A. Franchise expiration date: N.A. Began: N.A.
Channel capacity: 40. Channels available but not in use: 19.

Basic Service
Subscribers: 41.
Programming (received off-air): WHA-TV (P), WISC-TV (C), WKOW-TV (A), WMTV (N) Madison.
Programming (via satellite): WGN-TV (W) Chicago; A & E; American Movie Classics; CNN; Country Music TV; Discovery Channel; ESPN; Fox Family Channel; Lifetime; Nashville Network; Showtime; TBS Superstation; Turner Network TV; USA Network.
Fee: $50.00 installation; $30.00 monthly.

Miles of plant: 3.3 (coaxial). Homes passed: 232.
Manager: Jeff Anderson.
Ownership: Cable Systems Management of Iowa Inc. (MSO).

MARSHFIELD—Charter Communications Inc., 508 N. Central Ave., Marshfield, WI 54449. Phone: 715-384-5279. Fax: 715-389-2194. Counties: Marathon & Wood. Also serves Cameron (town), McMillan (town). ICA: WI0030.
TV Market Ranking: Below 100. Franchise award date: N.A. Franchise expiration date: N.A. Began: April 1, 1963.
Channel capacity: 57. Channels available but not in use: N.A.

Basic Service
Subscribers: 5,575; Commercial subscribers: 13.
Programming (received off-air): WEAU-TV (N) Eau Claire; WKBT (C) La Crosse; WCGV-TV (I) Milwaukee; WAOW-TV (A), WHRM-TV (P), WSAW-TV (C) Wausau-Rhinelander; 5 FMs.
Programming (via satellite): C-SPAN; C-SPAN 2; QVC.
Current originations: Automated time-weather; educational access; government access; local news.
Fee: $30.00 installation; $14.60 monthly; $1.50 converter.

Expanded Basic Service
Subscribers: 5,569.
Programming (via satellite): A & E; American Movie Classics; CNBC; CNN; Comedy Central; E! Entertainment TV; ESPN; EWTN; Fox Family Channel; Headline News; Lifetime; MTV; Nashville Network; Nickelodeon; The Weather Channel; Turner Network TV; USA Network; VH1.
Fee: $7.77 monthly.

Expanded Basic Service 2
Subscribers: N.A.
Programming (via satellite): WGN-TV (W) Chicago; Court TV; Discovery Channel; ESPN 2; The New Encore.
Fee: N.A.

Pay Service 1
Pay Units: 408.
Programming (via satellite): Cinemax.
Fee: $11.25 monthly.

Pay Service 2
Pay Units: 264.
Programming (via satellite): Disney Channel.
Fee: $9.25 monthly.

Pay Service 3
Pay Units: 626.
Programming (via satellite): HBO.
Fee: $11.25 monthly.

Pay Service 4
Pay Units: 104.
Programming (via satellite): The Movie Channel.
Fee: $11.25 monthly.

Pay Service 5
Pay Units: 407.
Programming (via satellite): Showtime.
Fee: $11.25 monthly.

Pay-Per-View
Viewer's Choice.

Local advertising: Yes. Available in locally originated programming.
Equipment: Scientific-Atlanta headend; C-COR amplifiers; Times Fiber cable; Texscan character generator; Pioneer set top converters; Pioneer addressable set top converters; Scientific-Atlanta satellite antenna; Scientific-Atlanta satellite receivers.
Miles of plant: 74.0 (coaxial). Additional miles planned: 8.0 (coaxial). Homes passed: 7,353. Total homes in franchised area: 8,637.
Manager: Norm D. Ruedinger. Chief technician: Mark Bartelt.
Ownership: Charter Communications Inc. (MSO). Purchased from Marcus Cable, April 1, 1999.

MAUSTON—Triax Cablevision, Box 110, 1504 2nd St. SE, Waseca, MN 56093. Phones: 507-835-5975; 800-332-0245. Fax: 507-835-4567. County: Juneau. Also serves Camp Douglas, Hustler, Juneau County (unincorporated areas), Necedah, New Lisbon. ICA: WI0084.
TV Market Ranking: Below 100 (Camp Douglas, Hustler); Outside TV Markets (Juneau County, Mauston, Necedah, New Lisbon). Franchise award date: N.A. Franchise expiration date: January 1, 2001. Began: April 1, 1977.
Channel capacity: 62 (2-way capable). Channels available but not in use: 1.

Basic Service
Subscribers: 2,653.
Programming (received off-air): WEAU-TV (N) Eau Claire; WKBT (C) La Crosse; WHA-TV (P), WISC-TV (C), WKOW-TV (A), WMSN-TV (F), WMTV (N) Madison; allband FM.
Programming (via satellite): C-SPAN; CNN; QVC.
Current originations: Educational access.
Fee: $35.16 installation; $9.59 monthly; $1.58 converter.

Expanded Basic Service
Subscribers: 2,542.
Programming (via satellite): WGN-TV (W) Chicago; A & E; American Movie Classics; Comedy Central; Country Music TV; Discovery Channel; ESPN; Fox Family Channel; Headline News; History Channel; Lifetime; MSNBC; Nashville Network; Odyssey; TBS Superstation; The Weather Channel; Turner Network TV; USA Network; VH1.
Fee: $14.91 monthly.

Pay Service 1
Pay Units: 864.
Programming (via satellite): Cinemax; Disney Channel; HBO; Showtime; The New Encore.
Fee: $5.00 monthly (Encore), $7.00 monthly (Disney), $11.00 monthly (Cinemax, HBO or Showtime).

Equipment: Scientific-Atlanta headend; Scientific-Atlanta amplifiers; Comm/Scope cable; Scientific-Atlanta set top converters; Eagle traps; RGH satellite antenna.
Miles of plant: 54.9 (coaxial).
Manager: Richard Giffen. Chief technician: Scott Walters.
City fee: 5%.
Ownership: Triax Telecommunications Co. LLC (MSO). See Cable System Ownership.

MAZOMANIE—Charter Communications Inc., Box 1127, 1348 Plainfield Ave., Janesville, WI 53545-1127. Phones: 608-754-3644; 800-652-9456. Fax: 608-754-8107. County: Dane. Also serves Black Earth. ICA: WI0116.
TV Market Ranking: 93. Franchise award date: N.A. Franchise expiration date: N.A. Began: January 1, 1983.
Channel capacity: 41 (not 2-way capable). Channels available but not in use: 5.

Basic Service
Subscribers: 727.
Programming (received off-air): WHPN-TV (U) Janesville; WHA-TV (P), WISC-TV (C), WKOW-TV (A), WMSN-TV (F), WMTV (N) Madison.
Programming (via satellite): WGN-TV (W) Chicago; QVC; TBS Superstation; The Weather Channel; USA Network.
Current originations: Automated time-weather; educational access; local news.
Fee: $11.19 monthly.

Expanded Basic Service
Subscribers: N.A.
Programming (via satellite): A & E; American Movie Classics; Bravo; C-SPAN; C-SPAN 2; CNBC; CNN; Comedy Central; Discovery Channel; Disney Channel; ESPN; ESPN 2; ESPNews; Fox Family Channel; Headline News; Home & Garden Television; Learning Channel; Lifetime; MSNBC; MTV; Nashville Network; Nick at Nite's TV Land; Nickelodeon; Turner Network TV; VH1.
Fee: $18.76 monthly.

Pay Service 1
Pay Units: 106.
Programming (via satellite): Cinemax.
Fee: $12.95 monthly.

Pay Service 2
Pay Units: 136.
Programming (via satellite): HBO.
Fee: $12.95 monthly.

Pay Service 3
Pay Units: 78.
Programming (via satellite): Showtime.
Fee: $12.95 monthly.

Equipment: Scientific-Atlanta headend; Scientific-Atlanta amplifiers; Times Fiber cable; Hamlin, Oak & Scientific-Atlanta set top converters; Scientific-Atlanta traps; Scientific-Atlanta satellite antenna; Scientific-Atlanta satellite receivers.
Miles of plant: 17.3 (coaxial). Homes passed: 1,183.
Manager: Marty Robinson. Chief technician: Tim Sanderson. Marketing director: Danette Knickmeier.
City fee: 3% of gross.
Ownership: Charter Communications Inc. (MSO). Purchased from Marcus Cable, April 1, 1999.

MEDFORD—Charter Communications Inc., Suite 20, 123 W. State St., Medford, WI 54451. Phone: 715-748-4140. Fax: 715-748-6981. County: Taylor. ICA: WI0074.
TV Market Ranking: Outside TV Markets. Franchise award date: July 7, 1981. Franchise expiration date: N.A. Began: July 1, 1982.
Channel capacity: 35 (not 2-way capable). Channels available but not in use: 1.

Basic Service
Subscribers: 1,360.

Programming (received off-air): WEAU-TV (N) Eau Claire; WAOW-TV (A), WHRM-TV (P), WJFW-TV (N), WSAW-TV (C) Wausau-Rhinelander.
Programming (via satellite): WGN-TV (W) Chicago; A & E; American Movie Classics; C-SPAN; CNN; Comedy Central; Discovery Channel; ESPN; Fox Family Channel; Fox-Net; Headline News; Lifetime; MTV; Nashville Network; Nickelodeon; QVC; TBS Superstation; The Weather Channel; Trinity Bcstg. Network; Turner Network TV; USA Network; VH1.
Current originations: Educational access; local news.
Fee: $42.95 installation; $23.50 monthly.
Pay Service 1
Pay Units: 215.
Programming (via satellite): Cinemax.
Fee: $19.95 installation; $12.50 monthly.
Pay Service 2
Pay Units: 155.
Programming (via satellite): Disney Channel.
Fee: $19.95 installation; $9.35 monthly.
Pay Service 3
Pay Units: 250.
Programming (via satellite): HBO.
Fee: $10.00 installation; $12.95 monthly.
Pay Service 4
Pay Units: 215.
Programming (via satellite): Showtime.
Fee: $10.00 installation; $12.50 monthly.
Equipment: Scientific-Atlanta headend; Scientific-Atlanta amplifiers; Times Fiber cable; Hamlin set top converters; Eagle traps; Scientific-Atlanta satellite antenna; Scientific-Atlanta satellite receivers.
Miles of plant: 29.0 (coaxial). Homes passed: 1,946.
Manager: Larry Kraklau. Chief technician: Bruce Wasleske. Marketing director: Susan Jirgl.
City fee: 3% of gross.
Ownership: Charter Communications Inc. (MSO). Purchased from Marcus Cable, April 1, 1999.

MELLEN—KRM Cablevision, Box 77, Mellen, WI 54546. Phone: 715-274-7631. County: Ashland. ICA: WI0165.
TV Market Ranking: Outside TV Markets. Franchise award date: March 1, 1978. Franchise expiration date: March 1, 2002. Began: March 1, 1979.
Channel capacity: 20 (not 2-way capable). Channels available but not in use: 3.
Basic Service
Subscribers: 350.
Programming (received off-air): KBJR-TV (N), KDLH (C), WDIO-TV (A,F) Duluth-Superior; WLEF-TV (P) Park Falls; WJFW-TV (N), WSAW-TV (C) Wausau-Rhinelander.
Programming (via satellite): WGN-TV (W) Chicago; CNN; Discovery Channel; ESPN; Fox Family Channel; Nashville Network; TBS Superstation; Turner Network TV; USA Network.
Fee: $35.00 installation; $14.00 monthly.
Pay Service 1
Pay Units: N.A.
Programming (via satellite): Disney Channel; The Movie Channel.
Fee: $8.00 monthly (Disney); $12.00 monthly (TMC).
Equipment: Scientific-Atlanta headend; Jerrold amplifiers.
Miles of plant: 11.0 (coaxial). Homes passed: 400. Total homes in franchised area: 400.
Manager: O. D. Miller. Chief technician: Keith Gehrett.
Ownership: KRM Cablevision (MSO).

MELROSE—Charter Communications Inc., Box 279, 314 Main St., Onalaska, WI 54650. Phones: 608-783-5255; 800-658-9473. Fax: 608-783-7033. County: Jackson. ICA: WI0202.
TV Market Ranking: Below 100. Franchise award date: N.A. Franchise expiration date: July 1, 2000. Began: October 31, 1985.
Channel capacity: 41 (not 2-way capable). Channels available but not in use: 23.
Basic Service
Subscribers: 150.
Programming (received off-air): WEAU-TV (N) Eau Claire; WHLA-TV (P), WKBT (C), WLAX (F), WXOW-TV (A) La Crosse.
Programming (via satellite): WGN-TV (W) Chicago; C-SPAN; C-SPAN 2.
Fee: $30.00 installation; $10.00 monthly; $1.80 converter.
Expanded Basic Service
Subscribers: 136.
Programming (via satellite): A & E; American Movie Classics; CNN; Country Music TV; Discovery Channel; Disney Channel; ESPN; ESPN 2; Fox Family Channel; Learning Channel; Lifetime; MTV; Midwest Sports Channel; Nashville Network; Nick at Nite's TV Land; Nickelodeon; TBS Superstation; The Weather Channel; Turner Network TV; USA Network.
Fee: $30.00 installation; $18.80 monthly.
Pay Service 1
Pay Units: 21.
Programming (via satellite): Showtime.
Fee: $20.00 installation; $12.95 monthly.
Pay Service 2
Pay Units: 22.
Programming (via satellite): HBO.
Fee: $20.00 installation; $12.95 monthly.
Equipment: Jerrold headend; Jerrold amplifiers; Comm/Scope & Belden cable; Magnavox cameras; Scientific-Atlanta set top converters; Eagle traps; Microdyne satellite antenna; Microdyne satellite receivers.
Miles of plant: 4.5 (coaxial); None (fiber optic). Homes passed: 215. Total homes in franchised area: 215.
Manager: Shirley Hehn Weibel. Chief technician: Tim Fischer.
Franchise fee: None.
Ownership: Charter Communications Inc. (MSO). Purchased from Marcus Cable, April 1, 1999.

MELVINA—Midwest Cable, Box 399, Sparta, WI 54656. Phone: 608-269-6247. County: Monroe. ICA: WI0231.
TV Market Ranking: Below 100. Franchise award date: N.A. Franchise expiration date: N.A. Began: January 1, 1980.
Channel capacity: 12. Channels available but not in use: 6.
Basic Service
Subscribers: 34.
Programming (received off-air): WEAU-TV (N) Eau Claire; WHLA-TV (P), WKBT (C), WLAX (F), WXOW-TV (A) La Crosse.
Fee: $20.00 installation; $7.00 monthly.
Pay Service 1
Pay Units: 7.
Programming (via satellite): Cinemax.
Fee: $10.00 monthly.
Homes passed: 43.
Manager: Roger H. Alderman.
Ownership: Midwest Cable (MSO).

MENOMONEE FALLS—Time Warner Cable, N. 84 W. 13540 Leon Rd., Menomonee Falls, WI 53051. Phone: 414-255-0117. Fax: 414-255-4612. County: Waukesha. Also serves Lannon. ICA: WI0027.
TV Market Ranking: 23. Franchise award date: N.A. Franchise expiration date: N.A. Began: September 1, 1981.
Channel capacity: 54 (not 2-way capable). Channels available but not in use: None.
Basic Service
Subscribers: 8,668.
Programming (received off-air): WPXE (X) Kenosha; WCGV-TV (I), WDJT-TV (C), WISN-TV (A), WITI (F), WMVS (P), WMVT (P), WTMJ-TV (N), WVCY-TV (I), WVTV (W) Milwaukee; WJJA (H) Racine.
Programming (via satellite): WGN-TV (W) Chicago; Home Shopping Network; Knowledge TV; QVC; TBS Superstation.
Current originations: Automated time-weather; public access; educational access; government access.
Fee: $27.50 installation; $23.10 monthly; $2.48 converter.
Expanded Basic Service
Subscribers: 8,500.
Programming (via satellite): A & E; American Movie Classics; C-SPAN; CNBC; CNN; CNN/SI; Cartoon Network; Court TV; Discovery Channel; E! Entertainment TV; ESPN; ESPN 2; EWTN; Fox Family Channel; Fox News Channel; Headline News; History Channel; Home Shopping Network 2; Learning Channel; Lifetime; MTV; Nashville Network; Nick at Nite; Nickelodeon; Sci-Fi Channel; TV Guide Channel; The Inspirational Network; The Weather Channel; Turner Network TV; USA Network; VH1.
Fee: N.A.
Pay Service 1
Pay Units: 424.
Programming (via satellite): Cinemax.
Fee: $10.00 installation; $9.95 monthly.
Pay Service 2
Pay Units: 480.
Programming (via satellite): Disney Channel.
Fee: $10.00 installation; $9.95 monthly.
Pay Service 3
Pay Units: 1,877.
Programming (via satellite): HBO.
Fee: $10.00 installation; $9.95 monthly.
Pay Service 4
Pay Units: 463.
Programming (via satellite): The Movie Channel.
Fee: $10.00 installation; $9.95 monthly.
Pay Service 5
Pay Units: 859.
Programming (via satellite): Showtime.
Fee: $10.00 installation; $9.95 monthly.
Pay-Per-View
Movies; special events.
Equipment: Scientific-Atlanta headend; Jerrold amplifiers; Comm/Scope cable; System Concepts character generator; Scientific-Atlanta addressable set top converters; Scientific-Atlanta satellite antenna; Scientific-Atlanta satellite receivers.
Miles of plant: 210.0 (coaxial). Homes passed: 11,200. Total homes in franchised area: 11,210.
Manager: Eric Kurtz. Chief technician: Don Guarisco. Marketing director: Shari Hahn.
City fee: 5% of gross.
Ownership: Time Warner Cable (MSO); Advance/Newhouse Partnership (MSO).

MENOMONIE—Charter Communications Inc., Suite 1A, 394 Red Cedar St., Menomonie, WI 54751. Phone: 715-235-6837. Fax: 715-235-1439. County: Dunn. Also serves Menomonie (town), Red Cedar (town), Tainter (town). ICA: WI0033.
TV Market Ranking: Below 100. Franchise award date: August 31, 1992. Franchise expiration date: N.A. Began: May 1, 1962.
Channel capacity: 60 (not 2-way capable). Channels available but not in use: 22.
Basic Service
Subscribers: 4,408.
Programming (received off-air): WEUX (F) Chippewa Falls; WEAU-TV (N), WQOW-TV (A) Eau Claire; WKBT (C) La Crosse; WHWC-TV (P) Menomonie; KARE (N), KMSP-TV (U), KSTP-TV (A), KTCA-TV (P), WCCO-TV (C) Minneapolis-St. Paul.
Programming (via satellite): WGN-TV (W) Chicago; TBS Superstation.
Fee: $42.95 installation; $11.32 monthly.
Expanded Basic Service
Subscribers: 4,008.
Programming (via satellite): A & E; American Movie Classics; C-SPAN; CNBC; CNN; Discovery Channel; ESPN; ESPN 2; Fox Family Channel; Headline News; Lifetime; MTV; Nashville Network; Nickelodeon; QVC; The Weather Channel; Turner Network TV; USA Network; VH1.
Fee: $42.95 installation; $17.18 monthly.
Pay Service 1
Pay Units: 535.
Programming (via satellite): Cinemax.
Fee: $19.95 installation; $12.50 monthly.
Pay Service 2
Pay Units: 598.
Programming (via satellite): Disney Channel.
Fee: $19.95 installation; $3.95 monthly.
Pay Service 3
Pay Units: 608.
Programming (via satellite): HBO.
Fee: $19.95 installation; $12.95 monthly.
Pay Service 4
Pay Units: 570.
Programming (via satellite): Showtime.
Fee: $19.95 installation; $12.50 monthly.
Pay Service 5
Pay Units: 49.
Programming (via satellite): DMX.
Fee: $6.95 monthly.
Local advertising: Yes. Available in satellite distributed programming. Rates: $3.00/30 Seconds. Local sales manager: Steve Kessler.
Equipment: Scientific-Atlanta amplifiers; Comm/Scope & Times Fiber cable; Texscan character generator; Scientific-Atlanta & Hamlin set top converters; Arcom & Eagle traps; Scientific-Atlanta satellite receivers.
Miles of plant: 100.0 (coaxial). Homes passed: 5,762.
Manager: Karen Sanderson. Chief technician: Pat Anderson.
City fee: 5% of gross.
Ownership: Charter Communications Inc. (MSO). Purchased from Marcus Cable, April 1, 1999.

MEQUON—Time Warner Cable, Box 3237, 1610 N. 2nd St., Milwaukee, WI 53201-3237. Phone: 414-271-9283. Fax: 414-224-6155. County: Ozaukee. Also serves Cedarburg. ICA: WI0041.
TV Market Ranking: 23. Franchise award date: N.A. Franchise expiration date: N.A. Began: March 1, 1985.
Channel capacity: 41. Channels available but not in use: N.A.
Basic Service
Subscribers: 6,784.
Programming (received off-air): WCGV-TV (I), WDJT-TV (C), WISN-TV (A), WITI (F), WMVS (P), WMVT (P), WTMJ-TV (N), WVTV (W) Milwaukee.
Programming (via satellite): WGN-TV (W) Chicago; A & E; Bravo; C-SPAN; CNBC; CNN; CNN/SI; Cartoon Network; Discovery Channel; ESPN; Fox Family Channel; Headline News; Lifetime; MTV; Nashville Network; Nickelodeon; TBS Superstation; The Weather Channel; Turner Network TV; USA Network; VH1.

Planned programming (via satellite): Fox Sports Net.
Fee: $25.00 installation; $8.28 monthly.
Pay Service 1
Pay Units: N.A.
Programming (via satellite): Cinemax; Disney Channel; HBO; Playboy TV; Showtime; The Movie Channel.
Fee: $10.45 monthly (each).
Miles of plant: 121.0 (coaxial).
Manager: Chris Garven. Engineering director: Randy Gicatello.
Ownership: Time Warner Cable (MSO).

MERCER—Karban TV Systems Inc., 73A S. Stevens St., Rhinelander, WI 54501. Phone: 715-277-2339. County: Iron. ICA: WI0264.
TV Market Ranking: Outside TV Markets. Franchise award date: N.A. Franchise expiration date: N.A. Began: March 1, 1988.
Channel capacity: 54. Channels available but not in use: 29.
Basic Service
Subscribers: 213.
Programming (received off-air): WLEF-TV (P) Park Falls; WAOW-TV (A), WJFW-TV (N), WSAW-TV (C) Wausau-Rhinelander.
Programming (via satellite): WGN-TV (W) Chicago; A & E; CNN; Discovery Channel; ESPN; Fox Family Channel; Headline News; Lifetime; Nashville Network; Nickelodeon; TBS Superstation; Turner Network TV; USA Network.
Fee: $75.00 installation; $24.00 monthly.
Pay Service 1
Pay Units: 7.
Programming (via satellite): Disney Channel.
Fee: $9.00 monthly.
Pay Service 2
Pay Units: 31.
Programming (via satellite): HBO.
Fee: $10.00 monthly.
Miles of plant: 16.0 (coaxial). Homes passed: 300.
Manager: John Karban.
Ownership: Karban TV Systems Inc. (MSO).

MERRILL—Warner Cable of Merrill, Box 430, Rte. 4, County Trunk E, Marshfield, WI 54449. Phone: 715-384-9711. Fax: 715-389-2194. County: Lincoln. ICA: WI0054.
TV Market Ranking: Below 100. Franchise award date: N.A. Franchise expiration date: N.A. Began: February 1, 1964.
Channel capacity: 38. Channels available but not in use: N.A.
Basic Service
Subscribers: 2,746; Commercial subscribers: 2.
Programming (received off-air): WEAU-TV (N) Eau Claire; WAOW-TV (A), WHRM-TV (P), WJFW-TV (N), WSAW-TV (C) Wausau-Rhinelander; 5 FMs.
Programming (via satellite): C-SPAN; Comedy Central; E! Entertainment TV; QVC; VH1.
Current originations: Automated time-weather; educational access.
Fee: $30.00 installation; $9.95 monthly.
Expanded Basic Service
Subscribers: 2,667.
Programming (via satellite): WGN-TV (W) Chicago; A & E; American Movie Classics; CNN; Discovery Channel; ESPN; Fox Family Channel; Headline News; Lifetime; MTV; Nashville Network; Nickelodeon; TBS Superstation; The Weather Channel; Turner Network TV; USA Network.
Fee: $13.95 monthly.
Pay Service 1
Pay Units: 143.
Programming (via satellite): Cinemax.
Fee: $10.95 monthly.
Pay Service 2
Pay Units: 120.
Programming (via satellite): Disney Channel.
Fee: $9.95 monthly.
Pay Service 3
Pay Units: 213.
Programming (via satellite): HBO.
Fee: $10.95 monthly.
Pay Service 4
Pay Units: 68.
Programming (via satellite): The Movie Channel.
Fee: $10.95 monthly.
Pay Service 5
Pay Units: 184.
Programming (via satellite): Showtime.
Fee: $10.95 monthly.
Pay-Per-View
Viewer's Choice.
Local advertising: Yes. Available in satellite distributed programming.
Equipment: CAS & SKL headend; SKL amplifiers; Superior & Times Fiber cable; Pioneer addressable traps; Scientific-Atlanta satellite antenna.
Miles of plant: 37.0 (coaxial). Additional miles planned: 9.0 (coaxial). Homes passed: 3,835. Total homes in franchised area: 4,694.
Manager: Norm D. Ruedinger. Chief technician: Mark Bartelt.
Ownership: Time Warner Cable (MSO). See Cable System Ownership.

MERRIMAC—Merrimac Area Cable, Box 40, 327 Palisade St., Merrimac, WI 53561. Phone: 608-493-2291. Fax: 608-493-9902. E-mail: bart@merr.com. Counties: Columbia & Sauk. Also serves Caledonia (town), Merrimac (town). ICA: WI0154.
TV Market Ranking: 93. Franchise award date: March 1, 1984. Franchise expiration date: March 1, 1999. Began: October 1, 1984.
Channel capacity: 36 (not 2-way capable). Channels available but not in use: N.A.
Basic Service
Subscribers: 425; Commercial subscribers: 2.
Programming (received off-air): WHA-TV (P), WISC-TV (C), WKOW-TV (A), WMSN-TV (F), WMTV (N) Madison; 5 FMs.
Programming (via satellite): WGN-TV (W) Chicago; C-SPAN; CNN; Discovery Channel; Disney Channel; ESPN; Fox Family Channel; Lifetime; MTV; Nashville Network; Nickelodeon; QVC; Sci-Fi Channel; TBS Superstation; The Weather Channel; Turner Network TV; USA Network.
Current originations: Automated time-weather; public access.
Fee: $25.00 installation; $26.00 monthly.
Commercial fee: $22.00 monthly.
Pay Service 1
Pay Units: 23.
Programming (via satellite): Cinemax.
Fee: $8.95 monthly.
Pay Service 2
Pay Units: 80.
Programming (via satellite): HBO (multiplexed).
Fee: $11.95 monthly.
Pay Service 3
Pay Units: 24.
Programming (via satellite): Showtime.
Fee: $9.95 monthly.
Local advertising: No.
Program Guide: Premium Channels.
Equipment: Scientific-Atlanta & Electrohome headend; Scientific-Atlanta amplifiers; Comm/Scope cable; Olson, Drake & RCA character generator; Panasonic set top converters; U.S. Robotics modems; Pico traps; Electrohome satellite receivers.
Miles of plant: 24.0 (coaxial). Homes passed: 650.
Manager: Bartlett Olson. Chief technician: Jim Paul.
Ownership: Merrimac Area Cable.

MIKANA—S & K TV Systems, Box 127, 503 W. Miner Ave., Ladysmith, WI 54848. Phones: 715-532-7321; 800-924-7880. County: Barron. ICA: WI0265.
TV Market Ranking: Outside TV Markets. Franchise award date: January 1, 1989. Franchise expiration date: January 1, 1999. Began: November 1, 1989.
Channel capacity: 36. Channels available but not in use: 14.
Basic Service
Subscribers: 138.
Programming (received off-air): WEUX (F) Chippewa Falls; WEAU-TV (N), WQOW-TV (A) Eau Claire; WHWC-TV (P) Menomonie; KMSP-TV (U), WCCO-TV (C) Minneapolis-St. Paul.
Programming (via satellite): WGN-TV (W) Chicago; A & E; American Movie Classics; CNN; Discovery Channel; Disney Channel; ESPN; Fox Family Channel; Nashville Network; Nick at Nite's TV Land; Nickelodeon; TBS Superstation; The Weather Channel; Turner Network TV; USA Network.
Fee: $22.95 monthly.
Pay Service 1
Pay Units: N.A.
Programming (via satellite): Cinemax.
Fee: N.A.
Manager: Randy Scott.
Ownership: S & K TV Systems (MSO).

MILLADORE (town)—Cable Systems Management of Iowa Inc., 3600 Kennebec Dr., Eagan, MN 55122. Phone: 612-688-2623. Fax: 612-688-2624. County: Wood. ICA: WI0221.
TV Market Ranking: Below 100. Franchise award date: N.A. Franchise expiration date: N.A. Began: N.A.
Channel capacity: 40. Channels available but not in use: 20.
Basic Service
Subscribers: 44.
Programming (received off-air): WEAU-TV (N) Eau Claire; WAOW-TV (A), WHRM-TV (P), WSAW-TV (C) Wausau-Rhinelander.
Programming (via satellite): WGN-TV (W) Chicago; A & E; American Movie Classics; CNN; Country Music TV; Discovery Channel; ESPN; Fox Family Channel; Headline News; Lifetime; Nashville Network; Showtime; TBS Superstation; Turner Network TV; USA Network.
Fee: $50.00 installation; $28.00 monthly.
Miles of plant: 3.2 (coaxial). Homes passed: 113.
Manager: Jeff Anderson.
Ownership: Cable Systems Management of Iowa Inc. (MSO).

MILWAUKEE—Time Warner Entertainment Co. LP, Box 3237, 1610 N. 2nd St., Milwaukee, WI 53212-3906. Phones: 414-271-9283; 800-627-2288. Fax: 414-224-6155. County: Milwaukee. ICA: WI0001.
TV Market Ranking: 23. Franchise award date: June 1, 1983. Franchise expiration date: July 1, 1999. Began: December 11, 1984.
Channel capacity: 56 (2-way capable; operating 2-way). Channels available but not in use: 6.
Basic Service
Subscribers: 377,416.
Programming (received off-air): WPXE (X) Kenosha; WHA-TV (P) Madison; WCGV-TV (I), WDJT-TV (C), WISN-TV (A), WITI (F), WMVS (P), WMVT (P), WTMJ-TV (N), WVCY-TV (I), WVTV (W) Milwaukee; WJJA (H) Racine; 5 FMs.
Programming (via satellite): BET; Bravo; C-SPAN; C-SPAN 2; EWTN; TV Guide Channel; The Weather Channel; Univision; ValueVision.
Current originations: Automated time-weather; public access; educational access; government access; leased access.
Fee: $41.00 installation; $10.20 monthly; $2.82 converter; $25.00 additional installation.
Expanded Basic Service
Subscribers: N.A.
Programming (via satellite): A & E; American Movie Classics; Animal Planet; CNBC; CNN; CNN/SI; Cartoon Network; Comedy Central; Court TV; Discovery Channel; ESPN; Fox Family Channel; Fox News Channel; Headline News; History Channel; Learning Channel; Lifetime; MSNBC; MTV; Midwest Sports Channel; Nashville Network; National Jewish TV; Nickelodeon; QVC; Sci-Fi Channel; Travel Channel; Turner Classic Movies; Turner Network TV; USA Network; VH1.
Fee: $19.54 monthly.
A la Carte 1
Subscribers: N.A.
Programming (via satellite): WGN-TV (W) Chicago; E! Entertainment TV; ESPN 2; TBS Superstation.
Fee: $0.90 monthly (each), $3.25 monthly (package).
Pay Service 1
Pay Units: N.A.
Programming (via satellite): Cinemax; Disney Channel; HBO; Playboy TV; Showtime; The Movie Channel.
Fee: $10.00 installation; $6.95 monthly (Disney), $11.95 monthly (Cinemax, HBO, Playboy, Showtime or TMC).
Pay-Per-View
Addressable homes: 2,592.
Local advertising: Yes.
Program Guide: The Entertainer.
Equipment: Scientific-Atlanta headend; Superior cable; Scientific-Atlanta satellite receivers.
Miles of plant: 1147.0 (coaxial).
Manager: Chris Garven. Engineering director: Randy Gicatello.
Ownership: Time Warner Cable (MSO).

MINDORO—Charter Communications Inc., Box 279, 314 Main St., Onalaska, WI 54650. Phones: 608-783-5255; 800-658-9473. Fax: 608-783-7033. County: La Crosse. ICA: WI0310.
TV Market Ranking: Below 100. Franchise award date: N.A. Franchise expiration date: N.A. Began: N.A.
Channel capacity: 52 (not 2-way capable). Channels available but not in use: 28.
Basic Service
Subscribers: 95.
Programming (received off-air): WEAU-TV (N) Eau Claire; WHLA-TV (P), WKBT (C), WLAX (F), WXOW-TV (A) La Crosse.
Programming (via satellite): WGN-TV (W) Chicago; C-SPAN; C-SPAN 2.
Fee: $30.00 installation; $10.00 monthly; $1.80 converter.
Expanded Basic Service
Subscribers: 91.
Programming (via satellite): A & E; American Movie Classics; CNN; Country Music TV; Discovery Channel; Disney Channel; ESPN; ESPN 2; ESPNews; Fox Family Channel;

Learning Channel; Lifetime; Midwest Sports Channel; Nashville Network; Nick at Nite's TV Land; Nickelodeon; TBS Superstation; The Weather Channel; Turner Network TV; USA Network.
Fee: $30.00 installation; $18.80 monthly.
Pay Service 1
Pay Units: 18.
Programming (via satellite): HBO.
Fee: $12.95 monthly.
Pay Service 2
Pay Units: 10.
Programming (via satellite): Showtime.
Fee: $20.00 installation; $12.95 monthly.
Local advertising: No.
Equipment: Jerrold headend; Jerrold amplifiers; Comm/Scope & Belden cable; Magnavox cameras; Scientific-Atlanta set top converters; Eagle traps; Microdyne satellite antenna; Microdyne satellite receivers.
Miles of plant: 3.1 (coaxial); None (fiber optic). Homes passed: 122. Total homes in franchised area: 122.
Manager: Shirley Hehn Weibel. Chief technician: Tim Fischer.
Ownership: Charter Communications Inc. (MSO). Purchased from Marcus Cable, April 1, 1999.

MINOCQUA—Charter Communications Inc., Box 1253, 1011 First Ave., Woodruff, WI 54568-1253. Phone: 800-581-0081. Fax: 715-356-4768. Counties: Oneida & Vilas. Also serves Arbor Vitae, Woodruff. ICA: WI0071.
TV Market Ranking: Below 100. Franchise award date: January 1, 1972. Franchise expiration date: N.A. Began: June 1, 1973.
Channel capacity: 35 (2-way capable). Channels available but not in use: None.
Basic Service
Subscribers: 1,732.
Programming (received off-air): WLEF-TV (P) Park Falls; WAOW-TV (A), WJFW-TV (N), WSAW-TV (C) Wausau-Rhinelander; allband FM.
Fee: $43.95 installation; $24.50 monthly.
Expanded Basic Service
Subscribers: N.A.
Programming (via satellite): WGN-TV (W) Chicago; A & E; American Movie Classics; CNBC; CNN; Comedy Central; Discovery Channel; ESPN; Fox Family Channel; Headline News; Lifetime; MTV; Nashville Network; Nickelodeon; QVC; TBS Superstation; The Weather Channel; Turner Network TV; USA Network; VH1.
Fee: $17.22 monthly.
Pay Service 1
Pay Units: 196.
Programming (via satellite): Cinemax.
Fee: $19.95 installation; $12.50 monthly.
Pay Service 2
Pay Units: 149.
Programming (via satellite): Disney Channel.
Fee: $19.95 installation; $9.35 monthly.
Pay Service 3
Pay Units: 224.
Programming (via satellite): HBO.
Fee: $19.95 installation; $12.95 monthly.
Pay Service 4
Pay Units: 242.
Programming (via satellite): Showtime.
Fee: $19.95 installation; $12.50 monthly.
Local advertising: Planned.
Equipment: Scientific-Atlanta headend; Theta-Com amplifiers; Anaconda & Times Fiber cable; Sony VTRs; Eagle traps; Scientific-Atlanta satellite antenna; Microdyne satellite receivers.
Miles of plant: 80.0 (coaxial); None (fiber optic). Homes passed: 1,984. Total homes in franchised area: 2,239.
Manager: Karen Sanderson. Chief technician: Pat Anderson.
City fee: 3% of gross.
Ownership: Charter Communications Inc. (MSO). Purchased from Marcus Cable, April 1, 1999.

MINONG—S & K TV Systems, Box 127, 503 W. Miner Ave., Ladysmith, WI 54848. Phones: 715-532-7321; 800-924-7880. Fax: 715-532-7538. County: Washburn. Also serves Trego. ICA: WI0317.
TV Market Ranking: Outside TV Markets. Franchise award date: N.A. Franchise expiration date: N.A. Began: N.A.
Channel capacity: 36. Channels available but not in use: 3.
Basic Service
Subscribers: 272.
Programming (received off-air): KBJR-TV (N), KDLH (C), WDIO-TV (A,F), WDSE-TV (P) Duluth-Superior; KSTP-TV (A) Minneapolis-St. Paul.
Programming (via satellite): WGN-TV (W) Chicago; A & E; American Movie Classics; CNN; Cartoon Network; Country Music TV; Discovery Channel; Disney Channel; ESPN; ESPN 2; Fox Family Channel; FoxNet; Goodlife TV Network; Headline News; History Channel; Home & Garden Television; Lifetime; Nashville Network; Nick at Nite's TV Land; Nickelodeon; Outdoor Channel; Sci-Fi Channel; TBS Superstation; The Weather Channel; Turner Classic Movies; Turner Network TV; USA Network.
Fee: $26.95 monthly.
Pay Service 1
Pay Units: N.A.
Programming (via satellite): Cinemax; HBO.
Fee: $6.95 monthly (Cinemax); $9.95 monthly (HBO).
Manager: Randy Scott.
Ownership: S & K TV Systems (MSO).

MISHICOT—Charter Communications Inc., Box 1197, 55 W. Scott St., Fond du Lac, WI 54936-1197. Phones: 920-923-7196; 800-581-0081. Fax: 920-923-1235. Web site: http://www.marcuscable.com. Counties: Kewaunee & Manitowoc. Also serves Carlton (town), Carlton Twp., Cooperstown (town), Coopertown Twp., Francis Creek Village, Gibson (town), Gibson Twp., Kossuth (town), Kossuth Twp., Maribel, Maribel Village, Mishicot (town), Mishicot (village), Mishicot Twp., South Mishicot. ICA: WI0083.
TV Market Ranking: 62. Franchise award date: N.A. Franchise expiration date: N.A. Began: November 4, 1987.
Channel capacity: 54 (2-way capable; operating 2-way). Channels available but not in use: 27.
Basic Service
Subscribers: 851.
Programming (received off-air): WACY (U) Appleton; WBAY-TV (A), WFRV-TV (C), WGBA (N), WLUK-TV (F), WPNE (P) Green Bay.
Programming (via satellite): WGN-TV (W) Chicago; C-SPAN; EWTN; Odyssey; TBS Superstation.
Current originations: Public access.
Fee: $56.73 installation; $7.75 monthly; $28.36 additional installation.
Expanded Basic Service
Subscribers: N.A.
Programming (via satellite): A & E; Animal Planet; CNN; Comedy Central; Country Music TV; Discovery Channel; Disney Channel; ESPN; ESPN 2; ESPNews; Fox Family Channel; Headline News; History Channel; Home & Garden Television; Learning Channel; Lifetime; MSNBC; MTV; Nashville Network; Nick at Nite's TV Land; Nickelodeon; Sci-Fi Channel; The Weather Channel; Turner Network TV; USA Network; VH1.
Fee: $19.20 monthly.
Pay Service 1
Pay Units: 119.
Programming (via satellite): Cinemax.
Fee: $12.95 monthly.
Pay Service 2
Pay Units: 189.
Programming (via satellite): HBO.
Fee: $12.95 monthly.
Pay Service 3
Pay Units: 71.
Programming (via satellite): Showtime.
Fee: $12.95 monthly.
Equipment: Scientific-Atlanta headend; Scientific-Atlanta amplifiers; Times Fiber & Comm/Scope cable; Commodore character generator; Scientific-Atlanta set top converters; Scientific-Atlanta satellite antenna; Scientific-Atlanta satellite receivers.
Miles of plant: 70.0 (coaxial). Homes passed: 1,600.
Manager: Lisa Washa. Chief technician: Jeff Gerner.
Ownership: Charter Communications Inc. (MSO). Purchased from Marcus Cable, April 1, 1999.

MONDOVI—Durand Cable Co. Inc., 318 3rd Ave. W, Durand, WI 54736. Phone: 715-672-5966. Fax: 715-672-4344. County: Buffalo. ICA: WI0112.
TV Market Ranking: Below 100. Franchise award date: N.A. Franchise expiration date: May 23, 2004. Began: September 1, 1970.
Channel capacity: 35 (not 2-way capable). Channels available but not in use: 12.
Basic Service
Subscribers: 850.
Programming (received off-air): WEUX (F) Chippewa Falls; WEAU-TV (N), WQOW-TV (A) Eau Claire; WKBT (C) La Crosse; WHWC-TV (P) Menomonie; KARE (N), KMSP-TV (U), KSTP-TV (A), WCCO-TV (C) Minneapolis-St. Paul; allband FM.
Programming (via satellite): WGN-TV (W) Chicago; A & E; American Movie Classics; CNN; Comedy Central; Country Music TV; Discovery Channel; ESPN; Fox Family Channel; Learning Channel; Lifetime; MTV; Nashville Network; Nick at Nite; Nickelodeon; TBS Superstation; The Weather Channel; Turner Network TV; USA Network; VH1.
Planned originations: Automated time-weather.
Fee: $15.00 installation; $17.50 monthly; $10.00 additional installation.
Pay Service 1
Pay Units: 30.
Programming (via satellite): Disney Channel.
Fee: $10.00 installation; $8.00 monthly.
Pay Service 2
Pay Units: 200.
Programming (via satellite): HBO.
Fee: $10.00 installation; $9.00 monthly.
Local advertising: No.
Equipment: Scientific-Atlanta headend; RCA amplifiers; Comm/Scope cable; Scientific-Atlanta set top converters; Pico traps; Microdyne & DH Satellite satellite antenna; Scientific-Atlanta & Standard Communications satellite receivers.
Miles of plant: 20.0 (coaxial). Homes passed: 900. Total homes in franchised area: 950.
Manager: Jerry Levenske. Chief technician: John Kurtzhals.
City fee: 1% of gross.
Ownership: Durand Cable Co. Inc. (MSO).

MONROE—Charter Communications Inc., Box 1127, 1348 Plainfield Ave., Janesville, WI 53547-1127. Phones: 608-754-3644; 800-942-6440. Fax: 608-754-8107. County: Green. Also serves Clarno (town), Monvae (town). ICA: WI0044.
TV Market Ranking: 93 (Clarno, Monroe, Monvae); 97 (Clarno, Monroe, Monvae). Franchise award date: N.A. Franchise expiration date: N.A. Began: February 1, 1984.
Channel capacity: 47 (not 2-way capable). Channels available but not in use: None.
Basic Service
Subscribers: 3,208; Commercial subscribers: 86.
Programming (received off-air): WIFR (C) Freeport-Rockford; WHA-TV (P), WISC-TV (C), WKOW-TV (A), WMSN-TV (F), WMTV (N) Madison; WQRF-TV (F), WREX-TV (N), WTVO (A) Rockford.
Current originations: Educational access; government access; local news.
Fee: N.A.
Expanded Basic Service
Subscribers: N.A.
Programming (via satellite): WGN-TV (W) Chicago; A & E; American Movie Classics; Animal Planet; Bravo; C-SPAN; C-SPAN 2; CNBC; CNN; Discovery Channel; Disney Channel; E! Entertainment TV; ESPN; ESPN 2; ESPNews; Fox Family Channel; Headline News; Home & Garden Television; Learning Channel; Lifetime; MSNBC; MTV; Nashville Network; Nick at Nite's TV Land; Nickelodeon; Odyssey; QVC; TBS Superstation; The Weather Channel; Turner Network TV; USA Network; VH1.
Fee: N.A.
Pay Service 1
Pay Units: 558.
Programming (via satellite): Cinemax.
Fee: $19.95 installation; $12.95 monthly.
Pay Service 2
Pay Units: 658.
Programming (via satellite): HBO.
Fee: $12.95 monthly.
Pay Service 3
Pay Units: 484.
Programming (via satellite): Showtime.
Fee: $12.95 monthly.
Local advertising: No. Local sales manager: Robert U'Ren.
Equipment: Scientific-Atlanta headend; Scientific-Atlanta amplifiers; Comm/Scope cable; Compuvid character generator; Pioneer addressable set top converters; Scientific-Atlanta satellite receivers.
Miles of plant: 77.9 (coaxial). Homes passed: 5,345.
Manager: Marty Robinson. Chief technician: Tim Sanderson. Marketing director: Danette Knickmeier.
City fee: 3% of gross.

Ownership: Charter Communications Inc. (MSO). Purchased from Marcus Cable, April 1, 1999.

MONTELLO—Charter Communications Inc., Box 1197, 55 W. Scott St., Fond du Lac, WI 54936-1197. Phones: 920-923-7196; 800-581-0081. Fax: 920-923-1235. County: Marquette. ICA: WI0122.

TV Market Ranking: Outside TV Markets. Franchise award date: N.A. Franchise expiration date: N.A. Began: June 30, 1983.

Channel capacity: 35 (not 2-way capable). Channels available but not in use: 3.

Basic Service

Subscribers: 567.

Programming (received off-air): WFRV-TV (C), WLUK-TV (F) Green Bay; WHA-TV (P), WISC-TV (C), WKOW-TV (A), WMSN-TV (F), WMTV (N) Madison; WVTV (W) Milwaukee.

Programming (via satellite): WGN-TV (W) Chicago; A & E; American Movie Classics; CNBC; CNN; Comedy Central; Discovery Channel; ESPN; ESPN 2; EWTN; Fox Family Channel; Headline News; Learning Channel; Lifetime; MTV; Nashville Network; Nickelodeon; QVC; TBS Superstation; Turner Network TV; USA Network; VH1.

Current originations: Public access; automated emergency alert; local news.

Fee: $34.95 installation; $9.51 monthly.

Pay Service 1

Pay Units: 92.

Programming (via satellite): Cinemax.

Fee: $14.95 installation; $12.50 monthly.

Pay Service 2

Pay Units: 58.

Programming (via satellite): Disney Channel.

Fee: $14.95 installation; $3.95 monthly.

Pay Service 3

Pay Units: 97.

Programming (via satellite): HBO.

Fee: $14.95 installation; $12.95 monthly.

Pay Service 4

Pay Units: 147.

Programming (via satellite): Showtime.

Fee: $14.95 installation; $12.50 monthly.

Local advertising: Yes. Available in character-generated programming.

Equipment: Scientific-Atlanta & Catel headend; Scientific-Atlanta amplifiers; Times Fiber cable; Texscan character generator; Scientific-Atlanta set top converters; Arcom & Eagle traps; Microdyne & Scientific-Atlanta satellite antenna; Scientific-Atlanta & Standard Communications satellite receivers.

Miles of plant: 16.0 (coaxial). Homes passed: 769.

Manager: Lisa Washa. Chief technician: Jeff Gerner.

City fee: 3% of gross.

Ownership: Charter Communications Inc. (MSO). Purchased from Marcus Cable, April 1, 1999.

MONTFORT—Spring Green CableComm, Box 609, 245 S. Winsted St., Spring Green, WI 53588-9431. Phone: 608-588-7454. Fax: 608-588-7067. Counties: Grant & Iowa. Also serves Cobb, Linden (town), Linden (village), Livingston. ICA: WI0266.

TV Market Ranking: Outside TV Markets. Franchise award date: March 1, 1986. Franchise expiration date: March 1, 2001. Began: August 1, 1986.

Channel capacity: 42 (not 2-way capable). Channels available but not in use: 10.

Basic Service

Subscribers: 568.

Programming (received off-air): WHA-TV (P), WISC-TV (C), WKOW-TV (A), WMSN-TV (F), WMTV (N) Madison.

Programming (via satellite): WGN-TV (W) Chicago; A & E; CNN; Discovery Channel; ESPN; Fox Family Channel; Headline News; Nashville Network; Nickelodeon; QVC; TBS Superstation; Turner Classic Movies; Turner Network TV; USA Network.

Fee: $49.95 installation; $29.85 monthly; $19.95 additional installation.

Pay Service 1

Pay Units: N.A.

Programming (via satellite): HBO.

Fee: $19.95 installation; $9.95 monthly.

Equipment: Scientific-Atlanta headend; Scientific-Atlanta amplifiers; Scientific-Atlanta cable; Intercept traps; Scientific-Atlanta satellite antenna; Scientific-Atlanta satellite receivers.

Miles of plant: 32.0 (coaxial).

Manager: Kevin Mayne. Chief technician: Ted Peak. Customer service manager: Liz Reuter.

City fee: None.

Ownership: Fanch Communications Inc. (MSO). See Cable System Ownership.

MONTICELLO—Triax Cablevision, Box 110, 1504 2nd St. SE, Waseca, MN 56093. Phones: 507-835-5975; 800-332-0245. Fax: 507-835-4567. County: Lafayette. ICA: WI0153.

TV Market Ranking: 97. Franchise award date: N.A. Franchise expiration date: June 22, 2013. Began: June 18, 1984.

Channel capacity: 37 (not 2-way capable). Channels available but not in use: 4.

Basic Service

Subscribers: 325.

Programming (received off-air): WIFR (C) Freeport-Rockford; WHA-TV (P), WISC-TV (C), WKOW-TV (A), WMSN-TV (F), WMTV (N) Madison; WQRF-TV (F), WREX-TV (N), WTVO (A) Rockford.

Programming (via satellite): WGN-TV (W) Chicago; A & E; American Movie Classics; Animal Planet; CNN; Country Music TV; Discovery Channel; ESPN; ESPN 2; Fox Family Channel; Home & Garden Television; Home Shopping Network; Lifetime; MTV; Nashville Network; Nickelodeon; Sci-Fi Channel; TBS Superstation; Trinity Bcstg. Network; Turner Network TV; USA Network.

Current originations: Local access.

Fee: $45.00 installation; $30.00 monthly.

Pay Service 1

Pay Units: 139.

Programming (via satellite): Cinemax; HBO.

Fee: $7.95 monthly (Cinemax), $11.99 monthly (HBO).

Equipment: Scientific-Atlanta headend; Scientific-Atlanta amplifiers; Scientific-Atlanta cable; Scientific-Atlanta set top converters; Vitek traps; Scientific-Atlanta satellite antenna; Scientific-Atlanta satellite receivers.

Miles of plant: 7.0 (coaxial). Homes passed: 451. Total homes in franchised area: 451.

Manager: Mike Nodgerson. Chief technician: Pat Alderman.

City fee: 3% of gross.

Ownership: Triax Telecommunications Co. LLC (MSO). See Cable System Ownership.

MOUNT HOREB—Charter Communications Inc., Box 1127, 1348 Plainfield Ave., Janesville, WI 53545-1127. Phone: 608-754-3644. Fax: 608-754-8107. County: Dane. ICA: WI0088.

TV Market Ranking: 93. Franchise award date: N.A. Franchise expiration date: N.A. Began: August 1, 1983.

Channel capacity: 40 (not 2-way capable). Channels available but not in use: None.

Basic Service

Subscribers: 1,365; Commercial subscribers: 13.

Programming (received off-air): WHA-TV (P), WISC-TV (C), WKOW-TV (A), WMSN-TV (F), WMTV (N) Madison.

Current originations: Automated time-weather; educational access; government access.

Fee: $7.95 monthly.

Expanded Basic Service

Subscribers: 1,280.

Programming (via satellite): WGN-TV (W) Chicago; A & E; Animal Planet; C-SPAN; C-SPAN 2; CNBC; CNN; Comedy Central; Discovery Channel; Disney Channel; ESPN; ESPN 2; ESPNews; Fox Family Channel; Headline News; Learning Channel; Lifetime; MSNBC; MTV; Nashville Network; Nickelodeon; Outdoor Life Network; QVC; TBS Superstation; The Weather Channel; Turner Network TV; USA Network; VH1.

Fee: $28.25 monthly.

Pay Service 1

Pay Units: 175.

Programming (via satellite): Cinemax.

Fee: $12.95 monthly.

Pay Service 2

Pay Units: 242.

Programming (via satellite): HBO.

Fee: $12.95 monthly.

Pay Service 3

Pay Units: 142.

Programming (via satellite): Showtime.

Fee: $12.95 monthly.

Equipment: Scientific-Atlanta headend; Texscan amplifiers; Times Fiber cable; Panasonic cameras; Panasonic VTRs; Texscan character generator; Pioneer set top converters; Microdyne satellite antenna; Scientific-Atlanta satellite receivers.

Miles of plant: 24.5 (coaxial). Homes passed: 2,282.

Manager: Marty Robinson. Chief technician: Tim Sanderson. Marketing director: Danette Knickmeier.

City fee: 3% of gross.

Ownership: Charter Communications Inc. (MSO). Purchased from Marcus Cable, April 1, 1999.

MUSKEGO—Time Warner Cable, 5475 W. Abbott Ave., Milwaukee, WI 53220-4900. Phone: 414-282-6300. Fax: 414-421-1206. Counties: Racine & Waukesha. Also serves Big Bend, Norway, Vernon, Waterford, Wind Lake. ICA: WI0051.

TV Market Ranking: 23. Franchise award date: N.A. Franchise expiration date: September 1, 1998. Began: February 15, 1984.

Channel capacity: 40. Channels available but not in use: N.A.

Basic Service

Subscribers: 10,637.

Programming (received off-air): WGN-TV (W) Chicago; WHA-TV (P) Madison; WCGV-TV (I), WDJT-TV (C), WISN-TV (A), WITI (F), WMVS (P), WMVT (P), WTMJ-TV (N), WVCY-TV (I), WVTV (W) Milwaukee; allband FM.

Programming (via satellite): C-SPAN; CNN/SI; TBS Superstation.

Fee: $40.00 installation; $8.37 monthly.

Expanded Basic Service

Subscribers: N.A.

Programming (via satellite): A & E; American Movie Classics; CNBC; CNN; Court TV; Discovery Channel; E! Entertainment TV; ESPN; EWTN; Fox Family Channel; Fox Sports Net; Goodlife TV Network; Headline News; Lifetime; MTV; Nashville Network; Nickelodeon; QVC; The Weather Channel; Turner Network TV; USA Network; VH1.

Fee: $12.87 monthly.

Pay Service 1

Pay Units: N.A.

Programming (via satellite): Cinemax; Disney Channel; HBO; Showtime; The Movie Channel.

Fee: $10.45 monthly (each).

Miles of plant: 104.8 (coaxial). Additional miles planned: 46.0 (coaxial).

Manager: Irene Picard. Chief technician: Rich Jaskowiak.

Ownership: Time Warner Cable (MSO).

NEW AUBURN—S & K TV Systems, Box 127, 503 W. Miner Ave., Ladysmith, WI 54848. Phones: 715-532-7321; 800-924-7880. Counties: Barron & Chippewa. ICA: WI0268.

TV Market Ranking: Below 100. Franchise award date: January 1, 1988. Franchise expiration date: January 1, 1998. Began: October 1, 1988.

Channel capacity: 36. Channels available but not in use: 14.

Basic Service

Subscribers: 127.

Programming (received off-air): WEUX (F) Chippewa Falls; WEAU-TV (N), WQOW-TV (A) Eau Claire; WKBT (C) La Crosse; WHWC-TV (P) Menomonie; KMSP-TV (U), KSTP-TV (A), WCCO-TV (C) Minneapolis-St. Paul.

Programming (via satellite): WGN-TV (W) Chicago; A & E; American Movie Classics; CNN; Discovery Channel; ESPN; Fox Family Channel; Nashville Network; TBS Superstation; Turner Network TV; USA Network.

Fee: $24.95 monthly.

Pay Service 1

Pay Units: N.A.

Programming (via satellite): HBO.

Fee: $9.95 monthly.

Manager: Randy Scott.

Ownership: S & K TV Systems (MSO).

NEW BERLIN—Time Warner Cable, Box 14924, 1138 S. 108th St., West Allis, WI 53214. Phone: 414-771-8400. Fax: 414-453-5405. Counties: Milwaukee & Waukesha. Also serves West Allis. ICA: WI0026.

TV Market Ranking: 23. Franchise award date: July 1, 1980. Franchise expiration date: N.A. Began: July 1, 1981.

Channel capacity: 42 (2-way capable; operating 2-way). Channels available but not in use: None.

Basic Service

Subscribers: 7,113; Commercial subscribers: 20.

Programming (via satellite): WGN-TV (W) Chicago; TBS Superstation; TV Guide Channel.

Current originations: Automated time-weather; public access; educational access; government access; automated emergency alert; local news.

Fee: $50.00 installation; $25.20 monthly; $20.00 additional installation.

Commercial fee: $30.00 monthly.

Expanded Basic Service

Subscribers: 7,094.

Programming (received off-air): WCGV-TV (I), WDJT-TV (C), WISN-TV (A), WITI (F), WMVS (P), WMVT (P), WTMJ-TV (N), WVCY-TV (I), WVTV (W) Milwaukee.

Programming (via satellite): A & E; American Movie Classics; C-SPAN; CNBC; CNN; Cartoon Network; Discovery Channel; Disney Channel; ESPN; EWTN; Fox Family Channel; Fox Sports Net; Headline News; Home Shopping Network; Knowledge TV; MTV; Nickelodeon; Odyssey; Sci-Fi Channel; Superaudio Cable Radio Service; The Weather Channel; Turner Network TV; USA Network; Univision; VH1.

Fee: N.A.

Pay Service 1
Pay Units: 632.
Programming (via satellite): Cinemax.
Fee: $9.95 monthly.
Pay Service 2
Pay Units: 2,814.
Programming (via satellite): HBO.
Fee: $9.95 monthly.
Pay Service 3
Pay Units: 456.
Programming (via satellite): The Movie Channel.
Fee: $9.95 monthly.
Pay Service 4
Pay Units: 1,474.
Programming (via satellite): Showtime.
Fee: $9.95 monthly.
Pay-Per-View
Addressable homes: 200.
Local advertising: Yes. Available in satellite distributed, locally originated & taped programming. Rates: $44.00/Minute; $22.00/30 Seconds. Local sales manager: Ann Holtz.
Program Guide: The Channel Guide.
Equipment: Scientific-Atlanta headend; Scientific-Atlanta amplifiers; Comm/Scope cable; Sony cameras; Sony VTRs; Compuvid character generator; Hamlin set top converters; Zenith addressable set top converters; Eagle traps; Scientific-Atlanta satellite antenna; Scientific-Atlanta satellite receivers; Channel-Matic commercial insert.
Miles of plant: 266.0 (coaxial). Homes passed: 12,555.
Manager: Joe Zuravle Jr. Chief technician: Denny Gorsuch. Program director: Ann Holtz. Marketing director: Mitch Miller.
City fee: 3% of gross.
Ownership: Time Warner Cable (MSO).

NEW FRANKEN—PTI TeleVideo, Box 126, 212 Church Ave., Casco, WI 54205-0126. Phone: 414-837-7474. Fax: 414-837-2330. County: Brown. Also serves Dykesville, Green Bay (portions). ICA: WI0269.
TV Market Ranking: 62. Franchise award date: N.A. Franchise expiration date: N.A. Began: October 1, 1989.
Channel capacity: 60 (not 2-way capable). Channels available but not in use: 30.
Basic Service
Subscribers: 640.
Programming (received off-air): WACY (U) Appleton; WBAY-TV (A), WFRV-TV (C), WGBA (N), WLUK-TV (F), WPNE (P) Green Bay.
Programming (via satellite): WGN-TV (W) Chicago; A & E; American Movie Classics; CNN; Discovery Channel; ESPN; Fox Family Channel; Headline News; Lifetime; MTV; Nashville Network; Nick at Nite; Nickelodeon; QVC; TBS Superstation; Turner Network TV; USA Network; VH1.
Current originations: Local news.
Fee: $25.00 installation; $17.50 monthly.
Pay Service 1
Pay Units: 109.
Programming (via satellite): Cinemax.
Fee: $8.95 monthly.
Pay Service 2
Pay Units: 41.
Programming (via satellite): Disney Channel.
Fee: $7.95 monthly.
Pay Service 3
Pay Units: 133.
Programming (via satellite): HBO.
Fee: $9.95 monthly.
Local advertising: No.
Equipment: Scientific-Atlanta headend; Scientific-Atlanta amplifiers; Comm/Scope cable; Scientific-Atlanta set top converters; Arcom traps; Scientific-Atlanta satellite receivers.
Miles of plant: 48.0 (coaxial). Homes passed: 800. Total homes in franchised area: 1,600.
Manager: Michael Gotstein. Chief technician: Matt Gunderson.
City fee: 3% of gross.
Ownership: Casco Telephone Co. (MSO).

NEW GLARUS—Charter Communications Inc., Box 1127, 1348 Plainfield Ave., Janesville, WI 53547-1127. Phone: 608-754-3644. Fax: 608-754-8107. County: Green. ICA: WI0117.
TV Market Ranking: 93. Franchise award date: N.A. Franchise expiration date: August 1, 1999. Began: December 15, 1984.
Channel capacity: 41. Channels available but not in use: 3.
Basic Service
Subscribers: 532.
Programming (received off-air): WIFR (C) Freeport-Rockford; WHA-TV (P), WISC-TV (C), WKOW-TV (A), WMSN-TV (F), WMTV (N) Madison; WREX-TV (N), WTVO (A) Rockford.
Current originations: Public access.
Fee: $42.95 installation; $10.52 monthly; $1.43 converter; $19.95 additional installation.
Expanded Basic Service
Subscribers: N.A.
Programming (via satellite): WGN-TV (W) Chicago; A & E; American Movie Classics; Bravo; C-SPAN; C-SPAN 2; CNBC; CNN; Comedy Central; Discovery Channel; Disney Channel; ESPN; ESPN 2; ESPNews; Fox Family Channel; Headline News; Home & Garden Television; Learning Channel; Lifetime; MSNBC; MTV; Nashville Network; Nickelodeon; QVC; TBS Superstation; The Weather Channel; Turner Network TV; USA Network; VH1.
Fee: $19.43 monthly.
Pay Service 1
Pay Units: 79.
Programming (via satellite): Cinemax.
Fee: $12.95 monthly.
Pay Service 2
Pay Units: 105.
Programming (via satellite): HBO.
Fee: $12.95 monthly.
Pay Service 3
Pay Units: 67.
Programming (via satellite): Showtime.
Fee: $12.95 monthly.
Equipment: Scientific-Atlanta headend; Scientific-Atlanta & Magnavox amplifiers; Comm/Scope cable; Scientific-Atlanta set top converters; Eagle traps; Scientific-Atlanta satellite antenna; Scientific-Atlanta satellite receivers.
Miles of plant: 10.0 (coaxial). Homes passed: 954.
Manager: Marty Robinson. Chief technician: Tim Sanderson. Marketing director: Danette Knickmeier.
City fee: 3% of gross.
Ownership: Charter Communications Inc. (MSO). Purchased from Marcus Cable, April 1, 1999.

NEW HOLSTEIN—Charter Communications Inc., 2230 Wisconsin Ave., New Holstein, WI 53061. Phone: 800-395-0995. Fax: 414-337-9251. County: Calumet. Also serves Kiel. ICA: WI0065.
TV Market Ranking: Below 100. Franchise award date: July 9, 1980. Franchise expiration date: N.A. Began: September 21, 1981.
Channel capacity: 35 (2-way capable; operating 2-way). Channels available but not in use: None.
Basic Service
Subscribers: 1,920.
Programming (received off-air): WBAY-TV (A), WFRV-TV (C), WGBA (N), WLUK-TV (F), WPNE (P) Green Bay; WISN-TV (A), WITI (F), WMVS (P), WTMJ-TV (N), WVTV (W) Milwaukee.
Programming (via satellite): WGN-TV (W) Chicago; A & E; American Movie Classics; C-SPAN; CNN; Discovery Channel; ESPN; EWTN; Fox Family Channel; Headline News; Lifetime; MTV; Nashville Network; Nick at Nite; Nickelodeon; QVC; TBS Superstation; The Weather Channel; Turner Network TV; USA Network.
Current originations: Automated time-weather.
Fee: $42.95 installation; $10.50 monthly.
Pay Service 1
Pay Units: 278.
Programming (via satellite): Cinemax.
Fee: $19.95 installation; $12.50 monthly.
Pay Service 2
Pay Units: 159.
Programming (via satellite): Disney Channel.
Fee: $19.95 installation; $9.35 monthly.
Pay Service 3
Pay Units: 326.
Programming (via satellite): HBO.
Fee: $19.95 installation; $12.95 monthly.
Pay Service 4
Pay Units: 309.
Programming (via satellite): Showtime.
Fee: $19.95 installation; $12.50 monthly.
Local advertising: No (locally produced). Available in character-generated programming.
Equipment: Scientific-Atlanta headend; Scientific-Atlanta amplifiers; Comm/Scope cable; Video Data Systems character generator; Hamlin set top converters; Eagle traps; Scientific-Atlanta satellite antenna; Microdyne satellite receivers.
Miles of plant: 35.0 (coaxial). Homes passed: 2,732. Total homes in franchised area: 2,732.
Manager: Jim Ebenhoe. Chief technician: Duane Hendricks.
City fee: 3% of gross.
Ownership: Charter Communications Inc. (MSO). Purchased from Marcus Cable, April 1, 1999.

NEW LONDON—Charter Communications Inc., Box 1818, 853 McIntosh St., Wausau, WI 54402-1818. Phones: 715-845-4223; 800-581-0081. Fax: 715-848-0081. Counties: Outagamie & Waupaca. Also serves Hortonia (town), Hortonville, Lebanon, Libery (town), Maple Creek (town), Mukwa, Northport (village), Royalton. ICA: WI0046.
TV Market Ranking: 62 (Hortonia, Hortonville, Libery, Maple Creek); Below 100 (Lebanon, Mukwa, New London, Northport, Royalton). Franchise award date: June 1, 1980. Franchise expiration date: N.A. Began: September 1, 1981.
Channel capacity: 36. Channels available but not in use: None.
Basic Service
Subscribers: 3,391.
Programming (received off-air): WACY (U) Appleton; WBAY-TV (A), WFRV-TV (C), WGBA (N), WLUK-TV (F), WPNE (P) Green Bay; WSAW-TV (C) Wausau-Rhinelander.
Programming (via satellite): Odyssey; TBS Superstation.
Current originations: Automated time-weather; educational access; automated emergency alert.
Fee: $56.73 installation; $6.81 monthly; $28.36 additional installation.
Expanded Basic Service
Subscribers: 3,337.
Programming (via satellite): WGN-TV (W) Chicago; A & E; American Movie Classics; C-SPAN; CNN; Discovery Channel; Disney Channel; ESPN; ESPN 2; Fox Family Channel; Headline News; Home Shopping Network; Knowledge TV; Lifetime; MTV; Nashville Network; Nickelodeon; Sci-Fi Channel; The Weather Channel; Turner Network TV; USA Network.
Fee: $13.00 monthly.
Pay Service 1
Pay Units: 850.
Programming (via satellite): Cinemax.
Fee: $12.50 monthly.
Pay Service 2
Pay Units: 944.
Programming (via satellite): HBO.
Fee: $12.95 monthly.
Pay Service 3
Pay Units: 408.
Programming (via satellite): Showtime.
Fee: $12.50 monthly.
Local advertising: Yes.
Equipment: Scientific-Atlanta headend; Scientific-Atlanta amplifiers; Comm/Scope cable; Oak set top converters; Scientific-Atlanta satellite antenna; Scientific-Atlanta satellite receivers.
Miles of plant: 88.5 (coaxial). Homes passed: 5,108.
Manager: Scott Behn. Chief technician: Bruce Wasleske. Marketing director: Tim Schieffer.
City fee: 3% of gross.
Ownership: Charter Communications Inc. (MSO). Purchased from Marcus Cable, April 1, 1999.

NEW RICHMOND—Frontier Cable, Box 318, 154 E. 2nd St., New Richmond, WI 54017. Phone: 715-246-2145. Fax: 715-246-7111. County: St. Croix. Also serves Richmond, Stanton, Star Prairie (town), Star Prairie (village). ICA: WI0077.
TV Market Ranking: 13. Franchise award date: March 1, 1983. Franchise expiration date: March 1, 1998. Began: February 1, 1984.
Channel capacity: 55 (not 2-way capable). Channels available but not in use: 19.
Basic Service
Subscribers: 2,223; Commercial subscribers: 64.
Programming (received off-air): WEAU-TV (N), WQOW-TV (A) Eau Claire; WKBT (C) La Crosse; WHWC-TV (P) Menomonie; KARE (N), KLGT (W), KMSP-TV (U), KSTP-TV (A), KTCA-TV (P), WCCO-TV (C), WFTC (F) Minneapolis-St. Paul.
Programming (via satellite): WGN-TV (W) Chicago; American Movie Classics; C-SPAN; CNBC; CNN; Discovery Channel; ESPN; Headline News; Lifetime; MTV; Midwest Sports Channel; Nashville Network; Nickelodeon; TBS Superstation; USA Network.
Current originations: Automated time-weather; public access; educational access; government access; leased access; automated emergency alert.
Fee: $20.00 installation; $13.25 monthly; $10.00 additional installation.
Commercial fee: $13.25 monthly.
Pay Service 1
Pay Units: N.A.
Programming (via satellite): Cinemax; Disney Channel; HBO; Showtime.
Fee: $7.00 installation; $7.00 monthly (Disney), $9.25 monthly (Cinemax or Showtime), $9.75 monthly (HBO).
Local advertising: No.
Equipment: Scientific-Atlanta headend; Scientific-Atlanta amplifiers; Comm/Scope cable; JVC cameras; JVC VTRs; Telpar character generator; Pioneer addressable set top con-

verters; Scientific-Atlanta satellite antenna; Scientific-Atlanta satellite receivers.
Miles of plant: 15.1 (coaxial). Homes passed: 1,800. Total homes in franchised area: 1,900.
Manager: Mary Hendrickson. Chief technician: Steve Brown.
City fee: 5% of gross.
Ownership: St. Croix Telephone Co.

NEWBURG—Time Warner Cable, Box 3237, 1610 N. 2nd St., Milwaukee, WI 53212-3906. Phone: 414-271-9283. Fax: 414-224-6155. Counties: Ozaukee & Washington. ICA: WI0270.
TV Market Ranking: 23. Franchise award date: November 1, 1985. Franchise expiration date: November 1, 2000. Began: April 1, 1986.
Channel capacity: 40. Channels available but not in use: N.A.
Basic Service
Subscribers: 211.
Programming (received off-air): WCGV-TV (I), WDJT-TV (C), WISN-TV (A), WITI (F), WMVS (P), WMVT (P), WTMJ-TV (N), WVCY-TV (I), WVTV (W) Milwaukee.
Programming (via satellite): WGN-TV (W) Chicago; A & E; C-SPAN; CNBC; CNN; CNN/SI; Discovery Channel; ESPN; Fox Family Channel; Lifetime; MTV; Nashville Network; Nickelodeon; TBS Superstation; The Weather Channel; Turner Network TV; USA Network; VH1.
Planned programming (via satellite): Fox Sports Net.
Fee: $25.00 installation; $7.91 monthly.
Pay Service 1
Pay Units: N.A.
Programming (via satellite): Cinemax; Disney Channel; HBO; Showtime; The Movie Channel.
Fee: $10.45 monthly (each).
Manager: Chris Garven. Engineering director: Randy Gicatello.
Ownership: Time Warner Cable (MSO).

NIAGARA—Niagara Community TV Co-op, Box 136, 1117 Main St., Niagara, WI 54151. Phone: 715-251-1526. Fax: 715-251-1527. County: Marinette. Also serves Niagara (town). ICA: WI0271.
TV Market Ranking: Below 100. Franchise award date: N.A. Franchise expiration date: September 21, 2002. Began: August 1, 1954.
Channel capacity: 52 (2-way capable; operating 2-way). Channels available but not in use: None.
Basic Service
Subscribers: 792.
Programming (received off-air): WJMN-TV (C) Escanaba; WBAY-TV (A), WLUK-TV (F), WPNE (P) Green Bay; WLUC-TV (N), WNMU-TV (P) Marquette; WJFW-TV (N) Wausau-Rhinelander; allband FM.
Programming (via translator): WGBA (N) Green Bay.
Programming (via satellite): WGN-TV (W) Chicago; CNN; ESPN; Fox Family Channel; Nashville Network; TBS Superstation; USA Network.
Current originations: Public access.
Fee: $100.00 installation; $14.94 monthly.
Pay Service 1
Pay Units: 56.
Programming (via satellite): Disney Channel.
Fee: $5.50 monthly.
Pay Service 2
Pay Units: 106.
Programming (via satellite): Showtime.
Fee: $6.50 monthly.
Pay Service 3
Pay Units: 30.
Programming (via satellite): HBO.
Fee: $10.00 monthly.
Local advertising: Yes. Available in character-generated programming. Local sales manager: Linda Weber.
Equipment: Electrohome, Jerrold & M/A-Com headend; Oak set top converters; Scientific-Atlanta satellite antenna; Automation Techniques, M/A-Com & Scientific-Atlanta satellite receivers.
Miles of plant: 19.5 (coaxial); None (fiber optic). Additional miles planned: 0.1 (coaxial). Homes passed: 900. Total homes in franchised area: 1,000.
Manager: Gerald Kallenbach. Program & marketing director: Linda Weber.
City fee: None.
Ownership: Niagara Community TV Co-op.

NORTH PRAIRIE—Time Warner Cable Communications Inc., Box 3237, 1610 N. 2nd St., Milwaukee, WI 53212-3906. Phone: 414-271-9283. Fax: 414-224-6155. Counties: Walworth & Waukesha. Also serves Delafield, Dousman, Eagle (town), Eagle (village), East Troy (town), East Troy (village), Genesee (town), Mukwonago (town), Ottawa (town). ICA: WI0272.
TV Market Ranking: 23. Franchise award date: N.A. Franchise expiration date: N.A. Began: N.A.
Channel capacity: 40. Channels available but not in use: N.A.
Basic Service
Subscribers: 11,456.
Programming (received off-air): WCGV-TV (I), WDJT-TV (C), WISN-TV (A), WITI (F), WMVS (P), WMVT (P), WTMJ-TV (N) Milwaukee.
Programming (via satellite): WGN-TV (W) Chicago; A & E; Bravo; C-SPAN; CNBC; CNN; CNN/SI; Discovery Channel; ESPN; Fox Family Channel; Headline News; Lifetime; MTV; Nashville Network; TBS Superstation; The Weather Channel; Turner Network TV; USA Network; VH1.
Planned programming (via satellite): Fox Sports Net.
Fee: $40.00 installation; $8.11 monthly.
Pay Service 1
Pay Units: N.A.
Programming (via satellite): Cinemax; Disney Channel; HBO; Playboy TV; Showtime; The Movie Channel.
Fee: $10.45 monthly (each).
Manager: Chris Garven. Engineering director: Randy Gicatello.
Ownership: Time Warner Cable (MSO).

NORWALK—Triax Cablevision, Box 110, 1504 2nd St. SE, Waseca, MN 56093. Phones: 507-835-5975; 800-332-0245. Fax: 507-835-4567. County: Monroe. ICA: WI0208.
TV Market Ranking: Below 100. Franchise award date: June 5, 1981. Franchise expiration date: March 1, 2001. Began: June 1, 1976.
Channel capacity: 62 (2-way capable). Channels available but not in use: N.A.
Basic Service
Subscribers: 166.
Programming (received off-air): WEAU-TV (N) Eau Claire; WHLA-TV (P), WKBT (C), WLAX (F), WXOW-TV (A) La Crosse.
Fee: $35.16 installation; $17.35 monthly.
Expanded Basic Service
Subscribers: 6.
Programming (via satellite): WGN-TV (W) Chicago; CNN; Discovery Channel; ESPN; Fox Family Channel; Nashville Network; TBS Superstation; Turner Network TV; USA Network.
Fee: $6.60 monthly.
Pay Service 1
Pay Units: 35.
Programming (via satellite): HBO.
Fee: $45.00 installation; $9.95 monthly.
Equipment: Blonder-Tongue & Scientific-Atlanta headend; Coral amplifiers; Comm/Scope cable; Arcom traps; Microdyne satellite antenna; Scientific-Atlanta satellite receivers.
Miles of plant: 5.8 (coaxial); None (fiber optic). Homes passed: 195. Total homes in franchised area: 195.
Manager: Richard Giffen. Chief technician: Scott Walters.
City fee: None.
Ownership: Triax Telecommunications Co. LLC (MSO). See Cable System Ownership.

OAKFIELD—Charter Communications Inc., Box 1197, 55 W. Scott St., Fond du Lac, WI 54936-1197. Phones: 920-923-7196; 800-581-0081. Fax: 920-923-1235. County: Fond du Lac. ICA: WI0167.
TV Market Ranking: Below 100. Franchise award date: October 1, 1981. Franchise expiration date: N.A. Began: December 1, 1983.
Channel capacity: 22 (not 2-way capable). Channels available but not in use: 3.
Basic Service
Subscribers: 227.
Programming (received off-air): WBAY-TV (A), WFRV-TV (C), WGBA (N), WLUK-TV (F), WPNE (P) Green Bay; WCGV-TV (I), WVTV (W) Milwaukee.
Programming (via satellite): WGN-TV (W) Chicago; CNN; ESPN; Fox Family Channel; Lifetime; Nashville Network; Nickelodeon; TBS Superstation; Turner Network TV; USA Network.
Fee: $34.95 installation; $18.34 monthly.
Pay Service 1
Pay Units: 52.
Programming (via satellite): Cinemax.
Fee: $12.15 installation; $12.50 monthly.
Pay Service 2
Pay Units: 58.
Programming (via satellite): HBO.
Fee: $12.95 monthly.
Local advertising: No.
Equipment: Scientific-Atlanta headend; Scientific-Atlanta amplifiers; Comm/Scope cable; Eagle traps; Microdyne satellite antenna; Microdyne satellite receivers.
Miles of plant: 7.0 (coaxial). Homes passed: 354. Total homes in franchised area: 385.
Manager: Lisa Washa. Chief technician: Jeff Gerner.
City fee: 3% of gross.
Ownership: Charter Communications Inc. (MSO). Purchased from Marcus Cable, April 1, 1999.

OCONOMOWOC LAKE—Warner Cable Communications, 5475 W. Abbott Ave., Greenfield, WI 53220-4900. Phone: 414-422-1088. Fax: 414-421-1206. Counties: Dodge, Jefferson & Waukesha. Also serves Ashippun, Chenequa, Ixonia, Merton (town), Nashota (town), Oconomowoc (town), Summit (town). ICA: WI0273.
TV Market Ranking: 23. Franchise award date: N.A. Franchise expiration date: N.A. Began: N.A.
Channel capacity: 40. Channels available but not in use: N.A.
Basic Service
Subscribers: 4,855.
Programming (received off-air): WCGV-TV (I), WDJT-TV (C), WISN-TV (A), WITI (F), WTMJ-TV (N), WVTV (W) Milwaukee.
Programming (via satellite): WGN-TV (W) Chicago; A & E; Bravo; C-SPAN; CNBC; CNN; CNN/SI; Discovery Channel; ESPN; Fox Family Channel; Headline News; Lifetime; MTV; Nashville Network; Nickelodeon; TBS Superstation; The Weather Channel; Turner Network TV; USA Network.
Planned programming (via satellite): Fox Sports Net.
Fee: $19.95 monthly.
Pay Service 1
Pay Units: N.A.
Programming (via satellite): Cinemax; Disney Channel; HBO.
Fee: $9.95 monthly (each).
Manager: Irene Picard. Chief technician: Rich Jaskowiak.
Ownership: Time Warner Cable (MSO).

OCONTO—Charter Communications Inc., Box 1818, 853 McIntosh St., Wausau, WI 54402-1818. Phones: 715-845-4223; 800-581-0081. Fax: 715-848-0081. County: Oconto. Also serves Gillett (town), Underhill (town), Underhill (village). ICA: WI0075.
TV Market Ranking: 62 (Gillett, Oconto, Underhill); Below 100 (Underhill). Franchise award date: February 16, 1983. Franchise expiration date: February 16, 1998. Began: September 1, 1981.
Channel capacity: 36 (2-way capable; operating 2-way). Channels available but not in use: 1.
Basic Service
Subscribers: 1,146.
Programming (received off-air): WACY (U) Appleton; WBAY-TV (A), WFRV-TV (C), WGBA (N), WLUK-TV (F), WPNE (P) Green Bay; 1 FM.
Programming (via satellite): WGN-TV (W) Chicago; TBS Superstation.
Current originations: Educational access.
Fee: $56.73 installation; $6.22 monthly; $28.36 additional installation.
Expanded Basic Service
Subscribers: 1,134.
Programming (via satellite): A & E; American Movie Classics; C-SPAN; CNBC; CNN; Discovery Channel; Disney Channel; ESPN; Fox Family Channel; Headline News; Lifetime; MTV; Nashville Network; Nickelodeon; Odyssey; Sci-Fi Channel; Turner Network TV; USA Network; VH1.
Fee: $13.69 monthly.
Pay Service 1
Pay Units: 189.
Programming (via satellite): Cinemax.
Fee: $12.50 monthly.
Pay Service 2
Pay Units: 296.
Programming (via satellite): HBO.
Fee: $12.95 monthly.
Pay Service 3
Pay Units: 200.
Programming (via satellite): Showtime.
Fee: $12.50 monthly.
Local advertising: No.
Equipment: Scientific-Atlanta headend; Scientific-Atlanta amplifiers; Times Fiber cable; Oak set top converters; Eagle traps.
Miles of plant: 32.9 (coaxial). Total homes in franchised area: 1,920.
Manager: Scott Behn. Chief technician: Bruce Wasleske. Marketing director: Tim Schieffer.
Ownership: Charter Communications Inc. (MSO). Purchased from Marcus Cable, April 1, 1999.

OCONTO FALLS—Oconto Falls Cable TV, Box 70, Oconto Falls, WI 54154. Phone: 920-846-4507. Fax: 920-846-4510. County: Oconto. ICA: WI0108.
TV Market Ranking: 62. Franchise award date: N.A. Franchise expiration date: N.A. Began: December 20, 1981.
Channel capacity: 52 (2-way capable; operating 2-way). Channels available but not in use: 16.

Basic Service

Subscribers: 899; Commercial subscribers: 16.

Programming (received off-air): WACY (U) Appleton; WBAY-TV (A), WFRV-TV (C), WLUK-TV (F), WPNE (P) Green Bay.

Programming (via satellite): WGN-TV (W) Chicago; A & E; CNN; Discovery Channel; ESPN; Lifetime; Nashville Network; Nickelodeon; TBS Superstation; The Weather Channel; Turner Network TV; USA Network.

Current originations: Automated time-weather.

Fee: $20.00 installation; $13.50 monthly; $5.00 additional installation.

Commercial fee: $13.50 monthly.

Pay Service 1

Pay Units: 61.

Programming (via satellite): Disney Channel.

Fee: $20.00 installation; $7.75 monthly.

Pay Service 2

Pay Units: 123.

Programming (via satellite): HBO.

Fee: $20.00 installation; $10.75 monthly.

Pay Service 3

Pay Units: 188.

Programming (via satellite): Showtime.

Fee: $20.00 installation; $10.75 monthly.

Equipment: Scientific-Atlanta & Triple Crown headend; Jerrold amplifiers; Jerrold cable; BEI character generator; Pioneer set top converters; Eagle & Pico traps; Scientific-Atlanta satellite antenna; Microdyne & Scientific-Atlanta satellite receivers.

Miles of plant: 18.0 (coaxial). Homes passed: 1,200. Total homes in franchised area: 1,200.

Manager: Pete Mann. Chief technician: Carl Volwinkez.

Ownership: Oconto Falls Cable TV.

OMRO—Charter Communications Inc., Box 1197, 55 W. Scott St., Fond du Lac, WI 54936-1197. Phones: 920-923-7196; 800-581-0081. Fax: 920-923-1235. County: Winnebago. Also serves Butte Des Morts, Oshkosh (town), Winneconne, Winneconne (village). ICA: WI0070.

TV Market Ranking: Below 100. Franchise award date: N.A. Franchise expiration date: N.A. Began: October 1, 1981.

Channel capacity: 35 (not 2-way capable). Channels available but not in use: 4.

Basic Service

Subscribers: 1,716.

Programming (received off-air): WBAY-TV (A), WFRV-TV (C), WGBA (N), WLUK-TV (F), WPNE (P) Green Bay.

Programming (via satellite): WGN-TV (W) Chicago; A & E; C-SPAN; CNN; Comedy Central; Discovery Channel; ESPN; EWTN; Fox Family Channel; Headline News; Lifetime; MTV; Nashville Network; Nickelodeon; QVC; TBS Superstation; The Weather Channel; Turner Network TV; USA Network; VH1.

Current originations: Automated time-weather; educational access.

Fee: $42.95 installation; $13.44 monthly.

Pay Service 1

Pay Units: 301.

Programming (via satellite): Cinemax.

Fee: $19.95 installation; $12.50 monthly.

Pay Service 2

Pay Units: 252.

Programming (via satellite): Disney Channel.

Fee: $19.95 installation; $9.35 monthly.

Pay Service 3

Pay Units: 348.

Programming (via satellite): HBO.

Fee: $19.95 installation; $12.95 monthly.

Pay Service 4

Pay Units: 402.

Programming (via satellite): Showtime.

Fee: $19.95 installation; $12.50 monthly.

Local advertising: Yes (locally produced). Available in character-generated programming.

Equipment: Scientific-Atlanta headend; Scientific-Atlanta amplifiers; Times Fiber cable; Texscan character generator; Scientific-Atlanta set top converters; Eagle & Arcom traps; Microdyne & Scientific-Atlanta satellite antenna; Microdyne satellite receivers.

Miles of plant: 42.0 (coaxial). Homes passed: 2,310.

Manager: Lisa Washa. Chief technician: Jeff Gerner.

City fee: 3% of gross.

Ownership: Charter Communications Inc. (MSO). Purchased from Marcus Cable, April 1, 1999.

ONALASKA—Charter Communications Inc., Box 279, 314 Main St., Onalaska, WI 54650. Phone: 800-658-9473. Fax: 608-783-7033. County: La Crosse. Also serves Bangor, Barre, Campbell, Hamilton, Holland, Holmen, La Crosse, Medary, Onalaska (town), West Salem. ICA: WI0024.

TV Market Ranking: Below 100. Franchise award date: October 1, 1973. Franchise expiration date: May 1, 1998. Began: November 1, 1974.

Channel capacity: 81 (2-way capable; operating 2-way). Channels available but not in use: 5.

Basic Service

Subscribers: 12,881.

Programming (received off-air): WEAU-TV (N) Eau Claire; KQEG-LP (I) La Crescent; WHLA-TV (P), WKBT (C), WLAX (F), WXOW-TV (A) La Crosse.

Programming (via satellite): WGN-TV (W) Chicago; Bravo; C-SPAN; C-SPAN 2; TV Guide Channel.

Current originations: Public access; educational access; government access; religious access; leased access; local access.

Fee: $64.57 installation; $7.60 monthly; $1.80 converter.

Expanded Basic Service

Subscribers: 11,867.

Programming (via satellite): A & E; American Movie Classics; Animal Planet; CNBC; CNN; Cartoon Network; Comedy Central; Country Music TV; Court TV; Discovery Channel; Disney Channel; E! Entertainment TV; ESPN; ESPN 2; ESPN Classic Sports; ESPNews; EWTN; FX; Fox Family Channel; Game Show Network; Golf Channel; Headline News; History Channel; Home & Garden Television; Home Shopping Network; Learning Channel; Lifetime; MSNBC; MTV; Midwest Sports Channel; Nashville Network; Nick at Nite's TV Land; Nickelodeon; Odyssey; Outdoor Life Network; QVC; Sci-Fi Channel; Speedvision; TBS Superstation; The Barker; The Weather Channel; Toon Disney; Travel Channel; Turner Classic Movies; Turner Network TV; USA Network; VH1; WB 100+ Station Group.

Fee: $64.57 installation; $25.60 monthly.

Pay Service 1

Pay Units: 1,238.

Programming (via satellite): Cinemax (multiplexed).

Fee: $20.00 installation; $12.95 monthly.

Pay Service 2

Pay Units: 118.

Programming (via satellite): DMX.

Fee: $20.00 installation; $6.95 monthly.

Pay Service 3

Pay Units: 1,522.

Programming (via satellite): HBO (multiplexed).

Fee: $20.00 installation; $12.95 monthly.

Pay Service 4

Pay Units: 1,132.

Programming (via satellite): Showtime.

Fee: $20.00 installation; $12.95 monthly.

Pay Service 5

Pay Units: N.A.

Programming (via satellite): The Movie Channel.

Fee: N.A.

Pay-Per-View

Addressable homes: 2,408.

Movies.

Local advertising: Yes. Available in satellite distributed programming. Local sales manager: Holly Hackner.

Equipment: Scientific-Atlanta headend; Scientific-Atlanta amplifiers; Times Fiber cable; Siecor fiber optic cable; JVC & Times Fiber cameras; JVC & Sony VTRs; Sony character generator; Scientific-Atlanta set top converters; General Instrument addressable set top converters; Scientific-Atlanta satellite antenna; Scientific-Atlanta satellite receivers.

Miles of plant: 330.0 (coaxial); 65.0 (fiber optic). Homes passed: 15,705. Total homes in franchised area: 15,705.

Manager: Shirley Hehn Weibel. Chief technician: Tim Fischer. Marketing director: Ellen Martin.

Ownership: Charter Communications Inc. (MSO). Purchased from Marcus Cable, April 1, 1999.

ONTARIO—Triax Cablevision, Box 110, 1504 2nd St. SE, Waseca, MN 56093. Phones: 507-835-5975; 800-332-0245. Fax: 507-835-4567. County: Vernon. ICA: WI0303.

TV Market Ranking: Below 100. Franchise award date: N.A. Franchise expiration date: February 9, 2009. Began: N.A.

Channel capacity: 62 (2-way capable; not operating 2-way). Channels available but not in use: N.A.

Basic Service

Subscribers: 167.

Programming (received off-air): WEAU-TV (N) Eau Claire; WHLA-TV (P), WKBT (C), WLAX (F), WXOW-TV (A) La Crosse; WKOW-TV (A), WMSN-TV (F), WMTV (N) Madison.

Fee: $35.16 installation; $9.03 monthly; $1.58 converter.

Expanded Basic Service

Subscribers: 162.

Programming (via satellite): WGN-TV (W) Chicago; A & E; CNN; Discovery Channel; ESPN; Fox Family Channel; Nashville Network; Nickelodeon; TBS Superstation; USA Network.

Fee: $14.92 monthly.

Pay Service 1

Pay Units: 31.

Programming (via satellite): HBO.

Fee: $10.45 monthly.

Miles of plant: 5.3 (coaxial). Homes passed: 190.

Manager: Richard Giffen. Chief technician: Scott Walters.

Ownership: Triax Telecommunications Co. LLC (MSO). See Cable System Ownership.

ORFORDVILLE—Triax Cablevision, Box 110, 1504 2nd St. SE, Waseca, MN 56093. Phones: 507-835-5975; 800-332-0245. Fax: 507-835-4567. County: Rock. Also serves Footville. ICA: WI0130.

TV Market Ranking: 93,97. Franchise award date: September 26, 1983. Franchise expiration date: April 6, 2014. Began: October 24, 1984.

Channel capacity: 37 (not 2-way capable). Channels available but not in use: None.

Basic Service

Subscribers: 511.

Programming (received off-air): WIFR (C) Freeport-Rockford; WHA-TV (P), WISC-TV (C), WKOW-TV (A), WMSN-TV (F), WMTV (N) Madison; WQRF-TV (F), WREX-TV (N), WTVO (A) Rockford.

Programming (via satellite): WGN-TV (W) Chicago; Home Shopping Network.

Fee: $45.00 installation; $13.50 monthly.

Expanded Basic Service

Subscribers: 495.

Programming (via satellite): A & E; American Movie Classics; CNN; Country Music TV; Discovery Channel; Disney Channel; ESPN; ESPN 2; FX; Fox Family Channel; History Channel; Lifetime; MTV; Nashville Network; Nickelodeon; Sci-Fi Channel; TBS Superstation; The Weather Channel; Trinity Bcstg. Network; Turner Network TV; USA Network.

Fee: $17.00 monthly.

Pay Service 1

Pay Units: 388.

Programming (via satellite): Cinemax; HBO; Showtime; Starz!; The New Encore.

Fee: $5.99 monthly (Encore & Starz), $7.95 monthly (Cinemax),$11.99 monthly (HBO or Showtime).

Equipment: Scientific-Atlanta headend; Scientific-Atlanta amplifiers; Scientific-Atlanta cable; Scientific-Atlanta set top converters; Vitek traps; Scientific-Atlanta satellite antenna; Scientific-Atlanta satellite receivers.

Miles of plant: 15.4 (coaxial). Homes passed: 673. Total homes in franchised area: 711.

Manager: Mike Nodgerson. Chief technician: Pat Alderman.

City fee: 3% of gross.

Ownership: Triax Telecommunications Co. LLC (MSO). See Cable System Ownership.

OXFORD—Cable Systems Management of Iowa Inc., 3600 Kennebec Dr., Eagan, MN 55122. Phone: 612-688-2623. Fax: 612-688-2624. County: Marquette. ICA: WI0314.

TV Market Ranking: Outside TV Markets. Franchise award date: N.A. Franchise expiration date: N.A. Began: N.A.

Channel capacity: N.A. Channels available but not in use: N.A.

Basic Service

Subscribers: 92.

Programming (received off-air): WHA-TV (P), WISC-TV (C), WKOW-TV (A), WMTV (N) Madison.

Programming (via satellite): WGN-TV (W) Chicago; A & E; American Movie Classics; CNN; Discovery Channel; Disney Channel; ESPN; Fox Family Channel; Learning Channel; Nashville Network; Showtime; TBS Superstation; Trinity Bcstg. Network; Turner Network TV; USA Network.

Fee: N.A.

Manager: Jeff Anderson.

Ownership: Cable Systems Management of Iowa Inc. (MSO).

PACKWAUKEE—Cable Systems Management of Iowa Inc., 3600 Kennebec Dr., Eagan, MN 55122. Phone: 612-688-2623. Fax: 612-688-2624. County: Marquette. ICA: WI0189.

TV Market Ranking: Outside TV Markets. Franchise award date: N.A. Franchise expiration date: N.A. Began: N.A.

Channel capacity: 40. Channels available but not in use: 19.

Basic Service

Subscribers: 55.

Programming (received off-air): WHA-TV (P), WISC-TV (C), WKOW-TV (A), WMTV (N) Madison.
Programming (via satellite): WGN-TV (W) Chicago; A & E; American Movie Classics; CNN; Country Music TV; Discovery Channel; E! Entertainment TV; ESPN; Fox Family Channel; Learning Channel; Nashville Network; Showtime; TBS Superstation; Trinity Bcstg. Network; Turner Network TV; USA Network.
Fee: $50.00 installation; $30.00 monthly.
Equipment: Nexus headend; Times Fiber cable.
Miles of plant: 9.8 (coaxial). Homes passed: 260.
Manager: Jeff Anderson.
Ownership: Cable Systems Management of Iowa Inc. (MSO).

PARK FALLS—Charter Communications Inc., 1725 S. Main St., Rice Lake, WI 54868-0539. Phones: 715-234-3821; 800-262-2578. Fax: 715-234-8537. County: Price. Also serves Eisenstein, Lake. ICA: WI0086.
TV Market Ranking: Outside TV Markets. Franchise award date: N.A. Franchise expiration date: N.A. Began: May 10, 1966.
Channel capacity: 60. Channels available but not in use: 30.
Basic Service
Subscribers: 1,285.
Programming (received off-air): WLEF-TV (P) Park Falls; WAOW-TV (A), WJFW-TV (N), WSAW-TV (C) Wausau-Rhinelander.
Programming (via satellite): WGN-TV (W) Chicago; C-SPAN; FoxNet.
Fee: $42.95 installation (aerial), $45.00 (underground); $8.93 monthly.
Expanded Basic Service
Subscribers: N.A.
Programming (via satellite): A & E; American Movie Classics; Animal Planet; Bravo; C-SPAN 2; CNBC; CNN; Comedy Central; Country Music TV; Discovery Channel; Disney Channel; ESPN; ESPN 2; FX; Fox Family Channel; Game Show Network; Headline News; Home & Garden Television; Learning Channel; Lifetime; MSNBC; MTV; Midwest Sports Channel; Nashville Network; Nick at Nite's TV Land; Nickelodeon; Outdoor Life Network; QVC; Speedvision; TBS Superstation; The Weather Channel; Toon Disney; Turner Network TV; USA Network; VH1.
Fee: $42.95 installation; $22.02 monthly.
Pay Service 1
Pay Units: 180.
Programming (via satellite): Cinemax.
Fee: $19.95 installation; $12.95 monthly.
Pay Service 2
Pay Units: 234.
Programming (via satellite): Showtime.
Fee: $19.95 installation; $12.95 monthly.
Pay Service 3
Pay Units: 207.
Programming (via satellite): HBO.
Fee: $19.95 installation; $12.95 monthly.
Local advertising: No.
Equipment: Scientific-Atlanta headend; Superior amplifiers; Times Fiber cable; Hamlin & Jerrold set top converters; Eagle traps; Scientific-Atlanta satellite antenna; Scientific-Atlanta satellite receivers.
Miles of plant: 28.5 (coaxial). Homes passed: 1,475.
Manager: Karen Sanderson. Chief technician: George Benjamin.
City fee: None.
Ownership: Charter Communications Inc. (MSO). Purchased from Marcus Cable, April 1, 1999.

PEPIN—US Cable, 128 W. Main St., Wabasha, MN 55981-1237. Phones: 651-565-4431; 800-642-5509. Fax: 651-565-2501. County: Pepin. ICA: WI0155.
TV Market Ranking: Below 100. Franchise award date: N.A. Franchise expiration date: N.A. Began: April 1, 1988.
Channel capacity: 29. Channels available but not in use: N.A.
Basic Service
Subscribers: 252.
Programming (received off-air): WEAU-TV (N) Eau Claire; WHLA-TV (P), WKBT (C), WXOW-TV (A) La Crosse; WISC-TV (C) Madison; KARE (N), KMSP-TV (U), WCCO-TV (C), WFTC (F) Minneapolis-St. Paul; KTTC (N) Rochester.
Fee: $17.00 monthly.
Pay Service 1
Pay Units: 100.
Programming (via satellite): Showtime.
Fee: $25.00 installation; $8.95 monthly.
Miles of plant: 3.5 (coaxial). Homes passed: 450.
Manager: Dennis Ender. Chief technician: Jim Ireland.
Ownership: US Cable Corp. (MSO). Purchased from Fanch Communications Inc., April 30, 1999.

PHELPS—Upper Peninsula Communications, U.S. Hwy. 41, Carney, MI 49812. Phone: 906-639-2194. County: Vilas. ICA: WI0176.
TV Market Ranking: Outside TV Markets. Franchise award date: N.A. Franchise expiration date: N.A. Began: N.A.
Channel capacity: 40. Channels available but not in use: 19.
Basic Service
Subscribers: 96.
Programming (received off-air): WJMN-TV (C) Escanaba; WLEF-TV (P) Park Falls; WJFW-TV (N), WSAW-TV (C) Wausau-Rhinelander.
Programming (via satellite): WGN-TV (W) Chicago; A & E; American Movie Classics; CNN; Country Music TV; Discovery Channel; ESPN; Fox Family Channel; Lifetime; Nashville Network; Showtime; TBS Superstation; Turner Network TV; USA Network.
Fee: $50.00 installation; $24.95 monthly.
Miles of plant: 16.2 (coaxial). Homes passed: 338.
Manager: Mark J. Rekers.
Ownership: Upper Peninsula Communications Inc. (MSO).

PHILLIPS—Price County Telephone Co., Box 108, 105 N. Avon Ave., Phillips, WI 54555. Phone: 715-339-2151. Fax: 715-339-4512. County: Price. ICA: WI0119.
TV Market Ranking: Outside TV Markets. Franchise award date: January 1, 1980. Franchise expiration date: January 1, 2000. Began: January 1, 1982.
Channel capacity: 35 (not 2-way capable). Channels available but not in use: 9.
Basic Service
Subscribers: 890.
Programming (received off-air): WEAU-TV (N) Eau Claire; WLEF-TV (P) Park Falls; WAOW-TV (A), WJFW-TV (N), WSAW-TV (C) Wausau-Rhinelander; allband FM.
Programming (via satellite): WGN-TV (W) Chicago; American Movie Classics; CNN; Discovery Channel; ESPN; FoxNet; Nashville Network; Nickelodeon; QVC; TBS Superstation; The Weather Channel; Turner Network TV; USA Network.
Current originations: Automated time-weather; local news; local sports.
Fee: $25.00 installation; $15.50 monthly; $1.50 converter.
Pay Service 1
Pay Units: 200.
Programming (via satellite): HBO.
Fee: $7.50 installation; $9.00 monthly.
Pay Service 2
Pay Units: N.A.
Programming (via satellite): Disney Channel.
Fee: N.A.
Local advertising: Planned. Local sales manager: John G. Mess.
Equipment: Scientific-Atlanta headend; Scientific-Atlanta amplifiers; Telpar character generator; Eagle traps; Scientific-Atlanta satellite antenna; Microdyne satellite receivers.
Miles of plant: 16.0 (coaxial). Homes passed: 950. Total homes in franchised area: 950.
Manager: John G. Mess. Chief technician: Larry Reuak.
Ownership: Price County Telephone Co.

PITTSVILLE—HLM Cable Corp., Box 620684, 2305-A Parview Rd., Middleton, WI 53562-0684. Phones: 608-831-7044; 800-451-5119. Fax: 608-836-5726. County: Wood. ICA: WI0183.
TV Market Ranking: Below 100. Franchise award date: January 1, 1987. Franchise expiration date: January 1, 2002. Began: January 1, 1988.
Channel capacity: 40 (not 2-way capable). Channels available but not in use: 12.
Basic Service
Subscribers: 204.
Programming (received off-air): WEAU-TV (N) Eau Claire; WAOW-TV (A), WHRM-TV (P), WSAW-TV (C) Wausau-Rhinelander.
Programming (via satellite): WGN-TV (W) Chicago; A & E; American Movie Classics; CNBC; CNN; Discovery Channel; ESPN; ESPN 2; Fox Family Channel; FoxNet; History Channel; Learning Channel; Lifetime; Nashville Network; Nick at Nite; Nick at Nite's TV Land; Nickelodeon; Sci-Fi Channel; TBS Superstation; The Weather Channel; Turner Network TV; USA Network; VH1.
Fee: $19.95 installation; $26.00 monthly; $1.50 converter.
Pay Service 1
Pay Units: 16.
Programming (via satellite): Disney Channel.
Fee: $14.95 installation; $6.95 monthly.
Pay Service 2
Pay Units: 51.
Programming (via satellite): Showtime.
Fee: $14.95 installation; $6.95 monthly.
Equipment: Scientific-Atlanta headend; Scientific-Atlanta amplifiers; Comm/Scope cable; Intercept traps; Scientific-Atlanta satellite antenna.
Miles of plant: 8.0 (coaxial). Homes passed: 300.
Manager: Robert E. Ryan.
City fee: None.
Ownership: H.L.M. Cable Co. (MSO).

PLAIN—Spring Green CableComm, Box 609, 245 S. Winsted St., Spring Green, WI 53588-9431. Phone: 608-588-7454. Fax: 608-588-7067. County: Sauk. ICA: WI0274.
TV Market Ranking: 93. Franchise award date: N.A. Franchise expiration date: N.A. Began: July 1, 1985.
Channel capacity: 42 (not 2-way capable). Channels available but not in use: 12.
Basic Service
Subscribers: 188.
Programming (received off-air): WHA-TV (P), WISC-TV (C), WKOW-TV (A), WMSN-TV (F), WMTV (N) Madison.
Programming (via satellite): WGN-TV (W) Chicago; A & E; CNN; Discovery Channel; ESPN; ESPN 2; Fox Family Channel; Headline News; Nashville Network; Nickelodeon; QVC; TBS Superstation; Turner Classic Movies; Turner Network TV; USA Network.
Fee: $49.95 installation; $29.85 monthly.
Pay Service 1
Pay Units: N.A.
Programming (via satellite): HBO.
Fee: $19.95 installation; $9.95 monthly.
Pay Service 2
Pay Units: N.A.
Programming (via satellite): Cinemax.
Fee: $9.95 monthly.
Miles of plant: 5.6 (coaxial).
Manager: Kevin Mayne. Chief technician: Tad Peak. Customer service manager: Liz Reuter.
Ownership: Fanch Communications Inc. (MSO). See Cable System Ownership.

PLATTEVILLE—CenturyTel TeleVideo, 135 N. Bonson St., Platteville, WI 53818. Phone: 608-326-2211. Fax: 608-348-2679. Counties: Grant & Lafayette. Also serves Evergreen Trailer Court, Platteville Twp. (eastern portion). ICA: WI0056.
TV Market Ranking: Below 100. Franchise award date: August 1, 1965. Franchise expiration date: N.A. Began: January 1, 1966.
Channel capacity: 60 (not 2-way capable). Channels available but not in use: 4.
Basic Service
Subscribers: 3,038.
Programming (received off-air): KCRG-TV (A), KGAN (C), KWWL (N) Cedar Rapids-Waterloo; KFXB (F) Dubuque; WHA-TV (P), WISC-TV (C), WKOW-TV (A), WMSN-TV (F), WMTV (N) Madison; 15 FMs.
Programming (via satellite): WGN-TV (W) Chicago; A & E; American Movie Classics; CNN; Discovery Channel; ESPN; Fox Family Channel; Lifetime; MTV; Nashville Network; Nickelodeon; TBS Superstation; The Weather Channel; Turner Network TV; USA Network.
Current originations: Automated time-weather; educational access.
Fee: $19.95 installation; $19.95 monthly.
Pay Service 1
Pay Units: 527.
Programming (via satellite): Cinemax.
Fee: $19.95 installation; $6.95 monthly.
Pay Service 2
Pay Units: 492.
Programming (via satellite): Showtime.
Fee: $19.95 installation; $6.95 monthly.
Local advertising: No.
Equipment: Jerrold & Scientific-Atlanta headend; Jerrold amplifiers; Times Fiber cable; Jerrold, Hamlin & RCA set top converters;

Arcom traps; Scientific-Atlanta satellite antenna; Scientific-Atlanta satellite receivers.
Miles of plant: 48.0 (coaxial). Homes passed: 3,700. Total homes in franchised area: 3,700.
Manager: Vicki Jernstrom. Chief technician: Mark Redfern.
City fee: 3% of gross.
Ownership: PTI Televideo Inc.

PLATTEVILLE—Triax Cablevision, Box 110, 1504 2nd St. SE, Waseca, MN 56093. Phones: 507-835-5975; 800-678-2798. Fax: 507-835-4567. Counties: Grant & Lafayette. Also serves Belmont, Benton, Cuba City, Darlington, Fennimore, Hazel Green, Muscoda, Potosi, Shullsburg, Tennyson. ICA: WI0320.
TV Market Ranking: Below 100 (Belmont, Benton, Cuba City, Darlington, Fennimore, Hazel Green, Platteville, Potosi, Shullsburg, Tennyson); Outside TV Markets (Muscoda). Franchise award date: N.A. Franchise expiration date: N.A. Began: N.A.
Channel capacity: N.A. Channels available but not in use: N.A.
Basic Service
Subscribers: 4,447.
Programming (received off-air): KGAN (C), KWWL (N) Cedar Rapids-Waterloo; KFXB (F) Dubuque; WHA-TV (P), WISC-TV (C), WKOW-TV (A), WMSN-TV (F), WMTV (N) Madison.
Programming (via satellite): WGN-TV (W) Chicago; American Movie Classics; QVC.
Fee: $11.45 monthly.
Expanded Basic Service
Subscribers: N.A.
Programming (via satellite): A & E; CNN; Country Music TV; Discovery Channel; Disney Channel; ESPN; Fox Family Channel; Headline News; Lifetime; MTV; Nashville Network; Nickelodeon; Odyssey; The Weather Channel; Turner Network TV; USA Network.
Fee: $16.50 monthly.
Pay Service 1
Pay Units: N.A.
Programming (via satellite): Cinemax; HBO; Showtime; The Movie Channel; The New Encore.
Fee: $5.95 monthly (Encore); $8.95 monthly (Cinemax); $11.95 monthly (HBO & Showtime).
Manager: Bob Ziel.
Ownership: Triax Telecommunications Co. LLC (MSO); InterMedia Partners (MSO). See Cable System Ownership.

PLUM CITY—Durand Cable Co. Inc., 318 3rd Ave. W, Durand, WI 54736. Phone: 715-672-5966. Fax: 715-672-4344. County: Pierce. ICA: WI0199.
TV Market Ranking: Outside TV Markets. Franchise award date: N.A. Franchise expiration date: October 3, 1999. Began: July 1, 1981.
Channel capacity: 40 (not 2-way capable). Channels available but not in use: 15.
Basic Service
Subscribers: 202.
Programming (received off-air): WEAU-TV (N), WQOW-TV (A) Eau Claire; WKBT (C) La Crosse; WHWC-TV (P) Menomonie; KARE (N), KMSP-TV (U), KSTP-TV (A), KTCA-TV (P), WCCO-TV (C), WFTC (F) Minneapolis-St. Paul; allband FM.
Programming (via satellite): WGN-TV (W) Chicago; A & E; American Movie Classics; CNN; Country Music TV; Discovery Channel; ESPN; Fox Family Channel; Nashville Network; TBS Superstation; Turner Network TV; USA Network.
Fee: $15.00 installation; $16.75 monthly.
Pay Service 1
Pay Units: 40.
Programming (via satellite): HBO.
Fee: $10.00 installation; $9.00 monthly.
Local advertising: No.
Equipment: Scientific-Atlanta headend; RCA amplifiers; Comm/Scope cable; Scientific-Atlanta set top converters; Eagle traps; Microdyne satellite antenna; Scientific-Atlanta & Standard Communications satellite receivers.
Miles of plant: 6.0 (coaxial). Additional miles planned: 1.0 (coaxial). Homes passed: 230.
Manager: Jerry Levenske. Chief technician: John Kurtzhals.
Village fee: $300 annually.
Ownership: Durand Cable Co. Inc. (MSO).

PLYMOUTH—Warner Cable, Box 224, Plymouth, WI 53073. Phone: 414-893-0542. Counties: Ozaukee & Sheboygan. Also serves Adell, Cascade, Elkhart Lake, Glenbeulah, Greenbush, Lima, Rhine, Waldo, Walibeka. ICA: WI0064.
TV Market Ranking: Below 100 (Elkhart Lake, Glenbeulah, Plymouth, Rhine, Walibeka); Outside TV Markets (Adell, Cascade, Greenbush, Lima, Waldo). Franchise award date: N.A. Franchise expiration date: N.A. Began: December 1, 1984.
Channel capacity: 46. Channels available but not in use: N.A.
Basic Service
Subscribers: 3,878.
Programming (received off-air): WBAY-TV (A), WFRV-TV (C), WGBA (N), WLUK-TV (F), WPNE (P) Green Bay; WCGV-TV (I), WISN-TV (A), WITI (F), WMVS (P), WMVT (P), WTMJ-TV (N), WVCY-TV (I) Milwaukee.
Programming (via satellite): WGN-TV (W) Chicago; A & E; C-SPAN; CNN; ESPN; Fox Family Channel; Headline News; Home Shopping Network; Learning Channel; Lifetime; MTV; Nashville Network; Nickelodeon; TBS Superstation; The Weather Channel; USA Network; VH1.
Fee: $75.00 installation; $10.47 monthly.
Pay Service 1
Pay Units: N.A.
Programming (via satellite): Cinemax; Disney Channel; HBO; Showtime; The Movie Channel.
Fee: $10.00 installation; $8.35 monthly (Disney), $10.45 monthly (Cinemax, HBO, Showtime or TMC).
Miles of plant: 60.8 (coaxial).
Manager: Norm Ruedinger.
Ownership: Time Warner Cable (MSO).

PORTAGE—Bresnan Communications Inc., Suite 150, 5618 Odana Rd., Madison, WI 53719. Phone: 608-274-3822. Fax: 608-274-1436. County: Columbia. Also serves Columbia County. ICA: WI0050.
TV Market Ranking: 93 (portions of Columbia County, Portage); Below 100 (portions of Columbia County); Outside TV Markets (portions of Columbia County). Franchise award date: N.A. Franchise expiration date: N.A. Began: September 1, 1975.
Channel capacity: 32. Channels available but not in use: N.A.
Basic Service
Subscribers: 2,462.
Programming (received off-air): WHA-TV (P), WISC-TV (C), WKOW-TV (A), WMSN-TV (F), WMTV (N) Madison; 14 FMs.
Programming (via satellite): WGN-TV (W) Chicago; C-SPAN; CNN; Discovery Channel; Fox Family Channel; Headline News; MTV; Nashville Network; Nickelodeon; QVC; TBS Superstation; The Weather Channel.
Current originations: Public access.
Fee: $60.00 installation; $10.00 monthly; $40.00 additional installation.
Expanded Basic Service
Subscribers: 2,275.
Programming (via satellite): A & E; American Movie Classics; ESPN; Lifetime; Turner Network TV; USA Network.
Fee: $1.75 monthly.
Pay Service 1
Pay Units: 141.
Programming (via satellite): Cinemax.
Fee: $12.90 monthly.
Pay Service 2
Pay Units: 108.
Programming (via satellite): Disney Channel.
Fee: N.A.
Pay Service 3
Pay Units: 517.
Programming (via satellite): HBO.
Fee: $12.90 monthly.
Pay Service 4
Pay Units: 178.
Programming (via satellite): Showtime.
Fee: $12.90 monthly.
Pay Service 5
Pay Units: 828.
Programming (via satellite): The New Encore.
Fee: N.A.
Local advertising: Yes.
Miles of plant: 37.0 (coaxial). Homes passed: 4,282. Total homes in franchised area: 4,282.
Manager: Brian Shirk. Chief technician: Jerry Myers. Marketing director: Tim Roehl.
Ownership: Bresnan Communications Co. LP (MSO). Purchased from Tele-Communications Inc, February 2, 1999. See Cable System Ownership.

POYNETTE—Charter Communications Inc., Box 1127, 1348 Plainfield Ave., Janesville, WI 53547-1127. Phone: 608-754-3644. Fax: 608-754-8107. County: Columbia. Also serves Arlington (village). ICA: WI0121.
TV Market Ranking: 93. Franchise award date: N.A. Franchise expiration date: N.A. Began: December 1, 1983.
Channel capacity: 40 (2-way capable; operating 2-way). Channels available but not in use: None.
Basic Service
Subscribers: 771.
Programming (received off-air): WHPN-TV (U) Janesville; WHA-TV (P), WISC-TV (C), WKOW-TV (A), WMSN-TV (F), WMTV (N) Madison.
Current originations: Local news.
Fee: $42.95 installation; $11.02 monthly.
Expanded Basic Service
Subscribers: 726.
Programming (via satellite): WGN-TV (W) Chicago; A & E; American Movie Classics; Animal Planet; C-SPAN; CNBC; CNN; Discovery Channel; Disney Channel; ESPN; ESPN 2; ESPNews; Fox Family Channel; Headline News; History Channel; Home & Garden Television; Learning Channel; Lifetime; MSNBC; MTV; Nashville Network; Nick at Nite's TV Land; Nickelodeon; Outdoor Life Network; QVC; TBS Superstation; The Weather Channel; Toon Disney; Turner Network TV; USA Network.
Fee: $30.45 monthly.
Pay Service 1
Pay Units: 124.
Programming (via satellite): Cinemax.
Fee: $12.95 monthly.
Pay Service 2
Pay Units: 163.
Programming (via satellite): HBO.
Fee: $12.95 monthly.
Pay Service 3
Pay Units: 109.
Programming (via satellite): Showtime.
Fee: $12.95 monthly.
Equipment: Scientific-Atlanta headend; Texscan amplifiers; Comm/Scope cable; Panasonic cameras; Panasonic VTRs; Texscan character generator; Oak set top converters; Eagle traps; Microdyne satellite antenna; Scientific-Atlanta satellite receivers.
Miles of plant: 10.0 (coaxial). Homes passed: 1,256.
Manager: Marty Robinson. Chief technician: Joe Browning. Marketing director: Danette Knickmeier.
City fee: 3% of gross.
Ownership: Charter Communications Inc. (MSO). Purchased from Marcus Cable, April 1, 1999.

PRAIRIE DU CHIEN—Triax Cablevision, Box 110, 1504 2nd St. SE, Waseca, MN 56093. Phones: 507-835-5975; 800-332-0245. Fax: 507-835-4567. Counties: Crawford & Grant, WI; Allamakee & Clayton, IA. Also serves Elkader, Guttenberg, Harpers Ferry, Lansing, Marquette, McGregor, Waukon Junction, IA; Boscobel, Bridgeport (town), Crawford County (unincorporated areas), DeSoto, Essman Island, Grant County (unincorporated areas), Prairie du Chien (town), WI. ICA: WI0066.
TV Market Ranking: Below 100 (portions of Crawford County, DeSoto, portions of Grant County, Guttenberg, Lansing); Outside TV Markets (Boscobel, Bridgeport, portions of Crawford County, Elkader, Essman Island, portions of Grant County, Harpers Ferry, Marquette, McGregor, Prairie Du Chien, Prairie du Chien, Waukon Junction). Franchise award date: N.A. Franchise expiration date: September 1, 2001. Began: February 1, 1968.
Channel capacity: 60. Channels available but not in use: 21.
Basic Service
Subscribers: 8,400.
Programming (received off-air): KCRG-TV (A), KGAN (C), KRIN (P), KWWL (N) Cedar Rapids-Waterloo; KFXB (F) Dubuque; WHLA-TV (P), WKBT (C), WLAX (F) La Crosse; WKOW-TV (A), WMTV (N) Madison; allband FM.
Fee: $8.00 monthly.
Expanded Basic Service
Subscribers: N.A.
Programming (via satellite): WGN-TV (W) Chicago; A & E; American Movie Classics; C-SPAN; CNBC; CNN; Country Music TV; Discovery Channel; ESPN; EWTN; Fox Family Channel; Headline News; Learning Channel; Lifetime; Nashville Network; Nickelodeon; Odyssey; TBS Superstation; TV Guide Channel; The Weather Channel; Trinity Bcstg. Network; Turner Network TV; USA Network; VH1.
Fee: N.A.
Pay Service 1
Pay Units: 1,004.
Programming (via satellite): Cinemax; Disney Channel; HBO; Showtime; The New Encore.
Fee: $20.00 installation; $10.00 monthly (HBO).
Local advertising: Yes. Rates: $7.00/Month.
Equipment: Jerrold headend; Jerrold amplifiers; Plastoid cable; Prodelin satellite antenna.
Miles of plant: 32.9 (coaxial).
Manager: Richard Giffen. Chief technician: Scott Walters.
City fee: $1.50 per first 400 subscribers.
Ownership: Triax Telecommunications Co. LLC (MSO). See Cable System Ownership.

PRAIRIE DU SAC—Charter Communications Inc., Box 1127, 1348 Plainfield Ave., Janes-

ville, WI 53547-1127. Phone: 608-754-3644. Fax: 608-754-8107. Counties: Columbia, Dane & Sauk. Also serves Prairie du Sac (town), Prairie du Sac (village), Roxbury, West Point Twp. ICA: WI0107.
TV Market Ranking: 93. Franchise award date: N.A. Franchise expiration date: N.A. Began: July 1, 1980.
Channel capacity: 41 (not 2-way capable). Channels available but not in use: None.
Basic Service
Subscribers: 905.
Programming (received off-air): WHA-TV (P), WISC-TV (C), WKOW-TV (A), WMSN-TV (F), WMTV (N) Madison.
Current originations: Educational access; local news.
Fee: $42.95 installation; $9.34 monthly.
Expanded Basic Service
Subscribers: 880.
Programming (via satellite): WGN-TV (W) Chicago; A & E; American Movie Classics; Animal Planet; C-SPAN; CNBC; CNN; Discovery Channel; Disney Channel; ESPN; ESPN 2; ESPNews; Fox Family Channel; Headline News; History Channel; Home & Garden Television; Learning Channel; Lifetime; MSNBC; MTV; Nashville Network; Nick at Nite's TV Land; Nickelodeon; QVC; TBS Superstation; The Weather Channel; Toon Disney; Turner Network TV; USA Network; VH1.
Fee: $20.61 monthly.
Pay Service 1
Pay Units: 107.
Programming (via satellite): Cinemax.
Fee: $12.95 monthly.
Pay Service 2
Pay Units: 153.
Programming (via satellite): HBO.
Fee: $12.95 monthly.
Pay Service 3
Pay Units: 92.
Programming (via satellite): Showtime.
Fee: $12.95 monthly.
Equipment: Scientific-Atlanta headend; Scientific-Atlanta amplifiers; Comm/Scope cable; Texscan character generator; Oak, Scientific-Atlanta & Hamlin set top converters; Eagle traps; Scientific-Atlanta satellite antenna; Scientific-Atlanta satellite receivers.
Miles of plant: 13.0 (coaxial). Homes passed: 1,501.
Manager: Marty Robinson. Chief technician: Joe Browning. Marketing director: Danette Knickmeier.
City fee: 3% of basic.
Ownership: Charter Communications Inc. (MSO). Purchased from Marcus Cable, April 1, 1999.

PRENTICE—KRM Cablevision, Box 77, Mellen, WI 54546. Phone: 715-274-7631. County: Price. ICA: WI0200.
TV Market Ranking: Outside TV Markets. Franchise award date: N.A. Franchise expiration date: N.A. Began: May 1, 1986.
Channel capacity: 18 (not 2-way capable). Channels available but not in use: 2.
Basic Service
Subscribers: N.A.
Programming (received off-air): WEAU-TV (N) Eau Claire; WLEF-TV (P) Park Falls; WAOW-TV (A), WJFW-TV (N), WSAW-TV (C) Wausau-Rhinelander.
Programming (via satellite): WGN-TV (W) Chicago; CNN; Comedy Central; Discovery Channel; ESPN; Nashville Network; TBS Superstation; Turner Network TV; USA Network.
Fee: $35.00 installation; $14.00 monthly.
Pay Service 1
Pay Units: N.A.
Programming (via satellite): Disney Channel; The Movie Channel.
Fee: $8.00 monthly (Disney); $12.00 monthly (TMC).
Equipment: Jerrold headend; Jerrold amplifiers; Plastoid cable; Arcom traps; Prodelin satellite antenna; Triple Crown satellite receivers.
Miles of plant: 6.0 (coaxial). Homes passed: 230.
Manager: O. D. Miller. Chief technician: Keith Gehrett.
Ownership: KRM Cablevision (MSO).

PULASKI—Net Cable Inc., Box 568, 122 S. Saint Augustine St., Pulaski, WI 54162-0568. Phone: 414-822-8121. Fax: 414-822-8665. E-mail: cbarnes@netnet.net. County: Brown. ICA: WI0114.
TV Market Ranking: 62. Franchise award date: January 1, 1981. Franchise expiration date: January 1, 2011. Began: January 1, 1982.
Channel capacity: 36 (not 2-way capable). Channels available but not in use: 1.
Basic Service
Subscribers: 860.
Programming (received off-air): WACY (U) Appleton; WBAY-TV (A), WFRV-TV (C), WGBA (N), WLUK-TV (F), WPNE (P) Green Bay.
Programming (via satellite): WGN-TV (W) Chicago; A & E; CNN; Country Music TV; Discovery Channel; Disney Channel; EWTN; Fox Family Channel; Lifetime; QVC; Sci-Fi Channel; TBS Superstation; The Weather Channel; Turner Network TV; USA Network; VH1.
Current originations: Automated time-weather; public access; educational access; government access; religious access; local news; local sports.
Fee: $20.00 installation; $17.65 monthly.
Expanded Basic Service
Subscribers: 825.
Programming (via satellite): American Movie Classics; CNN; ESPN; ESPN 2; Headline News; MTV; Nashville Network; Nickelodeon.
Fee: $7.50 installation; $4.00 monthly.
Pay Service 1
Pay Units: 150.
Programming (via satellite): Cinemax.
Fee: $7.50 installation; $9.95 monthly.
Pay Service 2
Pay Units: 175.
Programming (via satellite): HBO.
Fee: $7.50 installation; $9.95 monthly.
Local advertising: Yes. Available in character-generated programming. Local sales manager: Cheryl Barnes.
Equipment: Scientific-Atlanta headend; Scientific-Atlanta amplifiers; Oak set top converters; Pico traps; Scientific-Atlanta satellite antenna; Scientific-Atlanta satellite receivers.
Miles of plant: 13.0 (coaxial); None (fiber optic). Additional miles planned: 3.0 (coaxial). Homes passed: 1,175. Total homes in franchised area: 1,175.
Manager: Cheryl Barnes. Chief technician: Dave Willner.
Village fee: 3% of gross.
Ownership: Net Cable Inc.

RANDOLPH—Peoples Broadband Communications Systems Inc., Box 2, 121 Williams St., Randolph, WI 53956. Phone: 414-326-5859. Fax: 414-326-4127. Counties: Columbia & Dodge. Also serves Cambria, Courtland, Fall River, Fort Winnebago, Fountain Prairie, Fox Lake Twp., Lowville Twp., Marcellon, Otsego, Pacific Twp., Pardeeville, Rio, Wyocena Twp. ICA: WI0048.
TV Market Ranking: 93 (Cambria, Fall River, Fort Winnebago, Fountain Prairie, Fox Lake Twp., Lowville Twp., Marcellon, Otsego, Pacific Twp., Pardeeville, Randolph, Rio, Wyocena Twp.); Outside TV Markets (Courtland). Franchise award date: N.A. Franchise expiration date: N.A. Began: October 1, 1982.
Channel capacity: 36 (not 2-way capable). Channels available but not in use: 3.
Basic Service
Subscribers: 2,787.
Programming (received off-air): WHA-TV (P), WISC-TV (C), WKOW-TV (A), WMSN-TV (F), WMTV (N) Madison; WMVS (P), WTMJ-TV (N), WVTV (W) Milwaukee.
Programming (via satellite): WGN-TV (W) Chicago; A & E; American Movie Classics; C-SPAN; CNN; Comedy Central; Discovery Channel; ESPN; Fox Family Channel; Home Shopping Network; Learning Channel; Lifetime; MuchMusic Network; Nashville Network; Nickelodeon; Sci-Fi Channel; TBS Superstation; The Weather Channel; Turner Network TV; USA Network.
Current originations: Local news.
Fee: $15.95 monthly; $1.70 converter.
Pay Service 1
Pay Units: 460.
Programming (via satellite): Cinemax.
Fee: $8.95 monthly.
Pay Service 2
Pay Units: 189.
Programming (via satellite): Disney Channel.
Fee: $4.95 monthly.
Pay Service 3
Pay Units: 109.
Programming (via satellite): HBO.
Fee: $12.00 monthly.
Pay Service 4
Pay Units: 512.
Programming (via satellite): Showtime.
Fee: $9.95 monthly.
Local advertising: Yes. Available in character-generated programming.
Equipment: Scientific-Atlanta headend; Scientific-Atlanta amplifiers; Times Fiber & Comm/Scope cable; Oak, Hamlin & Scientific-Atlanta set top converters; Eagle traps; Scientific-Atlanta satellite antenna; Scientific-Atlanta satellite receivers.
Miles of plant: 104.3 (coaxial); 30.0 (fiber optic). Homes passed: 4,472. Total homes in franchised area: 4,472.
Manager: Gary Perleberg. Chief technician: Don Meinders. Marketing & program director: Jeffrey Beck.
Ownership: Pecoco Inc. (MSO).

RANDOM LAKE—Warner Cable, Box 224, Plymouth, WI 53073. Phone: 414-893-0542. Counties: Ozaukee & Sheboygan. Also serves Belgium, Cedar Grove, Dacada Village, Fredonia, Holland Twp., Oostburg, Sherman Twp. ICA: WI0059.
TV Market Ranking: 23 (Belgium, Dacada Village, Fredonia, Holland Twp.); Below 100 (Random Lake, Sherman Twp.); Outside TV Markets (Cedar Grove, Oostburg). Franchise award date: N.A. Franchise expiration date: January 1, 1999. Began: December 1, 1984.
Channel capacity: 44. Channels available but not in use: N.A.
Basic Service
Subscribers: 2,129.
Programming (received off-air): WACY (U) Appleton; WBAY-TV (A), WFRV-TV (C), WGBA (N), WLUK-TV (F) Green Bay; WCGV-TV (I), WISN-TV (A), WITI (F), WMVS (P), WMVT (P), WTMJ-TV (N), WVCY-TV (I), WVTV (W) Milwaukee.
Programming (via satellite): WGN-TV (W) Chicago; A & E; C-SPAN; CNBC; CNN; Discovery Channel; ESPN; EWTN; Fox Family Channel; Headline News; Home Shopping Network; Learning Channel; Lifetime; MTV; Nashville Network; Nickelodeon; TBS Superstation; The Weather Channel; USA Network; VH1.
Current originations: Public access; educational access.
Fee: $75.00 installation; $10.39 monthly.
Pay Service 1
Pay Units: N.A.
Programming (via satellite): Cinemax; Disney Channel; HBO; Showtime; The Movie Channel.
Fee: $10.00 installation; $8.35 monthly (Disney), $10.45 monthly (Cinemax, HBO, Showtime or TMC).
Pay-Per-View
Addressable homes: 1,824.
Miles of plant: 90.0 (coaxial). Homes passed: 3,188. Total homes in franchised area: 3,188.
Manager: Norm Ruedinger.
Ownership: Time Warner Cable (MSO).

REESEVILLE—Warner Cable Communications, 5475 W. Abbott Ave., Greenfield, WI 53220-4900. Phone: 414-282-6300. Fax: 414-421-1206. County: Dodge. Also serves Lowell. ICA: WI0151.
TV Market Ranking: 93. Franchise award date: N.A. Franchise expiration date: N.A. Began: N.A.
Channel capacity: 40. Channels available but not in use: N.A.
Basic Service
Subscribers: 226.
Programming (received off-air): WHA-TV (P), WISC-TV (C), WKOW-TV (A), WMSN-TV (F), WMTV (N) Madison; WCGV-TV (I), WISN-TV (A), WITI (F), WMVS (P), WTMJ-TV (N), WVTV (W) Milwaukee.
Programming (via satellite): WGN-TV (W) Chicago; CNBC; CNN; CNN/SI; Discovery Channel; ESPN; Fox Family Channel; MTV; Nashville Network; Nickelodeon; TBS Superstation; Turner Network TV; USA Network.
Planned programming (via satellite): Fox Sports Net.
Fee: $40.00 installation; $10.55 monthly.
Pay Service 1
Pay Units: N.A.
Programming (via satellite): Cinemax; Disney Channel; HBO; Showtime; The Movie Channel.
Fee: $10.45 monthly (each).
Miles of plant: 18.0 (coaxial). Homes passed: 472. Total homes in franchised area: 472.
Manager: Gary Owens. Chief technician: Rich Jaskowiak.
Ownership: Time Warner Cable (MSO). See Cable System Ownership.

RHINELANDER—Rhinelander Cable TV, Box 189, 821 Lincoln St., Rhinelander, WI 54501. Phone: 715-362-3942. Fax: 715-362-4441. Counties: Forest, Lincoln & Oneida. Also serves Argonne, Bradley, Bradley (Town), Crandon, Crescent, Heafford Junction, Lincoln, Monico, Newbold, Nokomis, Pelican, Pine Lake, Stella, Tomahawk, Wabeno. ICA: WI0037.
TV Market Ranking: Below 100. Franchise award date: N.A. Franchise expiration date: N.A. Began: February 1, 1954.
Channel capacity: 78 (2-way capable; not operating 2-way). Channels available but not in use: 35.

Basic Service
Subscribers: 8,300.
Programming (received off-air): WAOW-TV (A), WHRM-TV (P), WJFW-TV (N), WSAW-TV (C) Wausau-Rhinelander.
Programming (via satellite): WGN-TV (W) Chicago; A & E; C-SPAN; CNN; CNN International; CNNfn; Country Music TV; Court TV; Discovery Channel; ESPN; ESPN 2; ESPNews; EWTN; Fox Family Channel; Fox-Net; Headline News; History Channel; Home Shopping Network; Lifetime; MTV; Nashville Network; Nickelodeon; Sci-Fi Channel; TBS Superstation; The Weather Channel; Turner Classic Movies; Turner Network TV; USA Network; VH1.
Current originations: Educational access; religious access; leased access; automated emergency alert; local sports.
Fee: $40.00 installation; $26.95 monthly.
Pay Service 1
Pay Units: 157.
Programming (via satellite): Disney Channel.
Fee: $14.95 installation; $6.95 monthly.
Pay Service 2
Pay Units: 1,840.
Programming (via satellite): HBO (multiplexed).
Fee: $14.95 installation; $9.50 monthly.
Pay Service 3
Pay Units: 300.
Programming (via satellite): Showtime (multiplexed).
Fee: $14.95 installation; $6.95 monthly.
Local advertising: Yes. Available in locally originated, taped & automated programming. Local sales manager: Andrew Scrivener.
Equipment: Scientific-Atlanta & Drake headend; Scientific-Atlanta amplifiers; Comm/Scope cable; Lucent Technologies fiber optic cable; Scientific-Atlanta set top converters; Eagle traps; Scientific-Atlanta satellite antenna; Scientific-Atlanta & General Instrument satellite receivers.
Miles of plant: 300.0 (coaxial); 158.0 (fiber optic). Additional miles planned: 20.0 (coaxial); 14.0 (fiber optic).
Manager: Jeff Antonuk. Marketing director: Andrew Scrivener. Customer service manager: Michele DuFrane.
Ownership: Midwest Video Electronics Inc. (MSO).

RIB LAKE—Rib Lake Telecom Inc., Box 247, 1199 Fayette St., Rib Lake, WI 54470. Phone: 715-427-3737. Fax: 715-427-5117. County: Taylor. ICA: WI0177.
TV Market Ranking: Outside TV Markets. Franchise award date: November 1, 1979. Franchise expiration date: N.A. Began: November 1, 1984.
Channel capacity: 36 (not 2-way capable). Channels available but not in use: 4.
Basic Service
Subscribers: 285.
Programming (received off-air): WEAU-TV (N) Eau Claire; WAOW-TV (A), WHRM-TV (P), WJFW-TV (N), WSAW-TV (C) Wausau-Rhinelander; allband FM.
Programming (via satellite): WGN-TV (W) Chicago; C-SPAN; CNN; Discovery Channel; ESPN; ESPN 2; Fox Family Channel; Headline News; Learning Channel; Lifetime; Nashville Network; Nick at Nite; Nickelodeon; QVC; TBS Superstation; Turner Network TV; USA Network; VH1.
Current originations: Automated time-weather; public access; educational access; government access; library access; local sports.
Fee: $15.00 installation; $12.95 monthly; $2.00 converter; $9.95 additional installation.
Pay Service 1
Pay Units: 81.
Programming (via satellite): HBO.
Fee: $5.00 installation; $9.95 monthly.
Pay Service 2
Pay Units: 94.
Programming (via satellite): Showtime.
Fee: $5.00 installation; $8.95 monthly.
Pay Service 3
Pay Units: N.A.
Programming (via satellite): Disney Channel.
Fee: $4.95 monthly.
Local advertising: Yes (locally produced & insert). Available in locally originated & character-generated programming. Local sales manager: Clark Eckhoff.
Program Guide: The Cable Guide.
Equipment: Scientific-Atlanta headend; Scientific-Atlanta amplifiers; Telpar character generator; Pioneer set top converters; Scientific-Atlanta satellite receivers.
Miles of plant: 11.0 (coaxial). Additional miles planned: 4.0 (coaxial). Homes passed: 340. Total homes in franchised area: 345.
Manager: Clark Eckhoff. Chief technician: Michael Cihasky.
Ownership: Rib Lake Telephone Co. Inc.

RICE LAKE—Charter Communications Inc., 1725 S. Main St., Rice Lake, WI 54868-0539. Phones: 715-234-3821; 800-262-2578. Fax: 715-234-8537. Counties: Barron & Washburn. Also serves Barron, Barron (town), Chetek, Chetek (town), Cumberland, Long Lake, Rice Lake (town). ICA: WI0055.
TV Market Ranking: Below 100 (Chetek); Outside TV Markets (Barron, Cumberland, Long Lake, Rice Lake). Franchise award date: January 1, 1951. Franchise expiration date: July 10, 2001. Began: October 1, 1957.
Channel capacity: 35 (not 2-way capable). Channels available but not in use: None.
Basic Service
Subscribers: 6,400; Commercial subscribers: 318.
Programming (received off-air): WEUX (F) Chippewa Falls; WEAU-TV (N), WQOW-TV (A) Eau Claire; WKBT (C) La Crosse; WHWC-TV (P) Menomonie; KARE (N), KMSP-TV (U), KSTP-TV (A), KTCA-TV (P), WCCO-TV (C) Minneapolis-St. Paul; 8 FMs.
Programming (via satellite): WGN-TV (W) Chicago; Disney Channel; TBS Superstation.
Current originations: Public access; government access; automated emergency alert; local news.
Fee: $42.95 installation; $19.95 monthly.
Expanded Basic Service
Subscribers: 5,800.
Programming (via satellite): A & E; American Movie Classics; Animal Planet; Bravo; C-SPAN; C-SPAN 2; CNN; Cartoon Network; Comedy Central; Country Music TV; Court TV; Discovery Channel; E! Entertainment TV; ESPN; ESPN 2; ESPN Classic Sports; ESPNews; FX; Fox Family Channel; Game Show Network; Golf Channel; Headline News; History Channel; Home & Garden Television; Home Shopping Network; Learning Channel; Lifetime; MSNBC; MTV; Midwest Sports Channel; Nashville Network; Nick at Nite's TV Land; Nickelodeon; Outdoor Life Network; QVC; Sci-Fi Channel; Speedvision; TV Food Network; The Health Network; The Inspirational Network; The Weather Channel; Turner Classic Movies; Turner Network TV; USA Network; VH1.
Fee: $42.95 installation; $17.08 monthly.
Pay Service 1
Pay Units: 600.
Programming (via satellite): Cinemax (multiplexed).
Fee: $19.95 installation; $12.50 monthly.
Pay Service 2
Pay Units: 835.
Programming (via satellite): HBO (multiplexed).
Fee: $19.95 installation; $12.95 monthly.
Pay Service 3
Pay Units: 625.
Programming (via satellite): Showtime (multiplexed).
Fee: $19.95 installation; $12.50 monthly.
Pay-Per-View
Movies; special events.
Local advertising: Yes. Available in satellite distributed, taped & automated programming. Local sales manager: Andy Jerome.
Equipment: Jerrold headend; Jerrold amplifiers; Times Fiber cable; Scientific-Atlanta set top converters; Northeast Filter, PPC & Eagle traps; Scientific-Atlanta satellite antenna; M/A-Com & Scientific-Atlanta satellite receivers.
Miles of plant: 63.0 (coaxial); None (fiber optic). Homes passed: 7,706.
Manager: Scott Binder. Chief technician: George Benjamin.
City fee: 5% of gross.
Ownership: Charter Communications Inc. (MSO). Purchased from Marcus Cable, April 1, 1999.

RICHFIELD—Charter Communications Inc., Box 1197, 55 W. Scott St., Fond du Lac, WI 54936-1197. Phones: 920-923-7196; 800-581-0081. Fax: 920-923-1235. County: Washington. ICA: WI0276.
TV Market Ranking: 23. Franchise award date: N.A. Franchise expiration date: N.A. Began: August 1, 1990.
Channel capacity: 40. Channels available but not in use: 5.
Basic Service
Subscribers: 2,000.
Programming (received off-air): WCGV-TV (I), WDJT-TV (C), WISN-TV (A), WITI (F), WMVS (P), WTMJ-TV (N), WVCY-TV (I), WVTV (W) Milwaukee.
Programming (via satellite): WGN-TV (W) Chicago; A & E; American Movie Classics; C-SPAN; CNN; Country Music TV; Discovery Channel; ESPN; EWTN; Fox Family Channel; Headline News; Home Shopping Network; MTV; Nashville Network; Nickelodeon; Showtime; TBS Superstation; Travel Channel; Turner Network TV; USA Network; VH1.
Fee: $50.00 installation; $22.00 monthly.
Pay Service 1
Pay Units: N.A.
Programming (via satellite): Disney Channel; HBO; Showtime; The Movie Channel.
Fee: $5.95 monthly (each).
Local advertising: Yes. Available in character-generated programming.
Miles of plant: 163.0 (coaxial). Homes passed: 3,164.
Manager: Lisa Washa. Chief technician: Jeff Gerner.
Ownership: Charter Communications Inc. (MSO). Purchased from Marcus Cable, April 1, 1999.

RICHLAND CENTER—Bresnan Communications Co., Box 694, 170 N. Main St., Richland Center, WI 53581. Phones: 608-647-8857; 608-274-3822. Fax: 608-647-2203. County: Richland. ICA: WI0277.
TV Market Ranking: Outside TV Markets. Franchise award date: N.A. Franchise expiration date: N.A. Began: August 1, 1954.
Channel capacity: 54. Channels available but not in use: 26.
Basic Service
Subscribers: 2,080.
Programming (received off-air): WKBT (C) La Crosse; WHA-TV (P), WISC-TV (C), WKOW-TV (A), WMSN-TV (F), WMTV (N) Madison; 3 FMs.
Programming (via satellite): WGN-TV (W) Chicago; C-SPAN; CNN; Discovery Channel; Fox Family Channel; Lifetime; MTV; Nashville Network; QVC; TBS Superstation; The Weather Channel.
Current originations: Automated time-weather.
Fee: $30.00 installation; $10.00 monthly.
Expanded Basic Service
Subscribers: 1,944.
Programming (via satellite): A & E; American Movie Classics; Court TV; ESPN; Turner Network TV; USA Network.
Fee: $1.50 monthly.
Pay Service 1
Pay Units: 226.
Programming (via satellite): Cinemax.
Fee: $13.95 monthly.
Pay Service 2
Pay Units: 152.
Programming (via satellite): Disney Channel.
Fee: N.A.
Pay Service 3
Pay Units: 273.
Programming (via satellite): HBO.
Fee: $13.95 monthly.
Pay Service 4
Pay Units: 711.
Programming (via satellite): The New Encore.
Fee: N.A.
Local advertising: Yes.
Program Guide: The Cable Guide.
Equipment: Jerrold headend; Jerrold amplifiers; Plastoid cable; Hughes satellite antenna.
Miles of plant: 25.5 (coaxial). Total homes in franchised area: 2,405.
Manager: Brian Shirk.
Ownership: Bresnan Communications Co. LP (MSO). Purchased from Tele-Communications Inc, Febraury 2, 1999. See Cable System Ownership.

RIDGEWAY—Spring Green CableComm, Box 609, 245 S. Winsted St., Spring Green, WI 53588-9431. Phone: 608-588-7454. Fax: 608-588-7067. County: Iowa. Also serves Barneveld, Hollandale. Plans service to Blue Mounds. ICA: WI0278.
TV Market Ranking: 93. Franchise award date: N.A. Franchise expiration date: N.A. Began: June 1, 1989.
Channel capacity: 42 (not 2-way capable). Channels available but not in use: 10.
Basic Service
Subscribers: 570.
Programming (received off-air): WHA-TV (P), WISC-TV (C), WKOW-TV (A), WMSN-TV (F), WMTV (N) Madison.
Programming (via satellite): WGN-TV (W) Chicago; A & E; CNN; Discovery Channel; ESPN; Fox Family Channel; Headline News; Nashville Network; Nickelodeon; TBS Superstation; Turner Classic Movies; Turner Network TV; USA Network.
Fee: $49.95 installation; $29.85 monthly.
Pay Service 1
Pay Units: N.A.
Programming (via satellite): HBO.
Fee: $19.95 installation; $9.95 monthly.
Pay Service 2
Pay Units: N.A.
Programming (via satellite): Cinemax.
Fee: $9.95 monthly.
Miles of plant: 15.4 (coaxial).

Manager: Kevin Mayne. Customer service manager: Liz Reuter.
Ownership: Fanch Communications Inc. (MSO). See Cable System Ownership.

ROBERTS—Vision Communications, Box 355, 28 First Ave. W, Luck, WI 54853-0355. Phone: 715-472-2700. Fax: 715-472-2707. County: St. Croix. ICA: WI0184.
TV Market Ranking: 13. Franchise award date: N.A. Franchise expiration date: N.A. Began: January 1, 1986.
Channel capacity: 36. Channels available but not in use: 5.
Basic Service
Subscribers: 145.
Programming (received off-air): WEAU-TV (N), WQOW-TV (A) Eau Claire; WKBT (C) La Crosse; WHWC-TV (P) Menomonie; KARE (N), KLGT (W), KMSP-TV (U), KSTP-TV (A), KTCA-TV (P), WCCO-TV (C), WFTC (F) Minneapolis-St. Paul.
Fee: $49.95 installation; $14.95 monthly.
Expanded Basic Service
Subscribers: N.A.
Programming (via satellite): WGN-TV (W) Chicago; A & E; C-SPAN; CNN; Discovery Channel; ESPN; Fox Family Channel; Headline News; Home Shopping Network; Lifetime; MTV; Nashville Network; Nickelodeon; TBS Superstation; Turner Network TV; USA Network.
Fee: $6.55 monthly.
Pay Service 1
Pay Units: 23.
Programming (via satellite): Disney Channel.
Fee: $8.00 monthly.
Pay Service 2
Pay Units: 67.
Programming (via satellite): HBO.
Fee: $10.00 monthly.
Pay Service 3
Pay Units: 43.
Programming (via satellite): The Movie Channel.
Fee: $9.00 monthly.
Miles of plant: 4.5 (coaxial). Homes passed: 288.
Manager: John Blatt.
Ownership: Vision Communications LLC (MSO).

ROME TWP.—SCA Cable Inc., 1105 C.T.H. (D), Nekoosa, WI 54457. Phone: 715-325-3652. Fax: 715-325-7887. County: Adams. ICA: WI0279.
TV Market Ranking: Outside TV Markets. Franchise award date: N.A. Franchise expiration date: N.A. Began: January 1, 1984.
Channel capacity: 30. Channels available but not in use: N.A.
Basic Service
Subscribers: 641.
Programming (received off-air): WEAU-TV (N) Eau Claire; WAOW-TV (A), WHRM-TV (P), WSAW-TV (C) Wausau-Rhinelander.
Programming (via satellite): WGN-TV (W) Chicago; CNN; Cartoon Network; Lifetime; Nickelodeon; TBS Superstation; Turner Classic Movies; USA Network.
Fee: $20.00 installation; $17.75 monthly.
Pay Service 1
Pay Units: 127.
Programming (via satellite): Cinemax.
Fee: N.A.
Pay Service 2
Pay Units: 103.
Programming (via satellite): HBO.
Fee: N.A.
Miles of plant: 24.0 (coaxial).
Manager: Donn Smart.
Ownership: SCA Cable Inc.

ROSENDALE—Charter Communications Inc., Box 1197, 55 W. Scott St., Fond du Lac, WI 54936-1197. Phones: 920-923-7196; 800-581-0081. Fax: 920-923-1235. County: Fond du Lac. ICA: WI0193.
TV Market Ranking: Below 100. Franchise award date: N.A. Franchise expiration date: March 1, 1998. Began: December 1, 1983.
Channel capacity: 22 (not 2-way capable). Channels available but not in use: 6.
Basic Service
Subscribers: 171.
Programming (received off-air): WACY (U) Appleton; WBAY-TV (A), WFRV-TV (C), WGBA (N), WLUK-TV (F), WPNE (P) Green Bay.
Programming (via satellite): WGN-TV (W) Chicago; CNN; ESPN; Fox Family Channel; MTV; Nashville Network; Nickelodeon; TBS Superstation; Turner Network TV; USA Network.
Fee: $34.95 installation; $21.95 monthly.
Pay Service 1
Pay Units: 32.
Programming (via satellite): Cinemax.
Fee: $12.15 installation; $12.50 monthly.
Pay Service 2
Pay Units: 44.
Programming (via satellite): HBO.
Fee: $12.15 installation; $12.95 monthly.
Local advertising: No.
Equipment: Scientific-Atlanta amplifiers; Comm/Scope cable; Eagle traps; Scientific-Atlanta satellite antenna; DX Antenna satellite receivers.
Miles of plant: 8.0 (coaxial). Homes passed: 292.
Manager: Lisa Washa. Chief technician: Jeff Gerner.
City fee: 3% of gross.
Ownership: Charter Communications Inc. (MSO). Purchased from Marcus Cable, April 1, 1999.

ROSHOLT—Cable Systems Management of Iowa Inc., 3600 Kennebec Dr., Eagan, MN 55122. Phone: 612-688-2623. Fax: 612-688-2624. County: Portage. ICA: WI0280.
TV Market Ranking: Below 100. Franchise award date: N.A. Franchise expiration date: N.A. Began: N.A.
Channel capacity: 40. Channels available but not in use: 14.
Basic Service
Subscribers: 122.
Programming (received off-air): WEAU-TV (N) Eau Claire; WAOW-TV (A), WHRM-TV (P), WSAW-TV (C) Wausau-Rhinelander.
Programming (via satellite): WGN-TV (W) Chicago; A & E; American Movie Classics; CNN; Country Music TV; Discovery Channel; ESPN; Fox Family Channel; Headline News; Nashville Network; Showtime; TBS Superstation; Trinity Bcstg. Network; Turner Network TV; USA Network.
Fee: $50.00 installation; $24.00 monthly.
Miles of plant: 5.9 (coaxial). Homes passed: 225.
Manager: Jeff Anderson.
Ownership: Cable Systems Management of Iowa Inc. (MSO).

ROZELLVILLE—Cable Systems Management of Iowa Inc., 3600 Kennebec Dr., Eagan, MN 55122. Phone: 612-688-2623. Fax: 612-688-2624. County: Marathon. ICA: WI0281.
TV Market Ranking: Below 100. Franchise award date: N.A. Franchise expiration date: N.A. Began: N.A.
Channel capacity: 40. Channels available but not in use: 19.
Basic Service
Subscribers: 45.
Programming (received off-air): WEAU-TV (N) Eau Claire; WAOW-TV (A), WHRM-TV (P), WSAW-TV (C) Wausau-Rhinelander.
Programming (via satellite): WGN-TV (W) Chicago; A & E; American Movie Classics; CNN; Country Music TV; Discovery Channel; ESPN; Fox Family Channel; Headline News; Nashville Network; Showtime; TBS Superstation; Trinity Bcstg. Network; Turner Network TV; USA Network.
Fee: $50.00 installation; $30.00 monthly.
Miles of plant: 2.1 (coaxial). Homes passed: 90.
Manager: Jeff Anderson.
Ownership: Cable Systems Management of Iowa Inc. (MSO).

RUDOLPH—HLM Cable Corp., Box 620684, 2305-A Parview Rd., Middleton, WI 53562-2525. Phones: 608-831-7044; 800-451-5119. Fax: 608-836-5726. County: Wood. ICA: WI0217.
TV Market Ranking: Below 100. Franchise award date: N.A. Franchise expiration date: N.A. Began: N.A.
Channel capacity: 40 (not 2-way capable). Channels available but not in use: 12.
Basic Service
Subscribers: 134.
Programming (received off-air): WEAU-TV (N) Eau Claire; WAOW-TV (A), WHRM-TV (P), WJFW-TV (N), WSAW-TV (C) Wausau-Rhinelander.
Programming (via satellite): WGN-TV (W) Chicago; A & E; American Movie Classics; CNBC; CNN; Discovery Channel; ESPN; ESPN 2; Fox Family Channel; FoxNet; History Channel; Lifetime; Nashville Network; Nick at Nite; Nick at Nite's TV Land; Nickelodeon; Sci-Fi Channel; TBS Superstation; The Weather Channel; Turner Network TV; USA Network; VH1.
Fee: $19.95 installation; $25.00 monthly; $1.50 converter.
Pay Service 1
Pay Units: 18.
Programming (via satellite): Disney Channel.
Fee: $14.95 installation; $6.95 monthly.
Pay Service 2
Pay Units: 28.
Programming (via satellite): Showtime.
Fee: $14.95 installation; $6.95 monthly.
Homes passed: 150.
Manager: Robert E. Ryan.
Ownership: H.L.M. Cable Co. (MSO).

SAUK CITY—Bresnan Communications Inc., Suite 150, 5618 Odana Rd., Madison, WI 53719. Phone: 608-274-3822. Fax: 608-274-1436. County: Sauk. ICA: WI0090.
TV Market Ranking: 93. Franchise award date: N.A. Franchise expiration date: N.A. Began: December 1, 1980.
Channel capacity: 35. Channels available but not in use: 6.
Basic Service
Subscribers: 841.
Programming (received off-air): WHA-TV (P), WISC-TV (C), WKOW-TV (A), WMSN-TV (F), WMTV (N) Madison; 7 FMs.
Programming (via satellite): WGN-TV (W) Chicago; C-SPAN; CNN; Discovery Channel; Fox Family Channel; Knowledge TV; MTV; Nashville Network; Nickelodeon; QVC; TBS Superstation; The Weather Channel.
Current originations: Public access.
Fee: $60.00 installation; $10.00 monthly; $40.00 additional installation.
Expanded Basic Service
Subscribers: 783.
Programming (via satellite): A & E; American Movie Classics; ESPN; Lifetime; Turner Network TV; USA Network.
Fee: $1.75 monthly.
Pay Service 1
Pay Units: 54.
Programming (via satellite): Cinemax.
Fee: $12.90 monthly.
Pay Service 2
Pay Units: 45.
Programming (via satellite): Disney Channel.
Fee: N.A.
Pay Service 3
Pay Units: 159.
Programming (via satellite): HBO.
Fee: $12.90 monthly.
Pay Service 4
Pay Units: 67.
Programming (via satellite): Showtime.
Fee: $12.90 monthly.
Pay Service 5
Pay Units: 234.
Programming (via satellite): The New Encore.
Fee: N.A.
Miles of plant: 12.6 (coaxial). Homes passed: 1,396. Total homes in franchised area: 1,396.
Manager: Brian Shirk. Chief technician: Jerry Myers. Marketing director: Tim Roehl.
Ownership: Bresnan Communications Co. LP (MSO). Purchased from Tele-Communications Inc, February 2, 1999. See Cable System Ownership.

SAXEVILLE—Cable Systems Management of Iowa Inc., 3600 Kennebec Dr., Eagan, MN 55122. Phone: 612-688-2623. Fax: 612-688-2624. County: Waushara. ICA: WI0210.
TV Market Ranking: Below 100. Franchise award date: N.A. Franchise expiration date: N.A. Began: N.A.
Channel capacity: 40. Channels available but not in use: 19.
Basic Service
Subscribers: 53.
Programming (received off-air): WBAY-TV (A), WFRV-TV (C), WGBA (N), WLUK-TV (F), WPNE (P) Green Bay.
Programming (via satellite): WGN-TV (W) Chicago; A & E; American Movie Classics; CNN; Country Music TV; Discovery Channel; ESPN; Fox Family Channel; Headline News; Nashville Network; Showtime; TBS Superstation; Trinity Bcstg. Network; Turner Network TV; USA Network.
Fee: $30.00 monthly.
Miles of plant: 7.3 (coaxial). Homes passed: 183.
Manager: Jeff Anderson.
Ownership: Cable Systems Management of Iowa Inc. (MSO).

***SAYNER**—Northern Lights Cable Corp., Box 127, Presque Isle, WI 54557. Phone: 715-686-2938. Fax: 715-686-2080. County: Vilas. ICA: WI0283.
TV Market Ranking: Below 100. Franchise award date: N.A. Franchise expiration date: N.A. Scheduled to begin: N.A.
Channel capacity: 30. Channels available but not in use: N.A.
Basic Service
Subscribers: N.A.
Planned programming (received off-air): WLUC-TV (N) Marquette; WAOW-TV (A), WJFW-TV (N), WSAW-TV (C) Wausau-Rhinelander.
Planned originations: Automated time-weather; local news.
Fee: N.A.
Ownership: Northern Lights Cable Corp.

SENECA (village)—Dairyland Cable Systems Inc., 1140 Sextonville Rd., Richland Center, WI 53581. Phone: 608-647-6383. Fax: 608-647-7394. County: Crawford. Also serves Eastman (unincorporated areas), Lynxville (unincorporated areas), Mount Sterling (unincorporated areas). ICA: WI0316.

TV Market Ranking: Outside TV Markets. Franchise award date: N.A. Franchise expiration date: N.A. Began: N.A.

Channel capacity: N.A. Channels available but not in use: N.A.

Basic Service

Subscribers: 235.

Fee: $25.00 installation; $16.95 monthly.

Pay Service 1

Pay Units: 43.

Programming (via satellite): HBO.

Fee: $10.50 monthly.

Miles of plant: 17.0 (coaxial). Homes passed: 425.

Manager: Jim Atkinson. Chief technician: Dale Davenport.

Ownership: Dairyland Cable Systems Inc.

SEXTONVILLE—Spring Green CableComm, Box 609, 245 S. Winsted St., Spring Green, WI 53588-9431. Phone: 608-588-7454. Fax: 608-588-7067. County: Richland. Also serves Gotham. ICA: WI0284.

TV Market Ranking: Outside TV Markets. Franchise award date: N.A. Franchise expiration date: N.A. Began: N.A.

Channel capacity: 36 (not 2-way capable). Channels available but not in use: 8.

Basic Service

Subscribers: 193.

Programming (received off-air): WHA-TV (P), WISC-TV (C), WKOW-TV (A), WMSN-TV (F), WMTV (N) Madison.

Programming (via satellite): WGN-TV (W) Chicago; A & E; CNN; Discovery Channel; ESPN; Fox Family Channel; Lifetime; Nashville Network; Nickelodeon; QVC; TBS Superstation; Turner Network TV; USA Network; VH1.

Fee: $49.95 installation; $29.85 monthly.

Pay Service 1

Pay Units: N.A.

Programming (via satellite): HBO.

Fee: $19.95 installation; $9.95 monthly.

Miles of plant: 8.0 (coaxial).

Manager: Kevin Mayne. Chief technician: Tad Peak. Customer service manager: Liz Reuter.

Ownership: Fanch Communications Inc. (MSO). See Cable System Ownership.

SHARON—TCI Cablevision of Wisconsin Inc., Box 927, Section B, Walworth, WI 53184-0927. Phone: 414-275-2197. Fax: 414-275-3786. County: Walworth. ICA: WI0140.

TV Market Ranking: 97. Franchise award date: N.A. Franchise expiration date: N.A. Began: March 1, 1982.

Channel capacity: 60. Channels available but not in use: 10.

Basic Service

Subscribers: 365.

Programming (received off-air): WFLD (F), WGN-TV (W), WMAQ-TV (N), WTTW (P) Chicago; WIFR (C) Freeport-Rockford; WHA-TV (P), WISC-TV (C) Madison; WCGV-TV (I), WISN-TV (A), WITI (F), WTMJ-TV (N) Milwaukee; WQRF-TV (F), WREX-TV (N), WTVO (A) Rockford; 7 FMs.

Programming (via satellite): C-SPAN; CNN; Discovery Channel; MTV; Nashville Network; Nickelodeon; QVC; TBS Superstation.

Fee: $28.59 installation; $10.03 monthly.

Expanded Basic Service

Subscribers: 341.

Programming (via satellite): American Movie Classics; CNBC; Court TV; ESPN; Lifetime; Turner Network TV; USA Network.

Fee: $10.25 monthly.

Pay Service 1

Pay Units: 21.

Programming (via satellite): Disney Channel.

Fee: N.A.

Pay Service 2

Pay Units: 63.

Programming (via satellite): HBO.

Fee: $13.02 monthly.

Pay Service 3

Pay Units: 34.

Programming (via satellite): Showtime.

Fee: $13.02 monthly.

Pay Service 4

Pay Units: 36.

Programming (via satellite): The Movie Channel.

Fee: $13.02 monthly.

Pay Service 5

Pay Units: 149.

Programming (via satellite): The New Encore.

Fee: N.A.

Miles of plant: 7.3 (coaxial). Homes passed: 595.

Manager: Matt Forgas. Chief technician: Jeff Myers.

Ownership: AT&T Broadband & Internet Services (MSO). Purchased from Tele-Communications Inc., March 9, 1999.

SHAWANO—Charter Communications Inc., Box 1818, 853 McIntosh St., Wausau, WI 54402. Phones: 715-845-4223; 800-395-0995. Fax: 715-848-0081. County: Shawano. Also serves Richmond, Washington, Wescott. ICA: WI0040.

TV Market Ranking: 62 (Shawano, Washington, Wescott); Below 100 (Richmond). Franchise award date: May 7, 1980. Franchise expiration date: N.A. Began: December 1, 1980.

Channel capacity: 36. Channels available but not in use: None.

Basic Service

Subscribers: 3,579; Commercial subscribers: 8.

Programming (received off-air): WACY (U) Appleton; WBAY-TV (A), WFRV-TV (C), WGBA (N), WLUK-TV (F), WPNE (P) Green Bay; WSAW-TV (C) Wausau-Rhinelander.

Programming (via satellite): WGN-TV (W) Chicago; C-SPAN; TBS Superstation.

Current originations: Automated time-weather; public access; educational access; government access.

Fee: $56.73 installation; $6.82 monthly; $28.36 additional installation.

Expanded Basic Service

Subscribers: 3,488.

Programming (via satellite): A & E; American Movie Classics; CNBC; CNN; Discovery Channel; Disney Channel; ESPN; ESPN 2; Fox Family Channel; Headline News; Home Shopping Network; Knowledge TV; Lifetime; MTV; Nashville Network; Nickelodeon; Odyssey; Sci-Fi Channel; The Weather Channel; Turner Network TV; USA Network.

Fee: $13.03 monthly.

Pay Service 1

Pay Units: 583.

Programming (via satellite): Cinemax.

Fee: $12.50 monthly.

Pay Service 2

Pay Units: 886.

Programming (via satellite): HBO.

Fee: $12.95 monthly.

Pay Service 3

Pay Units: 547.

Programming (via satellite): Showtime.

Fee: $12.50 monthly.

Program Guide: Premium Channels.

Equipment: Scientific-Atlanta headend; Scientific-Atlanta amplifiers; Comm/Scope cable; Oak & Panasonic set top converters; Eagle traps; Scientific-Atlanta satellite antenna; Scientific-Atlanta & Standard Communications satellite receivers.

Miles of plant: 81.3 (coaxial). Additional miles planned: 5.0 (coaxial). Homes passed: 5,569.

Manager: Scott Behn. Chief technician: Bruce Wasleske. Marketing director: Tim Schieffer.

City fee: 3% of gross.

Ownership: Charter Communications Inc. (MSO). Purchased from Marcus Cable, April 1, 1999.

SHEBOYGAN—Charter Communications Inc., 55 W. Scott St., Fond du Lac, WI 54835. Phone: 920-923-7196. Fax: 920-923-1235. County: Sheboygan. Also serves Kohler (village), Lima (town), Sheboygan (town), Sheboygan Falls, Sheboygan Falls (town), Wilson. ICA: WI0014.

TV Market Ranking: Outside TV Markets. Franchise award date: N.A. Franchise expiration date: N.A. Began: May 1, 1982.

Channel capacity: 84 (2-way capable; operating 2-way). Channels available but not in use: 10.

Basic Service

Subscribers: 19,166; Commercial subscribers: 27.

Programming (received off-air): WBAY-TV (A), WFRV-TV (C), WGBA (N), WLUK-TV (F), WPNE (P) Green Bay; WCGV-TV (I), WDJT-TV (C), WISN-TV (A), WITI (F), WMVS (P), WMVT (P), WTMJ-TV (N), WVTV (W) Milwaukee.

Programming (via satellite): Knowledge TV; TV Guide Channel; WFMT Radio Networks.

Current originations: Public access; educational access; government access; religious access; leased access; automated emergency alert; local sports.

Fee: $42.95 installation; $10.03 monthly; $45.00 additional installation.

Commercial fee: $25.75 monthly.

Expanded Basic Service

Subscribers: 16,536.

Programming (via satellite): WGN-TV (W) Chicago; C-SPAN; C-SPAN 2; Cartoon Network; Court TV; Deutsche Welle TV; E! Entertainment TV; Goodlife TV Network; Home Shopping Network; NASA TV; Odyssey; TBS Superstation; The Weather Channel.

Fee: $60.10 installation; $4.92 monthly.

Expanded Basic Service 2

Subscribers: 15,829.

Programming (via satellite): A & E; American Movie Classics; Bravo; CNBC; CNN; Comedy Central; Country Music TV; Discovery Channel; ESPN; ESPN 2; EWTN; Fox Family Channel; Headline News; History Channel; International Channel; Learning Channel; Lifetime; MTV; Nashville Network; Nickelodeon; QVC; Sci-Fi Channel; Travel Channel; Turner Network TV; USA Network; Univision; VH1.

Fee: $60.10 installation; $12.22 monthly.

Pay Service 1

Pay Units: 3,192.

Programming (via satellite): Cinemax.

Fee: $45.00 installation; $12.50 monthly.

Pay Service 2

Pay Units: 482.

Programming (via satellite): Music Choice.

Fee: $6.95 monthly.

Pay Service 3

Pay Units: 2,220.

Programming (via satellite): Disney Channel.

Fee: $9.35 monthly.

Pay Service 4

Pay Units: 818.

Programming (via satellite): The New Encore.

Fee: $3.95 monthly.

Pay Service 5

Pay Units: 1,048.

Programming (via satellite): HBO.

Fee: $12.95 monthly.

Pay Service 6

Pay Units: 3,415.

Programming (via satellite): The Movie Channel.

Fee: $10.95 monthly.

Pay Service 7

Pay Units: 3,559.

Programming (via satellite): Showtime.

Fee: $12.50 monthly.

Pay Service 8

Pay Units: 718.

Programming (via satellite): Playboy TV.

Fee: $7.95 monthly.

Pay-Per-View

Special events.

Fee: Varies.

Local advertising: Yes. Available in locally originated, character-generated & automated programming.

Equipment: Scientific-Atlanta headend; Scientific-Atlanta amplifiers; Comm/Scope cable; Sony cameras; Sony VTRs; Video Data Systems character generator; Hamlin set top converters; Gardiner satellite antenna.

Miles of plant: 200.0 (coaxial). Homes passed: 25,000.

District manager: Lisa Washa. District engineer: Bill Whicher. Operations manager: Bob Lunda. Marketing manager: Jeff Lambert.

Ownership: Charter Communications Inc. (MSO). Purchased from Marcus Cable, April 1, 1999.

SIREN—Vision Communications, Box 355, 28 First Ave. W, Luck, WI 54853-0355. Phone: 715-472-2700. Fax: 715-472-2707. County: Burnett. Also serves Webster. ICA: WI0285.

TV Market Ranking: Outside TV Markets. Franchise award date: July 1, 1986. Franchise expiration date: July 1, 2001. Began: June 1, 1987.

Channel capacity: 36. Channels available but not in use: 5.

Basic Service

Subscribers: 279.

Programming (received off-air): KDLH (C) Duluth-Superior; WEAU-TV (N), WQOW-TV (A) Eau Claire; WHWC-TV (P) Menomonie; KARE (N), KLGT (W), KMSP-TV (U), KSTP-TV (A), KTCA-TV (P), KTCI-TV (P), WCCO-TV (C), WFTC (F) Minneapolis-St. Paul.

Fee: $49.95 installation; $14.95 monthly.

Expanded Basic Service

Subscribers: N.A.

Programming (via satellite): WGN-TV (W) Chicago; A & E; C-SPAN; CNN; Discovery Channel; ESPN; Fox Family Channel; Headline News; Home Shopping Network; Lifetime; MTV; Nashville Network; Nickelodeon; TBS Superstation; Turner Network TV; USA Network.

Fee: $6.55 monthly.

Pay Service 1

Pay Units: 51.

Programming (via satellite): Cinemax.

Fee: $9.00 monthly.

Pay Service 2

Pay Units: 19.

Programming (via satellite): Disney Channel.
Fee: $8.00 monthly.
Pay Service 3
Pay Units: 43.
Programming (via satellite): HBO.
Fee: $10.00 monthly.
Miles of plant: 21.5 (coaxial). Homes passed: 547.
Manager: John Klatt.
Ownership: Vision Communications LLC (MSO).

SISTER BAY—Charter Communications Inc., Box 1197, 55 W. Scott St., Fon Du Lac, WI 54936-1197. Phones: 920-923-7196; 800-581-0081. Fax: 920-920-1235. County: Door. Also serves Egg Harbor, Egg Harbor (town), Ephraim, Fish Creek, Liberty Grove. ICA: WI0309.
TV Market Ranking: Below 100. Franchise award date: N.A. Franchise expiration date: N.A. Began: N.A.
Channel capacity: 36. Channels available but not in use: 5.
Basic Service
Subscribers: 941.
Programming (received off-air): WBAY-TV (A), WFRV-TV (C), WGBA (N), WLUK-TV (F), WPNE (P) Green Bay.
Programming (via satellite): WGN-TV (W) Chicago; C-SPAN; QVC; TBS Superstation.
Current originations: Public access.
Fee: $47.00 installation; $19.13 monthly.
Expanded Basic Service
Subscribers: 922.
Programming (via satellite): A & E; CNN; Country Music TV; Discovery Channel; Disney Channel; ESPN; Fox Family Channel; MTV; Nashville Network; Nickelodeon; Sci-Fi Channel; The Weather Channel; Turner Network TV; USA Network; VH1.
Fee: $47.00 installation; $19.13 monthly.
Pay Service 1
Pay Units: 117.
Programming (via satellite): HBO.
Fee: $12.95 monthly.
Pay Service 2
Pay Units: 114.
Programming (via satellite): Showtime.
Fee: $12.50 monthly.
Manager: Lisa Washa. Chief technician: Jeff Gerner.
Ownership: Charter Communications Inc. (MSO). Purchased from Marcus Cable, April 1, 1999.

SOLON SPRINGS—Vision Communications, Box 355, 28 First Ave. W, Luck, WI 54853-0355. Phone: 715-472-2700. Fax: 715-472-2707. County: Douglas. ICA: WI0286.
TV Market Ranking: 89. Franchise award date: N.A. Franchise expiration date: N.A. Began: January 1, 1989.
Channel capacity: 36. Channels available but not in use: 13.
Basic Service
Subscribers: 174.
Programming (received off-air): KBJR-TV (N), KDLH (C), WDIO-TV (A,F), WDSE-TV (P) Duluth-Superior.
Programming (via satellite): WGN-TV (W) Chicago; Discovery Channel; ESPN; Fox Family Channel; FoxNet; Lifetime; Nashville Network; QVC.
Fee: $49.95 installation; $14.95 monthly.
Expanded Basic Service
Subscribers: N.A.
Programming (via satellite): C-SPAN; CNN; MTV; Midwest Sports Channel; Nickelodeon; TBS Superstation; Turner Network TV; USA Network.
Fee: $6.55 monthly.
Pay Service 1
Pay Units: 47.
Programming (via satellite): Cinemax.
Fee: $9.00 monthly.
Pay Service 2
Pay Units: 15.
Programming (via satellite): Disney Channel.
Fee: $8.00 monthly.
Pay Service 3
Pay Units: 41.
Programming (via satellite): HBO.
Fee: $10.00 monthly.
Miles of plant: 22.0 (coaxial). Homes passed: 354.
Manager: John Klatt.
Ownership: Vision Communications LLC (MSO).

SOMERSET—Somerset Communications, Box 159, 300 Spring St., Somerset, WI 54025. Phone: 715-247-3320. Fax: 715-247-3122. County: St. Croix. ICA: WI0146.
TV Market Ranking: 13. Franchise award date: N.A. Franchise expiration date: N.A. Began: November 1, 1988.
Channel capacity: N.A. Channels available but not in use: N.A.
Basic Service
Subscribers: 280.
Programming (received off-air): WEUX (F) Chippewa Falls; WEAU-TV (N), WQOW-TV (A) Eau Claire; WHWC-TV (P) Menomonie; KARE (N), KLGT (W), KMSP-TV (U), KSTP-TV (A), KTCA-TV (P), KTCI-TV (P), WCCO-TV (C), WFTC (F) Minneapolis-St. Paul.
Programming (via satellite): WGN-TV (W) Chicago; CNN; Discovery Channel; Disney Channel; ESPN; Fox Family Channel; Headline News; Home Shopping Network; Learning Channel; Lifetime; Midwest Sports Channel; Nashville Network; Nickelodeon; TBS Superstation; Turner Network TV; USA Network; VH1.
Fee: $25.00 installation; $19.95 monthly.
Pay Service 1
Pay Units: 20.
Programming (via satellite): Cinemax.
Fee: $9.25 monthly.
Pay Service 2
Pay Units: 60.
Programming (via satellite): HBO.
Fee: $9.75 monthly.
Homes passed: 512.
Manager: Victor Martinsen.
Ownership: Amery Telecom. Purchased from Somerset Communications.

SPARTA—Charter Communications Inc., Box 279, 314 Main St., Onalaska, WI 54650. Phones: 608-783-5255; 800-658-9473. Fax: 608-783-7033. County: Monroe. Also serves Angelo, Leon, Sparta (City), Sparta (Town). ICA: WI0058.
TV Market Ranking: Below 100. Franchise award date: September 9, 1964. Franchise expiration date: October 1, 2001. Began: December 15, 1965.
Channel capacity: 91 (2-way capable; operating 2-way). Channels available but not in use: 10.
Basic Service
Subscribers: 2,871.
Programming (received off-air): WEAU-TV (N) Eau Claire; KQEG-LP (I) La Crescent; WHLA-TV (P), WKBT (C), WLAX (F), WXOW-TV (A) La Crosse.
Programming (via satellite): WGN-TV (W) Chicago; Bravo; C-SPAN; C-SPAN 2; TV Guide Channel.
Current originations: Public access; educational access; leased access.
Fee: $64.57 installation; $8.57 monthly; $1.80 converter.
Expanded Basic Service
Subscribers: 2,664.
Programming (via satellite): A & E; American Movie Classics; Animal Planet; CNBC; CNN; Cartoon Network; Comedy Central; Country Music TV; Court TV; Discovery Channel; Disney Channel; E! Entertainment TV; ESPN; ESPN 2; ESPN Classic Sports; ESPNews; EWTN; FX; Fox Family Channel; Game Show Network; Golf Channel; Headline News; History Channel; Home & Garden Television; Home Shopping Network; Learning Channel; Lifetime; MSNBC; MTV; Midwest Sports Channel; Nashville Network; Nick at Nite's TV Land; Nickelodeon; Odyssey; Outdoor Life Network; QVC; Sci-Fi Channel; Speedvision; TBS Superstation; The Barker; The Weather Channel; Toon Disney; Travel Channel; Turner Classic Movies; Turner Network TV; USA Network; VH1; WB 100+ Station Group.
Current originations: Public access; educational access; automated emergency alert.
Fee: $24.63 monthly.
Pay Service 1
Pay Units: 340.
Programming (via satellite): Cinemax (multiplexed).
Fee: $20.00 installation; $12.95 monthly.
Pay Service 2
Pay Units: 382.
Programming (via satellite): HBO (multiplexed).
Fee: $20.00 installation; $12.95 monthly.
Pay Service 3
Pay Units: 307.
Programming (via satellite): Showtime (multiplexed).
Fee: $20.00 installation; $12.95 monthly.
Pay Service 4
Pay Units: 3.
Programming (via satellite): DMX.
Fee: $6.95 monthly.
Pay-Per-View
Addressable homes: 610.
Movies.
Local advertising: Yes. Available in satellite distributed & locally originated programming. Local sales manager: Holly Hockner.
Equipment: Scientific-Atlanta headend; Scientific-Atlanta amplifiers; Times Fiber cable; Siecor fiber optic cable; Scientific-Atlanta set top converters; General Instrument addressable set top converters; Scientific-Atlanta satellite antenna; Scientific-Atlanta satellite receivers.
Miles of plant: 68.0 (coaxial); 20.0 (fiber optic). Homes passed: 3,625. Total homes in franchised area: 3,625.
Manager: Shirley Hehn Weibel. Chief technician: Tim Fischer. Marketing coordinator: Ellen Martin.
Ownership: Charter Communications Inc. (MSO). Purchased from Marcus Cable, April 1, 1999.

SPENCER—Charter Communications Inc., 279 Trowbridge Dr., Fond du Lac, WI 54935. Phones: 920-926-1080; 800-581-0081. Fax: 920-926-1146. Counties: Clark & Marathon. Also serves Abbotsford, Athens, Colby, Dorchester, Edgar, Loyal, Marathon City, Neillsville, Owen, Spencer (village), Stratford, Unity, Withee. ICA: WI0034.
TV Market Ranking: Below 100 (Abbotsford, Athens, Colby, Dorchester, Edgar, Marathon City, Owen, Spencer, portions of Spencer, Stratford, Unity); Outside TV Markets (Loyal, Neillsville, portions of Spencer, Withee). Franchise award date: November 3, 1980. Franchise expiration date: N.A. Began: April 1, 1982.
Channel capacity: 35 (not 2-way capable). Channels available but not in use: 7.
Basic Service
Subscribers: 4,570.
Programming (received off-air): WEUX (F) Chippewa Falls; WEAU-TV (N) Eau Claire; WAOW-TV (A), WHRM-TV (P), WSAW-TV (C) Wausau-Rhinelander.
Programming (via satellite): WGN-TV (W) Chicago; C-SPAN.
Current originations: Leased access.
Fee: $60.48 installation; $8.57 monthly; $1.43 converter; $14.95 additional installation.
Expanded Basic Service
Subscribers: N.A.
Programming (via satellite): A & E; American Movie Classics; Animal Planet; CNBC; CNN; Comedy Central; Discovery Channel; Disney Channel; ESPN; ESPN 2; ESPNews; EWTN; Fox Family Channel; History Channel; Home & Garden Television; Learning Channel; Lifetime; MSNBC; MTV; Midwest Sports Channel; Nashville Network; Nickelodeon; QVC; TBS Superstation; The Weather Channel; Toon Disney; Trinity Bcstg. Network; Turner Network TV; USA Network.
Fee: $21.38 monthly.
Pay Service 1
Pay Units: 1,005.
Programming (via satellite): Cinemax.
Fee: $12.95 monthly.
Pay Service 2
Pay Units: N.A.
Programming (via satellite): Showtime.
Fee: $12.95 monthly.
Pay Service 3
Pay Units: 975.
Programming (via satellite): HBO.
Fee: $12.95 monthly.
Local advertising: No. Available in satellite distributed programming.
Equipment: Scientific-Atlanta headend; Texscan amplifiers; Comm/Scope cable; Panasonic cameras; Panasonic VTRs; MSI character generator; Pioneer, Scientific-Atlanta & Hamlin set top converters; Eagle traps; Scientific-Atlanta satellite antenna; Scientific-Atlanta satellite receivers.
Miles of plant: 112.8 (coaxial). Homes passed: 6,840.
Manager: Larry Kraklau. Chief technician: Bruce Wasleske. Marketing director: Susan Jirgl.
City fee: 3% of gross.
Ownership: Charter Communications Inc. (MSO). Purchased from Marcus Cable, April 1, 1999.

SPOONER—Charter Communications Inc., Box 539, 1725 S. Main St., Rice Lake, WI 54868-0539. Phones: 715-234-3821; 800-262-2578. Fax: 715-234-5077. County: Washburn. Also serves Shell Lake. ICA: WI0096.
TV Market Ranking: Outside TV Markets. Franchise award date: N.A. Franchise expiration date: March 20, 2013. Began: August 1, 1965.
Channel capacity: 36 (not 2-way capable). Channels available but not in use: None.
Basic Service
Subscribers: 1,500.
Programming (received off-air): WEUX (F) Chippewa Falls; KBJR-TV (N), KDLH (C), WDIO-TV (A,F) Duluth-Superior; WEAU-TV (N), WQOW-TV (A) Eau Claire; WHWC-TV (P) Menomonie; KARE (N), KMSP-TV (U), KSTP-TV (A), KTCA-TV (P), WCCO-TV (C) Minneapolis-St. Paul; allband FM.
Programming (via satellite): WGN-TV (W) Chicago; Disney Channel; TBS Superstation.

Current originations: Automated emergency alert.
Fee: $42.95 installation; $26.96 monthly.
Expanded Basic Service
Subscribers: 1,400.
Programming (via satellite): A & E; American Movie Classics; C-SPAN; CNN; Discovery Channel; ESPN; Fox Family Channel; Headline News; Lifetime; Nashville Network; Nick at Nite; Nickelodeon; QVC; The Weather Channel; Travel Channel; Turner Network TV; USA Network; VH1.
Fee: $42.95 installation; $14.53 monthly.
Pay Service 1
Pay Units: 170.
Programming (via satellite): Cinemax.
Fee: $19.95 installation; $12.50 monthly.
Pay Service 2
Pay Units: 250.
Programming (via satellite): HBO.
Fee: $19.95 installation; $12.95 monthly.
Pay Service 3
Pay Units: 160.
Programming (via satellite): Showtime.
Fee: $19.95 installation; $12.50 monthly.
Local advertising: No. Local sales manager: Andy Jerome.
Equipment: Blonder-Tongue, Jerrold & Scientific-Atlanta headend; Jerrold amplifiers; Times Fiber cable; Hamlin & Scientific-Atlanta set top converters; Eagle traps; Scientific-Atlanta satellite antenna; Scientific-Atlanta satellite receivers.
Miles of plant: 20.0 (coaxial). Homes passed: 1,176.
Manager: Scott Binder. Chief technician: George Benjamin.
City fee: $500 annually.
Ownership: Charter Communications Inc. (MSO). Purchased from Marcus Cable, April 1, 1999.

SPRING GREEN—Spring Green CableComm, Box 609, 245 S. Winsted St., Spring Green, WI 53588-9431. Phone: 608-588-7454. Fax: 608-588-7067. Counties: Richland & Sauk. Also serves Lone Rock, Spring Green (town), Spring Green Resort. ICA: WI0288.
TV Market Ranking: Outside TV Markets. Franchise award date: N.A. Franchise expiration date: N.A. Began: N.A.
Channel capacity: 42 (not 2-way capable). Channels available but not in use: 5.
Basic Service
Subscribers: 593.
Programming (received off-air): WHA-TV (P), WISC-TV (C), WKOW-TV (A), WMSN-TV (F), WMTV (N) Madison.
Programming (via satellite): WGN-TV (W) Chicago; A & E; CNN; Comedy Central; Discovery Channel; ESPN; ESPN 2; FX; Fox Family Channel; Headline News; Lifetime; Nashville Network; Nickelodeon; QVC; TBS Superstation; The Weather Channel; Turner Classic Movies; Turner Network TV; USA Network; VH1.
Fee: $49.95 installation; $29.85 monthly.
Pay Service 1
Pay Units: N.A.
Programming (via satellite): Cinemax; Disney Channel; HBO.
Fee: $19.95 installation; $6.95 monthly (Disney); $9.95 monthly (Cinemax or HBO).
Manager: Kevin Mayne. Chief technician: Tad Peak. Customer service manager: Liz Reuter.
Ownership: Fanch Communications Inc. (MSO). See Cable System Ownership.

SPRING VALLEY—DeMarce TV & Cable, Box 235, 116 S. Main St., Elmwood, WI 54740. Phone: 715-639-2121. Fax: 715-639-3026. County: Pierce. ICA: WI0289.
TV Market Ranking: Below 100. Franchise award date: January 1, 1963. Franchise expiration date: January 1, 2000. Began: January 1, 1963.
Channel capacity: 42 (not 2-way capable). Channels available but not in use: 4.
Basic Service
Subscribers: 385.
Programming (received off-air): WEUX (F) Chippewa Falls; WEAU-TV (N), WQOW-TV (A) Eau Claire; WKBT (C) La Crosse; WHWC-TV (P) Menomonie; KARE (N), KLGT (W), KMSP-TV (U), KSTP-TV (A), KTCA-TV (P), KVBM-TV (H), WCCO-TV (C), WFTC (F) Minneapolis-St. Paul.
Programming (via satellite): WGN-TV (W) Chicago; A & E; American Movie Classics; CNN; Country Music TV; Discovery Channel; ESPN; ESPN 2; Fox Family Channel; Headline News; History Channel; Learning Channel; Lifetime; MTV; Nashville Network; Nickelodeon; Sci-Fi Channel; TBS Superstation; The Weather Channel; Turner Network TV; USA Network; VH1.
Fee: $19.95 monthly; $1.50 converter.
Pay Service 1
Pay Units: 50.
Programming (via satellite): HBO.
Fee: $10.55 monthly.
Equipment: Philips amplifiers; Comm/Scope cable; Jerrold & Scientific-Atlanta set top converters; Eagle traps; Eagle addressable traps; ChannelMaster satellite antenna; Drake & Blonder-Tongue satellite receivers.
Miles of plant: 14.0 (coaxial); None (fiber optic). Total homes in franchised area: 431.
Manager: Mike DeMarce. Chief technician: Jeff DeMarce. Customer service manager: Janet DeMarce.
Ownership: DeMarce Cable TV (MSO).

ST. JOSEPH—Charter Communications Inc., Box 279, 314 Main St., Onalaska, WI 54650. Phones: 608-783-5255; 800-658-9473. Fax: 608-783-7033. County: La Crosse. ICA: WI0311.
TV Market Ranking: Below 100. Franchise award date: N.A. Franchise expiration date: N.A. Began: N.A.
Channel capacity: 51 (not 2-way capable). Channels available but not in use: 28.
Basic Service
Subscribers: 107.
Programming (received off-air): WEAU-TV (N) Eau Claire; WHLA-TV (P), WKBT (C), WLAX (F), WXOW-TV (A) La Crosse.
Programming (via satellite): WGN-TV (W) Chicago; Bravo; C-SPAN; C-SPAN 2.
Fee: $64.57 installation; $8.20 monthly; $1.10 converter.
Expanded Basic Service
Subscribers: 104.
Programming (via satellite): A & E; American Movie Classics; CNN; Discovery Channel; Disney Channel; ESPN; ESPN 2; ESPNews; Fox Family Channel; Learning Channel; MTV; Midwest Sports Channel; Nashville Network; Nick at Nite's TV Land; Nickelodeon; TBS Superstation; The Weather Channel; Turner Network TV; USA Network.
Fee: $21.95 monthly.
Pay Service 1
Pay Units: 25.
Programming (via satellite): HBO.
Fee: $20.00 installation; $12.95 monthly.
Local advertising: No. Local sales manager: Shirley Hehn Weibel.
Equipment: Jerrold headend; Triple Crown amplifiers; Comm/Scope & Belden cable; Magnavox cameras; Scientific-Atlanta set top converters; Eagle traps; Microdyne satellite antenna; Microdyne satellite receivers.
Miles of plant: 3.5 (coaxial); None (fiber optic). Homes passed: 125.
Manager: Shirley Hehn Weibel. Chief technician: Tim Fischer. Marketing coordinator: Ellen Martin.
Ownership: Charter Communications Inc. (MSO). Purchased from Marcus Cable, April 1, 1999.

ST. JOSEPH TWP.—Tele-Communications Cable Co., Box 193, Rte. 2, Fountain City, WI 54629. Phones: 608-687-6402; 608-526-3355. County: St. Croix. ICA: WI0290.
TV Market Ranking: 13. Franchise award date: July 1, 1990. Franchise expiration date: July 1, 2010. Began: April 1, 1990.
Channel capacity: 22. Channels available but not in use: N.A.
Basic Service
Subscribers: 64.
Programming (received off-air): WEAU-TV (N) Eau Claire; WHLA-TV (P), WKBT (C), WLAX (F), WXOW-TV (A) La Crosse.
Programming (via satellite): WGN-TV (W) Chicago; CNN; Discovery Channel; ESPN; MTV; Nashville Network; TBS Superstation; USA Network.
Fee: Free installation; $15.83 monthly.
Pay Service 1
Pay Units: 17.
Programming (via satellite): HBO.
Fee: $8.95 monthly.
Ownership: Dan Wolfe (MSO).

STANLEY—Charter Communications Inc., Box 539, 1725 S. Main St., Rice Lake, WI 54868 0539. Phones: 715-234-3821; 800-262-2578. Fax: 715-234-8537. County: Chippewa. ICA: WI0129.
TV Market Ranking: Below 100. Franchise award date: N.A. Franchise expiration date: June 5, 2000. Began: November 1, 1981.
Channel capacity: 36 (not 2-way capable). Channels available but not in use: None.
Basic Service
Subscribers: 529.
Programming (received off-air): WEUX (F) Chippewa Falls; WEAU-TV (N), WQOW-TV (A) Eau Claire; WKBT (C) La Crosse; WHWC-TV (P) Menomonie; WSAW-TV (C) Wausau-Rhinelander.
Programming (via satellite): WGN-TV (W) Chicago; A & E; CNN; Country Music TV; Discovery Channel; Disney Channel; E! Entertainment TV; ESPN; Fox Family Channel; FoxNet; Headline News; Learning Channel; MTV; Nashville Network; Nickelodeon; QVC; TBS Superstation; The Weather Channel; Turner Network TV; USA Network.
Fee: $42.95 installation; $27.97 monthly.
Pay Service 1
Pay Units: 41.
Programming (via satellite): Cinemax.
Fee: $19.95 installation; $12.50 monthly.
Pay Service 2
Pay Units: 50.
Programming (via satellite): HBO.
Fee: $19.95 installation; $12.95 monthly.
Pay Service 3
Pay Units: 63.
Programming (via satellite): Showtime.
Fee: $19.95 installation; $12.50 monthly.
Local advertising: No.
Equipment: Blonder-Tongue, Standard Communications & Triple Crown headend; Theta-Com & Triple Crown amplifiers; Comm/Scope cable; Hamlin & Scientific-Atlanta set top converters; Automation Techniques satellite receivers.
Miles of plant: 11.0 (coaxial). Homes passed: 702.
Manager: Scott Binder. Chief technician: George Benjamin.
City fee: 3% of gross.
Ownership: Charter Communications Inc. (MSO). Purchased from Marcus Cable, April 1, 1999.

STETSONVILLE—KRM Cablevision, Box 77, Mellen, WI 54546. Phone: 715-274-7631. County: Taylor. ICA: WI0291.
TV Market Ranking: Below 100. Franchise award date: N.A. Franchise expiration date: N.A. Began: October 1, 1988.
Channel capacity: 20. Channels available but not in use: 5.
Basic Service
Subscribers: N.A.
Programming (received off-air): WEAU-TV (N) Eau Claire; WAOW-TV (A), WHRM-TV (P), WSAW-TV (C) Wausau-Rhinelander.
Programming (via satellite): WGN-TV (W) Chicago; CNN; Comedy Central; Discovery Channel; ESPN; Nashville Network; TBS Superstation; Turner Network TV; USA Network.
Fee: $35.00 installation; $14.00 monthly.
Pay Service 1
Pay Units: N.A.
Programming (via satellite): Disney Channel; The Movie Channel.
Fee: $7.50 monthly (Disney), $9.50 monthly (TMC).
Manager: O. D. Miller. Chief technician: Keith Gehrett.
Ownership: KRM Cablevision (MSO).

STEUBEN—Steuben Community TV System, 207 Spencer, Woodman, WI 53827-0087. Phone: 608-533-2771. County: Crawford. ICA: WI0230.
TV Market Ranking: Outside TV Markets. Franchise award date: N.A. Franchise expiration date: N.A. Began: November 1, 1967.
Channel capacity: 12 (not 2-way capable). Channels available but not in use: 4.
Basic Service
Subscribers: 45.
Programming (received off-air): KCRG-TV (A), KWWL (N) Cedar Rapids-Waterloo; WKBT (C) La Crosse; WHA-TV (P), WISC-TV (C), WMSN-TV (F), WMTV (N) Madison.
Fee: $10.00 installation; $6.00 monthly.
Miles of plant: 2.0 (coaxial). Homes passed: 47.
Manager: Jerome Mezera.
Ownership: Steuben Community TV System.

STEVENS POINT—Charter Communications Inc., 2501 Church St., Stevens Point, WI 54481. Phone: 800-581-0081. Fax: 715-342-4366. County: Portage. Also serves Hull, Linwood, Park Ridge (village), Plover, Plover (village), Sharon (town), Stockton (town), Whiting (village). ICA: WI0019.
TV Market Ranking: Below 100 (Hull, Linwood, Park Ridge, Plover, Sharon, Stevens Point, Stockton, Whiting); Outside TV Markets (Plover). Franchise award date: October 1, 1977. Franchise expiration date: February 25, 2000. Began: February 25, 1985.
Channel capacity: 54 (2-way capable; operating 2-way). Channels available but not in use: 11.
Basic Service
Subscribers: 12,460.
Programming (received off-air): WEAU-TV (N) Eau Claire; WBAY-TV (A), WFRV-TV (C), WLUK-TV (F) Green Bay; WAOW-TV (A), WHRM-TV (P), WSAW-TV (C) Wausau-Rhinelander.
Programming (via microwave): WITI (F) Milwaukee.
Programming (via satellite): WGN-TV (W) Chicago; TBS Superstation.

Current originations: Automated time-weather; public access; educational access; government access; religious access; automated emergency alert; local sports.
Fee: $65.61 installation; $7.10 monthly.
Expanded Basic Service
Subscribers: 11,875.
Programming (via satellite): A & E; American Movie Classics; C-SPAN; CNBC; CNN; Discovery Channel; ESPN; ESPN 2; EWTN; Electronic Program Guide; Fox Family Channel; Headline News; Home Shopping Network; Learning Channel; Lifetime; MTV; Nashville Network; Nickelodeon; Odyssey; Sci-Fi Channel; The Weather Channel; Turner Network TV; VH1.
Fee: $15.13 monthly.
Pay Service 1
Pay Units: 1,580.
Programming (via satellite): Cinemax.
Fee: $10.00 installation; $12.50 monthly.
Pay Service 2
Pay Units: 2,150.
Programming (via satellite): HBO.
Fee: $10.00 installation; $12.95 monthly.
Pay Service 3
Pay Units: 1,340.
Programming (via satellite): Showtime.
Fee: $10.00 installation; $12.50 monthly.
Pay Service 4
Pay Units: 1,265.
Programming (via satellite): Disney Channel.
Fee: $10.00 installation; $2.95 monthly.
Local advertising: Yes (locally produced & insert). Available in satellite distributed & locally originated programming. Rates: $38.00/Minute; $19.00/30 Seconds. Local sales manager: Joan Welton.
Program Guide: The Entertainer.
Equipment: Scientific-Atlanta headend; Jerrold amplifiers; Comm/Scope cable; Sony cameras; Sony VTRs; MSI character generator; Oak set top converters; Arcom traps; Scientific-Atlanta satellite antenna; Microdyne satellite receivers; ChannelMatic commercial insert.
Miles of plant: 276.0 (coaxial). Homes passed: 17,570. Total homes in franchised area: 20,000.
Manager: Larry Kraklau. Chief technician: Bruce Wasleske. Marketing director: Susan Jirgl.
Ownership: Charter Communications Inc. (MSO). Purchased from Marcus Cable, April 1, 1999.

STODDARD—Triax Cablevision, Box 110, 1504 2nd St. SE, Waseca, MN 56093. Phones: 507-835-5975; 800-332-0245. Fax: 507-835-4567. County: Vernon. ICA: WI0161.
TV Market Ranking: Below 100. Franchise award date: July 3, 1979. Franchise expiration date: April 1, 2009. Began: February 1, 1969.
Channel capacity: 62 (2-way capable). Channels available but not in use: 42.
Basic Service
Subscribers: 257.
Programming (received off-air): WEAU-TV (N) Eau Claire; WHLA-TV (P), WKBT (C), WLAX (F), WXOW-TV (A) La Crosse.
Current originations: Public access.
Fee: $35.16 installation; $4.52 monthly; $1.58 converter.
Expanded Basic Service
Subscribers: 251.
Programming (via satellite): WGN-TV (W) Chicago; A & E; American Movie Classics; CNBC; CNN; Discovery Channel; ESPN; Fox Family Channel; Nashville Network; Nickelodeon; TBS Superstation; Turner Network TV; USA Network; VH1.
Fee: $18.53 monthly.
Pay Service 1
Pay Units: 60.
Programming (via satellite): HBO.
Fee: $23.44 installation; $11.00 monthly.
Miles of plant: 6.4 (coaxial). Homes passed: 372.
Manager: Richard Giffen. Chief technician: Scott Walters.
Ownership: Triax Telecommunications Co. LLC (MSO). See Cable System Ownership.

STURGEON BAY—Charter Communications Inc., 1009 Egg Harbor Rd., Sturgeon Bay, WI 54235. Phone: 800-581-0081. Fax: 414-743-5399. County: Door. Also serves Nasawapi, Remys, Sevastapol, Sturgeon Bay (town). ICA: WI0043.
TV Market Ranking: Outside TV Markets. Franchise award date: March 2, 1982. Franchise expiration date: N.A. Began: December 31, 1982.
Channel capacity: 42 (2-way capable; operating 2-way). Channels available but not in use: None.
Basic Service
Subscribers: 3,681.
Programming (received off-air): WACY (U) Appleton; WBAY-TV (A), WFRV-TV (C), WGBA (N), WLUK-TV (F), WPNE (P) Green Bay; allband FM.
Programming (via satellite): WGN-TV (W) Chicago; TBS Superstation; The Inspirational Network.
Fee: $56.73 installation; $6.82 monthly.
Expanded Basic Service
Subscribers: 3,484.
Programming (via satellite): A & E; American Movie Classics; C-SPAN; CNBC; CNN; Discovery Channel; Disney Channel; ESPN; ESPN 2; EWTN; Electronic Program Guide; Fox Family Channel; Headline News; Home Shopping Network; Knowledge TV; Lifetime; MTV; Nashville Network; Nickelodeon; Odyssey; Sci-Fi Channel; The Weather Channel; Turner Network TV; USA Network; VH1.
Fee: $13.64 monthly.
Pay Service 1
Pay Units: 662.
Programming (via satellite): Cinemax.
Fee: $12.50 monthly.
Pay Service 2
Pay Units: 799.
Programming (via satellite): HBO.
Fee: $12.95 monthly.
Pay Service 3
Pay Units: 479.
Programming (via satellite): Showtime.
Fee: $12.50 monthly.
Pay-Per-View
Addressable homes: 300.
Local advertising: Yes. Available in taped programming. Local sales manager: Brian Bertrand.
Program Guide: Premium Channels.
Equipment: Scientific-Atlanta headend; Scientific-Atlanta amplifiers; Times Fiber cable; Texscan character generator; Panasonic set top converters; Zenith addressable set top converters; Eagle traps.
Miles of plant: 81.3 (coaxial). Homes passed: 5,684.
Manager: Jim Ebenhoe. Chief technician: Duane Hendricks. Marketing director: Julie Stadtmueller.
City fee: 5% of gross.
Ownership: Charter Communications Inc. (MSO). Purchased from Marcus Cable, April 1, 1999.

SUGAR CREEK (town)—Mid-American Cable Systems, Box 71279, Des Moines, IA 50325. Phone: 800-320-5581. Fax: 515-270-9181. County: Walworth. ICA: WI0292.
TV Market Ranking: Outside TV Markets. Franchise award date: N.A. Franchise expiration date: N.A. Began: N.A.
Channel capacity: 37. Channels available but not in use: 2.
Basic Service
Subscribers: 408.
Programming (received off-air): WCGV-TV (I), WDJT-TV (C), WISN-TV (A), WITI (F), WMVS (P), WTMJ-TV (N), WVTV (W) Milwaukee.
Programming (via satellite): WGN-TV (W) Chicago; A & E; American Movie Classics; C-SPAN; CNBC; CNN; Country Music TV; Discovery Channel; ESPN; ESPN 2; Fox Family Channel; Learning Channel; Lifetime; MTV; Nashville Network; Nickelodeon; QVC; TBS Superstation; The Weather Channel; Trinity Bcstg. Network; Turner Network TV; USA Network; VH1.
Fee: $28.30 monthly.
Pay Service 1
Pay Units: N.A.
Programming (via satellite): Disney Channel; Showtime.
Fee: $5.95 monthly (Disney), $9.95 monthly (Showtime).
Miles of plant: 44.0 (coaxial). Homes passed: 1,300.
Manager: Mansell Nelson. Chief technician: Ron Enas. Marketing director: Dave Beasley.
Ownership: Mid American Cable Systems (MSO).

SURING—Wausaukee Cablevision Inc., Box 42, Rte. 3, Marinette, WI 54143. Phone: 715-735-9532. County: Oconto. ICA: WI0194.
TV Market Ranking: Below 100. Franchise award date: N.A. Franchise expiration date: N.A. Began: December 1, 1981.
Channel capacity: 12. Channels available but not in use: N.A.
Basic Service
Subscribers: 139.
Programming (received off-air): WBAY-TV (A), WFRV-TV (C), WLUK-TV (F), WPNE (P) Green Bay.
Programming (via satellite): WGN-TV (W) Chicago; TBS Superstation.
Fee: $25.00 installation; $8.95 monthly.
Pay Service 1
Pay Units: N.A.
Programming (via satellite): The Movie Channel.
Fee: $8.95 monthly.
Equipment: Scientific-Atlanta headend; Scientific-Atlanta amplifiers; Times Fiber cable.
Miles of plant: 6.0 (coaxial). Homes passed: 250. Total homes in franchised area: 250.
Manager: Carl Busch. Chief technician: Glen Mullen.
City fee: 3% of gross.
Ownership: Wausaukee Cablevision Inc. (MSO).

THORP—Century Tel, Box 307, 405 N. Washington St., Thorp, WI 54771. Phone: 715-669-5301. Fax: 715-669-5501. County: Clark. ICA: WI0139.
TV Market Ranking: Outside TV Markets. Franchise award date: June 23, 1981. Franchise expiration date: N.A. Began: October 1, 1982.
Channel capacity: 40 (not 2-way capable). Channels available but not in use: 21.
Basic Service
Subscribers: 521.
Programming (received off-air): WEAU-TV (N) Eau Claire; WKBT (C) La Crosse; WHWC-TV (P) Menomonie; WAOW-TV (A), WSAW-TV (C) Wausau-Rhinelander.
Programming (via satellite): CNN; ESPN; Fox Family Channel; TBS Superstation; Turner Network TV; USA Network.
Current originations: Automated time-weather; public access.
Fee: $10.00 installation; $15.50 monthly; $1.00 converter; $10.00 additional installation.
Expanded Basic Service
Subscribers: 251.
Programming (received off-air): WQOW-TV (A) Eau Claire.
Programming (via satellite): WGN-TV (W) Chicago; Lifetime; Nashville Network; Nickelodeon.
Fee: $7.50 installation; $3.00 monthly.
Pay Service 1
Pay Units: 36.
Programming (via satellite): Cinemax.
Fee: $7.50 installation; $9.25 monthly.
Pay Service 2
Pay Units: 57.
Programming (via satellite): Disney Channel.
Fee: $7.50 installation; $7.50 monthly.
Pay Service 3
Pay Units: 65.
Programming (via satellite): HBO.
Fee: $7.50 installation; $10.25 monthly.
Local advertising: Yes (locally produced). Local sales manager: Virginia Kodl.
Program Guide: Telescope.
Equipment: Scientific-Atlanta headend; GTE Sylvania amplifiers; Comm/Scope cable; Panasonic cameras; Panasonic VTRs; Texscan character generator; Texscan set top converters; Pico traps; Microdyne satellite antenna; Scientific-Atlanta satellite receivers.
Miles of plant: 14.0 (coaxial). Homes passed: 600. Total homes in franchised area: 600.
Manager: Dave M. Keating. Chief technician: Dean Benzschawel.
City fee: 3% of gross.
Ownership: Thorp Telephone Co.

THREE LAKES—Karban TV Systems Inc., 73A S. Stevens St., Rhinelander, WI 54501. Phone: 715-277-2339. County: Oneida. ICA: WI0293.
TV Market Ranking: Below 100. Franchise award date: N.A. Franchise expiration date: N.A. Began: January 1, 1986.
Channel capacity: 54 (not 2-way capable). Channels available but not in use: 29.
Basic Service
Subscribers: 163.
Programming (received off-air): WLEF-TV (P) Park Falls; WAOW-TV (A), WJFW-TV (N), WSAW-TV (C) Wausau-Rhinelander.
Programming (via satellite): WGN-TV (W) Chicago; A & E; CNN; Discovery Channel; ESPN; Fox Family Channel; Headline News; Lifetime; Nashville Network; Nickelodeon; TBS Superstation; Turner Network TV; USA Network.
Fee: $75.00 installation; $24.00 monthly.
Pay Service 1
Pay Units: 9.
Programming (via satellite): Disney Channel.
Fee: $9.00 monthly.
Pay Service 2
Pay Units: 25.
Programming (via satellite): HBO.
Fee: $10.00 monthly.
Miles of plant: 8.0 (coaxial). Homes passed: 210.
Manager: John Karban.
Ownership: Karban TV Systems Inc. (MSO).

TIGERTON—Charter Communications Inc., Box 1818, 853 McIntosh St., Wausau, WI 54402-

1818. Phones: 715-845-4223; 800-581-0081. Fax: 715-848-0081. County: Shawano. ICA: WI0169.

TV Market Ranking: Below 100. Franchise award date: October 5, 1982. Franchise expiration date: N.A. Began: May 1, 1982.

Channel capacity: 35 (2-way capable). Channels available but not in use: N.A.

Basic Service

Subscribers: 186.

Programming (received off-air): WACY (U) Appleton; WBAY-TV (A), WFRV-TV (C), WGBA (N), WLUK-TV (F), WPNE (P) Green Bay; WAOW-TV (A), WSAW-TV (C) Wausau-Rhinelander.

Programming (via satellite): WGN-TV (W) Chicago; TBS Superstation.

Current originations: Public access.

Fee: $56.73 installation; $9.72 monthly.

Expanded Basic Service

Subscribers: 180.

Programming (via satellite): A & E; CNN; Disney Channel; ESPN; Fox Family Channel; Headline News; Nashville Network; Nickelodeon; Sci-Fi Channel; Turner Network TV; USA Network; VH1.

Fee: $11.66 monthly.

Pay Service 1

Pay Units: 63.

Programming (via satellite): HBO.

Fee: $11.66 monthly.

Local advertising: No.

Equipment: Blonder-Tongue, Gardiner & Scientific-Atlanta headend; AEL & Winegard amplifiers; Intercept & Pico traps; Scientific-Atlanta satellite antenna; Gardiner & Scientific-Atlanta satellite receivers.

Miles of plant: 7.0 (coaxial). Homes passed: 375. Total homes in franchised area: 375.

Manager: Scott Behn. Chief technician: Bruce Wasleske. Marketing director: Tim Schieffer.

Ownership: Charter Communications Inc. (MSO). Purchased from Marcus Cable, April 1, 1999.

TOMAH—Charter Communications Inc., Box 279, 314 Main St., Onalaska, WI 54650. Phones: 608-783-5255; 800-658-9473. Fax: 608-783-7033.

Web site: http://www.chartercom.com.

County: Monroe. Also serves Greenfield (town), La Grange (town), Tomah (city), Tomah (town). ICA: WI0060.

TV Market Ranking: Below 100 (Greenfield); Outside TV Markets (Tomah). Franchise award date: February 9, 1965. Franchise expiration date: January 1, 1999. Began: February 1, 1967.

Channel capacity: 86 (2-way capable; operating 2-way). Channels available but not in use: 5.

Basic Service

Subscribers: 3,088.

Programming (received off-air): WEAU-TV (N) Eau Claire; KQEG-LP (I) La Crescent; WHLA-TV (P), WKBT (C), WLAX (F), WXOW-TV (A) La Crosse.

Programming (via satellite): WGN-TV (W) Chicago; Bravo; C-SPAN; C-SPAN 2; TV Guide Channel.

Current originations: Public access; automated emergency alert.

Fee: $64.57 installation; $6.71 monthly.

Expanded Basic Service

Subscribers: 2,777.

Programming (via satellite): A & E; American Movie Classics; Animal Planet; CNBC; CNN; Cartoon Network; Comedy Central; Country Music TV; Court TV; Discovery Channel; Disney Channel; E! Entertainment TV; ESPN; ESPN 2; ESPN Classic Sports; ESPNews; EWTN; FX; Fox Family Channel; Game Show Network; Golf Channel; Headline News; History Channel; Home & Garden Television; Home Shopping Network; Learning Channel; Lifetime; MSNBC; MTV; Midwest Sports Channel; Nashville Network; Nick at Nite's TV Land; Nickelodeon; Odyssey; Outdoor Life Network; QVC; Sci-Fi Channel; Speedvision; TBS Superstation; The Barker; The Weather Channel; Toon Disney; Travel Channel; Turner Classic Movies; Turner Network TV; USA Network; VH1; WB 100+ Station Group.

Fee: $64.57 installation; $26.49 monthly.

Pay Service 1

Pay Units: 435.

Programming (via satellite): Cinemax (multiplexed).

Fee: $20.00 installation; $12.95 monthly.

Pay Service 2

Pay Units: 499.

Programming (via satellite): HBO (multiplexed).

Fee: $20.00 installation; $12.95 monthly.

Pay Service 3

Pay Units: 398.

Programming (via satellite): Showtime.

Fee: $20.00 installation; $12.95 monthly.

Pay Service 4

Pay Units: 6.

Programming (via satellite): DMX.

Fee: $6.95 monthly.

Pay Service 5

Pay Units: N.A.

Programming (via satellite): The Movie Channel.

Fee: N.A.

Pay-Per-View

Addressable homes: 798.

Movies.

Local advertising: Yes. Available in satellite distributed programming. Local sales manager: Holly Hockner.

Equipment: Jerrold & Scientific-Atlanta headend; Scientific-Atlanta amplifiers; Systems Wire & Trilogy cable; Jerrold set top converters; Eagle traps; Scientific-Atlanta satellite antenna; Scientific-Atlanta satellite receivers.

Miles of plant: 62.0 (coaxial); 11.0 (fiber optic). Homes passed: 3,984. Total homes in franchised area: 4,610.

Manager: Shirley Hehn Weibel. Chief technician: Tim Fischer. Marketing coordinator: Ellen Martin.

Ownership: Charter Communications Inc. (MSO). Purchased from Marcus Cable, April 1, 1999.

TURTLE LAKE—Vision Communications LLC, Box 355, 28 First Ave. W, Luck, WI 54853-0355. Phone: 715-472-2700. Fax: 715-472-2707. Counties: Barron & Polk. ICA: WI0188.

TV Market Ranking: Outside TV Markets. Franchise award date: N.A. Franchise expiration date: N.A. Began: January 1, 1986.

Channel capacity: N.A. Channels available but not in use: N.A.

Basic Service

Subscribers: 137.

Programming (received off-air): WEAU-TV (N), WQOW-TV (A) Eau Claire; WHLA-TV (P) La Crosse; KSTP-TV (A), KTCI-TV (P), WCCO-TV (C), WFTC (F) Minneapolis-St. Paul.

Programming (via satellite): WGN-TV (W) Chicago; CNN; Discovery Channel; ESPN; Fox Family Channel; Headline News; Lifetime; MTV; Nashville Network; Nickelodeon; TBS Superstation; USA Network.

Fee: $45.00 installation; $18.95 monthly.

Pay Service 1

Pay Units: 9.

Programming (via satellite): Cinemax.

Fee: $8.00 monthly.

Pay Service 2

Pay Units: 15.

Programming (via satellite): Disney Channel.

Fee: $7.00 monthly.

Pay Service 3

Pay Units: 34.

Programming (via satellite): HBO.

Fee: $9.00 monthly.

Pay Service 4

Pay Units: 13.

Programming (via satellite): The Movie Channel.

Fee: $8.00 monthly.

Miles of plant: 5.0 (coaxial). Homes passed: 275.

Manager: John Klatt.

Ownership: Vision Communications LLC (MSO).

TUSTIN—Cable Systems Management of Iowa Inc., 3600 Kennebec Dr., Eagan, MN 55122. Phone: 612-688-2623. Fax: 612-688-2624. County: Waushara. Also serves Bloomfield (town). ICA: WI0225.

TV Market Ranking: Below 100. Franchise award date: N.A. Franchise expiration date: N.A. Began: N.A.

Channel capacity: 40. Channels available but not in use: 19.

Basic Service

Subscribers: 27.

Programming (received off-air): WACY (U) Appleton; WBAY-TV (A), WFRV-TV (C), WLUK-TV (F), WPNE (P) Green Bay.

Programming (via satellite): WGN-TV (W) Chicago; A & E; CNN; Country Music TV; Discovery Channel; ESPN; Fox Family Channel; Nashville Network; Showtime; TBS Superstation; Turner Network TV; USA Network.

Fee: $50.00 installation; $30.00 monthly.

Miles of plant: 2.8 (coaxial). Homes passed: 103.

Manager: Jeff Anderson.

Ownership: Cable Systems Management of Iowa Inc. (MSO).

TWO RIVERS—Charter Communications Inc., Box 1197, 55 W. Scott St., Fond du Lac, WI 54936-1197. Phones: 920-923-7196; 800-581-0081. Fax: 920-923-1235. County: Manitowoc. Also serves Two Rivers (town). ICA: WI0035.

TV Market Ranking: 62. Franchise award date: July 8, 1980. Franchise expiration date: N.A. Began: September 23, 1981.

Channel capacity: 42 (2-way capable; operating 2-way). Channels available but not in use: 1.

Basic Service

Subscribers: 3,888.

Programming (received off-air): WACY (U) Appleton; WBAY-TV (A), WFRV-TV (C), WGBA (N), WLUK-TV (F), WPNE (P) Green Bay; 18 FMs.

Programming (via satellite): WGN-TV (W) Chicago; C-SPAN; QVC.

Current originations: Educational access; leased access; automated emergency alert; local sports.

Fee: $56.73 installation; $8.16 monthly; $1.43 converter; $7.74 additional installation.

Expanded Basic Service

Subscribers: N.A.

Programming (via satellite): A & E; American Movie Classics; Animal Planet; CNBC; CNN; Comedy Central; Country Music TV; Discovery Channel; Disney Channel; ESPN; ESPN 2; ESPNews; EWTN; Fox Family Channel; Headline News; History Channel; Home & Garden Television; Learning Channel; Lifetime; MTV; Midwest Sports Channel; Nashville Network; Nick at Nite's TV Land; Nickelodeon; TBS Superstation; The Inspirational Network; The Weather Channel; Toon Disney; Turner Network TV; USA Network; VH1.

Fee: $21.52 monthly.

Pay Service 1

Pay Units: 590.

Programming (via satellite): Cinemax.

Fee: $15.00 installation; $12.95 monthly.

Pay Service 2

Pay Units: 824.

Programming (via satellite): Showtime.

Fee: $15.00 installation; $12.95 monthly.

Pay Service 3

Pay Units: 746.

Programming (via satellite): HBO.

Fee: $15.00 installation; $12.95 monthly.

Local advertising: Yes. Available in satellite distributed programming. Rates: $7.00/Minute; $4.00/30 Seconds. Local sales manager: John Welton.

Equipment: RCA & Scientific-Atlanta amplifiers; Comm/Scope & Times Fiber cable; Sony cameras; Sony VTRs; Video Data Systems character generator; Hamlin set top converters; Eagle traps; Hughes & Scientific-Atlanta satellite antenna; Standard Communications satellite receivers.

Miles of plant: 108.0 (coaxial). Homes passed: 6,205. Total homes in franchised area: 6,205.

Manager: Lisa Washa. Chief technician: Jeff Gerner.

City fee: 5% of gross.

Ownership: Charter Communications Inc. (MSO). Purchased from Marcus Cable, April 1, 1999.

VERONA—Charter Communications Inc., Box 1127, 1348 Plainfield Ave., Janesville, WI 53547-1127. Phone: 608-754-3644. Fax: 608-754-8107. County: Dane. Also serves Verona (town) (portions). ICA: WI0076.

TV Market Ranking: 93. Franchise award date: N.A. Franchise expiration date: N.A. Began: June 1, 1981.

Channel capacity: N.A. Channels available but not in use: N.A.

Basic Service

Subscribers: 1,580.

Programming (received off-air): WHA-TV (P), WISC-TV (C), WKOW-TV (A), WMSN-TV (F), WMTV (N) Madison; WMVS (P) Milwaukee.

Current originations: Educational access; government access; local news.

Fee: $42.95 installation; $33.75 monthly.

Expanded Basic Service

Subscribers: 1,517.

Programming (via satellite): WGN-TV (W) Chicago; A & E; American Movie Classics; C-SPAN; CNN; Comedy Central; Discovery Channel; ESPN; Fox Family Channel; Headline News; Learning Channel; Lifetime; MTV; Nashville Network; Nickelodeon; QVC; TBS Superstation; The Inspirational Network; The Weather Channel; Turner Network TV; USA Network.

Fee: N.A.

Pay Service 1

Pay Units: 186.

Programming (via satellite): Cinemax.

Fee: $12.95 monthly.

Pay Service 2

Pay Units: 285.

Programming (via satellite): HBO.

Fee: $12.95 monthly.

Pay Service 3

Pay Units: 164.

Programming (via satellite): Showtime.

Fee: $12.95 monthly.

Pay-Per-View

Addressable homes: 579.

Spice; Spice2; Viewer's Choice 1-4; movies.
Fee: $3.95-$34.95.
Equipment: Scientific-Atlanta headend; Scientific-Atlanta & Magnavox amplifiers; Times Fiber cable; Texscan character generator; Jerrold set top converters; Eagle traps; Scientific-Atlanta satellite receivers.
Miles of plant: 21.7 (coaxial). Additional miles planned: 2.0 (coaxial). Homes passed: 2,154.
Manager: Marty Robinson. Chief technician: Tim Sanderson. Marketing director: Danette Knickmeier.
City fee: 3% of gross.
Ownership: Charter Communications Inc. (MSO). Purchased from Marcus Cable, April 1, 1999.

VESPER—HLM Cable Corp., Box 620684, 2305-A Parview Rd., Middleton, WI 53562-0684. Phones: 608-831-7044; 800-451-5119. Fax: 608-836-5726. County: Wood. Also serves Arpin (village). ICA: WI0295.
TV Market Ranking: Below 100. Franchise award date: N.A. Franchise expiration date: N.A. Began: N.A.
Channel capacity: 40 (not 2-way capable). Channels available but not in use: 12.
Basic Service
Subscribers: 239.
Programming (received off-air): WEAU-TV (N) Eau Claire; WAOW-TV (A), WHRM-TV (P), WSAW-TV (C) Wausau-Rhinelander.
Programming (via satellite): WGN-TV (W) Chicago; A & E; American Movie Classics; CNBC; CNN; Discovery Channel; ESPN; ESPN 2; Fox Family Channel; FoxNet; History Channel; Learning Channel; Lifetime; Nashville Network; Nick at Nite; Nick at Nite's TV Land; Nickelodeon; Sci-Fi Channel; TBS Superstation; The Weather Channel; Turner Network TV; USA Network; VH1.
Fee: $19.95 installation; $26.00 monthly; $1.50 converter.
Pay Service 1
Pay Units: 23.
Programming (via satellite): Disney Channel.
Fee: $14.95 installation; $6.95 monthly.
Pay Service 2
Pay Units: 62.
Programming (via satellite): Showtime.
Fee: $14.95 installation; $6.95 monthly.
Manager: Robert E. Ryan.
Ownership: H.L.M. Cable Co. (MSO).

VIROQUA—Triax Cablevision, Box 110, 1504 2nd St. SE, Waseca, MN 56093. Phones: 507-835-5975; 800-332-0245. Fax: 507-835-4567. Counties: Crawford, La Crosse, Monroe, Richland & Vernon. Also serves Brookview Trailer Court, Cashton, Gays Mills, Greenfield (La Crosse County), La Crosse, La Farge, Readstown, Shelby, Soldier's Grove, Viola, Westby. ICA: WI0068.
TV Market Ranking: Below 100 (Brookview Trailer Court, Cashton, Greenfield, La Crosse, La Farge, Readstown, Shelby, Viola, Viroqua, Westby); Outside TV Markets (Gays Mills, Soldier's Grove). Franchise award date: N.A. Franchise expiration date: N.A. Began: January 1, 1968.
Channel capacity: 62 (2-way capable; operating 2-way). Channels available but not in use: 3.
Basic Service
Subscribers: 4,310.
Programming (received off-air): WEAU-TV (N) Eau Claire; WHLA-TV (P), WKBT (C), WLAX (F), WXOW-TV (A) La Crosse.
Programming (via satellite): C-SPAN; C-SPAN 2; Home Shopping Network; Knowledge TV; Odyssey; QVC.
Fee: $35.16 installation; $7.01 monthly; $1.58 converter.
Expanded Basic Service
Subscribers: 4,152.
Programming (via satellite): WGN-TV (W) Chicago; A & E; American Movie Classics; CNN; Cartoon Network; Comedy Central; Country Music TV; Discovery Channel; ESPN; Fox Family Channel; Goodlife TV Network; Headline News; History Channel; Home & Garden Television; Learning Channel; Lifetime; MSNBC; Nashville Network; Nickelodeon; TBS Superstation; TV Guide Channel; The Weather Channel; Turner Network TV; USA Network; VH1.
Fee: $17.94 monthly.
Pay Service 1
Pay Units: 1,133.
Programming (via satellite): Cinemax; Disney Channel; HBO; Showtime; The New Encore.
Fee: $10.00 installation; $8.95 monthly (Cinemax, Disney or Showtime), $9.95 monthly (HBO).
Equipment: Comtech satellite antenna.
Miles of plant: 108.0 (coaxial). Homes passed: 4,979.
Manager: Richard Giffen. Chief technician: Scott Walters.
Ownership: Triax Telecommunications Co. LLC (MSO). See Cable System Ownership.

WARRENS—Charter Communications, Box 279, 314 N. Main St., Onalaska, WI 54650. Phones: 608-783-5255; 800-658-9473. Fax: 608-783-7033.
Web site: http://www.chartercom.com.
County: Monroe. Also serves Oakdale. ICA: WI0319.
TV Market Ranking: Outside TV Markets. Franchise award date: N.A. Franchise expiration date: N.A. Began: N.A.
Channel capacity: N.A. Channels available but not in use: N.A.
Basic Service
Subscribers: 126.
Programming (received off-air): WEAU-TV (N) Eau Claire; KQEG-LP (I) La Crescent; WHLA-TV (P), WKBT (C), WLAX (F), WXOW-TV (A) La Crosse.
Programming (via satellite): WGN-TV (W) Chicago; Bravo; C-SPAN; C-SPAN 2; TV Guide Channel.
Current originations: Educational access.
Fee: $64.57 installation; $6.71 monthly; $1.80 converter; $32.29 additional installation.
Expanded Basic Service
Subscribers: 110.
Programming (via satellite): A & E; American Movie Classics; Animal Planet; CNBC; CNN; Cartoon Network; Comedy Central; Country Music TV; Court TV; Discovery Channel; Disney Channel; E! Entertainment TV; ESPN; ESPN 2; ESPNews; EWTN; FX; Fox Family Channel; Game Show Network; Headline News; History Channel; Home & Garden Television; Learning Channel; Lifetime; MSNBC; MTV; Midwest Sports Channel; Nashville Network; Nick at Nite's TV Land; Nickelodeon; Odyssey; QVC; Sci-Fi Channel; TBS Superstation; The Weather Channel; Toon Disney; Turner Network TV; USA Network; VH1; WB 100+ Station Group.
Fee: $24.49 monthly.
Pay Service 1
Pay Units: 15.
Programming (via satellite): Cinemax (multiplexed).
Fee: $20.00 installation; $12.95 monthly.
Pay Service 2
Pay Units: 16.
Programming (via satellite): HBO (multiplexed).
Fee: $20.00 installation; $12.95 monthly.
Pay Service 3
Pay Units: 14.
Programming (via satellite): Showtime.
Fee: $20.00 installation; $12.95 monthly.
Pay Service 4
Pay Units: N.A.
Programming (via satellite): The Movie Channel.
Fee: $20.00 installation; $12.95 monthly.
Miles of plant: 10.0 (coaxial). Homes passed: 206.
Manager: Shirley Nehn Weibel. Chief technician: Tim Fischer.
Ownership: Charter Communications Inc. (MSO).

WAUPACA—Charter Communications Inc., Box 1818, 853 McIntosh St., Wausau, WI 54402 1818. Phones: 715-845-4223; 800-581-0081. Fax: 715-848-0081. County: Waupaca. Also serves Dayton, Farmington, Lind (town), Royalton Twp., Weyauwega. ICA: WI0053.
TV Market Ranking: Below 100 (Lind, Royalton Twp., Waupaca, Weyauwega); Outside TV Markets (Dayton, Farmington). Franchise award date: April 1, 1978. Franchise expiration date: April 1, 1999. Began: June 1, 1979.
Channel capacity: 35 (not 2-way capable). Channels available but not in use: None.
Basic Service
Subscribers: 3,735.
Programming (received off-air): WACY (U) Appleton; WBAY-TV (A), WFRV-TV (C), WGBA (N), WLUK-TV (F), WPNE (P) Green Bay; WAOW-TV (A), WSAW-TV (C) Wausau-Rhinelander; 1 FM.
Programming (via satellite): WGN-TV (W) Chicago; C-SPAN; Home Shopping Network.
Current originations: Government access.
Fee: $60.48 installation; $7.55 monthly.
Expanded Basic Service
Subscribers: 3,520.
Programming (via satellite): A & E; American Movie Classics; CNN; Discovery Channel; Disney Channel; ESPN; ESPN 2; ESPNews; Fox Family Channel; Headline News; Home & Garden Television; Learning Channel; Lifetime; MSNBC; MTV; Midwest Sports Channel; Nashville Network; Nick at Nite; Nick at Nite's TV Land; Nickelodeon; Odyssey; QVC; TBS Superstation; The Weather Channel; Turner Network TV; USA Network; VH1.
Fee: $60.48 installation; $18.40 monthly.
Pay Service 1
Pay Units: 460.
Programming (via satellite): Cinemax.
Fee: $10.00 installation; $12.95 monthly.
Pay Service 2
Pay Units: 715.
Programming (via satellite): HBO.
Fee: $10.00 installation; $12.95 monthly.
Pay Service 3
Pay Units: 300.
Programming (via satellite): Showtime.
Fee: $10.00 installation; $12.95 monthly.
Local advertising: Yes. Available in satellite distributed & automated programming. Rates: $20.00/Minute; $10.00/30 Seconds. Local sales manager: John Welton.
Equipment: Scientific-Atlanta headend; Scientific-Atlanta amplifiers; Comm/Scope cable; Scientific-Atlanta set top converters; Scientific-Atlanta satellite antenna; Scientific-Atlanta & Standard Components satellite receivers; ChannelMatic & Sky Connect commercial insert.
Miles of plant: 105.0 (coaxial). Homes passed: 5,720.
Manager: Scott Behn. Chief technician: Bruce Wasleske. Marketing director: Tim Schieffer.
City fee: 3% of gross.
Ownership: Charter Communications Inc. (MSO). Purchased from Marcus Cable, April 1, 1999.

WAUSAU—Charter Communications Inc., Box 1818, 853 McIntosh St., Wausau, WI 54402-1818. Phones: 715-845-4223; 800-581-0081. Fax: 715-848-0081. Counties: Marathon & Shawano. Also serves Aniwa, Aniwa (village), Bergen Twp., Birnamwood, Bowler, Bowler (village), Brokaw, Hatley, Hatley (village), Kronenwetter, Maine Twp., Mattoon, Mattoon (village), Mosinee, Mosinee (town), Rib Mountain, Ringle (town), Rothschild, Schofield, Stettin, Texas (town), Wausau (town), Weston. ICA: WI0012.
TV Market Ranking: Below 100. Franchise award date: November 1, 1976. Franchise expiration date: April 14, 2008. Began: June 1, 1964.
Channel capacity: 35 (2-way capable; operating 2-way). Channels available but not in use: None.
Basic Service
Subscribers: 22,025.
Programming (received off-air): WFRV-TV (C) Green Bay; WAOW-TV (A), WHRM-TV (P), WJFW-TV (N), WSAW-TV (C) Wausau-Rhinelander.
Programming (via microwave): WITI (F) Milwaukee.
Programming (via satellite): WGN-TV (W) Chicago; TBS Superstation.
Current originations: Automated time-weather; public access; educational access; government access; automated emergency alert.
Fee: $65.61 installation; $6.80 monthly.
Expanded Basic Service
Subscribers: 21,680.
Programming (via satellite): A & E; American Movie Classics; C-SPAN; CNN; Discovery Channel; ESPN; ESPN 2; EWTN; Electronic Program Guide; Fox Family Channel; Headline News; Learning Channel; Lifetime; MTV; Nashville Network; Nickelodeon; The Weather Channel; Turner Network TV; USA Network; VH1.
Fee: $14.03 monthly.
Pay Service 1
Pay Units: 3,450.
Programming (via satellite): Cinemax.
Fee: $10.00 installation; $12.50 monthly.
Pay Service 2
Pay Units: 4,490.
Programming (via satellite): HBO.
Fee: $10.00 installation; $12.95 monthly.
Pay Service 3
Pay Units: 3,660.
Programming (via satellite): Showtime.
Fee: $10.00 installation; $12.50 monthly.
Pay Service 4
Pay Units: 2,570.
Programming (via satellite): Disney Channel.
Fee: $10.00 installation; $2.95 monthly.
Local advertising: Yes. Available in satellite distributed, locally originated & automated programming. Rates: $38.00/Minute; $19.00/30 Seconds. Local sales manager: John Welton.
Equipment: Scientific-Atlanta headend; Magnavox amplifiers; Comm/Scope cable; Panasonic cameras; Sony VTRs; Compuvid character generator; Oak set top converters;

Arcom traps; Scientific-Atlanta satellite antenna; Microdyne satellite receivers; ChannelMatic commercial insert.
Miles of plant: 489.0 (coaxial); 50.0 (fiber optic). Homes passed: 31,890. Total homes in franchised area: 32,700.
Manager: Scott Behn. Chief technician: Bruce Wasleske. Marketing director: Tim Schieffer.
City fee: 1% of gross.
Ownership: Charter Communications Inc. (MSO). Purchased from Marcus Cable, April 1, 1999.

WAUTOMA—Charter Communications Inc., Box 1197, 55 W. Scott St., Fond du Lac, WI 54936-1197. Phones: 920-923-7196; 800-581-0081. Fax: 920-923-1235. Counties: Marquette & Waushara. Also serves Coloma, Dakota, Hancock, Lohrville, Marion (town), Neshkoro, Plainfield, Redgranite, Wautoma (town), Westfield, Wild Rose. ICA: WI0057.
TV Market Ranking: Below 100 (Plainfield); Outside TV Markets (Coloma, Dakota, Hancock, Lohrville, Marion, Neshkoro, Redgranite, Wautoma, Westfield, Wild Rose). Franchise award date: N.A. Franchise expiration date: N.A. Began: April 1, 1980.
Channel capacity: 35 (not 2-way capable). Channels available but not in use: 4.

Basic Service
Subscribers: 2,790.
Programming (received off-air): WACY (U) Appleton; WBAY-TV (A), WFRV-TV (C), WGBA (N), WLUK-TV (F), WPNE (P) Green Bay; WISC-TV (C), WMTV (N) Madison; WSAW-TV (C) Wausau-Rhinelander.
Programming (via satellite): WGN-TV (W) Chicago; A & E; American Movie Classics; CNN; Discovery Channel; ESPN; ESPN 2; EWTN; Fox Family Channel; Learning Channel; Lifetime; MTV; Nashville Network; Nickelodeon; QVC; TBS Superstation; The Weather Channel; Turner Network TV; USA Network; VH1.
Current originations: Automated time-weather; automated emergency alert.
Fee: $34.95 installation; $12.09 monthly.

Pay Service 1
Pay Units: 548.
Programming (via satellite): Cinemax.
Fee: $14.95 installation; $12.50 monthly.

Pay Service 2
Pay Units: 637.
Programming (via satellite): HBO.
Fee: $14.95 installation; $12.95 monthly.

Pay Service 3
Pay Units: 271.
Programming (via satellite): Disney Channel.
Fee: $14.95 installation; $3.95 monthly.

Pay Service 4
Pay Units: 495.
Programming (via satellite): Showtime.
Fee: $14.95 installation; $12.50 monthly.
Local advertising: Yes. Available in character-generated programming.
Equipment: Scientific-Atlanta headend; Texscan amplifiers; Comm/Scope cable; Panasonic cameras; Panasonic VTRs; Texscan character generator; Scientific-Atlanta set top converters; Eagle traps; Scientific-Atlanta satellite antenna; Scientific-Atlanta satellite receivers.
Miles of plant: 94.8 (coaxial). Homes passed: 3,894.
Manager: Lisa Washa. Chief technician: Jeff Gerner.
City fee: 3% of gross.
Ownership: Charter Communications Inc. (MSO). Purchased from Marcus Cable, April 1, 1999.

WAUWATOSA—Time Warner Cable, 2767 N. Mayfair Rd., Wauwatosa, WI 53222-4403. Phone: 414-259-1234. Fax: 414-259-9230. Counties: Milwaukee, Ozaukee, Washington & Waukesha. Also serves Brookfield (town), Butler (village), Delafield, Elm Grove (village), Germantown (village), Hartland (village), Mequon, Merton (town), Mukwonago (village), Pewaukee (town), Pewaukee (village), Port Washington, Saukville (village), St. Francis, Theinsville (village), Waukesha, Waukesha (town), West Milwaukee (village). ICA: WI0004.
TV Market Ranking: 23. Franchise award date: N.A. Franchise expiration date: N.A. Began: December 1, 1978.
Channel capacity: 45. Channels available but not in use: None.

Basic Service
Subscribers: 50,000.
Programming (received off-air): WFLD (F), WGN-TV (W), WTTW (P) Chicago; WHA-TV (P) Madison; WCGV-TV (I), WISN-TV (A), WITI (F), WMVS (P), WMVT (P), WTMJ-TV (N), WVCY-TV (I), WVTV (W) Milwaukee; allband FM.
Programming (via satellite): A & E; Bravo; C-SPAN; CNBC; CNN; ESPN; Fox Family Channel; Headline News; Learning Channel; Lifetime; MTV; Nashville Network; Nickelodeon; TBS Superstation; The Weather Channel; USA Network; Univision; VH1.
Current originations: Public access; educational access; government access; religious access; automated emergency alert; local news.
Fee: $25.00 installation; $9.20 monthly.

Pay Service 1
Pay Units: N.A.
Programming (via satellite): Cinemax; Disney Channel; HBO; Playboy TV; Showtime; The Movie Channel.
Fee: $10.00 installation; $8.95 monthly (each).

Pay-Per-View
Addressable homes: 9,544.
Local advertising: Yes. Rates: $40.00/Minute; $20.00/30 Seconds.
Equipment: AML, Hughes & Jerrold headend; Jerrold amplifiers; Comm/Scope cable; Video Data Systems character generator; Jerrold set top converters; Tocom addressable set top converters; Vitek traps; Andrew & Simulsat satellite antenna; Scientific-Atlanta satellite receivers.
Miles of plant: 934.8 (coaxial). Additional miles planned: 10.0 (coaxial). Homes passed: 92,000.
Manager: Bill Rouggly. Chief technician: David Mueller. Marketing director: Sandy Fast.
City fee: 3% of gross.
Ownership: Century Communications Corp. (MSO); Time Warner Cable (MSO). See Cable System Ownership.

WEST BEND—Charter Communications Inc., Box 1197, 55 W. Scott St., Fond du Lac, WI 54936-1197. Phones: 920-923-7196; 800-581-0081. Fax: 920-923-1235. County: Washington. Also serves Addison (town), Allenton, Barton (town), Farmington (town), Jackson, Jackson Twp., Kewaskum, Polk (town), Trenton (town), West Bend (town). ICA: WI0020.
TV Market Ranking: 23. Franchise award date: September 10, 1979. Franchise expiration date: N.A. Began: October 30, 1980.
Channel capacity: 35 (not 2-way capable). Channels available but not in use: None.

Basic Service
Subscribers: 12,743; Commercial subscribers: 8.
Programming (received off-air): WCGV-TV (I), WDJT-TV (C), WISN-TV (A), WITI (F), WMVS (P), WMVT (P), WTMJ-TV (N), WVCY-TV (I), WVTV (W) Milwaukee.
Programming (via satellite): WGN-TV (W) Chicago; C-SPAN; C-SPAN 2; TBS Superstation; ValueVision.
Current originations: Automated time-weather; public access; educational access; government access; automated emergency alert; local news; local sports.
Fee: $34.95 installation; $9.59 monthly.

Expanded Basic Service
Subscribers: 11,976.
Programming (via satellite): A & E; American Movie Classics; Bravo; CNBC; CNN; Cartoon Network; Court TV; Discovery Channel; ESPN; ESPN 2; Fox Family Channel; Goodlife TV Network; Headline News; Home Shopping Network; Learning Channel; Lifetime; MTV; Nashville Network; Nickelodeon; Sci-Fi Channel; The Weather Channel; Turner Network TV; USA Network; VH1.
Fee: $21.37 monthly.

Pay Service 1
Pay Units: 1,524.
Programming (via satellite): Cinemax.
Fee: $13.12 installation; $12.50 monthly.

Pay Service 2
Pay Units: 625.
Programming (via satellite): Disney Channel.
Fee: $13.12 installation; $3.95 monthly.

Pay Service 3
Pay Units: 2,378.
Programming (via satellite): HBO.
Fee: $13.12 installation; $12.95 monthly.

Pay Service 4
Pay Units: 451.
Programming (via satellite): Showtime.
Fee: $13.12 installation; $12.50 monthly.

Pay Service 5
Pay Units: N.A.
Programming (via satellite): Music Choice; The New Encore.
Fee: $13.12 installation; $3.95 monthly (Encore), $6.95 monthly (Music Choice).

Pay-Per-View
Special events.
Fee: Varies.
Local advertising: Yes. Available in locally originated & automated programming.
Equipment: Scientific-Atlanta headend; Scientific-Atlanta amplifiers; Comm/Scope cable; Video Data Systems character generator; Hamlin set top converters; Eagle & Vitek traps; Scientific-Atlanta satellite antenna; Scientific-Atlanta satellite receivers.
Miles of plant: 468.0 (coaxial). Homes passed: 15,500. Total homes in franchised area: 16,988.
Manager: Lisa Washa. Chief technician: Jeff Gerner.
Ownership: Charter Communications Inc. (MSO). Purchased from Marcus Cable, April 1, 1999.

WEYERHAEUSER—S & K TV Systems, Box 127, 503 W. Miner Ave., Ladysmith, WI 54848. Phones: 715-523-7321; 800-924-7880. County: Rusk. ICA: WI0297.
TV Market Ranking: Outside TV Markets. Franchise award date: January 1, 1988. Franchise expiration date: January 1, 1998. Began: November 1, 1988.
Channel capacity: 36. Channels available but not in use: N.A.

Basic Service
Subscribers: 91.
Programming (received off-air): WEUX (F) Chippewa Falls; WEAU-TV (N), WQOW-TV (A) Eau Claire; WKBT (C) La Crosse; WHWC-TV (P) Menomonie.
Programming (via satellite): WGN-TV (W) Chicago; A & E; American Movie Classics; CNN; Discovery Channel; ESPN; Fox Family Channel; Nashville Network; TBS Superstation; Turner Network TV; USA Network.
Fee: $24.95 monthly.

Pay Service 1
Pay Units: N.A.
Programming (via satellite): HBO.
Fee: $9.95 monthly.
Manager: Randy Scott.
Ownership: S & K TV Systems (MSO).

WHITE LAKE—Northern Lakes Cable TV, Box 8, Bonduel, WI 54107. Phone: 715-758-2500. County: Langlade. ICA: WI0298.
TV Market Ranking: Below 100. Franchise award date: N.A. Franchise expiration date: N.A. Began: May 1, 1990.
Channel capacity: N.A. Channels available but not in use: N.A.

Basic Service
Subscribers: N.A.
Programming (received off-air): WACY (U) Appleton; WBAY-TV (A), WFRV-TV (C), WGBA (N), WLUK-TV (F) Green Bay; WLUC-TV (N) Marquette; WAOW-TV (A), WHRM-TV (P), WJFW-TV (N), WSAW-TV (C) Wausau-Rhinelander.
Programming (via satellite): WGN-TV (W) Chicago; CNN; Discovery Channel; ESPN; Fox Family Channel; MTV; Nashville Network; Nickelodeon; TBS Superstation; USA Network.
Fee: $15.95 monthly.

Pay Service 1
Pay Units: N.A.
Programming (via satellite): Cinemax; HBO.
Fee: $9.95 monthly (each).
Manager: Robert Steichen.
Ownership: Northern Lakes Cable TV (MSO).

WHITEWATER—Charter Communications Inc., 108 S. First St., Whitewater, WI 53190. Phone: 800-581-0081. Fax: 414-473-5426. Counties: Jefferson & Walworth. Also serves Palmyra (town), Palmyra (village), Whitewater (town). ICA: WI0045.
TV Market Ranking: 23 (Palmyra); 93 (Whitewater). Franchise award date: August 1, 1979. Franchise expiration date: N.A. Began: April 1, 1980.
Channel capacity: 95 (not 2-way capable). Channels available but not in use: None.

Basic Service
Subscribers: 3,311.
Programming (received off-air): WHPN-TV (U) Janesville; WPXE (X) Kenosha; WHA-TV (P), WISC-TV (C), WKOW-TV (A), WMTV (N) Madison; WCGV-TV (I), WDJT-TV (C), WISN-TV (A), WITI (F), WMVS (P), WTMJ-TV (N), WVTV (W) Milwaukee; allband FM.
Programming (via satellite): WGN-TV (W) Chicago; C-SPAN; C-SPAN 2; Home Shopping Network; QVC; TV Guide Channel.
Current originations: Public access; educational access; government access; local news.
Fee: $42.95 installation; $11.99 monthly.

Expanded Basic Service
Subscribers: N.A.
Programming (via satellite): A & E; American Movie Classics; Animal Planet; Bravo; CNBC; CNN; Cartoon Network; Comedy Central; Discovery Channel; Disney Channel; ESPN; ESPN 2; ESPN Classic Sports; ESPNews; EWTN; Fox Family Channel; Game Show Network; Headline News; History Channel; Home & Garden Television; Learning Channel; Lifetime; MSNBC; MTV; Midwest Sports Channel; Nashville Network; Nick at Nite's TV Land; Nickelodeon; Odyssey; Outdoor Life Network; Sci-Fi Channel; Speedvision; TBS Superstation; The Weather Channel;

Toon Disney; Turner Classic Movies; Turner Network TV; USA Network; VH1.
Fee: $21.26 monthly.

Pay Service 1
Pay Units: 558.
Programming (via satellite): Cinemax (multiplexed).
Fee: $25.00 installation; $12.95 monthly.

Pay Service 2
Pay Units: 717.
Programming (via satellite): HBO (multiplexed).
Fee: $12.95 monthly.

Pay Service 3
Pay Units: 733.
Programming (via satellite): Showtime (multiplexed).
Fee: $12.95 monthly.

Pay Service 4
Pay Units: N.A.
Programming (via satellite): MOVIEplex; Starz!; The Movie Channel; The New Encore.
Fee: $12.95 monthly (TMC), $12.95 monthly (Starz, Encore & MOVIEplex).

Pay-Per-View
Spice.

Local advertising: Yes. Available in locally originated programming. Local sales manager: Wisconsin Information Network.
Equipment: Scientific-Atlanta headend; Jerrold amplifiers; Comm/Scope cable; JVC VTRs; Portac character generator; Pioneer & Scientific-Atlanta set top converters; Eagle traps; Scientific-Atlanta satellite antenna; Scientific-Atlanta satellite receivers.
Miles of plant: 34.0 (coaxial). Homes passed: 5,459.
Manager: Marty Robinson. Chief technician: Joe Browning. Marketing director: Danette Knickmeier.
City fee: 3% of gross.
Ownership: Charter Communications Inc. (MSO). Purchased from Marcus Cable, April 1, 1999.

WILTON—Triax Cablevision, Box 110, 1504 2nd St. SE, Waseca, MN 56093. Phones: 507-835-5975; 800-332-0245. Fax: 507-835-4567. County: Monroe. ICA: WI0302.
TV Market Ranking: Below 100. Franchise award date: N.A. Franchise expiration date: N.A. Began: N.A.
Channel capacity: 21 (not 2-way capable). Channels available but not in use: 3.

Basic Service
Subscribers: 182.
Programming (received off-air): WEAU-TV (N) Eau Claire; WHLA-TV (P), WKBT (C), WLAX (F), WXOW-TV (A) La Crosse; WKOW-TV (A), WMSN-TV (F), WMTV (N) Madison.
Fee: $35.16 installation; $9.10 monthly; $1.58 converter.

Expanded Basic Service
Subscribers: 179.
Programming (via satellite): WGN-TV (W) Chicago; A & E; CNN; Discovery Channel; ESPN; Fox Family Channel; Nashville Network; TBS Superstation; Turner Network TV; USA Network.
Fee: $14.85 monthly.

Pay Service 1
Pay Units: 49.
Programming (via satellite): Disney Channel; HBO.
Fee: $7.00 monthly (Disney), 11.00 monthly (HBO).

Miles of plant: 6.9 (coaxial). Homes passed: 190.
Manager: Richard Giffen. Chief technician: Scott Walters.
Ownership: Triax Telecommunications Co. LLC (MSO). See Cable System Ownership.

WISCONSIN RAPIDS—Charter Communications Inc., 2140 8th St. S., Wisconsin Rapids, WI 54494. Phones: 715-424-2424; 800-581-0081. Fax: 715-423-1885. Counties: Portage & Wood. Also serves Biron, Grand Rapids, Grant, Nekoosa, Port Edwards, Port Edwards (village), Rudolph (town), Saratoga, Seneca. ICA: WI0022.
TV Market Ranking: Below 100 (Rudolph, Saratoga); Outside TV Markets (Biron, Grand Rapids, Grant, Nekoosa, Port Edwards, Seneca, Wisconsin Rapids). Franchise award date: February 1, 1974. Franchise expiration date: December 12, 2000. Began: February 1, 1972.
Channel capacity: 54 (2-way capable; operating 2-way). Channels available but not in use: 12.

Basic Service
Subscribers: 11,930.
Programming (received off-air): WEAU-TV (N) Eau Claire; WFRV-TV (C), WLUK-TV (F) Green Bay; WAOW-TV (A), WHRM-TV (P), WJFW-TV (N), WSAW-TV (C) Wausau-Rhinelander.
Programming (via satellite): WGN-TV (W) Chicago; Animal Planet; C-SPAN; TBS Superstation.
Current originations: Automated time-weather; public access; educational access; government access; religious access.
Fee: $60.48 installation; $7.67 monthly.

Expanded Basic Service
Subscribers: 11,500.
Programming (via satellite): A & E; American Movie Classics; Bravo; C-SPAN 2; CNBC; CNN; Comedy Central; Country Music TV; Court TV; Discovery Channel; ESPN; ESPN 2; ESPNews; EWTN; Fox Family Channel; Headline News; History Channel; Home & Garden Television; Home Shopping Network; Learning Channel; Lifetime; MSNBC; MTV; Midwest Sports Channel; Nashville Network; Nick at Nite's TV Land; Nickelodeon; QVC; Sci-Fi Channel; TV Guide Channel; The Weather Channel; Toon Disney; Turner Network TV; USA Network; VH1.
Fee: $21.18 monthly.

Expanded Basic Service 2
Subscribers: N.A.
Programming (via satellite): Cartoon Network; MOVIEplex; Outdoor Life Network; Starz!; The New Encore; Turner Classic Movies.
Fee: $7.95 monthly.

Pay Service 1
Pay Units: 1,680.
Programming (via satellite): Cinemax (multiplexed).
Fee: $10.00 installation; $12.95 monthly.

Pay Service 2
Pay Units: 2,160.
Programming (via satellite): HBO (multiplexed).
Fee: $10.00 installation; $12.95 monthly.

Pay Service 3
Pay Units: 1,425.
Programming (via satellite): Showtime (multiplexed).
Fee: $10.00 installation; $12.95 monthly.

Pay Service 4
Pay Units: N.A.
Programming (via satellite): DMX; The Movie Channel.
Fee: $10.00 installation; $9.95 monthly (DMX), $12.95 monthly (TMC).

Pay-Per-View
Spice; Spice2; movies.

Local advertising: Yes. Available in satellite distributed, locally originated & automated programming. Rates: $38.00/Minute; $19.00/30 Seconds. Local sales manager: John Welton.
Equipment: Scientific-Atlanta headend; Theta-Com amplifiers; Times Fiber cable; Panasonic cameras; Sony VTRs; Compuvid character generator; Oak set top converters; Arcom traps; Scientific-Atlanta satellite antenna; Microdyne satellite receivers; ChannelMatic commercial insert.
Miles of plant: 330.0 (coaxial). Homes passed: 15,085. Total homes in franchised area: 15,500.
Manager: Larry Kraklau. Chief technician: Bruce Wasleske. Marketing director: Susan Jirgl.
City fee: 2.5% of basic.
Ownership: Charter Communications Inc. (MSO). Purchased from Marcus Cable, April 1, 1999.

WITTENBERG—Wittenberg Cable TV, Box 309, 104 W. Walker, Wittenberg, WI 54499. Phone: 715-253-2828. Fax: 715-253-3497. County: Shawano. Also serves Bevent, Eland, Galloway, Hatley. ICA: WI0158.
TV Market Ranking: Below 100. Franchise award date: March 30, 1980. Franchise expiration date: March 15, 2000. Began: March 15, 1982.
Channel capacity: 36 (not 2-way capable). Channels available but not in use: 2.

Basic Service
Subscribers: 771; Commercial subscribers: 82.
Programming (received off-air): WBAY-TV (A), WFRV-TV (C), WGBA (N), WLUK-TV (F) Green Bay; WAOW-TV (A), WHRM-TV (P), WJFW-TV (N), WSAW-TV (C) Wausau-Rhinelander.
Programming (via satellite): WGN-TV (W) Chicago; A & E; Bloomberg Information News Service; CNN; Country Music TV; Discovery Channel; Disney Channel; ESPN; ESPN 2; Fox Family Channel; History Channel; Home Shopping Network; Learning Channel; MTV; Nashville Network; Nickelodeon; TBS Superstation; Turner Network TV; USA Network; VH1.
Fee: $35.00 installation; $19.60 monthly; $15.00 additional installation.
Commercial fee: $6.39 monthly.

Pay Service 1
Pay Units: 194.
Programming (via satellite): HBO.
Fee: $7.50 installation; $9.90 monthly.

Local advertising: No.
Equipment: Drake, Scientific-Atlanta & Cadco headend; Jerrold amplifiers; Times Fiber & Comm/Scope cable; Oak & Regal set top converters; Arcom traps; Scientific-Atlanta & Prodelin satellite antenna; Drake & Scientific-Atlanta satellite receivers.
Miles of plant: 19.0 (coaxial); 19.0 (fiber optic). Additional miles planned: 15.5 (coaxial); 10.5 (fiber optic). Homes passed: 1,005.
Manager: Allen Mahnke.
City fee: None.
Ownership: Wittenberg Telephone Co.

WOLF RIVER—Cable Systems Management of Iowa Inc., 3600 Kennebec Dr., Eagan, MN 55122. Phone: 612-688-2623. Fax: 612-688-2624. County: Winnebago. ICA: WI0185.
TV Market Ranking: Below 100. Franchise award date: N.A. Franchise expiration date: N.A. Began: N.A.
Channel capacity: 40. Channels available but not in use: 19.

Basic Service
Subscribers: 57.
Programming (received off-air): WACY (U) Appleton; WBAY-TV (A), WFRV-TV (C), WGBA (N), WLUK-TV (F), WPNE (P) Green Bay.
Programming (via satellite): WGN-TV (W) Chicago; A & E; American Movie Classics; CNN; Country Music TV; Discovery Channel; Fox Family Channel; Nashville Network; Showtime; TBS Superstation; Turner Network TV; USA Network.
Fee: $50.00 installation; $30.00 monthly.

Miles of plant: 6.7 (coaxial). Homes passed: 298.
Manager: Jeff Anderson.
Ownership: Cable Systems Management of Iowa Inc. (MSO).

WONEWOC—Spring Green CableComm, Box 609, 245 S. Winsted St., Spring Green, WI 53588-9431. Phone: 608-588-7454. Fax: 608-588-7067. County: Juneau. Also serves Union Center. ICA: WI0149.
TV Market Ranking: Outside TV Markets. Franchise award date: January 1, 1963. Franchise expiration date: August 1, 2001. Began: May 1, 1964.
Channel capacity: 42 (2-way capable). Channels available but not in use: 12.

Basic Service
Subscribers: 466.
Programming (received off-air): WEAU-TV (N) Eau Claire; WKBT (C) La Crosse; WHA-TV (P), WISC-TV (C), WKOW-TV (A), WMSN-TV (F), WMTV (N) Madison.
Programming (via satellite): WGN-TV (W) Chicago; A & E; CNN; Discovery Channel; ESPN; Fox Family Channel; Headline News; Home Shopping Network; Nashville Network; Nickelodeon; TBS Superstation; Turner Classic Movies; Turner Network TV; USA Network.
Fee: $49.95 installation; $29.85 monthly; $19.95 additional installation.

Pay Service 1
Pay Units: N.A.
Programming (via satellite): HBO.
Fee: $19.95 installation; $9.95 monthly.

Equipment: Scientific-Atlanta headend; Scientific-Atlanta amplifiers; M/A-Com cable; Pico traps; Harris satellite antenna; Scientific-Atlanta satellite receivers.
Miles of plant: 9.3 (coaxial). Homes passed: 480.
Manager: Kevin Mayne. Chief technician: Tad Peak. Customer service manager: Liz Reuter.
City fee: None.
Ownership: Fanch Communications Inc. (MSO). See Cable System Ownership.

WOODMAN—Woodman TV Cable System, 207 Spencer, Woodman, WI 53827-0087. Phone: 608-533-2771. County: Grant. ICA: WI0300.
TV Market Ranking: Outside TV Markets. Franchise award date: N.A. Franchise expiration date: N.A. Began: May 1, 1966.
Channel capacity: 12 (not 2-way capable). Channels available but not in use: 3.

Basic Service
Subscribers: 48.
Programming (received off-air): KCRG-TV (A), KRIN (P) Cedar Rapids-Waterloo; KFXB (F) Dubuque; WKBT (C) La Crosse; WHA-TV (P), WISC-TV (C), WKOW-TV (A), WMTV (N) Madison; KTTC (N) Rochester; allband FM.
Fee: $10.00 installation; $6.00 monthly.

Equipment: Blonder-Tongue headend; Magnavox amplifiers; Comm/Scope cable.
Miles of plant: 3.0 (coaxial). Homes passed: 48.
Manager: Jerome Mazera.
Ownership: Woodman TV Cable System.

WYOMING

Total Systems: 60
Total Communities Served: 124
Franchises Not Yet Operating: 0
Applications Pending: 0

Communities with Applications: 0
Number of Basic Subscribers: 118,793
Number of Expanded Basic Subscribers: 78,957
Number of Pay Units: 72,570

Top 100 Markets Represented: None.

For a list of all cable communities included in this section, see the Cable Community Index located in the back of this volume.
For explanation of terms used in cable system listings, see p. D-9.

AFTON—Blackstone Cable LLC, 1104 Ironwood Dr., Coeur d'Alene, ID 83814. Phone: 208-664-3370. Fax: 208-664-5888. County: Lincoln. ICA: WY0030.

TV Market Ranking: Outside TV Markets. Franchise award date: N.A. Franchise expiration date: July 1, 2009. Began: November 1, 1982.

Channel capacity: 20 (not 2-way capable). Channels available but not in use: None.

Basic Service

Subscribers: 333.

Programming (received off-air): KTWO-TV (N,W) Casper; KUSA-TV (N) Denver; KIDK (C), KIFI-TV (A) Idaho Falls-Pocatello.

Programming (via microwave): KRMA-TV (P) Denver.

Programming (via satellite): WGN-TV (W) Chicago; A & E; American Movie Classics; CNN; Discovery Channel; Disney Channel; ESPN; ESPN 2; Fox Family Channel; Fox News Channel; History Channel; Nashville Network; Nickelodeon; QVC; TBS Superstation; The Weather Channel; Turner Network TV; USA Network.

Fee: $35.00 installation; $27.55 monthly; $21.50 additional installation.

Pay Service 1

Pay Units: 18.

Programming (via satellite): HBO.

Fee: $12.95 monthly.

Pay Service 2

Pay Units: 23.

Programming (via satellite): Showtime.

Fee: $12.95 monthly.

Pay Service 3

Pay Units: 27.

Programming (via satellite): The Movie Channel.

Fee: $12.95 monthly.

Pay-Per-View

Addressable homes: 295.

Local advertising: No.

Miles of plant: 14.0 (coaxial). Homes passed: 632.

Manager: Ted W. Hughett. Technical manager: George Norcutt.

City fee: 1.5% of basic.

Ownership: Blackstone Cable LLC (MSO).

BIG PINEY—Blackstone Cable LLC, 1104 Ironwood Dr., Coeur d'Alene, ID 83814. Phone: 208-664-3370. Fax: 208-664-5888. County: Sublette. Also serves Marbleton. ICA: WY0037.

TV Market Ranking: Outside TV Markets. Franchise award date: N.A. Franchise expiration date: July 6, 2005. Began: January 1, 1979.

Channel capacity: 27 (not 2-way capable). Channels available but not in use: None.

Basic Service

Subscribers: 173.

Programming (received off-air): KTWO-TV (N,W) Casper; KSL-TV (N), KTVX (A), KUED (P), KUTV (C) Salt Lake City.

Programming (via microwave): KRMA-TV (P) Denver.

Programming (via satellite): WGN-TV (W) Chicago; ESPN; FoxNet; TBS Superstation; USA Network.

Fee: $35.00 installation; $11.95 monthly; $21.50 additional installation.

Expanded Basic Service

Subscribers: 142.

Programming (via satellite): KCNC-TV (C), KMGH-TV (A) Denver; A & E; Bravo; CNBC; CNN; Country Music TV; Discovery Channel; Disney Channel; FX; Fox Family Channel; Fox News Channel; Nashville Network; Nickelodeon; QVC; The Weather Channel; Turner Network TV.

Fee: N.A.

Pay Service 1

Pay Units: 13.

Programming (via satellite): HBO.

Fee: N.A.

Pay Service 2

Pay Units: 36.

Programming (via satellite): Showtime.

Fee: $12.95 monthly.

Pay Service 3

Pay Units: 17.

Programming (via satellite): The Movie Channel.

Fee: $12.95 monthly.

Local advertising: No.

Miles of plant: 24.0 (coaxial). Homes passed: 330.

Manager: Ted W. Hughett. Technical manager: George Norcutt.

City fee: 1% of gross.

Ownership: Blackstone Cable LLC (MSO).

BUFFALO—TCI Cablevision of Wyoming Inc., 410 W. Boxelder Rd., Gillette, WY 82718. Phones: 307-682-4303; 800-788-9457. Fax: 307-682-9631. County: Johnson. Also serves Johnson County. ICA: WY0019.

TV Market Ranking: Below 100 (Buffalo, portions of Johnson County); Outside TV Markets (portions of Johnson County). Franchise award date: N.A. Franchise expiration date: N.A. Began: April 1, 1964.

Channel capacity: 36 (not 2-way capable). Channels available but not in use: 5.

Basic Service

Subscribers: 1,460.

Programming (received off-air): KGWC-TV (C), KTWO-TV (N,W) Casper; KSGW-TV (A) Sheridan; 5 FMs.

Programming (via satellite): KCNC-TV (C), KDVR (F), KMGH-TV (A), KRMA-TV (P), KUSA-TV (N), KWGN-TV (W) Denver; FX; Intro TV; Lifetime; QVC.

Current originations: Automated time-weather.

Fee: $30.11 installation; $11.03 monthly; $15.04 additional installation.

Pay Service 1

Pay Units: 143.

Programming (via satellite): Disney Channel.

Fee: $14.95 installation; $9.95 monthly.

Pay Service 2

Pay Units: 316.

Programming (via satellite): HBO.

Fee: $14.95 installation; $11.20 monthly.

Pay Service 3

Pay Units: 469.

Programming (via satellite): The New Encore.

Fee: N.A.

Equipment: Jerrold & Tocom headend; Cascade & Tocom amplifiers; Vikoa cable; Andrew satellite antenna.

Miles of plant: 31.0 (coaxial); None (fiber optic). Homes passed: 1,565. Total homes in franchised area: 1,565.

Manager: Joe Conway. Chief technician: Richard Kuhn. Customer service manager: Doris Linderman.

City fee: 2% of gross.

Ownership: AT&T Broadband & Internet Services (MSO). Purchased from Tele-Communications Inc., March 9, 1999.

BURNS—B & C Cablevision Inc., 4683 Hwy. 6, Wiggins, CO 80654. Phone: 307-547-3328. Fax: 970-483-7822. E-mail: bccable@aol.com. County: Laramie. ICA: WY0070.

TV Market Ranking: Below 100. Franchise award date: August 18, 1994. Franchise expiration date: August 18, 2009. Began: May 1, 1995.

Channel capacity: 36 (not 2-way capable). Channels available but not in use: N.A.

Basic Service

Subscribers: 40.

Programming (received off-air): KGWN-TV (C), KKTU (N,W), KLWY (F) Cheyenne; KDVR (F), KMGH-TV (A), KRMA-TV (P), KUSA-TV (N), KWGN-TV (W) Denver.

Programming (via satellite): WGN-TV (W) Chicago; A & E; CNN; Discovery Channel; Disney Channel; ESPN; Fox Family Channel; Fox Sports Net Rocky Mountain; Nashville Network; TBS Superstation; The Weather Channel; Turner Classic Movies; Turner Network TV; USA Network.

Current originations: Automated time-weather.

Fee: $30.00 installation; $23.00 monthly; $3.00 converter.

Pay Service 1

Pay Units: 7.

Programming (via satellite): HBO.

Fee: $10.00 monthly.

Local advertising: No.

Equipment: Jerrold amplifiers; Drake satellite receivers.

Miles of plant: 3.0 (coaxial). Homes passed: 100. Total homes in franchised area: 100.

Manager: Bill Rogers. Chief technician: Harv Humphrey. Marketing director: Carol Rogers.

Franchise fee: 5% of gross.

Ownership: B & C Cablevision Inc. (MSO).

CASPER—TCI Cablevision of Casper, 451 S. Durbin, Casper, WY 82601-2899. Phone: 307-265-3130. Fax: 307-266-6821. County: Natrona. Also serves Bar Nunn, Evansville, Mills, Mountain View (Natrona County), Natrona County, Paradise Valley. ICA: WY0001.

TV Market Ranking: Below 100 (Bar Nunn, Casper, Evansville, Mills, Mountain View, portions of Natrona County, Paradise Valley); Outside TV Markets (portions of Natrona County). Franchise award date: N.A. Franchise expiration date: March 1, 2007. Began: December 24, 1953.

Channel capacity: 43 (2-way capable; operating 2-way). Channels available but not in use: None.

Basic Service

Subscribers: 17,000.

Programming (received off-air): K26ES (I), KFNB (A,F), KGWC-TV (C), KTWO-TV (N,W) Casper; KCWC-TV (P) Lander-Riverton; 6 FMS.

Programming (via satellite): WGN-TV (W) Chicago; KCNC-TV (C), KWGN-TV (W) Denver; C-SPAN; Discovery Channel; Learning Channel; QVC; TBS Superstation; TV Guide Channel; The Weather Channel.

Current originations: Educational access; government access.

Fee: $33.39 installation; $13.77 monthly; $3.00 converter.

Digital Basic Service

Subscribers: N.A.

Programming (via satellite): BBC America; Bravo; Discovery Health Channel; Discovery Kids Channel; Discovery People; Discovery Science Channel; ESPN Classic Sports; ESPNews; Encore Movie Networks; Fox Sports World; Game Show Network; History Channel; Home & Garden Television; Independent Film Channel; MuchMusic Network; Outdoor Life Network; Romance Classics; Sci-Fi Channel; The Barker; Turner Classic Movies.

Fee: N.A.

Expanded Basic Service

Subscribers: 15,600.

Programming (via satellite): A & E; American Movie Classics; Animal Planet; CNBC; CNN; Cartoon Network; Country Music TV; Disney Channel; ESPN; ESPN 2; FX; Fox Family Channel; Fox News Channel; Fox Sports Net Rocky Mountain; Headline News; Lifetime; MTV; Nashville Network; Nickelodeon; Turner Network TV; USA Network.

Fee: $16.78 monthly.

Pay Service 1

Pay Units: 1,411.

Programming (via satellite): Cinemax.

Fee: $2.00 installation; $11.45 monthly.

Pay Service 2

Pay Units: 3,560.

Programming (via satellite): HBO.

Fee: $2.00 installation; $11.45 monthly.

Pay Service 3

Pay Units: 1,203.

Programming (via satellite): Showtime (multiplexed).

Fee: $2.00 installation; $11.45 monthly.

Pay Service 4

Pay Units: N.A.

Programming (via satellite): Starz!; The New Encore.
Fee: N.A.
Digital Pay Service 1
Pay Units: N.A.
Programming (via satellite): HBO; Showtime; The Movie Channel.
Fee: N.A.
Pay-Per-View
Addressable homes: 6,500.
Spice delivered digitally; Viewer's Choice.
Local advertising: Yes (insert only). Available in satellite distributed & character-generated programming. Local sales manager: Paul Wilhelm.
Equipment: Scientific-Atlanta headend; Magnavox amplifiers; Comm/Scope & Times Fiber cable; Tektronix cameras; Sony VTRs; Video Data Systems character generator; Jerrold set top converters; Jerrold addressable set top converters; Andrew & Anixter-Mark satellite antenna.
Miles of plant: 358.8 (coaxial); 20.7 (fiber optic). Homes passed: 26,600. Total homes in franchised area: 26,600.
Manager: Jeff Frankenberger. Chief technician: John Miller.
City fee: 5% of gross.
Ownership: AT&T Broadband & Internet Services (MSO). Purchased from Tele-Communications Inc., March 9, 1999.

CHEYENNE—TCI Cablevision of Wyoming, Box 5389, Cheyenne, WY 82001-4840. Phone: 307-632-8114. Fax: 307-637-5973. Web site: http://www.tci.com. County: Laramie. Also serves Fox Farm College, Laramie County, South Greeley, Warren AFB. ICA: WY0002.
TV Market Ranking: Below 100 (Cheyenne, Fox Farm College, portions of Laramie County, South Greeley, Warren AFB); Outside TV Markets (portions of Laramie County). Franchise award date: N.A. Franchise expiration date: N.A. Began: December 1, 1968.
Channel capacity: 62. Channels available but not in use: N.A.
Basic Service
Subscribers: 23,000.
Programming (received off-air): KGWN-TV (C), KKTU (N,W), KLWY (F) Cheyenne; KCWC-TV (P) Lander-Riverton; 18 FMs.
Programming (via microwave): KCNC-TV (C), KMGH-TV (A), KRMA-TV (P), KUSA-TV (N), KWGN-TV (W) Denver.
Programming (via satellite): C-SPAN; C-SPAN 2; Discovery Channel; Discovery People; FX; Fox News Channel; Learning Channel; Odyssey; QVC; TBS Superstation; TV Guide Channel; Univision; WB 100+ Station Group.
Current originations: Automated time-weather; educational access; local news.
Fee: $60.00 installation; $11.84 monthly; $2.28 converter; $19.67 additional installation.
Digital Basic Service
Subscribers: N.A.
Programming (via satellite): BBC America; BET on Jazz; CNN/SI; Discovery Kids Channel; Discovery Science Channel; ESPN Classic Sports; ESPNews; Fox Sports World; Game Show Network; Golf Channel; Goodlife TV Network; History Channel; History Channel International; Independent Film Channel; Inspirational Life; International Channel; Kaleidoscope; Lifetime Movie Network; Nick at Nite's TV Land; Outdoor Channel; Outdoor Life Network; Ovation; Romance Classics; The Barker; The Biography Channel; The Health Network; Trinity Bcstg. Network; Turner Classic Movies; ZDTV.
Fee: N.A.
Expanded Basic Service
Subscribers: 20,277.
Programming (via satellite): A & E; American Movie Classics; Animal Planet; BET; CNBC; CNN; Cartoon Network; Comedy Central; Court TV; Discovery Channel; Disney Channel; E! Entertainment TV; ESPN; ESPN 2; Fox Family Channel; Fox Sports Net Rocky Mountain; Great American Country; Headline News; Home & Garden Television; Home Shopping Network; Lifetime; MSNBC; MTV; Nashville Network; Nickelodeon; Pax Net; Sci-Fi Channel; TV Food Network; The Weather Channel; Turner Network TV; USA Network; VH1.
Fee: $20.00 monthly.
Pay Service 1
Pay Units: 1,973.
Programming (via satellite): Cinemax.
Fee: $13.20 monthly.
Pay Service 2
Pay Units: 5,825.
Programming (via satellite): HBO.
Fee: $13.95 monthly.
Pay Service 3
Pay Units: 2,232.
Programming (via satellite): Showtime.
Fee: $13.20 monthly.
Pay Service 4
Pay Units: 10,424.
Programming (via satellite): The New Encore.
Fee: $1.75 monthly.
Pay Service 5
Pay Units: N.A.
Programming (via satellite): Starz!
Fee: $6.99 monthly.
Digital Pay Service 1
Pay Units: N.A.
Programming (via satellite): Bravo; DMX; Encore Love Stories; Encore Mystery; Encore Westerns; HBO (multiplexed); Showtime (multiplexed); Starz! (multiplexed); The Movie Channel.
Fee: N.A.
Pay-Per-View
Action PPV delivered digitally; Hot Choice delivered digitally; Playboy TV delivered digitally; Spice delivered digitally; Spice2 delivered digitally; Viewer's Choice Digital.
Local advertising: Yes.
Program Guide: The Cable Guide.
Equipment: Jerrold headend; Jerrold amplifiers; Times Fiber cable; Megadata character generator; Scientific-Atlanta satellite antenna.
Miles of plant: 382.4 (coaxial). Homes passed: 26,111.
Manager: Sandy Marquette. Chief technician: J. R. Johnston.
City fee: 2% of gross.
Ownership: AT&T Broadband & Internet Services (MSO). Purchased from Tele-Communications Inc., March 9, 1999.

CODY—TCI Cablevision of Wyoming, 2432 Sheridan Ave., Cody, WY 82414-4004. Phone: 307-587-2219. Fax: 307-587-5912. County: Park. Also serves Park County. ICA: WY0010.
TV Market Ranking: Outside TV Markets. Franchise award date: N.A. Franchise expiration date: N.A. Began: October 1, 1954.
Channel capacity: 37. Channels available but not in use: N.A.
Basic Service
Subscribers: 3,119.
Programming (via microwave): KTWO-TV (N,W) Casper; KSL-TV (N) Salt Lake City.
Programming (via translator): KTVQ (C), KULR-TV (N) Billings.
Programming (via satellite): KCNC-TV (C), KRMA-TV (P), KUSA-TV (N), KWGN-TV (W) Denver; C-SPAN; CNBC; CNN; Comedy Central; Discovery Channel; Fox Family Channel; FoxNet; Headline News; Knowledge TV; Lifetime; MTV; Nashville Network; Odyssey; QVC; TBS Superstation; The Weather Channel; VH1.
Current originations: Automated time-weather; local news.
Fee: $25.00 installation; $17.80 monthly; $3.00 converter.
Expanded Basic Service
Subscribers: 2,863.
Programming (via satellite): American Movie Classics; Court TV; ESPN; Fox Sports Net; Turner Network TV; USA Network.
Fee: N.A.
Pay Service 1
Pay Units: 139.
Programming (via satellite): Cinemax.
Fee: $13.20 monthly.
Pay Service 2
Pay Units: 215.
Programming (via satellite): Disney Channel.
Fee: $11.95 monthly.
Pay Service 3
Pay Units: 506.
Programming (via satellite): HBO.
Fee: $13.20 monthly.
Pay Service 4
Pay Units: 240.
Programming (via satellite): Showtime.
Fee: $13.20 monthly.
Pay Service 5
Pay Units: 1,188.
Programming (via satellite): The New Encore.
Fee: N.A.
Program Guide: The Cable Guide.
Equipment: Jerrold headend; Jerrold amplifiers; Times Fiber cable; Hughes satellite antenna.
Miles of plant: 73.4 (coaxial). Homes passed: 4,026. Total homes in franchised area: 4,026.
Manager: Jackie Valandingham. Chief technician: Dan Higgins.
City fee: 3% of gross.
Ownership: AT&T Broadband & Internet Services (MSO). Purchased from Tele-Communications Inc., March 9, 1999.

COKEVILLE—All West Inc., Box 588, 50 West 100 North, Kamas, UT 84036. Phone: 801-783-4371. County: Lincoln. ICA: WY0054.
TV Market Ranking: Outside TV Markets. Franchise award date: N.A. Franchise expiration date: N.A. Began: May 1, 1983.
Channel capacity: 22 (not 2-way capable). Channels available but not in use: None.
Basic Service
Subscribers: 174.
Programming (received off-air): KSL-TV (N), KSTU (F), KTVX (A), KUED (P), KUTV (C) Salt Lake City.
Programming (via satellite): WGN-TV (W) Chicago; American Movie Classics; CNN; Discovery Channel; ESPN; Fox Family Channel; Fox Sports Net; Nashville Network; Nickelodeon; TBS Superstation; Turner Network TV; USA Network.
Fee: $30.00 installation; $9.95 monthly.
Pay Service 1
Pay Units: 55.
Programming (via satellite): Disney Channel.
Fee: $9.95 monthly.
Pay Service 2
Pay Units: 39.
Programming (via satellite): HBO.
Fee: $12.00 monthly.
Miles of plant: 8.4 (coaxial); 15.0 (fiber optic). Homes passed: 200. Total homes in franchised area: 220.
Manager: Vernile Prince. Chief technician: Kelly Hoffman.
Ownership: All West/Utah Inc. (MSO).

COWLEY—Cowley Telecable Inc., Box 687, Cowley, WY 82420. Phone: 307-548-6457. Fax: 307-548-2728. County: Big Horn. ICA: WY0043.
TV Market Ranking: Outside TV Markets. Franchise award date: June 1, 1982. Franchise expiration date: N.A. Began: January 1, 1983.
Channel capacity: 12. Channels available but not in use: 3.
Basic Service
Subscribers: 114.
Programming (received off-air): KTVQ (C), KULR-TV (N) Billings; KTWO-TV (N,W) Casper; KHMT (F) Hardin.
Programming (via satellite): WGN-TV (W) Chicago; CNN; Discovery Channel; Disney Channel; ESPN; History Channel; Learning Channel; Nashville Network; Odyssey; TBS Superstation; Turner Classic Movies; Turner Network TV; USA Network.
Fee: $35.00 installation; $19.95 monthly.
Pay Service 1
Pay Units: N.A.
Programming (via satellite): HBO.
Fee: $11.95 monthly.
Miles of plant: 8.7 (coaxial). Additional miles planned: 1.0 (coaxial). Homes passed: 200. Total homes in franchised area: 200.
Manager: Jerri Townsend. Chief technician: Tim Townsend.
City fee: 1% of gross.
Ownership: Cowley Telecable Inc. (MSO).

DOUGLAS—CommuniComm Services, Suite A, 1135 College Ave., Fort Collins, CO 80524. Phone: 800-759-8448. County: Converse. ICA: WY0012.
TV Market Ranking: Outside TV Markets. Franchise award date: November 1, 1973. Franchise expiration date: N.A. Began: October 1, 1975.
Channel capacity: 75 (2-way capable; operating 2-way). Channels available but not in use: 14.
Basic Service
Subscribers: 1,803; Commercial subscribers: 426.
Programming (received off-air): KGWC-TV (C), KTWO-TV (N,W) Casper.
Programming (via microwave): KCNC-TV (C), KMGH-TV (A), KRMA-TV (P), KUSA-TV (N), KWGN-TV (W) Denver.
Programming (via satellite): WGN-TV (W) Chicago; A & E; American Movie Classics; Animal Planet; C-SPAN; C-SPAN 2; CNBC; CNN; Cartoon Network; Comedy Central; Country Music TV; Discovery Channel; Disney Channel; E! Entertainment TV; ESPN; ESPN 2; ESPNews; Fox Family Channel; Fox Sports Net; Headline News; History Channel; Home & Garden Television; Learning Channel; Lifetime; MTV; Nashville Network; Nickelodeon; Outdoor Life Network; QVC; Sci-Fi Channel; TBS Superstation; TV Guide Channel; The Weather Channel; Trinity Bcstg. Network; Turner Network TV; USA Network; VH1.
Current originations: Public access; leased access.
Fee: $32.95 installation; $31.95 monthly; $2.95 converter.
Commercial fee: $4.50 monthly.
Pay Service 1
Pay Units: 207.
Programming (via satellite): Cinemax.

Fee: $10.95 monthly.
Pay Service 2
Pay Units: 491.
Programming (via satellite): HBO.
Fee: $12.95 monthly.
Equipment: Jerrold headend; Jerrold amplifiers; Comm/Scope cable; Andrew satellite antenna.
Miles of plant: 32.0 (coaxial). Homes passed: 2,800.
Manager: Alan Price. Marketing director: Tracy Clodfelter.
City fee: 2% of gross.
Ownership: James Cable Partners (MSO).

DUBOIS—Blackstone Cable LLC, 1104 Ironwood Dr., Coeur d'Alene, ID 83814. Phone: 208-664-3370. Fax: 208-664-5888. County: Fremont. ICA: WY0040.
TV Market Ranking: Outside TV Markets. Franchise award date: N.A. Franchise expiration date: July 1, 2006. Began: March 17, 1972.
Channel capacity: 23 (not 2-way capable). Channels available but not in use: None.
Basic Service
Subscribers: 170.
Programming (received off-air): KTWO-TV (N,W) Casper; KCWC-TV (P) Lander-Riverton; 1 FM.
Programming (via microwave): KCNC-TV (C), KMGH-TV (A), KUSA-TV (N) Denver.
Programming (via satellite): WGN-TV (W) Chicago; A & E; Bravo; CNN; Discovery Channel; Disney Channel; ESPN; ESPN 2; Fox Family Channel; FoxNet; History Channel; Nashville Network; QVC; TBS Superstation; The Weather Channel; Turner Network TV; USA Network.
Fee: $35.00 installation; $27.55 monthly; $21.50 additional installation.
Pay Service 1
Pay Units: 13.
Programming (via satellite): The Movie Channel.
Fee: $5.00 installation; $12.95 monthly.
Pay Service 2
Pay Units: 16.
Programming (via satellite): Showtime.
Fee: $5.00 installation; $12.95 monthly.
Pay Service 3
Pay Units: 7.
Programming (via satellite): HBO.
Fee: $12.95 monthly.
Local advertising: No.
Equipment: Blonder-Tongue headend; Theta-Com amplifiers; Comm/Scope cable; Telemation cameras; Ampex VTRs; Prodelin satellite antenna.
Miles of plant: 9.9 (coaxial). Homes passed: 498.
Manager: Ted Hughett. Technical manager: George Norcutt.
City fee: 2% of gross.
Ownership: Blackstone Cable LLC (MSO).

EDGERTON—Tongue River Cable TV, Box 759, Ranchester, WY 82839. Phone: 307-655-9011. Fax: 307-655-9021. County: Natrona. Also serves Midwest. ICA: WY0032.
TV Market Ranking: Outside TV Markets. Franchise award date: September 17, 1979. Franchise expiration date: N.A. Began: August 1, 1980.
Channel capacity: 42 (not 2-way capable). Channels available but not in use: 9.
Basic Service
Subscribers: 144.
Programming (received off-air): KFNB (A,F), KGWC-TV (C), KTWO-TV (N,W) Casper.
Programming (via satellite): WGN-TV (W) Chicago; KRMA-TV (P) Denver; WWOR-TV (U) New York; A & E; American Movie Classics; Animal Planet; C-SPAN; CNN; Country Music TV; Discovery Channel; Disney Channel; E! Entertainment TV; ESPN; ESPN 2; Fox Family Channel; FoxNet; Headline News; History Channel; Learning Channel; Lifetime; MTV; Nashville Network; Nickelodeon; Outdoor Channel; QVC; TBS Superstation; The Weather Channel; Turner Network TV; USA Network.
Fee: $40.00 installation; $26.50 monthly; $15.00 additional installation.
Pay Service 1
Pay Units: 104.
Programming (via satellite): Cinemax; HBO; The New Encore.
Fee: $10.00 installation; $3.50 monthly (Encore), $8.50 monthly (Cinemax), $11.00 monthly (HBO).
Equipment: Scientific-Atlanta headend; Magnavox amplifiers; CCS Hatfield & Times Fiber cable; Eagle traps; Scientific-Atlanta & Prodelin satellite antenna; Scientific-Atlanta satellite receivers.
Miles of plant: 10.0 (coaxial). Homes passed: 450. Total homes in franchised area: 450.
Manager: Robert R. Jacobson.
City fee: 1% of gross over 400 subscribers.
Ownership: Lynda & Robert Jacobson (MSO).

EVANSTON—Century Communications, 1020 Main St., Evanston, WY 82930. Phones: 307-789-6138; 800-626-6299. Fax: 307-789-7754. Web site: http://www.centurycomm.com. County: Uinta. Also serves Uinta County (portions). ICA: WY0009.
TV Market Ranking: Outside TV Markets. Franchise award date: N.A. Franchise expiration date: August 24, 2002. Began: January 1, 1978.
Channel capacity: N.A. (not 2-way capable). Channels available but not in use: N.A.
Basic Service
Subscribers: 3,216.
Programming (via microwave): KTWO-TV (N,W) Casper; KJZZ-TV (U), KSL-TV (N), KSTU (F), KTVX (A), KUED (P), KUTV (C) Salt Lake City.
Programming (via satellite): WGN-TV (W) Chicago; A & E; American Movie Classics; Animal Planet; C-SPAN; CNBC; CNN; Country Music TV; Discovery Channel; Disney Channel; E! Entertainment TV; ESPN; ESPN 2; Fox News Channel; Headline News; History Channel; Learning Channel; Lifetime; MSNBC; MTV; Nickelodeon; Odyssey; Outdoor Life Network; QVC; Sci-Fi Channel; The Weather Channel; Toon Disney; USA Network; VH1.
Fee: $30.00 installation; $22.83 monthly; $1.65 converter.
Expanded Basic Service
Subscribers: N.A.
Programming (via satellite): Fox Family Channel; Nashville Network; TBS Superstation; Turner Network TV.
Fee: N.A.
Pay Service 1
Pay Units: 1,000.
Programming (via satellite): Cinemax; HBO.
Fee: $11.00 monthly (each).
Local advertising: No.
Equipment: Scientific-Atlanta headend; Oak set top converters.
Miles of plant: 88.0 (coaxial); None (fiber optic). Homes passed: 4,800.
Manager: Rick Darr. Chief technician: Tom Boley. Marketing director: Lavonda Short.
Ownership: Century Communications Corp. (MSO). See Cable System Ownership.

GARDENS NORTH—Galaxy Cablevision, 316 S. Lincoln Ave., York, NE 68467. Phone: 800-365-6988. County: Fremont. Also serves Riverton. ICA: WY0069.
TV Market Ranking: Below 100. Franchise award date: N.A. Franchise expiration date: February 23, 2001. Began: N.A.
Channel capacity: 15. Channels available but not in use: None.
Basic Service
Subscribers: 47.
Programming (received off-air): KSVI (A,F) Billings; KTWO-TV (N,W) Casper; KCWC-TV (P), KFNE (A), KGWL-TV (C) Lander-Riverton.
Programming (via satellite): WGN-TV (W) Chicago; CNN; Disney Channel; ESPN; Fox Family Channel; Nashville Network; TBS Superstation; USA Network.
Fee: $24.10 monthly.
Pay Service 1
Pay Units: N.A.
Programming (via satellite): HBO; The Movie Channel.
Fee: N.A.
Miles of plant: 2.0 (coaxial). Homes passed: 75.
State manager: Dave Walker. Technical manager: Jeff Pischer.
Ownership: Galaxy Cablevision (MSO).

GILLETTE—AT&T Cable Services, 410 W. Boxelder Rd., Gillette, WY 82718-5315. Phones: 307-682-4303; 800-788-9457. Fax: 307-682-9631. County: Campbell. Also serves Campbell County, Sleepy Hollow. ICA: WY0005.
TV Market Ranking: Outside TV Markets. Franchise award date: N.A. Franchise expiration date: February 1, 1998. Began: April 1, 1964.
Channel capacity: 86 (2-way capable; operating 2-way). Channels available but not in use: 6.
Basic Service
Subscribers: 10,013.
Programming (received off-air): KGWC-TV (C), KTWO-TV (N,W) Casper; KEVN-TV (F) Rapid City; KSGW-TV (A) Sheridan; 3 FMs.
Programming (via translator): KCWC-TV (P) Lander-Riverton.
Programming (via satellite): WGN-TV (W) Chicago; KCNC-TV (C), KDVR (F), KMGH-TV (A), KRMA-TV (P), KUSA-TV (N), KWGN-TV (W) Denver; A & E; C-SPAN; CNN; Discovery Channel; FX; Fox Family Channel; Fox News Channel; Game Show Network; Headline News; Home Shopping Network; Knowledge TV; Learning Channel; Lifetime; MSNBC; MTV; Nashville Network; Nickelodeon; Odyssey; Pax Net; QVC; TBS Superstation; TV Guide Channel; The Weather Channel; VH1.
Current originations: Public access; educational access; government access.
Fee: $28.91 installation; $20.14 monthly; $1.53 converter; $14.43 additional installation.
Digital Basic Service
Subscribers: N.A.
Programming (via satellite): BBC America; BET on Jazz; Bravo; CNN/SI; Discovery Civilization Channel; Discovery Health Channel; Discovery Home & Leisure Channel; Discovery Kids Channel; Discovery People; Discovery Science Channel; Discovery Wings Channel; ESPNews; Fox Sports World; Golf Channel; Goodlife TV Network; History Channel International; Independent Film Channel; Inspirational Life; International Channel; Kaleidoscope; Lifetime Movie Network; Nick at Nite's TV Land; Outdoor Channel; Outdoor Life Network; Ovation; Romance Classics; Speedvision; Sundance Channel; The Barker; The Biography Channel; The Health Network; Trinity Bcstg. Network; Turner Classic Movies; ZDTV.
Fee: $13.85 monthly.
Expanded Basic Service
Subscribers: 6,600.
Programming (via satellite): American Movie Classics; Animal Planet; C-SPAN 2; CNBC; Cartoon Network; Comedy Central; Country Music TV; Court TV; Disney Channel; E! Entertainment TV; ESPN; ESPN 2; ESPN Classic Sports; Encore Movie Networks; Fox Sports Net Rocky Mountain; History Channel; Home & Garden Television; Sci-Fi Channel; TV Food Network; The Health Network; Turner Network TV; USA Network.
Fee: $9.21 monthly.
Pay Service 1
Pay Units: 544.
Programming (via satellite): Cinemax.
Fee: $11.93 monthly.
Pay Service 2
Pay Units: 1,390.
Programming (via satellite): HBO.
Fee: $11.93 monthly.
Pay Service 3
Pay Units: 458.
Programming (via satellite): The Movie Channel.
Fee: $11.93 monthly.
Pay Service 4
Pay Units: 598.
Programming (via satellite): Showtime.
Fee: $11.93 monthly.
Pay Service 5
Pay Units: N.A.
Programming (via satellite): Starz!; The New Encore.
Fee: $1.75 monthly (Encore), $6.75 monthly (Starz).
Digital Pay Service 1
Pay Units: N.A.
Programming (via satellite): Cinemax (multiplexed); DMX; Encore Action; Encore Love Stories; Encore Mystery; Encore True Stories & Drama; Encore Westerns; HBO (multiplexed); Showtime (multiplexed); Starz! (multiplexed); The Movie Channel (multiplexed); The New Encore.
Fee: N.A.
Pay-Per-View
Addressable homes: 2,100.
Action PPV delivered digitally; Hot Choice delivered digitally; Playboy TV delivered digitally; Spice delivered digitally; Spice2 delivered digitally; Viewer's Choice Digital; special events.
Local advertising: Yes.
Program Guide: The Cable Guide.
Equipment: RCA headend; C-COR amplifiers; Comm/Scope cable; Jerrold & Panasonic set top converters; Jerrold addressable set top converters; Andrew satellite antenna.
Miles of plant: 233.0 (coaxial); 13.0 (fiber optic). Homes passed: 8,689. Total homes in franchised area: 8,689.
Manager: Joe Conway. Chief technician: Richard Kuhn. Customer service manager: Doris Linderman.
City fee: 2% of gross. County fee: 2% of gross.
Ownership: AT&T Broadband & Internet Services (MSO). Purchased from Tele-Communications Inc., March 9, 1999.

GLENDO—CommuniComm Services, Suite A, 113 S. College Ave., Fort Collins, CO 80524. Phone: 303-224-3325. County: Platte. ICA: WY0055.
TV Market Ranking: Outside TV Markets. Franchise award date: N.A. Franchise expiration date: N.A. Began: N.A.
Channel capacity: 13 (not 2-way capable). Channels available but not in use: N.A.

Basic Service
Subscribers: 68.
Programming (via satellite): KCNC-TV (C), KDVR (F), KMGH-TV (A), KRMA-TV (P), KUSA-TV (N), KWGN-TV (W) Denver; CNN; Discovery Channel; ESPN; Nashville Network; TBS Superstation.
Fee: $19.95 monthly.
Pay Service 1
Pay Units: 11.
Programming (via satellite): Cinemax.
Fee: $10.95 monthly.
Manager: Alan Price.
Ownership: James Cable Partners (MSO).

GLENROCK—CommuniComm Services, Suite A, 1135 College Ave., Fort Collins, CO 80524. Phone: 800-759-8448. County: Converse. Also serves Rolling Hills. ICA: WY0018.
TV Market Ranking: Below 100. Franchise award date: June 1, 1972. Franchise expiration date: N.A. Began: February 3, 1974.
Channel capacity: 45. Channels available but not in use: 3.
Basic Service
Subscribers: 869.
Programming (received off-air): KGWC-TV (C), KTWO-TV (N,W) Casper.
Programming (via microwave): KMGH-TV (A), KRMA-TV (P), KUSA-TV (N), KWGN-TV (W) Denver.
Programming (via satellite): WGN-TV (W) Chicago; A & E; American Movie Classics; Animal Planet; CNN; Cartoon Network; Country Music TV; Discovery Channel; Disney Channel; ESPN; ESPN 2; Fox Family Channel; Fox Sports Net; History Channel; Learning Channel; Lifetime; Nashville Network; Nickelodeon; QVC; Sci-Fi Channel; TBS Superstation; The Weather Channel; Turner Classic Movies; Turner Network TV; USA Network.
Current originations: Public access; leased access.
Fee: $32.95 installation; $32.95 monthly.
Pay Service 1
Pay Units: 141.
Programming (via satellite): Cinemax.
Fee: $10.95 monthly.
Pay Service 2
Pay Units: 170.
Programming (via satellite): HBO.
Fee: $12.95 monthly.
Equipment: Times Fiber cable.
Miles of plant: 28.0 (coaxial). Homes passed: 1,352. Total homes in franchised area: 1,622.
Manager: Alan Price. Marketing director: Tracy Clodfelter.
City fee: 2% of gross.
Ownership: James Cable Partners (MSO).

GRANGER—Union Cable Co., Box 160, Mountain View, WY 82939. Phone: 307-782-6131. Fax: 307-787-7043. County: Sweetwater. ICA: WY0050.
TV Market Ranking: Outside TV Markets. Franchise award date: N.A. Franchise expiration date: N.A. Began: January 1, 1983.
Channel capacity: 12 (not 2-way capable). Channels available but not in use: None.
Basic Service
Subscribers: 35.
Programming (received off-air): KCNC-TV (C), KMGH-TV (A), KRMA-TV (P), KUSA-TV (N) Denver.
Programming (via satellite): CNN; Discovery Channel; ESPN; FoxNet; Nashville Network; TBS Superstation.
Fee: $35.00 installation; $13.00 monthly.
Pay Service 1
Pay Units: 12.
Programming (via satellite): Cinemax.
Fee: $12.50 monthly.
Pay Service 2
Pay Units: 11.
Programming (via satellite): HBO.
Fee: $10.00 monthly.
Pay-Per-View
Addressable homes: 78.
Miles of plant: 3.7 (coaxial); None (fiber optic). Homes passed: 78.
Manager: John Woody. Chief technician: Chuck Fagnant. Marketing director: Gayle T. Walsh.
Ownership: Union Telephone Co. (MSO).

GREEN RIVER—Green River Cable TV Co., 151 E. Flaming Gorge Way, Green River, WY 82935. Phone: 307-875-2506. County: Sweetwater. Also serves James Town, Sweetwater County. ICA: WY0008.
TV Market Ranking: Below 100 (Green River, James Town, portions of Sweetwater County); Outside TV Markets (portions of Sweetwater County). Franchise award date: January 1, 1956. Franchise expiration date: January 1, 2005. Began: October 1, 1958.
Channel capacity: 45 (not 2-way capable). Channels available but not in use: 1.
Basic Service
Subscribers: 4,112.
Programming (received off-air): KGWR-TV (C) Rock Springs; 12 FMs.
Programming (via microwave): KTWO-TV (N,W) Casper; KSL-TV (N), KSTU (F), KTVX (A), KUED (P), KUTV (C) Salt Lake City.
Programming (via satellite): A & E; American Movie Classics; C-SPAN; CNBC; CNN; Country Music TV; Discovery Channel; ESPN; ESPN 2; Fox Family Channel; Fox News Channel; Fox Sports Net; Headline News; History Channel; Learning Channel; Lifetime; MTV; Nashville Network; Nick at Nite; Nickelodeon; Odyssey; QVC; Sci-Fi Channel; TBS Superstation; TV Guide Channel; The Weather Channel; Turner Network TV; USA Network; VH1.
Current originations: Automated time-weather; public access; educational access; government access; religious access; local news; local sports.
Fee: $27.50 installation; $20.95 monthly.
Pay Service 1
Pay Units: 230.
Programming (via satellite): Cinemax.
Fee: $7.95 installation; $9.95 monthly.
Pay Service 2
Pay Units: 1,670.
Programming (via satellite): HBO.
Fee: $12.50 installation; $9.95 monthly.
Pay Service 3
Pay Units: 154.
Programming (via satellite): Showtime.
Fee: $7.95 installation; $9.95 monthly.
Pay Service 4
Pay Units: 57.
Programming (via satellite): Music Choice.
Fee: $7.95 installation; $9.95 monthly.
Pay Service 5
Pay Units: 81.
Programming (via satellite): The New Encore.
Fee: $4.95 installation; $1.95 monthly.
Pay-Per-View
Addressable homes: 500.
Viewer's Choice.
Local advertising: Yes (locally produced). Available in satellite distributed, locally originated & character-generated programming. Rates: $125.00/30 Seconds. Local sales manager: Robin Vesco.
Equipment: General headend; General amplifiers; Times Fiber cable; Sony cameras; Sony VTRs; MSI character generator; General set top converters; Jerrold addressable set top converters; Hamlin traps; Andrew & Prodelin satellite antenna; Standard Communications satellite receivers.
Miles of plant: 56.0 (coaxial). Additional miles planned: 2.0 (coaxial). Homes passed: 5,000. Total homes in franchised area: 5,000.
Manager: Al Carollo Jr. Chief technician: Larry Gessner. Marketing & program director: John Carollo.
City fee: 2% of gross.
Ownership: Sweetwater Cable TV Co. Inc. (MSO).

GREYBULL—TCI Cablevision of Wyoming Inc., Box C, Worland, WY 82401-2606. Phone: 307-347-3244. Fax: 307-347-8349. County: Big Horn. Also serves Basin, Big Horn County. ICA: WY0022.
TV Market Ranking: Below 100 (portions of Big Horn County); Outside TV Markets (Basin, portions of Big Horn County, Greybull). Franchise award date: N.A. Franchise expiration date: N.A. Began: March 1, 1956.
Channel capacity: 42 (not 2-way capable). Channels available but not in use: 2.
Basic Service
Subscribers: 1,155.
Programming (received off-air): KTVQ (C) Billings; 5 FMs.
Programming (via microwave): KULR-TV (A) Billings; KTWO-TV (N,W) Casper.
Programming (via satellite): KCNC-TV (C), KMGH-TV (A), KRMA-TV (P), KWGN-TV (W) Denver; C-SPAN; Discovery Channel; FoxNet; Odyssey; QVC; TBS Superstation; The Weather Channel.
Current originations: Local news.
Fee: $44.95 installation; $13.42 monthly.
Expanded Basic Service
Subscribers: 1,065.
Programming (via satellite): American Movie Classics; Animal Planet; CNBC; CNN; Cartoon Network; Court TV; ESPN; ESPN 2; FX; Fox Family Channel; Fox News Channel; Headline News; Learning Channel; Lifetime; MOVIEplex; Nashville Network; Sci-Fi Channel; Turner Network TV; USA Network.
Fee: $16.09 monthly.
Pay Service 1
Pay Units: 120.
Programming (via satellite): Cinemax.
Fee: $12.95 installation; $12.75 monthly.
Pay Service 2
Pay Units: 123.
Programming (via satellite): Disney Channel.
Fee: $12.50 monthly.
Pay Service 3
Pay Units: 264.
Programming (via satellite): HBO.
Fee: $13.00 monthly.
Pay Service 4
Pay Units: 507.
Programming (via satellite): The New Encore.
Fee: $1.75 monthly.
Pay Service 5
Pay Units: 410.
Programming (via satellite): Starz!
Fee: $6.75 monthly.
Miles of plant: 28.0 (coaxial). Homes passed: 1,248. Total homes in franchised area: 1,248.
Manager: Clint Rodeman.
City fee: 2% of gross.
Ownership: AT&T Broadband & Internet Services (MSO). Purchased from Tele-Communications Inc., March 9, 1999.

GUERNSEY—Guernsey Community TV System, Box 518, Guernsey, WY 82214. Phone: 307-836-2314. Counties: Goshen & Platte. Also serves Fort Laramie, Hartville. ICA: WY0026.
TV Market Ranking: Outside TV Markets. Franchise award date: N.A. Franchise expiration date: N.A. Began: March 16, 1978.
Channel capacity: 21 (not 2-way capable). Channels available but not in use: N.A.
Basic Service
Subscribers: 423.
Programming (received off-air): KTNE-TV (P) Alliance; KTWO-TV (N,W) Casper; KGWN-TV (C) Cheyenne; KDUH-TV (A), KSTF (C) Scottsbluff; 2 FMs.
Programming (via microwave): KCNC-TV (C), KMGH-TV (A), KRMA-TV (P), KUSA-TV (N), KWGN-TV (W) Denver.
Programming (via satellite): CNN; Cartoon Network; ESPN; Fox Family Channel; Headline News; Nashville Network; TBS Superstation; Turner Classic Movies; Turner Network TV; USA Network.
Fee: $25.00 installation; $17.00 monthly.
Pay Service 1
Pay Units: 33.
Programming (via satellite): Disney Channel.
Fee: $20.00 installation; $9.90 monthly.
Pay Service 2
Pay Units: 184.
Programming (via satellite): HBO.
Fee: $20.00 installation; $12.00 monthly.
Local advertising: No.
Equipment: Blonder-Tongue, Jerrold & RCA headend; Jerrold amplifiers; Times Fiber cable; MSI & Texscan character generator; Jerrold set top converters; Intercept traps; Scientific-Atlanta satellite antenna; Scientific-Atlanta satellite receivers.
Miles of plant: 16.1 (coaxial). Homes passed: 796.
Manager: Rose Anderson. Chief technician, marketing & program director: John C. Harrison.
City fee: $200 (Guernsey); $50 (Hartville & Fort Laramie).
Ownership: John C. Harrison (MSO).

HULETT—Tongue River Cable TV Inc., Box 759, Ranchester, WY 82839. Phone: 307-655-9011. Fax: 307-655-9021. County: Crook. ICA: WY0044.
TV Market Ranking: Outside TV Markets. Franchise award date: N.A. Franchise expiration date: January 1, 2002. Began: N.A.
Channel capacity: 42 (not 2-way capable). Channels available but not in use: 7.
Basic Service
Subscribers: 133.
Programming (received off-air): KIVV-TV (F) Lead; KOTA-TV (A) Rapid City.
Programming (via satellite): WGN-TV (W) Chicago; KCNC-TV (C), KRMA-TV (P),

KUSA-TV (N), KWGN-TV (W) Denver; A & E; American Movie Classics; Animal Planet; C-SPAN; CNN; Country Music TV; Discovery Channel; Disney Channel; E! Entertainment TV; ESPN; ESPN 2; Fox Family Channel; Headline News; History Channel; Learning Channel; Lifetime; MTV; Nashville Network; Nickelodeon; Outdoor Channel; QVC; TBS Superstation; The Weather Channel; Trinity Bcstg. Network; Turner Network TV; USA Network.
Fee: $40.00 installation; $27.00 monthly; $15.00 additional installation.
Pay Service 1
Pay Units: 16.
Programming (via satellite): Cinemax.
Fee: $8.50 monthly.
Pay Service 2
Pay Units: 12.
Programming (via satellite): The New Encore.
Fee: $3.50 monthly.
Pay Service 3
Pay Units: 27.
Programming (via satellite): HBO.
Fee: $11.00 monthly.
Miles of plant: 4.0 (coaxial). Homes passed: 170.
Manager: Robert Jacobson.
Ownership: Lynda & Robert Jacobson (MSO).

JACKSON—AT&T Cable Services, Box 2650, 3575 S. Park Dr., Jackson, WY 83001-2650. Phone: 307-733-6030. Fax: 307-733-1805. County: Teton. Also serves Rafter J Ranch, South Park, Teton County, Teton Village, Wilson. ICA: WY0007.
TV Market Ranking: Below 100. Franchise award date: N.A. Franchise expiration date: N.A. Began: December 1, 1954.
Channel capacity: 41 (2-way capable; operating 2-way). Channels available but not in use: N.A.
Basic Service
Subscribers: 4,758.
Programming (received off-air): KTWO-TV (N,W) Casper; KJWY (N) Jackson; KCWC-TV (P) Lander-Riverton; KUED (P), KUTV (C) Salt Lake City; 15 FMs.
Programming (via microwave): KSL-TV (N), KUED (P), KUTV (C) Salt Lake City.
Programming (via translator): KIFI-TV (A) Idaho Falls-Pocatello.
Programming (via satellite): WGN-TV (W) Chicago; WPIX (W) New York; C-SPAN; Discovery Channel; FoxNet; Knowledge TV; TBS Superstation; The Weather Channel; WB 100+ Station Group.
Current originations: Automated time-weather; educational access; government access; local sports.
Fee: $43.50 installation (aerial), $65.00 (underground); $11.64 monthly; $3.50 converter; $21.75 additional installation.
Digital Basic Service
Subscribers: N.A.
Programming (via satellite): BBC America; Box Classic; Box Pulse; Bravo; CNN/SI; Discovery Civilization Channel; Discovery Health Channel; Discovery Home & Leisure Channel; Discovery Kids Channel; Discovery People; Discovery Science Channel; Discovery Wings Channel; ESPN Classic Sports; ESPNews; Fox Sports World; Game Show Network; Golf Channel; Goodlife TV Network; History Channel; Home & Garden Television; Independent Film Channel; Nick at Nite's TV Land; Outdoor Channel; Outdoor Life Network; Romance Classics; Sci-Fi Channel; Speedvision; The Health Network; The Inspirational Network; Trinity Bcstg. Network; Turner Classic Movies; ZDTV.
Fee: $12.95 installation; $10.00 monthly; $3.50 converter.
Expanded Basic Service
Subscribers: 4,176.
Programming (via satellite): A & E; American Movie Classics; Animal Planet; CNBC; CNN; Cartoon Network; Comedy Central; Country Music TV; Disney Channel; ESPN; ESPN 2; FX; Fox Family Channel; Fox News Channel; Fox Sports Net Rocky Mountain; Headline News; Learning Channel; Lifetime; MOVIEplex; MTV; Nashville Network; Nickelodeon; Pax Net; QVC; Turner Network TV; USA Network; VH1.
Fee: $17.94 monthly.
Pay Service 1
Pay Units: 1,041.
Programming (via satellite): HBO.
Fee: $13.70 monthly.
Pay Service 2
Pay Units: 493.
Programming (via satellite): Showtime.
Fee: $13.70 monthly.
Pay Service 3
Pay Units: 1,780.
Programming (via satellite): The New Encore.
Fee: $6.99 monthly.
Pay Service 4
Pay Units: N.A.
Programming (via satellite): Starz!; The Movie Channel.
Fee: $6.99 monthly (Starz), $13.70 monthly (TMC).
Digital Pay Service 1
Pay Units: N.A.
Programming (via satellite): DMX; Encore Love Stories; Encore Mystery; Encore Westerns; HBO (multiplexed); Showtime (multiplexed); Starz! Theater; The Movie Channel.
Fee: N.A.
Pay-Per-View
Playboy TV delivered digitally; Spice delivered digitally; movies delivered digitally.
Local advertising: Yes (locally produced & insert). Available in locally originated, taped & automated programming. Local sales manager: Jeff McDonald.
Program Guide: The Cable Guide.
Equipment: Jerrold headend; Jerrold amplifiers; Times Fiber cable; Jerrold set top converters; Eagle traps; AFC satellite antenna; Microdyne, Scientific-Atlanta & Standard Communications satellite receivers; Texscan commercial insert.
Miles of plant: 174.3 (coaxial). Additional miles planned: 11.0 (coaxial). Homes passed: 5,686. Total homes in franchised area: 6,537.
Manager: David Alexanderson. Chief technician: Tyler Peterson. Office manager: Dolores Coover.
City fee: 2% of gross.
Ownership: AT&T Broadband & Internet Services (MSO). Purchased from Tele-Communications Inc., March 9, 1999.

KEMMERER—Blackstone Cable LLC, 1104 Ironwood Dr., Coeur d'Alene, ID 83814. Phone: 208-664-3370. Fax: 208-664-5888. County: Lincoln. Also serves Diamondville, Frontier, Oakley. ICA: WY0021.
TV Market Ranking: Outside TV Markets. Franchise award date: N.A. Franchise expiration date: October 1, 2006. Began: August 1, 1955.
Channel capacity: 31 (not 2-way capable). Channels available but not in use: None.
Basic Service
Subscribers: 903.
Programming (received off-air): 5 FMs.
Programming (via microwave): KTWO-TV (N,W) Casper; KSL-TV (N), KTVX (A), KUED (P), KUTV (C) Salt Lake City.
Programming (via satellite): ESPN; FoxNet; QVC; TBS Superstation; USA Network.
Current originations: Automated time-weather; public access.
Fee: $35.00 installation; $11.95 monthly; $21.50 additional installation.
Expanded Basic Service
Subscribers: 824.
Programming (via satellite): WGN-TV (W) Chicago; A & E; American Movie Classics; C-SPAN; CNBC; CNN; Country Music TV; Discovery Channel; Disney Channel; ESPN 2; FX; Fox Family Channel; Fox News Channel; History Channel; Lifetime; MTV; Nashville Network; Nickelodeon; Sci-Fi Channel; The Weather Channel; Turner Classic Movies; Turner Network TV.
Fee: N.A.
Pay Service 1
Pay Units: 87.
Programming (via satellite): The Movie Channel.
Fee: $10.00 installation; $12.95 monthly.
Pay Service 2
Pay Units: 173.
Programming (via satellite): Showtime.
Fee: $10.00 installation; $12.95 monthly.
Pay Service 3
Pay Units: 96.
Programming (via satellite): HBO.
Fee: $10.00 installation; $12.95 monthly.
Local advertising: No.
Equipment: Anaconda & Catel headend; Jerrold & GTE Sylvania amplifiers; Times Fiber cable; Andrew satellite antenna.
Miles of plant: 28.0 (coaxial). Homes passed: 1,259. Total homes in franchised area: 1,791.
Manager: Ted W. Hughett. Technical manager: George Norcutt.
City fee: 2% of gross.
Ownership: Blackstone Cable LLC (MSO).

LA BARGE—Blackstone Cable LLC, 1104 Ironwood Dr., Coeur d'Alene, ID 83814. Phone: 208-664-3370. Fax: 208-664-5888. County: Lincoln. ICA: WY0042.
TV Market Ranking: Outside TV Markets. Franchise award date: N.A. Franchise expiration date: July 1, 2014. Began: July 1, 1979.
Channel capacity: 30 (not 2-way capable). Channels available but not in use: 5.
Basic Service
Subscribers: 70.
Programming (received off-air): KTWO-TV (N,W) Casper; KSL-TV (N), KTVX (A), KUED (P), KUTV (C) Salt Lake City.
Programming (via microwave): KCNC-TV (C), KMGH-TV (A), KUSA-TV (N) Denver.
Programming (via satellite): WGN-TV (W) Chicago; A & E; American Movie Classics; CNN; Discovery Channel; Disney Channel; ESPN; Fox Family Channel; FoxNet; Nashville Network; QVC; TBS Superstation; The Weather Channel; Turner Network TV; USA Network.
Fee: $35.00 installation; $27.55 monthly; $21.50 additional installation.
Pay Service 1
Pay Units: 10.
Programming (via satellite): The Movie Channel.
Fee: $10.00 installation; $12.95 monthly.
Pay Service 2
Pay Units: 10.
Programming (via satellite): Showtime.
Fee: $10.00 installation; $12.95 monthly.
Pay Service 3
Pay Units: 3.
Programming (via satellite): HBO.
Fee: $10.00 installation; $12.95 monthly.
Local advertising: No.
Miles of plant: 10.0 (coaxial). Homes passed: 226.
Manager: Ted W. Hughett. Technical manager: George Norcutt.
City fee: 1% of gross.
Ownership: Blackstone Cable LLC (MSO).

LANDER—TCI Cablevision of Wyoming Inc., 617 Main St., Lander, WY 82520. Phone: 307-332-4902. Fax: 307-332-7161. County: Fremont. Also serves Fremont County. ICA: WY0056.
TV Market Ranking: Below 100 (portions of Fremont County, Lander); Outside TV Markets (portions of Fremont County). Franchise award date: November 1, 1959. Franchise expiration date: October 1, 1999. Began: November 1, 1959.
Channel capacity: 48 (not 2-way capable). Channels available but not in use: N.A.
Basic Service
Subscribers: 2,207.
Programming (received off-air): KCWC-TV (P), KFNE (A), KGWL-TV (C) Lander-Riverton.
Programming (via microwave): KTWO-TV (N,W) Casper.
Programming (via satellite): KCNC-TV (C), KWGN-TV (W) Denver; C-SPAN; Discovery Channel; Odyssey; QVC; TBS Superstation; The Weather Channel; WB 100+ Station Group.
Current originations: Automated time-weather.
Fee: $44.95 installation; $12.76 monthly.
Expanded Basic Service
Subscribers: 2,073.
Programming (via satellite): A & E; American Movie Classics; Animal Planet; CNBC; CNN; Cartoon Network; Comedy Central; Country Music TV; Court TV; Disney Channel; ESPN; ESPN 2; Fox News Channel; Fox Sports Net; Headline News; History Channel; Home & Garden Television; Learning Channel; Lifetime; MOVIEplex; MSNBC; MTV; Nashville Network; Nickelodeon; Pax Net; Sci-Fi Channel; Turner Network TV; USA Network; VH1.
Fee: $20.99 monthly.
Pay Service 1
Pay Units: 140.
Programming (via satellite): Cinemax.
Fee: $13.00 monthly.
Pay Service 2
Pay Units: 300.
Programming (via satellite): HBO.
Fee: $13.83 monthly.
Pay Service 3
Pay Units: 150.
Programming (via satellite): Showtime.
Fee: $13.83 monthly.
Pay Service 4
Pay Units: 660.
Programming (via satellite): The New Encore.
Fee: $1.75 monthly.
Pay Service 5
Pay Units: 350.
Programming (via satellite): Starz!
Fee: $6.75 monthly.
Program Guide: The Cable Guide.
Equipment: Jerrold & Scientific-Atlanta headend; GTE Sylvania, Jerrold & Scientific-Atlanta amplifiers; Systems Wire & Times Fiber cable; Scientific-Atlanta satellite antenna.
Miles of plant: 42.3 (coaxial). Total homes in franchised area: 3,246.
Manager: Clint Rodeman. Chief technician: Don Gunsaullus. Office manager: Darlene Raymond.

City fee: 3% of gross.
Ownership: AT&T Broadband & Internet Services (MSO). Purchased from Tele-Communications Inc., March 9, 1999.

LARAMIE—TCI Cablevision of Wyoming, Box 640, Laramie, WY 82070-0640. Phone: 307-745-7333. Fax: 307-742-8002. County: Albany. Also serves Albany County. ICA: WY0003.
TV Market Ranking: Below 100 (portions of Albany County); Outside TV Markets (portions of Albany County, Laramie). Franchise award date: N.A. Franchise expiration date: N.A. Began: March 1, 1954.
Channel capacity: 42 (2-way capable; operating 2-way). Channels available but not in use: None.
Basic Service
Subscribers: 8,007.
Programming (received off-air): 4 FMs.
Programming (via microwave): KGWN-TV (C,A) Cheyenne.
Programming (via translator): KTWO-TV (N,W) Casper.
Programming (via satellite): WGN-TV (W) Chicago; KCNC-TV (C), KMGH-TV (A), KRMA-TV (P), KUSA-TV (N), KWGN-TV (W) Denver; A & E; C-SPAN; CNBC; CNN; Discovery Channel; Fox Family Channel; FoxNet; Headline News; Knowledge TV; Lifetime; MTV; Nashville Network; Nickelodeon; Odyssey; QVC; TBS Superstation; The Weather Channel.
Current originations: Automated time-weather; government access; automated emergency alert.
Fee: $19.95 installation; $22.00 monthly; $3.00 converter.
Expanded Basic Service
Subscribers: 6,867.
Programming (via satellite): American Movie Classics; ESPN; Fox Sports Net; Turner Network TV; USA Network; VH1.
Fee: N.A.
Pay Service 1
Pay Units: 616.
Programming (via satellite): Cinemax.
Fee: $20.00 installation; $13.20 monthly.
Pay Service 2
Pay Units: 636.
Programming (via satellite): Disney Channel.
Fee: N.A.
Pay Service 3
Pay Units: 1,614.
Programming (via satellite): HBO.
Fee: $13.20 monthly.
Pay Service 4
Pay Units: 600.
Programming (via satellite): Showtime.
Fee: $13.20 monthly.
Pay Service 5
Pay Units: 2,862.
Programming (via satellite): The New Encore.
Fee: N.A.
Local advertising: Yes.
Program Guide: The Cable Guide.
Equipment: Jerrold headend; GTE Sylvania amplifiers; Times Fiber cable; Scientific-Atlanta satellite antenna.
Miles of plant: 170.4 (coaxial). Homes passed: 10,470. Total homes in franchised area: 10,470.
Manager: Curtis Syme. Chief technician: Todd Lubbers.
City fee: 3% of gross.
Ownership: AT&T Broadband & Internet Services (MSO). Purchased from Tele-Communications Inc., March 9, 1999.

LOVELL—Lovell Cable TV Co., Box 415, Lovell, WY 82431. Phone: 307-548-6111. County: Big Horn. ICA: WY0024.
TV Market Ranking: Outside TV Markets. Franchise award date: January 1, 1973. Franchise expiration date: January 1, 2004. Began: May 1, 1974.
Channel capacity: 36 (2-way capable; operating 2-way). Channels available but not in use: 5.
Basic Service
Subscribers: 801.
Programming (via translator): KTVQ (C), KULR-TV (N) Billings; KTWO-TV (N,W) Casper.
Programming (via satellite): WGN-TV (W) Chicago; Fox Family Channel; TBS Superstation; Turner Classic Movies; USA Network.
Current originations: Automated time-weather.
Fee: $25.00 installation; $22.00 monthly.
Equipment: Drake & Scientific-Atlanta headend; Magnavox & Scientific-Atlanta amplifiers; Theta-Com & Comm/Scope cable; Scientific-Atlanta satellite antenna.
Miles of plant: 16.0 (coaxial); None (fiber optic). Homes passed: 900. Total homes in franchised area: 900.
Manager: John T. Nickle.
City fee: 2% of gross.
Ownership: John Nickle (MSO).

LUSK—CommuniComm Services, Suite A, 113 S. College Ave., Fort Collins, CO 80524. Phone: 303-224-3325. County: Niobrara. ICA: WY0027.
TV Market Ranking: Outside TV Markets. Franchise award date: November 1, 1978. Franchise expiration date: N.A. Began: May 1, 1980.
Channel capacity: 40 (not 2-way capable). Channels available but not in use: 2.
Basic Service
Subscribers: 592.
Programming (received off-air): KTWO-TV (N,W) Casper; KDUH-TV (A) Scottsbluff.
Programming (via microwave): KCNC-TV (C), KDVR (F), KMGH-TV (A), KRMA-TV (P), KUSA-TV (N), KWGN-TV (W) Denver.
Programming (via satellite): WGN-TV (W) Chicago; A & E; American Movie Classics; CNBC; CNN; Country Music TV; Discovery Channel; Disney Channel; ESPN; ESPN 2; Fox Family Channel; Fox Sports Net; Headline News; History Channel; Knowledge TV; Learning Channel; MTV; Nashville Network; Nickelodeon; QVC; Sci-Fi Channel; TBS Superstation; The Weather Channel; Turner Network TV; USA Network; VH1.
Fee: $32.95 installation; $28.95 monthly; $20.00 additional installation.
Pay Service 1
Pay Units: 129.
Programming (via satellite): HBO.
Fee: $12.95 monthly.
Pay Service 2
Pay Units: 137.
Programming (via satellite): Cinemax.
Fee: $10.95 monthly.
Equipment: Scientific-Atlanta headend; Jerrold amplifiers; CCS Hatfield & Times Fiber cable; Scientific-Atlanta satellite antenna.
Miles of plant: 17.0 (coaxial). Homes passed: 730. Total homes in franchised area: 800.
Manager: Alan Price.
City fee: $100 annually.
Ownership: James Cable Partners (MSO).

LYMAN—Blackstone Cable LLC, 1104 Ironwood Dr., Coeur d'Alene, ID 83814. Phone: 208-664-3370. Fax: 208-664-5888. County: Uinta. Also serves Bridger Valley, Fort Bridger, Uinta County, Urie. ICA: WY0057.
TV Market Ranking: Outside TV Markets. Franchise award date: N.A. Franchise expiration date: July 1, 2004. Began: December 1, 1981.
Channel capacity: 30 (not 2-way capable). Channels available but not in use: None.
Basic Service
Subscribers: 461.
Programming (received off-air): 6 FMs.
Programming (via microwave): KTWO-TV (N,W) Casper; KSL-TV (N), KTVX (A), KUED (P), KUTV (C) Salt Lake City.
Programming (via satellite): ESPN; FoxNet; QVC; TBS Superstation; USA Network.
Current originations: Automated time-weather; public access; local news.
Fee: $35.00 installation; $13.45 monthly; $21.50 additional installation.
Expanded Basic Service
Subscribers: 413.
Programming (via satellite): WGN-TV (W) Chicago; A & E; American Movie Classics; CNBC; CNN; Country Music TV; Discovery Channel; Disney Channel; ESPN 2; FX; Fox Family Channel; Fox News Channel; History Channel; Lifetime; MTV; Nashville Network; Nickelodeon; Sci-Fi Channel; The Weather Channel; Turner Network TV.
Fee: N.A.
Pay Service 1
Pay Units: 59.
Programming (via satellite): The Movie Channel.
Fee: $12.95 monthly.
Pay Service 2
Pay Units: 81.
Programming (via satellite): Showtime.
Fee: $12.95 monthly.
Pay Service 3
Pay Units: 48.
Programming (via satellite): HBO.
Fee: $12.95 monthly.
Local advertising: No.
Equipment: Catel, Rockwell & Scientific-Atlanta headend; Magnavox amplifiers; Compuvid character generator; Scientific-Atlanta satellite antenna; Rockwell satellite receivers.
Miles of plant: 30.0 (coaxial). Homes passed: 638.
Manager: Ted W. Hughett. Technical manager: George Norcutt.
City fee: 1% of gross.
Ownership: Blackstone Cable LLC (MSO).

MAMMOTH HOT SPRINGS—North Yellowstone Cable TV, Box 707, Gardiner, MT 59030. Phone: 406-848-7561. County: Park. ICA: WY0048.
TV Market Ranking: Outside TV Markets. Franchise award date: N.A. Franchise expiration date: N.A. Began: January 1, 1985.
Channel capacity: 12 (not 2-way capable). Channels available but not in use: None.
Basic Service
Subscribers: 70.
Programming (received off-air): KTVQ (C), KULR-TV (N) Billings; KIDK (C) Idaho Falls-Pocatello.
Programming (via satellite): WGN-TV (W) Chicago; KRMA-TV (P) Denver; CNN; Discovery Channel; ESPN; Fox Family Channel; Showtime; TBS Superstation.
Current originations: Government access.
Fee: $23.00 monthly.
Miles of plant: 3.5 (coaxial). Homes passed: 120.
Manager: George Buffington.
Ownership: Southwest Montana Corp. (MSO).

MEDICINE BOW—Blackstone Cable LLC, 1104 Ironwood Dr., Coeur d'Alene, ID 83814. Phone: 208-664-3370. Fax: 208-664-5888. County: Carbon. ICA: WY0045.
TV Market Ranking: Outside TV Markets. Franchise award date: N.A. Franchise expiration date: July 1, 2005. Began: February 3, 1981.
Channel capacity: 30 (not 2-way capable). Channels available but not in use: 8.
Basic Service
Subscribers: 57.
Programming (received off-air): KTWO-TV (N,W) Casper; KMGH-TV (A), KRMA-TV (P), KUSA-TV (N) Denver; KCWC-TV (P) Lander-Riverton.
Programming (via satellite): WGN-TV (W) Chicago; KCNC-TV (C), KDVR (F) Denver; A & E; American Movie Classics; CNN; Discovery Channel; Disney Channel; ESPN; FX; Fox Family Channel; Fox News Channel; Nashville Network; QVC; TBS Superstation; The Weather Channel; Turner Network TV; USA Network.
Fee: $35.00 installation; $27.55 monthly; $21.50 additional installation.
Pay Service 1
Pay Units: 5.
Programming (via satellite): The Movie Channel.
Fee: $10.00 installation; $9.95 monthly.
Pay Service 2
Pay Units: 14.
Programming (via satellite): Showtime.
Fee: $10.00 installation; $9.95 monthly.
Pay Service 3
Pay Units: 12.
Programming (via satellite): HBO.
Fee: $10.00 installation; $12.95 monthly.
Local advertising: No.
Equipment: Blonder-Tongue & Microdyne headend; Theta-Com amplifiers; CCS Hatfield cable; Prodelin satellite antenna.
Miles of plant: 4.0 (coaxial). Homes passed: 150.
Manager: Ted W. Hughett. Technical manager: George Norcutt.
City fee: 1.5% of gross.
Ownership: Blackstone Cable LLC (MSO).

MEETEETSE—Blackstone Cable LLC, 1104 Ironwood Dr., Coeur d'Alene, ID 83814. Phone: 208-664-3370. Fax: 208-664-5888. County: Park. ICA: WY0047.
TV Market Ranking: Outside TV Markets. Franchise award date: June 14, 1982. Franchise expiration date: December 23, 2004. Began: March 1, 1982.
Channel capacity: 20 (not 2-way capable). Channels available but not in use: None.
Basic Service
Subscribers: 102.
Programming (received off-air): KSVI (A,F), KTVQ (C), KULR-TV (N) Billings; KTWO-TV (N,W) Casper; KCWC-TV (P) Lander-Riverton.
Programming (via satellite): WGN-TV (W) Chicago; A & E; American Movie Classics; CNN; Discovery Channel; Disney Channel; ESPN; Fox Family Channel; FoxNet; Nashville Network; QVC; TBS Superstation; The Weather Channel; Turner Network TV; USA Network.
Fee: $35.00 installation; $27.55 monthly; $21.50 additional installation.
Pay Service 1
Pay Units: 13.
Programming (via satellite): The Movie Channel.
Fee: $10.00 installation; $9.95 monthly.
Pay Service 2
Pay Units: 6.
Programming (via satellite): HBO.

Fee: $10.00 installation; $10.95 monthly.
Local advertising: No.
Miles of plant: 4.0 (coaxial). Homes passed: 198.
Manager: Ted W. Hughett. Technical manager: George Norcutt.
City fee: 1.5% of gross.
Ownership: Blackstone Cable LLC (MSO).

MOORCROFT—TCI Cablevision of Wyoming Inc., 410 W. Boxelder Rd., Gillette, WY 82718. Phones: 307-682-4303; 800-788-9457. Fax: 307-682-9631. County: Crook. ICA: WY0033.
TV Market Ranking: Outside TV Markets. Franchise award date: N.A. Franchise expiration date: N.A. Began: January 1, 1979.
Channel capacity: 36 (not 2-way capable). Channels available but not in use: 7.
Basic Service
Subscribers: 260.
Programming (via translator): KGWC-TV (C), KTWO-TV (N,W) Casper; KEVN-TV (F), KOTA-TV (A) Rapid City.
Programming (via satellite): WGN-TV (W) Chicago; KRMA-TV (P) Denver; American Movie Classics; C-SPAN; CNBC; CNN; Court TV; Discovery Channel; ESPN; Fox Family Channel; FoxNet; Headline News; Knowledge TV; Lifetime; MTV; Nashville Network; Nickelodeon; QVC; TBS Superstation; The Weather Channel; Turner Network TV; USA Network.
Fee: $41.21 installation; $22.27 monthly; $20.59 additional installation.
Pay Service 1
Pay Units: 65.
Programming (via satellite): Disney Channel.
Fee: N.A.
Pay Service 2
Pay Units: 112.
Programming (via satellite): HBO.
Fee: $12.65 monthly.
Pay Service 3
Pay Units: 162.
Programming (via satellite): The New Encore.
Fee: N.A.
Miles of plant: 6.5 (coaxial); None (fiber optic). Homes passed: 433.
Manager: Joe Conway. Chief technician: Richard Kuhn. Customer service manager: Doris Linderman.
Ownership: AT&T Broadband & Internet Services (MSO). Purchased from Tele-Communications Inc., March 9, 1999.

MOUNTAIN VIEW (Uinta County)—Union Cable Co., Box 160, Mountain View, WY 82939. Phone: 307-782-6131. Fax: 307-787-7043. County: Uinta. ICA: WY0023.
TV Market Ranking: Outside TV Markets. Franchise award date: N.A. Franchise expiration date: N.A. Began: December 1, 1962.
Channel capacity: 27 (not 2-way capable). Channels available but not in use: None.
Basic Service
Subscribers: 264.
Programming (received off-air): KRMA-TV (P) Denver; KSL-TV (N), KTVX (A), KUTV (C) Salt Lake City.
Programming (via microwave): KTWO-TV (N,W) Casper.
Programming (via satellite): WGN-TV (W) Chicago; CNN; ESPN; Fox Family Channel; Fox Sports Net; Nashville Network; TBS Superstation; The Weather Channel; Turner Network TV.
Fee: $14.00 monthly.
Expanded Basic Service
Subscribers: 109.
Programming (via satellite): A & E; American Movie Classics; Country Music TV; Discovery Channel; ESPN 2; History Channel; Nickelodeon; VH1.
Fee: $8.00 monthly.
Pay Service 1
Pay Units: 65.
Programming (via satellite): Disney Channel.
Fee: $10.00 monthly.
Pay Service 2
Pay Units: 87.
Programming (via satellite): HBO.
Fee: $10.00 monthly.
Pay Service 3
Pay Units: N.A.
Programming (via satellite): Starz!; The New Encore.
Fee: $8.00 monthly.
Pay-Per-View
Addressable homes: 1,192.
Miles of plant: 14.9 (coaxial); None (fiber optic). Homes passed: 1,192. Total homes in franchised area: 1,192.
Manager: John Woody. Chief technician: Chuck Fagnant. Marketing director: Gayle T. Walsh.
Ownership: Union Telephone Co. (MSO).

NEWCASTLE—TCI Cablevision of Wyoming Inc., 410 W. Boxelder, Gillette, WY 82718. Phones: 800-788-9457; 307-682-4303. Fax: 307-682-9631. County: Weston. Also serves Weston County. ICA: WY0020.
TV Market Ranking: Below 100 (portions of Weston County); Outside TV Markets (Newcastle, portions of Weston County). Franchise award date: N.A. Franchise expiration date: N.A. Began: November 1, 1976.
Channel capacity: 34 (not 2-way capable). Channels available but not in use: N.A.
Basic Service
Subscribers: 1,218.
Programming (received off-air): KGWC-TV (C), KTWO-TV (N,W) Casper; KHSD-TV (A), KIVV-TV (F) Lead.
Programming (via satellite): WGN-TV (W) Chicago; C-SPAN; CNBC; CNN; Discovery Channel; Fox Family Channel; FoxNet; Headline News; Lifetime; MTV; Nashville Network; Nickelodeon; Odyssey; QVC; TBS Superstation; The Weather Channel.
Current originations: Automated time-weather; local news.
Fee: $60.00 installation; $20.39 monthly; $60.00 additional installation.
Expanded Basic Service
Subscribers: 1,052.
Programming (via satellite): A & E; Court TV; ESPN; Turner Network TV; USA Network.
Fee: $1.75 monthly.
Pay Service 1
Pay Units: 225.
Programming (via satellite): Disney Channel.
Fee: $10.00 installation; $9.00 monthly.
Pay Service 2
Pay Units: 406.
Programming (via satellite): HBO.
Fee: $10.00 installation; $12.65 monthly.
Pay Service 3
Pay Units: 694.
Programming (via satellite): The New Encore.
Fee: N.A.
Program Guide: The Cable Guide.
Equipment: Magnavox & Triple Crown headend; Magnavox amplifiers; Andrew satellite antenna.
Miles of plant: 57.0 (coaxial). Homes passed: 1,424. Total homes in franchised area: 1,424.
Manager: Joe Conway. Chief technician: Jackie Taylor.
City fee: None.
Ownership: AT&T Broadband & Internet Services (MSO). Purchased from Tele-Communications Inc., March 9, 1999.

OPAL—Union Cable Co., Box 160, Mountain View, WY 82939. Phone: 307-782-6131. Fax: 307-787-7043. County: Lincoln. ICA: WY0058.
TV Market Ranking: Outside TV Markets. Franchise award date: N.A. Franchise expiration date: N.A. Began: N.A.
Channel capacity: 12 (not 2-way capable). Channels available but not in use: None.
Basic Service
Subscribers: 14.
Programming (received off-air): KCNC-TV (C), KMGH-TV (A), KUSA-TV (N) Denver.
Programming (via satellite): CNN; Discovery Channel; ESPN; FoxNet; Nashville Network; TBS Superstation.
Fee: $35.00 installation; $13.00 monthly.
Pay Service 1
Pay Units: 3.
Programming (via satellite): Cinemax.
Fee: $12.50 monthly.
Pay Service 2
Pay Units: 1.
Programming (via satellite): Disney Channel.
Fee: $10.00 monthly.
Pay Service 3
Pay Units: 4.
Programming (via satellite): HBO.
Fee: $10.00 monthly.
Pay-Per-View
Addressable homes: 25.
Miles of plant: 2.5 (coaxial); None (fiber optic). Homes passed: 25. Total homes in franchised area: 25.
Manager: John Woody. Chief technician: Chuck Fagnant. Marketing director: Gayle T. Walsh.
Ownership: Union Telephone Co. (MSO).

OSAGE—Tongue River Cable TV Inc., Box 759, Ranchester, WY 82839. Phone: 307-655-9011. Fax: 307-655-9021. County: Weston. ICA: WY0049.
TV Market Ranking: Outside TV Markets. Franchise award date: N.A. Franchise expiration date: N.A. Began: January 1, 1983.
Channel capacity: 42 (not 2-way capable). Channels available but not in use: 9.
Basic Service
Subscribers: 52.
Programming (received off-air): KGWC-TV (C), KTWO-TV (N,W) Casper; KEVN-TV (F), KOTA-TV (A) Rapid City.
Programming (via satellite): WGN-TV (W) Chicago; KRMA-TV (P), KUSA-TV (N), KWGN-TV (W) Denver; A & E; American Movie Classics; C-SPAN; CNN; Country Music TV; Discovery Channel; Disney Channel; ESPN; Fox Family Channel; Headline News; Lifetime; Nashville Network; Nickelodeon; QVC; TBS Superstation; The Weather Channel; Turner Network TV; USA Network.
Fee: $40.00 installation; $24.50 monthly; $3.00 converter; $15.00 additional installation.
Pay Service 1
Pay Units: 10.
Programming (via satellite): Cinemax.
Fee: $10.00 installation; $8.50 monthly.
Pay Service 2
Pay Units: 8.
Programming (via satellite): The New Encore.
Fee: $3.50 monthly.
Pay Service 3
Pay Units: 9.
Programming (via satellite): HBO.
Fee: $11.00 monthly.
Local advertising: No.
Miles of plant: 3.5 (coaxial). Homes passed: 100.
Manager: Robert Jacobson.
Ownership: Lynda & Robert Jacobson (MSO).

PINE BLUFFS—Pine Bluffs Community TV System, Box 517, 210 Main St., Pine Bluffs, WY 82082. Phone: 307-245-3392. Fax: 307-245-3280. County: Laramie. ICA: WY0031.
TV Market Ranking: Outside TV Markets. Franchise award date: November 7, 1962. Franchise expiration date: N.A. Began: July 1, 1957.
Channel capacity: 26 (not 2-way capable). Channels available but not in use: None.
Basic Service
Subscribers: 383.
Programming (received off-air): KTNE-TV (P) Alliance; KTWO-TV (N,W) Casper; KGWN-TV (C) Cheyenne; KCNC-TV (C), KMGH-TV (A), KRMA-TV (P), KUSA-TV (N), KWGN-TV (W) Denver; KDUH-TV (A), KSTF (C) Scottsbluff; 4 FMs.
Programming (via satellite): CNN; ESPN; Fox Family Channel; Nashville Network; TBS Superstation; USA Network.
Current originations: Automated time-weather.
Fee: $25.00 installation; $24.95 monthly.
Pay Service 1
Pay Units: 17.
Programming (via satellite): Disney Channel.
Fee: $20.00 installation; $10.90 monthly.
Pay Service 2
Pay Units: 74.
Programming (via satellite): HBO.
Fee: $20.00 installation; $13.00 monthly.
Local advertising: Yes. Available in locally originated programming. Rates: $1.00/Day.
Equipment: Jerrold headend; Jerrold amplifiers; Times Fiber cable; MSI & Texscan character generator; Jerrold set top converters; Intercept traps; Scientific-Atlanta satellite antenna; Scientific-Atlanta satellite receivers.
Miles of plant: 8.1 (coaxial). Homes passed: 500.
Manager: Kathleen Reed. Chief technician, marketing & program director: John C. Harrison.
City fee: $25.00 annually.
Ownership: John C. Harrison (MSO).

PINE HAVEN—Tongue River Cable TV Inc., Box 759, Ranchester, WY 82839. Phone: 307-655-9011. Fax: 307-655-9021. County: Crook. ICA: WY0052.
TV Market Ranking: Outside TV Markets. Franchise award date: September 1, 1987. Franchise expiration date: N.A. Began: October 1, 1987.
Channel capacity: 42. Channels available but not in use: 10.
Basic Service
Subscribers: 53.
Programming (received off-air): KGWC-TV (C) Casper; KPSD-TV (P) Eagle Butte; KEVN-TV (F), KOTA-TV (A) Rapid City.
Programming (via satellite): WGN-TV (W) Chicago; KCNC-TV (C) Denver; WWOR-TV (U) New York; A & E; American Movie Classics; C-SPAN; CNN; Country Music TV; Discovery Channel; Disney Channel; ESPN; Fox Family Channel; FoxNet; Headline News; Lifetime; Nashville Network; Nickelodeon; QVC; TBS Superstation; The Weather Channel; Turner Network TV; USA Network.
Current originations: Automated time-weather.
Fee: $40.00 installation; $24.50 monthly; $3.00 converter; $15.00 additional installation.

CABLE & TELEVISION FACTBOOK
A LIST OF ALL CABLE COMMUNITIES INCLUDED IN THIS STATE IS AVAILABLE AT THE BACK OF THIS VOLUME.

Pay Service 1
Pay Units: 11.
Programming (via satellite): HBO.
Fee: $10.00 installation; $11.00 monthly.
Pay Service 2
Pay Units: 11.
Programming (via satellite): Cinemax.
Fee: $8.50 monthly.
Pay Service 3
Pay Units: 11.
Programming (via satellite): The New Encore.
Fee: $3.50 monthly.
Miles of plant: 6.0 (coaxial). Homes passed: 65.
Manager: Robert Jacobson.
Ownership: Lynda & Robert Jacobson (MSO).

PINEDALE—Blackstone Cable LLC, 1104 Ironwood Dr., Coeur d'Alene, ID 83814. Phone: 208-664-3370. Fax: 208-664-5888. County: Sublette. Also serves Sublette County. ICA: WY0025.
TV Market Ranking: Below 100 (portions of Sublette County); Outside TV Markets (Pinedale, portions of Sublette County). Franchise award date: N.A. Franchise expiration date: July 1, 2004. Began: January 1, 1979.
Channel capacity: 26 (not 2-way capable). Channels available but not in use: None.
Basic Service
Subscribers: 607.
Programming (received off-air): KTWO-TV (N,W) Casper; KSL-TV (N), KTVX (A), KUTV (C) Salt Lake City.
Programming (via microwave): KRMA-TV (P) Denver.
Programming (via satellite): WGN-TV (W) Chicago; ESPN; FoxNet; TBS Superstation; USA Network.
Fee: $35.00 installation; $13.55 monthly; $21.50 additional installation.
Expanded Basic Service
Subscribers: 528.
Programming (via satellite): KCNC-TV (C), KMGH-TV (A) Denver; A & E; American Movie Classics; C-SPAN; CNBC; CNN; Discovery Channel; Disney Channel; FX; Fox Family Channel; Fox News Channel; History Channel; Nashville Network; Nickelodeon; QVC; The Weather Channel; Turner Network TV.
Fee: N.A.
Pay Service 1
Pay Units: 37.
Programming (via satellite): The Movie Channel.
Fee: $12.95 monthly.
Pay Service 2
Pay Units: 78.
Programming (via satellite): Showtime.
Fee: $12.95 monthly.
Pay Service 3
Pay Units: 49.
Programming (via satellite): HBO.
Fee: $12.95 monthly.
Local advertising: No.
Miles of plant: 19.0 (coaxial). Homes passed: 897. Total homes in franchised area: 921.
Manager: Ted W. Hughett. Technical manager: George Norcutt.
City fee: 1% of gross.
Ownership: Blackstone Cable LLC (MSO).

POWELL—TCI Cablevision of Wyoming Inc., 880 E. 5th St., Powell, WY 82435-2106. Phone: 307-754-2219. County: Park. ICA: WY0015.
TV Market Ranking: Outside TV Markets. Franchise award date: N.A. Franchise expiration date: N.A. Began: December 1, 1965.
Channel capacity: 38. Channels available but not in use: N.A.
Basic Service
Subscribers: 1,681.
Programming (received off-air): KSVI (A,F) Billings.
Programming (via microwave): KTWO-TV (N,W) Casper; KSL-TV (N) Salt Lake City.
Programming (via translator): KTVQ (C), KULR-TV (N) Billings; KCWC-TV (P) Lander-Riverton.
Programming (via satellite): WGN-TV (W) Chicago; KRMA-TV (P), KUSA-TV (N), KWGN-TV (W) Denver; C-SPAN; CNBC; CNN; Comedy Central; Discovery Channel; Fox Family Channel; FoxNet; Headline News; Knowledge TV; Lifetime; MTV; Nashville Network; Nickelodeon; Odyssey; QVC; TBS Superstation; The Weather Channel; VH1.
Current originations: Local news.
Fee: $34.95 installation; $18.80 monthly.
Expanded Basic Service
Subscribers: 1,575.
Programming (via satellite): American Movie Classics; ESPN; Fox Sports Net; Turner Network TV; USA Network.
Fee: $3.43 monthly.
Pay Service 1
Pay Units: 97.
Programming (via satellite): Disney Channel.
Fee: N.A.
Pay Service 2
Pay Units: 271.
Programming (via satellite): HBO.
Fee: N.A.
Pay Service 3
Pay Units: 170.
Programming (via satellite): Showtime.
Fee: N.A.
Pay Service 4
Pay Units: 673.
Programming (via satellite): The New Encore.
Fee: N.A.
Program Guide: The Cable Guide.
Miles of plant: 23.6 (coaxial). Homes passed: 2,378. Total homes in franchised area: 2,378.
Manager: Jackie Zalendingham. Chief technician: Dan Higgins.
Ownership: AT&T Broadband & Internet Services (MSO). Purchased from Tele-Communications Inc., March 9, 1999.

RANCHESTER—Tongue River Cable TV Inc., Box 759, Ranchester, WY 82839. Phone: 307-655-9011. Fax: 307-655-9021. County: Sheridan. Also serves Dayton. ICA: WY0028.
TV Market Ranking: Below 100. Franchise award date: January 1, 1979. Franchise expiration date: March 1, 2000. Began: December 18, 1979.
Channel capacity: 54 (not 2-way capable). Channels available but not in use: 2.
Basic Service
Subscribers: 438.
Programming (received off-air): KTVQ (C) Billings; KGWC-TV (C), KTWO-TV (N,W) Casper; KHMT (F) Hardin; KCWC-TV (P) Lander-Riverton; KSGW-TV (A) Sheridan.
Programming (via satellite): WGN-TV (W) Chicago; KCNC-TV (C), KRMA-TV (P), KUSA-TV (N), KWGN-TV (W) Denver; KTLA (W) Los Angeles; WPIX (W) New York; A & E; American Movie Classics; Animal Planet; C-SPAN; C-SPAN 2; CNBC; CNN; Cartoon Network; Country Music TV; Court TV; Discovery Channel; Disney Channel; E! Entertainment TV; ESPN; ESPN 2; Fox Family Channel; Headline News; History Channel; Home & Garden Television; Knowledge TV; Learning Channel; Lifetime; MSNBC; MTV; Nashville Network; Nickelodeon; Odyssey; Outdoor Channel; QVC; Sci-Fi Channel; TBS Superstation; The Weather Channel; Travel Channel; Trinity Bcstg. Network; Turner Network TV; USA Network; VH1.
Current originations: Automated timeweather.
Fee: $40.00 installation; $27.00 monthly; $15.00 additional installation.
Pay Service 1
Pay Units: 51.
Programming (via satellite): Cinemax.
Fee: $10.00 installation; $8.50 monthly.
Pay Service 2
Pay Units: 31.
Programming (via satellite): The New Encore.
Fee: $10.00 installation; $3.50 monthly.
Pay Service 3
Pay Units: 54.
Programming (via satellite): HBO.
Fee: $10.00 installation; $11.00 monthly.
Equipment: Blonder-Tongue & Scientific-Atlanta headend; Magnavox amplifiers; Times Fiber cable; Oak set top converters; Intercept traps; Scientific-Atlanta satellite antenna.
Miles of plant: 24.0 (coaxial). Homes passed: 710. Total homes in franchised area: 800.
Manager: Robert Jacobson.
Franchise fee: $1000 per year.
Ownership: Lynda & Robert Jacobson (MSO).

RAWLINS—TCI Cablevision of Wyoming Inc., 409 6th St., Rawlins, WY 82301-5441. Phone: 307-324-2286. County: Carbon. Also serves Sinclair. ICA: WY0011.
TV Market Ranking: Below 100. Franchise award date: N.A. Franchise expiration date: N.A. Began: September 1, 1955.
Channel capacity: 38 (not 2-way capable). Channels available but not in use: N.A.
Basic Service
Subscribers: 3,112.
Programming (received off-air): KTWO-TV (N,W) Casper; KFNR (A) Rawlins; 3 FMs.
Programming (via satellite): WGN-TV (W) Chicago; KCNC-TV (C), KMGH-TV (A), KRMA-TV (P), KWGN-TV (W) Denver; C-SPAN; CNBC; CNN; Discovery Channel; Fox Family Channel; FoxNet; Headline News; Knowledge TV; Lifetime; MTV; Nashville Network; Nickelodeon; Odyssey; QVC; TBS Superstation; The Weather Channel; Univision.
Current originations: Automated timeweather; government access; local news.
Fee: $60.00 installation; $9.66 monthly; $60.00 additional installation.
Expanded Basic Service
Subscribers: 2,913.
Programming (via satellite): American Movie Classics; Court TV; ESPN; Fox Sports Net; Turner Network TV; USA Network.
Fee: $11.91 monthly.
Pay Service 1
Pay Units: 346.
Programming (via satellite): Disney Channel.
Fee: $19.95 installation; $11.95 monthly.
Pay Service 2
Pay Units: 722.
Programming (via satellite): HBO.
Fee: $12.59 monthly.
Pay Service 3
Pay Units: 147.
Programming (via satellite): The Movie Channel.
Fee: $12.59 monthly.
Pay Service 4
Pay Units: 365.
Programming (via satellite): Showtime.
Fee: $12.59 monthly.
Pay Service 5
Pay Units: 1,481.
Programming (via satellite): The New Encore.
Fee: N.A.
Local advertising: Yes.
Program Guide: The Cable Guide.
Equipment: Jerrold headend; Jerrold amplifiers; Times Fiber cable; Sony cameras; Sony VTRs; Andrew satellite antenna.
Miles of plant: 79.7 (coaxial). Homes passed: 4,016. Total homes in franchised area: 4,016.
Manager: Curtis Syme. Chief technician: Richard Wilson. Office manager: Bonnie Schwindt.
City fee: 5% of gross.
Ownership: AT&T Broadband & Internet Services (MSO). Purchased from Tele-Communications Inc., March 9, 1999.

RENO JUNCTION—TCI Cablevision of Wyoming Inc., 410 W. Boxelder Rd., Gillette, WY 82718. Phones: 307-682-4303; 800-788-9457. Fax: 307-682-9631. County: Campbell. Also serves Wright. ICA: WY0029.
TV Market Ranking: Outside TV Markets. Franchise award date: N.A. Franchise expiration date: N.A. Began: August 1, 1976.
Channel capacity: 36 (not 2-way capable). Channels available but not in use: 7.
Basic Service
Subscribers: 350.
Programming (received off-air): KTWO-TV (N,W) Casper; KEVN-TV (F) Rapid City; 1 FM.
Programming (via satellite): KCNC-TV (C), KDVR (F), KMGH-TV (A), KRMA-TV (P), KUSA-TV (N), KWGN-TV (W) Denver; American Movie Classics; CNN; Court TV; Discovery Channel; ESPN; Fox Family Channel; History Channel; Home & Garden Television; Intro TV; Learning Channel; Nashville Network; Odyssey; TBS Superstation; Turner Network TV; USA Network.
Fee: $22.16 installation; $19.60 monthly.
Pay Service 1
Pay Units: 116.
Programming (via satellite): Disney Channel.
Fee: N.A.
Pay Service 2
Pay Units: 184.
Programming (via satellite): HBO.
Fee: N.A.
Pay Service 3
Pay Units: 192.
Programming (via satellite): The New Encore.
Fee: N.A.
Pay Service 4
Pay Units: N.A.

Programming (via satellite): Starz!
Fee: N.A.
Miles of plant: 11.0 (coaxial); None (fiber optic). Homes passed: 589. Total homes in franchised area: 589.
Manager: Joe Conway. Chief technician: Richard Kuhn. Customer service manager: Doris Linderman.
Ownership: AT&T Broadband & Internet Services (MSO). Purchased from Tele-Communications Inc., March 9, 1999.

RIVERTON—TCI Cablevision of Wyoming Inc., Box 1730, Riverton, WY 82501-1730. Phone: 307-856-3248. Fax: 307-856-7156. County: Fremont. Also serves Fremont County. ICA: WY0059.
TV Market Ranking: Below 100 (portions of Fremont County, Riverton); Outside TV Markets (portions of Fremont County). Franchise award date: January 1, 1958. Franchise expiration date: December 18, 2000. Began: June 1, 1958.
Channel capacity: 60 (2-way capable; not operating 2-way). Channels available but not in use: 6.
Basic Service
Subscribers: 3,300.
Programming (received off-air): KCNC-TV (C) Denver; KCWC-TV (P), KFNE (A), KGWL-TV (C) Lander-Riverton.
Programming (via translator): KTWO-TV (N,W) Casper.
Programming (via satellite): KWGN-TV (W) Denver; C-SPAN; Discovery Channel; Odyssey; QVC; TBS Superstation; The Weather Channel; WB 100+ Station Group.
Fee: $44.95 installation; $13.52 monthly.
Expanded Basic Service
Subscribers: 2,901.
Programming (via satellite): A & E; American Movie Classics; Animal Planet; CNBC; CNN; Cartoon Network; Country Music TV; Court TV; Disney Channel; ESPN; ESPN 2; FX; Fox Family Channel; Fox News Channel; Fox Sports Net Rocky Mountain; Headline News; History Channel; Home & Garden Television; Learning Channel; Lifetime; MOVIEplex; MSNBC; MTV; Nashville Network; Nickelodeon; Outdoor Channel; Pax Net; Sci-Fi Channel; Turner Network TV; USA Network; VH1.
Fee: $18.91 monthly.
Pay Service 1
Pay Units: 350.
Programming (via satellite): Cinemax.
Fee: $12.95 installation; $13.00 monthly.
Pay Service 2
Pay Units: 850.
Programming (via satellite): HBO.
Fee: $12.95 installation; $13.83 monthly.
Pay Service 3
Pay Units: 350.
Programming (via satellite): Showtime.
Fee: $12.95 installation; $13.83 monthly.
Pay Service 4
Pay Units: 1,230.
Programming (via satellite): The New Encore.
Fee: $1.75 monthly.
Pay Service 5
Pay Units: 850.
Programming (via satellite): Starz!
Fee: $6.75 monthly.
Pay Service 6
Pay Units: N.A.
Programming (via satellite): DMX.
Fee: $12.95 monthly.
Pay-Per-View
Addressable homes: 100.
Local advertising: Yes. Local sales manager: Elliott Ramage.
Program Guide: The Cable Guide.
Equipment: Scientific-Atlanta headend; Jerrold amplifiers; Comm/Scope & Times Fiber cable; Texscan character generator; Hamlin, Jerrold & Scientific-Atlanta set top converters; Scientific-Atlanta addressable set top converters; Pico traps; Scientific-Atlanta satellite receivers.
Miles of plant: 63.5 (coaxial). Total homes in franchised area: 4,555.
Manager: Clint Rodeman. Chief technician: Don Gunsaullus.
City fee: 3% of gross.
Ownership: AT&T Broadband & Internet Services (MSO). Purchased from Tele-Communications Inc., March 9, 1999.

ROCK SPRINGS—Sweetwater Cable TV Co. Inc., Box 8, 602 Broadway, Rock Springs, WY 82901. Phone: 307-362-3773. Fax: 307-382-2781. County: Sweetwater. Also serves North Rock Springs, Reliance, Sweetwater County (unincorporated areas). ICA: WY0004.
TV Market Ranking: Below 100 (North Rock Springs, Reliance, Rock Springs, portions of Sweetwater County); Outside TV Markets (portions of Sweetwater County). Franchise award date: January 1, 1954. Franchise expiration date: January 1, 2005. Began: December 1, 1956.
Channel capacity: 45 (not 2-way capable). Channels available but not in use: N.A.
Basic Service
Subscribers: 7,816; Commercial subscribers: 160.
Programming (received off-air): KGWR-TV (C) Rock Springs; 12 FMs.
Programming (via microwave): KTWO-TV (N,W) Casper; KSL-TV (N), KSTU (F), KTVX (A), KUED (P), KUTV (C) Salt Lake City.
Programming (via satellite): A & E; American Movie Classics; C-SPAN; CNBC; CNN; Country Music TV; Discovery Channel; ESPN; ESPN 2; Fox Family Channel; Fox News Channel; Fox Sports Net; Headline News; History Channel; Learning Channel; Lifetime; MTV; Nashville Network; Nick at Nite; Nickelodeon; Odyssey; QVC; Sci-Fi Channel; TBS Superstation; TV Guide Channel; The Weather Channel; Turner Classic Movies; Turner Network TV; USA Network; VH1.
Current originations: Automated time-weather; public access; educational access; government access; religious access; local news; local sports.
Fee: $27.50 installation; $20.95 monthly; $15.00 additional installation.
Commercial fee: $20.95 monthly.
Pay Service 1
Pay Units: 487.
Programming (via satellite): Cinemax.
Fee: $7.95 installation; $9.95 monthly.
Pay Service 2
Pay Units: 3,189.
Programming (via satellite): HBO.
Fee: $9.95 monthly.
Pay Service 3
Pay Units: 212.
Programming (via satellite): The New Encore.
Fee: $12.50 installation; $9.95 monthly.
Pay Service 4
Pay Units: 334.
Programming (via satellite): Showtime.
Fee: $7.95 installation; $9.95 monthly.
Pay-Per-View
Addressable homes: 1,100.
Viewer's Choice.
Fee: Varies.
Local advertising: Yes (locally produced). Available in satellite distributed, locally originated, character-generated, taped & automated programming. Rates: $125.00/30 Seconds. Local sales manager: Robin Vesco.
Equipment: Jerrold headend; Jerrold amplifiers; Times Fiber cable; Sony cameras; Sony VTRs; Texscan character generator; Jerrold addressable set top converters; Pico traps; Andrew satellite antenna; Standard Communications satellite receivers; ChannelMatic commercial insert.
Miles of plant: 110.0 (coaxial). Homes passed: 9,000. Total homes in franchised area: 9,000.
Manager: Al Carollo Jr. Chief technician: Larry Gessner. Marketing & program director: John Carollo.
City fee: 2% of gross.
Ownership: Sweetwater Cable TV Co. Inc. (MSO).

SARATOGA—CommuniComm Services, Suite A, 1135 College Ave., Fort Collins, CO 80524. Phone: 800-759-8448. County: Carbon. Also serves Carbon County (portions), Elk Mountain, Elmo, Encampment, Hanna, Old Baldy, Riverside. ICA: WY0016.
TV Market Ranking: Below 100 (portions of Carbon County, Hanna, Saratoga); Outside TV Markets (portions of Carbon County, Elk Mountain, Elmo, Encampment, Old Baldy, Riverside). Franchise award date: N.A. Franchise expiration date: N.A. Began: November 1, 1979.
Channel capacity: 45. Channels available but not in use: 9.
Basic Service
Subscribers: 562.
Programming (via microwave): KTWO-TV (N,W) Casper; KCNC-TV (C), KMGH-TV (A), KRMA-TV (P), KUSA-TV (N), KWGN-TV (W) Denver.
Programming (via satellite): WGN-TV (W) Chicago; C-SPAN; CNN; Country Music TV; Court TV; Discovery Channel; Disney Channel; ESPN; ESPN 2; Fox Family Channel; Fox Sports Net; Headline News; Learning Channel; Nickelodeon; QVC; Sci-Fi Channel; TBS Superstation; The Weather Channel; Turner Network TV; USA Network.
Current originations: Public access.
Fee: $32.95 installation; $31.95 monthly; $2.95 converter; $15.00 additional installation.
Pay Service 1
Pay Units: 55.
Programming (via satellite): Cinemax.
Fee: $10.95 monthly.
Pay Service 2
Pay Units: 72.
Programming (via satellite): HBO.
Fee: $12.95 monthly.
Equipment: Jerrold headend; Magnavox amplifiers; Eagle traps; Hughes satellite antenna; Hughes satellite receivers.
Miles of plant: 30.0 (coaxial). Homes passed: 1,001.
Manager: Alan Price. Marketing director: Tracy Clodfelter.
City fee: 2% of gross.
Ownership: James Cable Partners (MSO).

SHERIDAN—AT&T Cable Services, Box A, 140 E. Loucks, Sheridan, WY 82801. Phone: 307-672-5841. Fax: 307-672-5844. County: Sheridan. Also serves Sheridan County. ICA: WY0006.
TV Market Ranking: Below 100 (Sheridan, portions of Sheridan County); Outside TV Markets (portions of Sheridan County). Franchise award date: N.A. Franchise expiration date: August 1, 2000. Began: September 1, 1955.
Channel capacity: 76 (2-way capable; operating 2-way). Channels available but not in use: None.
Basic Service
Subscribers: 6,095.
Programming (received off-air): KTVQ (C), KULR-TV (N) Billings; KTWO-TV (N,W) Casper; KCWC-TV (P) Lander-Riverton; KSGW-TV (A) Sheridan.
Programming (via satellite): KRMA-TV (P) Denver; FoxNet; QVC; TV Guide Channel; WB 100+ Station Group.
Current originations: Automated time-weather.
Fee: $27.76 installation; $8.10 monthly; $0.52 converter; $25.90 additional installation.
Expanded Basic Service
Subscribers: 5,628.
Programming (via satellite): A & E; American Movie Classics; Animal Planet; C-SPAN; C-SPAN 2; CNBC; CNN; CNN/SI; CNNfn; Cartoon Network; Comedy Central; Country Music TV; Discovery Channel; E! Entertainment TV; ESPN; ESPN 2; EWTN; Fox Family Channel; Fox News Channel; Golf Channel; Headline News; History Channel; Home & Garden Television; Learning Channel; Lifetime; MSNBC; MTV; Nashville Network; Nickelodeon; Odyssey; Outdoor Channel; Sci-Fi Channel; TBS Superstation; TV Food Network; TV Guide Sneak Prevue; The Weather Channel; Travel Channel; Turner Network TV; USA Network; VH1.
Fee: $21.64 monthly.
Pay Service 1
Pay Units: 420.
Programming (via satellite): Cinemax.
Fee: $10.95 monthly.
Pay Service 2
Pay Units: 244.
Programming (via satellite): Disney Channel.
Fee: $8.95 monthly.
Pay Service 3
Pay Units: 652.
Programming (via satellite): HBO.
Fee: $10.95 monthly.
Pay Service 4
Pay Units: 367.
Programming (via satellite): Showtime.
Fee: $10.95 monthly.
Pay-Per-View
Addressable homes: 1,112.
Hot Choice; Playboy TV; Viewer's Choice.
Fee: $3.99 (each).
Local advertising: Yes (locally produced). Available in locally originated & automated programming.
Equipment: Scientific-Atlanta headend; Magnavox amplifiers; Comm/Scope cable; Scientific-Atlanta & Jerrold set top converters; Scientific-Atlanta satellite antenna.
Miles of plant: 120.2 (coaxial); 21.7 (fiber optic). Homes passed: 8,797. Total homes in franchised area: 11,424.
Manager: James L. Wilhelm. Chief technician: Dave Siebert.
City fee: 3% of gross.
Ownership: AT&T Broadband & Internet Services (MSO). Purchased from Time Warner Cable, July 1, 1999.

SHOSHONI—Winhill Corp., Box 628, Riverton, WY 82501. Phone: 307-856-3322. County: Fremont. Also serves Hudson. ICA: WY0060.
TV Market Ranking: Below 100. Franchise award date: N.A. Franchise expiration date: N.A. Began: September 1, 1979.
Channel capacity: 36. Channels available but not in use: N.A.
Basic Service
Subscribers: N.A.
Programming (received off-air): KTWO-TV (N,W) Casper.

Programming (via satellite): TBS Superstation.
Fee: $40.00 installation; $10.00 monthly.
Pay Service 1
Pay Units: N.A.
Planned programming (via satellite): HBO.
Fee: N.A.
Equipment: Fort Worth Tower satellite antenna.
Manager: Darwin Hillberry.
Ownership: Darwin Hillberry.

STORY—Tongue River Cable TV Inc., Box 759, Ranchester, WY 82839. Phone: 307-655-9011. Fax: 307-655-9021. County: Sheridan. ICA: WY0034.
TV Market Ranking: Below 100. Franchise award date: N.A. Franchise expiration date: N.A. Began: July 1, 1980.
Channel capacity: 54 (not 2-way capable). Channels available but not in use: 2.
Basic Service
Subscribers: 314.
Programming (received off-air): KTVQ (C) Billings; KGWC-TV (C), KTWO-TV (N,W) Casper; KHMT (F) Hardin; KCWC-TV (P) Lander-Riverton; KSGW-TV (A) Sheridan.
Programming (via satellite): WGN-TV (W) Chicago; KCNC-TV (C), KRMA-TV (P), KUSA-TV (N), KWGN-TV (W) Denver; KTLA (W) Los Angeles; WPIX (W) New York; A & E; American Movie Classics; Animal Planet; C-SPAN; C-SPAN 2; CNBC; CNN; Cartoon Network; Country Music TV; Court TV; Discovery Channel; Disney Channel; E! Entertainment TV; ESPN; ESPN 2; Fox Family Channel; Headline News; History Channel; Home & Garden Television; Knowledge TV; Learning Channel; Lifetime; MSNBC; MTV; Nashville Network; Nickelodeon; Odyssey; Outdoor Channel; QVC; Sci-Fi Channel; TBS Superstation; The Weather Channel; Travel Channel; Trinity Bcstg. Network; Turner Network TV; USA Network; VH1.
Current originations: Automated time-weather; religious access.
Fee: $40.00 installation; $27.00 monthly; $15.00 additional installation.
Pay Service 1
Pay Units: 24.
Programming (via satellite): Cinemax.
Fee: $10.00 installation; $8.50 monthly.
Pay Service 2
Pay Units: 30.
Programming (via satellite): The New Encore.
Fee: $10.00 installation; $3.50 monthly.
Pay Service 3
Pay Units: 30.
Programming (via satellite): HBO.
Fee: $10.00 installation; $11.00 monthly.
Equipment: Scientific-Atlanta headend; Magnavox amplifiers; CCS Hatfield cable; Oak set top converters; Intercept traps; Scientific-Atlanta satellite antenna; Scientific-Atlanta satellite receivers.
Miles of plant: 13.0 (coaxial). Additional miles planned: 1.0 (coaxial). Homes passed: 410. Total homes in franchised area: 420.
Manager: Robert Jacobson.
City fee: None.
Ownership: Lynda & Robert Jacobson (MSO).

SUNDANCE—Sundance Cable TV Inc., Box 759, Ranchester, WY 82839. Phone: 307-655-9011. Fax: 307-655-9021. County: Crook. ICA: WY0061.
TV Market Ranking: Below 100. Franchise award date: N.A. Franchise expiration date: November 1, 2000. Began: November 1, 1980.
Channel capacity: 54 (not 2-way capable). Channels available but not in use: 2.
Basic Service
Subscribers: 416.
Programming (received off-air): KGWC-TV (C), KTWO-TV (N,W) Casper; KPSD-TV (P) Eagle Butte; KCWC-TV (P) Lander-Riverton; KIVV-TV (F) Lead; KOTA-TV (A) Rapid City.
Programming (via satellite): WGN-TV (W) Chicago; KCNC-TV (C), KUSA-TV (N), KWGN-TV (W) Denver; KTLA (W) Los Angeles; WPIX (W) New York; A & E; American Movie Classics; Animal Planet; C-SPAN; C-SPAN 2; CNBC; CNN; Cartoon Network; Country Music TV; Court TV; Discovery Channel; Disney Channel; E! Entertainment TV; ESPN; ESPN 2; Fox Family Channel; Headline News; History Channel; Home & Garden Television; Knowledge TV; Learning Channel; Lifetime; MSNBC; MTV; Nashville Network; Nickelodeon; Odyssey; Outdoor Channel; QVC; Sci-Fi Channel; TBS Superstation; The Weather Channel; Travel Channel; Trinity Bcstg. Network; Turner Network TV; USA Network; VH1.
Current originations: Automated time-weather.
Fee: $40.00 installation; $27.00 monthly; $15.00 additional installation.
Pay Service 1
Pay Units: 43.
Programming (via satellite): Cinemax.
Fee: $10.00 installation; $8.50 monthly.
Pay Service 2
Pay Units: 35.
Programming (via satellite): The New Encore.
Fee: $10.00 installation; $3.50 monthly.
Pay Service 3
Pay Units: 72.
Programming (via satellite): HBO.
Fee: $10.00 installation; $11.00 monthly.
Equipment: Scientific-Atlanta headend; Magnavox amplifiers; Scientific-Atlanta satellite antenna.
Manager: Robert Jacobson.
City fee: None.
Ownership: Lynda & Robert Jacobson (MSO).

TEN SLEEP—Ten Sleep Cablevision, Box 687, Cowley, WY 82420. Phone: 307-548-6457. Fax: 307-548-2728. County: Washakie. ICA: WY0046.
TV Market Ranking: Outside TV Markets. Franchise award date: N.A. Franchise expiration date: N.A. Began: October 5, 1983.
Channel capacity: N.A. Channels available but not in use: N.A.
Basic Service
Subscribers: 98.
Programming (received off-air): KULR-TV (N) Billings; KTWO-TV (N,W) Casper.
Programming (via satellite): WGN-TV (W) Chicago; KCNC-TV (C), KDVR (F), KMGH-TV (A) Denver; CNN; Discovery Channel; Disney Channel; ESPN; Fox Family Channel; History Channel; Learning Channel; Nashville Network; Odyssey; TBS Superstation; Turner Network TV; USA Network.
Fee: $35.00 installation; $19.95 monthly.
Pay Service 1
Pay Units: N.A.
Programming (via satellite): HBO.
Fee: $11.95 monthly.
Miles of plant: 3.1 (coaxial). Homes passed: 150.
Manager: Jerri Townsend.
Ownership: Cowley Telecable Inc. (MSO).

THERMOPOLIS—TCI Cablevision of Wyoming Inc., Box 1730, Riverton, WY 82501-1730. Phone: 307-856-3248. Fax: 307-856-7156. County: Hot Springs. Also serves East Thermopolis, Hot Springs County. ICA: WY0062.
TV Market Ranking: Below 100 (portions of Hot Springs County); Outside TV Markets (East Thermopolis, portions of Hot Springs County, Thermopolis). Franchise award date: N.A. Franchise expiration date: October 6, 2010. Began: July 1, 1957.
Channel capacity: 76 (not 2-way capable). Channels available but not in use: None.
Basic Service
Subscribers: 1,396.
Programming (received off-air): KTWO-TV (N,W) Casper; KCNC-TV (C) Denver; KCWC-TV (P), KFNE (A), KGWL-TV (C) Lander-Riverton; K32EL (I) Shoshoni.
Programming (via satellite): WGN-TV (W) Chicago; KWGN-TV (W) Denver; C-SPAN; CNN; Comedy Central; Court TV; Discovery Channel; Fox Family Channel; FoxNet; Headline News; Home Shopping Network; Lifetime; Nashville Network; Nickelodeon; Odyssey; QVC; TBS Superstation; The Weather Channel; VH1; WB 100+ Station Group.
Current originations: Automated time-weather; educational access; local access.
Fee: $44.95 installation; $20.40 monthly.
Expanded Basic Service
Subscribers: 1,300.
Programming (via satellite): A & E; American Movie Classics; Animal Planet; CNBC; Cartoon Network; Country Music TV; Court TV; Disney Channel; ESPN; ESPN 2; FX; Fox News Channel; Fox Sports Net Rocky Mountain; Home & Garden Television; Learning Channel; MOVIEplex; MSNBC; MTV; Pax Net; Sci-Fi Channel; Turner Network TV; USA Network.
Fee: $12.62 monthly.
Pay Service 1
Pay Units: 400.
Programming (via satellite): HBO.
Fee: $13.83 monthly.
Pay Service 2
Pay Units: 100.
Programming (via satellite): Showtime.
Fee: $13.83 monthly.
Pay Service 3
Pay Units: 500.
Programming (via satellite): The New Encore.
Fee: $1.75 monthly.
Pay Service 4
Pay Units: 80.
Programming (via satellite): Cinemax.
Fee: $13.00 monthly.
Pay Service 5
Pay Units: 340.
Programming (via satellite): Starz!
Fee: $6.75 monthly.
Pay-Per-View
Addressable homes: 50.
Program Guide: The Cable Guide.
Equipment: Jerrold headend; Jerrold amplifiers; Times Fiber & Comm/Scope cable; Scientific-Atlanta satellite antenna; Scientific-Atlanta satellite receivers.
Miles of plant: 18.5 (coaxial). Total homes in franchised area: 1,983.
Manager: Clint Rodeman. Chief technician: Don Gunsaullus.
City fee: 3% of gross.
Ownership: AT&T Broadband & Internet Services (MSO). Purchased from Tele-Communications Inc., March 9, 1999.

TORRINGTON—James Cable Partners, Box 837, 1942 East A St., Torrington, WY 82240. Phone: 307-532-2706. County: Goshen. Also serves Goshen County (unincorporated areas), Lingle, South Torrington. ICA: WY0014.
TV Market Ranking: Below 100 (portions of Goshen County, South Torrington, Torrington); Outside TV Markets (portions of Goshen County, Lingle). Franchise award date: January 1, 1962. Franchise expiration date: N.A. Began: November 1, 1964.
Channel capacity: 14. Channels available but not in use: N.A.
Basic Service
Subscribers: N.A.
Programming (received off-air): KTNE-TV (P) Alliance; KGWN-TV (C) Cheyenne; KDUH-TV (A), KSTF (C) Scottsbluff.
Programming (via microwave): KCNC-TV (C), KMGH-TV (A), KRMA-TV (P), KUSA-TV (N), KWGN-TV (W) Denver.
Programming (via satellite): ESPN; Fox Family Channel.
Current originations: Automated time-weather.
Fee: $30.00 installation; $17.95 monthly; $20.00 additional installation.
Pay Service 1
Pay Units: N.A.
Programming (via satellite): HBO; Showtime.
Fee: $11.00 monthly (each).
Pay-Per-View
Addressable homes: 1,300.
Viewer's Choice.
Equipment: Jerrold headend; Jerrold amplifiers; Times Fiber cable; Scientific-Atlanta satellite antenna.
Miles of plant: 67.0 (coaxial). Homes passed: 2,640.
Manager: John Friedlan.
City fee: 1% of gross.
Ownership: James Cable Partners (MSO).

UPTON—TCI Cablevision of Wyoming Inc., 410 W. Boxelder Rd., Gillette, WY 82718. Phones: 307-682-4303; 800-788-9457. Fax: 307-682-9631. County: Weston. ICA: WY0036.
TV Market Ranking: Outside TV Markets. Franchise award date: N.A. Franchise expiration date: N.A. Began: November 1, 1978.
Channel capacity: 35 (not 2-way capable). Channels available but not in use: 7.
Basic Service
Subscribers: 320.
Programming (received off-air): KEVN-TV (F), KOTA-TV (A) Rapid City.
Programming (via translator): KGWC-TV (C), KTWO-TV (N,W) Casper.
Programming (via satellite): KCNC-TV (C), KRMA-TV (P), KUSA-TV (N) Denver; A & E; American Movie Classics; Animal Planet; C-SPAN; C-SPAN 2; CNBC; CNN; Cartoon Network; Court TV; Discovery Channel; Disney Channel; E! Entertainment TV; ESPN; Fox Family Channel; Headline News; Learning Channel; Lifetime; MSNBC; MTV; Nashville Network; Nickelodeon; Odyssey; QVC; TBS Superstation; The Weather Channel; Turner Network TV; USA Network.
Fee: $46.95 installation; $26.75 monthly; $1.60 converter; $21.95 additional installation.
Pay Service 1
Pay Units: 90.
Programming (via satellite): HBO.
Fee: $13.05 monthly.
Pay Service 2
Pay Units: 143.
Programming (via satellite): The New Encore.
Fee: $1.75 monthly.

Miles of plant: 13.5 (coaxial); None (fiber optic). Homes passed: 342. Total homes in franchised area: 342.
Manager: Joe Conway. Chief technician: Richard Kuhn. Customer service manager: Doris Linderman.
Ownership: AT&T Broadband & Internet Services (MSO). Purchased from Tele-Communications Inc., March 9, 1999.

WAMSUTTER—Sweetwater Cable TV Co. Inc., Box 8, 602 Broadway, Rock Springs, WY 82901. Phone: 307-362-3773. Fax: 307-382-2781. County: Sweetwater. ICA: WY0039.
TV Market Ranking: Outside TV Markets. Franchise award date: N.A. Franchise expiration date: N.A. Began: April 26, 1981.
Channel capacity: 12 (not 2-way capable). Channels available but not in use: N.A.
Basic Service
Subscribers: 38; Commercial subscribers: 3.
Programming (received off-air): 5 FMs.
Programming (via microwave): KTWO-TV (N,W) Casper; KSL-TV (N), KSTU (F), KTVX (A), KUED (P), KUTV (C) Salt Lake City.
Programming (via satellite): CNN; ESPN; TBS Superstation.
Fee: $25.00 installation; $10.95 monthly.
Pay Service 1
Pay Units: 38.
Programming (via satellite): HBO.
Fee: $12.50 installation; $9.95 monthly.
Local advertising: No.
Equipment: Jerrold headend; Jerrold amplifiers; Times Fiber cable; Prodelin satellite antenna; Collins satellite receivers.
Miles of plant: 3.0 (coaxial). Homes passed: 300. Total homes in franchised area: 300.
Manager: Al Carollo Jr. Chief technician: Larry Gessner. Marketing & program director: John Carollo.
City fee: 2% of gross.
Ownership: Sweetwater Cable TV Co. Inc. (MSO).

WHEATLAND—CommuniComm Services, Suite A, 1135 College Ave., Fort Collins, CO 80524. County: Platte. Also serves Platte County (unincorporated areas). ICA: WY0017.
TV Market Ranking: Outside TV Markets. Franchise award date: January 1, 1962. Franchise expiration date: N.A. Began: September 1, 1963.
Channel capacity: 75. Channels available but not in use: 14.
Basic Service
Subscribers: 1,402.
Programming (received off-air): KTWO-TV (N,W) Casper; KGWN-TV (C) Cheyenne; KDUH-TV (A), KSTF (C) Scottsbluff.
Programming (via microwave): KRMA-TV (P) Denver.
Programming (via satellite): WGN-TV (W) Chicago; KCNC-TV (C), KMGH-TV (A), KUSA-TV (N), KWGN-TV (W) Denver; A & E; American Movie Classics; Animal Planet; C-SPAN; C-SPAN 2; CNBC; CNN; Cartoon Network; Country Music TV; Discovery Channel; Disney Channel; E! Entertainment TV; ESPN; ESPN 2; ESPNews; Fox Family Channel; Fox Sports Net; FoxNet; Headline News; History Channel; Home & Garden Television; Learning Channel; Lifetime; MTV; Nashville Network; Nickelodeon; Outdoor Life Network; QVC; Sci-Fi Channel; TBS Superstation; TV Guide Channel; The Weather Channel; Trinity Bcstg. Network; Turner Network TV; USA Network; Univision; VH1.
Current originations: Public access; leased access.
Fee: $32.95 installation; $30.95 monthly.
Pay Service 1
Pay Units: 243.
Programming (via satellite): Cinemax.
Fee: $10.95 monthly.
Pay Service 2
Pay Units: 211.
Programming (via satellite): HBO.
Fee: $12.95 monthly.
Equipment: Magnavox amplifiers; Times Fiber cable; Scientific-Atlanta satellite antenna.
Miles of plant: 41.0 (coaxial). Homes passed: 1,956.
Manager: Alan Price. Marketing director: Tracy Clodfelter.
City fee: 2% of gross.
Ownership: James Cable Partners (MSO).

WORLAND—TCI Cablevision of Wyoming Inc., Box C, Worland, WY 82401-2606. Phone: 307-347-3244. Fax: 307-347-8349. County: Washakie. Also serves Washakie County. ICA: WY0013.
TV Market Ranking: Outside TV Markets. Franchise award date: N.A. Franchise expiration date: N.A. Began: May 1, 1954.
Channel capacity: 47. Channels available but not in use: None.
Basic Service
Subscribers: 2,211.
Programming (received off-air): KGWL-TV (C) Lander-Riverton; 1 FM.
Programming (via microwave): KTWO-TV (N,W) Casper; KFNE (A) Lander-Riverton; KSL-TV (N) Salt Lake City.
Programming (via satellite): KCNC-TV (C), KRMA-TV (P), KWGN-TV (W) Denver; C-SPAN; Discovery Channel; FoxNet; Lifetime; Odyssey; QVC; TBS Superstation; The Weather Channel.
Current originations: Automated time-weather.
Fee: $44.95 installation; $11.06 monthly.
Expanded Basic Service
Subscribers: 2,051.
Programming (via satellite): A & E; American Movie Classics; Animal Planet; CNBC; CNN; Cartoon Network; Comedy Central; Court TV; ESPN; ESPN 2; FX; Fox Family Channel; Fox Sports Net; Headline News; Home & Garden Television; Learning Channel; MOVIEplex; MTV; Nashville Network; Nickelodeon; Sci-Fi Channel; Turner Network TV; USA Network; VH1.
Fee: $19.00 monthly.
Pay Service 1
Pay Units: 171.
Programming (via satellite): Cinemax.
Fee: $12.75 monthly.
Pay Service 2
Pay Units: 195.
Programming (via satellite): Disney Channel.
Fee: $12.50 monthly.
Pay Service 3
Pay Units: 501.
Programming (via satellite): HBO.
Fee: $14.19 monthly.
Pay Service 4
Pay Units: 238.
Programming (via satellite): Showtime.
Fee: $14.19 monthly.
Pay Service 5
Pay Units: 1,005.
Programming (via satellite): The New Encore.
Fee: $1.75 monthly.
Pay Service 6
Pay Units: N.A.
Programming (via satellite): Starz!
Fee: $6.75 monthly.
Program Guide: The Cable Guide.
Equipment: Jerrold headend; Jerrold amplifiers; Times Fiber cable; Scientific-Atlanta satellite antenna; Scientific-Atlanta satellite receivers.
Miles of plant: 33.3 (coaxial). Homes passed: 2,647. Total homes in franchised area: 2,710.
Manager: Clint Rodeman.
City fee: 3% of gross.
Ownership: AT&T Broadband & Internet Services (MSO). Purchased from Tele-Communications Inc., March 9, 1999.

WYODAK—Tongue River Cable TV Inc., Box 759, Ranchester, WY 82839. Phone: 307-655-9011. Fax: 307-655-9021. County: Campbell. ICA: WY0035.
TV Market Ranking: Outside TV Markets. Franchise award date: N.A. Franchise expiration date: December 1, 1999. Began: January 1, 1985.
Channel capacity: 42 (not 2-way capable). Channels available but not in use: 6.
Basic Service
Subscribers: 175.
Programming (received off-air): KGWC-TV (C), KTWO-TV (N,W) Casper; KIVV-TV (F) Lead; KOTA-TV (A) Rapid City.
Programming (via satellite): WGN-TV (W) Chicago; KCNC-TV (C), KRMA-TV (P), KUSA-TV (N), KWGN-TV (W) Denver; A & E; American Movie Classics; Animal Planet; C-SPAN; CNN; Cartoon Network; Country Music TV; Discovery Channel; Disney Channel; E! Entertainment TV; ESPN; ESPN 2; Fox Family Channel; Headline News; History Channel; Home & Garden Television; Learning Channel; Lifetime; MTV; Nashville Network; Nickelodeon; Outdoor Channel; QVC; Sci-Fi Channel; TBS Superstation; The Weather Channel; Trinity Bcstg. Network; Turner Network TV; USA Network.
Current originations: Automated time-weather.
Fee: $40.00 installation; $27.50 monthly; $15.00 additional installation.
Pay Service 1
Pay Units: 31.
Programming (via satellite): Cinemax.
Fee: $10.00 installation; $8.50 monthly.
Pay Service 2
Pay Units: 33.
Programming (via satellite): The New Encore.
Fee: $10.00 installation; $3.50 monthly.
Pay Service 3
Pay Units: 51.
Programming (via satellite): HBO.
Fee: $10.00 installation; $11.00 monthly.
Local advertising: No.
Equipment: Blonder-Tongue headend; Scientific-Atlanta cable; Miralite satellite antenna; Standard Communications satellite receivers.
Miles of plant: 15.0 (coaxial). Homes passed: 350. Total homes in franchised area: 350.
Manager: Rob Hium.
City fee: 2% of gross.
Ownership: Lynda & Robert Jacobson (MSO).

PUERTO RICO

Total Systems: 13
Total Communities Served: 73
Franchises Not Yet Operating: 0
Applications Pending: 0
Communities with Applications: 0
Number of Basic Subscribers: 278,592
Number of Expanded Basic Subscribers: 152,049
Number of Pay Units: 98,439

Top 100 Markets Represented: None.

For a list of all cable communities included in this section, see the Cable Community Index located in the back of this volume.
For explanation of terms used in cable system listings, see p. D-9.

AGUADILLA—Pegasus Cable Television, Box 5229, Hwy. 465 at Hwy. 110, Aguadilla, PR 00605. Phone: 787-882-7040. Fax: 787-882-3404. Also serves Aguada, Isabela, Moca, Quebradillas. ICA: PR0002.

TV Market Ranking: Below 100. Franchise award date: May 1, 1983. Franchise expiration date: May 1, 2003. Began: May 1, 1986.

Channel capacity: 54 (not 2-way capable). Channels available but not in use: None.

Basic Service

Subscribers: 22,074; Commercial subscribers: 20.

Programming (received off-air): W63BF (I) Aguada; WELU (E) Aguadilla; WOLE-TV (I) Aguadilla-Mayaguez; WUJA (E) Caguas; WMTJ (P), WPRV-TV (I) Fajardo; WIPM-TV (P), WORA-TV (I) Mayaguez; WSTE (I) Ponce; WAPA-TV (I), WTCV (N) San Juan.

Programming (via satellite): WGN-TV (W) Chicago; WNBC (N), WPIX (W) New York; WRAL-TV (C) Raleigh-Durham; A & E; CNN; Cartoon Network; CineLatino; Discovery Channel; ESPN; ESPN 2; EWTN; FoxNet; Gems Television; Headline News; History Channel; Learning Channel; Lifetime; MTV; Nickelodeon; QVC; TBS Superstation; The Weather Channel; Travel Channel; Trinity Bcstg. Network; Turner Network TV; USA Network; VH1.

Current originations: Public access; local news.

Fee: $25.75 installation; $28.84 monthly.

Commercial fee: $12.00 monthly.

Pay Service 1

Pay Units: 739.

Programming (via satellite): Cinemax (multiplexed).

Fee: $10.25 monthly.

Pay Service 2

Pay Units: 454.

Programming (via satellite): Disney Channel.

Fee: $7.21 monthly.

Pay Service 3

Pay Units: 1,531.

Programming (via satellite): HBO (multiplexed).

Fee: $10.25 monthly.

Pay Service 4

Pay Units: 589.

Programming (via satellite): Showtime; The Movie Channel.

Fee: $10.25 monthly.

Pay-Per-View

Addressable homes: 19,836.

Action Pay-Per-View; Playboy TV; Spice; Viewer's Choice.

Fee: $4.95-$6.95.

Pay-per-view manager: Hector Lamourt.

Local advertising: Yes. Available in satellite distributed programming. Local sales manager: Lillian Roman.

Equipment: Scientific-Atlanta & General headend; Scientific-Atlanta amplifiers; Scientific-Atlanta addressable set top converters; Eagle traps; Scientific-Atlanta satellite antenna; Scientific-Atlanta satellite receivers; Sony commercial insert.

Miles of plant: 546.0 (coaxial); None (fiber optic). Homes passed: 81,040. Total homes in franchised area: 83,291.

Manager: Vivian Smith. Chief technician: Ivan Rosa. Program director: Trina Vega. Marketing director: Lillian Roman. Customer service manager: Carmen Hernandez.

Franchise fee fee: 3% of gross.

Ownership: Pegasus Cable Television Inc. (MSO). Purchased from Cable Systems USA Partners, March 30, 1999.

ARECIBO—TCI Cablevision of Puerto Rico, Box 759, Arecibo, PR 00612-0759. Phone: 787-878-8303. Also serves Barceloneta, Camuy, Hatillo. ICA: PR0004.

TV Market Ranking: Below 100. Franchise award date: N.A. Franchise expiration date: N.A. Began: N.A.

Channel capacity: 36. Channels available but not in use: None.

Basic Service

Subscribers: 11,957.

Programming (received off-air): WCCV-TV (I) Arecibo; WLII (I) Caguas-San Juan; WMTJ (P), WPRV-TV (I) Fajardo; WSTE (I) Ponce; WAPA-TV (I), WIPR-TV (P), WKAQ-TV (O), WTCV (N) San Juan.

Programming (via satellite): WXIA-TV (N) Atlanta; WBBM-TV (C), WGN-TV (W) Chicago; WABC-TV (A) New York; BET; CNN; Comedy Central; Discovery Channel; EWTN; Fox Family Channel; Headline News; MTV; Nickelodeon; QVC; TBS Superstation; The Box; The Weather Channel; VH1.

Fee: $60.00 installation; $20.45 monthly.

Expanded Basic Service

Subscribers: 9,618.

Programming (via satellite): A & E; American Movie Classics; ESPN; Turner Network TV; USA Network.

Fee: $1.50 monthly.

Pay Service 1

Pay Units: 3,272.

Programming (via satellite): Cinemax.

Fee: N.A.

Pay Service 2

Pay Units: 696.

Programming (via satellite): Disney Channel.

Fee: N.A.

Pay Service 3

Pay Units: 2,240.

Programming (via satellite): The New Encore.

Fee: N.A.

Pay Service 4

Pay Units: 4,013.

Programming (via satellite): HBO.

Fee: N.A.

Pay Service 5

Pay Units: 1,385.

Programming (via satellite): Showtime.

Fee: N.A.

Program Guide: The Cable Guide.

Miles of plant: 318.2 (coaxial). Homes passed: 31,815. Total homes in franchised area: 34,721.

Chief technician: Edwin Rosario.

Ownership: AT&T Broadband & Internet Services (MSO). Purchased from Tele-Communications Inc., March 9, 1999.

BARRANQUITAS—BuenaVision, Box 8759, 4 Ave. Rafael Cordero, Caguas, PR 00726. Phone: 787-743-2600. Fax: 787-746-5717. Also serves Comerio, Naranjito. ICA: PR0012.

TV Market Ranking: Below 100. Franchise award date: N.A. Franchise expiration date: N.A. Began: N.A.

Channel capacity: 62 (2-way capable). Channels available but not in use: 2.

Basic Service

Subscribers: 756.

Programming (received off-air): WUJA (E) Caguas; WLII (I) Caguas-San Juan; WMTJ (P), WPRV-TV (I) Fajardo; WECN (I) Naranjito; WSTE (I) Ponce; WAPA-TV (I), WIPR-TV (P), WKAQ-TV (O), WRWR-TV (I), WTCV (N) San Juan.

Programming (via satellite): WGN-TV (W) Chicago; WABC-TV (A), WNBC (N), WPIX (W) New York; WRAL-TV (C) Raleigh-Durham; A & E; C-SPAN; CNBC; Cartoon Network; Disney Channel; EWTN; FoxNet; Gems Television; Learning Channel; QVC; TBS Superstation; TV Guide Channel; Turner Classic Movies; Turner Network TV.

Current originations: Automated time-weather; public access; educational access; religious access; leased access; local news.

Fee: $60.95 installation; $20.85 monthly.

Expanded Basic Service

Subscribers: 297.

Programming (via satellite): CBS TeleNoticias; CNN; CineLatino; Discovery Channel; ESPN; Flix; Fox Family Channel; Headline News; Lifetime; MTV; Nickelodeon; USA Network; VH1.

Fee: $8.95 monthly.

Pay Service 1

Pay Units: Included with Caguas, PR.

Programming (via satellite): Cinemax; HBO; Showtime; The Movie Channel; The New Encore.

Fee: $4.95 monthly (Encore), $12.50 monthly (Cinemax or HBO), $15.30 monthly (Showtime or TMC).

Pay-Per-View

Addressable homes: 756.

Action Pay-Per-View; Playboy TV; Spice.

Local advertising: Yes. Available in locally originated, character-generated, taped & automated programming. Rates: $60.00/30 Seconds.

Program Guide: TV Host.

Equipment: Jerrold & Scientific-Atlanta headend; Magnavox amplifiers; Comm/Scope cable; AT&T fiber optic cable; Texscan character generator; Jerrold set top converters; Jerrold addressable set top converters; Scientific-Atlanta satellite antenna; Scientific-Atlanta satellite receivers; Sony commercial insert.

Miles of plant: 33.2 (coaxial); 13.9 (fiber optic). Homes passed: 3,405.

Manager: Jose A. Romero. Chief technician: Adalberto Velez. Marketing director: Ricardo Ferrer. Customer service manager: Victor Jimenez.

Ownership: AT&T Broadband & Internet Services (MSO). Purchased from Tele-Communications Inc., March 9, 1999.

CAGUAS—BuenaVision, Box 8759, 4 Ave. Rafael Cordero, Caguas, PR 00726. Phone: 787-743-2600. Fax: 787-746-5717. Also serves Aguas Buenas, Cidra, Gurabo, Juncos, San Lorenzo. ICA: PR0013.

TV Market Ranking: Below 100. Franchise award date: N.A. Franchise expiration date: N.A. Began: January 1, 1984.

Channel capacity: 62 (2-way capable). Channels available but not in use: 2.

Basic Service

Subscribers: 15,789.

Programming (received off-air): WUJA (E) Caguas; WLII (I) Caguas-San Juan; WMTJ (P), WPRV-TV (I) Fajardo; WECN (I) Naranjito; WSTE (I) Ponce; WAPA-TV (I), WIPR-TV (P), WJPX (X), WKAQ-TV (O), WRWR-TV (I), WTCV (N) San Juan.

Programming (via satellite): WGN-TV (W) Chicago; WABC-TV (A), WNBC (N), WPIX (W) New York; WRAL-TV (C) Raleigh-Durham; A & E; C-SPAN; CNBC; Cartoon Network; Disney Channel; EWTN; FoxNet; Gems Television; Learning Channel; QVC; TBS Superstation; TV Guide Channel; Turner Classic Movies; Turner Network TV.

Current originations: Automated time-weather; public access; educational access; religious access; leased access; local news.

Fee: $60.95 installation; $20.85 monthly.

Expanded Basic Service

Subscribers: 6,717.

Programming (via satellite): CBS TeleNoticias; CNN; CineLatino; Discovery Channel; ESPN; Flix; Fox Family Channel; Headline News; Lifetime; MTV; Nickelodeon; USA Network; VH1.

Fee: $8.95 monthly.

Pay Service 1

Pay Units: 4,416. Includes figures for Barranquitas, Cayey & Humacao, PR.

Programming (via satellite): Cinemax.

Fee: $12.50 monthly.

Pay Service 2

Pay Units: 3,826. Includes figures for Barranquitas, Cayey & Humacao, PR.

Programming (via satellite): The New Encore.

Fee: $4.95 monthly.

Pay Service 3

Pay Units: 9,956. Includes figures for Barranquitas, Cayey & Humacao, PR.

Programming (via satellite): HBO.

Fee: $12.50 monthly.

Pay Service 4

Pay Units: 4,053. Includes figures for Barranquitas, Cayey & Humacao, PR.

Programming (via satellite): Showtime; The Movie Channel.

Fee: $15.30 monthly (each).

Pay-Per-View

Addressable homes: 15,789.

Action Pay-Per-View; Playboy TV; Spice.

Local advertising: Yes. Available in locally originated, character-generated, taped & automated programming. Rates: $60.00/30 Seconds.
Program Guide: TV Host.
Equipment: Jerrold & Scientific-Atlanta headend; Magnavox amplifiers; Comm/Scope cable; AT&T fiber optic cable; Texscan character generator; Jerrold set top converters; Jerrold addressable set top converters; Scientific-Atlanta satellite antenna; Scientific-Atlanta satellite receivers; Sony commercial insert.
Miles of plant: 462.0 (coaxial); None (fiber optic). Homes passed: 49,921.
Manager: Jose A. Romero. Chief technician: Adalberto Velez. Marketing director: Ricardo Ferrer. Customer service manager: Victor Jimenez.
Ownership: AT&T Broadband & Internet Services (MSO). Purchased from Tele-Communications Inc., March 9, 1999.

CAYEY—BuenaVision, Box 8759, 4 Ave. Rafael Cordero, Caguas, PR 00726. Phone: 787-743-2600. Fax: 787-746-5717. Also serves Aibonito. ICA: PR0014.
TV Market Ranking: Below 100. Franchise award date: N.A. Franchise expiration date: N.A. Began: N.A.
Channel capacity: 62 (2-way capable). Channels available but not in use: 2.

Basic Service
Subscribers: 4,702.
Programming (received off-air): WUJA (E) Caguas; WLII (I) Caguas-San Juan; WMTJ (P), WPRV-TV (I) Fajardo; WECN (I) Naranjito; WSTE (I) Ponce; WAPA-TV (I), WIPR-TV (P), WJPX (X), WKAQ-TV (O), WRWR-TV (I), WTCV (N) San Juan.
Programming (via satellite): WGN-TV (W) Chicago; WABC-TV (A), WNBC (N), WPIX (W) New York; WRAL-TV (C) Raleigh-Durham; A & E; C-SPAN; CNBC; Cartoon Network; Disney Channel; EWTN; FoxNet; Gems Television; Learning Channel; QVC; TBS Superstation; TV Guide Channel; Turner Classic Movies; Turner Network TV.
Current originations: Automated time-weather; public access; educational access; religious access; leased access; local news.
Fee: $60.95 installation; $20.85 monthly.

Expanded Basic Service
Subscribers: 1,753.
Programming (via satellite): CBS TeleNoticias; CNN; CineLatino; Discovery Channel; ESPN; Flix; Fox Family Channel; Headline News; Lifetime; MTV; Nickelodeon; USA Network; VH1.
Fee: $8.95 monthly.

Pay Service 1
Pay Units: Included with Caguas, PR.
Programming (via satellite): Cinemax; HBO; Showtime; The Movie Channel; The New Encore.
Fee: $4.95 monthly (Encore), $12.50 monthly (Cinemax or HBO),$15.30 monthly (Showtime or TMC).

Pay-Per-View
Addressable homes: 4,702.
Action Pay-Per-View; Playboy TV; Spice.
Local advertising: Yes. Available in locally originated, character-generated, taped & automated programming. Rates: $60.00/30 Seconds.
Program Guide: TV Host.
Equipment: Jerrold & Scientific-Atlanta headend; Magnavox amplifiers; Comm/Scope cable; AT&T fiber optic cable; Texscan character generator; Jerrold set top converters; Jerrold addressable set top converters; Scientific-Atlanta satellite antenna; Scientific-Atlanta satellite receivers; Sony commercial insert.
Miles of plant: 172.4 (coaxial); 34.0 (fiber optic). Homes passed: 16,364.
Manager: Jose A. Romero. Chief technician: Adalberto Velez. Marketing director: Ricardo Ferrer. Customer service manager: Victor Jimenez.
Ownership: AT&T Broadband & Internet Services (MSO). Purchased from Tele-Communications Inc., March 9, 1999.

CEIBA NAVAL BASE—Americable International Roosevelt Roads Inc., Roosevelt Road Naval Station, Langley Dr., Ceiba, PR 00735. Phone: 787-865-1280. Fax: 787-865-2660. ICA: PR0011.
TV Market Ranking: Below 100. Franchise award date: February 21, 1986. Franchise expiration date: N.A. Began: August 1, 1986.
Channel capacity: 63. Channels available but not in use: None.

Basic Service
Subscribers: 1,946.
Programming (received off-air): WTJX-TV (P) Charlotte Amalie; WAPA-TV (I), WKAQ-TV (O) San Juan.
Programming (via satellite): WXIA-TV (N) Atlanta; WGN-TV (W) Chicago; WABC-TV (A) New York; WRAL-TV (C) Raleigh-Durham; A & E; American Movie Classics; BET; C-SPAN; C-SPAN 2; CNBC; CNN; Country Music TV; Discovery Channel; E! Entertainment TV; ESPN; ESPN 2; Electronic Program Guide; fXM: Movies from Fox; Fox Family Channel; FoxNet; Headline News; Lifetime; MTV; Nashville Network; Nickelodeon; QVC; TBS Superstation; The Weather Channel; Trinity Bcstg. Network; Turner Classic Movies; Turner Network TV; USA Network; VH1.
Fee: $26.38 installation; $28.95 monthly.

Pay Service 1
Pay Units: 1,638.
Programming (via satellite): Disney Channel; HBO; Showtime; The Movie Channel; The New Encore.
Fee: $6.95 monthly (Encore), $9.95 monthly (Disney), $10.95 (Showtime or TMC), $12.95 monthly (HBO).
Equipment: Scientific-Atlanta headend; Magnavox amplifiers; Comm/Scope cable; Scientific-Atlanta set top converters; Standard Communications satellite receivers.
Miles of plant: 30.0 (coaxial). Homes passed: 2,752.
Manager: Serena Taylor. Chief technician: Dennis Lopez.
Ownership: Americable International Inc. (MSO).

HUMACAO—BuenaVision, Box 8759, 4 Ave. Rafael Cordero, Caguas, PR 00726. Phone: 787-743-2600. Fax: 787-746-5717. Also serves Las Piedras, Yabucoa. ICA: PR0015.
TV Market Ranking: Below 100. Franchise award date: N.A. Franchise expiration date: N.A. Began: N.A.
Channel capacity: 62 (2-way capable). Channels available but not in use: 2.

Basic Service
Subscribers: 2,752.
Programming (received off-air): WUJA (E) Caguas; WLII (I) Caguas-San Juan; WMTJ (P), WPRV-TV (I) Fajardo; WECN (I) Naranjito; WSTE (I) Ponce; WAPA-TV (I), WIPR-TV (P), WJPX (X), WKAQ-TV (O), WRWR-TV (I), WTCV (N) San Juan.
Programming (via satellite): WGN-TV (W) Chicago; WABC-TV (A), WNBC (N), WPIX (W) New York; WRAL-TV (C) Raleigh-Durham; A & E; C-SPAN; CNBC; Cartoon Network; Disney Channel; EWTN; FoxNet; Gems Television; Learning Channel; QVC; TBS Superstation; TV Guide Channel; Turner Classic Movies; Turner Network TV.
Current originations: Automated time-weather; public access; educational access; religious access; leased access; local news.
Fee: $60.95 installation; $20.85 monthly.

Expanded Basic Service
Subscribers: N.A.
Programming (via satellite): CBS TeleNoticias; CNN; CineLatino; Discovery Channel; ESPN; Flix; Fox Family Channel; Headline News; Lifetime; MTV; Nickelodeon; USA Network; VH1.
Fee: $8.95 monthly.

Pay Service 1
Pay Units: Included with Caguas, PR.
Programming (via satellite): Cinemax; HBO; Showtime; The Movie Channel; The New Encore.
Fee: $4.95 monthly (Encore), $12.50 monthly (Cinemax or HBO), $13.50 monthly (Showtime or TMC).

Pay-Per-View
Addressable homes: 2,752.
Action Pay-Per-View; Playboy TV; Spice.
Local advertising: Yes. Available in locally originated, character-generated, taped & automated programming. Rates: $60.00/30 Seconds.
Program Guide: TV Host.
Equipment: Jerrold & Scientific-Atlanta headend; Magnavox amplifiers; Comm/Scope cable; AT&T fiber optic cable; Jerrold set top converters; Jerrold addressable set top converters; Scientific-Atlanta satellite antenna; Scientific-Atlanta satellite receivers; Sony commercial insert.
Miles of plant: 310.2 (coaxial); None (fiber optic). Homes passed: 25,802.
Manager: Jose A. Romero. Chief technician: Adalberto Velez. Marketing director: Ricardo Ferrer. Customer service manager: Victor Jimenez.
Ownership: AT&T Broadband & Internet Services (MSO). Purchased from Tele-Communications Inc., March 9, 1999.

LEVITTOWN—Community Cablevision of Puerto Rico, Box 51508, Levittown, PR 00950. Phone: 787-261-0525. Fax: 787-784-2735. Also serves Catano, Toa Alta, Toa Baja. ICA: PR0009.
TV Market Ranking: Below 100. Franchise award date: N.A. Franchise expiration date: January 1, 2000. Began: January 1, 1980.
Channel capacity: 53 (not 2-way capable). Channels available but not in use: None.

Basic Service
Subscribers: 11,000.
Programming (received off-air): WLII (I) Caguas-San Juan; WSVI (A) Christiansted; WMTJ (P), WPRV-TV (I) Fajardo; WSTE (I) Ponce; WAPA-TV (I), WIPR-TV (P), WKAQ-TV (O), WRWR-TV (I), WTCV (N) San Juan.
Programming (via satellite): WPIX (W) New York; C-SPAN; Discovery Channel; Fox Family Channel; Headline News; Home Shopping Network; Lifetime; Nashville Network; TBS Superstation; TV Guide Channel.
Fee: $24.53 monthly.

Expanded Basic Service
Subscribers: 9,600.
Programming (via satellite): WGN-TV (W) Chicago; A & E; CNN; ESPN; MTV; Nickelodeon; USA Network.
Fee: $4.25 monthly.

Pay Service 1
Pay Units: N.A.
Programming (via satellite): Cinemax; Disney Channel; GalaVision; HBO.
Fee: $9.90 monthly (each).
Miles of plant: 160.0 (coaxial); 10.0 (fiber optic). Homes passed: 25,000. Total homes in franchised area: 50,000.
Manager: Francisco Toste Santana. Chief technician: Rafael Ventura. Marketing director: Gabriel Palerm.
Ownership: Century Communications Corp. (MSO). See Cable System Ownership.

LUQUILLO—TCI Cablevision of Puerto Rico, Box 719, Luquillo, PR 00773-0719. Phone: 787-889-3470. Also serves Canovanas, Ceiba, Fajardo, Loiza, Naguabo, Rio Grande. ICA: PR0003.
TV Market Ranking: Below 100. Franchise award date: N.A. Franchise expiration date: N.A. Began: December 1, 1985.
Channel capacity: 36 (not 2-way capable). Channels available but not in use: None.

Basic Service
Subscribers: 19,753.
Programming (received off-air): WCCV-TV (I) Arecibo; WLII (I) Caguas-San Juan; WMTJ (P), WPRV-TV (I) Fajardo; WSTE (I) Ponce; WAPA-TV (I), WIPR-TV (P), WKAQ-TV (O), WTCV (N) San Juan.
Programming (via satellite): WXIA-TV (N) Atlanta; WBBM-TV (C), WGN-TV (W) Chicago; WABC-TV (A) New York; BET; CNN; Comedy Central; Discovery Channel; EWTN; Fox Family Channel; Headline News; MTV; Nickelodeon; QVC; TBS Superstation; The Box; The Weather Channel; VH1.
Fee: $60.00 installation; $20.45 monthly; $2.00 converter; $15.00 additional installation.

Expanded Basic Service
Subscribers: 15,427.
Programming (via satellite): A & E; American Movie Classics; ESPN; Turner Network TV; USA Network.
Fee: $18.95 monthly.

Pay Service 1
Pay Units: 4,373.
Programming (via satellite): Cinemax.
Fee: $10.00 installation; $9.95 monthly.

Pay Service 2
Pay Units: 1,055.
Programming (via satellite): Disney Channel.
Fee: $10.00 installation; $9.95 monthly.

Pay Service 3
Pay Units: 3,925.
Programming (via satellite): The New Encore.
Fee: N.A.

Pay Service 4
Pay Units: 6,502.
Programming (via satellite): HBO.
Fee: $10.00 installation; $9.95 monthly.

Pay Service 5
Pay Units: 2,535.
Programming (via satellite): Showtime.
Fee: $10.00 installation; $9.95 monthly.
Local advertising: No.
Program Guide: The Cable Guide.
Equipment: AML, Jerrold & Hughes headend; Video Data Systems character generator; Jerrold addressable set top converters; Jerrold satellite receivers.
Miles of plant: 421.4 (coaxial). Homes passed: 51,663. Total homes in franchised area: 52,989.
Manager: Leonard Delgado. Marketing director: Lino Garcia.
Ownership: AT&T Broadband & Internet Services (MSO). Purchased from Tele-Communications Inc., March 9, 1999.

MAYAGUEZ—Pegasus Communications of Puerto Rico, Box 7994, Suite 201, Centro Comercial Vista Verde, Mayaguez, PR 00681. Phone: 787-265-6623. Fax: 787-265-2200. E-mail: rferrer@pgtv.com. Also serves Anasco, Caba Rojo, Guanica, Hormigueros, Lajas, Las

Marias, Maricao, Rincon, Sabanna Grande, San German. ICA: PR0008.

TV Market Ranking: Below 100. Franchise award date: June 1, 1984. Franchise expiration date: June 1, 2004. Began: June 16, 1986.

Channel capacity: 62 (2-way capable; operating 2-way). Channels available but not in use: None.

Basic Service

Subscribers: 28,100; Commercial subscribers: 50.

Programming (received off-air): W63BF (I) Aguada; WELU (E), WVEO (I) Aguadilla; WOLE-TV (I) Aguadilla-Mayaguez; WIPM-TV (P), WNJX (I), WORA-TV (I) Mayaguez; WJWN-TV (X) San Sebastian.

Programming (via satellite): WPIX (W) New York; A & E; American Movie Classics; Animal Planet; C-SPAN; CNN; Cartoon Network; Discovery Channel; E! Entertainment TV; ESPN; ESPN 2; EWTN; FX; Fox Family Channel; Headline News; Learning Channel; Lifetime; MTV; Nickelodeon; QVC; Sci-Fi Channel; TBS Superstation; TV Guide Channel; TV Guide Sneak Prevue; The Weather Channel; Travel Channel; Trinity Bcstg. Network; Turner Network TV; USA Network; VH1.

Current originations: Educational access; local access.

Fee: $59.95 installation; $28.65 monthly; $2.50 converter.

Commercial fee: $49.95 monthly.

A la Carte 1

Subscribers: N.A.

Programming (via satellite): Disney Channel.

Fee: N.A.

Pay Service 1

Pay Units: 1,746.

Programming (via satellite): Cinemax (multiplexed).

Fee: $11.95 monthly.

Pay Service 2

Pay Units: 3,641.

Programming (via satellite): HBO (multiplexed).

Fee: $11.95 monthly.

Pay Service 3

Pay Units: 1,475.

Programming (via satellite): The Movie Channel.

Fee: $8.95 monthly.

Pay Service 4

Pay Units: 1,557.

Programming (via satellite): Showtime.

Fee: $10.95 monthly.

Pay-Per-View

Addressable homes: 12,500.

Action Pay-Per-View; Playboy TV; Spice; Viewer's Choice.

Fee: $3.95 (Action or Viewer's Choice); $6.95 (Playboy); $7.95 (Spice).

Pay-per-view manager: Julia Aquilo.

Local advertising: Yes. Available in locally originated programming. Rates: $26.00/30 Seconds.

Equipment: Catel headend; Times Fiber & Comm/Scope cable; Scientific-Atlanta set top converters; Tocom addressable set top converters; Tocom addressable traps; Scientific-Atlanta satellite antenna; Scientific-Atlanta satellite receivers.

Miles of plant: 800.0 (coaxial); 750.0 (fiber optic). Additional miles planned: 50.0 (fiber optic). Homes passed: 85,000.

Manager: Ricardo Oerrer. Chief technician: Josue Digueroa. Program director: Yolanda Robins. Marketing director: Julia Aquilo. Customer service manager: Anabel Padilla.

Ownership: Pegasus Cable Television Inc. (MSO).

MERCEDITA—Teleponce Cable TV Inc., Box 204, Mercedita, PR 00715. Phone: 787-848-7745. Fax: 787-848-7757. Also serves Adjuntas, Arroyo, Coamo, Guayama, Guayanilla, Jayuya, Juana Diaz, Maunabo, Patillas, Penuelas, Playa de Ponce, Ponce, Salinas, Santa Isabel, Tallaboa, Villalba, Yauco. ICA: PR0005.

TV Market Ranking: Below 100. Franchise award date: January 1, 1978. Franchise expiration date: January 1, 1998. Began: September 1, 1979.

Channel capacity: 40. Channels available but not in use: N.A.

Basic Service

Subscribers: 27,067.

Programming (received off-air): WORA-TV (I) Mayaguez; WQTO (P), WSTE (I), WSUR-TV (I) Ponce.

Programming (via satellite): WGN-TV (W) Chicago; WPIX (W) New York; A & E; C-SPAN; CNN; ESPN; EWTN; Fox Family Channel; GalaVision; Headline News; Home Shopping Network; Lifetime; MTV; TBS Superstation; USA Network; VH1.

Current originations: Public access.

Fee: $20.00 installation (aerial), $63.95 (underground); $16.95 monthly.

Pay Service 1

Pay Units: 23,024.

Programming (via satellite): American Movie Classics; Bravo; Disney Channel; HBO; Playboy TV; Showtime.

Fee: N.A.

Local advertising: Yes (insert only). Available in satellite distributed programming. Rates: $12.00/30 Seconds. Local sales manager: Jeffrey Droz.

Program Guide: TV Host.

Equipment: Scientific-Atlanta headend; Jerrold amplifiers; Times Fiber cable; Sony VTRs; Texscan character generator; Scientific-Atlanta, Jerrold & Eagle set top converters; Scientific-Atlanta satellite antenna; Scientific-Atlanta satellite receivers; Arvis commercial insert.

Miles of plant: 1025.0 (coaxial). Additional miles planned: 125.0 (coaxial). Homes passed: 96,922. Total homes in franchised area: 157,602.

Manager: Albert N. Ferraro. Chief technician: John Green. Marketing director: Lourdes Estrada.

Franchise fee: 3% of gross.

Ownership: Teleponce/TPC Cable TV Inc.

SAN JUAN—Cable TV of Greater San Juan, Box 192296, San Juan, PR 00919-2296. Phone: 787-766-0909. Fax: 787-250-6532. Also serves Bayamon, Carolina, Guaynabo, Trujillo Alto. ICA: PR0001.

TV Market Ranking: Below 100. Franchise award date: January 1, 1971. Franchise expiration date: N.A. Began: April 1, 1972.

Channel capacity: 53 (2-way capable). Channels available but not in use: None.

Basic Service

Subscribers: 125,000.

Programming (received off-air): WCCV-TV (I) Arecibo; WDWL (I) Bayamon; WUJA (E) Caguas; WLII (I) Caguas-San Juan; WMTJ (P) Fajardo; WECN (I) Naranjito; WSTE (I) Ponce; WAPA-TV (I), WIPR-TV (P), WKAQ-TV (O), WTCV (N) San Juan.

Programming (via satellite): WSBK-TV (U) Boston; WGN-TV (W) Chicago; WPIX (W) New York; A & E; American Movie Classics; Bravo; C-SPAN; C-SPAN 2; CNN; Cartoon Network; Comedy Central; Discovery Channel; Disney Channel; E! Entertainment TV; ESPN; EWTN; Fox Family Channel; Gems Television; Headline News; Home Shopping Network; Learning Channel; Lifetime; MTV; Nickelodeon; QVC; TBS Superstation; TV Guide Channel; The Box; The Weather Channel; Trinity Bcstg. Network; Turner Network TV; USA Network; VH1.

Current originations: Automated time-weather; public access.

Fee: $41.00 installation; $32.71 monthly; $1.46 converter.

Expanded Basic Service

Subscribers: 102,000.

Programming (via satellite): Primetime 24.

Fee: $2.35 monthly.

Pay Service 1

Pay Units: N.A.

Programming (via satellite): Cinemax; HBO; Showtime; The Movie Channel.

Fee: $14.25 monthly (Cinemax, HBO or Showtime), $14.95 monthly (TMC).

Pay-Per-View

Addressable homes: 46,205.

Local advertising: Yes (locally produced). Available in satellite distributed programming. Local sales manager: David Saxon.

Equipment: Scientific-Atlanta headend; Theta-Com amplifiers; Times Fiber cable; Sony cameras; Panasonic VTRs; Texscan character generator; Oak set top converters; Eagle traps; Scientific-Atlanta satellite antenna; Hughes satellite receivers.

Miles of plant: 1250.0 (coaxial); 20.0 (fiber optic). Homes passed: 243,000. Total homes in franchised area: 317,228.

Manager: Francisco Toste Santana. Chief technician: Jerry Fitz. Marketing director: Gabriel Palerm.

City fee: 2% of gross.

Ownership: Century Communications Corp. (MSO). See Cable System Ownership.

VEGA BAJA—TCI Cablevision of Puerto Rico, Box 719, Luquillo, PR 00773-0719. Phone: 787-889-3470. Also serves Dorado, Manati, Vega Alta. ICA: PR0007.

TV Market Ranking: Below 100. Franchise award date: N.A. Franchise expiration date: N.A. Began: N.A.

Channel capacity: 36. Channels available but not in use: None.

Basic Service

Subscribers: 7,626.

Programming (received off-air): WCCV-TV (I) Arecibo; WLII (I) Caguas-San Juan; WMTJ (P), WPRV-TV (I) Fajardo; WSTE (I) Ponce; WAPA-TV (I), WIPR-TV (P), WKAQ-TV (O), WTCV (N) San Juan.

Programming (via satellite): WXIA-TV (N) Atlanta; WBBM-TV (C), WGN-TV (W) Chicago; WABC-TV (A) New York; BET; CNN; Comedy Central; Discovery Channel; EWTN; Fox Family Channel; Headline News; MTV; Nickelodeon; QVC; TBS Superstation; The Box; The Weather Channel; VH1.

Current originations: Public access.

Fee: $60.00 installation; $20.45 monthly.

Expanded Basic Service

Subscribers: 6,637.

Programming (via satellite): A & E; American Movie Classics; ESPN; Turner Network TV; USA Network.

Fee: $1.50 monthly.

Pay Service 1

Pay Units: 2,399.

Programming (via satellite): Cinemax.

Fee: N.A.

Pay Service 2

Pay Units: 644.

Programming (via satellite): Disney Channel.

Fee: N.A.

Pay Service 3

Pay Units: 1,728.

Programming (via satellite): The New Encore.

Fee: N.A.

Pay Service 4

Pay Units: 3,698.

Programming (via satellite): HBO.

Fee: N.A.

Pay Service 5

Pay Units: 1,329.

Programming (via satellite): Showtime.

Fee: N.A.

Miles of plant: 241.6 (coaxial). Homes passed: 25,244. Total homes in franchised area: 26,795.

Manager: Leonard Delgado. Marketing director: Lino Garcia.

Ownership: AT&T Broadband & Internet Services (MSO). Purchased from Tele-Communications Inc., March 9, 1999.

OTHER U.S. TERRITORIES AND POSSESSIONS

Total Systems: 5
Total Communities Served: 7
Franchises Not Yet Operating: 0
Applications Pending: 0
Communities with Applications: 0
Number of Basic Subscribers: 65,842
Number of Expanded Basic Subscribers: 22,354
Number of Pay Units: 21,824

Top 100 Markets Represented: None.

For a list of all cable communities included in this section, see the Cable Community Index located in the back of this volume.
For explanation of terms used in cable system listings, see p. D-9.

Cuba

GUANTANAMO BAY—Antilles Cable, 10 S. Franklin Turnpike, Ramsey, NJ 07446. Phone: 201-825-9090. Fax: 201-825-8794. County: Guantanamo Bay. ICA: CU0001.

TV Market Ranking: Outside TV Markets. Franchise award date: December 5, 1986. Franchise expiration date: N.A. Began: March 1, 1987.

Channel capacity: 35 (not 2-way capable). Channels available but not in use: 1.

Basic Service

Subscribers: 1,504.

Programming (received off-air): 3 FMs.

Programming (via satellite): WXIA-TV (N) Atlanta; WGN-TV (W) Chicago; WABC-TV (A) New York; WRAL-TV (C) Raleigh-Durham; A & E; BET; C-SPAN; CNN; Comedy Central; Country Music TV; Discovery Channel; ESPN; Electronic Program Guide; Fox Family Channel; FoxNet; Learning Channel; Lifetime; MTV; Nashville Network; Nickelodeon; TBS Superstation; Telemundo; VH1.

Current originations: Automated time-weather; local news.

Fee: $10.00 installation; $21.00 monthly; $3.00 converter; $7.00 additional installation.

Pay Service 1

Pay Units: 604.

Programming (via satellite): Cinemax.

Fee: $8.00 monthly.

Pay Service 2

Pay Units: 325.

Programming (via satellite): Disney Channel.

Fee: $8.00 monthly.

Pay Service 3

Pay Units: 1,023.

Programming (via satellite): HBO.

Fee: $8.00 monthly.

Pay Service 4

Pay Units: 434.

Programming (via satellite): The Movie Channel.

Fee: $8.00 monthly.

Pay Service 5

Pay Units: 532.

Programming (via satellite): Showtime.

Fee: $8.00 monthly.

Local advertising: No.

Program Guide: CableView.

Equipment: Magnavox amplifiers; M/A-Com cable; Zenith set top converters; Zenith addressable set top converters; Andrew, Scientific-Atlanta satellite antenna.

Miles of plant: 40.0 (coaxial). Homes passed: 3,000. Total homes in franchised area: 3,000.

Manager: Sean Feeney. Marketing & program director: John Finley.

Ownership: Phoenix Cable Inc. (MSO).

Guam

AGANA—Guam Cable TV, 530 W. O'Brien Dr., Agana, GU 96910. Phones: 671-477-7815; 617-477-7818. Fax: 671-477-7847. County: Guam. ICA: GU0001.

TV Market Ranking: Below 100. Franchise award date: N.A. Franchise expiration date: N.A. Began: October 1, 1970.

Channel capacity: 69 (2-way capable; not operating 2-way). Channels available but not in use: 4.

Basic Service

Subscribers: 29,485.

Programming (received off-air): KGTF (P), KUAM-TV (C,N,A) Agana; KTGM (A) Tamuning; allband FM.

Programming (via tape): KCET (P) Los Angeles; KFVE (U) Honolulu; KRCA (I) Riverside-Los An; KTLA (W) Los Angeles; KTTV (F) Los Angeles.

Programming (via satellite): A & E; Bravo; C-SPAN; CNBC; CNN; Cartoon Network; Comedy Central; Country Music TV; Discovery Channel; ESPN; ESPN 2; EWTN; Fox Family Channel; History Channel; International Channel; Learning Channel; Lifetime; MTV; Nashville Network; Nickelodeon; Sci-Fi Channel; TV Food Network; The Health Network; The Inspirational Network; The Weather Channel; USA Network; VH1.

Current originations: Automated time-weather; local news.

Fee: $31.95 installation; $28.95 monthly; $4.95 converter; $16.95 additional installation.

Pay Service 1

Pay Units: N.A.

Programming (via satellite): Cinemax; Disney Channel; HBO; Showtime; The Movie Channel.

Fee: $8.95 monthly (Disney), $11.95 monthly (Cinemax or TMC),$12.95 monthly (HBO or Showtime).

Pay-Per-View

Hot Choice; Viewer's Choice; special events.

Local advertising: Yes (locally produced & insert). Available in satellite distributed programming. Local sales manager: Jim Rapp.

Program Guide: TV Guam.

Equipment: Jerrold headend; Theta-Com amplifiers; General & Systems Wire cable; Hitachi cameras; Panasonic VTRs; 3M character generator; Magnavox set top converters; Harris satellite antenna.

Miles of plant: 709.0 (coaxial); 97.0 (fiber optic). Homes passed: 53,043.

Manager: Harrison Flora. Chief technician: Gary McEachern. Program & marketing director: Ernie Galito.

Territory fee: 4% of gross.

Ownership: Joan S. & Lee M. Holmes (MSO).

Mariana Islands

SAIPAN—Saipan Cable TV, Box 1015, San Jose, Saipan, MP 96950. Phone: 670-234-7350. Fax: 670-234-9828. County: Mariana Islands. Also serves Tinian. ICA: MR0001.

TV Market Ranking: Below 100. Franchise award date: N.A. Franchise expiration date: N.A. Began: June 1, 1976.

Channel capacity: 38 (2-way capable; operating 2-way). Channels available but not in use: None.

Basic Service

Subscribers: 6,580.

Programming (via tape): KABC-TV (A) Los Angeles; KCBS-TV (C) Los Angeles; KCOP-TV (I) Los Angeles; KNBC-TV (N) Los Angeles; KTLA (I) Los Angeles; KTTV (F) Los Angeles.

Programming (via satellite): A & E; Bravo; C-SPAN; Comedy Central; Country Music TV; Discovery Channel; ESPN; EWTN; Fox Family Channel; Goodlife TV Network; Learning Channel; Lifetime; MTV; Nashville Network; Nickelodeon; Sci-Fi Channel; The Inspirational Network; USA Network; VH1.

Current originations: Automated time-weather; educational access; government access.

Fee: $23.50 installation; $22.95 monthly; $1.95 converter.

Pay Service 1

Programming (via tape): Cinemax; HBO: Playboy TV, Showtime, The Movie Channel.

Fee: $10.95 installation; $8.95 monthly (Disney), $10.95 monthly (Showtime), $11.95 monthly (Cinemax, HBO or TMC).

Local advertising: Yes. Rates: $700.00/Hour.

Program Guide: TV Saipan.

Equipment: Phasecom & Scientific-Atlanta headend; Theta-Com & Magnavox amplifiers; Times Fiber & Trilogy cable; Panasonic cameras; Panasonic VTRs; ADM satellite antenna; Microdyne satellite receivers.

Miles of plant: 90.0 (coaxial); 20.0 (fiber optic). Additional miles planned: 25.0 (coaxial). Homes passed: 10,000. Total homes in franchised area: 11,000.

Manager: Fred Lord. Chief technician: Gary McEachern. Marketing director: Brad Cleven.

Ownership: Joan S. & Lee M. Holmes (MSO).

Virgin Islands

ST. CROIX—St. Croix Cable TV, 4501 Estate Diamond Christianste, St. Croix, VI 00820. Phone: 340-778-6701. Fax: 340-778-5230. County: Virgin Islands. ICA: VI0002.

TV Market Ranking: Below 100. Franchise award date: January 1, 1980. Franchise expiration date: January 1, 2015. Began: April 1, 1981.

Channel capacity: 60 (2-way capable; operating 2-way). Channels available but not in use: None.

Basic Service

Subscribers: 13,800.

Programming (received off-air): WTJX-TV (P) Charlotte Amalie; WSVI (A) Christiansted; WAPA-TV (I), WKAQ-TV (O) San Juan; 17 FMs.

Programming (via satellite): WGN-TV (W) Chicago; WNBC (N) New York; C-SPAN 2; Electronic Program Guide; FoxNet; TBS Superstation; TV Guide Sneak Prevue.

Current originations: Public access; government access.

Fee: $33.06 installation; $12.67 monthly; $9.84 additional installation.

Commercial fee: $24.00 monthly.

Expanded Basic Service

Subscribers: 9,172.

Programming (via satellite): A & E; BET; C-SPAN; CNBC; CNN; Discovery Channel; E! Entertainment TV; ESPN; Fox Family Channel; Goodlife TV Network; Headline News; Knowledge TV; Learning Channel; Lifetime; MTV; Nickelodeon; Sci-Fi Channel; TV Food Network; Travel Channel; Trinity Bcstg. Network; Turner Network TV; USA Network; VH1.

Fee: $27.52 monthly.

A la Carte 1

Subscribers: N.A.

Programming (via satellite): Bravo; Cartoon Network; Court TV; Flix; Fox Sports Net; Turner Classic Movies.

Fee: $5.25 monthly (package), $1.60 monthly (Bravo, Cartoon, Court or FSN), $2.65 monthly (Flix or TMC).

Pay Service 1

Pay Units: N.A.

Programming (via satellite): Cinemax; DMX; Disney Channel; HBO (multiplexed); Showtime (multiplexed).

Fee: $40.00 installation; $7.95 monthly (DMX), $9.54 monthly (Cinemax, Disney, or Showtime), $10.60 monthly (HBO).

Pay-Per-View

Addressable homes: 13,800.

Action Pay-Per-View; Spice Hot; Viewer's Choice; special events.

Fee: Varies.

Local advertising: Yes (locally produced & insert). Available in satellite distributed & locally originated programming. Rates: $5.58/Minute; $2.79/30 Seconds. Local sales manager: Lawrence Nyfield.

Equipment: Scientific-Atlanta headend; Scientific-Atlanta amplifiers; Comm/Scope cable; Sony VTRs; BEI character generator; Pioneer set top converters; Pioneer addressable set top converters; Scientific-Atlanta satellite antenna; Scientific-Atlanta satellite receivers; ChannelMatic commercial insert.

Miles of plant: 480.0 (coaxial). Additional miles planned: 10.0 (coaxial). Homes passed: 35,000.

Manager: Jack White. Chief technician: Don Bridgman. Marketing director: Amnerys A. Maldonado. Customer service manager: Ella-Sean Forbes.

City fee: 5% of gross.

Ownership: Innovative Communications Corp.

ST. THOMAS—Caribbean Communications Corp., 1 Beltjen Place, St. Thomas, VI 00802-6735. Phone: 809-776-2150. Fax: 809-774-5029. E-mail: info@cabletv.vi. Web site: http://www.cabletv.vi. County: Virgin Islands. Also serves St. John. ICA: VI0001.

TV Market Ranking: Below 100. Franchise award date: October 21, 1985. Franchise expiration date: October 20, 2000. Began: January 1, 1966.

Channel capacity: 77 (2-way capable; operating 2-way). Channels available but not in use: 5.

Basic Service

Subscribers: 14,084; Commercial subscribers: 389.

Programming (received off-air): WTJX-TV (P) Charlotte Amalie; WSVI (A) Christiansted; WAPA-TV (I), WKAQ-TV (O) San Juan; 23 FMs.
Programming (via satellite): WGN-TV (W) Chicago; WNBC (N), WPIX (W) New York; C-SPAN; C-SPAN 2; EWTN; FoxNet; Knowledge TV; Learning Channel; TBS Superstation; TV Guide Channel; TV Guide Sneak Prevue.
Current originations: Educational access; government access; religious access; leased access; local news.
Fee: $53.96 installation; $10.16 monthly; $3.05 converter.
Commercial fee: $10.16 monthly.

Expanded Basic Service
Subscribers: 13,182.
Programming (via satellite): A & E; American Movie Classics; BET; Bravo; C-SPAN; CNN; CNNfn; Cartoon Network; Comedy Central; Country Music TV; Court TV; Discovery Channel; Disney Channel; E! Entertainment TV; ESPN; ESPN 2; Fox Family Channel; Headline News; History Channel; International Channel; Lifetime; MTV; Nick at Nite's TV Land; Nickelodeon; QVC; Romance Classics; Sci-Fi Channel; The Inspirational Network; The Weather Channel; Travel Channel; Trinity Bcstg. Network; Turner Network TV; USA Network; VH1; Z Music Television.
Fee: $2.00 installation; $18.89 monthly.

Pay Service 1
Pay Units: 3,126.
Programming (via satellite): Cinemax.
Fee: $2.00 installation; $7.35 monthly.

Pay Service 2
Pay Units: 2,775.
Programming (via satellite): Starz!; The New Encore.
Fee: $2.00 installation; $9.45 monthly.

Pay Service 3
Pay Units: 6,538.
Programming (via satellite): HBO.
Fee: $2.00 installation; $12.08 monthly.

Pay Service 4
Pay Units: 2,875.
Programming (via satellite): Flix; The Movie Channel.
Fee: $2.00 installation; $9.45 monthly.

Pay Service 5
Pay Units: 3,592.
Programming (via satellite): Showtime.
Fee: $2.00 installation; $10.50 monthly.

Pay-Per-View
Addressable homes: 14,084.
Hot Choice; Playboy TV; Spice2; movies.
Fee: $5.95 (Hot Choice); $6.95 (Playboy TV); $7.95 (Spice2).

Local advertising: No.
Program Guide: TV Guide.
Equipment: General headend; General amplifiers; Comm/Scope cable; JVC & Ikegami cameras; Sony VTRs; Amiga character generator; Tocom & Jerrold addressable set top converters; Intercept traps; Scientific-Atlanta satellite antenna; General satellite receivers.
Miles of plant: 355.0 (coaxial); 5.0 (fiber optic). Homes passed: 26,591. Total homes in franchised area: 27,000.
Manager: Andrea L. Martin. Chief technician: Craig F. Nicastro.
Territory fee: 5% of gross.
Ownership: Caribbean Communications Corp.

Wireless Cable Systems

Asterisk (*) indicates planned system.

Alabama

ATHENS—Madison Communications Inc., 216 S. Marion St., Athens, AL 35611-2504. Phone: 205-536-3724. County: Limestone. ICA: AL0244.
Microwave channels reported: N.A.
Began: N.A.
Channel capacity: N.A.
Ownership: Madison Communications Inc.

BUCKS—Wireless One of Bucks, 5805 Hwy. 43 N, Satsuma, AL 36572. Phones: 334-675-7621; 888-947-3663. Fax: 334-679-8221. Web site: http://www.wirelessone.com. Counties: Baldwin, Mobile & Washington, AL; George & Greene, MS. Also serves Baldwin County (portions), Bay Minette, Citronelle, Daphne, Fairhope, Grand Bay, Loxley, Mobile, Mobile County, Perdido, Saraland, Satsuma, Semmes, Silverhill, Theodore, Washington County (portions), Wilmer, AL; George County (portions), Greene County (portions), MS. ICA: AL0245.
Total homes in service area: 113,102.
Microwave channels reported: N.A.
Began: March 1, 1996.
Channel capacity: 20. Channels available but not in use: None.
Basic Service
Subscribers: 1,581.
Programming (received off-air): WALA-TV (F), WEAR-TV (A), WEIQ (P), WKRG-TV (C), WPMI (N) Mobile-Pensacola.
Programming (via satellite): WGN-TV (W) Chicago; A & E; BET; CNN; Discovery Channel; Disney Channel; ESPN; Fox Family Channel; Fox Sports Net South; Lifetime; Nashville Network; Nick at Nite; Nickelodeon; QVC; TBS Superstation; The Weather Channel; Turner Network TV; USA Network.
Fee: $99.95 installation; $22.95 monthly.
Pay Service 1
Pay Units: N.A.
Programming (via satellite): HBO; Showtime.
Fee: $9.95 monthly (Showtime); $11.95 monthly (HBO).
Equipment: Jerrold set top converters.
Manager: Gerald Painter. Chief technician: Tom Hinricks. Marketing & program director: David Brown.
Ownership: Wireless One Inc. (MSO).

DEMOPOLIS—Wireless One of Demopolis, 306 Industrial Park N, Demopolis, AL 36732. Phones: 334-285-5290; 888-947-3663. Fax: 334-289-8237.
Web site: http://www.wirelessone.com. County: Marengo. ICA: AL0248.
Microwave channels reported: N.A.
Began: N.A.
Channel capacity: 31. Channels available but not in use: 3.
Basic Service
Subscribers: 792.
Programming (received off-air): WIIQ (P) Demopolis; WGBC (N), WTOK-TV (A,F) Meridian; WAKA (C) Montgomery-Selma.
Programming (via satellite): WGN-TV (W) Chicago; A & E; BET; C-SPAN; CNN; Country Music TV; Discovery Channel; Disney Channel; ESPN; Fox Family Channel; FoxNet; Headline News; History Channel; Learning Channel; Lifetime; Nashville Network; Nick at Nite; Nickelodeon; TBS Superstation; The Weather Channel; Turner Network TV; USA Network.
Fee: $99.95 installation; $22.95 monthly.
Pay Service 1
Pay Units: N.A.
Programming (via satellite): HBO; Showtime.
Fee: $9.95 monthly (Showtime); $11.95 monthly (HBO).
Pay-Per-View
Viewer's Choice.
Fee: $3.90.
Manager: John Vickeri. Chief technician: Dennis Soloman. Marketing & program director: David Brown.
Ownership: Wireless One Inc. (MSO).

DOTHAN—Wireless One of Dothan, 106 Eastland Dr., Dothan, AL 36303. Phones: 334-702-4111; 888-947-3663. Fax: 334-702-4379. Web site: http://www.wirelessone.com. County: Houston. ICA: AL0249.
Microwave channels reported: N.A.
Began: N.A.
Channel capacity: 31. Channels available but not in use: N.A.
Basic Service
Subscribers: 880.
Programming (received off-air): WDHN (A), WTVY (C) Dothan; WGIQ (P) Louisville; WSFA (N) Montgomery-Selma; WDFX-TV (F) Ozark.
Programming (via satellite): A & E; BET; CNN; Country Music TV; Discovery Channel; Disney Channel; ESPN; Fox Family Channel; Fox Sports Net South; History Channel; Lifetime; MTV; Nashville Network; Nick at Nite; Nickelodeon; QVC; TBS Superstation; The Weather Channel; Turner Network TV; USA Network.
Fee: $99.95 installation; $22.95 monthly.
Pay Service 1
Pay Units: N.A.
Programming (via satellite): HBO; Showtime (multiplexed).
Fee: $9.95 monthly (Showtime), $11.95 monthly (HBO).
Pay-Per-View
Viewer's Choice.
Fee: $3.90.
Manager: Randy Clark. Chief technician: Larry McAlpin. Marketing & program director: Susan Money.
Ownership: Wireless One Inc. (MSO).

FLORENCE—Wireless One of Florence, 510 Cherry St., Florence, AL 35630. Phones: 504-926-7778; 888-947-3663. Web site: http://www.wirelessone.com. County: Lauderdale. ICA: AL0253.
Microwave channels reported: N.A.
Began: N.A.
Channel capacity: N.A. Channels available but not in use: N.A.
Basic Service
Subscribers: N.A.
Programming (received off-air): WFIQ (P) Florence; WAAY-TV (A), WAFF (N), WHNT-TV (C), WZDX (F) Huntsville-Decatur.
Programming (via satellite): WGN-TV (W) Chicago; A & E; BET; C-SPAN; CNN; Cartoon Network; Country Music TV; Discovery Channel; Disney Channel; ESPN; Fox Family Channel; Fox Sports Net South; History Channel; Learning Channel; Lifetime; Nashville Network; Nickelodeon; TBS Superstation; The Weather Channel; Turner Network TV; USA Network; VH1.
Fee: $99.95 installation; $22.95 monthly.
Pay Service 1
Pay Units: N.A.
Programming (via satellite): Cinemax; HBO; Showtime.
Fee: $9.95 monthly (Showtime), $10.95 monthly (Cinemax), $11.95 monthly (HBO).
Pay-Per-View
Viewer's Choice.
Fee: $3.90.
Ownership: Wireless One Inc. (MSO).

GADSDEN—Wireless One of Gadsden, Suite 400, 2506 Lakeland Dr., Jackson, MS 39208. Phones: 504-926-7778; 888-947-3663. Web site: http://www.wirelessone.com. County: Etowah. ICA: AL0254.
Microwave channels reported: N.A.
Began: N.A.
Channel capacity: N.A. Channels available but not in use: N.A.
Basic Service
Subscribers: N.A.
Programming (received off-air): WJSU-TV (C) Anniston; WBRC-TV (F), WVTM-TV (N) Birmingham; WPXH (X) Gadsden; WCIQ (P) Mount Cheaha State Park.
Programming (via satellite): WGN-TV (W) Chicago; A & E; BET; C-SPAN; CNBC; CNN; Discovery Channel; ESPN; ESPN 2; Fox Family Channel; History Channel; Home Shopping Network; Learning Channel; Lifetime; Nashville Network; Nickelodeon; QVC; TBS Superstation; The Weather Channel; Turner Network TV; USA Network; VH1.
Fee: $99.95 installation; $28.95 monthly.
Pay Service 1
Pay Units: N.A.
Programming (via satellite): Cinemax; HBO; Showtime.
Fee: $9.95 monthly (Showtime), $10.95 monthly (Cinemax), $11.95 monthly (HBO).
Pay-Per-View
Viewer's Choice.
Fee: $3.90.
Ownership: Wireless One Inc. (MSO).

HUNTSVILLE—Wireless One of Huntsville, 113 Castle Dr., Madison, AL 35758. Phone: 205-430-5288. Fax: 205-430-3345. Counties: Limestone & Madison. Also serves Athens, Madison. ICA: AL0250.
Microwave channels reported: N.A.
Began: N.A.
Channel capacity: 31. Channels available but not in use: 4.
Basic Service
Subscribers: 4,182.
Programming (received off-air): WAAY-TV (A), WAFF (N), WHIQ (P), WHNT-TV (C), WZDX (F) Huntsville-Decatur.
Programming (via satellite): WGN-TV (W) Chicago; A & E; CNN; Cartoon Network; Country Music TV; Discovery Channel; Disney Channel; ESPN; Fox Family Channel; Fox Sports Net South; Learning Channel; Lifetime; Nashville Network; Nickelodeon; TBS Superstation; The Weather Channel; Turner Network TV; USA Network; VH1.
Fee: $19.95 monthly.
Pay Service 1
Pay Units: N.A.
Programming (via satellite): HBO; Showtime.
Fee: $7.95 monthly (Showtime), $9.95 monthly (HBO).
Pay-Per-View
Viewer's Choice.
Fee: $3.95.
Manager: Chuck Keeter. Chief technician: David Gregory. Marketing & program director: David Brown.
Ownership: Wireless One Inc. (MSO).

MOBILE—Mobile Wireless TV, 4123-A Government Blvd., Mobile, AL 36693. Phone: 334-602-1000. Fax: 334-602-1009. County: Mobile. Also serves Grand Bay, Irvington, Mobile County. ICA: AL0243.
Microwave channels reported: N.A.
Began: November 1, 1994.
Channel capacity: 11. Channels available but not in use: None.
Basic Service
Subscribers: 500.
Programming (received off-air): WJCT (P) Jacksonville; WALA-TV (F), WEAR-TV (A), WEIQ (P), WKRG-TV (C), WMPV-TV (T), WPMI (N) Mobile-Pensacola.
Programming (via satellite): CNN; Discovery Channel; ESPN; Fox Family Channel; Fox Sports Net South; Nashville Network; Nickelodeon; TBS Superstation; Turner Network TV.
Fee: $150.00 installation; $17.95 monthly.
Pay Service 1
Pay Units: 450.
Programming (via satellite): Showtime; The Movie Channel.
Fee: $7.95 monthly (each).
Manager: Dana Walters.
Ownership: Mobile Limited Liability.

TUSCALOOSA—Wireless One of Tuscaloosa, Suite 400, 2506 Lakeland Dr., Jackson, MS 39208. Phones: 504-926-7778; 888-947-3663. Web site: http://www.wirelessone.com. County: Tuscaloosa. ICA: AL0255.
Microwave channels reported: N.A.
Began: N.A.
Channel capacity: N.A. Channels available but not in use: N.A.
Basic Service
Subscribers: N.A.
Programming (received off-air): WBIQ (P), WBRC-TV (F), WIAT (C), WVTM-TV (N) Birmingham; WCFT-TV (C) Tuscaloosa.
Programming (via satellite): WGN-TV (W) Chicago; A & E; BET; CNN; Country Music

TV; Discovery Channel; E! Entertainment TV; ESPN; Fox Family Channel; Fox Sports Net South; History Channel; Learning Channel; Lifetime; Nashville Network; Nickelodeon; TBS Superstation; The Health Network; The Weather Channel; Turner Classic Movies; Turner Network TV; USA Network; VH1.
Fee: $99.95 installation; $22.95 monthly.
Pay Service 1
Pay Units: N.A.
Programming (via satellite): Disney Channel; HBO; Showtime.
Fee: $9.95 monthly (Showtime), $10.95 monthly (Disney), $11.95 monthly (HBO), $27.95 monthly (Disney, HBO & Showtime).
Pay-Per-View
Viewer's Choice; movies.
Fee: $3.90.
Ownership: Wireless One Inc. (MSO).

Alaska

ANCHORAGE—American Telecasting of Anchorage Inc., 1306 E. 74th Ave., Anchorage, AK 99518-3212. Phone: 907-349-0133. Fax: 907-349-0093. Web site: http://www.amtele.com. County: Anchorage. ICA: AK0045.
Microwave channels reported: N.A.
Began: N.A.
Channel capacity: 125 (not 2-way capable).
Manager: Rose Brock..
Ownership: American Telecasting Inc. (MSO). Sale pends to Sprint Corp.

ANCHORAGE—Alaskan Choice Television, Suite 100, 15-77 C St., Anchorage, AK 99501. Phone: 907-263-9910. Fax: 907-263-9911. Counties: Anchorage & Matanuska-Susitna. Also serves Wasilla. ICA: AK0047.
Microwave channels reported: N.A.
Began: N.A.
Channel capacity: 125 (not 2-way capable). Channels available but not in use: None.
Basic Service
Subscribers: N.A.
Programming (received off-air): KAKM (P), KIMO (A), KTUU-TV (N), KTVA (C), KYES (U,W) Anchorage.
Programming (via satellite): WGN-TV (W) Chicago; A & E; Animal Planet; BET; Bloomberg Information TV; C-SPAN; C-SPAN 2; CNBC; CNN; CNN/SI; CNNfn; Cartoon Network; Comedy Central; Country Music TV; Court TV; Discovery Channel; Disney Channel; E! Entertainment TV; ESPN; ESPN 2; ESPN Classic Sports; ESPNews; Fox Sports Net Northwest; Fox Sports Net West; Gala-Vision; Golf Channel; Headline News; History Channel; Home & Garden Television; Home Shopping Network; Learning Channel; Lifetime; MSNBC; MTV; Nashville Network; Outdoor Life Network; Ovation; QVC; Sci-Fi Channel; TV Food Network; The Health Network; The Inspirational Network; The Weather Channel; Turner Classic Movies; Turner Network TV; USA Network; VH1.
Current originations: Automated time-weather; educational access.
Fee: $35.00 monthly.
Pay Service 1
Pay Units: N.A.
Programming (via satellite): Cinemax (multiplexed); Encore Movie Networks; HBO The Works.
Fee: N.A.
Manager: Kate Giard. Chief engineer: Tom Peak. Program director & customer service manager: Betsy Hill. Marketing director: Steve Strait.
Ownership: Alaskan Choice Television (MSO).

FAIRBANKS—Alaskan Choice Television, 3532 International Way, Fairbanks, AK 99701. Phone: 907-459-2288. Fax: 907-456-5289. County: Fairbanks North Star. ICA: AK0048
Total homes in service area: 105,000.
Microwave channels reported: N.A.
Began: N.A.
Channel capacity: 120 (not 2-way capable). Channels available but not in use: 20.
Basic Service
Subscribers: N.A.
Programming (received off-air): KAKM (P), KIMO (A), KTUU-TV (N), KTVA (C), KYES (U,W) Anchorage.
Programming (via satellite): WGN-TV (W) Chicago; A & E; Animal Planet; BET; Bloomberg Information TV; C-SPAN; C-SPAN 2; CNBC; CNN; CNN/SI; CNNfn; Cartoon Network; Comedy Central; Country Music TV; Court TV; Discovery Channel; Disney Channel; E! Entertainment TV; ESPN; ESPN 2; ESPN Classic Sports; ESPNews; Fox Sports Net Northwest; Fox Sports Net West; Gala-Vision; Golf Channel; Headline News; History Channel; Home & Garden Television; Home Shopping Network; Learning Channel; Lifetime; MSNBC; MTV; Nashville Network; Outdoor Life Network; Ovation; QVC; Sci-Fi Channel; TV Food Network; The Health Network; The Inspirational Network; The Weather Channel; Turner Classic Movies; Turner Network TV; USA Network; VH1.
Current originations: Automated time-weather; educational access.
Fee: $35.00 monthly.
Pay Service 1
Pay Units: N.A.
Programming (via satellite): Cinemax (multiplexed); Encore Movie Networks; HBO (multiplexed); HBO The Works.
Fee: N.A.
Manager: Kate Giard. Chief technician: Tom Peak. Program & marketing director: Steve Strait.
Ownership: Alaskan Choice Television (MSO).

Arizona

FLAGSTAFF—Microwave Communication Services, Suite 900, 400 Perimeter Center Terrace NE, Atlanta, GA 30346. Phone: 404-804-6448. Fax: 404-409-0060. County: Coconino. ICA: AZ0116.
Microwave channels reported: N.A.
Channel capacity: N.A.
Ownership: Microwave Communication Services (MSO).

PHOENIX—People's Choice TV, 2921 N. 30th Ave., Phoenix, AZ 85017. Phone: 602-269-1350. Fax: 602-269-2045. County: Maricopa. ICA: AZ0120.
Microwave channels reported: N.A.
Channel capacity: N.A.
Manager: Steve Rawley.
Ownership: People's Choice TV Partners (MSO). Sale pends to Sprint Corp.

TUCSON—People's Choice TV, 5311 E. Broadway, Tucson, AZ 85711. Phone: 520-750-9900. County: Pima. ICA: AZ0118.
Microwave channels reported: N.A.
Channel capacity: N.A.
Ownership: People's Choice TV Partners (MSO). Sale pends to Sprint Corp.

VERDE VALLEY—Virginia Communications Inc., Suite B-1, 7621 E. Gray Rd., Scottsdale, AZ 85260-3423. Phone: 480-596-8283. Fax: 480-596-2973. County: Yavapai. ICA: AZ0121.
Microwave channels reported: N.A.
Channel capacity: N.A.
Ownership: Virginia Communications Inc.

YUMA—Microlink Television, No. 2, 1325 W. 16th St., Yuma, AZ 85364-4496. Phone: 520-783-2345. County: Yuma. ICA: AZ0119.
Microwave channels reported: N.A.
Channel capacity: N.A.
Ownership: Microlink Television.

Arkansas

FORT SMITH—Nucentrix Broadband Networks Inc., Suite 200, 200 Chisholm Place, Plano, TX 75075. Phone: 972-423-9494. Fax: 972-423-0819. County: Sebastian. ICA: AR0294.
Microwave channels reported: N.A.
Channel capacity: N.A.
Ownership: Nucentrix Broadband Networks (MSO).

LITTLE ROCK—American Telecasting of Little Rock Inc., Little Rock Corporate Center, Suite 43, 7123 I-30, Little Rock, AR 72209. Phones: 501-565-1400; 800-789-1440. Fax: 501-565-5740. Web site: http://www.amtele.com. County: Pulaski. ICA: AR0296.
Microwave channels reported: N.A.
Began: December 1, 1993.
Channel capacity: 33. Channels available but not in use: N.A.
Basic Service
Subscribers: 3,207; Commercial subscribers: 668.
Programming (received off-air): KARK-TV (N), KATV (A), KETS (P), KLRT (F), KTHV (C) Little Rock; KASN (U), KVTN (I) Pine Bluff.
Programming (via satellite): WGN-TV (W) Chicago; A & E; American Movie Classics; BET; CNN; Cartoon Network; Country Music TV; Discovery Channel; ESPN; ESPN 2; EWTN; Fox Family Channel; Headline News; Learning Channel; Lifetime; MTV; Nashville Network; Nickelodeon; Sci-Fi Channel; TBS Superstation; The Weather Channel; Turner Network TV; USA Network.
Fee: $199.95 installation; $21.95 monthly; $4.95 converter; $25.00 additional installation.
Pay Service 1
Pay Units: N.A.
Programming (via satellite): Disney Channel; HBO; Showtime.
Fee: $6.00 monthly (Disney), $6.95 monthly (Showtime), $10.95 monthly (HBO).
Manager: Bill Raschka. Chief technician: Dan Clark. Customer service manager: Connie Dobson.
Ownership: American Telecasting Inc. (MSO). Sale pends to Sprint Corp.

PARAGOULD—Nucentrix Broadband Networks Inc., Suite 200, 200 Chisholm Place, Plano, TX 75075. Phone: 972-423-9494. Fax: 972-423-0819. Counties: Clay, Craighead, Greene & Poinsett. Also serves Bono, Jonesboro, Marmaduke, Rector, Trumann. ICA: AR0295.
Total homes in service area: 28,227.
Microwave channels reported: N.A.
Began: April 1, 1992.
Channel capacity: 20. Channels available but not in use: None.
Basic Service
Subscribers: 1,962.
Programming (via satellite): WGN-TV (W) Chicago; A & E; CNN; Discovery Channel; Disney Channel; ESPN; Knowledge TV; Nashville Network; TBS Superstation; TV Guide Channel; The Weather Channel; USA Network.
Fee: $50.00 installation; $28.95 monthly.
Pay Service 1
Pay Units: 157.
Programming (via satellite): Cinemax.
Fee: $9.95 monthly.
Pay Service 2
Pay Units: 167.
Programming (via satellite): HBO.
Fee: $10.95 monthly.
Manager: Frederick Frank. Chief technician: Sam Schultz.
Ownership: Nucentrix Broadband Networks (MSO). Purchased from Heartland Wireless Communications Inc.

California

BAKERSFIELD—CS Wireless Systems Inc., Suite 101, 5610 District Blvd., Bakersfield, CA 93313. Phone: 805-397-2224. Fax: 805-397-2223. County: Kern West. ICA: CA0406.
Total homes in service area: 162,000.
Microwave channels reported: N.A.
Began: N.A.
Channel capacity: 42. Channels available but not in use: N.A.
Basic Service
Subscribers: 9,300.
Fee: N.A.
Ownership: CS Wireless Systems Inc. (MSO).

FRESNO—Choice TV, Box 2628, Fresno, CA 93745-2628. Phones: 209-442-1977; 800-794-6400. Fax: 209-442-1745. Web site: http://www.amtele.com. County: Fresno. Also serves Caruthers, Easton. ICA: CA0407.
Microwave channels reported: N.A.
Began: N.A.
Channel capacity: N.A. Channels available but not in use: N.A.
Basic Service
Subscribers: N.A.
Programming (received off-air): KGMC (W) Clovis-Fresno; K34AV (H), K69GV (I), KAIL (U), KFSN-TV (A), KJEO (C), KSEE (N), KVPT (P) Fresno; KFTV (S) Hanford-Fresno; KNSO (W) Merced; K66CQ (I) O'Neals; KPXF (X) Porterville; KMSG-TV (O) Sanger-Fresno; KNXT (E) Visalia; KMPH (F) Visalia-Fresno.
Programming (via satellite): A & E; American Movie Classics; CNN; Discovery Channel; ESPN; EWTN; Fox Family Channel; Fox Sports Net Bay Area; GalaVision; Headline News; Knowledge TV; Lifetime; NASA TV; Nashville Network; Nickelodeon; Sci-Fi Channel; TBS Superstation; TV Guide Channel; Turner Network TV; USA Network.
Current originations: Educational access.
Fee: N.A.
Manager: Maggie Gold. Customer service manager: Donna Kennedy.
Ownership: American Telecasting Inc. (MSO). Sale pends to Sprint Corp.

MERCED—Choice TV, Box 2628, Fresno, CA 93745. Phone: 559-442-1970. Fax: 559-442-1760. Web site: http://www.amtele.com. County: Merced. ICA: CA0436.
Microwave channels reported: N.A.
Began: N.A.
Channel capacity: N.A.
Ownership: American Telecasting Inc. (MSO). Sale pends to Sprint Corp.

MONTEREY—American Telecasting of Monterey Bay Inc., 536 Abbott St., Salinas, CA 93901. Phone: 408-751-7404. Fax: 408-751-

7410. Web site: http://www.amtele.com.
County: Monterey. ICA: CA0437.
Microwave channels reported: N.A.
Began: N.A.
Channel capacity: N.A.
Manager: Filomena Fagundes.
Ownership: American Telecasting Inc. (MSO). Sale pends to Sprint Corp.

REDDING—American Telecasting of Redding Inc., 20276 Skypark Dr., Redding, CA 96002. Phones: 530-221-8815; 800-683-8848. Fax: 530-221-8827. Web site: http://www.amtele.com. Counties: Shasta & Tehama. Also serves Anderson, Keswick, Olinda, Red Bluff, Round Mountain, Shingletown. ICA: CA0408.
Total homes in service area: 82,000.
Microwave channels reported: WLW740, F group, MMDS; WMH789, H1, MMDS; WMH781, H2, MMDS; WMH785, H3, MMDS.
Began: November 1, 1993.
Channel capacity: 32. Channels available but not in use: 20.
Basic Service
Subscribers: 169.
Programming (received off-air): KHSL-TV (C), KNVN (N) Chico; KCVU (U) Paradise; KIXE-TV (P) Redding; KRCR-TV (A) Redding-Chico.
Programming (via satellite): A & E; CNBC; CNN; Comedy Central; Discovery Channel; Disney Channel; E! Entertainment TV; ESPN; Home & Garden Television; Learning Channel; Lifetime; Nashville Network; Nickelodeon; Sci-Fi Channel; TBS Superstation; TV Guide Channel; Trinity Bcstg. Network; Turner Classic Movies; Turner Network TV; USA Network.
Fee: $19.95 installation; $20.95 monthly.
Pay Service 1
Pay Units: N.A.
Programming (via satellite): HBO; Showtime.
Fee: $8.50 monthly (Showtime), $10.95 monthly (HBO).
Local advertising: Yes. Regional interconnect: Northwest Cable Advertising.
Equipment: Jerrold set top converters.
Manager: Jack McCauley. Chief technician: Mike Beyer. Customer service manager: Linda Smith.
Ownership: American Telecasting Inc. (MSO). Sale pends to Sprint Corp.

RIVERSIDE & SAN BERNARDINO—Cross Country Wireless Cable, Suite B, 6177 Rivercrest Dr., Riverside, CA 92507. Phones: 909-653-4482; 909-653-4200. Fax: 909-656-9254. Counties: Riverside West & San Bernardino. ICA: CA0409.
Microwave channels reported: N.A.
Began: April 1, 1991.
Channel capacity: 31. Channels available but not in use: None.
Basic Service
Subscribers: 43,259.
Programming (received off-air): KABC-TV (A), KCAL-TV (I), KCBS-TV (C), KCOP (U), KMEX-TV (S), KNBC (N), KTLA (W), KTTV (F) Los Angeles; KVCR-TV (P) San Bernardino.
Programming (via satellite): WGN-TV (W) Chicago; American Movie Classics; BET; CNN; Discovery Channel; ESPN; Fox Family Channel; MTV; Nashville Network; Nickelodeon; TBS Superstation; TV Guide Channel; USA Network.
Fee: $49.95 installation; $18.95 monthly.
Pay Service 1
Pay Units: 36,750.
Programming (via satellite): Cinemax; Disney Channel; HBO; Showtime.
Fee: $4.00 monthly (Cinemax, Disney or Showtime), $7.00 monthly (HBO).
Pay-Per-View
Addressable homes: 42,000.
Action Pay-Per-View.
Manager: Gary Tapia. Chief technician: Sean Driscoll.
Ownership: SBC Media Ventures.

SACRAMENTO—Pacific West Cable TV, Suite 9, 1513 Sports Dr., Sacramento, CA 95834. Phones: 916-928-2500; 916-928-1454. Fax: 916-928-0825. Counties: El Dorado West, Placer, Sacramento & Yolo. Also serves El Dorado County (portions), Placer County (portions), Yolo County (portions). ICA: CA0410.
Total line of sight homes: 485,000. Total homes in service area: 507,000.
Microwave channels reported: N.A.
Began: March 18, 1994.
Channel capacity: 29 (not 2-way capable). Channels available but not in use: None.
Basic Service
Subscribers: 15,700; Commercial subscribers: 300.
Programming (received off-air): KCRA-TV (N), KOVR (C), KTXL (F), KVIE (P), KXTV (A) Sacramento-Stockton.
Programming (via satellite): WGN-TV (W) Chicago; A & E; BET; CNN; Discovery Channel; ESPN; Lifetime; MTV; Nashville Network; Nick at Nite; Nickelodeon; Sci-Fi Channel; TBS Superstation; TV Guide Channel; Turner Network TV; USA Network; VH1.
Fee: $60.00 installation; $21.95 monthly.
Commercial fee: $21.95 monthly.
Pay Service 1
Pay Units: 3,700.
Programming (via satellite): Cinemax.
Fee: $6.00 monthly.
Pay Service 2
Pay Units: 6,100.
Programming (via satellite): Disney Channel.
Fee: $3.00 monthly.
Pay Service 3
Pay Units: 6,000.
Programming (via satellite): HBO.
Fee: $8.00 monthly.
Pay Service 4
Pay Units: 3,800.
Programming (via satellite): Showtime.
Fee: $6.00 monthly.
Pay-Per-View
Special events.
Fee: Varies.
Equipment: Scientific-Atlanta headend; Microtek character generator; Superior satellite antenna; Scientific-Atlanta satellite receivers; ChannelMaster commercial insert.
Manager: Karen Parker. Customer service manager: Bonnie Simpson.
Ownership: Wireless Broadcasting Systems of America Inc. (MSO).

***SAN FRANCISCO**—Videowave Television, Box 640790, 821 Malcolm Rd., San Jose, CA 95164-0790. Phone: 415-259-7777. County: San Francisco. ICA: CA0411.
Microwave channels reported: N.A.
Scheduled to begin: N.A.
Channel capacity: N.A.
Manager: Brian Reynolds.
Ownership: Videowave Television (MSO).

SAN JOSE—Pacific Bell Video Services, 2410 Camino Ramon, San Ramon, CA 94583. Phone: 510-806-5818. County: Santa Clara. ICA: CA0441.
Microwave channels reported: N.A.
Began: N.A.
Channel capacity: N.A.
Ownership: SBC Media Ventures.

***SAN JOSE**—Videowave Television, Box 640790, 821 Malcolm Rd., San Jose, CA 95164-0790. Phone: 415-259-7777. County: Santa Clara. ICA: CA0412.
Microwave channels reported: N.A.
Scheduled to begin: N.A.
Channel capacity: N.A.
Manager: Brian Reynolds.
Ownership: Videowave Television (MSO).

SAN LUIS OBISPO—TVCN, Suite 300, 10020 E. Girard Ave., Denver, CO 80231. Phone: 303-751-2900. Fax: 303-751-1081. County: San Luis Obispo. ICA: CA0413.
Microwave channels reported: N.A.
Channel capacity: N.A.
Manager: Jackie Porter.
Ownership: TV Communications Network Inc.

***STOCKTON**—CAI Wireless Systems Inc., 18 Corporate Woods Blvd., Albany, NY 12211. Phone: 518-462-2632. Fax: 518-462-3045. County: San Joaquin. ICA: CA0438.
Microwave channels reported: N.A.
Scheduled to begin: N.A.
Channel capacity: N.A.
Ownership: CS Wireless Systems Inc. (MSO).

VISALIA—Choice TV, Box 2628, Fresno, CA 93745-2628. Phone: 209-442-1970. Web site: http://www.amtele.com. County: Tulare. ICA: CA0420.
Microwave channels reported: N.A.
Channel capacity: N.A.
Ownership: American Telecasting Inc. (MSO). Sale pends to Sprint Corp.

YUBA CITY—American Telecasting of Yuba City Inc., Suite E-5, 2947 Colusa Hwy., Yuba City, CA 95993. Phone: 916-755-2106. Fax: 916-751-0164. Web site: http://www.amtele.com. County: Sutter. ICA: CA0443.
Microwave channels reported: N.A.
Began: N.A.
Channel capacity: N.A.
Manager: Kevin McKnight.
Ownership: American Telecasting Inc. (MSO). Sale pends to Sprint Corp.

Colorado

COLORADO SPRINGS—American Telecasting of Colorado Springs Inc., Suite 500, 1096 Elkton Dr., Colorado Springs, CO 80907-3561. Phones: 719-535-8141; 800-878-4284. Fax: 719-535-2828.
Web site: http://www.amtele.com. Counties: Crowley, El Paso, Fremont, Otero & Pueblo. Also serves Avondale, Calhan, Ellicott, Fountain, Fowler, Monument, Ordway, Penrose, Pueblo, Rocky Ford, Rush, Yoder. ICA: CO0192.
Total line of sight homes: 190,000.
Microwave channels reported: N.A.
Began: November 1, 1989.
Channel capacity: 33 (2-way capable; not operating 2-way). Channels available but not in use: N.A.
Basic Service
Subscribers: 14,000.
Programming (received off-air): KKTV (C), KOAA-TV (N), KRDO-TV (A), KTSC (P), KXRM-TV (F,U) Colorado Springs-Pueblo.
Programming (via satellite): WGN-TV (W) Chicago; A & E; American Movie Classics; Animal Planet; CNBC; CNN; Cartoon Network; Discovery Channel; ESPN; ESPN 2; EWTN; Fox Family Channel; Fox Sports Net; Headline News; Learning Channel; Lifetime; MTV; Nashville Network; Nick at Nite; Nickelodeon; Sci-Fi Channel; TBS Superstation; TV Guide Channel; The Weather Channel; Turner Network TV; USA Network; VH1.
Current originations: Educational access.
Fee: $22.95 installation; $21.95 monthly.
Commercial fee: $21.95 monthly.
Pay Service 1
Pay Units: 12,500.
Programming (via satellite): Disney Channel; HBO; Showtime.
Fee: $6.00 monthly (Disney or Showtime), $10.95 monthly (HBO).
Pay-Per-View
Addressable homes: 12,500.
Spice; Viewer's Choice.
Fee: $3.95.
Local advertising: Yes. Available in satellite distributed programming.
Equipment: Emcee headend; Zenith set top converters.
Manager: Deborah Goth. Chief technician: Dan Royse.
Ownership: American Telecasting Inc. (MSO). Sale pends to Sprint Corp.

DENVER—American Telecasting of Denver Inc., 2175 S. Cherry St., Denver, CO 80222. Phones: 303-759-1204; 800-745-2740. Fax: 303-759-1222. Web site: http://www.amtele.com. County: Denver. ICA: CO0195.
Total line of sight homes: 550,000. Total homes in service area: 650,000.
Microwave channels reported: N.A.
Began: December 20, 1993.
Channel capacity: 32. Channels available but not in use: N.A.
Basic Service
Subscribers: N.A.
Programming (received off-air): KBDI-TV (P) Broomfield; KCNC-TV (C), KDVR (F), KMGH-TV (A), KRMA-TV (P), KTVD (U), KUSA-TV (N), KWGN-TV (W) Denver.
Programming (via satellite): WGN-TV (W) Chicago; A & E; CNBC; CNN; Country Music TV; Discovery Channel; ESPN; Fox Family Channel; Lifetime; MTV; Nickelodeon; Sci-Fi Channel; TBS Superstation; USA Network.
Fee: $39.95 installation; $17.95 monthly.
Pay Service 1
Pay Units: N.A.
Programming (via satellite): Disney Channel; HBO; Showtime.
Fee: $5.00 monthly (Showtime), $6.00 monthly (Disney), $10.95 monthly (HBO).
Manager: Paul Beckelheimer. Chief technician: Tom Hughes.
Ownership: American Telecasting Inc. (MSO). Sale pends to Sprint Corp.

FORT COLLINS—American Telecasting of Fort Collins Inc., 207 N. Summitview Dr., Fort Collins, CO 80524. Phones: 970-416-0085; 970-416-9440. Fax: 970-416-0093. Web site: http://www.amtele.com. County: Larimer. ICA: CO0197.
Microwave channels reported: N.A.
Channel capacity: N.A.
Chief technician: Matt Boutte.
Ownership: American Telecasting Inc. (MSO). Sale pends to Sprint Corp.

WRAY—Southwest Telecommunications, Box 309, Palisade, NE 69040. Phone: 308-285-3880. Fax: 308-285-3811. County: Yuma. Also serves Yuma County. ICA: CO0194.
Microwave channels reported: WHK934, E group, MMDS; WHK935, F group, MMDS.
Began: March 1, 1990.
Channel capacity: 11 (not 2-way capable). Channels available but not in use: None.
Basic Service
Subscribers: 239.

Programming (via satellite): CNN; Discovery Channel; ESPN; Fox Family Channel; Nashville Network; Nickelodeon; TBS Superstation; The Weather Channel; Turner Network TV.
Fee: $15.95 monthly.
Pay Service 1
Pay Units: 16.
Programming (via satellite): Disney Channel.
Fee: $8.95 monthly.
Pay Service 2
Pay Units: 34.
Programming (via satellite): HBO.
Fee: $10.95 monthly.
Equipment: Zenith set top converters.
Manager: Don Suda. Chief technician: Gary Hanken. Marketing director: Shannon Peuoteaux.
Ownership: Southwest Telecommunications Co-op Assn. Inc. (MSO).

Connecticut

***HARTFORD**—Connecticut Choice Television Inc., Suite One, 65 Louis St., Newington, CT 06111-4598. Phone: 860-667-9990. Fax: 860-667-4199. County: Hartford. ICA: CT0031.
Total homes in service area: 1,057,000.
Microwave channels reported: N.A.
Scheduled to begin: N.A.
Channel capacity: N.A.
Manager: Kevin O'Connell.
Ownership: CAI Wireless Systems Inc. (MSO). Sale pends to MCI WorldCom Inc.

District of Columbia

WASHINGTON—Washington Choice, 9246 Springhill Lane, Greenbelt, MD 20770. Phone: 301-513-0123. Fax: 301-513-0195. County: District of Columbia. ICA: DC0004.
Total line of sight homes: 1,295,000. Total homes in service area: 1,439,000.
Microwave channels reported: N.A.
Began: N.A.
Channel capacity: N.A. Channels available but not in use: N.A.
Basic Service
Subscribers: 2,000.
Programming (via satellite): BET; C-SPAN; C-SPAN 2; CNBC; CNN; ESPN; Home Team Sports; Nickelodeon; TBS Superstation.
Fee: $29.95 installation; $29.95 monthly.
Pay Service 1
Pay Units: N.A.
Programming (via satellite): Arabic Channel; HBO.
Fee: $10.00 monthly (HBO), $20.00 monthly (Arabic Channel).
Pay-Per-View
Special events.
Fee: Varies.
Manager: Eyob Gebrekidan.
Ownership: CAI Wireless Systems Inc. (MSO). Sale pends to MCI WorldCom Inc.

Florida

***BRADENTON**—American Telecasting Inc., Suite 500, 1096 Elkton Dr., Colorado Springs, CO 80907-3561. Phone: 719-632-5544. Fax: 719-632-5549. Web site: http://www.amtele.com. County: Manatee. ICA: FL0301.
Microwave channels reported: N.A.
Scheduled to begin: N.A.
Channel capacity: N.A.
Ownership: American Telecasting Inc. (MSO). Sale pends to Sprint Corp.

DAYTONA BEACH—American Telecasting of Daytona Beach, Suite B, 4700 L. B. McLeod Rd., Orlando, FL 32811. Phone: 904-322-8558. Web site: http://www.amtele.com. County: Volusia. ICA: FL0316.
Microwave channels reported: N.A.
Began: N.A.
Channel capacity: N.A. Channels available but not in use: N.A.
Basic Service
Subscribers: N.A.
Programming (received off-air): WKCF (W) Clermont; WCEU (P) New Smyrna Beach; WESH (N), WFTV (A), WKMG-TV (C), WMFE-TV (P), WOFL (F), WRBW (U) Orlando-Daytona Beach.
Programming (via satellite): WGN-TV (W) Chicago; Discovery Channel; ESPN; Headline News; Nashville Network; TBS Superstation; The Weather Channel; VH1.
Fee: N.A.
Pay Service 1
Pay Units: N.A.
Programming (via satellite): Showtime.
Fee: N.A.
Ownership: American Telecasting Inc. (MSO). Sale pends to Sprint Corp.

FORT MYERS—Superview of Fort Myers, 5500-2 Division Dr., Fort Myers, FL 33905. Phones: 941-693-1621; 941-693-5700. Fax: 941-693-7643. County: Lee. ICA: FL0302.
Microwave channels reported: N.A.
Began: August 1, 1991.
Channel capacity: N.A. Channels available but not in use: N.A.
Basic Service
Subscribers: 8,000.
Programming (received off-air): WFTX (F) Cape Coral; WBBH-TV (N), WINK-TV (C), WZVN-TV (A) Fort Myers-Naples; WRXY-TV (I) Tice.
Programming (via satellite): WGN-TV (W) Chicago; A & E; American Movie Classics; CNN; Discovery Channel; Disney Channel; ESPN; EWTN; Fox Family Channel; Headline News; Lifetime; NASA TV; Nashville Network; Nickelodeon; Sunshine Network; TBS Superstation; The Weather Channel; Turner Network TV; USA Network.
Fee: $29.95 installation; $22.45 monthly.
Pay Service 1
Pay Units: 2,939.
Programming (via satellite): HBO.
Fee: $10.95 monthly.
Pay Service 2
Pay Units: 4,928.
Programming (via satellite): Showtime.
Fee: $6.95 monthly.
Local advertising: Yes. Regional interconnect: Cable Advertising Sales.
Manager: John Brown. Chief technician: Joe Tineda.
Ownership: BellSouth Entertainment Inc.

FORT PIERCE—Wireless Broadcasting of Fort Pierce, Box 361056, Melbourne, FL 32936-1056. Phones: 561-871-1688; 561-871-0344. Fax: 561-340-7042. Counties: Martin & St. Lucie. Also serves Martin County, St. Lucie County. ICA: FL0303.
Total homes in service area: 150,000.
Microwave channels reported: N.A.
Began: May 15, 1992.
Channel capacity: 32. Channels available but not in use: 1.
Basic Service
Subscribers: 13,000.
Programming (received off-air): WTCE (E) Fort Pierce; WTVX (U) Fort Pierce-Vero Beach; WPBF (A) Tequesta-West Palm Beach; WFLX (F), WPEC (C), WPTV (N), WXEL-TV (P) West Palm Beach.
Programming (via satellite): A & E; CNN; Discovery Channel; ESPN; Fox Family Channel; Headline News; Lifetime; MTV; Nashville Network; Nickelodeon; Sunshine Network; TBS Superstation; The Weather Channel; Turner Classic Movies; Turner Network TV; USA Network.
Fee: $29.95 installation; $21.35 monthly.
Expanded Basic Service
Subscribers: 6,800.
Programming (via satellite): Disney Channel; Sci-Fi Channel.
Fee: $4.00 monthly.
Pay Service 1
Pay Units: 6,000.
Programming (via satellite): Cinemax.
Fee: $6.95 monthly.
Pay Service 2
Pay Units: 6,300.
Programming (via satellite): HBO.
Fee: $8.95 monthly.
Pay-Per-View
Special events.
Fee: Varies.
Manager: Luis Del Pino. Chief technician: Wayne Laloo.
Ownership: Wireless Broadcasting Systems of America Inc. (MSO).

FORT WALTON BEACH—Wireless One of Fort Walton Beach, 8804 A. Grow Dr., Pensacola, FL 32514-7050. Phones: 904-474-1110; 888-947-3663. Fax: 904-244-1704. County: Okaloosa. ICA: FL0337.
Total homes in service area: 54,584.
Microwave channels reported: N.A.
Began: N.A.
Channel capacity: 31. Channels available but not in use: N.A.
Basic Service
Subscribers: 779.
Programming (received off-air): WALA-TV (F), WEAR-TV (A), WKRG-TV (C), WPMI (N), WSRE (P) Mobile-Pensacola.
Programming (via satellite): WGN-TV (W) Chicago; A & E; C-SPAN; CNN; Cartoon Network; Country Music TV; Discovery Channel; Disney Channel; ESPN; Fox Family Channel; History Channel; Home Shopping Network; Lifetime; MTV; Nashville Network; Nickelodeon; Sunshine Network; TBS Superstation; The Weather Channel; Turner Network TV; USA Network.
Fee: $99.95 installation; $22.95 monthly.
Pay Service 1
Pay Units: N.A.
Programming (via satellite): HBO; Showtime; The Movie Channel.
Fee: $9.95 monthly (Showtime); $10.95 monthly (TMC); $11.95 monthly (HBO).
Pay-Per-View
Viewer's Choice.
Fee: $3.95.
Manager: George Barnett. Chief technician: Gary Gray. Marketing & program director: David Brown.
Ownership: Wireless One Inc. (MSO).

GAINESVILLE—Wireless One of Gainesville, Suite A6, 605 N.W. 53rd Ave., Gainesville, FL 32609. Phones: 352-376-5475; 888-947-3663. Fax: 352-395-6655.
Web site: http://www.wirelessone.com.
Counties: Alachua, Baker, Bradford, Columbia, Levy, Marion, Putnam & Union. Also serves Alachua County, Baker County (portions), Bradford County, Bronson, Citra, Columbia County (portions), Fort White, Hampton, Hawthorne, High Springs, Lake Butler, Lawtey, Levy County (portions), Melrose, Newberry, Putnam County (portions), Reddick, Starke, Union County, Waldo, Williston. ICA: FL0329.
Total homes in service area: 93,761.
Microwave channels reported: N.A.
Began: January 1, 1996.
Channel capacity: 14. Channels available but not in use: None.
Basic Service
Subscribers: 3,376.
Programming (received off-air): WCJB (A), WUFT (P) Gainesville; WGFL (W) High Springs; WJXT (C), WTLV (N) Jacksonville; WOGX (F) Ocala-Gainesville.
Programming (via satellite): WGN-TV (W) Chicago; A & E; C-SPAN; CNN; Cartoon Network; Country Music TV; Discovery Channel; Disney Channel; ESPN; Fox Family Channel; History Channel; Learning Channel; Lifetime; Nashville Network; Nickelodeon; Sunshine Network; TBS Superstation; The Weather Channel; Turner Network TV; USA Network; VH1.
Fee: $99.95 installation; $22.95 monthly.
Pay Service 1
Pay Units: 30.
Programming (via satellite): HBO.
Fee: $11.95 monthly.
Pay Service 2
Pay Units: N.A.
Programming (via satellite): Cinemax; Showtime.
Fee: $9.95 monthly (each).
Pay-Per-View
Viewer's Choice.
Fee: $3.90.
Manager: Marilyn Deas. Chief technician: Mike McCoy. Marketing & program director: David Brown.
Ownership: Wireless One Inc. (MSO).

JACKSONVILLE—American Telecasting of Jacksonville Inc., Suite 9, 8936 Western Way, Jacksonville, FL 32256. Phone: 904-464-0473. Fax: 904-464-0780.
Web site: http://www.amtele.com.
County: Duval. ICA: FL0317.
Total homes in service area: 352,729.
Microwave channels reported: N.A.
Began: March 1, 1994.
Channel capacity: 33. Channels available but not in use: N.A.
Basic Service
Subscribers: 1,558.
Programming (received off-air): WAWS-TV (F), WJCT (P), WJEB-TV (E), WJWB (W), WJXT (C), WTEV-TV (U), WTLV (N) Jacksonville.
Programming (via satellite): American Movie Classics; CNN; Discovery Channel; ESPN; Headline News; Nashville Network; Nickelodeon; Sunshine Network; TBS Superstation; The Weather Channel; Turner Network TV; USA Network; VH1.
Fee: $19.95 installation; $19.95 monthly.
Pay Service 1
Pay Units: 1,122.
Programming (via satellite): Showtime.
Fee: $6.00 monthly.
Pay-Per-View
Special events.
Equipment: Zenith set top converters.
Manager: Jim Cooper. Chief technician: Todd Senn. Customer service manager: Joanne McMillen.
Ownership: American Telecasting Inc. (MSO). Sale pends to Sprint Corp.

LAKELAND—American Telecasting of Lakeland Inc., Suite 14, 3705 U.S. Hwy. 98 S, Lakeland, FL 33813-4269. Phones: 941-668-9145; 941-667-0219. Fax: 941-667-0811.

Web site: http://www.amtele.com. County: Polk. ICA: FL0304.
Microwave channels reported: N.A.
Began: N.A.
Channel capacity: N.A.
Manager: Jim Cooper. Customer service manager: Michelle Eppink.
Ownership: American Telecasting Inc. (MSO). Sale pends to Sprint Corp.

MELBOURNE—Wireless Broadcasting of Melbourne, Suite 180, 4450 E. Eau Gallie Blvd., Melbourne, FL 32934. Phone: 407-255-0430. Fax: 407-254-0430. County: Brevard. Also serves Brevard County, Cocoa, Merritt Island, Palm Bay, Rockledge. ICA: FL0305.
Total homes in service area: 160,000.
Microwave channels reported: N.A.
Began: October 25, 1993.
Channel capacity: 30. Channels available but not in use: None.
Basic Service
Subscribers: 10,000.
Programming (received off-air): WKCF (W) Clermont; WBCC (E) Cocoa; WESH (N), WFTV (A), WKMG-TV (C), WMFE-TV (P), WOFL (F) Orlando-Daytona Beach.
Programming (via satellite): WGN-TV (W) Chicago; A & E; American Movie Classics; C-SPAN; C-SPAN 2; CNBC; CNN; Country Music TV; Discovery Channel; Disney Channel; ESPN; EWTN; Lifetime; MTV; Nashville Network; Nickelodeon; Sci-Fi Channel; Sunshine Network; TBS Superstation; The Weather Channel; Turner Network TV; USA Network.
Fee: $59.95 installation; $29.95 monthly; $10.00 additional installation.
Pay Service 1
Pay Units: 3,600.
Programming (via satellite): Cinemax.
Fee: $6.95 monthly.
Pay Service 2
Pay Units: 3,900.
Programming (via satellite): HBO.
Fee: $9.95 monthly.
Manager: Luis Del Pino.
Ownership: Wireless Broadcasting Systems of America Inc. (MSO).

ORLANDO—American Telecasting of Central Florida Inc., Suite B, 4700 L. B. McLeod Rd., Orlando, FL 32811. Phone: 904-322-8558. Web site: http://www.amtele.com. County: Orange. ICA: FL0306.
Microwave channels reported: N.A.
Began: N.A.
Channel capacity: N.A. Channels available but not in use: N.A.
Basic Service
Subscribers: N.A.
Programming (received off-air): WKCF (W) Clermont; W07BZ (O) Orlando; WESH (N), WFTV (A), WKMG-TV (C), WMFE-TV (P), WOFL (F), WRBW (U) Orlando-Daytona Beach.
Programming (via satellite): WGN-TV (W) Chicago; A & E; American Movie Classics; BET; C-SPAN; CNBC; CNN; Comedy Central; Discovery Channel; ESPN; ESPN 2; Fox Family Channel; MTV; Nashville Network; Nickelodeon; Sunshine Network; TBS Superstation; The Weather Channel; USA Network; Univision; VH1.
Current originations: Educational access.
Fee: N.A.
Pay Service 1
Pay Units: N.A.
Programming (via satellite): Disney Channel; HBO; Showtime.
Fee: N.A.
Ownership: American Telecasting Inc. (MSO). Sale pends to Sprint Corp.

PANAMA CITY—Wireless One of Panama City, 1117 Hwy. 390, Panama City, FL 32405. Phones: 904-747-1421; 800-236-1180. Fax: 904-747-0205. Web site: http://www.wirelessone.com. Counties: Bay, Calhoun, Gulf, Walton & Washington. Also serves Bay County, Calhoun County (portions), Chipley, Ebro, Fountain, Gulf County (portions), Lynn Haven, Vernon, Walton County (portions), Washington County (portions), Youngstown. ICA: FL0332.
Total homes in service area: 83,412.
Microwave channels reported: N.A.
Began: September 1, 1995.
Channel capacity: 24. Channels available but not in use: None.
Basic Service
Subscribers: 3,226.
Programming (received off-air): WTVY (C) Dothan; WFSG (P), WJHG-TV (N), WMBB (A), WPGX (F) Panama City.
Programming (via satellite): A & E; BET; CNN; Cartoon Network; Country Music TV; Discovery Channel; Disney Channel; ESPN; Fox Family Channel; History Channel; Lifetime; MTV; Nashville Network; Nick at Nite; Nickelodeon; QVC; Sunshine Network; TBS Superstation; The Weather Channel; Trinity Bcstg. Network; Turner Classic Movies; Turner Network TV; USA Network.
Fee: $99.95 installation; $22.95 monthly.
Pay Service 1
Pay Units: 349.
Programming (via satellite): HBO.
Fee: $11.95 monthly.
Pay Service 2
Pay Units: 498.
Programming (via satellite): Showtime.
Fee: $9.95 monthly.
Pay-Per-View
Viewer's Choice; movies.
Fee: $3.90.
Manager: Greg Bernard. Chief technician: Robert Williams. Marketing & program director: David Brown.
Ownership: Wireless One Inc. (MSO).

PENSACOLA—Wireless One of Pensacola, 8804 A. Grow Dr., Pensacola, FL 32514. Phones: 904-474-1110; 888-947-3663. Fax: 904-494-1199. Web site: http://www.wirelessone.com. Counties: Escambia & Santa Rosa. Also serves Escambia County, Gulf Breeze, Jay, McDavid, Santa Rosa (portions). ICA: FL0333.
Total homes in service area: 184,098.
Microwave channels reported: N.A.
Began: September 1, 1995.
Channel capacity: 28. Channels available but not in use: None.
Basic Service
Subscribers: 3,139.
Programming (received off-air): WALA-TV (F), WEAR-TV (A), WJTC (U), WKRG-TV (C), WPMI (N), WSRE (P) Mobile-Pensacola.
Programming (via satellite): A & E; BET; CNN; Discovery Channel; Disney Channel; ESPN; Headline News; MTV; Nashville Network; Nick at Nite; Nickelodeon; Odyssey; Playboy TV; QVC; Sunshine Network; TBS Superstation; The Weather Channel; Turner Network TV; USA Network.
Fee: $99.95 installation; $22.95 monthly.
Pay Service 1
Pay Units: 186.
Programming (via satellite): HBO.
Fee: $11.95 monthly.
Pay Service 2
Pay Units: 645.
Programming (via satellite): Flix; Showtime; Sundance Channel; The Movie Channel.
Fee: N.A.
Pay-Per-View
Viewer's Choice.
Manager: Fred Albertson. Chief technician: Thomas Winningham. Marketing & program director: David Brown.
Ownership: Wireless One Inc. (MSO).

POLK COUNTY—People's Wireless Cable, 3705 U.S. Hwy. 98 S, Lakeland, FL 33813-4269. Phone: 813-682-5453. County: Polk. ICA: FL0307.
Microwave channels reported: N.A.
Channel capacity: N.A.
Ownership: People's Cable TV Inc.

TALLAHASSEE—Wireless One of Tallahassee, 3970 Century Park Circle, Tallahassee, FL 32304. Phones: 904-575-9300; 888-947-3663. Web site: http://www.wirelessone.com. County: Leon. ICA: FL0340.
Microwave channels reported: N.A.
Began: N.A.
Channel capacity: N.A. Channels available but not in use: N.A.
Basic Service
Subscribers: N.A.
Programming (received off-air): WTLH (F) Bainbridge; WFSU-TV (P), WTWC (N), WTXL-TV (A) Tallahassee.
Programming (via satellite): A & E; CNN; Country Music TV; Discovery Channel; E! Entertainment TV; ESPN; Fox Family Channel; Knowledge TV; Learning Channel; Lifetime; Nashville Network; Nick at Nite; Nickelodeon; QVC; Sunshine Network; TBS Superstation; The Weather Channel; Turner Classic Movies; Turner Network TV; USA Network; VH1.
Current originations: Educational access.
Fee: $99.95 installation; $22.95 monthly.
Pay Service 1
Pay Units: N.A.
Programming (via satellite): Disney Channel; HBO; Showtime.
Fee: $9.95 monthly (Showtime), $10.95 monthly (Disney), $11.95 monthly (HBO), $27.95 monthly (Disney, HBO & Showtime).
Pay-Per-View
Viewer's Choice; movies.
Fee: $3.90.
Ownership: Wireless One Inc. (MSO).

TAMPA—Video Wave Television, 6840 Ulmerton Rd., Largo, FL 33771. Phone: 813-530-1812. Counties: Hillsborough, Pasco & Pinellas. Also serves Hillsborough County, Pasco County, Pinellas County. ICA: FL0309.
Total line of sight homes: 1,000,000. Total homes in service area: 1,000,000.
Microwave channels reported: N.A.
Began: April 1, 1995.
Channel capacity: 27 (not 2-way capable). Channels available but not in use: None.
Basic Service
Subscribers: 11,000; Commercial subscribers: 350.
Programming (received off-air): WFLA-TV (N), WFTS-TV (A), WTOG (U), WTSP (C), WTVT (F) Tampa-St. Petersburg.
Programming (via satellite): WGN-TV (W) Chicago; A & E; American Movie Classics; CNBC; CNN; Discovery Channel; ESPN; ESPN 2; Lifetime; MTV; Nashville Network; Nickelodeon; TBS Superstation; The Weather Channel; Turner Network TV; USA Network.
Fee: $29.95 installation; $17.95 monthly.
Commercial fee: $17.95 monthly.
Pay Service 1
Pay Units: 5,000.
Programming (via satellite): HBO.
Fee: $8.95 monthly.
Pay Service 2
Pay Units: 5,000.
Programming (via satellite): Cinemax.
Fee: $7.95 monthly.
Pay-Per-View
Addressable homes: 8,000.
Viewer's Choice.
Manager: Linda Cicro. Chief technician: Bob Stark.
Ownership: Wireless Holdings Inc. (MSO). Sale pends to Pacific Telesis.

Georgia

ALBANY—Wireless One of Albany, 944 W. Oglethorpe Blvd., Albany, GA 31701. Phones: 912-889-1100; 800-757-2593. Fax: 912-889-1822. Web site: http://www.wirelessone.com. County: Dougherty. ICA: GA0285.
Microwave channels reported: N.A.
Began: September 1, 1996.
Channel capacity: 30. Channels available but not in use: N.A.
Basic Service
Subscribers: 463.
Programming (received off-air): WALB-TV (N), WFXL (F) Albany; WTVM (A) Columbus; WABW-TV (P) Pelham; WCTV (C) Tallahassee-Thomasville.
Programming (via satellite): A & E; CNN; Discovery Channel; Disney Channel; ESPN; Fox Family Channel; Fox Sports Net South; Lifetime; Nashville Network; Nickelodeon; QVC; TBS Superstation; The Weather Channel; Turner Network TV; USA Network.
Fee: $99.95 installation; $22.95 monthly.
Pay Service 1
Pay Units: N.A.
Programming (via satellite): HBO.
Fee: $11.95 monthly.
Pay-Per-View
Viewer's Choice.
Fee: $3.90.
Manager: Robin Underwood. Chief technician: Barron Kendricks. Marketing & program director: David Brown.
Ownership: Wireless One Inc. (MSO).

ATLANTA—Bell South Entertainment, Suite 120, 660 Hembree Pkwy., Roswell, GA 30076. Phone: 770-242-1996. Fax: 770-409-3579. County: Fulton. ICA: GA0271.
Total homes in service area: 1,400,000.
Microwave channels reported: N.A.
Began: January 1, 1991.
Channel capacity: 27. Channels available but not in use: None.
Basic Service
Subscribers: 8,500.
Programming (received off-air): WAGA (F), WGNX (C), WPBA (P), WSB-TV (A), WTBS (I), WXIA-TV (N) Atlanta.
Programming (via satellite): WGN-TV (W) Chicago; A & E; BET; C-SPAN; C-SPAN 2; CNBC; CNN; Discovery Channel; ESPN; Fox Family Channel; Fox Sports Net South; Headline News; Lifetime; MTV; Nashville Network; Nickelodeon; The Weather Channel; Turner Network TV; USA Network.
Fee: $39.95 installation; $23.95 monthly.
Pay Service 1
Pay Units: 2,300.
Programming (via satellite): HBO.
Fee: $12.75 monthly.
Pay Service 2
Pay Units: 1,200.
Programming (via satellite): The Movie Channel.
Fee: $10.50 monthly.
Pay Service 3
Pay Units: 1,800.
Programming (via satellite): Showtime.
Fee: $10.50 monthly.

Equipment: General Instrument set top converters.
Manager: Rick Haney. Chief technician: Ted Stover. Program director: Jim Brown. Marketing director: Rick Kendrick.
Ownership: BellSouth Entertainment Inc. Purchased from Wireless Cable of Atlanta Inc.

CHARING—Wireless One of Charing, Suite 400, 2506 Lakeland Dr., Jackson, MS 39208. Phones: 504-926-7778; 888-947-3663. Web site: http://www.wirelessone.com. County: Taylor. ICA: GA0287.
Microwave channels reported: N.A.
Began: N.A.
Channel capacity: N.A. Channels available but not in use: N.A.
Basic Service
Subscribers: N.A.
Programming (received off-air): WJSP-TV (P), WLTZ (N), WRBL (C), WTVM (A), WXTX (F) Columbus.
Programming (via satellite): WGN-TV (W) Chicago; A & E; BET; CNN; Country Music TV; Discovery Channel; E! Entertainment TV; ESPN; Fox Family Channel; Fox Sports Net South; Headline News; History Channel; Home & Garden Television; Learning Channel; Lifetime; Nashville Network; Nick at Nite; Nickelodeon; QVC; TBS Superstation; The Health Network; The Weather Channel; Turner Classic Movies; Turner Network TV; USA Network; VH1.
Fee: $99.95 installation; $22.95 monthly.
Pay Service 1
Pay Units: N.A.
Programming (via satellite): Disney Channel; HBO; Showtime.
Fee: $9.95 monthly (Showtime), $10.95 monthly (Disney), $11.95 monthly (HBO), $27.95 monthly (Disney, HBO & Showtime).
Pay-Per-View
Viewer's Choice.
Fee: $3.90.
Ownership: Wireless One Inc. (MSO).

JEFFERSONVILLE—Wireless One of Jeffersonville, 2795 Laniar Heights Rd., Macon, GA 31217. Phones: 912-750-1115; 800-650-2331. Fax: 912-750-1125.
Web site: http://www.wirelessone.com.
Counties: Baldwin, Bibb, Butts, Houston, Jasper, Jones, Monroe, Peach, Twiggs & Wilkinson. Also serves Baldwin County, Bibb County, Butts County (portions), Byron, Danville, Forsyth, Gordon, Jasper County, Jones County, Lizella, Macon, Milledgeville, Monroe County, Monticello, Perry, Toomsboro, Twiggs County, Warner Robins, Wilkinson County. ICA: GA0284.
Total homes in service area: 145,777.
Microwave channels reported: N.A.
Began: March 1, 1996.
Channel capacity: 20. Channels available but not in use: None.
Basic Service
Subscribers: 1,427.
Programming (received off-air): WDCO-TV (P) Cochran; WGXA (F), WMAZ-TV (C), WMGT (N) Macon; WPGA (A) Perry.
Programming (via satellite): WGN-TV (W) Chicago; A & E; BET; C-SPAN; CNN; Country Music TV; Discovery Channel; ESPN; Fox Family Channel; Fox Sports Net South; History Channel; Home & Garden Television; Learning Channel; Lifetime; Nashville Network; Nickelodeon; TBS Superstation; The Weather Channel; Turner Network TV; USA Network; VH1.
Fee: $99.95 installation; $22.95 monthly.
Pay Service 1
Pay Units: N.A.
Programming (via satellite): Cinemax; Disney Channel; HBO; Showtime.
Fee: $9.95 monthly (Showtime); $10.95 monthly (Cinemax or Disney); $11.95 monthly (HBO).
Pay-Per-View
Viewer's Choice.
Fee: $3.90.
Manager: Corky Alford. Chief technician: Carl Briggs. Marketing & program director: Jim Colson.
Ownership: Wireless One Inc. (MSO).

Hawaii

HONOLULU—GTE Media Ventures, Suite 200, 1132 Bishop St., Honolulu, HI 96813. Phone: 808-566-6228. Fax: 808-566-6242. County: Honolulu. ICA: HI0017.
Microwave channels reported: N.A.
Channel capacity: N.A. Channels available but not in use: N.A.
Manager: Alaine Louchez. Chief technician: Daniel Baldwin.
Ownership: GTE Media Ventures (MSO).

MAUI—Maui Cablevision Corp., Suite 106, 350 Ward Ave., Honolulu, HI 96814-4004. Phone: 808-591-7787. County: Maui. ICA: HI0016.
Microwave channels reported: N.A.
Channel capacity: N.A.
Ownership: Maui Cablevision Corp.

Idaho

BOISE—Wireless Broadcasting Systems, Suite C, 3131 Lanark St., Meridian, ID 83642. Phones: 208-377-1266; 800-322-2538. Fax: 208-377-2605. Counties: Ada, Canyon, Gem & Payette. Also serves Caldwell, Emmett, Kuna, Meridian, Nampa, Payette. ICA: ID0086.
Total homes in service area: 120,000.
Microwave channels reported: N.A.
Began: December 1, 1992.
Channel capacity: 32 (not 2-way capable). Channels available but not in use: N.A.
Basic Service
Subscribers: 11,200.
Programming (received off-air): KAID (P), KBCI-TV (C), KTVB (N) Boise; KNIN-TV (U) Caldwell; KIVI (A), KTRV (F) Nampa.
Programming (via satellite): WGN-TV (W) Chicago; A & E; American Movie Classics; CNBC; CNN; Cartoon Network; Country Music TV; Discovery Channel; ESPN; EWTN; Fox Family Channel; Fox Sports Net Northwest; Headline News; History Channel; Knowledge TV; Learning Channel; Lifetime; MTV; Nashville Network; Nick at Nite; Nickelodeon; Sci-Fi Channel; Showtime; TBS Superstation; TV Guide Channel; Turner Network TV; USA Network; Univision.
Fee: $19.95 installation; $28.45 monthly.
Equipment: ITS headend; Regal set top converters.
Manager: Tami Morrison. Chief technician: Jim Parkinson.
Ownership: Wireless Broadcasting Systems of America Inc. (MSO).

TWIN FALLS—Teton Wireless Television, Box 5699, Twin Falls, ID 83303. Phone: 208-733-0500. Fax: 208-733-0535. County: Twin Falls. ICA: ID0087.
Microwave channels reported: N.A.
Channel capacity: N.A. Channels available but not in use: N.A.
Basic Service
Subscribers: 4,030.
Programming (received off-air): KIPT (P), KKVI (A,F), KMVT (C) Twin Falls.
Programming (via satellite): WGN-TV (W) Chicago; A & E; CNN; Cartoon Network; Comedy Central; Discovery Channel; ESPN; ESPN 2; Fox Family Channel; Fox Sports Net Northwest; Headline News; History Channel; Learning Channel; Lifetime; Nashville Network; Nick at Nite's TV Land; Nickelodeon; QVC; Sci-Fi Channel; TBS Superstation; TV Guide Channel; The New Encore; The Weather Channel; Trinity Bcstg. Network; Turner Classic Movies; Turner Network TV; USA Network; VH1.
Fee: $20.95 monthly.
Pay Service 1
Pay Units: N.A.
Programming (via satellite): Cinemax; Disney Channel; HBO.
Fee: N.A.
Manager: Thomas Carey.
Ownership: Teewinot Licensing Inc.

Illinois

BLOOMINGTON—Microwave Cable Corp., 1700 S. Morris Ave., Bloomington, IL 61701. Phone: 309-829-9949. Fax: 309-829-2870. County: McLean. Also serves Normal. ICA: IL0613.
Total homes in service area: 70,000.
Microwave channels reported: N.A.
Began: January 1, 1989.
Channel capacity: N.A. Channels available but not in use: N.A.
Basic Service
Subscribers: 3,100.
Programming (received off-air): WYZZ-TV (F) Bloomington; WEEK-TV (N), WHOI (A), WMBD-TV (C), WTVP (P) Peoria.
Programming (via satellite): WGN-TV (W) Chicago; CNN; Discovery Channel; ESPN; Fox Family Channel; Fox Sports Net Chicago; Nashville Network; Nickelodeon; TBS Superstation; The Weather Channel; USA Network.
Fee: $59.95 installation; $18.95 monthly.
Pay Service 1
Pay Units: N.A.
Programming (via satellite): Disney Channel; HBO.
Fee: N.A.
Equipment: Zenith set top converters.
Manager: Rod Harmon.
Ownership: Microwave Cable Corp.

CHAMPAIGN & URBANA—Nucentrix Broadband Networks Inc., Suite 200, 200 Chisholm Place, Plano, TX 75075. Phone: 972-423-9494. Fax: 972-423-0819. County: Champaign. ICA: IL0614.
Microwave channels reported: N.A.
Began: N.A.
Channel capacity: N.A. Channels available but not in use: N.A.
Basic Service
Subscribers: 1,600.
Fee: N.A.
Ownership: Nucentrix Broadband Networks (MSO).

CHICAGO—Preferred Entertainment of Chicago, 6260 Joliet Rd., Countryside, IL 60525. Phone: 312-463-6900. Fax: 312-482-0790. County: Cook. ICA: IL0615.
Microwave channels reported: N.A.
Began: N.A.
Channel capacity: 18. Channels available but not in use: N.A.
Marketing director: Dick Koeth.
Ownership: Preferred Entertainment Inc. (MSO).

FREEPORT—Nucentrix Broadband Networks Inc., Suite 200, 200 Chisholm Place, Plano, TX 75075. Phone: 972-423-9494. Fax: 972-423-0819. County: Stephenson. ICA: IL0643.
Microwave channels reported: N.A.
Began: N.A.
Channel capacity: N.A. Channels available but not in use: N.A.
Basic Service
Subscribers: N.A.
Programming (received off-air): KJMH (F) Burlington; KLJB-TV (F), KWQC-TV (N) Davenport; WQAD-TV (A) Moline; WHBF-TV (C) Rock Island; WREX-TV (N), WTVO (A) Rockford.
Programming (via satellite): WGN-TV (W) Chicago; A & E; CNN; Cartoon Network; Discovery Channel; ESPN; Fox Family Channel; Fox Sports Net Chicago; History Channel; MTV; Nashville Network; Nickelodeon; TBS Superstation; Turner Network TV; USA Network.
Fee: N.A.
Pay Service 1
Pay Units: N.A.
Programming (via satellite): Cinemax; HBO.
Fee: N.A.
Pay-Per-View
Viewer's Choice.
Manager: Andy Kallas. Chief technician: Dave Brust.
Ownership: Nucentrix Broadband Networks (MSO).

JACKSONVILLE—Nucentrix Broadband Networks Inc., Suite 200, 200 Chisholm Place, Plano, TX 75075. Phone: 972-423-9494. Fax: 972-423-0819. County: Morgan. ICA: IL0644.
Microwave channels reported: N.A.
Began: N.A.
Channel capacity: N.A. Channels available but not in use: N.A.
Basic Service
Subscribers: N.A.
Programming (received off-air): KHQA-TV (C) Quincy-Hannibal; WICS (N), WRSP-TV (F) Springfield; KDNL-TV (A) St. Louis.
Programming (via satellite): WGN-TV (W) Chicago; A & E; CNN; Discovery Channel; ESPN; ESPNews; Lifetime; Nashville Network; Nickelodeon; TBS Superstation; The Weather Channel; Turner Network TV; USA Network.
Fee: N.A.
Pay Service 1
Pay Units: N.A.
Programming (via satellite): Cinemax; HBO.
Fee: N.A.
Pay-Per-View
Viewer's Choice.
Manager: Todd Lehman. Chief technician: Jim Burt.
Ownership: Nucentrix Broadband Networks (MSO).

MACOMB—Nucentrix Broadband Networks Inc., Suite 200, 200 Chishom Place, Plano, TX 75075. Phone: 972-423-9494. Fax: 972-423-0819. County: McDonough. ICA: IL0645.
Microwave channels reported: N.A.
Began: N.A.
Channel capacity: N.A. Channels available but not in use: N.A.
Basic Service
Subscribers: N.A.
Programming (received off-air): KLJB-TV (F) Davenport; WQAD-TV (A) Moline; KHQA-TV (C) Quincy-Hannibal.
Programming (via satellite): WGN-TV (W) Chicago; CNN; Discovery Channel; ESPN; ESPNews; Lifetime; Nashville Network; Nick-

elodeon; TBS Superstation; The Weather Channel; Turner Network TV; USA Network.
Fee: $29.95 monthly.
Pay Service 1
Pay Units: N.A.
Programming (via satellite): Cinemax; HBO (multiplexed).
Fee: N.A.
Pay-Per-View
Viewer's Choice.
Manager: Todd Lehman. Chief technician: Mike Shelton.
Ownership: Nucentrix Broadband Networks (MSO).

McLEANSBORO—Nucentrix Broadband Networks Inc., Suite 200, 200 Chisholm Place, Plano, TX 75075. Phone: 972-423-9494. Fax: 972-423-0819. County: Hamilton. ICA: IL0635.
Microwave channels reported: N.A.
Channel capacity: N.A.
Ownership: Nucentrix Broadband Networks (MSO). Purchased from Heartland Wireless Communications Inc.

OLNEY—Nucentrix Broadband Networks Inc., Suite 200, 200 Chisholm Place, Plano, TX 75075. Phone: 972-423-9494. Fax: 972-423-0819. County: Richland. ICA: IL0638.
Microwave channels reported: N.A.
Channel capacity: N.A.
Ownership: Nucentrix Broadband Networks (MSO). Purchased from Heartland Wireless Communications Inc.

***PEORIA**—Nucentrix Broadband Networks Inc., Suite 200, 200 Chisholm Place, Plano, TX 75075. Phone: 972-423-9494. Fax: 972-423-0819. County: Peoria. ICA: IL0616.
Microwave channels reported: N.A.
Scheduled to begin: N.A.
Channel capacity: N.A.
Ownership: Nucentrix Broadband Networks (MSO).

ROCKFORD—Wireless Cable Systems Inc., Suite 6107, 350 5th Ave., New York, NY 10118. Phone: 212-268-2828. Fax: 212-268-5675. County: Winnebago. ICA: IL0617.
Microwave channels reported: N.A.
Channel capacity: N.A.
Ownership: Wireless Cable Systems Inc.

TAYLORVILLE—Nucentrix Broadband Networks Inc., Suite 200, 200 Chisholm Place, Plano, TX 75075. Phone: 972-423-9494. Fax: 972-423-0819. County: Christian. ICA: IL0636.
Microwave channels reported: N.A.
Channel capacity: N.A.
Ownership: Nucentrix Broadband Networks (MSO). Purchased from Heartland Wireless Communictions Inc.

VANDALIA—Nucentrix Broadband Networks Inc., Suite 200, 200 Chisholm Place, Plano, TX 75075. Phone: 972-423-9494. Fax: 972-423-0819. County: Fayette. ICA: IL0637.
Microwave channels reported: N.A.
Channel capacity: N.A.
Ownership: Nucentrix Broadband Networks (MSO). Purchased from Heartland Wireless Communications Inc.

Indiana

***ANDERSON**—Broadcast Cable Inc., 4109 E. 65th St., Indianapolis, IN 46220. Phone: 317-257-6934. County: Madison. ICA: IN0344.
Microwave channels reported: N.A.
Scheduled to begin: N.A.
Channel capacity: 23. Channels available but not in use: N.A.
Equipment: Comwave headend.
Manager: Thomas P. Farrell.
Ownership: Broadcast Cable Inc.

EVANSVILLE—Ohio Valley Wireless Ltd., 1420 N. Cullen Ave., Evansville, IN 47716. Phone: 812-471-7500. E-mail: ovc@ovcwireless.net. Web site: http://www.ovcwireless.net. County: Vanderburgh. ICA: IN0345.
Total homes in service area: 171,000.
Microwave channels reported: N.A.
Channel capacity: 31 (not 2-way capable). Channels available but not in use: 1.
Basic Service
Subscribers: 4,521.
Programming (received off-air): WEHT (A), WEVV (C), WFIE-TV (N), WNIN (P), WTVW (F), WWAZ-LP (U,W) Evansville.
Programming (via satellite): WGN-TV (W) Chicago; A & E; American Movie Classics; CNBC; CNN; Discovery Channel; ESPN; ESPN 2; Fox Family Channel; Nashville Network; Nickelodeon; Sci-Fi Channel; TBS Superstation; The Weather Channel; Trinity Bcstg. Network; Turner Classic Movies; Turner Network TV; USA Network; VH1.
Fee: $39.95 installation; $25.95 monthly; $3.00 converter.
Pay Service 1
Pay Units: 632.
Programming (via satellite): HBO.
Fee: $10.50 monthly.
Pay Service 2
Pay Units: 600.
Programming (via satellite): Showtime.
Fee: $9.50 monthly.
Local advertising: Yes. Rates: $6.00/Minute; $3.00/30 Seconds. Local sales manager: David Headlee.
Equipment: Comwave headend; Scientific-Atlanta set top converters.
Manager: Bradley Windell.
Ownership: Ohio Valley Wireless Ltd.

FORT WAYNE—Choice TV of Fort Wayne, 1909 Production Rd., Fort Wayne, IN 46808. Phone: 219-482-2020. Fax: 219-471-5406. E-mail: choicetv@fwi.com. Counties: Adams, Allen, De Kalb, Huntington, Noble, Wells & Whitley, IN; Defiance, Paulding & Van Wert, OH. Also serves Adams County, Allen County, De Kalb County, Huntington County, Noble County, Wells County, Whitley County, IN; Defiance County, Paulding County, Van Wert County, OH. ICA: IN0343.
Total homes in service area: 245,000.
Microwave channels reported: N.A.
Began: September 1, 1989.
Channel capacity: 33 (not 2-way capable). Channels available but not in use: 12.
Basic Service
Subscribers: 2,500; Commercial subscribers: 131.
Programming (received off-air): WANE-TV (C), WFFT-TV (F), WFWA (P), WKJG-TV (N), WPTA (A) Fort Wayne.
Programming (via satellite): WGN-TV (W) Chicago; A & E; CNN; Discovery Channel; Disney Channel; ESPN; EWTN; Fox Family Channel; Learning Channel; Lifetime; MTV; Nashville Network; Nickelodeon; TBS Superstation; The Weather Channel; Turner Classic Movies; Turner Network TV; USA Network.
Fee: $29.95 installation; $29.00 monthly.
Commercial fee: $29.45 monthly.
Pay Service 1
Pay Units: 325.
Programming (via satellite): HBO.
Fee: $13.00 monthly.
Pay Service 2
Pay Units: 425.
Programming (via satellite): Showtime.
Fee: $11.00 monthly.
Pay-Per-View
Addressable homes: 2,500.
Viewer's Choice.
Fee: Varies.
Local advertising: Yes.
Equipment: Comwave amplifiers; Zenith set top converters; Zenith addressable set top converters; Scientific-Atlanta satellite receivers.
Manager: William A. Millett. Chief technician: Kent Hull. Operations manager: Michelle L. Sweeney. Technical supervisor: Ron Enos.
Ownership: Fort Wayne Telsat Inc.

INDIANAPOLIS—People's Choice TV, Suite 212, 597 Industrial Dr., Carmel, IN 46032. Phone: 317-844-0002. Fax: 317-844-7177. County: Marion. ICA: IN0348.
Microwave channels reported: N.A.
Channel capacity: N.A.
Manager: Don Kent.
Ownership: People's Choice TV Partners (MSO). Sale pends to Sprint Corp.

MICHIANA—American Telecasting of Michiana Inc., Suite C, 5005 Lincoln Way E, Mishawaka, IN 46544. Phone: 219-258-6016. Fax: 219-258-6021. Web site: http://www.amtele.com. Counties: Elkhart, Kosciusko, La Porte, Marshall & St. Joseph, IN; Berrien & Cass, MI. Also serves Elkhart County, Kosciusko County, La Porte County, Marshall County, St. Joseph County, IN; Berrien County, Cass County, MI. ICA: IN0342.
Total homes in service area: 200,000.
Microwave channels reported: N.A.
Began: February 1, 1993.
Channel capacity: 33. Channels available but not in use: N.A.
Basic Service
Subscribers: 1,966; Commercial subscribers: 22.
Programming (received off-air): WFLD (F) Chicago; WHME-TV (W), WNDU-TV (N), WNIT-TV (P), WSBT-TV (C), WSJV (F) South Bend-Elkhart.
Programming (via satellite): WGN-TV (W) Chicago; TBS Superstation.
Fee: $35.00 installation; $12.95 monthly.
Commercial fee: $19.95 monthly.
Expanded Basic Service
Subscribers: 1,966.
Programming (via satellite): A & E; American Movie Classics; CNN; Discovery Channel; ESPN; EWTN; Fox Sports Net Chicago; Headline News; Lifetime; Nashville Network; Nickelodeon; Sci-Fi Channel; The Weather Channel; USA Network; VH1.
Fee: $35.00 installation; $7.00 monthly.
Pay Service 1
Pay Units: 1,481.
Programming (via satellite): Disney Channel.
Fee: $5.00 monthly.
Pay Service 2
Pay Units: 1,579.
Programming (via satellite): Showtime.
Fee: $5.00 monthly.
Pay Service 3
Pay Units: 150.
Programming (via satellite): HBO.
Fee: $9.95 monthly.
Equipment: ITS headend; Tocom addressable set top converters; DX Communications & Standard Communications satellite receivers.
Manager: John L. Smith. Customer service manager: Karen Guennel.
Ownership: American Telecasting Inc. (MSO). Sale pends to Sprint Corp.

SOUTH BEND—Choice TV, Box 2628, Fresno, CA 93745. Phone: 209-442-1977. Web site: http://www.amtele.com. County: St. Joseph. ICA: IN0355.
Microwave channels reported: N.A.
Channel capacity: N.A.
Ownership: American Telecasting Inc. (MSO). Sale pends to Sprint Corp.

Iowa

BATAVIA—Iowa Rural TV Inc., Box 160, 4th & Davis Sts., Batavia, IA 52533. Phone: 515-662-3400. Fax: 515-662-2511. Counties: Davis, Jefferson, Van Buren & Wapello. Also serves Agency, Bloomfield, Douds, Eldon, Fairfield, Floris, Libertyville, Ottumwa, Packwood, Pulaski, Troy. ICA: IA0549.
Total homes in service area: 19,157.
Microwave channels reported: N.A.
Began: September 1, 1993.
Channel capacity: 12 (not 2-way capable). Channels available but not in use: None.
Basic Service
Subscribers: 1,219.
Programming (received off-air): KCCI (C), WHO-TV (N) Des Moines; KTVO (A) Ottumwa-Kirksville.
Programming (via satellite): WGN-TV (W) Chicago; CNN; Discovery Channel; ESPN; Fox Family Channel; Nashville Network; Netlink International; TBS Superstation; USA Network.
Fee: $15.95 monthly.
Pay Service 1
Pay Units: 390.
Programming (via satellite): Showtime.
Fee: $7.95 monthly.
Pay-Per-View
Addressable homes: 1,164.
Equipment: ITS headend; Scientific-Atlanta set top converters; Scientific-Atlanta addressable set top converters; Prodelin satellite antenna; Scientific-Atlanta satellite receivers.
Manager: Dennis McKeever. Program & marketing director: Rhonda Bloomquist.
Ownership: Farmers Telephone Co.

EVERLY—Evertek, Box 358, 216 N. Main, Everly, IA 51338. Phone: 712-834-2255. County: Clay. ICA: IA0550.
Microwave channels reported: N.A.
Channel capacity: N.A.
Ownership: Evertek Inc.

RUTHAVEN—Terril Cable Systems, Box 100, Terril, IA 51364. Phone: 712-853-6121. Fax: 712-853-6185. Counties: Dickinson, Emmet, Kossuth & Palo Alto, IA; Blue Earth, Faribault & Martin, MN. Also serves Dickinson County, Emmet County, Kossuth County, Palo Alto County, IA; Blue Earth County, Faribault County, Martin County, MN. ICA: IA0551.
Total homes in service area: 137,000.
Microwave channels reported: WLW834, E group, MMDS; WMH424, F group, MMDS; WLW724, H1, MMDS; WLW728, H2, MMDS; WLW732, H3, MMDS.
Began: January 13, 1992.
Channel capacity: 11. Channels available but not in use: None.
Basic Service
Subscribers: 1,810.
Programming (received off-air): KAAL (A,F) Austin; KIMT (C) Mason City; KTTC (N) Rochester.
Programming (via satellite): WGN-TV (W) Chicago; CNN; Discovery Channel; ESPN;

Fox Family Channel; FoxNet; Nashville Network; TBS Superstation.
Fee: $50.00 installation; $13.95 monthly; $3.00 converter.
Pay Service 1
Pay Units: 554.
Programming (via satellite): HBO.
Fee: $9.95 monthly.
Equipment: Zenith set top converters.
Manager: Doug Nelson. Chief technician: Ivan Dalen. Marketing director: Carla Dyhrkopp.
Ownership: Ter Tel Enterprises (MSO).

STORY CITY—Nucentrix Broadband Networks Inc., Suite 200, 200 Chisholm Place, Plano, TX 75075. Phone: 972-423-9494. Fax: 972-423-0819. County: Story. ICA: IA0563.
Microwave channels reported: N.A.
Began: N.A.
Channel capacity: N.A. Channels available but not in use: N.A.
Basic Service
Subscribers: N.A.
Programming (received off-air): WOI-TV (A) Ames-Des Moines; KCRG-TV (A), KWWL (N) Cedar Rapids-Waterloo; KCCI (C), KDSM-TV (F,U), WHO-TV (N) Des Moines.
Programming (via satellite): WGN-TV (W) Chicago; A & E; CNN; Country Music TV; Discovery Channel; Disney Channel; ESPN; Fox Family Channel; Headline News; Learning Channel; Lifetime; Nashville Network; Nickelodeon; Speedvision; TBS Superstation; The Weather Channel; Trinity Bcstg. Network; Turner Classic Movies; Turner Network TV; USA Network.
Fee: $24.99 monthly.
Pay Service 1
Pay Units: N.A.
Programming (via satellite): HBO; Showtime.
Fee: N.A.
Ownership: Nucentrix Broadband Networks (MSO).

WATERLOO—Wireless Cable TV of Waterloo, 1463 Oakcrest Dr., Waterloo, IA 50701-1750. Phone: 319-234-0921. County: Black Hawk. ICA: IA0562.
Microwave channels reported: N.A.
Channel capacity: N.A.
Ownership: Wireless Cable TV of Waterloo.

Kansas

BELOIT—Nucentrix Broadband Networks Inc., Suite 200, 200 Chisholm Place, Plano, TX 75075. Phone: 972-423-9494. Fax: 972-423-0819. County: Mitchell. ICA: KS0441.
Microwave channels reported: N.A.
Began: N.A.
Channel capacity: N.A. Channels available but not in use: N.A.
Basic Service
Subscribers: N.A.
Programming (received off-air): KSNC (N) Great Bend; KBSH-TV (C) Hays; KAAS-TV (F) Salina.
Programming (via satellite): CNN; Country Music TV; Discovery Channel; ESPN; Fox Sports Net Rocky Mountain; Lifetime; Nashville Network; Nickelodeon; TBS Superstation; The Weather Channel; Turner Network TV; USA Network.
Fee: N.A.
Pay Service 1
Pay Units: N.A.
Programming (via satellite): Cinemax; HBO (multiplexed).
Fee: N.A.
Pay-Per-View
Viewer's Choice.
Manager: Coff Thomasson. Chief technician: Lonnie Alexander.
Ownership: Nucentrix Broadband Networks (MSO).

CHANUTE—Nucentrix Broadband Networks Inc., Suite 200, 200 Chisholm Place, Plano, TX 75075. Phone: 972-423-9494. Fax: 972-423-0819. County: Neosho. ICA: KS0438.
Microwave channels reported: N.A.
Began: N.A.
Channel capacity: N.A. Channels available but not in use: N.A.
Basic Service
Subscribers: N.A.
Programming (received off-air): KOAM-TV (C), KODE-TV (A), KSNF (N) Joplin-Pittsburg; KTWU (P) Topeka.
Programming (via satellite): WGN-TV (W) Chicago; A & E; American Movie Classics; CNBC; CNN; Cartoon Network; Country Music TV; Discovery Channel; Disney Channel; ESPN; ESPN 2; Fox Family Channel; FoxNet; History Channel; Lifetime; Nashville Network; Nickelodeon; TBS Superstation; TV Guide Channel; The Weather Channel; Trinity Bcstg. Network; Turner Network TV; USA Network.
Fee: $26.99 monthly.
Pay Service 1
Pay Units: N.A.
Programming (via satellite): Cinemax; HBO (multiplexed); Showtime.
Fee: $7.99 monthly (Showtime), $9.95 monthly (Cinemax), $10.95 monthly (HBO).
Pay-Per-View
Viewer's Choice.
Manager: Debbie Houston. Chief technician: Jim Bailey.
Ownership: Nucentrix Broadband Networks (MSO).

MANHATTAN—Nucentrix Broadband Networks Inc., Suite 200, 200 Chisholm Place, Plano, TX 75075. Phone: 972-423-9494. Fax: 972-423-0819. Counties: Pottawatomie & Riley. ICA: KS0425.
Microwave channels reported: N.A.
Channel capacity: N.A.
Ownership: Nucentrix Broadband Networks (MSO). Purchased from Heartland Wireless Communications Inc.

MARION—Nucentrix Broadband Networks Inc., Suite 200, 200 Chisholm Place, Plano, TX 75075. Phone: 972-423-9494. Fax: 972-423-0819. County: Marion. ICA: KS0439.
Microwave channels reported: N.A.
Began: N.A.
Channel capacity: N.A. Channels available but not in use: N.A.
Basic Service
Subscribers: N.A.
Programming (received off-air): KAKE-TV (A), KSAS-TV (F), KSNW (N), KWCH-TV (C) Wichita-Hutchinson.
Programming (via satellite): CNN; Discovery Channel; ESPN; Nashville Network; Nickelodeon; TBS Superstation; Trinity Bcstg. Network; Turner Network TV; USA Network.
Fee: $50.00 (underground); $29.95 monthly.
Pay Service 1
Pay Units: N.A.
Programming (via satellite): Cinemax; HBO.
Fee: N.A.
Manager: Rodney Stanfield.
Ownership: Nucentrix Broadband Networks (MSO).

MEDICINE LODGE—Nucentrix Broadband Networks Inc., Suite 200, 200 Chisholm Place, Plano, TX 75075. Phone: 972-423-9494. Fax: 972-423-0819. County: Barber. ICA: KS0440.
Microwave channels reported: N.A.
Began: N.A.
Channel capacity: N.A. Channels available but not in use: N.A.
Basic Service
Subscribers: N.A.
Programming (received off-air): KAKE-TV (A), KPTS (P), KSAS-TV (F), KSNW (N), KWCH-TV (C) Wichita-Hutchinson.
Programming (via satellite): A & E; CNN; Country Music TV; Discovery Channel; ESPN; Fox Sports Net Rocky Mountain; Lifetime; Nashville Network; Nickelodeon; TBS Superstation; The Weather Channel; Trinity Bcstg. Network; Turner Network TV; USA Network.
Fee: N.A.
Pay Service 1
Pay Units: N.A.
Programming (via satellite): Cinemax; HBO.
Fee: N.A.
Pay-Per-View
Viewer's Choice.
Manager: Justin Ellis. Chief technician: Roger Venscoy.
Ownership: Nucentrix Broadband Networks (MSO).

RICE COUNTY—Nucentrix Broadband Networks Inc., Suite 200, 200 Chisholm Place, Plano, TX 75075. Phone: 972-423-9494. Fax: 972-423-0819. County: Rice. ICA: KS0442.
Microwave channels reported: N.A.
Began: N.A.
Channel capacity: N.A. Channels available but not in use: N.A.
Basic Service
Subscribers: N.A.
Programming (received off-air): KAKE-TV (A), KSAS-TV (F), KSNW (N), KWCH-TV (C) Wichita-Hutchinson.
Programming (via satellite): CNN; Country Music TV; Discovery Channel; ESPN; Fox Sports Net Rocky Mountain; Lifetime; Nashville Network; Nickelodeon; TBS Superstation; The Weather Channel; Turner Network TV; USA Network.
Fee: $24.95 monthly.
Pay Service 1
Pay Units: N.A.
Programming (via satellite): Cinemax; HBO.
Fee: $5.00 monthly (HBO), $7.95 monthly (Cinemax).
Manager: Rodney Stanfield.
Ownership: Nucentrix Broadband Networks (MSO).

SALINA—TVCN, 2775 Arnold Ave., Salina, KS 67401-8159. Phone: 913-827-5551. County: Saline. ICA: KS0426.
Microwave channels reported: N.A.
Channel capacity: N.A.
Ownership: TV Communications Network Inc.

SHAW—Nucentrix Broadband Networks Inc., Suite 200, 200 Chisholm Place, Plano, TX 75075. Phone: 972-423-9494. Fax: 972-423-0819. Counties: Allen, Labette, Montgomery & Neosho. Also serves Chanute, Erie, Independence, Iola, Parsons, St. Paul. ICA: KS0427.
Total homes in service area: 12,733.
Microwave channels reported: N.A.
Began: July 1, 1991.
Channel capacity: 31. Channels available but not in use: None.
Basic Service
Subscribers: 3,447.
Programming (via satellite): WGN-TV (W) Chicago; KTLA (W) Los Angeles; WPIX (W) New York; A & E; American Movie Classics; CNBC; CNN; Country Music TV; Discovery Channel; Disney Channel; ESPN; Fox Family Channel; Fox Sports Net; Headline News; Knowledge TV; Lifetime; Nashville Network; Nickelodeon; TBS Superstation; TV Guide Channel; The Weather Channel; Trinity Bcstg. Network; USA Network; VH1.
Fee: $50.00 installation; $28.95 monthly; $7.50 additional installation.
Pay Service 1
Pay Units: 209.
Programming (via satellite): Cinemax.
Fee: $9.95 monthly.
Pay Service 2
Pay Units: 312.
Programming (via satellite): HBO.
Fee: $10.95 monthly.
Equipment: Jerrold addressable set top converters.
Manager: Frederick Frank. Chief technician: Sam Schultz.
Ownership: Nucentrix Broadband Networks (MSO). Purchased from Heartland Wireless Communications Inc.

WICHITA—American Telecasting of Wichita Inc., 519 N. Hydraulic, Wichita, KS 67214. Phones: 316-263-1900; 316-263-2337. Fax: 316-263-3338. Web site: http://www.amtele.com. County: Sedgwick. ICA: KS0428.
Microwave channels reported: N.A.
Began: N.A.
Channel capacity: 24. Channels available but not in use: N.A.
Basic Service
Subscribers: 6,000.
Fee: N.A.
Manager: Rhonda Crooms. Chief technician: Denis Frazier.
Ownership: American Telecasting Inc. (MSO). Sale pends to Sprint Corp.

Kentucky

LEXINGTON—Wireless Associates LP, Box 62889, Charleston, SC 29419. County: Fayette. ICA: KY0303.
Microwave channels reported: N.A.
Channel capacity: N.A.
Ownership: Wireless Associates LP.

LOUISVILLE—Superview of Louisville, 4211 Produce Rd., Louisville, KY 40218. Phone: 502-964-4600. Fax: 502-968-6966. County: Jefferson. ICA: KY0304.
Microwave channels reported: N.A.
Began: N.A.
Channel capacity: N.A. Channels available but not in use: N.A.
Basic Service
Subscribers: N.A.
Programming (received off-air): WAVE (N), WDRB (F), WHAS-TV (A), WKPC-TV (P), WLKY-TV (C) Louisville; WFTE (U) Salem.
Programming (via satellite): WGN-TV (W) Chicago; A & E; Animal Planet; BET; CNN; Country Music TV; Discovery Channel; ESPN; Nashville Network; Nickelodeon; Sci-Fi Channel; TBS Superstation; The Weather Channel; Turner Classic Movies; Turner Network TV; USA Network; VH1.
Fee: $49.95 installation; $18.95 monthly.
Pay Service 1
Pay Units: N.A.
Programming (via satellite): HBO; Showtime.

Fee: $6.00 monthly (Showtime), $8.95 monthly (HBO).
Manager: Ron Gibson. Chief technician: Gary Wright.
Ownership: BellSouth Entertainment Inc.

PADUCAH—NDW II Inc., 308 W. Main St., Durant, OK 74702. County: McCracken. ICA: KY0305.
Microwave channels reported: N.A.
Channel capacity: N.A.
Ownership: NDW II Inc.

Louisiana

ALEXANDRIA—Wireless One of Alexandria, Suite 400, 2506 Lakeland Dr., Jackson, MS 39208. Phones: 504-926-7778; 888-947-3663. Web site: http://www.wirelessone.com. County: Rapides. ICA: LA0230.
Microwave channels reported: N.A.
Began: N.A.
Channel capacity: N.A. Channels available but not in use: N.A.
Basic Service
Subscribers: N.A.
Programming (received off-air): KALB-TV (N), KLAX-TV (A), KLPA-TV (P) Alexandria; KNOE-TV (C) Monroe-El Dorado; WNTZ (F) Natchez.
Programming (via satellite): A & E; CNN; Discovery Channel; Disney Channel; ESPN; Fox Sports Net Southwest; Lifetime; Nashville Network; Nick at Nite; Nickelodeon; QVC; TBS Superstation; The Weather Channel; Turner Network TV; USA Network.
Fee: $99.95 installation; $22.95 monthly.
Pay Service 1
Pay Units: N.A.
Programming (via satellite): HBO.
Fee: $11.95 monthly.
Pay-Per-View
Viewer's Choice.
Fee: $3.90.
Ownership: Wireless One Inc. (MSO).

BUNKIE—Wireless One of Bunkie, 6611 Masonic Dr., Alexandria, LA 71301. Phones: 318-776-9000; 888-947-3663. Fax: 318-776-9009. Web site: http://www.wirelessone.com. Counties: Allen, Avoyelles, Evangeline, Rapides & St. Landry. Also serves Alexandria, Allen Parish (portions), Avoyelles Parish, Cheneyville, Cottonport, Evangeline Parish, Glenmora, Hessmer, Lecompte, Mamou, Marksville, Morrow, Opelousas, Palmetto, Pineville, Rapides Parish (portions), Simmesport, St. Landry, St. Landry Parish (portions), Vick, Washington. ICA: LA0223.
Total homes in service area: 81,752.
Microwave channels reported: N.A.
Began: November 1, 1995.
Channel capacity: 30. Channels available but not in use: 8.
Basic Service
Subscribers: 411.
Programming (received off-air): KALB-TV (N), KLAX-TV (A), KLPA-TV (P) Alexandria; KLFY-TV (C) Lafayette; WNTZ (F) Natchez.
Programming (via satellite): A & E; CNN; Country Music TV; Discovery Channel; Disney Channel; ESPN; Fox Sports Net Southwest; Nashville Network; Nick at Nite; Nickelodeon; QVC; TBS Superstation; The Weather Channel; Turner Network TV; USA Network.
Fee: $99.95 installation; $22.95 monthly.
Pay Service 1
Pay Units: 115.
Programming (via satellite): HBO.
Fee: $11.95 monthly.
Pay-Per-View
Viewer's Choice.
Fee: $3.90.
Equipment: Jerrold set top converters.
Manager: Sandy Naguin. Chief technician: David Van Mol. Marketing & program director: David Brown.
Ownership: Wireless One Inc. (MSO).

HOUMA—Wireless One of Houma, Suite B, 4027 Hwy. 90 E, Broussard, LA 70518-3509. Phones: 318-837-3777; 888-947-3663. Web site: http://www.wirelessone.com. County: Terrebonne. ICA: LA0225.
Microwave channels reported: N.A.
Began: June 1, 1996.
Channel capacity: 30. Channels available but not in use: 19.
Basic Service
Subscribers: 663.
Programming (received off-air): WBRZ (A), WLPB-TV (P), WVLA (N) Baton Rouge; WVUE (F), WWL-TV (C) New Orleans.
Programming (via satellite): WGN-TV (W) Chicago; A & E; BET; C-SPAN; CNN; Country Music TV; Discovery Channel; Disney Channel; ESPN; Fox Family Channel; Fox Sports Net Southwest; History Channel; Learning Channel; Lifetime; Nashville Network; Nickelodeon; TBS Superstation; The Weather Channel; Trinity Bcstg. Network; Turner Network TV; USA Network; VH1.
Fee: $99.95 installation; $22.95 monthly.
Pay Service 1
Pay Units: N.A.
Programming (via satellite): Cinemax; HBO; Showtime.
Fee: $9.95 monthly (Cinemax or Showtime), $11.95 monthly (HBO).
Pay-Per-View
Viewer's Choice.
Fee: $3.90.
Manager: Donnie Scioneaux. Chief technician: Kenneth Naquin. Marketing & program director: David Brown.
Ownership: Wireless One Inc. (MSO).

LAFAYETTE—Wireless One of Lafayette, Suite B, 4027 Hwy. 90 E, Broussard, LA 70518-3509. Phones: 318-837-3777; 888-947-3663. Fax: 318-837-3888. Web site: http://www.wirelessone.com. Counties: Acadia, Iberia, Lafayette, St. Landry, St. Martin & Vermilion. Also serves Acadia Parish (portions), Broussard, Crowley, Iberia, Lafayette Parish, Loreauville, New Iberia Parish, Opelousas, Rayne, St. Landry Parish (portions), St. Martin Parish, Vermilion Parish (portions), Youngsville. ICA: LA0221.
Total homes in service area: 144,222.
Microwave channels reported: N.A.
Began: December 1, 1993.
Channel capacity: 18 (not 2-way capable). Channels available but not in use: None.
Basic Service
Subscribers: 2,905.
Programming (received off-air): KADN (F), KATC (A), KLFY-TV (C), KLPB-TV (P) Lafayette; KPLC-TV (N) Lake Charles.
Programming (via satellite): A & E; BET; C-SPAN; CNN; Discovery Channel; ESPN; Fox Family Channel; Fox Sports Net South; History Channel; Home & Garden Television; Home Shopping Network; Learning Channel; Lifetime; Nashville Network; Nickelodeon; QVC; Showtime; TBS Superstation; The Weather Channel; Turner Network TV; USA Network.
Fee: $99.95 installation; $28.95 monthly.
Pay Service 1
Pay Units: N.A.
Programming (via satellite): Cinemax; Disney Channel; HBO; Showtime.
Fee: $9.95 monthly (Showtime); $10.95 monthly (Cinemax or Disney Channel); $11.95 monthly (HBO).
Pay-Per-View
Viewer's Choice.
Fee: $3.90.
Equipment: Jerrold set top converters.
Manager: Darnelle Delcambre. Chief technician: Gerard Barousse. Marketing & program director: David Brown. Customer service manager: Faye Thibodeaux.
Ownership: Wireless One Inc. (MSO).

LAKE CHARLES—Wireless One of Lake Charles, 4901 Common, Lake Charles, LA 70605. Phones: 318-477-4111; 888-947-3663. Fax: 318-477-4449.
Web site: http://www.wirelessone.com.
Counties: Allen, Beauregard, Calcasieu, Cameron & Jefferson Davis. Also serves Allen Parish (portions), Beauregard Parish (portions), Calcasieu Parish, Cameron Parish (portions), Elton, Iowa, Jefferson Davis Parish, Kinder, Longville, Mittie, Ragley, Roanoke, Singer, Starks, Sulphur, Vinton, Welsh. ICA: LA0220.
Total homes in service area: 89,248.
Microwave channels reported: N.A.
Began: April 1, 1994.
Channel capacity: 14. Channels available but not in use: None.
Basic Service
Subscribers: 4,754.
Programming (received off-air): KBMT (A) Beaumont-Port Arthur; KLFY-TV (C) Lafayette; KPLC-TV (N), KVHP (F) Lake Charles.
Programming (via satellite): A & E; BET; C-SPAN; CNN; Discovery Channel; Disney Channel; ESPN; Flix; Fox Family Channel; Fox Sports Net Southwest; History Channel; Learning Channel; Lifetime; MTV; Nashville Network; Nickelodeon; TBS Superstation; The Weather Channel; Turner Network TV; USA Network.
Fee: $99.95 installation; $22.95 monthly.
Pay Service 1
Pay Units: 84.
Programming (via satellite): HBO.
Fee: $11.95 monthly.
Pay Service 2
Pay Units: N.A.
Programming (via satellite): Showtime (multiplexed); Sundance Channel; The Movie Channel.
Fee: $12.95 monthly (package).
Pay-Per-View
Viewer's Choice.
Fee: $3.90.
Equipment: Jerrold set top converters.
Manager: Denise Mooring. Chief technician: Jonathan Guillory. Marketing & program director: David Brown. Customer service manager: Dawn Witherway.
Ownership: Wireless One Inc. (MSO).

MONROE—Wireless One of Monroe, Suite A, 505 N. 18th St., Monroe, LA 71201. Phones: 318-388-1533; 800-238-0320. Fax: 318-322-0785. Web site: http://www.wirelessone.com. Counties: Jackson, Lincoln, Morehouse, Ouachita, Richland, Union & West Carroll. Also serves Bastrop, Bonita, Choudrant, Collinston, Downsville, Eros, Farmerville, Jackson Parish (portions), Lincoln Parish (portions), Maugham, Marion, Mer Rouge, Morehouse Parish, Oak Ridge, Ouachita Parish, Rayville, Richland Parish, Ruston, Union Parish, West Carroll Parish (portions), West Monroe. ICA: LA0222.
Total homes in service area: 87,885.
Microwave channels reported: N.A.
Began: N.A.
Channel capacity: 20 (not 2-way capable). Channels available but not in use: None.
Basic Service
Subscribers: 3,500.
Programming (received off-air): KLAX-TV (A) Alexandria; KARD (F), KLTM-TV (P), KNOE-TV (C), KTVE (N) Monroe-El Dorado.
Programming (via satellite): A & E; BET; CNN; Discovery Channel; ESPN; Fox Family Channel; Lifetime; Nashville Network; Nick at Nite; Nickelodeon; Showtime; TBS Superstation; The Weather Channel; Turner Network TV; USA Network.
Fee: $99.95 installation; $22.95 monthly.
Pay Service 1
Pay Units: 145.
Programming (via satellite): HBO.
Fee: $11.95 monthly.
Pay-Per-View
Viewer's Choice.
Fee: $3.90.
Equipment: Jerrold set top converters.
Area manager: Denise Mooring. Chief technician: Stuart Williams. Marketing & program director: David Brown. Customer service manager: Julie Ticheli.
Ownership: Wireless One Inc. (MSO).

RAYVILLE—Cotton Country Cable, Box 698, Rayville, LA 71269. Phone: 318-728-3399. County: Richland. ICA: LA0219.
Microwave channels reported: N.A.
Began: N.A.
Channel capacity: N.A.
Ownership: Cotton Country Cable.

Maine

None reported.

Maryland

BALTIMORE—People's Choice TV, 5311 E. Broadway Blvd., Tucson, AZ 85711. Phone: 520-750-9900. Fax: 520-747-0832. County: Baltimore. ICA: MD0051.
Microwave channels reported: N.A.
Channel capacity: N.A.
Manager: Bob Boris.
Ownership: People's Choice TV Partners (MSO). Sale pends to Sprint Corp.

Massachusetts

None reported.

Michigan

BAY CITY & SAGINAW—Microcom, 2600 California Ave., Bay City, MI 48601. Phone: 517-777-8852. County: Bay. ICA: MI0386.
Microwave channels reported: N.A.
Channel capacity: N.A.
Ownership: Microcom Inc.

DETROIT—People's Choice TV, 1017 Naughton, Troy, MI 48083. Phone: 248-526-0910. Counties: Oakland & Wayne. Also serves Dearborn, Grosse Pointe, Southfield. ICA: MI0387.
Microwave channels reported: N.A.
Began: N.A.
Channel capacity: 12. Channels available but not in use: None.
Basic Service
Subscribers: 3,300; Commercial subscribers: 15.
Programming (received off-air): WDIV (N), WJBK (F), WKBD-TV (U), WTVS (P), WXYZ-TV (A) Detroit.

Programming (via satellite): WGN-TV (W) Chicago; BET; CNN; Discovery Channel; ESPN; Fox Family Channel; TBS Superstation; USA Network.
Fee: $25.00 installation; $15.95 monthly.
Pay Service 1
Pay Units: 1,705.
Programming (via satellite): HBO.
Fee: $8.00 monthly.
Pay Service 2
Pay Units: 1,692.
Programming (via satellite): Showtime.
Fee: $8.00 monthly.
Pay Service 3
Pay Units: 811.
Programming (via satellite): ANA Television Network.
Fee: $20.00 monthly.
Equipment: ITS headend; Zenith set top converters.
Manager: Nader Fakhouri. Chief technician: Jeff Deck.
Ownership: People's Choice TV Partners (MSO). Sale pends to Sprint Corp.

JACKSON—Wireless Cable Systems Inc., Suite 6107, 350 5th Ave., New York, NY 10118. Phone: 212-268-2828. Fax: 212-268-5675. County: Jackson. ICA: MI0390.
Microwave channels reported: N.A.
Channel capacity: N.A.
Ownership: Wireless Cable Systems Inc.

LANSING—American Telecasting of Lansing Inc., 2820 Alpha Access St., Lansing, MI 48910. Phone: 517-484-9200.
Web site: http://www.amtele.com.
Counties: Clinton, Eaton & Ingham. ICA: MI0394.
Total homes in service area: 300,000.
Microwave channels reported: N.A.
Began: August 1, 1994.
Channel capacity: 14. Channels available but not in use: N.A.
Basic Service
Subscribers: N.A.
Programming (received off-air): WPXD (X) Ann Arbor; WKAR-TV (P) East Lansing; WILX-TV (N), WLAJ (A), WLNS-TV (C), WSYM-TV (F) Lansing; WTCT (I) Marion.
Programming (via satellite): CNN; Discovery Channel; ESPN; Lifetime; Nashville Network; Nick at Nite; Nickelodeon; TBS Superstation; Turner Network TV; USA Network; VH1.
Fee: $39.95 installation; $18.95 monthly.
Pay Service 1
Pay Units: N.A.
Programming (via satellite): Disney Channel; HBO; Showtime.
Fee: $6.00 monthly (Showtime); $7.00 monthly (Disney); $11.00 monthly (HBO).
Manager: Mark Simmons. Chief technician: Alexander Fisher.
Ownership: American Telecasting Inc. (MSO). Sale pends to Sprint Corp.

MIDLAND—Microcom, 2600 California Ave., Saginaw, MI 48601. Phone: 517-777-8852. County: Midland. ICA: MI0388.
Microwave channels reported: N.A.
Channel capacity: N.A.
Operations manager: Tim Schobert. Chief technician: Randy Moldenhover.
Ownership: Microcom Inc.

Minnesota

ALEXANDRIA—Viking Vision, Suite 101, 901 Hwy. 29 N, Alexandria, MN 56308. Phone: 320-763-4122. County: Douglas. ICA: MN0392.
Microwave channels reported: N.A.
Channel capacity: N.A.
Ownership: Viking Vision.

BARNESVILLE—American Telecasting Inc., 2615 12th Ave. S., Moorhead, MN 56560. Phone: 218-937-5621. County: Clay. ICA: MN0271.
Microwave channels reported: N.A.
Began: January 14, 1991.
Channel capacity: N.A. Channels available but not in use: N.A.
Basic Service
Subscribers: N.A.
Programming (via satellite): WGN-TV (W) Chicago; CNN; Discovery Channel; ESPN; Fox Family Channel; Midwest Sports Channel; Nashville Network; USA Network.
Fee: $18.95 monthly.
Pay Service 1
Pay Units: N.A.
Programming (via satellite): Disney Channel; HBO.
Fee: $6.95 monthly (Disney), $9.95 monthly (HBO).
Manager: Bob Blair.
Ownership: American Telecasting Inc. (MSO). Sale pends to Sprint Corp.

MINNEAPOLIS/ST. PAUL—OmniVision, Suite 110, 1230 Eagan Industrial Rd., Eagan, MN 55121. Phone: 612-452-8010. Fax: 612-452-2814. County: Hennepin. ICA: MN0387.
Total homes in service area: 959,000.
Microwave channels reported: N.A.
Channel capacity: 33 (not 2-way capable). Channels available but not in use: 4.
Basic Service
Subscribers: 4,543.
Programming (via satellite): WGN-TV (W) Chicago; A & E; CNN; Discovery Channel; ESPN; Fox Family Channel; Knowledge TV; Lifetime; MTV; Midwest Sports Channel; Nashville Network; Nickelodeon; TBS Superstation; The Box; The Weather Channel; Turner Network TV; USA Network.
Fee: $9.95 installation; $18.95 monthly.
Pay Service 1
Pay Units: N.A.
Programming (via satellite): Disney Channel; HBO; Showtime; The Movie Channel.
Fee: $9.95 monthly (Disney, Showtime or TMC), $12.00 monthly (HBO).
Equipment: Comwave headend; Tocom addressable set top converters; Standard Communications satellite receivers.
Manager: Dan Johnson. Chief technician: Jeff Aspnes.
Ownership: CS Wireless Systems Inc. (MSO).

WINDOM—American Telecasting of Minnesota Inc., Suite A, 2615 12th Ave. S, Moorhead, MN 56560. Phone: 218-233-3848. Fax: 218-233-4225. Web site: http://www.amtele.com. Counties: Cottonwood & Watonwan. Also serves St. James. ICA: MN0388.
Microwave channels reported: N.A.
Began: N.A.
Channel capacity: N.A. Channels available but not in use: N.A.
Basic Service
Subscribers: N.A.
Programming (received off-air): KEYC-TV (C) Mankato; KARE (N), KSTP-TV (A) Minneapolis-St. Paul; KELO-TV (C), KSFY-TV (A) Sioux Falls-Mitchell.
Programming (via satellite): WGN-TV (W) Chicago; CNN; Discovery Channel; ESPN; Fox Family Channel; Midwest Sports Channel; Nashville Network; Nickelodeon; USA Network.
Fee: N.A.
Pay Service 1
Pay Units: N.A.
Programming (via satellite): HBO.
Fee: N.A.
Manager: Ron Groslie.
Ownership: American Telecasting Inc. (MSO). Sale pends to Sprint Corp.

Mississippi

GULF COAST AREA—Wireless One of Gulf Coast, Suite A, 920 Cedar Lake Rd., Biloxi, MS 39532. Phones: 601-392-7870; 888-947-3663. Fax: 601-392-8445. Web site: http://www.wirelessone.com. Counties: Hancock, Harrison & Jackson. ICA: MS0200.
Microwave channels reported: N.A.
Began: N.A.
Channel capacity: 31. Channels available but not in use: 2.
Basic Service
Subscribers: 4,053.
Programming (received off-air): WLOX-TV (A), WMAH-TV (P) Biloxi; WXXV-TV (F) Gulfport; WDAM-TV (N) Laurel-Hattiesburg; WKRG-TV (C) Mobile-Pensacola.
Programming (via satellite): WGN-TV (W) Chicago; A & E; C-SPAN; CNN; Country Music TV; Discovery Channel; E! Entertainment TV; ESPN; Fox Family Channel; History Channel; Learning Channel; Lifetime; Nashville Network; Nickelodeon; TBS Superstation; The Health Network; The Weather Channel; Turner Classic Movies; Turner Network TV; USA Network; VH1.
Fee: $99.95 installation; $22.95 monthly.
Pay Service 1
Pay Units: N.A.
Programming (via satellite): Disney Channel; HBO; Showtime.
Fee: $9.95 monthly (Showtime); $10.95 monthly (Disney); $11.95 monthly (HBO).
Pay-Per-View
Viewer's Choice.
Fee: $3.95.
Manager: Cliff Thomas. Chief technician: Tom Ambron. Marketing & program director: David Brown.
Ownership: Wireless One Inc. (MSO).

HATTIESBURG—Wireless One of Hattiesburg, Suite 400, 2506 Lakeland Dr., Jackson, MS 39208. Phones: 504-926-7778; 888-947-3663. Web site: http://www.wirelessone.com. Counties: Forrest & Lamar. ICA: MS0210.
Microwave channels reported: N.A.
Began: N.A.
Channel capacity: N.A. Channels available but not in use: N.A.
Basic Service
Subscribers: N.A.
Programming (received off-air): WLOX-TV (A), WMAH-TV (P) Biloxi; WXXV-TV (F) Gulfport; WHLT (C) Hattiesburg; WDAM-TV (N) Laurel-Hattiesburg.
Programming (via satellite): WGN-TV (W) Chicago; A & E; C-SPAN; CNN; Country Music TV; Discovery Channel; ESPN; Fox Family Channel; Fox Sports Net South; History Channel; Home Shopping Network; Learning Channel; Lifetime; Nashville Network; Nickelodeon; QVC; TBS Superstation; The Weather Channel; Turner Network TV; USA Network; VH1.
Fee: $99.95 installation; $28.95 monthly.
Pay Service 1
Pay Units: N.A.
Programming (via satellite): Cinemax; Disney Channel; HBO; Showtime.
Fee: $9.95 monthly (Showtime), $10.95 monthly (Cinemax or Disney), $11.95 monthly (HBO).
Pay-Per-View
Viewer's Choice.
Fee: $3.90.
Ownership: Wireless One Inc. (MSO).

INVERNESS—Wireless One of Inverness, Suite 400, 2506 Lakeland Dr., Jackson, MS 39208. Phones: 504-926-7778; 888-947-3663. Web site: http://www.wirelessone.com. County: Sunflower. ICA: MS0206.
Microwave channels reported: N.A.
Began: N.A.
Channel capacity: N.A. Channels available but not in use: N.A.
Basic Service
Subscribers: N.A.
Programming (received off-air): WXVT (C) Greenville; WABG-TV (A) Greenwood; WLBT-TV (N) Jackson.
Programming (via satellite): WGN-TV (W) Chicago; A & E; BET; C-SPAN; CNN; Country Music TV; Discovery Channel; Disney Channel; ESPN; Fox Family Channel; FoxNet; Fox Sports Net South; History Channel; Learning Channel; Lifetime; Nashville Network; Nickelodeon; TBS Superstation; The Weather Channel; Turner Network TV; USA Network; VH1.
Current originations: Educational access.
Fee: $99.95 installation; $22.95 monthly.
Pay Service 1
Pay Units: N.A.
Programming (via satellite): Cinemax; HBO; Showtime.
Fee: $9.95 monthly (Showtime), $10.95 monthly (Cinemax), $11.95 monthly (HBO).
Pay-Per-View
Viewer's Choice.
Fee: $3.90.
Ownership: Wireless One Inc. (MSO).

JACKSON—Wireless One of Jackson, Suite H, 181 Davis Johnson Dr., Jackson, MS 39218. Phones: 601-936-7403; 888-947-3663. Fax: 601-936-9355.
Web site: http://www.wirelessone.com.
County: Hinds. ICA: MS0194.
Microwave channels reported: N.A.
Began: N.A.
Channel capacity: 30. Channels available but not in use: N.A.
Basic Service
Subscribers: 15,157.
Programming (received off-air): WAPT (A), WBMS-LP (I), WDBD (F), WJTV (C), WLBT-TV (N), WMPN-TV (P) Jackson.
Programming (via satellite): A & E; BET; C-SPAN; CNBC; CNN; Country Music TV; Discovery Channel; Disney Channel; ESPN; Fox Family Channel; Fox Sports Net South; History Channel; Learning Channel; Lifetime; Nashville Network; Nickelodeon; TBS Superstation; The Weather Channel; Turner Network TV; USA Network; VH1.
Fee: $99.95 installation; $28.95 monthly.
Pay Service 1
Pay Units: N.A.
Programming (via satellite): Cinemax; HBO; Showtime.
Fee: $9.95 monthly (Showtime); $10.95 monthly (Cinemax); $11.95 monthly (HBO).
Pay-Per-View
Viewer's Choice.
Fee: $3.95.
Manager: Tim Reilly. Chief technician: Sam Robertson. Marketing & program director: David Brown.
Ownership: Wireless One Inc.

MERIDIAN—Wireless One of Meridian, 2590 Sellers Dr., Meridian, MS 39301. Phones: 601-482-0220; 888-947-3663. Fax: 601-482-6225. County: Lauderdale. ICA: MS0205.
Microwave channels reported: N.A.
Began: N.A.
Channel capacity: 31. Channels available but not in use: 1.
Basic Service
Subscribers: 750.
Programming (received off-air): WGBC (N), WMAW-TV (P), WMDN (C), WTOK-TV (A,F) Meridian.
Programming (via satellite): WGN-TV (W) Chicago; A & E; BET; C-SPAN; CNN; Country Music TV; Discovery Channel; E! Entertainment TV; ESPN; Fox Family Channel; Fox Sports Net South; FoxNet; History Channel; Learning Channel; Lifetime; Nashville Network; Nickelodeon; QVC; TBS Superstation; The Health Network; The Weather Channel; Turner Classic Movies; Turner Network TV; USA Network; VH1.
Fee: $22.95 monthly.
Pay Service 1
Pay Units: N.A.
Programming (via satellite): Disney Channel; HBO; Showtime.
Fee: $9.95 monthly (Showtime), $10.95 monthly (Disney), $11.95 monthly (HBO), $27.95 monthly (Disney, HBO & Showtime).
Pay-Per-View
Viewer's Choice.
Manager: Lex Guellette. Operations manager: Jeff Peeples. Chief technician: Bryant Gunn. Marketing director: Walt Eilers.
Ownership: Wireless One Inc. (MSO).

NATCHEZ—Wireless One of Natchez, 611 Main St. N, Meadville, MS 39653. Phones: 601-936-1515; 888-947-3663. Fax: 601-936-1517. Web site: http://www.wirelessone.com. Counties: Adams, Panola & Sunflower. Also serves Delta, Indianola. ICA: MS0202.
Microwave channels reported: N.A.
Began: N.A.
Channel capacity: N.A. Channels available but not in use: N.A.
Basic Service
Subscribers: N.A.
Programming (received off-air): WAPT (A), WJTV (C), WLBT-TV (N) Jackson; WNTZ (F) Natchez.
Programming (via satellite): A & E; BET; C-SPAN; CNN; Country Music TV; Discovery Channel; Disney Channel; ESPN; Fox Family Channel; History Channel; Home Shopping Network; Learning Channel; Lifetime; Nashville Network; Nickelodeon; QVC; TBS Superstation; The Weather Channel; Turner Network TV; USA Network; VH1.
Fee: $99.95 installation; $22.95 monthly.
Pay Service 1
Pay Units: N.A.
Programming (via satellite): Cinemax; HBO; Showtime.
Fee: $9.95 monthly (Showtime); $10.95 monthly (Cinemax); $11.95 monthly (HBO).
Pay-Per-View
Viewer's Choice.
Fee: $3.90.
Ownership: Wireless One Inc. (MSO).

OXFORD—Wireless One of Oxford, 179 Hwy. 6 E, Oxford, MS 38655. Phones: 601-281-1020; 888-947-3663. Fax: 601-281-1024. Web site: http://www.wirelessone.com. County: Lafayette. ICA: MS0203.
Microwave channels reported: N.A.
Began: N.A.
Channel capacity: 31. Channels available but not in use: 7.
Basic Service
Subscribers: N.A.
Programming (received off-air): WHBQ-TV (F), WMC-TV (N), WPTY-TV (A), WREG-TV (C) Memphis; WMAV-TV (P) Oxford.
Programming (via satellite): A & E; BET; C-SPAN; CNN; Discovery Channel; Disney Channel; E! Entertainment TV; ESPN; Fox Family Channel; History Channel; Learning Channel; Nashville Network; Nickelodeon; TBS Superstation; The Health Network; The Weather Channel; Turner Classic Movies; Turner Network TV; USA Network; VH1.
Fee: $99.95 installation; $22.95 monthly.
Pay Service 1
Pay Units: N.A.
Programming (via satellite): HBO.
Fee: $11.95 monthly.
Pay-Per-View
Viewer's Choice.
Fee: $3.90.
Manager: Louis McOray. Chief technician: Michael Mullins. Marketing & program director: David Brown.
Ownership: Wireless One Inc. (MSO).

STARKVILLE—Wireless One of Starkville, 637 S. Frontage Rd., Columbia, MS 39701. Phones: 601-241-0037; 888-947-3663. Fax: 601-329-0021. Web site: http://www.wirelessone.com. Counties: Lowndes & Oktibbeha. Also serves Columbus. ICA: MS0204.
Microwave channels reported: N.A.
Began: N.A.
Channel capacity: 31. Channels available but not in use: 1.
Basic Service
Subscribers: N.A.
Programming (received off-air): WAAY-TV (A), WAFF (N), WHNT-TV (C), WZDX (F) Huntsville-Decatur.
Programming (via satellite): WGN-TV (W) Chicago; A & E; BET; C-SPAN; CNN; Country Music TV; Discovery Channel; E! Entertainment TV; ESPN; Fox Family Channel; Fox Sports Net South; Headline News; History Channel; Learning Channel; Lifetime; Nashville Network; Nickelodeon; QVC; TBS Superstation; The Health Network; The Weather Channel; Turner Classic Movies; Turner Network TV; USA Network; VH1.
Fee: $99.95 installation; $22.95 monthly.
Pay Service 1
Pay Units: N.A.
Programming (via satellite): Disney Channel; HBO; Showtime.
Fee: $9.95 monthly (Showtime); $10.95 monthly (Disney); $11.95 monthly (HBO).
Pay-Per-View
Viewer's Choice.
Fee: $3.90.
Manager: Murry Tate. Chief technician: Heather Dusenberry. Marketing & program director: David Brown.
Ownership: Wireless One Inc. (MSO).

TUPELO—Wireless One of Tupelo, 1935 McCullough Blvd., Tupelo, MS 38801. Phones: 601-840-5100; 888-947-3663. Fax: 601-840-9789. Web site: http://www.wirelessone.com. County: Lee. ICA: MS0207.
Microwave channels reported: N.A.
Began: N.A.
Channel capacity: N.A.
Basic Service
Subscribers: N.A.
Programming (received off-air): WMAE-TV (P) Booneville; WCBI-TV (C), WTVA (N) Columbus-Tupelo; WPTY-TV (A) Memphis; WLOV-TV (F) Tupelo.
Programming (via satellite): WGN-TV (W) Chicago; A & E; BET; C-SPAN; CNN; Country Music TV; Discovery Channel; E! Entertainment TV; ESPN; Fox Family Channel; Fox Sports Net South; Headline News; History Channel; Learning Channel; Lifetime; Nashville Network; Nickelodeon; QVC; TBS Superstation; The Health Network; The Weather Channel; Turner Classic Movies; Turner Network TV; USA Network; VH1.
Fee: $99.95 installation; $22.95 monthly.
Pay Service 1
Pay Units: N.A.
Programming (via satellite): Disney Channel; HBO; Showtime.
Fee: $9.95 monthly (Showtime), $10.95 monthly (Disney), $11.95 monthly (HBO), $27.95 monthly (Disney, HBO & Showtime).
Pay-Per-View
Viewer's Choice.
Fee: $3.90.
Office manager: Sandy Harmon. Chief technician: Van McRay.
Ownership: Wireless One Inc. (MSO).

Missouri

KANSAS CITY—People's Choice TV, 5301 E. Broadway Blvd., Tucson, AZ 85711-3710. Phone: 520-519-4400. Fax: 520-747-6830. County: Clay. ICA: MO0453.
Microwave channels reported: N.A.
Channel capacity: N.A. Channels available but not in use: N.A.
Manager: Larry De Alba. Chief technician: Mike Denny.
Ownership: Matthew Oristano.

MALDEN—Broadcast Cablevision, Drawer 377, Malden, MO 63863. Phone: 573-276-3025. County: Dunklin. ICA: MO0449.
Microwave channels reported: N.A.
Channel capacity: N.A.
Ownership: Broadcast Cablevision.

MONROE CITY—Nucentrix Broadband Networks Inc., Suite 200, 200 Chisholm Place, Plano, TX 75075. Phone: 972-423-9494. Fax: 972-423-0819. County: Monroe. ICA: MO0460.
Microwave channels reported: N.A.
Began: September 9, 1995.
Channel capacity: N.A. Channels available but not in use: N.A.
Basic Service
Subscribers: N.A.
Programming (received off-air): KTVO (A) Ottumwa-Kirksville.
Programming (via satellite): WGN-TV (W) Chicago; A & E; American Movie Classics; CNN; Cartoon Network; Country Music TV; Discovery Channel; Disney Channel; ESPN; Fox Family Channel; Fox Sports Net Midwest; FoxNet; History Channel; Learning Channel; Lifetime; Nashville Network; Nickelodeon; Sci-Fi Channel; TBS Superstation; The Weather Channel; Turner Network TV; USA Network.
Fee: $28.65 monthly.
Pay Service 1
Pay Units: N.A.
Programming (via satellite): Cinemax; HBO (multiplexed); Showtime.
Fee: N.A.
Pay-Per-View
Viewer's Choice.
Manager: Melissa Hawker. Chief technician: Kevin Wilke.
Ownership: Nucentrix Broadband Networks (MSO). Purchased from Heartland Wireless Communications Inc.

MONTGOMERY CITY—Nucentrix Broadband Networks Inc., Suite 200, 200 Chisholm Place, Plano, TX 75075. Phone: 972-423-9494. Fax: 972-423-0819. County: Montgomery. ICA: MO0459.
Microwave channels reported: N.A.
Began: October 1, 1996.
Channel capacity: N.A. Channels available but not in use: N.A.
Basic Service
Subscribers: N.A.
Programming (received off-air): KDNL-TV (A), KETC (P), KMOV (C), KSDK (N), KTVI (F) St. Louis.
Programming (via satellite): WGN-TV (W) Chicago; A & E; CNN; Discovery Channel; Disney Channel; ESPN; Fox Sports Net Midwest; Lifetime; Nashville Network; Nickelodeon; TBS Superstation; The Weather Channel; Turner Classic Movies; Turner Network TV; USA Network.
Fee: N.A.
Pay Service 1
Pay Units: N.A.
Programming (via satellite): Cinemax; HBO (multiplexed).
Fee: N.A.
Pay-Per-View
Viewer's Choice.
Manager: Melissa Hawker. Chief technician: Kevin Wilke.
Ownership: Nucentrix Broadband Networks (MSO). Purchased from Heartland Wireless Communications Inc.

SIKESTON—Nucentrix Broadband Networks Inc., Suite 200, 200 Chisholm Place, Plano, TX 75075. Phone: 972-423-9494. Fax: 972-423-0819. Counties: Dunklin, Mississippi, New Madrid & Scott. Also serves East Prairie, Malden, Miner, Portageville. ICA: MO0451.
Total homes in service area: 9,359.
Microwave channels reported: WLX-380, A-1-4, ITFS; WLX-377, B-1-4, ITFS, WLX-376, C-1-4, ITFS, WLX-378, D-1-4, ITFS.
Began: January 1, 1992.
Channel capacity: 20. Channels available but not in use: None.
Basic Service
Subscribers: 1,699.
Programming (via satellite): WGN-TV (W) Chicago; A & E; CNN; Discovery Channel; Disney Channel; ESPN; Knowledge TV; Nashville Network; TBS Superstation; TV Guide Channel; The Weather Channel; USA Network.
Fee: $50.00 installation; $28.95 monthly.
Pay Service 1
Pay Units: 170.
Programming (via satellite): Cinemax.
Fee: $9.95 monthly.
Pay Service 2
Pay Units: 150.
Programming (via satellite): HBO.
Fee: $10.95 monthly.
Equipment: Jerrold set top converters.
Manager: Frederick Frank. Chief technician: Sam Schultz.
Ownership: Nucentrix Broadband Networks (MSO). Purchased from Heartland Wireless Communications Inc.

ST. LOUIS—People's Choice TV of St. Louis, 818 Horan Dr., St. Louis, MO 63026. Phone: 314-343-7288. Fax: 314-343-5732. Counties: Madison, Monroe & St. Clair, IL; Jefferson, St. Charles & St. Louis, MO. Also serves Madison County, Monroe County, St. Clair County, IL; Jefferson County, St. Charles County, St. Louis County, MO. ICA: MO0454.
Total homes in service area: 985,000.
Microwave channels reported: WQQ64, Ch. 1, MDS; WHT651, E group, MMDS; WHJ915, H2, MMDS.
Began: July 1, 1994.

Channel capacity: 39. Channels available but not in use: 6.

Basic Service

Subscribers: 6,100.

Programming (received off-air): KDNL-TV (A), KETC (P), KMOV (C), KPLR-TV (W), KSDK (N), KTVI (F) St. Louis.

Programming (via satellite): WGN-TV (W) Chicago; A & E; BET; CNBC; CNN; Discovery Channel; ESPN; Fox Family Channel; Fox Sports Net Midwest; Headline News; Learning Channel; Lifetime; MTV; Nashville Network; Nickelodeon; TBS Superstation; TV Guide Channel; Turner Network TV; USA Network.

Fee: $25.00 installation; $22.00 monthly; $3.95 converter.

Pay Service 1

Pay Units: 1,986.

Programming (via satellite): Cinemax.

Fee: $7.95 monthly.

Pay Service 2

Pay Units: 756.

Programming (via satellite): Disney Channel.

Fee: $7.95 monthly.

Pay Service 3

Pay Units: 3,450.

Programming (via satellite): HBO.

Fee: $7.95 monthly.

Pay-Per-View

Action Pay-Per-View; Playboy TV; Spice.

Fee: Varies.

Local advertising: Yes.

Equipment: Jerrold set top converters.

Manager: Rodney Stage. Chief technician: Dale Ross. Program director: Rodney Stouge. Marketing director: Nicole Wydra.

Ownership: People's Choice TV Partners (MSO). Sale pends to Sprint Corp.

Montana

BILLINGS—American Telecasting of Billings Inc., 1115 First Ave. N, Billings, MT 59101-2664. Phones: 406-248-9001; 406-248-9887. Fax: 406-248-8137.

Web site: http://www.amtele.com.

Counties: Carbon & Yellowstone. Also serves Carbon County (portions), Yellowstone County (portions). ICA: MT0120.

Total homes in service area: 52,000.

Microwave channels reported: N.A.

Began: January 1, 1991.

Channel capacity: 33. Channels available but not in use: 5.

Basic Service

Subscribers: 3,940; Commercial subscribers: 20.

Programming (received off-air): KSVI (A,F), KTVQ (C), KULR-TV (N) Billings.

Programming (via microwave): KUSM (P) Bozeman.

Programming (via translator): KWGN-TV (W) Denver.

Programming (via satellite): WGN-TV (W) Chicago; A & E; American Movie Classics; CNBC; CNN; Discovery Channel; Disney Channel; ESPN; Fox Family Channel; Headline News; Learning Channel; Lifetime; Nashville Network; Nickelodeon; Sci-Fi Channel; TBS Superstation; TV Guide Channel; The Weather Channel; Turner Network TV; USA Network; VH1.

Fee: $19.95 installation; $22.95 monthly. Commercial fee: $20.95 monthly.

Pay Service 1

Pay Units: 1,000.

Programming (via satellite): HBO.

Fee: $10.00 monthly.

Pay Service 2

Pay Units: 1,500.

Programming (via satellite): Showtime.

Fee: $6.00 monthly.

Equipment: General Instrument set top converters.

Manager: Lori Beck. Chief technician: Chuck Davis. Program director: Chris Clark. Marketing director: Clay Montague.

Ownership: American Telecasting Inc. (MSO). Sale pends to Antilles Wireless LLC.

Nebraska

BARTLEY—Southwest Telecommunications, Box 309, Palisade, NE 69040. Phone: 308-285-3880. Fax: 308-285-3811. Counties: Frontier & Red Willow. Also serves Frontier County. ICA: NE0344.

Microwave channels reported: WLW999, E group, MMDS; WHK929, F group, MMDS; WNEX783, H1, MMDS.

Began: March 1, 1990.

Channel capacity: 11 (not 2-way capable). Channels available but not in use: None.

Basic Service

Subscribers: 346; Commercial subscribers: 1.

Programming (via satellite): CNN; Discovery Channel; ESPN; Fox Family Channel; Nashville Network; Nickelodeon; TBS Superstation; The Weather Channel; Turner Network TV.

Fee: $15.95 monthly.

Pay Service 1

Pay Units: 24.

Programming (via satellite): Disney Channel.

Fee: $8.95 monthly.

Pay Service 2

Pay Units: 34.

Programming (via satellite): HBO.

Fee: $10.95 monthly.

Equipment: Zenith set top converters.

Manager: Don Suda. Chief technician: Gary Hanken. Marketing director: Shannon Pevoteaux.

Ownership: Southwest Telecommunications Co-op Assn. Inc. (MSO).

GENEVA—American Telecasting of Grand Island/Geneva/Omaha, 123 N. Lexington, Hastings, NE 68901. Phones: 402-463-0641; 800-950-3038. Fax: 402-463-0620. Web site: http://www.amtele.com. County: Fillmore. ICA: NE0352.

Microwave channels reported: N.A.

Began: N.A.

Channel capacity: N.A. Channels available but not in use: N.A.

Basic Service

Subscribers: N.A.

Programming (received off-air): KGIN (C) Grand Island; KHAS-TV (N), KHNE-TV (P) Hastings; KHGI-TV (A) Kearney; KLNE-TV (P) Lexington; KLKN (A), KOLN (C) Lincoln; KSNB-TV (F) Superior.

Programming (via satellite): WGN-TV (W) Chicago; CNN; Discovery Channel; ESPN; Nashville Network; USA Network.

Fee: N.A.

Pay Service 1

Pay Units: N.A.

Programming (via satellite): HBO; Showtime.

Fee: N.A.

Ownership: American Telecasting Inc. (MSO). Sale pends to Sprint Corp.

GRAND ISLAND—American Telecasting of Grand Island/Geneva/Omaha, 123 N. Lexington, Hastings, NE 68901. Phones: 402-463-0641; 800-950-3038. Fax: 402-463-0620. Web site: http://www.amtele.com. County: Hall. ICA: NE0345.

Microwave channels reported: N.A.

Began: N.A.

Channel capacity: N.A. Channels available but not in use: N.A.

Basic Service

Subscribers: N.A.

Programming (received off-air): KGIN (C) Grand Island; KHAS-TV (N), KHNE-TV (P) Hastings; KHGI-TV (A) Kearney; KLNE-TV (P) Lexington; KLKN (A), KOLN (C) Lincoln; KSNB-TV (F) Superior.

Programming (via satellite): WGN-TV (W) Chicago; A & E; American Movie Classics; CNBC; CNN; Country Music TV; Discovery Channel; Disney Channel; ESPN; Fox Family Channel; Fox Sports Net; Lifetime; Nashville Network; Nickelodeon; TBS Superstation; The Weather Channel; USA Network; VH1.

Fee: N.A.

Pay Service 1

Pay Units: N.A.

Programming (via satellite): HBO; Showtime.

Fee: N.A.

Ownership: American Telecasting Inc. (MSO). Sale pends to Antilles Wireless LLC.

KEARNEY—Cable USA, 809 Central Ave., Kearney, NE 68847. Phone: 308-234-6428. County: Buffalo. ICA: NE0346.

Microwave channels reported: N.A.

Channel capacity: N.A.

Ownership: Cable USA Inc.

LINCOLN—American Telecasting of Nebraska Inc., 2441 N. 9th St., Lincoln, NE 68521. Phones: 402-435-4920; 800-950-3038. Fax: 402-435-5078.

Web site: http://www.amtele.com.

County: Lancaster. ICA: NE0350.

Microwave channels reported: N.A.

Channel capacity: N.A.

Manager: Chip Spann. Chief technician: Jim Gary.

Ownership: American Telecasting Inc. (MSO). Sale pends to Sprint Corp.

NORTH PLATTE—Southwest Telecommunications, Box 309, Palisade, NE 69040. Phone: 308-285-3880. Fax: 308-285-3811. County: Lincoln. ICA: NE0347.

Microwave channels reported: WHK928, E group, MMDS; WHK923, F group, MMDS; WNEX785, H1, MMDS.

Began: March 1, 1990.

Channel capacity: 11 (not 2-way capable). Channels available but not in use: None.

Basic Service

Subscribers: 448.

Programming (via satellite): CNN; Discovery Channel; ESPN; Fox Family Channel; Nashville Network; Nickelodeon; TBS Superstation; The Weather Channel; Turner Network TV.

Fee: $15.95 monthly.

Pay Service 1

Pay Units: 32.

Programming (via satellite): Disney Channel.

Fee: $8.95 monthly.

Pay Service 2

Pay Units: 45.

Programming (via satellite): HBO.

Fee: $10.95 monthly.

Equipment: Zenith set top converters.

Manager: Don Suda. Chief technician: Gary Hanken. Marketing director: Shannon Pevoteaux.

Ownership: Southwest Telecommunications Co-op Assn. Inc. (MSO).

OMAHA—Digital Broadcast Corp., 111 Great Neck Rd., Great Neck, NY 11021. Phone: 516-466-1932. Fax: 800-565-0410. County: Douglas. ICA: NE0354.

Microwave channels reported: N.A.

Channel capacity: N.A.

Ownership: Digital Broadcast Corp.

OSHKOSH—Southwest Telecommunications, Box 309, Palisade, NE 69040. Phone: 308-285-3880. Fax: 308-285-3811. County: Garden. ICA: NE0348.

Microwave channels reported: WLW997, E group, MMDS; WLW964, F group, MMDS.

Began: March 1, 1990.

Channel capacity: 11 (not 2-way capable). Channels available but not in use: None.

Basic Service

Subscribers: 293; Commercial subscribers: 2.

Programming (via satellite): CNBC; CNN; Discovery Channel; ESPN; Fox Family Channel; Nashville Network; Nickelodeon; TBS Superstation; Turner Network TV.

Fee: $15.95 monthly.

Pay Service 1

Pay Units: 17.

Programming (via satellite): Disney Channel.

Fee: $8.95 monthly.

Pay Service 2

Pay Units: 41.

Programming (via satellite): HBO.

Fee: $10.95 monthly.

Equipment: Zenith set top converters.

Manager: Don Suda. Chief technician: Gary Hanken. Marketing director: Shannon Pevoteaux.

Ownership: Southwest Telecommunications Co-op Assn. Inc. (MSO).

WAUNETA—Southwest Telecommmunications, Box 309, Palisade, NE 69040. Phone: 308-285-3880. Fax: 308-285-3511. County: Chase. Also serves Chase County. ICA: NE0355.

Microwave channels reported: WLW998, E group, MMDS; WHK926, F group, MMDS; WNEX784, H1, MMDS.

Began: March 1, 1990.

Channel capacity: 11 (not 2-way capable). Channels available but not in use: None.

Basic Service

Subscribers: 322.

Programming (via satellite): CNN; Discovery Channel; ESPN; Fox Family Channel; Nashville Network; Nickelodeon; TBS Superstation; The Weather Channel; Turner Network TV.

Fee: $15.95 monthly.

Pay Service 1

Pay Units: 18.

Programming (via satellite): Disney Channel.

Fee: $8.95 monthly.

Pay Service 2

Pay Units: 65.

Programming (via satellite): HBO.

Fee: $10.95 monthly.

Local advertising: Yes.

Equipment: Zenith set top converters.

Manager: Don Suda. Chief technician: Gary Hanken. Marketing director: Shannon Pevoteaux.

Ownership: Southwest Telecommunications Co-op Assn. Inc. (MSO).

Nevada

CARSON CITY—Quadravision, 1345 Airmotive Way, Reno, NV 89502. Phone: 702-686-5580.

Fax: 702-686-5590. County: Carson City. ICA: NV0051.
Microwave channels reported: N.A.
Began: N.A.
Channel capacity: N.A. Channels available but not in use: N.A.
Basic Service
Subscribers: N.A.
Programming (received off-air): KNPB (P), KOLO-TV (A), KRNV (N), KRXI (F), KTVN (C) Reno.
Fee: $24.95 installation; $4.95 monthly.
Expanded Basic Service
Subscribers: N.A.
Programming (via satellite): WGN-TV (W) Chicago; A & E; CNN; Discovery Channel; Disney Channel; ESPN; Knowledge TV; Learning Channel; Nashville Network; Nickelodeon; Sci-Fi Channel; TBS Superstation; The Weather Channel; Turner Classic Movies; Turner Network TV; USA Network.
Fee: $24.95 installation; $7.95 monthly.
Pay Service 1
Pay Units: N.A.
Programming (via satellite): Cinemax; HBO.
Fee: $8.00 monthly (Cinemax); $9.95 monthly (HBO).
Pay-Per-View
Movies; special events.
Fee: Varies.
Ownership: Quadravision (MSO).

LAS VEGAS—Superchannels of Las Vegas, Suite 101, 975 American Pacific Dr., Henderson, NV 89014. Phones: 775-566-9414; 775-566-9268. Fax: 775-566-9424. E-mail: bharris@amtele.com.
Web site: http://www.amtele.com.
County: Clark. ICA: NV0055.
Total homes in service area: 395,000.
Microwave channels reported: N.A.
Began: N.A.
Channel capacity: 23 (not 2-way capable). Channels available but not in use: None.
Basic Service
Subscribers: 4,977.
Programming (via satellite): WGN-TV (W) Chicago; A & E; Animal Planet; BET; CNBC; CNN; Discovery Channel; Disney Channel; ESPN; EWTN; Fox Sports Net West; Lifetime; MTV; Nashville Network; Nickelodeon; Sci-Fi Channel; TBS Superstation; Turner Classic Movies; Turner Network TV; USA Network; Univision.
Fee: $69.95 installation; $22.95 monthly.
Pay Service 1
Pay Units: 2,341.
Programming (via satellite): Showtime.
Fee: $7.00 monthly.
Pay Service 2
Pay Units: 1,251.
Programming (via satellite): HBO.
Fee: $10.00 monthly.
Pay Service 3
Pay Units: 2,396.
Programming (via satellite): Starz!
Fee: $5.00 monthly.
Pay-Per-View
Viewer's Choice.
Local advertising: No.
Equipment: California Amplifier addressable set top converters.
Manager: Dalen Lawrence. Chief technician: Dan Lawrence Jr. Marketing & program director: Bill Gerski. Operations manager: Bob Harris.
Ownership: American Telecasting Inc. (MSO). Sale pends to Sprint Corp.

RENO—Quadravision, 1345 Airmotive Way, Reno, NV 89502. Phone: 702-686-5580. Fax: 702-686-5590. County: Washoe. ICA: NV0053.
Microwave channels reported: N.A.
Began: N.A.
Channel capacity: N.A. Channels available but not in use: N.A.
Basic Service
Subscribers: N.A.
Programming (received off-air): KNPB (P), KOLO-TV (A), KRNV (N), KRXI (F), KTVN (C) Reno.
Fee: $4.95 monthly.
Expanded Basic Service
Subscribers: N.A.
Programming (via satellite): WGN-TV (W) Chicago; A & E; CNN; Discovery Channel; Disney Channel; ESPN; Knowledge TV; Learning Channel; MTV; Nashville Network; Nickelodeon; Sci-Fi Channel; TBS Superstation; The Weather Channel; Turner Network TV; USA Network.
Fee: $20.95 monthly.
Pay Service 1
Pay Units: N.A.
Programming (via satellite): HBO; Showtime.
Fee: $8.00 monthly (Showtime), $9.95 monthly (HBO).
Pay-Per-View
Playboy TV; movies; special events.
Fee: $2.95-$9.95.
Ownership: Quadravision (MSO).

New Jersey

ATLANTIC CITY—OrionVision, 101 Pleasant Ave., Absecon, NJ 08201. Phones: 609-485-0099; 609-926-8599. Fax: 609-569-1512. Counties: Atlantic, Cape May & Cumberland. Also serves Atlantic County, Cape May County, Cumberland County. ICA: NJ0064.
Total homes in service area: 485,000.
Microwave channels reported: WMI383, Ch. 1, MDS; WMI837, Ch. 2A, MDS; WHT752, E group, MMDS; WMI280, F group, MMDS; WNTH892, H1, MMDS; WLX-491, D-1-4, ITFS.
Began: January 1, 1991.
Channel capacity: 31. Channels available but not in use: 4.
Basic Service
Subscribers: 2,000; Commercial subscribers: 1,136.
Programming (received off-air): KYW-TV (C), WCAU (N), WPHL-TV (W), WPSG (U), WPVI-TV (A), WTXF-TV (F) Philadelphia; WMGM-TV (N) Wildwood; WHYY-TV (P) Wilmington.
Programming (via satellite): A & E; American Movie Classics; CNBC; CNN; Discovery Channel; Disney Channel; E! Entertainment TV; ESPN; ESPN 2; EWTN; Fox Family Channel; Fox Sports Net; Headline News; Knowledge TV; MTV; NASA TV; Nashville Network; Netlink International; Nick at Nite; Nickelodeon; QVC; Sci-Fi Channel; TBS Superstation; The Weather Channel; Turner Network TV; USA Network.
Fee: $69.00 installation; $19.93 monthly; $0.93 converter.
Commercial fee: $4.40 monthly.
Pay Service 1
Pay Units: 68.
Programming (via satellite): The Movie Channel.
Fee: N.A.
Pay Service 2
Pay Units: 357.
Programming (via satellite): Showtime.
Fee: $6.95 monthly.
Pay Service 3
Pay Units: N.A.
Programming (via satellite): Flix.
Fee: N.A.
Equipment: Jerrold & Tocom set top converters.
Manager: Michael Myers. Chief technician: Joe Mignogma. Marketing director: Christopher Beausang.
Ownership: Orion Broadcasting Systems (MSO).

New Mexico

ALBUQUERQUE—Multimedia Development Corp., Suite 300, 13170-B Central Ave. SE, Albuquerque, NM 87123. County: Bernalillo. ICA: NM0100.
Microwave channels reported: N.A.
Channel capacity: N.A.
Ownership: Multimedia Development Corp.

LAS CRUCES—Santa Fe Wireless Cable TV, Box 878, Sandia Park, NM 87047. Phone: 505-524-7625. County: Dona Ana. ICA: NM0097.
Microwave channels reported: N.A.
Began: N.A.
Channel capacity: N.A.
Ownership: Santa Fe Wireless Cable TV.

ROSWELL—Microwave Communication Services, Suite 900, 400 Perimeter Center Terrace NE, Atlanta, GA 30346. Phone: 404-804-6448. Fax: 404-409-0060. County: Chaves. ICA: NM0098.
Microwave channels reported: N.A.
Channel capacity: N.A.
Ownership: Microwave Communication Services (MSO).

SANTA FE—Santa Fe Wireless Cable TV, Box 878, Sandia Park, NM 87047. Phone: 505-524-7625. County: Santa Fe. ICA: NM0099.
Microwave channels reported: N.A.
Channel capacity: N.A.
Ownership: Santa Fe Wireless Cable TV.

New York

ALBANY—Capital Choice Television Inc., 7 Hemphill Place, Ballston Spa, NY 12020. Phone: 518-899-2222. Fax: 518-899-9456. County: Albany. ICA: NY0264.
Total homes in service area: 444,000.
Microwave channels reported: N.A.
Began: August 1, 1993.
Channel capacity: 32. Channels available but not in use: 1.
Basic Service
Subscribers: 4,843.
Programming (via satellite): WSBK-TV (U) Boston; A & E; American Movie Classics; BET; C-SPAN; C-SPAN 2; CNBC; CNN; Discovery Channel; ESPN; Fox Family Channel; Headline News; Lifetime; MTV; Nashville Network; Nickelodeon; TBS Superstation; The Weather Channel; USA Network; VH1.
Fee: $49.95 installation; $18.75 monthly.
Pay Service 1
Pay Units: 716.
Programming (via satellite): Disney Channel.
Fee: $7.99 monthly.
Pay Service 2
Pay Units: 867.
Programming (via satellite): The New Encore.
Fee: $3.95 monthly.
Pay Service 3
Pay Units: 1,045.
Programming (via satellite): HBO.
Fee: $11.00 monthly.
Pay Service 4
Pay Units: 789.
Programming (via satellite): Showtime.
Fee: $8.95 monthly.
Pay-Per-View
Addressable homes: 3,800.
Special events.
Fee: Varies.
Equipment: Scientific-Atlanta set top converters.
Manager: George Williams. Staff engineer: Steve Leszczynski.
Ownership: CAI Wireless Systems Inc. (MSO). Sale pends to MCI WorldCom Inc.

BROOKLYN—CellularVision of New York, Loft 9W, 140 58th St., Brooklyn, NY 11220. Phone: 718-439-2360. Fax: 718-439-9740. County: Kings. ICA: NY0276.
Total homes in service area: 3,200,000.
Microwave channels reported: N.A.
Began: N.A.
Channel capacity: 49 (2-way capable). Channels available but not in use: N.A.
Basic Service
Subscribers: 12,500.
Programming (received off-air): WABC-TV (A), WCBS-TV (C), WNBC (N), WNYW (F), WPIX (W), WWOR-TV (U) New York; WNET (P) New York-Newark.
Programming (via satellite): A & E; BET; C-SPAN; CNBC; CNN; Comedy Central; Court TV; Discovery Channel; Disney Channel; E! Entertainment TV; ESPN; Headline News; International Channel; Learning Channel; Lifetime; MSNBC; MTV; Nickelodeon; QVC; TBS Superstation; TV Food Network; TV Guide Channel; Telemundo; The Weather Channel; USA Network; VH1.
Fee: N.A.
Expanded Basic Service
Subscribers: 3,750.
Programming (via satellite): ESPN 2; MOVIEplex; Madison Square Garden Network; Sci-Fi Channel; Starz!; The New Encore; Turner Classic Movies; Turner Network TV.
Fee: N.A.
Pay Service 1
Pay Units: N.A.
Programming (via satellite): Cinemax; Ethnic-American Broadcasting; Flix; HBO; Playboy TV; Showtime; The Movie Channel.
Fee: N.A.
Pay-Per-View
Addressable homes: 5,000.
Movies.
Equipment: Samsung set top converters.
Manager: John Walber. Chief technician: Ed Bogdan. Program director: George Parise. Marketing director: Gary McGregor.
Ownership: CellularVision USA Inc.

CAZENOVIA—Selectavision of Cazenovia & Nelson Inc., Box 642, Cazenovia, NY 13035. Phone: 315-655-3555. Fax: 315-655-4400. County: Madison. Also serves Cazenovia (village), Nelson (town). ICA: NY0127.
Microwave channels reported: N.A.
Channel capacity: 25. Channels available but not in use: N.A.
Basic Service
Subscribers: N.A.
Programming (received off-air): WBNG-TV (C) Binghamton; WCNY-TV (P), WIXT (A), WSTM-TV (N), WTVH (C) Syracuse; WKTV (N), WUTR (A) Utica; CKWS-TV Kingston.
Programming (via microwave): WSBK-TV (U) Boston; WPIX (W) New York.
Programming (via satellite): TBS Superstation.
Fee: N.A.
Manager: Caroline Barilla.
Ownership: William Canley.

NEW YORK—Wireless Cable of New York,. Counties: Kings, New York & Queens. ICA: NY0265.
Total homes in service area: 5,000,000.
Microwave channels reported: WQQ79, Ch. 1, MDS; WLK227, Ch. 2, MDS; KRS-81, A-4, ITFS; K2E-20, B-1 & 3-4, ITFS; WHR-691, B2, ITFS; WHR-829, C-2, ITFS; WHR-828, C-4, ITFS; WHR-520, D-1-4, ITFS; KRS-82, E-1-4, ITFS.
Began: January 1, 1987.
Channel capacity: 17. Channels available but not in use: N.A.
Note: System not operational, pending reorganization.
Basic Service
Subscribers: 25,000; Commercial subscribers: 100.
Programming (received off-air): WABC-TV (A), WCBS-TV (C), WNBC (N), WNYW (F), WPIX (W), WPXN-TV (X), WWOR-TV (U) New York; WHSE-TV (H), WNET (P), WNJU (O) New York-Newark; WXTV (S) New York-Paterson.
Programming (via satellite): BET; CNN; Discovery Channel; ESPN; MTV; Madison Square Garden Network; Nickelodeon; TBS Superstation; Turner Network TV; USA Network.
Fee: $24.95 installation; $20.95 monthly.
A la Carte 1
Subscribers: 26,000.
Programming (via satellite): KTLA (W) Los Angeles; Fox Sports Net New York.
Fee: $4.50 monthly (package).
Pay-Per-View
Addressable homes: 25,000.
Special events.
Fee: Varies.
Equipment: Zenith set top converters.
Manager: Mark Patrick Hyland. Chief technician: Jim Baumann. Marketing & program director: Gary Linieman.
Ownership: CAI Wireless Systems Inc. (MSO). Sale pends to MCI WorldCom Inc.

ROCHESTER—Rochester Choice TV, Suite D, 565 Blossom Rd., Rochester, NY 14610-1859. Phone: 716-654-5120. Fax: 716-654-6625. Counties: Monroe, Ontario & Wayne. Also serves Farmington (town), Monroe County (portions), Ontario County (portions), Wayne County (portions). ICA: NY0269.
Total homes in service area: 449,000.
Microwave channels reported: N.A.
Began: July 1, 1994.
Channel capacity: 26. Channels available but not in use: N.A.
Basic Service
Subscribers: N.A.
Programming (received off-air): WHEC-TV (N), WOKR (A), WROC-TV (C), WUHF (F,U), WXXI-TV (P) Rochester.
Programming (via satellite): WPIX (W) New York; A & E; BET; C-SPAN; CNBC; CNN; Discovery Channel; Disney Channel; ESPN; Fox Family Channel; Headline News; Lifetime; MTV; Nashville Network; Nickelodeon; TBS Superstation; TV Guide Channel; The Weather Channel; USA Network; VH1.
Fee: $150.00 installation; $21.95 monthly.
Commercial fee: $26.95 monthly.
Pay Service 1
Pay Units: N.A.
Programming (via satellite): HBO; Showtime; The Movie Channel.
Fee: $7.00 (Showtime or TMC), $11.95 monthly (HBO).
Pay-Per-View
Action Pay-Per-View.
Fee: Varies.
Manager: George Williams. Chief technician: Steve Leszczynski.
Ownership: CAI Wireless Systems Inc. (MSO). Sale pends to MCI WorldCom Inc.

North Carolina

CHARLOTTE—CAI Wireless Systems Inc., 18 Corporate Woods Blvd., Albany, NY 12211. Phone: 518-462-2632. Fax: 518-462-3045. County: Mecklenburg. ICA: NC0241.
Microwave channels reported: N.A.
Channel capacity: N.A.
Ownership: CAI Wireless Systems Inc. (MSO). Sale pends to CS Wireless.

WILMINGTON—Microwave Communication Services, Suite 900, 400 Perimeter Center Terrace NE, Atlanta, GA 30346. Phone: 404-804-6448. Fax: 404-409-0060. County: New Hanover. ICA: NC0228.
Microwave channels reported: N.A.
Channel capacity: N.A.
Ownership: Microwave Communication Services (MSO).

North Dakota

BOWBELLS—Northwest Communications Cooperative, Box 38, 111 Railroad Ave., Ray, ND 58849-0038. Phone: 701-568-3331. Fax: 701-568-7777. County: Burke. ICA: ND0221.
Microwave channels reported: N.A.
Began: N.A.
Channel capacity: N.A. Channels available but not in use: N.A.
Basic Service
Subscribers: 763.
Programming (received off-air): KMCY (A), KMOT (N), KSRE (P), KXMC-TV (C) Minot.
Programming (via satellite): WGN-TV (W) Chicago; CNN; Country Music TV; Discovery Channel; Disney Channel; ESPN; Fox Family Channel; FoxNet; Nashville Network; Nickelodeon; TBS Superstation; The Weather Channel; Turner Network TV; USA Network.
Fee: $19.95 monthly.
Pay Service 1
Pay Units: N.A.
Programming (via satellite): Showtime.
Fee: $8.00 monthly.
Operations manager: Myron Ranum. Plant supervisor: Gary Hansen. Office manager: Michael Steffan.
Ownership: Northwest Communications Cooperative (MSO).

CARRINGTON—Central Dakota TV Inc., Box 299, Carrington, ND 58421. Phone: 701-674-8122. Fax: 701-674-8121. County: Foster. ICA: ND0212.
Microwave channels reported: WLW751, E group, MMDS; WLW752, F group, MMDS.
Began: October 1, 1990.
Channel capacity: 23. Channels available but not in use: 5.
Basic Service
Subscribers: 891.
Programming (received off-air): KFYR-TV (N) Bismarck; WDAZ-TV (A) Devils Lake; KXJB-TV (C) Valley City.
Programming (via satellite): CNN; Discovery Channel; ESPN; Nashville Network; TBS Superstation; Turner Network TV; USA Network.
Current originations: Educational access.
Fee: $100.00 installation; $18.00 monthly.
Pay Service 1
Pay Units: 317.
Programming (via satellite): HBO.
Fee: $8.50 monthly.
Pay-Per-View
Addressable homes: 1,022.
Equipment: Zenith set top converters.
Manager: Robert Hill. Chief technician: Dave Wolf. Customer service manager: Brenda Neumiller.
Ownership: Central Dakota TV Inc.

EPPING—Northwest Communications Cooperative, Box 38, 111 Railroad Ave., Ray, ND 58849-0038. Phone: 701-568-3331. Fax: 701-568-7777. County: Williams. ICA: ND0220.
Microwave channels reported: N.A.
Began: N.A.
Channel capacity: N.A. Channels available but not in use: N.A.
Basic Service
Subscribers: 574.
Programming (received off-air): KMCY (A) Minot.
Programming (via satellite): WGN-TV (W) Chicago; CNN; Country Music TV; Discovery Channel; Disney Channel; ESPN; Fox Family Channel; FoxNet; Midwest Sports Channel; Nashville Network; Nickelodeon; TBS Superstation; The Weather Channel; Turner Network TV; USA Network.
Fee: $19.95 monthly.
Pay Service 1
Pay Units: N.A.
Programming (via satellite): Showtime.
Fee: N.A.
Operations manager: Myron Ranum. Plant supervisor: Gary Hansen. Office manager: Michael Steffan.
Ownership: Northwest Communications Cooperative (MSO).

FARGO—American Telecasting of Barnesville, Suite A, 2615 12th Ave. South, Moorehead, MN 56560. Phone: 218-233-3848. Fax: 218-233-4225. Web site: http://www.amtele.com. County: Cass. ICA: ND0214.
Microwave channels reported: N.A.
Began: N.A.
Channel capacity: N.A. Channels available but not in use: N.A.
Basic Service
Subscribers: N.A.
Programming (received off-air): KFME (P), KVLY-TV (N), KVRR (F), WDAY-TV (A) Fargo; KXJB-TV (C) Valley City.
Programming (via satellite): WGN-TV (W) Chicago; CNN; Discovery Channel; Disney Channel; ESPN; Fox Family Channel; Midwest Sports Channel; Nashville Network; USA Network.
Fee: N.A.
Pay Service 1
Pay Units: N.A.
Programming (via satellite): HBO.
Fee: N.A.
Manager: Ron Groslie.
Ownership: American Telecasting Inc. (MSO). Sale pends to Sprint Corp.

GRAND FORKS—Microwave Communication Services, Suite 900, 400 Perimeter Center Terrace NE, Atlanta, GA 30346. Phone: 404-804-6448. Fax: 404-409-0060. County: Grand Forks. ICA: ND0215.
Microwave channels reported: N.A.
Channel capacity: N.A.
Ownership: Microwave Communication Services (MSO).

KILLDEER—Consolidated Telephone Cooperative, Box 1408, Dickinson, ND 58602. Phone: 701-225-6061. County: Dunn. ICA: ND0216.
Microwave channels reported: N.A.
Began: N.A.
Channel capacity: 15 (not 2-way capable). Channels available but not in use: N.A.
Basic Service
Subscribers: 337.
Fee: N.A.
Manager: Dan Wilhelmson.
Ownership: Consolidated Telephone Cooperative.

LANGDON—United Telephone Mutual Aid Corp., Box 729, 411 7th Ave., Langdon, ND 58249-0729. Phone: 701-256-5156. Fax: 701-256-1121. Counties: Cavalier, Pembina, Ramsey, Rolette, Towner & Walsh. Also serves Cavalier County, Pembina County, Ramsey County, Rolett County, Towner County, Walsh County. ICA: ND0217.
Total homes in service area: 6,000.
Microwave channels reported: WLW984, E group, MMDS; WLW986, E group, MMDS; WLW982, F group, MMDS; WNEZ913, H1, MMDS, WNEZ907, H2, MMDS; WNTC633, H3, MMDS; WNTC634, H3, MMDS.
Began: June 1, 1990.
Channel capacity: 19 (not 2-way capable). Channels available but not in use: None.
Basic Service
Subscribers: 1,481.
Programming (received off-air): WDAZ-TV (A) Devils Lake; KVLY-TV (N) Fargo; KNRR (F) Pembina; KXJB-TV (C) Valley City.
Programming (via satellite): WGN-TV (W) Chicago; CNN; Discovery Channel; ESPN; FX; Nashville Network; TBS Superstation.
Fee: $15.00 monthly.
Expanded Basic Service
Subscribers: 1,222.
Programming (via satellite): A & E; Country Music TV; Disney Channel; Fox Family Channel; The Weather Channel; Turner Classic Movies; Turner Network TV; USA Network.
Fee: $10.00 monthly.
Pay Service 1
Pay Units: 374.
Programming (via satellite): Showtime.
Fee: $10.00 monthly.
Equipment: Zenith set top converters.
Manager: Kenneth Carlson. Chief technician, marketing & program director: Dennis Hansel.
Ownership: United Telephone Mutual Aid Corp.

LEFOR—Consolidated Telephone Cooperative, Box 1077, Dickinson, ND 58602. Phone: 701-225-6061. County: Stark. ICA: ND0218.
Microwave channels reported: N.A.
Began: N.A.
Channel capacity: N.A.
Basic Service
Subscribers: 657.
Fee: N.A.
Manager: Dan Wilhelmson.
Ownership: Consolidated Telephone Cooperative.

MINOT—Microwave Communication Services, Suite 900, 400 Perimeter Center Terrace NE, Atlanta, GA 30346. Phone: 404-804-6448. Fax: 404-409-0060. County: Ward. ICA: ND0219.
Microwave channels reported: N.A.
Channel capacity: N.A.
Ownership: Microwave Communication Services (MSO).

Ohio

BUCYRUS—Nucentrix Broadband Network Inc., Suite 200, 200 Chisholm Place, Plano, TX 75075. Phone: 972-423-9494. Fax: 972-423-0819. County: Crawford. ICA: OH0395.
Microwave channels reported: N.A.
Began: N.A.
Channel capacity: N.A.

Basic Service
Subscribers: N.A.
Programming (via satellite): WGN-TV (W) Chicago; A & E; American Movie Classics; CNN; Cartoon Network; Country Music TV; Discovery Channel; Disney Channel; ESPN; History Channel; Nashville Network; Nickelodeon; Sci-Fi Channel; TBS Superstation; The Weather Channel; Turner Network TV; USA Network.
Fee: N.A.
Pay Service 1
Pay Units: N.A.
Programming (via satellite): Cinemax; HBO.
Fee: N.A.
Manager: Chad Carter. Chief technician: Mike Remy.
Ownership: Nucentrix Broadband Networks.

CLEVELAND—Popvision, Suite 355, 303 Ken-Mar Industrial Pkwy., Broadview Heights, OH 44147. Phones: 216-575-8000; 216-575-8016. Fax: 216-662-7165. County: Cuyahoga. Also serves Brook Park, Brooklyn, Brooklyn Heights, Newburgh Heights. ICA: OH0386.
Total line of sight homes: 1,062,200. Total homes in service area: 1,178,000.
Microwave channels reported: N.A.
Began: N.A.
Channel capacity: 33. Channels available but not in use: N.A.
Basic Service
Subscribers: 24,000.
Programming (received off-air): WBNX-TV (W,F) Akron; WEWS-TV (A), WJW (F), WKYC-TV (N), WQHS-TV (H), WVIZ-TV (P) Cleveland; WUAB (U) Lorain-Cleveland; WOIO (C) Shaker Heights.
Programming (via satellite): WGN-TV (W) Chicago; A & E; American Movie Classics; BET; CNBC; CNN; Discovery Channel; ESPN; Fox Family Channel; Fox Sports Net Ohio; Lifetime; MTV; Nashville Network; Nickelodeon; TBS Superstation; TV Guide Channel; The Weather Channel; Turner Network TV; USA Network; Univision.
Fee: $49.95 installation; $18.50 monthly.
Pay Service 1
Pay Units: N.A.
Programming (via satellite): Disney Channel; HBO; Showtime.
Fee: N.A.
Pay-Per-View
Movies.
Local advertising: Yes.
Manager: Robert Patterson. Chief technician: George Hollender.
Ownership: CS Wireless Systems Inc. (MSO).

COLUMBUS—American Telecasting of Columbus Inc., 1080 Rarig Ave., Columbus, OH 43219. Phones: 614-251-8170; 800-465-8200. Fax: 614-251-8178.
Web site: http://www.amtele.com.
County: Franklin. ICA: OH0390.
Microwave channels reported: N.A.
Began: February 1, 1994.
Channel capacity: N.A.
Basic Service
Subscribers: 4,000.
Programming (received off-air): WBNS-TV (C), WCMH-TV (N), WOSU-TV (P), WSYX (A), WTTE (F,U) Columbus.
Programming (via satellite): WGN-TV (W) Chicago; A & E; CNBC; CNN; Country Music TV; Discovery Channel; ESPN; EWTN; Fox Family Channel; Fox Sports Net Ohio; Learning Channel; Lifetime; MTV; Nickelodeon; Sci-Fi Channel; TBS Superstation; The Weather Channel; VH1.
Fee: $19.95 installation; $19.95 monthly.
Pay Service 1
Pay Units: N.A.
Programming (via satellite): Disney Channel; HBO; Showtime.
Fee: $7.00 monthly (Showtime), $8.00 monthly (Disney), $10.95 monthly (HBO).
Manager: Bob Lunda. Chief technician: Ed Huston.
Ownership: American Telecasting Inc. (MSO). Sale pends to Sprint Corp.

DAYTON—CS Wireless Systems Inc., 1101 Summit Ave., Plano, TX 75074. Phone: 972-730-3300. County: Montgomery. Also serves Miamisburg. ICA: OH0394.
Microwave channels reported: N.A.
Began: November 1, 1993.
Channel capacity: 32. Channels available but not in use: None.
Basic Service
Subscribers: N.A.
Programming (received off-air): WDTN (A), WHIO-TV (C), WKEF (N), WPTD (P), WRGT-TV (F,U) Dayton; WPTO (P) Oxford.
Programming (via satellite): WGN-TV (W) Chicago; A & E; CNN; Discovery Channel; ESPN; Fox Family Channel; Headline News; Knowledge TV; Learning Channel; Lifetime; MTV; Nashville Network; Nickelodeon; QVC; Sci-Fi Channel; TBS Superstation; The Weather Channel; Turner Network TV; USA Network.
Fee: $19.95 installation; $19.72 monthly.
Pay Service 1
Pay Units: N.A.
Programming (via satellite): Cinemax; Disney Channel; HBO.
Fee: $8.40 monthly (Disney), $10.60 monthly (Cinemax or HBO).
Pay-Per-View
Viewer's Choice.
Fee: $3.95.
Manager: Wes Duvall. Chief technician: Terry Burns.
Ownership: CS Wireless Systems Inc. (MSO).

LIMA—W.A.T.C.H. TV, 3225 W. Elm St., Lima, OH 45805. Phone: 419-227-2266. Fax: 419-999-2140. E-mail: watchtmk@bright.net. Web Site: http://www.watch.net. County: Allen. ICA: OH0387.
Total line of sight homes: 150,000.
Microwave channels reported: N.A.
Began: April 1, 1992.
Channel capacity: 33 (not 2-way capable). Channels available but not in use: None.
Basic Service
Subscribers: 10,284.
Programming (received off-air): WBGU-TV (P) Bowling Green; WBNS-TV (C) Columbus; WFFT-TV (F), WPTA (A) Fort Wayne; WLIO (N), WOHL-LP (F) Lima.
Programming (via satellite): WGN-TV (W) Chicago; Knowledge TV; TBS Superstation; TV Guide Channel.
Fee: $69.99 installation; $4.95 monthly.
Expanded Basic Service
Subscribers: 10,276.
Programming (via satellite): A & E; Discovery Channel; ESPN; ESPN 2; Fox Family Channel; Fox Sports Net Ohio; Headline News; Home Shopping Network; Lifetime; Nashville Network; Nickelodeon; TBS Superstation; Turner Classic Movies; Turner Network TV; USA Network; VH1.
Fee: $29.95 installation; $22.97 monthly.
Pay Service 1
Pay Units: 1,145.
Programming (via satellite): Cinemax.
Fee: $6.95 monthly.
Pay Service 2
Pay Units: 981.
Programming (via satellite): Disney Channel.
Fee: $8.95 monthly.
Pay Service 3
Pay Units: 1,960.
Programming (via satellite): HBO.
Fee: $9.95 monthly.
Pay Service 4
Pay Units: 1,481.
Programming (via satellite): Showtime.
Fee: $5.99 monthly.
Pay-Per-View
Addressable homes: 9,500.
Viewer's Choice.
Local advertising: Yes. Available in satellite distributed programming.
Equipment: Jerrold set top converters.
Manager: Thomas N. Knippen. Chief technician: Mike Birkemeier. Marketing director: Melissa Caldwell. Customer service manager: Kay Walters.
Ownership: Benton Ridge Telephone Co.

LYKENS—Nucentrix Broadband Networks Inc., Suite 200, 200 Chisholm Place, Plano, TX 75075. Phone: 972-423-9494. Fax: 972-423-0819. Counties: Crawford, Marion & Wyandot. Also serves Bucyrus, Caledonia, New Washington, Upper Sandusky. ICA: OH0388.
Total homes in service area: 78,675.
Microwave channels reported: WLX-527, A-1-4, ITFS; WLX-885, B-1-4, ITFS; WLX-532, C-1-4, ITFS; WLX-528, D-1-4, ITFS, WLX-529, G-1-4, ITFS.
Began: September 1, 1992.
Channel capacity: 20. Channels available but not in use: None.
Basic Service
Subscribers: 827.
Programming (via satellite): WGN-TV (W) Chicago; A & E; C-SPAN; CNN; Country Music TV; Discovery Channel; Disney Channel; ESPN; Knowledge TV; Nashville Network; Nickelodeon; QVC; TBS Superstation; TV Guide Channel; The Weather Channel; USA Network.
Fee: $50.00 installation; $28.95 monthly.
Pay Service 1
Pay Units: 36.
Programming (via satellite): Cinemax.
Fee: $9.95 monthly.
Pay Service 2
Pay Units: 159.
Programming (via satellite): HBO.
Fee: $10.95 monthly.
Equipment: Jerrold set top converters.
Manager: Chad Carter. Chief technician: Mike Remy.
Ownership: Nucentrix Broadband Networks (MSO). Purchased from LDH Inc.

TOLEDO—American Telecasting of Toledo, 716 N. Westwood Ave., Toledo, OH 43607. Phone: 419-534-2474. Fax: 419-534-2472. Web site: http://www.amtele.com. Counties: Monroe, MI; Lucas & Wood, OH. Also serves Monroe, MI; Bowling Green, Maumee, Perrysburg, OH. ICA: OH0392.
Total homes in service area: 351,000.
Microwave channels reported: N.A.
Began: June 1, 1993.
Channel capacity: 12. Channels available but not in use: None.
Basic Service
Subscribers: N.A.
Programming (received off-air): WGTE-TV (P), WNWO-TV (N), WTOL-TV (C), WTVG (A), WUPW (F) Toledo; CBET Windsor.
Programming (via satellite): CNN; Discovery Channel; ESPN; Lifetime; Nashville Network; Nick at Nite; Nickelodeon; TBS Superstation; Turner Network TV; USA Network.
Fee: $69.95 installation; $16.95 monthly.
Commercial fee: $5.95 monthly.
Pay Service 1
Pay Units: N.A.
Programming (via satellite): HBO; Showtime.
Fee: $6.00 monthly (Showtime), $11.00 monthly (HBO).
Pay-Per-View
Viewer's Choice.
Equipment: General Instrument & Jerrold set top converters.
Manager: Mark W. Simmons. Chief technician: Joel Tegtmeier.
Ownership: American Telecasting Inc. (MSO). Sale pends to Sprint Corp.

YOUNGSTOWN—American Telecasting of Youngstown Inc., 50 Karago Dr., Boardman, OH 44512. Phones: 330-629-7550; 800-261-7550. Fax: 330-629-7560.
E-mail: cmatgsevace@amtele.com Web site: http://www.amtele.com.
Counties: Columbiana, Mahoning & Trumbull, OH; Mercer, PA. Also serves Columbiana County (portions), Mahoning County (portions), Trumbull County (portions), OH; Mercer County (portions), PA. ICA: OH0389.
Total homes in service area: 100,000.
Microwave channels reported: N.A.
Began: N.A.
Channel capacity: 30 (2-way capable; not operating 2-way). Channels available but not in use: 33.
Basic Service
Subscribers: 3,600.
Programming (received off-air): WNEO (P) Alliance; WUAB (U) Lorain-Cleveland; WPGH-TV (F) Pittsburgh; WFMJ-TV (N), WKBN-TV (C), WYTV (A,F) Youngstown.
Programming (via satellite): WGN-TV (W) Chicago; A & E; American Movie Classics; Animal Planet; BET; C-SPAN; CNBC; CNN; Cartoon Network; Discovery Channel; ESPN; Fox Family Channel; Fox Sports Net Ohio; Learning Channel; Lifetime; Nickelodeon; Sci-Fi Channel; TBS Superstation; The Health Network; The Weather Channel; USA Network.
Planned originations: Educational access.
Fee: $21.95 monthly.
Pay Service 1
Pay Units: N.A.
Programming (via satellite): Disney Channel; HBO; Showtime.
Fee: $7.00 (Disney or Showtime); $10.95 monthly (HBO).
Pay-Per-View
Addressable homes: 3,000.
Viewer's Choice.
Manager: Michael Battel. Chief technician: Chris Matesevac.
Ownership: American Telecasting Inc. (MSO). Sale pends to Sprint Corp.

Oklahoma

ADA—Nucentrix Broadband Networks Inc., Suite 200, 200 Chisholm Place, Plano, TX 75075. Phone: 972-423-9494. Fax: 972-423-0819. County: Pontotoc. ICA: OK0346.
Microwave channels reported: N.A.
Channel capacity: N.A.
Ownership: Nucentrix Broadband Networks (MSO).

ARDMORE—Nucentrix Broadband Networks Inc., Suite 200, 200 Chisholm Place, Plano, TX 75075. Phone: 972-423-9494. Fax: 972-423-0819. County: Carter. ICA: OK0359.
Microwave channels reported: N.A.
Began: N.A.
Channel capacity: N.A. Channels available but not in use: N.A.

Basic Service
Subscribers: N.A.
Programming (received off-air): KTEN (A,N,F) Ada; KFOR-TV (N), KOCO-TV (A), KOKH-TV (F), KWTV (C) Oklahoma City; KXII (C) Sherman.
Programming (via satellite): A & E; BET; CNN; Cartoon Network; Country Music TV; Discovery Channel; Disney Channel; ESPN; Fox Family Channel; Fox Sports Net Southwest; History Channel; Lifetime; Nashville Network; Nickelodeon; TBS Superstation; The Weather Channel; Trinity Bcstg. Network; Turner Network TV; USA Network.
Fee: $25.00 installation; $28.84 monthly.
Pay Service 1
Pay Units: N.A.
Programming (via satellite): HBO; Showtime.
Fee: N.A.
Pay-Per-View
Viewer's Choice.
Manager: Mike Massey. Chief technician: Jerry Dunn.
Ownership: Nucentrix Broadband Networks (MSO).

CLAYTON—Star Search Rural TV Inc., Box 399, Clayton, OK 74536. Phone: 918-569-4111. County: Pushmataha. ICA: OK0329.
Microwave channels reported: N.A.
Channel capacity: N.A.
Manager: Cindy Garrison. Chief technician: Darrell Kirkes. Marketing director: Phillis Van Horn.
Ownership: Oklahoma Western Telephone Co.

ENID—Nucentrix Broadband Networks Inc., Suite 200, 200 Chisholm Place, Plano, TX 75075. Phone: 972-423-9494. Fax: 972-423-0819. County: Garfield. ICA: OK0347.
Microwave channels reported: N.A.
Channel capacity: N.A.
Ownership: Nucentrix Broadband Networks (MSO). Purchased from Heartland Wireless Communications Inc.

KINGFISHER—Nucentrix Broadband Networks, Suite 200, 200 Chisholm Place, Plano, TX 75075. Phone: 972-423-9494. Fax: 972-423-0819. County: Kingfisher. ICA: OK0331.
Microwave channels reported: N.A.
Channel capacity: N.A.
Ownership: Nucentrix Broadband Networks.

LAWTON—Nucentrix Broadband Networks Inc., Suite 200, 200 Chisholm Place, Plano, TX 75075. Phone: 972-423-9494. Fax: 972-423-0819. County: Comanche. ICA: OK0348.
Microwave channels reported: N.A.
Channel capacity: N.A.
Ownership: Nucentrix Broadband Networks (MSO). Purchased from Heartland Broadband Networks Inc.

LINDSAY—Nucentrix Broadband Networks Inc., Suite 200, 200 Chisholm Place, Plano, TX 75075. Phone: 972-423-9494. Fax: 972-423-0819. County: Garvin. ICA: OK0332.
Microwave channels reported: N.A.
Channel capacity: N.A.
Ownership: Nucentrix Broadband Networks (MSO). Purchased from Heartland Wireless Communications Inc.

MUSKOGEE—Nucentrix Broadband Networks Inc., Suite 200, 200 Chisholm Place, Plano, TX 75075. Phone: 972-423-9494. Fax: 972-423-0819. County: Muskogee. ICA: OK0361.
Microwave channels reported: N.A.
Began: N.A.
Channel capacity: N.A. Channels available but not in use: N.A.
Basic Service
Subscribers: N.A.
Programming (received off-air): KJRH (N), KOKI-TV (F), KOTV (C), KTUL (A) Tulsa.
Programming (via satellite): CNN; Country Music TV; Discovery Channel; ESPN; Fox Sports Net Southwest; Lifetime; Nashville Network; Nickelodeon; TBS Superstation; The Weather Channel; Turner Network TV; USA Network.
Fee: N.A.
Pay Service 1
Pay Units: N.A.
Programming (via satellite): Cinemax; HBO (multiplexed).
Fee: N.A.
Pay-Per-View
Viewer's Choice.
Manager: Ken Merlin. Chief technician: Rick Gardner.
Ownership: Nucentrix Broadband Networks (MSO).

OKLAHOMA CITY—American Telecasting of Oklahoma City Inc., 4224-FN Santa Fe, Oklahoma City, OK 73118. Phones: 405-525-1000; 405-525-2032. Fax: 405-525-7000. Web site: http://www.amtele.com. Counties: Canadian, Cleveland & Oklahoma. ICA: OK0333.
Microwave channels reported: N.A.
Began: N.A.
Channel capacity: 23. Channels available but not in use: N.A.
Basic Service
Subscribers: 13,300.
Fee: N.A.
Manager: Bill Raschka. Chief technician: Steve Housley.
Ownership: American Telecasting Inc. (MSO). Sale pends to Sprint Corp.

STILLWATER—Nucentrix Broadband Networks Inc., Suite 200, 200 Chisholm Place, Plano, TX 75075. Phone: 972-423-9494. Fax: 972-423-0819. County: Payne. ICA: OK0349.
Microwave channels reported: N.A.
Channel capacity: N.A.
Ownership: Nucentrix Broadband Networks (MSO). Purchased from Heartland Wireless Communications Inc.

TULSA—Nucentrix Broadband Networks Inc., Suite 200, 200 Chisholm Place, Plano, TX 75075. Phone: 972-423-9494. Fax: 972-423-0819. County: Osage. ICA: OK0362.
Microwave channels reported: N.A.
Began: N.A.
Channel capacity: N.A.
Basic Service
Subscribers: N.A.
Programming (via satellite): WGN-TV (W) Chicago; A & E; American Movie Classics; CNN; Cartoon Network; Country Music TV; Discovery Channel; Disney Channel; ESPN; Fox Family Channel; Fox Sports Net Midwest; Headline News; History Channel; Lifetime; MTV; Nashville Network; Nickelodeon; Sci-Fi Channel; TBS Superstation; The Weather Channel; Turner Network TV; USA Network.
Fee: N.A.
Pay Service 1
Pay Units: N.A.
Programming (via satellite): Cinemax; HBO (multiplexed).
Fee: N.A.
Manager: Paul Saunders. Chief technician: Terry Davis.
Ownership: Nucentrix Broadband Networks (MSO).

WEATHERFORD—Nucentrix Broadband Networks Inc., Suite 200, 200 Chisholm Place, Plano, TX 75075. Phone: 972-423-9494. Fax: 972-423-0819. E-mail: gmwood@nwoknet.net. County: Blaine. ICA: OK0363.
Microwave channels reported: N.A.
Began: N.A.
Channel capacity: 31. Channels available but not in use: N.A.
Basic Service
Subscribers: N.A.
Programming (received off-air): KETA (P), KFOR-TV (N), KOCO-TV (A), KOKH-TV (F), KWTV (C) Oklahoma City.
Programming (via satellite): WGN-TV (W) Chicago; A & E; CNN; Cartoon Network; Country Music TV; Discovery Channel; Disney Channel; ESPN; Fox Family Channel; Fox Sports Net Midwest; Headline News; History Channel; Learning Channel; Lifetime; Nashville Network; Nickelodeon; Sci-Fi Channel; TBS Superstation; The Weather Channel; Turner Classic Movies; Turner Network TV; USA Network.
Fee: $26.99 monthly.
Pay Service 1
Pay Units: N.A.
Programming (via satellite): Cinemax; HBO (multiplexed); Showtime.
Fee: N.A.
Pay-Per-View
Viewer's Choice.
Manager: Douglas E. Stavig. Chief technician: Jeremy Jacobs.
Ownership: Nucentrix Broadband Networks (MSO).

WOODWARD—Nucentrix Broadband Networks Inc., Suite 200, 200 Chisholm Place, Plano, TX 75075. Phone: 927-423-9494. Fax: 972-423-0819. E-mail: gmwood@nwoknet.net. Counties: Dewey, Ellis & Woodward. Also serves Arnett, Fort Supply, Gage, Mooreland, Mutual, Seiling, Sharon, Shattuck, Vici. ICA: OK0364.
Total homes in service area: 13,000.
Microwave channels reported: N.A.
Began: N.A.
Channel capacity: 31. Channels available but not in use: None.
Basic Service
Subscribers: 2,300.
Programming (received off-air): KFOR-TV (N), KOCO-TV (A), KOKH-TV (F), KWTV (C) Oklahoma City.
Programming (via satellite): WGN-TV (W) Chicago; A & E; CNN; Cartoon Network; Country Music TV; Discovery Channel; Disney Channel; ESPN; ESPN 2; Fox Family Channel; Fox Sports Net Southwest; Learning Channel; Lifetime; Nashville Network; Nickelodeon; Sci-Fi Channel; TBS Superstation; The Weather Channel; Trinity Bcstg. Network; Turner Classic Movies; Turner Network TV; USA Network.
Fee: $26.99 monthly.
Pay Service 1
Pay Units: 2,300.
Programming (via satellite): Cinemax; HBO (multiplexed).
Fee: $5.00 monthly (each).
Pay-Per-View
Viewer's Choice.
Manager: Douglas E. Stavig. Chief technician: Jeremy Jacobs.
Ownership: Nucentrix Broadband Networks (MSO). Purchased from Heartland Wireless Communications Inc.

Oregon

BEND—American Telecasting of Bend, Deschutes Business Park, Suite F-7, 20332 Empire Ave., Bend, OR 97701. Phone: 541-382-4031. Fax: 541-382-6835. Web site: http://www.amtele.com. County: Deschutes. ICA: OR0164.
Total homes in service area: 45,000.
Microwave channels reported: N.A.
Began: April 1, 1994.
Channel capacity: N.A.
Basic Service
Subscribers: 3,700.
Programming (received off-air): KOAB-TV (P), KTVZ (N) Bend; KATU (A), KOIN (C) Portland; KPDX (F) Vancouver.
Programming (via satellite): WGN-TV (W) Chicago; A & E; American Movie Classics; Blazer Vision; CNBC; CNN; Discovery Channel; ESPN; ESPN 2; Fox Family Channel; Nashville Network; Nick at Nite; Nickelodeon; Sci-Fi Channel; TBS Superstation; The Weather Channel; Turner Network TV; USA Network; VH1.
Fee: $39.95 installation; $19.95 monthly.
Pay Service 1
Pay Units: 592.
Programming (via satellite): Disney Channel.
Fee: $6.00 monthly.
Pay Service 2
Pay Units: 1,068.
Programming (via satellite): Showtime.
Fee: $5.00 monthly.
Pay Service 3
Pay Units: 460.
Programming (via satellite): HBO.
Fee: $10.95 monthly.
Pay-Per-View
Boxing.
Manager: Betsy Berens. Chief technician & program director: Bruce Danielson. Marketing director: Bob Finley.
Ownership: American Telecasting Inc. (MSO). Sale pends to Sprint Corp.

PRINEVILLE—Central Vision, Box 5393, Bend, OR 97708-5393. Phone: 503-382-4031. County: Crook. ICA: OR0169.
Microwave channels reported: N.A.
Channel capacity: N.A.
Ownership: Central Vision.

REDMOND—Central Vision, Box 5393, Bend, OR 97708-5393. Phone: 503-382-4031. County: Deschutes. ICA: OR0166.
Microwave channels reported: N.A.
Channel capacity: N.A.
Ownership: Central Vision.

Pennsylvania

GREENVILLE—Nucentrix Broadband Networks Inc., Suite 200, 200 Chisholm Place, Plano, TX 75075. Phone: 972-423-9494. Fax: 972-423-0819. County: Mercer. ICA: PA0443.
Microwave channels reported: N.A.
Began: N.A.
Channel capacity: N.A.
Basic Service
Subscribers: N.A.
Programming (received off-air): WJW (F) Cleveland; WJET-TV (A) Erie; WUAB (U) Lorain-Cleveland; WFMJ-TV (N), WKBN-TV (C) Youngstown.
Programming (via satellite): CNN; Discovery Channel; Disney Channel; ESPN; Lifetime; Nashville Network; Nickelodeon; TBS Superstation; The Weather Channel; Turner Network TV; USA Network.
Fee: N.A.
Pay Service 1
Pay Units: N.A.
Programming (via satellite): Cinemax; HBO (multiplexed).
Fee: N.A.

Manager: Pete Nealy. Chief technician: Chris Nowakowski.
Ownership: Nucentrix Broadband Networks (MSO).

PHILADELPHIA—Popvision, 2510 Metropolitan Dr., Trevose, PA 19053-6738. Phone: 215-396-9400. Fax: 215-396-9550. County: Philadelphia. ICA: PA0429.
Total homes in service area: 2,200,000.
Microwave channels reported: WPE97, Ch. 1, MDS; WLK234, Ch. 2, MDS; WHT643, E group, MMDS; WHT644, F group, MMDS: WNEY590, H1, MMDS; WAU-29, A-1-4, ITFS; WLX-924, A-3-4, ITFS; WLX-578, B-3-4, ITFS; WLX-825, C-1-4, ITFS; WHR-527, G-1-4, ITFS.
Began: September 1, 1989.
Channel capacity: 27 (not 2-way capable). Channels available but not in use: 3.
Basic Service
Subscribers: 53,000; Commercial subscribers: 600.
Programming (via satellite): A & E; American Movie Classics; BET; C-SPAN; CNBC; CNN; Discovery Channel; ESPN; ESPN 2; Fox Family Channel; Lifetime; MTV; Nashville Network; Nick at Nite; Nickelodeon; QVC; TBS Superstation; Turner Network TV; USA Network; Univision.
Fee: $38.66 installation; $27.61 monthly.
Pay Service 1
Pay Units: N.A.
Programming (via satellite): Cinemax; Disney Channel; HBO; Showtime.
Fee: $9.49 monthly (each).
Pay-Per-View
Addressable homes: 53,000.
Viewer's Choice.
Fee: $3.95.
Local advertising: Yes. Regional interconnect: Metrobase Cable Advertising.
Equipment: Tocom set top converters; Simulsat satellite antenna; Scientific-Atlanta satellite receivers.
Manager: Mike Louella. Chief technician: Jim Gracie. Marketing director: Peter Hasse.
Ownership: CAI Wireless Systems Inc. (MSO). Sale pends to MCI WorldCom Inc.

READING—Digital Wireless Systems, Box 15065, Reading, PA 19612. Phones: 610-921-9500; 610-921-5555. Fax: 610-921-0290. County: Berks. ICA: PA0430.
Total homes in service area: 325,000.
Microwave channels reported: N.A.
Began: N.A.
Channel capacity: 8. Channels available but not in use: None.
Basic Service
Subscribers: 685; Commercial subscribers: 5.
Programming (via satellite): CNN; ESPN; Nashville Network; Nickelodeon; Showtime; TBS Superstation; The Movie Channel; USA Network.
Fee: $24.95 installation; $17.95 monthly.
Manager: Joseph Paradis. Marketing director: Stephanie Snyder.
Ownership: Digital Wireless Systems Inc.

Rhode Island

None reported.

South Carolina

None reported.

South Dakota

ABERDEEN & BATH—Northern Rural Cable TV Cooperative Inc., 39456 133rd St., Bath, SD 57427. Phones: 605-225-0310; 800-529-0310. Fax: 605-225-1684. Counties: Brown, Day, Edmunds, Faulk, Marshall, McPherson & Spink. Also serves Amherst, Andover, Ashton, Athol, Barnard, Brown County, Chelsea, Claremont, Columbia, Conde, Cresbard, Day County (portions), Edmunds County (portions), Faulk County (portions), Ferney, Groton, Hecla, Houghton, Ipswich, Langford, Leola, Mansfield, Marshall County (portions), McPherson County (portions), Mina, Pierpoint, Putney, Spink County (portions), Stratford, Turton, Verdon, Warner, Westport, Wetonka. ICA: SD0226.
Total homes in service area: 3,300.
Microwave channels reported: WLK408, E group, MMDS; WLK409, F group, MMDS.
Began: December 2, 1988.
Channel capacity: 29 (not 2-way capable). Channels available but not in use: None.
Basic Service
Subscribers: 2,199.
Programming (via satellite): WGN-TV (W) Chicago; WDIV (N) Detroit; CNN; ESPN; Fox Family Channel; Nashville Network; Nickelodeon; TBS Superstation.
Fee: $15.00 monthly.
Expanded Basic Service
Subscribers: 971.
Programming (received off-air): KTTW (F) Sioux Falls-Mitchell.
Programming (via satellite): A & E; Country Music TV; Discovery Channel; Lifetime; Midwest Sports Channel; The Weather Channel; Turner Classic Movies; Turner Network TV; USA Network.
Fee: $5.00 monthly.
Expanded Basic Service 2
Subscribers: 693.
Programming (via satellite): Disney Channel; History Channel; Learning Channel; VH1.
Fee: $4.00 monthly.
Pay Service 1
Pay Units: 704.
Programming (via satellite): Showtime.
Fee: $8.00 monthly.
Pay-Per-View
Addressable homes: 2,650.
Manager: Larry Petrich. Marketing director: Dennis W. Hagny. Customer service manager: Mark Fisher.
Ownership: Northern Electric Cooperative Inc.

CLEAR LAKE—HD Electric Cooperative, Box 1007, Clear Lake, SD 57226. Phone: 605-874-2171. Fax: 605-874-8173. County: Deuel. ICA: SD0227.
Microwave channels reported: N.A.
Channel capacity: N.A.
Manager: Gary Cramer. Chief technician: Jim Resman.
Ownership: HD Electric Cooperative.

COLMAN—Sioux Valley Wireless, Box 20, Colman, SD 57017. Phone: 605-534-3241. Fax: 605-256-1691. E-mail: jbrick@svswe.com. Web Site: http://www.svtv.com. Counties: Brookings, Lake & Moody, SD.; Pipestone, MN. Also serves Pipestone County (portions), MN; Brookings County (portions), Lake County (portions), Moody County (portions), SD. ICA: SD0228.
Total homes in service area: 5,000.
Microwave channels reported: WHI959, F group, MMDS; WNEX781, H1, MMDS; WNEX689, H2, MMDS; WNTA301, H3, MMDS.
Began: June 6, 1989.
Channel capacity: 33 (2-way capable; not operating 2-way). Channels available but not in use: None.
Basic Service
Subscribers: 2,400.
Programming (received off-air): KDLT-TV (N) Sioux Falls; KELO-TV (C), KSFY-TV (A), KTTW (F) Sioux Falls-Mitchell.
Programming (via satellite): WGN-TV (W) Chicago; A & E; CNN; Country Music TV; Discovery Channel; Disney Channel; ESPN; ESPN 2; Fox Family Channel; History Channel; Home & Garden Television; Learning Channel; Lifetime; MTV; Nashville Network; Nick at Nite; Nickelodeon; Sci-Fi Channel; TBS Superstation; TV Guide Channel; The Weather Channel; Toon Disney; Turner Network TV; USA Network.
Fee: $25.00 installation; $28.95 monthly.
Pay Service 1
Pay Units: 640.
Programming (via satellite): Cinemax; HBO.
Fee: $9.95 monthly (Cinemax); $10.95 monthly (HBO).
Pay-Per-View
Addressable homes: 5,000.
Viewer's Choice.
Fee: $3.95.
Equipment: California Amplifier set top converters.
Manager: Joel Brick.
Ownership: Sioux Valley Rural Television Inc. (MSO).

DE SMET—Kingsbury Electric, Box E, De Smet, SD 57231. Phone: 605-854-3522. County: Kingsbury. ICA: SD0229.
Microwave channels reported: N.A.
Channel capacity: N.A.
Ownership: Kingsbury Electric.

HURON—Northeast TV Cooperative, Box 850, Watertown, SD 57201. Phone: 605-352-8591. County: Beadle. ICA: SD0230.
Microwave channels reported: N.A.
Channel capacity: N.A.
Ownership: Northeast TV Cooperative.

RAPID CITY—American Telecasting, 2491 W. Chicago St., Rapid City, SD 57702. Phones: 605-348-4810; 605-348-6255. Fax: 605-348-7104. County: Pennington. ICA: SD0233.
Microwave channels reported: N.A.
Channel capacity: 30 (not 2-way capable). Channels available but not in use: 3.
Basic Service
Subscribers: 4,800.
Fee: $22.95 monthly.
Pay-Per-View
Addressable homes: 4,800.
Viewer's Choice.
Fee: $3.95.
Equipment: ITS headend; General Instrument set top converters.
Manager: J. Mathew Boutte. Customer service manager: Sue Rutowski.
Ownership: American Telecasting Inc. (MSO). Sale pends to Antilles Wireless LLC.

REDFIELD—Spink Electric, Box 40, Redfield, SD 57469. Phone: 605-472-0380. County: Spink. ICA: SD0234.
Microwave channels reported: N.A.
Channel capacity: N.A.
Ownership: Spink Electric.

ROWENA—Sioux Valley Wireless, Box 20, Colman, SD 57017. Phone: 605-534-3241. Fax: 605-256-1691. E-mail: jbrick@svswe.com. Web site: http://www.svtv.com. Counties: Lincoln & Minnehaha. Also serves Lincoln County (portions), Minnehaha County (portions). ICA: SD0241.
Microwave channels reported: WMX358, E group, MMDS; WMX344, F group, MMDS; WMX347, H1, MMDS; WMX348, H2, MMDS; WMX349, H3, MMDS.
Began: May 1, 1994.
Channel capacity: 11 (not 2-way capable). Channels available but not in use: None.
Basic Service
Programming (received off=air): KDLT-TV (N) Sioux Falls; KELO-TV (C), KSFY-TV (A), KTTW (F) Sioux Falls-Mitchell.
Subscribers: 2,450.
Programming (received off-air): KDLT-TV (N) Sioux Falls; KELO-TV (C), KSFY-TV (A), KTTW (F) Sioux Falls-Mitchell.
Programming (via satellite): WGN-TV (W) Chicago; A & E; CNN; Country Music TV; Discovery Channel; Disney Channel; ESPN; ESPN 2; Fox Family Channel; History Channel; Home & Garden Television; Learning Channel; Lifetime; MTV; Nashville Network; Nick at Nite; Nickelodeon; Sci-Fi Channel; TBS Superstation; TV Guide Channel; The Weather Channel; Toon Disney; Turner Network TV; USA Network.
Fee: $25.00 installation; $28.95 monthly.
Pay Service 1
Pay Units: 400.
Programming (via satellite): Cinemax; HBO.
Fee: $9.95 monthly (Cinemax); $10.95 monthly (HBO).
Pay-Per-View
Viewer's Choice.
Fee: $3.95.
Equipment: Emcee headend; California Amplifier set top converters.
Manager: Joel Brick. Chief technician: Marvin Luke.
Ownership: Sioux Valley Rural Television Inc. (MSO).

SISSETON—Northeast TV Cooperative, Box 850, Watertown, SD 57201. Phone: 605-886-5706. County: Roberts. ICA: SD0236.
Microwave channels reported: N.A.
Channel capacity: N.A.
Ownership: Northeast TV Cooperative.

WATERTOWN—Northeast TV Cooperative, Box 850, Watertown, SD 57201. Phone: 605-886-5706. County: Codington. ICA: SD0237.
Microwave channels reported: N.A.
Channel capacity: N.A.
Ownership: Northeast TV Cooperative (MSO).

WEBSTER—Lake Region Electric, Box 341, Webster, SD 57274. Phone: 605-345-3379. Fax: 605-345-4442. County: Day. ICA: SD0238.
Microwave channels reported: N.A.
Channel capacity: N.A.
Manager: Jim Tomkins.
Ownership: Lake Region Electric.

WILLOW LAKE—Northeast TV Cooperative, Box 850, Watertown, SD 57201. Phone: 605-886-5706. County: Clark. ICA: SD0239.
Microwave channels reported: N.A.
Channel capacity: N.A.
Ownership: Northeast TV Cooperative.

YANKTON—Sioux Valley Wireless, Box 20, Colman, SD 57017. Phone: 605-534-3241. Fax: 605-534-3522. E-mail: jbrick@svswe.com. Web site: http://www.svtv.com. County: Yankton. ICA: SD0240.
Microwave channels reported: N.A.
Began: N.A.
Channel capacity: 25 (2-way capable). Channels available but not in use: N.A.
Basic Service
Subscribers: 1,100.
Programming (received off-air): KDLV-TV (N), KELO-TV (C), KSFY-TV (A), KTTW (F)

Sioux Falls-Mitchell; KUSD-TV (P) Vermillion.
Programming (via satellite): WGN-TV (W) Chicago; CNN; Discovery Channel; ESPN; Fox Family Channel; Midwest Sports Channel; Nashville Network; Nickelodeon; TBS Superstation; USA Network.
Fee: N.A.
Pay Service 1
Pay Units: N.A.
Programming (via satellite): Showtime.
Fee: N.A.
Manager: Joel Brick. Chief technician: Marvin Luke.
Ownership: Sioux Valley Rural Television Inc. (MSO).

Tennessee

CLARKSVILLE—Digital Wireless Systems, Box 15065, Reading, PA 19612. Phones: 610-921-5555; 610-921-9500. County: Montgomery. ICA: TN0182.
Microwave channels reported: N.A.
Channel capacity: N.A.
Manager: Joseph Cunningham.
Ownership: Virginia Communications Inc.

KNOXVILLE—Tennessee Wireless Inc., 6330 Baum Dr., Knoxville, TN 37919. Phone: 423-584-1234. Fax: 423-588-9336. Counties: Blount, Jefferson, Knox & Loudon. Also serves Blount, Jefferson, Knox, Loudon. ICA: TN0180.
Microwave channels reported: N.A.
Began: February 1, 1990.
Channel capacity: 31. Channels available but not in use: None.
Basic Service
Subscribers: 1,380; Commercial subscribers: 858.
Programming (via satellite): WGN-TV (W) Chicago; A & E; American Movie Classics; BET; C-SPAN; CNBC; CNN; Country Music TV; Discovery Channel; ESPN; Fox Family Channel; Fox Sports Net South; Headline News; Knowledge TV; Learning Channel; Lifetime; MTV; Nashville Network; Nickelodeon; Odyssey; TBS Superstation; TV Guide Channel; The Weather Channel; USA Network.
Fee: $59.95 installation; $21.95 monthly.
Pay Service 1
Pay Units: 238.
Programming (via satellite): Cinemax.
Fee: $8.95 monthly.
Pay Service 2
Pay Units: 102.
Programming (via satellite): Disney Channel.
Fee: $8.95 monthly.
Pay Service 3
Pay Units: 358.
Programming (via satellite): HBO.
Fee: $8.95 monthly.
Pay-Per-View
Viewer's Choice.
Manager: Tracy Evans. Chief technician: Kevin Gladfelder. Marketing director: Chris Scurto.
Ownership: Tennessee Wireless Inc.

LAWRENCEBURG—Wireless One of Lawrenceburg, 1403 Buffalo Rd., Lawrenceburg, TN 38464. Phones: 615-762-7549; 888-947-3663. Fax: 615-708-3660.
Web site: http://www.wirelessone.com.
County: Lawrence. ICA: TN0188.
Microwave channels reported: N.A.
Began: N.A.
Channel capacity: 31. Channels available but not in use: 11.
Basic Service
Subscribers: N.A.
Programming (received off-air): WAFF (N), WHNT-TV (C), WZDX (F) Huntsville-Decatur; WDCN (P), WKRN-TV (A) Nashville.
Programming (via satellite): WGN-TV (W) Chicago; CNN; Cartoon Network; Discovery Channel; ESPN; Fox Family Channel; Nashville Network; Nickelodeon; TBS Superstation; Trinity Bcstg. Network; Turner Classic Movies; Turner Network TV; USA Network.
Fee: $99.95 installation; $22.95 monthly.
Pay Service 1
Pay Units: N.A.
Programming (via satellite): Showtime.
Fee: $9.95 monthly.
Pay-Per-View
Viewer's Choice.
Fee: $3.90.
Manager: Will Good. Chief technician: Jackie Schultz. Marketing & program director: David Brown.
Ownership: Wireless One Inc. (MSO).

NASHVILLE—Nashville Wireless Associates, Suite 408, 475 Metroplex Dr., Nashville, TN 37211. Phone: 615-333-9288. Fax: 615-333-5983. Counties: Davidson, Sumner, Williamson & Wilson. Also serves Sumner County, Williamson County, Wilson County. ICA: TN0183.
Microwave channels reported: N.A.
Began: January 1, 1992.
Channel capacity: 31 (not 2-way capable). Channels available but not in use: None.
Basic Service
Subscribers: 2,973.
Programming (received off-air): WUPN-TV (U) Greensboro-High Point; WDCN (P), WKRN-TV (A), WSMV (N), WTVF (C), WZTV (F) Nashville.
Programming (via satellite): WGN-TV (W) Chicago; A & E; C-SPAN; CNN; Country Music TV; Discovery Channel; Disney Channel; ESPN; Fox Family Channel; Fox Sports Net South; Headline News; Lifetime; MTV; Nashville Network; Nickelodeon; QVC; Sci-Fi Channel; TBS Superstation; TV Guide Channel; The Weather Channel; Trinity Bcstg. Network; Turner Network TV; USA Network.
Fee: $22.95 monthly.
Pay Service 1
Pay Units: N.A.
Programming (via satellite): HBO; Showtime; The Movie Channel.
Fee: N.A.
Equipment: Comwave headend; Scientific-Atlanta amplifiers; Tocom set top converters; Eagle traps.
Manager: Danny Crowson.
Ownership: Nashville Wireless Cable Inc.

TULLAHOMA—Wireless One of Tullahoma, 101 S. Woodland St., Manchester, TN 37355. Phones: 615-723-2111; 888-947-3663. Fax: 615-723-0844.
Web site: http://www.wirelessone.com.
Counties: Bedford, Cannon, Coffee, Franklin, Grundy, Marion, Moore, Rutherford & Warren. Also serves Bedford County, Beersheba Springs, Bell Buckle, Cannon County, Coffee County, Decherd, Estill Springs, Franklin County, Grundy County, Lynchburg, Manchester, Marion County (portions), Monteagle, Morrison, Rockvale, Rutherford County, Shelbyville, Tracy City, Unionville, Warren County, Winchester, Woodbury. ICA: TN0187.
Total homes in service area: 151,082.
Microwave channels reported: N.A.
Began: November 1, 1995.
Channel capacity: 21 (not 2-way capable). Channels available but not in use: None.
Basic Service
Subscribers: 2,446.
Programming (received off-air): WDCN (P), WKRN-TV (A), WSMV (N), WTVF (C), WZTV (F) Nashville.
Programming (via satellite): A & E; BET; CNN; Country Music TV; Discovery Channel; Disney Channel; ESPN; Fox Sports Net South; Nashville Network; Nickelodeon; QVC; TBS Superstation; The Weather Channel; Turner Network TV; USA Network.
Fee: $99.95 installation; $22.95 monthly.
Pay Service 1
Pay Units: 856.
Programming (via satellite): HBO.
Fee: $11.95 monthly.
Pay-Per-View
Addressable homes: 2,368.
Viewer's Choice.
Fee: $3.90.
Equipment: Jerrold set top converters.
Manager: Mike Brown. Chief technician: Doug Breed. Marketing & program director: David Brown.
Ownership: Wireless One Inc. (MSO).

UNION CITY—MetroVision, Box 117, Union City, TN 38261. Phone: 901-885-4922. County: Obion. ICA: TN0181.
Microwave channels reported: N.A.
Began: N.A.
Channel capacity: N.A. Channels available but not in use: N.A.
Basic Service
Subscribers: N.A.
Programming (via satellite): WGN-TV (W) Chicago; A & E; CNN; Fox Family Channel; Nashville Network; TBS Superstation; USA Network.
Fee: $15.00 installation; $29.00 monthly.
Pay Service 1
Pay Units: N.A.
Programming (via satellite): Showtime.
Fee: $10.00 installation; $17.50 monthly.
Ownership: Time Warner Cable (MSO).

Texas

ABILENE—Nucentrix Broadband Networks Inc., Suite 200, 200 Chisholm Place, Plano, TX 75075. Phone: 972-423-9494. Fax: 972-423-0819. County: Taylor. ICA: TX0925.
Microwave channels reported: N.A.
Channel capacity: N.A.
Ownership: Nucentrix Broadband Networks (MSO).

AUSTIN—Nucentrix Broadband Networks Inc., Suite 200, 200 Chisholm Place, Plano, TX 75075. Phone: 972-423-9494. Fax: 972-423-0819. County: Travis. ICA: TX0889.
Microwave channels reported: N.A.
Began: N.A.
Channel capacity: 31. Channels available but not in use: N.A.
Basic Service
Subscribers: 10,000.
Fee: N.A.
Pay Service 1
Pay Units: N.A.
Programming (via satellite): Cinemax; HBO (multiplexed); Showtime.
Fee: $9.00 monthly (each).
Manager: Charlie Todd. Chief technician: Mike Stizakos. Marketing director: Tom Strubbe.
Ownership: Nucentrix Broadband Networks (MSO).

BIG COUNTRY—Nucentrix Broadband Networks Inc., Suite 200, 200 Chisholm Place, Plano, TX 75075. Phone: 972-423-9494. Fax: 972-423-0819. County: Eastland. ICA: TX0948.
Microwave channels reported: N.A.
Began: N.A.
Channel capacity: N.A.
Basic Service
Subscribers: N.A.
Programming (received off-air): KDFW (F), KTVT (C), KXAS-TV (N), WFAA-TV (A) Dallas-Fort Worth.
Programming (via satellite): CNN; Country Music TV; Discovery Channel; ESPN; Fox Sports Net Southwest; Lifetime; Nashville Network; Nickelodeon; TBS Superstation; The Weather Channel; Turner Network TV; USA Network.
Fee: $24.95 monthly.
Pay Service 1
Pay Units: N.A.
Programming (via satellite): Cinemax; HBO.
Fee: $7.95 monthly (Cinemax), $9.95 monthly (HBO).
Pay-Per-View
Viewer's Choice.
Manager: Tamela King. Chief Technician: James Southall.
Ownership: Nucentrix Broadband Networks (MSO).

BRENHAM—Wireless One, Suite D, 580 Graham Rd., College Station, TX 77845. Phones: 409-690-2121; 888-947-3663. Fax: 409-690-0741. Web site: http://www.wirelessone.com. Counties: Austin, Brazos, Burleson, Colorado, Fayette, Grimes, Waller & Washington. Also serves Austin County (portions), Brazos County (portions), Burleson County (portions), Colorado County (portions), Fayette County (portions), Grimes County (portions), Navasota, Waller County (portions), Washington County (portions). ICA: TX0934.
Total homes in service area: 38,038.
Microwave channels reported: N.A.
Began: February 1, 1996.
Channel capacity: 22. Channels available but not in use: None.
Basic Service
Subscribers: 2,068.
Programming (received off-air): KBTX-TV (C) Bryan; KPRC-TV (N), KRIV (F), KTRK-TV (A), KUHT (P) Houston.
Programming (via satellite): A & E; BET; CNN; Country Music TV; Discovery Channel; Disney Channel; ESPN; Fox Sports Net Southwest; Nashville Network; TBS Superstation; The Weather Channel; Turner Network TV; USA Network.
Fee: $99.95 installation; $22.95 monthly.
Pay Service 1
Pay Units: 23.
Programming (via satellite): HBO.
Fee: $11.95 monthly.
Pay-Per-View
Viewer's Choice.
Fee: $3.90.
Equipment: Jerrold set top converters.
Manager: Scott Sewell. Chief technician: Mark Hill. Marketing & program director: David Brown.
Ownership: Wireless One Inc. (MSO).

BRYAN—Wireless One of Bryan, Suite D, 580 Graham Rd., College Station, TX 77845. Phones: 409-690-2121; 888-947-3663. Fax: 409-690-0741. Web site: http://www.wirelessone.com. Counties: Brazos, Burleson, Grimes, Madison, Milam, Robertson & Washington. Also serves Brazos County (portions), Burleson County (portions), College Station, Grimes County (portions), Madison County (portions), Milam County (portions), Robertson County (portions), Washington County (portions). ICA: TX0935.

Total homes in service area: 92,408.
Microwave channels reported: N.A.
Began: May 1, 1995.
Channel capacity: 34. Channels available but not in use: None.

Basic Service
Subscribers: 4,582.
Programming (received off-air): KBTX-TV (C), KYLE (W) Bryan; KAMU-TV (P) College Station; KCEN-TV (N), KXXV (A) Waco-Temple.
Programming (via satellite): A & E; BET; C-SPAN; CNN; Country Music TV; Discovery Channel; Disney Channel; ESPN; Fox Sports Net Southwest; Headline News; History Channel; Learning Channel; Lifetime; MTV; Nashville Network; Nickelodeon; QVC; TBS Superstation; The New Encore; The Weather Channel; Turner Network TV; USA Network; Univision.
Fee: $99.95 installation; $22.95 monthly.

Pay Service 1
Pay Units: 449.
Programming (via satellite): HBO.
Fee: $11.95 monthly.

Pay Service 2
Pay Units: N.A.
Programming (via satellite): Showtime.
Fee: $9.95 monthly.

Pay Service 3
Pay Units: 358.
Programming (via satellite): Starz!
Fee: $6.95 monthly.

Pay-Per-View
Addressable homes: 4,500.
Viewer's Choice.
Fee: $3.90.
Equipment: Jerrold set top converters.
Manager: Scott Sewell. Chief technician: Mark Hill. Marketing & program director: David Brown.
Ownership: Wireless One Inc. (MSO).

CORPUS CHRISTI—Nucentrix Broadband Networks Inc., Suite 200, 200 Chisholm Place, Plano, TX 75075. Phone: 972-423-9494. Fax: 972-423-0819. County: Nueces. ICA: TX0890.
Microwave channels reported: N.A.
Channel capacity: N.A.
Ownership: Nucentrix Broadband Networks (MSO). Purchased from Heartland Wireless Communications Inc.

CORSICANA—Nucentrix Broadband Networks Inc., Suite 200, 200 Chisholm Place, Plano, TX 75075. Phone: 972-423-9494. Fax: 972-423-0819. County: Navarro. ICA: TX0938.
Microwave channels reported: N.A.
Began: N.A.
Channel capacity: N.A.

Basic Service
Subscribers: N.A.
Programming (received off-air): KDFW (F), KTVT (C), KXAS-TV (N), WFAA-TV (A) Dallas-Fort Worth.
Programming (via satellite): CNN; Country Music TV; Discovery Channel; ESPN; Fox Sports Net Southwest; Lifetime; Nashville Network; Nickelodeon; TBS Superstation; The Weather Channel; Turner Network TV; USA Network.
Fee: $37.00 monthly.

Pay Service 1
Pay Units: N.A.
Programming (via satellite): Cinemax; HBO (multiplexed).
Fee: N.A.

Pay-Per-View
Viewer's Choice.
Manager: Fred Santiago. Chief technician: Bruce McManus.
Ownership: Nucentrix Broadband Networks (MSO).

DALLAS—Nucentrix Broadband Networks Inc., Suite 200, 200 Chisholm Place, Plano, TX 75075. Phone: 972-423-9494. Fax: 972-423-0819. County: Dallas. ICA: TX0922.
Microwave channels reported: N.A.
Channel capacity: N.A.
Ownership: Nucentrix Broadband Networks (MSO).

FORT WORTH—CS Wireless Systems Inc., 1101 Summit Ave., Plano, TX 75074. Phone: 972-730-3300. County: Tarrant. ICA: TX0891.
Total homes in service area: 440,000.
Microwave channels reported: WJM75, Ch. 1, MDS; WFY900, Ch. 2, MDS, WHR883, C-1-4, ITFS.
Began: January 1, 1992.
Channel capacity: 33. Channels available but not in use: N.A.

Basic Service
Subscribers: 1,600.
Programming (received off-air): KDAF (W), KDFI-TV (I), KDFW (F), KDTX-TV (T), KERA-TV (P), KFWD (O), KTVT (C), KTXA (U), KXAS-TV (N), KXTX-TV (I), WFAA-TV (A) Dallas-Fort Worth; KDTN (P) Denton; KHSX-TV (H) Irving.
Programming (via satellite): WGN-TV (W) Chicago; CNN; Country Music TV; Discovery Channel; ESPN; Fox Sports Net Southwest; Nashville Network; Nickelodeon; TBS Superstation; The Weather Channel; USA Network.
Fee: $49.95 installation; $16.95 monthly.

Pay Service 1
Pay Units: 1,300.
Programming (via satellite): Disney Channel; Showtime.
Fee: $7.95 monthly.

Pay Service 2
Pay Units: 400.
Programming (via satellite): HBO.
Fee: $10.00 monthly.
Equipment: Comwave headend; Tocom addressable set top converters; Scientific-Atlanta satellite antenna; Standard Communications satellite receivers.
Manager: Steve Moncreiff. Chief technician: Jim Galbraith. Customer service manager: Michele Russell.
Ownership: CS Wireless Systems Inc. (MSO).

FREEPORT—Wireless One of Freeport, Suite 400, 2506 Lakeland Dr., Jackson, MS 39208. Phones: 504-326-7778; 888-947-3663. Web site: http://www.wirelessone.com. County: Brazoria. ICA: TX0971.
Microwave channels reported: N.A.
Began: N.A.
Channel capacity: N.A.

Basic Service
Subscribers: N.A.
Programming (received off-air): KHTV (W), KPRC-TV (N), KRIV (F), KTRK-TV (A), KTXH (U), KUHT (P) Houston.
Programming (via satellite): WGN-TV (W) Chicago; A & E; C-SPAN; CNN; Cartoon Network; Discovery Channel; ESPN; Fox Family Channel; Fox Sports Net Southwest; History Channel; Home Shopping Network; Learning Channel; Lifetime; Nashville Network; Nickelodeon; QVC; TBS Superstation; The Weather Channel; Turner Network TV; USA Network; Univision.
Fee: $99.95 installation; $28.95 monthly.

Pay Service 1
Pay Units: N.A.
Programming (via satellite): Cinemax; HBO; Showtime.
Fee: $9.95 monthly (Showtime), $10.95 monthly (Cinemax), $11.95 monthly (HBO), $25.95 monthly (Cinemax, HBO & Showtime).

Pay-Per-View
Viewer's Choice.
Fee: $3.90.
Ownership: Wireless One Inc. (MSO).

GAINESVILLE—Nucentrix Broadband Networks Inc., Suite 200, 200 Chisholm Place, Plano, TX 75075. Phone: 972-423-9494. Fax: 972-423-0819. County: Cooke. ICA: TX0939.
Microwave channels reported: N.A.
Began: N.A.
Channel capacity: N.A.

Basic Service
Subscribers: N.A.
Programming (received off-air): WFAA-TV (A) Dallas-Fort Worth; KXII (C) Sherman; KFDX-TV (N), KJTL (F,U) Wichita Falls-Lawton.
Programming (via satellite): A & E; CNN; Country Music TV; Discovery Channel; Disney Channel; ESPN; Fox Family Channel; Learning Channel; Nashville Network; Nickelodeon; Sci-Fi Channel; TBS Superstation; The Weather Channel; Turner Network TV; USA Network.
Fee: N.A.

Pay Service 1
Pay Units: N.A.
Programming (via satellite): Cinemax; HBO (multiplexed).
Fee: N.A.
Manager: Troy McLain.
Ownership: Nucentrix Broadband Networks (MSO).

GEORGE WEST—Nucentrix Broadband Networks Inc., Suite 200, 200 Chisholm Place, Plano, TX 75075. Phone: 972-423-9494. Fax: 972-423-0819. County: Live Oak. ICA: TX0940.
Microwave channels reported: N.A.
Began: N.A.
Channel capacity: N.A.

Basic Service
Subscribers: N.A.
Programming (received off-air): KIII (A), KRIS-TV (N), KZTV (C) Corpus Christi; KABB (F) San Antonio.
Programming (via satellite): WGN-TV (W) Chicago; A & E; CNN; Cartoon Network; Country Music TV; Discovery Channel; ESPN; Fox Sports Net Southwest; Lifetime; Nashville Network; Nickelodeon; TBS Superstation; Telemundo; The Weather Channel; Turner Network TV; USA Network; Univision.
Fee: $25.00 (underground); $24.95 monthly.

Pay Service 1
Pay Units: N.A.
Programming (via satellite): Cinemax; Disney Channel; HBO.
Fee: N.A.
Manager: Mike Dougherty. Chief technician: Brian Hayes. Marketing director: Mike Lind. Customer service manager: Rita Bowen.
Ownership: Nucentrix Broadband Networks (MSO).

GOLDTHWAITE—Central Texas Wireless, Box 627, 1012 Reilly St., Goldthwaite, TX 76844. Phone: 915-648-2213. County: Mills. ICA: TX0892.
Microwave channels reported: N.A.
Channel capacity: N.A.
Ownership: Central Texas Wireless TV Inc.

HAMILTON—Nucentrix Broadband Networks Inc., Suite 200, 200 Chisholm Place, Plano, TX 75075. Phone: 927-423-9494. Fax: 927-423-0819. County: Hamilton. ICA: TX0957.
Microwave channels reported: N.A.
Began: N.A.
Channel capacity: N.A.

Basic Service
Subscribers: N.A.
Programming (received off-air): KXAS-TV (N), WFAA-TV (A) Dallas-Fort Worth; KWKT (F), KWTX-TV (C) Waco-Temple.
Programming (via satellite): A & E; American Movie Classics; CNN; Country Music TV; Discovery Channel; Disney Channel; ESPN; Fox Family Channel; Fox Sports Net; Learning Channel; Lifetime; MTV; Nashville Network; Nickelodeon; TBS Superstation; The Weather Channel; Trinity Bcstg. Network; Turner Network TV; USA Network.
Fee: $60.00 installation; $24.99 monthly.

Pay Service 1
Pay Units: N.A.
Programming (via satellite): Cinemax; HBO (multiplexed).
Fee: $5.00 monthly (Cinemax), $10.00 monthly (HBO).
Manager: Duane Doyal.
Ownership: Nucentrix Broadband Networks (MSO).

HOUSTON—People's Choice TV of Houston, 7272 Pinemont Dr., Houston, TX 77040. Phone: 713-690-4500. Fax: 713-895-8852. Counties: Galveston & Harris. Also serves Galveston (portions). ICA: TX0893.
Total homes in service area: 1,100,000.
Microwave channels reported: N.A.
Began: March 1, 1994.
Channel capacity: N.A. Channels available but not in use: N.A.

Basic Service
Subscribers: N.A.
Programming (received off-air): KETH (E), KHOU-TV (C), KHTV (W), KPRC-TV (N), KRIV (F), KTRK-TV (A), KTXH (U), KUHT (P) Houston; KNWS-TV (I) Katy.
Programming (via satellite): WGN-TV (W) Chicago; WPIX (W) New York; A & E; BET; CNBC; CNN; Country Music TV; Discovery Channel; ESPN; Fox Family Channel; Fox Sports Net Southwest; Headline News; Home Shopping Network; Lifetime; MTV; Nashville Network; Nickelodeon; TBS Superstation; TV Guide Channel; Telemundo; USA Network; Univision.
Fee: $19.75 monthly.

Pay Service 1
Pay Units: N.A.
Programming (via satellite): Cinemax; Disney Channel; HBO.
Fee: $7.95 monthly (each).

Pay-Per-View
Playboy TV; Spice; special events.
Fee: Varies.
Ownership: People's Choice TV Partners (MSO). Sale pends to Sprint Corp.

JOURDANTON—Nucentrix Broadband Networks Inc., Suite 200, 200 Chisholm Place, Plano, TX 75075. Phone: 972-423-9494. Fax: 972-423-0819. County: Atascosa. ICA: TX0941.
Microwave channels reported: N.A.
Began: N.A.
Channel capacity: N.A. Channels available but not in use: N.A.

Basic Service
Subscribers: N.A.
Programming (received off-air): KABB (F), KENS-TV (C), KMOL-TV (N), KSAT-TV (A) San Antonio.
Programming (via satellite): A & E; CNN; Country Music TV; Discovery Channel; ESPN; Fox Sports Net Southwest; Nashville Network; Nickelodeon; TBS Superstation; The Weather Channel; Turner Network TV; USA Network; Univision.
Fee: N.A.

Pay Service 1
Pay Units: N.A.
Programming (via satellite): Cinemax; HBO.
Fee: N.A.
Pay-Per-View
Viewer's Choice.
Manager: Fred Santiago. Chief technician: Luis Morales.
Ownership: Nucentrix Broadband Networks (MSO).

KERRVILLE—Nucentrix Broadband Networks Inc., Suite 200, 200 Chisholm Place, Plano, TX 75075. Phone: 972-423-9494. Fax: 972-423-0819. County: Kerr. ICA: TX0942.
Microwave channels reported: N.A.
Began: N.A.
Channel capacity: N.A. Channels available but not in use: N.A.
Basic Service
Subscribers: N.A.
Programming (received off-air): KABB (F), KENS-TV (C), KMOL-TV (N), KSAT-TV (A) San Antonio.
Programming (via satellite): CNN; Country Music TV; Discovery Channel; ESPN; Fox Sports Net Southwest; Lifetime; Nashville Network; Nickelodeon; TBS Superstation; The Weather Channel; Turner Network TV; USA Network.
Fee: N.A.
Pay Service 1
Pay Units: N.A.
Programming (via satellite): Cinemax; HBO.
Fee: N.A.
Pay-Per-View
Viewer's Choice.
Manager: Graydon Vaught. Chief technician: Monty Baker.
Ownership: Nucentrix Broadband Networks (MSO).

KINGSVILLE—Nucentrix Broadband Networks Inc., Suite 200, 200 Chisholm Place, Plano, TX 75075. Phone: 972-423-9494. Fax: 972-423-0819. County: Kleberg. ICA: TX0943.
Microwave channels reported: N.A.
Began: N.A.
Channel capacity: N.A. Channels available but not in use: N.A.
Basic Service
Subscribers: N.A.
Programming (received off-air): KIII (A), KRIS-TV (N), KZTV (C) Corpus Christi.
Programming (via satellite): WGN-TV (W) Chicago; CNN; Discovery Channel; ESPN; Learning Channel; Lifetime; Nashville Network; Nickelodeon; TBS Superstation; Telemundo; The Weather Channel; Turner Network TV; USA Network.
Fee: N.A.
Pay Service 1
Pay Units: N.A.
Programming (via satellite): Cinemax; HBO.
Fee: N.A.
Manager: Mike Daugherty. Chief technician: Amado Delagarza.
Ownership: Nucentrix Broadband Networks (MSO).

LAREDO—Nucentrix Broadband Networks Inc., Suite 200, 200 Chisholm Place, Plano, TX 75075. Phone: 972-423-9494. Fax: 972-423-0819. County: Webb. ICA: TX0927.
Microwave channels reported: N.A.
Channel capacity: N.A.
Ownership: Nucentrix Broadband Networks (MSO). Purchased from Heartland Wireless Communications Inc.

LUBBOCK—Nucentrix Broadband Networks Inc., Suite 200, 200 Chisholm Place, Plano, TX 75075. Phone: 972-423-9494. Fax: 972-423-0819. County: Lubbock. Also serves O'Donnel, Olton. ICA: TX0944.
Microwave channels reported: N.A.
Began: N.A.
Channel capacity: N.A. Channels available but not in use: N.A.
Basic Service
Subscribers: N.A.
Programming (received off-air): KAMC (A), KCBD-TV (N), KJTV (F), KLBK-TV (C), KTXT-TV (P) Lubbock.
Programming (via satellite): A & E; BET; CNBC; CNN; Cartoon Network; Country Music TV; Discovery Channel; Disney Channel; ESPN; Fox Family Channel; Fox Sports Net Southwest; Headline News; Lifetime; MTV; Nashville Network; Nickelodeon; TBS Superstation; Telemundo; The Box; The Weather Channel; Turner Network TV; USA Network; Univision.
Fee: N.A.
Pay Service 1
Pay Units: N.A.
Programming (via satellite): Cinemax; HBO; Showtime.
Fee: N.A.
Manager: Wayne Kreller. Chief technician: Chris Hernandez.
Ownership: Nucentrix Broadband Networks (MSO).

MIDLAND—Nucentrix Broadband Networks Inc., Suite 200, 200 Chisholm Place, Plano, TX 75075. Phone: 972-423-9494. Fax: 972-423-0819. County: Midland. ICA: TX0928.
Microwave channels reported: N.A.
Channel capacity: N.A.
Ownership: Nucentrix Broadband Networks (MSO). Purchased from Heartland Wireless Communications Inc.

MILANO—Wireless One of Milano, Suite D, 580 Graham Rd., College Station, TX 77845. Phones: 409-690-2121; 800-921-1103. Fax: 409-690-0741. Web site: http://www.wirelessone.com. Counties: Bell, Burleson, Lee, Milam, Robertson & Williamson. Also serves Bell County (portions), Burleson County (portions), Cameron, Giddings, Hearne, Lee County, Milam County, Robertson County (portions), Rockdale, Williamson County (portions). ICA: TX0894.
Total homes in service area: 36,792.
Microwave channels reported: WLX-440, A-1-4, ITFS; WLX-442, B-1-4, ITFS; WLX-454, C-1-4, ITFS; WLX-398, D-1-4, ITFS; WLX-441, G-1-4, ITFS.
Began: March 1, 1992.
Channel capacity: 19. Channels available but not in use: None.
Basic Service
Subscribers: 1,958.
Programming (received off-air): KEYE-TV (C), KLRU (P), KTBC (F), KVUE-TV (A), KXAN-TV (N) Austin.
Programming (via satellite): WGN-TV (W) Chicago; American Movie Classics; CNN; Discovery Channel; Disney Channel; ESPN; Fox Sports Net Southwest; Nashville Network; TBS Superstation; TV Guide Channel; The Weather Channel; Turner Network TV; USA Network.
Fee: $99.95 installation; $22.95 monthly.
Pay Service 1
Pay Units: 511.
Programming (via satellite): HBO.
Fee: $11.95 monthly.
Pay-Per-View
Viewer's Choice.
Fee: $3.90.
Local advertising: Yes. Regional interconnect: Cabletime.
Equipment: Jerrold set top converters.
Manager: Scott Sewell. Chief technician: Mark Hill. Marketing & program director: David Brown.
Ownership: Wireless One Inc. (MSO).

MOUNT PLEASANT—Nucentrix Broadband Networks Inc., Suite 200, 200 Chisholm Place, Plano, TX 75075. Phone: 972-423-9494. Fax: 972-423-0819. County: Titus. ICA: TX0929.
Microwave channels reported: N.A.
Channel capacity: N.A.
Ownership: Nucentrix Broadband Networks (MSO). Purchased from Heartland Wireless Communications Inc.

OLTON—Nucentrix Broadband Networks Inc., Suite 200, 200 Chisholm Place, Plano, TX 75075. Phone: 972-423-9494. Fax: 972-423-0819. County: Lamb. ICA: TX0930.
Microwave channels reported: N.A.
Channel capacity: N.A.
Ownership: Nucentrix Broadband Networks (MSO). Purchased from Heartland Wireless Communications Inc.

PARIS—Nucentrix Broadband Networks Inc., Suite 200, 200 Chisholm Place, Plano, TX 75075. Phone: 972-423-9494. Fax: 972-423-0819. County: Lamar. ICA: TX0945.
Microwave channels reported: N.A.
Began: N.A.
Channel capacity: N.A. Channels available but not in use: N.A.
Basic Service
Subscribers: N.A.
Programming (received off-air): KTEN (A,N,F) Ada; KXII (C) Sherman.
Programming (via satellite): A & E; CNN; Cartoon Network; Country Music TV; Discovery Channel; ESPN; Fox Sports Net Southwest; Headline News; MTV; Nashville Network; Nickelodeon; TBS Superstation; The Weather Channel; Turner Network TV; USA Network.
Fee: N.A.
Pay Service 1
Pay Units: N.A.
Programming (via satellite): Cinemax; HBO.
Fee: N.A.
Pay-Per-View
Viewer's Choice.
Manager: Ken Murlin. Chief technician: David Taylor.
Ownership: Nucentrix Broadband Networks (MSO).

SAN ANGELO—Sterling Wireless Cable, Box 5248, San Angelo, TX 76902. Phone: 915-944-0037. County: Tom Green. ICA: TX0931.
Microwave channels reported: N.A.
Channel capacity: N.A.
Ownership: Sterling Wireless Cable.

SAN ANTONIO—CS Wireless Systems Inc., 1101 Sumitt Ave., Plano, TX 75074. Phone: 972-730-3300. County: Bexar. ICA: TX0896.
Microwave channels reported: N.A.
Channel capacity: N.A.
Ownership: CS Wireless Systems Inc. (MSO).

SNYDER—Snyder Microwave Communications LC, Box 940008, Plano, TX 75094. Phone: 214-424-1661. Counties: Borden, Fisher, Mitchell, Nolan & Scurry. Also serves Colorado City, Gail, Hermleigh, Ira, Loraine, Roby, Roscoe, Rotan, Sweetwater, Westbrook. ICA: TX0897.
Microwave channels reported: WMI373, E group, MMDS; WMI377, F group, MMDS; WNTK882, H group, MMDS.
Began: N.A.
Channel capacity: 11.
Manager: Leo H. Thomasian.
Ownership: Snyder Microwave Communications LC.

TEMPLE—Nucentrix Broadband Networks Inc., Suite 200, 200 Chisholm Place, Plano, TX 75075. Phone: 972-423-9494. Fax: 972-423-0819. County: Bell. ICA: TX0932.
Microwave channels reported: N.A.
Channel capacity: N.A.
Ownership: Nucentrix Broadband Networks (MSO). Purchased from Heartland Wireless Communications Inc.

TEXARKANA—Nucentrix Broadband Networks Inc., Suite 200, 200 Chisholm Place, Plano, TX 75075. Phone: 972-423-9494. Fax: 972-423-0819. Counties: Bowie & Cass. Also serves Bowie County, Cass County. ICA: TX0924.
Microwave channels reported: N.A.
Began: N.A.
Channel capacity: 22. Channels available but not in use: N.A.
Basic Service
Subscribers: 808.
Fee: N.A.
Ownership: Nucentrix Broadband Networks (MSO).

TEXOMA—Nucentrix Broadband Networks Inc., Suite 200, 200 Chisholm Place, Plano, TX 75075. Phone: 972-423-9494. Fax: 972-423-0819. Counties: Bryan, OK; Sherman, TX. Also serves Durant, OK. ICA: TX0947.
Microwave channels reported: N.A.
Began: N.A.
Channel capacity: N.A. Channels available but not in use: N.A.
Basic Service
Subscribers: N.A.
Programming (received off-air): KTEN (A,N,F) Ada; KDFW (F), KXAS-TV (N), KXTX-TV (I), WFAA-TV (A) Dallas-Fort Worth; KXII (C) Sherman.
Programming (via satellite): WGN-TV (W) Chicago; A & E; CNN; Cartoon Network; Country Music TV; Discovery Channel; ESPN; EWTN; Fox Family Channel; Fox Sports Net Southwest; Learning Channel; MTV; Nashville Network; Nickelodeon; TBS Superstation; The Weather Channel; Turner Network TV; USA Network.
Fee: $24.99 monthly.
Pay Service 1
Pay Units: N.A.
Programming (via satellite): Cinemax; HBO.
Fee: $5.00 monthly.
Manager: Kenny Beddow. Chief Technician: Jeff Zebonik.
Ownership: Nucentrix Broadband Networks (MSO).

UVALDE—Nucentrix Broadband Networks Inc., Suite 200, 200 Chisholm Place, Plano, TX 75075. Phone: 972-423-9494. Fax: 972-423-0819. County: Uvalde. ICA: TX0946.
Microwave channels reported: N.A.
Began: N.A.
Channel capacity: N.A. Channels available but not in use: N.A.
Basic Service
Subscribers: N.A.
Programming (received off-air): KABB (F), KENS-TV (C), KMOL-TV (N), KSAT-TV (A) San Antonio.
Programming (via satellite): A & E; CNN; Country Music TV; Discovery Channel; ESPN; Fox Sports Net Southwest; Nashville Network; Nickelodeon; TBS Superstation; The Weather Channel; Turner Network TV; USA Network; Univision.
Fee: $24.95 monthly.

Pay Service 1
Pay Units: N.A.
Programming (via satellite): Cinemax; HBO.
Fee: $10.00 monthly.
Pay-Per-View
Viewer's Choice.
Ownership: Nucentrix Broadband Networks (MSO).

WACO—Nucentrix Broadband Networks Inc., Suite 200, 200 Chisholm Place, Plano, TX 75075. Phone: 972-423-9494. Fax: 972-423-0819. County: McLennan. ICA: TX0899.
Microwave channels reported: N.A.
Channel capacity: N.A.
Ownership: Nucentrix Broadband Networks (MSO). Purchased from Heartland Wireless Communications Inc.

WHARTON—Wireless One of Wharton, Suite D, 580 Graham Rd., College Station, TX 77845-9661. Phones: 409-690-2121; 800-921-1103. Fax: 409-690-0741. Web site: http://www.wirelessone.com. Counties: Austin, Brazoria, Colorado, Fort Bend, Matagorda & Wharton. Also serves Brazoria County (portions), Colorado County (portions), Eagle Lake, El Campo, Matagorda County (portions), Richmond, Rosenberg, Sealy, West Columbia, Wharton County. ICA: TX0936.
Total homes in service area: 92,027.
Microwave channels reported: N.A.
Began: June 1, 1994.
Channel capacity: 24. Channels available but not in use: None.
Basic Service
Subscribers: 2,586.
Programming (received off-air): KHOU-TV (C), KPRC-TV (N), KRIV (F), KTRK-TV (A), KUHT (P) Houston.
Programming (via satellite): A & E; BET; CNN; Country Music TV; Discovery Channel; ESPN; Fox Sports Net Southwest; Nashville Network; Nickelodeon; TBS Superstation; The Weather Channel; Turner Network TV; USA Network; Univision.
Fee: $99.95 installation; $19.95 monthly.
Pay Service 1
Pay Units: 471.
Programming (via satellite): HBO.
Fee: $11.95 monthly.
Pay Service 2
Pay Units: 613.
Programming (via satellite): Showtime.
Fee: $9.95 monthly.
Pay-Per-View
Viewer's Choice.
Fee: $3.90.
Local advertising: Yes. Regional interconnect: Cabletime.
Equipment: Jerrold set top converters.
Manager: Terri Quinn. Chief technician: Scott Sewell. Marketing & program director: David Brown.
Ownership: Wireless One Inc. (MSO).

WICHITA FALLS—Nucentrix Broadband Networks Inc., Suite 200, 200 Chisholm Place, Plano, TX 75075. Phone: 972-423-9494. Fax: 972-423-0819. County: Wichita. ICA: TX0933.
Microwave channels reported: N.A.
Channel capacity: N.A.
Ownership: Nucentrix Broadband Networks (MSO). Purchased from Heartland Wireless Communications Inc.

Utah

SALT LAKE CITY—TechniVision Inc., 120 Floral Ave., New Providence, NJ 07974. Phone: 908-665-0343. County: Salt Lake. ICA: UT0082.
Microwave channels reported: N.A.
Channel capacity: N.A.
Ownership: Technivision Inc.

ST. GEORGE—Sky-View Technologies, Box 1207, 845 E. Skyline Dr., St. George, UT 84770. Phone: 801-674-0320. Fax: 801-674-7679. County: Washington. ICA: UT0079.
Total homes in service area: 20,000.
Microwave channels reported: N.A.
Began: January 1, 1989.
Channel capacity: 32. Channels available but not in use: N.A.
Basic Service
Subscribers: N.A.
Programming (received off-air): KVBC (N) Las Vegas; KTLA (W) Los Angeles; KSL-TV (N), KTVX (A), KUTV (C) Salt Lake City.
Programming (via satellite): WGN-TV (W) Chicago; A & E; American Movie Classics; CNN; Country Music TV; Discovery Channel; ESPN; Fox Family Channel; Headline News; History Channel; Learning Channel; Nashville Network; Nickelodeon; Sci-Fi Channel; TBS Superstation; Turner Classic Movies; USA Network.
Fee: $30.00 installation; $21.50 monthly.
Pay Service 1
Pay Units: N.A.
Programming (via satellite): Showtime; The Movie Channel.
Fee: $9.50 monthly (each).
Ownership: American Wireless Inc.

Vermont

MOUNT ASCUTNEY—New England Wireless Inc., 56 Green St., Bellows Falls, VT 05101. Phone: 802-463-2228. Fax: 802-463-2232. County: Windsor. ICA: VT0091.
Microwave channels reported: N.A.
Channel capacity: N.A.
Ownership: New England Wireless Inc.

RUTLAND—Satellite Signals of New England, 178 N. Main St., Rutland, VT 05701. Phone: 802-775-4112. Fax: 802-775-1041. County: Rutland. ICA: VT0086.
Microwave channels reported: N.A.
Channel capacity: N.A.
Manager: Louis Jaffe.
Ownership: Satellite Signals of New England Inc.

Virginia

CHARLOTTESVILLE—CFW Communications, Suite 1, 1145 River Rd., Charlottesville, VA 22901. Phone: 804-977-6111. Fax: 804-977-1665. Counties: Albemarle, Buckingham, Fluvanna, Goochland, Greene, Louisa, Nelson & Orange. Also serves Albemarle County, Buckingham County, Fluvanna County, Goochland County (portions), Greene County, Louisa County, Nelson County (portions), Orange County. ICA: VA0163.
Total homes in service area: 105,251.
Microwave channels reported: WPX69, Ch. 1, MDS; WMH388, E group, MMDS; WLW840, F group, MMDS; WNTH948, H group, MMDS; WLX-523, A-1-4, ITFS; WLX-519, B-1-4, ITFS; WLX-518, C-1-4, ITFS; WLX-524, D-1-4, ITFS; WLX-517, G-1-4, ITFS.
Began: February 19, 1992.
Channel capacity: 32 (not 2-way capable). Channels available but not in use: None.
Basic Service
Subscribers: 7,329.
Programming (received off-air): WHTJ (P), WVIR-TV (N) Charlottesville; WRIC-TV (A), WRLH-TV (F), WTVR-TV (C) Richmond-Petersburg.
Programming (via satellite): A & E; BET; C-SPAN; CNN; Comedy Central; Discovery Channel; ESPN; Fox Family Channel; Headline News; Home Team Sports; Learning Channel; Lifetime; MTV; Nashville Network; Nickelodeon; TBS Superstation; The Weather Channel; Turner Classic Movies; Turner Network TV; USA Network; VH1.
Fee: $20.00 installation; $23.75 monthly; $3.95 converter.
Pay Service 1
Pay Units: 1,184.
Programming (via satellite): Cinemax.
Fee: $10.50 monthly.
Pay Service 2
Pay Units: 615.
Programming (via satellite): Disney Channel.
Fee: $9.00 installation; $9.95 monthly.
Pay Service 3
Pay Units: 1,947.
Programming (via satellite): HBO.
Fee: $10.50 monthly.
Pay Service 4
Pay Units: 1,054.
Programming (via satellite): Showtime.
Fee: $10.50 monthly.
Pay-Per-View
Addressable homes: 4,939.
Movies; special events.
Fee: Varies.
Equipment: Jerrold set top converters.
Manager: Dan Meenan. Chief technician: Jay D. Chupp. Marketing & program director: Casey Good.
Ownership: CFW Communications (MSO).

FAIRFAX—Capitol Connection, George Mason University, Kelley Dr., Fairfax, VA 22030-4444. Phones: 703-993-3100; 703-691-1119. Fax: 703-273-2417. Counties: Alexandria City, Arlington, Fairfax & Fairfax City, VA; District of Columbia; Montgomery & Prince George's, MD. Also serves Washington, DC, Montgomery County (portions), Prince George's County (portions), MD; Alexandria, Arlington County, Fairfax City, Fairfax County, VA. ICA: VA0164.
Microwave channels reported: N.A.
Channel capacity: N.A. Channels available but not in use: N.A.
Basic Service
Subscribers: 1,780.
Programming (received off-air): WBDC-TV (W), WDCA (U), WETA-TV (P), WHUT-TV (P), WJLA-TV (A), WRC-TV (N), WTTG (F), WUSA (C) Washington.
Programming (via satellite): C-SPAN; C-SPAN 2; CNBC; CNN.
Current originations: Educational access; government access.
Fee: $49.95 monthly.
Expanded Basic Service
Subscribers: N.A.
Programming (via satellite): BET; ESPN; Home Team Sports; MTV; Nickelodeon; TBS Superstation.
Fee: N.A.
Manager: Julia Morelli. Chief technician: Kirk Tatem.
Ownership: George Mason U. Instructional Foundation.

HARRISONBURG—CFW Communications, Suite 1, 1145 River Rd., Charlottesville, VA 22901. Phone: 804-977-6111. Fax: 804-977-1665. Counties: Augusta, Page, Rockingham, Shenandoah & Waynesboro City. Also serves Augusta County, Page County, Rockingham County, Shenandoah County, Staunton, Waynesboro. ICA: VA0179.
Total homes in service area: 71,532.
Microwave channels reported: WMI-916, Ch. 1, MDS; WMX-331, E group, MMDS; WMX-327, F group, MMDS; WMX-366, H group, MMDS; WNL-649, A-1-4, ITFS; WNL-650, B-1-4, ITFS; WNL-651, C-1-4, ITFS; WNL-652, D-1-4, ITFS.
Began: November 1, 1994.
Channel capacity: 32. Channels available but not in use: 4.
Basic Service
Subscribers: 4,110.
Programming (received off-air): WVIR-TV (N) Charlottesville; WHSV-TV (A,F) Harrisonburg; WTVR-TV (C) Richmond-Petersburg; WVPT (P) Staunton; WTTG (F) Washington.
Programming (via satellite): A & E; C-SPAN; CNN; Country Music TV; Discovery Channel; ESPN; Fox Family Channel; Home Team Sports; Learning Channel; MTV; Nashville Network; Nickelodeon; Odyssey; Showtime; TBS Superstation; The Weather Channel; Turner Classic Movies; Turner Network TV; USA Network.
Fee: $20.00 installation; $23.75 monthly; $3.95 converter.
Pay Service 1
Pay Units: 453.
Programming (via satellite): Cinemax.
Fee: $10.50 monthly.
Pay Service 2
Pay Units: 348.
Programming (via satellite): Disney Channel.
Fee: $8.95 monthly.
Pay Service 3
Pay Units: 709.
Programming (via satellite): HBO.
Fee: $10.50 monthly.
Pay Service 4
Pay Units: 6.
Programming (via satellite): Showtime.
Fee: $10.50 monthly.
Pay-Per-View
Addressable homes: 3,095.
Movies; special events.
Fee: Varies.
Equipment: Jerrold set top converters.
Manager: Dan Meenan. Chief technician: Jay D. Chupp. Marketing & program director: Casey Good.
Ownership: CFW Communications (MSO).

NORFOLK & VIRGINIA BEACH—Hampton Roads Wireless, Suite 102, 12 Corporate Woods Blvd., Albany, NY 12211. Phone: 518-462-2632. Fax: 518-462-3045. Counties: Norfolk City & Virginia Beach City. ICA: VA0171.
Total homes in service area: 573,000.
Microwave channels reported: N.A.
Began: July 1, 1994.
Channel capacity: N.A. Channels available but not in use: N.A.
Equipment: Jerrold set top converters.
Manager: Roddy Edge.
Ownership: CAI Wireless Systems Inc. (MSO). Sale pends to MCI WorldCom Inc.

RICHMOND—CFW Communications, 485 South Lake Blvd., Richmond, VA 23236. Phone: 804-378-8687. Fax: 804-378-8903. Counties: Amelia, Caroline, Chesterfield, Dinwiddie, Hanover, Henrico, King William, Nottoway, Powhatan & Prince George. Also serves Amelia County, Caroline County, Chesterfield County, Dinwiddie County, Hanover County, King William County, Nottoway County, Powhatan County, Prince George County. ICA: VA0181.
Total homes in service area: 379,360.

Microwave channels reported: WHT735, E group, MDS; WHT736, F group, MMDS; WNTJ713, H1, MMDS; WNL-491, B-1-4, ITFS; WNL-638, C-1-2, ITFS; WNL-489, D-3-4, ITFS; WNL-686, G-3-4, ITFS.
Began: November 1, 1995.
Channel capacity: 22. Channels available but not in use: None.
Basic Service
Subscribers: 1,260.
Programming (received off-air): WCVE-TV (P), WRIC-TV (A), WRLH-TV (F), WTVR-TV (C), WWBT (N) Richmond-Petersburg.
Programming (via satellite): A & E; BET; CNBC; CNN; Discovery Channel; Disney Channel; ESPN; Learning Channel; MTV; Nashville Network; Nickelodeon; TBS Superstation; The Weather Channel; Turner Network TV; USA Network.
Fee: $100.00 installation; $22.10 monthly.
Pay Service 1
Pay Units: 445.
Programming (via satellite): Cinemax.
Fee: $9.50 monthly.
Manager: Mark Barber. Chief technician: Stan Alexander. Marketing director: Casey Wilkinson. Customer service manager: Candice M. Diehl.
Ownership: CFW Communications (MSO).

ROANOKE—R & B Cable, Box 174, Daleville, VA 24083. Phone: 540-992-3300. Fax: 540-992-3094. Counties: Botetourt, Franklin, Montgomery & Roanoke. Also serves Botetourt County, Franklin County, Montgomery County, Roanoke County, Salem, Vinton. ICA: VA0173.
Total homes in service area: 92,000.
Microwave channels reported: N.A.
Began: February 5, 1996.
Channel capacity: 31. Channels available but not in use: 18.
Local advertising: No.
Manager: Robert F. Nay. Chief technician: Charles Richardson.
Ownership: R & B Communications.

Washington

***SEATTLE**—American Telecasting Inc., Suite 300, 5575 Tech Center Dr., Colorado Springs, CO 80919-2351. Phone: 719-260-5533. Fax: 719-632-5549. County: King. ICA: WA0197.
Microwave channels reported: N.A.
Scheduled to begin: N.A.
Channel capacity: N.A.
Ownership: American Telecasting Inc. (MSO). Sale pends to Sprint Corp.

SPOKANE—Video Wave Television, 933 E. 3rd Ave., Spokane, WA 99202. Phone: 509-534-7500. Fax: 509-534-1266. E-mail: videowave@aol.com. Counties: Spokane & Stevens, WA; Kootenai, ID. Also serves Coeur d'Alene, Post Falls, ID; Airway Heights, Chattaroy, Cheney, Deer Park, Fairchild, Greenacres, Medical Lake, Rockford, WA. ICA: WA0190.
Microwave channels reported: N.A.
Began: N.A.
Channel capacity: 31 (not 2-way capable). Channels available but not in use: N.A.
Basic Service
Subscribers: 7,501.
Programming (received off-air): KWSU-TV (P) Pullman; KAYU-TV (F), KHQ-TV (N), KREM-TV (C), KSKN (U,W), KSPS-TV (P), KXLY-TV (A) Spokane.
Programming (via satellite): WGN-TV (W) Chicago; A & E; CNN; Cartoon Network; Country Music TV; Discovery Channel; ESPN; ESPN 2; EWTN; Fox Family Channel; Fox Sports Net Northwest; Headline News; Learning Channel; Lifetime; NASA TV; Nashville Network; Nickelodeon; Sci-Fi Channel; TBS Superstation; Turner Classic Movies; Turner Network TV; USA Network.
Current originations: Educational access.
Fee: $21.95 installation; $24.95 monthly.
Pay Service 1
Pay Units: 2,671.
Programming (via satellite): Cinemax.
Fee: $6.95 monthly.
Pay Service 2
Pay Units: 970.
Programming (via satellite): Disney Channel.
Fee: $6.95 monthly.
Pay Service 3
Pay Units: 3,176.
Programming (via satellite): HBO.
Fee: $7.95 monthly.
Pay-Per-View
Addressable homes: 7,501.
Action Pay-Per-View.
Fee: Varies.
Pay-per-view manager: Erica Buschhorn.
Equipment: Comwave headend; Comwave amplifiers; Times Fiber cable; Jerrold set top converters; Jerrold addressable set top converters.
Manager: Rene Wokich. Chief technician: Gerald Becker. Marketing director & customer service manager: Erica Buschhorn.
Ownership: Wireless Holdings Inc. (MSO).

YAKIMA—Wireless Broadcasting Systems of Yakima Inc., 1514 S. First St., Yakima, WA 98901. Phone: 509-248-9038. Fax: 509-575-4658. County: Yakima. ICA: WA0191.
Total homes in service area: 85,000.
Microwave channels reported: N.A.
Began: N.A.
Channel capacity: 24. Channels available but not in use: N.A.
Basic Service
Subscribers: 7,280.
Programming (received off-air): KAPP (A), KIMA-TV (C), KNDO (N), KYVE-TV (P) Yakima.
Programming (via satellite): WGN-TV (W) Chicago; A & E; CNN; Cartoon Network; Discovery Channel; ESPN; EWTN; Fox Family Channel; MTV; Nashville Network; Nickelodeon; QVC; Sci-Fi Channel; TBS Superstation; Turner Network TV; USA Network; Univision.
Fee: $9.95 installation; $27.95 monthly; $3.50 converter.
Pay Service 1
Pay Units: 400.
Programming (via satellite): Disney Channel.
Fee: N.A.
Pay Service 2
Pay Units: 800.
Programming (via satellite): HBO.
Fee: N.A.
Pay-Per-View
Special events.
Manager: Steve Pecaut. Chief technician: Lonnie Tomerline. Marketing & program director: Chris Scurio.
Ownership: Wireless Broadcasting Systems of America Inc.

Wisconsin

GREEN BAY—American Telecasting of Green Bay, 1861 Enterprise Dr., De Pere, WI 54115. Phone: 800-873-9277. County: Brown. ICA: WI0305.
Microwave channels reported: N.A.
Began: N.A.
Channel capacity: N.A. Channels available but not in use: N.A.
Basic Service
Subscribers: 3,000.
Programming (received off-air): WACY (U) Appleton; WBAY-TV (A), WFRV-TV (C), WGBA (N), WLUK-TV (F), WPNE (P) Green Bay.
Programming (via satellite): WGN-TV (W) Chicago; CNN; Discovery Channel; ESPN; Nashville Network; Nickelodeon; USA Network.
Fee: $14.95 installation; $21.95 monthly.
Pay Service 1
Pay Units: 1,200.
Programming (via satellite): HBO.
Fee: $11.00 monthly.
Pay Service 2
Pay Units: 2,000.
Programming (via satellite): Showtime.
Fee: $5.00 monthly.
Manager: Dennis Beaulieu. Chief technician: Tim Calnin.
Ownership: American Telecasting Inc. (MSO). Sale pends to Sprint Corp.

JANESVILLE—Wireless Cable Systems Inc., Suite 6107, 350 5th Ave., New York, NY 10118. Phone: 212-268-2828. Fax: 212-268-5675. County: Rock. ICA: WI0307.
Microwave channels reported: N.A.
Channel capacity: N.A.
Ownership: Wireless Cable Systems Inc.

MADISON—Skycable TV of Madison, 2520 Todd Dr., Madison, WI 53713. Phone: 608-271-6999. Fax: 608-271-2256. E-mail: kegan@skycabletv.com. Web site: http://www.skycabletv.com. Counties: Dane & Green. Also serves Green County. ICA: WI0306.
Total homes in service area: 250,000.
Microwave channels reported: WDU380, E group, MMDS; WHT772, F group, MMDS; WNTJ388, H1, MMDS; WNTJ432, H2, MMDS; WNTJ374, H3, MMDS; WHR-626, B-1-4, ITFS; WHR-671, G-1-4, ITFS.
Began: January 1, 1987.
Channel capacity: 31 (not 2-way capable). Channels available but not in use: 9.
Basic Service
Subscribers: 3,300.
Programming (received off-air): WHA-TV (P), WISC-TV (C), WKOW-TV (A), WMSN-TV (F), WMTV (N) Madison.
Programming (via satellite): WGN-TV (W) Chicago; A & E; CNN; Discovery Channel; ESPN; ESPN 2; Nashville Network; Nickelodeon; TBS Superstation; The Weather Channel; Turner Classic Movies; Turner Network TV; USA Network; VH1.
Current originations: Public access.
Fee: $25.00 installation; $19.95 monthly.
Pay Service 1
Pay Units: N.A.
Programming (via satellite): Cinemax; HBO (multiplexed).
Fee: $10.00 monthly (each).
Pay-Per-View
Addressable homes: 3,000.
Equipment: Jerrold set top converters.
Manager: Kim A. Egan. Chief technician: Doug Timmens. System manager: Carrie M. Freidig. Marketing director: Pat Whaley.
Ownership: Skycable TV of Madison LLC.

Wyoming

SHERIDAN—American Telecasting of Sheridan, Suite 11, 23 N. Scott St., Sheridan, WY 82801. Phone: 307-672-9781. Fax: 307-672-9782. Web site: http://www.amtele.com. County: Sheridan. ICA: WY0068.
Microwave channels reported: N.A.
Channel capacity: N.A. Channels available but not in use: N.A.
Ownership: American Telecasting Inc. (MSO). Sale pends to Sprint Corp.

Puerto Rico

SAN JUAN—WHTV Broadcasting Corp., 1409 Ponce de Leon Ave., Santurce, PR 00910. Phone: 787-722-7815. Fax: 787-721-0444. County: Puerto Rico. Also serves Aguas Buenas, Bayamon, Caguas, Carolina, Guaynabo, Rio Piedras, Trujillo Alto. Total homes in service area: 500,000. ICA: PR0016.
Microwave channels reported: WHT654, E group, MMDS; WHT655, F group, MMDS; WLX-315, C-1-4, ITFS; WLX-321, A-1-4, ITFS; WLX-322, D-1-4, ITFS; WLX-323, B-1-4, ITFS.
Began: January 1, 1987.
Channel capacity: 27. Channels available but not in use: N.A.
Basic Service
Subscribers: 6,000; Commercial subscribers: 60.
Programming (via satellite): WSBK-TV (U) Boston; WGN-TV (W) Chicago; WPIX (W) New York; CNN; Discovery Channel; Headline News; MTV; Nick at Nite; Nickelodeon; Primetime 24; TBS Superstation; Turner Network TV; USA Network.
Fee: $60.00 installation; $24.95 monthly.
Commercial fee: $39.95 monthly.
Pay Service 1
Pay Units: 1,259.
Programming (via satellite): Cinemax.
Fee: $10.00 monthly.
Pay Service 2
Pay Units: 992.
Programming (via satellite): Disney Channel.
Fee: $10.00 monthly.
Pay Service 3
Pay Units: 1,343.
Programming (via satellite): HBO.
Fee: $10.00 monthly.
Pay-Per-View
Special events.
Fee: $29.95.
Equipment: General set top converters.
Manager: Jose Sala. Chief technician: Ralph Diaz. Marketing & program director: Pedro Figueroa.
Ownership: WHTV Broadcasting Corp.

Cable System Franchises and Applications

Within system listings, franchises are noted with an asterisk (*); applications with a dagger (†).

CABLE FRANCHISES LISTED

CALIFORNIA

LOS TRANCOS WOODS—TCI Cablevision.

GEORGIA

CHAMBLEE—BellSouth.

ILLINOIS

DES PLAINES—Americast.
PROSPECT HEIGHTS—Americast.
SCHAUMBURG—Ameritech New Media Inc.
VALMEYER—WestCom.
VERNON HILLS—Americast.

MAINE

BELMONT (TOWN)—FrontierVision Partners LP.
DEDHAM (TOWN)—FrontierVision Partners LP.

MICHIGAN

CUB LAKE—Mid Lakes CableComm.
RIVERVIEW—Americast.

NEW HAMPSHIRE

JEFFERSON (TOWN)—FrontierVision Partners LP.

NEW YORK

SOUTH DAYTON (VILLAGE)—Hometown Cablevision.

OHIO

BRICE—Americast.
DUBLIN—Americast.
MADISON TWP. (FRANKLIN COUNTY)—Americast.
MARSEILLES—Paxton Cable.
NEW ROME—Americast.
PRAIRIE TWP.—Americast.
WESTLAKE—Americast.

VERMONT

ALBANY TWP.—FrontierVision Partners LP.
ALBURG TWP.—FrontierVision Partners LP.
BAKERSFIELD TWP.—FrontierVision Partners LP.
BARNARD TWP.—FrontierVision Partners LP.
BARNET TWP.—FrontierVision Partners LP.
BLOOMFIELD TWP.—FrontierVision Partners LP.
CABOT TWP.—FrontierVision Partners LP.
CHARLESTON TWP.—FrontierVision Partners LP.
COVENTRY TWP.—FrontierVision Partners LP.
EAST MONTPELIER TWP.—FrontierVision Partners LP.
FAIRFAX TWP.—FrontierVision Partners LP.
FAIRLEE TWP.—FrontierVision Partners LP.
FLETCHER TWP.—FrontierVision Partners LP.
GRAND ISLE TWP.—FrontierVision Parners LP.
GUILFORD TWP.—FrontierVision Partners LP.
HARTLAND TWP.—FrontierVision Partners LP.
IRASBURG TWP.—FrontierVision Partners LP.
JAMAICA TWP.—FrontierVision Partners LP.
LONDONDERRY TWP.—FrontierVision Partners LP.
LUNENBURG TWP.—FrontierVision Partners LP.
MIDDLETOWN SPRINGS TWP.—FrontierVision Partners LP.
NEWPORT TWP.—FrontierVision Partners LP.
ORWELL TWP.—FrontierVision Partners LP.
PEACHAM TWP.—FrontierVision Partners LP.
RUPERT TWP.—FrontierVision Partners LP.
RYEGATE TWP.—FrontierVision Partners LP.
STAMFORD TWP.—FrontierVision Partners LP.
THETFORD TWP.—FrontierVision Partners LP.
TOWNSHEND TWP.—FrontierVision Partners LP.
TROY TWP.—FrontierVision Partners LP.
WARDSBORO TWP.—FrontierVision Partners LP.
WESTFORD TWP.—FrontierVision Partners LP.
WESTMINSTER TWP.—FrontierVision Partners LP.
WINDHAM TWP.—FrontierVision Partners LP.

WASHINGTON

TACOMA—Tacoma City Light.

WISCONSIN

SAYNER—Northern Lights Cable Corp.

CABLE APPLICATIONS LISTED

None listed

Ownership of Cable Systems in the United States

Comprises all persons or companies with interest in cable systems, wireless cable systems or franchises. Ownership of all systems is assumed to be 100% unless otherwise noted.

ABC CABLE TV

1103 2nd St. W
Roundup, MT 59072
Phone: 406-323-2016
Ownership: Gary Toombs & Peggy Toombs, 100% jointly.
Cable Systems (1):
Montana: Lavina.
Total Basic Subscribers: 24.
Total Pay Units: 4.

A. D. MANAGEMENT INC.

Box 932
Fayette, AL 35555
Phone: 205-932-7264
Officers:
Joe D. Acker, Chmn., Pres. & Chief Exec. Officer
David Oswalt, Chief Financial Officer
Ownership: Joe D. Acker.
Represented (legal): Holder, Moore & Lawrence.
Cable Systems (5):
Alabama: Addison, Ashville, Good Hope, Hayden, Margaret.
Total Basic Subscribers: 7,100.
Total Pay Units: 3,000.

ADAMS CATV INC.

9 N. Main St.
Carbondale, PA 18407-2303
Phone: 717-282-6121
Fax: 717-282-3787
Officers:
Dorotha T. Adams, Pres.
Douglas V.R. Adams, V.P.
Ownership: Dorotha T. Adams.
Represented (legal): Cohen & Berfield PC.
Cable Systems (6):
New York: Windsor (town).
Pennsylvania: Carbondale, Forest City, Loomis Lake, New Milford Twp., Thompson Twp.
Total Basic Subscribers: 29,078 (0.04% of total cable households).
Total Pay Units: 3,200.

ADAMS TELCOM INC.

Box 248
Golden, IL 62339
Phone: 217-696-2701
Fax: 217-696-4811
Officers:
Dennis Cornwell, Pres.
Walter Rowland, Chief Operating Officer
Vern Lubker, V.P.
Bill Scranton, Secy.-Treas.
Ownership: Adams Telephone Cooperative Inc.
Cable Systems (1):
Illinois: Golden.
Total Basic Subscribers: 1,177.
Total Pay Units: 701.
Other Holdings:
Telephone.
Cellular radio.

ADELPHIA COMMUNICATIONS CORP.

Main @ Water St.
Coudersport, PA 16915-1141
Phones: 814-274-6273; 814-274-9830
Fax: 814-274-6372; 814-274-8631
Officers:
John J. Rigas, Chmn., Pres. & Chief Exec. Officer
Daniel Milliard, Sr. V.P. & Secy.
James Rigas, V.P., Strategic Development
Michael Rigas, V.P., Operations
Daniel Liberatore, V.P., Engineering
Orby Kelly, V.P., Human Resources
James R. Brown, V.P., Finance
Timothy Rigas, Chief Financial Officer
Ownership: John J. Rigas & family, 67%; remainder publicly held. The Rigas family owns the NHL's Buffalo Sabres.
Represented (legal): Buchanan Ingersoll PC; Fleischman & Walsh LLP.
Cable Systems (162):
Florida: Banyon Springs, Boca Raton, Brandon (portions), Chase Wood, Delray Beach, Forest Glen, Gator Trace, Golf Village, Greenacres City, Highland Beach, Indian Springs, Indiantown, Inverness, Kissimmee, Madeira Beach, Miami, Moon River, Orange County (portions), Osceola County (unincorporated areas), Palm Beach County, Palm Beach Gardens, Palm Chase, Palm Springs, Sand-n-Sea, St. Lucie West, Stuart, Tequesta, Woodfield.
Massachusetts: Falmouth, Marshfield, Martha's Vineyard, North Adams.
Michigan: Kalamazoo, Lawton, Pioneer.
New Hampshire: Alstead, Andover (town), Campton, Claremont, Cornish, Grantham, Greenville, Hinsdale, Milan (town), Peterborough.
New Jersey: Berkeley Twp., Crestwood Village.
New York: Branchport, Buffalo 66.7%, Dunkirk 66.7%, Evans (town) 66.7%, Gorham, Hammondsport, Lancaster (town) 66.7%, Niagara Falls, Olean, Penn Yan, Saranac Lake (resort), Silver Creek, Springville (village) 66.7%, Wellsville, Westfield 66.7%.
North Carolina: Ahoskie, Elizabeth City, Murfreesboro.
Ohio: Concord Twp. (Lake County) 66.7%, Conneaut 66.7%, Geneva 66.7%, Greenwood (village), Lorain 66.7%, Macedonia, Madison Twp. (Lake County) 66.7%, Mantua, Plymouth Twp. (Ashtabula County) 66.7%, Vermilion.
Pennsylvania: Adams Twp. (Cambria County), Aultman, Beaver Valley, Bethel Park, Blairsville, Coudersport, Du Bois, Dunmore, East Conemaugh, Freeport, Green Twp. (Indiana County), Harborcreek Twp. 66.7%, Kittanning, Lansdale, Mahaffey, Midway, Monroeville, Montgomery, Mount Oliver, Murrysville, Nanty Glo, New Bethlehem, New Castle, Portage, Punxsutawney, Robinson Twp. (Allegheny County), Rochester, Scranton, West Mifflin, West Newton.
South Carolina: Hilton Head Island.
Vermont: Bellows Falls, Bennington, Braintree, Brattleboro, Burlington, Fair Haven, Grafton, Killington, Manchester, Middlebury, Milton, Montpelier, Mount Ascutney, Newport, Pawlet, Pittsford, Reading, Richmond, Rochester, Rutland, Shelburne, Weston.
Virginia: Amherst County (southern portion), Blacksburg, Brookneal, Buena Vista, Charlottesville, Craigsville, Crozet, Danville, Dinwiddie, Emporia, Front Royal, Galax, Glasgow, Grundy, Harrisonburg, Independence, Keen Mountain, Lexington, Louisa, Luray, Lynchburg, Marion, Martinsville, McKenney, Pulaski, Richlands, Salem, Shenandoah, South Boston, South Hill, Staunton, Tazewell, Troutville 50.5%, Winchester.
Total Basic Subscribers: 2,304,325 (3.36% of total cable households).
Total Pay Units: 1,083,359.
Cable Holdings:
50% of St. Marys TV, see listing.
33.3% of MetroCast Cablevision of New Hampshire LLC, see listing.
Other Holdings:
Program source: Interest in Music Choice.

ADVANCED CABLE TECHNOLOGIES

5940 Zangs Dr.
San Antonio, TX 78238
Phone: 210-521-1500
Fax: 210-681-6239
Cable Systems (1):
Texas: Medina.
Total Basic Subscribers: 52.

ADVANCED TECHNOLOGIES & TECHNICAL RESOURCES INC.

380 E. 12th St.
Flora, IL 62839
Phone: 618-662-6038
Fax: 618-662-2499
Ownership: Jon Fopay.
Cable Systems (3):
Illinois: Iuka, Ste. Marie Twp., Willow Hill Twp.
Total Basic Subscribers: N.A.

ADVANCE/NEWHOUSE PARTNERSHIP

5015 Campuswood Dr.
East Syracuse, NY 13057
Phone: 315-463-7675
Cable Systems (187):
Alabama: Birmingham 33.33%, Eufaula 33.33%, Wetumpka 33.33%.
California: Avenal 33.33%, Bakersfield 33.33%, Barstow 33.33%, Canyon Country 33.33%, Coronado 33.33%, Palm Springs 33.33%, San Diego 33.33%, South Pasadena 33.33%, Taft 33.33%, Tehachapi 33.33%.
Florida: Apollo Beach 33.33%, Barefoot Bay 33.33%, Bradenton 33.33%, Century 33.33%, De Land 33.33%, Dunedin 33.33%, Geneva 33.33%, Homosassa 33.33%, Lakeland 33.33%, Marion Oaks 33.33%, Melbourne 33.33%, Orange County (southwestern portion) 33.33%, Orlando 33.33%, Ormond Beach 33.33%, Pinellas County 33.33%, Plant City (portions) 33.33%, Silver Springs 33.33%, Wildwood 33.33%, Winter Garden 33.33%, Winter Haven 33.33%.
Indiana: Carmel 33.33%, Hendricks County 33.33%, Indianapolis (portions) 33.33%.
Louisiana: Houma 33.33%, La Place 33.33%.
Massachusetts: Orange 33.33%, Pittsfield 33.33%.
Michigan: Farmington 33.33%, Livonia 33.33%, Redford 33.33%.
Nebraska: Auburn 33.33%, Columbus 33.33%, Fairbury 33.33%, Falls City 33.33%, Fremont 33.33%, Lincoln 33.33%, York 33.3%.
New Jersey: Palisades Park 33.33%.
New York: Albany 33.33%, Albion 33.33%, Alden 33.33%, Battenkill 33.33%, Binghamton 33.33%, Carthage 33.33%, Champlain 33.33%, Corning 33.33%, Elmira 33.33%, Fredonia (village) 33.33%, Fulton 33.33%, Geneva 33.33%, Glens Falls 33.33%, Ilion 33.33%, Ithaca 33.33%, Jamestown 33.33%, Malone 33.33%, Massena 33.33%, Mexico (village) 33.33%, Ogdensburg 33.33%, Oneida 33.33%, Oneonta 33.33%, Oswego 33.33%, Owego (village) 33.33%, Potsdam 33.33%, Rochester 33.33%, Rome 33.33%, Saratoga Springs 33.33%, Schenectady 33.33%, Stafford 33.33%, Syracuse 33.33%, Troy 33.33%, Walton (village) 33.33%, Whitney Point (village) 33.33%.
North Carolina: Albemarle 33.33%, Archdale 33.33%, Asheboro 33.33%, Belmont 33.33%, Bladenboro 33.33%, Burlington 33.33%, Carrboro 33.33%, Cary 33.33%, Chapel Hill 33.33%, Charlotte 33.33%, Cherry Point 33.33%, Cramerton 33.33%, Dobson 33.33%, Durham 33.33%, Farmville 33.33%, Fayetteville 33.33%, Garner 33.33%, Gastonia 33.33%, Goldsboro 33.33%, Greensboro 33.33%, Henderson 33.33%, High Point 33.33%, Jacksonville 33.33%, Kannapolis 33.33%, Kings Mountain 33.33%, Lumberton 33.33%, Mecklenburg 33.33%, Monroe 33.33%, Morehead City 33.33%, Raleigh 33.33%, Red Springs 33.33%, Reidsville 33.33%, Rockingham 33.33%, Salisbury 33.33%, Selma 33.33%, Shelby 33.33%, Southern Pines 33.33%, Wake Forest 33.33%, Whiteville 33.33%, Wilmington 33.33%, Wilson 33.33%, Winston-Salem 33.33%.
Ohio: Green Twp. (Hamilton County) 33.33%.
Pennsylvania: Montrose 33.33%, Sayre 33.33%.
South Carolina: Batesburg 33.33%, Clover 33.33%, Columbia 33.33%, Florence 33.33%, Kingstree 33.33%, Lake City 33.33%, Manning 33.33%, Myrtle Beach 33.33%, Orangeburg 33.33%, St. Matthews 66.67%, Sumter 33.33%, Surfside Beach 33.33%.
Texas: Austin 33.33%, Bartlett, Bastrop 33.33%, Beaumont 16.67%, Brownsville 16.67%, Columbus 16.67%, Commerce 16.67%, Coppell 16.67%, Crystal City 16.67%, Cuero 16.67%, Del Rio 16.67%, Eagle Pass 16.67%, El Paso 16.67%, Florence, Fort Hood 33.33%, Gonzales 16.67%, Graham 16.67%, Granada Hills 33.33%, Grapevine 16.67%, Greenville 16.67%, Harlingen 16.67%, Houston 16.67%, Irving 16.67%, Kerrville 16.67%, Killeen 33.33%, Kyle, Liberty 16.67%, Liberty Hill, Lockhart 33.33%, Luling 33.33%, Northeast Hays 33.3%, Orange 16.67%, Palestine 16.67%, Pearsall 16.67%, Pharr 16.67%, Port Arthur 16.67%, Rio Grande

City 16.67%, Roma 16.67%, Temple 33.33%, Thorndale 33.3%, Uvalde 16.67%, Waco 33.33%, Wichita Falls 33.33%, Yoakum 16.67%.
Wisconsin: Menomonee Falls 33.33%.
Total Basic Subscribers: 6,058,001 (8.84% of total cable households).
Total Pay Units: 2,736,748.
Cable Holdings:
Viewer's Choice, 33%.
Other Holdings:
Cable Network: 25% of Discovery Channel; interest in Viewer's Choice.
On Line Service: 9% of Road Runner.

ADVENT CHRISTIAN VILLAGE INC.

Hwy. 136
Dowling Park, FL 32060
Phone: 904-658-3333
Officer:
Tim Goyette, Dir., Operations
Cable Systems (1):
Florida: Advent Christian Village.
Total Basic Subscribers: 420.

ALASKAN CHOICE TELEVISION

Suite 100
1577 C St.
Anchorage, AK 99501
Phones: 907-263-9900; 907-263-9910
Fax: 907-263-9911
Officers:
Jim Hillyard, Chief Exec. Officer
Kate Giard, Chief Operating Officer
Steven R. Strait, V.P., Mktg.
Ownership: ATU Telecommunications, 33%; Goldbelt Inc. (see LPTV ownership), 33%; Viatek, 33%.
Wireless Cable Systems (2):
Alaska: Anchorage, Fairbanks.
Total Basic Subscribers: N.A.

ALBERT CITY COMMUNICATIONS INC.

Box 133
Albert, IA 50510
Phone: 712-843-2211
Fax: 712-843-5439
Ownership: John Hopkins & Al Romo, 100% jointly.
Cable Systems (1):
Iowa: Albert City.
Total Basic Subscribers: 253.
Total Pay Units: 97.

ALBION TELEPHONE CO.

Box 98
Hwy. 77
Albion, ID 83311
Phone: 208-673-5300
Ownership: Odeen Redman, Principal.
Cable Systems (1):
Idaho: Albion.
Total Basic Subscribers: 90.
Total Pay Units: 42.

ALEXCOM LTD. PARTNERSHIP

Suite 1701
745 5th Ave.
New York, NY 10151-0008
Phone: 212-421-9870
Fax: 212-688-3043
Officers:
Richard Treibick, Chmn. & Chief Exec. Officer
Rust Muirhead, Pres.
Rory Phillips, Sr. V.P., Finance
Wendell Dean, V.P., Operations
Yin Chan, V.P., Engineering
Amy Treibick Caplan, V.P., Mktg.
Represented (legal): Cole, Raywid & Braverman LLP.
Cable Systems (1):
Tennessee: Oak Ridge.
Total Basic Subscribers: 19,635 (0.03% of total cable households).
Total Pay Units: 7,372.

ALHAMBRA-GRANTFORK TELEHPONE CO.

Box 207
Alhambra, IL 62001
Phone: 618-488-2165
Cable Systems (1):
Illinois: Grantfork (village).
Total Basic Subscribers: 48.

ALL-TECH CATV CONSTRUCTORS INC.

5065 W. Homosassa Trail
Lecanto, FL 34461-9116
Phone: 904-621-0505
Officer:
Richard Jobe, Gen. Mgr.
Cable Systems (2):
Florida: Florida Highlands, Ozello.
Total Basic Subscribers: 427.
Total Pay Units: 72.

ALLEGHANY CABLEVISION INC.

Box 429
105 N. Main St.
Sparta, NC 28675
Phone: 336-372-5801
Ownership: George L. Sheets, Pres.
Cable Systems (1):
North Carolina: Sparta.
Total Basic Subscribers: 895.
Total Pay Units: 275.

ALLEN'S TV CABLE SERVICE INC.

Box 2643
611 Everett St.
Morgan City, LA 70381
Phone: 504-384-8335
Fax: 504-384-5243
Officers:
Gregory A. Price, Pres.
Chris Price, V.P.
Elizabeth Price, Secy.-Treas.
Ownership: Elizabeth Price & Gregory A. Price, 100% jointly.
Represented (legal): Cole, Raywid & Braverman LLP.
Cable Systems (6):
Louisiana: Arnaudville, Bayou l'Ourse, Grand Coteau, Morgan City, Pierre Part, Port Barre.
Total Basic Subscribers: 12,121 (0.02% of total cable households).
Total Pay Units: 3,400.

ALLTEL CORP.

1705 Lillian
Bolivar, MO 65613
Phone: 417-326-8000
Fax: 417-326-8439
Officer:
Barry Bishop, Area Mgr.
Ownership: Publicly held.
Cable Systems (2):
Missouri: Bolivar, Stockton.
Total Basic Subscribers: 3,595.
Total Pay Units: 710.
Other Holdings:
Telephone.

ALL WEST/UTAH INC.

Box 588
Kamas, UT 84036
Phone: 801-783-4371
Fax: 801-783-4928
Officers:
Carl Clark, Chmn. & Chief Exec. Officer
Vernile Prince, Pres.
Tony DiStefano, V.P., Operations
Lynne Pappas, V.P., Finance
Ownership: Carl Clark, Principal.
Cable Systems (3):
Utah: Kamas, Randolph.
Wyoming: Cokeville.
Total Basic Subscribers: 1,029.
Total Pay Units: 332.
Other Holdings:
Telephone.

ALPINE CABLE TELEVISION LC

Box 71604
Des Moines, IA 50325
Phone: 515-251-2659
Officer:
Mick Herke, Gen. Mgr.
Ownership: Alpine Communications. Also has telephone holdings.
Cable Systems (13):
Iowa: Arlington, Aurora, Clermont, Earlville, Garber, Greeley, Lamont, Lawler, Sherrill, St. Lucas, Volga, Wadena (village), Westgate (village).
Total Basic Subscribers: 924.

CITY OF ALTAMONT CABLE TV

Box 305
500 S. Huston
Altamont, KS 67330
Phone: 316-784-5612
Officer:
Lizabeth Finley, City Clerk
Ownership: Community owned.
Cable Systems (1):
Kansas: Altamont.
Total Basic Subscribers: 390.
Total Pay Units: 123.

ALTRO TV INC.

Box 9
Altro Rd.
Altro, KY 41306
Phones: 606-398-2282; 606-398-2360
Ownership: Clarence Gabbard, Pres. & Secy.-Treas.
Cable Systems (1):
Kentucky: Altro.
Total Basic Subscribers: 685.

AMERICABLE INTERNATIONAL INC.

Suite B130
10735 S.W. 216th St.
Miami, FL 33170
Phone: 305-256-6844
Fax: 305-256-3824
Officers:
Joan A. Hermanowski, Pres. & Chief Exec. Officer
William J. McCarthy, V.P. & Chief Operating Officer
Kim Hermanowski, V.P., Sales
Gary Babb, V.P., West Coast
Ownership: Joan A. Hermanowski, 51%; Charles C. Hermanowski, 29%; Joy A. Hermanowski, 5%; Jean A. Hermanowski, 5%; Kim E. Hermanowski, 5%; Charles A. Hermanowski, 5%.
Represented (legal): Kelly & Jackson; James E. Meyers.
Cable Systems (23):
Alabama: Chancellor.
Arizona: Cordes Lakes, Fort Mohave Mesa, Golden Shores, Golden Valley, Quartzsite (unincorporated areas).
California: Long Beach Naval Base, Moffett Field Naval Air Station, Petaluma Coast Guard Station, San Diego Naval Base, Vandenberg AFB.
Colorado: Peterson AFB, Pueblo Army Depot.
Florida: River Ranch, South Miami, Sunny Hills, Westville.
Hawaii: Bellows AFB.
Massachusetts: Fort Devens.
New Jersey: Lakehurst Naval Air Station.
New York: Fort Hamilton Army Base.
Ohio: Fort Recovery (village).
Puerto Rico: Ceiba Naval Base.
Total Basic Subscribers: 25,000 (0.04% of total cable households).
Total Pay Units: 9,000.

AMERICABLE USA INC.

3630 S. Main St.
Akron, OH 44319
Phone: 330-644-5459
Cable Systems (1):
Ohio: North Baltimore.
Total Basic Subscribers: 1,550.

AMERICAN CABLE ENTERTAINMENT

Suite 302
4 Landmark Square
Stamford, CT 06901
Phone: 203-323-1100
Fax: 203-325-3110
Officers:
Bruce A. Armstrong, Pres. & Chief Exec. Officer
Day Patterson, Sr. V.P. & General Counsel
Steven Fox, V.P., Engineering
Jerry Earl, V.P., Engineering
John M. Flanagan Jr., Chief Financial Officer
Ownership: Bruce A. Armstrong, Principal.
Represented (legal): Cole, Raywid & Braverman LLP.
Cable Systems (18):
Arkansas: Crossett, Fordyce.
California: Meyers.
Colorado: Cortez.
Louisiana: Jena, Marksville, Winnsboro.
Nebraska: Chadron, Crawford, Gordon.
New Mexico: Alamogordo, Carrizozo, High Rolls Mountain Park, Truth or Consequences.
North Dakota: Dickinson.
Ohio: Bellefontaine.
Texas: Harris County (northern portion).
Virginia: Radford.
Total Basic Subscribers: 108,302 (0.16% of total cable households).
Total Pay Units: 34,894.

AMERICAN CABLEVISION SERVICES INC.

900 Towne Center Dr.
Poinciana, FL 34759
Phone: 407-933-5308
Fax: 407-870-5006
Officers:
Dennis Getman, Pres.
Jeffrey Fashley, V.P.
Ownership: Avatar Holdings Inc.
Cable Systems (1):
Florida: Poinciana.

Total Basic Subscribers: 3,668.
Total Pay Units: 1,480.

AMERICAN TELECASTING INC.

Suite 300
5575 Tech Center Dr.
Colorado Springs, CO 80919
Phones: 719-260-5533; 800-225-1683
Fax: 719-260-5010; 719-260-5012
Officers:
Donald R. DePriest, Chmn.
Brian E. Gast, Pres. & Chief Exec. Officer
Richard F. Seney, Vice Chmn. & Secy.
Gary Jaeckel, V.P. Finance
David Sentman, Chief Financial Officer
Christopher Clark, Dir., Communications
Ownership: Charles Mauszycki, Principal.
Cable Systems (12):
Minnesota: Avoca, Bigelow, Chandler, Dundee, Iona, Leota, Magnolia, Reading.
South Dakota: Hudson, Lesterville, Monroe, Volin.
Wireless Cable Systems (35):
Alaska: Anchorage.
Arkansas: Little Rock.
California: Fresno, Merced, Monterey, Redding, Visalia, Yuba City.
Colorado: Colorado Springs, Denver, Fort Collins.
Florida: Daytona Beach, Jacksonville, Lakeland, Orlando.
Indiana: Michiana, South Bend.
Kansas: Wichita.
Michigan: Lansing.
Minnesota: Barnesville, Windom.
Montana: Billings.
Nebraska: Geneva, Grand Island, Lincoln.
Nevada: Las Vegas.
North Dakota: Fargo.
Ohio: Columbus, Toledo, Youngstown.
Oklahoma: Oklahoma City.
Oregon: Bend.
South Dakota: Rapid City.
Wisconsin: Green Bay.
Wyoming: Sheridan.
Planned Wireless Cable Systems (2):
Florida: Bradenton.
Washington: Seattle.
Total Cable Subscribers: 107,000 (0.16% of total cable households).
Total Pay Units: 34,987.
Other Holdings:
LPTV, MDS, MMDS, see listings.
ITFS.
Note: Sold to Sprint Corp. 1999.

AMERITECH NEW MEDIA INC.

18th Floor
300 S. Riverside Plaza
Chicago, IL 60606
Phone: 312-526-8000
Fax: 312-526-8565
Officer:
Ali Shadman, Pres.
Ownership: Publicly held.
Cable Systems (52):
Illinois: Arlington Heights, Elgin, Glen Ellyn, Glendale Heights, Naperville.
Michigan: Allen Park, Berkley, Canton Twp., Clawson, Clinton, Eastpointe, Ferndale, Fraser, Garden City, Huntington Woods, Lincoln Park, Madison Heights, Melvindale, Mount Clemens, Northville, Northville Twp., Pleasant Ridge, Plymouth, Plymouth Twp., Roseville, Royal Oak, Southgate, St. Clair Shores, Sterling Heights, Trenton, Troy, Utica, Warren, Wayne, Westland.
Ohio: Berea, Blendon Twp., Clinton Twp., Columbus, Fairview Park, Franklin Twp., Hilliard, Jackson Twp., Mifflin Twp., North Olmsted, Norwich Twp., Perry Twp., Riverlea, Sharon Twp., Upper Arlington, Valleyview, Worthington.
Cable Franchises (11):
Illinois: Des Plaines, Prospect Heights, Schaumburg, Vernon Hills.
Michigan: Riverview.
Ohio: Brice, Dublin, Madison Twp. (Franklin County), New Rome, Prairie Twp., Westlake.
Total Basic Subscribers: 250,000 (0.36% of total cable households).

AMERY TELECOM

116 N. Harriman Ave.
Amery, WI 54001
Phone: 715-268-7101
Ownership: Amery Telephone Co. Amery also owns Northwest Community Communications Inc., see listing.
Cable Systems (1):
Wisconsin: Somerset.
Total Basic Subscribers: 280.
Total Pay Units: 80.
Other Holdings:
Telephone.

AMHERST TELEPHONE CO.

Box 279
120 Mill St.
Amherst, WI 54406
Phone: 715-824-5529
Fax: 715-824-2050
Officers:
Carl F. Bohman, Pres.
Charles Iverson Jr., V.P.
Rita L. Danielson, Secy.-Treas.
Cable Systems (1):
Wisconsin: Amherst (village).
Total Basic Subscribers: 562.
Total Pay Units: 123.
Other Holdings:
Cellular radio.

AMRAC TELECOMMUNICATIONS LP

470 Totten Pond Rd.
Waltham, MA 02154
Phone: 617-890-9191
Fax: 617-890-6239
Officer:
David Slifka, Chief Financial Officer
Ownership: Sidney Whiting, Gen. Partner.
Represented (legal): Posternak, Blankstein & Lund.
Cable Systems (1):
Massachusetts: Belchertown.
Total Basic Subscribers: 4,679.
Total Pay Units: 1,400.

AMW CABLEVISION LP

912 N. Chrisman Ave.
Cleveland, MS 38732-2111
Phone: 601-846-5363
Cable Systems (7):
Mississippi: Benoit, Cary, Gunnison, Mayersville, Oakland, Pace, Winstonville.
Total Basic Subscribers: 573.

WILBUR L. ANDERSON

Box 2040
San Angelo, TX 76902
Phone: 915-884-3406
Fax: 915-655-1185
Cable Systems (2):
Texas: Big Lake, Hamilton 50%.
Total Basic Subscribers: 2,190.
Total Pay Units: 1,396.

ANDREW TELEPHONE CO. INC.

Box 510
Andrew, IA 52030
Phone: 319-672-3277
Officers:
Milton Cornelius, Pres.
Pat Cornelius, Secy.
Wilson Cornelius, Treas.
Cable Systems (1):
Iowa: Andrew.
Total Basic Subscribers: 121.
Total Pay Units: 33.

ANGOON CABLEVISION

Box 189
Angoon, AK 99820
Phone: 907-788-3653
Officer:
Dennis McGuire, Chief Operating Officer
Ownership: Community owned.
Cable Systems (1):
Alaska: Angoon.
Total Basic Subscribers: 85.

KEITH ANTCLIFF

Box 157
Dugway, UT 84022
Phone: 801-831-4404
Cable Systems (2):
Utah: Dugway.
Washington: Newport.
Total Basic Subscribers: 1,471.

ARAPAHOE TELEPHONE CO.

Box 300
Arapahoe, NE 68922-0300
Phone: 308-962-6060
Fax: 308-962-5373
Ownership: John Koller, Gen. Mgr.
Cable Systems (3):
Nebraska: Arapahoe, Elwood, Holbrook.
Total Basic Subscribers: 776.
Total Pay Units: 221.

ARK MO CABLE TV INC.

Box 70
Houston, MO 65483
Phone: 417-967-4422
Fax: 417-967-4840
Cable Systems (1):
Missouri: Rolla.
Total Basic Subscribers: N.A.

ARLINGTON TELEPHONE CO.

Box 400
1638 Lincoln St.
Blair, NE 68008
Phone: 402-533-1000
Fax: 402-426-6196
Officers:
Hugh W. Hunt, Chmn.
Richard A. Hunt, Vice Chmn.
Michael A. Jacobson, Pres. & Treas.
Michael A. Mines, V.P., Mktg.
Karen B. Aman, Secy.
Douglas L. Davidson, Chief Financial Officer
Ownership: Hugh W. Hunt & Richard A. Hunt.
Cable Systems (1):
Nebraska: Arlington.
Total Basic Subscribers: 348.
Total Pay Units: 170.
Other Holdings:
Cellular radio.

ARLINGTON TV COOPERATIVE INC.

Box 184
Arlington, OR 97812
Phone: 503-454-2707
Officers:
Richard Rende, Pres.
Steve Conlee, Chief Operating Officer
Della Foster, Secy.-Treas.
Ownership: Subscriber owned.
Cable Systems (1):
Oregon: Arlington.
Total Basic Subscribers: 170.
Total Pay Units: 71.

ARMSTRONG GROUP OF COMPANIES

One Armstrong Place
Butler, PA 16001
Phone: 724-283-0925
Fax: 724-283-2602
Officers:
Jay L. Sedwick, Chmn.
Dru A. Sedwick, Pres.
Kirby J. Campbell, Chief Executive Officer
William C. Stewart, Chief Operating Officer
A. Dean Busatto, V.P., Operations
Edgar E. Hassler Jr., V.P., Engineering
Jud D. Stewart, V.P., Mktg.
Bryan Cipoletti, Chief Financial Officer
Ownership: Armstrong Holdings.
Represented (legal): Ross & Hardies.
Cable Systems (17):
Kentucky: Boyd County, Greenup.
Ohio: Ashland, Austintown Twp., Boardman, Medina, Orrville, South Point.
Pennsylvania: Butler, California, Connellsville, Ellwood City, Grove City, Meadville, Oxford, Zelienople.
West Virginia: Hamlin.
Total Basic Subscribers: 201,981 (0.29% of total cable households).
Total Pay Units: 93,698.

CHARLES WINS ASHWORTH II

Box 1048
Littleton, NC 27850
Phone: 919-586-7156
Fax: 919-586-6997
Cable Systems (2):
Virginia: Jarratt, Lake Gaston.
Total Basic Subscribers: 720.
Total Pay Units: 146.
Other Holdings:
Cable construction: CWA Enterprises.

AT&T BROADBAND & INTERNET SERVICES

Box 5630
Denver, CO 80217-5630
Phones: 720-875-5500; 720-875-5659
Fax: 720-875-5389
Officers:
C. Michael Armstrong, Chmn., AT&T Corp.
Daniel Somers, Interim Pres.
Curt Hockemeier, Exec. V.P. & Chief Operating Officer, Telephony Operations
Lela Cocoros, Exec. V.P., Corporate Communications
LaRae Marsik, V.P., Media Relations
Ownership: AT&T Corp., publicly held; Microsoft, 3%.
Represented (legal): Sherman & Howard; Shea & Gould.
Cable Systems (1106):
Alabama: Auburn, Bay Minette, Center Point, Clanton, Elba, Fairfield, Fairhope, Florala, Hoover, Montgomery, Red Bay, Samson, Selma, Slocomb, Sylacauga, Troy.
Arizona: Douglas, Green Valley, Patagonia, Santa Rita Bel Aire, Willcox.
Arkansas: Ravenden, Walnut Ridge.

California: Adobe Wells Mobile Home Park, Alameda, Alturas, Burlingame, Camarillo, Cape Cod Mobile Home Park, Casa De Amigos Mobile Home Park, Colton, Concord, Daly City, Davis, East San Fernando Valley, Foster City, Franciscan Mobile Home Park, Fremont, Georgian Manor Mobile Home Park, Glenwood, Grass Valley, Hacienda Heights, Hayward, Hemet, Knightsen, Lake Wildwood, Los Gatos, Marin County (southeastern portion), Marsh Creek Motor Home Park, Merced, Milpitas, Mission Bay Mobile Home Park, Monterey, Mountain View, Napa, Newark, Newman, North Star, Oakland, Ojai, Oroville, Pacifica, Paradise Park, Perris, Petaluma, Pico Rivera, Pittsburg, Pleasant Hill, Rasnow, Redlands, Richmond, Rio Vista, San Bernardino, San Francisco, San Jose, San Mateo, Santa Clara, Santa Cruz, Saratoga, Sierra Madre, Sonora, South Lake Tahoe, South San Francisco, Spanish Ranch Mobile Home Park, Sunnyvale, Thousand Oaks, Tracy, Travis AFB, Tri-Valley, Twain Harte, Union City, Vacaville, Vallejo, Walnut Creek, Willow Ranch Mobile Home Park.

Colorado: Alamosa, Antonito, Aspen, Avon, Basalt, Bennett, Boulder, Brighton, Broomfield, Buena Vista, Canon City, Carbondale, Castle Rock, Colorado City, Columbine Valley, Craig, Del Norte, Delta, Denver, Dillon, Dolores, Dove Creek, Durango, Durango West, Empire, Evergreen, Fort Collins, Fort Morgan, Fowler, Frederick, Genesee, Glen wood Springs, Granby, Grand Junction, Greeley, Hayden, Highlands Ranch, Idaho Springs, Kremmling, La Junta, Lakewood, Lamar, Leadville, Manassa, Mancos, Manzanola, Meeker, Monte Vista, Montrose, New Castle, Nucla, Paonia, Penrose (unincorporated areas), Pueblo, Pueblo West, Rangely, Rifle, Rocky Ford, Roxborough Park, Salida, San Luis, Silt, Steamboat Springs, Sterling, Victor, Walden, Walsenburg, Wheat Ridge, Windsor, Winter Park.

Connecticut: Branford, Hartford, Sharon, Vernon.

District of Columbia: Washington.

Florida: Blountstown, Cantonment, Chattahoochee, Chipley, Fort Pierce, Hollywood, Islamorada, Kendall, Key Colony Beach, Key Largo, Key West, Little Torch Key, Margate, Miami, North Miami, Ocean Reef, Vero Beach.

Georgia: Albany, Americus, Ashburn, Bainbridge, Camilla, Columbus, Cordele, Dawson, Eastman, Enigma, Fitzgerald, Hazlehurst, Lakeland, Lenox, McRae, Moultrie, Nashville, Pearson, Sandersville, Sylvester, Thomasville, Tifton, Valdosta.

Idaho: Blackfoot, Boise, Burley, Caldwell, Fish Haven, Idaho Falls, Lewiston, Pocatello, Preston, Salmon, St. Anthony.

Illinois: Alton, Arlington Heights, Aurora, Barrington Hills, Batavia, Belleville, Belvidere, Bloomington, Breese, Bushnell, Cahokia, Campton Twp., Canton, Carbondale, Carlyle, Carpentersville, Carthage, Casey, Charleston, Chicago (area 1) 45%, Chicago (area 4), Chicago (area 5) 80%, Chicago Heights, Coal Valley, Custer Park, Danville, De Kalb, Decatur, Dixon, East Dubuque, East St. Louis 80%, Effingham, Elgin, Galena, Galesburg, Glendale Heights, Glenview, Great Lakes Naval Training Center, Greenup, Hanover, Harrisburg, Harvard, Harvey, Herrin, Herscher, Highland Park, Homer, Kankakee, La Harpe, Ladd, Lake Holiday, Lake Zurich, Lansing, Lewistown, Libertyville, Lisle, Louisville, Macomb, Marion, Martinsville, Matteson, Mattoon, Maywood, McHenry, Mendota, Millington, Minooka, Moline, Monmouth, Morris, Mount Prospect, Mount Pulaski, Naperville, Neoga, Newman, Niantic, North Utica, Oak Forest, Oak Lawn, Onarga, Oregon, Orland Park, Palos Hills, Park Forest, Peoria, Peru, Piper City, Plano, Princeton, Ridge Farm, Robbins, Rock Island, Sangamon County, Schaumburg, Scott AFB, Skokie, South Holland, Springfield, Sterling, Strasburg, Streamwood, Urbana, Villa Park, Waukegan, West Chicago, Western Springs, Wilmington, Windsor, Woodstock.

Indiana: Alexandria 50%, Anderson 50%, Attica 50%, Bedford 50%, Bloomfield 50%, Bloomington 50%, Boonville 50%, Bristol, Dublin 50%, Elkhart, Elwood 50%, Evansville 50%, Fort Branch 50%, Franklin 50%, Gary, Greencastle 50%, Greenfield 50%, Greensburg 50%, Hammond, Hartford City 50%, Hebron, Jasper 50%, Jefferson Twp. (Elkhart County), Jeffersonville 50%, Kokomo 50%, La Porte, Lafayette 50%, Lake of the Four Seasons, Lebanon 50%, Linton 50%, Lynn 50%, Martinsville 50%, Merrillville, Michigan City, Middlebury, Monroe County (portions), Mount Vernon 50%, New Castle 50%, Noblesville 50%, Owensville 50%, Portage, Poseyville 50%, Princeton 50%, Richmond 50%, Salem 50%, South Bend, Sullivan 50%, Wa karusa, Winchester 50%.

Iowa: Ackley, Adel, Albia, Algona, Ames, Asbury, Atalissa, Atlantic, Audubon, Avoca, Bedford, Belle Plaine, Blakesburg, Bloom field, Boone, Burlington, Bussey, Carroll, Cascade, Cedar Falls, Cedar Rapids, Cen terville, Chariton, Charles City, Cherokee, Clare, Clarinda, Clarion, Clinton, Colfax, Columbus Junction, Conesville, Corning, Cory don, Creston, Davis City, Decatur, Delta, Denison, Denmark, Des Moines, Dexter, Drakesville, Dubuque, Dyersville, Eddyville, Eldon, Eldora, Fairfield, Forest City, Fort Dodge, Fort Madison, Garner, Glenwood, Granger, Greenfield, Grinnell, Grundy Center, Guthrie Center, Hampton, Harlan, Hawarden, Hills, Humboldt, Independence, Indianola, Iowa City, Iowa Falls, Jefferson, Kellerton, Keokuk, Keswick, Knoxville, Lamoni, Laurens, Lavinia, Le Mars, Leon, Lisbon, Madrid, Maquoketa, Marengo, Marshalltown, Mason City, Melcher, Monroe, Morning Sun, Moulton, Mount Ayr, Mount Pleasant, Muscatine, Newton, North Liberty, Northwood, Oelwein, Osage, Osceola, Oskaloosa, Ottumwa, Oxford, Parkersburg, Pella, Perry, Pleasantville, Pocahontas, Pulaski, Red Oak, Reinbeck, Sheldahl, Shenandoah, Solon, Storm Lake, Story City, Swisher, Toledo, Traer, Villisca, Vinton, Wapello, Washington, Waterloo, Waverly, Webster City, West Branch, Wilton, Winterset.

Kansas: Arma, Beattie, Caney, Cherryvale, Chetopa, Erie, Fredonia, Garnett, Greenleaf, Hanover, Humboldt, Linn, Maple Hill, Marysville, Yates Center.

Kentucky: Dawson Springs 50%, Henderson 50%, Providence 50%.

Louisiana: Baker, Baton Rouge, Bossier City 20%, Denham Springs, Donaldsonville, Erwinville, Gonzales, Gramercy, Lake Charles 20%, Plaquemine, Port Allen, Rosedale, St. Gabriel, Sulphur 20%, White Castle.

Maryland: Baltimore, Elkton, Lexington Park, Ocean City.

Michigan: Adrian, Battle Creek, Burt, Cassopolis, Chesaning, Clarkston, Commerce Twp., Devils Lake, East Lansing, Edwardsburg, Elsie, Fennville, Fremont, Grand Rapids, Lake Orion, Montrose, Muskegon, Niles, Royal Oak, South Haven, St. Joseph Twp., Thetford Twp., Three Oaks, Woodhaven.

Minnesota: Aitkin, Albany, Babbitt, Benson, Blue Earth, Browerville, Browns Valley, Crookston, Ely, Glenwood, Kerkhoven, Little Falls, Littlefork, Long Prairie, Melrose, Ortonville, Osakis, Park Rapids, Rollingstone, Sauk Centre, Staples, Tower.

Mississippi: Hattiesburg 33.33%.

Missouri: Arnold, Centralia, Columbia, Ferguson 66.67%, Hannibal, Hermann, Holts Summit, Jefferson City, Louisiana, Mexico, Moberly, Monroe City, Springfield, St. Charles, St. Louis, St. Louis County, Tarkio.

Montana: Anaconda, Billings, Boulder, Bozeman, Broadus 10%, Butte, Cascade, Chinook, Choteau, Conrad, Cut Bank, Deer Lodge, Dillon, Fairfield, Fort Benton, Glasgow, Glendive, Great Falls, Hamilton, Harlem, Havre, Helena, Kalispell, Lewistown, Livingston, Malmstrom AFB, Malta, Manhattan, Miles City, Missoula, Montana City, Opportunity, Polson, Shelby, Sidney, Stevensville, Terry, Thompson Falls, Townsend, Wolf Point.

Nebraska: Adams, Bayard, Bridgeport, Broken Bow, Cortland, Firth, Kimball, Lexington, McCook, Minatare, Mitchell, Morrill, Shelton, St. Paul, Talmage.

Nevada: Battle Mountain, Carlin, Carson City, Crystal Bay, Dayton, Elko, Fallon, Fernley, Gardnerville, Hawthorne, Lockwood, Reno, Silver Springs, Sparks City, Spring Creek, Washoe County, Wells.

New Jersey: Avalon, Gloucester, Long Beach Twp., Maple Shade Twp., Wildwood.

New Mexico: Cimarron, Clovis 20%, Eunice, Farmington, Gallup, Jal, Las Cruces, Raton, Red River, Santa Fe, Springer.

New York: Buffalo 33.3%, Camden, Dunkirk 33.3%, Evans (town) 33.3%, Lancaster (town) 33.3%, Leyden, Lowville, Rhinebeck (town), Springville (village) 33.3%, Watertown 33%, Westfield 33.3%.

North Dakota: Arvilla, Bismarck 50%, Cavalier Air Force Station, Forest River, Gilby, Grand Forks, Grand Forks AFB, Lakota, Larimore, Manvel, Minot, Minto, Wahpeton, Williston.

Ohio: Adena, Amsterdam, Barnesville, Bazetta Twp., Bellaire, Belmont, Bridgeport, Cadiz, Carrollton, Concord Twp. (Lake County) 33.3%, Conneaut 33.3%, East Liverpool, East Palestine, Fairfield Twp. (Butler County), Flushing, Freeport Twp., Geneva 33.3%, Glencoe, Golf Manor, Hopedale, Irondale, Jewett, Leesville, Lorain 33.3%, Madison Twp. (Lake County) 33.3%, Marietta, Martins Ferry, Minerva, Newton Falls, Plymouth Twp. (Ashtabula County) 33.3%, Port William, Salineville, Scio, Sebring, Shadyside, Springfield Twp. (Mahoning County), St. Clairsville, Steubenville, Tappen Lake, Wilmington.

Oklahoma: Bixby, Claremore, Coweta, Tulsa.

Oregon: Adams, Baker, Beaverton, Burns, Corvallis, Eugene, Hermiston, Lakeview, Lebanon, Milton-Freewater, Milwaukie, Newberg, Portland, Salem, St. Helens, Sweet Home, Union, Weston, Yachats.

Pennsylvania: Aliquippa, Baden, Beaver Falls, Bedford, Berlin Borough, Bethel, Bigler Twp., Canonsburg, Carnegie, Carrolltown Borough, Castle Shannon, Central City Borough, Clarion Borough, Clinton Twp. (Lycoming County), Coraopolis, Curtin Twp., Darlington Twp. (Beaver County), East Hills, Elderton Borough, Elizabethtown, Gallitzin Twp., Glassport, Greensburg, Hamburg, Harborcreek Twp. 33.3%, Hyndman Borough, Kane, Kiskiminetas Twp., Lebanon, Levittown, Lewistown, Limestone Twp. (Lycoming County), Lock Haven 20%, McDonald, McKees Rocks, McKeesport, Midland, Mon Valley, Mount Morris, Oil City, Philipsburg Borough, Pittsburgh, Pottsville, Reading, Ridgway Borough, Rose Twp., Ross Twp. (Allegheny County), Rural Valley, Saltsburg, Shippingport Borough, Shirley Twp., Smethport, Somerset Borough, South Fork, Spring Twp. (Crawford County), St. Petersburg, State College, Toby Twp., Towanda, Tyrone, Washington, Waynesburg, West Wheatfield Twp. (Indiana County).

South Dakota: Belle Fourche, Black Hawk, Brookings 50%, Custer, Deadwood, Hot Springs, Madison, Milbank, Mitchell 50%, Mobridge, Rapid City, Rosholt, Sioux Falls 50%, Sisseton, Spearfish, Sturgis, Watertown, Wilmot.

Texas: Abilene 20%, Alice, Allen, Alton 50%, Amarillo 20%, Andrews 20%, Arlington, Asherton 50%, Athens 20%, Ballinger 20%, Beaumont 50%, Bedford, Beeville, Benavides, Big Spring 20%, Bishop, Brownsville 50%, Bruni, Carrollton, Charlotte 50%, Columbus 50%, Commerce 50%, Coppell 50%, Corpus Christi, Cotulla 50%, Crystal City 50%, Cuero 50%, Dalhart 20%, Dallas, De Kalb 20%, De Soto, Del Rio 50%, Dilley 50%, Eagle Lake 50%, Eagle Pass 50%, Edcouch 50%, El Paso 50%, Encinal 50%, Falfurrias, Farmers Branch, Flower Mound, Floydada 20%, Freer, Gainesville 20%, Garland, George West, Gladewater 20%, Gonzales 50%, Graham 50%, Grand Prairie, Grapevine 50%, Greenville 50%, Harlingen 50%, Hebbronville, Henderson 20%, Hidalgo 50%, Honey Grove 20%, Hooks 20%, Houston 50%, Irving 50%, Jacksonville 20%, Kerrville 50%, La Coste, La Grulla 50%, Lakehills, Lancaster, Leon Springs, Lewisville 50%, Liberty 50%, Los Fresnos 50%, Mathis, Maud 20%, McKinney, Mesquite, Miles 20%, Mineola 20%, Mineral Wells 20%, Mount Pleasant 20%, Mount Vernon 20%, New Boston 20%, Oilton, Orange 50%, Orange Grove, Palestine 50%, Paris 20%, Pearsall 50%, Perryton 20%, Pharr 50%, Pittsburg 20%, Plainview 20%, Plano, Port Arthur 50%, Port Isabel 50%, Port O'Connor, Poteet 50%, Premont, Quemado 50%, Raymondville 50%, Refugio, Rio Grande City 50%, Rockwell 20%, Roma 50%, San Angelo 20%, San Patricio, San Ygnacio, Seadrift, Seguin, Snyder 20%, Somerset, South Padre Island 50%, Stockdale, Stonebridge Ranch, Sullivan City 50%, Sulphur Springs 20%, Sweetwater 20%, The Colony, Tyler 20%, Uvalde 50%, Weslaco 50%, Whitesboro 20%, Winters 20%, Wylie, Yoakum 50%, Zapata.

Utah: Bear River City, Brigham City, Cedar City, Coalville, Delta, Farmington, Fielding, Fruit Heights, Grantsville, Heber City, Hooper, Lewiston, Morgan City, Morgan County, Nephi, Park City, Provo, Richmond, Riverdale, Salem, Salt Lake City, Sandy, Stansbury Park, Tooele, Tremonton, Vernal, Wendover, West Valley City, Willard.

Virginia: Culpeper, Orange.

Washington: Aberdeen, Anacortes, Arlington, Auburn, Bellingham, Blaine, Bremerton, Burlington, Centralia-Chehalis, Cle Elum, Clinton, Coupeville, Dixie, Elmer, Ferndale, Freeland, Grand Coulee, Grandview, Leavenworth, Lynden, Maple Falls, McChord Air Force Base, Mineral, Montesano, Mossyrock, Nespelem, Olympia, Omak, Oroville, Poulsbo, Prescott, Raymond, Redmond, Rochester, Ruston, Ryderwood, Seattle, Shelton, Spokane 99%, Starbuck, Sudden Valley, Tacoma, Tonasket, Toppenish, Vancouver, Waitsburg, Washtucna, Westport, Winlock.

West Virginia: Chester, Fork Ridge, Moundsville, New Cumberland, Parsons, Romney, St. Marys, Weirton, Wellsburg, Wheeling.
Wisconsin: Fountain City, Genoa City, Sharon.
Wyoming: Buffalo, Casper, Cheyenne, Cody, Gillette, Greybull, Jackson, Lander, Laramie, Moorcroft, Newcastle, Powell, Rawlins, Reno Junction, Riverton, Sheridan, Thermopolis, Upton, Worland.
Puerto Rico: Arecibo, Barranquitas, Caguas, Cayey, Humacao, Luquillo, Vega Baja.
Cable Franchises (1):
California: Los Trancos Woods.
Wireless Cable Systems (1):
Texas: Roma.
Total Basic Subscribers: 10,843,000 (15.82% of total cable households).
Total Pay Units: 10,678,000.
Cable Holdings:
Bresnan Communications Co. LP (50%), see listing; Cablevision Systems Corp. (25%), see listing; Falcon Communications LP (46%), see listing; Kansas City Cable Partners (50%), see listing; Lenfest Communications Inc. (50%), see listing; Susquehanna Cable Co. (through Lenfest Communications Inc.), see listing; AT&T also has interest in Videopole, French cable co.; TeleWest Communications Group Ltd., United Kingdom cable operator; CableVision of Buenos Aires; Bresnan International Partners LP (Poland); HKP Partners of New Zealand., Pacific Communications Inc, cable sales & video production co.; Compania de Telecomunicaciones de Chile (largest Chilean MSO).
Other Holdings:
Broadcast holdings: Minority interest in News Corp., owner of Fox Television Stations Inc., see listing.
Program source (through subsidiary New Liberty Media Group): BET Holdings (35%), Discovery (49%), Encore Media, QVC (43%), TCI Music (86%), Telemundo (50%), Time Warner/Turner Programming (9%), USA Networks (21%).
Common Carrier: Southern Satellite Systems (CC).
Telecommunications company: 30% of Teleport Communications Group; Cable Adnet Inc. (cable ad sales representative), Jupiter Telecommunications Co. Ltd. (Asia & Australia).
Manufacturer: Owns 49% of TSX Corp.

ATC CABLEVISION INC.
Box 248
Ayrshire, IA 50515
Phone: 712-426-2815
Officer:
John Higgins, Pres.
Ownership: Ayrshire Farmers Mutual Telephone Co.
Cable Systems (4):
Iowa: Ayrshire, Cylinder, Gillett Grove, Whittemore.
Total Basic Subscribers: 384.
Total Pay Units: 94.

ATKINS TELEPHONE CO.
Box 157
85 Maine Ave.
Atkins, IA 52206
Phone: 319-446-7331
Fax: 319-446-9100
Cable Systems (1):
Iowa: Atkins.
Total Basic Subscribers: 283.
Total Pay Units: 96.

ATLANTIC TELEPHONE MEMBERSHIP CORP.
Box 3198
620 Whiteville Rd. NW
Shallotte, NC 28459
Phone: 919-754-4311
Fax: 919-754-5499
Officers:
Carol Danford, Pres.
Russell Price, Chief Operating & Financial Officer
Cable Systems (1):
North Carolina: Shallotte.
Total Basic Subscribers: 15,039 (0.02% of total cable households).
Total Pay Units: 5,511.
Other Holdings:
Telephone.

ATWOOD CABLE SYSTEMS INC.
423 State St.
Atwood, KS 67730
Phone: 913-626-3261
Fax: 913-626-9005
Officers:
Harold Dunker, Pres.
Robert J. Dunker, V.P.
Craig H. Dunker, Secy.-Treas.
Ownership: Harold Dunker.
Cable Systems (1):
Kansas: Atwood.
Total Basic Subscribers: 520.
Total Pay Units: 89.

AVALON CABLE
Suite 3100
800 3rd Ave.
New York, NY 10022
Phone: 212-421-0600
Fax: 212-421-1742
Officers:
David W. Unger, Chmn.
Joel C. Cohen, Pres. & Chief Exec. Officer
Ownership: ABRY Partners Inc., principal investor.
Cable Systems (86):
Connecticut: Winsted.
Massachusetts: Charlton, Hinsdale, Lanesboro, West Stockbridge.
Michigan: Allegan, Allendale, Ashley, Baldwin, Barryton, Bear Lake, Benona Twp., Big Prairie Twp., Big Star Lake, Billings, Bingham Twp. (Clinton County), Broomfield Valley Trailer Park, Cadillac, Caro, Carson City, Cass City, Chester Twp. (Ottawa County), Coldwater, Country Acres, Custer, Delton, Durand, Evart, Fife Lake, Fine Lake, Fowler, Garfield Twp. (Clare County), Gilmore Twp. (Isabella County), Gladwin, Grand Lake, Grant, Grayling, Greenville, Hamlin Twp. (Mason County), Harrison, Higgins Lake, Houghton Lake, Howard City, Indian River, Ionia, Johnstown Twp., Kaleva (village), Lake George, Lakeview, Lapeer, Mancelona, Manistee, Manton, Maple Rapids, Marion, McBain, Mecosta, Mesick, Middleville/Caledonia, Monroe, Montague, Nashville, Pellston, Pentwater, Perrinton, Posen, Reed City, Remus, Riverdale, Rockford, Rogers City, Roscommon, Rutland Twp., Sanford, Skidway Lake, St. Helen, Standish, Stanton, Surrey Twp., Traverse City, Vassar, Weidman, West Branch, Whitehall, Woodland (village).
New York: Chatham.
Total Basic Subscribers: 260,000 (0.38% of total cable households).
Note: Sold to Charter Communications Inc.

AVENUE TV CABLE SERVICE INC.
Box 1458
1954 E. Main St.
Ventura, CA 93002-1458
Phone: 805-643-9971
Fax: 805-643-1284
Officers:
John G. George, Pres.
Stephen J. George, V.P.
N. Fern George, Secy.-Treas.
Ownership: John G. George.
Represented (legal): Baraff, Koerner & Olender PC.
Cable Systems (2):
California: New Cuyama, Ventura.
Total Basic Subscribers: 11,010 (0.02% of total cable households).
Total Pay Units: 2,747.

BAGLEY PUBLIC UTILITIES
Box M
18 Main Ave. S
Bagley, MN 56621
Phone: 218-694-2300
Fax: 218-694-6632
Officers:
Dave Lee, Chmn.
Hank Dewey, Secy.-Treas.
Michael Monsrud, Superintendent
Ownership: Community owned.
Cable Systems (1):
Minnesota: Bagley.
Total Basic Subscribers: 558.
Total Pay Units: 203.

BAHAKEL COMMUNICATIONS LTD.
Box 32488
Charlotte, NC 28232
Phone: 704-372-4434
Fax: 704-335-9904; 704-375-5890
Officers:
Cy N. Bahakel, Pres.
Beverly Bahakel Poston, Exec. V.P.
Cullie Tarleton, V.P., Television
Steve Bahakel, V.P., Radio
Russell Schwartz, V.P., Business Affairs & Gen. Counsel
Stan Dyl, Chief Financial Officer
Ownership: The Cy N. Bahakel Revocable Trust.
Represented (legal): Fleischman & Walsh LLP.
Cable Systems (13):
Virginia: Appomattox, Blackstone, Crewe, Timberlake.
West Virginia: Craigsville, Fanrock, Herndon, Hotchkiss, Mullens, Oakvale, Oceana, Pineville, Ravencliff.
Total Basic Subscribers: 17,497 (0.03% of total cable households).
Total Pay Units: 2,359.
Other Holdings:
TV, see listing.
Radio holdings: Radio stations.

BAILEY CABLE TV INC.
807 Church St.
Port Gibson, MS 39150
Phone: 601-437-8300
Ownership: David A. Bailey.
Cable Systems (6):
Louisiana: Angola, St. Francisville.
Mississippi: Crystal Springs, Hazlehurst, Magee, Mendenhall.
Total Basic Subscribers: 4,262.
Total Pay Units: 1,854.

LEON M. BAILEY JR.
Box 368
115 N. Main St.
Ripley, MS 38663
Phone: 601-837-4881
Cable Systems (1):
Mississippi: Ripley.
Total Basic Subscribers: 3,389.
Total Pay Units: 1,130.

BAKER CABLEVISION
Box 4
Baker, CA 92309
Phone: 760-733-4560
Cable Systems (1):
California: Baker.
Total Basic Subscribers: 100.

BALDWIN TELECOM INC.
930 Maple St.
Baldwin, WI 54002
Phone: 715-684-3346
Fax: 715-684-4747
Officer:
Bill Hawley, Pres.
Ownership: Publicly held.
Cable Systems (2):
Wisconsin: Baldwin (village), Knapp (village).
Total Basic Subscribers: 1,550.
Total Pay Units: 780.
Other Holdings:
Telephone.
Cellular radio.

HEATHER BALOCK
Box 252
Melstone, MT 59054
Phone: 406-358-2200
Cable Systems (2):
Montana: Melstone 50%, Twin Bridges 25%.
Total Basic Subscribers: 163.
Total Pay Units: 132.

JOHN BALOCK JR.
Box 252
Melstone, MT 59054
Phone: 406-358-2200
Cable Systems (2):
Montana: Melstone 50%, Twin Bridges 25%.
Total Basic Subscribers: 163.
Total Pay Units: 132.

B & C CABLE
Box 548
Norwood, CO 81423
Phones: 970-327-4000; 970-327-4521
Fax: 970-327-4080
Officers:
Craig Greager, Pres.
Mediatrica Greager, V.P.
Ownership: Craig Greager, 50%; Mediatrica Greager, 50%.
Cable Systems (1):
Colorado: Norwood.
Total Basic Subscribers: 145.
Total Pay Units: 68.

B & C CABLEVISION INC.
4683 Hwy. 6
Wiggins, CO 80654
Phone: 970-483-7820
Fax: 970-483-7822
Officers:
Carol Rogers, Pres.
Bill Rogers, Secy.-Treas.
Ownership: Bill Rogers & Carol Rogers, Principals.

Cable Systems (5):
Colorado: Arriba, Kit Carson, Merino, Seibert.
Wyoming: Burns.
Total Basic Subscribers: 296.
Total Pay Units: 100.

B & L COMMUNICATIONS
Box 970
Andalusia, AL 36420
Phone: 334-222-6110
Fax: 334-222-2159
Officers:
Chris Alexander, Pres.
Maurice Rabren, V.P.
Linda Rabren, Secy.-Treas.
Allen Sharp, Asst. Secy.

Branch Office:
Box 580
Orangeville, UT 84537
Phone: 801-748-2345
Ownership: Chris Alexander, Linda Rabren, Maurice Rabren & Allen Sharp, Principals.
Represented (legal): Mark Murphy; David Green.
Cable Systems (11):
Alabama: Beatrice, Castleberry, Hayneville, Heath, McKenzie, Red Level, Selbrook.
Florida: Baker, Milton (eastern portion).
Utah: Cleveland, Escalante.
Total Basic Subscribers: 4,658.
Total Pay Units: 1,809.
Other Holdings:
SMATV.

BARBOURVILLE UTILITY COMMISSION
Box 1600
Barbourville, KY 40906
Phone: 606-546-4127
Fax: 606-546-4848
Officers:
Randall Young, Superintendent
Wilhem Brewer, Asst. Superintendent
Ownership: Community owned.
Cable Systems (1):
Kentucky: Barbourville.
Total Basic Subscribers: 2,700.
Total Pay Units: 338.

CITY OF BARDSTOWN
Box 368
220 N. 5th St.
Bardstown, KY 40004
Phone: 502-348-9711
Fax: 502-348-2433
Officers:
Henry S. Spalding, Mayor & Chief Exec. Officer.
Lawrence A. Hamilton, City Administrator & Chief Operating Officer
Lonnie G. Parrott, City Clerk & Chief Financial Officer
Ownership: Community owned.
Cable Systems (1):
Kentucky: Bardstown.
Total Basic Subscribers: 7,209.
Total Pay Units: 1,475.

JERRY BARNES
218 Main St.
Oriskany Falls, NY 13425
Phone: 315-821-7225
Cable Systems (1):
New York: Oriskany Falls.
Total Basic Subscribers: 1,220.

CITY OF BARNESVILLE
Box 550
Barnesville, MN 56514
Phone: 218-354-7671
Cable Systems (1):
Minnesota: Barnesville.
Total Basic Subscribers: 550.
Total Pay Units: 63.

BARRETT'S TV CABLE SYSTEM
Box 197
RD 1
Troy, PA 16947
Phone: 717-297-3607
Ownership: Joseph K. Barrett.
Cable Systems (2):
Pennsylvania: Big Pond, West Burlington Twp.
Total Basic Subscribers: 70.

BARROW CABLE TV
Box 489
1230 Agvik St.
Barrow, AK 99723
Phones: 907-852-5511; 907-852-8633
Fax: 907-852-5510
Officers:
Glenn R. Edwards, Pres. & Chief Operating Officer
Thomas Leavitt, V.P.
Mike Stotts, Secy.-Treas.
Ownership: Arctic Slope Regional Corp.
Cable Systems (1):
Alaska: Barrow.
Total Basic Subscribers: 1,127.
Total Pay Units: 800.
Other Holdings:
SMATV.

KEN BARTLETT
503 N. Logan
Danville, IL 61832
Phone: 217-442-0751
Fax: 217-442-0866
Cable Systems (1):
Illinois: Longview.
Total Basic Subscribers: 40.

BASCO ELECTRONICS INC.
420 W. 2nd St.
Weston, WV 26452
Phone: 304-269-7530
Officers:
Wilfred L. Sholes, Pres.
Virginia Sue Sholes, Secy.-Treas.
Ownership: Virginia Sue Sholes & Wilfred L. Sholes, 100% jointly.
Represented (legal): Hogan & Hartson LLP.
Cable Systems (4):
West Virginia: Alum Bridge, Broad Run, Ireland, Salem College.
Total Basic Subscribers: 991.
Total Pay Units: 202.

BASE CABLEVISION INC.
Box 710
Farmington, MO 63640-0710
Phone: 314-756-8616
Fax: 314-756-0123
Officers:
Larry V. Jones, Acting Pres.
John Scott, Secy.
Gerald Gamble, Treas.
Cable Systems (1):
Missouri: Hornersville.
Total Basic Subscribers: 229.
Total Pay Units: 36.

BASTRESS TV CABLE
Box 85
Loganton, PA 17747
Phone: 717-725-2733
Officer:
Robert Wenner, Pres.
Ownership: Community owned.
Cable Systems (1):
Pennsylvania: Bastress Twp.
Total Basic Subscribers: 30.

BATH TV SERVICE CORP.
45 Liberty St.
Bath, NY 14810
Phone: 607-776-4861
Fax: 607-766-1152; 607-776-7577
Officers:
William G. Conley, Pres., Chief Exec. & Operating Officer
Harold Brown, V.P.
Mildred B. Murphy, Secy.-Treas.
Ownership: Mildred B. Murphy, 46.7%; William G. Conley, 18.6%; Harold Brown, 8.5%; Bath TV & Service, 26.4%.
Cable Systems (1):
New York: Bath.
Total Basic Subscribers: 3,902.
Total Pay Units: 491.

WILLIAM D. BAUER
760 M St.
Gering, NE 69341
Phone: 308-436-4650
Cable Systems (1):
Nebraska: Lyman.
Total Basic Subscribers: 204.
Total Pay Units: 50.
Other Holdings:
Multimedia: InterTECH Interactive Technologies Inc.

CITY OF BAXTER SPRINGS
Box 577
1445 Military
Baxter Springs, KS 66713
Phone: 316-856-2114
Fax: 316-856-2460
Ownership: Community owned.
Cable Systems (1):
Kansas: Baxter Springs.
Total Basic Subscribers: 1,450.
Total Pay Units: 1,153.

BAY CABLE INC.
Suite 202
2444 Solomons Island Rd.
Annapolis, MD 21401
Phone: 410-266-9393
Fax: 410-266-9054
Ownership: Roy E. Hayes Jr., Pres., Principal.
Cable Systems (14):
Alabama: Allgood.
District of Columbia: U.S. Soldiers' & Airmen's Home.
Mississippi: Evergreen, Mooreville.
North Carolina: Bunnlevel, Columbus County (central portion), Duncan, Orrum, Robeson County (western portion), Vass.
Texas: Argyle, Boyd, Pelican Bay, Ponder.
Total Basic Subscribers: 15,532 (0.02% of total cable households).
Cable Holdings:
Constel Communications LP & Johnston County Cable LP, see listings.

BAYOUVISION
105 Steen Dr.
Lafayette, LA 70508
Phone: 318-989-2768
Cable Systems (1):
Louisiana: Estherwood.
Total Basic Subscribers: N.A.

BAYSIDE 1989-I LP
Box 2330
Gulf Shores, AL 36547
Phone: 205-968-6424
Fax: 205-968-5415
Officers:
Gregory B. Armstrong, Pres. & Chief Exec. Officer
Delbert W. Layne, Chief Operating Officer
Ownership: Gregory B. Armstrong & Delbert W. Layne, Principals.
Cable Systems (2):
Oklahoma: Catoosa, Tulsa County (western portion).
Total Basic Subscribers: 3,337.
Total Pay Units: 711.

BEAVER SPRINGS MUTUAL TV ASSN.
Box 460
RD 1
Beaver Springs, PA 17812
Phone: 717-658-8403
Fax: 717-658-7413
Officers:
Bob Herbster, Pres.
Jean Woodling, Secy.-Treas.
Ownership: Community owned.
Cable Systems (1):
Pennsylvania: Beaver Springs.
Total Basic Subscribers: 290.
Total Pay Units: 95.

BEAVER VALLEY CABLE INC.
Box 60D
RD 2
Rome, PA 18837
Phone: 717-247-2512
Cable Systems (3):
Pennsylvania: Estella, Little Meadows, Rome.
Total Basic Subscribers: 894.

BEAVERCREEK COOPERATIVE TELEPHONE CO.
Box 69
Beavercreek, OR 97004
Phone: 503-632-3113
Fax: 503-632-4159
Officers:
Art Keller, Chmn.
Tom Linstron, Chief Operating Officer
John Rosebrook, Secy.-Treas.

Branch Office:
Oregon City, OR 97045
Cable Systems (1):
Oregon: Beavercreek.
Total Basic Subscribers: 2,550.
Total Pay Units: 556.

LARRY K. BECK
Box 300A
RR 2
Ramsey, IL 62080
Phone: 618-423-2844
Cable Systems (1):
Illinois: Panama.
Total Basic Subscribers: 220.
Total Pay Units: 96.

BEE LINE INC.
Box 859
Houlton, ME 04730
Phone: 207-532-7070
Fax: 207-532-7062
Officers:
Owen F. Hannigan, Pres.
Madeline S. Hannigan, V.P.

Paul W. Hannigan, V.P., Finance
Ownership: Owen F. Hannigan, 75%; Madeline S. Hannigan, 10%; Paul W. Hannigan, 5%.
Represented (legal): Haley, Bader & Potts PLC.
Cable Systems (3):
Maine: Farmington, Madison, Millinocket.
Total Basic Subscribers: 9,758.
Total Pay Units: 2,414.

BEK COMMUNICATIONS COOPERATIVE
Box 230
Steele, ND 58482
Phone: 701-475-2361
Ownership: Jerome Tishmack, Principal.
Cable Systems (6):
North Dakota: Hazelton, Robinson, Strasburg, Tappen, Tuttle, Wing.
Total Basic Subscribers: 298.
Total Pay Units: 220.
Other Holdings:
Telephone.

B.E.K. INC.
Box 307
Denton, MT 59430
Phone: 406-538-3050
Officers:
Wayne Boling, Chief Exec. Officer
Richard Ronish, Chief Operating Officer
Betty Patterson, Secy.-Treas.
Ownership: Wayne Boling, 50%; Marcella Boling, 50%.
Cable Systems (1):
Montana: Stanford.
Total Basic Subscribers: 224.
Total Pay Units: 193.

BELHAVEN CABLE TV INC.
245 E. Main St.
Belhaven, NC 27810
Phone: 919-943-3736
Fax: 919-943-3738
Officers:
Guinn Leverett, Pres. & Chief Exec. Officer
Glenn Tomlinson, Chief Operating Officer
Corki Leverett, Secy.-Treas.
Cable Systems (1):
North Carolina: Belhaven.
Total Basic Subscribers: 1,600.
Total Pay Units: 800.

BELLEVILLE CATV INC.
7713 Hillcrest Ave.
Middleton, WI 53562
Phone: 608-233-5245
Fax: 608-836-1840
Officer:
Rosemary E. Gall, Secy.-Treas.
Ownership: Richard C. Gall, 52.5%; Rosemary Gall, 25%; local investors, 22.5%.
Cable Systems (1):
Wisconsin: Belleville.
Total Basic Subscribers: 607.
Total Pay Units: 195.

BELLEVUE MUNICIPAL CABLE
106 N. 3rd St.
Bellevue, IA 52031
Phone: 319-872-4456
Fax: 319-872-4094
Ownership: Community owned.
Cable Systems (1):
Iowa: Bellevue.
Total Basic Subscribers: 1,110.

BELLSOUTH ENTERTAINMENT INC.
Suite 414, 1100 Abernathy Rd. NE
500 Northpark Town Center
Atlanta, GA 30328
Phone: 770-673-2800
Fax: 770-392-4575
Officers:
Robert J. Frame, Pres.
Thompson T. Rawls II, V.P. & Gen. Counsel
Howard J. Haug, Chief Financial Officer
Ownership: BellSouth Corp.
Cable Franchises (1):
Georgia: Chamblee.
Wireless Cable Systems (3):
Florida: Fort Myers.
Georgia: Atlanta.
Kentucky: Louisville.
Total Basic Subscribers: 16,500.
Total Pay Units: 7,867.
Other Holdings:
MDS, MMDS, see listing.

BENCHMARK COMMUNICATIONS
21545 Ridgetop Circle
Sterling, VA 20166-6504
Phone: 703-444-1800
Fax: 703-444-9797
Officers:
Colleen Millsap, Pres.
Philip Rainwater, Chief Exec. Officer
Ownership: C. P. Rainwater & R. Calvin Sutliff, Gen. Partners.
Represented (legal): Cole, Raywid & Braverman LLP.
Cable Systems (27):
Florida: Mims.
Georgia: Clermont, Jackson County, Lula, Statham, Winder.
Mississippi: Kossuth, Pontotoc.
North Carolina: Camp Wesley, Craven, Gold Hill, King, Lake Waccamaw, Mocksville, Raeford, Rowland, Rural, Tabor City, Wayne County (northern portion).
Oklahoma: Rogers County (northern portion).
South Carolina: Browns Ferry, Debordieu Colony, McClellanville, Sampit, The Summit.
Virginia: Loudoun County, Powhatan.
Total Basic Subscribers: 34,000 (0.05% of total cable households).
Total Pay Units: 52,364.
Other Holdings:
SMATV.

BENHAM CABLE TV
Box 487
Benham, KY 40807
Phone: 606-848-2904
Officer:
E. L. Cannon, Secy.-Treas.
Ownership: Community owned.
Cable Systems (1):
Kentucky: Benham.
Total Basic Subscribers: 282.
Total Pay Units: 188.

BENKELMAN TELEPHONE CO.
Box 684
Benkelman, NE 69021
Phone: 308-423-2000
Fax: 308-423-2399
Cable Systems (3):
Nebraska: Benkelman, Haigler, Wauneta.
Total Basic Subscribers: 857.
Total Pay Units: 302.

BENTLEYVILLE TELEPHONE CO.
608 Main St.
Bentleyville, PA 15314
Phones: 412-239-2501; 800-239-2501
Fax: 412-239-1000
Officers:
Clyde Watson, Chmn.
Richard D'Antonio, Pres. & Chief Exec. Officer
Richard Watson, V.P., Operations
Jim Kail, Chief Financial Officer
Cable Systems (1):
Pennsylvania: Bentleyville.
Total Basic Subscribers: 1,136.
Total Pay Units: 444.

BENTON COOPERATIVE TELEPHONE CO.
2220 125th St. NW
Rice, MN 56367-9701
Phone: 320-393-2115
Fax: 320-393-2221
Officers:
Ray Thompson, Pres.,
Joe Wollak, Secy.-Treas.,
Cable Systems (1):
Minnesota: Rice.
Total Basic Subscribers: 1,045.
Total Pay Units: 369.

BENTON RIDGE TELEPHONE CO.
3225 W. Elm St.
Lima, OH 45805
Phone: 419-859-2144
Fax: 419-859-2150
Officers:
William Jones, Chmn.
Thomas N. Knippen, V.P. & Gen. Mgr.
Kimberly Horne, Secy.-Treas.
Represented (legal): Thompson, Hine & Flory LLP.
Cable Systems (1):
Ohio: Benton Ridge.
Wireless Cable Systems (1):
Ohio: Lima.
Total Basic Subscribers: 10,835 (0.02% of total cable households).
Total Pay Units: 5,685.
Other Holdings:
Security system: B. R. Security Co.
MMDS, W.A.T.C.H. TV Co., see listing.

BERESFORD CABLEVISION INC.
101 N. 3rd St.
Beresford, SD 57004
Phone: 605-763-2500
Ownership: Community owned.
Cable Systems (1):
South Dakota: Beresford.
Total Basic Subscribers: 743.
Total Pay Units: 358.

BERKELEY CABLE TV CO. INC.
Box 1257
Moncks Corner, SC 29461
Phone: 803-761-8188
Ownership: Robert L. Helmly, Pres. Helmly is also Pres. & Gen. Mgr. of the Home Telephone Co. Inc., Moncks Corner, SC.
Cable Systems (1):
South Carolina: Moncks Corner.
Total Basic Subscribers: 6,055.
Total Pay Units: 2,691.

BEULAH LAND COMMUNICATIONS INC.
Box 188
Beulah, CO 81023
Phone: 719-485-2400
Ownership: Richard Sellers, Principal.
Cable Systems (1):
Colorado: Beulah.
Total Basic Subscribers: 264.
Total Pay Units: 38.

BIG SANDY TELECOMMUNICATIONS INC.
Box 218
Simla, CO 80835
Phone: 719-541-2261
Officer:
Bob Lunday, Pres.
Cable Systems (2):
Colorado: Calhan, Simla.
Total Basic Subscribers: 473.
Total Pay Units: 218.

CLIFF BILBREY
1034 E. Main St.
Livingston, TN 38570
Phones: 931-823-1114; 931-823-1123
Cable Systems (1):
Tennessee: Livingston.
Total Basic Subscribers: 2,572.
Total Pay Units: 516.

BILTMORE-HOLIDAY CORP.
300 E. 3rd St.
Lordsburg, NM 88045
Phone: 505-542-3584
Fax: 505-542-3535
Officer:
Suila Depaoli, Pres.
Cable Systems (1):
New Mexico: Lordsburg.
Total Basic Subscribers: 1,000.
Total Pay Units: 420.

JOSEPH R. BIONDO
605 Pennsylvania Ave.
Matamoras, PA 18336
Phone: 717-491-4837
Cable Systems (3):
New Jersey: Montague Twp.
New York: Minisink.
Pennsylvania: Matamoras.
Total Basic Subscribers: 2,795.
Total Pay Units: 590.

BISHOP COMMUNICATIONS INC.
9938 State Hwy. 55 NW
Annandale, MN 55302
Phone: 612-274-5800
Officers:
John M. Bishop, Chief Exec. Officer
Gene R. South Sr., Chief Operating Officer
Cable Systems (1):
Minnesota: Annandale.
Total Basic Subscribers: 532.
Total Pay Units: 135.

BISHOP TV CLUB INC.
Box 71
Bishop, VA 24604-0071
Phone: 703-988-2182
Officers:
James C. Shrader, Chmn. & Pres.
Rommel Hargrove, V.P.
Glenda Cox, Secy.-Treas. & Chief Financial Officer
Ownership: Community owned.
Cable Systems (1):
Virginia: Bishop.
Total Basic Subscribers: 170.
Total Pay Units: 55.

BLACK ROCK CABLE INC.
2544 Mount Baker Hwy.
Bellingham, WA 98226

Phone: 360-734-7930
Total Basic Subscribers: N.A.
Cable Holdings:
Granted certification on April 22, 1999 to operate an Open Video System in Skagit County (Anacortes, Burlington, Mount Vernon, Sedro Wooley); Snohomish County (Arlington, Bothell, Brier, Edmonds, Everett, Lynnwood, Marysville, Mill Creek, Monroe, Mountainlake Terrace, Mukilteo, Snohomish, Woodway); Whatcom County (Blaine, Everson, Ferndale, Lynden, Nooksack, Sumas).

BLACKDUCK TELEPHONE CO.

Box 325
50 Margaret Ave. E
Blackduck, MN 56630
Phone: 218-835-7890
Fax: 218-835-3299
Ownership: Blackduck Telephone Co.
Cable Systems (1):
Minnesota: Blackduck.
Total Basic Subscribers: 375.
Total Pay Units: 108.

BLACKSTONE CABLE LLC

1104 W. Ironwood Dr.
Coeur d'Alene, ID 83814-2605
Phone: 208-664-3370
Fax: 208-664-5888
Officers:
Ted W. Hughett, Managing Agent
Tom Tupper, Chief Financial Officer
Ownership: Stratlyn Inc., Gen. Partner.
Represented (legal): Baker & Hostetler.
Cable Systems (92):
Alabama: Marlow, Perdido Beach, Stapleton.
California: Cedarville, Dorris, Fall River Mills, Happy Camp, Herlong (Sierra Army Depot), Klamath, Orick, Trinity Center, Tulelake, Willow Creek.
Georgia: Abbeville, Gibson, Gordon, Guyton, Lake Blackshear, Laurens County (eastern portion), Leslie, Midville, Plains, Portal, Sardis, Smithville, Surrency.
Idaho: Arco, Ashton, Bancroft, Challis, Downey, Driggs, Georgetown, Grace, Lava Hot Springs, Mackay, Malad City, McCammon, Montpelier, Paris, Soda Springs, Victor.
Montana: Belt, Billings (western portion), Chester, Culbertson, Dutton, Fromberg, Hysham, Joliet, Poplar, Scobey, Sun Prairie, Valier.
Oregon: Bonanza, Chiloquin, Cove, Haines, Imbler, Malin, Merrill, North Powder, Sumpter.
South Carolina: Branchville, Santee, Summerton.
Utah: Beaver, Brian Head, Central, Enoch, Enterprise, Eureka, Glenwood, Goshen, Kanarraville, Lyman, Mona, Monroe, New Harmony, Panguitch, Paragonah, Parowan, Santaquin.
Wyoming: Afton, Big Piney, Dubois, Kemmerer, La Barge, Lyman, Medicine Bow, Meeteetse, Pinedale.
Total Basic Subscribers: 24,193 (0.04% of total cable households).
Total Pay Units: 6,324.

BLADE COMMUNICATIONS INC.

541 N. Superior St.
Toledo, OH 43660
Phone: 419-724-6035
Fax: 419-724-6167
Officers:
William Block, Chmn.
Allan Block, Vice Chmn.
William Block Jr., Pres.
John R. Block, Exec. V.P.
Gary J. Blair, V.P. & Treas.
Fritz Byers, Secy.
Ownership: William Block Sr. & William Block Jr., Trustees, 50% jointly; Allan Block, 25%; John R. Block, 25%.
Represented (legal): Dow, Lohnes & Albertson PLLC.
Cable Systems (3):
Michigan: Monroe.
Ohio: Sandusky, Toledo.
Total Basic Subscribers: 159,891 (0.23% of total cable households).
Total Pay Units: 62,468.
Other Holdings:
TV, LPTV, see listings.
Community Communications Services, advertising distribution company.
Newspapers.

BLAKELY CABLE TV INC.

2115 W. Liberty St.
Blakely, GA 31723
Phone: 912-723-3555
Officer:
Charles Deloach Jr., Pres.
Ownership: Charles Deloach Jr., 51%; Wayne R. Foster, 49%.
Cable Systems (1):
Georgia: Blakely.
Total Basic Subscribers: 1,761.
Total Pay Units: 825.

BLEDSOE TELEPHONE CO.

Box 609
203 Cumberland Ave.
Pikeville, TN 37367
Phone: 423-447-2121
Fax: 423-447-2498
Officers:
John Lee Downey, Chmn.
Gregory Anderson, Chief Exec. Officer
Nell Morgan, Secy.-Treas.
Cable Systems (2):
Tennessee: Dunlap, Pikeville.
Total Basic Subscribers: 4,556 as of October 30, 1998.
Total Pay Units: 555.

BLOCK ISLAND CABLE TV

Drawer A2
New Shoreham
Block Island, RI 02807
Phone: 401-466-2479
Fax: 401-596-7366
Officers:
William Bendokas, Chmn. & Chief Exec. Officer
Lois Bendokas, Chief Operating Officer
Dean Martin, Chief Financial Officer
Ownership: William Bendokas & Lois Bendokas, Principals.
Cable Systems (1):
Rhode Island: New Shoreham.
Total Basic Subscribers: 495.

BLOOMINGDALE TELEPHONE CO. INC.

Box 187
Bloomingdale, MI 49026
Phone: 616-521-3000
Fax: 616-521-3500
Ownership: William Godfrey, Pres.
Cable Systems (1):
Michigan: Bloomingdale.
Total Basic Subscribers: 500.
Total Pay Units: 192.

BLOOMVILLE CABLE

Box 137
Halcottsville, NY 12438
Phone: 607-326-4514
Ownership: Lynn George.
Cable Systems (1):
New York: Bloomville.
Total Basic Subscribers: 140.

BLUE EARTH VALLEY TEL CO.

55 First St. SE
Wells, MN 56097-1601
Phone: 507-553-3144
Fax: 507-553-6700
Cable Systems (1):
Minnesota: Minnesota Lake.
Total Basic Subscribers: 272.

BLUE MOUNTAIN TV CABLE CO.

Box 267
Mount Vernon, OR 97865
Phone: 503-932-4613
Ownership: Jack McKenna.
Cable Systems (4):
Oregon: Dayville, Mount Vernon, Prairie City, Seneca.
Total Basic Subscribers: 1,715.

BLUE RIDGE COMMUNICATIONS

444 Sunrise Ave.
Honesdale, PA 18431-1034
Phone: 570-253-3451
Fax: 570-253-2355
Officer:
Bill Taninies, Chief Exec. Officer
Cable Systems (1):
Pennsylvania: Honesdale.
Total Basic Subscribers: N.A.

BLUEBONNET RURAL DEVELOPMENT CORP.

Box 240
Giddings, TX 78942
Phone: 409-542-3151
Fax: 409-522-1187
Officers:
David W. Peterson, Gen. Mgr.
James Havran, Mgr., Finance & Accounting
Tommy Frizell, Mgr., Corporate Services
Cable Systems (7):
Texas: Birch Creek, Burton, Carmine, Chappell Hill, Dime Box, Indian Lake/Lake Thunderbird, Lake Thunderbird Estates.
Total Basic Subscribers: 1,105.
Total Pay Units: 233.

BLY CABLE CO.

2809 Montelius St.
Klamath Falls, OR 97601
Phone: 503-884-9880
Officers:
William J. Jones, Chmn. & Chief Operating Officer
Joyce E. Jones, Chief Financial Officer
Ownership: Joyce E. Jones & William J. Jones, 100% jointly.
Cable Systems (1):
Oregon: Bly.
Total Basic Subscribers: 115.

BLYTHEVILLE TV CABLE CO.

Box 127
121 S. 2nd St.
Blytheville, AR 72315
Phone: 501-763-6688
Officers:
Harold Sudbury, Pres.
Ross Holt, V.P.
Ownership: Harold Sudbury, 50%; Ross Holt, 50%. Sudbury owns KLCN(AM) & KHLS(FM) Blytheville; KAWW-AM-FM Heber Springs; KHPA(FM) Hope; KNBY(AM) & KOKR(FM) Newport; KTPA(AM) Prescott; KSUD(AM) West Memphis, all AR. Holt has 50% interest in Decatur, AR telephone co.
Cable Systems (2):
Arkansas: Blytheville, Dell.
Total Basic Subscribers: 6,813.
Total Pay Units: 3,020.

BMI CABLEVISION

Box 1424
Huron, SD 57350
Phone: 605-352-4014
Fax: 605-352-6509
Ownership: John Rearick, 50%; Dick Shelton, 50%. Rearick & Shelton also own 50% each of Frontier Cable Inc., see listing.
Cable Systems (1):
Alaska: Adak.
Total Basic Subscribers: 20.
Total Pay Units: 3.

BOB BOALDIN

Box 1260
610 S. Cosmos
Elkhart, KS 67950
Phone: 316-697-4466
Cable Systems (1):
Kansas: Elkhart.
Total Basic Subscribers: 1,133.
Total Pay Units: 406.

VILLAGE OF BOAZ

Rte. 1
Muscoda, WI 53573
Phone: 608-536-3493
Ownership: Local investors.
Cable Systems (1):
Wisconsin: Boaz.
Total Basic Subscribers: 63.
Total Pay Units: 23.

BOCCO CABLE

Box 215
RR 2
Valley Grove, WV 26060
Phone: 304-336-7086
Fax: 304-336-7086
Ownership: Basil O. Ellis, Chief Exec. Officer.
Cable Systems (1):
West Virginia: Bethany.
Total Basic Subscribers: 79.
Total Pay Units: 23.

BONDUEL CABLE TV

Box 8
Bonduel, WI 54107
Phone: 715-758-2500
Ownership: Geraldine Steichen & Robert Steichen, 100% jointly.
Cable Systems (1):
Wisconsin: Bonduel.
Total Basic Subscribers: 262.
Total Pay Units: 86.

ALAN BOOKER

Box 466
Marion, LA 71260
Phone: 318-292-4774
Cable Systems (5):
Arkansas: Huttig, Strong.
Louisiana: Marion, Rocky Branch, Sterlington.
Total Basic Subscribers: 1,761.

BOULDER RIDGE CABLE TV

Box 609

4120 Citrus Ave.
Rocklin, CA 95677
Phone: 916-652-1267
Fax: 916-652-0133
Officers:
Dean Hazen, Chmn.
Zoe Hazen, Pres. & Chief Exec. Officer
D. Jack Stock, Sr. V.P., Chief Financial Officer
A. Dean Henderson, V.P. & Gen. Mgr.
Ownership: Dean Hazen & Zoe Hazen, 100% jointly.
Represented (legal): Cole, Raywid & Braverman LLP.
Cable Systems (3):
California: Garberville, Placer County (southwestern portion).
Hawaii: Hickam AFB 75%.
Total Basic Subscribers: 17,909 (0.03% of total cable households).
Total Pay Units: 5,992.

BOWEN CABLEVISION INC.
Box 130
Wilkinson, WV 25653-0130
Phone: 304-752-3023
Cable Systems (4):
West Virginia: Crawley Creek Road, Lyburn, Mud River, Six Mile.
Total Basic Subscribers: N.A.

DAN BOWLING
Box 522
Hyden, KY 41749-0522
Phone: 606-672-2808
Cable Systems (1):
Kentucky: Hyden.
Total Basic Subscribers: 922.
Total Pay Units: 151.

GENE BOWMAN
Box 437
Booneville, KY 41314
Phone: 606-593-5465
Cable Systems (1):
Kentucky: Lerose.
Total Basic Subscribers: 215.

BOYCOM CABLEVISION INC.
Box 333
Rural Rte. 10
Poplar Bluff, MO 63901
Phones: 314-686-3218; 314-686-9101
Fax: 314-686-4722
Officers:
Steven D. Boyers, Chmn. & Pres.
Patricia Jo Boyers, V.P. & Secy.-Treas.
Ownership: Steven D. Boyers, 50%; Patricia Jo Boyers, 50%.
Cable Systems (1):
Missouri: Butler County.
Total Basic Subscribers: 347.
Total Pay Units: 69.

BRADLEY'S INC.
Box 41
Wharton, WV 25208
Phone: 304-247-6231
Officer:
Robert Legg Jr., V.P., Operations
Ownership: Charles M. Bradley.
Cable Systems (3):
West Virginia: Bandytown, Meadow Bridge, Union.
Total Basic Subscribers: 1,029.
Total Pay Units: 188.

BRANCH CABLE INC.
Suite 1100
125 S. Congress St.
Jackson, MS 39021-3306
Phone: 601-355-1522
Fax: 601-353-0950
Ownership: James Creekmore, Wade Creekmore Sr. & Wade Creekmore Jr., Principals.
Cable Systems (8):
Mississippi: Ackerman-Weir, Crosby, Isola-Inverness, Louise, Meadville-Bude, New Augusta, New Hebron, Roxie.
Total Basic Subscribers: 3,042.
Total Pay Units: 1,232.

BRANDYWINE CABLEVISION
Box 248
Brandywine, WV 26802-0248
Phone: 304-249-5610
Ownership: Harry Lee Scott & Richard Short, 100% jointly.
Cable Systems (1):
West Virginia: Brandywine.
Total Basic Subscribers: 350.

BRESNAN COMMUNICATIONS CO. LP
709 Westchester Ave.
White Plains, NY 10604
Phones: 914-993-6600; 914-993-6624
Fax: 914-993-6601; 914-993-6602
Officers:
William J. Bresnan, Pres. & Chief Exec. Officer
Jeffrey S. DeMond, Sr. V.P. & Chief Financial Officer
Daniel J. Bresnan, Sr. V.P., Business Development
Michael J. Bresnan, Sr. V.P., Domestic Div.
Janice L. Barning, V.P., Human Resoruces
Barbara Bodart, V.P., International Development
Patrick J. Bresnan, V.P., Community Development
Robert V. Bresnan, V.P. & Gen. Counsel
Claudia Chifos, V.P., Finance & Asst. Treas.
Eric D. Cunningham, V.P., Finance & Asst. Treas.
Lenny Higgins, V.P., Telephone & Data Services
Andrew Kober, V.P. & Controller
Joe Lawson, V.P., Mktg.
Gary McIntosh, V.P., Engineering
Suzanne Thompson, V.P., Public Affairs
Terry St. Marie, V.P., International Operations
John Wade, V.P., Midwest Development
Roger Worboys, V.P., Domestic Operations
Ownership: AT&T Broadband & Internet Services, 50%; Blackstone Capital Partners III Merchant Banking Fund LP, 40%; Bresnan Communications Co., managing partner, 10%. BCC ownership: William J. Bresnan, 51%; TCI/Liberty Holdings Co., 49%.
Cable Systems (86):
Michigan: Alba, Alma, Alpena, Bay City, Beaver Twp. (Bay County), Bergland, Big Rapids, Boardman Twp., Bridgeport Twp., Butman Twp., Canadian Lakes, Charlevoix, Cheboygan, Chippewa Twp. (Isabella County), East Jordan, Escanaba, Ewen, Gagetown, Gaylord, Harbor Beach, Hermansville, Hope Twp. (Midland County), Houghton, Iron Mountain, Ironwood, Jamestown Twp., Kincheloe, Levering, Ludington, Mackinac Island, Mackinaw City, Manistique, Marquette, Midland (portions), Mount Pleasant, Newberry, Olive Twp. (Ottawa County), Omer, Ontonagon, Owosso, Petoskey, Pickford Twp., Reese, Sage Twp., Saginaw, Sault Ste. Marie, St. Ignace, St. Johns, Thomas Twp., Watersmeet.
Michigan: Whittemore.
Minnesota: Albert Lea, Alexandria, Austin, Brainerd, Buffalo, Duluth, Faribault, Fergus Falls, Glencoe, International Falls, Mankato, Marshall, Montevideo, Owatonna, Rochester, St. Cloud, Wadena, Willmar, Winona.
Nebraska: Alliance, Beatrice, Grand Island, Hastings, North Platte, Ogallala, Scottsbluff, Sidney.
Wisconsin: Baraboo, Columbus, La Crosse, Lake Nebagamon, Madison, Portage, Richland Center, Sauk City.
Total Basic Subscribers: 639,000 (0.93% of total cable households).
Total Pay Units: 255,000.
Other Holdings:
Bresnan International Partners has cable systems in Chile.

BRISTER'S CABLE TV
364 Blue Island St.
Fairhope, AL 36532
Phone: 205-928-5541
Cable Systems (1):
Alabama: Baldwin County (unincorporated areas).
Total Basic Subscribers: 200.

BRISTOL BAY TELEPHONE COOPERATIVE INC.
Box 259
King Salmon, AK 99613
Phone: 907-246-3403
Fax: 907-246-1115
Officers:
Dennis Niedermeyer, Pres.
Duane C. Durand, Chief Exec. Officer & Gen. Mgr.
Marlene Swain, V.P.
Pete Hill, Secy.-Treas.
Marilyn Sessions, Chief Financial Officer
Ownership: Subscriber owned.
Cable Systems (1):
Alaska: King Salmon.
Total Basic Subscribers: 380.

BROADCAST CABLEVISION
Drawer 377
Malden MO, 63863
Phone: 573-276-3025
Wireless Cable Systems (1):
Missouri: Malden.
Total Basic Subscribers: N.A.

BROCKWAY TV INC.
501 Main St.
Brockway, PA 15824
Phone: 814-268-6565
Officers:
L. F. Robertson, Chmn. & Chief Exec. Officer
James McMeekin, Vice-Chmn.
Joseph Bruno Jr., Secy.-Treas.
Ownership: Subscriber owned.
Represented (legal): R. Edward Ferraro.
Cable Systems (1):
Pennsylvania: Brockway.
Total Basic Subscribers: 1,872.
Total Pay Units: 355.

BRONSON CABLEVISION INC.
Box 128
Brooker, FL 32622
Phone: 904-485-1362
Ownership: Tom Hulett, Pres. & Chief Exec. Officer.
Represented (legal): James F. Lang.
Cable Systems (1):
Florida: Brooker.
Total Basic Subscribers: 360.
Total Pay Units: 109.

MARTIN P. BROPHY
38 N. Main St.
Shenandoah, PA 17976
Phone: 570-462-1911
Fax: 570-462-1948
Represented (legal): Frank Toole.
Cable Systems (1):
Pennsylvania: Shenandoah.
Total Basic Subscribers: 3,900.
Total Pay Units: 700.

JERRY BROWERS
Box 282
Plumerville, AR 72127
Phone: 501-354-6152
Cable Systems (4):
Mississippi: Crowder, Friars Point, Jonestown, Lula.
Total Basic Subscribers: 733.
Total Pay Units: 170.

NORMAN BROWNING
Box 6
Mecosta, MI 49332
Phone: 616-972-7111
Cable Systems (2):
Michigan: Leroy (village) 45%, St. James Twp. 45%.
Total Basic Subscribers: 621.
Total Pay Units: 284.

BROWNWOOD TV CABLE SERVICE INC.
Box 1149
310 Carnegie
Brownwood, TX 76801
Phone: 915-646-3576
Fax: 915-643-2846
Officers:
Mrs. J. Andrews, Pres.
Johnnie A. Andrews, V.P.
Ownership: Mrs. J. Andrews, 95%; Johnnie A. Andrews, 5%.
Represented (legal): Cole, Raywid & Braverman LLP.
Cable Systems (4):
Texas: Baird, Brownwood, Rising Star, Santa Anna.
Total Basic Subscribers: 11,097 (0.02% of total cable households).
Total Pay Units: 2,242.
Other Holdings:
Cable construction, equipment manufacturer.

BRUSH VALLEY CABLEVISION INC.
Box 147 A
RD 7
Somerset, PA 15530
Phone: 800-535-7249
Cable Systems (1):
Pennsylvania: Brush Valley Twp.
Total Basic Subscribers: 370.
Total Pay Units: 109.

BUD-ALPOCA TV CABLE CLUB INC.
Box 188
Bud, WV 24716
Phone: 304-294-5365
Ownership: Community owned.
Cable Systems (1):
West Virginia: Bud.
Total Basic Subscribers: 108.

BUD'S ELECTRIC SERVICE INC.
Box 51
RD 3

Clearfield, PA 16830
Phone: 814-765-5018
Fax: 814-765-9831
Officers:
Alfred E. Swatsworth, Pres.
Freda C. Swatsworth, Secy.-Treas.
Ownership: Alfred E. Swatsworth & Freda C. Swatsworth, Principals.
Cable Systems (1):
Pennsylvania: Glen Richey.
Total Basic Subscribers: 379.
Total Pay Units: 70.

BUENAVISION TELECOMMUNICATIONS INC.

912 N. Eastern Ave.
Los Angeles, CA 90063
Phone: 213-269-8251
Fax: 213-269-8257
Officers:
Moctesuma Esparza, Pres.
Benjamin Ochoa, V.P. & Gen. Mgr.
Ownership: Moctesuma Esparza & David Ochoa, Principals.
Cable Systems (1):
California: Los Angeles.
Total Basic Subscribers: 10,000.

BUFORD TELEVISION INC.

Box 9090
Tyler, TX 75711
Phones: 903-561-4411; 903-581-2121
Fax: 903-561-4031
Officers:
Robert P. Buford, Chmn.
Geoffrey Buford, Vice Chmn.
Ben Hooks, Pres. & Chief Exec. Officer
Ron Martin, Exec. V.P. & Chief Operating Officer
Kay Monigold, V.P. & Chief Administration Officer
Tom Seale, V.P. & Chief Financial Officer
Ownership: Buford Holding Corp. BHC ownership: Robert Buford, Pres., 49.89%; Geoffrey Buford, V.P. & Secy.-Treas., 49.89%, Ross P. Buford Trust, 0.1%.
Represented (legal): Cole, Raywid & Braverman LLP.
Cable Systems (249):
Arkansas: Almyra, Altheimer, Atkins, Baxter County (unincorporated areas), Bearden, Biscoe, Bono, Bradley, Cabot, Carthage, Chidester, Clarendon, Coal Hill, Conway (eastern portion), Crawfordsville, Danville, Delight, Des Arc, Dover, Emerson, Emmet, Fouke, Fountain Hill, Garland City, Grady, Hamburg, Harmony Grove, Harrell, Harrisburg, Hazen, Hector, Hermitage, Higginson, Holly Grove, Hughes, Humnoke, Humphrey, Jasper, Junction City, Knobel, Lake City, Lake Erling, Leola, Leslie, Lewisville, Locust Bayou, London, Lynn, Magazine, Manila, Marked Tree, Mayflower, McDougal, Mount Ida, Nashville, O'Kean, Osceola, Ozark Acres, Palestine, Pine Bluff (southern portion), Pinebergen, Plainview, Ravenden Springs, Sedgwick, Sheridan, Smackover, Stephens, Taylor, Thornton, Traskwood, Trumann, Turrell, Western Grove, Wheatley, Whitehall, Wilmar.
Louisiana: Bernice, Boyce, Brouillette, Calvin, Clayton, Cloutierville, Colfax, Cotton Valley, Dodson, Dry Prong, Effie, Georgetown, Gibsland, Haughton, Krotz Springs, Lake Claiborne, Lake St. John, Lecompte, Marksville, McIntyre, Melville, Monterey, Montgomery, Moreauville, Natchez, Newellton, Robeline, Rodessa, Sibley, St. Joseph, Turkey Creek, Wallace Ridge, Waterproof.
Missouri: Clever, Coffman Bend, Conway, Fair Play, Fordland, Gainesville, Galena, Gravois Mills, Hartville, Highway DD, Ivy Bend, Joplin, Lampe, Macks Creek, Mindenmines, Missionary, Niangua, Niangua Bridge, Northshore, Norwood, Pleasant Hope, Porter Mill, Powersite, Sheldon, Sparta, Stotts City, Urbana, Wilson Bend.
Texas: Adkins, Alba, Albany, Allendale, Alto, Anahuac, Anna, Anson, Arp, Atascosa, Avinger, Aztec, Beach City, Beaumont Colony, Ben Wheeler, Breckenridge, Brookeland, Burkburnett, Caddo Peak, Cedar Springs, Center, Central, Cheek, Chester, Clarksville, Clifton, Colmesneil, Cumby, Cushing, Cypress, De Leon, Diana, Eastland, Ector, Egan, Electra, Elmo, Fannett, Fruitvale, Garrison, Gary, Golden, Gorman, Grapeland, Groveton, Hamlin, Hawkins, Henrietta, Homer, Hull, Iowa Park, Josephine, Katy (southern portion), Kenefick, Kilgore, Krum, Lake Cherokee, Laneville, Lansing, Las Gallinas, Leonard, Lost Pines, Lovelady, Lowry Crossing, Lucas, Magnolia, Mart, Mauriceville, Moss Bluff, Mount Enterprise, Myrtle Springs, New Summerfield, Nocona, Nome, North Silsbee, Oklahoma, Olney, Pilot Point, Plum Grove, Porter, Pottsboro, Powderly, Price, Quinlan, Raywood, Redwater, Reklaw, Reno (Parker County), Riverside, Rose City, Rotan, Royse City, Rusk, San Augustine, Seymour, Sherwood Shores, South Silsbee, Splendora, Tenaha, Terrell, Timpson, Toledo Village, Trinity, Vernon, Vidor (southern portion), Wells, West, Wildwood Resort City, Woden, Wolfe City, Woodville, Zavalla.
Total Basic Subscribers: 166,133 (0.24% of total cable households).
Total Pay Units: 73,198.
Note: Sold to Classic Cable 1999.

BULLSKIN CABLE TV

River St.
Oneida, KY 40972
Phones: 606-598-3444; 606-847-4358
Ownership: John Russell Brown & Vernon Gay, 100% jointly.
Cable Systems (1):
Kentucky: Bullskin Creek.
Total Basic Subscribers: 115.

BURRIS COMMUNICATIONS

525 Eastwood Dr.
Albemarle, NC 28001-8187
Phone: 704-982-1323
Ownership: John Burris.
Cable Systems (1):
California: Plantation-by-the-Lake.
Total Basic Subscribers: 141.
Total Pay Units: 30.

LON BURZYCKI

4 Reynolds St.
Alfred, NY 14802
Phone: 607-587-9313
Cable Systems (1):
New York: Alfred.
Total Basic Subscribers: 370.
Total Pay Units: 68.

BUTLER-BREMER MUTUAL TELEPHONE CO.

Box 86
716 Main St.
Plainfield, IA 50666
Phone: 319-276-4458
Fax: 319-276-7530
Officers:
Wendall Kuethe, Pres.
Donald White, V.P.
J. W. Lynes, Secy.-Treas.
Cable Systems (1):
Iowa: Tripoli.
Total Basic Subscribers: 669.
Total Pay Units: 164.

BYERS-PETROLIA CABLE TV CO. INC.

Box 308
220 Main St.
Byers, TX 76357
Phone: 817-529-6123
Fax: 817-529-6125
Officers:
Johnnie Ruhl, Chief Exec. Officer
Charlotte Helt, Cable Coordinator
Ownership: Pioneer Telephone Cooperative Inc.
Cable Systems (1):
Texas: Byers.
Total Basic Subscribers: 400.
Total Pay Units: 312.

CABLE AMERICA CORP.

Suite 200
2720 E. Camelback Rd.
Phoenix, AZ 85016-4317
Phone: 602-957-2500
Fax: 602-957-2555
Officers:
William G. Jackson, Pres.
Christopher A. Dyrek, V.P., Finance
Gloria J. Jackson, Secy.-Treas.
Ownership: William G. Jackson, 90%; Gloria J. Jackson, 10%.
Represented (legal): Cole, Raywid & Braverman LLP.
Cable Systems (11):
Arizona: Coolidge, Gila Bend, Mesa.
California: Rancho Cordova.
Michigan: Eagle Harbor Twp.
Missouri: Dixon, Doolittle, Maryland Heights, Republic, Richland, St. Robert.
Total Basic Subscribers: 43,500 (0.06% of total cable households).
Total Pay Units: 23,000.
Other Holdings:
SMATV.

CABLE & COMMUNICATIONS CORP.

Box 280
106 2nd Ave. S
Circle, MT 59215
Phone: 406-485-3301
Fax: 406-485-2924
Officers:
Fulton Castleberry, Pres.
Doug Senner, V.P.
Kevin Braun, Secy.-Treas.
Ownership: Mid-Rivers Telephone Cooperative Inc.
Cable Systems (6):
Montana: Circle, Ekalaka, Jordan, Richey, Savage, Wibaux.
Total Basic Subscribers: 1,142.
Total Pay Units: 437.
Other Holdings:
Telephone.
Cellular radio.

CABLE COMMUNICATIONS OF PALO ALTO INC.

3200 Park Blvd.
Palo Alto, CA 94306
Phone: 415-856-3553
Fax: 415-856-8244
Officers:
John Kelley, Pres.
Bradley E. Anderson, Chief Exec. Officer
Seth Fearey, Secy.
Mark Rogowsky, Chief Financial Officer
Represented (legal): Cole, Raywid & Braverman LLP.
Cable Systems (1):
California: Palo Alto.
Total Basic Subscribers: 28,432 (0.04% of total cable households).
Total Pay Units: 17,901.

CABLE COMMUNICATIONS OF WILLSBORO INC.

Box 625
9 Lakeshore Rd.
Willsboro, NY 12996
Phone: 518-963-4116
Fax: 518-963-7405
Officers:
Herb Longware, Pres.
Shirley Longware, Chief Financial Officer
Ownership: Herb Longware, 60%; John Longware & Shirley Longware, 40% jointly.
Cable Systems (1):
New York: Willsboro (town).
Total Basic Subscribers: 453.
Total Pay Units: 230.

CABLE COOPERATIVE INC.

23 E. College St.
Oberlin, OH 44074
Phone: 216-775-4001
Fax: 216-775-1635
Officers:
Andrew Ruckman, Chmn.
Ralph Potts, Chief Operating Officer
Dayton Livingston, Chief Financial Officer
Ownership: Subscriber-owned.
Cable Systems (1):
Ohio: Oberlin.
Total Basic Subscribers: 1,743.
Total Pay Units: 804.

CABLE ENTERTAINMENT CO.

Box 282
Plumerville, AR 72127
Phone: 501-354-6152
Ownership: Jerry Browers.
Cable Systems (3):
Arkansas: Elaine, Lake View, Plumerville.
Total Basic Subscribers: 1,633.
Total Pay Units: 386.

CABLE MANAGEMENT ASSOC.

Box 802068
Dallas N. Pkwy.
Dallas, TX 75380
Phone: 972-233-9616
Fax: 972-385-9601
Officers:
Nathan A. Levine, Chmn. & Chief Exec. Officer
Douglas K. Bridges, Chief Operating Officer
M. Jane Ketcham, V.P., Mktg.
Stan Jones, V.P., Operations
Bill Teeling, Chief Financial Officer
Ownership: Nathan A. Levine.
Represented (legal): Dow, Lohnes & Albertson PLLC.
Cable Systems (47):
Louisiana: Belle Chasse, Blanchard, Braithwaite, Calhoun, Columbia, Delhi 95%, Empire, Farmerville, Haynesville, Homer, Lake Providence, Logansport, Mansfield, Mooringsport, North Monroe, Oak Grove 95%, Pointe a la Hache, Rayville 95%, South Monroe, Springhill, Tallulah, Vivian, Wisner.
Mississippi: Anguilla, Arcola, Hollandale, Leland, Quitman, Waynesboro.
Nevada: Laughlin.
Texas: Angleton, Bellville, Blackwell, Bronte, Buffalo Gap, China, Grape Creek, Hempstead, Joaquin, Kingsville, La Grange, Lawn,

Merkel, Robert Lee, Roscoe, Sour Lake, Tuscola.
Total Basic Subscribers: 50,903 (0.07% of total cable households).
Total Pay Units: 24,049.
Other Holdings:
Service company: 50% of Alpha Data Systems Inc., national computer company specializing in cellular telephone billing services and third party administration for insurance companies; Credit Protection Assoc. Inc., collection agency for cable receivables.
Retail operation: Blockbuster Video stores in Washington, DC; Louisiana, Texas, Canada & the United Kingdom.

CABLE MICHIGAN—Sold to Avalon Cable 1998.

CABLE ONE INC.
1314 N. 3rd St.
Phoenix, AZ 85004
Phone: 602-364-6000
Fax: 602-364-6010
Officers:
Thomas O. Might, Pres.
Patrick Dolohanty, V.P. & Treas.
Ronald Pancratz, V.P., Advertising
Alan Silverman, V.P. & Gen. Counsel
Tom Basinger, V.P., Central Div.
Mitch Bland, V.P., Northwest Div.
John Gosch, V.P., Southwest Div.
Gerald McKenna, V.P., Strategic Mktg.
Tommy Hill, V.P., Engineering
Ownership: The Washington Post Co. The Washington Post Co. has broadcast, newspaper, periodical, publishing and other interests, see listing for Post-Newsweek Stations Inc. in Commercial TV Station Ownership.
Represented (legal): Fleischman & Walsh LLP.
Cable Systems (68):
Alabama: Anniston.
Arizona: Bisbee, Clifton, Cornville, Globe-Miami, Holbrook, Page, Prescott, Safford, Show Low, Winslow.
California: Modesto & Oakdale, Santa Rosa.
Indiana: Greenwood.
Iowa: Sioux City.
Louisiana: Vidalia.
Minnesota: Moorhead.
Mississippi: Batesville, Biloxi, Brookhaven, Bruce, Caledonia, Clarksdale, Cleveland, Columbus, Grenada, Gulfport/Long Beach, Hamilton, Lambert, McComb, Natchez, Pascagoula, Yazoo City.
Missouri: Joplin, Kirksville.
Nebraska: Norfolk.
New Mexico: Rio Rancho, Roswell.
North Dakota: Fargo.
Ohio: Green Twp. (Summit County).
Oklahoma: Ada, Altus, Ardmore, Bartlesville, Clinton, Cordell, Duncan, Elk City, Frederick, Hobart, Idabel, Madill, Mangum, Marietta, Miami, Nowata, Ponca City, Sayre, Vinita.
Tennessee: Dyersburg.
Texas: Aransas Pass, Bonham, Livingston, Odessa, Port Lavaca, Sherman, Texarkana, Whitewright.
Total Basic Subscribers: 736,843 (1.07% of total cable households).
Total Pay Units: 412,413.

CABLE OPTIONS INC.
Box 1404
Fairhope, AL 36533
Phone: 205-928-5770
Officer:
J. Alex Bowab, Chief Operating Officer
Ownership: Alex Bowab & John Riley, Principals.
Cable Systems (1):
Alabama: Baldwin County (portions).
Total Basic Subscribers: 450.

CABLE PLUS
Suite 120
11400 S.E. 6th St.
Bellevue, WA 98004
Phone: 206-462-2090
Fax: 206-462-2092
Cable Systems (5):
Washington: Creston, Easton, Maltby, Thorp, Whatcom County (portions).
Total Basic Subscribers: 3,125.
Total Pay Units: 95.

CABLE PROPERTIES INC.
Box 386
North Branch, MI 48461
Phone: 313-688-3059
Fax: 313-688-3336
Officers:
J. David Giesy, Pres.
Carol M. Davis, V.P.
Ownership: Carol Davis & David Giesy, 100% jointly.
Represented (legal): Pelavin & Powers.
Cable Systems (9):
Michigan: Applegate, Forester Twp., Forestville, Frost Twp., Goodells, Merritt Twp., Minden City, Rives Junction, Wisner (village).
Cable Franchises (1):
Michigan: Cub Lake.
Total Basic Subscribers: 2,980.
Total Pay Units: 1,495.

CABLE SERVICES INC.
Box 608
308 2nd St. NW
Jamestown, ND 58401
Phone: 701-252-5281
Officer:
Roy A. Sheppard, Chief Exec. & Operating Officer
Cable Systems (8):
North Dakota: Ellendale, Jamestown, Kulm, Lisbon, Medina, Oakes, Sanborn, Valley City.
Total Basic Subscribers: 9,300.
Total Pay Units: 1,450.
Others Holdings:
LPTV, see listing.

CABLE SYSTEMS MANAGEMENT OF IOWA INC.
3600 Kennebec Dr.
Eagan, MN 55122
Phone: 612-688-2623
Officers:
Mark Fisher, Pres.
Clifford Plagman, V.P.
Robert Smith, Secy.
Wally Wells, Treas.
Ownership: Cable Systems Services.
Cable Systems (38):
Iowa: Blairsburg, Gilmore City, Lake Park, Marcus, Paulina, Peterson, Sioux Rapids, Sutherland, Thor.
Minnesota: Canosia Twp., Finland, French River Twp., Knife Lake Twp., Knife River, Long Lake, Round Lake Twp., Rutledge (village), Shultz Lake Twp., Willow River, Wrenshall.
Wisconsin: Almond, Bancroft, Briggsville, Dalton, Doylestown, Endeavor, Granton, Kellnersville, Kingston, Marquette, Milladore (town), Oxford, Packwaukee, Rosholt, Rozellville, Saxeville, Tustin, Wolf River.
Total Basic Subscribers: 5,156.
Total Pay Units: 850.

CABLE TV ASSOC. INC.
124 E. 7th Ave.
Redfield, SD 57469
Phone: 605-472-3415
Cable Systems (18):
Nebraska: Atkinson.
South Dakota: Avon, Britton, Burke, Clark, Clear Lake, Edgemont, Eureka, Faulkton, Frankfort, Gregory, Lake Andes, Mellette, Platte, Tripp, Tyndall, Wagner, West Whitlock.
Total Basic Subscribers: 5,669.
Total Pay Units: 1,306.

CABLE TV OF THE KENNEBUNKS
35 Forest Hill Lane
Kennebunk, ME 04043
Phone: 207-967-5212
Fax: 207-967-0591
E-mail: cabletv@kbunktv.com
Web site: http://www.kbunktv.com
Officers:
Kenneth Thompson, Chief Exec. Officer
Claudia Richards, Chief Operating Officer
Lynn McKellar, Chief Financial Officer
Ownership: Ltd. partnership. Kenneth Thompson, Gen. Partner, 70%.
Cable Systems (1):
Maine: Kennebunk.
Total Basic Subscribers: 8,200.
Total Pay Units: 3,500.

CABLE TV OF STANTON
Box 716
Stanton, NE 68779-0716
Phone: 402-439-5000
Officers:
Bernard Paden, Pres.
Leona Paden, Secy.
Ownership: Bernard Paden & Leona Paden, 55% jointly; John Paden, 15%; Richard A. Paden, 15%; Robert J. Paden, 15%.
Cable Systems (1):
Nebraska: Stanton.
Total Basic Subscribers: 532.
Total Pay Units: 212.

CABLE T.V. SERVICES INC.
Box 420
301 W. Jasper Hwy. 24 W
Goodland, IN 47948-0420
Phone: 219-297-3400
Fax: 219-474-6332
Officers:
Richard Mailloux, Chief Exec. & Financial Officer
Steve Mailloux, Chief Operating Officer
Ownership: Joanne Mailloux & Richard Mailloux, 100% jointly.
Cable Systems (1):
Indiana: Boswell.
Total Basic Subscribers: 2,129.
Total Pay Units: 566.

CABLE USA INC.
Box 1448
Kearney, NE 68848-1448
Phones: 308-234-6428; 308-995-6156
Fax: 308-234-6452
Officers:
Russell G. Hilliard, Pres., Chief Exec. & Financial Officer
Stuart Gilbertson, Corp. Engineer
Ownership: Russell G. Hilliard.
Represented (legal): Cole, Raywid & Braverman LLP.
Cable Systems (60):
California: Bombay Beach, Borrego Springs, Calipatria, Ocotillo, Salton Sea Beach.
Colorado: Canterbury Park, Constitution Hills Mobile Home Park, Fleming, Holyoke, Julesburg.
Iowa: Missouri Valley, Onawa.
Nebraska: Amherst, Ansley, Axtell, Bee (village), Bennington, Bertrand, Blair, Cairo, Cedar Bluffs, Chappell, Cozad, Dannebrog, Davey (village), Dwight (village), Elba, Elm Creek, Fort Calhoun, Goehner (village), Gothenburg, Herman (village), Hildreth, Holdrege, Johnson Lake, Juniata, Kearney, Kennard, Lake Cunningham, Lake Maloney, Litchfield, Loomis, Loup City, Mason City, Mead, Minden, Oakland, Oconto, Ord, Oshkosh, Overton, Phillips, Pleasanton, Ravenna, St. Libory, Sumner, Tekamah, Washington (village), Wilcox, Yutan.
Wireless Cable Systems (1):
Nebraska: Kearney.
Total Cable Subscribers: 34,434 (0.05% of total cable households).
Total Pay Units: 10,000.
Other Holdings:
MDS, see listing.

CABLE VENTURES LTD.
5151 Reed Rd.
Columbus, OH 43220
Phone: 800-582-0504
Fax: 614-457-2567
Ownership: William Mayes, Managing Gen. Partner.
Cable Systems (6):
Texas: Gustine, Hasse, Lake Brownwood, May, South Shores, Thunderbird Bay.
Total Basic Subscribers: 1,037.
Total Pay Units: 309.

CABLE VISION SERVICES INC.
1701 Cogswell Ave.
Pell City, AL 35125
Phone: 205-884-4549
Officer:
Art Smith, Pres.
Cable Systems (1):
Alabama: Odenville.
Total Basic Subscribers: 1,433.
Total Pay Units: 477.

CABLE VUE TV
Box 660
103 Parker St.
Baxley, GA 31515
Phone: 912-367-9811
Cable Systems (2):
Georgia: Baxley, Blackshear.
Total Basic Subscribers: 3,400.

CABLESTAR INC.
Box 145
Ragland, AL 35131-0145
Phone: 205-472-2141
Ownership: Bob Dickinson, Principal.
Cable Systems (1):
Alabama: Ragland.
Total Basic Subscribers: 700.
Total Pay Units: 320.
Other Holdings:
Telephone.

CABLETEX SYSTEMS INC.
Box 547
Riesel, TX 76682
Phone: 254-896-2818

Ownership: Pete Bingham.
Cable Systems (1):
Texas: Riesel.
Total Basic Subscribers: N.A.

CABLETRONIX
Box 133
Cedar Bluff, VA 24609
Phone: 703-783-6181
Ownership: Robert Waldron.
Cable Systems (1):
Virginia: Rosedale 50%.
Total Basic Subscribers: N.A.

CABLEVISION COMMUNICATIONS INC.
Box 477
Cloudcroft, NM 88317
Phone: 505-682-2528
Ownership: James Howard, Pres.
Cable Systems (5):
New Mexico: Cloudcroft, Elephant Butte, Twin Forks.
New York: Ramapo.
Tennessee: Mountain City.
Total Basic Subscribers: 28,416 (0.04% of total cable households).
Total Pay Units: 13,353.

CABLE-VISION LTD.
Box 757
Gatesville, TX 76528
Phone: 817-865-6542
Officer:
Phil Bone, Pres.
Ownership: Martha Bone, 50%; Cris Bone, 16%; Jan Bone, 16%; Phil Bone, 16%.
Cable Systems (3):
Texas: Edna, Ganado, Lexington.
Total Basic Subscribers: N.A.

CABLEVISION SYSTEMS CORP.
One Media Crossways
Woodbury, NY 11797
Phone: 516-803-2300
Fax: 516-803-1196
Officers:
Corporate Executives:
Charles F. Dolan, Chmn.
James Dolan, Chief Exec. Officer
William J. Bell, Vice Chmn.
Bill Quinn, Pres., Cable Operations
Joseph Azznara, Pres., Telecommunications Services
Robert Lemle, Exec. V.P. & Secy.
Margaret Albergo, Sr. V.P., Planning & Performance
Joseph Cece, Sr. V.P., Strategic Planning
Thomas Dolan, Sr. V.P., Chief Information Officer
Sheila Mahoney, Sr. V.P., Government Relations & Public Affairs
Barry J. O'Leary, Sr. V.P. Finance & Treas.
Irwin Polinsky, Sr. V.P., Administration
Andrew Rosengard, Sr. V.P. & Controller
Cable Operations:
Patricia Falese, Sr. V.P., Regional Operations for New York City &
Wayne Barnett, Regional V.P., Ohio
Kathleen Mayo, Regional V.P., Boston, Brookline & suburban Massachusetts
Rainbow Media Holdings Inc.
Joshua Sapan, Chief Exec. Officer, Rainbow Media Holdings Inc.
Hank Ratner, Exec. V.P., Rainbow Media Holdings Inc.
Ownership: Publicly held. Charles F. Dolan, majority stockholder; AT&T Broadband & Internet Services, see listing, 25%; National Broadcasting Co., 25%.
Represented (legal): Mintz, Levin, Cohn, Ferris, Glovsky & Popeo; Piper & Marbury LLP.
Cable Systems (62):
Connecticut: Bridgeport 50%, Litchfield, Norwalk.
Massachusetts: Boston, Braintree, Danvers, Fitchburg, Framingham, Haverhill, Lexington, Maynard, Norwood, Peabody, Westford.
Michigan: Kalamazoo.
New Jersey: Allamuchy Twp., Bayonne, Bergenfield, Dover, Elizabeth, Freehold, Hamilton Twp. (Mercer County), Hoboken, Millstone Twp., Monmouth County, Newark, Oakland, Paterson, Piscataway.
New York: Bronx, Brookhaven, Brooklyn, Cobleskill (town), Dover Plains, East Hampton, Islip, Lynbrook, Mamaroneck, Mount Kisco, North Salem, Port Chester, Riverhead, Rockland, Stamford, Suffolk County, Warwick, Woodbury (Nassau County), Yonkers, Yorktown.
Ohio: Bainbridge Twp. (Geauga County), Bath Twp. (Summit County), Brecksville, Brook Park, Brunswick, Chardon, Cleveland, Cleveland Heights, Garfield Heights, North Olmsted, Sheffield Lake, Solon, Strongsville.
Total Basic Subscribers: 3,438,000 (5.02% of total cable households).
Total Pay Units: 5,555,000.
Other Holdings:
Program source: Rainbow Media Holdings Inc., American Movie Classics, Bravo, 6 regional Fox Sports channels (minority interest), Madison Square Garden Network (majority interest), Metro Channels, Much Music, News 12 Bronx, News 12 Connecticut, News 12 Long Island, News 12 New Jersey, News 12 Westchester, Romance Classics, The Independent Film Channel.
New York: Madison Square Garden, Radio City Music Hall.
Cable advertising representative: Rainbow Advertising Sales Corp.
Common Carrier: License for personal communications network (PCN) to provide experimental carriage of telephony via cable.
Motion picture holdings: Clearview motion picture theaters in New York.
Professional sports team: Majority interest in New York Knicks & New York Rangers.
Data service: @Home.
Telecommunications company: Lightpath CLEC.

CAI WIRELESS SYSTEMS INC.
Suite 102
12 Corporate Woods Blvd.
Albany, NY 12211
Phone: 518-462-2632
Fax: 518-462-3045
Officers:
Jared Abbruzzese, Chmn. & Chief Exec. Officer
John Prico, Pres.
James Ashman, Sr. V.P., Corp. Finance & Acquisitions
Timothy Santora, Sr. V.P., Spectrum Acquisition
John Brinker, V.P., Operations
George Williams, Chief Financial Officer

Engineering Offices:
Suite 100
Arlington, VA 22201
Phone: 703-812-8800
Fax: 703-812-8808
Ownership: MCI WorldCom, 62%.
Wireless Cable Systems
District of Columbia: Washington.
New York: Albany, New York, Rochester.
North Carolina: Charlotte.
Pennsylvania: Philadelphia.
Virginia: Norfolk & Virginia Beach.
Planned Wireless Cable Systems (1):
Connecticut: Hartford.
Total Basic Subscribers: 65,700 (0.10% of total cable households).
Total Pay Units: 29,417.
Other Holdings:
LPTV, MDS, MMDS, see listings.
CS Wireless Systems Inc., 90%, see listing.

CALAVISION
Suite 90036
5670 Wilshire Blvd.
Los Angeles, CA 90036
Phone: 323-965-5400
Fax: 323-965-5411
Officers:
Garry Spire, Chmn.
Ira Wechsler, Pres.
Paul Koplin, Chief Exec. Officer
Bill Chen, Chief Operating Officer
Ownership: Lawrence Rogow, Garry Spire & Ira Wechsler, Principals. For Rogow's & Spire's other interests, see Venture Technologies Group Inc. in TV & LPTV Ownership.
Represented (legal): Arter & Hadden LLP; Rogers & Wells.
Cable Systems (2):
California: Calabasas Park, Thousand Palms.
Total Basic Subscribers: 3,090.
Total Pay Units: 1,622.

CALIFORNIA-OREGON BROADCASTING INC.
Box 1489
125 S. Fir St.
Medford, OR 97501
Phone: 541-779-5555
Fax: 541-779-1151
Officers:
Patricia C. Smullin, Pres.
Doreeta Domke, V.P.
Carol Anne Smullin Brown, Secy.
Ownership: Patricia C. Smullin, 50%; Carol Anne Smullin Brown, 50%.
Represented (legal): Wiley, Rein & Fielding.
Cable Systems (4):
Oregon: Enterprise, La Pine, Madras, Prineville.
Total Basic Subscribers: 10,171.
Total Pay Units: 2,409.
Other Holdings:
TV, LPTV, see listings.

JEWEL B. CALLAHAM REVOCABLE TRUST
Box 548
Broken Bow, OK 74728
Phone: 405-584-3340
Ownership: Esta Callaham, John B. Callaham & Angela G. Wisenhunt, Trustees.
Cable Systems (1):
Oklahoma: Broken Bow.
Total Basic Subscribers: N.A.
Other Holdings:
LPTV, see listing.
Pine Telephone Co. Inc.

CALLAIS CABLEVISION INC.
Drawer 788
Golden Meadow, LA 70357
Phone: 504-594-6823
Officers:
Harold J. Callais, Pres.
Peter Callais, Chief Operating Officer
Ronald L. Callais, Secy.-Treas.
Ownership: Harold J. Callais.
Cable Systems (1):
Louisiana: Golden Meadow.
Total Basic Subscribers: 11,200 (0.02% of total cable households).
Total Pay Units: 4,400.

CALVIN CABLE SYSTEM INC.
Box 96
Calvin, PA 16222
Phone: 814-643-0438
Fax: 814-643-0438
Officers:
Harold Colbert, Pres.
Judy Colbert, Secy.
Ownership: Harold Colbert & Judy Colbert, 100% jointly.
Cable Systems (1):
Pennsylvania: Union Twp. (Huntingdon County).
Total Basic Subscribers: 900.
Total Pay Units: 512.

CAMBRIDGE TELEPHONE CO.
130 Superior St.
Cambridge, ID 83610
Phone: 208-257-3314
Cable Systems (1):
Idaho: Cambridge.
Total Basic Subscribers: 111.
Total Pay Units: 62.

DON CAMPBELL
Box 70
Idaho City, ID 83631
Phone: 208-392-4290
Fax: 208-392-4505
Cable Systems (1):
Idaho: Idaho City.
Total Basic Subscribers: 200.
Total Pay Units: 143.

CANBY TELEPHONE ASSN.
Box 850
184 N. Grant
Canby, OR 97013
Phone: 503-656-8343
Cable Systems (1):
Oregon: Canby.
Total Basic Subscribers: N.A.

C & W CABLE INC.
7920 Hwy. 30W
Annville, KY 40402-9748
Phone: 606-364-5357
Officers:
Don Williams, Pres. & Chief Exec. & Operating Officer
Judy C. Williams, V.P., Secy.-Treas. & Chief Financial Officer
Ownership: Don Williams & Judy C. Williams.
Cable Systems (2):
Kentucky: Bond, Burning Springs.
Total Basic Subscribers: 2,350.

WILLIAM CANLEY
Town & Country Plaza
Rte. 20 E
Cazenovia, NY 13035
Phone: 315-655-3555
Wireless Cable Systems (1):
New York: Cazenovia.
Total Basic Subscribers: 856.

CANNON VALLEY CABLEVISION
Box 337
Bricelyn, MN 56014
Phone: 507-653-4444
Officer:
Scott Johnson, Pres.

Cable Systems (2):
Minnesota: Bricelyn, Morristown.
Total Basic Subscribers: 960.
Total Pay Units: 303.

CAPP'S TV ELECTRONICS INC.
1399 Arundell Ave.
Ventura, CA 93003
Phones: 805-642-0241; 800-227-7747
Fax: 805-650-1869
Officers:
Earl (Capp) Loughboro, Chmn., Pres. & Chief Exec. Officer
William G. Loughboro, V.P.
Dolly M. Loughboro, Chief Financial Officer
Cable Systems (2):
California: Camarillo, Lake Hughes.
Total Basic Subscribers: 335.
Total Pay Units: 66.

CARIBBEAN COMMUNICATIONS CORP.
One Beltjen Place
St. Thomas, VI 00802
Phone: 340-776-2150
Fax: 340-774-5029
Officers:
Jeffrey Prosser, Chmn.
Thomas Minnich, Chief Operating Officer
Ownership: Innovative Communication Corp.
Represented (legal): Pepper & Corazzini LLP.
Cable Systems (1):
Virgin Islands: St. Thomas.
Total Basic Subscribers: 14,512 (0.02% of total cable households).
Total Pay Units: 18,868.

CAROLINA COUNTRY CABLE
1070 Jonathan Creek Rd.
Waynesville, NC 28786
Phone: 704-926-2288
Fax: 704-926-2835
Officer:
Stewart Corbett, Pres.
Ownership: Stewart Corbett, Gerald Aldridge & Ed Stark, Principals. Corbett & Stark are also principals of Kudzu Cable TV Inc., see listing.
Cable Systems (4):
Georgia: Bent Tree Community.
North Carolina: Ironduff, Waynesville.
Tennessee: Turtletown.
Total Basic Subscribers: 2,719.
Total Pay Units: 125.

CARSON COMMUNICATIONS LLC
Box 214
Wetmore, KS 66550
Phone: 785-866-2133
Fax: 785-866-2144
Ownership: Robert C. Carson, principal. Carson is also principal of C.L.R. Video LLC, see listing.
Cable Systems (19):
Kansas: Baileyville, Bern, Denison, Emmett, Fairview, Goff, Hiawatha, Highland, Lake Dabinawa, Morrill, Muscotah, Randolph, Reserve, Summerfield, Troy, Vermillion, Wathena, White Cloud, Whiting.
Total Basic Subscribers: 2,764.

DAVID CARTER
Box 2326
Natchitoches, LA 71457
Phone: 318-352-8321
Cable Systems (1):
Louisiana: Natchitoches (portions).
Total Basic Subscribers: 42.
Total Pay Units: 6.

CASCADE CABLE SYSTEMS
Box 397
The Dalles, OR 97058
Phone: 503-298-4983
Ownership: James F. Roth.
Cable Systems (3):
Oregon: Tygh Valley.
Washington: Lyle, Wishram.
Total Basic Subscribers: 407.
Total Pay Units: 81.

CITY OF CASCADE LOCKS CABLE TV
Box 308
Cascade Locks, OR 97014
Phone: 541-374-8484
Officer:
Mike Bridges, Chief Exec. Officer
Ownership: Municipally owned.
Cable Systems (1):
Oregon: Cascade Locks.
Total Basic Subscribers: 395.
Total Pay Units: 216.

CASCO TELEPHONE CO.
Box 126
212 Church Ave.
Casco, WI 54205-0126
Phone: 414-837-7474
Fax: 414-837-2330
Officer:
Michael A. Gotstein, Regional Dir.-CATV
Ownership: Pacific Telecom Inc., see listing.
Cable Systems (2):
Wisconsin: Casco, New Franken.
Total Basic Subscribers: 1,230.
Total Pay Units: 615.
Other Holdings:
Cellular radio.

CASEY MUTUAL TELEPHONE CO.
108 E. Logan St.
Casey, IA 50048
Phone: 515-746-2222
Fax: 515-746-2221
Officer:
John Breining, Mgr.
Cable Systems (1):
Iowa: Casey.
Total Basic Subscribers: 181.
Total Pay Units: 42.

CASPIAN COMMUNITY TV CORP.
Box 240
Caspian, MI 49915
Phone: 906-265-4840
Officers:
Joseph Sabol, Pres.
John Regozzi, V.P.
Susan Sundquist, Secy.-Treas.
Ownership: Subscriber owned.
Cable Systems (1):
Michigan: Caspian.
Total Basic Subscribers: 800.
Total Pay Units: 103.

CASS CABLE TV INC.
Box 200
100 Redbud Rd.
Virginia, IL 62691
Phone: 217-452-7725
Fax: 217-452-7797
Officers:
Gerald E. Gill, Chmn. & Pres.
Donald L. Bell, V.P. & Chief Exec. Officer
Marvin Seward, V.P. & Gen. Mgr.
Thomas D. Allen, Chief Financial Officer
Donna Troutman, Mktg. Dir.
Ownership: Gerald E. Gill. Gill owns Cass Telephone Co., Cass Long Distance, Cass Communications Management Inc. & has cellular telephone holdings.
Represented (legal): Cole, Raywid & Braverman LLP.
Cable Systems (15):
Illinois: Baylis (village), Beardstown, Chatham, Easton, Havana, Kampsville (village), Manito, Milton, Mount Sterling, Oakford (village), Pittsfield, Rushville, Versailles, Virginia.
Missouri: Palmyra.
Total Basic Subscribers: 16,573 (0.02% of total cable households).
Total Pay Units: 8,476.

CASS COUNTY CABLE INC.
Box 293
Greenwood, MO 64034
Phone: 816-537-8356
Officer:
Daryl Granzella, Mgr.
Cable Systems (3):
Missouri: Cass County (northwestern portion), Hume, Newton.
Total Basic Subscribers: 259.
Total Pay Units: 190.
Other Holdings:
Cable construction.

CATALINA CABLE TV CO.
Box 2143
222 Metropole Ave.
Avalon, CA 90704
Phone: 310-510-0255
Fax: 310-510-2565
Officer:
Ralph J. Morrow, Jr., Chief Exec. Officer
Ownership: Patricia L. Morrow & Ralph J. Morrow Jr., 100% jointly.
Cable Systems (1):
California: Avalon/Catalina Island.
Total Basic Subscribers: 1,354.
Total Pay Units: 429.

CATAWBA SERVICES INC.
203 Saluda St.
Rock Hill, SC 29731
Phones: 803-324-6222; 803-482-2222
Fax: 803-324-2600
Officers:
F. S. Barnes Jr., Chmn.
J. M. Barnes, Pres.
W. C. Beaty Jr., V.P. & Gen. Mgr.
E. L. Barnes, Secy.-Treas.
Ownership: Edwin L. Barnes, Frank S. Barnes Jr. & John M. Barnes, Principals. Barnes' have interest in Video Vision Inc. (see listing) & are affiliated with telephone companies in Fort Mill, Lancaster & Rock Hill, SC.
Cable Systems (4):
South Carolina: Great Falls, Rock Hill, Winnsboro, York.
Total Basic Subscribers: 46,249 (0.07% of total cable households).
Total Pay Units: 26,263.

CATV SERVICE INC.
115 Mill St.
Danville, PA 17821
Phone: 717-275-8410
Fax: 717-275-3888
Officer:
Margaret Walsonavich, Pres.
Ownership: Margaret Walsonavich.
Represented (legal): Pepper & Corazzini.
Cable Systems (2):
Pennsylvania: Danville, Lewisburg.
Total Basic Subscribers: 17,000 (0.02% of total cable households).
Total Pay Units: 4,000.

CAWKER CITY
Box 2
804 Locust St.
Cawker City, KS 67430
Phone: 913-781-4713
Fax: 913-781-4436
Officer:
Wayne Musgrove, Gen. Mgr.
Ownership: Community owned.
Represented (legal): Tracy J. Thull.
Cable Systems (1):
Kansas: Cawker City.
Total Basic Subscribers: 267.
Total Pay Units: 269.

C.E.D. ENTERPRISES INC.
115 First Ave. W
Rock Rapids, IA 51246-1501
Phone: 712-472-3816
Fax: 712-472-3604
Ownership: Carl De Jongh, Chmn. & Chief Exec. Officer.
Cable Systems (1):
Iowa: Rock Rapids.
Total Basic Subscribers: 970.
Total Pay Units: 321.

CEDAR FALLS MUNICIPAL COMMUNICATIONS UTILITY
Box 769
Utility Pkwy.
Cedar Falls, IA 50613
Phone: 319-266-1761
Officers:
Jerry Shoff, Chief Exec. Officer
Doris J. Kelley, Mktg. Coordinator
Cable Systems (1):
Iowa: Cedar Falls.
Total Basic Subscribers: 6,609.

CELLULARVISION USA INC.
140 58th St.
Brooklyn, NY 11220
Phone: 718-439-2360
Fax: 718-439-9740
Wireless Cable Systems (1):
New York: Brooklyn.
Total Basic Subscribers: 12,500 (0.02% of total cable households).

CENCOM INC.
Box 40
Jackson, NE 68743
Phone: 402-632-4811
Officer:
Howard Rasmussen, Pres.
Cable Systems (4):
Nebraska: Clearwater, Coleridge, Newcastle, Wynot.
Total Basic Subscribers: 514.
Total Pay Units: 172.

CENTER CABLE TV
Box 117
Greeley, NE 68842
Phone: 308-428-5925
Ownership: Martin Callahan, 50%; Thomas Callahan, 50%.
Cable Systems (1):
Nebraska: Greeley.
Total Basic Subscribers: 145.

CENTER JUNCTION TELEPHONE CO.

513 Main St.
Center Junction, IA 52212
Phone: 319-487-2631
Fax: 319-487-3701
Officers:
John Gray, Pres.
Judy Paulson, Secy.-Treas.
Cable Systems (1):
Iowa: Center Junction.
Total Basic Subscribers: 51.

CENTER MUNICIPAL CABLE SYSTEM

Box 400
400 S. Worth St.
Center, CO 81125
Phone: 719-754-3497
Fax: 719-754-3379
Ownership: Community owned.
Cable Systems (1):
Colorado: Center.
Total Basic Subscribers: 617.
Total Pay Units: 407.

CENTRAL DAKOTA TV INC.

Box 299
630 N. 5th St.
Carrington, ND 58421
Phone: 701-674-8122
Officers:
Robert Hill, Chief Exec. Officer
Gerald Eissinger, Pres.
Doug Wede, Secy.-Treas.
Dave Wolf, Chief Plant Officer
Keith Larson, Chief Financial Officer
Cindy Hewitt, Commerical Mgr.
Tricia Jeske, Accounting Mgr.
Ownership: Dakota Central Telecommunications Cooperative.
Represented (legal): Fabian Noack.
Cable Systems (6):
North Dakota: Bowdon, Cleveland, Glenfield, Sykeston, Woodworth, Ypsilanti.
Wireless Cable Systems (1):
North Dakota: Carrington.
Total Cable Subscribers: 1,232.
Total Pay Units: 678.
Other Holdings:
MMDS, see listing.

CENTRAL TEXAS WIRELESS TV INC.

Box 509
Goldthwaite, TX 76844
Phone: 915-648-2213
Wireless Cable Systems (1):
Texas: Goldthwaite.
Total Basic Subscribers: N.A.

CENTRAL VALLEY CABLE TV LLC

Suite 102
375 Woodworth Ave.
Clovis, CA 93612
Phone: 209-298-1464
Fax: 209-298-1329
Ownership: Tom Gelardi, Chief Operating Officer.
Cable Systems (4):
California: Coalinga, Huron, Riverdale, Williams.
Total Basic Subscribers: 5,010.
Total Pay Units: 1,773.

CENTRAL VISION

Box 5393
Bend OR, 97708-5393
Phone: 503-382-4031
Wireless Cable Systems (2):
Oregon: Prineville, Redmond.
Total Basic Subscribers: N.A.

CENTROVISION INC.

Box 3157
Temple, TX 76501
Phone: 817-773-1163
Ownership: Alton Shepard, Pres. & Principal.
Cable Systems (7):
Texas: Little River-Academy, Moody, Morgan's Point Resort, Rogers, Salado, Temple, Troy.
Total Basic Subscribers: 1,617.

CENTURY COMMUNICATIONS CORP.

50 Locust Ave.
New Canaan, CT 06840
Phone: 203-966-8746
Fax: 203-966-9228
Officers:
Leonard Tow, Chmn. & Chief Exec. Officer
Bernard P. Gallager, Pres. & Chief Operating Officer
Andrew Tow, Exec. V.P.
Michael G. Harris, Sr. V.P., Engineering
Scott N. Schneider, Sr. V.P. & Treas.
Daniel E. Gold, Sr. V.P.
Claire L. Tow, Sr. V.P.
George Franciscovich, V.P.
Geoffrey R. Broom, V.P., Human Resources
William Rosendahl, V.P., Corp. Affairs
Robert J. Larson, V.P. & Controller
Katherine Caminiti, V.P., Asst. Controller
David Z. Rosensweig, Secy.
Cable Television Division:
Daniel E. Gold, Pres.
Judith Allen, Sr. V.P., Mktg. & Programming
George Franciscovich, Sr. V.P., Legal Affairs
Frank Tow, Exec. Dir., Century Advertising
Sharon O'Malley, V.P., Legal Affairs
Joe DiBacco, V.P., Southwestern Region
Ken Rhoades, V.P., Eastern Region
Paco Toste, V.P., Caribbean Region
William Shreffler, V.P., Western Region
Jeffrey Butler, Mgr., Bay Area Region
Richard Sander, V.P., Controller
Ownership: Publicly held., Leonard Tow, majority shareholder.
Represented (legal): Fleischman & Walsh LLP; Leavy, Rosensweig & Hyman (New York).
Cable Systems (109):
Alabama: Blountsville, Cullman, Enterprise, Fort Payne.
Arizona: Yuma.
California: Anaheim, Benicia, Brea, Burney, Chino, Diamond Bar, El Centro, Fairfield, Glendora, Hermosa Beach, Los Angeles, Redondo Beach, Rohnert Park, San Pablo, Susanville, Ukiah, Ventura, Yorba Linda, Yountville, Yucca Valley.
Colorado: Colorado Springs, Gunnison, Telluride, Trinidad.
Connecticut: Norwich, Old Lyme.
Florida: Archer, Dunnellon, Trenton, Williston, Yankeetown, Yulee.
Georgia: Brunswick 50%.
Idaho: Bonners Ferry, Coeur d'Alene, Moscow, Mountain Home, Twin Lakes.
Indiana: De Soto, Huntington, Muncie, Newburgh.
Kansas: Liberal.
Kentucky: Clay, Corydon, Dixon, Garrison, Henderson (town), Owensboro 50%, Vanceburg, Whitesburg.
Massachusetts: Great Barrington.
Mississippi: Greenwood, Indianola.
Montana: Libby.
New Mexico: Angel Fire, Deming, Hatch, Las Vegas, Los Alamos, Lovington, Pecos, Portales, Questa, Silver City, Taos, Tucumcari.
New York: Norwich.
North Carolina: Laurinburg.
Ohio: Portsmouth, Struthers 80%.
Pennsylvania: Lykens, Sharon.
South Carolina: Cheraw, Dillon, Hartsville, Mullins.
Virginia: Ben Hur, Clintwood, Coeburn, Duffield, Norton, Pennington Gap.
Washington: Friday Harbor, Longview.
West Virginia: Arnettsville, Brookhaven, Clarksburg, Colfax, Easton, Grafton, Huntington, Hutchinson, Meadowdale, Monongah, Morgantown, Red House, Westover, Whitehall, Worthington.
Wisconsin: Wauwatosa 50%.
Wyoming: Evanston.
Puerto Rico: Levittown 50%, San Juan.
Total Basic Subscribers: 1,338,000 (1.95% of total cable households).
Total Pay Units: 448,000.
Radio Stations:
Kentucky: WVJS(AM), Owensboro; WSTO(FM), Owensboro.
Other Holdings:
Cellular telephone: Has 33% interest in Centennial Cellular Corp., serving AR, IN, LA, NC & VA.
Cable: Owns license to distribute satellite pay TV in Australia.
Note: Sold to Adelphia Communications Corp. 1999.

CFW COMMUNICATIONS

Box 1990
Waynesboro, VA 22980
Phone: 540-946-3500
Fax: 540-946-3599
Officers:
Robert S. Yeago Jr., Chmn.
James S. Quarforth, Pres. & Chief Exec. Officer
Carl A. Rosberg, Sr. V.P.
Christina S. Smith, Secy.-Treas.
Michael B. Moneymaker, Chief Financial Officer
Ownership: Publicly owned.
Cable Systems (1):
Virginia: Covington.
Wireless Cable Systems (3):
Virginia: Charlottesville, Harrisonburg, Richmond.
Total Cable Subscribers: 19,699 (0.03% of total cable households).
Total Pay Units: 8,218.
Other Holdings:
MDS, MMDS, see listing.
Paging service.
Data service: Internet access.
Cellular telephone, ITFS.

CHAMBERS COMMUNICATIONS CORP.

Box 7009
Suite 200
2295 Coburg Rd.
Eugene, OR 97401
Phone: 541-485-5611
Fax: 541-342-1568
Officers:
Carolyn S. Chambers, Chmn. & Chief Exec. Officer
Scott Chambers, Pres.
Bill Nagy, Chief Operating Officer
Jack Lawrence, Exec. V.P.
James L. Plummer, V.P., Finance
John C. Ohm, Secy.
Ownership: Carolyn S. Chambers.
Represented (legal): Arnold, Gallagher, Saydack, Percell & Roberts.
Cable Systems (8):
California: Chico, Novato.
Idaho: Marsing, Payette.
Oregon: Huntington, Ontario, Sunriver.
Washington: Edmonds.
Total Basic Subscribers: 80,781 (0.12% of total cable households).
Total Pay Units: 18,959.
Other Holdings:
TV, LPTV, see listings.
Multimedia: Chambers Production Group, Chambers Multimedia Connection Inc.

CHANNEL 4 TV INC.

Box 648
Eureka, MT 59917
Phone: 406-889-3099
Ownership: Rob Little.
Cable Systems (1):
Montana: Eureka.
Total Basic Subscribers: 560.
Total Pay Units: 155.

CHARITON VALLEY COMMUNICATIONS CORP.

Box 470
Hwy. 129 N
Bucklin, MO 64631
Phone: 816-695-9930
Fax: 816-695-4403
Officer:
William Biere, Gen. Mgr.
Ownership: Chariton Valley Telephone Corp. Has telephone & cellular radio holdings.
Cable Systems (3):
Missouri: Bevier, Bucklin, New Cambria.
Total Basic Subscribers: 589.
Total Pay Units: 249.

CHARTER COMMUNICATIONS INC.

Suite 400
12444 Powerscourt Dr.
St. Louis, MO 63131
Phone: 314-965-0555
Fax: 314-543-2477; 314-965-6640
Officers:
Paul Allen, Chmn.
Barry L. Babcock, Vice Chmn.
Howard Wood, Vice Chmn.
Jerald L. Kent, Pres. & Chief Exec. Officer
Curtis Shaw, Sr. V.P., Gen. Counsel & Secy.
Kent Kalkwarf, Sr. V.P. & Chief Financial Officer
Thomas R. Jokerst, Sr. V.P., Advanced Technology Development
Mary Pat Blake, Sr. V.P., Mktg. & Programming
Ralph G. Kelly, Sr. V.P. & Treas.
Steve Silva, V.P., New Product Development
Don Johnson, V.P., Human Resources
Patricia L. McCaskill, V.P., Programming & PPV
Anita B. Lamont, Dir., Communications
Donald J. Vollmayer, Controller

Branch Offices:

941 Charter Commons Dr.
Town and Country, MO 63017
Phone: 314-207-7044

Metroplex Regional
4800 Blue Mound Rd.
Ft. Worth, TX 76106
Phone: 817-509-6272

North Central Regional
440 Science Dr.
Suite 302
Madison, WI 53711
Phone: 608-238-9690

Northeast
11 Commerce Rd.
Newtown, CT 06470-1655
Phone: 203-270-8665

South Central I
One River Chase Office Plaza
Suite 126
Birmingham, AL 35244
Phone: 205-733-0703

Southeast Regional Office
883 N.E. Main St.
Simpsonville, SC 29681
Phone: 864-967-2730

Southern
2269 Wilma Rudolph Blvd.
Suite 103
Clarksville, TN 37040-5841
Phone: 931-906-6641

California I
2215 W. Mission Rd.
Alhambra, CA 91803
Phone: 626-537-6100

California II
6680 View Park Court
Riverside, CA 92503
Phone: 909-687-2721

Long Beach
2931 Redondo Ave.
Long Beach, CA 90806
Phone: 562-424-4657

Illinois
210 W. Division St.
Maryville, IL 62062
Phone: 618-345-2205
Ownership: Paul Allen.
Cable Systems (324):
Alabama: Albertville, Alexander City, Arab, Baileyton, Berry, Beulah, Bradford, Brookwood, Carbon Hill, Centreville, Childersburg, Columbiana, Cordova, Curry, Double Springs, Gardendale, Guntersville, Haleyville, Harpersville, Hartselle, Heflin, Henagar, Hokes Bluff, Jasper, Limestone County (western portion), Locust Fork, Maytown, Montevallo, Morgan City, Moulton, Mountain Brook, Oakman, Ozark, Pence, Russellville, Shelby County (northern portion), Shelby Lake, Southside, Sumiton, Talladega, Thorsby, Tuscaloosa County, Tuskegee, Warrior, West Blocton.
California: Alhambra, Auburn, Azusa, Crescent Mills, Duarte, Glendale, Livingston, Long Beach, Pasadena, Portola, Quincy (portions), Rancho Yolo Mobile Home Park, Rio Vista, Riverbank, Riverside, San Bernardino, San Luis Obispo, Turlock, Victorville, Watsonville, West Sacramento, Whittier.
Colorado: Fort Carson.
Connecticut: Ashford, Newtown.
Georgia: Ambrose, Carrollton, Columbus, Cusseta, Douglas, Dublin, Greenville, Grovetown, La Grange, Manchester, Newnan, Pine Mountain, Stockbridge, Thomaston, Tignall, Waverly Hall, West Point.
Illinois: Alhambra, Genoa, Hamel, Marengo, Marine, Maryville, New Douglas, Roscoe, Sorento, St. Jacob, Waterloo, Worden.
Indiana: Adamsboro, Akron, Batesville, Brookville, Columbus, Connersville, Covington, Crawfordsville, Frankfort 80%, Lake Cicott, Liberty, Logansport, Monticello, New Albany, North Vernon, Peru, Rushville, Seymour, Silver Lake, Veedersburg, Wabash, Warsaw, Westport.
Kansas: Fort Riley.
Kentucky: Eminence, Hopkinsville, Middlesboro, Shelbyville.
Louisiana: Bogalusa, Folsom, Hammond, Lafourche Parish, Pointe Coupee, St. Landry Parish, St. Tammany Parish.
Massachusetts: Chicopee, Pepperell, Rutland (town), Uxbridge, Wales, Westport.
Minnesota: Northfield, Red Wing, Rosemount, Stockton.
Mississippi: Osyka, Picayune.
Missouri: Barnhart, Bowling Green, Canton, Chesterfield, Flat River, Frankford, Kirkwood, La Belle, Terre du Lac, Troy, Villa Ridge, Warrenton.
Montana: Alberton, Arlee, Big Flat, Grant Creek, Lolo, Milltown, Nine Mile, Polson, Ronan, Seeley Lake, St. Marie, Superior, Victor.
North Carolina: Anderson Creek, Benson, Black Mountain, Buies Creek, Burnsville, Camp Lejeune, Hickory, Kenly, Lenoir, Lincolnton, Lynn, Marshall, Newton Grove, Princeton, Sanford, Spruce Pine, Waynesville.
South Carolina: Abbeville, Anchor Point, Belton, Camden, Chester, Gaffney, Gray Court, Greer, Hartwell Villas, Iva, Laurens, Lockhart, Pickens, Salem, Travelers Rest, Union, West Pelzer, Whitmire, Williamston.
Tennessee: Anthony Hill, Ashland City, Bristol, Clarksville, Jackson, Johnson City, Montgomery County, Morristown, Sneedville.
Texas: Alvarado, Borger, Carrollton, Cleburne, Cleveland, Combine, Crandall, Denton, Dumas, Duncanville, Fort Worth, Frost, Godley, Hubbard, Jasper, Kennedale, Mansfield, McLean, Pampa, South Weatherford, Trophy Club, University Park, Waxahachie, Weatherford, Whitney.
Utah: Logan.
Wisconsin: Adams, Algoma, Algoma Twp., Antigo, Ashland, Beloit, Berlin, Black Creek, Black River Falls, Bloomer, Boyd/Cadott, Brandon, Brillion, Brodhead, Chilton, Clintonville, Coleman, Colfax, Cornell, Dane, Denmark, Dresser, Eagle River, Eau Claire, Fitchburg, Fond du Lac, Gillett, Green Lake, Gresham, Hayward, Hustisford, Janesville, Kewaunee, Ladysmith, Lafayette, Lena, Markesan, Marshfield, Mazomanie, Medford, Melrose, Menomonie, Mindoro, Minocqua, Mishicot, Monroe, Montello, Mount Horeb, New Glarus, New Holstein, New London, Oakfield, Oconto, Omro, Onalaska, Park Falls, Poynette, Prairie du Sac, Rice Lake, Richfield, Rosendale, Shawano, Sheboygan, Sister Bay, Sparta, Spencer, Spooner, St. Joseph, Stanley, Stevens Point, Sturgeon Bay, Tigerton, Tomah, Two Rivers, Verona, Warrens, Waupaca, Wausau, Wautoma, West Bend, Whitewater, Wisconsin Rapids.
Total Basic Subscribers: 2,364,113 (3.45% of total cable households).
Total Pay Units: 1,346,627.

CHAUTAUQUA & ERIE TELEPHONE CO.

Box B
30 E. Main St.
Westfield, NY 14787
Phone: 716-326-2121
Fax: 716-326-3166
Cable Systems (1):
New York: Clymer.
Total Basic Subscribers: 628.
Total Pay Units: 130.

CHEROKEE CABLEVISION INC.

Box 487
Cherokee, NC 28719
Phone: 704-497-4861
Ownership: Ken Blankenship, Pres.
Cable Systems (1):
North Carolina: Cherokee Indian Reservation.
Total Basic Subscribers: 2,690.
Total Pay Units: 921.

CHEYENNE RIVER SIOUX TRIBE TELEPHONE AUTHORITY

Box 810
Eagle Butte, SD 57625
Phones: 605-964-2600; 605-964-3307
Cable Systems (3):
South Dakota: Cherry Creek, Eagle Butte, Takini.
Total Basic Subscribers: 758.
Total Pay Units: 346.

CHIBARDUN CABLE TV COOPERATIVE

Box 164
110 N. 2nd Ave.
Dallas, WI 54733
Phone: 715-837-1011
Officers:
James Johnson, Pres.
Ricky S. Vergin, Chief Exec. Officer
Scott J. Hickok, Chief Operating Officer
Donald Featherly, Chief Financial Officer
Ownership: James Johnson, Principal.
Cable Systems (2):
Wisconsin: Barron, Dallas.
Total Basic Subscribers: 2,082.
Total Pay Units: 1,147.

CHICAGO CABLE TV

5711 S. Western Ave.
Chicago, IL 60636
Phone: 312-525-8653
Officer:
Mike Green, Mgr.
Ownership: Local investors.
Cable Systems (1):
Illinois: Chicago (area 1) 5%.
Total Basic Subscribers: 71,020 (0.10% of total cable households).
Total Pay Units: 79,475.

CHINOOK PROGRESSIVE CLUB TV

Box 15
Chinook, WA 98614
Phone: 206-777-8412
Officers:
Terry Eager, Chmn.
Terry Krager, Pres.
Dale Hughes, Chief Exec. Officer
Trophy W. Hughes, Chief Operating Officer
Rhoda Hughes, Secy.-Treas.
Ownership: Subscriber owned.
Cable Systems (1):
Washington: Chinook.
Total Basic Subscribers: 280.
Total Pay Units: 165.

CHRISTIAN ENTERPRISES

Box 300
Pioche, NV 89043
Phone: 702-726-3100
Officers:
John Christian, Pres.
Paul Christian, V.P.
Cable Systems (4):
Nevada: Alamo, Caliente, Panaca, Pioche.
Total Basic Subscribers: 587.
Total Pay Units: 198.

ROGER CHUMLEY

Box 12215
Lexington, KY 40581
Phone: 606-263-5516
Cable Systems (1):
Kentucky: Millville.
Total Basic Subscribers: N.A.

CIM TEL CABLE INC.

Box 266
Manford, OK 74044
Phone: 918-865-3314
Officers:
V. David Miller II, Pres.
H. Gene Baldwin, Chief Exec. Officer
Dan Overland, Chief Financial Officer
Ownership: MBO Corp.
Cable Systems (7):
Oklahoma: Cleveland, Fairfax, Jennings, Mannford, Osage, Pawnee, Westport.
Total Basic Subscribers: 4,757.
Total Pay Units: 2,071.

CITIZENS TELEPHONE CO.

Box 1177
Brevard, NC 28712
Phone: 704-884-2671
Fax: 704-885-2300
Officers:
C. W. Pickelsimer Jr., Pres.
Joseph Pickelsimer, V.P.
D. O. Albertson, Secy.-Treas.
Represented (legal): Dow, Lohnes & Albertson PLLC.
Cable Systems (2):
North Carolina: Brevard, Lake Toxaway.
Total Basic Subscribers: 8,934.
Total Pay Units: 2,506.

CITIZENS TELEPHONE CORP.

Box 330
426 N. Wayne St.
Warren, IN 46792
Phone: 219-375-2115
Fax: 219-375-2244
Officer:
Gordon L. Laymon, Chief Exec. Officer & Gen. Mgr.
Cable Systems (1):
Indiana: Warren.
Total Basic Subscribers: 670.
Total Pay Units: 419.

CITIZENS UTILITY

Drawer 1600
Window Rock, AZ 86515
Phone: 520-871-5581
Fax: 520-871-3779
Officers:
Bill Kirby, V.P.
Joe Hausner, V.P., Operations
Laura L. Young, Operations Mgr.
Cable Systems (10):
Arizona: Chinle, Kayenta, Tsaile.
California: Needles.
New Mexico: Navajo, Ramah, Shiprock, To-hatchi, Yah-Ta-Hey, Zuni.
Total Basic Subscribers: 7,273.
Total Pay Units: 3,891.

CLARENCE TELEPHONE CO. INC.

Box 246
608 Lombard St.
Clarence, IA 52216
Phone: 319-452-3852
Fax: 319-452-3883
Cable Systems (1):
Iowa: Clarence.
Total Basic Subscribers: 385.
Total Pay Units: 177.

CLARENDON TV ASSOCIATION
Box 315
Clarendon, PA 16313
Phone: 814-723-4735
Ownership: Subscriber owned.
Cable Systems (1):
Pennsylvania: Clarendon.
Total Basic Subscribers: 395.

CLARKS TELECOMMINICATIONS CO.
Box 126
Clarks, NE 68628
Phone: 308-548-2251
Fax: 308-548-2400
Officers:
Timothy D. Bittinger, Pres.
Cindy L. Bittinger, Secy.-Treas.
Cable Systems (1):
Nebraska: Clarks.
Total Basic Subscribers: 138.
Total Pay Units: 41.

CLASSIC CABLE
Box 429
605 N.W. 3rd St.
Plainville, KS 67663
Phones: 785-434-7620; 800-999-8876
Fax: 785-434-4932
Officers:
Steve Seach, Pres.
Merritt Belisle, Chief Exec. Officer
Ownership: Brera Capital Partners, 64.4%; Ponca/Universal Holdings Inc., 35.6%.
Cable Systems (296):
Arkansas: Charleston, De Witt, England, Lonoke, Stuttgart, Waldron.
Colorado: Breckenridge, Fairplay, Wray.
Kansas: Abilene, Almena, Andale, Anthony, Argonia, Arlington, Ashland, Attica, Bazine, Beloit, Bucklin, Burrton, Caldwell, Clay Center, Coldwater, Colwich, Concordia, Dighton, Downs, Ellsworth, Fort Scott, Frontenac, Garden Plain, Geneseo, Girard, Jetmore, Kensington, Kiowa, La Cygne, Leoti, Lincoln, Lindsborg, Louisburg, Luray, Macksville, McDonald, Mount Hope, Natoma, Ness City, Norton, Norwich, Oberlin, Osawatomie, Paola, Phillipsburg, Plainville, Pleasanton, Pretty Prairie, Protection, Sharon Springs, Smith Center, South Haven, Spring Hill, St. Francis, St. John, Sterling, Stockton, Sylvan Grove, Tipton, Tribune, Victoria.
Missouri: Armstrong, Boonville, Brookfield, Cole County (portions), Drexel, Fair Grove, Fayette, Glasgow, Lebanon, Lexington, Maryville, Neosho, Noel, Ozark, Seneca, Trenton, Wellington.
Nebraska: Alma, Beaver City, Culbertson, Franklin, Indianola, Orleans, Oxford, Red Cloud.
New Mexico: Fort Sumner, Melrose, Santa Rosa, Tatum, Vaughn.
Oklahoma: Ames, Anadarko, Arapaho, Arnett, Beaver, Bessie, Billings, Binger, Blanchard, Boise City, Bokoshe, Breckenridge, Buffalo, Burns Flat, Byars, Cache, Calumet, Camargo, Canute, Carmen, Cashion, Cherokee, Comanche, Corn, Covington, Custer City, Cyril, Dacoma, Dill City, Dover, Drummond, Elgin, Erick, Eufaula, Fairview, Fargo, Fort Sill, Freedom, Geary, Goltry, Goodwell, Hammon, Hardesty, Healdton, Heavener, Helena, Hennessey, Hollis, Hooker, Hugo, Hunter, Jet, Jones, Kingfisher, Kremlin, Lahoma, Laverne, Leedey, Marshall, Maysville, Medicine Park, Meridian, Nash, Newcastle, Noble, Okarche, Okeene, Paoli, Piedmont, Pond Creek, Poteau, Purcell, Ringwood, Roosevelt, Rush Springs, Ryan, Sallisaw, Seiling, Shattuck, Spiro, Terral, Thomas, Union City, Velma, Vici, Wakita, Walters, Wanette, Washington, Watonga, Watts, Waukomis, Waurika, Wayne, Weatherford, Woodward.
Texas: Abernathy, Anton, Aqua Vista, Barstow, Bellevue, Bloomington, Booker, Brady, Buffalo Springs Lake, Caldwell, Camp Wood, Canadian, Carlsbad, Center Point, Childress, Chillicothe, Christoval, Clarendon, Claude, Comfort, Country Haven, Crane, Crosbyton, Crowell, Darrouzett, Dickens, Dimmitt, Eden, Eldorado, Flatonia, Follett, Friona, Gardendale, Goat Creek, Goldsmith, Grandfalls, Groom, Hale Center, Happy, Hart, Hedley, Higgins, Howardwick, Idalou, Imperial, Ingram, Junction, Kenedy, Kermit, Knox City, Kress, Lampasas, Lefors, Lockney, Lorenzo, Lubbock, Lubbock County (southeastern portion), Lyons, Mason, Matador, Memphis, Menard, Mertzon, Monahans, Montague, Muleshoe, Nixon, Olton, Paducah, Pecos, Petersburg, Plains, Post, Quanah, Quitaque, Ralls, Roaring Springs, Roby, Rock Springs, Rockdale, Runge, San Saba, Shamrock, Silverton, Skellytown, Sonora, Spearman, Spur, St. Jo, Sterling City, Stratford, Sundown, The Woods, Tulia, Wellington, Whiteface, Wickett, Wink, Woodrow, Yorktown.
Total Basic Subscribers: 186,371 (0.27% of total cable households).
Total Pay Units: 69,093.

CLEARVIEW CABLE TV INC.
Box 247 AA
Rte. 4
Lewisburg, WV 24901
Phone: 304-645-1397
Ownership: Chip James & Shawn James, 100% jointly.
Cable Systems (2):
Virginia: Callaghan.
West Virginia: Frankford.
Total Basic Subscribers: 1,686.
Total Pay Units: 3,217.

CLEARVIEW PARTNERS
394 Highland Dr.
Mountville, PA 17554
Phone: 717-299-0123
Officer:
William B. Domurad, Pres.
Ownership: Clearview CATV Inc., 70%; Lenfest Communications Inc., see listing, 30%. CCATVI ownership: William B. Domurad & Alvin Miller, Principals.
Cable Systems (2):
Maryland: Bel Air.
Pennsylvania: Fawn Grove.
Total Basic Subscribers: 10,116.
Total Pay Units: 3,223.

CLEARWATER CABLEVISION
112 S. Lee St.
Clearwater, KS 67026
Phones: 316-584-2255; 800-362-2396
Fax: 316-584-2260
Ownership: Evelyn L. Mikesell, 25%; Gordon G. Mikesell, 25%; Maxine Mikesell, 25%; remainder undisclosed.
Cable Systems (4):
Kansas: Belle Plaine, Burden, Clearwater, Leon.
Total Basic Subscribers: 1,575.
Total Pay Units: 638.

CLIMAX TELEPHONE CO.
110 N. Main
Climax, MI 49034
Phone: 616-746-4411
Fax: 616-746-9914
Officers:
Gilbert A. Collver, Pres.
Frank Bindi, V.P.
Ownership: CTS Communications Corp.
Cable Systems (1):
Michigan: Climax Twp.
Total Basic Subscribers: 575.
Total Pay Units: 270.

CLINTON CABLE TV CO. INC.
Box 665
Terre Haute, IN 47808
Phone: 765-832-3586
Officers:
George O. Nichols, Chief Exec. Officer
William F. George, Chief Operating Officer
Ownership: George O. Nichols, John Nichols & Steven Nichols, 100% jointly.
Cable Systems (1):
Indiana: Clinton.
Total Basic Subscribers: 4,530.
Total Pay Units: 1,750.

JIM CLOUD
137 Mountain Park Place NW
Albuquerque, NM 87114
Phone: 505-275-3466
Fax: 505-293-9415
Cable Systems (10):
Arizona: Grand Missouri Mobile Home Park.
California: El Toro Estates, Riverside Meadows.
New Mexico: Cuba, Four Hills, Maxwell, Mora, San Antonio, Santa Barbara, Wagon Mound.
Total Basic Subscribers: 1,550.
Total Pay Units: 749.

C.L.R. VIDEO LLC
Box 214
Wetmore, KS 66550
Phones: 913-548-7511; 800-346-9084
Fax: 913-548-7517
Ownership: Lynch Multi-Media Corp.; Rainbow Communications & Electronics; Robert C. Carson. Carson is also principal of Carson Communications LLC, see listing.
Cable Systems (20):
Kansas: Axtell, Belvue, Centralia, Easton, Effingham, Frankfort, Holton, Horton, Hoyt, Leonardville, Mayetta, McLouth, Nortonville, Olsburg, Oskaloosa, Ozawkie, Valley Falls, Westmoreland, Wetmore, Winchester.
Total Basic Subscribers: 4,326.
Total Pay Units: 1,588.

CND ACQUISITION CO. LLC
Box 880
400 Chickamauga Ave.
Rossville, GA 30741
Phone: 423-866-0901
Fax: 423-866-0902
Ownership: William J. Cooke & David P. Daniel, 100% jointly.
Cable Systems (2):
North Carolina: Andrews, Murphy.
Total Basic Subscribers: 1,900.

COAXIAL CABLE TV CORP.
105 Walker Dr.
Edinboro, PA 16412
Phone: 814-734-1424
Fax: 814-734-8898
Officers:
Michael Mead, Pres.
Edward M. Mead, Exec. V.P.
Ownership: Mead Newspapers. Mead Newspapers owns Erie (PA) News, Times & Times News; Warren (PA) Times-Observer.
Represented (legal): The McDonald Group.
Cable Systems (1):
Pennsylvania: Edinboro.
Total Basic Subscribers: 4,800.
Total Pay Units: 995.

COAXIAL COMMUNICATIONS
Suite 280
700 Ackerman Rd.
Columbus, OH 43202
Phone: 614-263-6100
Fax: 614-263-7299
Officers:
Barry Silverstein, Chmn.
Joel S. Rudich, Pres. & Chief Exec. Officer
Thomas Wilson, Executive V.P. & Chief Financial Officer
Steve Crane, Sr. V.P. & Chief Operating Officer
Gregg Graff, Sr. V.P., Sales & Mktg.
Daniel McKay, V.P., Technical Operations
Ownership: Barry Silverstein, 67.5%; Dennis McGillicuddy, 22.5%; Steve McVoy, 10%. McGillicuddy, McVoy & Silverstein have interest in Paxton Cable Television Inc., see listing.
Represented (legal): Fleischman & Walsh LLP.
Cable Systems (10):
Ohio: Amelia, Collinsville, Columbus 25%, Fairfield (Butler County), Lebanon, Liberty Twp. (Butler County), Morrow, Ross Twp. (Butler County).
West Virginia: Flat Rock, Snowshoe.
Total Basic Subscribers: 44,776 (0.07% of total cable households).
Total Pay Units: 23,979.

COAXIAL PROPERTIES INC.
Suite 805
4564 Telephone Rd.
Ventura, CA 93003
Phone: 805-658-1579
Cable Systems (1):
California: Point Mugu Naval Air Station.
Total Basic Subscribers: 652.
Total Pay Units: 478.

WILLIAM J. COLE
Box 219
Outer Holland St.
Alexandria Bay, NY 13607
Phone: 315-482-9975
Cable Systems (1):
New York: Alexandria Bay.
Total Basic Subscribers: 1,008.
Total Pay Units: 586.

CITY OF COLERAINE
Box 670
302 Roosevelt Ave.
Coleraine, MN 55722
Phone: 218-245-2112
Fax: 218-245-2123
Officers:
Peter Axford, Mayor, Chmn.
Patricia Decoster, Chief Financial Officer
Ownership: Municipally owned.
Represented (legal): Kent Nyberg.
Cable Systems (1):
Minnesota: Coleraine.
Total Basic Subscribers: 371.
Total Pay Units: 127.

COLFAX HIGHLINE CABLE CO.
Box 187
Colfax, WA 99111
Phone: 509-397-2211
Fax: 509-397-2274
Ownership: St. John Cable Co. Inc., 50%; Ken Julian, 50%.
Cable Systems (1):
Washington: Colfax.

Total Basic Subscribers: 985.
Total Pay Units: 435.

CITY OF COLLINS

Box 400
City Hall
Collins, MS 39428
Phone: 601-765-4491
Fax: 609-765-0050
Officers:
V. O. Smith, Mayor & Mgr.
Debbie Lundy, Cable Clerk
Ownership: Municipally owned.
Cable Systems (1):
Mississippi: Collins.
Total Basic Subscribers: 902.
Total Pay Units: 271.

COLLINSVILLE TV CABLE

Box 272
Collinsville, AL 35961
Phone: 205-524-2267
Ownership: Mary Ann Pendergrass, Principal.
Cable Systems (1):
Alabama: Collinsville.
Total Basic Subscribers: 420.
Total Pay Units: 100.

COLSTRIP CABLE TV CO. INC.

2930 Grand Ave.
Billings, MT 59102
Phone: 406-656-8024
Ownership: Norman Mills, Pres. & Chief Exec. Officer.
Cable Systems (1):
Montana: Colstrip.
Total Basic Subscribers: 400.
Total Pay Units: 204.

COLUMBUS CABLEVISION

300 E. Maple St.
Columbus, KS 66725
Phone: 316-429-2159
Fax: 316-429-1159
Ownership: Community owned.
Cable Systems (1):
Kansas: Columbus.
Total Basic Subscribers: 1,180.
Total Pay Units: 559.

COLUMBUS GROVE TELEPHONE CO.

112 W. Sycamore St.
Columbus Grove, OH 45840
Phone: 419-659-2111
Fax: 419-659-5001
Cable Systems (1):
Ohio: Columbus Grove (village).
Total Basic Subscribers: N.A.

COMCAST CABLE COMMUNICATIONS INC.

1500 Market St.
Philadelphia, PA 19102
Phones: 215-665-1700; 215-981-7619
Fax: 215-981-7793
Comcast Corporation Officers:
Ralph J. Roberts, Chmn.
Julian A. Brodsky, Vice Chmn.
Brian L. Roberts, Pres.
Lawrence S. Smith, Exec. V.P.
John R. Alchin, Sr. V.P. & Treas.
David N. Watson, Sr. V.P., Mktg.
Stanley L. Wang, Sr. V.P., Gen. Counsel & Secy.
Joseph J. Euteneuer, V.P. & Controller
Joseph W. Waz Jr., V.P., External Affairs & Public Policy Counsel
Arthur R. Block, V.P. & Sr. Deputy Gen. Counsel
Robert S. Pick, V.P., Corporate Development
C. Stephen Backstrom, V.P., Taxation
Amy L. Banse, V.P.
William E. Dordelman, V.P., Finance
Kenneth Mikalauskas, V.P., Finance
Richard A. Petrino, V.P., Human Resources & Planning & Development
Mark A. Coblitz, V.P., Strategic Planning
Comcast Cable Communications Officers:
Michael S. Tallent, Sr. V.P., Accounting & Administration
Bradley P. Dusto, Sr. V.P., Engineering
Filemon Lopez, Sr. V.P., Advertising Sales
Thomas Hurley, Sr. V.P., Programming
Regional Management:
David A. Scott, Sr. V.P., South Central Region
Michael A. Doyle, Sr. V.P., East West Region
Stephen A. Burch, Sr. V.P., Mid-Atlantic/Midwest Region
William R. Goetz Jr., Sr. V.P., Southeast Region
Ownership: Comcast Corp. Comcast Corp. has interest in wired telecommunications including telephone services; wireless telecommunications including cellular, personal communications services and direct-to-home satellite television; and content through principal ownership of QVC.
Represented (legal): Dow, Lohnes & Albertson PLLC; LeBoeuf, Lamb, Greene & MacRae LLP.
Cable Systems (183):
Alabama: Cloverdale, Dauphin Island, Dothan, Florence, Gadsden, Huntsville, Mobile, Tuscaloosa.
Arkansas: Little Rock, North Little Rock.
California: Buena Park, Lompoc, Newport Beach, Ontario, Sacramento, San Bernardino, Santa Ana, Santa Maria, Seal Beach, Simi Valley.
Colorado: Berthoud, Erie, Fort Lupton, Lafayette, Longmont, Louisville, Loveland, Parachute.
Connecticut: Clinton, Danbury, Groton, Middletown, New Haven.
Delaware: Dover, Harrington, Rehoboth Beach.
Florida: Alford, Arcadia, Avon Park Air Force Base, Bartow, Boca Raton, Brighton (Kissimmee River Resort), Broward County, Crawfordville, De Bary, Englewood, Fort Lauderdale, Hallandale, Hickory Lakes Estates, Hidden Acres, Jasper, Lake Placid, Lake Rosalie, Lake Wales, Leesburg, Lehigh Acres, Madison, Marianna, Midway, North Miami Beach, Panama City, Perry, Port Charlotte, Quincy, Sarasota, Sebring, Silver Springs Shores, Spring Lake, Tallahassee, Three World Recreational Vehicle Park, Venice, Wauchula, West Palm Beach, Zolfo Springs.
Georgia: Adrian, Blue Ridge, Bowman, Calhoun, Chamblee, Claxton, Dallas, Elberton, Glennville, Hartwell, Hickory Level, Homerville, La Fayette, Louisville, Metter, Millen, Montezuma, Monticello, Mount Vernon, Mount Zion, Quitman, Rome, Rossville, Soperton, Sylvania, Tallapoosa, Twin City, Walton County, Warrenton, Washington, Waynesboro, Whitesburg, Wrightsville.
Indiana: Avilla, Fort Wayne, Indianapolis, Monroeville (town), Monrovia, Tell City.
Kentucky: Campbellsville, Elizabethtown, Glasgow, Greenville, Hodgenville, Horse Cave, Leitchfield, Paducah.
Maryland: Aberdeen, Cambridge, Ellicott City, Pocomoke, Salisbury, Towson.
Michigan: Burton, Clinton Twp. (Macomb County), Detroit, East Detroit, Grosse Pointe Woods, Hillsdale, Pontiac, Shelby Twp. (Macomb County), St. Clair Shores, Sterling Heights, Taylor, Warren.
Mississippi: Corinth, Fulton, Hattiesburg 33.33%, Laurel, Meridian, Tupelo.
New Jersey: Bay Head, Carlstadt Borough, Cherry Hill, East Windsor, Eatontown, Jersey City, North Plainfield, Port Murray, Trenton, Union, Willingboro, Woodbury.
New York: Watertown 33%.
Pennsylvania: Lower Merion Twp., Philadelphia (area 3), Philadelphia (area 4), Tarentum Borough, Willow Grove.
South Carolina: Calhoun Falls, Charleston, Newberry, Walterboro.
Tennessee: Athens, Benton, Chattanooga, Gray, Harriman, Knoxville, La Follette, Livingston, Maynardville, Norris, Rockwood, Walden Creek.
Virginia: Chesterfield County, Glade Spring.
West Virginia: Bluefield, Kimball.
Total Basic Subscribers: 5,500,000 (8.02% of total cable households).
Total Pay Units: 3,953,000.
Cable Holdings:
Jones Intercable, 57% (see listing).
Other Holdings:
Professional sports: Owns 66% of sports venture that includes Philadelphia Flyers (hockey team), Philadelphia 76ers (basketball team); CoreStates Center & CoreStates Spectrum (sports arenas); Phantoms of American Hockey League; Spectator.

COM-LINK INC.

1500 E. Conecuh
Union Springs, AL 36089
Phone: 205-738-2204
Ownership: Ropir Industries & Mrs. R. M. Pirnie, Principals. Pirnie has telephone holdings.
Cable Systems (13):
Alabama: Autaugaville, Lake Martin Resort, Midway, Notasulga, Union Springs.
Colorado: Bayfield, Black Hawk, Creede, Eagle, Nederland, Pagosa Springs, Silverton, South Fork.
Total Basic Subscribers: 7,699.
Total Pay Units: 3,306.

COMMUNICATIONS & CABLE OF CHICAGO

5711 S. Western Ave.
Chicago, IL 60636
Phone: 773-434-8614
Cable Systems (1):
Illinois: Chicago (area 1) 5%.
Total Basic Subscribers: 71,020 (0.10% of total cable households).
Total Pay Units: 79,475.

COMMUNITY ANTENNA SYSTEM INC.

655 Hill Ave.
Hillsboro, WI 54634
Phone: 608-489-2321
Officers:
Eugene Kubarski, Chmn.
Bernice Kubarski, Pres.
Randall Kubarski, V.P.
Gregory Kubarski, V.P.
Cable Systems (4):
Wisconsin: Cazenovia, Elroy, Hillsboro, Kendall.
Total Basic Subscribers: 1,551.
Total Pay Units: 409.

COMMUNITY ANTENNA SYSTEMS INC.

1809 North St.
Belleville, KS 66935
Phone: 913-527-2226
Ownership: Robert K. Weary Jr., Principal, see listing.
Cable Systems (2):
Kansas: Council Grove, St. Marys.
Total Basic Subscribers: 1,540.
Total Pay Units: 256.

COMMUNITY CABLE CORP. OF PENNSYLVANIA

RD 2
Mansfield, PA 16933
Phone: 570-549-3805
Fax: 570-549-2500
Officers:
Robert H. Wagner, Pres.
Howard M. Selleck, V.P.

Branch Office:

Prattsburgh, NY 14873
Phone: 607-522-3712
Ownership: North Penn Telephone Co.
Cable Systems (1):
Pennsylvania: East Smithfield.
Total Basic Subscribers: 136.
Other Holdings:
Telephone.

COMMUNITY CABLE TV CORP.

Box J
102 Main St.
Sanborn, IA 51248
Phone: 712-729-5160
Ownership: Community owned.
Cable Systems (1):
Iowa: Sanborn.
Total Basic Subscribers: 890.
Total Pay Units: 372.

COMMUNITY CABLEVISION CO.

Box 307
Skiatook, OK 74070-0307
Phone: 918-396-3019
Ownership: Ann Hamilton & George C. Hamilton, 100% jointly.
Cable Systems (12):
Oklahoma: Avant, Barnsdall, Collinsville, Copan, Hominy, Kaw City, Ochelata, Oilton, Ramona, Skiatook, Wynona, Yale.
Total Basic Subscribers: 4,903.
Total Pay Units: 3,368.

COMMUNITY COMMUNICATIONS CO.

110 W. McCloy St.
Monticello, AR 71655
Phones: 501-367-2633; 501-376-7300
Fax: 501-376-9770
Officers:
Christine Gardner, Pres.
Paul Gardner, V.P.
Ownership: Christine Gardner, 50%; Paul Gardner, 50%.
Represented (legal): Pepper & Corazzini.
Cable Systems (30):
Arkansas: Amity, Arkansas City, Aubrey, Bismarck, Carpenter Dam, Curtis, East Camden, Eudora, Friendship, Gillett, Glenwood, Gould, Hooker/Ladd, Jones Mill, Keo, Magic Springs, Monticello, Norman, Pearcy, Reed, Rison, Rondo, Rosston, Royal, Saline County (unincorporated areas), Star City, Warren, Watson.
Louisiana: Kilbourne.
Mississippi: Rosedale.
Total Basic Subscribers: 12,191 (0.02% of total cable households).
Total Pay Units: 2,396.

THE COMMUNITY DEVELOPMENT CORP.
311 2nd
Edgeley, ND 58433
Phone: 701-493-2241
Ownership: Subscriber owned.
Cable Systems (1):
North Dakota: Edgeley.
Total Basic Subscribers: 297.
Total Pay Units: 30.

COMMUNITY TV
Box 85
Loganton, PA 17747
Phone: 717-725-2733
Officer:
Robert Mills, Pres.
Ownership: Community owned.
Cable Systems (1):
Pennsylvania: Tylersville.
Total Basic Subscribers: N.A.

COMMUNITY TV CO.
5 College St.
Ellijay, GA 30540
Officers:
Albert E. Harrison, Pres.
Marion Harrison, Secy.
Ownership: Albert E. Harrison, 36.3%; Marion Harrison, 35.2%; John Harrison, 28.5%.
Cable Systems (1):
Georgia: Ellijay.
Total Basic Subscribers: 3,593.

COMMUNITY TV INC.
364 Riverside Dr.
Hazard, KY 41701
Phone: 606-436-4593
Officer:
Jesse Feltner, Pres.
Ownership: Non-profit organization.
Cable Systems (1):
Kentucky: Walkertown Station.
Total Basic Subscribers: 500.

COMMUNITY TV SYSTEMS CABLE CO.
3845 Wintergreen Blvd.
Columbus, OH 43230
Phone: 740-635-9680
Officers:
David Fekete, Pres., Chief Exec. & Financial Officer
Dom Cavicchia, Chief Operating Officer

Branch Office:
Martins Ferry, OH 43935
Ownership: David Fekete & Dom Cavicchia.
Cable Systems (2):
Ohio: Mount Pleasant Twp. (Jefferson County).
Pennsylvania: West Alexander.
Total Basic Subscribers: 1,013.
Total Pay Units: 474.

COMSERV LTD.
Box 310
111 W. 2nd St.
Schaller, IA 51053
Phone: 712-275-4215
Fax: 712-275-4121
Officer:
Steven Reimers, Chmn.
Ownership: Schaller Telephone Co.
Represented (legal): Steven Reimers.
Cable Systems (11):
Iowa: Anthon, Correctionville, Cushing, Holstein, Ida Grove, Kingsley, Kiron, Lake View, Moville, Odebolt, Schaller.
Total Basic Subscribers: 3,701.
Total Pay Units: 975.

COMSOUTH TELECABLE
Box 1198
910 Carrol St.
Perry, GA 31069
Phone: 912-987-3444
Officer:
William K. Mitchell, Pres. & Chief Exec. Officer
Ownership: United Cable Co. Inc.
Cable Systems (1):
Georgia: Perry.
Total Basic Subscribers: 5,850.
Total Pay Units: 1,458.

COMSTAR CABLE TV INC.
Box 975
Beatrice, NE 68310
Phone: 402-228-0683
Ownership: Tim Schwarz, Pres.
Cable Systems (4):
Nebraska: Daykin, Filley, Pickrell, Swanton.
Total Basic Subscribers: 237.
Total Pay Units: 87.

COMSTOCK COMMUNITY TV INC.
Box 9
Virginia City, NV 89440
Phone: 702-847-0958
Officers:
Anna Perry, Chmn. & Chief Exec. Officer
Barbara Bowers, Secy.-Treas.
Ownership: Non-profit organization.
Cable Systems (1):
Nevada: Virginia City.
Total Basic Subscribers: 390.

CONSOLIDATED CABLE INC.
Box 6147
Lincoln, NE 68506
Phone: 800-432-2773
Cable Systems (10):
Nebraska: Anselmo, Ashton, Big Springs, Comstock, Elsie, Farnam, Lewellen, Madrid, Merna, Wallace.
Total Basic Subscribers: 722.

CONSOLIDATED CABLEVISION
2373 State Rte. 44
New Smyrna Beach, FL 32168
Phone: 904-427-0909
Ownership: Dave Carlton.
Cable Systems (1):
Florida: Samsula.
Total Basic Subscribers: 202.

CONSOLIDATED TELEPHONE COOPERATIVE
Box 1408
507 S. Main Ave.
Dickinson, ND 58601-1408
Phone: 701-225-6061
Fax: 701-225-0001
Wireless Cable Systems (2):
North Dakota: Killdeer, Lefor.
Total Basic Subscribers: 994.
Other Holdings:
MMDS, see listing.

CONSTEL COMMUNICATIONS LP
Suite 202
2444 Solomons Island Rd.
Annapolis, MD 21401-3715
Phone: 410-266-9393
Fax: 410-266-9054
Officer:
Roy E. Hayes Jr., Pres.
Ownership: Bay Cable Inc., Gen. Partner, see listing.
Cable Systems (6):
Florida: Brooksville (unincorporated portions), Christmas, Lake Mary Jane, Lake Padgett Estates East, Zellwood.
Total Basic Subscribers: N.A.

CONWAY CORP.
Box 99
1307 Prairie St.
Conway, AR 72033
Phone: 501-450-6000
Officers:
Richard Arnold, Chief Exec. Officer
Roger Q. Mills Jr., Chief Operating Officer
Bret Carroll, Chief Financial Officer
Ownership: Community owned.
Cable Systems (1):
Arkansas: Conway.
Total Basic Subscribers: 16,783 (0.02% of total cable households).
Total Pay Units: 3,767.

COON CREEK TELEPHONE & CABLEVISION
Box D
310 Locust St.
Blairstown, IA 52209
Phone: 319-454-6234
Cable Systems (1):
Iowa: Blairstown.
Total Basic Subscribers: 450.
Total Pay Units: 115.

COON RAPIDS MUNICIPAL CABLE SYSTEM
Box 207
123 3rd Ave.
Coon Rapids, IA 50058
Phone: 712-684-2225
Officers:
Dan Pomeroy, Chmn.
Brad Honold, Chief Exec. Officer
Kevin Dorpinghaus, Chief Operating Officer
Philip R. Wernsman, Chief Financial Officer
Ownership: Community owned.
Cable Systems (1):
Iowa: Coon Rapids.
Total Basic Subscribers: 479.
Total Pay Units: 250.

COON VALLEY CABLEVISION
516 Sherman St.
Menlo, IA 50164
Phone: 515-524-2111
Fax: 515-524-2112
Officer:
Jim Nelson, Gen. Mgr.
Cable Systems (1):
Iowa: Menlo.
Total Basic Subscribers: 80.
Total Pay Units: 62.

COONEY CABLE ASSOC. INC.
228 Park Ave.
Worcester, MA 01609
Phone: 508-754-5865
Fax: 508-752-7342
Officers:
John B. Cooney, Pres. & Treas.
Karen A. Perrone, V.P. & Secy.
Ownership: John B. Cooney.
Represented (legal): Cameron & Mittleman.
Cable Systems (12):
New York: Warsaw (village).
Pennsylvania: Coalport.
Virginia: Bastian, Birchleaf, Hot Springs, Lebanon (portions), Speedwell.
West Virginia: Beech Creek, Bruno, Delbarton, Hanover, Varney.
Total Basic Subscribers: 9,682.
Total Pay Units: 2,590.

ARTHUR R. COOPER
Box 282
Rte. 1
Washington, WV 26181-9801
Phone: 304-485-8922
Cable Systems (4):
West Virginia: Cottageville, Murphytown, Tunnelton, Washington.
Total Basic Subscribers: 4,222.

COOSA CABLE CO.
1701 Cogswell Ave.
Pell City, AL 35125
Phone: 205-884-4545
Officers:
Arthur M. Smith, Pres.
Jeff Smith, V.P.
Jacqueline I. Smith, Secy.-Treas.
Ownership: Arthur M. Smith, 53%; Jeff Smith, 30%; N. L. Smith, 15%; Jacqueline I. Smith, 2%. Arthur M. Smith is 50% owner of Trinity Cablevision Inc., see listing.
Cable Systems (1):
Alabama: Pell City.
Total Basic Subscribers: 7,298.
Total Pay Units: 2,161.

COPPER MOUNTAIN CONSOLIDATED METROPOLITAN DISTRICT
Box 3002
Copper Mountain, CO 80443
Phone: 303-668-2882
Officers:
Thomas J. Malmgren, Chmn. & Chief Exec. Officer
Elizabeth Black, Chief Operating & Financial Officer
Ownership: Community owned.
Cable Systems (1):
Colorado: Copper Mountain.
Total Basic Subscribers: 900.

COTTON COUNTRY CABLE
Box 698
Rayville, LA 71269
Phone: 318-728-3399
Wireless Cable Systems (1):
Louisiana: Rayville.
Total Basic Subscribers: N.A.

EDGAR COUCH
Box 180
Rte. 1
Viper, KY 41774
Phone: 606-436-5188
Cable Systems (1):
Kentucky: Bonnyman 50%.
Total Basic Subscribers: 205.

LEONARD COUCH
Box 180
Rte. 1
Viper, KY 41774
Phone: 606-436-5188

Cable Systems (1):
Kentucky: Bonnyman 50%.
Total Basic Subscribers: 205.

COUNTRY CABLE INC.

6839 Convoy Court
San Diego, CA 92111
Phone: 619-292-8032
Officers:
Bruce O. Witte, Pres.
Constantine G. Pappas, V.P.-Secy.
Ownership: Constantine G. Pappas, 75%; Bruce O. Witte, 25%.
Cable Systems (1):
California: San Diego Country Estates.
Total Basic Subscribers: 2,600.
Total Pay Units: 1,000.

COUNTRY CABLEVISION

Box 355
Tipton, IN 46072
Phone: 317-675-9033
Cable Systems (3):
Indiana: Kempton, Michigantown, Tipton.
Total Basic Subscribers: N.A.

COUNTRY CABLEVISION LTD.

Box 12038
Salem, OR 97309-0038
Phone: 503-588-8247
Ownership: John P. Johnson, Chief Exec., Operating & Financial Officer.
Represented (legal): Doug Vande Griend.
Cable Systems (4):
Oregon: Brooks, Gilchrist, Macleay, South Salem.
Total Basic Subscribers: 2,200.
Total Pay Units: 825.

COUNTRY COMMUNICATIONS INC.

RR 3
Box 144-A
Hunlock Creek, PA 18621
Phone: 717-477-5305
Ownership: David Martin, Pres.
Cable Systems (1):
Pennsylvania: Huntington Twp. (Luzerne County).
Total Basic Subscribers: 300.
Total Pay Units: 92.

COURTLAND CABLE TV

City Hall, Main St.
Courtland, KS 66939
Phone: 913-374-4260
Officers:
Tim Garman, Chief Exec. Officer
Ruth Sederlin, Chief Financial Officer
Ownership: Community owned.
Cable Systems (1):
Kansas: Courtland.
Total Basic Subscribers: N.A.

COVINGTON CABLE TV

1167 Pace St.
Covington, GA 30209
Phone: 404-786-5324
Ownership: Community owned.
Represented (legal): Ed Crudup.
Cable Systems (1):
Georgia: Covington.
Total Basic Subscribers: 9,159.
Total Pay Units: 3,925.

COWLEY TELECABLE INC.

Box 687
Cowley, WY 82420
Phone: 307-548-6457
Officers:
Jerrie Townsend, Pres.
Tim Townsend, Chief Exec. Officer
Ownership: Jerri Townsend & Tim Townsend, 100% jointly.
Cable Systems (4):
Montana: Belfry, Drummond.
Wyoming: Cowley, Ten Sleep.
Total Basic Subscribers: 363.
Total Pay Units: 112.

COX COMMUNICATIONS INC.

1400 Lake Hearn Dr.
Atlanta, GA 30319
Phone: 404-843-5000
Fax: 404-843-5777
Officers:
James C. Kennedy, Chmn.
James O. Robbins, Pres. & Chief Exec. Officer
Maggie Bellville, Exec. V.P., Operations
Ajit Dalvi, Sr. V.P., Strategy & Programming
Alex Best, Sr. V.P., Engineering
David Woodrow, Sr. V.P., Broadband Services
Jason Juraska, V.P., Operations
Claus Kroeger, V.P., Operations
James A. Hatcher, V.P., Legal & Regulatory Affairs
Scott Hatfield, V.P. & Chief Information Officer
Patrick J. Esser, V.P., Advertising Sales
David Andersen, V.P., Public Affairs
Dallas Clement, Treas.
Jimmy Hayes, Chief Financial Officer
Ownership: Publicly held. Cox Enterprises (see listing in Commercial TV Station Ownership), majority stockholder.
Represented (legal): Dow, Lohnes & Albertson PLLC.
Cable Systems (59):
Arizona: Avondale, Carefree, Casa Grande, Gilbert, Luke AFB, Phoenix, Rio Verde, Sierra Vista, Tucson.
California: Bakersfield, El Cajon, Eureka, Irvine, Orange County, Palos Verdes Peninsula, Rancho Santa Margarita, Santa Barbara.
Connecticut: Enfield, Manchester, Meriden.
Florida: Crestview 50%, Destin 50%, Eglin Air Force Base 50%, Fort Walton Beach 50%, Gainesville, Niceville 50%, Ocala, Pensacola.
Georgia: Macon.
Louisiana: Jefferson Parish, New Orleans, St. Bernard Parish, St. Charles Parish.
Massachusetts: Holland.
Nebraska: Omaha.
Nevada: Las Vegas.
New York: Staten Island 50%.
Ohio: Bluffton, Greenfield, Parma, Sugarcreek.
Oklahoma: Oklahoma City.
Rhode Island: Cranston, Johnston, Newport & Lincoln, Providence, Westerly.
Texas: Lubbock, Midland 99.6%.
Virginia: Gloucester County, Hampton, Hampton Roads, James City County, New Kent, Newport News, Poquoson, Roanoke, West Point, Williamsburg.
Total Basic Subscribers: 3,855,582 (5.62% of total cable households).
Total Pay Units: 2,239,247.
Cable Holdings:
Australian cable interests.
Other Holdings:
Program source: Equity interest in The Discovery Channel, E! Entertainment TV, QVC Network, The Sunshine Network, Viewer's Choice & other pay-per-view networks, 13.3% of Flextech, Britain.
Cable advertising representative: CableRep.
Common Carrier: Licenses for personal communications network (PCN) for experimental carriage of telephony via cable in New York & San Diego.
Service company: K-Prime Partners/Prime Star satellite services.

ARCHILLES CRAFT

Box 275
H.C. 64
Yeaddiss, KY 41777
Phone: 606-279-4478
Cable Systems (1):
Kentucky: Cutshin.
Total Basic Subscribers: 100.

CRAIG CABLE TV INC.

Box 131
Craig, AK 99921
Phone: 907-826-3470
Cable Systems (1):
Alaska: Craig.
Total Basic Subscribers: 450.

CRAW-KAN TELEPHONE CO.

200 N. Ozark
Girard, KS 66743
Phones: 316-724-8235; 800-362-0316
Fax: 316-724-4099
Ownership: Cooperative.
Cable Systems (2):
Kansas: Edna, McCune.
Total Basic Subscribers: 160.

WILLIS J. CRISP

Box 502
Pocahontas, AR 72455
Phone: 501-892-4862
Cable Systems (1):
Arkansas: Oak Grove Heights.
Total Basic Subscribers: 163.
Total Pay Units: 85.

CRISWELL GROUP

513 Jordan Ave.
Montoursville, PA 17754
Phone: 717-368-3266
Fax: 717-368-8154
Officers:
Roxanne Criswell, Pres.
C. Dale Criswell, Chief Exec. Officer
Timothy J. Criswell, Chief Operating Officer
Ownership: C. Dale Criswell, Roxanne Y. Criswell & Timothy J. Criswell, 100% jointly.
Cable Systems (4):
Pennsylvania: Anthony Twp., Laporte Borough, Summerville, Timblin Borough.
Total Basic Subscribers: 2,239.
Total Pay Units: 850.

CROSSLAKE MUNICIPAL TELEPHONE CO.

Box 70
Crosslake, MN 56442
Phone: 218-692-2777
Fax: 218-692-2410
Officer:
Kevin T. Larson, Gen. Mgr.
Ownership: Community owned.
Cable Systems (1):
Minnesota: Crosslake.
Total Basic Subscribers: 1,925.
Total Pay Units: 404.

CROSSROADS TV CABLE PARTNERSHIP

511 Broadway Ave.
Bridgeport, WV 26330-1201
Phone: 304-662-6115
Cable Systems (1):
West Virginia: Crossroads.
Total Basic Subscribers: 60.

KEVIN L. CROWNINGSHIELD

Box 617
740 Tea St.
Charlemont, MA 01339
Phone: 413-339-8759
Cable Systems (1):
Massachusetts: Charlemont.
Total Basic Subscribers: 110.

CROWNPOINT CABLE TV INC.

Box 210
Crownpoint, NM 87313
Phones: 505-534-4778; 505-786-5541
Cable Systems (1):
New Mexico: Crownpoint.
Total Basic Subscribers: 325.

CRYSTAL CABLE TV INC.

Box 365
122 Lake St.
Crystal, MI 48818
Phone: 517-235-6100
Fax: 517-235-6247
Officers:
W. Rex Skea, Pres.
Allen C. Horak, V.P.
Kimberly Marks, Secy.-Treas.
Ownership: W. Rex Skea & Allen C. Horak, Principals. Skea is principal of Great Lakes Communication Co., telephone consulting & contracting service.
Represented (legal): William Van Eck.
Cable Systems (1):
Michigan: Crystal Twp.
Total Basic Subscribers: 560.
Total Pay Units: 228.
Other Holdings:
Plans to extend cable service through LPTV.

CITY OF CRYSTAL FALLS

401 Superior Ave.
Crystal Falls, MI 49920
Phone: 906-875-3212
Ownership: Community owned.
Cable Systems (1):
Michigan: Crystal Falls.
Total Basic Subscribers: 878.
Total Pay Units: 228.

CS WIRELESS SYSTEMS INC.

1101 Summit Ave.
Plano, TX 75074
Phone: 972-398-5300
Fax: 972-398-1112

Branch Office:

2101 Wilson Blvd.
Arlington, VA 22201
Ownership: CAI Wireless Systems Inc., see listing, 90%; BANX Partnership, 10%.
Wireless Cable Systems (6):
California: Bakersfield.
Minnesota: Minneapolis/St. Paul.
Ohio: Cleveland, Dayton.
Texas: Fort Worth, San Antonio.
Planned Wireless Cable Systems (1):
California: Stockton.
Total Basic Subscribers: 64,862 (0.09% of total cable households).
Other Holdings:
MDS, MMDS, see listing.

C T & R CABLE LLC

29 Water St.
Petersburg, WV 26847
Phone: 304-257-2085
Ownership: Matthew Alt, 50%; Terry Hinkle, 50%.
Cable Systems (2):

West Virginia: Dorcas, Rig.
Total Basic Subscribers: 535.
Total Pay Units: 110.

C T & T INC.

4512 Burrow Dr.
North Little Rock, AR 72116
Phone: 501-758-5698
Ownership: Larry Clary, Doug Martin, John Tarkington & Harry Thomas, majority owners.
Cable Systems (2):
Arkansas: Greenbrier, Greers Ferry.
Total Basic Subscribers: 1,164.

CUNNINGHAM TELEPHONE & CABLE CO.

Box 108
Glen Elder, KS 67446
Phone: 785-545-3215
Ownership: David Cunningham & John Cunningham.
Cable Systems (8):
Kansas: Delphos, Formoso, Glasco, Glen Elder, Jamestown, Jewell, Randall, Scandia.
Total Basic Subscribers: 1,100.

CURTIS TELEPHONE CO. INC.

Box 8
Curtis, NE 69025
Phone: 308-367-8600
Officers:
Ed Cole, Chief Exec. Officer.
Marion Johnson, Pres.
Cable Systems (1):
Nebraska: Curtis.
Total Basic Subscribers: 485.
Total Pay Units: 125.
Other Holdings:
Cellular telephone.

CVF CABLEVISION

Suite 212
8301 Edgewater Dr.
Oakland, CA 94621
Phones: 510-569-7537; 800-331-6832
Cable Systems (1):
Oregon: Lacomb.
Total Basic Subscribers: 279.
Total Pay Units: 202.

DAIRYLAND CABLE SYSTEMS INC.

1140 Sextonville Rd.
Richland Center, WI 53581
Phone: 608-647-6383
Fax: 608-647-7394
Ownership: Lonnie Freeman, Principal.
Cable Systems (5):
Wisconsin: Bagley (village), Blue River (village), Ironton, Loganville (village), Seneca (village).
Total Basic Subscribers: 584.
Total Pay Units: 112.

DAK COMMUNICATIONS INC.

Box 218
Murrieta, CA 92564-0218
Phone: 909-677-2147
Fax: 909-677-1819
Officers:
Edward W. Ellis, Pres.
Tom Thomas, V.P.

Branch Office:

Murrieta, CA 92562
Phone: 909-677-9593
Ownership: Edward W. Ellis, 50%; Jeanne M. Ellis, 50%.
Represented (legal): Edward Nowakoski.
Cable Systems (1):
California: Rainbow.
Total Basic Subscribers: 111.
Other Holdings:
SMATV: Park Place Mobile Home Park, CA.

DAKOTA TELECOM INC.

Box 127
Irene, SD 57037
Phone: 605-263-3921
Fax: 605-263-7195
Officers:
Clark McLeod, Chmn.
Tomas W. Hertz, Pres. & Chief Exec. Officer
Bill Heaston, V.P. & Secy.-Treas.
Ownership: McLeod USA Inc.
Represented (legal): Bill Heaston.
Cable Systems (14):
Iowa: Inwood, Larchwood.
Minnesota: Adrian, Currie, Edgerton, Ellsworth, Hills, Jasper.
South Dakota: Alcester, Colton, Humboldt, Tabor, Valley Springs, Viborg.
Total Basic Subscribers: 6,811.
Total Pay Units: 2,706.

DALEVILLE CITY CABLE

Box 188
Daleville, AL 36322
Phone: 334-598-1119
Fax: 334-598-1200
Officers:
Wes Etheredge, Mayor
Ownership: Community owned.
Represented (legal): Steagall & Filmore.
Cable Systems (1):
Alabama: Daleville.
Total Basic Subscribers: 1,439.
Total Pay Units: 1,910.

DALTON CABLE TELEVISION INC.

Box 37
321 Lessman St.
Dalton, NE 69131
Phone: 308-377-2311
Fax: 308-377-2611
Officers:
Lowell L. Swanson, Chmn., Pres. & Chief Exec. Officer
Mildred R. Swanson, Chief Operating & Financial Officer
Ownership: Lowell Swanson & Mildred Swanson.
Cable Systems (5):
Nebraska: Dalton, Dix, Gurley, Lodgepole, Potter.
Total Basic Subscribers: 452.

DANIELS COMMUNICATIONS INC.

Suite 500
3200 Cherry Creek S Dr.
Denver, CO 80209
Phone: 303-778-5555
Fax: 303-778-5500; 760-438-8461
Officers:
Bill Daniels, Chmn.
H. Dewitt Mitchell, Pres. & Chief Exec. Officer
Kenneth Farabee, Secy.
James P. Hanson, Treas.

Branch Office:

5720 El Camino Real
Carlsbad, CA 92008
Phone: 619-438-7741
Ownership: Bill Daniels.
Cable Systems (2):
California: Carlsbad, Desert Hot Springs.
Total Basic Subscribers: 72,057 (0.11% of total cable households).
Total Pay Units: 28,296.

DATA VIDEO SYSTEMS INC.

Box 45
Parkers Prairie, MN 56361
Phone: 218-338-4000
Fax: 218-338-3297
Officers:
George M. Revering, Pres.
Rodney Scheel, Chief Exec. Officer
Dave Lehrke, V.P., Administration
Mark Roach, Controller
Ownership: North Central Utilities Inc.
Cable Systems (1):
Minnesota: Parkers Prairie.
Total Basic Subscribers: 627.
Total Pay Units: 168.
Other Holdings:
Telephone: Osakis Telephone Co., Osakis, MN;, Midwest Telephone Co., Parkers Prairie, MN;, Means-Polaris long distance company.
Cellular telephone: Cellular Five Partnership (Lowry, MN).
Telecommunications company: Central Minnesota Network Systems.
Publishing: IIS telephone directory publishing.
Data service: Midwest Information Systems Inc.

DAVI COMMUNICATIONS INC.

Box 104
Verona, VA 24482
Phone: 703-248-3400
Ownership: Sally M. Davison, Pres.
Cable Systems (1):
Virginia: Crawford Manor.
Total Basic Subscribers: 140.
Total Pay Units: 47.

DAVIS COMMUNICATIONS INC.

Box 117
Cheney, WA 99004
Phone: 509-235-5144
Ownership: Elizabeth Davis, 20%; John Davis, 20%; Mary Ann Davis, 20%; Patrick Davis, 20%; Thomas Davis, 20%.
Cable Systems (4):
Washington: Big Lake, Cheney, Lake Goodwin, Medical Lake.
Total Basic Subscribers: 10,524 (0.02% of total cable households).
Total Pay Units: 2,093.

LANE E. DAVIS

c/o Houston Newspapers
Box 70
Houston, MO 65483
Phone: 417-967-3358
Cable Systems (2):
Missouri: Houston 25%, Licking 50%.
Total Basic Subscribers: 559.
Other Holdings:
Publishing holdings: 50% of Houston Newspapers Inc., publisher of The Herald & The Republican, Houston, MO.

MICKEY DAVIS

Box 237
314 W. Main St.
Mountain View, OK 73062
Phone: 405-347-2111
Cable Systems (1):
Oklahoma: Mountain View.
Total Basic Subscribers: 334.
Total Pay Units: 67.

ROBERT L. DAVIS

Box 70
Houston, MO 65483
Phone: 417-967-3358
Cable Systems (1):
Missouri: Houston 75%.
Total Basic Subscribers: N.A.

CITY OF DAYTON (IA)

Box 45
101 S. Main St.
Dayton, IA 50530-0045
Phone: 515-547-3342
Officers:
Kenny Sanders, Chief Exec. Officer
Randy Danielson, Chief Financial Officer
Ownership: Municipally-owned.
Cable Systems (1):
Iowa: Dayton.
Total Basic Subscribers: 285.
Total Pay Units: 122.

DEAN HILL CABLE

Box 128
Parkdale, AR 71661
Phone: 501-473-2802
Officer:
Phillip Johnson, Mgr.
Cable Systems (1):
Arkansas: Wilmot.
Total Basic Subscribers: 110.

DEANS CABLEVISION INC.

115 S. Linden St.
Lamoni, IA 50140
Phones: 515-784-6764; 800-798-5488
Fax: 515-784-7327
Officer:
Robert Dean Pierce, Chmn., Pres. & Chief Operating Officer
Ownership: Greta Pierce & Robert Dean Pierce, 100% jointly.
Cable Systems (9):
Iowa: Blockton, Clearfield, Diagonal, Grand River, Van Wert.
Missouri: Conception Junction, Parnell, Ravenwood, Sheridan.
Total Basic Subscribers: 888.
Total Pay Units: 174.

DEARY TV CO-OP INC.

Box 105
Deary, ID 83823
Ownership: Non-profit organization.
Cable Systems (1):
Idaho: Deary.
Total Basic Subscribers: 185.

DONALD G. DEE

Box 38
Houlton, ME 04730
Phone: 207-532-4451
Cable Systems (1):
Maine: Mattawamkeag (town).
Total Basic Subscribers: 332.
Total Pay Units: 54.

DEEP RIVER TELEPHONE CO.

Box 211
Deep River, IA 52222
Phone: 515-595-4000
Cable Systems (1):
Iowa: Deep River.
Total Basic Subscribers: 172.

DEER RIVER CABLEVISION
Box 367
209 2nd St. SE
Deer River, MN 56636
Phone: 218-246-8228
Fax: 218-246-2075
Ownership: Deer River Telephone Co.
Cable Systems (1):
Minnesota: Deer River.
Total Basic Subscribers: 438.
Total Pay Units: 170.

DEFIANCE TELEPHONE CO.
Box 399
300 Main Ave.
Defiance, IA 51527
Phone: 712-748-3511
Officer:
James E. Bieker, Chief Exec. Officer
Cable Systems (1):
Iowa: Defiance.
Total Basic Subscribers: 113.
Total Pay Units: 43.

DELTA CABLE COMMUNICATIONS LTD.
5381 48th Ave.
Delta BC V4K 1W7
Canada
Phone: 604-946-1144
Fax: 604-946-5627
Officers:
W. Stan Thomas, Chmn.
John S. Thomas, Pres. & Chief Exec. Officer
Monica Barrett, Secy.-Treas. & Chief Financial Officer
Ownership: Thomas Investments Ltd., 77.5%; John S. Thomas, 12%; Coast Communications Ltd., 5%; others, 5.5%. TIL ownership: W. S. Thomas & John S. Thomas, Principals. TIL owns 80% of Northwest Communications Ltd., television production and post-production company. John S. Thomas owns 20% of Coast Cable Communications Ltd. (Canadian MSO) & 51% of Coast Communications Ltd.
Cable Systems (1):
Washington: Point Roberts.
Total Basic Subscribers: 716.
Total Pay Units: 30.
Cable Holdings:
Canada: Delta, BC.

DELTA COMMUNICATIONS INC.
6301 Broad Branch Rd.
Chevy Chase, MD 20815
Cable Systems (2):
California: Earlimart.
Michigan: Munising.
Total Basic Subscribers: 1,600.
Total Pay Units: 451.

DEMARCE CABLE TV
116 S. Main
Elmwood, WI 54740
Phone: 715-639-2121
Fax: 715-639-2121
Officers:
Mike DeMarce, Chmn., Pres., Chief Exec. & Operating Officer
Dianne DeMarce, V.P.
Jeff DeMarce, Secy.-Treas.
Ownership: Jeff DeMarce, 50%; Micke DeMarce, 50%.
Cable Systems (3):
Wisconsin: Elmwood, Glenwood City, Spring Valley.
Total Basic Subscribers: 1,140.
Total Pay Units: 105.

DEMOPOLIS CATV CO.
Box 477
Demopolis, AL 36732
Phone: 205-289-0727
Officers:
Lynn Goldman, Pres. & Chief Exec. Officer
Debbie Goldman, V.P.
Richard Manley, Secy.-Treas.
Ownership: Lynn Goldman, 99.5%; Richard Manley, 0.5%.
Cable Systems (1):
Alabama: Demopolis.
Total Basic Subscribers: 2,525.
Total Pay Units: 244.

DENISON COMMUNICATIONS INC.
Suite B
11919 Sunray Ave.
Baton Rouge, LA 70816
Phone: 504-291-9698
Cable Systems (4):
Mississippi: McLaurin, Sanford, Seminary, Sunrise.
Total Basic Subscribers: 583.

DEPOSIT TV INC.
20 Elm St.
Deposit, NY 13754
Phone: 607-467-2105
Officers:
Ralph Kaplan, Pres.
Charles Kaplan, V.P.
Helen Kaplan, Secy.-Treas.
Ownership: Ralph Kaplan, 50%; Charles Kaplan, 49%; Helen Kaplan, 1%.
Cable Systems (1):
New York: Deposit.
Total Basic Subscribers: 800.
Total Pay Units: 260.

G. EUGENE DERRICKSON
Box 297
Licking, MO 65542
Phone: 314-674-3515
Cable Systems (1):
Missouri: Licking 50%.
Total Basic Subscribers: 559.
Total Pay Units: 120.

MARLA L. & DONALD L. DESHAW
Box 242
11 5th St. NE
Harlowton, MT 59036-0242
Phone: 406-632-4300
Fax: 406-632-4309
Officers:
Donald L. DeShaw, Pres.
Marla L. DeShaw, Secy.-Treas.
Cable Systems (2):
Montana: Harlowton, Ryegate.
Total Basic Subscribers: 436.
Total Pay Units: 92.

ALLEN DETWILER
Box 43
RD 1
New Enterprise, PA 16664
Phone: 814-766-2614
Cable Systems (1):
Pennsylvania: Woodbury.
Total Basic Subscribers: 750.
Total Pay Units: 72.

DICKEY RURAL SERVICES INC.
Box 69
9628 Hwy. 281
Ellendale, ND 58436
Phone: 701-349-3687
Fax: 701-783-4300
Officer:
Kent Klima, Pres.
Ownership: Dickey Rural Telephone Co-op.
Represented (legal): Mark Scallon.
Cable Systems (6):
North Dakota: Forman, Gwinner, Litchville, Marion, Milnor, Wyndmere.
Total Basic Subscribers: 944.
Total Pay Units: 539.
Other Holdings:
Telephone.

DIGITAL BROADCAST CORP.
Box 37100
Omaha, NE 68137-2357
Phone: 402-592-3436
Wireless Cable Systems (1):
Nebraska: Omaha.
Total Basic Subscribers: N.A.

DIGITAL WIRELESS SYSTEMS INC.
55 Auburn Rd.
Londonderry, NH 03053
Phone: 603-432-1176
Fax: 603-432-3881
Officers:
David D. Schlueter, Chmn. & Chief Exec. Officer
Joseph R. Paradis, Pres. & Chief Operating Officer

Corporate Office:
Reading, PA 19612
Phone: 610-921-9500
Wireless Cable Systems (1):
Pennsylvania: Reading.
Total Basic Subscribers: 2,400.
Other Holdings:
MMDS, see listing.

DIODE CABLE CO. INC.
Box 236
Diller, NE 68342
Phone: 402-793-5330
Ownership: Diller Telephone Co.
Cable Systems (9):
Kansas: Home, Morrowville, Oketo, Republic.
Nebraska: Alexandria, Diller, Hardy, Jansen, Ruskin.
Total Basic Subscribers: 559.
Total Pay Units: 60.
Other Holdings:
Telephone.

DIVERSE COMMUNICATIONS INC.
246 N. Division St.
Woodhull, IL 61490
Phone: 309-334-2150
Fax: 309-334-2989
Officers:
Jerry Krueger, Pres.
Roscoe Lowrey, Exec. V.P.
Robert L. Johnson, Secy.-Treas.
Ownership: Woodhull Community Telephone Com.
Cable Systems (1):
Illinois: Alpha.
Total Basic Subscribers: 646.
Total Pay Units: 710.

DIXIE CABLE TV INC.
Box 97
Alma, GA 31510
Phone: 912-632-4241
Officers:
Jack Bennett, Pres.
Kevin K. Brooks, Chief Exec. Officer
Ownership: Charlene Bennett & Jack Bennett, 100% jointly.
Cable Systems (1):
Georgia: Alma.
Total Basic Subscribers: 1,675.
Total Pay Units: 600.

DIXON TELEPHONE CO.
Box 10
608 Davenport St.
Dixon, IA 52745
Phone: 319-843-2901
Officer:
Bob Dahms, Pres.
Cable Systems (4):
Iowa: Dixon, Donahue, Maysville, New Liberty.
Total Basic Subscribers: 122.

ALBERT DOBITZ
Regent, ND 58650
Phone: 701-563-4626
Cable Systems (1):
North Dakota: Regent.
Total Basic Subscribers: 82.
Total Pay Units: 50.

DODGE COUNTY CABLEVISION
Box 620343
Middleton, WI 53562-0343
Phone: 608-831-7044
Fax: 608-836-5726
Ownership: Robert E. Ryan; David G. Walsh; WMC Properties Ltd.
Represented (legal): Foley & Lardner.
Cable Systems (1):
Wisconsin: Brownsville.
Total Basic Subscribers: 368.
Total Pay Units: 119.

ROBERT DOERR
Box 6
Mecosta, MI 49332
Phone: 616-972-7111
Cable Systems (2):
Michigan: Leroy (village) 40%, St. James Twp. 45%.
Total Basic Subscribers: 621.
Total Pay Units: 284.

CITY OF DOERUN
Box 37
223 W. Broad Ave.
Doerun, GA 31744
Phone: 912-782-5444
Fax: 912-782-5224
Ownership: Community owned.
Cable Systems (1):
Georgia: Doerun.
Total Basic Subscribers: 347.

JOHN DONOFRIO JR.
57 Everett St.
Warren, RI 02885
Phone: 401-247-2250
Represented (legal): William C. Maaia Assoc.
Cable Systems (1):
Rhode Island: Warren.
Total Basic Subscribers: 12,600 (0.02% of total cable households).
Total Pay Units: 7,000.

LEE C. DORMAN
196 S. Main St.
Pleasant Gap, PA 16823
Phone: 814-359-3161
Fax: 814-359-2145
Cable Systems (1):
Pennsylvania: Union Twp. (Centre County).
Total Basic Subscribers: 894.
Total Pay Units: 205.

KEN DOUVIA
730 Burlington
Grand Ridge, IL 61325
Phone: 815-249-5517
Represented (legal): Tim Creedon.
Cable Systems (1):
Illinois: Grand Ridge.
Total Basic Subscribers: 302.
Total Pay Units: 80.

DOWNIEVILLE TV CORP.
Box 393
Downieville, CA 95936
Phone: 916-289-3619
Officers:
Thomas Vilas, Chmn.
Rae Kalustian, Secy.-Treas.
Ownership: 77 Stockholders.
Cable Systems (1):
California: Downieville.
Total Basic Subscribers: 210.

DOWNSVILLE COMMUNITY ANTENNA SYSTEM INC.
Box 197
HC 89
Downsville, NY 13755
Phone: 607-363-7717
Officers:
Arthur Merrill, Chief Exec. Officer
Stacey Mattson, Secy.-Treas.
Ownership: Community owned.
Cable Systems (1):
New York: Downsville.
Total Basic Subscribers: 404.
Total Pay Units: 255.

DRESDEN CABLE INC.
106 W. Maple
Dresden, TN 38225
Phone: 901-364-5259
Ownership: Richard Hutcherson, Pres.
Cable Systems (1):
Tennessee: Dresden.
Total Basic Subscribers: N.A.

DREWRY COMMUNICATIONS
Box 708
Lawton, OK 73502
Phones: 405-355-7000; 580-353-2250
Fax: 405-357-3811
Officers:
Robert H. Drewry, Chmn.
Larry Patton, V.P.
Ownership: Robert T. Drewry & William T. Drewry, 79.4% jointly; William A. Scott, 6.09%; Judy W. Bryan, 5.77%; James T. Warkentin, 5.76%; Drewry Family Ltd. Partnership, 2.41%; Edith Scott, 0.57%.
Cable Systems (1):
Oklahoma: Lawton.
Total Basic Subscribers: 25,000 (0.04% of total cable households).
Total Pay Units: 5,500.
Other Holdings:
TV, see listing.

DUBOIS COMMUNICATIONS INC.
50 Tipp St.
Dubois, PA 15801
Phone: 814-371-1925
Fax: 814-371-3052
Officer:
Rodney R. Preston, Pres.
Ownership: Rodney R. Preston.
Represented (legal): David Hopkins.
Cable Systems (8):
Pennsylvania: Caledonia, Hazen, New Freeport, Rogersville, Sabula, Spartansburg, Weedville, Wind Ridge.
Total Basic Subscribers: 2,543.
Total Pay Units: 560.

DUMONT TELEPHONE CO.
Box 349
506 Pine St.
Dumont, IA 50625
Phone: 515-857-3211
Fax: 515-857-3300
Officers:
William Blakley, Chmn. & Chief Exec. Officer
Elmer Garrels, Pres.
Arnold Miller, Secy.-Treas.
Ownership: Shareholder owned.
Cable Systems (3):
Iowa: Bristow, Dumont, Geneva.
Total Basic Subscribers: 429.
Total Pay Units: 186.

CLIFFORD DUNCAN
Box 685
Wilmington, VT 05363
Phone: 802-464-2233
Cable Systems (1):
Vermont: Wilmington.
Total Basic Subscribers: 1,000.
Total Pay Units: 265.

DUNKERTON TELEPHONE COOPERATIVE
701 S. Canfield Rd.
Dunkerton, IA 50626
Phone: 319-822-4512
Fax: 319-822-2206
Officer:
Ron Reil, Pres.
Cable Systems (1):
Iowa: Dunkerton.
Total Basic Subscribers: 218.
Total Pay Units: 62.

DURAND CABLE CO. INC.
320 3rd Ave. W
Durand, WI 54736
Phone: 715-672-5966
Officers:
Henry W. Niehoff, Pres.
Gerald Hanson, Secy.-Treas.
Ownership: Gerald Hanson, 50%; Henry W. Niehoff, 50%.
Cable Systems (3):
Wisconsin: Durand, Mondovi, Plum City.
Total Basic Subscribers: 2,002.
Total Pay Units: 460.

RAY S. DYER JR.
Box 157
Locke, NY 13092
Phone: 315-497-0444
Cable Systems (1):
New York: Moravia.
Total Basic Subscribers: 950.

DYNAX COMMUNICATIONS INC.
201 S. Main St.
Waldorf, MN 59091
Phone: 507-239-2359
Cable Systems (1):
Minnesota: Waldorf.
Total Basic Subscribers: 84.
Total Pay Units: 23.

EAGLE CABLEVISION (MT)
Box 159
Laurel, MT 59044
Phone: 406-628-2974
Ownership: Cliff Schollmeyer, Principal.
Cable Systems (5):
Montana: Lame Deer, Lodge Grass, White Sulphur Springs.
North Dakota: Dunn Center, Taylor.
Total Basic Subscribers: 910.
Total Pay Units: 210.

EAGLE CABLEVISION INC.
Box 39
First & Cedar St.
Remer, MN 56672
Phone: 218-566-2302
Officers:
Conrad Johnson, Pres.
Ron Johnson, V.P.
Donna Gunderson, Secy.
Ownership: Conrad Johnson, Donna Johnson, Dwayne Johnson, Lowell Johnson & Ronald Johnson, 100% jointly. Lowell & Ronald Johnson are execs. with the Johnson Telephone Co., Remer, MN.
Cable Systems (2):
Minnesota: Remer.
Montana: Philipsburg.
Total Basic Subscribers: 488.
Total Pay Units: 107.

EAGLE COMMUNICATIONS INC. (KS)
Box 817
2703 Hall
Hays, KS 67601
Phone: 785-625-4000
Fax: 785-625-8030
Officers:
Robert E. Schmidt, Chmn. & Chief Exec. Officer
Gary Shorman, Pres.
Kenneth R. Braun, Secy.-Treas.
Ownership: Robert E. Schmidt.
Represented (legal): Wiley, Rein & Fielding.
Cable Systems (5):
Kansas: Goodland, Hays, Hoxie, Russell, Wakeeney.
Total Basic Subscribers: 12,300 (0.02% of total cable households).
Total Pay Units: 3,066.
Cable Holdings:
Manages Eagle West LLC, see listing.

EAGLE VALLEY COMMUNICATIONS
Box 178
109 Main St.
Richland, OR 97870
Phone: 541-893-6111
Fax: 541-893-6202
Cable Systems (1):
Oregon: Richland.
Total Basic Subscribers: 140.

EAGLE WEST LLC
No. 36
9333 E. Apache Trail
Mesa, AZ 85207
Phone: 480-380-5855
Fax: 480-380-5877
Officers:
James F. Collins, Chief Exec. Officer
Al H. Williams, Chief Operating Officer
Ken Robinson, Chief Financial Officer

Branch Offices:
Eagar, AZ
Phone: 520-333-1444

123 S. 3rd St.
Williams, AZ
Phone: 520-635-2360
Ownership: Privately held. Managed by Eagle Communications Inc. (KS), see listing.
Represented (legal): Kenda, Austerman, Mitchell & Zuercher.
Cable Systems (16):
Arizona: Alpine, Bagdad, Bear Flats, Black Canyon City, Casa Grande (northern portion), Concho Valley, Eagar, East Mesa, Florence (northern portion), Saddle Mountain, St. Johns, Williams, Yarnell.
New Mexico: Glenwood, Rancho Grande Estates, Reserve.
Total Basic Subscribers: 8,487.
Total Pay Units: 1,303.

EAST BUCHANAN TELEPHONE COOPERATIVE
Box 147
Winthrop, IA 50682
Phone: 319-935-3011
Cable Systems (1):
Iowa: Winthrop.
Total Basic Subscribers: 425.
Total Pay Units: 108.

EAST CLEVELAND CABLE TV LLC
1395 Hayden Ave.
East Cleveland, OH 44112
Phone: 216-851-2215
Fax: 216-851-0231
Ownership: Jerry Smart & Alan Thompson.
Cable Systems (1):
Ohio: East Cleveland.
Total Basic Subscribers: 3,708.
Total Pay Units: 2,429.

EASTERN CONNECTICUT CABLE TV INC.
Box 6001
61 Myrock Ave.
Waterford, CT 06385
Phone: 860-442-8525
Fax: 860-443-6031
Officers:
Ralph A. Mariani, Chmn. & Pres.
Edmund W. O'Brien, Secy.
L. James Carroll, Chief Financial Officer
Represented (legal): Piper & Marbury LLP; Day Berry & Howard.
Cable Systems (2):
Connecticut: New London.
Rhode Island: Newport.
Total Basic Subscribers: 45,228 (0.07% of total cable households).
Total Pay Units: 25,541.

EASTERN NEBRASKA TELEPHONE CO.
1638 Lincoln St.
Blair, NE 68008
Phone: 402-426-2101
Officers:
Hugh W. Hunt, Pres.
Mike Jacobson, Chief Exec. Officer

Richard A. Hunt, Exec. V.P.
Karen Hunt, V.P.
Michael A. Mines, V.P., Mktg.
Douglas L. Davidson, Chief Financial Officer
Ownership: Hugh W. Hunt & Richard A. Hunt. The Hunts also own Arlington Telephone Co. & Rock County Telephone Co., see listings.
Cable Systems (2):
Nebraska: Carroll, Osmond.
Total Basic Subscribers: 441.
Total Pay Units: 178.

EASTON UTILITIES COMMISSION
Box 1189
Easton, MD 21601
Phone: 410-822-6110
Cable Systems (1):
Maryland: Easton.
Total Basic Subscribers: 4,856.
Total Pay Units: 2,515.

EASTVILLE TV CABLE
Box 85
Loganton, PA 17747
Phone: 717-725-2733
Officer:
James Gounet, Pres.
Ownership: Community owned.
Cable Systems (1):
Pennsylvania: Eastville.
Total Basic Subscribers: N.A.

MARVEL EBENHAHN
Box 175
Sheyenne, ND 58374
Phone: 701-996-3131
Cable Systems (1):
North Dakota: Sheyenne.
Total Basic Subscribers: 95.
Total Pay Units: 37.

ECONOCO INC.
Box 147
Rte. 61
Kincaid, WV 25119
Phone: 304-469-2817
Ownership: Sheila Bills, Principal.
Cable Systems (6):
West Virginia: Canvas, Gandeeville, Goldtown, Left Hand, Maysel, Mount Lookout.
Total Basic Subscribers: 2,138.
Total Pay Units: 284.

RICHARD EKSTRAND
Box 304
Emery, SD 57332
Phone: 605-449-4203
Fax: 605-449-4329
Cable Systems (1):
South Dakota: Emery.
Total Basic Subscribers: 155.
Total Pay Units: 40.

EL-MAR COMMUNICATIONS CO.
143 Wellsville St.
Bolivar, NY 14715
Phones: 716-928-2812; 800-836-0420
Fax: 716-928-1962
Ownership: Lance Shaner & Fred Shaner, 100% jointly.
Cable Systems (3):
New York: Cohocton, Friendship, Limestone.
Total Basic Subscribers: 1,706.
Total Pay Units: 517.

ELDORADO CABLE TV INC.
2103 Ave. Vista Grande
Santa Fe, NM 87505
Phone: 505-988-1302
Officer:
James W. Harper, Chief Operating Officer
Cable Systems (1):
New Mexico: Eldorado.
Total Basic Subscribers: 860.
Total Pay Units: 180.

ELECTRONIC CABLE COMMUNICATIONS INC.
Box 454
715 Main St.
Haines, AK 99827
Phone: 907-766-2137
Fax: 907-766-2345
Officers:
Larry D. Glackin, Pres.
Patty A. Glackin, Secy.-Treas.
Ownership: Larry D. Glackin, 50%; Patty Glackin, 50%.
Cable Systems (2):
Alaska: Haines, Skagway.
Total Basic Subscribers: 500.
Total Pay Units: 150.

ELGIN TV ASSN. INC.
Box 246
830 Alder
Elgin, OR 97827
Phone: 503-437-4575
Officers:
Allen Williams, Pres.
Allen Williams, V.P.
Carl Schmittle, Secy.-Treas.
Ownership: Subscriber owned.
Cable Systems (1):
Oregon: Elgin.
Total Basic Subscribers: 689.
Total Pay Units: 350.

ELK RIVER TV CABLE CO.
822 N. Cleveland
Moscow, ID 83843
Phones: 208-826-3370; 208-882-2710
Ownership: Dewayne Allert.
Cable Systems (1):
Idaho: Elk River.
Total Basic Subscribers: 65.
Total Pay Units: 11.

CLIFTON ELLER
Box 872100
Wasilla, AK 99687-3809
Phone: 907-373-6007
Fax: 907-373-5599
Cable Systems (2):
Alaska: Tanana, Whittier.
Total Basic Subscribers: 159.
Total Pay Units: 364.

L. E. ELLIOTT
Box 368
115 N. Main St.
Ripley, MS 38663
Phone: 601-837-4881
Cable Systems (1):
Mississippi: Ripley.
Total Basic Subscribers: 3,389.
Total Pay Units: 1,130.

ELLIS ENGINEERING & CONSTRUCTION CO.
Drawer B
Riverton, KS 66770
Phone: 316-848-3494
Ownership: Holland Ellis.
Cable Systems (2):
Kansas: Lowell, Weir.
Total Basic Subscribers: N.A.

EMILY COOPERATIVE TELEPHONE CO.
Box 100
Emily, MN 56447
Phone: 218-763-3000
Fax: 218-763-2042
Officers:
Thomas Stevens, Pres.
Sharon Libby Nix, Secy.-Treas.
Ownership: Subscriber owned.
Represented (legal): Moss & Barnett (Minneapolis, MN).
Cable Systems (1):
Minnesota: Emily.
Total Basic Subscribers: 882.
Total Pay Units: 140.
Other Holdings:
Cellular radio.

JAMES ENGLISH
4363-C Leisure Time Dr.
Diamondhead, MS 39525
Phone: 601-255-3381
Cable Systems (1):
Mississippi: Diamondhead.
Total Basic Subscribers: 2,834.
Total Pay Units: 967.

ENTERTAINMENT EXPRESS LTD.
3275 M St. NW
Washington, DC 20007
Phone: 202-333-0902
Officers:
Richard Sklar, Chmn. & Chief Exec. Officer
Marc Sklar, Chief Operating Officer
Cable Systems (1):
California: Mountain Meadows.
Total Basic Subscribers: 1,838.
Total Pay Units: 605.

EQC CABLE INC.
Box 8
50 W. Oak St.
Campbellsburg, IN 47108
Phone: 812-755-4786
Officers:
Bert Engler, Pres.
John Engler, V.P.
Ownership: Bert Engler & John Engler, Principals.
Cable Systems (3):
Indiana: Campbellsburg, Medora, Saltillo.
Total Basic Subscribers: 762.

ERIE TELECOMMUNICATIONS INC.
3627 Zimmerman Rd.
Erie, PA 16510-2642
Phone: 814-453-4553
Fax: 814-456-5162
Ownership: Time Warner Cable, see listing, 54.19%; Times Publishing Co., 29.18%; Greater Erie Economic Development Corp., 10%; Gregory Baldwin, 4.64%; Bruce W. Baldwin, 1.32%; Ann Elizabeth Baldwin, 0.66%.
Total Basic Subscribers: 30,400 (0.04% of total cable households).
Total Pay Units: 14,735.

DALLAS R. EUBANKS
Box 126
Corbin, KY 40701
Phone: 606-528-6400
Cable Systems (1):
Kentucky: Gray.
Total Basic Subscribers: 2,413.
Total Pay Units: 474.

EUSTIS TELEPHONE EXCHANGE
Box 127
Brady, NE 69123
Phone: 308-584-3313
Ownership: Rodney E. Chrisp, Chmn. & Pres.
Cable Systems (3):
Nebraska: Brady, Eustis, Maxwell.
Total Basic Subscribers: 422.
Total Pay Units: 245.

EVERTEK INC.
Box 270
216 N. Main St.
Everly, IA 51338
Phone: 712-834-2255
Ownership: Doug Gathman, Jack Hames, Wayne Johnson, Willie Hartman & Ron Schoenewe, 100% jointly.
Cable Systems (1):
Iowa: Everly.
Total Basic Subscribers: 256.
Other Holdings:
MMDS, see listings.

EYECOM INC.
2121 Abbott Rd.
Anchorage, AK 99507
Phone: 907-349-2400
Fax: 907-349-1858
Officers:
Jack Rhyner, Chmn., Pres.
Daniel W. Gordon, Chief Operating Officer
David J. Goggins, V.P., Plant
Michael C. Burke, Chief Financial Officer
Ownership: TelAlaska Inc.
Represented (legal): Heather H. Grahame.
Cable Systems (4):
Alaska: Galena, Girdwood, Port Lions, Unalaska.
Total Basic Subscribers: 1,638.
Total Pay Units: 1,221.

FAIRBANKS COMMUNICATIONS INC.
Suite 103
3071 Continental Dr.
West Palm Beach, FL 33407
Phone: 561-844-5330
Fax: 561-844-4402
Officers:
Richard M. Fairbanks, Chmn., Pres. & Chief Exec. Officer
Roger S. Snowdon, Chief Financial Officer
Richard C. Hindes, V.P., Controller
Mary P. Knight, Assistant Controller

Branch Offices:
Suite 304
Indianapolis, IN 46260
Phone: 317-846-7111

10778 Randall Ave.
Aurora, IN 47001
Phone: 812-926-3694
Ownership: Richard Fairbanks.
Represented (legal): Haley Bader & Potts PLC.
Cable Systems (6):
Indiana: Bright, Dillsboro, Lawrenceburg, Milan, Osgood, Rising Sun.
Total Basic Subscribers: 11,400 (0.02% of total cable households).
Total Pay Units: 3,300.

Radio Stations:
Florida: WJNO(AM), West Palm Beach.

FALCON/CAPITAL CABLE PARTNERS LP

Suite 220
906 S. Kirkwood Rd.
St. Louis, MO 63122
Phone: 314-909-8444
Fax: 314-909-8459
Officers:
Scott R. Widham, Pres. & Chief Operating Officer
Mary Meier, V.P., Mktg.
Roland Van Heest, Chief Financial Officer

Branch Office:

1510 Boone Industrial Dr.
Columbia, MO 63202
Phone: 314-875-8875
Ownership: Falcon Communications LP, 50%; private investors, 50%.
Cable Systems (64):
Illinois: Albion, Brownstown, Carmi, Crossville, Effingham County, Enfield, Kinmundy, Newton, Norris City, Patoka, Ramsey, St. Francisville, Sumner, Vandalia, Watson.
Indiana: New Harmony.
Iowa: Allerton, Cincinnati, Garden Grove, Humeston, Lineville, Moravia, Mystic, Russell, Seymour.
Kansas: Conway Springs, Douglass, Kansas City (portions), La Harpe, Lake of the Forest, Oxford.
Kentucky: Sebree.
Missouri: Belle, Boone County, Braymer, Breckenridge, Cainsville, Cairo, Chamois, Clarence, Cuba, Eagleville, Elsberry, Gerald, Gilman City, Hamilton, Hardin, La Plata, Laredo, Lathrop, Linn, Linneus, Milan, Mountain Grove, New Hampton, New Haven, Orrick, Polo, Renick, Ridgeway, Spickard, Stewartsville, Vandalia, Viburnum.
Total Basic Subscribers: 22,337 (0.03% of total cable households).
Total Pay Units: 10,395.

FALCON COMMUNICATIONS LP

Suite 200
474 S. Raymond Ave.
Pasadena, CA 91105
Phone: 626-792-7132
Fax: 626-793-5143
Web site: http://www.falconcable.com
Officers:
Marc B. Nathanson, Chmn. & Chief Exec. Officer
Frank J. Intiso, Pres. & Chief Operating Officer
Michael K. Menerey, Chief Financial Officer
Falcon Cable Group
Joan Scully, V.P., Human Resources
Raymond J. Tyndall, V.P., Engineering
Jon Lunsford, V.P., Finance & Corporate Development
Ownership: Falcon Cable TV, managing partner, 54%; AT&T Broadband & Information Services, see listing, 46%.
Cable Systems (319):
Alabama: Altoona, Athens, Attalla, Cedar Bluff, Centre, Cherokee, Decatur, Elgin, Gurley, Leighton, Mobile County, Piedmont, Rainsville, Scottsboro.
Arkansas: Ashdown, Beebe, Hardy, Maumelle, McAlmont, Shannon Hills, Vilonia, West Pulaski.
California: Adelanto, Agoura Hills, Big Bear Lake, Boron, Box Canyon, Calabasas, California City, California Hot Springs, Crescent City, Gilroy, Greenfield, Guadalupe, Hesperia, Hidden Hills, Jack Ranch/Posey, King City, Lake Arrowhead, Los Alamos, Lost Hills, Malibu, Mojave, North Edwards, Phelan, Porterville, Redding, San Luis Obispo County, Soledad, Thousand Oaks, Topanga Canyon.
Florida: Palm Bay, Sebastian.
Georgia: Cave Spring, Cedartown, Dalton, Lake Park, Moody Air Force Base, Ringgold, Rockmart, Valdosta, Villa Rica.
Idaho: Cascade, Council, Donnelly, Emmett, McCall, New Meadows, Weiser.
Illinois: Anna 65%, Carlinville, Cisne, Fairfield, Farmersville, Flora, Gillespie, Girard, Hillsboro, Jerseyville, Litchfield, Mount Carmel, Noble, Nokomis, Pana, Raymond, Salem, Shelbyville, Taylorville, Xenia.
Kentucky: Bell County, Benton, Bradfordsville, Bryantsville, Burnside, Calvert City, Columbia, Corbin, Cumberland, Eubank, Fulton, Greensburg, Hustonville, Liberty, McKinney, Monticello, Mount Vernon, Paint Lick, Parksville, Russell Springs, Somerset, Summersville, Whitley City, Williamsburg.
Louisiana: Arcadia, Benton, Choudrant, Dixie Inn, Greensburg, Mangham, Oak Ridge, Plain Dealing, Start.
Maryland: Centreville, Crisfield.
Michigan: Akron/Fairgrove, Au Gres, Coleman, Hale, Linwood, Rosebush, Sterling, Unionville.
Mississippi: Belmont, Burnsville.
Missouri: Alton, Annapolis, Bell City, Benton, California, Cape Girardeau, Chaffee, Charleston, Clinton, Dexter, El Dorado Springs, Eldon, Fisk, Fredericktown, Gower, Harrisonville, Holden, Ironton, Knob Noster, Lesterville, Malden, Marble Hill, Maysville, Nevada, New Madrid, Osage Beach, Pacific, Perryville, Plattsburg, Pomme de Terre, Poplar Bluff, Potosi, Qulin, Rockwood Point, Scott City, Sedalia, Sikeston, St. Clair, St. James, Ste. Genevieve, Steelville, Sullivan, Thayer, Tipton, Versailles, Wappapello, Warrensburg, Warsaw, Washington, West Plains.
Missouri: Willow Springs, Windsor.
Nevada: Mesquite, Overton.
New York: Beekmantown, Jay, Long Lake, Plattsburgh (town), Westport (village).
North Carolina: Burke County, Buxton, Carolina Beach, Chinquapin, Corolla, Faison, Gates County, Manteo, North Wilkesboro, Olde Point, Roaring Gap, Snow Hill, Surf City, Warsaw.
Oklahoma: Earlsboro, Meeker, Prague, Shawnee, Stratford.
Oregon: Astoria, Bandon, Bear Mountain, Brickyard Road, Brookings, Brownsville, Cave Junction, Clatskanie, Coos Bay, Coquille, Cottage Grove, Dallas, Drain, Florence, Gold Beach, Grants Pass, Halfway, Hauser, Hood River, Klamath Falls, La Grande, Lincoln City, Mapleton, Medford, Myrtle Creek, Myrtle Point, Nehalem, Netarts, Newport, Pendleton, Powers 89, Reedsport, Roseburg, Sandy, Silverton, Sutherlin, The Dalles, Tillamook, Tillamook County (southwestern portion), Veneta.
South Carolina: Beaufort, Chesterfield, Daufuskie Island, Kershaw, Pageland, River Hills.
Tennessee: Bolivar, Bradford, Brownsville, Covington, Dyer, Jellico, Ripley.
Texas: Atlanta, Batesville, Big Wells, Brackettville, Carthage, Castroville, Comanche, Devine, Goliad, Hallsville, Hondo, Jefferson, La Pryor, Marshall, Palacios, Pleasanton, Port Aransas, Portland, Rockport, Sabinal, Shiner, Sinton, Sweeny, Three Rivers, Tilden, West Columbia, Wharton.
Utah: Green River, Hurricane, Ivins, Leeds, Rockville, St. George.
Virginia: Accomac, Belle Haven, Chincoteague, Franklin, Suffolk 80%, Tangier Island.
Washington: Cathlamet, Colville, Ellensburg, Holly, Kennewick, Long Beach, Loon Lake, Naselle, Northport, Port Orchard, Prosser, Sunnyside, Walla Walla, Wenatchee, Yakima.
Total Basic Subscribers: 1,093,444 (1.60% of total cable households).
Total Pay Units: 312,839.
Cable Holdings:
Falcon/Capital Cable Partners LP, 50%, see listing.
Note: Sold to Charter Communications Inc. 1999.

FANCH COMMUNICATIONS INC.

Suite 1550
1873 S. Bellaire St.
Denver, CO 80222
Phone: 303-756-5600
Fax: 303-756-5774
Officers:
Robert C. Fanch, Chmn. & Chief Exec. Officer
Jack T. Pottle, Pres. & Chief Operating Officer
Terry J. Adams, Chief Financial Officer
Ownership: Robert C. Fanch.
Represented (legal): Cole, Raywid & Braverman LLP.
Cable Systems (307):
Colorado: Burlington, Estes Park, Las Animas, Springfield.
Delaware: Middletown 50.5%.
Florida: Deer Creek Golf RV Resort.
Indiana: Crawford County 50.5%, Edinburgh 50.5%, Elberfeld 50.5%, French Lick, Hatfield 50.5%, Hendricks County (southern portion), Loogootee 50.5%, Lynnville 50.5%, Marshall County 50.5%, Oakland City 50.5%, Petersburg 50.5%, Prince's Lakes, Santa Claus, Troy 50.5%, Williamsburg 69.5%.
Kansas: Atchison 50.5%, Ellinwood, Fowler, Greensburg, Kismet, Meade, Minneola, Plains, Scott City, Sedan.
Kentucky: Bulan 69.5%, Flat Lick 69.5%, Fogertown 69.5%, Garrard 69.5%, Hartford 69.5%, Madisonville 50.5%, Mayfield 69.5%, Murray 69.5%, Paintsville 50.5%.
Louisiana: Basile 50.5%, Bunkie 50.5%, Cameron 50.5%, Hackberry 50.5%, Iota 50.5%, Iowa 50.5%, Merryville 59.5%, Pine Prairie 50.5%.
Maryland: Cumberland 50.5%.
Michigan: Almont 50.5%, Attica Twp. 50.5%, Berlin Twp. (St. Clair County) 50.5%, Davison 50.5%, Fenton 50.5%, Hamburg Twp. 69.5%, Highland Park 50.5%, Imlay City 50.5%, Kingston Twp. 50.5%, Mayville 49.5%, Metamora, Mio, North Branch 50.5%, Oscoda 50.5%, Oxford 69.5%, Rose City 50.5%.
Mississippi: Columbia 50.5%, Fayette.
Missouri: Camden Point 50.5%.
New Mexico: Clayton, Logan.
New York: Allentown, Angelica 69.5%, Avoca 69.5%, Bolivar 69.5%, Cortland 50.5%, Dansville 69.5%, Dresden 69.5%, Dundee 69.5%, Fillmore, Hornell 50.5%, Hume 69.5%, Jasper 69.5%, Johnstown (city) 50.5%, Lindley (town), Naples 69.5%, Salamanca 50.5%, Troupsburg 69.5%, Wallace, Woodhull 69.5%.
North Carolina: Bayboro 50.5%, Carthage 50.5%, Davidson County 50.5%, Denton 50.5%, Eden 50.5%, Liberty 50.5%, Madison 50.5%, Mebane 50.5%, Wadesboro 50.5%, Youngsville 50.5%.
Ohio: Anna 69.5%, Ashley 69.5%, Atwater Twp. 50.5%, Belle Center 69.5%, Bettsville 50.5%, Bowling Green 50.5%, Chippewa Twp. 50.5%, Columbus, Crooksville 50.5%, Dresden 50.5%, Frazeysburg 50.5%, Green Cove Condominiums 50.5%, Guilford Lake 50.5%, Hayden Heights 69.5%, La Rue 69.5%, Lake Mohawk Mobile Home Park 50.5%, Lindsey (Sandusky County) 50.5%, Marengo 69.5%, Nashport 50.5%, Nelson Mobile Home Park 50.5%, New Concord 50.5%, Philo (portions) 50.5%, Rising Sun 50.5%, Robbins Mobile Home Park 50.5%, Salem 50.5%, St. Marys, Waynesfield, West Mansfield, Willows Mobile Home Park 50.5%, Zanesville 50.5%.
Oklahoma: Adair 50.5%, Afton 50.5%, Agra 50.5%, Beggs 50.5%, Bernice, Boynton 50.5%, Cameron 50.5%, Carney 50.5%, Chelsea 50.5%, Chouteau 50.5%, Colcord 50.5%, Cromwell 50.5%, Delaware 50.5%, Depew 50.5%, Dustin 50.5%, Fort Gibson 50.5%, Gans 50.5%, Glencoe 50.5%, Gore 50.5%, Grand Lake-Monkey Island 50.5%, Grove 50.5%, Hartshorne, Hulbert 50.5%, Inola 50.5%, Kansas 50.5%, Kellyville 50.5%, Keota 50.5%, Ketchum 50.5%, Langston 50.5%, Longtown 50.5%, Luther 50.5%, Marland 50.5%, Milburn 50.5%, Morris 50.5%, Morrison 50.5%, Mounds 50.5%, Okay 50.5%, Oologah 50.5%, Porter 50.5%, Porum 50.5%, Quinton 50.5%, Ralston 50.5%, Salina 50.5%, Savanna 50.5%, Schulter 50.5%, Spavinaw 50.5%, Stilwell 50.5%, Strang 50.5%, Tryon 50.5%, Turpin, Tyrone 50.5%, Verdigris 50.5%, Vian 50.5%, Welch 50.5%, Weleetka 50.5%, Westville 50.5%, Wilburton 50.5%, Wyandotte 50.5%.
Pennsylvania: Altoona 50.5%, Bradford 50.5%, Clearfield 50.5%, Elkland 69.5%, Johnstown 50.5%, Lawrenceville 69.5%, Lewistown 50.5%, Mifflinburg 50.5%, Tioga, Ulysses, Warren 50.5%.
Texas: Aspermont, Azle, Bedias 50.5%, Bridge City 50.5%, Brownfield 50.5%, Centerville 50.5%, Coleman 50.5%, Colorado City 50.5%, Emory 50.5%, Ennis 50.5%, Evant, Garfield 50.5%, Goldthwaite, Granbury, Haskell 50.5%, Johnson City, Joshua, Kosse, Kountze 50.5%, Leona 50.5%, Levelland 50.5%, Littlefield 50.5%, Lometa, Loraine 50.5%, Manor 50.5%, Meridian 50.5%, Midway 50.5%, Morton 50.5%, Munday 50.5%, Mustang Ridge 50.5%, Normangee 50.5%, North Zulch 50.05%, O'Donnell 50.5%, Oakwood 50.5%, Parkway Village 50.5%, Preston Peninsula 50.5%, Richland Springs, Rockwall 50.5%, Slaton 50.5%, Spicewood Beach, Stamford 50.5%, Stanton 50.5%, Tahoka 50.5%, Texline, Valley Mills, Vidor 50.5%, Wills Point 50.5%, Wilson 50.5%, Winnie 50.5%.
Virginia: Bedford County (southwestern portion), Bowling Green 50.5%, Clarksville 50.5%, Colonial Beach 50.5%, Drakes Branch 50.5%, Farmville 50.5%, Kenbridge 50.5%, Keysville 50.5%, Lawrenceville 50.5%, Tappahannock 50.5%, Warsaw 50.5%, Wytheville 50.5%.
West Virginia: Alkol 50.5%, Beckley 50.5%, Belington 50.5%, Bergoo 50.5%, Charleston 50.5%, Chattaroy 50.5%, Chelyan 50.5%, Cowen 50.5%, Curtin 50.5%, Davis 50.5%, Dixie 50.5%, Gassaway 50.5%, Independent Mountain 50.5%, Indore 50.5%, Jodie 50.5%, Julian 50.5%, Lewisburg 50.5%, Logan 50.5%, Loudendale 50.5%, New Martinsville 50.5%, Nitro 50.5%, Parkersburg 50.5%, Paw Paw 50.5%, Pax, Pond Gap 50.5%, Princeton 50.5%, Robson, Sand Fork 50.5%, Summersville 50.5%, Vaughan, Webster

Springs 50.5%, Weston 50.5%, Whitesville 50.5%.
Wisconsin: Arena, Avoca, Bay City, Cassville, Dickeyville, Dodgeville, Highland, La Valle, Lancaster, Montfort, Plain, Ridgeway, Sextonville, Spring Green, Wonewoc.
Total Basic Subscribers: 499,004 (0.73% of total cable households).
Total Pay Units: 190,000.
Note: Sold to Charter Communications Inc. 1999.

FANNETTSBURG CABLE TV CO.

Box 202
Fannettsburg, PA 17221
Phone: 717-349-7775
Officers:
John Baker, Pres.
Wilbur Barrick, V.P.
Ownership: Community owned.
Cable Systems (1):
Pennsylvania: Fannettsburg.
Total Basic Subscribers: N.A.

FANNON CABLE TV CO.

Box 1526
120 Main St.
New Tazewell, TN 37825
Phone: 423-626-9107
Fax: 423-626-6304
Officer:
Ray Fannon, Chmn. & Chief Exec. Officer
Ownership: Charles Chadwell, 33%; Hollis Bush, 17%; Letton Bush, 17%; Bill Fannon, 11%; Bob Fannon, 11%; Ray Fannon, 11%.
Cable Systems (1):
Tennessee: New Tazewell.
Total Basic Subscribers: 5,746.
Total Pay Units: 1,309.

FARMERS' & BUSINESSMEN'S TELEPHONE CO.

Box 307
103 Main St.
Wheatland, IA 52777
Phone: 319-374-1236
Cable Systems (4):
Iowa: Bennett, Delmar, Lowden, Wheatland.
Total Basic Subscribers: 621.

FARMERS & MERCHANTS MUTUAL TELEPHONE CO.

210 W. Main St.
Wayland, IA 52654
Phone: 319-256-2736
Cable Systems (1):
Iowa: Wayland.
Total Basic Subscribers: 399.
Total Pay Units: 263.

FARMERS COOPERATIVE TELEPHONE CO.

Box 280
332 Main St.
Dysart, IA 52224
Phone: 319-476-7800
Cable Systems (1):
Iowa: Clutier.
Total Basic Subscribers: 66.

FARMERS MUTUAL COOPERATIVE TELEPHONE CO.

Box 311
Harlan, IA 51537
Phone: 712-744-3131
Fax: 712-744-3100
Officers:
Rex G. Adams, Pres.
Thomas Conry, Chief Exec. Officer
Roger Schmitz, Secy.-Treas.
Cable Systems (3):
Iowa: Earling, New Market, Stanton.
Total Basic Subscribers: 857.
Total Pay Units: 236.

FARMERS MUTUAL TELEPHONE CO.

608 E. Congress
Nora Springs, IA 50458
Phone: 515-749-2531
Officer:
Ron Laudner, Mgr.
Cable Systems (4):
Iowa: Littleton, Marble Rock, Plymouth, Rudd.
Total Basic Subscribers: 317.

FARMERS TELEPHONE CO.

Box 160
404 4th St.
Batavia, IA 52533
Phone: 515-662-3400
Fax: 515-662-2511
Officers:
Max Willhoit, Pres.
Steve Dallner, V.P.
Stuart Taylor, Secy-Treas.
Represented (legal): David Miller (Libertyville, IA); Davis, Hockenberg, Wine (Des Moines, IA; Rosenman & Colin Washington, DC).
Wireless Cable Systems (1):
Iowa: Batavia.
Total Basic Subscribers: 585.
Total Pay Units: 320.
Other Holdings:
Cellular radio, ITFS.

FARMERS TELEPHONE CO-OP INC.

Box 588
1101 E. Main St.
Kingstree, SC 29556
Phone: 803-382-2333
Officers:
Newell Myers, Chmn.
Johnny L. McDaniel, Chief Exec. Officer
Jeff Lawrimire, Chief Financial Officer
Cable Systems (1):
South Carolina: Turbeville.
Total Basic Subscribers: 585.
Total Pay Units: 339.

FARMINGTON CABLEVISION INC.

Box 710
403 E. Karsch Blvd.
Farmington, MO 63640
Phone: 314-756-8616
Officers:
Tom Legan, Pres.
Larry Jones, V.P.
Paul Storey, Secy.
Cable Systems (2):
Missouri: Bismarck, Farmington.
Total Basic Subscribers: 4,717.
Total Pay Units: 1,404.

FENTON COOPERATIVE TELEPHONE CO.

Box 77
Fenton, IA 50539
Phone: 515-889-2785
Cable Systems (1):
Iowa: Fenton.
Total Basic Subscribers: 137.
Total Pay Units: 20.

FIDELITY CABLEVISION INC.

Box 857
1304 Hwy. 72 E
Rolla, MO 65401
Phone: 314-364-5206
Cable Systems (1):
Missouri: Rolla.
Total Basic Subscribers: 5,299.
Total Pay Units: 2,294.

THEODORE W. FILSON

Suite 19
215 W. Kellner Blvd.
Rensselaer, IN 47978
Phone: 219-866-7101
Fax: 219-866-5785

Branch Office:

Winamac, IN 46996
Phone: 219-946-3813
Cable Systems (3):
Indiana: Morocco, Rensselaer, Winamac.
Total Basic Subscribers: 4,201.
Total Pay Units: 993.

FINCOM CORP.

Box 21300
Canton, OH 44701
Phone: 216-430-3517
Fax: 216-430-3511
Officers:
Norman E. Jackson, Chmn.
James R. Fink, Pres. & Chief Exec. Officer
Carl Sorensen, Secy.-Treas.
Cable Systems (7):
Ohio: Pine Lake Trailer Park.
West Virginia: Clarksburg, Coalton, Diana, Glen Dale, West Liberty, Wyatt.
Total Basic Subscribers: 2,940.
Total Pay Units: 550.

FIRST CABLE OF MISSOURI INC.

Box 1010
605 Concannon
Moberly, MO 65270
Phones: 816-263-6300; 800-892-7139
Fax: 816-263-3238
Officers:
Alan D. Steinbach, Pres.
Jesse W. Wamsley, V.P.
Craig H. Plaster, Secy.-Treas.
Ownership: Alan D. Steinbach, Jesse W. Wamsley & Craig H. Plaster, each, 33.33%. Principals also own Mississippi Valley Communications Inc., regional CATV contracting firm.
Represented (legal): McDowell, Rice & Smith; Blackwell, Sanders, Matheny, Weary & Lombardi.
Cable Systems (16):
Missouri: Argyle, Clarksburg, Clarksville, Curryville, Eolia, Eugene, Gasconade, Harrisburg, Hawk Point, Jacksonville, Loose Creek, Middletown, Mokane, Silex, St. Thomas, Syracuse.
Total Basic Subscribers: 1,095.
Total Pay Units: 475.

1ST COMMONWEALTH COMMUNICATIONS INC.

Box 857
Summerville Plantation
Gloucester, VA 23061
Phone: 804-693-3535
Fax: 804-693-2885
Officers:
Donald A. Perry, Chmn. & Chief Exec. Officer
Patricia Gibbs, V.P.
Britt Belyea, V.P., Engineering
Ownership: Donald A. Perry, 76%; Britt Belyea, 24%. Perry owns Donald A. Perry & Assoc., CATV broker, see listing.
Represented (legal): Michael T. Sobench.
Cable Systems (2):
Virginia: Lancaster County, Middlesex County.
Total Basic Subscribers: 4,612.
Total Pay Units: 1,806.

GARY FISKE

Box 576
Enosburg Falls, VT 05450
Phone: 802-933-8843
Cable Systems (1):
Vermont: Enosburg Falls.
Total Basic Subscribers: 862.
Total Pay Units: 234.

LARRY FITZGERALD

Box 40
Guthrie, TX 79236
Phone: 806-596-4459
Cable Systems (1):
Texas: Guthrie.
Total Basic Subscribers: 54.

JAMES W. FITZPATRICK

Box 35
Whitesville, NY 14897
Phone: 607-356-3117
Cable Systems (1):
New York: Whitesville.
Total Basic Subscribers: 165.

KEVIN FLANNIGAN

Box 67
993 Commerce Dr.
Grafton, OH 44044
Phone: 440-926-3230
Fax: 440-926-2889
Cable Systems (2):
Ohio: Grafton, Wellington.
Total Basic Subscribers: 6,841.

DENNIS FLEMING

Drawer M
Haysi, VA 24256
Phone: 703-865-4253
Cable Systems (1):
Virginia: Haysi.
Total Basic Subscribers: 200.
Total Pay Units: 18.

FLIGHT SYSTEMS CABLEVISION

505 Fishing Creek Rd.
Lewisberry, PA 17339
Phone: 717-932-9919
Fax: 717-932-9925
Officers:
Robert Shaffner, Chmn. & Chief Exec. Officer
Robert York, V.P.
Bob Rothermel, Chief Financial Officer

Branch Office:

P2-101
Baltimore, MD 21230
Phone: 410-576-0710

Represented (legal): Goldberg, Katzman & Shipman.
Cable Systems (1):
Maryland: Baltimore (Inner Harbor).
Total Basic Subscribers: 650.

FLINT CABLE TELEVISION INC.

Box 669
Reynolds, GA 31076
Phone: 912-847-3101
Officers:
Donald E. Bond, Pres.
James L. Bond, Chief Operating Officer
E. Kelly Bond, V.P.
Cable Systems (4):
Georgia: Buena Vista, Butler, Reynolds, Roberta.
Total Basic Subscribers: 1,502.

FLORIDA CABLE TV NETWORK INC.

Box 498
Hwy. 40
Astor, FL 32002
Fax: 352-759-3577
Officers:
Walter Tucker, Pres.
Bob Samuel, Secy.-Treas.
Ownership: Walter Tucker & Bob Samuel.
Cable Systems (1):
Florida: Astor.
Total Basic Subscribers: 427.

FORT JENNINGS TELEPHONE CO.

Box 146
Fort Jennings, OH 45844
Phone: 419-286-2181
Fax: 419-286-2193
Officer:
Shirley A. Berelsman, Chief Exec. Officer & Secy.-Treas.
Cable Systems (1):
Ohio: Fort Jennings.
Total Basic Subscribers: 440.
Total Pay Units: 275.

FORT MORGAN CABLE TV INC.

6930 State Hwy. 180
Gulf Shores, AL 36542-8066
Phone: 334-540-7221
Officers:
Peter Mallory, Chmn. & Chief Exec. Officer
Cason Woodyard, Chief Financial Officer
Ownership: Peter Mallory, Principal.
Cable Systems (1):
Alabama: Fort Morgan.
Total Basic Subscribers: 260.
Total Pay Units: 23.

FORT WAYNE TELSAT INC.

1909 Production Rd.
Fort Wayne, IN 46808
Phone: 219-471-2324
Fax: 219-471-5406
Officers:
Richard R. Corwin, Chmn.
James A. Simon, Pres.
William A. Millett, V.P.
Wireless Cable Systems (1):
Indiana: Fort Wayne.
Total Basic Subscribers: 2,500.
Total Pay Units: 1,000.

FOSSIL COMMUNITY TV INC.

Box 209
Fossil, OR 97830
Phone: 503-763-4404
Officers:
Vern W. Kirby, Pres. & Mgr.
Robert M. Boyles, V.P.
W. L. Reinhart, Secy.-Treas.
Ownership: Non-profit organization.
Cable Systems (1):
Oregon: Fossil.
Total Basic Subscribers: N.A.

CITY OF FOSSTON CABLE TV

220 E. First St.
Fosston, MN 56542
Phone: 218-435-1737
Ownership: Community owned.
Cable Systems (1):
Minnesota: Fosston.
Total Basic Subscribers: 633.
Total Pay Units: 150.

FOSTER COMMUNICATIONS INC.

818 W. Hillsboro St.
El Dorado, AR 71730-7047
Phone: 501-862-6750
Officer:
Phoenix Foster, Pres.
Cable Systems (3):
Mississippi: Coles Point, Harmontown, Mooreville.
Total Basic Subscribers: 386.

FRANKFORT PLANT BOARD

306 Hickory Dr.
Frankfort, KY 40601
Phone: 502-227-4125
Fax: 502-223-4449
Officers:
Bruce Dungan, Chmn.
David Sandidge, Chief Operating Officer
Ownership: Community owned.
Represented (legal): Hobson & Bowman.
Cable Systems (1):
Kentucky: Frankfort.
Total Basic Subscribers: 17,400 (0.03% of total cable households).
Total Pay Units: 8,967.

HAROLD FREEMAN

Box 1228
Troy, AL 36081
Phone: 205-566-3310
Cable Systems (1):
Alabama: Troy.
Total Basic Subscribers: 2,977.

HERSHEL W. FREEMAN

Box 855
Coupeville, WA 98239
Phone: 360-678-3712
Cable Systems (1):
Washington: Greenbank.
Total Basic Subscribers: 57.
Total Pay Units: 30.

FRONTIER CABLE INC.

Box 1424
Huron, SD 57350
Phone: 605-352-4014
Ownership: John Rearick, 50%; Dick Shelton, 50%. Rearick & Shelton own BMI Cablevision, see listing.
Cable Systems (10):
Alaska: Gambell, Hooper Bay, Kipnuk, Quinhagak, Savoonga, St. Marys, Togiak, Toksook Bay, Tununak, Unalakleet.
Total Basic Subscribers: 340.

FRONTIERVISION PARTNERS LP

Suite P-200
1777 S. Harrison St.
Denver, CO 80210
Phone: 303-757-1588
Fax: 303-757-6105
Officers:
James C. Vaughn, Pres. & Chief Exec. Officer
John S. Koo, Sr. V.P. & Chief Financial Officer
William J. Mahon Jr., V.P., Operations
James W. McHose, V.P. & Treas.
Ownership: Jim Vaughn, Principal; J.P. Morgan Capital, Brown Bros. Harriman, Olympus Partners & First Union Capital Partners, Ltd. Partners.
Cable Systems (271):
Indiana: Madison, Vevay.
Kentucky: Ashland, Beattyville, Burnaugh, Campton, Carlisle, Carrollton, Cynthiana, Falmouth, Flemingsburg, Frenchburg, Georgetown, Jackson, Lebanon, Leslie County (northern portion), London, Maloneton, Midway, Morehead, Mount Sterling, Mozelle, New Haven, Nicholasville, North Middletown, Olive Hill, Owingsville, Paris, Pine Hill, Richmond, Sandy Hook, Sharpsburg, Soldier, Stanton, Tollesboro, Versailles, Wallins Creek, Warsaw, West Liberty, Winchester.
Maine: Addison, Ashland, Augusta, Avon, Bangor, Belgrade, Bethel, Blue Hill (town), Boothbay, Bridgton, Bristol, Buckfield, Buxton, Calais, Canton (town), Carrabassett Valley, Castine, Cornish (town), Denmark, Eagle Lake, Easton, Fort Kent, Franklin (town), Friendship (town), Glenburn (town), Greenbush (town), Greene (town), Hancock, Hermon, Jay, Kenduskeag, Lewiston, Lovell (town), Madawaska, Mapleton, Mars Hill, Milo, Mount Desert (town), New Sharon (town), Newcastle, North Anson, Norway, Pittsfield, Poland, Portage, Rangeley (town), Rockland, Rumford, Searsmont, Sebago (town), Sidney (town), Smithfield (town), Sorrento, St. Francis, Stockholm (town), Stockton Springs, Stonington, Temple (town), Trenton, Union (town), Van Buren, Vinalhaven, Warren (town), Washburn, Waterville, Weld, Windham.
Maryland: Accident, Deep Creek Lake, Grantsville.
Michigan: Bedford Twp. (Monroe County), Hartland, Hudson, Springfield Twp. (Oakland County).
New Hampshire: Bath (village), Carroll, Conway, Freedom (town), Hill (town), Lebanon, Lincoln, Littleton, Madison (town), Monroe (town), Moultonborough (town), New London, Newport, Plainfield (town), Plymouth, Stratford (town), Sugar Hill (town), Wakefield (town), Wentworth (town).
North Carolina: Aulander, Bailey, Bunn, Dortches, Fountain, Halifax, Hollister, Lake Gaston, Littleton, MacCripines, Meat Camp, Mid Lakes Trailer Park, Oak City, Pink Hill, Roan Fork, Santree Mobile Home Park, Simpson, Spring Hope, Whitakers, Zionville.
Ohio: Ada, Albany, Allen Twp. (Ottawa County), Ashley Corner, Bainbridge, Bolivar, Bryan, Cambridge, Carey, Celina, Chillicothe, Circleville (portions), Clarington, Commercial Point, Coshocton, Crown City, Defiance, Delhi Twp., Dellroy, Deshler, Dunkirk, Edon, Enterprise, Eureka, Fayette, Frankfort, Franklin Furnace, Fulton Twp., Glenmont, Guernsey County (portions), Guysville, Hanibal, Hanover (village), Hide-A-Way Hills, Howard, Huntington Twp., Ironton, Jackson, Kingston, Lick Twp. (Jackson County), Licking County (northeastern portion), Licking County (northwestern portion), Logan, Luckey, Manchester, Margaretta Twp., Marion, Mcconnelsville, Metamora, Millersburg, Minster, Mowrystown, Murray City, Muskingum County (portions), Napoleon, New Holland, New Matamoras, New Philadelphia, Newark, Newport, Northwood, Oak Harbor, Oak Hill, Oakland, Paint Twp. (Highland County), Paulding, Pedro, Pioneer, Port Clinton, Porterfield, Put-in-Bay, Richmond Dale, Rio Grande, Ripley (Brown County), Scipio Twp. (Meigs County), Swanton, Van Wert, Versailles, Wakeman, Washington Court House, Watertown, Waterville, Waverly.
Pennsylvania: Markleysburg, Meyersdale, Rockwood.
Tennessee: Bean Station, Friendsville, Greeneville, Laurel Bloomery, Simmerly Creek, Whitesburg.
Vermont: Hardwick, Morrisville, St. Albans (city).
Virginia: Amelia County (portions), Bristol, Charles City County (portions), Dillwyn, Gordonsville, Heathsville, Lacey Spring, Lake Holston, Mathews, Montross, Mount Clinton, New Market, Rockingham, Stanardsville, Stuart, Woodstock.
West Virginia: Apple Grove, Centerville, Cyrus, Friendly, Graysville, Ragland, Salt Rock.
Cable Franchises (37):
Maine: Belmont (town), Dedham (town).
New Hampshire: Jefferson (town).
Vermont: Albany Twp., Alburg Twp., Bakersfield Twp., Barnard Twp., Barnet Twp., Bloomfield Twp., Cabot Twp., Charleston Twp., Coventry Twp., East Montpelier Twp., Fairfax Twp., Fairlee Twp., Fletcher Twp., Grand Isle Twp., Guilford Twp., Hartland Twp., Irasburg Twp., Jamaica Twp., Londonderry Twp., Lunenburg Twp., Middletown Springs Twp., Newport Twp., Orwell Twp., Peacham Twp., Rupert Twp., Ryegate Twp., Stamford Twp., Thetford Twp., Townshend Twp., Troy Twp., Wardsboro Twp., Westford Twp., Westminster Twp., Windham Twp.
Total Basic Subscribers: 694,584 (1.01% of total cable households).
Total Pay Units: 292,982.
Note: Sold to Adelphia Communications Corp. 1999.

THEODORE FULLER

Box 218
Fedscreek, KY 41524
Phone: 606-835-4811
Cable Systems (1):
Kentucky: Fedscreek.
Total Basic Subscribers: 180.

FUTURE COMMUNICATIONS INC.

Suite 100
3617 Kim Dr.
Irving, TX 75061
Phone: 972-986-0243
Officer:
Sergio Bosco, Pres.
Ownership: Publicly held.
Cable Systems (1):
Texas: Wilmer.
Total Basic Subscribers: N.A.

G-FORCE LLC

3022 Peleke St.
Lihue, HI 96766-2199
Phone: 808-246-9315
Cable Systems (1):
Hawaii: Kauai Island.
Total Basic Subscribers: 17,420 (0.03% of total cable households).
Total Pay Units: 6,734.

GAINES WATROUS TV ASSOCIATION INC.

RD Box 30
Gaines, PA 16921
Phone: 814-435-6578
Fax: 814-435-8585
Officers:
Nancy Holleran, Pres.
Melvin Lowrey, Chief Operating Officer
Amy Smith, Secy.-Treas.
Ownership: Subscriber owned.
Cable Systems (1):
Pennsylvania: Gaines.
Total Basic Subscribers: 317.
Total Pay Units: 60.

GALAXY AMERICAN COMMUNICATIONS

1220 N. Main
Sikeston, MO 63801
Phone: 573-472-8200
Fax: 573-471-7281
Officers:
Jerry W. Strasser, Pres.
J. Keith Davidson, Chief Financial Officer
Ownership: Galaxy Cablevision, Managing Partner, 40%; Mid American Cable Systems & New Path Communications LC, 60% jointly, see listings.
Cable Systems (7):
Illinois: Ava, Vergennes.
Indiana: Fulton, Richland, Williamsburg.
Missouri: Amsterdam, Centerview.
Total Basic Subscribers: 642.

GALAXY CABLEVISION

1220 N. Main
Sikeston, MO 63801
Phone: 573-472-8200
Fax: 573-471-7281
Officers:
Tommy L. Gleason Jr., Chmn., Pres. & Chief Exec. Officer
James M. Gleason, Chief Operating Officer.
Thomas M. Morris, V.P., Operations
Ron Voss, V.P., Corp. Development
Terry Cordova, V.P., Engineering
J. Keith Davidson, Chief Financial Officer

Branch Offices:

Wickliffe, KY 42087
Phone: 502-335-5158

Hwy. 431 N
Box 8
Headland, AL 36345
Phone: 334-693-2610
Ownership: Galaxy Telecom LP.
Represented (legal): Clayton Vandivort.
Cable Systems (385):
Alabama: Abbeville, Arley, Ashford, Butler, Clayton, Cottonwood, Cuba, Fulton, Grove Hill, Headland, Nauvoo, Orrville, Pennington, Pine Hill, Ranburne, Thomaston, Uniontown.
Colorado: Cheyenne Wells, Coal Creek Canyon, Deer Trail, Eads, Flagler, Granada, Holly, Hugo, Limon, Lyons, Ordway, Silver Cliff, Stratton, Walsh, Wiley.
Florida: Anthony, Bostwick, Bronson, Citra, Esto, Greenville, Greenwood, Hampton, Lawtey, Melrose, Middleburg, Nobleton, Paisley.
Georgia: Arnoldsville, Attapulgus, Avalon, Berlin, Bishop, Chauncey, Climax, Colquitt, Danville, Dry Branch, Flint River, Hayneville, Iron City, Jackson Lake, Lincolnton, Pineview, Pitts, Rebecca, Sanford, Seminole County, Warwick.
Illinois: Alexander County, Allendale, Arrowsmith (village), Bartelso, Beecher City, Bellmont, Bluford, Bone Gap, Bonnie, Browns, Calhoun, Carriers Mills, Chestnut, Cissna Park (village), Claremont, Cowden, Creal Springs, Dahlgren, Dongola, Edgewood, Flat Rock, Freeman Spur, Galatia, Golconda, Goreville, Ina, Irvington, Jackson County, Karnak, Keensburg, Keyesport, Lake Camelot, Mill Shoals, Mulberry Grove, Olmsted, Parkersburg, Pittsburg, Pocahontas, Richview, Rosiclare, Tamaroa, Triangle Mobile Home Park, Vienna, Watseka, West Salem, Willisville.
Kansas: Admire, Alma, Alta Vista, Americus, Barnes, Basehor, Benton, Blue Rapids, Bronson, Chapman, Clifton, Colony, Cuba, Durham, Dwight, Eskridge, Florence, Hartford, Harveyville, Hillsboro, Hope, Lake Wabaunsee, Lincolnville, Marion, McFarland, Melvern, Meriden, Milford, Minneapolis, Moran, Morganville, Neosho Rapids, Olpe, Onaga, Overbrook, Paxico, Pomona, Potwin, Quenemo, Reading, Richmond, Riley, Rossville, Sabetha, Seneca, Solomon, Strong City, Tampa, Tonganoxie, Vassar, Wakefield, Walton, Waverly, White City, Whitewater, Williamsburg, Woodbine.
Kentucky: Arlington, Bardwell, Clinton, Eddyville, Graves County, Hazel, Hickman, Kevil, Wickliffe.
Louisiana: Kentwood, Leesville, Simpson.
Mississippi: Aberdeen, Amory, Ashland, Baldwyn, Bassfield, Bentonia, Booneville, Calhoun City, Canton, Charleston, Chunky, Coffeeville, De Kalb, Durant, Eupora, Hickory Flat, Holly Springs, Itta Bena, Iuka, Jumpertown, Lake, Lauderdale, Leakesville, Lexington, Lumberton, Macedonia, Macon, Monticello, Moselle, Mound Bayou, Nettleton, New Albany, Oxford, Pachuta, Pickens, Poplarville, Prentiss, Richton, Shelby, Shubuta, State Line, Sumner, Sumrall, Taylorsville, Tchula, Tylertown, Victoria, Walnut Grove, Winona.
Missouri: Adrian, Alma, Atlanta, Baring, Blackburn, Blackwater, Bogard, Bosworth, Brooking Park, Browning, Buffalo, Calhoun, Chula, Clark, Cole Camp, Concordia, Creighton, Crocker, Downing, Durham, East Lynne, Emma, Ewing, Ferrelview, Freeburg, Gallatin, Galt, Garden City, Gilliam, Gorin, Green Castle, Green Ridge, Greentop, Hale, Hallsville, Higbee, Higginsville, Houstonia, Hurdland, Iberia, Jamesport, Jamestown, Jefferson Park, Keytesville, Knox City, La Monte, Laclede, Lancaster, Leeton, Lincoln, Mayview, Meadville, Memphis, Mercer, Meta, Monticello, New Bloomfield, New Franklin, Novinger, Otterville, Princeton, Russellville, Slater, Smithton, Stover, Sweet Springs, Taos, Urich, Vienna, Waverly, Westphalia, Wheeling, Wyaconda.
Nebraska: Albion, Arcadia, Arnold, Beaver Crossing, Bellwood, Benedict, Bradshaw, Brainard, Burwell, Byron, Callaway, Cedar Rapids, Central City, Ceresco, Chester, Clay Center, Deshler, Duncan, Fullerton, Garland, Geneva, Genoa, Glenvil, Grand Island (southern portion), Gresham, Gretna, Hay Springs, Humphrey, Malcolm, Meadow Grove, Mullen, Nelson, Newman Grove, North Loup, Osceola, Peru, Polk, Raymond, Sargent, Schuyler, Scotia, Shelby, Silver Creek, St. Edward, Staplehurst, Stromsburg, Syracuse, Taylor, Ulysses, Utica, Valparaiso, Waco, Western, Wilber, Wymore.
South Carolina: Coward, Cross Hill, Dovesville, Five Points, Hilda, Lynchburg, Pine Grove, Plum Branch, Society Hill, Wallace, Ware Place.
South Dakota: Boulder Canyon, Country Village/Prairie Acres Mobile Home Park, Countryside Mobile Home Park, Hill City, Newell, Rimrock, Whitewood.
Texas: Bremond, Calvert, Cameron, Chilton, Crawford, Franklin, Lorena, Lott.
Wyoming: Gardens North.
Total Basic Subscribers: 180,572 (0.26% of total cable households).
Total Pay Units: 106,059.
Cable Holdings:
40% interest in & managing partner of Galaxy American Communications, see listing.
Other Holdings:
Marketing company: Galaxy Cablevision Mktg.

GALI ESTATE

c/o Skyview TV Cable
Box 445
Broadus, MT 59317
Phone: 406-436-2820
Cable Systems (1):
Montana: Broadus 45%.
Total Basic Subscribers: 268.
Total Pay Units: 70.

GALVA CABLE CO. INC.

Box 8
Galva, KS 67443
Phone: 316-654-3673
Fax: 316-654-3122
Officers:
Robert Baldwin, Chief Exec. Officer
Nancy Flaherty, Secy.-Treas.
Ownership: Home Enterprises.
Cable Systems (4):
Kansas: Assaria, Galva, Gypsum, Smolan.
Total Basic Subscribers: 435.
Total Pay Units: 43.

G & K COMMUNICATIONS

Box 404
Ness City, KS 67560
Phone: 785-798-2836
Cable Systems (1):
Kansas: McCracken.
Total Basic Subscribers: 268.
Total Pay Units: 65.

GANS MULTIMEDIA PARTNERSHIP

217 E. 9th St.
Hazleton, PA 18201
Phone: 717-455-6851
Fax: 717-459-0963
Officers:
Joseph S. Gans Sr., Chmn. & Pres.
Joseph W. Aman, Chief Operating Officer
Larry S. Shewalk, V.P., Engineering
Terrance Herron Sr., Legal
John T. Howell, Chief Financial Officer
Ownership: Joseph S. Gans Sr.
Cable Systems (12):
Arizona: Sells, Tucson Estates, Wellton.
Maryland: Boones Mobile Home Estates, Calvert Beach, St. Marys County.
Pennsylvania: Berwick, Crosby, Pocono, Spruce Creek Twp., Sugar Grove, Three Springs.
Total Basic Subscribers: 28,438 (0.04% of total cable households).
Total Pay Units: 11,075.
Other Holdings:
LPTV, see listing.

GAP CABLE TV INC.

3925 Hill Church Rd.
Lebanon, PA 17042
Phone: 717-865-0511
Officers:
Carolyn A. Bryce, Pres.
George Bryce, Chief Operating Officer
Ray Funck, V.P.
Ruth Ann Funck, Secy.
Ownership: Carolyn A. Bryce, Pres.
Cable Systems (1):
Pennsylvania: Fort Indiantown Gap.
Total Basic Subscribers: 300.
Total Pay Units: 50.

GARDEN VALLEY TELEPHONE CO.

201 Ross Ave.
Erksine, MN 56535
Phone: 218-687-5251
Officers:
George Fish, Gen. Mgr.
Randy Versdahl, Facilities Mgr.
Cable Systems (6):
Minnesota: Clearbrook, Erskine, Grygla, Oklee, Shevlin, St. Hilaire.
Total Basic Subscribers: 2,004.
Total Pay Units: 413.

WILLIAM H. GARNER

Box 483
McCalla, AL 35111
Phone: 205-477-6210
Cable Systems (1):
Alabama: Abernant.
Total Basic Subscribers: 970.

GATEWAY CABLEVISION CORP.

6 Genessee Lane
Amsterdam, NY 12010
Phone: 518-842-6803
Fax: 518-842-0737
Officers:
Joseph M. Isabel, Chmn. & Pres.
Ernest W. Scialabba, V.P.
Carol Scialabba, Secy.-Treas.

Branch Office:

Box 271
W. Dover, VT 05356
Phone: 802-464-5200
Represented (legal): Vorys, Sater, Seymour & Pease.
Cable Systems (4):
New York: Northville.
Vermont: Jacksonville, West Dover, Whitingham.
Total Basic Subscribers: 2,680.
Total Pay Units: 248.
Radio Station:
New York: WCSS(AM), Amsterdam.

CHARLES F. GAUTHIER

Box 399
Lac du Flambeau, WI 54538
Phone: 715-588-3580
Cable Systems (1):
Wisconsin: Lac Du Flambeau.
Total Basic Subscribers: N.A.

G. C. ASSOC.—Sold to Cox Communications Inc. 1998.

GENERAL COMMUNICATION INC.

Suite 1000
2550 Denali St.
Anchorage, AK 99503
Phone: 907-265-5676
Officers:
Carter F. Page, Chmn.
Ronald A. Duncan, Pres. & Chief Exec. Officer
G. Wilson Hughes, Chief Operating Officer
Riley Snell, V.P., Cable/Entertainment
John M. Lowber, Secy.-Treas. & Chief Financial Officer

Represented (legal): Hartig Rhodes Norman & Mahoney.
Cable Systems (14):
Alaska: Anchorage, Cordova, Fairbanks, Homer, Juneau, Ketchikan, Kodiak, Kotzebue, Nome, Petersburg, Seward, Sitka, Valdez, Wrangell.
Total Basic Subscribers: 108,600 (0.16% of total cable households).
Total Pay Units: 75,700.

GENESIS COMMUNICATIONS LLC—Sold to Benchmark Communications 1999.

DENISE & ROY GEORGE
Rte. 28
Margaretville, NY 12445
Phone: 914-586-4721
Cable Systems (2):
New York: Andes, Margaretville.
Total Basic Subscribers: N.A.

GEORGE MASON U. INSTRUCTIONAL FOUNDATION
George Mason University
4400 University Dr. MS#1D2
Fairfax, VA 22030-4444
Phone: 703-993-3100
Fax: 703-993-3115
Officers:
Alan G. Merten, Chmn.
Michael R. Kelley, Pres.
Kirk Tatem, V.P., Engineering
Otis D. Coston, Treas.
Roland Saldana, Chief Financial Officer
Represented (legal): Goldberg, Godles, Wiener & Wright.
Wireless Cable Systems (1):
Virginia: Fairfax.
Total Basic Subscribers: 1,780.
Other Holdings:
MMDS: Owns F Corp. MMDS LC, see listing.
ITFS.

T. W. GIENCKE
6485 46th Ave. SE
St. Cloud, MN 56304-8522
Phone: 612-252-8219
Cable Systems (1):
Minnesota: St. Joseph.
Total Basic Subscribers: N.A.

BARBARA GIESE
Phone: 701-579-4444
Cable Systems (1):
North Dakota: New England.
Total Basic Subscribers: 220.

GLENN GIESE
Cable Systems (2):
North Dakota: Flasher, New England.
Total Basic Subscribers: 289.
Total Pay Units: 99.

GLASGOW ELECTRIC PLANT BOARD-CATV DIVISION
100 Mallory Dr.
Glasgow, KY 42141
Phone: 502-651-8341
Fax: 502-651-1638
Officers:
William J. Ray, Chief Exec. Officer
Chappy Rice, Chief Operating Officer
Jim Searcy, Chief Financial Officer
Ownership: Community owned.
Represented (legal): H. Jeff Herbert.
Cable Systems (1):
Kentucky: Glasgow.
Total Basic Subscribers: 3,401.
Total Pay Units: 1,935.

GLASS ANTENNA SYSTEMS INC.
602 N. Jackson St.
Greencastle, IN 46135-1035
Phone: 765-653-5541
Fax: 765-653-8262
Officers:
Richard L. Glass, Pres.
Larry Glass, Chief Operating Officer
Dorothy Glass, Chief Financial Officer
Ownership: Richard L. Glass, Pres.
Cable Systems (2):
Indiana: Fillmore, Heritage Lake.
Total Basic Subscribers: 505.
Total Pay Units: 145.

GLENWOOD TELECOMMUNICATIONS
Box 357
510 W. Gage St.
Blue Hill, NE 68930
Phone: 402-756-3130
Fax: 402-756-3134
Officers:
Doug Zuellner, Pres.
Ron Ostdiek, Secy.-Treas.
Ownership: Glenwood Telephone Membership Corp.
Represented (legal): Charles W. Hastings.
Cable Systems (3):
Nebraska: Blue Hill, Funk, Guide Rock.
Total Basic Subscribers: 1,076.
Total Pay Units: 425.
Other Holdings:
Telephone.

GLIDE CABLEVISION
Box 609
731 Grandview
Glide, OR 97443
Phone: 541-496-0515
Ownership: Richard Arwood Sr. & Gean M. Arwood, Principals.
Cable Systems (1):
Oregon: Glide.
Total Basic Subscribers: 325.
Total Pay Units: 77.

GOLDEN BELT TELEPHONE COMMUNICATIONS INC.
Box 229
103 Lincoln
Rush Center, KS 67575
Phones: 316-525-6267; 913-372-4236
Fax: 316-525-6294
Officers:
Don Nuckolls, Pres.
Emmet J. Bauer, V.P.
Raymond L. Patterson, Secy.
Ownership: Don Nuckolls, 8%; Raymond L. Bauer & Thelda R. Bauer, 8% jointly; Burdett State Bank, 8%; Emmet J. Bauer, 4%; Raymond L. Patterson, 1%; 12 others, none with more than 4%.
Cable Systems (5):
Kansas: Munjor, Pawnee Rock, Rush Center, Schoenchen, Utica.
Total Basic Subscribers: 570.
Total Pay Units: 172.

GOLDEN WEST CABLEVISION
Box 411
Wall, SD 57790-0411
Phone: 605-279-2161
Officers:
Wayne Livermont, Pres.
Richard Hagen, Secy.-Treas.
Ownership: Golden West Companies.
Represented (legal): Meyers & Rogers.
Cable Systems (14):
South Dakota: Buffalo Gap, Evergreen Housing, Kadoka, Kyle, Manderson-White Horse Creek, Martin, Midland, New Underwood, Oelrichs, Philip, Springfield, Wall, Wanblee, White River.
Total Basic Subscribers: 2,963.
Total Pay Units: 2,083.
Other Holdings:
Cellular radio.
DirecTV DBS franchise.

GOLDFIELD COMMUNICATION SERVICES CORP.
Box 67
536 N. Main
Goldfield, IA 50542
Phone: 515-825-3888
Fax: 515-825-3801
Officers:
Kenneth Axon, Pres.
John Whyte, Secy.-Treas.
Ownership: Goldfield Telephone Co.
Cable Systems (3):
Iowa: Badger, Goldfield, Woolstock.
Total Basic Subscribers: 465.
Total Pay Units: 140.
Other Holdings:
Cellular telephone.

RODNEY GORGES
1694 6th St.
Coachella, CA 92236
Phone: 619-347-1955
Cable Systems (1):
California: Mecca.
Total Basic Subscribers: N.A.

GOWRIE CABLEVISION
Box 145
1112 1/2 Beek St.
Gowrie, IA 50543
Phone: 515-352-5227
Ownership: Paul Johnson, Pres.
Cable Systems (2):
Iowa: Gowrie, Paton.
Total Basic Subscribers: 386.

GPA CABLE
Box 943
Osprey, FL 34229
Phone: 813-924-8882
Officers:
George Pancner, Chmn.
Robert J. Zimmer, Chief Operating Officer
Ownership: George Pancner, Principal.
Cable Systems (1):
Virginia: Madison.
Total Basic Subscribers: 969.

GRAND MOUND COOPERATIVE TELEPHONE ASSN.
Box 316
705 Clinton St.
Grand Mound, IA 52751
Phone: 319-847-3000
Fax: 319-847-3001
Cable Systems (1):
Iowa: Grand Mound.
Total Basic Subscribers: 220.

GREAT PLAINS CABLE TV
Box 500
1635 Front St.
Blair, NE 68008
Phone: 402-426-9511
Ownership: Great Plains Communications Inc.
Cable Systems (15):
Nebraska: Bancroft, Bloomfield, Chapman, Creighton, Grant, Hayes Center, Imperial, Neligh, Niobrara, Oakdale, Plainview, Ponca, Stapleton, Venango, Wolbach.
Total Basic Subscribers: 4,272.
Total Pay Units: 1,457.

GREAT SOUTHERN PRINTING & MANUFACTURING CO.
Box 398
442 W. Patrick St.
Frederick, MD 21705-0398
Phone: 301-662-6822
Fax: 301-662-1307
Officers:
Robert W. Cole, Pres.
George B. Delaplaine Jr., Chief Exec. Officer
Marlene B. Young, Secy.
Philip W. Hammond, Treas.

Branch Offices:
2720 Baltimore Pike
Gettysburg, PA 17325
Phone: 707-337-1630

Virginia Division
12196 Alum Springs Rd.
Culpepper, VA 22701
Phone: 540-829-0791

West Virginia Division
302 N. Mildred St.
Ranson, WV 25438
Phone: 304-725-9185
Represented (legal): Cole, Raywid & Braverman LLP; Hogan & Hartson LLP.
Cable Systems (8):
Maryland: Frederick.
Pennsylvania: Dillsburg, Gettysburg, Glen Rock.
Virginia: Culpeper County.
West Virginia: Charles Town, Inwood, Martinsburg.
Total Basic Subscribers: 115,049 (0.17% of total cable households).
Total Pay Units: 46,005.
Newspapers:
Maryland: Frederick Post, Frederick News.

GREAT WESTERN PROPERTIES INC.
32700 Desert Moon Dr.
Thousand Palms, CA 92276
Phone: 714-343-3497
Cable Systems (1):
California: Tri-Palm Estates.
Total Basic Subscribers: N.A.

GREATER MEDIA INC.
Box 1059
2 Kennedy Blvd.
East Brunswick, NJ 08816
Phone: 732-247-6161
Fax: 732-247-0215
Officers:
Frank Kabela, Pres.
Thomas J. Milewski, Exec. V.P. & Chief Operating Officer
John Zielinski, V.P. & Chief Financial Officer
Milford K. Smith, V.P., Radio Engineering
Walter Veth, Group V.P., Cable Div.
Richard Kirsche, V.P., Engineering
Barbara Burns, V.P. & Gen. Counsel

Edward Nolan, Controller, Cable
Ownership: Peter A. Bordes Family. Sold Massachusetts holdings to Charter Communications Inc. & Pennsylvania holdings to Comcast Cable Communications Inc. 1999.
Represented (legal): Cole, Raywid & Braverman LLP; Schwartz, Woods & Miller.
Cable Systems (2):
Massachusetts: Worcester.
Pennsylvania: Philadelphia (area 1).
Total Basic Subscribers: 252,515 (0.37% of total cable households).
Total Pay Units: 211,555.
Newspapers:
New Jersey: East Brunswick Sentinel, Suburban (weekly), Recorder (weekly), Freehold News Transcript, Middletown Independent, The Examiner.
Other Holdings:
Printing company: Greater Jersey Press, East Brunswick, NJ.
Telecommunications company: Greater Star Link & Motower (Detroit, MI).
Radio Stations; SMATV systems.
MDS; MMDS, see listings.

BILL GREEN

Box 658
c/o Dale Miller
Rayville, LA 71269
Phone: 318-559-1212
Cable Systems (4):
Louisiana: Delhi 5%, Lake Providence, Oak Grove 5%, Rayville 5%.
Total Basic Subscribers: 4,964.
Total Pay Units: 612.

GREEN HILLS COMMUNICATIONS INC.

Box 227
7926 N.E. State Rte. M
Breckenridge, MO 64625
Phone: 660-644-2000
Fax: 660-644-5464
Officers:
Lloyd Riley, Pres.
Steven Tarr, Secy.
Ownership: Green Hills Telephone Corporation.
Cable Systems (6):
Missouri: Cowgill, Easton, Kingston, Lake Viking, Tina, Utica.
Total Basic Subscribers: 427.
Total Pay Units: 135.

GREEN RIVER CABLE TV INC.

Box 310
Fort Gay, WV 25514
Phone: 502-866-2655
Officer:
Gary Yocum, Pres.
Cable Systems (1):
Kentucky: Louisa.
Total Basic Subscribers: 260.
Total Pay Units: 60.

GREEN TREE CABLE TV INC.

Box 85
Franklin Furnace, OH 45629
Phone: 614-354-9195
Ownership: Donna Lycans.
Cable Systems (2):
Ohio: Proctorville.
West Virginia: Twelve Pole.
Total Basic Subscribers: 485.

GREENBURR TV CABLE

Box 85
Loganton, PA 17747
Phone: 717-725-2733
Officer:
Paul Rhinehart, Pres.
Ownership: Community owned.
Cable Systems (1):
Pennsylvania: Greenburr.
Total Basic Subscribers: 138.

GREENE CABLEVISION CO.

50 Genesee St.
Greene, NY 13778
Phone: 607-656-8717
Officers:
Michael J. Csigi, Pres.
Dorothy M. Csigi, Secy.-Treas.
Ownership: Michael J. Csigi & Dorothy M. Csigi, 100% jointly.
Cable Systems (1):
New York: Greene.
Total Basic Subscribers: 900.
Total Pay Units: 350.

GREENE COMMUNICATIONS INC. (AL)

2400 Sportsman Dr.
Phenix City, AL 36868
Phone: 334-298-7000
Fax: 334-298-0833
Officers:
Roy M. Greene, Chmn.
Lynne G. Frakes, Pres.
Vicki Abbot, Chief Operating Officer
Cable Systems (2):
Alabama: Hatchechubbee, Phenix City.
Total Basic Subscribers: 16,560 (0.02% of total cable households).
Total Pay Units: 13,869.
Other Holdings:
LPTV, see listing.

GREENE COMMUNICATIONS INC. (VA)

Suite 2
8902 Seminole Trail
Ruckersville, VA 22968-3318
Phone: 804-985-2266
Officers:
Frank L. Lamb, Chmn.
William G. Downey, Vice Chmn.
Richard Herring, Pres.
David C. Dickey, Secy.
Michael Snow, Treas.
Cable Systems (1):
Virginia: Greene County.
Total Basic Subscribers: 1,800.
Total Pay Units: 820.

GREENE COUNTY PARTNERS INC.

2663 Farragut Dr.
Springfield, IL 62704
Phones: 217-793-8939; 800-274-5789
Officers:
John Beck, Pres.
Doug Foster, V.P.
Annette Beck, Secy.
Ownership: John Beck, Doug Foster & Annette Beck, Principals.
Cable Systems (9):
Illinois: Athens, Carrollton, Greenville, Mason City, Petersburg, Riverton, Roodhouse, Williamsville.
Michigan: Benton Harbor.
Total Basic Subscribers: 16,450 (0.02% of total cable households).
Total Pay Units: 9,288.

GRISWOLD CO-OP TELEPHONE CO.

Box 640
607 Main St.
Griswold, IA 51535
Phone: 712-778-2122
Cable Systems (2):
Iowa: Elliott, Griswold.
Total Basic Subscribers: 496.
Other Holdings:
MMDS, see listing.

GROVE CABLE CO.

115 Glenwood Rd.
Marquette, MI 49855
Phone: 906-249-1057
Ownership: Robert Grove.
Cable Systems (4):
Michigan: Grand Marais, Republic Twp., Seney Twp., Shingleton.
Total Basic Subscribers: 532.
Total Pay Units: 207.

GRUVER CABLEVISION INC.

308 Main St.
Gruver, TX 79040
Phone: 806-733-5295
Ownership: E. J. Riley & Roy Riley, 100% jointly.
Cable Systems (2):
Texas: Gruver, Vega.
Total Basic Subscribers: 701.
Total Pay Units: 390.

GTE MEDIA VENTURES

Suite 300
100 E. Royal Lane
Irving, TX 76051
Phone: 972-465-4125
Fax: 972-465-4972
Officers:
William D. Wilson, Pres.
James Miles, V.P.
Gerald L. Edgar, Secy.
Larry G. Manion, Chief Financial Officer
Ownership: GTE Corp.
Represented (legal): Gerald L. Edgar.
Cable Systems (3):
California: Cerritos, Thousand Oaks.
Florida: Tampa Bay.
Wireless Cable Systems (1):
Hawaii: Honolulu.
Total Cable Subscribers: 58,832 (0.09% of total cable households).
Total Pay Units: 53,783.
Other Holdings:
MDS, MMDS, see listings.

GUADALUPE VALLEY COMMUNICATIONS SYSTEMS INC.

100 FM 3159
New Braunfels, TX 78132-1604
Phone: 512-885-4411
Fax: 830-885-2100
Officers:
Arley Sueltenfuss, Pres.
Tom See, Chief Operating Officer
Robert Hunt, Exec. V.P.
L. Charles Billings, V.P.
Laverne Cydabec, Secy.-Treas.
Ownership: Community owned.
Cable Systems (2):
Texas: Boerne, Canyon Lake.
Total Basic Subscribers: 6,510.
Total Pay Units: 4,010.
Other Holdings:
Telephone.

GULF SOUTH CABLE INC.

Box 80277
Lafayette, LA 70598
Phone: 800-848-6692
Ownership: Scott Smith, Principal.
Cable Systems (2):
Louisiana: Livingston, Walker.
Total Basic Subscribers: N.A.

HADLAND COMMUNICATIONS INC.

Box 1286
Bayfield, WI 54814
Phone: 715-779-5840
Fax: 715-779-5846
Ownership: Bob Hadland, Chief Exec. Officer.
Cable Systems (1):
Wisconsin: Bayfield.
Total Basic Subscribers: 311.
Total Pay Units: 246.

HAEFELE TV INC.

Box 368
24 E. Tioga St.
Spencer, NY 14883
Phone: 607-589-6235
Ownership: Lee Haefele, Principal.
Cable Systems (10):
New York: Alpine, Berkshire, Burdett, Enfield, McDonough, Orange (town), Reading, Smithville Flats, Spencer, Tioga.
Total Basic Subscribers: 4,698.
Total Pay Units: 3,520.

LLOYD L. HALL

Box 707
Bovill, ID 83806
Phone: 208-826-3234
Cable Systems (1):
Idaho: Bovill.
Total Basic Subscribers: 40.
Total Pay Units: 8.

HAMDEN COMMUNITY TV CLUB INC.

Box 14 A
RD 1
Hamden, NY 13782
Phone: 607-746-2342
Officers:
Wayne E. Marshfield, Pres.
Donald Crawford, V.P.
Virginia MacNaught, Secy.-Treas.
Ownership: Subscriber owned.
Cable Systems (1):
New York: Hamden.
Total Basic Subscribers: 300.
Total Pay Units: 125.

HAMILTON COUNTY/GORE MOUNTAIN CABLE TV INC.

1430 Balltown Rd.
Schenectady, NY 12309
Phone: 518-381-4832
Fax: 518-381-4833
Officers:
Paul F. Schonewolf, Pres. & Chief Operating Officer
George M. Williams, Chief Financial Officer
Ownership: Paul F. Schonewolf, 80.01%; George M. Williams, 19.9%.
Represented (legal): Baraff, Koerner & Olender PC.
Cable Systems (3):
New York: Indian Lake (town), Johnsburg (town), Wells.
Total Basic Subscribers: 1,548.
Total Pay Units: 385.

STEVE HAMILTON
Box 6
Mecosta, MI 49332
Cable Systems (1):
Michigan: Leroy (village) 10%.
Total Basic Subscribers: 523.
Total Pay Units: 224.

N. R. HAMM CONTRACTORS INC.
Box 17
Perry, KS 66073
Phone: 913-597-5111
Fax: 913-597-5117
Officers:
N. Rodney Hamm, Pres.
Deloris Myers, Secy.
Ownership: N. Rodney Hamm.
Cable Systems (1):
Kansas: Perry.
Total Basic Subscribers: 490.
Total Pay Units: 216.

HANCEL INC.
Box 608
6 Read St.
Hancock, NY 13783-0608
Phone: 607-637-2568
Officers:
Robert C. Wrighter Sr., Chmn. & Pres.
Gary P. Schoonmaker, Chief Operating Officer
Elizabeth B. Clark, Chief Financial Officer
Ownership: Hancock Telephone Co.
Cable Systems (2):
New York: Hancock.
Pennsylvania: Lakewood.
Total Basic Subscribers: 1,290.
Total Pay Units: 514.

H & B CABLE SERVICE INC.
Box 108
Holyrood, KS 67450
Phones: 913-252-3251; 913-252-4000
Officers:
Betty L. Koch, Chmn.
Robert Koch, Pres.
Del Jeane Nash, Secy.-Treas.
Ownership: Betty Koch & Harold Koch, 100% jointly.
Cable Systems (1):
Kansas: Holyrood.
Total Basic Subscribers: 850.
Total Pay Units: 276.

HANSON COMMUNICATIONS
Central CableLand T.V.
Box 217
Alexandria, SD 57311
Phone: 605-239-4302
Fax: 605-239-4301
Officers:
Ronald Sardine, Chmn.
Lanny Johnson, Chief Exec. Officer
Cable Systems (2):
South Dakota: Alexandria, Spencer.
Total Basic Subscribers: 284.
Total Pay Units: 96.

HARGRAY TELEPHONE CO.
Box 5519
Hilton Head Island, SC 29938
Phone: 803-785-2166
Ownership: Gloria R. Shepherd, Principal.
Cable Systems (4):
South Carolina: Bluffton, Estill, Hardeeville, Ridgeland.
Total Basic Subscribers: 3,606.
Total Pay Units: 1,376.

HARLAN COMMUNITY TV INC.
Box 592
First & Eversole Sts.
Harlan, KY 40831
Phone: 606-573-2945
Officers:
James Morgan, Pres.
Wade McCorkle, V.P.
Charles Hale, Secy.-Treas.
Ownership: Subscriber owned.
Represented (legal): James S. Greene Jr.
Cable Systems (1):
Kentucky: Harlan.
Total Basic Subscribers: 3,212.
Total Pay Units: 300.

HARMAN CABLE CORP.
Box 98
Main St.
Harman, WV 26270
Phone: 304-227-4143
Officers:
Klare Cooper, Pres.
Lila Lee Ray, Secy.-Treas.
Cable Systems (1):
West Virginia: Harman.
Total Basic Subscribers: 96.

HARMON CABLE COMMUNICATIONS
Suite 6900
8480 E. Orchard Rd.
Englewood, CO 80111
Phone: 303-773-3821
Fax: 303-773-0839
Officers:
James R. Jackman, Pres. & Chief Operating Officer
Robert M. Fukumoto, Chief Financial Officer
Ownership: Harmon Family.
Represented (legal): Cole, Raywid & Braverman LLP.
Cable Systems (15):
Minnesota: Balaton, Canby, Cottonwood, Tracy.
Nebraska: Ashland, Greenwood, Lake Ventura, Louisville, Plattsmouth, Springfield, Wahoo, Waverly.
North Dakota: West Fargo.
Oklahoma: Elmore City, Sulphur.
Total Basic Subscribers: 33,800 (0.05% of total cable households).
Total Pay Units: 15,000.

MITCHELL HARPER
Box 67
Harper, TX 78631
Phone: 512-864-4040
Cable Systems (1):
Texas: Harper.
Total Basic Subscribers: 200.
Total Pay Units: 45.

J. D. HARRISON
Strawn, TX 76475
Phones: 254-672-5296; 254-672-5653
Cable Systems (1):
Texas: Strawn 50%.
Total Basic Subscribers: 190.
Total Pay Units: 43.

JOHN C. HARRISON
Box 517
210 Main St.
Pine Bluffs, WY 82082
Phone: 307-245-3392
Fax: 307-245-3280
Represented (legal): Pepper & Corazzini.
Cable Systems (2):
Wyoming: Guernsey, Pine Bluffs.
Total Basic Subscribers: 806.
Total Pay Units: 308.

HARRON COMMUNICATIONS CORP.
Box 3022
70 E. Lancaster Ave.
Frazer, PA 19355
Phone: 610-644-7500
Fax: 610-644-2790; 610-993-1100
Web site: http://www.harron.com
Officers:
Paul F. Harron Jr., Pres. & Chief Exec. Officer
Gregory Raymond, Sr. V.P.
Andrew J. Walton, V.P., Operations
Patricia Imbesi, V.P. & Secy.
Linda C. Stuchell, V.P., Programming & Public Affairs
Ron Enas, V.P., Engineering
John F. Quigley III, Chief Financial Officer
Represented (legal): Hogan & Hartson LLP.
Cable Systems (32):
Massachusetts: Pembroke.
Michigan: Bad Axe, Brown City, Capac, Caseville, Croswell, Deckerville, Marlette, New Haven, Pigeon, Port Austin, Port Hope, Port Huron, Sandusky, Sebewaing, Ubly, Yale.
New Hampshire: Londonderry, Merrimack, New Boston.
New York: Argyle, Auburn, Canajoharie, Edinburg (town), Forestport, Granville, Hartford (town), Old Forge, Queensbury, Utica.
Pennsylvania: Kennett Square, Malvern.
Total Basic Subscribers: 283,928 (0.41% of total cable households).
Total Pay Units: 132,301.
Other Holdings:
TV, see listing.
Cable advertising representative: Radius Communications.
SMATV systems.
Note: Sold to Adelphia Communications Corp. 1999.

CONNIE HARTIN III
Box 839
111 N. College St.
Georgetown, TX 78627
Phone: 512-930-3085
Fax: 512-869-2962
Cable Systems (1):
Texas: Pflugerville 5%.
Total Basic Subscribers: 10,000.
Total Pay Units: 4,637.

HARTINGTON TELEPHONE CO.
Box 157
Hartington, NE 68739
Phone: 402-254-3933
Cable Systems (1):
Nebraska: Hartington.
Total Basic Subscribers: 616.
Total Pay Units: 343.

HARTLEY MUNICIPAL CABLE TV
11 S. Central Ave.
Hartley, IA 51346
Phone: 712-728-2240
Fax: 712-728-2878
Officers:
Bryan Gerritson, Chief Exec. Officer
Rodney Roth, Chief Operating Officer
Ownership: Community owned.
Cable Systems (1):
Iowa: Hartley.
Total Basic Subscribers: 702.
Total Pay Units: 326.

JAMES DALE HASLETT
Box 386
Waldport, OR 97394
Phone: 503-528-7341
Cable Systems (1):
Oregon: Waldport.
Total Basic Subscribers: 950.

JOHN HASTINGS
Box 900
Clinton, AR 72031
Phone: 501-745-4040
Fax: 501-745-4966
Cable Systems (1):
Arkansas: Clinton.
Total Basic Subscribers: 1,074.

HAVILAND TELEPHONE CO.
Box 308
Haviland, KS 67059
Phone: 316-862-5211
Officer:
Robert Ellis, Pres.
Cable Systems (1):
Kansas: Haviland.
Total Basic Subscribers: 214.
Total Pay Units: 65.

CITY OF HAWARDEN
Box 231
Hawarden, IA 51023
Phone: 712-551-2565
Fax: 712-551-1117
Officers:
Mose V. Hendricks, Chief Exec. Officer
Tim Waddell, City Clerk
Cable Systems (1):
Iowa: Hawarden.
Total Basic Subscribers: 794.
Other Holdings:
Telephone.

HAWKEYE TV CO.
Box 250
115 Main St.
Hawkeye, IA 52142
Phone: 319-427-3222
Fax: 319-427-2553
Officers:
William Strudthoff, Pres.
Chuck Gray, Chief Exec. & Financial Officer & Secy.-Treas.
Michael Johnson, Chief Operating Officer
Ownership: Hawkeye Telephone Co.
Cable Systems (1):
Iowa: Hawkeye.
Total Basic Subscribers: 170.
Total Pay Units: 65.

JIM HAYS
Box 186
232 Broadway
Irvine, KY 40336
Phone: 606-723-4240
Cable Systems (3):
Kentucky: Clover Bottom, Irvine, McKee.
Total Basic Subscribers: 4,829.

HAYWOOD CABLEVISION INC.
Box 778
Waynesville, NC 28786
Phone: 709-926-2288
Cable Systems (1):
North Carolina: Cruso.
Total Basic Subscribers: 592.
Total Pay Units: 114.

HAZARD TV CABLE CO. INC.
Box 929

Gorman Ridge
Hazard, KY 41702-0828
Phone: 606-436-2522
Fax: 606-436-3447
Officers:
William D. Gorman Sr., Chmn. & Chief Exec. Officer
William D. Gorman Jr., Chief Operating Officer
Ownership: William D. Gorman Sr., 52%; D. A. Davis Estate, 48%.
Cable Systems (1):
Kentucky: Hazard.
Total Basic Subscribers: 800.
Total Pay Units: 150.

HD ELECTRIC COOPERATIVE
Box 307
Clear Lake SD, 57226
Phone: 605-874-2171
Fax: 605-874-8173
Wireless Cable Systems (1):
South Dakota: Clear Lake.
Total Basic Subscribers: N.A.

HDC CABLE
8518 Lynnwood Dr.
Catlettsburg, KY 41129
Phone: 606-739-6445
Ownership: Doug Jones, Principal.
Cable Systems (1):
Tennessee: Altamont.
Total Basic Subscribers: 315.
Total Pay Units: 51.

HEARTLAND CABLE INC. (FLORIDA)
10001 U.S. 27 S
Sebring, FL 33870
Phone: 813-655-1122
Officer:
John Greytak, Chief Exec. Officer
Ownership: Marvin Burton, Principal.
Cable Systems (1):
Florida: Buttonwood Bay Mobile Home Park.
Total Basic Subscribers: 284.

HEARTLAND CABLE INC. (ILLINOIS)
167 W. 5th
Minonk, IL 61760
Phone: 309-432-2075
Fax: 309-432-2500
Officers:
Steve Allen, Chief Exec. & Operating Officer
Marshall Smith, V.P. & Asst. Secy.
Ken Nevius, Secy. & Asst. Treas.
Ownership: Steve Allen, Ken Nevius & Marshall Smith, Principals.
Represented (legal): David Davis (Bloomington, IL).
Cable Systems (5):
Illinois: Armington (village), Flanagan, Kenney, Sibley (village), Sublette (village).
Total Basic Subscribers: 981.
Total Pay Units: 150.

STEVEN HECK
Box 517
601 7th St.
Armstrong, IA 50514
Phone: 712-864-3431
Cable Systems (4):
Iowa: Lakota, Renwick, Woden.
Minnesota: Emmons.
Total Basic Subscribers: 550.
Total Pay Units: 100.

HELICON CORP.
630 Palisades Ave.
Englewood Cliffs, NJ 07632
Phone: 201-568-7720
Fax: 201-568-6228
Officers:
Theodore Baum, Chmn. & Pres.
Gregory Kriser, Exec. V.P. & Chief Operating Officer
Herbert Roberts, Sr. V.P., Treas. & Chief Financial Officer
Ruth Baum, V.P.
Dick Clark, V.P., Mktg.
David M. Baum, V.P., Operations
Thomas Gimbel, V.P., Engineering
George Psyllos, V.P. & Controller
Richard Hainbach, Secy. & Gen. Counsel
Ownership: Baum Family, 69%; Corporate management, 7%; others, 24%.
Represented (legal): Cole, Raywid & Braverman LLP.
Cable Systems (38):
Alabama: Skyline.
Georgia: Chatsworth, Menlo, Summerville, Trenton.
Louisiana: Terrebonne Parish.
North Carolina: Boone, Creston (southern portion), Roanoke Rapids, Roxboro.
Pennsylvania: Paint Twp. (Clarion County), Uniontown.
South Carolina: Anderson.
Tennessee: Calhoun, Dayton, Decatur, Jasper, Kingston.
Vermont: Barre, Bradford, Chelsea, St. Johnsbury.
West Virginia: Ansted, Burnsville, Camden on Gauley, Dorothy, Elizabeth, Elkview, Ellenboro, Glenville, Grant Town, Grantsville, Harrisville, Hinton, Page, Pipestem, Scarbro, Spencer.
Total Basic Subscribers: 174,041 (0.25% of total cable households).
Total Pay Units: 65,434.
Note: Sold to Charter Communications Inc. 1999.

HELIX COMMUNICATIONS
Box 326
200 Concord St.
Helix, OR 97835
Phone: 541-457-2385
Officers:
James A. Smith, Pres.
Timothy J. Smith, Secy.-Treas.
Ownership: James A. Smith, 50%; Timothy J. Smith, 50%.
Cable Systems (1):
Oregon: Helix.
Total Basic Subscribers: 60.

HENDERSON COOPERATIVE TELEPHONE CO.
1000 N. Main St.
Henderson, NE 68371
Phone: 402-723-4448
Fax: 402-723-4451
Cable Systems (1):
Nebraska: Henderson.
Total Basic Subscribers: 390.
Total Pay Units: 121.

JOHN HENNING
Box 222
Sulphur, LA 70664
Phone: 318-583-4973
Cable Systems (1):
Louisiana: Carlyss.
Total Basic Subscribers: 1,750.
Total Pay Units: 1,213.

HEPPNER TV INC.
162 N. Main
Heppner, OR 97836
Phone: 541-676-9663
Fax: 541-676-9655
Officers:
Gregory Sweek, Pres.
Judith Laughlin, Secy.-Treas. & Chief Financial Officer
Ownership: Cooperative.
Represented (legal): Kuhn & Spicer.
Cable Systems (1):
Oregon: Heppner.
Total Basic Subscribers: 614.
Total Pay Units: 244.

WILLIAM HERBOLICH
Box 343
509 First St. E
Whitehall, MT 59759
Phone: 406-287-3913
Cable Systems (1):
Montana: Whitehall.
Total Basic Subscribers: 283.
Total Pay Units: 90.

HEREFORD CABLE TV INC.
Box 1656
119 E. 4th St.
Hereford, TX 79045
Phone: 806-364-3912
Fax: 806-364-7147
Officer:
Clint Formby, Chmn. & Chief Exec. Officer
Cable Systems (1):
Texas: Hereford 80%.
Total Basic Subscribers: 4,188.
Total Pay Units: 1,000.

HERMOSA CABLEVISION
355 Animosa Dr.
Durango, CO 81301
Phone: 303-259-3810
Officers:
Doug Hawks, Pres.
Randy Hawks, Chief Operating Officer & Secy.-Treas.
Ownership: R. L. Hawks, 50%; Doug Hawks, 8.33%; Kim Hawks, 8.33%; Pam Hawks, 8.33%; Randy Hawks, 8.33%; Steve Hawks, 8.33%; Tim Hawks, 8.33%.
Cable Systems (1):
Colorado: Hermosa.
Total Basic Subscribers: 904.
Total Pay Units: 360.

HERR CABLE CO.
Box 717
RR 4
Montoursville, PA 17754-9665
Phone: 717-433-3111
Ownership: Ralph Herr, 51%; Rita Herr, 49%.
Cable Systems (7):
Pennsylvania: Barbours, Bodines, Brookside, Eldred Twp. (Lycoming County), Hillsgrove, Lairdsville, Waterville.
Total Basic Subscribers: 1,422.

EDWARD HEWSON
Box 1569
Ocean Shores, WA 98569
Phone: 206-289-2252
Cable Systems (1):
Washington: Ocean Shores.
Total Basic Subscribers: 2,311.
Total Pay Units: 696.

HFU TV
No. 26 HFU Circle
Coleville, CA 96107
Phone: 916-495-2224
Officers:
James W. Charlton, Co-Pres.
David Scott Charlton, Co-Pres.
Ownership: James W. Charlton, 50%; David Scott Charlton, 48%; HFU Inc., 2%.
Cable Systems (2):
California: Coleville.
Nevada: Topaz Lake.
Total Basic Subscribers: 1,101.
Total Pay Units: 763.

HIGH MOUNTAIN COMMUNICATIONS INC.
Box 267
West Yellowstone, MT 59758
Phone: 800-326-4343
Fax: 406-646-4048
Cable Systems (10):
Montana: Charlo, Darby, Ennis, Hot Springs, Marion, Paradise, Plains, St. Ignatius, St. Regis, West Yellowstone.
Total Basic Subscribers: 1,954.
Total Pay Units: 962.

HIGH PLAINS CABLEVISION INC.
Box 310
116 S. Main St.
Lockney, TX 79241
Phone: 806-652-3328
Ownership: Jim Doucette, Principal.
Cable Systems (5):
Texas: Adrian, Cactus, Channing, Nazareth, Turkey.
Total Basic Subscribers: 569.
Total Pay Units: 78.

HIGHLAND CABLE
317 N. Farr St.
San Angelo, TX 76903
Phone: 915-655-5795
Ownership: John W. Jones, Chief Exec. Officer.
Cable Systems (1):
Texas: Highland Range.
Total Basic Subscribers: 100.

HIGHLAND COMMUNICATIONS COOPERATIVE INC.
Box 339
Monterey, VA 24465
Phone: 540-468-3390
Cable Systems (1):
Virginia: Monterey.
Total Basic Subscribers: 347.
Total Pay Units: 88.

DARWIN HILLBERRY
Box 628
Riverton, WY 82501
Phone: 307-856-3322
Cable Systems (1):
Wyoming: Shoshoni.
Total Basic Subscribers: N.A.

THE HILLIARD GROUP
Box 427
222 W. First St.
Laurel, MT 59044
Phone: 406-628-2100
Fax: 406-628-8181
Officers:
Leslie P. Hilliard, Pres.
Maggie Hilliard, Chief Exec. Officer & Secy.-Treas.
Ken Young, Chief Operating Officer
Greg Herbert, Chief Financial Officer

Ownership: Leslie P. Hilliard.
Represented (legal): Cole, Raywid & Braverman LLP.
Cable Systems (11):
Montana: Absarokee, Big Timber, Columbus, Forsyth, Hardin, Laurel, Missoula, Park City, Red Lodge.
Texas: Silsbee.
Washington: Fairchild AFB.
Total Basic Subscribers: 16,511 (0.02% of total cable households).
Total Pay Units: 5,392.

HILLSIDE CATV INC.
1114 Bermuda Run
Advance, NC 27006
Phone: 919-998-5182
Cable Systems (1):
Virginia: Goshen.
Total Basic Subscribers: 185.
Total Pay Units: 64.

HILLTOP COMMUNICATIONS INC.
Box 352
Germantown, NY 12526
Phone: 518-537-6257
Fax: 518-537-6700
Officers:
Madeline Bohnsack, Pres.
Bruce Bohnsack, V.P. & Gen. Mgr.
A. Joel Bohnsack, Secy.-Treas.
Ownership: Germantown Telephone Inc.
Cable Systems (1):
New York: Germantown.
Total Basic Subscribers: 1,024.
Total Pay Units: 837.
Other Holdings:
Telephone.
Cellular radio.

BOB HILLYER JR.
5834 J St.
Lincoln, NE 68510
Phone: 402-488-2965
Cable Systems (9):
Nebraska: Cedar Creek, Cook, Davenport, Johnson, Lake Waconda, Murray, Nehawka, Unadilla, Union.
Total Basic Subscribers: 937.
Total Pay Units: 500.

HINTON CATV CO.
Box 70
Hinton, OK 73047
Phone: 405-542-3211
Officers:
J. R. Hollis, Pres.
Del Hollis, V.P.
Kenneth Doughty, Secy.-Treas.
Cable Systems (2):
Oklahoma: Eakly, Hinton.
Total Basic Subscribers: 606.
Total Pay Units: 451.

H.L.M. CABLE CO.
Box 620684
Middleton, WI 53562-0684
Phone: 608-831-7044
Fax: 608-836-5726
Officers:
David Walsh, Chmn. & Chief Exec. Officer
Robert E. Ryan, Chief Operating Officer
Ownership: Glenna J. Miller, D. G. Walsh & Robert E. Ryan, Principals.
Represented (legal): Robert M. Foley.
Cable Systems (8):
Illinois: Gem Suburban Mobile Home Park.
Wisconsin: Auburndale, Bluffview, Darien, Junction City, Pittsville, Rudolph, Vesper.
Total Basic Subscribers: 2,074.
Total Pay Units: 869.

E. D. HOFFMAN
Box 839
111 N. College St.
Georgetown, TX 87627
Phone: 512-869-1505
Fax: 512-869-2962
Cable Systems (4):
Texas: Georgetown 5%, Jarrell 5%, Leander 5%, Pflugerville 5%.
Total Basic Subscribers: 24,152 (0.04% of total cable households).
Total Pay Units: 10,388.

JOAN S. & LEE M. HOLMES
530 W. O'Brien Dr.
Agana, GU 96910
Phone: 671-477-7815
Fax: 671-477-7847
Represented (legal): Brown, Nietert & Kaufman, Chartered.
Cable Systems (2):
Guam: Agana.
Mariana Island: Saipan.
Total Basic Subscribers: 36,065 (0.05% of total cable households).
Total Pay Units: 15,277.
Radio Stations:
Guam: KOKU(FM), Agana.
Other Holdings:
Broadcast holdings: Interest in licensee of KFVE(TV) Honolulu, HI.

HOME TOWN CABLE
Box 216
Little River, KS 67457
Phone: 316-897-6255
Ownership: Sheldon Smith & Russell Stephenson, Principals.
Cable Systems (1):
Kansas: Little River.
Total Basic Subscribers: 198.
Total Pay Units: 58.

HOMETOWN CABLEVISION
48 Maple St.
South Dayton, FL 14138
Phone: 716-988-3188
Ownership: John Storms, Principal.
Cable Franchises (1):
New York: South Dayton (village).

HOOD CANAL COMMUNICATIONS
Box 249
Union, WA 98592
Phone: 360-898-2481
Fax: 360-898-2244
Officer:
Rick Buechel, Pres.
Cable Systems (1):
Washington: Union.
Total Basic Subscribers: 2,100.
Total Pay Units: 664.
Other Holdings:
Cellular radio.

HOONAH COMMUNITY TV
Box 510
Hoonah, AK 99829
Phone: 907-945-3600
Ownership: Tlingit & Haida Community Council.
Cable Systems (1):
Alaska: Hoonah.
Total Basic Subscribers: 110.
Total Pay Units: 40.

HOOPER TELEPHONE CO.
Box 47
101 N. Elm St.
Hooper, NE 68031-0047
Phone: 402-654-3344
Officer:
Dave Nilles, Office Mgr.
Ownership: Privately held.
Cable Systems (1):
Nebraska: Hooper.
Total Basic Subscribers: 244.
Total Pay Units: 105.

JUNE HOOVER
Box 186
RR 4
Shickshinny, PA 18655
Phone: 717-256-3437
Cable Systems (3):
Pennsylvania: Camp Hill Correctional Institute, Dallas Correctional Institute, Retreat Correctional Institution.
Total Basic Subscribers: 1,636.
Total Pay Units: 539.

HORIZON CABLEVISION INC.—Sold to Millennium Digital Media LLC 1999.

HORRY TELEPHONE COOPERATIVE INC.
Box 1820
3480 Hwy. 701 N
Conway, SC 29528-1820
Phone: 843-365-2151
Fax: 843-365-1111
Officers:
H. G. McNeill, Pres., Board of Directors
Curley P. Huggins, Chief Exec. Officer
O'Neal Miller, Chief Exec., Financial Operations
Lowell Carter, Chief Exec., Engineering
Brent D. Groome, Chief Exec., Customer Operations
Ownership: Subscriber owned.
Cable Systems (1):
South Carolina: Homewood.
Total Basic Subscribers: 23,869 (0.03% of total cable households).
Total Pay Units: 7,831.

HORSESHOE BAY-APPLEHEAD CABLEVISION
Box 8859
Horseshoe Bay, TX 78654
Phone: 512-598-2535
Ownership: Norman C. Hurd, Trustee.
Cable Systems (1):
Texas: Applehead.
Total Basic Subscribers: 11.

BOB HOUGHTON
Box 389
Birch River, WV 26610
Phone: 304-649-2447
Cable Systems (1):
West Virginia: Tanner.
Total Basic Subscribers: 740.
Total Pay Units: 74.

RUTH HOWARD
Box 229
Rte. 40
Salyersville, KY 41465
Phone: 606-349-3317
Cable Systems (1):
Kentucky: Salyersville.
Total Basic Subscribers: N.A.

MARTIN HOWSER
729 S. Bernard St.
Spokane, WA 99204
Phone: 509-624-4140
Cable Systems (10):
Washington: Connell, Ione, Kahlotus, Liberty Lake, Lind, Metaline Falls, Odessa, Ritzville, Tekoa, Warden.
Total Basic Subscribers: 4,420.
Total Pay Units: 2,281.

HTC CABLECOM
Box 142
Hospers, IA 51238
Phone: 712-752-8100
Ownership: Hospers Telephone Exchange Inc.
Cable Systems (3):
Iowa: Hospers, Sheldon, Sibley.
Total Basic Subscribers: 2,627 as of November 1, 1995.
Total Pay Units: 930.

HUBBARD CO-OP CABLE
306 E. Maple St.
Hubbard, IA 50122
Phone: 515-864-2216
Fax: 515-864-2666
Cable Systems (1):
Iowa: Hubbard.
Total Basic Subscribers: 260.
Total Pay Units: 38.

KEN & SUE HULA
Box 424
128 Walnut
Waterville, KS 66548
Phone: 913-785-2646
Cable Systems (1):
Kansas: Waterville.
Total Basic Subscribers: 225.
Total Pay Units: 87.

HUNTERS CREEK COMMUNICATIONS CORP.
14078 Water Plant Dr.
Orlando, FL 32837-6107
Phone: 407-240-4040
Fax: 407-856-8265
Ownership: Bill Strickler, Pres.
Cable Systems (1):
Florida: Hunters Creek.
Total Basic Subscribers: 3,635.

HUNTINGDON TV CABLE CO. INC.
170 Penn St.
Huntingdon, PA 16652
Phone: 814-643-3498
Officers:
J. Melvin Isett, Chmn.
Chester P. Isett, Pres.
Eileen Moore, V.P. & Treas.
Judy Collins, Secy.
Represented (legal): Dow, Lohnes & Albertson PLLC.
Cable Systems (1):
Pennsylvania: Huntingdon.
Total Basic Subscribers: 7,550.

HURLEY CABLEVISION
Box 404
Panther, WV 24872
Phone: 304-938-5264
Ownership: Thurman Hurley, Principal.
Cable Systems (2):

West Virginia: Davy, Panther.
Total Basic Subscribers: 377.

WALTER E. HUSSMAN JR.

2nd Floor
115 E. Capitol St.
Little Rock, AR 72203
Officers:
Walter E. Hussman Jr., Pres.
Jim Wilbanks, Exec. V.P.
Allen Berry, Chief Financial Officer
Cable Systems (1):
Arkansas: Camden 19%.
Total Basic Subscribers: 5,793.
Total Pay Units: 2,399.
Cable Holdings:
WEHCO Video Inc., see listing.
Other Holdings:
Broadcast holdings: KTAL-TV Inc., see listing.

ILLINET COMMUNICATIONS OF CENTRAL ILLINOIS INC.

Bldg. 6
11260 Aurora Ave.
Urbandale, IA 50322
Phone: 515-276-3069
Fax: 515-270-9181
Ownership: Jay Eliason, Principal. Eliason also has interest in Illini Cablevision of Illinois Inc., Mid American Cable Systems, New Path Communications LC, TelePartners, Telnet Communications & Westcom LC, see listings.
Cable Systems (5):
Illinois: Cerro Gordo, Hume (village), Monticello, Sidell (village), Tolono.
Total Basic Subscribers: 2,708.

ILLINI CABLEVISION INC.

Box 1005
595 San Antonio Ave.
Many, LA 71449
Phone: 318-256-2097
Fax: 318-256-9536
Ownership: Edwin T. Baldridge, 75%; Tedd Dumas, 25%.
Represented (legal): Cole, Raywid & Braverman LLP.
Cable Systems (1):
Colorado: Olathe.
Total Basic Subscribers: 395 (0.02% of total cable households).
Total Pay Units: 67.

ILLINI CABLEVISION OF ILLINOIS INC.

Box 71279
Des Moines, IA 50325
Phone: 515-276-3174
Officer:
Jay Eliason, Secy.
Ownership: Jay Eliason, Principal. Eliason also has interest in Illinet Communications of Central Illinois Inc., Mid American Cable Systems, New Path Communications LC, TelePartners, Telnet Communications & Westcom LC, see listings.
Cable Systems (1):
Illinois: Tuscola.
Total Basic Subscribers: 5,371.

INDEPENDENCE COUNTY CABLE TV INC.

Box 3799
2700 N. St. Louis
Batesville, AR 72501-0869
Phone: 501-793-4174
Fax: 501-793-7439
Officers:
J. D. Pierce, Pres.
Boyce E. Barnett, Secy.-Treas.
Ownership: J. D. Pierce, 50%; Boyce E. Barnett, 50%.
Cable Systems (26):
Arkansas: Alpena, Black Rock, Bradford, Caldwell, Calico Rock, Cave City, Cushman, Diamond City, Evening Shade, Guion, Gum Springs, Huntsville, Melbourne, Moro, Mount Pleasant, Mountain View, Newark, Oil Trough, Pangburn, Plainview, Pleasant Plains, Russell, Tumbling Shoals, Tupelo, Weavers Chapel, Yellville.
Total Basic Subscribers: 11,808 (0.02% of total cable households).
Total Pay Units: 2,798.

INDEVIDEO CO. INC.

Box 56339
Phoenix, AZ 85079
Phone: 602-248-8333
Fax: 602-248-0690

Branch Office:

Tuba City, AZ 86045
Phone: 602-283-5164
Fax: 602-283-5648
Cable Systems (8):
Arizona: Gisela, Grand Canyon, Keams Canyon, Leupp, Shonto, Tuba City, Tusayan.
New Mexico: Fort Wingate.
Total Basic Subscribers: 4,141.
Total Pay Units: 1,283.

INDEX CABLE TV INC.

941 Iowa Heights Rd.
Sedro Woolley, WA 98284
Phone: 205-724-3802
Cable Systems (3):
Washington: Guemes Island, Index, Skykomish.
Total Basic Subscribers: 383.
Total Pay Units: 65.

INNOVATIVE COMMUNICATIONS CORP.

4501 Estate Diamond
Christiansted, VI 00820
Phone: 340-778-6701
Fax: 340-778-5230
Cable Systems (1):
Virgin Islands: St. Croix.
Total Basic Subscribers: 13,800 (0.02% of total cable households).

INSIGHT COMMUNICATIONS CO.

126 E. 56th St.
New York, NY 10022
Phone: 212-371-2266
Fax: 212-371-1549
Web site: http://www.insight_com.com
Officers:
Sidney R. Knafel, Chmn.
Michael S. Willner, Pres. & Chief Exec. Officer
Kim D. Kelly, Exec. V.P., Chief Operating & Financial Officer
Pamela N. Euler Halling, Sr. V.P., Mktg. & Programming
Steve Sklar, Sr. V.P., Finance & Business Development
Scott Cooley, Sr. V.P., Operations, Indiana State Office
Colleen Quinn, Sr. V.P., Corporate Relations
Charles Dietz, Sr. V.P., Engineeering
James A. Stewart, Sr. V.P., Operations

Indiana State Office:

Suite 320
Indianapolis, IN 46240
Phone: 317-469-2700
Ownership: Vestar Capital Partners, Sidney R. Knafel & Michael S. Willner, Principals.
Represented (legal): Fleischman & Walsh LLP.
Cable Systems (49):
California: Artesia, Bell, Claremont.
Georgia: Griffin.
Illinois: Rockford.
Indiana: Alexandria 50%, Anderson 50%, Attica 50%, Bedford 50%, Bloomfield 50%, Bloomington 50%, Boonville 50%, Brownstown, Dublin 50%, Elwood 50%, Evansville 50%, Fort Branch 50%, Franklin 50%, Greencastle 50%, Greenfield 50%, Greensburg 50%, Hartford City 50%, Henryville, Jasper 50%, Jeffersonville 50%, Kokomo 50%, Lafayette 50%, Lebanon 50%, Linton 50%, Lynn 50%, Martinsville 50%, Monroe County (southern portion), Mount Vernon 50%, New Castle 50%, Noblesville 50%, Owensville 50%, Pekin, Portland, Poseyville 50%, Princeton 50%, Richmond 50%, Salem 50%, Scottsburg, Sullivan 50%, Winchester 50%.
Kentucky: Dawson Springs 50%, Henderson 50%, Providence 50%.
Ohio: Columbus 75%.
Total Basic Subscribers: 513,003 (0.75% of total cable households).
Total Pay Units: 410,210.

INTER-COUNTY CABLE CO.

127 Jackson St.
Brooklyn, IA 52211
Phone: 515-522-7000
Fax: 515-522-5001
Ownership: Brooklyn Mutual Telephone Co.
Cable Systems (1):
Iowa: Brooklyn.
Total Basic Subscribers: 1,038.
Total Pay Units: 172.

INTERLAKE CABLEVISION INC.

Box 540
Pequot Lakes, MN 56472
Phone: 218-568-5454
Fax: 218-568-2125

Branch Office:

Madison, WI
Phone: 608-845-4000
Ownership: TDS Telecom.
Cable Systems (2):
Minnesota: Hackensack, Pequot Lakes.
Total Basic Subscribers: 6,225.
Total Pay Units: 1,177.
Other Holdings:
Telephone.

INTERMEDIA PARTNERS

Suite 420
235 Montgomery St.
San Francisco, CA 94104
Phones: 415-616-4600; 415-616-4621
Fax: 415-397-4706; 415-397-3406
Officers:
F. Steven Crawford, Chief Operating Officer
Edon V. Smith, Chief Financial Officer
Ken Wright, Chief Technical Officer & Dir., Technology
Rodney M. Royse, Exec. Dir., Business Development

Branch Office:

Suite 1600
Nashville, TN 37219
Phone: 615-244-2300
Ownership: Robert J. Lewis, Managing Gen. Partner.
Represented (legal): Pillsbury, Madison & Sutro LLP; Fletcher, Heald & Hildreth PLC.
Cable Systems (86):
Georgia: Athens, Comer, Cuthbert, Donalsonville, Fairburn, Gainesville, Grantville, Milledgeville, Peachtree City, Powder Springs, Watkinsville.
Illinois: Abingdon 60.5%, Lacon 60.5%, Mahomet 60.5%, Momence 60.5%, Paxton 60.5%, Roanoke 60.5%, Standard 60.5%, Watseka 60.5%.
Iowa: Anamosa 60.5%, Blue Grass 60.5%, Clayton 60.5%, Garnavillo 60.5%, Lansing 60.5%, Manchester 60.5%, Monticello 60.5%, New Albin 60.5%, Tipton 60.5%, Waukon 60.5%.
Minnesota: Chisholm, Hancock, Hoyt Lakes, Redwood Falls.
North Carolina: Asheville, Elkin, Marion, Mount Airy.
South Carolina: Edgefield, Greenville, McCormick, Saluda, Spartanburg, Ware Shoals.
Tennessee: Alcoa, Carthage, Cleveland, Clifton, Crossville, Dickson, Gallatin, Gatlinburg, Greenbrier, Hartsville, Henderson, Hendersonville, Hohenwald, Joelton, Kingsport, Lafayette, Lewisburg, Lexington, Loretto, Loudon, Lynchburg, Madisonville, Martin, McEwen, McKenzie, Monterey, Mount Juliet, Murfreesboro, Nashville, Parsons, Portland, Red Boiling Springs, Savannah, Seymour, Smithville, Smyrna, Waverly, Waynesboro, Westmoreland, Westpoint, Winchester, Woodbury.
Wisconsin: Platteville 60.5%.
Total Basic Subscribers: 1,308,128 (1.91% of total cable households).
Total Pay Units: 919,594.
Note: Sold to Charter Communications Inc. & AT&T Broadband & Internet Services 1999.

INTERMEDIA PARTNERS VI LP

Suite 1600
424 Church St.
Nashville, TN 37219
Phone: 615-244-2300
Ownership: Blackstone Capital Partners Merchant Banking Fund LP, 49.5%; AT&T Broadband & Internet Services, see listing, 49.5%; InterMedia Partners, see listing, 1%. Blackstone & InterMedia sold their interests to Insight Communications Co. 1999. Resulting AT&T ownership: 50%.
Cable Systems (18):
Kentucky: Bloomfield, Bowling Green, Brandenburg, Bullitt, Covington, Danville, Five Star, Fort Campbell, Harrodsburg, Lawrenceburg, Lebanon Junction, Lexington, Louisville, Newport, Perryville, Radcliff, Stanford, Taylorsville.
Total Basic Subscribers: 425,000 (0.62% of total cable households).

INTER-MOUNTAIN CABLE INC.

Box 159
Harold, KY 41635
Phone: 606-478-9406
Fax: 606-478-3650
Officers:
Paul R. Gearheart, Pres.
Paul D. Gearheart, V.P.
Elaine Gearheart, Secy.-Treas.
James O. Campbell, Dir., Operations
Ownership: Elaine Gearhart, 50%; Paul R. Gearhart, 50%.
Cable Systems (1):
Kentucky: Martin.

Total Basic Subscribers: 22,800 (0.03% of total cable households).
Total Pay Units: 1,300.

INTERSTATE CABLEVISION INC.

605 Morton Ave.
Emerson, IA 51533
Phone: 712-824-7227
Cable Systems (9):
Iowa: Carson, Emerson, Martensdale, Murray, New Virginia, Silver City, St. Charles, Sun Valley Lake, Truro.
Total Basic Subscribers: 1,352.
Total Pay Units: 303.
Other Holdings:
Telephone: Interstate '35' Telephone Co., Truro, IA;, Southwest Telephone Exchange Inc., Emerson, IA (affiliated with independent telephone cos.).

IONE CITY TV CO-OP

Box 154
Ione, OR 97843
Phone: 503-422-7456
Officers:
Don Ball, Pres.
Edith Matthews, Secy.-Treas.
Ownership: Non-profit organization.
Cable Systems (1):
Oregon: Ione.
Total Basic Subscribers: N.A.

IRON RIVER COOPERATIVE TV ANTENNA CORP.

316 N. 2nd Ave.
Iron River, MI 49935
Phone: 906-265-3810
Fax: 906-265-3020
Officers:
Richard Brewster, Pres.
Lisa Powell, Secy.-Treas.
Ownership: Subscriber owned.
Cable Systems (1):
Michigan: Iron River.
Total Basic Subscribers: 1,505.
Total Pay Units: 455.

JEREMY ISIP

3003 N. Garfield Rd.
Traverse City, MI 49686
Phone: 616-947-5834
Cable Systems (1):
Michigan: Frederic Twp.
Total Basic Subscribers: 99.

JACKPOT ANTENNA-VISION INC.

Box 516
Ontario, OR 97914
Phone: 503-889-3173
Officers:
Lee Smith, Chmn. & Chief Exec. Officer
Donna Smith, Chmn. & Chief Operating Officer
David Smith, Pres.
Judy Surmeier, Secy.-Treas.
Ownership: Jody Aronson, 25%; David Smith, 25%; Judy Surmeier, 25%; Donna Smith, 12.5%; Lee Smith, 12.5%.
Cable Systems (1):
Nevada: Jackpot.
Total Basic Subscribers: 322.
Total Pay Units: 240.

JACKSON CABLE

Box 8196
Clinton, LA 70722
Phone: 504-683-9297
Officers:
V. F. Jackson Sr., Pres.
V. F. Jackson Jr., V.P.
James Jackson, Secy.
Cable Systems (1):
Louisiana: Clinton.
Total Basic Subscribers: 1,756.
Total Pay Units: 685.

JACKSON MUNICIPAL TV SYSTEM

80 W. Ashley St.
Jackson, MN 56143
Phone: 507-847-3225
Fax: 507-847-5586
Ownership: Community owned.
Cable Systems (1):
Minnesota: Jackson.
Total Basic Subscribers: 1,550.
Total Pay Units: 573.

LYNDA & ROBERT JACOBSON

Box 759
Ranchester, WY 82839
Phone: 307-655-9011
Fax: 307-655-9021
Officers:
Robert Jacobson, Pres.
Lynda Lee Jacobson, Secy.-Treas.
Cable Systems (8):
Wyoming: Edgerton, Hulett, Osage, Pine Haven, Ranchester, Story, Sundance, Wyodak.
Total Basic Subscribers: 1,752.
Total Pay Units: 700.

JADE COMMUNICATIONS LLC

Box 1035
Alamosa, CO 81101-1035
Phone: 719-379-5233
Cable Systems (1):
Colorado: Blanca.
Total Basic Subscribers: 200.
Total Pay Units: 96.

JAMES CABLE PARTNERS

Suite 180
710 N. Woodward
Bloomfield Hills, MI 48304
Phone: 248-647-1080
Fax: 248-647-1321
Ownership: William R. James, 91.5%; C. Timothy Trenary, 7.5%; Daniel K. Shoemaker, 1%.
Represented (legal): Cole, Raywid & Braverman LLP.
Cable Systems (63):
Alabama: Ashland, Dadeville, Guin, Hackleburg, Hollis Crossroads, Lafayette, Phil Campbell, Roanoke, Sulligent, Wadley, Wedowee.
Colorado: Akron, Otis, Yuma.
Florida: Alachua, Branford, Chiefland, Cross City, Hawthorne, High Springs, Micanopy, Orange Lake, Steinhatchee.
Georgia: Crawford, Crawfordville, Eatonton, Forsyth, Gray, Hawkinsville, Pinehurst, Unadilla.
Louisiana: De Quincy, Kinder, Lake Arthur, Vinton, Welsh, Westlake.
Oklahoma: Achille, Atoka, Coalgate, Colbert, Durant, Kingston, Sandpoint, Stonewall, Stringtown, Tishomingo, Wapanucka.
Tennessee: Byrdstown, Wartburg.
Texas: Bowie, Decatur, Huntington, Jacksboro, Kirbyville, Springtown.
Wyoming: Douglas, Glendo, Glenrock, Lusk, Saratoga, Torrington, Wheatland.
Total Basic Subscribers: 78,197 (0.11% of total cable households).
Total Pay Units: 24,076.

JAMES VALLEY COOPERATIVE TELEPHONE CO.

Box 260
235 E. First Ave.
Groton, SD 57445-0260
Phone: 605-397-2323
Fax: 605-397-2350
Officers:
Robert A. Johnson, Chmn. & Pres.
Alfred Larson, V.P.
Duane Jark, Secy.
Keith J. Taylor, Treas.
Ownership: Subscriber owned.
Represented (legal): Hyde & Allred (Aberdeen, SD).
Cable Systems (1):
South Dakota: Groton.
Total Basic Subscribers: 778.
Total Pay Units: 158.
Other Holdings:
Telephone: Accent Communications Inc.
Cellular radio.

J & N CABLE CO.

614 S. Columbus
Goldendale, WA 98620
Phone: 509-773-5359
Fax: 509-773-5554
Officer:
John Kusky, Pres.
Ownership: John Kusky & Nancy Kusky, 100% jointly.
Cable Systems (3):
Oregon: Condon, Wasco.
Washington: Yacolt.
Total Basic Subscribers: 412.

JAYROC INC.

Box 6575
Abilene, TX 79608
Phone: 915-691-5787
Fax: 915-676-2882
Officers:
Dorton Canon, Chmn. & Chief Exec. Officer
Judy Canon, V.P. & Secy.-Treas.
Ownership: Dorton Canon & Judy Canon.
Cable Systems (10):
Texas: Benjamin, Goree, Hawley, Jayton, Lueders, Moran, Potosi, Rochester, Trent, Weinert.
Total Basic Subscribers: 875.
Total Pay Units: 350.

J. B. CABLE

Box 268
Minersville, PA 17954
Phone: 717-544-5582
Ownership: John Dunleavy, 50%; Thomas O'Brien, 50%.
Cable Systems (1):
Pennsylvania: Primrose.
Total Basic Subscribers: 591.

JEFFERSON CABLE TV CORP.

216 Estelle St.
Wrens, GA 30833
Phone: 404-547-6651
Cable Systems (1):
Georgia: Wrens.
Total Basic Subscribers: 600.

JEFFERSON COUNTY CABLE INC.

116 S. 4th
Toronto, OH 43964
Phone: 614-537-2214
Ownership: Marvin L. Bates Sr., Principal.
Cable Systems (7):
Ohio: Rush Run, Toronto.
Pennsylvania: Avella, Burgettstown, Claysville.
West Virginia: Beech Bottom, Colliers.
Total Basic Subscribers: N.A.

JEFFERSON TELEPHONE CO. INC.

Box 128
311 Main St.
Jefferson, SD 57038
Phone: 605-966-5631
Cable Systems (1):
South Dakota: Jefferson.
Total Basic Subscribers: 125.

JESUP FARMER'S MUTUAL TELEPHONE CO.

Box 249
Jesup, IA 50648-0249
Phone: 319-827-3434
Officers:
Gerald Bloes, Pres.
Russell Rock, Chief Operating Officer
Ownership: Cooperative.
Cable Systems (1):
Iowa: Jesup.
Total Basic Subscribers: 740.
Total Pay Units: 388.

KEVIN JOHNSON

Box 789
Mitchell, SD 57301
Phone: 605-996-7683
Cable Systems (1):
South Dakota: Armour.
Total Basic Subscribers: 296.
Total Pay Units: 48.

ROBERT JOHNSON

One BET Plaza
1900 W Place NE
Washington, DC 20018-1211
Phones: 202-608-2000; 202-608-2171
Cable System (1):
District of Columbia: Washington (minority interest).
Total Basic Subscribers: 106,240 (0.16% of total cable households).
Total Pay Units: 168,927.
Other Holdings:
Cable Network: 64% of Black Entertainment Network.

JOHNSONBURG COMMUNITY TV CO. INC.

Box 248
424 Center St.
Johnsonburg, PA 15845
Phone: 814-965-4888
Officers:
Archie Shuer, Pres.
Harry Horne, Chief Operating Officer & Secy.
Sam Guaglianone, Chief Financial Officer
Ownership: Community owned.
Cable Systems (1):
Pennsylvania: Johnsonburg.
Total Basic Subscribers: 1,577.
Total Pay Units: 1,800.

JOHNSTON COUNTY CABLE LP

Suite 202
2444 Solomons Island Rd.
Annapolis, MD 21401-3715
Phone: 410-266-9393
Fax: 410-266-9054
Ownership: Bay Cable Inc., Gen. Partner.
Cable Systems (2):

North Carolina: Dover, Smithfield.
Total Basic Subscribers: 3,361.
Total Pay Units: 2,345.

BILLY R. JONES

Box 1470
Stockbridge, GA 30281
Phone: 404-389-9999
Represented (legal): Kilpatrick & Cody.
Cable Systems (1):
Virginia: King George.
Total Basic Subscribers: 3,000.
Total Pay Units: 594.

EUGENE JONES

Box 8
Rte. 1
Folsum, WV 26348
Phone: 304-334-6504
Cable Systems (1):
West Virginia: Folsom.
Total Basic Subscribers: 200.

JONES INTERCABLE INC.

9697 E. Mineral Ave.
Englewood, CO 80112
Phone: 303-792-3111
Officers:
Glenn R. Jones, Chmn. & Chief Exec. Officer
James B. O'Brien, Pres. & Chief Operating Officer
Chris Bowick, Group V.P., Technology
Kevin Coyle, Group V.P., Finance
George Newton, Group V.P., Telecommunications
Ray Vigil, Group V.P., Human Resources
Ruth E. Warren, Group V.P., Operations
Cindy Winning, Group VP, Marketing
Elizabeth M. Steele, V.P. & Secy.
Roy Pottle, V.P. & Treas.
Ownership: Comcast Cable Communications Inc., see listing, 57%.
Represented (legal): Davis Graham & Stubbs LLP.
Cable Systems (44):
Arizona: Oro Valley.
California: Oxnard, Palmdale, Roseville.
Florida: Brighton Seminole Reserve, Celebration, Fort Myers, Panama City Beach.
Georgia: Augusta, Colonels Island, Eulonia, Hinesville, Jesup, Savannah, Waynesville, Woodbine.
Kansas: Olathe.
Maryland: Annapolis (portions), Anne Arundel County (portions), Prince Frederick, Prince George's County (portions), Waldorf.
Michigan: Dowagiac, Jones, Three Rivers, Watervliet.
Missouri: Independence.
Nebraska: South Sioux City.
New Mexico: Albuquerque, Edgewood, Grants, Isleta, Moriarty, Placitas, Socorro, Thoreau, Tijeras.
South Carolina: Hampton.
Virginia: Alexandria, Fort Belvoir Army Base, Manassas, Reston.
Washington: Loomis.
Wisconsin: Manitowoc.
Total Basic Subscribers: 1,055,614 (1.54% of total cable households).
Total Pay Units: 861,570.
Other Holdings:
SMATV systems.
Data service: Jones Internet Channel.

ONIE D. JONES

Box 246
Desert Center, CA 92239
Phone: 760-227-3245
Cable Systems (1):
California: Desert Center.
Total Basic Subscribers: 40.
Total Pay Units: 12.

RICHARD C. JONES

111 N. Rice
Hamilton, TX 76531
Phone: 817-386-3418
Cable Systems (1):
Texas: Hamilton 50%.
Total Basic Subscribers: 1,125.
Total Pay Units: 205.

JSV CABLE

213 First St.
Soldier, IA 51572
Phone: 712-884-2203
Fax: 712-884-2205
Officer:
Heather Leisinger, Secy.
Ownership: LongLines Ltd.; WIPCO.
Cable Systems (3):
Iowa: Moorhead, Soldier, Ute.
Total Basic Subscribers: 250.
Total Pay Units: 135.

CITY OF KAHOKA

c/o Sandra Wagers
250 N. Morgan
Kahoka, MO 63445
Phone: 816-727-3711
Fax: 816-727-3750
Officers:
S. W. Waschenbach, Chmn.
Larry Young, Mayor
Sandie Hopp, Cable Dir.
Sandra L. Wagers, Chief Financial Officer
Ownership: Community owned.
Cable Systems (1):
Missouri: Kahoka.
Total Basic Subscribers: 769.
Total Pay Units: 331.

KALIDA TELEPHONE CO.

Box 267
Kalida, OH 45853
Phone: 419-532-3218
Cable Systems (1):
Ohio: Kalida.
Total Basic Subscribers: 835.
Total Pay Units: 145.

KANSAS CITY CABLE PARTNERS

6550 Winchester Ave.
Kansas City, MO 64133
Phone: 816-358-5360
Fax: 816-358-5815
Officers:
Robert Niles, Pres.
Stephanie Christensen, V.P., Customer Service
Jeff Johnston, V.P., Mktg. & Division Affairs
Ownership: AT&T Broadband & Internet Services, 50%; Time Warner Cable, 50%, see listings.
Cable Systems (2):
Kansas: Overland Park.
Missouri: Kansas City.
Total Basic Subscribers: 299,000 (0.44% of total cable households).
Total Pay Units: 227,542.

KARBAN TV SYSTEMS INC.

73A St. Stevens St.
Rhinelander, WI 54501
Phone: 715-362-4550
Ownership: John Karban.
Cable Systems (4):
Wisconsin: Boulder Junction, Land O'Lakes, Mercer, Three Lakes.
Total Basic Subscribers: 635.
Total Pay Units: 117.

ROGER KAUFMAN

Box 247
Gridley, IL 61744
Phone: 309-747-2324
Cable Systems (1):
Illinois: Gridley.
Total Basic Subscribers: 545.
Total Pay Units: 165.
Other Holdings:
Telephone: Roger Kaufman is Pres. of the Gridley Telephone Co., Gridley, IL.

KELLOGG COMMUNICATIONS

RD 1
Box 774
Shinglehouse, PA 16748
Phone: 814-697-7163
Cable Systems (1):
Pennsylvania: Oswayo.
Total Basic Subscribers: N.A.

KENNEBEC CATV CO.

Box 158
Kennebec, SD 57544
Phone: 605-869-2229
Officers:
Delores Johnstone, Chmn. & Chief Exec. Officer
Rod Bowar, Chief Operating Officer
Ownership: Dolores Johnstone, 85%; Rod Bowar, 15%.
Cable Systems (1):
South Dakota: Kennebec.
Total Basic Subscribers: 89.
Total Pay Units: 38.

J. ROGER KENNEDY JR.

Box 1310
Hwy. 280 W
Reidsville, GA 30453
Phone: 912-557-6133
Fax: 912-557-6545
Cable Systems (2):
Georgia: Pembroke, Reidsville.
Total Basic Subscribers: 2,631.
Total Pay Units: 1,357.
Other Holdings:
Kennedy Cable Construction Inc.

KENTUCKY/WEST VIRGINIA CABLE INC.

Box 216
Louisa, KY 41230
Phone: 606-638-3432
Cable Systems (3):
Kentucky: Blaine, Lawrence County (southern portion).
West Virginia: Glenhayes.
Total Basic Subscribers: 770.
Total Pay Units: 329.

KETNER ELECTRONICS INC.

Box 96
708 N. Vine St.
Stella, NE 68442
Phone: 402-883-2435
Fax: 402-883-2004
Officer:
George W. Ketner, Chief Exec. Officer
Ownership: Public corporation.
Cable Systems (1):
Nebraska: Stella.
Total Basic Subscribers: 65.
Total Pay Units: 63.

KEYSTONE FARMERS COOPERATIVE TELEPHONE CO.

86 Main St.
Keystone, IA 52249
Phone: 319-442-3241
Officer:
DuWayne Schirm, Pres.
Cable Systems (1):
Iowa: Keystone.
Total Basic Subscribers: 402.
Total Pay Units: 213.
Other Holdings:
Cellular radio.

KEYSTONE WILCOX CABLE TV INC.

Box 134
Ridgway, PA 15853
Phone: 814-371-1550
Officers:
James A. Rickard Jr., Pres. & Chief Operating Officer
Shirley A. McCoy, Secy.-Treas.

Branch Office:

Dubois, PA 15801
Phone: 814-371-2939
Ownership: Shirley A. McCoy, 50%; James Rickard Jr., 50%.
Cable Systems (2):
Pennsylvania: Westline, Wilcox.
Total Basic Subscribers: 481.
Total Pay Units: 240.
Other Holdings:
SMATV.

J. R. KING ENTERPRISES INC.

620 South
1310 Ranch Rd.
Austin, TX 78734
Phone: 512-263-9194
Fax: 512-263-3445
Officers:
J. R. King, Chmn. & Chief Exec. Officer
Kerri King, Chief Operating Officer
Ownership: J. R. King.
Cable Systems (1):
Texas: Lakeway.
Total Basic Subscribers: 5,200.
Total Pay Units: 4,000.

KINGSBURY ELECTRIC

Box E
De Smet SD, 57231
Phone: 605-854-3522
Wireless Cable Systems (1):
South Dakota: De Smet.
Total Basic Subscribers: N.A.

GEORGE KIRKPATRICK

7300 Col. Greirson Dr.
Spanish Fort, AL 36527
Phone: 334-937-2675
Fax: 334-937-2675
Cable Systems (1):
Alabama: Baldwin County (northwestern portion).
Total Basic Subscribers: 55.
Total Pay Units: 38.

PATRICIA KIRKPATRICK

Box 848
1402 E. Main
Magnolia, AR 71753
Phone: 501-234-5555
Cable Systems (1):

Arkansas: McNeil.
Total Basic Subscribers: 129.

KLAMRON ENTERPRISES INC.
Box 418
Chatham, LA 71226
Phone: 318-249-2111
Ownership: H. Alton Spillers Jr., Pres.
Cable Systems (1):
Louisiana: Chatham.
Total Basic Subscribers: 162.

DON KLINE
110 E. 10th St.
Kinsley, KS 67547
Phone: 316-659-3527
Cable Systems (2):
Kansas: Lewis, Offerle.
Total Basic Subscribers: 250.

RON KLINGENSTEIN
Box 148
204 E. Main St.
Dayton, WA 99328
Phone: 509-382-2132
Cable Systems (1):
Washington: Dayton.
Total Basic Subscribers: N.A.

KLM TELEPHONE CO.
Box 30
Rich Hill, MO 64779
Phone: 417-395-2121
Fax: 417-395-2120
Cable Systems (2):
Missouri: Rich Hill, Rockville.
Total Basic Subscribers: 404.
Total Pay Units: 171.

KNOWLEDGY
1241 O. G. Skinner Dr.
West Point, GA 31833
Phone: 706-645-3986
Ownership: Greg Orr, Charles Hilton & Allan Bense, 100% jointly.
Cable Systems (4):
Alabama: Huntsville, Montgomery.
Florida: Panama City Beach.
Georgia: Columbus.
Total Basic Subscribers: 54,975 (0.08% of total cable households).
Total Pay Units: 38,028.

RUTH I. KOLPIN
Box 696
Carthage, MO 64836
Phone: 417-358-3002
Cable Systems (3):
Missouri: Carthage, Lamar, Monett.
Total Basic Subscribers: 12,012 (0.02% of total cable households).
Total Pay Units: 3,231.
Other Holdings:
MDS, see listing.
Note: Sale pends to TCA Cable TV Inc.

ARTHUR J. KRAUS
Box 11
Manhattan, IL 60442
Phone: 815-357-6678
Cable Systems (3):
Illinois: Gardner, Manhattan, Seneca.
Total Basic Subscribers: 1,783.
Total Pay Units: 525.

KRM CABLEVISION
Box 648
Mellen, WI 54546
Phone: 715-274-7631
Cable Systems (10):
Wisconsin: Augusta, Butternut, Fall Creek, Fifield, Glidden, Greenwood, Hawkins (village), Mellen, Prentice, Stetsonville.
Total Basic Subscribers: N.A.

KUDZU CABLE TV INC.
Box 180-B
Rte. 6
Murphy, NC 28906
Phone: 704-494-4020
Officers:
Verner Free, Pres.
Ed Stark, Secy.
Ownership: Stewart Corbett, Verner Free & Ed Stark, 100% jointly. Corbett & Stark are also principals of Carolina Country Cable, see listing.
Cable Systems (1):
North Carolina: Ranger.
Total Basic Subscribers: 9.

KUESTER LAKE INC.
20 Kuesters Lake
Grand Island, NE 68801
Phone: 308-381-5501
Ownership: Robert D. Kutz.
Cable Systems (1):
Nebraska: Kuesters Lake.
Total Basic Subscribers: 69.

KUHN COMMUNICATIONS
Box 277
301 W. Main St.
Walnut Bottom, PA 17266
Phone: 717-532-8857
Ownership: Earl Kuhn.
Cable Systems (3):
Pennsylvania: Newburg, Orrstown, Walnut Bottom.
Total Basic Subscribers: N.A.

LAKE AREA TV CABLE
5203 E. Hwy. 45
Fort Smith, AR 72901
Phone: 501-648-1966
Ownership: Bob D. Griffith, Pres.
Cable Systems (1):
Oklahoma: White Horn Cove.
Total Basic Subscribers: 523.
Total Pay Units: 421.

LAKE REGION ELECTRIC
Box 341
Webster SD, 57274
Phone: 605-345-3379
Wireless Cable Systems (1):
South Dakota: Webster.
Total Basic Subscribers: N.A.

CITY OF LAKEFIELD PUBLIC UTILITIES
Box 1023
301 Main St.
Lakefield, MN 56150
Phone: 507-662-5457
Fax: 507-662-5990
Officers:
Stanley Sievert, Chmn.
Mark Steffen, Vice Chmn.
Mark Erickson, Secy.
Joni Hanson, Treas.
Cable Systems (1):
Minnesota: Lakefield.
Total Basic Subscribers: 715.
Total Pay Units: 161.

LAKELAND CABLE TV INC.
Box 118
Crowder, OK 74430
Phone: 918-334-6200
Officers:
Charles O. Smith, Chmn.
Janet Brooks, Secy.
Ownership: Charles Smith, Betty Smith & Orlean Smith, Principals. Charles Smith is Pres. & Gen. Mgr. and Betty Smith is exec. of the Canadian Valley Telephone Co., Crowder, OK.
Cable Systems (1):
Oklahoma: Canadian.
Total Basic Subscribers: 616.
Total Pay Units: 313.

ROGER LAMASTUS
Box 905
Pineville, WV 24874
Phone: 304-732-8626
Cable Systems (1):
West Virginia: Keyrock.
Total Basic Subscribers: N.A.

RICHARD LANDY
Box 453
Stowe, VT 05672
Phone: 802-253-9282
Cable Systems (2):
Vermont: Jeffersonville, Stowe.
Total Basic Subscribers: 160.

LAUREL CABLE LP
Box 42
Berlin, PA 15530
Phones: 814-443-6250; 800-732-5604
Cable Systems (1):
Pennsylvania: New Baltimore.
Total Basic Subscribers: 130.
Total Pay Units: 40.

LAUREL HIGHLAND TV CO.
Box 168
Stahlstown, PA 15687
Phone: 724-593-2411
Fax: 724-593-2423
Officers:
J. Paul Kalp, Pres.
Morgan F. Withrow, V.P. & Treas.
Mary Lou Barnhart, Secy.
Ownership: J. Paul Kalp, 37%; M. Graham Hunter, 25%; Mary Lou Barnhart, 19%; Morgan F. Withrow, 12%; William I. Piper, 6%.
Cable Systems (1):
Pennsylvania: Indian Creek.
Total Basic Subscribers: 3,817.
Total Pay Units: 1,075.

LEAF RIVER TELEPHONE CO.
Box 249
102 W. 2nd St.
Leaf River, IL 61047
Phone: 815-738-2211
Fax: 815-738-6060
Cable Systems (1):
Illinois: Leaf River.
Total Basic Subscribers: 121.
Total Pay Units: 64.

DON T. LEAP
Box 703
Hyndman, PA 15545
Phone: 814-842-3370
Cable Systems (1):
Pennsylvania: Londonderry Twp. (Bedford County).
Total Basic Subscribers: 130.
Total Pay Units: 30.

LEE'S CABLE INC.
Box 703
La Veta, CO 81055
Phone: 719-742-3000
Cable Systems (2):
Colorado: Cuchara Valley, La Veta.
Total Basic Subscribers: 206.

LEESBURG LAKESHORE MOBILE HOME PARK
1208 N. Lee St.
Leesburg, FL 34748
Phone: 904-787-6966
Ownership: Thomas N. Grizzard, 33%; Sally G. Reeves, 33%; Beverly Grizzard Trust, 34%.
Cable Systems (1):
Florida: Leesburg Lakeshore Mobile Home Park.
Total Basic Subscribers: 183.

LEHIGH SERVICES INC.
Box 137
Lehigh, IA 50557
Phone: 515-359-2211
Fax: 515-359-2424
Ownership: Lehigh Valley Cooperative Telephone Assn.
Cable Systems (1):
Iowa: Lehigh.
Total Basic Subscribers: 550.
Total Pay Units: 150.

LENFEST COMMUNICATIONS INC.
Box 989
200 Cresson Blvd.
Oaks, PA 19456-0989
Phone: 610-650-3000
Fax: 610-650-3011
Officers:
H. F. Lenfest, Chmn., Pres. & Chief Exec. Officer
Robert Lawrence, Exec. V.P.
Maryann Bryla, Sr. V.P., Treas. & Chief Financial Officer
Chris Patterson, Engineering V.P.
Samuel W. Morris Jr., Secy.
Ownership: H. F. Lenfest, & family, 50%; AT&T Broadband & Internet Services, 50%.
Represented (legal): Fleischman & Walsh LLP; Saul, Ewing & Saul Remick.
Cable Systems (25):
Delaware: Wilmington.
New Jersey: Cherry Hill 50%, Franklinville, Lambertville, Pleasantville, Salem, Turnersville, Vineland.
Pennsylvania: Bensalem Twp., Carlisle, Chambersburg, Chester County, Fort Loudon, Harrisburg, Hershey, Holland, Jamison, King of Prussia, Lancaster, McConnellsburg, Newtown, Norristown, Pottstown, Sellersville, Wallingford.
Total Basic Subscribers: 1,213,522 (1.77% of total cable households).
Total Pay Units: 712,486.
Other Holdings:
Cable interconnect: Radius Communications Inc.
Cable: Interest in Videopole, French cable co., 30% of Susquehanna Cable, see listing.
Note: Sale pends to Comcast Communications.

LENOX MUNICIPAL CABLEVISION
Box 96
Lenox, IA 50851
Phone: 515-333-2550
Cable Systems (1):

Iowa: Lenox.
Total Basic Subscribers: 525.
Total Pay Units: 132.

LEWIS COUNTY CABLE TV CO.

Box 90
Greig, NY 13345
Phone: 315-348-4033
Ownership: Robert Greiner, Pres. & Gen. Partner.
Cable Systems (2):
New York: Greig, Henderson (town).
Total Basic Subscribers: 875.
Total Pay Units: 343.

LEWISPORT TELEPHONE CO.

Box 338
Lewisport, KY 42351
Phone: 502-295-3232
Cable Systems (1):
Kentucky: Lewisport.
Total Basic Subscribers: 674.
Total Pay Units: 305.

LEXANDER CABLEVISION

Box 1681
Quincy, FL 32351-5681
Phone: 912-246-5937
Ownership: Alex Brown & Emerson Brown, 100% jointly.
Cable Systems (1):
Georgia: Whigham.
Total Basic Subscribers: N.A.

CITY OF LINCOLN

Box 172
Hwy. 78 W, Municipal Complex
Lincoln, AL 35096
Phone: 205-763-7777
Fax: 205-763-7394
Officers:
C. L. Watson, Chmn. & Chief Exec. Officer
L. Carmack, Chief Operating & Financial Officer
Ownership: Community owned.
Cable Systems (1):
Alabama: Lincoln.
Total Basic Subscribers: 1,384.
Total Pay Units: 487.

LINCOLN TELEPHONE CO.

Box 1
HCR-30
Lincoln, MT 59639
Phone: 406-362-4216
Officers:
John P. Mulcare, Pres.
Robert G. Orr, Chief. Exec. Officer
Richard L. Knight, Secy.-Treas.
Ownership: Stockholder owned.
Cable Systems (1):
Montana: Lincoln.
Total Basic Subscribers: 500.
Total Pay Units: 200.

LINCOLNVILLE COMMUNICATIONS INC.

Box 200
Lincolnville Center, ME 04850
Phone: 207-763-9900
Fax: 207-763-3028
Officers:
Jethro Pease, Chmn.
Shirley Manning, Pres. & Chief Exec. Officer
Ronald McIntyre, Chief Financial Officer
Ownership: Lincolnville Telephone Co.
Cable Systems (1):
Maine: Lincolnville.
Total Basic Subscribers: 835.
Total Pay Units: 280.
Other Holdings:
Telephone.

LIVERMORE CABLE

Box 163
806 Okoboji Ave.
Milford, IA 51351
Phone: 712-338-4967
Ownership: Cliff Plagman, Principal. Plagman also has interest in Milford Cable TV, see listing.
Cable Systems (1):
Iowa: Livermore.
Total Basic Subscribers: 150.

L.N. SATELLITE COMMUNICATIONS CO.

Box 97
Lost Nation, IA 52254
Phone: 319-678-2470
Fax: 319-678-2300
Officers:
Gerald Wirth, Pres.
Alvin Weirup, V.P.
Duane Rutenbeck, Secy.-Treas.
Ownership: Lost Nation-Elwood Telephone.
Cable Systems (1):
Iowa: Lost Nation.
Total Basic Subscribers: 308.
Total Pay Units: 71.
Other Holdings:
Telephone.

MARY S. LOAR

Box 222
Soper, OK 74759
Phone: 405-345-2898
Cable Systems (1):
Oklahoma: Soper.
Total Basic Subscribers: 98.

LOCKESBURG CABLEVISION

Box 14
Lockesburg, AR 71846
Phone: 501-289-3261
Officers:
Loyd E. Montgomery, Chmn.
Cliff Pounds, Chief Operating Officer
L. DeAnne Robbins, Chief Financial Officer
Ownership: Community owned.
Cable Systems (1):
Arkansas: Lockesburg.
Total Basic Subscribers: 313.
Total Pay Units: 140.

LOLITA CABLE TV INC.

Box 120
La Ward, TX 77970
Phone: 512-872-2362
Cable Systems (1):
Texas: Lolita.
Total Basic Subscribers: 298.
Total Pay Units: 155.

LONE PINE TV INC.

Box 867
310 Jackson St.
Lone Pine, CA 93545
Phone: 760-876-5461
Fax: 760-876-9101
Officers:
Bruce J. Branson, Chmn., Pres. & Secy.-Treas.
Timothy W. Branson, V.P. & Chief Operating Officer
Virgil J. Branson, Chief Financial Officer
Ownership: Bruce Branson & Timothy Branson.
Cable Systems (2):
California: Alabama Hills, Lone Pine.
Total Basic Subscribers: 724.
Total Pay Units: 250.

GENELLE LOTT

102 S. Hayden St.
Belzoni, MS 39038
Phone: 601-247-1834
Officers:
De Lott, Pres.
Genelle Lott, Secy.-Treas. & Chief Financial Officer
Cable Systems (1):
Mississippi: Belzoni.
Total Basic Subscribers: 625.

CITY OF LOWELL CABLE TV DEPT.

Box 229
127 N. Broadway
Lowell, MI 49331-0229
Phone: 616-897-8405
Fax: 616-897-4082
Ownership: Community owned.
Represented (legal): Dickinson, Wright, Moon, VanDuessen & Freeman.
Cable Systems (1):
Michigan: Lowell.
Total Basic Subscribers: 2,300.
Total Pay Units: 749.

LOWELL COMMUNITY TV CORP.

Box 364
Water St.
Lowell, OH 45744
Phone: 614-896-2626
Officers:
Dan Flickman, Pres.
Debbie Cline, Secy.-Treas.
Ownership: Subscriber owned.
Cable Systems (1):
Ohio: Lowell.
Total Basic Subscribers: 315.

LYNCH TV INC.

Box 698
Lynch, KY 40855
Phone: 606-848-2977
Officers:
Joe Takacs, Co-Chmn.
Carl Collins, Co-Chmn.
Linda Goins, Secy.-Treas. & Chief Financial Officer
Ownership: Non-profit organization.
Cable Systems (1):
Kentucky: Lynch.
Total Basic Subscribers: 369.
Total Pay Units: 48.

DAN MACY

Box 520
Warm Springs, OR 97761
Phone: 503-553-1597
Cable Systems (1):
Oregon: Warm Springs.
Total Basic Subscribers: N.A.

GILBERT MACY

630 Oak St.
Mansfield, OH 44907
Phone: 419-526-4591
Cable Systems (1):
Ohio: Greenfield Estates.
Total Basic Subscribers: N.A.

MADDOCK AREA DEVELOPMENT CORP.

Box 1
Maddock, ND 58348
Phone: 701-438-2541
Cable Systems (1):
North Dakota: Maddock.
Total Basic Subscribers: 205.
Total Pay Units: 127.

MADISON COMMUNICATIONS

Box 158
Hamel, IL 62046
Phone: 618-633-2267
Cable Systems (1):
Illinois: Staunton.
Total Basic Subscribers: 890.

MADISON COMMUNICATIONS INC.

216 S. Marion St.
Athens, AL 35611-2504
Phone: 256-536-3724
Wireless Cable Systems (1):
Alabama: Athens.
Total Basic Subscribers: N.A.

MAGNOLIA CABLE CO.

Box 7084
Tupelo, MS 38802
Phone: 601-844-3530
Officers:
Duncan Chalk, Pres.
Gerald Hanna, Secy.
Ownership: Duncan Chalk, Gerald Hanna & Tim Hester, Principals.
Cable Systems (2):
Mississippi: Artesia, Crawford.
Total Basic Subscribers: 100.

WILLIAM MAHOWALD

617 Arbor Ave.
Minot, ND 58701
Phone: 701-852-8288
Cable Systems (1):
North Dakota: Velva.
Total Basic Subscribers: 300.
Total Pay Units: 80.

KASMIR MAJEWSKI

356 Table Rock Lane
Warwood, WV 26003
Phone: 304-277-3314
Cable Systems (5):
Ohio: Barton 33.33%, Maynard, Powhaton Point.
West Virginia: Warwood, Windsor Heights.
Total Basic Subscribers: N.A.

MALLARD CABLEVISION

Box 1460
El Campo, TX 77437
Phone: 409-543-9711
Fax: 409-541-5592
Officer:
William R. Jenkins, Pres.
Ownership: William R. Jenkins & Mike Sydow.
Represented (legal): Verner Liipfert Bernhard McPherson & Hand.
Cable Systems (8):
Texas: Burleson, Gordon, Millsap, Palo Pinto, Perrin, River Oaks (Tarrant County), Santo, Willow Park.
Total Basic Subscribers: 5,000.
Total Pay Units: 1,783.

MANAWA TELECOM INC.

Box 130
Manawa, WI 54949

Phone: 414-596-2700
Fax: 414-596-3775
Officers:
Thomas R. Squires, Pres.
Robert E. Squires, V.P.
Brian J. Squires, Secy.-Treas.
Ownership: Manawa Telecommunications Inc.
Cable Systems (1):
Wisconsin: Manawa.
Total Basic Subscribers: 647.
Total Pay Units: 331.
Other Holdings:
Telephone.

MANILLA MUNICIPAL CABLE

Box 398
City Hall
Manilla, IA 51454
Phone: 712-654-2632
Officers:
Jon Uennink, Chief Exec. Officer
Charles Sahram, Chief Operating Officer
Ownership: Community owned.
Cable Systems (1):
Iowa: Manilla.
Total Basic Subscribers: 320.
Total Pay Units: 120.

MANNING MUNICIPAL COMMUNICATION & TV SYSTEM UTILITY

Box 386
719 3rd St.
Manning, IA 51455
Phone: 712-653-3214
Officer:
Dean Fara, Chmn.
Ownership: Community owned.
Cable Systems (1):
Iowa: Manning.
Total Basic Subscribers: 600.
Total Pay Units: 174.

MANNINGTON TV INC.

206 Pleasant St.
Mannington, WV 26582
Phone: 304-986-1650
Ownership: James A. Sturm, 50%; James A. Sturm Jr., 50%.
Cable Systems (1):
West Virginia: Mannington.
Total Basic Subscribers: 1,372.

MAPLETON COMMUNICATIONS INC.

513 Main
Mapleton, IA 51034
Phone: 712-882-1351
Fax: 712-882-2726
Officers:
Thomas LeFebvre, Chmn.
Betty Castle, Secy.-Treas.
Ownership: City owned.
Cable Systems (1):
Iowa: Mapleton.
Total Basic Subscribers: 538.
Total Pay Units: 206.

MARBLE CABLE TV SYSTEMS

Box 38
Marble, MN 55764
Phone: 218-247-7147
Officer:
Rodger L. Brown, Chmn.
Ownership: Community owned.
Cable Systems (1):
Minnesota: Marble.
Total Basic Subscribers: 374.
Total Pay Units: 149.

MARCUS CABLE—Sold to Charter Communications Inc. 1999.

MARK TWAIN RURAL TELEPHONE CO.

Box 68
Hurdland, MO 63547
Phone: 816-423-5211
Cable Systems (1):
Missouri: Brashear.
Total Basic Subscribers: 100.
Total Pay Units: 37.

MARK'S CABLEVISION

Box 535
9155-D Deschutes Rd.
Palo Cedro, CA 96073
Phone: 916-547-5438
Fax: 916-547-4948
Officer:
Sean M. Hogue, Regional Operations Mgr.
Cable Systems (7):
California: Bear Valley, Forest Falls, Hayfork, Lewiston, Palo Cedro, Tehama, Weaverville.
Total Basic Subscribers: 5,991.
Total Pay Units: 1,768.

MARNE & ELK HORN TELEPHONE CO.

Box 120
4242 Main St.
Elk Horn, IA 51531
Phone: 712-764-6161
Fax: 712-764-2773
Officers:
Merlyn Knudsen, Pres.
Dallas Hansen, V.P.
Leroy Pedersen, Secy.
Daryle Moeller, Treas.
Cable Systems (3):
Iowa: Elk Horn, Exira, Shelby.
Total Basic Subscribers: 1,114.
Total Pay Units: 416.

MARTELL TELECOMMUNICATIONS INC.

Box 1056
Glenns Ferry, ID 83623
Phone: 208-366-2700
Ownership: James R. Martell.
Cable Systems (1):
Idaho: Glenns Ferry.
Total Basic Subscribers: 397.
Total Pay Units: 125.

MARTELLE COOPERATIVE TELEPHONE ASSOCIATION

Box 128
204 South St.
Martelle, IA 52305
Phone: 319-482-2381
Fax: 319-482-3018
Officers:
John O. Miller, Pres.
Richard Strother, Secy.-Treas.
Ownership: Sandra Davis, Principal.
Cable Systems (1):
Iowa: Martelle.
Total Basic Subscribers: 495.
Total Pay Units: 294.

MARSHALL C. MARTIN

514 Forest Ave.
Luverne, AL 36049
Phone: 205-335-5059
Cable Systems (1):
Alabama: Luverne.
Total Basic Subscribers: 1,550.
Total Pay Units: 314.

M.A.S. CO.

Box 4005
Bisbee, AZ 85603-4005
Phone: 520-366-5608
Ownership: Kent Daniel Stoner.
Cable Systems (3):
Arizona: Bisbee Junction, Hereford, Moson Road.
Total Basic Subscribers: 179.
Total Pay Units: 71.

MASSILLON CABLE TV INC.

Box 1000
814 Cable Court NW
Massillon, OH 44648-1000
Phone: 330-833-4134
Fax: 330-833-7522
Officers:
Richard W. Gessner, Pres. & Treas.
Robert B. Gessner, V.P.
Susan R. Gessner, Secy.
Ownership: Richard W. Gessner & Susan R. Gessner, 54% jointly; 100 stockholders, each with less than 5%.
Represented (legal): Vorys, Sater, Seymour & Pease.
Cable Systems (2):
Ohio: Massillon, Wooster.
Total Basic Subscribers: 45,200 (0.07% of total cable households).
Total Pay Units: 11,840.

MASTERTECH INC.

Box 995
355 Broadway
Estacada, OR 97023
Phone: 503-630-2565
Ownership: Duane Day, Principal.
Cable Systems (1):
Oregon: Estacada.
Total Basic Subscribers: 913.
Total Pay Units: 320.

MASTERVISION CABLE CO.

Box 518
Tioga, PA 16946
Phone: 717-827-2259
Ownership: Chris Caldwell.
Cable Systems (1):
Pennsylvania: Bentley Creek.
Total Basic Subscribers: N.A.

WALTER MATKOVICH

Box 67
Powhatan, OH 43942
Phone: 614-795-5005
Cable Systems (3):
Ohio: Barton 33.33%, Maynard, Powhaton Point.
Total Basic Subscribers: 215.

MATRIX CABLEVISION INC.

12333 S. Saratoga-Sunnyvale Rd.
Saratoga, CA 95070
Phone: 408-253-6590
Officers:
Brad Daniel, Pres. & Chief Exec. Officer
Julie Daniel, Secy.-Treas.
Ownership: Brad Daniel.
Cable Systems (2):
California: Aldercroft Heights, Menlo Park.
Total Basic Subscribers: 913.
Total Pay Units: 380.

EDWARD MATTOX

Box 435
Parsons, KS 67357
Phone: 316-421-1577
Cable Systems (1):
Kansas: St. Paul.
Total Basic Subscribers: 192.
Total Pay Units: 100.

MAUI CABLEVISION CORP.

Suite 106
350 Ward Ave.
Honolulu HI, 96814-4004
Phone: 808-591-7787
Wireless Cable Systems (1):
Hawaii: Maui.
Total Basic Subscribers: N.A.

MAXTEL CABLEVISION

Palm Court, Suite 50
8600 Hidden River Pkwy.
Tampa, FL 33637
Phone: 813-978-8000
Fax: 813-971-6904
Officers:
Robert R. Swander, Chief Exec. Officer
Robert Moore, Chief Financial Officer

Branch Offices:

6330 E. 75th St.
Suite 306
Indianapolis, IN 46250
Phone: 317-576-8010

Eastern Region
5500 Oakbrook Pkwy.
Suite 275
Norcross, GA 30093
Phone: 404-446-8222
Ownership: Robert Swander, Principal.
Cable Systems (2):
Florida: Beverly Beach, Rima Ridge.
Total Basic Subscribers: 418.
Total Pay Units: 125.

MCA CABLE INC.

Box 978
Wise, VA 24293
Phone: 703-328-5248
Fax: 703-395-5713
Officers:
Freddie Dean, Pres. & Chief Exec. Officer
Don Green, Secy.-Treas.
Ownership: 28 local stockholders.
Represented (legal): William J. Sturgill & Assoc.
Cable Systems (1):
Virginia: Wise.
Total Basic Subscribers: 1,285.
Total Pay Units: 427.

GARFIELD McCLAIN

Box 8
118 Yocum St.
Evarts, KY 40828
Phone: 606-837-2505
Cable Systems (1):
Kentucky: Evarts.
Total Basic Subscribers: 750.

M. K. McDANIEL

Box 839
111 N. College St.
Georgetown, TX 78627
Phone: 512-869-1505
Fax: 512-869-2962
Cable Systems (4):
Texas: Georgetown 54%, Jarrell 54%, Leander 83%, Pflugerville 78%.
Total Basic Subscribers: 24,152 (0.04% of total cable households).
Total Pay Units: 7,267.

JOE McGEE

Box 117
Woodville, AL 35776
Phone: 256-533-0611
Cable Systems (1):
Alabama: Woodville.
Total Basic Subscribers: 161.

McNABB CABLE & SATELLITE INC.

Box 218
McNabb, IL 61335
Phone: 815-882-2202
Fax: 815-882-2141
Officers:
Leslie K. Troyon, Pres.
Brooks Whitney, Chief Financial Officer
Ownership: McNabb Telephone Co.
Cable Systems (4):
Illinois: Cedar Point, Kickapoo, Malden, McNabb.
Total Basic Subscribers: 354.
Total Pay Units: 214.

MCT COMMUNICATIONS INC.

2300 S. Chilton
Tyler, TX 75701
Phone: 214-825-2371
Officer:
John R. McGeehan, Chief Exec. Officer
Cable Systems (1):
New Hampshire: Warner Twp.
Total Basic Subscribers: 2,028.
Total Pay Units: 687.

JOSEPH McTAGUE

3301 Carmen Rd.
Schenectady, NY 12303
Phone: 518-658-9047
Fax: 518-584-6573
Ownership: Sold to Avalon Cable 1999.
Cable Systems (1):
New York: Berlin (town).
Total Basic Subscribers: 410.

MEAD ENTERTAINMENT & INFORMATION CABLE INC.

Box 593
339 4th St.
Mead, CO 80542
Phone: 303-535-4618
Cable Systems (1):
Colorado: Mead.
Total Basic Subscribers: 160.
Total Pay Units: 33.

MECHANICSVILLE TELEPHONE CO.

107 N. John
Mechanicsville, IA 52306
Phone: 319-432-7221
Fax: 319-432-7721
Officers:
William Woods, Pres.
Robert G. Horner, Secy.-Treas.
Cable Systems (1):
Iowa: Mechanicsville.
Total Basic Subscribers: 420.
Total Pay Units: 273.

MEDIA GENERAL INC.

Box 85333
Richmond, VA 23293-0001
Phones: 703-378-8400; 804-649-6103
Fax: 703-378-3498; 703-378-3840
Officers:
J. Stewart Bryan III, Chmn., Pres. & Chief Exec. Officer
Marshall N. Morton, Sr. V.P.
H. Graham Woodlief Jr., V.P.
Robert W. Pendergast, V.P.
George L. Mahoney, Secy.
Stephen R. Zacharias, Treas.
Media General Cable
Thomas E. Waldrop, Chmn. & Chief Exec. Officer
Don Mathison, Sr. V.P., Mktg. & Programming
Linda Clark, V.P., Human Resources
Janet Kohler Dueweke, Mktg. & Public Relations Dir.
David DeJesus, Chief Financial Officer
Ownership: Publicly held.
Represented (legal): Christian & Barton.
Cable Systems (2):
Virginia: Fairfax County, Fredericksburg.
Total Basic Subscribers: 259,149 (0.38% of total cable households).
Total Pay Units: 347,789.
Other Holdings:
TV, see listing.
Magazine: Virginia Business Magazine.
Newspapers.
Printing company: Beacon Press Inc.-Richmond.
Service company: Garden State Paper Company Inc. (Garfield, NJ), Southeast Paper Manufacturing Co. (33%), GSP Recycling Corp. (Elmwood Park, NJ).
Finance service: Media General Financial Services-Richmond.
Note: Cable holdings sold to Cox Communications Inc. 1999.

MEDIACOM LLC

100 Crystal Run Rd.
Middletown, NY 10941
Phone: 914-695-2600
Fax: 914-695-2699
Web site: http://www.mediacomllc.com
Officers:
Rocco B. Commisso, Pres. & Chief Exec. Officer
Joseph Van Loan, Sr. V.P., Technology
Italia Commisso-Weinard, Sr. V.P., Programming & Human Resources
Jim Carey, Sr. V.P., Operations
John Pascarelli, V.P., Mktg.
Mark Stephen, Chief Financial Officer
Ownership: Rocco B. Commisso, Principal.
Represented (legal): Fleischman & Walsh LLP.
Cable Systems (155):
Alabama: Ardmore, Atmore, Big Cove, Brewton, Camden, Citronelle, Daphne, Evergreen, Greensboro, Gulf Shores, Huntsville, Jackson, Linden, Livingston, McIntosh, Mobile County, Monroeville, Mount Vernon, Robertsdale, Satsuma, Spanish Cove, Thomasville.
Arizona: Ajo, Nogales, Rio Rico.
California: Clearlake Oaks, Kern River Valley, Ridgecrest, Sun City, Valley Center.
Delaware: Dagsboro.
Florida: Alligator Point, Apalachicola, Bonifay, Cape San Blas, Carrabelle, Eastpoint, Greensboro, Gretna, Gulf Breeze, Havana, Mexico Beach, Milton, Sandestin Beach Resort, Southport, St. Georges Island, Tyndall AFB, Vernon, Walton County (southern portion), Wewahitchka.
Illinois: Cobden, Coulterville, Mounds, Red Bud, Zeigler.
Kansas: Altoona, Baldwin City, Burlington, Eureka, Galena, Hamilton, Madison, Osage City, Oswego, Thayer, Toronto.
Kentucky: Albany, Bremen, Burkesville, Cadiz, Edmonton, Elkton, Gilbertsville, Hardin, Marion, Munfordville, Nebo, Nortonville, Oak Grove, Pembroke, Princeton, Tompkinsville.
Mississippi: Beaumont, Decatur, Houston, Louisville, Lucedale, Newton, Pearlington, Pontotoc, St. Andrews, Union, Water Valley, Waveland, Wiggins.
Missouri: Alba, Albany, Anderson, Appleton City, Archie, Ava, Bethany, Billings, Brunswick, Butler, Cabool, Cameron, Carl Junction, Carrollton, Caruthersville, Cassville, Crane, Diamond, Duquesne, Everton, Excelsior Springs, Forsyth, Goodman, Granby, Jasper, Kimberling City, Liberal, Lowry City, Mansfield, Marceline, Marshfield, Norborne, Osceola, Purdy, Richmond, Rogersville, Salisbury, Sarcoxie, Seymour, Strafford.
North Carolina: Arrowhead Beach, Camden County, Columbia, Conway, Currituck County (southern portion), Edenton, Franklin, Hendersonville, Lansing, Nebo, Plymouth, Powellsville, Rich Square, Sparta, Sylva, West Jefferson, Windsor.
Oklahoma: Picher.
Tennessee: Dover, Huntland.
Total Basic Subscribers: 360,000 (0.53% of total cable households).
Total Pay Units: 412,000.

MEDIAONE GROUP

5th Floor
188 Inverness Dr. W
Englewood, CO 80112
Phone: 303-858-3404
Fax: 303-858-3445
Officers:
Chuck Lillis, Chmn. & Chief Exec. Officer
Roger Christensen, Exec. V.P. & Chief Administrative Officer
Frank Eichler, Exec. V.P., Law and Public Policy & Gen. Counsel
Doug Holmes, Exec. V.P., Strategy & Business Development
Patti Klinge, Exec. V.P. & Chief Human Resources Officer
Rick Post, Exec. V.P. & Chief Financial Officer
Bud Wonsiewicz, Sr. V.P. & Chief Technical Officer
Ownership: Publicly held.
Cable Systems (160):
California: Banning, Carson, Compton, Corona, Costa Mesa, Covina, Cypress, Downey, Fresno, Hanford, Kyburz, Lake Elsinore, Lakewood, Lodi, Los Angeles, Manteca, Mendota, Parlier, Placerville, Pomona, Reedley, San Andreas, Sanger, Santa Clarita, Selma, Stockton, Strawberry, Tulare, Tustin, Wilmington, Yuba City.
Florida: Bonita Springs, Callahan, Crescent City, Everglades City, Fernandina Beach, Hastings, Hialeah, Hilliard, Jacksonville, Jacksonville Beach, Lake Butler, MacClenny, Naples, Orange Park, Pine Island, Plantation, Pompano Beach, Ponte Vedra Beach, Sanibel Island, Waldo, Welaka.
Georgia: Atlanta, Folkston, Nahunta, Woodstock.
Idaho: Aberdeen, American Falls, Fairfield, Filer, Oakley.
Illinois: Dolton, Elmhurst, Freeport, Kewanee, Lincoln, Morton, Morton Grove, Pekin, Peotone, Quincy, Rolling Meadows, Romeoville.
Massachusetts: Amherst, Andover, Attleboro 49%, Bernardston, Beverly, Brockton 99%, Cambridge, Chester, Conway, Dedham, Fairhaven, Foxborough, Hopkinton, Lawrence, Longmeadow, Lowell, Marion, Marlborough, Mashpee, Medford, Middleborough, Milford, Nantucket, Natick, New Bedford, Newburyport, Newton, North Andover, North Attleboro, Orleans, Phillipston, Quincy, Saugus, Scituate, South Yarmouth, Springfield, Sterling, Stoughton, Taunton, Waltham, Watertown, Westfield, Weymouth, Winchendon, Woburn.
Michigan: Ann Arbor, Birmingham, Brighton, Brooklyn (Irish Hills), Dearborn, Dearborn Heights, Eaton Rapids, Hazel Park, Holland, Jackson, Lansing, Madison Heights, Plymouth, Romulus, Roseville, Saline, Southfield, Summit-Leoni, Wayne, West Bloomfield Twp.
Minnesota: Brooklyn Park, Roseville, St. Croix, St. Paul.
Missouri: Lake St. Louis.
New Hampshire: Concord, Derry, Hampstead, Manchester, Nashua, Portsmouth.
New York: Ossining.
Ohio: Amherst, Bay Village, Elyria, Fairborn, Mentor, Springfield, Vandalia.
Virginia: Henrico County, Richmond 90%, Yorktown.
Total Basic Subscribers: 4,966,000 (7.24% of total cable households).
Total Pay Units: 4,181,600.
Cable Holdings:
25.51% of Time Warner Entertainment Co. LP, majority owner of Time Warner Cable, see listing.
Other Holdings:
Program source: 50% of New England Cable News, 11% of Viewer's Choice.
International Cable: 29.99% of Telewest (United Kingdom), 25% of Telenet (Belgium), 97% of Cable Plus (Czech Republic), 25% of TITUS (Japan), 19.14% of Chofu Cable (Japan), 25% of Singapore Cablevision, 35% of PT ARIAWEST International (fixed wireline).
Note: Sale pends to AT&T Broadband & Internet Services.

MEDIAPOLIS CABLEVISION CO.

652 Main St.
Mediapolis, IA 52637
Phone: 319-394-3996
Fax: 319-394-9155
Officer:
William Malcom, Gen. Mgr.
Ownership: Mediapolis Telephone Co.
Cable Systems (1):
Iowa: Mediapolis.
Total Basic Subscribers: 657.
Total Pay Units: 493.

MERCOM INC.— Sold to Avalon Cable 1998.

MERRIMAC AREA CABLE

327 Palisade St.
Merrimac, WI 53561
Phone: 608-493-9470
Fax: 608-493-9902
Officer:
Bart Olson, Chmn.
Ownership: Bartlett Olson & Charlotte Olson, 100% jointly.
Represented (legal): Bartlett Olson.
Cable Systems (1):
Wisconsin: Merrimac.
Total Basic Subscribers: 425.
Total Pay Units: 171.

METROCAST CABLEVISION OF NEW HAMPSHIRE LLC

9 Apple Rd.
Belmont, NH 03220
Phones: 603-524-4425; 800-952-1001
Fax: 603-524-5190
Officers:
Bill Luby, Pres.
Terry Hicks, V.P.
Ownership: Communications Equity Associates Inc., 33.33%; Adelphia Communica-

tions Corp., see listing, 33.33%; TL Ventures, 33.33%.
Cable Systems (5):
New Hampshire: Alton, Deerfield, Franklin, Laconia, Pittsfield.
Total Basic Subscribers: 28,991 (0.04% of total cable households).
Total Pay Units: 6,568.

JOHN METZLER
Box 535
Beulah, MI 49617-0535
Phone: 616-882-7969
Cable Systems (1):
Michigan: Thompsonville/Copemish.
Total Basic Subscribers: 96.

MEYERHOFF CABLE SYSTEMS
Box 340
Mi-Wuk Village, CA 95346
Phone: 209-586-7622
Ownership: Rich Meyerhoff, Principal.
Cable Systems (2):
California: Long Barn, Pinecrest.
Total Basic Subscribers: 737.

MICROCOM INC.
Box 2108
Saginaw, MI 48605-2108
Phone: 517-777-8852
Fax: 517-777-8862
Officer:
David A. Bradford, Pres. & Chief Exec. Officer
Represented (legal): Pepper & Corazzini.
Wireless Cable Systems (2):
Michigan: Bay City & Saginaw, Midland.
Total Basic Subscribers: 3,200.
Total Pay Units: 1,600.
Other Holdings:
MDS, see listing.

MICROLINK TELEVISION
Suite 2
1325 W. 16th St.
Yuma, AZ 85364-4496
Phone: 520-783-2345
Ownership: Cardiff Communications Partners II, see listing in MMDS Ownership.
Wireless Cable Systems (1):
Arizona: Yuma.
Total Basic Subscribers: N.A.

MICROWAVE CABLE CORP.
1700 S. Morris Ave.
Bloomington IL, 61701
Phone: 309-829-9949
Fax: 309-829-2870
Wireless Cable Systems (1):
Illinois: Bloomington.
Total Basic Subscribers: 3,100.

MICROWAVE COMMUNICATION SERVICES
Suite 900
400 Perimeter Center Terrace NE
Atlanta, GA 30346
Phone: 404-804-6448
Fax: 404-409-0060
Officer:
Larry Bowman, Pres.
Wireless Cable Systems (5):
Arizona: Flagstaff.
New Mexico: Roswell.
North Carolina: Wilmington.
North Dakota: Grand Forks, Minot.
Total Basic Subscribers: N.A.

MICROWAVE DISTRIBUTION SERVICES INC.
Box 640
Ignacio, CO 81137-0640
Phone: 303-563-9593
Fax: 303-563-9381
Officers:
Christopher L. May, Pres.
Nancy Howley, Secy.
Represented (legal): Christopher L. May.
Cable Systems (2):
Colorado: Ignacio, Sunnyside.
Total Basic Subscribers: 320.
Total Pay Units: 307.

MID AMERICAN CABLE SYSTEMS
Box 71279
Des Moines, IA 50325
Phone: 800-320-5581
Officers:
Ken Anderson, Chmn.
Jay R. Eliason, Pres.
Don McConkey, Secy.-Treas. & Chief Financial Officer
Ownership: Jay Eliason, Principal. Eliason also has interest in Illinet Communications of Central Illinois Inc., Illini Cablevision of Illinois Inc., New Path Communications LC, TelePartners, Telnet Communications & Westcom LC, see listings.
Cable Systems (70):
Illinois: Bonfield (village), Burlington (village), Caledonia, Chemung, Cortland (village), Garden Prairie, Grand Detour, Grant Park (village), Hebron (village), Hooppole, La Moille (village), Lee (village), Long Point (village), Magnolia (village), Mazon (village), Ohio, Pawpaw (village), Ringwood, Seatonville (village), Shady Oaks Trailer Park, Sheridan (village), South Wilmington (village), Spring Grove (village), Steward (village), Troy Grove (village).
Indiana: Amboy, Andrews, Ashley, Claypool, Clear Lake, Francesville, Gaston, Hamlet, Hillsboro, Hoagland, Kewanna, Kingman, Kouts, La Fontaine, Lagro, Malden, Markle, Matthews, Medaryville, Mellot, Mentone, Orland, Perrysville, Royal Center, San Pierre, Shipshewana, Somerset, Topeka, Urbana, Van Buren, Walton, Waveland, Westville, Wheatfield, Yoder, Zanesville.
Iowa: Albion, Alta Vista (town), Colesburg, Ely, Ionia, Union, Walford (town).
Michigan: Montgomery.
Wisconsin: Sugar Creek (town).
Total Basic Subscribers: 12,319 (0.02% of total cable households).
Total Pay Units: 6,452.
Cable Holdings:
Galaxy American Communications, see listing.

MID COAST CABLE TV INC.
1905 W. Loop
Box 1269
El Campo, TX 77437
Phone: 409-543-6858
Officers:
Clive Runnells, Chmn.
J. H. Landrum, V.P.
Ownership: Clive Runnells, Principal.
Represented (legal): Dow, Lohnes & Albertson PLLC.
Cable Systems (3):
Texas: Blessing, El Campo, Louise.
Total Basic Subscribers: 4,310.
Total Pay Units: 1,078.

MIDCONTINENT COMMUNICATIONS
Suite 1100
7900 Xerxes Ave. S
Minneapolis, MN 55431
Fax: 612-844-2660
Officers:
N. L. Bentson, Chmn. & Chief Exec. Officer
Joseph H. Floyd, Pres. & Chief Operating Officer
Mark S. Niblick, Exec. V.P.
Patrick McAdaragh, V.P., Operations
Rick Reed, V.P., Engineering & Technical Operations
Dick Busch, V.P., Information Technology
Steven E. Grosser, Corporate Controller
Rod Carlson, Dir., Community Relations
Lee Johnson, Dir., Mktg.
Leigh Anglin, Dir., Advertising Sales
Ownership: Midcontinent Media Inc.
Represented (legal): Dow, Lohnes & Albertson PLLC.
Cable Systems (157):
Minnesota: Hallock, Oslo, Sabin.
Montana: Fairview.
Nebraska: Ainsworth, Cody, Long Pine, Naper, O'Neill, Springview, Valentine.
North Dakota: Alexander, Anamoose, Aneta, Arthur, Ashley, Beach, Belfield, Beulah, Binford, Bisbee, Bismarck 50%, Bottineau, Bowman, Buffalo, Burlington, Buxton, Cando, Carrington, Casselton, Center, Columbus, Cooperstown, Crosby, Devils Lake, Dodge, Drake, Drayton, Dunseith, Edmore, Esmond, Fairmount, Fessenden, Gackle, Galesburg, Garrison, Gladstone, Glen Ullin, Glenburn, Golden Valley, Goodrich, Grafton, Grandin, Halliday, Hankinson, Hannaford, Harvey, Harwood, Hatton, Hazen, Hebron, Hettinger, Hillsboro, Hope, Horace, Hunter, Kenmare, Kensal, Killdeer, La Moure, Langdon, Lansford, Leeds, Lehr, Leonard, Lidgerwood, Lignite, Linton, Mapleton, Max, Mayville, McClusky, Minnewaukan, Minot AFB, Mohall, Mott, Napoleon, New Rockford, New Salem, Page, Pick City, Portland, Reeder, Reynolds, Rhame, Richardton, Riverdale, Rolette, Rolla, Rugby, Ruthville, Scranton, Selfridge, Solen, South Heart, St. John, Stanton, Starkweather, Streeter, Surrey, Thompson, Tioga, Towner, Turtle Lake, Underwood, Walhalla, Washburn, Watford City, Willow City, Wilton, Wimbledon, Wishek, Zap, Zeeland.
South Dakota: Aberdeen, Bath, Bowdle, Bristol, Buffalo, Canton, Doland, Faith, Fort Pierre, Frederick, Gettysburg, Huron, Ipswich, Java, Lemmon, McIntosh, McLaughlin, Miller, Mina, Mitchell 50%, Pierre, Redfield, Roscoe, Roslyn, Selby, Sioux Falls 50%, St. Lawrence, Timber Lake, Warner, Waubay, Webster, Winner, Wolsey.
Total Basic Subscribers: 131,577 (0.19% of total cable households).
Total Pay Units: 53,450.

MID-HUDSON CABLEVISION INC.
Box 399
200 Jefferson Heights
Catskill, NY 12414
Phone: 518-943-6600
Fax: 518-943-6603
Officers:
James M. Reynolds, Chief Exec. Officer
Stuart W. Smith, Operations Mgr.
Anthony J. Bajoreck, Chief Financial Officer
Cable Systems (1):
New York: Catskill.
Total Basic Subscribers: 19,500 (0.03% of total cable households).
Total Pay Units: 18,250.

MID-IOWA COMMUNICATIONS INC.
Box 13
Gilman, IA 50106
Phone: 515-498-7701
Fax: 515-498-7308
Officer:
Don Jennings, Mgr.
Cable Systems (1):
Iowa: Gilman.
Total Basic Subscribers: 1,079.
Total Pay Units: 453.
Other Holdings:
Telephone.

MID-KANSAS CABLE SERVICES INC.
Box 960
109 N. Christian Ave.
Moundridge, KS 67107
Phone: 316-345-2831
Fax: 316-345-6106
Officers:
Carl Krehbiel, Pres.
Kathryn Krehbiel, Secy.-Treas.
Ownership: Carl C. Krehbiel Trust, 50%; Kathryn Krehbiel Trust, 50%.
Cable Systems (2):
Kansas: Goessel, Moundridge.
Total Basic Subscribers: 433.
Total Pay Units: 114.
Other Holdings:
Telephone.
Cellular radio.

MID-MISSOURI TELEPHONE CO.
Box 38
Pilot Grove, MO 65276
Phone: 816-834-3311
Fax: 816-834-6632
Officer:
Harold A. Jones, Chief Exec. Officer
Cable Systems (2):
Missouri: Bunceton, Pilot Grove.
Total Basic Subscribers: 387.
Total Pay Units: 223.

MID SOUTH CABLE TV INC.
Box 910
McKenzie, TN 38201
Phones: 901-352-2980; 800-541-4208
Fax: 901-352-3533
Officer:
Gary Blount, Pres.
Ownership: Gary Blount, Paul Field & Dave Pardonner, Principals.
Represented (legal): Fleischman & Walsh LLP.
Cable Systems (3):
Tennessee: Celina, Eagleville, Pleasant Hill.
Total Basic Subscribers: 4,861.
Total Pay Units: 755.

MID-SOUTH CABLEVISION CO.
Box 136
Rienzi, MS 38865-0136
Phone: 601-568-3310
Ownership: Rochester Telephone Co.
Cable Systems (1):
Mississippi: Rienzi.
Total Basic Subscribers: 148.
Total Pay Units: 41.
Other Holdings:
Telephone.

MID-STATE COMMUNITY TV INC.

1001 12th St.
Aurora, NE 68818
Phone: 402-694-5101
Fax: 402-694-2848
Officers:
Phillip C. Nelson, Pres.
Betty Van Luchene, Secy.
Ownership: Phillip C. Nelson. Nelson is Pres. of the Hamilton Telephone Co., Aurora, NE.
Cable Systems (6):
Nebraska: Aurora, Doniphan, Giltner, Hordville, Marquette, Trumbull.
Total Basic Subscribers: 2,108.
Total Pay Units: 569.

MIDVALE TELEPHONE EXCHANGE INC.

Box 7
Midvale, ID 83645
Phone: 208-355-2211
Fax: 208-355-2222
Officers:
Lane Williams, Pres. & Chief Operating Officer
Mary Williams, Chief Financial Officer
Cable Systems (1):
Idaho: Midvale.
Total Basic Subscribers: 60.
Total Pay Units: 16.

MIDWAY CABLE TV CO.

Box 1034
Hays, KS 67601
Phone: 913-625-8900
Ownership: Patrick Dechant, 50%; Ron Legleiter, 50%.
Cable Systems (7):
Kansas: Abbyville, Canton, Cunningham, Iuka, Marquette, Sylvia, Turon.
Total Basic Subscribers: 1,056.
Total Pay Units: 325.

MIDWEST CABLE

Box 399
Sparta, WI 54656
Phone: 608-269-6247
Ownership: Roger H. Alderman, Principal.
Cable Systems (2):
Wisconsin: Bloomingdale, Melvina.
Total Basic Subscribers: 64.
Total Pay Units: 14.

MIDWEST CABLE COMMUNICATIONS INC.

Box 337
314 3rd St.
Bemidji, MN 56601
Phone: 218-751-5507
Ownership: Jon P. Langhout, Pres.
Cable Systems (2):
Minnesota: Bemidji, Cass Lake.
Total Basic Subscribers: 5,523.
Total Pay Units: 1,644.

MIDWEST VIDEO ELECTRONICS INC.

Box 6478
Rochester, MN 55903-6478
Phone: 507-287-0880
Officers:
Patricia A.P. Likos, Pres.
Richard H. Plunkett Jr., V.P.
Pamela Kyzer, Secy.
Ownership: Plunkett Children's Trust, 66.6%; Irene Dohrmann & John Dohrmann, 33.3% jointly.
Cable Systems (1):
Wisconsin: Rhinelander.
Total Basic Subscribers: 8,300.
Total Pay Units: 2,297.

MIKE'S TV INC.

Box J
Morton, WA 98356
Phone: 360-496-5635
Fax: 360-496-5635
Officers:
Esper M. Fairhart, Pres. & Chief Exec. Officer
Shirley M. Fairhart, V.P.
Sheryl K. Fairhart, Secy.-Treas.
Ownership: Esper M. Fairhart, 51%; Shirley M. Fairhart, 49%.
Represented (legal): William Boehm.
Cable Systems (1):
Washington: Morton.
Total Basic Subscribers: 647.
Total Pay Units: 174.

MILE HI CABLE PARTNERS LP

1617 S. Acoma St.
Denver, CO 80223
Phone: 303-778-2978
Fax: 303-778-2912
Ownership: Robert Johnson.
Cable Systems (1):
Colorado: Denver.
Total Basic Subscribers: 450,000 (0.66% of total cable households).
Total Pay Units: 94,517.

MILESTONE COMMUNICATIONS LP

Suite 200
1850 Woodmoor Dr.
Monument, CO 80132
Phone: 719-488-2916
Fax: 719-488-3629
Officers:
Michael W. Drake, Pres.
Valerie Drake, Secy.
Ownership: Milestone Media Management Inc., Gen. Partner; Michael W. Drake, Ltd. Partner; 25 E. Erie Corp., Ltd. Partner. MMMI ownership: Michael W. Drake, Principal.
Represented (legal): Bienstock and Clark.
Cable Systems (12):
New York: Burlington (town), Cuyler, Durham, Otselic, Summit.
Pennsylvania: Canoe Creek, Hartslog, McAlevys Fort, Warriors Mark.
West Virginia: Cass, Durbin, Marlinton.
Total Basic Subscribers: 4,000.

MILFORD CABLE TV

Box 163
806 Okoboji Ave.
Milford, IA 51351
Phone: 712-338-4967
Cable Systems (1):
Iowa: Milford.
Total Basic Subscribers: 900.

MILLENNIUM DIGITAL MEDIA LLC

Suite 150
120 S. Central
Clayton, MO 63105
Phone: 314-802-2400
Fax: 314-802-2300
Officers:
Charles J. Payer Jr., Chmn.
Kelvin R. Westbrook, Pres. & Chief Exec. Officer
John K. Brooks, Chief Operating Officer
Peter C. Smith, Sr. V.P., Mktg.
J. Richard Beard, Sr. V.P., Operations
Thomas G. Jordan, Sr. V.P., Business Development
Steven S. Cochran, V.P. & Controller
Jeffrey C. Saunders, Chief Financial Officer

Branch Offices:

406 Headquarters Dr.
Millersville, MD 21108
Phone: 410-987-8400

Central Region
2598 Lansing Rd.
Charlotte, MI 48813
Phone: 517-543-1245

Northwest Region
3633 136th Place SE
Suite 107
Bellevue, WA 98006-1451
Phone: 425-747-4600
Ownership: Jeff Brooks, Chuck Payer Jr., Jeff Sanders & Kelvin Westbrook.
Cable Systems (58):
Idaho: Buhl, Castleford, Hagerman, Hazelton, Richfield, Shoshone.
Maryland: Millersville.
Michigan: Albion, Bath, Charlotte, Clarksville, Concord, Eagle Twp., Grass Lake, Hastings, Lake Odessa, Leslie, Marshall, Mason, Olivet, Pewamo, Portland, Potterville, Saranac, South Lyon, Sunfield, Twin Lake, Union City, Vermontville, Watertown Twp. (Clinton County), Williamston.
Oregon: Depoe Bay, Rose Lodge, Siletz, Southbeach.
Washington: Anderson Island, Brewster, Bucoda, Carson, Chelan, Concrete, Darrington, Duvall, Entiat, Forks, Glenoma, Kala Point, Lake Bay, Marblemount, Napavine, Packwood, Pe Ell, Port Townsend, Seattle (Central District), Twisp, Vader, Waterville, Whidbey Island.
Total Basic Subscribers: 144,000 (0.21% of total cable households).
Total Pay Units: 96,700.
Other Holdings:
Data service: OneNet Communications Inc., Northwest Link.

MARY E. MILLER

3190 Bahia Vista
Sarasota, FL 33580
Phone: 813-959-4501
Cable Systems (1):
Florida: Saralake Estates.
Total Basic Subscribers: 191.

RAY V. MILLER GROUP

1000 Pensacola Hwy.
Burnsville, NC 28714
Phone: 704-682-4074
Fax: 704-682-6895
Officers:
Ray V. Miller, Chmn.
Randall Miller, Pres.
Bryan Hyder, Secy.-Treas.
Represented (legal): Dusenbury, Hendricks & Little; Cole, Raywid & Braverman LLP.
Cable Systems (3):
North Carolina: Atlantic Beach, Burnsville.
South Carolina: Briarcliff Acres.
Total Basic Subscribers: 9,635.
Total Pay Units: 8,496.
Other Holdings:
Cable Network: Interest in "The Outdoor Channel".
Telecommunications company: Interest in World Multicast.Com Inc.

V. DAVID & BILLIE LYNN MILLER

Box 509
Warner, OK 74469
Phone: 918-463-2921
Fax: 918-463-2551
Represented (legal): Mike Norman.
Cable Systems (1):
Oklahoma: Warner.
Total Basic Subscribers: 407.
Total Pay Units: 216.

MILLERSBURG TV CO.

Box 66
804 Plum St.
Millersburg, PA 17061
Phone: 717-692-4772
Officers:
William B. Helwig, Chief Exec. Officer
David Hawley, Dir. & Secy.
Ownership: David Hawley, 20%; Thomas Long, 20%; Robert E. Woodside, 20%; William Helwig, 20%; Donald Miller, 20%.
Represented (legal): Fleischman & Walsh LLP.
Cable Systems (1):
Pennsylvania: Millersburg.
Total Basic Subscribers: 4,620.
Total Pay Units: 390.

MILLHEIM TV TRANSMISSION CO.

Box 365
Millheim, PA 16854
Phone: 814-349-5394
Officers:
Earl Heckman, Pres.
Harold Benfer, Secy.-Treas.
Ownership: Subscriber owned.
Cable Systems (1):
Pennsylvania: Millheim.
Total Basic Subscribers: 372.
Total Pay Units: 342.

MILLINGTON CATV INC.

Box 399
5115 Easley
Millington, TN 38083
Phone: 901-872-3600
Fax: 901-872-6703
Officers:
Holly Starnes, Pres.
Laura Howard, Secy.

Branch Office:

Munford, TN 38058
Phone: 901-873-3131
Ownership: Holly Starnes, 25%; 3 others, each with 25%.
Represented (legal): J. Houston Gordon.
Cable Systems (1):
Tennessee: Millington.
Total Basic Subscribers: 7,700.
Total Pay Units: 3,369.

MIM CABLE

Box 834
Fair Bluff, NC 28439
Phone: 919-649-7112
Ownership: Gloria Martinez & Mike Martinez, 100% jointly.
Cable Systems (1):
North Carolina: Fair Bluff.
Total Basic Subscribers: N.A.

MINBURN CABLEVISION INC.

Box 206
416 Chestnut St.
Minburn, IA 50167-0206

Phone: 515-677-2100
Fax: 515-677-2007
Officers:
Richard H. Cockrum, Pres.
William Wright, V.P.
Karen P. Taylor, Secy.-Treas.
Ownership: Minburn Telephone Co.
Cable Systems (1):
Iowa: Minburn.
Total Basic Subscribers: 104.
Total Pay Units: 69.

MINDEN CABLEVISION

Box 107
Avoca, IA 51521
Phone: 712-343-3007
Ownership: Kenny Hertz.
Cable Systems (1):
Iowa: Minden.
Total Basic Subscribers: 130.
Total Pay Units: 100.

MINERVA VALLEY CABLEVISION INC.

104 N. Pine
Zearing, IA 50278
Phone: 515-487-7399
Fax: 515-487-7611
Cable Systems (1):
Iowa: Zearing.
Total Basic Subscribers: 207.

MOBILE LIMITED LIABILITY

4123A Government Blvd.
Mobile, AL 36693
Phone: 334-602-1000
Fax: 334-602-1009
Wireless Cable Systems (1):
Alabama: Mobile.
Total Basic Subscribers: 500.
Total Pay Units: 450.

MOBILE PARK PROPERTIES INC.

950 Ridgewood Ave.
Venice, FL 33595
Phone: 813-485-5441
Ownership: English S. Deschamps, 13%; James M. Doss, 13%; Fred H. Lindstrom, 13%; John M. Miller, 13%; Wesley L. Peterson, 13%; Latimer Turner, 13%; Leo H. Wilson, 13%; Stuart W. Gregory, 7%.
Cable Systems (1):
Florida: Bay Indies Mobile Home Park.
Total Basic Subscribers: 1,309.
Total Pay Units: 70.

MOFFAT COMMUNICATIONS LTD.

4103 W. Lake Houston Pkwy.
Houston, TX 77339
Phones: 204-788-3440; 281-360-7500
Fax: 204-956-2710; 281-360-1320
Officers:
Randall L. Moffat, Chmn. & Pres.
William A. Davis, V.P., Finance
Steve Wotherspoon, Dir., Finance
Ownership: Privately held.
Cable Systems (6):
Florida: Palm Coast, Pasco County (central & eastern portions).
Texas: Conroe West, Kingwood, Shepherd, Walden.
Total Basic Subscribers: 59,114 (0.09% of total cable households).
Total Pay Units: 19,517.
Other Holdings:
Canadian cable: Flin Flon, Snow Lake, Thompson & Winnipeg, MB; Atikokan, Dryden & Fort Frances, ON.; Winnipeg Videon Ltd., cable system owner.
Cable Network: 68.4% of WTN-Women's Television Network.
Broadcast holdings: See CKY-TV, Winnipeg, MB in Canadian TV Stations.

JAMES MOGG TV

Box 328
Cheyenne, OK 73628
Phone: 405-497-2157
Officers:
James M. Mogg, Pres.
Lura Mae Mogg, V.P.
Ownership: James M. Mogg, 50%; Lura Mae Mogg, 50%.
Cable Systems (1):
Oklahoma: Cheyenne.
Total Basic Subscribers: 404.

MONROE AREA COMMUNICATIONS INC.

Box 130
140 S. 5th St.
Monroe, OR 97456
Phone: 503-847-5135
Officers:
John H. Dillard, Chmn.
John T. Dillard, Pres.
Donna M. Dillard, Secy.-Treas.
Ownership: Monroe Telephone Co.
Cable Systems (1):
Oregon: Monroe.
Total Basic Subscribers: 300.
Total Pay Units: 123.
Other Holdings:
Telephone.

JAMES A. MONROE

9795 E. Caron
Scottsdale, AZ 85258-5602
Phone: 602-391-1904
Fax: 602-451-7712
Cable Systems (2):
Arizona: San Carlos.
California: Julian.
Total Basic Subscribers: 1,787.
Total Pay Units: 935.

LAJUNTA K. MONROE

Box 100
San Carlos, AZ 85550
Phone: 602-475-2550
Fax: 602-451-7712
Cable Systems (1):
Arizona: San Carlos.
Total Basic Subscribers: 1,100.
Total Pay Units: 850.

CITY OF MONROE, WATER, LIGHT & GAS COMMISSION

Box 725
215 N. Broad St.
Monroe, GA 30655
Phone: 770-267-3429
Fax: 770-267-3698
Officers:
Eugene Kelly Jr., Chmn.
Mark S. Ennis, Pres.
Michele A. Bowman, Financial Mgr.
Ownership: Community owned.
Represented (legal): Benton & Preston PC.
Cable Systems (1):
Georgia: Monroe.
Total Basic Subscribers: 5,091.
Total Pay Units: 3,383.

MONTROSE MUTUAL TELEPHONE CO.

Box 4
Dieterich, IL 62424
Phone: 217-925-5246
Cable Systems (3):
Illinois: Dieterich, Montrose, Shumway.
Total Basic Subscribers: 239.

MONUMENT TV

Box 85
Loganton, PA 17747
Phone: 717-725-2733
Officer:
Earnest Hanley, Pres.
Ownership: Community owned.
Cable Systems (1):
Pennsylvania: Monument.
Total Basic Subscribers: N.A.

DAVID P. MOONEY

Box 1004
111 Marshall
Gilmer, TX 75644
Phone: 903-843-5597
Represented (legal): Cole, Raywid & Braverman LLP.
Cable Systems (5):
Arkansas: Hope 5.72%, Hot Springs 20%, Prescott 20%.
Texas: East Mountain, Gilmer.
Total Basic Subscribers: 29,385 (0.04% of total cable households).
Total Pay Units: 9,510.

GENE MOOS

Box 191
Ashland, MT 59003
Phone: 406-436-2820
Cable Systems (1):
Montana: Ashland 50%.
Total Basic Subscribers: 225.
Total Pay Units: 95.

MOOSEHEAD ENTERPRISES INC.

Main St.
Greenville, ME 04441
Phone: 207-695-3337
Officers:
Scott Richardson, Chmn. & Chief Exec. Officer
Earl Richardson Jr., Pres. & Chief Operating & Financial
Ownership: Earl Richardson.
Cable Systems (2):
Maine: Guilford, Jackman.
Total Basic Subscribers: 967.
Cable Holdings:
Manages cable system in Pleasant Ridge Plantation, ME.
Other Holdings:
SMATV.

MOREHEAD STATE UNIVERSITY

Box 916
Morehead, NC 40351
Phone: 606-783-2141
Cable Systems (1):
Kentucky: Morehead State University.
Total Basic Subscribers: N.A.

WAYNE E. MORGAN

85 Cordell Lane
Coos Bay, OR 97420
Phone: 503-267-4788
Cable Systems (1):
Oregon: Greenacres.
Total Basic Subscribers: 129.

CITY OF MORGANTON

201 W. Meeting St.
Morganton, NC 28655
Phone: 704-438-5353
Officer:
Tom Peeler, Chief Exec. Officer
Ownership: Community owned.
Cable Systems (1):
North Carolina: Morganton.
Total Basic Subscribers: 6,734.
Total Pay Units: 2,947.

MORO TV CLUB

Box 371
Moro, OR 97039
Phone: 541-565-3353
Officers:
Larry Triebelhorn, Pres.
Ernie Moore, First V.P.
Eileen Moreau, Second V.P.
Jerrilea Mayfield, Secy.
Larry Hoctor, Treas.
Ownership: Community owned.
Cable Systems (1):
Oregon: Moro.
Total Basic Subscribers: 127.
Total Pay Units: 127.

MOULTRIE TELECOMMUNICATIONS INC.

Box 350
199 S. Broadway
Lovington, IL 61937
Phone: 217-873-5215
Fax: 217-873-4990
Officer:
David A. Bowers, Pres.
Represented (legal): John V. Freeman.
Cable Systems (1):
Illinois: Lovington.
Total Basic Subscribers: 486.
Total Pay Units: 202.

MOUNT DUTTON CABLE CORP.

Box 38
King Cove, AK 99612
Phone: 907-497-2346
Fax: 907-497-2444
Officer:
Kenneth Mack, Chmn. & Chief Exec. Officer
Ownership: King Cove Corp.
Represented (legal): Wagstaff, Pope & Rogers.
Cable Systems (1):
Alaska: King Cove.
Total Basic Subscribers: 125.
Total Pay Units: 125.

MOUNTAIN CABLE

Box 1271
Clifton, CO 81520
Phone: 970-434-4249
Fax: 970-434-1571
Ownership: Arnold Moore, 50%; Diana Moore, 50%.
Cable Systems (1):
Colorado: Collbran.
Total Basic Subscribers: 120.
Total Pay Units: 56.

MOUNTAIN CABLE SYSTEMS INC.

Box 761
Pikeville, KY 41502
Phone: 606-631-1890
Officer:
A. R. Phillips, Pres.
Ownership: Publicly held.

Cable Systems (1):
Kentucky: Upper Johns Creek.
Total Basic Subscribers: 106.

MOUNTAIN VIEW CABLE
Box 1254
Angels Camp, CA 95222
Phone: 209-728-2349
Fax: 209-728-1512
Ownership: Mountainview Cable, 75%; Robert Casanieda, 25%.
Cable Systems (1):
California: Copper Cove Copperopolis.
Total Basic Subscribers: N.A.

MOUNTAIN ZONE TV SYSTEMS
Box 1377
307 East Ave. E
Alpine, TX 79831
Phone: 915-837-2300
Fax: 915-837-5423
Officers:
Janet Neu, Pres.
Lawrence Neu, Secy.
Steve Neu, Treas.
Ownership: Janet Neu, Principal.
Represented (legal): Kenneth DeHart.
Cable Systems (6):
Texas: Balmorhea, Fort Davis, Marathon, Marfa, Presidio, Valentine.
Total Basic Subscribers: 1,823.
Total Pay Units: 222.

M-TEK SYSTEMS
Box 109
200 Lake Dr.
Redwood Falls, MN 56283
Phone: 507-637-8351
Fax: 507-637-8351
Officers:
LuVerne Maserek, Chmn.
Magdalen Maserek, Chief Financial Officer
Ownership: LuVerne Maserek, 50%; Magdalen Maserek, 50%.
Cable Systems (8):
Minnesota: Belview, Clements, Comfrey, Courtland, Echo, Hanska, Nicollet, Wood Lake.
Total Basic Subscribers: 958.
Total Pay Units: 100.

MULLAN TV CO.
Box 615
202 2nd St.
Mullan, ID 83846
Phone: 208-744-1223
Officers:
John F. Erickson, Chmn. & Pres.
William Lindroos, Secy.-Treas.
Ownership: Non-profit organization.
Cable Systems (1):
Idaho: Mullan.
Total Basic Subscribers: 357.
Total Pay Units: 174.

MULLINVILLE CABLE TV
Box 92
Mullinville, KS 67109
Phone: 316-548-2537
Officers:
Ron Freeman, Pres.
Scott Brown, V.P.
Paul Kendall, Secy.
Ownership: Rick Sherer, Scott Brown, Paul Kendall, Ron Freeman, Paul Hayse, Marvin Price, Don Douglass & others, percentages undisclosed.
Cable Systems (1):
Kansas: Mullinville.
Total Basic Subscribers: 111.

MULTICHANNEL TV INC.
Box 41
200 W. Commercial St.
Miami, TX 79059
Phone: 806-868-3151
Officer:
Robert Tipps, Pres.
Cable Systems (1):
Texas: Miami.
Total Basic Subscribers: 225.
Total Pay Units: 162.

MULTIMEDIA CABLEVISION INC.
Box 3027
701 E. Douglas
Wichita, KS 67201
Phone: 316-262-4270
Fax: 316-262-2309
Officers:
Mike Burrus, Pres.
David P. Fleming, V.P. & Gen. Counsel
Steve Yates, V.P. & Business Mgr.
Patsy Selby, V.P., Programming & Corp. Administration
Cliff Waggoner, V.P., Technology & Development

Branch Offices:
Rocky Mount, NC 27801
Phone: 252-443-4019
Fax: 252-443-5932
Bruce Mears, V.P. & Regional Mgr.

820 W. Irish Lane
Edmond, OK 73083
Phone: 405-348-5750
Fax: 405-348-8059
Terry Gorsuch, V.P. & Regional Mgr.
Ownership: Gannett Broadcasting Group. see listing in Commercial TV Station Ownership.
Cable Systems (69):
Kansas: Andover, Arkansas City, Auburn, Augusta, Buhler, Cheney, Coffeyville, Dodge City, El Dorado, Garden City, Goddard, Great Bend, Harper, Haven, Herington, Hutchinson, Inman, Iola, Junction City, Kingman, Kinsley, La Crosse, Lyons, Manhattan, McPherson, Medicine Lodge, Newton, Nickerson, Ottawa, Pauline, Peabody, Pittsburg, Pratt, Rose Hill, Salina, Sharon, Shawnee County (northern portion), Tecumseh, Topeka, Wichita, Winfield.
North Carolina: Clinton, Enfield, Greenville, Kinston, New Bern, Parmele, Rocky Mount, Scotland Neck, Tarboro, Washington.
Oklahoma: Bethany, Chickasha, Choctaw, Crescent, Del City, Edmond, El Reno, Guthrie, Lindsay, Midwest City, Moore, Mustang, Newkirk, Nichols Hills, Norman, Pauls Valley, Warr Acres, Yukon.
Total Basic Subscribers: 515,451 (0.75% of total cable households).
Total Pay Units: 302,632.
Note: Sale to Cox Communications Inc. pends.

MULTIMEDIA DEVELOPMENT CORP.
9500 Montgomery NE
Suite 121
Albuquerque, NM 87111
Phone: 505-237-0525
Fax: 505-237-0575
Officers:
Hazel Mickelson, Chmn.
Walter K. Mickelson, Pres.
Thor Mickelson, Secy.-Treas.
Ownership: Hazel Mickelson & Walter K. Mickelson, 73% jointly; Les Gutierrez & Veronica Gutierrez, 23% jointly; Bill Simons & Terri Simons, 2% jointly; Thor Mickelson, 2%. The Mickelsons are also execs. of Santa Fe Wireless Cable TV, see listing.
Represented (legal): Rini, Coran & Lancellotta PC.
Cable Systems (2):
New Mexico: Estancia, Mountainair.
Wireless Cable Systems (1):
New Mexico: Albuquerque.
Total Cable Subscribers: 327.
Total Pay Units: 149.
Other Holdings:
MDS, MMDS, see listing.

MULTI-TECH COMMUNICATIONS
Box 219
Sligo, PA 16255
Phone: 814-745-2426
Ownership: Donald McCall & Richard McHenry, Principals.
Cable Systems (4):
Pennsylvania: Clintonville, Limestone, Monterey, Ninevah.
Total Basic Subscribers: 2,117.
Total Pay Units: 211.

JOHN MURAGLIA
Box 839
111 N. College St.
Georgetown, TX 78627
Phone: 512-869-1505
Cable Systems (4):
Texas: Georgetown 41%, Jarrell 41%, Leander 12%, Pflugerville 12%.
Total Basic Subscribers: 24,152 (0.04% of total cable households).
Total Pay Units: 7,267.

LUKE MURPHY
6449 Hwy. 140
Midpines, CA 95345
Phone: 209-966-3895
Cable Systems (1):
California: Midpines.
Total Basic Subscribers: 70.
Total Pay Units: 20.

MURRAY CABLE TV INC.
108 W. Peoria St.
Paola, KS 66071
Phone: 913-294-3961
Ownership: Gene Murray, Principal.
Cable Systems (3):
Kansas: Fontana, Greeley, Rantoul.
Total Basic Subscribers: 380.

MYVOCOM
Box 127
Manila, UT 84046
Phone: 801-784-3175
Ownership: Patrick Asbill & Sandy Asbill, 100% jointly.
Cable Systems (1):
Utah: Manila.
Total Basic Subscribers: N.A.

NASHVILLE WIRELESS CABLE INC.
Suite 408
475 Metroplex Dr.
Nashville, TN 37211
Phone: 615-333-9288
Fax: 615-333-5983
Officers:
Henry Hunter, Pres.
Jim Feeney, Chief Financial Officer
Wireless Cable Systems (1):
Tennessee: Nashville.
Total Basic Subscribers: 2,973.

NATIONAL CABLE
Suite 106-A
5151 Reed Rd.
Columbus, OH 43220
Phones: 614-442-5890; 800-582-0504
Fax: 614-457-2567
Cable Systems (49):
Georgia: Avera, Browns Crossing, Oconee.
Kansas: Arcadia, Blue Mound, Buffalo, Lane, Mound Valley, Parker, Prescott, Uniontown, Walnut.
Missouri: Chilhowee.
Ohio: Bladensburg, Martinsburg, Mount Eaton, Winesburg.
Texas: Ackerly, Anderson, Arrowhead Addition, Ben Bolt, Buckholts, Coleto Creek, Cranfills Gap, Ellinger, Fentress, Flat, Floresville, Garwood, Gause, Golinda, Green Acres/Zion Hill, Iola, Kempner, Moulton, Mound, New Ulm, Nordheim, Nursery, Realitos, Rio Vista, Sandia, Sheridan, Smiley, Snook, Tuleta, Waelder, Walnut Springs, Westhoff.
Total Basic Subscribers: 2,505.

NDW II INC.
Suite 200
200 Chisholm Place
Plano, TX 75075
Phone: 405-924-4638
Wireless Cable Systems (1):
Kentucky: Paducah.
Total Basic Subscribers: N.A.
Other Holdings:
MMDS, see listing.

CITY OF NEGAUNEE CABLE TV
Box 70
City Hall, Silver St.
Negaunee, MI 49866
Phone: 906-475-7700
Fax: 906-475-0178
Ownership: Community owned.
Represented (legal): Tom Solka.
Cable Systems (1):
Michigan: Negaunee.
Total Basic Subscribers: 1,298.
Total Pay Units: 333.

JAMES NEHIL
3921 Tupelo Dr.
Midland, MI 48642
Phone: 517-832-2235
Cable Systems (1):
Michigan: Beaverton.
Total Basic Subscribers: 602.
Total Pay Units: 327.

NELSON COUNTY CABLEVISION CORPORATION
Box 395
Lovingston, VA 22949
Phone: 804-263-4805
Fax: 804-263-4821
Officers:
Joe Lee McClellan, Chmn. & Pres.
W. Burkes Fortune, V.P. & Treas.
Ownership: Joe Lee McClellan.
Cable Systems (2):
Virginia: Scottsville, Wintergreen.
Total Basic Subscribers: 342.
Total Pay Units: 154.

NELSONVILLE TV CABLE INC.
One W. Columbus St.

Nelsonville, OH 45764
Phone: 614-753-2686
Officers:
Eugene R. Edwards, Pres.
Betty Edwards, Secy.-Treas.
Ownership: Eugene R. Edwards, 99.6%; Betty Edwards, 0.4%.
Cable Systems (1):
Ohio: Nelsonville.
Total Basic Subscribers: 6,500.
Total Pay Units: 2,427.

NEPSK INC.

Box 1149
Presque Isle, ME 04769
Phone: 207-764-4461
Fax: 207-764-5329
Officers:
Peter P. Kozloski, Pres.
Catherine Donovan, V.P., Chief Financial Officer
Carole M. Kozloski, V.P.

Branch Office:

Box 610
Houlton, ME 04730
Phone: 207-532-2579
Fax: 207-532-4025
Ownership: Peter P. Kozloski.
Cable Systems (8):
Maine: Danforth, Houlton, Howland, Island Falls, Medway, Monticello (town), Oakfield, Patten.
Total Basic Subscribers: 4,369.
Total Pay Units: 766.
Other Holdings:
TV, see listing.

NET CABLE INC.

Box 568
122 S. St. Augustine St.
Pulaski, WI 54162-0568
Phone: 920-822-8121
Fax: 920-822-8665
Officers:
Patrick D. Riordan, Exec. V.P. & Chief Exec. Officer
Robert H. Riordan, Exec. V.P.
Mark Naze, Chief Financial Officer
Ownership: Northeast Communications of Wisconsin Inc. Affiliated with Northeast Telephone Co., Pulaski, WI.
Represented (legal): Vande Castle and Warpinski.
Cable Systems (1):
Wisconsin: Pulaski.
Total Basic Subscribers: 875.
Total Pay Units: 344.

NETWORK CABLE INC.

12507 263rd Ave. SE
Monroe, WA 98272
Phone: 800-526-9924
Fax: 360-794-7958
Officers:
Debra Kolrud, Pres.
Connie Hooker, V.P.
Ownership: Debra Kolrud, 50%; Connie Hooker, 50%.
Cable Systems (1):
Washington: Maxwelton.
Total Basic Subscribers: 450.

NEW ENGLAND CABLEVISION INC.

Box 7437
121 Free St.
Portland, ME 04112
Phone: 207-842-5400
Fax: 207-842-5410
Officers:
Lee Stanley, Pres. & Chief Exec. Officer
Timothy Baker, V.P. & Controller
Paul Clancy, Treas.
Ownership: Diversified Communications Inc., see listing in Ownership of LPTV Stations & Commercial TV Stations.
Represented (legal): Irwin, Campbell & Tannenwald PC.
Cable Systems (2):
Maine: Sanford.
New Hampshire: Rochester.
Total Basic Subscribers: 25,756 (0.04% of total cable households).
Total Pay Units: 11,336.

NEW ENGLAND CABLEVISION OF MASSACHUSETTS INC.

38 Blackburn Center
Gloucester, MA 01930
Phone: 508-281-0811
Fax: 508-281-8679
Ownership: William Russell & Jack Pierce, Principals.
Cable Systems (2):
Massachusetts: Amesbury, Gloucester.
Total Basic Subscribers: 25,615 (0.04% of total cable households).
Total Pay Units: 13,945.

NEW ENGLAND WIRELESS INC.

Box 470
Rte. 5 S
Ascutney, VT 05030
Phone: 802-674-2206
Fax: 802-674-2751
Officers:
Alan R. Ackerman, Chmn.
Scott A. Wendel, Pres. & Chief Exec. Officer
Michael Tedesco, Chief Operating Officer
Lorry A. Lachapelle, Secy.-Treas.
Harold Doran, Chief Financial Officer

Branch Office:

Route 15
Box 218
Jericho, VT 05465
Phone: 802-899-1301
Wireless Cable Systems (1):
Vermont: Mount Ascutney.
Total Basic Subscribers: N.A.
Other Holdings:
LPTV, MDS, MMDS, see listings.

NEW HOPE TELEPHONE COOPERATIVE

Box 452
New Hope, AL 35760
Phone: 205-723-4211
Officers:
Loyd Atchley, Pres.
Billy Tucker, V.P.
Johnny Cobb, Secy.
Bobby Salmon, Treas.
Cable Systems (2):
Alabama: Grant, New Hope.
Total Basic Subscribers: 3,000.
Total Pay Units: 1,250.

NEW KNOXVILLE TELEPHONE CO.

301 West St.
New Knoxville, OH 45871
Phone: 419-753-2457
Fax: 419-753-2950
Officers:
Preston Meyer, Chief Exec. Officer
John H. Hoge, Secy.-Treas.
Cable Systems (1):
Ohio: New Knoxville.
Total Basic Subscribers: 1,172.
Total Pay Units: 197.

NEW PARIS TELEPHONE CO.

Box 7
New Paris, IN 46553
Phone: 219-831-2225
Officers:
Mark Grady, V.P.
Myrna Rapp, Chief Financial Officer
Cable Systems (1):
Indiana: New Paris.
Total Basic Subscribers: 1,607.
Total Pay Units: 400.

NEW PATH COMMUNICATIONS LC

Bldg. 6
11260 Aurora Ave.
Urbandale, IA 50322
Phone: 515-276-3069
Fax: 515-270-9181
Officers:
Ken Anderson, Chmn.
Jay Eliason, Pres.
Ken Thompson, V.P.
Donald McConkey, Chief Financial Officer
Ownership: Jay Eliason, Principal. Eliason also has interest in Illinet Communications of Central Illinois Inc., Illini Cablevision of Illinois Inc., Mid American Cable Systems, TelePartners, Telnet Communications & Westcom LC, see listings.
Cable Systems (178):
Illinois: Adair (unincorporated areas), Bardolph, Beaverville Twp., Biggsville, Boody, Bryant (village), Cisco (village), Donovan Twp., Gays (village), Henning (village), Iroquois (village), Joy, Keithsburg, Kirkwood, La Place, Lerna, Martinton (village), New Boston, Penfield, Prairie City, Redmon, Royal, Sadorus, Seymour (village), Smithfield, Table Grove, Thawville, Vermillion (village), West Union, White Heath.
Indiana: Arlington, Birdseye, Bretzville, Brooklyn, Cataract Lake, Center Point, Chrisney, Cloverdale, Coal City, Corunna, Crane, Dana, Decker, Dubois County, Dupont, Economy, Freetown, Gentryville, Glenwood, Greens Fork, Griffin, Hardinsburg, Hayden, Hill Lake Resorts, Hillsdale, Holland, Holton, Homer, Kimmel, Knapp Lake, Lake Santee, Larwill, Laurel Twp., Leavenworth, Leiters Ford, Liberty Mills, Loon Lake, Merom, Metamora, Miami, Milroy, Mongo, Monterey, Montgomery, Morristown, Newport, Oliver Lake, Otwell, Owensburg, Paint Mill Lake, Patricksburg, Pine Village, Pretty Lake, Roann, Royer Lake, Spurgeon, Talma, Trafalgar, Twelve Mile, Twin Lakes, Waldron, West Lebanon, Westpoint, Yankeetown, Young America.
Iowa: Adair, Afton, Alexander, Batavia, Bridgewater, Bronson, Chester, Crawfordsville, Crescent, Cumberland, Danbury, Donnellson, Fonda, Goodell (village), Grandview, Gravity, Hastings, Henderson, Holland, Hornick, Joice (village), Lawton, Ledyard (village), Letts, Lincoln, Little Sioux, Logan, Lytton, Massena, Milton, Mondamin, Muscatine County, Newell, Oakville, Orient, Pacific Junction, Pisgah, Pomeroy, Prescott, Rake (village), Randolph, Rowan (village), Rowley (village), Salem, Smithland, Swaledale (village), Underwood, Whiting, Winfield, Woodbine.
Kentucky: Corinth, Cromwell, Island, Lafayette, Nelson, Pleasant Ridge, Rochester, Slaughters, Welchs Creek.
Michigan: Allen (village), Amboy Twp., Cambria Twp., Camden Twp., Gilead, Kinderhook Twp., Matteson Lake Twp., Sherwood Twp.
Missouri: Barnard, Bolckow, Burlington Junction, Clarksdale, De Kalb, Faucett, Grant City, Holt, Hopkins, King City, Mound City, Osborn, Stanberry, Trimble, Westboro.
Ohio: Scott (village).
Total Basic Subscribers: 15,467 (0.02% of total cable households).
Total Pay Units: 2,662.
Cable Holdings:
Galaxy American Communications, see listing.

NEW ULM TELECOM INC.

400 2nd St. N
New Ulm, MN 56073-1600
Phone: 507-354-4111
Fax: 507-354-1982
Cable Systems (4):
Minnesota: Jeffers, Lake Wilson, Sanborn, Wabasso.
Total Basic Subscribers: 733.
Total Pay Units: 145.

NEW WILMINGTON BOROUGH CABLE TV

134 High St.
New Wilmington, PA 16142
Phone: 412-946-8167
Ownership: Community owned.
Cable Systems (1):
Pennsylvania: New Wilmington.
Total Basic Subscribers: 900.
Total Pay Units: 198.

CITY OF NEWBERRY

Box 368
Newberry, FL 32669
Phone: 904-472-2473
Ownership: Community owned.
Cable Systems (1):
Florida: Newberry.
Total Basic Subscribers: 700.
Total Pay Units: 200.

NEWBURG CABLE TV SYSTEM

Box K
2nd & Main St.
Newburg, MO 65550
Phone: 314-762-2315
Ownership: Community owned.
Cable Systems (1):
Missouri: Newburg.
Total Basic Subscribers: 250.

TOM NEWMAN

Box 3
Waterfall, PA 16689
Phone: 814-685-3464
Cable Systems (1):
Pennsylvania: Waterfall.
Total Basic Subscribers: 288.

NEWS PRESS & GAZETTE CO.

Box 29
825 Edmond St.
St. Joseph, MO 64502
Phone: 816-271-8500
Fax: 816-271-8695
Officers:
Henry H. Bradley, Chmn., V.P. & Treas.
David R. Bradley Jr., Pres., Editor & Publisher
Lyle E. Leimkuhler, V.P., Finance & Secy.
Ownership: David R. Bradley Jr.; Henry H. Bradley.

Cable Systems (13):
Arizona: Bullhead City, Flagstaff, Kingman, Lake Havasu City, Munds Park, Parker, Payson, Pine, Sedona.
California: Blythe, Mammoth Lakes.
Missouri: Macon, St. Joseph.
Total Basic Subscribers: 115,000 (0.17% of total cable households).
Total Pay Units: 38,134.
Other Holdings:
TV, see listing.
Newspapers, radio.

NIAGARA COMMUNITY TV CO-OP
Box 136
1117 Main St.
Niagara, WI 54151
Phone: 715-251-1526
Fax: 715-251-1527
Officers:
Mike Westrich, Pres.
Bill Collinson, V.P.
Lori Tanko, Secy.
Bruce Nygard, Treas.
Ownership: Subscriber owned.
Cable Systems (1):
Wisconsin: Niagara.
Total Basic Subscribers: 792.
Total Pay Units: 200.

JOHN NICKLE
Box 415
Lovell, WY 82431
Phones: 307-548-6111; 406-356-7518
Cable Systems (2):
Montana: Baker 33.3%.
Wyoming: Lovell.
Total Basic Subscribers: 1,421.
Total Pay Units: 166.

NITTANY MEDIA INC.
Box III
Lewistown, PA 17044
Phone: 717-248-3733
Ownership: Harry J. Hain & Anna A. Hain, Principals. Hains have application for TV station for State College, PA.
Cable Systems (10):
Pennsylvania: Beavertown, Granville Twp., Ickesburg, McAlisterville, McClure, Mifflintown, New Bloomfield, Old Port, Port Royal, Thompsontown.
Total Basic Subscribers: 653.

JOHN NORCUTT
Suite 800
5335 Wisconsin Ave. NW
Washington, DC 20015
Phone: 202-364-3511
Cable Systems (1):
District of Columbia: Bolling AFB.
Total Basic Subscribers: 1,449.
Other Holdings:
Cable: Norcutt is principal of OnePoint Communications, see listing.

NORDLY'S TELECOM INC.
Box 133
414 Florence Ave.
Lowry, MN 56349
Cable Systems (1):
Minnesota: Lowry.
Total Basic Subscribers: N.A.

NORMAN & ASSOCIATES INC.
Box 870227
Stone Mountain, GA 30087-0006
Phone: 904-263-1442
Officers:
Dale H. Norman, Pres.
Debi F. Norman, Chief Financial Officer
Ownership: Dale H. Norman.
Cable Systems (2):
Alabama: Gordon.
Florida: Campbellton.
Total Basic Subscribers: 181.
Total Pay Units: 68.

NORTH AMERICAN CABLEVISION
No. F
13240 S Ave.
Chicago, IL 60633
Phone: 312-221-7200
Cable Systems (1):
Indiana: La Porte Mobile Home Park.
Total Basic Subscribers: N.A.

NORTH AMERICAN COMMUNICATIONS CORP.
Box 387
Hector, MN 55342
Phones: 612-848-6231; 800-982-8038
Fax: 612-848-2702
Officers:
Curtis A. Sampson, Chmn.
Avis J. Johnson, V.P., Administration & Secy.
Paul N. Hanson, Chief Financial Officer
Ownership: Hector Communications Corp.
Represented (legal): Lindquist & Vennum.
Cable Systems (29):
Minnesota: Big Falls, Bigfork, Bovey, Cologne, Delavan, Dexter, Easton, Eitzen, Fountain, Garden City, Green Isle, Hayward, Kelliher, Lewisville, Madison Lake, Mapleview, Mayer, New Auburn, New Market, Ostrander, Plato, Racine, Red Rock, Rose Creek, Vernon Center, Warsaw, Washington Twp., Wykoff.
Wisconsin: Hudson (town).
Total Basic Subscribers: 3,848.
Total Pay Units: 399.

NORTH BONNEVILLE COMMUNITY CABLE TV SYSTEM
Box 7
North Bonneville, WA 98639
Phone: 509-427-8182
Fax: 509-427-7214
Ownership: Community owned.
Represented (legal): Kielpinski & Woodrich.
Cable Systems (1):
Washington: North Bonneville.
Total Basic Subscribers: 187.
Total Pay Units: 46.

NORTH STAR CABLE INC.
Box 169
Fremont, MI 49412-0169
Phones: 616-924-8060; 800-443-0758
Fax: 616-924-4882
Officer:
Charles Lathrop, Pres.
Ownership: Charles Lathrop, Pres.
Cable Systems (3):
Michigan: Freeport, Lewiston, Mears.
Total Basic Subscribers: 1,804.

NORTH TEXAS COMMUNICATIONS CO.
Drawer 587
250 N. Walnut St.
Muenster, TX 76252
Phone: 940-736-2255
Fax: 940-759-5557
Officers:
Alvin M. Fuhrman, Pres. & Mgr.
Gene Fuhrman, Dir., Operations
Ellen Grace Fuhrman, Dir., Administration & Finance
Ownership: Alvin M. Fuhrman, 50%; Ellen G. Fuhrman, 50%. Fuhrmans are affiliated with the Muenster Telephone Corp., Muenster, TX.
Cable Systems (4):
Texas: Collinsville, Lake Kiowa, Muenster, Valley View.
Total Basic Subscribers: 1,995.
Total Pay Units: 542.

NORTH VALLEY CABLE SYSTEMS INC.
Box 303
Waterbury, VT 05676
Phone: 802-476-6357
Cable Systems (1):
Vermont: Williamstown (portions).
Total Basic Subscribers: 18.

NORTHEAST CABLE TV
Box 4095
Youngstown, OH 44515
Phone: 216-793-7434
Ownership: Albert F. Pezzenti.
Cable Systems (4):
Ohio: Brookfield Twp. (Trumbull County), Hubbard Twp. (Trumbull County), Warren Twp. (Trumbull County), Weathersfield Twp. (Trumbull County).
Total Basic Subscribers: N.A.

NORTHEAST IOWA TELEPHONE CO.
113 N. Page
Monona, IA 52159
Phone: 319-539-2111
Fax: 319-539-2003
Officers:
Ronald Sass, Pres.
Arlyn Schroeder, Secy-Treas.
Cable Systems (1):
Iowa: Monona.
Total Basic Subscribers: 830.
Total Pay Units: 365.

NORTHEAST LOUISIANA TELEPHONE CO. INC.
Drawer 185
6403 Howell Ave.
Collinston, LA 71229
Phone: 318-874-7011
Fax: 318-874-2041
Officers:
Rector L. Hopgood, Pres.
Tim Andrews, Chief Operating Officer
William A. Norsworthy, V.P.
William M. George, Treas.
Dorothy Anne George, Secy.
Ownership: Rector L. Hopgood, 50%; William A. Norsworthy, 50%.
Cable Systems (1):
Louisiana: Collinston.
Total Basic Subscribers: 374.
Total Pay Units: 291.

NORTHEAST TV COOPERATIVE
Box 850
7 8th Ave. SE
Watertown, SD 57201-0850
Phone: 605-886-5706
Wireless Cable Systems (4):
South Dakota: Huron, Sisseton, Watertown, Willow Lake.
Total Basic Subscribers: N.A.

NORTHERN CABLE CO. INC.
Box 267
Ontonagon, MI 49953
Phone: 906-884-2037
Ownership: Ralph Baker & Scott Baker, 100% jointly.
Cable Systems (1):
Michigan: Mass City.
Total Basic Subscribers: 320.

NORTHERN ELECTRIC COOPERATIVE INC.
Hwy. 12
Box 488
Bath, SD 57427
Phone: 605-225-0310
Fax: 605-229-5927
Officers:
Dale Engelhart, Chmn. & Pres.
Dennis W. Hagny, Chief Exec. Officer
Wireless Cable Systems (1):
South Dakota: Aberdeen & Bath.
Total Basic Subscribers: 2,199.
Total Pay Units: 640.
Other Holdings:
MMDS, see listing.

NORTHERN LAKES CABLE TV
Box 8
Bonduel, WI 54107
Phone: 715-758-2500
Ownership: Charles Mullen, 50%; Robert Steichen, 50%.
Cable Systems (5):
Wisconsin: Bear Creek, Elcho (town), Goodman, Laona, White Lake.
Total Basic Subscribers: 668.

NORTHERN LIGHTS CABLE CORP.
Box 127
Presque Isle, WI 54557
Phone: 715-686-2938
Officers:
Carl F. Forster, Pres.
Mrs. H. O. Reitch, V.P.
Betty D. Hollingsworth, Secy.-Treas.
Cable Franchises (1):
Wisconsin: Sayner.
Total Basic Subscribers: N.A.

NORTHLAND COMMUNICATIONS CORP.
Suite 3600
1201 3rd Ave.
Seattle, WA 98101
Phone: 206-621-1351
Fax: 206-623-9015
Officers:
John S. Whetzell, Chmn., Pres. & Chief Exec. Officer
Richard I. Clark, V.P. & Treas.
Richard J. Dyste, V.P., Technical Services
Gary S. Jones, V.P. & Controller
James A. Penney, V.P. & Gen. Counsel
James A. Hanlon, Div. V.P., Operations
H. Lee Johnson, Div. V.P., Operations
Wayne F. Schattenkerk, Div. V.P., Operations

Branch Offices:
Box 538
Flint, TX 75762
Phone: 903-894-8200
James E. Hanlon, Div. V.P.

32 E. Vine
Statesboro, GA 30458
Phone: 912-489-1065
H. Lee Johnson, Div. V.P.
Represented (legal): Arent Fox Kintner Plotkin & Kahn; Cairncross & Hempleman.
Cable Systems (98):
Alabama: Aliceville, Eutaw, Marion, Millport, Reform.
California: Chowchilla, Coarsegold, Fish Camp, Le Grand, Lushmeadows, Mariposa, Mount Shasta, Oakhurst, Planada, Yreka.
Georgia: Clayton, Royston, Statesboro, Swainsboro, Toccoa, Vidalia.
Idaho: Clark Fork, Garfield Bay, Priest River, Sandpoint.
Mississippi: Carthage, Forest, Kosciusko, Maben, Philadelphia, Raleigh, Sandersville, Starkville.
North Carolina: Forest City, Highlands.
Oregon: Woodburn.
South Carolina: Aiken, Barnwell, Bennettsville, Greenwood, Liberty, Seneca.
Texas: Bay City, Berryville, Brenham, Brookshire, Buchanan Dam, Buffalo, Burnet, Chandler, Coolidge, Corsicana, Crockett, Cut and Shoot, Dixie, Dublin, Fairfield, Flint, Gun Barrel City, Hico, Hillsboro, Horseshoe Bay, Huffman, Jackson's Landing, Jewett, Kaufman, Kerens, Kingsland, Lake Palestine, Lamesa, Madisonville, Malakoff, Marble Falls, Marlin, Matagorda, Mexia, Montgomery, Navasota, New Caney, New Chapel Hill, Oak Grove, Red Ackers, Rice, Stephenville, Trenton, Waller, Waterwood, Wortham.
Washington: Bainbridge Island, Bayview, Camano Island, Clallam Bay, Ephrata, La Conner, Moses Lake, Othello, Port Angeles, Sequim.
Total Basic Subscribers: 268,276 (0.39% of total cable households).
Total Pay Units: 98,859.
Radio Stations:
Texas: KAND-AM-FM, Corsicana.

NORTHLAND COMMUNICATIONS INC.
Box 66
Clear Lake, IA 50428
Phones: 515-357-2111; 800-944-8993
Officers:
Marcia A. Connell, Pres.
Doug Kline, Chief Financial Officer
Ownership: Clear Lake Telephone Co.
Cable Systems (2):
Iowa: Meservey, Thornton.
Total Basic Subscribers: 181.

NORTHSIDE TV CORP.
521 Vulcan St.
Iron Mountain, MI 49801-2333
Phone: 906-774-1351
Ownership: Subscriber owned.
Cable Systems (1):
Michigan: Iron Mountain.
Total Basic Subscribers: 928.
Total Pay Units: 217.

NORTHSTAR CABLE INC.
Box 880
Kingston, WA 98346
Phone: 360-297-2295
Officers:
Robert J. Smiley, Pres. & Chief Exec. Officer
Sandra D. Smiley, Secy.-Treas.
Ownership: Mary Smiley, 50%; Robert J. Smiley, 50%.
Cable Systems (2):
Washington: Hansville, Kingston.
Total Basic Subscribers: 1,496.
Total Pay Units: 167.

NORTHSTATE CABLEVISION CO.
Box 297
Dufur, OR 97021
Phone: 503-467-2409
Officers:
J. W. Damon, Pres.
Barbara Damon, V.P.
Helen Saunders, Secy.-Treas.
Cable Systems (1):
Oregon: Dufur.
Total Basic Subscribers: 278.
Total Pay Units: 86.
Other Holdings:
Telephone: Northstate Telephone Co., Dufur, OR.

NORTHWEST CABLE LTD. PARTNERSHIP
Box 618
Lockney, TX 79241-0618
Phone: 509-534-3766
Ownership: Bill Yusko, Gen. Partner.
Cable Systems (10):
Idaho: Worley.
Washington: Fairfield, Garfield, Harrington, Oakesdale, Reardan, Rosalia, Spangle, Sprague, Springdale.
Total Basic Subscribers: 1,280.
Total Pay Units: 696.

NORTHWEST COMMUNICATIONS COOPERATIVE
Box 38
Ray, ND 58849
Phone: 701-568-3331
Fax: 701-568-7777
Ownership: Estate of G. Russell Chambers, 33.3%; Francis E. Martin, 33.3%; Thomas E. Bird, 33.3%.
Cable Systems (5):
North Dakota: Bowbells, Grenora, Powers Lake, Ray, Wildrose.
Wireless Cable Systems (2):
North Dakota: Bowbells, Epping.
Total Cable Subscribers: 1,310.
Total Pay Units: 247.
Other Holdings:
MDS, MMDS, see listing.
Telephone.

NORTHWEST COMMUNICATIONS INC. (BOZEMAN, MT)
Box 3839
Bozeman, MT 59772
Phone: 406-587-2213
Ownership: Dan Edwards, Bob Fredericks, Dan Kamp, John Kamp & Anthony Storti, Principals.
Cable Systems (2):
Montana: Four Corners, Riverside Greens.
Total Basic Subscribers: N.A.

NORTHWEST COMMUNICATIONS INC. (HAVELOCK, IA)
Box 186
Havelock, IA 50546
Phone: 712-776-2222
Fax: 712-776-4444
Officers:
Thomas Eberle, Pres.
Donald D. Miller, Chief Exec. Officer
Gerald Thatcher, Secy.-Treas.
Ownership: Northwest Telephone Cooperative.
Cable Systems (1):
Iowa: Havelock.
Total Basic Subscribers: 803.
Total Pay Units: 316.

NORTHWEST COMMUNITY COMMUNICATIONS INC.
116 N. Harriman Ave.
Amery, WI 54001
Phone: 715-268-7101
Ownership: Amery Telephone Co. Amery also owns Amery Telecom, see listing.
Cable Systems (1):
Wisconsin: Amery.
Total Basic Subscribers: 1,980.
Total Pay Units: 861.
Other Holdings:
Telephone.

NORTHWEST IOWA TELEPHONE CO.
428 Evans St.
Sloan, IA 51055
Phone: 712-943-5566
Cable Systems (1):
Iowa: Salix.
Total Basic Subscribers: 631.
Total Pay Units: 251.

NORTHWOODS CABLE INC.
Box 508
20938 Washington Ave.
Onaway, MI 49765-0508
Phone: 517-733-2630
Fax: 517-733-2455
Officers:
Peter J. Christiano, Pres.
Christopher Christiano, V.P.
Ownership: Christopher Christiano & Peter J. Christiano, Principals.
Represented (legal): Cameron & Mittleman.
Cable Systems (6):
Michigan: Atlanta, Clark Twp., Drummond Island, Hillman Twp., Mullett Twp., Onaway.
Total Basic Subscribers: 2,381.

CITY OF NORWAY CATV
Box 99
Norway, MI 49870
Phone: 906-563-9641
Ownership: Community owned.
Cable Systems (1):
Michigan: Norway.
Total Basic Subscribers: 1,550.
Total Pay Units: 546.

NORWAY RURAL TELEPHONE CO.
105 S. Main
Kanawha, IA 50447
Phone: 515-762-3772
Fax: 515-762-8201
Officers:
Bob Howlett, Chmn. & Chief Exec. Officer
Bill Johnson, Chief Financial Officer
Cable Systems (2):
Iowa: Kanawha, Klemme.
Total Basic Subscribers: 428.
Total Pay Units: 92.
Other Holdings:
Cellular radio.

NOVA CABLE MANAGEMENT INC.— Sold to Avalon Cable 1999.

NOVA CABLEVISION INC.
Box 1412
Galesburg, IL 61402
Phone: 309-342-9681
Ownership: Robert G. Fischer Jr., Chief Exec. & Operating Officer, 100%.
Cable Systems (5):
Illinois: Cameron, Gladstone, Little York, Norris, Trivoli.
Total Basic Subscribers: 712.
Total Pay Units: 256.

HAROLD NOWELL
Box 345
Hwy. 45
Trenton, TN 38382
Phone: 901-855-2808
Cable Systems (1):
Tennessee: Trenton.
Total Basic Subscribers: 2,164.

NUCENTRIX BROADBAND NETWORKS
Suite 200
200 Chisholm Place
Plano, TX 75075
Phone: 972-423-9494
Fax: 972-423-0819
Officers:
Carroll D. McHenry, Chmn., Pres., Chief Exec. & Financial Officer
Randall C. May, V.P., Operations
Wayne M. Taylor, V.P., Administration
J. Curtis Henderson, V.P., Gen. Counsel & Secy.

Branch Office:
224 W. Evergreen
Durant, OK 74701
Phone: 405-924-6220
Ownership: David E. Webb; L. Allen Wheeler; Hunt Capital Group LLC; Jupiter Partners.
Wireless Cable Systems (59):
Arkansas: Fort Smith, Paragould.
Illinois: Champaign & Urbana, Freeport, Jacksonville, Macomb, McLeansboro, Olney, Taylorville, Vandalia.
Iowa: Story City.
Kansas: Beloit, Chanute, Manhattan, Marion, Medicine Lodge, Rice County, Shaw.
Missouri: Monroe City, Montgomery City, Sikeston.
Ohio: Bucyrus, Lykens.
Oklahoma: Ada, Ardmore, Enid, Kingfisher, Lawton, Lindsay, Muskogee, Stillwater, Tulsa, Weatherford, Woodward.
Pennsylvania: Greenville.
Texas: Abilene, Austin, Big Country, Corpus Christi, Corsicana, Dallas, Gainesville, George West, Hamilton, Jourdanton, Kerrville, Kingsville, Laredo, Lubbock, Midland, Mount Pleasant, Olton, Paris, Temple, Texarkana, Texoma, Uvalde, Waco, Wichita Falls.
Planned Wireless Cable Systems (1):
Illinois: Peoria.
Total Basic Subscribers: 197,446 (0.29% of total cable households).
Other Holdings:
MDS, MMDs, see listing.
International Cable: 49% of Television Interactiva del Norte ("Telinor").
Telecommunications company: 20% of Wireless One Inc.
Note: Nucentrix was formerly known as Heartland Wireless Communications Inc.

NUSHAGAK TELEPHONE COOPERATIVE INC.
Box 350
Dillingham, AK 99576
Phone: 907-842-5295
Fax: 907-842-2799

Officers:
Norman Heyano, Pres.
Anna May Sorensen, V.P.
Rob Carpenter, Secy.
Raebelle S. Whitcomb, Treas.
Cable Systems (1):
Alaska: Dillingham.
Total Basic Subscribers: 536.

N.W. COMMUNICATIONS INC.
Box 103
Rte. 2
Bourbon, MO 65441
Phone: 314-468-4646
Officers:
Evan Copsey, Pres.
Bruce Copsey, Secy.-Treas.
Ownership: RBJ Corp. RBJ ownership: Copsey Family, Principals.
Cable Systems (2):
Missouri: Maitland, Skidmore.
Total Basic Subscribers: 116.

OAK CABLE SYSTEMS INC.
Box 203
Huxley, IA 50124
Phone: 515-597-3385
Fax: 515-597-2415
Ownership: Mike Heggen & Doug Sheldahl, Principals.
Cable Systems (7):
Iowa: Alden, Coulter, Dows, Latimer, Steamboat Rock, Wellsburg, Williams.
Total Basic Subscribers: 900.

CLARENCE & LOIS OBEY
Box 181
Jenkinjones, WV 24848
Phone: 304-383-2245
Cable Systems (1):
West Virginia: Jenkinjones.
Total Basic Subscribers: 62.
Total Pay Units: 29.

OCONTO FALLS CABLE TV
Box 70
Oconto Falls, WI 54154
Phone: 414-846-2911
Officer:
Peter Mann, Mgr.
Ownership: Community owned.
Cable Systems (1):
Wisconsin: Oconto Falls.
Total Basic Subscribers: 899.
Total Pay Units: 372.

OGDEN TELEPHONE CO.
Box 457
113 S.W. 3rd St.
Ogden, IA 50212-0457
Phone: 515-275-2050
Cable Systems (1):
Iowa: Ogden.
Total Basic Subscribers: 530.
Total Pay Units: 241.

OHIO VALLEY WIRELESS LTD.
1420 N. Cullen Ave.
Evansville IN, 47716
Phone: 812-471-7500
Officers:
Dave Barning, Chmn.
Richard K. Gunderson, Chief Exec. Officer
Edgar Kuhlenschmidt, Pres.
Dale Weideman, V.P., OVC
C. A. Robinson, Secy.-Treas.
Wireless Cable Systems (1):
Indiana: Evansville.
Total Basic Subscribers: 5,100.
Total Pay Units: 1,100.

OKLAHOMA WESTERN TELEPHONE CO.
Box 398
Clayton, OK 74536
Officer:
Pauline Van Horne, Pres.
Wireless Cable Systems (1):
Oklahoma: Clayton.
Total Basic Subscribers: N.A.
Other Holdings:
MMDS, see listing.

OLDTOWN COMMUNITY SYSTEMS INC.
Box 75
Oldtown, MD 21555
Phone: 301-478-5700
Fax: 301-478-5711
Officers:
David Bennett, Pres.
Jacqueline Malcolm, Treas.
Ownership: Non-profit cooperative.
Cable Systems (1):
Maryland: Oldtown.
Total Basic Subscribers: 775.
Total Pay Units: 151.

OLLIG UTILITIES CO.
Box 98
525 E. 4th St.
Dell Rapids, SD 57022
Phone: 605-428-5421
Officer:
K. P. Ellefson, V.P.
Represented (legal): Moss & Barnett.
Cable Systems (14):
Minnesota: Ada, Dilworth, Fertile, Gary, Hawley, Mahnomen, Oakport, Pelican Lake, Pelican Rapids, Ulen.
North Dakota: Finley.
South Dakota: Corsica, Dell Rapids, Montrose.
Total Basic Subscribers: 2,654.
Total Pay Units: 1,859.

OLMSTED CABLE CO. CORP.
1801 E. 9th St.
Suite 1710
Cleveland, OH 44114
Phone: 216-522-0800
Ownership: Gary Brookins & Bob Reed, Principals.
Represented (legal): Robert C. Reed.
Cable Systems (1):
Ohio: Olmsted Twp.
Total Basic Subscribers: 800.

ROY OLSEN
Box 1134
East Corinth, VT 05040
Phone: 802-439-5737
Cable Systems (1):
Vermont: East Corinth.
Total Basic Subscribers: 29.

OMEGA CABLE
Box 627
404 Denver
Saguache, CO 81149
Phone: 719-655-2470
Ownership: Scott Alexander & Dale Hazard, Principals.
Cable Systems (1):
Colorado: Saguache.
Total Basic Subscribers: 230.
Total Pay Units: 81.

OMEGA COMMUNICATIONS INC.
Box 1766
29 E. Maryland St.
Indianapolis, IN 46206
Phone: 317-264-4000
Fax: 317-264-4020
Officers:
Robert E. Schloss, Chmn., Chief Exec. & Operating Officer
James Jones, Chief Financial Officer
Ownership: Schloss family, majority interest.
Cable Systems (6):
Illinois: Hoopeston, Paris, Westville.
Indiana: Brazil, Cordry/Sweetwater Conservancy District, Mitchell.
Total Basic Subscribers: 48,840 (0.07% of total cable households).
Total Pay Units: 14,843.
Other Holdings:
SMATV.

OMNI III CABLE TV INC.
224 S. 4th St.
Jay, OK 74346
Phone: 918-253-4545
Fax: 918-253-3400
Officers:
Teresa A. Aubrey, Pres.
Rex Ray Brixey, Exec. V.P. & Treas.
Tim Etris, V.P., Operations
Norma R. Holt, V.P., Industry Relations
Sherri Stephens, Secy.
Ownership: Teresa Aubrey, 51%; Norma Holt, 49%. Aubrey & Holt are execs. with the Grand Telephone Co., Jay, OK.
Cable Systems (1):
Oklahoma: Disney.
Total Basic Subscribers: 247.
Total Pay Units: 51.
Other Holdings:
Cellular radio.

ONEIDA TELEPHONE EXCHANGE
Box 445
Oneida, IL 61467
Phone: 309-483-3111
Officer:
David Olson, Gen. Mgr.
Cable Systems (1):
Illinois: Oneida.
Total Basic Subscribers: 266.
Total Pay Units: 100.

ONEONTA TELEPHONE CO. INC.
Box 1500
Oneonta, AL 35121
Phone: 205-625-3591
Officers:
R. C. Corr, Chmn. & Chief Exec. Officer
Bryan Corr, Pres.
Doris Corr, V.P. & Secy.-Treas.
Cable Systems (1):
Alabama: Oneonta.
Total Basic Subscribers: 2,545.
Total Pay Units: 606.
Other Holdings:
Cellular radio.

ONEPOINT COMMUNICATIONS
Suite 750
5335 Wisconsin Ave. NW
Washington, DC 20015
Phone: 202-364-3511
Fax: 202-364-3520
Officers:
John C. Norcutt, Pres.
Joan H. Miller, Chief Operating Officer
M. John Lubetkin, V.P., Business Development
John Long, Chief Financial Officer
Ownership: Mid-Atlantic Cable, 50%; Telcom Plus, 50%. MAC ownership: John C. Norcutt, Gen. Partner, see listing.
Cable Systems (5):
Maryland: Howard County, Warwick.
Virginia: King William (portions), River Oaks, Ruther Glen.
Total Basic Subscribers: 42,288 (0.06% of total cable households).
Total Pay Units: 23,617.
Other Holdings:
SMATV.

ONIDA CABLE TV
Box 285
Onida, SD 57564
Phone: 605-258-2874
Ownership: Terry Thomas, 50%; Ken Miles, 50%.
Cable Systems (1):
South Dakota: Onida.
Total Basic Subscribers: 210.
Total Pay Units: 108.

ONSLOW COOPERATIVE TELEPHONE ASSOCIATION
Box 6
102 Anamosa Ave.
Onslow, IA 52321
Phone: 319-485-2833
Fax: 319-485-3891
Officer:
Ron Fagan, Chmn.
Cable Systems (1):
Iowa: Onslow.
Total Basic Subscribers: 81.

OPP CABLEVISION
Box 610
Opp, AL 36467
Phone: 205-493-4571
Fax: 205-493-6666
Ownership: Community owned.
Cable Systems (1):
Alabama: Opp.
Total Basic Subscribers: 3,527.
Total Pay Units: 1,061.

OPTEL CABLE
Suite 100
1111 W. Mockingbird Lane
Dallas, TX 75247
Phones: 214-634-3800; 800-487-3321
Web site: http://www.optelinc.com
Cable Systems (4):
California: Cabazon.
Illinois: Palos Park, Union.
Washington: Suncrest.
Total Basic Subscribers: 1,844.
Total Pay Units: 1,009.

KEITH O'QUINN
1135 S. First St.
Jesup, GA 31545
Phone: 912-427-4221
Cable Systems (1):
Georgia: Patterson.
Total Basic Subscribers: 350.
Total Pay Units: 31.

OREGON COMMUNITY CABLE TV INC.
13909 S.E. Stark St.
Portland, OR 97233
Phone: 503-252-6080
Cable Systems (1):
Oregon: Boring.
Total Basic Subscribers: N.A.

ORION BROADCASTING SYSTEMS
Suite 208B
7231 S. Eastern Ave.
Las Vegas, NV 89119-0451
Phone: 800-356-1825
Ownership: Orionvision.
Wireless Cable Systems (1):
New Jersey: Atlantic City.
Total Basic Subscribers: 2,000.
Total Pay Units: 425.
Other Holdings:
MDS, MMDS, see listing.

MATTHEW ORISTANO
5301 E. Broadway Blvd.
Tucson, AZ 85711-3710
Phone: 520-519-4400
Fax: 520-747-6830
Wireless Cable Systems (1):
Missouri: Kansas City.
Total Basic Subscribers: N.A.
Other Holdings:
MDS, MMDS, see listing.
Oristano is the Chmn. of Preferred Entertainment Inc., see listing.

ORVISTON TV
Box 85
Loganton, PA 17747
Phone: 717-725-2733
Officer:
Lester Rhodes, Pres.
Ownership: Community owned.
Cable Systems (1):
Pennsylvania: Orviston.
Total Basic Subscribers: N.A.

ORWELL TELEPHONE CO.
Box 337
70 S. Maple St.
Orwell, OH 44076-0337
Phone: 440-437-6111
Fax: 440-437-1000
Officers:
Donald Pokorny, Pres.
Albert Leonetti, Exec. V.P.
Frank Leonetti Jr., V.P. & Secy.
Cable Systems (2):
Ohio: Leipsic, Orwell.
Total Basic Subscribers: 2,888.
Total Pay Units: 1,404.
Other Holdings:
Cellular radio.

OTEC COMMUNICATIONS CO.
Box 427
245 W. 3rd St.
Ottoville, OH 45876-0427
Phone: 419-453-3324
Officers:
Basil Alt, Pres.
Ray Kaufman, Secy.-Treas.
Ownership: Non-profit organization.
Cable Systems (1):
Ohio: Ottoville.
Total Basic Subscribers: 850.
Total Pay Units: 389.

TODD OVERTON
Box 1135
Baker, MT 59313
Phone: 406-778-2937
Cable Systems (1):
Montana: Baker 33.3%.
Total Basic Subscribers: 620.
Total Pay Units: 166.

TOM OVERTON
Box 1135
Baker, MT 59313
Phone: 406-778-2937
Cable Systems (1):
Montana: Baker 33.3%.
Total Basic Subscribers: 6200.
Total Pay Units: 166.

PACIFIC COAST CABLE CO.
Box 1018
Ione, CA 95640
Phone: 209-274-2660
Ownership: George F. Laine III.
Cable Systems (1):
California: Ione.
Total Basic Subscribers: 870.
Total Pay Units: 435.

PACIFIC TELECOM INC.
Box 9901
805 Broadway St.
Vancouver, WA 98668-8701
Phone: 206-696-0983
Fax: 206-696-6912
Officers:
Charles Robinson, Chmn., Pres. & Chief Exec. Officer
C. E. Peterson, Exec. V.P.
Ownership: Pacific Corp., 80%; remainder undisclosed.
Cable Systems (1):
Colorado: Lake City.
Total Basic Subscribers: 799.
Total Pay Units: 180.
Other Holdings:
Cable: Casco Telephone Co.; Thorp Telephone Co., see listings.

PALMER MUTUAL TELEPHONE CO.
306 Main St.
Palmer, IA 50571
Phone: 712-359-2411
Officer:
Verne Metzger, Pres.
Cable Systems (1):
Iowa: Palmer.
Total Basic Subscribers: 90.
Total Pay Units: 23.

PALMETTO CABLE TV INC.
Suite 1500
101 Allison St.
Fort Mill, SC 29715
Phones: 803-547-2510; 803-548-6000
Ownership: Robert L. Helmly, 50%; Fort Mill Trust Co., 50%.
Cable Systems (2):
South Carolina: Fort Mill, Regent Park.
Total Basic Subscribers: 7,659.
Total Pay Units: 4,610.

PALO COOPERATIVE TELEPHONE ASSN.
Box 252
Palo, IA 52324
Phone: 319-851-3431
Fax: 319-851-6970
Officers:
Wayne McVay, Pres.
Robbi Kane, Chief Operating Officer
John Huntington, Secy.-Treas.
Cable Systems (1):
Iowa: Palo.
Total Basic Subscribers: 210.
Total Pay Units: 84.

PANORA COOPERATIVE CABLEVISION ASSN. INC.
Box 217
114 E. Main
Panora, IA 50216
Phone: 515-755-2200
Fax: 515-755-2425
Officer:
Ron Reynolds, Chmn.
Cable Systems (3):
Iowa: Bagley, Jamaica, Panora.
Total Basic Subscribers: 1,373.
Total Pay Units: 535.
Other Holdings:
Telephone.
Cellular radio.

PARAGOULD CITY LIGHT & WATER COMMISSION
1901 Jones Rd.
Paragould, AR 72450
Phone: 501-239-7700
Fax: 501-239-7798
Cable Systems (1):
Arkansas: Paragould.
Total Basic Subscribers: 8,658.
Total Pay Units: 5,696.

PARK TV & ELECTRONICS INC.
Box 423
120 S. 2nd
Cissna Park, IL 60924
Phone: 815-457-2659
Cable Systems (3):
Illinois: Buckley (village), Potomac (village), Rankin (village).
Total Basic Subscribers: 676.

PAT'S INC.
Box 555
Linden, TN 37096
Phone: 615-589-2696
Ownership: Bert Patterson & Mrs. Edwin Patterson, Principals.
Cable Systems (3):
Tennessee: Linden, Lobelville, Scotts Hill.
Total Basic Subscribers: N.A.

MYRON PATTISON
Box 794
120 S. Washington St.
Crawfordsville, IN 47933
Phone: 317-362-6161
Represented (legal): Dow, Lohnes & Albertson PLLC.
Cable Systems (1):
Indiana: Frankfort 10%.
Total Basic Subscribers: 5,050.
Total Pay Units: 2,483.

PAXTON CABLE TELEVISION INC.
Suite 280
700 Ackerman Rd.
Columbus, OH 43202
Phone: 614-263-6100
Officers:
Susan McVoy, Chmn. & Chief Exec. Officer
Steve McVoy, Chief Operating Officer
Ownership: Dennis McGillicuddy, Steve McVoy, Susan McVoy & Barry Silverstein, Principals. Dennis McGillicuddy, Steve McVoy & Barry Silverstein have interest in Coaxial Communications, see listing.
Cable Systems (17):
Illinois: Shawneetown.
Indiana: Elizabeth.
Kentucky: Barrallton, Dunmor, Stonewall Estates, Sturgis.
Ohio: Big Island Twp., Caledonia, Canaan Twp. (Madison County), Morral.
West Virginia: Ballard, Birch River, Ellamore, Gassaway, Leivasy, Nettie, Summers County (portions).
Cable Franchises (1):
Ohio: Marseilles.
Total Basic Subscribers: 4,002.
Total Pay Units: 1,488.

TRAVIS PAYNE
Box 156
Due West, SC 29639
Phone: 803-379-2174
Cable Systems (1):
South Carolina: Due West.
Total Basic Subscribers: 574.
Total Pay Units: 90.

PCL CABLE
Box 1328
Athens, AL 35612
Phones: 256-232-4009; 256-353-1100
Fax: 256-232-4020
Cable Systems (1):
Alabama: Athens.
Total Basic Subscribers: N.A.

P.D.Q. CABLE TV INC.
Box 780
17755 W. Hwy. 40
Dunnellon, FL 32630
Phone: 904-489-5924
Fax: 904-489-4294
Officers:
Kenneth R. Carroll Sr., Pres.
Teresa P. Carroll, V.P.
Represented (legal): Chris S. Egan.
Cable Systems (4):
Florida: Florahome, Holopaw, Kenansville, Orange Springs.
Total Basic Subscribers: 1,350.
Total Pay Units: 352.
Other Holdings:
P.D.Q. Cable Construction Inc.
P.D.Q. CATV Supply Inc.

PEAK CABLEVISION LLC
Suite 304
5655 S. Yosemite St.
Englewood, CO 80111
Phone: 303-721-0914
Officers:
Donne F. Fisher, Chief Exec. Officer
Blake Fisher, Chief Operating Officer
William K. Fisher, Chief Financial Officer

Branch Office:
Box 471467
Tulsa, OK 74147-1467
Phone: 918-627-9406
Fax: 918-627-9407
Steven Murphy, Sr. V.P., Operations
Ownership: AT&T Broadband & Internet Services, majority equity interest, see listing.
Represented (legal): Cole, Raywid & Braverman LLP.
Cable Systems (93):
Arizona: Fredonia.
Arkansas: Beaver Lake, Benton County, Cedarville, Daisy, De Queen, Dierks, Fulton, Hatfield, Huntington, Mansfield, McCaskill, Midland, Mineral Springs, Mulberry, Murfreesboro, Prairie Grove, Rogers, Rudy/Highway 71, Salem, West Fork, Winslow.
Missouri: Seligman.
Nevada: Ely, Eureka, McGill, Ruth, Wendover.
Oklahoma: Allen, Alva, Antlers, Bennington, Boswell, Braggs, Bristow, Calvin, Caney,

Chandler, Clayton, Cushing, Drumright, Enid, Grove, Haskell, Henryetta, Holdenville, Howe, Konawa, Lake Tenkiller, Maud, McAlester, McCurtain, Muskogee, Okemah, Okmulgee, Panama, Pawhuska, Perry, Porum Landing, Pryor (outside areas), Rattan, Seminole, Stigler, Stillwater, Stroud, Stuart, Talihina, Valiant, Wagoner, Wellston, Wetumka, Wewoka, Wister, Wright City.
Utah: Blanding, Castle Dale, Duchesne, East Carbon, Ephraim, Ferron, Fillmore, Gunnison, Kanab, Milford, Minersville, Moab, Monticello, Moroni, Mount Pleasant, Price, Richfield, Roosevelt, Salina.
Total Basic Subscribers: 123,678 (0.18% of total cable households).
Total Pay Units: 82,323.
Note: Sale to Cox Communications Inc. pends.

PEC CABLE
Eastdale Plaza
1700 First Ave., No. 1
Iowa City, IA 52240
Phone: 319-351-2297
Fax: 319-358-5810
Officers:
Jim Peterson, Pres.
Joe Peterson, V.P.
Cable Systems (1):
Iowa: Nichols.
Total Basic Subscribers: 99.
Total Pay Units: 57.

PECOCO INC.
Box 1
121 Williams St.
Randolph, WI 53956
Phone: 414-326-5808
Fax: 414-326-4125
Officers:
Ben Olson, Chmn.
Elizabeth Burke, Pres.
Gary Perleberg, Chief Operating Officer
Bryan Woltman, Chief Financial Officer

Branch Office:
Randolph, WI 53956
Phone: 414-326-3151
Represented (legal): Michaelbest & Friedrich.
Cable Systems (2):
Wisconsin: Fair Water, Randolph.
Total Basic Subscribers: 2,853.
Total Pay Units: 1,270.
Other Holdings:
Telephone: Peoples Telephone Co., Fairwater-Brandon-Alto Telephone Co., Brandon, WI, Peoples Cellular, an unincorporated division of Peoples Telephone.
Cable Layers Inc., utility & construction for telephone & cable.
Outdoor advertising.

PEGASUS CABLE TELEVISION INC.
Suite 200
225 City Line Ave.
Bala Cynwyd, PA 19004
Phone: 610-934-7000
Fax: 610-934-7121
Officers:
Howard Verlin, Pres.
Marshall W. Pagon, Chief Exec. Officer
Alan E. Burch, Sr. V.P.
Robert Verdecchio, Chief Financial Officer

Branch Offices:
Box 7998
Mayaguez, PR 00680
Phone: 787-834-8550

San German Shopping Center No. 4
Box 360
San German, PR 00683
Phone: 787-892-1827
Ownership: Pegasus Communications Corp.
Represented (legal): Vorys, Sater, Seymour & Pease.
Cable Systems (2):
Puerto Rico: Aguadilla, Mayaguez.
Total Basic Subscribers: 52,000 (0.08% of total cable households).
Total Pay Units: 15,000.
Other Holdings:
DBS: Pegasus Satelline Television.

PEMBINA CABLE
Phone: 701-746-5771
Ownership: Clayton Kleppen, David Sunsdahl & Robert Weise. Sunsdahl owns 51% of Stephen Cable TV Inc., see listing.
Cable Systems (1):
North Dakota: Pembina.
Total Basic Subscribers: 240.
Total Pay Units: 82.

PENCOR SERVICES INC.
Box 215
471 Delaware Ave.
Palmerton, PA 18071
Phone: 610-826-2552
Fax: 610-826-7626
Officers:
Donald G. Reinhard, Pres.
Styles S. Butz, V.P.
Fred A. Reinhard, Secy.
Alex Kaslik, Treas.
Cable Systems (19):
Pennsylvania: Beach Lake, Duncannon, Dushore, Ephrata, Galeton, Greentown, Hawley, Hemlock Farms Development, Lansford, Leroy Twp., Mansfield, Meshoppen, Milford, Newberry Twp., Noxen, Palmerton, Stroudsburg, Sweet Valley, Troy.
Total Basic Subscribers: 156,000 (0.23% of total cable households).
Total Pay Units: 65,000.
Newspapers:
Pennsylvania: Lehighton Times News.
Other Holdings:
Telephone: Palmerton Telephone Co.

CLAUDE A. PENNINGTON
Box 301
Rte. 2
Jonesville, VA 24263
Phone: 703-346-1288
Cable Systems (1):
Virginia: Jonesville.
Total Basic Subscribers: N.A.

PEOPLE'S CABLE TV INC.
Suite 14
3705 US Hwy. 98 S
Lakeland, FL 33813
Phone: 813-647-5226
Ownership: Patrick D. McConnell, Managing Partner.
Wireless Cable Systems (1):
Florida: Polk County.
Total Basic Subscribers: N.A.

PEOPLE'S CHOICE TV PARTNERS
Suite 249
2 Corporate Dr.
Shelton, CT 06484-6239
Phone: 203-929-2800
Fax: 203-929-1454

Officer:
Joel A. Strasser, Dir., Corp. Communications
Wireless Cable Systems (7):
Arizona: Phoenix, Tucson.
Indiana: Indianapolis 73.5%.
Maryland: Baltimore.
Michigan: Detroit.
Missouri: St. Louis.
Texas: Houston.
Total Basic Subscribers: 75,200 (0.11% of total cable households).
Total Pay Units: 371.
Other Holdings:
MMDS, see listing.
Cable: Preferred Entertainment Inc., see listing.
Note: Sold to Sprint Corp. 1999.

PEOPLES TELEPHONE CO. (IOWA)
221 Main St.
Aurelia, IA 51005
Phone: 712-434-5989
Fax: 712-434-5555
Officers:
James P. Jensen, Chmn.
Bill Otis, Pres. & Chief Exec. Officer
Ralph Watts, Secy.
Cable Systems (1):
Iowa: Aurelia.
Total Basic Subscribers: 365.
Total Pay Units: 117.

PEOPLES TELEPHONE CO. INC. (TENNESSEE)
Box 310
Main St.
Erin, TN 37061
Phone: 615-289-4221
Fax: 615-289-4220
Officers:
Joseph D. Fail, Chmn. & Pres.
James H. Coakley Jr., Chief Operating Officer
Harvey Poole, Chief Financial Officer
Cable Systems (2):
Tennessee: Henry, Tennessee Ridge.
Total Basic Subscribers: 1,745.
Total Pay Units: 1,135.

PETTY GENERAL CONSTRUCTION CO. INC.
Box 507
511 8th St.
Comfort, TX 78013
Phone: 830-995-2813
Fax: 830-995-2245
Ownership: Hazel Petty, Principal.
Cable Systems (1):
Texas: Lavernia.
Total Basic Subscribers: 119.

PHELPS DODGE CORP.
Box 67
Playas, NM 88009
Phone: 505-436-2211
Cable Systems (1):
New Mexico: Playas.
Total Basic Subscribers: 275.

PHILIPPI COMMUNICATIONS SYSTEM
Box 460
108 N. Main St.
Philippi, WV 26416
Phone: 304-457-3700
Fax: 304-457-2703
Officer:
Carl Radcliff, Chief Operating Officer
Ownership: Community owned.
Cable Systems (1):
West Virginia: Philippi.
Total Basic Subscribers: 1,312.
Total Pay Units: 335.

PHOENIX CABLE INC.
10 S. Franklin Turnpike
Ramsey, NJ 07446
Phone: 201-825-9090
Fax: 201-825-8794
Officers:
James Feeney, Pres.
Parie Choksi, V.P., Finance
Charles D. Himelrich, Asst. V.P., Operations
Maryanne Lyman, Asst. Corp. Secy.
Ownership: Phoenix Leasing Inc.
Represented (legal): Cole, Raywid & Braverman LLP.
Cable Systems (37):
Cuba: Guantanamo Bay.
Georgia: Arabi, Baldwin County (portions), Collins.
Indiana: Darlington, Frankton, Jamestown, Lapel, Montezuma, New Market, Oxford, Roachdale, Sheridan, Summitville, Waynetown, Whitestown, Worthington.
New York: Augusta, De Ruyter, Guilford (town), Minerva (town), Newcomb, Peterboro, Preble (town), Scott.
North Carolina: Ellenboro, Fairfield Mountain, Sapphire.
Oregon: Butte Falls, Glendale, Prospect, Shady Cove.
South Carolina: Holly Hill, St. George.
Tennessee: Fairfield Glade.
Washington: Chattaroy, Diamond Lake.
Total Basic Subscribers: 28,652 (0.04% of total cable households).
Total Pay Units: 13,772.

PHONOSCOPE LTD.
6105 Westline Dr.
Houston, TX 77036
Phone: 713-272-4600
Fax: 713-271-4334
Officers:
Lee Cook, Chmn. & Chief Exec. Officer
Rhonda Druke, Pres.
Ted Viens, Research & Development
Jim Cox, Technical Dir.
Ownership: Partnership.
Cable Systems (1):
Texas: Houston.
Total Basic Subscribers: 3,000.
Other Holdings:
Internet, private data networks.
Videoconferencing.

PICKWICK CABLEVISION
Box 12
18455 Old SR 57
Pickwick Dam, TN 38365-0012
Phone: 901-689-5722
Ownership: Bob Campbell.
Cable Systems (1):
Tennessee: Counce.
Total Basic Subscribers: 840.

PIEDMONT CABLE CORP.
768 Marshall Mill Rd.
Fort Valley, GA 31030
Phone: 912-825-3578
Officers:
D. Mark Baxter, Pres. & Chief Exec. Officer
J. Roger Kennedy Jr., Chief Operating Officer
Denice B. Morgan, Secy.-Treas. & Chief Financial Officer
Ownership: D. Mark Baxter & J. Roger Kennedy Jr., Principals.
Cable Systems (1):
Georgia: Crawford County (eastern portion).

Total Basic Subscribers: 620.
Total Pay Units: 138.

PIEDMONT TELEPHONE MEMBERSHIP CORP.
Box 2066
Lexington, NC 27293-2066
Phone: 910-787-5433
Fax: 910-787-5246
Officers:
Fred L. Mock, Chmn.
Grady L. Leonard, Pres.
Elbert R. Perrell, Chief Exec. Officer
Represented (legal): Crisp, Davis, Schwentker, Page, Currin & Nich (ols).
Cable Systems (1):
North Carolina: Reeds Cross Roads.
Total Basic Subscribers: 3,194.
Total Pay Units: 2,332.

PIKE'S PEAK TV ASSN.
General Delivery
Herndon, PA 17830
Phone: 717-758-1777
Officer:
Andrew Bobb, Pres.
Ownership: Subscriber owned.
Cable Systems (1):
Pennsylvania: Herndon.
Total Basic Subscribers: N.A.

PINE ISLAND TELEPHONE CO.
Box 588
108 S.W. 2nd St.
Pine Island, MN 55963
Phone: 507-356-8302
Fax: 507-356-4001
Officers:
Curtis Sampson, Chmn. & Chief Exec. Officer
Steve Sjogren, Chief Operating Officer
Cable Systems (1):
Minnesota: Pine Island.
Total Basic Subscribers: 1,095.
Total Pay Units: 385.
Other Holdings:
Cellular.

PINE RIDGE CABLE TV
Box 420
Billy Mills Hall
Pine Ridge, SD 57770
Phone: 605-867-1166
Ownership: Warren Chord.
Cable Systems (1):
South Dakota: Pine Ridge.
Total Basic Subscribers: 470.
Total Pay Units: 290.

PINE TREE CABLEVISION
Suite 223
400 E. Lancaster Ave.
Wayne, PA 19087
Phone: 610-688-6051
Officers:
Walter E. Kemmerer, Pres.
Tom Cataldo, Operations Mgr.
Ownership: Pine Tree Management.
Cable Systems (23):
Maine: Eastport, Jonesport, Lubec, Machias, Milbridge, Pembroke, Winter Harbor.
New Hampshire: Nelson (town), Spofford, Stoddard, Troy.
South Carolina: Bethune, Cottageville, Cross, Elloree, Gaston, Hopkins, Jefferson, Lamar, North, St. Stephen, Swansea, Wagener.
Total Basic Subscribers: 8,888.
Total Pay Units: 2,682.

PINPOINT COMMUNICATIONS INC.
Box 490
611 Patterson
Cambridge, NE 69022
Phone: 308-697-3375
Fax: 308-697-3631
Officers:
J. Richard Shoemaker, Pres.
Roger Hoffman, Exec. V.P.
Steve Hunter, V.P., Mktg.

Branch Office:
McCook, NE 69001
Phone: 308-345-3870
Ownership: PinPoint Holdings Inc.
Cable Systems (1):
Nebraska: Cambridge.
Total Basic Subscribers: 628.
Total Pay Units: 214.

PIONEER COMMUNICATIONS
Box 707
120 W. Kansas Ave.
Ulysses, KS 67880-2001
Phone: 316-356-3211
Fax: 316-356-3242
Officers:
Earl B. Williams, Pres.
Richard K. Veach, Chief Exec. Officer
Williams Nicholas, V.P.
Leon Young, Secy.-Treas.

Branch Offices:
Hugoton, KS 67951
Phone: 316-544-4392

201 N. Main
Lakin, KS 67860
Phone: 316-355-7355

402 Main St.
Scott City, KS 67871
Phone: 316-872-2998

212 N. Main
Syracuse, KS 67878
Phone: 316-384-7721
Represented (legal): Lukas, McGowan, Nace & Gutierrez.
Cable Systems (9):
Kansas: Deerfield, Holcomb, Hugoton, Johnson, Lakin, Satanta, Sublette, Syracuse, Ulysses.
Total Basic Subscribers: 8,839.
Total Pay Units: 4,757.

PITCAIRN COMMUNITY ANTENNA SYSTEM
582 6th St.
Pitcairn, PA 15140
Phone: 412-372-6500
Officers:
Orelio Vecchio, Pres.
Josephine Higgins, Secy.-Treas.
Ownership: Community owned.
Cable Systems (1):
Pennsylvania: Pitcairn.
Total Basic Subscribers: 1,554.
Total Pay Units: 853.

PLAINS CABLE SYSTEMS
Box 267
Spirit Lake, IA 51360
Phone: 712-336-5151
Ownership: E. M. Parsen, 90%; Jerry Kittelson, 10%.
Cable Systems (2):
Iowa: Spirit Lake.
Minnesota: Mountain Lake.
Total Basic Subscribers: 4,367.
Total Pay Units: 1,137.

PLANTATION CABLEVISION INC.
Box 494
Eatonton, GA 31024
Phone: 706-485-7740
Fax: 706-485-2590
Officers:
James H. Hall, Pres.
Joel H. Hall, Chief Operating Officer
John H. Hall, V.P., Engineering
Cable Systems (1):
Georgia: Greene County (unincorporated areas).
Total Basic Subscribers: 1,800.
Total Pay Units: 630.

PLEASANT RIDGE CABLEVISION INC.
c/o Assessor's Office
Bingham, ME 04920
Phone: 207-672-3738
Officer:
Jenis M. Robinson, Mgr.
Ownership: Community owned.
Cable Systems (1):
Maine: Pleasant Ridge Plantation.
Total Basic Subscribers: 40.
Total Pay Units: 40.

PLENTYWOOD CABLE TV CO.
Box 128
Plentywood, MT 59259
Phone: 406-765-1199
Officers:
Ernest Berland, Pres.
Robert Schultz, Secy.-Treas.
Ownership: Ernest Berland, Tom Overton & Robert Schultz, Principals.
Cable Systems (1):
Montana: Plentywood.
Total Basic Subscribers: 650.
Total Pay Units: 210.

KENNETH W. POINDEXTER
Box 878
Marshall, TX 75671
Phone: 903-935-9355
Fax: 903-935-0963
Cable Systems (1):
Arkansas: Hope 5.72%.
Total Basic Subscribers: 3,801.
Total Pay Units: 1,687.

POND BRANCH CABLE
121 Centerville Rd.
Gilbert, SC 29054
Phone: 803-892-6600
Fax: 803-892-5592
Ownership: Pond Branch Telephone Co.
Cable Systems (1):
South Carolina: Gilbert.
Total Basic Subscribers: 647.
Total Pay Units: 279.

PONDEROSA CABLESYSTEMS LTD.
Suite 340
1855 Gateway Blvd.
Concord, CA 94520
Phone: 415-820-3000
Officer:
Claude B. Cody, Chief Exec. Officer
Ownership: Ponderosa Equipment Corp.
Cable Systems (1):
California: Tassajara Valley.
Total Basic Subscribers: 1,000.

POOLE'S INC.
3100 Turner Rd. SE
Salem, OR 97302
Phone: 503-363-7717
Cable Systems (1):
Oregon: Salem (southeastern portion).
Total Basic Subscribers: 395.

CHARLES PORTER
Box 580
Omar, WV 25638
Phone: 304-946-2147
Cable Systems (1):
West Virginia: Sarah Ann.
Total Basic Subscribers: N.A.

POST CABLEVISION OF NEBRASKA LP
Suite 16A
14818 W. 6th Ave.
Golden, CO 80401
Phones: 303-278-9660; 800-344-5404
Ownership: John Post, Pres.
Cable Systems (3):
Nebraska: Brule, Paxton, Stratton.
Total Basic Subscribers: 2,777.
Total Pay Units: 849.

POSTVILLE TELEPHONE CO.
Box 39
Postville, IA 52162-0039
Phone: 319-864-7211
Officers:
Lyle E. Zieman, Chmn. & Chief Exec. Officer
Edward W. Kozelka, Chief Financial Officer
Cable Systems (1):
Iowa: Postville.
Total Basic Subscribers: 625.
Total Pay Units: 294.

HOWARD POWELL
North Lowndes Cable Co.
Box 880
Hayneville, AL 36040
Phone: 205-875-5459
Cable Systems (1):
Alabama: Mosses.
Total Basic Subscribers: 420.
Total Pay Units: 400.

PREFERRED ENTERTAINMENT INC.
6260 Joliet Rd.
Countryside, IL 60525
Phones: 312-463-6900; 708-579-8168
Fax: 708-482-0790
Officers:
Mathew Oristano, Chmn.
Fred Atchity, Chief Exec. Officer
Paul McCarthy, Chief Operating Officer
Charles Schwartz, Chief Financial Officer
Ownership: People's Choice TV Partners, see listing.
Wireless Cable Systems (1):
Illinois: Chicago.
Total Basic Subscribers: 6,000.

PREMIER COMMUNICATIONS INC.
339 First Ave. NE
Sioux Center, IA 51250
Phone: 712-722-3451
Fax: 712-722-1113
Cable Systems (2):
Iowa: Doon, Sioux Center.

Total Basic Subscribers: 2,986.
Total Pay Units: 873.
Other Holdings:
Telephone.

PRESTIGE CABLE TV INC.

Box 2950
406 Old Mill Rd.
Cartersville, GA 30120
Phone: 770-382-0531
Fax: 770-386-2540
Officers:
Jon Oscher, Chmn. & Pres.
Lorri McClain, V.P. & Chief Operating Officer
Bob Buckfelder, V.P. & Chief Financial Officer
Ownership: Jon Oscher, Principal.
Represented (legal): Kilpatrick & Cody; Fleischman & Walsh LLP.
Cable Systems (9):
Georgia: Canton, Cartersville, Cumming.
Maryland: Carroll County.
North Carolina: Lake Norman, Mooresville, Statesville.
Virginia: Spotsylvania, Warrenton.
Total Basic Subscribers: 161,000 (0.23% of total cable households).
Total Pay Units: 77,000.

PRICE COUNTY TELEPHONE CO.

Box 108
105 N. Avon
Phillips, WI 54555
Phone: 715-339-2151
Cable Systems (1):
Wisconsin: Phillips.
Total Basic Subscribers: 890.
Total Pay Units: 200.

PRIME CABLE

Suite 3000
600 Congress Ave.
Austin, TX 78701
Phone: 512-476-7888
Fax: 512-320-4059
Officers:
Robert W. Hughes, Chmn.
Greg Marchbanks, Pres.
C. Ronald Dorchester, Exec. Advisor
Jerry Lindauer, Sr. V.P.
Allan Barnes, V.P., Operations
William Glasgow, V.P., Finance
Mark Greenburg, V.P., Mktg.
Dan Pike, V.P., Engineering
Shirley Barnes, Treas.
Diane Wigington, Contracts Mgr.
Ownership: Robert W. Hughes, C. R. Dorchester, Greg Marchbank & Jerry Lindauer, Principals.
Represented (legal): Hogan & Hartson LLP.
Cable Systems (3):
Illinois: Chicago (areas 2 & 3).
Maryland: Montgomery County.
Virginia: Arlington.
Total Basic Subscribers: 542,993 (0.79% of total cable households).
Total Pay Units: 395,627.
Other Holdings:
Cellular.
Retail operation: Video stores.
Note: Sale to Comcast Communications Inc. pends.

PRINCETOWN CABLE CO.

Box 1225
Schenectady, NY 12301-1225
Phone: 518-346-1107
Ownership: Barbara Price, Principal.
Cable Systems (1):
New York: Princetown (town).
Total Basic Subscribers: 564.
Total Pay Units: 252.

PRIVATE CABLE COMMUNITIES INC.

11546 Hwy. 17 Bypass S
Murrells Inlet, SC 29576
Phone: 803-237-1569
Officers:
Neil Lewis, Chmn.
John L. Dumas, Chief Exec. Officer
Jack Bodner, Chief Operating & Financial Officer
Ownership: John Dumas, Principal.
Cable Systems (1):
South Carolina: Pawleys Island.
Total Basic Subscribers: 400.
Total Pay Units: 67.

MORRIS G. PRIZER

Box 2169
224 Laguna Trail
Frazier Park, CA 93225
Phone: 805-245-3946
Cable Systems (1):
California: Frazier Park 5%.
Total Basic Subscribers: 1,400.
Total Pay Units: 312.

PROGRESSIVE CABLE COMMUNICATIONS INC.

Box 131689
Tyler, TX 75713
Phone: 800-653-7059
Fax: 903-561-9503
Ownership: Steve Houston, 50%; Velma Houston, 50%.
Cable Systems (1):
Texas: Thornton.
Total Basic Subscribers: 124.
Total Pay Units: 52.
Other Holdings:
LPTV, see listing.

PROJECT SERVICES INC.

Box 686
110 Cedar Ave. E
Hector, MN 55342
Phone: 612-848-6227
Officers:
Avis J. Johnson, Pres., Chief Exec. Officer & Secy.
Arland Johnson, Chief Operating Officer
Kirk A. Johnson, V.P. & Programming Dir.
Kim Johnson, V.P., Engineering
Kwen M. Johnson, Treas. & Chief Financial Officer
Ownership: Kae J. Hall, Kirk A. Johnson, Arland C. Johnson, Avis J. Johnson, Kim A. Johnson, Kwen M. Johnson, Pamela J. Johnson & Mabel L. Larson, 100% jointly.
Cable Systems (4):
Minnesota: Hanley Falls, Lake Lillian, Raymond, Watson.
Total Basic Subscribers: 573.
Total Pay Units: 160.

CITY OF PROTIVIN

Box 53
117 N. Main
Protivin, IA 52163
Phone: 319-569-8401
Ownership: Community owned.
Cable Systems (1):
Iowa: Protivin.
Total Basic Subscribers: 124.
Total Pay Units: 40.

PTI TELEVIDEO INC.

135 N. Bonson St.
Platteville, WI 53818
Phone: 608-348-3048
Cable Systems (1):
Wisconsin: Platteville.
Total Basic Subscribers: 3,038.
Total Pay Units: 1,019.

BILL PURCELL

Box 2405
King, NC 27021
Phone: 336-983-2121
Fax: 336-983-0980
Cable Systems (1):
North Carolina: Goldston.
Total Basic Subscribers: 5,500.
Total Pay Units: 1,726.

QUADRAVISION

1345 Air Motive Way
Reno, NV 89502
Phone: 702-686-5580
Fax: 702-686-5590
Wireless Cable Systems (2):
Nevada: Carson City, Reno.
Total Basic Subscribers: N.A.

QUALITY CABLEVISION OF OKLAHOMA INC.

Box 315
816-D N. Date
Jenks, OK 74037
Cable Systems (3):
Oklahoma: Hectorville, Preston, Talala.
Total Basic Subscribers: 572.

QUALITY ENTERTAINMENT CORP.

Suite 512
Central Mall Plaza
Fort Smith, AR 72903
Phone: 501-452-1998
Fax: 501-452-6430
Officers:
Brent Lewis, Pres., Chief Exec. & Operating Officer
Randall Hinton, V.P.
Ownership: Brent Lewis.
Cable Systems (16):
Arkansas: Been Ridge, Booneville Human Development Center, Casa, Knoxville, Pencil Bluff/Oden, Ratcliff, Scranton, Subiaco, Witcherville.
Oklahoma: Chicken Creek, Cookson, Cumberland, Elk Creek, Paradise Hill, Park Hill, Woodall.
Total Basic Subscribers: 1,750.
Total Pay Units: 240.

BILL QUARLES

1616 Calhoun Rd.
Greenwood, SC 29649
Phone: 803-229-3638
Cable Systems (1):
South Carolina: Little River.
Total Basic Subscribers: N.A.

QUINCY COMMUNITY TV ASSN. INC.

Box 834
81 Bradley St.
Quincy, CA 95971
Phone: 916-283-2330
Officers:
Max Frantz, Pres.
Art Griffin, V.P.
Berle Brents, Secy.
Terry Kidd, Treas.
Ownership: Subscriber owned.
Cable Systems (1):
California: Quincy.
Total Basic Subscribers: 1,953.
Total Pay Units: 623.

QUINTER CABLE CO.

419 Main St.
Quinter, KS 67752
Phone: 913-754-3480
Officers:
Kenneth L. Cooksey, Pres.
Lela Cooksey, Secy.-Treas.
Ownership: Kenneth L. Cooksey & Lela Cooksey, 100% jointly.
Cable Systems (1):
Kansas: Quinter.
Total Basic Subscribers: 345.
Total Pay Units: 114.

RADCLIFFE CABLEVISION INC.

Box 130
Radcliffe, IA 50230
Phone: 515-899-2341
Officers:
Richard R. Drake, Chmn. & Chief Exec. Officer
Ed Drake, Chief Operating Officer
Cable Systems (1):
Iowa: Radcliffe.
Total Basic Subscribers: 135.
Total Pay Units: 23.

RAE CABLE

#3 Lake Metigoshe Park
Bottineau, ND 58318
Phone: 701-263-4607
Ownership: Russell L. Ray, Chmn.
Represented (legal): John Gregg.
Cable Systems (4):
North Dakota: Balta, Newburg, Souris, Upham.
Total Basic Subscribers: 115.
Total Pay Units: 21.

GLENN R. RAMSEY

Box 331
Toledo, WA 98591
Phone: 206-864-4553
Cable Systems (1):
Washington: Toledo.
Total Basic Subscribers: 343.
Total Pay Units: 48.

R & B COMMUNICATIONS

Box 174
1000 Roanoke Rd.
Daleville VA, 24083
Phone: 540-992-2211
Fax: 540-992-3094
Officers:
Ira D. Layman, Chmn.
J. Allen Layman, Pres. & Chief Exec. Officer
Robert F. Nay, V.P., Mktg.
Chris C. Foster, Chief Financial Officer
Represented (legal): Gurman, Blask & Freedman, Chartered.
Wireless Cable Systems (1):
Virginia: Roanoke.
Total Basic Subscribers: 1,000.
Total Pay Units: 250.
Other Holdings:
ITFS.

R & R CABLE CO. INC.

Box 610
Roslyn, WA 98941
Phone: 509-649-2212
Fax: 509-649-3111

Officers:
Alan F. Weis, Pres.
Douglas W. Weis, V.P.
Nathan R. Weis, Secy.-Treas.

Branch Office:
Uniontown, WA 99179
Phone: 509-229-3311
Ownership: Western Elite Inc. Services.
Cable Systems (1):
Washington: Roslyn.
Total Basic Subscribers: 750.
Total Pay Units: 41.

RANGE TV CABLE CO. INC.
Box 189
1818 3rd Ave. E
Hibbing, MN 55746
Phone: 218-262-7072
Fax: 218-263-8340
Officers:
Frank Befera, Chmn. & Chief Exec. Officer
Robert S. Nickoloff, Secy.-Treas.
Ownership: Frank Befera, 54%; Robert S. Nickoloff, 26.8%; Ben P. Owens, 10%; James Parise, 5%; Charles Henry, 2.1%; James Klungness, 2.1%.
Cable Systems (1):
Minnesota: Hibbing.
Total Basic Subscribers: 5,500.
Total Pay Units: 1,606.

RAPID COMMUNICATIONS PARTNERS LP
1311 S. Victor St.
Aurora, CO 80012
Phones: 303-751-4847; 303-751-5333
Fax: 303-751-5221
Officers:
Tom Semptimphelter, Pres.
Beth Semptimphelter, Secy.
Steve Rice, Dir., Technical Operations
Kit Halgrimson, Dir., Administrative Affairs

Branch Office:
Branson, MO 65616
Phone: 417-334-7897
Fax: 417-334-7897
Ownership: TS Communications Inc., 1.09%; limited partners, 98.91%.
Represented (legal): Parcel, Mauro, Hultin & Spaanstra; Wiley, Rein & Fielding.
Cable Systems (55):
Colorado: Hotchkiss.
Illinois: Galena.
Kentucky: Big Clifty, Caneyville, Casey County (southwestern portion), Henderson (southern portion), Lincoln County (eastern portion), Rough River Dam, Russell County (unincorporated areas), Upton, Whitesville, Whitley County (unincorporated areas).
Missouri: Branson 99%, Hollister, Indian Point 99%, Rockaway Beach 99%.
Oklahoma: Blair 99%, Butler, Canton, Carter, Chattanooga, Cleo Springs, Davidson, Duke, Eldorado, Fort Cobb, Fort Supply, Garber, Geronimo, Gotebo, Gracemont, Granite, Lamont, Lone Wolf, Longdale, Martha, Mountain Park, Ninnekah, Olustee, Pocasset, Rocky, Sentinel, Snyder, Tipton, Verden.
Tennessee: Niota, Tellico Plains, Vonore.
Texas: Bentsen Grove, Blanket, Pleasant Valley, Progreso, San Carlos, Sebastian.
Virginia: Chesapeake.
Total Basic Subscribers: 24,220 (0.04% of total cable households).
Total Pay Units: 7,150.

RAYSTAY CO.— Sold to Lenfest Communications Corp. 1999.

RCN CORP.
105 Carnegie Center
Princeton, NJ 08540
Phone: 609-734-3737
Fax: 609-734-3713
Web site: http://www.rcn.com
Officers:
David C. McCourt, Chmn. & Chief Exec. Officer
Dennis Spina, Vice Chmn. & Pres., Internet Services
Michael J. Mahoney, Pres. & Chief Operating Officer
Bruce C. Godfrey, Exec. V.P. & Chief Financial Officer
Michael A. Adams, Exec. V.P. & Pres., Technology & Network
Mark Haverkate, Exec. V.P., Business Development
Sal Quadrino, Exec. V.P. & Chief Administrative Officer
Paul Sigmund, Exec. V.P., RCN International Holdings
Cable Systems (5):
New Jersey: Hillsborough, Long Hill Twp., Princeton.
New York: Carmel.
Pennsylvania: Northampton.
Total Basic Subscribers: 203,912 (0.30% of total

READLYN TELEPHONE CO.
Box 159
121 Main St.
Readlyn, IA 50668
Phone: 319-279-3375
Fax: 319-279-7575
Officer:
Burton Thies, Pres.
Ownership: Cooperative.
Cable Systems (1):
Iowa: Readlyn.
Total Basic Subscribers: 285.
Total Pay Units: 135.

RED RIVER CABLE TV
Box 674
Coushatta, LA 71019
Phone: 318-932-4991
Ownership: Jim Hardy, Principal.
Cable Systems (4):
Louisiana: Campti, Clarence, Coushatta, Hall Summit.
Total Basic Subscribers: 891.

RED'S TV CABLE INC.
Box 202
Farmville, NC 27828
Phone: 919-753-3074
Ownership: Frank Styers.
Cable Systems (1):
North Carolina: Bath.
Total Basic Subscribers: 115.

LEON REED
15 Crofton St.
Wellsboro, PA 16901
Phone: 717-724-4516
Cable Systems (2):
Pennsylvania: Arnot, Wellsboro.
Total Basic Subscribers: 3,110.

RENAISSANCE MEDIA HOLDINGS LLC— Sold to Charter Communications Inc. 1999

RENO CABLE CO.
111 2nd St.
Reno, PA 16343
Phone: 814-676-3115
Ownership: Walter Ebbert, 50%; Charles Stormer, 50%.
Cable Systems (1):
Pennsylvania: Reno.
Total Basic Subscribers: N.A.

RESERVATION TELEPHONE COOPERATIVE
Box 68
Parshall, ND 58770
Phone: 701-862-3115
Fax: 701-862-3008
Cable Systems (1):
North Dakota: Parshall.
Total Basic Subscribers: 1,038.
Total Pay Units: 559.

RETEL TV CABLE CO. INC.
1836 Hayes Ave.
Wiliamsport, PA 17701
Phone: 717-494-0500
Fax: 717-673-7039
Officer:
Terry Hughes, Pres.

Branch Office:
62 Troy St.
Canton, PA 17724
Phone: 717-673-5326
Ownership: George L. Hughes, 50%; Vera P. Hughes, 50%.
Cable Systems (3):
Pennsylvania: Canton, Cogan Station, Ralston.
Total Basic Subscribers: 2,685.
Total Pay Units: 800.

REYNOLDS CABLE TV INC.
Box 782
Swainsboro, GA 30401
Phone: 912-237-2853
Officer:
Terry Reynolds, Chmn., Pres. & Chief Exec. Officer
Ownership: Terry Reynolds, 51%; Randy Forehand, 44%; Bill McWhorter, 5%.
Represented (legal): Reddy, Begley & McCormick.
Cable Systems (1):
Georgia: Bolingbroke.
Total Basic Subscribers: 685.
Total Pay Units: 170.

RIB LAKE TELEPHONE CO. INC.
Box 247
1199 Fayette St.
Rib Lake, WI 54470
Phone: 715-427-3737
Fax: 715-427-5117
Officers:
Clark J. Eckhoff, Pres. & Chief Exec. Officer
Leslie H. Eckhoff, Secy.-Treas.
Ownership: Rhinelander Telecommunications Inc.
Represented (legal): Donald S. Rush.
Cable Systems (1):
Wisconsin: Rib Lake.
Total Basic Subscribers: 285.
Total Pay Units: 175.
Other Holdings:
Cellular.

PAUL E. RICHARDS
Drawer 2
Jerusalem, OH 43747
Phone: 614-926-1742
Cable Systems (3):
Ohio: Malaga Twp., New Athens.
West Virginia: Middlebourne.
Total Basic Subscribers: 819.

RICHLAND GRANT TELEPHONE CO-OP INC.
Box 67
Blue River, WI 53518
Phone: 608-537-2461
Officers:
Lorraine J. Orrick, Pres.
David J. Lull, Chief Exec. & Operating Officer
Byron Hillberry, Secy.-Treas.
Robert P. Cary, Chief Financial Officer
Cable Systems (1):
Wisconsin: Bell Center.
Total Basic Subscribers: 33.
Total Pay Units: 10.
Other Holdings:
Paging service.

RIDGEVILLE TELEPHONE CO.
Box A
Ridgeville Corners, OH 43555
Phone: 419-267-5185
Officer:
Donald Benecke, Pres.
Cable Systems (1):
Ohio: Ridgeville Twp.
Total Basic Subscribers: 139.
Total Pay Units: 60.

RIFKIN & ASSOCIATES INC.
Suite 600
360 S. Monroe St.
Denver, CO 80209
Phone: 303-333-1215
Fax: 303-322-3553
Officers:
Monroe M. Rifkin, Chmn. & Chief Exec. Officer
Jeffrey D. Bennis, Pres. & Chief Operating Officer
Kevin B. Allen, Pres., R & A Enterprises Inc.
Steve Hattrup, Sr. V.P., Operations
Dale D. Wagner, Sr. V.P., Finance & Administration
Paul A. Bambei, V.P., Operations
Suzanne Cyman, V.P., Programming
Peter N. Smith, V.P., Engineering
Lee A. Clayton, V.P., Mktg.
Bruce A. Rifkin, V.P., Operations
Ownership: Limited partnerships. Rifkin & Assoc., Principal.
Represented (legal): Cole, Raywid & Braverman LLP.
Cable Systems (219):
Arkansas: Ash Flat, Biggers, Briarcliff, Gosnell, Horseshoe Bend, Marmaduke, Maynard, Oxford, Piggott, Rector, Viola.
Florida: Miami Beach.
Georgia: Gwinnett County (portions), Roswell.
Illinois: Argenta, Augusta, Barry, Bethany, Blue Mound, Bluffs, Brighton, Cairo, Camp Point, Centralia, Chester, Evansville, Findlay, Grafton, Grayville, Greenfield, Griggsville, Hardin, Kinderhook, Lawrenceville, Lenzburg, Liberty, Maroa, McLeansboro, Mount Vernon, Moweaqua, Murrayville, Nashville, Okawville, Palmyra, Payson, Pleasant Hill, Sesser, Sparta, Steeleville, Tamms, Warrensburg, Waverly, Wayne City, Winchester, Woodlawn.
Indiana: Bainbridge, Bicknell, Carlisle, Clay City, Cynthiana, Dugger, Francisco, Gosport, Jasonville, Knightstown, Lyons, Middle-

town, Monroe City, Mount Summit, Oaktown, Odon, Patoka, Rockville, Rosedale, Shelburn, Shoals, Spencer, Vincennes, Washington, Wilkinson.
Kentucky: Black Mountain, Eolia, Fallsburg, Greenup, Inez, Jenkins, Prestonsburg, Varney, Wallins.
Maryland: Oakland.
Missouri: Advance, Bernie, Birch Tree, Bunker, Clarkton, Doniphan, Dudley, Ellington, Ellsinore, Eminence, Essex, Fremont, Fulton, Greenville, Mountain View, Naylor, Parma, Piedmont, Portageville, Puxico, Salem, Steele, Summersville, Van Buren, Wardell, Williamsville, Winona.
New Mexico: Ruidoso.
Ohio: Andover, Ava, Cameron, Corning, Cumberland, Kinsman, Middleburg (Noble County), Sarahsville, Senecaville, Summerfield, Warner, Woodsfield.
Pennsylvania: Boyers, Brave, Callensburg, Chicora, Cooperstown, Eau Claire, Garland, Grampian, Jamestown, Karthaus, Kellettville, Linesville, Marienville, Mill Village, North Clarion, Pinoak, Plumer, Rockmere, Sandy Lake, Snow Shoe, Somerset, Tidioute, Titusville, Townville, Wattsburg.
Tennessee: Alexandria, Columbia, Cookeville, Fayetteville, Kentucky Lake, Lawrenceburg, Lebanon, Manchester, McMinnville, Paris, Piney Flats, Shelbyville, Tiptonville, Tullahoma.
Texas: Spring.
Virginia: Bedford, Buchanan, Damascus, Franklin County, Lebanon, Pearisburg.
West Virginia: Alderson, Auburn, Bens Creek, Beverly, Buckhannon, Cairo, Cameron, Dingess, Dunlow, Farmington, Flemington, Franklin, Gilbert, Greenacres, Kermit, Kingwood, Lenore, Littleton, Madison, Matewan, Milton, Moorefield, Oak Hill, Panther, Pennsboro, Petersburg, Peterstown, Pine Grove, Point Pleasant, Pricetown, Pullman, Richwood, Rupert, Salem, Shinnston, Smithfield, Upper Tract, Wayne, West Milford, West Union, White Sulphur Springs, Wileyville, Williamson.
Total Basic Subscribers: 533,000 (0.78% of total
Total Pay Units: 261,200.

RIGEL COMMUNICATIONS INC.
70 Leach Hollow Rd.
Sherman, CT 06784
Phones: 203-354-9945; 212-686-2330
Fax: 212-545-0883
Officers:
Gordon Werner, Chmn.
Douglas Feltman, Chief Exec., Operating & Financial Officer

Branch Offices:
Gordon, GA 31031
Phone: 912-628-2434

Gulf Cable TV
503 3rd St.
Port St. Joe, FL 32456
Phone: 904-229-8880
Ownership: Douglas Feltman.
Cable Systems (14):
Florida: Port St. Joe.
Georgia: Haddock, Hoboken, Jeffersonville, Milan, Oak Park, Port Wentworth (portions), Rhine, Rochelle, Sparta, Stapleton, Stillmore, Toomsboro, Uvalda.
Total Basic Subscribers: 4,593.
Total Pay Units: 2,057.

JOHN C. RILEY
Rte. 1
Box 280
Dix, IL 62830
Phone: 618-266-7892
Cable Systems (1):
Illinois: Dix.
Total Basic Subscribers: 115.

RILEY VIDEO SERVICES
Box 5865
Athens, OH 45701-5865
Phone: 614-698-5510
Cable Systems (1):
Ohio: Amesville.
Total Basic Subscribers: 83.
Total Pay Units: 38.

RINGSTED CABLEVISION LTD.
Box 187
Ringsted, IA 50578
Phone: 712-866-1456
Fax: 712-866-0002
Officer:
Dale Johansen, Chmn. & Chief Exec. Officer
Ownership: Ringsted Telephone Co.
Represented (legal): Anderson, Pelzer & Hart.
Cable Systems (1):
Iowa: Ringsted.
Total Basic Subscribers: 213.
Total Pay Units: 56.
Other Holdings:
Cellular.
Telephone.

RIO CABLEVISION
Box 1412
Galesburg, IL 61402
Phone: 309-342-9681
Fax: 309-342-4408
Officer:
Robert G. Fischer Jr., Chief Exec. Officer
Cable Systems (4):
Illinois: Lake Bracken, Rio, Taylor Ridge, Wee-Ma-Tuk Hills.
Total Basic Subscribers: 838.
Total Pay Units: 253.

RIVER VALLEY CABLE TV INC.
1410 A Washington Blvd.
Williamsport, PA 17701
Phone: 570-322-4700
Fax: 570-601-1902
Officers:
John M. Roskowski, Pres.
Ken R. Michaels, V.P.
Represented (legal): Wiley, Rein & Fielding.
Cable Systems (1):
Pennsylvania: Mill Hall.
Total Basic Subscribers: 3,900.
Total Pay Units: 475.

RIVERTON CABLE TV INC.
Box 598
115 Riverton Ave.
Wagram, NC 28396
Phone: 919-369-2051
Officers:
Ernest Persinger, Pres.
Glenn White, V.P.
Ownership: Ernest Persinger.
Cable Systems (1):
North Carolina: Wagram.
Total Basic Subscribers: 182.

RIVIERA TELEPHONE CO.
Box 997
Riviera, TX 78379
Phone: 512-296-3232
Ownership: Bill Colston Jr., Pres.
Cable Systems (2):
Texas: Ricardo, Riviera.
Total Basic Subscribers: 88.

RIVIERA UTILITIES CABLE TV
Box 2050
413 E. Laurel Ave.
Foley, AL 36536
Phone: 334-943-5001
Fax: 334-943-5275
Officer:
H. Sewell St. John Jr., Chief Exec. Officer & Secy.-Treas.
Ownership: Community owned.
Represented (legal): Bryan Cave LLP.
Cable Systems (1):
Alabama: Foley.
Total Basic Subscribers: 6,511.
Total Pay Units: 6,400.

JIM ROBY
Suite 103
301 E. Hwy. 243
Canton, TX 75103
Phone: 903-567-2260
Cable Systems (1):
Texas: Canton.
Total Basic Subscribers: 1,370.

ROCK COUNTY TELEPHONE CO.
Box 400
1638 Lincoln St.
Blair, NE 68008
Phone: 402-533-1000
Officers:
Hugh W. Hunt, Chmn.
Richard A. Hunt, Vice Chmn.
Michael A. Jacobson, Pres. & Treas.
Michael A. Mines, V.P., Mktg.
Karen B. Aman, Secy.
Douglas L. Davidson, Chief Financial Officer
Ownership: Hugh W. Hunt & Richard A. Hunt, Principals. H. Hunt & R. Hunt also own Arlington Telephone Co., Eastern Nebraska Telephone Co. (see listings) & The Blair Telephone Co.
Cable Systems (1):
Nebraska: Bassett.
Total Basic Subscribers: 365.
Total Pay Units: 149.

ROCKPORT TELEPHONE CO.
Box 147
107 Opp St.
Rockport, MO 64482
Phone: 816-744-5311
Fax: 816-744-2120
Officers:
Robert L. Stanton, Pres.
Richard S. Garst, V.P.
Robert H. Fay, Secy.
James R. Amthor, Treas.
Cable Systems (1):
Missouri: Rockport.
Total Basic Subscribers: N.A.

ROGERS AMERICAN CABLESYSTEMS INC.
333 Bloor St. E, 10th Floor
Toronto, ON M4W 1G9
Canada
Phone: 416-935-3500
Fax: 416-935-3502
Officer:
Philip B. Lind, Chmn.

Branch Office:
Box 873107
Wasilla, AK 99687-3107
Phone: 907-373-5028
Ownership: Rogers Communications Inc. Rogers owns Canadian cable systems.
Represented (legal): Cole, Raywid & Braverman LLP.
Cable Systems (1):
Alaska: Palmer.
Total Basic Subscribers: 6,500.
Total Pay Units: 2,720.

RONCEVERTE TELEVISION CORP.
Box 525
Ronceverte, WV 24970-0525
Phone: 304-647-5455
Officers:
Donald R. Honaker, Pres.
Keith E. Morgan, Secy.-Treas.
Ownership: Subscriber owned.
Cable Systems (1):
West Virginia: Ronceverte.
Total Basic Subscribers: 1,010.
Total Pay Units: 218.

ROOME TELECOMMUNICATIONS INC.
Box 227
707 W. First St.
Halsey, OR 97348
Phone: 503-369-2211
Officer:
Randal L. Roome, Chief Exec. Officer
Cable Systems (1):
Oregon: Halsey.
Total Basic Subscribers: 170.
Total Pay Units: 95.
Other Holdings:
Telephone.

ROUNDUP CABLE INC.
1813 3rd St. W
Roundup, MT 59072-1559
Phone: 406-323-1787
Cable Systems (1):
Montana: Roundup.
Total Basic Subscribers: 439.
Total Pay Units: 235.

ROYAL TELEPHONE CO.
Box 182
Royal, IA 51357
Phone: 712-933-2615
Cable Systems (1):
Iowa: Royal.
Total Basic Subscribers: 182.

RUBY VALLEY CABLE CO. INC.
Box 153
Sheridan, MT 59749
Phone: 406-842-5941
Cable Systems (1):
Montana: Sheridan.
Total Basic Subscribers: 176.

RUNESTONE TELEPHONE ASSOCIATION
Box 336
123 Memorial Dr.
Hoffman, MN 56339
Phone: 612-986-6602
Cable Systems (3):
Minnesota: Barrett, Carlos, Elbow Lake.
Total Basic Subscribers: 1,910.
Total Pay Units: 143.

RURAL TELEPHONE SERVICE CO.

Box 234
Lenora, KS 67645
Phone: 785-567-4281
Cable Systems (13):
Kansas: Burr Oak, Edmond, Gorham, Grainfield, Herndon, Hill City, Kirwin, Lebanon, McDonald, Norcatur, Woodston.
Nebraska: Republican City, Stamford.
Total Basic Subscribers: N.A.

RUSSELL MUNICIPAL CABLE TV

Box 408
65 Main St.
Russell, MA 01071
Phone: 413-862-4707
Fax: 413-862-3103
E-mail: russell3@exit3.com
Officers:
Louis E. Garlo, Chief Exec. Officer
Susan B. Maxwell, Chief Operating Officer
Ownership: Community owned.
Cable Systems (1):
Massachusetts: Russell.
Total Basic Subscribers: 475.
Total Pay Units: 325.

S CORPORATION

Box 956
Paintsville, KY 41240
Phone: 606-789-3455
Officer:
Paul D. Butcher, V.P.
Cable Systems (1):
Kentucky: Van Lear.
Total Basic Subscribers: 2,820.
Total Pay Units: 770.

SAC COUNTY MUTUAL TELEPHONE CO.

Box 582
108 S. Maple St.
Odebolt, IA 51458
Phone: 712-668-2200
Fax: 712-668-2100
Officer:
Dale Schaefer, Mgr.
Ownership: Publicly owned.
Cable Systems (2):
Iowa: Arthur, Battle Creek.
Total Basic Subscribers: 329.
Total Pay Units: 142.

JAMES P. SAGE

Box 234A
228 Sage Rd.
Rural Retreat, VA 24368
Phone: 540-686-5242
Cable Systems (1):
Virginia: Rural Retreat.
Total Basic Subscribers: 700.
Total Pay Units: 250.

SALTILLO TV CABLE CORP.

Box 176
Saltillo, PA 17253
Phone: 814-448-3839
Officer:
Rodney Thomas, Pres.
Cable Systems (1):
Pennsylvania: Saltillo.
Total Basic Subscribers: 210 as of June 27, 1999.
Total Pay Units: 145.

CITY OF SAN BRUNO MUNICIPAL CABLE TV

398 El Camino Real
San Bruno, CA 94066
Phone: 415-877-8889
Fax: 415-871-5526
Ownership: Community owned.
Cable Systems (1):
California: San Bruno.
Total Basic Subscribers: 12,200 (0.02% of total
Total Pay Units: 6,506.

SAN JUAN CABLE & CONSTRUCTION

2568 1/2 MacKenzie Rd.
Bellingham, WA 98226
Phone: 206-758-7879
Officers:
Fred J. Morgan, Chmn.
Roy M. Budde, Chief Exec. Officer
Edward Warner, Chief Operating Officer
Richard Warbus, Chief Financial Officer
Cable Systems (1):
Washington: Lummi Indian Reservation.
Total Basic Subscribers: 217.
Total Pay Units: 104.

SAN SIMEON COMMUNITY CABLE INC.

Box 84
San Simeon, CA 93452
Phone: 805-927-5555
Cable Systems (1):
California: San Simeon Acres.
Total Basic Subscribers: N.A.

SANBORN TELEPHONE COOPERATIVE

Box 67
Woonsocket, SD 57385
Phone: 605-796-4411
Officer:
Gene Kroell, Gen. Mgr.
Cable Systems (5):
South Dakota: Canova, Ethan, Mitchell, Mount Vernon, Woonsocket.
Total Basic Subscribers: 2,282.

S & K TV SYSTEMS

5164 E. 5th St. N
Ladysmith, WI 54848
Phone: 715-532-3039
Officer:
Randy Scott, Mgr.
Ownership: Randy Scott & Tom Krenz.
Cable Systems (8):
Wisconsin: Anson Twp., Cable, Downsville, Lake Holcombe, Mikana, Minong, New Auburn, Weyerhaeuser.
Total Basic Subscribers: 1,417.
Total Pay Units: 235.

S & T COMMUNICATIONS OF NORTHWEST KANSAS

Box 99
Brewster, KS 67732
Phone: 913-694-7060
Cable Systems (5):
Kansas: Brewster, Grinnell, Healy, Kanorado, Winona.
Total Basic Subscribers: 340.
Total Pay Units: 55.

SANTA FE WIRELESS CABLE TV

Box 14670
Albuquerque, NM 87191
Phones: 505-237-2123; 800-698-3740
Officers:
Hazel Mickelson, Chmn.
Walter Mickelson, Pres.
Jane Scofield, Chief Exec. Officer
Thor Mickelson, V.P.
Jenni Olson, Chief Financial Officer
Wireless Cable Systems (2):
New Mexico: Las Cruces, Santa Fe.
Total Basic Subscribers: 1,470 as of July 13, 1999.
Other Holdings:
Multimedia Development Corp., see listing.

SATELLITE CABLE SERVICES INC.

Box 106
Brookings, SD 57006-0106
Phone: 605-692-5508
Officers:
Richard Cutler, Pres. & Chief Financial Officer
Doug Bierschbach, V.P.
Ownership: Richard Cutler, Robert Hayes, David Knutson & David Bozied, 100% jointly.
Cable Systems (40):
South Dakota: Ashton, Astoria, Brookings, Bruce, Bryant, Carthage, Castlewood, Cavour, Chamberlain, Chester, Colman, Conde, Eden, Estelline, Florence, Freeman, Gary, Hayti, Henry, Howard, Iroquois, Lake Norden, New Effington, Oldham, Pierpont, Prairiewood Village, Pukwana, Ramona, Raymond, Revillo, South Shore, Summit, Toronto, Trent, Wentworth, Wessington Springs, White, White Lake, Willow Lake, Yale.
Total Basic Subscribers: 15,214 (0.02% of total cable households).
Total Pay Units: 6,046.

SATELLITE OPERATIONS INC.

517 Petrie Ave.
St. Joseph, MI 49085-1927
Phone: 616-983-0206
Ownership: Tim Olmstead, 50%; Art Schmidt Jr., 50%.
Cable Systems (1):
Michigan: Keeler Twp.
Total Basic Subscribers: 500.
Total Pay Units: 540.

SATELLITE SIGNALS OF NEW ENGLAND INC.

168 N. Main St.
Rutland, VT 05701
Phone: 802-775-4112
Ownership: E. Nicholas Sangrunetti.
Wireless Cable Systems (1):
Vermont: Rutland.
Total Basic Subscribers: N.A.
Other Holdings:
MMDS, see listing.

SATTERLEE LEASING CORP.

RD No. 1
Box 173
Rochester Mills, PA 15771
Phone: 412-397-2400
Officers:
Dan Satterlee, Pres.
David Satterlee, V.P.
Gary Satterlee, V.P.
Ownership: Dan Satterlee, Principal.
Cable Systems (2):
Pennsylvania: Rayne Twp., Sandy Twp. (Clearfield County).
Total Basic Subscribers: N.A.

SAVAGE COMMUNICATIONS INC.

Box 810
206 Power Ave. N
Hinckley, MN 55037
Phone: 320-384-7442
Fax: 320-384-7446
Officers:
Ronald W. Savage, Pres.
Mike Danielson, V.P., Operations
Paula Savage, Secy.-Treas.
Ownership: Ron Savage, Principal; Mike Danielson, Pat McCabe & Jerry Meier.
Cable Systems (16):
Minnesota: Barnum, East Gull Lake, Floodwood, Hill City, Isle, McGregor, Motley, Pengilly, Pillager, Sandstone, Stacy, Taylors Falls, Verndale.
South Dakota: Mission, Rosebud, St. Francis.
Total Basic Subscribers: 6,450.
Total Pay Units: 1,960.

SAVANNAH QUARTERS CABLE TV

2 Southbridge Blvd.
Savannah, GA 31405
Phone: 912-651-5400
Fax: 912-651-5444
Cable Systems (1):
Georgia: Southbridge.
Total Basic Subscribers: N.A.

SBC MEDIA VENTURES

20 W. Gude Dr.
Rockville, MD 20850
Phone: 301-294-7633
Fax: 301-309-5033; 301-251-1635
Officers:
Edward E. Whitacre, Chmn. & Chief Exec. Officer
Jameson Scott, V.P., Mktg. & Programming
Steve Dimmitt, Dir., Strategic Business Development
Ownership: SBC Communications Inc. SBCCI has 10% interest in Compagnie Generale des Videocommunications, French cable operator; 50% interest in SBC CableComs, United Kingdom cable & telephone company; 10% interest in Societe Francaise du Radiocommunication, French cellular communications company; 40% interest in VTR Inversiones, Chilean telecommunications company. SBCCI is also parent of Southwestern Bell Telephone Co. & Southwestern Bell Mobile Systems. 30% TelKom (South Africa).
Represented (legal): Fleischman & Walsh LLP.
Wireless Cable Systems (2):
California: Riverside & San Bernardino, San Jose.
Total Basic Subscribers: 269,056 (0.39% of total
Total Pay Units: 279,733.
Other Holdings:
MDS, MMDS, see listing.
Note: Sold to Prime Cable Corp. 1998.

SCA CABLE INC.

1105 C.T.H. (D)
Nekoosa, WI 54457
Phone: 715-325-3652
Cable Systems (1):
Wisconsin: Rome Twp.
Total Basic Subscribers: 641.
Total Pay Units: 230.

NEAL SCHNOG

7120 Buckingham Blvd.
Berkeley, CA 94705
Phone: 801-745-0745

Fax: 310-530-5603
Cable Systems (1):
Utah: Huntsville.
Total Basic Subscribers: 275.
Total Pay Units: 40.
Other Holdings:
Schnog is publisher of the Cable Yellow Pages.

SCHURZ COMMUNICATIONS INC.

225 W. Colfax Ave.
South Bend, IN 46626
Phone: 219-287-1001
Fax: 219-287-2257
Officers:
Franklin D. Schurz Jr., Pres.
James M. Schurz, Sr. V.P., Newspapers
James D. Freeman, Sr. V.P., Bcstg.
E. Berry Smith, Sr. V.P.
Mary Schurz, V.P. & Secy.
Scott C. Schurz, V.P.
David C. Ray, V.P.
James G. Young Jr., Treas. & Chief Financial Officer
Ownership: Schurz Investment Partnership, 75.17%; others, 24.83%.
Represented (legal): Hogan & Hartson LLP; Bryan Cave LLP.
Cable Systems (4):
Florida: Coral Springs, Weston.
Maryland: Fort Ritchie, Hagerstown.
Total Basic Subscribers: 81,858 (0.12% of total cable households).
Total Pay Units: 52,228.
Other Holdings:
TV, see listing.
Newspapers, radio stations.

SCI CABLE INC.

No. 203
536 N.W. Tyler Court
Topeka, KS 66608
Phone: 913-234-4253
Officer:
Kirk A. Keberlein, Pres.
Represented (legal): Robert North.
Cable Systems (2):
Kansas: Grantville, St. George.
Total Basic Subscribers: 663.

SCIO CABLEVISION INC.

Box 210
Scio, OR 97374
Phones: 503-394-2995; 503-394-3366
Fax: 503-394-3999
Officers:
Mike Glaser, Chmn.
Gary Clevenger, Chief Exec. Officer
Danny Dutey, Chief Operating Officer
Joyce Morse, Secy.-Treas.
Tom Rogers, Chief Financial Officer
Cable Systems (1):
Oregon: Scio.
Total Basic Subscribers: 430.
Total Pay Units: 122.
Other Holdings:
Telephone.

SCOPE CABLE TV OF NEBRASKA

Box 500
1635 Front St.
Blair, NE 68008
Phone: 402-426-6434
Ownership: Nebraska Partnership; J. J. Garrigan; S. M. Jensen, Principals. Garrigan & Jensen are affiliated with Great Plains Communications Inc., an independent telephone co.
Cable Systems (6):
Nebraska: Elgin, Hershey, North Bend, Palisade, Scribner, Sutherland.
Total Basic Subscribers: 3,165.
Total Pay Units: 1,733.

SCOTT TELECOM & ELECTRONICS INC.

Box 489
Gate City, VA 24251-0489
Phone: 540-452-2201
Fax: 540-452-2447
Officers:
John Kilgore, Pres.
William J. Franklin, Exec. V.P.
Daniel E. Odom, Asst. Exec. V.P.
John Brickey Jr., V.P.
John Ferguson, Secy.-Treas.
Ownership: Scott County Telephone Cooperative.
Cable Systems (1):
Virginia: Weber City.
Total Basic Subscribers: 3,777.
Total Pay Units: 380.
Other Holdings:
Manufacturer.

SCRANTON TELEPHONE CO.

Box 8
1200 Main St.
Scranton, IA 51462
Phone: 712-652-3355
Fax: 712-652-3777
Cable Systems (1):
Iowa: Scranton.
Total Basic Subscribers: 225.
Total Pay Units: 50.

SCS COMMUNICATIONS & SECURITY

Box 477
475 N. 2nd
Stayton, OR 97383
Phone: 503-769-7388
Ownership: Stayton Cooperative Telephone Co.
Cable Systems (2):
Oregon: Idanha, Sublimity.
Total Basic Subscribers: 5,761.
Total Pay Units: 1,164.
Other Holdings:
Telephone.

SEARLE COMMUNICATION INC.

Box 39
47 3rd St.
Monument, CO 80132
Phone: 719-481-2451
Officers:
Robert Searle, Pres.
Stan Searle, Chief Exec. Officer
Rebecca Hendricks, Chief Financial Officer
Ownership: Stan Searle & Lorna Searle, 100% jointly.
Cable Systems (2):
Colorado: Cheyenne Mountain Estates, Monument.
Total Basic Subscribers: 5,424.
Total Pay Units: 705.

SEMO COMMUNICATIONS INC.

Box C
Sikeston, MO 63801
Phone: 573-471-6594
Fax: 573-471-6878
Officers:
Travis E. Garrett, Chmn.
Tyrone Garrett, Pres.
Shannon Garrett, V.P. & Secy.-Treas.
Ownership: Travis E. Garrett, 50.1%; Tyrone Garrett, 21.3%; Shannon Garrett, 14.3%; Denise Antrobus, 14.3%.
Represented (legal): William Clayton Vandivort.
Cable Systems (6):
Missouri: Anniston, Delta, Matthews, Morley, Pocahontas, Wyatt.
Total Basic Subscribers: 1,673.
Total Pay Units: 497.
Other Holdings:
Cable construction.

SERVICE ELECTRIC CABLE TV INC.

201 W. Centre St.
Mahanoy City, PA 17948
Phones: 570-773-2585; 570-874-1010
Fax: 570-773-0276
Officers:
John Walson Jr., Pres.
Hoyt Walter, V.P.
Margaret Walson, Secy.
Ownership: Margaret Walson.
Represented (legal): Pepper & Corazzini.
Cable Systems (13):
New Jersey: Phillipsburg, Sparta.
Pennsylvania: Birdsboro, Bloomsburg, Easton, Emmaus, Fleetwood, Hazleton, Kutztown, Lehigh Valley, Mahanoy City, Sunbury, Wilkes-Barre.
Total Basic Subscribers: 292,000 (0.43% of total
Total Pay Units: 120,000.
Other Holdings:
Common Carrier.

SHADE GAP TV ASSN.

HC 83 Box 398
Shade Gap, PA 17255
Phone: 814-259-3673
Officers:
Richard Price, Pres.
Mary McMullen, Secy.-Treas.
Ownership: Community owned.
Cable Systems (1):
Pennsylvania: Shade Gap.
Total Basic Subscribers: 120.
Total Pay Units: 29.

VIOLA M. SHAFFER & FAMILY

Box 237
512 Church St.
Waynoka, OK 73860
Phone: 580-824-9311
Cable Systems (1):
Oklahoma: Waynoka.
Total Basic Subscribers: N.A.

VICTOR E. SHARER

Box 100
San Carlos, AZ 85550
Phone: 602-475-2550
Cable Systems (1):
Arizona: San Carlos.
Total Basic Subscribers: 1,100.
Total Pay Units: 850.

R. J. SHELLEY CATV

Box 243
Mount Pleasant Mills, PA 17853
Phone: 717-539-8511
Ownership: Russell J. Shelley.
Cable Systems (2):
Pennsylvania: Mount Pleasant Mills, Richfield.
Total Basic Subscribers: N.A.

SHELLSBURG CABLEVISION INC.

Box 390
Shellsburg, IA 53332
Phone: 319-436-2224
Officers:
Roy M. Fish, Pres.
Rex Miller, V.P.
Robert H. Smith, Secy.
Warren Richart, Treas.
Ownership: Community owned.
Cable Systems (8):
Iowa: Central City, Coggon, Delhi, Hopkinton, Luxemburg, Ryan, Shellsburg, Worthington.
Total Basic Subscribers: 2,421.
Total Pay Units: 1000.
Other Holdings:
Telephone.

SHENANDOAH TELECOMMUNICATIONS INC.

Box 459
Edinburg, VA 22824
Phone: 703-984-4140
Cable Systems (1):
Virginia: Edinburg.
Total Basic Subscribers: 2,700.
Total Pay Units: 430.
Other Holdings:
Telephone: Shenandoah Telephone Co.

SHERMAN CABLEVISION

Box 38
Houlton, ME 04730
Phone: 207-532-3320
Ownership: Ronald Dee.
Cable Systems (1):
Maine: Sherman Mills.
Total Basic Subscribers: 211.

SHERWOOD TELEPHONE CO.

Box 4574
Sherwood, OH 43556
Phone: 419-899-2121
Fax: 419-899-4567
Cable Systems (1):
Ohio: Sherwood.
Total Basic Subscribers: 115.

R. EDWARD SHIELDS

Box 87-B
RD No. 1
McClure, PA 17841
Phone: 717-543-5972
Cable Systems (2):
Pennsylvania: Honey Grove, Walnut.
Total Basic Subscribers: N.A.

SHOALS CABLE TV INC.

Box 267
Russellville, AL 35653
Phone: 205-332-9730
Officers:
John Dennis, Pres.
Jerold Rogers, Secy.-Treas.
Ownership: Jerold Rogers, 50%; John Dennis, 50%.
Cable Systems (2):
Alabama: Hawk Pride Mountain, Hillsboro.
Total Basic Subscribers: 800.
Total Pay Units: 200.
Cable Holdings:
CATV Unlimited Inc., cable construction co.

JOHN P. SHOEMAKER JR.

Box 5064
Martinsville, VA 24115
Phone: 804-685-1521
Cable Systems (1):
Virginia: Brosville.
Total Basic Subscribers: 1,666.
Total Pay Units: 775.

SHREWSBURY'S COMMUNITY CABLEVISION
100 Maple Ave.
Shrewsbury, MA 01545
Phone: 508-755-5450
Fax: 508-842-9419
Officer:
Richard A. Corbi, Finance & Administration
Ownership: Community owned.
Cable Systems (1):
Massachusetts: Shrewsbury.
Total Basic Subscribers: 10,446 (0.02% of total
Total Pay Units: 8,157.

GARY SIEBRING
Box 36
301 S. Main St.
George, IA 51237
Phone: 712-475-3747
Fax: 712-475-2517
Cable Systems (1):
Iowa: George.
Total Basic Subscribers: 395.
Total Pay Units: 206.

SIERRA DAWN ESTATES HOMEOWNERS ASSN.
950 S. Lyon
Hemet, CA 92343
Phones: 714-925-6026; 714-925-6502
Cable Systems (1):
California: Sierra Dawn Estates.
Total Basic Subscribers: 1,474.

SIOUX VALLEY RURAL TELEVISION INC.
Box 20
Colman, SD 57017
Phone: 605-534-3241
Fax: 605-534-3522
E-mail: jbrick@svswe.com
Web site: http://www.svtv.com
Officers:
James Kiley, Chief Exec. Officer
Joel Brick, Dir., Telecommunications
Ownership: Sioux Valley Empire Electric Assn.
Represented (legal): Lukas, McGowan, Nace & Gutierrez.
Wireless Cable Systems (3):
South Dakota: Colman, Rowena, Yankton.
Total Basic Subscribers: 6,000.
Total Pay Units: 2,000.
Other Holdings:
MMDS, see listing.

SISKIYOU CABLEVISION INC.
Box 399
11903 Main St.
Fort Jones, CA 96032-0399
Phone: 916-468-5666
Fax: 916-468-5401
Officers:
Betty Hendricks, Chief Exec. Officer
Jim G. Hendricks, Chief Financial Officer
Cable Systems (1):
California: Fort Jones.
Total Basic Subscribers: 953.
Total Pay Units: 289.

SIX MILE RUN TV CORP.
Six Mile Run, PA 16679
Phone: 814-928-4897
Ownership: Community owned.
Cable Systems (1):
Pennsylvania: Six Mile Run.
Total Basic Subscribers: 64.

SJOBERG'S CABLE TV INC.
315 N. Main
Thief River Falls, MN 56701
Phone: 218-681-3044
Officers:
Richard Sjoberg, Pres.
Stan Sjoberg, Secy.-Treas.
Ownership: Richard Sjoberg, 50%; Stan Sjoberg, 50%.
Represented (legal): Cole, Raywid & Braverman LLP.
Cable Systems (11):
Minnesota: Badger, Baudette, Greenbush, Karlstad, Middle River, Newfolden, Red Lake Falls, Roseau, Thief River Falls, Warren, Warroad.
Total Basic Subscribers: 7,934.

SKISAT
10 Abbott Park
Providence, RI 02903
Phone: 401-272-2558
Ownership: Tom Corcoran, 50%; Philip R. DeSano, 50%.
Cable Systems (1):
New Hampshire: Waterville Valley.
Total Basic Subscribers: 1,150.
Total Pay Units: 250.

SKYCABLE TV OF MADISON LLC
2520 Todd Dr.
Madison, WI 53713
Phone: 608-271-6999
Fax: 608-271-2256
Officer:
Kim A. Egan, Managing Partner
Ownership: Wisconsin Wireless Partners.
Represented (legal): Murphy & Desmond.
Wireless Cable Systems (1):
Wisconsin: Madison.
Total Basic Subscribers: 6,000.
Total Pay Units: 3,000.
Other Holdings:
MMDS, see listing.

SKY CABLEVISION LTD.
Box 65
Meridian, MS 39302
Phone: 601-485-6980
Fax: 601-483-0103
Ownership: Berry Ward.
Cable Systems (5):
Alabama: Bellamy, Boligee, Forkland, Providence, Sweet Water.
Total Basic Subscribers: 300.

SKY SCAN CABLE CO.
Box 57
Creighton, NE 68729-0057
Phone: 402-358-3510
Fax: 402-358-3864
Ownership: Douglas Laflin, Pres.
Cable Systems (17):
Iowa: Blencoe.
Nebraska: Allen, Bristow Twp., Brunswick, Chambers, Columbus (portions), Creston, Hadar, Page (village), Palmer, Pilger, Spalding, Uehling, Winside.
South Dakota: Fairfax, Geddes, Pickstown.
Total Basic Subscribers: 2,135.
Total Pay Units: 561.

SLEDGE TELEPHONE CO.
Box 68
Sunflower, MS 38778
Phone: 601-569-3311
Cable Systems (1):
Mississippi: Sunflower.
Total Basic Subscribers: N.A.

SLEEPY EYE TELEPHONE CO.
Box 306
Sleepy Eye, MN 56085
Phone: 507-794-3361
Fax: 507-794-2351
Officers:
Curtis A. Sampson, Chmn.
Steven H. Sjogren, Pres.
Bob Weiss, V.P., Operations
Dennis Spetser, Secy.-Treas.
Cable Systems (1):
Minnesota: Goodhue.
Total Basic Subscribers: 185.
Total Pay Units: 38.

RAHE SLOVER
Phone: 830-775-3567
Cable Systems (1):
Texas: Sheffield.
Total Basic Subscribers: 65.

SMALL TOWN CABLE CORP.
225 Highland Villa
Nashville, TN 37211
Phone: 877-368-2110
Officers:
Doc Collins, V.P.
T. Hasbrouck, Controller
Ownership: Vince King, Managing Partner.
Cable Systems (6):
Tennessee: Chapel Hill, Cornersville, Lynnville, Pulaski, Rogersville, Summertown.
Total Basic Subscribers: 3,700.
Total Pay Units: 1,500.

RAY SMEAL
100 Curtis St.
Philipsburg, PA 16866
Phone: 814-342-3868
Cable Systems (1):
Pennsylvania: Graham Twp.
Total Basic Subscribers: 392.
Total Pay Units: 137.

SMITH, DEMARCO & CO.
Suite 17
5635 Westfield Ave.
Pennsauken, NJ 08110
Phone: 609-663-3311
Officer:
Edward J. DeMarco, Pres.
Cable Systems (1):
Massachusetts: North Brookfield.
Total Basic Subscribers: N.A.

SMS CABLE CO.
Box 1119
30 W. Main
Carnegie, OK 73015
Phone: 405-654-1571
Officers:
H. S. Scott, Pres.
Troy Scott, V.P.
Wade Scott, V.P.
Suzanne Scott, Secy.-Treas.
Ownership: H. S. Scott, 97%; Troy Scott, 1%; Wade Scott, 1%; Suzanne Scott, 1%.
Cable Systems (1):
Oklahoma: Carnegie.
Total Basic Subscribers: 850.
Total Pay Units: 360.

CASSON F. SNYDER
Box 207
Hornell, NY 14843
Phone: 607-478-8969
Cable Systems (2):
New York: Canaseraga, Greenwood.
Total Basic Subscribers: 306.
Total Pay Units: 78.

SNYDER MICROWAVE COMMUNICATIONS LC
Box 940008
Plano, TX 75094
Phone: 214-424-1661
Wireless Cable Systems (1):
Texas: Snyder.
Total Basic Subscribers: N.A.

DOUG SODEN
RD 2
Box 60-D
Rome, PA 18837
Phone: 717-247-2512
Cable Systems (1):
Pennsylvania: Ulster.
Total Basic Subscribers: 400.
Total Pay Units: 420.

SOMERFIELD CABLE TV CO.
6511 National Pike
Addison, PA 15411
Phone: 814-395-3084
Ownership: Michael J. Diehl, Chmn. & Chief Exec. Officer.
Cable Systems (1):
Pennsylvania: Addison Twp. (southern portion).
Total Basic Subscribers: 675.
Total Pay Units: 150.

SONIC COMMUNICATIONS—Sold to Charter Communications Inc. 1998.

SOURIS RIVER TELECOMMUNICATIONS COOPERATIVE
Box 2027
Minot, ND 58702-2027
Phone: 701-858-5300
Fax: 701-722-1225
Officers:
Dennis Erber, Pres.
Warren Hight, Chief Exec. Officer
Steve Lysne, Chief Operating Officer
Marvin Thom, Secy.-Treas.
John Reiser, Chief Financial Officer
Ownership: Subscriber owned.
Represented (legal): Pringle Herigstad.
Cable Systems (11):
North Dakota: Berthold, Butte, Carpio, Des Lacs, Donnybrook, Granville, Karlsruhe, Maxbass, Metigoshe, Sherwood, Westhope.
Total Basic Subscribers: 1,042.
Total Pay Units: 293.
Other Holdings:
Telephone.

SOUTH BUFFALO CABLEVISION
259 Horseshoe Dr.
Freeport, PA 16229
Phone: 412-295-3466
Ownership: Richard P. Koglman, Principal.
Cable Systems (1):
Pennsylvania: South Buffalo Twp.
Total Basic Subscribers: 162.

SOUTH CHICAGO CABLE INC.
721 E. 112th St.
Chicago, IL 60628
Phone: 312-468-6628
Cable Systems (1):
Illinois: Chicago (area 5) 20%.
Total Basic Subscribers: 74,000 (0.11% of total cable households).
Total Pay Units: 115,669.

SOUTH HOLT CABLEVISION INC.
Box 227
Oregon, MO 64473
Phone: 816-446-3391
Ownership: Robert Williams, Chmn. & Chief Exec. Officer.
Cable Systems (1):
Missouri: Oregon.
Total Basic Subscribers: 425.
Total Pay Units: 182.

SOUTH KENTUCKY SERVICES
Box 910
Somerset, KY 42502
Phone: 606-387-6476
Fax: 606-679-8279
Ownership: South Kentucky Rural Electric Co-operative Corp.
Cable Systems (1):
Kentucky: Clinton County.
Total Basic Subscribers: N.A.

SOUTH SHORE CABLE TV INC.
6301 Broad Branch Rd.
Chevy Chase, MD 20815
Cable Systems (4):
Georgia: Luthersville.
Illinois: Mason.
New York: Cato (town).
Texas: Glen Rose.
Total Basic Subscribers: 2,465.
Total Pay Units: 1,112.

SOUTH SIDE TV ASSN.
Church St.
Sheffield, PA 16347
Phone: 814-968-3806
Officers:
Robert W. McMillen, Pres.
Jody Nuhfer, Secy.-Treas.
Ownership: Non-profit organization.
Cable Systems (1):
Pennsylvania: Sheffield.
Total Basic Subscribers: 350.

SOUTHEAST CABLE TV INC.
Suite 200
3902 Corporex Park Dr.
Tampa, FL 33619-1132
Phone: 813-630-5500
Officers:
James F. Cavanaugh, Pres.
Bob Heide, V.P.

Branch Office:
Boston, GA 31626-0584
Phone: 912-498-4191
Represented (legal): MacFarland, Ferguson, Allison & Kelly.
Cable Systems (7):
Florida: Hosford, Keaton Bead, White Springs.
Georgia: Boston, Coolidge, Ochlocknee, Pavo.
Total Basic Subscribers: 1,600.
Total Pay Units: 600.

SOUTHERN CABLE COMMUNICATIONS
Box 1998
Georgetown, SC 29442
Phone: 803-546-2200
Fax: 803-527-2314
Officers:
Ron Charlton Sr., Pres.
Ron Charlton Jr., Chief Exec. Officer
Robert Adkison, Chief Operating Officer
Keith Harper, Chief Financial Officer

Branch Offices:
Summerton, SC 29198
Phone: 803-478-2823

Hwy. 17-401
North Myrtle Beach, SC 29556
Phone: 803-399-9222
Ownership: Bonnie Charlton & Ron Charlton Sr., 100% jointly. Ron Charlton Sr. is also a principal of Southern Wireless Co. Inc., see listing in MDS/MMDS Ownership.
Represented (legal): Pepper & Corazzini.
Cable Systems (3):
North Carolina: Bald Head Island.
South Carolina: Dunes West, Lake View.
Total Basic Subscribers: 943.
Total Pay Units: 435.
Other Holdings:
Telephone.

SOUTHERN CABLEVISION INC.
Box 106
165 E. Lee St.
Dawson, GA 31742
Phone: 912-995-3373
Fax: 912-995-6224
Officers:
Milton F. Foster, Pres.
Pamela S. Foster, Secy.-Treas.
Ownership: Milton Foster.
Represented (legal): W.T. Gamble III.
Cable Systems (4):
Georgia: Bronwood, Preston, Sasser.
Minnesota: Grand Meadow.
Total Basic Subscribers: 403.
Total Pay Units: 202.

SOUTHERN KANSAS TELEPHONE CO.
112 S. Lee
Clearwater, KS 67026
Phones: 316-584-2255; 800-362-2396
Fax: 316-584-2260
Cable Systems (11):
Kansas: Atlanta, Cedar Vale, Dearing, Dexter, Elk City, Grenola, Howard, Longton, Moline, Severy, Viola.
Total Basic Subscribers: 1,388.

SOUTHERN NEW ENGLAND TELECOMMUNICATIONS CORP.
227 Church St.
New Haven, CT 06510
Phone: 203-771-4474
Fax: 203-772-3998
Ownership: SBC Communications Inc.
Represented (legal): Fleischman & Walsh LLP.
Cable Systems (1):
Connecticut: Unionville.
Total Basic Subscribers: N.A.

SOUTHERN VERMONT CABLE CO.
Box 166
Bondville, VT 05340-0166
Phone: 518-843-3037
Officers:
Herbert Scialabba, Chmn.
Ernest Scialabba, Pres.
Carol Scialabba, Secy.-Treas.
Ownership: Ernest Scialabba & Herbert Scialabba.
Cable Systems (2):
Vermont: Newfane, Putney.
Total Basic Subscribers: 841.
Total Pay Units: 113.

SOUTHWEST MONTANA CORP.
Box 707
Gardiner, MT 59030
Phone: 406-848-7561
Officer:
Ken Dixon, Pres.
Cable Systems (2):
Montana: Gardiner.
Wyoming: Mammoth Hot Springs.
Total Basic Subscribers: 325.
Total Pay Units: 80.

SOUTHWEST TELECOMMUNICATIONS CO-OP ASSN. INC.
Box 309
Palisade, NE 69040
Phone: 308-285-3880
Fax: 308-285-3811
Officer:
David Fahrenbruch, Chief Financial Officer
Represented (legal): Burger & Bennet.
Wireless Cable Systems (5):
Colorado: Wray.
Nebraska: Bartley, North Platte, Oshkosh, Wauneta.
Total Basic Subscribers: 1,648.
Total Pay Units: 326.
Other Holdings:
MMDS, see listing.

SOUTHWESTERN CABLE INVESTMENTS CORP.
Box 1656
119 E. 4th St.
Hereford, TX 79045
Phone: 806-364-3912
Fax: 806-364-7147
Officer:
Wendell Mayes Jr., Chief Exec. Officer
Cable Systems (1):
Texas: Hereford 20%.
Total Basic Subscribers: 4,188.
Total Pay Units: 1,000.

SOUTHWESTERN CATV INC.
One Big Rock Blvd.
Medicine Park, OK 73557
Phone: 405-529-2288
Ownership: Edward Hillary & Steven Hillary, Principals.
Cable Systems (7):
Oklahoma: Alex, Apache, Cement, Grandfield, Randlett, Sterling, Tuttle.
Total Basic Subscribers: 1,359.
Total Pay Units: 37.

CHARLIE SPERR
Box 10
Government Camp, OR 97028
Phone: 503-272-3333
Cable Systems (1):
Oregon: Government Camp.
Total Basic Subscribers: 65.
Total Pay Units: 65.

SPILLWAY CABLEVISION INC.
Box 337
Maringouin, LA 70757
Phone: 504-625-2311
Officers:
Craig Greene, Pres.
Mark Greene, Secy.-Treas.
Ownership: Craig Greene & Mark Greene, Principals.
Cable Systems (2):
Louisiana: Innis, Maringouin.
Total Basic Subscribers: 1,601.
Total Pay Units: 1,166.

SPINK ELECTRIC
Box 40
Redfield SD, 57469
Phone: 605-472-0380
Wireless Cable Systems (1):
South Dakota: Redfield.
Total Basic Subscribers: N.A.

SPLITROCK TELECOM COOPERATIVE INC.
612 3rd St.
Garretson, SD 57030
Phone: 605-594-3411
Fax: 605-594-6776
Cable Systems (1):
South Dakota: Garretson.
Total Basic Subscribers: 1,941.
Total Pay Units: 740.
Other Holdings:
Telephone.

SPRING CITY CABLE TV INC.
Box 729
Spring City, TN 37381
Phone: 423-365-7288
Cable Systems (1):
Tennessee: Spring City.
Total Basic Subscribers: 2,000.
Total Pay Units: 692.

SPRING MILLS TV CO.
RD 1
Box 241
Spring Mills, PA 16875
Phone: 814-422-8460
Officers:
Neal Roy Thompson, Pres.
Schenley Johnson, Secy.
Ownership: Community owned.
Cable Systems (1):
Pennsylvania: Spring Mills.
Total Basic Subscribers: 192.

CITY OF SPRINGFIELD
3529 E. 3rd St.
Panama City, FL 32401
Phone: 904-785-9516
Ownership: Community owned.
Cable Systems (1):
Florida: Springfield.
Total Basic Subscribers: 2,509.

SPRINGPORT TELEPHONE CO.
Box 208
137 E. Main St.
Springport, MI 49284
Phone: 517-857-3500
Cable Systems (1):
Michigan: Springport Twp.
Total Basic Subscribers: N.A.

SPRINGVILLE COOPERATIVE TELEPHONE ASSN. INC.
207 Broadway
Springville, IA 52336
Phone: 319-854-6500
Cable Systems (1):
Iowa: Springville.
Total Basic Subscribers: 556.
Total Pay Units: 329.

DANNY SPURLOCK
Box 268
Groesbeck, TX 76642
Phone: 817-729-2221

Cable Systems (1):
Texas: Rosebud.
Total Basic Subscribers: 340.
Total Pay Units: 100.

SRW INC.

71 Cedar Ave.
Hershey, PA 17033
Phone: 717-533-3322
Fax: 717-533-3344
Officers:
Richard Snyder, Pres.
John Weidman, V.P. & Secy.
Ownership: Richard L. Snyder & John P. Weidman, 100% jointly.
Cable Systems (3):
Pennsylvania: Broad Top City 50%, Mill Creek, Williamsburg (Blair County).
Total Basic Subscribers: 13,700 (0.02% of total
Total Pay Units: 3,200.

ST. CROIX TELEPHONE CO.

Box 318
154 E. 2nd St.
New Richmond, WI 54017
Phone: 715-246-2145
Fax: 715-246-7111
Ownership: Rochester (NY) Telephone.
Cable Systems (1):
Wisconsin: New Richmond.
Total Basic Subscribers: 2,223.
Total Pay Units: 576.
Other Holdings:
Cellular.

ST. JOHN CABLE CO. INC.

Box 268
St. John, WA 99171
Phone: 509-648-3322
Cable Systems (1):
Washington: St. John.
Total Basic Subscribers: 513.
Other Holdings:
Telephone.
50% interest in Colfax Highline Cable Co., see listing.

ST. MARYS TV

314 S. Michael St.
St. Marys, PA 15857
Phone: 814-781-1466
Fax: 814-834-1706
Officers:
Frank A. Vitarelli, Pres.
Cletas Heller, Secy.-Treas.
Ownership: Adelphia Communications Corp., see listing, 50%; Cletas Heller, 50%.
Cable Systems (1):
Pennsylvania: St. Marys.
Total Basic Subscribers: 6,810.
Total Pay Units: 3,042.

STANDARD TOBACCO CO. INC.

Box 100
626 Forest Ave.
Maysville, KY 41056
Phone: 606-564-5678
Officers:
James A. Finch, Chmn., Pres. & Chief Exec. Officer
Ivan Cracraft, Chief Operating & Financial Officer
Ronald Buerkley, V.P., Cable
Karen Campbell, Secy.
Ownership: James A. Finch Jr., 90%; Barbara Tucker, 10%. Finch owns WFTM-AM-FM, Maysville, KY.
Represented (legal): Rose, Zweigant & Kirk.
Cable Systems (4):
Kentucky: Augusta, Brooksville, Maysville, Mount Olivet.
Total Basic Subscribers: 6,402.
Total Pay Units: 1,716.

STANLEY CABLEVISION INC.

Box 400
Stanley, ND 58784
Phone: 701-628-3333
Ownership: Fred Beehler, Gordon Wilhelmi, James Wilhelmi & Mark Wilhelmi, 100% jointly.
Cable Systems (1):
North Dakota: Stanley.
Total Basic Subscribers: 558.

STAR CABLE ASSOCIATES

100 Greentree Commons
381 Mansfield Ave.
Pittsburgh, PA 15220
Phone: 412-937-0099
Fax: 412-937-0145
Officers:
James C. Roddey, Chmn. & Chief Exec. Officer
Michael R. Haislip, Pres. & Chief Operating Officer
Richard W. Talarico, Chief Financial Officer
Daniel G. Skantar, Dir., Communications

Branch Offices:

Ville Platte, LA 70586

800 Hwy. 36 N
Bldg. 3, Suite 132
Brazoria, TX 77422

4720 Mahoning Ave.
Box 4458
Youngstown, OH 44515

200 Scurry St.
Box 626
Daingerfield, TX 75638
Ownership: The Hawthorne Group; James C. Roddey, Principals.
Represented (legal): Wiley, Rein & Fielding; Hogan & Hartson LLP.
Cable Systems (40):
Louisiana: Fort Polk, Lydia, Many, Ville Platte, Zwolle.
Ohio: Auburn Twp., Berlin Twp. (Mahoning County), Bloomingdale, Coitsville Twp., Denmark Twp., Knoxville, Nelson Twp., Newton Twp., Rock Creek, Thompson Twp. (Geauga County), Vernon.
Texas: Algoa, Arcola, Boling, Brazoria, Crystal Beach, Daingerfield, Goodrich, Guy, Heights, Hemphill, Holiday Lakes, Indian Springs, Linden, Liverpool, Mont Belvieu, Naples, Ore City, Oyster Creek, Pineland, Pleak, San Leon, Santa Fe, Sargent, Wallis.
Total Basic Subscribers: 42,866 (0.06% of total
Total Pay Units: 22,484.
Note: Sale to Classic Cable pends.

STAR SATELLITE TV & CABLE

410 E. Walnut St.
Glenwood City, WI 54013
Phones: 715-643-2419; 715-643-2822
Fax: 715-643-2822
Ownership: Steve Schmidt, Pres. & Gen. Mgr.
Cable Systems (1):
Wisconsin: Boyceville.
Total Basic Subscribers: 110.
Total Pay Units: 18.

WILLIAM STARK

Box 7477
Omar, WV 25638
Phone: 304-946-2871
Cable Systems (2):
West Virginia: Hampden, Omar.
Total Basic Subscribers: 172.
Total Pay Units: 21.

STARVISION INC.

Box 319
Clinton, NC 28329
Phone: 910-564-7888
Fax: 910-564-5410
Cable Systems (2):
North Carolina: Garland, Roseboro.
Total Basic Subscribers: 811.
Total Pay Units: 335.

STARWEST INC.

Box 98
Atkins, IA 52206
Phone: 319-446-7858
Ownership: John Stookesberry, Principal.
Cable Systems (8):
Iowa: Birmingham, Brighton, Fairfax, Farmington, Fremont, Hedrick, Keosauqua, Richland.
Total Basic Subscribers: 1,078.

STATE CABLE TV CORP.—Sold to FrontierVision Partners LP 1998.

RODNEY E. STEORTS

Box 685
Sutton, WV 26601
Phone: 304-765-2527
Cable Systems (1):
West Virginia: Little Otter.
Total Basic Subscribers: 100.
Total Pay Units: 17.

STEPHEN CABLE TV INC.

Box 9
Stephen, MN 56757
Phone: 218-478-2216
Officers:
David Sunsdahl, Pres.
L. C. Sunsdahl, V.P.
Phyllis Sunsdahl, Secy.
Carrol Sunsdahl, Treas.
Ownership: David Sunsdahl, 51%; L. C. Sunsdahl, 49%. David Sunsdahl has interest in Pembina Cable, see listing.
Cable Systems (6):
Minnesota: Alvarado, Argyle, Kennedy, Lake Bronson, Lancaster, Stephen.
Total Basic Subscribers: 1,003.
Total Pay Units: 310.

STERLING WIRELESS CABLE

Box 5248
San Angelo, TX 76902
Phone: 915-944-0037
Wireless Cable Systems (1):
Texas: San Angelo.
Total Basic Subscribers: N.A.

STEUBEN COMMUNITY TV SYSTEM

207 Spencer
Woodman, WI 53827-0082
Phone: 608-533-2771
Officer:
Jerome Mezera, Mgr.
Ownership: Community owned.
Cable Systems (1):
Wisconsin: Steuben.
Total Basic Subscribers: 45.

STRATFORD MUTUAL TELEPHONE

Box 438
1001 Tennyson St.
Stratford, IA 50249
Phone: 515-838-2390
Officers:
Gary W. Davis, Chief Exec. Officer
Dave Prichard, Chief Operating Officer
Cable Systems (5):
Iowa: Gilbert, Jewell, Roland, State Center, Stratford.
Total Basic Subscribers: 1,808.
Total Pay Units: 781.

STUCK ELECTRIC INC.

128 N. Bridge St.
Sheridan, OR 97378
Phone: 503-843-2322
Officer:
Donald Stuck, Pres.
Ownership: Donald Stuck & Velna N. Stuck, 100% jointly.
Cable Systems (1):
Oregon: Sheridan.
Total Basic Subscribers: 1,623.

RICHARD STURTZ

Box 445
Broadus, MT 59317
Phone: 406-436-2820
Cable Systems (2):
Montana: Ashland 50%, Broadus 45%.
Total Basic Subscribers: 493.
Total Pay Units: 165.

SUFFOLK CABLEVISION INC.

Box 348
216 Moore Ave.
Suffolk, VA 23434
Phone: 804-539-8307
Ownership: Local investors.
Cable Systems (1):
Virginia: Suffolk 20%.
Total Basic Subscribers: 7,084.
Total Pay Units: 5,388.

SUL ROSS STATE UNIVERSITY

Box C-107
Alpine, TX 79832
Phone: 915-837-8011
Officers:
Dr. R. Vic Morgan, Chmn.
Mickey C. Havens, Chief Operating Officer
Cable Systems (1):
Texas: Alpine.
Total Basic Subscribers: 343.

SULLIVAN COMMUNICATIONS

Box 1039
Bastrop, TX 78602-1039
Phones: 512-303-1190; 800-396-4439
Fax: 512-303-1190
Officers:
Jeff Sullivan, Chmn., Pres. & Chief Exec. Officer
Marie Sullivan, V.P., Chief Operating Officer & Secy.-Treas.
Ownership: Jeff Sullivan & Marie Sullivan, Principals.
Represented (legal): Fleckman & Schless.
Cable Systems (1):
Texas: Alum Creek.
Total Basic Subscribers: 273.

SULLY BUTTES TELEPHONE COOPERATIVE INC.
Box 157
Highmore, SD 57345
Phone: 605-852-2224
Officers:
Harry Thomas, Pres.
Randy Houdek, Chief Exec. Officer
Randy Olson, Chief Operating Officer
Represented (legal): Meyers & Rogers.
Cable Systems (12):
South Dakota: Blunt, Harrold, Highmore, Hitchcock, Hoven, Langford, Onaka, Ree Heights, Seneca, Tolstoy, Tulare, Wessington.
Total Basic Subscribers: 1,261.
Total Pay Units: 330.
Other Holdings:
Cellular.

CITY OF SUMAS TV CABLE SYSTEM
Box 9
433 Cherry St.
Sumas, WA 98295
Phone: 360-988-5711
Fax: 360-988-8855
Ownership: Community owned.
Cable Systems (1):
Washington: Sumas.
Total Basic Subscribers: 360.
Total Pay Units: 99.

SUMMIT COMMUNICATIONS INC.— Sold to Millennium Digital Media LLC 1999.

SUMNER CABLE TV CO.
117 W. Harvey
Wellington, KS 67152
Phone: 316-326-8989
Fax: 316-326-3290
Ownership: Jack Mitchell & Jeanne Mitchell, 100% jointly.
Cable Systems (1):
Kansas: Wellington.
Total Basic Subscribers: 3,250.
Total Pay Units: 1,000.

SUN CABLE TV
Box 589
300 Quetiloquasoon No. 2
Manson, WA 98831
Phone: 509-687-3325
Ownership: Steven Byquist & Earl R. Gors, 100% jointly.
Cable Systems (2):
Washington: Mansfield, Manson.
Total Basic Subscribers: 935.
Total Pay Units: 100.

SUN COUNTRY CABLE
7901 Stoneridge Dr.
Suite 404
Pleasanton, CA 94588-3600
Phone: 925-463-1919
Fax: 925-463-9627
Officers:
David D. Kinley, Pres.
David Smart, Sr. V.P., Operations
Melana Matthews, Controller

Branch Offices:
7 D St. SW
Quincy, WA 48848
Phone: 509-787-3543

18638 Main St.
Groveland, CA 95321
Phone: 209-962-6373
Ownership: David D. Kinley.
Represented (legal): Mintz, Levin, Cohn, Ferris, Glovsky & Popeo.
Cable Systems (16):
California: Groveland, Los Altos Hills.
Oregon: Knappa, Rainier, Westport.
Washington: Almira, Coulee City, Davenport, Deer Park, Malaga, Mattawa, Orcas Island, Quincy, Royal City, Wilbur, Wilson Creek.
Total Basic Subscribers: 9,047.
Total Pay Units: 2,038.

SUNFLOWER CABLEVISION
Box 808
644 New Hampshire St.
Lawrence, KS 66044
Phone: 913-841-2100
Fax: 913-832-6363
Officers:
Dolph C. Simons Jr., Pres.
Marie N. Simons, Secy.-Treas.
Represented (legal): Wiley, Rein & Fielding.
Cable Systems (1):
Kansas: Lawrence.
Total Basic Subscribers: 30,807 (0.04% of total cable households).
Total Pay Units: 7,420.
Newspapers:
Kansas: Lawrence Journal-World.

SUNMAN TELECOMMUNICATIONS INC.
Box 145
Sunman, IN 47041
Phone: 812-623-2122
Officers:
Robert T. Miles Jr., Chmn. & Chief Exec. Officer
Mike Fledderman, Chief Operating Officer
Barbara Miles, Secy.-Treas.
Tim Miles, Chief Financial Officer
Represented (legal): Kreig, DeVault, Alexander & Capehart.
Cable Systems (2):
Indiana: New Point, Sunman.
Total Basic Subscribers: 449.
Total Pay Units: 198.
Other Holdings:
Telephone.
Cellular.

SUNNYSIDE CABLE TV CO.
5361 Hwy. 238
Jacksonville, OR 97530
Phone: 503-899-1341
Ownership: David P. Johnson & Helene B. Johnson, Principals.
Cable Systems (1):
Oregon: Ruch.
Total Basic Subscribers: 350.
Total Pay Units: 95.

SUNTEL COMMUNICATIONS LLC
Suite 404
7901 Stoneridge Dr.
Pleasanton, CA 94588-3600
Phone: 925-463-1919
Fax: 925-463-9627
Officers:
David D. Kinley, Pres.
David Smart, Sr. V.P.
Ownership: David D. Kinley.
Cable Systems (2):
California: Dire Mountain.
Nevada: Winnemucca.
Total Basic Subscribers: 5,205.
Total Pay Units: 2,192.

SUSQUEHANNA CABLE CO.
140 E. Market St.
York, PA 17401
Phone: 717-848-5500
Fax: 717-771-1440
Officers:
Louis J. Appell Jr., Chmn.
Peter P. Brubaker, Pres. & Chief Exec. Officer
James D. Munchel, Sr. V.P., Operations
W. Jeffrey Tate, V.P., Engineering & Technology
Ownership: Susquehanna Media Co.; Lenfest Communications, see listing, 30%. SMC Ownership: Susquehanna Pfaltzgraff.
Represented (legal): Wiley, Rein & Fielding.
Cable Systems (16):
Illinois: Benton, Du Quoin, Olney, Pinckneyville.
Indiana: Flat Rock, Shelbyville.
Maine: Brunswick, Freeport, Harpswell, Woolwich.
Mississippi: Pearl, Puckett.
Pennsylvania: Avis, Muncy, Williamsport, York.
Total Basic Subscribers: 184,777 (0.27% of total cable households).
Total Pay Units: 69,766.

SWAYZEE TELE BROADBAND
Box 70
Swayzee, IN 46986
Phone: 317-922-7928
Fax: 317-922-7966
Officer:
S. M. Samuels, Pres.
Cable Systems (1):
Indiana: Swayzee.
Total Basic Subscribers: 463.
Total Pay Units: 154.
Other Holdings:
Telephone.

SWEETWATER CABLE TV CO. INC.
Box 8
602 Broadway
Rock Springs, WY 82901
Phone: 307-362-3773
Officers:
Albert M. Carollo Sr., Chmn.
Albert M. Carollo Jr., Pres.
John B. Carollo, Chief Operating Officer
James R. Carollo, V.P.
Leona Carollo, Secy.-Treas.
Ownership: Albert M. Carollo Jr., 25%; James R. Carollo, 25%; John B. Carollo, 25%; Albert M. Carollo Sr., 25%. Carollo family owns 100% of Pilot Butte Transmission Co. (CC); TV translator station K12FH Superior, WY.
Represented (legal): Cole, Raywid & Braverman LLP.
Cable Systems (3):
Wyoming: Green River, Rock Springs, Wamsutter.
Total Basic Subscribers: 11,928 (0.02% of total cable households).
Total Pay Units: 6,677.

TACOMA CITY LIGHT
3628 S. 35th St.
Tacoma, WA 98409
Phone: 800-752-6745
Fax: 253-502-8349
Cable Franchises (1):
Washington: Tacoma.
Total Basic Subscribers: N.A.

CITY OF TACONITE CABLE TV
Box 137
Taconite, MN 55786
Phone: 218-245-1831
Ownership: Community owned.
Cable Systems (1):
Minnesota: Taconite.
Total Basic Subscribers: 110.

ALBERT A. TALLEY
Box 48
Strawn, TX 76475
Phones: 254-672-5296; 254-672-5653
Cable Systems (1):
Texas: Strawn 50%.
Total Basic Subscribers: 190.
Total Pay Units: 43.

TALOGA CABLE TV
Box 218
Taloga, OK 73667
Phone: 405-328-5262
Ownership: Glenn Gore.
Represented (legal): Graft & Rodolph.
Cable Systems (1):
Oklahoma: Taloga.
Total Basic Subscribers: 143.
Total Pay Units: 162.

T. A. T. CABLEVISION
Box 197
467 First St.
Flora, MS 39071
Phone: 601-879-3288
Ownership: Robert Taylor & Terry Taylor, 100% jointly.
Cable Systems (1):
Mississippi: Flora.
Total Basic Subscribers: 225.
Total Pay Units: 131.

KEN TAYLOR
Box 6
Mecosta, MI 49332
Phone: 616-972-7111
Cable Systems (1):
Michigan: St. James Twp. 10%.
Total Basic Subscribers: 143.
Total Pay Units: 60.

TCA CABLE PARTNERS
Box 130489
Tyler, TX 75713-0489
Phone: 903-595-3701
Fax: 903-595-1929
Officer:
See TCA Cable TV Inc.,
Ownership: TCA Cable TV Inc., see listing, managing partner, 75%; Donrey Media Group, 25%. Donrey has newspaper holdings in Arkansas, California, Hawaii, Indiana, Iowa, Kentucky, Mississippi, Missouri, Nevada, New Mexico, North Carolina, Oklahoma, Tennessee, Texas & Washington & outdoor advertising holdings. TCA Cable TV Inc. became a subsidiary of Cox Communications Inc. 1999.
Cable Systems (49):
Arkansas: Arkadelphia, Batesville, Bella Vista, Bentonville, Berryville, Booneville, Clarksville, Corning, Dardanelle, Dermott, El Dorado, Eureka Springs, Fairfield Bay, Fayetteville, Fort Smith, Gurdon, Harrison, Heber Springs, Helena, Hickory Creek, Hot Springs Village, Jonesboro, Lake Village, Lavaca, Magnolia, Malvern, Marvell, McCrory, McGehee, Mena, Moorefield, Morrilton, Mountain Home, Newport, Ozark, Paris, Pocahontas, Russellville, Siloam Springs, Springdale, Tontitown, Tuckerman, Van Buren.
Mississippi: Greenville.
Oklahoma: Blackwell, Guymon.
Texas: Corrigan, Hudson, Kilgore 50%.

Total Basic Subscribers: 217,875 (0.32% of total cable households).
Total Pay Units: 62,449.

TCA CABLE TV INC.

Box 130489
Tyler, TX 75713-0489
Phone: 903-595-3701
Fax: 903-596-9008
Officers:
Robert M. Rogers, Chmn. & Chief Exec. Officer
Fred R. Nichols, Pres. & Chief Operating Officer
Jimmie F. Taylor, V.P., Treas. & Chief Financial Officer
Jerry Yandell, V.P., Operations
Mel Jenschke, V.P., Engineering
Karen Garrett, Secy.
Ownership: Louise Rogers; Chieftain Capital Management; Fidelity Management; Warren Buffett, 8.1%; remainder publicly held. TCA Cable TV became a subsidiary of Cox Communications Inc. 1999.
Represented (legal): Cole, Raywid & Braverman LLP.
Cable Systems (67):
Arkansas: Excelsior, Sonora.
Idaho: Ketchum.
Louisiana: Abbeville, Bastrop, Bossier City 80%, Crowley, De Ridder, Franklin, Jonesboro, Lafayette, Lake Charles 80%, Minden, Natchitoches, New Iberia, Patterson, Pineville, Rayne, Ruston, St. Martinville, Sulphur 80%, Winnfield.
New Mexico: Clovis 80%.
Oklahoma: Pocola.
Texas: Abilene 80%, Amarillo 80%, Andrews 80%, Athens 80%, Ballinger 80%, Big Spring 80%, Bryan, Canyon, Conroe, Dalhart 80%, De Kalb 80%, Floydada 80%, Gainesville 80%, Gatesville, Gladewater 80%, Hearne, Henderson 80%, Honey Grove 80%, Hooks 80%, Huntsville, Jacksonville 80%, Maud 80%, Miles 80%, Mineola 80%, Mineral Wells 80%, Mount Pleasant 80%, Mount Vernon 80%, Nacogdoches, New Boston 80%, Paris 80%, Perryton 80%, Pittsburg 80%, Plainview 80%, Rockwell 80%, Roxton, San Angelo 80%, Snyder 80%, Sulphur Springs 80%, Sweetwater 80%, Tyler 80%, Victoria, Whitesboro 80%, Winters 80%.
Total Basic Subscribers: 872,182 (1.27% of total cable households).
Total Pay Units: 549,099.

TCD CORP.

Box 550366
Atlanta, GA 30355-2866
Phone: 404-396-1088
Fax: 404-396-1283
Officer:
Thomas C. Dowden, Chmn. & Chief Exec. Officer

Branch Office:

900 Airport Dr.
Springfield, IL 62707
Phone: 217-523-5968
Fax: 217-522-6761
Ownership: Thomas C. Dowden, Gen. Partner.
Represented (legal): Zukowski, Rogers, Flood & McArdle; Cole, Raywid & Braverman LLP.
Cable Systems (4):
Illinois: German Valley, Manlius (village), Pearl City (village), Winslow.
Total Basic Subscribers: 1,009.
Total Pay Units: 203.

TECHNIVISION INC.

5541 Bear Lane
No. 3100
Corpus Christi, TX 78405
Phone: 512-289-0303
Fax: 512-289-2921
Officers:
Robert Bilodeau, Chmn.
Scott Augustine, V.P.
Represented (legal): Brown, Nietert & Kaufman, Chartered.
Wireless Cable Systems (1):
Utah: Salt Lake City.
Total Basic Subscribers: N.A.

TEEWINOT LICENSING INC.

Box 1550
Port Orchard, WA 98366
Phone: 360-871-5981
Officers:
Willis E. Twiner, Pres.
Patrick J. Carey, Chief Exec. Officer
Thomas Carey, Chief Operating Officer
Sheryll Curtis, Secy.-Treas. & Chief Financial Officer
Wireless Cable Systems (1):
Idaho: Twin Falls.
Total Basic Subscribers: 13,000 (0.02% of total cable households).
Other Holdings:
MDS, MMDS, see listings.

TEKSTAR CABLEVISION INC.

150 2nd Ave. SW
Perham, MN 56573
Phone: 218-346-2288
Fax: 218-346-5510
Officers:
Eleanor Arvig, Chmn.
Allen Arvig, Pres.
Donna Ward, V.P.
Carmen Arvig, Secy.
Nancy Ettish, Treas.
Ownership: Arvig Enterprises Inc.
Cable Systems (4):
Minnesota: Perham, Twin Valley, Walker, Wall Lake.
Total Basic Subscribers: 16,300 (0.02% of total cable households).
Total Pay Units: 4,000.

TELECOMMUNICATIONS DEVELOPMENT CORP.

Box 208
Minot, ND 58701
Phone: 701-838-5776
Cable Systems (1):
North Dakota: Minot.
Total Basic Subscribers: 200.
Total Pay Units: 72.

TELE-COMMUNICATIONS INC.— Sold to AT&T Broadband & Internet Services 1999.

TELE-MEDIA CORP.

Box 5301
320 W. College Ave.
Pleasant Gap, PA 16823-5301
Phone: 814-359-3481
Fax: 814-359-5390
Officers:
Robert E. Tudek, Chmn., Pres. & Chief Exec. Officer
Everett I. Mundy, Vice-Chmn.
Russell G. Bamburger, Sr. V.P. & Pres., Tele-Media Constructors
Tony S. Swain, Sr. V.P. & Dir. of Engineering
Frank R. Vincente, Sr. V.P., Operations
Douglas F. Best III, Sr. V.P., Business Development
Robert D. Stemler, Sr. V.P., Finance & Treas.
Allen C. Jacobson, V.P., Legal Affairs & Asst. Secy.
Charles J. Hilderbrand, V.P. & Gen. Mgr.
Wayne P. Harrison, V.P. & Gen. Mgr.
James R. Guthrie, V.P. & Gen. Mgr.
Richard W. Shore, V.P., Corp. Development & Tax Affairs
Robert H. Stewart, V.P. & Dir., Purchasing
William S. Dunlop, V.P. & Gen. Mgr.
Robert R. Shepherd, V.P. & Gen. Sales Mgr.
Steven E. Koval, V.P., Information Technology
Thomas E. Mundy, V.P.
Tony V. Masella Jr., Asst. V.P., Mktg.
Jean C. Brown, Administrative V.P. & Asst. Secy.
Elsie M. Tudek, Administrative V.P., Asst. Secy.-Treas.
Ownership: Robert E. Tudek, 50%; Everett I. Mundy, 50%.
Represented (legal): Fleischman & Walsh LLP.
Cable Systems (38):
Connecticut: Seymour, Waterbury.
Indiana: Rockport.
Kentucky: Adairville, Auburn, Brownsville, Cloverport, Elkhorn City, Frakes, Franklin, Greasy Creek, Hardinsburg, Hawesville, Irvington, Livermore, Marrowbone, Morgantown, Pathfork, Pikeville, Pineville, Russellville, Scottsville.
Maryland: Hancock.
North Carolina: Bryson City, Robbins, Robbinsville.
Pennsylvania: Dallas, Walker Twp. (Centre County).
Tennessee: White House.
Virginia: Chase City, Ewing, Hopewell, Petersburg, Victoria.
West Virginia: Augusta, Iaeger, Keyser, Northfork.
Total Basic Subscribers: 266,188 (0.39% of total cable households).
Total Pay Units: 83,736.

TELEPARTNERS

Bldg. 12
11260 Aurora Ave.
Urbandale, IA 50322
Phone: 515-276-3069
Fax: 515-270-9181
Ownership: Jay Eliason, Principal. Eliason also has interest in Illinet Communications of Central Illinois Inc., Illin Cablevision of Illinois Inc., Mid American Cable Systems, New Path Communications LC, Telnet Communications & Westcom LC, see listings.
Cable Systems (9):
Nebraska: Beemer, Craig, Dodge, Emerson, Laurel, Lyons, Pender, Wakefield.
South Dakota: Elk Point.
Total Basic Subscribers: 2,248.
Total Pay Units: 778.

TELEPONCE/TPC CABLE TV INC.

Box 204
X-1 Vayas Torres
Mercedita, PR 00715-0204
Phone: 787-848-7745
Fax: 787-848-7757
Officers:
Hector R. Gonzalez, Pres., Chief Exec. & Financial Officer
Albert N. Ferraro, V.P. & Gen. Mgr.
Jose S. Mendez, V.P., Technical Operations
Roberto Vargas, V.P., Legal
Provita T. Gonzalez, Secy.

Branch Offices:

CSO-Ponce Region
Ponce, PR 00731
Phone: 787-844-7700

Yauco Plaza Shopping Center
CSO-Yauco Region
Yauco, PR 00698
Phone: 787-856-6024
Ownership: TPC Communications PR Inc. TPC Ownership: Hector R. Gonzales, Principal.
Represented (legal): Lukas, McGowan, Nace & Gutierrez.
Cable Systems (1):
Puerto Rico: Mercedita.
Total Basic Subscribers: 33,554 (0.05% of total cable households).
Total Pay Units: 26,156.

TELEPRO COMMUNICATIONS

Suite 310
4122 128th Ave. SE
Bellevue, WA 98006
Phone: 206-957-4730
Fax: 206-957-0119

Branch Office:

Suite 222
Torrance, CA 90505
Phone: 310-375-6212
Ownership: John F. Craig, Pres., majority stockholder.
Represented (legal): James Stefnik.
Cable Systems (1):
Washington: Clyde Hill.
Total Basic Subscribers: 3,300.
Total Pay Units: 1,600.
Other Holdings:
SMATV.

TELESAT CABLE

Suite B
2901 Washington St.
Burlington, KY 41005-8211
Phone: 606-283-6780
Officer:
Larry Boisvert, Chief Exec. Officer
Cable Systems (1):
Kentucky: Crittenden.
Total Basic Subscribers: 7,000.
Total Pay Units: 1,400.

TELE-SERVICES LTD.

Box 38
Farragut, IA 51639-0038
Phone: 712-382-1773
Ownership: Ott Boeckman, Principal.
Cable Systems (15):
Iowa: Bayard, Breda, Farragut, Grand Junction, Hamburg, Lohrville, Malvern, Neola, Oakland, Sidney, Tabor, Thurman, Treynor, Westside.
Nebraska: Beaver Lake.
Total Basic Subscribers: 1,709.
Other Holdings:
Telephone.

TELESYSTEMS INC.

401 N. Division
Kellogg, ID 83837
Phone: 208-786-6762
Cable Systems (2):
Idaho: Cataldo, Prichard.
Total Basic Subscribers: 224.
Total Pay Units: 49.

TELEVIEW INC.

Box 400
2000 Industrial Ave.
Cornelia, GA 30531
Phones: 706-776-4494; 800-345-3874

Fax: 706-778-5684
Officer:
Harris L. Bagley, Pres. & Chief Exec. Officer
Ownership: Alltel Communications.
Represented (legal): Cole, Raywid & Braverman LLP.
Cable Systems (10):
Georgia: Big Canoe, Blairsville, Cleveland, Commerce, Cornelia, Dahlonega, Dawsonville, Helen, Hiawassee, Jefferson.
Total Basic Subscribers: 30,300 (0.04% of total cable households).
Total Pay Units: 11,280.
Other Holdings:
Telephone: Standard Telephone Co. & long distance reseller.
Cellular.
Paging service.

TELEVISION ASSN. OF REPUBLIC

Box 555
N. 147 Clark
Republic, WA 99166
Phone: 509-775-3822
Officers:
Ken Coyle, Chmn. & Pres.
Charles Edward Yost, Chief Financial Officer
Cable Systems (1):
Washington: Republic.
Total Basic Subscribers: 574.
Total Pay Units: 338.

TELEVISTA COMMUNICATIONS INC.

Box 250429
Franklin, MI 48025-0429
Phone: 313-753-3455
Ownership: Michael Turner, Pres., 87.5%; remainder undisclosed.
Cable Systems (1):
Michigan: York Twp.
Total Basic Subscribers: 3,286.
Total Pay Units: 3,800.

TELNET COMMUNICATIONS

11260 Aurora Ave., Bldg. 6
Urbandale, IA 50322
Phone: 319-382-3560
Ownership: Jay Eliason, Principal. Eliason also has interest in Illinet Communications of Central Illinois Inc., Illini Cablevision of Illinois Inc., Mid American Cable Systems, New Path Communications LC, TelePartners & Westcom LC, see listings.
Cable Systems (2):
Iowa: Decorah, Preston.
Total Basic Subscribers: 3,737.
Total Pay Units: 864.

TEL-STAR CABLEVISION INC.

RR 5
Box 205
Metamora, IL 61548-8416
Phone: 309-699-9509
Fax: 309-698-9371
Officers:
James Perley, Chmn. & Chief Exec. Officer
Barbara A. Perley, Chief Financial Officer
Ownership: Barbara Perley.
Cable Systems (7):
Illinois: Congerville, Edwards, Heritage Lake, La Rose, Lowpoint, Mapleton, Woodland Heights.
Total Basic Subscribers: 1,181.
Total Pay Units: 452.

TEMPLETON TELEPHONE CO.

Box 77
115 Main
Templeton, IA 51463
Phone: 712-669-3311
Fax: 712-669-3312
Officer:
Loretta Friedman, Chmn. & Pres.
Cable Systems (2):
Iowa: Dedham, Templeton.
Total Basic Subscribers: 219.
Total Pay Units: 79.

TENNESSEE WIRELESS INC.

6330 Baum Dr.
Knoxville, TN 37919-9505
Phone: 423 -584-1234
Wireless Cable Systems (1):
Tennessee: Knoxville.
Total Basic Subscribers: 1,380.
Total Pay Units: 698.

TER TEL ENTERPRISES

Box 100
Terril, IA 51364
Phone: 712-853-6121
Fax: 712-853-6185
Cable Systems (4):
Iowa: Terril.
Minnesota: Trimont, Truman, Welcome.
Wireless Cable Systems (1):
Iowa: Ruthven.
Total Cable Subscribers: 3,002.
Total Pay Units: 923.
Other Holdings:
Telephone.

TGN CABLE

Box 110
Rte. 2
Olney, TX 76374
Phone: 940-873-4423
Cable Systems (1):
Texas: Throckmorton.
Total Basic Subscribers: 670.

THOMPSON CABLEVISION CO. INC.

Box 13309
Sissonville, WV 25360
Phone: 304-984-0025
Fax: 304-984-0002
Officer:
Allen D. Thompson, Pres.
Ownership: Allen B. Thompson, Principal.
Cable Systems (7):
Kentucky: Grayson.
Ohio: Gallipolis, Mount Orab.
West Virginia: Clay, Pocatalico, War, Welch.
Total Basic Subscribers: 15,289 (0.02% of total cable households).
Total Pay Units: 1,323.

THORNE BAY COMMUNITY TV INC.

Box 434
Thorne Bay, AK 99919
Phone: 907-828-3938
Ownership: Subscriber owned.
Cable Systems (1):
Alaska: Thorne Bay.
Total Basic Subscribers: 107.

THORNTOWN TELEPHONE CO.

115 E. Bow
Thorntown, IN 46071
Phone: 765-436-2273
Fax: 765-436-7979
Ownership: Rochester Telephone Corp.
Cable Systems (1):
Indiana: Thorntown.
Total Basic Subscribers: 925.
Total Pay Units: 196.

THORP TELEPHONE CO.

Box 307
405 N. Washington St.
Thorp, WI 54771
Phone: 715-669-5301
Fax: 715-669-5501
Officer:
Michael Gotstein, Pres.
Ownership: Pacific Telecom Inc., see listing.
Cable Systems (1):
Wisconsin: Thorp.
Total Basic Subscribers: 521.
Total Pay Units: 158.

3D CABLE INC.

Box 4145
Dalton, GA 30719
Phone: 404-334-4200
Ownership: William R. Dempsey.
Cable Systems (1):
Georgia: Ranger.
Total Basic Subscribers: 99.
Total Pay Units: 130.

THREE SIXTY CORP.

120 Floral Ave.
New Providence, NJ 07974
Phone: 908-665-0094
Fax: 908-665-0343
Officers:
Robert Bilodeau, Pres.
Salvatore LaMarca, V.P. & Chief Operating Officer
Roy Tartaglia, V.P.
Robert Greenwood, Secy. & Legal Counsel
Ronald Rizzo, Chief Financial Officer
Ownership: Robert Bilodeau, Burr Egan Delage Co. & Robert Greenwood, Principals.
Cable Systems (1):
California: El Monte.
Total Basic Subscribers: 12,245 (0.02% of total cable households).
Total Pay Units: 13,000.
Other Holdings:
MMDS, see listing.
SMATV.

TIME WARNER CABLE

290 Harbor Dr.
Stamford, CT 06902
Phones: 203-328-0600; 203-328-0613
Fax: 203-328-0650
Officers:
Joseph J. Collins, Chmn. & Chief Exec. Officer
Glenn A. Britt, Pres.
Jeffrey A. Schwall, Pres., International
Thomas Rutledge, Sr. Exec. V.P.
John Bickham, Exec. V.P.
James P. Cottingham, Exec. V.P.
Theodore J. Cutler, Exec. V.P.
Charles W. Ellis, Exec. V.P.
John F. Gault, Exec. V.P., Strategic Planning
Carl U.J. Rossetti, Exec. V.P.
Marc Apfelbaum, Sr. V.P., Gen. Counsel & Secy.
James A. Chiddix, Sr. V.P., Engineering & Technology, Chief Technical Officer
Richard J. Davies, Sr. V.P., Corp. Development
Fred M. Dressler, Sr. V.P., Programming
Kevin J. Leddy, Sr. V.P., Mktg.
Edward O. McCarthy, Sr. V.P., Management Information Services
John Newton, Sr. V.P.
David E. O'Hayre, Sr. V.P., Investments
Richard M. Petty, Sr. V.P. & Controller
Lynn M. Yaeger, Sr. V.P., Public Affairs
Donald B. Armour, Treas.
Tommy J. Harris, Chief Financial Officer

Branch Office:

160 Inverness Dr., W
Englewood, CO 80112
Phone: 303-799-1200
Ownership: Time Warner Entertainment Co. LP. TWE ownership: Time Warner Inc., 74.49%; MediaOne Group Inc., 25.51%.
Represented (legal): Fleischman & Walsh LLP.
Cable Systems (785):
Alabama: Birmingham 66.67%, Clio, Daleville, Eufaula 66.67%, Fort Deposit, Geneva, Georgiana, Greenville, Wetumpka 66.67%.
Arkansas: Parkin, West Memphis.
California: Avenal 66.67%, Bakersfield 66.67%, Barstow 66.67%, Canyon Country 66.67%, Coronado 66.67%, Orange County (western portion), Palm Desert, Palm Springs 66.67%, San Diego 66.67%, San Fernando, San Marino, South Pasadena 66.67%, Taft 66.67%, Tehachapi 66.67%, Torrance, West San Fernando Valley.
Delaware: Middletown 49.5%.
Florida: Altamonte Springs, Alva, Apollo Beach 66.67%, Barefoot Bay 66.67%, Belle Glade, Bowling Green, Bradenton 66.67%, Cape Coral, Cedar Key, Century 66.67%, Clewiston, Cloverleaf Mobile Home Park, Crestview 50%, Daytona Beach, De Funiak Springs, De Land 66.67%, Deer Creek Golf RV Resort, Destin 50%, Dunedin 66.67%, Eglin Air Force Base 50%, Flagler Beach, Fort McCoy, Fort Walton Beach 50%, Geneva 66.67%, Golden Gate, Hernando County, Homosassa 66.67%, Immokalee, Isla del Sol, Jennings, Keystone Heights, La Belle, Lake City, Lakeland 66.67%, Live Oak, Marion Oaks 66.67%, Mayo, Melbourne 66.67%, Monticello, Moore Haven, Niceville 50%, Okeechobee, Orange County (southwestern portion) 66.67%, Orlando 66.67%, Ormond Beach 66.67%, Ortona, Oviedo, Palatka, Pinellas County 66.67%, Plant City (portions) 66.67%, Port Richey, Rainbow Park, Salt Springs, Silver Springs 66.67%, Southgate, St. Augustine, Venice, Wildwood 66.67%, Winter Garden 66.67%, Winter Haven 66.67%.
Georgia: Brunswick 50%, Fort Benning.
Hawaii: Hawaii Kai, Hawi, Hilo, Honolulu, Kailua Kona, Maui, Maui Island, Pahala.
Illinois: Altamont, Kingston Mines.
Indiana: Carmel 66.67%, Crawford County 49.5%, Edinburgh 49.5%, Elberfeld 49.5%, Fortville, Hatfield 49.5%, Hendricks County 66.67%, Indianapolis (portions) 66.67%, Loogootee 49.5%, Lynnville 49.5%, Marion, Marshall County 49.5%, Oakland City 49.5%, Petersburg 49.5%, Terre Haute, Troy 49.5%, Union City, Williamsburg 30.5%, Zionsville.
Kansas: Atchison 49.5%, Chanute, Colby, Emporia, Independence, Neodesha, Oakley, Parsons.
Kentucky: Bulan 30.5%, Flat Lick 30.5%, Fogertown 30.5%, Garrard 30.5%, Hartford 30.5%, Madisonville 49.5%, Mayfield 30.5%, Murray 30.5%, Owensboro 50%, Paintsville 49.5%, White Plains, Williamsburg.
Louisiana: Basile 49.5%, Bunkie 49.5%, Calhoun, Cameron 49.5%, Cheniere, Hackberry 49.5%, Hosston, Houma 66.67%, Iota 49.5%, Iowa 49.5%, La Place 66.67%, Merryville 49.5%, Pine Prairie 49.5%, Shreveport, Stonewall, Swartz, West Monroe.
Maine: Biddeford, Caribou, Portland, Saco, Wells.
Maryland: Cumberland 49.5%.

Massachusetts: Orange 66.67%, Pittsfield 66.67%.
Michigan: Almont 49.5%, Attica Twp. 49.5%, Berlin Twp. (St. Clair County) 49.5%, Davison 49.5%, Farmington 66.67%, Fenton 49.5%, Hamburg Twp. 30.5%, Highland Park 49.5%, Imlay City 49.5%, Kingston Twp. 49.5%, Livonia 66.67%, Mayville 49.5%, Mio, North Branch 49.5%, Oscoda 49.5%, Oxford 30.5%, Redford 66.67%, Rose City 49.5%.
Minnesota: Bloomington, Chaska, Fridley, Jordan, Madelia, Minneapolis, Montrose, New Prague, New Ulm, Shakopee, St. Louis Park.
Mississippi: Bolton, Brownfield, Columbia 49.5%, Edwards, Hattiesburg 33.33%, Jackson, Raymond, Southaven.
Missouri: Camden Point 49.5%, Chillicothe, Kennett, Marshall.
Nebraska: Auburn 66.67%, Columbus 66.67%, Fairbury 66.67%, Falls City 66.67%, Fremont 66.67%, Humboldt, Lincoln 66.67%, Trenton, York 66.67%.
New Hampshire: Berlin, Groveton, Keene.
New Jersey: Palisades Park 66.67%.
New York: Adams (town), Albany 66.67%, Albion 66.67%, Alden 66.67%, Amsterdam, Angelica 30.5%, Avoca 30.5%, Bainbridge, Baldwinsville, Battenkill 66.67%, Binghamton 66.67%, Bolivar 30.5%, Brookfield, Carthage 66.67%, Champlain 66.67%, Chaumont, Constantia (town), Cooperstown, Corning 66.67%, Cortland 49.5%, Crown Point (town), Dansville 30.5%, Delhi, Dresden 30.5%, Dundee 30.5%, Ellenville, Elmira 66.67%, Fredonia (village) 66.67%, Fulton 66.67%, Geneva 66.67%, Glens Falls 66.67%, Harrisville, Highland Falls (village), Hornell 49.5%, Hume 30.5%, Hunter (village), Ilion 66.67%, Ithaca 66.67%, Jamestown 66.67%, Jasper 30.5%, Johnstown (city) 49.5%, Kingston, Malone 66.67%, Massena 66.67%, Mexico (village) 66.67%, Middletown (Orange County), Morris, Mount Tremper, Mount Vernon, Naples 30.5%, New Berlin, New Paltz, New York, Newark Valley (town), Newburgh, Ogdensburg 66.67%, Olive, Oneida 66.67%, Oneonta 66.67%, Oswego 66.67%, Owego (village) 66.67%, Oxford (town), Phoenicia, Pine Hill, Port Henry (village), Port Jervis, Potsdam 66.67%, Poughkeepsie, Rensselaer, Rochester 66.67%, Rome 66.67%, Rosendale, Salamanca 49.5%, Saratoga Springs 66.67%, Saugerties (town), Schenectady 66.67%, Schroeppel, Schroon (town), Sidney, Stafford 66.67%, Staten Island 50%, Sullivan (town), Sullivan County, Syracuse 66.67%, Syracuse 66.67%, Ticonderoga (village), Troupsburg 30.5%, Troy 66.67%, Tusten, Walden, Walton (village) 66.67%, Washingtonville, Watertown 33%, Whitehall (town), Whitney Point (village) 66.67%, Woodhull 30.5%, Woodridge, Woodstock (town).
North Carolina: Albemarle 66.67%, Archdale 66.67%, Asheboro 66.67%, Aurora, Bayboro 49.5%, Belmont 66.67%, Bladenboro 66.67%, Burlington 66.67%, Carrboro 66.67%, Carthage 49.5%, Cary 66.67%, Chapel Hill 66.67%, Charlotte 66.67%, Cherry Point 66.67%, Cramerton 66.67%, Creedmoor, Davidson County 49.5%, Denton 49.5%, Dobson 66.67%, Durham 66.67%, Eden 49.5%, Farmville 66.67%, Fayetteville 66.67%, Franklinton, Garner 66.67%, Gastonia 66.67%, Goldsboro 66.67%, Greensboro 66.67%, Henderson 66.67%, High Point 66.67%, Holden Beach, Jacksonville 66.67%, Kannapolis 66.67%, Kings Mountain 66.67%, Liberty 49.5%, Louisburg, Lumberton 66.67%, Madison 49.5%, Mebane 49.5%, Mecklenburg 66.67%, Monroe 66.67%, Morehead City 66.67%, Oxford, Pinehurst, Raleigh 66.67%, Red Springs 66.67%, Reidsville 66.67%, Rockingham 66.67%, Salisbury 66.67%, Selma 66.67%, Seven Lakes, Shelby 66.67%, Southern Pines 66.67%, Stoneville, Wadesboro 49.5%, Wake Forest 66.67%, Walnut Cove, Whiteville 66.67%, Wilmington 66.67%, Wilson 66.67%, Winston-Salem 66.67%, Youngsville 49.5%, Zebulon.
Ohio: Akron, Anna 30.5%, Ashley 30.5%, Athens, Attica, Atwater Twp. 49.5%, Baltimore, Belle Center 30.5%, Bellevue, Bettsville 49.5%, Bloomville, Bowling Green 49.5%, Bucyrus, Canton, Centerburg, Chippewa Twp. 49.5%, Cincinnati, Circleville, Columbus, Congress, Craig Beach 49.5%, Crooksville 49.5%, Danville, Dayton, Delphos, Dresden 49.5%, Findlay, Forest 49.5%, Fort Shawnee, Fostoria, Frazeysburg 49.5%, Fredericktown, Friendship, Galion, Gambier, Germantown, Goshen Twp. (Clermont County), Green Cove Condominiums 49.5%, Green Meadows, Green Twp. (Hamilton County) 66.67%, Greenville, Guilford Lake 49.5%, Hamilton, Hayden Heights 30.5%, Hillsboro, Jeromesville, Johnstown, Kent, Kenton, Kettering, Kirkersville, La Rue 30.5%, Lake Mohawk Mobile Home Park 49.5%, Lancaster, Leesburg, Lewisburg, Liberty Twp. (Butler County), Lima, Lindsey (Sandusky County) 49.5%, Lisbon 49.5%, Lodi, London, Loudonville, Lucasville, Lynchburg, Mansfield, Marengo 30.5%, Marysville, Middletown, Monroe Twp. (Miami County), Mount Gilead, Mount Sterling (Muskingum County), Mount Vernon, Nashport 49.5%, Nelson Mobile Home Park 49.5%, New Concord 49.5%, New Lexington (Perry County), New London, Norwalk, Norwich 49.5%, Ottawa, Owensville, Oxford, Pataskala, Peebles, Philo (portions) 49.5%, Piketon, Piqua, Polk, Richwood, Rising Sun 49.5%, Robbins Mobile Home Park 49.5%, Rockford 49.5%, Salem 49.5%, Seaman, Shelby, Shreve, Sidney, Somerset, St. Marys, St. Paris, Sycamore, Thornville, Tipp City, Troy, Upper Sandusky, Urbana, Utica, Wapakoneta, Warren, Waynesfield 49.5%, West Lafayette, West Mansfield 49.5%, West Union, Willard, Willows Mobile Home Park 49.5%, Worthington Arms, Yellow Springs, Youngstown, Zanesville 49.5%.
Oklahoma: Adair 49.5%, Afton 49.5%, Agra 49.5%, Beggs 49.5%, Boynton 49.5%, Cameron 49.5%, Carney 49.5%, Chelsea 49.5%, Chouteau 49.5%, Colcord 49.5%, Cromwell 49.5%, Delaware 49.5%, Depew 49.5%, Dustin 49.5%, Fort Gibson 49.5%, Gans 49.5%, Glencoe 49.5%, Gore 49.5%, Grand Lake-Monkey Island 49.5%, Grove 49.5%, Hulbert 49.5%, Inola 49.5%, Kansas 49.5%, Kellyville 49.5%, Keota 49.5%, Ketchum 49.5%, Langston 49.5%, Longtown 49.5%, Luther 49.5%, Marland 49.5%, Milburn 49.5%, Morris 49.5%, Morrison 49.5%, Mounds 49.5%, Okay 49.5%, Oologah 49.5%, Porter 49.5%, Porum 49.5%, Pryor, Quinton 49.5%, Ralston 49.5%, Salina 49.5%, Savanna 49.5%, Schulter 49.5%, Spavinaw 49.5%, Stilwell 49.5%, Strang 49.5%, Tryon 49.5%, Tyrone 49.5%, Verdigris 49.5%, Vian 49.5%, Welch 49.5%, Weleetka 49.5%, Westville 49.5%, Wilburton 49.5%, Wyandotte 49.5%.
Pennsylvania: Altoona 49.5%, Bradford 49.5%, Clearfield 49.5%, Corry, Elkland 30.5%, Franklin (Venango County), Greenville, Johnstown 49.5%, Lawrenceville 30.5%, Lewistown 49.5%, Mifflinburg 49.5%, Montrose 66.67%, Philadelphia (area 2), Reedsville, Sayre 66.67%, Warren 49.5%.
South Carolina: Batesburg 66.67%, Bishopville, Clover 66.67%, Columbia 66.67%, Florence 66.67%, Georgetown, Johnsonville, Kingstree 66.67%, Lake City 66.67%, Lane, Manning 66.67%, Myrtle Beach 66.67%, Orangeburg 66.67%, Ridgeville, St. Matthews 66.67%, Summerville, Sumter 66.67%, Surfside Beach 66.67%.
Tennessee: Alamo, Braden, Camden, Grand Junction, Memphis, Middleton, Newbern, Selmer, Somerville, Whiteville.
Texas: Alton 50%, Archer City, Asherton 50%, Aspermont, Austin 66.67%, Bandera, Bartlett, Bastrop 66.67%, Beaumont 33.33%, Bedias 49.5%, Bertram, Bridge City 49.5%, Brownfield 49.5%, Brownsville 33.33%, Centerville 49.5%, Charlotte 50%, Coleman 49.5%, Colorado City 49.5%, Columbus 33.33%, Commerce 33.33%, Coppell 33.33%, Cotulla 50%, Crystal City 33.33%, Cuero 33.33%, Del Rio 33.33%, Dilley 50%, Eagle Lake 50%, Eagle Pass 33.33%, Edcouch 50%, El Paso 33.33%, Elgin, Emory 49.5%, Encinal 50%, Ennis 49.5%, Florence, Fort Hood 66.67%, Fredericksburg, Garden Ridge, Garfield 49.5%, Gonzales 33.33%, Graham 33.33%, Granada Hills 66.67%, Grapevine 33.33%, Greenville 33.33%, Harlingen 33.33%, Haskell 49.5%, Hidalgo 50%, Holliday, Houston 33.33%, Irving 33.33%, Kerrville 33.33%, Killeen 66.67%, Kountze 49.5%, Kyle, La Grulla 50%, Lake Arrowhead, Laredo, Leona 49.5%, Levelland 49.5%, Lewisville 50%, Liberty 33.33%, Liberty Hill, Littlefield 49.5%, Lockhart 66.67%, Loraine 49.5%, Los Fresnos 50%, Luling 66.67%, Manor 49.5%, Meridian 49.5%, Midway 49.5%, Morton 49.5%, Munday 49.5%, Mustang Ridge 49.5%, New Braunfels, Normangee 49.5%, North Zulch 49.5%, Northeast Hays 66.6%, O'Donnell 49.5%, Oakwood 49.5%, Orange 33.33%, Palestine 33.33%, Parkway Village 49.5%, Pearsall 33.33%, Pharr 33.33%, Port Arthur 33.33%, Port Isabel 50%, Poteet 50%, Preston Peninsula 49.5%, Quemado 50%, Raymondville 50%, Rio Grande City 33.33%, Rockwall 49.5%, Roma 33.33%, San Antonio, San Marcos, Slaton 49.5%, South Padre Island 50%, Stamford 49.5%, Stanton 49.5%, Sullivan City 50%, Tahoka 49.5%, Taylor, Temple 66.67%, Thorndale 66.6%, Trumbull, Uvalde 33.33%, Vidor 49.5%, Waco 66.67%, Weslaco 50%, Wichita Falls 66.67%, Wills Point 49.5%, Wilson 49.5%, Wimberley, Winnie 49.5%, Yoakum 33.33%.
Virginia: Altavista, Bowling Green 49.5%, Clarksville 49.5%, Colonial Beach 49.5%, Drakes Branch 49.5%, Farmville 49.5%, Floyd, Fort Chiswell, Hurt, Kenbridge 49.5%, Keysville 49.5%, Lawrenceville 49.5%, Newcastle, Tappahannock 49.5%, Troutville 49.5%, Warsaw 49.5%, Wytheville 49.5%.
West Virginia: Alkol 49.5%, Beckley 49.5%, Belington 49.5%, Bergoo 49.5%, Charleston 49.5%, Chattaroy 49.5%, Chelyan 49.5%, Clarksburg, Cowen 49.5%, Curtin 49.5%, Davis 49.5%, Dixie 49.5%, Fairmont, Gassaway 49.5%, Independent Mountain 49.5%, Indore 49.5%, Jodie 49.5%, Julian 49.5%, Lewisburg 49.5%, Logan 49.5%, Loudendale 49.5%, New Martinsville 49.5%, Nitro 49.5%, Parkersburg 49.5%, Paw Paw 49.5%, Pond Gap 49.5%, Princeton 49.5%, Sand Fork 49.5%, Summersville 49.5%, Webster Springs 49.5%, Weston 49.5%, Whitesville 49.5%.
Wisconsin: Appleton, Brookfield, Burlington, Cedarburg, Greenfield (Milwaukee County), Howards Grove, Iron Ridge, Kenosha, Marinette, Menomonee Falls 66.67%, Mequon, Merrill, Milwaukee, Muskego, New Berlin, Newburg, North Prairie, Oconomowoc Lake, Plymouth, Random Lake, Reeseville, Wauwatosa 50%.
Wireless Cable Systems (1):
Tennessee: Union City.
Total Basic Subscribers: 12,600,000 (18.38% of total cable households).
Cable Holdings:
16.67%, CAT Partnership, 50%, Century Venture Corporation, 54.19%, Erie Communications Inc., 50%, Kansas City Cable Partners.
Other Holdings:
Cable: CiteReseau, S.A. (France), 49.88%, Rhone Vision Cable S.A.S. (France).
Program source: Cinemax, 50% of Comedy Central, 50% of Court TV, Home Box Office, 40% of HBO Asia, 23% of HBO Brasil, HBO Independent Productions, 33.46% of HBO Ole, HB TVKO Pay-Per-View, New York City 1 News.
Telephone: Offers local telephone service through Austin & Houston, TX; New York & Rochester, NY; Orlando & Tampa Bay, FL systems.
Production: 50% of Bel-Air Entertainment, Looney Tunes, Telepictures Productions, Warner Bros. Television, Warner Bros. Television Animation, Warner Home Video, WarnerVision Entertainment, WB Television Network.
Publishing: 50% of DC Comics.
Retail operation: Warner Brothers Consumer Products, Warner Brothers Studio Stores.
Data service: 46.47% of Road Runner, Warner Brothers Online.

TIP TOP COMMUNICATION

200 Center St.
Arcadia, IA 51480
Phone: 712-689-2238
Fax: 712-689-2600
Ownership: Arcadia Telephone Cooperative.
Cable Systems (6):
Iowa: Charter Oak, Deloit, Dow City, Dunlap, Schleswig, Vail.
Total Basic Subscribers: 1,158.
Total Pay Units: 379.

BOB TIPS

Box 7
Canadian, TX 79014
Phone: 407-423-7583
Cable Systems (1):
Texas: Texhoma.
Total Basic Subscribers: N.A.

TITONKA TELEPHONE CO.

Box 321
247 Main St.
Titonka, IA 50480
Phone: 515-928-2120
Fax: 515-928-2897
Officers:
Gerrit DeWaard, Chmn. & Chief Exec. Officer
Vicky Nelson, Secy.-Treas.
Cable Systems (1):
Iowa: Titonka.
Total Basic Subscribers: 247.
Total Pay Units: 48.
Other Holdings:
Telephone: The Burt Telephone Co.

TOMOKA CABLE TV

1951 State Rd. 40
Ormond Beach, FL 32174
Phone: 904-672-7573
Ownership: J. Stanley Shirah, 50%; Steve P. Shirah, 50%.
Cable Systems (1):
Florida: Ormond Beach (western portion).
Total Basic Subscribers: 3,015.
Total Pay Units: 865.

TORRENCE CABLE INC.
Box 1167
Ridgeland, MS 39158
Phones: 601-981-6900; 800-977-8849
Officers:
Kim A. Torrence, Chmn., Pres. & Chief Exec. Officer
Barry Breithaupt, Chief Operating Officer
Lisa P. McDaniel, Chief Financial Officer
Cable Systems (79):
Alabama: Akron, Appleton, Chatom, Coden, Freemanville, Millry, North Brewton, Pollard, St. Elmo.
Florida: Bratt.
Georgia: Draketown.
Louisiana: Cecilia, Coteau Holmes, Egan, Ethel, Forked Island, Four Corners, Grand Chenier, Grand Lake, Henry, Lebeau, Mire, Norwood, Pecaniere, Sweetwater, Wilson.
Mississippi: Bay St. Louis, Beulah, Carrierre, Centreville, Cruger, Franklin Creek, Glen Allan, Kiln, Lucedale, McAdams, Morgantown, Picayune, Project Road, Schlater, West.
Texas: Bailey, Berclair, Blue Ridge, Bluff Dale, Campbell, Campbellton, Campo Alto, Capisallo Park, Cedar Creek, Cedar Creek Lake, Country Club Shores, Cresson, Dodd City, Eustace, Faysville, Forsan, Garden City, Harbor Point, Knippa, Lasara, Loop, Malone, Maxwell, Monte Alto, Oglesby, Paradise, Pecan Gap, Pettus, Placedo, Randolph, Richards, Santa Maria/Bluetown, Seven Points, St. Francis Village, Welch, Wellman, Westbrook, Westminster.
Total Basic Subscribers: 5,667.
Total Pay Units: 865.

TOTAL LOCAL COMMUNICATIONS INC.
Box 929
La Junta, CO 81050
Phone: 719-384-9898
Fax: 719-384-7320
Officers:
Leo D. Holt, Pres.
Brad Buck, V.P.
Norman Bailey, Secy.-Treas.
Cable Systems (5):
Colorado: Aguilar, Avondale, Boone, Oak Creek, Olney Springs.
Total Basic Subscribers: 1,085.
Total Pay Units: 517.

TOTAL TV OF CALIFORNIA INC.
Box 1749
Monument, CO 80132-1749
Phone: 719-488-8670
Officers:
James F. Fitzgerald Sr., Chmn.
James F. Fitzgerald, Pres.
Ownership: James F. Fitzgerald Sr., James F. Fitzgerald Jr. & Brian Fitzgerald. 100% jointly.
Cable Systems (1):
California: Fort Irwin.
Total Basic Subscribers: 2,600.

BILL TRACY
Box 1058
Marsing, ID 83639
Phones: 208-336-2958; 208-455-5100
Cable Systems (1):
Idaho: Ada County (unincorporated areas).
Total Basic Subscribers: 131.
Total Pay Units: 58.

DAVID TRAISER
3300 38th Ave. NW
Minot, ND 58703
Phone: 701-839-5926
Cable Systems (1):
North Dakota: Sawyer.
Total Basic Subscribers: 79.
Total Pay Units: 38.

TRANS-VIDEO INC.
Village Common
Northfield, VT 05663
Phone: 802-485-3811
Officers:
George L. Goodrich Jr., Pres.
Robert H. Goodrich, V.P.
Ownership: George L. Goodrich Jr., 50%; Robert H. Goodrich, 50%.
Represented (legal): Young, Monte & Lyford.
Cable Systems (1):
Vermont: Northfield (village).
Total Basic Subscribers: 1,650.
Total Pay Units: 215.

TREECE TV CABLE SERVICE
Box 167
Hwy. 65-S
Marshall, AR 72650
Phone: 870-448-2550
Ownership: Bobbie Treece.
Cable Systems (1):
Arkansas: Marshall.
Total Basic Subscribers: 625.

TRIANGLE COMMUNICATION SYSTEMS INC.
Box 1140
Havre, MT 59501
Phone: 406-265-7807
Fax: 406-265-7801
Officers:
Verlin Reichelt, Pres.
John Magyar, Chief Exec. Officer & Gen. Mgr.
Merlyn Huso, Chief Financial Officer
Ownership: Triangle Telephone Cooperative Assn. Inc.
Cable Systems (1):
Montana: Big Sandy.
Total Basic Subscribers: 170.
Total Pay Units: 38.
Other Holdings:
Telephone.
Cellular.

TRIAX TELECOMMUNICATIONS CO. LLC
Suite 600
100 Fillmore St.
Denver, CO 80206
Phones: 303-333-2424; 800-541-7056
Fax: 303-333-1110
Officers:
James DeSorrento, Chmn. & Chief Exec. Officer
Jay R. Busch, Pres.
Samuel S. Street, Exec. V.P. & Dir., Operations
Christopher R. O'Toole, Sr. V.P., Finance & Chief Financial
Angela Borrillo, Dir., Programming & Public Relations
Mark G. Sanford, V.P., Engineering

Branch Offices:
1102 N. 4th St.
Box 334
Chillicothe, IL 61523-0334
Phone: 309-274-4500
Fax: 309-274-3188
Dave Finch, Regional Mgr.

Minnesota Area
1504 2nd St. SE
Waseca, MN 56093
Phone: 507-835-2356
Fax: 507-835-4567
Richard Hanson, Regional Mgr.
Ownership: James DeSorrento, Member; Jay R. Busch, Member. Sold to Mediacom LLC 1999.
Represented (legal): Gallop, Johnson & Neuman (St. Louis, MO).
Cable Systems (303):
Arizona: Apache Junction, Queen Valley.
Illinois: Abingdon 39.5%, Alexis, Altona, Andover, Apollo Acres, Arenzville, Astoria, Atlanta, Avon, Bradford, Brimfield, Buffalo, Bureau, Cantrall, Chapin, Chatsworth, Chillicothe, Clinton, Coffeen, Colfax, Cornell, Cullom, Dallas City, Danvers, Deer Creek, Delavan, Downs, Dunlap, Durand, Dwight, Elizabeth, Elkhart Twp., Elmwood, Fairbury, Fairview, Farmer City, Farmington, Galva, Gibson City, Gilberts, Glasford, Good Hope, Greenview, Hampshire, Hartsburg, Harvel, Herrick, Heyworth, Hudson, Industry, Ipava, Irving, Jacksonville, Kincaid, Kirkland, Lacon 39.5%, Le Roy, Leland, Lena, Lexington, Loami, London Mills, Mahomet 39.5%, Malta, Mansfield, Maquon, Melvin, Middletown, Mineral, Minier, Momence 39.5%, Morrisonville, Mount Auburn, Mount Carroll, Nauvoo, New Berlin, New Holland, Oconee, Odell, Oquawka, Ottawa, Palmer, Paxton 39.5%, Pecatonica, Pontiac, Poplar Grove, Princeville, Rantoul, Rapids City, River Oaks (village), Roanoke 39.5%, Robinson, Roseville, Saybrook, Shipman, St. David, Standard 39.5%, Stockton, Streator, Stronghurst, Sugar Grove, Sullivan, Tampico, Towanda, Tower Hill, Varna, Vermont, Victoria, Viola, Walnut, Warren, Washington Park, Wataga, Waterman, Watseka 39.5%, Weldon, Williamsfield, Wilsonville, Wolfe Road, Wyoming.
Indiana: Albion, Angola, Argos, Auburn, Bluffton, Bourbon, Bremen, Butler, Churubusco, Columbia City, Culver, Harlan, Kendallville, Kentland, Knox, Lagrange, Lakeville, Ligonier, North Manchester, North Webster, Rome City, Roselawn, South Whitley, Syracuse, Walkerton.
Iowa: Amana, Anamosa 39.5%, Armstrong, Bancroft, Blue Grass 39.5%, Bonaparte, Buffalo Center, Burt, Calmar, Clarksville, Clayton 39.5%, Cresco, Eagle Grove, Edgewood, Elgin, Elma, Emmetsburg, Estherville, Fairbank, Fayette, Fredericksburg, Garnavillo 39.5%, Gladbrook, Greene, Hudson, Kalona, Keota, La Porte City, Lansing 39.5%, Lime Springs, Lone Tree, Lowden, Manchester 39.5%, Manly, Maynard, Montezuma, Monticello 39.5%, Montrose, Nashua, New Albin 39.5%, New Hampton, New Hartford, New Sharon, Newhall, North English, Oxford Junction, Riceville, Riverside, Sheffield, Sigourney, Spencer, St. Ansgar, Stacyville, Stanwood, Strawberry Point, Sully, Sumner, Swea City, Tipton 39.5%, Waukon 39.5%, West Union, What Cheer, Williamsburg.
Michigan: Marcellus, Mattawan, Mendon.
Minnesota: Adams, Appleton, Belgrade, Belle Plaine, Blooming Prairie, Brooten, Brownsville, Brownton, Caledonia, Cannon Falls, Canton, Chatfield, Chisago City, Chokio, Clara City, Clinton, Cloquet, Concord, Cook, Cosmos, Dakota, Dawson, Dodge Center, Eveleth, Fulda, Gaylord, Graceville, Grand Marais, Grand Rapids, Granite Falls, Grove City, Hector, Hokah, Houston, Hutchinson, Ivanhoe, Janesville, Keewatin, Kenyon, Lafayette, Lake City, Lake Crystal, Lake Minnetonka, Lanesboro, Le Roy, Le Sueur, Lester Prairie, Litchfield, Lyle, Mabel, Madison, Moose Lake, Morris, Olivia, Paynesville, Peterson, Pipestone, Prior Lake, Proctor, Silver Bay, Slayton, Spring Grove, Springfield, St. James, St. Peter, Starbuck, Two Harbors, Waseca, Wells, Wheaton, Winnebago.
Ohio: Hicksville.
Wisconsin: Albany, Argyle, Blanchardville, Chaseburg, Coon Valley, Fort Mccoy, Fremont, Iola, Mauston, Monticello, Norwalk, Ontario, Orfordville, Platteville 39.5%, Prairie du Chien, Stoddard, Viroqua, Wilton.
Total Basic Subscribers: 341,876 (0.50% of total cable households).
Total Pay Units: 171,691.

TRI-CABLE INC.
3600 Kennebec Dr.
Eagan, MN 55122
Phone: 612-432-1729
Officer:
Lanny Sparks, Pres.
Ownership: Robert Smith, 75%; Lanny Sparks, 25%.
Cable Systems (3):
Minnesota: Elko, Hayfield, Montgomery.
Total Basic Subscribers: 392.
Total Pay Units: 202.

TRI-COM CABLE
Box 135
716 N. College Ave.
Geneseo, IL 61254
Phone: 309-944-5685
Fax: 309-944-5686
Ownership: William L. Kepper, John B. Tupper & Robert Van Der Heyden, Principals.
Cable Systems (1):
Illinois: Geneseo.
Total Basic Subscribers: 2,400.
Total Pay Units: 820.

TRI-COUNTY COMMUNICATIONS CORP.
Box 186
New Richmond, IN 47967
Phone: 317-339-4651
Fax: 317-339-7999
Officer:
Robert V. Warnick, Pres.
Ownership: Tri-County Telephone Co. Inc.
Cable Systems (1):
Indiana: Linden.
Total Basic Subscribers: 1,686.
Total Pay Units: 1,214.
Other Holdings:
Telephone.

TRI-COUNTY COMMUNICATIONS INC.
Box 460
Belhaven, NC 27810
Phone: 252-964-2100
Fax: 252-964-2211
Officer:
Dennis M. Wallace Jr., Chief Exec. Officer
Represented (legal): Harvey W. Raynor III.
Cable Systems (1):
North Carolina: Sidney.
Total Basic Subscribers: 1,809.
Total Pay Units: 952.

TRINITY CABLEVISION INC.
1701 Cogswell Ave.
Pell City, AL 35125
Phone: 205-884-4549
Ownership: Alton D. Elliot, 50%; Arthur M. Smith, 50%. Smith is principal of Coosa Cable Inc., see listing.

Cable Systems (1):
Alabama: Trinity.
Total Basic Subscribers: 1,037.
Total Pay Units: 352.

TRISTAR CABLE INC.

Box 1829
Junction City, KS 66441-6829
Phone: 913-238-3099
Fax: 913-238-7190
Officers:
Ted B. Gleason, Chmn.
Kenneth L. Trimble, Chief Exec. Officer
Ownership: Ted Gleason, 28%; John More, 28%; Larry Trimble, 28%; Vic Davis, 16%.
Represented (legal): Weary, Davis, Henry, Struebling & Troup.
Cable Systems (7):
Oregon: Crabtree, Elkton, Lookingglass, Pioneer Mobile Home Park, St. Paul (town), Tenmile.
Washington: Hood Canal.
Total Basic Subscribers: 1,937.

TRI-STATE CABLE TV

1020 Daniel Mountain
Wallins Creek, KY 40873-8856
Ownership: Alan Harris, Pres.
Cable Systems (1):
Kentucky: Martins Fork.
Total Basic Subscribers: 110.

TROY TELEVISION CO. INC.

Box 37
Troy, ID 83871
Phone: 208-835-4422
Ownership: Community owned.
Cable Systems (1):
Idaho: Troy.
Total Basic Subscribers: 295.
Total Pay Units: 96.

TS COMMUNICATIONS INC.

310 Walnut Extension
Branson, MO 65616
Phones: 417-339-2200; 417-334-7897
Fax: 417-334-7899
Officers:
Thomas G. Semptimphelter, Pres. & Chief Exec. Officer
Robert N. Hymson, Chief Operating Officer
Beth Semptimphelter, Secy.-Treas.
Cable Systems (19):
Oklahoma: Blair 1%, Cleo Springs, Davidson, Duke, Fort Cobb, Fort Supply, Geronimo, Gotebo, Gracemont, Granite, Lone Wolf, Martha, Ninnekah, Olustee, Rocky, Sentinel, Snyder, Tipton, Verden.
Total Basic Subscribers: 36,240 (0.05% of total cable households).
Total Pay Units: 7,403.

THE TULALIP TRIBE INC.

6326 33rd Ave. N
Marysville, WA 98270
Phone: 206-653-4585
Officers:
Stanley G. Jones Sr., Chmn.
Chris Henry, Chief Exec. Officer
Represented (legal): Bell & Ingram.
Cable Systems (1):
Washington: Tulalip Indian Reservation.
Total Basic Subscribers: 1,654
Total Pay Units: 795.

TURIN CABLE TV

4793 Creaser Rd.
Westmoreland, NY 13490
Phone: 315-376-7800
Ownership: Al Szablak, Principal.
Cable Systems (1):
New York: Turin (town).
Total Basic Subscribers: 100.

ROBERT E. TURNER

Rte. 4
Windom, MN 56101
Phone: 507-831-4176
Cable Systems (3):
Minnesota: Lamberton, Revere, Walnut Grove.
Total Basic Subscribers: 625.
Total Pay Units: 77.

TV ASSOCIATION OF COULEE DAM

Box 67
Coulee Dam, WA 99116-0067
Phone: 509-633-2283
Officers:
Jim Manning, Pres.
Frank Ayers, V.P.
Walt Netzel, Secy.-Treas.
Ownership: Subscriber owned.
Cable Systems (1):
Washington: Coulee Dam.
Total Basic Subscribers: 517.
Total Pay Units: 225.

TV CABLE ASSOCIATES INC.

Box 101
Loganton, PA 17747
Phone: 717-725-2733
Officer:
William Sayers, Pres.
Ownership: Community owned.
Cable Systems (1):
Pennsylvania: Loganton.
Total Basic Subscribers: 165.
Total Pay Units: 165.

TV CABLE CO. OF ANDALUSIA INC.

Box 34
Andalusia, AL 36420
Phone: 205-222-6464
Officers:
J. Dige Bishop, Pres.
Ivan H. Bishop, Exec. V.P.
Ownership: Ivan Bishop, 23.35%; Linda Whitman, 18.82%; Julia H. Bishop Trust, 16.09%; John Anderson, 9.86%; Jane Anthony, 7.42%; William H. Albritton, 6.97%; Ophelia Albritton, 5.34%; Ann L. Albritton, 4.25%; Virginia & Thomas Broughton, 2.53%; Drew Cowen, 2.26%; Tyler Cowen, 2.26%; J. Dige Bishop Trust, 0.9%.
Cable Systems (1):
Alabama: Andalusia.
Total Basic Subscribers: 4,299.
Total Pay Units: 1,181.

TV COMMUNICATIONS NETWORK INC.

Suite 300
10020 E. Girard Ave.
Denver, CO 80231
Phone: 303-751-2900
Fax: 303-751-1081
Officers:
Omar A. Duwaik, Pres. & Chief Exec. Officer
Geir Hauge, V.P., Engineering
Ken Roznoy, V.P., Business Development & Secy.
Ownership: Omar Duwaik, 90%; remainder publicly held.
Represented (legal): Fleischman & Walsh LLP.
Wireless Cable Systems (2):
California: San Luis Obispo.
Kansas: Salina.
Total Basic Subscribers: N.A.
Other Holdings:
MMDS, see listing.

TV SERVICE INC.

Box 1410
Hwy. 550
Hindman, KY 41822
Phone: 606-785-3450
Officers:
Robert C. Thacker, Pres., Chief Operating & Financial Officer
Archie W. Everage, V.P., Operations
Junell Thacker, Secy.-Treas.
Ownership: Robert C. Thacker, Thacker is part owner of Thacker-Grigsby Telephone Co., Hindman, KY.
Represented (legal): Weinberg, Pratt & Campbell; Slone & Slone.
Cable Systems (1):
Kentucky: Hindman.
Total Basic Subscribers: 13,500 (0.02% of total cable households).
Total Pay Units: 729.
Other Holdings:
Telephone.

TVC INC.

Box 338
Lennon, MI 48449
Phone: 810-638-7288
Fax: 810-621-9600
Cable Systems (1):
Michigan: New Lothrop.
Total Basic Subscribers: 230.

21ST CENTURY CABLE TV INC.

Suite 600
350 N. Orleans
Chicago, IL 60654
Phone: 312-470-2100
Cable Systems (1):
Illinois: Chicago (area 1) 45%.
Total Basic Subscribers: 71,020 (1.03% of total cable households).
Total Pay Units: 79,475.

TWIN VALLEY COMMUNICATIONS INC.

22 Spruce St.
Miltonvale, KS 67466
Phones: 785-427-2288; 800-515-3311
Fax: 785-427-2216
Officers:
John F. Gisselbeck, Chmn. & Pres.
Michael J. Foster, Chief Operating Officer
Jackie L. Foster, Secy.-Treas.
Ownership: John G. Foster, 11%; Joe Foster, 11%; Peggy S. Foster, 11%; Lulu R. Foster, 11%; Mildred H. Foster, 11%; Michael J. Foster, 11%; Jackie L. Foster, 11%; John F. Gisselbeck, 11%; Penny L. Gisselbeck, 11%. Michael J. Foster is an executive with the Twin Valley Telephone Co., Miltonvale, KS. John F. Gisselbeck is an executive with the Twin Valley Telephone Co., Miltonvale, KS.
Cable Systems (8):
Kansas: Barnard, Bennington, Beverly, Miltonvale, New Cambria, Red Bud Lake, Talmage, Tescott.
Total Basic Subscribers: 585.
Total Pay Units: 226.

TYKESON & ASSOCIATES

Box 5067
63090 Sherman Rd.
Bend, OR 97708-5067
Phone: 503-382-5551
Fax: 503-385-3271
Officers:
Donald E. Tykeson, Chmn.
Amy C. Tykeson, Chief Exec. Officer
William P. Morton, Pres. & Chief Operating Officer
Michael Puckett, V.P., Advertising Sales
Ann Lum, Secy.-Treas.
Thomas H. Palmer, Chief Financial Officer
Daniel Heller, Dir., Engineering Operations
Ownership: Donald E. Tykeson. Tykeson has TV interests.
Represented (legal): Wiley, Rein & Fielding.
Cable Systems (2):
Oregon: Bend, Redmond.
Total Basic Subscribers: 23,472 (0.03% of total cable households).
Total Pay Units: 8,000.

ULTRONICS INC.

396 E St.
Chula Vista, CA 91910-2619
Phone: 619-422-0776
Fax: 619-422-4060
Cable Systems (1):
California: Chula Vista.
Total Basic Subscribers: 4,367.

UNEV COMMUNICATIONS INC.

Box 1077
Lovelock, NV 89419
Phone: 702-273-2020
Ownership: Tom Mitchell.
Cable Systems (2):
Nevada: Lovelock.
Texas: Ozona.
Total Basic Subscribers: 2,281.
Total Pay Units: 1,268.

UNION TELEPHONE CO.

Box 160
Mountain View, WY 82939
Phone: 307-782-6131
Officer:
Howard D. Woody, Pres.
Cable Systems (3):
Wyoming: Granger, Mountain View (Uinta County), Opal.
Total Basic Subscribers: 313.
Total Pay Units: 183.

CITY OF UNIONVILLE MISSOURI CATV

Box 255
1611 Grant
Unionville, MO 63565
Phone: 816-947-3818
Fax: 816-947-2438
Officer:
Jerry Tilden, Chief Operating Officer
Represented (legal): Sam Frank.
Cable Systems (1):
Missouri: Unionville.
Total Basic Subscribers: 1,032.
Total Pay Units: 488.

UNITED CABLE MANAGEMENT

Box 14375
Grand Forks, ND 58208-4375
Phone: 701-772-7191
Ownership: David A. Ramage.
Cable Systems (3):
Nevada: Indian Springs, Indian Springs AFB, Nellis AFB.
Total Basic Subscribers: 1600.

UNITED COMMUNICATIONS ASSN. INC.

1107 McArtor Rd.
Dodge City, KS 67801
Phone: 316-227-8645
Fax: 316-227-7032
Officers:
Laurence Vierthaler, Pres.
Don Howell, V.P.
Sharon Batman, Secy.-Treas.
Ownership: Subscriber owned.
Cable Systems (8):
Kansas: Cimarron, Copeland, Ensign, Ford, Hanston, Ingalls, Montezuma, Spearville.
Total Basic Subscribers: 1,420.
Total Pay Units: 557.

UNITED SATELLITE AMERICA INC.

36380 Garfield Rd.
Clinton Twp., MI 48035
Phone: 810-790-3971
Fax: 810-790-3778
Cable Systems (3):
Iowa: Fontanelle.
Missouri: Kinloch, Wellston.
Total Basic Subscribers: 571.
Total Pay Units: 397.

UNITED STATES GYPSUM CO.

Box 130
Hwy. 447 N
Empire, NV 89405
Phone: 702-557-2341
Fax: 702-557-2138
Cable Systems (1):
Nevada: Empire.
Total Basic Subscribers: 122.
Total Pay Units: 124.

UNITED TELEPHONE MUTUAL AID CORP.

Box 729
411 7th Ave.
Langdon, ND 58259
Phone: 701-256-5156
Fax: 701-256-5150
E-mail: utc@utma.com
Web Site: http://www.utma.com
Officer:
Kenneth Carlson, Pres.
Ownership: Community cooperative.
Represented (legal): Scott R. Stewart.
Cable Systems (1):
North Dakota: Munich.
Wireless Cable Systems (1):
North Dakota: Langdon.
Total Cable Subscribers: 1,697.
Total Pay Units: 403.
Other Holdings:
MDS, MMDS, see listing.

UNITY CABLE TV INC.

Box 643
15 Main St.
Unity, ME 04988
Phone: 207-948-2288
Ownership: Bert Clifford, Raymond McCormack & Rick O'Connor, Principals.
Cable Systems (1):
Maine: Unity.
Total Basic Subscribers: 540.
Total Pay Units: 159.

UNIVERSAL CABLE INC.

495 Ginger Lane
Apt. 17
Calumet City, IL 60409
Phone: 708-862-4004
Ownership: Renald Banks & Barbara Vary, 100% jointly.
Cable Systems (1):
Illinois: Ginger Ridge.
Total Basic Subscribers: N.A.

UNIVERSAL CABLEVISION INC.

4440 26th St. W
Bradenton, FL 33507
Phone: 813-756-5460
Officers:
John L. Manny, Chmn., Chief Exec., Operating & Financial Officer
Bonnie J. Manny, V.P.
Ownership: Bonnie J. Manny & John L. Manny, Principals.
Cable Systems (1):
Florida: Bradenton (unincorporated areas).
Total Basic Subscribers: 374 as of August 1, 1993.
Total Pay Units: 65.

UPPER PENINSULA COMMUNICATIONS INC.

U.S. Hwy. 41
Carney, MI 49812
Phone: 906-639-2194
Ownership: Louis DuPont & L. G. Matthews, Principals.
Cable Systems (14):
Michigan: Alpha (village), Amasa, Champion Twp., De Tour (village), Engadine, Garden Twp., Germfask, Marenisco Twp., Mellen Twp., Michigamme Twp., Portage Twp., Powers, Wolverine (village).
Wisconsin: Phelps.
Total Basic Subscribers: 1,714.
Total Pay Units: 213.

UPSALA COOPERATIVE TELEPHONE ASSOCIATION

Box 366
119 S. Main St.
Upsala, MN 56384
Phone: 320-573-2122
Cable Systems (3):
Minnesota: Grey Eagle, Randall, Swanville.
Total Basic Subscribers: 305.
Total Pay Units: 30.

US CABLE CORP.

Montvale Plaza
28 W. Grand Ave.
Montvale, NJ 07645
Phone: 201-930-9000
Fax: 201-930-9232
Officers:
Stephen E. Myers, Chmn.
James D. Pearson, Pres. & Chief Exec. Officer
Michael C. Anderson, Exec. V.P.
G. Joseph Appio, V.P., Operations
Ownership: Stephen E. Myers, 88%; Michael C. Anderson, 10%; James D. Pearson, 2%.
Represented (legal): Dow, Lohnes & Albertson PLLC.
Cable Systems (83):
Colorado: Bailey, Conifer, Cripple Creek, Eaton, Evergreen, Gilcrest, Hudson, Johnstown, Kersey, Laporte, Loveland (Columbine Mobile Home Park), Marshdale, Table Mountain, Woodland Park.
Georgia: Darien, Jekyll Island, Skidaway Island, St. Marys, Tybee Island.
Minnesota: Alden, Avon, Baldwin, Blue Hill Twp., Brewster, Cambridge, Ceylon, Clarkfield, Crown, Dunnell, Forest Lake, Glenville, Granada, Hendricks, Heron Lake, Howard Lake, Livonia, Mazeppa, Minneota, Norwood, Onamia, Plainview, Renville, Round Lake, St. Francis, Storden, Wabasha, Wanamingo, Westbrook.
Missouri: Edina, Farber, Jonesburg, Madison, Montgomery City, Paris, Perry, Shelbina, Winfield.
New Mexico: Artesia, Brazos, Carlsbad, Chama, Dixon, Espanola, Hobbs, Los Ojos, Santa Clara Indian Reservation, Tierra Amarilla.
South Carolina: Awendaw, Edisto Beach, Folly Beach, Fripp Island, Hollywood, Johns Island, Lady's Island, Wild Dunes.
Texas: Ector County, Odessa (western portion), Seminole, West Alpine, West Odessa.
Wisconsin: Alma, Ellsworth, Pepin.
Total Basic Subscribers: 51,100 (0.07% of total cable households).
Total Pay Units: 23,873.
Other Holdings:
SMATV systems.

US CABLE INC.

3926 Hwy. 79
O'Fallon, MO 63366
Phone: 314-272-2020
Fax: 314-272-2022
Cable Systems (2):
Missouri: Lake Sherwood, Portage Des Sioux.
Total Basic Subscribers: 1,600.
Total Pay Units: 407.
Cable Holdings:
Interest in Dodge County Cablevision, see listing.

USA MEDIA GROUP LLC

Suite 22
6490 S. McCarran Blvd.
Reno, NV 89509
Phone: 775-825-3111
Fax: 775-825-1332
Officers:
Christian Hilliard, Pres. & Chief Exec. Officer
Jim Faircloth, Exec. V.P. & Chief Operating Officer
John Bailey, Exec. V.P. & Chief Financial Officer
Ownership: Christian Hilliard (see listing in LPTV Ownership), Jim Faircloth; & John Bailey, jointly.
Represented (legal): Davis Wright Tremaine LLP.
Cable Systems (32):
California: Big Pine, Bishop, Bridgeport, Chalfant Valley, Crowley Lake, Foresthill, Fort Ord, Half Moon Bay, Independence, Lake Of The Pines, Lee Vining, Meadow Vista, Round Valley, Shaver Lake, Truckee.
Idaho: Burke, Culdesac, Elk City, Kooskia, Orofino, Osburn, Riggins, Spirit Lake, St. Maries, Twin Lakes.
New Mexico: Belen.
Oregon: Boardman, Umatilla.
Washington: Benton City, Chinook Pass, Goldendale, Naches.
Total Basic Subscribers: 55,503 (0.08% of total cable households).
Total Pay Units: 18,841.

UTE MOUNTAIN INDIAN TRIBE

Box 33
Towaoc, CO 81334
Phone: 303-565-9574
Cable Systems (1):
Colorado: Towaoc.
Total Basic Subscribers: 298.
Total Pay Units: 163.

VALLEY CABLE & SATELLITE COMMUNICATIONS

Box 7
102 S. Main St.
Herreid, SD 57632-0007
Phone: 605-437-2615
Fax: 605-437-2220
Officers:
Dean Wessel, Pres.
Charles Wolf, Secy.-Treas.
Ownership: Valley Telco Co-op Assn. Inc.
Represented (legal): Meyers & Rogers.
Cable Systems (5):
South Dakota: Glenham, Herreid, Hosmer, Leola, Pollock.
Total Basic Subscribers: 652.
Total Pay Units: 94.
Other Holdings:
Telephone.

VALLEY CABLE SYSTEMS

Box 78
Doylesburg, PA 17219
Phone: 717-349-7717
Ownership: Barry L. Kepner, Chmn., 50%; Sandy Kepner, 50%.
Cable Systems (7):
Pennsylvania: Allensville, Doylesburg, East Waterford, Fannettsburg, Neelyton.
West Virginia: Capon Bridge, Wardensville.
Total Basic Subscribers: 1,107.
Total Pay Units: 152.

VALLEY CABLE TV INC. I

602 College St.
Fort Valley, GA 31030
Phone: 912-825-3626
Cable Systems (1):
Georgia: Fort Valley.
Total Basic Subscribers: 1,808.

VALLEY TV CO-OP INC.

Box 450
Parkdale, OR 97401
Phone: 503-352-6760
Cable Systems (2):
Oregon: Odell, Parkdale.
Total Basic Subscribers: 790.
Total Pay Units: 350.

VALPARAISO COMMUNICATION SYSTEMS

Box 296
465 Valparaiso Pkwy.
Valparaiso, FL 32580
Phone: 904-729-5404
Officer:
Helen J. Bourgeois, Chief Financial Officer & City Clerk
Ownership: Community owned.
Cable Systems (1):
Florida: Valparaiso.
Total Basic Subscribers: 1,641.
Total Pay Units: 855.

VAN HORNE TELEPHONE CO.

204 Main St.
Van Horne, IA 52346
Phone: 319-228-8791
Fax: 319-228-8784
Officers:
Ralph Petersen, Pres.
Wayne Eichmeyer, V.P., Van Horne Telephone & Cablevision
Daniel O'Brien, Secy.-Treas.
Cable Systems (1):
Iowa: Van Horne.
Total Basic Subscribers: 254.
Total Pay Units: 134.

Other Holdings:
Telephone: Benton Telemarketing Center Inc.
Cellular: Navenroh Communications Inc.

W. ADDINGTON VANCE
122 S. Washington St.
Crawfordsville, IN 47933
Phone: 317-362-6161
Cable Systems (1):
Indiana: Frankfort 10%.
Total Basic Subscribers: 5,050.
Total Pay Units: 2,483.

VENTURE ASSOC. CORP.
2661 N.W. 60th Ave.
Ocala, FL 34482
Phone: 352-732-9898
Fax: 352-732-5994
Cable Systems (1):
Florida: Palm Cay.
Total Basic Subscribers: 850.
Total Pay Units: 200.

VERNON COMMUNICATIONS & TV
Box 267
309 Main St.
Sanborn, IA 51248
Phones: 712-729-5333; 800-642-4088
Fax: 712-729-3331
Officers:
Ross K. Vernon, Chmn., Pres. & Chief Exec. Officer
Thurlow Beimers, Chief Operating Officer
Doug Boone, Chief Financial Officer
Ownership: Ross K. Vernon. Vernon is Pres. & Gen. Mgr. of Northern Iowa Telephone Co., Sioux Center, IA.
Cable Systems (12):
Iowa: Akron, Ashton, Boyden, Dickens, Hinton, Ireton, Little Rock, Maurice, Melvin, Merrill, Ocheyedan, Webb.
Total Basic Subscribers: 1,960.
Total Pay Units: 630.

VERNONIA CATV INC.
536 S. First Ave.
Vernonia, OR 97064
Phone: 503-427-8327
Ownership: Bud Foster.
Cable Systems (1):
Oregon: Vernonia.
Total Basic Subscribers: 503.

VERTO COMMUNICATIONS—Sold to Adelphia Communications Corp. 1999.

VIDEO ENGINEERING INC.
12333 S. Sunnyville-Saratoga Rd.
Saratoga, CA 95070
Phone: 415-883-9251
Ownership: Ken Daniel, Principal.
Cable Systems (1):
California: Hamilton AFB.
Total Basic Subscribers: 242.
Total Pay Units: 66.

VIDEO INC.
Box 708
Bay Springs, MS 39422
Phone: 601-764-3143
Fax: 601-764-4900
Officers:
Joseph D. Fail, Pres. & Chief Exec. Officer
R. A. McFarland, V.P.
D. Wayne Skelton, Secy.-Treas.
Robert J. Healea, Chief Financial Officer
Ownership: Telephone Electronics Corp. Affiliated with the Bay Springs Telephone Co. Inc., Bay Springs, MS.
Cable Systems (1):
Mississippi: Bay Springs.
Total Basic Subscribers: 2,045.
Total Pay Units: 1,240.

VIDEO SERVICES LTD.
Box 123
Bode, IA 50519
Phone: 515-379-1558
Ownership: Mark Steil, Principal.
Cable Systems (2):
Iowa: Bode, Lu Verne.
Total Basic Subscribers: 291.
Total Pay Units: 25.

VIDEO VISION INC.
Box 11703
Rock Hill, SC 29731
Phone: 803-285-1561
Ownership: F. S. Barnes Jr. & John M. Barnes, Principals. Barnes have interest in Catabwa Services Inc., see listing.
Cable Systems (1):
South Carolina: Lancaster.
Total Basic Subscribers: 10,257.
Total Pay Units: 4,708.

VIDEOWAVE TELEVISION
2387 Midway Rd.
Carson, TX 75006
Phone: 650-631-9190
Fax: 415-631-9188
Ownership: Videotron.
Planned Wireless Cable Systems (2):
California: San Francisco, San Jose.
Total Basic Subscribers: N.A.

VIKING ELECTRONICS INC.
Box 35
110 4th St.
Park River, ND 58270
Phone: 701-284-7221
Cable Systems (12):
North Dakota: Adams, Cavalier, Crystal, Edinburg, Fordville, Hoople, Michigan, Neche, Osnabrock, Park River, Petersburg, St. Thomas.
Total Basic Subscribers: 2,554.
Total Pay Units: 873.

VIKING VISION
Suite 101
901 Hwy. 29 N
Alexandria, MN 56308
Phone: 320-763-4122
Wireless Cable Systems (1):
Minnesota: Alexandria.
Total Basic Subscribers: N.A.
Other Holdings:
MMDS, see listing.

VILLAGE CABLE CO. (ANCHORAGE, AK)
Box 93250
Anchorage, AK 99509-3250
Phone: 907-522-4796
Fax: 907-349-3558
Officers:
Paul H. Davis, Chmn. & Pres.
William C. Newell, Chief Exec. Officer
Ownership: Paul H. Davis, William C. Newell, David Vatz & James F. Williamson, Principals.
Cable Systems (1):
Alaska: Mountain Village.
Total Basic Subscribers: 90.
Total Pay Units: 172.

VILLAGE CABLE CO. (PALMETTO, LA)
Box 97
Palmetto, LA 71358
Phone: 318-623-4426
Fax: 318-623-3138
Ownership: Community owned.
Represented (legal): Earl B. Taylor.
Cable Systems (1):
Louisiana: Palmetto.
Total Basic Subscribers: 101.
Total Pay Units: 28.

H. A. VIRDELL JR.
Drawer F
Hwy. 80
Sierra Blanca, TX 79851
Phone: 915-369-2341
Represented (legal): Fletcher, Heald & Hildreth PLC.
Cable Systems (1):
Texas: Sierra Blanca.
Total Basic Subscribers: 135.

VIRGINIA COMMUNICATIONS INC.
6330 E. Mockingbird Lane
Scottsdale, AZ 85253
Phone: 602-948-3776
Fax: 602-991-6797
Ownership: Virginia Merrill, Pres.
Represented (legal): Pepper & Corazzini.
Wireless Cable Systems (2):
Arizona: Verde Valley.
Tennessee: Clarksville.
Total Basic Subscribers: N.A.
Other Holdings:
MDS, MMDS, see listing.

VISION COMMUNICATIONS LLC
Box 355
Luck, WI 54853
Phone: 715-472-2700
Officers:
John Klatt, Pres.
Larry Knegendorf, V.P.
Dana Olson, Secy.-Treas.
Ownership: Alden Telecom, 16.66%; Amery Telcom, 16.66%; Clearlake Telephone, 16.66%; Farmers Independent Telephone Co. of Grantsburg, 16.66%; Luck Telephone, 16.66%; Milltown Mutual Telephone, 16.66%.
Cable Systems (6):
Wisconsin: Grantsburg, Luck, Roberts, Siren, Solon Springs, Turtle Lake.
Total Basic Subscribers: 2,070.
Total Pay Units: 1,593.

VISION ELECTRONICS
14707 N. 72nd St.
Omaha, NE 68122
Phone: 402-571-7590
Fax: 402-571-2801
Ownership: John W. Smith, Pres., Principal.
Cable Systems (8):
Nebraska: Butte, Clarkson, Decatur, Ewing, Spencer, Stuart, Verdigre, Wausa.
Total Basic Subscribers: 1,641.
Total Pay Units: 693.

VISTA BROADBAND COMMUNICATIONS LLC
Box 1587
Smyrna, GA 30081
Phone: 770-433-2338
Fax: 770-433-2453
Officer:
Neil McHugh, Pres.
Ownership: Boston Ventures LP V; Neil R. McHugh.
Cable Systems (1):
Georgia: Smyrna.
Total Basic Subscribers: 26,700 (0.04% of total cable households).
Total Pay Units: 16,500.
Note: Sold to Charter Communications Inc. 1999.

VI-TEL INC.
Box 789
223 Broadway
Davenport, OK 74026-0789
Phone: 918-377-2347
Fax: 918-377-2506
Officers:
Steven Guest, Pres.
David Guest, V.P.
Ownership: Central Oklahoma Telephone Co.
Cable Systems (1):
Oklahoma: Davenport.
Total Basic Subscribers: 301.
Total Pay Units: 141.
Other Holdings:
Telephone.

VLCEK CABLE CO.
Box 548
Wilson, KS 67490
Phone: 913-658-2490
Officer:
Douglas Vlcek, Pres.
Ownership: Douglas Vlcek & Susan Vlcek, 100% jointly.
Cable Systems (2):
Kansas: Lucas, Wilson.
Total Basic Subscribers: N.A.

VOLCANO COMMUNICATIONS CO.
Box 890
Pine Grove, CA 95665
Phone: 209-296-2288
Ownership: Sharon Lundgren, Chmn., Principal.
Represented (legal): Beck & Ackerman.
Cable Systems (1):
California: Pine Grove.
Total Basic Subscribers: 3,850.
Total Pay Units: 1,470.
Other Holdings:
Telephone: Volcano Telephone Co.
Cellular: Volcano Cellular Inc.

DAVID WAGNER
4413 Sourdough Rd.
Bozeman, MT 59715
Phone: 406-995-4075
Cable Systems (1):
Montana: Big Sky.
Total Basic Subscribers: 920.
Total Pay Units: 180.

BERNARD H. WAINWRIGHT
Box 865
Rte. 7
Baxley, GA 31513
Phone: 912-367-2479
Cable Systems (2):
Georgia: Funston, Norman Park.
Total Basic Subscribers: 400.
Total Pay Units: 90.

WAITSFIELD-FAYSTON TELEPHONE CO.
Box 9

Waitsfield, VT 05673
Phone: 802-496-5800
Cable Systems (1):
Vermont: Waitsfield.
Total Basic Subscribers: 3,268.
Total Pay Units: 2,748.

VIC WALDRON
Box 133
Cedar Bluff, VA 24609
Phone: 703-964-5946
Cable Systems (1):
Virginia: Rosedale 50%.
Total Basic Subscribers: N.A.

WALKER CABLEVISION
1734 Smyrna Rd.
Uvalda, GA 30473
Phone: 912-584-8103
Ownership: Wilbur Walker, 55%; James Eudy, 45%.
Cable Systems (3):
Georgia: Davisboro, Harrison, Kite.
Total Basic Subscribers: 348.
Total Pay Units: 108.

WALL LAKE CABLE TV SYSTEM
City Hall
Wall Lake, IA 51466
Phone: 712-664-2216
Ownership: Community owned.
Cable Systems (1):
Iowa: Wall Lake.
Total Basic Subscribers: 265.

WALNUT CREEK COMMUNICATIONS INC.
Box 70
Huxley, IA 50124
Phones: 515-597-2212; 800-231-4922
Fax: 515-597-2899
Officers:
Dean Lester, Pres.
D. R. Reinertson, Exec. V.P.
Dave Halverson, Secy.-Treas.
Ownership: Huxley Cooperative Telephone Co.
Cable Systems (10):
Iowa: Alleman, Cambridge, Collins, Colo, Hartford, Kelley, Lacona, Maxwell, Milo, Runnells.
Total Basic Subscribers: 1,000.

WALNUT TELEPHONE CO.
Box 346
Walnut, IA 51577-0346
Phone: 712-784-2211
Fax: 712-784-2010
Officer:
Bruce Heyne, Pres.
Cable Systems (1):
Iowa: Walnut.
Total Basic Subscribers: 290.
Total Pay Units: 226.
Other Holdings:
Cellular.

WAMEGO COMMUNITY ANTENNA SYSTEMS INC.
1410 Lilac Lane
Wamego, KS 66547
Phone: 913-456-8356
Officers:
Robert K. Weary Sr., Pres.
Robert H. Morse, V.P.
Robert K. Weary Jr., Secy.
Ownership: Robert K. Weary Jr., see listing, 32.5%; Ralph L. Weir Jr., 32.5%; Robert H. Morse Sr., 12.5%; Dale Ann Clore, 12.5%; Weldon S. Johnson, 5%; John Monroe, 5%.
Cable Systems (1):
Kansas: Wamego.
Total Basic Subscribers: 1,689.
Total Pay Units: 286.

WANDER TELECOMMUNICATIONS
Box 200
The Sea Ranch, CA 95497-0200
Phones: 415-921-2138; 208-453-1025
Ownership: Dr. Gerhard J. Hanneman, Pres., Chief Exec. Officer & Gen. Partner.
Represented (legal): Cole, Raywid & Braverman LLP.
Cable Systems (27):
Arizona: Arizona City, Cave Creek, Dolan Springs, Dudleyville, Eloy, Heber, Kearny, Mammoth, Oracle, Peach Springs, Perryville, San Manuel, Superior.
California: Cow Creek, Grapevine, The Sea Ranch.
Nevada: Beatty, Blue Diamond, Boulder City (northern portion), Cal-Nev-Ari, Callville Bay, Gabbs, Goldfield, Hadley, Pahrump, Silverpeak, Tonopah.
Total Basic Subscribers: 6,795.
Total Pay Units: 1,491.

WARD COMMUNICATIONS
Box 3393
Williamsport, PA 17701
Phones: 717-435-2035; 800-257-2288
Ownership: Neal W. Kimberling, Pres.
Cable Systems (1):
Pennsylvania: Pulaski.
Total Basic Subscribers: 840.
Total Pay Units: 245.

WARMATH COMMUNICATIONS INC.
Box 408
Humboldt, TN 38343
Phone: 901-784-5000
Fax: 901-784-7474
Officer:
John Warmath, Pres.
Ownership: J. Frank Warmath Estate, 70.66%; John F. Warmath, 14.67%; James C. Warmath, 14.67%. John F. Warmath also has MDS holdings, see listing.
Cable Systems (1):
Tennessee: Humboldt.
Total Basic Subscribers: 4,483.
Total Pay Units: 901.
Newspapers:
Tennessee: The Courier-Chronicle.

JAMES R. WATKINS
Box 464
Rte. 2
Booneville, KY 41314
Phone: 606-593-6490
Cable Systems (1):
Kentucky: Island City.
Total Basic Subscribers: 244.

JAMES WATSON
RR1
Box 94
Somonauk, IL 60552
Phone: 815-498-3195
Cable Systems (2):
Illinois: Compton, Kingston.
Total Basic Subscribers: N.A.

WAUSAUKEE CABLEVISION INC.
Box 166
W. 1597 Hwy. 64
Marinette, WI 54143
Phone: 715-735-9532
Ownership: H. C. Lock.
Cable Systems (2):
Michigan: Stephenson.
Wisconsin: Suring.
Total Basic Subscribers: 597.
Total Pay Units: 170.

WAYCROSS CABLE CO. INC.
126 Havanna Ave.
Waycross, GA 31501
Phone: 912-283-2332
Officer:
John Stembler, Pres.
Cable Systems (1):
Georgia: Waycross 89%.
Total Basic Subscribers: 11,047 (0.02% of total cable households).
Total Pay Units: 2,400.

WAYSIDE TELEPHONE CO.
7235 County Rd. W
Greenleaf, WI 54126-9499
Phone: 920-864-2105
Cable Systems (1):
Wisconsin: Greenleaf.
Total Basic Subscribers: 130.

WCS INC.
Suite 101
105 W. 23rd St.
Hastings, MN 55033
Phones: 612-438-3507; 612-438-3510
Fax: 612-438-3526; 800-347-0323
Officer:
Hubertus Sarrazin, Pres.
Cable Systems (4):
Minnesota: Hampton, Randolph, Ravenna, Vermillion.
Total Basic Subscribers: 417.

W. E. COMMUNICATIONS INC.
Box 308
35 First Ave. NE
Harmony, MN 55939
Phone: 507-886-2525
Officers:
Kenneth L. Halverson, Chief Exec. Officer
Linda L. Halverson, Chief Financial Officer
Cable Systems (1):
Minnesota: Harmony.
Total Basic Subscribers: 411.
Total Pay Units: 139.
Other Holdings:
Harmony Telephone Co.

ROBERT K. WEARY JR.
1809 N St.
Belleville, KS 66935
Phone: 913-527-2226
Cable Systems (4):
Kansas: Belleville, Mankato, Washington.
Nebraska: Hebron.
Total Basic Subscribers: 2,616.
Total Pay Units: 620.
Cable Holdings:
Wamego Community Antenna Systems Inc, see listing, 32.50%.

WEHCO VIDEO INC.
Box 2221
Little Rock, AR 72203
Phone: 501-378-3529
Fax: 501-376-8594
Officers:
Walter E. Hussman Jr., Chmn. & Chief Exec. Officer
J. P. Morbeck, Chief Operating Officer
Allen Berry, Chief Financial Officer
Ownership: KCMC Inc. Walter E. Hussman Jr., Principal. Hussman owns KTAL-TV Inc., see listing.
Represented (legal): Covington & Burling.
Cable Systems (16):
Arkansas: Augusta, Bald Knob, Brinkley, Camden 81%, Forrest City, Hope 80%, Hot Springs 80%, Marianna, Pine Bluff, Prescott 80%, Searcy, Wynne.
Mississippi: Vicksburg.
Oklahoma: Tahlequah.
Texas: Kilgore 50%, Longview 75%.
Total Basic Subscribers: 116,480 (0.17% of total cable households).
Total Pay Units: 41,166.
Newspapers:
Arkansas: Hot Springs Sentinel Record, El Dorado News-Times, Little Rock Arkansas Democrat, Magnolia Banner-News, Hope Star (25%), Texarkana Gazette.
Texas: Jacksonville Progress (25%).
Other Holdings:
Common Carrier: Owns 81% of United WEHCO Inc.
Theater: Minority interest in Home Theatres Inc., Little Rock, AR.

ROBERT WEISBERG
Suite PHA
145 E. 92nd St.
New York, NY 10128
Phone: 212-722-2990
Cable Systems (1):
California: Frazier Park 95%.
Total Basic Subscribers: 1,400.
Total Pay Units: 350.

WESLEY CABLE TV OF WESLEY IOWA INC.
Box 97
207 Main St.
Wesley, IA 50483
Phone: 515-679-4225
Cable Systems (2):
Iowa: Corwith, Wesley.
Total Basic Subscribers: 200.
Total Pay Units: 91.

DONALD WESLEY
Box 100
Sweet Valley, PA 18656
Phone: 717-925-5720
Cable Systems (1):
Pennsylvania: Sugarloaf Twp.
Total Basic Subscribers: 208.
Total Pay Units: 50.

WEST ALABAMA TV CABLE CO. INC.
108 First St. SW
Fayette, AL 35555
Phone: 205-932-4100
Ownership: Stephen W. Vaughan, Pres.
Cable Systems (3):
Alabama: Fayette, Hamilton, Winfield.
Total Basic Subscribers: 6,773.
Total Pay Units: 1,317.

WEST CENTRAL ELECTRIC COOPERATIVE INC.
Box 17
Murdo, SD 57559
Phone: 605-669-2472
Fax: 605-669-2358

Cable Systems (5):
South Dakota: Kimball, Murdo, Oacoma, Presho, Reliance.
Total Basic Subscribers: 601.

WEST CENTRAL TELEPHONE ASSN.

Box 312
Sebeka, MN 56477
Phone: 218-837-5155
Fax: 218-837-5001
Officers:
Jerome Schermerhorn, Pres.
Anthony Mayer, Chief Exec. Officer
Cable Systems (1):
Minnesota: Menahga.
Total Basic Subscribers: 742.
Total Pay Units: 155.

UNIVERSITY OF WEST FLORIDA

Instructional Media Center
11000 University Pkwy.
Pensacola, FL 32514
Phone: 904-474-2501
Cable Systems (1):
Florida: University of West Florida.
Total Basic Subscribers: 424.
Radio Stations:
Florida: WUWF-FM, Pensacola.

WEST IOWA TELEPHONE CO.

12 E. 3rd St.
Remsen, IA 51050
Phone: 712-786-1181
Fax: 712-786-2400
Cable Systems (1):
Iowa: Anita.
Total Basic Subscribers: 352.
Total Pay Units: 91.

JOE WEST

Box 2150
Hwy. 195
Trinity, TX 75862
Phone: 409-594-2405
Cable Systems (1):
Texas: Carolina Cove.
Total Basic Subscribers: 42.
Total Pay Units: 52.

WEST RIVER COOPERATIVE TELEPHONE CO.

Box 39
Bison, SD 57620
Phone: 605-244-5213
Fax: 605-244-7288
Cable Systems (1):
South Dakota: Bison.
Total Basic Subscribers: 168.
Total Pay Units: 93.

WEST SIDE TV CORP.

Box 812
Sheffield, PA 16347
Phone: 814-968-3394
Officers:
Charles Culbertson, Pres.
John Buck, V.P.
Peggy Dunn, Secy.
Tammy Mangina, Treas.
Ownership: Subscriber owned.
Cable Systems (1):
Pennsylvania: Sheffield.
Total Basic Subscribers: 420.

WEST TENNESSEE WIRELESS

Phone: 901-427-7037
Wireless Cable Systems (1):
Tennessee: Jackson.
Total Basic Subscribers: N.A.

WESTCOM LC

Box 71279
Des Moines, IA 50325
Phone: 515-276-3174
Ownership: Jay Eliason, Principal. Eliason also has interest in Illinet Communications of Central Illinois Inc., Illini Cablevision of Illinois Inc., Mid American Cable Systems, New Path Communications LC, TelePartners & Telnet Communications, see listings.
Cable Systems (73):
Illinois: Addieville, Alsey Twp., Chesterfield (village), Cypress (village), Dubois (village), East Carondelet (town), Eldred, Ellis Grove, Fayetteville, Fieldon, Fillmore, Gorham Twp., Grand Chain (town), Grand Tower (village), Hettick (village), Hoffman, Hoyleton, Joppa, Logan (village), Manchester (village), Medora, New Burnside, New Haven (village), New Minden, Omaha, Pierron, Sims, St. Libory, Stonefort, Waltonville, Wolf Lake.
Kansas: Bentley, Brookville, Burns, Haddam, Mahaska, Mulvane, Munden, Partridge, Princeton, Rosalia, Sedgwick County (portions), Wilsey.
Michigan: Barton City, Brethren, Free Soil, Glennie (village), Lilley Twp., Luzerne, Prescott (village), Wellston.
Missouri: Amazonia, Craig, Ste. Genevieve.
Nebraska: Avoca, Brock, Dawson, Dubois, Endicott, Otoe, Prague, Rulo, Salem, Shubert, Tobias, Verdon, Weston.
Oklahoma: Asher, Deer Creek, Meno, Orlando, Red Rock, Ripley.
Cable Franchises (1):
Illinois: Valmeyer.
Total Basic Subscribers: 4,928.

WESTERN CABLE COMMUNICATIONS

13450 S. Weber Rd.
Plainfield, IL 60504
Phone: 815-886-2311
Fax: 815-886-0909
Officers:
Dan Houghton, V.P.
Tony Fischietto, Chief Financial Officer
Cable Systems (1):
Illinois: Plainfield.
Total Basic Subscribers: 3,121.

WESTERN DAKOTA CABLE INC.

Box 58
Elgin, ND 58533
Phone: 701-584-3113
Officers:
Clara Messmer, Pres.
Patsy A. Kochel, Secy.-Treas.
Ownership: Patsy A. Kochel, Timothy F. Kochel, Clara Messmer & Vic Messmer, 100% jointly.
Represented (legal): Ron Weikum.
Cable Systems (3):
North Dakota: Carson, Elgin, New Leipzig.
Total Basic Subscribers: 400.
Total Pay Units: 46.

WESTERN WISCONSIN COMMUNICATIONS COOPERATIVE

Box 846
202 Whitehall Rd.
Independence, WI 54747
Phone: 715-985-3004
Ownership: Subscriber owned.
Represented (legal): Fleischman & Walsh LLP.
Cable Systems (1):
Wisconsin: Independence.
Total Basic Subscribers: 6,628.
Total Pay Units: 3,222.

WESTFIELD COMMUNITY ANTENNA ASSN. INC.

121 Strang St.
Westfield, PA 16950
Phone: 814-367-5190
Fax: 814-367-5586
Ownership: Subscriber owned.
Cable Systems (1):
Pennsylvania: Westfield.
Total Basic Subscribers: 1,027.
Total Pay Units: 362.

THE WESTSTAR COMPANIES—Sold to USA Media Group LLC 1999.

WETHERELL CABLE TV SYSTEM

Box 188
Cleghorn, IA 51014
Phone: 712-436-2266
Ownership: Ronald Wetherell & Todd Wetherell, 100% jointly.
Cable Systems (1):
Iowa: Cleghorn.
Total Basic Subscribers: N.A.

WFL CABLE TELEVISION ASSOCIATES INC.

114 N. Rutherford St.
Wadesboro, NC 28170
Phone: 704-694-9409
Fax: 704-694-6803
Officers:
William F. Lee, Pres.
H. P. Taylor Jr., Chief Operating Officer
Ownership: William F. Lee, 50%; H. P. Taylor Jr., 50%.
Represented (legal): Taylor & Bower.
Cable Systems (1):
North Carolina: Morven.
Total Basic Subscribers: 550.
Total Pay Units: 250.

WHEAT STATE TELECABLE INC.

Box 357
106 W. First St.
Udall, KS 67146
Phone: 316-782-3347
Fax: 316-782-3302
Officers:
Greg Reed, Chmn., Pres. & Chief Exec. Officer
Arturo Macias, Chief Operating Officer & Secy.-Treas.
Ownership: Golden Wheat Inc. Also owns Wheat State Telephone Co.
Represented (legal): James Caplinger.
Cable Systems (1):
Kansas: Udall.
Total Basic Subscribers: 240.
Total Pay Units: 85.

WHEELER TV SYSTEM INC.

Box 380
S. Hwy. 83
Wheeler, TX 79096
Phone: 806-826-3026
Ownership: N. D. Ware.
Cable Systems (1):
Texas: Wheeler.
Total Basic Subscribers: 440.

WHITE SANDS CABLE CO. INC.

Box 70
White Sands Missile Range, NM 88002
Phone: 505-382-5077
Officers:
Homer Harmon, Chief Exec. Officer
R. Harmon, Chief Operating Officer
Ownership: Homer Harmon & Kathy Harmon, 100% jointly.
Cable Systems (1):
New Mexico: White Sands.
Total Basic Subscribers: 905.
Total Pay Units: 807.

TIMOTHY A. WHITNEY

Box 47
Keene Valley, NY 12943
Phone: 518-576-4510
Cable Systems (1):
New York: Keene Valley.
Total Basic Subscribers: 305.

DALE L. WHITTINGTON CORP.

684 Dyson Rd.
Haines City, FL 33844
Phone: 813-421-4528
Cable Systems (1):
Florida: Sweetwater Golf & Tennis Club East.
Total Basic Subscribers: 109.

WHTV BROADCASTING CORP.

Box 8437
Fernandez Juncos Station
San Juan, PR 00910-8437
Phone: 787-722-7815
Officers:
Dr. Luis F. Sala, Chmn. & Chief Exec. Officer
Abelardo Le Compte, Chief Operating Officer
Jorge P. Sala, Chief Financial Officer
Ownership: Sala Business Corp., 80%; Ponce Broadcasting Corp., 20%.
Wireless Cable Systems (1):
Puerto Rico: San Juan.
Total Basic Subscribers: 6,000.
Total Pay Units: 3,594.
Other Holdings:
MMDS, see listing.

WIGGINS TELEPHONE CO.

414 Main St.
Wiggins, CO 80654
Phone: 970-483-7345
Fax: 970-483-7345
Cable Systems (1):
Colorado: Wiggins.
Total Basic Subscribers: 146.
Total Pay Units: 38.

WILCOP CABLE TV

Box 558
Brodhead, KY 40409
Phone: 606-758-8320
Ownership: Johnny Wilcop.
Cable Systems (2):
Kentucky: Brodhead, Crab Orchard.
Total Basic Subscribers: 458.

WILLIAMSON ROAD TV CO. INC.

Box 45
Blossburg, PA 16912
Phone: 717-638-2490
Officers:

Jerome Ogden, Pres.
Conrad E. Lindquist, Chief Exec. Officer
Leonard S. Mahosky, Secy.-Treas.
Ownership: Community owned.
Cable Systems (1):
Pennsylvania: Blossburg.
Total Basic Subscribers: 640.
Total Pay Units: 153.

CITY OF WILLIAMSTOWN CABLE TV

Box 147
400 N. Main St.
Williamstown, KY 41097
Phone: 606-824-3633
Fax: 606-824-6320
Officers:
Chuck Hudson, Chmn., Chief Exec. & Operating Officer
Angel Crouch, Chief Financial Officer
Ownership: Community owned.
Cable Systems (1):
Kentucky: Williamstown.
Total Basic Subscribers: 1,016.
Total Pay Units: 332.

WINDOM CABLE COMMUNICATIONS

Box 38
444 9th St.
Windom, MN 56101
Phone: 507-831-2363
Ownership: Community owned.
Cable Systems (1):
Minnesota: Windom.
Total Basic Subscribers: 1,632.
Total Pay Units: 400.

SCOTT WINGER

210 N. Main St.
Sweetser, IN 46937
Phone: 317-384-5444
Cable Systems (1):
Indiana: Sweetser.
Total Basic Subscribers: 1,190.
Total Pay Units: 411.

WINNEBAGO COOPERATIVE TELEPHONE ASSN.

704 E. Main
Lake Mills, IA 50450
Phone: 515-592-1000
Fax: 515-592-6102
Ownership: Subscriber owned.
Cable Systems (1):
Iowa: Thompson.
Total Basic Subscribers: 1,325.
Total Pay Units: 419.

WIRE TELE-VIEW CORP.

603 E. Market St.
Pottsville, PA 17901
Phone: 717-622-4501
Officers:
Deborah A. Stabinsky, Pres.
J. Richard Kirn, Secy.
Mary Louise Schoffstall, Treas.
Ownership: Mary Louise Schoffstall, 30.4%; Deborah A. Stabinsky, 12.2%; J. Richard Kirn, 9.6%; remainder undisclosed.
Cable Systems (2):
Pennsylvania: Pottsville, Tremont.
Total Basic Subscribers: 2,525.
Total Pay Units: 400.

WIRELESS ASSOCIATES LP

Box 62889
Charleston, SC 29419
Wireless Cable Systems (1):
Kentucky: Lexington.
Total Basic Subscribers: N.A.

WIRELESS BROADCASTING SYSTEMS OF AMERICA INC.

Suite 325
9250 E. Costilla Ave.
Englewood, CO 80112
Phone: 303-649-1195
Fax: 303-649-1196
Officers:
William Kingery, Chief Exec. Officer
Sharan Wilson, Chief Operating Officer
Chris Scurto, V.P., Mktg.
Peer Pedersen, Secy.-Treas.
Jeb Dickey, Chief Financial Officer
Ownership: WBS America LLC.
Wireless Cable Systems (5):
California: Sacramento.
Florida: Fort Pierce, Melbourne.
Idaho: Boise.
Washington: Yakima.
Total Basic Subscribers: 75,000 (0.11% of total cable households).
Total Pay Units: 51,000.
Other Holdings:
LPTV, MDS, MMDS, see listings.

WIRELESS CABLE SYSTEMS INC.

Phone: 212-268-2828
Fax: 212-268-5675
Wireless Cable Systems (3):
Illinois: Rockford.
Michigan: Jackson.
Wisconsin: Janesville.
Total Basic Subscribers: N.A.
Other Holdings:
MMDS, see listing.

WIRELESS CABLE TV OF WATERLOO

c/o Group Communications Inc.
1463 Oak Crest Dr.
Waterloo, IA 50701-1750
Phone: 319-234-0921
Officer:
William D. Silverson III, Chief Exec. Officer
Wireless Cable Systems (1):
Iowa: Waterloo.
Total Basic Subscribers: N.A.

WIRELESS HOLDINGS INC.

500 Clyde Ave.
Mountain View, CA 94043
Officers:
Brian Reynolds, Chief Operating Officer
Francois Labonte, V.P., Control
Ownership: Groupe Videotron Ltd.; Transworld Telecommunications Inc.
Wireless Cable Systems (2):
Florida: Tampa.
Washington: Spokane.
Total Basic Subscribers: 21,000 (0.03% of total cable households).
Total Pay Units: 10,000.

WIRELESS ONE INC.

Suite 400
2506 Lakeland Dr.
Jackson, MS 39208
Phones: 504-926-7778; 601-933-6879
Fax: 504-926-7583
Officers:
Hans Sternberg, Chmn.
Henry Burkhalter, Vice Chmn. & Pres.
Sean Reilly, Chief Exec. Officer
Alton C. Rye, Exec. V.P., Operations
Henry Schopfer, Exec. V.P. & Chief Financial Officer
Ownership: Nucentrix Broadband Networks, see listing, 20%.

Branch Offices:

Suite B
Crowley, LA
1106 Richmond Rd.
Wharton, TX 77488
580 A. Graham Rd.
College Station, TX 77845
8804 B. Grow Rd.
Pensacola, FL 32514
Represented (legal): Pepper & Corazzini.
Wireless Cable Systems (37):
Alabama: Bucks, Demopolis, Dothan, Florence, Gadsden, Huntsville, Tuscaloosa.
Florida: Fort Walton Beach, Gainesville, Panama City, Pensacola, Tallahassee.
Georgia: Albany, Charing, Jeffersonville.
Louisiana: Alexandria, Bunkie, Houma, Lafayette, Lake Charles, Monroe.
Mississippi: Gulf Coast Area, Hattiesburg, Inverness, Jackson, Meridian, Natchez, Oxford, Starkville, Tupelo.
Tennessee: Lawrenceburg, Tullahoma.
Texas: Brenham, Bryan, Freeport, Milano, Wharton.
Total Basic Subscribers: 114,020 (0.17% of total cable households).
Total Pay Units: 4,836.
Other Holdings:
MDS, MMDS, see listing.

WITTENBERG TELEPHONE CO.

Box 309
Wittenberg, WI 54499
Phone: 715-253-2828
Fax: 715-253-3497
Officers:
Gordon Cowles, Pres.
Allen Mahnke, V.P.
Sydney R. Peterson, Secy.
M. Owen Wilkins, Treas.
Cable Systems (1):
Wisconsin: Wittenberg.
Total Basic Subscribers: 771.
Total Pay Units: 246.

WMW CABLE TV

Box 151
103 E. First St.
Hartford, SD 57033
Phone: 605-528-3211
Officers:
William G. Haugen, Pres.
Marilyn M. Haugen, Secy.-Treas. & Chief Financial Officer
Ownership: Marilyn Haugen & William G. Haugen.
Cable Systems (1):
South Dakota: Hartford.
Total Basic Subscribers: 640.
Total Pay Units: 280.

WOLFE BROADCASTING CORP.

905 W. State St.
Fremont, OH 43420
Phone: 419-332-8218
Cable Systems (1):
Ohio: Fremont.
Total Basic Subscribers: 7,400.
Radio Stations:
Ohio: WFRO-AM-FM, Fremont.

DAN WOLFE

Box 193
Rte. 2
Fountain City, WI 54629
Phone: 608-687-6402
Cable Systems (1):
Wisconsin: St. Joseph Twp.
Total Basic Subscribers: 64.
Total Pay Units: 17.

WOODMAN TV CABLE SYSTEM

207 Spencer
Woodman, WI 53827-0087
Phone: 608-533-2771
Ownership: Subscriber owned.
Cable Systems (1):
Wisconsin: Woodman.
Total Basic Subscribers: 48.

WOODSTOCK TELEPHONE CO.

Box C
Ruthton, MN 56170
Phones: 507-658-3830; 800-752-9397
Officers:
Ken Knuth, Chief Exec. & Financial Officer
Doug Folkerts, Chief Operating Officer
Ben Knuth, Mktg. Dir.
Dave Berkowski, Engineering Dir.
Cable Systems (5):
Minnesota: Good Thunder, Lismore, Rushmore, Ruthton, Wilmont.
Total Basic Subscribers: 760.
Total Pay Units: 240.

WORTH ENTERPRISE

Box 2056
Darien, GA 31305
Phone: 912-437-3422
Fax: 912-437-2065
Ownership: Dennis B. Wortham.
Cable Systems (1):
Georgia: Townsend (unincorporated areas).
Total Basic Subscribers: 300.
Total Pay Units: 48.

WOZNIAK TV

1133 Nickerson Ave.
Trinidad, CO 81082
Phone: 719-846-2798
Ownership: Steve A. Blasi.
Cable Systems (1):
Colorado: Valdez.
Total Basic Subscribers: 145.
Total Pay Units: 45.

WRIGHT CABLEVISION

Box 447
Cathlamet, WA 98612
Phone: 206-795-8636
Ownership: Art Wright, 50%; Don Wright, 50%.
Cable Systems (1):
Washington: Skamokawa.
Total Basic Subscribers: 47.

WYANDOTTE MUNICIPAL SERVICE COMMISSION

3005 Biddle Ave.
Wyandotte, MI 48192
Phone: 313-282-7100
Ownership: Community owned.
Cable Systems (1):
Michigan: Wyandotte.
Total Basic Subscribers: 10,173.
Total Pay Units: 5,958.

Y CO. INC.
Box 6478
215 Rochester Bank & Trust
Rochester, MN 55903-6478
Phone: 507-287-0880
Fax: 507-288-9207
Officer:
Rick Plunkett, Chief Exec. Officer
Cable Systems (2):
Minnesota: Fairmont, Sherburn.
Total Basic Subscribers: 4,334.
Total Pay Units: 989.

LEALON YARBER
Box 96
Belmont, MS 38827
Phone: 601-454-7285
Cable Systems (1):
Alabama: Waterloo.
Total Basic Subscribers: 80.

YAZOO ANSWER CALL INC.
Box 399
Rolling Fork, MS 39159
Phone: 601-873-2841
Ownership: L. T. Wade Jr., Principal.
Cable Systems (1):
Mississippi: Rolling Fork.
Total Basic Subscribers: 577.
Total Pay Units: 150.

BRUCE YERKS
Box 620
Pleasant Valley, NY 12569
Phone: 914-635-3835
Fax: 914-635-8362
Cable Systems (1):
New York: Pleasant Valley.
Total Basic Subscribers: N.A.

YOUNGSVILLE TV CORP.
3 W. Main St.
Youngsville, PA 16371
Phone: 814-563-3336
Officers:
Felix Matthews, Pres.
Robert Mourer, Chief Operating Officer
William Olewine, V.P.
Dan Sowa, Secy.
Ownership: Community owned.
Cable Systems (1):
Pennsylvania: Youngsville.
Total Basic Subscribers: 1,200.
Total Pay Units: 601.

ZAMPELLI TV
Box 261
RR 6
Lewistown, PA 17044-9806
Phone: 717-248-4465
Ownership: Frank P. Zampelli, Principal.
Cable Systems (3):
Pennsylvania: Belleville, Liverpool, McVeytown.
Total Basic Subscribers: N.A.

TOM ZELKA
Box 338
Hardin, MT 59034
Phone: 406-665-2103
Cable Systems (1):
Montana: Crow Agency.
Total Basic Subscribers: 210.
Total Pay Units: 105.

ZYLSTRA COMMUNICATIONS CORP.
Box 178
Yankton, SD 57078-0178
Phone: 605-665-8030
Fax: 605-665-0683
Officers:
J. W. Abbott, Pres. & Chief Operating Officer
Brian P. Steward, Chief Finanical Officer
Ownership: J. W. Abbott, Trustee.
Represented (legal): Cole, Raywid & Braverman LLP.
Cable Systems (5):
Iowa: Orange City.
Minnesota: Luverne, Worthington.
South Dakota: Vermillion, Yankton.
Total Basic Subscribers: 14,709 (0.02% of total cable households).
Total Pay Units: 4,931.
Note: Sold to MediaCom LLC 1999.

Cable Ownership Category Index

Cable Companies with Broadcast Interests

Bahakel Communications Ltd.
Blade Communications Inc.
California-Oregon Broadcasting Inc.
Century Communications Corp.
Chambers Communications Corp.
Cox Communications Inc.
Drewry Communications
Eagle Communications Inc. (KS)
Fairbanks Communications Inc.
Gannett Broadcasting Group
Greater Media Inc.
Harron Communications Corp.
Walter E. Hussman Jr.
Media General Inc.
Moffat Communications Ltd.
NEPSK Inc.
News Press & Gazette Co.
Northland Communications Corp.
Schurz Communications Inc.
Time Warner Cable
WEHCO Video Inc.
Wolfe Broadcasting Corp.

Cable Companies with Telephone, Cellular Radio and/or PCS Holdings

Adams Telcom Inc.
Albion Telephone Co.
Alhambra-Grantfork Telehpone Co.
Alltel Corp.
All West/Utah Inc.
Ameritech New Media Inc.
Amery Telecom
Amherst Telephone Co.
Andrew Telephone Co. Inc.
Arapahoe Telephone Co.
Arlington Telephone Co.
Armstrong Group of Companies
AT&T Broadband & Internet Services
Atlantic Telephone Membership Corp.
Baldwin TeleCom Inc.
Beavercreek Cooperative Telephone Co.
BEK Communications Cooperative
Benkelman Telephone Co.
Bentleyville Telephone Co.
Benton Cooperative Telephone Co.
Benton Ridge Telephone Co.
Blackduck Telephone Co.
Bledsoe Telephone Co.
Bloomingdale Telephone Co. Inc.
Blue Earth Valley Tel Co.
Bristol Bay Telephone Cooperative Inc.
Butler-Bremer Mutual Telephone Co.
Cable & Communications Corp.
Cablestar Inc.
Cablevision Systems Corp.
Jewel B. Callaham Revocable Trust
Cambridge Telephone Co.
Canby Telephone Assn.
Caribbean Communications Corp.
Casco Telephone Co.
Casey Mutual Telephone Co.
Cass Cable TV Inc.
Cedar Falls Municipal Communications Utility
Center Junction Telephone Co.
CFW Communications
Chariton Valley Communications Corp.
Chautauqua & Erie Telephone Co.
Cheyenne River Sioux Tribe Telephone Authority
Chibardun Cable TV Cooperative
Citizens Telephone Co.
Citizens Telephone Corp.
Clarence Telephone Co. Inc.
Clarks Telecommunications Co.
Climax Telephone Co.
C.L.R. Video LLC
Columbus Grove Telephone Co.
Com-Link Inc.
Community Cable Corp. of Pennsylvania
Comserv Ltd.
Consolidated Telephone Cooperative
Coon Creek Telephone & Cablevision
Cox Communications Inc.
Craw-Kan Telephone Co.
Crosslake Municipal Telephone Co.
Crystal Cable TV Inc.
Curtis Telephone Co. Inc.
Dakota Telecom Inc.
Data Video Systems Inc.
Deep River Telephone Co.
Defiance Telephone Co.
Delta County Cooperative Telephone Co.
Dickey Rural Services Inc.
Diode Cable Co. Inc.
Dixon Telephone Co.
Dubois Telephone Exchange Inc.
Dumont Telephone Co.
Dunkerton Telephone Cooperative
East Buchanan Telephone Cooperative
Eastern Nebraska Telephone Co.
Emily Cooperative Telephone Co.
Eustis Telephone Exchange
Farmers' & Businessmen's Telephone Co.
Farmers & Merchants Mutual Telephone Co.
Farmers Cooperative Telephone Co.
Farmers Mutual Cooperative Telephone Co.
Farmers Mutual Telephone Co.
Farmers Telephone Co.
Farmers Telephone Co-op Inc.
Fenton Cooperative Telephone Co.
Fort Jennings Telephone Co.
Garden Valley Telephone Co.
Glenwood Telecommunications
Golden Belt Telephone Communications Inc.
Golden West Cablevision
Goldfield Communication Services Corp.
Grand Mound Cooperative Telephone Assn.
Great Plains Cable TV
Griswold Co-op Telephone Co.
GTE Media Ventures
Guadalupe Valley Communications Systems Inc.
Hargray Telephone Co.
Hartington Telephone Co.
Haviland Telephone Co.
City of Hawarden
Hawkeye TV Co.
Helix Communications
Henderson Cooperative Telephone Co.
Hilltop Communications Inc.
Hood Canal Communications
Hooper Telephone Co.
Horry Telephone Cooperative Inc.
Interlake Cablevision Inc.
Interstate Cablevision Inc.
James Valley Cooperative Telephone Co.
Jefferson Telephone Co. Inc.
Jesup Farmer's Mutual Telephone Co.
JSV Cable
Kalida Telephone Co.
Roger Kaufman
Keystone Farmers Cooperative Telephone Co.
KLM Telephone Co.
Lehigh Services Inc.
Lewisport Telephone Co.
Lincoln Telephone Co.
Lincolnville Communications Inc.
L.N. Satellite Communications Co.
Manawa Telecom Inc.
Mark Twain Rural Telephone Co.
Marne & Elk Horn Telephone Co.
Martelle Cooperative Telephone Association
McNabb Cable & Satellite Inc.
Mechanicsville Telephone Co.
MediaOne Group
Mediapolis Cablevision Co.
Midcontinent Communications
Mid-Iowa Communications Inc.
Mid-Kansas Cable Services Inc.
Mid-Missouri Telephone Co.
Mid-South Cablevision Co.
Midvale Telephone Exchange Inc.
Ray V. Miller Group
Minburn Cablevision Inc.
Monroe Area Communications Inc.
Montrose Mutual Telephone Co.
Net Cable Inc.
New Hope Telephone Cooperative
New Knoxville Telephone Co.
New Paris Telephone Co.
New Path Communications LC
New Ulm Telecom Inc.
North Texas Communications Co.
Northeast Iowa Telephone Co.
Northeast Louisiana Telephone Co. Inc.
Northland Communications Inc.
Northstate Cablevision Co.
Northwest Communications Cooperative
Northwest Communications Inc. (Havelock, IA)
Northwest Community Communications Inc.
Northwest Iowa Telephone Co.
Norway Rural Telephone Co.
Nushagak Telephone Cooperative Inc.
Ogden Telephone Co.
Omni III Cable TV Inc.
Oneida Telephone Exchange
Oneonta Telephone Co. Inc.
OnePoint Communications
Onslow Cooperative Telephone Association
Orwell Telephone Co.
Palmer Mutual Telephone Co.
Palo Cooperative Telephone Assn.
Panora Cooperative Cablevision Assn. Inc.
Pecoco Inc.
Pencor Services Inc.
Peoples Telephone Co. (Iowa)
Peoples Telephone Co. Inc. (Tennessee)
Piedmont Telephone Membership Corp.
Pine Island Telephone Co.
PinPoint Communications Inc.
Pioneer Communications
Postville Telephone Co.
Premier Communications Inc.
Price County Telephone Co.
Prime Cable
Readlyn Telephone Co.
Reservation Telephone Cooperative
Rib Lake Telephone Co. Inc.
Richland Grant Telephone Co-op Inc.
Ridgeville Telephone Co.
Ringsted Cablevision Ltd.
Riviera Telephone Co.
Rock County Telephone Co.
Rockport Telephone Co.
Roome Telecommunications Inc.
Royal Telephone Co.
Sac County Mutual Telephone Co.
Sanborn Telephone Cooperative
SBC Media Ventures
Scio Cablevision Inc.
Scranton Telephone Co.
SCS Communications & Security
Shellsburg Cablevision Inc.
Shenandoah Telecommunications Inc.
Sherwood Telephone Co.
Sledge Telephone Co.
Sleepy Eye Telephone Co.
Souris River Telecommunications Cooperative
South Holt Cablevision Inc.
Southern Cable Communications
Southern New England Telecommunications Corp.
Splitrock Telecom Cooperative Inc.
Springport Telephone Co.
Springville Cooperative Telephone Assn. Inc.
St. Croix Telephone Co.
St. John Cable Co. Inc.
Stratford Mutual Telephone
Sully Buttes Telephone Cooperative Inc.
Sunman Telecommunications Inc.
Swayzee Tele Broadband
Tele-Services Ltd.
Teleview Inc. (GA)
Templeton Telephone Co.
Ter Tel Enterprises
Thorntown Telephone Co.
Thorp Telephone Co.
Three Sixty Corp.
Time Warner Cable
Tip Top Communication
Titonka Telephone Co.
Triangle Communication Systems Inc.
Tri-County Communications Corp.
TV Service Inc.
Union Telephone Co.
United Telephone Mutual Aid Corp.
Upsala Cooperative Telephone Association
Valley Cable & Satellite Communications
Van Horne Telephone Co.
Vernon Communications & TV
Video Inc.
Vi-Tel Inc.
Volcano Communications Co.
Waitsfield-Fayston Telephone Co.
Walnut Telephone Co.
Wayside Telephone Co.
W. E. Communications Inc.
West Central Telephone Assn.

West Iowa Telephone Co.
West River Cooperative Telephone Co.
Wheat State Telecable Inc.
Winnebago Cooperative Telephone Assn.
Wittenberg Telephone Co.
WMW Cable TV
Woodstock Telephone Co.

Cable Companies with MDS and/or MMDS Holdings

American Telecasting Inc.
BellSouth Entertainment Inc.
Benton Ridge Telephone Co.
Cable USA Inc.
Jewel B. Callaham Revocable Trust
Central Dakota TV Inc.
CFW Communications
Consolidated Telephone Cooperative
Daniels Communications Inc.
Evertek Inc.
Flight Systems Cablevision
Galaxy Cablevision
Greater Media Inc.
Griswold Co-op Telephone Co.
GTE Media Ventures
Ruth I. Kolpin
Multimedia Development Corp.
Northwest Communications Cooperative
Omni III Cable TV Inc.
Sanborn Telephone Cooperative
SBC Media Ventures
Three Sixty Corp.
United Telephone Mutual Aid Corp.
Warmath Communications Inc.

Wireless Cable Companies

Alaskan Choice Television
American Telecasting Inc.
Antilles Wireless LLC
Benton Ridge Telephone Co.
Broadcast Cable Inc.
Broadcast Cablevision
CAI Wireless Systems Inc.
William Canley
CellularVision USA Inc.
Central Dakota TV Inc.
Central Texas Wireless TV Inc.
Central Vision
CFW Communications
Consolidated Telephone Cooperative
Cotton Country Cable
CS Wireless Systems Inc.
Digital Broadcast Corp.
Digital Wireless Systems Inc.
Farmers Telephone Co.
Fort Wayne Telsat Inc.
George Mason U. Instructional Foundation
GTE Media Ventures
HD Electric Cooperative
Kingsbury Electric
Lake Region Electric
Madison Communications Inc.
Maui Cablevision Corp.
Microcom Inc.
Microlink Television
Microwave Cable Corp.
Microwave Communication Services
Mobile Limited Liability
Nashville Wireless Cable Inc.
NDW II Inc.
New England Wireless Inc.
Northeast TV Cooperative
Northern Electric Cooperative Inc.
Northwest Communications Cooperative
Nucentrix Broadband Networks
Ohio Valley Wireless Ltd.
Oklahoma Western Telephone Co.
Orion Broadcasting Systems
Matthew Oristano
People's Cable TV Inc.
People's Choice TV Partners
Pioneer Communications
Preferred Entertainment Inc.
Quadravision
Quality Cable Inc.
R & B Communications
Santa Fe Wireless Cable TV
Satellite Signals of New England Inc.
SBC Media Ventures
Sioux Valley Rural Television Inc.
Skycable TV of Madison LLC
Snyder Microwave Communications LC
Southwest Telecommunications Co-op Assn. Inc.
Spink Electric
Sprint Corp.
Sterling Wireless Cable
SunCoast Wireless Cable
Technivision Inc.
Teewinot Licensing Inc.
Tennessee Wireless Inc.
TV Communications Network Inc.
Valley Wireless Cable Holding Inc.
Videowave Television
Viking Vision
Virginia Communications Inc.
West Tennessee Wireless
WHTV Broadcasting Corp.
Wireless Associates LP
Wireless Broadcasting Systems of America Inc.
Wireless Cable Systems Inc.
Wireless Cable TV of Waterloo
Wireless Holdings Inc.
Wireless One Inc.

Multipoint Distribution Service

(2150-2160 MHz)

MDS is a point to point microwave frequency service authorized to transmit single channel specialized private TV programming or data and facsimile transmissions to customer selected locations within a metropolitan area. This section lists MDS licensees & conditional licenses. Channel numbers, station locations, power, latitudes & longitudes have been included. For ownership of stations, see MDS & MMDS Ownership.

Alaska

Anchorage—KFC63 (Ch. 1). MDS Systems, Box 190929, Anchorage, AK 99519-0929. Authorized power: 20-w. Antenna: 99-ft. above ground. Lat. 61° 06' 25", long. 149° 44' 16". Transmitter: 7460 Upper Huffman Rd. Equipment: Emcee transmitter; Andrew antenna. Ownership: MDS Systems.

Fairbanks—WPY44 (Ch. 1). Alaska Wireless Cable Inc., 3055 Braddock St., Fairbanks, AK 99701. Phone: 907-456-6160. Authorized power: 100-w. Lat. 64° 52' 39", long. 148° 02' 24". Transmitter: Ester Dome. Equipment: Emcee transmitter; Andrew antenna. Ownership: Alaska Wireless Cable Inc.

Juneau—WLW796 (Ch. 1). Ronald D. Ward, 10010 Crazy Horse Dr., Juneau, AK 99801. Phone: 907-789-9867. Authorized power: 10-w. Antenna: 66-ft. above ground. Lat. 58° 22' 12", long. 134° 36' 21". Transmitter: 10010 Crazy Horse Dr. Equipment: ITS transmitter; Bogner antenna. Ownership: Ronald D. Ward.

Juneau—WLW792 (Ch. 2A). Edward F. Shilling, Box 1087, Petersburg, AK 99833. Phone: 907-789-9867. Authorized power: 10-w. Antenna: 66-ft. above ground. Lat. 58° 22' 12", long. 134° 36' 21". Transmitter: 10010 Crazy Horse Dr. Equipment: ITS transmitter; Bogner antenna. Ownership: Edward F. Shilling.

Arizona

Bullhead City—WMI394 (Ch. 1). MWTV Inc., 3401 E. Cholla St., Phoenix, AZ 85028. Phone: 602-867-7351. Authorized power: 50-w. Antenna: 125-ft. above ground. Lat. 35° 01' 58", long. 114° 21' 57". Transmitter: KRCY-FM Tower, Oatman Peak. Equipment: Comwave transmitter; Bogner antenna. Ownership: MWTV Inc.

Phoenix—WPF47 (Ch. 1). Alda Wireless Holdings Inc., 5301 E. Broadway Blvd., Tucson, AZ 85711-3710. Phone: 520-519-4400. Fax: 520-747-6830. Authorized power: 100-w. Antenna: 96-ft. above ground. Lat. 33° 20' 02", long. 112° 03' 44". Transmitter: 10660 S. Central. Equipment: Comwave transmitter; Andrew antenna. Ownership: Matthew Oristano.
Leased to American Cable Television Inc., 17602 N. Black Canyon Hwy., Phoenix, AZ 85023.

Phoenix—WHB522 (Ch. 2A). Phoenix MDS Co., 114 Sutton Manor Rd., New Rochelle, NY 10801. Phone: 914-576-6622. Fax: 914-576-6689. Authorized power: 100-w. Antenna: 96-ft. above ground. Lat. 33° 20' 02", long. 112° 03' 44". Transmitter: 10660 S. Central. Equipment: Emcee transmitter; Andrew antenna. Ownership: Broadcast Data Corp.; Phoenix MDS Co.; Private Networks Inc.

Sierra Vista—WMY446 (Ch. 1). John McLain, 7110 Jaxel Rd., Hereford, AZ 85616. Phone: 520-378-3349. Authorized power: 10-w. Antenna: 50-ft. above ground. Lat. 31° 28' 49", long. 109° 57' 30". Transmitter: Mule Mountain. Equipment: Comwave transmitter; Andrew antenna. Ownership: John McLain.

Tucson—WMH229 (Ch. 1). Alda Tucson Inc., 5301 E. Broadway Blvd., Tucson, AZ 85711-3710. Phone: 520-519-4400. Fax: 520-747-6830. Authorized power: 50-w. Antenna: 200-ft. above ground. Lat. 32° 14' 56", long. 111° 06' 57". Transmitter: 1720 W. Lost Canyon Dr. Equipment: Comwave transmitter; Andrew antenna. Ownership: Matthew Oristano.
Leased to People's Choice TV Corp., 5301 E. Broadway Blvd., Tucson, AZ 85711. Phone: 520-519-4400.

Tucson—WMI956 (Ch. 2A). Alda Tucson Inc., 5301 E. Broadway Blvd., Tucson, AZ 85711-3710. Phone: 520-519-4400. Fax: 520-747-6830. Authorized power: 50-w. Antenna: 112-ft. above ground. Lat. 32° 14' 56", long. 111° 06' 57". Transmitter: 1720 W. Lost Canyon Dr. Equipment: Comwave transmitter; Andrew antenna. Ownership: Matthew Oristano.

Arkansas

Hot Springs—WKW790 (Ch. 1). Masscom, 1023 51st St., Moline, IL 61265. Phone: 309-764-6886. Authorized power: 10-w. Antenna: 150-ft. above ground. Lat. 34° 30' 19", long. 93° 05' 06". Transmitter: West Mountain. Equipment: Comwave transmitter; Andrew antenna. Ownership: Masscom.

California

Anaheim—KFI79 (Ch. 1). Earl S. Kim, Box 1503, Running Springs, CA 92382-1503. Phone: 909-867-5874. Fax: 909-867-5484. Authorized power: 100-w. Antenna: 108-ft. above ground. Lat. 33° 58' 24", long. 117° 56' 31". Transmitter: 1518 Skyline Dr., La Habra Heights. Equipment: Micro-Link transmitter; Andrew antenna. Ownership: Earl S. Kim.
Leased to Access West, 8502 E. Chapman Ave., Suite 220, Orange, CA 92869. Phone: 714-639-6502.

Anaheim—WGX394 (Ch. 2). DCT Los Angeles LLC, No. 454, 10040 E. Happy Valley Rd., Scottsdale, AZ 85255. Phone: 480-515-0913. Fax: 480-515-4632. E-mail: jimwies@aol.com. Authorized power: 100-w. Antenna: 100-ft. above ground. Lat. 33° 58' 24", long. 117° 56' 31". Transmitter: La Habra Heights. Equipment: Emcee transmitter; Andrew antenna. Ownership: DCT Los Angeles LLC.

Bakersfield—WMH877 (Ch. 1). CS Wireless Systems Inc., 1101 Summit Ave., Plano, TX 75074. Phone: 972-730-3300. Authorized power: 50-w. Antenna: 365-ft. above ground. Lat. 35° 16' 52", long. 119° 04' 41". Transmitter: 8101 Ashe Rd. Equipment: ITS transmitter; Andrew antenna. Ownership: CS Wireless Systems Inc.

Bakersfield—WMI942 (Ch. 2A). CS Wireless Systems Inc., 1101 Summit Ave., Plano, TX 75074. Phone: 972-730-3300. Authorized power: 10-w. Antenna: 365-ft. above ground. Lat. 35° 16' 52", long. 119° 04' 41". Transmitter: 8101 Ashe Rd. Equipment: ITS transmitter; Andrew antenna. Ownership: CS Wireless Systems Inc.

Clayton—KFF68 (Ch. 1). Hubbard Trust, 26573 Basswood Ave., Rancho Palos Verdes, CA 90275. Phone: 310-373-6234. Fax: 310-373-6234. E-mail: hubbardtech@earthlink.net. Authorized power: 10-w. Antenna: 433-ft. above ground. Lat. 37° 52' 54", long. 121° 55' 05". Transmitter: Summit Rd., Clayton. Equipment: Emcee transmitter; Andrew antenna. Requests change to 443-ft. Above ground. Ownership: Hubbard Trust.
Leased to National Micro Vision Systems Inc., 3140 Red Hill St., Suite 200, Costa Mesa, CA 92676. Phone: 714-752-2807.

Cummings Valley—WGW348 (Ch. 1). Densen Enterprises Inc., 710 Brundage Lane, Bakersfield, CA 93304. Authorized power: 10-w. Lat. 35° 09' 09", long. 118° 34' 50". Transmitter: El Rancho Peak. Ownership: Densen Enterprises Inc.

El Centro—WGW408 (Ch. 1). SBC, Suite 204, 3628 Lynoak, Claremont, CA 91711. Phone: 909-621-1004. Fax: 909-624-2257. Authorized power: 10-w. Antenna: 60-ft. above ground. Lat. 32° 56' 43", long. 115° 47' 48". Transmitter: Superstition Mountain, Westmoreland. Equipment: Emcee transmitter; Andrew antenna. Ownership: Hydra Communications.

Gilroy—WDU424 (Ch. 1). American Telecasting of Monterey Inc., Suite 300, 5575 Tech Center Dr., Colorado Springs, CO 80919. Phone: 719-260-5533. Fax: 719-260-5010. Authorized power: 10-w. Antenna: 16-ft. above ground. Lat. 37° 01' 31", long. 121° 29' 02". Transmitter: Eggs Ranch, 5-mi. E of Gilroy. Equipment: Emcee transmitter; Andrew antenna. Ownership: American Telecasting Inc.

Lancaster—WGW239 (Ch. 1). SBC, Suite 204, 3628 Lynoak, Claremont, CA 91711. Phone: 909-621-1004. Fax: 909-624-2257. Authorized power: 10-w. Antenna: 30-ft. above ground. Lat. 34° 32' 43", long. 118° 12' 43". Transmitter: Hauser Mountain. Equipment: Emcee transmitter; Andrew antenna. Ownership: Hydra Communications.

Los Angeles—KFF79 (Ch. 1). Earl S. Kim, Box 1503, Running Springs, CA 92382-1503. Phone: 909-867-5874. Fax: 909-867-5484. Authorized power: 100-w. Antenna: 72-ft. above ground. Lat. 34° 07' 08", long. 118° 23' 30". Transmitter: 2555 Briarcrest Rd. Equipment: Micro-Link transmitter; Andrew antenna. Ownership: Earl S. Kim.
Leased to Armenian TV Products, 13441 Sherman Way, North Hollywood, CA 91605. Phone: 818-982-1979.

Los Angeles—WHD479 (Ch. 2). Los Angeles MDS Co. Inc., Suite 6C, 104 E. 68th St., New York, NY 10021. Phone: 212-288-2356. Fax: 212-288-2312. Authorized power: 100-w. Antenna: 75-ft. above ground. Lat. 34° 07' 08", long. 118° 23' 30". Transmitter: 2555 Briarcrest Rd. Equipment: Emcee transmitter; Andrew antenna. Ownership: Los Angeles MDS Co. Inc.

Monterey—WPX66 (Ch. 1). Broadcast Data Corp., Suite 247, 189 Berdan Ave., Wayne, NJ 07470. Phone: 201-831-7407. Authorized power: 10-w. Antenna: 194-ft. above ground. Lat. 36° 31' 48", long. 121° 36' 31". Transmitter: Mount Toro, Salinas. Equipment: Emcee transmitter; Bogner antenna. Ownership: Broadcast Data Corp.

Mount San Bruno—WLK228 (Ch. 2). San Francisco MDS Inc., Suite 301, 276 5th Ave., New York, NY 10001. Phone: 212-777-4740. Authorized power: 10-w. Lat. 37° 52' 58", long. 122° 13' 11". Transmitter: Grizzly Peak Blvd., Vollmer Peak, Orinda. Equipment: Emcee transmitter; Andrew antenna. Requests change to 1401-ft. above ground, lat. 37° 41' 17", long. 122° 26' 07"; transmitter to Tower 6, San Bruno Mountain, 6.1-mi. S of San Francisco. Ownership: Private Networks Inc.

Oro Grande—WDU486 (Ch. 1). Hubbard Trust, 26573 Basswood, Ranchos Palos Verdes, CA 90275. Phone: 310-373-6234. Fax: 310-373-6234. E-mail: hubbardtech@earthlink.net. Authorized power: 10-w. Antenna: 1200-ft. above ground. Lat. 34° 36' 38", long. 117° 17' 19". Transmitter: Quartzite Mountain. Equipment: Emcee transmitter; Andrew antenna. Ownership: Hubbard Trust.
Leased to National Micro Vision Systems, Inc., 3140 Red Hill St., Suite 200, Costa Mesa, CA 92626. Phone: 714-752-2807.

Palm Springs—WSL86 (Ch. 1). Desert MDS Co., Box 163, Tupelo, MS 38801. Authorized power: 10-w. Lat. 33° 51' 58", long. 116° 26' 03". Transmitter: Edom Hill, 6-mi. NE of Palm Desert. Equipment: Emcee transmitter; Andrew antenna. Ownership: Microwave Service Co.; Palmer Communications Inc.

Palo Alto—WFY976 (Ch. 1). Bay Area Cablevision Inc., 130 Kearny St., San Francisco, CA 94108. Authorized power: 10-w. Antenna: 100-ft. above ground. Lat. 37° 29' 07", long. 121° 51' 57". Equipment: Emcee transmitter; Andrew antenna. Ownership: Bay Area Cablevision Inc.

Palo Alto—WJL36 (Ch. 1). Bay Area Cablevision Inc., 975-H Industrial Rd., San Carlos, CA 94070. Phone: 415-631-9190. Authorized power: 10-w. Antenna: 350-ft. above ground. Lat. 37° 29' 17", long. 121° 51' 59". Transmitter: Monument Peak, 11-mi. N of San Jose. Equipment: ITS transmitter; Andrew antenna. Requests change to 100-ft. above ground; California Amplifier antenna. Ownership: Bay Area Cablevision Inc.

Riverside—WPW94 (Ch. 1). Pacific Telesis Southern Wireless Video Inc., 130 Kearny St., San Francisco, CA 94108. Phone: 415-394-3000. Authorized power: 10-w. Antenna: 30-ft. above ground. Lat. 34° 01' 20", long. 117° 17' 46". Transmitter: Blue Mountain, 1.2-mi. SE of Grand Terrace. Equipment: Emcee transmitter; Andrew antenna. Ownership: SBC Media Ventures.

Sacramento—WSL88 (Ch. 1). Sacramento Wireless Co., c/o Broadcast Data Corp., 25 Rockwood Place, Englewood, NJ 07631. Phone: 201-894-8000. Authorized power: 330-w. Lat. 38° 38' 54", long. 121° 28' 40". Transmitter: 0.25-mi. W of Gate. Equipment: Varian/Micro-Link transmitter; Andrew antenna. Ownership: Sacramento Wireless Co.
Leased to Pacific West Cable TV, 1513 Sports Dr., No. 9, Sacramento, CA 98534. Phone: 916-928-2500.

Sacramento—WGW352 (Ch. 2). Wireless Broadband Services of America LLC, Suite 325, 9250 E. Costilla Ave., Englewood, CO 80112. Phone: 303-649-1195. Fax: 303-649-1196. Authorized power: 100-w. Antenna: 450-ft. above ground. Lat. 38° 38' 54", long. 121° 28' 40". Transmitter: 0.25-mi. W of N. Market & Gate Sts. Equipment: Comwave transmitter; Andrew antenna. Ownership: Wireless Broadcasting Systems of America Inc.

San Bernardino—WHT573 (Ch. 2). DCT Los Angeles LLC, No. 454, 10400 E. Happy Valley Rd., Scottsdale, AZ 85255. Phone: 480-515-0913. Fax: 480-515-4632. E-mail: jimwies@aol.com. Authorized power: 100-w. Antenna: 35-ft. above ground. Lat. 34° 14' 10", long. 117° 19' 01". Transmitter: Playground Rd. Equipment: Emcee transmitter; Andrew antenna. Ownership: DCT Los Angeles LLC.

San Diego—WFY435 (Ch. 1). Via/Net Companies, 836 E. Washington St., San Diego, CA 92103. Phone: 619-260-0110. Authorized power: 100-w. Lat. 32° 41' 48", long. 116° 56' 10". Transmitter: San Miguel Mountain. Equipment: Emcee transmitter; Bogner antenna. Ownership: Via/Net Companies.

San Diego—WHT559 (Ch. 2). San Diego MDS Co., 1761 Fairfield Beach Rd., Fairfield, CT 06430. Lat. 32° 41' 48", long. 116° 56' 10". Transmitter: San Miguel Mountain. Ownership: Cross Country Network Inc.; Broadcast Data Corp.; Private Networks Inc.

San Francisco—KFF81 (Ch. 1). Bay Area Cablevision Inc., 975-H Industrial Rd., San Carlos, CA 94070. Phone: 415-631-9190. Authorized power: 10-w. Antenna: 160-ft. above ground. Lat. 37° 41' 17", long. 122° 26' 07". Transmitter: Tower 6, San Bruno Mountain. Equipment: ITS transmitter; Andrew antenna. Requests change to 100-ft. above ground; California Amplifier antenna. Ownership: Bay Area Cablevision Inc.

San Marcos—WPX85 (Ch. 1). Hubbard Trust, 26573 Basswood Ave., Rancho Palos Verdes, CA 90275. Phone: 310-373-6234. Fax: 310-373-6234. E-mail: hubbardtech@earthlink.net. Authorized power: 100-w. Antenna: 1665-ft. above ground. Lat. 33° 06' 39", long. 117° 09' 10". Transmitter: Mount Whitney, 21851 Washingtonian Dr. Equipment: Emcee & Comwave transmitter; Andrew antenna. Ownership: Hubbard Trust.
Leased to National Micro Vision Systems Inc., 3140 Red Hill St., Suite 200, Costa Mesa, CA 92626. Phone: 714-752-2807.

San Pedro—WPY40 (Ch. 1). Earl S. Kim, Box 1503, Running Springs, CA 92382-1503. Phone: 909-867-5874. Fax: 909-867-5484. Authorized power: 100-w. Antenna: 50-ft. above ground. Lat. 33° 44' 46", long. 118° 20' 07". Transmitter: 2555 Briarcrest Rd. Equipment: Emcee transmitter; Andrew antenna. Ownership: Earl S. Kim.

Stockton—WPW84 (Ch. 1). CS Wireless Systems Inc., 1101 Summit Ave., Plano, TX 75074. Phone: 972-730-3300. Authorized power: 100-w. Antenna: 496-ft. above ground. Lat. 37° 43' 44", long. 121° 07' 34". Transmitter: 1220 S. Acacia Ave. Equipment: ITS transmitter; Andrew antenna. Ownership: CS Wireless Systems Inc.

Colorado

Colorado Springs—WPW97 (Ch. 1). American Telecasting of Colorado Springs Inc., Suite 300, 5575 Tech Center Dr., Colorado Springs, CO 80919. Phone: 719-260-5533. Fax: 719-260-5010. Authorized power: 100-w. Lat. 38° 44' 42", long. 104° 51' 39". Transmitter: 11 Transmitter Lane, Cheyenne Mountain. Equipment: Micro-Link transmitter; Andrew antenna. Ownership: American Telecasting Inc.

Colorado Springs—WPG39 (Ch. 2). American Telecasting Inc., Suite 300, 5575 Tech Center Dr., Colorado Springs, CO 80919. Phone: 719-260-5533. Fax: 719-260-5010. Authorized power: 10-w. Antenna: 110-ft. above ground. Lat. 38° 44' 46", long. 104° 51' 37". Transmitter: 6233 Transmitter Lane, Cheyenne Mountain. Equipment: Emcee transmitter; Bogner antenna. Ownership: American Telecasting Inc.

Denver—WPY32 (Ch. 1). American Telecasting of Denver Inc., Suite 300, 5575 Tech Center Dr., Colorado Springs, CO 80919. Phone: 719-260-5533. Fax: 719-260-5010. Authorized power: 100-w. Lat. 39° 54' 48", long. 105° 17' 32". Transmitter: Eldorado Mountain. Equipment: Micro-Link transmitter; Andrew antenna. Ownership: American Telecasting Inc.

Denver—WMY475 (Ch. 2). American Telecasting of Denver Inc., Suite 300, 5575 Tech Center Dr., Colorado Springs, CO 80919. Phone: 719-260-5533. Fax: 719-260-5010. Authorized power: 100-w. Antenna: 48-ft. above ground. Lat. 39° 54' 48", long. 105° 17' 32". Transmitter: Eldorado Mountain. Equipment: Comwave transmitter; Bogner antenna. Requests change to 60-ft. Above ground. Ownership: American Telecasting Inc.

Grand Junction—WFY716 (Ch. 1). Progressive Technologies Co. Authorized power: 10-w. Lat. 39° 05' 20", long. 108° 13' 35". Transmitter: 17-mi. E of Grand Junction. Ownership: Progressive Technologies Co.

Prowers City—WMX339 (Ch. 1). Eagle Television Inc., Box 35, Eads, CO 81036-0035. Phone: 719-438-2221. Fax: 719-438-5592. Authorized power: 10-w. Antenna: 105-ft. above ground. Lat. 39° 10' 19", long. 102° 40' 50". Transmitter: 4240 Rd. PP, Wiley. Equipment: Comwave transmitter; Andrew antenna. Ownership: Eagle Television Inc.

Trinidad—WMY410 (Ch. 1). Satellite Microcable Partners. Authorized power: 10-w. Antenna: 140-ft. above ground. Lat. 37° 08' 45", long. 104° 30' 42". Transmitter: 100 Fisher Dr. Equipment: Comwave transmitter; Bogner antenna. Ownership: Satellite Microcable Partners.

District of Columbia

Washington—WOI93 (Ch. 1). Washington License Inc., Suite 100, 2101 Wilson Blvd., Arlington, VA 22201. Phone: 703-812-8800. Fax: 703-812-8808. Authorized power: 100-w. Antenna: 732-ft. above ground. Lat. 38° 57' 49", long. 77° 06' 18". Transmitter: 5202 River Rd., Bethesda, MD. Equipment: ITS transmitter; Andrew antenna. Ownership: CAI Wireless Systems Inc.

Washington—WHT747 (Ch. 2). Washington MDS Co., Box 206, Prince Frederick, MD 20678. Phone: 410-535-7091. Authorized power: 100-w. Antenna: 809-ft. above ground. Lat. 38° 57' 49", long. 77° 06' 18". Transmitter: 5202 River Rd., Bethesda, MD. Equipment: Emcee transmitter; Andrew antenna. Ownership: Broadcast Data Corp.; KC Corp.; Multipoint Information Systems Inc.; Private Networks Inc.; Vidicom Inc.

Florida

Daytona Beach—WLK243 (Ch. 1). BellSouth Wireless Cable Inc., Suite 414, 1100 Abernathy Rd. NE, Atlanta, GA 30328. Phone: 770-673-2800. Authorized power: 50-w. Antenna: 445-ft. above ground. Lat. 29° 10' 29", long. 81° 09' 32". Transmitter: Indian Lake Rd., 7-mi. WSW of Daytona Beach. Equipment: Comwave transmitter; Andrew antenna. Ownership: BellSouth Corp.

Jacksonville—WMH805 (Ch. 1). Eagleview Technologies Inc., Suite 6-271, 5030 Champion Blvd., Boca Raton, FL 33496. Authorized power: 10-w. Antenna: 633-ft. above ground. Lat. 30° 19' 33", long. 81° 39' 32". Transmitter: One Independent Dr. Equipment: Emcee transmitter; Andrew antenna. Ownership: Eagleview Technologies Inc.

Marco Island—WFY577 (Ch. 1). Marco Island MDS Co., 301 Tower Rd., Naples, FL 33962. Authorized power: 100-w. Antenna: 140-ft. above ground. Lat. 25° 56' 11", long. 81° 44' 00". Transmitter: Sombrero Beach Rd., 1-mi. SE of Marathon. Ownership: Palmer Communications Inc.; Qualicom Electronics.

Miami—WLJ79 (Ch. 1). South Florida Television Inc., Suite 414, 1100 Abernathy Rd. NE, Atlanta, GA 30328. Phone: 770-673-2800. Authorized power: 100-w. Antenna: 453-ft. above ground. Lat. 25° 46' 23", long. 80° 25' 17". Transmitter: 2-mi. W of Sweetwater. Equipment: Emcee transmitter; Andrew antenna. Ownership: BellSouth Corp.

Okeechobee—WFY524 (Ch. 1). MDS Services of Okeechobee Inc., 1120 Royal Palm Beach Blvd., Okeechobee, FL 33411. Phone: 561-439-0090. Lat. 27° 13' 02", long. 80° 49' 51". Transmitter: Okeechobee. Ownership: Robert Gordon.

Orlando—WFY742 (Ch. 1). Orange County, 201 S. Rosalind Ave., Orlando, FL 32801. Phone: 407-836-7300. Fax: 407-836-5888. Authorized power: 10-w. Antenna: 341-ft. above ground. Lat. 28° 36' 33", long. 81° 27' 12". Transmitter: Pine Hills & Clarcona. Equipment: Emcee transmitter; Andrew antenna. Ownership: Orange County Board of Commissioners.

Orlando—WGW518 (Ch. 2A). Orange County, 201 S. Rosalind Ave., Orlando, FL 32801. Phone: 407-836-7300. Fax: 407-836-5888. Authorized power: 10-w. Antenna: 341-ft. above ground. Lat. 28° 36' 33", long. 81° 27' 12". Transmitter: Pine Hills & Clarcona. Equipment: Comwave transmitter; Andrew antenna. Ownership: Orange County Board of Commissioners.

Pensacola—WDU502 (Ch. 1). Communication Innovations Corp., Suite 401, 145 Huguenot St., New Rochelle, NY 10801. Phone: 914-576-6622. Fax: 914-576-6689. Authorized power: 10-w. Antenna: 315-ft. above ground. Lat. 30° 30' 50", long. 87° 17' 45". Transmitter: 1.5-mi. W of Hwy. 29. Equipment: Emcee transmitter; Andrew antenna. Ownership: Communication Innovations Corp.

Pompano Beach—KFJ28 (Ch. 1). Eagleview Technologies Inc., Suite 6-271, 5030 Champion Blvd., Boca Raton, FL 33496. Phone: 561-274-4233. Authorized power: 10-w. Antenna: 297-ft. above ground. Lat. 26° 13' 55", long. 80° 05' 28". Transmitter: 1360 S. Ocean Blvd. Equipment: Emcee transmitter; Andrew antenna. Requests change to lat. 26° 12' 45", long. 80° 05' 33". Ownership: Eagleview Technologies Inc.

Stuart—WFY650 (Ch. 1). MDS Services of Stuart Inc., 1120 Royal Palm Beach Blvd., Royal Palm Beach, FL 33411. Phone: 561-439-0090. Authorized power: 10-w. Lat. 27° 07' 20", long. 80° 23' 21". Transmitter: 8-mi. SW of Stuart. Equipment: Emcee transmitter; Andrew antenna. Ownership: Robert Gordon.

Tampa-St. Petersburg—WOF43 (Ch. 1). Communication Innovations Corp., 145 Huguenot St., New Rochelle, NY 10801. Phone: 914-576-6622. Fax: 914-576-6689. Authorized power: 100-w. Antenna: 592-ft. above ground. Lat. 27° 56' 50", long. 82° 27' 35". Transmitter: 111 Madison St., Tampa. Equipment: Emcee transmitter; Andrew antenna. Ownership: Communication Innovations Corp.

West Palm Beach—WPY38 (Ch. 1). Communication Innovations Corp., 145 Huguenot St., New Rochelle, NY 10801. Phone: 914-576-6622. Fax: 914-576-6689. Authorized power: 100-w. Antenna: 500-ft. above ground. Lat. 26° 34' 37", long. 80° 14' 32". Transmitter: 11200 Malrite Rd. Equipment: Emcee transmitter; Andrew antenna. Ownership: Communication Innovations Corp.

West Palm Beach—WGW504 (Ch. 2A). Communication Innovations Corp., 145 Huguenot St., New Rochelle, NY 10801. Phone: 914-576-6622. Fax: 914-576-6689. Authorized power: 100-w. Antenna: 1533-ft. above ground. Lat. 26° 34' 37", long. 80° 14' 32". Transmitter: 11200 Malrite Rd. Equipment: Comwave transmitter; Andrew antenna. Ownership: Communication Innovations Corp.

Georgia

Atlanta—WQR43 (Ch. 1). BellSouth Corp., Suite 414, 1100 Abernathy Rd. NE, Atlanta, GA 30328. Phone: 770-673-2800. Authorized power: 100-w. Antenna: 1017-ft. above ground. Lat. 33° 46' 15", long. 84° 23' 19". Transmitter: NationsBank Plaza. Equipment: Emcee transmitter; Andrew antenna. Ownership: BellSouth Corp.

Atlanta—WGW309 (Ch. 2). Atlanta MDS Co. Inc., Suite 6-C, 104 E. 68th St., New York, NY 10021. Phone: 212-288-2356. Authorized power: 50-w. Antenna: 1017-ft. above ground. Lat. 33° 46' 15", long. 84° 23' 10". Transmitter: NationsBank Plaza. Equipment: Emcee transmitter; Andrew antenna. Requests change to 942-ft. above ground; transmitter to 600 Peachtree Rd. Ownership: Atlanta MDS Co.

Valdosta—WLW877 (Ch. 1). Wireless One Licensing Venture Inc., Suite 403, 2506 Lakeland Dr., Jackson, MS 39208. Authorized power: 10-w. Antenna: 707-ft. above ground. Lat. 31° 16' 18", long. 83° 21' 57". Transmitter: 4.5-mi. E of Sparks. Equipment: Comwave transmitter; Bogner antenna. Requests change to lat. 31° 10' 06", long. 83° 21' 50"; transmitter to 1-mi. SSE of Barnesdale. Ownership: Wireless One Inc.

Hawaii

Honolulu—WMY434 (Ch. 1). WC Wireless, 6902 Compton Lane, Naples, FL 34104. Phone: 941-352-7849. Authorized power: 10-w. Antenna: 70-ft. above ground. Lat. 21° 24' 24", long. 158° 06' 02". Transmitter: Palikea Ridge on Palehua Rd. Equipment: Comwave transmitter; Andrew antenna. Ownership: WC Wireless.

Honolulu—WMY435 (Ch. 2A). GTE Media Ventures Inc., Suite 300, 100 E. Royal Lane, Irving, TX 75028. Phone: 972-443-0400. Fax: 972-443-0562. E-mail: webmaster@cc.gte.com. Web site: http://www.cc.gte.com. Authorized power: 15-w. Antenna: 78-ft. above ground. Lat. 21° 24' 24", long. 158° 06' 02". Transmitter: Palikea Ridge on Palehua Rd. Equipment: Comwave transmitter; Andrew antenna. Ownership: GTE Media Ventures.

Idaho

Boise—WMH801 (Ch. 1). WBSB Licensing Corp., Suite 325, 9250 E. Costilla Ave., Englewood, CO 80112. Phone: 303-649-1195. Fax: 303-649-1196. Authorized power: 50-w. Antenna: 22-ft. above ground. Lat. 43° 45' 18", long. 116° 05' 52". Transmitter: 11-mi. NE of Boise. Equipment: ITS transmitter; Andrew antenna. Ownership: Wireless Broadcasting Systems of America Inc.

Payette—WGW349 (Ch. 1). TV2S, 1811 D. Roache Harbor Rd., Friday Harbor, WA 98250. Authorized power: 100-w. Antenna: 161-ft. above ground. Lat. 44° 03' 47", long. 116° 54' 23". Transmitter: 1-mi. SE of Payette. Equipment: Emcee transmitter; Andrew antenna. Ownership: TV2S.

Twin Falls—WKR64 (Ch. 1). Teewinot Licensing Inc., Box 1550, Port Orchard, WA 98366. Phone: 360-871-5981. Authorized power: 20-w. Antenna: 135-ft. above ground. Lat. 42° 43' 54", long. 114° 25' 04". Transmitter: 0.15-mi. WSW of Flat Top Butte. Equipment: Emcee transmitter; Andrew antenna. Ownership: Teewinot Licensing Inc.

Illinois

Casey—WLW800 (Ch. 1). Bolin Enterprises Inc., Box 133, Old Rte. 40 E, Casey, IL 62420. Phone: 217-932-4533. Authorized power: 10-w. Antenna: 250-ft. above ground. Lat. 39° 12' 55", long. 88° 13' 49". Transmitter: 1.6-mi. E of Jewett. Equipment: Comwave transmitter; Andrew antenna. Ownership: Bolin Enterprises Inc.

Casey—WLW804 (Ch. 2A). Bolin Enterprises Inc., Box 133, Old Rte. 40 E, Casey, IL 62420. Phone: 217-932-4533. Authorized power: 10-w. Antenna: 200-ft. above ground. Lat. 39° 12' 55", long. 88° 13' 49". Transmitter: 1.6-mi. E of Jewett. Equipment: Varian transmitter; Andrew antenna. Ownership: Bolin Enterprises Inc.

Champaign—WLW763 (Ch. 1). Specchio Developers Ltd., Box 846, 233 N. Garrard, Rantoul, IL 61866. Phone: 217-892-8888. Authorized power: 10-w. Antenna: 175-ft. above ground. Lat. 40° 09' 50", long. 88° 17' 47". Transmitter: RR 2. Equipment: Comwave transmitter; Andrew antenna. Ownership: Specchio Developers Ltd.

Chicago—WOF49 (Ch. 1). Tribune Regional Programming Inc., Suite 114, 2000 York Rd., Oak Brook, IL 60521. Phone: 630-368-4394. Fax: 630-571-0489. E-mail: charrison@tribune.com. Authorized power: 100-w. Antenna: 1121-ft. above ground. Lat. 41° 53' 56", long. 87° 37' 23". Transmitter: John Hancock Center, 875 Michigan Ave. Equipment: Comwave transmitter; Andrew antenna. Ownership: Tribune Broadcasting Co.

Chicago—WHT562 (Ch. 2). Chicago MDS Co., 1761 Fairfield Beach Rd., Fairfield, CT 06430. Phone: 203-256-1302. Authorized power: 100-w. Antenna: 1456-ft. above ground. Lat. 41° 52' 44", long. 87° 38' 10". Transmitter: 101 S. Wacker Dr. Equipment: Comwave transmitter; Andrew antenna. Requests change to 1121-ft. above ground. Ownership: Broadcast Data Corp.; Cross Country Network Inc.; Private Networks Inc.

Olney—WFY537 (Ch. 1). Red Hill Telecommunications Corp., 120 W. Mack Ave., Olney, IL 62450. Authorized power: 10-w. Lat. 38° 43' 54", long. 87° 48' 58". Transmitter: 7.3-mi. W of Lawrenceville. Equipment: Andrew antenna. Ownership: Red Hill Telecommunications Corp.

Peoria—WPX72 (Ch. 1). Evans Microwave, Box 181, Savoy, IL 61874. Phone: 303-792-3111. Authorized power: 10-w. Antenna: 320-ft. above ground. Lat. 40° 39' 11", long. 89° 35' 13". Transmitter: 500 N. Stewart St., Creve Coeur. Equipment: Emcee transmitter; Andrew antenna. Ownership: Evans Microwave Inc.

Urbana—KEW94 (Ch. 2A). Board of Trustees of U. of Illinois, Room 354, Henry Admin Bldg., 506 S. Wright St., Urbana, IL 61801. Phone: 217-333-1000. Authorized power: 10-w. Antenna: 135-ft. above ground. Lat. 46° 06' 44", long. 88° 13' 33". Transmitter: U. of Illinois. Equipment: Emcee transmitter; Andrew antenna. Ownership: Board of Trustees of U. of Illinois.

Waukegan—WGW344 (Ch. 1). Tribune Regional Programming Inc., Suite 114, 2000 York Rd., Oak Brook, IL 60521. Phone: 630-368-4394. Fax: 630-571-0489. E-mail: charrison@tribune.com. Authorized power: 10-w. Antenna: 174-ft. above ground. Lat. 42° 21' 35", long. 87° 49' 38". Transmitter: 4 S. Genesee St. Equipment: Emcee transmitter; Andrew antenna. Ownership: Tribune Broadcasting Co.

Indiana

Fort Wayne—WGW300 (Ch. 1). James A. Simon. Authorized power: 100-w. Antenna: 538-ft. above ground. Lat. 41° 06' 25", long. 85° 11' 46". Transmitter: 3431 Hillegas Rd. Equipment: Comwave transmitter; Andrew antenna. Ownership: James A. Simon.

Fort Wayne—WHD358 (Ch. 2A). James A. Simon. Authorized power: 100-w. Antenna: 538-ft. above ground. Lat. 41° 06' 25", long. 85° 11' 46". Transmitter: 3431 Hillegas Rd. Equipment: Comwave transmitter; Andrew antenna. Ownership: James A. Simon.

Indianapolis—WPX33 (Ch. 1). Alda Wireless Holdings Inc., 5301 E. Broadway Blvd., Tucson, AZ 85711-8181. Phone: 520-519-4400. Fax: 520-747-6830. Authorized power: 100-w. Lat. 39° 46' 12", long. 86° 09' 20". Transmitter: Indiana National Bank Tower, Ohio & Pennsylvania Aves. Equipment: Emcee transmitter; Andrew antenna. Requests change to 823-ft. above ground, lat. 39° 46' 11", long. 86° 09' 26"; transmitter to 111 Monument Circle. Ownership: Matthew Oristano.

Indianapolis—WLK246 (Ch. 2). Indianapolis MDS Co., Box 023707, Brooklyn, NY 11201. Phone: 212-777-4740. Authorized power: 10-w. Antenna: 522-ft. above ground. Lat. 39° 46' 12", long. 86° 09' 20". Transmitter: 300 N. Delaware St. Equipment: Emcee transmitter; Andrew antenna. Ownership: Broadcast Data Corp.; Private Networks Inc.

Iowa

Davenport—WFY595 (Ch. 1). Virginia Communications Inc., 6330 E. Mockingbird Lane, Scottsdale, AZ 85253. Phone: 602-948-3776. Fax: 602-991-6797. Authorized power: 100-w. Antenna: 495-ft. above ground. Lat. 41° 36' 13", long. 90° 26' 01". Transmitter: 8212 Wells Ferry Rd., Bettendorf. Equipment: Emcee transmitter; Andrew antenna. Ownership: Virginia Communications Inc.

Des Moines—WMH232 (Ch. 2A). Distinctive Sound, 1205 31st St., West Des Moines, IA 50266. Phone: 515-253-9020. E-mail: distsound@aol.com. Authorized power: 100-w. Antenna: 162-ft. above ground. Lat. 41° 35' 12", long. 93° 40' 24". Transmitter: 4111 Ingersoll Ave. Equipment: ITS transmitter; Andrew antenna. Ownership: Distinctive Sound.

Kansas

Effingham—WMH876 (Ch. 1). CS Wireless Systems Inc., 1101 Summit Ave., Plano, TX 75074. Phone: 972-730-3300. Authorized power: 50-w. Antenna: 700-ft. above ground. Lat. 39° 30' 02", long. 95° 29' 37". Transmitter: 5-mi. WSW of Effingham. Equipment: Comwave transmitter; Andrew antenna. Ownership: CS Wireless Systems Inc.

Garden City—WMI903 (Ch. 1). C & G Communications, 1205 2nd St., Moundsville, WV 26041. Phone: 304-845-7694. Authorized power: 10-w. Antenna: 420-ft. above ground. Lat. 37° 56' 40", long. 100° 51' 59". Transmitter: 2-mi. S of Garden City. Equipment: Comwave transmitter; Andrew antenna. Ownership: C & G Communications.

Garden City—WMI943 (Ch. 2A). C & G Communications, 1205 2nd St., Moundsville, WV 26041. Phone: 304-845-7694. Authorized power: 10-w. Antenna: 420-ft. above ground. Lat. 37° 56' 40", long. 100° 51' 59". Transmitter: 2-mi. S of Garden City. Equipment: Comwave transmitter; Andrew antenna. Ownership: C & G Communications.

Kentucky

Harrodsburg—WFY837 (Ch. 1). Yates Enterprises Inc. Authorized power: 10-w. Antenna: 304-ft. above ground. Lat. 37° 45' 00", long. 84° 50' 50". Transmitter: 0.5-mi. S of Hwy. 127. Equipment: Emcee transmitter; Andrew antenna. Ownership: Yates Enterprises Inc.

Louisville—KOA86 (Ch. 1). BellSouth Wireless Cable Inc., 1100 Abernathy Rd. NE, Atlanta, GA 30328. Phone: 770-673-2800. Authorized power: 100-w. Antenna: 374-ft. above ground. Lat. 38° 10' 25", long. 85° 54' 50". Transmitter: Doolittle & Corner. Equipment: Comwave transmitter; Bogner antenna. Ownership: BellSouth Corp.

Paducah—WMX910 (Ch. 1). Libmot Communications Partnership, 2700 Chain Bridge Rd. NW, Washington, DC 20016. Phone: 202-966-2167. Fax: 202-237-7742. Authorized power: 10-w. Antenna: 417-ft. above ground. Lat. 37° 05' 55", long. 88° 37' 19". Transmitter: 1700 N. A St. Equipment: ITS transmitter; Andrew antenna. Ownership: Libmot Communications Partnership.
Leased to Heartland Wireless Communications Inc., 200 Chisholm Place, Suite 200, Plano, TX 75075. Phone: 972-423-9494.

Paducah—WMX911 (Ch. 2A). Libmot Communications Partnership, 2700 Chain Bridge Rd. NW, Washington, DC 20016. Phone: 202-966-2167. Fax: 202-237-7742. Authorized power: 10-w. Antenna: 417-ft. above ground. Lat. 37° 05' 55", long. 88° 37' 19". Transmitter: 1700 N. A St. Equipment: ITS transmitter; Andrew antenna. Ownership: Libmot Communications Partnership.
Leased to Nucentrix, 200 Chisholm Place, Suite 200, Plano, TX 75075. Phone: 972-423-9494.

Parkers Lake—WMX332 (Ch. 1). CNI Wireless Inc., Box 643, 310 W. Columbia St., Somerset, KY 42501. Phone: 606-679-8917. Fax: 606-678-3018. Authorized power: 50-w. Antenna: 503-ft. above ground. Lat. 36° 50' 27", long. 84° 26' 41". Transmitter: 2.1-mi. E of Parkers Lake. Equipment: Comwave transmitter; Andrew antenna. Ownership: CNI Wireless Inc.

Louisiana

Alexandria—WFY645 (Ch. 1). Satellite Vision Broadcasting Co., 377 Browns Bend Rd., Alexandria, LA 71303-4138. Phone: 318-442-

6714. Authorized power: 10-w. Lat. 31° 16' 04", long. 92° 26' 24". Transmitter: 2910 Duhon Lane. Equipment: Emcee transmitter; Andrew antenna. Ownership: Satellite Vision Broadcasting Co.

Baton Rouge—WPW96 (Ch. 1). K-Towers Partnership, 123 N. Easy St., Lafayette, LA 70506. Authorized power: 10-w. Lat. 30° 24' 47", long. 91° 05' 50". Transmitter: 4041 Essen Lane. Equipment: Emcee transmitter; Andrew antenna. Ownership: K-Towers Partnership.

Harahan—WLK290 (Ch. 2). Radiofone Inc., 3130 N. I-10 Service Rd., Metairie, LA 70002. Phone: 504-830-5400. Authorized power: 10-w. Antenna: 714-ft. above ground. Lat. 29° 57' 00", long. 90° 04' 16". Transmitter: 1001 Howard Ave. Equipment: ITS transmitter; Andrew antenna. Requests change to 110-ft. above ground, lat. 29° 57' 07", long. 90° 11' 14". Ownership: James D. & Lawrence D. Garvey.

New Orleans—WKR26 (Ch. 1). The Microband Companies Inc., Box 6099, 800 W. Airport Freeway, Irving, TX 75062. Authorized power: 100-w. Lat. 29° 54' 36", long. 90° 11' 48". Transmitter: 0.4-mi. W of Avondale Railroad Yard, Avondale. Equipment: Micro-Link transmitter; Andrew antenna. Ownership: The Microband Companies Inc.

Rayville—WFY896 (Ch. 1). Communications Towers Inc. of Texas. Authorized power: 10-w. Antenna: 300-ft. above ground. Lat. 32° 27' 22", long. 91° 39' 27". Transmitter: 5-mi. E of Rayville on Hwy. 20. Equipment: Emcee transmitter; Andrew antenna. Ownership: Communications Towers Inc. of Texas.

Maine

Augusta-Belgrade—KNJ27 (Ch. 1). Tel-Radio Communications Properties Inc., 301 S. Westfield Rd., Madison, WI 53705. Authorized power: 10-w. Lat. 44° 28' 44", long. 69° 52' 34". Transmitter: 12.5-mi. NW of Augusta. Equipment: Emcee transmitter; Andrew antenna. Ownership: Tel-Radio Communications Properties Inc.

Maryland

Baltimore—WHT571 (Ch. 2). Atlantic Microsystems Inc., Suite 100, 2101 Wilson Blvd., Arlington, VA 22201. Phone: 703-812-8800. Fax: 703-812-8808. Authorized power: 100-w. Antenna: 710-ft. above ground. Lat. 39° 20' 10", long. 76° 38' 59". Transmitter: WBFF(TV) tower. Equipment: ITS transmitter; Andrew antenna. Ownership: CAI Wireless Systems Inc.

Massachusetts

Boston—WSL33 (Ch. 1). Commonwealth License Inc., Suite 100, 2101 Wilson Blvd., Arlington, VA 22201. Phone: 703-812-8800. Fax: 703-812-8808. Authorized power: 100-w. Antenna: 679-ft. above ground. Lat. 42° 21' 08", long. 71° 03' 25". Transmitter: One Financial Center. Equipment: ITS transmitter; Andrew antenna. Ownership: CAI Wireless Systems Inc.

Michigan

Cadillac—WLW902 (Ch. 1). JB Wireless, 7 Roundtree Dr., Melville, NY 11747. Phone: 516-643-8349. Fax: 516-643-8349. Authorized power: 10-w. Antenna: 242-ft. above ground. Lat. 44° 22' 11", long. 85° 12' 54". Transmitter: 320 Central. Equipment: Comwave transmitter; Andrew antenna. Ownership: JB Wireless.

Detroit—WHT594 (Ch. 2). Detroit MDS Co., Box 1059, East Brunswick, NJ 08816. Phone: 212-288-2356. Fax: 212-288-2312. Authorized power: 200-w. Antenna: 850-ft. above ground. Lat. 42° 27' 13", long. 83° 09' 50". Transmitter: One Radio Plaza. Equipment: Comwave transmitter; Andrew antenna. Ownership: Broadcast Data Corp.

Ironwood—WHT576 (Ch. 1). Superior Communications Systems, 4141 Elkhorn Dr., Cedar Rapids, IA 52411. Phone: 319-393-0094. Authorized power: 100-w. Lat. 46° 29' 30", long. 90° 01' 29". Transmitter: 1-mi. NE of Bessemer. Ownership: Superior Communications Systems.

Royal Oak Twp.—WJM22 (Ch. 1). Alda Wireless Holdings Inc., 5301 E. Broadway Blvd., Tucson, AZ 85711-3710. Phone: 520-519-4400. Fax: 520-747-6830. Authorized power: 200-w. Antenna: 850-ft. above ground. Lat. 42° 27' 13", long. 83° 09' 50". Transmitter: One Radio Plaza. Equipment: Comwave transmitter; Andrew antenna. Requests change to 95-ft. above ground. Ownership: Matthew Oristano.

Saginaw—WLW833 (Ch. 1). ALCH Inc., 2600 California St., Saginaw, MI 48640. Authorized power: 50-w. Antenna: 874-ft. above ground. Lat. 43° 28' 24", long. 83° 50' 40". Transmitter: 6-mi. E of Saginaw. Equipment: Comwave transmitter; Andrew antenna. Ownership: ALCH Inc.

Saginaw—WMI947 (Ch. 2A). Microcom Inc., 3735 Bern Dr., Bay City, MI 48706-9275. Authorized power: 50-w. Antenna: 874-ft. above ground. Lat. 43° 28' 24", long. 83° 50' 40". Transmitter: 6-mi. E of Saginaw. Equipment: Comwave transmitter; Andrew antenna. Ownership: Microcom Inc.

Minnesota

Fairmont—WMI359 (Ch. 2A). Starcom Inc., Box 87, 106 E. Robins Ave., Graettinger, IA 51342. Phone: 712-859-3700. Fax: 712-859-3711. Authorized power: 50-w. Antenna: 5000-ft. above ground. Lat. 43° 33' 20", long. 94° 29' 11". Transmitter: 5.8-mi. S of Fairmont. Equipment: ITS transmitter; Andrew antenna. Ownership: Starcom Inc.

Minneapolis—WPE99 (Ch. 1). CS Wireless Systems Inc., 1101 Summit Ave., Plano, TX 75074. Phone: 972-730-3300. Authorized power: 100-w. Antenna: 811-ft. above ground. Lat. 44° 58' 32", long. 93° 16' 18". Transmitter: IDS Bldg., 7th & Marquette. Equipment: Comwave transmitter; Andrew antenna. Ownership: CS Wireless Systems Inc.

Minneapolis—WCU552 (Ch. 2). Minneapolis MDS Co., Suite 247, 189 Berdan Ave., Wayne, NJ 07470. Phone: 201-831-7404. Authorized power: 100-w. Antenna: 815-ft. above ground. Lat. 44° 58' 32", long. 93° 16' 18". Transmitter: 80 S. 8th St. Equipment: Comwave transmitter; Andrew antenna. Ownership: Minneapolis MDS Co.

Missouri

Carthage—WDU466 (Ch. 1). Southwest Missouri Cable TV Inc., Box 696, Carthage, MO 64836. Phone: 417-358-3002. Fax: 417-358-1845. Authorized power: 100-w. Antenna: 475-ft. above ground. Lat. 37° 10' 58", long. 94° 21' 35". Transmitter: Hwy. 96, 2-mi. W of Carthage. Equipment: Andrew antenna. Ownership: Ruth I. Kolpin.

Fordland—WMH812 (Ch. 1). Champion Industries Inc., 300 W. Mission Dr., Chandler, AZ 85224. Phone: 602-497-5774. Authorized power: 20-w. Antenna: 259-ft. above ground. Lat. 37° 12' 42", long. 93° 16' 53". Transmitter: 405 N. Sherman Dr. Equipment: Emcee transmitter; Andrew antenna. Requests change to 770-ft. above ground, lat. 37° 12' 06", long. 92° 56' 33"; transmitter to 3-mi. N of Fordland. Ownership: Champion Industries Inc.

Kansas City—KOB43 (Ch. 1). CS Wireless Systems Inc., 1101 Summit Ave., Plano, TX 75074. Phone: 972-730-3300. Authorized power: 100-w. Antenna: 616-ft. above ground. Lat. 39° 05' 58", long. 94° 34' 57". Transmitter: 2100 Stark St. Equipment: Emcee transmitter; Andrew antenna. Ownership: CS Wireless Systems Inc.

Lake of the Ozarks (Osage Beach)—WOG68 (Ch. 1). Microwave Movies Inc. Authorized power: 100-w. Lat. 39° 09' 23", long. 92° 36' 43". Transmitter: Lake Rd. 54-22 & Sunset Dr., Osage Beach. Equipment: Emcee transmitter; Andrew antenna. Ownership: Microwave Movies Inc.

Maysville—WMX936 (Ch. 1). CS Wireless Systems Inc., 1101 Summit Ave., Plano, TX 75074. Phone: 972-730-3300. Authorized power: 10-w. Antenna: 300-ft. above ground. Lat. 39° 52' 04", long. 94° 22' 14". Transmitter: 0.5-mi. W of Hwy. 33. Equipment: Comwave transmitter; Andrew antenna. Ownership: CS Wireless Systems Inc.

St. Louis—WQQ64 (Ch. 1). Alda Wireless Holdings Inc., 5301 E. Broadway Blvd., Tucson, AZ 85711-3710. Phone: 520-519-4400. Fax: 520-747-6830. Authorized power: 50-w. Antenna: 769-ft. above ground. Lat. 38° 28' 56", long. 90° 23' 53". Transmitter: 3-mi. N of Arnold. Equipment: Townsend, Micro-Link transmitter; Andrew antenna. Ownership: Matthew Oristano.

Leased to People's Choice TV of St. Louis, 11737 Administration Dr., St. Louis, MO 63146. Phone: 314-993-5767.

St. Louis—WHT702 (Ch. 2). St. Louis MDS Co., Box 023707, Brooklyn, NY 11201. Authorized power: 10-w. Lat. 38° 38' 51", long. 90° 20' 13". Transmitter: Clayton Inn Center, Clayton. Equipment: Emcee transmitter; Andrew antenna. Ownership: Private Networks Inc.

Montana

Billings—WFY748 (Ch. 1). American Telecasting of Billings Inc., Suite 300, 5575 Tech Center Dr., Colorado Springs, CO 80919. Phone: 719-260-5533. Fax: 719-260-5010. Authorized power: 10-w. Antenna: 200-ft. above ground. Lat. 45° 45' 34", long. 108° 27' 10". Transmitter: Westergard Hill, Billings. Equipment: Emcee transmitter; Andrew antenna. Ownership: American Telecasting Inc.

Glasgow—WHC973 (Ch. 1). Telecrafter Communications Group. Authorized power: 10-w. Lat. 48° 01' 52", long. 106° 18' 29". Transmitter: 6.5-mi. NE of Fort Peck. Ownership: Telecrafter Services Corp.

Kalispell—WMY216 (Ch. 1). Grand Alliance Kalispell (F) Partnership, Suite 400, 2001 Pennsylvania Ave. NW, Washington, DC 20036. Phone: 202-887-0600. Authorized power: 10-w. Antenna: 100-ft. above ground. Lat. 48° 30' 42", long. 144° 22' 14". Transmitter: Big Mount, 6.2-mi. N of Whitefish. Equipment: Comwave transmitter; Andrew antenna. Ownership: Grand Alliance Kalispell (F) Partnership.

Kalispell—WMY220 (Ch. 2A). Grand Alliance Kalispell (F) Partnership, Suite 400, 2001 Pennsylvania Ave. NW, Washington, DC 20036. Phone: 202-887-0600. Authorized power: 10-w. Antenna: 100-ft. above ground. Lat. 48° 30' 42", long. 114° 22' 14". Transmitter: Big Mount, 6.2-mi. N of Whitefish. Equipment: Comwave transmitter; Andrew antenna. Ownership: Grand Alliance Kalispell (F) Partnership.

Nebraska

Kearney—WFY431 (Ch. 1). Cable USA Inc., Box 1448, Kearney, NE 68848-1448. Lat. 40° 43' 38", long. 99° 07' 40". Transmitter: Junction of Hwys. 10A & 30. Ownership: Cable USA Inc.

North Platte—WFY765 (Ch. 1). Mid-Nebraska Telecommunications Inc. Authorized power: 10-w. Antenna: 194-ft. above ground. Lat. 41° 12' 49", long. 100° 43' 48". Transmitter: 3.5-mi. N of North Platte. Equipment: Emcee transmitter; Andrew antenna. Ownership: Mid-Nebraska Telecommunications Inc.

Nevada

Carson City—WJL89 (Ch. 1). Jonsson Communications Corp., Suite 900, 233 Wilshire Blvd., Santa Monica, CA 90401. Phone: 310-451-3230. Authorized power: 100-w. Antenna: 67-ft. above ground. Lat. 39° 15' 25", long. 119° 42' 37". Transmitter: 6.9-mi. NE of Carson City. Equipment: ITS transmitter; Bogner antenna. Ownership: Jonsson Communications Corp.

Ely—WLW905 (Ch. 2A). LC Communications, 7 Roundtree Dr., Melville, NY 11747. Phone: 516-643-8349. Fax: 516-643-8349. Authorized power: 10-w. Antenna: 77-ft. above ground. Lat. 39° 14' 46", long. 114° 55' 39". Transmitter: Saxton Peak. Equipment: Varian transmitter; Andrew antenna. Ownership: LC Communications.

Las Vegas—WWZ51 (Ch. 1). Tekkom Inc., 836 E. Washington St., San Diego, CA 92103. Phone: 619-260-0110. Authorized power: 100-w. Lat. 35° 56' 50", long. 115° 03' 01". Transmitter: Black Mountain. Equipment: Emcee transmitter; Andrew antenna. Ownership: Carl B. Hilliard Jr.

Las Vegas—WKR65 (Ch. 2). American Telecasting Inc., Suite 300, 5575 Tech Center Dr., Colorado Springs, CO 80919. Phone: 719-260-5533. Fax: 719-260-5010. Authorized power: 10-w. Antenna: 67-ft. above ground. Lat. 36° 00' 30", long. 115° 00' 20". Transmitter: Black Mountain. Equipment: ITS transmitter; Andrew antenna. Ownership: American Telecasting Inc.

Leased to Superchannels of Las Vegas Inc., 31 Cactus Garden, Henderson, NV 89014. Phone: 702-456-6969.

Reno—WFY434 (Ch. 1). Jonsson Communications Corp., Suite 900, 233 Wilshire Blvd., Santa Monica, CA 90401. Authorized power:

10-w. Lat. 39° 35' 03", long. 119° 47' 52". Transmitter: Red Peak, 4-mi. N of Reno. Equipment: Emcee transmitter; Andrew antenna. Ownership: Jonsson Communications Corp.

Reno—WFY553 (Ch. 2A). Dynamic Sound, No. 108, 4910 Aircenter Circle, Reno, NV 89502. Authorized power: 93-w. Antenna: 157-ft. above ground. Lat. 39° 18' 47", long. 119° 52' 59". Transmitter: Slide Mountain, 15-mi. SSW of Reno. Equipment: Comwave transmitter; Andrew antenna. Ownership: Dynamic Sound.

New Jersey

Atlantic City—WMI383 (Ch. 1). Orion Broadcasting Systems Inc., No. 208 B, 7231 S. Eastern Ave., Las Vegas, NV 89119-0451. Phone: 800-356-1825. Authorized power: 10-w. Antenna: 365-ft. above ground. Lat. 39° 22' 51", long. 74° 27' 02". Transmitter: 1701 Absecon Blvd. Equipment: Emcee transmitter; Andrew antenna. Ownership: Orion Broadcasting Systems.

Atlantic City—WMI387 (Ch. 2A). Orion Broadcasting Systems Inc., No. 208 B, 7231 S. Eastern Ave., Las Vegas, NV 89119-0451. Phone: 800-356-1825. Authorized power: 10-w. Antenna: 365-ft. above ground. Lat. 39° 22' 51", long. 74° 27' 02". Transmitter: 1701 Absecon Blvd. Equipment: Emcee transmitter; Andrew antenna. Ownership: Orion Broadcasting Systems.

New Brunswick—WCU573 (Ch. 1). New York License Inc., Suite 100, 2101 Wilson Blvd., Arlington, VA 22201. Phone: 703-812-8800. Fax: 703-812-8808. Authorized power: 20-w. Antenna: 85-ft. above ground. Lat. 40° 42' 42", long. 74° 21' 12". Transmitter: 99 Beauvoir Ave., Summit. Equipment: ITS transmitter; Andrew antenna. Ownership: CAI Wireless Systems Inc.

Trenton—KHH87 (Ch. 1). Micro TV Inc., 300 Domino Lane, Philadelphia, PA 19128. Authorized power: 10-w. Lat. 40° 13' 14", long. 74° 46' 03". Transmitter: 28 W. State St. Ownership: 216 Paoli Ave. Corp.

New Mexico

Albuquerque—KFK32 (Ch. 1). Multimedia Development Corp., Box 14670, Albuquerque, NM 87191. Phone: 505-237-2123. Fax: 505-237-0575. E-mail: yguado@aol.com. Web site: http://www.tvwest.com. Authorized power: 10-w. Antenna: 79-ft. above ground. Lat. 35° 13' 00", long. 106° 27' 07". Transmitter: Sandia Crest. Equipment: Emcee transmitter; Andrew antenna. Ownership: Multimedia Development Corp.

Albuquerque—WLW898 (Ch. 2A). Cox Music & Sound, Box 8083, Albuquerque, NM 87198-8083. Phone: 505-268-7700. Authorized power: 100-w. Antenna: 36-ft. above ground. Lat. 35° 12' 51", long. 106° 27' 02". Transmitter: 7-mi. NE of Albuquerque. Equipment: ITS transmitter; Andrew antenna. Ownership: Cox Music & Sound.

Deming—WHD499 (Ch. 1). Tel Master. Authorized power: 10-w. Lat. 32° 12' 00", long. 107° 36' 00". Transmitter: 12.5-mi. SE of Deming. Ownership: Tel Master.

Greenfield—WMY421 (Ch. 1). RVS Holdings Corp., Suite 200, 200 Chisholm Place, Plano, TX 75075. Phone: 972-423-9494. Fax: 972-423-0819. Authorized power: 50-w. Antenna: 493-ft. above ground. Lat. 33° 12' 10", long. 104° 17' 29". Transmitter: 4-mi. NE of Greenfield. Equipment: ITS transmitter; Andrew antenna. Ownership: Nucentrix Broadband Networks Inc.

Greenfield—WMY422 (Ch. 2A). RVS Holdings Corp., Suite 200, 200 Chisholm Place, Plano, TX 75075. Phone: 972-423-9494. Fax: 972-423-0819. Authorized power: 50-w. Antenna: 493-ft. above ground. Lat. 33° 12' 10", long. 104° 17' 29". Transmitter: 4-mi. NE of Greenfield. Equipment: ITS transmitter; Andrew antenna. Ownership: Nucentrix Broadband Networks Inc.

Hobbs—WMY449 (Ch. 1). Blake Twedt, 5102 Rosegreen Court, Tampa, FL 33624. Phone: 727-587-9959. Authorized power: 10-w. Antenna: 290-ft. above ground. Lat. 32° 48' 59", long. 103° 13' 56". Transmitter: Hwy. 18, 0.25-mi. N of Hobbs. Equipment: Emcee transmitter; Andrew antenna. Ownership: Blake Twedt.

Las Cruces—WJM88 (Ch. 1). Multimedia Development Corp., Suite 300, 13170B Central SE, Albuquerque, NM 87123. Phone: 505-237-0525. Fax: 505-237-0575. E-mail: tvwest@tvwest.com. Web site: http://www.tvwest.com. Authorized power: 10-w. Lat. 32° 17' 08", long. 106° 41' 48". Transmitter: 4-mi. SE of Las Cruces. Equipment: Comwave transmitter; Andrew antenna. Ownership: Multimedia Development Corp.

Pinos Altos-Silver City—WGW313 (Ch. 1). Tel Master. Authorized power: 10-w. Lat. 32° 50' 50", long. 108° 14' 18". Transmitter: 10-mi. N of Silver City. Equipment: Andrew antenna. Ownership: Tel Master.

Tucumcari—WMY408 (Ch. 1). RVS Holdings Corp., Suite 200, 200 Chisholm Place, Plano, TX 75075. Phone: 972-423-9494. Fax: 972-423-0819. Authorized power: 50-w. Antenna: 706-ft. above ground. Lat. 35° 13' 47", long. 103° 44' 11". Transmitter: 4-mi. N of Tucumcari. Equipment: ITS transmitter; Andrew antenna. Ownership: Nucentrix Broadband Networks Inc.

Tucumcari—WMY407 (Ch. 2A). RVS Holdings Corp., Suite 200, 200 Chisholm Place, Plano, TX 75075. Phone: 972-423-9494. Fax: 972-423-0819. Authorized power: 50-w. Antenna: 706-ft. above ground. Lat. 35° 13' 47", long. 103° 44' 11". Transmitter: 4-mi. N of Tucumcari. Equipment: ITS transmitter; Andrew antenna. Ownership: Nucentrix Broadband Networks Inc.

New York

Albany—KFK28 (Ch. 1). Eastern Microwave Inc., Box 4872, 3 Northern Concourse, Syracuse, NY 13221. Authorized power: 100-w. Lat. 42° 38' 55", long. 73° 45' 58". Transmitter: Empire Plaza, Tower Bldg. Equipment: Emcee transmitter; Andrew antenna. Ownership: Eastern Microwave Inc.

Albany—WHI966 (Ch. 2). Greater Albany License Inc., Suite 100, 2101 Wilson Blvd., Arlington, VA 22201. Phone: 703-812-8800. Fax: 703-812-8808. Authorized power: 50-w. Antenna: 103-ft. above ground. Lat. 42° 38' 09", long. 74° 00' 04". Transmitter: Pinnacle Rd., New Scotland. Equipment: ITS transmitter; Andrew antenna. Ownership: CAI Wireless Systems Inc.

Corning—WMH869 (Ch. 1). KA3B2 Television Partnership, No. 238, 2219 Thousand Oaks Blvd., Thousand Oaks, CA 91362. Phone: 800-388-7371. Authorized power: 20-w. Antenna: 100-ft. above ground. Lat. 42° 06' 20", long. 76° 52' 17". Transmitter: Hawley Hill, 3-mi. WNW of Elmira. Equipment: ITS transmitter; Andrew antenna. Requests change to 600-ft. Above ground. Ownership: KA3B2 Television Partnership.

Long Island—WJM64 (Ch. 1). Lipper Communications Inc., 74 Trinity Place, New York, NY 10006. Phone: 212-393-1300. Authorized power: 20-w. Antenna: 292-ft. above ground. Lat. 40° 48' 11", long. 73° 12' 26". Transmitter: St. John's Cemetery, Central Islip. Equipment: ITS transmitter; Andrew antenna. Ownership: Lipper Communications.

New York—WQQ79 (Ch. 1). New York License Inc., Suite 100, 2101 Wilson Blvd., Arlington, VA 22201. Phone: 703-812-8800. Fax: 703-812-8808. Authorized power: 100-w. Antenna: 922-ft. above ground. Lat. 40° 44' 54", long. 73° 59' 10". Transmitter: Empire State Bldg., 34th St. & 5th Ave. Equipment: Townsend transmitter; Andrew antenna. Ownership: CAI Wireless Systems Inc.

New York—WLK227 (Ch. 2). New York MDS Inc. Authorized power: 100-w. Antenna: 1472-ft. above ground. Lat. 40° 44' 54", long. 73° 59' 10". Transmitter: Empire State Bldg., 34th & 5th Ave. Equipment: Comwave transmitter; Andrew antenna. Ownership: New York MDS Inc.

Leased to Wireless Cable of New York, 286 Elridge Rd., Fairfield, NJ 07004. Phone: 973-808-3700.

Syracuse—WHC998 (Ch. 1). Syracuse License Inc., Suite 100, 2101 Wilson Blvd., Arlington, VA 22201. Phone: 703-812-8800. Fax: 703-812-8808. Authorized power: 50-w. Antenna: 801-ft. above ground. Lat. 42° 52' 50", long. 76° 11' 59". Transmitter: 4-mi. S of Kingsley Rd. Equipment: ITS transmitter; Andrew antenna. Ownership: CAI Wireless Systems Inc.

North Carolina

Charlotte—WGW715 (Ch. 1). CS Wireless Systems Inc., 1101 Summit Ave., Plano, TX 75074. Phone: 972-730-3300. Authorized power: 100-w. Antenna: 936-ft. above ground. Lat. 35° 17' 14", long. 80° 41' 45". Transmitter: 12541 Caldwell Rd. Equipment: ITS transmitter; Andrew antenna. Ownership: CS Wireless Systems Inc.

Greensboro—WFY738 (Ch. 1). Greensboro License Inc., Suite 100, 2101 Wilson Blvd., Arlington, VA 22201. Phone: 703-812-8800. Fax: 703-812-8808. Authorized power: 50-w. Antenna: 950-ft. above ground. Lat. 35° 56' 43", long. 79° 51' 44". Transmitter: Greensboro. Equipment: Emcee transmitter; Andrew antenna. Ownership: CAI Wireless Systems Inc.

Nags Head—WFY686 (Ch. 1). John H. Bond Jr., 7822 Eastdale Rd., Baltimore, MD 21224. Authorized power: 100-w. Lat. 35° 51' 51", long. 75° 39' 01". Transmitter: Hwy. 345, Wanchese. Equipment: Emcee transmitter. Ownership: John H. Bond Jr.

Raleigh—WMX524 (Ch. 1). Carolina Media Group Inc. Authorized power: 10-w. Antenna: 1104-ft. above ground. Lat. 35° 40' 29", long. 78° 31' 38". Transmitter: U.S. Rte. 70, 2-mi. SE of Auburn. Equipment: Comwave transmitter; Andrew antenna. Ownership: Carolina Media Group Inc.

Winston-Salem—WMH664 (Ch. 1). Winston-Choice License Inc., Suite 100, 2101 Wilson Blvd., Arlington, VA 22201. Phone: 703-812-8800. Fax: 703-812-8808. Authorized power: 10-w. Antenna: 224-ft. above ground. Lat. 36° 05' 51", long. 80° 14' 51". Transmitter: 310 W. 4th St. Equipment: ITS transmitter; Andrew antenna. Ownership: CAI Wireless Systems Inc.

Winston-Salem—WMH668 (Ch. 2A). Winston-Choice License Inc., Suite 100, 2101 Wilson Blvd., Arlington, VA 22201. Phone: 703-812-8800. Fax: 703-812-8808. Authorized power: 10-w. Antenna: 224-ft. above ground. Lat. 36° 05' 51", long. 80° 14' 51". Transmitter: 310 W. 4th St. Equipment: ITS transmitter; Andrew antenna. Ownership: CAI Wireless Systems Inc.

North Dakota

Bismarck—WMH904 (Ch. 2A). American Telecasting Inc., Suite 300, 5575 Tech Center Dr., Colorado Springs, CO 80919. Phone: 719-260-5533. Fax: 719-260-5010. Authorized power: 10-w. Antenna: 919-ft. above ground. Lat. 46° 56' 31", long. 100° 41' 38". Transmitter: 10-mi. N of Bismarck. Equipment: Comwave transmitter; Andrew antenna. Ownership: American Telecasting Inc.

Bowbells—WMX955 (Ch. 1). Northwest Communications Corp., Box 38, Ray, ND 58849. Phone: 701-568-3331. Fax: 701-568-7777. Authorized power: 50-w. Antenna: 435-ft. above ground. Lat. 48° 43' 58", long. 102° 28' 11". Transmitter: 10-mi. W & 5-mi. S of Bowbells. Equipment: ITS transmitter; Andrew antenna. Ownership: Northwest Communications Cooperative.

Cando—WMY208 (Ch. 1). United Telephone Mutual Aid Corp., Box 729, 411 7th Ave., Langdon, ND 58249. Phone: 701-256-5156. Fax: 701-256-5150. Authorized power: 50-w. Antenna: 485-ft. above ground. Lat. 48° 37' 58", long. 99° 06' 05". Transmitter: W. Hwy. 66. Equipment: ITS transmitter; Andrew antenna. Ownership: United Telephone Mutual Aid Corp.

Langdon—WMY447 (Ch. 1). United Telephone Mutual Aid Corp., Box 729, 411 7th Ave., Langdon, ND 58249. Phone: 701-256-5156. Fax: 701-256-5150. Authorized power: 50-w. Antenna: 405-ft. above ground. Lat. 48° 37' 44", long. 98° 00' 35". Transmitter: 1.2-mi. E of Milton. Equipment: ITS transmitter; Andrew antenna. Ownership: United Telephone Mutual Aid Corp.

Ohio

Canton—WSL34 (Ch. 1). Multipoint Information Systems Inc., Suite 6C, 104 E. 68th St., New York, NY 10021. Phone: 212-288-2356. Fax: 212-288-2312. Authorized power: 10-w. Lat. 40° 43' 16", long. 81° 22' 51". Transmitter: 5950 Briggle, East Sparta. Equipment: Emcee transmitter; Andrew antenna. Ownership: Multipoint Information Systems Inc.

Cincinnati—WOG60 (Ch. 1). American Telecasting of Cincinnati Inc., Suite 300, 5575 Tech Center Dr., Colorado Springs, CO 80919. Phone: 719-260-5533. Fax: 719-260-5010. Authorized power: 10-w. Antenna: 669-ft. above ground. Lat. 39° 06' 17", long. 84° 33' 23". Transmitter: 810 Matson Place. Equipment: Emcee transmitter; Andrew antenna. Ownership: American Telecasting Inc.

Cleveland—WQQ66 (Ch. 1). CS Wireless Systems Inc., 1101 Summit Ave., Plano, TX 75074. Authorized power: 50-w. Antenna: 625-ft. above ground. Lat. 41° 22' 58", long. 81° 42' 07". Transmitter: 2861 W. Ridgewood Dr. Equipment: ITS transmitter; Andrew antenna. Ownership: CS Wireless Systems Inc.

Columbus—WDU606 (Ch. 2). Broadcast Data Corp., Suite 247, 189 Berdan Ave., Wayne, NJ 07470. Phone: 201-831-7407. Authorized power: 10-w. Lat. 39° 57' 48", long. 83° 00' 17". Transmitter: Leveque-Lincoln Bldg. Equipment: Andrew antenna. Ownership: Broadcast Data Corp.

Dayton—WMX909 (Ch. 1). CS Wireless Systems Inc., 1101 Summit Ave., Plano, TX 75074. Phone: 972-730-3300. Authorized power: 100-w. Antenna: 810-ft. above ground. Lat. 39° 43' 16", long. 84° 15' 00". Transmitter: 3901 Guthrie Rd. Equipment: Emcee transmitter; Andrew antenna. Ownership: CS Wireless Systems Inc.

Lima—WMI386 (Ch. 1). W.A.T.C.H. TV Co., 3225 W. Elm St, Lima, OH 45805. Phone: 419-999-2824. Fax: 419-999-2140. E-mail: WATCHTMK@bright.net. Authorized power: 50-w. Antenna: 1082-ft. above ground. Lat. 40° 38' 03", long. 84° 12' 29". Transmitter: 19507 State Rte. 501. Equipment: Comwave transmitter; Andrew antenna. Requests change to 1107-ft. above ground; transmitter to 3.3-mi. SW of Lima. Ownership: W.A.T.C.H. TV Co.

Lima—WMI390 (Ch. 2). W.A.T.C.H. TV Co., 3225 W. Elm St., Lima, OH 45805. Phone: 419-999-2824. Fax: 419-999-2140. E-mail: WATCHTMK@bright.net. Authorized power: 50-w. Antenna: 1082-ft. above ground. Lat. 40° 38' 03", long. 84° 12' 29". Transmitter: 19507 State Rte. 501. Equipment: Comwave transmitter; Andrew antenna. Requests change to 1107-ft. above ground; transmitter to 3.3-mi. SW of Lima. Ownership: W.A.T.C.H. TV Co.

Lykens—WMX938 (Ch. 1). RVS Holdings Corp., Suite 200, 200 Chisholm Place, Plano, TX 75075. Phone: 972-423-9494. Fax: 972-423-0819. Authorized power: 10-w. Antenna: 300-ft. above ground. Lat. 40° 54' 23", long. 83° 03' 04". Transmitter: 2-mi. W of Broken Sword. Equipment: Comwave transmitter; Andrew antenna. Ownership: Nucentrix Broadband Networks Inc.

Toledo—KFK31 (Ch. 1). Media Broadcasting Inc., 2049 Robinwood Ave., Toledo, OH 43620. Authorized power: 10-w. Antenna: 334-ft. above ground. Lat. 41° 38' 48", long. 83° 36' 22". Transmitter: 716 Westwood Ave. Equipment: Emcee transmitter; Andrew antenna. Requests change to 415-ft. above ground. Ownership: Media Broadcasting Inc.

Youngstown—WDU693 (Ch. 1). WKBN Broadcasting Corp., Box 59, 3930 Sunset Blvd., Youngstown, OH 44501. Phone: 216-782-1144. Fax: 216-782-3504. Authorized power: 10-w. Antenna: 264-ft. above ground. Lat. 41° 03' 24", long. 80° 38' 44". Transmitter: 3930 Sunset Blvd. Equipment: Harris transmitter; Andrew antenna. Requests change to 469-ft. above ground, lat. 41° 03' 26", long. 80° 38' 22"; transmitter to 4040 Simon Rd. Ownership: WKBN Broadcasting Corp.

Oklahoma

Ada—WMI932 (Ch. 1). Barry James. Authorized power: 10-w. Antenna: 407-ft. above ground. Lat. 34° 43' 31", long. 96° 42' 14". Transmitter: 2.8-mi. SSW of Ada. Equipment: Varian transmitter; Andrew antenna. Ownership: Barry James.

Enid—WLW787 (Ch. 1). Libmot Communications Partnership, 2700 Chain Bridge Rd. NW, Washington, DC 20016. Phone: 202-966-2167. Fax: 202-237-7742. Authorized power: 10-w. Antenna: 75-ft. above ground. Lat. 36° 23' 50", long. 97° 52' 38". Transmitter: 114 E. Broadway. Equipment: Varian transmitter; Andrew antenna. Ownership: Libmot Communications Partnership.
Leased to Nucentrix Broadband Networks, 200 Chisholm Place, Suite 200, Plano, TX 75075. Phone: 972-423-9494.

Guymon—WMY224 (Ch. 1). Pioneer Telephone Cooperative Inc., Box 539, Kingfisher, OK 73750. Phone: 405-375-4111. Authorized power: 10-w. Antenna: 403-ft. above ground. Lat. 36° 40' 37", long. 101° 33' 36". Transmitter: 3-mi. W of Guymon. Equipment: Comwave transmitter; Andrew antenna. Ownership: Pioneer Telephone Cooperative Inc.

Oklahoma City—WJL99 (Ch. 1). Antenna Vision, 4224-F N. Santa Fe, Oklahoma City, OK 73118-8527. Phone: 405-525-1000. Authorized power: 100-w. Antenna: 509-ft. above ground. Lat. 35° 28' 06", long. 97° 30' 51". Transmitter: Liberty Tower, 100 Broadway. Equipment: Varian transmitter; Andrew antenna. Ownership: Antenna Vision.

Oklahoma City—WFY642 (Ch. 2). Broadcast Data Corp., Suite 247, 189 Berdan Ave., Wayne, NJ 07470. Phone: 201-831-7407. Lat. 35° 28' 06", long. 97° 30' 51". Transmitter: Oklahoma City. Ownership: Broadcast Data Corp.

Tulsa—WPG45 (Ch. 2A). Eagleview Technologies Inc., Suite 6-271, 5030 Champion Blvd., Boca Raton, FL 33496. Authorized power: 10-w. Antenna: 305-ft. above ground. Lat. 36° 10' 49", long. 95° 47' 02". Transmitter: 177th & Pine Sts. Equipment: ITS transmitter; Andrew antenna. Ownership: Eagleview Technologies Inc.

Oregon

Bend—WHA674 (Ch. 1). American Telecasting of Bend Inc., Suite 300, 5575 Tech Center Dr., Colorado Springs, CO 80919. Phone: 719-260-5533. Fax: 719-260-5010. Authorized power: 50-w. Antenna: 75-ft. above ground. Lat. 44° 26' 17", long. 120° 57' 13". Transmitter: Grizzly Mountain. Equipment: Comwave transmitter; Andrew antenna. Ownership: American Telecasting Inc.

Coos Bay—WLW906 (Ch. 1). JB Wireless, 7 Roundtree Dr., Melville, NY 11747. Phone: 516-643-8349. Fax: 516-643-8349. Authorized power: 10-w. Antenna: 120-ft. above ground. Lat. 44° 14' 53", long. 124° 23' 56". Transmitter: 116 W. Harris St. Equipment: Comwave transmitter; Andrew antenna. Ownership: JB Wireless.

Medford—WMX333 (Ch. 1). American Telecasting of Medford Inc., Suite 300, 5575 Tech Center Dr., Colorado Springs, CO 80919. Phone: 719-260-5533. Fax: 719-260-5010. Authorized power: 20-w. Antenna: 80-ft. above ground. Lat. 42° 21' 23", long. 122° 58' 33". Transmitter: John's Peak. Equipment: ITS transmitter; Andrew antenna. Ownership: American Telecasting Inc.

Portland—WPY39 (Ch. 1). Microband Corp. of America. Authorized power: 100-w. Lat. 45° 29' 23", long. 122° 41' 47". Transmitter: 4650 S.W. Council Crest Dr. Equipment: Emcee transmitter; Andrew antenna. Ownership: The Microband Companies Inc.

The Dalles—WLW746 (Ch. 1). G/S The Dalles E Settlement Group, Box 6219, Springfield, IL 62708. Phone: 217-341-0721. Fax: 217-528-8827. Authorized power: 10-w. Antenna: 100-ft. above ground. Lat. 45° 35' 56", long. 121° 10' 29". Transmitter: 719 E. 2nd. Equipment: Comwave transmitter; Andrew antenna. Ownership: G/S The Dalles E Settlement Group.

Pennsylvania

Philadelphia—WPE97 (Ch. 1). PC License Inc., Suite 100, 2101 Wilson Blvd., Arlington, VA 22201. Phone: 703-812-8800. Fax: 703-812-8808. Authorized power: 100-w. Antenna: 175-ft. above ground. Lat. 40° 02' 21", long. 75° 14' 13". Transmitter: 216 Paoli Ave. Equipment: Emcee transmitter; Andrew antenna. Ownership: CAI Wireless Systems Inc.

Philadelphia—WLK231 (Ch. 2). Philadelphia MDS Co., Box 023707, Brooklyn, NY 11201. Phone: 212-777-4740. Authorized power: 100-w. Lat. 40° 00' 17", long. 75° 12' 10". Transmitter: 3600 Conshohocken Ave. Equipment: Emcee transmitter; Andrew antenna. Ownership: Broadcast Data Corp.; Greater Media Inc.; Multipoint Information Systems Inc.; Private Networks Inc.
Leased to Popvision, 2510 Metropolitan Dr., Trevose, PA 19053. Phone: 215-396-9400.

Pittsburgh—WPF48 (Ch. 1). Pittsburgh License Inc., Suite 100, 2101 Wilson Blvd., Arlington, VA 22201. Phone: 703-812-8800. Fax: 703-812-8808. Authorized power: 100-w. Antenna: 279-ft. above ground. Lat. 40° 26' 46", long. 79° 57' 51". Transmitter: 2850 Burthold St. Equipment: Varian transmitter; Andrew antenna. Ownership: CAI Wireless Systems Inc.

Rhode Island

Providence—KNV65 (Ch. 1). Eastern New England License Inc., Suite 100, 2101 Wilson Blvd., Arlington, VA 22201. Phone: 703-812-8800. Fax: 703-812-8808. Authorized power: 100-w. Antenna: 872-ft. above ground. Lat. 41° 52' 14", long. 71° 17' 45". Transmitter: 33 Pine St., Rehoboth. Equipment: ITS transmitter; Andrew antenna. Ownership: CAI Wireless Systems Inc.

South Dakota

Bath—WMY463 (Ch. 1). Northern Rural Cable TV Cooperative Inc., Box 488, Bath, SD 57427. Phone: 605-225-0310. Fax: 605-225-1684. Authorized power: 50-w. Antenna: 412-ft. above ground. Lat. 45° 27' 57", long. 98° 20' 12". Transmitter: 0.25-mi. W of Bath. Equipment: ITS transmitter; Andrew antenna. Requests change to 488-ft. above ground, lat. 45° 27' 57", long. 98° 20' 08". Ownership: Northern Rural Cable TV Cooperative.

Tennessee

Chattanooga—WPE83 (Ch. 1). Eagleview Technologies Inc., Suite 6-271, 5030 Champion Blvd., Boca Raton, FL 33496. Authorized power: 10-w. Antenna: 180-ft. above ground. Lat. 35° 09' 28", long. 85° 18' 36". Transmitter: Wilson Ave. at Clegg St., Walden. Equipment: Emcee transmitter; Andrew antenna. Ownership: Eagleview Technologies Inc.

Johnson City—WMI904 (Ch. 1). WCTV Partners, 1616 Parkins Mill Rd., Greenville, SC 29607. Phone: 803-288-0930. Authorized power: 10-w. Antenna: 358-ft. above ground. Lat. 36° 16' 07", long. 82° 20' 21". Transmitter: Buffalo Mountain. Equipment: Comwave transmitter; Andrew antenna. Ownership: WCTV Partners.

Johnson City—WMH905 (Ch. 2A). Grand Alliance Johnson City (E) Partnership, Suite 660, 1920 N St. NW, Washington, DC 20036. Phone: 202-887-0600. Authorized power: 10-w. Antenna: 358-ft. above ground. Lat. 36° 16' 07", long. 82° 20' 21". Transmitter: Buffalo Mountain. Equipment: Emcee transmitter; Bogner antenna. Ownership: Macro Distribution Systems Inc.

Memphis—WJM63 (Ch. 1). Nucentrix Spectrum Resources Inc., Suite 200, 200 Chisholm Place, Plano, TX 75075. Phone: 972-423-9494. Fax: 972-423-0819. Authorized power: 100-w. Lat. 35° 06' 45", long. 89° 53' 32". Transmitter: 5100 Poplar, Memphis. Equipment: Emcee transmitter; Andrew antenna. Ownership: Nucentrix Broadband Networks Inc.

Somerville—WFY989 (Ch. 1). Austin Campbell Lewis & John Franklin Warmath, Box 740, 2606 East End Dr., Humboldt, TN 38343. Authorized power: 10-w. Antenna: 252-ft. above ground. Lat. 35° 13' 41", long. 89° 17' 36". Transmitter: 3.5-mi. SE of Somerville. Equipment: Comwave transmitter; Andrew antenna. Ownership: Austin C. Lewis; John F. Warmath.

Union City—WGW505 (Ch. 1). Union City Microvision, Box 117, Union City, TN 38261. Phone: 901-885-4922. Authorized power: 100-w. Lat. 36° 23' 47", long. 89° 10' 47". Transmitter: Troy-Hickman Rd., 5-mi. SW of Union City. Equipment: Emcee transmitter; Andrew antenna. Ownership: Union City Microvision.

Texas

Abilene—WPY36 (Ch. 1). Hallicrafters of Florida. Authorized power: 10-w. Antenna: 376-ft. above ground. Lat. 32° 30' 37", long. 99° 44' 28". Transmitter: S of I-20. Equipment: Varian transmitter; Andrew antenna. Ownership: Hallicrafters of Florida.

Abilene—WLW920 (Ch. 2A). New Hampshire Wireless Inc., Box 168, Derry, NH 03038. Phone: 603-893-1995. Authorized power: 10-w. Antenna: 408-ft. above ground. Lat. 32° 17' 06", long. 99° 38' 38". Transmitter: 13-mi. SSE of Abilene. Equipment: Varian transmitter; Andrew antenna. Ownership: New Hampshire Wireless.

Amarillo—WCZ53 (Ch. 1). Heartland Wireless Commercial Channels Inc., Suite 200, 200 Chisholm Place, Plano, TX 75075. Phone: 972-423-9494. Fax: 972-423-0819. Authorized power: 10-w. Antenna: 550-ft. above ground. Lat. 35° 20' 33", long. 101° 49' 20". Transmitter: 1.32-mi. NE of State Hwy. 286 & Givens Ave. Equipment: Emcee transmitter; Andrew antenna. Ownership: Heartland Wireless Commercial Channels Inc.

Austin—WJM66 (Ch. 1). CS Wireless Systems Inc., 1101 Summit Ave., Plano, TX 75074.

Phone: 972-730-3300. Authorized power: 100-w. Antenna: 289-ft. above ground. Lat. 30° 19' 20", long. 97° 48' 03". Transmitter: 2724 G Trial of Madrones, Travis. Equipment: Comwave transmitter; Andrew antenna. Ownership: CS Wireless Systems Inc.

Austin—WLW975 (Ch. 2A). Nucentrix Spectrum Resources Inc. Suite 200, 200 Chisholm Place, Plano, TX 75075. Phone: 972-423-9494. Fax: 972-423-0819. Authorized power: 10-w. Antenna: 360-ft. above ground. Lat. 30° 18' 18", long. 97° 50' 18". Transmitter: Bee Cave & St. Stephens School Rds. Equipment: ITS transmitter; Andrew antenna. Ownership: Nucentrix Broadband Networks Inc.

Bay City—WHT625 (Ch. 1). Communication Security Enterprises. Authorized power: 10-w. Antenna: 350-ft. above ground. Lat. 29° 02' 47", long. 96° 16' 24". Transmitter: County Rd. 441 S. Equipment: Comwave transmitter; Bogner antenna. Ownership: Communication Security Enterprises.

Beaumont—WJL88 (Ch. 1). AmeriComm Inc., 568 Spyglass Lane, Thousand Oaks, CA 91360. Phone: 818-597-1837. Fax: 818-597-3221. Authorized power: 10-w. Lat. 30° 04' 45", long. 94° 07' 58". Transmitter: 27 Sawyer St. Equipment: Emcee transmitter; Andrew antenna. Ownership: AmeriComm Inc.

Beeville—WLK317 (Ch. 1). Oakland Communications. Authorized power: 10-w. Lat. 28° 28' 26", long. 97° 48' 39". Transmitter: 2824 Farm Rd., 5.1-mi. N of Beeville. Equipment: Emcee transmitter; Bogner antenna. Ownership: Patrick W. Haug.

Brady—WMI987 (Ch. 1). Central Texas Telephone Co-op Inc., Box 627, Goldthwaite, TX 76844. Phone: 915-648-2237. Authorized power: 10-w. Antenna: 520-ft. above ground. Lat. 31° 15' 28", long. 99° 23' 35". Transmitter: 6-mi. off Hwy. 283. Equipment: Comwave transmitter; Andrew antenna. Ownership: Central Texas Telephone Co-op Inc.

Brenham—WLW857 (Ch. 1). Brenham Broadcast Communications Inc., 128 Redbird Trail, Georgetown, TX 78628. Phone: 512-863-3146. Authorized power: 20-w. Antenna: 439-ft. above ground. Lat. 30° 10' 28", long. 96° 27' 43". Transmitter: Hwy. 290, 3.9-mi. W of Brenham. Equipment: ITS transmitter; Andrew antenna. Ownership: Brenham Broadcast Communications Inc.

Bryan—WMI960 (Ch. 1). Becker Broadcasting, Box 12641, El Paso, TX 79912. Phone: 915-585-1178. Fax: 915-585-1179. Authorized power: 10-w. Antenna: 499-ft. above ground. Lat. 30° 39' 37", long. 96° 25' 01". Transmitter: 0.6-mi. E of Hwy. 21 & 28th St. Equipment: Comwave transmitter; Andrew antenna. Ownership: Becker Broadcasting.

Leased to Wireless One Inc., 5551 Corporate Blvd., Baton Rouge, LA 70808. Phone: 504-916-7770.

Corpus Christi—WDU282 (Ch. 1). CS Wireless Systems Inc., 1101 Summit Ave., Plano, TX 75074. Phone: 972-730-3300. Authorized power: 100-w. Antenna: 264-ft. above ground. Lat. 27° 47' 45", long. 97° 23' 46". Transmitter: 600 Leopard Ave. Equipment: Comwave transmitter; Andrew antenna. Ownership: CS Wireless Systems Inc.

Corsicana—WMH217 (Ch. 1). Heartland Wireless Commercial Channels Inc., Suite 200, 200 Chisholm Place, Plano, TX 75075. Phone: 972-423-9494. Fax: 972-423-0819. Authorized power: 10-w. Antenna: 705-ft. above ground. Lat. 32° 01' 40", long. 96° 11' 03". Transmitter: approx. 1-mi. SW of Round Prairie. Equipment: ITS transmitter; Andrew antenna. Ownership: Heartland Wireless Commercial Channels Inc.

Dallas—WQQ65 (Ch. 1). CS Wireless Systems Inc., 1101 Summit Ave., Plano, TX 75074. Phone: 972-730-3300. Authorized power: 50-w. Antenna: 299-ft. above ground. Lat. 32° 51' 57", long. 96° 48' 01". Transmitter: Preston Tower Bldg., 6211 W. Northwest Hwy. Equipment: Comwave transmitter; Andrew antenna. Ownership: CS Wireless Systems Inc.

Dallas—WHT564 (Ch. 2). CS Wireless Systems Inc., 1101 Summit Ave., Plano, TX 75074. Phone: 972-730-3300. Authorized power: 50-w. Antenna: 299-ft. above ground. Lat. 32° 51' 57", long. 96° 48' 01". Transmitter: 6211 W. Northwest Hwy. Equipment: Emcee transmitter; Andrew antenna. Ownership: CS Wireless Systems Inc.

Decatur—WMX334 (Ch. 1). Richard D. Morgese Trust, Box 14187, San Francisco, CA 94114. Phone: 415-285-1739. Authorized power: 10-w. Antenna: 420-ft. above ground. Lat. 33° 40' 17", long. 97° 37' 16". Transmitter: 6.5-mi. W of St. Jo. Equipment: Comwave transmitter; Bogner antenna. Ownership: Richard D. Morgese.

Dilley—WMH433 (Ch. 1). Ultra Vision of Texas Inc., Box 1538, 100 E. Kleberg, Kingsville, TX 78363. Phone: 512-851-8588. Authorized power: 10-w. Antenna: 459-ft. above ground. Lat. 28° 39' 40", long. 99° 13' 45". Transmitter: 3.3-mi. WSW of Dilley. Equipment: Comwave transmitter; Bogner antenna. Ownership: Ultra Vision of Texas.

Edgewood—WMI852 (Ch. 1). Richard D. Morgese Trust, Box 14187, San Francisco, CA 94114. Phone: 415-285-1739. Authorized power: 10-w. Antenna: 153-ft. above ground. Lat. 32° 42' 52", long. 95° 47' 49". Transmitter: 2-mi. N of Edgewood. Equipment: Comwave transmitter; Andrew antenna. Ownership: Richard D. Morgese.

El Paso—WSL59 (Ch. 1). CS Wireless Systems Inc., 1101 Summit Ave., Plano, TX 75074. Phone: 972-730-3300. Authorized power: 10-w. Antenna: 5100-ft. above ground. Lat. 31° 47' 34", long. 106° 28' 47". Transmitter: Mount Franklin. Equipment: Comwave transmitter; Andrew antenna. Ownership: CS Wireless Systems Inc.

Falfurrias—WLW936 (Ch. 1). Ultra Vision of Texas Inc., Box 1538, 100 E. Kleberg, Kingsville, TX 78383. Phone: 512-851-8588. Authorized power: 100-w. Antenna: 499-ft. above ground. Lat. 27° 15' 18", long. 98° 05' 46". Transmitter: 5-mi. NE of Falfurrias. Equipment: Comwave transmitter; Bogner antenna. Ownership: Ultra Vision of Texas.

Farwell—WMI980 (Ch. 1). AMV Comm., 2113 Coolidge Dr., Santa Clara, CA 95051. Phone: 408-996-5716. Authorized power: 10-w. Antenna: 465-ft. above ground. Lat. 34° 32' 26", long. 102° 47' 56". Transmitter: 5.5-mi. ENE of Bovine. Equipment: Comwave transmitter; Andrew antenna. Ownership: AMV Comm.

Fort Worth—WJM75 (Ch. 1). CS Wireless Systems Inc., 1101 Summit Ave., Plano, TX 75074. Phone: 972-730-3300. Authorized power: 50-w. Antenna: 541-ft. above ground. Lat. 35° 45' 01", long. 97° 20' 03". Transmitter: Suite 2355, 801 Cherry St. Equipment: Comwave transmitter; Andrew antenna. Ownership: CS Wireless Systems Inc.

Leased to American Wireless, 501 106th St., Arlington, TX 76011. Phone: 817-633-2131.

Fort Worth—WFY900 (Ch. 2). CS Wireless Systems Inc., 1101 Summit Ave., Plano, TX 75074. Phone: 972-509-2634. Authorized power: 50-w. Antenna: 541-ft. above ground. Lat. 35° 45' 01", long. 97° 20' 03". Transmitter: Suite 2355, 801 Cherry St. Equipment: Comwave transmitter; Andrew antenna. Ownership: CS Wireless Systems Inc.

Galveston—WDU206 (Ch. 1). Alda Gold Inc., 5301 E. Broadway Blvd., Tucson, AZ 85711-3710. Phone: 520-519-4400. Fax: 520-747-6830. Authorized power: 7.5-w. Antenna: 214-ft. above ground. Lat. 29° 16' 21", long. 94° 49' 03". Transmitter: 5220 Seawall Blvd. Equipment: Comwave transmitter; Andrew antenna. Ownership: Matthew Oristano.

George West—WMI392 (Ch. 1). Ultra Vision of Texas Inc., Box 1538, 100 E. Kleberg, Kingsville, TX 78363. Phone: 512-851-8588. Authorized power: 100-w. Antenna: 620-ft. above ground. Lat. 28° 17' 37", long. 98° 13' 17". Transmitter: 7-mi. WSW of George West. Equipment: Comwave transmitter; Andrew antenna. Ownership: Ultra Vision of Texas.

Goldthwaite—WMI995 (Ch. 1). Central Texas Telephone Co-op Inc., Box 627, Goldthwaithe, TX 76844. Phone: 915-648-2237. Authorized power: 10-w. Antenna: 399-ft. above ground. Lat. 31° 27' 13", long. 98° 33' 21". Transmitter: Hwy. 84. Equipment: Comwave transmitter; Andrew antenna. Requests change to lat. 31° 27' 21", long. 98° 33' 19"; transmitter to U.S. Rte. 84 & State Rte. 2005 intersection. Ownership: Central Texas Telephone Co-op Inc.

Goldthwaite—WMI991 (Ch. 2A). Central Texas Telephone Co-op Inc., Box 627, Goldthwaite, TX 76844. Phone: 915-648-2237. Authorized power: 10-w. Antenna: 399-ft. above ground. Lat. 31° 27' 13", long. 98° 33' 21". Transmitter: Hwy. 84, 1-mi. E of Goldthwaite. Equipment: Comwave transmitter; Andrew antenna. Ownership: Central Texas Telephone Co-op Inc.

Greenville—WMI915 (Ch. 1). Richard Daniel Morgese Revocable Inter Vivos Trust, Suites 302-304, 630 Alvarado St., San Francisco, CA 94114. Phone: 415-285-1739. Authorized power: 10-w. Antenna: 420-ft. above ground. Lat. 33° 00' 06", long. 96° 10' 48". Transmitter: 6-mi. S of Greenville. Equipment: Comwave transmitter; Andrew antenna. Ownership: Richard D. Morgese.

Houston—WOF76 (Ch. 1). Alda Gold Inc., 5301 E. Broadway Blvd., Tucson, AZ 85711. Phone: 520-519-4400. Fax: 520-747-6830. Authorized power: 20-w. Antenna: 995-ft. above ground. Lat. 29° 45' 30", long. 95° 22' 03". Transmitter: 1000 Louisiana St. Equipment: Comwave transmitter; Andrew antenna. Requests change to 300-ft. above ground. Ownership: Taft Broadcasting Co.

Houston—WHT570 (Ch. 2). Private Networks Inc., Box 012707, 28 Old Fulton St., Brooklyn, NY 11201. Phone: 212-777-4740. Authorized power: 100-w. Antenna: 994-ft. above ground. Lat. 29° 45' 30", long. 95° 22' 03". Transmitter: Olympic Blvd. Equipment: Comwave transmitter; Andrew antenna. Ownership: Private Networks Inc.

Ingram—WMX935 (Ch. 1). RVS Holdings Corp., Suite 200, 200 Chisholm Place, Plano, TX 75075. Phone: 972-423-9494. Fax: 972-423-0819. Authorized power: 20-w. Antenna: 695-ft. above ground. Lat. 30° 01' 10", long. 99° 20' 09". Transmitter: Moore Ranch. Equipment: Comwave transmitter; Andrew antenna. Ownership: Nucentrix Broadband Networks Inc.

Jasper—WMI994 (Ch. 1). CMG Enterprises III, 1715 Hollis Rd., Westlake, IA 70669. Phone: 318-477-1218. Authorized power: 10-w. Antenna: 356-ft. above ground. Lat. 30° 55' 11", long. 93° 58' 13". Transmitter: Hwy. 190 E. Equipment: Comwave transmitter; Andrew antenna. Ownership: CMG Enterprises III.

Karnes City—WMI396 (Ch. 1). Ultra Vision of Texas Inc., Box 1538, 100 E. Kleberg, Kingsville, TX 78363. Phone: 512-851-8588. Authorized power: 100-w. Antenna: 620-ft. above ground. Lat. 28° 53' 50", long. 97° 52' 26". Transmitter: 7-mi. WSW of Karnes City. Equipment: Comwave transmitter; Andrew antenna. Ownership: Ultra Vision of Texas.

Killeen—WDU302 (Ch. 1). CS Wireless Systems Inc., 1101 Summit Ave., Plano, TX 75074. Phone: 972-730-3300. Authorized power: 10-w. Antenna: 1304-ft. above ground. Lat. 31° 05' 23", long. 97° 35' 55". Transmitter: Farm Rd. 439, 0.7-mi. NNE of Nolandville. Equipment: Comwave transmitter; Andrew antenna. Ownership: CS Wireless Systems Inc.

Longview—WMI933 (Ch. 1). Southwest Cable Inc. Authorized power: 10-w. Antenna: 820-ft. above ground. Lat. 32° 36' 04", long. 94° 52' 15". Transmitter: 7-mi. NW of Longview. Equipment: ITS transmitter; Andrew antenna. Ownership: Southwest Cable Inc.

Longview—WMI929 (Ch. 2A). Southwest Cable Inc. Authorized power: 10-w. Antenna: 820-ft. above ground. Lat. 32° 36' 04", long. 94° 52' 15". Transmitter: 7-mi. NW of Longview. Equipment: ITS transmitter; Andrew antenna. Ownership: Southwest Cable Inc.

Loraine—WMX952 (Ch. 1). RVS Holdings Corp., Suite 200, 200 Chisholm Place, Plano, TX 75075. Phone: 972-423-9494. Fax: 972-423-0819. Authorized power: 10-w. Antenna: 300-ft. above ground. Lat. 32° 28' 26", long. 100° 44' 35". Transmitter: 3.8-mi. N of I-80. Equipment: Comwave transmitter; Andrew antenna. Ownership: Nucentrix Broadband Networks Inc.

Lubbock—WDU247 (Ch. 1). Nucentrix Spectrum Resources Inc., Suite 200, 200 Chisholm Place, Plano, TX 75075. Phone: 972-423--9494. Fax: 972-423-0819. Authorized power: 10-w. Lat. 33° 28' 10", long. 101° 47' 25". Transmitter: 3.5-mi. E of Rte. 87. Requests change to 304-ft. above ground, lat. 33° 35' 07", long. 101° 50' 49", transmitter to 1220 Broadway, Metro Tower. Ownership: Nucentrix Broadband Networks Inc.

McAllen—WDU443 (Ch. 1). Tri-County Communications Inc., Box 1065, Weslaco, TX 78596. Authorized power: 10-w. Antenna: 445-ft. above ground. Lat. 26° 15' 23", long. 98° 13' 49". Transmitter: 3.5-mi. N of 23rd St. Equipment: Varian transmitter; Andrew antenna. Ownership: Tri-County Communications Inc. (TX).

Mineral Wells—WMI906 (Ch. 1). Richard Daniel Morgese Revocable Inter Vivos Trust, Suites 302-304, 630 Alvarado St., San Francisco, CA 94114. Phone: 415-285-1739. Authorized power: 10-w. Antenna: 200-ft. above ground. Lat. 32° 48' 42", long. 98° 06' 11".

Transmitter: N.E. 11th Ave. Equipment: Comwave transmitter; Andrew antenna. Ownership: Richard D. Morgese.

Mount Pleasant—WMI920 (Ch. 1). Ron Pingel, 8018 Simpson Dr., Amarillo, TX 79121. Phone: 806-371-9666. Authorized power: 10-w. Antenna: 919-ft. above ground. Lat. 33° 04' 36", long. 95° 14' 26". Transmitter: 1.5-mi. SE of Purley. Equipment: ITS transmitter; Andrew antenna. Ownership: Ron Pingel.

Pampa—WLW861 (Ch. 1). Nucentrix Spectrum Resources Inc., Suite 200, 200 Chisholm Place, Plano, TX 75075. Phone: 972-423-9494. Fax: 972-423-0819. Authorized power: 10-w. Antenna: 340-ft. above ground. Lat. 35° 32' 43", long. 100° 55' 15". Transmitter: Hwy. 60 on Loop 171. Equipment: ITS transmitter; Andrew antenna. Ownership: Nucentrix Broadband Networks Inc.
Leased to Town & Country Wireless, 4104 W. 33rd St., Amarillo, TX 79109. Phone: 806-354-0798.

Plainview—WMH201 (Ch. 1). Masscom, 1023 51st St., Moline, IL 61265. Phone: 309-764-6886. Authorized power: 10-w. Antenna: 300-ft. above ground. Lat. 34° 15' 45", long. 101° 40' 05". Transmitter: 4.1-mi. NE of Plainview. Equipment: Comwave transmitter; Andrew antenna. Ownership: Masscom.

Plainview—WMH488 (Ch. 2A). Masscom, 1023 51st St., Moline, IL 61265. Phone: 309-764-6886. Authorized power: 10-w. Antenna: 300-ft. above ground. Lat. 34° 15' 45", long. 101° 40' 05". Transmitter: 4.1-mi NE of Plainview. Equipment: Varian transmitter; Andrew antenna. Ownership: Masscom.

San Angelo—WML478 (Ch. 1). Estate of Charles R. Jones, 5588 Westside Dr., El Paso, TX 79932. Phone: 915-584-1848. Authorized power: 10-w. Antenna: 520-ft. above ground. Lat. 31° 25' 16", long. 100° 32' 36". Transmitter: Hwy. 67 W. Equipment: Emcee transmitter; Andrew antenna. Ownership: Estate of Charles R. Jones.

San Angelo—WMH397 (Ch. 2A). LC Communications, 7 Roundtree Dr., Melville, NY 11747. Phone: 516-643-8349. Fax: 516-643-8349. Authorized power: 10-w. Antenna: 250-ft. above ground. Lat. 31° 42' 11", long. 100° 19' 20". Transmitter: 3.5-mi. N of Orient. Equipment: Varian transmitter; Andrew antenna. Ownership: LC Communications.

San Antonio—WJM80 (Ch. 1). CS Wireless Systems Inc., 1101 Summit Ave., Plano, TX 75074. Phone: 972-730-3300. Authorized power: 100-w. Antenna: 1192-ft. above ground. Lat. 29° 25' 22", long. 98° 29' 28". Transmitter: Tower Life Bldg., 310 Villita St. Equipment: Comwave transmitter; Andrew antenna. Requests change to 185-ft. above ground, lat. 29° 33' 13", long. 98° 21' 15"; transmitter to 12544 Judson Rd. Ownership: CS Wireless Systems Inc.

San Antonio—WFY852 (Ch. 2). CS Wireless Systems Inc., 1101 Summit Ave., Plano, TX 75074. Phone: 972-730-3300. Authorized power: 100-w. Antenna: 185-ft. above ground. Lat. 29° 33' 13", long. 98° 21' 15". Transmitter: 12544 Judson Rd. Equipment: Varian transmitter; Andrew antenna. Ownership: CS Wireless Systems Inc.

San Saba—WMI944 (Ch. 1). Central Texas Telephone Co-op Inc., Box 627, Goldthwaite, TX 76844. Phone: 915-648-2237. Authorized power: 10-w. Antenna: 308-ft. above ground. Lat. 31° 09' 52", long. 98° 37' 39". Transmitter: Fm. 580, off Hwy. 190. Equipment: Comwave transmitter; Andrew antenna. Ownership: Central Texas Telephone Co-op Inc.

Sumner—WMX939 (Ch. 1). RVS Holdings Corp., Suite 200, 200 Chisholm Place, Plano, TX 75075. Phone: 972-423-9494. Fax: 972-423-0819. Authorized power: 20-w. Antenna: 605-ft. above ground. Lat. 33° 46' 33", long. 95° 37' 22". Transmitter: 5-mi. W of U.s. Hwy. 271. Equipment: Comwave transmitter; Andrew antenna. Ownership: Nucentrix Broadband Networks Inc.

Tyler—WMI973 (Ch. 1). BGR Wireless, 3804 Southview Dr., San Diego, CA 92117. Phone: 619-270-7615. Authorized power: 10-w. Antenna: 619-ft. above ground. Lat. 32° 19' 21", long. 95° 14' 08". Transmitter: 960 County Rd. 219. Equipment: Comwave transmitter; Andrew antenna. Ownership: BGR Wireless.
Leased to Mitchell Communications Corp., 6 Concourse Pkwy., Suite 2120, Atlanta, GA 30328. Phone: 404-395-2700.

Tyler—WMI930 (Ch. 2A). BPJ-TV, 2603 E. Doublegate Dr., Albany, GA 31707. Phone: 912-436-7019. Authorized power: 10-w. Antenna: 619-ft. above ground. Lat. 32° 19' 21", long. 95° 14' 08". Transmitter: 960 County Rd. 219. Equipment: Varian transmitter; Andrew antenna. Ownership: BPJ-TV.

Uvalde—WLW868 (Ch. 1). Sea Shore Communications, 1905 Spring Lake Court, Birmingham, AL 35215. Phone: 205-854-6472. Authorized power: 10-w. Antenna: 283-ft. above ground. Lat. 29° 11' 46", long. 99° 46' 48". Transmitter: 828 S. Getty St. Equipment: Comwave transmitter; Andrew antenna. Ownership: Sea Shore Communications.

Victoria—WGW374 (Ch. 1). CS Wireless Systems Inc., 1101 Summit Ave., Plano, TX 75074. Phone: 972-730-3300. Authorized power: 10-w. Antenna: 574-ft. above ground. Lat. 28° 46' 42", long. 96° 58' 08". Transmitter: 3112 Pleasant Green Rd. Equipment: Emcee transmitter; Andrew antenna. Ownership: CS Wireless Systems Inc.

Wellington—WMI976 (Ch. 1). Cable Media Systems Inc., 405 N. Avenue E, Olney, TX 76374-1421. Phone: 817-564-5688. Authorized power: 10-w. Antenna: 300-ft. above ground. Lat. 35° 01' 24", long. 100° 13' 16". Transmitter: 11.6-mi. N of Wellington. Equipment: ITS transmitter; Andrew antenna. Ownership: Cable Media Systems Inc.

Wellington—WMI972 (Ch. 2A). Cable Media Systems Inc., 405 N. Avenue E, Olney, TX 76374-1421. Phone: 817-564-5688. Authorized power: 10-w. Antenna: 300-ft. above ground. Lat. 35° 01' 24", long. 100° 13' 16". Transmitter: 11.6-mi. N of Wellington. Equipment: ITS transmitter; Andrew antenna. Ownership: Cable Media Systems Inc.

Utah

Cedar City—WMI364 (Ch. 1). Grand Alliance Cedar City (E) Partnership, Suite 660, 1920 N St. NW, Washington, DC 20036. Phone: 202-887-0600. Authorized power: 200-w. Antenna: 84-ft. above ground. Lat. 37° 40' 12", long. 113° 04' 59". Transmitter: 589 South 1750 West. Equipment: Comwave transmitter; Andrew antenna. Ownership: Macro Distribution Systems Inc.

Cedar City—WMI368 (Ch. 2A). Grand Alliance Cedar City (E) Partnership, Suite 660, 1920 N St. NW, Washington, DC 20036. Phone: 202-887-0600. Authorized power: 200-w. Antenna: 84-ft. above ground. Lat. 37° 40' 12", long. 113° 04' 59". Transmitter: 589 South 1750 West. Equipment: Comwave transmitter; Andrew antenna. Ownership: Macro Distribution Systems Inc.

Logan—WLW932 (Ch. 2A). Token Partnership, 1201 7th St., East Moline, IL 61244. Authorized power: 10-w. Antenna: 358-ft. above ground. Lat. 41° 40' 30", long. 111° 56' 06". Transmitter: 2.4-mi. N of Wellsville. Equipment: Varian transmitter; Andrew antenna. Ownership: Token Partnership.

Ogden—WFY786 (Ch. 1). Ogden MDS Co., Box 627, Claremont, CA 91711. Phone: 909-621-1004. Fax: 909-624-2257. Authorized power: 10-w. Lat. 41° 09' 49", long. 112° 01' 28". Transmitter: 5500 South 1900 West, Roy. Equipment: Andrew antenna. Ownership: Hydra Communications.

Park City—WGW291 (Ch. 1). Transworld Wireless Television Inc., Suite 320, 102 West 500 South, Salt Lake City, UT 84101. Authorized power: 10-w. Antenna: 41-ft. above ground. Lat. 40° 41' 58", long. 111° 31' 21". Transmitter: Quarry Mountain, 2-mi. N of Park City. Equipment: Comwave transmitter; Andrew antenna. Ownership: Channel View Inc.

Salt Lake City—KEW74 (Ch. 1). Alda Wireless Holdings Inc., 5301 E. Broadway Blvd., Tucson, AZ 85711. Phone: 520-519-4400. Fax: 520-747-6830. Web site: http://www.pchoicetv.com. Authorized power: 100-w. Antenna: 423-ft. above ground. Lat. 40° 39' 28", long. 111° 53' 27". Transmitter: 5200 S. Main St., Murray. Equipment: Emcee transmitter; Andrew antenna. Requests change to 77-ft. above ground, lat. 40° 39' 35", long. 112° 12' 05"; transmitter to Farnsworth Peak. Ownership: Matthew Oristano.
Leased to People's Choice TV Corp., 5301 E. Broadway Blvd., Tucson, AZ 85711. Phone: 520-519-4400.

St. George—WMI946 (Ch. 1). American Wireless Inc., Box 2500, 845 E. Skyline Dr., St. George, UT 84771. Phone: 435-674-0320. Fax: 435-674-7679. Authorized power: 50-w. Antenna: 45-ft. above ground. Lat. 37° 03' 49", long. 113° 34' 20". Transmitter: 2.4-mi. S of St. George. Equipment: ITS transmitter; Andrew antenna. Ownership: American Wireless Inc.

Vermont

Rutland—WMH868 (Ch. 1). Sanguinetti Investment Corp., 168 N. Main St., Rutland, VT 05701. Phone: 802-773-2163. Authorized power: 50-w. Antenna: 297-ft. above ground. Lat. 43° 39' 32", long. 73° 06' 25". Transmitter: Granpa's Knob. Equipment: ITS transmitter; Andrew antenna. Ownership: Sanguinetti Investment Corp.

Rutland—WMI343 (Ch. 2A). Sanguinetti Investment Corp., 168 N. Main St., Rutland, VT 05701. Phone: 802-773-2163. Authorized power: 50-w. Antenna: 297-ft. above ground. Lat. 43° 39' 32", long. 73° 06' 25". Transmitter: Granpa's Knob. Equipment: ITS transmitter; Andrew antenna. Ownership: Sanguinetti Investment Corp.

Windsor—WMI410 (Ch. 1). New England Wireless Inc., Box 470, Rte. 5 S, Ascutney, VT 05030. Phone: 802-674-2206. Fax: 802-674-2751. Authorized power: 10-w. Antenna: 414-ft. above ground. Lat. 43° 26' 15", long. 72° 27' 09". Transmitter: 4-mi. SW of Windsor. Equipment: ITS transmitter; Andrew antenna. Ownership: New England Wireless Inc.

Windsor—WMI418 (Ch. 2A). New England Wireless Inc., Box 470, Rte. 5 S, Ascutney, VT 05030. Phone: 802-674-2206. Fax: 802-674-2751. Authorized power: 10-w. Antenna: 414-ft. above ground. Lat. 43° 26' 15", long. 72° 27' 09". Transmitter: 4-mi. SW of Windsor. Equipment: ITS transmitter; Andrew antenna. Ownership: New England Wireless Inc.

Virginia

Basye—WMI910 (Ch. 1). R. Stanley Allen, 4408 E. Conway Dr. NW, Atlanta, GA 30327-3531. Authorized power: 10-w. Antenna: 192-ft. above ground. Lat. 38° 51' 32", long. 78° 48' 20". Transmitter: 4.1-mi. NNE of Bayshore. Equipment: ITS transmitter; Andrew antenna. Ownership: R. Stanley Allen.

Bridgewater—WMI916 (Ch. 1). CFW Licenses Inc., Suite 300, 401 Spring Lane, Waynesboro, VA 22980. Phone: 540-946-1890. Authorized power: 10-w. Antenna: 107-ft. above ground. Lat. 38° 23' 27", long. 78° 59' 40". Transmitter: 1.5-mi. NW of Bridgewater. Equipment: Emcee transmitter; Andrew antenna. Requests change to 122-ft. above ground, lat. 38° 23' 36", long. 78° 46' 12". Ownership: CFW Communications.

Charlottesville—WPX69 (Ch. 1). CFW Cable, Suite 300, 401 Spring Lane, Waynesboro, VA 22980. Phone: 540-946-1890. Fax: 804-977-1665. E-mail: cfwcable@cfw.com. Authorized power: 10-w. Antenna: 305-ft. above ground. Lat. 37° 59' 00", long. 78° 28' 54". Transmitter: Carter Mountain. Equipment: Varian transmitter; Andrew antenna. Ownership: CFW Communications.

Culpeper—WMI908 (Ch. 1). American Telecasting Inc., Suite 300, 5575 Tech Center Dr., Colorado Springs, CO 80919. Phone: 719-260-5533. Fax: 719-260-5010. Authorized power: 10-w. Antenna: 157-ft. above ground. Lat. 38° 36' 15", long. 78° 05' 41". Transmitter: 9-mi. NW of Culpeper. Equipment: Emcee transmitter; Andrew antenna. Ownership: American Telecasting Inc.

Wytheville—WMI922 (Ch. 1). American Telecasting Inc., Suite 300, 5575 Tech Center Dr., Colorado Springs, CO 80919. Phone: 719-260-5533. Fax: 719-260-5010. Authorized power: 10-w. Antenna: 120-ft. above ground. Lat. 36° 54' 30", long. 81° 04' 15". Transmitter: 2.7-mi. S of Wytheville. Equipment: Emcee transmitter; Andrew antenna. Ownership: American Telecasting Inc.

Washington

Bellingham—WDU571 (Ch. 1). Telecomm Systems Inc., Box 7222, Menlo Park, CA 94026. Authorized power: 100-w. Antenna: 403-ft. above ground. Lat. 48° 40' 48", long. 122° 50' 24". Transmitter: 0.05-mi. NW of Lookout Tower. Equipment: Emcee transmitter; Bogner antenna. Ownership: Telecommunications Systems Inc.

Ephrata—WMH669 (Ch. 1). Paul M. Benson, 5178 Griffin Lane, Vacaville, CA 95688. Phone: 209-384-7448. Authorized power: 10-w. Antenna: 214-ft. above ground. Lat. 47° 06' 57", long. 119° 15' 31". Transmitter: Marsh Island at Moses Lake. Equipment: Comwave transmitter; Bogner antenna. Ownership: Paul M. Benson.

Ephrata—WMH665 (Ch. 2A). Paul M. Benson, 5178 Griffin Lane, Vacaville, CA 95688. Phone: 209-384-7448. Authorized power: 10-w. Antenna: 214-ft. above ground. Lat. 47° 06' 57", long. 119° 15' 31". Transmitter: Marsh Island at Moses Lake. Equipment: Comwave transmitter; Bogner antenna. Ownership: Paul M. Benson.

Seattle—WMI902 (Ch. 1). American Telecasting of Seattle Inc., Suite 300, 5575 Tech Center Dr., Colorado Springs, CO 80919. Phone: 719-260-5533. Fax: 719-260-5010. E-mail: jimwies@aol.com. Authorized power: 100-w. Antenna: 450-ft. above ground. Lat. 47° 36' 57", long. 122° 18' 26". Transmitter: 145 Dexter Ave. N. Equipment: ITS transmitter; Andrew antenna. Ownership: American Telecasting Inc.

Leased to American Telecasting of Seattle Inc.

Yakima—WKR57 (Ch. 1). WBSY Licensing Corp., Suite 325, 9250 E. Costilla Ave., Englewood, CO 80112. Authorized power: 0.05-w. Antenna: 30-ft. above ground. Lat. 46° 38' 09", long. 120° 28' 42". Transmitter: 3.2-mi. ESE of Selah. Equipment: NSI antenna. Ownership: WBS America LLC.

West Virginia

Huntington—WMH656 (Ch. 1). Virginia Communications Inc., 6330 E. Mockingbird Lane, Scottsdale, AZ 85253. Phone: 602-948-3776. Authorized power: 20-w. Antenna: 1342-ft. above ground. Lat. 38° 25' 11", long. 82° 24' 06". Transmitter: Rotary Park. Equipment: ITS transmitter; Andrew antenna. Ownership: Virginia Communications Inc.

Martinsburg—WHT629 (Ch. 1). Shannondale Wireless, 3623 Parklane Rd., Fairfax, VA 22030. Phone: 703-691-1119. Fax: 703-691-8938. E-mail: mkelley@gmu.edu. Authorized power: 50-w. Antenna: 195-ft. above ground. Lat. 39° 25' 16", long. 78° 05' 19". Transmitter: North Mountain. Equipment: Comwave transmitter; Bogner antenna. Ownership: Shannondale Wireless.

Leased to CFW Cable, 401 Spring Lane, Suite 300, Waynesboro, VA 22940. Phone: 540-946-1890.

Martinsburg—WLK242 (Ch. 2). Shannondale Wireless, 3623 Parklane Rd., Fairfax, VA 22030. Phone: 703-691-1119. Fax: 703-691-8938. E-mail: mkelley@gmu.edu. Authorized power: 50-w. Antenna: 195-ft. above ground. Lat. 39° 25' 16", long. 78° 05' 19". Transmitter: North Mountain. Equipment: Comwave transmitter; Bogner antenna. Ownership: Shannondale Wireless.

Leased to CFW Cable, 401 Spring Lane, Suite 300, Waynesboro, VA 22980. Phone: 540-946-1890.

Parkersburg—WMH661 (Ch. 1). Parkersburg Wireless LLC, 1025 Thomas Jefferson St. NW, Washington, DC 20007. Authorized power: 20-w. Antenna: 172-ft. above ground. Lat. 39° 18' 36", long. 81° 35' 49". Transmitter: 1.4-mi. N of Belpre. Equipment: ITS transmitter; Andrew antenna. Ownership: Parkersburg Wireless LLC.

Wheeling—WDU369 (Ch. 1). Hallicrafters of Florida. Authorized power: 10-w. Antenna: 150-ft. above ground. Lat. 40° 03' 26", long. 80° 42' 31". Transmitter: Old Hubbard Rd. exit. Equipment: Emcee transmitter; Andrew antenna. Ownership: Hallicrafters of Florida.

Wisconsin

Eau Claire—WMH884 (Ch. 1). Grand Alliance Eau Claire (F) Partnership, Suite 660, 1920 N St. NW, Washington, DC 20036. Phone: 202-887-0600. Authorized power: 10-w. Antenna: 506-ft. above ground. Lat. 44° 57' 39", long. 91° 40' 05". Transmitter: 3.9-mi. SE of Colfax. Equipment: Emcee transmitter; Andrew antenna. Ownership: Macro Distribution Systems Inc.

Eau Claire—WMH885 (Ch. 2A). Grand Alliance Eau Claire (F) Partnership, Suite 660, 1920 N St. NW, Washington, DC 20036. Phone: 202-887-0600. Lat. 44° 57' 39", long. 91° 40' 05". Transmitter: 3.9-mi. SE of Colfax. Equipment: Emcee transmitter; Andrew antenna. Ownership: Macro Distribution Systems Inc.

Green Bay—WQQ77 (Ch. 1). Joseph L. Roffers, 327 S. Superior St., De Pere, WI 54155. Phone: 414-336-0947. Fax: 414-336-9036. E-mail: jroffers@netnet.net. Authorized power: 10-w. Antenna: 1120-ft. above ground. Lat. 44° 24' 01", long. 88° 00' 37". Transmitter: Scray Hill. Equipment: Emcee transmitter; Andrew antenna. Ownership: Joseph L. Roffers.

Janesville-Beloit—WFY430 (Ch. 1). Tel-Radio Communications Properties Inc., 301 S. Westfield Rd., Madison, WI 53705. Authorized power: 100-w. Lat. 42° 41' 47", long. 88° 56' 59". Transmitter: 4634 Case Dr., Janesville. Equipment: Emcee transmitter; Andrew antenna. Ownership: Tel-Radio Communications Properties Inc.

La Crosse—WLW742 (Ch. 1). Grand Alliance La Crosse (F) Partnership, Suite 660, 1920 N St. NW, Washington, DC 20036. Phone: 202-887-0600. Authorized power: 10-w. Antenna: 219-ft. above ground. Lat. 43° 48' 44", long. 91° 11' 59". Transmitter: 93 Hixon Rd. Equipment: Emcee transmitter; Andrew antenna. Ownership: Macro Distribution Systems Inc.

La Crosse—WMH901 (Ch. 2A). Grand Alliance La Crosse (F) Partnership, Suite 660, 1920 N St. NW, Washington, DC 20036. Phone: 202-887-0600. Authorized power: 10-w. Antenna: 232-ft. above ground. Lat. 43° 48' 44", long. 91° 11' 59". Transmitter: 93 Hixon Rd. Equipment: Emcee transmitter; Andrew antenna. Ownership: Macro Distribution Systems Inc.

Madison—WPY30 (Ch. 1). Tel-Radio Communications Properties Inc., 301 S. Westfield Rd., Madison, WI 53705. Authorized power: 100-w. Lat. 43° 04' 18", long. 89° 23' 11". Transmitter: 110 S. Henry St. Equipment: Emcee transmitter; Andrew antenna. Ownership: Tel-Radio Communications Properties Inc.

Milwaukee—WKR27 (Ch. 1). Alda Wireless Holdings Inc., 5301 E. Broadway Blvd., Tucson, AZ 85711-3710. Phone: 520-519-4400. Fax: 520-747-6830. Authorized power: 100-w. Antenna: 594-ft. above ground. Lat. 43° 02' 18", long. 87° 54' 05". Transmitter: First Wisconsin Center. Equipment: Townsend transmitter; Andrew antenna. Ownership: Matthew Oristano.

Milwaukee—WHT566 (Ch. 2). Milwaukee MDS Co., 25 Rockwood Place, Englewood, NJ 07631. Authorized power: 100-w. Antenna: 593-ft. above ground. Lat. 43° 02' 18", long. 87° 54' 05". Transmitter: Wisconsin Center. Equipment: ITS transmitter; Andrew antenna. Ownership: Broadcast Data Corp.

Sturgeon Bay—WHA706 (Ch. 1). William A. Everson, Rte. 5, 6284 Carnot Rd., Sturgeon Bay, WI 54235. Lat. 44° 54' 21", long. 87° 22' 15". Transmitter: 5-mi. N of Sturgeon Bay. Ownership: William A. Everson.

Wyoming

Cheyenne—WLW901 (Ch. 2A). Super Comm, 738 Intrepid Way, Davidsonville, MD 21035. Phone: 310-261-4766. Authorized power: 10-w. Antenna: 288-ft. above ground. Lat. 41° 03' 09", long. 104° 49' 53". Transmitter: 1.9-mi. W of U.S. 85 on State Rte. 223. Equipment: Varian transmitter; Andrew antenna. Ownership: Super Comm.

Cody—WHD367 (Ch. 1). ROB-ART Inc., Box 85, Cody, WY 82414. Phone: 307-587-6449. Authorized power: 10-w. Lat. 44° 29' 48", long. 109° 09' 07". Transmitter: Cedar Mountain, 4-mi. SW of Cody. Ownership: ROB-ART Inc.

Evanston—WMI408 (Ch. 1). G/S Evanston F Settlement Group, 11600 Pinehaven Ave., Bakersfield, CA 93312. Authorized power: 10-w. Antenna: 175-ft. above ground. Lat. 41° 21' 13", long. 110° 54' 31". Transmitter: 6.4-mi. NNE of Evanston. Equipment: Comwave transmitter; Andrew antenna. Ownership: G/S Evanston F Settlement Group.

Riverton—WMI404 (Ch. 1). G/S Riverton F Settlement Group, 2120 E. Prien Lake Rd., Lake Charles, LA 70601. Phone: 318-477-1218. Authorized power: 10-w. Antenna: 132-ft. above ground. Lat. 42° 43' 10", long. 108° 08' 41". Transmitter: Beaver Rim. Equipment: Comwave transmitter; Andrew antenna. Ownership: G/S Riverton F Settlement Group.

Guam

Barigada—WLW921 (Ch. 1). Victor J. Toth, 2719 Soapstone Dr., Reston, VA 22091. Phone: 703-476-5515. Authorized power: 10-w. Antenna: 92-ft. above ground. Lat. 13° 29' 17", long. 144° 49' 30". Transmitter: Mount Barigada. Equipment: ITS transmitter; Andrew antenna. Ownership: Victor J. Toth.

Puerto Rico

Caguas—WFY859 (Ch. 1). Caguas/Humacao Cable Systems, Rafael Cordero No. 4 Santa Juana, Caguas, PR 00626. Phone: 809-746-0454. Fax: 809-746-5717. Authorized power: 10-w. Antenna: 164-ft. above ground. Lat. 18° 14' 53", long. 66° 01' 22". Transmitter: Rafael Cordero Ave. Equipment: Emcee transmitter; Andrew antenna. Ownership: Caguas-/Humacao Cable Systems.

Fajardo—WGX581 (Ch. 1). All-Star Communications, Box 487, Fajardo, PR 00648. Authorized power: 10-w. Lat. 18° 19' 45", long. 65° 40' 12". Transmitter: 1.2-mi. W of Fajardo. Equipment: Emcee transmitter; Bogner antenna. Ownership: All-Star Communications.

Mayaguez—WFY444 (Ch. 1). Caribbean MDS Co., 1725 Andres Bello, San Juan, PR 00926. Authorized power: 10-w. Antenna: 235-ft. above ground. Lat. 18° 19' 06", long. 67° 10' 42". Transmitter: 8-mi. S of Aguadilla. Equipment: Emcee transmitter; Andrew antenna. Ownership: San Juan MDS Inc.

Ponce—WFY440 (Ch. 1). Caribbean MDS Co., 1725 Andres Bello, San Juan, PR 00926. Authorized power: 10-w. Antenna: 200-ft. above ground. Lat. 18° 10' 30", long. 66° 35' 22". Transmitter: Punta Peak. Equipment: Emcee transmitter; Andrew antenna. Ownership: San Juan MDS Inc.

San Juan-Ponce-Mayaguez—WPW98 (Ch. 1). San Juan MDS Inc., 1725 Andres Bello, San Juan, PR 00926. Authorized power: 100-w. Lat. 18° 19' 05", long. 66° 03' 21". Transmitter: 0.84-mi. E of Rte. 842, Caimito Alto. Equipment: Emcee transmitter; Andrew antenna. Ownership: San Juan MDS Inc.

Multichannel Multipoint Distribution Service

(2596-2644 MHz)

MMDS is a point-to-point microwave frequency service authorized by the FCC in 1983 to transmit multiple channel specialized private TV programming or data and facsimile transmissions to customer selected locations within a metropolitan area. This section lists MMDS licenses & conditional licenses. E & F groups are four-channel clusters; H is composed of three channels, which are frequently licensed singly. For ownership of stations, see MDS & MMDS Ownership.

Alabama

Andalusia—WNTM544 (H group). NBI TV Partners, 2570 Chateau Way, Livermore, CA 94550. Phone: 510-443-1415. Authorized power: 200-w. each. Antenna: 265-ft. above ground. Lat. 31° 18' 10", long. 86° 29' 10". Transmitter: 508 Auburn Ave. Equipment: Comwave transmitter; Andrew antenna. Ownership: NBI TV Partners.

Auburn—WMH568 (E group). Wireless One PCS Inc., Suite 400, 2506 Lakeland Dr., Jackson, MS 39208. Phone: 601-933-6879. Authorized power: 12-w. each. Antenna: 204-ft. above ground. Lat. 32° 45' 30", long. 85° 28' 21". Transmitter: 1022 Chambers County Hwy. Equipment: Emcee transmitter; Andrew antenna. Ownership: Wireless One Inc..

Auburn—WMH985 (F group). Wireless One PCS Inc., Suite 400, 2506 Lakeland Dr., Jackson, MS 39208. Phone: 601-933-6879. Authorized power: 10-w. each. Antenna: 904-ft. above ground. Lat. 32° 45' 30", long. 85° 28' 21". Transmitter: 1022 Chambers County Hwy. Equipment: Emcee transmitter; Andrew antenna. Ownership: Wireless One Inc..

Birmingham—WHT710 (F group). Wireless One PCS Inc., Suite 400, 2506 Lakeland Dr., Jackson, MS 39208. Phone: 601-933-6879. Authorized power: 100-w. each. Antenna: 824-ft. above ground. Lat. 33° 29' 04", long. 86° 48' 25". Transmitter: Red Mountain. Equipment: Emcee transmitter; Andrew antenna. Ownership: Wireless One Inc.

Birmingham—WNTJ807 (H2). Libmot Communications Partnership, 2700 Chain Bridge Rd. NW, Washington, DC 20016. Phone: 202-966-2167. Fax: 202-237-7742. Authorized power: 10-w. Antenna: 190-ft. above ground. Lat. 33° 22' 01", long. 86° 57' 14". Transmitter: 1000 Raimund Muscoda Rd. Equipment: Emcee transmitter; Andrew antenna. Ownership: Libmot Communications Partnership.
Leased to Wireless One.

Birmingham—WNTH399 (H3). MMDS Inc. Authorized power: 10-w. Antenna: 709-ft. above ground. Lat. 33° 27' 37", long. 86° 51' 07". Transmitter: WABM(TV) tower. Equipment: Emcee transmitter; Andrew antenna. Ownership: MMDS Inc.
Leased to Wireless One of Birmingham Inc.

Demopolis—WMI379 (E group). Arvol M. Hyatt, Box 429, Arlington, WA 98223. Authorized power: 50-w. each. Antenna: 943-ft. above ground. Lat. 33° 22' 01", long. 87° 52' 03". Transmitter: Rte. 1, Box 122. Equipment: Comwave transmitter; Andrew antenna. Ownership: Arvol M. Hyatt.
Leased to Stuart Barron, 607 80 W, Demopolis, AL 36732.

Demopolis—WLW737 (F group). Louis F. Powell, 202 Bluffview Dr., Belleair Bluffs, FL 34640. Phone: 813-581-1996. Antenna: 946-ft. above ground. Lat. 32° 22' 01", long. 87° 52' 03". Transmitter: Rte. 1. Equipment: Comwave transmitter; Bogner antenna. Ownership: Louis F. Powell.

Dothan—WLW709 (E group). National TV Co., Drawer B, Kingsville, TX 78363. Phone: 512-595-5673. Fax: 512-595-0151. Authorized power: 50-w. each. Antenna: 900-ft. above ground. Lat. 31° 15' 07", long. 85° 17' 12". Transmitter: Hwy. 52, 5.5-mi. NE of Dothan. Equipment: ITS transmitter; Andrew antenna. Ownership: National TV Co.

Dothan—WNTH963 (H3). Wireless One PCS Inc., Suite 400, 2506 Lakeland Dr., Jackson, MS 39208. Phone: 601-933-6879. Authorized power: 50-w. Antenna: 900-ft. above ground. Lat. 31° 15' 07", long. 85° 17' 12". Transmitter: Hwy. 52, 5.5-mi. NE of Dothan. Equipment: ITS transmitter; Andrew antenna. Ownership: Wireless One Inc.

Huntsville—WLR564 (E group). Theodore D. Little, 15917 E. Lincoln Rd., Spokane, WA 99217. Phone: 509-921-9733. Fax: 509-926-1110. E-mail: tdlittle@msn.com. Authorized power: 50-w. each. Antenna: 760-ft. above ground. Lat. 34° 49' 05", long. 86° 44' 16". Transmitter: Capshaw Mountain. Equipment: ITS transmitter; Andrew antenna. Ownership: T. D. Little.
Leased to Wireless One, 11301 Industriplex Blvd., Suite 4, Baton Rouge, LA 70809. Phone: 205-536-3724.

Huntsville—WLW773 (F group). Private Networks Inc., Box 023707, Brooklyn, NY 11201. Phone: 212-777-4740. Authorized power: 50-w. each. Antenna: 688-ft. above ground. Lat. 34° 49' 05", long. 86° 44' 16". Transmitter: Capshaw Mountain. Equipment: ITS transmitter; Andrew antenna. Ownership: Private Networks Inc.

Huntsville—WNTF818 (H1). Wireless One, Suite 4, 11301 Industriplex Blvd., Baton Rouge, LA 70809. Phone: 504-293-5000. Fax: 504-293-5400. Authorized power: 50-w. Antenna: 350-ft. above ground. Lat. 34° 49' 05", long. 86° 44' 16". Transmitter: Capshaw Mountain. Equipment: ITS transmitter; Andrew antenna. Ownership: Wireless One Inc.

Huntsville—WNTG248 (H2). Wireless One, Suite 4, 11301 Industriplex Blvd., Baton Rouge, LA 70809. Phone: 504-293-5000. Fax: 504-293-5400. Authorized power: 50-w. Antenna: 688-ft. above ground. Lat. 34° 49' 05", long. 86° 44' 16". Transmitter: Capshaw Mountain. Equipment: ITS transmitter; Andrew antenna. Ownership: Wireless One Inc.

Huntsville—WNTG242 (H3). Wireless One, Suite 4, 11301 Industriplex Blvd., Baton Rouge, LA 70809. Phone: 504-293-5000. Fax: 504-293-5400. Authorized power: 50-w. Antenna: 688-ft. above ground. Lat. 34° 49' 05", long. 86° 44' 16". Transmitter: Capshaw Mountain. Equipment: ITS transmitter; Andrew antenna. Ownership: Wireless One Inc.

Mobile—WHT773 (E group). TV Communications Network Inc., Suite 300, 10020 E. Girard Ave., Denver, CO 80231. Phone: 303-751-2900. Fax: 303-751-1081. E-mail: kroznoy@Plinet.com. Authorized power: 10-w. each. Antenna: 492-ft. above ground. Lat. 30° 44' 44", long. 88° 05' 40". Transmitter: Talisman Lane, Pritchard. Equipment: Emcee transmitter; Bogner antenna. Ownership: TV Communications Network Inc.
Leased to Wireless Cable of Mobile.

Mobile—WMH408 (F group). Multi-Channel MDS Inc., Box 258, Rd. 2, Elverson, PA 19520. Authorized power: 10-w. each. Antenna: 148-ft. above ground. Lat. 30° 41' 30", long. 88° 02' 27". Transmitter: 103 Dauphin St. Equipment: Emcee transmitter; Andrew antenna. Requests change to 492-ft. above ground. Ownership: Multi-Channel MDS Inc.

Mobile—WMX263 (H1). Advanced Wireless Systems Inc., No. 1, 4123-A Government Blvd., Mobile, AL 36693. Phone: 334-602-1000. Antenna: 190-ft. above ground. Lat. 30° 44' 44", long. 88° 05' 40". Transmitter: Whistler Ave. & William St. intersection. Ownership: Advanced Wireless Systems Inc.

Mobile—WMX259 (H2). Advanced Wireless Systems Inc., No. 1, 4123-A Government Blvd., Mobile, AL 36693. Phone: 334-602-1000. Authorized power: 10-w. Antenna: 639-ft. above ground. Lat. 30° 35' 03", long. 88° 12' 31". Transmitter: 7100 Lenardo. Equipment: Comwave transmitter; Andrew antenna. Ownership: Advanced Wireless Systems Inc.

Mobile—WMX267 (H3). Advanced Wireless Systems Inc., No. 1, 4123-A Government Blvd., Mobile, AL 36693. Phone: 334-602-1000. Authorized power: 10-w. Antenna: 639-ft. above ground. Lat. 30° 35' 03", long. 88° 12' 31". Transmitter: 7100 Lenardo. Equipment: Comwave transmitter; Andrew antenna. Ownership: Advanced Wireless Systems Inc.

Montgomery—WMH505 (E group). Line of Site Inc., 8601 E. Santa Catalina Dr., Scottsdale, AZ 85255. Phone: 602-585-1839. Authorized power: 50-w. each. Antenna: 810-ft. above ground. Lat. 32° 24' 11", long. 86° 11' 48". Transmitter: 1369 Adrian Lane. Equipment: Comwave transmitter; Andrew antenna. Requests change to 720-ft. above ground, lat. 32° 20' 06", long. 86° 17' 16". Ownership: Line of Site Inc.

Montgomery—WLW867 (F group). WCSC Inc., Box 160005, Charleston, SC 29416-6005. Authorized power: 10-w. each. Antenna: 1935-ft. above ground. Lat. 31° 58' 32", long. 86° 09' 46". Transmitter: Collier Rd., 29-mi. SSE of Montgomery. Equipment: Emcee transmitter; Andrew antenna. Ownership: WCSC Inc.

Montgomery—WNTJ725 (H1). George Kern, Bldg. 1, No. 11, 12945 Seminole Blvd., Largo, FL 33778. Authorized power: 50-w. Antenna: 810-ft. above ground. Lat. 32° 24' 11", long. 86° 11' 48". Transmitter: 1369 Adrian Lane. Equipment: Comwave transmitter; Andrew antenna. Requests change to 720-ft. above ground, lat. 32° 20' 06", long. 86° 17' 16". Ownership: George Kern.

Montgomery—WNTJ802 (H2). John Dudeck, 11672 Harborside Circle, Largo, FL 33773. Authorized power: 50-w. Antenna: 810-ft. above ground. Lat. 32° 24' 11", long. 86° 11' 48". Transmitter: 1369 Adrian Lane. Equipment: Comwave transmitter; Andrew antenna. Requests change to 720-ft. above ground, lat. 32° 20' 06", long. 86° 17' 16". Ownership: John Dudeck.

Montgomery—WNTJ773 (H3). Melissa S. Wilson, 701 Grant St., Harvard, IL 60033. Phone: 312-288-0336. Authorized power: 50-w. Antenna: 810-ft. above ground. Lat. 32° 24' 11", long. 86° 11' 48". Transmitter: 1369 Adrian Lane. Equipment: Comwave transmitter; Andrew antenna. Requests change to 720-ft. above ground, lat. 32° 20' 06", long. 86° 17' 16". Ownership: Melissa S. Wilson.

Alaska

Anchorage—WHD477 (E group). Echonet Corp., Box 255, Evergreen, CO 80439. Phone: 303-526-1039. Authorized power: 10-w. each. Antenna: 280-ft. above ground. Lat. 61° 12' 57", long. 149° 53' 26". Transmitter: 550 W. 7th Ave. Equipment: Comwave transmitter; Bogner antenna. Ownership: Echonet Corp.

Anchorage—WMX529 (F group). JRH/BDC Partnership, 3850 Aircraft Dr., Anchorage, AK 99502. Authorized power: 10-w. each. Antenna: 93-ft. above ground. Lat. 61° 06' 30", long. 149° 44' 23". Transmitter: 7460 Upper Huffman Rd. Equipment: Comwave transmitter; Andrew antenna. Ownership: JRH/BDC Partnership.

Fairbanks—WMI316 (E group). Wireless Supervision TV, Box 1789, 921 Carroll St., Perry, GA 31069. Phone: 912-987-7055. Authorized power: 10-w. each. Antenna: 205-ft. above ground. Lat. 64° 52' 48", long. 147° 40' 29". Transmitter: 303 Farmers Loop Rd. Equipment: Comwave transmitter; Andrew antenna. Ownership: Wireless Supervision TV Inc.

Fairbanks—WMY297 (F group). Maurice P. O'Connell, 2203 Pasadena Place, Gulfport, FL 33707. Phone: 727-347-3266. Fax: 727-347-4649. E-mail: bonniedo@tampabay.rr.com. Authorized power: 10-w. each. Antenna: 100-ft. above ground. Lat. 64° 54' 42", long. 147° 36' 30". Transmitter: U. of Alaska. Equipment: Comwave transmitter; Bogner antenna. Ownership: Maurice P. O'Connell.
Leased to Alaska Wireless, 1190 Mendell St., Box 2222, El Granada, CA 94018. Phone: 415-726-3087.

Homer—WLK270 (F group). MDS Systems, Box 190929, Anchorage, AK 99519-0929. Authorized power: 10-w. each. Antenna: 40-ft. above ground. Lat. 59° 38' 26", long. 151° 27' 28". Transmitter: 2.8-mi. SE of Homer. Equipment: Emcee transmitter; Andrew antenna. Ownership: MDS Systems.

Kenai—WMH736 (E group). Jody Barnes, Box 1102, Claremont, CA 91711. Phone: 909-

625-2988. Authorized power: 10-w. each. Antenna: 75-ft. above ground. Lat. 60° 38' 08", long. 151° 21' 19". Transmitter: Rte. 1. Equipment: Emcee transmitter; Andrew antenna. Ownership: Jody Barnes.

Arizona

Casa Grande—WMI839 (E group). Virginia Communications Inc., Suite B1, 7621 E. Gray Rd., Scottsdale, AZ 85260. Phone: 480-596-8283. Fax: 480-596-2973. Authorized power: 10-w. each. Antenna: 78-ft. above ground. Lat. 32° 49' 27", long. 111° 42' 09". Transmitter: 3-mi. SE of Casa Grande. Equipment: Comwave transmitter; Andrew antenna. Requests change to 75-ft. above ground. Ownership: Virginia Communications Inc.

Casa Grande—WMH344 (F group). MWTV Inc., 3401 E. Cholla St., Phoenix, AZ 85028. Phone: 602-996-3871. Authorized power: 10-w. each. Antenna: 78-ft. above ground. Lat. 32° 49' 27", long. 111° 42' 09". Transmitter: 3-mi. SE of Casa Grande. Equipment: Comwave transmitter; Andrew antenna. Requests change to 75-ft. above ground. Ownership: MWTV Inc.

Flagstaff—WMI320 (E group). Kannew Broadcast Technologies, Suite 425, 1200 L St. NW, Washington, DC 20005. Phone: 202-289-6300. Authorized power: 10-w. each. Antenna: 68-ft. above ground. Lat. 35° 14' 29", long. 111° 36' 35". Transmitter: Devils Head Peak. Equipment: Comwave transmitter; Andrew antenna. Ownership: Kannew Broadcast Technologies.

Flagstaff—WLW970 (F group). Multi-Micro Inc., Suite 120, 4700 S. McClintock, Tempe, AZ 85282. Phone: 480-755-7524. Fax: 480-755-7534. Authorized power: 10-w. each. Antenna: 68-ft. above ground. Lat. 35° 14' 02", long. 111° 36' 25". Transmitter: Devils Head Mountain. Equipment: Comwave transmitter; Andrew antenna. Ownership: Multi-Micro Inc.

Flagstaff—WNTH876 (H1). Fortuna Systems Corp. Authorized power: 10-w. Antenna: 119-ft. above ground. Lat. 35° 14' 28", long. 111° 36' 35". Transmitter: Devils Head Peak. Equipment: Comwave transmitter; Andrew antenna. Ownership: Fortuna Systems Corp.

Globe—WMH512 (E group). Line of Site Inc., 8611 E. Santa Catalina Dr., Scottsdale, AZ 85255-2870. Phone: 602-951-8245. Authorized power: 10-w. each. Antenna: 88-ft. above ground. Lat. 33° 17' 37", long. 110° 50' 09". Transmitter: Signal Peak. Equipment: Emcee transmitter; Andrew antenna. Ownership: Line of Site Inc.

Globe—WLR480 (F group). Line of Site Inc., 8611 E. Santa Catalina Dr., Scottsdale, AZ 85255-2870. Phone: 602-951-8245. Authorized power: 50-w. each. Antenna: 100-ft. above ground. Lat. 33° 17' 37", long. 110° 50' 09". Transmitter: Signal Peak. Equipment: ITS transmitter; Andrew antenna. Ownership: Line of Site Inc.

Phoenix—WHK556 (H1). Alda Gold Inc., 5301 E. Broadway Blvd., Tucson, AZ 85711-3710. Phone: 520-519-4400. Fax: 520-747-6830. Authorized power: 100-w. Antenna: 96-ft. above ground. Lat. 33° 20' 02", long. 112° 03' 44". Transmitter: 10660 S. Central. Equipment: Comwave transmitter; Andrew antenna. Ownership: Matthew Oristano.

Prescott—WMH800 (E group). Virginia Communications Inc., Suite B1, 7621 E. Gray Rd., Scottsdale, AZ 85260. Phone: 480-596-8283. Fax: 480-596-2973. Authorized power: 50-w. each. Antenna: 54-ft. above ground. Lat. 34° 13' 58", long. 112° 22' 13". Transmitter: NW of Crown King. Equipment: Emcee transmitter; Andrew antenna. Ownership: Virginia Communications Inc.

Prescott—WNTJ440 (H group). Virginia Communications Inc., Suite B1, 7621 E. Gray Rd., Scottsdale, AZ 85260. Phone: 480-596-8283. Fax: 480-596-2973. Authorized power: 10-w. each. Antenna: 86-ft. above ground. Lat. 34° 42' 17", long. 112° 06' 55". Transmitter: South Peak-Mingus Mountain. Equipment: Emcee transmitter; Andrew antenna. Ownership: Virginia Communications Inc.

Shaw Butte—WHT685 (E group). Alda Gold Inc., 5301 E. Broadway Blvd., Tucson, AZ 85711-3710. Phone: 520-519-4400. Fax: 520-747-6830. Authorized power: 100-w. each. Antenna: 46-ft. above ground. Lat. 33° 35' 38", long. 112° 05' 11". Transmitter: 9-mi. N of Phoenix. Equipment: Comwave transmitter; Andrew antenna. Ownership: Matthew Oristano.
Leased to People's Choice TV Partners, 2 Corporate Dr., Suite 249, Shelton, CT 06484-6239. Phone: 203-929-2800. Fax: 203-929-1454.

Shaw Butte—WHT686 (F group). Alda Gold Inc., 5301 E. Broadway Blvd., Tucson, AZ 85711-3710. Phone: 520-519-4400. Fax: 520-747-6830. Authorized power: 100-w. each. Antenna: 46-ft. above ground. Lat. 33° 35' 38", long. 112° 05' 11". Transmitter: 9-mi. N of Phoenix. Equipment: Comwave transmitter; Andrew antenna. Ownership: Matthew Oristano.

Shaw Butte—WHJ902 (H2). Alda Gold Inc., 5301 E. Broadway Blvd., Tucson, AZ 85711-3710. Phone: 520-519-4400. Fax: 520-747-6830. Authorized power: 100-w. Antenna: 45-ft. above ground. Lat. 33° 35' 38", long. 112° 05' 11". Transmitter: 9-mi. N of Phoenix. Equipment: Comwave transmitter; Andrew antenna. Ownership: Matthew Oristano.
Leased to People's Choice TV Partners, 2 Corporate Dr., Suite 249, Shelton, CT 06484-6239. Phone: 203-929-2800. Fax: 203-929-1454.

Shaw Butte—WNTL436 (H3). Alda Gold Inc., 5301 E. Broadway Blvd., Tucson, AZ 85711-3710. Phone: 520-519-4400. Fax: 520-747-6830. Antenna: 45-ft. above ground. Lat. 33° 35' 38", long. 112° 05' 11". Transmitter: 9-mi. N of Phoenix. Equipment: Townsend, Micro-Link transmitter; Andrew antenna. Ownership: Matthew Oristano.

Sierra Vista—WMI375 (E group). John McLain, 7110 Jaxel Rd., Hereford, AZ 85615. Phone: 602-378-6549. Authorized power: 10-w. each. Antenna: 120-ft. above ground. Lat. 31° 28' 49", long. 109° 57' 30". Transmitter: Mule Mountain, Bisbee. Equipment: ITS transmitter; Andrew antenna. Ownership: John McLain.

Sierra Vista—WMI371 (F group). John McLain, 7110 Jaxel Rd., Hereford, AZ 85615. Phone: 602-378-6549. Authorized power: 10-w. each. Antenna: 120-ft. above ground. Lat. 31° 28' 49", long. 109° 57' 30". Transmitter: Mule Mountain, Bisbee. Equipment: ITS transmitter; Andrew antenna. Ownership: John McLain.

Sierra Vista—WNTI467 (H1). John McLain, 7110 Jaxel Rd., Hereford, AZ 85615. Phone: 520-378-3349. Authorized power: 10-w. Antenna: 50-ft. above ground. Lat. 31° 28' 49", long. 109° 57' 30". Transmitter: Mule Mountain, Bisbee. Equipment: Comwave transmitter; Andrew antenna. Ownership: John McLain.

Sierra Vista—WNTI488 (H2). Norman R. Herrington, 144-12 159th St., Springfield Garden, NY 11434. Phone: 718-712-3109. Authorized power: 10-w. Antenna: 120-ft. above ground. Lat. 31° 28' 49", long. 109° 57' 30". Transmitter: Mule Mountain, Bisbee. Equipment: Comwave transmitter; Andrew antenna. Ownership: Norman R. Herrington.

Sierra Vista—WNTI399 (H3). Jeffrey D. Grumm, Box 2982, Sierra Vista, AZ 85636. Phone: 520-459-0459. Authorized power: 10-w. Antenna: 50-ft. above ground. Lat. 31° 28' 49", long. 109° 57' 30". Transmitter: Mule Mountain, Bisbee. Equipment: Comwave transmitter; Andrew antenna. Ownership: Jeffrey D. Grumm.

Tucson—WHT696 (E group). Red Tucson E Partnership, 248 King George St., Annapolis, MD 21401. Phone: 410-626-1200. Fax: 410-626-1266. Authorized power: 50-w. each. Antenna: 132-ft. above ground. Lat. 32° 14' 56", long. 111° 06' 57". Transmitter: 7120 W. Lost Canyon Dr. Equipment: Emcee transmitter; Andrew antenna. Ownership: Multichannel Media Inc., 33.3%; MHW Associates, 33.3%; National Wireless Video, 33.3%.
Leased to People's Choice TV Partners, 2 Corporate Dr., Suite 249, Shelton, CT 06484-6239. Phone: 203-929-2800. Fax: 203-929-1454.

Tucson—WHK994 (F group). Omega Radiotelephone, 1601 Neptune Dr., San Leandro, CA 94577. Phone: 510-895-9500. Authorized power: 50-w. each. Antenna: 122-ft. above ground. Lat. 32° 14' 56", long. 111° 06' 57". Transmitter: 7120 W. Lost Canyon Dr. Equipment: Emcee transmitter; Andrew antenna. Ownership: Omega Radiotelephone.

Tucson—WEH249 (H group). Arizona Board of Regents for the U. of Arizona, No. 255, Modern Languages Bldg., Tucson, AZ 85721. Phone: 602-621-7365. Authorized power: 50-w. each. Antenna: 132-ft. above ground. Lat. 32° 14' 55", long. 111° 06' 57". Transmitter: 1720 W. Lost Canyon Dr. Equipment: Comwave transmitter; Andrew antenna. Ownership: Arizona University Board of Regents.

Verde Valley—WMI827 (E group). Virginia Communications Inc., Suite B1, 7621 E. Gray Rd., Scottsdale, AZ 85260. Phone: 480-596-8283. Fax: 480-596-2973. Authorized power: 10-w. each. Antenna: 86-ft. above ground. Lat. 34° 42' 17", long. 112° 06' 55". Transmitter: South Peak-Mingus Mountain. Equipment: Emcee transmitter; Andrew antenna. Ownership: Virginia Communications Inc.

Verde Valley—WMI864 (F group). Virginia Communications Inc., Suite B1, 7621 E. Gray Rd., Scottsdale, AZ 85260. Phone: 480-596-8283. Fax: 480-596-2973. Authorized power: 10-w. each. Antenna: 86-ft. above ground. Lat. 34° 42' 17", long. 112° 06' 55". Transmitter: South Peak-Mingus Mountain. Equipment: Emcee transmitter; Andrew antenna. Ownership: Virginia Communications Inc.

Yuma—WLW829 (E group). Cardiff Communications Partners II, 1830 E. Willow Glen Circle, Sandy, UT 84093. Phone: 801-561-9995. Authorized power: 10-w. each. Antenna: 114-ft. above ground. Lat. 32° 40' 22", long. 114° 20' 14". Transmitter: Telegraph Pass Communications Site. Equipment: Emcee transmitter; Andrew antenna. Ownership: Cardiff Communications Partners II.

Yuma—WLW826 (F group). Cardiff Communications Partners II, 1830 E. Willow Glen Circle, Sandy, UT 84093. Phone: 801-561-9995. Authorized power: 10-w. each. Antenna: 114-ft. above ground. Lat. 32° 40' 22", long. 114° 20' 14". Transmitter: Telegraph Pass Communications Site. Equipment: Emcee transmitter; Andrew antenna. Ownership: Cardiff Communications Partners II.

Yuma—WNTI531 (H group). Cardiff Communications Partners II, 1830 E. Willow Glen Circle, Sandy, UT 84093. Phone: 801-561-9995. Authorized power: 10-w. each. Antenna: 40-ft. above ground. Lat. 32° 40' 22", long. 114° 20' 14". Transmitter: Telegraph Pass Communications Site. Equipment: Emcee transmitter; Andrew antenna. Ownership: Cardiff Communications Partners II.

Arkansas

El Dorado—WMY298 (F group). JCL El Dorado Arkansas F Grand Alliance, 2203 Pasadena Place, Gulfport, FL 33707. Phone: 727-347-3266. Fax: 727-347-4649. E-mail: bonniedo@tampabay.rr.com. Authorized power: 10-w. each. Antenna: 400-ft. above ground. Lat. 33° 16' 19", long. 92° 42' 11". Transmitter: 5.5-mi. N of Hwys. 335 & 82 junction. Equipment: Comwave transmitter; Bogner antenna. Ownership: JCL El Dorado Arkansas F Grand Alliance.
Leased to Nucentrix Broadband Networks, 200 Chisholm Place, Suite 200, Plano, TX 75075. Phone: 972-423-9494.

El Dorado—WNTM542 (H2). NBI TV Partners, 2570 Chateau Way, Livermore, CA 94550. Phone: 702-597-9875. Authorized power: 200-w. Antenna: 600-ft. above ground. Lat. 33° 16' 19", long. 92° 42' 11". Transmitter: 5.5-mi. N of Hwys. 335 & 82 junction. Equipment: Comwave transmitter; Andrew antenna. Ownership: NBI TV Partners.

Fayetteville—WMI821 (E group). People's Choice TV Inc., Suite 249, 2 Corporate Dr., Shelton, CT 06484-6239. Phone: 203-929-2800. Fax: 203-929-1454. Authorized power: 10-w. each. Antenna: 100-ft. above ground. Lat. 36° 08' 50", long. 94° 11' 14". Transmitter: 4201 S. 56th St. Equipment: Comwave transmitter; Andrew antenna. Ownership: People's Choice TV Partners.

Fayetteville—WMI881 (F group). Fayetteville Wireless TV Inc., 2014 Rock Creek Dr., Arlington, TX 76010. Phone: 817-469-8687. Authorized power: 20-w. each. Antenna: 155-ft. above ground. Lat. 36° 12' 16", long. 94° 06' 04". Transmitter: 2499-A Dodd Ave. Equipment: Comwave transmitter; Scala antenna. Ownership: Fayetteville Wireless TV Inc.

Fort Smith—WLK312 (E group). Virginia Communications Inc., Suite B1, 7621 E. Gray Rd., Scottsdale, AZ 85260. Phone: 480-596-8283. Fax: 480-596-2973. Authorized power: 10-w. each. Antenna: 270-ft. above ground. Lat. 35° 26' 50", long. 94° 21' 54". Transmitter: 100-ft. E of Pernot St., Van Buren. Equipment: Comwave transmitter; Andrew antenna. Ownership: Virginia Communications Inc.
Leased to American Wireless, 7426 Stetson Dr., Suite 220, Scottsdale, AZ 85251. Phone: 602-994-4301.

Fort Smith—WLK316 (F group). Smithco of Fort Smith Inc., 6609 Rogers Ave., Fort Smith, AR 72903. Phone: 501-452-1681. Authorized power: 1-w. each. Antenna: 270-ft. above ground. Lat. 35° 26' 50", long. 94° 21' 54". Transmitter: 100-ft. E of Pernot St., Van Buren. Equipment: Comwave transmitter; Andrew antenna. Ownership: Smithco of Fort Smith Inc.

Gurdon—WMX227 (H1). Arthur L. Dalton, Box 516, Pago Pago, AS 96799. Authorized power: 10-w. Antenna: 150-ft. above ground. Lat. 33° 56' 42", long. 93° 10' 43". Transmitter: 2-mi. NW of Gurdon. Equipment: Emcee transmitter; Bogner antenna. Ownership: Arthur L. Dalton.

Gurdon—WMX222 (H2). Arthur L. Dalton, Box 516, Pago Pago, AS 96799. Authorized power: 10-w. Antenna: 150-ft. above ground. Lat. 33° 56' 42", long. 93° 10' 43". Transmitter: 2-mi. NW of Gurdon. Equipment: Emcee transmitter; Bogner antenna. Ownership: Arthur L. Dalton.

Gurdon—WMX226 (H3). Arthur L. Dalton, Box 516, Pago Pago, AS 96799. Authorized power: 10-w. Antenna: 150-ft. above ground. Lat. 33° 56' 42", long. 93° 10' 43". Transmitter: 2-mi. NW of Gurdon. Equipment: Emcee transmitter; Bogner antenna. Ownership: Arthur L. Dalton.

Hot Springs—WLW705 (F group). Masscom, 1023 51st St., Moline, IL 61265. Phone: 309-764-6886. Authorized power: 10-w. each. Antenna: 200-ft. above ground. Lat. 34° 30' 19", long. 93° 05' 06". Transmitter: West Mountain. Equipment: Comwave transmitter; Bogner antenna. Ownership: Masscom.

Jonesboro—WMH420 (E group). Lawrence N. Brandt, Suite 220, 3201 New Mexico Ave. NW, Washington, DC 20016. Phone: 202-363-1100. Authorized power: 10-w. each. Antenna: 506-ft. above ground. Lat. 35° 47' 56", long. 90° 44' 31". Transmitter: 3-mi. SW of Jonesboro. Equipment: Comwave transmitter; Bogner antenna. Ownership: Lawrence N. Brandt.

Jonesboro—WNTH815 (H2). John Dudeck, 11672 Harborside Circle, Largo, FL 33773. Authorized power: 50-w. Antenna: 421-ft. above ground. Lat. 35° 47' 56", long. 90° 44' 31". Transmitter: 3-mi. S of Jonesboro. Equipment: Comwave transmitter; Bogner antenna. Ownership: John Dudeck.

Jonesboro—WNTH889 (H3). Blake Twedt, 5102 Rosegreen Court, Tampa, FL 33624. Phone: 727-587-9959. Authorized power: 50-w. Antenna: 421-ft. above ground. Lat. 35° 47' 56", long. 90° 44' 31". Transmitter: 3-mi. S of Jonesboro. Equipment: Comwave transmitter; Bogner antenna. Ownership: Blake Twedt.

Little Rock—WHT723 (E group). Stephen Communications Inc., 1152 Gilmer Dr., Salt Lake City, UT 84105. Phone: 801-582-0381. Authorized power: 50-w. each. Antenna: 650-ft. above ground. Lat. 34° 47' 57", long. 92° 29' 29". Transmitter: Shinall Mountain. Equipment: Emcee transmitter; Andrew antenna. Ownership: Stephen Communications Inc.

Little Rock—WMI816 (F group). Paul M. Moore, 716 N. Westwood Ave., Toledo, OH 43607. Authorized power: 50-w. each. Antenna: 650-ft. above ground. Lat. 34° 47' 57", long. 92° 29' 29". Transmitter: 1501 N. University. Equipment: Emcee transmitter; Andrew antenna. Ownership: Paul M. Moore.

Russellville—WNTL298 (H group). Ark-Star Partners-Gamma, 276 W. 20th St., Tracy, CA 95376. Phone: 209-836-3316. Fax: 209-832-2153. Authorized power: 10-w. each. Antenna: 160-ft. above ground. Lat. 35° 13' 09", long. 93° 15' 13". Transmitter: Mount Nebo. Equipment: ITS transmitter; Bogner antenna. Ownership: Ark-Star Partners-Gamma.

California

Bakersfield—WHT584 (E group). CS Wireless Systems Inc., 1100 Summit Ave., Plano, TX 75074. Phone: 972-730-3300. Authorized power: 50-w. each. Antenna: 355-ft. above ground. Lat. 35° 16' 52", long. 119° 04' 41". Transmitter: 8101 Ashe Rd. Equipment: ITS transmitter; Andrew antenna. Ownership: CS Wireless Systems Inc.

Bakersfield—WHT585 (F group). CS Wireless Systems Inc., 1100 Summit Ave., Plano, TX 75074. Phone: 972-730-3300. Authorized power: 20-w. each. Antenna: 355-ft. above ground. Lat. 35° 16' 52", long. 119° 04' 41". Transmitter: 8101 Ashe Rd. Equipment: ITS transmitter; Andrew antenna. Ownership: CS Wireless Systems Inc.

Bishop—WMI389 (E group). Government Enterprises Inc. Authorized power: 10-w. each. Antenna: 36-ft. above ground. Lat. 37° 24' 48", long. 118° 11' 08". Transmitter: 12-mi. NE of Bishop. Equipment: Scientific-Atlanta transmitter; Andrew antenna. Ownership: Government Enterprises Inc.

Bishop—WMI385 (F group). Government Enterprises Inc. Authorized power: 10-w. each. Antenna: 36-ft. above ground. Lat. 37° 24' 48", long. 118° 11' 08". Transmitter: Silver Peak, 12-mi. NE of Bishop. Equipment: Scientific-Atlanta transmitter; Andrew antenna. Ownership: Government Enterprises Inc.

Bishop—WNTJ493 (H group). Government Enterprises Inc. Authorized power: 10-w. each. Antenna: 36-ft. above ground. Lat. 37° 24' 48", long. 118° 11' 08". Transmitter: Silver Peak, 12-mi. NE of Bishop. Equipment: Scientific-Atlanta transmitter; Andrew antenna. Ownership: Government Enterprises Inc.

Chico—WMI407 (E group). Jack G. Hubbard, 8793 Ranch Dr., Chesterland, OH 44026. Phone & fax: 216-729-7282. Authorized power: 20-w. each. Antenna: 199-ft. above ground. Lat. 39° 57' 29", long. 121° 42' 50". Transmitter: 10895 Cohasset Rd. Equipment: Comwave transmitter; Andrew antenna. Ownership: Jack G. Hubbard.
Leased to Centimeter Wave Television Inc., 2512 Chambers Rd., Suite 208, Tustin, CA 92680. Phone: 714-252-2190.

Chico—WNTD890 (H1). Token Partnership, 1201 7th St., East Moline, IL 61244. Phone: 309-755-1472. Authorized power: 20-w. Antenna: 180-ft. above ground. Lat. 39° 57' 29", long. 121° 42' 50". Transmitter: 10895 Cohasset Rd. Equipment: Comwave transmitter; Andrew antenna. Ownership: Token Partnership.

Chico—WNTD875 (H2). North Florida MMDS Partnership, Box 4935, Rte. 1, Williston, FL 32696. Phone: 813-360-2416. Authorized power: 20-w. Antenna: 180-ft. above ground. Lat. 39° 57' 29", long. 121° 42' 50". Transmitter: 10895 Cohasset Rd. Equipment: Comwave transmitter; Andrew antenna. Ownership: North Florida MMDS Partners.

El Centro—WMH640 (F group). Video/Multipoint Inc., 2809 Pine St., San Francisco, CA 94115-2501. Phone: 415-775-9552. Fax: 415-775-9536. E-mail: bill@sauro.com. Authorized power: 10-w. each.Antenna: 163-ft. above ground. Lat. 32° 46' 30", long. 115° 30' 22". Transmitter: NE of 17th & C Rds. intersection. Equipment: Emcee transmitter; Andrew antenna. Ownership: Video/Multipoint Inc.
Leased to Bloomer & Associates.

Fresno—WHT715 (E group). Via/Net Companies, 836 E. Washington St., San Diego, CA 92103. Phone: 619-260-0110. Authorized power: 50-w. each. Antenna: 100-ft. above ground. Lat. 36° 55' 49", long. 119° 38' 16". Transmitter: Owens Mountain. Equipment: Comwave transmitter; Andrew antenna. Ownership: Via/Net Companies.

Fresno—WLW816 (F group). Fresno MMDS Associates, Box 2628, Fresno, CA 93725-2628. Phone: 209-442-1970. Authorized power: 20-w. each. Antenna: 96-ft. above ground. Lat. 36° 55' 49", long. 119° 38' 26". Transmitter: Owens Mountain. Equipment: ITS transmitter; Andrew antenna. Ownership: Fresno MMDS Associates.

Fresno—WNEZ574 (H1). Via/Net Companies, 836 E. Washington St., San Diego, CA 92103. Phone: 619-260-0110. Authorized power: 20-w. Antenna: 96-ft. above ground. Lat. 36° 55' 49", long. 119° 38' 26". Transmitter: Owens Mountain. Equipment: ITS transmitter; Andrew antenna. Ownership: Via/Net Companies.

Fresno—WNTA439 (H2). Robert Hostetler, 17215 Colonial Park Dr., Monument, CO 80132. Authorized power: 20-w. Antenna: 100-ft. above ground. Lat. 36° 55' 49", long. 119° 38' 16". Transmitter: Owens Mountain. Equipment: Loma Scientific transmitter; Andrew antenna. Ownership: Robert Hostetler.

Grand Terrace—WHT636 (E group). Integration Communications International Inc., Suite 103, 6507 Ridge St., McLean, VA 22101. Phone: 202-628-2832. Fax: 202-628-2833. Authorized power: 50-w. each. Antenna: 30-ft. above ground. Lat. 34° 01' 20", long. 117° 17' 46". Transmitter: Blue Mountain, 0.7-mi. SE of Grand Terrace. Equipment: ITS transmitter; Andrew antenna. Ownership: Integration Communications International.
Leased to Cross Country Wireless Cable, 130 Kearny St., San Francisco, CA 94108.

Grand Terrace—WHT637 (F group). Metrocall of Nevada General Partnership II, 6677 Richmond Hwy., Alexandria, VA 22306. Phone: 703-660-6677. Authorized power: 50-w. each. Antenna: 30-ft. above ground. Lat. 34° 01' 20", long. 117° 17' 46". Transmitter: Blue Mountain, 1.2-mi. SE of Grand Terrace. Equipment: ITS transmitter; Andrew antenna. Ownership: Metrocall of Nevada General Partnership II.

La Habra—WNET335 (H3). Pacific Telesis Southern Wireless Video Inc., 130 Kearny St., San Francisco, CA 94108. Authorized power: 50-w. Antenna: 104-ft. above ground. Lat. 33° 58' 24", long. 117° 56' 31". Transmitter: 1518 Skyline Dr. Equipment: ITS transmitter; Andrew antenna. Ownership: SBC Media Ventures.

Merced—WNTK866 (H1). Fresno MMDS Associates, Box 2628, Fresno, CA 93725-2628. Phone: 209-442-1970. Authorized power: 50-w. Antenna: 125-ft. above ground. Lat. 37° 31' 59", long. 120° 01' 32". Transmitter: 6282 Morrissey Rd. Equipment: ITS transmitter; Andrew antenna. Ownership: Fresno MMDS Associates.

Merced—WNTK887 (H2). Terry J. Holmes, 423 E. Edgemont Dr., Fresno, CA 93720. Authorized power: 50-w. Antenna: 125-ft. above ground. Lat. 37° 31' 59", long. 120° 01' 32". Transmitter: 6286 Morrissey Rd. Equipment: ITS transmitter; Andrew antenna. Ownership: Terry J. Holmes.

Merced—WNTK983 (H3). Fresno MMDS Associates, 17215 Colonial Park Dr., Monument, CO 80132. Authorized power: 50-w. Antenna: 125-ft. above ground. Lat. 37° 31' 59", long. 120° 01' 32". Transmitter: 6286 Morrissey Rd. Equipment: ITS transmitter; Andrew antenna. Ownership: Fresno MMDS Associates.

Modesto—WGW513 (E group). Golden Bear Communications Inc., 6781 Coffee Rd., Bakersfield, CA 93308. Phone: 805-325-8655. Authorized power: 100-w. each. Antenna: 496-ft. above ground. Lat. 37° 43' 44", long. 121° 07' 34". Transmitter: 1220 S. Acacia Ave. Equipment: ITS transmitter; Andrew antenna. Ownership: Golden Bear Communications Inc.

Modesto—WNTJ742 (H1). Golden Bear Communications Inc., 6781 Coffee Rd., Bakersfield, CA 93308. Phone: 805-325-8655. Authorized power: 20-w. Antenna: 385-ft. above ground. Lat. 37° 43' 44", long. 121° 07' 34". Transmitter: 1220 S. Acacia Ave. Equipment: ITS transmitter; Andrew antenna. Ownership: Golden Bear Communications Inc.

Modesto—WNTJ756 (H3). Golden Bear Communications Inc., 6781 Coffee Rd., Bakersfield, CA 93308. Phone: 805-325-8655. Authorized power: 100-w. Antenna: 496-ft. above ground. Lat. 37° 43' 44", long. 121° 07' 34". Transmitter: 1220 S. Acacia Ave. Equipment: ITS transmitter; Andrew antenna. Ownership: Golden Bear Communications Inc.

Mount San Bruno—WHT653 (E group). Alda Wireless Holdings Inc., 5301 E. Broadway Blvd., Tucson, AZ 85711-3710. Phone: 520-519-4400. Fax: 520-747-6830. Authorized power: 40-w. each. Antenna: 135-ft. above ground. Lat. 37° 41' 17", long. 122° 26' 07". Transmitter: 6.1-mi. S of San Francisco. Equipment: ITS transmitter; Andrew antenna. Ownership: Matthew Oristano.

Mount Wilson—WBB785 (H2). Pacific Telesis Southern Wireless Video Inc., 130 Kearny St., San Francisco, CA 94108. Authorized power: 10-w. Antenna: 111-ft. above ground. Lat. 33° 58' 24", long. 117° 56' 31". Transmitter: 1518 Skyline Dr., Anaheim. Equipment: ITS transmitter; Andrew antenna. Ownership: SBC Media Ventures.

Redding—WMH681 (E group). American Telecasting of Redding Inc., Suite 300, 5575 Tech Center Dr., Colorado Springs, CO 80919. Phone: 719-260-5004. Fax: 719-260-5010. Authorized power: 50-w. each. Antenna: 194-ft. above ground. Lat. 40° 39' 14", long. 122° 31' 12". Transmitter: South Fort Mountain, 2.5-mi. NE of Whiskeytown. Equipment: Comwave transmitter; Andrew antenna. Ownership: American Telecasting Inc.

Redding—WLW740 (F group). American Telecasting of Redding Inc., Suite 300, 5575 Tech Center Dr., Colorado Springs, CO 80919. Phone: 719-260-5004. Fax: 719-260-5010. Authorized power: 50-w. each. Antenna: 194-ft. above ground. Lat. 40° 39' 14", long. 122° 31' 12". Transmitter: South Fort Mountain, 2.5-mi. NE of Whiskeytown. Equipment: Comwave transmitter; Andrew antenna. Ownership: American Telecasting Inc.

Redding—WMH789 (H1). Cardiff Broadcasting Group, Suite 224, 2010 Jimmy Durante Blvd., Del Mar, CA 92014. Phone: 619-481-3410. Authorized power: 20-w. Antenna: 20-ft. above ground. Lat. 40° 33' 46", long. 122° 27' 07". Transmitter: 6188 Placer St. Equipment: ITS transmitter; Andrew antenna. Ownership: Cardiff Communications Partners II.

Redding—WMH781 (H2). Cardiff Broadcasting Group, Suite 224, 2010 Jimmy Durante Blvd., Del Mar, CA 92014. Phone: 619-481-3410. Authorized power: 20-w. Antenna: 20-ft. above ground. Lat. 40° 33' 46", long. 122° 27' 07". Transmitter: 6188 Placer St. Equipment: ITS transmitter; Andrew antenna. Ownership: Cardiff Communications Partners II.

Redding—WMH785 (H3). Cardiff Broadcasting Group, Suite 224, 2010 Jimmy Durante Blvd., Del Mar, CA 92014. Phone: 619-481-3410. Authorized power: 20-w. Antenna: 20-ft. above ground. Lat. 40° 33' 46", long. 122° 27' 07". Transmitter: 6188 Placer St. Equipment: ITS transmitter; Andrew antenna. Ownership: Cardiff Communications Partners II.

Riverside—WNTD998 (H2). Pacific Telesis Southern Wireless Video Inc., 130 Kearny St., San Francisco, CA 94108. Phone: 415-394-3000. Authorized power: 50-w. Antenna: 30-ft. above ground. Lat. 34° 01' 20", long. 117° 17' 46". Transmitter: Blue Mountain, 1.2-mi. SE of Grand Terrace. Equipment: ITS transmitter; Andrew antenna. Ownership: SBC Media Ventures.

Riverside—WNTL542 (H3). Pacific Telesis Southern Wireless Video Inc., 130 Kearny St., San Francisco, CA 94108. Phone: 415-394-3000. Authorized power: 50-w. Antenna: 30-ft. above ground. Lat. 34° 01' 20", long. 117° 17' 46". Transmitter: Blue Mountain, 1.2-mi. SE of Grand Terrace. Equipment: ITS transmitter; Andrew antenna. Ownership: SBC Media Ventures.

Sacramento—WHT689 (E group). WBSS Licensing Corp., Suite 325, 9250 E. Costilla Ave., Englewood, CO 80112. Phone: 509-248-9038. Authorized power: 50-w. each. Antenna: 24-ft. above ground. Lat. 38° 38' 54", long. 121° 28' 40". Transmitter: N. Market St., 0.24-mi. W of Gate St. Equipment: Comwave transmitter; Andrew antenna. Ownership: Wireless Broadcasting Systems of America Inc.

Sacramento—WHT690 (F group). American Telecasting Inc., Suite 300, 5575 Tech Center Dr., Colorado Springs, CO 80919. Phone: 719-260-5533. Fax: 719-260-5010. Authorized power: 50-w. each. Antenna: 450-ft. above ground. Lat. 38° 38' 54", long. 121° 28' 40". Transmitter: N. Market St., 0.24-mi. W of Gate St. Equipment: Comwave transmitter; Andrew antenna. Ownership: American Telecasting Inc..

Leased to Wireless Broadcasting Systems of Sacramento Inc., 1513 Sports Dr., Suite 9, Sacramento, CA 95834. Phone: 916-928-2500.

Sacramento—WNET337 (H1). WBSS Licensing Corp., Suite 325, 9250 E. Costilla Ave., Englewood, CO 80112. Authorized power: 50-w. Antenna: 450-ft. above ground. Lat. 38° 38' 54", long. 121° 28' 40". Transmitter: N. Market St., 0.24-mi. W of Gate St. Equipment: Emcee transmitter; Andrew antenna. Ownership: Wireless Broadcasting Systems of America Inc.

Sacramento—WNTB228 (H2). Via/Net Companies, 836 E. Washington St., San Diego, CA 92103. Phone: 619-260-0110. Authorized power: 50-w. Antenna: 450-ft. above ground. Lat. 38° 38' 54", long. 121° 28' 40". Transmitter: N. Market St., 0.24-mi. W of Gate St. Equipment: Emcee transmitter; Andrew antenna. Ownership: Via/Net Companies.

Salinas—WMI322 (E group). The Kenneth H. Iscol 1990 Trust for Kiva Iscol, 63 Lyndel Rd., Pound Ridge, NY 10576. Authorized power: 10-w. each. Antenna: 194-ft. above ground. Lat. 36° 31' 48", long. 121° 36' 31". Transmitter: Mount Toro. Equipment: Comwave transmitter; Bogner antenna. Ownership: The Kenneth H. Iscol 1990 Trust for Kiva Iscol.

Salinas—WMI278 (F group). Video/Multipoint Inc., 2809 Pine St., San Francisco, CA 94115-2501. Phone: 415-775-9552. Fax: 415-775-9536. E-mail: bill@sauro.com. Authorized power: 10-w. each. Antenna: 194-ft. above ground. Lat. 36° 31' 48", long. 121° 36' 31". Transmitter: Mount Toro. Equipment: Emcee transmitter; Andrew antenna. Ownership: Video/Multipoint Inc.

Leased to American Telecasting Inc., 5575 Tech Center Dr., Suite 300, Colorado Springs, CO 80919. Phone: 719-260-5533. Fax: 719-260-5010.

San Diego—WMI355 (E group). William A. Brandt Jr., c/o Development Specialists Inc., Suite 900, 200 S. Biscayne Blvd., Miami, FL 33134-2312. Phone: 305-374-2717. Authorized power: 10-w. each. Antenna: 160-ft. above ground. Lat. 33° 18' 32", long. 116° 50' 38". Transmitter: 3.8-mi. S of Palomar Mountain, Escondido. Equipment: Emcee transmitter; Andrew antenna. Requests change to 97-ft. above ground, lat. 32° 41' 49", long. 116° 56' 09"; transmitter to San Miguel Mountain. Ownership: William A. Brandt Jr.

San Diego—WMH541 (F group). U.S. Satellite Corp., 935 W. Bullion St., Murray, UT 84123. Phone: 801-263-0519. Fax: 801-263-0796. Authorized power: 10-w. each. Antenna: 100-ft. above ground. Lat. 32° 41' 48", long. 116° 56' 10". Transmitter: San Miguel Mountain. Equipment: Emcee transmitter; Andrew antenna. Ownership: U.S. Satellite Corp.

Leased to WHI-San Diego Inc./Wireless Holdings Inc., 102 West 500 South, Suite 320, Salt Lake City, UT 84101. Phone: 801-328-5619.

San Diego—WHJ908 (H2). Alda Wireless Holdings Inc., 5301 E. Broadway Blvd., Tucson, AZ 85711-3710. Phone: 520-519-4400. Fax: 520-747-6830. Antenna: 410-ft. above ground. Lat. 32° 42' 58", long. 117° 09' 45". Transmitter: 1010 2nd Ave. Ownership: Matthew Oristano.

Leased to People's Choice TV Partners, 2 Corporate Dr., Suite 249, Shelton, CT 06484-6239. Phone: 203-929-2800. Fax: 203-929-1454.

San Francisco—WMY498 (F1 & 3). Bay Area Cablevision Inc., 975-H Industrial Rd., San Carlos, CA 94070. Phone: 415-631-9190. Authorized power: 40-w. each. Antenna: 135-ft. above ground. Lat. 37° 41' 17", long. 122° 26' 07". Transmitter: San Bruno Mountain. Equipment: ITS transmitter; Andrew antenna. Ownership: Bay Area Cablevision Inc.

San Francisco—WMY499 (F2 & 4). Bay Area Cablevision Inc., 975-H Industrial Rd., San Carlos, CA 94070. Phone: 415-631-9190. Authorized power: 10-w. each. Antenna: 300-ft. above ground. Lat. 37° 29' 17", long. 121° 51' 59". Transmitter: 10.6-mi. N of San Francisco. Equipment: ITS transmitter; Andrew antenna. Ownership: Bay Area Cablevision Inc.

San Francisco—WNTB230 (H1). Via/Net Companies, 836 E. Washington St., San Diego, CA 92103. Phone: 619-260-0110. Authorized power: 40-w. Antenna: 135-ft. above ground. Lat. 37° 41' 17", long. 122° 26' 07". Transmitter: 6.1-mi. S of San Francisco. Equipment: ITS transmitter; Bogner antenna. Ownership: Via/Net Companies.

San Francisco—WNTA514 (H2). Pacific Telesis Southern Wireless Video Inc., 130 Kearny St., San Francisco, CA 94108. Antenna: 256-ft. above ground. Lat. 37° 41' 17", long. 122° 26' 07". Transmitter: San Bruno Mountain, 6.1-mi. S of San Francisco. Equipment: ITS transmitter; Bogner antenna. Ownership: SBC Media Ventures.

San Francisco—WHJ909 (H3). Alda Wireless Holdings Inc., 5301 E. Broadway Blvd., Tucson, AZ 85711-3710. Phone: 520-519-4400. Fax: 520-747-6830. Authorized power: 40-w. Antenna: 150-ft. above ground. Lat. 37° 41' 17", long. 122° 26' 07". Transmitter: 6.1-mi. S of San Francisco. Equipment: ITS transmitter; Bogner antenna. Ownership: Matthew Oristano.

San Francisco (south)—WNEJ497 (H1). Bay Area Cablevision, 130 Kearney St., San Francisco, CA 94108. Authorized power: 10-w. Antenna: 300-ft. above ground. Lat. 37° 29' 17", long. 121° 51' 59". Transmitter: 10.6-mi. N of San Jose. Equipment: ITS transmitter; Bogner antenna. Ownership: Bay Area Cablevision Inc.

San Jose—WNTM579 (H2). Bay Area Cablevision Inc., 130 Kearny St., San Francisco, CA 94108. Authorized power: 10-w. Antenna: 300-ft. above ground. Lat. 37° 29' 17", long. 121° 51' 59". Transmitter: 10.6-mi. N of Sab Jose. Equipment: ITS transmitter; Bogner antenna. Ownership: Bay Area Cablevision Inc.

San Luis Obispo—WGW606 (E group). TV Communications Network Inc., Suite 300, 10020 E. Girard Ave., Denver, CO 80231. Phone: 303-751-2900. Fax: 303-751-1081. E-mail: kroznoy@Plinet.com. Authorized power: 10-w. each.Antenna: 50-ft. above ground. Lat. 35° 21' 38", long. 120° 39' 21". Transmitter: Cuesta Peak, Los Padres National Forest, 5.5-mi. N of San Luis Obispo. Equipment: Emcee transmitter; Bogner antenna. Ownership: TV Communications Network Inc.

Santa Barbara—WLW891 (F). McDonald Group, Suite 300, One Office Park Circle, Birmingham, AL 35223. Authorized power: 10-w. each. Antenna: 450-ft. above ground. Lat. 34° 24' 37", long. 119° 42' 26". Transmitter: 730 Miramonte Dr. Equipment: Emcee transmitter; Bogner antenna. Ownership: McDonald Group.

Santa Barbara—WMX215 (H3). Mester's TV, Box 300406, 682 Argyle Rd., Brooklyn, NY 11230-0406. Phone: 718-282-9090. Fax: 718-469-0881. Authorized power: 10-w. Antenna: 60-ft. above ground. Lat. 34° 27' 58", long. 119° 40' 37". Transmitter: 3-mi. NW of Montecito. Equipment: Emcee transmitter; Andrew antenna. Ownership: Mester's TV.

Santa Barbara-Santa Maria-Lompoc—WLK217 (E group). Mester's TV, Box 300406, 682 Argyle Rd., Brooklyn, NY 11230-0406. Phone: 718-282-9090. Fax: 718-469-0881. Authorized power: 10-w. each. Antenna: 2145-ft. above ground. Lat. 34° 27' 55", long. 119° 40' 38". Transmitter: Gibraltar Peak, Santa Barbara. Equipment: Comwave transmitter; Andrew antenna. Requests change to 150-ft. above ground, lat. 34° 31' 32", long. 119° 57' 28"; transmitter to 1.2-mi. E of Santa Ynez, Santa Barbara. Ownership: Mester's TV.

Stockton—WHT786 (F). Golden Bear Communications, 6781 Coffee Rd., Bakersfield, CA 93308. Phone: 805-325-8655. Authorized power: 100-w. each. Antenna: 496-ft. above ground. Lat. 37° 43' 44", long. 121° 07' 34". Transmitter: 1220 S. Acacia Ave. Equipment: Emcee transmitter; Andrew antenna. Ownership: Golden Bear Communications Inc.

Ukiah—WNTF690 (H1). North Florida MMDS Partners, Box 4935, Rte. 1, Williston, FL 32696. Phone: 904-528-2290. Authorized power: 10-w. Antenna: 100-ft. above ground. Lat. 39° 07' 44", long. 123° 04' 30". Transmitter: Cow Mountain. Equipment: Comwave transmitter; Bogner antenna. Ownership: North Florida MMDS Partners.

Visalia—WGW280 (E group). American Telecasting Inc., Suite 300, 5575 Tech Center Dr., Colorado Springs, CO 80919. Phone: 719-260-5533. Fax: 719-260-5010. Authorized power: 20-w. each. Antenna: 142-ft. above ground. Lat. 36° 06' 26", long. 119° 01' 45". Transmitter: Republican Hill. Equipment: ITS transmitter; Andrew antenna. Requests change to 72-ft. above ground. Ownership: American Telecasting Inc.

Leased to Fresno MMDS Associates, 22245 Sunset Lane, Elkhart, IN 46516. Phone: 219-294-2522.

Visalia—WHF413 (F group). Manabi Hirasaki, 862 Camino Concordia, Camarillo, CA 93031. Authorized power: 10-w. each. Antenna: 305-ft. above ground. Lat. 36° 19' 37", long. 119° 33' 58". Transmitter: Hwy. 198 at 6th Ave. Equipment: Townsend transmitter; Bogner antenna. Ownership: Manabi Hirasaki.

Visalia—WNTM603 (H2). FMA Licensee Subsidiary Inc., 3526 E. Church St., Fresno, CA 93725. Phone: 209-442-1977. Fax: 209-442-1745. Authorized power: 20-w. Antenna: 75-ft. above ground. Lat. 36° 06' 25", long. 119° 01' 45". Transmitter: 21.7-mi. SE of Visalia. Equipment: ITS transmitter; Andrew antenna. Ownership: FMA Licensee Subsidiary Inc.

Leased to Fresno MMDS Associates, dba Choice TV, Box 2628, Fresno, CA 93725-2628. Phone: 209-442-1970.

Visalia—WNTM668 (H3). FMA Licensee Subsidiary Inc., 3526 E. Church St., Fresno, CA 93725. Phone: 209-442-1977. Fax: 209-442-1745. Authorized power: 50-w. Antenna: 453-ft. above ground. Lat. 36° 06' 25", long. 119° 01' 45". Transmitter: 21.7-mi. SE of Visalia. Equipment: ITS transmitter; Andrew antenna. Requests change to 20-w., 72-ft. above ground, lat. 36° 16' 25", long. 119° 01' 45". Ownership: FMA Licensee Subsidiary Inc.

Yuba City—WMH384 (E group). American Telecasting of Yuba City Inc., Suite 300, 5575 Tech Center Dr., Colorado Springs, CO 80919. Phone: 719-260-5533. Fax: 719-260-5010. Authorized power: 20-w. each. Antenna: 24-ft. above ground. Lat. 39° 12' 21", long. 121° 49' 10". Transmitter: South Butte of Sutter Buttes. Equipment: Emcee transmitter; Andrew antenna. Ownership: American Telecasting Inc.

Yuba City—WMH381 (F group). American Telecasting of Yuba City Inc., Suite 300, 5575 Tech Center Dr., Colorado Springs, CO 80919. Phone: 719-260-5533. Fax: 719-260-5010. Authorized power: 10-w. each. Antenna: 28-ft. above ground. Lat. 39° 12' 21", long. 121° 49' 10". Transmitter: South Butte of Sutter Buttes. Equipment: ITS transmitter; Andrew antenna. Requests change to 20-w., 24-ft. above ground. Ownership: American Telecasting Inc.

Colorado

Alamosa—WMY299 (F group). JCL Alamosa Colorado F Grand Alliance, 2203 Pasadena Place, Gulfport, FL 33707. Phone: 727-347-3266. Fax: 727-347-4649. E-mail: bonniedo@tampabay.rr.com. Authorized power: 10-w. each. Antenna: 100-ft. above ground. Lat. 37° 31' 30", long. 105° 54' 30". Transmitter: 2.5-mi. N of Alamosa. Equipment: Comwave transmitter; Bogner antenna. Ownership: JCL Alamosa Colorado F Grand Alliance.

Alamosa—WMX527 (H1). Grand Alliance Alamosa (E) Partnership, Box 660, 1920 N St.

NW, Washington, DC 20036. Phone: 202-887-0600. Authorized power: 15-w. Antenna: 100-ft. above ground. Lat. 37° 31' 30", long. 105° 54' 30". Transmitter: 2.5-mi. N of Alamosa. Equipment: Comwave transmitter; Andrew antenna. Ownership: Macro Distribution Systems Inc.

Alamosa—WMX256 (H2). Grand Alliance Alamosa (E) Partnership, Suite 660, 1920 N St. NW, Washington, DC 20036. Phone: 202-887-0600. Authorized power: 15-w. Antenna: 100-ft. above ground. Lat. 37° 31' 30", long. 105° 54' 30". Transmitter: 2.5-mi. N of Alamosa. Equipment: Comwave transmitter; Andrew antenna. Ownership: Macro Distribution Systems Inc.

Alamosa—WMX525 (H3). Grand Alliance Alamosa (E) Partnership, Suite 660, 1920 N St. NW, Washington, DC 20036. Phone: 202-887-0600. Authorized power: 15-w. Antenna: 100-ft. above ground. Lat. 37° 31' 30", long. 105° 54' 30". Transmitter: 2.5-mi. N of Alamosa. Equipment: Comwave transmitter; Andrew antenna. Ownership: Macro Distribution Systems Inc.

Burlington—WMY396 (E group). Laurence E. Wolff, Box 787, Gillette, WY 82717. Authorized power: 20-w. each. Antenna: 125-ft. above ground. Lat. 39° 17' 10", long. 102° 16' 30". Transmitter: Rtes. 385 & 70 Grain Elevator. Equipment: ITS transmitter; Andrew antenna. Ownership: Laurence E. Wolff.

Colorado Springs—WHT756 (E group). Thomas M. Glab, Box 627, Claremont, CA 91711. Phone: 909-621-1004. Fax: 909-624-2257. Authorized power: 10-w. each. Antenna: 132-ft. above ground. Lat. 38° 44' 46", long. 104° 51' 37". Transmitter: 6325 Transmitter Lane, Cheyenne Mountain. Equipment: Comwave transmitter; Bogner antenna. Ownership: Thomas M. Glab.

Colorado Springs—WHT758 (F group). American Telecasting of Colorado Springs Inc., Suite 300, 5575 Tech Center Dr., Colorado Springs, CO 80919. Phone: 719-260-5533. Fax: 719-260-5010. Authorized power: 10-w. each. Antenna: 117-ft. above ground. Lat. 38° 44' 46", long. 104° 51' 37". Transmitter: 6325 Transmitter Lane, Cheyenne Mountain. Equipment: Emcee transmitter; Bogner antenna. Ownership: American Telecasting Inc.

Colorado Springs—WNTA854 (H1). American Telecasting of Colorado Springs Inc., Suite 300, 5575 Tech Center Dr., Colorado Springs, CO 80919. Phone: 719-260-5533. Fax: 719-260-5010. Authorized power: 10-w. Antenna: 117-ft. above ground. Lat. 38° 44' 46", long. 104° 51' 37". Transmitter: 6325 Transmitter Lane, Cheyenne Mountain. Equipment: Emcee transmitter; Bogner antenna. Ownership: American Telecasting Inc.

Colorado Springs—WNTG791 (H2). American Telecasting of Colorado Springs Inc., Suite 300, 5575 Tech Center Dr., Colorado Springs, CO 80919. Phone: 719-260-5533. Fax: 719-260-5010. Authorized power: 50-w. Antenna: 132-ft. above ground. Lat. 38° 44' 46", long. 104° 51' 37". Transmitter: 6325 Transmitter Lane, Cheyenne Mountain. Equipment: Comwave transmitter; Bogner antenna. Ownership: American Telecasting Inc.

Colorado Springs—WNTG790 (H3). American Telecasting of Colorado Springs Inc., Suite 300, 5575 Tech Center Dr., Colorado Springs, CO 80919. Phone: 719-260-5533. Fax: 719-260-5010. Authorized power: 50-w. Antenna: 132-ft. above ground. Lat. 38° 44' 46", long. 104° 51' 37". Transmitter: 6325 Transmitter Lane, Cheyenne Mountain. Equipment: Comwave transmitter; Bogner antenna. Ownership: American Telecasting Inc.

Craig—WMI888 (E group). Kelli Bohrisch, 5178 Griffin Lane, Vacaville, CA 95688. Phone: 702-831-8335. Authorized power: 10-w. each. Antenna: 57-ft. above ground. Lat. 40° 33' 51", long. 107° 36' 37". Transmitter: Cedar Mountain. Equipment: Scientific-Atlanta transmitter; Andrew antenna. Ownership: Kelli Bohrisch.

Craig—WMI892 (F group). James H. Schroeder, 980 Meadow Lane, Fond du Lac, WI 54935. Phone: 414-922-6130. Authorized power: 10-w. each. Antenna: 57-ft. above ground. Lat. 40° 33' 51", long. 107° 36' 37". Transmitter: Cedar Mountain. Equipment: Scientific-Atlanta transmitter; Andrew antenna. Ownership: James H. Schroeder.

Denver—WLK321 (E group). American Telecasting of Denver Inc., Suite 300, 5575 Tech Center Dr., Colorado Springs, CO 80919. Phone: 719-260-5533. Fax: 719-260-5010. Authorized power: 50-w. each. Antenna: 60-ft. above ground. Lat. 39° 54' 48", long. 105° 17' 32". Transmitter: Eldorado Mountain. Equipment: Emcee transmitter; Andrew antenna.

Denver—WHK938 (F). Heritage Broadcasting Group, Box 627, Cadillac, MI 49601-0627. Authorized power: 10-w. each. Antenna: 60-ft. above ground. Lat. 39° 54' 48", long. 105° 17' 32". Transmitter: Eldorado Mountain. Equipment: Emcee transmitter; Bogner antenna. Ownership: Heritage Broadcasting Group.

Denver—WNTH953 (H1). American Telecasting of Denver Inc., Suite 300, 5575 Tech Center Dr., Colorado Springs, CO 80919. Phone: 719-260-5533. Fax: 719-260-5010. Authorized power: 50-w. Antenna: 60-ft. above ground. Lat. 39° 54' 48", long. 105° 17' 32". Transmitter: Eldorado Mountain. Equipment: Emcee transmitter; Andrew antenna. Ownership: American Telecasting Inc.

Denver—WNTH998 (H2). American Telecasting of Denver Inc., Suite 300, 5575 Tech Center Dr., Colorado Springs, CO 80919. Phone: 719-260-5533. Fax: 719-260-5010. Authorized power: 50-w. Antenna: 60-ft. above ground. Lat. 39° 54' 48", long. 105° 17' 32". Transmitter: Eldorado Mountain. Equipment: Emcee transmitter; Andrew antenna. Ownership: American Telecasting Inc.

Denver—WNEY681 (H3). American Telecasting Inc., Suite 300, 5575 Tech Center Dr., Colorado Springs, CO 80919. Phone: 719-260-5533. Fax: 719-260-5010. Authorized power: 50-w. Antenna: 60-ft. above ground. Lat. 39° 54' 48", long. 105° 17' 32". Transmitter: Eldorado Mountain. Equipment: Emcee transmitter; Andrew antenna. Ownership: American Telecasting Inc.

Fort Collins—WMH400 (E group). National Wireless Cable, 63 Dombey Circle, Thousand Oaks, CA 91360. Authorized power: 10-w. each. Antenna: 180-ft. above ground. Lat. 40° 20' 43", long. 105° 16' 16". Transmitter: 2-mi. N of Fort Collins. Equipment: Comwave transmitter; Bogner antenna. Ownership: National Wireless Cable.

Grand Junction—WLW761 (E group). Kravetz Media Corp., 5130 S. Hanover, Englewood, CO 80111. Authorized power: 10-w. each. Antenna: 80-ft. above ground. Lat. 39° 05' 20", long. 108° 13' 35". Transmitter: Grand Mesa. Equipment: Comwave transmitter; Bogner antenna. Ownership: Kravetz Media Corp.

Grand Junction—WMH720 (F group). Echonet Corp., Box 255, Evergreen, CO 80439. Authorized power: 10-w. each. Antenna: 206-ft. above ground. Lat. 39° 05' 41", long. 108° 34' 41". Transmitter: 1-mi. NW of Grand Junction. Equipment: Comwave transmitter; Bogner antenna. Ownership: Echonet Corp.

Greeley—WLW976 (E group). Pro-Communications Inc., 233 N. Garrard, Rantoul, IL 61866. Phone: 217-893-8730. Authorized power: 10-w. each. Antenna: 305-ft. above ground. Lat. 40° 29' 36", long. 105° 10' 53". Transmitter: Milner Mountain, Fort Collins. Equipment: Comwave transmitter; Bogner antenna. Ownership: Pro-Communications Inc.

Greeley—WMH425 (F group). Debra Chavez, Box 852, Morrison, CO 80465. Phone: 303-988-0234. Fax: 303-988-3019. Authorized power: 10-w. each. Antenna: 305-ft. above ground. Lat. 40° 22' 42", long. 104° 49' 56". Transmitter: County Rd. 25 & Rte. 54. Equipment: Comwave transmitter; Bogner antenna. Ownership: Debra Chavez.

La Junta—WMX202 (E group). JCL La Junta Colorado E Grand Alliance, 2203 Pasadena Place, Gulfport, FL 33707. Phone: 727-347-3266. Fax: 727-347-4649. E-mail: bonniedo@tampabay.rr.com. Authorized power: 20-w. each. Antenna: 394-ft. above ground. Lat. 37° 58' 43", long. 103° 34' 48". Transmitter: 1-mi. W, 0.25-mi. S on Rd. 27. Equipment: Veltek transmitter; Veltek antenna. Ownership: JCL La Junta Colorado E Grand Alliance.

La Junta—WMX201 (F group). JCL La Junta Colorado E Grand Alliance, 2203 Pasadena Place, Gulfport, FL 33707. Phone: 727-347-3266. Fax: 727-347-4649. E-mail: bonniedo@tampabay.rr.com. Authorized power: 20-w. each. Antenna: 394-ft. above ground. Lat. 37° 58' 43", long. 103° 34' 48". Transmitter: 1-mi. W, 0.25-mi. S on Rd. 27. Equipment: Veltek transmitter; Veltek antenna. Ownership: JCL La Junta Colorado E Grand Alliance.

Lamar—WMX203 (E group). JCL Lamar Colorado E Grand Alliance, 11611 Harborview Dr., Cleveland, OH 44102. Authorized power: 10-w. each. Antenna: 294-ft. above ground. Lat. 38° 10' 19", long. 102° 40' 50". Transmitter: 2-mi. S of Lamar. Equipment: Comwave transmitter; Bogner antenna. Ownership: JCL Lamar Colorado E Grand Alliance.

Lamar—WMX200 (F group). JCL Lamar Colorado E Grand Alliance, 11611 Harborview Dr., Cleveland, OH 44102. Authorized power: 10-w. each. Antenna: 294-ft. above ground. Lat. 38° 10' 19", long. 102° 40' 50". Transmitter: 2-mi. S of Lamar. Equipment: Comwave transmitter; Bogner antenna. Ownership: JCL Lamar Colorado E Grand Alliance.

Leadville—WMH700 (E group). Colowave Inc., Box F, Shawnee, CO 80475. Authorized power: 10-w. each. Antenna: 33-ft. above ground. Lat. 39° 11' 41", long. 106° 10' 44". Transmitter: 2.3-mi. W of Leavick. Equipment: Emcee transmitter; Andrew antenna. Ownership: Colowave Inc.

Mancos—WLW762 (F group). Multi-Point TV Distributors Inc., 331 Sea Ridge Dr., La Jolla, CA 92037. Phone: 619-488-2324. Authorized power: 10-w. each. Antenna: 46-ft. above ground. Lat. 37° 20' 26", long. 108° 13' 51". Transmitter: 3.8-mi. E of Mancos. Equipment: Comwave transmitter; Andrew antenna. Ownership: Multi-Point TV Distributors Inc.

Prowers City—WLW726 (H1). Eagle Television Inc., Box 35, Eads, CO 81036-0035. Phone: 719-438-2221. Fax: 719-438-5592. Authorized power: 10-w. Antenna: 194-ft. above ground. Lat. 38° 10' 19", long. 102° 40' 50". Transmitter: 4240 Road PP. Equipment: Comwave transmitter; Andrew antenna. Ownership: Eagle Television Inc.

Prowers City—WLW730 (H2). Eagle Television Inc., Box 35, Eads, CO 81036-0035. Phone: 719-438-2221. Fax: 719-438-5592. Authorized power: 10-w. Antenna: 194-ft. above ground. Lat. 38° 10' 19", long. 102° 40' 50". Transmitter: 4240 Road PP. Equipment: Comwave transmitter; Andrew antenna. Ownership: Eagle Television Inc.

Prowers City—WLW734 (H3). Eagle Television Inc., Box 35, Eads, CO 81036-0035. Phone: 719-438-2221. Fax: 719-438-5592. Authorized power: 10-w. Antenna: 194-ft. above ground. Lat. 38° 10' 19", long. 102° 40' 50". Transmitter: 4240 Road PP. Equipment: Comwave transmitter; Andrew antenna. Ownership: Eagle Television Inc.

Pueblo—WMH393 (E group). National Wireless Cable, 63 Dombey Circle, Thousand Oaks, CA 91360. Authorized power: 10-w. each. Antenna: 80-ft. above ground. Lat. 38° 02' 29", long. 105° 11' 05". Transmitter: 10-mi. W of Beulah. Equipment: Comwave transmitter; Bogner antenna. Ownership: National Wireless Cable.

Pueblo—WLW883 (F group). Lawrence N. Brandt, Suite 220, 3201 New Mexico Ave. NW, Washington, DC 20016. Phone: 202-363-1100. Authorized power: 50-w. each. Antenna: 190-ft. above ground. Lat. 38° 12' 18", long. 104° 42' 24". Transmitter: Jackson Hill. Equipment: Emcee transmitter; Andrew antenna. Ownership: Lawrence N. Brandt.

Sterling—WMX216 (F group). Grand Alliance Sterling (F) Partnership, Suite 660, 1920 N St. NW, Washington, DC 20036. Phone: 202-887-0600. Fax: 202-457-0126. Authorized power: 10-w. each. Antenna: 300-ft. above ground. Lat. 40° 36' 56", long. 103° 02' 02". Transmitter: 8.2-mi. E of Sterling. Equipment: Emcee transmitter; Andrew antenna. Ownership: Macro Distribution Systems Inc.

Sterling—WMX934 (H3). Grand Alliance Sterling (F) Partnership, Suite 660, 1920 N St. NW, Washington, DC 20036. Phone: 202-887-0600. Fax: 202-457-0126. Authorized power: 200-w. Antenna: 300-ft. above ground. Lat. 40° 36' 56", long. 103° 02' 02". Transmitter: 8.2-mi. E of Sterling. Equipment: Comwave transmitter; Andrew antenna. Ownership: Macro Distribution Systems Inc.

Vail—WLW971 (E group). Patrick/Hybl Communications. Authorized power: 10-w. each. Antenna: 530-ft. above ground. Lat. 39° 38' 08", long. 106° 26' 46". Transmitter: 2-mi. W of Vail. Equipment: Comwave transmitter; Bogner antenna. Ownership: Patrick/Hybl Communications.

Wray—WHK934 (E group). Southwest Telecommunications Cooperative Assn. Inc., Box 309, Palisade, NE 69040-0366. Phone: 308-285-3880. Fax: 308-285-3811. Authorized power: 50-w. each. Antenna: 490-ft. above ground. Lat. 40° 00' 40", long. 102° 19' 31". Transmitter: 4.9-mi. W, 4.5-mi. S of Wray. Equipment: Emcee transmitter; Andrew antenna. Ownership: Southwest Telecommunications Co-op Assn. Inc.

Wray—WHK935 (F group). Nebraska Telecommunications Inc., 616 Chestnut Dr., Loveland, CO 80538. Phone: 303-663-1072. Authorized power: 50-w. each. Antenna: 490-ft. above ground. Lat. 40° 00' 40", long. 102° 19' 31". Transmitter: 4.9-mi. W, 4.5-mi. S of Wray.

Equipment: Emcee transmitter; Andrew antenna. Ownership: Nebraska Telecommunications Inc.
Leased to Southwest Telecommunications Corp., 215 N. Main St., Palisade, NE 69040. Phone: 308-285-3295.

Wray—WNEX782 (H1 & 3)). Southwest Telecommunications Cooperative Assn. Inc., 215 N. Main St., Palisade, NE 69040. Phone: 308-285-3880. Fax: 308-285-3811. Authorized power: 10-w. each. Antenna: 485-ft. above ground. Lat. 40° 00' 40", long. 102° 19' 31". Transmitter: 4.9-mi. W, 4.5-mi. S of Wray. Equipment: Emcee/ITS transmitter; Andrew antenna. Ownership: Southwest Telecommunications Co-op Assn. Inc.

Wray—WNEX651 (H2). Nebraska Telecommunications Inc., 616 Chestnut Dr., Loveland, CO 80538. Phone: 303-663-1072. Authorized power: 10-w. Antenna: 485-ft. above ground. Lat. 40° 00' 40", long. 102° 19' 31". Transmitter: 4.9-mi. W, 4.5-mi. S of Wray. Equipment: Emcee transmitter; Andrew antenna. Ownership: Nebraska Telecommunications Inc.
Leased to Southwest Telecommunications Corp., 215 N. Main St., Palisade, NE 69040. Phone: 800-535-7823.

Connecticut

Farmington—WHT672 (F group). Connecticut License Inc., Suite 100, 2101 Wilson Blvd., Arlington, VA 22201. Phone: 703-812-8800. Fax: 703-812-8808. Authorized power: 10-w. each. Antenna: 300-ft. above ground. Lat. 41° 40' 48", long. 72° 49' 34". Transmitter: N. Mountain Rd., 1-mi. from Rte. 372. Equipment: Comwave transmitter; Bogner antenna. Ownership: CAI Wireless Systems Inc.
Leased to Housatonic Wireless Inc., c/o George W. Bott, Box 186, Rexford, NY 12148.

Farmington—WNTG352 (H2). Connecticut License Inc., Suite 100, 2101 Wilson Blvd., Arlington, VA 22201. Phone: 703-812-8800. Fax: 703-812-8808. Authorized power: 10-w. Antenna: 300-ft. above ground. Lat. 41° 40' 48", long. 72° 49' 34". Transmitter: N. Mountain Rd., 1-mi. from Rte. 372. Equipment: Comwave transmitter; Bogner antenna. Requests change to 351-ft. above ground, lat. 41° 42' 13", long. 72° 49' 57"; transmitter to Rattlesnake Mountain Rd.; Andrew antenna. Ownership: CAI Wireless Systems Inc.

Hartford—WHT671 (E group). Thomas M. Glab, Box 627, Claremont, CA 91711. Phone: 909-621-1004. Fax: 909-624-2257. Authorized power: 10-w. each. Antenna: 626-ft. above ground. Lat. 41° 46' 30", long. 72° 48' 04". Transmitter: 580 Deercliff Rd. Equipment: Emcee transmitter; Andrew antenna. Ownership: Thomas M. Glab.

New Haven—WMI358 (F group). MCI Telecommunications Corp., 1133 19th St. NW, Washington, DC 20036. Phone: 202-736-6757. Fax: 202-736-6408. E-mail: brae@Harrisondigital.com. Web Site: http://www.mci.com. Authorized power: 10-w. each. Antenna: 199-ft. above ground. Lat. 41° 18' 33", long. 72° 55' 26". Transmitter: 234 Church St. Equipment: Emcee transmitter; Andrew antenna. Ownership: MCI Telecommunications Corp.

District of Columbia

Washington—WHT659 (F group). F Corp., George Mason U., Kelley Dr., Fairfax, VA 22030-4444. Phone: 703-993-3100. Fax: 703-273-2417. E-mail: mkelley@gmu.edu. Authorized power: 50-w. each. Antenna: 635-ft. above ground. Lat. 38° 57' 49", long. 77° 06' 18". Transmitter: 5202 River Rd., Bethesda. Equipment: ITS transmitter; Andrew antenna. Ownership: F Corp.
Leased to CAI Wireless Systems, 2101 Wilson Blvd., Suite 100, Arlington, VA 22201. Phone: 703-812-8800. Fax: 703-812-8808.

Florida

Bradenton—WMH513 (E group). Fortuna Systems Corp. Authorized power: 10-w. each. Antenna: 639-ft. above ground. Lat. 27° 29' 08", long. 82° 32' 00". Transmitter: 2404 13th Ave. E. Equipment: Emcee transmitter; Andrew antenna. Ownership: Fortuna Systems Corp.

Bradenton—WNTK634 (H3). Senvista General Partnership, 7521 E. Edgemont, Scottsdale, AZ 85257. Phone: 602-994-0919. Authorized power: 50-w. Antenna: 295-ft. above ground. Lat. 27° 28' 30", long. 82° 31' 47". Transmitter: 2800 27th St. E. Equipment: Emcee transmitter; Andrew antenna. Requests change to 10-w, 296-ft. above ground, lat. 27° 29' 08", long. 82° 32' 00". Ownership: Senvista General Partnership.

Daytona Beach—WHT761 (E group). Line of Site Inc., 8611 E. Santa Catalina Dr., Scottsdale, AZ 85255. Phone: 602-585-1839. Authorized power: 10-w. each. Antenna: 445-ft. above ground. Lat. 29° 10' 29", long. 81° 09' 32". Transmitter: Indian Lake Rd. Equipment: ITS transmitter; Andrew antenna. Ownership: Line of Site Inc.

Daytona Beach—WHT762 (F group). BellSouth Wireless Cable Inc., Suite 414, 1100 Abernathy Rd. NE, Atlanta, GA 30328. Phone: 770-673-2800. Authorized power: 10-w. each. Antenna: 445-ft. above ground. Lat. 29° 10' 29", long. 81° 09' 32". Transmitter: Indian Lake Rd. Equipment: Comwave transmitter; Andrew antenna. Ownership: BellSouth Entertainment Inc.

Daytona Beach—WMX941 (H1). BellSouth Wireless Cable Inc., Suite 414, 1100 Abernathy Rd. NE, Atlanta, GA 30328. Phone: 770-673-2800. Authorized power: 10-w. Antenna: 445-ft. above ground. Lat. 29° 10' 29", long. 81° 09' 32". Transmitter: Indian Lake Rd. Equipment: Emcee transmitter; Andrew antenna. Ownership: BellSouth Entertainment Inc.

Daytona Beach—WNEY905 (H2). BellSouth Wireless Cable Inc., Suite 414, 1100 Abernathy Rd. NE, Atlanta, GA 30328. Phone: 770-673-2800. Authorized power: 10-w. Antenna: 445-ft. above ground. Lat. 29° 10' 29", long. 81° 09' 32". Transmitter: Indian Lake Rd. Equipment: Comwave transmitter; Andrew antenna. Ownership: BellSouth Entertainment Inc.

Daytona Beach—WNEZ718 (H3). BellSouth Wireless Cable Inc., Suite 414, 1100 Abernathy Rd. NE, Atlanta, GA 30328. Phone: 770-673-2800. Authorized power: 10-w. Antenna: 445-ft. above ground. Lat. 29° 10' 29", long. 81° 09' 32". Transmitter: Indian Lake Rd. Equipment: Emcee transmitter; Andrew antenna. Ownership: BellSouth Entertainment Inc.

Fort Myers—WHK973 (E group). Columbia Wireless Corp., Suite 501, 1100 17th St. NW, Washington, DC 20036-4646. Phone: 202-223-4449. Fax: 202-223-4450. E-mail: rgould@cwix.com. Authorized power: 10-w. each. Antenna: 492-ft. above ground. Lat. 26° 43' 35", long. 81° 47' 12". Transmitter: N end of Bahia Vista, Fort Myers (Lee County), FL. Equipment: Emcee transmitter. Requests change to 50-w. each, 489-ft. above ground. Ownership: Columbia Wireless Corp.
Leased to BellSouth Entertainment Inc., 1100 Abernathy Rd., Suite 414, Atlanta, GA 30328. Phone: 770-392-4575.

Fort Myers—WHK974 (F group). MMDS Fort Myers Inc., 2700 Chain Bridge Rd. NW, Washington, DC 20016. Phone: 202-293-0700. Fax: 202-237-7742. E-mail: nevisbill@aol.com. Authorized power: 10-w. each. Antenna: 492-ft. above ground. Lat. 26° 43' 35", long. 81° 47' 12". Transmitter: N end of Bahia Vista. Equipment: ITS transmitter; Bogner antenna. Requests change to 50-w. each, 489-ft. above ground, Emcee transmitter; Andrew antenna. Ownership: MDS Signal Group.
Leased to BellSouth Entertainment South.

Fort Myers—WMX373 (H1). BellSouth Wireless Cable Inc., Suite 414, 1100 Abernathy Rd. NE, Atlanta, GA 30328. Phone: 770-673-2800. Authorized power: 50-w. Antenna: 492-ft. above ground. Lat. 26° 43' 35", long. 81° 47' 12". Transmitter: N end of Bahia Vista. Equipment: Emcee transmitter; Andrew antenna. Requests change to 489-ft. above ground. Ownership: BellSouth Entertainment Network.

Fort Myers—WNTH636 (H2). Lee County Board of Commissioners, Box 398, 1540 Broadway, Fort Myers, FL 33902. Phone: 941-338-3208. Authorized power: 50-w. Antenna: 489-ft. above ground. Lat. 26° 43' 35", long. 81° 47' 12". Transmitter: N end of Bahia Vista. Equipment: Emcee transmitter; Andrew antenna. Ownership: Lee County Board of Commissioners.

Fort Myers—WMX338 (H3). BellSouth Wireless Cable Inc., Suite 414, 1100 Abernathy Rd. NE, Atlanta, GA 30328. Phone: 770-673-2800. Authorized power: 50-w. Antenna: 492-ft. above ground. Lat. 26° 43' 35", long. 81° 47' 12". Transmitter: N end of Bahia Vista. Equipment: Emcee transmitter; Bogner antenna. Requests change to 489-ft. above ground, Andrew antenna. Ownership: BellSouth Entertainment Inc.

Fort Pierce—WLW758 (E group). WBSFP Licensing Corp., Box 7307, Port St. Lucie, FL 34985. Phone: 407-871-1688. Fax: 407-871-0155. Authorized power: 10-w. each. Antenna: 18-ft. above ground. Lat. 27° 19' 17", long. 80° 18' 49". Transmitter: 37th St. Equipment: Emcee transmitter; Andrew antenna. Requests change to 50-w. each, 500-ft. above ground, lat. 27° 19' 27", long. 80° 18' 49"; transmitter to 1100 Dyer Rd.; Comwave transmitter. Ownership: Wireless Broadcasting Systems of America Inc. Sale pends to Boston Ventures Co. LP IV.
Leased to Coastal Wireless Cable Television, 8423 S. U.S. Rte. 1, Box 7307, Port St. Lucie, FL 34985. Phone: 407-871-1688.

Fort Pierce—WLK308 (F group). WBSFP Licensing Corp., 8423 U.S. Rte. 1, Port St. Lucie, FL 34952. Phone: 407-871-1688. Authorized power: 10-w. each. Antenna: 296-ft. above ground. Lat. 27° 19' 17", long. 80° 18' 49". Transmitter: Old WOVV(FM) Tower, 37th St. Equipment: Emcee transmitter; Andrew antenna. Ownership: WJB-TV Fort Pierce Inc.

Fort Pierce—WNTJ380 (H1). WBSFP Licensing Corp., 8423 S. U.S. Rte. 1, Port St. Lucie, FL 34952. Phone: 407-871-1688. Authorized power: 50-w. Antenna: 524-ft. above ground. Lat. 27° 19' 27", long. 80° 18' 49". Transmitter: 1100 Dyer Rd. Equipment: Comwave transmitter; Andrew antenna. Ownership: WJB-TV Fort Pierce Inc.
Leased to Coastal Wireless Cable Television, 8423 S. U.S. Rte. 1, Box 7307, Port St. Lucie, FL 34985. Phone: 407-871-1688.

Fort Walton Beach—WNTJ427 (H1). Wireless One PCS Inc., Suite 400, 2506 Lakeland Dr., Jackson, MS 39208. Phone: 601-933-6879. Authorized power: 50-w. Antenna: 275-ft. above ground. Lat. 30° 27' 03", long. 86° 34' 17". Transmitter: Shalimar Elementary, Elgin Pkwy. Equipment: Comwave transmitter; Andrew antenna. Ownership: Wireless One Inc.

Fort Pierce—WNTI841 (H2). WBSFP Licensing Corp., 8423 S. U.S. Rte. 1, Port St. Luice, FL 34952. Phone: 407-871-1688. Antenna: 518-ft. above ground. Lat. 27° 26' 05", long. 80° 21' 42". Transmitter: 37th St. Equipment: Emcee transmitter; Andrew antenna. Ownership: WJB-TV Fort Pierce Inc.
Leased to Coastal Wireless Cable Television, 8423 S. U.S. Rte. 1, Box 7307, Port St. Lucie, FL 34985. Phone: 407-871-1688.

Fort Walton Beach—WNTJ426 (H2). Wireless One PCS Inc., Suite 400, 2506 Lakeland Dr., Jackson, MS 39208. Phone: 601-933-6879. Authorized power: 50-w. Antenna: 275-ft. above ground. Lat. 30° 27' 03", long. 86° 34' 17". Transmitter: Shalimar Elementary School. Equipment: Comwave transmitter; Andrew antenna. Ownership: Wireless One Inc.

Fort Walton Beach—WNTJ383 (H3). Wireless One PCS Inc., Suite 400, 2506 Lakeland Dr., Jackson, MS 39208. Phone: 601-933-6879. Authorized power: 50-w. Antenna: 275-ft. above ground. Lat. 30° 27' 03", long. 86° 34' 17". Transmitter: Shalimar Elementary, Elgin Pkwy. Equipment: Comwave transmitter; Andrew antenna. Ownership: Wireless One Inc.

Gainesville—WGW515 (E group). Wireless One PCS Inc., Suite 400, 2506 Lakeland Dr., Jackson, MS 39208. Phone: 601-933-6879. Authorized power: 50-w. each. Antenna: 706-ft. above ground. Lat. 29° 56' 29", long. 82° 23' 51". Transmitter: 1.3-mi. NE of State Rte. 18. Equipment: ITS transmitter; Andrew antenna. Ownership: Wireless One Inc.

Gainesville—WMH620 (F group). Wireless One PCS Inc., Suite 400, 2506 Lakeland Dr., Jackson, MS 39208. Phone: 601-933-6879. Authorized power: 50-w. each. Antenna: 706-ft. above ground. Lat. 29° 56' 29", long. 82° 23' 51". Transmitter: 1.3-mi. NE of State Rte. 18. Equipment: ITS transmitter; Andrew antenna. Ownership: Wireless One Inc.

Jacksonville—WHT675 (E group). BellSouth Wireless Cable Inc., Suite 414, 1100 Abernathy Rd. NE, Atlanta, GA 30328. Phone: 770-673-2800. Authorized power: 100-w. each. Antenna: 600-ft. above ground. Lat. 30° 16' 51", long. 81° 34' 12". Transmitter: Hogan County Rd. Equipment: Emcee transmitter; Andrew antenna. Ownership: BellSouth Entertainment Inc.

Jacksonville—WHT676 (F group). BellSouth Wireless Cable Inc., Suite 414, 1100 Abernathy Rd. NE, Atlanta, GA 30328. Phone: 770-673-2800. Authorized power: 100-w. each. Antenna: 1030-ft. above ground. Lat. 30° 16' 53", long. 81° 34' 15". Transmitter: Hogan County Rd. Equipment: Emcee transmitter; Andrew antenna. Requests change to 600-ft. above ground, lat. 30° 16' 51", long. 81° 34'

21"; transmitter to 8675 Hogan Rd. Ownership: BellSouth Entertainment Inc.
Leased to American Telecasting Inc., 5575 Tech Center Dr., Suite 300, Colorado Springs, CO 80919. Phone: 719-260-5533. Fax: 719-260-5010.

Jacksonville—WNTJ809 (H1). Lynn Twedt, 701 Grant St., Harvard, IL 60033. Phone: 815-943-4760. Authorized power: 10-w. Antenna: 257-ft. above ground. Lat. 30° 19' 10", long. 81° 38' 18". Transmitter: 100 Festival Park Ave. Equipment: Emcee transmitter; Andrew antenna. Requests change to 600-ft. above ground, lat. 30° 16' 51", long. 81° 34' 12"; transmitter to 8675 Hogan Rd. Ownership: Lynn Twedt.

Jacksonville—WMX382 (H2). BellSouth Wireless Cable Inc., Suite 414, 1100 Abernathy Rd. NE, Atlanta, GA 30328. Phone: 770-673-2800. Authorized power: 100-w. Antenna: 1030-ft. above ground. Lat. 30° 16' 53", long. 81° 34' 15". Transmitter: Hogan County & Old Hogan Rds. Equipment: Emcee transmitter; Andrew antenna. Requests change to 600-ft. above ground, lat. 30° 16' 51", long. 81° 34' 12"; transmitter to 8675 Hogan Rd. Ownership: BellSouth Entertainment Inc.

Jacksonville—WMX383 (H3). BellSouth Wireless Cable Inc., Suite 414, 1100 Abernathy Rd. NE, Atlanta, GA 30328. Phone: 770-675-2800. Authorized power: 100-w. Antenna: 1030-ft. above ground. Lat. 30° 16' 53", long. 81° 34' 15". Transmitter: Hogan County & Old Hogan Rds. Equipment: Emcee transmitter; Andrew antenna. Requests change to 600-ft. above ground, lat. 30° 16' 51", long. 81° 34' 12"; transmitter to 8675 Hogan Rd. Ownership: BellSouth Entertainment Inc.

Key West—WMH604 (E group). Thomas M. Glab, 2129 San Marcos Place, Claremont, CA 91711. Phone: 909-621-1004. Fax: 909-624-2257. Authorized power: 10-w. each. Antenna: 40-ft. above ground. Lat. 24° 33' 16", long. 81° 48' 07". Transmitter: 513 Flemming. Equipment: Emcee transmitter; Andrew antenna. Ownership: Thomas M. Glab.

Key West—WMY476 (F group). Wireless 2000 Partnership, 1440 Chattahoochee Run Dr., Suwanee, GA 30174. Phone: 770-932-5452. Authorized power: 10-w. each. Antenna: 115-ft. above ground. Lat. 24° 33' 18", long. 81° 48' 07". Transmitter: 527 Southard St. Equipment: Comwave transmitter; Andrew antenna. Ownership: Wireless 2000 Partnership.

Lake City—WNTM541 (H group). NBI TV Partners, 2570 Chateau Way, Livermore, CA 94550. Phone: 510-443-1415. Authorized power: 200-w. each. Antenna: 535-ft. above ground. Lat. 30° 07' 44", long. 82° 52' 49". Transmitter: Rte. 49, 8-mi. S of Lake City. Equipment: Comwave transmitter; Andrew antenna. Ownership: NBI TV Partners.

Lakeland—WHK925 (E group). Lakeland BDC-MMDS Co., 28 Cadman Plaza W, Brooklyn, NY 11201. Phone: 718-935-1502. Authorized power: 15.8-w. each. Antenna: 399-ft. above ground. Lat. 27° 59' 35", long. 81° 53' 23". Transmitter: 3433 Winter Lake Rd. Equipment: Comwave transmitter; Andrew antenna. Ownership: Broadcast Data Corp.

Lakeland—WMI397 (H1). BellSouth Wireless Cable Inc., Suite 414, 1100 Abernathy Rd. NE, Atlanta, GA 30328. Phone: 770-673-2800. Authorized power: 50-w. Antenna: 399-ft. above ground. Lat. 27° 59' 35", long. 81° 53' 23". Transmitter: 0.38-mi. SE of Lakeland. Equipment: Emcee transmitter; Andrew antenna. Ownership: BellSouth Entertainment Inc.

Lakeland—WMY472 (H2). BellSouth Wireless Cable, Suite 414, 1100 Abernathy Rd. NE, Atlanta, GA 30328. Phone: 770-673-2800. Authorized power: 50-w. Antenna: 399-t. above ground. Lat. 27° 59' 35", long. 81° 53' 23". Transmitter: 3433 Winter Lake Rd. Equipment: Emcee transmitter; Andrew antenna. Ownership: BellSouth Entertainment Inc.

Lakeland—WMI401 (H3). BellSouth Wireless Cable Inc., Suite 414, 1100 Abernathy Rd. NE, Atlanta, GA 30328. Phone: 770-673-2800. Authorized power: 50-w. Antenna: 399-ft. above ground. Lat. 27° 57' 35", long. 81° 53' 23". Transmitter: 0.38-mi. SE of Lakeland. Equipment: Emcee transmitter; Andrew antenna. Ownership: BellSouth Entertainment Inc.

Lakeland-Winter Haven—WHK958 (F group). Delta Band Services Ltd., Box 1241, Suess Path, Quogue, NY 11909. Phone: 516-563-9354. Authorized power: 50-w. each. Antenna: 399-ft. above ground. Lat. 27° 59' 35", long. 81° 53' 23". Transmitter: 0.4-mi. SE of Lakeland. Equipment: ITS transmitter; Andrew antenna. Ownership: Delta Band Services Ltd.

Melbourne—WMI887 (E group). WBSM Licensing Corp., Suite 325, 9250 E. Costilla Ave., Englewood, CO 80112. Phone: 303-649-1195. Fax: 303-649-1196. Authorized power: 50-w. each. Antenna: 500-ft. above ground. Lat. 28° 08' 15", long. 80° 42' 11". Transmitter: 1865 Harlock Rd. Equipment: Emcee transmitter; Andrew, Bogner antenna. Requests change to 496-ft. above ground. Ownership: Wireless Broadcasting Systems of America Inc. Sale pends to Boston Ventures Co. LP IV.
Leased to Coastal Wireless Cable Television, 4450 E. Eau Galle Blvd., Suite 180, Melbourne, FL 32934. Phone: 407-254-0430.

Melbourne—WMI891 (F group). WBSM Licensing Corp., Suite 325, 9250 E. Costilla Ave., Englewood, CO 80112. Phone: 303-649-1195. Fax: 303-649-1196. Authorized power: 50-w. each. Antenna: 500-ft. above ground. Lat. 28° 08' 15", long. 80° 42' 11". Transmitter: 1865 Harlock Rd. Equipment: Emcee transmitter; Andrew, Bogner antenna. Requests change to 496-ft. above ground. Ownership: Wireless Broadcasting Systems of America Inc. Sale pends to Boston Ventures Co. LP IV.
Leased to Coastal Wireless Cable Television, 4450 E. Eau Galle Blvd., Suite 180, Melbourne, FL 32934. Phone: 407-254-0430.

Melbourne—WNTJ436 (H1). WBSM Licensing Corp., Suite 325, 9250 E. Costilla Ave., Englewood, CO 80112. Phone: 303-649-1195. Fax: 303-649-1196. Authorized power: 50-w. Antenna: 500-ft. above ground. Lat. 28° 08' 15", long. 80° 42' 11". Transmitter: 1865 Harlock Rd. Equipment: Emcee transmitter; Andrew, Bogner antenna. Ownership: Wireless Broadcasting Systems of America Inc. Sale pends to Boston Ventures Co. LP IV.
Leased to Coastal Wireless Cable Television, 4450 E. Eau Galle Blvd., Suite 180, Melbourne, FL 32934. Phone: 407-254-0430.

Melbourne—WNTM547 (H3). WBSM Licensing Corp., Suite 325, 9250 E. Costilla Ave., Englewood, CO 80112. Phone: 303-649-1195. Fax: 303-649-1196. Authorized power: 50-w. Antenna: 500-ft. above ground. Lat. 28° 08' 15", long. 80° 42' 11". Transmitter: 1865 Harlock Rd. Equipment: Emcee transmitter; Andrew, Bogner antenna. Requests change to 496-ft. above ground. Ownership: Wireless Broadcasting Systems of America Inc. Sale pends to Boston Ventures Co. . LP IV.
Leased to Coastal Wireless Cable Television, 4450 E. Eau Galle Blvd., Suite 180, Melbourne, FL 32934. Phone: 407-254-0430.

Miami—WHT639 (F group). Private Networks Inc., Box 023707, Brooklyn, NY 11201. Phone: 212-777-4740. Authorized power: 10-w. each. Antenna: 411-ft. above ground. Lat. 25° 46' 25", long. 80° 11' 18". Transmitter: 2 S. Biscayne Blvd. Equipment: Comwave transmitter; Bogner antenna. Requests change to 403-ft. above ground. Ownership: Private Networks Inc.

Miami—WNEK346 (H1). South Florida Television Inc., Suite 2001, 156 W. 56th St., New York, NY 10019. Authorized power: 20-w. Antenna: 763-ft. above ground. Lat. 25° 46' 20", long. 80° 11' 20". Transmitter: Biscayne Blvd. & First St. SE. Equipment: Comwave transmitter; Andrew antenna. Ownership: BellSouth Entertainment Inc.

Miami—WHJ893 (H2). South Florida Television, Suite 2001, 156 W. 56th St., New York, NY 10019. Antenna: 476-ft. above ground. Lat. 25° 46' 25", long. 80° 11' 18". Transmitter: 2 S. Biscayne Blvd. Ownership: BellSouth Corp.

Miami—WEF376 (H3). Metropolitan Dade County, 5680 S.W. 87th Ave., Miami, FL 33173. Phone: 305-596-8898. Authorized power: 10-w. Antenna: 527-ft. above ground. Lat. 25° 46' 30", long. 80° 11' 49". Transmitter: 111 N.W. First Ave. Equipment: ITS transmitter; Andrew antenna. Ownership: Metropolitan Dade County.

Naples—WNTI465 (H1). American Telecasting Development Inc., Suite 300, 5575 Tech Center Dr., Colorado Springs, CO 80919. Phone: 719-260-5533. Fax: 719-260-5010. Antenna: 305-ft. above ground. Lat. 26° 19' 00", long. 81° 47' 13". Transmitter: Channel 30 Dr. Equipment: Emcee transmitter; Andrew antenna. Ownership: American Telecasting Inc.

Naples—WNTI333 (H3). American Telecasting Development Inc., Suite 300, 5575 Tech Center Dr., Colorado Springs, CO 80919. Phone: 719-260-5533. Fax: 719-260-5010. Authorized power: 50-w. Antenna: 305-ft. above ground. Lat. 26° 19' 00", long. 81° 47' 13". Transmitter: Channel 30 Dr. Equipment: Emcee transmitter; Andrew antenna. Ownership: American Telecasting Inc.

Ocala—WLW911 (F group). Nucentrix Spectrum Resources Inc., Suite 200, 200 Chisholm Place, Plano, TX 75075. Phone: 972-423-9494. Fax: 972-423-0819. Authorized power: 10-w. each. Antenna: 421-ft. above ground. Lat. 29° 10' 59", long. 82° 02' 15". Transmitter: 3-mi. SW of Junction SR 417. Equipment: Comwave transmitter; Andrew antenna. Ownership: Nucentrix Broadband Networks.

Ocala—WNTF688 (H1). North Florida MMDS Partnership, Box 4935, Rte. 1, Williston, FL 32696. Authorized power: 10-w. Antenna: 296-ft. above ground. Lat. 29° 10' 59", long. 82° 02' 15". Transmitter: W of Alvarez, 4th & 5th Sts. SE. Equipment: Comwave transmitter; Andrew antenna. Ownership: North Florida MMDS Partners.

Oldsmar—WHT700 (E group). Bay Area License Inc., 18940 U.S. 19 N, Clearwater, FL 34624. Phone: 813-530-1812. Authorized power: 100-w. each. Antenna: 636-ft. above ground. Lat. 28° 02' 20", long. 82° 39' 29". Transmitter: 105 Dunbar Ave. Equipment: Emcee transmitter; Andrew antenna. Ownership: Videotron (Bay Area) Inc.

Oldsmar—WNTB227 (H1). Quadrangle Communications Inc., 836 E. Washington St., San Diego, CA 92103. Phone: 619-260-0165. Authorized power: 100-w. Antenna: 636-ft. above ground. Lat. 28° 02' 20", long. 82° 39' 29". Transmitter: 105 Dunbar Ave. Equipment: Comwave transmitter; Andrew antenna. Ownership: Quadrangle Communications Inc.

Oldsmar—WHJ947 (H3). Via/Net Companies, 836 E. Washington St., San Diego, CA 92103. Phone: 619-260-0110. Authorized power: 100-w. Antenna: 636-ft. above ground. Lat. 28° 02' 20", long. 82° 39' 29". Transmitter: 105 Dunbar Ave. Equipment: Comwave transmitter; Andrew antenna. Ownership: Via/Net Companies.

Orlando—WHT731 (E group). Line of Site Inc., 8611 E. Santa Catalina Dr., Scottsdale, AZ 85255-2870. Phone: 602-585-1837. Authorized power: 50-w. each. Antenna: 402-ft. above ground. Lat. 28° 32' 22", long. 81° 22' 46". Transmitter: 200 S. Orange Ave. Equipment: Emcee transmitter; Andrew antenna. Ownership: Line of Site Inc.

Orlando—WHT732 (F group). Orlando BDC-MMDS Co. Authorized power: 50-w. each. Antenna: 402-ft. above ground. Lat. 28° 32' 22", long. 81° 22' 46". Transmitter: 200 S. Orange Ave. Equipment: Comwave transmitter; Andrew antenna. Ownership: Orlando BDC-MMDS Co.

Orlando—WNEY682 (H1). BellSouth Wireless Cable Inc., Suite 414, 1100 Abernathy Rd. NE, Atlanta, GA 30328. Phone: 770-673-2827. Authorized power: 50-w. Antenna: 402-ft. above ground. Lat. 28° 32' 22", long. 81° 22' 46". Transmitter: 200 S. Orange Ave. Equipment: Emcee transmitter; Andrew antenna. Ownership: BellSouth Entertainment Inc.

Orlando—WNTG591 (H2). BellSouth Wireless Cable Inc., Suite 414, 1100 Abernathy Rd. NE, Atlanta, GA 30328. Phone: 770-673-2827. Authorized power: 50-w. Antenna: 402-ft. above ground. Lat. 28° 32' 22", long. 81° 22' 46". Transmitter: 200 S. Orange Ave. Equipment: Emcee transmitter; Andrew antenna. Ownership: BellSouth Entertainment Inc.

Orlando—WNEZ716 (H3). BellSouth Wireless Cable Inc., Suite 414, 1100 Abernathy Rd. NE, Atlanta, GA 30328. Phone: 770-673-2827. Authorized power: 50-w. Antenna: 402-ft. above ground. Lat. 28° 32' 22", long. 81° 22' 46". Transmitter: 200 S. Orange Ave. Equipment: Emcee transmitter; Andrew antenna. Ownership: BellSouth Entertainment Inc.

Panama City—WNTJ390 (H1). Maddox Nachman Kern Partnership, 10300 97th St. N, Seminole, FL 34643. Authorized power: 50-w. Antenna: 500-ft. above ground. Lat. 30° 19' 43", long. 85° 41' 25". Transmitter: 2-mi. W of Vicksburg. Equipment: ITS transmitter; Andrew antenna. Ownership: Maddox Nachman Kern Partnership. Sale pends to Wireless One Inc.

Panama City—WNTJ386 (H2). Rocz Dudeck Leas Partnership, 11672 Harborside Circle, Largo, FL 33773-4439. Authorized power: 50-w. Antenna: 500-ft. above ground. Lat. 30° 19' 43", long. 85° 41' 25". Transmitter: 2-mi. W of Vicksburg. Equipment: ITS transmitter; Andrew antenna. Ownership: Rocz Dudeck Leas Partnership. Sale pends to Wireless One Inc.

Panama City—WNTJ377 (H3). Crossfield Wilson Blake Partnership. Authorized power: 50-w. Antenna: 500-ft. above ground. Lat. 30° 19' 43", long. 85° 41' 25". Transmitter: 2-mi. W of Vicksburg. Equipment: ITS transmitter; Andrew antenna. Ownership: Crossfield Wilson Blake Partnership. Sale pends to Wireless One Inc.

Pensacola—WMI847 (E group). Wireless One Inc., Suite 400, 2506 Lakeland Dr., Jackson,

MS 39208. Phone: 601-933-6871. Authorized power: 50-w. each. Antenna: 499-ft. above ground. Lat. 30° 39' 23", long. 87° 11' 42". Transmitter: 1687 Quintet Rd. Equipment: Emcee transmitter; Bogner antenna. Ownership: Wireless One Inc.

Pensacola—WMH721 (F group). Stephanie Engstrom, Apt. 204, 420 S. Catalina Ave., Redondo Beach, CA 90277. Phone & fax: 310-540-9867. Authorized power: 50-w. each. Antenna: 499-ft. above ground. Lat. 30° 39' 23", long. 87° 11' 42". Transmitter: 1687 Quintet Rd. Equipment: Emcee transmitter; Bogner antenna. Ownership: Stephanie Engstrom.

Sarasota—WMI303 (E group). Paradise Cable Inc. Authorized power: 50-w. each. Antenna: 305-ft. above ground. Lat. 27° 07' 56", long. 82° 23' 43". Transmitter: 2000 Border Rd. Equipment: Comwave transmitter; Andrew antenna. Ownership: Multi-Point TV Distributors Inc.

Tampa—WHT699 (F group). Mars Communications Inc., Suite 3300, 101 E. Kennedy Blvd., Tampa, FL 33602. Phone: 813-222-8844. Fax: 813-225-1513. Authorized power: 10-w. each. Antenna: 636-ft. above ground. Lat. 28° 02' 20", long. 82° 39' 29". Transmitter: 105 Dunbar Ave., Oldsmar. Equipment: Comwave transmitter; Andrew antenna. Ownership: Mars Communications Inc.
Leased to Videotron (Bay Area) Inc., 18940 U.S. 19 N., Clearwater, FL 34624. Phone: 813-530-1812.

Tampa—WNEY710 (H2). Wireless Cable International Inc., 67-A Mountain Blvd. Ext., Warren, NJ 07059. Phone: 908-271-4880. Authorized power: 100-w. Antenna: 636-ft. above ground. Lat. 28° 02' 20", long. 82° 39' 29". Transmitter: 105 Dunbar Ave., Oldsmar. Equipment: Comwave transmitter; Andrew antenna. Ownership: Wireless Cable International Inc.

West Palm Beach—WMI841 (E group). WBSWP Licensing Corp., Suite 325, 9250 E. Costilla Ave., Englewood, CO 80112. Phone: 303-649-1195. Fax: 303-649-1196. Authorized power: 10-w. each. Antenna: 208-ft. above ground. Lat. 26° 44' 02", long. 80° 04' 55". Transmitter: 2425 Presidential Way. Equipment: Comwave transmitter; Bogner antenna. Requests change to 396-ft. above ground, lat. 26° 31' 22", long. 80° 05' 29"; transmitter to 505 S. Congress Ave., Boynton Beach; Andrew antenna. Ownership: Wireless Broadcasting Systems of America Inc. Sale pends to Boston Ventures Co. LP IV.

West Palm Beach—WHT697 (F). Sherry Rullman, 2129 San Marcus Place, Claremont, CA 91711-1766. Phone: 714-625-2988. Fax: 714-624-3993. Authorized power: 10-w. each. Antenna: 40-ft. above ground. Lat. 26° 40' 31", long. 80° 03' 34". Transmitter: 1897 Palm Beach Lake Bldg. Equipment: Emcee transmitter; Andrew antenna. Ownership: Sherry Rullman.

Georgia

Albany—WNTC449 (H1). WCTV Partners, 1616 Parkins Mill Rd., Greenville, SC 29607. Phone: 803-288-0930. Authorized power: 50-w. Antenna: 453-ft. above ground. Lat. 31° 37' 40", long. 84° 11' 45". Transmitter: 3333 Palmyra Rd. Equipment: ITS transmitter; Andrew antenna. Ownership: WCTV Partners.

Albany—WNTC450 (H2). Token Partnership, 1023 51st St., Moline, IL 61265. Authorized power: 50-w. Antenna: 453-ft. above ground. Lat. 31° 37' 40", long. 84° 11' 45". Transmitter: 3333 Palmyra Rd. Equipment: ITS transmitter; Andrew antenna. Ownership: Token Partnership.

Athens—WMI284 (E group). BellSouth Wireless Cable Inc., Suite 414, 1100 Abernathy Rd. NE, Atlanta, GA 30328. Phone: 770-673-2827. Authorized power: 50-w. each. Antenna: 1240-ft. above ground. Lat. 34° 12' 27", long. 83° 37' 48". Transmitter: NE of Pendergrass. Equipment: Emcee transmitter; Andrew antenna. Ownership: BellSouth Entertainment Inc.

Athens—WMI824 (F). BellSouth Wireless Cable Inc., Suite 414, 1100 Abernathy Rd. NE, Atlanta, GA 30328. Phone: 770-673-2827. Authorized power: 10-w. each. Antenna: 1189-ft. above ground. Lat. 34° 05' 02", long. 83° 19' 18". Transmitter: Nice Commerce Rd. & Hwy. 106. Equipment: Emcee transmitter; Andrew antenna. Requests change to 1100-ft. above ground, lat. 34° 12' 27", long. 83° 37' 48"; transmitter to NE of Pendergrass, Athens. Ownership: BellSouth Entertainment Inc.

Athens—WNTM819 (H2). BellSouth Wireless Cable Inc., Suite 414, 1100 Abernathy Rd., Atlanta, GA 30328. Phone: 770-673-2827. Authorized power: 10-w. Antenna: 1189-ft. above ground. Lat. 34° 05' 02", long. 83° 19' 18". Transmitter: Batwall Rd., Hwy. 106. Equipment: Emcee transmitter; Andrew antenna. Ownership: BellSouth Entertainment Inc.

Atlanta—WHT663 (E group). BellSouth Corp., Suite 414, 1100 Abernathy Rd. NE, Atlanta, GA 30328. Phone: 770-673-2800. Authorized power: 200-w. each. Antenna: 1017-ft. above ground. Lat. 33° 46' 15", long. 84° 23' 10". Transmitter: 600 Peachtree Rd. Equipment: Emcee transmitter; Andrew antenna. Ownership: BellSouth Entertainment Inc.

Atlanta—WHT664 (F group). National TV Co., Drawer B, Kingsville, TX 78363. Phone: 512-595-5673. Fax: 512-595-0151. Authorized power: 200-w. each. Antenna: 1017-ft. above ground. Lat. 33° 46' 15", long. 84° 23' 10". Transmitter: 600 Peachtree Rd. Equipment: Emcee transmitter; Andrew antenna. Ownership: National TV Co.
Leased to BellSouth Entertainment Inc.

Atlanta—WNTA434 (H1). BellSouth Corp., Suite 414, 1100 Abernathy Rd. NE, Atlanta, GA 30328. Phone: 770-673-2800. Authorized power: 200-w. Antenna: 1017-ft. above ground. Lat. 33° 46' 15", long. 84° 23' 10". Transmitter: 600 Peachtree Rd. Equipment: Emcee transmitter; Andrew antenna. Ownership: BellSouth Entertainment Inc.

Atlanta—WHJ940 (H2). Via/Net Companies, 836 E. Washington St., San Diego, CA 92103. Phone: 619-260-0110. Authorized power: 200-w. Antenna: 1017-ft. above ground. Lat. 33° 46' 15", long. 84° 23' 10". Transmitter: 600 Peachtree Rd. Equipment: Emcee transmitter; Andrew antenna. Ownership: Via/Net Companies.

Atlanta—WNTB872 (H3). BellSouth Corp., Suite 414, 1100 Abernathy Rd. NE, Atlanta, GA 30328. Phone: 770-673-2800. Authorized power: 200-w. Antenna: 1017-ft. above ground. Lat. 33° 46' 15", long. 84° 23' 10". Transmitter: 600 Peachtree Rd. Equipment: Emcee transmitter; Andrew antenna. Ownership: BellSouth Entertainment Inc.

Augusta—WHT561 (E group). Sunbelt Entertainment Corp. Authorized power: 10-w. each. Antenna: 272-ft. above ground. Lat. 33° 30' 00", long. 81° 56' 03". Transmitter: 1-mi. E of Augusta. Equipment: Emcee transmitter; Bogner antenna. Requests change to 193-ft. above ground, lat. 33° 29' 19", long. 82° 04' 25"; transmitter to 3609 Walton Way. Ownership: Sunbelt Entertainment Corp.

Augusta—WMX233 (H2). Blake Twedt, 5102 Rosegreen Court, Tampa, FL 33624. Phone: 727-587-9959. Authorized power: 10-w. Antenna: 650-ft. above ground. Lat. 33° 24' 29", long. 81° 50' 36". Transmitter: Pine Log Rd. Equipment: Emcee transmitter; Andrew antenna. Ownership: Blake Twedt.

Brunswick—WLW907 (F group). Mickelson Media Inc., 50 Locust Ave., New Canaan, CT 06840. Phone: 203-966-8746. Authorized power: 10-w. each. Antenna: 362-ft. above ground. Lat. 31° 09' 39", long. 81° 28' 47". Transmitter: 2005 Harvey St. Equipment: Emcee transmitter; Andrew antenna. Ownership: Mickelson Media Inc.

Carrollton—WMX932 (H3). Southern Wireless Cable Partnership, 605 Lake Shore Dr., Maitland, FL 32751. Phone: 407-647-3952. Authorized power: 10-w. Antenna: 190-ft. above ground. Lat. 33° 24' 52", long. 85° 15' 08". Transmitter: 0.6-mi. NNE of Carrollton. Equipment: Comwave transmitter; Andrew antenna. Ownership: Southern Wireless Cable Partners.

Chatsworth—WMY417 (H1). Paul Jackson Enterprises, Box 2279, Rte. 2, Chatsworth, GA 30705. Authorized power: 10-w. Antenna: 180-ft. above ground. Lat. 34° 45' 06", long. 84° 42' 54". Transmitter: 3.3-mi. SSW of Chatsworth. Equipment: ITS transmitter; Andrew antenna. Ownership: Paul Jackson Enterprises.

Chatsworth—WMY416 (H2). Paul Jackson Enterprises, Box 2279, Rte. 2, Chatsworth, GA 30705. Authorized power: 10-w. Antenna: 180-ft. above ground. Lat. 34° 45' 06", long. 84° 42' 54". Transmitter: 3.3-mi. SSW of Chatsworth. Equipment: ITS transmitter; Andrew antenna. Ownership: Paul Jackson Enterprises.

Chatsworth—WMY415 (H3). Paul Jackson Enterprises, Box 2279, Rte. 2, Chatsworth, GA 30705. Authorized power: 10-w. Antenna: 180-ft. above ground. Lat. 34° 45' 06", long. 84° 42' 54". Transmitter: 3.3-mi. SSW of Chatsworth. Equipment: ITS transmitter; Andrew antenna. Ownership: Paul Jackson Enterprises.

Columbus—WLW935 (F group). Stella A. Pappas, 500 S. Chinowth Rd., Visalia, CA 93277. Phone: 209-733-7800. Fax: 209-627-5363. Authorized power: 10-w. each. Antenna: 335-ft. above ground. Lat. 32° 27' 55", long. 85° 03' 28". Transmitter: Womack Rd. & Hwy. 80. Equipment: Emcee transmitter; Andrew antenna. Ownership: Stella A. Pappas.
Leased to Wireless One Inc., 5551 Corporate Blvd., Suite 2-K, Baton Rouge, LA 70808. Phone: 504-926-7778.

Hoggard Mill—WMY455 (H1). RVS Holdings Corp., Suite 200, 200 Chisholm Place, Plano, TX 75075. Phone: 972-423-9494. Fax: 972-423-0819. Authorized power: 10-w. Antenna: 132-ft. above ground. Lat. 31° 13' 47", long. 84° 34' 40". Transmitter: 1.9-mi. NW of Cooktown. Equipment: ITS transmitter; Andrew antenna. Ownership: Nucentrix Broadband Networks Inc.

Hoggard Mill—WMY456 (H3). RVS Holdings Corp., Suite 200, 200 Chisholm Place, Plano, TX 75075. Phone: 972-423-9494. Fax: 972-423-0819. Authorized power: 10-w. Antenna: 132-ft. above ground. Lat. 31° 13' 47", long. 84° 34' 40". Transmitter: 1.9-mi. NW of Cooktown. Equipment: ITS transmitter; Andrew antenna. Ownership: Nucentrix Broadband Networks Inc.

Jeffersonville—WMH545 (E group). Wireless One PCS Inc., Suite 400, 2506 Lakeland Dr., Jackson, MS 39208. Phone: 601-933-6879. Authorized power: 50-w. each. Antenna: 450-ft. above ground. Lat. 32° 51' 07", long. 83° 39' 12". Transmitter: 2262 Rogers Place. Equipment: Emcee transmitter; Andrew antenna. Ownership: Wireless One Inc.

Jeffersonville—WMI857 (F group). Wireless One PCS Inc., Suite 400, 2506 Lakeland Dr., Jackson, MS 39208. Phone: 601-933-6879. Authorized power: 50-w. each. Antenna: 706-ft. above ground. Lat. 32° 44' 00", long. 83° 19' 16". Transmitter: 3.6-mi. NNE of SR 96 & U.S. 80. Equipment: Emcee transmitter; Andrew antenna. Ownership: Wireless One Inc.

Jeffersonville—WNTJ428 (H1). Michael J. Carter, 1010 Samy Dr., Tampa, FL 33613. Phone: 813-962-1473. Authorized power: 50-w. Antenna: 706-ft. above ground. Lat. 32° 44' 00", long. 83° 19' 16". Transmitter: 3.6-mi. NNE of SR 96 & U.S. 80. Equipment: Emcee transmitter; Andrew antenna. Ownership: Michael J. Carter.
Leased to Wireless One, 2506 Lakeland Dr., No. 403, Jackson, MS 39208. Phone: 601-933-6871.

Jeffersonville—WNTJ424 (H2). Blake Twedt, 5102 Rosegreen Court, Tampa, FL 33624. Phone: 727-587-9959. Authorized power: 50-w. Antenna: 706-ft. above ground. Lat. 32° 44' 00", long. 83° 19' 16". Transmitter: 3.6-mi. NNE of State Rd. 96 & U.S. 80. Equipment: Emcee transmitter; Andrew antenna. Ownership: Blake Twedt.

Jeffersonville—WNTJ384 (H3). Michael J. Carter, 1010 Samy Dr., Tampa, FL 33613. Phone: 813-962-1473. Authorized power: 50-w. Antenna: 706-ft. above ground. Lat. 32° 44' 00", long. 83° 19' 16". Transmitter: 3.6-mi. NNE of SR 96 & U.S. 80. Equipment: Emcee transmitter; Andrew antenna. Ownership: Michael J. Carter.
Leased to Wireless One, 2506 Lakeland Dr., No. 403, Jackson, MS 39208. Phone: 601-933-6871.

Rome—WMI338 (E group). BellSouth Wireless Cable Inc., Suite 414, 1100 Abernathy Rd. NE, Atlanta, GA 30328. Phone: 770-673-2800. Authorized power: 10-w. each. Antenna: 205-ft. above ground. Lat. 34° 02' 06", long. 85° 15' 04". Transmitter: 413 Lakeview Dr. Equipment: Emcee transmitter; Bogner antenna. Ownership: BellSouth Entertainment Inc.

Sandersville—WNTM820 (H group). Gateway Partners, 3543 Remco St., Castro Valley, CA 94546. Antenna: 500-ft. above ground. Lat. 33° 03' 39", long. 82° 47' 07". Transmitter: Hwy. 15, 5-mi. N of Sandersville. Ownership: Gateway Partners.

Savannah—WLW749 (E group). Inner City Broadcasting Corp., 40th Floor, 3 Park Ave., New York, NY 10016. Phone: 212-447-1000. Authorized power: 50-w. each. Antenna: 464-ft. above ground. Lat. 32° 05' 48", long. 81° 19' 17". Transmitter: Hwy. 16 & Cross Rd. Equipment: Emcee transmitter; Andrew antenna. Ownership: Inner City Broadcasting Corp.

Savannah—WMX341 (H2). Blake Twedt, 5102 Rosegreen Court, Tampa, FL 33624. Phone:

727-587-9959. Authorized power: 10-w. Antenna: 464-ft. above ground. Lat. 32° 05' 48", long. 81° 19' 17". Transmitter: Hwy. 16 & Cross Rd. Equipment: Emcee transmitter; Andrew antenna. Ownership: Blake Twedt.

Savannah—WMX340 (H3). Blake Twedt, 5102 Rosegreen Court, Tampa, FL 33624. Phone: 727-587-9959. Authorized power: 10-w. Antenna: 464-ft. above ground. Lat. 32° 05' 48", long. 81° 19' 17". Transmitter: Hwy. 16 & Cross Rd. Equipment: Emcee transmitter; Andrew antenna. Ownership: Blake Twedt.

Swainsboro—WMY295 (E group). Bonnie D. O'Connell, 2203 Pasadena Place, Gulfport, FL 33707. Phone: 727-347-3266. Fax: 727-347-4649. E-mail: bonniedo@tampabay.rr.com. Authorized power: 10-w. each. Antenna: 180-ft. above ground. Lat. 32° 34' 52", long. 82° 23' 14". Transmitter: 2-mi. E of Swainsboro on Hills Bridge Rd. Equipment: Comwave transmitter; Bogner antenna. Ownership: Bonnie D. O'Connell.
Leased to Wireless One, 11301 Industriplex Blvd., Suite 4, Baton Rouge, LA 70809 4115. Phone: 504-293-5000.

Valdosta—WLW881 (E group). Wireless One Licensing Venture Inc., Suite 403, 2506 Lakeland Dr., Jackson, MS 39208. Authorized power: 10-w. each. Antenna: 707-ft. above ground. Lat. 31° 10' 06", long. 83° 21' 50". Transmitter: 1-mi. SSE of Barnesdale. Equipment: Comwave transmitter; Bogner antenna. Ownership: Wireless One Inc.

Valdosta—WLW848 (F group). Wireless One Licensing Venture Inc., Suite 403, 2506 Lakeland Dr., Jackson, MS 39208. Authorized power: 10-w. each. Antenna: 707-ft. above ground. Lat. 31° 10' 06", long. 83° 21' 50". Transmitter: 1-mi. SSE of Barnesdale. Equipment: Comwave transmitter; Bogner antenna. Ownership: Wireless One Inc.

Hawaii

Honolulu—WMX211 (E group). Moloka'i Network Corp., Box 47397, St. Petersburg, FL 33743. Phone: 813-345-8044. Authorized power: 20-w. each. Antenna: 70-ft. above ground. Lat. 21° 24' 24", long. 158° 06' 02". Transmitter: Palikea Ridge, Palehua Rd. Equipment: Comwave transmitter; Andrew antenna. Ownership: Moloka'i Network Corp.

Honolulu—WHT718 (F group). GTE Media Ventures, 600 Hidden Ridge, Irving, TX 75028. Phone: 972-718-4666. Authorized power: 10-w. each. Antenna: 78-ft. above ground. Lat. 21° 24' 24", long. 158° 06' 02". Transmitter: Palikea Ridge, Palehua Rd. Equipment: Emcee transmitter; Andrew antenna. Requests change to 16-ft. above ground, lat. 21° 16' 11", long. 157° 42' 18"; transmitter to Kokohead Natural Park, 0.9-mi. S of Hawaii Kai; Andrew antenna. Ownership: GTE Media Ventures.

Honolulu—WNTH954 (H1). Honolulu Cablevision Corp., Suite 900, 1350 Connecticut Ave. NW, Washington, DC 20036. Phone: 202-296-2007. Authorized power: 20-w. Antenna: 78-ft. above ground. Lat. 21° 24' 24", long. 158° 06' 02". Transmitter: Palikea Ridge, Palehua Rd. Equipment: Comwave transmitter; Andrew antenna. Ownership: Honolulu Cablevision Corp.

Honolulu—WNTI201 (H2). Honolulu Cablevision Corp., Suite 900, 1350 Connecticut Ave. NW, Washington, DC 20036. Phone: 202-296-2007. Authorized power: 20-w. Antenna: 78-ft. above ground. Lat. 21° 24' 24", long. 158° 06' 02". Transmitter: Palikea Ridge, Palehua Rd. Equipment: Comwave transmitter; Andrew antenna. Requests change to 16-ft. above ground, lat. 21° 16' 11", long. 157° 42' 18"; transmitter to Kokohead Natural Park, 0.9-mi. S of Hawaii Kai. Ownership: Honolulu Cablevision Corp.

Kahului—WNTH288 (H2). American Telecasting of Hawaii Inc., Suite 300, 5575 Tech Center Dr., Colorado Springs, CO 80919. Phone: 719-260-5533. Fax: 719-260-5010. Authorized power: 10-w. Antenna: 184-ft. above ground. Lat. 20° 49' 24", long. 156° 27' 27". Transmitter: Thompson Ranch Rd., Mount Haleakala. Equipment: Emcee transmitter; Andrew antenna. Ownership: American Telecasting Inc.

Kahului—WNTH270 (H3). American Telecasting of Hawaii Inc., Suite 300, 5575 Tech Center Dr., Colorado Springs, CO 80919. Phone: 719-260-5533. Fax: 719-260-5010. Authorized power: 10-w. Antenna: 184-ft. above ground. Lat. 20° 49' 24", long. 156° 27' 27". Transmitter: Thompson Ranch Rd., Mount Haleakala. Equipment: Emcee transmitter; Andrew antenna. Ownership: American Telecasting Inc.

Koloa—WMH745 (F group). Super Comm, 738 Intrepid Way, Davidsonville, MD 21035. Phone: 301-261-4766. Authorized power: 10-w. each. Antenna: 250-ft. above ground. Lat. 21° 53' 37", long. 159° 33' 27". Transmitter: 6-mi. SW of Koloa. Equipment: Comwave transmitter; Andrew antenna. Ownership: Super Comm.

Maui—WMH637 (E group). Kelly L. Briggs, 3100 Gold Nugget Rd., Placerville, CA 95667. Authorized power: 10-w. each. Antenna: 60-ft. above ground. Lat. 20° 42' 38", long. 156° 15' 34". Transmitter: Kolekole Park. Equipment: Emcee transmitter; Andrew antenna. Ownership: Kelly L. Briggs.

Maui—WMH484 (F). Phillip D. Perry, 2346 La Lima Way, Sacramento, CA 95833. Phone: 916-955-4512. Authorized power: 10-w. each. Antenna: 28-ft. above ground. Lat. 20° 42' 26", long. 156° 21' 41". Transmitter: Thompson Ranch Rd. Equipment: ITS transmitter; Bogner antenna. Ownership: Phillip D. Perry.
Leased to Maui Cablevision Corp., 350 Ward Ave., Suite 106, Honolulu, HI 96814.

Maui—WNTH468 (H1). Brett Meyer, 2695 S. Kihei Rd., Maui, HI 96753. Authorized power: 10-w. Antenna: 184-ft. above ground. Lat. 20° 49' 24", long. 156° 27' 27". Transmitter: Thompson Ranch Rd. Equipment: Emcee transmitter; Andrew antenna. Ownership: Brett Meyer.

Idaho

Boise—WHT797 (E group). WBSB Licensing Corp., Suite 325, 9250 E. Costilla Ave., Englewood, CO 80112. Phone: 303-649-1195. Fax: 303-649-1196. Authorized power: 20-w. each. Antenna: 37-ft. above ground. Lat. 43° 45' 18", long. 116° 05' 52". Transmitter: Deer Point, 10-mi. NE of Boise. Equipment: ITS transmitter; Andrew antenna. Ownership: Wireless Broadcasting Systems of America Inc. Sale pends to Boston Ventures Co. LP IV.

Boise—WLW924 (F group). WBSB Licensing Corp., Suite 325, 9250 E. Costilla Ave., Englewood, CO 80112. Phone: 303-649-1195. Fax: 303-649-1196. Authorized power: 20-w. each. Antenna: 40-ft. above ground. Lat. 43° 45' 18", long. 116° 05' 52". Transmitter: Deer Point, 10-mi. NE of Boise. Equipment: ITS transmitter; Andrew antenna. Ownership: Wireless Broadcasting Systems of America Inc. Sale pends to Boston Ventures Co. LP IV.
Leased to Northwest Cable TV, 10338 Fairview Ave., Boise, ID 83704. Phone: 208-377-1266.

Boise—WNTJ839 (H1). Tharrell D. Ming. Authorized power: 20-w. Antenna: 298-ft. above ground. Lat. 43° 45' 18", long. 116° 05' 52". Transmitter: Deer Point, 10-mi. NE of Boise. Equipment: ITS transmitter; Andrew antenna. Ownership: Tharrell D. Ming.
Leased to Northwest Cable TV, 10338 Fairview Ave., Boise, ID 83704. Phone: 208-377-1266.

Boise—WNTJ729 (H2). Tharrell D. Ming. Authorized power: 20-w. Antenna: 298-ft. above ground. Lat. 43° 45' 18", long. 116° 05' 52". Transmitter: Deer Point, 10-mi. NE of Boise. Equipment: ITS transmitter; Andrew antenna. Ownership: Tharrell D. Ming.
Leased to Northwest Cable TV, 10338 Fairview Ave., Boise, ID 83704. Phone: 208-377-1266.

Boise—WNTJ801 (H3). Richard J. Amons Jr., 6507 Ridge St., McLean, VA 22101. Authorized power: 20-w. Antenna: 298-ft. above ground. Lat. 43° 45' 18", long. 116° 05' 52". Transmitter: Deer Point, 10-mi. NE of Boise. Equipment: ITS transmitter; Andrew antenna. Ownership: Richard J. Amons Jr.
Leased to Northwest Cable TV, 10338 Fairview Ave., Boise, ID 83704. Phone: 208-377-1266.

Idaho Falls—WLR468 (E group). Vicki Sardinas. Phone: 414-233-5054. Authorized power: 50-w. each. Antenna: 127-ft. above ground. Lat. 43° 21' 06", long. 112° 00' 22". Transmitter: Taylor Mountain. Equipment: Comwave transmitter; Andrew antenna. Ownership: Vicki Sardinas.

Idaho Falls—WMX247 (F group). Teewinot Licensing Inc., Box 1508, Twin Falls, ID 83303. Phone: 208-733-0500. Authorized power: 50-w. each. Antenna: 127-ft. above ground. Lat. 43° 21' 06", long. 112° 00' 22". Transmitter: Taylor Mountain. Equipment: Comwave transmitter; Andrew antenna. Ownership: Teewinot Licensing Inc.

Pocatello—WMH981 (E group). Thomas M. Glab, Box 627, Claremont, CA 91711. Phone: 909-621-1004. Fax: 909-624-2257. Authorized power: 10-w. each. Antenna: 243-ft. above ground. Lat. 42° 51' 57", long. 112° 30' 46". Transmitter: Howard Mountain. Equipment: Emcee transmitter; Andrew antenna. Ownership: Thomas M. Glab.

Pocatello—WMX243 (F group). Hubbard Trust, 26573 Basswood Ave., Rancho Palos Verdes, CA 90275. Phone & fax: 310-373-6234. E-mail: hubbardtech@earthlink.net. Authorized power: 10-w. each. Antenna: 200-ft. above ground. Lat. 42° 51' 57", long. 112° 30' 46". Transmitter: Howard Mountain. Equipment: Comwave transmitter; Andrew antenna. Requests change to 30-ft. above ground, lat. 42° 53' 03", long. 112° 26' 55"; transmitter to 456 Yellowstone. Ownership: Hubbard Trust. Sale pends to Direct Communications Wireless Cable LLC.
Leased to Direct Communications Wireless Cable LLC, 231 W. Center, Suite B, Rockland, ID 83271. Phone: 208-548-9911.

Pocatello—WNTH957 (H1). Ivan Nachman, 10300 97th St. N, Seminole, FL 34643. Phone: 813-392-0335. Authorized power: 10-w. Antenna: 200-ft. above ground. Lat. 42° 51' 57", long. 112° 30' 46". Transmitter: Howard Mountain. Equipment: Comwave transmitter; Andrew antenna. Ownership: Ivan Nachman.

Pocatello—WNTH960 (H2). Blake Twedt, 5102 Rosegreen Court, Tampa, FL 33624. Phone: 727-587-9959. Authorized power: 10-w. Antenna: 200-ft. above ground. Lat. 42° 51' 57", long. 112° 30' 46". Transmitter: Howard Mountain. Equipment: Comwave transmitter; Andrew antenna. Ownership: Blake Twedt.

Pocatello—WNTI229 (H3). John Dudeck, 11662 Harborside Circle, Largo, FL 33773. Authorized power: 10-w. Antenna: 200-ft. above ground. Lat. 42° 51' 57", long. 112° 30' 46". Transmitter: Howard Mountain. Equipment: Comwave transmitter; Andrew antenna. Ownership: John Dudeck.

Salmon—WMY426 (E group). John C. Landy, 11611 Harbour View Dr., Cleveland, OH 44102. Authorized power: 10-w. each. Antenna: 250-ft. above ground. Lat. 45° 11' 35", long. 113° 51' 00". Transmitter: E of Salmon Cemetery. Equipment: Comwave transmitter; Bogner antenna. Ownership: John C. Landy.

Twin Falls—WLW965 (E group). Teewinot Licensing Inc., Box 1550, Port Orchard, WA 98366. Phone: 360-870-5981. Authorized power: 10-w. each. Antenna: 135-ft. above ground. Lat. 42° 43' 54", long. 114° 25' 04". Transmitter: 0.15-mi. WSW of Flat Top Butte. Equipment: Emcee transmitter; Andrew antenna. Ownership: Teewinot Licensing Inc.

Twin Falls—WMI391 (F group). New Hampshire Wireless Inc., Box 168, Derry, NH 03038. Phone: 603-893-1995. Authorized power: 20-w. each. Antenna: 135-ft. above ground. Lat. 42° 43' 54", long. 114° 25' 04". Transmitter: 0.15-mi. WSW of Flat Top Butte. Equipment: Emcee transmitter; Andrew antenna. Ownership: New Hampshire Wireless.

Illinois

Bloomington-Normal—WHI968 (E group). Prairieland Cable Partnership No. 1. Authorized power: 10-w. each. Antenna: 303-ft. above ground. Lat. 40° 28' 59", long. 88° 59' 43". Transmitter: Intersection of Center & Mulberry. Equipment: Comwave transmitter; Bogner antenna. Ownership: Prairieland Cable Partnership.

Bloomington-Normal—WHI964 (F group). Krisar Inc., 320 Hamilton St., Albion, NY 14411. Phone: 716-964-9121. Fax: 716-589-9091. E-mail: topperiai@aol.com. Authorized power: 10-w. each. Antenna: 303-ft. above ground. Lat. 40° 28' 59", long. 88° 59' 43". Equipment: Comwave transmitter; Bogner antenna. Ownership: Krisar Inc.
Leased to Microwave Cable Corp., 1700 S. Morris Ave., Bloomington, IL 61701.

Casey—WLW821 (E group). Everett Bolin Jr., Box 133, Casey, IL 62420. Authorized power: 50-w. each. Antenna: 356-ft. above ground. Lat. 39° 12' 55", long. 88° 13' 49". Transmitter: 1.6-mi. E of Jewett. Equipment: ITS transmitter; Andrew antenna. Ownership: Bolin Enterprises Inc.

Casey—WMI896 (F group). Bolin Enterprises Inc., Box 133, Casey, IL 62420. Authorized power: 50-w. each. Antenna: 356-ft. above ground. Lat. 39° 12' 55", long. 88° 13' 49". Transmitter: 1.6-mi. E of Jewett. Equipment: ITS transmitter; Andrew antenna. Ownership: Bolin Enterprises Inc.

Casey—WNTB224 (H3). Bolin Enterprises, Box 133, Casey, IL 62420. Authorized power: 50-w. Antenna: 356-ft. above ground. Lat. 39° 12' 55", long. 88° 13' 49". Transmitter:

1.6-mi. E of Jewett. Equipment: ITS transmitter; Andrew antenna. Ownership: Bolin Enterprises Inc.

Champaign—WLW779 (E group). Line of Site Inc., 8611 E. Santa Catalina Dr., Scottsdale, AZ 85255-2870. Phone: 602-951-8243. Authorized power: 10-w. each. Antenna: 354-ft. above ground. Lat. 40° 10' 51", long. 88° 19' 04". Transmitter: 6-mi. NW of Champaign. Equipment: Comwave transmitter; Andrew antenna. Ownership: Line of Site Inc.

Champaign—WNTA368 (H1). Timothy A. Mathews, Box 181, Savoy, IL 61874. Authorized power: 10-w. Antenna: 338-ft. above ground. Lat. 40° 10' 51", long. 88° 19' 04". Transmitter: 6-mi. NW of Champaign. Equipment: Comwave transmitter; Andrew antenna. Ownership: Timothy A. Mathews.

Champaign—WNTA575 (H2). Specchio Developers Ltd., 233 N. Garrard, Rantoul, IL 61860. Authorized power: 50-w. Antenna: 338-ft. above ground. Lat. 40° 10' 51", long. 88° 19' 04". Transmitter: 6-mi. NW of Champaign. Equipment: Comwave transmitter; Andrew antenna. Ownership: Specchio Developers Ltd.

Champaign—WNTA478 (H3). Robert E. Terres, 2430 Norwood Ave., Pennsauken, NJ 08109. Authorized power: 50-w. Antenna: 338-ft. above ground. Lat. 40° 10' 51", long. 88° 19' 04". Transmitter: 6-mi. NW of Champaign. Equipment: Comwave transmitter; Andrew antenna. Ownership: Robert E. Terres.

Champaign-Urbana—WLK292 (F group). Presco Corp., 4547 4th Ave. NE, Seattle, WA 98105. Phone: 206-545-0268. Authorized power: 10-w. each. Antenna: 338-ft. above ground. Lat. 10° 10' 51", long. 88° 19' 04". Transmitter: Rd. 900 E, Champaign. Equipment: Emcee transmitter; Andrew antenna. Ownership: Presco Corp.

Chicago—WHK999 (F group). Audrey Malkan, 304 Crestwood Dr., Fort Worth, TX 76107. Phone: 817-626-0931. Authorized power: 10-w. each. Antenna: 1456-ft. above ground. Lat. 41° 52' 44", long. 87° 38' 10". Transmitter: 101 S. Wacker Dr. Equipment: Comwave transmitter; Andrew antenna. Ownership: Audrey Malkan.

Chicago—WMX255 (H1). Alda Wireless Holdings Inc., 5301 E. Broadway Blvd., Tucson, AZ 85711-3710. Phone: 520-519-4400. Fax: 520-747-6830. Authorized power: 10-w. Antenna: 1456-ft. above ground. Lat. 41° 52' 44", long. 87° 38' 10". Transmitter: 101 S. Wacker Dr. Equipment: Comwave transmitter; Andrew antenna. Ownership: Matthew Oristano.

Chicago—WNEL393 (H2). American Communications Services Inc., Box 753, Elmhurst, IL 60126-0753. Authorized power: 100-w. Antenna: 1456-ft. above ground. Lat. 41° 52' 44", long. 87° 38' 10". Transmitter: 101 S. Wacker St. Equipment: Comwave transmitter; Andrew antenna. Ownership: American Communications Services Inc.

Chicago—WNET334 (H3). Alda Wireless Holdings Inc., 5301 E. Broadway Blvd., Tucson, AZ 85711-3710. Phone: 520-519-4400. Fax: 520-747-6830. Authorized power: 100-w. Antenna: 1456-ft. above ground. Lat. 41° 52' 44", long. 87° 38' 10". Transmitter: 101 S. Wacker Dr. Equipment: Emcee transmitter; Andrew antenna. Ownership: Matthew Oristano.

Decatur—WHT634 (E group). Private Networks Inc., Box 23707, Brooklyn, NY 11201. Phone: 212-777-4740. Authorized power: 10-w. each. Antenna: 425-ft. above ground. Lat. 39° 51' 46", long. 88° 58' 06". Transmitter: 2044 Walnut Grove. Equipment: Comwave transmitter; Bogner antenna. Ownership: Private Networks Inc.

Galesburg—WMH557 (E group). Todd Communications Inc., 6545 Cecilia Circle, Minneapolis, MN 55435. Phone: 612-941-0556. Authorized power: 10-w. each. Antenna: 70-ft. above ground. Lat. 40° 47' 50", long. 90° 24' 07". Transmitter: Edge of Abingdon City. Equipment: ITS transmitter; Bogner antenna. Ownership: Todd Communications Inc.

Jewett—WNTB577 (H1). Everett Bolin Jr., Box 133, Old Rte. 40 E, Casey, IL 62420. Authorized power: 50-w. Antenna: 356-ft. above ground. Lat. 39° 12' 55", long. 88° 13' 49". Transmitter: 1.6-mi. E of Jewett. Equipment: ITS transmitter; Andrew antenna. Ownership: Bolin Enterprises Inc.

Jewett—WNTB476 (H2). Everett Bolin Jr., Box 133, Old Rte. 40 E, Casey, IL 62420. Authorized power: 50-w. Antenna: 356-ft. above ground. Lat. 39° 12' 55", long. 88° 13' 49". Transmitter: 1.6-mi. E of Jewett. Equipment: ITS transmitter; Andrew antenna. Ownership: Bolin Enterprises Inc.

Ladd/Streator—WMH577 (E group). Todd Communications, 6545 Cecilia Circle, Minneapolis, MN 55435. Phone: 612-941-0556. Authorized power: 50-w. each. Antenna: 600-ft. above ground. Lat. 41° 18' 05", long. 88° 57' 11". Transmitter: 3-mi. E of Hwy. 178. Equipment: ITS transmitter; Andrew antenna. Ownership: Todd Communications Inc.

McLeansboro—WNTI571 (H1). Nucentrix Spectrum Resources Inc., Suite 200, 200 Chisholm Place, Plano, TX 75075. Phone: 972-423-9494. Fax: 972-423-0819. Authorized power: 12.6-w. Antenna: 495-ft. above ground. Lat. 38° 06' 36", long. 88° 32' 09". Transmitter: 1.1-mi. N of McLeansboro. Equipment: Comwave transmitter; Andrew antenna. Ownership: Nucentrix Broadband Networks.

McLeansboro—WNTF548 (H2). Nucentrix Spectrum Resources Inc., Suite 200, 200 Chisholm Place, Plano, TX 75075. Phone: 972-423-9494. Fax: 972-423-0819. Authorized power: 50-w. Antenna: 495-ft. above ground. Lat. 38° 06' 36", long. 88° 32' 09". Transmitter: 1.1-mi. N of McLeansboro. Equipment: Comwave transmitter; Andrew antenna. Ownership: Nucentrix Broadband Networks.

McLeansboro—WNTF515 (H3). Nucentrix Spectrum Resources Inc. Suite 200, 200 Chisolm Place, Plano, TX 75075. Phone: 972-423-9494. Fax: 972-423-0819. Authorized power: 50-w. Antenna: 495-ft. above ground. Lat. 38° 06' 36", long. 88° 32' 09". Transmitter: 1.1-mi. N of McLeansboro. Equipment: Comwave transmitter; Andrew antenna. Ownership: Nucentrix Broadband Networks.

Mount Sterling—WMH256 (E group). Todd Communications Inc., 6545 Cecilia Circle, Minneapolis, MN 55435. Phone: 612-941-0556. Authorized power: 10-w. each. Antenna: 490-ft. above ground. Lat. 39° 59' 16", long. 90° 43' 10". Transmitter: 1.5-mi. E of Mount Sterling. Equipment: ITS transmitter; Bogner antenna. Ownership: Todd Communications Inc.

Peoria—WMH380 (E group). Nucentrix Spectrum Resources Inc., Suite 200, 200 Chisholm Place, Plano, TX 75075. Phone: 972-423-9494. Fax: 972-423-0819. Authorized power: 10-w. each. Antenna: 606-ft. above ground. Lat. 40° 41' 44", long. 89° 35' 11". Transmitter: Fayette St. Equipment: Emcee transmitter; Andrew antenna. Ownership: Nucentrix Broadband Networks.

Leased to American Telecasting Inc., 5575 Tech Center Dr., Suite 300, Colorado Springs, CO 80919. Phone: 719-260-5533. Fax: 719-260-5010.

Peoria—WMH200 (F group). Nucentrix Spectrum Resources Inc., Suite 200, 200 Chisholm Place, Plano, TX 75075. Phone: 972-423-9494. Fax: 972-423-0819. Authorized power: 10-w. each. Antenna: 55-ft. above ground. Lat. 40° 41' 44", long. 89° 35' 11". Transmitter: 321 Sayette Bldg. Equipment: Emcee transmitter; Andrew antenna. Ownership: Nucentrix Broadband Networks.

Quincy—WLW887 (E group). TV Communications Network Inc., Suite 300, 10020 E. Girard Ave., Denver, CO 80231. Phone: 303-751-2900. Fax: 303-751-1081. E-mail: kroznoy@Plinet.com. Authorized power: 10-w. each. Antenna: 230-ft. above ground. Lat. 39° 58' 22", long. 91° 19' 54". Transmitter: 510 Maine. Equipment: Emcee transmitter; Bogner antenna. Ownership: Multichannel Distribution of America Inc.

Rockford—WMH333 (E group). Wireless CATV Systems Inc., Suite 6107, 350 5th Ave., New York, NY 10118. Phone: 212-268-2828. Fax: 212-268-5675. E-mail: kevinlim@idt.net. Web Site: http://www.lvwi.net. Authorized power: 10-w. each. Antenna: 199-ft. above ground. Lat. 42° 16' 02", long. 89° 04' 12". Transmitter: 1415 E. State St. Equipment: Emcee transmitter; Andrew antenna. Requests modification of license for change to 450-ft. above ground, lat. 42° 17' 48", long. 89° 10' 15". Ownership: Wireless Cable Systems Inc.

Rockford—WMI326 (F group). Wireless CATV Systems Inc., Suite 6107, 350 5th Ave., New York, NY 10118. Phone: 212-268-2828. Fax: 212-268-5675. E-mail: kevinlim@idt.net. Web Site: http://www.lvwi.net. Authorized power: 50-w. each. Antenna: 390-ft. above ground. Lat. 42° 22' 02", long. 89° 05' 13". Transmitter: 2430 Latham Rd. Equipment: ITS transmitter; Andrew antenna. Ownership: Wireless Cable Systems Inc.

Rockford—WNTI207 (H1). Alice Twedt, 701 Park St., Harvard, IL 60033. Authorized power: 50-w. Antenna: 390-ft. above ground. Lat. 42° 22' 02", long. 89° 05' 13". Transmitter: 2430 Latham Rd. Equipment: ITS transmitter; Andrew antenna. Ownership: Alice Twedt.

Rockford—WNTI343 (H2). John Dudeck, 11672 Harborside Court, Largo, FL 33773. Authorized power: 50-w. Antenna: 390-ft. above ground. Lat. 42° 22' 02", long. 89° 05' 13". Transmitter: 2430 Latham Rd. Equipment: ITS transmitter; Andrew antenna. Ownership: John Dudeck.

Rockford—WNTI287 (H3). John Dudeck, 11672 Harborside Court, Largo, FL 33773. Authorized power: 50-w. Antenna: 390-ft. above ground. Lat. 42° 22' 02", long. 89° 05' 13". Transmitter: 2430 Latham Rd. Ownership: John Dudeck.

Salem—WMI346 (E group). Nucentrix Spectrum Resources Inc., Suite 200, 200 Chisholm Place, Plano, TX 75075. Phone: 972-423-9494. Fax: 972-423-0819. Authorized power: 10-w. each. Antenna: 500-ft. above ground. Lat. 38° 06' 36", long. 88° 32' 09". Transmitter: 1.1-mi. N of McLeansboro. Equipment: Comwave transmitter; Andrew antenna. Ownership: Nucentrix Broadband Networks.

Salem—WMI327 (F group). Nucentrix Spectrum Resources Inc., Suite 200, 200 Chisholm Place, Plano, TX 75075. Phone: 972-423-9494. Fax: 972-423-0819. Authorized power: 50-w. each. Antenna: 495-ft. above ground. Lat. 38° 06' 36", long. 88° 32' 09". Transmitter: 1.1-mi. N of McLeansboro. Equipment: Comwave transmitter; Andrew antenna. Ownership: Nucentrix Broadband Networks.

Springfield—WMY460 (H2). Springfield One Partnership, Suite 501, 1100 17th St. NW, Washington, DC 20036-4601. Phone: 202-223-4449. Fax: 202-223-4450. E-mail: rgould@cwix.com. Authorized power: 20-w. Antenna: 220-ft. above ground. Lat. 39° 47' 36", long. 89° 36' 18". Transmitter: 712 S. Dirkson Pkwy. Equipment: Emcee transmitter; Andrew antenna. Ownership: Springfield One Partnership.

Witt—WMH565 (E group). Todd Communications Inc., 6545 Cecilia Circle, Minneapolis, MN 55435. Phone: 612-941-0556. Authorized power: 20-w. each. Antenna: 346-ft. above ground. Lat. 39° 10' 46", long. 89° 17' 07". Transmitter: 6.5-mi. SW of Witt. Equipment: ITS transmitter; Andrew antenna. Ownership: Todd Communications Inc.

Indiana

Anderson—WMH569 (E group). Walter Communications Inc., Suite 120, 4700 S. McClintock, Tempe, AZ 85282. Phone: 602-755-7524. Fax: 602-755-7534. Authorized power: 10-w. each. Antenna: 534-ft. above ground. Lat. 40° 03' 43", long. 85° 42' 34". Transmitter: Hwys. 9 & 69. Equipment: Emcee transmitter; Andrew antenna. Ownership: Walter Communications Inc.

Leased to Broadcast Cable Inc., 4109 E. 65th St., Indianapolis, IN 46220. Phone: 317-257-6934.

Anderson—WMI874 (F group). Krisar Inc., 320 Hamilton St., Albion, NY 14411. Phone: 716-964-9121. Fax: 716-589-9094. E-mail: topperiai.aol.com. Authorized power: 10-w. Antenna: 534-ft. above ground. Lat. 40° 03' 43", long. 85° 42' 34". Transmitter: Near Rd. 300 S. Equipment: Comwave transmitter; Bogner antenna. Ownership: Krisar Inc.

Anderson—WNTA435 (H1). Sue A. Lemna, 4432 Shenandoah Circle, Fort Wayne, IN 46835. Phone: 219-486-1405. Authorized power: 20-w. Antenna: 474-ft. above ground. Lat. 40° 03' 43", long. 85° 42' 34". Transmitter: 2500 W. 53rd St. Equipment: Comwave transmitter; Andrew antenna. Ownership: Sue A. Lemna.

Anderson—WNTA436 (H2). Lauren F. Griffith, 3427 Rockwood Dr., Fort Wayne, IN 46815. Phone: 219-483-2325. Authorized power: 20-w. Antenna: 474-ft. above ground. Lat. 40° 03' 43", long. 85° 42' 34". Transmitter: 2500 W. 53rd St. Equipment: Comwave transmitter; Andrew antenna. Ownership: Lauren F. Griffith.

Anderson—WNTG393 (H3). Alda Wireless Holdings Inc., 5301 E. Broadway Blvd., Tucson, AZ 85711-8181. Phone: 520-519-4400. Fax: 520-747-6830. Authorized power: 20-w. Antenna: 474-ft. above ground. Lat. 40° 03' 43", long. 85° 42' 34". Transmitter: 2500 W. 53rd St. Equipment: Comwave transmitter; Andrew antenna. Ownership: Matthew Oristano.

Bloomington—WLW973 (F group). Broadcast Data Corp., Suite 247, 189 Berdan Ave., Wayne, NJ 07470. Phone: 201-831-7407.

Authorized power: 10-w. each. Antenna: 104-ft. above ground. Lat. 39° 09' 56", long. 86° 32' 06". Transmitter: 205 N. College Ave. Equipment: Comwave transmitter; Bogner antenna. Ownership: Broadcast Data Corp.

Bloomington—WNTM675 (H1 & 2)). Alda Wireless Holdings Inc., 5301 E. Broadway Blvd., Tucson, AZ 85711-8181. Phone: 520-519-4400. Fax: 520-747-6830. Antenna: 800-ft. above ground. Lat. 39° 24' 22", long. 86° 08' 37". Transmitter: 0.8-mi. SSE of Trafalgar. Ownership: Matthew Oristano.

Bloomington—WNTG394 (H3). Alda Wireless Holdings Inc., 5301 E. Broadway Blvd., Tucson, AZ 85711-8181. Phone: 520-519-4400. Fax: 520-747-6830. Authorized power: 50-w. Antenna: 404-ft. above ground. Lat. 39° 08' 32", long. 86° 29' 43". Transmitter: 2897 S. Sare Rd. Equipment: Comwave transmitter; Andrew antenna. Ownership: Matthew Oristano.

Elkhart—WMH360 (E group). American Telecasting of Michiana Inc., Suite 300, 5575 Tech Center Dr., Colorado Springs, CO 80919. Phone: 719-260-5533. Fax: 719-260-5010. Authorized power: 10-w. each. Antenna: 296-ft. above ground. Lat. 41° 40' 28", long. 85° 56' 51". Transmitter: 1246 E. Indiana Ave. Equipment: Emcee transmitter; Andrew antenna. Ownership: American Telecasting Inc.

Evansville—WMI378 (E group). Tri-State Public Teleplex Inc., 405 Carpenter St., Evansville, IN 47708. Phone: 812-423-2973. Fax: 812-428-7548. Authorized power: 50-w. each. Antenna: 595-ft. above ground. Lat. 37° 59' 13", long. 87° 16' 11". Transmitter: New Hope Rd. Equipment: ITS transmitter; Andrew antenna. Ownership: Southwest Indiana Public Broadcasting Inc.
Leased to Ohio Valley Wireless Ltd., 1420 N. Cullen, Box 5518, Evansville, IN 47716. Phone: 812-471-7500.

Evansville—WLW799 (F group). Multi-Micro, Suite 120, 4700 S. McClintock, Tempe, AZ 85282. Phone: 480-755-7524. Fax: 480-755-7534. Authorized power: 10-w. each. Antenna: 595-ft. above ground. Lat. 37° 59' 13", long. 87° 16' 11". Transmitter: New Hope Rd. Equipment: Comwave transmitter; Andrew antenna. Ownership: Multi-Micro Inc.
Leased to Ohio Valley Wireless Ltd., 1420 N. Cullen Ave., Box 5518, Evansville, IN 47716. Phone: 812-471-7500.

Evansville—WNTJ744 (H2). Thomas Crossfield, Suite 201, 7800 113th St. N, Seminole, FL 34642. Phone: 813-392-1681. Authorized power: 50-w. Antenna: 595-ft. above ground. Lat. 37° 59' 13", long. 87° 16' 11". Transmitter: New Hope Rd. Equipment: Emcee transmitter; Andrew antenna. Ownership: Thomas Crossfield.

Evansville—WNTJ711 (H3). Wayland Blake, Box 67, Forest City, IA 50436. Authorized power: 31.6-w. Antenna: 595-ft. above ground. Lat. 37° 59' 13", long. 87° 16' 11". Transmitter: New Hope Rd. Equipment: Comwave transmitter; Andrew antenna. Ownership: Wayland Blake.

Fort Wayne—WHT767 (E group). Wireless Entertainment Systems Inc., Suite 104, 3501 N. Campbell, Tucson, AZ 85719. Authorized power: 100-w. each. Antenna: 300-ft. above ground. Lat. 41° 06' 25", long. 85° 11' 46". Transmitter: 3431 Hillegas Rd. Equipment: Comwave transmitter; Bogner antenna. Ownership: Wireless Entertainment Systems Inc.

Fort Wayne—WHT768 (F group). Via/Net Companies, 836 E. Washington St., San Diego, CA 92103. Phone: 619-260-0110. Authorized power: 100-w. each. Antenna: 300-ft. above ground. Lat. 41° 06' 25", long. 85° 11' 46". Transmitter: 3431 Hillegas Rd. Equipment: Comwave transmitter; Bogner antenna. Ownership: Via/Net Companies.
Leased to People's Chocie TV Partners, 2 Corporate Dr., Suite 249, Shelton, CT 06484-6239. Phone: 203-929-2800. Fax: 203-929-1454.

Indianapolis—WHT673 (E group). Affiliated MDS Corp., One Financial Center, Boston, MA 02111. Phone: 617-856-8400. Authorized power: 100-w. each. Antenna: 824-ft. above ground. Lat. 39° 46' 11", long. 86° 09' 26". Transmitter: 111 Monument Circle. Equipment: Comwave transmitter; Andrew antenna. Requests change to 10-w. each, 533-ft. above ground, lat. 39° 46' 13", long. 86° 09' 20"; transmitter to Indianapolis Square. Ownership: Affiliated MDS Corp.
Leased to People's Choice TV Partners, 2 Corporate Dr., Suite 249, Shelton, CT 06484-6239. Phone: 203-929-2800. Fax: 203-929-1454.

Indianapolis—WHT674 (F group). Alda Wireless Holdings Inc., 5301 E. Broadway Blvd., Tucson, AZ 85711-3710. Phone: 520-519-4400. Fax: 520-747-6830. Authorized power: 10-w. each. Antenna: 823-ft. above ground. Lat. 39° 46' 11", long. 86° 09' 26". Transmitter: 111 Monument Circle. Equipment: Emcee transmitter; Andrew antenna. Ownership: Matthew Oristano.

Indianapolis—WMY204 (H1). Alda Wireless Holdings Inc., 5301 E. Broadway Blvd., Tucson, AZ 85711-8181. Phone: 520-519-4400. Fax: 520-747-6830. Authorized power: 100-w. Antenna: 823-ft. above ground. Lat. 39° 46' 11", long. 86° 09' 26". Transmitter: 111 Monument Circle. Equipment: Comwave transmitter; Andrew antenna. Ownership: Matthew Oristano.

Indianapolis—WMY205 (H2). Alda Wireless Holdings Inc., 5301 E. Broadway Blvd., Tucson, AZ 85711-8181. Phone: 520-519-4400. Fax: 520-747-6830. Authorized power: 50-w. Antenna: 823-ft. above ground. Lat. 39° 46' 11", long. 86° 09' 26". Transmitter: 111 Monument Circle. Equipment: Comwave transmitter; Andrew antenna. Ownership: Matthew Oristano.

Indianapolis—WMY203 (H3). Alda Wireless Holdings Inc., 5301 E. Broadway Blvd., Tucson, AZ 85711-8181. Phone: 520-519-4400. Fax: 520-747-6830. Authorized power: 50-w. Antenna: 823-ft. above ground. Lat. 39° 46' 11", long. 86° 09' 26". Transmitter: 111 Monument Circle. Equipment: Comwave transmitter; Andrew antenna. Ownership: Matthew Oristano.

Kokomo—WMH997 (E group). Belwen Inc., 7 Boyle Rd., Scotia, NY 12302. Phone: 518-393-7428. Authorized power: 10-w. each. Antenna: 345-ft. above ground. Lat. 40° 28' 18", long. 86° 09' 52". Transmitter: 1100 S. Dixon. Equipment: Comwave transmitter; Bogner antenna. Ownership: Belwen Inc.

Kokomo—WMI877 (F group). Krisar Inc., 320 Hamilton St., Albion, NY 14411. Phone: 716-964-9121. Fax: 716-589-9094. E-mail: topperiai@aol.com. Authorized power: 50-w. each. Antenna: 474-ft. above ground. Lat. 40° 28' 18", long. 86° 09' 52". Transmitter: 1100 S. Dixon. Equipment: Comwave transmitter; Andrew antenna. Ownership: Krisar Inc.
Leased to People's Choice TV Partners, 2 Corporate Dr., Suite 249, Shelton, CT 06484-6239. Phone: 203-929-2800. Fax: 203-929-1454.

Lafayette—WMH572 (E group). Cossa Enterprise, 7212 Palm Tree Circle, Bakersfield, CA 93308. Phone: 661-399-8182. E-mail: cgbowser5@aol.com. Authorized power: 10-w. each. Antenna: 407-ft. above ground. Lat. 40° 17' 50", long. 86° 54' 05". Transmitter: 8-mi. S of Lafayette. Equipment: Emcee transmitter; Andrew antenna. Ownership: Cossa Enterprise.
Leased to People's Choice TV, 2 Corporate Dr., Suite 249, Shelton, CT 06484-6239. Phone: 203-929-2800. Fax: 203-929-1454.

Lafayette—WLW814 (F group). Universal Wireless Television Corp. Authorized power: 100-w. each. Antenna: 383-ft. above ground. Lat. 40° 23' 24", long. 86° 51' 53". Transmitter: 2510 S. 30th St. Equipment: ITS transmitter; Andrew antenna. Ownership: Universal Wireless Television Corp.

Lafayette—WNTJ438 (H group). Cossa Enterprise, 7212 Palm Tree Circle, Bakersfield, CA 93308. Phone: 661-399-8182. E-mail: cgbowser5@aol.com. Authorized power: 100-w. each. Antenna: 383-ft. above ground. Lat. 40° 23' 24", long. 86° 51' 53". Transmitter: 250 S. 30th St. Equipment: ITS transmitter; Andrew antenna. Ownership: Cossa Enterprise.
Leased to People's Choice TV, 2 Corporate Dr., Suite 249, Shelton, CT 06484-6239. Phone: 203-929-2800. Fax: 203-929-1454.

Lyford—WNTJ462 (H group). Multi-Micro Inc., Suite 120, 4700 S. McClintock, Tempe, AZ 85282. Phone: 480-755-7524. Fax: 480-755-7534. Authorized power: 100-w. each. Antenna: 440-ft. above ground. Lat. 39° 30' 26", long. 87° 31' 50". Transmitter: 30th Ave. & 71st Place intersection. Equipment: Comwave transmitter; Andrew antenna. Ownership: Multi-Micro Inc.

Muncie—WMH689 (E group). Century Microwave Corp., 51 Locust Ave., New Canaan, CT 06840. Authorized power: 10-w. each. Antenna: 300-ft. above ground. Lat. 40° 09' 55", long. 85° 25' 13". Transmitter: Middletown Rd. & CR 2005. Equipment: Emcee transmitter; Andrew antenna. Ownership: Century Microwave Corp.

New Albany—WNTA919 (H3). BellSouth Wireless Cable Inc., Suite 414, 1100 Abernathy Rd. NE, Atlanta, GA 30328. Phone: 770-673-2800. Authorized power: 20-w. Antenna: 273-ft. above ground. Lat. 38° 10' 25", long. 85° 54' 50". Transmitter: Doolittle Rd. & Lohicks Corner Rd. Equipment: Comwave transmitter; Andrew antenna. Ownership: BellSouth Entertainment Inc.

South Bend—WMI307 (E group). Jack G. Hubbard, 8793 Ranch Dr., Chesterland, OH 44026. Phone & fax: 216-729-7282. Authorized power: 10-w. each. Antenna: 70-ft. above ground. Lat. 41° 40' 51", long. 86° 15' 07". Transmitter: 120 W. La Salle. Equipment: Emcee transmitter; Andrew antenna. Ownership: Jack G. Hubbard.
Leased to National Micro Vision Systems Inc., 270 Bristol St., Suite 101, Costa Mesa, CA 92626. Phone: 714-708-8637.

South Bend—WMI853 (F group). Krisar Inc., 320 Hamilton St., Albion, NY 14411. Phone: 716-964-9121. Fax: 716-589-9094. E-mail: topperiai@aol.com. Authorized power: 50-w. each. Antenna: 750-ft. above ground. Lat. 41° 36' 59", long. 86° 11' 43". Transmitter: 16965 Johnson Rd. Equipment: ITS transmitter; Andrew antenna. Ownership: Krisar Inc.
Leased to American Telecasting Inc., 5575 Tech Center Dr., Suite 300, Colorado Springs, CO 80919. Phone: 719-260-5533.

South Bend—WNTM640 (H2). Mary C. Salvato, 8811 Angoff Dr., New Port Richey, FL 34653. Phone: 813-376-9284. Authorized power: 50-w. Antenna: 750-ft. above ground. Lat. 41° 36' 59", long. 86° 11' 43". Transmitter: 16965 Johnson Rd. Equipment: ITS transmitter; Andrew antenna. Ownership: Mary C. Salvato.

Terre Haute—WMI833 (E group). Alda Multichannels Ltd., 5301 E. Broadway Blvd., Tucson, AZ 85711-3710. Phone: 520-519-4400. Fax: 520-747-6830. Authorized power: 10-w. each. Antenna: 689-ft. above ground. Lat. 39° 30' 14", long. 87° 26' 37". Transmitter: 3-mi. E of 150, N of Sycamore. Equipment: Comwave transmitter; Bogner antenna. Ownership: Matthew Oristano.

Iowa

Batavia—WLW851 (E group). CDV Inc., 2414 S. Halliburton, Kirksville, MO 63501. Authorized power: 50-w. each. Antenna: 460-ft. above ground. Lat. 40° 56' 10", long. 92° 10' 16". Transmitter: 4.5-mi. S of Batavia. Equipment: ITS transmitter; Andrew antenna. Ownership: CDV Inc.

Britt—WMH553 (E group). Todd Communications Inc., 6545 Cecilia Circle, Minneapolis, MN 55435. Phone: 612-941-0556. Authorized power: 10-w. each. Antenna: 490-ft. above ground. Lat. 43° 07' 40", long. 93° 44' 50". Transmitter: 1-mi. N of Hwy. 18, 2-mi. E of Britt. Equipment: ITS transmitter; Bogner antenna. Ownership: Todd Communications Inc.

Britt—WMH676 (F group). Walter L. Bush Jr., 5704 Camelback Dr., Minneapolis, MN 55436. Phone: 612-944-7885. Authorized power: 10-w. each. Antenna: 490-ft. above ground. Lat. 43° 07' 40", long. 93° 44' 50". Transmitter: 1-mi. N of Hwy. 18, 2-mi. E of Britt. Equipment: ITS transmitter; Bogner antenna. Ownership: Walter L. Bush Jr.

Cedar Rapids—WMI345 (E group). Virginia Communications Inc., Suite B1, 7621 E. Gray Rd., Scottsdale, AZ 85260. Phone: 480-596-8283. Fax: 480-596-2973. Authorized power: 50-w. each. Antenna: 353-ft. above ground. Lat. 41° 54' 33", long. 91° 39' 17". Transmitter: 6301 Kirkwood Blvd. SW. Equipment: Emcee transmitter; Andrew antenna. Ownership: Virginia Communications Inc.

Davenport—WLW894 (F group). MWTV Inc., 3401 E. Cholla St., Phoenix, AZ 85028. Phone: 602-867-7351. Authorized power: 10-w. each. Antenna: 910-ft. above ground. Lat. 41° 31' 58", long. 90° 34' 40". Transmitter: 317 W. 13th St. Equipment: Emcee transmitter; Andrew antenna. Ownership: MWTV Inc.

Davenport—WNTJ387 (H1). Virginia Communications Inc., Suite B1, 7621 E. Gray Rd., Scottsdale, AZ 85260. Phone: 480-596-8283. Fax: 480-596-2973. Authorized power: 50-w. Antenna: 354-ft. above ground. Lat. 41° 32' 48", long. 90° 27' 56". Transmitter: 500 Belmont Rd., Bettendorf. Equipment: Emcee transmitter; Andrew antenna. Ownership: Virginia Communications Inc.

Davenport—WNTJ392 (H2). Virginia Communications Inc., Suite B1, 7621 E. Gray Rd., Scottsdale, AZ 85260. Phone: 480-596-8283. Fax: 480-596-2973. Authorized power: 50-w. Antenna: 354-ft. above ground. Lat. 41° 32' 48", long. 90° 27' 56". Transmitter: 500 Belmont Rd., Bettendorf. Equipment: Emcee transmitter; Andrew antenna. Ownership: Virginia Communications Inc.

Davenport—WNTJ376 (H3). Virginia Communications Inc., Suite B1, 7621 E. Gray Rd., Scottsdale, AZ 85260. Phone: 480-596-8283. Fax: 480-596-2973. Authorized power: 50-w. Antenna: 360-ft. above ground. Lat. 41° 32' 48", long. 90° 27' 56". Transmitter: 500 Belmont Rd., Bettendorf. Equipment: Emcee transmitter; Andrew antenna. Ownership: Virginia Communications Inc.

Davenport, IA-Rock Island-Moline, IL—WHT588 (E group). Virginia Communications Inc., Suite B1, 7621 E. Gray Rd., Scottsdale, AZ 85260. Phone: 480-596-8283. Fax: 480-596-2973. Authorized power: 10-w. each. Antenna: 910-ft. above ground. Lat. 41° 31' 58", long. 90° 34' 40". Transmitter: 317 W. 13th St., Davenport. Equipment: ITS transmitter; Andrew antenna. Ownership: Virginia Communications Inc.

Dubuque—WMI281 (F group). Broadcast Data Corp., Suite 247, 189 Berdan Ave., Wayne, NJ 07470. Phone: 201-831-7407. Authorized power: 10-w. each. Antenna: 409-ft. above ground. Lat. 42° 30' 10", long. 90° 42' 24". Transmitter: 2763 Penn Ave. Equipment: Comwave transmitter; Bogner antenna. Ownership: Broadcast Data Corp.

Grimes—WMX356 (H1). Des Moines One Partnership, 2700 Chain Bridge Rd. NW, Washington, DC 20016. Phone: 202-659-4400. Fax: 202-237-7742. Authorized power: 10-w. Antenna: 675-ft. above ground. Lat. 41° 42' 01", long. 93° 51' 55". Transmitter: 3.5-mi. WNW of Grimes. Equipment: Comwave transmitter; Andrew antenna. Ownership: Des Moines One Partnership.

Leased to Nucentrix Broadband Networks, 200 Chisholm Place, Suite 200, Plano, TX 75075. Phone: 972-423-9494. Fax: 972-423-0819.

Grimes—WMX357 (H2). Des Moines One Partnership, 2700 Chain Bridge Rd. NW, Washington, DC 20016. Phone: 202-659-4400. Fax: 202-237-7742. Authorized power: 10-w. Antenna: 675-ft. above ground. Lat. 41° 42' 01", long. 93° 51' 55". Transmitter: 3.5-mi. WNW of Grimes. Equipment: Comwave transmitter; Andrew antenna. Ownership: Des Moines One Partnership.

Leased to Nucentrix Broadband Networks, 200 Chisholm Place, Suite 200, Plano, TX 75075. Phone: 972-423-9494. Fax: 972-423-0819.

Grimes—WMX355 (H3). Des Moines One Partnership, 2700 Chain Bridge Rd. NW, Washington, DC 20016. Phone: 202-659-4400. Fax: 202-237-7742. Authorized power: 10-w. Antenna: 675-ft. above ground. Lat. 41° 42' 01", long. 93° 51' 55". Transmitter: 3.5-mi. WNW of Grimes. Equipment: Comwave transmitter; Andrew antenna. Ownership: Des Moines One Partnership.

Leased to Nucentrix Broadband Networks, 200 Chisholm Place, Suite 200, Plano, TX 75075. Phone: 972-423-9494. Fax: 972-423-0819.

Griswold—WMY432 (E group). Griswold Cooperative Telephone Co., Box 640, 607 Main St., Griswold, IA 51535. Phone: 712-778-2122. Authorized power: 50-w. each. Antenna: 195-ft. above ground. Lat. 41° 17' 05", long. 94° 44' 59". Transmitter: 3-mi. NE of Massena. Equipment: ITS transmitter; Andrew antenna. Ownership: Griswold Co-op Telephone Co.

Marion—WNTH585 (H1). Virginia Communications Inc., Suite B1, 7621 E. Gray Rd., Scottsdale, AZ 85260. Phone: 480-596-8283. Fax: 480-596-2973. Authorized power: 50-w. Antenna: 353-ft. above ground. Lat. 41° 54' 33", long. 91° 39' 17". Transmitter: 6301 Kirkwood Blvd. Equipment: Emcee transmitter; Andrew antenna. Ownership: Virginia Communications Inc.

Marion—WNTI403 (H3). Virginia Communications Inc., Suite B1, 7621 E. Gray Rd., Scottsdale, AZ 85260. Phone: 480-596-8283. Fax: 480-596-2973. Authorized power: 50-w. Antenna: 353-ft. above ground. Lat. 41° 54' 33", long. 91° 39' 17". Transmitter: 6301 Kirkwood Blvd. Equipment: Emcee transmitter; Andrew antenna. Ownership: Virginia Communications Inc.

Palmer—WLK383 (E group). Evertek Inc., Box 270, 216 N. Main St., Everly, IA 51338. Phone: 712-834-2255. Authorized power: 10-w. each.Antenna: 482-ft. above ground. Lat. 42° 38' 00", long. 94° 38' 03". Transmitter: Hwy. 315, 1.5-mi. W of Palmer. Equipment: ITS transmitter; Andrew antenna. Ownership: Evertek Inc.

Palmer—WLK386 (F group). Evertek Inc., Box 270, 216 N. Main St., Everly, IA 51338. Phone: 712-834-2255. Authorized power: 10-w. each. Antenna: 490-ft. above ground. Lat. 42° 38' 00", long. 94° 38' 03". Transmitter: Hwy. 315, 1.5-mi. W of Palmer. Equipment: ITS transmitter; Bogner antenna. Requests change to 482-ft. above ground; Andrew antenna. Ownership: Evertek Inc.

Palmer—WNEZ929 (H1). Evertek Inc., Box 270, 216 N. Main St., Everly, IA 51338. Phone: 712-834-2255. Authorized power: 10-w. Antenna: 482-ft. above ground. Lat. 42° 38' 00", long. 94° 38' 03". Transmitter: Hwy. 315, 1.5-mi. W of Palmer. Equipment: ITS transmitter; Andrew antenna. Ownership: Evertek Inc.

Palmer—WNTB279 (H). Evertek Inc., Box 270, 216 N. Main St., Everly, IA 51338. Phone: 712-834-2255. Authorized power: 10-w. Antenna: 483-ft. above ground. Lat. 42° 38' 00", long. 94° 38' 03". Transmitter: 1.5-mi. W on Hwy. 315. Equipment: ITS transmitter; Andrew antenna. Ownership: Evertek Inc.

Palmer—WNTB791 (H3). Evertek Inc., Box 270, 216 N. Main St., Everly, IA 51338. Phone: 712-834-2255. Authorized power: 10-w. Antenna: 482-ft. above ground. Lat. 42° 38' 00", long. 94° 38' 03". Transmitter: Hwy. 315, 1.5-mi. W of Palmer. Equipment: ITS transmitter; Andrew antenna. Ownership: Evertek Inc.

Postville—WLW767 (E group). Northeast Iowa TV Inc., Box 289, RR 1, Postville, IA 52162. Phone: 319-864-3104. Authorized power: 10-w. each. Antenna: 305-ft. above ground. Lat. 43° 04' 48", long. 91° 33' 32". Transmitter: Hwy. 52. Equipment: ITS transmitter; Andrew antenna. Ownership: Northeast Iowa TV Inc.

Radcliffe—WLW731 (E group). Central Iowa TV Inc., Box 548, Bath, SD 57427. Phone: 605-229-2412. Authorized power: 10-w. each. Antenna: 491-ft. above ground. Lat. 42° 20' 10", long. 93° 28' 00". Transmitter: 1.5-mi. W, 1.5-mi. N of Radcliffe. Equipment: ITS transmitter; Andrew antenna. Ownership: TC Communications Inc.

Radcliffe—WLW727 (F group). Central Iowa TV Inc., Box 548, Bath, SD 57427. Phone: 605-229-2412. Authorized power: 10-w. each. Antenna: 491-ft. above ground. Lat. 42° 20' 10", long. 93° 28' 00". Transmitter: 1.5-mi. W, 1.5-mi. N of Radcliffe. Equipment: ITS transmitter; Andrew antenna. Ownership: Central Iowa TV Inc.

Radcliffe—WNTE611 (H3). Central Iowa TV Inc., Box 548, Bath, SD 57427. Phone: 605-229-2412. Authorized power: 10-w. Antenna: 485-ft. above ground. Lat. 42° 20' 10", long. 93° 28' 00". Transmitter: 1.5-mi. W, 1.5-mi. N of Radcliffe. Equipment: ITS transmitter; Andrew antenna. Ownership: Central Iowa TV Inc.

Sioux City—WMH468 (E group). Grand Alliance Sioux City (E) Partnership, Suite 660, 1920 N St. NW, Washington, DC 20036. Authorized power: 10-w. each. Antenna: 154-ft. above ground. Lat. 42° 29' 39", long. 96° 24' 10". Transmitter: 4th & Jackson Sts., Badgerow Bldg. Equipment: Emcee transmitter; Andrew antenna. Ownership: Macro Distribution Systems Inc.

Sioux City—WLW956 (F group). Thomas F. Lennon, Receiver. Authorized power: 10-w. each. Antenna: 156-ft. above ground. Lat. 42° 29' 39", long. 96° 24' 10". Transmitter: 4th & Jackson Sts. Equipment: Comwave transmitter; Bogner antenna. Ownership: Continental Wireless Cable Television Inc.

Spencer—WLK403 (E group). Evertek Inc., Box 270, 216 N. Main St., Everly, IA 51338. Phone: 712-834-2255. Authorized power: 10-w. each. Antenna: 440-ft. above ground. Lat. 43° 09' 53", long. 95° 19' 29". Transmitter: 7.7-mi. W of Spencer. Equipment: ITS transmitter; Andrew antenna. Ownership: Evertek Inc.

Spencer—WLK267 (F group). Evertek Inc., Box 270, 216 N. Main St., Everly, IA 51338. Phone: 712-834-2255. Authorized power: 10-w. each. Antenna: 440-ft. above ground. Lat. 43° 09' 53", long. 95° 19' 29". Transmitter: 7.7-mi. W of Spencer. Equipment: ITS transmitter; Andrew antenna. Ownership: Evertek Inc.

Spencer—WNEZ928 (H1). Evertek Inc., Box 270, 216 N. Main St., Everly, IA 51338. Phone: 712-834-2255. Authorized power: 10-w. Antenna: 440-ft. above ground. Lat. 43° 09' 53", long. 95° 19' 29". Transmitter: 7.7-mi. W of Spencer. Equipment: ITS transmitter; Andrew antenna. Ownership: Evertek Inc.

Spencer—WNTB278 (H2). Evertek Inc., Box 270, 216 N. Main St., Everly, IA 51338. Phone: 712-834-2255. Authorized power: 10-w. Antenna: 440-ft. above ground. Lat. 43° 09' 53", long. 95° 19' 29". Transmitter: 7.7-mi. W of Spencer. Equipment: ITS transmitter; Andrew antenna. Ownership: Evertek Inc.

Spencer—WNTB792 (H3). Evertek Inc., Box 270, 216 N. Main St., Everly, IA 51338. Phone: 712-834-2255. Authorized power: 10-w. Antenna: 440-ft. above ground. Lat. 43° 09' 53", long. 95° 19' 29". Transmitter: 7.7-mi. W of Spencer. Equipment: ITS transmitter; Andrew antenna. Ownership: Evertek Inc.

Waterloo-Cedar Falls—WHK956 (E group). Group Communications Inc., 1463 Oak Crest Dr., Waterloo, IA 50701. Phone: 319-232-3696. Authorized power: 10-w. each. Antenna: 430-ft. above ground. Lat. 42° 52' 05", long. 92° 40' 40". Transmitter: 5-mi. N of Clarksville on Rte. 64, Waterloo. Equipment: ITS transmitter; Bogner antenna. Ownership: Group Communications Inc.

Kansas

Anthony—WMY441 (H1). Heartland Cable, 2908 S. Santa Fe St., Chanute, KS 66720. Phone: 800-221-6788. Authorized power: 25-w. Antenna: 854-ft. above ground. Lat. 37° 23' 10", long. 98° 15' 43". Transmitter: approx. 3.6-mi. S of Zenda. Equipment: Andrew antenna. Ownership: Heartland Cable Inc. (Kansas).

Anthony—WMY442 (H3). Heartland Cable, 2908 S. Santa Fe St., Chanute, KS 66720. Phone: 800-221-6788. Authorized power: 25-w. Antenna: 854-ft. above ground. Lat. 37° 23' 10", long. 98° 15' 43". Transmitter: approx. 3.6-mi. S of Zenda. Equipment: Andrew antenna. Ownership: Heartland Cable Inc. (Kansas).

Dodge City—WMI275 (E group). Kannew Broadcast Technologies, Suite 425, 1220 L St. NW, Washington, DC 20005. Phone: 202-289-6300. Authorized power: 10-w. each. Antenna: 500-ft. above ground. Lat. 37° 46' 46", long. 100° 08' 28". Transmitter: 2.4-mi. E of Howell. Equipment: Comwave transmitter; Andrew antenna. Ownership: Kannew Broadcast Technologies.

Dover—WNTH894 (H1). Blake Twedt, 5102 Rosegreen Court, Tampa, FL 33624. Phone: 727-587-9959. Authorized power: 50-w. Antenna: 855-ft. above ground. Lat. 39° 01' 34", long. 95° 54' 58". Transmitter: 2280 W. Union Rd. Equipment: Comwave transmitter; Andrew antenna. Ownership: Blake Twedt.

Durham—WMY300 (H3). RVC Holdings Inc., Suite 200, 200 Chisholm Place, Plano, TX 75075. Phone: 972-423-9494. Fax: 972-423-0819. Authorized power: 10-w. Antenna: 30-ft. above ground. Lat. 38° 28' 29", long. 97° 16' 55". Transmitter: 3.2-mi. E of Hwy. 15. Equipment: Comwave transmitter; Andrew antenna. Ownership: Nucentrix Broadband Networks Inc.

Erie—WNTG293 (H1). Nucentrix Spectrum Resources Inc., Suite 200, 200 Chisholm Place, Plano, TX 75075. Phone: 972-423-9494. Fax: 972-423-0819. Antenna: 1680-ft. above ground. Lat. 37° 36' 11", long. 95° 16' 20". Transmitter: 3-mi. NW of Erie. Equipment: Andrew antenna. Ownership: Nucentrix Broadband Networks.

Erie—WNTG290 (H2). Nucentrix Spectrum Resources Inc., Suite 200, 200 Chisholm Place, Plano, TX 75075. Phone: 972-423-9494. Fax: 972-423-0819. Lat. 37° 36' 11", long. 95° 16' 20". Transmitter: 3-mi. NW of Erie. Equipment: Andrew antenna. Ownership: Nucentrix Broadband Networks.

Erie—WNTG289 (H3). Nucentrix Spectrum Resources Inc., Suite 200, 200 Chisholm Place, Plano, TX 75075. Phone: 972-423-9494. Fax: 972-633-0074. Web site: http://www.heartland-wireless.com. Antenna: 1680-ft. above ground. Lat. 37° 36' 11", long. 95° 16' 20". Transmitter: 3-mi. NW of Erie. Ownership: Nucentrix Broadband Networks.

Griswold—WMY432 (H1). Willian H. Benson, 6th Floor, 5520 LBJ Freeway, Dallas, TX 75240. Phone: 214-715-2103. Authorized power: 50-w. Antenna: 326-ft. above ground. Lat. 37° 41' 53", long. 97° 19' 11". Transmitter: 1510 E. Murdock. Equipment: ITS transmitter; Bogner antenna. Ownership: William H. Benson.

Hays—WHT621 (E group). TV Communications Network Inc., Suite 300, 10020 E. Girard Ave., Denver, CO 80231. Phone: 303-751-2900. Fax: 303-751-1081. E-mail: kroznoy@Plinet.com. Authorized power: 10-w. each. Antenna: 450-ft. above ground. Lat. 38° 55' 20", long. 99° 21' 11". Transmitter: Bird Farm Rd., 0.75-mi.

N of I-70. Equipment: Emcee transmitter; Bogner antenna. Ownership: TV Communications Network Inc.

Hoisington—WMH712 (E group). Danel Co., 265 W. Broadway, Hoisington, KS 67544. Authorized power: 10-w. each. Antenna: 403-ft. above ground. Lat. 38° 32' 49", long. 98° 45' 59". Transmitter: Susan Rd., 1.75-mi. N of Hoisington. Equipment: Emcee transmitter; Bogner antenna. Ownership: Danel Co.

Salina—WHT623 (E group). TV Communications Network Inc., Suite 300, 10020 E. Girard Ave., Denver, CO 80231. Phone: 303-751-2900. Fax: 303-751-1081. E-mail: kroznoy@Plinet.com. Authorized power: 10-w. each. Antenna: 440-ft. above ground. Lat. 38° 55' 55", long. 97° 35' 27". Transmitter: 4-mi. N of Salina on Ohio St. Equipment: Emcee transmitter; Bogner antenna. Ownership: TV Communications Network Inc.

Salina—WLW885 (F group). Token Partnership, 1201 7th St., East Moline, IL 61244. Authorized power: 10-w. each. Antenna: 440-ft. above ground. Lat. 38° 55' 55", long. 97° 35' 27". Transmitter: 4-mi. N of Salina on Ohio St. Equipment: Emcee transmitter; Bogner antenna. Ownership: Token Partnership.

Topeka—WMI290 (F group). Sherry Rullman, 2129 San Marcos Place, Claremont, CA 91711-1766. Phone: 714-625-2988. Fax: 714-624-3993. Authorized power: 10-w. each. Antenna: 90-ft. above ground. Lat. 39° 03' 00", long. 95° 04' 12". Transmitter: Capital Tower Bldg. Equipment: Emcee transmitter; Andrew antenna. Ownership: Sherry Rullman.

Wichita—WHT743 (E group). Paging Systems Inc., Box 4249, Burlingame, CA 94010. Authorized power: 50-w. each. Antenna: 500-ft. above ground. Lat. 37° 41' 53", long. 97° 19' 11". Transmitter: 1510 E. Murdock. Equipment: ITS transmitter; Bogner antenna. Ownership: Paging Systems Inc.

Wichita—WHT744 (F group). Omega Radiotelephone, 1601 Neptune Dr., San Leandro, CA 94577. Authorized power: 10-w. each. Antenna: 494-ft. above ground. Lat. 37° 41' 53", long. 97° 19' 11". Transmitter: Wichita. Equipment: Emcee transmitter; Bogner antenna. Ownership: Omega Radiotelephone.

Wichita—WNTB419 (H1). American Telecasting of Oklahoma Inc., Suite 300, 5575 Tech Center Dr., Colorado Springs, CO 80919. Phone: 719-260-5533. Fax: 719-260-5010. Authorized power: 50-w. Antenna: 326-ft. above ground. Lat. 37° 41' 53", long. 97° 19' 11". Transmitter: 1510 E. Murdock. Equipment: ITS transmitter; Bogner antenna. Ownership: American Telecasting Inc.

Wichita—WNTM611 (H2). JRZ Associates, 210 W. 4th St., Greenville, NC 27858. Authorized power: 50-w. Antenna: 326-ft. above ground. Lat. 37° 41' 43", long. 97° 19' 05". Transmitter: 1510 E. Murdock. Equipment: ITS transmitter; Bogner antenna. Ownership: JRZ Associates.

Wichita—WNTU661 (H3). American Telecasting of Oklahoma Inc., Suite 300, 5575 Tech Center Dr., Colorado Springs, CO 80919. Phone: 719-260-5533. Fax: 719-260-5010. Authorized power: 50-w. Antenna: 326-ft. above ground. Lat. 37° 41' 53", long. 97° 19' 11". Transmitter: 1510 E. Murdock. Equipment: Bogner antenna. Ownership: American Telecasting Inc.

Kentucky

Columbia—WMI419 (E group). Microwave Broadcast Services Inc., Suite 200, 5505 South 900 East, Salt Lake City, UT 84117. Phone: 801-288-1760. Authorized power: 20-w. each. Antenna: 900-ft. above ground. Lat. 37° 10' 05", long. 85° 18' 32". Transmitter: 4.1-mi. N of Columbia. Equipment: ITS transmitter; Andrew antenna. Ownership: Microwave Broadcast Services Inc.

Columbia—WMI415 (F group). Microwave Broadcast Services Inc., Suite 200, 5505 South 900 East, Salt Lake City, UT 84117. Phone: 801-288-1760. Authorized power: 20-w. each. Antenna: 900-ft. above ground. Lat. 37° 10' 05", long. 85° 18' 32". Transmitter: 4.1-mi. N of Columbia. Equipment: ITS transmitter; Andrew antenna. Ownership: Microwave Broadcast Services Inc.

Lexington—WMH573 (E group). David Weichman, 8929 Etiwanda Ave., Northridge, CA 91325. Authorized power: 10-w. each. Antenna: 90-ft. above ground. Lat. 38° 02' 55", long. 84° 29' 48". Transmitter: 163 W. Short. Equipment: Emcee transmitter; Andrew antenna. Ownership: David Weichman.

Lexington—WLR484 (F group). Video/Multipoint Inc., 2809 Pine St., San Francisco, CA 94115-2501. Phone: 415-775-9552. Fax: 415-775-9536. E-mail: bill@sauro.com. Authorized power: 10-w. each. Antenna: 754-ft. above ground. Lat. 38° 02' 22", long. 84° 24' 11". Transmitter: Rte. 60, 2.8-mi. E of New Circle. Equipment: Comwave transmitter; Andrew antenna. Ownership: Video/Multipoint Inc.

Lexington—WNTJ726 (H1). Libmot Communications Partnership, 2700 Chain Bridge Rd. NW, Washington, DC 20016. Phone: 202-293-0700. Authorized power: 10-w. Antenna: 503-ft. above ground. Lat. 38° 00' 54", long. 84° 26' 18". Transmitter: 2599 Palumbo Dr. Equipment: Comwave transmitter; Andrew antenna. Ownership: Libmot Communications Partnership.

Lexington—WNTJ752 (H2). G & Y Communications, Suite 501, 1100 17th St. NW, Washington, DC 20036-4646. Phone: 202-223-4449. Fax: 202-223-4450. E-mail: rgould@cwix.com. Authorized power: 50-w. Antenna: 503-ft. above ground. Lat. 38° 00' 54", long. 84° 26' 18". Transmitter: 0.4-mi. S of Liberty Rd. Equipment: ITS transmitter; Andrew antenna. Ownership: G & Y Communications.
Leased to Wireless Cable of Lexington Inc., 1600 McScimming, Aspen, CO 81611. Phone: 970-920-4604.

Lexington—WNTJ710 (H3). Blake Twedt, 5102 Rosegreen Court, Tampa, FL 33624. Phone: 727-587-9959. Authorized power: 50-w. Antenna: 503-ft. above ground. Lat. 38° 00' 54", long. 84° 26' 18". Transmitter: 0.4-mi. S of Liberty Rd. Equipment: ITS transmitter; Andrew antenna. Ownership: Blake Twedt.

Louisville—WHT725 (E group). BellSouth Wireless Cable Inc., Suite 414, 1100 Abernathy Rd. NE, Atlanta, GA 30328. Phone: 770-673-2800. Authorized power: 50-w. each. Antenna: 374-ft. above ground. Lat. 38° 10' 25", long. 85° 54' 50". Transmitter: Doolittle & Lohicks Corner, New Albany, IN. Equipment: Comwave transmitter; Bogner antenna. Ownership: BellSouth Entertainment Inc.

Louisville—WNEZ577 (H1). BellSouth Wireless Cable Inc., Suite 414, 1100 Abernathy Rd. NE, Atlanta, GA 30328. Phone: 770-673-2800. Authorized power: 50-w. Antenna: 377-ft. above ground. Lat. 38° 10' 25", long. 85° 54' 50". Transmitter: Doolittle & Lohicks Corner, New Albany, IN. Equipment: Comwave transmitter; Bogner antenna. Ownership: BellSouth Entertainment Inc.

Louisville—WNEZ666 (H2). BellSouth Wireless Cable Inc., Suite 414, 1100 Abernathy Rd. NE, Atlanta, GA 30328. Phone: 470-673-2800. Authorized power: 50-w. Antenna: 374-ft. above ground. Lat. 38° 10' 25", long. 85° 54' 50". Transmitter: Doolittle & Lohicks Corner, New Albany, IN. Equipment: Comwave transmitter; Bogner antenna. Ownership: BellSouth Entertainment Inc.

Owensboro—WLW852 (E group). Belwen Inc., 7 Boyle Rd., Scotia, NY 12302. Phone: 518-393-7428. Authorized power: 10-w. each. Antenna: 1103-ft. above ground. Lat. 37° 36' 29", long. 87° 03' 15". Transmitter: 3.2-mi. ENE of Owensboro. Equipment: Comwave transmitter; Bogner antenna. Ownership: Belwen Inc.

Paducah—WLW995 (E group). Kannew Broadcast Technologies, Suite 425, 1220 L St. NW, Washington, DC 20005. Phone: 202-293-0700. Authorized power: 10-w. each. Antenna: 495-ft. above ground. Lat. 37° 08' 32", long. 88° 39' 01". Transmitter: WRIK-FM tower, Metropolis, IL. Equipment: ITS transmitter; Andrew antenna. Ownership: Kannew Broadcast Technologies.

Paducah—WLW755 (F group). Baypoint TV Inc., 2700 Chain Bridge Rd. NW, Washington, DC 20016. Phone: 202-659-4400. Fax: 202-237-7742. Authorized power: 10-w. each. Antenna: 495-ft. above ground. Lat. 37° 08' 32", long. 88° 39' 01". Transmitter: WRIL(FM) tower, Metropolis, IL. Equipment: ITS transmitter; Andrew antenna. Ownership: Baypoint TV Inc.
Leased to Nucentrix Broadband Networks, 200 Chisholm Place, Suite 200, Plano, TX 75075. Phone: 972-423-9494.

Paducah—WNTH444 (H1). JRZ Associates, Box 8026, Greenville, NC 27835-8026. Phone: 252-757-0279. Fax: 252-752-9155. E-mail: LBAgrp@LBAgroup.com. Web site: http://www.LBAgroup.com. Authorized power: 10-w. Antenna: 495-ft. above ground. Lat. 37° 08' 32", long. 88° 39' 01". Transmitter: WRIK-FM tower, Metropolis, IL. Equipment: ITS transmitter; Andrew antenna. Ownership: JRZ Associates.

Paducah—WNTH681 (H2). Libmot Communications Partnership, 2700 Chain Bridge Rd. NW, Washington, DC 20016. Phone: 202-966-2167. Fax: 202-237-7742. Authorized power: 10-w. Antenna: 495-ft. above ground. Lat. 37° 08' 32", long. 88° 39' 01". Transmitter: WRIK-FM tower, Metropolis, IL. Equipment: ITS transmitter; Andrew antenna. Ownership: Libmot Communications Partnership.
Leased to Nucentrix Broadband Networks, 200 Chisholm Place, Suite 200, Plano, TX 75075. Phone: 972-423-9494.

Paducah—WNTH387 (H3). G & Y Communications, Suite 501, 1100 17th St. NW, Washington, DC 20036-4646. Phone: 202-223-4449. Fax: 202-223-4450. E-mail: rgould@cwix.com. Authorized power: 10-w. Antenna: 495-ft. above ground. Lat. 37° 08' 32", long. 88° 39' 01". Transmitter: WKPD-TV tower, Metropolis, IL. Equipment: ITS transmitter; Andrew antenna. Ownership: G & Y Communications.
Leased to Nucentrix Broadband Networks, 200 Chisholm Place, Suite 200, Plano, TX 75075. Phone: 972-423-9494.

Somerset—WLR488 (F group). Agnes C. Kozel, 1434 Grant Ave., San Francisco, CA 94133. Phone: 415-567-9132. Authorized power: 10-w. each. Antenna: 200-ft. above ground. Lat. 37° 06' 09", long. 84° 35' 51". Transmitter: Rockquarry Rd. Equipment: Comwave transmitter; Bogner antenna. Ownership: Agnes C. Kozel.

Louisiana

Alexandria—WMI870 (F group). Video/Multipoint Inc., 2809 Pine St., San Francisco, CA 94115-2501. Phone: 415-775-9552. Fax: 415-775-9536. E-mail: bill@sauro.com. Authorized power: 50-w. each. Antenna: 1304-ft. above ground. Lat. 31° 33' 56", long. 92° 32' 50". Transmitter: 1.4-mi. SW of Dry Prong. Equipment: Comwave transmitter; Andrew antenna. Ownership: Video/Multipoint Inc.
Leased to Wireless One, 11301 Industriplex Blvd., Suite 4, Baton Rouge, LA 70809. Phone: 504-293-5000.

Baton Rouge—WHT707 (E group). Wireless Advantage Inc., 2155 Main St., Sarasota, FL 34237. Authorized power: 50-w. each. Antenna: 631-ft. above ground. Lat. 30° 17' 49", long. 91° 11' 40". Transmitter: 2.2-mi. NE of Plaquemine. Equipment: Emcee transmitter; Andrew antenna. Ownership: Wireless Advantage Inc.

Baton Rouge—WHT708 (F group). Digital Wireless Systems Inc., 1800 N. 12th St., Reading, PA 19604. Phone: 610-921-9500. Fax: 610-921-0290. Authorized power: 50-w. each. Antenna: 631-ft. above ground. Lat. 30° 17' 49", long. 91° 11' 40". Transmitter: 2.2-mi. NE of Plaquemine. Equipment: Emcee transmitter; Andrew antenna. Ownership: Digital Wireless Systems Inc.

Baton Rouge—WNTJ395 (H2). Blake Twedt, 5102 Rosegreen Court, Tampa, FL 33624. Phone: 727-587-9959. Lat. 30° 25' 56", long. 91° 11' 06". Transmitter: 1650 Highland. Ownership: Blake Twedt.

Baton Rouge—WNTJ409 (H3). John Dudeck, 11672 Harborside Circle, Largo, FL 33773. Lat. 30° 25' 56", long. 91° 11' 06". Transmitter: 1650 Highland. Ownership: John Dudeck.

Crowley/Eunice—WLW878 (E group). National Wireless Cable, 63 Dombey Circle, Thousand Oaks, CA 91360. Authorized power: 10-w. each. Antenna: 500-ft. above ground. Lat. 30° 11' 32", long. 92° 37' 16". Transmitter: Mermentau. Equipment: Comwave transmitter; Bogner antenna. Ownership: National Wireless Cable.

Houma—WMI831 (E group). Virginia Communications Inc., Suite B1, 7621 E. Gray Rd., Scottsdale, AZ 85260. Phone: 480-596-8283. Fax: 480-596-2973. Authorized power: 50-w. each. Antenna: 709-ft. above ground. Lat. 29° 41' 39", long. 90° 59' 58". Transmitter: 0.6-mi. N of U.S. 90 & State Rte. Equipment: Emcee transmitter; Andrew antenna. Ownership: Virginia Communications Inc.

Houma—WNTK965 (H2 & 3). Glenn Burke, 725 Yucca Dr., El Centro, CA 92243. Phone: 619-353-1537. Authorized power: 50-w. each. Antenna: 496-ft. above ground. Lat. 29° 41' 39", long. 90° 59' 58". Transmitter: N of U.S. 90 & State Rte. 20. Equipment: Comwave transmitter; Andrew antenna. Ownership: Glenn Burke.

Jennings—WMY436 (H1). RVS Holdings Corp., Suite 200, 200 Chisholm Place, Plano, TX 75075. Phone: 972-423-9494. Fax: 972-423-0819. Antenna: 30-ft. above ground. Lat. 30° 17' 48", long. 92° 40' 46". Transmitter:

4.5-mi. N of Jennings. Ownership: Nucentrix Broadband Networks Inc.

Jennings—WMY437 (H2). RVS Holdings Corp., Suite 200, 200 Chisholm Place, Plano, TX 75075. Phone: 972-423-9494. Fax: 972-423-0819. Antenna: 30-ft. above ground. Lat. 30° 17' 48", long. 92° 40' 46". Transmitter: 4.5-mi. N of Jennings. Ownership: Nucentrix Broadband Networks Inc.

Lafayette—WMH361 (F group). MWTV Inc., 3401 E. Cholla St., Phoenix, AZ 85028. Phone: 602-867-7351. Authorized power: 10-w. each. Antenna: 588-ft. above ground. Lat. 30° 02' 54", long. 91° 59' 49". Transmitter: 3.2-mi. S of Guillotte Rd. Equipment: Emcee transmitter; Andrew antenna. Ownership: MWTV Inc.

Lafayette—WNTJ425 (H2). Blake Twedt, 5102 Rosegreen Court, Tampa, FL 33624. Phone: 727-587-9959. Authorized power: 10-w. Antenna: 588-ft. above ground. Lat. 30° 02' 54", long. 91° 59' 49". Transmitter: 3.2-mi. S of Guillotte Rd. Equipment: Emcee transmitter; Andrew antenna. Ownership: Blake Twedt.

Lafayette—WNTJ385 (H3). Mahrle Gilders Rocz Partnership, Suite 201, 7800 113th St. N, Seminole, FL 34642. Phone: 813-855-1718. Authorized power: 10-w. Antenna: 588-ft. above ground. Lat. 30° 02' 54", long. 91° 59' 49". Transmitter: 123 N. Easy St. Equipment: Emcee transmitter; Andrew antenna. Ownership: Mahrle Gilders Rocz Partnership.

Lake Charles—WMH708 (E group). Wireless One of Lake Charles Inc., Suite 400, 2506 Lakeland Dr., Jackson, MS 39208. Phone: 601-933-6879. Authorized power: 50-w. each. Antenna: 407-ft. above ground. Lat. 30° 11' 50", long. 93° 13' 12". Transmitter: 129 W. Prien Lake. Equipment: Emcee transmitter; Andrew antenna. Ownership: Wireless One Inc.

Lake Charles—WLW801 (F group). Wireless One of Lake Charles Inc., Suite 400, 2506 Lakeland Dr., Jackson, MS 39208. Phone: 601-933-6879. Authorized power: 50-w. each. Antenna: 407-ft. above ground. Lat. 30° 11' 50", long. 93° 13' 12". Transmitter: 129 W. Prien Lake. Equipment: Comwave transmitter; Andrew antenna. Ownership: Wireless One Inc.

Lake Charles—WNTH956 (H1). Ivan C. Nachman, Suite 201, 7800 113th St. N, Seminole, FL 34642. Phone: 813-392-1681. Authorized power: 50-w. Antenna: 407-ft. above ground. Lat. 30° 11' 50", long. 93° 13' 12". Transmitter: 129 W. Prien Lake. Equipment: Emcee transmitter; Andrew antenna. Ownership: Ivan Nachman.

Lake Charles—WNTH843 (H2). Blake Twedt, 5102 Rosegreen Court, Tampa, FL 33624. Phone: 727-587-9959. Authorized power: 50-w. Antenna: 407-ft. above ground. Lat. 30° 11' 50", long. 93° 13' 12". Transmitter: 129 W. Prien Lake. Equipment: Emcee transmitter; Andrew antenna. Ownership: Blake Twedt.

Lake Charles—WNTJ459 (H3). Wireless One of Lake Charles Inc., Suite 400, 2506 Lakeland Dr., Jackson, MS 39208. Phone: 601-933-6879. Authorized power: 50-w. Antenna: 407-ft. above ground. Lat. 30° 11' 50", long. 93° 13' 12". Transmitter: 129 W. Prien Lake. Equipment: Emcee transmitter; Andrew antenna. Ownership: Wireless One Inc.

Monroe—WMH357 (E group). National Wireless Video, 63 Dombey Circle, Thousand Oaks, CA 91360. Authorized power: 10-w. each. Antenna: 900-ft. above ground. Lat. 32° 39' 38", long. 91° 59' 28". Transmitter: 10-mi. N of Monroe. Equipment: Emcee transmitter; Bogner antenna. Ownership: National Wireless Video.

Monroe—WMH413 (F group). Nucentrix Spectrum Resources Inc., Suite 200, 200 Chisholm Place, Plano, TX 75075. Phone: 972-423-9494. Fax: 972-423-0819. Authorized power: 50-w. each. Antenna: 655-ft. above ground. Lat. 32° 39' 38", long. 91° 59' 28". Transmitter: 10-mi. N of Monroe. Equipment: Comwave transmitter; Andrew antenna. Ownership: Nucentrix Broadband Networks.

Monroe—WNTH893 (H1). Blake Twedt, 5102 Rosegreen Court, Tampa, FL 33624. Phone: 727-587-9959. Authorized power: 50-w. Antenna: 134-ft. above ground. Lat. 32° 39' 38", long. 91° 59' 28". Transmitter: 2.7-mi. ENE of Fairbanks. Equipment: Emcee transmitter; Andrew antenna. Ownership: Blake Twedt.

Monroe—WNTI518 (H2). Aerie Communications Inc. Authorized power: 50-w. Antenna: 906-ft. above ground. Lat. 32° 39' 38", long. 91° 59' 28". Transmitter: 10-mi. N of Monroe. Equipment: Comwave transmitter; Andrew antenna. Ownership: Aerie Comm Inc.

Natchitoches—WNTN322 (H2). Skyline Broadcasting. Authorized power: 50-w. Antenna: 405-ft. above ground. Lat. 31° 47' 56", long. 93° 28' 54". Transmitter: 1.7-mi. E of Pleasant Hills. Equipment: Comwave transmitter; Andrew antenna. Ownership: Skyline Broadcasting.

New Orleans—WHT681 (E group). BellSouth Wireless Cable Inc., Suite 414, 1100 Abernathy Rd. NE, Atlanta, GA 30328. Phone: 770-673-2800. Authorized power: 50-w. each. Antenna: 657-ft. above ground. Lat. 29° 57' 07", long. 90° 04' 13". Transmitter: 201 St. Charles Ave. Ownership: BellSouth Entertainment Inc.

New Orleans—WLW963 (F group). BellSouth Wireless Cable Inc., Suite 414, 1100 Abernathy Rd. NE, Atlanta, GA 30328. Phone: 770-673-2800. Authorized power: 50-w. each. Antenna: 657-ft. above ground. Lat. 29° 57' 07", long. 90° 04' 13". Transmitter: 201 St. Charles Ave. Equipment: Emcee transmitter; Bogner antenna. Ownership: BellSouth Entertainment Inc.

New Orleans—WNTB691 (H1). BellSouth Wireless Cable Inc., Suite 414, 1100 Abernathy Rd. NE, Atlanta, GA 30328. Phone: 770-673-2800. Authorized power: 50-w. Antenna: 657-ft. above ground. Lat. 29° 57' 07", long. 90° 04' 13". Transmitter: 201 St. Charles Ave. Equipment: Comwave transmitter; Andrew antenna. Ownership: BellSouth Entertainment Inc.

New Orleans—WNEZ351 (H2). BellSouth Wireless Cable Inc., Suite 414, 1100 Abernathy Rd. NE, Atlanta, GA 30328. Phone: 770-673-2800. Authorized power: 50-w. Antenna: 657-ft. above ground. Lat. 29° 57' 07", long. 90° 04' 13". Transmitter: 201 St. Charles Ave. Equipment: Comwave transmitter; Andrew antenna. Ownership: BellSouth Entertainment Inc.

Shreveport—WLK223 (E group). Line of Site Inc., 8611 E. Santa Catalina Dr., Scottsdale, AZ 85255-2870. Phone: 602-951-8243. Authorized power: 10-w. each. Antenna: 600-ft. above ground. Lat. 32° 34' 32", long. 93° 52' 06". Transmitter: 1902 Park Ave. Equipment: Emcee transmitter; Andrew antenna. Ownership: Line of Site Inc.

Shreveport—WNTD716 (H1). Token Partnership, 1201 7th St., East Moline, IL 61244. Phone: 309-764-6886. Authorized power: 50-w. Antenna: 920-ft. above ground. Lat. 32° 34' 32", long. 93° 52' 06". Transmitter: 0.6-mi. S of Pine Hills Rd. Equipment: Emcee transmitter; Andrew antenna. Ownership: Token Partnership.

Shreveport—WNTI842 (H2). Blake Twedt, 5102 Rosegreen Court, Tampa, FL 33624. Phone: 727-587-9959. Authorized power: 10-w. Antenna: 600-ft. above ground. Lat. 32° 34' 32", long. 93° 52' 05". Transmitter: 3.1-mi. S of Pine Hills Rd. Equipment: Emcee transmitter; Andrew antenna. Ownership: Blake Twedt.

Shreveport—WNTG414 (H3). Digital Wireless Systems Inc., 1800 N. 12th St., Reading, PA 19604. Phone: 610-921-9500. Fax: 610-921-0290. Authorized power: 50-w. Antenna: 600-ft. above ground. Lat. 32° 34' 32", long. 93° 52' 06". Transmitter: 3.1-mi. S of Pine Hills Rd. Equipment: Emcee transmitter; Andrew antenna. Ownership: Digital Wireless Systems Inc.

Maine

Augusta—WMI878 (E group). Kannew Broadcast Technologies, Box 15129, Chevy Chase, MD 20825. Authorized power: 10-w. each. Antenna: 115-ft. above ground. Lat. 44° 18' 51", long. 69° 50' 03". Transmitter: 8-mi. WNW of Augusta. Equipment: Comwave transmitter; Bogner antenna. Requests change to 179-ft. above ground, lat. 44° 17' 30", long. 69° 46' 27"; transmitter to Dr. Mam Rd. Ownership: Kannew Broadcast Technologies.

Augusta—WMH221 (F group). Broadcast Data Corp., Suite 247, 189 Berdan Ave., Wayne, NJ 07470. Phone: 201-831-7407. Authorized power: 10-w. each. Antenna: 115-ft. above ground. Lat. 44° 18' 51", long. 69° 50' 03". Transmitter: 8-mi. WNW of Augusta. Equipment: Comwave transmitter; Bogner antenna. Ownership: Broadcast Data Corp.

Bangor—WLW836 (F group). Whitcom Partners, Time Life Bldg. Room 4310, 110 W. 51st St., New York, NY 10020. Phone: 212-582-2300. Fax: 212-582-2310. Authorized power: 10-w. each. Antenna: 62-ft. above ground. Lat. 44° 45' 14", long. 68° 33' 59". Transmitter: Blackcap Mountain. Equipment: Emcee transmitter; Andrew antenna. Ownership: Whitcom Partners.

Camden—WMH300 (F group). Donald King Pendleton, Box 258, Islesboro, ME 04848. Authorized power: 10-w. each. Antenna: 98-ft. above ground. Lat. 44° 12' 45", long. 69° 09' 04". Transmitter: Ragged Mountain. Equipment: Townsend transmitter; Bogner antenna. Ownership: Donald K. Pendleton.

Maryland

Baltimore—WHT630 (E group). Baltimore Wireless Cable, 3511 Rue de Fleur, Columbus, OH 43221. Phone: 614-457-7045. Authorized power: 10-w. each. Antenna: 418-ft. above ground. Lat. 39° 17' 21", long. 76° 36' 53". Transmitter: 10 Light St. Equipment: Emcee transmitter; Andrew antenna. Ownership: Johanna Destefano.

Baltimore—WHT631 (F group). American Telecasting Development Inc., Suite 300, 5575 Tech Center Dr., Colorado Springs, CO 80919. Phone: 719-260-5533. Fax: 719-260-5010. Authorized power: 15-w. each. Antenna: 1259-ft. above ground. Lat. 39° 20' 10", long. 76° 38' 59". Transmitter: Hooper Ave. & 41st St. Equipment: Comwave transmitter; Andrew antenna. Ownership: American Telecasting Inc.
Leased to People's Choice TV Partners, 2 Corporate Dr., Suite 249, Shelton, CT 06484 6239. Phone: 203-929-2800. Fax: 203-929-1454.

Baltimore—WNEK883 (H1). Baltimore License Inc., Suite 100, 2101 Wilson Blvd., Arlington, VA 22201. Phone: 703-812-8800. Fax: 703-812-8808. Authorized power: 50-w. Antenna: 710-ft. above ground. Lat. 39° 20' 10", long. 76° 38' 59". Equipment: Comwave transmitter; Andrew antenna. Ownership: CAI Wireless Systems Inc.

Bethesda—WHJ920 (H3). Washington License Inc., Suite 100, 2101 Wilson Blvd., Arlington, VA 22201. Phone: 703-812-8800. Fax: 703-812-8808. Authorized power: 50-w. Antenna: 635-ft. above ground. Lat. 38° 57' 49", long. 77° 06' 18". Transmitter: 5202 River Rd. Equipment: ITS transmitter; Andrew antenna. Ownership: CAI Wireless Systems Inc.

Salisbury—WNTK594 (H3). NVJ Com, 15071 Becky Lane, Monte Soreno, CA 95030. Phone: 408-268-3908. Authorized power: 50-w. Antenna: 390-ft. above ground. Lat. 38° 24' 26", long. 75° 35' 57". Transmitter: Naylor Mill/Jersey. Equipment: Comwave transmitter; Andrew antenna. Ownership: NVJ Com.

Massachusetts

Boston—WMI863 (E group). Commonwealth License Inc., Suite 100, 2101 Wilson Blvd., Arlington, VA 22201. Phone: 703-812-8800. Fax: 703-812-8808. Authorized power: 100-w. each. Antenna: 679-ft. above ground. Lat. 42° 21' 08", long. 71° 03' 25". Transmitter: One Financial Center. Equipment: ITS transmitter; Andrew antenna. Ownership: CAI Wireless Systems Inc.

Boston—WNTB229 (H1). Commonwealth License Inc., Suite 100, 2101 Wilson Blvd., Arlington, VA 22201. Phone: 703-812-8800. Fax: 703-812-8808. Authorized power: 100-w. Antenna: 679-ft. above ground. Lat. 42° 21' 08", long. 71° 03' 35". Transmitter: One Financial Center. Equipment: ITS transmitter; Andrew antenna. Ownership: CAI Wireless Systems Inc.

Boston—WHJ868 (H2). AMI License Corp., Suite 100, 2101 Wilson Dr., Arlington, VA 22201. Phone: 703-812-8800. Fax: 703-812-8808. Authorized power: 100-w. Antenna: 679-ft. above ground. Lat. 42° 21' 08", long. 71° 03' 25". Transmitter: One Financial Center. Equipment: ITS transmitter; Andrew antenna. Ownership: CAI Wireless Systems Inc.

Boston—WNEK864 (H3). MultiChannel Media Inc., 248 King George St., Annapolis, MD 21401. Phone: 410-626-1200. Fax: 410-626-1266. Authorized power: 100-w. Antenna: 679-ft. above ground. Lat. 42° 18' 12", long. 71° 13' 08". Transmitter: One Financial Center. Equipment: Omni transmitter; Andrew antenna. Ownership: CAI Wireless Systems Inc.

Deerfield—WNTI337 (H1). John Dudeck, 11672 Harborside Circle, Largo, FL 33773. Authorized power: 10-w. Antenna: 45-ft. above ground. Lat. 42° 32' 05", long. 72° 35' 32". Transmitter:

1-mi. SE of Deerfield. Equipment: Emcee transmitter; Andrew antenna. Ownership: John Dudeck.

Deerfield—WNTI260 (H2). Ivan Nachman, 10300 97th St. N, Seminole, FL 34643. Phone: 813-392-0335. Authorized power: 10-w. Antenna: 45-ft. above ground. Lat. 42° 32' 05", long. 72° 35' 32". Transmitter: 1-mi. SE of Deerfield. Equipment: Emcee transmitter; Andrew antenna. Ownership: Ivan Nachman.

Deerfield—WNTH970 (H3). Blake Twedt, 5102 Rosegreen Court, Tampa, FL 33624. Phone: 727-587-9959. Authorized power: 10-w. Antenna: 45-ft. above ground. Lat. 42° 32' 05", long. 72° 35' 32". Transmitter: 1-mi. SE of Deerfield. Equipment: Emcee transmitter; Andrew antenna. Ownership: Blake Twedt.

Hyannis—WLK314 (E group). Satellite Signals of New England Inc., 168 N. Main St., Rutland, VT 05701. Phone: 802-775-4112. Authorized power: 10-w. each. Antenna: 220-ft. above ground. Lat. 41° 41' 24", long. 70° 11' 31". Transmitter: 19 Dupont Ave. Equipment: Comwave transmitter; Bogner antenna. Ownership: Satellite Signals of New England Inc.

New Bedford—WLK212 (F group). Champion Industries Inc., 300 W. Mission Dr., Chandler, AZ 85225. Phone: 602-497-5774. Authorized power: 100-w. each. Antenna: 872-ft. above ground. Lat. 41° 52' 14", long. 71° 17' 45". Transmitter: 33 Pine St. Equipment: Emcee transmitter; Andrew antenna. Ownership: Champion Industries Inc.

Pittsfield—WMI289 (E group). Belwen Inc., 7 Boyle Rd., Scotia, NY 12302. Phone: 518-393-7428. Authorized power: 20-w. each. Antenna: 158-ft. above ground. Lat. 42° 24' 44", long. 73° 17' 05". Transmitter: Bousquet Ski Area, Dan Fox Dr. Equipment: Comwave transmitter; Bogner antenna. Ownership: Belwen Inc.

Rehoboth—WLW859 (E group). Eastern New England License Inc., Suite 100, 2101 Wilson Blvd., Arlington, VA 22201. Phone: 703-812-8800. Fax: 703-812-8808. Authorized power: 100-w. each. Antenna: 905-ft. above ground. Lat. 41° 52' 14", long. 71° 17' 45". Transmitter: 33 Pine St. Equipment: Comwave transmitter; Andrew antenna. Ownership: Eastern New England License Inc.

Springfield—WLK255 (E group). Virginia Communications Inc., Suite B1, 7621 E. Gray Rd., Scottsdale, AZ 85260. Phone: 480-596-8283. Fax: 480-596-2973. Authorized power: 10-w. each. Antenna: 353-ft. above ground. Lat. 42° 06' 32", long. 72° 36' 44". Transmitter: 101 West St. Equipment: Emcee transmitter; Andrew antenna. Ownership: Virginia Communications Inc.

Springfield—WLK226 (F group). Springfield License Inc., Suite 101, 2101 Wilson Blvd., Arlington, VA 22201. Phone: 703-812-8800. Fax: 703-812-8808. Authorized power: 10-w. each. Antenna: 310-ft. above ground. Lat. 42° 06' 08", long. 72° 35' 33". Transmitter: 1500 Main St. Equipment: Emcee transmitter; Andrew antenna. Ownership: CAI Wireless Systems Inc.

Worcester—WMH752 (E group). Commonwealth License Inc., Suite 100, 2101 Wilson Blvd., Arlington, VA 22201. Phone: 703-812-8800. Fax: 703-812-8808. Authorized power: 10-w. each. Antenna: 442-ft. above ground. Lat. 42° 30' 27", long. 71° 49' 39". Transmitter: 4-mi. S of Fitchburg. Equipment: Emcee transmitter; Andrew antenna. Ownership: CAI Wireless Systems Inc.

Worcester—WMI893 (F group). Commonwealth License Inc., Suite 100, 2101 Wilson Blvd., Arlington, VA 22201. Phone: 703-812-8800. Fax: 703-812-8808. Authorized power: 50-w. each. Antenna: 263-ft. above ground. Lat. 42° 18' 13", long. 71° 53' 51". Transmitter: 99 Asnebumskit Rd., Paxton. Equipment: Emcee transmitter; Andrew antenna. Ownership: CAI Wireless Systems Inc.

Michigan

Bad Axe—WMH641 (E group). Dennis A. Puvalowski, 1910 Sand Beach Rd., Bad Axe, MI 48413. Phone: 517-269-7709. Authorized power: 50-w. each. Antenna: 490-ft. above ground. Lat. 43° 48' 15", long. 82° 54' 26". Transmitter: Hwy. 142, 4-mi. E of Bad Axe. Equipment: ITS transmitter; Andrew antenna. Ownership: Dennis A. Puvalowski.

Bad Axe—WMH636 (F group). Dennis A. Puvalowski, 1910 Sand Beach Rd., Bad Axe, MI 48413. Phone: 517-269-7709. Authorized power: 50-w. each. Antenna: 490-ft. above ground. Lat. 43° 48' 15", long. 82° 54' 26". Transmitter: Hwy. 142, 4-mi. E of Bad Axe. Equipment: ITS transmitter; Andrew antenna. Requests to change transmitter to 3.9-mi. E of Hwy. 142. Ownership: Dennis A. Puvalowski.

Bad Axe—WNTL898 (H group). Dennis A. Puvalowski, 1910 Sand Beach Rd., Bad Axe, MI 48413. Phone: 517-269-7709. Authorized power: 50-w. each. Antenna: 490-ft. above ground. Lat. 43° 48' 15", long. 82° 54' 26". Transmitter: Hwy. 142, 4-mi. E of Bad Axe. Equipment: ITS transmitter; Andrew antenna. Ownership: Dennis A. Puvalowski.

Battle Creek—WLK256 (E group). Figgie International Inc. Authorized power: 10-w. each. Antenna: 209-ft. above ground. Lat. 42° 19' 01", long. 85° 11' 01". Transmitter: 25 N. Michigan Mall. Equipment: Comwave transmitter; Bogner antenna. Ownership: Figgie International Inc.

Battle Creek—WLK260 (F group). Multi-Point TV Distributors Inc., 331 Sea Ridge Dr., La Jolla, CA 92037. Phone: 619-488-9428. Authorized power: 10-w. each. Antenna: 967-ft. above ground. Lat. 42° 34' 15", long. 85° 28' 11". Transmitter: Mullen & Norris Rds. Equipment: Emcee transmitter; Andrew antenna. Ownership: Multi-Point TV Distributors Inc.

Cheboygan—WMI283 (F group). Donald E. Benson, 4755 Clydesdale, Lansing, MI 48906. Authorized power: 10-w. each. Antenna: 150-ft. above ground. Lat. 45° 39' 38", long. 84° 29' 26". Transmitter: 1758 Mackinaw Ave. Equipment: Emcee transmitter; Andrew antenna. Ownership: Donald E. Benson.

Detroit—WLK367 (E group). Wayne State U. Authorized power: 40-w. each. Lat. 42° 19' 45", long. 83° 02' 25". Equipment: Bogner antenna. Ownership: Daniels Communications Inc.

Detroit—WLK238 (F group). Alda Wireless Holdings Inc., 5301 E. Broadway Blvd., Tucson, AZ 85711-3710. Phone: 520-519-4400. Fax: 520-747-6830. Authorized power: 40-w. each. Antenna: 18-ft. above ground. Lat. 42° 19' 45", long. 83° 02' 25". Transmitter: Renaissance Center. Equipment: ITS transmitter; Andrew antenna. Ownership: Matthew Oristano.

Detroit—WNTK656 (H1). Alda Wireless Holdings Inc., 5301 E. Broadway Blvd., Tucson, AZ 85711-3710. Phone: 520-519-4400. Fax: 520-747-6830. Authorized power: 50-w. Antenna: 875-ft. above ground. Lat. 42° 27' 13", long. 83° 09' 50". Transmitter: One Radio Plaza. Equipment: ITS transmitter; Andrew antenna. Ownership: Matthew Oristano.

Detroit—WHJ878 (H2). Alda Wireless Holdings Inc., 5301 E. Broadway Blvd., Tucson, AZ 85711-3710. Phone: 520-519-4400. Fax: 520-747-6830. Authorized power: 50-w. Antenna: 875-ft. above ground. Lat. 42° 27' 13", long. 83° 09' 50". Transmitter: One Radio Plaza. Equipment: ITS transmitter; Andrew antenna. Ownership: Matthew Oristano.

Detroit—WNEK611 (H3). Alda Wireless Holdings Inc., 5301 E. Broadway Blvd., Tucson, AZ 85711-3710. Phone: 520-519-4400. Fax: 520-747-6830. Authorized power: 50-w. Antenna: 875-ft. above ground. Lat. 42° 27' 13", long. 83° 09' 50". Transmitter: One Radio Plaza. Equipment: ITS transmitter; Andrew antenna. Ownership: Matthew Oristano.

Escanaba—WMI279 (E group). Charles D. Benson, 4228 Barton, Lansing, MI 48917. Authorized power: 10-w. each. Antenna: 240-ft. above ground. Lat. 45° 49' 57", long. 87° 04' 03". Transmitter: 0.5-mi. S of West Gladstone. Equipment: Emcee transmitter; Andrew antenna. Ownership: Charles D. Benson.

Flint—WLK200 (F group). BF Investments Inc., 7521 E. Edgemont, Scottsdale, AZ 85257. Authorized power: 10-w. each. Antenna: 321-ft. above ground. Lat. 43° 00' 57", long. 83° 41' 24". Transmitter: One E. First St. Equipment: Emcee transmitter; Andrew antenna. Ownership: Hisol LP.

Gaylord—WLW797 (F group). Marilyn A. Benson, 4228 Barton, Lansing, MI 48917. Authorized power: 10-w. each. Antenna: 350-ft. above ground. Lat. 45° 02' 23", long. 84° 50' 23". Transmitter: 7-mi. W of Gaylord. Equipment: Emcee transmitter; Andrew antenna. Ownership: Marilyn A. Benson.

Ironwood—WGW502 (E group). Superior Communications System, 4140 Elkhorn Dr., Cedar Rapids, IA 52411. Phone: 319-393-0094. Authorized power: 100-w. each. Antenna: 200-ft. above ground. Lat. 46° 29' 30", long. 90° 01' 29". Transmitter: 1-mi. NE of Bessemer. Equipment: Emcee transmitter; Bogner antenna. Ownership: Superior Communications Systems.

Jackson—WMI843 (E group). Alda Wireless Holdings Inc., 5301 E. Broadway Blvd., Tucson, AZ 85711-3710. Phone: 520-519-4400. Fax: 520-747-6830. Authorized power: 10-w. each. Antenna: 315-ft. above ground. Lat. 42° 04' 53", long. 84° 35' 03". Transmitter: 2.1-mi. SE of Hanover. Equipment: Comwave transmitter; Bogner antenna. Ownership: Matthew Oristano.

Jackson—WMH517 (F group). American Telecasting of Jackson Inc., Suite 300, 5575 Tech Center Dr., Colorado Springs, CO 80919. Phone: 719-260-5533. Fax: 719-260-5010. Authorized power: 50-w. each. Antenna: 196-ft. above ground. Lat. 42° 09' 22", long. 84° 23' 39". Transmitter: 0.05-mi. S of Hau & Kimmer. Equipment: Comwave transmitter; Andrew antenna. Ownership: American Telecasting Inc.

Kalamazoo—WMH593 (E group). Belwen Inc., 7 Boyle Rd., Scotia, NY 12302. Phone: 518-393-7428. Authorized power: 10-w. Antenna: 305-ft. above ground. Lat. 42° 19' 36", long. 85° 31' 39". Transmitter: Near Stears Lake. Equipment: Comwave transmitter; Bogner antenna. Ownership: Belwen Inc.

Kalamazoo—WMH652 (F group). MWTV Inc., 3401 E. Cholla St., Phoenix, AZ 85028. Phone: 602-867-7351. Authorized power: 10-w. each. Antenna: 286-ft. above ground. Lat. 42° 28' 32", long. 85° 29' 22". Transmitter: 2.9-mi. SSW of Prairieville. Equipment: Emcee transmitter; Andrew antenna. Ownership: MWTV Inc.

Lansing—WLK205 (E group). Figgie International Inc. Authorized power: 10-w. each. Antenna: 397-ft. above ground. Lat. 42° 43' 58", long. 84° 33' 13". Transmitter: 124 W. Allegan St. Equipment: ITS transmitter; Andrew antenna. Ownership: Figgie International Inc.

Lansing—WMH808 (F group). SunAmerica Inc., Century City, One SunAmerica Center, Los Angeles, CA 90067-6002. Phone: 310-772-6000. Authorized power: 10-w. each. Antenna: 397-ft. above ground. Lat. 42° 43' 58", long. 84° 33' 13". Transmitter: Capital & Allegan Sts. Equipment: Emcee transmitter; Bogner antenna. Ownership: SunAmerica Inc.

Lansing—WNTM549 (H2). Paul G. Herrick, 1249 Forge Rd., Cherry Hill, NJ 08034. Phone: 609-795-2576. Authorized power: 20-w. Antenna: 350-ft. above ground. Lat. 42° 43' 58", long. 84° 33' 13". Transmitter: 124 W. Allegan St. Equipment: ITS transmitter; Andrew antenna. Ownership: Paul G. Herrick.

Manistique—WLW809 (F group). Donald E. Benson, 4755 Clydesdale Rd., Lansing, MI 48906. Authorized power: 10-w. each. Antenna: 295-ft. above ground. Lat. 45° 57' 33", long. 86° 13' 45". Transmitter: E edge of Manistique. Equipment: Emcee transmitter; Andrew antenna. Ownership: Donald E. Benson.

Marquette—WLC270 (F group). Broadcast Data Corp., Suite 247, 189 Berdan Ave., Wayne, NJ 07470. Phone: 201-831-7407. Authorized power: 10-w. each. Antenna: 1101-ft. above ground. Lat. 46° 21' 09", long. 87° 51' 32". Transmitter: 7-mi. E of Republic. Equipment: Comwave transmitter; Bogner antenna. Ownership: Broadcast Data Corp.

Muskegon—WMH509 (E group). Line of Site Inc., 8611 E. Santa Catalina Dr., Scottsdale, AZ 85255-2870. Phone: 602-951-8243. Authorized power: 10-w. each. Antenna: 303-ft. above ground. Lat. 43° 16' 35", long. 86° 15' 10". Transmitter: 517 Giles Rd. Equipment: Emcee transmitter; Andrew antenna. Ownership: Line of Site Inc.

Muskegon—WMH389 (F group). WBSM Licensing Corp., Suite 325, 9250 E. Costilla Ave., Englewood, CO 80112. Authorized power: 10-w. each. Antenna: 303-ft. above ground. Lat. 43° 16' 35", long. 86° 15' 10". Transmitter: 3565 Green St. Equipment: Emcee transmitter; Andrew antenna. Ownership: Wireless Broadcasting Systems of America Inc.

Petoskey—WMI317 (E group). Marylan J. Benson, 4755 Clydesdale, Lansing, MI 48906. Authorized power: 10-w. each. Antenna: 70-ft. above ground. Lat. 45° 28' 00", long. 84° 54' 04". Transmitter: Nubbs Knob. Equipment: Emcee transmitter; Andrew antenna. Ownership: Marylan J. Benson.

Saginaw—WGW275 (E group). Paul Communications Inc., 7555 Pebble Beach Dr., Reno, NV 89502. Phone: 602-319-3311. Authorized power: 10-w. each. Antenna: 874-ft. above ground. Lat. 43° 28' 24", long. 83° 50' 40". Transmitter: 6-mi. E of Saginaw. Equipment: Comwave transmitter; Andrew antenna. Ownership: Paul Communications Inc.

Saginaw—WMI369 (F group). BF Investments Inc., 7521 E. Edgemont, Scottsdale, AZ 85257. Phone: 602-992-3493. Authorized power: 10-w. each. Antenna: 423-ft. above ground. Lat. 43° 28' 38", long. 83° 57' 00". Transmitter: Tittabawasee Rd. Equipment: Emcee transmitter; Andrew antenna. Ownership: Hisol LP.

Saginaw—WNTD763 (H2). ALCH Inc., 2600 California St., Saginaw, MI 48640. Authorized power: 50-w. Antenna: 680-ft. above ground. Lat. 43° 28' 24", long. 83° 50' 40". Transmitter: 6-mi. E of Saginaw. Equipment: Comwave transmitter; Andrew antenna. Ownership: ALCH Inc.

Traverse City—WMI854 (F group). Broadcast Data Corp., Suite 247, 189 Berdan Ave., Wayne, NJ 07470. Phone: 201-831-7407. Authorized power: 10-w. each. Antenna: 304-ft. above ground. Lat. 44° 46' 11", long. 85° 41' 43". Transmitter: 2-mi. NW of Traverse City. Equipment: Comwave transmitter; Bogner antenna. Ownership: Broadcast Data Corp.

Minnesota

Appleton—WMH313 (E group). Todd Communications Inc., 6545 Cecilia Circle, Minneapolis, MN 55435. Phone: 612-941-0556. Authorized power: 10-w. each. Antenna: 500-ft. above ground. Lat. 45° 10' 46", long. 95° 59' 35". Transmitter: 1-mi. SE of Appleton on Hwy. 7. Equipment: ITS transmitter; Bogner antenna. Ownership: Todd Communications Inc.

Appleton—WMH329 (F group). Walter L. Bush Jr. Authorized power: 10-w. each. Antenna: 500-ft. above ground. Lat. 45° 10' 46", long. 95° 59' 35". Transmitter: 1-mi. SE of Appleton on Hwy. 7. Equipment: ITS transmitter; Bogner antenna. Ownership: Walter L. Bush Jr.

Austin—WMH316 (E group). Todd Communications Inc., 6545 Cecilia Circle, Minneapolis, MN 55435. Phone: 612-941-0556. Authorized power: 10-w. each. Antenna: 350-ft. above ground. Lat. 43° 38' 18", long. 93° 08' 49". Transmitter: 7.3-mi. W of Austin. Equipment: ITS transmitter; Bogner antenna. Ownership: Todd Communications Inc.

Austin—WMH332 (F group). Walter L. Bush Jr. Authorized power: 10-w. each. Antenna: 350-ft. above ground. Lat. 43° 38' 18", long. 93° 08' 49". Transmitter: 7.3-mi. W of Austin. Equipment: ITS transmitter; Bogner antenna. Ownership: Walter L. Bush Jr.

Bagley—WMH373 (F group). Wild Rice Electric Co-op Inc., Box 438, Mahnomen, MN 56557. Phone: 218-935-2517. Authorized power: 10-w. each. Antenna: 488-ft. above ground. Lat. 47° 37' 07", long. 95° 24' 16". Transmitter: 6-mi. N of Bagley. Equipment: ITS transmitter; Bogner antenna. Ownership: Wild Rice Electric Co-op Inc.

Barnesville—WNTH394 (H2). American Telecasting of Minnesota Inc., Suite 300, 5575 Tech Center Dr., Colorado Springs, CO 80919. Phone: 719-260-5533. Fax: 719-260-5010. Authorized power: 50-w. Antenna: 190-ft. above ground. Lat. 46° 42' 11", long. 96° 12' 57". Transmitter: 2-mi. N of Rtes. 32 & 34. Equipment: Emcee transmitter. Ownership: American Telecasting Inc.

Barnesville—WNTH396 (H3). American Telecasting of Minnesota Inc., Suite 300, 5575 Tech Center Dr., Colorado Springs, CO 80919. Phone: 719-260-5533. Fax: 719-260-5010. Authorized power: 50-w. Antenna: 190-ft. above ground. Lat. 46° 42' 11", long. 96° 12' 57". Transmitter: 2-mi. N of Rtes. 32 & 34. Ownership: American Telecasting Inc.

Brainerd—WMH317 (E group). Todd Communications Inc., 6545 Cecilia Circle, Minneapolis, MN 55435. Phone: 612-941-0556. Authorized power: 10-w. each. Antenna: 500-ft. above ground. Lat. 46° 19' 19", long. 94° 09' 55". Transmitter: 1-mi. E, 1-mi. S of Brainerd. Equipment: ITS transmitter; Bogner antenna. Ownership: Todd Communications Inc.

Byron—WNTJ817 (H group). CS Wireless Systems Inc., 1101 Summit, Plano, TX 75074. Phone: 972-509-2634. Authorized power: 50-w. each. Antenna: 495-ft. above ground. Lat. 44° 01' 59", long. 92° 36' 10". Transmitter: 2.3-mi. E of Byron. Equipment: Emcee transmitter; Andrew antenna. Ownership: CS Wireless Systems Inc.

Duluth—WMH605 (E group). Lawrence N. Brandt, Suite 220, 3201 New Mexico Ave. NW, Washington, DC 20016. Phone: 202-363-1100. Authorized power: 10-w. each. Antenna: 503-ft. above ground. Lat. 46° 47' 41", long. 92° 07' 05". Transmitter: 1603 N. First Ave. Equipment: Comwave transmitter; Bogner antenna. Ownership: Lawrence N. Brandt.

Erskine—WMH989 (F group). Wild Rice Electric Co-op Inc., Box 438, Mahnomen, MN 56557. Phone: 218-935-2517. Authorized power: 10-w. each. Antenna: 491-ft. above ground. Lat. 47° 39' 26", long. 95° 59' 31". Transmitter: 5-mi. S & 0.5-mi. E of Erskine. Equipment: ITS transmitter; Andrew antenna. Ownership: Wild Rice Electric Co-op Inc.

Fairmont—WLW834 (E group). Starcom Inc., Box 8, 11 Robbins Ave., Graettinger, IA 51342. Phone: 712-859-3300. Fax: 712-859-3290. E-mail: riverval@netins.net. Authorized power: 50-w. each. Antenna: 500-ft. above ground. Lat. 43° 33' 20", long. 94° 29' 11". Transmitter: 5.8-mi. S of Fairmont. Equipment: ITS transmitter; Andrew antenna. Ownership: Starcom Inc.

Fairmont—WMH424 (F group). Walter L. Bush Jr. Authorized power: 50-w. each. Antenna: 500-ft. above ground. Lat. 43° 33' 20", long. 94° 29' 11". Transmitter: 5.8-mi. S of Fairmont. Equipment: ITS transmitter; Andrew antenna. Ownership: Walter L. Bush Jr.

Fairmont—WLW724 (H1). Starcom Inc., Box 8, 11 Robbins Ave., Graettinger, IA 51342. Phone: 712-859-3300. Fax: 712-859-3290. E-mail: riverval@netins.net. Authorized power: 50-w. Antenna: 500-ft. above ground. Lat. 43° 33' 20", long. 94° 29' 11". Transmitter: 5.8-mi. S of Fairmont. Equipment: ITS transmitter; Andrew antenna. Ownership: Starcom Inc.

Fairmont—WLW728 (H2). Starcom Inc., Box 8, 11 Robbins Ave., Graettinger, IA 51342. Phone: 712-859-3300. Fax: 712-859-3290. E-mail: riverval@netins.net. Authorized power: 50-w. Antenna: 500-ft. above ground. Lat. 43° 33' 20", long. 94° 29' 11". Transmitter: 5.8-mi. S of Fairmont. Equipment: ITS transmitter; Andrew antenna. Ownership: Starcom Inc.

Fairmont—WLW732 (H3). Starcom Inc., Box 8, 11 Robbins Ave., Graettinger, IA 51342. Phone: 712-859-3300. Fax: 712-859-3290. E-mail: riverval@netins.net. Authorized power: 50-w. Antenna: 500-ft. above ground. Lat. 43° 33' 20", long. 94° 29' 11". Transmitter: 5.8-mi. S of Fairmont. Equipment: ITS transmitter; Andrew antenna. Ownership: Starcom Inc.

Garfield—WLW783 (E group). Patricia A. Anderson, Emmetsburg, IA 50536. Authorized power: 20-w. each. Antenna: 453-ft. above ground. Lat. 45° 55' 55", long. 95° 26' 42". Transmitter: 6-mi. NW of Alexandria. Equipment: ITS transmitter; Andrew antenna. Ownership: Patricia A. Anderson.

Garfield—WLW784 (F group). Patricia A. Anderson, Emmetsburg, IA 50536. Authorized power: 50-w. each. Antenna: 453-ft. above ground. Lat. 45° 55' 55", long. 95° 26' 42". Transmitter: 6-mi. NW of Alexandria. Equipment: ITS transmitter; Andrew antenna. Ownership: Patricia A. Anderson.

Granite Falls—WMH481 (E group). Todd Communications Inc., 6545 Cecilia Circle, Minneapolis, MN 55435. Phone: 612-941-0556. Authorized power: 10-w. each. Antenna: 300-ft. above ground. Lat. 44° 48' 01", long. 95° 34' 21". Transmitter: 1-mi. W of Granite Falls. Equipment: ITS transmitter; Bogner antenna. Ownership: Todd Communications Inc.

Granite Falls—WMH480 (F group). Walter L. Bush Jr. Authorized power: 10-w. each. Antenna: 300-ft. above ground. Lat. 44° 48' 01", long. 95° 34' 21". Transmitter: 1-mi. W of Granite Falls. Equipment: ITS transmitter; Bogner antenna. Ownership: Walter L. Bush Jr.

Jeffers—WNTK426 (H group). American Telecasting of Minnesota Inc., Suite 300, 5575 Tech Center Dr., Colorado Springs, CO 80919. Phone: 719-260-5533. Fax: 719-260-5010. Authorized power: 50-w. each. Antenna: 20-ft. above ground. Lat. 44° 00' 14", long. 95° 12' 04". Transmitter: 4-mi. S of Jeffers. Equipment: Comwave transmitter; Andrew antenna. Ownership: American Telecasting Inc.

Mankato—WNTG603 (E group). Tele-Acquisitions LLC, 4404-B Dunwoody Park, Dunwoody, GA 30338. Phone: 770-396-1888. Authorized power: 10-w. each. Antenna: 485-ft. above ground. Lat. 44° 36' 34", long. 94° 20' 39". Transmitter: 6-mi. W & 3-mi. N of Mankato. Equipment: ITS transmitter; Andrew antenna. Ownership: Tele-Acquisitions LLC.

Mankato—WLW853 (F group). MMDS Mankato Inc. (a Delaware Corp.), 2700 Chain Bridge Rd. NW, Washington, DC 20016. Phone: 202-966-2167. Fax: 202-237-7742. Authorized power: 10-w. each. Antenna: 415-ft. above ground. Lat. 44° 08' 34", long. 94° 00' 08". Transmitter: State U. Campus. Equipment: ITS transmitter; Bogner antenna. Ownership: MDS Signal Group.

Leased to American Telecasting.

Mankato—WNTH469 (H1). Tele-Acquisitions LLC, 4004-B Dunwoody Park, Dunwoody, GA 30338. Phone: 770-396-1888. Authorized power: 415-w. Antenna: 50-ft. above ground. Lat. 44° 08' 34", long. 94° 00' 08". Transmitter: Minnesota State U. campus. Equipment: Emcee transmitter; Andrew antenna. Ownership: Tele-Acquisitions LLC.

Mankato—WNTH575 (H2). Tele-Acquisitions LLC, 4404-B Dunwoody Park, Dunwoody, GA 30338. Phone: 770-396-1888. Authorized power: 50-w. Antenna: 415-ft. above ground. Lat. 44° 08' 34", long. 94° 00' 08". Transmitter: Minnesota State U. campus. Equipment: Emcee transmitter; Andrew antenna. Ownership: Tele-Acquisitions LLC.

Mankato—WNTH457 (H3). Tele-Acquisitions LLC, 4404-B Dunwoody Park, Dunwoody, GA 30338. Phone: 770-396-1888. Authorized power: 50-w. Antenna: 415-ft. above ground. Lat. 44° 08' 34", long. 94° 00' 08". Transmitter: State University campus. Equipment: Emcee transmitter; Andrew antenna. Ownership: Tele-Acquisitions LLC.

Mankato/Gaylord—WNTG601 (H3). Tele-Acquisitions LLC, 4004-B Dunwoody Park, Dunwoody, GA 30338. Phone: 770-396-1888. Authorized power: 10-w. Antenna: 485-ft. above ground. Lat. 44° 36' 54", long. 94° 20' 39". Transmitter: 6-mi. W & 3-mi. N of Gaylord. Equipment: ITS transmitter; Andrew antenna. Ownership: Tele-Acquisitions LLC.

Mankato/Waterville—WLW862 (E group). National Wireless Cable, 63 Dombey Circle, Thousand Oaks, CA 91360. Authorized power: 10-w. each. Antenna: 240-ft. above ground. Lat. 44° 07' 43", long. 94° 02' 01". Transmitter: 2-mi. S of Mankato. Equipment: Comwave transmitter; Bogner antenna. Ownership: National Wireless Cable.

Marshall—WMH549 (E group). Todd Communications Inc., 6545 Cecilia Circle, Minneapolis, MN 55435. Phone: 612-941-0556. Authorized power: 10-w. each. Antenna: 400-ft. above ground. Lat. 44° 24' 26", long. 95° 51' 50". Transmitter: 2-mi. NE of Lynd on Hwy. 23. Equipment: ITS transmitter; Bogner antenna. Ownership: Todd Communications Inc.

Marshall—WMH677 (F group). Walter L. Bush Jr. Authorized power: 10-w. each. Antenna: 400-ft. above ground. Lat. 44° 24' 33", long. 95° 51' 46". Transmitter: 2-mi. NE of Lynd on Hwy. 23. Equipment: ITS transmitter; Bogner antenna. Ownership: Walter L. Bush Jr.

Minneapolis—WHT677 (E group). CS Wireless Systems Inc., 1101 Summit Ave., Plano, TX 75074. Phone: 972-509-2634. Authorized power: 10-w. each. Antenna: 811-ft. above ground. Lat. 44° 58' 32", long. 93° 16' 18". Transmitter: IDS Center, 80 S. 8th St. Equipment: Comwave transmitter; Andrew antenna. Ownership: CS Wireless Systems Inc.

Minneapolis—WHT678 (F group). CS Wireless Systems Inc., 1101 Summit Ave., Plano, TX 75074. Phone: 972-509-2634. Authorized power: 50-w. each. Antenna: 811-ft. above ground. Lat. 44° 58' 32", long. 93° 16' 18". Transmitter: 80 S. 8th St. Equipment: Comwave transmitter; Andrew antenna. Ownership: CS Wireless Systems Inc.

Minneapolis—WNEY683 (H1). Broadcast Data Corp., Suite 247, 189 Berdan Ave., Wayne, NJ 07470. Phone: 201-831-7407. Authorized power: 50-w. Antenna: 811-ft. above ground. Lat. 44° 58' 32", long. 93° 16' 18". Transmitter: 80 S. 8th St. Equipment: Comwave transmitter; Andrew antenna. Ownership: Broadcast Data Corp.

Minneapolis—WNEZ819 (H2). CS Wireless Systems Inc., 1101 Summit Ave., Plano, TX 75074. Phone: 972-509-2634. Authorized power: 50-w. Antenna: 811-ft. above ground. Lat. 44° 58' 32", long. 93° 16' 18". Transmitter: 80 S. 8th St. Equipment: Comwave transmitter; Andrew antenna. Ownership: CS Wireless Systems Inc.

Minneapolis—WNTA934 (H3). CS Wireless Systems Inc., 1101 Summit Ave., Plano, TX 75074. Phone: 972-509-2634. Authorized power: 50-w. Antenna: 811-ft. above ground. Lat. 44° 58' 32", long. 93° 16' 18". Transmitter: 80 S. 8th St. Equipment: Comwave transmitter; Andrew antenna. Ownership: CS Wireless Systems Inc.

St. Cloud—WMI286 (F group). MWTV Inc., 3401 E. Cholla St., Phoenix, AZ 85028. Phone: 602-867-7351. Authorized power: 10-w. each. Antenna: 513-ft. above ground. Lat. 45° 31' 00", long. 94° 13' 52". Transmitter: 3299 Granite View Rd. Equipment: Emcee transmitter; Andrew antenna. Ownership: MWTV Inc.

St. James—WMH533 (E group). Todd Communications Inc., 6545 Cecilia Circle, Minneapolis, MN 55435. Phone: 612-941-0556. Authorized power: 10-w. each. Antenna: 1000-ft. above ground. Lat. 44° 06' 27", long. 94° 35' 43". Transmitter: 1-mi. E of Godahl. Equipment: ITS transmitter; Bogner antenna. Ownership: Todd Communications Inc.

Ulm/James/Winthrop—WLW870 (F group). Mickelson Media Inc., 50 Locust Ave., New Canaan, CT 06840. Authorized power: 10-w. each. Antenna: 380-ft. above ground. Lat. 44° 15' 56", long. 94° 25' 52". Transmitter: Hwys. 68 & 15. Equipment: Emcee transmitter; Bogner antenna. Ownership: Mickelson Media Inc.

Wadena—WHT607 (F group). Walter L. Bush Jr. Authorized power: 10-w. each. Antenna: 270-ft. above ground. Lat. 46° 22' 15", long. 95° 08' 58". Transmitter: 4-mi. S of city limits. Equipment: ITS transmitter; Bogner antenna. Ownership: Walter L. Bush Jr.

Waterville—WMH244 (F group). Walter L. Bush Jr. Authorized power: 10-w. each. Antenna: 490-ft. above ground. Lat. 44° 15' 48", long. 93° 35' 17". Transmitter: 3-mi. N of Waterville. Equipment: ITS transmitter; Bogner antenna. Ownership: Walter L. Bush Jr.

Willmar—WMH540 (E group). Rural Television Inc., Box 726, Spicer, MN 56288. Phone: 320-796-7881. Authorized power: 10-w. each. Antenna: 500-ft. above ground. Lat. 45° 09' 58", long. 95° 02' 41". Transmitter: 3-mi. N of Willmar. Equipment: ITS transmitter; Bogner antenna. Ownership: Rural Television Inc.

Willmar—WMH352 (F group). Viking Vision. Authorized power: 50-w. each. Antenna: 460-ft. above ground. Lat. 45° 11' 52", long. 94° 56' 59". Transmitter: 6.5-mi. N of Willmar. Equipment: ITS transmitter; Andrew antenna. Ownership: Viking Vision.

Windom—WLW990 (E group). American Telecasting of Minnesota Inc., Suite 300, 5575 Tech Center Dr., Colorado Springs, CO 80919. Phone: 719-260-5533. Fax: 719-260-5010. Authorized power: 50-w. each. Antenna: 274-ft. above ground. Lat. 44° 00' 14", long. 95° 12' 04". Transmitter: 4-mi. S of Jeffers. Equipment: Comwave transmitter; Andrew antenna. Ownership: American Telecasting Inc.

Windom—WLW989 (F group). American Telecasting of Minnesota Inc., Suite 300, 5575 Tech Center Dr., Colorado Springs, CO 80919. Phone: 719-260-5533. Fax: 719-260-5010. Authorized power: 50-w. each. Antenna: 274-ft. above ground. Lat. 44° 00' 14", long. 95° 12' 04". Transmitter: 4-mi. S of Jeffers. Equipment: Comwave transmitter; Andrew antenna. Ownership: American Telecasting Inc.

Worthington—WMH680 (F group). Walter L. Bush Jr. Authorized power: 10-w. each. Antenna: 500-ft. above ground. Lat. 43° 36' 11", long. 95° 42' 10". Transmitter: 2-mi. S & 2-mi. W of Worthington. Equipment: ITS transmitter; Bogner antenna. Ownership: Walter L. Bush Jr.

Mississippi

Biloxi—WLW725 (E group). National Television Co., Meeting House Farm, Lincoln, VA 22078. Phone: 703-338-3750. Fax: 703-338-4525. Authorized power: 50-w. each. Antenna: 1285-ft. above ground. Lat. 30° 45' 14", long. 88° 56' 44". Transmitter: 12-mi. ENE of McHenry. Equipment: ITS transmitter; Andrew antenna. Ownership: National TV Co.

Biloxi—WMI886 (F group). StarChannels Associates LP. Authorized power: 10-w. each. Antenna: 220-ft. above ground. Lat. 30° 23' 21", long. 89° 06' 23". Transmitter: 39th St. & 34th Ave. intersection, Gulfport. Equipment: Emcee transmitter; Andrew antenna. Ownership: StarChannels Associates LP.

Clarksdale—WNTG905 (H1). Wireless One PCS Inc., Suite 400, 2506 Lakeland Dr., Jackson, MS 39208. Phone: 601-933-6879. Authorized power: 50-w. Antenna: 805-ft. above ground. Lat. 33° 22' 34", long. 90° 32' 32". Transmitter: 3.2-mi. NE of Inverness. Equipment: Emcee transmitter; Andrew antenna. Ownership: Wireless One Inc.

Clarksdale—WNTJ875 (H2). Wireless One PCS Inc., Suite 400, 2506 Lakeland Dr., Jackson, MS 39208. Phone: 601-933-6879. Authorized power: 50-w. Antenna: 905-ft. above ground. Lat. 33° 22' 34", long. 90° 32' 32". Transmitter: 3.2-mi. NE of Inverness. Equipment: Emcee transmitter; Andrew antenna. Ownership: Wireless One Inc.

Clarksdale—WNTJ746 (H3). Wireless One PCS Inc., Suite 400, 2506 Lakeland Dr., Jackson, MS 39208. Phone: 601-933-6879. Authorized power: 10-w. Antenna: 490-ft. above ground. Lat. 34° 09' 22", long. 90° 37' 52". Transmitter: Hwy. 61, 4-mi. S of Clarksdale. Equipment: Emcee transmitter; Andrew antenna. Ownership: Wireless One Inc.

Hattiesburg—WNTH936 (H3). Rosemarie Kosman, Apt. 204, 1635 E. 13 Mile Rd., Madison Heights, MI 48071. Authorized power: 50-w. Antenna: 1021-ft. above ground. Lat. 31° 25' 50", long. 89° 08' 50". Transmitter: 8-mi. NE of Petal. Equipment: ITS transmitter; Andrew antenna. Ownership: Rosemarie Kosman.

Meridian—WMX933 (H3). Grand Spectrum Alliance Meridian (E) Partnership, Suite 660, 1920 N St. NW, Washington, DC 20036. Phone: 202-887-0600. Authorized power: 10-w. Antenna: 300-ft. above ground. Lat. 32° 18' 43", long. 88° 41' 33". Transmitter: Hwy. 45, S of Meridian. Equipment: Emcee transmitter; Andrew antenna. Ownership: Macro Distribution Systems Inc.

Pascagoula—WMH401 (E group). National TV Co., Meeting House Farm, Lincoln, VA 22078. Phone: 703-338-3750. Fax: 703-338-4525. Authorized power: 10-w. each. Antenna: 365-ft. above ground. Lat. 30° 26' 54", long. 88° 33' 15". Transmitter: 3.5-mi. N of Pascagoula. Equipment: Emcee transmitter; Bogner antenna. Ownership: National TV Co.

Pascagoula—WLR618 (F group). Broadcast Data Corp., Suite 247, 189 Berdan Ave., Wayne, NJ 07470. Phone: 201-831-7407. Authorized power: 10-w. each. Antenna: 365-ft. above ground. Lat. 30° 26' 54", long. 88° 33' 15". Transmitter: 3520 Dale Ave. Equipment: Comwave transmitter; Bogner antenna. Ownership: Broadcast Data Corp.

Tupelo—WNTH472 (H2). John Dudeck, Suite 201, 7800 113th St. N, Seminole, FL 34643. Phone: 813-397-2759. Authorized power: 50-w. Antenna: 534-ft. above ground. Lat. 34° 19' 24", long. 88° 42' 39". Transmitter: 2.5-mi. N of Tupelo. Equipment: ITS transmitter; Andrew antenna. Ownership: John Dudeck.

Vicksburg—WLK203 (E group). TruVision Wireless Inc., Suite 403, 2506 Lakeland Dr., Jackson, MS 39208. Phone: 601-933-6871. Authorized power: 10-w. each. Antenna: 800-ft. above ground. Lat. 32° 16' 53", long. 90° 17' 41". Transmitter: 140 Alphal Rd. Equipment: Comwave transmitter; Andrew antenna. Requests change to 175-ft. above ground, lat. 32° 20' 42", long. 90° 52' 55"; transmitter to 799 Bridge St.; Comm. & Energy Corp. antenna. Ownership: Virginia Communications Inc.

Leased to Wireless Communications Inc., 308 W. Main, Durant, OK 74701. Phone: 405-921-4627.

Vicksburg—WLW835 (F group). TruVision Wireles Inc., Suite 403, 2506 Lakeland Dr., Jackson, MS 39208. Phone: 601-933-6871. Authorized power: 10-w. each. Antenna: 1080-ft. above ground. Lat. 32° 16' 53", long. 90° 17' 41". Transmitter: 140 Alphal Rd. Equipment: Comwave transmitter; Andrew antenna. Requests change to 175-ft. above ground, lat. 32° 20' 42", long. 90° 52' 55"; transmitter to 799 Bridge St.; Comm. & Energy Corp. antenna. Ownership: Kannew Broadcast Technologies.

Vicksburg—WNTJ282 (H1). TruVision Wireless Inc., Suite 403, 2506 Lakeland Dr., Jackson, MS 39208. Phone: 601-933-6871. Antenna: 1040-ft. above ground. Lat. 32° 16' 53", long. 90° 17' 41". Transmitter: 1.9-mi. SW of State Rtes. 18-I & 20. Requests change to 175-ft. above ground, lat. 32°20'42", long. 90°52'55"; transmitter to 799 Bridge St.; Comm. & Energy Corp. antenna. Ownership: Ivan C. Nachman.

Missouri

Appleton City—WNTM561 (H group). Stephen L. & Susan W. Whitman, 206 Grove St., Westwood, MA 02090. Phone: 617-329-2004. Authorized power: 50-w. each. Antenna: 468-ft. above ground. Lat. 38° 13' 21", long. 94° 18' 19". Transmitter: 2.5-mi. S of Rte. 52. Equipment: Comwave transmitter; Bogner antenna. Ownership: Stephen L. & Susan W. Whitman.

Bellflower—WMY439 (H1). RVC Holdings Corp., Suite 200, 200 Chisholm Place, Plano, TX 75075. Phone: 972-423-9494. Fax: 972-423-0819. Antenna: 300-ft. above ground. Lat. 39° 00' 46", long. 91° 18' 07". Transmitter: 2.9-mi. E of Bellflower. Requests change to 704-ft. above ground, transmitter to 3-mi. ENE of Bellflower; Andrew antenna. Ownership: Nucentrix Broadband Networks Inc.

Bellflower—WMY440 (H2). RVC Holdings Corp., Suite 200, 200 Chisholm Place, Plano, TX 75075. Phone: 972-423-9494. Fax: 972-423-0819. Antenna: 300-ft. above ground. Lat. 39° 00' 46", long. 91° 18' 07". Transmitter: 2.9-mi. E of Bellflower. Requests change to 704-ft. above ground, transmitter to 3-mi. ENE of Bellflower; Andrew antenna. Ownership: Nucentrix Broadband Networks Inc.

Bellflower—WMY438 (H3). RVC Holdings Corp., Suite 200, 200 Chisholm Place, Plano, TX 75075. Phone: 972-423-9494. Fax: 972-423-0819. Antenna: 300-ft. above ground. Lat. 39° 00' 46", long. 91° 18' 07". Transmitter: 2.9-mi. E of Bellflower. Requests change to 704-ft. above ground, transmitter to 3-mi. ENE of Bellflower; Andrew antenna. Ownership: Nucentrix Broadband Networks Inc.

Columbia—WMH504 (F group). Nucentrix Spectrum Resources Inc., Suite 200, 200 Chisholm Place, Plano, TX 75075. Phone: 972-423-9494. Fax: 972-423-5010. Authorized power: 10-w. each. Antenna: 110-ft. above ground. Lat. 38° 57' 03", long. 92° 19' 43". Transmitter: 23 S. 8th St. Equipment: Emcee transmitter; Bogner antenna. Ownership: Nucentrix Broadband Networks.

Columbia—WNTI251 (H1). Nucentrix Spectrum Resources Inc., Suite 200, 200 Chisholm Place, Plano, TX 75075. Phone: 972-423-9494. Fax: 972-423-0819. Authorized power: 50-w. Antenna: 947-ft. above ground. Lat. 38° 46' 29", long. 92° 33' 22". Transmitter: 3.5-mi. W of Jamestown. Equipment: Comwave transmitter; Andrew antenna. Ownership: Nucentrix Broadband Networks.

Elmo—WMI405 (E group). National MicroVision Systems Inc. Authorized power: 10-w. each. Antenna: 487-ft. above ground. Lat. 40° 33' 12", long. 95° 07' 18". Transmitter: 2.4 mi. N of Elmo. Equipment: Comwave transmitter; Bogner antenna. Ownership: National Micro Vision Systems Inc.

Elmo—WMI409 (F group). National MicroVision Systems Inc. Authorized power: 10-w. each. Antenna: 487-ft. above ground. Lat. 40° 33' 12", long. 95° 07' 18". Transmitter: 2.4-mi. N of Elmo. Equipment: Comwave transmitter; Bogner antenna. Ownership: National Micro Vision Systems Inc.

Fulton—WMH257 (F group). Microwave Movies Inc. Authorized power: 10-w. each. Antenna: 495-ft. above ground. Lat. 38° 52' 35", long. 91° 54' 12". Transmitter: Hwy. 2.1-mi. E of Fulton. Equipment: Emcee transmitter; Andrew antenna. Ownership: Microwave Movies Inc.

Jefferson City—WMI323 (E group). People's Choice TV Inc., 2 Corporate Dr., Suite 249, Shelton, CT 06484-6239. Phone: 203-929-2800. Fax: 203-929-1454. Authorized power: 10-w. each. Antenna: 220-ft. above ground. Lat. 38° 34' 45", long. 92° 14' 02". Transmitter: 3103 S. Ten Mile Dr. Equipment: Comwave transmitter; Bogner antenna. Ownership: People's Choice TV Partners.

Kansas City—WHT790 (E group). CS Wireless Systems Inc., 1101 Summit Ave., Plano, TX 75074. Phone: 972-509-2634. Authorized power: 10-w. each. Antenna: 616-ft. above ground. Lat. 39° 05' 58", long. 94° 34' 57". Transmitter: Manchester & Front Sts. Equipment: Comwave transmitter; Andrew antenna. Ownership: CS Wireless Systems Inc.

Kansas City—WLK282 (F group). CS Wireless Systems Inc., 1101 Summit Ave., Plano, TX 75074. Phone: 972-509-2634. Authorized power: 10-w. each. Antenna: 616-ft. above ground. Lat. 39° 05' 58", long. 94° 34' 57". Transmitter: Commerce Towers. Equipment: Comwave transmitter; Andrew antenna. Ownership: CS Wireless Systems Inc.

Kirksville—WMH621 (E group). CDV Inc., 2414 S. Halliburton, Kirksville, MO 63501. Phone: 816-665-0300. Fax: 816-665-9121. Authorized power: 20-w. each. Antenna: 400-ft. above ground. Lat. 40° 14' 34", long. 92° 25' 42". Transmitter: Hwy. 11 E, 8.5-mi. ENE of Kirksville. Equipment: ITS transmitter; Andrew antenna. Requests change to 600-ft. above ground. Ownership: CDV Inc.

Kirksville—WMI895 (F group). CDV Inc., 2414 S. Halliburton, Kirksville, MO 63501. Phone: 816-665-0300. Fax: 816-665-9121. Authorized power: 50-w. each. Antenna: 600-ft. above ground. Lat. 40° 14' 34", long. 92° 25' 42". Transmitter: Hwy. 11 E, 8.5-mi. ENE of Kirksville. Equipment: Comwave transmitter; Andrew antenna. Ownership: CDV Inc.

Kirksville—WNTJ368 (H group). CDV Inc., 2414 S. Halliburton, Kirksville, MO 63501. Phone: 816-665-0300. Fax: 816-665-9121. Authorized power: 20-w. each. Antenna: 400-ft. above ground. Lat. 40° 14' 34", long. 92° 25' 42". Transmitter: Hwy. 11 E, 8.5-mi ENE of Kirksville. Equipment: ITS transmitter; Andrew antenna. Requests change to 600-ft. above ground. Ownership: CDV Inc.

Lake Ozark—WLW937 (E group). Microwave Movies Inc. Authorized power: 10-w. each. Antenna: 400-ft. above ground. Lat. 38° 09' 23", long. 92° 36' 43". Transmitter: Lake Rd. 54-22 & Sunset Dr., Osage Beach. Equipment: Emcee transmitter; Andrew antenna. Ownership: Microwave Movies Inc.

Malden—WMX953 (F group). Donald J. Kunkle, 2565 Colt Rd., Rancho Palos Verdes, CA 90274. Authorized power: 10-w. each. Antenna: 300-ft. above ground. Lat. 36° 45' 46", long. 90° 26' 03". Transmitter: 0.5-mi. W of Poplar Bluff. Equipment: Comwave transmitter; Andrew antenna. Ownership: Donald J. Kunkle.

Malden—WNTJ367 (H3). BCW Systems Inc., 118 N. Madison, Malden, MO 63863. Phone: 573-276-3025. Authorized power: 50-w. Antenna: 275-ft. above ground. Lat. 36° 35' 11", long. 90° 04' 07". Transmitter: Crowleys Ridge. Equipment: Emcee transmitter; Andrew antenna. Requests change to 460-ft. above ground, lat. 36° 35' 11", long. 90° 04' 06"; Bogner antenna. Ownership: BCW Systems Inc.

Maysville—WMX926 (H1). CS Wireless Systems Inc., 1101 Summit Ave., Plano, TX 75074. Phone: 972-509-2634. Authorized power: 10-w. Antenna: 100-ft. above ground. Lat. 39° 52' 04", long. 94° 22' 14". Transmitter: 0.5-mi. W of Hwy. 33. Equipment: Comwave transmitter; Andrew antenna. Ownership: CS Wireless Systems Inc.

Maysville—WMX928 (H2). CS Wireless Systems Inc., 1101 Summit Ave., Plano, TX 75074. Phone: 972-509-2634. Authorized power: 10-w. Antenna: 100-ft. above ground. Lat. 39° 52' 04", long. 94° 22' 14". Transmitter: 0.5-mi. W of Hwy. 33. Equipment: Comwave transmitter; Andrew antenna. Ownership: CS Wireless Systems Inc.

Maysville—WMX927 (H3). CS Wireless Systems Inc., 1101 Summit Ave., Plano, TX 75074. Phone: 972-509-2634. Authorized power: 10-w. Antenna: 100-ft. above ground. Lat. 39° 52' 04", long. 94° 22' 14". Transmitter: 0.5-mi. W of Hwy. 33. Equipment: Comwave transmitter; Andrew antenna. Ownership: CS Wireless Systems Inc.

Nevada—WMH744 (F group). Baillon MDS Corp., 1218 Pioneer Bldg., 336 N. Roberts St., St. Paul, MN 55101. Phone: 612-222-5555. Authorized power: 10-w. each. Antenna: 295-ft. above ground. Lat. 37° 51' 37", long. 94° 22' 54". Transmitter: 0.75-mi. NW of Nevada. Equipment: Emcee transmitter; Andrew antenna. Ownership: Baillon MDS Corp.

Sikeston—WMH440 (E group). Jerry Albert Payne, 1840 Barron Rd., Poplar Bluff, MO 63907. Phone: 314-785-0756. Authorized power: 50-w. each. Antenna: 275-ft. above ground. Lat. 36° 35' 11", long. 90° 04' 06". Transmitter: Crowleys Ridge. Equipment: Emcee transmitter; Andrew antenna. Ownership: Jerry A. Payne.
Leased to Broadcast Cablevision.

Springfield—WMX370 (H1). Springfield One Partnership, Suite 501, 1100 17th St. NW, Washington, DC 20036. Phone: 202-223-4449. Fax: 202-223-4450. E-mail: rggould@mindspring.com. Authorized power: 20-w. Antenna: 1000-ft. above ground. Lat. 37° 11' 40", long. 92° 56' 04". Transmitter: 2.5-mi. N of Fordland. Equipment: Emcee transmitter; Andrew antenna. Requests change to 770-ft. above ground, lat. 37° 12' 06", long. 92° 56' 33"; transmitter to 3-mi. N of Fordland. Ownership: Springfield One Partnership.
Leased to Nucentrix Broadband Networks, 200 Chisholm Place, Suite 200, Plano, TX 75075. Phone: 972-633-4011.

Springfield—WMX371 (H2). Springfield One Partnership, Suite 501, 1100 17th St. NW, Washington, DC 20036. Phone: 202-223-4449. Fax: 202-223-4450. E-mail: rggould@mindspring.com. Authorized power: 20-w. Antenna: 228-ft. above ground. Lat. 37° 12' 42", long. 93° 16' 53". Transmitter: 403 Sherman Ave. Equipment: Emcee transmitter; Andrew antenna. Requests change to 770-ft. above ground, lat. 37° 12' 06", long. 92° 56' 33"; transmitter to 3-mi. N of Fordland. Ownership: Springfield One Partnership.

Springfield—WMX372 (H3). Springfield One Partnership, Suite 501, 1100 17th St., Washington, DC 20036. Phone: 202-223-4449. Fax: 202-223-4450. E-mail: rggould@mindspring.com. Authorized power: 20-w. Antenna: 228-ft. above ground. Lat. 37° 12' 42", long. 93° 16' 53". Transmitter: 403 Sherman Ave. Equipment: Emcee transmitter; Andrew antenna. Requests change to 770-ft. above ground, lat. 37° 12' 06", long. 92° 56' 33"; transmitter to 3-mi. N of Fordland. Ownership: Springfield One Partnership.

St. Joseph—WMI293 (E group). Belwen Inc., 7 Boyle Rd., Scotia, NY 12302. Phone: 518-393-7428. Authorized power: 10-w. each. Antenna: 496-ft. above ground. Lat. 39° 40' 51", long. 94° 46' 47". Transmitter: N of Pigeonhill Wildlife Area. Equipment: Comwave transmitter; Bogner antenna. Ownership: Belwen Inc.

St. Louis—WHT651 (E group). Louis R. du Treil, 201 Fletcher Ave., Sarasota, FL 34237. Phone: 941-329-6000. Fax: 941-329-6030. E-mail: bobsr@dlr.com. Authorized power: 200-w. each. Antenna: 790-ft. above ground. Lat. 38° 28' 56", long. 90° 23' 53". Transmitter: 5489 Butler Hill Rd. Equipment: Comwave transmitter; Andrew antenna. Ownership: Louis R. du Treil.
Leased to People's Choice TV Partners, 2 Corporate Dr., Suite 249, Shelton, CT 064846239. Phone: 203-929-2800.

St. Louis—WLK422 (F group). Baypoint TV Inc., 2700 Chain Bridge Rd. NW, Washington, DC 20016. Phone: 202-659-4400. Fax: 202-237-7742. Authorized power: 10-w. Antenna: 790-ft. above ground. Lat. 38° 28' 56", long. 90° 23' 53". Transmitter: 5489 Butler Hill Rd. Equipment: Comwave transmitter; Andrew antenna. Ownership: Baypoint TV Inc.
Leased to Nucentrix Broadband Network, 200 Chisholm Place, Suite 200, Plano, TX 75075. Phone: 972-423-9494.

St. Louis—WBF80 (H1). City of St. Louis Metropolitan Police Dept., 1200 Clark, St. Louis, MO 63103. Phone: 314-444-5657. Fax: 314-444-5689. E-mail: epolice@stlouis.missouri.org. Authorized power: 200-w. Antenna: 790-ft. above ground. Lat. 38° 28' 56", long. 90° 23' 53". Transmitter: 5489 Butler Rd. Equipment: Comwave transmitter; Andrew antenna. Ownership: City of St. Louis Metropolitan Police Dept.
Leased to People's Choice TV Partners, 2 Corporate Dr., Suite 249, Shelton, CT 064846239. Phone: 203-929-2800. Fax: 203-929-1454.

St. Louis—WHJ915 (H2). Alda Gold, 5301 E. Broadway Blvd., Tucson, AZ 85711-3710. Phone: 520-519-4400. Fax: 520-747-6830. Authorized power: 200-w. Antenna: 790-ft. above ground. Lat. 38° 28' 56", long. 90° 23' 53". Transmitter: 5489 Butler Rd. Equipment: Comwave transmitter; Andrew antenna. Ownership: Matthew Oristano.
Leased to People's Choice TV Partners, 2 Corporate Dr., Suite 249, Shelton, CT 064846239. Phone: 203-929-2800. Fax: 203-929-1454.

St. Louis—WNEK905 (H3). Group W Television, Suite 506, 1025 Connecticut Ave. NW, Washington, DC 20036. Phone: 202-857-5160. Authorized power: 200-w. Antenna: 790-ft. above ground. Lat. 38° 28' 56", long. 90° 23' 53". Transmitter: 5489 Butler Rd. Equipment: Comwave transmitter; Andrew antenna. Ownership: Group W Televison.

Trenton—WMH585 (F group). Wireless Supervision TV Inc. Authorized power: 10-w. each. Antenna: 360-ft. above ground. Lat. 40° 05' 00", long. 93° 33' 30". Transmitter: 0.5-mi. N of Hwy. 6. Equipment: Comwave transmitter; Andrew antenna. Ownership: Wireless Supervision TV Inc.

Montana

Billings—WFY603 (E group). American Telecasting of Billings Inc., Suite 300, 5575 Tech Center Dr., Colorado Springs, CO 80919. Phone: 719-260-5533. Fax: 719-260-5010. Authorized power: 20-w. each. Antenna: 194-ft. above ground. Lat. 45° 46' 04", long. 108° 27' 27". Transmitter: 1613 Coburn Rd. Equipment: Comwave transmitter; Andrew antenna. Ownership: American Telecasting Inc.

Billings—WLW837 (F group). American Telecasting of Billings Inc., Suite 300, 5575 Tech Center Dr., Colorado Springs, CO 80919. Phone: 719-260-5533. Fax: 719-260-5010. Authorized power: 20-w. each. Antenna: 181-ft. above ground. Lat. 45° 46' 04", long. 108° 27' 27". Transmitter: 1613 Coburn Rd. Equipment: Comwave transmitter; Andrew antenna. Ownership: American Telecasting Inc.

Billings—WNTA626 (H1). Touch Tel Corp., Box 4008, Burlingame, CA 94011. Phone: 415-697-1000. Authorized power: 20-w. Antenna: 181-ft. above ground. Lat. 45° 46' 04", long. 108° 27' 27". Transmitter: 1613 Coburn Rd. Equipment: Comwave transmitter; Andrew antenna. Ownership: Touch Tel Corp.

Billings—WNTA982 (H2). American Telecasting of Billings Inc., Suite 300, 5575 Tech Center Dr., Colorado Springs, CO 80919. Phone: 719-260-5533. Fax: 719-260-5010. Authorized power: 20-w. Antenna: 181-ft. above ground. Lat. 45° 46' 04", long. 108° 27' 27". Transmitter: 1613 Coburn Rd. Equipment: Comwave transmitter; Andrew antenna. Ownership: American Telecasting Inc.

Bozeman—WMI851 (F group). Stephen Rullman, Box 1102, Claremont, CA 91711. Phone: 909-621-1004. Authorized power: 10-w. each. Antenna: 50-ft. above ground. Lat. 45° 40' 17", long. 111° 02' 49". Transmitter: Farm Bureau Professional Office. Equipment: Emcee transmitter; Andrew antenna. Ownership: Stephen Rullman.

Butte—WLW793 (F group). Broadcast Data Corp., Suite 247, 189 Berdan Ave., Wayne, NJ 07470. Phone: 201-831-7407. Authorized power: 10-w. each. Antenna: 100-ft. above ground. Lat. 46° 00' 22", long. 112° 26' 30". Transmitter: 3-mi. E of Butte. Equipment: Comwave transmitter; Bogner antenna. Ownership: Broadcast Data Corp.

Dillon—WMX921 (H1). G/S Dillon F Settlement Group, 3423 Rolston St., Fort Wayne, IN 46805. Phone: 219-483-2741. Authorized power: 10-w. Antenna: 8-ft. above ground. Lat. 45° 14' 22", long. 112° 40' 03". Transmitter: 1-mi. NW of Dillon. Equipment: Comwave transmitter; Andrew antenna. Ownership: G/S Dillon F Settlement Group.

Dillon—WMX922 (H2). G/S Dillon F Settlement Group, 3423 Rolston St., Fort Wayne, IN 46805. Phone: 219-483-2741. Authorized power: 10-w. Antenna: 8-ft. above ground. Lat. 45° 14' 22", long. 112° 40' 03". Transmitter: 1-mi. NW of Dillon. Equipment: Comwave transmitter; Andrew antenna. Ownership: G/S Dillon F Settlement Group.

Dillon—WMX920 (H3). G/S Dillon F Settlement Group, 3423 Rolston St., Fort Wayne, IN 46805. Phone: 219-483-2741. Authorized power: 10-w. Antenna: 8-ft. above ground. Lat. 45° 14' 22", long. 112° 40' 03". Transmitter: 1-mi. NW of Dillon. Equipment: Comwave transmitter; Andrew antenna. Ownership: G/S Dillon F Settlement Group.

Lewistown—WMY423 (E group). Super Wireless TV, 214 Broadway, Millbrae, CA 94030. Authorized power: 10-w. each. Antenna: 200-ft. above ground. Lat. 47° 04' 13", long. 109° 24' 26". Transmitter: 1.2-mi. NE of Courthouse. Equipment: Comwave transmitter; Andrew antenna. Ownership: Super Wireless TV.

Lewistown—WMX918 (H1). G/S Lewistown F Settlement Group, 11600 Pinehaven Ave., Bakersfield, CA 93312. Phone: 805-589-1240. Authorized power: 10-w. Antenna: 200-ft. above ground. Lat. 47° 04' 13", long. 109° 24' 26". Transmitter: 1.2-mi. NE of Courthouse. Equipment: Comwave transmitter; Andrew antenna. Ownership: G/S Lewistown F Settlement Group.

Lewistown—WMX917 (H2). G/S Lewistown F Settlement Group, 11600 Pinehaven Ave., Bakersfield, CA 93312. Phone: 805-589-1240. Authorized power: 10-w. Antenna: 200-ft. above ground. Lat. 47° 04' 13", long. 109° 24' 26". Transmitter: 1.2-mi. NE of Courthouse. Equipment: Comwave transmitter; Andrew antenna. Ownership: G/S Lewistown F Settlement Group.

Lewistown—WMX916 (H3). G/S Lewistown F Settlement Group, 11600 Pinehaven Ave., Bakersfield, CA 93312. Phone: 805-589-1240. Authorized power: 10-w. Antenna: 200-ft. above ground. Lat. 47° 04' 13", long. 109° 24' 26". Transmitter: 1.2-mi. NE of Courthouse. Equipment: Comwave transmitter; Andrew antenna. Ownership: G/S Lewistown F Settlement Group.

Miles City—WLR476 (F group). Richard Daniel Morgese Revocable Inter Vivos Trust, Suites 302-304, 630 Alvarado St., San Francisco, CA 94114. Phone: 415-285-1739. Authorized power: 10-w. each. Antenna: 628-ft. above ground. Lat. 46° 24' 04", long. 105° 39' 06". Transmitter: Government Hill Rd. Equipment: Comwave transmitter; Andrew antenna. Ownership: Richard D. Morgese.

Miles City—WMX364 (H1). Richard Daniel Morgese Revocable Inter Vivos Trust, Suites 302-304, 630 Alvarado St., San Francisco, CA 94114. Phone: 415-285-1739. Antenna: 30-ft. above ground. Lat. 46° 25' 40", long. 105° 53' 08". Transmitter: Hangar area, Miles City Airport. Equipment: Comwave transmitter; Andrew antenna. Ownership: Richard D. Morgese.

Miles City—WMX365 (H2). Richard Daniel Morgese Revocable Inter Vivos Trust, Suites 302-304, 630 Alvarado St., San Francisco, CA 94114. Phone: 415-285-1739. Antenna: 30-ft. above ground. Lat. 46° 25' 40", long. 105° 53' 08". Transmitter: Hangar area, Miles City Airport. Equipment: Comwave transmitter; Andrew antenna. Ownership: Richard D. Morgese.

Miles City—WMX362 (H3). Richard Daniel Morgese Revocable Inter Vivos Trust, Suites 302-304, 630 Alvarado St., San Francisco, CA 94114. Phone: 415-285-1739. Antenna: 30-ft. above ground. Lat. 46° 25' 40", long. 105° 53' 08". Transmitter: Hangar area, Miles City Airport. Equipment: Comwave transmitter; Andrew antenna. Ownership: Richard D. Morgese.

Missoula—WMH729 (F group). Echonet Corp., Box 255, Evergreen, CO 80439. Authorized power: 10-w. each. Antenna: 249-ft. above ground. Lat. 47° 02' 24", long. 113° 59' 00". Transmitter: 11-mi. N of Missoula. Equipment: Comwave transmitter; Bogner antenna. Ownership: Echonet Corp.

Nebraska

Bartley—WLW999 (E group). Nebraska Telecommunications Inc., 616 Chestnut Dr., Loveland, CO 80538. Phone: 303-663-1072. Authorized power: 10-w. each. Antenna: 490-ft. above ground. Lat. 40° 21' 53", long. 100° 17' 43". Transmitter: 7.5-mi. N of Bartley. Equipment: Emcee transmitter; Bogner antenna. Ownership: Nebraska Telecommunications Inc.
Leased to Southwest Telecommunications Corp., 212 N. Main St., Palisade, NE 69040. Phone: 800-535-7823.

Bartley—WHK929 (F group). Southwest Telecommunications Cooperative Assn. Inc., Box 309, Palisade, NE 69040-0366. Phone: 308-285-3880. Fax: 308-285-3811. Authorized power: 50-w. each. Antenna: 490-ft. above ground. Lat. 40° 21' 53", long. 100° 17' 43". Transmitter: 7.5-mi. N of Bartley. Equipment: Emcee transmitter; Bogner antenna. Ownership: Southwest Telecommunications Co-op Assn. Inc.

Bartley—WNEX783 (H1). Southwest Telecommunications Cooperative Assn. Inc., 215 N. Main St., Palisade, NE 69040. Phone: 308-285-3880. Fax: 308-285-3811. Authorized power: 10-w. Antenna: 485-ft. above ground. Lat. 40° 21' 53", long. 100° 17' 43". Transmitter: 7.5-mi. N of Bartley. Equipment: Emcee transmitter; Bogner antenna. Ownership: Southwest Telecommunications Co-op Assn. Inc.

Bartley—WNEX653 (H2). Nebraska Telecommunications Inc., 616 Chestnut Dr., Loveland, CO 80538. Phone: 303-663-1072. Antenna: 490-ft. above ground. Lat. 40° 21' 53", long. 100° 17' 43". Transmitter: 7.5-mi. N of Bartley. Equipment: Emcee transmitter; Bogner antenna. Requests change to 10-w., 485-ft. above ground. Ownership: Nebraska Telecommunications Inc.
Leased to Southwest Telecommunications Corp., 212 N. Main St., Palisade, NE 69040. Phone: 800-535-7823.

Chadron—WMI292 (E group). Eugene Kozel, 560 W. Franklin St., Monterey, CA 93940. Phone: 408-375-7125. Authorized power: 10-w. each. Antenna: 400-ft. above ground. Lat. 42° 38' 06", long. 103° 05' 30". Transmitter: 14-mi. SW of Chadron. Equipment: Comwave transmitter; Bogner antenna. Ownership: Eugene Kozel.

Chadron—WMI296 (F group). Rima Kozel, 560 W. Franklin St., Monterey, CA 93940. Phone: 408-375-7125. Authorized power: 10-w. each. Antenna: 400-ft. above ground. Lat. 42° 38' 06", long. 103° 05' 30". Transmitter: 14-mi. SW of Chadron. Equipment: Comwave transmitter; Bogner antenna. Ownership: Rima Kozel.

Geneva—WMH765 (E group). American Telecasting of Nebraska Inc., Suite 300, 5575 Tech Center Dr., Colorado Springs, CO 80919. Phone: 719-260-5533. Fax: 719-260-5010. Authorized power: 10-w. each. Antenna: 431-ft. above ground. Lat. 40° 28' 02", long. 97° 35' 32". Transmitter: 4-mi. S of Geneva. Equipment: ITS transmitter; Andrew antenna. Ownership: American Telecasting Inc.

Geneva—WMH768 (F group). American Telecasting of Nebraska Inc., Suite 300, 5575 Tech Center Dr., Colorado Springs, CO 80919. Phone: 719-260-5533. Fax: 719-260-5010. Authorized power: 10-w. each. Antenna: 431-ft. above ground. Lat. 40° 28' 02", long. 97° 35' 32". Transmitter: 4-mi. S of Geneva. Equipment: ITS transmitter; Andrew antenna. Ownership: American Telecasting Inc.

Grand Island—WLW974 (E group). Kannew Broadcast Technologies, Suite 425, 1220 L St. NW, Washington, DC 20005. Phone: 202-289-6300. Authorized power: 100-w. each. Antenna: 495-ft. above ground. Lat. 40° 41' 30", long. 98° 23' 20". Transmitter: Grand Island. Equipment: Comwave transmitter; Andrew antenna. Ownership: Kannew Broadcast Technologies.

Grand Island—WLW922 (F group). American Telecasting of Nebraska, Suite 300, 5575 Tech Center Dr., Colorado Springs, CO 80919. Phone: 719-260-5533. Fax: 719-260-5010. Authorized power: 100-w. each. Antenna: 495-ft. above ground. Lat. 40° 41' 30", long. 98° 23' 20". Transmitter: Grand Island. Equipment: ITS transmitter; Andrew antenna. Ownership: American Telecasting Inc.

Grand Island—WNTG845 (H1). Fortuna Systems Corp., Suite 200, 2000 L St. NW, Washington, DC 20036. Phone: 202-293-0972. Authorized power: 100-w. Antenna: 495-ft. above ground. Lat. 40° 41' 30", long. 98° 23' 20". Transmitter: Grand Island, NE Adams. Equipment: ITS transmitter; Andrew antenna. Ownership: Fortuna Systems Corp.

Grand Island—WNTH847 (H2). Integration Communications, Suite 200, 2000 L St. NW, Washington, DC 20036. Phone: 202-293-0972. Authorized power: 100-w. Antenna: 495-ft. above ground. Lat. 40° 41' 30", long. 98° 23' 20". Transmitter: Grand Island, NE Adams. Equipment: ITS transmitter; Andrew antenna. Ownership: Integration Communications International.

Grand Island—WNTH392 (H3). Richard J. Amons Jr., 6507 Ridge St., McLean, VA 22101. Authorized power: 100-w. Antenna: 495-ft. above ground. Lat. 40° 41' 30", long. 98° 23' 20". Transmitter: Grand Island, NE Adams. Equipment: ITS transmitter; Andrew antenna. Ownership: Richard J. Amons Jr.

Lincoln—WDU307 (E group). Affiliated Communications Corp., 33 S. Service Rd., Jericho, NY 11753-1006. Phone: 516-333-2000. Fax: 516-333-7555. Authorized power: 50-w. each. Antenna: 497-ft. above ground. Lat. 40° 43' 45", long. 96° 36' 44". Transmitter: Near Beal Slough Creek. Equipment: Comwave transmitter; Andrew antenna. Ownership: Affiliated Communications Corp.
Leased to American Telecasting of Green Bay Inc., 5575 Tech Center Dr., Suite 300, Colorado Springs, CO 80919. Phone: 719-260-5533. Fax: 719-260-5010.

Lincoln—WNTF780 (H1). Fortuna Systems Corp., Suite 200, 2000 L St. NW, Washington, DC 20036. Phone: 202-293-0972. Authorized power: 50-w. Antenna: 246-ft. above ground. Lat. 40° 43' 38", long. 96° 39' 49". Transmitter: Near Beal Slough Creek. Equipment: Comwave transmitter; Andrew antenna. Ownership: Fortuna Systems Corp.

Lincoln—WNTH475 (H2). John Dudeck, 11672 Harborside Circle, Largo, FL 33773. Authorized power: 50-w. Antenna: 246-ft. above ground. Lat. 40° 43' 38", long. 96° 36' 49". Transmitter: Near Beal Slough Creek. Equipment: Comwave transmitter; Andrew antenna. Ownership: John Dudeck.

Lincoln—WNTH745 (H3). Blake Twedt, 5102 Rosegreen Court, Tampa, FL 33624. Phone: 727-587-9959. Authorized power: 50-w. Antenna: 246-ft. above ground. Lat. 40° 43' 38", long. 96° 36' 49". Transmitter: Near Beal Slough Creek. Equipment: Comwave transmitter; Andrew antenna. Ownership: Blake Twedt.

North Platte—WHK928 (E group). Nebraska Telecommunications Inc., 616 Chestnut Dr., Loveland, CO 80538. Phone: 303-663-1072. Authorized power: 50-w. each. Antenna: 410-ft. above ground. Lat. 41° 13' 22", long. 100° 41' 17". Transmitter: 6-mi. N, 2.5-mi. E of North Platte. Equipment: Emcee transmitter; Bogner antenna. Ownership: Nebraska Telecommunications Inc.
Leased to Southwest Telecommunications Corp., 212 N. Main St., Palisade, NE 69040. Phone: 800-535-7823.

North Platte—WHK923 (F group). Southwest Telecommunications Cooperative Assn. Inc., Box 309, Palisade, NE 69040-0366. Phone: 308-285-3880. Fax: 308-285-3811. Authorized power: 50-w. each. Antenna: 410-ft. above ground. Lat. 41° 13' 22", long. 100° 41' 17". Transmitter: 6-mi. N, 2.5-mi. E of North Platte. Equipment: Emcee transmitter; Bogner antenna. Ownership: Southwest Telecommunications Co-op Assn. Inc.

North Platte—WNEX785 (H1). Southwest Telecommunications Cooperative Assn. Inc., 215 N. Main St., Palisade, NE 69040. Phone: 308-285-3880. Fax: 308-285-3811. Authorized power: 10-w. Antenna: 405-ft. above ground. Lat. 41° 13' 22", long. 100° 41' 17". Transmitter: 6-mi. N, 2.5-mi. E of North Platte. Equipment: Emcee transmitter; Bogner antenna. Ownership: Southwest Telecommunications Co-op Assn. Inc.

North Platte—WNEX655 (H2). Nebraska Telecommunications Inc., 616 Chestnut Dr., Loveland, CO 80538. Phone: 308-663-1072. Authorized power: 10-w. Antenna: 405-ft. above ground. Lat. 41° 13' 22", long. 100° 41' 17". Transmitter: 6-mi. N, 2.5-mi. E of North Platte. Equipment: Emcee transmitter; Bogner antenna. Ownership: Nebraska Telecommunications Inc.
Leased to Southwest Telecommunications Corp., 212 N. Main, Palisade, NE 69040. Phone: 800-535-7823.

Omaha—WHT777 (E group). Line of Site Inc., 8611 E. Santa Catalina Dr., Scottsdale, AZ 85255-2870. Phone: 602-951-8243. Authorized power: 10-w. each. Antenna: 489-ft. above ground. Lat. 41° 15' 28", long. 95° 56' 19". Transmitter: 1700 Farnham St. Equipment: Emcee transmitter; Andrew antenna. Ownership: Line of Site Inc.

Omaha—WLW992 (F group). Ron Abboud, 3208 S. 121st St., Omaha, NE 68137. Phone: 402-330-3474. Authorized power: 10-w. each. Antenna: 163-ft. above ground. Lat. 41° 12' 39", long. 96° 05' 14". Transmitter: 108th & L Sts. Equipment: Emcee transmitter; Andrew antenna. Ownership: Ron Abboud.

Omaha—WNTF452 (H1). Young Communications, 2715 Jenifer St. NW, Washington, DC 20015. Phone: 202-537-1264. Fax: 202-537-1264. Authorized power: 20-w. Antenna: 1839-ft. above ground. Lat. 41° 04' 15", long. 96° 13' 30". Transmitter: 19801 Pflug Rd. Equipment: Comwave transmitter; Andrew antenna. Ownership: Young Communications.
Leased to American Telecasting of Lincoln Inc., 5575 Tech Center Dr., Suite 300, Colorado Springs, CO 80918. Phone: 719-260-5533. Fax: 719-260-5010.

Oshkosh—WLW997 (E group). Nebraska Telecommunications Inc., 616 Chestnut Dr., Loveland, CO 80358. Phone: 303-663-1072. Authorized power: 50-w. each. Antenna: 460-ft. above ground. Lat. 41° 20' 25", long. 102° 23' 57". Transmitter: 4.3-mi. S, 3-mi. W of Oshkosh. Equipment: Emcee transmitter; Bogner antenna. Ownership: Nebraska Telecommunications Inc.
Leased to Southwest Telecommunications Corp., 212 N. Main St., Palisade, NE 69040. Phone: 800-535-7823.

Oshkosh—WLW964 (F group). Southwest Telecommunications Cooperative Assn. Inc., Box 309, Palisade, NE 69040-0366. Phone: 308-285-3880. Fax: 308-285-3811. Authorized power: 50-w. each. Antenna: 460-ft. above ground. Lat. 41° 20' 25", long. 102° 23' 57". Transmitter: 4.3-mi. S, 3-mi. W of Oshkosh. Equipment: Emcee transmitter; Bogner antenna. Ownership: Southwest Telecommunications Co-op Assn. Inc.

Oshkosh—WNEZ240 (H1). Southwest Telecommunications Cooperative Assn. Inc., 215 N. Main St., Palisade, NE 69040-0366. Phone: 308-285-3880. Fax: 308-285-3811. Authorized power: 10-w. Antenna: 455-ft. above ground. Lat. 41° 20' 25", long. 102° 23' 57". Transmitter: 4.3-mi. S & 3-mi. W of Oshkosh. Equipment: Emcee transmitter; Bogner antenna. Ownership: Southwest Telecommunications Co-op Assn. Inc.

Oshkosh—WNEX652 (H2). Nebraska Telecommunications Inc., 616 Chestnut Dr., Loveland, CO 80538. Phone: 303-663-1072. Authorized power: 10-w. Antenna: 455-ft. above ground. Lat. 41° 20' 25", long. 102° 23' 57". Transmitter: 4.3-mi. S, 3-mi. W of Oshkosh. Equipment: Emcee transmitter; Bogner antenna. Ownership: Nebraska Telecommunications Inc.
Leased to Southwest Telecommunications Corp., 212 N. Main St., Palisade, NE 69040. Phone: 800-535-7823.

Peru—WMY301 (H1). RVC Holdings Corp., Suite 200, 200 Chisholm Place, Plano, TX 75075. Phone: 972-423-9494. Fax: 972-423-0819. Authorized power: 10-w. Antenna: 100-ft. above ground. Lat. 40° 26' 18", long. 95° 44' 57". Transmitter: 3.8-mi SW of Peru. Equipment: Comwave transmitter; Andrew antenna. Ownership: Nucentrix Broadband Networks Inc.

Peru—WMY302 (H2). RVC Holdings Corp., Suite 200, 200 Chisholm Place, Plano, TX 75075. Phone: 972-423-9494. Fax: 972-423-0819. Authorized power: 10-w. Antenna: 100-ft. above ground. Lat. 40° 26' 18", long. 95° 44' 57". Transmitter: 3.8-mi. SW of Peru. Equipment: Comwave transmitter; Andrew antenna. Ownership: Nucentrix Broadband Networks Inc.

Peru—WMY303 (H3). RVC Holdings Corp., Suite 200, 200 Chisholm Place, Plano, TX 75075. Phone: 972-423-9494. Fax: 972-423-0819. Authorized power: 10-w. Antenna: 100-ft. above ground. Lat. 40° 26' 18", long. 95° 44' 57". Transmitter: 3.8-mi. SW of Peru. Equipment: Comwave transmitter; Andrew antenna. Ownership: Nucentrix Broadband Networks Inc.

Silver Creek—WMX945 (H1). RVC Holdings Corp., Suite 200, 200 Chisolm Place, Plano, TX 75075. Phone: 972-423-9494. Fax: 972-423-0819. Authorized power: 10-w. Antenna: 100-ft. above ground. Lat. 41° 15' 04", long. 97° 38' 07". Transmitter: 5-mi. NNE of Silver Creek. Equipment: Comwave transmitter; Andrew antenna. Ownership: Nucentrix Broadband Networks Inc.

Silver Creek—WMX946 (H2). RVC Holdings Corp., Suite 200, 200 Chisholm Place, Plano, TX 75075. Phone: 972-423-9494. Fax: 972-423-0819. Authorized power: 10-w. Antenna: 100-ft. above ground. Lat. 41° 15' 04", long. 97° 38' 07". Transmitter: 5-mi. NNE of Silver Creek. Equipment: Comwave transmitter; Andrew antenna. Ownership: Nucentrix Broadband Networks Inc.

Silver Creek—WMX944 (H3). RVC Holdings Corp., Suite 200, 200 Chisholm Place, Plano, TX 75075. Phone: 972-423-9494. Fax: 972-423-0819. Authorized power: 10-w. Antenna: 100-ft. above ground. Lat. 41° 15' 04", long. 97° 38' 07". Transmitter: 5-mi. NNE of Silver Creek. Equipment: Comwave transmitter; Andrew antenna. Ownership: Nucentrix Broadband Networks Inc.

Wauneta—WLW998 (E group). Nebraska Telecommunications Inc., 616 Chestnut Dr., Loveland, CO 80538. Phone: 303-663-1072. Authorized power: 10-w. each. Antenna: 460-ft. above ground. Lat. 40° 28' 54", long. 101° 23' 06". Transmitter: 4.5-mi. N, 0.5-mi. W of Wauneta. Equipment: Emcee transmitter; Andrew antenna. Ownership: Nebraska Telecommunications Inc.
Leased to Southwest Telecommunications Corp., 212 N. Main St., Palisade, NE 69040. Phone: 800-535-7823.

Wauneta—WHK926 (F group). Southwest Telecommunications Cooperative Assn. Inc., Box 309, Palisade, NE 69040-0366. Phone: 308-285-3880. Fax: 308-285-3811. Authorized power: 50-w. each. Antenna: 460-ft. above ground. Lat. 40° 28' 54", long. 101° 23' 06". Transmitter: 4.5-mi. N, 0.5-mi. W of Wauneta. Equipment: Emcee transmitter; Andrew antenna. Ownership: Southwest Telecommunications Co-op Assn. Inc.

Wauneta—WNEX784 (H1). Southwest Telecommunications Cooperative Assn. Inc., 215 N. Main St., Palisade, NE 69040. Phone: 308-285-3880. Fax: 308-285-3811. Authorized power: 10-w. Antenna: 455-ft. above ground. Lat. 40° 28' 54", long. 101° 23' 06". Transmitter: 4.5-mi. N, 0.5-mi. W of Wauneta. Equipment: Emcee transmitter; Andrew antenna. Ownership: Southwest Telecommunications Co-op Assn. Inc.

Wauneta—WNEX654 (H2). Nebraska Telecommunications Inc., 616 Chestnut Dr., Loveland, CO 89538. Phone: 303-663-1072. Authorized power: 10-w. Antenna: 455-ft. above ground. Lat. 40° 28' 54", long. 101° 23' 06". Transmitter: 4.5-mi. N, 0.5-mi. W of Wauneta. Equipment: Emcee transmitter; Andrew antenna. Ownership: Nebraska Telecommunications Inc.
Leased to Southwest Telecommunications Corp., 212 N. Main St., Palisade, NE 69040. Phone: 800-535-7823.

Nevada

Carson City—WMH705 (E group). Jonsson Communications Corp., Suite 900, 233 Wilshire Blvd., Santa Monica, CA 90401. Phone: 310-451-3230. Authorized power: 100-w. each. Antenna: 190-ft. above ground. Lat. 39° 15' 33", long. 119° 42' 12". Transmitter: 7.2-mi. NE of Carson City. Equipment: ITS transmitter; Andrew antenna. Ownership: Jonsson Communications Corp.

Carson City—WMH709 (F group). Broadcast Data Corp., Suite 247, 189 Berdan Ave., Wayne, NJ 07470. Phone: 201-831-7407. Authorized power: 10-w. each. Antenna: 140-ft. above ground. Lat. 39° 15' 25", long. 119° 42' 37". Transmitter: 6.9-mi. NE of Carson City. Equipment: ITS transmitter; Bogner antenna. Ownership: Broadcast Data Corp.

Carson City—WNTL575 (H group). Jonsson Communications Corp., Suite 900, 233 Wilshire Blvd., Santa Monica, CA 90401. Phone: 310-451-3230. Authorized power: 100-w. each. Antenna: 187-ft. above ground. Lat. 39° 15' 33", long. 119° 42' 12". Transmitter: 7.2-mi. NNE of Carson City. Equipment: ITS transmitter; Andrew antenna. Ownership: Jonsson Communications Corp.

Elko—WLW721 (E group). Carol A. Baglia, 7097 Brightwood Dr., Concord, OH 44077. Phone: 216-357-5834. Authorized power: 10-w. each. Antenna: 194-ft. above ground. Lat. 40° 50' 37", long. 115° 44' 58". Transmitter: 1800 Idaho St. Equipment: Comwave transmitter; Andrew antenna. Ownership: Carol A. Baglia.

Fallon—WLW698 (E group). Four Pro Plus Partners, 3175 Callecita St., Sacramento, CA 95815. Authorized power: 10-w. each. Antenna: 253-ft. above ground. Lat. 39° 29' 47", long. 118° 48' 50". Transmitter: 1155 Gummow Dr. Equipment: Loma Scientific transmitter; Bogner antenna. Ownership: Four Pro Plus Partners.

Fallon—WMX350 (H1). Holub Wamack Partnership, 6919 Laurel Oak Way, Fair Oaks, CA 95628. Phone: 916-965-3895. Authorized power: 10-w. Antenna: 255-ft. above ground. Lat. 39° 29' 47", long. 118° 48' 50". Transmitter: 1155 Gummow Dr. Equipment: ITS transmitter; Andrew antenna. Ownership: Holub Wamack Partnership.

Fallon—WMX352 (H3). Holub Wamack Partnership, 6919 Laurel Oak Way, Fair Oaks, CA 95628. Phone: 916-965-3895. Authorized power: 10-w. Antenna: 255-ft. above ground. Lat. 39° 29' 47", long. 118° 48' 50". Transmitter: 1155 Gummow Dr. Equipment: ITS transmitter; Andrew antenna. Ownership: Holub Wamack Partnership.

Hawthorne—WMY399 (E group). Patricia M. DeLovely, 9503 Lawnsberry Terrace, Silver Spring, MD 20901. Authorized power: 10-w. each. Antenna: 60-ft. above ground. Lat. 38° 31' 23", long. 118° 37' 27". Transmitter: Corner of 4th & Sierra Way. Equipment: Comwave transmitter; Bogner antenna. Ownership: Patricia M. DeLovely.

Hawthorne—WMY400 (F group). Joseph W. St. Clair, 2 Locke Circle, Medford, NJ 08055-3905. Authorized power: 10-w. each. Antenna: 60-ft. above ground. Lat. 38° 31' 23", long. 118° 37' 27". Transmitter: Corner of 4th & Sierra Way. Equipment: Comwave transmitter; Bogner antenna. Ownership: Joseph W. St. Clair.

Henderson—WNTH951 (H1). Via/Net Companies, 836 E. Washington St., San Diego, CA 92103. Phone: 619-260-0110. Authorized power: 50-w. Antenna: 85-ft. above ground. Lat. 36° 00' 32", long. 115° 00' 22". Transmitter: Black Mountain. Equipment: Comwave transmitter; Andrew antenna. Ownership: Via/Net Companies.

Henderson—WNTH999 (H2). Quadrangle Communications Inc., 836 E. Washington St., San Diego, CA 92103. Phone: 619-260-0110. Fax: 619-260-0791. Authorized power: 50-w. Antenna: 85-ft. above ground. Lat. 36° 00' 32", long. 115° 00' 22". Transmitter: Black Mountain. Equipment: Comwave transmitter; Andrew antenna. Ownership: Quadrangle Communications Inc.

Henderson—WNTH881 (H3). Bruce Merrill, Suite B1, 7621 E. Gray Rd., Scottsdale, AZ 85260. Phone: 480-596-8283. Fax: 480-596-2973. Antenna: 85-ft. above ground. Lat. 36° 00' 31", long. 115° 00' 22". Transmitter: Black Mountain. Ownership: Bruce Merrill.

Las Vegas—WHT721 (E group). Line of Site Inc., 8611 E. Santa Catalina Dr., Scottsdale, AZ 85255-2870. Phone: 602-951-8243. Authorized power: 10-w. each. Antenna: 85-ft. above ground. Lat. 36° 00' 32", long. 115° 00' 22". Transmitter: Black Mountain Peak. Equipment: Emcee transmitter; Andrew antenna. Ownership: Line of Site Inc.

Las Vegas—WHT722 (F group). MMDS-Las Vegas Inc., 2700 Chain Bridge Rd. NW, Washington, DC 20016. Phone: 202-966-2167. Fax: 202-237-7742. Authorized power: 25-w. each. Antenna: 280-ft. above ground. Lat. 36° 00' 32", long. 115° 00' 22". Transmitter: Black Mountain. Equipment: Comwave transmitter; Andrew antenna. Ownership: MDS Signal Group.
Leased to Super Channels of Nevada.

Las Vegas—WNTJ881 (H3). Bruce Merrill, Suite B1, 7621 E. Gray Rd., Scottsdale, AZ 85260. Phone: 480-596-8283. Fax: 480-596-2973. Authorized power: 25-w. Antenna: 85-ft. above ground. Lat. 36° 00' 32", long. 115° 00' 22". Transmitter: Mount Henderson. Equipment: Comwave transmitter; Andrew antenna. Ownership: Bruce Merrill.

Reno—WHT781 (E group). Jonsson Communications Corp., Suite 900, 233 Wilshire Blvd., Santa Monica, CA 90401. Phone: 310-451-3230. Authorized power: 100-w. each. Antenna: 184-ft. above ground. Lat. 39° 35' 03", long. 119° 47' 52". Transmitter: 4.15-mi. NNW of Sparks. Equipment: ITS transmitter; Bogner antenna. Ownership: Jonsson Communications Corp.

Reno—WHT782 (F group). Jonsson Communications Corp., Suite 900, 233 Wilshire Blvd., Santa Monica, CA 90401. Phone: 310-451-3230. Authorized power: 100-w. each. Antenna: 184-ft. above ground. Lat. 39° 35' 03", long. 119° 47' 52". Transmitter: 4-mi. N of Reno. Equipment: Emcee transmitter; Bogner antenna. Ownership: Jonsson Communications Corp.

New Hampshire

Manchester—WMH548 (E group). StarChannels Associates LP Authorized power: 10-w. each. Antenna: 100-ft. above ground. Lat. 43° 13' 00", long. 71° 34' 34". Transmitter: Little Pond Rd. Equipment: Emcee transmitter; Andrew antenna. Ownership: StarChannels Associates LP.

Plymouth—WMH252 (E group). Whitcom Partners, Room 4310, Time Life Bldg., 110 W. 51st St., New York, NY 10020. Phone: 212-582-2300. Fax: 212-582-2310. Authorized power: 10-w. each. Antenna: 20-ft. above ground. Lat. 43° 46' 10", long. 71° 40' 20". Transmitter: 1-mi. NE of Plymouth. Equipment: Emcee transmitter; Bogner antenna. Ownership: Whitcom Partners.

Portsmouth—WLW855 (E group). Nucentrix Spectrum Resources Inc., Suite 200, 200 Chisolm Place, Plano, TX 75075. Phone: 972-423-9494. Fax: 972-423-0819. Authorized power: 50-w. Antenna: 400-ft. above ground. Lat. 43° 03' 11", long. 70° 46' 04". Transmitter: 815 W. Lafayette Rd. Equipment: Comwave transmitter; Andrew antenna. Ownership: Nucentrix Broadband Networks.

Portsmouth—WNTH586 (H1). Ivan C. Nachman, Suite 201, 7800 113th St. N, Seminole, FL 34642. Phone: 813-392-1681. Authorized power: 50-w. Antenna: 400-ft. above ground. Lat. 43° 03' 11", long. 70° 46' 04". Transmitter: 815 Lafayette Rd. Equipment: Emcee transmitter; Andrew antenna. Ownership: Ivan Nachman.

Portsmouth—WNTH471 (H2). John Dudeck, 11672 Harborside Circle, Largo, FL 33773. Authorized power: 50-w. Antenna: 400-ft. above ground. Lat. 43° 03' 11", long. 70° 46' 04". Transmitter: 815 Lafayette Rd. Equipment: Emcee transmitter; Andrew antenna. Ownership: John Dudeck.

Portsmouth—WNTH747 (H3). Blake Twedt, 5102 Rosegreen Court, Tampa, FL 33624. Phone: 727-587-9959. Authorized power: 50-w. Antenna: 400-ft. above ground. Lat. 43° 03' 11", long. 70° 46' 04". Transmitter: 815 Lafayette Rd. Equipment: Emcee transmitter; Andrew antenna. Ownership: Blake Twedt.

New Jersey

Atlantic City—WHT752 (E group). Orion Broadcasting Systems Inc., Suite B-14, 2700 E. Sunset Blvd., Las Vegas, NV 89120. Phone: 800-356-1825. Authorized power: 10-w. each. Antenna: 365-ft. above ground. Lat. 39° 22' 51", long. 74° 27' 02". Transmitter: 1701 Absecon Blvd. Equipment: Emcee transmitter; Andrew antenna. Ownership: Orion Broadcasting Systems.

Atlantic City—WMI280 (F group). Orion Broadcasting Systems Inc., Suite B-14, 2700 E. Sunset Blvd., Las Vegas, NV 89120. Phone: 800-356-1825. Authorized power: 50-w. each. Antenna: 499-ft. above ground. Lat. 39° 19' 15", long. 74° 46' 17". Transmitter: 1.6-mi. NW of Atlantic City. Equipment: Emcee transmitter; Andrew antenna. Ownership: Orion Broadcasting Systems.

Atlantic City—WNTH892 (H1). Orion Vision, 201 Tilton Rd. , Northfield, NJ 08225. Phone: 609-485-0099. Fax: 609-569-1512. E-mail: mike@orionvision.com. Web site: http://www.orionvision.com. Authorized power: 50-w. Antenna: 500-ft. above ground. Lat. 39°

22' 51", long. 74° 27' 02". Transmitter: Corbin City. Equipment: Emcee transmitter; Andrew antenna. Ownership: Orion Broadcasting Systems.

Leased to Orion Broadcasting Systems Inc., 201 Tilton Rd., Northfield, NJ 08225. Phone: 609-485-0099.

Atlantic City—WNTJ652 (H3). Orion Broadcasting Systems Inc., Suite B-14, 2700 E. Sunset Blvd., Las Vegas, NV 89120. Phone: 800-356-1825. Authorized power: 50-w. Antenna: 499-ft. above ground. Lat. 39° 19' 15", long. 74° 46' 17". Transmitter: 1.6-mi. NW of Atlantic City. Equipment: Emcee transmitter; Andrew antenna. Ownership: Orion Broadcasting Systems.

New Mexico

Albuquerque—WHT661 (E group). Multi-Channel MDS Inc., Box 385, Rd. 2, Elverson, PA 19520. Phone: 610-286-0425. Authorized power: 50-w. each. Antenna: 163-ft. above ground. Lat. 35° 06' 38", long. 106° 33' 27". Transmitter: 2633 Tennessee St. Equipment: Emcee transmitter; Andrew antenna. Ownership: Multi-Channel MDS Inc.

Albuquerque—WHT662 (F group). Paul M. Kimball, Suite A, 1012 N.W. Grand Blvd., Oklahoma City, OK 73118-6038. Phone: 405-848-1874. Fax: 405-840-1164. E-mail: pmkimball@aol.com. Authorized power: 50-w. each. Antenna: 163-ft. above ground. Lat. 35° 06' 38", long. 106° 33' 27". Transmitter: 2633 Tennessee St. Equipment: Emcee transmitter; Andrew antenna. Ownership: Paul M. Kimball.

Leased to Jones Intercable.

Albuquerque—WNTF451 (H1). Multimedia Development Corp. Authorized power: 20-w. Antenna: 28-ft. above ground. Lat. 35° 13' 02", long. 106° 27' 06". Transmitter: Sandia Crest. Equipment: Emcee transmitter; Andrew antenna. Ownership: Multimedia Development Corp.

Albuquerque—WMX359 (H2). Blake Twedt, 5102 Rosegreen Court, Tampa, FL 33624. Phone: 727-587-9959. Authorized power: 20-w. Antenna: 22-ft. above ground. Lat. 35° 13' 02", long. 106° 27' 06". Transmitter: Sandia Crest. Equipment: Emcee transmitter; Andrew antenna. Ownership: Blake Twedt.

Albuquerque—WNTF306 (H3). Multimedia Development Corp. Authorized power: 20-w. Antenna: 28-ft. above ground. Lat. 35° 13' 02", long. 106° 27' 06". Transmitter: Sandia Crest. Equipment: Emcee transmitter; Andrew antenna. Ownership: Multimedia Development Corp.

Clayton—WMY433 (F group). G/S Sandpoint F Settlement Group, Box 6219, Springfield, IL 62708. Authorized power: 10-w. each. Antenna: 50-ft. above ground. Lat. 48° 19' 54", long. 116° 41' 35". Transmitter: 6.8-mi. WNW of Sandpoint. Equipment: Comwave transmitter; Bogner antenna. Ownership: G/S Sandpoint F Settlement Group.

Deming—WHT597 (E group). Martin V. Rosales, Box 211, Lordsburg, NM 88045. Authorized power: 10-w. each. Lat. 32° 12' 00", long. 107° 36' 00". Transmitter: 12.5-mi. SE of Deming. Equipment: Comwave transmitter; Andrew antenna. Ownership: Martin V. Rosales.

Farmington—WLW778 (F group). Broadcast Data Corp., Suite 247, 189 Berdan Ave., Wayne, NJ 07470. Phone: 201-831-7407. Lat. 36° 41' 45", long. 108° 13' 23". Ownership: Broadcast Data Corp.

Gallup—WMH348 (F group). New Mexico Media Ltd., Box 4816, Sante Fe, NM 87502. Authorized power: 10-w. each. Antenna: 200-ft. above ground. Lat. 35° 22' 02", long. 108° 42' 22". Transmitter: 9-mi. S of Gallup. Equipment: Emcee transmitter; Andrew antenna. Ownership: New Mexico Media Ltd.

Gallup—WNTI529 (H2). John Dudeck, 11672 Harborside Circle, Largo, FL 33773. Authorized power: 10-w. Antenna: 184-ft. above ground. Lat. 35° 22' 02", long. 108° 42' 22". Transmitter: 9-mi. S of Gallup. Equipment: Emcee transmitter; Andrew antenna. Ownership: John Dudeck.

Hobbs—WMY420 (E group). Hobbs NM E Group MMDS Settlement Partnership, Suite 201, 7800 113th St. N, Seminole, FL 33772. Authorized power: 10-w. each. Antenna: 290-ft. above ground. Lat. 32° 17' 34", long. 106° 41' 48". Transmitter: Tortugas Mountain. Equipment: Comwave transmitter; Andrew antenna. Ownership: Hobbs NM E Group MMDS Settlement Partnership.

Las Cruces—WHK962 (E group). National Wireless Video, 63 Dombey Circle, Thousand Oaks, CA 91360. Authorized power: 20-w. each. Antenna: 77-ft. above ground. Lat. 32° 17' 34", long. 106° 41' 48". Transmitter: Tortugas Mountain. Equipment: Comwave transmitter; Andrew antenna. Ownership: National Wireless Video.

Las Cruces—WHK961 (F group). Multimedia Development Corp. Authorized power: 20-w. each. Antenna: 77-ft. above ground. Lat. 32° 17' 34", long. 106° 41' 48". Transmitter: Tortugas Mountain. Equipment: Comwave transmitter; Andrew antenna. Ownership: Multimedia Development Corp.

Las Cruces—WMI332 (H1). Multimedia Development Corp. Authorized power: 10-w. Antenna: 81-ft. above ground. Lat. 32° 17' 34", long. 106° 41' 48". Transmitter: Tortugas Mountain. Equipment: Comwave transmitter; Andrew antenna. Ownership: Multimedia Development Corp.

Las Cruces—WMI336 (H2). Multimedia Development Corp. Authorized power: 10-w. Antenna: 81-ft. above ground. Lat. 32° 17' 34", long. 106° 41' 48". Transmitter: Tortugas Mountain. Equipment: Comwave transmitter; Andrew antenna. Ownership: Multimedia Development Corp.

Las Cruces—WMI340 (H3). Multimedia Development Corp. Authorized power: 10-w. Antenna: 81-ft. above ground. Lat. 32° 17' 34", long. 106° 41' 48". Transmitter: Tortugas Mountain. Equipment: Comwave transmitter; Andrew antenna. Ownership: Multimedia Development Corp.

Las Vegas—WMH296 (F group). Mickelson Media Inc., 50 Locust Ave., New Canaan, CT 06840. Authorized power: 10-w. each. Antenna: 282-ft. above ground. Lat. 35° 35' 59", long. 105° 15' 16". Transmitter: Creston Mountain. Equipment: Emcee transmitter; Bogner antenna. Ownership: Mickelson Media Inc.

Las Vegas—WNTL418 (H1 & 3). Las Vegas Wireless Cable Inc. Authorized power: 50-w. each. Antenna: 103-ft. above ground. Lat. 35° 36' 16", long. 105° 15' 35". Transmitter: 0.5-mi. W of State Hospital. Equipment: Comwave transmitter; Andrew antenna. Ownership: National Cable & Television Services Group.

Los Alamos—WMH297 (F group). Mickelson Media Corp., 50 Locust Ave., New Canaan, CT 06840. Authorized power: 10-w. each. Antenna: 50-ft. above ground. Lat. 35° 52' 37", long. 106° 17' 08". Equipment: Emcee transmitter; Bogner antenna. Ownership: Mickelson Media Inc.

Roswell—WMH421 (F group). Broadcast Data Corp., Suite 247, 189 Berdan Ave., Wayne, NJ 07470. Phone: 201-831-7407. Authorized power: 10-w. Antenna: 241-ft. above ground. Lat. 33° 24' 05", long. 104° 22' 45". Transmitter: Comanche Hill. Equipment: Comwave transmitter; Bogner antenna. Ownership: Broadcast Data Corp.

Roswell—WNTI462 (H3). Blake Twedt, 5102 Rosegreen Court, Tampa, FL 33724. Phone: 727-587-9959. Authorized power: 10-w. Antenna: 238-ft. above ground. Lat. 33° 24' 05", long. 104° 22' 45". Transmitter: Comanche Hill. Equipment: Andrew antenna. Ownership: Blake Twedt.

Santa Fe—WLW782 (E group). Nancy & Ted Phillips Co., Box 431 121 N. Main St., Seminole, OK 74868. Phone: 405-382-1100. Authorized power: 10-w. each. Antenna: 57-ft. above ground. Lat. 35° 47' 09", long. 105° 46' 54". Transmitter: Tesuque Peak. Equipment: Emcee transmitter; Andrew antenna. Ownership: Nancy & Ted Phillips Co.

Santa Fe—WMI325 (F group). New Mexico Media Ltd., Box 4816, Santa Fe, NM 87502. Phone: 505-473-2200. Authorized power: 10-w. each. Antenna: 57-ft. above ground. Lat. 35° 47' 09", long. 105° 46' 54". Transmitter: Tesuque Peak. Equipment: Emcee transmitter; Andrew antenna. Ownership: New Mexico Media Ltd.

Santa Fe—WNTI583 (H1). Blake Twedt, 5102 Rosegreen Court, Tampa, FL 33624. Phone: 727-589-9959. Authorized power: 10-w. Antenna: 57-ft. above ground. Lat. 35° 47' 09", long. 105° 46' 54". Transmitter: Tesuque Peak. Equipment: Emcee transmitter; Andrew antenna. Ownership: Blake Twedt.

Santa Fe—WNTF247 (H2). Les Gutierrez, No. 300, 13170-B Central SE, Albuquerque, NM 87123. Phone: 505-281-4302. Authorized power: 10-w. Antenna: 60-ft. above ground. Lat. 35° 47' 09", long. 105° 46' 54". Transmitter: Tesuque Peak. Equipment: Emcee transmitter; Andrew antenna. Ownership: Les Gutierrez.

Santa Fe—WNTI521 (H3). John Dudeck, 11672 Harborside Circle, Largo, FL 33773. Authorized power: 10-w. Antenna: 57-ft. above ground. Lat. 35° 47' 09", long. 105° 46' 54". Transmitter: Tesuque Peak. Equipment: Emcee transmitter; Andrew antenna. Ownership: John Dudeck.

Silver City—WHT598 (E group). Rural Television System, Box L, Lordsburg, NM 88045. Phone: 505-542-3508. Fax: 505-542-3535. Authorized power: 10-w. each. Antenna: 40-ft. above ground. Lat. 32° 50' 50", long. 108° 14' 18". Transmitter: 5-mi. N of Silver City. Equipment: Comwave transmitter; Andrew antenna. Ownership: Rural Television System Inc.

Socorro—WMI416 (E group). Socorro Satellite Systems Inc., 215 E. Manzanares Ave., Socorro, NM 87801. Phone: 505-835-0560. Authorized power: 20-w. each. Antenna: 41-ft. above ground. Lat. 34° 04' 18", long. 106° 57' 44". Transmitter: 4-mi. W of Socorro. Equipment: Emcee transmitter; Andrew antenna. Ownership: Socorro Satellite Systems Inc.

Socorro—WMI417 (F group). Socorro Satellite Systems Inc., 215 E. Manzanares Ave., Socorro, NM 87801. Phone: 505-835-0560. Authorized power: 20-w. each. Antenna: 41-ft. above ground. Lat. 34° 04' 18", long. 106° 57' 44". Transmitter: 4-mi. W of Socorro. Equipment: Emcee transmitter; Andrew antenna. Ownership: Socorro Satellite Systems Inc.

Socorro—WNTK750 (H group). Socorro Satellite Systems, 215 E. Manzanares Ave., Socorro, NM 87801. Phone: 505-835-0560. Authorized power: 20-w. each. Antenna: 41-ft. above ground. Lat. 34° 04' 18", long. 106° 57' 44". Transmitter: 4-mi. W of Socorro. Equipment: Emcee transmitter; Andrew antenna. Ownership: Socorro Satellite Systems Inc.

Truchas-Taos—WMH476 (E group). Colowave Inc., Box F, Shawnee, CO 80475. Authorized power: 10-w. each. Antenna: 33-ft. above ground. Lat. 36° 02' 27", long. 105° 50' 38". Transmitter: 1.8-mi. W of Truchas. Equipment: Emcee transmitter; Andrew antenna. Ownership: Colowave Inc.

Tucumcari—WMX929 (H1). RVC Holdings Corp., Suite 200, 200 Chisholm Place, Plano, TX 75075. Phone: 972-423-9494. Fax: 972-423-0819. Authorized power: 10-w. Antenna: 706-ft. above ground. Lat. 35° 13' 47", long. 103° 44' 11". Transmitter: 4-mi. N of Tucumcari. Equipment: ITS transmitter; Andrew antenna. Ownership: Nucentrix Broadband Networks Inc.

Tucumcari—WMX930 (H2). RVC Holdings Corp., Suite 200, 200 Chisholm Place, Plano, TX 75075. Phone: 972-423-9494. Fax: 972-423-0819. Authorized power: 10-w. Antenna: 706-ft. above ground. Lat. 35° 13' 47", long. 103° 44' 11". Transmitter: 4-mi. N of Tucumcari. Equipment: ITS transmitter; Andrew antenna. Ownership: Nucentrix Broadband Networks Inc.

Tucumcari—WMX931 (H3). RVC Holdings Corp., Suite 200, 200 Chisholm Place, Plano, TX 75075. Phone: 972-423-9494. Fax: 972-423-0819. Authorized power: 10-w. Antenna: 706-ft. above ground. Lat. 35° 13' 47", long. 103° 44' 11". Transmitter: 4-mi. N of Tucumcari. Equipment: ITS transmitter; Andrew antenna. Ownership: Nucentrix Broadband Networks Inc.

New York

Albany—WHT750 (E group). Greater Albany License Inc., Suite 100, 2101 Wilson Blvd., Arlington, VA 22201. Phone: 703-812-8800. Fax: 703-812-8808. Authorized power: 50-w. each. Antenna: 103-ft. above ground. Lat. 42° 38' 09", long. 74° 00' 04". Transmitter: Pinnacle Rd., New Scotland. Equipment: ITS transmitter; Andrew antenna. Ownership: CAI Wireless Systems Inc.

Albany—WHT751 (F group). Greater Albany License Inc., Suite 100, 2101 Wilson Blvd., Arlington, VA 22201. Phone: 703-812-8800. Fax: 703-812-8808. Authorized power: 50-w. each. Antenna: 103-ft. above ground. Lat. 42° 38' 09", long. 74° 00' 04". Transmitter: Pinnacle Rd., New Scotland. Equipment: ITS transmitter; Andrew antenna. Ownership: CAI Wireless Systems Inc.

Albany—WNTA920 (H1). Greater Albany License Inc., Suite 100, 2101 Wilson Blvd., Arlington, VA 22201. Phone: 703-812-8800. Fax: 703-812-8808. Authorized power: 50-w. Antenna: 115-ft. above ground. Lat. 42° 38' 09", long. 74° 00' 04". Transmitter: Pinnacle

Rd., New Scotland. Equipment: ITS transmitter; Andrew antenna. Ownership: CAI Wireless Systems Inc.

Albany—WNTA389 (H2). Greater Albany License Inc., Suite 100, 2101 Wilson Blvd., Arlington, VA 22201. Phone: 703-812-8800. Fax: 703-812-8808. Authorized power: 50-w. Antenna: 103-ft. above ground. Lat. 42° 38' 09", long. 74° 00' 04". Transmitter: Pinnacle Rd., New Scotland. Equipment: ITS transmitter; Andrew antenna. Ownership: CAI Wireless Systems Inc.

Albany—WNEZ721 (H3). Greater Albany License Inc., Suite 100, 2101 Wilson Blvd., Arlington, VA 22201. Phone: 703-812-8800. Fax: 703-812-8808. Authorized power: 50-w. Antenna: 103-ft. above ground. Lat. 42° 38' 09", long. 74° 00' 04". Transmitter: Pinnacle Rd., New Scotland. Equipment: ITS transmitter; Andrew antenna. Ownership: CAI Wireless Systems Inc.

Binghamton—WLK276 (F group). Krisar Inc., 320 Hamilton St., Albion, NY 14411. Phone: 716-964-9121. Fax: 716-589-9091. E-mail: topperiai@aol.com. Authorized power: 10-w. each. Antenna: 934-ft. above ground. Lat. 42° 03' 22", long. 75° 56' 39". Transmitter: Ingraham Hill Rd. Equipment: Comwave transmitter; Bogner antenna. Ownership: Krisar Inc.

Corning—WNTK908 (H group). KA3B2 TV Partners, No. 238, 2219 Thousand Oaks Blvd., Thousand Oaks, CA 91362. Phone: 800-388-7371. Authorized power: 50-w. each. Antenna: 100-ft. above ground. Lat. 42° 09' 45", long. 77° 02' 15". Transmitter: Denmark Hill. Equipment: ITS transmitter; Andrew antenna. Ownership: KA3B2 Television Partnership.

Elmira—WMH417 (E group). Lawrence N. Brandt, Suite 220, 3201 New Mexico Ave. NW, Washington, DC 20016. Phone: 202-363-1100. Authorized power: 10-w. each. Antenna: 140-ft. above ground. Lat. 42° 01' 55", long. 76° 47' 02". Transmitter: Comfort Rd. Equipment: Comwave transmitter; Bogner antenna. Ownership: Lawrence N. Brandt.

Fairport—WHT688 (F group). Robert S. Moore, 316 N. Westwood Ave., Toledo, OH 43603. Phone: 419-531-1440. Authorized power: 100-w. each. Antenna: 317-ft. above ground. Lat. 43° 02' 10", long. 77° 25' 24". Transmitter: 975 Thayer Rd. Equipment: Emcee transmitter; Andrew antenna. Ownership: Robert S. Moore.

Fairport—WNTE275 (H1). Rochester License Inc., Suite 100, 2101 Wilson Blvd., Arlington, VA 22201. Phone: 703-812-8800. Fax: 703-812-8808. Authorized power: 100-w. Antenna: 317-ft. above ground. Lat. 43° 02' 10", long. 77° 25' 24". Transmitter: 975 Thayer Rd. Equipment: Andrew antenna. Ownership: CAI Wireless Systems Inc.

Fairport—WNTG719 (H2). Rochester License Inc., Suite 100, 2101 Wilson Blvd., Arlington, VA 22201. Phone: 703-812-8800. Fax: 703-812-8808. Authorized power: 100-w. Antenna: 317-ft. above ground. Lat. 43° 02' 10", long. 77° 25' 24". Transmitter: 975 Thayer Rd. Equipment: ITS transmitter; Andrew antenna. Ownership: CAI Wireless Systems Inc.

Fairport—WNTD891 (H3). Rochester License Inc., Suite 100, 2101 Wilson Blvd., Arlington, VA 22201. Phone: 703-812-8800. Fax: 703-812-8808. Authorized power: 100-w. Antenna: 317-ft. above ground. Lat. 43° 02' 10", long. 77° 25' 24". Transmitter: 975 Thayer Rd. Equipment: ITS transmitter; Andrew antenna. Ownership: CAI Wireless Systems Inc.

Glens Falls—WMI301 (F group). Glens Falls BDC-MMDS Co., Suite 247, 189 Berdan Ave., Wayne, NJ 07470. Phone: 201-616-1168. Authorized power: 10-w. Antenna: 223-ft. above ground. Lat. 43° 18' 17", long. 73° 45' 07". Transmitter: 5-mi. W of Glens Falls. Equipment: Emcee transmitter; Bogner antenna. Ownership: Broadcast Data Corp., 33.3%; Private Networks Inc., 66.7%.

Grand Island—WHT665 (E group). Buffalo License Inc., Suite 100, 2101 Wilson Blvd., Arlington, VA 22201. Phone: 703-812-8800. Fax: 703-812-8808. Authorized power: 20-w. each. Antenna: 796-ft. above ground. Lat. 43° 01' 48", long. 78° 55' 15". Transmitter: 871 Whitehaven Rd. Equipment: ITS transmitter; Bogner antenna. Requests to change to transmitter to 0.6-mi. NNE of Whitehaven & Harvey Rds.; Andrew antenna. Ownership: CAI Wireless Systems Inc.

Grand Island—WNEK802 (H2). Buffalo License Inc., Suite 100, 2101 Wilson Blvd., Arlington, VA 22201. Phone: 703-812-8800. Fax: 703-812-8808. Authorized power: 20-w. Antenna: 796-ft. above ground. Lat. 43° 01' 48", long. 78° 55' 15". Transmitter: 871 Whitehaven Rd. Equipment: Comwave transmitter; Bogner antenna. Requests to change to transmitter to 0.6-mi. NNE of Whitehaven & Harvey Rds.; Andrew antenna. Ownership: CAI Wireless Systems Inc.

Ithaca—WMI294 (F group). Private Networks Inc., Box 023707, Brooklyn, NY 11201. Phone: 212-777-4740. Authorized power: 10-w. each. Antenna: 75-ft. above ground. Lat. 42° 23' 13", long. 76° 40' 10". Transmitter: Conn Hill Rd. Equipment: Comwave transmitter; Bogner antenna. Ownership: Private Networks Inc.

Jamestown—WLR464 (F group). Gate City General Partnership Authorized power: 10-w. each. Antenna: 29-ft. above ground. Lat. 42° 06' 51", long. 79° 12' 18". Transmitter: 1395 E. 2nd St. Equipment: Comwave transmitter; Bogner antenna. Ownership: Gate City General Partnership.

Middleville—WMI820 (F group). United Communications. Authorized power: 10-w. each. Antenna: 379-ft. above ground. Lat. 43° 08' 46", long. 75° 10' 40". Transmitter: Smith Hill Rd., Utica. Equipment: Emcee transmitter; Andrew antenna. Ownership: United Communications Ltd.

Middleville—WNTJ461 (H group). United Communications Authorized power: 10-w. each. Antenna: 379-ft. above ground. Lat. 43° 08' 46", long. 75° 10' 40". Transmitter: Smith Hill Rd., Utica. Equipment: Comwave transmitter; Andrew antenna. Ownership: United Communications Ltd.

New York—WLR500 (E group). Red New York E Partnership, 248 King George St., Annapolis, MD 21401. Phone: 410-626-1200. Fax: 410-626-1266. Authorized power: 10-w. each. Antenna: 921-ft. above ground. Lat. 40° 44' 54", long. 73° 59' 10". Transmitter: Empire State Bldg. Equipment: Emcee transmitter; Bogner antenna. Ownership: Red New York E Partnership.

New York—WMY467 (F group). Grand MMDS Alliance New York F/P Partnership, 40 Woodland St., Hartford, CT 06105. Authorized power: 10-w. each. Antenna: 922-ft. above ground. Lat. 40° 44' 54", long. 73° 59' 10". Transmitter: Empire State Bldg. Equipment: ITS transmitter; Andrew antenna. Ownership: Grand MMDS Alliance New York F/P Partnership.

New York—WHJ897 (H2). New York License Inc., Suite 100, 2101 Wilson Blvd., Arlington, VA 22201. Phone: 703-812-8800. Fax: 703-812-8808. Authorized power: 10-w. Antenna: 921-ft. above ground. Lat. 40° 44' 54", long. 73° 59' 10". Transmitter: Empire State Building. Equipment: ITS transmitter; Andrew antenna. Ownership: CAI Wireless Systems Inc.

New York—WNTQ214 (H3). New York License Inc., Suite 100, 2101 Wilson Blvd., Arlington, VA 22201. Phone: 703-812-8800. Fax: 703-812-8808. Authorized power: 10-w. Antenna: 921-ft. above ground. Lat. 40° 44' 54", long. 73° 59' 10". Transmitter: Empire State Bldg. Equipment: ITS transmitter; Andrew antenna. Ownership: CAI Wireless Systems Inc.

Poughkeepsie—WMH804 (E group). Paul Communications Inc., 7555 Pebble Beach Dr., Reno, NV 89502. Phone: 602-319-3311. Authorized power: 10-w. each. Antenna: 300-ft. above ground. Lat. 41° 43' 04", long. 73° 59' 49". Transmitter: Illinois Mountain. Equipment: Emcee transmitter; Andrew antenna. Ownership: Paul Communications Inc.

Poughkeepsie—WLW939 (F group). Low Power Technology Inc., No. 307, 225 Congress, Austin, TX 78701. Authorized power: 10-w. each. Antenna: 300-ft. above ground. Lat. 41° 43' 04", long. 73° 59' 49". Transmitter: Illinois Mountain. Equipment: Emcee transmitter; Andrew antenna. Ownership: Low Power Technology Inc.

Selden—WNTM910 (H2). NEW Com, 11645 Putter Way, Los Altos, CA 94024. Authorized power: 10-w. Antenna: 328-ft. above ground. Lat. 40° 50' 32", long. 73° 02' 23". Transmitter: Adirondack Dr. & Midvale. Equipment: ITS transmitter; Andrew antenna. Ownership: NEW Com.

Syracuse—WHT739 (E group). Line of Site Inc., 8611 E. Santa Catalina Dr., Scottsdale, AZ 85255-2870. Phone: 602-951-8243. Authorized power: 10-w. each. Antenna: 1019-ft. above ground. Lat. 42° 52' 50", long. 76° 11' 46". Transmitter: Barker St., Otisco Turnpike. Equipment: Comwave transmitter; Andrew antenna. Ownership: Line of Site Inc.

Syracuse—WHT740 (F group). Video/Multipoint Inc., 2809 Pine St., San Francisco, CA 94115-2501. Phone: 415-775-9552. Fax: 415-775-9536. E-mail: bill@sauro.com. Authorized power: 10-w. Antenna: 800-ft. above ground. Lat. 42° 52' 50", long. 76° 11' 46". Transmitter: Barker St., Otisco Turnpike. Equipment: Comwave transmitter; Andrew antenna. Ownership: Video/Multipoint Inc.
Leased to Syracuse Wireless LLC.

Watertown—WNTM557 (H group). Daniel J. Demers, Trustee for Northeast Telecom Inc., Suite 155, 1433 N. Jones Blvd., Las Vegas, NV 89108. Authorized power: 8-w. each. Antenna: 300-ft. above ground. Lat. 44° 03' 18", long. 75° 57' 14". Transmitter: Rte. 12 & Perch Lake Rd. Equipment: Comwave transmitter; Andrew antenna. Ownership: Northeast Telecom Inc.

North Carolina

Asheville—WLW938 (F group). MWTV Inc., 3401 E. Cholla St., Phoenix, AZ 85028. Phone: 602-867-7351. Authorized power: 10-w. each. Antenna: 25-ft. above ground. Lat. 35° 36' 02", long. 82° 39' 07". Transmitter: Spivey Mountain Rd. Equipment: ITS transmitter; Andrew antenna. Ownership: MWTV Inc.

Asheville—WMX214 (H2). Asheville (E) Wireless Cable Partnership, 55 Auburn Rd., Londonderry, NH 03053. Phone & fax: 603-434-3881. Authorized power: 10-w. Antenna: 40-ft. above ground. Lat. 35° 37' 14", long. 82° 31' 59". Transmitter: 14-1/2 Crowning Way Dr. Equipment: Comwave transmitter; Andrew antenna. Ownership: Asheville (E) Wireless Cable Partnership.

Burlington—WHK991 (E group). Visionaire Inc., 63 Lyndel Rd., Pound Ridge, NY 10576. Authorized power: 10-w. each. Antenna: 400-ft. above ground. Lat. 35° 56' 26", long. 79° 25' 40". Transmitter: Cane Creek Mountain. Equipment: Comwave transmitter; Bogner antenna. Ownership: Visionaire Inc.

Charlotte—WHT667 (E group). Wireless One of North Carolina LLC, Suite 4, 11301 Industriplex Blvd., Baton Rouge, LA 70809. Phone: 504-293-5000. Fax: 504-293-5400. Authorized power: 10-w. each. Antenna: 500-ft. above ground. Lat. 35° 15' 06", long. 80° 41' 12". Transmitter: 8050 Hood Rd. Equipment: Townsend transmitter; Bogner antenna. Ownership: Wireless One Inc.

Gastonia—WNTM681 (H group). Dynasty Partners II, Suite A-12, 2700 E. Sunset Blvd., Las Vegas, NV 89120. Authorized power: 200-w. each. Antenna: 294-ft. above ground. Lat. 36° 30' 12", long. 77° 44' 47". Transmitter: Hwy. 46, 3.2-mi. E of Vultare. Equipment: Andrew antenna. Ownership: Dynasty Partners II.

Greensboro—WMH597 (E group). Greensboro Wireless Inc. Authorized power: 10-w. each. Antenna: 199-ft. above ground. Lat. 36° 04' 11", long. 79° 47' 25". Transmitter: 301 S. Elm St. Equipment: Comwave transmitter; Bogner antenna. Ownership: Greensboro Wireless Inc.

Greensboro—WMH600 (F group). Greensboro Wireless Inc. Authorized power: 10-w. each. Antenna: 203-ft. above ground. Lat. 36° 04' 11", long. 79° 47' 25". Transmitter: 301 S. Elm St. Equipment: Comwave transmitter; Bogner antenna. Ownership: Greensboro Wireless Inc.

Greenville—WLW777 (E group). Lawrence N. Brandt, Suite 220, 3201 New Mexico Ave. NW, Washington, DC 20016. Phone: 202-363-1100. Authorized power: 10-w. each. Antenna: 499-ft. above ground. Lat. 35° 36' 58", long. 77° 22' 14". Transmitter: State Rd. 1214, 1.5-mi. N of Greenville. Equipment: Emcee transmitter; Andrew antenna. Ownership: Lawrence N. Brandt.

Greenville—WMI838 (F group). Baypoint TV Inc., 2700 Chain Bridge Rd. NW, Washington, DC 20016. Phone: 202-659-4400. Fax: 202-237-7742. Authorized power: 10-w. each. Antenna: 195-ft. above ground. Lat. 35° 36' 25", long. 77° 28' 05". Transmitter: WRQR(FM) transmitter site. Equipment: Emcee transmitter; Andrew antenna. Ownership: Baypoint TV Inc.
Leased to Wireless One of North Carolina.

Jacksonville—WMH601 (E group). National TV Co., Meeting House Farm, Lincoln, VA 22078. Phone: 703-338-3750. Fax: 703-338-4525. Authorized power: 50-w. each. Antenna: 147-ft. above ground. Lat. 34° 44' 56", long. 77° 24' 51". Transmitter: 904 Lejeune

Blvd. Equipment: Comwave transmitter; Bogner antenna. Ownership: National TV Co.

King—WNTM578 (H1). JRZ Associates, Suite 810, 1627 Eye St. NW, Washington, DC 20006. Phone: 202-293-0700. Authorized power: 10-w. Antenna: 180-ft. above ground. Lat. 36° 22' 31", long. 80° 22' 27". Transmitter: Sauratown Mountain. Equipment: Emcee transmitter; Andrew antenna. Ownership: JRZ Associates.

Morganton—WMH693 (F group). Broadcast Data Corp., Suite 247, 189 Berdan Ave., Wayne, NJ 07470. Phone: 201-831-7407. Authorized power: 10-w. each. Antenna: 385-ft. above ground. Lat. 34° 45' 09", long. 81° 43' 19". Transmitter: 2-mi. N of Morganton. Equipment: Comwave transmitter; Bogner antenna. Ownership: Broadcast Data Corp.

New Bern—WMX320 (H2). Ronald W. Benfield Partnership, 702 Hartness Rd., Statesville, NC 28677. Phone: 704-878-9004. Authorized power: 10-w. Antenna: 300-ft. above ground. Lat. 35° 00' 02", long. 76° 49' 58". Transmitter: 1.8-mi. S of Arapahoe. Equipment: ITS transmitter; Andrew antenna. Ownership: Ronald W. Benfield Partnership.

Raleigh—WMH536 (E group). Thomas Alexander & Associates. Authorized power: 10-w. each. Antenna: 992-ft. above ground. Lat. 35° 41' 07", long. 78° 43' 14". Transmitter: Intersection of 1377 & 1378. Equipment: Comwave transmitter; Andrew antenna. Ownership: Thomas Alexander & Associates.

Raleigh—WHT734 (F group). Wireless One of North Carolina LLC, Suite 4, 11301 Industriplex Blvd., Baton Rouge, LA 70809. Phone: 504-293-5000. Fax: 504-293-5400. Authorized power: 10-w. each. Antenna: 390-ft. above ground. Lat. 35° 46' 15", long. 78° 38' 23". Transmitter: Fayetteville St. Mall. Equipment: Comwave transmitter; Andrew antenna. Ownership: Wireless One Inc.

Raleigh—WNTA867 (H1). Wireless One of North Carolina LLC, Suite 4, 11301 Industriplex Blvd., Baton Rouge, LA 70809. Phone: 504-293-5000. Fax: 504-293-5400. Authorized power: 10-w. Antenna: 380-ft. above ground. Lat. 35° 46' 43", long. 78° 38' 23". Equipment: Comwave transmitter; Andrew antenna. Ownership: Wireless One Inc.

Roanoke Rapids—WMH756 (E group). National MicroVision Systems Inc. Phone: 714-752-1055. Authorized power: 10-w. each. Antenna: 500-ft. above ground. Lat. 36° 27' 38", long. 77° 33' 52". Transmitter: 1710 Birdsong St. Equipment: Comwave transmitter; Bogner antenna. Ownership: National MicroVision Systems Inc.

Rockingham—WNTK909 (H1). Wireless One of North Carolina, Suite 4, 11301 Industriplex Blvd., Baton Rouge, LA 70809. Phone: 504-293-5000. Fax: 504-293-5400. Authorized power: 10-w. Antenna: 198-ft. above ground. Lat. 34° 57' 40", long. 79° 50' 28". Transmitter: 2-mi. E of Rockingham. Equipment: ITS transmitter; Andrew antenna. Ownership: Wireless One Inc.

Rockingham—WMX943 (H2). CS Wireless Systems Inc., 1101 Summit, Plano, TX 75074. Phone: 972-730-3300. Antenna: 187-ft. above ground. Lat. 34° 57' 40", long. 79° 50' 28". Transmitter: Old River Rd., 2-mi. W of Hwy. 74. Ownership: CS Wireless Systems Inc.

Rockingham—WMX942 (H3). CS Wireless Systems Inc., 1101 Summit, Plano, TX 75074. Phone: 972-730-3300. Antenna: 187-ft. above ground. Lat. 34° 57' 40", long. 79° 50' 28". Transmitter: Old River Rd., 2-mi. W of Hwy 74. Ownership: CS Wireless Systems Inc.

Wilmington—WMI297 (E group). Belwen Inc., 7 Boyle Rd., Scotia, NY 12302. Phone: 518-393-7428. Authorized power: 50-w. each. Antenna: 357-ft. above ground. Lat. 34° 10' 30", long. 77° 56' 30". Transmitter: River Rd. Equipment: Emcee transmitter; Bogner antenna. Ownership: Belwen Inc.

Wilmington—WMI295 (F group). Broadcast Data Corp., Suite 247, 189 Berdan Ave., Wayne, NJ 07470. Phone: 201-831-7407. Authorized power: 10-w. each. Antenna: 357-ft. above ground. Lat. 34° 10' 30", long. 77° 56' 30". Transmitter: River Rd. Equipment: Comwave transmitter; Bogner antenna. Ownership: Broadcast Data Corp.

North Dakota

Amenia—WMY320 (H1). Cass County Electric Corp. Inc., Box 676, Kindred, ND 58051-0008. Phone: 701-277-4400. Fax: 701-277-4500. Authorized power: 10-w. Antenna: 496-ft. above ground. Lat. 47° 00' 48", long. 97° 11' 37". Transmitter: 1.25-mi. E of Amenia. Equipment: ITS transmitter; Andrew antenna. Ownership: Cass County Electric Corp. Inc.

Amenia—WMY312 (H2). Cass County Electric Corp. Inc., Box 676, Kindred, ND 58051-0008. Phone: 701-277-4400. Fax: 701-277-4500. Authorized power: 10-w. Antenna: 496-ft. above ground. Lat. 47° 00' 48", long. 97° 11' 37". Transmitter: 1.25-mi. E of Amenia. Equipment: ITS transmitter; Andrew antenna. Ownership: Cass County Electric Corp. Inc.

Amenia—WMY316 (H3). Cass County Electric Corp. Inc., Box 496, Kindred, ND 58051-0008. Phone: 701-277-4400. Fax: 701-277-4500. Authorized power: 10-w. Antenna: 496-ft. above ground. Lat. 47° 00' 48", long. 97° 11' 37". Transmitter: 1.25-mi. E of Amenia. Equipment: ITS transmitter; Andrew antenna. Ownership: Cass County Electric Corp. Inc.

Bismarck—WMY448 (E group). Family Entertainment Network, 30 N. Harmon, Mitchell, SD 57301. Authorized power: 10-w. each. Antenna: 183-ft. above ground. Lat. 46° 56' 31", long. 100° 41' 38". Transmitter: 10-mi. N of Bismarck. Equipment: Comwave transmitter; Andrew antenna. Ownership: Family Entertainment Network Inc.

Bismarck—WMI866 (F group). American Telecasting Inc., Suite 300, 5575 Tech Center Dr., Colorado Springs, CO 80919. Phone: 719-260-5533. Fax: 719-260-5010. Authorized power: 10-w. each. Antenna: 919-ft. above ground. Lat. 46° 56' 31", long. 100° 41' 38". Transmitter: 10-mi. N of Bismarck. Equipment: Comwave transmitter; Andrew antenna. Ownership: American Telecasting Inc.

Bowbells—WLW987 (E group). Northwest Communications Cooperative, Box 38, Ray, ND 58849. Phone: 701-568-3331. Authorized power: 50-w. each. Antenna: 441-ft. above ground. Lat. 48° 43' 58", long. 102° 28' 11". Transmitter: 10-mi. W, 5-mi. S of Bowbells. Equipment: ITS transmitter; Andrew antenna. Ownership: Northwest Communications Cooperative.

Cando—WLW986 (E group). United Telephone Mutual Aid Corp., Box 729, 411 7th Ave., Langdon, ND 58249. Phone: 701-256-5156. Fax: 701-256-5150. E-mail: utc@utma.com. Web site: http://www.utma.com. Authorized power: 50-w. each. Antenna: 491-ft. above ground. Lat. 48° 37' 58", long. 99° 06' 05". Transmitter: Hwy. 66 & Egeland Rd. Equipment: ITS transmitter; Andrew antenna. Ownership: United Telephone Mutual Aid Corp.

Cando—WLW982 (F group). United Telephone Mutual Aid Corp., Box 729, 411 7th Ave., Langdon, ND 58249. Phone: 701-256-5156. Fax: 701-256-5150. E-mail: utc@utma.com. Web site: http://www.utma.com. Authorized power: 50-w. each. Antenna: 491-ft. above ground. Lat. 48° 37' 58", long. 99° 06' 05". Transmitter: Hwy. 66 & Egeland Rd. Equipment: ITS transmitter; Andrew antenna. Ownership: United Telephone Mutual Aid Corp.

Carrington—WLW751 (E group). Central Dakota TV, 630 N. 5th St., Carrington, ND 58421. Phone: 701-674-8122. Web site: http://www.daktel.com. Authorized power: 50-w. each. Antenna: 490-ft. above ground. Lat. 47° 13' 36", long. 99° 12' 03". Transmitter: 14.5-mi. S, 3-mi. E of Carrington. Equipment: ITS transmitter; Bogner antenna. Ownership: Central Dakota TV Inc.

Carrington—WLW752 (F group). Central Dakota TV, 630 N. 5th St., Carrington, ND 58421. Phone: 701-674-8122. Web site: http://www.daktel.com. Authorized power: 50-w. each. Antenna: 490-ft. above ground. Lat. 47° 13' 36", long. 99° 12' 03". Transmitter: 14.5-mi. S, 3-mi. E of Carrington. Equipment: Emcee transmitter; Andrew antenna. Ownership: Central Dakota TV Inc.

Egeland—WNTA554 (H1). United Telephone Mutual Aid Corp., Box 729, 411 7th Ave., Langdon, ND 58249. Phone: 701-256-5156. Fax: 701-256-5150. E-mail: utc@utma.com. Web site: http://www.utma.com. Authorized power: 10-w. Antenna: 485-ft. above ground. Lat. 48° 37' 58", long. 99° 06' 05". Transmitter: W. Hwy. 66. Equipment: ITS transmitter; Andrew antenna. Ownership: United Telephone Mutual Aid Corp.

Egeland—WNTA471 (H2). United Telephone Mutual Aid Corp., Box 729, 411 7th Ave., Langdon, ND 58249. Phone: 701-256-5156. Fax: 701-256-5150. E-mail: utc@utma.com. Web site: http://www.utma.com. Authorized power: 50-w. Antenna: 485-ft. above ground. Lat. 48° 37' 58", long. 99° 06' 05". Transmitter: W. Hwy. 66. Equipment: ITS transmitter; Andrew antenna. Ownership: United Telephone Mutual Aid Corp.

Egeland—WNTC634 (H3). United Telephone Mutual Aid Corp., Box 729, 411 7th Ave., Langdon, ND 58249. Phone: 701-256-5156. Fax: 701-256-5150. E-mail: utc@utma.com. Web site: http://www.utma.com. Authorized power: 50-w. Antenna: 485-ft. above ground. Lat. 48° 37' 58", long. 99° 06' 05". Transmitter: W. Hwy. 66. Equipment: ITS transmitter; Andrew antenna. Ownership: United Telephone Mutual Aid Corp.

Fargo—WLW839 (E group). American Telecasting of Minnesota Inc., Suite 300, 5575 Tech Center Dr., Colorado Springs, CO 80919. Phone: 719-260-5533. Fax: 719-260-5010. Authorized power: 10-w. each. Antenna: 190-ft. above ground. Lat. 46° 42' 11", long. 96° 12' 57". Transmitter: Main St. Equipment: Comwave transmitter; Andrew antenna. Ownership: American Telecasting Inc.

Fargo, ND-Moorhead, MN—WLK300 (F group). Joseph W. Hubbard, 26573 Basswood, Rancho Palos Verdes, CA 90274. Phone: 310-373-6234. E-mail: hubbardtech@earthlink.net. Authorized power: 50-w. each. Antenna: 190-ft. above ground. Lat. 46° 42' 11", long. 96° 12' 57". Transmitter: 6-mi. E of Barnesville on Rte. 32. Equipment: Comwave transmitter; Andrew antenna. Ownership: Joseph W. Hubbard. Leased to American Telecasting Inc., 5575 Tech Center Dr., Suite 300, Colorado Springs, CO 80919. Phone: 719-260-5533. Fax: 719-260-5010.

Fort Ransom—WMI875 (E group). Southeast Rural Vision Enterprises Co., Box 7, Kindred, ND 58051. Phone: 701-277-4400. Fax: 701-277-4500. E-mail: shandy@kwh.com. Web site: http://www.kwh.com. Authorized power: 50-w. each. Antenna: 451-ft. above ground. Lat. 46° 31' 25", long. 97° 57' 25". Transmitter: 1.5-mi. W of Fort Ransom. Equipment: ITS transmitter; Andrew antenna. Ownership: Southeast Rural Vision Enterprises Co.

Fort Ransom—WMI879 (F group). Southeast Rural Vision Enterprises Co., Box 7, Kindred, ND 58051. Phone: 701-277-4400. Fax: 701-277-4500. E-mail: shandy@kwh.com. Web site: http://www.kwh.com. Authorized power: 50-w. each. Antenna: 451-ft. above ground. Lat. 46° 31' 25", long. 97° 57' 25". Transmitter: 1.5-mi. W of Fort Ransom. Equipment: ITS transmitter; Andrew antenna. Ownership: Southeast Rural Vision Enterprises Co.

Fort Ransom—WNTK290 (H group). Southeast Rural Vision Enterprises Co., Box 7, Kindred, ND 58051. Phone: 701-277-4400. Fax: 701-277-4500. E-mail: shandy@kwh.com. Web site: http://www.kwh.com. Authorized power: 50-w. each. Antenna: 451-ft. above ground. Lat. 46° 31' 25", long. 97° 57' 25". Transmitter: 1.5-mi. W of Fort Ransom. Equipment: ITS transmitter; Andrew antenna. Ownership: Southeast Rural Vision Enterprises Co.

Grand Forks—WLW888 (F group). Fortuna Systems Corp. Authorized power: 10-w. each. Antenna: 420-ft. above ground. Lat. 47° 52' 33", long. 97° 02' 50". Transmitter: 47th & Hwy. 81 S. Equipment: Comwave transmitter; Andrew antenna. Ownership: Fortuna Systems Corp.

Hazen—WLR508 (H1). West River Telecommunications Cooperative, Box 467, Hazen, ND 58545. Phone: 701-748-2211. Fax: 701-748-6800. Authorized power: 20-w. Antenna: 500-ft. above ground. Lat. 47° 16' 11", long. 101° 25' 39". Transmitter: 9.1-mi. WNW of Hazen. Equipment: ITS transmitter; Andrew antenna. Ownership: West River Telecommunications Cooperative.

Hazen—WLR504 (H3). West River Telecommunications Cooperative, Box 467, Hazen, ND 58545. Phone: 701-748-2211. Fax: 701-748-6800. Authorized power: 20-w. Antenna: 500-ft. above ground. Lat. 47° 16' 11", long. 101° 25' 39". Transmitter: 9.1-mi. WNW of Hazen. Equipment: ITS transmitter; Andrew antenna. Ownership: West River Telecommunications Cooperative.

Killdeer—WLW766 (E group). Consolidated Telephone Cooperative, Box 1077, Dickinson, ND 58602. Phone: 701-225-6061. Authorized power: 10-w. each. Antenna: 411-ft. above ground. Lat. 47° 28' 17", long. 102° 55' 39". Transmitter: 9-mi. N, 9-mi. W of Killdeer. Equipment: Comwave transmitter; Andrew antenna. Ownership: Consolidated Telephone Cooperative.

Killdeer—WLW765 (F group). Consolidated Telephone Cooperative, Box 1077, Dickinson, ND 58602. Phone: 701-225-6061. Authorized power: 10-w. each. Antenna: 411-ft. above ground. Lat. 47° 28' 17", long. 102° 55' 39". Transmitter: 9-mi. N, 9-mi. W of Killdeer. Equipment: ITS transmitter; Andrew antenna. Ownership: Consolidated Telephone Cooperative.

Langdon—WLW984 (E group). United Telephone Mutual Aid Corp., Box 729, 411 7th Ave., Langdon, ND 58249. Phone: 701-256-5156. Fax: 701-256-5150. E-mail: utc@utma.com. Web site: http://www.utma.com. Authorized power: 50-w. each. Antenna: 405-ft. above ground. Lat. 48° 37' 44", long. 98° 00' 35". Transmitter: 1.2-mi. E of Milton. Equipment: ITS transmitter; Andrew antenna. Ownership: United Telephone Mutual Aid Corp.

Langdon—WLW985 (F group). United Telephone Mutual Aid Corp., Box 729, 411 7th Ave., Langdon, ND 58259. Phone: 701-256-5156. Fax: 701-256-5150. E-mail: utc@utma.com. Web site: http://www.utma.com. Authorized power: 50-w. each. Antenna: 411-ft. above ground. Lat. 48° 37' 44", long. 98° 00' 35". Transmitter: 1.2-mi. E of Milton. Equipment: ITS transmitter; Andrew antenna. Ownership: United Telephone Mutual Aid Corp.

Lefor—WLW771 (E group). Consolidated Telephone Cooperative, Box 1077, Dickinson, ND 58601. Phone: 701-225-6061. Authorized power: 50-w. each. Antenna: 485-ft. above ground. Lat. 46° 41' 37", long. 102° 37' 10". Transmitter: 3-mi. W, 1-mi. N of Lefor. Equipment: ITS transmitter; Andrew antenna. Ownership: Consolidated Telephone Cooperative.

Lefor—WLW764 (F group). Consolidated Telephone Cooperative, Box 1077, Dickinson, ND 58602. Phone: 701-225-6061. Authorized power: 50-w. each. Antenna: 491-ft. above ground. Lat. 46° 41' 37", long. 102° 37' 10". Transmitter: 3-mi. W, 1-mi. N of Lefor. Equipment: ITS transmitter; Andrew antenna. Ownership: Consolidated Telephone Cooperative.

Lefor—WNTB961 (H1). Consolidated Telephone Cooperative, Box 1077, 507 S. Main, Dickinson, ND 58601. Phone: 701-225-6061. Authorized power: 50-w. Antenna: 485-ft. above ground. Lat. 46° 41' 37", long. 102° 37' 10". Transmitter: 3-mi. W, 1-mi. N of Lefor. Equipment: Comwave transmitter; Andrew antenna. Ownership: Consolidated Telephone Cooperative.

Lefor—WNTB636 (H2). Consolidated Telephone Cooperative, Box 1077, 507 S. Main St., Dickinson, ND 58601. Authorized power: 50-w. Antenna: 485-ft. above ground. Lat. 46° 41' 37", long. 102° 37' 10". Transmitter: 3-mi. W, 1-mi. N of Lefor. Equipment: Comwave transmitter; Andrew antenna. Ownership: Consolidated Telephone Cooperative.

Lefor—WNTC624 (H3). United Telephone Mutual Aid Corp., Box 729, 411 7th Ave., Langdon, ND 58249. Phone: 701-256-5156. Fax: 701-256-5150. E-mail: utc@utma.com. Web site: http://www.utma.com. Authorized power: 50-w. Antenna: 485-ft. above ground. Lat. 46° 41' 37", long. 102° 37' 10". Transmitter: 3-mi. W, 1-mi. N of Lefor. Equipment: Comwave transmitter; Andrew antenna. Ownership: United Telephone Mutual Aid Corp.

Milton—WNEZ913 (H1). United Telephone Mutual Aid Corp., Box 729, 411 7th Ave., Langdon, ND 58249. Phone: 701-256-5156. Fax: 701-256-5150. E-mail: utc@utma.com. Web site: http://www.utma.com. Authorized power: 50-w. Antenna: 405-ft. above ground. Lat. 48° 37' 44", long. 98° 00' 35". Transmitter: 1.2-mi. E of Milton. Equipment: ITS transmitter; Andrew antenna. Ownership: United Telephone Mutual Aid Corp.

Milton—WNEZ907 (H2). United Telephone Mutual Aid Corp., Box 729, 411 7th Ave., Langdon, ND 58259. Phone: 701-256-5156. Fax: 701-256-5150. E-mail: utc@utma.com. Web site: http://www.utma.com. Authorized power: 10-w. Antenna: 405-ft. above ground. Lat. 48° 37' 44", long. 98° 00' 35". Transmitter: 1.2-mi. E of Milton. Equipment: ITS transmitter; Andrew antenna. Ownership: United Telephone Mutual Aid Corp.

Milton—WNTC633 (H3). United Telephone Mutual Aid Corp., Box 729, 411 7th Ave., Langdon, ND 58259. Phone: 701-256-5156. Fax: 701-256-5150. E-mail: utc@utma.com. Web site: http://www.utma.com. Authorized power: 50-w. Antenna: 405-ft. above ground. Lat. 48° 37' 44", long. 98° 00' 35". Transmitter: 1.2-mi. E of Milton. Equipment: ITS transmitter; Andrew antenna. Ownership: United Telephone Mutual Aid Corp.

Minot—WMI313 (E group). Lawrence N. Brandt, Suite 220, 3201 New Mexico Ave. NW, Washington, DC 20016. Phone: 202-363-1100. Authorized power: 10-w. each. Antenna: 69-ft. above ground. Lat. 48° 15' 07", long. 101° 17' 44". Transmitter: 1505 N. Broadway. Equipment: Comwave transmitter; Bogner antenna. Ownership: Lawrence N. Brandt.

Minot—WLC269 (F group). Broadcast Data Corp., Suite 247, 189 Berdan Ave., Wayne, NJ 07470. Phone: 201-831-7407. Authorized power: 10-w. each. Antenna: 66-ft. above ground. Lat. 48° 15' 07", long. 101° 17' 44". Transmitter: 1505 N. Broadway. Equipment: Comwave transmitter; Bogner antenna. Ownership: Broadcast Data Corp.

Scranton—WLW770 (E group). Consolidated Telephone Cooperative, Box 1077, Dickinson, ND 58601. Phone: 701-225-6061. Authorized power: 50-w. each. Antenna: 491-ft. above ground. Lat. 46° 10' 57", long. 103° 02' 56". Transmitter: 4.5-mi. E, 2.5-mi. N of Scranton. Equipment: Comwave transmitter; Andrew antenna. Ownership: Consolidated Telephone Cooperative.

Scranton—WLW769 (F group). Slope Electric Cooperative Inc., Box 338, New England, ND 58647. Phone: 701-225-6061. Authorized power: 50-w. each. Antenna: 485-ft. above ground. Lat. 46° 10' 57", long. 103° 02' 56". Transmitter: 4.5-mi. E, 2.5-mi. N of Scranton. Equipment: Comwave transmitter; Andrew antenna. Ownership: Slope Electric Cooperative Inc.

Williston—WLW748 (E group). Northwest Communications Cooperative, Box 38, Ray, ND 58849. Phone: 701-568-3331. Authorized power: 50-w. each. Antenna: 491-ft. above ground. Lat. 48° 09' 49", long. 103° 22' 06". Transmitter: 8-mi. S of Epping. Equipment: ITS transmitter; Bogner antenna. Ownership: Northwest Communications Cooperative.

Williston—WLW968 (F group). Northwest Communications Cooperative, Box 38, Ray, ND 58849. Phone: 701-568-3331. Authorized power: 50-w. each. Antenna: 491-ft. above ground. Lat. 48° 09' 49", long. 103° 22' 06". Transmitter: 8-mi. S of Epping. Equipment: ITS transmitter; Andrew antenna. Ownership: Northwest Communications Cooperative, 45.5%; Burke-Divide Electric Cooperative Inc., 27.25%; Mountrail-Williams Electric Cooperative Inc., 27.25%.

Ohio

Cincinnati—WHT632 (E group). American Telecasting of Cincinnati Inc., Suite 300, 5575 Tech Center Dr., Colorado Springs, CO 80919. Phone: 719-260-5533. Fax: 719-260-5510. Authorized power: 100-w. each. Antenna: 830-ft. above ground. Lat. 39° 12' 01", long. 84° 31' 22". Transmitter: 6015 Winton Rd. Equipment: Emcee transmitter; Andrew antenna. Ownership: American Telecasting Inc.

Cincinnati—WHT633 (F group). American Telecasting of Cincinnati Inc., Suite 300, 5575 Tech Center Dr., Colorado Springs, CO 80919. Phone: 719-260-5533. Fax: 719-260-5510. Authorized power: 100-w. each. Antenna: 830-ft. above ground. Lat. 39° 12' 01", long. 84° 31' 22". Transmitter: 6015 Winton Rd. Equipment: Emcee transmitter; Andrew antenna. Ownership: American Telecasting Inc.

Cincinnati—WNTI621 (H2). Ivan C. Nachman, Suite 201, 113th St. N, Seminole, FL 34642. Phone: 813-392-1681. Authorized power: 10-w. Antenna: 15-ft. above ground. Lat. 39° 07' 44", long. 84° 31' 01". Transmitter: Calhoun Hall. Equipment: Emcee transmitter; Andrew antenna. Ownership: Ivan Nachman.

Cleveland—WLK310 (E group). CS Wireless Systems Inc., 1101 Summit Ave., Plano, TX 75074. Phone: 972-509-2634. Fax: 703-812-8808. Authorized power: 50-w. each. Antenna: 600-ft. above ground. Lat. 41° 23' 02", long. 81° 42' 06". Transmitter: 2861 W. Ridgewood Dr., Parma. Equipment: Emcee transmitter; Bogner antenna. Ownership: CS Wireless Systems Inc.

Cleveland—WLK306 (F group). Krisar Inc., 320 Hamilton St., Albion, NY 14411. Phone: 716-964-9121. Fax: 716-589-9091. E-mail: topperiai@aol.com. Authorized power: 50-w. each. Antenna: 1029-ft. above ground. Lat. 41° 23' 02", long. 81° 42' 06". Transmitter: 2861 W. Ridgewood Dr., Parma. Equipment: Emcee transmitter; Bogner antenna. Ownership: Krisar Inc.
Leased to Popvision (ACS Enterprises).

Columbus—WHT669 (E group). Baltimore Wireless Cable, 3511 Rue de Fleur, Columbus, OH 43221. Phone: 614-457-7045. Authorized power: 10-w. each. Antenna: 607-ft. above ground. Lat. 39° 57' 44", long. 83° 00' 08". Transmitter: 50 W. Broad St. Equipment: Emcee transmitter; Andrew antenna. Ownership: Johanna Destefano.

Columbus—WHT670 (F group). Champion Industries Inc., 300 W. Mission Dr., Chandler, AZ 85225. Phone: 602-497-5774. Authorized power: 50-w. each. Antenna: 603-ft. above ground. Lat. 39° 57' 44", long. 83° 00' 08". Transmitter: 50 W. Broad St. Equipment: ITS transmitter; Andrew antenna. Ownership: Champion Industries Inc. Sale pends to American Telecasting of Columbus Inc.

Columbus—WMH816 (H1). American Telecasting of Columbus Inc., Suite 300, 5575 Tech Center Dr., Colorado Springs, CO 80919. Phone: 719-260-5533. Fax: 719-260-5010. Authorized power: 50-w. Antenna: 573-ft. above ground. Lat. 39° 57' 44", long. 83° 00' 08". Transmitter: 50 W. Broad St. Equipment: Emcee transmitter; Andrew antenna. Ownership: American Telecasting Inc.

Columbus—WNTE288 (H2). Klondike Data Systems, 1909 Production Rd., Fort Wayne, IN 46808. Phone: 219-484-6474. Authorized power: 50-w. Antenna: 573-ft. above ground. Lat. 39° 57' 44", long. 83° 00' 08". Transmitter: 50 W. Broad St. Equipment: ITS transmitter; Andrew antenna. Ownership: Klondike Data Systems.

Dayton—WHT713 (E group). CS Wireless Systems Inc., 1101 Summit Ave., Plano, TX 75074. Phone: 972-509-2634. Fax: 703-812-8808. Authorized power: 100-w. each. Antenna: 817-ft. above ground. Lat. 39° 43' 16", long. 84° 15' 00". Transmitter: 3901 Guthrie Rd. Equipment: Emcee transmitter; Andrew antenna. Ownership: CS Wireless Systems Inc.

Dayton—WHT714 (F group). Progressive MDS & Assoc., Suite 214, 7617 Reading Rd., Cincinnati, OH 45237. Authorized power: 100-w. each. Antenna: 817-ft. above ground. Lat. 39° 43' 16", long. 84° 15' 00". Transmitter: 3901 Guthrie Rd. Equipment: Comwave transmitter; Andrew antenna. Ownership: Progressive Communications Inc.

Dayton—WNTB420 (H1). CS Wireless Systems Inc., 1101 Summit Ave., Plano, TX 75074. Phone: 972-509-2634. Fax: 703-812-8808. Authorized power: 100-w. Antenna: 879-ft. above ground. Lat. 39° 43' 16", long. 84° 15' 00". Transmitter: 3901 Guthrie Rd. Equipment: Emcee transmitter; Andrew antenna. Ownership: CS Wireless Systems Inc.

Dayton—WNEX725 (H2). CS Wireless Systems Inc., 1101 Summit Ave., Plano, TX 75074 Phone: 972-509-2634. Fax: 703-812-8808. Authorized power: 100-w. Antenna: 810-ft. above ground. Lat. 39° 43' 16", long. 84° 15' 00". Transmitter: 3901 Guthrie Rd. Equipment: Emcee transmitter; Andrew antenna. Ownership: CS Wireless Systems Inc.

Dayton—WNTB689 (H3). CS Wireless Systems Inc., 1101 Summit Ave., Plano, TX 75074 Phone: 972-509-2634. Fax: 703-812-8808. Authorized power: 100-w. Antenna: 817-ft. above ground. Lat. 39° 43' 16", long. 84° 15' 00". Transmitter: 3901 Guthrie Rd. Equipment: Emcee transmitter; Andrew antenna. Ownership: CS Wireless Systems Inc.

Lima—WMH228 (E group). Line of Site Inc., 6048 E. Kathleen Rd., Scottsdale, AZ 85254. Phone: 602-995-2711. Authorized power: 10-w. each. Antenna: 200-ft. above ground. Lat. 40° 38' 03", long. 84° 12' 29". Transmitter: 19507 State Rte. 501. Equipment: ITS transmitter; Andrew antenna. Requests change to 1108-ft. above ground; transmitter to 3.3-mi. SW of Lima. Ownership: Line of Site Inc.

Lima—WMH528 (F group). W.A.T.C.H. TV Co., 3225 W. Elm St., Lima, OH 45805. Phone: 419-999-2824. Fax: 419-999-2140. Authorized power: 10-w. each. Antenna: 200-ft. above ground. Lat. 40° 38' 03", long. 84° 12' 29". Transmitter: 19507 State Rte. 501. Equipment: ITS transmitter; Andrew antenna. Requests change to 1107-ft. above ground; transmitter to 3.3-mi. SW of Lima. Ownership: W.A.T.C.H. TV Co.

Lima—WNTH924 (H group). W.A.T.C.H. TV Co., 3225 W. Elm St., Lima, OH 45805. Phone: 419-999-2824. Fax: 419-999-2140. E-mail: watchtmk@bright.net. Authorized power: 50-w. each. Antenna: 1082-ft. above ground. Lat. 40° 38' 03", long. 84° 12' 29". Transmitter: 19507 State Rte. 501. Equipment: Comwave transmitter; Andrew antenna. Requests change to 1107-ft. above ground; transmitter to 3.3-mi. SW of Lima. Ownership: W.A.T.C.H. TV Co.

Mansfield—WLK210 (F group). Presco Corp., 4547 4th Ave. NE, Seattle, WA 98105. Phone: 206-545-0268. Authorized power: 10-w. each. Antenna: 373-ft. above ground. Lat. 40° 42' 33", long. 82° 29' 11". Transmitter: 3.6-mi. SSE of Mansfield. Equipment: ITS transmitter; Andrew antenna. Ownership: Presco Corp.

Nelsonville—WMH385 (F group). James W. Feasel, 13549 Morse Rd., Pataskala, OH 43062. Authorized power: 10-w. each. Antenna: 199-ft. above ground. Lat. 39° 26' 20", long. 82°

13' 13". Transmitter: 209 Robbins Rd. Equipment: Emcee transmitter; Andrew antenna. Ownership: James W. Feasel.

Oregon—WNTH748 (H3). Blake Twedt, 5102 Rosegreen Court, Tampa, FL 33624 Phone: 727-587-9959. Authorized power: 50-w. Antenna: 434-ft. above ground. Lat. 41° 38' 43", long. 83° 36' 22". Transmitter: 4818 Angola Rd., Toledo. Equipment: Emcee transmitter; Andrew antenna. Ownership: Blake Twedt.

Otway—WNTK907 (H group). KA3B2 Television Partnership, Suite 238, 2219 Thousand Oaks Blvd., Thousand Oaks, CA 91362. Phone: 602-898-9428. Authorized power: 10-w. each. Antenna: 117-ft. above ground. Lat. 38° 43' 19", long. 82° 59' 52". Transmitter: Southshore, Portsmouth. Equipment: Comwave transmitter; Andrew antenna. Ownership: KA3B2 Television Partnership.

Parma—WHJ951 (H2). CS Wireless Systems Inc., 1101 Summit Ave., Plano, TX 75074. Phone: 972-509-2634. Authorized power: 50-w. Antenna: 600-ft. above ground. Lat. 41° 22' 58", long. 81° 42' 07". Transmitter: 2861 W. Ridgewood Dr. Equipment: Emcee transmitter; Andrew antenna. Ownership: CS Wireless Systems Inc.

Springfield—WNTJ743 (H1). American Telecasting of Toledo Inc., Suite 300, 5575 Tech Center Dr., Colorado Springs, CO 80919. Phone: 719-260-5533. Fax: 719-260-5010. Authorized power: 50-w. Antenna: 434-ft. above ground. Lat. 41° 38' 43", long. 83° 36' 22". Transmitter: 4818 Angola Rd. Equipment: Emcee transmitter; Andrew antenna. Ownership: American Telecasting Inc.

Steubenville—WLW747 (E group). Belwen Inc., 7 Boyle Rd., Scotia, NY 12302. Phone: 518-393-7428. Authorized power: 10-w. each. Antenna: 266-ft. above ground. Lat. 40° 26' 49", long. 80° 34' 06". Transmitter: Weirton, WV. Equipment: Comwave transmitter; Bogner antenna. Ownership: Belwen Inc.

Steubenville—WMI885 (F group). Multi-Micro Inc., Suite 120, 4700 S. McClintock, Tempe, AZ 85282. Phone: 602-755-7524. Fax: 602-755-7534. Authorized power: 10-w. each. Antenna: 138-ft. above ground. Lat. 40° 23' 05", long. 80° 35' 45". Transmitter: McKim Ridge Rd., 2-mi. S of Weirton, WV. Equipment: Emcee transmitter; Andrew antenna. Ownership: Multi-Micro Inc.
Leased to Interactive Communications, 8432 Sterling, Suite 204, Irving, TX 75063. Phone: 214-915-0145.

Toledo—WHT741 (E group). Jody Barnes, Box 1102, Claremont, CA 91711. Phone: 909-625-2988. Authorized power: 50-w. each. Antenna: 434-ft. above ground. Lat. 41° 38' 43", long. 83° 36' 22". Transmitter: 4818 Angola Rd. Equipment: Emcee transmitter; Andrew antenna. Requests change to 415-ft. above ground, lat. 41° 38' 48", long. 83° 36' 22"; transmitter to 716 Westwood Ave. Ownership: Jody Barnes.

Toledo—WHT742 (F group). American Telecasting of Toledo Inc., Suite 300, 5575 Tech Center Dr., Colorado Springs, CO 80919. Phone: 719-260-5533. Fax: 719-260-5010. Authorized power: 10-w. each. Antenna: 434-ft. above ground. Lat. 41° 38' 43", long. 83° 36' 22". Transmitter: 4818 Angola Rd. Equipment: Emcee transmitter; Andrew antenna. Requests change to 415-ft. above ground, lat. 41° 38' 48", long. 83° 36' 22"; transmitter to 716 Westwood Ave. Ownership: American Telecasting Inc.

Youngstown—WMI374 (E group). American Telecasting of Youngstown, OH, Suite 300, 5575 Tech Center Dr., Colorado Springs, CO 80919. Phone: 719-260-5533. Fax: 719-260-5010. Authorized power: 10-w. each. Antenna: 259-ft. above ground. Lat. 41° 06' 00", long. 80° 39' 01". Transmitter: One Federal Plaza W. Equipment: Emcee transmitter; Andrew antenna. Ownership: American Telecasting Inc.

Youngstown—WMI899 (F group). MWTV Inc., 3401 E. Cholla St., Phoenix, AZ 85028. Phone: 602-867-7351. Authorized power: 50-w. each. Antenna: 469-ft. above ground. Lat. 41° 03' 26", long. 80° 38' 22". Transmitter: 4040 Simon Rd. Equipment: Comwave transmitter; Andrew antenna. Ownership: MWTV Inc.

Youngstown—WNTJ727 (H1). Lynn Twedt, 701 Grant St., Harvard, IL 60033. Phone: 815-943-4760. Authorized power: 50-w. Antenna: 683-ft. above ground. Lat. 41° 03' 26", long. 80° 38' 22". Transmitter: 4040 Simon Rd. Equipment: Comwave transmitter; Andrew antenna. Ownership: Lynn Twedt.

Youngstown—WNTH500 (H3). Libmot Communications Partnership, 2700 Chain Bridge Rd. NW, Washington, DC 20016. Phone: 202-966-2167. Fax: 202-237-7742. Authorized power: 50-w. Antenna: 683-ft. above ground. Lat. 41° 03' 26", long. 80° 38' 22". Transmitter: 4040 Simon Rd. Equipment: Comwave transmitter; Andrew antenna. Ownership: Libmot Communications Partnership.
Leased to American Telecasting.

Oklahoma

Ada—WMH337 (E group). Nucentrix Spectrum Resources Inc., Suite 200, 200 Chisholm Place, Plano, TX 75075. Phone: 972-423-9494. Fax: 972-423-0819. Web site: http://www.heartland-wireless.com. Authorized power: 10-w. each. Antenna: 407-ft. above ground. Lat. 34° 43' 31", long. 96° 42' 14". Transmitter: 2.75-mi. SSW of Ada. Equipment: Comwave transmitter; Andrew antenna. Ownership: Nucentrix Broadband Networks.

Ada—WMH336 (F group). Frankie Cornelison, 1948 W. Live Oak, Durant, OK 74701. Phone: 405-924-2420. Authorized power: 10-w. each. Antenna: 407-ft. above ground. Lat. 34° 43' 31", long. 96° 42' 14". Transmitter: 2.75-mi. SSW of Ada. Equipment: Comwave transmitter; Andrew antenna. Ownership: Frankie Cornelison. Sale pends to Nucentrix Broadband Networks.

Ada—WNTH577 (H1). Nucentrix Spectrum Resources Inc., Suite 200, 200 Chisholm Place, Plano, TX 75075. Phone: 972-423-9494. Fax: 972-423-0819. Authorized power: 10-w. Antenna: 407-ft. above ground. Lat. 34° 43' 31", long. 96° 42' 14". Transmitter: 2.75-mi. SSW of Ada. Equipment: Comwave transmitter; Andrew antenna. Ownership: Nucentrix Broadband Networks.

Ada—WNTH573 (H2). Frankie Cornelison, 1948 W. Live Oak, Durant, OK 74701. Phone: 405-924-2420. Authorized power: 10-w. Antenna: 407-ft. above ground. Lat. 34° 43' 31", long. 96° 42' 14". Transmitter: 2.75-mi. SSW of Ada. Equipment: Comwave transmitter; Andrew antenna. Ownership: Frankie Cornelison. Sale pends to Nucentrix Broadband Networks.

Ada—WNTH576 (H3). Bob C. Story, Box 1307, Durant, OK 74701. Phone: 405-920-0788. Authorized power: 10-w. Antenna: 400-ft. above ground. Lat. 34° 43' 31", long. 96° 42' 14". Transmitter: 2.75-mi. SSW of Ada. Equipment: Comwave transmitter; Andrew antenna. Ownership: Bob C. Story. Sale pends to Nucentrix Broadband Networks.

Broken Bow/Idabel—WMH376 (E group). Jewel B. Callaham Revocable Trust, Box 548, Broken Bow, OK 74728. Phone: 405-584-3355. Authorized power: 10-w. each. Antenna: 499-ft. above ground. Lat. 34° 12' 31", long. 94° 46' 58". Transmitter: Hairpin Mountain. Equipment: Comwave transmitter; Andrew antenna. Ownership: Jewel B. Callaham Revocable Trust.

Clayton—WLK382 (E group). Oklahoma Western Telephone Co., Box 398, Clayton, OK 74536. Authorized power: 10-w. each. Antenna: 103-ft. above ground. Lat. 34° 36' 08", long. 95° 24' 28". Transmitter: 3.2-mi. W of Flagpole Mountain. Equipment: Emcee transmitter; Andrew antenna. Ownership: Oklahoma Western Telephone Co.

Colony—WMI311 (F group). Nucentrix Spectrum Resources Inc., Suite 200, 200 Chisholm Place, Plano, TX 75075. Phone: 972-423-9494. Fax: 972-423-0819. Authorized power: 50-w. each. Antenna: 484-ft. above ground. Lat. 35° 51' 99", long. 98° 34' 36". Transmitter: 9.5-mi. W of Colony. Equipment: Comwave transmitter; Andrew antenna. Ownership: Nucentrix Broadband Networks.

Enid—WMH653 (E group). Nucentrix Spectrum Resources Inc., Suite 200, 200 Chisholm Place, Plano, TX 75075. Phone: 972-423-9494. Fax: 972-423-0819. Authorized power: 10-w. each. Antenna: 500-ft. above ground. Lat. 36° 25' 14", long. 98° 01' 12". Transmitter: 6.5-mi. W of Enid. Equipment: Emcee transmitter; Bogner antenna. Ownership: Nucentrix Broadband Networks.

Enid—WMH701 (F group). Baypoint TV Inc., 2700 Chain Bridge Rd. NW, Washington, DC 20016. Phone: 202-659-4400. Fax: 202-237-7742. Authorized power: 50-w. each. Antenna: 500-ft. above ground. Lat. 36° 25' 14", long. 98° 01' 12". Transmitter: 6.5-mi. W of Enid. Equipment: Comwave transmitter; Andrew antenna. Ownership: Baypoint TV Inc.
Leased to Nucentrix Broadband Networks, 200 Chisholm Place, Suite 200, Plano, TX 75075. Phone: 972-423-9494. Fax: 972-423-0819

Enid—WNTI252 (H group). Nucentrix Spectrum Resources Inc., Suite 200, 200 Chisholm Place, Plano, TX 75075. Phone: 972-423-9494. Fax: 972-423-0819. Authorized power: 50-w. each. Antenna: 515-ft. above ground. Lat. 36° 25' 14", long. 98° 01' 12". Transmitter: 6.5-mi. W of Enid. Equipment: Comwave transmitter; Andrew antenna. Ownership: Nucentrix Broadband Networks.

Glencoe—WNTH362 (H3). Harold Coates, 908 Biscayne, Austin, TX 78734. Authorized power: 25-w. Antenna: 854-ft. above ground. Lat. 36° 11' 12", long. 96° 50' 17". Transmitter: 6-mi. E of Stillwater. Equipment: Comwave transmitter; Andrew antenna. Ownership: Harold Coates.

Jay, OK-Decatur, AR—WLW846 (E group). Grand Telephone Co. Inc., Box 308, Jay, OK 74346. Phone: 918-253-4231. Authorized power: 50-w. each. Antenna: 495-ft. above ground. Lat. 36° 27' 17", long. 94° 46' 45". Transmitter: 1.7-mi. N of Jay. Equipment: Comwave transmitter; Andrew antenna. Ownership: Grand Telephone Co. Inc.

Lawton—WMH613 (E group). NDW Co. Inc., Box 448, Durant, OK 74702. Phone: 405-924-0900. Authorized power: 10-w. each. Antenna: 500-ft. above ground. Lat. 34° 35' 27", long. 98° 21' 10". Transmitter: 5-mi. SW of Lawton. Equipment: Emcee transmitter; Bogner antenna. Ownership: NDW Inc.
Leased to Nucentrix Broadband Networks, 200 Chisholm Place, Suite 200, Plano, TX 75075. Phone: 972-423-9494. Fax: 972-423-0819

Lawton—WMI298 (F group). Private Networks Inc., Box 023707 Brooklyn, NY 11201. Phone: 212-777-4740. Authorized power: 10-w. each. Antenna: 496-ft. above ground. Lat. 34° 36' 27", long. 98° 16' 26". Transmitter: Hwy. 7 & Trial Ridge Rd. Equipment: Comwave transmitter; Bogner antenna. Ownership: Private Networks Inc.

Lawton—WNTJ492 (H2 & H3). Nucentrix Spectrum Resources Inc., Suite 200, 200 Chisholm Place, Plano, TX 75075. Phone: 972-423-9494. Fax: 972-423-0819. Authorized power: 50-w. each Antenna: 500-ft. above ground. Lat. 34° 36' 27", long. 98° 16' 26". Transmitter: Hwy. 7 & Trail Ridge Rd. Equipment: Comwave transmitter; Andrew antenna. Ownership: Nucentrix Broadband Networks.

Lindsay—WLW828 (E group). Heartland Wireless Commercial Channels Inc., Suite 200, 200 Chisholm Place, Plano, TX 75075. Phone: 972-423-9494 Fax: 972-423-0819 Authorized power: 50-w. each. Antenna: 491-ft. above ground. Lat. 34° 37' 59", long. 97° 36' 33". Transmitter: 14.4-mi. S of Lindsay. Equipment: ITS transmitter; Andrew antenna. Ownership: Nucentrix Broadband Networks Inc.

Lindsay—WLW983 (F group). Rural Electric Cooperative Inc., Box 609, Lindsay, OK 73052. Phone: 405-756-3104. Authorized power: 50-w. each. Antenna: 491-ft. above ground. Lat. 34° 37' 59", long. 97° 36' 33". Transmitter: 14.4-mi. S of Lindsay. Equipment: ITS transmitter; Andrew antenna. Ownership: Rural Electric Cooperative Inc.

Lindsay—WNTA265 (H2). Nucentrix Spectrum Resources Inc., Suite 200, 200 Chisholm Place, Plano, TX 75075. Phone: 972-423-9494. Fax: 972-423-0819. Authorized power: 50-w. Antenna: 485-ft. above ground. Lat. 34° 37' 59", long. 97° 36' 33". Transmitter: 14.4-mi. S of Lindsay. Equipment: ITS transmitter; Andrew antenna. Ownership: Nucentrix Broadband Networks.

Lindsay—WNTD985 (H3). Nucentrix Spectrum Resources Inc., Suite 200, 200 Chisholm Place, Plano, TX 75075. Phone: 972-423-9494. Fax: 972-423-0819. Authorized power: 50-w. Antenna: 485-ft. above ground. Lat. 34° 37' 59", long. 97° 36' 33". Transmitter: 14.4-mi. S of Lindsay. Equipment: ITS transmitter. Ownership: Nucentrix Broadband Networks.

Oklahoma City—WHT683 (E group). Hinton CATV Co. Inc., Box 70, Hinton, OK 73047. Authorized power: 100-w. each. Antenna: 511-ft. above ground. Lat. 35° 28' 06", long. 97° 30' 51". Transmitter: 100 N. Broadway. Equipment: Emcee transmitter; Bogner antenna. Ownership: Hinton Telephone Co. Inc.

Oklahoma City—WHT684 (F group). American Telecasting of Oklahoma Inc., Suite 300, 5575 Tech Center Dr., Colorado Springs, CO 80919. Phone: 719-260-5533. Fax: 719-260-5010. Authorized power: 100-w. each. Antenna: 508-ft. above ground. Lat. 35° 28' 06", long. 97° 30' 51". Transmitter: 100 N. Broadway. Equipment: Emcee transmitter; Bogner antenna. Ownership: American Telecasting Inc.

Oklahoma City—WNEX724 (H2). American Telecasting of Oklahoma Inc., Suite 300, 5575 Tech Center Dr., Colorado Springs, CO 80919. Phone: 719-260-5533. Fax: 719-260-5010. Authorized power: 10-w. Antenna: 508-ft. above ground. Lat. 35° 28' 06", long. 97° 30' 51". Transmitter: 100 N. Broadway. Equipment: Andrew antenna. Ownership: American Telecasting Inc.

Oklahoma City—WNTM545 (H3). American Telecasting of Oklahoma Inc., Suite 300, 5575 Tech Center Dr., Colorado Springs, CO 80919. Phone: 719-260-5533. Fax: 719-260-5010. Authorized power: 100-w. Antenna: 513-ft. above ground. Lat. 35° 28' 06", long. 97° 30' 51". Transmitter: 100 N. Broadway. Equipment: ITS transmitter; Andrew antenna. Ownership: American Telecasting Inc.

Salina/Langley—WLW874 (F group). Salina-Spavinaw Telephone Co., Box 600, 109 Evanjoy Rd., Salina, OK 74365-0600. Authorized power: 50-w. each. Antenna: 495-ft. above ground. Lat. 36° 27' 17", long. 94° 46' 44". Transmitter: 1.7-mi. N of Jay. Equipment: Emcee transmitter; Andrew antenna. Ownership: Salina-Spavinaw Telephone Co. Inc.

Watonga—WNTI666 (H3). Nucentrix Spectrum Resources Inc., Suite 200, 200 Chisholm Place, Plano, TX 75075. Phone: 972-423-9494. Fax: 972-423-0819. Authorized power: 50-w. Antenna: 484-ft. above ground. Lat. 35° 51' 19", long. 98° 34' 36". Transmitter: 8.9-mi. W of Watonga. Equipment: Comwave transmitter; Andrew antenna. Ownership: Nucentrix Broadband Networks.

Woodward—WMH761 (E group). TV Communications Network Inc., Suite 300, 10020 E. Girard Ave., Denver, CO 80231. Phone: 303-751-2900. Fax: 303-751-1081. E-mail: kroznoy@Plinet.com. Authorized power: 50-w. each. Antenna: 348-ft. above ground. Lat. 36° 23' 26", long. 99° 20' 54". Transmitter: I-270 & 34 junction. Equipment: ITS transmitter; Andrew antenna. Ownership: Multichannel Distribution of America Inc.

Leased to Nucentrix Broadband Networks, 200 Chisholm Place, Suite 200, Plano, TX 75075. Phone: 972-423-9494. Fax: 972-423-0819

Woodward—WMX578 (H1). Nucentrix Spectrum Resources Inc., Suite 200, 200 Chisholm Place, Plano, TX 75075. Phone: 972-423-9494. Fax: 972-423-0819. Authorized power: 22-w. Antenna: 344-ft. above ground. Lat. 36° 23' 26", long. 99° 20' 54". Equipment: Comwave transmitter; Andrew antenna. Ownership: Nucentrix Broadband Networks.

Woodward—WMX579 (H2). Nucentrix Spectrum Resources Inc., Suite 200, 200 Chisholm Place, Plano, TX 75075. Phone: 972-423-9494. Fax: 972-423-0819. Authorized power: 22-w. Antenna: 487-ft. above ground. Lat. 36° 23' 20", long. 99° 20' 26". Transmitter: 4.3-mi. SE of Woodward. Equipment: Comwave transmitter; Andrew antenna. Ownership: Nucentrix Broadband Networks.

Woodward—WMX577 (H3). Nucentrix Spectrum Resources Inc., Suite 200, 200 Chisholm Place, Plano, TX 75075. Phone: 972-423-9494. Fax: 972-423-0819. Authorized power: 22-w. Antenna: 344-ft. above ground. Lat. 36° 23' 26", long. 99° 20' 54". Transmitter: 2.5-mi. SE of Woodward. Equipment: Comwave transmitter; Andrew antenna. Ownership: Nucentrix Broadband Networks.

Oregon

Bend—WLW954 (F group). American Telecasting of Bend Inc., Suite 300, 5575 Tech Center Dr., Colorado Springs, CO 80919. Phone: 719-260-5533. Fax: 719-260-5010. Authorized power: 50-w. each. Antenna: 80-ft. above ground. Lat. 44° 26' 15", long. 120° 57' 11". Transmitter: Grizzly Mountain, 10.8-mi. NNW of Bend. Equipment: Comwave transmitter; Andrew antenna. Ownership: American Telecasting Inc.

Bend—WNTJ728 (H1). American Telecasting of Bend Inc., Suite 300, 5575 Tech Center Dr., Colorado Springs, CO 80919. Phone: 719-260-5533. Fax: 719-260-5010. Authorized power: 50-w. Antenna: 57-ft. above ground. Lat. 44° 26' 17", long. 120° 57' 13". Transmitter: Grizzly Mountain, 10.8-mi. NNW of Bend. Equipment: Comwave transmitter; Andrew antenna. Ownership: American Telecasting Inc.

Bend—WLR492 (H2). American Telecasting of Bend Inc., Suite 300, 5575 Tech Center Dr., Colorado Springs, CO 80919. Phone: 719-260-5533. Fax: 719-260-5010. Authorized power: 50-w. Antenna: 80-ft. above ground. Lat. 44° 26' 15", long. 120° 57' 11". Transmitter: Grizzly Mountain, 10.8-mi. NNW of Bend. Equipment: Comwave transmitter; Andrew antenna. Ownership: American Telecasting Inc.

Medford—WLK249 (E group). American Telecasting of Medford Inc., Suite 300, 5575 Tech Center Dr., Colorado Springs, CO 80919. Phone: 719-260-5533. Fax: 719-260-5010. Authorized power: 20-w. each. Antenna: 58-ft. above ground. Lat. 42° 21' 23", long. 122° 58' 33". Transmitter: John's Peak, N of Medford. Equipment: ITS transmitter; Andrew antenna. Ownership: American Telecasting Inc.

Medford—WLK253 (F group). American Telecasting of Medford, Suite 300, 5575 Tech Center Dr., Colorado Springs, CO 80919. Phone: 719-260-5533. Fax: 719-260-5010. Authorized power: 20-w. each. Antenna: 80-ft. above ground. Lat. 42° 21' 23", long. 122° 58' 33". Transmitter: John's Peak, N of Medford. Equipment: ITS transmitter; Andrew antenna. Ownership: American Telecasting Inc.

Leased to Cardiff Communications Partners III, 2010 Jimmy Durante Blvd., Suite 224, Del Mar, CA 92014. Phone: 800-444-3410.

Medford—WNTJ458 (H group). American Telecasting of Medford Inc., Suite 300, 5575 Tech Center Dr., Colorado Springs, CO 80919. Phone: 719-260-5533. Fax: 719-260-5010. Authorized power: 20-w. each. Antenna: 80-ft. above ground. Lat. 42° 21' 23", long. 122° 58' 33". Transmitter: John's Peak, N of Medford. Equipment: ITS transmitter; Andrew antenna. Ownership: American Telecasting Inc.

Portland—WHT647 (E group). AESCO Systems Inc., 14 S. Bryn Mawr Ave., Bryn Mawr, PA 19010. Phone: 610-527-6640. Fax: 610-525-8610. Authorized power: 50-w. each. Antenna: 494-ft. above ground. Lat. 45° 29' 20", long. 122° 41' 40". Transmitter: 4700 S.W. Council Crest Dr. Equipment: Emcee transmitter; Andrew antenna. Ownership: Aesco Systems Inc.

Leased to American Telecasting of Portland Inc., 5575 Tech Center Dr., Suite 300, Colorado Springs, CO 80919. Phone: 719-260-5533. Fax: 719-260-5010

Portland—WHT648 (F group). American Telecasting of Portland Inc., Suite 300, 5575 Tech Center Dr., Colorado Springs, CO 80919. Phone: 719-260-5533. Fax: 719-260-5010. Authorized power: 50-w. each. Antenna: 494-ft. above ground. Lat. 45° 29' 20", long. 122° 41' 40". Transmitter: 4700 S.W. Council Crest Dr. Equipment: Emcee transmitter; Andrew antenna. Ownership: American Telecasting of Portland Inc.

Portland—WMX947 (H1). American Telecasting of Portland Inc., Suite 300, 5575 Tech Center Dr., Colorado Springs, CO 80919. Phone: 719-260-5533. Fax: 719-260-5010. Authorized power: 50-w. Antenna: 494-ft. above ground. Lat. 45° 29' 20", long. 122° 41' 40". Transmitter: 4700 S.W. Council Crest Dr. Equipment: Emcee transmitter; Andrew antenna. Ownership: American Telecasting of Portland Inc.

Portland—WMX948 (H2). American Telecasting of Portland Inc., Suite 300, 5575 Tech Center Dr., Colorado Springs, CO 80919. Phone: 719-260-5533. Fax: 719-260-5010. Authorized power: 50-w. Antenna: 494-ft. above ground. Lat. 45° 29' 20", long. 122° 41' 40". Transmitter: 4700 S.W. Council Crest Dr. Equipment: Emcee transmitter; Andrew antenna. Ownership: American Telecasting of Portland Inc.

Portland—WNTF447 (H3). American Telecasting of Portland Inc., Suite 300, 5575 Tech Center Dr., Colorado Springs, CO 80919. Phone: 719-260-5533. Fax: 719-260-5010. Authorized power: 50-w. Antenna: 494-ft. above ground. Lat. 45° 29' 20", long. 122° 41' 40". Transmitter: 4700 S.W. Council Crest Dr. Equipment: Emcee transmitter; Andrew antenna. Ownership: American Telecasting of Portland Inc.

Prineville—WHK953 (E group). American Telecasting of Bend Inc., Suite 300, 5575 Tech Center Dr., Colorado Springs, CO 80919. Phone: 719-260-5533. Fax: 719-260-5010. Authorized power: 50-w. each. Antenna: 80-ft. above ground. Lat. 44° 26' 15", long. 120° 57' 11". Transmitter: Grizzly Mountain, 10.8-mi. NNW of Bend. Equipment: Comwave transmitter; Andrew antenna. Ownership: American Telecasting Inc.

Leased to Central Vision, Box 5393, Bend, OR 97708-5393. Phone: 503-282-4031.

Prineville—WLR496 (H3). American Telecasting of Bend Inc., Suite 300, 5575 Tech Center Dr., Colorado Springs, CO 80919. Phone: 719-260-5533. Fax: 719-260-5010. Authorized power: 50-w. Antenna: 57-ft. above ground. Lat. 44° 26' 17", long. 120° 57' 13". Transmitter: Grizzly Mountain, 10.8-mi. NNW of Bend. Equipment: Comwave transmitter; Andrew antenna. Ownership: American Telecasting Inc.

Salem—WMI302 (F group). American Telecasting Inc., Suite 300, 5575 Tech Center Dr., Colorado Springs, CO 80919. Phone: 719-260-5533. Fax: 719-260-5010. Authorized power: 50-w. each. Antenna: 268-ft. above ground. Lat. 44° 51' 17", long. 123° 07' 17". Transmitter: Prospect Hill. Equipment: Emcee transmitter; Andrew antenna. Ownership: American Telecasting Inc.

The Dalles—WMX221 (H1). G/S The Dalles E Settlement Group, Box 6219, 60-C Washington Park, Springfield, IL 62708. Phone: 217-341-0721. Fax: 217-528-8827. Authorized power: 10-w. Antenna: 35-ft. above ground. Lat. 45° 35' 56", long. 121° 10' 29". Transmitter: 719 E. 2nd. Equipment: Comwave transmitter; Andrew antenna. Ownership: G/S The Dalles E Settlement Group.

The Dalles—WMX218 (H2). G/S The Dalles E Settlement Group, Box 6219, 60-C Washington Park, Springfield, IL 62708. Phone: 217-341-0721. Fax: 217-528-8827. Authorized power: 10-w. Antenna: 35-ft. above ground. Lat. 45° 35' 56", long. 121° 10' 29". Transmitter: 719 E. 2nd. Equipment: Comwave transmitter; Andrew antenna. Ownership: G/S The Dalles E Settlement Group.

The Dalles—WMX217 (H3). G/S The Dalles E Settlement Group, Box 6219, 60-C Washington Park, Springfield, IL 62708. Phone: 217-341-0721. Fax: 217-528-8827. Authorized power: 10-w. Antenna: 35-ft. above ground. Lat. 45° 35' 56", long. 121° 10' 29". Transmitter: 719 E. 2nd. Equipment: Comwave transmitter; Andrew antenna. Ownership: G/S The Dalles E Settlement Group.

Pennsylvania

Allentown—WLK357 (E group). Fortuna Systems Corp. Authorized power: 10-w. each. Lat. 40° 34' 01", long. 75° 26' 05". Transmitter: 550 E. Rock Dr. Equipment: Emcee transmitter; Andrew antenna. Ownership: Fortuna Systems Corp.

Altoona—WLK302 (E group). Virginia Communications Inc., Suite B1, 7621 E. Gray Rd., Scottsdale, AZ 85260. Phone: 480-596-8283. Fax: 480-596-2973. Authorized power: 10-w. each. Antenna: 176-ft. above ground. Lat. 40° 34' 03", long. 78° 26' 42". Transmitter: Wopononock Mountain, 4-mi. NW of Altoona. Equipment: Emcee transmitter; Andrew antenna. Ownership: Virginia Communications Inc.

Erie—WLK405 (E group). Marrco Communications Inc., Suite 211, 3419 Via Lido, Newport Beach, CA 92693. Authorized power: 10-w. each. Antenna: 400-ft. above ground. Lat. 42° 02' 20", long. 80° 03' 45". Transmitter: 2.25-mi. SE of Kearsarge. Equipment: Comwave transmitter; Andrew antenna. Ownership: Marrco Communications Inc.

Erie—WMH780 (F group). Krisar Inc., 320 Hamilton St., Albion, NY 14411. Phone: 716-964-9121. Fax: 716-589-9094. E-mail: topperiai@aol.com. Authorized power: 10-w. each. Antenna: 500-ft. above ground. Lat. 42° 02' 20", long. 80° 03' 45". Transmitter: 8631 Peach St. Equipment: Comwave transmitter; Bogner antenna. Ownership: Krisar Inc.

Harrisburg—WMH648 (E group). Walter Communications Inc., Suite 120, 4700 S. McClintock, Tempe, AZ 85282. Phone: 602-755-7524. Fax: 602-755-7534. Authorized power: 10-w. each. Antenna: 387-ft. above ground. Lat. 40° 15' 41", long. 76° 52' 48". Transmitter: 333 Market St. Equipment: Emcee transmitter; Andrew antenna. Ownership: Walter Communications Inc.

Leased to Wireless Advantage Inc.

Johnstown—WMH372 (E group). Belwen Inc., 7 Boyle Rd., Scotia, NY 12302. Phone: 518-393-7428. Authorized power: 10-w. each. Antenna: 90-ft. above ground. Lat. 40° 19' 36", long. 78° 50' 02". Transmitter: Near Strip Mine & Conrail. Equipment: Comwave transmitter; Bogner antenna. Ownership: Belwen Inc.

Lancaster—WLW811 (E group). Broadcast Data Corp., Suite 247, 189 Berdan Ave., Wayne, NJ 07470. Phone: 201-831-7407. Lat. 40° 02' 17", long. 76° 18' 23". Ownership: Broadcast Data Corp.

Lancaster—WMH737 (F group). Champion Industries Inc., 300 W. Mission Dr., Chandler, AZ 85224. Phone: 602-497-5774. Fax: 602-345-4450. Authorized power: 10-w. each. Antenna: 170-ft. above ground. Lat. 39° 56' 40", long. 76° 08' 16". Transmitter: Mine Ridge Mountain. Equipment: Emcee transmitter; Andrew antenna. Ownership: Champion Industries Inc.

Philadelphia—WHT643 (E group). PC License Inc., Suite 100, 2101 Wilson Blvd., Arlington, VA 22201. Phone: 703-812-8800. Fax: 703-812-8808. Authorized power: 100-w. each. Antenna: 1166-ft. above ground. Lat. 40° 02' 21", long. 75° 14' 13". Transmitter: 216 Paoli Ave. Equipment: ITS transmitter; Andrew antenna. Ownership: CAI Wireless Systems Inc.

Philadelphia—WHT644 (F group). Northwest Communications Inc., 7900 Germantown Ave., Philadelphia, PA 19118. Phone: 215-242-2017. Fax: 215-242-6061. Authorized power: 100-w. each. Antenna: 1075-ft. above ground. Lat. 40° 02' 21", long. 75° 14' 13". Transmitter: 216 Paoli Ave. Equipment: ITS transmitter; Andrew antenna. Ownership: Northwest Communications Inc.
Leased to CAI Wireless, 2510 Metropolitan Dr., Trevose, PA 19053. Phone: 215-396-9400.

Philadelphia—WNEY590 (H1). PC License Inc., Suite 100, 2101 Wilson Blvd., Arlington, VA 22201. Phone: 703-812-8800. Fax: 703-812-8808. Authorized power: 100-w. Antenna: 1075-ft. above ground. Lat. 40° 02' 21", long. 75° 14' 13". Transmitter: 216 Paoli Ave. Equipment: ITS transmitter; Andrew antenna. Ownership: CAI Wireless Systems Inc.

Philadelphia—WNET336 (H2). PC License Inc., Suite 100, 2101 Wilson Blvd., Arlington, VA 22201. Phone: 703-812-8800. Fax: 703-812-8808. Authorized power: 100-w. Antenna: 1075-ft. above ground. Lat. 40° 02' 21", long. 75° 14' 13". Transmitter: 216 Paoli Ave. Equipment: ITS transmitter; Andrew antenna. Ownership: CAI Wireless Systems Inc.

Pittsburgh—WHT645 (E group). Pittsburgh License Inc., Suite 100, 2101 Wilson Blvd., Arlington, VA 22201. Phone: 703-812-8800. Fax: 703-812-8808. Authorized power: 50-w. each. Antenna: 279-ft. above ground. Lat. 40° 26' 46", long. 79° 57' 51". Transmitter: 2850 Burthold St. Equipment: ITS transmitter; Andrew antenna. Ownership: CAI Wireless Systems Inc.

Pittsburgh—WHT646 (F group). Pittsburgh License Inc., Suite 100, 2101 Wilson Blvd., Arlington, VA 22201. Phone: 703-812-8800. Fax: 703-812-8808. Authorized power: 50-w. each. Antenna: 279-ft. above ground. Lat. 40° 26' 46", long. 79° 57' 51". Transmitter: QED Tower. Equipment: ITS transmitter; Andrew antenna. Ownership: CAI Wireless Systems Inc.

Pittsburgh—WBD240 (H2). Associated Information Services Corp., 200 Gateway Towers, Pittsburgh, PA 15202. Antenna: 531-ft. above ground. Lat. 40° 26' 31", long. 80° 00' 01". Transmitter: One Oliver Plaza. Ownership: Associated Information Services Corp.

Pittsburgh—WNTI200 (H3). Pittsburgh License Inc., Suite 100, 2101 Wilson Blvd., Arlington, VA 22201. Phone: 703-812-8800. Fax: 703-812-8808. Authorized power: 50-w. Antenna: 279-ft. above ground. Lat. 40° 26' 46", long. 79° 57' 51". Transmitter: QED Tower. Equipment: ITS transmitter; Andrew antenna. Ownership: CAI Wireless Systems Inc.

Reading—WMI314 (E group). Digital Wireless Systems Inc., 1800 N. 12th St., Reading, PA 19604. Phone: 610-921-9500. Fax: 610-921-0290. Authorized power: 20-w. each. Antenna: 140-ft. above ground. Lat. 40° 21' 14", long. 75° 53' 56". Transmitter: Skyline Dr., Mount Penn. Equipment: Emcee transmitter; Andrew antenna. Ownership: Digital Wireless Systems Inc.

Reading—WMI393 (F group). Digital Wireless Systems Inc., 1800 N. 12th St., Reading, PA 19604. Phone: 610-921-9500. Fax: 610-921-0290. Authorized power: 10-w. each. Antenna: 155-ft. above ground. Lat. 40° 21' 15", long. 75° 53' 56". Transmitter: Mount Penn. Equipment: Emcee transmitter; Andrew antenna. Ownership: Digital Wireless Systems Inc.
Leased to The Cellular Group Inc., 2155 Main St., Sarasota, FL 34237. Phone: 813-957-0065.

Scranton—WLK221 (E group). The Kenneth H. Iscol 1990 Trust for Kiva Iscol, 63 Lyndel Rd., Pound Ridge, NY 10576. Authorized power: 10-w. each. Antenna: 823-ft. above ground. Lat. 41° 10' 58", long. 75° 52' 21". Transmitter: Electronic Heights. Equipment: Emcee transmitter; Andrew antenna. Ownership: Visionaire Inc.

Scranton—WLK222 (F group). Stephen Rullman, Box 1102, Claremont, CA 91711. Phone: 909-621-1004. Authorized power: 50-w. each. Antenna: 347-ft. above ground. Lat. 41° 26' 06", long. 75° 43' 35". Transmitter: Dewey Mountain. Equipment: Emcee transmitter; Bogner antenna. Ownership: Stephen Rullman.

Sharon—WMI291 (F group). Broadcast Data Corp., Suite 247, 189 Berdan Ave., Wayne, NJ 07470. Phone: 201-831-7407. Authorized power: 10-w. each. Antenna: 93-ft. above ground. Lat. 41° 13' 57", long. 80° 30' 30". Transmitter: 30 E. State St. Equipment: Comwave transmitter; Bogner antenna. Ownership: Broadcast Data Corp.

State College—WMI366 (F group). Krisar Inc., 320 Hamilton St., Albion, NY 14411. Phone: 716-964-9121. Fax: 716-589-9094. E-mail: topperiai@aol.com. Authorized power: 10-w. each. Antenna: 160-ft. above ground. Lat. 40° 45' 08", long. 77° 45' 16". Transmitter: Little Flat. Equipment: Comwave transmitter; Bogner antenna. Ownership: Krisar Inc.
Leased to Randall Ratton.

Williamsport—WMI282 (F group). National Television Co., Meeting House Farm, Lincoln, VA 22078. Phone: 703-338-3750. Fax: 703-338-9525. Authorized power: 10-w. each. Antenna: 140-ft. above ground. Lat. 41° 14' 24", long. 77° 00' 20". Transmitter: W. 4th & William Sts. Equipment: Emcee transmitter; Bogner antenna. Ownership: National TV Co.

York—WMI365 (F group). BF Investments Inc., 7521 E. Edgemont, Scottsdale, AZ 85257. Phone: 602-992-3493. Authorized power: 10-w. each. Antenna: 120-ft. above ground. Lat. 39° 56' 25", long. 76° 41' 59". Transmitter: 2005 Queen St. Equipment: Emcee transmitter; Bogner antenna. Ownership: BF Investments Inc.

Rhode Island

Providence—WHT650 (F group). Multichannel Networks, 527 Shore Acres Dr., Mamaroneck, NY 10543-4008. Phone: 212-975-1771. Fax: 914-698-3943. E-mail: tfdelaney@cbs.com. Authorized power: 10-w. each. Antenna: 541-ft. above ground. Lat. 41° 48' 18", long. 71° 28' 24". Transmitter: Neutaconkanut Hill. Equipment: ITS transmitter; Andrew antenna. Ownership: Multichannel Networks.

Providence—WNTI210 (H1). Alice Twedt, 701 Grant St., Harvard, IL 60033. Authorized power: 10-w. Antenna: 650-ft. above ground. Lat. 41° 35' 48", long. 71° 11' 24". Transmitter: Lafayette Rd., 1.8-mi. N of Tiverton. Equipment: Emcee transmitter; Andrew antenna. Ownership: Alice Twedt.

Tiverton—WNTI314 (H3). Eastern New England License Inc., Suite 100, 2101 Wilson Blvd., Arlington, VA 22201. Phone: 703-812-8800. Fax: 703-802-8808. Authorized power: 100-w. Antenna: 900-ft. above ground. Lat. 41° 35' 48", long. 71° 11' 24". Transmitter: Lafayette Rd. Equipment: ITS transmitter; Andrew antenna. Ownership: CAI Wireless Systems Inc.

South Carolina

Augusta Road—WMY462 (H3). Blake Twedt, 5102 Rosegreen Court, Tampa, FL 33621. Phone: 727-587-9959. Authorized power: 10-w. Antenna: 650-ft. above ground. Lat. 33° 24' 29", long. 81° 50' 36". Transmitter: Pine Log Rd., Beech Island. Equipment: Emcee transmitter; Andrew antenna. Ownership: Blake Twedt.

Charleston—WHT799 (E group). Meadow Microwave, Box 8909, Aspen, CO 81612. Phone: 800-826-1997. Authorized power: 10-w. each. Antenna: 1611-ft. above ground. Lat. 32° 56' 24", long. 79° 41' 45". Transmitter: Mount Pleasant. Equipment: Comwave transmitter; Bogner antenna. Ownership: Meadow Microwave.

Charleston—WFY743 (F group). Red Charleston F Partnership, 248 King George St., Annapolis, MD 21401. Phone: 410-626-1200. Fax: 410-626-1266. Authorized power: 50-w. each. Antenna: 394-ft. above ground. Lat. 32° 48' 07", long. 80° 01' 26". Transmitter: 40 Wallace School Rd. Equipment: Comwave transmitter; Andrew antenna. Ownership: Red Charleston F Partnership.

Charleston—WMX207 (H1). Cindy L. Barnes, Box 8909, Aspen, CO 81612. Phone: 303-927-1460. Authorized power: 50-w. Antenna: 394-ft. above ground. Lat. 32° 48' 07", long. 80° 01' 26". Transmitter: 40 Wallace School Rd. Equipment: Comwave transmitter; Andrew antenna. Ownership: Cindy Barnes. Sale pends to Eagle Properties LLC.

Charleston—WMX206 (H3). Cindy L. Barnes, Box 8909, Aspen, CO 81612. Phone: 303-927-1460. Authorized power: 10-w. Antenna: 394-ft. above ground. Lat. 32° 48' 07", long. 80° 01' 26". Transmitter: 40 Wallace School Rd. Equipment: Comwave transmitter; Andrew antenna. Ownership: Cindy Barnes. Sale pends to Eagle Properties LLC.

Columbia—WMH508 (E group). Morris Communications Inc., 1508 W. Blue Ridge Dr., Greenville, SC 29611. Authorized power: 10-w. each. Antenna: 264-ft. above ground. Lat. 34° 08' 39", long. 81° 03' 25". Transmitter: Hwy. 38, 0.75-mi. W of U.S. 321. Equipment: Emcee transmitter; Andrew antenna. Ownership: Morris Communications Inc.

Columbia—WMH501 (F group). Sun Multi-Channel MDS Inc., Suite 500, 3200 Cherry Creek South Dr., Denver, CO 80209. Authorized power: 10-w. each. Antenna: 747-ft. above ground. Lat. 34° 03' 23", long. 80° 58' 49". Transmitter: 5807 Shakespeare Rd. Equipment: Emcee transmitter; Bogner antenna. Ownership: Sun Multi-Channel MDS Inc.

Florence—WMI309 (F group). Lawrence N. Brandt, Suite 220, 3201 New Mexico Ave. NW, Washington, DC 20016. Phone: 202-363-1100. Authorized power: 10-w. each. Antenna: 796-ft. above ground. Lat. 34° 16' 46", long. 79° 44' 37". Transmitter: 5-mi. NE of Florence. Equipment: Comwave transmitter; Bogner antenna. Ownership: Lawrence N. Brandt.

Georgetown—WMH616 (F group). Southern Wireless Co. Inc., Box 1998, Georgetown, SC 29442. Phone: 803-546-2200. Fax: 803-527-2314. Authorized power: 10-w. each. Antenna: 104-ft. above ground. Lat. 33° 25' 06", long. 79° 17' 04". Transmitter: Junction of Rtes. 701 & 51. Equipment: ITS transmitter; Andrew antenna. Ownership: Southern Wireless Co. Inc.

Georgetown—WMX235 (H2). James Necaise, Box 1998, Georgetown, SC 29442. Phone: 803-546-2200. Fax: 803-527-2314. Authorized power: 10-w. Antenna: 100-ft. above ground. Lat. 33° 25' 06", long. 79° 17' 04". Transmitter: Junction of Rtes. 701 & 51. Equipment: ITS transmitter; Andrew antenna. Ownership: James Necaise.

Georgetown—WMX234 (H3). James Necaise, Box 1998, Georgetown, SC 29442. Phone: 803-546-2200. Fax: 803-527-2314. Authorized power: 10-w. Antenna: 100-ft. above ground. Lat. 33° 25' 06", long. 79° 17' 04". Transmitter: Junction of Rtes. 701 & 51. Equipment: ITS transmitter; Andrew antenna. Ownership: Southern Wireless Co. Inc.

Greenville—WLW738 (E group). TCI Acquisition Corp., 975-H Industrial Rd., San Carlos, CA 94070. Phone: 415-631-9190. Authorized power: 10-w. each. Antenna: 245-ft. above ground. Lat. 34° 56' 26", long. 82° 24' 38". Transmitter: Paris Mountain. Equipment: Emcee transmitter; Andrew antenna. Ownership: TCI Acquisition Corp.

Greenville—WNTH789 (H1). BF Investments Inc., 7521 E. Edgemont, Scottsdale, AZ 85257. Phone: 602-994-3493. Authorized power: 20-w. Antenna: 245-ft. above ground. Lat. 34° 56' 26", long. 82° 24' 38". Transmitter: Paris Mountain. Equipment: ITS transmitter; Andrew antenna. Ownership: BF Investments Inc.

Myrtle Beach—WLK351 (E group). TV Communications Network Inc., Suite 300, 10020 E. Girard, Denver, CO 80231. Phone: 303-751-2900. Fax: 303-751-1081. E-mail: kroznoy@Plinet.com. Authorized power: 10-w. each. Antenna: 100-ft. above ground. Lat. 33° 50' 58", long. 79° 04' 11". Transmitter: 1721 Hwy. 501 W. Equipment: ITS transmitter; Bogner antenna. Ownership: Multichannel Distribution of America Inc.

Myrtle Beach—WLW977 (F group). SE/USA Broadcasting Co. Inc., 201 Fletcher Ave., Sarasota, FL 34237. Phone: 813-329-6000. Fax: 813-329-6030. E-mail: bobsr@dlr.com. Authorized power: 10-w. each. Antenna: 150-ft. above ground. Lat. 33° 42' 58", long. 78° 52' 32". Transmitter: 29th Ave., North Extension. Equipment: Emcee transmitter; Andrew antenna. Ownership: SE/USA MDS Co.

Orangeburg—WHT952 (E group). MMDS Orangeburg Inc., 7711 Wessex Lane, Columbia, SC 29223. Authorized power: 10-w. each. Antenna: 305-ft. above ground. Lat. 33° 31' 02", long. 80° 52' 09". Transmitter: Hwy. 178 Bypass. Equipment: Townsend transmitter; Andrew antenna. Ownership: MMDS Orangeburg Inc.

South Dakota

Aberdeen—WLK408 (E group). Northern Rural Cable TV Cooperative Inc., Box 488, Bath, SD 57427. Phone: 605-225-0310. Fax: 605-225-1684. Authorized power: 50-w. each. Antenna: 488-ft. above ground. Lat. 45° 27' 57", long. 98° 20' 08". Transmitter: 0.25-mi. W of Bath. Equipment: Andrew antenna. Ownership: Northern Electric Cooperative Inc.

Aberdeen—WLK409 (F group). Northern Rural Cable TV Cooperative Inc., Box 488, Bath, SD 57427. Phone: 605-225-0310. Fax: 605-225-1684. Authorized power: 50-w. each. Antenna: 488-ft. above ground. Lat. 45° 27' 57", long. 98° 20' 08". Transmitter: 0.25-mi. W of Bath. Equipment: Andrew antenna. Ownership: Northern Electric Cooperative Inc.

Aberdeen—WNEX765 (H2). Northern Rural Cable TV Cooperative, Box 488, Bath, SD 57427. Phone: 605-225-0310. Fax: 605-225-1684. Authorized power: 50-w. Antenna: 489-ft. above ground. Lat. 45° 27' 57", long. 98° 20' 08". Transmitter: 1.25-mi W of Bath. Equipment: Andrew antenna. Ownership: Northern Electric Cooperative Inc.

Aberdeen—WNTI409 (H3). Northern Rural Cable TV Cooperative Inc., Box 488, Bath, SD 57427. Phone: 605-225-0310. Fax: 605-225-1684. Authorized power: 50-w. Antenna: 488-ft. above ground. Lat. 45° 27' 57", long. 98° 20' 08". Transmitter: 0.25-mi W of Bath. Equipment: Emcee transmitter; Andrew antenna. Ownership: Northern Rural Cable TV Cooperative.

Bath—WNEX688 (H1). Northern Electric Cooperative Inc., Box 457, Bath, SD 57427. Phone: 605-225-0310. Fax: 605-225-1684. Authorized power: 50-w. Antenna: 488-ft. above ground. Lat. 45° 27' 57", long. 98° 20' 08". Transmitter: 0.25-mi. W of Bath. Equipment: Andrew antenna. Ownership: Northern Electric Cooperative Inc.

Colman—WHI959 (F group). Sioux Valley Rural Television Inc., Box 20, Colman, SD 57017. Phone: 605-534-3241. Fax: 605-534-3522. E-mail: jbrick@svswe.com. Web Site: http://www.svtv.com. Authorized power: 50-w. each. Antenna: 404-ft. above ground. Lat. 43° 59' 31", long. 96° 46' 11". Transmitter: 1-mi. NNW of I-29 & State Rte. 34 intersection. Equipment: Emcee transmitter; Andrew antenna. Ownership: Sioux Valley Rural Television Inc.

Colman—WNEX781 (H1). Sioux Valley Rural Television Inc., Box 20, Colman, SD 57017. Phone: 605-534-3241. Fax: 605-534-3522. E-mail: jbrick@svswe.com. Web site: http://www.svtv.com. Authorized power: 50-w. Antenna: 404-ft. above ground. Lat. 43° 59' 31", long. 96° 46' 11". Transmitter: 1-mi. NNW of I-29 & State Rte. 34 intersection. Equipment: Emcee transmitter; Andrew antenna. Ownership: Sioux Valley Rural Television Inc.

Colman—WNEX689 (H2). Sioux Valley Rural Television Inc., Box 20, Colman, SD 57017. Phone: 605-534-3241. Fax: 605-534-3522. E-mail: jbrick@svswe.com. Web site: http://www.svtv.com. Authorized power: 50-w. Antenna: 404-ft. above ground. Lat. 43° 59' 31", long. 96° 46' 10". Transmitter: 1-mi. NNW of I-29 & State Rte. 34 intersection. Equipment: Emcee transmitter; Andrew antenna. Ownership: Sioux Valley Rural Television Inc.

Colman—WNTA301 (H3). Sioux Valley Rural Television Inc., Box 20, Colman, SD 57017. Phone: 605-534-3241. Fax: 605-534-3522. E-mail: jbrick@svswe.com. Web site: http://www.svtv.com. Authorized power: 50-w. Antenna: 404-ft. above ground. Lat. 43° 59' 31", long. 96° 46' 10". Transmitter: 1-mi. NNW of I-29 & State Rte. 34 intersection. Equipment: Emcee transmitter; Andrew antenna. Ownership: Sioux Valley Rural Television Inc.

Mitchell—WGW419 (E group). Communications Enterprises, Box 67, S. Main St., Woonsocket, SD 57385-0067. Phone: 605-796-4411. Authorized power: 10-w. each. Lat. 43° 30' 40", long. 98° 15' 51". Transmitter: 12-mi. S of I-90, Mount Vernon. Equipment: Emcee transmitter; Andrew antenna. Ownership: Communications Enterprises Inc.

Mitchell—WHD364 (F group). Communications Enterprises Inc., Box 67, S. Main St., Woonsocket, SD 57385-0067. Phone: 605-796-4411. Authorized power: 10-w. each. Antenna: 160-ft. above ground. Lat. 43° 30' 40", long. 98° 15' 51". Transmitter: 12-mi. S of I-90, Mount Vernon. Equipment: Emcee transmitter; Andrew antenna. Ownership: Communications Enterprises Inc.

Mobridge—WMY424 (E group). John C. Landy, 11611 Harbor View Dr., Cleveland, OH 44102. Authorized power: 10-w. each. Antenna: 200-ft. above ground. Lat. 45° 32' 20", long. 100° 22' 08". Transmitter: 4.6-mi. W of Mobridge. Equipment: Comwave transmitter; Bogner antenna. Ownership: John C. Landy.

Pierre—WMX354 (H2). TMT Partnership, 25 Alexander Ave., Carlisle, PA 17013. Phone: 717-243-7893. Authorized power: 10-w. Antenna: 140-ft. above ground. Lat. 44° 21' 30", long. 100° 23' 20". Transmitter: 1000-ft. S of U.S. 14 & Cedar Hill. Equipment: ITS transmitter; Bogner antenna. Ownership: TMT Partnership.

Pierre—WMX353 (H3). TMT Partnership, 25 Alexander Ave., Carlisle, PA 17013. Phone: 717-243-7893. Authorized power: 10-w. Antenna: 140-ft. above ground. Lat. 44° 21' 30", long. 100° 23' 20". Transmitter: 1000-ft. S of U.S. 14 & Cedar Hill. Equipment: ITS transmitter; Bogner antenna. Ownership: TMT Partnership.

Rapid City—WMI825 (E group). American Telecasting of Rapid City Inc., Suite 300, 5575 Tech Center Dr., Colorado Springs, CO 80919. Phone: 719-260-5533. Fax: 719-260-5010. Authorized power: 20-w. each. Antenna: 300-ft. above ground. Lat. 44° 02' 48", long. 103° 14' 46". Transmitter: Skyline Dr., 2-mi. S of Rapid City. Equipment: ITS transmitter; Bogner antenna. Ownership: American Telecasting Inc.

Rapid City—WMI884 (F group). American Telecasting of Rapid City Inc., Suite 300, 5575 Tech Center Dr., Colorado Springs, CO 80919. Phone: 719-260-5533. Fax: 719-260-5010. Authorized power: 20-w. each. Antenna: 300-ft. above ground. Lat. 44° 02' 48", long. 103° 14' 46". Transmitter: Skyline Dr., 2-mi. S of Rapid City. Equipment: ITS transmitter; Bogner antenna. Ownership: American Telecasting Inc.

Rapid City—WMH817 (H1). American Telecasting of Rapid City Inc., Suite 300, 5575 Tech Center Dr., Colorado Springs, CO 80919. Phone: 719-260-5533. Fax: 719-260-5010. Authorized power: 10-w. Antenna: 500-ft. above ground. Lat. 44° 02' 48", long. 103° 14' 46". Transmitter: 2-mi. S of Rapid City. Equipment: Comwave transmitter; Bogner antenna. Ownership: American Telecasting Inc.

Rapid City—WMH813 (H2). American Telecasting of Rapid City Inc., Suite 300, 5575 Tech Center Dr., Colorado Springs, CO 80919. Phone: 719-260-5533. Fax: 719-260-5010. Authorized power: 10-w. Antenna: 500-ft. above ground. Lat. 44° 02' 48", long. 103° 14' 46". Transmitter: 2-mi. S of Rapid City. Equipment: Comwave transmitter; Bogner antenna. Ownership: American Telecasting Inc.

Sioux Falls—WMX358 (E group). Sioux Valley Rural Television Inc., Box 216, Colman, SD 57017. Phone: 605-534-3241. Fax: 605-534-3522. E-mail:jbrick@svswe.com. Web site:http://www.svtv.com. Authorized power: 50-w. each. Antenna: 622-ft. above ground. Lat. 43° 30' 11", long. 96° 34' 38". Transmitter: 1.5-mi. SW of Rowena. Equipment: Emcee transmitter; Andrew antenna. Ownership: Sioux Valley Rural Television Inc.

Sioux Falls—WMX344 (F group). Sioux Valley Rural Television Inc., Box 216, Colman, SD 57017. Phone: 605-534-3241. Fax: 605-534-3522. E-mail: jbrick@svswe.com. Web site: http://www.svtv.com. Authorized power: 50-w. each. Antenna: 622-ft. above ground. Lat. 43° 30' 11", long. 96° 34' 38". Transmitter: 1.5-mi. SW of Rowena. Equipment: Emcee transmitter; Andrew antenna. Ownership: Sioux Valley Rural Television Inc.

Sioux Falls—WMX347 (H1). Sioux Valley Rural Television Inc., Box 216, Colman, SD 57017. Phone: 605-534-3241. Fax: 605-534-3522. E-mail:jbrick@svswe.com. Web site:http://www.svtv.com. Authorized power: 50-w. Antenna: 622-ft. above ground. Lat. 43° 30' 11", long. 96° 34' 38". Transmitter: 1.5-mi. SW of Rowena. Equipment: Emcee transmitter; Andrew antenna. Ownership: Sioux Valley Rural Television Inc.

Sioux Falls—WMX348 (H2). Sioux Valley Rural Television Inc., Box 216, Colman, SD 57017. Phone: 605-534-3241. Fax: 605-534-3522. E-mail:jbrick@svswe.com. Web site:http://www.svtv.com. Authorized power: 50-w. Antenna: 622-ft. above ground. Lat. 43° 30' 11", long. 96° 34' 38". Transmitter: 1.5-mi. SW of Rowena. Equipment: Emcee transmitter; Andrew antenna. Ownership: Sioux Valley Rural Television Inc.

Sioux Falls—WMX349 (H3). Sioux Valley Rural Television Inc., Box 216, Colman, SD 57017. Phone: 605-534-3241. Fax: 605-534-3522. E-mail:jbrick@svswe.com. Web site:http://www.svtv.com. Authorized power: 50-w. Antenna: 622-ft. above ground. Lat. 43° 30' 11", long. 96° 34' 38". Transmitter: 1.5-mi. SW of Rowena. Equipment: Emcee transmitter; Andrew antenna. Ownership: Sioux Valley Rural Television Inc.

Sisseton—WLK365 (E group). North East TV Cooperative Inc., Box 850, Watertown, SD 57201. Phone: 605-886-5706. Authorized power: 10-w. each. Antenna: 405-ft. above ground. Lat. 45° 39' 50", long. 97° 10' 08". Transmitter: 5.8-mi. W of Sisseton. Equipment: ITS transmitter; Bogner antenna. Ownership: HD Electric.

Sisseton—WLK366 (F group). North East TV Cooperative Inc., Box 850, Watertown, SD 57201. Phone: 605-886-5706. Authorized power: 10-w. each. Antenna: 405-ft. above ground. Lat. 45° 39' 50", long. 97° 10' 08". Transmitter: 5.8-mi. W of Sisseton. Equipment: ITS transmitter; Bogner antenna. Ownership: HD Electric.

Watertown—WLK330 (E group). North East TV Cooperative Inc., Box 850, Watertown, SD 57201. Phone: 605-886-5706. Authorized power: 10-w. each. Antenna: 412-ft. above ground. Lat. 44° 55' 15", long. 96° 53' 33". Transmitter: 1-mi. E, 2.5-mi. N of Watertown. Equipment: Emcee transmitter; Bogner antenna. Ownership: HD Electric.

Watertown—WLK327 (F group). North East TV Cooperative Inc., Box 850, Watertown, SD 57201. Phone: 605-886-5706. Authorized power: 50-w. each. Antenna: 405-ft. above ground. Lat. 44° 55' 15", long. 96° 53' 33". Transmitter: 1-mi. E, 2.25-mi. N of Watertown. Equipment: ITS transmitter; Bogner antenna. Ownership: HD Electric.

Willow Lake—WLK323 (E group). North East TV Cooperative Inc., Box 850, Watertown, SD 57201. Phone: 605-886-5706. Authorized power: 50-w. each. Antenna: 1840-ft. above ground. Lat. 44° 35' 24", long. 97° 40' 45". Transmitter: 2.5-mi. S, 2.25-mi. W of Willow Lake. Equipment: ITS transmitter; Bogner antenna. Ownership: HD Electric.

Willow Lake—WLK319 (F group). North East TV Cooperative Inc., Box 850, Watertown, SD 57201. Phone: 605-886-5706. Authorized power: 50-w. each. Antenna: 1840-ft. above ground. Lat. 44° 35' 24", long. 97° 40' 45". Transmitter: 2.5-mi. S, 2.25-mi. W of Willow Lake. Equipment: ITS transmitter; Bogner antenna. Ownership: HD Electric.

Yankton—WLK384 (E group). Sioux Valley Rural Television Inc., Box 20, Colman, SD 57017. Phone: 605-534-3241. Fax: 605-534-3522. E-mail: jbrick@svcwe.com. Web site: http://www.svtv.com. Authorized power: 50-w. each. Antenna: 190-ft. above ground. Lat. 43° 14' 38", long. 97° 22' 38". Transmitter: U.S. Hwy. 18, 2-mi. E of Hwy. 81. Equipment: Emcee transmitter; Bogner antenna. Ownership: Sioux Valley Rural Television Inc.

Yankton—WLK328 (F group). Sioux Valley Rural Television Inc., Box 20, Colman, SD 57017. Phone: 605-534-3241. Fax: 605-534-3522. E-mail: jbrick@svcwe.com. Web site: http://www.svtv.com. Authorized power: 50-w. each. Antenna: 190-ft. above ground. Lat. 43° 14' 38", long. 97° 22' 38". Transmitter: U.S. Hwy. 18, 2-mi. E of Hwy. 81. Equipment: Emcee transmitter; Bogner antenna. Ownership: Sioux Valley Rural Television Inc.

Yankton—WNTK311 (H group). Sioux Valley Rural Television Inc., Box 20, Colman, SD 57017. Phone: 605-534-3241. Fax: 605-534-3522. E-mail: jbricksvcwe.com. Web site: http://www.svtv.com. Authorized power: 50-w. each. Antenna: 190-ft. above ground. Lat. 43° 14' 38", long. 97° 22' 38". Transmitter: E of Hwys. 81 & 18 junction. Equipment:

Comwave transmitter; Andrew antenna. Ownership: Sioux Valley Rural Television Inc.

Tennessee

Chattanooga—WMI898 (F group). Greater Media MDS Inc., Box 1059, 2 Kennedy Blvd., East Brunswick, NJ 08816. Phone: 732-247-6161. Fax: 732-247-4956. Authorized power: 50-w. each. Antenna: 309-ft. above ground. Lat. 35° 12' 34", long. 85° 16' 39". Transmitter: 12-mi. N of Chattanooga. Equipment: Emcee transmitter; Andrew antenna. Ownership: Greater Media Inc.

Leased to Chattanooga Wireless Communications, 7800 113th St. N, Suite 201, Seminole, FL 34642.

Chattanooga—WNTJ389 (H1). Maddox Nachman Partnership, Suite 201, 7800 113th St. N, Seminole, FL 34642. Authorized power: 10-w. Antenna: 180-ft. above ground. Lat. 35° 09' 39", long. 85° 18' 53". Transmitter: 1.75-mi. NE of Chattanooga. Equipment: Emcee transmitter; Andrew antenna. Ownership: Maddox Nachman Partnership.

Chattanooga—WNTJ433 (H2). John Dudeck, 11672 Harborside Court, Largo, FL 33773. Authorized power: 10-w. Antenna: 180-ft. above ground. Lat. 35° 09' 39", long. 85° 18' 53". Transmitter: 1.75-mi. NE of Chattanooga. Equipment: Emcee transmitter; Andrew antenna. Ownership: John Dudeck

Clarksville—WLW966 (E group). Virginia Communications Inc., Suite B1, 7621 E. Gray Rd., Scottsdale, AZ 85260. Phone: 480-596-8283. Fax: 480-596-2973. Authorized power: 20-w. each. Antenna: 480-ft. above ground. Lat. 36° 26' 00", long. 87° 25' 22". Transmitter: Hackberry-Clarksville. Equipment: Comwave transmitter; Andrew antenna. Ownership: Virginia Communications Inc.

Clarksville—WLW969 (F group). Virginia Communications Inc., Suite B1, 7621 E. Gray Rd., Scottsdale, AZ 85260. Phone: 480-596-8283. Fax: 480-596-2973. Authorized power: 20-w. each Antenna: 480-ft. above ground. Lat. 36° 26' 00", long. 87° 25' 22". Transmitter: Hackberry-Clarksville. Equipment: Comwave transmitter; Andrew antenna. Ownership: Virginia Communications Inc.

Clarksville—WNTJ418 (H1). Digital Wireless Systems Inc., Box 15065, Reading, PA 19612-5065. Phone: 610-921-9500. Authorized power: 20-w. Antenna: 480-ft. above ground. Lat. 36° 26' 00", long. 87° 25' 22". Transmitter: 0.7-mi. S of Vernon Creek & Addway, Hackberry. Equipment: Comwave transmitter; Andrew antenna. Ownership: Digital Wireless Systems Inc.

Clarksville—WNTF896 (H2). Virginia Communications Inc., Suite B1, 7621 E. Gray Rd., Scottsdale, AZ 85260. Phone: 480-596-8283. Fax: 480-596-2973. Authorized power: 20-w. Antenna: 480-ft. above ground. Lat. 36° 26' 00", long. 87° 25' 22". Transmitter: Hackberry-Clarksville. Equipment: Comwave transmitter; Andrew antenna. Ownership: Virginia Communications Inc.

Clarksville—WNTF893 (H3). Digital Wireless Systems Inc., Box 15065, Reading, PA 19612-5065. Phone: 610-921-9500. Authorized power: 20-w. Antenna: 480-ft. above ground. Lat. 36° 26' 00", long. 87° 25' 22". Transmitter: 7-mi. S of Vernon Creek & Addway. Equipment: Comwave transmitter; Andrew antenna. Ownership: Digital Wireless Systems Inc.

Fairmont—WMI855 (E group). Wireless One PCS Inc., Suite 400, 2506 Lakeland Dr., Jackson, MS 39208. Phone: 601-933-6879. Authorized power: 20-w. each. Antenna: 309-ft. above ground. Lat. 35° 12' 34", long. 85° 16' 39". Transmitter: 3-mi. NE of Fairmont. Equipment: Emcee transmitter; Andrew antenna. Ownership: Wireless One Inc.

Fairmont—WNTJ382 (H3). Blake Twedt, 5102 Rosegreen Court Tampa, FL 33629. Phone: 727-587-9959. Authorized power: 10-w. Antenna: 180-ft. above ground. Lat. 35° 09' 39", long. 85° 18' 53". Transmitter: 1.75-mi. NE of Chattanooga. Equipment: Emcee transmitter; Andrew antenna. Ownership: Blake Twedt.

Johnson City—WMH469 (E group). Grand Alliance Johnson City (E) Partnership, Suite 660, 1920 N St. NW, Washington, DC 20036. Phone: 202-887-0600. Authorized power: 10-w. each Antenna: 160-ft. above ground. Lat. 36° 26' 04", long. 82° 08' 06". Transmitter: Holston Mountain. Equipment: Emcee transmitter; Bogner antenna. Ownership: Macro Distribution Systems Inc.

Knoxville—WLW953 (E group). Belwen Inc., 7 Boyle Rd., Scotia, NY 12302. Phone: 518-393-7428. Authorized power: 50-w. each. Antenna: 456-ft. above ground. Lat. 36° 00' 10", long. 83° 56' 40". Transmitter: 331 Sharp's Ridge Rd. Equipment: ITS transmitter; Bogner antenna. Ownership: Belwen Inc.

Knoxville—WHT720 (F group). Disney Enterprises Inc., 500 S. Buena Vista St., Burbank, CA 91521. Phone: 818-560-1000. Authorized power: 10-w. each. Antenna: 456-ft. above ground. Lat. 36° 00' 10", long. 83° 56' 40". Transmitter: 331 Sharp's Ridge Rd. Equipment: Comwave transmitter; Bogner antenna. Ownership: Disney Enterprises Inc.

Knoxville—WNTF779 (H2). George W. Bott, 320 Hamilton St., Albion, NY 14411-9383. Phone: 518-374-0651. Authorized power: 50-w. Antenna: 456-ft. above ground. Lat. 36° 00' 10", long. 83° 56' 40". Transmitter: 331 Sharp's Ridge Rd. Equipment: Comwave transmitter; Bogner antenna. Ownership: George W. Bott

Knoxville—WNTE475 (H3). Woodrow A. Baker, 13979 Allen Rd., Albion, NY 14411. Phone: 716-589-9295. Authorized power: 50-w. Antenna: 460-ft. above ground. Lat. 36° 00' 10", long. 83° 56' 40". Transmitter: 331 Sharp's Ridge Rd. Equipment: Comwave transmitter; Bogner antenna. Ownership: Woodrow A. Baker.

Memphis—WMI883 (E group). Wireless One PCS Inc., Suite 400, 2506 Lakeland Dr., Jackson, MS 39208. Phone: 601-933-6871. Authorized power: 10-w. each. Antenna: 412-ft. above ground. Lat. 35° 06' 45", long. 89° 53' 32". Transmitter: 5100 Poplar Ave. Equipment: Emcee transmitter; Andrew antenna. Ownership: Wireless One Inc.

Memphis—WHT728 (F group). Red Memphis F Partnership, 248 King George St., Annapolis, MD 21401. Phone: 410-626-1200. Fax: 410-626-1266. Authorized power: 10-w. each. Antenna: 412-ft. above ground. Lat. 35° 06' 45", long. 89° 53' 32". Transmitter: 5100 Poplar Ave. Equipment: Emcee transmitter; Andrew antenna. Ownership: Red Memphis F Partnership.

Memphis—WNTH952 (H2). Wireless One PCS Inc., Suite 400, 2506 Lakeland Dr., Jackson, MS 39208. Phone: 601-933-6879. Authorized power: 10-w. Antenna: 412-ft. above ground. Lat. 35° 06' 45", long. 89° 53' 32". Transmitter: 100 N. Main St. Equipment: Comwave transmitter; Andrew antenna. Ownership: Wireless One Inc.

Memphis—WNTI565 (H3). Wireless One PCS Inc., Suite 400, 2506 Lakeland Dr., Jackson, MS 39208. Phone: 601-933-6879. Authorized power: 10-w. Antenna: 500-ft. above ground. Lat. 35° 08' 53", long. 90° 03' 05". Transmitter: 100 N. Main St. Equipment: Comwave transmitter; Andrew antenna. Ownership: Wireless One Inc.

Mount Pleasant—WNTM643 (H2). Dynasty Partners II, Suite A-12, 2700 E. Sunset Rd., Las Vegas, NV 89120. Phone: 702-597-9875. Authorized power: 200-w. Antenna: 100-ft. above ground. Lat. 35° 31' 15", long. 87° 12' 30". Transmitter: Glass St. Equipment: Comwave transmitter; Andrew antenna. Ownership: Dynasty Partners II.

Mount Pleasant—WNTM644 (H3). Dynasty Partners II, Suite A-12, 2700 E. Sunset Rd., Las Vegas, NV 89120. Phone: 702-597-9875. Authorized power: 200-w. Antenna: 100-ft. above ground. Lat. 35° 31' 15", long. 87° 12' 30". Transmitter: Glass St. Equipment: Comwave transmitter; Andrew antenna. Ownership: Dynasty Partners II.

Nashville—WHT680 (E group). Jack G. Hubbard, 8793 Ranch Dr., Chesterland, OH 44026. Phone & Fax: 216-729-7282. Authorized power: 10-w. each. Antenna: 1550-ft. above ground. Lat. 35° 55' 22", long. 86° 42' 38". Transmitter: 3.2-mi. SW of Nolensville. Equipment: Comwave transmitter; Andrew antenna. Ownership: Jack G. Hubbard.

Leased to Nashville Wireless Cable TV, Inc., 475 Metroplex Dr., Suite 408, Nashville, TN 37211. Phone: 615-333-9288.

Nashville—WHT679 (F group). Presco Corp., 4547 4th Ave. NE, Seattle, WA 98105. Phone: 206-545-0268. Authorized power: 10-w. each Antenna: 400-ft. above ground. Lat. 35° 55' 22", long. 86° 42' 38". Transmitter: 3.2-mi. SW of Nolensville. Equipment: Comwave transmitter; Andrew antenna. Ownership: Presco Corp.

Nashville—WNTM642 (H1). Thomas F. Lennon. Authorized power: 50-w. Antenna: 373-ft. above ground. Lat. 35° 55' 22", long. 86° 42' 38". Transmitter: 3.2-mi. SW of Nolensville. Equipment: Comwave transmitter; Andrew antenna. Ownership: Continental Wireless Cable Television Inc.

Nashville—WNTE429 (H2). Thomas F. Lennon. Authorized power: 50-w. Antenna: 373-ft. above ground. Lat. 35° 55' 22", long. 86° 42' 38". Transmitter: 3.2-mi. SW of Nolensville. Equipment: Comwave transmitter; Andrew antenna. Ownership: Continental Wireless Cable Television Inc.

Nashville—WNTE741 (H3). Thomas F. Lennon. Authorized power: 1-w. Antenna: 380-ft. above ground. Lat. 35° 55' 22", long. 86° 42' 38". Transmitter: 3.2-mi. SW of Nolensville. Equipment: Comwave transmitter; Bogner antenna. Ownership: Continental Wireless Cable Television Inc.

Union City—WGW628 (E group). Union City Microvision, Box 709, Union City, TN 38261. Phone: 901-885-4922. Authorized power: 10-w. each. Antenna: 289-ft. above ground. Lat. 36° 23' 47", long. 89° 10' 47". Transmitter: Troy-Hickman Dr. Equipment: Emcee transmitter; Andrew antenna. Ownership: Union City Microvision.

Union City—WNTK889 (H group). Union City Microvision, Box 709, Union City, TN 38261. Phone: 901-885-4922. Authorized power: 50-w. each. Antenna: 305-ft. above ground. Lat. 36° 23' 47", long. 89° 10' 47". Transmitter: 5-mi. W of Union City. Equipment: ITS transmitter; Andrew antenna. Ownership: Union City Microvision.

Texas

Amarillo—WHT794 (E group). Nucentrix Spectrum Resources Inc., Suite 200, 200 Chisholm Place, Plano, TX 75075. Phone: 972-423-9494. Fax: 972-423-0819. Authorized power: 20-w. each. Antenna: 550-ft. above ground. Lat. 35° 20' 33", long. 101° 49' 20". Transmitter: 1.32-mi. NE of State Hwy. 286 & Givens Ave. Equipment: ITS transmitter; Andrew antenna. Ownership: Nucentrix Broadband Networks.

Amarillo—WNTP928 (H3). JRZ Associates, Box 8026, Greenville, NC 27835-8026. Phone: 252-757-0279. Fax: 252-752-9155. E-mail: lbagrp@lbagroup.com. Web site: http://www.lbagroup.com. Authorized power: 50-w. Antenna: 550-ft. above ground. Lat. 35° 20' 33", long. 101° 49' 20". Transmitter: 1.4-mi. NNE of Hwy. 286. Equipment: Comwave transmitter; Andrew antenna. Ownership: JRZ Associates.

Austin—WHT705 (E group). Grand MMDS Alliance Austin E/P Partnership, Suite 660, 1920 N St. NW, Washington, DC 20036. Phone: 202-887-0600. Fax: 202-457-0126. Authorized power: 20-w. each. Antenna: 340-ft. above ground. Lat. 30° 18' 18", long. 97° 50' 18". Transmitter: Bee Cave & Stephen School Rds. Equipment: ITS transmitter; Andrew antenna. Ownership: Jonathan M. Levy.

Austin—WHT706 (F group). Columbia Wireless Corp., Suite 501, 1100 17th St. NW, Washington, DC 20036-4646. Phone: 202-223-4449. Fax: 202-223-4450. E-mail: rgould@cwix.com. Authorized power: 20-w. each. Antenna: 360-ft. above ground. Lat. 30° 18' 18", long. 97° 50' 18". Transmitter: Bee Cave & Stephen School Rds., Austin (Travis City), TX. Equipment: ITS transmitter; Andrew antenna. Ownership: Columbia Wireless Corp.

Leased to Nucentrix Broadband Networks, 200 Chisholm Place, Suite 200, Plano, TX 75075. Phone: 972-423-9494. Fax:972-423-0819

Beaumont—WLW931 (F group). Multichannel Media Inc., 248 King George St., Annapolis, MD 21401. Phone: 410-626-1200. Fax: 410-626-1266. Authorized power: 10-w. each. Antenna: 500-ft. above ground. Lat. 30° 05' 18", long. 93° 57' 13". Transmitter: Jap Lane. Equipment: Emcee transmitter; Andrew antenna. Ownership: Multichannel Media Inc.

Beaumont—WNTJ712 (H1). AmeriComm Inc., 568 Spyglass Lane, Newbury Park, CA 91230. Phone: 805-499-5525. Fax: 805-499-3083. Authorized power: 10-w. Antenna: 283-ft. above ground. Lat. 30° 04' 45", long. 94° 07' 58". Transmitter: 27 Sawyer St. Equipment: Emcee transmitter; Andrew antenna. Requests change to 280-ft. above ground. Ownership: AmeriComm Inc.

Beaumont—WNTJ737 (H2). AmeriComm Inc., 568 Spyglass Lane, Newbury Park, CA 91320. Phone: 805-499-5525. Fax: 805-499-3083. Authorized power: 50-w. Antenna: 423-ft. above ground. Lat. 30° 05' 18", long. 93° 57' 12". Transmitter: 1.5-mi. E of FM 1135. Equipment: Emcee transmitter; Andrew antenna. Ownership: AmeriComm Inc.

Brazoria—WNTH877 (H2). Robert A. Hart IV, Box 66436, 4615 N Blvd., Baton Rouge, LA 70896. Antenna: 300-ft. above ground. Lat. 29° 03' 55", long. 95° 35' 55". Transmitter: 4.3-mi. SE of Wharton. Ownership: Robert A. Hart IV.

Brownsville—WLR463 (F group). Warren F. Ache, 3206 Rustic Villa Dr., Kingwood, TX 77345. Phone: 281-360-7365. Authorized power: 20-w. Antenna: 484-ft. above ground. Lat. 25° 57' 49", long. 97° 31' 11". Transmitter: 4-mi. N of Brownsville. Equipment: Comwave transmitter; Andrew antenna. Requests change to 493-ft. above ground; transmitter to 1-mi. N of Brownsville. Ownership: Warren F. Ache.
Leased to United States Wireless Systems, Inc., 1083 West Ave., Austin, TX 78701.

Brownsville—WNTV757 (H1). Blake Twedt, 5102 Rosegreen Court, Tampa, FL 33624. Phone: 727-587-9959. Authorized power: 20-w. Antenna: 300-ft. above ground. Lat. 25° 57' 49", long. 97° 31' 11". Transmitter: 5-mi. N of Brownsville. Equipment: Comwave transmitter; Andrew antenna. Requests change to 493-ft. above ground. Ownership: Blake Twedt.

Brownsville-Harlingen—WLK284 (E group). United States Wireless Systems Inc., 1803 West Ave., Austin, TX 78701. Phone: 956-423-6566. Fax: 956-425-8470. Authorized power: 20-w.each. Antenna: 493-ft. above ground. Lat. 25° 57' 49", long. 97° 31' 11". Transmitter: 1-mi. N of Brownsville. Equipment: Alan Dick & Co. transmitter; Andrew antenna. Ownership: United States Wireless Systems Inc.

Bryan—WLW979 (E group). Becker Broadcasting, Box 12641, El Paso, TX 79912. Phone: 915-585-1178. Fax: 915-585-1179. Authorized power: 10-w. each. Antenna: 484-ft. above ground. Lat. 30° 39' 37", long. 96° 25' 01". Transmitter: 0.6-mi. E of Hwy. 21 & 28th St. Equipment: Emcee transmitter; Bogner antenna. Ownership: Becker Broadcasting.
Leased to Wireless One Inc., 11301 Industriplex Blvd., Suite 4, Baton Rouge, LA 70809. Phone: 504-293-5001. Fax: 509-293-5400.

Bryan—WNTG864 (H1). Becker Broadcasting, Box 12641, El Paso, TX 79912. Phone: 915-585-1178. Fax: 915-585-1179. Antenna: 484-ft. above ground. Lat. 30° 39' 37", long. 96° 25' 01". Transmitter: 6-mi. E of Hwy. 21. Equipment: Comwave transmitter; Andrew antenna. Ownership: Becker Broadcasting.
Leased to Wireless One Inc., 11301 Industriplex Blvd, Suite 4, Baton Rouge, LA 70809. Phone: 504-293-5001. Fax: 509-293-5400

Bryan—WNTH502 (H2). Libmot Communications Partnership, 2700 Chain Bridge Rd. NW, Washington, DC 20016. Phone: 202-966-2167. Fax: 202-237-7742. Antenna: 499-ft. above ground. Lat. 30° 39' 37", long. 96° 25' 01". Transmitter: 6-mi. E of Hwy. 21. Equipment: Comwave transmitter; Andrew antenna. Ownership: Libmot Communications Partnership.
Leased to Wireless One Inc., 11301 Industriplex Blvd., Suite 4, Baton Rouge, LA 70809. Phone: 504-293-5001. Fax: 504-293-5400.

Bryan—WNTH514 (H3). Becker Broadcasting, Box 12641, El Paso, TX 79912. Phone: 915-585-1178. Fax: 915-585-1179. Antenna: 484-ft. above ground. Lat. 30° 39' 37", long. 96° 25' 01". Transmitter: 6-mi. E of Hwy. 21. Equipment: Comwave transmitter; Andrew antenna. Ownership: Becker Broadcasting.
Leased to Wireless One Inc., 11301 Industriplex Blvd., Suite 4, Baton Rouge, LA 70809. Phone: 504-293-5001. Fax: 504-293-+5400.

Bryan-College Station—WLW978 (F group). Becker Broadcasting, Box 12641, El Paso, TX 79912. Phone: 915-585-1178. Fax: 915-585-1179. Authorized power: 10-w. each. Antenna: 484-ft. above ground. Lat. 30° 39' 37", long. 96° 25' 01". Transmitter: 0.6-mi. E of Hwy. 21 & 28th St. Equipment: Comwave transmitter; Andrew antenna. Ownership: Becker Broadcasting.
Leased to Wireless One Inc., 11301 Industriplex Blvd., Suite 4, Baton Rouge, LA 70809. Phone: 504-293-5001. Fax: 504-293-+5400.

Carrizo Springs—WMH261 (E group). National Wireless Cable, 63 Dombey Circle, Thousand Oaks, CA 91360. Authorized power: 10-w. each. Antenna: 440-ft. above ground. Lat. 28° 29' 51", long. 99° 53' 21". Transmitter: 1.6-mi. WSW of Carrizo Springs. Equipment: Comwave transmitter; Bogner antenna. Ownership: National Wireless Cable.

Corpus Christi—WHT711 (E group). Three Sixty Corp. Authorized power: 50-w. each. Antenna: 333-ft. above ground. Lat. 27° 47' 50", long. 97° 23' 48". Transmitter: 802 N. Carancahua St. Equipment: Emcee transmitter; Andrew antenna. Ownership: Three Sixty Corp.

Corpus Christi—WHT712 (F group). StarChannels Associates LP. Authorized power: 50-w. each. Antenna: 333-ft. above ground. Lat. 27° 47' 50", long. 97° 23' 48". Transmitter: 802 N. Carancahua St. Equipment: Emcee transmitter; Andrew antenna. Ownership: StarChannels Associates LP.

Corpus Christi—WNTB460 (H1). Nucentrix Spectrum Resources Inc., Suite 200, 200 Chisholm Place, Plano, TX 75075. Phone: 972-423-9494. Fax: 972-423-0819. Authorized power: 50-w. Antenna: 333-ft. above ground. Lat. 27° 47' 50", long. 97° 23' 48". Transmitter: 802 N. Carancahua St. Equipment: Emcee transmitter; Andrew antenna. Ownership: Nucentrix Broadband Networks.

Corpus Christi—WNTB468 (H2). Thomas H. Schitzions, Suite 2450, 717 Louisiana St., Houston, TX 77002. Phone: 713-222-2170. Authorized power: 50-w. Antenna: 333-ft. above ground. Lat. 27° 47' 50", long. 97° 23' 48". Transmitter: 802 N. Carancahua St. Equipment: Emcee transmitter; Andrew antenna. Ownership: Thomas H. Schitzions.

Corpus Christi—WNTB410 (H3). Nucentrix Spectrum Resources Inc., Suite 200, 200 Chisholm Place, Plano, TX 75075. Phone: 972-423-9494. Fax: 972-423-0819. Authorized power: 50-w. Antenna: 333-ft. above ground. Lat. 27° 47' 50", long. 97° 23' 48". Transmitter: 802 N. Carancahua St. Equipment: Emcee transmitter; Andrew antenna. Ownership: Nucentrix Broadband Networks.

Corsicana—WNTM673 (H1). Nucentrix Spectrum Resources Inc., Suite 200, 200 Chisholm Place, Plano, TX 75075. Phone: 972-423-9494. Fax: 972-423-0819. Authorized power: 10-w. Antenna: 270-ft. above ground. Lat. 32° 08' 48", long. 95° 58' 25". Transmitter: Country Rd., 2.5-mi. SE of Malakoff. Equipment: ITS transmitter; Andrew antenna. Requests change to 705-ft. above ground, lat. 32° 01' 40", long. 96° 11' 03"; transmitter to to approx. 1-mi. SW of Round Prairie. Ownership: Nucentrix Broadband Networks.

Corsicana—WNTM838 (H3). Nucentrix Spectrum Resources Inc., Suite 200, 200 Chisholm Place, Plano, TX 75075. Phone: 972-423-9494. Fax: 972-423-0819. Authorized power: 10-w. Antenna: 705-ft. above ground. Lat. 32° 01' 40", long. 96° 11' 03". Transmitter: approx. 1-mi. SW of Round Prairie. Equipment: ITS transmitter; Andrew antenna. Ownership: Nucentrix Broadband Networks.

Dallas—WMY464 (E group). Global Information Technologies Inc., Suite 2530, 111 Congress Ave., Austin, TX 78701. Phone: 512-478-3400. Authorized power: 10-w. each. Antenna: 300-ft. above ground. Lat. 32° 51' 58", long. 96° 48' 00". Transmitter: 6211 W. Northwest Hwy. Equipment: Comwave transmitter; Andrew antenna. Requests change to 314-ft. above ground. Ownership: Global Information Technologies Inc.; Paging Systems Inc.

Dallas—WHJ873 (H2). CS Wireless Systems Inc., 1101 Summit Ave., Plano, TX 75074. Phone: 972-509-2634. Authorized power: 10-w. Antenna: 299-ft. above ground. Lat. 32° 51' 57", long. 96° 48' 01". Transmitter: 6211 Northwest Hwy. Equipment: Comwave transmitter; Andrew antenna. Ownership: CS Wireless Systems Inc.

Dallas—WNTD967 (H3). CS Wireless Systems Inc., 1101 Summit Ave., Plano, TX 75074. Phone: 972-509-2634. Authorized power: 50-w. Antenna: 299-ft. above ground. Lat. 32° 51' 57", long. 96° 48' 01". Transmitter: 6211 W. Northwest Hwy. Equipment: Comwave transmitter; Andrew antenna. Ownership: CS Wireless Systems Inc.

Dallas/Fort Worth—WHT789 (F group). CS Wireless Systems Inc., 1101 Summit Ave., Plano, TX 75074. Phone: 972-509-2634. Authorized power: 10-w. each. Antenna: 515-ft. above ground. Lat. 32° 45' 11", long. 97° 19' 46". Transmitter: 777 Main St. Equipment: Comwave transmitter; Andrew antenna. Ownership: CS Wireless Systems Inc.

Decatur—WMI361 (E group). Rural Wireless South Inc., Suite 200, 200 Chisholm Place, Plano, TX 75075. Phone: 972-423-9494. Fax: 972-423-0819. Authorized power: 10-w. each. Antenna: 150-ft. above ground. Lat. 33° 40' 17", long. 97° 37' 16". Transmitter: 6.3-mi. W of Decatur. Equipment: Emcee transmitter; Bogner antenna. Ownership: Heartland Wireless Commercial Channels Inc.

Decatur—WMI357 (F group). Rural Wireless South Inc., Suite 200, 200 Chisholm Place, Plano, TX 75075. Phone: 972-423-9494. Fax: 972-423-0819. Authorized power: 10-w. each. Antenna: 150-ft. above ground. Lat. 33° 40' 17", long. 97° 37' 16". Transmitter: 6.3-mi. W of Decatur. Equipment: Emcee transmitter; Bogner antenna. Ownership: Heartland Wireless Commercial Channels Inc.

Denison—WLW760 (F group). Broadcast Data Corp., 25 Rockford Place, Englewood, NJ 07631. Phone: 201-894-8000. Authorized power: 50-w. each. Antenna: 446-ft. above ground. Lat. 33° 40' 34", long. 96° 35' 04". Transmitter: E of Frisco. Equipment: Comwave transmitter; Andrew antenna. Ownership: Broadcast Data Corp.

Denison—WNEZ899 (H1). Nucentrix Spectrum Resources Inc., Suite 200, 200 Chisholm Place, Plano, TX 75075. Phone: 972-423-9494. Fax: 972-423-0819. Authorized power: 50-w. Antenna: 446-ft. above ground. Lat. 33° 40' 34", long. 96° 35' 04". Transmitter: E. of Frisco. Equipment: Comwave transmitter; Andrew antenna. Ownership: Nucentrix Broadband Networks.

Denison—WNTB287 (H2). Nucentrix Spectrum Resources Inc., Suite 200, 200 Chisholm Place, Plano, TX 75075. Phone: 972-423-9494. Fax: 972-423-0819. Authorized power: 50-w. Antenna: 446-ft. above ground. Lat. 33° 40' 34", long. 96° 35' 04". Transmitter: E of Frisco. Equipment: Comwave transmitter; Andrew antenna. Ownership: Nucentrix Broadband Networks.

Denison—WNEX639 (H3). Supreme Cable Co., Suite 200, 200 Chisholm Place, Plano, TX 75075. Phone: 972-423-9494. Authorized power: 50-w. Antenna: 446-ft. above ground. Lat. 33° 40' 34", long. 96° 35' 04". Transmitter: E of Frisco. Equipment: Comwave transmitter; Andrew antenna. Ownership: Supreme Cable Co. Inc.

El Paso—WHK950 (E group). Via/Net Companies, 836 E. Washington St., San Diego, CA 92103. Phone: 619-260-0110. Authorized power: 10-w. each. Antenna: 100-ft. above ground. Lat. 31° 47' 16", long. 106° 28' 46". Transmitter: 0.4-mi. from Scenic Dr. Equipment: Emcee transmitter; Andrew antenna. Ownership: Via/Net Companies.

El Paso—WHT766 (F group). Red El Paso F Partnership, 248 King George St., Annapolis, MD 21401. Phone: 410-626-1200. Fax: 410-626-1266. Authorized power: 10-w. each. Antenna: 100-ft. above ground. Lat. 31° 47' 16", long. 106° 28' 46". Transmitter: 0.4-mi. from Scenic Dr. Equipment: Emcee transmitter; Andrew antenna. Ownership: MDS Signal Group, 33.3%; Multichannel Media Inc., 33.3%; StarChannels Associates LP, 33.3%.

El Paso—WNTB422 (H1). William H. Benson, Suite 600, 5520 LBJ Freeway, Dallas, TX 75240-6294. Authorized power: 10-w. Antenna: 65-ft. above ground. Lat. 31° 47' 46", long. 106° 28' 57". Transmitter: Comanche Peak. Equipment: Emcee transmitter; Andrew antenna. Ownership: Willam H. Benson. Sale pends to Heartland Commercial Channels Inc.

El Paso—WNEX722 (H2). Specchio Developers Ltd., 233 N. Garrard, Rantoul, IL 61866. Authorized power: 10-w. Antenna: 65-ft. above ground. Lat. 31° 47' 46", long. 106° 28' 57". Transmitter: Comanche Peak. Equipment: Emcee transmitter; Andrew antenna. Ownership: Specchio Developers Ltd. Sale pends to Heartland Wireless Commercial Channels Inc.

El Paso—WNTB687 (H3). Nucentrix Spectrum Resources Inc., Suite 200, 200 Chisholm Place, Plano, TX 75075. Phone: 972-423-9494. Fax: 972-423-0819. Authorized power: 10-w. Antenna: 65-ft. above ground. Lat. 31° 47' 46", long. 106° 28' 57". Transmitter: Comanche Peak. Equipment: Emcee transmitter; Andrew antenna. Ownership: Nucentrix Broadband Networks.

Falfurrias—WLW892 (E group). Ultra Vision of Texas Inc., Box 1538, 100 E. Kleberg, Kingsville, TX 78383. Phone: 512-851-8588. Authorized power: 10-w. each. Antenna: 499-ft. above ground. Lat. 27° 15' 18", long. 98° 05' 46". Transmitter: 5-mi. NE of Falfurrias. Equipment: Comwave transmitter; Bogner antenna. Ownership: Ultra Vision of Texas.

Falfurrias—WLW896 (F group). Ultra Vision of Texas Inc., Box 1538, 100 E. Kleberg, Kingsville, TX 78383. Phone: 512-851-8588. Authorized power: 100-w. each. Antenna: 499-ft. above ground. Lat. 27° 15' 18", long. 98° 05' 46". Transmitter: 5-mi. NE of Falfurrias. Equipment: Comwave transmitter; Bogner antenna. Ownership: Ultra Vision of Texas.

Fort Stockton—WMY445 (E group). Tide Microcable Partnership, 67-755 Peineta Rd., Palm Springs, CA 92262. Antenna: 305-ft. above ground. Lat. 30° 56' 47", long. 102° 52' 27". Transmitter: Fort Stockton. Ownership: Tide Microcable Partnership.

Freeport—WNTI238 (H1). Elsie Burkhardt, 7 Roundtree Dr., Melville, NY 11747. Phone & fax: 516-643-8349. Antenna: 303-ft. above ground. Lat. 28° 59' 23", long. 95° 14' 25". Transmitter: State Rte. 3005 W, 7.4-mi. ENE of Freeport. Ownership: LC Communications.

Freeport—WNTH938 (H3). Frederick M. Ganz, 15 Gallahad Lane, Nesconset, NY 11767. Antenna: 303-ft. above ground. Lat. 28° 59' 23", long. 95° 14' 25". Transmitter: State Rte. 3005 W, 7.4-mi. ENE of Freeport. Ownership: Frederick M. Ganz.

George West—WLW900 (E group). Ultra Vision of Texas Inc., Box 1538, 100 E. Kleberg, Kingsville, TX 78363. Phone: 512-851-8588. Authorized power: 100-w. each. Antenna: 620-ft. above ground. Lat. 28° 17' 37", long. 98° 13' 17". Transmitter: 7-mi. WSW of George West. Equipment: Comwave transmitter; Bogner antenna. Ownership: Ultra Vision of Texas.

George West—WLW904 (F group). Ultra Vision of Texas Inc., Box 1538, 100 E. Kleberg, Kingsville, TX 78363. Phone: 512-851-8588. Authorized power: 100-w. each. Antenna: 620-ft. above ground. Lat. 28° 17' 37", long. 98° 13' 17". Transmitter: 7-mi. WSW of George West. Equipment: Comwave transmitter; Bogner antenna. Ownership: Ultra Vision of Texas.

George West—WLW743 (H1). Ultra Vision of Texas Inc., Box 1538, 100 E. Kleberg, Kingsville, TX 78363. Phone: 512-851-8588. Authorized power: 100-w. Antenna: 620-ft. above ground. Lat. 28° 17' 37", long. 98° 13' 17". Transmitter: 7-mi. WSW of George West. Equipment: Comwave transmitter; Andrew antenna. Ownership: Ultra Vision of Texas.

George West—WLW735 (H2). Ultra Vision of Texas Inc., Box 1538, 100 E. Kleberg, Kingsville, TX 78363. Phone: 512-851-8588. Authorized power: 100-w. Antenna: 620-ft. above ground. Lat. 28° 17' 37", long. 98° 13' 17". Transmitter: 7-mi. WSW of George West. Equipment: Comwave transmitter; Andrew antenna. Ownership: Ultra Vision of Texas.

George West—WLW739 (H3). Ultra Vision of Texas Inc., Box 1538, 100 E. Kleberg, Kingsville, TX 78363. Phone: 512-851-8588. Authorized power: 100-w. Antenna: 620-ft. above ground. Lat. 28° 17' 37", long. 98° 13' 17". Transmitter: 7-mi. WSW of George West. Equipment: Comwave transmitter; Andrew antenna. Ownership: Ultra Vision of Texas.

Houston—WLK305 (E group). Block & Assoc., 3605 Frost Lane, Reno, NV 89511. Phone: 702-852-6604. Authorized power: 100-w. each. Antenna: 991-ft. above ground. Lat. 29° 45' 30", long. 95° 22' 03". Transmitter: 11811 Olympic Blvd. Equipment: Comwave transmitter; Andrew antenna. Ownership: Block & Assoc.

Houston—WMI812 (F group). Robert S. Moore, 716 N. Westwood Ave., Toledo, OH 43607. Phone: 419-531-1440. Authorized power: 100-w. each. Antenna: 991-ft. above ground. Lat. 29° 45' 30", long. 93° 22' 03". Transmitter: 11811 Oympic Blvd. Equipment: Comwave transmitter; Andrew antenna. Ownership: Robert S. Moore.

Houston—WHJ887 (H2). Alda Gold, 5301 E. Broadway Blvd., Tucson, AZ 85711-3710. Phone: 520-519-4400. Fax: 520-747-6830. Antenna: 991-ft. above ground. Lat. 29° 45' 30", long. 95° 22' 03". Transmitter: 1000 Louisiana St. Ownership: Matthew Oristano. Leased to People's Choice TV Partners, 2 Corporate Dr., Suite 249, Shelton, CT 06484-6239. Phone: 203-929-2800. Fax: 203-929-1454.

Ingram—WMY304 (H1). RVS Holdings Corp., Suite 200, 200 Chisholm Place, Plano, TX 75075. Phone: 972-423-9494. Fax: 972-423-0819. Authorized power: 10-w. Antenna: 300-ft. above ground. Lat. 30° 01' 09", long. 99° 20' 08". Transmitter: 1.6-mi. E of SR 39. Equipment: Comwave transmitter; Andrew antenna. Ownership: Nucentrix Broadband Networks Inc.

Kerrville—WMI897 (E group). Minority MDS. Authorized power: 10-w. each. Antenna: 459-ft. above ground. Lat. 30° 06' 18", long. 99° 04' 34". Transmitter: Hwy. 16, 5-mi. N of Kerrville. Equipment: Emcee transmitter; Andrew antenna. Ownership: Minority MDS.

Kerrville—WMH288 (F group). Becker Broadcasting, Box 12641, 106 Castellano, El Paso, TX 79912. Phone: 915-585-1178. Authorized power: 10-w. each. Antenna: 459-ft. above ground. Lat. 30° 06' 18", long. 99° 04' 34". Transmitter: Hwy. 16, 5-mi. NE of Kerrville. Equipment: Comwave transmitter; Bogner antenna. Ownership: Becker Broadcasting.

Laredo—WLR467 (F group). Baypoint TV Inc., Suite 810, 1627 Eye St. NW, Washington, DC 20067. Phone: 202-293-0700. Authorized power: 10-w. each. Antenna: 459-ft. above ground. Lat. 27° 24' 09", long. 99° 26' 49". Transmitter: 6-mi. S of Laredo on Pinta. Equipment: Emcee transmitter; Andrew antenna. Ownership: Baypoint TV Inc.

Leon Springs—WNTA693 (H1). CS Wireless Systems Inc., 1101 Summit Ave., Plano, TX 75074. Phone: 972-509-2634. . Authorized power: 10-w. Antenna: 367-ft. above ground. Lat. 29° 38' 00", long. 98° 37' 50". Transmitter: KCYY Tower, 2.1-mi. S of Leon Springs. Equipment: Comwave transmitter; Andrew antenna. Ownership: CS Wireless Systems Inc.

Longview—WMH477 (E group). Gary Golden, 6500 Torrey Pines Cove, Austin, TX 78746. Authorized power: 10-w. each. Antenna: 253-ft. above ground. Lat. 32° 33' 44", long. 94° 28' 40". Transmitter: Hynson Springs Rd. Equipment: Emcee transmitter; Andrew antenna. Ownership: Gary Golden.

Longview—WMI306 (F group). Gary Golden, 6500 Torrey Pines Cove, Austin, TX 78746. Authorized power: 10-w. each. Antenna: 309-ft. above ground. Lat. 32° 33' 44", long. 94° 28' 40". Transmitter: Hynson Springs Rd. Equipment: Emcee transmitter; Andrew antenna. Ownership: Gary Golden.

Lubbock—WMX239 (E group). Broadcast Data Corp., Suite 247, 189 Berdan Ave., Wayne, NJ 07470. Phone: 201-831-7407. Authorized power: 10-w. each. Antenna: 130-ft. above ground. Lat. 33° 33' 43", long. 101° 51' 06". Transmitter: 1511 35th St. Equipment: Comwave transmitter; Bogner antenna. Ownership: Broadcast Data Corp.

Lubbock—WMH608 (F group). National Television Co., Meeting House Farm, Lincoln, VA 22078. Phone: 703-338-3750. Fax: 703-338-4525. Authorized power: 10-w. each. Antenna: 303-ft. above ground. Lat. 33° 29' 38", long. 101° 44' 01". Transmitter: 6-mi. SE of Lubbock. Equipment: Emcee transmitter; Bogner antenna. Ownership: National TV Co.

Lubbock—WNEZ900 (H1). Nucentrix Spectrum Resources Inc., Suite 200, 200 Chisholm Place, Plano, TX 75075. Phone: 972-423-9494. Fax: 972-423-0819. Authorized power: 20-w. Antenna: 442-ft. above ground. Lat. 33° 28' 10", long. 101° 47' 25". Transmitter: Rte. 1585, 9-mi. SSE of Lubbock. Equipment: ITS transmitter; Andrew antenna. Ownership: Nucentrix Broadband Networks.

Lubbock—WNTB289 (H2). Nucentrix Spectrum Resources Inc., Suite 200, 200 Chisholm Place, Plano, TX 75075. Phone: 972-423-9494. Fax: 972-423-0819. Authorized power: 20-w. Antenna: 442-ft. above ground. Lat. 33° 28' 10", long. 101° 47' 25". Transmitter: Rte. 1585, 9-mi. SSE of Lubbock. Equipment: ITS transmitter; Andrew antenna. Requests change to 404-ft. above ground. Ownership: Nucentrix Broadband Networks.

Lubbock—WNEY638 (H3). Nucentrix Spectrum Resources Inc., Suite 200, 200 Chisholm Place, Plano, TX 75075. Phone: 972-423-9494. Fax: 972-423-0819. Authorized power: 20-w. Antenna: 442-ft. above ground. Lat. 33° 28' 10", long. 101° 47' 25". Transmitter: Rte. 1585, 9-mi. SSE of Lubbock. Equipment: ITS transmitter; Andrew antenna. Ownership: Nucentrix Broadband Networks.

Lufkin—WMI807 (E group). Lipscomb Interests Partnership, 2306 Brookhollow, Witchita Falls, TX 76308. Authorized power: 10-w. each. Antenna: 460-ft. above ground. Lat. 31° 40' 58", long. 94° 41' 55". Transmitter: 2.5-mi. NW of Nacogdoches. Equipment: Comwave transmitter; Bogner antenna. Ownership: Lipscomb Interests Partnership.

Lufkin—WMH993 (F group). L. M. Beal Jr., 2514 Broadmoor, Bryan, TX 77802. Authorized power: 10-w. each Antenna: 631-ft. above ground. Lat. 31° 24' 28", long. 94° 45' 53". Transmitter: State Hwy. 103. Equipment: ITS transmitter; Andrew antenna. Ownership: L. M. Beal Jr.

McAllen—WMH576 (E group). American Telecasting Development Inc., Suite 300, 5575 Tech Center Dr., Colorado Springs, CO 80919. Phone: 719-260-5533. Fax: 719-260-5010. Authorized power: 10-w. each. Antenna: 440-ft. above ground. Lat. 26° 15' 57", long. 98° 10' 43". Transmitter: Hwy. 281, 2-mi. S of Edinburg. Equipment: Comwave transmitter; Andrew antenna. Ownership: American Telecasting Inc.

McAllen—WLR475 (F group). Warren F. Ache, 3206 Rustic Villa Dr., Kingwood, TX 77345. Phone: 713-874-2493. Authorized power: 20-w. each. Antenna: 440-ft. above ground. Lat. 26° 15' 57", long. 98° 10' 43". Transmitter: Hwy. 281, 2-mi S. of Edinburg. Equipment: Andrew antenna. Ownership: Warren F. Ache. Leased to United States Wireless Systems Inc., 1803 West Ave., Austin, TX 78701.

Midland—WLW875 (E group). Edna Cornaggia, Space 345, 4095 Fruit St., LaVerne, CA 91750. Phone: 714-593-0175. Authorized power: 10-w. each. Antenna: 30-ft. above ground. Lat. 31° 59' 31", long. 102° 06' 54". Transmitter: 3515 W. Illinois. Equipment: Emcee transmitter; Andrew antenna. Ownership: Edna Cornaggia.

Nelsonville—WMY293 (H2). RVS Holdings Corp., Suite 200, 200 Chisholm Place, Plano, TX 75075. Phone: 972-423-9494. Fax: 972-423-0819. Authorized power: 10-w. Antenna: 30-ft. above ground. Lat. 30° 00' 01", long. 96° 26' 15". Transmitter: 1.3-mi. NW of junction of SR 2754 & SR 2502. Equipment: Comwave transmitter; Andrew antenna. Ownership: Nucentrix Broadband Networks Inc.

Nelsonville—WMY294 (H3). RVS Holdings Corp., Suite 200, 200 Chisholm Place, Plano, TX 75075. Phone: 972-423-9494. Fax: 972-423-0819. Authorized power: 10-w. Antenna: 360-ft. above ground. Lat. 30° 00' 01", long. 96° 26' 15". Transmitter: 1.3-mi. NW of junction of SR 2754 & SR 2502. Equipment: Comwave transmitter; Andrew antenna. Ownership: Nucentrix Broadband Networks Inc.

Nolanville—WMI835 (E group). The Kenneth H. Iscol 1990 Trust for Kiva Iscol, 63 Lyndel Rd., Pound Ridge, NY 10576. Authorized power: 10-w. Antenna: 518-ft. above ground. Lat. 31° 05' 23", long. 97° 35' 55". Transmitter: Farm Rd. 439, 1.2-mi. NE of Killeen. Equipment: ITS transmitter; Andrew antenna. Requests change to 400-ft. above ground. Ownership: Visionaire Inc.

Nolanville—WMI869 (F group). Krisar Inc., 320 Hamilton St., Albion, NY 14411. Phone: 716-964-9121. Fax: 716-598-9094. E-mail: topperiai@aol.com. Authorized power: 10-w. each. Antenna: 498-ft. above ground. Lat. 31° 05' 23", long. 97° 35' 55". Transmitter: Farm Rd. 439, 1.2-mi. NE of Killeen. Equipment: ITS transmitter; Andrew antenna. Requests change to 400-ft. above ground. Ownership: Krisar Inc.
Leased to Nucentrix Broadband Networks, 200 Chisholm Place, Suite 200, Plano, TX 75075. Phone: 972-423-9494. Fax: 972-423-0819.

Nolanville—WNEZ717 (H3). Nucentrix Spectrum Resources Inc., Suite 200, 200 Chisholm Place, Plano, TX 75075. Phone: 972-423-9494. Fax: 972-423-0819. Authorized power: 50-w. Antenna: 400-ft. above ground. Lat. 31° 05' 23", long. 97° 35' 55". Transmitter: Farm Rd. 439, 1.2-mi. NE of Nolanville. Equipment: ITS transmitter; Andrew antenna. Ownership: Nucentrix Broadband Networks.

Pampa—WMX231 (H2). Ron Pingel. Authorized power: 10-w. Antenna: 330-ft. above ground. Lat. 35° 32' 43", long. 100° 55' 15". Transmitter: 1-mi. N of Hwy. 60 in Loop 171. Equipment: ITS transmitter; Andrew antenna. Ownership: Ron Pingel.

Paris—WMH697 (E group). Chaney Communications Inc. Authorized power: 10-w. each. Antenna: 150-ft. above ground. Lat. 33° 47' 24", long. 95° 30' 27". Transmitter: 7-mi. NNE of Paris. Equipment: Emcee transmitter; Bogner antenna. Ownership: Chaney Communications Inc.

Pecos—WMH797 (F group). Merrifield Partnership, 1004 E. Tate, Broomfield, TX 79316. Authorized power: 10-w. each. Antenna: 160-ft. above ground. Lat. 31° 26' 09", long. 103° 30' 14". Transmitter: 1-mi. N. on Carlsbad Hwy. Equipment: Comwave transmitter; Andrew antenna. Ownership: Merrifield Partnership.

Roma—WLW940 (E group). Tele-View Inc., Box 186, Roma, TX 78584. Phone: 512-849-1740. Authorized power: 10-w. each. Antenna: 300-ft. above ground. Lat. 26° 24' 50", long. 99° 01' 25". Transmitter: Estrella & Nicks Station. Equipment: Comwave transmitter; Andrew antenna. Ownership: Tele-View Inc.

San Angelo—WMX908 (E group). Estate of Charles R. Jones, 5588 Westside Dr., San Angelo, TX 79932. Phone: 915-584-1848. Authorized power: 10-w. each. Antenna: 508-ft. above ground. Lat. 31° 25' 16", long. 100° 32' 36". Transmitter: Hwy. 67, W of San Angelo. Equipment: Comwave transmitter; Andrew antenna. Ownership: Estate of Charles R. Jones.

San Angelo—WLW827 (F group). Joseph L. Calibani, 1521 Mackenzie St., San Angelo, TX 76901. Phone: 915-658-5111. Authorized power: 10-w. each. Antenna: 370-ft. above ground. Lat. 31° 24' 46", long. 100° 32' 58". Equipment: Comwave transmitter; Andrew antenna. Ownership: Joseph L. Calibani.

San Angelo—WNTC543 (H1). Estate of Charles R. Jones, 5588 Westside Dr., San Angelo, TX 79932. Phone: 915-584-1848. Authorized power: 10-w. Antenna: 508-ft. above ground. Lat. 31° 25' 16", long. 100° 32' 36". Transmitter: Hwy. 67, W of San Angelo. Equipment: Comwave transmitter; Andrew antenna. Ownership: Estate of Charles R. Jones.

San Angelo—WMH612 (H3). Estate of Charles R. Jones, 5588 Westside Dr., San Angelo, TX 79932. Phone: 915-584-1848. Authorized power: 20-w. Antenna: 520-ft. above ground. Lat. 31° 25' 16", long. 100° 32' 36". Transmitter: Hwy. 67, W of San Angelo. Equipment: Emcee transmitter; Andrew antenna. Ownership: Estate of Charles R. Jones.

San Antonio—WHT693 (E group). Larsen MMDS Inc., Suite 2130, 2180 State Rd. 434 W, Longwood, FL 32779. Phone: 407-862-5130. Fax: 407-862-8151. Authorized power: 50-w. each. Antenna: 185-ft. above ground. Lat. 29° 33' 13", long. 98° 21' 15". Transmitter: 12544 Judson Rd. Equipment: ITS transmitter; Andrew antenna. Ownership: Larsen MMDS Inc.

San Antonio—WHT694 (F group). Omega Radiotelephone, 1601 Neptune Dr., San Leandro, CA 94577. Phone: 510-895-9500. Authorized power: 10-w. each. Antenna: 185-ft. above ground. Lat. 29° 33' 13", long. 98° 21' 15". Transmitter: 12544 Judson Rd. Equipment: ITS transmitter; Andrew antenna. Ownership: Omega Radiotelephone.

San Antonio—WNEY637 (H2 & 3). CS Wireless Systems Inc., 1101 Summit Ave., Plano, TX 75074. Phone: 972-509-2634. Antenna: 185-ft. above ground. Lat. 29° 33' 13", long. 98° 21' 15". Transmitter: 12544 Judson Rd. Ownership: CS Wireless Systems Inc.

Santa Anna—WMY236 (H2). Coleman County Telephone Cooperative Inc., Box 608, 215 N. 2nd St., Santa Anna, TX 76878. Phone: 915-348-3124. Authorized power: 10-w. Antenna: 302-ft. above ground. Lat. 31° 44' 48", long. 99° 19' 25". Transmitter: 0.2-mi. NNW of Parker & 2nd Sts. Equipment: Comwave transmitter; Andrew antenna. Ownership: Coleman County Telephone Cooperative Inc.

Santa Anna—WMY240 (H3). Coleman County Telephone Cooperative Inc., Box 608, 215 N. 2nd St., Santa Anna, TX 76878. Phone: 915-348-3124. Authorized power: 10-w. Antenna: 302-ft. above ground. Lat. 31° 44' 48", long. 99° 19' 25". Transmitter: 0.2-mi. NNW of Parker & 2nd Sts. Equipment: Comwave transmitter; Andrew antenna. Ownership: Coleman County Telephone Cooperative Inc.

Snyder—WMI373 (E group). Tex-Star Wireless Communications Alpha, Box 940008, Plano, TX 75094-0008. Authorized power: 10-w. each. Antenna: 430-ft. above ground. Lat. 32° 45' 53", long. 100° 53' 08". Transmitter: 2.5-mi. N of 8th & Ennis Creek. Equipment: ITS transmitter; Andrew antenna. Ownership: Tex-Star Wireless Communications Alpha.
Leased to Snyder Microwave Communications LC, Box 940008, Plano, TX 75094.

Snyder—WMI377 (F group). Tex-Star Wireless Communications Beta, Box 940008, Plano, TX 75094-0008. Authorized power: 10-w. each. Antenna: 430-ft. above ground. Lat. 32° 45' 53", long. 100° 53' 08". Transmitter: 2.5-mi. N of 8th & Ennis Creek. Equipment: ITS transmitter; Andrew antenna. Ownership: Tex-Star Wireless Communications Beta.
Leased to Snyder Microwave Communications LC, Box 940008, Plano, TX 75094.

Snyder—WNTK882 (H group). Tex-Star Wireless Communications-Gamma, Box 940008, Plano, TX 75094-0008. Authorized power: 10-w. each. Antenna: 430-ft. above ground. Lat. 32° 45' 53", long. 100° 53' 08". Transmitter: 2.5-mi. N of 8th and Ennis Creek. Equipment: ITS transmitter; Andrew antenna. Ownership: Tex-Star Wireless Communications Gamma.
Leased to Snyder Microwave Communications LC, Box 940008, Plano, TX 75094.

Texarkana—WMH396 (E group). Visionaire Inc., 63 Lyndel Rd., Pound Ridge, NY 10576. Authorized power: 10-w. each. Antenna: 280-ft. above ground. Lat. 33° 25' 49", long. 94° 03' 25". Transmitter: 15th St. & Kansas City RR. Equipment: Comwave transmitter; Bogner antenna. Ownership: Visionaire Inc.

Texarkana—WMH516 (F group). Stephanie Engstrom, Apt. 104, 420 S. Catalina Ave., Redondo Beach, CA 90277. Phone & fax: 310-540-9867. Authorized power: 10-w. each. Antenna: 450-ft. above ground. Lat. 33° 25' 48", long. 94° 05' 08". Transmitter: North U.S. Hwy. 82. Equipment: Emcee transmitter; Andrew antenna. Ownership: Stephanie Engstrom.

Texarkana—WNTH836 (H1). JRZ Associates, Box 8026, 3400 Tupper Dr., Greenville, NC 27834. Phone: 919-757-0279. Authorized power: 20-w. Antenna: 450-ft. above ground. Lat. 33° 25' 48", long. 94° 05' 08". Transmitter: N. U.S. Hwy. 82. Equipment: ITS transmitter; Andrew antenna. Ownership: JRZ Associates.

Texarkana—WNTI234 (H2). Libmot Communications Partnership, 2700 Chain Bridge Rd. NW, Washington, DC 20016. Phone: 202-966-2167. Fax: 202-237-7742. Authorized power: 20-w. Antenna: 450-ft. above ground. Lat. 33° 25' 48", long. 94° 05' 08". Transmitter: N. U.S. Hwy. 82. Equipment: ITS transmitter; Andrew antenna. Ownership: Libmot Communications Partnership.
Leased to Nucentrix Broadband Networks, 200 Chisholm Place, Suite 200, Plano, TX 75075. Phone: 972-423-9494. Fax: 972-423-0819.

Victoria—WLW927 (E group). Friendly Community Television Services, Box 632, Palmer Rd., Cuero, TX 77954. Phone: 512-275-8332. Authorized power: 50-w. each. Antenna: 505-ft. above ground. Lat. 28° 49' 00", long. 97° 03' 56". Transmitter: FM 1685, 5-mi. W of Victoria. Equipment: Comwave transmitter; Andrew antenna. Ownership: Friendly Community Television Services.

Victoria—WNTH481 (H1). United States Wireless Systems Inc., 1803 West Ave., Austin, TX 78701. Phone: 956-423-6566. Fax: 956-425-8470. Authorized power: 50-w. Antenna: 505-ft. above ground. Lat. 28° 49' 00", long. 97° 03' 56". Transmitter: FM 1685, 5-mi. W of Victoria. Equipment: Emcee transmitter; Andrew antenna. Ownership: United States Wireless Systems Inc.

Victoria—WNTJ758 (H2). United States Wireless Systems Inc., 1803 West Ave., Austin, TX 78701. Phone: 956-423-6566. Fax: 956-425-8470. Authorized power: 50-w. Antenna: 505-ft. above ground. Lat. 28° 49' 00", long. 97° 03' 56". Transmitter: FM 1685, 5-mi. W of Victoria. Equipment: Comwave transmitter; Andrew antenna. Ownership: United States Wireless Systems Inc.

Victoria—WNTH388 (H3). United States Wireless Systems Inc., 1803 West Ave., Austin, TX 78701. Phone: 956-423-6566. Fax: 956-425-8470. Authorized power: 50-w. Antenna: 505-ft. above ground. Lat. 28° 49' 00", long. 97° 03' 56". Transmitter: FM 1685, 5-mi. W of Victoria. Equipment: Comwave transmitter; Andrew antenna. Ownership: United States Wireless Systems Inc.
Leased to Golden Crescent Wireless Cable, 13004 N. Navarro, Victoria, TX 77904.

Waco—WHI625 (E group). Alda Wireless Holdings Inc., 5301 E. Broadway Blvd., Tucson, AZ 85711-3710. Phone: 520-519-4400. Fax: 520-747-6830. Authorized power: 10-w. each. Antenna: 494-ft. above ground. Lat. 31° 49' 29", long. 97° 09' 33". Transmitter: 4.3-mi. NW of West Waco. Equipment: ITS transmitter; Andrew antenna. Ownership: Matthew Oristano.

Waco—WMI865 (F group). American Telecasting Development Inc., Suite 300, 5575 Tech Center Dr., Colorado Springs, CO 80919. Phone: 719-260-5533. Fax: 719-260-5010. Authorized power: 10-w. each. Antenna: 99-ft. above ground. Lat. 31° 49' 29", long. 97° 09' 33". Transmitter: 4.3-mi. NW of West Waco. Equipment: ITS transmitter; Andrew antenna. Ownership: American Telecasting Inc.
Leased to Galaxy Cablevision LP, 1220 N. Main, Sikeston, MO 63801. Phone: 314-471-5022.

West Waco—WNTA620 (H group). Nucentrix Spectrum Resources Inc., Suite 200, 200 Chisholm Place, Plano, TX 75075. Phone: 972-423-9494. Fax: 972-423-0819. Authorized power: 50-w. each. Antenna: 400-ft. above ground. Lat. 31° 49' 29", long. 97° 09' 33". Transmitter: 4.3-mi. NW of West Waco. Equipment: ITS transmitter; Andrew antenna. Ownership: Nucentrix Broadband Networks.

Wharton—WMX228 (H1). Wireless One Inc., Suite 400, 2506 Lakeland Dr., Jackson, MS 39208. Phone: 601-933-6879. Authorized power: 10-w. Antenna: 204-ft. above ground. Lat. 29° 13' 30", long. 96° 15' 47". Transmitter: 1504 E. Jackson, El Campo. Equipment: ITS transmitter; Andrew antenna. Requests change to 50-w., 349-ft. above ground, lat. 26° 16' 53", long. 96° 02' 27"; transmitter to 4.3-mi. SE of Wharton. Ownership: Wireless One Inc.

Wharton—WMX229 (H3). Wireless One Inc., Suite 400, 2506 Lakeland Dr., Jackson, MS 39208. Phone: 601-933-6879. Authorized power: 10-w. Antenna: 204-ft. above ground. Lat. 29° 13' 30", long. 96° 15' 47". Transmitter: 1504 E. Jackson, El Campo. Equipment: ITS transmitter; Andrew antenna. Requests change to 50-w., 349-ft. above ground, lat. 29° 16' 53", long. 96° 02' 27"; transmitter to 4.3-mi. SE of Wharton. Ownership: Wireless One Inc.

Wichita Falls—WMI354 (E group). Mester's TV, Box 300406, 682 Argyle Rd., Brooklyn, NY 11230-0406. Phone: 718-282-9090. Fax: 718-469-0881. Authorized power: 10-w. each. Antenna: 449-ft. above ground. Lat. 33° 53' 00", long. 98° 36' 10". Transmitter: 4000 N Hwy. 369/277. Equipment: ITS transmitter; Andrew antenna. Ownership: Mester's TV.
Leased to Heartland Wireless Commercial Channels Inc., 200 Chisholm Place, Suite 200, Plano, TX 75075. Phone: 972-423-9494. Fax: 972-423-0819.

Wichita Falls—WMH356 (F group). Microband Corp. of America. Authorized power: 20-w. each. Antenna: 449-ft. above ground. Lat. 33° 53' 00", long. 98° 36' 10". Transmitter: 4000 N. Hwy. 369/277. Equipment: ITS transmitter; Andrew antenna. Ownership: The Microband Companies Inc.

Wichita Falls—WNTJ391 (H1). John Dudeck, 11672 Harborside Court, Largo, FL 33773. Phone: 813-397-2759. Authorized power: 50-w. Antenna: 445-ft. above ground. Lat. 33° 53' 00", long. 98° 36' 10". Transmitter: 4000 N. Hwy. 369/277. Equipment: Comwave transmitter; Andrew antenna. Ownership: John Dudeck.

Wichita Falls—WNTJ394 (H2). Blake Twedt, 5102 Rosegreen Court, Tampa, FL 33624. Phone: 727-587-9959. Authorized power: 50-w. Antenna: 445-ft. above ground. Lat. 33° 53' 00", long. 98° 36' 10". Transmitter: 4000 N. Hwy. 369/277. Equipment: Comwave transmitter; Andrew antenna. Ownership: Blake Twedt.

Utah

Cedar City—WMH289 (F group). Communication Innovations Corp., 145 Huguenot St., New Rochelle, NY 10801. Phone: 914-576-6622. Authorized power: 10-w. each. Antenna: 84-ft. above ground. Lat. 37° 40' 12", long. 113° 04' 59". Transmitter: 1-mi. SW of Cedar City. Equipment: Comwave transmitter; Andrew antenna. Ownership: Communication Innovations Corp.

Delta—WMI395 (F group). Pisces Microcable Partnership, 67-755 Peineta Rd., Palm Springs, CA 92262. Phone: 619-323-2199. Authorized power: 10-w. each. Antenna: 50-ft. above ground. Lat. 39° 21' 29", long. 112° 34' 52". Transmitter: UPRR Depot. Equipment: Scientific-Atlanta transmitter; Andrew antenna. Ownership: Pisces Microcable Partnership.

Magna—WLW775 (E group). Alda Wireless Holdings Inc., 5301 E. Broadway Blvd., Tucson, AZ 85711. Phone: 520-519-4400. Fax: 520-747-6830. Web site: http://www.pchoice.tv.com. Authorized power: 10-w. each. Antenna: 75-ft. above ground. Lat. 40° 39' 35", long. 112° 12' 05". Transmitter: Farnsworth Peak. Equipment: Emcee transmitter; Andrew antenna. Ownership: Matthew Oristano.
Leased to People's Choice TV Corp., 5301 E. Broadway Blvd., Tucson, AZ 85711. Phone: 520-519-4400.

Magna—WHT692 (F group). Alda Wireless Holdings Inc., 5301 E. Broadway Blvd., Tucson, AZ 85711. Phone: 520-519-4400. Fax: 520-747-6830. Authorized power: 10-w. each. Antenna: 75-ft. above ground. Lat. 40° 39' 35", long. 112° 12' 05". Transmitter: Farnsworth Peak. Equipment: Emcee transmitter; Andrew antenna. Ownership: Matthew Oristano.

Magna—WNTB421 (H1). Alda Wireless Holdings Inc., 5301 E. Broadway Blvd., Tucson, AZ 85711. Phone: 520-519-4400. Fax: 520-747-6830. Web site: http://www.pchoice.tv.com. Authorized power: 10-w. Antenna: 75-ft. above ground. Lat. 40° 39' 35", long. 112° 12' 05". Transmitter: Farnsworth Peak. Equipment: Emcee transmitter; Andrew antenna. Ownership: Matthew Oristano.
Leased to People's Choice TV Corp., 5301 E. Broadway Blvd., Tucson, AZ 85711. Phone: 520-519-4400.

Magna—WNTB690 (H2). Alda Wireless Holdings Inc., 5301 E. Broadway Blvd., Tucson, AZ 85711. Phone: 520-519-4400. Fax: 520-747-6830. Authorized power: 100-w. Antenna: 77-ft. above ground. Lat. 40° 39' 35", long. 112° 12' 05". Transmitter: Farnsworth Peak. Equipment: ITS transmitter; Andrew antenna. Ownership: Matthew Oristano.

Magna—WNTB688 (H3). Alda Wireless Holdings Inc., 5301 E. Broadway Blvd., Tucson, AZ 85711. Phone: 520-519-4400. Fax: 520-747-6830. Web site: http://www.pchoice.tv.com. Authorized power: 10-w. Antenna: 75-ft. above ground. Lat. 40° 39' 35", long. 112° 12' 05". Transmitter: Farnsworth Peak. Equipment: Emcee transmitter; Andrew antenna. Ownership: Matthew Oristano.

Leased to People's Choice TV Corp., 5301 E. Broadway Blvd., Tucson, AZ 85711. Phone: 520-519-4400.

Provo-Orem—WMH776 (E group). Timpview Wireless Inc., 845 E. Skyline Dr., St. George, UT 84770. Authorized power: 10-w. each. Antenna: 69-ft. above ground. Lat. 40° 05' 17", long. 111° 49' 16". Transmitter: West Mountain, SW of Provo. Equipment: Comwave transmitter; Andrew antenna. Ownership: Timpview Wireless Inc.

Provo-Orem—WMH696 (F group). Timpview Wireless Inc., 845 E. Skyline Dr., St. George, UT 84770. Authorized power: 50-w. each. Antenna: 75-ft. above ground. Lat. 40° 05' 17", long. 111° 49' 16". Transmitter: West Mountain, SW of Provo. Equipment: Emcee transmitter; Andrew antenna. Ownership: Champion Industries Inc.

Santaquin—WNTJ437 (H3). SenVista General Partnership, 7521 E. Edgemont, Scottsdale, AZ 85257. Phone: 602-994-3493. Authorized power: 10-w. Antenna: 193-ft. above ground. Lat. 39° 58' 40", long. 111° 46' 26". Transmitter: 1000-ft. N of Rte. 6. Equipment: Comwave transmitter; Andrew antenna. Ownership: SenVista General Partnership.

St. George—WMI367 (E group). American Wireless Inc., Box 2500, 845 E. Skyline Dr., St. George, UT 84771. Phone: 435-674-0320. Fax: 435-674-7679. Authorized power: 50-w. each. Antenna: 40-ft. above ground. Lat. 37° 03' 49", long. 113° 34' 20". Transmitter: 2.4-mi. S of St. George. Equipment: ITS transmitter; Andrew antenna. Ownership: American Wireless Inc.

St. George—WMI363 (F group). American Wireless Inc., Box 2500, 845 E. Skyline Dr., St. George, UT 84771. Phone: 435-674-0320. Fax: 435-674-7679. Authorized power: 50-w. each. Antenna: 40-ft. above ground. Lat. 37° 03' 49", long. 113° 34' 20". Transmitter: 2.4-mi. S of St. George. Equipment: ITS transmitter; Andrew antenna. Ownership: American Wireless Inc.

St. George—WNTJ366 (H group). American Wireless Inc., Box 2500, 845 E. Skyline Dr., St. George, UT 84771. Phone: 435-674-0320. Fax: 435-674-7679. Authorized power: 50-w. each. Antenna: 40-ft. above ground. Lat. 37° 03' 49", long. 113° 34' 20". Transmitter: 2.4-mi. S of St. George. Equipment: ITS transmitter; Andrew antenna. Ownership: American Wireless Inc.

Vermont

Baltimore/White River Junction—WLW890 (E group). Satellite Signals of New England Inc., 168 N. Main St., Rutland, VT 05701. Phone: 802-775-4112. Authorized power: 10-w. each. Antenna: 50-ft. above ground. Lat. 43° 22' 05", long. 72° 34' 49". Transmitter: Hawks Mountain. Equipment: Emcee transmitter; Bogner antenna. Ownership: Satellite Signals of New England Inc.

Burlington—WMI818 (E group). Lawrence N. Brandt, Suite 220, 3201 New Mexico Ave. NW, Washington, DC 20016. Phone: 202-363-1100. Authorized power: 10-w. each. Antenna: 362-ft. above ground. Lat. 44° 27' 03", long. 73° 11' 51". Transmitter: Joy Dr. Equipment: Comwave transmitter; Bogner antenna. Ownership: Lawrence N. Brandt.

Burlington—WNTI675 (H1). Ivan Nachman, Suite 201, 7800 113th St. N, Seminole, FL 34642. Phone: 813-392-1681. Authorized power: 20-w. Antenna: 88-ft. above ground. Lat. 44° 31' 32", long. 72° 48' 54". Transmitter: 20-mi. E of Burlington. Equipment: ITS transmitter; Andrew antenna. Ownership: Ivan Nachman.

Burlington—WNTI680 (H2). Blake Twedt, 5102 Rosegreen Court, Tampa, FL 33624. Phone: 727-587-9959. Authorized power: 20-w. Antenna: 88-ft. above ground. Lat. 44° 31' 32", long. 72° 48' 54". Transmitter: 20-mi. E of Burlington. Equipment: ITS transmitter; Andrew antenna. Ownership: Blake Twedt.

Burlington—WNTH842 (H3). John Dudeck, 11672 Harborside Court, Largo, FL 33773. Authorized power: 20-w. Antenna: 88-ft. above ground. Lat. 44° 31' 32", long. 72° 48' 54". Transmitter: 20-mi. E of Burlington. Equipment: ITS transmitter; Andrew antenna. Ownership: John Dudeck.

Cornwall—WMH308 (E group). Satellite Signals of New England Inc., 168 N. Main St., Rutland, VT 05701. Phone: 802-775-4112. Authorized power: 10-w. each. Antenna: 50-ft. above ground. Lat. 43° 59' 46", long. 73° 12' 30". Transmitter: 3-mi. N of Cornwall. Equipment: Emcee transmitter; Bogner antenna. Ownership: Satellite Signals of New England Inc.

East Enosburg—WMH464 (E group). Satellite Signals of New England Inc., 168 N. Main St., Rutland, VT 05701. Phone: 802-775-4112. Authorized power: 10-w. each. Antenna: 50-ft. above ground. Lat. 44° 53' 03", long. 72° 42' 07". Transmitter: 2-mi. NE of East Enosburg. Equipment: Emcee transmitter; Bogner antenna. Ownership: Satellite Signals of New England Inc.

Lyndonville—WLR471 (H2). New England Wireless Inc., Box 470, Rte. 5 S, Ascutney, VT 05030. Phone: 802-674-2206. Fax: 802-674-2751. Authorized power: 20-w. Antenna: 128-ft. above ground. Lat. 44° 34' 16", long. 71° 53' 39". Transmitter: 6-mi. ENE of Lyndonville. Equipment: ITS transmitter; Andrew antenna. Ownership: New England Wireless Inc.

Lyndonville—WLR479 (H3). New England Wireless Inc., Box 470, Rte. 5 S, Ascutney, VT 05030. Phone: 802-674-2206. Fax: 802-674-2751. Authorized power: 20-w. Antenna: 128-ft. above ground. Lat. 44° 34' 16", long. 71° 53' 39". Transmitter: 6-mi. ENE of Lyndonville. Equipment: ITS transmitter; Andrew antenna. Ownership: New England Wireless Inc.

Rutland—WLK341 (E group). Satellite Signals of New England Inc., Box 608, Barre, VT 05641. Phone: 802-476-3426. Authorized power: 50-w. each. Antenna: 125-ft. above ground. Lat. 43° 39' 32", long. 73° 06' 25". Transmitter: Grandpa's Knob. Equipment: Comwave transmitter; Andrew antenna. Ownership: Satellite Signals of New England Inc.

Rutland—WNTI856 (H group). Satellite Signals of New England Inc., Box 608, Barre, VT 05641. Phone: 802-476-3426. Authorized power: 50-w. each. Antenna: 125-ft. above ground. Lat. 43° 39' 32", long. 73° 06' 25". Transmitter: Grandpa's Knob. Equipment: ITS transmitter; Andrew antenna. Ownership: Satellite Signals of New England Inc.

Virginia

Bridgewater—WMX331 (E group). CFW Licenses, Suite 300, 401 Spring Lane, Waynesboro, VA 22980. Phone: 540-946-3500. Fax: 540-946-3599. Authorized power: 10-w. each. Antenna: 104-ft. above ground. Lat. 38° 23' 27", long. 78° 59' 40". Transmitter: 1.5-mi. NW of Bridgewater. Equipment: Emcee transmitter; Andrew antenna. Ownership: CFW Communications.

Leased to CFW Cable Inc.

Bridgewater—WMX327 (F group). CFW Licenses, Suite 300, 401 Spring Lane, Waynesboro, VA 22980. Phone: 540-946-3500. Fax: 540-946-3599. Authorized power: 10-w. each. Antenna: 122-ft. above ground. Lat. 38° 23' 36", long. 78° 46' 12". Transmitter: 1.5-mi. NW of Bridgewater. Equipment: Emcee transmitter; Andrew antenna. Ownership: CFW Communications.

Leased to CFW Cable Inc.

Buchanan—WNTH926 (H1). Richard Amons Jr., Box 174, 100 Roanoke Rd., Daleville, VA 24083-0174. Phone: 540-992-2211. Authorized power: 50-w. Antenna: 174-ft. above ground. Lat. 37° 30' 57", long. 79° 40' 37". Transmitter: 0.7-mi. S of Buchanan. Equipment: Comwave transmitter; Andrew antenna. Ownership: R & B Communications Inc.

Charlottesville—WMH388 (E group). CFW Licenses Inc., Suite 300, 401 Spring Lane, Waynesboro, VA 22980. Phone: 540-946-3500. Fax: 540-946-3599. Authorized power: 50-w. each. Antenna: 273-ft. above ground. Lat. 37° 58' 57", long. 78° 28' 58". Transmitter: Carters Mountain. Equipment: ITS transmitter; Andrew antenna. Requests change to 92-ft. above ground, lat. 38° 04' 17", long. 78° 42' 17"; transmitter to 0.25-mi. WNW of Crozet. Ownership: CFW Communications.

Leased to CFW Cable Inc.

Charlottesville—WLW840 (F group). CFW Licenses Inc., Suite 300, 401 Spring Lane, Waynesboro, VA 22980. Phone: 540-946-3599. Fax: 540-946-3599. Authorized power: 50-w. each. Antenna: 273-ft. above ground. Lat. 37° 58' 57", long. 78° 28' 58". Transmitter: Carters Mountain. Equipment: ITS transmitter; Andrew antenna. Requests change to 92-ft. above ground, lat. 38° 04' 17", long. 78° 42' 17", transmitter to 0.25-mi.WNW of Crozct.Equipment: Mark antenna. Ownership: CFW Communications.

Charlottesville—WNTH948 (H group). CFW Licenses Inc., Suite 300, 401 Spring Lane, Waynesboro, VA 22980. Phone: 540-946-3500. Fax: 540-946-3599. Antenna: 199-ft. above ground. Lat. 37° 58' 57", long. 78° 28' 58". Transmitter: Carters Mountain. Equipment: ITS transmitter; Andrew antenna. Requests change to 92-ft. above ground, lat. 38° 04' 17", long. 78° 42' 17"; transmitter to 0.25-mi. WNW of Crozet. Ownership: CFW Communications.

Danville—WLW697 (E group). Alda Wireless Holdings Inc., 5301 E. Broadway Blvd., Tucson, AZ 85711-8181. Phone: 520-519-4400. Fax: 520-747-6830. Authorized power: 10-w. each. Antenna: 324-ft. above ground. Lat. 36° 44' 28", long. 79° 23' 05". Transmitter: White Oak Mountain. Equipment: Comwave transmitter; Bogner antenna. Ownership: Matthew Oristano.

Danville—WMI381 (F group). Broadcast Data Corp., Suite 247, 189 Berdan Ave., Wayne, NJ 07470. Phone: 201-831-7407. Authorized power: 10-w. each. Antenna: 324-ft. above ground. Lat. 36° 44' 28", long. 79° 23' 05". Transmitter: 6-mi. N of Danville. Equipment: Comwave transmitter; Bogner antenna. Ownership: Broadcast Data Corp.

Driver—WHT729 (E group). Jody Barnes c/o Secure Business Communications, Suite 204, 3628 Lynoak, Claremont, CA 91711. Phone: 909-621-1004. Authorized power: 50-w. each. Antenna: 801-ft. above ground. Lat. 36° 48' 56", long. 76° 28' 00". Transmitter: WTKR(TV) Tower, 2-mi. E of Driver. Equipment: Comband (GE) transmitter; Andrew antenna. Ownership: Jody Barnes.

Driver—WHT730 (F group). East West Communications Inc., Suite 102-D, 1682 E. Gude Dr., Rockville, MD 20850. Phone: 301-251-1020. Fax: 301-251-0716. Authorized power: 50-w. each. Antenna: 801-ft. above ground. Lat. 36° 48' 56", long. 76° 28' 00". Transmitter: WTKR(TV) tower, 2-mi. E of Driver. Equipment: Comband (GE) transmitter; Andrew antenna. Ownership: East West Communications Inc.

Leased to CAI Wireless Systems Inc., 2101 Wilson Blvd., Suite 100, Arlington, VA 22201. Phone: 703-812-8800.

Driver—WNTB576 (H1). Hampton Roads License Inc., Suite 100, 2101 Wilson Blvd., Arlington, VA 22201. Phone: 703-875-7682. Authorized power: 50-w. Antenna: 801-ft. above ground. Lat. 36° 48' 56", long. 76° 28' 00". Transmitter: WTKR(TV) tower, 2-mi. E of Driver. Equipment: ITS transmitter; Andrew antenna. Ownership: Hampton Roads License Inc.

Driver—WNTB962 (H2). Libmot Communications Partnership, 2700 Chain Bridge Rd. NW, Washington, DC 20016. Phone: 202-966-2167. Fax: 202-237-7742. Authorized power: 50-w. Antenna: 801-ft. above ground. Lat. 36° 48' 56", long. 76° 28' 00". Transmitter: WTKR(TV) tower, 2-mi. E of Driver. Equipment: Comband transmitter; Andrew antenna. Ownership: Libmot Communications Partnership.

Leased to Hampton Roads Wireless Inc., 2101 Wilson Blvd., Suite 100, Arlington, VA 22201. Phone: 703-812-8800.

Driver—WNTB262 (H3). Cotopaxi Communications Corp., 60 Jefferson Davis Dr., Martinsville, VA 24112. Authorized power: 50-w. Antenna: 801-ft. above ground. Lat. 36° 48' 56", long. 76° 28' 00". Transmitter: WTKR(TV) tower, 2-mi. E of Driver. Equipment: ITS transmitter; Andrew antenna. Ownership: Cotopaxi Communications.

Lexington—WMX242 (H1). Wireless Properties of Virginia Inc., Suite 201, 4065 N. Sinton Rd., Colorado Springs, CO 80907. Phone: 719-632-5544. Fax: 719-632-5549. Antenna: 50-ft. above ground. Lat. 37° 47' 15", long. 79° 29' 11". Transmitter: 3-mi. W of Lexington. Ownership: American Telecasting Inc.

Lexington—WMX241 (H2). Wireless Properties of Virginia Inc., Suite 201, 4065 N.

Sinton Rd., Colorado Springs, CO 80907. Phone: 719-632-5544. Fax: 719-632-5549. Antenna: 50-ft. above ground. Lat. 37° 47' 15", long. 79° 29' 11". Transmitter: 3-mi. W of Lexington. Ownership: American Telecasting Inc.

Lexington—WMX240 (H3). Wireless Properties of Virginia Inc., Suite 201, 4065 N. Sinton Rd., Colorado Springs, CO 80907. Phone: 719-632-5544. Fax: 719-632-5549. Antenna: 50-ft. above ground. Lat. 37° 47' 15", long. 79° 29' 11". Transmitter: 3-mi. W of Lexington. Ownership: American Telecasting Inc.

Lynchburg—WNTU756 (H1). Ivan C. Nachman, Suite 201, 7800 113th St. N, Seminole, FL 34642. Phone: 813-392-1681. Authorized power: 10-w. Antenna: 195-ft. above ground. Lat. 37° 33' 47", long. 79° 11' 38". Transmitter: High Peak Mountain. Equipment: ITS transmitter; Andrew antenna. Ownership: Ivan C. Nachman.

Lynchburg—WNTH817 (H2). John Dudeck, 11672 Harborside Circle N, Largo, FL 33773. Authorized power: 10-w. Antenna: 195-ft. above ground. Lat. 37° 33' 47", long. 79° 11' 38". Transmitter: High Peak Mountain. Equipment: ITS transmitter; Andrew antenna. Ownership: John Dudeck.

Richmond—WHT735 (E group). Grand MMDS Alliance Richmond E/P Partnership, Box 300406, Brooklyn, NY 11230. Phone: 718-253-1880. Fax: 718-468-0881. Authorized power: 50-w. each. Antenna: 1003-ft. above ground. Lat. 37° 30' 15", long. 77° 42' 13". Transmitter: 201 Dry Bridge Rd. Equipment: Emcee transmitter; Andrew antenna. Ownership: Macro Distribution Systems Inc.
Leased to CFW Communications Inc./CFW Cable Inc., 401 Spring Lane, Suite 300, Waynesboro, VA 22980-7590. Phone: 540-946-3500. Fax: 540-946-3599.

Richmond—WHT736 (F group). CFW Licenses Inc., Suite 300, 401 Spring Lane, Waynesboro, VA 22980-7590. Phone: 540-946-3500. Fax: 540-946-3599. Authorized power: 50-w. each. Antenna: 1003-ft. above ground. Lat. 37° 30' 15", long. 77° 42' 13". Transmitter: 201 Dry Bridge Rd. Equipment: ITS transmitter; Andrew antenna. Ownership: CFW Communications.
Leased to CFW Cable Inc.

Richmond—WNTJ713 (H1). Blake Twedt, 5102 Rosegreen Court, Tampa, FL 33624. Phone: 727-587-9959. Authorized power: 50-w. Antenna: 1003-ft. above ground. Lat. 37° 30' 15", long. 77° 42' 13". Transmitter: Richmond. Equipment: Emcee transmitter; Andrew antenna. Ownership: Blake Twedt.

Richmond—WNTJ739 (H3). Blake Twedt, 5102 Rosegreen Court, Tampa, FL 33624. Phone: 727-587-9959. Authorized power: 50-w. Antenna: 1003-ft. above ground. Lat. 37° 30' 15", long. 77° 42' 13". Transmitter: Richmond. Equipment: Emcee transmitter; Andrew antenna. Ownership: Blake Twedt.

Roanoke—WGW371 (F group). Steven A. Davie, Suite F, Medical Arts Bldg., 3708 S. Main St., Blacksburg, VA 24060. Phone: 540-552-6220. Authorized power: 10-w. each. Antenna: 166-ft. above ground. Lat. 37° 11' 35", long. 80° 09' 29". Transmitter: Poor Mountain. Equipment: Emcee transmitter; Andrew antenna. Ownership: Steven A. Davie.

Roanoke—WNTH507 (H2). Libmot Communications Partnership, 2700 Chain Bridge Rd. NW, Washington, DC 20016. Phone: 202-966-2167. Fax: 202-237-7742. Antenna: 199-ft. above ground. Lat. 37° 11' 35", long. 80° 09' 29". Transmitter: Poor Mountain. Equipment: Emcee transmitter; Andrew antenna. Ownership: Libmot Communications Partnership.
Leased to Digital Broadcast Corp., 1010 Northern Blvd., Suite 208, Great Neck, NY 11021.

West Augusta—WMX366 (H group). CFW Licenses, Suite 300, 401 Spring Lane, Waynesboro, VA 22980. Phone: 540-946-3500. Fax: 540-946-3599. Antenna: 122-ft. above ground. Lat. 38° 23' 36", long. 78° 46' 12". Transmitter: Rte. 250, 2.8-mi. NW of West Augusta. Ownership: CFW Communications.
Leased to CFW Cable Inc.

Winchester—WNTI796 (H group). Wireless Properties of Virginia Inc., Suite 201, 4065 N. Sinton Rd., Colorado Springs, CO 80907. Phone: 719-632-5544. Fax: 719-632-5549. Antenna: 195-ft. above ground. Lat. 39° 25' 16", long. 78° 05' 12". Transmitter: County Rtes. 45/9 & 45/14. Ownership: American Telecasting Inc.

Wytheville—WNTI942 (H group). CFW Licenses, Suite 300, 401 Spring Lane, Waynesboro, VA 22980. Phone: 540-946-3500. Fax: 540-946-3599. Authorized power: 10-w. each. Antenna: 120-ft. above ground. Lat. 36° 54' 30", long. 81° 04' 15". Transmitter: 2.7-mi. S of Wytheville. Equipment: Comwave transmitter; Andrew antenna. Ownership: CFW Communications.

Washington

Bellingham—WLW741 (E group). TV2S, 1811 D. Roache Harbor Rd., Friday Harbor, WA 98250. Authorized power: 10-w. each. Antenna: 100-ft. above ground. Lat. 48° 29' 01", long. 122° 19' 24". Transmitter: 0.5-mi. N of Bellingham. Equipment: Emcee transmitter; Andrew antenna. Ownership: TV2S.

Bellingham—WLW745 (F group). American Telecasting Development Inc., Suite 300, 5575 Tech Center Dr., Colorado Springs, CO 80919. Phone: 719-260-5533. Fax: 719-260-5010. Authorized power: 100-w. each. Antenna: 400-ft. above ground. Lat. 48° 40' 45", long. 122° 50' 31". Transmitter: Mount Constitution. Equipment: Emcee transmitter; Andrew antenna. Ownership: American Telecasting Inc.

Bremerton—WMI890 (E group). Sun Multi-Channel MDS Inc., Suite 500, 3200 Cherry Creek S Dr., Denver, CO 80209. Authorized power: 10-w. each. Antenna: 497-ft. above ground. Lat. 47° 32' 53", long. 122° 48' 22". Transmitter: Gold Mountain, 3-mi. W of Bremerton. Equipment: Emcee transmitter; Bogner antenna. Ownership: Sun Multi-Channel MDS Inc.

Ephrata—WMI411 (E group). Paul M. Benson, 5178 Griffin Lane, Vacaville, CA 95688. Phone: 209-384-7448. Authorized power: 10-w. each. Antenna: 310-ft. above ground. Lat. 47° 06' 16", long. 119° 17' 32". Transmitter: Marsh Island. Equipment: Scientific-Atlanta transmitter; Andrew antenna. Ownership: Paul M. Benson.

Kennewick—WNTJ460 (H group). WBSY Licensing Corp., Suite 120, 4700 S. McClintock, Tempe, AZ 85282. Phone & fax: 602-755-7524. Authorized power: 10-w. each. Antenna: 84-ft. above ground. Lat. 46° 06' 12", long. 119° 07' 45". Transmitter: Jump off Joe Butte. Equipment: Comwave transmitter; Andrew antenna. Ownership: Multi-Micro Inc. Sale pends to Boston Ventures Co. LP IV.
Leased to Cardiff Broadcasting Group.

Olympia—WMI350 (E group). Jack G. Hubbard, 8793 Ranch Dr., Chesterland, OH 44026. Phone & Fax: 216-729-7282. Authorized power: 10-w. each. Antenna: 50-ft. above ground. Lat. 46° 58' 22", long. 123° 08' 17". Transmitter: Capitol Peak Point, Section 12. Equipment: Comwave transmitter; Bogner antenna. Ownership: Jack G. Hubbard.
Leased to National Micro Vision Systems Inc., 270 Bristol St., Suite 101, Costa Mesa, CA 92626. Phone: 714-708-8637.

Olympia—WMH725 (F group). Stephanie Engstrom, Apt. 204, 420 S. Catalina Ave., Redondo Beach, CA 90277. Phone & fax: 310-540-9867. Authorized power: 10-w. each. Antenna: 50-ft. above ground. Lat. 46° 58' 22", long. 123° 08' 17". Transmitter: Capitol Peak Point, Section 12. Equipment: Comwave transmitter; Bogner antenna. Ownership: Stephanie Engstrom.

Richland—WML477 (E group). National Wireless Video Inc., 24 Oak Dr., Durham, NC 27707. Authorized power: 10-w. each. Antenna: 84-ft. above ground. Lat. 46° 06' 12", long. 119° 07' 45". Transmitter: Jump off Joe Butte, near Richland. Equipment: Emcee transmitter; Bogner antenna. Ownership: National Wireless Video.

Seattle—WHT656 (E group). Jack G. Hubbard, 8793 Ranch Dr., Chesterland, OH 44026. Phone & fax: 216-729-7282. Authorized power: 10-w. each. Antenna: 954-ft. above ground. Lat. 47° 36' 17", long. 122° 19' 46". Transmitter: 701 5th Ave. Equipment: Emcee transmitter; Andrew antenna. Ownership: Jack G. Hubbard.
Leased to American Telecasting Inc., 5575 Tech Center Dr., Suite 300, Colorado Springs, CO 80918. Phone: 719-260-5533. Fax: 719-260-5010.

Seattle—WHT657 (F group). Sherry Rullman, Box 345, Claremont, CA 91711. Phone: 909-625-2988. Antenna: 954-ft. above ground. Lat. 47° 36' 17", long. 122° 19' 46". Transmitter: 701 5th Ave. Equipment: Emcee transmitter; Andrew antenna. Requests change to 10-w. each, lat. 47° 12' 52", long. 122° 27' 53". Ownership: Sherry Rullman.

Seattle—WHJ910 (H2). Associated Information Services Corp., 200 Gateway Towers, Pittsburgh, PA 15222. Antenna: 556-ft. above ground. Lat. 47° 36' 23", long. 122° 19' 51". Transmitter: 900 4th Ave. Ownership: Associated Information Services Corp.

Spokane—WHT783 (E group). Haddonfield Wireless Co., Box 7999, Suite 165, Mayaguez, PR 00681. Phone: 609-881-9360. E-mail: jdecelis@msn.com. Authorized power: 50-w. each. Antenna: 194-ft. above ground. Lat. 47° 34' 58", long. 117° 17' 37". Transmitter: Krell Hill, 4-mi. SE of Spokane. Equipment: Comwave transmitter; Andrew antenna. Ownership: Haddonfield Wireless Co.
Leased to Videotron/Wireless Holdings.

Spokane—WHT784 (F group). Stephanie Engstrom, Apt. 204, 420 S. Catalina Ave., Redondo Beach, CA 90277. Phone & fax: 310-540-9867. Authorized power: 50-w. each. Antenna: 194-ft. above ground. Lat. 47° 34' 58", long. 117° 17' 37". Transmitter: Krell Hill, 4-mi. SE of Spokane. Equipment: Comwave transmitter; Andrew antenna. Ownership: Stephanie Engstrom.

Spokane—WNTJ347 (H1). Spokane H Group Partnership, Suite 1-11, 12945 Seminole Blvd., Largo, FL 33778. Authorized power: 50-w. Antenna: 194-ft. above ground. Lat. 47° 34' 58", long. 117° 17' 37". Transmitter: Krell Hill, 4-mi. SE of Spokane. Ownership: Ivan Nachman.

Spokane—WNTJ346 (H2). Spokane H Group Partnership, Suite 1-11, 12945 Seminole Blvd., Largo, FL 33778. Authorized power: 50-w. Antenna: 194-ft. above ground. Lat. 47° 34' 58", long. 117° 17' 37". Transmitter: Krell Hill, 4-mi. SE of Spokane. Ownership: Ivan Nachman.

Spokane—WNTJ345 (H3). Spokane H Group Partnership, Suite 1-11, 12945 Seminole Blvd., Largo, FL 33778. Authorized power: 50-w. Antenna: 194-ft. above ground. Lat. 47° 34' 58", long. 117° 17' 37". Transmitter: Krell Hill, 4-mi. SE of Spokane. Ownership: Ivan Nachman.

Yakima—WLK396 (E group). WBSY Licensing Corp., Suite 325, 9250 E. Costilla Ave., Englewood, CO 80112. Phone: 509-248-9038. Authorized power: 50-w. each. Antenna: 114-ft. above ground. Lat. 46° 31' 01", long. 120° 24' 02". Transmitter: Rattlesnake Ridge. Equipment: Emcee transmitter; Andrew antenna. Ownership: Wireless Broadcasting Systems of America Inc. Sale pends to Boston Ventures Co. LP IV.

Yakima—WLW944 (F group). Presco Corp., 4547 4th Ave. NE, Seattle, WA 98105. Phone: 206-545-0268. Authorized power: 50-w. each. Antenna: 114-ft. above ground. Lat. 46° 31' 01", long. 120° 24' 02". Transmitter: Rattlesnake Ridge. Equipment: Emcee transmitter; Andrew antenna. Ownership: Presco Corp.

Yakima—WNTJ283 (H1). Ivan C. Nachman, 10300 97th St. N, Seminole, FL 34643. Phone: 813-392-0335. Authorized power: 50-w. Antenna: 114-ft. above ground. Lat. 46° 31' 01", long. 120° 24' 02". Transmitter: Rattlesnake Ridge. Equipment: Emcee transmitter; Andrew antenna. Ownership: Ivan Nachman.

Yakima—WNTI815 (H2). Tharrell D. Ming. Authorized power: 20-w. Antenna: 117-ft. above ground. Lat. 46° 31' 01", long. 120° 24' 02". Transmitter: Rattlesnake Ridge. Equipment: ITS transmitter; Andrew antenna. Ownership: Tharrell D. Ming.

Yakima—WNTI804 (H3). John Dudeck, 1162 Haborside Circle, Largo, FL 33773. Authorized power: 20-w. Antenna: 114-ft. above ground. Lat. 46° 31' 01", long. 120° 24' 02". Transmitter: Rattlesnake Ridge. Equipment: ITS transmitter; Andrew antenna. Ownership: John Dudeck.

West Virginia

Charleston—WMY398 (E group). Nucentrix Spectrum Resources Inc., Suite 200, 200 Chisholm Place, Plano, TX 75075. Phone: 972-423-9494. Fax: 972-423-0819. Authorized power: 10-w. each. Antenna: 247-ft. above ground. Lat. 38° 23' 58", long. 81° 46' 43". Transmitter: Golf Mountain Rd., 8-mi. WNW of Charleston. Equipment: Emcee transmitter; Bogner antenna. Ownership: Nucentrix Broadband Networks.

Martinsburg—WMY290 (E group). Wireless Properties of Virginia Inc., Suite G-100, 625 Slaters Lane, Alexandria, VA 22314. Phone: 703-683-8726. Authorized power: 10-w. each. Antenna: 100-ft. above ground. Lat. 38° 58' 30", long. 78° 29' 56". Transmitter: 5-mi. W of Strasburg. Equipment: Emcee transmitter; Andrew antenna. Ownership: American Telecasting Inc.

Martinsburg—WMY291 (F group). Wireless Properties of Virginia Inc., Suite G-100, 625 Slaters Lane, Alexandria, VA 22314. Phone: 703-683-8726. Authorized power: 10-w. each.

Antenna: 100-ft. above ground. Lat. 38° 58' 30", long. 78° 29' 56". Transmitter: 5-mi. W of Strasburg. Equipment: Emcee transmitter; Andrew antenna. Ownership: American Telecasting Inc.

Martinsburg—WMY489 (H1). Shannondale Wireless, 3623 Parklane Rd., Fairfax, VA 22030. Phone: 703-691-1119. Fax: 703-691-8938. E-mail: mkelley@gmu.edu. Authorized power: 50-w. Antenna: 195-ft. above ground. Lat. 39° 25' 16", long. 78° 05' 19". Transmitter: North Mountain. Equipment: Comwave transmitter; Bogner antenna. Ownership: Michael R. Kelley.
Leased to CFW Cable Inc., 401 Spring Lane, Suite 300, Waynesboro, VA 22980. Phone: 540-946-3511.

Morgantown—WMH412 (F group). MDS Signal Group, Suite 810, 1627 Eye St. NW, Washington, DC 20006. Phone: 202-293-0700. Authorized power: 10-w. each. Antenna: 468-ft. above ground. Lat. 39° 17' 27", long. 80° 18' 56". Transmitter: 8-mi. SE of Morgantown. Equipment: ITS transmitter; Bogner antenna. Ownership: MDS Signal Group.

Parkersburg—WMI413 (F group). Parkersburg Wireless LLC, Suite 400E, 1025 Thomas Jefferson St. NW, Washington, DC 20007. Phone: 202-965-8126. Authorized power: 10-w. each. Antenna: 172-ft. above ground. Lat. 39° 18' 36", long. 81° 35' 49". Transmitter: 1.4-mi. N of Belpre. Equipment: Emcee transmitter; Andrew antenna. Ownership: Parkersburg Wireless LLC.

Wheeling—WLK289 (E group). Paul Communications Inc., 7555 Pebble Beach Dr., Reno, NV 89502. Phone: 602-319-3311. Authorized power: 10-w. each. Antenna: 355-ft. above ground. Lat. 40° 03' 41", long. 80° 45' 08". Transmitter: 0.5-mi. S of Bridgeport. Equipment: Emcee transmitter; Andrew antenna. Ownership: Paul Communications Inc.

Wisconsin

Appleton—WMI331 (F group). Family Entertainment Network Inc., 30 N. Harmon, Mitchell, SD 57301. Authorized power: 10-w. each. Antenna: 500-ft. above ground. Lat. 44° 15' 45", long. 88° 21' 55". Transmitter: 2727 E. Radio Rd. Equipment: Emcee transmitter; Andrew antenna. Ownership: Family Entertainment Network Inc.

Ashland—WMI337 (E group). Ashland Partners Alpha, 8027 Northbridge Dr., Spring, TX 77379. Phone: 713-370-7444. Authorized power: 10-w. each. Antenna: 604-ft. above ground. Lat. 46° 36' 55", long. 90° 49' 25". Transmitter: One E. Mack Rd. Equipment: ITS transmitter; Andrew antenna. Ownership: Ashland Partners Alpha.

Ashland—WMI341 (F group). Ashland Partners Beta, 8027 Northbridge Dr., Spring, TX 77379. Phone: 713-370-7444. Authorized power: 10-w. each. Antenna: 604-ft. above ground. Lat. 46° 36' 55", long. 90° 49' 25". Transmitter: One E. Mack Rd. Equipment: ITS transmitter; Andrew antenna. Ownership: Ashland Partners Beta.

Eau Claire—WMH497 (E group). MRC Telecommunications Inc., 275 N. Corporate Dr., Brookfield, WI 53045. Phone: 414-792-9700. Fax: 414-792-7712. Authorized power: 10-w. each. Antenna: 78-ft. above ground. Lat. 44° 47' 41", long. 90° 30' 40". Transmitter: 900 W. Clairemont. Equipment: Emcee transmitter; Andrew antenna. Ownership: MRC Telecommunications Inc.

Green Bay—WLW981 (E group). Fortuna Systems Corp., Box 1669, 819 Belleview Ave., Crested Butte, CO 81224. Phone: 970-349-5849. Authorized power: 50-w. each. Antenna: 604-ft. above ground. Lat. 44° 21' 32", long. 87° 58' 58". Transmitter: Scray's Hill. Equipment: Comwave transmitter; Andrew antenna. Ownership: Fortuna Systems Corp.

Green Bay—WLW980 (F group). MWTV Inc., 3401 E. Cholla St., Phoenix, AZ 85028. Phone: 602-996-3871. Authorized power: 50-w. each. Antenna: 604-ft. above ground. Lat. 44° 21' 32", long. 87° 58' 58". Transmitter: Scray's Hill. Equipment: Comwave transmitter; Andrew antenna. Ownership: MWTV Inc. Sale pends to American Telecasting of Green Bay Inc.

Green Bay—WMX342 (H2). Ivan C. Nachman, Suite 201, 7800 113th St. N, Seminole, FL 34642. Phone: 813-392-1681. Authorized power: 50-w. Antenna: 604-ft. above ground. Lat. 44° 21' 32", long. 87° 58' 58". Transmitter: Scray's Hill. Equipment: Comwave transmitter; Andrew antenna. Requests change to 374-ft. above ground. Ownership: Ivan Nachman.

Green Bay—WMH660 (H3). American Telecasting of Green Bay Inc., Suite 300, 5575 Tech Center Dr., Colorado Springs, CO 80919. Phone: 719-260-5533. Fax: 719-260-5010. Authorized power: 50-w. Antenna: 604-ft. above ground. Lat. 44° 21' 32", long. 87° 58' 58". Transmitter: Scray's Hill. Equipment: Comwave transmitter; Andrew antenna. Ownership: American Telecasting Inc.

La Crosse—WMH473 (E group). Tel-Com Wireless Cable TV Corp., 1506 N.E. 162nd St., North Miami Beach, FL 33162. Phone: 305-947-3010. Fax: 305-919-8154. E-mail: info@tel-com.net. Web site: http://tel-com.net. Authorized power: 10-w. each. Antenna: 211-ft. above ground. Lat. 43° 48' 44", long. 91° 11' 59". Transmitter: 93 Hixon Rd. Equipment: Emcee transmitter; Andrew antenna. Ownership: Tel-Com Wireless Cable TV Corp.
Leased to Wisconsin Wireless Cable TV, 335 Lang Dr., La Crosse, WI 54603. Phone: 608-782-4100.

La Crosse—WMH472 (F group). Tel-Com Wireless Cable TV Corp., 1506 N.E. 162nd St., North Miami Beach, FL 33162. Phone: 305-947-3010. Fax: 305-919-8154. E-mail: info@telcom.net. Web site: http://www.tel-com.net. Authorized power: 10-w. each. Antenna: 211-ft. above ground. Lat. 43° 48' 44", long. 91° 11' 59". Transmitter: 93 Hixon Rd. Equipment: Emcee transmitter; Andrew antenna. Ownership: Tel-Com Wireless Cable TV Corp.

La Crosse—WNTI731 (H group). Tel-Com Wireless Cable TV Corp., 1506 N.E. 162nd St., North Miami Beach, FL 33162. Phone: 305-947-3010. Fax: 305-919-8154. E-mail: info@tel-com.net. Web site: http://tel-com.net. Authorized power: 10-w. each. Antenna: 211-ft. above ground. Lat. 43° 48' 44", long. 91° 11' 59". Transmitter: 93 Hixon Rd. Equipment: Emcee transmitter; Andrew antenna. Ownership: Tel-Com Wireless Cable TV Corp.
Leased to Wisconsin Wireless Cable TV, 335 Lang Dr., La Crosse, WI 54603. Phone: 608-782-4100.

Madison—WDU380 (E group). Edna Cornaggia, 3628 Lynoak, Claremont, CA 91711. Authorized power: 50-w. each. Antenna: 1097-ft. above ground. Lat. 43° 03' 21", long. 89° 32' 05". Transmitter: 8559 Mineral Point Rd. Equipment: Comwave transmitter; Andrew antenna. Ownership: Edna Cornaggia.

Madison—WHT772 (F group). Skycable TV of Madison LLC, 2520 Todd Dr., Madison, WI 53713. Phone: 608-271-6999. Fax: 608-271-2256. E-mail: kegan@skycabletv.com. Web site: http://www.skycabletv.com. Authorized power: 50-w. each. Antenna: 1107-ft. above ground. Lat. 43° 03' 21", long. 89° 32' 06". Transmitter: 8559 Mineral Point Rd. Equipment: Comwave transmitter; Andrew antenna. Ownership: Skycable TV of Madison LLC.

Madison—WNTJ388 (H1). Skycable TV of Madison LLC, 2520 Todd Dr., Madison, WI 53713. Phone: 608-271-6999. Fax: 608-271-2256. E-mail: kegan@skycabletv.com. Web site: http://www.skycabletv.com. Authorized power: 50-w.Antenna: 1107-ft. above ground. Lat. 43° 03' 21", long. 89° 32' 05". Transmitter: 8559 Mineral Point Rd. Equipment: Comwave transmitter; Andrew antenna. Ownership: Skycable TV of Madison LLC.

Madison—WNTJ432 (H2). Skycable TV of Madison LLC, 2520 Todd Dr., Madison, WI 53713. Phone: 608-271-6999. Fax: 608-271-2256. E-mail: kegan@skycabletv.com, Web site: http://www.skycabletv.com. Authorized power: 50-w. Antenna: 1107-ft. above ground. Lat. 43° 03' 21", long. 89° 32' 05". Transmitter: 8500 Mineral Point Rd. Equipment: Comwave transmitter; Andrew antenna. Ownership: Skycable TV of Madison LLC.

Madison—WNTJ374 (H3). Skycable TV of Madison LLC, 2520 Todd Dr., Madison, WI 53713. Phone: 608-271-6999. Fax: 608-271-2256. E-mail: kegan@skycabletv.com. Web site: http://www.skycabletv.com. Authorized power: 50-w. Antenna: 1107-ft. above ground. Lat. 43° 03' 21", long. 89° 32' 05". Transmitter: 8500 Mineral Point Rd. Equipment: Comwave transmitter; Andrew antenna. Ownership: Skycable TV of Madison LLC.

Milwaukee—WLW871 (E group). Kansas City Microwave Communications Inc., 114 W. 11th St., Kansas City, MO 64105. Phone: 816-556-0325. Authorized power: 100-w. each. Antenna: 594-ft. above ground. Lat. 43° 02' 18", long. 87° 54' 05". Transmitter: First Wisconsin Center. Equipment: Comwave transmitter; Bogner antenna. Ownership: Kansas City Microwave Communications Inc.

Milwaukee—WHT641 (F group). al Charles H. Wilson, Sally K. Bang & Benito Gaguine, Co-personal Representatives of the Estate of John H. Wilson, 5th Floor, 1201 Pennsylvania Ave. NW, Washington, DC 20004. Phone: 202-626-6290. Authorized power: 100-w. each. Antenna: 594-ft. above ground. Lat. 43° 02' 18", long. 87° 54' 05". Transmitter: First Wisconsin Center. Equipment: Comwave transmitter; Bogner antenna. Ownership: John Hobart Wilson Estate.

Sheboygan—WMI362 (E group). American Telecasting of Green Bay Inc., Suite 300, 5575 Tech Center Dr., Colorado Springs, CO 80919. Phone: 719-260-5533. Fax: 719-260-5010. Authorized power: 10-w. each. Antenna: 230-ft. above ground. Lat. 43° 43' 53", long. 88° 17' 34". Transmitter: 8-mi. SE of Fond du Lac. Equipment: Comwave transmitter; Andrew antenna. Ownership: American Telecasting Inc.

Sheboygan—WMH688 (F group). American Telecasting of Green Bay Inc., Suite 300, 5575 Tech Center Dr., Colorado Springs, CO 80919. Phone: 719-260-5533. Fax: 719-260-5010. Authorized power: 10-w. each. Antenna: 230-ft. above ground. Lat. 43° 43' 53", long. 88° 17' 34". Transmitter: 8-mi. SE of Fond du Lac. Equipment: Comwave transmitter; Andrew antenna. Ownership: American Telecasting Inc.

Sheboygan—WNTK964 (H group). American Telecasting of Green Bay Inc., Suite 300, 5575 Tech Center Dr., Colorado Springs, CO 80919. Phone: 719-260-5533. Fax: 719-260-5010. Authorized power: 10-w. each. Antenna: 230-ft. above ground. Lat. 43° 43' 53", long. 88° 17' 34". Transmitter: 8-mi. SE of Fond du Lac. Equipment: Comwave transmitter; Bogner antenna. Ownership: American Telecasting Inc.

Wausau—WMH248 (E group). Ina M. Kozel, 560 W. Franklin, Monterey, CA 93940. Authorized power: 10-w. each. Antenna: 455-ft. above ground. Lat. 44° 58' 58", long. 89° 36' 06". Transmitter: Coates Lane. Equipment: Comwave transmitter; Bogner antenna. Ownership: Ina M. Kozel.

Wyoming

Casper—WHK936 (F group). Echonet Corp., Box 255, Evergreen, CO 80439. Phone: 303-526-1039. Authorized power: 10-w. each. Antenna: 100-ft. above ground. Lat. 42° 44' 37", long. 106° 18' 26". Transmitter: Casper Mountain, 7.7-mi. S of Casper. Equipment: Comwave transmitter; Bogner antenna. Ownership: Echonet Corp.

Cody—WLW729 (F group). Agnes C. Kozel, 1434 Grant Ave., San Francisco, CA 94133. Phone: 415-567-9132. Authorized power: 10-w. each. Antenna: 25-ft. above ground. Lat. 44° 29' 48", long. 109° 09' 07". Transmitter: 3-mi. W of Cody. Equipment: Comwave transmitter; Bogner antenna. Ownership: Agnes C. Kozel.

Jackson Hole—WLR472 (F group). Chesterfield Communications, 2401 Wisteria Lane, Muncie, IN 47302. Phone: 317-289-0683. Authorized power: 10-w. each. Antenna: 15-ft. above ground. Lat. 43° 35' 48", long. 110° 52' 11". Transmitter: Rendezvous Mountain. Equipment: Comwave transmitter; Bogner antenna. Ownership: Chesterfield Communications.

Newcastle—WMX919 (H3). G/S Newcastle F Settlement Group, 11600 Pinehaven Ave., Bakersfield, CA 93312. Phone: 805-589-1240. Authorized power: 10-w. Antenna: 160-ft. above ground. Lat. 43° 50' 28", long. 104° 13' 55". Transmitter: 227 Kenwood Dr. Equipment: Comwave transmitter; Andrew antenna. Ownership: G/S Newcastle F Settlement Group.

Pinedale—WMY404 (F group). Audrey B. Warwick, 8140 W. Linvale Place, Denver, CO 80231. Authorized power: 10-w. each. Antenna: 197-ft. above ground. Lat. 42° 56' 19", long. 109° 52' 55". Transmitter: 5-mi. W of Pinedale. Equipment: Comwave transmitter; Bogner antenna. Ownership: Audrey B. Warwick.

Riverton—WMX914 (H1). G/S Riverton F Settlement Group, 3423 Rolston St., Fort Wayne, IN 46805. Phone: 318-477-1218. Authorized power: 10-w. Antenna: 123-ft. above ground. Lat. 42° 43' 10", long. 108° 08' 41". Transmitter: Beaver Rim. Equipment: Comwave transmitter; Andrew antenna. Ownership: G/S Riverton F Settlement Group.

Riverton—WMX912 (H2). G/S Riverton F Settlement Group, 3423 Rolston St., Fort Wayne, IN 46805. Phone: 318-477-1218. Authorized power: 10-w. Antenna: 123-ft. above ground. Lat. 42° 43' 10", long. 108° 08' 41". Transmitter: Beaver Rim. Equipment: Comwave transmitter; Andrew antenna. Ownership: G/S Riverton F Settlement Group.

Riverton—WMX913 (H3). G/S Riverton F Settlement Group, 3423 Rolston St., Fort Wayne, IN 46805. Phone: 318-477-1218. Authorized power: 10-w. Antenna: 123-ft. above ground. Lat. 42° 43' 10", long. 108° 08' 41". Transmitter: Beaver Rim. Equipment: Comwave transmitter; Andrew antenna. Ownership: G/S Riverton F Settlement Group.

Sheridan—WLW824 (E group). American Telecasting of Sheridan Inc., Suite 300, 5575 Tech Center Dr., Colorado Springs, CO 80919. Phone: 719-260-5533. Fax: 719-260-5010. Authorized power: 10-w. each. Antenna: 96-ft. above ground. Lat. 44° 37' 20", long. 107° 06' 57". Transmitter: 12-mi. S & 8-mi. W of Sheridan. Equipment: Comwave transmitter; Bogner antenna. Ownership: American Telecasting Inc.

Sheridan—WLW820 (F group). American Telecasting of Sheridan Inc., Suite 300, 5575 Tech Center Dr., Colorado Springs, CO 80919. Phone: 719-260-5533. Fax: 719-260-5010. Authorized power: 10-w. each. Antenna: 96-ft. above ground. Lat. 44° 37' 20", long. 107° 06' 57". Transmitter: 12-mi. S & 8-mi. W of Sheridan. Equipment: Comwave transmitter; Bogner antenna. Ownership: American Telecasting Inc.

Worland—WMI333 (F group). Unity Cable Partners. Authorized power: 10-w. each. Antenna: 60-ft. above ground. Lat. 44° 04' 06", long. 107° 51' 57". Transmitter: 5.5-mi. E of Worland. Equipment: Comwave transmitter; Andrew antenna. Ownership: Unity Cable Partners.

American Samoa

Pago Pago—WMH584 (E group). Ultracom Cablevision, Suite 634, 700 7th St. SW, Washington, DC 20024. Phone: 202-479-4658. Authorized power: 95-w. each. Antenna: 95-ft. above ground. Lat. 14° 19' 21", long. 170° 45' 45". Transmitter: NW of Pago Pago Airport. Equipment: ITS transmitter; Andrew antenna. Ownership: Ultracom Cablevision.

Pago Pago—WNTK888 (H group). Arthur L. Dalton Authorized power: 10-w. each. Antenna: 150-ft. above ground. Lat. 14° 17' 41", long. 170° 39' 44". Transmitter: Lauli'i Village. Equipment: Comwave transmitter; Andrew antenna. Ownership: Arthur L. Dalton.

Guam

Agana—WMI810 (E group). JJJ Partnership, Box 24881, GMF, GU 96921. Phone: 671-646-8886. Fax: 671-646-4723. Authorized power: 10-w. each. Antenna: 30-ft. above ground. Lat. 13° 29' 20", long. 144° 49' 36". Transmitter: Mount Barrigada. Equipment: ITS transmitter; Andrew antenna. Ownership: JJJ Partnership.

Agana—WMI814 (F group). Victor J. Toth, 2719 Soapstone Dr., Reston, VA 22091. Phone: 703-476-5515. Authorized power: 10-w. each. Antenna: 30-ft. above ground. Lat. 13° 29' 20", long. 144° 49' 36". Transmitter: Mount Barrigada. Equipment: ITS transmitter; Andrew antenna. Ownership: Victor J. Toth.

Puerto Rico

Aguadilla—WMH325 (E group). Belwen Inc., 7 Boyle Rd., Scotia, NY 12302. Phone: 518-393-7428. Authorized power: 10-w. each. Antenna: 100-ft. above ground. Lat. 18° 24' 30", long. 67° 09' 44". Transmitter: Near Victoria. Equipment: Comwave transmitter; Bogner antenna. Ownership: Belwen Inc.

Arecibo—WMH292 (F group). Placido Gonzales Cordova, Box 1161, Caguas, PR 00626. Authorized power: 10-w. each. Antenna: 250-ft. above ground. Lat. 18° 26' 12", long. 66° 47' 11". Transmitter: Plaza Atlantica. Equipment: Emcee transmitter; Andrew antenna. Ownership: Placido G. Cordova.

Mayaguez—WMH225 (F group). San Juan MDS Inc., 1725 Andrees Bello Cupey, San Juan, PR 00926. Authorized power: 10-w. each. Antenna: 50-ft. above ground. Lat. 18° 12' 26", long. 67° 08' 48". Transmitter: Darlington Bldg., Mendez Vigo St. Equipment: Comwave transmitter; Bogner antenna. Ownership: San Juan MDS Inc.

San German—WNTK992 (H group). Caribbean MMDS Partnership, Box 940008, Plano, TX 75094. Authorized power: 50-w. each. Antenna: 30-ft. above ground. Lat. 18° 03' 37", long. 60° 00' 20". Transmitter: Carretera 118. Ownership: Caribbean MMDS Partnership.

San German—WLW576 (E group). Robert J. Walser, Box 366236, San Juan, PR 00936. Authorized power: 50-w. each. Antenna: 103-ft. above ground. Lat. 18° 03' 37", long. 67° 00' 20". Transmitter: Carretera 118. Equipment: Andrew antenna. Requests change to Scale Antenna. Ownership: Robert J. Walser.

San Juan—WHT654 (E group). Victor Ginorio Gomez, Box 307, Rd. 924, KM 1.7, Humacao, PR 00791-0307. Phone: 809-722-7815. Authorized power: 50-w. each. Antenna: 128-ft. above ground. Lat. 18° 16' 51", long. 66° 06' 38". Transmitter: Cerro Marquesa Mountain, 5.35-mi. NW of San Juan. Equipment: Emcee transmitter; Andrew antenna. Ownership: Victor Ginorio Gomez.

Leased to WHTV Broadcasting Corp., Box 8437, San Juan, PR 00907- 8437. Phone: 787-722-7815.

San Juan—WHT655 (F group). Fundacion Sala Inc., 1409 Ponce de Leon Ave., Santurce, PR 00907. Phone: 809-722-7815. Authorized power: 10-w. each. Lat. 18° 16' 51", long. 66° 06' 38". Transmitter: Cerro Marquesa Mountain, 5.35-mi. NW of San Juan. Equipment: ITS transmitter; Bogner antenna. Requests change to 128-ft. above ground, Andrew antenna. Ownership: WHTV Broadcasting Corp.

San Juan—WNTF632 (H1). Fundacion Sala Inc., 1409 Ponce de Leon Ave., Santurce, PR 00907. Phone: 809-722-7815. Authorized power: 50-w. Antenna: 128-ft. above ground. Lat. 18° 16' 51", long. 66° 06' 38". Transmitter: Cerro Marquesa Mountain, 5.35-mi. NW of San Juan. Equipment: Emcee transmitter; Andrew antenna. Requests change to 54-ft. above ground. Ownership: WHTV Broadcasting Corp.

San Juan—WNTB423 (H2). Fundacion Sala Inc., 1409 Ponce de Leon Ave., Santurce, PR 00907. Phone: 809-722-7815. Authorized power: 10-w. Antenna: 57-ft. above ground. Lat. 18° 16' 51", long. 66° 06' 38". Transmitter: 1-mi NNW of Aguas Buenas. Equipment: Emcee transmitter; Andrew antenna. Requests change to 54-ft. above ground,; transmitter to Cerro Marquesa Mountain, 5.35-mi. NW of San Juan. Ownership: WHTV Broadcasting Corp.

San Juan—WNTB467 (H3). Fundacion Sala Inc., 1409 Ponce de Leon Ave., Santurce, PR 00907. Phone: 809-722-7815. Authorized power: 10-w. Antenna: 62-ft. above ground. Lat. 18° 16' 51", long. 66° 06' 38". Transmitter: 1-mi. NNW of Aguas Buenas. Equipment: Emcee transmitter; Andrew antenna. Requests change to 54-ft. above ground,; transmitter to Cerro Marquesa Mountain, 5.35-mi. NW of San Juan. Ownership: WHTV Broadcasting Corp.

Virgin Islands

St. Croix—WMH685 (E group). Cabarrus TV Corp., Box WKPT, 222 Commerce St., Kingsport, TN 37662. Phone: 423-246-9578. Fax: 423-246-6261. E-mail: gdv@wkpttv.com. Web site: http://www.wkpttv.com. Authorized power: 10-w. each. Antenna: 50-ft. above ground. Lat. 17° 45' 25", long. 64° 48' 00". Transmitter: Blue Mountain, 5.5-mi. W of Christiansted. Equipment: Emcee transmitter; Bogner antenna. Ownership: Glenwood Communications Corp.

St. John/St. Thomas—WLW886 (F group). Walter L. Bush Jr. Authorized power: 10-w. each. Antenna: 20-ft. above ground. Lat. 18° 20' 00", long. 64° 47' 12". Transmitter: 0.5-mi. E of Cruz Bay. Equipment: ITS transmitter; Bogner antenna. Ownership: Walter L. Bush Jr.

Instructional Television

(2,500 MHz)

As of August 1999

Alabama

Bankston—WNC-677 (Channels A-1-4). Berry High School, 103 First Ave. NW, Fayette, AL 35555. Phone: 205-689-4467. Fax: 205-689-8819. Authorized power: 50-w. each. Antenna: 495-ft. above ground. Lat. 33° 54' 43", long. 87° 33' 45". Transmitter: S side of U.S. 78, 0.25-mi. W of city boundary, Kansas. Equipment: Comwave transmitter; Andrew antenna.

Bankston—WNC-281 (Channels C-1-4). Lamar County Board of Education, Hwy. 18 W, Vernon, AL 35592. Phone: 205-695-7615. Fax: 205-695-7678. Authorized power: 50-w. each. Antenna: 495-ft. above ground. Lat. 33° 54' 34", long. 87° 33' 45". Transmitter: S side of U.S. 78, 0.25-mi. W of city boundary, Kansas. Equipment: Comwave transmitter; Andrew antenna.

Bankston—WNC-230 (Channels D-1-4). Marion County Board of Education, Room 107, Courthouse, Hamilton, AL 35570. Phone: 205-921-3191. Fax: 205-921-7336. Authorized power: 50-w. each. Antenna: 495-ft. above ground. Lat. 33° 54' 34", long. 87° 33' 45". Transmitter: S side of U.S. 78, 0.25-mi. W of city boundary, Kansas. Equipment: Comwave transmitter; Andrew antenna.
Leased to Wireless One Inc., 11301 Industriplex Blvd., Suite 4, Baton Rouge, LA 70809-4115. Phone: 504-293-5000.

Bankston—WNC-365 (Channels G-1-4). Walker County Board of Education. Authorized power: 50-w. each. Antenna: 495-ft. above ground. Lat. 33° 54' 34", long. 87° 33' 45". Transmitter: S side of U.S. 78, 0.25-mi. W of city boundary, Kansas. Equipment: Comwave transmitter; Andrew antenna.

Birmingham—WND-234 (Channels A-1-4). Jefferson State Community College, 2601 Carson Rd., Birmingham, AL 35215-3098. Authorized power: 100-w. each. Antenna: 1831-ft. above ground. Lat. 33° 29' 04", long. 86° 48' 25". Transmitter: Red Mountain. Equipment: Emcee transmitter; Andrew antenna.

Birmingham—WBN-31 (Channels B-1-4). Board of Trustees U. of Alabama, 909 S. 18th St., Birmingham, AL 35294. Phone: 205-934-4067. Fax: 205-975-2534. Authorized power: 100-w. each. Antenna: 879-ft. above ground. Lat. 33° 29' 04", long. 86° 48' 25". Transmitter: Red Mountain. Equipment: Emcee transmitter; Andrew antenna.

Birmingham—WND-235 (Channels C-1-4). U. of Alabama School of Medicine, 909 S. 18th St., Birmingham, AL 35294. Authorized power: 100-w. each. Antenna: 879-ft. above ground. Lat. 33° 29' 04", long. 86° 48' 25". Transmitter: Red Mountain. Equipment: Emcee transmitter; Andrew antenna.

Birmingham—WND-236 (Channels D-1-4). Jess Lanier High School, 100 High School Dr., Bessemer, AL 35023. Authorized power: 2.3-w. each. Antenna: 1099-ft. above ground. Lat. 33° 26' 38", long. 86° 52' 47". Transmitter: 0.25-mi. SW of Spring Gap. Equipment: Emcee transmitter; Andrew antenna.

Birmingham—KLC-77 (Channels E-1-4). Board of Education of Birmingham, 2015 7th Ave. N, Birmingham, AL 35202. Phone: 205-583-4697. Fax: 205-581-5233. Authorized power: 10-w. each. Antenna: 111-ft. above ground. Lat. 33° 33' 39", long. 86° 48' 20". Transmitter: Wharton lookout tower. Equipment: Comwave transmitter.

Birmingham—KZW-56 (Channels G-1-4). Board of Education of Birmingham, 2015 7th Ave. N, Birmingham, AL 35202. Phone: 205-583-4697. Fax: 205-581-5233. Authorized power: 1-w. each. Antenna: 85-ft. above ground. Lat. 33° 31' 25", long. 86° 48' 20". Transmitter: Phillips High School, 2316 N. 7th Ave., Birmingham. Equipment: Emcee transmitter.

Bucks—WNC-634 (Channels A-1-4). Alba High School, 288 S. Wintzell Ave., Bayou La Batre, AL 36509. Authorized power: 10-w. each. Antenna: 859-ft. above ground. Lat. 31° 08' 47", long. 88° 03' 37". Transmitter: 1.4-mi. S of Fairford. Equipment: Comwave transmitter; Andrew antenna.

Bucks—WNC-635 (Channels B-1-4). Blount High, 838 W. Main St., Pritchard, AL 36610. Authorized power: 10-w. each. Antenna: 859-ft. above ground. Lat. 31° 08' 47", long. 88° 03' 37". Transmitter: Approx. 1.4-mi. S of Fairford. Equipment: Comwave transmitter; Andrew antenna.

Bucks—WNC-459 (Channels C-1-4). McIntosh High School, Box 359, Hwy. 43, McIntosh, AL 36553. Phone: 334-944-2441. Fax: 334-944-8779. Authorized power: 50-w. each. Antenna: 994-ft. above ground. Lat. 31° 08' 47", long. 88° 03' 37". Transmitter: 1.4-mi. S of Fairford. Equipment: Emcee transmitter; Andrew antenna.

Bucks—WLX-963 (Channels D-1-4). McIntosh Christian Academy, Box 416, McIntosh, AL 36553. Phone: 205-944-2298. Authorized power: 50-w. each. Antenna: 994-ft. above ground. Lat. 31° 08' 47", long. 88° 03' 37". Transmitter: 1.4-mi. S of Fairford. Equipment: Emcee transmitter; Andrew antenna.
Leased to RuralVision South Inc., Box 1482, Canyon Lake, TX 78130.

Bucks—WNC-460 (Channels G-1-4). Washington County High School, Box 1329, Hwy. 56, Chatom, AL 36518. Authorized power: 50-w. each. Antenna: 994-ft. above ground. Lat. 31° 08' 47", long. 88° 03' 37". Transmitter: 1.4-mi. S of Fairford. Equipment: Emcee transmitter; Andrew antenna.

Burnsville—WNC-603 (Channels A-1-4). Hale County High School, Hwy. 69 N, Moundville, AL 35474. Authorized power: 10-w. each. Antenna: 624-ft. above ground. Lat. 32° 23' 26", long. 86° 47' 33". Transmitter: 1.7-mi. SW of Peace. Equipment: Comwave transmitter; Andrew antenna.

Burnsville—WNC-604 (Channels B-1-4). Hale County Board of Education, Box 360, Greensboro, AL 36744. Authorized power: 10-w. each. Antenna: 859-ft. above ground. Lat. 32° 27' 12", long. 86° 55' 07". Transmitter: 2.5-mi. SW of Peace. Equipment: Comwave transmitter; Andrew antenna.

Burnsville—WNC-488 (Channels C-1-4). Lawrence County Board of Education, 14131 Market St., Moulton, AL 35650. Authorized power: 10-w. each. Antenna: 855-ft. above ground. Lat. 32° 27' 12", long. 86° 55' 07". Transmitter: 0.1-mi. NW of State Rte. 14, 2.5-mi. SW of Burnsville. Equipment: Comwave transmitter; Andrew antenna.

Demopolis—WNC-420 (Channels A-1-4). Wilcox County Board of Education. Authorized power: 25-w. each. Antenna: 1207-ft. above ground. Lat. 32° 22' 01", long. 87° 52' 03". Transmitter: 0.25-mi. NE of Rtes. 28 & 43. Equipment: Comwave transmitter; Andrew antenna.

Demopolis—WNC-331 (Channels B-1-4). Demopolis City Board of Education, Drawer 759, Demopolis, AL 36732. Authorized power: 25-w. each. Antenna: 946-ft. above ground. Lat. 32° 22' 01", long. 87° 52' 03". Transmitter: Rte. One. Equipment: Comwave transmitter; Andrew antenna.

Demopolis—WNC-330 (Channels C-1-4). Marengo County Board of Education, Box 480339, Linden, AL 36748-0339. Authorized power: 25-w. each. Antenna: 1207-ft. above ground. Lat. 32° 22' 01", long. 87° 52' 03". Transmitter: Rte. One. Equipment: Comwave transmitter; Andrew antenna.

Demopolis—WNC-329 (Channels D-1-4). Linden City Board of Education, Box 480609, Linden, AL 36748-0609. Authorized power: 25-w. each. Antenna: 1207-ft. above ground. Lat. 32° 22' 01", long. 87° 52' 03". Transmitter: Rte. One. Equipment: Comwave transmitter; Andrew antenna.

Demopolis—WNC-332 (Channels G-1-4). Sumter County Board of Education, Box 10, Livingston, AL 35470. Authorized power: 25-w. each. Antenna: 1207-ft. above ground. Lat. 32° 22' 01", long. 87° 52' 03". Transmitter: Choctaw, Linden Sumter, Marengo. Equipment: Comwave transmitter; Andrew antenna.

Dothan—WNC-535 (Channels A-1-4). Houston Academy, 1001 Buena Vista Dr., Dothan, AL 36303. Authorized power: 50-w. each. Antenna: 899-ft. above ground. Lat. 31° 15' 07", long. 85° 17' 12". Transmitter: WOOF-FM tower, Hwy. 52, 5.5-mi. NE of Dothan. Equipment: ITS transmitter; Andrew antenna.

Dothan—WNC-720 (Channels B-1-4). Houston County Board of Education, Box 1688, Dothan, AL 36302. Authorized power: 50-w. each. Antenna: 899-ft. above ground. Lat. 31° 15' 07", long. 85° 17' 12". Transmitter: WOOF-FM tower, Hwy. 52, 5.5-mi. NE of Dothan. Equipment: ITS transmitter; Andrew antenna.

Dothan—WND-247 (Channels C-1-4). Troy State U.-Dothan, Box 8368, Dothan, AL 36304. Authorized power: 50-w. each. Antenna: 899-ft. above ground. Lat. 31° 15' 07", long. 85° 17' 12". Transmitter: WOOF-FM tower, Hwy. 52, 5.5-mi. NE of Dothan. Equipment: ITS transmitter; Andrew antenna.

Dothan—WNC-692 (Channels D-1-4). Dothan City Board of Education, 500 Dusy St., Dothan, AL 36301. Authorized power: 50-w. each. Antenna: 899-ft. above ground. Lat. 31° 15' 07", long. 85° 17' 12". Transmitter: WOOF-FM Tower, Hwy. 52, 5.5-mi. NE of Dothan. Equipment: ITS transmitter; Andrew antenna.

Dothan—WNC-752 (Channels G-1-4). George C. Wallace State Community College, Wallace College, Dothan, AL 36303. Authorized power: 50-w. each. Antenna: 899-ft. above ground. Lat. 31° 15' 07", long. 85° 17' 12". Transmitter: WOOF-FM tower, Hwy. 52, 5.5-mi. NE of Dothan. Equipment: ITS transmitter; Andrew antenna.

Eutaw—WLX-846 (Channels A-1-4). Eutaw High School, 220 Main St., Eutaw, AL 35462. Authorized power: 50-w. each. Antenna: 761-ft. above ground. Lat. 33° 03' 15", long. 87° 32' 57". Transmitter: Rte. 69, Moundville. Equipment: Comwave transmitter; Andrew antenna.

Eutaw—WNC-421 (Channels B-1-4). Carver Elementary School, Box 659, Eutaw, AL 35462. Authorized power: 10-w. each. Antenna: 485-ft. above ground. Lat. 32° 52' 57", long. 87° 51' 18". Transmitter: 0.65-mi. E on County Hwy. 138, off U.S. Hwy. 43. Equipment: Comwave transmitter; Andrew antenna.

Eutaw—WNC-397 (Channels C-1-4). Paramount Unit School, Box 188, Boligee, AL 35443. Phone: 205-336-8557. Fax: 205-336-8571. Authorized power: 10-w. each. Antenna: 405-ft. above ground. Lat. 32° 50' 00", long. 87° 52' 38". Transmitter: Carver Elementary School, 527 Greenshore Ave. Equipment: Comwave transmitter; Andrew antenna.

Eutaw—WNC-433 (Channels D-1-3). West Alabama Health Services Inc., Box 711, Eutaw, AL 35462. Phone: 205-372-4770. Fax: 205-372-4498. Authorized power: 10-w. each. Antenna: 485-ft. above ground. Lat. 32° 52' 57", long. 87° 51' 18". Transmitter: 0.65-mi. E on County Hwy. 138, off U.S. Hwy. 43. Equipment: Comwave transmitter; Andrew antenna.
Leased to Black Warrior Telecommunications Consortium, Box 686, Demopolis, AL 36732. Phone: 334-289-1976.

Eutaw—WNC-372 (Channels G-2-4). Greene County Hospital, 509 Wilson Ave., Eutaw, AL 35462. Authorized power: 10-w. each. Antenna: 485-ft. above ground. Lat. 32° 52' 57", long. 87° 51' 18". Transmitter: 0.65-mi. E on County Hwy. 138, off U.S. Hwy. 43. Equipment: Comwave transmitter; Andrew antenna.

Gadsden—WNC-317 (Channels A-1-4). Coosa Christian School, 771 Whites Chapel Rd., Gadsden, AL 35901. Phone: 205-547-3714. Authorized power: 50-w. each. Antenna: 256-ft.

above ground. Lat. 33° 55' 59", long. 85° 54' 12". Transmitter: 100 Cellular Tower Rd., Glencoe. Equipment: Comwave transmitter; Andrew antenna.

Gadsden—WNC-747 (Channels B-1-4). Jacksonville State U., 700 Pelham Rd. N, Jacksonville, AL 36265. Authorized power: 50-w. each. Antenna: 256-ft. above ground. Lat. 33° 55' 59", long. 85° 54' 12". Transmitter: 100 Cellular Tower Rd., Glencoe. Equipment: Comwave transmitter; Andrew antenna.

Gadsden—WNC-318 (Channels C-1-4). Westbrook Christian School, 100 Westminster Dr., Rainbow City, AL 35906. Authorized power: 50-w. each. Antenna: 256-ft. above ground. Lat. 33° 55' 59", long. 85° 54' 12". Transmitter: 100 Cellular Tower Rd., Glencoe. Equipment: Comwave transmitter; Andrew antenna.

Gadsden—WNC-287 (Channels D-1-4). Gadsden State Community College, Box 227, 1001 George Wallace Dr., Gadsden, AL 35902-0227. Phone: 205-549-8439. Fax: 205-549-8404. Authorized power: 50-w. each. Antenna: 256-ft. above ground. Lat. 33° 55' 59", long. 85° 54' 12". Transmitter: 100 Cellular Tower Rd., Glencoe. Equipment: Comwave transmitter; Andrew antenna.

Holly Springs—WNC-396 (Channels G-1-4). Curry High School, Box 311, Jasper, AL 35502. Authorized power: 50-w. each. Antenna: 854-ft. above ground. Lat. 33° 48' 57", long. 86° 27' 19". Transmitter: Blount Mountain, 1.4-mi. E of Holly Springs. Equipment: Comwave transmitter; Andrew antenna.

Huntsville—WLX-290 (Channels A-1-4). Martin Methodist College, 433 W. Madison St., Pulaski, TN 38478. Authorized power: 50-w. each. Antenna: 350-ft. above ground. Lat. 34° 49' 05", long. 86° 44' 16". Transmitter: Capshaw Mountain. Equipment: ITS transmitter; Andrew antenna.

Huntsville—WLX-293 (Channels B-1-4). Limestone County Board of Education, 300 S. Jefferson St., Athens, AL 35611. Phone: 256-232-5353. Fax: 256-233-6461. Authorized power: 50-w. each. Antenna: 350-ft. above ground. Lat. 34° 49' 05", long. 86° 44' 16". Transmitter: Capshaw Mountain. Equipment: ITS transmitter; Andrew antenna.

Leased to Madison Communications Inc., Box 1069, Athens, AL 35611. Phone: 205-232-1822.

Huntsville—WLX-294 (Channels C-1-4). Madison Academy Inc., 325 Slaughter Rd., Madison, AL 35758. Phone: 256-971-1619. Fax: 256-971-1436.

E-mail: rburton@macademy.org.

Web site: http://www.macademy.org.

Authorized power: 50-w. each. Antenna: 350-ft. above ground. Lat. 34° 49' 05", long. 86° 44' 16". Equipment: ITS transmitter; Andrew antenna.

Leased to Wireless One, 113 Castle Dr., Madison, AL 35758. Phone: 256-430-2588.

Huntsville—KHU-75 (Channels D-1-4). City Board of Education of Huntsville, 706 Read Dr., Huntsville, AL 35801. Phone: 205-532-3006. Fax: 205-532-3007. Authorized power: 10-w. each. Antenna: 290-ft. above ground. Lat. 34° 44' 16", long. 86° 32' 02". Transmitter: WHIQ(TV), 706 Read Dr. Equipment: ITS transmitter; Andrew antenna.

Huntsville—WLX-289 (Channels G-1-4). Athens Bible School, 507 Hoffman Rd., Athens, AL 35611. Authorized power: 50-w. each. Antenna: 350-ft. above ground. Lat. 34° 49' 05", long. 86° 44' 16". Transmitter: Capshaw Mountain, Wall Triana Hwy. Equipment: ITS transmitter; Andrew antenna.

Mobile—WNC-633 (Channels A-1-4). Hispanic Information & Telecommunications Network Inc., 3rd Floor, 449 Broadway, New York, NY 10013. Phone: 212-966-5660. Fax: 212-966-5725.

E-mail: email@hitn.org.

Web site: http://www.hitn.org.

Authorized power: 10-w. each. Antenna: 429-ft. above ground. Lat. 30° 44' 44", long. 88° 05' 40". Transmitter: Whistler Ave. at William, Pritchard, AL. Equipment: Emcee transmitter; Andrew antenna.

Leased to Distance Learning Services Inc., 1155 Connecticut Ave. NW, Suite 300, Washington, DC 20036. Phone: 202-467-8500.

Mobile—WNC-873 (Channels B-1-4). Baldwin County Catholic Schools, 308 S. Dearborn St., Mobile, AL 36601. Authorized power: 10-w. each. Antenna: 249-ft. above ground. Lat. 30° 44' 44", long. 88° 05' 40". Transmitter: 2300 Smiley Lane, Pritchard. Equipment: Emcee transmitter; Andrew antenna.

Mobile—WNC-874 (Channels C-1-4). Faulkner State Community College, 1900 Hwy. 315, Bay Minette, AL 36507. Phone: 334-580-2203. Fax: 334-580-2253.

E-mail: margaret@faulkner.cc.al.us.

Web site: http://www.faulkner.cc.al.us.

Authorized power: 10-w. each. Antenna: 249-ft. above ground. Lat. 30° 44' 44", long. 88° 05' 40". Transmitter: 2300 Smiley Lane, Pritchard. Equipment: Emcee transmitter; Andrew antenna.

Mobile—WNC-875 (Channels D-1-4). Bayside Academy, Box 2590, Dryer Ave., Daphne, AL 36526. Authorized power: 10-w. each. Antenna: 249-ft. above ground. Lat. 30° 44' 44", long. 88° 05' 40". Transmitter: 2300 Smiley Lane, Pritchard. Equipment: Emcee transmitter; Andrew antenna.

Mobile—WLX-648 (Channels G-1-4). Inc. North American Catholic Educational Programming Foundation, Box 40026, Providence, RI 02940-0026. Authorized power: 10-w. each. Antenna: 499-ft. above ground. Lat. 30° 35' 03", long. 88° 12' 31". Transmitter: Whistler Ave. at William. Equipment: Comwave transmitter; Andrew antenna.

Montevallo—WND-277 (Channels A-1-4). Hoover City Board of Education, Suite 200, 100 Municipal Dr., Hoover, AL 35216. Authorized power: 1-w. each. Antenna: 23-ft. above ground. Lat. 33° 07' 06", long. 86° 46' 00". Transmitter: 1.6-mi. NW of Hwy. 25 & U.S. 31 intersection. Equipment: Emcee transmitter; Andrew antenna.

Montevallo—WND-279 (Channels C-1-4). Tulane U. of Louisiana, 6823 St. Charles Ave., New Orleans, LA 70118. Authorized power: 1-w. each. Antenna: 7-ft. above ground. Lat. 33° 07' 06", long. 86° 46' 00". Transmitter: 1.6-mi. NW of Rte. 25 & U.S. 31 intersection. Equipment: Andrew transmitter; Andrew antenna.

Montevallo—WND-280 (Channels D-1-4). Indian Springs School, 190 Woodward Dr., Indian Springs, AL 35124. Authorized power: 1-w. each. Antenna: 23-ft. above ground. Lat. 33° 07' 06", long. 86° 46' 00". Transmitter: 1.6-mi. NW of Hwy. 25 & U.S. 31 intersection. Equipment: Emcee transmitter; Andrew antenna.

Montevallo—WND-281 (Channels G-1-4). Shelby County Board of Education, 410 E. College St., Columbiana, AL 35051. Authorized power: 1-w. each. Antenna: 23-ft. above ground. Lat. 33° 07' 06", long. 86° 46' 00". Transmitter: 1.6-mi. NW of Hwy. 25 & U.S. 31 intersection. Equipment: Emcee transmitter; Andrew antenna.

Montgomery—WNC-347 (Channels A-1-4). Montgomery Public School System, 307 S. Decatur St., Montgomery, AL 36104. Authorized power: 50-w. each. Antenna: 1169-ft. above ground. Lat. 32° 24' 11", long. 86° 11' 47". Transmitter: 1.8-mi. NE of Hwys. 152 & 80 intersection. Equipment: ITS transmitter; Andrew antenna. Requests change to 926-ft. above ground, lat. 32° 20' 06", long. 86° 17' 16"; transmitter to 1369 Adrian Lane.

Montgomery—WNC-679 (Channels B-1-4). Autauga County Private School Foundation, 497 Golson Rd., Prattville, AL 36067. Authorized power: 50-w. each. Antenna: 1168-ft. above ground. Lat. 32° 24' 11", long. 86° 11' 48". Transmitter: 1.8-mi. NE of Hwys. 152 & 80 intersection. Equipment: ITS transmitter; Andrew antenna.

Montgomery—WNC-346 (Channels C-1-4). Lowndes County Public Schools, 105 E. Tuskeena St., Haynesville, AL 36040. Authorized power: 50-w. each. Antenna: 1168-ft. above ground. Lat. 32° 24' 11", long. 86° 11' 48". Transmitter: 1.8-mi. NE of Hwys. 152 & 80 intersection. Equipment: ITS transmitter; Andrew antenna. Requests change to 926-ft. above ground, lat. 32° 20' 06", long. 86° 17' 16"; transmitter to 1369 Adrian Lane.

Montgomery—WNC-701 (Channels D-1-4). The Lowndes County Private School Foundation, Box 68, Lowndesboro, AL 36752. Authorized power: 50-w. each. Antenna: 1168-ft. above ground. Lat. 32° 24' 11", long. 86° 11' 48". Transmitter: 1.8-mi. NE of Hwys. 152 & 80 intersection. Equipment: ITS transmitter; Andrew antenna.

Montgomery—WNC-219 (Channels G-1-4). Autauga County School District, 153 W. 4th St., Prattville, AL 36067. Authorized power: 50-w. each. Antenna: 900-ft. above ground. Lat. 32° 24' 11", long. 86° 11' 48". Transmitter: 1.8-mi. NE of Hwys. 152 & 80 intersection. Equipment: Andrew antenna. Requests change to 926-ft. above ground, lat. 32° 20' 06", long. 86° 17' 16"; transmitter to 1369 Adrian Lane.

Muscle Shoals—WNC-713 (Channels A-1-4). U. of North Alabama, Wesleyan Ave., Florence, AL 35632. Authorized power: 10-w. each. Antenna: 833-ft. above ground. Lat. 34° 40' 24", long. 87° 42' 56". Transmitter: Florence. Equipment: ITS transmitter; Andrew antenna.

Muscle Shoals—WNC-832 (Channels C-1-4). International Bible College, 3625 Helton Dr., Florence, AL 35630. Authorized power: 10-w. each. Antenna: 673-ft. above ground. Lat. 34° 40' 24", long. 87° 42' 56". Transmitter: 4-mi. S of Milk Springs Rd. Equipment: ITS transmitter; Andrew antenna.

Muscle Shoals—WNC-831 (Channels D-1-4). Northwest Alabama Community College. Authorized power: 10-w. each. Antenna: 673-ft. above ground. Lat. 34° 40' 24", long. 87° 42' 56". Transmitter: 4-mi. S of Milk Springs Rd. Equipment: ITS transmitter; Andrew antenna.

Opelika—WND-320 (Channels A-1-4). Lee-Scott Academy, 2307 E. Glen Ave., Auburn, AL 36830. Authorized power: 50-w. each. Antenna: 709-ft. above ground. Lat. 32° 45' 30", long. 85° 28' 21". Transmitter: Chambers County Hwy. 1022. Equipment: Emcee transmitter; Andrew antenna.

Opelika—WND-321 (Channels B-1-4). Shekinah Network, 14875 Powerline Rd., Atascadero, CA 93442. Phone & fax: 805-438-3341. Authorized power: 50-w. each. Antenna: 709-ft. above ground. Lat. 32° 45' 30", long. 85° 28' 21". Transmitter: Chambers County Hwy. 1022. Equipment: Emcee transmitter; Andrew antenna.

Opelika—WND-322 (Channels C-1-4). Southern Union State Community College-Opelika Technical, 1701 Lafayette Pkwy., Opelika, AL 36803. Authorized power: 50-w. each. Antenna: 709-ft. above ground. Lat. 32° 45' 30", long. 85° 28' 21". Transmitter: Chambers County Hwy. 1022. Equipment: Emcee transmitter; Andrew antenna.

Opelika—WND-323 (Channels D-1-4). Southern Union State Community College, Roberts St., Waley, AL 36276. Authorized power: 50-w. each. Antenna: 709-ft. above ground. Lat. 32° 45' 30", long. 85° 28' 21". Transmitter: Chambers County Hwy. 1022. Equipment: Emcee transmitter; Andrew antenna.

Opelika—WND-324 (Channels G-1-4). The Clarendon Foundation, Suite 826, 4201 S. 31st St., Arlington, VA 22206. Authorized power: 50-w. each. Antenna: 709-ft. above ground. Lat. 32° 45' 30", long. 85° 28' 21". Transmitter: Chambers County Hwy. 1022. Equipment: Emcee transmitter; Andrew antenna.

Phenix City—WNC-734 (Channels C-1-4). Booker T. Washington, 3803 Martin Luther King Hwy., Tuskegee Institute, AL 36088. Authorized power: 50-w. each. Antenna: 448-ft. above ground. Lat. 32° 20' 42", long. 85° 00' 41". Transmitter: Summerville Rd. Equipment: Emcee transmitter; Andrew antenna.

Phenix City—WNC-733 (Channels D-1-4). Notasulga High School, E. Main St., Notasulga, AL 36866. Authorized power: 50-w. each. Antenna: 448-ft. above ground. Lat. 32° 20' 42", long. 85° 00' 41". Transmitter: Summerville Rd. Equipment: Emcee transmitter; Andrew antenna.

Six Mile—WNC-395 (Channels A-1-4). Bibb County High School, 214 Birmingham Rd., Centerville, AL 35042. Authorized power: 100-w. each. Antenna: 324-ft. above ground. Lat. 33° 29' 04", long. 86° 48' 25". Transmitter: Red Mountain. Equipment: ITS transmitter; Andrew antenna.

Six Mile—WNC-393 (Channels C-1-4). Henry County Board of Education, Box 635, Abbeville, AL 36310. Authorized power: 100-w. each. Antenna: 324-ft. above ground. Lat. 33° 29' 04", long. 86° 48' 25". Transmitter: Red Mountain. Equipment: ITS transmitter; Andrew antenna.

Six Mile—WNC-391 (Channels G-1-4). West Blocton High School, 100 School St., West Blocton, AL 35184. Authorized power: 100-w. each. Antenna: 324-ft. above ground. Lat. 33° 29' 04", long. 86° 48' 25". Transmitter: Red Mountain. Equipment: ITS transmitter; Andrew antenna.

Tuscaloosa—WNC-485 (Channels B-1-4). American Christian Academy, 701 Martin Luther King Blvd., Northport, AL 35476. Authorized power: 10-w. each. Antenna: 398-ft. above ground. Lat. 33° 12' 05", long. 87° 32' 00". Transmitter: 15th St. & Forest Lake intersection. Equipment: ITS transmitter; Andrew antenna.

Alaska

Anchorage—WNC-732 (Channels A-1-4). Shekinah Network, 14875 Powerline Rd., Atascadero, CA 93422. Phone & fax: 805-438-3341.: Authorized power: 20-w. each. Antenna: 101-ft. above ground. Lat. 61° 06' 25", long. 149° 44' 16". Transmitter: 7460 Upper Huffman Rd. Equipment: ITS transmitter; Andrew antenna.

Anchorage—WLX-586 (Channels B-1-4). Views on Learning Inc., 200 Kenyon Ave., Elkhart, IN 46516. Phone & fax: 219-522-1725.
E-mail: jrueff@lsoc-vol.org.
Web site: http://www.lsoc-vol.org.
Authorized power: 20-w. each. Antenna: 102-ft. above ground. Lat. 61° 06' 25", long. 149° 44' 16". Transmitter: 7460 Upper Hoffman Rd. Equipment: ITS transmitter; Andrew antenna.

Anchorage—WLX-344 (Channels C-1-4). North American Catholic Educational Programming Foundation Inc., Box 40026, Providence, RI 02940-0026. Phone: 401-729-0900. Lat. 61° 06' 25", long. 149° 44' 16". Requests change to 20-w each, 93-ft. above ground, transmitter to 7460 Upper Huffman Rd., ITS transmitter, Andrew antenna.

Anchorage—WNC-386 (Channels D-1-4). The Clarendon Foundation, Suite 826, 4201 S. 31st. St., Arlington, VA 22026. Authorized power: 20-w. each. Antenna: 93-ft. above ground. Lat. 61° 06' 25", long. 149° 44' 16". Transmitter: 7460 Upper Huffman Rd. Equipment: ITS transmitter; Andrew antenna.

Fairbanks—WNC-773 (Channels A-1-4). Shekinah Network, 14875 Powerline Rd., Atascadero, CA 93422. Phone & fax: 805-438-3341. Authorized power: 20-w. each. Antenna: 120-ft. above ground. Lat. 64° 52' 44", long. 148° 03' 10". Transmitter: Ester Dome, 10-mi. WNW of Fairbanks. Equipment: ITS transmitter; Andrew antenna.

Fairbanks—WLX-453 (Channels B-1-4). Views on Learning Inc., 200 Kenyon Ave., Elkhart, IN 46516. Phone & fax: 219-522-1725.
E-mail: jrueff@lsoc-vol.org.
Web site: http://www.lsoc-vol.org.
Authorized power: 20-w. each. Antenna: 96-ft. above ground. Lat. 64° 52' 44", long. 148° 03' 10". Transmitter: Ester Dome, 10-mi. WNW of Fairbanks. Equipment: ITS transmitter; Andrew antenna.
Leased to Alaska Wireless Cable, Box 2222, El Granada, CA 94018. Phone: 415-824-0314.

Fairbanks—WNC-768 (Channels C-1-4). Morningstar Educational Network, 4012 Morningstar, Huntington Beach, CA 92649. Authorized power: 20-w. each. Antenna: 120-ft. above ground. Lat. 64° 52' 44", long. 148° 03' 10". Transmitter: Ester Dome, 10-mi. WNW of Fairbanks. Equipment: ITS transmitter; Andrew antenna.

Fairbanks—WNC-772 (Channels D-1-4). Information Resource Foundation, 1360 East 4325 South, Salt Lake City, UT 84124. Authorized power: 20-w. each. Antenna: 121-ft. above ground. Lat. 64° 52' 44", long. 148° 03' 10". Transmitter: Ester Dome, 10-mi. WNW of Fairbanks. Equipment: ITS transmitter; Andrew antenna.

Fairbanks—WNC-729 (Channels G-1-4). The Clarendon Foundation, Suite 826, 4201 S. 31st St., Arlington, VA 22206. Authorized power: 20-w. each. Antenna: 120-ft. above ground. Lat. 64° 52' 44", long. 148° 03' 10". Transmitter: Ester Dome, 10-mi. WNW of Fairbanks. Equipment: ITS transmitter; Andrew antenna.

Arizona

Bisbee—WNC-340 (Channels C-1-4). First Baptist Christian Academy, 1447 S. 7th St., Sierra Vista, AZ 85635. Phone: 520-458-2983. Authorized power: 10-w. each. Antenna: 135-ft. above ground. Lat. 31° 28' 49", long. 109° 57' 30". Transmitter: Mule Mountain. Equipment: Comwave transmitter; Andrew antenna.
Leased to Nucentrix Broadband Networks, 200 Chisholm Place, Suite 200, Plano, TX 75075. Phone: 972-423-9494. Fax: 972-423-0819.

Bisbee—WNC-234 (Channels D-2-4). Nova School Inc., 241 W. Hwy. 90, Sierra Vista, AZ 85635. Authorized power: 10-w. each. Antenna: 135-ft. above ground. Lat. 31° 28' 49", long. 109° 57' 30". Transmitter: Mule Mountain. Equipment: Comwave transmitter; Andrew antenna.

Bisbee—WLX-886 (Channels G-1-4). Montessori School of Flagstaff, 575 W. University Ave., Flagstaff, AZ 86001. Authorized power: 10-w. each. Antenna: 63-ft. above ground. Lat. 31° 28' 49", long. 109° 57' 30". Transmitter: Mule Mountain. Equipment: Comwave transmitter; Andrew antenna.

Bullhead City—WNC-657 (Channels B-1-4). American Foundation for Instructional TV, 1413 Belmont Lane, Helena, AL 35080-4009. Phone: 205-621-8432.
E-mail: agpiazza@bellsouth.net.
Authorized power: 50-w. each. Antenna: 125-ft. above ground. Lat. 35° 01' 58", long. 114° 21' 57". Transmitter: Oatman Peak Electronic Site, 14-mi. SE of Bullhead City. Equipment: Comwave transmitter; Andrew antenna.

Bullhead City—WLX-503 (Channels C-1-4). North American Catholic Educational Programming Foundation Inc., Box 40026, Providence, RI 02940-0026. Authorized power: 50-w. each. Antenna: 125-ft. above ground. Lat. 35° 01' 58", long. 114° 21' 57". Transmitter: Oatman Peak Electronic Site, 14-mi. SE of Bullhead City. Equipment: Comwave transmitter; Andrew antenna.

Bullhead City—WNC-656 (Channels D-1-4). Excellence in Education Network, 5700 Belmont Dr., Irondale, AL 35210. Authorized power: 50-w. each. Antenna: 45-ft. above ground. Lat. 35° 01' 58", long. 114° 21' 57". Transmitter: Oatman Peak Electronic Site, 14-mi. SE of Bullhead City. Equipment: Comwave transmitter; Andrew antenna.

Bullhead City—WNC-655 (Channels G-1-4). Foreign Language & Cultural Foundation, 850 Fay Rd., Syracuse, NY 13219. Authorized power: 50-w. each. Antenna: 125-ft. above ground. Lat. 35° 01' 58", long. 114° 21' 57". Transmitter: Oatman Peak Electronic Site, 14-mi. SE of Bullhead City. Equipment: Comwave transmitter; Andrew antenna.

Casa Grande—WNC-350 (Channels B-1-4). Southwestern Academy, Beaver Creek Ranch Campus, Rimrock, AZ 86355. Phone: 520-567-4581. Fax: 520-567-4436.
E-mail: vvschool@sedona.net.
E-mail: kveronda@southwesternacademy.edu.
Web site: http://www.southwesternacademy.edu.
Authorized power: 10-w. each. Antenna: 854-ft. above ground. Lat. 32° 47' 43", long. 111° 46' 48". Transmitter: 0.4-mi. NW of Shedd & Thornton Rds. intersection. Equipment: Comwave transmitter; Andrew antenna.

Casa Grande—WNC-351 (Channels C-1-4). Discovery Montessori-Cedar, 2212 E. Cedar, Flagstaff, AZ 86004. Authorized power: 10-w. each. Antenna: 854-ft. above ground. Lat. 32° 47' 43", long. 111° 46' 48". Transmitter: 0.4-mi. NW of Shedd & Thornton Rds. intersection. Equipment: Comwave transmitter; Andrew antenna.

Casa Grande—WNC-467 (Channels D-1-3). Verde Valley School, 3511 Verde Valley School Rd., Sedona, AZ 86351. Phone: 520-284-2272. Fax: 520-284-0432. Authorized power: 10-w. each. Antenna: 854-ft. above ground. Lat. 32° 47' 43", long. 111° 46' 48". Transmitter: 0.4-mi. NW of Shedd & Thornton Rds. intersection. Equipment: Comwave transmitter; Andrew antenna.
Leased to People's Choice TV Corp., 5301 E. Broadway Blvd., Tucson, AZ 85711. Phone: 520-519-4400.

Flagstaff—WNC-320 (Channels A-1-4). Northern Arizona U., Box 5751, Flagstaff, AZ 86011. Authorized power: 10-w. each. Antenna: 97-ft. above ground. Lat. 35° 11' 22", long. 111° 39' 13". Transmitter: Sechrist Hall, Northern Arizona U. Campus. Equipment: Emcee transmitter; Andrew antenna.

Flagstaff—WNC-312 (Channels B-1-4). Northern Arizona U., Babbitt Administration Bldg., Flagstaff, AZ 86011. Authorized power: 10-w. each. Antenna: 97-ft. above ground. Lat. 35° 11' 22", long. 111° 39' 13". Transmitter: Sechrist Hall, Northern Arizona U. Campus. Equipment: Emcee transmitter; Andrew antenna.

Flagstaff—WNC-319 (Channels C-1-4). Mount Calvary Lutheran School, 2605 N. Fort Valley Rd., Flagstaff, AZ 86001. Authorized power: 10-w. each. Antenna: 64-ft. above ground. Lat. 35° 14' 29", long. 111° 36' 35". Transmitter: Devils Head Peak. Equipment: Emcee transmitter; Andrew antenna.

Flagstaff—WNC-288 (Channels D-1-4). The Clarendon Foundation, Suite 826, 4201 S. 31st. St., Arlington, VA 22206. Authorized power: 10-w. each. Antenna: 64-ft. above ground. Lat. 35° 14' 29", long. 111° 36' 35". Transmitter: Devils Head Peak. Equipment: Emcee transmitter; Andrew antenna.

Flagstaff—WNC-258 (Channels G-1-4). Verde Valley School, 3511 Verde Valley School Rd., Sedona, AZ 86351. Phone: 520-284-2272. Fax: 520-284-0432.
E-mail: vvschool@sedona.net.
Authorized power: 10-w. each. Antenna: 68-ft. above ground. Lat. 35° 14' 29", long. 111° 36' 35". Transmitter: 1.5-mi. N of Flagstaff. Equipment: Comwave transmitter; Andrew antenna.

Lake Havasu City—WLX-450 (Channels A-1-4). North American Catholic Educational Programming Foundation Inc., Box 40026, Providence, RI 02940-0026. Authorized power: 50-w. each. Antenna: 72-ft. above ground. Lat. 34° 33' 06", long. 114° 11' 37". Transmitter: Crossman Peak Electronic Site, 9-mi. NE of Lake Hauasu City. Equipment: Comwave transmitter; Andrew antenna.

Lake Havasu City—WNC-641 (Channels B-1-4). Foreign Language & Cultural Foundation, 850 Fay Rd., Syracuse, NY 13219. Phone: 205-491-6220. Authorized power: 50-w. each. Antenna: 72-ft. above ground. Lat. 34° 33' 06", long. 114° 11' 37". Transmitter: Crossman Peak Electronic Site, 9-mi. NE of Lake Havasu City. Equipment: Comwave transmitter; Andrew antenna.

Lake Havasu City—WND-285 (Channels C-1-4). Needles Unified School District, 1900 Erin Dr., Needles, CA 92363. Authorized power: 50-w. each. Antenna: 72-ft. above ground. Lat. 34° 33' 06", long. 114° 11' 37". Transmitter: Crossman Peak Electronic Site, 9-mi. NE of Lake Havasu City. Equipment: Comwave transmitter; Andrew antenna.

Lake Havasu City—WNC-642 (Channels G-1-4). Excellence in Education Network, 5700 Belmont Dr., Irondale, AL 35210. Authorized power: 50-w. each. Antenna: 39-ft. above ground. Lat. 34° 33' 06", long. 114° 11' 37". Transmitter: Crossman Peak Electronic Site, 9-mi. NE of Lake Havasu City. Equipment: Comwave transmitter; Andrew antenna.

Phoenix—WNC-663 (Channels A-1-4). Arizona State Board of Regents for Arizona State U., Tempe, AZ 85287. Phone: 480-965-6738. Fax: 480-965-1371.
Web site: http://asuonline.asu.edu.
Authorized power: 0.3-w. each. Antenna: 50-ft. above ground. Lat. 33° 35' 38", long. 112° 05' 11". Transmitter: Shaw Butte, 9-mi. N of Phoenix. Equipment: Comwave transmitter; Andrew antenna.
Leased to People's Choice TV, 5301 E. Broadway, Tucson, AZ 85711. Phone: 520-519-4400.

Phoenix—WLX-815 (Channels B-1-4). Arizona State U., Tempe, AZ 85287-2904. Phone: 480-965-6738. Fax: 480-965-1371.
Web site: http://asuonline.asu.edu.
Authorized power: 100-w. each. Antenna: 170-ft. above ground. Lat. 33° 20' 02", long. 112° 03' 44". Transmitter: 10660 S. Central, South Mountain Park. Equipment: Comwave transmitter; Andrew antenna.
Leased to People's Choice TV, 5301 East Broadway, Tucson, AZ 85711. Phone: 520-519-4400.

Phoenix—WNC-664 (Channels B-1-4). Arizona State Board of Regents for Arizona State U., Tempe, AZ 85257. Phone: 480-965-6738. Fax: 480-965-1371.
Web site: http://asuonline.asu.edu.
Authorized power: 0.3-w. each. Antenna: 50-ft. above ground. Lat. 33° 35' 38", long. 112° 05' 11". Transmitter: Shaw Butte, 9-mi. N of Phoenix. Equipment: Comwave transmitter; ITS antenna.
Leased to People's Choice TV, 5301 E. Broadway, Tucson, AZ 85711. Phone: 520-519-4400.

Phoenix—WHR-919 (Channels C-1-4). North American Catholic Educational Programming Foundation Inc., Box 40026, Providence, RI 02940-0026. Authorized power: 100-w. each. Antenna: 95-ft. above ground. Lat. 33° 20' 02", long. 112° 03' 44". Transmitter: 10660 S. Central, South Mountain Park. Equipment: Comwave transmitter; Andrew antenna.

Phoenix—WLX-816 (Channels D-1-4). Instructional Telecom Foundation Inc., Box 6060, Boulder, CO 80306. Phone: 303-442-2707. Fax: 303-442-6472.
E-mail: itf@fstv.org.
Authorized power: 100-w. each. Antenna: 98-ft. above ground. Lat. 33° 20' 02", long. 100° 03' 44". Transmitter: 10660 S. Central, South Mountain Park, 8.2-mi. SW of Phoenix. Equipment: Comwave transmitter; Andrew antenna.
Leased to People's Choice TV Corp., 5301 E. Broadway, Tucson, AZ 85711. Phone: 520-519-4400.

Phoenix—WNC-558 (Channels G-3-4). Hispanic Information & Telecommunications Network Inc., 3rd Floor, 449 Broadway, New York, NY 10013. Phone: 212-966-5660. Fax: 212-966-5725.
E-mail: email@hitn.org.
Web site: http://www.hitn.org.
Authorized power: 100-w. each. Antenna: 98-ft. above ground. Lat. 33° 20' 02", long. 112° 03'

44". Transmitter: 10660 S. Central, South Mountain Park. Equipment: Comwave transmitter; Andrew antenna.

Leased to People's Choice TV Corp., 5301 E. Broadway, Tucson, AZ 85711. Phone: 520-519-4400.

Phoenix (metropolitan area)—WHF-226 (Channels A-1-4). Arizona Board of Regents, Arizona State U., Tempe, AZ 85287-2904. Phone: 480-965-6738. Fax: 480-965-1371.

Web site: http://www.asuonline.asu.edu.

Authorized power: 100-w. each. Lat. 33° 20' 00", long. 112° 03' 46". Transmitter: 10660 S. Central, South Mountain Park. Equipment: Comwave transmitter; Andrew antenna.

Leased to People's Choice TV, 5301 E. Broadway, Tucson, AZ 85711. Phone: 520-519-4400.

Phoenix, Scottsdale, Glendale, Peoria & Paradise Valley—WHF-227 (Channels E-1-4). Arizona Board of Regents, Arizona State U., Tempe, AZ 85287-1405. Phone: 602965-3506. Fax: 602-965-1000. Authorized power: 10-w. each. Antenna: 50-ft. above ground. Lat. 33° 35' 38", long. 112° 05' 11". Transmitter: Shaw Butte, 9-mi. N of downtown Phoenix.

Prescott—WND-276 (Channels G-1-4). Yavapai County Community College District, 1100 E. Sheldon St., Prescott, AZ 86301. Authorized power: 10-w. each. Antenna: 148-ft. above ground. Lat. 34° 42' 04", long. 112° 07' 04". Transmitter: Mingus Mountain, Prescott. Equipment: Bogner transmitter; Bogner antenna.

Shaw Butte—WND-496 (Channels A-1-4). Arizona State U. Board of Regents, Arizona State U., Tempe, AZ 85287. Phone: 480-965-6738. Fax: 480-965-1371.

Web site: http://asuonline.asu.edu.

Authorized power: 2.5-w. each. Antenna: 46-ft. above ground. Lat. 33° 35' 38", long. 112° 05' 11". Transmitter: 9-mi. N of Phoenix. Equipment: Comwave transmitter; Andrew antenna.

Leased to People's Choice TV, 5301 E. Broadway, Tucson, AZ 85711. Phone: 520-519-4400.

Shaw Butte—WND-497 (Channels B-1-4). Arizona State U. Board of Regents, Arizona State U., Tempe, AZ 85287. Phone: 480-965-6738. Fax: 480-965-1371.

Web site: http://asuonline.asu.edu.

Authorized power: 2.5-w. each. Antenna: 46-ft. above ground. Lat. 33° 35' 38", long. 112° 05' 11". Transmitter: 9-mi. N of Phoenix. Equipment: Comwave transmitter; Andrew antenna.

Leased to People's Choice TV, 5301 E. Broadway, Tucson, AZ 85711. Phone: 520-519-4400.

Shaw Butte—WND-498 (Channels G-1-2). Valley Lutheran High School, 525 W. Colter, Phoenix, AZ 85013. Authorized power: 2.5-w. each. Antenna: 46-ft. above ground. Lat. 33° 35' 38", long. 112° 05' 11". Transmitter: 9-mi. N of Phoenix. Equipment: Comwave transmitter; Andrew antenna.

Shaw Butte—WND-499 (Channels G-3-4). Hispanic Information & Telecommunications Network Inc., 3rd Floor, 449 Broadway, New York, NY 10013. Phone: 212-966-5660. Fax: 212-966-5725.

E-mail: email@hitn.org.

Web site: http://www.hitn.org.

Authorized power: 2.12-w. each. Antenna: 46-ft. above ground. Lat. 33° 35' 38", long. 112° 05' 11". Transmitter: 9-mi. N of Phoenix. Equipment: Comwave transmitter; Shadowmaster antenna.

Leased to People's choice TV, 5301 E. Broadway, Tucson, AZ 85711. Phone: 520-519-4400.

Sierra Vista—WHR-942 (Channel D-1). Arizona Board of Regents for Benefit of U. of Arizona, KUAT-TV, Modern Languages Bldg., Room 222, Tucson, AZ 85721. Phone: 520-621-7365. Fax: 520-621-3360. Authorized power: 10-w. Antenna: 24-ft. above ground. Lat. 31° 32' 29", long. 110° 24' 04". Transmitter: TV Hill, Fort Huachuca. Equipment: Comwave transmitter; Andrew antenna. Requests change to 20-ft. above ground.

Tempe—WHF-225 (Channels G-1-2). Valley Lutheran High School, 525 W. Colter, Phoenix, AZ 85013. Authorized power: 100-w. each. Antenna: 95-ft. above ground. Lat. 33° 20' 02", long. 112° 03' 44". Transmitter: 10660 S. Central, South Mountain Park.

Tucson—WHR-964 (Channels A-1-4). Arizona Board of Regents for Benefit of U. of Arizona, KUAT-TV, Modern Languages Bldg., Room 222, Tucson, AZ 85721. Phone: 520-621-7365. Fax: 520-621-3360. Authorized power: 50-w. each. Antenna: 275-ft. above ground. Lat. 32° 14' 56", long. 111° 06' 57". Transmitter: 7120 W. Lost Canyon Dr., Tucson Mountain Communications Site. Equipment: Comwave transmitter.

Leased to People's Choice TV Corp., 5301 E. Broadway Blvd., Tucson, AZ 85711. Phone: 520-519-4400.

Tucson—WHR-962 (Channels B-1-4). Arizona Board of Regents for Benefit of U. of Arizona, Modern Languages Bldg., Room 222, Tucson, AZ 85721. Phone: 520-621-7635. Fax: 520-621-3360. Authorized power: 50-w. each. Antenna: 290-ft. above ground. Lat. 32° 14' 56", long. 111° 06' 57". Transmitter: 7120 W. Lost Canyon Dr., Tucson Mountain Communications Site. Equipment: Comwave transmitter; Andrew antenna.

Leased to People's Choice TV Corp., 5301 E. Broadway Blvd., Tucson, AZ 85711. Phone: 520-519-4400.

Tucson—WLX-470 (Channels C-1-4). Hispanic Information & Telecommunications Network Inc., 3rd Floor, 449 Broadway, New York, NY 10013. Phone: 212-966-5660. Fax: 212-966-5725.

E-mail: email@hitn.org.

Web site: http://www.hitn.org.

Authorized power: 50-w. each. Antenna: 132-ft. above ground. Lat. 32° 14' 56", long. 111° 06' 57". Transmitter: 7120 W. Lost Canyon Dr. Equipment: Comwave transmitter; Andrew antenna.

Leased to People's Choice TV Corp., 5301 E. Broadway Blvd., Tucson, AZ 85711. Phone: 520-519-4400.

Tucson—WHR-621 (Channels D-1-4). Arizona Board of Regents for Benefit of U. of Arizona KAUT-TV, Modern Languages Bldg., Room 222, Tucson, AZ 85721. Phone: 520-621-7635. Fax: 520-621-3360. Authorized power: 50-w. each. Antenna: 132-ft. above ground. Lat. 32° 14' 56", long. 111° 06' 57". Transmitter: 7120 W. Lost Canyon Dr., Tucson Mountain Communications Site. Equipment: Comwave transmitter; Andrew antenna.

Leased to People's Choice TV Corp., 5301 E. Broadway Blvd., Tucson, AZ 85711. Phone: 520-519-4400.

Tucson—WHR-963 (Channels G-1-4). Arizona Board of Regents for Benefit of U. of Arizona, KAUT-TV, Modern Languages Bldg., Room 222, Tucson, AZ 85721. Phone: 520-621-7365. Fax: 520-621-3360. Authorized power: 50-w. each. Lat. 32° 14' 56", long. 111° 06' 57". Transmitter: 7120 W. Lost Canyon Dr., Tucson Mountain Communications Site. Equipment: Comwave transmitter; Andrew antenna.

Leased to People's Choice TV Corp., 5301 E. Broadway Blvd., Tucson, AZ 85711. Phone: 529-519-4400.

Yuma—WLX-919 (Channels A-1-4). Shekinah Network, 14875 Powerline Rd., Atascadero, CA 93422. Phone & fax: 805-438-3341. Authorized power: 50-w. each. Antenna: 76-ft. above ground. Lat. 32° 40' 24", long. 114° 20' 13". Transmitter: Yuma County. Equipment: Andrew transmitter; Comwave antenna.

Leased to Cardiff Broadcasting, 2110 Jimmy Durante Blvd., Suite 224, Del Mar, CA 92014. Phone: 800-444-3410.

Yuma—WND-375 (Channels B-1-4). Hispanic Information & Telecommunications Network, 3rd Floor, 449 Broadway, New York, NY 10013. Phone: 212-966-5660. Fax: 212-966-5725.

E-mail: email@hitn.org.

Web site: http://www.hitn.org.

Authorized power: 50-w. each. Antenna: 75-ft. above ground. Lat. 32° 40' 24", long. 114° 20' 13". Transmitter: Wellton, AZ. Equipment: Comwave transmitter; Andrew antenna.

Leased to Distance Learning Services, 1155 Connecticut Ave. NW, Suite 300, Washington, DC 20036. Phone: 202-467-8500.

Yuma—WND-233 (Channels G-1-4). Seniors' Advocate, 13422 Elliott An Court, Herndon, VA 22071. Authorized power: 50-w. each. Antenna: 98-ft. above ground. Lat. 32° 40' 22", long. 114° 20' 14". Transmitter: Telegraph Pass Communications Site. Equipment: Emcee transmitter; Andrew antenna.

Arkansas

El Dorado—WNC-429 (Channels C-1-4). Southern Arkansas U., SAU Box 1392, Hwy. 19 N, Magnolia, AR 71753. Authorized power: 10-w. each. Antenna: 404-ft. above ground. Lat. 33° 16' 19", long. 92° 42' 11". Transmitter: Rte. 335, 8-mi. NNW of El Dorado. Equipment: Comwave transmitter; Andrew antenna.

El Dorado—WNC-428 (Channels D-1-4). El Dorado School District No. 15, 220 W. Oak, El Dorado, AR 71730. Authorized power: 10-w. each. Antenna: 620-ft. above ground. Lat. 33° 16' 19", long. 92° 42' 11". Transmitter: Rte. 335, 8-mi. NNW of El Dorado. Equipment: Comwave transmitter; Andrew antenna.

Forrest City—WLX-533 (Channels A-1-4). Crawfordsville School District, 100 Ward St., Crawfordsville, AR 72327. Authorized power: 39.8-w. each. Antenna: 495-ft. above ground. Lat. 35° 01' 22", long. 90° 45' 59". Transmitter: 1.1-mi. SSE of State Rte. 284 & I-40 intersection. Equipment: Comwave transmitter; Andrew antenna.

Forrest City—WLX-730 (Channels B-1-4). Earle School District, Box 637, Earle, AR 72331. Authorized power: 39.8-w. each. Antenna: 495-ft. above ground. Lat. 35° 01' 22", long. 90° 45' 59". Transmitter: 1.1-mi. SSE of State Rte. 284 & I-40 intersection. Equipment: Comwave transmitter; Andrew antenna.

Forrest City—WLX-582 (Channels C-1-4). Cross County School District, Box 158, Cherry Valley, AR 72324. Authorized power: 40-w. each. Antenna: 495-ft. above ground. Lat. 35° 01' 22", long. 90° 45' 59". Transmitter: 1.1-mi. SSE of State Rte. 284 & I-40 intersection. Equipment: Comwave transmitter; Omni antenna.

Forrest City—WLX-561 (Channels D-1-4). Hughes School District No. 27, One College St., Hughes, AR 72348. Authorized power: 39.8-w. each. Antenna: 495-ft. above ground. Lat. 35° 01' 22", long. 90° 45' 59". Transmitter: 1.1-mi. SSE of Rte. 284 & I-40 intersection. Equipment: Comwave transmitter; Andrew antenna.

Forrest City—WNC-364 (Channels G-1-4). Turrell School District, Box 369, Turrell, AR 72384. Authorized power: 40-w. each. Antenna: 495-ft. above ground. Lat. 35° 01' 22", long. 90° 45' 59". Transmitter: 1.1-mi. SSE of State Rte. 284 & I-40 intersection. Equipment: Comwave transmitter; Andrew antenna.

Fort Smith & Van Buren—WNC-445 (Channels A-1-4). Van Buren Public Schools, 2221 Pointer Trail, Van Buren, AR 72956. Authorized power: 10-w. each. Antenna: 156-ft. above ground. Lat. 35° 26' 51", long. 94° 21' 54". Transmitter: Crawford County. Equipment: ITS transmitter; Andrew antenna.

Fort Smith & Van Buren—WNC-388 (Channels B-1-4). Carl Albert State College, 1507 S. McKenna St., Poteau, OK 74953. Phone: 918-647-1200. Fax: 918-647-1266. Authorized power: 10-w. each. Antenna: 156-ft. above ground. Lat. 35° 26' 51", long. 94° 21' 54". Transmitter: Crawford County. Equipment: ITS transmitter; Andrew antenna.

Leased to Liberty South Cable, 6609 Rogers Ave., Fort Smith, AR 72907. Phone: 501-452-1681.

Fort Smith & Van Buren—WNC-468 (Channels C-1-4). Fort Smith Public School, 3205 Jenny Lind Ave., Fort Smith, AR 72901. Authorized power: 10-w. each. Antenna: 156-ft. above ground. Lat. 35° 26' 51", long. 94° 21' 54". Transmitter: Crawford County. Equipment: ITS transmitter; Andrew antenna.

Fort Smith & Van Buren—WNC-383 (Channels D-1-4). Carl Albert State College, 304 Harriet, Salisaw, OK 74955. Authorized power: 10-w. each. Antenna: 156-ft. above ground. Lat. 35° 26' 51", long. 94° 21' 54". Transmitter: Crawford County. Equipment: ITS transmitter; Andrew antenna.

Fort Smith & Van Buren—WNC-479 (Channels G-1-4). Hackett Public School, Box 188, Hackett, AR 72937. Authorized power: 10-w. each. Antenna: 238-ft. above ground. Lat. 35° 26' 51", long. 94° 21' 54". Equipment: ITS transmitter; Andrew antenna.

Hot Springs—WND-347 (Channels A-1-4). The Clarendon Foundation, Suite 826, 4201 S. 31st St., Arlington, VA 22206. Authorized power: 5-w. each. Antenna: 299-ft. above ground. Lat. 34° 30' 19", long. 93° 05' 06". Transmitter: West Mountain No. 1, 1-mi. NW of Hot Springs. Equipment: Comwave transmitter; Andrew antenna.

Hot Springs—WND-348 (Channels B-1-4). Shekinah Network, 14875 Powerline Rd., Atascadero, CA 93422. Authorized power: 5-w. each. Antenna: 299-ft. above ground. Lat. 34° 30' 19", long. 93° 05' 06". Transmitter: West Mountain No. 1, 1-mi. NW of Hot Springs. Equipment: Comwave transmitter; Andrew antenna.

Hot Springs—WND-350 (Channels D-1-4). Center for Economic & Social Justice, Box 40849, Washington, DC 20016. Authorized power: 5-w. each. Antenna: 299-ft. above ground. Lat. 34° 30' 19", long. 93° 05' 06". Transmitter: West Mountain No. 1, 1-mi. NW of Hot Springs. Equipment: Comwave transmitter; Andrew antenna.

Hot Springs—WND-351 (Channels G-1-4). Lake Hamilton Schools, 300 Wolf St., Pearcy, AR 71964. Authorized power: 5-w. each. Antenna: 299-ft. above ground. Lat. 34° 30' 19", long.

93° 05' 06". Transmitter: West Mountain No. 1, 1-mi. NW of Hot Springs. Equipment: Comwave transmitter; Andrew antenna.

Little Rock—WNC-466 (Channels C-1-4). North American Catholic Educational Programming Foundation, Box 40026, Providence, RI 02940-0026. Authorized power: 10-w. each. Antenna: 650-ft. above ground. Lat. 34° 47' 57", long. 92° 29' 21". Transmitter: 11711 W. Markham. Equipment: Emcee transmitter; Andrew antenna.

Magnolia—WND-228 (Channels A-1-4). Southern Arkansas U., Hwy. 19 N, Magnolia, AR 71753. Authorized power: 50-w. each. Antenna: 361-ft. above ground. Lat. 33° 11' 28", long. 93° 08' 09". Transmitter: County Rd. 11. Equipment: Comwave transmitter; Andrew antenna.

Magnolia—WND-229 (Channels B-1-4). Stephens County School District, Box 427, Stephens, AR 71764. Authorized power: 50-w. each. Antenna: 361-ft. above ground. Lat. 33° 11' 28", long. 93° 08' 09". Transmitter: County Rd. 11. Equipment: Comwave transmitter; Andrew antenna.

Magnolia—WND-230 (Channels C-1-4). Emerson School District No. 66, Box 129, Emerson, AR 71740. Phone: 870-547-2218. Fax: 870-547-2017. Authorized power: 50-w. each. Antenna: 361-ft. above ground. Lat. 33° 11' 28", long. 93° 08' 09". Transmitter: County Rd. 11. Equipment: Comwave transmitter; Andrew antenna.
Leased to Nucentrix Broadband Network, 200 Chisholm Place, Suite 200, Plano, TX 75075. Phone: 972-423-9494. Fax: 972-423-0819.

Magnolia—WND-231 (Channels D-1-4). Southern Arkansas U., 100 Carr Rd., Camden, AR 71701. Phone: 870-574-4500. Fax: 870-574-4520.
E-mail: rworsley@titus.sautech.edu.
Web site: http://www.sautech.edu.
Authorized power: 50-w. each. Antenna: 135-ft. above ground. Lat. 33° 11' 28", long. 93° 08' 09". Transmitter: County Rd. 11. Equipment: Comwave transmitter; Andrew antenna.

Magnolia—WND-232 (Channels G-1-4). Southern Arkansas U. Alumni Assn, Box 1416, Magnolia, AR 71753. Authorized power: 50-w. each. Antenna: 361-ft. above ground. Lat. 33° 11' 28", long. 93° 08' 09". Transmitter: County Rd. 11. Equipment: Comwave transmitter; Andrew antenna.

Paragould—WLX-387 (Channels A-1-4). Buffalo Island School District, Hwy. 18, Monette, AR 72447. Authorized power: 100-w. each. Antenna: 495-ft. above ground. Lat. 36° 05' 57", long. 90° 34' 31". Transmitter: Crowleys Ridge, 5.5-mi. WNW of Paragould. Equipment: Comwave transmitter; Andrew antenna. Requests change to 39.8-w. each, lat. 36° 06' 26", long. 90° 34' 45"; transmitter to Crowleys Ridge, 6.1-mi. NW of Paragould.

Paragould—WLX-388 (Channels B-1-4). Clay County Central School District, Box 368, Rector, AR 72461. Authorized power: 100-w. each. Antenna: 495-ft. above ground. Lat. 36° 05' 57", long. 90° 34' 31". Transmitter: Crowleys Ridge, 5.5-mi. WNW of Paragould. Equipment: Comwave transmitter; Andrew antenna. Requests change to 398-w. each lat. 36° 06' 26", long. 90° 34' 45"; transmitter to Crowleys Ridge, 6.1-mi. NW of Paragould.

Paragould—WLX-390 (Channels C-1-4). Hoxie School District No. 46, Alice & Gibson Sts., Hoxie, AR 72433. Authorized power: 100-w. each. Antenna: 500-ft. above ground. Lat. 36° 05' 57", long. 90° 34' 31". Transmitter: Crowleys Ridge, 5.5-mi. WNW of Paragould. Equipment: Comwave transmitter; Andrew antenna. Requests change to 39.8-w each, lat. 36° 06' 26", long. 90° 34' 45"; transmitter to Crowleys Ridge, 6.1-mi. NW of Paragould.

Paragould—WLX-386 (Channels D-1-4). Paragould School District, 631 W. Court St., Paragould, AR 72450. Phone: 870-239-2105. Fax: 870-239-4697.
E-mail: tkimb@rams.nesd.kl2.ar.us.
Web site: http://www.rams.nesd.kl2.ar.us.
Authorized power: 100-w. each. Lat. 36° 05' 57", long. 90° 34' 31". Transmitter: Crowleys Ridge, 5.5-mi. WNW of Paragould. Equipment: Comwave transmitter; Andrew antenna. Requests change to 39.8-w. each, 495-ft. above ground, lat. 36° 06' 26", long. 90° 34' 45"; transmitter to Crowleys Ridge, 6.1-mi. NW of Paragould.
Leased to James Wells, Rte. 4, Box 210, Paragould, AR 72450.

Paragould—WLX-389 (Channels G-1-4). Delaplaine School District, Hwy. 90, Delaplaine, AR 72425. Authorized power: 100-w. each. Lat. 36° 05' 57", long. 90° 34' 31". Transmitter: Crowleys Ridge, 5.5-mi. WNW of Paragould. Equipment: Comwave transmitter; Andrew antenna. Requests change to 39.8-w. each 495-ft. above ground, lat. 36° 06' 26", long. 90° 34' 45"; transmitter to Crowley's Ridge, 6.1-mi. NW of Paragould.

Pine Bluff—WND-286 (Channels A-1-4). Jefferson County Regional Adult Education Center, 414 Walnut St., Pine Bluff, AR 71601. Authorized power: 10-w. each. Antenna: 105-ft. above ground. Lat. 34° 09' 56", long. 91° 50' 27". Transmitter: Hwy 65, 10-mi. SE of Pine Bluff. Equipment: Comwave transmitter; Andrew antenna.

Pine Bluff—WND-287 (Channels B-1-4). Dollarway School District, 4900 Dollarway Rd., Pine Bluff, AR 71602. Authorized power: 10-w. each. Antenna: 105-ft. above ground. Lat. 34° 09' 56", long. 91° 50' 27". Transmitter: Hwy. 65, 10-mi. SE of Pine Bluff. Equipment: Comwave transmitter; Andrew antenna.

Pine Bluff—WND-376 (Channels C-1-4). Altheimer Unified School District, 102 Orchard, Altheimer, AR 72004. Authorized power: 10-w. each. Antenna: 105-ft. above ground. Lat. 34° 09' 56", long. 91° 50' 27". Transmitter: Hwy. 65, 10-mi. SE of Pine Bluff. Equipment: Comwave transmitter; Andrew antenna.

Pine Bluff—WND-377 (Channels G-1-4). White Hall School District, 1020 W. Holland, White Hall, AR 71602. Phone: 870-247-2002. Fax: 870-247-3707. Authorized power: 10-w. each. Antenna: 105-ft. above ground. Lat. 34° 09' 56", long. 91° 50' 27". Transmitter: Hwy. 65, 10-mi. SE of Pine Bluff. Equipment: Comwave transmitter; Andrew antenna.

Springdale—WND-223 (Channels A-1-4). Elkins School District No. 10, Box 322, Elkins, AR 72727. Authorized power: 50-w. each. Antenna: 98-ft. above ground. Lat. 36° 08' 50", long. 94° 11' 14". Transmitter: 4201 S. 56th St. Equipment: Emcee transmitter; Andrew antenna.

Springdale—WND-224 (Channels B-1-4). Gentry Public Schools, Drawer 159, Gentry, AR 72734. Authorized power: 50-w. each. Antenna: 1446-ft. above ground. Lat. 36° 08' 50", long. 94° 11' 14". Transmitter: 4201 S. 56th St. Equipment: Emcee transmitter; Andrew antenna.

Springdale—WND-225 (Channels C-1-4). Lincoln Public Schools, 502 E. P. Rothrock, Lincoln, AR 72744. Authorized power: 50-w. each. Antenna: 98-ft. above ground. Lat. 36° 08' 50", long. 94° 11' 14". Transmitter: 4201 S. 56th St. Equipment: Emcee transmitter; Andrew antenna.

Springdale—WND-226 (Channels D-1-4). Prairie Grove School District, 820 N. Mock St., Prairie Grove, AR 72753. Authorized power: 50-w. each. Antenna: 1446-ft. above ground. Lat. 36° 08' 50", long. 94° 11' 14". Transmitter: 4201 S. 56th St. Equipment: Emcee transmitter; Andrew antenna.

Springdale—WND-227 (Channels G-1-4). Siloam Springs School District, Box 798, 847 S. Dogwood, Siloam Springs, AR 72761. Authorized power: 50-w. each. Antenna: 1446-ft. above ground. Lat. 36° 08' 50", long. 94° 11' 14". Transmitter: 4201 S. 56th St. Equipment: Emcee transmitter; Andrew antenna.

Texarkana—WNC-469 (Channels C-1-4). Texarkana School District No. 7, 3512 Grand, Texarkana, AR 75505. Authorized power: 50-w. each. Antenna: 450-ft. above ground. Lat. 33° 25' 48", long. 94° 05' 08". Transmitter: N of U.S. Hwy. 92. Equipment: Comwave transmitter; Andrew antenna.

Toltec—WLX-954 (Channels A-1-4). Pulaski County Special School District, 925 E. Dixon Rd., Little Rock, AR 72216. Authorized power: 50.8-w. each. Antenna: 1266-ft. above ground. Lat. 34° 47' 57", long. 92° 29' 29". Transmitter: Shinall Mountain TV Tower. Equipment: Emcee transmitter; Andrew antenna.

Toltec—WLX-955 (Channels B-1-4). Lonoke School District, 411 Holly St., Lonoke, AR 72086. Authorized power: 50-w. each. Antenna: 655-ft. above ground. Lat. 34° 47' 57", long. 92° 29' 29". Transmitter: Shinall Mountain TV Tower. Equipment: Emcee transmitter; Andrew antenna.

Toltec—WLX-953 (Channels G-1-4). Little Rock School District, 801 W. Markham, Little Rock, AR 72201. Phone: 501-324-2020. Fax: 501-324-2032. Authorized power: 100-w. each. Antenna: 500-ft. above ground. Lat. 34° 39' 09", long. 92° 03' 01". Transmitter: 1800-ft. E of U.S. Hwy. 165. Equipment: Comwave transmitter; Andrew antenna.
Leased to American Telecasting, 5575 Tech Center Dr., Suite 300, Colorado Springs, CO 80919. Phone: 719-632-5544.

California

Anaheim—KUZ-56 (Channels A-1-4). Anaheim City School District, 1001 S. East St., Anaheim, CA 92805. Phone: 714-517-8500. Authorized power: 0.25-w. each. Transmitter: 412 E. Broadway.

Bakersfield—WHR-797 (Channels A-1-4). California State U., 9001 Stockdale Hwy., Bakersfield, CA 93311-1099. Phone: 661-664-2448. Fax: 661-664-2449.
E-mail: tbulaski@csubak.edu.
Web site: http://www.csubak.edu.
Authorized power: 50-w. each. Antenna: 355-ft. above ground. Lat. 35° 16' 52", long. 119° 04' 41". Transmitter: 8101 Ashe Rd. Equipment: ITS transmitter; Andrew antenna.
Leased to Popvision, 3115 Select Ave., Bakersfield, CA 93304. Phone: 661-638-2222.

Bakersfield—WLX-345 (Channels B-1-4). Kern Community College District, 2100 Chester Ave., Bakersfield, CA 93301. Authorized power: 50-w. each. Antenna: 355-ft. above ground. Lat. 35° 16' 52", long. 119° 04' 41". Transmitter: 8101 Ashe Rd. Equipment: ITS transmitter; Andrew antenna.

Bakersfield—WLX-372 (Channels C-1-4). Kern High School District, 2000 24th St., Bakersfield, CA 93301. Authorized power: 50-w. each. Antenna: 360-ft. above ground. Lat. 35° 16' 52", long. 119° 04' 41". Transmitter: 8101 Ashe Rd. Equipment: ITS transmitter; Andrew antenna.

Bakersfield—WLX-550 (Channels D-1-4). Panama-Buena Vista Union School District, 4200 Ashe Rd., Bakersfield, CA 93313. Phone: 805-831-8331. Fax: 805-398-2141. Authorized power: 50-w. each. Antenna: 355-ft. above ground. Lat. 35° 16' 52", long. 119° 04' 41". Transmitter: 8101 Ashe Rd. Equipment: ITS transmitter; Andrew antenna.

Barstow—WHR-832 (Channels G-1-4). California State U.-San Bernardino, 5500 University Pkwy., San Bernardino, CA 92407-2397. Phone: 909-880-5619. Fax: 909-880-7075.
E-mail: scooper@wiley.csusb.edu.
Web site: http://www.acm.csusb.edu.
Authorized power: 50-w. each. Antenna: 105-ft. above ground. Lat. 34° 36' 38", long. 117° 17' 17". Transmitter: N of Barstow. Equipment: Comwave transmitter; Andrew antenna.
Leased to Transworld Telecommunications Inc., 102 West 500 South, Suite 320, Salt Lake City, UT 84101.

Bear Mountain—WHR-454 (Channels A-1-2). California State U.-Fresno, MS 121, 2225 E. San Ramon, Fresno, CA 93740. Phone: 209-278-2058. Fax: 209-278-7026. Authorized power: 60-w. each. Antenna: 1703-ft. above ground. Lat. 36° 55' 49", long. 119° 38' 26". Transmitter: Owens Mountain, Fresno. Equipment: Comwave transmitter; Andrew antenna.

Beaumont—WHR-927 (Channels B-1-4). Caritas Telecommunications, 1201 E. Highland Ave., San Bernardino, CA 92404. Phone: 909-475-5350. Fax: 909-475-5357.
E-mail: caritasctn@aol.com.
Authorized power: 10-w. each. Antenna: 38-ft. above ground. Lat. 33° 54' 29", long. 116° 59' 46". Transmitter: Mount Davis, 2.2-mi. SW of Beaumont. Equipment: Comwave transmitter; Bogner antenna.
Leased to Craig Broadcast Systems, 2940 Victoria Ave., Brandon, MB R7B 3Y3. Phone: 202-728-1150.

Berkeley—WAC-273 (Channels A-1-2). Regents of the U. of California, 1111 Franklin St., Oakland, CA 94607. Authorized power: 40-w. each. Antenna: 256-ft. above ground. Lat. 37° 41' 17", long. 122° 26' 07". Transmitter: San

Bruno Mountain, 6.1-mi. S of San Francisco. Equipment: ITS transmitter; Bogner, Andrew antenna.

Berry Creek—WHR-796 (Channels A-1-4). Butte Community College District, 3536 Butte Campus Dr., Oroville, CA 95965. Phone: 530-895-2344. Fax: 530-895-2413.
E-mail: web@bctv.net.
Web site: http://www.bctv.net.
Authorized power: 10-w. each. Antenna: 2000-ft. above ground. Lat. 39° 39' 04", long. 121° 27' 43". Transmitter: Top of Bloomer Hill, Oroville. Equipment: Comwave transmitter; Andrew antenna.

Butte—WHQ-374 (Channel D-2). Regents of the U. of California, 1111 Franklin St., Oakland, CA 94607. Authorized power: 10-w. Antenna: 160-ft. above ground. Lat. 39° 12' 21", long. 121° 49' 10". Transmitter: Sutter Buttes, 12-mi. W of Yuba City.

Calaveras & Tuolumne Counties—WHG-340 (Channel E-1). California State College, 801 W. Monte Vista Ave., Turlock, CA 95380. Authorized power: 10-w. Antenna: 20-ft. above ground. Lat. 38° 01' 52", long. 120° 21' 02". Transmitter: Telegraph Hill, 2.5-mi. E of Columbia.

Carson—WHG-267 (Channels A-1-4). California State Universities & Colleges, 400 Golden Shore, Long Beach, CA 90802. Authorized power: 10-w. each. Lat. 33° 51' 53", long. 118° 15' 18". Transmitter: 1000 E. Victoria St. Equipment: Emcee transmitter.

Chatsworth—WHR-664 (Channels D-2-4). U. of Southern California, Room 108, Olin Hall, 3650 McClintock Ave., OHE 108, Los Angeles, CA 90089. Authorized power: 10-w. each. Antenna: 340-ft. above ground. Lat. 34° 19' 26", long. 118° 34' 34". Transmitter: Oat Mountain, 4.9-mi. N of Chatsworth. Equipment: Andrew transmitter. Requests change to 20-w. each.

Chatsworth—WHG-229 (Channels F-1-4). California State U. of Northridge, Oviatt Library-4A, 18111 Nordhoff St., Northridge, CA 91330-8324. Phone: 818-885-2355. Fax: 818-885-2316. Authorized power: 50-w. each. Antenna: 320-ft. above ground. Lat. 34° 13' 37", long. 118° 03' 58". Transmitter: Oat Mountain, 4.9-mi. N of Chatsworth, Allcom Bldg. Equipment: ITS transmitter; Andrew antenna.
Leased to Cross Country Wireless Cable, 67A Mountain Blvd. Warren, NJ 07059.

Chico—WND-221 (Channels B-1-4). Butte County Office of Education, 5 County Center Dr., Oroville, CA 95965. Authorized power: 10-w. each. Antenna: 3491-ft. above ground. Lat. 39° 57' 29", long. 121° 42' 50". Transmitter: 10895 Cohasset Rd. Equipment: ITS transmitter; Andrew antenna.

Chico—WND-222 (Channels D-1-4). Paradise Unified School District, 565 Recreation Dr., Paradise, CA 95969. Authorized power: 10-w. each. Antenna: 3491-ft. above ground. Lat. 39° 57' 29", long. 121° 42' 50". Transmitter: 10895 Cohasset Rd. Equipment: ITS transmitter; Andrew antenna.

Chico—WLX-458 (Channels G-1-4). North American Catholic Educational Programming Foundation Inc., Box 40026, Providence, RI 02940-0026. Phone: 401-729-0900. Authorized power: 10-w. each. Antenna: 290-ft. above ground. Lat. 39° 56' 46", long. 121° 43' 17". Transmitter: 10575 Cohasset Rd. Equipment: Emcee transmitter; Lance antenna.

El Centro—WNC-886 (Channels A-1-4). Imperial County Office of Education, 1398 Sperber Rd., El Centro, CA 92243. Authorized power: 20-w. each. Antenna: 289-ft. above ground. Lat. 32° 46' 56", long. 115° 31' 51". Transmitter: Corner of Dogwood & Rodd Rds. Equipment: Comwave transmitter; Andrew antenna.

El Centro—WNC-887 (Channels B-1-4). Central Union High School District, 351 Ross Ave., El Centro, CA 92243. Authorized power: 20-w. each. Antenna: 252-ft. above ground. Lat. 32° 46' 56", long. 115° 31' 51". Transmitter: Corner of Dogwood & Rodd Rds. Equipment: Comwave transmitter; Andrew antenna.

El Centro—WNC-888 (Channels C-1-4). Imperial Community College District, Box 158, El Centro, CA 92243. Authorized power: 20-w. each. Antenna: 252-ft. above ground. Lat. 32° 46' 56", long. 115° 31' 51". Transmitter: Corner of Dogwood & Rodd Rds. Equipment: Comwave transmitter; Andrew antenna.

El Centro—WNC-889 (Channels D-1-4). Meadows Union School District, 2059 Browker Rd., El Centro, CA 92243. Phone: 760-352-7512. Fax: 760-337-1275. Authorized power: 20-w. each. Antenna: 291-ft. above ground. Lat. 32° 46' 56", long. 115° 31' 51". Transmitter: Corner of Dogwood & Rodd Rds. Equipment: Comwave transmitter; Andrew antenna.

El Centro—WNC-890 (Channels G-1-4). Seeley Union School District, Box 868, 1812 W. Rio Vista, Seeley, CA 92273. Authorized power: 20-w. each. Antenna: 246-ft. above ground. Lat. 32° 46' 56", long. 115° 31' 51". Transmitter: Corner of Dogwood & Rodd Rds. Equipment: Comwave transmitter; Andrew antenna.

El Dorado—WHR-925 (Channel D-3). Los Rios Community College District, 1919 Spanos Court, Sacramento, CA 95825. Phone: 916-688-7280. Fax: 916-688-7476.
E-mail: caldwej@crc.losrios.cc.ca.us.
Authorized power: 10-w. Antenna: 508-ft. above ground. Lat. 38° 37' 49", long. 120° 51' 20". Transmitter: El Dorado. Equipment: Comwave transmitter; Bogner antenna.

Elverta—WLX-735 (Channels D-1-4). California Human Development Corp., 3315 Airway Dr., Santa Rosa, CA 95403. Authorized power: 50-w. each. Antenna: 453-ft. above ground. Lat. 38° 38' 54", long. 121° 28' 40". Transmitter: N. Market, 0.25-mi. W of Gate St. Equipment: Comwave transmitter; Andrew antenna.

Encino—KSW-92 (Channels D-1-4). Archdiocese of Los Angeles Education & Welfare Corp., 1530 W. 9th St., Los Angeles, CA 90015. Phone: 213-251-3308. Fax: 213-386-8667. Authorized power: 10-w. each. Antenna: 40-ft. above ground. Lat. 34° 09' 43", long. 118° 31' 07". Transmitter: 17750 Ventura Blvd., Encino. Equipment: Emcee transmitter; Taco antenna.

Eureka—WND-237 (Channels C-1-4). Humboldt County Office of Education, 901 Myrtle Ave., Eureka, CA 95501. Authorized power: 10-w. each. Antenna: 194-ft. above ground. Lat. 40° 43' 36", long. 123° 58' 26". Transmitter: 10-mi. E of Eureka. Equipment: Emcee transmitter; Bogner antenna.

Eureka—WNC-737 (Channels D-1-4). College of the Redwoods, Tompkins Hills Rd., Eureka, CA 95501. Authorized power: 10-w. each. Antenna: 200-ft. above ground. Lat. 40° 43' 36", long. 123° 58' 26". Transmitter: 10-mi. E of Eureka. Equipment: Comwave transmitter; Bogner antenna.

Eureka—WND-238 (Channels G-1-4). The Clarendon Foundation, Suite 826, 4201 S. 31st St., Arlington, VA 22206. Authorized power: 10-w. each. Antenna: 194-ft. above ground. Lat. 40° 42' 58", long. 124° 12' 11". Transmitter: End of Humboldt Rd. Equipment: Comwave transmitter; Andrew antenna.

Flea Mountain—WLX-522 (Channels C-1-4). California State U. Chico, Instructional Media Center, Chico, CA 95929. Phone: 916-898-6112. Fax: 916-898-5369.
Web site: http://www.csuchico.edu.
Authorized power: 100-w. each. Antenna: 97-ft. above ground. Lat. 39° 49' 45", long. 121° 28' 16". Transmitter: Butte County. Equipment: Comwave transmitter; Andrew antenna.

Fresno—WLX-962 (Channels A-3-4). Madera Unified School District, 1902 Howard Rd., Madera, CA 93637. Authorized power: 20-w. each. Antenna: 96-ft. above ground. Lat. 36° 55' 49", long. 119° 38' 26". Transmitter: Owens Mountain. Equipment: ITS transmitter; Andrew antenna.

Fresno—WLX-351 (Channels B-1-2). North American Catholic Educational Programming Foundation Inc., Box 40026, Providence, RI 02940-0026. Phone: 401-729-0900. Authorized power: 20-w. each. Antenna: 96-ft. above ground. Lat. 36° 55' 49", long. 119° 38' 26". Equipment: ITS transmitter; Andrew antenna.

Fresno—WLX-671 (Channels D-1-4). Hispanic Information & Telecommunications Network Inc., 3rd Floor, 449 Broadway, New York, NY 10013. Phone: 212-966-5660. Fax: 212-966-5725.
E-mail: E-mail@hitn.org.
Web site: http://www.hitn.org.
Authorized power: 10-w. each. Antenna: 345-ft. above ground. Lat. 36° 44' 09", long. 119° 47' 59". Transmitter: E & G Sts. Equipment: Emcee transmitter; Andrew antenna.
Leased to People's Choice TV Corp., 5301 E. Broadway Blvd., Tucson, AZ 85711. Phone: 520-519-4400.

Fresno—WHR-462 (Channel E-1). California State U. Fresno, Computing, Communication & Media Service, Fresno, CA 93740-0050. Phone: 209-278-3923. Fax: 209-278-7026. Authorized power: 10-w. Antenna: 90-ft. above ground. Lat. 36° 48' 42", long. 119° 44' 43". Transmitter: Speech Arts Bldg., California State U., Fresno. Equipment: Comwave transmitter; Bogner antenna.

Fresno—KVK-21 (Channels G-3-4). Fresno County Superintendent of Schools, 1111 Van Ness Ave., Fresno, CA 93721. Phone: 209-265-3058. Fax: 209-497-3899.
E-mail: spassmore@fcoe.k12.ca.us.
Web site: http://www.fcoe@k12.ca.us.
Authorized power: 20-w. each. Antenna: 96-ft. above ground. Lat. 36° 55' 49", long. 119° 38' 26". Transmitter: Owens Mountain. Equipment: ITS transmitter; Andrew antenna.

Fullerton—WHR-667 (Channels A-1-4). California State U.-Fullerton, 800 N. State Blvd., Fullerton, CA 92634-5000. Phone: 714-773-2623. Fax: 714-773-3892.
E-mail: w1reeder@fullerton.edu.
Web site: http://www.fullerton.edu.
Authorized power: 10-w. each. Antenna: 100-ft. above ground. Lat. 33° 52' 55", long. 117° 53' 05". Transmitter: Corner of Nutwood Ave. & State College Blvd. Equipment: Global System transmitter; Andrew antenna.
Leased to Pac-Bell Video Services, 2000 E. McFadden Ave., Room 136, Santa Ana, CA 92705. Phone: 714-245-1000.

Fullerton—KVP-26 (Channels F-1-4). Anaheim City School District, 1001 S. East St., Anaheim, CA 92805. Phone: 714-517-8500. Authorized power: 9-w. each. Lat. 33° 53' 30.8", long. 117° 54' 04". Transmitter: Motorola Site No. 2, Modjeska Peak. Equipment: ITS transmitter; Bogner antenna.

Gilroy—WHR-644 (Channels G-2-3). Santa Clara County Board of Education, 1290 Ridder Park Dr., San Jose, CA 95131-2304. Phone: 408-453-6800. Fax: 408-453-6659.
Web site: http://www.sccoe.k12.ca.us.
Authorized power: 10-w. each. Antenna: 30-ft. above ground. Lat. 37° 03' 35", long. 121° 37' 30". Transmitter: 1.6-mi. W of Hwy. 101 & Church Ave. intersection. Equipment: Emcee transmitter; Bogner antenna.
Leased to Wireless Holdings Inc., 975-H Industrial Rd., San Carlos, CA 94070. Phone: 415-631-9190.

Gilroy (rural area)—WHR-827 (Channels C-1-4). Leland Stanford Jr. U., 857 Sierra St., Stanford, CA 94305. Authorized power: 10-w. each. Antenna: 17-ft. above ground. Lat. 37° 09' 06", long. 121° 36' 32". Transmitter: Canada Rd., 4.9-mi. E of Gilroy. Equipment: Comwave transmitter; Lance antenna.

Gonzales—WHR-909 (Channels B-1-4). Hartnell College, 156 Homestead Ave., Salinas, CA 93901. Authorized power: 20-w. each. Lat. 36° 34' 54", long. 121° 26' 34". Transmitter: E side of Parsons Hill. Equipment: Comwave transmitter; Andrew antenna.

Grand Terrace—WND-392 (Channels A-1-4). California State Polytechnic U., 3801 W. Temple Ave., Pamona, CA 91768. Authorized power: 0.3-w. each. Antenna: 29-ft. above ground. Lat. 34° 01' 20", long. 117° 17' 46". Transmitter: Blue Mountain, 1.2-mi. SE of Grand Terrace. Equipment: ITS transmitter; Andrew antenna.

Grand Terrace—WND-381 (Channel B-1). San Bernardino Community College District, 701 S. Mount Vernon Ave., San Bernardino, CA 92410. Authorized power: 0.3-w. Antenna: 29-ft. above ground. Lat. 34° 01' 20", long. 117° 17' 46". Transmitter: Blue Mountain, 1.2-mi. SE of Grand Terrace. Equipment: ITS transmitter; Andrew antenna.

Grand Terrace—WND-384 (Channels C-1-4). Hispanic Information & Telecommunications Network, 3rd Floor, 449 Broadway, New York, NY 10013. Phone: 212-966-5660. Fax: 212-966-5725.
E-mail: email@hitn.org.
Web site: http://www.hitn.org.
Authorized power: 0.3-w. each. Antenna: 29-ft. above ground. Lat. 34° 01' 20", long. 117° 17' 46". Transmitter: Atop Blue Mountain. Equipment: ITS transmitter; Andrew antenna.
Leased to PVBS, 2000 E. McFadden Ave., Santa Ana, CA 92705. Phone: 714-245-1000.

Grand Terrace—WND-385 (Channels D-1-4). Caritas Telecommunications, 1201 E. Highland Ave., San Bernardino, CA 92404. Phone: 909-475-5350. Fax: 909-475-5357.
E-mail: cmcolella@esbdiocese.org.
Authorized power: 0.3-w. each. Antenna: 29-ft. above ground. Lat. 34° 01' 20", long. 117° 17' 46". Transmitter: Blue Mountain, 1.2-mi. SE of Grand Terrace. Equipment: ITS transmitter; Andrew antenna.
Leased to Cross Country Wireless (Prime One), 6177 Rivercrest Dr., Suite B, Riverside, CA 92507. Phone: 909-653-4499.

Grand Terrace—WND-383 (Channels G-1, 3-4). San Bernardino Community College District,

701 S. Mount Vernon Ave., San Bernardino, CA 92410. Authorized power: 0.3-w. each. Antenna: 29-ft. above ground. Lat. 34° 01' 20", long. 117° 17' 46". Equipment: ITS transmitter; Andrew antenna.

Greenfield—WHR-910 (Channels A-1-4). Hartnell College, 156 Homestead Ave., Salinas, CA 93901. Authorized power: 10-w. each. Antenna: 30-ft. above ground. Lat. 36° 19' 36.3", long. 121° 14' 43". Transmitter: Greenfield High School. Equipment: Comwave transmitter.

Joaquin Ridge—WHR-819 (Channels D-1-2). California State U.-Fresno, Computing, Communication & Media Service, Fresno, CA 93740. Phone: 209-278-3923. Fax: 209-278-7026. Authorized power: 50-w. each. Antenna: 27-ft. above ground. Lat. 36° 17' 58", long. 120° 23' 55". Transmitter: 12-mi. NW of Coalinga. Equipment: Comwave transmitter; Bogner antenna.

Kelseyville—WNC-409 (Channels B-1-4). Yuba Community College District, 2088 N. Beale Rd., Marysville, CA 95901. Phone: 530-741-6757. Fax: 530-741-6824.
E-mail: scato@mail2.yuba.cc.ca.us.
Web site: http://www.yuba.cc.ca.us.
Authorized power: 15-w. each. Antenna: 20-ft. above ground. Lat. 38° 59' 23", long. 122° 46' 04". Transmitter: Mount Konocit, Buckingham Peak, W shore of Clear Lake. Equipment: Comwave transmitter; Bogner antenna.

Livermore—WBY-28 (Channel B-4). Regents of the U. of California, 2200 University Ave., Berkeley, CA 94720. Authorized power: 10-w. Antenna: 75-ft. above ground. Lat. 37° 49' 17", long. 121° 46' 49". Transmitter: 10-mi. N of Livermore. Equipment: Emcee transmitter; Andrew antenna.

Long Beach—WHR-679 (Channels B-3-4). California State U., 400 Golden Shore, Long Beach, CA 90802. Authorized power: 10-w. each. Antenna: 105-ft. above ground. Lat. 33° 46' 37", long. 118° 06' 47". Transmitter: Bellflower Blvd.

Long Beach—WFD-555 (Channels G-1-4). Long Beach Unified School District of Los Angeles County, 701 Locust Ave., Long Beach, CA 90813. Authorized power: 0.1-w. each. Antenna: 26-ft. above ground. Lat. 33° 46' 37", long. 118° 11' 23". Transmitter: 878 Locust Ave.

Los Altos—WHR-464 (Channels A-1-4). Assn. for Continuing Education, 404A Durand Bldg., Stanford, CA 94305. Authorized power: 10-w. each. Antenna: 80-ft. above ground. Lat. 37° 23' 48", long. 122° 06' 14". Transmitter: 5050 El Camino Real.

Los Altos—WHR-466 (Channels A-1-4). Assn. for Continuing Education, 5050 El Camino Real, Los Altos, CA 94022. Authorized power: 10-w. each. Antenna: 2723-ft. above ground. Lat. 37° 29' 17", long. 121° 51' 59". Transmitter: Monument Peak, 10.6-mi. N of San Jose.

Los Altos—WHR-467 (Channels C-1-4). Assn. for Continuing Education, 5050 El Camino Real, Los Altos, CA 94022. Authorized power: 10-w. each. Antenna: 285-ft. above ground. Lat. 37° 29' 17", long. 121° 51' 59". Transmitter: 10.6-mi. N of San Jose. Equipment: ITS transmitter; Andrew antenna.

Los Angeles—KWE-33 (Channels B-1-4). U. of Southern California, OHE 212, University Park, Los Angeles, CA 90089. Authorized power: 50-w. each. Antenna: 321-ft. above ground. Lat. 34° 13' 37", long. 118° 03' 56". Transmitter: Allcom Bldg. Equipment: ITS transmitter; Andrew antenna.

Los Angeles—WLX-482 (Channels D-1-2). U. of Southern California, MC-1455, OHE 100, Los Angeles, CA 90089-1455. Authorized power: 50-w. each. Antenna: 211-ft. above ground. Lat. 34° 13' 37", long. 118° 03' 58". Transmitter: Allcom Bldg. Equipment: ITS transmitter; Andrew antenna.

Los Angeles—KSW-93 (Channels G-1-4). Archdiocese of Los Angeles Education & Welfare Corp., 1530 W. 9th St., Los Angeles, CA 90015. Phone: 213-251-3308. Fax: 213-386-8667. Authorized power: 50-w. each. Antenna: 321-ft. above ground. Lat. 34° 13' 27", long. 118° 03' 58". Transmitter: Allcom Bldg. Equipment: ITS transmitter; Andrew antenna.

Mariposa—WHR-654 (Channel A-1-4). Mariposa County United School District, Box 8, 5082 Old Highway N, Mariposa, CA 95338. Phone: 209-742-0250. Fax: 209-966-4549. Authorized power: 50-w. Antenna: 128-ft. above ground. Lat. 37° 32' 00", long. 120° 01' 29". Transmitter: 6286 Morrissey Rd. Equipment: ITS transmitter; Andrew antenna.

Mariposa—WLX-916 (Channels B-1-4). Mariposa County Unified School District, 5081 Hwy. 40, Mariposa, CA 95338. Authorized power: 50-w. each. Antenna: 125-ft. above ground. Lat. 37° 31' 59", long. 120° 01' 32". Transmitter: 6286 Morissey Rd. Equipment: ITS transmitter; Andrew antenna.

Mariposa—WLX-873 (Channels C-1-4). Views on Learning Inc., 200 Kenyon Ave., Elkhart, IN 46514. Phone & fax: 219-522-1725.
E-mail: jrueff@lsoc-vol.org.
Web site: http://www.lsoc-vol.org.
Authorized power: 50-w. each. Antenna: 4285-ft. above ground. Lat. 37° 31' 59", long. 120° 01' 32". Transmitter: 6286 Morrissey Rd. Equipment: ITS transmitter; Andrew antenna.
Leased to Choice TV, 3526 E. Church, Fresno, CA 93725. Phone: 209-442-1970.

Mariposa—WNC-213 (Channels D-1-4). Madera County Superintendent of Schools, 28123 Ave. 14, Madera, CA 93638. Phone: 209-673-6051. Fax: 209-673-5569.
E-mail: srobison@maderacoe.k12.ca.us.
Web site: http://www.maderacoe.k12.ca.us.
Authorized power: 50-w. each. Antenna: 141-ft. above ground. Lat. 37° 31' 59", long. 120° 01' 32". Transmitter: 6286 Morrissey Rd. Equipment: ITS transmitter; Andrew antenna.
Leased to Choice TV, 3526 E. Church, Fresno, CA 93725. Phone: 209-442-1970.

Merced—WND-215 (Channels A-1-4). California State U.-Stanislaus, 801 W. Monte Vista Ave., Turlock, CA 95382. Authorized power: 50-w. each. Antenna: 4272-ft. above ground. Lat. 37° 31' 59", long. 120° 01' 32". Transmitter: 6286 Morrissey Rd. Equipment: ITS transmitter; Andrew antenna.

Merced—WND-216 (Channels G-1-4). Merced County Superintendent of Schools, 632 W. 13th St., Merced, CA 95340. Phone: 209-381-6635. Fax: 209-381-6773.
E-mail: gstallin@mcoe.merced.k12.ca.us.
Web site: http://www.merced.k12.ca.us.
Authorized power: 50-w. each. Antenna: 4272-ft. above ground. Lat. 37° 31' 59", long. 120° 01' 32". Transmitter: 6286 Morrissey Rd. Equipment: ITS transmitter; Andrew antenna.

Milpitas—WHG-338 (Channels B-1-4). Santa Clara County Board of Education, 1290 Ridder Park Dr., San Jose, CA 95131. Phone: 408-453-6800. Fax: 408-453-6815.
Web site: http://www.sccoe.k12.ca.us.
Authorized power: 10-w. each. Antenna: 302-ft. above ground. Lat. 37° 29' 17", long. 121° 51' 59". Transmitter: Monument Peak, 10.6-mi. N of San Jose. Equipment: ITS transmitter; Bogner antenna.
Leased to Wireless Holdings Inc., 975-H Industrial Rd., San Carlos, CA 94070. Phone: 415-631-9190.

Mission Viejo—WHR-654 (Channel A-1). Saddleback Community College District, 28000 Marguerite Pkwy., Mission Viejo, CA 92692. Authorized power: 1-w. Antenna: 55-ft. above ground. Lat. 33° 33' 12", long. 117° 39' 54". Transmitter: 28000 Marguerite Pkwy.

Modjeska—WHR-854 (Channels B-1-4). California State U. -Fullerton, 800 N. State College Blvd., Fullerton, CA 92634-5000. Phone: 714-773-2623. Fax: 714-773-3892.
E-mail: w1reeder@fullerton.edu.
Authorized power: 50-w. each. Antenna: 98-ft. above ground. Lat. 33° 42' 45", long. 117° 33' 13". Transmitter: Motorola Site No. 2. Equipment: Loma Scientific transmitter; Bogner antenna.

Modjeska Peak—WDD-655 (Channels A-1-4). U. of Southern California, OHE 212, University Park, Los Angeles, CA 90089. Authorized power: 50-w. each. Antenna: 98-ft. above ground. Lat. 33° 42' 43", long. 117° 33' 13". Transmitter: Motorola Site No. 2. Equipment: ITS transmitter; Bogner antenna.

Modjeska Peak—WSJ-70 (Channels C-1-4). Santa Ana Unified School District, 1601 E. Chestnut Ave., Santa Ana, CA 92701-6322. Phone: 714-558-5641. Fax: 714-480-5301.
E-mail: breed@cyber.k12.ca.us.
Web site: http://www.sausd.k12.ca.us.
Authorized power: 50-w. each. Antenna: 5015-ft. above ground. Lat. 33° 42' 43", long. 117° 33' 13". Transmitter: Motorola Site No. 2. Equipment: ITS transmitter; Bogner antenna.
Leased to Pacific Bell Video Services, 2000 E. McFadden Ave., Room 201, Santa Ana, CA 92705-4706. Phone: 714-245-1121.

Modjeska Peak—KZH-31 (Channels D-1-4). Long Beach Unified School District, 1515 Hughes Way, Long Beach, CA 90810. Authorized power: 50-w. each. Antenna: 5015-ft. above ground. Lat. 33° 42' 43", long. 117° 33' 13". Transmitter: Motorola Site No. 2. Equipment: ITS transmitter; Bogner antenna.

Modjeska Peak—WHG-396 (Channels G-1-2). Diocese of Orange Education & Welfare Corp., Box 14195, 2811 E. Villa Real Dr., Orange, CA 92613-1595. Phone: 714-282-3000. Fax: 714-282-3029. Authorized power: 10-w. each. Antenna: 55-ft. above ground. Lat. 33° 42' 58", long. 117° 32' 52". Transmitter: Modjeska Peak, border of Orange & Riverside Counties.
Leased to Pacific Telesis Group, 130 Kearney St., San Francisco, CA 94108. Phone: 510-806-4131.

Mount Bullion, Mariposa & Merced Counties—WHG-342 (Channel F-1). California State Universities & Colleges, 801 W. Monte Vista Ave., Turlock, CA 95380. Authorized power: 10-w. Antenna: 20-ft. above ground. Lat. 37° 32' 05", long. 120° 01' 46". Transmitter: Mount Bullion.

Mount Davis—WHR-686 (Channels G-1-4). California State U., 5500 University Pkwy., San Bernardino, CA 92407. Phone: 909-880-5619. Fax: 909-880-7075.
E-mail: scooper@wiley.csusb.edu.
Web site: http://www.acm.csusb.edu.
Authorized power: 10-w. each. Antenna: 46-ft. above ground. Lat. 34° 02' 32", long. 117° 06' 09". Transmitter: Crafton Hills. Equipment: Comwave transmitter; Bogner antenna.

Mount Diablo—WGV-621 (Channels C-1-4). Roman Catholic Communications Corp., 324 Middlefield Rd., Menlo Park, CA 94025. Phone: 650-326-7850. Fax: 650-326-4605.
E-mail: ctn@impresso.com.
Web site: http://www.ctnba.org.
Authorized power: 10-w. each. Antenna: 70-ft. above ground. Lat. 37° 52' 54", long. 121° 55' 05". Transmitter: 7-mi. E of Walnut Creek.
Leased to Bay Area Cablevision Inc./Wavepath, 500 Clyde Ave., Mountain View, CA 94043. Phone: 650-237-9744.

Mount Laguna—WFW-588 (Channels A-1-2). Board of Trustees, California State U.-San Diego, 5200 Campanile Dr., San Diego, CA 92182. Authorized power: 10-w. each. Antenna: 20-ft. above ground. Lat. 32° 53' 31", long. 116° 25' 10". Transmitter: Monument Peak, Cleveland National Forest. Equipment: Emcee transmitter; Mark antenna.

Mount Whitney & San Diego County—WHM-928 (Channel A-1). Diocese of San Diego Education & Welfare Corp., Box 80428, Alcala Park, San Diego, CA 92138. Authorized power: 10-w. Antenna: 35-ft. above ground. Lat. 33° 06' 39", long. 117° 09' 11". Transmitter: 21851 Washingtonian Dr., 900-ft. NE of Mount Whitney.

Mount Wilson—WHR-463 (Channel A-1 & 4). California State U.-Los Angeles, 5151 State University Dr., Los Angeles, CA 90032. Phone: 213-343-3901. Authorized power: 50-w. Antenna: 141-ft. above ground. Lat. 34° 13' 34", long. 118° 03' 57". Transmitter: Pacific Bell Tower. Equipment: ITS transmitter; Andrew antenna.

Mount Wilson—WHR-505 (Channels A-2-3). California State Polytechnic U.-Pomona, B-66, 3801 W. Temple Ave., Pomona, CA 91768. Phone: 909-869-3916. Fax: 909-869-3933.
E-mail: arvargas@csupomona.edu.
Web site: http://www.itac.csupomona.edu.
Authorized power: 50-w. each. Antenna: 16-ft. above ground. Lat. 34° 13' 34", long. 118° 03' 57". Transmitter: Pacific Bell Tower. Equipment: ITS transmitter; Andrew antenna.
Leased to Pacific Bell Video Services, 2000 E. McFadden Ave., Santa Ana, CA 92705. Phone: 714-245-1000.

Mount Wilson—WHR-802 (Channel C-4). Intelecom Intelligent Telecommunications, Suite 300, 150 E. Colorado Blvd., Pasadena, CA 91105-1932. Phone: 818-796-7300. Fax: 818-577-4282.
Web site: http://www.intelcom.org.
Authorized power: 50-w. Antenna: 5691-ft. above ground. Lat. 34° 13' 34", long. 118° 03' 57". Transmitter: Pacific Bell Tower. Equipment: ITS transmitter; Andrew antenna.
Leased to Pacific Bell Video Services, 2000 E. McFadden Ave., Santa Ana, CA 92705. Phone: 714-245-1000.

Mount Wilson—WHG-268 (Channels E-1-4). California State U., 400 Golden Shore, Long Beach, CA 90802. Authorized power: 50-w. each. Antenna: 5691-ft. above ground. Lat. 34° 13' 34", long. 118° 03' 57". Transmitter: Pacific Bell Tower. Equipment: ITS transmitter; Andrew antenna.

Nevada County—WHG-371 (Channel B-4). California State Universities & Colleges, 6000 J St., Sacramento, CA 95819. Phone: 916-

278-5764. Fax: 916-278-5644. Authorized power: 10-w. Antenna: 2653-ft. above ground. Lat. 39° 08' 00", long. 121° 05' 57". Transmitter: 6-mi. S of Grass Valley. Equipment: Emcee transmitter; Andrew antenna.

New Almaden—WHR-453 (Channels A-1-4). San Jose State U., IRC 310, One Washington Square, San Jose, CA 95192-0169. Phone: 408-924-2636. Fax: 408-924-2881.
E-mail: bcbenson@sjsu.edu.
Web site: http://www.sjsu.edu/depts/ten.
Authorized power: 10-w. each. Antenna: 200-ft. above ground. Lat. 37° 06' 40", long. 121° 50' 29". Transmitter: Peak Loma Prieta, 4.6-mi. SW of New Almaden. Equipment: ITS transmitter; Andrew antenna.

North Palm Springs—WHR-904 (Channels G-1-4). Caritas Telecommunications, 1201 E. Highland Ave., San Bernardino, CA 92404. Phone: 909-475-5350. Fax: 909-475-5357.
E-mail: caritasctn@aol.com.
Authorized power: 10-w. each. Antenna: 50-ft. above ground. Lat. 33° 55' 20", long. 116° 37' 00". Transmitter: North Palm Springs. Equipment: Comwave transmitter; Bogner antenna.

Northridge—WHG-227 (Channels A-1-4). California State U.-Northridge, Oviatt Library-4A, 18111 Nordhoff St., Northridge, CA 91330. Phone: 818-885-2355. Fax: 818-885-2316. Authorized power: 1-w. each. Antenna: 78-ft. above ground. Lat. 34° 14' 25", long. 118° 31' 43". Transmitter: 18111 Nordhoff St., Northridge. Equipment: ITS transmitter; Mark antenna.

Oakland & Alameda County—WHG-348 (Channels A-3-4). Peralta Community College District, 333 E. 8th St., Oakland, CA 94606. Authorized power: 40-w. each. Antenna: 256-ft. above ground. Lat. 37° 41' 17", long. 122° 26' 07". Transmitter: San Bruno Mountain, 6.1-mi. S of San Francisco. Equipment: ITS transmitter; Anixter antenna.

Orange—WHG-395 (Channels B-1-2). Diocese of Orange Education & Welfare Corp., 2811 E. Villa Real Dr., Orange, CA 92667. Authorized power: 10-w. each. Antenna: 17-ft. above ground. Lat. 33° 49' 48", long. 117° 49' 28". Transmitter: 2811 E. Villa Real Dr.

Palmdale—WHR-502 (Channels C-1-4). Television California State U.-Northridge, Continuing Education, Oviatt Library-4A, 18111 Nordhoff St., Northridge, CA 91330-8324. Phone: 818-885-2355. Fax: 818-885-2316. Authorized power: 10-w. each. Antenna: 66-ft. above ground. Lat. 34° 32' 52", long. 118° 12' 53". Transmitter: Hauser Mountain. Equipment: Global System transmitter; Andrew antenna.

Palm Springs—WHR-659 (Channel C-1). California State U. -San Bernardino, 5500 University Pkwy., San Bernardino, CA 92407. Phone: 909-880-5619. Fax: 909-880-7075.
E-mail: scooper@wiley.csusb.edu.
Web site: http://www.acm.csusb.edu.
Authorized power: 10-w. Antenna: 60-ft. above ground. Lat. 33° 55' 25", long. 116° 36' 57". Transmitter: White Water Hill at Hwys. 10 & 62 junction. Equipment: Comwave transmitter; Bogner antenna.

Pleasanton—WHR-814 (Channels G-1-4). Leland Stanford Jr. U., 401 Durand Bldg., Stanford, CA 94305. Phone: 650-725-3000. Fax: 650-725-2868. Authorized power: 2-w. each. Antenna: 67-ft. above ground. Lat. 37° 37' 13", long. 121° 55' 16". Transmitter: Sunol Ridge, 4-mi. SW of Pleasanton. Equipment: Comwave transmitter; Bogner antenna.

Point Mugu—WAQ-324 (Channels E-1-2). Regents of U. of California, 1111 Franklin St., Oakland, CA 94607. Authorized power: 10-w. each. Antenna: 20-ft. above ground. Lat. 34° 06' 30", long. 119° 03' 50". Transmitter: 3.3-mi. E of Naval Air Station Point Mugu, Laguna Peak.

Ramona & San Diego County—WHG-344 (Channels C-3-4). California State U.-San Diego, 5200 Campanile Dr., San Diego, CA 92182. Authorized power: 10-w. each. Antenna: 45-ft. above ground. Lat. 33° 00' 33", long. 116° 58' 13". Transmitter: Mount Woodson.

Redding—WBS-390 (Channels A-1-4). California State U.-Chico, Instructional Media Center, Chico, CA 95929-0005. Phone: 916-898-6112. Fax: 916-898-5369.
Web site: http://www.csuchico.edu.
Authorized power: 50-w. each. Antenna: 194-ft. above ground. Lat. 40° 39' 14", long. 122° 31' 12". Transmitter: 8-mi. NW of Redding. Equipment: Comwave transmitter; Andrew antenna.
Leased to American Telecasting Inc., 5575 Tech Center Dr., Suite 300, Colorado Springs, CO 80919. Phone: 719-260-5533.

Redding—WND-262 (Channels B-1-2). Northern California Educational TV Assn., 603 N. Market St., Redding, CA 96003. Authorized power: 50-w. each. Antenna: 236-ft. above ground. Lat. 40° 39' 14", long. 122° 31' 12". Transmitter: Southfork Mountain. Equipment: Comwave transmitter; Andrew antenna.

Redding—WND-263 (Channels B-3-4). Northern California Educational TV Assn., 603 N. Market St., Redding, CA 96003. Authorized power: 50-w. each. Antenna: 236-ft. above ground. Lat. 40° 39' 14", long. 122° 31' 12". Transmitter: Southfork Mountain. Equipment: Comwave transmitter; Andrew antenna.

Redding—WHR-569 (Channels C-1-4). Northern California Educational TV Assn. Inc., 603 N. Market St., Redding, CA 96003. Phone: 530-243-5493. Fax: 530-243-7443.
Web site: http://www.kixe.pbs.org.
Authorized power: 10-w. each. Antenna: 40-ft. above ground. Lat. 40° 36' 09", long. 122° 39' 01". Transmitter: KIXE-TV tower, 13-mi. W of Redding.
Leased to American Telecasting Inc. 5575 Tech Center Dr., Suite 300, Colorado Springs, CO 80919. Phone: 719-260-5533.

Redding—WNC-407 (Channels G-1-4). Shekinah Network, 14875 Powerline Rd., Atascadero, CA 93422-6424. Phone: 805-438-3341. Authorized power: 50-w. each. Antenna: 196-ft. above ground. Lat. 40° 39' 14", long. 122° 31' 12". Transmitter: 8-mi. NW of Anderson. Equipment: Comwave transmitter; Andrew antenna.

Reedley—KZM-21 (Channels C-1-4). Fresno County Superintendent of Schools, 1111 Van Ness Ave., Fresno, CA 93721. Phone: 209-265-3058. Fax: 209-497-3899.
E-mail: spassmore@fcoe.k12.ca.us.
Web site: http://www.fcoe.k12.ca.us.
Authorized power: 20-w. each. Antenna: 96-ft. above ground. Lat. 36° 55' 49", long. 119° 38' 26". Transmitter: Owens Mountain. Equipment: ITS transmitter; Andrew antenna.

Ridgecrest—WNC-625 (Channels D-1-4). Kern Education Telecom Consortium, 1300 17th St., City Centre, Bakersfield, CA 93301-4533. Phone: 805-636-4758. Fax: 805-636-4656.
E-mail: laciecalone@kern.org.
Web site: http://www.kern.org.
Authorized power: 10-w. each. Antenna: 140-ft. above ground. Lat. 35° 28' 39", long. 117° 41' 57". Transmitter: El Paso Peak, 12-mi. SW of Ridgecrest. Equipment: Emcee transmitter; Andrew antenna.

Ripon—WGV-750 (Channel A-1-4). California State U.-Stanislaus, 801 W. Monte Vista Ave., Turlock, CA 95380. Authorized power: 10-w. Antenna: 20-ft. above ground. Lat. 37° 30' 16", long. 120° 51' 04". Transmitter: 1220 S. Acacia Ave. Equipment: ITS transmitter; Andrew antenna.

Ripon—WHR-656 (Channel B-1). California State U. & Colleges-Stanislaus, 801 W. Monte Vista Ave., Turlock, CA 95380. Authorized power: 100-w. Antenna: 495-ft. above ground. Lat. 37° 43' 44", long. 121° 07' 34". Transmitter: 1220 S. Acacia Ave. Equipment: ITS transmitter; Andrew antenna.

Ripon—WND-211 (Channels B-2-4). Yosemite Community College, 2201 Blue Gum Ave., Modesto, CA 95358. Authorized power: 100-w. each. Antenna: 436-ft. above ground. Lat. 37° 43' 44", long. 121° 07' 34". Transmitter: 1220 S. Acacia Ave. Equipment: ITS transmitter; Andrew antenna.

Ripon—WGV-751 (Channel D-1-4). California State U.-Stanislaus, 801 W. Monte Vista Ave., Turlock, CA 95380. Phone: 209-667-3171. Fax: 209-667-3356. Authorized power: 100-w. Antenna: 436-ft. above ground. Lat. 37° 43' 44", long. 121° 07' 34". Transmitter: 1220 S. Acacia Ave. Equipment: ITS transmitter; Andrew antenna.

Ripon—WHR-474 (Channels G-1-4). San Joaquin Delta Community College, 5151 Pacific Ave., Stockton, CA 95207. Authorized power: 100-w. each. Antenna: 492-ft. above ground. Lat. 37° 43' 44", long. 121° 07' 34". Transmitter: 1220 S. Acacia Ave. Equipment: ITS transmitter; Andrew antenna.

Riverside—WLX-257 (Channels A-1-4). California State Polytechnic U., 3801 W. Temple Ave., Pomona, CA 91768. Authorized power: 50-w. each. Antenna: 304-ft. above ground. Lat. 33° 57' 57", long. 117° 17' 05". Transmitter: Box Springs Mountain. Equipment: ITS transmitter; Andrew antenna.

Riverside—WHR-928 (Channels B-2-4 & G-2). Regents of the U. of California, 1111 Franklin St., Oakland, CA 94607. Authorized power: 50-w. each. Antenna: 304-ft. above ground. Lat. 33° 57' 55", long. 117° 17' 03". Transmitter: Box Spring Mountain. Equipment: ITS transmitter; Andrew antenna.

Riverside-San Bernardino—WLX-367 (Channels C-1-4). Hispanic Information & Telecommunications Network Inc., 3rd Floor, 449 Broadway, New York, NY 10013. Phone: 212-966-5660. Fax: 212-966-5725.
E-mail: email@hitn.org.
Web site: http://www.hitn.org.
Authorized power: 50-w. each. Antenna: 414-ft. above ground. Lat. 33° 57' 55", long. 117° 17' 03". Transmitter: Box Springs Mountain. Equipment: ITS transmitter; Andrew antenna.
Leased to Pacific Bell Video Services, 2000 E. McFadden Ave., Santa Ana, CA 92705. Phone: 714-245-1000.

Sacramento—WHG-370 (Channel A-1-4). California State Universities & Colleges, 6000 J St., Sacramento, CA 95819. Phone: 916-2785764. Fax: 916-278-5644.
E-mail: kirkbriderd@csus.edu.
Authorized power: 50-w. Antenna: 453-ft. above ground. Lat. 38° 38' 54", long. 121° 28' 40". Transmitter: N. Market St., 0.25-mi. W of Gate St. Equipment: ITS transmitter; Andrew antenna.

Sacramento—WSA-40 (Channels B-1-4). Regents of the U. of California, 1111 Franklin St., Oakland, CA 94607. Authorized power: 50-w. each. Antenna: 471-ft. above ground. Lat. 38° 38' 54", long. 121° 28' 40". Transmitter: N. Market St., 0.25-mi. W of Gate St. Equipment: Comwave transmitter; Andrew antenna. Requests change to 540-ft. above ground.

Sacramento—WHR-512 (Channels C-1-4). Instructional Telecommunications Foundation Inc., Box 6060, Boulder, CO 80306. Phone: 303-442-4180. Fax: 303-442-6472.
E-mail: itf@fstv.org.
Authorized power: 50-w. each. Antenna: 541-ft. above ground. Lat. 38° 38' 54", long. 121° 28' 40". Transmitter: N. Market St., 0.25-mi. W of Gate St. Equipment: Comwave transmitter; Andrew antenna.
Leased to Wireless Broadcasting Systems, 1513 Sports Dr. No. 9, Sacramento, CA 95834. Phone: 916-928-2614.

Sacramento—WLX-720 (Channels D-1-3). Hispanic Information & Telecommunications Network Inc., 3rd Floor, 449 Broadway, New York, NY 10013. Phone: 212-966-5660. Fax: 212-966-5725.
E-mail: email@hitn.org.
Web site: http://www.hitn.org.
Authorized power: 50-w. each. Antenna: 450-ft. above ground. Lat. 38° 38' 54", long. 121° 28' 40". Transmitter: N. Market St., 0.25-mi. W of Gate St. Equipment: Comwave transmitter; Andrew antenna.
Leased to Wireless Broadcasting Systems of Sacramento, Inc., 9250 E. Costilla Ave., Suite 325, Englewood, CO 80112. Phone: 303-649-1195.

Sacramento—WHR-772 (Channels G-1-4). Los Rios Community College District, 1919 Spanos Court, Sacramento, CA 95825. Phone: 916-688-7280. Fax: 916-688-7476.
E-mail: caldwej@crc.losrios.cc.ca.us.
Authorized power: 100-w. each. Antenna: 453-ft. above ground. Lat. 38° 38' 54", long. 121° 28' 40". Transmitter: N. Market, 0.25-mi. W of Gate St. Equipment: Comwave transmitter; Andrew antenna.
Leased to Wireless Broadcasting Systems of Sacramento Inc., 9250 E. Costilla Ave., Suite 325, Englewood, CO 80112. Phone: 303-649-1195.

Sacramento—WSA-39 (Channel G-1). Regents of U. of California, 1111 Franklin St., Oakland, CA 94607. Authorized power: 10-w. Antenna: 84-ft. above ground. Lat. 38° 32' 25", long. 121° 44' 52". Transmitter: Hutchison Hall, U. of California-Davis.

Salinas—WLX-996 (Channels C-1-4). Views on Learning Inc., 200 Kenyon Ave., Elkhart, IN 46516. Phone & fax: 219-522-1725.
E-mail: jrueff@lsoc-vol.org.
Web site: http://www.lsoc-vol.org.
Authorized power: 50-w. each. Antenna: 154-ft. above ground. Lat. 36° 31' 48", long. 121° 36' 31". Transmitter: Mount Toro. Equipment: ITS transmitter; Andrew antenna.
Leased to American Telecasting Inc., 5575 Tech Center Dr., Suite 300, Colorado Springs, CO 80919. Phone: 719-260-5533.

Salinas—WNC-787 (Channels C-1-2). Shekinah Network, 14875 Powerline Rd., Atascadero, CA 93422. Phone: 805-438-3341. Fax: 805-438-3341. Authorized power: 20-w. each. Antenna: 75-ft. above ground. Lat. 36° 06' 25", long. 119° 01' 45". Transmitter: 21.7 mi. SE of Visalia. Equipment: ITS transmitter; Andrew antenna.

Salinas—WHR-911 (Channels D-1-4). Hartnell College, 156 Homestead Ave., Salinas, CA 93901. Authorized power: 10-w. each. Antenna: 49-ft. above ground. Lat. 36° 40' 22", long. 121° 40' 00". Equipment: Comwave transmitter; Andrew antenna.

Salinas—WNC-788 (Channels D-1-4). Santa Cruz County Superintendent of Schools, 809 Bay Ave., Capitola, CA 95010. Authorized power: 50-w. each. Antenna: 199-ft. above ground. Lat. 36° 31' 48", long. 121° 36' 31". Transmitter: 10-mi. S of Salinas. Equipment: Emcee transmitter; Andrew antenna.
Leased to American Telecasting Inc., 5575 Tech Center Dr., Suite 300 Colorado Springs, CO. 80919. Phone: 719-260-5533.

Salinas—WNC-366 (Channels G-1-4). Monterey County Superintendent of Schools, Box 80851, 901 Blanco Circle, Salinas, CA 93912-0851. Authorized power: 50-w. each. Antenna: 194-ft. above ground. Lat. 36° 31' 48", long. 121° 36' 31". Transmitter: Mount Toro. Equipment: ITS transmitter; Andrew antenna.

San Bernardino—WHR-658 (Channel A-1). California State U.-San Bernardino, 5500 University Pkwy., San Bernardino, CA 92407. Phone: 909-880-5619. Fax: 909-880-7075.
E-mail: scooper@wiley.csusb.edu.
Web site: http://www.acm.csusb.edu.
Authorized power: 10-w. Antenna: 110-ft. above ground. Lat. 34° 10' 57", long. 117° 19' 23". Transmitter: 5500 University Pkwy. Equipment: Comwave transmitter; Anixter antenna.

San Bernardino—WHR-661 (Channels A-1-4). California State U.-San Bernardino, 5500 University Pkwy., San Bernardino, CA 92407. Phone: 714-880-5060.
E-mail: scooper@wiley.csusb.edu.
Web site: http://www.acm.csusb.com.
Authorized power: 10-w. each. Antenna: 67-ft. above ground. Lat. 33° 55' 25", long. 116° 36' 57". Transmitter: Mount Davis, 2.2-mi. SW of Beaumont. Equipment: Comwave transmitter; Bogner antenna. Requests modification of license for change to lat. 33° 54' 30", long. 116° 59' 46".

San Bernardino—WHR-834 (Channels A-1-4). California State U.-San Bernardino, 5500 University Pkwy., San Bernardino, CA 92407. Phone: 909-880-5619. Fax: 909-880-7075.
E-mail: scooper@wiley.csusb.edu.
Web site: http://www.acm.csusb.edu.
Authorized power: 10-w. each. Lat. 34° 14' 04", long. 117° 08' 24". Transmitter: Heaps Peak, SE Lake Arrowhead on State Rte. 18. Equipment: Comwave transmitter; Anixter antenna. Requests change to 50-w., 103-ft. above ground, lat. 34° 36' 38", long. 117° 17' 17"; transmitter to Quartzite Mountain; Andrew antenna.
Leased to Transworld Telecommunications Inc., 102 West 500 South, Suite 300, Salt Lake City, UT 84101.

San Bernardino—WHM-937 (Channel B-1). San Bernardino Community College District, 701 S. Mount Vernon Ave., San Bernardino, CA 92410. Phone: 909-888-6511. Authorized power: 50-w. Antenna: 304-ft. above ground. Lat. 33° 57' 55", long. 117° 17' 03". Transmitter: Box Springs Mountain, Riverside. Equipment: ITS transmitter; Andrew antenna.
Leased to Cross Country Wireless Inc., 6177 River Crest Dr., Suite B, Riverside, CA 92507. Phone: 714-245-1126.

San Bernardino—WHR-929 (Channels G-1&3-4). San Bernardino Community College District, 701 S. Mount Vernon Ave., San Bernardino, CA 92410. Phone: 909-888-6511. Authorized power: 50-w. each. Antenna: 415-ft. above ground. Lat. 33° 57' 55", long. 117° 17' 03". Transmitter: Box Springs Mountain, Riverside. Equipment: ITS transmitter; Andrew antenna.
Leased to Cross Country Wireless Inc., 6177 River Crest Dr., Suite B, Riverside, CA 92504. Phone: 714-245-1126.

San Bernardino-Riverside—WLX-238 (Channels D-1-4). Caritas Telecommunications, 1201 E. Highland Ave., San Bernardino, CA 92404. Phone: 909-475-5350. Fax: 909-475-5357.
E-mail: caritasctn@aol.com.
Authorized power: 50-w. each. Antenna: 304-ft. above ground. Lat. 33° 57' 55", long. 117° 17' 03". Transmitter: Box Springs Mountain. Equipment: ITS transmitter; Andrew antenna.

San Diego—WBS-375 (Channels A-1-4). San Diego County Office of Education, 6401 Linda Vista Rd., San Diego, CA 92111. Phone: 619-292-3788. Fax: 619-467-1549. Authorized power: 50-w. each. Antenna: 80-ft. above ground. Lat. 32° 41' 48", long. 116° 56' 10". Transmitter: San Miguel Mountain 13-mi. SE of San Diego. Equipment: ITS transmitter; Andrew antenna.

San Diego—WHR-611 (Channels B-1-4). Board of Trustees, California State U. & Colleges of San Diego State U., 5200 Campanile Dr., San Diego, CA 92182. Authorized power: 20-w. each. Antenna: 2677-ft. above ground. Lat. 32° 41' 48", long. 116° 56' 10". Transmitter: San Miguel Mountain 13-mi. SE of San Diego. Equipment: ITS transmitter; Andrew antenna.

San Diego—WDD-752 (Channels C-1-4). San Diego County Office of Education, 6401 Linda Vista Rd., San Diego, CA 92111. Phone: 619-292-3788. Fax: 619-467-1549. Authorized power: 50-w. each. Antenna: 118-ft. above ground. Lat. 32° 41' 48", long. 116° 56' 10". Transmitter: San Miguel Mountain, 13-mi. SE of San Diego. Equipment: ITS transmitter; Andrew antenna.

San Diego—WND-372 (Channel D-1). Hispanic Information & Telecommunications Network, 3rd Floor, 449 Broadway, New York, NY 10013. Phone: 212-966-5660. Fax: 212-966-5725. Authorized power: 50-w. Antenna: 118-ft. above ground. Lat. 32° 41' 48", long. 116° 56' 10". Transmitter: San Miguel Mountain, 13-mi. SE of San Diego. Equipment: ITS transmitter; Andrew antenna.
Leased to Pacific Bell Video Services, 2000 McFadden Ave., Santa Ana, CA 92705. Phone: 714-245-1000.

San Diego—WND-373 (Channels D-2-4). San Diego Community College District, 3375 Camino Del Rio S, San Diego, CA 92108. Authorized power: 50-w. each. Antenna: 115-ft. above ground. Lat. 32° 41' 48", long. 116° 56' 10". Transmitter: San Miguel Mountain, 13-mi. SE of San Diego. Equipment: ITS transmitter; Andrew antenna.

San Diego—WBM-726 (Channels E-1-3). Board of Trustees, California State U.-San Diego, 5200 Campanile Dr., San Diego, CA 92182. Antenna: 56-ft. above ground. Lat. 32° 41' 47", long. 116° 56' 07". Transmitter: San Miguel Mountain 13-mi. SE of San Diego. Equipment: Andrew antenna.

San Diego & San Diego County (north)—WHG-343 (Channels B-1-2). Board of Trustees, California State U., 5200 Campanile Dr., San Diego, CA 92182.
Web site: http://www.kpbs.org.
Authorized power: 10-w. each. Antenna: 56-ft. above ground. Lat. 32° 46' 35", long. 117° 04' 17". Transmitter: San Diego U., 5300 Campanile Dr.

San Francisco—KZB-23 (Channels B-1-4). Roman Catholic Communications Corp., 324 Middlefield Rd., Menlo Park, CA 94025. Phone: 650-326-7850. Fax: 650-326-4605.
E-mail: ctn@impresso.com.
Web site: http://www.ctnba.com.
Authorized power: 40-w. each. Antenna: 256-ft. above ground. Lat. 37° 41' 17", long. 122° 26' 07". Transmitter: San Bruno Mountain, 6-mi. S of San Francisco. Equipment: ITS transmitter.

San Francisco—KZB-24 (Channels D-1-4). Roman Catholic Communications Corp., 324 Middlefield Rd., Menlo Park, CA 94025. Phone: 650-326-7850. Fax: 650-326-4605.
E-mail: ctn@impresso.com.
Web site: http://www.ctnba.org.
Authorized power: 10-w. each. Antenna: 20-ft. above ground. Lat. 37° 55' 44", long. 122° 35' 11". Transmitter: Mount Tamalpais. Equipment: Comwave transmitter; Andrew & Taco antenna.

San Francisco—WNC-824 (Channels D-1-3). Roman Catholic Communications Corp., 324 Middlefield Rd., Menlo Park, CA 94025. Phone: 650-326-7850. Fax: 650-326-4605.
E-mail: ctn@impresso.com.
Web site: http://www.ctnba.org.
Authorized power: 40-w. each. Antenna: 256-ft. above ground. Lat. 37° 41' 17", long. 122° 26' 07". Transmitter: San Bruno Mountain, 6.1-mi. S of San Francisco. Equipment: ITS transmitter.
Leased to Bay Area Cablevision Inc./Wavepath, 500 Clyde Ave., Mountain View, CA 94043. Phone: 650-237-9744.

San Francisco—KHU-89 (Channel F-2). Regents of U. of California, 1111 Franklin St., Oakland, CA 94607. Authorized power: 40-w. Antenna: 256-ft. above ground. Lat. 37° 41' 17", long. 122° 26' 07". Transmitter: San Bruno Mountain, 6.1-mi. S of San Francisco. Equipment: ITS transmitter.

San Francisco—KTB-97 (Channel F-1 & 3). Regents of U. of California, 1111 Franklin St., Oakland, CA 94607. Authorized power: 40-w. Antenna: 256-ft. above ground. Lat. 37° 41' 17", long. 122° 26' 07". Transmitter: San Bruno Mountaink, 6.1-mi. S of San Francisco. Equipment: ITS transmitter.

San Francisco—WHR-760 (Channels G-1-4). Assn. for Continuing Education, 5050 El Camino Real, Los Altos, CA 94022. Authorized power: 40-w. each. Antenna: 256-ft. above ground. Lat. 37° 41' 17", long. 122° 26' 07". Transmitter: San Bruno Mountain, 6.1-mi. S of San Francisco. Equipment: ITS transmitter.

San Francisco Bay—KGG-38 (Channels E-1-4). Leland Stanford Jr. U., Stanford Instructional TV Network, Stanford, CA 94305. Phone: 650-725-3000. Fax: 650-725-2868. Authorized power: 10-w. each. Antenna: 62-ft. above ground. Lat. 37° 19' 18", long. 122° 08' 47". Transmitter: Montebello Rd., 7.9-mi. SSE of Stanford. Equipment: ITS transmitter; Andrew antenna.

San Jose—KZB-25 (Channels D-1-4). Roman Catholic Communications Corp., 324 Middlefield Rd., Menlo Park, CA 94025. Phone: 650-326-7850. Fax: 650-326-4605.
E-mail: ctn@impresso.com.
Web site: http://www.ctnba.org.
Authorized power: 10-w. each. Antenna: 2740-ft. above ground. Lat. 37° 29' 17", long. 121° 51' 59". Transmitter: Monument Peak, 10.6-mi. N of San Jose. Equipment: ITS transmitter; Andrew antenna.
Leased to Bay Area Cablevision Inc./Wavepath, 500 Clyde Ave., Mountain View, CA 94043. Phone: 650-237-9744.

San Jose—WHR-460 (Channels G-1-4). San Jose State University, IRC 310, One Washington Square, San Jose, CA 95192-0169. Phone: 408-924-2636. Fax: 408-924-2881.
E-mail: bcbenson@sjsu.edu.
Web site: http://www.sjsu.edu/depts/ten.
Authorized power: 1-w. each. Antenna: 65-ft. above ground. Lat. 37° 20' 10", long. 121° 54' 03". Transmitter: 125 S. 7th St. Requests change to 285-ft. above ground, lat. 37° 29' 17", long. 121° 51' 59"; transmitter to Monument Peak, 10-mi. N of San Jose, ITS transmitter, Bogner antenna.
Leased to Bay Area Cablevision Inc./Wavepath, 500 Clyde Ave., Mountain View, CA 94043. Phone: 650-237-9744.

San Luis Obispo—WNC-286 (Channels D-1-4). Lucia Mar Unified School District, 602 Orchard St., Arroyo Grande, CA 93420-4099. Authorized power: 100-w. each. Antenna: 103-ft. above ground. Lat. 35° 21' 28", long. 120° 39' 21". Transmitter: Cuesta Electronic Site, 5.5-mi. N of San Luis Obispo. Equipment: ITS transmitter; Andrew antenna.

San Marcos—WGR-706 (Channel A-3). Palomar Community College District, 1140 W. Mission Rd., San Marcos, CA 92069-1487. Phone: 760-744-1150. Fax: 760-761-3519.
E-mail: tvoffice@palomar.edu.
Web site: http://www.palomar.edu.
Authorized power: 0.1-w. Antenna: 50-ft. above ground. Lat. 33° 09' 03", long. 117° 10' 53". Transmitter: 1140 W. Mission Rd. Equipment: Emcee transmitter; Andrew antenna.

San Marcos—WCX-487 (Channel F-1). San Diego County Office of Education, 6401 Linda Vista Rd., San Diego, CA 92111. Phone: 619-292-3788. Fax: 619-467-1549. Authorized power: 10-w. Antenna: 30-ft. above ground. Lat. 33° 06' 32", long. 117° 09' 16". Transmitter: Mount Whitney. Equipment: Emcee transmitter; Andrew antenna.

San Marcos—WGR-707 (Channel F-4). Palomar Community College District, 1140 W. Mission Rd., San Marcos, CA 92069-1487. Phone: 760-744-1150. Fax: 760-761-3519.
E-mail: tvoffice@palomar.edu.
Web site: http://www.palomar.edu.
Authorized power: 10-w. Antenna: 30-ft. above ground. Lat. 33° 06' 32", long. 117° 09' 16". Transmitter: Mount Whitney. Equipment: Emcee transmitter; Andrew antenna.

San Marcos & San Diego County (north)—WHG-345 (Channels B-3-4). Board of Trustees, California State U. & Colleges for San Diego State U., 5200 Campanile Dr., San Diego, CA 92182. Authorized power: 10-w. each. Antenna: 80-ft. above ground. Lat. 33° 06' 55", long. 117° 09' 01". Transmitter: 321 Washington Dr.

San Mateo County—KZB-22 (Channels G-1-4). Roman Catholic Communications Corp., 324 Middlefield Rd., Menlo Park, CA 94025. Phone: 650-326-7850. Fax: 650-326-4605.
E-mail: ctn@impresso.com.
Web site: http://www.ctnba.org.

Authorized power: 40-w. each. Antenna: 256-ft. above ground. Lat. 37° 41' 17", long. 122° 26' 07". Transmitter: San Bruno Mountain, 6.1-mi. S of San Francisco.
Leased to Bay Area Cablevision Inc./Wavepath, 500 Clyde Ave., Mountain View, CA 94043. Phone: 650-237-9744.

San Miguel Mountain-San Diego County—WHQ-403 (Channels G-1-4). California State U. & Colleges for San Diego, 5300 Campanile Dr., San Diego, CA 92182. Authorized power: 50-w. each. Antenna: 112-ft. above ground. Lat. 32° 41' 48", long. 116° 56' 10". Transmitter: San Miguel Mountain. Equipment: ITS transmitter; Andrew antenna.

Santa Barbara—WAQ-323 (Channels A-1-2). Regents of U. of California, 1111 Franklin St., Oakland, CA 94607. Authorized power: 10-w. each. Antenna: 93-ft. above ground. Lat. 34° 24' 50", long. 119° 50' 24". Transmitter: Engineering Bldg., U. of California at Santa Barbara, Goleta.

Santa Barbara—WLX-994 (Channels C-1-4). Shekinah Network, 14875 Powerline Rd., Atascadero, CA 93422. Phone & fax: 805-438-3341. Authorized power: 20-w. each. Antenna: 150-ft. above ground. Lat. 34° 31' 32", long. 119° 57' 28". Transmitter: Broadcast Peak, Santa Ynez Mountains. Equipment: ITS transmitter; Bogner antenna.
Leased to American Telecasting Inc., 5575 Tech Center Dr., Suite 300, Colorado Springs, CO 80919. Phone: 719-260-5533.

Santa Barbara—WHR-839 (Channels D-1-4). Archdiocese of Los Angeles Education & Welfare Corp., 1530 W. 9th St., Los Angeles, CA 90015. Phone: 213-251-3308. Fax: 213-386-8667. Authorized power: 10-w. each. Antenna: 35-ft. above ground. Lat. 34° 31' 32", long. 119° 57' 28". Transmitter: Broadcast Peak, 9.5-mi. NW of Goleta.

Santa Paula—WHR-902 (Channels B-1-4). Archdiocese of Los Angeles Education & Welfare Corp., 1530 W. 9th St., Los Angeles, CA 90015. Phone: 213-251-3308. Fax: 213-386-8667. Authorized power: 10-w. each. Antenna: 253-ft. above ground. Lat. 34° 19' 49", long. 119° 01' 24". Transmitter: South Mountain, 3-mi. SE of Santa Paula.

Santa Paula—WHG-228 (Channels C-1-4). California State U.-Northridge, Continuing Education, Oviatt Library-4A, 18111 Nordhoff St., Northridge, CA 91330-8324. Phone: 818-885-2355. Fax: 818-885-2316. Authorized power: 10-w. each. Antenna: 60-ft. above ground. Lat. 34° 19' 52", long. 119° 01' 17". Transmitter: South Mountain, 3-mi. SE of Santa Paula. Equipment: ITS transmitter; Andrew antenna.

Santa Rosa—WHR-761 (Channels B-1-4). Rural California Broadcasting Corp., 5850 Labath Ave., Rohnert Park, CA 94928. Phone: 707-585-8522. Fax: 707-585-1363.
E-mail: larry-stratton@kccb.pbs.org.
Authorized power: 10-w. each. Antenna: 40-ft. above ground. Lat. 38° 20' 54", long. 122° 34' 37". Transmitter: End of Sonoma Mountain. Equipment: Comwave transmitter; Andrew antenna.
Leased to Wireless Holdings Inc., 500 Clyde Ave., Mountain View, CA 94043. Phone: 650-237-9744.

Santa Rosa—WLX-642 (Channels D-1-4). North American Catholic Educational Programming Foundation Inc., Box 40026, Providence, RI 02940-0026. Phone: 401-729-0900. Authorized power: 10-w. each. Antenna: 75-ft. above ground. Lat. 38° 39' 22", long. 122° 36' 57". Transmitter: Mount St. Helena. Equipment: Emcee transmitter; Andrew antenna.

Santiago—WHR-655 (Channel D-4). Saddleback Community College, 28000 Marguerite Pkwy., Mission Viejo, CA 92692. Authorized power: 1-w. Antenna: 20-ft. above ground. Lat. 33° 42' 38", long. 117° 32' 01". Transmitter: Bldg. 5, Santiago Peak.

South Palm Springs—WNC-684 (Channels D-2-4). Caritas Telecommunications Corp., 1201 E. Highland Ave., San Bernadino, CA 92404. Phone: 909-475-5350. Fax: 909-475-5357.
E-mail: caritasctn@aol.com.
Authorized power: 10-w. each. Antenna: 56-ft. above ground. Lat. 33° 52' 03", long. 116° 25' 58". Transmitter: Edom Hill, South Palm Springs area. Equipment: Comwave transmitter; Scala antenna.
Leased to Wireless Telecommunications Inc., 4000 E. Market St., York, PA 17402. Phone: 717-757-9660.

Spring Hill—WLX-974 (Channels A-1-4). California State U.-Northridge, Continuing Education, 18111 Nordhoff St., Northridge, CA 91330. Phone: 818-885-2355. Fax: 818-885-2316. Equipment: Emcee transmitter; Andrew antenna. Requests change to 10-w., 15-ft. above ground, lat. 35° 28' 48", long. 117° 40' 55"; transmitter to Laurel Mountain, 10-mi. S of Ridgecrest; ITS transmitter; Andrew antenna.

Sutter—WLX-737 (Channels C-1-4). Yuba Community College District, 2088 N. Beale Rd., Marysville, CA 95901. Phone: 530-741-6757. Fax: 530-741-6824.
E-mail: scato@mail2.yuba.cc.ca.us.
Web site: http://www.yuba.cc.ca.us.
Authorized power: 20-w. each. Antenna: 30-ft. above ground. Lat. 39° 12' 21", long. 121° 49' 10". Transmitter: South Butte at Sutter Buttes. Equipment: Comwave transmitter; Andrew antenna.
Leased to American Telecasting Inc., 5575 Tech Center Dr., Suite 300, Colorado Springs, CO 80919. Phone: 719-260-5533.

Tehachapi—WNC-691 (Channels B-1-4). Kern Educational Telecommunication Consortium, 5801 Sunvale Ave., Bakersfield, CA 93309. Authorized power: 10-w. each. Antenna: 18.2-ft. above ground. Lat. 35° 04' 47", long. 118° 21' 44". Transmitter: Oak Peak, 6-mi. SE of Tehachapi. Equipment: Emcee transmitter; Andrew antenna.

Torrance—WAU-30 (Channels C-1-4). Torrance Unified School District, 2336 Plaza del Amo, Torrance, CA 90501. Phone: 310-533-4619. Fax: 310-533-4700.
E-mail: ngriffith@tusd.k12.ca.us.
Web site: http://www.tusd.k12.ca.us.
Transmitter: Educational Materials Bldg., 2336 Plaza del Amo.

Ukiah—WNC-893 (Channels A-1-4). Shekinah Network, 14875 Powerline Rd., Atascadero, CA 93422. Authorized power: 10-w. each. Antenna: 98-ft. above ground. Lat. 39° 07' 44", long. 123° 04' 30". Transmitter: Cow Mountain Antenna Farm. Equipment: Emcee transmitter; Bogner antenna.

Ukiah—WND-284 (Channels B-1-4). College of the Redwoods, Tompkins Hills Rd., Eureka, CA 95501. Authorized power: 10-w. each. Antenna: 98-ft. above ground. Lat. 39° 07' 44", long. 123° 04' 30". Transmitter: Cow Mountain Antenna. Equipment: Emcee transmitter; Bon antenna.

Ukiah—WNC-894 (Channels D-1-4). Views on Learning Inc., 200 Kenyon Ave., Elkhart, IN 46516. Authorized power: 10-w. each. Antenna: 86-ft. above ground. Lat. 39° 07' 44", long. 123° 04' 30". Transmitter: Cow Mountain Antenna Farm. Equipment: Comwave transmitter; Andrew antenna.

Ukiah—WND-421 (Channels G-1-4). Mendocino County Office of Education, 2240 Eastside Rd., Ukiah, CA 95482. Authorized power: 10-w. each. Antenna: 98-ft. above ground. Lat. 39° 07' 44", long. 123° 04' 30". Transmitter: Cow Mountain. Equipment: Emcee transmitter; Bogner antenna.

Victorville—WLX-814 (Channels B-1-4). Franciscan Canticle Inc. Authorized power: 10-w. each. Antenna: 103-ft. above ground. Lat. 34° 36' 38", long. 117° 17' 17". Transmitter: Quartzite Mountain. Equipment: ITS transmitter; Andrew antenna. Requests change to 50-w. each; Comwave transmitter.

Victorville—WHR-835 (Channels C-1-4). California State U.-San Bernardino., 5500 State University Pkwy., San Bernardino, CA 92407. Phone: 909-880-5619. Fax: 909-880-7075.
E-mail: scooper@wiley.csusb.edu.
Web site: http://www.acm.csusb.edu.
Authorized power: 50-w. each. Antenna: 108-ft. above ground. Lat. 34° 36' 38", long. 117° 17' 17". Transmitter: Quartzite Mountain. Equipment: ITS transmitter; Andrew antenna.
Leased to Transworld Telecommunications Inc., 102 West 500 South, Suite 320, Salt Lake City, UT 84101.

Victorville—WHG-356 (Channels D-1-4). Caritas Telecommunications, 1201 E. Highland Ave., San Bernardino, CA 92404. Phone: 909-475-5350. Fax: 909-475-5357.
E-mail: caritasctn@aol.com.
Authorized power: 50-w. each. Antenna: 105-ft. above ground. Lat. 34° 36' 38", long. 117° 17' 20". Transmitter: Quartzite Mountain, Victorville. Equipment: ITS transmitter; Andrew antenna.
Leased to Wireless Holdings Inc., 975 H Industrial Rd., San Carlos, CA 94070. Phone: 415-631-9190.

Visalia—WLX-864 (Channels A-3-4). Views on Learning Inc., 200 Kenyon Ave., Elkhart, IN 46516. Phone & fax: 219-522-1725.
E-mail: jrueff@lsoc-vol.org.
Web site: http://www.lsoc-vol.org.
Authorized power: 20-w. each. Antenna: 76-ft. above ground. Lat. 36° 06' 26", long. 119° 01' 45". Transmitter: 21.7-mi. SE of Visalia. Equipment: ITS transmitter; Andrew antenna.
Leased to Choice TV, 3526 E. Church, Fresno, CA 93725. Phone: 209-442-1970.

Visalia—WNC-785 (Channels B-1-4). Kings County Superintendent of Schools, 1144 W. Lacey Blvd., Hanford, CA 93230. Authorized power: 20-w. each. Antenna: 75-ft. above ground. Lat. 36° 06' 25", long. 119° 01' 45". Transmitter: 21.7 mi. SE of Visalia. Equipment: ITS transmitter; Andrew antenna.

Visalia—WLX-926 (Channels C-3-4). Views on Learning Inc., 200 Kenyon Ave., Elkhart, IN 46516. Phone & fax: 219-522-1725.
E-mail: jrueff@lsoc-vol.org.
Web site: http://www.lsoc-vol.org.
Authorized power: 20-w. each. Antenna: 76-ft. above ground. Lat. 36° 06' 26", long. 119° 01' 45". Transmitter: 21.7-mi. SE of Visalia. Equipment: ITS transmitter; Andrew antenna.
Leased to Choice TV, 3526 E. Church, Fresno, CA 93725. Phone: 209-442-1970.

Visalia—WNC-789 (Channels D-1-4). College of the Sequoias, 915 S. Money Blvd., Visalia, CA 93277. Authorized power: 20-w. each. Antenna: 75-ft. above ground. Lat. 36° 06' 25", long. 119° 01' 45". Transmitter: 21.7-mi. SE of Visalia. Equipment: ITS transmitter; Andrew antenna.

Visalia—WNC-790 (Channels G-1-4). Tulare County Superintendent of Schools, Education Bldg., Civic Center, Visalia, CA 93291. Phone: 209-733-6300. Fax: 209-627-4670.
E-mail: jimv@tcoe.k12.ca.us.
Web site: http://www.tcoe.k12.ca.us.
Authorized power: 20-w. each. Antenna: 75-ft. above ground. Lat. 36° 06' 25", long. 119° 01' 45". Transmitter: 21.7-mi. SE of Visalia. Equipment: ITS transmitter; Andrew antenna.
Leased to Fresno MMDS Associates, 3526 E. Church Ave., Fresno, CA 93725. Phone: 209-442-1970.

Walnut Grove—WHR-848 (Channels C-2-4). Roman Catholic Communications Corp., 324 Middlefield Rd., Menlo Park, CA 94025. Phone: 650-326-7850. Fax: 650-326-4605.
E-mail: ctn@impresso.com.
Web site: http://www.ctnba.org.
Authorized power: 100-w. each. Antenna: 495-ft. above ground. Lat. 37° 43' 44", long. 121° 07' 34". Transmitter: 1220 S. Acacia Ave., Ripon. Equipment: ITS transmitter; Andrew antenna.
Leased to Bay Area Cablevision Inc./Wavepath, 500 Clyde Ave., Mountain View, CA 94043. Phone: 650-237-9744.

Yuba City—WNC-614 (Channels A-1-4). North American Catholic Educational Programming Foundation, Box 40026, Providence, RI 02940. Phone: 401-729-0900. Authorized power: 20-w. each. Antenna: 30-ft. above ground. Lat. 39° 12' 21", long. 121° 49' 10". Transmitter: Sutter Buttes, South Butte. Equipment: Emcee transmitter; Andrew antenna.

Yuba City—WNC-615 (Channels B-1-3). California Human Development Corp., 3315 Airway Dr., Santa Rosa, CA 95403. Authorized power: 20-w. each. Antenna: 30-ft. above ground. Lat. 39° 12' 21", long. 121° 49' 10". Transmitter: Sutter Buttes, South Butte. Equipment: Emcee transmitter; Andrew antenna.

Yuba City—WAQ-325 (Channels D-1, 3&4). California State U. & Colleges-Chico, Instructional Media Center, W. First & Normal Sts., Chico, CA 95929-0005. Phone: 916-898-6112. Fax: 916-898-5369. Authorized power: 50-w. each. Antenna: 24-ft. above ground. Lat. 39° 12' 21", long. 121° 49' 10". Transmitter: Sutter Buttes, South Butte. Equipment: ITS transmitter; Andrew antenna.
Leased to American Telecasting Inc., 5575 Tech Center Dr., Suite 300, Colorado Springs, CO 80919. Phone: 719-260-5533.

Yuba City—WLX-808 (Channels G-1-4). Education North Valley Inc., Box 348721, Sacramento, CA 95834. Authorized power: 50-w. each. Antenna: 24-ft. above ground. Lat. 39° 12' 21", long. 121° 49' 10". Transmitter: Sutter Buttes, South Butte. Equipment: Emcee transmitter; Andrew antenna. Requests change to 20-w. each, 28-ft. above ground.

Colorado

Alamosa—WNC-775 (Channels B-1-4). Alamosa School District, 209 Victoria, Alamosa, CO 81101. Authorized power: 50-w. each. Antenna: 151-ft. above ground. Lat. 37° 28' 12", long. 105° 53' 00". Transmitter: 400 Washington St. Equipment: Emcee transmitter; Andrew antenna.

Alamosa—WNC-795 (Channels C-1-4). Trinidad State Jr. College, 1101 Main St., Alamosa, CO 81101. Authorized power: 50-w. each. Antenna: 151-ft. above ground. Lat. 37° 28' 12", long. 105° 53' 00". Transmitter: 400 Washington St. Equipment: Emcee transmitter; Andrew antenna.

Alamosa—WNC-802 (Channels D-1-4). The Clarendon Foundation, Suite 826, 4201 S. 31st St., Arlington, VA 22206. Authorized power: 50-w. each. Antenna: 151-ft. above ground. Lat. 37° 28' 12", long. 105° 53' 00". Transmitter: 400 Washington St. Equipment: Emcee transmitter; Andrew antenna.

Aspen—WND-368 (Channels A-1-4). Shekinah Network, 14875 Powerline Rd., Atascadero, CA 93422. Authorized power: 10-w. each. Antenna: 46-ft. above ground. Lat. 39° 13' 33", long. 106° 50' 00". Transmitter: Lower Red Mountain tower, Aspen. Equipment: Emcee transmitter; Andrew antenna.

Boulder—WHA-72 (Channels A-1-4). Board of Regents, U. of Colorado, Campus Box 379, ces, Boulder, CO 80309-0379. Phone: 303-492-2677. Fax: 303-492-7017.
E-mail: shaun.dalrymple@colorado.edu.
Web site: http://www.colorado.edu.
Authorized power: 50-w. each. Antenna: 55-ft. above ground. Lat. 39° 54' 48", long. 105° 17' 32". Transmitter: Patty's Peak, near Boulder. Equipment: Comwave transmitter; Andrew antenna.
Leased to American Telecasting Inc., 5575 Tech Center Dr., Suite 300, Colorado Springs, CO 80919. Phone: 719-260-5533.

Colorado Springs—WLX-245 (Channels A-1-4). Pikes Peak Community College, Campus Box 10, 5675 S. Academy Blvd., Colorado Springs, CO 80906. Phone: 719-540-7509. Fax: 719-540-7532. Authorized power: 50-w. each. Antenna: 117-ft. above ground. Lat. 38° 44' 46", long. 104° 51' 37". Transmitter: 6325 Transmitter Lane. Equipment: Emcee transmitter; Bogner antenna.
Leased to American Telecasting Inc., 5575 Tech Center Dr., Suite 300, Colorado Springs, CO 80919. Phone: 719-260-5533.

Colorado Springs—WLX-314 (Channels B-1-4). North American Catholic Educational Programming Foundation Inc., Box 40026, Providence, RI 02940-0026. Authorized power: 50-w. each. Antenna: 117-ft. above ground. Lat. 38° 44' 46", long. 104° 51' 37". Transmitter: 6325 Transmitter Lane. Equipment: Comwave transmitter; Bogner antenna.

Colorado Springs—WHR-694 (Channels D-1-4). Board of Regents, U. of Colorado, Campus Box 379, ces, Boulder, CO 80309. Phone: 303-492-8282. Fax: 303-492-7017.
E-mail: shaun.dalrymple@colorado.edu.
Authorized power: 50-w. each. Antenna: 131-ft. above ground. Lat. 38° 44' 46", long. 104° 51' 37". Transmitter: Austin Bluffs. Equipment: Emcee transmitter; Bogner antenna.

Colorado Springs—WLX-361 (Channels G-1-4). Hispanic Information & Telecommunications Network Inc., 3rd Floor, 449 Broadway, New York, NY 10013. Phone: 212-966-5660. Fax: 212-966-5725.
E-mail: email@hitn.org.
Web site: http://www.hitn.org.
Authorized power: 50-w. each. Antenna: 117-ft. above ground. Lat. 38° 44' 46", long. 104° 51' 37". Transmitter: 6325 Transmitter Lane. Equipment: Comwave transmitter; Bogner antenna.
Leased to American Telecasting Inc., 5575 Tech Center Dr., Colorado Springs, CO 80919. Phone: 719-260-5533.

Denver—WHR-521 (Channels C-1-3). Front Range Educational Media Corp., Box 1740, Denver, CO 80201. Phone: 303-296-1212. Fax: 303-296-6650.
E-mail: channel12@kbdi.pbs.org.
Web site: http://www.kbdi.edu.
Authorized power: 10-w. each. Antenna: 60-ft. above ground. Lat. 39° 54' 48", long. 105° 17' 32". Transmitter: El Dorado Mountain, El Dorado Springs. Equipment: ITS transmitter; Andrew antenna. Requests change to 50-w. each, 64.5-ft. above ground; Emcee transmitter.
Leased to American Telecasting, 5575 Tech Center Dr., Suite 300, Colorado Springs, CO 80919. Phone: 719-260-5533.

Denver—WHR-781 (Channels D-1-4). Colorado School District No. 1 in City & County of Denver & State of, 900 Grant St., Denver, CO 80203. Authorized power: 10-w. each. Antenna: 70-ft. above ground. Lat. 39° 44' 30", long. 104° 59' 40". Transmitter: KRMA-TV studio, 13th & Welton Sts.

Denver—WHR-488 (Channels D-1-4). Denver Area Educational Telecommunications Consortium Inc., Box 6060, Denver, CO 80306. Phone: 303-442-4180. Fax: 303-442-6472. Authorized power: 50-w. each. Antenna: 59-ft. above ground. Lat. 39° 54' 48", long. 105° 17' 32". Transmitter: Eldorado Mountain. Equipment: Comwave transmitter; Andrew antenna.
Leased to American Telecasting of Denver Inc. (ATI), 12600 E. Arapahoe Rd., Englewood, CO 80112. Phone: 303-566-4117.

Denver—WHR-780 (Channels G-1-4). Colorado School District No. 1 in City & County of Denver & State of, 900 Grant St., Denver, CO 80203. Authorized power: 50-w. each. Antenna: 64.5-ft. above ground. Lat. 39° 54' 30", long. 105° 17' 32". Transmitter: Eldorado Mountain. Equipment: Emcee transmitter; Andrew antenna.

Eldorado Springs—WLX-526 (Channel C-4). North American Catholic Educational Programming Foundation Inc., Box 40026, Providence, RI 02940-0026. Phone: 401-729-0900. Authorized power: 50-w. Antenna: 65-ft. above ground. Lat. 39° 54' 48", long. 105° 17' 32". Transmitter: Jefferson County. Equipment: Comwave transmitter; Bogner antenna. Requests change to 50-w. each, 64.5-ft. above ground, Emcee; Andrew antenna.

Fort Collins—WNC-611 (Channels C-1-4). Weld County School District RE-4, 1020 Main St., Windsor, CO 80550. Authorized power: 20-w. each. Antenna: 64-ft. above ground. Lat. 40° 29' 36", long. 105° 10' 53". Transmitter: Milner Mountain. Equipment: ITS transmitter; Bogner antenna.

Fort Collins—WNC-613 (Channels D-1-4). Thompson School District R2-J, 535 N. Douglas Ave., Loveland, CO 80533. Authorized power: 20-w. each. Antenna: 64-ft. above ground. Lat. 40° 29' 36", long. 105° 10' 53". Transmitter: Milner Mountain. Equipment: ITS transmitter; Andrew antenna.

Fort Collins—WNC-612 (Channels G-1-4). Colorado State Board of Agriculture/Colorado State U., Suite 640, 110 16th St., Denver, CO 80202. Phone: 970-491-1325. Fax: 970-491-6989.
E-mail: lpreuss@vines.colostate.edu.
Authorized power: 20-w. each. Antenna: 67-ft. above ground. Lat. 40° 29' 36", long. 105° 10' 15". Transmitter: Milner Mountain. Equipment: ITS transmitter; Andrew antenna.
Leased to American Telecasting Inc., 5575 Tech Center Dr., Suite 300, Colorado Springs, CO 80919. Phone: 719-260-5533.

Greeley—WNC-607 (Channels A-1-4). Weld County School District RE-SJ, 3 N. Jay, Johnstown, CO 80534. Authorized power: 20-w. each. Antenna: 305-ft. above ground. Lat. 40° 22' 42", long. 104° 49' 56". Transmitter: County Rd. 25 & State Rte. 54. Equipment: ITS transmitter; Bogner antenna.

Greeley—WNC-518 (Channels B-1-4). Poudre School District R-1, 2407 LaPorte Ave., Fort Collins, CO 80521. Phone: 970-490-3630. Fax: 970-490-3001.
E-mail: judym@psd.k12.co.us.
Web site: http://www.psd.k12.co.us.
Authorized power: 20-w. each. Antenna: 64-ft. above ground. Lat. 40° 29' 36", long. 105° 10' 53". Transmitter: Milner Mountain. Equipment: ITS transmitter; Andrew antenna.
Leased to American Telecasting Inc., 5575 Tech Center Dr., Suite 300, Colorado Springs, CO 80919. Phone: 719-260-5533.

Greeley—WNC-465 (Channels B-1-4). Weld County School District No. 6, 811 15th St., Greeley, CO 80631. Authorized power: 20-w. each. Antenna: 280-ft. above ground. Lat. 40° 22' 42", long. 104° 49' 56". Transmitter: 8-mi. WSW of Greeley. Equipment: ITS transmitter; Andrew antenna.

Greeley—WNC-610 (Channels C-1-4). Board of Trustees, Carter Hall, U. of North Colorado, Greeley, CO 80639. Phone: 970-351-2885. Fax: 970-351-2983.
E-mail: rscamp@bentley.univnorthco.edu.
Web site: http://www.univnorthco.edu.
Authorized power: 20-w. each. Antenna: 364-ft. above ground. Lat. 40° 22' 42", long. 104° 49' 56". Transmitter: Greeley/Fort Collins. Equipment: ITS transmitter; Andrew antenna.
Leased to American Telecasting Inc., 5575 Twcvh Center Dr., Suite 300, Colorado Springs, CO 80919. Phone: 719-260-5533.

Greeley—WNC-609 (Channels D-1-4). Aims Junior College District, 5401 W. 20th St., Greeley, CO 80634. Phone: 970-330-8008. Fax: 970-339-6664.
E-mail: kfsauer@hades.aims.edu.
Web site: http://www.aims.edu.
Authorized power: 20-w. each. Antenna: 307.5-ft. above ground. Lat. 40° 22' 42", long. 104° 49' 56". Equipment: ITS transmitter; Andrew antenna.
Leased to American Telecasting Inc., 5575 Tech Center Dr., Suite 300, Colorado Springs, CO 80919. Phone: 719-260-5533.

Greeley—WNC-608 (Channels G-1-4). Weld County School District RE-1, 1055 Birch St., Gilcrest, CO 80623. Authorized power: 20-w. each. Antenna: 305-ft. above ground. Lat. 40° 22' 42", long. 104° 49' 56". Transmitter: Country Rd. 25 & State Rte. 54 intersection. Equipment: ITS transmitter; Andrew antenna.

Pueblo—WNC-908 (Channels B-1-4). State Board of Agriculture, 2200 Bonforte Blvd., Pueblo, CO 81001. Phone: 719-543-8800. Fax: 719-549-2208. Authorized power: 50-w. each. Antenna: 190-ft. above ground. Lat. 38° 12' 18", long. 104° 42' 24". Transmitter: Jackson Hill, SW of Pueblo. Equipment: Emcee transmitter; Andrew antenna.

Pueblo—WNC-910 (Channels D-1-4). U. of Southern Colorado, 220 Bonforte Blvd., Pueblo, CO 81001. Phone: 719-543-8800. Fax: 719-549-2208. Authorized power: 50-w. each. Antenna: 190-ft. above ground. Lat. 38° 12' 18", long. 104° 42' 24". Transmitter: Jackson Hill, SW of Pueblo. Equipment: Emcee transmitter; Andrew antenna.

Pueblo—WNC-911 (Channels G-1-4). Pueblo School District No. 70, 24951 Hwy. 50 E, Pueblo, CO 81006. Authorized power: 50-w. each. Antenna: 190-ft. above ground. Lat. 38° 12' 18", long. 104° 42' 24". Transmitter: Jackson Hill, SW of Pueblo. Equipment: Emcee transmitter; Andrew antenna.

Vail—WND-352 (Channels A-1-4). Shekinah Network, 14875 Powerline Rd., Atascadero, CA 93422. Authorized power: 10-w. each. Antenna: 249-ft. above ground. Lat. 39° 38' 05", long. 106° 26' 47". Transmitter: Approx. 2-mi. W of Vail. Equipment: Emcee transmitter; Andrew antenna.

Wiley—WNC-857 (Channels A-1-4). Lamar Community College, 2401 S. Main, Lamar, CO 81052. Authorized power: 10-w. each. Antenna: 4166-ft. above ground. Lat. 38° 10' 19", long. 102° 40' 50". Transmitter: 4240 Rd. PP. Equipment: Comwave transmitter; Andrew antenna.

Wiley—WNC-858 (Channels G-1-4). Wiley Consolidated Schools, 505 Ward Rd., Wiley, CO 81092. Authorized power: 10-w. each. Antenna: 4166-ft. above ground. Lat. 38° 10' 19", long. 102° 40' 50". Transmitter: 4240 Rd. PP. Equipment: Comwave transmitter; Andrew antenna.

Connecticut

Ashford—WHR-888 (Channels D-1-4). Connecticut Educational Telecommunications Corp., 24 Summit St., Hartford, CT 06106. Phone: 860-278-5310. Fax: 860-278-2157. Authorized power: 10-w. each. Antenna: 687-ft. above ground. Lat. 41° 51' 51", long. 72° 07' 19". Transmitter: Punkin Hill. Equipment: ITS transmitter; Andrew antenna.

Bozrah—WLX-228 (Channels C-1-2). Board of Trustees, Community Technical College, 61 Woodland St., Hartford, CT 06150. Authorized power: 50-w. each. Antenna: 431-ft. above ground. Lat. 41° 31' 11", long. 72° 10' 04". Transmitter: WEDN(TV) tower, 3.2-mi. SSW of Fitchville & 0.5-mi. from Bishop Rd. Equipment: Comwave transmitter; Andrew antenna.

Bozrah—WHF-277 (Channels E-1-2). Connecticut Educational Telecommunications Corp., 24 Summit St., Hartford, CT 06106. Phone: 860-278-5310. Fax: 860-278-2157. Authorized power: 10-w. each. Antenna: 250-ft. above ground. Lat. 41° 31' 11", long. 72° 10' 04". Transmitter: 3.2-mi. SSW of Fitchville. Equipment: Comwave transmitter.

Brookfield—WHR-840 (Channels D-3-4). Connecticut Educational Telecommunications Corp., 240 New Britain Ave., Hartford, CT 06126. Phone: 860-278-5310. Fax: 860-278-2157. Authorized power: 10-w. each. Antenna: 250-ft. above ground. Lat. 41° 27' 35", long. 73° 22' 07". Transmitter: Tower Rd. Equipment: Emcee transmitter; Andrew antenna.

Brooklyn—WLX-241 (Channels D-3-4). Connecticut Public Broadcasting Inc., 240 New Britain Ave., Hartford, CT 06106. Phone: 860-278-5310. Fax: 860-278-2157. Authorized power: 2-w. each. Antenna: 255-ft. above ground. Lat. 41° 48' 59", long. 71° 58' 37". Transmitter: State Police Tower, Bush Hill. Equipment: Emcee transmitter; Andrew antenna.

Cornwall—WHR-804 (Channels A-1-4). Connecticut Educational Telecommunications Corp., 24 Summit St., Hartford, CT 06106. Phone: 860-278-5310. Fax: 860-278-2157. Authorized power: 10-w. each. Antenna: 752-ft. above ground. Lat. 41° 49' 17", long. 73° 17' 52". Transmitter: End of Mattatuck Rd., 2.3-mi. SE of Cornwall. Equipment: ITS transmitter; Andrew antenna.

Farmington—WLX-229 (Channels D-1-2). Board of Trustees, Community Technical College, 61 Woodland St., Hartford, CT 06105. Phone: 203-725-6618. Fax: 203-566-6624. Authorized power: 50-w. each. Antenna: 603-ft. above ground. Lat. 41° 42' 02", long. 72° 49' 57". Transmitter: WVIT(TV) transmitter site, Rattlesnake Mountain. Equipment: Comwave transmitter; Andrew antenna.

Farmington—WHF-271 (Channels E-1-2). Connecticut Public Broadcasting Inc., 24 Summit St., Hartford, CT 06106. Phone: 860-278-5310. Fax: 860-278-2157. Authorized power: 50-w. each. Antenna: 1005-ft. above ground. Lat. 41° 42' 02", long. 72° 49' 57". Transmitter: WVIT(TV) transmitter site, Rattlesnake Mountain. Equipment: Comwave transmitter; Andrew antenna.

Glastonbury—WHF-276 (Channels C-1-4). Connecticut Public Broadcasting Inc., 24 Summit St., Hartford, CT 06106. Phone: 860-278-5310. Fax: 860-278-2156. Authorized power: 10-w. each. Antenna: 548-ft. above ground. Lat. 41° 42' 32", long. 72° 28' 30". Transmitter: John Tom Hill, Birch Mountain Rd. & Hebron Ave. intersection. Equipment: ITS transmitter; Andrew antenna.

Haddam—WHR-673 (Channels A-1-4). Connecticut Public Broadcasting Inc., 24 Summit St., Hartford, CT 06106. Phone: 860-278-5310. Fax: 860-278-2157. Authorized power: 10-w. each. Antenna: 493-ft. above ground. Lat. 41° 26' 36", long. 72° 34' 02". Transmitter: Porkorny Rd. Equipment: Comwave transmitter; Andrew antenna.

Hartford—WLX-569 (Channels B-1-4). Archdiocese of Hartford School Office of Communications. Authorized power: 26.3-w. each. Antenna: 350-ft. above ground. Lat. 41° 42' 13", long. 72° 49' 57". Transmitter: Rattlesnake Mountain, Rte. 6, Colt Hwy. Equipment: Comwave transmitter; Bogner antenna.

Hartford—WLX-572 (Channels C-1-4). Counterpoint Communications Inc. Authorized power: 26.3-w. each. Antenna: 350-ft. above ground. Lat. 41° 42' 13", long. 72° 49' 57". Transmitter: Rattlesnake Mountain, Rte. 6, Colt Hwy. Equipment: Comwave transmitter; Cablewave antenna.

Hartford—WNC-321 (Channels D-1-2). Hispanic Information & Telecommunications Network Inc., 3rd Floor, 449 Broadway, New York, NY 10013. Phone: 212-966-5660. Fax: 212-966-5725.

E-mail: email@hitn.org.

Web site: http://www.hitn.org.

Authorized power: 26.3-w. each. Antenna: 350-ft. above ground. Lat. 41° 42' 13", long. 72° 49' 57". Transmitter: Rattlesnake Mountain. Equipment: Comwave transmitter; Andrew antenna.

Leased to CAI Wireless Systems Inc., 2101 Wilson Blvd., Suite 100, Arlington, VA 22201. Phone: 703-812-8800.

Naugatuck—WHR-767 (Channels A-1-4). Connecticut Public Broadcasting Inc., 24 Summit St., Hartford, CT 06106. Phone: 860-278-5310. Fax: 860-278-2157. Authorized power: 27-w. each. Antenna: 514-ft. above ground. Lat. 41° 31' 05", long. 73° 01' 06". Transmitter: 520-ft. SE from towns of intersection of Naugatuck, Waterbury & Prospect. Equipment: ITS transmitter; Omni antenna.

New Britain—WLX-531 (Channels A-3-4). Albion Community Development Corp., 51 N. Main St., Albion, NY 14411. Authorized power: 26.3-w. each. Antenna: 350-ft. above ground. Lat. 41° 42' 13", long. 72° 49' 57". Transmitter: Rattlesnake Mountain, Rte. 6, Colt Hwy. Equipment: Comwave transmitter; Cablewave antenna.

New Britain—WLX-831 (Channels D-3-4). National Conference on Citizenship, Suite 1150, 4770 Biscayne Blvd., Miami, FL 33137. Phone: 305-576-4310. Fax: 305-576-7412 Authorized power: 26.3-w. each. Antenna: 339-ft. above ground. Lat. 41° 42' 13", long. 72° 49' 57". Transmitter: Rattle Snake Mountain, Rte. 6 & Colt Hwy. Equipment: Comwave transmitter; Andrew antenna.

New Haven—WHR-893 (Channels B-1-4). Archdiocese of Hartford. Authorized power: 10-w. each. Antenna: 255-ft. above ground. Lat. 41° 20' 58", long. 72° 58' 27". Transmitter: 1055 Wintergreen Ave. Equipment: Emcee transmitter; Andrew antenna.

New Haven—WHR-841 (Channels D-3-4). Connecticut Educational Telecommunications Corp., 24 Summit St., Hartford, CT 06106. Phone: 860-278-5310. Fax: 860-278-2157. Authorized power: 10-w. each. Antenna: 279-ft. above ground. Lat. 41° 19' 42", long. 72° 54' 25". Transmitter: 7-mi. ENE of New Haven. Equipment: Emcee transmitter; Andrew antenna.

Seymour—WHF-270 (Channels C-1-2). Connecticut Educational Telecommunications Corp., 24 Summit St., Hartford, CT 06106. Phone: 860-278-5310. Fax: 860-278-2157. Authorized power: 50-w. each. Antenna: 415-ft. above ground. Lat. 41° 21' 43", long. 72° 06' 48". Transmitter: 80 Great Hill Rd. Equipment: Comwave transmitter; Andrew antenna.

Seymour—WLX-230 (Channels C-3-4). Board of Trustees, Community Technical Colleges, 61 Woodland St., Hartford, CT 06105. Authorized power: 10-w. each. Antenna: 170-ft. above ground. Lat. 41° 21' 43", long. 73° 06' 48". Transmitter: 80 Great Hill Rd. Equipment: Comwave transmitter; Andrew antenna.

Thompson—WLX-771 (Channels G-3-4). Connecticut Public Broadcasting Inc., 240 New Britain Ave., Hartford, CT 06126. Phone: 860-278-5310. Fax: 860-244-9624. Authorized power: 2-w. each. Antenna: 251-ft. above ground. Lat. 41° 58' 45", long. 71° 51' 12". Transmitter: Telemedia Cable Tower on Davis Rd. Equipment: Comwave transmitter; Andrew antenna.

Trumbull—WHR-842 (Channels G-1-2). Connecticut Educational Telecommunications Corp., 24 Summit St., Hartford, CT 06106. Phone: 860-278-5310. Fax: 860-278-2157. Authorized power: 10-w. each. Antenna: 602-ft. above ground. Lat. 41° 16' 43", long. 73° 11' 09". Transmitter: Video Lane, off Booth Hill Rd. Equipment: Comwave transmitter; Andrew antenna.

Wilton—WLX-565 (Channels G-3-4). Connecticut Educational Telecommunication Corp., 24 Summit St., Hartford, CT 06106. Phone: 860-278-5310. Fax: 860-278-2157. Authorized power: 10-w. each. Antenna: 266-ft. above ground. Lat. 41° 10' 30", long. 73° 26' 03". Transmitter: Beldon Hill Rd. Equipment: Comwave transmitter; Andrew antenna.

Delaware

Wilmington—WLX-571 (Channels B-1-4). WHYY Inc., 150 N. 6th St., Philadelphia, PA 19106. Authorized power: 10-w. each. Antenna: 531-ft. above ground. Lat. 29° 03' 57", long. 95° 19' 17". Transmitter: 2021 County Rd. 227. Equipment: Emcee transmitter; Bogner antenna.

District of Columbia

Washington—WHG-442 (Channels D-1-4). George Washington U., 2121 Eye St. NW, Washington, DC 20052. Phone: 202-994-2083. Fax: 202-994-5048.

E-mail: tchriste@gwtv.gwu.edu.

Web site: http://www.gwu.edu.

Authorized power: 50-w. each. Antenna: 635-ft. above ground. Lat. 38° 57' 49", long. 77° 06' 18". Transmitter: 5202 River Rd. Equipment: ITS transmitter; Andrew antenna.

Leased to CAI Wireless Systens, 2101 Wilson Blvd., Suite 100, Arlington, VA 22201. Phone: 703-812-8800.

Washington—WHG-443 (Channels E-1-4). George Washington U., Room T306, 801 22nd St. NW, Washington, DC 20052. Phone: 202-994-2083. Fax: 202-994-5048.

E-mail: tchriste@gwtv.gwu.edu.

Web site: http://www.gwu.edu/~gwtv.

Authorized power: 50-w. each. Antenna: 636-ft. above ground. Lat. 38° 57' 49", long. 77° 06' 18". Transmitter: 5202 River Rd., Bethesda, MD. Equipment: ITS transmitter; Andrew antenna.

Leased to CAI, 2101 Wilson Blvd., Suite 100, Arlington, VA 22201. Phone: 703-812-8800.

Washington—WHR-461 (Channels G-1-4). Network for Instructional TV Inc., Suite 110, 11490 Commerce Park Dr., Reston, VA 20191. Phone: 703-860-9200. Fax: 703-860-9237. Authorized power: 50-w. each. Antenna: 639-ft. above ground. Lat. 38° 57' 49", long. 77° 06' 18". Transmitter: 5202 River Rd., WDCA(TV) tower. Equipment: Emcee transmitter; Andrew antenna.

Leased to CAI Wireless Systems, 2101 Wilson Blvd., Suite 100, Arlington, VA 22201. Phone: 703-812-8800.

Florida

Bell—WNC-264 (Channel C-1). Lake City Community College, Box 1030, Rte. 19, Lake City, FL 32025. Phone: 904-752-1822. Fax: 904-755-1002.

E-mail: mckeem@mail.firn.edu.

Authorized power: 10-w. Antenna: 209-ft. above ground. Lat. 29° 45' 08", long. 82° 51' 35". Transmitter: Bell Full Service School. Equipment: Comwave transmitter; Andrew antenna.

Belle Glade—KZB-28 (Channel A-4). Palm Beach County School Board, 3304 Forest Hill Blvd., West Palm Beach, FL 33406-5813. Phone: 407-738-2702. Fax: 407-738-2901. Authorized power: 10-w. Antenna: 250-ft. above ground. Lat. 26° 42' 24", long. 80° 40' 49". Transmitter: State Rd. 175, 1-mi. N of State Rtes. 717 & 715 intersection. Equipment: Emcee transmitter; Andrew antenna.

Boca Raton—WHR-877 (Channels A-1-4). Florida Board of Regents/Florida Atlantic U., Bldg. 4, Rm. 239, 777 Glades Rd., Boca Raton, FL 33431. Authorized power: 1-w. each. Antenna: 100-ft. above ground. Lat. 26° 22' 17", long. 80° 06' 14". Transmitter: Campus of Florida Atlantic U. Equipment: Comwave transmitter; Andrew antenna.

Boca Raton—WHR-894 (Channels D-1-4). Florida Board of Regents, Florida Atlantic U., Bldg. 4, Rm. 239, 777 Glades Rd., Boca Raton, FL 33431. Authorized power: 1-w. each. Antenna: 100-ft. above ground. Lat. 26° 22' 17", long. 80° 06' 14". Transmitter: Campus of Florida Atlantic U. Equipment: Comwave transmitter; Andrew antenna.

Boca Raton—WHR-895 (Channels G-1-4). Florida Board of Regents, Florida Atlantic U., Bldg. 4, Rm. 239, 777 Glades Rd., Boca Raton, FL 33431. Authorized power: 1-w. each. Antenna: 155-ft. above ground. Lat. 26° 07' 12", long. 80° 08' 28". Transmitter: University Tower, 220 S.E. 2nd Ave., Fort Lauderdale. Equipment: Comwave transmitter; Andrew antenna.

Bonita Springs—WLX-678 (Channels A-1-4). Collier County Public Schools, 3710 Estey Ave., Naples, FL 33942. Phone: 813-436-6441. Fax: 813-643-7751. Authorized power: 50-w. each. Antenna: 322-ft. above ground. Lat. 26° 19' 00", long. 81° 47' 13". Transmitter: Channel 30 Dr. Equipment: Emcee transmitter; Andrew antenna.

Leased to American Telecasting Inc., 5575 Tech Center Dr., Suite 300, Colorado Springs, CO 80919. Phone: 719-260-5533.

Bonita Springs—WNC-676 (Channels B-1-4). Community School of Naples, 3521 Pine Ridge Rd., Naples, FL 33942. Authorized power: 50-w. each. Antenna: 322-ft. above ground. Lat. 26° 19' 00", long. 81° 47' 13". Transmitter: Channel 30 Dr. Equipment: Emcee transmitter; Andrew antenna.

Bonita Springs—WNC-803 (Channels C-1-4). Seacrest County Day School, 7100 Davis Blvd., Naples, FL 34104. Phone: 941-793-1986. Fax: 941-793-1460.

E-mail: hruisi@seacrest.org.

Authorized power: 50-w. each. Antenna: 322-ft. above ground. Lat. 26° 07' 33", long. 81° 43' 17". Transmitter: Channel 30 Dr. Equipment: Emcee transmitter; Andrew antenna.

Bonita Springs—WNC-260 (Channels D-1-4). The Montessori School of Fort Myers, 2151 Crystal Dr. SE, Fort Myers, FL 33907-4147. Authorized power: 50-w. each. Antenna: 322-ft. above ground. Lat. 26° 07' 33", long. 81° 43' 17". Transmitter: Channel 30 Dr. Equipment: Emcee transmitter; Andrew antenna.

Bonita Springs—WND-240 (Channels G-1-4). Edison Community College, Box 06210, 8099 College Pkwy. SW, Fort Myers, FL 33906-6210. Phone: 941-489-9264. Fax: 941-489-9021.

E-mail: bo'neill@Edison.edu.

Web site: http://edison.edu.

Authorized power: 50-w. each. Antenna: 305-ft. above ground. Lat. 26° 19' 00", long. 81° 47' 13". Transmitter: Channel 30 Dr. Equipment: Emcee transmitter; Andrew antenna.
Leased to Bell South/American Telecasting Inc., 4700 L.B. McLeod Rd., Suite B, Orlando, FL 32811. Phone: 407-648-5702.

Boynton Beach—KHU-90 (Channels E-1-4). Palm Beach County School Board, 3304 Forest Hill Blvd., West Palm Beach, FL 33406-5813. Phone: 407-738-2702. Fax: 407-738-2901. Authorized power: 10-w. each. Antenna: 235-ft. above ground. Lat. 26° 31' 22", long. 80° 05' 28". Transmitter: 505 S. Congress Ave. Equipment: Emcee transmitter; Andrew antenna.

Bradenton—WHR-838 (Channels A-1-4). School Board of Manatee County, 215 Manatee Ave. W, Bradenton, FL 33505. Authorized power: 1-w. each. Antenna: 80-ft. above ground. Lat. 27° 29' 35", long. 82° 33' 56". Transmitter: 215 Manatee Ave. W. Equipment: Emcee transmitter; Andrew antenna.

Bradenton—WLX-724 (Channels D-1-4). North American Catholic Educational Programming Foundation Inc., Box 40026, Providence, RI 02940-0026. Phone: 401-729-0900. Authorized power: 10-w. each. Antenna: 296-ft. above ground. Lat. 27° 29' 08", long. 82° 32' 00". Transmitter: 2404 13th Ave. E. Equipment: Emcee transmitter; Andrew antenna.

Bradenton—WHR-873 (Channels G-1-2). School Board of Manatee County, 215 Manatee Ave. W, Bradenton, FL 33505. Phone: 941-741-3470. Fax: 941-741-3480. Authorized power: 10-w. each. Antenna: 299-ft. above ground. Lat. 27° 28' 30", long. 82° 31' 47".

Bradfordville—WLX-924 (Channels C-1-4). Maclay School, 3737 N. Meridian Rd., Tallahassee, FL 32312. Phone: 904-893-2138. Authorized power: 50-w. each. Antenna: 706-ft. above ground. Lat. 30° 29' 32", long. 84° 17' 13". Transmitter: 123 Ridgewood Rd., Tallahassee. Equipment: Comwave transmitter; Andrew antenna.

Brooksville—WHR-749 (Channel E-4). Hernando County School Board, 919 N. Broad St., Brooksville, FL 33512. Phone: 352-797-7009. Fax: 352-797-7109. Authorized power: 10-w. Antenna: 116-ft. above ground. Lat. 28° 31' 34", long. 82° 23' 44". Transmitter: Repeater station K-RJ804.

Chipley—WHR-800 (Channels G-1-4). Panhandle Area Educational Consortium, 753 West Blvd., Chipley, FL 32428. Phone: 904-638-6131. Fax: 904-638-6135.
E-mail: everitr@mail.firn.edu.
Web site: http://www.paec.org.
Authorized power: 10-w. each. Antenna: 155-ft. above ground. Lat. 30° 46' 34", long. 85° 33' 04".
Leased to Wireless One Inc., 5551 Corporate Blvd., Suite 2K, Baton Rouge, LA 70808. Phone: 504-926-7778.

Clearwater—WLX-226 (Channel D-1 & 4). School Board of Pinellas County, 1960 E. Druid Rd., Clearwater, FL 34618. Authorized power: 100-w. Antenna: 640-ft. above ground. Lat. 28° 02' 20", long. 82° 39' 29". Transmitter: 103 Dunbar Ave., Oldsmar. Equipment: Comwave transmitter; Andrew antenna.

Cocoa—WLX-949 (Channels A-1-4). Brevard Community College, 1519 Clearlake Rd., Cocoa, FL 32922. Phone: 407-632-1111. Fax: 407-634-3724.
E-mail: carlsona@brevard.cc.fl.us.
Authorized power: 50-w. each. Antenna: 490-ft. above ground. Lat. 28° 16' 42", long. 80° 42' 03". Transmitter: 1865 Harlock Rd. Equipment: Emcee transmitter; Bogner antenna.

Cocoa—WLX-989 (Channels C-1-4). Brevard Community College, 1519 Clearlake Rd., Cocoa, FL 32922. Phone: 407-632-1111.
E-mail: carlsona@brevard.cc.fl.us.
Authorized power: 50-w. each. Antenna: 488-ft. above ground. Lat. 28° 16' 42", long. 80° 42' 11". Transmitter: 1865 Harlock Rd. Equipment: Emcee transmitter; Bogner antenna.
Leased to Wireless Broadcasting Systems, 4450 W. Eau Gallie Blvd., Melbourne, FL 32934. Phone: 407-255-0430.

Cocoa—WHR-494 (Channels G-1-4). U. of Central Florida, Clearlake Rd., Cocoa, FL 32922. Authorized power: 50-w. each. Antenna: 496-ft. above ground. Lat. 28° 08' 15", long. 80° 42' 11". Transmitter: 1865 Harlock Rd. Equipment: Emcee transmitter; Bogner antenna.

Cottondale—WND-293 (Channels B-1-4). Washington County District School Board. Authorized power: 50-w. each. Antenna: 505-ft. above ground. Lat. 30° 46' 02", long. 85° 17' 14". Transmitter: 1.2-mi. S of Hwy. 90, 2-mi. W of Hwy. 27. Equipment: Emcee transmitter; Bogner antenna.

Cottondale—WND-294 (Channels D-1-4). Jackson County District School Board, 2903 Jefferson St., Marianna, FL 32446. Authorized power: 50-w. each. Antenna: 505-ft. above ground. Lat. 30° 46' 02", long. 85° 17' 14". Transmitter: 1.2-mi. S of Hwy. 90, 2-mi. W of Hwy. 27. Equipment: Emcee transmitter; Bogner antenna.

Daytona Beach—WBE-795 (Channel A-1). Volusia County School Board, Box 2118, 230 N. Stone St., De Land, FL 32720. Authorized power: 10-w. Antenna: 185-ft. above ground. Lat. 29° 11' 55", long. 81° 01' 42". Transmitter: Loomis & Lockhart Sts.

Daytona Beach—WHR-779 (Channels D-1-4). Daytona Beach Community College, Box 2811, 1200 International Speedway Blvd, Daytona Beach, FL 32120-2811. Phone: 904-254-4413. Fax: 904-947-3175. Authorized power: 10-w. each. Antenna: 190-ft. above ground. Lat. 29° 12' 11", long. 81° 03' 02". Transmitter: 1200 International Speedway Dr. Equipment: ITS transmitter; Bogner antenna.

Daytona Beach—WGV-765 (Channel E-1). Volusia County School Board, Box 1910, Daytona Beach, FL 32015. Authorized power: 0.1-w. Antenna: 95-ft. above ground. Lat. 29° 11' 44", long. 81° 03' 05". Transmitter: Mainland Senior High School.

DeBary—WLX-320 (Channels B-1-2). Daytona Beach Community College, Box 2811, 1200 International Speedway Blvd., Daytona Beach, FL 32120-2811. Phone: 904-254-4413. Fax: 904-947-3175. Authorized power: 10-w. each. Antenna: 260-ft. above ground. Lat. 28° 53' 29", long. 81° 17' 06". Transmitter: 336 E. Highbanks Rd. Equipment: Emcee transmitter; Bogner antenna.

De Funiak Springs—WHR-880 (Channels A-1-4). Panhandle Area Educational Consortium, 753 West Blvd., Chipley, FL 32428. Phone: 904-638-6131. Fax: 904-638-6135.
E-mail: everitr@mail.firn.edu.
Web site: http://www.paec.org.
Authorized power: 10-w. each. Antenna: 307-ft. above ground. Lat. 30° 43' 13", long. 86° 05' 57". Transmitter: Walton County Vocational Technical School, Park Ave.

De Land—WHR-768 (Channels B-3-4). Daytona Beach Community College, Box 2811, 1200 International Speedway Blvd, Daytona Beach, FL 32120-2811. Phone: 904-254-4413. Fax: 904-947-3175. Authorized power: 10-w. each. Antenna: 142-ft. above ground. Lat. 29° 00' 46", long. 81° 14' 35". Transmitter: 1135 County Rd. 4139. Equipment: ITS transmitter; Bogner antenna.

De Land—WBK-225 (Channel E-1). Volusia County School Board, Box 2118, 230 N. Stone St., De Land, FL 32720. Authorized power: 10-w. Antenna: 120-ft. above ground. Lat. 29° 01' 49", long. 81° 19' 01". Transmitter: 230 N. Stone St.

De Leon Springs—WLX-225 (Channel A-3). School Board of Volusia County, 200 N. Clara Ave., De Land, FL 32721. Authorized power: 10-w. Antenna: 128-ft. above ground. Lat. 29° 07' 25", long. 81° 21' 05". Transmitter: McInnis Elementary School, 5175 N. Hwy. 17. Equipment: Emcee transmitter; ITS antenna.

Flagler Beach—WHR-783 (Channels B-1-2). Daytona Beach Community College, Box 2811, 1200 International Speedway Blvd, Daytona Beach, FL 32120-2811. Phone: 904-254-4413. Fax: 904-947-3175. Authorized power: 10-w. each. Antenna: 236-ft. above ground. Lat. 29° 33' 16", long. 81° 11' 45". Transmitter: 3000 Palm Coast Pkwy. E, Palm Coast. Equipment: Emcee transmitter; Bogner antenna.

Fort Lauderdale—KLC-80 (Channels B-1-4). The School Board of Broward County, ITV Center, 6600 S.W. Nova Dr., Fort Lauderdale, FL 33312. Phone: 954-370-8350. Fax: 954-370-1648.
Web site: http://www.becon-itv.org.
Authorized power: 50-w. each. Antenna: 253-ft. above ground. Lat. 26° 05' 09", long. 80° 14' 08". Transmitter: 6600 S.W. Nova Dr. Equipment: Comwave transmitter; Andrew antenna.

Fort Lauderdale—WHR-897 (Channels C-1-4). Florida Board of Regents, Florida Atlantic U., Bldg. 4, Rm. 239, 777 Glades Rd., Boca Raton, FL 33431. Authorized power: 10-w. each. Antenna: 340-ft. above ground. Lat. 26° 06' 54", long. 80° 08' 30". Transmitter: 110 S.E. 6th St. Equipment: Comwave transmitter; Andrew antenna.

Fort Lauderdale—KTZ-22 (Channels G-1-4). School Board of Broward County, ITV Center, 6600 S.W. Nova Dr., Fort Lauderdale, FL 33312. Phone: 954-370-8350. Fax: 954-370-1648.
Web site: http://www.becon-itv.org.
Authorized power: 50-w. each. Antenna: 253-ft. above ground. Lat. 26° 05' 09", long. 80° 14' 08". Transmitter: 6600 S.W. Nova Dr. Equipment: Comwave transmitter; Andrew antenna.

Fort Myers—WND-291 (Channels A-1-4). Edison Community College, Box 06210, 8099 College Pkwy. SW, Fort Myers, FL 33906. Authorized power: 50-w. each. Antenna: 476-ft. above ground. Lat. 26° 43' 35", long. 81° 47' 12". Transmitter: N end of Bahia Vista. Equipment: Emcee transmitter; Andrew antenna.

Fort Myers—WBE-805 (Channel B-1). Lee County School Board, 3308 Canal St., Fort Myers, FL 33901. Authorized power: 10-w. Antenna: 140-ft. above ground. Lat. 26° 38' 53", long. 81° 51' 12". Transmitter: Southern Cablevision Tower, 2931 Michigan Ave.

Fort Myers—WLX-273 (Channels C-1-4). U. of South Florida, 4202 E. Fowler Ave., Tampa, FL 33620. Phone: 813-974-7984. Fax: 813-974-7272.
Web site: http://www.outreach.usf.edu.
Authorized power: 15-w. each. Antenna: 492-ft. above ground. Lat. 26° 43' 35", long. 81° 47' 12". Transmitter: N end of Bahia Vista. Equipment: Emcee transmitter; Andrew antenna. Requests change to 50-w. each.
Leased to American Telecasting Inc., 2500 N. Orange Blossom Trail, Orlando, FL 32804. Phone: 407-650-4684.

Fort Myers—WND-292 (Channels D-1-4). Views on Learning Inc., 200 Kenyon Ave., Elkhart, IN 46516. Authorized power: 50-w. each. Antenna: 476-ft. above ground. Lat. 26° 43' 35", long. 81° 47' 12". Transmitter: N end of Bahia Vista. Equipment: Emcee transmitter; Andrew antenna.

Fort Myers—WLX-354 (Channels G-1-4). North American Catholic Educational Programming Foundation Inc., Box 40026, Providence, RI 02940-0026. Phone: 401-729-0900. Authorized power: 50-w. each. Antenna: 492-ft. above ground. Lat. 26° 43' 35", long. 81° 47' 12". Transmitter: N end of Bahia Vista. Equipment: Emcee transmitter; Andrew antenna.

Fort Pierce—WLX-510 (Channels G-1-4). North American Catholic Educational Programming Foundation Inc., Box 40026, Providence, RI 02940-0026. Phone: 401-729-0900. Authorized power: 50-w. each. Antenna: 496-ft. above ground. Lat. 27° 19' 27", long. 80° 18' 49". Transmitter: 1100 Dyer Rd. Equipment: Emcee transmitter; Andrew antenna.
Leased to Coastal Wireless Cable Television, 8423 S. U.S. Rte. 1, Box 7307, Port St. Lucie, FL 34985. Phone: 407-871-0155.

Islamorada—WNC-899 (Channels D-1-4). Views on Learning Inc., 200 Kenyon Ave., Elkhart, IN 46516. Authorized power: 20-w. each. Antenna: 167-ft. above ground. Lat. 24° 56' 12", long. 80° 37' 02". Transmitter: 500-ft. N of U.S. Hwy. 1, Islamorada. Equipment: ITS transmitter; Bogner antenna.

Islamorda—WNC-900 (Channels G-1-4). Island Christian High School, 83400 Overseas Hwy., Islamorda, FL 33036. Authorized power: 20-w. each. Antenna: 10-ft. above ground. Lat. 24° 56' 12", long. 80° 37' 02". Transmitter: 500-ft. N of U.S. 1. Equipment: ITS transmitter; Bogner antenna.

Jacksonville—WHA-934 (Channel A-1). Florida Junior College at Jacksonville, 501 W. State St., Jacksonville, FL 32202. Authorized power: 100-w. Antenna: 50-ft. above ground. Lat. 30° 20' 04", long. 81° 39' 40". Transmitter: 101 S. State St.

Jacksonville—WHA-933 (Channels A-2-3). Florida Junior College at Jacksonville, 501 W. State St., Jacksonville, FL 32202. Authorized power: 100-w. each. Antenna: 248-ft. above ground. Lat. 30° 19' 45", long. 81° 39' 27". Transmitter: Charter Security Life Bldg., Church St., near Main St.

Jacksonville—WLX-922 (Channels A-1-4). Duval County School Board, 1701 Prudential Dr., Jacksonville, FL 32207. Authorized power: 100-w. each. Antenna: 600-ft. above ground. Lat. 30° 16' 53", long. 81° 34' 15". Transmitter: 400-ft. N of Hogan County Rd. & Old Hogan County Rds. intersection. Equipment: Emcee transmitter; Andrew antenna.

Jacksonville—WLX-538 (Channels B-1-3). Hispanic Information & Telecommunications Network Inc., 3rd Floor, 449 Broadway, New York, NY 10013. Phone: 212-966-5660. Fax: 212-966-5725.
E-mail: email@hitn.org.
Web site: http://www.hitn.org.

Authorized power: 10-w. each. Antenna: 537-ft. above ground. Lat. 30° 19' 33", long. 81° 39' 32". Transmitter: One Independent Dr. Equipment: Emcee transmitter; Andrew antenna. Requests change to 50-w. each, 564-ft. above ground lat. 30° 16' 53" long. 81° 34' 12"; transmitter to 400-ft. N of Hogan County & Old County Rds. intersection.

Leased to BellSouth, 1100 Abernathy Rd., Suite 414, Atlanta, GA 30328. Phone: 770-481-2990.

Jacksonville—WLX-651 (Channel B4). U. of North Florida, 4567 St. Johns Bluff Rd. S, Jacksonville, FL 32216-6699. Phone: 904-646-2710. Fax: 904-646-2505. Authorized power: 100-w. Antenna: 600-ft. above ground. Lat. 30° 16' 53", long. 81° 34' 15". Transmitter: 400-ft. N of Hogan County & Old Hogan County Rds. intersection. Equipment: Emcee transmitter; Andrew antenna.

Jacksonville—WNC-678 (Channels D-1-4). WJCT Inc., 100 Festival Park Ave., Jacksonville, FL 32202. Phone: 904-353-7770. Fax: 904-358-6345. Authorized power: 100-w. each. Antenna: 613-ft. above ground. Lat. 30° 16' 53", long. 81° 34' 15". Transmitter: 400-ft. N of Hogan County & Old Hogan County Rds. Equipment: Emcee transmitter; Andrew antenna.

Jacksonville—WHR-541 (Channels E-1-4). WJCT Inc., 100 Festival Park Ave., Jacksonville, FL 32202. Phone: 904-353-7770. Fax: 904-358-6345. Authorized power: 10-w. each. Antenna: 260-ft. above ground. Lat. 30° 19' 10", long. 81° 38' 18". Transmitter: 2037 Main St.

Jacksonville—WHR-858 (Channels G-1-2). Jacksonville U., Howard Administration Bldg., 2800 University Blvd., Jacksonville, FL 32211. Authorized power: 50-w. each. Antenna: 653-ft. above ground. Lat. 30° 16' 53", long. 81° 34' 15". Transmitter: 500-ft. N of Hogan County & Old Hogan County Rds. intersection. Requests change to 100-w. each, 600-ft. above ground, transmitter to 400-ft. N of Hogan County & Old Hogan County Rds.

Jacksonville—WLX-930 (Channels G-3-4). U. of North Florida, 4567 St. Johns Bluff Rd. S, Jacksonville, FL 32216-6699. Phone: 904-646-2710. Fax: 904-646-2505. Authorized power: 15.8-w. each. Antenna: 220-ft. above ground. Lat. 30° 16' 27", long. 81° 30' 28". Transmitter: 4567 St. Johns Bluff Rd. S. Equipment: Emcee transmitter; Andrew antenna.

Lake City—WLX-966 (Channels C-1-4). Lake City Community College, U.S. Hwy. 90 E, Lake City, FL 32025. Authorized power: 50-w. each. Antenna: 489-ft. above ground. Lat. 30° 14' 40", long. 82° 40' 11". Transmitter: U.S. 41 & I-10. Equipment: Emcee transmitter; Andrew antenna.

Lakeland—WLX-275 (Channels A-1-4). Polk Community College, 999 Ave. H NE, Winter Haven, FL 33881. Phone: 941-297-1041. Fax: 941-297-1065.

Web site: http://www.polk.cc.fl.us.

Authorized power: 50-w. each. Antenna: 399-ft. above ground. Lat. 27° 59' 35", long. 81° 53' 23". Transmitter: 0.4-mi. SW of Lakeland. Equipment: ITS transmitter; Andrew antenna.

Leased to American Telecasting Inc., 5575 Tech Center Dr., Suite 300, Colorado Springs, CO 80919. Phone: 407-648-0106.

Lakeland—WLX-385 (Channels B-1-4). Radio Training Network Inc., Suite 104, 5015 S. Florida Ave., Lakeland, FL 33813. Phone: 941-644-3464. Fax: 941-646-5326.

E-mail: gosrad@aol.com.

Authorized power: 50-w. each. Antenna: 399-ft. above ground. Lat. 27° 59' 35", long. 81° 53' 23". Transmitter: 0.4-mi. SW of Lakeland. Equipment: Comwave transmitter; Andrew antenna.

Leased to BellSouth Entertainment Inc., 1100 Abernathy Rd., No. 414, Atlanta, GA 30328. Phone: 407-648-8595.

Lakeland—WLX-270 (Channels D-1-4). Southeastern College of the Assemblies of God Inc., 100 Longfellow Blvd., Lakeland, FL 33801. Authorized power: 50-w. each. Antenna: 399-ft. above ground. Lat. 27° 59' 35", long. 81° 53' 23". Transmitter: 0.4-mi. SW of Lakeland. Equipment: ITS transmitter; Andrew antenna.

Lakeland—WHR-943 (Channels G-1-4). U. of South Florida, 8111 College Pkwy., Fort Myers, FL 33901. Phone: 813-432-5531. Authorized power: 50-w. each. Antenna: 399-ft. above ground. Lat. 27° 59' 35", long. 81° 53' 23". Transmitter: 0.4-mi. SW of Lakeland. Equipment: ITS transmitter; Andrew antenna.

Lakeland-Winterhaven—WLX-272 (Channels C-1-4). Diocese of Orlando, 321 E. Robinson St., Orlando, FL 32801. Authorized power: 50-w. each. Antenna: 399-ft. above ground. Lat. 27° 59' 35", long. 81° 53' 23". Transmitter: 0.4-mi. SW of Lakeland. Equipment: ITS transmitter; Andrew antenna.

Leesburg—WLX-240 (Channel B-1). District Board of Trustees, Sumter Community College, 9501 U.S. Hwy. 441, Leesburg, FL 34788. Phone: 352-365-3566. Fax: 352-365-3501.

E-mail: longordt@lscc.cc.fl.us.

Web site: http://www.lscc.cc.fl.us.

Authorized power: 1-w. Antenna: 99-ft. above ground. Lat. 28° 49' 41", long. 81° 47' 49". Transmitter: Lake Sumter Community College Campus Multi-Purpose Bldg. 9501, Hwy. 441. Equipment: Emcee transmitter; Mark/Lance antenna. Requests change to 101-ft. above ground.

Leesburg—WHR-770 (Channels D-1-4). Lake Sumter Community College, 9501 Hwy. 441, Leesburg, FL 34788. Phone: 352-365-3566. Fax: 352-365-3501.

E-mail: longordt@lscc.cc.fl.us.

Web site: http://www.lscc.cc.fl.us.

Authorized power: 10-w. each. Antenna: 275-ft. above ground. Lat. 28° 48' 54", long. 81° 52' 38". Transmitter: 425 N. 3rd St. Equipment: ITS Comwave transmitter; Bogner antenna.

Loxahatchee—KZB-30 (Channels H-1-3). Palm Beach County School Board, 3304 Forest Hill Blvd., West Palm Beach, FL 33406-5813. Phone: 407-738-2702. Fax: 407-738-2901. Authorized power: 10-w. each. Antenna: 250-ft. above ground. Lat. 26° 41' 42", long. 80° 16' 08". Transmitter: 0.75-mi. N of Hwys. 441 & 98. Equipment: Emcee transmitter; Andrew antenna.

Marianna—WHR-879 (Channels A-1-4). Panhandle Area Educational Consortium, 753 West Blvd., Chipley, FL 32428. Phone: 904-638-6131. Fax: 904-638-6135.

E-mail: everitr@mail.firn.edu.

Web site: http://www.paec.org.

Authorized power: 10-w. each. Antenna: 307-ft. above ground. Lat. 30° 47' 07", long. 85° 14' 29". Transmitter: Frank M. Golson Elementary School, 800 2nd Ave.

Leased to Wireless One Inc., 5551 Corporate Blvd., Suite 2K, Baton Rouge, LA 70808. Phone: 504-926-7778.

Marion County—WHR-486 (Channels A-1-4). Marion County School Board, 512 S.E. 3rd St., Ocala, FL 32671. Phone: 904-620-7763. Fax: 904-620-7788. Authorized power: 50-w. each. Antenna: 606-ft. above ground. Lat. 29° 10' 59", long. 82° 02' 15". Transmitter: 101 S.E. 68th Court. Equipment: Comwave transmitter; Andrew antenna.

Melbourne—WNC-267 (Channels B-1-4). Inc. North American Catholic Educational Programming Foundation. Authorized power: 50-w. each. Antenna: 496-ft. above ground. Lat. 28° 08' 15", long. 80° 42' 11". Transmitter: 1865 Harlock Rd. Equipment: Emcee transmitter; Bogner antenna.

Melbourne—WLX-990 (Channels D-1-4). Especially for Children Inc., 1230 Banana River Dr., Indian Harbor Beach, FL 32937. Authorized power: 50-w. each. Antenna: 488-ft. above ground. Lat. 28° 08' 15", long. 80° 42' 11". Transmitter: 1865 Harlock Rd. Equipment: Emcee transmitter; Bogner antenna.

Miami—WHA-956 (Channels A-1-4). School Board of Dade County, 172 N.E. 15th St., Miami, FL 33132. Phone: 305-995-2259. Fax: 305-995-2299. Authorized power: 50-w. each. Antenna: 527-ft. above ground. Lat. 25° 46' 30", long. 80° 11' 49". Transmitter: 111 N.W. First Ave. Equipment: ITS transmitter; Bogner antenna.

Leased to National Wireless Holdings Inc., 233 N. Garrard, Rantoul, IL 61866. Phone: 217-893-8730.

Miami—WHR-866 (Channels B-1-4). Friends of WLRN Inc., 172 N.E. 15th St., Miami, FL 33132. Phone: 305-995-2259. Fax: 305-995-2299. Authorized power: 50-w. each. Antenna: 527-ft. above ground. Lat. 25° 46' 30", long. 80° 11' 49". Transmitter: 111 N.W. First Ave. Equipment: ITS transmitter; Bogner antenna.

Leased to National Wireless Holdings Inc., 233 N. Garrard St., Rantoul, IL 62866. Phone: 217-893-8730.

Miami—WHG-230 (Channels C-1-4). School Board of Dade County, 172 N.E. 15th St., Miami, FL 33132. Phone: 305-995-2259. Fax: 305-995-2290. Authorized power: 50-w. each. Antenna: 525-ft. above ground. Lat. 25° 46' 30", long. 80° 11' 49". Transmitter: 111 N.W. First Ave. Equipment: ITS transmitter; Bogner antenna.

Leased to National Wireless Holdings Inc., 233 N. Garrard, Rantoul, IL 61866. Phone: 217-893-8730.

Miami—WHR-790 (Channels D-1-4). Southern Florida Instructional TV Inc., 172 N.E. 15th St., Miami, FL 33132. Phone: 305-995-2259. Fax: 305-995-2299. Authorized power: 50-w. each. Antenna: 527-ft. above ground. Lat. 25° 46' 30", long. 80° 11' 49". Transmitter: 111 N.W. First Ave. Equipment: ITS transmitter; Bogner antenna.

Leased to National Wireless Holdings Inc., 233 N. Garrard, Rantoul, IL 61866. Phone: 217-893-8730.

Miami—KTB-84 (Channels F-1-4). School Board of Dade County, 172 N.E. 15th St., Miami, FL 33132. Phone: 305-995-2259. Fax: 305-995-2299.

Web site: http://www.wlrn.org.

Authorized power: 10-w. each. Antenna: 527-ft. above ground. Lat. 25° 46' 30", long. 80° 11' 49". Transmitter: 111 N.W. First Ave. Equipment: Emcee transmitter; Bogner antenna.

Leased to National Wireless Holdings Inc., 233 N. Garrard, Rantoul, IL 61866. Phone: 217-893-8730.

Miami—KTB-85 (Channels F-1-4). School Board of Dade County, 172 N.E. 15th St., Miami, FL 33132. Phone: 305-995-2259. Fax: 305-995-2249.

Web site: http://www.wlrn.org.

Authorized power: 200-w. each. Antenna: 774-ft. above ground. Lat. 25° 46' 20", long. 80° 11' 20". Transmitter: 200 S. Biscayne Blvd. Equipment: Comwave transmitter; Andrew antenna.

New Smyrna Beach—WLX-780 (Channels G-1-4). Daytona Beach Community College, Box 2811, 1200 W. International Speedway Blvd., Daytona Beach, FL 32120-2811. Phone: 904-254-4413. Fax: 904-947-3175. Authorized power: 10-w. each. Antenna: 152-ft. above ground. Lat. 28° 59' 52", long. 80° 55' 34". Transmitter: 940 10th St. Equipment: ITS transmitter; Bogner antenna.

Ocala—WLX-593 (Channels B-1-4). North American Catholic Educational Programming Foundation Inc. Phone: 401-729-0900. Authorized power: 10-w. each. Antenna: 603-ft. above ground. Lat. 29° 10' 59", long. 82° 02' 15". Transmitter: 101 S.E. 68th Court. Equipment: Comwave transmitter; Andrew antenna.

Ocala—WLX-279 (Channels C-1-4). The School Board of Marion County, 512 S.E. 3rd St., Ocala, FL 32671. Phone: 904-620-7763. Fax: 904-620-7788. Authorized power: 10-w. each. Antenna: 300-ft. above ground. Lat. 29° 10' 57", long. 82° 08' 00". Equipment: Emcee transmitter; Andrew antenna. Requests change to 50-w. each., 606-ft. above ground, lat. 29° 10' 59", long. 82° 02' 15"; transmitter to 101 S.E. 68th Court. Equipment: Comwave transmitter.

Ocala—WND-218 (Channels D-1-4). Tulane U. of Louisiana, 6823 St. Charles Ave., New Orleans, LA 70118. Authorized power: 10-w. each. Antenna: 600-ft. above ground. Lat. 29° 10' 59", long. 82° 02' 15". Transmitter: 101 S.E. 68th Court. Equipment: Comwave transmitter; Andrew antenna.

Ocala—WLX-832 (Channels G-1-4). The School Board of Marion County, 512 S.E. 3rd. St., Ocala, FL 32671. Authorized power: 50-w. each. Antenna: 606-ft. above ground. Lat. 29° 10' 59", long. 82° 02' 15". Transmitter: 101 S.E. 68th Court. Comwave transmitter. Equipment: Comwave transmitter; Andrew antenna.

Oldsmar—WFW-689 (Channels A-2-3). St. Petersburg Junior College, Box 13489, St. Petersburg, FL 33733. Phone: 727-394-6126. Fax: 727-394-6124.

E-mail: steersm@mail.spjc.cc.fl.us.

Web site: http://www.spjc.edu.

Authorized power: 100-w. each. Antenna: 636-ft. above ground. Lat. 28° 02' 20", long. 82° 39' 29". Transmitter: 105 Dunbar Ave., Oldsmar, FL. Equipment: Comwave transmitter; Andrew antenna.

Leased to Videotron Inc., 6840 Ulmerton Rd., Largo, FL 33771. Phone: 727-532-3100.

Oldsmar—WGV-752 (Channel D-2-3). St. Petersburg Junior College, Box 13489, St. Petersburg, FL 33733. Phone: 727-394-6126. Fax: 727-394-6124.

E-mail: steersm@mail.spjc.cc.fl.us.

Web site: http://www.spjc.edu.

Authorized power: 100-w. each. Antenna: 636-ft. above ground. Lat. 28° 02' 20", long. 82° 39' 49". Transmitter: 105 Dunbar Ave., Oldsmar, FL. Equipment: Comwave transmitter; Andrew antenna.

Leased to Videotron Inc., 6840 Ulmerton Rd., Largo, FL 33771. Phone: 727-532-3100.

Old Town—WHR-976 (Channels G-1-4). Tri-County Media Associates, 808 N. Main St., Chiefland, FL 32626. Phone: 352-493-6037.

Fax: 352-493-6038. Authorized power: 50-w. each. Antenna: 377-ft. above ground. Lat. 29° 33' 32", long. 82° 58' 19". Transmitter: 0.8-mi. E of Hwy. 349, Old Town. Equipment: Emcee transmitter; Andrew antenna.

Leased to Nucentrix Broadband Networks, 200 Chisolm Place, Suite 200, Plano, TX 75075. Phone: 972-423-9494. Fax: 972-423-0819.

Orange City—WHR-499 (Channel G-1). U. of Central Florida, Box 25000, Orlando, FL 32816. Phone: 407-823-6778. Fax: 407-823-6710.
E-mail: joel@pegasus.cc.ucf.edu.
Web site: http://www.ucf.edu.
Authorized power: 10-w. Antenna: 225-ft. above ground. Lat. 28° 53' 29", long. 81° 17' 06". Transmitter: High Banks Rd., Daytona Beach Community College, Debory Campus. Equipment: Emcee transmitter; Anixter antenna.
Leased to American Telecasting Inc., 4700 L.B. McLeod Rd., Orlando, FL 32811 6433. Phone: 407-648-0106.

Orlando—WHR-536 (Channels A-1-4). Valencia Community College, Box 3028, Orlando, FL 32802. Phone: 407-299-5000. Fax: 407-299-5000. Authorized power: 10-w. each. Antenna: 300-ft. above ground. Lat. 28° 31' 22", long. 81° 28' 00". Transmitter: 1800 S. Kirkman Rd.

Orlando—WLX-362 (Channels B-1-4). Hispanic Information & Telecommunications Network Inc., 3rd Floor, 449 Broadway, New York, NY 10013. Phone: 212-966-5660. Fax: 212-966-5725.
E-mail: email@hitn.org.
Web site: http://www.hitn.org.
Authorized power: 50-w. each. Antenna: 420-ft. above ground. Lat. 28° 32' 22", long. 81° 22' 46". Transmitter: 200 S. Orange Ave. Equipment: ITS transmitter; Andrew antenna.
Leased to American Telecasting Inc., 5575 Tech Center Dr., Suite 300, Colorado Springs, CO 80919. Phone: 719-260-5010.

Orlando—WHR-493 (Channels C-1-4). U. of Central Florida, LIB 107, 4000 Central Florida Blvd., Orlando, FL 32816-2191. Phone: 407-823-2571. Fax: 407-823-2109. Authorized power: 50-w. each. Antenna: 403-ft. above ground. Lat. 28° 32' 22", long. 81° 22' 46". Transmitter: 200 S. Orange Ave. Equipment: ITS transmitter; Andrew antenna.

Orlando—WLX-309 (Channels D-1-4). U. of Central Florida, 4000 Central Florida Blvd., Orlando, FL 32816. Phone: 407-823-2571. Fax: 407-823-2109. Authorized power: 50-w. each. Antenna: 403-ft. above ground. Lat. 28° 32' 22", long. 81° 22' 46". Transmitter: 200 S. Orange Ave. Equipment: ITS transmitter; Andrew antenna.

Orlando—WLX-773 (Channels G-1-4). Northern Arizona U. Foundation, Box 5751, Flagstaff, AZ 86011. Authorized power: 50-w. each. Antenna: 440-ft. above ground. Lat. 28° 32' 22", long. 81° 22' 46". Transmitter: 200 S. Orange Ave. Equipment: ITS transmitter; Andrew antenna.

Palatka—WLX-242 (Channel G-1-3-4). Putnam County School District, 200 S. 7th St., Palatka, FL 32177. Authorized power: 10-w. Antenna: 300-ft. above ground. Lat. 29° 36' 47", long. 81° 40' 25". Transmitter: Palatka Cablevision Tower, Cable Tower Rd. Equipment: Emcee transmitter; Andrew antenna.

Palatka—WLX-443 (Channel G-2). Putnam County School District, 200 S. 7th St., Palatka, FL 32177. Authorized power: 1-w. Antenna: 44-ft. above ground. Lat. 29° 38' 45", long. 81° 38' 11". Transmitter: Campbell Administration Bldg., 200 S. 7th St. Equipment: Emcee transmitter; Anixter-Mark antenna.

Palm Beach—WLX-269 (Channels A-1-4). Florida Board of Regents, Florida Atlantic U., Bldg. 4, Rm. 239, 777 Glades Rd., Boca Raton, FL 33431. Authorized power: 2-w. each. Antenna: 82-ft. above ground. Lat. 26° 50' 38", long. 80° 05' 01". Transmitter: Palm Beach Community College North Campus, Palm Beach Gardens. Equipment: Comwave transmitter; Andrew antenna.

Palm Beach County—WHR-896 (Channels B-1-4). Florida Board of Regents, Florida Atlantic U., Bldg. 4, Rm. 239, 777 Glades Rd., Boca Raton, FL 33431. Authorized power: 2-w. each. Antenna: 182-ft. above ground. Lat. 26° 31' 22", long. 80° 05' 29". Transmitter: Palm Beach County ITV Center, 505 Congress Ave., Boynton Beach. Equipment: Comwave transmitter; Andrew antenna. Requests change to 15-w., 396-ft. above ground.

Palm Beach Gardens—WHR-901 (Channels C-1-4). Florida Atlantic U., 500 N.W. 20th St., Boca Raton, FL 33431. Authorized power: 10-w. each. Antenna: 224-ft. above ground. Lat. 26° 46' 50", long. 80° 05' 41". Transmitter: SE Corner of Blue Heron Blvd. & Military Trail. Equipment: Comwave transmitter; Andrew antenna. Requests change to 374-ft. above ground, lat. 26° 46' 17", long. 80° 05' 55"; transmitter to 2455 Port West Blvd.

Panama City—WLX-265 (Channels B-1-4). Bay District Instructional Media Services, 1110 W. 17th St., Panama City, FL 32405. Phone: 850-872-4756. Fax: 850-872-4887.
E-mail: toolebg@mail.bay.k12.fl.us.
Web site: http://www.bay.k12.fl.us/district/bdims/.
Authorized power: 10-w. each. Antenna: 204-ft. above ground. Lat. 30° 11' 06", long. 85° 43' 36". Transmitter: Gulf Coast Community College, U.S. Hwy. 98. Equipment: Emcee transmitter; Andrew antenna.
Leased to Wireless One, Box 97209, Jackson, MS 39288. Phone: 888-947-3663.

Panama City—WNC-200 (Channels C-1-4). Bay Communications Foundation Inc. Authorized power: 50-w. each. Antenna: 450-ft. above ground. Lat. 30° 19' 43", long. 85° 41' 25". Transmitter: Bay County. Equipment: ITS transmitter; Andrew antenna.

Panama City—WHR-801 (Channels G-1-4). Panhandle Area Educational Consortium, 411 West Blvd., Chipley, FL 32428. Phone: 904-638-6131. Fax: 904-638-6135.
E-mail: everitr@mail.firn.edu.
Web site: http://www.paec.org.
Authorized power: 50-w. each. Antenna: 499-ft. above ground. Lat. 30° 19' 43", long. 85° 41' 25".
Leased to Wireless One Inc., 5551 Corporate Blvd., Suite 2K, Baton Rouge, LA 70808. Phone: 504-926-7778.

Pensacola—WNC-236 (Channels A-1-4). Santa Rosa County School Board, 603 Canal St., Milton, FL 32570. Phone: 904-983-5110. Fax: 904-983-5114.
E-mail: kosticl@mail.santarosa.k12.fl.us.
Authorized power: 50-w. each. Antenna: 493-ft. above ground. Lat. 30° 39' 23", long. 87° 11' 42". Transmitter: WXBM-FM tower, 1687 Quintet Rd. Equipment: Emcee transmitter; Bogner antenna. Requests change to 496-ft. above ground.
Leased to Wireless One, 8804 A Grow Dr., Pensacola, FL 32514. Phone: 904-474-1110.

Pensacola—WNC-237 (Channels B-1-4). Escambia Christian Schools Authorized power: 50-w. each. Antenna: 499-ft. above ground. Lat. 30° 39' 23", long. 87° 11' 42". Transmitter: WXBM-FM tower, 1687 Quintet Rd. Equipment: Emcee transmitter; Bogner antenna. Requests change to 496-ft. above ground; Andrew antenna.

Pensacola—WNC-231 (Channels C-1-2 & D-3-4). Troy State U., No. 247, Adams Administrative Bldg., Troy, AL 36082. Authorized power: 50-w. each. Antenna: 496-ft. above ground. Lat. 30° 39' 23", long. 87° 11' 42". Transmitter: WXBM-FM tower, 1687 Quintet Rd. Equipment: Emcee transmitter; Bogner antenna.
Leased to Wireless One, 5551 Corporate Blvd., Suite 2K, Baton Rouge, LA 70809. Phone: 504-926-7778.

Pensacola—WNC-238 (Channels C-3-4 & D1). Troy State U., Adams Administration Bldg., Room 247, Troy, AL 36082. Authorized power: 50-w. each. Antenna: 496-ft. above ground. Lat. 30° 39' 23", long. 87° 11' 42". Transmitter: WXBM-FM tower, 1687 Quintet Rd. Equipment: Emcee transmitter; Andrew antenna. Requests change to 499-ft. above ground.

Port St. Lucie—WLX-391 (Channels A-1-4). School Board of St. Lucie County Florida, 2909 Delaware Ave., Fort Pierce, FL 34947. Phone: 561-468-5160. Fax: 561-468-5181. Authorized power: 50-w. each. Antenna: 497-ft. above ground. Lat. 27° 19' 27", long. 80° 18' 49". Transmitter: 1100 Dryer Rd. Equipment: Comwave transmitter; Andrew antenna.
Leased to Wireless Broadcast Systems Inc., 8423 S. U.S. Rte. One, Box 7307, Port St. Luice, FL 34985. Phone: 561-871-1688.

Port St. Lucie—WLX-392 (Channels B-1-4). School Board of St. Lucie County Florida, 2909 Delaware Ave., Port Pierce, FL 34947. Phone: 561-468-5160. Fax: 561-468-5181. Authorized power: 50-w. each. Antenna: 497-ft. above ground. Lat. 27° 19' 27", long. 80° 18' 49". Transmitter: 1100 Dryer Rd. Equipment: Emcee transmitter; Andrew antenna.
Leased to Wireless Broadcast Systems Inc., 8423 S. U.S. Rte. One, Box 7307, Port St. Lucie, FL 34985. Phone: 561-871-0155.

Port St. Lucie—WLX-943 (Channels C-1-4). Indian River Community College, 3209 Virginia Ave., Fort Pierce, FL 34981. Authorized power: 50-w. each. Antenna: 497-ft. above ground. Lat. 27° 19' 27", long. 80° 18' 49". Transmitter: 1100 Dryer Rd. Equipment: Emcee transmitter; Andrew antenna.
Leased to Coastal Wireless Cable Television, 8423 S. U.S. Rte. One, Box 7307, Port St. Lucie, FL 34985. Phone: 561-871-0344.

Port St. Lucie—WLX-941 (Channels D-1-4). Indian River Community College, 3209 Virginia Ave., Fort Pierce, FL 34981. Authorized power: 50-w. each. Antenna: 497-ft. above ground. Lat. 27° 19' 27", long. 80° 18' 49". Transmitter: 1100 Dryer Rd. Equipment: Emcee transmitter; Andrew antenna.
Leased to Coastal Wireless Cable Television, 8423 S. U.S. Rte. One, Box 7307, Port St. Lucie, FL 34985. Phone: 561-871-0344.

Riverview—WHR-820 (Channels B-1-4). U. of South Florida, 8111 College Pkwy., Fort Myers, FL 33901. Phone: 813-432-5531. Authorized power: 10-w. each. Antenna: 299-ft. above ground. Lat. 27° 28' 30", long. 82° 31' 47". Transmitter: Matzke Complex, 2800 27th St. E, Bradenton. Equipment: Emcee transmitter; Andrew antenna.

Riverview—WHR-736 (Channels D-1-4). U. of South Florida, 8111 College Pkwy., Fort Myers, FL 33901. Phone: 813-432-5531. Authorized power: 10-w. each. Antenna: 1020-ft. above ground. Lat. 27° 50' 53", long. 82° 15' 48". Transmitter: 4-mi. E of Riverview on Boyette Rd. Equipment: Emcee transmitter; Anixter-Mark antenna.

Riviera Beach—KZB-29 (Channels G-1-4). Palm Beach County School Board, 3304 Forest Hill Blvd., West Palm Beach, FL 33406-5813. Phone: 407-738-2702. Fax: 407-738-2901. Authorized power: 10-w. each. Antenna: 400-ft. above ground. Lat. 26° 46' 10", long. 80° 05' 51". Transmitter: Riviera Beach. Equipment: Emcee transmitter; Andrew antenna.

Sarasota—WLX-404 (Channels C-1-4). Sarasota School Board, 1960 Landings Blvd., Sarasota, FL 34231-3302. Phone: 941-361-6355. Fax: 941-361-6358. Authorized power: 10-w. each. Antenna: 299-ft. above ground. Lat. 27° 17' 08", long. 82° 30' 10".

Sebring—WNC-902 (Channels B-1-4). South Florida Community College, 600 W. College Dr., Avon Park, FL 33825. Phone: 941-453-6661. Fax: 941-382-3111.
E-mail: esfahani-r@popmail.fivn.edu.
Web site: http://www.sfcc.cc.fl.us.
Authorized power: 10-w. each. Antenna: 335-ft. above ground. Lat. 27° 29' 39", long. 81° 25' 00". Transmitter: 1000 Sheriff's Tower Rd. Equipment: Emcee transmitter; Andrew antenna.

Sebring—WNC-905 (Channels G-1-4). Views on Learning Inc., 200 Kenyon Ave., Elkhart, IN 46516. Authorized power: 10-w. each. Antenna: 335-ft. above ground. Lat. 27° 29' 39", long. 81° 25' 00". Transmitter: 1000 Sheriff's Tower Rd. Equipment: Emcee transmitter; Andrew antenna.

Shalimar—WNC-884 (Channels A-1-4). Walton County School District, Suite 5, 145 Park St., De Funiak Springs, FL 32433. Authorized power: 50-w. each. Antenna: 276-ft. above ground. Lat. 30° 27' 03", lat. 86° 34' 17". Transmitter: Shalimar Elementary School, Elgin Pkwy. Equipment: Emcee transmitter; Andrew antenna.

Shalimar—WLX-834 (Channels B-1-4). Okaloosa County School Board, 461 W. School Ave., Crestview, FL 32536. Phone: 904-689-7138. Fax: 904-689-7140. Authorized power: 50-w. each. Antenna: 276-ft. above ground. Lat. 30° 27' 03", long. 86° 34' 17". Transmitter: Shalimar Elementary School, Elgin Pkwy.

Equipment: Emcee transmitter; Andrew antenna.

Leased to Wireless One of Fort Walton Inc., 11301 Industriplex Blvd., Suite 4, Baton Rouge, LA 70809. Phone: 504-293-5000.

Shalimar—WLX-837 (Channels C-1-4). Okaloosa Communication Foundation Inc., 120 Lowery Place, Fort Walton, FL 32548. Phone: 904-689-7138. Fax: 904-689-7140. Authorized power: 50-w. each. Antenna: 297-ft. above ground. Lat. 30° 29' 59", long. 86° 34' 27". Transmitter: Elgin Pkwy. at Shalimar. Equipment: Emcee transmitter; Andrew antenna. Requests change to 85-ft. above ground, lat. 30° 27' 03", long. 86° 34' 17"; transmitter to Shalimar Elementary School, Elgin Pkwy.

Leased to Wireless One of Fort Walton, Inc., 11301 Industriplex Blvd., Suite 4, Baton Rouge, LA 70809. Phone: 504-293-5000.

Shalimar—WLX-931 (Channels D-1-4). Okaloosa Walton Community College, 100 College Blvd., Niceville, FL 32578. Phone: 850-678-5111. Fax: 850-729-5295.

E-mail: tripplg@owcc.net.

Web site: http://www.owcc.cc.fl.us.

Authorized power: 50-w. each. Antenna: 318-ft. above ground. Lat. 30° 27' 03", long. 86° 34' 17". Transmitter: Shalimar Elementary School, Eglin Pkwy. Equipment: Emcee transmitter; Andrew antenna.

Leased to Wireless One, Box 97209, Jackson, MS 39288. Phone: 601-933-6767.

Shalimar—WNC-885 (Channels G-1-4). Okaloosa-Walton Community College, 100 College Blvd., Niceville, FL 32578. Phone: 850-678-5111. Fax: 850-729-5295.

E-mail: tripplg@owcc.net.

Web site: http://www.owcc.cc.fl.us.

Authorized power: 50-w. each. Antenna: 318-ft. above ground. Lat. 30° 27' 03", long. 86° 34' 17". Transmitter: Shalimar Elementary School, Eglin Pkwy. Equipment: Emcee transmitter; Andrew antenna.

Leased to Wireless One, Box 97209, Jackson, MS 39288. Phone: 601-933-6767.

Spring Hill—WLX-794 (Channels G-1-4). Eckerd Family Youth Alternative Inc., 3112 Friendship Rd., Milton, FL 32570. Phone: 904-675-4512. Fax: 904-675-1230. Authorized power: 50-w. each. Antenna: 496-ft. above ground. Lat. 30° 39' 23", long. 87° 11' 42". Transmitter: WXBM-FM Tower. Equipment: Emcee transmitter; Bogner antenna.

St. Petersburg—WLX-227 (Channels A-3-4). School Board of Pinellas County, 1960 E. Druid Rd., Clearwater, FL 34618. Authorized power: 100-w. each. Antenna: 640-ft. above ground. Lat. 28° 02' 20", long. 82° 39' 29". Transmitter: 103 Dunbar Ave., Oldsmar. Equipment: Comwave transmitter; Andrew antenna.

St. Petersburg—WHG-239 (Channels F-1-2). U. of South Florida, 8111 College Pkwy., Fort Myers, FL 33901. Phone: 813-432-5531. Authorized power: 10-w. each. Antenna: 287-ft. above ground. Lat. 27° 46' 14", long. 82° 38' 03". Transmitter: Bayfront Towers, One Beach Dr. SE.

Tallahassee—WHF-229 (Channels A-1-2). Leon County School Board, 2757 W. Pensacola St., Tallahassee, FL 32304. Phone: 904-922-0199. Fax: 904-487-6710.

E-mail: bigal@dmc.leon.k12.fl.us.

Authorized power: 50-w. each. Antenna: 607-ft. above ground. Lat. 30° 29' 32", long. 84° 17' 13". Transmitter: 123 Ridgeland Rd. Equipment: Comwave transmitter; Andrew antenna.

Leased to Wireless One Inc., Box 97209, Jackson, MS 39288. Phone: 601-933-6767.

Tallahassee—WHR-959 (Channels A-3-4). Leon County School Board, 2757 W. Pensacola St., Tallahassee, FL 32304. Phone: 904-922-0199. Fax: 904-487-6710.

Web site: http://www.dmc.leon.k12.fl.us.

Authorized power: 1-w. each. Antenna: 186-ft. above ground. Lat. 30° 26' 27", long. 84° 20' 06". Transmitter: 3955 W. Pensacola St. Equipment: Emcee transmitter.

Tallahassee—WNC-856 (Channels B-1-4). Wakulla County School Board, 126 High Dr., Crawfordville, FL 32326. Authorized power: 50-w. each. Antenna: 607-ft. above ground. Lat. 30° 29' 32", long. 84° 17' 13". Transmitter: 123 Ridgeland Rd. Equipment: Comwave transmitter; Andrew antenna.

Tallahassee—WHR-748 (Channels G-1-2). Gadsden County School Board, 35 Experiment Rd., Quincy, FL 32351. Phone: 904-627-9651. Fax: 904-627-2760. Authorized power: 50-w. each. Antenna: 607-ft. above ground. Lat. 30° 29' 32", long. 84° 17' 13". Transmitter: 123 Ridgeland Rd. Equipment: Comwave transmitter; Andrew antenna.

Tallahassee—WHR-757 (Channels G-3-4). Jefferson County School Board, 1490 W. Washington St., Monticello, FL 32344. Phone: 850-342-0100. Fax: 850-342-0108. Authorized power: 50-w. each. Antenna: 607-ft. above ground. Lat. 30° 29' 32", long. 84° 17' 13". Transmitter: 123 Ridgeland Rd. Equipment: Comwave transmitter; Andrew antenna.

Leased to Phipps Wireless Cable, 1306 Thomasville Rd., Tallahassee, FL 32303.

Tampa—WHF-223 (Channels B-1-2). U. of South Florida, 8111 College Pkwy., Fort Myers, FL 33901. Phone: 813-432-5531. Authorized power: 10-w. each. Antenna: 355-ft. above ground. Lat. 28° 04' 04", long. 82° 24' 56". Transmitter: U. of South Florida campus, 4202 Fowler Ave.

Tampa—WHR-518 (Channels C-1-4). Network for Instructional TV Inc., Suite 110, 11490 Commerce Park Dr., Reston, VA 20191. Phone: 703-860-9200. Fax: 703-860-9237. Authorized power: 100-w. each. Antenna: 640-ft. above ground. Lat. 28° 02' 20", long. 82° 39' 29". Transmitter: 103 Dunbar Ave. Equipment: ITS transmitter; Andrew antenna.

Leased to Videotron-Bay Area, 18940 U.S. 19 N, Clearwater, FL 34624. Phone: 813-532-3100.

Tampa—WHB-828 (Channels G-1-4). U. of South Florida, 8111 College Pkwy., Fort Myers, FL 33901. Phone: 813-432-5531. Lat. 28° 04' 04", long. 82° 24' 56".

Venice—WNC-778 (Channels A-1-4). Manatee Community College, 5840 26th St. W, Bradenton, FL 84207. Authorized power: 50-w. each. Antenna: 571-ft. above ground. Lat. 27° 07' 56", long. 82° 23' 43". Transmitter: 2000 Border Rd. Equipment: ITS transmitter; Bogner antenna.

Venice—WND-370 (Channels B-1-4). U. of South Florida, 4202 E. Fowler Ave., Tampa, FL 33620. Phone: 813-974-7984. Fax: 813-974-7272.

Web site: http://www.outreach.usf.edu.

Authorized power: 50-w. each. Antenna: 305-ft. above ground. Lat. 27° 07' 56", long. 82° 23' 43". Transmitter: 2000 Border Rd. Equipment: Emcee transmitter; Andrew antenna.

Leased to Wireless Cable of Florida, 1950 Landings Blvd., Sarasota, FL 34231.

Venice—WNC-980 (Channels D-1-4). U. of Sarasota, 5250 17th St., Sarasota, FL 34325. Authorized power: 50-w. each. Antenna: 322-ft. above ground. Lat. 27° 07' 56", long. 82° 23' 43". Transmitter: 2000 Border Rd. Equipment: Emcee transmitter; Andrew antenna.

Venice—WND-369 (Channels G-1-4). Out-of-Door Academy, 444 Reid St., Sarasota, FL 34242. Phone: 941-349-3223. Fax: 941-349-8133.

E-mail: dbrock@oda.edu.

Web site: http://www.oda.edu.

Authorized power: 50-w. each. Antenna: 318-ft. above ground. Lat. 27° 07' 56", long. 82° 23' 43". Transmitter: 2000 Border Rd. Equipment: ITS transmitter; Bogner antenna.

Leased to Wireless Cable of Florida Inc., 2477 Stickney Point Rd., Suite 201B, Sarasota, FL 34231.

West Palm Beach—WHR-973 (Channels G-1-2). School Board of Palm Beach County, 505 S. Congress Ave., Boynton Beach, FL 33426. Phone: 561-738-2747. Fax: 561-738-2901. Authorized power: 1-w. each. Antenna: 168-ft. above ground. Lat. 26° 42' 55", long. 80° 03' 12". Transmitter: Dixie Hwy. & 3rd St. intersection. Equipment: Emcee transmitter; Andrew antenna.

West Palm Beach—WHR-994 (Channels G-3-4). School Board of Palm Beach County, 505 S. Congress Ave., Boynton Beach, FL 33427. Phone: 561-738-2747. Fax: 561-738-2901. Authorized power: 1-w. each. Antenna: 154-ft. above ground. Lat. 26° 41' 28", long. 80° 05' 55". Transmitter: Emergency Operations Center. Equipment: Emcee transmitter; Andrew antenna.

Wewahitchka—WHR-878 (Channels A-1-4). Panhandle Area Educational Consortium, 753 West Blvd., Chipley, FL 32428. Phone: 904-638-6131. Fax: 904-638-6135.

E-mail: everitr@mail.firn.edu.

Web site: http://www.paec.org.

Authorized power: 10-w. each. Antenna: 407-ft. above ground. Lat. 30° 06' 18", long. 85° 12' 00". Transmitter: Wewahitchka School Site, State Rte. 6 S.

Leased to Wireless One, Inc., 5551 Corporate Blvd., Suite 2K, Baton Rouge, LA 70808. Phone: 504-926-7778.

Wewahitchka—WNC-895 (Channels G-1-4). Liberty County District School Board. Authorized power: 50-w. each. Antenna: 404-ft. above ground. Lat. 30° 06' 18", long. 85° 12' 00". Transmitter: Wewahitchka School, State Rte. 6 S. Equipment: Emcee transmitter; Bogner antenna.

Worthington Springs—WNC-441 (Channels A-2-4). Westwood Hills Church of God, 1512 N.W. 31st. Ave., Gainesville, FL 32605. Authorized power: 50-w. each. Antenna: 706-ft. above ground. Lat. 29° 56' 29", long. 82° 23' 51". Transmitter: 1.3-mi. NE of State Rte. 18 & County Rd. 5-18A intersection. Equipment: ITS transmitter; Andrew antenna.

Worthington Springs—WNC-222 (Channels B-1-4). Orange Park Christian Academy, 1324 Kingsley Ave., Orange Park, FL 32073. Authorized power: 50-w. each. Antenna: 705-ft. above ground. Lat. 29° 56' 29", long. 82° 23' 51". Transmitter: County Rd. 5-18A, 1.3-mi. NE of Union County line & State Rd. 18. Equipment: Comwave transmitter; Andrew antenna.

Worthington Springs—WLX-998 (Channels C-1-4). Heritage Christian Academy, 4325 Hwy. 17 S, Orange Park, FL 32073. Authorized power: 50-w. each. Antenna: 705-ft. above ground. Lat. 29° 56' 29", long. 82° 23' 51". Transmitter: County Rd. 5-18A, 1.3-mi. NE of Union County line & State Rd. 18. Equipment: Comwave transmitter; Andrew antenna.

Worthington Springs—WNC-637 (Channels D-1-4). Orange Park High, 2300 Kinsley Ave., Orange Park, FL 32043. Phone: 904-272-8110. Fax: 904-272-5327. Authorized power: 50-w. each. Antenna: 705-ft. above ground. Lat. 29° 56' 29", long. 82° 23' 51". Transmitter: County Rd. 5-18A, 1.3-mi. NE of Union County line & State Rd. 18. Equipment: Comwave transmitter; Andrew antenna.

Worthington Springs—WNC-639 (Channels G-1-4). Clay High, 2025 Hwy. 16 W, Green Cove Springs, FL 32043. Authorized power: 50-w. each. Antenna: 705-ft. above ground. Lat. 29° 56' 29", long. 82° 23' 51". Transmitter: County Rd. 5-18A, 1.3-mi. NE of Union County line & State Rd. 18. Equipment: Comwave transmitter; Andrew antenna.

Youngstown—WHR-899 (Channels D-1-4). Panhandle Area Educational Consortium, 411 West Blvd., Chipley, FL 32428. Phone: 904-638-6131. Fax: 904-638-6135.

E-mail: everitr@mail.firn.edu.

Web site: http://www.paec.org.

Authorized power: 50-w. each. Antenna: 152-ft. above ground. Lat. 30° 19' 43", long. 85° 41' 25". Transmitter: 0.4-mi. N of County Rd. 388 & 2-mi. W of Vicksburg.

Georgia

Albany—WNC-294 (Channels A-1-4). Lee County Board of Education, Box 236, Leesburg, GA 31763. Authorized power: 50-w. each. Antenna: 453-ft. above ground. Lat. 31° 37' 40", long. 84° 11' 45". Transmitter: 3333 Palmyra Rd. Equipment: ITS transmitter; Andrew antenna.

Albany—WNC-367 (Channels B-1-4). Deerfield-Windsor School, Box 71149, Albany, GA 31707-0020. Authorized power: 50-w. each. Antenna: 453-ft. above ground. Lat. 31° 37' 40", long. 84° 11' 45". Transmitter: 3333 Palmyra Rd. Equipment: ITS transmitter; Andrew antenna.

Albany—WNC-355 (Channels C-1-4). Mitchell County Board of Education, Box 588, Camilla, GA 31730. Authorized power: 50-w. each. Antenna: 453-ft. above ground. Lat. 31° 37' 40", long. 84° 11' 45". Transmitter: 3333 Palmyra Rd. Equipment: ITS transmitter; Andrew antenna.

Albany—WNC-425 (Channels D-1-4). Baker County Board of Education, Box 40, Newton, GA 31770. Authorized power: 50-w. each. Antenna: 453-ft. above ground. Lat. 31° 37' 40", long. 84° 11' 45". Transmitter: 3333 Palmyra Rd. Equipment: ITS transmitter; Andrew antenna.

Albany—WNC-669 (Channels G-1-4). Calhoun County Board of Education, Box 38, Morgan, GA 31766. Authorized power: 10-w. each. Antenna: 518-ft. above ground. Lat. 31° 37' 40", long. 84° 11' 45". Transmitter: 3333 Palmyra Rd. Equipment: ITS transmitter; Andrew antenna.

Atlanta—KVI-65 (Channels A-1-4). Emory U., 1440 Clifton Rd. NE, Atlanta, GA 30322. Authorized power: 200-w. each. Antenna: 1017-ft. above ground. Lat. 33° 46' 15", long. 84° 23' 10". Transmitter: Nations Bank Plaza. Equipment: ITS transmitter; Andrew antenna.

Atlanta—WHR-755 (Channels B-1-4). Atlanta Interfaith Broadcasters Inc., 1075 Spring St., Atlanta, GA 30309. Phone: 404-892-0454. Fax: 404-892-8687.
E-mail: aib@mindspring.com.
Web site: http://www.atlconnect.org.
Authorized power: 200-w. each. Antenna: 1017-ft. above ground. Lat. 33° 46' 15", long. 84° 23' 10". Transmitter: Nations Bank Bldg., 600 Peachtree St. Equipment: ITS transmitter; Andrew antenna.

Atlanta—WNC-560 (Channels C-1-4). Georgia State U. Board of Regents, University System of Georgia. Authorized power: 200-w. each. Antenna: 1017-ft. above ground. Lat. 33° 46' 15", long. 84° 23' 10". Transmitter: Nations Bank Plaza. Equipment: ITS transmitter; Andrew antenna.

Atlanta—WNC-567 (Channels D-1-3). Dekalb College, The University System of Georgia. Authorized power: 50-w. each. Antenna: 1031-ft. above ground. Lat. 33° 46' 15", long. 84° 23' 10". Transmitter: NationsBank Plaza. Equipment: Emcee transmitter; Andrew antenna.

Atlanta—WNC-804 (Channels D-1-4). Atlanta Educational Services Inc., 740 Bismarck Rd. NE, Atlanta, GA 30324. Authorized power: 10-w. each. Antenna: 302-ft. above ground. Lat. 33° 45' 52", long. 84° 23' 02". Transmitter: Renaissance Square Center. Equipment: Emcee transmitter; Andrew antenna.

Atlanta—WGV-663 (Channels E-1-4). Georgia Institute of Technology. Authorized power: 0.1-w. each. Antenna: 52-ft. above ground. Lat. 33° 46' 20", long. 84° 23' 45". Transmitter: Engineering Science & Mechanics Bldg., Cherry St.

Atlanta—WNC-561 (Channels G-1-4). Georgia Institute of Technology. Authorized power: 200-w. each. Antenna: 1017-ft. above ground. Lat. 33° 46' 15", long. 84° 23' 10". Transmitter: Nations Bank Plaza. Equipment: ITS transmitter; Andrew antenna.

Barnesdale—WNC-843 (Channels A-1-4). Berrien County Board of Education, Box 625, Nashville, GA 31639. Authorized power: 50-w. each. Antenna: 705-ft. above ground. Lat. 31° 10' 18", long. 83° 21' 57". Transmitter: Approx. 1-mi. SSE of Barnesdale. Equipment: Emcee transmitter; Andrew antenna.

Barnesdale—WLX-597 (Channels B-1-4). Cook County Schools, Box 152, Adel, GA 31620. Phone: 912-896-2294. Fax: 912-896-3443. Authorized power: 50-w. each. Antenna: 934-ft. above ground. Lat. 31° 10' 18", long. 83° 21' 57". Transmitter: Approx. 1-mi. SSE of Barnesdale. Equipment: Emcee transmitter; Andrew antenna.
Leased to Wireless One Inc., 2506 Lakeland Dr., Suite 403, Jackson, MS 39208. Phone: 601-933-6871.

Barnesdale—WNC-844 (Channels C-1-4). Tift County Board of Education, 207 N. Ridge Ave., Tifton, GA 31793. Authorized power: 50-w. each. Antenna: 587-ft. above ground. Lat. 31° 10' 18", long. 83° 21' 57". Transmitter: Approx. 1-mi. SSE of Barnesdale. Equipment: Emcee transmitter; Andrew antenna.

Barnesdale—WLX-676 (Channels D-1-4). Lowndes Middle School, 506 Copeland Rd., Valdosta, GA 31601. Authorized power: 50-w. each. Antenna: 706-ft. above ground. Lat. 31° 10' 18", long. 83° 21' 57". Transmitter: 1-mi. SSE of Barnesdale. Equipment: ITS transmitter; Andrew antenna.

Barnesdale—WLX-574 (Channels G-1-4). Lanier County Board of Education, 406 E. Church St., Lakeland, GA 31635. Authorized power: 50-w. each. Antenna: 705-ft. above ground. Lat. 31° 10' 08", long. 83° 21' 47". Transmitter: Approx. 1-mi. SSE of Barnesdale. Equipment: ITS transmitter; Andrew antenna.
Leased to Nucentrix Broadband Networks, 200 Chisolm Place, Suite 200, Plano, TX 75075. Phone: 972-423-9494. Fax: 972-423-0819.

Bloomingdale—WLX-698 (Channels C-1-4). Evans County School System, Box 826, 613 W. Main St., Claxton, GA 30417. Authorized power: 50-w. each. Antenna: 706-ft. above ground. Lat. 32° 05' 48", long. 81° 19' 17". Transmitter: Hwy. 16 & Cross Rd. Equipment: Comwave transmitter; Andrew antenna.

Calhoun—WLX-797 (Channels A-1-4). West Georgia RESA, 99 Brown School Dr., Grantville, GA 30220. Authorized power: 50-w. each. Antenna: 706-ft. above ground. Lat. 34° 27' 32", long. 84° 53' 05". Transmitter: 1.8-mi. E of State Rte. 53 & I-75 junction. Equipment: ITS transmitter; Andrew antenna.

Calhoun—WLX-766 (Channels C-1-4). Etowah High School, 1895 Eagle Dr., Woodstock, GA 30188. Authorized power: 50-w. each. Antenna: 296-ft. above ground. Lat. 34° 27' 32", long. 84° 53' 05". Transmitter: 1.8-mi. ESE of State Rte. 53 & I-75 junction. Equipment: ITS transmitter; Andrew antenna.

Calhoun—WLX-701 (Channels D-1-4). Academy Elementary School, 450 Academy Dr. SW, Calhoun, GA 30701. Authorized power: 50-w. each. Antenna: 910-ft. above ground. Lat. 34° 27' 32", long. 84° 53' 05". Transmitter: 1.8-mi. ESE of State Rte. 53 & I-75 junction. Equipment: ITS transmitter; Andrew antenna.

Calhoun—WLX-765 (Channels G-1-4). Bartow County School System, 65 Gilreath Rd. NW, Cartersville, GA 30120. Authorized power: 50-w. each. Antenna: 295-ft. above ground. Lat. 34° 27' 32", long. 84° 53' 05". Transmitter: 1.8-mi. ESE of State Rte. 53 & I-75 junction. Equipment: ITS transmitter; Andrew antenna.

Charing—WLX-604 (Channels A-1-4). Webster County Board of Education, Box 149, Preston, GA 31824. Authorized power: 50-w. each. Antenna: 706-ft. above ground. Lat. 32° 25' 21", long. 84° 23' 19". Transmitter: Approx. 0.1-mi. NW of State Rte. 137, 0.2-mi. NE of the Taylor/Marion County line. Equipment: ITS transmitter; Andrew antenna.

Charing—WLX-600 (Channels B-1-4). Central Elementary & High School, State Hwy. 41 N, Talbotton, GA 31827. Phone: 706-665-8577. Fax: 706-665-3946. Authorized power: 50-w. each. Antenna: 706-ft. above ground. Lat. 32° 25' 21", long. 84° 23' 19". Transmitter: Approx. 0.1-mi. NW of State Rte. 137, 0.2-mi. NE of the Taylor/Marion County line. Equipment: ITS transmitter; Andrew antenna.

Charing—WNC-945 (Channels C-1-4). Schley County Board of Education, Box 66, Ellaville, GA 31806. Authorized power: 50-w. each. Antenna: 705-ft. above ground. Lat. 32° 25' 21", long. 84° 23' 21". Transmitter: Hwy. 137, 4-mi. SW of Charing. Equipment: Emcee transmitter; Andrew antenna.

Charing—WNC-944 (Channels D-1-4). Taylor County Board of Education, 229 Mulberry St., Butler, GA 31006. Authorized power: 50-w. each. Antenna: 705-ft. above ground. Lat. 32° 25' 21", long. 84° 23' 21". Transmitter: Hwy. 137, 4-mi. SW of Charing. Equipment: Emcee transmitter; Andrew antenna.

Charing—WLX-615 (Channels G-1-4). Crawford City Comprehensive High School, Agency St., Roberta, GA 31078. Fax: 912-836-3795. Authorized power: 50-w. each. Antenna: 706-ft. above ground. Lat. 32° 25' 21", long. 84° 23' 19". Transmitter: Approx. 0.1-mi. NW of State Rte. 137, 0.2-mi. NE of the Taylor/Marion County line. Equipment: ITS transmitter; Andrew antenna.

Columbus—WND-487 (Channels B-1-4). Chattahoochee-Flint RESA, 203 E. College St., Ellaville, GA 31806. Authorized power: 10-w. each. Antenna: 338-ft. above ground. Lat. 32° 27' 55", long. 85° 03' 28". Transmitter: Womack Rd. & Hwy. 80, Phenix City, AL. Equipment: Emcee transmitter; Andrew antenna.

Columbus—WND-483 (Channels G-1-4). Troy State U., Room 247, Adams Administration Bldg., Troy, GA 36082. Authorized power: 10-w. each. Antenna: 338-ft. above ground. Lat. 32° 27' 55", long. 85° 03' 28". Transmitter: Womack Rd. & Hwy. 80, Phenix City, AL. Equipment: Emcee transmitter; Andrew antenna.

Franklin—WNC-390 (Channels A-1-4). West Georgia RESA, 99 Brown School Dr., Grantville, GA 30220. Phone: 404-583-2528. Authorized power: 50-w. each. Antenna: 709-ft. above ground. Lat. 33° 16' 18", long. 85° 05' 12". Transmitter: 0.1-mi. N of U.S. Rte. 27, 0.8-mi. SE of Rte. 27 & State Rte. 34. Equipment: ITS transmitter; Andrew antenna.

Franklin—WLX-861 (Channels B-1-4). Heard High & Middle School, 545 Main St., Franklin, GA 30217. Authorized power: 50-w. each. Antenna: 706-ft. above ground. Lat. 33° 16' 18", long. 85° 05' 12". Transmitter: 0.1-mi. N of U.S. Rte. 27, 0.8-mi. SE of Rte. 27 & State Rte. 34. Equipment: ITS transmitter; Comwave antenna.

Franklin—WNC-389 (Channels C-1-4). West Georgia RESA, 99 Brown School Dr., Grantville, GA 30220. Phone: 404-583-2528. Authorized power: 50-w. each. Antenna: 709-ft. above ground. Lat. 33° 16' 18", long. 85° 05' 12". Transmitter: 0.1-mi. N of U.S. Rte. 27, 0.8-mi. SE of U.S. Rte. 27 & State Rte. 34. Equipment: ITS transmitter; Andrew antenna.

Franklin—WLX-866 (Channels D-1-4). Hogansville High School, 611 E. Main St., Hogansville, GA 30230. Authorized power: 50-w. each. Antenna: 706-ft. above ground. Lat. 33° 16' 18", long. 85° 05' 12". Transmitter: 0.1-mi. N of U.S. Rte. 27, 0.8-mi. SE of U.S. Rte. 27 & State Rte. 34 intersection. Equipment: ITS transmitter; Andrew antenna.

Franklin—WLX-795 (Channels G-1-4). Heard County School System, Box 1330, Franklin, GA 30217-1330. Phone: 706-675-3320. Fax: 706-675-3357. Authorized power: 50-w. each. Antenna: 709-ft. above ground. Lat. 33° 16' 18", long. 85° 05' 12". Transmitter: 0.1-mi. N of U.S. Rte. 27, 0.8-mi. SE of U.S. Rte. 27 & State Rte. 34. Equipment: ITS transmitter; Andrew antenna.
Leased to Bell South Entertainment, 500 North Park Town Center, 1100 Abernathy Rd. NE, Suite 414, Atlanta, GA 30328. Phone: 770-392-4575.

Jeffersonville—WNC-335 (Channels A-1-4). Laurens County Schools, Box 2128, Dublin, GA 31040. Authorized power: 50-w. each. Antenna: 706-ft. above ground. Lat. 32° 44' 00", long. 83° 19' 16". Transmitter: 3.6-mi. NNE of State Rte. 96 & U.S. Rte. 80 intersection. Equipment: ITS transmitter; Andrew antenna.

Jeffersonville—WLX-652 (Channels B-1-4). West Laurens High School, Box 138, Rte. 3, Dublin, GA 31021. Authorized power: 50-w. each. Antenna: 706-ft. above ground. Lat. 32° 44' 00", long. 83° 19' 16". Transmitter: Approx. 3.6-mi. NNE of State Rte. 96 & U.S. Rte. 80 intersection. Equipment: ITS transmitter; Andrew antenna.

Jeffersonville—WLX-695 (Channels C-1-4). Beckley County Schools, 909 N.E. Dykes St., Cochran, GA 31014.
E-mail: sbleckley@peachnet.campus.mci.net.
Web site: http://www.bleckley.k12ga.us/.
Authorized power: 50-w. each. Antenna: 706-ft. above ground. Lat. 32° 41' 47", long. 83° 19' 50". Transmitter: 3.6-mi. NNE of State Rte. 96 & U.S. Rte. 80 intersection. Equipment: ITS transmitter; Andrew antenna.
Leased to Wireless One Inc., 1080 River Oaks Dr., Suite A 150, Jackson, MS 39208. Phone: 601-936-1515.

Jeffersonville—WNC-324 (Channels D-1-4). Twiggs County High School, E. Main St., Jeffersonville, GA 31044. Authorized power: 50-w. each. Antenna: 706-ft. above ground. Lat. 32° 44' 00", long. 83° 19' 16". Transmitter: 3.6-mi. NNE of State Rte. 96 & U.S. Rte. 80 intersection. Equipment: ITS transmitter; Andrew antenna.

Jeffersonville—WLX-666 (Channels G-1-4). Twiggs County Middle School, Watson Blvd., Jeffersonville, GA 31044. Phone: 912-945-3112. Authorized power: 50-w. each. Antenna: 706-ft. above ground. Lat. 32° 44' 00", long. 83° 19' 16". Transmitter: Approx. 3.6-mi. NNE of State Rte. 96 & U.S. Rte. 80 intersection. Equipment: ITS transmitter; Andrew antenna.

Madison—WLX-784 (Channels A-1-4). Rutledge Academy, 4031 Davis Academy Rd., Rutledge, GA 30665. Authorized power: 50-w. each. Antenna: 464-ft. above ground. Lat. 33° 29' 34", long. 83° 28' 07". Transmitter: 5-mi. W of Pierce Dairy Rd., 4-mi. along a bearing of 177 °T from the I-20 & U.S. Rte. 441 intersection, Godfrey Division, Morgan County. Equipment: ITS transmitter; Andrew antenna.

Madison—WLX-788 (Channels B-1-4). Piedmont Academy, Box 231, 126 Hwy. 212 W, Monticello, GA 31064. Phone: 706-468-8818. Fax: 706-468-8884. Authorized power: 50-w. each. Antenna: 453-ft. above ground. Lat. 33° 29' 27", long. 83° 28' 20". Transmitter: 4-mi. S of I-20 & U.S. Rte. 441. Equipment: ITS transmitter; Andrew antenna.

Madison—WLX-856 (Channels D-1-4). Morgan County Middle School, 920 Pearl St., Madison, GA 30650. Authorized power: 50-w. each. Antenna: 706-ft. above ground. Lat. 33° 29' 34", long. 83° 28' 07". Transmitter: 0.5-mi. W of Pierce Dairy Rd., 4-mi. along a bearing of 177 °T from the I-20 & U.S. Rte. 441 intersection, Godfrey Division, Morgan County. Equipment: ITS transmitter; Andrew antenna.

Madison—WLX-867 (Channels G-1-4). Newton County School System, 3187 Newton Dr. NE, Covington, GA 30209. Authorized power: 50-w. each. Antenna: 464-ft. above ground. Lat. 33° 29' 34", long. 83° 28' 07". Transmitter: 0.5-mi. W of Madison. Equipment: ITS transmitter; Andrew antenna.

Matthews—WLX-862 (Channels A-1-4). Wrens High School, 210 Griffin St., Wrens, GA 30833. Authorized power: 50-w. each. Antenna: 699-ft. above ground. Lat. 33° 15' 33", long. 82° 17' 09". Transmitter: 4.5-mi. NNE of Matthews, 1-mi. S of U.S. 1. Equipment: Emcee transmitter; Andrew antenna.

Pembroke—WLX-599 (Channels A-1-4). Effingham County Middle School, 1290 Hwy.

119 S, Springfield, GA 31329. Phone: 912-754-3332. Authorized power: 50-w. each. Antenna: 706-ft. above ground. Lat. 32° 08' 15", long. 81° 36' 39". Transmitter: Approx. 0.7-mi. ENE of the State Rte. 119 & U.S. Rte. 280 intersection. Equipment: ITS transmitter; Andrew antenna.

Pembroke—WLX-601 (Channels G-1-4). Statesboro High School, 10 Lester Rd., Statesboro, GA 30458. Authorized power: 50-w. each. Antenna: 706-ft. above ground. Lat. 32° 08' 15", long. 81° 36' 39". Transmitter: Approx. 0.7-mi. ENE of State Rte. 119 & U.S. Rte. 280 intersection. Equipment: ITS transmitter; Andrew antenna.

Pendergrass—WND-494 (Channels A-1-4). Jackson County Board of Education, 1660 Winder Hwy., Jefferson, GA 30549. Authorized power: 50-w. each. Antenna: 1122-ft. above ground. Lat. 34° 12' 27", long. 83° 37' 48". Transmitter: NE of Pendergrass. Equipment: Comwave transmitter; Andrew antenna.

Stone Mountain—WHM-938 (Channels G-1-4). Georgia Institute of Technology. Authorized power: 10-w. each. Antenna: 420-ft. above ground. Lat. 33° 48' 18", long. 84° 08' 40". Transmitter: 15.8-mi. E of Atlanta. Equipment: Emcee transmitter; Andrew antenna.

Tarboro—WLX-623 (Channels A-1-3). Glynn County Middle School, 902 George St., Brunswick, GA 31520. Authorized power: 50-w. each. Antenna: 702-ft. above ground. Lat. 31° 09' 13", long. 81° 58' 00". Transmitter: 1.7-mi. E of Hickox. Equipment: Comwave transmitter; Andrew antenna.

Tarboro—WNC-289 (Channels B-1-4). Brunswick High School, 3920 Habersham St., Brunswick, GA 31520. Authorized power: 50-w. each. Antenna: 706-ft. above ground. Lat. 31° 04' 32", long. 81° 50' 33". Transmitter: 4.5-mi. NW of Tarboro. Equipment: ITS transmitter; Andrew antenna.

Tarboro—WLX-683 (Channels C-1-4). Brantley County Board of Education, Box 613, Nahunta, GA 31553. Phone: 912-462-6176. Fax: 912-462-6731. Authorized power: 50-w. each. Antenna: 702-ft. above ground. Lat. 31° 09' 13", long. 81° 58' 00". Transmitter: 1.7-mi. E of Hickox. Equipment: Comwave transmitter; Andrew antenna.

Leased to Wireless One, 2506 Lakeland Dr., Jackson, MS 39208. Phone: 601-936-1515.

Tarboro—WLX-680 (Channels D-1-4). Charlton County High School, 500 N. Cross St., Folkston, GA 31537. Phone: 912-496-2041. Authorized power: 50-w. each. Antenna: 702-ft. above ground. Lat. 31° 09' 13", long. 80° 58' 00". Transmitter: 1.7-mi. E of Hickox. Equipment: Comwave transmitter; Andrew antenna.

Tarboro—WLX-632 (Channels G-1-4). Folkston Middle School, 810 N. 3rd St., Folkston, GA 31537. Phone: 912-496-2360. Fax: 912-496-3766. Authorized power: 50-w. each. Antenna: 702-ft. above ground. Lat. 31° 09' 13", long. 81° 58' 00". Transmitter: 1.7-mi. E of Hickox. Equipment: Comwave transmitter; Andrew antenna.

Thomasville—WNC-415 (Channels A-1-4). West Georgia RESA, 123 La Grange St., Grantville, GA 30220. Authorized power: 50-w. each. Antenna: 504-ft. above ground. Lat. 30° 49' 09", long. 83° 59' 49". Transmitter: U.S. Hwy. 319 & Pine Tree Blvd. Equipment: Comwave transmitter; Andrew antenna.

Thomasville—WNC-416 (Channels B-1-4). West Georgia RESA, 123 La Grange St., Grantville, GA 30220. Authorized power: 50-w. each. Antenna: 504-ft. above ground. Lat. 30° 49' 09", long. 83° 59' 49". Transmitter: U.S. Hwy. 319 & Pine Tree Blvd. Equipment: Comwave transmitter; Andrew antenna.

Thomasville—WNC-417 (Channels C-1-4). Troup County Schools, 611A E. Main St., Hogansville, GA 30230. Authorized power: 50-w. each. Antenna: 504-ft. above ground. Lat. 30° 49' 09", long. 83° 59' 49". Transmitter: U.S. Hwy. 319 & Pine Tree Blvd. Equipment: Comwave transmitter; Andrew antenna.

Thomasville—WNC-418 (Channels D-1-4). Bulloch County Board of Education, 500 Northside Dr. E, Statesboro, GA 30458. Authorized power: 50-w. each. Antenna: 504-ft. above ground. Lat. 30° 49' 09", long. 83° 59' 49". Transmitter: U.S. Hwy. 319 & Pine Tree Blvd. Equipment: Comwave transmitter; Andrew antenna.

Thomasville—WNC-419 (Channels G-1-4). Effingham County Board of Education, 305 Ash St., Springfield, GA 31329. Authorized power: 50-w. each. Antenna: 504-ft. above ground. Lat. 30° 49' 09", long. 83° 59' 49". Transmitter: U.S. Hwy. 319 & Pine Tree Blvd. Equipment: Comwave transmitter; Andrew antenna.

Vidette—WLX-852 (Channels B-1-4). Glascock County Schools, Box 205, Gibson, GA 30810. Authorized power: 50-w. each. Antenna: 619-ft. above ground. Lat. 33° 01' 36", long. 82° 15' 17". Transmitter: 0.87-mi. SSW of Vidette, off Middle Ground Rd. Equipment: ITS transmitter; Andrew antenna.

Leased to Rural Vision, Box 1482, Canyon Lake, TX 78130. Phone: 210-964-2211.

Vidette—WLX-839 (Channels C-1-4). Louisville High School, School St., Louisville, GA 30434. Authorized power: 50-w. each. Antenna: 619-ft. above ground. Lat. 33° 01' 36", long. 82° 15' 17". Transmitter: 0.87-mi. SSW of Vidette, off Middle Ground Rd. Equipment: ITS transmitter; Andrew antenna.

Vidette—WNC-452 (Channels D-1-4). Burke County Middle School, Box 849, Park Dr., Waynesboro, GA 30830. Authorized power: 50-w. each. Antenna: 447-ft. above ground. Lat. 33° 15' 33", long. 82° 17' 09". Transmitter: 4.5-mi. NNE of Matthews. Equipment: Emcee transmitter; Andrew antenna.

Vidette—WNC-451 (Channels G-1-4). Burke County Comprehensive High, Box 51-D, Rte. 6, Waynesboro, GA 30830. Authorized power: 50-w. each. Antenna: 624-ft. above ground. Lat. 33° 01' 36", long. 82° 15' 17". Transmitter: 0.9-mi. SSW of Vidette. Equipment: ITS transmitter; Andrew antenna.

Waleska—WNC-414 (Channels A-1-4). West Georgia RESA, 99 Brown School Dr., Grantville, GA 30220. Authorized power: 50-w. each. Antenna: 295-ft. above ground. Lat. 34° 18' 48", long. 84° 38' 56". Transmitter: Approx. 4.5-mi. ESE of State Rte. 140 & U.S. Rte. 411 intersection, Bear Mountain. Equipment: ITS transmitter; Andrew antenna.

Waleska—WNC-668 (Channels C-1-4). Etowan High School, 1895 Eagle Dr., Woodstock, GA 30137. Authorized power: 50-w. each. Antenna: 295-ft. above ground. Lat. 34° 18' 47", long. 84° 38' 55". Transmitter: 4.5-mi. ESE of State Rte. 140 & U.S. 411 intersection, Bear Mountain. Equipment: ITS transmitter; Andrew antenna.

Waleska—WNC-665 (Channels D-1-4). Academy Elementary School, 450 Academy Dr. SW, Calhoun, GA 30701. Authorized power: 50-w. each. Antenna: 295-ft. above ground. Lat. 34° 18' 47", long. 084° 38' 55". Transmitter: 4.5-mi. ESE of State Rte. 140 & U.S. 411 intersection, Bear Mountain. Equipment: ITS transmitter; Andrew antenna.

Waleska—WNC-666 (Channels G-1-4). Bartow County School System, 65 Gilbreath Rd., Cartersville, GA 30120. Authorized power: 50-w. each. Antenna: 295-ft. above ground. Lat. 34° 18' 47", long. 84° 38' 55". Transmitter: 4.5-mi. ESE of State Rte. 140 & U.S. 411 intersection, Bear Mountain. Equipment: ITS transmitter; Andrew antenna.

Hawaii

Hilo—WNC-806 (Channels A-1-4). Transition Network Inc., Box 10068, Hilo, HI 96720. Authorized power: 50-w. each. Antenna: 194-ft. above ground. Lat. 19° 35' 33", long. 155° 07' 36". Transmitter: 2.7-mi. N of Mountain View, N. Kulani Rd. Equipment: Emcee transmitter; Andrew antenna.

Hilo—WNC-809 (Channels B-1-4). Spiritual Assembly of the Baha'is of Puma, Box 906, Keaau, HI 96744. Authorized power: 50-w. each. Antenna: 194-ft. above ground. Lat. 19° 35' 33", long. 155° 07' 36". Transmitter: 2.7-mi. N of Mountain View, N. Kulani Rd. Equipment: Emcee transmitter; Andrew antenna.

Hilo—WNC-218 (Channels C-1-4). North American Catholic Educational Programming Foundation Inc., Box 40026, Providence, RI 02940-0026. Phone: 401-729-0900. Authorized power: 100-w. each. Antenna: 199-ft. above ground. Lat. 19° 35' 33", long. 155° 07' 36". Transmitter: Near Leleiwi Point, 2-mi. E of Hilo. Equipment: ITS transmitter; Andrew antenna.

Hilo—WHR-708 (Channels G-1-4). U. of Hawaii, BA 11-2, 1630 Bachman Place, Honolulu, HI 96822. Authorized power: 10-w. each. Antenna: 25-ft. above ground. Lat. 19° 42' 19", long. 155° 04' 58". Transmitter: U. of Hawaii, Hilo Campus. Equipment: Emcee transmitter; Bogner antenna.

Honolulu—WNC-786 (Channels A-1-4). Sacred Hearts Academy, 3253 Waialae Ave., Honolulu, HI 96816. Authorized power: 10-w. each. Antenna: 140-ft. above ground. Lat. 21° 24' 24", long. 158° 06' 02". Transmitter: Palikea Ridge on Palehue Rd. Equipment: Comwave transmitter; Andrew antenna.

Honolulu—WHR-716 (Channels B-1-4). U. of Hawaii, BA 11-2, 1630 Bachman Place, Honolulu, HI 96822. Authorized power: 15-w. each. Antenna: 69-ft. above ground. Lat. 21° 24' 24", long. 158° 06' 02". Transmitter: Ala Noana Hotel, 410 Atkinson Dr. Equipment: Comwave transmitter; Andrew antenna.

Honolulu—WNC-261 (Channels D-1-4). Hawaii Pacific U., 1166 Fort Street Mall, Honolulu, HI 96813. Authorized power: 15-w. each. Antenna: 69-ft. above ground. Lat. 21° 24' 24", long. 158° 06' 02". Transmitter: Palikea Ridge on Palehua Rd., Motorola site. Equipment: Comwave transmitter; Andrew antenna.

Honolulu—WHR-713 (Channels G-1-4). U. of Hawaii, BA 11-2, 1630 Bachman Place, Honolulu, HI 96822. Authorized power: 100-w. each. Antenna: 30-ft. above ground. Lat. 21° 19' 49", long. 157° 45' 24". Transmitter: Wilwilinui Ridge.

Kealakekua—WLX-988 (Channels C-1-4). North American Catholic Educational Programming Foundation Inc., Box 40026, Providence, RI 02940-0026. Phone: 401-729-0900. Authorized power: 10-w. each. Antenna: 250-ft. above ground. Lat. 19° 31' 10", long. 155° 55' 08". Transmitter: Mamalahoa Hwy. Equipment: ITS transmitter; Andrew antenna.

Kona—WHR-710 (Channels A-1-4). U. of Hawaii, BA 11-2, 1630 Bachman Place, Honolulu, HI 96822. Authorized power: 10-w. each. Antenna: 104-ft. above ground. Lat. 19° 43' 10", long. 155° 54' 41". Transmitter: Kaupulehu Crater. Equipment: Comwave transmitter.

Lanai—WHR-717 (Channels A-1-4). U. of Hawaii, BA 11-2, 1630 Bachman Place, Honolulu, HI 96822. Authorized power: 10-w. each. Antenna: 130-ft. above ground. Lat. 20° 50' 45", long. 156° 54' 06". Transmitter: Puu Kilea. Equipment: Comwave transmitter.

Lihue—WHR-709 (Channels A-1-4). U. of Hawaii, BA 11-2, 1630 Bachman Place, Honolulu, HI 96822. Authorized power: 10-w. each. Antenna: 100-ft. above ground. Lat. 21° 59' 41", long. 159° 24' 36". Transmitter: Kilohana Radio Site. Equipment: Comwave transmitter.

Puhi—WHR-712 (Channels A-1-4). U. of Hawaii, BA 11-2, 1630 Bachman Place, Honolulu, HI 96822. Authorized power: 100-w. each. Antenna: 30-ft. above ground. Lat. 21° 58' 20", long. 159° 29' 55". Transmitter: Puhi Kawai.

Puunene—WNC-807 (Channels A-1-3). Sylvan Learning Center. Authorized power: 10-w. each. Antenna: 184-ft. above ground. Lat. 20° 49' 24", long. 156° 27' 27". Transmitter: Thompson Ranch Rd. Equipment: Emcee transmitter; Andrew antenna.

Puunene—WNC-791 (Channels B-1-4). First Assembly of God, 95 S. Kane St., Kahului, HI 96732. Authorized power: 10-w. each. Antenna: 184-ft. above ground. Lat. 20° 49' 24", long. 156° 27' 27". Transmitter: Puunene. Equipment: Emcee transmitter; Andrew antenna.

Puunene—WLX-793 (Channels D-1-4). Saint Anthony Jr. Senior High School, 1618 Lower Main St., Wailuku, HI 96793. Phone: 808-244-4190. Fax: 808-242-8081. Authorized power: 10-w. each. Antenna: 184-ft. above ground. Lat. 20° 49' 24", long. 156° 27' 27". Transmitter: 3-mi. S of Puunene. Equipment: Comwave transmitter; Andrew antenna.

Waialua—WHR-714 (Channels G-1-4). U. of Hawaii, 2350 Dole St., Honolulu, HI 96822. Authorized power: 15-w. each. Antenna: 69-ft. above ground. Lat. 21° 24' 24", long. 158° 06' 02". Transmitter: Palikea Ridge on Palehua Rd. Equipment: Comwave transmitter; Andrew antenna.

Wailuku—WHR-711 (Channels A-1-4). U. of Hawaii, BA 11-2, 1630 Bachman Place, Honolulu, HI 96822. Authorized power: 100-w. each. Antenna: 30-ft. above ground. Lat. 20° 53' 31", long. 156° 28' 37". Transmitter: Maui Community College, Maui.

Wailuku—WHR-707 (Channels G-1-4). U. of Hawaii, BA 11-2, 1630 Bachman Place, Honolulu, HI 96822. Authorized power: 100-w. each. Antenna: 30-ft. above ground. Lat. 20° 42' 40", long. 156° 15' 34". Transmitter: Haleakala, Kolekole Crater.

Waipahu—WLX-384 (Channels C-1-4). Catholic Diocese of Honolulu, 1184 Bishop St., Honolulu, HI 96813. Authorized power: 15-w.

each. Antenna: 70-ft. above ground. Lat. 21° 24' 24", long. 158° 06' 02". Transmitter: Palikea Ridge on Palehua Rd. Equipment: Comwave transmitter; Andrew antenna.

Idaho

Boise—WLX-813 (Channels A-1-4). North American Catholic Educational Programming Foundation Inc., Box 40026, Providence, RI 02940-0026. Phone: 401-729-0900. Authorized power: 20-w. each. Antenna: 96-ft. above ground. Lat. 43° 45' 18", long. 116° 05' 52". Transmitter: Deer Point, 10-mi. NE of Boise. Equipment: ITS transmitter; Andrew antenna.
Leased to Northwest Cable TV, 10338 Fairview Ave., Boise, ID 83704. Phone: 208-377-1266.

Boise—WHR-688 (Channels B-1-2). Idaho State Board of Education, 1910 University Dr., Boise, ID 83725. Phone: 208-373-7220. Fax: 208-373-7245. Authorized power: 20-w. each. Antenna: 39-ft. above ground. Lat. 43° 45' 18", long. 116° 05' 52". Transmitter: 1910 University Dr.

Boise—WNC-735 (Channels D-1-2). Canyon County School, 1101 Cleveland Blvd., Caldwell, ID 83605. Phone: 208-455-3300. Authorized power: 20-w. each. Antenna: 39-ft. above ground. Lat. 43° 45' 18", long. 116° 05' 52". Transmitter: Deer Point, 10-mi. NE of Boise. Equipment: Andrew transmitter; Andrew antenna.

Boise—WHR-689 (Channels D-3-4). State Board of Education IE/PBS, 1910 University Dr., Boise, ID 83725. Authorized power: 20-w. each. Antenna: 32.5-ft. above ground. Lat. 43° 45' 18", long. 116° 05' 52". Transmitter: Deer Point TV Lot No. 3, 11-mi. NE of Boise. Equipment: ITS transmitter; Andrew antenna.

Idaho Falls—WND-470 (Channels A-1-4). Regents of U. of Idaho, VSS 215, Media Services Center, Moscow, ID 83844. Authorized power: 50-w. each. Antenna: 128-ft. above ground. Lat. 43° 21' 06", long. 112° 00' 22". Equipment: ITS transmitter; Andrew antenna.

Idaho Falls—WND-473 (Channels D-1-4). Hope Lutheran School, 2071 12th St., Idaho Falls, ID 83404. Authorized power: 50-w. each. Antenna: 128-ft. above ground. Lat. 43° 21' 08", long. 112° 00' 22". Transmitter: Tavior Mountain. Equipment: ITS transmitter; Andrew antenna.

Lewiston—WND-403 (Channels A-1-4). Clarendon Foundation, Suite 826, 4201 S. 31st St., Arlington, VA 22206. Authorized power: 10-w. each. Antenna: 66-ft. above ground. Lat. 46° 27' 41", long. 117° 00' 36". Transmitter: 2.5-mi. N of Lewiston. Equipment: Comwave transmitter; Andrew antenna.

Lewiston—WNC-769 (Channels D-1-4). Views on Learning Inc., 1401 N. Meridian St., Indianapolis, IN 46202. Authorized power: 10-w. each. Antenna: 66-ft. above ground. Lat. 46° 27' 41", long. 117° 00' 36". Transmitter: 2.5-mi. N of Lewiston. Equipment: Comwave transmitter; Andrew antenna.

Lewiston—WND-404 (Channels G-1-4). Center for Economic & Social Justice, Box 40711, Washington, DC 20016. Phone: 703-243-5155. Fax: 703-243-5935.
E-mail: thirdwag@cesj.org.
Web site: http://www.cesj.org.
Authorized power: 10-w. each. Antenna: 66-ft. above ground. Lat. 46° 27' 41", long. 117° 00' 36". Transmitter: 2.5-mi. N of Lewiston. Equipment: Comwave transmitter; Andrew antenna.
Leased to American Telecasting Inc., 4065 N. Sinton Rd., Suite 201, Colorado Springs, CO 80907.

Pocatello—WHR-585 (Channels A-1-4). State Board of Education, 1910 University Dr., Boise, ID 83725. Authorized power: 10-w. each. Antenna: 30-ft. above ground. Lat. 42° 51' 55", long. 112° 29' 28". Transmitter: 3-mi. W of Pocatello.

Pocatello—WND-465 (Channels A-1-4). Shekinah Network, 14875 Powerline, Atascadero, CA 93422. Authorized power: 50-w. each. Antenna: 200-ft. above ground. Lat. 42° 51' 57", long. 112° 30' 46". Transmitter: Howard Mountain. Equipment: ITS transmitter; Andrew antenna.

Pocatello—WND-466 (Channels B-1-3). Views on Learning Inc., 200 Kenyon Ave., Elkhart, IN 46516. Authorized power: 50-w. each. Antenna: 200-ft. above ground. Lat. 42° 51' 57", long. 112° 30' 46". Transmitter: Howard Mountain. Equipment: ITS transmitter; Andrew antenna.

Pocatello—WND-467 (Channels C-1-4). Morningstar Educational Network, 4012 Morningstar, Huntington Beach, CA 92649. Authorized power: 50-w. each. Antenna: 200-ft. above ground. Lat. 42° 51' 57", long. 112° 30' 46". Transmitter: Howard Mountain. Equipment: ITS transmitter; Andrew antenna.

Pocatello—WND-468 (Channels D-1-4). Del-Jen Inc., Suite 401, 28441 Highridge Rd., Rolling Hills Estate, CA 90274. Authorized power: 50-w. each. Antenna: 200-ft. above ground. Lat. 42° 51' 57", long. 112° 30' 46". Transmitter: Howard Mountain. Equipment: ITS transmitter; Andrew antenna.

Twin Falls—WNC-801 (Channels A-1-4). Twin Falls Public School District No. 411, 201 Main Ave. W, Twin Falls, ID 83301. Authorized power: 20-w. each. Antenna: 403-ft. above ground. Lat. 42° 43' 54", long. 114° 25' 04". Transmitter: 11-mi. N of Twin Falls. Equipment: ITS transmitter; Andrew antenna.

Twin Falls—WNC-738 (Channels B-1-4). College of Southern Idaho, 315 Falls Ave. W, Twin Falls, ID 83301. Authorized power: 20-w. each. Antenna: 39-ft. above ground. Lat. 42° 43' 54", long. 114° 25' 04". Transmitter: 11-mi. N of Twin Falls. Equipment: ITS transmitter; Andrew antenna.

Twin Falls—WNC-731 (Channels G-1-4). Idaho State U., Campus Box 8064, Pocatello, ID 83209. Authorized power: 20-w. each. Antenna: 402-ft. above ground. Lat. 42° 43' 54", long. 114° 25' 04". Transmitter: 11-mi. N of Twin Falls. Equipment: ITS transmitter; Andrew antenna.

Illinois

Bloomington—WLX-610 (Channels A-1-4). Lincoln Christian College & Seminary, 100 Campus View Dr., Lincoln, IL 62656. Phone: 217-732-3168. Fax: 217-732-5914. Authorized power: 10-w. each. Antenna: 283-ft. above ground. Lat. 40° 28' 59", long. 88° 59' 43". Transmitter: Center & Mulberry Sts. Equipment: Emcee transmitter; Bogner antenna.
Leased to Microwave Cable. Phone: 309-829-9949.

Bluffs—WLX-595 (Channels A-1-4). Beardstown Community United School District No. 15, E 15th St., Beardstown, IL 62367. Authorized power: 39-w. each. Antenna: 495-ft. above ground. Lat. 39° 41' 19", long. 90° 34' 04". Transmitter: 4.5-mi. SSW of Bluffs. Equipment: Comwave transmitter.

Bluffs—WLX-603 (Channels B-1-4). Liberty Community United School District No. 2, RR 1, Liberty, IL 62347. Authorized power: 39.8-w. each. Antenna: 495-ft. above ground. Lat. 39° 41' 16", long. 90° 33' 48". Transmitter: E side of State Rte. 100, 4.5-mi. SSW of Bluffs. Equipment: Comwave transmitter; Andrew antenna.

Bluffs—WLX-594 (Channels C-1-4). Scott-Morgan Community United School District No. 2, 100 W. Rockwood, Bluffs, IL 62621. Authorized power: 40-w. each. Antenna: 495-ft. above ground. Lat. 39° 41' 19", long. 90° 34' 04". Transmitter: E side of Illinois Rte. 100, 4.5-mi. SSW of Bluffs. Equipment: Comwave transmitter; Andrew antenna.

Bluffs—WLX-732 (Channels D-1-4). Waverly Community Unit School District No. 6, 201 N. Miller, Waverly, IL 62692. Phone: 217-435-2211. Fax: 217-435-3431.
E-mail: jbailey@roe46.k12.il.us.
Authorized power: 39.8-w. each. Antenna: 495-ft. above ground. Lat. 39° 41' 19", long. 90° 34' 04". Transmitter: E side of Rte. 100, Scott County. Equipment: Comwave transmitter; Andrew antenna.
Leased to Nucentrix Broadband Networks, 200 Chisolm Place, Suite 200, Plano, TX 75075. Phone: 972-423-9494. Fax: 972-423-0819.

Champaign—WLX-278 (Channels C-1-4). Network for Instructional TV Inc., Suite 110, 11490 Commerce Park Dr., Reston, VA 22091. Phone: 703-860-9200. Fax: 703-860-9237. Authorized power: 50-w. each. Antenna: 338-ft. above ground. Lat. 40° 10' 51", long. 88° 19' 04". Transmitter: 0.6-mi. N of I-74, 3-mi. NW of Champaign. Equipment: Comwave transmitter; Andrew antenna.
Leased to Nucentrix Broadband Networks, 200 Chisholm Place, Suite 200, Plano, TX 75075. Phone: 972-423-9494. Fax: 972-423-0819.

Champaign—WLX-918 (Channels G-1-4). Parkland College, 2400 W. Bradley Ave., Champaign, IL 61821. Authorized power: 50-w. each. Antenna: 338-ft. above ground. Lat. 40° 10' 51", long. 88° 19' 04". Transmitter: 0.6-mi. N of I-74, 3-mi. NW of Champaign. Equipment: Comwave transmitter; Andrew antenna.

Chicago—KGZ-66 (Channels A-1-4). New Trier Twp. High School District 203, 385 Winnetka Ave., Winnetka, IL 60093. Phone: 847-446-9440. Fax: 847-446-5285.
E-mail: hausfelj@nttc.org.
Authorized power: 100-w. each. Antenna: 1467-ft. above ground. Lat. 41° 52' 44", long. 87° 38' 10". Transmitter: Sears Tower, 101 S. Wacker Dr. Equipment: Comwave transmitter; Andrew antenna.
Leased to People's Choice TV, 5301 E. Broadway Blvd., Tucson, AZ 85711. Phone: 520-519-4400.

Chicago—WHM-934 (Channels B-1-2). Triton College, 2000 5th Ave., River Grove, IL 60171. Authorized power: 100-w. each. Antenna: 1467-ft. above ground. Lat. 41° 52' 44", long. 87° 38' 10". Transmitter: Sears Tower, 101 S. Wacker Dr. Equipment: Comwave transmitter; Andrew antenna.

Chicago—WHR-498 (Channels B-3-4). Community College District 535, 1600 E. Golf Rd., Des Plaines, IL 60016. Phone: 847-635-1640. Fax: 847-635-1987.
E-mail: garyn@oakton.edu.
Authorized power: 100-w. each. Antenna: 1709-ft. above ground. Lat. 41° 52' 44", long. 87° 38' 10". Transmitter: Sears Tower, 101 S. Wacker Dr. Equipment: Comwave transmitter; Andrew antenna.
Leased to Preferred Entertainment, 6260 Joliet Rd., Countryside, IL 60525. Phone: 708-482-0770.

Chicago—WAC-262 (Channels C-1-4). The Catholic Bishop of Chicago, Box 1979, Chicago, IL 60690. Authorized power: 50-w. each. Antenna: 1709-ft. above ground. Lat. 41° 52' 44", long. 87° 38' 10". Transmitter: Sears Bldg., 101 S. Wacker Dr. Equipment: Comwave transmitter; Andrew antenna.

Chicago—WLX-630 (Channels D-1 & 3). Chicago Instructional Technology Foundation Inc., 1813 W. Cortland, Chicago, IL 60622. Authorized power: 100-w. each. Antenna: 1467-ft. above ground. Lat. 41° 52' 44", long. 87° 38' 10". Transmitter: Sears Tower, 101 S. Wacker Dr. Equipment: Comwave transmitter; Andrew antenna.

Chicago—WNC-263 (Channel D-2 & 4). Chicago Instructional Technology Foundation, 1813 W. Cortland, Chicago, IL 60622. Authorized power: 50-w. each Antenna: 1709-ft. above ground. Lat. 41° 52' 44", long. 87° 38' 10". Transmitter: Sears Tower, 101 Wacker Dr. Equipment: Comwave transmitter; Bogner antenna.

Chicago—WBM-648 (Channels E-1-4). Illinois Institute of Technology, 3300 S. Federal St., Chicago, IL 60616. Authorized power: 100-w. each. Antenna: 1709-ft. above ground. Lat. 41° 52' 44", long. 87° 38' 10". Transmitter: Sears Tower, 101 S. Wacker Dr. Equipment: Comwave transmitter; Andrew antenna.

Chicago—WHG-269 (Channels G-1-4). Illinois Institute of Technology, 3300 S. Federal St., Chicago, IL 60616. Authorized power: 100-w. each. Antenna: 1467-ft. above ground. Lat. 41° 52' 44", long. 87° 38' 10". Transmitter: Sears Tower, 101 S. Wacker Dr. Equipment: Comwave transmitter; Andrew antenna.

Danville—WNC-552 (Channels D-1-4). Shekinah Network, 14875 Powerline Rd., Atascadero, CA 93422. Phone: 805-438-3341. Fax: 805-438-3341. Authorized power: 50-w. each. Antenna: 338-ft. above ground. Lat. 40° 10' 51", long. 88° 19' 04". Transmitter: 0.6-mi. N of I-74, 3-mi. NW of Champaign. Equipment: Comwave transmitter; Andrew antenna.

Dundas—WLX-555 (Channels A-1-4). Red Hill Community United School District No. 10, 1250 Judy Ave., Bridgeport, IL 62417. Authorized power: 25-w. each. Antenna: 702-ft. above ground. Lat. 38° 51' 09", long. 88° 07' 06". Transmitter: Approx. 2-mi. NW of Dundas. Equipment: Comwave transmitter; Andrew antenna.
Leased to Nucentrix Broadband Networks, 200 Chisolm Place, Suite 200, Plano, TX 75075. Phone: 972-423-9494. Fax: 972-423-0819.

Dundas—WLX-733 (Channels B-1-4). Oblong Community United School District No. 4, 600 W. Main, Oblong, IL 62449. Authorized power: 25-w. each. Antenna: 702-ft. above ground. Lat. 38° 51' 09", long. 88° 07' 06". Transmitter: 2-mi. NW of Dundas. Equipment: Comwave transmitter; Andrew antenna.

Dundas—WLX-796 (Channels C-1-4). Newton Community High School, West End Ave., Newton, IL 62448. Authorized power: 25-w. each. Antenna: 702-ft. above ground. Lat. 38° 51'

09", long. 88° 07' 06". Transmitter: 2-mi. NW of Dundas. Equipment: Comwave transmitter; Andrew antenna.

Dundas—WLX-734 (Channels D-1-4). Robinson High School, 2000 N. Cross, Robinson, IL 62454. Authorized power: 25-w. each. Antenna: 702-ft. above ground. Lat. 38° 51' 09", long. 88° 07' 06". Transmitter: Approx. 2-mi. NW of Dundas. Equipment: Comwave transmitter; Andrew antenna.

Dundas—WLX-548 (Channels G-1-4). Hutsonville Community United School District No. One, W. Clover St., Hutsonville, IL 62433. Phone: 618-563-4912. Fax: 618-563-9122. Authorized power: 25-w. each. Antenna: 705-ft. above ground. Lat. 38° 51' 12", long. 88° 07' 22". Transmitter: Approx. 2-mi. NW of Dundas. Equipment: Comwave transmitter; Andrew antenna.

Golden—WLX-646 (Channels A-1-4). Community Unit School District No. 337, Box 236, One High School Rd., Augusta, IL 62311. Authorized power: 50-w. each. Antenna: 495-ft. above ground. Lat. 40° 06' 37", long. 91° 01' 47". Transmitter: 301 N. Rte. 94. Equipment: Comwave transmitter; Andrew antenna.

Golden—WLX-644 (Channels B-1-4). Community Unit School District No. 337, Box 236, One High School Rd., Augusta, IL 62311. Authorized power: 50-w. each. Antenna: 499-ft. above ground. Lat. 40° 06' 37", long. 91° 01' 47". Transmitter: 301 N. Rte. 94. Equipment: ITS transmitter; Andrew antenna.

Golden—WLX-643 (Channels C-1-4). Community United School District No. 4, Box 218, 380 Collins, Mendon, IL 63251. Authorized power: 50-w. each. Antenna: 493-ft. above ground. Lat. 40° 06' 37", long. 91° 01' 47". Transmitter: 301 N. Rte. 94. Equipment: Comwave transmitter; Andrew antenna.

Golden—WLX-717 (Channels D-1-4). Community Unit School District No. 3, Box 163-A, Camp Point, IL 62320. Authorized power: 50-w. each. Antenna: 475-ft. above ground. Lat. 40° 06' 37", long. 91° 01' 47". Transmitter: 301 N. Rte. 94, Adams County. Equipment: Comwave transmitter; Andrew antenna.

Golden—WLX-713 (Channels G-1-4). Brown City Community Unit School District No. 1, 214 E. North, Mount Sterling, IL 62353. Authorized power: 50-w. each. Antenna: 493-ft. above ground. Lat. 40° 06' 37", long. 91° 01' 47". Transmitter: 301 N. Rte. 94, Adams County. Equipment: Comwave transmitter; Andrew antenna.

Harper—WNC-254 (Channels A-1-4). Lena-Winslow Community Unit School District No. 202, 517 Fremont, Lena, IL 61048. Authorized power: 10-w. each. Antenna: 855-ft. above ground. Lat. 42° 07' 14", long. 89° 44' 39". Transmitter: 0.6-mi. N of Locust Rd. & 4.7-mi. NW of Brookville. Equipment: Comwave transmitter; Andrew antenna.

Harper—WNC-255 (Channels B-1-4). Lee Center Community Unit School District No. 271, Box 508, Paw Paw, IL 61353. Phone: 815-627-2841. Fax: 815-728-2971.
E-mail: tomcat@theramp.net.
Web site: http://2paws.net.
Authorized power: 10-w. each. Antenna: 855-ft. above ground. Lat. 42° 07' 14", long. 89° 44' 39". Transmitter: 0.6-mi. N of Locust Rd. & 4.7-mi. NW of Brookville. Equipment: Comwave transmitter; Andrew antenna.

Harper—WNC-256 (Channels C-1-4). Eastland Community Unit School District No. 308, 200 S. School St., Lanark, IL 61046. Phone: 815-493-6301. Fax: 815-493-6303. Authorized power: 10-w. each. Antenna: 855-ft. above ground. Lat. 42° 07' 14", long. 89° 44' 39". Transmitter: 0.6-mi. N of Locust Rd. & 4.7-mi. NW of Brookville. Equipment: Comwave transmitter; Andrew antenna.
Leased to Nucentrix Broadband Networks, 200 Chisolm Place, Suite 200, Plano, TX 75075. Phone: 972-423-9494. Fax: 972-423-0819.

Harper—WNC-257 (Channels G-1-4). Savanna Community Unit School District No. 300, 18 Adams St., Savanna, IL 61074. Authorized power: 10-w. each. Antenna: 496-ft. above ground. Lat. 42° 07' 14", long. 89° 44' 39". Transmitter: Shannon Rd. Equipment: Comwave transmitter; Andrew antenna.

McLeansboro—WNC-339 (Channels A-1-4). Odin High School, 100 Merritt St., Odin, IL 62870. Authorized power: 12.6-w. each. Antenna: 500-ft. above ground. Lat. 38° 06' 36", long. 88° 32' 09". Transmitter: Kaskaskia College District 501. Equipment: Comwave transmitter; Andrew antenna.

McLeansboro—WLX-619 (Channels B-1-4). Webber Township High School District No. 204, Box 97, Bluford, IL 62814. Phone: 618-732-6121. Fax: 618-732-8784. Authorized power: 12.6-w. each. Antenna: 495-ft. above ground. Lat. 38° 06' 36", long. 88° 32' 09". Transmitter: 800-ft. E of State Rte. 142, 1.1-mi. N of McLeansboro. Equipment: Comwave transmitter; Andrew antenna.

McLeansboro—WLX-710 (Channels C-1-4). Mount Vernon Township High School District No. 201, 320 S. 7th, Mount Vernon, IL 62864. Phone: 618-244-3700. Fax: 618-244-8047. Authorized power: 12.6-w. each. Antenna: 495-ft. above ground. Lat. 38° 06' 36", long. 88° 32' 09". Transmitter: Hamilton County. Equipment: Comwave transmitter; Andrew antenna.
Leased to Nucentrix Broadband Networks, 200 Chisolm Place, Suite 200, Plano, TX 75075. Phone: 972-423-9494. Fax: 972-423-0819.

McLeansboro—WNC-644 (Channels D-1-2). South Central Community United School District No. 401, 800 N. Washington, Farina, IL 62838. Authorized power: 12-w. each. Antenna: 499-ft. above ground. Lat. 38° 06' 36", long. 88° 32' 09". Transmitter: 1.1-mi. N of McLeansboro, near State Rte. 142. Equipment: Comwave transmitter; Andrew antenna.

McLeansboro—WLX-677 (Channels D-1-4). North Wayne Community Unit School District No. 200, Box 235, Cisne, IL 62823. Phone: 618-673-2151. Fax: 618-673-2152.
E-mail: cisnems@wabash.net.
Authorized power: 12.6-w. each. Antenna: 495-ft. above ground. Lat. 38° 06' 36", long. 88° 32' 09". Transmitter: 800-ft. E of State Rte. 142, 1.1-mi. N of McLeansboro. Equipment: Comwave transmitter; Andrew antenna.

McLeansboro—WLX-768 (Channels G-1-4). Norris City-Omaha-Enfield CUSD No. 3, East St., Norris City, IL 62869. Authorized power: 12.6-w. each. Antenna: 500-ft. above ground. Lat. 38° 06' 36", long. 88° 32' 09". Transmitter: 800-ft. E of Illinois Rte. 1. Equipment: Comwave transmitter; Andrew antenna.

Metropolis—WLX-625 (Channels A-1-4). Carlisle County School District, Box 267, Rte. 1, Bardwell, KY 42033. Phone: 502-628-5476. Fax: 502-628-5477. Authorized power: 50-w. each. Antenna: 495-ft. above ground. Lat. 37° 08' 32", long. 88° 39' 01". Transmitter: Approx. 4-mi. E of Metropolis. Equipment: Comwave transmitter; Andrew antenna.

Metropolis—WNC-524 (Channels B-1-4). Mayfield Independent School District, 709 S. 8th, Mayfield, KY 42006. Authorized power: 50-w. each. Antenna: 495-ft. above ground. Lat. 37° 08' 32", long. 88° 39' 01". Transmitter: Approx. 4-mi. E of Metropolis. Equipment: Comwave transmitter; Andrew antenna.

Metropolis—WLX-702 (Channels D-1-4). McCracken School District, 260 Bleich Rd., Paducah, KY 42003. Phone: 502-554-6800. Fax: 502-554-6810.
E-mail: ecool@mccracken.k12.ky.us.
Web site: http://www.mccracken.k12.ky.us.
Authorized power: 50-w. each. Antenna: 495-ft. above ground. Lat. 37° 08' 32", long. 88° 39' 01". Transmitter: Approx. 4-mi. E of Metropolis. Equipment: Comwave transmitter; Andrew antenna.
Leased to Ruralvision.

Metropolis—WLX-774 (Channels G-1-4). Fulton County Schools, Rte. 4, Hickman, KY 42050. Authorized power: 50-w. each. Antenna: 495-ft. above ground. Lat. 37° 08' 32", long. 88° 39' 01". Transmitter: Approx. 4-mi. E of Metropolis. Equipment: Comwave transmitter; Andrew antenna.

Moline—WND-204 (Channels C-1-4). Black Hawk College, 6600 34th Ave., Moline, IL 61265. Authorized power: 10-w. each. Antenna: 279-ft. above ground. Lat. 41° 28' 30", long. 90° 26' 44". Transmitter: Black Hawk College Campus. Equipment: ITS transmitter; Andrew antenna.

Moline—WND-205 (Channels D-1-4). Black Hawk College, 6600 34th Ave., Moline, IL 61265. Authorized power: 10-w. each. Antenna: 279-ft. above ground. Lat. 41° 28' 30", long. 90° 26' 44". Transmitter: Black Hawk College Campus. Equipment: ITS transmitter; Andrew antenna.

Moline—WLX-262 (Channels G-1-2). West Central Illinois Educational Telecommunications Corp., Box 6248, Springfield, IL 62708. Phone: 217-786-6647. Fax: 217-786-7267. Lat. 41° 28' 30", long. 90° 26' 44".

Morton—WLX-887 (Channels B-1-4). Midstate College, 411 West Northmoor Rd., Peoria, IL 61614. Phone: 309-692-4092. Fax: 309-692-3893.
E-mail: midstatec@aol.com.
Web site: http://midstate.edu.
Authorized power: 10-w. each. Antenna: 170-ft. above ground. Lat. 40° 38' 27", long. 89° 24' 33". Transmitter: Rte. One at Lakeland Rd. Equipment: ITS transmitter; Andrew antenna.
Requests change to 50-w. each; 463-ft. above ground; lat. 40° 37' 44", long. 89° 34' 12".
Leased to Heartland Wireless of Peoria, 618 W. Jackson St., Morton, IL 61550. Phone: 309-263-0351.

Morton—WLX-983 (Channels D-1-4). Heartland Community College, 1540 College Ave., Normal, IL 61701. Phone: 309-827-0500. Fax: 309-823-4346.
E-mail: carolyno@hcc.cc.il.us.
Authorized power: 50-w. each. Antenna: 463-ft. above ground. Lat. 40° 37' 44", long. 89° 34' 12". Transmitter: 2600 Cole Hollow Rd. Equipment: Comwave transmitter; Andrew antenna.
Leased to Nucentrix Broadband Networks, 200 Chisolm Place, Suite 200, Plano, TX 75075. Phone: 972-423-9494. Fax: 972-423-0819.

Morton—WLX-841 (Channels G-1-4). Eureka College, 300 E. College Ave., Eureka, IL 61530. Authorized power: 50-w. each. Antenna: 463-ft. above ground. Lat. 40° 37' 44", long. 89° 34' 12". Transmitter: 2600 Cole Hollow Rd. Equipment: Comwave transmitter; Andrew antenna.

Mundelein—WAH-800 (Channels F-1-4). The Catholic Bishop of Chicago, Box 1979, Chicago, IL 60690. Authorized power: 10-w. each. Antenna: 280-ft. above ground. Lat. 42° 17' 13", long. 87° 59' 40". Transmitter: St. Mary of the Lake Seminary. Equipment: Varian/Micro-Link transmitter; Alford antenna.

Ottawa—WND-416 (Channels B-1-3). Ohio Community Consolidated School District No. 17, 103 Memorial, Ohio, IL 61349. Authorized power: 50-w. each. Antenna: 404-ft. above ground. Lat. 41° 15' 38", long. 88° 47' 18". Transmitter: 5-mi. SE of Ottawa. Equipment: Comwave transmitter; Andrew antenna.

Ottawa—WND-419 (Channels G-1-4). Earlville C.U. School District, 415 W. Union, Earlville, IL 60518. Authorized power: 50-w. each. Antenna: 404-ft. above ground. Lat. 41° 15' 38", long. 88° 47' 18". Transmitter: 5-mi. SE of Ottawa. Equipment: Comwave transmitter; Andrew antenna.

Peoria—KTZ-30 (Channels C-1-4). Bradley U., 1501 W. Bradley Ave., Peoria, IL 61606. Phone: 309-677-2767. Authorized power: 50-w. each. Antenna: 463-ft. above ground. Lat. 40° 37' 44", long. 89° 34' 12". Transmitter: 2600 Cole Hollow Rd. Equipment: Comwave transmitter; Andrew antenna.
Leased to Nucentrix Broadband Networks, 200 Chisolm Place, Suite 200, Plano, TX 75075. Phone: 972-423-9494. Fax: 972-423-0819.

Quincy—WND-417 (Channels C-1-4). Ohio Community High School District, 103 Memorial St., Ohio, IL 61349. Authorized power: 50-w. each. Antenna: 403-ft. above ground. Lat. 41° 15' 38", long. 88° 47' 18". Transmitter: approx. 5-mi. SW of Ottawa. Equipment: Comwave transmitter; Andrew antenna.

Rockford—WNC-724 (Channels A-2-4). Durand Communications Unit School District 322. Authorized power: 10-w. each. Antenna: 152-ft. above ground. Lat. 42° 22' 02", long. 89° 05' 13". Transmitter: 2430 Latham Rd. Equipment: ITS transmitter; Andrew antenna.

Rockford—WNC-748 (Channels B-1-4). Pecatonica Community Unified School District 321, 1200 Main St., Pecatonica, IL 61063. Authorized power: 10-w. each. Antenna: 497-ft. above ground. Lat. 42° 22' 02", long. 89° 05' 13". Transmitter: 2430 Latham Rd. Equipment: ITS transmitter; Andrew antenna.

Rockford—WNC-464 (Channels C-1-2). Rockford College, 5050 E. State St., Rockford, IL 61108. Authorized power: 10-w. each. Antenna: 450-ft. above ground. Lat. 42° 17' 48", long. 89° 10' 15". Transmitter: W of Rockford, 3-mi. SSE of Meridian & Auburn Rds. Equipment: ITS transmitter; Andrew antenna.

Rockford—WND-253 (Channels C-3-4). Rockford College, 5050 E. State St., Rockford, IL 61108. Authorized power: 50-w. each. Antenna: 1223-ft. above ground. Lat. 42° 22' 02", long. 89° 05' 13". Transmitter: 2430 Latham Rd. Equipment: ITS transmitter; Andrew antenna.

Rockford—WNC-538 (Channels D-1-4). Harlem Consolidated School District 122, 8065 N. 2nd St., Machesney Park, IL 61115. Phone: 815-654-4500. Fax: 815-654-4600.
E-mail: jcanova@harlem.winbgo.k12.il.us.
Web site: http://www.harlem.winbgo.k12.il.us.
Authorized power: 10-w. each. Antenna: 500-ft. above ground. Lat. 42° 22' 02", long. 89° 05' 13". Transmitter: 2430 Latham Rd. Equipment: ITS transmitter; Andrew antenna.
Leased to U.S. Wireless Cable, 1803 W. Avenue, Austin, TX 78701. Phone: 512-320-8522.

Rockford—WND-208 (Channels G-1-2). Winnebago County United School District No. 323, 100 E. McNair Rd., Winnebago, IL 61088. Authorized power: 50-w. each. Antenna: 387-ft. above ground. Lat. 42° 22' 02", long. 89° 05' 13". Transmitter: 2430 Latham Rd. Equipment: ITS transmitter; Andrew antenna.

Rockford—WND-209 (Channels G-3-4). Rock Valley College, 3301 N. Mulford, Rockford, IL 61111. Authorized power: 50-w. each. Antenna: 387-ft. above ground. Lat. 42° 22' 02", long. 89° 05' 13". Transmitter: 2430 Latham Rd. Equipment: ITS transmitter; Andrew antenna.
Leased to Wireless Cable of Rockford.

South Holland—WLX-940 (Channels B-1-2). South Suburban College, 15800 S. State St., South Holland, IL 60473. Phone: 708-210-5767. Fax: 708-210-5758. Authorized power: 50-w. each. Antenna: 200-ft. above ground. Lat. 41° 36' 17", long. 87° 37' 16". Transmitter: 15800 S. State St. Equipment: ITS transmitter; Andrew antenna.

Sugar Grove—WHR-850 (Channels A-1-4). Waubonsee Community College, Communications Technology Inc., 6213 Middleton Springs Dr., Middleton, WI 53562. Authorized power: 10-w. each. Antenna: 180-ft. above ground. Lat. 41° 47' 50", long. 88° 27' 25". Transmitter: Rte. 47 & Harter Rd. intersection, Sugar Bush.
Leased to Nucentrix Broadband Networks, 200 Chisholm Place, Suite 200, Plano, TX 75075. Phone: 972-423-9494. Fax: 972-423-0819.

Taylorville—WLX-725 (Channels A-1-4). Pana Community Unit School District No. 8, 14 E. Main, Pana, IL 62557. Phone: 217-562-3976. Fax: 217-562-3375. Authorized power: 39.8-w. each. Antenna: 495-ft. above ground. Lat. 39° 33' 52", long. 89° 11' 44". Transmitter: 5.3-mi. at 76° from Taylorville. Equipment: Comwave transmitter; Andrew antenna.

Taylorville—WLX-670 (Channels B-1-4). Edinburg Community Unit School District No. 4, 100 E. Martin St., Edinburg, IL 62531. Authorized power: 39.8-w. each. Antenna: 495-ft. above ground. Lat. 39° 33' 52", long. 89° 11' 44". Transmitter: 5.3-mi. at 76° from Taylorville. Equipment: Comwave transmitter; Andrew antenna.

Taylorville—WLX-739 (Channels C-1-4). South Fork School District No. 14, Box 20, Kincaid, IL 62540. Phone: 217-237-4333. Fax: 217-237-4370. Authorized power: 100-w. each. Antenna: 495-ft. above ground. Lat. 39° 33' 59", long. 89° 11' 47". Transmitter: 5.3-mi. at 76° from Taylorville. Equipment: Comwave transmitter; Andrew antenna.

Taylorville—WLX-781 (Channels D-1-4). Divernon Community Unit School District No. 13, Box 20, Divernon, IL 62530. Phone: 217-628-3414. Fax: 217-628-3814. Authorized power: 39.8-w. each. Antenna: 495-ft. above ground. Lat. 39° 33' 59", long. 89° 11' 47". Transmitter: 5.3-mi. E of Taylorville. Equipment: Comwave transmitter; Andrew antenna.

Taylorville—WLX-854 (Channels G-1-4). Morrisonville Community Unit District No. One, 301 School St., Morrisonville, IL 62546. Phone: 217-526-4431. Fax: 217-526-4433. Authorized power: 100-w. each. Antenna: 495-ft. above ground. Lat. 39° 33' 59", long. 89° 11' 47". Transmitter: 5.3-mi. at 76° from Taylorville. Equipment: Comwave transmitter; Andrew antenna.
Leased to Nucentrix Broadband Networks, 200 Chisolm, Suite 200, Plano, TX 75075. Phone: 972-423-9494. Fax: 972-423-0819.

Tilden—WLX-719 (Channels A-1-4). Christian Fellowship School, Box 227, Du Quoin, IL 62832. Authorized power: 10-w. each. Antenna: 496-ft. above ground. Lat. 38° 18' 47", long. 89° 36' 47". Transmitter: 8-mi. NE of Tilden off Hwy. 153, near Lively Grove. Equipment: ITS transmitter; Andrew antenna.

Tilden—WLX-723 (Channels B-1-4). De Soto Consolidated School District No. 86, 406 E. Washington St., De Soto, IL 62924. Phone: 618-867-2413. Fax: 618-867-3233.
E-mail: rkoehn@desoto.jacksn.k12.il.us.
Authorized power: 10-w. each. Antenna: 496-ft. above ground. Lat. 38° 18' 47", long. 89° 36' 47". Transmitter: 8-mi. NE of Tilden off Hwy. 153, near Lively Grove. Equipment: ITS transmitter; Andrew antenna.
Leased to Rural Vision Central Inc., Box 1482, Canyon Lake, TX 78130. Phone: 210-967-2211.

Tilden—WLX-715 (Channels C-1-4). Nashville Community United School District No. 99, Rte. 3, Nashville, IL 62263. Authorized power: 10-w. each. Antenna: 496-ft. above ground. Lat. 38° 18' 47", long. 89° 36' 47". Transmitter: 8-mi. NE of Tilden off Hwy. 153, near Lively Grove. Equipment: ITS transmitter; Andrew antenna.

Tilden—WLX-711 (Channels D-1-4). Waltonville Community Unit School District No. One, 804 West Knob, Waltonville, IL 62894. Phone: 618-279-7211. Fax: 618-279-7212. Authorized power: 10-w. each. Antenna: 496-ft. above ground. Lat. 38° 18' 47", long. 89° 36' 47". Transmitter: 8-mi. NE of Tilden off Hwy. 153, near Lively Grove. Equipment: ITS transmitter; Andrew antenna.

Tilden—WLX-707 (Channels G-1-4). Sesser-Valier Community Unit School District No. 196, Box 465, Sesser, IL 62884. Phone: 618-625-5105. Fax: 618-625-6696.
E-mail: dthomas@SV.frnkln.k12.il.us.
Authorized power: 10-w. each. Antenna: 496-ft. above ground. Lat. 38° 18' 47", long. 89° 36' 47". Transmitter: 8-mi. NE of Tilden off Hwy. 153, near Lively Grove. Equipment: ITS transmitter; Andrew antenna.

University Park—WND-289 (Channels A-1-4). The Board of Education of Township High School, 385 Winnetka Ave., Chicago, IL 60093. Phone: 847-446-9440. Fax: 847-446-5285.
E-mail: hausfeld@nitc.org.
Web site: http://www.nitc.org.
Authorized power: 50-w. each. Antenna: 495-ft. above ground. Lat. 41° 27' 15", long. 87° 43' 22". Transmitter: Governors State U. campus. Equipment: Comwave transmitter; Bogner antenna.
Leased to PCTV, 5301 E. Broadway Blvd., Tucson, AZ 85711. Phone: 520-519-4400.

University Park—WLX-476 (Channels B-3-4). Board of Trustees of Governors State U., University Pkwy., University Park, IL 60466. Phone: 708-534-5000. Fax: 708-534-8956. Authorized power: 50-w. each. Antenna: 499-ft. above ground. Lat. 41° 27' 15", long. 87° 43' 22". Transmitter: Governors State U. Equipment: ITS transmitter; Andrew antenna.

Vandalia—WLX-913 (Channels A-1-4). Brownstown Community School District No. 201, 421 S. College Ave., Brownstown, IL 62418. Phone: 618-427-3355. Fax: 618-427-3704.
E-mail: jjones@mail.fayette.k12.il.us.
Authorized power: 20-w. each. Antenna: 705-ft. above ground. Lat. 38° 53' 52", long. 88° 59' 51". Transmitter: Approx. 2-mi. NNE of Augsburg. Equipment: Comwave transmitter; Andrew antenna.
Leased to Nucentrix Broadband Networks, 200 Chisolm Place, Suite 200, Plano, TX 75075. Phone: 972-423-9494. Fax: 972-423-0819.

Vandalia—WLX-912 (Channels B-1-4). Patoka Community Unit School District No. 204, 1220 Kinoka Rd., Patoka, IL 62875. Phone: 618-432-5440. Fax: 618-432-5306. Authorized power: 20-w. each. Antenna: 705-ft. above ground. Lat. 38° 53' 52", long. 88° 59' 51". Transmitter: Approx. 2-mi. NNE of Augsburg. Equipment: Comwave transmitter; Andrew antenna.
Leased to Nucentrix Broadband Networks, 200 Chisolm Place, Suite 200, Plano, TX 75075. Phone: 972-423-9494. Fax: 972-423-0819.

Vandalia—WLX-767 (Channels C-1-4). Altamont Community Unit School District No. 10, 7 S. Ewing St., Altamont, IL 62411. Authorized power: 20-w. each. Antenna: 705-ft. above ground. Lat. 38° 53' 52", long. 88° 59' 51". Transmitter: Approx 2-mi. NNE of Augsburg. Equipment: Comwave transmitter; Andrew antenna.

Vandalia—WLX-910 (Channels D-1-4). Mulberry Grove Community Unit School District No. 1, Box 327, Rural Rte. 2, Mulberry Grove, IL 62262. Phone: 618-326-8812. Fax: 618-326-8482. Authorized power: 20-w. each. Antenna: 705-ft. above ground. Lat. 38° 53' 52", long. 88° 59' 51". Transmitter: Approx. 2-mi. NNE of Augsburg. Equipment: Comwave transmitter; Andrew antenna.

Vandalia—WLX-911 (Channels G-1-4). Salem Community High School, 1200 N. Broadway, Salem, IL 62881. Phone: 618-548-0727. Fax: 618-548-8021.
E-mail: salem@schs.marion.k12.81.us.
Web site: http://www.salemhigh.com.
Authorized power: 20-w. each. Antenna: 705-ft. above ground. Lat. 38° 53' 52", long. 88° 59' 51". Transmitter: Approx. 2-mi. NNE of Augsburg. Equipment: Comwave transmitter; Andrew antenna.
Leased to Nucentrix Broadband Networks, 200 Chisolm Place, Suite 200, Plano, TX 75075. Phone: 972-423-9494. Fax: 972-423-0819.

Walnut Grove—WLX-559 (Channels A-1-4). Alexis Community Unit School District No. 400, Box 599, Holloway St., Alexis, IL 61412. Authorized power: 20-w. each. Antenna: 704-ft. above ground. Lat. 40° 41' 10", long. 90° 35' 13". Transmitter: 3.1-mi. S of State Rd. 116, 5-mi. NNW of Walnut Grove. Equipment: Comwave transmitter; Andrew antenna.

Walnut Grove—WLX-540 (Channels B-1-4). Union Community Unit School District No. 115, Box 72, RR 1, Biggsville, IL 61418. Phone: 309-627-2371. Authorized power: 20-w. each. Antenna: 704-ft. above ground. Lat. 40° 41' 10", long. 90° 35' 13". Transmitter: 3.1-mi. S of State Rd. 116, 5-mi. NNW of Walnut Grove. Equipment: Comwave transmitter; Andrew antenna.

Walnut Grove—WLX-558 (Channels C-1-4). V.I.T. Community Unit School District No. 2, Box 7, Rte. 1, Table Grove, IL 61482. Phone: 309-758-5138. Fax: 309-758-5298.
E-mail: vit.k-12.il.us.
Authorized power: 20-w. each. Antenna: 704-ft. above ground. Lat. 40° 41' 03", long. 90° 35' 28". Transmitter: 3.1-mi. S of State Rd. 116, 5-mi. NNW of Walnut Grove. Equipment: Comwave transmitter; Andrew antenna.
Leased to Nucentrix Broadband Networks, 200 Chisolm Place, Suite 200, Plano, TX 75075. Phone: 972-423-9494. Fax: 972-423-0819.

Walnut Grove—WLX-551 (Channels D-1-4). Avon Community Unit School District No. 176, 320 E. Wood St., Avon, IL 61415. Phone: 309-465-3708. Fax: 309-465-9030. Authorized power: 20-w. each. Antenna: 704-ft. above ground. Lat. 40° 41' 03", long. 90° 35' 28". Transmitter: 3.1-mi. S of State Rd. 116, 5-mi. NNW of Walnut Grove. Equipment: Comwave transmitter; Andrew antenna.
Leased to Nucentrix Broadband Networks, 200 Chisolm Place, Suite 200, Plano, TX 75075. Phone: 972-423-9494. Fax: 972-423-0819.

Walnut Grove—WLX-541 (Channels G-1-4). Schuyler County Community Unit School District No. 1, 215 W. Washington, Rushville, IL 62681. Authorized power: 20-w. each. Antenna: 704-ft. above ground. Lat. 40° 41' 03", long. 90° 35' 28". Transmitter: approx. 5-mi. NNW of Walnut Grove. Equipment: Comwave transmitter; Andrew antenna.
Leased to Nucentrix Broadband Networks, 200 Chisolm Place, Suite 200, Plano, TX 75075. Phone: 972-423-9494. Fax: 972-423-0819.

Woodford—KVO-30 (Channels E-1-2). Bradley U., 1501 W. Bradley Ave., Peoria, IL 61606. Lat. 40° 50' 00", long. 89° 19' 08". Transmitter: 3.2-mi. NE of Metamora.

Wyoming—KVO-29 (Channels A-1-2). Bradley U., 1501 W. Bradley Ave., Peoria, IL 61606. Transmitter: 0.7-mi. N of Wyoming.

Indiana

Anderson—WND-449 (Channels A-1-4). Ball State U., Office of the President, Muncie, IN 47306. Authorized power: 20-w. each. Antenna: 472-ft. above ground. Lat. 40° 03' 43", long. 85° 42' 34". Transmitter: 2500 W. 53rd St. Equipment: Comwave transmitter; Andrew antenna.

Anderson—WFD-457 (Channels B-1-4). Trustees of Indiana U., Indiana Higher Education Telecommunications Systems, 957 W. Michigan St., Indianapolis, IN 46202. Phone: 317-263-8923. Fax: 317-263-8831. Authorized power: 20-w. each. Antenna: 472-ft. above ground. Lat. 40° 03' 43", long. 85° 42' 34". Transmitter: 2500 W. 53rd St. Equipment: Comwave transmitter; Andrew antenna.
Leased to PCTV, 597 Industrial Dr., Suite 212, Carmel, IN 46032 4207. Phone: 317-844-0202.

Anderson—WHR-826 (Channels C-1-4). Metro Indianapolis Bcstg. Inc., 1401 N. Meridian St., Indianapolis, IN 46202. Phone: 317-636-2020. Fax: 317-633-7418. Authorized power: 100-w. each. Antenna: 1043-ft. above ground. Lat. 39° 46' 11", long. 86° 09' 26". Transmitter: Bank One Bldg., 111 Monument Circle. Equipment: Comwave transmitter; Andrew antenna.
Leased to Broadcast Cable Inc., 4109 E. 65th St., Indianapolis, IN 46220. Phone: 317-257-6934.

Anderson—WLX-951 (Channels D-1-4). Network for Instructional TV Inc., Suite 110, 11490 Commerce Park Dr., Reston, VA 20191. Phone: 703-860-9200. Fax: 703-860-9237. Authorized power: 10-w. each. Antenna: 534-ft. above ground. Lat. 40° 03' 43", long. 85° 42' 34". Transmitter: 2500 W. 53rd St. Equipment: Comwave transmitter; Andrew antenna.
Leased to People's Choice TV of Indianapolis Inc., 2 Corporate Dr., Suite 249, Shelton, CT 06484. Phone: 203-292-2800.

Bedford—WLX-252 (Channels G-1-4). Trustees of Indiana U., Indiana Higher Education Telecommunications Systems, 957 W. Michigan St., Indianapolis, IN 46202. Phone: 317-263-8923. Fax: 317-263-8831. Authorized power: 10-w. each. Antenna: 277-ft. above ground. Lat. 38° 44' 05", long. 86° 34' 43". Transmitter: 1.5-mi. N of Hwy. 60. Equipment: Comwave transmitter; Andrew antenna.

Bloomington—WFD-422 (Channels A-1-4). Trustees of Indiana U, Indiana Higher Education Telecommunications Systems, 957 W. Michigan St., Indianapolis, IN 46202. Phone: 317-263-8923. Fax: 317-263-8831. Authorized power: 50-w. each. Antenna: 590-ft. above ground. Lat. 39° 08' 32", long. 86° 29' 43". Transmitter: Sare Rd., 2.7-mi. SE of Bloomington. Equipment: Comwave transmitter; Andrew antenna.

Bloomington—WND-450 (Channels B-1-4). Ball State U., Office of the President, Muncie, IN 47306. Authorized power: 50-w. each. Antenna: 590-ft. above ground. Lat. 39° 08' 32", long. 86° 29' 43". Transmitter: 2.7-mi. SE of Bloomington. Equipment: Comwave transmitter; Andrew antenna.

Bloomington—WFD-424 (Channels C-1-4). Trustees of Indiana U., Indiana Higher Education Telecommunications Systems, 957 W. Michigan St., Indianapolis, IN 46202. Phone: 317-263-8923. Fax: 317-263-8831. Authorized power: 50-w. each. Antenna: 408-ft. above ground. Lat. 39° 08' 32", long. 86° 29' 43". Transmitter: Ballantine Hill, Indiana U. campus antenna. Equipment: Comwave transmitter; Omni antenna.

Cedar Lake—KPD-40 (Channels A-1-4). Trustees of Indiana U., Indiana Higher Education Telecommunications Systems, 957 W. Michigan St., Indianapolis, IN 46202. Phone: 317-263-8923. Fax: 317-263-8831. Authorized power: 50-w. each. Antenna: 500-ft. above ground. Lat. 41° 21' 09", long. 87° 24' 18". Transmitter: Lake Central High School, St. John. Equipment: Comwave transmitter; Omni antenna.

Columbus—WHB-821 (Channels B-1-4). Trustees of Indiana U., Indiana Higher Education Telecommunications Systems, 957 W. Michigan St., Indianapolis, IN 46202. Phone: 317-263-8923. Fax: 317-263-8831. Authorized power: 50-w. each. Antenna: 357-ft. above ground. Lat. 39° 11' 50", long. 85° 48' 32". Transmitter: 2-mi. E of Jewell Village. Equipment: Comwave transmitter; Omni antenna.

Columbus—WHR-889 (Channels G-1-4). Trustees of Indiana U., Indiana Higher Education Telecommunications Systems, 957 W. Michigan St., Indianapolis, IN 46202. Phone: 317-263-8923. Fax: 317-263-8831. Authorized power: 2-w. each. Antenna: 44-ft. above ground. Lat. 39° 14' 39", long. 85° 54' 09". Equipment: Comwave transmitter. Requests change to 450-ft. above ground, lat. 30° 19' 43", long. 85° 41' 25"; transmitter to 0.4-mi. N of Rte. 388.

Elkhart—WLX-457 (Channels A-1-4). North American Catholic Educational Programming Foundation Inc., Box 40026, Providence, RI 02940-0026. Phone: 401-729-0900. Authorized power: 10-w. each. Antenna: 296-ft. above ground. Lat. 41° 40' 28", long. 85° 56' 51". Transmitter: 1246 E. Indiana Ave. Equipment: Andrew antenna.

Elkhart—WLX-423 (Channels C-1-4). The Learning Society of Elkhart Inc., 200 Kenyon Ave., Elkhart, IN 46516. Phone: 219-522-1725. Fax: 219-522-1725.
E-mail: jrueff@lsoc-vol.org.
Web site: http://www.lsoc-vol.org.
Authorized power: 50-w. each. Antenna: 750-ft. above ground. Lat. 41° 36' 59", long. 85° 11' 43". Transmitter: 16965 Johnson Rd. Equipment: ITS transmitter; Andrew antenna.
Leased to American Telecasting Inc., 5575 Tech Center Dr., Suite 300, Colorado Springs, CO 80919. Phone: 719-260-5533.

Evansville—WBX-204 (Channels B-1-4). Trustees of Indiana U., Indiana Higher Education Telecommunications Systems, 957 W. Michigan St., Indianapolis, IN 46202. Phone: 317-263-8923. Fax: 317-263-8831. Authorized power: 1-w. each. Antenna: 130-ft. above ground. Lat. 37° 57' 46", long. 87° 40' 42". Transmitter: Hwy. 62 & Schatte Rd., Indiana U. regional campus. Equipment: Comwave transmitter.

Evansville—WBX-205 (Channels D-1-4). Trustees of Indiana U., Indiana Higher Education Telecommunications Systems, 957 W. Michigan St., Indianapolis, IN 46202. Phone: 317-263-8923. Fax: 317-263-8831. Authorized power: 50-w. each. Antenna: 600-ft. above ground. Lat. 37° 59' 13", long. 87° 16' 11". Transmitter: Old National Bank Bldg., 420 Main St. Equipment: Comwave transmitter; Andrew antenna.

Fort Wayne—WBX-213 (Channels A-1-4). Trustees of Indiana U., Indiana Higher Education Telecommunications Systems, 957 W. Michigan St., Indianapolis, IN 46202. Phone: 317-263-8923. Fax: 317-263-8831. Authorized power: 100-w. each. Antenna: 525-ft. above ground. Lat. 41° 06' 25", long. 85° 11' 46". Transmitter: 3431 Hillegas Rd. Equipment: Comwave transmitter; Bogner antenna.

Fort Wayne—WLX-833 (Channels B-1-4). Views on Learning Inc., 200 Kenyon Ave., Elkhart, IN 46516. Phone: 219-522-1725. Fax: 219-522-1725.
E-mail: jrueff@lsoc-vol.org.
Web site: http://www.lsoc-vol.org.
Authorized power: 100-w. each. Antenna: 523-ft. above ground. Lat. 41° 06' 25", long. 85° 11' 46". Transmitter: 3431 Hillegas Rd. Equipment: Comwave transmitter; Bogner antenna.
Leased to Choice TV of Ft. Wayne, 1909 Production Rd., Fort Wayne, IN 46508. Phone: 219-436-9794.

Fort Wayne—WLX-236 (Channels C-1-4). Trustees of Indiana U., Indiana Higher Education Telecommunications Systems, 957 W. Michigan St., Indianapolis, IN 46202. Phone: 317-263-8923. Fax: 317-263-8831. Authorized power: 100-w. each. Antenna: 525-ft. above ground. Lat. 41° 06' 25", long. 85° 11' 46". Transmitter: 3431 Hillegas Rd. Equipment: Comwave transmitter; Bogner antenna.

Fort Wayne—WHR-798 (Channels D-1-4). Trustees of Indiana U., Indiana Higher Education Telecommuni, cations Systems, Indiana U., Bloomington, IN 47401. Phone: 317-263-8923. Fax: 317-263-8831. Authorized power: 100-w. each. Antenna: 522-ft. above ground. Lat. 41° 06' 25", long. 85° 11' 46". Transmitter: 3431 Hillegas Rd. Equipment: Comwave transmitter; Bogner antenna.

Fort Wayne—WLX-306 (Channels G-1-4). North American Catholic Educational Programming Foundation Inc., Box 40026, Providence, RI 02940. Phone: 401-729-0900. Lat. 41° 06' 25", long. 85° 11' 46".

Franklin—WFD-456 (Channels D-1-4). Network for Instructional TV Inc., 11490 Commerce Park Dr., Reston, VA 22091. Authorized power: 10-w. each. Antenna: 150-ft. above ground. Lat. 39° 28' 45", long. 86° 02' 45". Transmitter: Franklin College Campus. Equipment: Comwave transmitter.

Greencastle—WHR-824 (Channels D-1-4). Trustees of Indiana U., Indiana Higher Education Telecommunications Systems, 957 W. Michigan St., Indianapolis, IN 46202. Phone: 317-263-8923. Fax: 317-263-8831. Authorized power: 50-w. each. Antenna: 237-ft. above ground. Lat. 39° 41' 18", long. 86° 45' 29". Transmitter: 5.2-mi. NE of Greencastle. Equipment: Comwave transmitter; Omni antenna.

Indianapolis—WBX-257 (Channels A-1-4). Trustees of Indiana U., Indiana Higher Education Telecommunications Systems, 957 W. Michigan St., Indianapolis, IN 46202. Phone: 317-263-8923. Fax: 317-263-8831. Authorized power: 50-w. each. Antenna: 523-ft. above ground. Lat. 39° 46' 13", long. 86° 09' 20". Transmitter: One Indiana Square. Equipment: Comwave transmitter; Omni antenna.

Indianapolis—WHR-808 (Channels B-1-4). Trustees of Indiana U., Indiana Higher Education Telecommunications Systems, 957 W. Michigan St., Indianapolis, IN 46202. Phone: 317-263-8923. Fax: 317-263-8831. Authorized power: 100-w. each. Antenna: 2703-ft. above ground. Lat. 39° 46' 11", long. 86° 09' 26". Transmitter: Bank One Bldg., 111 Monument Circle. Equipment: Comwave transmitter; Andrew antenna.

Indianapolis—WAT-21 (Channels E-1-2). Trustees of Indiana U., Indiana Higher Education Telecommunications Systems, 957 W. Michigan St., Indianapolis, IN 46202. Phone: 317-263-8923. Fax: 317-263-8831. Authorized power: 10-w. each. Antenna: 140-ft. above ground. Lat. 39° 46' 30", long. 86° 10' 34". Transmitter: Indiana U. Hospital, Indiana U. Medical Center. Equipment: Emcee transmitter; Omni antenna.

Indianapolis—WHR-509 (Channels G-1-4). Instructional Telecommunications Foundation Inc., Box 6060, Boulder, CO 30306. Phone: 303-442-4180. Fax: 303-442-6472.
E-mail: ITF@fstv.org.
Authorized power: 10-w. each. Antenna: 524-ft. above ground. Lat. 39° 46' 13", long. 86° 09' 20". Transmitter: Indiana Bank tower, One Indiana Square.
Leased to PCTV, 597 Industrial Dr., Suite 212, Carmel, IN 46032 4207. Phone: 317-844-0002.

Jasper—WGR-704 (Channel F-1). Board of Trustees of Vincennes U., 1001 N. First St., Vincennes, IN 47591. Authorized power: 0.1-w. Antenna: 300-ft. above ground. Lat. 38° 22' 31", long. 86° 54' 07". Transmitter: 1.8-mi. N of Huntingburg on U.S. Rte. 231.

Kokomo—WND-298 (Channels C-1-4). Metropolitan Indianapolis Public Broadcasting, 1401 N. Meridian St., Indianapolis, IN 46202. Authorized power: 50-w. each. Antenna: 472-ft. above ground. Lat. 40° 26' 58", long. 86° 04' 57". Transmitter: 2386 E. 200 South Rd. Equipment: Comwave transmitter; Andrew antenna.

Kokomo—WHB-846 (Channels D-1-4). Trustees of Indiana U., Indiana Higher Education Telecommunications Systems, 957 W. Michigan St., Indianapolis, IN 46202. Phone: 317-263-8923. Fax: 317-263-8831. Authorized power: 50-w. each. Antenna: 472-ft. above ground. Lat. 40° 26' 58", long. 86° 04' 57". Transmitter: 1400-ft. W of 500 East Rd. & 800-ft. N of 200 South Rd. Equipment: Andrew transmitter; Omni antenna.
Leased to Broadcast Cable Inc., 4109 E. 65th St., Indianapolis, IN 46220. Phone: 317-257-6934.

Kokomo—WHB-845 (Channels G-1-4). Purdue U., 1063 Horde Hall, West Lafayette, IN 47907. Authorized power: 50-w. each. Antenna: 472-ft. above ground. Lat. 40° 27' 38", long. 86° 07' 55". Transmitter: 2386 S.E. 200 South Rd. Equipment: Comwave transmitter; Andrew antenna.

La Porte—WHR-643 (Channels F-1-2). Northwest Indiana Public Broadcasting Inc., 6100 Southport Rd., Portage, IN 46368-6409. Lat. 41° 34' 29", long. 86° 39' 02".

Lafayette—WND-434 (Channels A-1-4). Ball State U., Muncie, IN 47306. Authorized power: 100-w. each. Antenna: 394-ft. above ground. Lat. 40° 23' 24", long. 86° 51' 53". Transmitter: 2510 S. 30th St. Equipment: ITS transmitter; Andrew antenna.

Lafayette—WND-295 (Channels G-1-4). Lafayette School Corp., 230 Cason St., Lafayette, IN 47904. Authorized power: 50-w. each. Antenna: 3232-ft. above ground. Lat. 40° 23' 24", long. 86° 51' 53". Transmitter: 2510 S. 30th St. Equipment: ITS transmitter; Andrew antenna.

Madison—WHG-341 (Channels C-1-4). Trustees of Indiana U., Indiana Higher Education Telecommunications Systems, 957 W. Michigan St., Indianapolis, IN 46202. Phone: 317-263-8923. Fax: 317-263-8831. Authorized power: 10-w. each. Antenna: 220-ft. above ground. Lat. 38° 47' 41", long. 85° 25' 31". Transmitter: West Rd., 600-ft. S of North Rd. Equipment: Comwave transmitter; Omni antenna.

Merrillville—WHR-645 (Channels F-1-2). Northwest Indiana Public Broadcasting Inc., 6100 Southport Rd., Portage, IN 46368-6409. Transmitter: Hwy. 70.

Napoleon—WNC-277 (Channels A-1-4). Anna Local School District, Box 169, One McRill Way, Anna, OH 45302. Phone: 513-394-2011. Fax: 513-394-7658.
E-mail: al supt@woco.ohio.gov.
Authorized power: 50-w. each. Antenna: 859-ft. above ground. Lat. 39° 16' 43", long. 85° 19' 22". Transmitter: County Rds. 850E & 400S intersection. Equipment: Comwave transmitter; Andrew antenna.

Napoleon—WNC-276 (Channels B-1-4). Benjamin Logan Local School District, 2091 State Rte. 47E, Bellfontaine, OH 43311. Authorized power: 50-w. each. Antenna: 859-ft. above ground. Lat. 39° 16' 43", long. 85° 19' 22". Transmitter: County Rds. 850E & 400S intersection. Equipment: Comwave transmitter; Andrew antenna.

Napoleon—WNC-278 (Channels C-1-4). Jackson Center Local School District, 204 S. Linden, Jackson Center, OH 45334. Phone: 513-596-6053. Authorized power: 50-w. each. Antenna: 859-ft. above ground. Lat. 39° 16' 43", long. 85° 19' 22". Transmitter: County Rds. 850E & 400S intersection. Equipment: Comwave transmitter; Andrew antenna.

Napoleon—WNC-284 (Channels D-1-4). Waynes-Goshen Local School District, Box 370, N. Westminster St., Waynesfield, OH 45896. Phone: 419-568-4451. Authorized power: 50-w. each. Antenna: 859-ft. above ground. Lat. 39° 16' 43", long. 85° 19' 22". Transmitter: County Rds. 850E & 400S intersection. Equipment: Comwave transmitter; Andrew antenna.

Napoleon—WNC-283 (Channels G-1-4). Graham Local School District, 104 W. Main St., St. Paris, OH 43072. Phone: 513-663-4123. Authorized power: 50-w. each. Antenna: 859-ft. above ground. Lat. 39° 16' 43", long. 85° 19' 22". Transmitter: County Rds. 850E & 400S intersection. Equipment: Comwave transmitter; Andrew antenna.

New Albany—WBX-215 (Channels G-1-4). Trustees of Indiana U., Indiana Higher Education Telecommunications Systems, 957 W. Michigan St., Indianapolis, IN 46202. Phone: 317-263-8923. Fax: 317-263-8831. Authorized power: 50-w. each. Antenna: 377-ft. above ground. Lat. 38° 10' 25", long. 85° 54' 50". Transmitter: Rte. 1, Bald Knob Rd. Equipment: Comwave transmitter; Bogner antenna.

Pelzer—WLX-881 (Channels A-1-2). U. of Southern Indiana, 8600 University Blvd., Evansville, IN 47712. Phone: 812-464-1968. Fax: 812-465-7061.
E-mail: kbonnel.usc@smpt.usi.edu.
Authorized power: 50-w. each. Antenna: 595-ft. above ground. Lat. 37° 59' 13", long. 87° 16' 11". Transmitter: 0.7-mi. WSW of Pelzer. Equipment: Comwave transmitter; Andrew antenna.
Leased to Ohio Valley Cable Ltd., 1420 N. Cullen Ave., Evansville, IN 47715. Phone: 812-471-7500.

Pelzer—WLX-880 (Channels A-3-4). U. of Southern Indiana, 8600 University Blvd., Evansville, IN 47712. Phone: 812-464-1968. Fax: 812-465-7061.
E-mail: kbonnell.ucs@smtp.usi.edu.
Authorized power: 50-w. each. Antenna: 600-ft. above ground. Lat. 37° 59' 13", long. 87° 16' 11". Transmitter: New Hope Rd., 0.7-mi. WSW of Pelzer. Equipment: ITS transmitter; Andrew antenna.
Leased to Ohio Valley Cable Ltd., 1420 N. Cullen Ave., Evansville, IN 47715. Phone: 812-471-7500.

Pelzer—WLX-878 (Channels C-1-4). U. of Southern Indiana, 8600 University Blvd., Evansville, IL 47712. Phone: 812-464-1968. Fax: 812-465-7061.
E-mail: kbonnell.usc@smtp.usi.edu.
Authorized power: 50-w. each. Antenna: 593-ft. above ground. Lat. 37° 59' 13", long. 87° 16' 11". Transmitter: 0.7-mi. WSW of Pelzer. Equipment: Comwave transmitter; Andrew antenna.
Leased to Ohio Valley Cable Ltd., 1420 N. Cullen Ave., Evansville, IN 47715. Phone: 812-471-7500.

Pelzer—WLX-883 (Channels G-1-4). Northern Arizona U. Foundation, Babbit Administration Bldg., Flagstaff, AZ 86011. Authorized power: 50-w. each. Antenna: 595-ft. above ground. Lat. 37° 59' 13", long. 87° 16' 11". Transmitter: 0.7-mi. WSW of Pelzer. Equipment: Comwave transmitter; Andrew antenna.

Plainville—WHR-926 (Channels A-1-4). Board of Trustees of Vincennes U., 1002 N. First St., Vincennes, IN 47591. Authorized power: 10-w. each. Antenna: 200-ft. above ground. Lat. 38° 51' 00", long. 87° 17' 52". Transmitter: 700 North Rd., 7-mi. N of Washington & 0.25-mi. W of U.S. Rtes. 57 & 150. Equipment: Comwave transmitter; Andrew antenna.

Plainville—WBS-405 (Channels C-1-4). Board of Trustees of Vincennes U., 1002 N. First St., Vincennes, IN 47591. Phone: 812-888-8888. Authorized power: 10-w. each. Antenna: 200-ft. above ground. Lat. 38° 51' 00", long. 87° 17' 52". Transmitter: 700 North Rd., 7-mi. N of Washington & 0.25-mi. W of U.S. Rtes. 57 & 150. Equipment: Comwave transmitter; Andrew antenna.

Princeton—WOX-84 (Channel A-1). North Gibson School Corp., Water & West Sts., Princeton, IN 47670. Authorized power: 10-w. Antenna: 100-ft. above ground. Lat. 38° 21' 56", long. 87° 34' 54". Transmitter: Princeton Community High School, Embree & Warnock Sts.

Rensselaer—WHR-825 (Channels C-1-4). Trustees of Indiana U., Indiana Higher Education Telecommunications Systems, 957 W. Michigan St., Indianapolis, IN 46202. Phone: 317-263-8923. Fax: 317-263-8831. Authorized power: 50-w. each. Antenna: 409-ft. above ground. Lat. 40° 55' 17", long. 87° 08' 51". Transmitter: 0.4-mi. S of Rensselaer. Equipment: Comwave transmitter; Omni antenna.

Richmond—WFD-423 (Channel D-1). Trustees of Indiana U., Indiana Higher Education Telecommunications Systems, 957 W. Michigan St., Indianapolis, IN 46202. Phone: 317-263-8923. Fax: 317-263-8831. Authorized power: 50-w. Antenna: 349-ft. above ground. Lat. 39° 52' 18", long. 84° 52' 49". Transmitter: 0.4-mi. E of U.S. 27. Equipment: Comwave transmitter; Omni antenna.
Leased to Wireless Cablecom Ltd.

Rochester—WHR-944 (Channels G-1-4). Trustees of Indiana U., Indiana Higher Education Telecommunications Systems, 957 W. Michigan St., Indianapolis, IN 46202. Phone: 317-263-8923. Fax: 317-263-8831. Authorized power: 50-w. each. Antenna: 761-ft. above ground. Lat. 41° 46' 41", long. 86° 04' 48". Transmitter: 0.3-mi. N of Lovers Lane Rd. & County Rd. 190. Equipment: Comwave transmitter; Andrew antenna.
Leased to American Telecasting Inc., 5575 Tech Center Dr., Suite 300, Colorado Springs, CO 80919. Phone: 719-260-5533.

South Bend—WHR-490 (Channels B-1-4). Trustees of Indiana U., Indiana Higher Education Telecommunications Systems, 957 W. Michigan St., Indianapolis, IN 46202. Phone: 317-263-8923. Fax: 317-263-8831. Authorized power: 50-w. each. Antenna: 680-ft. above ground. Lat. 41° 36' 59", long. 86° 11' 43". Transmitter: 16965 Johnson Rd., Mishawaka. Equipment: Comwave transmitter; Omni antenna.
Leased to American Telecasting Inc., 5575 Tech Center Dr., Suite 300, Colorado Springs, CO 80919. Phone: 719-260-5533.

South Bend—WHR-489 (Channels D-1-4). Trustees of Indiana U., Indiana Higher Education Telecommunications Systems, 957 W. Michigan St., Indianapolis, IN 46202. Phone: 317-263-8923. Fax: 317-263-8831. Authorized power: 50-w. each. Antenna: 751-ft. above ground. Lat. 41° 36' 59", long. 86° 11' 43". Transmitter: 1700 Mishawaka Ave. Equipment: ITS transmitter; Andrew antenna.

South Bend—WHR-491 (Channels G-1-4). Trustees of Indiana U., Indiana Higher Education Telecommunications Systems, 957 W. Michigan St., Indianapolis, IN 46202. Phone: 317-263-8923. Fax: 317-263-8831. Authorized power: 50-w. each. Antenna: 679-ft. above ground. Lat. 41° 36' 59", long. 86° 11' 43". Transmitter: 16965 Johnson Rd., Mishawaka. Equipment: Comwave transmitter; Andrew antenna.

Terre Haute—WBG-606 (Channels A-1-4). Trustees of Indiana U, Indiana Higher Education Telecommunications Systems, 957 W. Michigan St., Indianapolis, IN 46202. Phone: 317-263-8923. Fax: 317-263-8831. Authorized power: 100-w. each. Antenna: 407-ft. above ground. Lat. 39° 30' 26", long. 87° 31' 50". Transmitter: 30th Ave. & 71st Place. Equipment: Comwave transmitter; Andrew antenna.

Terre Haute—WHR-953 (Channels D-1-4). Trustees of Indiana U., Indiana Higher Telecommunications Systems, 957 W. Michigan St., Indianapolis, IN 46202. Phone: 317-263-8923. Fax: 317-263-8831. Authorized power: 100-w. each. Antenna: 440-ft. above ground. Lat. 39° 30' 26", long. 87° 31' 50". Transmitter: 30th Ave. & 71st Place. Equipment: Comwave transmitter; Andrew antenna.

Versailles—WHR-823 (Channels G-1-4). Trustees of Indiana U., Indiana Higher Education Telecommunications Systems, 957 W. Michigan St., Indianapolis, IN 46202. Phone: 317-263-8923. Fax: 317-263-8831. Authorized power: 50-w. each. Antenna: 307-ft. above ground. Lat. 39° 04' 04", long. 85° 15' 57". Transmitter: 0.5-mi. W of Versailles. Equipment: Comwave transmitter; Omni antenna.

Vincennes—WLX-231 (Channels B-1-4). Board of Trustees, Vincennes U., 1002 N. First St., Vincennes, IN 47541. Phone: 812-888-8888. Authorized power: 10-w. each. Antenna: 200-ft. above ground. Lat. 38° 51' 00", long. 87° 17' 52". Transmitter: 700 North Rd., 7-mi. N of Washington & 0.25-mi. W of U.S. Rtes. 57 & 150. Equipment: Comwave transmitter; Andrew antenna.

Vincennes—WBS-404 (Channels G-1-4). Vincennes U., 1002 N. First St., Vincennes, IN 47591. Authorized power: 50-w. each. Antenna: 423-ft. above ground. Lat. 38° 39' 06", long. 87° 28' 37". Transmitter: Vincennes U. Campus, 0.3-mi. SW of Hwy. 61. Equipment: Comwave transmitter; Andrew antenna.

Warsaw—WLX-462 (Channels D-1-4). Trustees of Indiana U., Indiana Higher Telecommunications Systems, 957 W. Michigan St., Indianapolis, IN 46202. Phone: 317-263-8923. Fax: 317-263-8831. Authorized power: 10-w. each. Antenna: 224-ft. above ground. Lat. 41° 14' 11", long. 85° 52' 27". Transmitter: 1401 W. Center St. Equipment: Comwave transmitter; Omni antenna.

West Lafayette—WGI-228 (Channel B-1). Trustees of Indiana U., Indiana Higher Education Telecommunications Systems, 957 W. Michigan St., Indianapolis, IN 46202. Phone: 317-263-8923. Fax: 317-263-8831. Authorized power: 50-w. Antenna: 409-ft. above ground. Lat. 40° 17' 50", long. 86° 54' 05". Transmitter: 8-mi. S of Lafayette. Equipment: Comwave transmitter; Omni antenna.
Leased to Universal Wireless Television.

West Lafayette—WGI-229 (Channels D-1-4). Trustees of Indiana U., Indiana Higher Telecommunications Systems, 957 W. Michigan St., Indianapolis, IN 46202. Phone: 317-263-8923. Fax: 317-263-8831. Authorized power: 1-w. each. Antenna: 85-ft. above ground. Lat. 40° 25' 30", long. 86° 54' 45". Transmitter: Stewart Center, Purdue U. campus. Equipment: Comwave transmitter.

Iowa

Allison—WLX-210 (Channels G-3-4). Hawkeye Institute of Technology, 1501 E. Orange Rd., Waterloo, IA 50704. Authorized power: 10-w. each. Antenna: 362-ft. above ground. Lat. 42° 41' 47", long. 92° 47' 27". Equipment: ITS transmitter; Andrew antenna.

Anamosa—WGW-944 (Channel C-3). Kirkwood Community College, 6301 Kirkwood Blvd. SW, Cedar Rapids, IA 52406. Phone: 319-398-5663.
E-mail: othein@kirkwood.cc.ia.us.
Authorized power: 10-w. . Antenna: 297-ft. above ground. Lat. 42° 06' 35", long. 91° 16' 16". Transmitter: 209 Sadie St. Equipment: Emcee transmitter; Andrew antenna.

Batavia—WMX-648 (Channels D-1-4). Iowa Rural TV Inc., 404 4th St., Batavia, IA 52533. Phone: 515-662-3400. Fax: 515-662-2511.
E-mail: mckeever@notins.net.
Authorized power: 50-w. each. Antenna: 460-ft. above ground. Lat. 40° 56' 10", long. 92° 10' 16". Transmitter: 4.5-mi. S of Batavia. Equipment: ITS transmitter; Andrew antenna.

Batavia—WMX-649 (Channels G-1-4). Iowa Rural TV Inc., Box 160, 404 4th St., Batavia, IA 52533. Phone: 515-662-3400. Fax: 515-662-2511. Authorized power: 50-w. each. Antenna: 460-ft. above ground. Lat. 40° 56' 10", long. 92° 10' 16". Transmitter: 4.5-mi. S of Batavia. Equipment: ITS transmitter; Andrew antenna.

Bettendorf—WHR-479 (Channels A-1-4). Eastern Iowa Community College District, 306 W. River Dr., Davenport, IA 52801. Phone: 319-322-5105. Authorized power: 50-w. each. Antenna: 361-ft. above ground. Lat. 41° 32' 48", long. 90° 27' 56". Transmitter: Scott Community College, 500 Belmont Rd. Equipment: Emcee transmitter; Andrew antenna.

Cedar Rapids—WGR-762 (Channels A-1-4). Kirkwood Community College, 6301 Kirkwood Blvd. SW, Cedar Rapids, IA 52406. Phone: 319-398-5663.
E-mail: othein@kirkwood.cc.ia.us.
Authorized power: 10-w. each. Antenna: 1194-ft. above ground. Lat. 41° 54' 33", long. 91° 39' 18". Transmitter: Kirkwood Community College, 3601 Kirkwood Blvd. SW. Equipment: Emcee transmitter; Andrew antenna.

Clinton—WHR-510 (Channels F-1-4). Eastern Iowa Community College District, 306 W. River Dr., Davenport, IA 52801. Phone: 319-322-5105. Authorized power: 10-w. each. Antenna: 350-ft. above ground. Lat. 41° 50' 02", long. 90° 12' 40". Transmitter: 1000 Lincoln Blvd. Equipment: Emcee transmitter; Andrew antenna.

Des Moines—WNC-203 (Channels A-1-4). North American Catholic Educational Programming Foundation Inc., Box 40026, Providence, RI 02940-0026. Phone: 401-729-0900. Authorized power: 50-w. each. Antenna: 673-ft. above ground. Lat. 41° 41' 59", long. 93° 51' 36". Transmitter: 14-mi. NNW of Des. Moines. Equipment: Comwave transmitter; Andrew antenna.

Eagle Grove—WHR-875 (Channel D1). Iowa Central Community College, 330 Ave. M, Fort Dodge, IA 50501. Authorized power: 10-w. Antenna: 186-ft. above ground. Lat. 42° 40' 14", long. 93° 54' 16". Transmitter: Grain elevator, 7th & Arthur Sts.

Estherville—WHR-247 (Channels A-1-4). Iowa Lakes Community College, 300 S. 18th St., Estherville, IA 51334. Authorized power: 50-w. each. Antenna: 350-ft. above ground. Lat. 43° 22' 25", long. 94° 49' 39". Transmitter: 2-mi. S of Estherville. Equipment: Emcee transmitter.

Fort Dodge—WHR-891 (Channel G1). Iowa Central Community College, 330 Ave. M, Fort Dodge, IA 50501. Authorized power: 10-w. Antenna: 328-ft. above ground. Lat. 42° 29' 23", long. 94° 12' 21". Transmitter: 330 Ave. M. Equipment: ITS transmitter; Andrew antenna.

Grimes—WND-401 (Channels G-1-4). Shekinah Network, 14875 Powerline Rd., Atascadero, CA 93422. Authorized power: 20-w. each. Antenna: 672-ft. above ground. Lat. 41° 41' 59", long. 93° 51' 36". Transmitter: 14-mi. NNW of Des Moines. Equipment: Comwave transmitter; Andrew antenna.

Grundy Center—WLX-213 (Channels A-3-4). Hawkeye Institute of Technology, 1501 E. Orange Rd., Waterloo, IA 50704. Phone: 319-296-2320. Authorized power: 10-w. each. Antenna: 343-ft. above ground. Lat. 42° 45' 27", long. 92° 26' 04". Equipment: ITS transmitter; Andrew antenna.

Humboldt—WHR-747 (Channel D1). Iowa Central Community College, 330 Ave. M, Fort Dodge, IA 50501. Authorized power: 10-w. Antenna: 299-ft. above ground. Lat. 42° 42' 48", long. 94° 13' 48". Transmitter: Humboldt High School, Hwy. 169 S.

Independence—WLX-211 (Channels A-3-4). Hawkeye Community College, 1501 E. Orange Rd., Waterloo, IA 50704. Phone: 319-296-2320. Fax: 319-296-4018. Authorized power: 10-w. each. Antenna: 362-ft. above ground. Lat. 42° 29' 23", long. 91° 51' 50". Transmitter: 1.83-mi. NE of courthouse. Equipment: ITS transmitter; Andrew antenna.

Iowa City—WGR-761 (Channel C4). Kirkwood Community College, 6301 Kirkwood Blvd. SW, Cedar Rapids, IA 52406. Phone: 319-398-5663.
E-mail: othein@kirkwood.cc.ia.us.
Authorized power: 10-w. Antenna: 287-ft. above ground. Lat. 41° 41' 57", long. 91° 28' 46". Transmitter: Rapid Creek Rd. Equipment: Emcee transmitter; Andrew antenna.

Iowa City—WHR-685 (Channels G-1-4). U. of Iowa, 710 S. Clinton Street Bldg., Iowa City, IA 52242. Phone: 319-335-5730. Fax: 319-335-6116.
E-mail: tedmonds@icaen.viowa.edu.
Authorized power: 10-w. each. Antenna: 300-ft. above ground. Lat. 41° 42' 37", long. 91° 35' 57". Transmitter: Corner of Oakdale Blvd. & Crosspark Rd. Equipment: ITS transmitter; Andrew antenna.

Jefferson—WHR-745 (Channels B-1-4). Iowa Central Community College, 330 Ave. M, Fort Dodge, IA 50501. Authorized power: 50-w. each. Antenna: 307-ft. above ground. Lat. 42° 00' 03", long. 94° 22' 10". Transmitter: Jefferson High School, 100 Sunset.

Muscatine—WHR-478 (Channels D-1-4). Eastern Iowa Community College District, 306 W. River Dr., Davenport, IA 52801. Authorized power: 10-w. each. Antenna: 270-ft. above ground. Lat. 41° 26' 23", long. 91° 01' 32". Transmitter: 152 Colorado St.

Pocahontas—WHR-785 (Channels C-1-4). Iowa Central Community College, 330 Ave. M, Fort Dodge, IA 50501. Authorized power: 50-w. each. Antenna: 187-ft. above ground. Lat. 42° 44' 01", long. 94° 40' 12". Transmitter: Farmers Cooperative elevator 1-mi. N of Hwy. 3 & 0.45-mi. N of Hwy. 4.

Radcliffe—WND-402 (Channels A-1-4). Hubbard-Radcliffe Community School, 200 Chestnut St., Hubbard, IA 50122. Authorized power: 10-w. each. Antenna: 482-ft. above ground. Lat. 42° 20' 10", long. 93° 28' 00". Transmitter: 1.5-mi. W & 1.5-mi. N of Radcliffe. Equipment: ITS transmitter; Andrew antenna.

Radcliffe—WNC-855 (Channels B-1-4). South Hamilton Community School District, Box 100, Jewell, IA 50130. Authorized power: 10-w. each. Antenna: 482-ft. above ground. Lat. 42° 20' 10", long. 93° 28' 00". Transmitter: 1.5-mi. W, 1.5-mi. N of Radcliffe. Equipment: ITS transmitter; Andrew antenna.

Radcliffe—WND-398 (Channels G-1-4). Roland-Story Community School District, 1009 Story St., Story City, IA 50248. Authorized power: 10-w. each. Antenna: 482-ft. above ground. Lat. 42° 20' 10", long. 93° 28' 00". Transmitter: 1.5-mi. W & 1.5-mi. N of Radcliffe. Equipment: ITS transmitter; Andrew antenna.

Rockwell City—WHR-763 (Channels B-1-4). Iowa Central Community College, 330 Ave. M, Fort Dodge, IA 50501. Authorized power: 50-w. each. Antenna: 205-ft. above ground. Lat. 42° 23' 36", long. 94° 38' 57". Transmitter: Rockwell City High School, Tonawanda.

Sac City—WHR-744 (Channels D-1-4). Iowa Central Community College, 330 Ave. M, Fort Dodge, IA 50501. Authorized power: 50-w. each. Antenna: 266-ft. above ground. Lat. 42° 24' 54", long. 95° 00' 17". Transmitter: Sac Community Elementary School, S. 16th St.

Spencer—WHF-247 (Channel A-4). Iowa Lakes Community College, 300 S. 18th St., Estherville, IA 51334. Authorized power: 10-w. Antenna: 440-ft. above ground. Lat. 43° 09' 53", long. 95° 19' 29". Transmitter: 7.7-mi. W of Spencer. Equipment: ITS transmitter; Andrew antenna.

Spencer—WND-326 (Channels B-1-4). Hartley-Melvin-Sandon, Box 206, 600 3rd St. NW, Hartley, IA 51346. Authorized power: 10-w. each. Antenna: 440-ft. above ground. Lat. 43° 09' 53", long. 95° 19' 29". Transmitter: 7.7-mi. W of Spencer, near Everly. Equipment: ITS transmitter; Andrew antenna.

Spencer—WND-327 (Channels D-1-4). Clay Central/Everly C. School District, Box 110, 306 E. 2, Everly, IA 51338. Authorized power: 10-w. each. Antenna: 440-ft. above ground. Lat. 43° 09' 53", long. 95° 19' 29". Transmitter: 7.7-mi. W of Spencer, near Everly. Equipment: ITS transmitter; Andrew antenna.

Storm Lake—WHR-876 (Channel A-1). Iowa Central Community College, 330 Ave. M, Fort Dodge, IA 50501. Authorized power: 10-w. Antenna: 326-ft. above ground. Lat. 42° 38' 09", long. 95° 11' 12". Transmitter: 1103 E. Lakeshore Dr.

Tipton—WGW-943 (Channel C-1). Kirkwood Community College, 6301 Kirkwood Blvd. SW, Cedar Rapids, IA 52406. Phone: 319-398-5663.
E-mail: othein@kirkwood.cc.ia.us.
Authorized power: 10-w. Antenna: 232-ft. above ground. Lat. 41° 46' 22", long. 91° 07' 08". Transmitter: 400 E. 6th St. Equipment: Emcee transmitter; Andrew antenna.

Vinton—WGW-945 (Channel C-1). Kirkwood Community College, 6301 Kirkwood Blvd. SW, Cedar Rapids, IA 52406. Phone: 319-398-5663.
E-mail: othein@kirkwood.cc.ia.us.
Authorized power: 10-w. Antenna: 297-ft. above ground. Lat. 42° 09' 22", long. 92° 01' 15". Transmitter: 213 W. 15th St. Equipment: Emcee transmitter; Andrew antenna.

Washington—WHA-816 (Channel C-2). Kirkwood Community College, 6301 Kirkwood Blvd. SW, Cedar Rapids, IA 52406. Phone: 319-398-5663.
E-mail: othein@kirkwood.cc.ia.us.
Authorized power: 10-w. Antenna: 197-ft. above ground. Lat. 41° 23' 43", long. 91° 39' 05". Transmitter: 313 S. 4th St. Equipment: Emcee transmitter; Andrew antenna.

Waterloo—WLX-209 (Channels A-1-2). Hawkeye Community College, 1501 E. Orange Rd., Waterloo, IA 50704. Phone: 319-296-2320. Fax: 319-296-4018. Authorized power: 10-w. each. Antenna: 350-ft. above ground. Lat. 42° 25' 44", long. 92° 19' 21". Equipment: Emcee transmitter; Andrew antenna.

Waverly—WLX-212 (Channels A-3-4). Hawkeye Institute of Technology, 1501 E. Orange Rd., Waterloo, IA 50704. Lat. 42° 45' 27", long. 92° 26' 04".

Webster City & surrounding area—WHR-898 (Channel C-1). Iowa Central Community College, 330 Ave. M, Fort Dodge, IA 50501. Authorized power: 10-w. Antenna: 205-ft. above ground. Lat. 42° 27' 33", long. 93° 50' 18". Transmitter: 1725 Beach St.

Williamsburg—WGW-951 (Channel C-3). Kirkwood Community College, 6301 Kirkwood Blvd. SW, Cedar Rapids, IA 52406. Phone: 319-398-5663.
E-mail: othein@kirkwood.cc.ia.us.
Authorized power: 10-w. Antenna: 247-ft. above ground. Lat. 41° 39' 44", long. 92° 01' 13". Transmitter: 810 Walnut St. Equipment: Emcee transmitter; Andrew antenna. Requests change to 244-ft. above ground.

Williamsburg—WNC-854 (Channel D-1). Kirkwood Community College, Box 2068, 6301 Kirkwood Blvd., Cedar Rapids, IA 52406. Phone: 319-398-5663. Fax: 319-398-5413.
E-mail: othein@kirkwood.cc.ia.us.
Authorized power: 10-w. Antenna: 246-ft. above ground. Lat. 41° 39' 44", long. 92° 01' 13". Transmitter: 810 Walnut St. Equipment: Emcee transmitter; Andrew antenna.

Kansas

Dover—WLX-904 (Channels B-1-4). Silver Lake Unified School District No. 372, 200 Rice Rd., Silver Lake, KS 66539. Phone: 913-582-4026. Fax: 913-582-5259. Authorized power: 50-w. each. Antenna: 997-ft. above ground. Lat. 39° 01' 34", long. 95° 54' 58". Transmitter: 2280 W. Union Rd. Equipment: Comwave transmitter; Andrew antenna.
Leased to Nucentrix Broadband Networks, 200 Chisolm Place, Suite 200, Plano, TX 75075. Phone: 972-423-9494. Fax: 972-423-0819.

Dover—WLX-714 (Channels C-1-3). Auburn-Washburn U.S.D. 437, 5928 S.W. 53rd St., Topeka, KS 66610-9451. Phone: 913-862-0419. Fax: 913-862-3800. Authorized power: 50-w. each. Antenna: 997-ft. above ground. Lat. 39° 01' 34", long. 95° 54' 58". Transmitter: 2280 W. Union Rd. Equipment: Comwave transmitter; Andrew antenna.

Dover—WND-448 (Channels D-1-3). Rossville United School District No. 321, 800 S. Main St., Rossville, KS 66533. Phone: 913-584-6193. Authorized power: 50-w. each. Antenna: 997-ft. above ground. Lat. 39° 01' 34", long. 95° 54' 58". Transmitter: 2280 W. Union Rd. Equipment: Comwave transmitter; Andrew antenna.

Dover—WNC-430 (Channels G-1-3). Seaman Unified School District 345, 901 N.W. Lyman Rd., Topeka, KS 66608. Authorized power: 50-w. each. Antenna: 997-ft. above ground. Lat. 39° 01' 34", long. 95° 54' 58". Transmitter: 2280 W. Union Rd., Dover. Equipment: Comwave transmitter; Andrew antenna.

Durham—WNC-333 (Channels A-1-4). Unified School District No. 398, 506 Elm St., Peabody, KS 66866. Authorized power: 25-w. each. Antenna: 1455-ft. above ground. Lat. 38° 28' 29", long. 97° 16' 55". Transmitter: 3.2-mi. E of Hwy. 15. Equipment: Comwave transmitter; Andrew antenna.

Durham—WNC-334 (Channels B-1-4). Unified School District No. 410, 812 E. A St., Hillsboro, KS 67063. Phone: 316-947-3184. Fax: 316-947-3263.
E-mail: gordon@tetn.k12.ks.us.
Web site: http://www2.southwind.net/~usd410.
Authorized power: 25-w. each. Antenna: 853-ft. above ground. Lat. 38° 28' 33", long. 97° 17' 17". Transmitter: NW corner of Marion County. Equipment: Comwave transmitter; Andrew antenna.
Leased to Nucentrix Broadband Networks, 200 Chisolm Place, Suite 200, Plano, TX 75075. Phone: 972-423-9494. Fax: 972-423-0819.

Durham—WNC-323 (Channels C-1-4). Herington Unified School District No. 487, 19 N. Broadway, Herington, KS 67449. Phone: 785-258-2263. Fax: 785-258-3552. Authorized power: 25-w. each. Antenna: 856-ft. above ground. Lat. 38° 28' 33", long. 97° 17' 17". Transmitter: NW corner of Marion County. Equipment: Comwave transmitter; Andrew antenna.

Durham—WNC-376 (Channels G-1-4). Marion-Florence Unified School District, 601 E. Main, Marion, KS 68861. Phone: 316-382-2117. Authorized power: 25-w. each. Antenna: 859-ft. above ground. Lat. 38° 28' 29", long. 97° 16' 55". Transmitter: 3.2-mi. E of Hwy. 15. Equipment: Comwave transmitter; Andrew antenna.

Effingham—WLX-473 (Channels A-1-4). Trinity Lutheran, 609 N. 8th, Atchison, KS 66002. Phone: 913-367-4263. Authorized power: 10-w. each. Antenna: 694-ft. above ground. Lat. 39° 30' 02", long. 95° 29' 37". Transmitter: 3-mi. S of U.S. 159, 5-mi. WSW of Effingham. Equipment: Comwave transmitter; Andrew antenna.

Effingham—WLX-329 (Channels B-1-4). Holton Unified School District, 515 Pennsylvania, Holton, KS 66436. Phone: 785-364-3650. Fax: 785-364-3975.
E-mail: jfuqua@mail.holton.k12.ks.us.
Web site: http://www.holton.k12.ks.us/frames.html.
Authorized power: 10-w. each. Antenna: 694-ft. above ground. Lat. 39° 30' 02", long. 95° 29' 37". Transmitter: 3-mi. S of U.S. 159, 5-mi.

WSW of Effingham. Equipment: Comwave transmitter; Andrew antenna.

Effingham—WLX-339 (Channels C-1-4). Easton Unified School District No. 449, 32502 Easton Rd., Easton, KS 66020. Phone: 913-651-9740. Fax: 913-651-6740.
E-mail: eboeaston@wwgv.com.
Authorized power: 10-w. each. Antenna: 694-ft. above ground. Lat. 39° 30' 02", long. 95° 29' 37". Transmitter: 3-mi. S of U.S. 159, 5-mi. WSW of Effingham. Equipment: Comwave transmitter; Andrew antenna.

Effingham—WLX-340 (Channels D-1-4). Mayetta Unified School District No. 337, Box 117, Mayetta, KS 66509. Authorized power: 10-w. each. Antenna: 694-ft. above ground. Lat. 39° 30' 02", long. 95° 29' 37". Transmitter: 3-mi. S of U.S. 159 & 5-mi. WSW of Effingham. Equipment: Comwave transmitter; Andrew antenna.

Effingham—WLX-360 (Channels G-1-4). Sabetha Unified School District No. 441, 107 Oregon St., Sabetha, KS 66534. Authorized power: 10-w. each. Antenna: 694-ft. above ground. Lat. 39° 31' 22", long. 95° 25' 22". Transmitter: 3-mi. S of U.S. 159, 5-mi. WSW of Effingham. Equipment: Comwave transmitter; Andrew antenna.
Leased to American Telecasting Inc., 519 N. Hydraulic, Wichita, KS 67214. Phone: 316-263-2337.

Emporia—WLX-461 (Channels G-1-4). North American Catholic Educational Programming Foundation Inc., Box 40026, Providence, RI 02940-0026. Phone: 401-729-0900. Authorized power: 1-w. each. Antenna: 344-ft. above ground. Lat. 38° 23' 10", long. 96° 10' 36". Transmitter: Soden's Grove. Equipment: Plessey transmitter; Andrew antenna.

Erie—WLX-280 (Channels A-1-4). Neosho County Community College, 1000 S. Allen St., Chanute, KS 66720. Authorized power: 50-w. each. Antenna: 700-ft. above ground. Lat. 37° 36' 11", long. 95° 16' 20". Transmitter: 0.2-mi. N of State Rd. 146, 3-mi. NW of Erie. Equipment: Comwave transmitter; Andrew antenna.

Erie—WLX-281 (Channels B-1-4). Unified School District No. 413, 410 S. Evergreen, Chanute, KS 66720. Phone: 316-432-2500. Fax: 316-431-6810. Authorized power: 50-w. each. Antenna: 692-ft. above ground. Lat. 37° 36' 16", long. 95° 16' 30". Transmitter: 1-mi. S of Rte. 146 & 4-mi. E of Erie. Equipment: Comwave transmitter; Andrew antenna.
Leased to Nucentrix Broadband Networks, 200 Chisolm Place, Suite 200, Plano, TX. Phone: 972-423-9494. Fax: 972-423-0819.

Erie—WLX-283 (Channels C-1-4). Unified School District No. 101, Box 37, 205 S. Main, Erie, KS 66733. Authorized power: 50-w. each. Antenna: 700-ft. above ground. Lat. 37° 36' 11", long. 95° 16' 20". Transmitter: 0.2-mi. N of State Rd. 146, 3-mi. NW of Erie. Equipment: Comwave transmitter; Andrew antenna. Requests change to lat. 37° 36' 16", long. 95° 16' 30".

Erie—WLX-282 (Channels D-1-4). Unified School District No. 248, 401-415 N. Summit, Girard, KS 66743. Phone: 316-724-4325. Fax: 316-724-8446. Authorized power: 50-w. each. Antenna: 213-ft. above ground. Lat. 37° 36' 16", long. 95° 16' 30". Transmitter: 0.1-mi. S of Rte. 146, 4-mi. E of Erie. Equipment: Comwave transmitter; Andrew antenna.

Erie—WLX-296 (Channels G-1-4). Southeast Kansas Educational Service, Box 189, Girard, KS 66743. Lat. 37° 35' 17", long. 95° 10' 09". Requests change to lat. 37° 36' 16", long. 95° 16' 30".

Garden City—WNC-765 (Channels A-1-4). Hispanic Information & Telecommunications Network Inc., 3rd Floor, 449 Broadway, New York, NY 10013. Phone: 212-966-5660. Fax: 212-966-5725.
E-mail: E-mail@hitn.org.
Web site: http://www.hitn.org.
Authorized power: 10-w. each. Antenna: 360-ft. above ground. Lat. 37° 56' 40", long. 100° 51' 59". Transmitter: 1.5-mi. S of Garden City. Equipment: ITS transmitter; Andrew antenna.
Leased to Distance Learning Services Inc., 1155 Connecticut Ave. NW, Washington, DC 20036. Phone: 202-467-8500.

Great Bend—WND-486 (Channels B-1-4). Barton County Community College, Box 1367, Rte. 3, Great Bend, KS 67530. Phone: 316-792-2701. Authorized power: 50-w. each. Antenna: 853-ft. above ground. Lat. 38° 23' 58", long. 98° 43' 58". Transmitter: 2.5-mi. N of Breat Bend. Equipment: Comwave transmitter; Andrew antenna.

Great Bend—WND-485 (Channels C-1-4). Unified School District, 201 Patton Rd., Great Bend, KS 67530. Authorized power: 50-w. each. Antenna: 853-ft. above ground. Lat. 38° 23' 58", long. 98° 43' 58". Transmitter: 2.5-mi. N of Great Bend. Equipment: Comwave transmitter; Andrew antenna.

Great Bend—WLX-525 (Channels D-1-4). North American Catholic Educational Programming Foundation Inc., Box 40026, Providence, RI 02940-0026. Phone: 401-729-0900. Authorized power: 50-w. each. Antenna: 853-ft. above ground. Lat. 38° 23' 58", long. 98° 43' 58". Transmitter: 2.5-mi. N of Great Bend. Equipment: Comwave transmitter; Andrew antenna.

Great Bend—WND-484 (Channels G-1-4). Unified School District No. 431, 106 N. Main, Hoisington, KS 67554. Authorized power: 50-w. each. Antenna: 853-ft. above ground. Lat. 38° 23' 58", long. 98° 43' 58". Transmitter: 2.5-mi. N of Great Bend. Equipment: Comwave transmitter; Andrew antenna.

Hays—WND-490 (Channels B-1-4). Unified School District No. 407, 802 N. Main, Russell, KS 67665. Phone: 785-483-2173. Fax: 785-483-2175.
E-mail: ddegenhardt@eaglecom.net.
Web site: http://www.usd407.org.
Authorized power: 50-w. each. Antenna: 499-ft. above ground. Lat. 38° 51' 27", long. 99° 04' 33". Transmitter: 0.5-mi. S of Walker. Equipment: Comwave transmitter; Andrew antenna.

Hays—WND-488 (Channels C-1-4). Fort Hays State U., 600 Park St., Hays, KS 67601. Authorized power: 50-w. each. Antenna: 499-ft. above ground. Lat. 38° 51' 27", long. 99° 04' 33". Transmitter: 0.5-mi. S of Walker. Equipment: Comwave transmitter; Andrew antenna.

Hays—WLX-504 (Channels D-1-4). North American Catholic Educational Programming Foundation Inc., Box 40026, Providence, RI 02940-0026. Phone: 401-729-0900. Authorized power: 1-w. each. Antenna: 250-ft. above ground. Lat. 38° 55' 20", long. 99° 21' 11". Transmitter: 2.2-mi. NNW of Hays. Equipment: Plessey transmitter; Andrew antenna.

Hays—WND-489 (Channels G-1-4). Barton County Community College, Box 1367, Rte. 3, Great Bend, KS 67530. Authorized power: 50-w. each. Antenna: 499-ft. above ground. Lat. 38° 51' 27", long. 99° 04' 33". Transmitter: 0.5-mi. S of Walker. Equipment: Comwave transmitter; Andrew antenna.

Hutchinson—WLX-333 (Channel A1). Wichita State U., 1845 Fairmount, Wichita, KS 67208. Phone: 316-689-3575. Fax: 316-689-3560. Authorized power: 10-w. Antenna: 300-ft. above ground. Lat. 38° 03' 21", long. 97° 46' 35". Transmitter: 4th & Buhler Rds. intersection. Equipment: Comwave transmitter; Andrew antenna.

Nickerson—WLX-622 (Channels A-2-4). Unified School District No. 401 Chase-Raymond, Box 366, Chase, KS 67524. Authorized power: 7.6-w. each. Antenna: 854-ft. above ground. Lat. 38° 13' 06", long. 98° 05' 26". Transmitter: 6-mi. N of Kansas Hwy. 96, 4.5-mi. N of Nickerson. Equipment: Comwave transmitter; Andrew antenna.

Nickerson—WLX-624 (Channels B-1-4). Claflin Unified School District No. 354, Box 346, Claflin, KS 67525. Authorized power: 25-w. each. Antenna: 341-ft. above ground. Lat. 38° 13' 03", long. 97° 59' 39". Transmitter: 6-mi. NE of Nickerson. Equipment: Comwave transmitter; Andrew antenna.

Nickerson—WLX-700 (Channels C-1-4). Pretty Prairie No. 311, Box 218, Pretty Prairie, KS 67570. Phone: 316-459-6241. Fax: 316-459--6810.
E-mail: usd311@dtc.net.
Authorized power: 5-w. each. Antenna: 440-ft. above ground. Lat. 38° 13' 06", long. 98° 05' 26". Transmitter: 4.5-mi. N of Nickerson. Equipment: Comwave transmitter; Andrew antenna.
Leased to Nucentrix Broadband Networks, 200 Chisolm Place, Suite 200, Plano, TX 75075. Phone: 972-423-9494. Fax: 972-423-0819.

Nickerson—WLX-716 (Channels D-1-4). Unified School District No. 312, 414 W. Main, Haven, KS 67543. Authorized power: 25-w. each. Antenna: 341-ft. above ground. Lat. 38° 13' 03", long. 97° 59' 39". Transmitter: approx. 6-mi. NE of Nickerson. Equipment: Comwave transmitter; Andrew antenna.
Leased to Nucentrix Broadband Networks, 200 Chisolm Place, Suite 200, Plano, TX 75075. Phone: 972-423-9494. Fax: 972-423-0819.

Nickerson—WLX-657 (Channels G-1-4). Unified School District No. 355, Box 368, Ellinwood, KS 67526. Authorized power: 25-w. each. Antenna: 341-ft. above ground. Lat. 38° 13' 03", long. 97° 59' 39". Transmitter: approx. 6-mi. NE of Nickerson. Equipment: Comwave transmitter; Andrew antenna.

Ottawa—WLX-330 (Channels A-1-4). Santa Fe Trail Unified School District No. 434, Box 310, Carbondale, KS 66414. Phone: 913-665-7168. Fax: 913-665-7164. Authorized power: 10-w. each. Antenna: 855-ft. above ground. Lat. 38° 41' 48", long. 94° 58' 24". Transmitter: 6-mi. ESE of Wellsville; Comwave transmitter. Equipment: Comwave transmitter; Andrew antenna.
Leased to CS Wireless, 1101 Summit Ave., Plano, TX 75074. Phone: 972-730-3300.

Ottawa—WLX-331 (Channels B-1-4). Marais des Cygnes Valley Unified School District No. 456, Box 158, Melvern, KS 66510. Authorized power: 10-w. each. Antenna: 1021-ft. above ground. Lat. 38° 41' 48", long. 94° 58' 24". Transmitter: Malvern Area. Equipment: Comwave transmitter; Andrew antenna.

Ottawa—WLX-327 (Channels C-1-4). Eudora Unified School Distrct No. 491, Box 500, Eudora, KS 66025. Phone: 785-542-4910. Fax: 785-542-4909. Authorized power: 10-w. each. Antenna: 350-ft. above ground. Lat. 38° 38' 28", long. 95° 19' 07". Transmitter: 3-mi. NW of Ottawa, near Baxter School. Equipment: ITS transmitter. Requests change to 855-ft. above ground, lat. 38° 41' 48", long. 94° 58' 24"; transmitter to 6-mi. ESE of Wellsville; Comwave transmitter; Andrew antenna.

Ottawa—WLX-335 (Channels D-1-4). Garnett Unified School District No. 365, Box 328, 114 W. 5th St., Garnett, KS 66032. Authorized power: 10-w. each. Antenna: 350-ft. above ground. Lat. 38° 41' 48", long. 94° 58' 24". Transmitter: 6-mi. ESE of Wellsville. Equipment: ITS transmitter.

Randolph—WLX-783 (Channels A-1-4). Unified School District No. 379, Box 379, Clay Center, KS 67432. Authorized power: 50-w. each. Antenna: 645-ft. above ground. Lat. 39° 26' 47", long. 96° 48' 07". Transmitter: 1.6-mi. NW of Randolph, 0.07-mi. N of State Hwy. 16. Equipment: Comwave transmitter; Andrew antenna.

Randolph—WLX-776 (Channels B-1-4). Unified School District No. 378, 12451 Fairview Church Rd., Riley, KS 66531. Phone: 913-485-2818. Fax: 913-485-2860. Authorized power: 50-w. each. Antenna: 645-ft. above ground. Lat. 39° 26' 47", long. 96° 48' 07". Transmitter: 1.6-mi. NW of Randolph. Equipment: Comwave transmitter; Andrew antenna.
Leased to Nucentrix Broadband Networks, 200 Chisolm Place, Suite 200, Plano, TX 75075. Phone: 972-423-9494. Fax: 972-423-0819.

Randolph—WLX-835 (Channels C-1-4). Blue Valley Unified School District No. 384, One Ram Way, Randolph, KS 66554. Phone: 913-293-5256. Fax: 913-293-5607.
Web site: http://www.usd384.k12.ks.us.
Authorized power: 50-w. each. Antenna: 855-ft. above ground. Lat. 39° 26' 47", long. 96° 48' 07". Transmitter: 1.6-mi. NW of Randolph, 0.7-mi. N of State Hwy. 16. Equipment: Comwave transmitter; Andrew antenna.

Randolph—WLX-927 (Channels D-1-4). Washington United School District No. 222, Box 275, Washington, KS 66968. Phone: 913-325-2261. Fax: 913-325-2138. Authorized power: 50-w. each. Antenna: 645-ft. above ground. Lat. 39° 26' 47", long. 96° 48' 07". Transmitter: 1.6-mi. NW of Randolph, 0.07-mi. N of State Hwy. 16. Equipment: Comwave transmitter; Andrew antenna.

Randolph—WLX-782 (Channels G-1-4). Rock Creek Unified School District No. 323, 201 S. 3rd, Westmoreland, KS 66549. Phone: 913-457-3732. Fax: 913-457-3701. Authorized power: 50-w. each. Antenna: 645-ft. above ground. Lat. 39° 26' 47", long. 96° 48' 07". Transmitter: 1.6-mi. NW of Randolph, 0.07-mi.

N of State Hwy. 16. Equipment: Comwave transmitter; Andrew antenna.

Salina—WLX-898 (Channels B-1-4). Salina Public Schools Unified School District No. 305, 300 W. Ash, Salina, KS 67401. Authorized power: 10-w. each. Antenna: 434-ft. above ground. Lat. 38° 55' 55", long. 97° 35' 27". Transmitter: 5-mi. N of Salina. Equipment: ITS transmitter; Andrew antenna.

Salina—WLX-562 (Channels D-1-4). North American Catholic Educational Programming Foundation Inc., Box 40026, Providence, RI 02940-0026. Phone: 401-729-0900. Authorized power: 1-w. each. Antenna: 434-ft. above ground. Lat. 38° 55' 55", long. 97° 35' 27". Transmitter: 5-mi. N of Salina. Equipment: Plessey transmitter; Andrew antenna.

Teterville—WLX-243 (Channels A-1-4). Butler Community College, 901 S. Haverhill Rd., El Dorado, KS 67042. Phone: 316-322-3179. Fax: 316-322-3267.
E-mail: jhostetl@butler.buccc.cc.ks.us.
Authorized power: 10-w. each. Antenna: 197-ft. above ground. Lat. 38° 02' 17", long. 96° 25' 22". Transmitter: Greenwood County. Equipment: Comwave transmitter; Mark V antenna.

Tipton—WLX-602 (Channels A-1-4). Unified School District No. 273, Box 547, Beloit, KS 67420. Phone: 913-738-3261. Fax: 913-738--4103.
E-mail: usd273@nckcn.com.
Authorized power: 33.5-w. each. Antenna: 814-ft. above ground. Lat. 39° 19' 13", long. 98° 23' 53". Transmitter: 4.5-mi. SE of Tipton. Equipment: Comwave transmitter; Andrew antenna.
Leased to RuralVision, Box 1482, Canyon Lake, TX 78130.

Tipton—WLX-607 (Channels B-1-4). Unified School District No. 299, Box 308, Sylvan Grove, KS 67481. Authorized power: 50-w. each. Antenna: 1205-ft. above ground. Lat. 39° 19' 19", long. 98° 23' 48". Transmitter: Approx. 4.5-mi. SE of Tipton. Equipment: Comwave transmitter; Andrew antenna.

Tipton—WLX-692 (Channels C-1-4). Unified School District No. 392, Box 209, 134 N. 3rd St., Osborne, KS 67473. Phone: 913-346-2145. Fax: 913-346-2448. Authorized power: 33.5-w. each. Antenna: 814-ft. above ground. Lat. 39° 19' 13", long. 98° 23' 53". Transmitter: Approx. 4.5-mi. SW of Tipton. Equipment: Comwave transmitter; Andrew antenna.
Leased to Cable Equity, Box 1482, Canyon Lake, TX 78130. Phone: 913-964-2211.

Tipton—WLX-869 (Channels D-1-4). Unified School District No. 298, 145 E. Lincoln Ave., Lincoln, KS 67455. Phone: 913-524-4436. Fax: 913-524-3080. Authorized power: 33.5-w. each. Antenna: 814-ft. above ground. Lat. 39° 19' 13", long. 98° 23' 53". Transmitter: Approx. 4.5-mi. SW of Tipton. Equipment: Comwave transmitter; Andrew antenna.

Tipton—WLX-614 (Channels G-1-4). Unified School District No. 272, Box 326, 708 Locust, Cawker City, KS 67430. Phone: 913-781-4328. Fax: 913-781-4318. Authorized power: 33.5-w. each. Antenna: 814-ft. above ground. Lat. 39° 19' 13", long. 98° 23' 53". Transmitter: Approx. 4.5-mi. SW of Tipton. Equipment: Comwave transmitter; Andrew antenna.
Leased to Ruralvision Central Inc., Box 1482, Canyon Lake, TX 78130. Phone: 210-964-2211.

Topeka—WLX-588 (Channels A-1-4). Shawnee Heights U.S.D. 450, 4401 S.E. Shawnee Heights Rd., Tecumseh, KS 66542. Phone: 785-379-5800. Fax: 785-379-5810. Authorized power: 50-w. each. Antenna: 175-ft. above ground. Lat. 39° 02' 05", long. 95° 38' 39". Transmitter: 200-ft. S of I-70 on Golden St. Equipment: ITS transmitter; Home Made antenna. Requests change to 1000-ft. above ground, lat. 39° 01' 34", long. 95° 54' 58"; transmitter to 2280 W. Union Rd., Dover; Comwave transmitter; Andrew antenna.

Wellsville—WNC-431 (Channels G-1-4). Ottawa Unified School District 290. Authorized power: 50-w. each. Antenna: 859-ft. above ground. Lat. 38° 41' 48", long. 94° 58' 24". Transmitter: 3.8-mi. SW of Interstate 35. Equipment: Comwave transmitter; Andrew antenna.

Wichita—WHR-934 (Channels A-3-4). Butler County Community College, 901 S. Haverhill Rd., El Dorado, KS 67042. Phone: 316-322-3179. Fax: 316-322-3267.
E-mail: jhostetl@butler.buccc.cc.ks.us.
Authorized power: 50-w. each. Antenna: 495-ft. above ground. Lat. 37° 41' 43", long. 97° 19' 05". Transmitter: 1510 E. Murdock St. Equipment: ITS transmitter; Bogner antenna.

Wichita—WLX-214 (Channels B-1-4). Wichita Public School District No. 259, 217 N. Water St., Wichita, KS 67202. Phone: 316-833-2075. Fax: 316-833-2181. Authorized power: 50-w. each. Antenna: 988-ft. above ground. Lat. 37° 41' 53", long. 97° 19' 11". Transmitter: 1510 E. Murdock St. Equipment: ITS transmitter; Bogner antenna.
Leased to American Telecasting Inc., 5575 Tech Center Dr., Suite 300, Colorado Springs, CO 80919. Phone: 719-632-5544.

Wichita—WHR-970 (Channels C-1-4). Wichita State U., 1845 Fairmount, Wichita, KS 67208. Phone: 316-978-3575. Fax: 316-978-3560.
E-mail: myersc@twsuvm.uc.twsu.eou.
Authorized power: 50-w. each. Antenna: 495-ft. above ground. Lat. 37° 41' 53", long. 97° 19' 11". Transmitter: 1510 E. Murdock St. Equipment: ITS transmitter; Bogner antenna.
Leased to American Telecasting Inc., 519 N. Hydraulic, Wichita, KS 67214. Phone: 316-263-1900.

Wichita—WHR-981 (Channels D-1-4). Catholic Diocese of Wichita, Newman College, 424 N. Broadway, Wichita, KS 62702. Authorized power: 50-w. each. Antenna: 495-ft. above ground. Lat. 37° 41' 53", long. 97° 19' 11". Transmitter: 1510 E. Murdock St. Equipment: ITS transmitter; Bogner antenna.

Wichita—WHR-977 (Channels G-1-4). Friends U., 2100 University, Wichita, KS 67213. Authorized power: 50-w. each. Antenna: 495-ft. above ground. Lat. 37° 41' 53", long. 97° 19' 11". Transmitter: 1510 E. Murdock St. Equipment: ITS transmitter; Bogner antenna.

Zenda—WLX-628 (Channels A-1-4). Kingman Unified School District No. 331, Box 416, Kingman, KS 67068. Authorized power: 25-w. each. Antenna: 856-ft. above ground. Lat. 37° 23' 10", long. 98° 15' 43". Transmitter: Near the southern border of Kingman County. Equipment: Comwave transmitter; Andrew antenna.

Zenda—WLX-611 (Channels B-1-4). Unified School District No. 332, Box 67, Cunningham, KS 67035. Authorized power: 25-w. each. Antenna: 854-ft. above ground. Lat. 37° 23' 09", long. 98° 16' 05". Transmitter: 3.8-mi. S of Hwy. 42, 3.8-mi. S of Zenda. Equipment: Comwave transmitter; Andrew antenna.

Zenda—WLX-892 (Channels C-1-4). Argonia Unified School District No. 359, Box 72A, Rte. 1, Argonia, KS 76004. Phone: 316-435-6311. Fax: 316-435-6322. Authorized power: 25-w. each. Antenna: 856-ft. above ground. Lat. 37° 23' 10", long. 98° 15' 43". Transmitter: approx. 3.8-mi. S of Zenda. Equipment: Comwave transmitter; Andrew antenna.

Zenda—WLX-952 (Channels D-1-4). Unified School District No. 511, 718 N. Main, Attica, KS 67009. Authorized power: 25-w. each. Antenna: 856-ft. above ground. Lat. 37° 23' 10", long. 98° 15' 43". Transmitter: Approx. 3.8-mi. S of Zenda. Equipment: Comwave transmitter; Andrew antenna.

Kentucky

Bowling Green—WHR-723 (Channels A-1-3). Western Kentucky U., One Big Red Way, Bowling Green, KY 42101. Phone: 502-745-2400. Fax: 502-745-2084.
E-mail: wkyutv@wku.edu.
Web site: http://www.wku.edu/wkyo.tv.
Authorized power: 10-w. each. Antenna: 74-ft. above ground. Lat. 36° 59' 15", long. 86° 27' 05". Transmitter: Cherry Hall, Western Kentucky U. campus.

Lexington—WLX-914 (Channels A-1-4). Clark County Board of Education, 1600 W. Lexington Ave., Winchester, KY 40391. Authorized power: 50-w. each. Antenna: 531-ft. above ground. Lat. 38° 00' 54", long. 84° 26' 18". Transmitter: Lexington. Equipment: ITS transmitter; Andrew antenna.

Lexington—WLX-906 (Channels B-1-4). Jessamine County Board of Education, 501 E. Maple St., Nicholasville, KY 40356. Authorized power: 50-w. each. Antenna: 531-ft. above ground. Lat. 38° 00' 54", long. 84° 26' 18". Transmitter: 2940 Bryant Rd. Equipment: ITS transmitter; Andrew antenna.

Lexington—WNC-572 (Channels C-1-4). Eastern Kentucky U., Perkins Bldg. 102, Richmond, VA 40475. Phone: 606-622-2474. Fax: 606-622-6276.
E-mail: clmrkollf@acs.eku.edu.
Authorized power: 50-w. each. Antenna: 530-ft. above ground. Lat. 38° 00' 03", long. 84° 26' 18". Transmitter: 2599 Palumbo Dr. Equipment: ITS transmitter.
Leased to Wireless Cable of Lexington LLC.

Lexington—WLX-848 (Channels G-1-4). Scott County Board of Education, 1036 Longlick Pike, Georgetown, KY 40324. Authorized power: 50-w. each. Antenna: 531-ft. above ground. Lat. 38° 00' 54", long. 84° 26' 18". Transmitter: Lexington. Equipment: ITS transmitter; Andrew antenna.

Louisville—WHR-769 (Channels A-1-4). Views on Learning Inc., 200 Kenyon Ave., Elkhart, IN 46516. Authorized power: 10-w. each. Antenna: 162-ft. above ground. Lat. 38° 11' 54", long. 85° 41' 07". Transmitter: 4421 Bishops Lane.
Leased to American Telecasting of Louisville Inc., 5575 Tech Center Dr., Suite 300, Colorado Springs, CO 80919. Phone: 719-260-5533.

Louisville—WHB-211 (Channels B-1-4). Jefferson County Board of Education, 3001 Crittenden Dr., Louisville, KY 40209. Authorized power: 25-w. each. Antenna: 159-ft. above ground. Lat. 38° 11' 54", long. 85° 41' 07". Transmitter: 4301 Bishops Lane. Equipment: Comwave transmitter; Bogner antenna.

Louisville—WLX-337 (Channels C-1-4). Kentucky Authority for Educational TV, 600 Cooper Dr., Lexington, KY 40502. Phone: 606-258-7192. Fax: 606-258-7390.
E-mail: stalbert@ket.org.
Web site: http://www.ket.org.
Authorized power: 50-w. each. Antenna: 374-ft. above ground. Lat. 38° 10' 25", long. 85° 54' 50". Transmitter: New Albany, IN. Equipment: Comwave transmitter; Bogner antenna.
Leased to American Telecasting of Louisville, 4211 Produce Rd., Louisville, KY 40218. Phone: 502-964-4600.

Louisville—WBX-203 (Channels D-1-4). U. of Louisville, 2301 S. 3rd St., Louisville, KY 40208. Authorized power: 10-w. each. Antenna: 132-ft. above ground. Lat. 38° 13' 10", long. 85° 45' 32". Transmitter: 2301 S. 3rd St.

Louisville—WAY-655 (Channels F-1-4). Jefferson County Board of Education, 3001 Crittenden Dr., Louisville, KY 40209. Authorized power: 10-w. each. Antenna: 103-ft. above ground. Lat. 38° 10' 40", long. 85° 50' 41". Transmitter: Western High School, 2501 Rockford Lane.

Parkers Lake—WND-282 (Channels B-1-4). Wayne County Board of Education, Box 437, Monticello, KY 42633. Authorized power: 50-w. each. Antenna: 502-ft. above ground. Lat. 36° 50' 27", long. 84° 26' 41". Transmitter: 2.1-mi. E of Parkers Lake. Equipment: Comwave transmitter; Andrew antenna.

Parkers Lake—WND-283 (Channels D-1-4). Wayne County Hospital Inc., 166 Hospital St., Monticello, KY 42633. Phone: 606-348-9343. Fax: 606-348-5796.
E-mail: wchhospital@kih.net.
Web site: http://www.users.kih.net/2wchospital/.
Authorized power: 50-w. each. Antenna: 502-ft. above ground. Lat. 36° 50' 27", long. 84° 26' 41". Transmitter: 2.1-mi. E of Parkers Lake. Equipment: Comwave transmitter; Andrew antenna.

Parkers Lake—WND-366 (Channels G-1-4). Center for Kentucky Rural Development. Authorized power: 50-w. each. Antenna: 502-ft. above ground. Lat. 36° 50' 27", long. 84° 26' 41". Transmitter: 2.1-mi. E of Parkers Lake. Equipment: Comwave transmitter; Andrew antenna.

Louisiana

Alexandria—WHR-468 (Channel F-1). Louisiana ETV Authority, 7860 Anselmo Lane, Baton Rouge, LA 70810. Authorized power: 10-w. Antenna: 200-ft. above ground. Lat. 31° 18' 29", long. 92° 26' 42". Transmitter: 1210 6th St. Equipment: Emcee transmitter; Andrew antenna.

Baton Rouge—WHR-813 (Channels D-1-4). Louisiana State U., 99 Lakeshore Dr., Baton Rouge, LA 70803. Authorized power: 10-w. each. Antenna: 131-ft. above ground. Lat. 30° 24' 37", long. 91° 10' 37". Transmitter: Choppin Hall, Louisiana State U.

Blond—WND-353 (Channels A-1-4). Southeastern Louisiana U., SLU-858, Hammond, LA 70402. Authorized power: 10-w. each. Antenna: 302-ft. above ground. Lat. 30° 36' 32", long. 90° 06' 26". Transmitter: 500 S. Kramer Rd. Equipment: Comwave transmitter; Andrew antenna.

Blond—WND-354 (Channels B-1-4). Tulane Regional Primate Research Center, Room H128, Gibson Hall, New Orleans, LA 70118. Authorized power: 10-w. each. Antenna: 302-ft. above ground. Lat. 30° 36' 32", long. 90° 06' 26". Transmitter: 500 S. Kramer Rd. Equipment: Comwave transmitter; Andrew antenna.

Blond—WND-355 (Channels C-1-4). Oaks Montessori School, 43283 S. Range Rd., Hammond, LA 70403. Authorized power: 10-w. each. Antenna: 302-ft. above ground. Lat. 30° 36' 32", long. 90° 06' 26". Transmitter: 500 S. Kramer Rd. Equipment: Comwave transmitter; Andrew antenna.

Blond—WND-356 (Channels D-1-4). Trafton Academy, Drawer 2845, Hammond, LA 70404. Phone: 504-542-7212. Fax: 504-542-7213. Authorized power: 10-w. each. Antenna: 302-ft. above ground. Lat. 30° 36' 32", long. 90° 06' 26". Transmitter: 500 S. Kramer Rd. Equipment: Comwave transmitter; Andrew antenna.

Blond—WND-357 (Channels G-1-4). Louisiana ETV Authority, 7860 Anselmo Lane, Baton Rouge, LA 70810. Authorized power: 10-w. each. Antenna: 302-ft. above ground. Lat. 30° 36' 32", Long. 90° 06' 26". Transmitter: 500 S. Kramer Rd. Equipment: Comwave transmitter; Andrew antenna.

Bunkie—WLX-757 (Channels A-1-4). Avoyelles Parish School Board, 201 Tunica Dr. W, Marksville, LA 71351. Authorized power: 50-w. each. Antenna: 705-ft. above ground. Lat. 30° 57' 53", long. 92° 07' 15". Transmitter: 2.9-mi. E of Bunkie, 4-mi. SW of Boggy Lake. Equipment: Comwave transmitter; Andrew antenna.

Bunkie—WLX-760 (Channels B-1-4). Ville Platte High School, 210 W. Cotton, Ville Platte, LA 70586. Authorized power: 50-w. each. Antenna: 705-ft. above ground. Lat. 30° 57' 53", long. 92° 07' 15". Transmitter: 2.9-mi. E of Bunkie, 4-mi. SW of Boggy Lake. Equipment: Comwave transmitter; Andrew antenna.

Bunkie—WLX-838 (Channels C-1-4). Basile High School, 2nd St., Basile, LA 70515. Authorized power: 50-w. each. Lat. 30° 57' 47", long. 92° 07' 35". Transmitter: 2.5-mi. E of Bunkie. Equipment: Comwave transmitter; Andrew antenna.

Bunkie—WLX-972 (Channels D-1-4). Sacred Heart Elementary, 532 E. Main St., Ville Platte, LA 70586. Authorized power: 50-w. each. Antenna: 705-ft. above ground. Lat. 30° 57' 47", long. 92° 07' 35". Transmitter: 3.1-mi. E of Bunkie, next to Cypress Lake. Equipment: Comwave transmitter; Andrew antenna.

Bunkie—WLX-761 (Channels G-1-4). Westminster Christian Academy, 186 Westminster Dr., Opelousas, LA 70570. Phone: 318-948-8600. Authorized power: 50-w. each. Antenna: 705-ft. above ground. Lat. 30° 57' 53", long. 92° 07' 15". Transmitter: 2.9-mi. E of Bunkie, 4-mi. SW of Boggy Lake. Equipment: Comwave transmitter; Andrew antenna.

Buras—WND-435 (Channels A-1-4). Light Tabernacle Christian Academy, Box 1153, Port Sulphur, LA 70083. Authorized power: 50-w. each. Antenna: 194-ft. above ground. Lat. 29° 20' 15", long. 89° 28' 46". Transmitter: Adjacent to Mississippi River across from the east edge of Buras. Equipment: Emcee transmitter; Andrew antenna.

Buras—WND-436 (Channels B-1-4). Solid Rock Academy, Box 67, Port Sulphur, LA 70082. Authorized power: 50-w. each. Antenna: 194-ft. above ground. Lat. 29° 20' 15", long. 89° 28' 46". Transmitter: Adjacent to Mississippi River across from the east edge of Buras. Equipment: Emcee transmitter; Andrew antenna.

Delhi—WND-429 (Channels D-1-4). Tulane U. of Louisiana, 6823 St. Charles Ave., New Orleans, LA 70118. Authorized power: 10-w. each. Antenna: 79-ft. above ground. Lat. 32° 24' 56", long. 92° 29' 28". Equipment: Comwave transmitter; Andrew antenna.

Delhi—WND-506 (Channels G-1-4). Northwestern State U. of Louisiana, Box 5273, Natchitoches, LA 71497. Authorized power: 10-w. each. Antenna: 79-ft. above ground. Lat. 32° 24' 56", long. 91° 29' 28". Transmitter: 3-mi. S of Delhi. Equipment: Comwave transmitter; Andrew antenna.

Dry Prong—WND-503 (Channels A-1-4). Louisiana ETV Authority, 7860 Anselmo Lane, Baton Rouge, LA 70810. Authorized power: 50-w. each. Antenna: 1329-ft. above ground. Lat. 31° 33' 56", long. 92° 32' 50". Transmitter: 1.4-mi. SW of Dry Prong. Equipment: Comwave transmitter; Andrew antenna.

Dry Prong—WNC-492 (Channels B-1-4). Foundation for Excellence in Louisiana Public Broadcasting, 7860 Anselmo Lane, Baton Rouge, LA 70810. Authorized power: 50-w. each. Antenna: 1329-ft. above ground. Lat. 31° 33' 56", long. 92° 32' 50". Transmitter: 1.4-mi. SW of Dry Prong. Equipment: Comwave transmitter; Andrew antenna.

Dry Prong—WNC-507 (Channels C-1-4). Louisiana Independent Higher Education Research Foundation, 650 N. 10th St., Baton Rouge, LA 70802. Phone: 504-389-9885. Fax: 504-389-0149.
E-mail: laicu@ix.netcom.com.
Authorized power: 50-w. each. Antenna: 1306-ft. above ground. Lat. 31° 33' 56", long. 92° 32' 50". Equipment: Comwave transmitter; Andrew antenna.
Leased to Wireless One Inc., 11301 Industriplex Blvd., Suite 4, Baton Rouge, LA 70809-4115. Phone: 504-293-5000.

Dry Prong—WNC-643 (Channels D-1-4). Louisiana State U. Alumni Assn., 3960 W. Lakeshore Dr., Baton Rouge, LA 70808. Authorized power: 50-w. each. Antenna: 1306-ft. above ground. Lat. 31° 33' 56", long. 92° 32' 50". Transmitter: 1.4-mi. SW of Dry Prong. Equipment: Comwave transmitter; Andrew antenna.

Ferriday—WND-330 (Channels A-1-4). Louisiana ETV Authority, 7860 Anselmo Lane, Baton Rouge, LA 70810. Authorized power: 10-w. each. Antenna: 262-ft. above ground. Lat. 31° 40' 08", long. 91° 41' 30". Transmitter: 4.4-mi. SW of Dunbarton. Equipment: Comwave transmitter; Andrew antenna.

Ferriday—WND-331 (Channels B-1-4). Foundation for Excellence in Louisiana Public Broadcasting, 7860 Anselmo Lane, Baton Rouge, LA 70810. Authorized power: 10-w. each. Antenna: 262-ft. above ground. Lat. 31° 40' 08", long. 91° 41' 30". Transmitter: 4.4-mi. SW of Dunbarton. Equipment: Comwave transmitter; Andrew antenna.

Ferriday—WND-424 (Channels D-1-4). Northwestern State U. of Louisiana, Box 5273, Natchitoches, LA 71457. Authorized power: 10-w. each. Antenna: 262-ft. above ground. Lat. 31° 40' 08", long. 91° 41' 30". Transmitter: 4.4-mi. SW of Dunbarton. Equipment: Comwave transmitter; Andrew antenna.

Ferriday—WND-332 (Channels G-1-4). Tulane U. of Louisiana, 6823 St. Charles Ave., New Orleans, LA 70118. Authorized power: 10-w. each. Antenna: 262-ft. above ground. Lat. 31° 40' 08", long. 91° 41' 30". Transmitter: 4.4-mi. SW of Dunbarton. Equipment: Comwave transmitter; Andrew antenna.

Gibson—WND-206 (Channels A-1-4). Thibodaux High School, 1355 Tiger Dr., Thibodaux, LA 70301. Authorized power: 50-w. each. Antenna: 499-ft. above ground. Lat. 29° 41' 39", long. 90° 59' 58". Transmitter: 0.7-mi. SE of Gibson, 0.6-mi. N of U.S. 90 & State Rte. 20 intersection. Equipment: Comwave transmitter; Andrew antenna.

Gibson—WLX-612 (Channels B-1-4). Central Lafourche High School, 4820 Hwy. 1, Mathews, LA 70375. Authorized power: 50-w. each. Antenna: 705-ft. above ground. Lat. 29° 41' 39", long. 90° 59' 58". Transmitter: 0.7-mi. SE of Gibson, 0.6-mi. N of intersection of U.S. 90 & State Rte. 20. Equipment: Comwave transmitter; Andrew antenna.

Gibson—WLX-844 (Channels C-1-4). Assumption High School, Box 338, Hwy. 308, Napoleonville, LA 70390. Authorized power: 50-w. each. Antenna: 705-ft. above ground. Lat. 29° 41' 39", long. 90° 59' 58". Transmitter: 0.7-mi. SE of Gibson, 0.6-mi. N of U.S. 90 & State Rte. 20 intersection. Equipment: Comwave transmitter; Andrew antenna.

Gibson—WND-207 (Channels D-1-4). Nicholls State U., University Station, Hwy. One, Thibodaux, LA 70310. Authorized power: 50-w. each. Antenna: 499-ft. above ground. Lat. 29° 41' 39", long. 90° 59' 58". Transmitter: 0.7-mi. SE of Gibson, 0.6-mi. N of U.S. 90 & SR 20 intersection. Equipment: Comwave transmitter; Andrew antenna.

Gibson—WLX-769 (Channels G-1-4). Jefferson Davis Parish School, 203 E. Plaquemine, Jennings, LA 70546. Authorized power: 50-w. each. Antenna: 496-ft. above ground. Lat. 29° 41' 39", long. 90° 59' 58". Transmitter: 0.7-mi. SE of Gibson, 0.6-mi. N of U.S. 90 & State Rte. 20 intersection. Equipment: Comwave transmitter; Andrew antenna.

Husser—WLX-656 (Channels A-1-4). Bowling Green School, 700 Varnado St., Franklinton, LA 70438. Phone: 504-839-5317. Fax: 504-839-5668.
E-mail: bowlingg@cmq.com.
Authorized power: 10-w. each. Antenna: 302-ft. above ground. Lat. 30° 16' 30", long. 89° 47' 38". Transmitter: West & Martin Sts. Equipment: Comwave transmitter; Andrew antenna.

Husser—WLX-655 (Channels B-1-4). Northlake Christian School, 70104 Wolverine Dr., Covington, LA 70433. Phone: 504-892-2683. Fax: 504-893-4363. Authorized power: 10-w. each. Antenna: 302-ft. above ground. Lat. 30° 16' 30", long. 89° 47' 38". Transmitter: West & Martin Sts. Equipment: Comwave transmitter; Andrew antenna.
Leased to Wireless One Inc., 11301 Industriplex Blvd., Suite 4, Baton Rouge, LA 70809-4115. Phone: 504-293-5000.

Husser—WLX-696 (Channels C-1-4). St. Helena Central High School, Box 490, Greensburg, LA 70441. Authorized power: 10-w. each. Antenna: 302-ft. above ground. Lat. 30° 16' 30", long. 89° 47' 38". Transmitter: West & Martin Sts. Equipment: Comwave transmitter; Andrew antenna.

Husser—WLX-665 (Channels G-1-4). Oak Forest Academy, 600 Walnut St., Amite, LA 70422. Phone: 504-748-4321. Fax: 504-748-4320. Authorized power: 10-w. each. Antenna: 302-ft. above ground. Lat. 30° 16' 30", long. 89° 47' 38". Transmitter: West & Martin Sts. Equipment: Comwave transmitter; Andrew antenna.
Leased to Wireless One Inc., 11301 Industriplex Blvd., Suite 4, Baton Rouge, LA 70809. Phone: 504-293-5000.

Jennings—WLX-634 (Channels A-1-4). Jefferson Davis Parish School, Box 640, Jennings, LA 70546. Authorized power: 50-w. each. Antenna: 410-ft. above ground. Lat. 30° 11' 50", long. 93° 13' 12". Transmitter: 129 W. Prien Lake. Equipment: Comwave transmitter; Andrew antenna.

Jennings—WLX-675 (Channels C-1-4). Oakdale High School, 101 S. 13th St., Oakdale, LA 71463. Phone: 318-335-2338. Fax: 318-335-3257. Authorized power: 50-w. each. Antenna: 354-ft. above ground. Lat. 31° 03' 01", long. 93° 16' 35". Transmitter: KVVP(FM) tower, 7-mi. SSW of Leesville. Equipment: Comwave transmitter; Andrew antenna.

Jennings—WNC-293 (Channels D-1-4). Church Point High School, 305 E. Lougarre St., Church Point, LA 70525. Authorized power: 50-w. each. Antenna: 587-ft. above ground. Lat. 30° 02' 54", long. 91° 59' 49". Transmitter: 4.5-mi. N of Jennings. Equipment: Comwave transmitter; Andrew antenna.

Jennings—WLX-633 (Channels G-1-4). Elizabeth High School, Live Oak St., Elizabeth, LA 70638. Authorized power: 50-w. each. Antenna: 354-ft. above ground. Lat. 31° 03' 01", long. 93° 16' 35". Transmitter: KVVP(FM) tower, 7-mi. SSW of Leesville. Equipment: Comwave transmitter; Andrew antenna.

Lafayette—WHR-670 (Channels B-1-4). Bishop J. Jeanmard, 450 E. Farrel Rd., Lafayette, LA 70508. Phone: 318-988-1572. Authorized power: 50-w. each. Antenna: 587-ft. above ground. Lat. 30° 02' 54", long. 91° 59' 49". Transmitter: 2.7-mi. ENE of Ridge. Equipment: Comwave transmitter; Andrew antenna.

Lake Charles—WNC-750 (Channels B-1-4). Sulphur High School, 600 Sycamore St., Sulphur, LA 70663. Authorized power: 50-w. each. Antenna: 410-ft. above ground. Lat. 30° 11' 50", long. 93° 13' 12". Transmitter: 129 W. Prien Lake. Equipment: Emcee transmitter; Andrew antenna.

Lake Charles—WNC-751 (Channels C-1-4). Delta School of Business and Technology, 517 E. Broad St., Lake Charles, LA 70601. Phone: 318-439-5765. Fax: 318-436-5151.
Web site: http://www.deltatech-lc.com.
Authorized power: 50-w. each. Antenna: 460-ft. above ground. Lat. 30° 11' 50", long. 93° 13' 12". Transmitter: 129 W. Prien Lake. Equipment: Emcee transmitter; Andrew antenna.

Lake Charles—WNC-749 (Channels D-1-4). McNeese State U., Box 92940, Lake Charles, LA 70609. Authorized power: 50-w. each. Antenna: 409-ft. above ground. Lat. 30° 11' 50", long. 93° 13' 12". Transmitter: 129 W. Prien Lake. Equipment: Emcee transmitter; Andrew antenna.

Lake Charles—WHR-484 (Channel E-1). Louisiana ETV Authority, 7860 Anselmo Lane, Baton Rouge, LA 70810. Phone: 504-767-5660. Fax: 504-767-4277. Authorized power: 10-w. Antenna: 474-ft. above ground. Lat. 30° 13' 48", long. 93° 12' 57". Transmitter: 320 Division St.

Lake Charles—WNC-779 (Channels G-1-4). Louisiana ETV Authority, 7860 Anselmo Lake, Baton Rouge, LA 70810. Phone: 504-767-5660. Fax: 504-767-4277. Authorized power: 50-w. each. Antenna: 460-ft. above ground. Lat. 30° 11' 50", long. 93° 13' 12". Transmitter: 129 W. Prien Lake. Equipment: Emcee transmitter; Andrew antenna.

Leesville—WND-343 (Channels A-1-4). Vernon Parish School Board, 201 Belview Rd., Leesville, LA 71446. Authorized power. 50-w. each. Antenna: 354-ft. above ground. Lat. 31° 03' 01", long. 93° 16' 35". Transmitter: 7-mi. SSW of Leesville. Equipment: Comwave transmitter; Andrew antenna.

Leesville—WND-345 (Channels D-1-4). Louisiana Educational Television Authority, 7860 Anselmo Lane, Baton Rouge, LA 70809. Authorized power: 50-w. each. Antenna: 354-ft. above ground. Lat. 31° 03' 01", long. 93° 16' 35". Transmitter: 7-mi. SSW of Leesville. Equipment: Comwave transmitter; Andrew antenna.

Natchitoches—WNC-626 (Channels D-1-3). Northwestern State U. of Louisiana, Natchitoches, LA 71497. Phone: 318-357-6441. Fax: 318-357-4223.
E-mail: mcbride@alpha.nsula.edu, webb@alpha.nslua.edu.
Authorized power: 10-w. each. Antenna: 403-ft. above ground. Lat. 31° 47' 16", long. 93° 08' 38". Transmitter: 0.2-mi. E of State Rd. Equipment: ITS transmitter; Andrew antenna.
Leased to Nucentrix Broadband Networks, 200 Chisolm Place, Suite 200, Plano, TX 75075. Phone: 972-423-9494. Fax: 972-423-0819.

New Orleans—WHR-912 (Channels A-1-4). St. Bernard Parish School Board, 67 E. Chalmette Circle, Chalmette, LA 70043. Authorized power: 10-w. each. Antenna: 651-ft. above ground. Lat. 29° 57' 07", long. 90° 04' 13". Transmitter: Avondale Shipyard S. Equipment: ITS transmitter; Andrew antenna. Requests change to 20-w. each.

New Orleans—WHR-918 (Channels B-1-4). New Orleans Educational Telecommunications Consortium Inc., Suite 2038, 2 Canal St., New Orleans, LA 70130. Phone: 504-524-0350. Fax: 504-524-0327.
E-mail: blucas@iamerica.net.
Authorized power: 10-w. each. Antenna: 651-ft. above ground. Lat. 29° 57' 07", long. 90° 04' 13". Transmitter: Bank One Center. Equipment: ITS transmitter; Andrew antenna. Requests change to 20-w. each.
Leased to Bell South Entertainment, 101 Teal St., St. Rose, LA 70087. Phone: 504-712-4808.

New Orleans—WHR-681 (Channels C-1-4). Hispanic Information & Telecommunications Network Inc., 3rd Floor, 449 Broadway, New York, NY 10013. Phone: 212-966-5660. Fax: 212-966-5725.
E-mail: email@hitn.org.
Web site: http://www.hitn.org.
Authorized power: 50-w. each. Antenna: 662-ft. above ground. Lat. 29° 57' 07", long. 90° 04' 13". Transmitter: Place St. Charles, 201 St. Charles Ave. Equipment: ITS transmitter; Andrew antenna.
Leased to Bell South Wireless Cable Inc., 1100 Abernathy Rd., Suite 414, Atlanta, GA 30328. Phone: 770-481-2990.

New Orleans—WHR-513 (Channels D-1-4). Network for Instructional TV Inc., Suite 110, 11490 Commerce Park Dr., Reston, VA 20191. Phone: 703-860-9200. Fax: 703-860-9237. Authorized power: 10-w. each. Antenna: 651-ft. above ground. Lat. 29° 57' 07", long. 90° 04' 13". Transmitter: Avondale Shipyard, SE of New Orleans. Equipment: ITS transmitter; Andrew antenna. Requests change to 20-w. each.
Leased to Crescent Broadcasting (Continental), 800 W. Airport Freeway, Irving, TX 75065. Phone: 214-445-4110.

New Orleans—WHR-913 (Channels G-1-4). Focus on Education, 2300 Energy Center, 1100 Poydras St., New Orleans, LA 70163-2000. Authorized power: 10-w. each. Antenna: 651-ft. above ground. Lat. 29° 57' 07", long. 90° 04' 13". Transmitter: Avondale Shipyard S. Equipment: ITS transmitter; Andrew antenna.

Plaquemine—WLX-971 (Channels D-1-4). Louisiana State U. & Agricultural & Mechanical College,. Authorized power: 50-w. each. Antenna: 630-ft. above ground. Lat. 30° 17' 49", long. 91° 11' 40". Transmitter: 2.2-mi. NE of Plaquemine. Equipment: Emcee transmitter; Andrew antenna.

Rayville—WNC-534 (Channels B-1-4). Ouachita Academy of Arts & Science, 224 Auburn Ave., Monroe, LA 71201. Authorized power: 10-w. each. Antenna: 304-ft. above ground. Lat. 32° 27' 22", long. 91° 39' 27". Transmitter: 5-mi. E of Hwy. 20. Equipment: Emcee transmitter; Andrew antenna.

Shreveport—WND-507 (Channels D-1-4). Springhill High School, 507 W. Church St., Springhill, LA 71075. Phone: 318-539-2563. Authorized power: 50-w. each. Antenna: 600-ft. above ground. Lat. 32° 34' 32", long. 93° 52' 06". Transmitter: 0.6-mi. S of Pine Hills Rd. Equipment: Emcee transmitter; Andrew antenna.

Shreveport—WHR-475 (Channel E-1). Louisiana ETV Authority, 7860 Anselmo Lane, Baton Rouge, LA 70810. Authorized power: 10-w. Antenna: 281-ft. above ground. Lat. 32° 30' 50", long. 93° 44' 54". Transmitter: 425 Edwards St. Equipment: Emcee transmitter; Andrew antenna.

Youngsville—WLX-616 (Channels A-1-4). Acadia Parish School Board, 2402 N. Parkerson Ave., Crowley, LA 70526. Authorized power: 50-w. each. Antenna: 587-ft. above ground. Lat. 30° 02' 54", long. 91° 59' 49". Transmitter: 3.2-mi. S of Guillotte. Equipment: Comwave transmitter; Andrew antenna.

Youngsville—WND-431 (Channels C-1-4). U. of Southwestern Louisiana, 104 University Circle, Lafayette, LA 70504. Authorized power: 20-w. each. Antenna: 443-ft. above ground. Lat. 30° 02' 54", long. 91° 59' 49". Transmitter: 10.2-mi. S of Youngsville. Equipment: Comwave transmitter; Bogner antenna.

Maine

Augusta—WHR-969 (Channels G-1-4). U. of Maine System, 46 University Dr., Augusta, ME 04330. Phone: 207-621-3377. Fax: 207-621-3420.
E-mail: sgjurich@maine.edu.
Web site: http://www.unet.maine.edu.
Authorized power: 10-w. each. Antenna: 155-ft. above ground. Lat. 44° 19' 51", long. 69° 46' 31". Transmitter: Sand Hill, Forest Ave. Equipment: Comwave & Emcee transmitter; Andrew & Bogner antenna.

Blue Hill—WLX-215 (Channels A-1-4). U. of Maine System, 46 University Dr., Augusta, ME 04330. Phone: 207-621-3377. Fax: 207-621-3420.
E-mail: sgjurich@maine.edu.
Web site: http://www.unet.maine.edu.
Authorized power: 10-w. each. Antenna: 57-ft. above ground. Lat. 44° 26' 02", long. 68° 35' 33". Equipment: Comwave & Emcee transmitter; Bogner antenna.

Bridgewater—WHR-999 (Channels A-1-4). U. of Maine System, 46 University Dr., Augusta, ME 04330. Phone: 207-621-3377. Fax: 207-621-3420.
E-mail: sgjurich@maine.edu.
Web site: http://www.unet.maine.edu.
Authorized power: 10-w. each. Antenna: 69-ft. above ground. Lat. 46° 25' 17", long. 68° 01' 28". Transmitter: No. 9 mountain, near Bridgewater. Equipment: Comwave & Emcee transmitter; Bogner antenna.

Buckfield—WLX-305 (Channels D-1-4). U. of Maine System, 46 University Dr., Augusta, ME 04330. Phone: 207-621-3377. Fax: 207-621-3420.
E-mail: sgjurich@maine.edu.
Web site: http://www.unet.maine.edu.
Authorized power: 10-w. each. Antenna: 100-ft. above ground. Lat. 44° 14' 56", long. 70° 25' 25". Transmitter: Streaked Mountain. Equipment: Comwave & Emcee transmitter; Bogner antenna.

Camden—WHR-965 (Channels D-1-4). U. of Maine System, 46 University Dr., Augusta, ME 04330. Phone: 207-621-3377. Fax: 207-621-3420.
E-mail: sgjurich@maine.edu.
Web site: http://www.unet.maine.edu.
Authorized power: 10-w. each. Antenna: 107-ft. above ground. Lat. 44° 12' 40", long. 69° 09' 06". Transmitter: Summit of Ragged Mountain. Equipment: Emcee & Comwave transmitter; Bogner antenna.

Carrabassett—WLX-580 (Channels A-1-4). U. of Maine System, 46 University Dr., Augusta, ME 04330. Phone: 207-621-3377. Fax: 207-621-3420.
E-mail: sgjurich@maine.edu.
Web site: http://www.unet.maine.edu.
Authorized power: 10-w. each. Antenna: 50-ft. above ground. Lat. 45° 01' 54", long. 70° 18' 50". Transmitter: Sugarloaf Mountain. Equipment: Comwave & Emcee transmitter; Bogner & Mark antenna.

Charleston—WHR-983 (Channels G-1-4). U. of Maine System, 46 University Dr., Augusta, ME 04330. Phone: 207-621-3377. Fax: 207-621-3420.
E-mail: sgjurich@maine.edu.
Web site: http://www.unet.maine.edu.
Authorized power: 10-w. each. Antenna: 186-ft. above ground. Lat. 45° 05' 40", long. 69° 05' 18". Transmitter: Bull Hill, Charleston. Equipment: Comwave & Emcee transmitter; Andrew antenna.

Cooper—WLX-216 (Channels A-1-2). U. of Maine System, 46 University Dr., Augusta, ME 04330. Phone: 207-621-3377. Fax: 207-621-3420.
E-mail: sgjurich@maine.edu.
Web site: http://www.unet.maine.edu.
Authorized power: 10-w. each. Antenna: 107-ft. above ground. Lat. 44° 59' 13", long. 67° 28' 01". Transmitter: Machias. Equipment: Comwave & Emcee transmitter; Bogner & Andrew antenna. Requests modification of license for change to add Channels A-3-4.

Daigle—WLX-219 (Channels C-1-4). U. of Maine System, 46 University Dr., Augusta, ME 04330. Phone: 207-621-3377. Fax: 207-621-3420.
E-mail: sgjurich@maine.edu.
Web site: http://www.unet.maine.edu.
Authorized power: 10-w. each. Antenna: 157-ft. above ground. Lat. 42° 12' 05", long. 68° 27' 25". Transmitter: Stockholm. Equipment: Comwave & Emcee transmitter; Bogner & Mark antenna.

Dixmont Center—WHR-992 (Channels C-1-4). U. of Maine System, 46 University Dr., Augusta, ME 04330. Phone: 207-621-3377. Fax: 207-621-3420.
E-mail: sgjurich@maine.edu.
Web site: http://www.unet.maine.edu.
Authorized power: 10-w. each. Antenna: 107-ft. above ground. Lat. 44° 42' 08", long. 69° 04' 47". Transmitter: Peaked Mountain. Equipment: Comwave & Emcee transmitter; Bogner & Mark antenna.

East Eddington—WHR-988 (Channels D-1-4). U. of Maine System, 46 University Dr., Augusta, ME 04330. Phone: 207-621-3377. Fax: 207-621-3420.
E-mail: sgjurich@maine.edu.
Web site: http://www.unet.maine.edu.
Authorized power: 50-w. each. Antenna: 133-ft. above ground. Lat. 44° 45' 36", long. 68° 33' 59". Transmitter: Black Cap Mountain. Equipment: Comwave & Emcee transmitter; Bogner antenna.

East Machias—WLX-217 (Channels G-1-4). U. of Maine System, 46 University Dr., Augusta, ME 04330. Phone: 207-621-3377. Fax: 207-621-3420.
E-mail: sgjurich@maine.edu.
Web site: http://www.unet.maine.edu.
Authorized power: 10-w. each. Antenna: 127-ft. above ground. Lat. 44° 43' 48", long. 67° 24' 40". Transmitter: East Machias. Equipment: Comwave & Emcee transmitter; Bogner & Andrew antenna.

Fort Kent—WHR-996 (Channels A-1-4). U. of Maine System, 46 University Dr., Augusta, ME 04330. Phone: 207-621-3377. Fax: 207-621-3420.
E-mail: sgjurich@maine.edu.
Web site: http://www.unet.maine.edu.
Authorized power: 10-w. each. Antenna: 157-ft. above ground. Lat. 47° 15' 30", long. 68° 33' 30". Transmitter: Charette Hill. Equipment: Comwave & Emcee transmitter; Bogner antenna.

Greenville—WLX-203 (Channels A-1-4). U. of Maine System, 46 University Dr., Augusta, ME 04330. Phone: 207-621-3377. Fax: 207-621-3420.
E-mail: sgjurich@maine.edu.
Web site: http://www.unet.maine.edu.
Authorized power: 10-w. each. Antenna: 97-ft. above ground. Lat. 45° 27' 46", long. 69° 33' 23". Transmitter: Greenville Airport. Equipment: Comwave & Emcee transmitter; Bogner antenna.

Greenwood—WHR-984 (Channels A-1-2). U. of Maine System, 46 University Dr., Augusta, ME 04330. Phone: 207-621-3377. Fax: 207-621-3420.
E-mail: sgjurich@maine.edu.
Web site: http://www.unet.maine.edu.
Authorized power: 10-w. each. Antenna: 75-ft. above ground. Lat. 44° 22' 11", long. 70° 42' 48". Transmitter: Mount Abrams. Equipment: Comwave transmitter; Bogner antenna.

Kittery—WHR-706 (Channels G-1-4). U. of New Hampshire, Box 1100, Durham, NH 03824. Authorized power: 10-w. each. Antenna: 80-ft. above ground. Lat. 43° 13' 25", long. 70° 41' 32". Transmitter: Mount Agamenticus, 9.5-mi. NNE of Portsmouth, NH. Equipment: ITS transmitter; Andrew antenna.

Lewiston—WHR-967 (Channels C-1-4). U. of Maine System, 46 University Dr., Augusta, ME 04330. Phone: 207-621-3377. Fax: 207-621--3420.
E-mail: sgjurich@maine.edu.
Web site: http://www.unet.maine.edu.
Authorized power: 10-w. each. Antenna: 157-ft. above ground. Lat. 44° 05' 18", long. 70° 11' 33". Transmitter: Apple Sas Hill, Moun-

tainview Ave. Equipment: Comwave & Emcee transmitter; Bogner antenna.

Lincoln—WHR-991 (Channels B-1-4). U. of Maine System, 46 University Dr., Augusta, ME 04330. Phone: 207-621-3377. Fax: 207-621--3420.
E-mail: sgjurich@maine.edu.
Web site: http://www.unet.maine.edu.
Authorized power: 10-w. each. Antenna: 137-ft. above ground. Lat. 45° 20' 43", long. 68° 30' 28". Transmitter: Fish Hill. Equipment: Comwave & Emcee transmitter; Anixter-Mark & Bogner antenna.

Litchfield—WHR-968 (Channels A-1-4). U. of Maine System, 46 University Dr., Augusta, ME 04330. Phone: 207-621-3377. Fax: 207-621-3420.
E-mail: sgjurich@maine.edu.
Web site: http://www.unet.maine.edu.
Authorized power: 50-w. each. Antenna: 250-ft. above ground. Lat. 44° 09' 16", long. 70° 00' 37". Transmitter: Summit of Danforth Hill. Equipment: Emcee & Comwave transmitter; Bogner antenna.

Millinocket—WLX-204 (Channels G-1-4). U. of Maine System, 46 University Dr., Augusta, ME 04330. Phone: 207-621-3377. Fax: 207-621-3420.
E-mail: sgjurich@maine.edu.
Web site:http://www.unet.maine.edu.
Authorized power: 10-w. each. Antenna: 254-ft. above ground. Lat. 45° 38' 52", long. 68° 45' 08". Transmitter: Quakish Lake. Equipment: Comwave & Emcee transmitter; Bogner antenna.

New Sharon—WHR-985 (Channels C-1-4). U. of Maine System, 46 University Dr., Augusta, ME 04330. Phone: 207-621-3377. Fax: 207-621-3420.
E-mail: sgjurich@maine.edu.
Web site: http://www.unet.maine.edu.
Authorized power: 10-w. each. Antenna: 157-ft. above ground. Lat. 44° 35' 48", long. 69° 58' 25". Transmitter: York Hill. Equipment: Comwave & Emcee transmitter; Bogner & Andrew antenna.

Portland—WHR-982 (Channels B-1-4). U. of Maine System, 46 University Dr., Augusta, ME 04330. Phone: 207-621-3377. Fax: 207-621-3420.
E-mail: sgjurich@maine.edu.
Web site: http://www.unet.maine.edu.
Authorized power: 50-w. each. Antenna: 97-ft. above ground. Lat. 43° 39' 38", long. 70° 16' 50". Transmitter: Portland Law Bldg. Equipment: Comwave & Emcee transmitter; Bogner & Andrew antenna.

Presque Isle—WHR-987 (Channels B-1-4). U. of Maine System, 46 University Dr., Augusta, ME 04330. Phone: 207-621-3377. Fax: 207-621-3420.
E-mail: sgjurich@maine.edu.
Web site: http://www.unet.maine.edu.
Authorized power: 10-w. each. Antenna: 139-ft. above ground. Lat. 46° 44' 25", long. 67° 55' 53". Transmitter: Parkhurst. Equipment: Emcee & Comwave transmitter; Bogner antenna.

Presque Isle—WHR-998 (Channels G-1-4). U. of Maine System, 46 University Dr., Augusta, ME 04330. Phone: 207-621-3377. Fax: 207-621-3420.
E-mail: sgjurich@maine.edu.
Web site: http://www.unet.maine.edu.
Authorized power: 10-w. each. Antenna: 47-ft. above ground. Lat. 46° 36' 13", long. 68° 00' 25". Transmitter: Quaggy Joe Mountain. Equipment: Comwave & Emcee transmitter; Bogner & Mark antenna.

Rumford—WHR-989 (Channels G-1-4). U. of Maine System, 46 University Dr., Augusta, ME 04330. Phone: 207-621-3377. Fax: 207-621-3420.
E-mail: sgjurich@maine.edu.
Web site: http://www.unet.maine.edu.
Authorized power: 10-w. each. Antenna: 163-ft. above ground. Lat. 44° 35' 01", long. 70° 38' 17". Transmitter: Black Mountain. Equipment: Comwave & Emcee transmitter; Bogner antenna.

Sebago—WLX-205 (Channels G-1-4). U. of Maine System, 46 University Dr., Augusta, ME 04330. Phone: 207-621-3377. Fax: 207-621-3420.
E-mail: sgjurich@maine.edu.
Web site: http://www.unet.maine.edu.
Authorized power: 10-w. each. Antenna: 302-ft. above ground. Lat. 43° 51' 32", long. 70° 42' 40". Transmitter: Winn Mountain. Equipment: Comwave & Emcee transmitter; Bogner antenna.

Smyrna—WHR-986 (Channels C-1-4). U. of Maine System, 46 University Dr., Augusta, ME 04330. Phone: 207-621-3377. Fax: 207-621-3420.
E-mail: sgjurich@maine.edu.
Web site: http://www.unet.maine.edu.
Authorized power: 10-w. each. Antenna: 52-ft. above ground. Lat. 46° 09' 48", long. 68° 05' 45". Transmitter: Smyrna Center. Equipment: Emcee & Comwave transmitter; Bogner antenna.

Topsfield—WLX-218 (Channels D-1-4). U. of Maine System, 46 University Dr., Augusta, ME 04330. Phone: 207-621-3377. Fax: 207-621-3420.
E-mail: sgjurich@maine.edu.
Web site: http://www.unet.maine.edu.
Authorized power: 10-w. each. Antenna: 103-ft. above ground. Lat. 45° 23' 20", long. 67° 47' 50". Transmitter: Musquash Mountain. Equipment: Comwave & Emcee transmitter; Andrew antenna.

Vassalboro—WHR-966 (Channels B-1-4). U. of Maine System, 46 University Dr., Augusta, ME 04330. Phone: 207-621-3377. Fax: 207-621-3420.
E-mail: sgjurich@maine.edu.
Web site: http://www.unet.maine.edu.
Authorized power: 10-w. each. Antenna: 107-ft. above ground. Lat. 44° 29' 22", long. 69° 39' 04". Transmitter: Summit of Cook Hill, North Vassalboro. Equipment: Comwave & Emcee transmitter; Bogner antenna.

York—WLX-202 (Channels D-1-4). U. of Maine System, 46 University Dr., Augusta, ME 04330. Phone: 207-621-3377. Fax: 207-621-3420.
E-mail: sgjurich@maine.edu.
Web site: http://www.unet.maine.edu.
Authorized power: 10-w. each. Antenna: 107-ft. above ground. Lat. 43° 13' 23", long. 70° 41' 35". Transmitter: Mount Agamenticus. Equipment: Comwave & Emcee transmitter; Bogner antenna.

Maryland

Annapolis—WLX-336 (Channels B-1-4). U. of Maryland, Glen L. Martin Engineering Bldg., College Park, MD 20742. Phone: 301-405-4910. Fax: 301-314-9639.
E-mail: a520@umail.umd.edu.
Authorized power: 0.001-w. each. Antenna: 99-ft. above ground. Lat. 38° 59' 03", long. 76° 33' 29". Transmitter: S side of MD 450, 2000-ft. W of MD 178. Equipment: California Amplifier transmitter; Andrew antenna.

Baltimore—WNC-708 (Channels A-1-4). U. of Maryland-College Park, College of Engineering, Room 2015, Bldg. 088.
E-mail: a520@umail.umd.edu.
Authorized power: 50-w. each. Antenna: 1000-ft. above ground. Lat. 39° 20' 10", long. 76° 38' 59". Transmitter: WBFF(TV) tower. Equipment: Comwave transmitter; Andrew antenna.

Baltimore—WHR-807 (Channels B-1-4). U. of Maryland, Glen L. Martin Engineering Bldg., College Park, MD 20742. Phone: 301-405-4910. Fax: 301-314-9639.
E-mail: a520@umail.umd.edu.
Authorized power: 50-w. each. Antenna: 710-ft. above ground. Lat. 39° 20' 10", long. 76° 38' 59". Transmitter: WBFF(TV) tower. Equipment: Comwave transmitter; Andrew antenna.

Baltimore—WLX-789 (Channels C-1-4). U. of Maryland, Glen L. Martin Engineering Bldg., College Park, MD 20742. Phone: 301-405-4910. Fax: 301-314-9639.
E-mail: a520@umail.umd.edu.
Authorized power: 10-w. each. Antenna: 227-ft. above ground. Lat. 39° 15' 38", long. 76° 47' 49". Transmitter: U. of Maryland, Baltimore. Equipment: Emcee transmitter; Andrew antenna.

Baltimore—WHR-917 (Channels D-1-4). Maryland State Dept. of Education, 200 W. Baltimore St., Baltimore, MD 21201. Authorized power: 50-w. each. Antenna: 712-ft. above ground. Lat. 39° 20' 10", long. 76° 38' 59". Transmitter: WBFF(TV) tower. Equipment: Comwave transmitter; Andrew antenna.

Baltimore—WLX-790 (Channels G-1-4). Catonsville Community College, 800 S. Rolling Rd., Catonsville, MD 21228. Authorized power: 50-w. each. Antenna: 710-ft. above ground. Lat. 39° 20' 10", long. 76° 38' 59". Transmitter: WBFF(TV) tower. Equipment: Comwave transmitter; Andrew antenna.

Bethesda—WLX-235 (Channel C-4). The George Mason U. Instructional Foundation Inc., 4400 University Dr., Fairfax, VA 22030. Phone: 703-993-3100. Fax: 703-273-2417.
E-mail: mkelley@gmu.edu.
Authorized power: 50-w. Antenna: 809-ft. above ground. Lat. 38° 57' 49", long. 77° 06' 18". Transmitter: 5202 River Rd. Equipment: ITS transmitter; Andrew antenna.
Leased to CAI Wireless Systems, 2101 Wilson Blvd., Suite 100, Arlington, VA 22201. Phone: 703-812-8800.

Clear Spring—WHR-727 (Channels C-1-4). U. of Maryland, Glen L. Martin Engineering Bldg., College Park, MD 20742. Phone: 301-405-4910. Fax: 301-314-9639.
E-mail: a520@umail.umd.edu.
Authorized power: 10-w. each. Antenna: 200-ft. above ground. Lat. 39° 39' 04", long. 77° 58' 15". Transmitter: 3-mi. W of Clear Spring.

College Park—WDT-880 (Channels E-3-4). U. of Maryland, Glen L. Martin Engineerng Bldg., College Park, MD 20742. Phone: 301-405-4910. Fax: 301-314-9639.
E-mail: a520@umail.umd.edu.
Authorized power: 0.1-w. each. Antenna: 132-ft. above ground. Lat. 38° 59' 32", long. 76° 56' 32". Transmitter: Centreville Hall.

Crownsville—WGI-231 (Channels E-1-2). U. of Maryland, Glen L. Martin Engineering Bldg., College Park, MD 20742. Phone: 301-405-4910. Fax: 301-314-9639.
E-mail: a520@umail.umd.edu.
Authorized power: 10-w. each. Lat. 39° 00' 36", long. 76° 36' 33". Transmitter: Crownsville Hospital grounds, 1.2-mi. SSW of Crownsville.

Fort Meade—WHQ-240 (Channels E-1-4). U. of Maryland, Glen L. Martin Engineering Bldg., College Park, MD 20742. Phone: 301-405-4910. Fax: 301-314-9639.
E-mail: a520@umail.umd.edu.
Authorized power: 0.1-w. each. Antenna: 280-ft. above ground. Lat. 39° 06' 18", long. 76° 46' 01". Transmitter: Fort George G. Meade Military Reservation.

Gaithersburg—WHQ-379 (Channels E-1-4). U. of Maryland, Glen L. Martin Engineering Bldg., College Park, MD 20742. Phone: 301-405-4910. Fax: 301-314-9639.
E-mail: a520@umail.umd.edu.
Authorized power: 0.1-w. each. Antenna: 142-ft. above ground. Lat. 38° 08' 07", long. 77° 12' 58". Transmitter: National Bureau of Standards Bldg.

Salisbury—WNC-437 (Channels B-1-4). U. of Maryland Eastern Shore, Princess Anne, MD 21853. Authorized power: 50-w. each. Antenna: 390-ft. above ground. Lat. 38° 24' 26", long. 75° 35' 57". Transmitter: Naylor Mill & Jersey Rds. Equipment: Comwave transmitter; Bogner antenna.

Salisbury—WNC-463 (Channels C-1-4). WOR-WIC Community Authorized power: 50-w. each. Antenna: 390-ft. above ground. Lat. 38° 24' 26", long. 75° 35' 57". Transmitter: Naylor Mill & Jersey Rds. Equipment: Comwave transmitter; Bogner antenna.

Waldorf—WLX-829 (Channels C-1-4). U. of Maryland, Glen L. Martin Engineering Bldg., College Park, MD 20742. Phone: 301-405-4910. Fax: 301-314-9639.
E-mail: a520@umail.umd.edu.
Authorized power: 50-w. each. Antenna: 600-ft. above ground. Lat. 38° 37' 07", long. 76° 50' 42". Transmitter: 2.2-mi. E of State Rte. 5. Equipment: Comwave transmitter; Andrew antenna.

Wheaton—WDT-881 (Channels A-1-4). U. of Maryland, Glen L. Martin Engineering Bldg., College Park, MD 20742. Phone: 301-405-4910. Fax: 301-314-9639.
E-mail: a520@umail.umd.edu.
Authorized power: 10-w. each. Antenna: 323-ft. above ground. Lat. 39° 02' 26", long. 77° 03' 19". Transmitter: 2647 University Blvd. W.

Wye Mills—WHR-764 (Channels A-1-4). Chesapeake College, Box 8, Wye Mills, MD 21679. Phone: 410-822-5400. Authorized power: 200-w. each. Lat. 38° 56' 55", long. 76° 05' 00". Transmitter: Rtes. 50 & 213 intersection at Wye Mills Chesapeake College.

Massachusetts

Agawam—WND-414 (Channels C-1-4). WGBY-TV, 44 Hampden St., Springfield, MA 01103. Phone: 413-781-2801.
Web site: http://www.wgby.org.
Authorized power: 100-w. each. Antenna: 351-ft. above ground. Lat. 42° 05' 05", long. 72° 44' 14". Transmitter: Provin Mountain, 591 Northwest St. Equipment: ITS transmitter; Andrew antenna.

Leased to CAI Wireless Systems, 2101 Wilson Blvd., Suite 100, Arlington, VA 22201. Phone: 703-812-8800.

Amherst—WHR-792 (Channels G-1-4). U. of Massachusetts-Amherst, 131 Marston Hall, Amherst, MA 01003. Authorized power: 10-w. each. Antenna: 563-ft. above ground. Lat. 42° 23' 23", long. 72° 31' 44". Transmitter: Library Bldg., U. of Massachusetts.

Andover—WND-257 (Channels A-1-2). Boston Catholic TV Center Inc., Box 56, 55 Chapel St., Newton, MA 02160. Authorized power: 14.1-w. each. Antenna: 226-ft. above ground. Lat. 42° 39' 17", long. 71° 13' 13". Transmitter: Wood Hill. Equipment: ITS transmitter; Andrew antenna.

Andover—WND-255 (Channels B-1-4). Northeastern U., Church Hall, Boston, MA 02115. Authorized power: 14.1-w. each. Antenna: 226-ft. above ground. Lat. 42° 39' 17", long. 71° 13' 13". Transmitter: Wood Hill. Equipment: ITS transmitter; Andrew antenna.

Andover—KMA-57 (Channels F-1-4). Boston Catholic TV Center Inc., Box 56, 55 Chapel St., Newton, MA 02160. Authorized power: 10-w. each. Antenna: 228-ft. above ground. Lat. 42° 39' 17", long. 71° 13' 13". Transmitter: Wood Hill.

Boston—WHR-758 (Channel C-1). Emerson College, 100 Beacon St., Boston, MA 02116. Authorized power: 100-w. Antenna: 366-ft. above ground. Lat. 42° 18' 12", long. 71° 13' 08". Transmitter: 144 Cabot St. Equipment: ITS transmitter; Andrew antenna.

Boston—WBB-421 (Channels C-2-4). President & Fellows of Harvard College, Harvard U., 17 Quincy St., Cambridge, MA 02138. Phone: 617-495-2857. Fax: 617-495-9837. Authorized power: 100-w. each. Antenna: 679-ft. above ground. Lat. 42° 21' 08", long. 71° 03' 25". Transmitter: One Financial Center. Equipment: ITS transmitter; Andrew antenna.
Leased to CAI Wireless Systems, 2101 Wilson Blvd., Suite 100, Arlington, VA 22201. Phone: 703-812-8800..

Boston—WND-258 (Channels D-1-4). Boston Catholic TV Center Inc. Box 56, 55 Chapel St., Newton, MA 02160. Authorized power: 14-w. each. Antenna: 358-ft. above ground. Lat. 42° 39' 17", long. 71° 13' 13". Transmitter: Wood Hill. Equipment: ITS transmitter; Andrew antenna.

Boston—WND-259 (Channels D-1-4). Boston Catholic TV Center Inc., Box 56, 55 Chapel St., Newton, MA 02160. Authorized power: 11-w. each. Antenna: 679-ft. above ground. Lat. 42° 20' 46", long. 71° 27' 05". Equipment: ITS transmitter; Andrew antenna.

Boylston—WHA-817 (Channels D-1-4). Boston Catholic TV Center Inc., Box 56, 55 Chapel St., Newton, MA 02160. Lat. 42° 20' 01", long. 71° 42' 53". Transmitter: Stiles Hill, Cross St., 2.6-mi. N of Shrewsbury.

Danvers—WAL-20 (Channels G-1-4). Boston Catholic TV Center Inc., Box 56, 55 Chapel St., Newton, MA 02160. Authorized power: 10-w. each. Antenna: 102-ft. above ground. Lat. 42° 34' 57", long. 70° 59' 15". Transmitter: Catholic Chapel, Danvers State Hospital.

Dartmouth—WHR-837 (Channels G-1-3). Southeastern Massachusetts U., Old Westport Rd., North Dartmouth, MA 02747. Authorized power: 10-w. each. Antenna: 240-ft. above ground. Lat. 41° 37' 43", long. 71° 00' 25". Equipment: Emcee transmitter; Andrew antenna.

Dartmouth—WOG-94 (Channel G-4). Southeastern Massachusetts U., Old Westport Rd., North Dartmouth, MA 02747. Authorized power: 10-w. Antenna: 250-ft. above ground. Lat. 41° 37' 43", long. 71° 00' 25". Transmitter: Old Westport Rd.

Framingham—WND-261 (Channels A-1-2). Boston Catholic TV Center Inc., Box 56, Chapel St., Newton, MA 02160. Authorized power: 11.2-w. each. Antenna: 79-ft. above ground. Lat. 42° 20' 46", long. 71° 27' 05". Transmitter: Nobscott Hill. Equipment: ITS transmitter; Andrew antenna.

Framingham—WND-256 (Channels B-1-4). Northeastern U., Church Hall, Boston, MA 02115. Authorized power: 11.2-w. each. Antenna: 79-ft. above ground. Lat. 42° 20' 46", long. 71° 27' 05". Transmitter: Nobscot Hill. Equipment: ITS transmitter; Andrew antenna.

Great Blue Hill—WHR-789 (Channels A-1-4). WGBH Educational Foundation, 125 Western Ave., Boston, MA 02134. Authorized power: 10-w. each. Antenna: 129-ft. above ground. Lat. 42° 20' 50", long. 71° 04' 59". Transmitter: Great Blue Hill near Milton.

Holyoke—WHR-793 (Channels A-1-4). WGBH Educational Foundation, 125 Western Ave., Boston, MA 02134. Authorized power: 10-w. each. Antenna: 100-ft. above ground. Lat. 42° 14' 30", long. 72° 38' 54". Transmitter: Mount Tom.

Milton—WND-254 (Channels B-1-4). Northeastern U., Church Hall, Boston, MA 02115. Authorized power: 5.6-w. each. Antenna: 105-ft. above ground. Lat. 42° 14' 42", long. 71° 06' 51". Transmitter: Great Blue Hill. Equipment: ITS transmitter; Andrew antenna.

Needham—KQT-47 (Channels A-1-2). Boston Catholic TV Center Inc., Box 57, 55 Chapel St., Newton, MA 02160. Authorized power: 10-w. each. Antenna: 679-ft. above ground. Lat. 42° 21' 08", long. 71° 03' 25". Transmitter: One Financial Center, Boston. Equipment: ITS transmitter; Andrew antenna.

Needham—KYP-23 (Channels B-1-4). Northeastern U., 111 Hayden Hall, Boston, MA 02115. Phone: 617-373-4441. Fax: 617-373-2661.
E-mail: gherman@lynx.neu.edu.
Authorized power: 50-w. each. Antenna: 679-ft. above ground. Lat. 42° 21' 08", long. 71° 03' 25". Transmitter: One Financial Center, Boston. Equipment: ITS transmitter; Bogner antenna.
Leased to CAI Wireless Systems, 2101 Wilson Blvd., Suite 100, Arlington, VA 22201. Phone: 703-812-8800..

Needham—KVQ-24 (Channels D-1-4). Boston Catholic TV Center Inc., Box 57, 55 Chapel St., Newton, MA 02160. Authorized power: 50-w. each. Antenna: 679-ft. above ground. Lat. 42° 21' 08", long. 71° 03' 25". Transmitter: One Financial Center, Boston. Equipment: ITS transmitter. Andrew antenna.

Needham—KLC-85 (Channels G-1-4). Boston Catholic TV Center Inc., Box 56, 55 Chapel St., Newton, MA 02160. Authorized power: 10-w. each. Antenna: 696-ft. above ground. Lat. 42° 21' 08", long. 71° 03' 25". Transmitter: One Financial Center, Boston. Equipment: ITS transmitter; Andrew antenna.

Pittsfield—WND-413 (Channels B-1-4). Albion Community Development Corp., 51 N. Main St., Albion, NY 14411. Authorized power: 20-w. each. Antenna: 39-ft. above ground. Lat. 42° 26' 53", long. 73° 14' 20". Transmitter: Lyman St. Equipment: ITS transmitter; Bogner antenna.

Pittsfield—WND-412 (Channels D-1-4). Rockne Educational Television, 908 Madison Ave., Albany, NY 12208. Authorized power: 20-w. each. Antenna: 39-ft. above ground. Lat. 42° 26' 53", long. 73° 14' 20". Transmitter: Lyman St. Equipment: ITS transmitter; Bogner antenna.

Pittsfield—WND-411 (Channels G-1-4). Counterpoint Communications Inc., 15 Peach Orchard Rd., Prospect, CT 06712. Authorized power: 20-w. each. Antenna: 39-ft. above ground. Lat. 42° 26' 53", long. 73° 14' 20". Transmitter: Lyman St. Equipment: ITS transmitter; Bogner antenna.

Rehoboth—WND-425 (Channels G-1-4). U. of Massachusetts-Dartmouth, 285 Old Westport Rd., North Dartmouth, MA 02747. Authorized power: 100-w. each. Antenna: 905-ft. above ground. Lat. 41° 52' 14", long. 71° 17' 45". Transmitter: 33 Pine St. Equipment: ITS transmitter; Andrew antenna.

West Barnstable—WHR-833 (Channels D-1-4). Southeastern Massachusetts U., Old Westport Rd., North Dartmouth, MA 02747. Authorized power: 10-w. each. Antenna: 99-ft. above ground. Lat. 41° 41' 29", long. 70° 20' 18". Transmitter: Cape Cod Community College Arts Center. Equipment: Emcee transmitter; Andrew antenna.

Worcester County—WHR-788 (Channels A-1-4). WGBH Educational Foundation, 125 Western Ave., Boston, MA 02134. Authorized power: 10-w. each. Antenna: 200-ft. above ground. Lat. 42° 18' 10", long. 71° 53' 51". Transmitter: Mount Asnebumskit, Paxton.

Michigan

Bad Axe—WNC-439 (Channels A-1-4). Cross Lutheran School, 7274 Hartley St., Pigeon, MI 48755. Phone & fax: 517-453-3331.
E-mail: crossls@avci.net.
Authorized power: 50-w. each. Antenna: 489-ft. above ground. Lat. 43° 48' 15", long. 82° 54' 26". Transmitter: Hwy. 142, 4-mi. E of Bad Axe. Equipment: ITS transmitter; Andrew antenna.
Leased to Thumb Wireless Cable, 2900 Sand Beach Rd., Bad Axe, MI 48755. Phone: 517-269-6677.

Bad Axe—WNC-442 (Channels B-1-4). Zion Lutheran School, 299 Garden St., Harbor Beach, MI 48441. Authorized power: 50-w. each. Antenna: 489-ft. above ground. Lat. 43° 48' 15", long. 82° 54' 26". Transmitter: Hwy. 142, 4-mi. E of Bad Axe. Equipment: ITS transmitter; Andrew antenna.

Bad Axe—WNC-438 (Channels C-1-4). St. John's Lutheran School, 7379 Berne Rd., Pigeon, MI 48755. Authorized power: 50-w. each. Antenna: 489-ft. above ground. Lat. 43° 48' 15", long. 82° 54' 26". Transmitter: Hwy. 142, 4-mi. E of Bad Axe. Equipment: ITS transmitter; Andrew antenna.

Bad Axe—WNC-400 (Channels D-1-4). Our Lady of Lake Huron Catholic School, 222 Court St., Harbor Beach, MI 48441. Phone: 517-479-3427. Authorized power: 50-w. each. Antenna: 489-ft. above ground. Lat. 43° 48' 15", long. 82° 54' 26". Transmitter: Hwy. 142, 4-mi. E of Bad Axe. Equipment: ITS transmitter; Andrew antenna.

Barnesville—WNC-632 (Channels A-1-4). Concordia College, 901 S. 8th St., Moorhead, MN 56562. Phone: 218-299-4202. Authorized power: 50-w. each. Antenna: 179-ft. above ground. Lat. 46° 42' 11", long. 96° 12' 57". Transmitter: 2-mi. N of Rtes. 32 & 34 intersection. Equipment: Comwave transmitter; Andrew antenna.

Cass City—WLX-304 (Channels G-1-4). Regional Educational Media Center 10, 4415 S. Seeger St., Cass City, MI 48726. Phone: 517-872-4901. Fax: 517-872-2226.
E-mail: tvonhs8054@aol.com.
Authorized power: 50-w. each. Antenna: 460-ft. above ground. Lat. 43° 35' 35", long. 83° 10' 49". Equipment: Comwave transmitter; Bogner antenna.

Charlevoix—WNC-702 (Channel A-2). Cheboygan-Ostego-Presque Isle Intermediate School District, 6065 Learning Lane, Indian River, MI 49749. Phone: 616-238-9394. Fax: 616-238-7153.
E-mail: maniadl@pace.k12.mi.us.
Web site: http://www.pace.k12.mi.us.
Authorized power: 20-w. Antenna: 18-ft. above ground. Lat. 45° 20' 05", long. 85° 14' 48". Transmitter: 8568 Mercer Blvd. Equipment: Comwave transmitter; Anixter-Mark antenna.

Clinton Twp.—WHR-914 (Channels B-3-4). Macomb Intermediate School District, 44001 Garfield Rd., Clinton Twp., MI 48038. Phone: 810-228-3401. Fax: 810-286-1523. Authorized power: 50-w. each. Antenna: 1000-ft. above ground. Lat. 42° 27' 13", long. 83° 09' 50". Transmitter: One Radio Plaza, Royal Oak Twp. Equipment: ITS transmitter; Alford antenna.

Detroit—WAK-57 (Channels B-1-2). Wayne State U., 70 W. Palmer, Detroit, MI 48202. Authorized power: 50-w. each. Antenna: 1000-ft. above ground. Lat. 42° 27' 13", long. 83° 09' 50". Transmitter: One Radio Plaza, Royal Oak Twp.

Detroit—KTB-98 (Channels C-2-3). Detroit Board of Education, 5057 Woodward St., Detroit, MI 48202. Authorized power: 50-w. each. Antenna: 1000-ft. above ground. Lat. 42° 27' 13", long. 83° 09' 50". Transmitter: One Radio Plaza, Royal Oak Twp. Equipment: ITS transmitter; Alford antenna.

Emmett—WHR-610 (Channels D-1-3). Archdiocese of Detroit, 305 Michigan Ave., Detroit, MI 48226. Phone: 313-237-5938. Fax: 313-237-5928. Authorized power: 10-w. each. Antenna: 300-ft. above ground. Lat. 42° 59' 37", long. 82° 43' 48". Transmitter: SE corner of Brandon & Bricker Rds.

Grand Rapids—WLX-950 (Channels G-1-4). Shekinah Network, 14875 Powerline Rd., Atascadero, CA 93422. Phone: 805-438-3341. Authorized power: 10-w. each. Antenna: 197-ft. above ground. Lat. 42° 47' 56", long. 85° 38' 51". Transmitter: 1200-ft. N of 92nd St. & Hwy. 131. Equipment: Emcee transmitter; Andrew antenna.

Leased to American Telecasting Inc., 5575 Tech Center Dr., Suite 300, Colorado Springs, CO 80919. Phone: 719-632-5544.

Jackson—WNC-509 (Channels C-1-4). Vandercook Lake Public Schools, 1000 Golf Ave., Jackson, MI 49203. Authorized power: 10-w. each. Antenna: 272-ft. above ground. Lat. 42° 13' 16", long. 84° 26' 03". Transmitter: Jackson County. Equipment: ITS transmitter; Andrew antenna.

Jackson—WNC-863 (Channels D-1-4). Napoleon County Schools, 212 East Ave., Napoleon, MI 49261. Authorized power: 10-w. each. Antenna: 197-ft. above ground. Lat. 42° 13' 16", long. 84° 26' 03". Transmitter: Hague Rd., 6-mi. S of Jackson. Equipment: Comwave transmitter; Andrew antenna.

Jackson—WNC-379 (Channels G-1-4). Columbia School District, 11775 Hewitt St., Brooklyn, MI 49230. Authorized power: 50-w. each. Antenna: 200-ft. above ground. Lat. 42° 09' 22", long. 84° 23' 39". Transmitter: 0.5-mi. S of Hague & Kimmer Rds. Equipment: Comwave transmitter; Andrew antenna.

Lansing—WLX-481 (Channels A-1-4). North American Catholic Educational Programming Foundation Inc., Box 40026, Providence, RI 02940-0026. Phone: 401-729-0900. Authorized power: 20-w. each. Antenna: 350-ft. above ground. Lat. 42° 43' 58", long. 84° 33' 13". Transmitter: 124 W. Allegan St. Equipment: ITS transmitter; Andrew antenna.

Lansing—WND-410 (Channels C-1-4). Grand Ledge Public Schools. Authorized power: 1-w. each. Antenna: 351-ft. above ground. Lat. 42° 43' 58", long. 84° 33' 13". Transmitter: 124 W. Allegan St. Equipment: Emcee transmitter; Andrew antenna.

Lansing—WND-334 (Channels G-1-4). Views on Learning Inc., 200 Kenyon Ave., Elkhart, IN 46516. Authorized power: 1-w. each. Antenna: 351-ft. above ground. Lat. 42° 43' 58", long. 84° 33' 13". Transmitter: 124 W. Allegan St. Equipment: Emcee transmitter; Andrew antenna.

Milford—WHR-633 (Channels B-1-2). Oakland Schools, 2100 Pontiac Lake Rd., Waterford, MI 48328. Phone: 248-209-2285. Fax: 248-209-2021.

E-mail: jan.vandam@oakland.k12.mi.us.

Web site: http://www.oakland.k12.mi.us.

Authorized power: 10-w. each. Antenna: 300-ft. above ground. Lat. 42° 34' 55", long. 83° 36' 34". Transmitter: E. L. Johnson School, 515 General Motors Rd.

Moline—WLX-981 (Channels A-1-4). Hopkins Public School, 400 Clark St., Hopkins, MI 49328. Phone: 616-793-7261. Fax: 616-793-3154. Authorized power: 10-w. each. Antenna: 853-ft. above ground. Lat. 42° 39' 01", long. 85° 31' 37". Transmitter: 0.9-mi. E of Patterson Rd. & 1-mi. E of Allegan & Barry County Line, near Bowens. Equipment: Comwave transmitter; Andrew antenna.

Moline—WNC-290 (Channels B-1-4). Hastings Area School System, 232 W. Grand St., Hastings, MI 49058. Phone: 616-948-4400. Fax: 616-948-4425. Authorized power: 10-w. each. Antenna: 853-ft. above ground. Lat. 42° 39' 01", long. 85° 31' 37". Transmitter: 0.9-mi. E of Patterson Rd. & 1-mi. E of Allegan Barry County line, near Bowens. Equipment: Comwave transmitter; Andrew antenna.

Leased to Nucentrix Broadband Networks, 200 Chisolm Place, Suite 200, Plano, TX 75075. Phone: 972-423-9494. Fax: 972-423-0819.

Moline—WNC-483 (Channels C-1-4). Otsego Public Schools, 540 Washington St., Otsego, MI 49078. Authorized power: 10-w. each. Antenna: 853-ft. above ground. Lat. 42° 39' 01", long. 85° 31' 37". Transmitter: 0.9-mi. E of Patterson Rd. & 1-mi. E of Allegan & Barry County line. Equipment: Comwave transmitter; Andrew antenna.

Moline—WNC-359 (Channels D-1-3). Plainwell Community Schools, 600 School Dr., Plainwell, MI 49080. Authorized power: 10-w. each. Antenna: 853-ft. above ground. Lat. 42° 39' 01", long. 85° 31' 37". Transmitter: 0.9-mi. E of Patterson Rd. & 1-mi. E of Allegan & Barry County line, near Bowens. Equipment: Comwave transmitter; Andrew antenna.

Mount Pleasant—WNC-270 (Channels A-1-4). Alma College, 614 W. Superior, Alma, MI 48801. Authorized power: 10-w. each. Antenna: 264-ft. above ground. Lat. 43° 37' 29", long. 85° 04' 04". Transmitter: 4-mi. E & 2-mi. N of Remus. Equipment: Emcee transmitter; Andrew antenna.

Mount Pleasant—WNC-271 (Channels B-1-4). Mount Pleasant Baptist Academy, 1802 E. High St., Mount Pleasant, MI 48858. Authorized power: 10-w. each. Antenna: 264-ft. above ground. Lat. 43° 37' 29", long. 85° 04' 04". Transmitter: 4-mi. E & 2-mi. N of Remus. Equipment: Emcee transmitter; Andrew antenna.

Mount Pleasant—WNC-272 (Channels C-1-4). Mount Pleasant Public Schools, 201 S. University, Mount Pleasant, MI 48858. Authorized power: 10-w. each. Antenna: 264-ft. above ground. Lat. 43° 37' 29", long. 85° 04' 04". Transmitter: 4-mi. E & 2-mi. N of Remus. Equipment: Emcee transmitter; Andrew antenna.

Mount Pleasant—WNC-273 (Channels D-1-4). Central Michigan U. Authorized power: 10-w. each. Antenna: 264-ft. above ground. Lat. 43° 37' 29", long. 85° 04' 04". Transmitter: 4-mi. E & 2-mi. N of Remus. Equipment: Emcee transmitter; Andrew antenna.

Muskegon—WNC-689 (Channels A-1-4). Mona Shores Public Schools, 3374 McCracken, Muskegon, MI 49441. Authorized power: 50-w. each. Antenna: 152-ft. above ground. Lat. 43° 13' 47", long. 86° 05' 05". Transmitter: SE Corner of Hwy. 46 & Hilton Park Rd. Equipment: Comwave transmitter; Andrew antenna.

Muskegon—WNC-707 (Channels C-1-4). Greater Muskegon Catholic Schools, 1145 W. Luketon Ave., Muskegon, MI 49441. Authorized power: 50-w. each. Antenna: 400-ft. above ground. Lat. 43° 13' 47", long. 86° 05' 05". Transmitter: SE Corner of Hwy. 46 & Hilton Park Rd. Equipment: Comwave transmitter; Andrew antenna.

Petoskey—WLX-374 (Channels C-1-4). Pace Telecommunications Consortium, 6065 Learning Lane, Indian River, MI 49749. Phone: 616--238-9394. Fax: 616-238-7153.

E-mail: maniadl@pace.k12.mi.us.

Web site: http://www.pace.k12.mi.us.

Authorized power: 50-w. each. Antenna: 595-ft. above ground. Lat. 45° 19' 28", long. 84° 52' 58". Transmitter: E of Klass Rd. Equipment: Comwave transmitter; Andrew antenna.

Pontiac—WHR-508 (Channels B-3-4). Oakland Schools, 2100 Pontiac Lake Rd., Waterford, MI 48328. Phone: 248-209-2285. Fax: 248-209-2021.

E-mail: jan.vandam@oakland.k12.mi.us.

Web site: http://www.oakland.k12.mi.us.

Authorized power: 50-w. each. Antenna: 1000-ft. above ground. Lat. 42° 27' 13", long. 83° 09' 50". Transmitter: One Radio Plaza, Royal Oak Twp. Equipment: ITS transmitter; Alford antenna.

Portage Twp.—WNC-753 (Channels A-1-4). Copper County Intermediate School District, 602 Hecla St., Hancock, MI 49930. Authorized power: 50-w. each. Antenna: 402-ft. above ground. Lat. 47° 06' 13", long. 88° 34' 04". Transmitter: 0.2-mi. S on Hwy. P102. Equipment: Emcee transmitter; Andrew antenna.

Portage Twp.—WNC-756 (Channels B-1-4). Regional Educational Media Center No. One, Box 270, 602 Hecla St., Hancock, MI 49930. Authorized power: 50-w. each. Antenna: 402-ft. above ground. Lat. 47° 06' 13", long. 88° 34' 04". Transmitter: 0.2-mi. S on Hwy. P102. Equipment: Emcee transmitter; Andrew antenna.

Portage Twp.—WNC-755 (Channels C-1-4). Regional Educational Media Center No. One, Box 270, 602 Hecla St., Hancock, MI 49930. Authorized power: 50-w. each. Antenna: 402-ft. above ground. Lat. 47° 06' 13", long. 88° 34' 04". Transmitter: 0.2-mi. S on Hwy. P102. Equipment: Emcee transmitter; Andrew antenna.

Portage Twp.—WNC-754 (Channels D-1-4). Michigan Technological U., 1400 Townsend Dr., Houghton, MI 49931. Authorized power: 50-w. each. Antenna: 402-ft. above ground. Lat. 47° 06' 13", long. 88° 34' 04". Transmitter: 0.2-mi. S on Hwy. P102. Equipment: Emcee transmitter; Andrew antenna.

Portage Twp.—WNC-762 (Channels G-1-4). Adams Twp. School District, Goodell St., Painesdale, MI 49955. Authorized power: 50-w. each. Antenna: 402-ft. above ground. Lat. 47° 06' 13", long. 88° 34' 04". Transmitter: 0.2-mi. S on Hwy. P102. Equipment: Emcee transmitter; Andrew antenna.

Royal Oak Twp.—WHQ-422 (Channels A-1-4). Archdiocese of Detroit, 305 Michigan Ave., Detroit, MI 48226. Phone: 313-237-5938. Fax: 313-237-5928. Authorized power: 200-w. each. Antenna: 459-ft. above ground. Lat. 42° 27' 13", long. 83° 09' 50". Transmitter: One Radio Plaza. Equipment: Comwave transmitter; Andrew antenna.

Royal Oak Twp.—WHR-916 (Channel C-1 & 4). Wayne County Intermediate School District, 33500 Van Born Rd., Wayne, MI 48184. Phone: 313-467-1308. Fax: 313-326-0857. Authorized power: 50-w. Antenna: 1000-ft. above ground. Lat. 42° 27' 13", long. 83° 09' 50". Transmitter: One Radio Plaza. Equipment: Comwave transmitter; Andrew antenna.

Saginaw—WLX-253 (Channels A-1-4). Great Lakes College, 3555 E. Patrick, Midland, MI 48642. Phone: 517-835-5588. Fax: 517-835-8363. Authorized power: 50-w. each. Antenna: 680-ft. above ground. Lat. 43° 28' 24", long. 83° 50' 40". Transmitter: 5720 Becker Rd. Equipment: Comwave transmitter; Andrew antenna.

Saginaw—WLX-291 (Channels C-1-4). Network for Instructional TV Inc., Suite 110, 11490 Commerce Park Dr., Reston, VA 20191. Phone: 703-860-9200. Fax: 703-860-9237. Authorized power: 50-w. each. Antenna: 680-ft. above ground. Lat. 43° 28' 24", long. 83° 50' 40". Equipment: Comwave transmitter; Andrew antenna.

Saginaw—WLX-292 (Channels D-1-4). Network for Instructional TV Inc., Suite 110, 11490 Commerce Park Dr., Reston, VA 20191. Phone: 703-860-9200. Fax: 703-860-9237. Authorized power: 50-w. each. Antenna: 874-ft. above ground. Lat. 43° 28' 24", long. 83° 50' 40". Transmitter: 5720 Becker Rd. Equipment: Comwave transmitter; Andrew antenna.

Leased to Microcom Wireless Cable, 2600 California St., Saginaw, MI 48601. Phone: 517-777-8852.

Saginaw—WLX-460 (Channels G-1-4). Regional Educational Media, 6235 Gratiot Rd., Saginaw, MI 48603. Phone: 517-799-4321. Fax: 517-799-5991. Authorized power: 10-w. each. Antenna: 280-ft. above ground. Lat. 43° 24' 49", long. 84° 02' 24". Transmitter: Saginaw. Equipment: Comwave transmitter; Andrew antenna.

Southfield—WHR-915 (Channels D-2-4). Detroit Educational TV Foundation, 7441 2nd Blvd., Detroit, MI 48202. Phone: 313-873-7200. Authorized power: 50-w. each. Antenna: 1000-ft. above ground. Lat. 42° 27' 13", long. 83° 09' 50". Transmitter: One Radio Plaza, Royal Oak Twp. Equipment: ITS transmitter; Alford antenna.

Leased to Community Telecommunications Network, c/o Wayne State., U. of Detroit, MI 48202. Phone: 313-577-2085.

Springfield—WHR-924 (Channels B-3-4). Oakland Schools, 2100 Pontiac Lake Rd., Waterford, MI 48328. Phone: 248-209-2285. Fax: 248-209-2021.

E-mail: jan.vandam@oakland.k12.mi.us.

Web site: http://www.oakland.k12.mi.us.

Authorized power: 10-w. each. Antenna: 300-ft. above ground. Lat. 42° 46' 20", long. 83° 28' 00". Transmitter: Bridge Lake & Rattalee Lake Rds. Equipment: Emcee transmitter; Bogner antenna.

St. Joseph—WND-415 (Channels A-1-4). Benton Harbor Area Schools, 711 E. Brittain, Benton Harbor, MI 49023. Authorized power: 20-w. each. Antenna: 269-ft. above ground. Lat. 42° 04' 19", long. 86° 22' 14". Transmitter: WIRX(FM) tower. Equipment: Comwave transmitter; Bogner antenna.

St. Joseph—WND-426 (Channels B-1-4). St. Joseph Public Schools, 2214 S. State St., St. Joseph, MI 49085. Authorized power: 20-w. each. Antenna: 269-ft. above ground. Lat. 42° 04' 19", long. 86° 22' 14". Transmitter: WIRX(FM) tower. Equipment: Comwave transmitter; Bogner antenna.

St. Joseph—WND-427 (Channels C-1-4). Coloma Community Schools, 2518 Boyer Rd., Coloma, MI 49038. Authorized power: 20-w. each. Antenna: 269-ft. above ground. Lat. 42° 04' 19", long. 86° 22' 14". Transmitter: WIRX(FM) tower. Equipment: Comwave transmitter; Bogner antenna.

St. Joseph—WND-428 (Channels D-1-4). Niles Community Schools, 111 Spruce St., Niles, MI 49120. Authorized power: 20-w. each. Antenna: 269-ft. above ground. Lat. 42° 04' 19", long. 86° 22' 14". Transmitter: WIRX(FM) tower. Equipment: Comwave transmitter; Bogner antenna.

Topinabee—WHR-997 (Channels A-1 & 3-4). Cheboygan-Ostego-Presque Isle, 6065 Learning Lane, Indian River, MI 49749. Phone: 616-238-9394. Fax: 616-238-7153.
E-mail: maniadl@pace.k12.mi.us.
Web site: http://www.pace.k12.mi.us.
Authorized power: 100-w. each. Antenna: 495-ft. above ground. Lat. 45° 27' 40", long. 84° 36' 47". Transmitter: 6065 Learning Lane, Indian River. Equipment: SBS transmitter; Andrew antenna.

Traverse City—KQI-29 (Channels C-1-4). Federal Bcstg. Co., 1533 N. Woodward Ave., Bloomfield Hills, MI 48034. Lat. 44° 46' 36", long. 85° 41' 02".

University Center—WHA-955 (Channels B-1-4). Delta College, WDCQ-TV, University Center, MI 48710. Phone: 517-686-9350. Fax: 517-686-0155. Authorized power: 10-w. each. Antenna: 260-ft. above ground. Lat. 43° 33' 43", long. 83° 58' 54". Transmitter: Delta Rd., 5.5-mi. SSW of Bay City. Equipment: Emcee transmitter; Andrew antenna.

Minnesota

Appleton—WHR-859 (Channels A-1-4). West Central Minnesota ETV Corp., 25 S. Miles St., Appleton, MN 56208. Phone: 320-289-2622. Fax: 320-289-2634.
E-mail: yourtv@pioneer.org.
Web site: http://www.pioneer.org.
Authorized power: 10-w. each. Antenna: 437-ft. above ground. Lat. 45° 10' 04", long. 95° 59' 54". Transmitter: 2.8-mi. S of Appleton. Equipment: Andrew antenna.

Appleton—WHR-678 (Channels C-1-4). West Central Minnesota ETV Corp., 25 S. Miles St., Appleton, MN 56208. Phone: 320-289-2622. Fax: 320-289-2634.
E-mail: yourtv@pioneer.org.
Web site: http://www.pioneer.org.
Authorized power: 50-w. each. Antenna: 440-ft. above ground. Lat. 45° 10' 04", long. 95° 59' 54". Transmitter: 2.8-mi. S of Appleton.

Ashby—WHR-743 (Channels C-1-4). Independent School District No. 261, 300 Birch St., Ashby, MN 56309. Phone: 218-747-2257. Fax: 218-747-2289. Authorized power: 10-w. each. Antenna: 300-ft. above ground. Lat. 46° 09' 38", long. 95° 44' 24". Transmitter: 6-mi. from Ashby. Equipment: Emcee transmitter; Bogner antenna.

Austin—WNC-589 (Channels G-1-4). Independent School District No. 492, 202 4th St. NE, Austin, MN 55912. Phone: 507-433-0966. Fax: 507-433-0950. Authorized power: 20-w. each. Antenna: 122-ft. above ground. Lat. 43° 40' 33", long. 93° 00' 09". Transmitter: 2000 8th St. NW. Equipment: ITS transmitter; Andrew antenna.

Barnesville—WNC-228 (Channels D-1-4). Northwest Technical College-Moorehead, 1900 28th Ave. S, Moorehead, MN 56560. Authorized power: 50-w. each. Antenna: 179-ft. above ground. Lat. 46° 42' 11", long. 96° 12' 11". Transmitter: 2-mi. N of Barnesville at Rtes. 32 & 34 intersection. Equipment: Comwave transmitter; Andrew antenna.

Barnesville—WNC-548 (Channels G-1-4). Independent School District, Box 189, Barnesville, MN 56514. Authorized power: 50-w. each. Antenna: 190-ft. above ground. Lat. 46° 42' 11", long. 96° 12' 57". Transmitter: 2-mi. N of Barnesville at Rtes. 32 & 34 intersection. Equipment: Comwave transmitter; Andrew antenna.

Bertha, Eagle Bend & Clarissa—WHB-843 (Channel A-1). Minnesota Independent School District No. 786, Bertha, MN 56437. Authorized power: 0.1-w. Antenna: 145-ft. above ground. Lat. 46° 15' 51", long. 95° 03' 43". Transmitter: Bertha-Hewitt School Bldg.

Buffalo—WHR-847 (Channels G-1-4). Sherburne Wright Educational Technical Cooperative, 1400 Hwy. 25 N, Buffalo, MN 55313. Phone: 612-682-4112. Fax: 612-682-4113.
E-mail: jim.mecklenburg@wtc.k12.mn.us.
Authorized power: 10-w. each. Antenna: 253-ft. above ground. Lat. 45° 11' 31", long. 93° 52' 18". Transmitter: Hwy. 25, North Buffalo.

Byron—WLX-455 (Channels A-1-4). Stewartville School District No. 534, 500 4th St. SW, Stewartville, MN 55976. Authorized power: 50-w. each. Antenna: 495-ft. above ground. Lat. 44° 01' 59", long. 92° 36' 10". Transmitter: 2.3-mi. E of Byron. Equipment: Emcee transmitter; Andrew antenna.

Byron—WLX-469 (Channels C-1-4). Pine Island Public Schools, Box 398, 223 First Ave. SE, Pine Island, MN 55963. Phone: 507-356-4849. Fax: 507-356-8827. Authorized power: 50-w. each. Antenna: 495-ft. above ground. Lat. 44° 01' 59", long. 92° 36' 10". Transmitter: 2.3-mi. E of Byron. Equipment: Emcee transmitter; Andrew antenna.

Byron—WLX-511 (Channels D-1-4). Byron Independent School District No. 531, Box 157, Byron, MN 55920. Phone: 507-775-2301. Fax: 507-775-2303. Authorized power: 50-w. each. Antenna: 495-ft. above ground. Lat. 44° 01' 59", long. 92° 36' 10". Transmitter: 2.3-mi. E of Byron. Equipment: Emcee transmitter; Andrew antenna.

Clarissa—WHB-842 (Channel A-3). Minnesota Independent School District No. 2759, Leslie St., Clarissa, MN 56440. Authorized power: 0.1-w. Antenna: 145-ft. above ground. Lat. 46° 07' 30", long. 94° 57' 14". Transmitter: Clarissa Public School.

Deer Creek—WHR-742 (Channel G-1). Minnesota Independent School District No. 543, Deer Creek Public School, Deer Creek, MN 56527. Authorized power: 10-w. Antenna: 88-ft. above ground. Lat. 46° 23' 24", long. 95° 19' 33". Transmitter: Deer Creek School.

Duluth—WHR-627 (Channels B-1-4). State of Wisconsin Educational Communications Board, 3319 W. Beltline Hwy., Madison, WI 53713. Phone: 608-264-9636. Fax: 608-264-9664.
E-mail: ecbweb@mail.state.wi.us.
Web site: http://www.wecb.org.
Authorized power: 10-w. each. Antenna: 50-ft. above ground. Lat. 46° 47' 21", long. 92° 06' 52". Equipment: Comwave transmitter; Bogner antenna.

Duluth—WHR-751 (Channels G-1-4). Minnesota Public Radio, 45 E. 7th St., St. Paul, MN 55101. Phone: 651-290-1259. Fax: 651-290-1342. Authorized power: 10-w. each. Antenna: 330-ft. above ground. Lat. 46° 47' 20", long. 92° 07' 04". Transmitter: Orange & 13th Sts.
Leased to Digital & Wireless Television, Box 1460, El Campo, TX 77437. Phone: 409-543-9711.

Eagle Bend—WND-408 (Channels B-1-2). Bertha Hewitt Public School District, 211 Central Ave., Bertha, MN 56437. Authorized power: 10-w. each. Antenna: 377-ft. above ground. Lat. 46° 10' 00", long. 95° 02' 40". Transmitter: Park Ave. & Maine St. Equipment: ITS transmitter; Andrew antenna.

Eagle Bend—WND-409 (Channels B-3-4). Clarissa Public School District No. 789, 789 Frank St. N, Clarissa, MN 56440. Authorized power: 10-w. each. Antenna: 377-ft. above ground. Lat. 46° 10' 00", long. 95° 02' 40". Transmitter: Park Ave. & Main St. Equipment: ITS transmitter; Andrew antenna.

Eagle Bend—WND-407 (Channels D-1-2). Parkers Prairie Public Schools, 411 S. Otter Ave., Parkers Prairie, MN 56351. Authorized power: 10-w. each. Antenna: 377-ft. above ground. Lat. 46° 10' 00", long. 95° 02' 40". Transmitter: Park Ave. & Maine St. Equipment: ITS transmitter; Andrew antenna.

Eagle Bend—WND-406 (Channels D-3-4). Staples Motley Independent School District No. 2170, 401 Centennial Lane, Staples, MN 56479. Authorized power: 10-w. each. Antenna: 377-ft. above ground. Lat. 46° 10' 00", long. 95° 02' 40". Transmitter: Park Ave. & Maine St. Equipment: ITS transmitter; Andrew antenna.

Eagle Bend, Bertha-Hewitt & Clarissa—WHG-355 (Channels C-1-4). Minnesota Independent School District No. 2759, Park Ave. & Main St., Eagle Bend, MN 56446. Authorized power: 10-w. each. Antenna: 135-ft. above ground. Lat. 46° 09' 55", long. 95° 02' 31". Transmitter: Eagle Bend Public School Bldg.

Fairmont—WND-328 (Channels D-1-4). Morningstar Educational Network, 4012 Morningstar, Huntington Beach, CA 92649. Authorized power: 50-w. each. Antenna: 486-ft. above ground. Lat. 43° 33' 20", long. 94° 29' 11". Transmitter: 5.8-mi. S of Fairmont. Equipment: ITS transmitter; Andrew antenna.

Fairmont—WND-405 (Channels G-1-4). Minnesota Tele-Media, Box 547, Southwest State U., Marshall, MN 56258. Authorized power: 50-w. each. Antenna: 486-ft. above ground. Lat. 43° 33' 20", long. 94° 29' 11". Transmitter: 5.8-mi. S of Fairmont. Equipment: ITS transmitter; Andrew antenna.

Howard Lake—WND-309 (Channels A-1-4). Howard Lake-Waverly Public Schools, Box 708, 8th St. & 8th Ave., Howard, MN 55349. Phone: 320-543-3471. Fax: 320-543-3590.
E-mail: hlww@cmgate.com.
Web site: http://www.hlww.k12.mn.us.
Authorized power: 1-w. each. Antenna: 72-ft. above ground. Lat. 45° 03' 29", long. 94° 04' 06". Transmitter: Howard Lake-Waverly High School. Equipment: Emcee transmitter; Andrew antenna.

Ivanhoe—WHR-853 (Channels A-1-4). Minnesota Tele-Media, Southwest State U., Marshall, MN 56258. Authorized power: 10-w. each. Antenna: 294-ft. above ground. Lat. 44° 00' 14", long. 95° 12' 04". Transmitter: 4-mi. S of Jeffers, NW of town hall.

Jeffers—WHR-660 (Channels B-1-4). Minnesota Tele-Media, Southwest State U., Marshall, MN 56258. Authorized power: 10-w. each. Antenna: 276-ft. above ground. Lat. 44° 00' 14", long. 95° 12' 04". Transmitter: 4-mi. S of Jeffers. Equipment: Comwave transmitter; Andrew antenna.

Jeffers—WHR-805 (Channels C-1-4). Minnesota Tele-Media, Southwest State U., Marshall, MN 56258. Authorized power: 10-w. each. Antenna: 300-ft. above ground. Lat. 44° 03' 36", long. 95° 11' 44". Transmitter: Clark St. Equipment: Bogner antenna.

Jeffers—WHR-905 (Channels D-1-4). Minnesota Tele-Media, Southwest State U., Marshall, MN 56258. Authorized power: 10-w. each. Antenna: 276-ft. above ground. Lat. 44° 00' 14", long. 95° 12' 04". Transmitter: 4-mi. S of Jeffers. Equipment: Comwave transmitter; Andrew antenna.

Magnolia—WHR-663 (Channels D-1-4). Minnesota Tele-Media, Southwest State U., Marshall, MN 56258. Authorized power: 10-w. each. Antenna: 200-ft. above ground. Lat. 43° 38' 45", long. 96° 05' 02". Transmitter: Magnolia Public School.

Mankato—WHR-754 (Channels A-1-4). Minnesota Public Radio, 45 E. 7th St., St. Paul, MN 55101. Phone: 651-290-1259. Fax: 651-290-1342. Authorized power: 10-w. each. Antenna: 290-ft. above ground. Lat. 44° 08' 34", long. 93° 00' 08". Transmitter: 734 Marsh St. Equipment: Emcee transmitter; Andrew antenna.
Leased to American Telecasting Inc., 5575 Tech Center Dr., Suite 300, Colorado Springs, CO 80919. Phone: 719-632-5544.

Mankato—WLX-513 (Channels B-1-4). Gaylord Public Schools, 500 Court Ave., Gaylord, MN 55334. Phone: 612-237-5511. Fax: 612-237-3300. Authorized power: 50-w. each. Antenna: 413-ft. above ground. Lat. 44° 08' 34", long. 94° 00' 08". Transmitter: Minnesota State U. campus. Equipment: Emcee transmitter; Andrew antenna.

Melrose—WND-310 (Channel A-3). Melrose Area Public Schools, District 740, 546 N. 5th Ave. E, Melrose, MN 56352. Authorized power: 1-w. Antenna: 164-ft. above ground. Lat. 45° 45' 06", long. 94° 48' 30". Transmitter: Near Hwy. 94. Equipment: Emcee transmitter; Andrew antenna.

Minneapolis—WLX-299 (Channels A-1-4). Minnesota Public Radio, 45 E. 7th St., St. Paul, MN 55101. Phone: 651-290-1500. Fax: 651-290-1342. Authorized power: 50-w. each. Antenna: 800-ft. above ground. Lat. 44° 58' 32", long. 93° 16' 18". Transmitter: 80 S. 8th St. Equipment: Comwave transmitter; Andrew antenna.

Minneapolis—WLX-200 (Channels D-1-4). Board of Education, Special School District No. 1, 807 N.E. Broadway, Minneapolis, MN 55413. Authorized power: 50-w. each. Antenna: 814-ft. above ground. Lat. 44° 58' 32", long. 93° 16' 18". Transmitter: IDS Bldg. at 80 S. 8th St. Equipment: Comwave transmitter; Andrew antenna.

Minneapolis—WHR-487 (Channels G-1-4). Twin Cities Schools Telecommunications Group Inc., No. 19, 16526 W. 78th St., Eden Prairie, MN 55346. Authorized power: 50-w. each. Antenna: 1808-ft. above ground. Lat. 44° 58' 32", long. 93° 16' 18". Transmitter: IDS Center, 80 S. 8th St. Equipment: Comwave transmitter; Andrew antenna.

Okabena—WHR-803 (Channels C-1-4). Minnesota Tele-Media, Southwest State U., Marshall, MN 56258. Authorized power: 10-w. each. Antenna: 351-ft. above ground. Lat. 44° 03' 36", long. 95° 11' 44". Transmitter: Sioux City Ave. & Milbrath St. Equipment: M/A-Com transmitter; Andrew antenna.

Parkers Prairie—WHR-730 (Channel A-2). Independent School District No. 2759, Park Ave. & Main St., Eagle Bend, MN 56446. Authorized power: 1-w. Antenna: 75-ft. above ground. Lat. 46° 09' 01", long. 95° 19' 40". Transmitter: W. Elm St. & Otter Ave., Eagle Bend.

Rochester—WHR-753 (Channels B-1-4). Minnesota Public Radio, 45 E. 7th St., St. Paul, MN

55101. Phone: 651-290-1259. Fax: 651-290-1342. Authorized power: 10-w. each. Antenna: 130-ft. above ground. Lat. 44° 01' 11", long. 92° 28' 39". Transmitter: 4th St. & 10th Ave.

St. Cloud—WHR-750 (Channels B-1-4). Minnesota Public Radio, 45 E. 7th St., St. Paul, MN 55101. Phone: 651-290-1259. Fax: 651-290-1342. Authorized power: 10-w. each. Antenna: 118-ft. above ground. Lat. 45° 33' 36", long. 94° 09' 20". Transmitter: 400 First St. S.

St. Paul—WHR-497 (Channels B-1-4). Minnesota Public Radio, 45 E. 7th St., St. Paul, MN 55101. Phone: 651-290-1259. Fax: 651-290-1342. Authorized power: 10-w. each. Antenna: 811-ft. above ground. Lat. 44° 58' 32", long. 93° 16' 18". Transmitter: 80 S. 7th St., Minneapolis. Equipment: Comwave transmitter; Andrew antenna.
Leased to CS Wireless Systems Inc., 1101 Summit Ave., Plano, TX 75074. Phone: 972-730-3300.

St. Paul-Minneapolis—WHR-636 (Channels C-1-4). Regents of the U. of Minnesota, 100 Church St. SE, Minneapolis, MN 55455. Phone: 612-624-2332. Fax: 612-626-0761.
Web site: http://www.unite.umn.edu.
Authorized power: 50-w. each. Antenna: 810-ft. above ground. Lat. 44° 58' 32", long. 93° 16' 18". Transmitter: IDS Bldg., 80 S. 8th St. Equipment: Comwave transmitter; Andrew antenna.
Leased to CS Wireless Systems Inc., 1101 Summit Ave., Plano, TX 75074. Phone: 972-730-3300.

Staples—WHR-731 (Channel A-4). Independent School District No. 790, Park Ave. & Main St., Eagle Bend, MN 56446. Authorized power: 1-w. Antenna: 160-ft. above ground. Lat. 46° 21' 36", long. 94° 47' 39". Transmitter: 3rd St. N.

Upsala—WND-311 (Channels A-1-4). Melrose Area Public Schools District 740, 546 N. 5th Ave. E, Melrose, MN 56352. Authorized power: 1-w. each. Antenna: 344-ft. above ground. Lat. 45° 49' 07", long. 94° 34' 39". Transmitter: 1-mi. W & 0.5-mi. N of Upsala. Equipment: Emcee transmitter; Andrew antenna.

Upsala—WLX-472 (Channels B-1-4). Swanville Public Schools, Box 98, Swanville, MN 56382. Authorized power: 1-w. each. Antenna: 345-ft. above ground. Lat. 45° 49' 07", long. 94° 34' 39". Transmitter: 1-mi. W, 0.5-mi. N of Upsala. Equipment: Plessy transmitter; Andrew antenna.

Upsala—WLX-300 (Channels D-1-4). Upsala Area Schools, Box 190, Upsala, MN 56384. Lat. 45° 49' 07", long. 94° 34' 39".

Upsala—WLX-303 (Channels G-1-4). Holdingford Public School, Box 250, Holdingford, MN 56340. Phone & fax: 612-746-2221. Lat. 45° 49' 07", long. 94° 34' 39".
Leased to Upsala Telephone Co., Main St., Box 366, Upsala, MN 56385. Phone: 612-573-2122.

Waseca—WLX-659 (Channels C-1-4). Janesville-Waldorf-Pemberton District No. 283, 110 E. 3rd St., Janesville, MN 56048. Authorized power: 50-w. each. Antenna: 413-ft. above ground. Lat. 44° 08' 34", long. 94° 00' 08". Transmitter: Minnesota State U. campus. Equipment: Emcee transmitter; Andrew antenna.

Waseca—WLX-449 (Channels D-1-4). Waseca Public Schools, 501 E. Elm Ave., Waseca, MN 56093. Authorized power: 50-w. each. Antenna: 413-ft. above ground. Lat. 44° 08' 34", long. 94° 00' 08". Transmitter: Minnesota State U. campus. Equipment: Emcee transmitter; Andrew antenna. Requests change to lat. 44° 15' 00", long. 93° 28' 42"; transmitter to of State Rtes. 16 & 14, NE of Waseca.

Willmar—WHR-784 (Channels G-1-4). Minnesota Tele-Media, Southwest State U., Marshall, MN 56258. Authorized power: 50-w. each. Antenna: 459-ft. above ground. Lat. 45° 11' 52", long. 94° 56' 59". Transmitter: Approx. 6.8-mi. NE of Willmar. Equipment: ITS transmitter; Andrew antenna.

Winthrop—WLX-687 (Channels G-1-4). GFW High School, N. Cottonwood, Winthrop, MN 55396. Authorized power: 50-w. each. Antenna: 410-ft. above ground. Lat. 44° 08' 34", long. 94° 00' 08". Transmitter: Minnesota State U. campus. Equipment: Emcee transmitter; Andrew antenna.

Mississippi

Ackerman—WLX-414 (Channels A-1-4). Mississippi Authority for ETV, 3825 Ridgewood Rd., Jackson, MS 39211. Phone: 601-982-6565. Fax: 601-982-6311. Lat. 33° 21' 07", long. 89° 08' 56".
Leased to Truvision Wireless Inc., 1080 River Oaks Dr., Suite A-150, Jackson, MS 39208. Phone: 601-936-1515.

Ackerman—WLX-489 (Channels B-1-4). State Board for Community & Jr. Colleges, Box 3, 3825 Ridgewood Rd., Jackson, MS 39211. Phone: 601-982-6565. Authorized power: 50-w. each. Antenna: 805-ft. above ground. Lat. 33° 21' 07", long. 89° 08' 56". Transmitter: Ackerman TV tower, 2.75-mi. NNE of Ackerman. Equipment: Emcee transmitter; Andrew antenna.

Ackerman—WLX-416 (Channels C-1-4). State Board of Education, 501 Sillers Office Bldg., Jackson, MS 39205. Lat. 33° 21' 07", long. 89° 08' 56".

Ackerman—WLX-746 (Channels D-1-4). Mississippi Ednet Institute Inc., Box 24, 3825 Ridgewood Rd., Jackson, MS 39211. Phone: 601-982-6565. Fax: 601-982-6311. Authorized power: 50-w. each. Antenna: 800-ft. above ground. Lat. 33° 21' 07", long. 89° 08' 56". Transmitter: 2.75-mi. NNE of Ackerman. Equipment: ITS transmitter; Andrew antenna.

Ackerman—WLX-415 (Channels G-1-4). Board of Trustees, State Institute of Higher Learning, 3825 Ridgewood Rd., Jackson, MS 39211. Lat. 33° 21' 07", long. 89° 08' 56".

Booneville—WLX-413 (Channels A-1-4). Mississippi Authority for ETV, 3825 Ridgewood Rd., Jackson, MS 39211. Phone: 601-982-6565. Fax: 601-982-6311. Lat. 34° 40' 00", long. 88° 45' 05".
Leased to Truvision Wireless Inc., 1080 River Oaks Dr., Suite A-150, Jackson, MS 39208. Phone: 601-936-1515.

Booneville—WLX-474 (Channels B-1-4). State Board for Community & Jr. College, 3825 Ridgewood Rd., Jackson, MS 39211. Phone: 601-982-6565. Authorized power: 50-w. each. Antenna: 541-ft. above ground. Lat. 34° 19' 24", long. 88° 42' 39". Transmitter: Booneville TV Tower, 10.5-mi. W of Booneville. Equipment: Emcee transmitter; Andrew antenna.

Booneville—WLX-411 (Channels C-1-4). State Board of Education, 501 Sillers Office Bldg., Jackson, MS 39205. Lat. 34° 40' 00", long. 88° 45' 05".

Booneville—WLX-745 (Channels D-1-4). Mississippi Ednet Institute Inc., Box 24, 3825 Ridgewood Rd., Jackson, MS 39211. Phone: 601-982-6565. Fax: 601-982-6311. Authorized power: 50-w. each. Antenna: 320-ft. above ground. Lat. 34° 40' 00", long. 88° 45' 05". Transmitter: 10.5-mi. W of Booneville. Equipment: ITS transmitter; Andrew antenna.
Leased to Truvision Wireless Inc., 1080 River Oaks Dr., Suite A-150, Jackson, MS 39208. Phone: 601-936-1515.

Booneville—WLX-412 (Channels G-1-4). Mississippi Board of Trustees, State Institute of Higher Learning, 3825 Ridgewood Rd., Jackson, MS 39211. Lat. 34° 40' 00", long. 88° 45' 05".

Bruce—WND-440 (Channels A-1-4). TruVision Wireless Inc., Suite 403, 2506 Lakeland Dr., Jackson, MS 39208. Authorized power: 1-w. each. Antenna: 299-ft. above ground. Lat. 34° 01' 29", long. 89° 21' 10". Transmitter: Bruce & surrounding area. Equipment: Comwave transmitter; Andrew antenna.

Bude—WLX-497 (Channels A-1-4). Mississippi Authority for ETV, 3825 Ridgewood Rd., Jackson, MS 39211. Phone: 601-982-6565. Fax: 601-982-6311. Authorized power: 50-w. each. Antenna: 1066-ft. above ground. Lat. 31° 22' 19", long. 90° 45' 05". Transmitter: Bude TV tower, 8.3-mi. SE of Bude on Hwy. 98. Equipment: Emcee transmitter; Andrew antenna.
Leased to TruVision Wireless Inc., 1080 River Oaks Dr., Suite A-150, Jackson, MS 39208. Phone: 601-936-1515.

Bude—WLX-488 (Channels B-1-4). State Board for Community & Jr. Colleges, Box 3, 3825 Ridgewood Rd., Jackson, MS 39211. Authorized power: 50-w. each. Antenna: 1066-ft. above ground. Lat. 31° 22' 19", long. 90° 45' 05". Transmitter: Bude TV tower, 8.3-mi. SE of Bude, on Hwy. 98. Equipment: Emcee transmitter; Andrew antenna.

Bude—WLX-498 (Channels C-1-4). State Board of Education, 501 Sillers Office Bldg., Jackson, MS 39205. Authorized power: 50-w. each. Antenna: 479-ft. above ground. Lat. 31° 22' 19", long. 90° 45' 05". Transmitter: Bude TV tower, 8.3-mi. SE of Bude on Hwy. 98. Equipment: Emcee transmitter; Andrew antenna.

Bude—WLX-741 (Channels D-1-4). Mississippi Ednet Institute Inc., Box 24, 3825 Ridgewood Rd., Jackson, MS 39211. Phone: 601-982-6565. Fax: 601-982-6311. Authorized power: 50-w. each. Antenna: 1066-ft. above ground. Lat. 31° 22' 19", long. 90° 45' 05". Transmitter: 8.3-mi. SE of Bude on Hwy. 98. Equipment: ITS transmitter; Andrew antenna.
Leased to TruVision Wireless Inc., 1080 River Oaks Dr., Suite A-150, Jackson, MS 39208. Phone: 601-936-1515.

Bude—WLX-496 (Channels G-1-4). Board of Trustees, State Institute of Higher Learning, 3825 Ridgewood Rd., Jackson, MS 38211. Authorized power: 50-w. each. Antenna: 1066-ft. above ground. Lat. 31° 22' 19", long. 90° 45' 05". Transmitter: Bude TV tower, 8.3-mi. SE of Bude on Hwy. 98. Equipment: Emcee transmitter; Andrew antenna.

Clarksdale—WND-447 (Channels A-1-4, B-1-4, C-1-4, D-1-4, G-1-4). TruVision Wireless Inc., Suite 100, 2506 Lakeland Dr., Jackson, MS 39208. Phone: 601-936-1515. Authorized power: 1-w. each. Antenna: 299-ft. above ground. Lat. 34° 12' 29", long. 90° 33' 36". Transmitter: 1.2-mi. W of U.S. 61 & State Rte. 6. Equipment: Comwave transmitter; Andrew antenna.

Forest—WND-445 (Channels A-1-4, B-1-4, C-1-4). TruVision Wireless Inc., Suite 100, 2506 Lakeland Dr., Jackson, MS 39208. Phone: 601-936-1515. Authorized power: 1-w. each. Antenna: 302-ft. above ground. Lat. 33° 21' 48", long. 89° 25' 29". Transmitter: Hwy. 80 E, approx. 3-mi. E of Forest. Equipment: Comwave transmitter; Andrew antenna.

Grenada—WND-439 (Channels A-1-4, B-1-4, C-1-4). TruVision Wireless Inc., Suite 100, 2506 Lakeland Dr., Jackson, MS 39208. Phone: 601-936-1515. Authorized power: 1-w. each. Antenna: 299-ft. above ground. Lat. 33° 45' 06", long. 89° 51' 12". Transmitter: 2.5-mi. S of Grenada. Equipment: Comwave transmitter; Andrew antenna.

Inverness—WLX-467 (Channels A-1-4). Mississippi Authority for ETV, 3825 Ridgewood Rd., Jackson, MS 39211. Authorized power: 50-w. each. Antenna: 1062-ft. above ground. Lat. 33° 22' 34", long. 90° 32' 32". Transmitter: 3.2-mi. NE of Inverness. Equipment: Emcee transmitter; Andrew antenna.

Inverness—WLX-465 (Channels B-1-4). State Board for Community & Jr. Colleges, 3825 Ridgewood Rd., Jackson, MS 39211. Authorized power: 50-w. each. Antenna: 1062-ft. above ground. Lat. 33° 22' 34", long. 90° 32' 32". Transmitter: Inverness TV tower, 3.2-mi. NE of Inverness. Equipment: Emcee transmitter; Andrew antenna.

Inverness—WLX-468 (Channels C-1-4). State Board of Education, 501 Sillers Office Bldg., Jackson, MS 39205. Authorized power: 50-w. each. Antenna: 1062-ft. above ground. Lat. 33° 22' 34", long. 90° 32' 32". Transmitter: 3.2-mi. NE of Inverness. Equipment: Emcee transmitter; Andrew antenna.

Inverness—WLX-750 (Channels D-1-4). Mississippi Ednet Institute Inc., Box 24, 3825 Ridgewood Rd., Jackson, MS 39211. Phone: 601-982-6565. Fax: 601-982-6311. Authorized power: 50-w. each. Antenna: 1062-ft. above ground. Lat. 33° 22' 34", long. 90° 32' 32". Transmitter: 3.2-mi. NE of Inverness. Equipment: Emcee transmitter; Andrew antenna.
Leased to TruVision Wireless Inc., 2506 Lakeland Dr., Suite 100, Jackson, MS 39208. Phone: 601-936-1515.

Inverness—WLX-509 (Channels G-1-4). Board of Trustees, State Institute of Higher Learning, 3825 Ridgewood Rd., Jackson, MS 39211. Authorized power: 50-w. each. Antenna: 1062-ft. above ground. Lat. 33° 22' 34.2", long. 90° 32' 31.5". Transmitter: Inverness TV tower, 3.2-mi. NE of Inverness. Equipment: Emcee transmitter; Andrew antenna.

Jackson—WLX-420 (Channels A-1-4). Mississippi Authority for ETV, 3825 Ridgewood Rd., Jackson, MS 39211. Phone: 601-982-6565. Fax: 601-982-6311. Antenna: 1040-ft. above ground. Lat. 32° 16' 53", long. 90° 17' 41". Transmitter: Jackson FM tower, 1.9-mi. SW of State Rte. 18 & I-20 intersection. Equipment: Andrew antenna.
Leased to TruVision Wireless Inc., 2506 Lakeland Dr., Suite 100, Jackson, MS 39208. Phone: 601-936-1515.

Jackson—WLX-478 (Channels B-1-4). State Board for Community & Jr. Colleges, Box 3, 3825 Ridgewood Rd., Jackson, MS 39211. Authorized power: 50-w. each. Antenna: 1040-ft. above ground. Lat. 32° 16' 53", long. 90° 17' 41". Transmitter: Jackson FM tower, 1.9-mi. SW of State Rte. 18 & I-20 intersection. Equipment: Emcee transmitter; Andrew antenna.

Jackson—WLX-421 (Channels C-1-4). State Board of Education, 501 Sillers Office Bldg., Jackson, MS 39205. Antenna: 1040-ft. above ground. Lat. 32° 16' 53", long. 90° 17' 41". Transmitter: Jackson FM tower, 1.9-mi. SW of State Rte. 18 & I-20. Equipment: Andrew antenna.

Jackson—WLX-744 (Channels D-1-4). Mississippi Ednet Institute Inc., Box 24, 3825 Ridgewood Rd, Jackson, MS 39211. Phone: 601-982-6565. Fax: 601-982-6311. Authorized power: 50-w. each. Antenna: 1040-ft. above ground. Lat. 32° 16' 53", long. 90° 17' 41". Transmitter: Jackson FM tower, 1.9-mi. SW of State Rte. 18 & I-20 intersection. Equipment: Emcee transmitter; Andrew antenna.

Leased to TruVision Wireless Inc., 2506 Lakeland Dr., Suite 100, Jackson, MS 39208. Phone: 601-936-1515.

Jackson—WLX-422 (Channels G-1-4). Board of Trustees, State Institute of Higher Learning, 3825 Ridgewood Rd., Jackson, MS 39211. Antenna: 1040-ft. above ground. Lat. 32° 16' 53", long. 90° 17' 41". Transmitter: Jackson FM tower, 1.9-mi. SW of State Rte. 18 & I-20 intersection. Equipment: Andrew antenna.

Louisville—WND-444 (Channels A-1-4, B-1-4, C-1-4). TruVision Wireless Inc., Suite 100, 2506 Lakeland Dr., Jackson, MS 39208. Phone: 601-936-1515. Authorized power: 1-w. each. Lat. 33° 06' 45", long. 89° 02' 53". Transmitter: 0.1-mi. S of intersection of State Hwys. 14 & 15. Equipment: Comwave transmitter; Andrew antenna.

Magee—WND-433 (Channels A-1-4, B-1-4, C-1-4). TruVision Wireless Inc., Suite 100, 2506 Lakeland Dr., Jackson, MS 39208. Phone: 601-936-1515. Authorized power: 1-w. each. Antenna: 302-ft. above ground. Lat. 31° 53' 14", long. 89° 43' 38". Transmitter: Colonial Dr., approx. 1-mi. NNE of Magee. Equipment: Comwave transmitter; Andrew antenna.

McHenry—WLX-419 (Channels A-1-4). Mississippi Authority for ETV, 3825 Ridgewood Rd., Jackson, MS 39211. Phone: 601-982-6565. Fax: 601-982-6311. Lat. 30° 45' 14", long. 88° 56' 44".

Leased to TruVision Wireless Inc., 2506 Lakeland Dr., Suite 100, Jackson, MS 39208. Phone: 601-936-1515.

McHenry—WLX-466 (Channels B-1-4). State Board for Community & Jr. Colleges, 3825 Ridgewood Rd., Jackson, MS 39211. Authorized power: 50-w. each. Antenna: 1285-ft. above ground. Lat. 30° 45' 14", long. 88° 56' 44". Transmitter: McHenry TV tower, 12-mi. ENE of McHenry. Equipment: Emcee transmitter; Andrew antenna.

McHenry—WLX-418 (Channels C-1-4). State Board of Education, 501 Sillers Office Bldg., Jackson, MS 39205. Lat. 30° 45' 14", long. 88° 56' 44".

McHenry—WLX-736 (Channels D-1-4). Mississippi Ednet Institute Inc., Box 24, 3825 Ridgewood Rd., Jackson, MS 39211. Phone: 601-982-6565. Fax: 601-982-6311. Authorized power: 50-w. each. Antenna: 1785-ft. above ground. Lat. 30° 45' 14", long. 88° 56' 44". Transmitter: 12-mi. ENE of McHenry. Equipment: ITS transmitter; Andrew antenna.

Leased to TruVision Wireless Inc., 2506 Lakeland Dr., Suite 100, Jackson, MS 39208. Phone: 601-936-1515.

McHenry—WLX-417 (Channels G-1-4). Board of Trustees, State Institute for Higher Learning, 3825 Ridgewood Rd., Jackson, MS 39211. Lat. 30° 45' 14", long. 88° 56' 44".

Melba—WLX-501 (Channels A-1-4). Mississippi Authority for ETV, 3825 Ridgewood Rd., Jackson, MS 39211. Phone: 601-982-6565. Fax: 601-982-6311. Authorized power: 50-w. each. Antenna: 1266-ft. above ground. Lat. 31° 25' 50", long. 89° 08' 50". Transmitter: Melba microwave tower, 5.3-mi. WNW of Sumrall on Hwy. 42. Equipment: ITS transmitter; Andrew antenna.

Leased to TruVision Wireless Inc., 2506 Lakeland Dr., Suite 100, Jackson, MS 39208. Phone: 601-936-1515.

Melba—WLX-500 (Channels B-1-4). State Board for Community & Jr. Colleges, 3825 Ridgewood Rd., Jackson, MS 39211. Authorized power: 20-w. each. Antenna: 257-ft. above ground. Lat. 31° 25' 47", long. 89° 38' 14". Transmitter: Melba microwave tower, 5.3-mi. WNW of Sumrall on Hwy. 42. Equipment: Emcee transmitter; Andrew antenna.

Melba—WLX-502 (Channels C-1-4). State Board of Education, Box 771, 501 Sillers Office Bldg., Jackson, MS 39205. Phone: 601-359-3954. Fax: 601-359-2040. Authorized power: 50-w. each. Antenna: 1266-ft. above ground. Lat. 31° 25' 50", long. 89° 08' 51". Transmitter: Melba microwave tower, 5.3-mi. WNW of Sumrall on Hwy. 42. Equipment: ITS transmitter; Andrew antenna.

Melba—WLX-748 (Channels D-1-4). Mississippi Ednet Institute Inc., Box 24, 3825 Ridgewood Rd., Jackson, MS 39211. Phone: 601-982-6565. Fax: 601-982-6311. Authorized power: 50-w. each. Antenna: 1260-ft. above ground. Lat. 31° 25' 50", long. 89° 08' 50". Transmitter: Melba Microwave tower, 5.3-mi. WNW of Sumrall. Equipment: ITS transmitter; Andrew antenna.

Leased to TruVision Wireless Inc., 2506 Lakeland Dr., Suite 100, Jackson, MS 39208. Phone: 601-936-1515.

Melba—WLX-499 (Channels G-1-4). Board of Trustees, State Institute of Higher Learning, 3825 Ridgewood Rd., Jackson, MS 39211. Authorized power: 50-w. each. Antenna: 1266-ft. above ground. Lat. 31° 25' 50", long. 89° 08' 51". Transmitter: Melba microwave tower, 5.3-mi. WNW of Sumrall on Hwy. 42. Equipment: ITS transmitter; Andrew antenna.

Natchez—WND-437 (Channels A-1-4, B-1-4, C-1-4). TruVision Wireless Inc., Suite 100, 2506 Lakeland Dr., Jackson, MS 39208. Phone: 601-936-1515. Authorized power: 1-w. each. Antenna: 236-ft. above ground. Lat. 31° 30' 33", long. 91° 24' 19". Equipment: AML transmitter; Andrew antenna.

Oxford—WLX-408 (Channels A-1-4). Mississippi Authority for ETV, 3825 Ridgewood Rd., Jackson, MS 39211. Phone: 601-982-6565. Fax: 601-982-6311. Authorized power: 50-w. each. Antenna: 1319-ft. above ground. Lat. 34° 17' 26", long. 89° 42' 24". Transmitter: Oxford TV tower, 7-mi. WNW of Taylor. Equipment: Emcee transmitter; Andrew antenna.

Leased to TruVision Wireless Inc., 2506 Lakeland Dr., Suite 100, Jackson, MS 39208. Phone: 601-936-1515.

Oxford—WLX-479 (Channels B-1-4). State Board for Community & Jr. Colleges, Box 3, 3825 Ridgewood Rd., Jackson, MS 39211. Authorized power: 50-w. each. Antenna: 1319-ft. above ground. Lat. 34° 17' 26", long. 89° 42' 24". Transmitter: Oxford TV tower, 7-mi. WNW of Taylor. Equipment: Emcee transmitter; Andrew antenna.

Oxford—WLX-410 (Channels C-1-4). State Board of Education, 501 Sillers Office Bldg., Jackson, MS 39205. Authorized power: 50-w. each. Antenna: 1319-ft. above ground. Lat. 34° 17' 26", long. 89° 42' 24". Transmitter: Oxford TV tower, 7-mi. WNW of Taylor. Equipment: Emcee transmitter; Andrew antenna.

Oxford—WLX-740 (Channels D-1-4). Mississippi Ednet Institute Inc., Box 24, 3825 Ridgewood Rd., Jackson, MS 39211. Phone: 601-982-6565. Fax: 601-982-6311. Authorized power: 50-w. each. Antenna: 1319-ft. above ground. Lat. 34° 17' 26", long. 89° 42' 24". Transmitter: Oxford TV tower, 7-mi. WNW of Taylor. Equipment: Emcee transmitter; Andrew antenna.

Leased to TruVision Wireless Inc., 2506 Lakeland Dr., Suite 100, Jackson, MS 39208. Phone: 601-936-1515.

Oxford—WLX-409 (Channels G-1-4). Board of Trustees, Institute of Higher Learning, 3825 Ridgewood Rd., Jackson, MS 39211. Authorized power: 50-w. each. Antenna: 1319-ft. above ground. Lat. 34° 17' 26", long. 89° 42' 24". Transmitter: Oxford TV tower, 7-mi. WNW of Taylor. Equipment: Emcee transmitter; Andrew antenna.

Philadelphia—WND-446 (Channels A-1-4, B-1-4, C-1-4). TruVision Wireless Inc., Suite 100, 2506 Lakeland Dr., Jackson, MS 39208. Phone: 601-936-1515. Authorized power: 1-w. each. Antenna: 233-ft. above ground. Lat. 32° 47' 12", long. 89° 04' 48". Transmitter: 104 Magnolia St. Equipment: Comwave transmitter; Andrew antenna.

Picayune—WND-441 (Channels A-1-4, B-1-4, C-1-4). TruVision Wireless Inc., Suite 100, 2506 Lakeland Dr., Jackson, MS 39208. Phone: 601-936-1515. Authorized power: 1-w. each. Antenna: 299-ft. above ground. Lat. 30° 34' 21", long. 89° 37' 54". Transmitter: Approx. 7.3-mi. E of I-59 & 0.644-mi. NNW of Sycamore. Equipment: Comwave transmitter; Andrew antenna.

Rose Hill—WLX-485 (Channels A-1-4). Mississippi Authority for ETV, 3825 Ridgewood Rd., Jackson, MS 39211. Phone: 601-982-6565. Fax: 601-982-6311. Authorized power: 50-w. each. Antenna: 427-ft. above ground. Lat. 32° 19' 44", long. 88° 41' 31". Transmitter: Rose Hill TV tower, 5.5-mi. W of Rose Hill. Equipment: ITS transmitter; Andrew antenna.

Leased to TruVision Wireless Inc., 2506 Lakeland Dr., Suite 100, Jackson, MS 39208. Phone: 601-936-1515.

Rose Hill—WLX-475 (Channels B-1-4). State Board for Community & Jr. Colleges, Box 3, 3825 Ridgewood Rd., Jackson, MS 39211. Authorized power: 50-w. each. Antenna: 427-ft. above ground. Lat. 32° 19' 44", long. 88° 41' 31". Transmitter: Rose Hill TV tower, 5.5-mi. W of Rose Hill. Equipment: ITS transmitter; Andrew antenna.

Rose Hill—WLX-484 (Channels C-1-4). State Board of Education, Suite 501, Box 7, Sillers Office Bldg., Jackson, MS 39205. Authorized power: 50-w. each. Antenna: 427-ft. above ground. Lat. 32° 19' 44", long. 88° 41' 31". Transmitter: Rose Hill TV tower, 5.5-mi. W of Rose Hill. Equipment: ITS transmitter; Andrew antenna.

Rose Hill—WLX-742 (Channels D-1-4). Mississippi Ednet Institute Inc., Box 24, 3825 Ridgewood Rd., Jackson, MS 39211. Phone: 601-982-6565. Fax: 601-982-6311. Authorized power: 50-w. each. Antenna: 427-ft. above ground. Lat. 32° 19' 44", long. 88° 41' 31". Transmitter: 5.5-mi. W of Rose Hill. Equipment: ITS transmitter; Andrew antenna.

Leased to TruVision Wireless Inc., 2506 Lakeland Dr., Suite 100, Jackson, MS 39208. Phone: 601-936-1515.

Rose Hill—WLX-483 (Channels G-1-4). Board of Trustees, State Institute of Higher Learning, 3825 Ridgewood Rd., Jackson, MS 39211. Authorized power: 50-w. each. Antenna: 430-ft. above ground. Lat. 32° 19' 44", long. 88° 41' 31". Transmitter: Rose Hill TV tower, 5.5-mi. W of Rose Hill. Equipment: ITS transmitter; Andrew antenna.

Sharon—WLX-464 (Channels A-1-4). Mississippi Authority for ETV, 3825 Ridgewood Rd., Jackson, MS 39215. Phone: 601-982-6565. Fax: 601-982-6311. Authorized power: 20-w. each. Antenna: 320-ft. above ground. Lat. 32° 39' 49", long. 89° 55' 12". Transmitter: E side of Hwy. 43. Equipment: Emcee transmitter; Andrew antenna.

Leased to TruVision Wireless Inc., 2506 Lakeland Dr., Suite 100, Jackson, MS 39208. Phone: 601-936-1515.

Sharon—WLX-512 (Channels B-1-4). State Board for Community & Jr. Colleges, Box 3, 3825 Ridgewood Rd., Jackson, MS 39211. Authorized power: 20-w. each. Antenna: 317-ft. above ground. Lat. 32° 39' 49", long. 89° 55' 12". Transmitter: E side of Hwy. 43, 1-mi. E of Sharon. Equipment: Emcee transmitter; Andrew antenna.

Sharon—WLX-463 (Channels C-1-4). Mississippi State Board of Education, 501 Sillers Office Bldg., Jackson, MS 39205. Authorized power: 20-w. each. Antenna: 320-ft. above ground. Lat. 32° 39' 49", long. 89° 55' 12". Equipment: Emcee transmitter; Andrew antenna.

Sharon—WLX-749 (Channels D-1-4). Mississippi Ednet Institute Inc., Box 24, 3825 Ridgewood Rd., Jackson, MS 39211. Phone: 601-928-6565. Fax: 601-928-6311. Authorized power: 20-w. each. Antenna: 317-ft. above ground. Lat. 32° 39' 49", long. 89° 55' 12". Transmitter: E side of Hwy. 43, Madison County. Equipment: Emcee transmitter; Andrew antenna.

Sharon—WLX-471 (Channels G-1-4). Board of Trustees, State Institute of Higher Learning, 3825 Ridgewood Rd., Jackson, MS 39211. Authorized power: 20-w. each. Antenna: 317-ft. above ground. Lat. 32° 39' 49", long. 89° 55' 12". Transmitter: Sharon microwave tower, E side of Hwy. 43, 1-mi. E of Sharon. Equipment: Emcee transmitter; Andrew antenna.

Starkville—WLX-493 (Channels A-1-4). Mississippi Authority for ETV, 3825 Ridgewood Rd., Jackson, MS 39215. Phone: 601-982-6565. Fax: 601-982-6311. Authorized power: 50-w. each. Antenna: 654-ft. above ground. Lat. 33° 20' 40", long. 88° 32' 47". Transmitter: Columbus MHP tower, 2-mi. N of Starkville. Equipment: Emcee transmitter; Andrew antenna.

Leased to TruVision Wireless Inc., 2506 Lakeland Dr., Suite 100, Jackson, MS 39208. Phone: 601-936-1515.

Starkville—WLX-477 (Channels B-1-4). State Board for Community & Jr. Colleges, Box 3, 3825 Ridgewood Rd., Jackson, MS 39211. Authorized power: 50-w. each. Antenna: 679-ft. above ground. Lat. 33° 20' 40", long. 88° 32' 47". Transmitter: Columbus MHP tower, 2-mi. N of Starkville. Equipment: Emcee transmitter; Andrew antenna.

Starkville—WLX-492 (Channels C-1-4). State Board of Education, Suite 501, Box 771, Sillers Office Bldg., Jackson, MS 39205-0771. Phone: 601-359-3954. Fax: 601-359-2040. Authorized power: 50-w. each. Antenna: 679-ft. above ground. Lat. 33° 20' 40", long. 88° 32' 47". Transmitter: Columbus MHP tower, 2-mi. N of Starkville. Equipment: Emcee transmitter; Andrew antenna.

Starkville—WLX-738 (Channels D-1-4). Mississippi Ednet Institute Inc., Box 24, 3825 Ridgewood Rd., Jackson, MS 39211. Phone: 601-928-6565. Fax: 601-928-6311. Authorized power: 50-w. each. Antenna: 256-ft. above ground. Lat. 33° 20' 40", long. 88° 32' 47". Transmitter: Columbus MHP Tower, 2-mi. N of Starkville. Equipment: ITS transmitter; Andrew antenna.

Leased to TruVision Wireless Inc., 2506 Lakeland Dr., Suite 100, Jackson, MS 39208. Phone: 601-936-1515.

Starkville—WLX-494 (Channels G-1-4). Board of Trustees, State Institute of Higher Learning, 3825 Ridgewood Rd., Jackson, MS 39211. Authorized power: 50-w. each. Antenna: 679-ft. above ground. Lat. 33° 20' 40", long. 88° 32' 47". Transmitter: Columbus MHP Tower, 2-mi. N of Starkville. Equipment: ITS transmitter; Andrew antenna.

Waynesboro—WND-438 (Channels A-1-4, B-1-4, C-1-4). TruVision Wireless Inc., Suite 100, 2506 Lakeland Dr., Jackson, MS 39028. Phone: 601-936-1515. Authorized power: 1-w. each. Antenna: 300-ft. above ground. Lat. 31° 41' 17", long. 88° 41' 24". Transmitter: 2.5-mi. NW of Waynesboro. Equipment: Comwave transmitter; Andrew antenna.

Winona—WND-443 (Channels A-1-4, B-1-4, C-1-4). TruVision Wireless Inc., Suite 403, 2506 Lakeland Dr., Jackson, MS 39208. Authorized power: 1-w. each. Antenna: 367-ft. above ground. Lat. 33° 34' 56", long. 89° 44' 52". Transmitter: Approx. 6-mi. N of U.S. Hwys. 51 & 82. Equipment: Comwave transmitter; Andrew antenna.

Missouri

Bellflower—WLX-446 (Channels A-1-4). Silex R-1 School District, Box 46, 64 Hwy. UU, Silex, MO 63377. Authorized power: 50-w. each. Antenna: 704-ft. above ground. Lat. 39° 00' 46", long. 91° 18' 07". Transmitter: 2.9-mi. ENE of Bellflower. Equipment: Comwave transmitter; Andrew antenna.

Leased to Nucentrix Broadband Networks, 200 Chisolm Place, Suite 200, Plano, TX 75075. Phone: 972-423-9494. Fax: 972-423-0819.

Bellflower—WLX-447 (Channels B-1-4). Gasconade County R-1, Hwy. 100 W, Hermann, MO 65041. Phone: 573-486-2116. Fax: 573-486-3032. Authorized power: 50-w. each. Antenna: 704-ft. above ground. Lat. 39° 00' 46", long. 91° 18' 07". Transmitter: 2.9-mi. ENE of Bellflower. Equipment: Comwave transmitter; Andrew antenna.

Leased to Nucentrix Broadband Networks, 200 Chisolm Place, Suite 200, Plano, TX 75075. Phone: 972-423-9494. Fax: 972-423-0819.

Bellflower—WLX-444 (Channels C-1-4). Wellsville Middletown R-1, Burlington Rd., Wellsville, MO 63384. Authorized power: 50-w. each. Antenna: 704-ft. above ground. Lat. 39° 00' 46", long. 91° 18' 07". Transmitter: 2.9-mi. ENE of Bellflower. Equipment: Comwave transmitter; Andrew antenna.

Bellflower—WLX-445 (Channels D-1-4). Warren County R-3 School District, 302 Kuhl Ave., Warrenton, MO 63383. Phone: 314-456-4311. Fax: 314-456-7687. Authorized power: 50-w. each. Antenna: 704-ft. above ground. Lat. 39° 00' 46", long. 91° 18' 07". Transmitter: 2.9-mi. ENE of Bellflower. Equipment: Comwave transmitter; Andrew antenna.

Bellflower—WLX-448 (Channels G-1-4). Van-Far R-1 School District, 2200 Hwy. 54 W, Vandalia, MO 63382. Authorized power: 50-w. each. Antenna: 704-ft. above ground. Lat. 39° 00' 46", long. 91° 18' 07". Transmitter: 2.9-mi. ENE of Bellflower. Equipment: Comwave transmitter; Andrew antenna.

Columbia—KXY-61 (Channels C-1-2). The Curators of the U. of Missouri, 225 University Hall, Columbia, MO 65211. Phone: 573-882-3652. Fax: 573-882-6110.

E-mail: dunkind@missouri.edu.

Lat. 38° 56' 43", long. 92° 19' 43".

Creve Coeur—WHR-864 (Channels G-1-4). Cooperating School Districts, St. Louis Suburban Area Inc., 1460 Craig Rd., St. Louis, MO 63146. Authorized power: 10-w. each. Antenna: 1004-ft. above ground. Lat. 38° 34' 24", long. 90° 19' 30". Transmitter: Lodestar tower, 7555 MacKenzie Rd., St. Louis.

Fordland—WNC-384 (Channels G-1-4). Greene County School District R-8, Box 587, 104 N. Beatie St., Rogersville, MO 65742. Phone: 417-753-2891. Fax: 417-753-3063.

E-mail: dhayter@lrhs.greene-r8.k12.mo.us.

Web site: http://www.oznet.com/rogersville.

Authorized power: 20-w. each. Antenna: 554-ft. above ground. Lat. 37° 11' 40", long. 92° 56' 04". Transmitter: 2.6-mi. N of Fordland. Equipment: Emcee transmitter; Andrew antenna.

Leased to Nucentrix Broadband Networks, 200 Chisolm Place, Suite 200, Plano, TX 75075. Phone: 972-423-9494. Fax: 972-423-0819.

Jamestown—WNC-411 (Channels D-1-4). Columbia College, 1001 Rogers St., Columbia, MO 65216. Phone: 573-875-7200. Fax: 573-449-7769. Authorized power: 50-w. each. Antenna: 948-ft. above ground. Lat. 38° 46' 29", long. 92° 33' 22". Transmitter: Approx. 3.5-mi. W of Jamestown. Equipment: Comwave transmitter; Andrew antenna.

Leased to Nucentrix Broadband Networks, 200 Chisolm Place, Plano, TX 75075. Phone: 972-423-9494. Fax: 972-423-0819.

Jamestown—WNC-406 (Channels G-1-4). Southern Boone County R-I School District, 303 N. Main, Ashland, MO 65010. Authorized power: 50-w. each. Antenna: 948-ft. above ground. Lat. 38° 46' 29", long. 92° 33' 22". Transmitter: Approx. 3.5-mi. W of Jamestown. Equipment: Comwave transmitter; Andrew antenna.

Joplin—WHR-956 (Channels A-1-4). Board of Regents-Missouri Southern State College, Newman & Duquesne Rds., Joplin, MO 64801. Phone: 417-625-9792. Fax: 417-625-9742. Authorized power: 20-w. each. Antenna: 171-ft. above ground. Lat. 37° 05' 48", long. 94° 27' 51". Transmitter: TV studio, 3950 E. Newman Rd. Equipment: Emcee transmitter; Andrew antenna.

Joplin—WLX-879 (Channels B-1-4). Carl Junction R-1 School District, W. Allen, Carl Junction, MO 64834. Authorized power: 20-w. each. Antenna: 340-ft. above ground. Lat. 37° 05' 48", long. 94° 27' 51". Transmitter: Newman & Duquesne Rds. Equipment: Emcee transmitter; Andrew antenna.

Joplin—WLX-877 (Channels C-1-4). Carthage R-9 School District, 714 S. Main, Carthage, MO 64836. Phone: 417-359-7000. Fax: 417-359-7004. Authorized power: 20-w. each. Antenna: 340-ft. above ground. Lat. 37° 05' 48", long. 94° 27' 51". Transmitter: Newman & Duquesne Rds. Equipment: Emcee transmitter; Andrew antenna.

Joplin—WLX-876 (Channels D-1-4). Lamar R-1 School District, 503 Maple, Lamar, MO 64759. Phone: 417-682-3527. Authorized power: 20-w. each. Antenna: 350-ft. above ground. Lat. 37° 05' 48", long. 94° 27' 51". Transmitter: Newman & Duquesne Rds. Equipment: Emcee transmitter; Andrew antenna.

Joplin—WLX-875 (Channels G-1-4). Monett R-1 School District, 8th & Scott, Monett, MO 65708. Authorized power: 20-w. each. Antenna: 340-ft. above ground. Lat. 37° 05' 48", long. 94° 27' 51". Transmitter: Newman & Duquesne Rds. Equipment: Emcee transmitter; Andrew antenna.

Kansas City—WHR-531 (Channels A-1-4). Public TV 19 Inc., 125 E. 31st St., Kansas City, MO 64108. Phone: 816-756-3580. Fax: 816-931-2500. Authorized power: 10-w. each. Antenna: 361-ft. above ground. Lat. 39° 04' 15", long. 94° 34' 57". Transmitter: 125 E. 31st St. Equipment: Emcee transmitter; Bogner antenna.

Kansas City—WLX-709 (Channels B-1-4). Hispanic Information & Telecommunications Network Inc., 3rd Floor, 449 Broadway, New York, NY 10013. Phone: 212-966-5660. Fax: 212-966-5725.

E-mail: email@hitn.org.

Web site: http://www.hitn.org.

Authorized power: 10-w. each. Antenna: 438-ft. above ground. Lat. 39° 06' 12", long. 94° 34' 57". Transmitter: 911 Main St. Equipment: Emcee transmitter; Andrew antenna.

Leased to Nucentrix Broadband Networks, 200 Chisolm Place, Suite 200, Plano, TX 75075. Phone: 972-423-9494. Fax: 972-423-0819.

Kansas City—WHR-511 (Channels C-1-4). Instructional Telecommunications Foundation Inc., Box 6060, Boulder, CO 80306. Phone: 303-442-4180. Fax: 303-442-6472.

E-mail: itf@fstv.org.

Authorized power: 10-w. each. Antenna: 464-ft. above ground. Lat. 39° 06' 12", long. 94° 34' 57". Transmitter: 911 Main St. Equipment: Comwave transmitter; Andrew antenna.

Leased to People's Choice TV Corp., 5301 E. Broadway Blvd., Tucson, AZ 85711. Phone: 520-519-4400.

Kansas City—WHR-523 (Channels D-1-4). Network for Instructional TV Inc., Suite 110, 11490 Commerce Park Dr., Reston, VA 20191. Phone: 703-860-9200. Fax: 703-860-9237. Authorized power: 10-w. each. Antenna: 421-ft. above ground. Lat. 39° 06' 12", long. 94° 34' 57". Transmitter: 911 Main St.

Leased to People's Choice TV Corp., 5301 E. Broadway Blvd., Tucson, AZ 85711. Phone: 520-519-4400.

Kansas City—WLX-575 (Channels G-1-4). Junior College District of Metropolitan Kansas City, 3200 Broadway, Kansas City, MO 64111. Phone: 816-759-4367. Fax: 816-759-4489.

E-mail: gosselin@pennvalley.cc.mo.us.

Authorized power: 10-w. each. Antenna: 361-ft. above ground. Lat. 39° 04' 15", long. 94° 34' 57". Transmitter: 125 E. 31st St. Equipment: Comwave transmitter; Bogner antenna.

Lakenan—WLX-917 (Channels A-1-4). Madison C-III School District, Box 123, 401 W. Cooper St., Madison, MO 65263. Authorized power: 10-w. each. Antenna: 863-ft. above ground. Lat. 39° 40' 21", long. 91° 58' 35". Transmitter: Approx. 1.3-mi. W of Lakenan. Equipment: Comwave transmitter; Andrew antenna.

Lakenan—WLX-920 (Channels B-1-4). Marion County R-II School, Box 100, Hwy. D, Philadelphia, MO 63463. Phone: 314-439-5913. Fax: 314-439-5914. Authorized power: 10-w. each. Antenna: 863-ft. above ground. Lat. 39° 40' 21", long. 91° 58' 35". Transmitter: Approx. 1.3-mi. W of Lakenan. Equipment: Comwave transmitter; Andrew antenna.

Leased to Rural Vision, Box 1482, Canyon Lake, TX 78130. Phone: 210-964-2211.

Lakenan—WNC-204 (Channels C-1-4). Monroe City R-I School District, Hwys. 24 & 36 E, Monroe City, MO 63456. Authorized power: 10-w. each. Antenna: 863-ft. above ground. Lat. 39° 40' 21", long. 91° 58' 35". Transmitter: Approx. 0.6-mi. S of U.S. 36, 1.3-mi. W of Lakenan. Equipment: Comwave transmitter; Andrew antenna.

Lakenan—WNC-412 (Channels D-1-3). Shelby County C-1 Schools, Box 142, Hwy. 15, Shelbyville, MO 63469. Phone: 573-633-2410. Fax: 573-633-2138.

E-mail: lsmoot@nshelby.k12.mo.us.

Authorized power: 10-w. each. Antenna: 863-ft. above ground. Lat. 39° 40' 21", long. 91° 58' 35". Transmitter: Approx. 1.3-mi. W of Lakenan. Equipment: Comwave transmitter; Andrew antenna.

Leased to Nucentrix Broadband Networks, 200 Chisolm Place, Suite 200, Plano, TX 75075. Phone: 972-423-9494. Fax: 972-423-0819.

Lakenan—WNC-403 (Channels G-1-4). Shelby County R-IV Schools, Hwy. 36 W, Shelbina, MO 63468. Authorized power: 10-w. each. Antenna: 860-ft. above ground. Lat. 39° 40' 21", long. 91° 58' 35". Transmitter: Approx. 1.3-mi. W of Lakenan. Equipment: Comwave transmitter; Andrew antenna.

Maysville—WLX-626 (Channels A-1-4). Winston R-VI School District, Box 38, Winston, MO 64689. Authorized power: 20-w. each. Antenna: 854-ft. above ground. Lat. 39° 52' 04", long. 94° 22' 14". Transmitter: 0.5-mi. W of State Hwy. 33, 1.3-mi. SSW of Maysville. Equipment: Comwave transmitter; Andrew antenna.

Maysville—WLX-842 (Channels B-1-4). Stewartsville C-II School, 902 Buchanan St., Stewartsville, MO 64490. Phone: 816-669-3792.

Fax: 816-669-8125. Authorized power: 20-w. each. Antenna: 854-ft. above ground. Lat. 39° 52' 04", long. 92° 22' 14". Transmitter: 1.3-mi. SSW of Maysville. Equipment: Comwave transmitter; Andrew antenna.

Maysville—WLX-821 (Channels C-1-4). Union Star R-II School District, 6132 N.W. State Rte. 2, Union Star, MO 64494. Phone: 816-593-2294. Fax: 816-593-4427. Authorized power: 20-w. each. Antenna: 854-ft. above ground. Lat. 39° 52' 04", long. 94° 22' 14". Transmitter: 0.5-mi. W of State Rte. 33 & 1.3-mi. SSW of Maysville. Equipment: Comwave transmitter; Andrew antenna.

Maysville—WLX-868 (Channels D-1-4). Gallatin R.V. School District, 602 S. Olive, Gallatin, MO 64640. Authorized power: 20-w. each. Antenna: 854-ft. above ground. Lat. 39° 52' 04", long. 94° 22' 14". Transmitter: 0.5-mi. W of Hwy. 33, Dekalb County. Equipment: Comwave transmitter; Andrew antenna.

Maysville—WLX-785 (Channels G-1-4). Harrison County R-4 School District, 141 Lindsay Ave., Gilman City, MO 64642. Phone: 816-876-5221. Authorized power: 20-w. each. Antenna: 854-ft. above ground. Lat. 39° 52' 04", long. 94° 22' 14". Transmitter: 0.5-mi. N of State Hwy., 1.3-mi. SSW of Maysville. Equipment: Comwave transmitter; Andrew antenna.

Peaksville—WNC-221 (Channels A-1-4). Canton R-V School District, 200 S. 4th St., Canton, MO 63435. Phone: 314-288-5216. Fax: 314-288-5442. Authorized power: 10-w. each. Antenna: 856-ft. above ground. Lat. 40° 35' 01", long. 91° 45' 16". Transmitter: Approx. 6-mi. NE of Peaksville. Equipment: Comwave transmitter; Andrew antenna.

Peaksville—WNC-380 (Channels B-1-4). Clark County R-I School District, 427 W. Chestnut St., Kahoka, MO 63445. Authorized power: 10-w. each. Antenna: 856-ft. above ground. Lat. 40° 35' 01", long. 91° 45' 16". Transmitter: Approx. 6-mi. NE of Peaksville. Equipment: Comwave transmitter; Andrew antenna.

Peaksville—WNC-214 (Channels C-1-4). Luray No. 33 School District, Box 248, Luray, MO 63453. Phone: 660-866-2222. Fax: 660-866-2233. Authorized power: 10-w. each. Antenna: 856-ft. above ground. Lat. 40° 35' 01", long. 91° 45' 16". Transmitter: Approx. 6-mi. NE of Peaksville. Equipment: Comwave transmitter; Andrew antenna.

Peaksville—WLX-995 (Channels D-1-3). Revere C-3 School District, One Circle Dr., Revere, MO 63465. Phone: 816-948-2621. Fax: 816-948-2623. Authorized power: 10-w. each. Antenna: 856-ft. above ground. Lat. 40° 35' 01", long. 91° 45' 16". Transmitter: Approx. 6-mi. NE of Peaksville. Equipment: Comwave transmitter; Andrew antenna.

Purdin—WLX-960 (Channels A-1-4). Grundy County R-V Schools, Box 6, Galt, MO 64641. Authorized power: 50-w. each. Antenna: 704-ft. above ground. Lat. 39° 55' 46", long. 93° 10' 13". Transmitter: W side of Missouri Hwy. 5, 1.6-mi. S of Purdin. Equipment: Comwave transmitter; Andrew antenna.

Purdin—WLX-811 (Channels B-1-4). Milan C-2 Schools, 373 S. Market St., Milan, MO 63556. Authorized power: 50-w. each. Antenna: 704-ft. above ground. Lat. 39° 55' 46", long. 93° 10' 13". Transmitter: 1.6-mi. S of Purdin. Equipment: Comwave transmitter; Andrew antenna.

Purdin—WLX-826 (Channels C-1-4). Meadville R-IV School District, 101 W. Crandall, Meadville, MO 64659. Authorized power: 50-w. each. Antenna: 704-ft. above ground. Lat. 39° 55' 46", long. 93° 10' 13". Transmitter: 1.6-mi. S of Purdin. Equipment: Comwave transmitter; Andrew antenna.

Purdin—WLX-865 (Channels D-1-4). Linn County R-I Public School, Box 130, Purdin, MO 64674. Authorized power: 50-w. each. Antenna: 704-ft. above ground. Lat. 39° 55' 46", long. 93° 10' 13". Transmitter: 1.6-mi. S of Purdin. Equipment: Comwave transmitter; Andrew antenna.

Purdin—WLX-985 (Channels G-1-4). Tri-County R-VII Schools, Main St., Jamesport, MO 64648. Authorized power: 50-w. each. Antenna: 704-ft. above ground. Lat. 39° 55' 46", long. 93° 10' 13". Transmitter: W side of Missouri Hwy. 5 & 1.6-mi. S of Purdin. Equipment: Comwave transmitter; Andrew antenna.

Sikeston—WLX-380 (Channels A-1-4). Scott County R-5 School District, Rte. 1, Hwy. 61 N, Sikeston, MO 63801. Authorized power: 50-w. each. Antenna: 704-ft. above ground. Lat. 36° 47' 17", long. 89° 32' 04". Transmitter: W side of I-55, 6.8-mi. SSE of Sikeston. Equipment: Comwave transmitter; Andrew antenna. Requests change to lat. 36° 47' 13", long. 89° 32' 00".

Sikeston—WLX-377 (Channels B-1-4). East Prairie R-2 School District, 304 E. Walnut, East Prairie, MO 63845. Authorized power: 50-w. each. Antenna: 704-ft. above ground. Lat. 36° 47' 17", long. 89° 32' 04". Transmitter: W side of I-55, 6.8-mi. SSE of Sikeston. Equipment: Comwave transmitter; Andrew antenna. Requests change to lat. 36° 47' 13", long. 89° 32' 00".

Sikeston—WLX-376 (Channels C-1-4). Richland R-1 School District, Hwy. 114, Essex, MO 63846. Authorized power: 50-w. each. Antenna: 704-ft. above ground. Lat. 36° 47' 17", long. 89° 32' 04". Transmitter: W side of I-55, 6.8-mi. SSE of Sikeston. Equipment: Comwave transmitter; Andrew antenna. Requests change to lat. 36° 47' 13", long. 89° 32' 00".

Sikeston—WLX-378 (Channels D-1-4). Bell City R-2 School District, Hwy. 91, Bell City, MO 63735. Authorized power: 50-w. each. Antenna: 704-ft. above ground. Lat. 36° 47' 17", long. 89° 32' 04". Transmitter: W side of I-55, 6.8-mi. SSE of Sikeston. Equipment: Comwave transmitter; Andrew antenna. Requests change to lat. 36° 47' 13", long. 89° 32' 00".

Sikeston—WLX-379 (Channels G-1-4). Oran R-3 School District, Box 250, Church St., Oran, MO 63771. Phone: 314-262-2330. Authorized power: 50-w. each. Antenna: 704-ft. above ground. Lat. 36° 47' 17", long. 89° 32' 04". Transmitter: W side of I-55, 6.8-mi. SSE of Sikeston. Equipment: Comwave transmitter; Andrew antenna. Requests change to lat. 36° 47' 13", long. 89° 32' 00".

Leased to Rural Vision South, 1465 FM 2673, Canyon Lake, TX 78130. Phone: 210-964-2211.

Springfield—WND-335 (Channels A-1-4). Strafford R-VI School District, McCabe St., Strafford, MO 65757. Authorized power: 50-w. each. Antenna: 308-ft. above ground. Lat. 37° 12' 37", long. 93° 16' 16". Transmitter: 1359 St. Louis St. Equipment: Emcee transmitter; Andrew antenna.

St. Joseph—WLX-668 (Channels A-1-4). Board of Regents, Missouri West State College, 4525 Downs Dr., St. Joseph, MO 64507. Phone: 816-271-5874. Fax: 816-271-4295.
E-mail: schlesin@griffon.mwsc.edu.
Authorized power: 10-w. each. Antenna: 484-ft. above ground. Lat. 39° 44' 19", long. 94° 45' 09". Transmitter: St. Joseph Cablevision tower, E of Pickett & Riverside Rds. Equipment: Comwave transmitter; Andrew antenna.

St. Louis—WHG-332 (Channels A-1-4). St. Louis Regional Educational & Public TV Commission, 3655 Olive St., St. Louis, MO 63108. Phone: 314-512-9000. Fax: 314-512-9005.
E-mail: letters@ketc.pbs.org.
Web site: http://www.ketc.org.
Authorized power: 200-w. each. Antenna: 1073-ft. above ground. Lat. 38° 28' 56", long. 90° 23' 53". Transmitter: 5489 Butler Hill Rd.

St. Louis—WHR-806 (Channels B-1-4). Human Instructional TV Educational Center. Authorized power: 20-w. each. Antenna: 1073-ft. above ground. Lat. 38° 28' 56", long. 90° 23' 53". Transmitter: 5489 Butler Hill Rd. Equipment: Comwave transmitter; Andrew antenna.

St. Louis—WHR-588 (Channels C-1-4). St. Louis Community College, 300 S. Broadway, St. Louis, MO 63102. Authorized power: 200-w. each. Antenna: 1073-ft. above ground. Lat. 38° 28' 56", long. 90° 23' 53". Transmitter: KETC(TV) tower, 5489 Butler Hill Rd. at Hageman, 14-mi. SW of St. Louis. Equipment: Comwave transmitter; Andrew antenna.

St. Louis—WLX-759 (Channels D-1-4). Network for Instructional TV Inc., Suite 110, 11490 Commerce Park Dr., Reston, VA 20191. Phone: 703-860-9200. Fax: 703-860-9237. Authorized power: 10-w. each. Antenna: 761-ft. above ground. Lat. 38° 28' 56", long. 90° 23' 53". Transmitter: 5489 Butler Hill Rd. Equipment: Comwave transmitter; Andrew antenna.

Leased to People's Choice TV of St. Louis, 2 Corporate Woods Blvd., Suite 249, Shelton, CT 06484. Phone: 203-929-2800.

St. Louis—WHR-865 (Channels G-1-2). Missouri Baptist College ITFS Inc., 12542 Conway Rd., St. Louis, MO 63141. Authorized power: 200-w. each. Antenna: 1073-ft. above ground. Lat. 38° 28' 56", long. 90° 23' 53". Transmitter: 5489 Butler Hill Rd. Equipment: Comwave transmitter; Andrew antenna.

Sweet Springs—WLX-669 (Channels A-1-4). Marshall School District, 468 S. Jefferson, Marshall, MO 65340. Phone: 816-886-7414. Fax: 816-886-5641. Authorized power: 20-w. each. Antenna: 750-ft. above ground. Lat. 38° 53' 19", long. 93° 29' 50". Transmitter: 3.25-mi. W of State Hwy. 127, 5.5-mi. SW of Sweet Springs. Equipment: Comwave transmitter; Andrew antenna.

Sweet Springs—WLX-606 (Channels B-1-4). Sweet Springs VII School District, 105 Main, Sweet Springs, MO 65351. Phone: 816-335-6341. Fax: 816-335-4378. Authorized power: 20-w. each. Antenna: 854-ft. above ground. Lat. 38° 53' 19", long. 93° 29' 50". Transmitter: 3.25-mi. W of State Hwy. 127, 5.5-mi. SW of Sweet Springs. Equipment: Comwave transmitter; Andrew antenna.

Sweet Springs—WLX-693 (Channels C-1-4). Concordia Reorganized School District No. 2, 117 W. 11th St., Concordia, MO 64020. Phone: 816-463-7235. Authorized power: 20-w. each. Antenna: 750-ft. above ground. Lat. 38° 53' 19", long. 93° 29' 50". Transmitter: 3.25-mi. W of State Hwy. 127, 5.5-mi. SW of Sweet Springs. Equipment: Comwave transmitter; Andrew antenna.

Sweet Springs—WLX-658 (Channels D-1-4). Lamonte School District, 301 S. Washington, La Monte, MO 65337. Phone: 816-347-5439. Fax: 816-347-5467.
E-mail: bcx010@mail.connect.more.net.
Authorized power: 20-w. each. Antenna: 750-ft. above ground. Lat. 38° 53' 19", long. 93° 29' 50". Transmitter: 5.5-mi. SW of Sweet Springs. Equipment: Comwave transmitter; Andrew antenna.

Sweet Springs—WLX-620 (Channels G-1-4). Leeton R-X School District, Box 9A, Rte. 2, Leeton, MO 64761. Authorized power: 20-w. each. Antenna: 750-ft. above ground. Lat. 38° 53' 19", long. 93° 29' 50". Transmitter: 3.25-mi. W of State Hwy. 127, 5.5-mi. SW of Sweet Springs. Equipment: Comwave transmitter; Andrew antenna.

Trimble—WLX-343 (Channels C-2-4). The Curators of the U. of Missouri, 225 University Hall, Columbia, MO 65211. Phone: 573-882-2706. Fax: 573-884-5255.
E-mail: brennemant@umkc.edu.
Web site: http://www.umkc.edu/ivn.
Authorized power: 10-w. each. Antenna: 163-ft. above ground. Lat. 37° 57' 35", long. 91° 46' 19". Transmitter: Trimble, MO. Equipment: Comwave transmitter; Andrew antenna.

Montana

Billings—WHR-682 (Channels A-1-4). St. Vincent Hospital & Health Center, Box 35200, Billings, MT 59107-5200. Authorized power: 10-w. each. Antenna: 200-ft. above ground. Lat. 45° 46' 04", long. 108° 27' 27". Transmitter: Sacrifice Cliff. Equipment: Comwave transmitter.

Billings—WNC-588 (Channels B-1-4). Excellence in Education Network, 5700 Belmont Dr., Birmingham, AL 35210. Authorized power: 10-w. each. Antenna: 200-ft. above ground. Lat. 45° 46' 04", long. 108° 27' 27". Transmitter: Near Sacriffe Cliff. Equipment: Comwave transmitter; Andrew antenna.

Billings—WNC-233 (Channels C-1-4). Foreign Language & Cultural Foundation, 850 Fay Rd., Syracuse, NY 13219. Authorized power: 50-w. each. Antenna: 210-ft. above ground. Lat. 45° 46' 04", long. 108° 27' 27". Transmitter: Near Sacrifice Cliff. Equipment: Emcee transmitter; Andrew antenna.

Billings—WNC-229 (Channels D-1-4). American Foundation for Instructional TV, 1413 Belmont Lane, Helena, AL 35080-4009. Phone: 205-621-8432.
E-mail: agpiazza@bellsouth.net.
Authorized power: 20-w. each. Antenna: 210-ft. above ground. Lat. 45° 46' 04", long. 108° 27' 27". Transmitter: Near Sacrifice Cliff. Equipment: Emcee transmitter; Andrew antenna.

Leased to American Telecasting Inc., 5575 Tech Center Dr., Suite 300, Colorado Springs, CO 80919. Phone: 719-260-5533.

Bozeman—WNC-740 (Channels A-1-4). Montana State U., Room 172, Visual Communications Bldg., Bozeman, MT 59717. Phone: 406-994-3437. Authorized power: 20-w. each. Antenna: 377-ft. above ground. Lat. 45° 40' 24", long. 110° 52' 02". Transmitter: 7.7-mi. E of Bozeman. Equipment: ITS transmitter; Andrew antenna.

Bozeman—WNC-739 (Channels B-1-4). Bozeman School District No. 7, 404 W. Main, Bozeman, MT 59771.
E-mail: isday@hawks.bps.montana.edu.
Web site: http://ww.bps.montana.edu.
Authorized power: 20-w. each. Antenna: 377-ft. above ground. Lat. 45° 40' 24", long. 110° 52'

02". Transmitter: 7.7-mi. E of Bozeman. Equipment: ITS transmitter; Andrew antenna.
Leased to U.S. Wireless Cable Inc., 1803 West Ave., Austin, TX 78701.

Bozeman—WNC-736 (Channels C-1-4). Monforton School, 6001 Monforton School Rd., Bozeman, MT 59715. Authorized power: 20-w. each. Antenna: 376-ft. above ground. Lat. 45° 40' 24", long. 110° 52' 02". Transmitter: 7.7-mi. E of Bozeman. Equipment: ITS transmitter; Andrew antenna.

Bozeman—WNC-743 (Channels D-1-4). Montana State U., Room 172, Visual Communications Bldg., Bozeman, MT 59717. Phone: 406-994-3437. Authorized power: 20-w. each. Antenna: 377-ft. above ground. Lat. 45° 40' 24", long. 110° 52' 02". Transmitter: 7.7-mi E of Bozeman. Equipment: ITS transmitter; Andrew antenna.

Bozeman—WNC-741 (Channels G-1-4). Bozeman School District No. 7, 404 W. Main, Bozeman, MT 59771.
E-mail: isday@hawks.bps.montana.edu.
Web site: http://www.bps.montana.edu.
Authorized power: 20-w. each. Antenna: 377-ft. above ground. Lat. 45° 40' 24", long. 110° 52' 02". Transmitter: 7.7-mi E of Bozeman. Equipment: ITS transmitter; Andrew antenna.
Leased to U.S. Wireless Cable Inc., 1803 West Ave., Austin, TX 78701.

Great Falls—WNC-812 (Channels A-1-4). Sun River Valley School District 55F, Box 38, Simms, MT 59477. Authorized power: 50-w. each. Antenna: 489-ft. above ground. Lat. 47° 32' 23", long. 111° 17' 06". Transmitter: W side of Bootlegger Trail. Equipment: Comwave transmitter; Andrew antenna.

Great Falls—WNC-794 (Channels B-1-4). Fort Benton School, 1820 Washington, Fort Benton, MT 59442. Authorized power: 50-w. each. Antenna: 489-ft. above ground. Lat. 47° 32' 23", long. 111° 17' 06". Transmitter: W side of Bootlegger Trail. Equipment: Comwave transmitter; Andrew antenna.

Great Falls—WNC-777 (Channels C-1-4). Belt Public Schools, Box 197, Belt, MT 59412. Authorized power: 50-w. each. Antenna: 3232-ft. above ground. Lat. 47° 32' 23", long. 111° 17' 06". Transmitter: W side of Bootlegger Trail. Equipment: Comwave transmitter; Andrew antenna.

Great Falls—WNC-814 (Channels D-1-4). Cascade Public Schools, Box 307, Cascade, MT 59421. Authorized power: 50-w. each. Antenna: 489-ft. above ground. Lat. 47° 32' 23", long. 111° 17' 06". Transmitter: W side of Bootlegger Trail. Equipment: Comwave transmitter; Andrew antenna.

Great Falls—WNC-813 (Channels G-1-4). Montana State U., 2100 16th Ave. S, Great Falls, MT 59405. Authorized power: 50-w. each. Antenna: 489-ft. above ground. Lat. 47° 32' 23", long. 111° 17' 06". Transmitter: W side of Bootlegger Trail. Equipment: Comwave transmitter; Andrew antenna.

Missoula—WNC-728 (Channels A-1-4). Frenchtown High School, 17620 Frontage Rd., Frenchtown, MT 59834. Authorized power: 50-w. each. Antenna: 120-ft. above ground. Lat. 46° 48' 09", long. 113° 58' 21". Transmitter: Dean Stone Mountain. Equipment: ITS transmitter; Andrew antenna.

Missoula—WNC-763 (Channels B-1-4). Frenchtown Elementary School, 16495 Main St., Frenchtown, MT 59834. Authorized power: 50-w. each. Antenna: 121-ft. above ground. Lat. 46° 48' 09", long. 113° 58' 21". Transmitter: Dean Stone Mountain. Equipment: ITS transmitter; Andrew antenna.

Missoula—WNC-761 (Channels D-1-4). Florence-Carlton High School, 5602 Old Hwy. 93, Florence, MT 59833. Authorized power: 50-w. each. Antenna: 121-ft. above ground. Lat. 46° 48' 09", long. 113° 58' 21". Transmitter: Dean Stone Mountain. Equipment: ITS transmitter; Andrew antenna.

Missoula—WNC-764 (Channels G-1-4). Florence-Carlton Elementary School, 5602 Old Hwy. 93, Florence, MT 59833. Authorized power: 50-w. each. Antenna: 121-ft. above ground. Lat. 46° 48' 09", long. 113° 58' 21". Transmitter: Dean Stone Mountain. Equipment: ITS transmitter; Andrew antenna.

Nebraska

Angora—WHR-452 (Channel F-1). U. of Nebraska Board of Regents, 3835 Holdrege St., Lincoln, NE 68583. Authorized power: 10-w. Lat. 41° 50' 24", long. 103° 03' 18". Transmitter: 4-mi. E of Angora on County Rd.

Bluffs—WLX-712 (Channels G-1-4). Franklin Community United School District No. 1, Box 188, Franklin, IL 62638. Authorized power: 40-w. each. Antenna: 495-ft. above ground. Lat. 39° 41' 16", long. 90° 33' 48". Transmitter: E side of State Rte. 100. Equipment: Comwave transmitter; Andrew antenna.

Elkhorn—WHR-890 (Channels G-1-4). Metropolitan Community College, Box 3777, Omaha, NE 68103-0777. Phone: 402-289-1214. Fax: 402-289-1276.
E-mail: ccarlson@metropo.mccneb.edu.
Web site: http://www.mccneb.edu.
Authorized power: 10-w. each. Antenna: 400-ft. above ground. Lat. 41° 15' 52", long. 96° 14' 25". Transmitter: 206 W. Dodge Rd. Equipment: ITS transmitter; Andrew antenna.

Gibbon—WLX-903 (Channels C-1-4). Silver Lake Public Schools, 201 S. Lincoln Ave., Roseland, NE 68973. Phone: 402-756-6611. Fax: 402-756-6613. Authorized power: 20-w. each. Antenna: 91-ft. above ground. Lat. 40° 44' 30", long. 99° 22' 40". Transmitter: 0.6-mi. S of Interstate 80. Equipment: Andrew transmitter; Andrew antenna.
Leased to Antilles Wireless LLS, 809 Central Ave., Kearney, NE 68847.

Hastings—WLX-894 (Channels A-1-4). Central Catholic High School Foundation, 1200 N. Ruby, Grand Island, NE 68803. Authorized power: 50-w. each. Antenna: 197-ft. above ground. Lat. 40° 41' 30", long. 98° 23' 20". Transmitter: 5-mi. S of Grand Island. Equipment: ITS transmitter; Andrew antenna.

Hastings—WLX-891 (Channels B-1-4). Hastings Catholic Schools, 521 N. Kansas, Hastings, NE 68901. Phone: 402-462-2105. Fax: 402-462-2106.
E-mail: mbutler@esu9.k12.ne.us.
Web site: http://www.esu9.k12.ne.us/~hes.
Authorized power: 100-w. each. Antenna: 499-ft. above ground. Lat. 40° 41' 30", long. 98° 23' 20". Transmitter: Grand Island. Equipment: ITS transmitter; Andrew antenna.
Leased to American Telecasting Inc., 5575 Tech Center Dr., Suite 300, Colorado Springs, CO 80919. Phone: 719-260-5533.

Hastings—WNC-821 (Channels C-1-2). Campbell School District R-13, Box 218, Campbell, NE 68932. Authorized power: 50-w. each. Antenna: 197-ft. above ground. Lat. 40° 41' 30", long. 98° 23' 20". Transmitter: 0.38-mi. W of Hwy. 34 & 281. Equipment: ITS transmitter; Andrew antenna.

Hastings—WNC-822 (Channels C-3-4). Adams Central Jr.-Sr. High School, Box 1088, Hastings, NE 68902. Authorized power: 50-w. each. Antenna: 197-ft. above ground. Lat. 40° 41' 30", long. 98° 23' 20". Transmitter: 0.38-mi. W of Hwy. 34 & 281. Equipment: ITS transmitter; Andrew antenna.

Hastings—WNC-503 (Channels D-1-4). Kearney State College Foundation, Box 113, Kearney, NE 68849. Authorized power: 100-w. each. Antenna: 499-ft. above ground. Lat. 40° 41' 30", long. 98° 23' 20". Transmitter: Grand Island. Equipment: ITS transmitter; Andrew antenna.

Kearney—WLX-893 (Channels A-1-4). Kearney State College Foundation, Box 113, Kearney, NE 68849. Authorized power: 20-w. each. Antenna: 192-ft. above ground. Lat. 40° 44' 30", long. 99° 22' 40". Transmitter: 1.5-mi. N of Elm Creek, NW. Equipment: ITS transmitter; Andrew antenna.

Kearney—WNC-505 (Channels B-1-4). Wilcox School District R-2, Box 190, Wilcox, NE 68982. Phone: 308-478-5265. Fax: 308-478-5260.
Web site:
http://www.esull.k12.ne.us/wilcox/home.html.
Authorized power: 20-w. each. Antenna: 300-ft. above ground. Lat. 40° 44' 30", long. 99° 22' 40". Transmitter: 1.5-mi. N of Elm Creek. Equipment: ITS transmitter; Andrew antenna.
Leased to USA Wireless.

Kearney—WLX-986 (Channels D-1-4). Kearney Catholic Foundation, 2202 Central Ave., Kearney, NE 68847. Authorized power: 20-w. each. Antenna: 294-ft. above ground. Lat. 40° 44' 30", long. 99° 22' 40". Transmitter: 1.5-mi. N of Elm Creek. Equipment: ITS transmitter; Andrew antenna.

Kearney—WNC-504 (Channels G-1-4). Hildreth Public Schools, Box 157, Hildreth, NE 68947. Phone: 308-938-3825. Fax: 308-938-5335. Authorized power: 20-w. each. Antenna: 300-ft. above ground. Lat. 40° 44' 30", long. 99° 22' 40". Transmitter: 1.5-mi. N of Elm Creek. Equipment: ITS transmitter; Andrew antenna.

Lincoln—WCG-671 (Channel A-1). U. of Nebraska Board of Regents, 3835 Holdrege St., Lincoln, NE 68583. Authorized power: 10-w. Antenna: 178-ft. above ground. Lat. 40° 49' 11", long. 96° 42' 11". Transmitter: Oldfather Hall, 610 N. 12th. Equipment: ITS transmitter; Andrew antenna.

Lincoln—WNC-623 (Channel A-2). Norris School District 160, RR 1, Firth, NE 68358. Phone: 402-791-0000. Fax: 402-791-0025. Authorized power: 50-w. Antenna: 503-ft. above ground. Lat. 40° 43' 45", long. 96° 36' 44". Transmitter: 0.7-mi S of State Rte. 2, 0.1-mi. S of Burlington Northern Railroad, near Beal Slough Creek. Equipment: Comwave transmitter; Andrew antenna.
Leased to American Telecasting Inc., 5575 Tech Center Dr., Suite 300, Colorado Springs, CO 80919. Phone: 719-260-5533.

Lincoln—WNC-621 (Channels A-3-4). Southeast Community College, 8800 O St., Lincoln, NE 68520. Authorized power: 50-w. each. Antenna: 503-ft. above ground. Lat. 40° 43' 45", long. 96° 36' 44". Transmitter: 0.7-mi S of State Rte. 2, 0.1-mi. S of Burlington Northern Railroad, near Beal Slough Creek. Equipment: Comwave transmitter; Andrew antenna.

Lincoln—WNC-620 (Channels B-1-2). Malcolm School District 148, 10004 N.W. 112th St., Malcolm, NE 68402. Phone: 402-796-2152. Fax: 402-796-2178. Authorized power: 50-w. each. Antenna: 246-ft. above ground. Lat. 40° 43' 38", long. 96° 36' 49". Transmitter: 4100 Industrial Ave. Equipment: Comwave transmitter; Andrew antenna.

Lincoln—WNC-622 (Channels B-3-4). Pius X High School. Authorized power: 50-w. each. Antenna: 503-ft. above ground. Lat. 40° 43' 45", long. 96° 36' 44". Transmitter: 0.7-mi S of State Rte. 2, 0.1-mi. S of Burlington Northern Railroad, near Beal Slough Creek. Equipment: Comwave transmitter; Andrew antenna.

Lincoln—WNC-616 (Channels C-1-4). Concordia Teachers College, 800 N. Columbia Ave., Seward, NE 68434. Authorized power: 10-w. each. Antenna: 499-ft. above ground. Lat. 40° 43' 38", long. 96° 36' 49". Transmitter: 7900 Yankee Hill Rd. Equipment: ITS transmitter; Andrew antenna.

Lincoln—WNC-618 (Channels D-1-2). Raymond Central Public School District 161, Box 180A, Rte. 1, Raymond, NE 68428. Authorized power: 50-w. each. Antenna: 503-ft. above ground. Lat. 40° 43' 45", long. 96° 36' 44". Transmitter: 0.7-mi S of State Rte. 2, 0.1-mi. S of Burlington Northern Railroad, near Beal Slough Creek. Equipment: Comwave transmitter; Andrew antenna.

Lincoln—WNC-617 (Channels D-3-4). Kearney State College Foundation, 905 W. 25th St., Kearney, NE 68849. Authorized power: 50-w. each. Antenna: 503-ft. above ground. Lat. 40° 43' 45", long. 96° 36' 44". Transmitter: 0.7-mi S of State Rte. 2, 0.1-mi. S of Burlington Northern Railroad, near Beal Slough Creek. Equipment: Comwave transmitter; Andrew antenna.

Lincoln—WHB-820 (Channels F-1-4). U. of Nebraska Board of Regents, 3835 Holdrege St., Lincoln, NE 68583. Authorized power: 10-w. each. Antenna: 89-ft. above ground. Lat. 40° 49' 52", long. 96° 40' 18". Transmitter: 1800 N. 33rd St. Equipment: Emcee transmitter; Andrew antenna.

Lincoln—WCG-672 (Channels G-1-3). U. of Nebraska Board of Regents, 3835 Holdrege St., Lincoln, NE 68583. Authorized power: 0.002-w. each. Antenna: 138-ft. above ground. Lat. 40° 49' 09", long. 96° 41' 48". Transmitter: Cather Hall, 17th & Vine Sts.

Lincoln—WLX-948 (Channels G-1-4). Waverly School District 145, 14541 Castlewood, Waverly, NE 68462. Authorized power: 20-w. each. Antenna: 152-ft. above ground. Lat. 40° 43' 48", long. 96° 36' 49". Transmitter: 0.68-mi. S of State Rte. 2, near Beal Slough Creek. Equipment: Comwave transmitter; Andrew antenna.

Memphis—WHG-314 (Channel F-1). U. of Nebraska Board of Regents, 3835 Holdrege St., Lincoln, NE 68583. Authorized power: 10-w. Antenna: 122-ft. above ground. Lat. 41° 08' 18", long. 96° 27' 19". Transmitter: 1.25-mi. W, 3-mi. N of Memphis. Equipment: Emcee transmitter; Andrew antenna.

Omaha—KWU-42 (Channels A-1-4). Omaha City School District, 3215 Cuming St., Omaha, NE 68131. Phone: 402-557-2222. Authorized power: 10-w. each. Antenna: 105-ft. above ground. Lat. 41° 17' 09", long. 95° 59' 36". Transmitter: Maple & 52nd Sts.

Omaha—WHR-812 (Channels B-1-4). U. of Nebraska Board of Regents, 3835 Holdrege St., Lincoln, NE 68583. Phone: 402-472-3611.
E-mail: wramsay@unlinfo.unl.edu.
Authorized power: 100-w. each. Antenna: 320-ft. above ground. Lat. 41° 15' 28", long. 96° 00' 32". Transmitter: U. of Nebraska-Omaha.

Omaha—WHR-724 (Channels C-1-4). U. of Nebraska Board of Regents, 3835 Holdrege St., Lincoln, NE 68583. Phone: 402-472-3611. Fax: 402-472-1785.
E-mail: wramsay@unlinfo.unl.edu.
Authorized power: 100-w. each. Antenna: 320-ft. above ground. Lat. 41° 15' 28", long. 96° 00' 32". Transmitter: U. of Nebraska-Omaha.

Omaha—KWU-43 (Channels D-1-2). Omaha City School District, 3215 Cumming St., Omaha, NE 68131. Phone: 402-557-2222. Authorized power: 10-w. each. Antenna: 45-ft. above ground. Lat. 41° 15' 43", long. 96° 06' 04". Transmitter: 12200 Burke Blvd.

Omaha—WGZ-636 (Channel F-1 & 4). U. of Nebraska, Board of Regents, 3835 Holdredge St., Lincoln, NE 68583. Authorized power: 10-w. each. Antenna: 320-ft. above ground. Lat. 41° 15' 28", long. 96° 00' 32". Equipment: Emcee transmitter; Andrew antenna.

Peru—WNC-432 (Channels C-1-4). Johnson-Brock Public Schools, Box 186, Johnson, NE 68378. Phone: 402-868-5235. Fax: 402-868-4785. Authorized power: 50-w. each. Antenna: 854-ft. above ground. Lat. 40° 26' 18", long. 95° 44' 57". Transmitter: 3.75-mi. NW of U.S. 136 & State Rte. 67 intersection, 3-mi. SSW of Peru. Equipment: Comwave transmitter; Andrew antenna.
Leased to Nucentrix Broadband Networks, 200 Chisholm Place, Suite 200, Plano, TX 75075. Phone: 972-423-9494. Fax: 972-423-0819.

Scottsbluff—WNC-776 (Channels D-1-4). Western Nebraska Community College, 1601 E. 27th St., Scottsbluff, NE 69361. Authorized power: 10-w. each. Antenna: 157-ft. above ground. Lat. 41° 56' 28", long. 103° 39' 21". Transmitter: 3.6-mi. N of Scottsbluff. Equipment: ITS transmitter; Andrew antenna.

Silver Creek—WNC-482 (Channels A-1-2). Stromsburg School District No. 10, 401 E. 4th St., Stromsburg, NE 68666. Authorized power: 50-w. each. Antenna: 751-ft. above ground. Lat. 41° 14' 41", long. 97° 31' 23". Transmitter: Approx. 1-mi. SE of Nebraska Rd. 39. Equipment: Comwave transmitter; Andrew antenna.

Silver Creek—WNC-475 (Channels A-3-4). Scotus Central Catholic, Box 644, 1554 18th Ave., Columbus, NE 68601. Authorized power: 50-w. each. Antenna: 751-ft. above ground. Lat. 41° 14' 41", long. 97° 31' 23". Transmitter: Approx. 1-mi. SE of Nebraska Rd. 39. Equipment: Comwave transmitter; Andrew antenna.

Silver Creek—WNC-474 (Channels B-1-2). Clarks Schools District No. 11, Box 205, Clarks, NE 68628. Authorized power: 50-w. each. Antenna: 751-ft. above ground. Lat. 41° 14' 41", long. 97° 31' 23". Transmitter: Approx. 1-mi. SE of Nebraska Rd. 39. Equipment: Comwave transmitter; Andrew antenna.

Silver Creek—WNC-477 (Channels B-3-4). Aquinas High School, Box 149, Hwy. 14, David City, NE 68632. Authorized power: 50-w. each. Antenna: 751-ft. above ground. Lat. 41° 14' 41", long. 97° 31' 23". Transmitter: Approx. 1-mi. SE of Nebraska Rd. 39. Equipment: Comwave transmitter; Andrew antenna.

Silver Creek—WNC-481 (Channels C-1-2). Palmer School District No. 49, Box 248, Palmer, NE 68864. Authorized power: 50-w. each. Antenna: 751-ft. above ground. Lat. 41° 14' 41", long. 97° 31' 23". Transmitter: Approx. 1-mi. SE of Nebraska Rd. 39. Equipment: Comwave transmitter; Andrew antenna.

Silver Creek—WNC-476 (Channels C-3-4). Comunity College Foundation, Suite 211, 2727 W. 2nd St., Hastings, NE 68901. Authorized power: 50-w. each. Antenna: 751-ft. above ground. Lat. 41° 14' 41", long. 97° 31' 23". Transmitter: Approx. 1-mi. SE of Nebraska Rd. 39. Equipment: Comwave transmitter; Andrew antenna.

Silver Creek—WLX-679 (Channels D-1-4). Polk-Hordville School District, Box 29, 260 S. Pine, Polk, NE 68654. Authorized power: 50-w. each. Antenna: 751-ft. above ground. Lat. 41° 14' 41", long. 97° 31' 23". Transmitter: Approx. 1-mi. SE of Nebraska Rd. 39 Creek. Equipment: Comwave transmitter; Andrew antenna.

Silver Creek—WNC-480 (Channels G-1-4). Shelby School District No. 32, 650 N. Walnut, Shelby, NE 68662. Authorized power: 50-w. each. Antenna: 751-ft. above ground. Lat. 41° 14' 41", long. 97° 31' 23". Transmitter: Approx. 1-mi. SE of Nebraska Rd. 39. Equipment: Comwave transmitter; Andrew antenna.

Tecumseh—WNC-556 (Channels A-1-4). Southeast Community College, W. Scott & Hwy. 136, Beatrice, NE 68310. Phone: 402-228-3468. Authorized power: 10-w. each. Antenna: 413-ft. above ground. Lat. 40° 14' 54", long. 96° 47' 37". Transmitter: Beatrice. Equipment: Comwave transmitter; Andrew antenna.

Tecumseh—WNC-985 (Channels C-1-4). Southern Public School District No. 1, 115 11th St., Wymore, NE 68466. Authorized power: 50-w. each. Antenna: 495-ft. above ground. Lat. 40° 28' 43", long. 96° 12' 21". Transmitter: 6.3-mi. NNE of Tecumseh. Equipment: Comwave transmitter; Andrew antenna.

Tecumseh—WNC-554 (Channels D-1-4). Adams Public School District No. 30, No. 30, 415 8th St., Adams, NE 68301. Authorized power: 50-w. each. Antenna: 500-ft. above ground. Lat. 40° 28' 43", long. 96° 12' 21". Transmitter: 6.3-mi. NNE of Tecumseh. Equipment: Comwave transmitter; Andrew antenna.

Tecumseh—WNC-506 (Channels G-1-4). Beatrice City School District No. 15, 213 N. 5th St., Beatrice, NE 68310. Phone: 402-223-1500. Fax: 402-223-1509. Authorized power: 50-w. each. Antenna: 500-ft. above ground. Lat. 40° 28' 43", long. 96° 12' 21". Transmitter: 6.3-mi. NNE of Tecumseh. Equipment: Comwave transmitter; Andrew antenna.

Nevada

Boulder City—WNC-682 (Channels A-1-4). Clark County School District, 2832 E. Flamingo Rd., Las Vegas, NV 89121. Phone: 702-799-1010. Fax: 702-799-5586. Authorized power: 20-w. each. Antenna: 26-ft. above ground. Lat. 35° 59' 45", long. 114° 51' 46". Equipment: Emcee transmitter; Andrew antenna.

Carson City—WHR-774 (Channels C-1-4). U. of Nevada at Reno. Authorized power: 100-w. each. Antenna: 79-ft. above ground. Lat. 39° 15' 25", long. 119° 42' 37". Transmitter: McClellan Peak, 6.9-mi. NNE of Carson City. Equipment: ITS transmitter; Bogner antenna.

Eagle Ridge—WLX-266 (Channel B-1). Western Nevada Community College. Authorized power: 50-w. Antenna: 32-ft. above ground. Lat. 39° 29' 13", long. 119° 19' 04". Transmitter: 7.7-mi. SSW of Fernley. Equipment: Comwave transmitter; Andrew antenna.

Gardnerville—WHR-775 (Channels A-1-4). U. of Nevada. Authorized power: 20-w. each. Antenna: 27-ft. above ground. Lat. 38° 57' 20", long. 119° 45' 57". Transmitter: Douglas County Law Enforcement, 1625 8th St., Minden.

Henderson—WLX-803 (Channels D-1-4). The Clarendon Foundation, Suite 826, 4201 S. 31st St., Arlington, VA 22206. Authorized power: 50-w. each. Antenna: 75-ft. above ground. Lat. 36° 00' 32", long. 115° 00' 22". Transmitter: Black Mountain, Henderson site. Equipment: Comwave transmitter; Andrew antenna.

Las Vegas—KZH-33 (Channels A-1-4). Clark County School District, 2832 E. Flamingo Rd., Las Vegas, NV 89121. Phone: 702-799-1010. Fax: 702-799-5586. Authorized power: 10-w. each. Antenna: 258-ft. above ground. Lat. 36° 10' 11", long. 115° 08' 31". Transmitter: Fitzgerald Hotel, 301 E. Fremont St. Equipment: Emcee transmitter.

Las Vegas—WLX-370 (Channels B-1-4). Hispanic Information & Telecommunications Network Inc., 3rd Floor, 449 Broadway, New York, NY 10003. Phone: 212-966-5660. Fax: 212-966-5725.
E-mail: email@hitn.org.
Web site: http://www.hitn.org.
Authorized power: 50-w. each. Antenna: 85-ft. above ground. Lat. 36° 00' 32", long. 115° 00' 22". Transmitter: Black Mountain, Henderson site. Equipment: Comwave transmitter; Andrew antenna.
Leased to American Telecasting Inc., 5575 Tech Center Dr., Suite 300, Colorado Springs, CO 80919. Phone: 719-260-5533.

Las Vegas—KZH-32 (Channels C-1-4). Clark County School District, 4210 Channel 10 Dr., Las Vegas, NV 89119. Phone: 702-799-1010. Fax: 702-799-5586. Authorized power: 10-w. each. Antenna: 482-ft. above ground. Lat. 36° 10' 11", long. 115° 08' 31". Transmitter: Fitzgerald Hotel, E. Fremont St. Equipment: ITS transmitter; Andrew antenna.

Las Vegas—WLX-694 (Channels G-1-4). Instructional Telecommunications Network Inc., Box 6060, Boulder, CO 80306. Phone: 303-442-4180. Fax: 303-442-6472.
E-mail: itf@fstv.org.
Authorized power: 50-w. each. Antenna: 75-ft. above ground. Lat. 36° 00' 32", long. 115° 00' 22". Transmitter: Black Mountain, Henderson site Equipment: Comwave transmitter; Andrew antenna.
Leased to American Telecasting Inc., 5575 Tech Center Dr., Suite 300, Colorado Springs, CO 80919. Phone: 719-260-5533.

Mesquite—WNC-934 (Channels B-1-4). Clark County School District, 2832 E. Flamingo Rd., Las Vegas, NV 89121. Authorized power: 10-w. each. Antenna: 36-ft. above ground. Lat. 36° 48' 45", long. 114° 04' 20". Transmitter: Water tank site, 0.6-mi. NW of Mesquite. Equipment: ITS transmitter; Andrew antenna.

Pahrump—WNC-842 (Channels C-1-4). Clark County School District, 2832 Flamingo Rd., Las Vegas, NV 89121. Authorized power: 10-w. each. Antenna: 2644-ft. above ground. Lat. 36° 12' 17", long. 115° 57' 50". Transmitter: 771 Panorama Rd. Equipment: ITS transmitter; Mark antenna.

Reno—WHR-773 (Channels A-1-4). U. of Nevada. Authorized power: 20-w. each. Antenna: 38-ft. above ground. Transmitter: Red Peak, 3.2-mi. N of Reno.

Reno—WND-476 (Channels A-1-4). Shekinah Network, 14875 Powerline Rd., Atascadero, CA 93422. Authorized power: 100-w. each. Antenna: 190-ft. above ground. Lat. 39° 15' 33", long. 119° 42' 12". Transmitter: 7.2-mi. NNE of Carson City. Equipment: ITS transmitter; Andrew antenna.

Rural—WND-312 (Channels B-1-4). Washoe County School District, 425 E. 9th St., Reno, NV 89520. Authorized power: 100-w. each. Antenna: 187-ft. above ground. Lat. 39° 15' 33", long. 119° 42' 12". Transmitter: 7.2-mi. NNE of Carson City. Equipment: ITS transmitter; Andrew antenna.

Singatse Peak—WLX-259 (Channel A-2). Western Nevada Community College. Lat. 38° 59' 13", long. 119° 14' 27".

Southsmoke—WLX-324 (Channel B-2). U. of Nevada, 2601 Enterprise Rd., Reno, NV 89512. Authorized power: 10-w. Antenna: 20-ft. above ground. Lat. 38° 56' 35", long. 119° 54' 24". Transmitter: East Peak, 2.7-mi. SE of Southsmoke. Equipment: Comwave transmitter.

Talpoos—WLX-326 (Channel B-1). U. of Nevada, 2601 Enterprise Rd., Reno, NV 89512. Authorized power: 50-w. Antenna: 34-ft. above ground. Lat. 39° 29' 03", long. 119° 18' 01". Transmitter: Talpoos. Equipment: Comwave transmitter.

Toulon Peak—WLX-325 (Channel C-3). U. of Nevada. Authorized power: 10-w. Antenna: 20-ft. above ground. Lat. 40° 07' 05", long. 118° 43' 39". Transmitter: Toulon Peak, 14-mi. SW of Lovelock. Equipment: Comwave transmitter.

New Jersey

Atlantic City—WNC-266 (Channels A-1-4). Views on Learning Inc., 200 Kenyon Ave., Elkhart, IN 46516. Phone & Fax: 219-522-1725.
E-mail: jrueff@lsoc-vol.org.
Web site: http://www.lsoc-vol.org.
Authorized power: 50-w. each. Antenna: 499-ft. above ground. Lat. 39° 19' 15", long. 74° 46' 17". Transmitter: Abescon Blvd. Equipment: Emcee transmitter; Andrew antenna.
Leased to Orion Broadcasting Systems Inc., 2700 E. Sunset Rd., Suite A-12, Las Vegas, NV 89020. Phone: 800-356-1825.

Atlantic City—WLX-491 (Channels D-1-4). North American Catholic Educational Programming Foundation Inc., Box 40026, Providence, RI 02940-0026. Phone: 401-729-0900. Authorized power: 50-w. each. Antenna: 499-ft. above ground. Lat. 39° 19' 15", long. 74° 46' 17". Transmitter: Hwy. 50, 1.6-mi. NW of Atlantic City. Equipment: Emcee transmitter; Andrew antenna.

Montclair—WHR-821 (Channels G-1-4). New Jersey Public Bcstg. Authority, 25 S. Stockton St., Trenton, NJ 08638. Phone: 609-777-5000. Fax: 609-633-2921.
Web site: http://www.njn.org.
Authorized power: 10-w. each. Antenna: 297-ft. above ground. Lat. 40° 51' 53", long. 74° 12' 03". Transmitter: 42 Clove Rd. Equipment: Comwave transmitter; Bogner antenna.

Pemberton—WNC-308 (Channels A-1-4). Burlington County College, Pemberton-Brown Mills Rd., Pemberton, NJ 08068. Phone: 609-894-9311. Fax: 609-894-9440. Authorized power: 20-w. each. Antenna: 180-ft. above ground. Lat. 39° 58' 13", long. 74° 38' 34". Transmitter: County Rte. 530. Equipment: ITS transmitter; Bogner antenna.

Piscataway—WHR-872 (Channel C-2 & 4). Rutgers, The State U. of New Jersey, Office of Radio & TV, Alexander Johnson Hall, New Brunswick, NJ 08903. Authorized power: 10-w. Antenna: 204-ft. above ground. Lat. 40° 31' 29", long. 74° 25' 53". Transmitter: Rutgers Television Bldg., Berrue Circle.

Toms River—WND-374 (Channels A-1-4). St. Rose Church Schools, 603 7th Ave., Belmar, NJ 07719. Authorized power: 50-w. each. Antenna: 202-ft. above ground. Lat. 39° 56' 52", long. 74° 12' 03". Transmitter: Toms River. Equipment: Comwave transmitter; Bogner antenna.

Trenton—WLX-250 (Channels C-2-4). New Jersey Public Broadcasting Authority, CN 777, Trenton, NJ 08625. Phone: 609-777-5165. Fax: 609-777-5400. Authorized power: 10-w. each. Antenna: 492-ft. above ground. Lat. 40° 16' 58", long. 74° 41' 11". Transmitter: 3260 Brunswick Pike. Equipment: Comwave transmitter; Andrew antenna.

Union City—WGM-95 (Channel C-1). Union Twp. Schools, 2369 Morris Ave., Union, NJ 07083. Authorized power: 10-w. Antenna: 77-ft. above ground. Lat. 40° 44' 54", long. 73° 59' 10". Transmitter: 3rd St., Union.

Warren Twp.—WHR-822 (Channels G-1-4). New Jersey Public Broadcasting Authority, CN 777, 25 S. Stockton St., Trenton, NJ 08625-0777. Phone: 609-777-5000. Fax: 609-633-2920. Authorized power: 10-w. each. Antenna: 342-ft. above ground. Lat. 40° 37' 17", long. 74° 30' 10". Transmitter: 204-A Mount Horeb Rd. Equipment: Comwave transmitter; Bogner antenna.

Leased to CAI Wireless Systems Inc., 2101 Wilson Blvd., Suite 100, Arlington, VA 22201. Phone: 703-812-8800.

West Windsor Twp.—WOW-99 (Channel B-1). Mercer County Community College, 1200 Old Trenton Rd., Trenton, NJ 08690. Authorized power: 10-w. Antenna: 204-ft. above ground. Lat. 40° 15' 30", long. 73° 38' 59". Transmitter: 1200 Old Trenton Rd.

New Mexico

Alamogordo—WNC-963 (Channels B-1-4). Silver Consolidated Schools, 2810 N. Swan St., Silver City, NM 88061. Authorized power: 50-w. each. Antenna: 49-ft. above ground. Lat. 32° 49' 49", long. 105° 53' 25". Transmitter: Long Ridge. Equipment: Emcee transmitter; Andrew antenna.

Albuquerque—WLX-673 (Channels A-1-4). Hispanic Information & Telecommunications Network Inc., 3rd Floor, 449 Broadway, New York, NY 10013. Phone: 212-966-5660. Fax: 212-966-5725.

E-mail: email@hitn.org.

Web site: http://www.hitn.org.

Authorized power: 10-w. each. Antenna: 23-ft. above ground. Lat. 35° 13' 02", long. 106° 27' 06". Transmitter: Site 35B, Sandia Crest. Equipment: Emcee transmitter; Andrew antenna.

Leased to People's Choice TV, 5301 E. Broadway Blvd., Tucson, AZ 85711. Phone: 520-519-4400.

Albuquerque—WHR-551 (Channels B-1-4). Regents of the U. of New Mexico & Board of Education of the City of Albuquerque (KNME-TV), Albuquerque Public Schools, 1130 University Blvd. NE, Albuquerque, NM 87102. Phone: 505-277-2121. Fax: 505-277-2191.

E-mail: jon@knmel.unm.edu.

Web site: http://www.pbs.org/knme/.

Authorized power: 10-w. each. Antenna: 48-ft. above ground. Lat. 35° 12' 45", long. 106° 26' 58". Transmitter: Sandia Crest, approximately 13-mi. NE of Albuquerque. Equipment: Comwave transmitter; Bogner antenna.

Albuquerque—WNC-275 (Channels C-1-4). North American Catholic Educational Programming Foundation Inc., Box 40026, Providence, RI 02940-0026. Phone: 401-729-0900. Authorized power: 20-w. each. Antenna: 22-ft. above ground. Lat. 35° 13' 02", long. 106° 27' 06". Transmitter: Sandia Crest. Equipment: ITS transmitter; Andrew antenna.

Albuquerque—WLX-992 (Channel D-1). North American Catholic Educational Programming Foundation Inc., Box 40026, Providence, RI 02940-0026. Phone: 401-729-0900. Authorized power: 20-w. Antenna: 22-ft. above ground. Lat. 35° 13' 02", long. 106° 27' 06". Transmitter: Sandia Crest. Equipment: ITS transmitter; Andrew antenna.

Albuquerque—WNC-373 (Channels D-2-4). Shekinah Network, 14875 Powerline Rd., Atascadero, CA 93422. Authorized power: 20-w. each. Antenna: 22-ft. above ground. Lat. 35° 13' 02", long. 106° 27' 06". Transmitter: Sandia Crest. Equipment: ITS transmitter; Andrew antenna.

Albuquerque—WHR-672 (Channels G-1-4). Regents of U. of New Mexico & Board of Education of the City of Albuquerque (KNME-TV), Albuquerque Public Schools, 1130 University Blvd. NE, Albuquerque, NM 87102. Phone: 505-277-2121. Fax: 505-277-2191.

E-mail: jon@knmel.unm.edu.

Web site: http://www.pbs.org.

Authorized power: 10-w. each. Antenna: 88-ft. above ground. Lat. 35° 12' 44", long. 106° 26' 57". Transmitter: KNME-TV transmitter site. Equipment: Comwave transmitter; Bogner antenna.

Carlsbad—WNC-378 (Channels B-1-4). Loving Municipal Schools, Box 98, Loving, NM 88256. Authorized power: 50-w. each. Antenna: 497-ft. above ground. Lat. 32° 25' 14", long. 104° 10' 19". Transmitter: 3.5-mi. NE of U.S. Rtes. 285 & 180/62 intersection. Equipment: ITS transmitter; Andrew antenna.

Carlsbad—WLX-997 (Channels C-1-4). Bethel Christian School. Authorized power: 50-w. each. Antenna: 497-ft. above ground. Lat. 32° 25' 14", long. 104° 10' 19". Transmitter: 3.5-mi. NE of U.S. Rtes. 285 & 180/62 intersection. Equipment: ITS transmitter; Andrew antenna.

Carlsbad—WNC-533 (Channels D-1-4). Shekinah Network, 14875 Powerline Rd., Atascadero, CA 93422. Authorized power: 10-w. each. Antenna: 458-ft. above ground. Lat. 32° 26' 30", long. 104° 10' 30". Transmitter: 3-mi. E of Carlsbad. Equipment: Emcee transmitter; Andrew antenna.

Carlsbad—WLX-961 (Channels G-1-4). Victory Christian Academy, 2107 W. Church, Carlsbad, NM 88220. Phone: 505-887-3777. Authorized power: 50-w. each. Antenna: 497-ft. above ground. Lat. 32° 25' 14", long. 104° 10' 19". Transmitter: 3.5-mi. NE of U.S. Rtes. 285 & 180/62 intersection. Equipment: ITS transmitter; Andrew antenna.

Clovis—WNC-215 (Channels B-1-4). Floyd Municipal School, Box 75, Hwy. 267, Floyd, NM 88118. Phone: 505-478-2211. Fax: 505-478-2811. Authorized power: 50-w. each. Antenna: 616-ft. above ground. Lat. 34° 22' 12", long. 103° 13' 14". Transmitter: 0.1-mi. E of railroad tracks & approx. 2-mi. S of Clovis. Equipment: ITS transmitter; Andrew antenna.

Leased to MultiMedia Development Corp., 13170-B Central Ave. SE, Suite 300, Albuquerque, NM 87123. Phone: 505-281-4302.

Clovis—WLX-958 (Channels C-1-4). Portales High School, 201 S. Knoxville, Portales, NM 88130. Authorized power: 50-w. each. Antenna: 706-ft. above ground. Lat. 34° 22' 12", long. 103° 13' 14". Transmitter: 0.1-mi. E of railroad tracks, approx. 2-mi. S of Clovis. Equipment: ITS transmitter; Andrew antenna.

Clovis—WNC-268 (Channels D-1-4). Texico Municipal School, Box 327, 520 N. Griffin, Texico, NM 88135. Phone: 505-482-3228. Fax: 505-482-3801. Authorized power: 50-w. each. Antenna: 616-ft. above ground. Lat. 34° 22' 12", long. 103° 13' 14". Transmitter: 0.1-mi. E of railroad tracks & approximately 2-mi. S of Clovis. Equipment: ITS transmitter; Andrew antenna.

Leased to Nucentrix Broadband Networks, 200 Chisholm Place, Suite 200, Plano, TX 75075. Phone: 972-423-0819. Fax: 972-423-0819.

Clovis—WLX-932 (Channels G-1-4). Melrose Municipal Schools, 100 E. Missouri, Melrose, NM 88124. Authorized power: 50-w. each. Lat. 34° 22' 12", long. 103° 13' 14". Transmitter: 0.1-mi. E of railroad. Equipment: ITS transmitter; Andrew antenna.

Elida—WLX-261 (Channels C-1-4). Board of Regents, Eastern New Mexico U., Portales, NM 88130. Authorized power: 25-w. each. Antenna: 140-ft. above ground. Lat. 33° 54' 15", long. 103° 30' 41".

Farmington—WNC-601 (Channels B-1-4). Bethel Christian School. Authorized power: 50-w. each. Antenna: 409-ft. above ground. Lat. 36° 41' 02", long. 108° 12' 50". Transmitter: 3.5-mi. S of Farmington. Equipment: ITS transmitter; Andrew antenna.

Farmington—WNC-361 (Channels C-1-4). Espanola Public Schools, 714 Calle don Diego, Espanola, NM 87532. Authorized power: 50-w. each. Antenna: 494-ft. above ground. Lat. 36° 41' 02", long. 108° 12' 50". Transmitter: San Juan County. Equipment: ITS transmitter; Andrew antenna.

Farmington—WNC-712 (Channels D-1-4). Victory Christian Academy, 2107 W. Church St., Carlsbad, NM 88220. Phone: 505-887-3777. Authorized power: 50-w. each. Antenna: 499-ft. above ground. Lat. 36° 40' 37", long. 108° 13' 17". Transmitter: 3.5-mi. S of Farmington. Equipment: ITS transmitter; Andrew antenna.

Farmington—WNC-313 (Channels G-1-4). Tucumcari Municipal School, Box 1046, 902 S. 11th St., Tucumcari, NM 88401. Phone: 505-461-3910. Fax: 505-461-3554. Authorized power: 50-w. each. Antenna: 495-ft. above ground. Lat. 36° 40' 37", long. 108° 13' 17". Transmitter: Farmington. Equipment: ITS transmitter; Andrew antenna.

Greenfield—WNC-447 (Channels B-1-4). Hagerman High School, 406 N. Cambridge, Hagerman, NM 88232. Authorized power: 50-w. each. Antenna: 706-ft. above ground. Lat. 33° 12' 22", long. 104° 12' 30". Transmitter: 8.5-mi. ENE of Greenfield. Equipment: ITS transmitter; Andrew antenna.

Greenfield—WNC-446 (Channels D-1-4). Hagerman Municipal Schools, Drawer B, Hagerman, NM 88232. Authorized power: 50-w. each. Antenna: 177-ft. above ground. Lat. 33° 22' 16", long. 104° 38' 10". Transmitter: 3930 S. Brown Rd. Equipment: Emcee transmitter; Andrew antenna.

Greenfield—WLX-925 (Channels G-1-4). Portales High School, 201 S. Knoxville, Portales, NM 88130. Authorized power: 50-w. each. Antenna: 706-ft. above ground. Lat. 33° 12' 22", long. 104° 12' 30". Transmitter: 8.5-mi. ENE of Greenfield. Equipment: ITS transmitter; Andrew antenna.

Hobbs—WNC-454 (Channels A-1-4). Denver City Junior High, 419 Mustang Ave., Denver City, TX 79323. Authorized power: 50-w. each. Antenna: 558-ft. above ground. Lat. 32° 37' 03", long. 103° 01' 46". Transmitter: 15-mi. NE of State Rte. 18. Equipment: Emcee transmitter; Andrew antenna.

Hobbs—WNC-453 (Channels B-1-4). Denver City High School, 601 Mustang Ave., Denver City, TX 79323. Authorized power: 50-w. each. Antenna: 558-ft. above ground. Lat. 32° 43' 43", long. 102° 56' 17". Transmitter: 4.6-mi. NE of State Rte. 18. Equipment: Emcee transmitter; Andrew antenna.

Hobbs—WNC-328 (Channels G-1-4). Seminole Independent School District, 207 S.W. 6th, Seminole, TX 79360. Phone: 915-758-3662. Fax: 915-758-6249.

E-mail: rgryan@tenet.edu.

Authorized power: 50-w. each. Antenna: 558-ft. above ground. Lat. 32° 43' 43", long. 102° 56' 17". Transmitter: 4.6-mi. NE of State Rte. 18. Equipment: Emcee transmitter; Andrew antenna.

Leased to Leaco Rural Telephone Co-op Inc., 1500 N. Love, Lovington, NM 88260. Phone: 505-396-6209.

Las Cruces—WNC-224 (Channels A-1-4). Onate High School, 1700 E. Spruce, Las Cruces, NM 88005. Authorized power: 50-w. each. Antenna: 82-ft. above ground. Lat. 32° 17' 34", long. 106° 41' 48". Transmitter: Tortugas Mountain. Equipment: ITS transmitter; Andrew antenna.

Las Cruces—WNC-726 (Channels B-1-4). Seminole High School, 2100 N.W. Ave. D, Seminole, TX 79360. Phone: 915-758-5873. Fax: 915-758-8146. Authorized power: 50-w. each. Antenna: 321-ft. above ground. Lat. 32° 24' 17", long. 106° 45' 38". Transmitter: Twin Peaks. Equipment: ITS transmitter; Andrew antenna.

Leased to Multimedia Development Corp., 13170-B Central SE, Suite 300, Albuquerque, NM 87123. Phone: 505-281-4302.

Las Cruces—WNC-259 (Channels C-1-4). Gadsden Independent School District, Drawer 70, Anthony, NM 88021. Phone: 505-882-6240. Fax: 505-882-6250. Authorized power: 20-w. each. Antenna: 75-ft. above ground. Lat. 32° 17' 34", long. 106° 41' 48". Transmitter: Tortugas Mountain. Equipment: Emcee transmitter; Andrew antenna.

Leased to MultiMedia Development Corp., 13170-B Central SE, No. 300, Albuquerque, NM 87123. Phone: 505-281-4302.

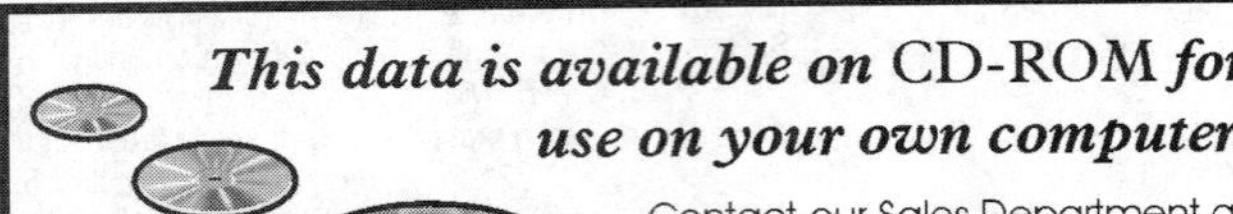

Las Cruces—WNC-337 (Channels D-1-4). International Business College New Mexico Inc., Suite F, 650 E. Montana, Las Cruces, NM 88001. Phone: 505-526-5579. Fax: 505-523-7144. Authorized power: 20-w. each. Antenna: 75-ft. above ground. Lat. 32° 17' 34", long. 106° 41' 48". Transmitter: Tortugas Mountain. Equipment: Emcee transmitter; Andrew antenna.

Leased to Multimedia Development Corp., 13170-B Central SE, No. 300, Albuquerque, NM 87123. Phone: 505-281-4302.

Las Cruces—WLX-806 (Channels G-1-4). Hispanic Information & Telecommunications Network Inc., 3rd Floor, 449 Broadway, New York, NY 10013. Phone: 212-966-5660. Fax: 212-966-5725.

E-mail: email@hitn.org.

Web site: http://www.hitn.org.

Authorized power: 20-w. each. Antenna: 75-ft. above ground. Lat. 32° 17' 34", long. 106° 41' 48". Transmitter: Tortugas Mountain. Equipment: Emcee transmitter; Andrew antenna.

Leased to Multichannel Media, 13170-B Central Ave. SE, Suite 300, Albuquerque, NM 87123. Phone: 505-281-4302.

Las Vegas—WNC-943 (Channels A-1 & 3-4). Morningstar Educational Network, 4012 Morningstar, Huntington Beach, CA 92649. Authorized power: 50-w. each. Antenna: 102-ft. above ground. Lat. 35° 36' 16", long. 105° 15' 35". Transmitter: 0.5-mi. W of State Hospital. Equipment: Emcee transmitter; Andrew antenna.

Las Vegas—WHR-975 (Channel A-2). Luna Vocational Technical Institute. Authorized power: 10-w. Antenna: 44-ft. above ground. Lat. 35° 37' 46", long. 105° 14' 09". Equipment: Comwave transmitter; Bogner antenna.

Los Alamos—WHR-756 (Channel C-4). Regents of U. of New Mexico & Board of Education of the City of Albuquerque (KNME-TV), Albuquerque Public Schools, 1130 University Blvd. NE, Albuquerque, NM 87102. Phone: 505-277-2121. Fax: 505-277-2191.

E-mail: jon@knmel.unm.edu.

Web site: http://www.pbs.org/knme/.

Authorized power: 10-w. Antenna: 50-ft. above ground. Lat. 35° 51' 15", long. 106° 16' 53". Transmitter: Los Alamos National Lab, Bldg. TA-46. Equipment: Comwave transmitter; Andrew antenna.

Lovington—WNC-279 (Channels D-1-4). Lovington Municipal Schools, Box 1537, Lovington, NM 88260. Phone: 505-396-2891. Fax: 505-396-6450. Authorized power: 50-w. each. Antenna: 558-ft. above ground. Lat. 32° 43' 43", long. 102° 56' 17". Transmitter: 7.9-mi. SE of State Rte. 18 & U.S. Rte. 18. Equipment: Emcee transmitter; Andrew antenna.

Leased to Leaco Communications, 1500 N. Love, Lovington, NM 88260. Phone: 505-396-6209.

Maljamar—WNC-300 (Channels C-1-4). Board of Regents, Eastern New Mexico U., Portales, NM 88130. Authorized power: 10-w. each. Antenna: 440-ft. above ground. Lat. 32° 54' 55", long. 103° 46' 31". Transmitter: KMTH-FM transmitter site, 3-mi. NE of Maljamar. Equipment: Comwave transmitter; Andrew antenna.

Portales—WLX-234 (Channels A-1-4). Board of Regents Eastern New Mexico U., Portales, NM 88130. Authorized power: 50-w. each. Antenna: 305-ft. above ground. Lat. 34° 10' 27", long. 103° 21' 03". Transmitter: KENW-(TV) studios, Eastern New Mexico U. Equipment: Comwave transmitter; Bogner antenna.

Raton—WNC-800 (Channels A-1-4). Board of Regents Eastern New Mexico U., Portales, NM 88130. Authorized power: 10-w. each. Antenna: 150-ft. above ground. Lat. 36° 52' 14", long. 104° 25' 58". Transmitter: 2.2-mi S of Police Office, U.S. I-25. Equipment: Comwave transmitter; Andrew antenna.

Roswell—WNC-301 (Channels C-1-4). Board of Regents, Eastern New Mexico U., Portales, NM 88130. Authorized power: 12-w. each. Antenna: 70-ft. above ground. Lat. 33° 18' 25", long. 104° 31' 27". Transmitter: Eastern New Mexico U., Roswell Campus. Equipment: Comwave transmitter; Andrew antenna.

Ruidoso—WNC-402 (Channels A-1-4). Board of Regents, Eastern New Mexico U., Portales, NM 88130. Lat. 33° 24' 14", long. 105° 46' 55". Transmitter: Buck Mountain, 9.5-mi. NW of Ruidoso. Equipment: Comwave transmitter; Andrew antenna.

Santa Fe—WNC-687 (Channels B-1-4). College of Santa Fe, 1600 St. Michael's Dr., Santa Fe, NM 87501. Authorized power: 10-w. each. Antenna: 56-ft. above ground. Lat. 35° 47' 09", long. 105° 46' 54". Transmitter: Horse Head Ranch. Equipment: Emcee transmitter; Andrew antenna.

Santa Fe—WNC-852 (Channels C-1-4). Pojoaque Valley Schools, Box 3468, Pojoaque Station, Santa Fe, NM 87501. Authorized power: 10-w. each. Antenna: 11985-ft. above ground. Lat. 35° 47' 09", long. 105° 46' 54". Transmitter: Tesuque Peak. Equipment: ITS transmitter; Andrew antenna.

Santa Fe—WNC-636 (Channels D-1-4). Santa Fe Community College, 6401 Richards Ave., Santa Fe, NM 87505. Phone: 505-438-1319. Fax: 505-438-1237. Authorized power: 10-w. each. Antenna: 56-ft. above ground. Lat. 35° 47' 09", long. 105° 46' 54". Transmitter: Horse Head Ranch. Equipment: Emcee transmitter; Andrew antenna.

Leased to Multimedia Development Corp., 12443 N. Hwy. 14, Box 878, Sancha Park, NM 87047. Phone: 505-281-4302.

Silver City—WNC-969 (Channels G-1-4). Western New Mexico U., 1000 College Ave., Silver City, NM 88062. Authorized power: 50-w. each. Antenna: 30-ft. above ground. Lat. 32° 50' 50", long. 108° 14' 18". Transmitter: 5-mi. N of Silver City. Equipment: Emcee transmitter; Bogner antenna.

Socorro—WNC-841 (Channels C-1-4). Socorro Consolidated Schools, 700 Franklin, Socorro, NM 87801. Authorized power: 20-w. each. Antenna: 36-ft. above ground. Lat. 34° 04' 18", long. 106° 57' 44". Transmitter: 4-mi. W of Socorro. Equipment: Emcee transmitter; Lance antenna.

Tucumcari—WNC-455 (Channels B-1-4). House Municipal School, Box 673, Hwy. 252 & Apple St., House, NM 88121. Authorized power: 50-w. each. Antenna: 706-ft. above ground. Lat. 35° 13' 47", long. 103° 44' 11". Transmitter: 4-mi. N of Tucumcari & 0.7-mi. S of Quay County border. Equipment: ITS transmitter; Andrew antenna.

Tucumcari—WNC-458 (Channels A-1-4). House High School, Box 673, House, NM 88121. Authorized power: 50-w. each. Antenna: 706-ft. above ground. Lat. 35° 13' 47", long. 103° 44' 11". Transmitter: 4-mi. N of Tucumcari & 0.7-mi. S of Quay County border. Equipment: ITS transmitter; Andrew antenna.

Tucumcari—WLX-882 (Channels C-1-4). Logan Municipal Schools, Box 67, Logan, NM 88426. Authorized power: 50-w. each. Antenna: 706-ft. above ground. Lat. 35° 13' 47", long. 103° 44' 11". Transmitter: 4-mi. N of Tucumcari. Equipment: ITS transmitter; Andrew antenna.

Tucumcari—WLX-938 (Channels D-1-4). San Jon Municipal Schools, Box 5, 7th & Elm Sts., San Jon, NM 88434. Authorized power: 50-w. each. Antenna: 706-ft. above ground. Lat. 35° 13' 47", long. 103° 44' 11". Transmitter: 4-mi. N of Tucumcari & 0.7-mi. S of Quay County border. Equipment: ITS transmitter; Andrew antenna.

Tucumcari—WLX-980 (Channels G-1-4). Tucumcari Municipal Schools, Box 1046, 902 S. 11th, Tucumcari, NM 88401. Phone: 505-461-3910. Fax: 505-461-3554. Authorized power: 50-w. each. Antenna: 706-ft. above ground. Lat. 35° 13' 47", long. 103° 44' 11". Transmitter: 4-mi. N of Tucumcari & 0.7-mi. S of Quay County border. Equipment: ITS transmitter; Andrew antenna.

New York

Albany—WHR-930 (Channels B-1-4). Hispanic Information & Telecommunications Network Inc., 3rd Floor, 449 Broadway, New York, NY 10013. Phone: 212-966-5660. Fax: 212-966-5725.

E-mail: email@hitn.org.

Web site: http://www.hitn.org.

Authorized power: 50-w. each. Antenna: 115-ft. above ground. Lat. 42° 38' 09", long. 74° 00' 04". Transmitter: Pinnacle Rd. Equipment: ITS transmitter; Andrew antenna.

Leased to CAI Wireless Systems Inc., 2101 Wilson Blvd., Suite 100, Arlington, VA 22201. Phone: 703-812-8800.

Albany—WHR-885 (Channels D-1-4). National Conference on Citizenship, Suite 1150, 4770 Biscayne Blvd., Miami, FL 33137. Phone: 305-576-4310. Fax: 305-576-7412. Authorized power: 50-w. each. Antenna: 120-ft. above ground. Lat. 42° 38' 09", long. 74° 00' 04". Transmitter: Pinnacle Rd., NE of Camp Pinnacle. Equipment: ITS transmitter; Andrew antenna.

Leased to CAI Wireless Systems Inc., 2101 Wilson Blvd., Suite 100, Arlington, VA 22201. Phone: 703-812-8800.

Albany—WHR-886 (Channels G-1-4). Northern Arizona U. Foundation, Box 4114, Flagstaff, AZ 86011. Authorized power: 50-w. each. Antenna: 120-ft. above ground. Lat. 42° 38' 09", long. 74° 00' 04". Transmitter: Pinnacle Rd. Equipment: ITS transmitter; Andrew antenna.

Amityville—WHR-845 (Channels G-1-4). Roman Catholic Diocese of Rockville Centre, 50 N. Park Ave., Rockville Centre, NY 11570. Authorized power: 20-w. each. Antenna: 100-ft. above ground. Lat. 40° 48' 11", long. 73° 12' 26". Transmitter: Central Islip. Equipment: ITS transmitter; Andrew antenna.

Leased to CAI Wireless Systmes Inc., 2101 Wilson Blvd., Suite 100, Arlington, VA 22201. Phone: 703-812-8800.

Beacon—KRS-85 (Channels E-1-4). Department of Education, Archdiocese of New York, 215 Seminary Ave., Yonkers, NY 10704. Phone: 914-968-7800. Fax: 914-968-2075. Authorized power: 10-w. each. Antenna: 310-ft. above ground. Lat. 41° 29' 19", long. 73° 56' 52". Transmitter: Mount Beacon. Equipment: Emcee transmitter; Andrew antenna.

Leased to Magnavision Corp., 1725 Hwy. 35, Wall, NJ 07719.

Binghamton—WNC-979 (Channels A-1-4). Universal Education Foundation Co., 850 Fay Rd., Syracuse, NY 13219. Authorized power: 10-w. each. Antenna: 2165-ft. above ground. Lat. 42° 03' 22", long. 75° 56' 39". Transmitter: Ingraham Hill Rd. Equipment: Andrew transmitter.

Binghamton—WNC-964 (Channels D-1-4). Rockne Educational Television, 320 Hamilton St., Albion, NY 14411. Authorized power: 10-w. each. Antenna: 404-ft. above ground. Lat. 42° 03' 22", long. 75° 56' 39". Transmitter: 3000 Ingraham Hill Rd. Equipment: Comwave transmitter; Bogner antenna.

Binghamton—WND-400 (Channels G-1-4). Catholic Communications of Western New York, 795 Main St., Buffalo, NY 14203. Authorized power: 10-w. each. Antenna: 403-ft. above ground. Lat. 42° 03' 22", long. 75° 56' 39". Transmitter: 3000 Ingram Hill Rd. Equipment: Comwave transmitter; Bogner antenna.

Brooklyn—KNZ-69 (Channels B-1-4). Trans Video Communications Inc., 1712 10th Ave., Brooklyn, NY 11215. Phone: 718-499-9705. Fax: 718-499-2406. Authorized power: 10-w. each. Antenna: 353-ft. above ground. Lat. 40° 39' 20", long. 73° 58' 56". Transmitter: 19th & Prospect Park W.

Leased to CAI Wireless Systems Inc., 2101 Wilson Blvd., Suite 100, Arlington, VA 22201. Phone: 703-812-8800.

Brooklyn—KVS-31 (Channels F-1-4). Trans Video Communications Inc., 1712 10th Ave., Brooklyn, NY 11215. Phone: 718-499-9705. Fax: 718-499-2406. Authorized power: 5-w. each. Antenna: 142-ft. above ground. Lat. 40° 43' 09", long. 73° 56' 32". Transmitter: 1-15 Monitor St.

Leased to CAI Wireless Systems Inc., 2101 Wilson Blvd., Suite 100, Arlington, VA 22201. Phone: 703-812-8800.

Buffalo—WLX-584 (Channels A-1-2). Albion Community Development Corp., 51 Main St., Albion, NY 14411. Authorized power: 40-w. each. Antenna: 353-ft. above ground. Lat. 42° 53' 10", long. 78° 52' 26". Transmitter: Washington St. & Broadway. Equipment: Comwave transmitter; Bogner antenna.

Buffalo—WDG-55 (Channel G-1). State U. of New York, Parker Engineering Bldg., Buffalo, NY 14214. Authorized power: 10-w. Antenna: 150-ft. above ground. Lat. 42° 57' 20", long. 78° 49' 01". Transmitter: 3415 Main St.

Buffalo—WLX-770 (Channels G-2-4). Hispanic Information & Telecommunications Network Inc., 3rd. Floor, 449 Broadway, New York, NY 10013. Phone: 212-966-5660. Fax: 212-966-5725.
E-mail: email@hitn.org.
Web site: http://www.hitn.org.
Authorized power: 20-w. each. Antenna: 797-ft. above ground. Lat. 43° 01' 48", long. 78° 55' 15". Transmitter: Marine Midland Center. Equipment: Emcee transmitter; Bogner antenna.
Leased to CAI Wireless Systems Inc., 2101 Wilson Blvd., Suite 100, Arlington, VA 22201. Phone: 703-812-8800.

Central Islip—KNZ-68 (Channels B-1-4). Roman Catholic Diocese of Rockville TV, 1200 Glenn Curtiss Blvd., Uniondale, NY 11553. Antenna: 300-ft. above ground. Lat. 40° 48' 11", long. 73° 12' 24". Transmitter: Wheeler Rd. & Motor Pkwy. intersection (St. John's Cemetery).
Leased to CAI Wireless Systmes Inc., 2101 Wilson Blvd., Suite 100, Arlington, VA 22201. Phone: 703-812-8800.

Deerfield—WNC-992 (Channels A-1-4). Counterpoint Communications Inc. Authorized power: 50-w. each. Antenna: 253-ft. above ground. Lat. 43° 08' 34", long. 75° 10' 34". Transmitter: 269 Grace Rd. Equipment: Comwave transmitter; Bogner antenna.

Deerfield—WNC-514 (Channels D-1-4). Rockne Educational Television, 320 Hamilton St., Albion, NY 14411. Phone: 716-589-9295. Fax: 716-589-9094. Authorized power: 50-w. each. Antenna: 253-ft. above ground. Lat. 43° 08' 34", long. 75° 10' 34". Transmitter: 269 Grace Rd. Equipment: Comwave transmitter; Bogner antenna.

Deerfield—WNC-991 (Channels G-1-4). Catholic Communications of Western New York, 795 Main St., Buffalo, NY 14203. Authorized power: 50-w. each. Antenna: 253-ft. above ground. Lat. 43° 08' 34", long. 75° 10' 34". Transmitter: 269 Grace Rd. Equipment: Comwave transmitter; Bogner antenna.

Fairport—WLX-613 (Channels A-1-4). Rockne Educational Television, 320 Hamilton St., Albion, NY 14411. Phone: 716-589-9295. Fax: 716-589-9094.
E-mail: topper1a1@AOL.
Authorized power: 100-w. each. Antenna: 247-ft. above ground. Lat. 43° 02' 10", long. 77° 25' 24". Transmitter: 935 Thayer Rd. Equipment: ITS transmitter; Andrew antenna.
Leased to CAI Wireless, 2101 Wilson Blvd., Suite 100, Arlington, VA 22201. Phone: 703-812-8800.

Fairport—WLX-536 (Channels B-1-4). Albion Community Development Corp., 51 N. Main St., Albion, NY 14411. Authorized power: 100-w. each. Antenna: 247-ft. above ground. Lat. 43° 02' 10", long. 77° 25' 24". Transmitter: 935 Thayer Rd. Equipment: ITS transmitter; Andrew antenna.

Fairport—WLX-870 (Channels D-1-4). Northern Arizona U. Foundation, Box 4094, Flagstaff, AZ 86011. Authorized power: 100-w. each. Antenna: 244-ft. above ground. Lat. 43° 02' 10", long. 77° 25' 24". Transmitter: 935 Thayer Rd. Equipment: ITS transmitter; Andrew antenna.

Fairport—WLX-543 (Channels G-1-4). National Conference on Citizenship, Suite 1150, 4770 Biscayne Blvd., Miami, FL 33137. Phone: 305-576-4310. Fax: 305-576-7412. Authorized power: 100-w. each. Antenna: 244-ft. above ground. Lat. 43° 02' 10", long. 77° 25' 24". Transmitter: 935 Thayer Rd. Equipment: ITS transmitter; Andrew antenna.
Leased to CAI Wireless Systmes INc., 2101 Wilson Blvd, Suite 100, Arlington, VA 22201. Phone: 703-812-8800.

Franklin Square—KHD-21 (Channels A-2-3). Sewanhaka Central High School District of Elmont & New Hyde Park, 555 Ridge Rd., Elmont, NY 11003. Phone: 516-539-9497. Fax: 516-565-4351. Transmitter: 230 Poppy Ave.

Fredonia—WAQ-310 (Channel C-1). BOCES of Chautauqua County, Box 250, Fredonia, NY 14063. Phone: 716-672-4371. Fax: 716-672--2393.
E-mail: plester@e2ccboces.wnyric.org.
Authorized power: 10-w. Antenna: 200-ft. above ground. Lat. 42° 25' 08", long. 79° 18' 40". Transmitter: BOCES Center, SE of Water St. & Webster Rd.

Gloversville—WHR-900 (Channel C-2). Gloversville School District, 90 N. Main St., Gloversville, NY 12078. Phone: 518-725-2210. Fax: 518-725-3611. Authorized power: 10-w. Antenna: 147-ft. above ground. Lat. 43° 02' 37", long. 74° 22' 11". Transmitter: 524 N. Perry St. Equipment: Emcee transmitter; Andrew antenna.

Grand Island—WNC-353 (Channels A-3-4). Rockne Educational Television, 320 Hamilton St., Albion, NY 14411. Phone 716-589-9295. Fax: 716-589-9094. Authorized power: 20-w. each. Antenna: 546-ft. above ground. Lat. 43° 01' 48", long. 78° 55' 15". Transmitter: 871 Whitehaven Rd. Equipment: Comwave transmitter; Andrew antenna.
Leased to CAI Wireless, 2101 Wilson Blvd., Suite 100, Arlington, VA 22201. Phone: 703-812-8800.

Grand Island—WNC-435 (Channels B-1-4). Diocese of Buffalo, NY, 795 Main St., Buffalo, NY 14203. Authorized power: 25-w. each. Antenna: 577-ft. above ground. Lat. 43° 01' 48", long. 78° 55' 15". Transmitter: 871 Whitehaven Rd. Equipment: Comwave transmitter; Bogner antenna.
Leased to CAI Wireless Systems Inc., 2101 Wilson Blvd., Suite 100, Arlington, VA 22201. Phone: 703-812-8800.

Grand Island—WNC-202 (Channels C-1-4). Catholic Communications of Western New York Inc., 795 Main St., Buffalo, NY 14203. Authorized power: 20-w. each. Antenna: 1123-ft. above ground. Lat. 43° 01' 48", long. 78° 55' 15". Transmitter: 871 Whitehaven Rd. Equipment: Comwave transmitter; Bogner antenna.
Leased to CAI Wireless Systems Inc., 2101 Wilson Blvd., Suite 100, Arlington, VA 22201. Phone: 703-812-8800.

Grand Island—WNC-338 (Channels D-1-4). National Conference on Citizenship, Suite 1150, 4770 Biscayne Blvd., Miami, FL 33137. Phone: 305-576-4310. Fax: 305-576-7412. Authorized power: 20-w. each. Antenna: 546-ft. above ground. Lat. 43° 01' 48", long. 78° 55' 15". Transmitter: 871 Whitehaven Rd. Equipment: Comwave transmitter; Andrew antenna.

Grand Island—WNC-239 (Channel G-1). Christ the King Seminary, 711 Knox Rd., East Aurora, NY 14052. Authorized power: 20-w. Antenna: 577-ft. above ground. Lat. 45° 01' 48", long. 78° 55' 15". Transmitter: 871 Whitehaven Rd. Equipment: Comwave transmitter; Andrew antenna.
Leased to CAI Wireless Systems Inc., 2101 Wilson Blvd., Suite 100, Arlington, VA 22201. Phone: 703-812-8800.

Haverstraw—KRS-84 (Channels A-1-4). Department of Education, Archdiocese of New York, 215 Seminary Ave., Yonkers, NY 10204. Phone: 914-968-7800. Fax: 914-968-2075. Authorized power: 10-w. each. Antenna: 310-ft. above ground. Lat. 41° 12' 15", long. 74° 02' 49". Transmitter: Cheesecote Mountain, Peekskill. Equipment: Emcee transmitter; RCA antenna.
Leased to Magnavision Corp., 1725 Hwy. 35, Wall, NJ 07719.

Highland—WLX-207 (Channels B-1-2). Dutchess Community College, 53 Pendell Rd., Poughkeepsie, NY 12601. Phone: 914-431-8947. Fax: 914-431-8985.
E-mail: simpson@sunydutchess.edu.
Authorized power: 10-w. each. Antenna: 135-ft. above ground. Lat. 41° 43' 10", long. 73° 59' 45". Transmitter: Illinois Mountain, 1.5-mi. W of Highland. Equipment: Emcee transmitter; Andrew antenna.

Kenmore—KWE-21 (Channels A-1-2). Union Free School District, 50 N. Park Ave, Rockville Centre, Long Island, NY 11570. Authorized power: 1-w. each. Lat. 49° 48' 11", long. 73° 12' 26". Transmitter: Administration Bldg., 1500 Colvin Blvd.

Long Island—KNZ-67 (Channels A-1-4). Roman Catholic Diocese of Rockville TV, 50 N. Park Ave., Rockville Center, NY 11750. Phone: 516-536-3409. Authorized power: 20-w. each. Antenna: 291-ft. above ground. Lat. 40° 48' 11", long. 73° 12' 26". Transmitter: Central Islip. Equipment: ITS transmitter; Andrew antenna.
Leased to CAI Wireless Systems Inc., 2101 Wilson Blvd., Suite 100, Arlington, VA 22201. Phone: 703-812-8800.

Loomis—KRW-67 (Channels A-1-3). Department of Education, Archdiocese of New York, 215 Seminary Ave., Yonkers, NY 10204. Phone: 914-968-7800. Fax: 914-968-2075. Authorized power: 10-w. each. Antenna: 310-ft. above ground. Lat. 41° 48' 17", long. 74° 47' 07". Transmitter: 2-mi. W of Liberty. Equipment: RCA transmitter; RCA antenna.
Leased to Magnavision Corp., 1725 Hwy. 35, Wall, NJ 07719.

Mineola—KNZ-71 (Channels G-1-4). Union Free School District No. 10., 200 Emory Rd., Mineola, NY 11501. Phone: 516-741-1631. Fax: 516-741-1860.
E-mail: jcollinstv@aol.com.
Web site: http://www.mineola.k12.ny.us/avtv.
Authorized power: 10-w. each. Antenna: 921-ft. above ground. Lat. 40° 44' 54", long. 73° 59' 10". Transmitter: 350 5th Ave., New York. Equipment: ITS transmitter; Andrew antenna.
Leased to CAI, 2101 Wilson Blvd., Suite 100, Arlington, VA 22201. Phone: 703-812-8800.

New Scotland—WHR-729 (Channels A-1-4). American Red Cross, Schenectady County Chapter, 1040 State St., Schenectady, NY 12307-1508. Phone: 518-393-3606. Authorized power: 50-w. each. Antenna: 120-ft. above ground. Lat. 42° 38' 09", long. 74° 00' 04". Transmitter: Pinnacle Rd. Equipment: ITS transmitter; Andrew antenna.

New Scotland—WHR-586 (Channels C-1-4). Faculty Student Assn. of Hudson Valley Community College Inc., Vandenburgh Ave., Troy, NY 12180. Phone: 518-270-7307. Fax: 518-270-7586. Authorized power: 50-w. each. Antenna: 190-ft. above ground. Lat. 42° 38' 09", long. 74° 00' 04". Transmitter: 2.5-mi. SW of New Salem on Pinnacle Rd. Equipment: ITS transmitter; Andrew antenna.
Leased to Niskayvna Assoc., Box 186, Rexford, NY 12148. Phone: 518-374-0651.

New York—KRS-81 (Channels A-1-4). Department of Education, Archdiocese of New York, 215 Seminary Rd., Yonkers, NY 10704. Phone: 914-968-7800. Fax: 914-968-2075. Authorized power: 10-w. each. Antenna: 1087-ft. above ground. Lat. 40° 44' 54", long. 73° 59' 10". Transmitter: Empire State Bldg. Equipment: Emcee transmitter; RCA antenna.
Leased to Magnavision Corp., 1725 Hwy. 35, Wall, NJ 07719.

New York—WHR-691 (Channel B-2). Trans Video Communications Inc., 1712 10th Ave., Brooklyn, NY 11215. Phone: 718-499-9705. Fax: 718-499-2406. Authorized power: 1-w. Antenna: 1680-ft. above ground. Lat. 40° 42' 54", long. 73° 59' 47". Transmitter: Confucius Plaza, Bowery & Division Sts. Equipment: Bogner antenna.
Leased to CAI Wireless Systems Inc., 2101 Wilson Blvd., Suite 100, Arlington, VA 22201. Phone: 703-812-8800.

New York—WHR-829 (Channels C-2-3). Hispanic Information & Telecommunications Network Inc., 3rd Floor, 449 Broadway, New York, NY 10013. Phone: 212-966-5660. Fax: 212-966-5725.
E-mail: email@hitn.org.
Web site: http://www.hitn.org.
Authorized power: 10-w. each. Antenna: 925-ft. above ground. Lat. 40° 44' 54", long. 73° 59' 10". Transmitter: Empire State Bldg., 350 5th Ave. Equipment: Andrew antenna.
Leased to CAI Wireless Systems Inc., 2101 Wilson Blvd., Suite 100, Arlington, VA 22201. Phone: 703-812-8800.

New York—WHR-828 (Channel C-4). Educational Bcstg. Corp., 356 W. 58th St., New York, NY 10019. Phone: 212-560-2000. Fax: 212-582-3297. Authorized power: 10-w. Antenna: 925-ft. above ground. Lat. 40° 44' 54", long. 73° 59' 10". Transmitter: Empire State Bldg., 350 5th Ave.
Leased to New York License Inc., 2101 Wilson Blvd., Suite 100, Arlington, VA 22201. Phone: 703-812-8800.

New York—WHR-520 (Channels D-1-4). Network for Instructional TV Inc., Suite 110, 11490 Commerce Park Dr., Reston, VA 20191. Phone: 703-860-9200. Fax: 703-860-9237. Authorized power: 10-w. each. Antenna: 924-ft. above ground. Lat. 40° 44' 54", long. 73° 59' 10". Transmitter: Empire State Bldg., 350 5th Ave. Equipment: Bogner transmitter; Andrew antenna.
Leased to CAI Wireless Systems Inc., 2101 Wilson Blvd., Suite 100, Arlington, VA 22201. Phone: 703-812-8800.

New York—KRS-82 (Channels E-1-4). Department of Education, Archdiocese of New York, 215 Seminary Ave., Yonkers, NY 10704. Phone: 914-968-7800. Fax: 914-968-2075. Authorized power: 10-w. each. Antenna: 310-ft. above ground. Lat. 40° 35' 51", long. 74° 06' 53". Transmitter: Todt Hill Rd., St. Francis Seminary. Equipment: Emcee transmitter; RCA antenna.
Leased to Magnavision Corp., 1725 Hwy. 35, Wall, NJ 07719.

New York—KNZ-70 (Channels F-1-4). Trans Video Communications Inc.,, 1712 10th Ave., Brooklyn, NY 11215. Phone: 718-499-9705. Fax: 718-499-2406. Authorized power: 10-w. each. Antenna: 277-ft. above ground. Lat. 40° 42' 47", long. 73° 47' 13". Transmitter: 176-21 Wexford Terrace, Jamaica. Equipment: Comwave transmitter; Andrew antenna.

Leased to CAI Wireless Systems Inc., 2101 Wilson Blvd., Suite 100 Arlington, VA 22201. Phone: 703-812-8800.

Newburgh—KTN-66 (Channels D-1-2). Newburgh City School District, 98 Grand Ave., Newburgh, NY 12550. Transmitter: Newburgh Free Academy, Fullerton Ave.

Olean—WBB-433 (Channel A-1). Cattaraugus, Allegany, Erie, Wyoming BOCES, 1825 Windfall Rd., Olean, NY 14760. Phone: 716-372-8293. Fax: 716-372-2500. Authorized power: 110-w. Antenna: 245-ft. above ground. Lat. 42° 03' 18", long. 78° 27' 28". Transmitter: 1.5-mi. NE of Olean.

Plainview—KHC-94 (Channels B-1-2). Plainview-Old Bethpage Public Schools, Administrative Bldg., Jamaica Ave., Plainview, NY 11803. Authorized power: 5-w. each. Lat. 40° 46' 53", long. 73° 27' 35". Transmitter: J. F. Kennedy High School, Washington Ave. & Kennedy Dr.

Plattsburgh—WBK-219 (Channel A-1). State U. of New York. Authorized power: 10-w. Antenna: 131-ft. above ground. Lat. 44° 41' 40", long. 73° 27' 56". Transmitter: Kehoe Administration Bldg., State U. of New York-Plattsburgh.

Poughkeepsie—WHR-978 (Channels C-1-2). Dutchess Community College, Pendell Rd., Poughkeepsie, NY 12601. Phone: 914-471-4500. Fax: 914-471-4869.
E-mail: simpson@sunydutchess.edu.
Authorized power: 10-w. each. Antenna: 494-ft. above ground. Lat. 41° 43' 36", long. 73° 54' 16". Transmitter: Dutchess Community College, Poughkeepsie. Equipment: Emcee transmitter; Andrew antenna.

Queens—KZE-20 (Channels B-1-4). Tran Video Communications Inc., 1712 10th Ave., Brooklyn, NY 11215. Phone: 718-499-9705. Fax: 718-499-2406. Authorized power: 1-w. each. Antenna: 293-ft. above ground. Lat. 40° 44' 05", long. 73° 51' 53". Transmitter: One Lefrak City Plaza. Equipment: Comwave transmitter; Andrew antenna.
Leased to CAI Wireless, 18 Corporate Woods Bldg., Albany, NY 12211. Phone: 518-462-2632.

Rhinecliff—KRS-86 (Channels A-1-4). Department of Education, Archdiocese of New York, 215 Seminary Ave., Yonkers, NY 10704. Phone: 914-968-7800. Fax: 914-968-2075. Authorized power: 10-w. each. Antenna: 310-ft. above ground. Lat. 41° 54' 02", long. 73° 56' 39". Transmitter: Morton Rd. Equipment: Emcee transmitter; RCA antenna.
Leased to Magnavision Corp., 1725 Hwy. 35, Wall, NJ 07719.

Rochester—WLX-753 (Channels C-1-4). Hispanic Information & Telecommunications Network Inc., 3rd Floor, 449 Broadway, New York, NY 10013. Phone: 212-966-5660. Fax: 212-966-5725.
E-mail: email@hitn.org.
Web site: http://www.hitn.org.
Authorized power: 100-w. each. Antenna: 154-ft. above ground. Lat. 43° 02' 10", long. 77° 25' 24". Transmitter: 935 Thayer Rd. Equipment: ITS transmitter; Andrew antenna.
Leased to CAI Wireless Systems Inc., 2101 Wilson Blvd., Suite 100, Arlington, VA 22201. Phone: 703-812-8800.

Sentinel Heights—WHR-641 (Channels G-1-4). Public Bcstg. Council of Central New York Inc., 506 Old Liverpool Rd., Syracuse, NY 13220-2400. Phone: 315-453-2424. Fax: 315-451-8824.
E-mail: wcny-online@wcny.pbs.org.
Web site: http://www.wcny.org.
Authorized power: 10-w. each. Antenna: 170-ft. above ground. Lat. 42° 56' 45", long. 76° 07' 09". Transmitter: 0.3-mi. S of Sentinel Heights. Equipment: Emcee transmitter; Andrew antenna.

Syracuse—WNC-472 (Channels A-1-4). Classical Education Foundation Corp., 850 Fay Rd., Syracuse, NY 13219. Authorized power: 50-w. each. Antenna: 2431-ft. above ground. Lat. 42° 52' 50", long. 76° 11' 59". Transmitter: to 3-mi. SW of Syracuse on Makyes Rd. Equipment: ITS transmitter; Andrew antenna.

Syracuse—WNC-919 (Channels B-1-4). Sacred Heart School, 1001 Park Ave., Syracuse, NY 13201. Authorized power: 50-w. each. Antenna: 2430-ft. above ground. Lat. 42° 52' 50", long. 76° 11' 59.00". Transmitter: 3-mi. SW of Syracuse on Makyes Rd. Equipment: ITS transmitter; Andrew antenna.

Syracuse—WLX-929 (Channels C-1-4). Albion Community Development Corp., 51 N. Main St., Albion, NY 14411. Authorized power: 50-w. each. Antenna: 810-ft. above ground. Lat. 42° 52' 50", long. 76° 11' 59". Transmitter: Barker St., 2.4-mi. S of U.S. 20. Equipment: ITS transmitter; Andrew antenna.

Syracuse—WLX-682 (Channels D-1-4). Hispanic Information & Telecommunications Network Inc., 3rd Floor, 449 Broadway, New York, NY 10013. Phone: 212-966-5660. Fax: 212-966-5725.
E-mail: email@hitn.org.
Web site: http://www.hitn.org.
Authorized power: 50-w. each. Antenna: 810-ft. above ground. Lat. 42° 52' 50", long. 76° 11' 59". Transmitter: Barker St., 2.4-mi. S of U.S. 20. Equipment: ITS transmitter; Andrew antenna.
Leased to CAI Wireless Systems Inc., 2101 Wilson Blvd., Suite 100, Arlington, VA 22201. Phone: 703-812-8800.

Syracuse—WLX-840 (Channels G-1-4). Rockne Educational Television, 320 Hamilton St., Albion, NY 14411. Authorized power: 50-w. each. Antenna: 810-ft. above ground. Lat. 42° 52' 50", long. 76° 11' 59". Transmitter: Barker St., 2.4-mi. S of U.S. 20. Equipment: ITS transmitter; Andrew antenna.

Uniondale—KNZ-65 (Channels E-1-4). Roman Catholic Diocese of Rockville TV, 1200 Glenn Curtiss Blvd., Uniondale, NY 11553. Lat. 40° 42' 59", long. 73° 34' 54".
Leased to Telicare, 1200 Glenn Curtiss Blvd., Uniondale, NY 11553. Phone: 516-538-8700.

Utica—WNC-699 (Channels B-1-4). Board of Cooperative Educational Services, Box 70, 70 Middle Sett Rd., New Hartford, NY 13413. Phone: 315-793-8503. Fax: 315-793-8554. Authorized power: 20-w. each. Antenna: 383-ft. above ground. Lat. 43° 08' 46", long. 75° 10' 40". Transmitter: Smith Hill, 5-mi. NE of Utica. Equipment: Emcee transmitter; Andrew antenna.

Utica—WNC-675 (Channels C-1-4). Utica College of Syracuse U., Burrstone Rd., Utica, NY 13502. Authorized power: 20-w. each. Antenna: 383-ft. above ground. Lat. 43° 08' 46", long. 75° 10' 40". Transmitter: Smith Hill, 5-mi. NE of Utica. Equipment: Emcee transmitter; Andrew antenna.

Westbury—KNU-43 (Channels D-1-4). BOCES of Nassau County, Valentine Rd. & Plain Rd., Westbury, NY 11590. Phone: 516-622-5678. Fax: 516-742-5406.
E-mail: charles@villagenet.com.
Web site: http://www.nassauboces.org.
Authorized power: 20-w. each. Antenna: 291-ft. above ground. Lat. 40° 48' 11", long. 73° 12' 26". Transmitter: Nassau County School District. Equipment: ITS transmitter; Andrew antenna.
Leased to CAI Wireless Systems, 2101 Wilson Blvd., Suite 100, Arlington, VA 22201. Phone: 703-812-8800.

Yonkers—KRS-83 (Channels E-1-4). Department of Education, Archdiocese of New York, 215 Seminary Ave., Yonkers, NY 10704. Phone: 914-968-7800. Fax: 914-968-2075. Authorized power: 10-w. each. Antenna: 315-ft. above ground. Lat. 40° 55' 54", long. 73° 51' 47". Transmitter: 215 Seminary Ave. Equipment: Emcee transmitter; RCA antenna.
Leased to Magnavision Corp., 1725 Hwy. 35, Wall, NJ 07719.

North Carolina

Asheville—WHR-598 (Channels A-1-4). U. of North Carolina, Box 3508, Chapel Hill, NC 27515. Authorized power: 10-w. each. Antenna: 35-ft. above ground. Lat. 35° 35' 53", long. 82° 38' 34". Transmitter: North Carolina Forest Service Lookout Tower, Spivey Mountain.

Charlotte—WHR-535 (Channels A-1-4). Charlotte Mecklenburg Public Bcstg., 3242 Commonwealth Ave., Charlotte, NC 28205. Phone: 704-372-2442. Fax: 704-335-1358.
Web site: http://www.wtvi.org.
Authorized power: 10-w. each. Antenna: 200-ft. above ground. Lat. 35° 12' 25", long. 80° 47' 30". Transmitter: WTVI(TV) transmitter site. Equipment: Emcee transmitter; Andrew antenna.
Leased to CAI Wireless Inc., 18 Corporate Woods Blvd., Albany, NY 12211. Phone: 800-884-2297.

Charlotte & Mecklenburg County—WHR-657 (Channels C-1-4). U. of North Carolina-Charlotte, Office of the Vice Chancellor for Research & Public Service, Charlotte, NC 28223. Authorized power: 10-w. each. Antenna: 408-ft. above ground. Lat. 35° 18' 00", long. 80° 44' 51". Transmitter: W. Harris Blvd. between Hwys. 49 & 29, E of Charlotte.

Durham—WLX-436 (Channels A-1-4). U. of North Carolina-Center for Public Television, 10 TW Alexander Dr., Research Triangle Park, NC 27709. Authorized power: 50-w. each. Antenna: 404-ft. above ground. Lat. 35° 46' 43", long. 78° 38' 23". Transmitter: Research Triangle Park. Equipment: Emcee transmitter; Andrew antenna.

Durham—WHR-697 (Channels B-1-4). U. of North Carolina, General Administration, 910 Raleigh Rd., Chapel Hill, NC 27514. Phone: 919-549-7000. Authorized power: 50-w. each. Antenna: 374-ft. above ground. Lat. 36° 03' 32", long. 78° 57' 13". Transmitter: Alexander Dr., Research Triangle Park. Equipment: Comwave transmitter; Andrew antenna.

Fayetteville—WND-361 (Channels A-1-4). Fayetteville Technical Community College, 2201 Hull Rd., Fayetteville, NC 28303. Authorized power: 50-w. each. Antenna: 457-ft. above ground. Lat. 35° 02' 42", long. 78° 58' 47". Transmitter: Hwys. 59 & 401 S. Equipment: Emcee transmitter; Andrew antenna.

Fayetteville—WND-362 (Channels B-1-4). Bladen Community College, Hwy. 41, Dublin, NC 28332. Authorized power: 50-w. each. Antenna: 457-ft. above ground. Lat. 35° 02' 42", long. 78° 58' 47". Transmitter: Hwys. 59 & 401 S. Equipment: Emcee transmitter; Andrew antenna.

Fayetteville—WND-364 (Channels C-1-4). Sampson Community College, Hwy. 24, Clinton, NC 28328. Phone: 910-592-8081. Fax: 910-592-8048.
E-mail: dgrubb@sampson.cc.nc.us.
Web site: http://www.sampson.cc.nc.us.
Authorized power: 50-w. each. Antenna: 457-ft. above ground. Lat. 35° 02' 42", long. 78° 58' 47". Transmitter: Hwys. 59 & 401 S. Equipment: Emcee transmitter; Andrew antenna.

Fayetteville—WND-360 (Channels D-1-4). Robeson Community College, U.S. 301 N at I-95, Lunberton, NC 28358. Authorized power: 50-w. each. Antenna: 457-ft. above ground. Lat. 35° 02' 42", long. 78° 58' 47". Transmitter: Hwys. 59 & 401 S. Equipment: Emcee transmitter; Andrew antenna.

Fayetteville—WND-363 (Channels G-1-4). U. of North Carolina, Box 2688, Chapel Hill, NC 27515. Authorized power: 50-w. each. Antenna: 457-ft. above ground. Lat. 35° 02' 42", long. 78° 58' 47". Transmitter: Hwys. 59 & 401 S. Equipment: Emcee transmitter; Andrew antenna.

Gaston—WND-303 (Channels A-1-4). Vance-Granville Community College, SR 1126, Henderson, NC 27536. Authorized power: 50-w. each. Antenna: 315-ft. above ground. Lat. 36° 30' 12", long. 77° 44' 47". Transmitter: Hwy. 46, Gaston. Equipment: Emcee transmitter; Andrew antenna.

Gaston—WND-304 (Channels B-1-4). Nash Community College, Box 744, Old Carriage Rd., Rocky Mount, NC 27804. Authorized power: 50-w. each. Antenna: 315-ft. above ground. Lat. 36° 30' 12", long. 77° 44' 47". Transmitter: Hwy. 46, Gaston. Equipment: Emcee transmitter; Andrew antenna.

Gaston—WND-305 (Channels C-1-4). Edgecomb Community College, 2009 W. Wilson St., Tarboro, NC 27886. Authorized power: 50-w. each. Antenna: 315-ft. above ground. Lat. 36° 30' 12", long. 77° 44' 47". Transmitter: Hwy. 46, Gaston. Equipment: Emcee transmitter; Andrew antenna.

Gaston—WND-307 (Channels D-1-4). U. of North Carolina, Box 2688, Chapel Hill, NC 27515. Authorized power: 50-w. each. Antenna: 315-ft. above ground. Lat. 36° 30' 12", long. 77° 44' 47". Transmitter: Hwy. 46. Equipment: Emcee transmitter; Andrew antenna.

Gaston—WND-306 (Channels G-1-4). Roanoke Rapids Graded School District, 536 Hamilton St., Roanoke Rapids, NC 27870. Authorized power: 50-w. each. Antenna: 315-ft. above ground. Lat. 36° 30' 12", long. 77° 44' 47". Transmitter: Hwy. 46. Equipment: Emcee transmitter; Andrew antenna.

Greensboro—WHR-649 (Channels A-1-4). U. of North Carolina, 910 Raleigh Rd., Chapel Hill, NC 27514. Authorized power: 10-w. each. Antenna: 200-ft. above ground. Lat. 36° 04' 51", long. 79° 46' 10". Transmitter: North Carolina Agricultural & Technical U.

Greensboro—WHR-683 (Channels C-1-4). North Carolina Agricultural & Technical State U., 316 Dowdy Bldg., 1601 E. Market St., Greensboro, NC 27411. Phone: 910-334-7810. Authorized power: 10-w. each. Antenna: 400-ft. above ground. Lat. 36° 04' 58", long. 79° 46' 08". Transmitter: Lindsay St. & Hwy. 29.

Greenville—WHR-596 (Channels A-1-4). U. of North Carolina, 910 Raleigh Rd., Chapel Hill, NC 27514. Authorized power: 10-w. each. Antenna: 251-ft. above ground. Lat. 35° 34' 15", long. 77° 22' 49". Transmitter: S. Evans St., 2-mi. S of Greenville Equipment: Comwave transmitter; Andrew antenna.

Greenville—WND-299 (Channels B-1-4). East Carolina U., 5th St., Greenville, NC 27858. Authorized power: 10-w. each. Antenna: 228-ft. above ground. Lat. 35° 34' 15", long. 77° 22' 49". Transmitter: S. Evan St., 2-mi. S of Greenville. Equipment: Comwave transmitter; Andrew antenna.

Greenville—WND-300 (Channels C-1-4). Wayne Community College, 3000 Wayne Memorial Dr., Goldsboro, NC 27533. Authorized power: 10-w. each. Antenna: 228-ft. above ground. Lat. 35° 34' 15", long. 77° 22' 49". Transmitter: S. Evan St., 2-mi. S of Greenville. Equipment: Comwave transmitter; Andrew antenna.

Greenville—WND-302 (Channels D-1-4). Pitt Community College, Drawer 7007, Hwy. 11 S, Greenville, NC 27835. Authorized power: 10-w. each. Antenna: 228-ft. above ground. Lat. 35° 34' 15", long. 77° 22' 49". Transmitter: S. Evans St., 2-mi. S of Greenville. Equipment: Comwave transmitter; Andrew antenna.

Greenville—WND-301 (Channels G-1-4). Wilson Tech Community College, 902 Herring Ave., Wilson, NC 27893. Authorized power: 4-w. each. Antenna: 228-ft. above ground. Lat. 35° 34' 15", long. 77° 22' 49". Transmitter: S. Evans St., 2-mi. S of Greenville. Equipment: Comwave transmitter; Andrew antenna.

McCain—WND-394 (Channels B-1-4). Sandhills Community College, 2200 Airport Rd., Pinehurst, NC 28374. Authorized power: 50-w. each. Antenna: 315-ft. above ground. Lat. 35° 02' 43", long. 79° 19' 36". Transmitter: 1500-ft. NE of Hwy. 211. Equipment: Emcee transmitter; Andrew antenna.

McCain—WND-396 (Channels C-1-4). Central Carolina Community College, 1105 Kelley Dr., Sanford, NC 27330. Authorized power: 50-w. each. Antenna: 315-ft. above ground. Lat. 35° 02' 43", long. 79° 19' 36". Transmitter: 1500-ft. NE of Hwy 211. Equipment: Emcee transmitter; Andrew antenna.

McCain—WND-395 (Channels D-1-4). Hoke County Board of Education, 310 Wooley St., Raeford, NC 28376. Authorized power: 50-w. each. Antenna: 315-ft. above ground. Lat. 35° 02' 43", long. 79° 19' 36". Transmitter: 1500-ft. NE of Hwy. 211. Equipment: Emcee transmitter; Andrew antenna.

McCain—WND-399 (Channels G-1-4). Moore County Schools, 160 Pickney Rd., Carthage, NC 28327. Authorized power: 50-w. each. Antenna: 315-ft. above ground. Lat. 35° 02' 43", long. 79° 19' 36". Transmitter: 1500-ft. NE of Hwy. 211. Equipment: Emcee transmitter; Andrew antenna.

Raleigh—WHR-590 (Channels E-1-4). U. of North Carolina, 910 Raleigh Rd., Chapel Hill, NC 27514. Authorized power: 10-w. each. Antenna: 190-ft. above ground. Lat. 35° 47' 00", long. 78° 41' 15". Transmitter: Raleigh Studio, U. of North Carolina, Western Blvd.

Raleigh & Wake County—WHR-619 (Channels C-1-4). North Carolina State U., Room 202, McKimmon Center, Raleigh, NC 27695-7401. Phone: 919-515-7730. Fax: 919-515-5778.
E-mail: tom_russell@ncsu.edu.
Web site: http://www2.ncsu.edu/oit.
Authorized power: 50-w. each. Antenna: 404-ft. above ground. Lat. 35° 46' 43", long. 78° 38' 23". Transmitter: D. H. Hill Library, Hillsborough St., North Carolina State U. campus. Equipment: Comwave transmitter; Andrew antenna.

Wilmington—WND-461 (Channels A-1-4). Cape Fear Community College, 411 N. Front St., Wilmington, NC 28401. Phone: 910-251-5130. Authorized power: 50-w. each. Antenna: 436-ft. above ground. Lat. 34° 12' 35", long. 77° 56' 53". Transmitter: Adams St. & Burnett Blvd. Equipment: Emcee transmitter; Andrew antenna.

Wilmington—WND-463 (Channels C-1-4). The Crary School, 1739 Point Winward Place, Shallotte, NC 28459. Authorized power: 50-w. each. Antenna: 436-ft. above ground. Lat. 34° 12' 35", long. 77° 56' 53". Transmitter: Adams St. & Burnett Blvd. Equipment: Emcee transmitter; Andrew antenna.

Wilmington—WND-459 (Channels D-1-4). U. of North Carolina, Box 2688, Chapel Hill, NC 27515. Authorized power: 50-w. each. Antenna: 285-ft. above ground. Lat. 34° 10' 30", long. 77° 56' 30". Transmitter: 0.5-mi. S of Wilmington. Equipment: Comwave transmitter; Bogner antenna.

Winston-Salem—WHR-818 (Channels B-1-4). Winston-Salem State U., Box 19473, Winston-Salem, NC 27110. Phone: 336-750-2680. Fax: 336-750-2636.
E-mail: edwardsr@wssumits.wssu.edu.
Web site: http://www.wssu.edu.
Authorized power: 10-w. each. Antenna: 327-ft. above ground. Lat. 36° 05' 24", long. 80° 13' 20". Transmitter: Winston-Salem State U. campus, off Reynolds Park Rd.

North Dakota

Amenia—WNC-357 (Channels A-1-4). Northern Cass School District No. 97, 135 2nd Ave., Arthur, ND 58006. Phone: 701-967-8344. Fax: 701-967-8931.
E-mail: hhaberma@sendit.nodak.edu.
Web site: http://northerncass.k12.nd.us.
Authorized power: 20-w. each. Antenna: 496-ft. above ground. Lat. 47° 00' 48", long. 97° 13' 07". Transmitter: 1.25-mi. E of Amenia. Equipment: ITS transmitter; Andrew antenna.
Leased to Cass County Electronic Cooperative, 1442 W. Main Ave., West Fargo, ND 58078. Phone: 701-428-3292.

Amenia—WNC-569 (Channels B-1-4). Cass Valley North No. 76, Box 38, 306 Aldrich, Argusville, ND 58005. Phone: 701-484-5511. Authorized power: 20-w. each. Antenna: 1178-ft. above ground. Lat. 47° 00' 48", long. 97° 11' 37". Transmitter: 1.25-mi. E of Amenia. Equipment: ITS transmitter; Andrew antenna.
Leased to Cass County Electronic Cooperative, 4100 32nd Ave. SW, Fargo, ND 58102. Phone: 701-277-4400.

Amenia—WLX-999 (Channels D-1-4). Page Public Schools, 630 May Ave., Page, ND 58064. Authorized power: 20-w. each. Antenna: 496-ft. above ground. Lat. 47° 00' 48", long. 97° 11' 37". Transmitter: 1.25-mi. E of Amenia. Equipment: ITS transmitter; Andrew antenna.

Bowdon—WLX-944 (Channel A-4). Bowdon Public Schools, Box 429, Bowdon, ND 58418. Phone: 701-962-3477. Fax: 701-962-3476. Authorized power: 50-w. Antenna: 90-ft. above ground. Lat. 47° 28' 13", long. 99° 42' 18". Transmitter: Adjacent to Bowdon Public School. Equipment: ITS transmitter; Andrew antenna.

Carrington—WLX-909 (Channels C-1-4). New Rockford Public Schools, 430 First Ave. N, New Rockford, ND 58356. Phone: 701-947-5036. Fax: 701-947-2195. Authorized power: 50-w. each. Antenna: 496-ft. above ground. Lat. 47° 13' 41", long. 99° 12' 01". Transmitter: 14.5-mi. S & 3-mi. W of Carrington. Equipment: Emcee transmitter; Andrew antenna. Sale pends to Wimbledon/Courtenay Public School District, 208 Center St., Carrington, ND 58421.

Carrington—WLX-439 (Channels G-1-2). Jamestown High School, Box 269, Jamestown, ND 58402. Authorized power: 50-w. each. Antenna: 490-ft. above ground. Lat. 47° 13' 41", long. 99° 12' 01". Transmitter: 14.5-mi. S, 3-mi. E of Carrington. Equipment: Emcee transmitter; Andrew antenna.

Carrington—WNC-543 (Channels G-3-4). Midkota Public School, Box 98, Glenfield, ND 58443. Authorized power: 50-w. each. Antenna: 496-ft. above ground. Lat. 47° 13' 41", long. 99° 12' 01". Transmitter: 14.5-mi. S, 3-mi. E of Carrington. Equipment: Emcee transmitter; Andrew antenna.

Fargo—WHR-602 (Channels A-1-4). Prairie Public Television, 207 N. 5th St., Fargo, ND 58108-3240. Phone: 701-239-7504. Fax: 701-239-7655.
E-mail: jackanderson@pol.org.
Authorized power: 10-w. each. Antenna: 250-ft. above ground. Lat. 46° 40' 03", long. 96° 48' 06". Transmitter: 2.5-mi. S of Fargo on U.S. Hwy. 81.

Fargo—WHR-765 (Channels C-1-4). Minnesota Public Radio, 45 E. 7th St., St. Paul, MN 55101. Phone: 651-290-1259. Fax: 651-290-1260. Authorized power: 50-w. each. Antenna: 1716-ft. above ground. Lat. 46° 42' 11", long. 96° 12' 57". Transmitter: 101 S. 2nd. Equipment: Comwave transmitter; Andrew antenna.
Leased to American Telecasting Inc., 5575 Tech Center Dr., Suite 300, Colorado Springs, CO 80919. Phone: 719-632-5544.

Fessenden—WLX-921 (Channel A-1). Fessenden Public Schools, Box 67, Fessenden, ND 58438. Phone: 701-547-3296. Fax: 701-547-3125. Authorized power: 2-w. Antenna: 90-ft. above ground. Lat. 47° 39' 07", long. 99° 37' 35". Transmitter: Adjacent to Fessenden Public School. Equipment: ITS transmitter; Andrew antenna.

Fort Ransom—WNC-274 (Channels A-1-4). Marion School. Authorized power: 50-w. each. Antenna: 445-ft. above ground. Lat. 46° 31' 25", long. 97° 57' 25". Transmitter: 1.5-mi. W of Fort Ransom. Equipment: ITS transmitter; Andrew antenna.

Fort Ransom—WNC-606 (Channels D-1-4). Enderlin School, 410-20 Bluff St., Enderlin, ND 58027. Phone: 701-437-2240. Authorized power: 50-w. each. Antenna: 451-ft. above ground. Lat. 46° 31' 25", long. 97° 57' 25". Transmitter: 1.5-mi. W of Fort Ransom. Equipment: ITS transmitter; Andrew antenna.

Inkster—WNC-443 (Channels D-1-4). Larimore Public School District No. 44, 300 Booth Ave., Larimore, ND 58251. Authorized power: 50-w. each. Antenna: 854-ft. above ground. Lat. 48° 10' 43", long. 97° 44' 16". Transmitter: 1.1-mi. S of Walsh & Grand Forks Counties boundary & 1.6-mi. W of Forrest River Colony. Equipment: ITS transmitter; Andrew antenna.

Inkster—WNC-444 (Channels G-1-4). Northwood Public School District No. 129, 204 S. Doheny St., Northwood, ND 58267. Authorized power: 50-w. each. Antenna: 854-ft. above ground. Lat. 48° 10' 43", long. 97° 44' 16". Transmitter: 1.1-mi. S of Walsh & Grand Forks Counties boundary & 1.6-mi. W of Forrest River Colony. Equipment: ITS transmitter; Andrew antenna.

Jamestown—WLX-942 (Channel A-3). Jamestown High School, Box 269, Jamestown, ND 58402. Authorized power: 5-w. Antenna: 150-ft. above ground. Lat. 46° 45' 13", long. 98° 43' 06". Transmitter: Adjacent to Jamestown High School. Equipment: ITS transmitter; Andrew antenna.

Kensal—WLX-982 (Channel D-4). Kensal Public School, Box 8, Kensal, ND 58455. Phone: 701-435-2857. Authorized power: 50-w. Antenna: 496-ft. above ground. Lat. 47° 13' 41", long. 99° 12' 01". Transmitter: 14.5-mi. S & 3-mi. E of Carrington. Equipment: Emcee transmitter; Andrew antenna. Sale pends to Pingree/Buchanan Public School District, 111 Lincoln Ave., Pingree, ND 58421.

Killdeer—WNC-745 (Channels B-1-4). Halliday High School, 188 4th St. S, Halliday, ND 58636. Authorized power: 50-w. each. Antenna: 409-ft. above ground. Lat. 47° 28' 17", long. 102° 55' 39". Transmitter: 8-mi. N & 9-mi. W of Killdeer. Equipment: Comwave transmitter; Andrew antenna.

Lefor—WLX-506 (Channels D-1-4). Trinity High School, Empire Rd. & 8th Ave. W, Dickinson, ND 58601. Authorized power: 50-w. each. Antenna: 485-ft. above ground. Lat. 46° 41' 37", long. 102° 37' 10". Transmitter: 3-mi. W, 1-mi. N of Lefor. Equipment: ITS transmitter; Andrew antenna.

Milton—WNC-553 (Channels C-1-4). Grafton Public School District No. 3, 1548 School Rd., Grafton, ND 58237. Phone: 701-352-1930. Fax: 701-352-1943.
E-mail: jubjorns@sendit.nodak.edu.
Authorized power: 50-w. each. Antenna: 411-ft. above ground. Lat. 48° 37' 44", long. 98° 00' 35". Transmitter: 1.2-mi. E of Milton. Equipment: ITS transmitter; Andrew antenna.

Pingree—WLX-970 (Channel B-3). Pingree-Buchanan Public Schools, 111 Lincoln Ave., Pingree, ND 58476. Phone: 701-252-5563. Fax: 701-252-2245.
E-mail: pbhs@daktel.com.
Authorized power: 5-w. Antenna: 66-ft. above ground. Lat. 47° 09' 39", long. 98° 54' 34". Transmitter: adjacent to Pingree Public Schools. Equipment: ITS transmitter; Mark antenna.

Scranton—WNC-744 (Channels B-1-4). Scranton High School, First & Fries Sts., Scranton, ND 58653. Phone: 701-275-8897. Authorized power: 50-w. each. Antenna: 491-ft. above ground. Lat. 46° 10' 57", long. 103° 02' 56". Transmitter: 4.5-mi. E & 2.5-mi. N of Scranton. Equipment: Comwave transmitter; Andrew antenna.
Leased to CTC, 507 S. Main, Dickinson, ND 58601. Phone: 701-225-6061.

Walcott—WNC-573 (Channels C-1-4). Wahpeton School District, 1505 N. 11th, Wahpeton, ND 58075. Authorized power: 50-w. each. Antenna: 300-ft. above ground. Lat. 46° 32' 29", long. 96° 57' 36". Transmitter: 1.2-mi. WSW of Walcott. Equipment: ITS transmitter; Andrew antenna.

Ohio

Akron—WHN-707 (Channel G-2 & 4). Greater Cleveland Hospital Assn., 1226 Huron Rd., Cleveland, OH 44115. Authorized power: 10-w. Antenna: 939-ft. above ground. Lat. 41° 05' 00", long. 81° 37' 57". Transmitter: Driesbach Dr. Equipment: Emcee transmitter; Andrew antenna.

Belpre—WNC-938 (Channels B-1-4). Mountain State College, Spring at 16th, Parkersburg, WV 26101. Authorized power: 50-w. each. Antenna: 1801-ft. above ground. Lat. 39° 18' 36", long. 81° 35' 49". Transmitter: 2101 S. Cleveland-Massillon. Equipment: Comwave transmitter; Andrew antenna.

Bowling Green—WHR-617 (Channel B-1 & 3). Bowling Green State U., Bowling Green, OH 43403. Phone: 419-372-2700. Fax: 419-372-7048.
E-mail: info@wbgu.bgsu.edu.
Web site: http://www.wbgu.bgsu.edu.
Authorized power: 10-w. Antenna: 146-ft. above ground. Lat. 41° 22' 21", long. 83° 38' 30". Transmitter: Bowling Green.

Cincinnati—KHX-47 (Channels A-1-2). Board of Directors, U. of Cincinnati, Clifton Ave., Cincinnati, OH 45221. Phone: 513-558-5672. Fax: 513-558-4120. Authorized power: 100-w. each. Antenna: 177-ft. above ground. Lat. 39° 12' 01", long. 84° 31' 22". Transmitter: Sanders Hall, U. of Cincinnati. Equipment: Emcee transmitter; Andrew antenna.
Leased to Interactive Communications Inc.

Cincinnati—WHR-662 (Channels A-3-4). Board of Directors, U. of Cincinnati, College of Medicine, Mail Location 573, Cincinnati, OH 45267. Phone: 513-558-5672. Fax: 513-558-4120. Authorized power: 100-w. each. Antenna: 830-ft. above ground. Lat. 39° 12' 01", long. 84° 31' 22". Transmitter: 6015 Winston Rd. Equipment: Emcee transmitter; Andrew antenna.
Leased to Interactive Communications Inc.

Cincinnati—WND-313 (Channels B-1-4). Board of Education. Authorized power: 100-w. each. Antenna: 830-ft. above ground. Lat. 39° 12' 01", long. 84° 31' 22". Transmitter: 6015 Winton Rd. Equipment: Emcee transmitter; Andrew antenna.

Cincinnati—WLX-805 (Channels D-1-4). Board of Trustees, Mail Location 573, College of Medicine, Cincinnati, OH 45267. Authorized power: 100-w. each. Antenna: 839-ft. above ground. Lat. 39° 12' 01", long. 84° 31' 22". Transmitter: Sanders Hall, U. of Cincinnati. Equipment: Emcee transmitter; Andrew antenna.

Cincinnati—WLX-435 (Channels G-1-4). Hispanic Information & Telecommunications Network Inc., 3rd Floor, 449 Broadway, New York, NY 10016. Phone: 212-966-5660. Fax: 212-966-5725.
E-mail: email@hitn.org.
Web site: http://www.hitn.org.
Authorized power: 10-w. each. Antenna: 174-ft. above ground. Lat. 39° 06' 17", long. 84° 33' 23". Transmitter: 810 Matson Place. Equipment: Comwave transmitter; Andrew antenna.
Leased to People's Choice TV Corp., 5301 E. Broadway, Tucson, AZ 85711. Phone: 520-519-4400.

Cleveland—WAJ-20 (Channels A-1-4). ETV Assn. of Metropolitan Cleveland, 4300 Brookpark Rd., Cleveland, OH 44134. Phone: 216-398-2800. Fax: 216-749-2560.
E-mail: feedback@wviz.org.
Web site: http://www.wviz.org.
Authorized power: 50-w. each. Antenna: 1029-ft. above ground. Lat. 41° 23' 02", long. 81° 42' 06". Transmitter: 2861 W. Ridgewood Dr.
Leased to Popvision, 303 Ken-Mar Industrial Pkwy, Suite 355, Broadview Heights, OH 44147. Phone: 888-904-8862.

Cleveland—WHR-675 (Channel C-2 & 4). Greater Cleveland Hospital Assn., Playhouse Square, 1226 Huron Rd., Cleveland, OH 44115. Authorized power: 0.1-w. Antenna: 68-ft. above ground. Lat. 41° 30' 00", long. 81° 40' 58". Transmitter: 1226 Huron Rd. Equipment: Emcee transmitter; Anixter-Mark antenna.

Cleveland—WHR-776 (Channels D-1-4). Greater Cleveland Hospital Assn., Playhouse Square, 1226 Huron Rd., Cleveland, OH 44115. Authorized power: 10-w. each. Antenna: 190-ft. above ground. Lat. 41° 26' 48", long. 81° 30' 20". Transmitter: Robert Bishop Dr., Warrensville. Equipment: ITS transmitter; Andrew antenna.

Columbus—WLX-592 (Channels A-1-4). Views on Learning Inc., 200 Kenyon Ave., Elkhart, IN 46516. Phone & fax: 219-522-1725.
E-mail: jrueff@lsoc-vol.org.
Web site: http://www.lsoc-vol.org.
Authorized power: 50-w. each. Antenna: 573-ft. above ground. Lat. 39° 57' 44", long. 83° 00' 08". Transmitter: 50 W. Broad St. Equipment: ITS transmitter; Andrew antenna.
Leased to American Telecasting Inc., 5575 Tech Center Dr., Suite 300, Colorado Springs, CO 80919. Phone: 719-260-5533.

Columbus—WHR-532 (Channels B-1-4). Ohio State U., Telecommunications Center, 2400 Olentangy River Rd., Columbus, OH 43210. Authorized power: 10-w. each. Antenna: 149-ft. above ground. Lat. 40° 00' 41", long. 83° 01' 17". Transmitter: 125 E. 31st St. Equipment: Comwave transmitter; Andrew antenna.

Columbus—WLX-539 (Channels C-1-4). North American Catholic Educational Programming Foundation Inc., Box 40026, Providence, RI 02940-0026. Phone: 401-729-0900. Authorized power: 50-w. each. Antenna: 573-ft. above ground. Lat. 39° 57' 44", long. 83° 00' 08". Transmitter: 50 W. Broad St. Equipment: ITS transmitter; Andrew antenna.

Columbus—WGW-946 (Channels D-1-4). Ohio State U., College of Medicine, Columbus, OH 43210. Authorized power: 10-w. each. Antenna: 132-ft. above ground. Lat. 39° 59' 45", long. 83° 01' 04". Transmitter: Ohio State U., College of Medicine.

Columbus—WHR-523 (Channels F-1-4). Ohio State U. Telecommunications Center, Columbus, OH 43210. Authorized power: 10-w. each. Antenna: 146-ft. above ground. Lat. 40° 00' 41", long. 83° 01' 17". Transmitter: Fawcett Center for Tomorrow, Ohio State U. campus, Columbus. Equipment: Emcee transmitter; Andrew antenna.

Copley—WNC-926 (Channels B-1-4). Northeastern Educational TV of Ohio, Box 5191, 1750 Campus Center Dr., Kent, OH 44240. Authorized power: 50-w. each. Antenna: 1801-ft. above ground. Lat. 41° 04' 58", long. 81° 38' 00". Transmitter: 2101 Cleveland-Massillion Rd. Equipment: Emcee transmitter; Bogner antenna.

Copley—WNC-940 (Channels D-1-4). Copley-Fairlawn City Schools, 3797 Ridgewood Rd., Copley, OH 44321. Authorized power: 50-w. each. Antenna: 1801-ft. above ground. Lat. 41° 04' 58", long. 81° 38' 00". Transmitter: 2101 S. Cleveland-Massillon Rd. Equipment: Emcee transmitter; Bogner antenna.

Copley—WNC-939 (Channels G-1-4). Revere Local Schools, 3496 Everett Rd., Bath, OH 44210. Authorized power: 50-w. each. Antenna: 1801-ft. above ground. Lat. 41° 04' 58", long. 81° 38' 00". Transmitter: 2101 S. Cleveland-Massillon. Equipment: Emcee transmitter; Bogner antenna.

Cridersville—WLX-987 (Channels A-1-4). Cory Rawson Local School, 3930 County Rd. 26, Rawson, OH 45881. Phone: 419-963-3415. Fax: 419-963-4400. Authorized power: 50-w. each. Antenna: 1108-ft. above ground. Lat. 40° 38' 03", long. 84° 12' 29". Transmitter: 19507 State Rte. 501. Equipment: Comwave transmitter; Andrew antenna. Requests change to 63-w. each; 245-ft. above ground, lat. 40° 22' 21", long. 83° 39' 26"; transmitter to 0.13-mi. S of Rtes. 540 & 533 intersection.
Leased to W.A.T.C.H. TV, 3225 W. Elm St., Lima, OH 45805. Phone: 419-999-2824.

Cridersville—WLX-979 (Channels B-1-4). Indian Lake Local Schools, 6210 State Rte. 235 N, Lewiston, OH 43333. Authorized power: 50-w. each. Antenna: 1108-ft. above ground. Lat. 40° 38' 03", long. 84° 12' 29". Transmitter: 19507 State Rte. 501. Equipment: Comwave transmitter; Andrew antenna. Requests change to 63-w. each; 245-ft. above ground, lat. 40° 22' 21", long. 83° 39' 26"; transmitter to 0.13-mi. S of intersection of Rtes. 540 & 533.

Cridersville—WLX-977 (Channels C-1-4). St. Mary's City Schools, 101 W. South St., St. Mary's, OH 45885. Phone: 419-394-4312. Fax: 419-394-5638. Authorized power: 50-w. each. Antenna: 1108-ft. above ground. Lat. 40° 38' 03", long. 84° 12' 29". Transmitter: 19507 State Rte. 501. Equipment: Comwave transmitter; Andrew antenna. Requests change to 63-w. each; 245-ft. above ground, lat. 40° 22' 21", long. 83° 39' 26"; transmitter to 0.13-mi. S of Rtes. 540 & 533 intersection.

Cridersville—WLX-762 (Channels D-1-4). Parkway Local Schools, 401 S. Franklin St., Rockford, OH 45882. Authorized power: 50-w. each. Antenna: 1108-ft. above ground. Lat. 40° 38' 03", long. 84° 12' 29". Transmitter: Rte. 501. Equipment: Comwave transmitter; Andrew antenna. Requests change to 63-w. each; 245-ft. above ground, lat. 40° 22' 21", long. 83° 39' 26"; transmitter to 0.13-mi. S of Rtes. 540 & 533 intersection.

Dayton—WHR-537 (Channels A-1-4). Greater Dayton Public Television Inc., 110 S. Jefferson St., Dayton, OH 45402-2415. Phone: 513-220-1600. Fax: 513-220-1642. Authorized power: 50-w. each. Antenna: 825-ft. above ground. Lat. 39° 43' 16", long. 85° 15' 00". Transmitter: WPTD(TV) tower, near Lyleburn Rd., 4-mi. SW of Dayton. Equipment: ITS transmitter; Andrew antenna.

Dayton—WLX-573 (Channels B-1-4). Sinclair Community College, 444 W. 3rd St., Dayton, OH 45402. Phone: 937-226-3050. Fax: 937-226-3080.
E-mail: sjonas@sinclair.edu.
Web site: http://www.sinclair.edu.
Authorized power: 50-w. each. Antenna: 817-ft. above ground. Lat. 39° 43' 16", long. 84° 15' 00". Transmitter: 3896 Guthrie Rd. Equipment: ITS transmitter; Andrew antenna.
Leased to Technivision Inc., 800 W. Airport Freeway, Suite 414, Irving, TX 75602.

Dayton—WHR-939 (Channels C-1-4). Greater Dayton Public Television Inc., 110 S. Jefferson St., Dayton, OH 45402-2415. Phone: 513-220-1600. Fax: 513-220-1642. Authorized power: 50-w. each. Antenna: 825-ft. above ground. Lat. 39° 43' 16", long. 85° 15' 00". Transmitter: WPTD(TV) tower, near Lyleburn Rd., 4-mi. SW of Dayton. Equipment: ITS transmitter; Andrew antenna.

Dayton—WLX-568 (Channels D-1-4). Wright State U., 104 TV Center, Dayton, OH 45435. Phone: 513-873-3685. Fax: 513-873-4891. Authorized power: 50-w. each. Antenna: 817-ft. above ground. Lat. 39° 43' 16", long. 85° 15' 00". Transmitter: 3896 Guthrie Rd. Equipment: ITS transmitter; Andrew antenna.
Leased to Omni-Vision of Dayton, 37 Lawrence Ave., Miamisburg, OH 45342. Phone: 513-866-7600.

Dayton—WLX-375 (Channels G-1-4). Hispanic Information & Telecommunications Network Inc., 3rd Floor, 449 Broadway, New York, NY 10013. Phone: 212-966-5660. Fax: 212-966-5725.
E-mail: email@hitn.org.
Web site: http://www.hitn.org.
Authorized power: 100-w. each. Antenna: 823-ft. above ground. Lat. 39° 43' 16", long. 84° 15' 00". Transmitter: 3896 Guthrie Rd. Equipment: Emcee transmitter; Andrew antenna.
Leased to CS Wireless Systems Inc., 1101 Summit Ave., Plano, TX 75074. Phone: 972-398-5300.

Elyria—WHR-517 (Channels D-2-4). Greater Cleveland Hospital Assn., 1226 Huron Rd., Cleveland, OH 44115. Lat. 41° 21' 57", long. 82° 05' 52".

Elyria—WHR-777 (Channels G-1-4). Lorain County Community College, 1500 N. Abbe Rd., Elyria, OH 44035. Phone: 440-366-4027. Fax: 440-366-4071.
E-mail: tbedocs@lorainccc.edu.
Authorized power: 10-w. each. Antenna: 299-ft. above ground. Lat. 41° 24' 38", long. 82° 04' 11". Transmitter: 1005 N. Abbe Rd. Equipment: Emcee transmitter; Andrew antenna.

Gageville—WHR-450 (Channel B-1). Catholic Diocese of Youngstown, 144 W. Wood St., Youngstown, OH 44503. Phone: 216-553-2243. Fax: 216-533-1076. Authorized power: 10-w. Antenna: 377-ft. above ground. Lat. 41° 51' 39", long. 80° 40' 44". Transmitter: Wright St. between Gulf Rd. & I-90.

Kirtland—WHN-700 (Channels G-2-4). Greater Cleveland Hospital Assn., Playhouse Square, 1226 Huron Rd., Cleveland, OH 44115. Authorized power: 10-w. each. Antenna: 190-ft. above ground. Lat. 41° 26' 48", long. 81° 30' 20". Transmitter: Robert Bishop Dr., Warrensville.

Lykens—WLX-527 (Channels A-1-4). Buckeye Central Local School District, 306 S. Kibler, New Washington, OH 44854. Authorized power: 10-w. each. Antenna: 696-ft. above ground. Lat. 40° 54' 13", long. 83° 03' 13". Transmitter: Bethel Rd., 2-mi. W of Broken Sword. Equipment: Emcee transmitter; Andrew antenna.

Lykens—WLX-885 (Channels B-1-4). New Riegel Local School District, 44 N. Perry St., New Riegel, OH 44853. Authorized power: 10-w. each. Antenna: 696-ft. above ground. Lat. 40° 54' 13", long. 83° 03' 13". Transmitter: Bethel Rd., 2-mi. W of Broken Sword. Equipment: Comwave transmitter; Andrew antenna.

Lykens—WLX-532 (Channels C-1-4). Mohawk Local School District, 295 S. No. 231, Sycamore, OH 44882. Phone: 419-927-2414. Fax: 419-927-2393. Authorized power: 10-w. each.

Antenna: 696-ft. above ground. Lat. 40° 54' 13", long. 83° 03' 13". Transmitter: Bethel Rd., 2-mi. W of Broken Sword. Equipment: Emcee transmitter; Andrew antenna.
Leased to Nucentrix Broadband Networks, 200 Chisholm Place, Suite 200, Plano, TX 75075. Phone: 972-423-9494. Fax: 972-423-0819.

Lykens—WLX-528 (Channels D-1-4). Carey Exempted Village Schools. Authorized power: 10-w. each. Antenna: 696-ft. above ground. Lat. 40° 54' 13", long. 83° 03' 13". Transmitter: Bethel Rd., 2-mi. W of Broken Sword. Equipment: Emcee transmitter; Andrew antenna.

Lykens—WLX-529 (Channels G-1-4). Seneca East School District, 109 Seneca, Attica, OH 44854. Authorized power: 10-w. each. Antenna: 696-ft. above ground. Lat. 40° 54' 13", long. 83° 03' 13". Transmitter: Bethel Rd., 2-mi. W of Broken Sword. Equipment: ITS transmitter; Emcee antenna.

New Jerusalem—WNC-627 (Channels A-1-4). Cory Rawson Local School, 3930 County Rd., Rawson, OH 45881. Authorized power: 100-w. each. Antenna: 250-ft. above ground. Lat. 40° 22' 21", long. 83° 39' 26". Transmitter: 0.13-mi. S of Rtes. 540 & 533 intersection. Equipment: Comwave transmitter; Andrew antenna.

New Jerusalem—WNC-628 (Channels B-1-4). Indian Lake Local Schools, 6210 State Rte. 235 N, Lewiston, OH 43333. Authorized power: 100-w. each. Antenna: 250-ft. above ground. Lat. 40° 22' 21", long. 83° 39' 26". Transmitter: 0.13-mi. S of Rtes. 540 & 533 intersection. Equipment: Comwave transmitter; Andrew antenna.

New Jerusalem—WNC-525 (Channels C-1-4). St. Mary's City Schools, 101 W. South St., St. Mary's, OH 45885. Authorized power: 63-w. each. Antenna: 250-ft. above ground. Lat. 40° 22' 21", long. 83° 39' 26". Transmitter: 0.13-mi. S of Rtes. 540 & 533 intersection. Equipment: Comwave transmitter; Andrew antenna.

New Jerusalem—WNC-630 (Channels D-1-4). Parkway Local Schools, 401 S. Franklin St., Rockford, OH 45882. Authorized power: 0.1-w. each. Antenna: 76.2-ft. above ground. Lat. 40° 22' 21", long. 83° 39' 26". Transmitter: 0.13-mi. S of Rtes. 540 & 533 intersection. Equipment: Comwave transmitter; Andrew antenna.

New Jerusalem—WNC-629 (Channels G-1-4). Lima City Schools, 515 S. Camulet Ave., Lima, OH 45804. Authorized power: 100-w. each. Antenna: 250-ft. above ground. Lat. 40° 22' 21", long. 83° 39' 26". Transmitter: 0.13-mi. S of Rtes. 540 & 533 intersection. Equipment: Comwave transmitter; Andrew antenna.

Oxford—WHR-584 (Channels C-1-4). Greater Dayton Public Television Inc., 110 S. Jefferson St., Dayton, OH 45402. Phone: 937-220-1600. Fax: 937-220-1642. Authorized power: 100-w. each. Antenna: 280-ft. above ground. Lat. 39° 12' 01", long. 84° 31' 22". Transmitter: 310 Oak St. Equipment: Emcee transmitter; Andrew antenna.

Parma—KNZ-60 (Channel A-1). Parma Board of Education, Parma City School District, 6726 Ridge Rd., Parma, OH 44129. Phone: 440-885-8381. Fax: 440-885-2452. Lat. 41° 22' 18", long. 81° 41' 48". Transmitter: 3600 Dentzler Rd.
Leased to CS Wireless Systems Inc., 1101 Summit Ave., Plano, TX 75074. Phone: 972-730-3300.

Parma—WNC-508 (Channels D-1-4). Rockne Educational Television, 320 Hamilton St., Albion, NY 14411. Authorized power: 50-w. each. Antenna: 600-ft. above ground. Lat. 41° 23' 02", long. 81° 42' 06". Transmitter: 2861 W. Ridgewood Dr. Equipment: Emcee transmitter; Bogner antenna.

Parma—WGM-96 (Channel F-3). Parma Board of Education, Parma City School District, 6726 Ridge Rd., Parma, OH 44129. Phone: 216-885-8381. Fax: 216-885-8307. Authorized power: 0.0018-w. Antenna: 35-ft. above ground. Lat. 41° 21' 44", long. 81° 41' 56". Transmitter: Normandy H.S., 2400 W. Pleasant Valley Rd.
Leased to Metro-Ten, 5400 Transportation Blvd., Garfield Heights, OH 44125. Phone: 216-662-7125.

Salem—WHR-696 (Channel A-1). Catholic Diocese of Youngstown, 144 W. Wood St., Youngstown, OH 44503. Phone: 216-533-2243. Fax: 216-533-1907. Lat. 40° 54' 23", long. 80° 54' 40".
Leased to American Telecasting Inc., 5575 Tech Center Dr., Suite 300, Colorado Springs, CO 80919. Phone: 719-260-5533.

Toledo—WNC-247 (Channels A-1-4). Springfield Board of Education, 6900 Hall St., Holland, OH 43528. Authorized power: 50-w. each. Antenna: 419-ft. above ground. Lat. 41° 38' 48", long. 83° 36' 22". Transmitter: 716 Westwood Ave. Equipment: Emcee transmitter; Andrew antenna.

Toledo—WNC-246 (Channels B-1-4). Washington Local Schools, 3505 W. Lincolnshire Blvd., Toledo, OH 43606. Authorized power: 10-w. each. Antenna: 500-ft. above ground. Lat. 41° 40' 19", long. 83° 25' 07". Transmitter: Point Rd. Equipment: ITS transmitter; Andrew antenna.

Toledo—WNC-249 (Channels D-1-4). Swanton Local Schools, 108 N. Main St., Swanton, OH 43558. Authorized power: 50-w. each. Antenna: 419-ft. above ground. Lat. 41° 38' 48", long. 83° 36' 22". Transmitter: 716 Westwood Ave. Equipment: Emcee transmitter; Andrew antenna.

Toledo—WNC-248 (Channels G-1-4). Maumee Local Schools, 2345 Detroit Ave., Maumee, OH 43537. Authorized power: 20-w. each. Antenna: 508-ft. above ground. Lat. 41° 40' 09", long. 83° 25' 07". Transmitter: Point Rd. Equipment: ITS transmitter; Andrew antenna.

Wayne—WNC-360 (Channels A-1-4). Champion Local School District, 5759 Mahoning Ave. NW, Warren, OH 44483. Lat. 41° 31' 12", long. 80° 31' 41". Transmitter: 0.9-mi. S of Simmons Rd. & U.S. 322 intersection, 1-mi. W of Pymatuning Reservoir. Equipment: Comwave transmitter; Andrew antenna.

Wayne—WNC-232 (Channels C-1-4). Hubbard Exempted School District, 150 Hall Ave., Hubbard, OH 44425. Phone: 216-534-1921. Authorized power: 50-w. each. Antenna: 449-ft. above ground. Lat. 41° 31' 12", long. 80° 31' 41". Transmitter: 1-mi. W of Pymatuning Reservoir. Equipment: Comwave transmitter; Andrew antenna.

Wayne—WNC-387 (Channels D-1-4). Ledgemont Local School, 16200 Burrows Rd., Thompson, OH 44086. Authorized power: 50-w. each. Antenna: 859-ft. above ground. Lat. 41° 31' 12", long. 80° 31' 41". Transmitter: 0.9-mi. S of Simmons Rd. & U.S. 322 intersection, 10-mi. W of Pymatuning Reservoir. Equipment: Comwave transmitter; Andrew antenna.

Wick—WNC-315 (Channels G-1-4). Bloomfield-Mespo Local Schools, Box 229, Mesopotamia, OH 44439. Phone: 216-693-4125. Lat. 41° 31' 12", long. 80° 31' 41". Transmitter: 0.9-mi. S of Simmons Rd. & U.S. 322 intersection, 1-mi. W of Pymatuning Reservoir. Equipment: Comwave transmitter; Andrew antenna.

Youngstown—WNC-297 (Channels A-1-4). Boardman Local School District, 7410 Market St., Youngstown, OH 44512. Authorized power: 50-w. each. Antenna: 469-ft. above ground. Lat. 41° 03' 26", long. 80° 38' 22". Transmitter: 4040 Simon Rd. Equipment: Comwave transmitter; Andrew antenna.
Leased to American Telecasting of Youngstown Inc., 50 Karago Dr., Youngstown, OH 44512. Phone: 216-629-7550.

Youngstown—WLX-456 (Channels B-1-4). Catholic Diocese of Youngstown, 144 W. Wood St., Youngstown, OH 44503. Phone: 216-533-2243. Fax: 216-533-1907. Authorized power: 50-w. each. Antenna: 680-ft. above ground. Lat. 41° 03' 26", long. 80° 38' 22". Transmitter: Youngstown. Equipment: Emcee transmitter; ITS antenna.
Leased to American Telecasting, Inc., 50 Karago, Boardman, OH 44512. Phone: 330-629-7550.

Youngstown—WLX-851 (Channels C-1-4). North American Catholic Educational Programming Foundation Inc., Box 40026, Providence, RI 02940-0026. Phone: 401-729-0900. Authorized power: 50-w. each. Antenna: 469-ft. above ground. Lat. 41° 03' 26", long. 80° 38' 32". Transmitter: Youngstown. Equipment: Comwave transmitter; Andrew antenna.

Youngstown—WHN-701 (Channel C-1-4). Catholic Diocese of Youngstown, Box 430, Cansfield, OH 44406. Phone: 216-533-2243. Fax: 216-533-1907.
E-mail: ctny@connectinc.com.
Authorized power: 10-w. Antenna: 710-ft. above ground. Lat. 41° 03' 31", long. 80° 38' 47". Transmitter: 3930 Sunset Blvd., Youngstown.
Leased to American Telecasting Inc., 5575 Tech Center Dr., Suite 300, Colorado Springs, CO 80919. Phone: 719-260-5533.

Youngstown—WNC-298 (Channels D-1-4). Northeastern Educational TV of Ohio Inc., 1750 Campus Center Dr., Kent, OH 44240. Phone: 216-677-4549. Fax: 216-672-7995. Authorized power: 50-w. each. Antenna: 469-ft. above ground. Lat. 41° 03' 26", long. 80° 38' 22". Transmitter: 4040 Simon Rd. Equipment: Comwave transmitter; Andrew antenna.
Leased to American Telecasting of Youngstown, 50 Karago Dr., Boardman, OH 44512. Phone: 216-629-7550.

Youngstown—WNC-299 (Channels G-1-4). Youngstown State U., 410 Wick Ave., Youngstown, OH 44555. Authorized power: 50-w. each. Antenna: 469-ft. above ground. Lat. 41° 03' 26", long. 80° 38' 22". Transmitter: 4040 Simon Rd. Equipment: Comwave transmitter; Andrew antenna.

Oklahoma

Ada—WLX-650 (Channels A-1-4). Stratford Public School, 341 N. Oak, Stratford, OK 74872. Authorized power: 10-w. each. Antenna: 400-ft. above ground. Lat. 34° 43' 31", long. 96° 42' 14". Transmitter: Pontotoc County. Equipment: Comwave transmitter; Andrew antenna.

Ada—WLX-923 (Channels B-1-4). Valley View Regional Hospital, 430 N. Monta Vista, Ada, OK 74820. Authorized power: 10-w. each. Antenna: 400-ft. above ground. Lat. 34° 43' 31", long. 96° 42' 14". Transmitter: 2.75-mi. SSW of Ada. Equipment: Comwave transmitter; Andrew antenna.
Leased to Nucentrix Broadband Networks, 200 Chisholm Place, Suite 200, Plano, TX 75075. Phone: 972-423-9494. Fax: 972-423-0819.

Ada—WLX-812 (Channels C-1-4). Ada Public Schools, 1400 Stadium Dr., Ada, OK 74820. Authorized power: 10-w. each. Antenna: 400-ft. above ground. Lat. 34° 43' 31", long. 96° 42' 14". Transmitter: 2.75-mi. SSW of Ada. Equipment: Comwave transmitter; Andrew antenna.

Ada—WLX-935 (Channels D-1-4). Byng Public Schools, Rte. 3, Ada, OK 74820. Phone: 580-436-3020. Fax: 580-436-3052.
E-mail: byngsupt@chickasaw.com.
Authorized power: 10-w. each. Antenna: 400-ft. above ground. Lat. 34° 43' 31", long. 96° 42' 14". Transmitter: 2.75-mi. SSW of Ada. Equipment: Comwave transmitter; Andrew antenna.

Ada—WNC-362 (Channels G-1-4). East Central U., 104 Administration Bldg., Ada, OK 74820. Authorized power: 10-w. each. Antenna: 400-ft. above ground. Lat. 34° 43' 31", long. 96° 42' 14". Transmitter: 2.75-mi. SSW of Ada. Equipment: Comwave transmitter; Andrew antenna.

Altus—KGF-23 (Channels A-1-3). Oklahoma State Regents for Higher Education, State Capitol Complex, 500 Education Bldg., Oklahoma City, OK 73105. Phone: 405-524-9168. Fax: 405-521-6125. Authorized power: 10-w. each. Antenna: 90-ft. above ground. Lat. 34° 40' 14", long. 99° 20' 13". Equipment: Andrew antenna.

Altus—WNC-714 (Channels A-1-4). Altus Public School District 18, Box 558, 219 N. Lee, Altus, OK 73521. Authorized power: 10-w. each. Antenna: 20-ft. above ground. Lat. 34° 40' 52", long. 99° 09' 14". Transmitter: 9-mi. NE of Altus Municipal Airport runway. Equipment: Comwave transmitter; Andrew antenna.

Altus—WNC-758 (Channels B-1-4). Southwestern Oklahoma State U., 100 Campus Dr., Weatherford, OK 73096. Authorized power: 10-w. each. Antenna: 20-ft. above ground. Lat. 34° 40' 52", long. 99° 09' 14". Transmitter: 9-mi. NE of Altus Municipal Airport. Equipment: Comwave transmitter; Andrew antenna.

Altus—WNC-424 (Channels C-1-4). Navajo Public Schools, Box 84A, Rte. 2, Altus, OK 73521. Phone: 405-482-7742. Fax: 405-482-7749. Authorized power: 10-w. each. Antenna: 15-ft. above ground. Lat. 34° 40' 52", long. 99° 09' 14". Transmitter: 9-mi. NE of Altus Municipal Airport. Equipment: Comwave transmitter; Andrew antenna.

Altus—WNC-576 (Channels D-1-4). Southwest Area Vocational-Technical Center, 711 W. Tamarack, Altus, OK 73522. Authorized power: 10-w. each. Antenna: 20-ft. above ground. Lat. 34° 40' 52", long. 99° 09' 14". Transmitter: 9-mi. NE of Altus. Equipment: Comwave transmitter; Andrew antenna.

Altus—WNC-549 (Channels G-1-4). Olustee Public School, 606 E. 6th, Olustee, OK 73560. Authorized power: 10-w. each. Antenna: 20-ft. above ground. Lat. 34° 40' 52", long. 99° 09' 14". Transmitter: 9-mi. NE of Altus. Equipment: Comwave transmitter; Andrew antenna.

Ardmore—WAH-871 (Channels A-3-4). Oklahoma State Regents for Higher Education, State Capitol Complex, 500 Education Bldg., Oklahoma City, OK 73105. Phone: 405-524-9168. Fax: 405-521-6125. Authorized power: 10-w. each. Antenna: 312-ft. above ground. Lat. 34° 11' 10", long. 97° 04' 59". Transmitter: 1-mi. E of Ardmore.

Leased to Nucentrix Broadband Networks, 200 Chisholm Place, Suite 200, Plano, TX 75075. Phone: 972-423-9494.

Ardmore—WNC-498 (Channels B-1-4). East Central U., 104 Administration Bldg., Ada, OK 74820. Authorized power: 50-w. each. Antenna: 400-ft. above ground. Lat. 34° 21' 48", long. 97° 10' 48". Transmitter: 9-mi. NW of Ardmore. Equipment: Comwave transmitter; Andrew antenna.

Ardmore—WNC-497 (Channels G-1-4). Wilson School Independent School District No. 43, Box 730, Wilson, OK 73463. Phone: 405-668-2356. Fax: 405-668-2055.

E-mail: wilsonc@onenet.net.

Web site: http://www.onenet.net/~wilsonc/.

Authorized power: 50-w. each. Antenna: 400-ft. above ground. Lat. 34° 21' 48", long. 97° 10' 48". Transmitter: 9-mi. NW of Ardmore. Equipment: Comwave transmitter; Andrew antenna.

Bartlesville—WGM-91 (Channels C-1-3). Oklahoma State Regents for Higher Education, State Capitol Complex, 500 Education Bldg., Oklahoma City, OK 73105. Phone: 405-524-9169. Fax: 405-524-6125. Authorized power: 10-w. each. Antenna: 300-ft. above ground. Lat. 36° 45' 22", long. 95° 50' 51". Transmitter: 5-mi. E of Bartlesville. Equipment: Andrew antenna.

Leased to Nucentrix Broadband Networks, 200 Chisholm Place, Suite 200, Plano, TX 75075. Phone: 972-423-9494.

Broken Bow—WNC-973 (Channels C-1-4). Idabel Public Schools, Box 29, Idabel, OK 74745. Authorized power: 10-w. each. Antenna: 1102-ft. above ground. Lat. 34° 12' 31", long. 94° 46' 58". Transmitter: Hairpin Mountain. Equipment: Comwave transmitter; Andrew antenna.

Broken Bow—WNC-972 (Channels G-1-4). McCurtain County Higher Education Program, Box 178, Rte. 3, Idabel, OK 74745. Phone: 580-286-9431. Fax: 580-286-5247.

Web site: http://www.mchep.osrhe.edu.

Authorized power: 10-w. each. Antenna: 1102-ft. above ground. Lat. 34° 12' 31", long. 94° 46' 58". Transmitter: Hairpin Mountain. Equipment: Comwave transmitter; Andrew antenna.

Corn—WNC-577 (Channels C-1-4). Clinton Public Schools, Box 729, Clinton, OK 73601. Phone: 580-323-1800. Fax: 580-323-1804.

E-mail: eclinton@k12.ok.us.

Authorized power: 20-w. each. Antenna: 350-ft. above ground. Lat. 35° 23' 55", long. 98° 46' 55". Transmitter: 1.7-mi. N of Corn. Equipment: ITS transmitter; Andrew antenna.

Leased to Nucentrix Spectrum Resources Inc., 200 Chisholm Place, Suite 200, Plano, TX 75076. Phone: 972-633-2086.

Corn—WNC-580 (Channels D-1-4). Western Oklahoma Area Vocational-Technical School, Box 1469, Burns Flat, OK 73624. Authorized power: 20-w. each. Antenna: 348-ft. above ground. Lat. 35° 23' 55", long. 98° 46' 55". Transmitter: 1.7-mi. N of Corn. Equipment: Omni transmitter; Andrew antenna.

Enid—WNC-683 (Channels B-1-4). St. John Private School, 202 S. 5th, Okarche, OK 73762. Phone: 405-263-4488. Authorized power: 20-w. each. Antenna: 203-ft. above ground. Lat. 36° 23' 01", long. 97° 57' 43". Transmitter: 2.5-mi. WSW of Enid. Equipment: Comwave transmitter; Andrew antenna.

Enid—WNC-568 (Channels D-1-4). Phillips U., 100 S. University Ave., Enid, OK 73701. Authorized power: 50-w. each. Antenna: 1289-ft. above ground. Lat. 36° 25' 14", long. 98° 01' 12". Transmitter: 4-mi. SSW of County Rds. 45 & 132 intersection. Equipment: Comwave transmitter; Andrew antenna.

Fort Gibson—WNC-542 (Channels A-2-4). Okay Public Schools, Box 830, Okay, OK 74446. Authorized power: 10-w. each. Antenna: 407-ft. above ground. Lat. 35° 47' 38", long. 95° 06' 20". Transmitter: Red Berry Mountain. Equipment: Comwave transmitter; Andrew antenna.

Fort Gibson—WNC-516 (Channels C-1-4). Indian Capital Area Voc-Tech, 2403 N. 41st St. E, Muskogee, OK 74403. Phone: 918-682-1965. Fax: 918-682-5595. Authorized power: 10-w. each. Antenna: 407-ft. above ground. Lat. 35° 47' 38", long. 95° 06' 20". Transmitter: Red Berry Mountain, 7.5-mi. E of Fort Gibson. Equipment: Comwave transmitter; Andrew antenna.

Glencoe—WLX-845 (Channels A-1-4). Perry Public Schools, 900 Fir Ave., Perry, OK 73077. Authorized power: 25-w. each. Antenna: 345-ft. above ground. Lat. 36° 12' 17", long. 96° 59' 54". Transmitter: 1.3-mi. S of Stillwater Connection Rd. Equipment: Comwave transmitter; Andrew antenna. Requests change to 854-ft. above ground, lat. 36° 11' 12", long. 96° 50' 17"; transmitter to 6-mi. E of Stillwater & 5-mi. N of Hwy. 51.

Glencoe—WLX-890 (Channels B-1-4). Morrison Public Schools, Box 176, Morrison, OK 73061. Phone: 580-724-3390. Fax: 580-724-3004. Authorized power: 25-w. each. Antenna: 345-ft. above ground. Lat. 36° 12' 17", long. 96° 59' 54". Transmitter: 1.3-mi. S of Stillwater Connection Rd. & 4.4-mi. WSW of Glencoe. Equipment: Comwave transmitter; Andrew antenna. Requests change to 854-ft. above ground, lat. 36° 11 12", long. 96° 50' 17"; transmitter to 6-mi. E of Stillwater & 5-mi. N of Hwy. 51.

Leased to Nucentrix Broadband Networks, 200 Chisholm Place, Suite 200, Plano, TX 75075. Phone: 972-423-9494. Fax: 972-423-0819.

Glencoe—WNC-227 (Channels C-1-4). Ripley Schools, Box 97, Ripley, OK 74062. Phone: 918-372-4242. Fax: 918-372-4608. Authorized power: 25-w. each. Antenna: 854-ft. above ground. Lat. 36° 12' 17", long. 96° 59' 54". Transmitter: 6-mi. E of Stillwater & 5-mi. N of Hwy. 51, near Glencoe. Equipment: Comwave transmitter; Andrew antenna.

Leased to Nucentrix Broadband Networks, 200 Chisholm Place, Suite 200, Plano, TX 75075. Phone: 972-423-9494. Fax: 972-423-0819.

Glencoe—WNC-280 (Channels D-1-4). Frontier Public Schools, Box 130, Red Rock, OK 74651. Phone: 580-723-4361. Fax: 580-723-4516.

E-mail: shiever@pc253.frontier.osrhe.edu.

Web site: http://pc65.frontier.osrhe.edu.

Authorized power: 25-w. each. Antenna: 854-ft. above ground. Lat. 36° 11' 12", long. 96° 50' 17". Transmitter: 6-mi. E of Stillwater, 5-mi. N of Hwy. 51. Equipment: Comwave transmitter; Andrew antenna.

Leased to Nucentrix Broadband Networks, 200 Chisholm Place, Suite 200, Plano, TX 75075. Phone: 972-423-9494. Fax: 972-423-0819.

Glencoe—WLX-849 (Channels G-1-4). Yale Public Schools, 315 E. Chicago, Yale, OK 74085. Phone: 918-387-2334. Fax: 918-387-2503. Authorized power: 25-w. each. Antenna: 345-ft. above ground. Lat. 36° 12' 17", long. 96° 59' 54". Transmitter: 1.3-mi. S of Stillwater Connection Rd. Equipment: Comwave transmitter; Andrew antenna. Requests change to 854-ft. above ground, lat. 36° 11' 12", long. 96° 50' 17"; transmitter to 6-mi. E of Stillwater & 5-mi. N of Hwy. 51.

Leased to Nucentrix Broadband Networks, 200 Chisholm Place, Suite 200, Plano, TX 75075. Phone: 972-423-9494. Fax: 972-423-0819.

Heavener—KGF-24 (Channels A-1-2). Oklahoma State Regents for Higher Education, State Capitol Complex, 500 Education Bldg., Oklahoma City, OK 73105. Phone: 405-524-9169. Fax: 405-524-6125. Authorized power: 10-w. each. Antenna: 110-ft. above ground. Lat. 34° 56' 35", long. 94° 33' 09". Transmitter: Poteau Mountain. Equipment: Andrew antenna.

Hocker—WNC-520 (Channel A1-). Western Oklahoma Area Vocational-Technical School, Box 1469, 621 Sooner, Burns Flat, OK 73624. Phone: 405-562-3184. Authorized power: 20-w. Antenna: 358-ft. above ground. Lat. 35° 18' 04", long. 99° 30' 32". Transmitter: Hwys. 152 & 34. Equipment: ITS transmitter; Andrew antenna.

Hocker—WNC-562 (Channels B-1-4). Southern Oklahoma State U., 100 Campus Dr., Weatherford, OK 73096. Authorized power: 20-w. each. Antenna: 678-ft. above ground. Lat. 35° 18' 04", long. 99° 30' 32". Transmitter: 3800-ft. NNW of Hwys. 152 & 34 junction. Equipment: ITS transmitter; Andrew antenna.

Hocker—WNC-722 (Channels D-1-4). Oklahoma State U., 107 Whitehurst Hall, Stillwater, OK 74078. Authorized power: 20-w. each. Antenna: 109-ft. above ground. Lat. 35° 18' 04", long. 99° 30' 32". Transmitter: 3800-ft. NNW of Hwys. 154 & 34 junction. Equipment: ITS transmitter; Andrew antenna.

Holdenville—WLX-553 (Channels A-1-4). Holdenville School District, 415 Grimes, Holdenville, OK 74848. Authorized power: 50-w. each. Antenna: 704-ft. above ground. Lat. 35° 03' 30", long. 96° 18' 32". Transmitter: 2-mi. S of U.S. Hwy. 270, 5.5-mi. ESE of Holdenville. Equipment: Comwave transmitter; Andrew antenna.

Holdenville—WLX-554 (Channels B-1-4). Wewoka Public Schools, 1121 S. Okfuskee, Wewoka, OK 74884. Authorized power: 50-w. each. Antenna: 704-ft. above ground. Lat. 35° 03' 30", long. 96° 18' 32". Transmitter: 2-mi. S of U.S. Hwy. 270, 5.5-mi. ESE of Holdenville. Equipment: Comwave transmitter; Andrew antenna.

Holdenville—WLX-507 (Channels C-1-4). Mass Public Schools, Box 57, Rte. 2, Holdenville, OK 74848. Phone: 405-379-2273. Fax: 405-379-2333. Authorized power: 50-w. each. Antenna: 704-ft. above ground. Lat. 35° 03' 30", long. 96° 18' 32". Transmitter: 2-mi. S of U.S. Hwy. 270, 5.5-mi. ESE of Holdenville. Equipment: Comwave transmitter; Andrew antenna.

Holdenville—WLX-505 (Channels D-1-4). Wetumpka Public Schools I-005, 410 E. Benson, Wetumpka, OK 74883. Authorized power: 50-w. each. Antenna: 704-ft. above ground. Lat. 35° 03' 30", long. 96° 18' 32". Transmitter: 2-mi. S of U.S. Hwy. 270, 5.5-mi. ESE of Holdenville. Equipment: Comwave transmitter; Andrew antenna.

Lawton—WAH-862 (Channels A-1-2). Oklahoma State Regents for Higher Education, State Capitol Complex, 500 Education Bldg., Oklahoma City, OK 73105. Phone: 405-524-9169. Fax: 405-521-6125. Authorized power: 50-w. each. Antenna: 348-ft. above ground. Lat. 34° 36' 27", long. 98° 16' 26". Transmitter: SE 1/4 sec. 20, T2N, R10W, approximately 7-mi. E of Lawton. Equipment: Andrew antenna.

Leased to Nucentrix Broadband Networks, 200 Chisholm Place, Suite 200, Plano, TX 75075. Phone: 972-423-9494. Fax: 972-423-0819.

Lawton—WNC-499 (Channels A-3-4). Oklahoma State U., 107 Whitehurst Hall, Stillwater, OK 74078. Authorized power: 50-w. each. Antenna: 500-ft. above ground. Lat. 34° 26' 27", long. 98° 16' 26". Transmitter: Hwy. 7 & Trail Ridge Rd. Equipment: Comwave transmitter; Andrew antenna.

Lawton—WNC-757 (Channels B-1-4). Red River Area Vocational Technical School, 3300 W. Bois D'Arc, Duncan, OK 73533. Authorized power: 50-w. each. Antenna: 499-ft. above ground. Lat. 34° 36' 27", long. 98° 16' 26". Transmitter: Hwy. 7 & Trail Ridge Rd. intersection. Equipment: Comwave transmitter; Andrew antenna.

Lawton—WLX-350 (Channels C-1-4). Inc. North American Catholic Educational Programming Foundation, Box 40026, Providence, RI 02940-0026. Phone: 401-729-0900. Lat. 34° 36' 27", long. 98° 16' 26".

Lawton—WNC-545 (Channels G-1-4). Marlow Public Schools Independent School District, Box 73, Marlow, OK 73055. Authorized power: 10-w. each. Antenna: 500-ft. above ground. Lat. 34° 26' 27", long. 98° 16' 26". Transmitter: Hwy. 7 & Trail Ridge Rd. Equipment: ITS transmitter; Bogner antenna.

Lenapah—WLX-596 (Channels A-1-4). Nowata Public Schools, 707 W. Osage Ave., Nowata, OK 74048. Authorized power: 50-w. each. Antenna: 495-ft. above ground. Lat. 36° 55' 25", long. 95° 41' 39". Transmitter: 5.5-mi. NW of Lenapah. Equipment: Comwave transmitter. Requests change to lat. 36° 55' 01", long. 95° 04' 47". Equipment: Andrew antenna.

Leased to Nucentrix Broadband Networks, 200 Chisholm Place, Suite 200, Plano, TX 75075. Phone: 972-423-9494. Fax: 972-423-0819.

Lenapah—WLX-605 (Channels B-1-4). Unified School District No. 286, 416 E. Elm St., Sedan, KS 67361. Phone: 316-725-3186. Fax: 316-725-3188. Authorized power: 50-w. each. Antenna: 495-ft. above ground. Lat. 36° 55' 25", long. 95° 41' 36". Transmitter: 5.5-mi. NW of Lenapah. Equipment: Comwave transmitter; Andrew antenna. Requests change to lat. 36° 55' 01", long. 95° 41' 47".

Lenapah—WNC-322 (Channels G-1-4). Caney Valley Unified School District 436, 109 W. 4th St., Caney, KS 67333. Authorized power: 50-w. each. Antenna: 495-ft. above ground. Lat. 36° 55' 01", long. 95° 41' 47". Transmitter: 5.5-mi. NW of Lenapah. Equipment: Comwave transmitter; Andrew antenna.

Lindsay—WLX-772 (Channels B-1-4). Rush Springs Public Schools, Box 308, Rush Springs, OK 73082. Phone: 405-476-3929. Fax: 405-476-2018.

E-mail: chambwp@yahoo.com.

Authorized power: 50-w. each. Antenna: 485-ft. above ground. Lat. 34° 37' 59", long. 97° 36' 33". Transmitter: 14.4-mi. S of Lindsay. Equipment: ITS transmitter; Andrew antenna.

Leased to Nucentrix Broadband Networks, 200 Chisholm Place, Suite 200, Plano, TX 75075. Phone: 972-423-9494. Fax: 972-423-0819.

Lindsay—WLX-895 (Channels C-1-3). Paoli Public Schools, 211 W. Stewart, Paoli, OK 73074. Authorized power: 10-w. each. Antenna: 343-ft. above ground. Lat. 33° 28' 59", long. 97° 26' 50". Transmitter: 14.4-mi. S of Lindsay. Equipment: ITS transmitter; Andrew antenna.

Lindsay—WNC-690 (Channels D-1-4). Pauls Valley Public Schools, Box 780, Pauls Valley, OK 73075. Phone: 405-238-6453. Fax: 405-238-4178. Authorized power: 50-w. each. Antenna: 705-ft. above ground. Lat. 34° 37' 59", long. 97° 36' 33". Transmitter: 2.35-mi. from Hwys. 59 & 59B intersection. Equipment: Comwave transmitter; Andrew antenna.

Leased to Nucentrix Broadband Networks, 200 Chisholm Place, Suite 200, Plano, TX 75025. Phone: 972-423-9494. Fax: 972-423-0819.

McAlester—KGF-21 (Channels A-1-2). Oklahoma State Regents for Higher Education, State Capitol Complex, 500 Education Bldg., Oklahoma City, OK 73105. Phone: 405-524-9169. Fax: 405-521-6125. Authorized power: 10-w. each. Antenna: 384-ft. above ground. Lat. 34° 58' 37", long. 95° 43' 01". Transmitter: 2.9-mi. NE of McAlester. Equipment: Andrew antenna.

Leased to Nucentrix Broadband Networks, 200 Chisholm Place, Suite 200, Plano, TX 75075. Phone: 972-423-9494.

McAlester—WNC-295 (Channels B-1-4). McAlester Public School Independent District No. 80, 200 E. Adams, McAlester, OK 74502. Authorized power: 10-w. each. Antenna: 185-ft. above ground. Lat. 34° 59' 13", long. 95° 42' 10". Transmitter: Pittsburg County. Equipment: Comwave transmitter; Andrew antenna.

McAlester—WNC-660 (Channels C-1-4). Kiowa Public Schools, Box 6, Kiowa, OK 74533. Authorized power: 10-w. each. Antenna: 381-ft. above ground. Lat. 34° 59' 13", long. 95° 42' 10". Transmitter: 4.7-mi. NNE of McAlester. Equipment: Comwave transmitter; Andrew antenna.

McAlester—WNC-696 (Channels D-1-4). East Central U., 104 Administration Bldg., Ada, OK 74820. Authorized power: 10-w. each. Antenna: 116-ft. above ground. Lat. 34° 59' 13", long. 95° 42' 10". Transmitter: 4.7-mi. NNE of McAlester. Equipment: Comwave transmitter; Andrew antenna.

Miami—WNC-544 (Channels A-1-4). Miami Public Schools, 418 G St. SE, Miami, OK 74354. Authorized power: 10-w. each. Antenna: 407-ft. above ground. Lat. 36° 48' 38", long. 94° 55' 36". Transmitter: U.S. 59 & 69 S. Equipment: Comwave transmitter; Andrew antenna.

Miami—WNC-410 (Channels C-1-4). Northeast Oklahoma Area Vocational-Technical School, Box 487, Pryor, OK 74362-0487. Authorized power: 10-w. each. Antenna: 404-ft. above ground. Lat. 36° 48' 38", long. 94° 55' 36". Transmitter: U.S. Rtes. 59 & 69 S, 5.5-mi. SSW of Miami. Equipment: Comwave transmitter; Andrew antenna.

Muskogee—KGF-22 (Channels A-1-2). Oklahoma State Regents for Higher Education, State Capitol Complex, 500 Education Bldg., Oklahoma City, OK 73105. Phone: 405-524-9169. Fax: 405-521-6125. Authorized power: 10-w. each. Antenna: 80-ft. above ground. Lat. 35° 45' 54", long. 95° 24' 51". Transmitter: Muskogee V.A. Hospital. Equipment: Andrew antenna.

Oklahoma City—WGM-93 (Channels A-1-3). Oklahoma State Regents for Higher Education, State Capitol Complex, 500 Education Bldg., Oklahoma City, OK 73105. Phone: 405-524-9169. Fax: 405-521-6125. Authorized power: 10-w. each. Antenna: 304-ft. above ground. Lat. 35° 29' 00", long. 97° 29' 53". Transmitter: 14th St. & Phillips Ave. Equipment: Andrew antenna.

Leased to Nucentrix Broadband Networks, 200 Chisholm Place, Suite 200, Plano, TX 75075. Phone: 972-423-9494. Fax: 972-423-0819.

Oklahoma City—WHR-791 (Channels B-1-4). Trustees of Oklahoma City U., 2501 N. Blackwelder, Oklahoma City, OK 73106. Phone: 405-521-5433. Fax: 405-521-5928. Authorized power: 10-w. each. Antenna: 513-ft. above ground. Lat. 35° 28' 06", long. 97° 30' 51". Transmitter: 2501 N. Blackwelder, Oklahoma City 73106. Equipment: Emcee transmitter; Bogner antenna.

Leased to American Telecasting, 4224-F N. Santa Fe, Oklahoma City, OK 73118 8527. Phone: 405-525-1000.

Oklahoma City—WHR-559 (Channels C-1-4). Oklahoma Educational Television Authority, 7403 N. Kelley Ave., Oklahoma City, OK 73113. Authorized power: 100-w. each. Antenna: 513-ft. above ground. Lat. 35° 28' 06", long. 97° 30' 51". Transmitter: 100 Broadway. Equipment: ITS transmitter; Bogner antenna.

Oklahoma City—WLX-672 (Channels D-1-4). Hispanic Information & Telecommunications Network Inc., 3rd Floor, 449 Broadway, New York, NY 10013. Phone: 212-966-5660. Fax: 212-966-5725.

E-mail: email@hitn.org.

Authorized power: 100-w. each. Antenna: 506-ft. above ground. Lat. 35° 28' 06", long. 97° 30' 51". Transmitter: 100 N. Broadway. Equipment: ITS transmitter; Andrew antenna.

Leased to American Telecasting Inc., 5575 Tech Center Dr., Suite 300, Colorado Springs, CO 80919. Phone: 719-260-5533.

Oklahoma City—WLX-251 (Channels G-1-4). The Trustees of Oklahoma City U., 2501 N. Blackwelder, Oklahoma City, OK 73106. Phone: 405-521-5433. Fax: 405-521-5928. Authorized power: 10-w. each. Antenna: 513-ft. above ground. Lat. 35° 28' 06", long. 97° 30' 51". Transmitter: 120 N. Robinson. Equipment: ITS transmitter; Bogner antenna.

Leased to American Telecasting, 4224-F N. Santa Fe, Oklahoma City, OK 73118 8527. Phone: 405-525-1000.

Ponca City—WAH-861 (Channels A-1-2). Oklahoma State Regents for Higher Education, 500 Education Bldg., State Capitol Complex, Oklahoma City, OK 73105. Phone: 405-524-9169. Fax: 405-521-6125. Authorized power: 10-w. each. Antenna: 200-ft. above ground. Lat. 36° 48' 49", long. 96° 59' 33". Transmitter: Continental Oil Community Center, 1000 S. Pine. Equipment: Andrew antenna.

Leased to Nucentrix Broadband Networks, 200 Chisholm Place, Suite 200, Plano, TX 75075. Phone: 972-423-9494. Fax: 972-423-0819.

Tulsa—WGM-92 (Channels A-1-4). Oklahoma State Regents for Higher Education, State Capitol Complex, 500 Education Bldg., Oklahoma City, OK 73105. Phone: 405-524-9169. Fax: 405-521-6125. Authorized power: 50-w. each. Antenna: 594-ft. above ground. Lat. 36° 07' 57", long. 96° 04' 16". Transmitter: Atlanta & Marshall Sts. Equipment: ITS transmitter; Andrew antenna.

Leased to Nucentrix Broadband Networks, 200 Chisholm Place, Suite 200, Plano, TX 75075. Phone: 972-423-9494. Fax: 972-423-0819.

Tulsa—WNC-356 (Channels B-1-4). Owasso Public School, Independent School District No. 11, 1501 N. Ash, Owasso, OK 74055. Authorized power: 50-w. each. Antenna: 594-ft. above ground. Lat. 36° 07' 57", long. 96° 04' 16". Transmitter: Wilson Center, 101 E. 2nd St. Equipment: ITS transmitter; Andrew antenna.

Tulsa—WLX-397 (Channels D-1-4). Platt College, 3801 S. Sheridan Rd., Tulsa, OK 74145-1111. Phone: 918-663-9000. Lat. 36° 09' 19", long. 95° 59' 23".

Tulsa—WLX-534 (Channels G-1-4). Hispanic Information & Telecommunications Network Inc., 3rd Floor, 449 Broadway, New York, NY 10013. Phone: 212-966-5660. Fax: 212-966-5725.

E-mail: email@hitn.org.

Web site: http://www.hitn.org.

Authorized power: 50-w. each. Antenna: 604-ft. above ground. Lat. 36° 07' 57", long. 96° 04' 16". Transmitter: 6800 W. 22nd St. Equipment: ITS transmitter; Andrew antenna. Requests change to 594-ft. above ground, lat. 36° 07' 52", long. 96° 04' 13"; transmitter to 5100 W. 21st St.

Leased to People's Choice TV Corp., 5301 E. Broadway, Tucson, AZ 85711. Phone: 520-519-4400.

Warner—WNC-662 (Channels A-3-4). Morris School District, 307 S. 6th, Morris, OK 74445. Authorized power: 50-w. each. Antenna: 476-ft. above ground. Lat. 35° 29' 28", long. 95° 13' 13". Transmitter: Rabbit Hill, approx. 4.7-mi. E of Warner. Equipment: Comwave transmitter; Andrew antenna.

Warner—WNC-377 (Channels B-1-4). Gore Public School, Box 580, Gore, OK 74435. Phone: 918-489-5587. Authorized power: 50-w. each. Antenna: 476-ft. above ground. Lat. 35° 29' 28", long. 95° 13' 13". Transmitter: Rabbit Hill, approx. 4.7-mi. E of Warner. Equipment: Comwave transmitter; Andrew antenna.

Warner—WNC-528 (Channels C-1-4). Fort Gibson Schools, Corner of Ross & East Aves., Fort Gibson, OK 74434. Authorized power: 50-w. each. Antenna: 476-ft. above ground. Lat. 35° 29' 28", long. 95° 13' 13". Transmitter: Rabbit Hill, 4.7-mi. E of Warner. Equipment: Comwave transmitter; Andrew antenna.

Warner—WNC-697 (Channels D-1-4). Haskell School District, Box 278, Hwy. 64 N, Haskell, OK 74436. Phone: 918-482-5221. Fax: 918-482-3346. Authorized power: 50-w. each. Antenna: 476-ft. above ground. Lat. 35° 29' 28", long. 95° 13' 13". Transmitter: Rabbit Hill, approx. 4.7-mi. E of Warner. Equipment: Comwave transmitter; Andrew antenna.

Warner—WNC-555 (Channels G-1-4). Warner Public Schools, Box 1240, Rte. 1, Warner, OK 74469. Phone: 918-463-5171. Fax: 918-463-2542. Authorized power: 50-w. each. Antenna: 476-ft. above ground. Lat. 35° 29' 28", long. 95° 13' 13". Transmitter: Rabbit Hill, approx. 4.7-mi. E of Warner. Equipment: Comwave transmitter; Andrew antenna.

Weatherford—WNC-579 (Channels A-1-4). Weatherford Public Schools, 516 n. Broadway, Weatherford, OK 73096. Phone: 580-772-3327. Authorized power: 50-w. each. Antenna: 348-ft. above ground. Lat. 35° 23' 55", long. 98° 46' 55". Transmitter: 1.7-mi. N of Corn. Equipment: Omni transmitter; Andrew antenna.

Weatherford—WNC-581 (Channels B-1-4). Southwestwestern Oklahoma State U., 100 Campus Dr., Weatherford, OK 73096. Phone: 405-774-3795. Authorized power: 20-w. each. Antenna: 350-ft. above ground. Lat. 35° 23' 55", long. 98° 46' 55". Transmitter: 1.7-mi. N of Corn. Equipment: ITS transmitter; Andrew antenna.

Wewoka—WNC-262 (Channels G-1-4). Allen Public Schools, Box 430, Allen, OK 74825. Phone: 405-857-2416. Fax: 405-857-2636. Authorized power: 10-w. each. Antenna: 420-ft. above ground. Lat. 35° 05' 31", long. 96° 32' 30". Transmitter: Seminole County. Equipment: Comwave transmitter; Andrew antenna.

Woodward—WLX-947 (Channels A-1-4). Arnett Public Schools, Box 317, Arnett, OK 73832. Authorized power: 100-w. each. Antenna: 490-ft. above ground. Lat. 36° 23' 20", long. 99° 20' 36". Transmitter: 3-mi. NW of Woodward. Equipment: Comwave transmitter; Andrew antenna.

Woodward—WNC-225 (Channels D-1-4). Mooreland Public Schools, Box 75, Mooreland, OK 73851-0075. Authorized power: 100-w. each. Antenna: 489-ft. above ground. Lat. 36° 23' 20", long. 99° 20' 36". Transmitter: Woodward. Equipment: Comwave transmitter; Andrew antenna.

Woodward—WLX-965 (Channels G-1-4). Seiling Public Schools, Box 780, Seiling, OK 73663-0780. Authorized power: 100-w. each. Antenna: 489-ft. above ground. Lat. 36° 23' 20", long. 99° 20' 36". Transmitter: Woodward. Equipment: Comwave transmitter; Andrew antenna.

Leased to Nucentrix Broadband Networks Inc., 200 Chisholm Place, Suite 200, Plano, TX 75075. Phone: 972-423-9494. Fax: 972-423-0819.

Oregon

Benton Center—WNC-540 (Channels G-1-4). Benton Center, 630 NW 7th, Corvallis, OR 97330. Authorized power: 50-w. each. Antenna: 100-ft. above ground. Lat. 44° 11' 52", long. 122° 59' 06". Transmitter: Buck Mountain, 11-mi. NE of Benton Center. Equipment: ITS transmitter; Andrew antenna.

Eugene—WNC-527 (Channels A-1-4). Oregon State U., Kidder Hall 109, Corvallis, OR 97331. Authorized power: 50-w. each. Antenna: 100-ft. above ground. Lat. 44° 11' 52", long. 122° 59' 06". Transmitter: Buck Mountain, 11-mi. NE of Eugene. Equipment: ITS transmitter; Andrew antenna.

Eugene—WNC-526 (Channels B-1-4). U. of Oregon, Knight Library, Eugene, OR 94403. Phone: 541-346-2682. Fax: 541-346-1872. Authorized power: 50-w. each. Antenna: 100-ft. above ground. Lat. 44° 00' 08", long. 123° 06' 50". Transmitter: Blanton Heights, 3-mi. SW of Eugene. Equipment: ITS transmitter; Andrew antenna.
Leased to American Telecasting Inc., 5575 Tech Center Dr., Suite 300, Colorado Springs, CO 80919. Phone: 719-260-5533.

Eugene—WNC-574 (Channels C-1-4). Oregon State System of Higher Education, No. 342, 1431 Johnson Lane, Eugene, OR 97403. Authorized power: 50-w. each. Antenna: 312-ft. above ground. Lat. 44° 00' 08", long. 123° 06' 50". Transmitter: 4555 Blanton Rd. Equipment: Emcee transmitter; Andrew antenna.

Eugene—WNC-487 (Channels D-1-4). Lane Community College, 4000 E. 30th Ave., Eugene, OR 97405. Phone: 541-726-2260. Fax: 541-744-3974.
E-mail: leathersc@laneec.edu.
Authorized power: 50-w. each. Antenna: 95-ft. above ground. Lat. 44° 00' 08", long. 123° 06' 50". Transmitter: Blanton Heights, 4555 Blanton Rd., Eugene OR. Equipment: ITS transmitter; Andrew antenna.
Leased to American Telecasting Inc., 5575 Tech Center Dr., Suite 300, Colorado Springs, CO 80919. Phone: 719-260-5533.

La Grande—WNC-956 (Channels G-1-4). Shekinah Network, 14875 Powerline Rd., Atascadero, CA 93422. Authorized power: 10-w. each. Lat. 45° 26' 15", long. 118° 05' 27". Transmitter: La Grande. Equipment: Emcee transmitter; Andrew antenna.

Medford—WLX-975 (Channels B-1-4). Shekinah Network, 9126 Santa Margarita Rd., Atascadero, CA 93422. Phone: 805-438-3341. Authorized power: 20-w. each. Antenna: 66-ft. above ground. Lat. 42° 21' 23", long. 122° 58' 33". Transmitter: John's Peak, Jackson County. Equipment: ITS transmitter; Andrew antenna.
Leased to Cardiff Bcstg., 2110 Jimmy Durante Blvd., Suite 224, Del Mar, CA 92014. Phone: 800-444-3410.

Portland—WHR-543 (Channels A-1-4). Oregon Public Bcstg., 7140 S.W. Macadam Ave., Portland, OR 97219. Phone: 503-244-9900. Fax: 503-293-4877. Authorized power: 10-w. each. Antenna: 604-ft. above ground. Lat. 45° 29' 20", long. 122° 41' 40". Transmitter: 4700 SW Council Crest Dr. Equipment: Emcee transmitter; Andrew antenna.
Leased to American Telecasting Inc., 5575 Tech Center Dr., Suite 300, Colorado Springs, CO 80919. Phone: 719-260-5533.

Portland—WND-505 (Channels B-1-2). Portland Community College, Box 19000, Portland, OR 97280. Authorized power: 0.059-w. each. Antenna: 23-ft. above ground. Lat. 45° 18' 24", long. 120° 47' 52". Transmitter: 18-mi. SSW of Portland. Equipment: Comwave transmitter; Andrew antenna.

Portland—WLX-237 (Channels B-3-4). Portland Community College, 12000 S.W. 49th Ave., Portland, OR 97219. Phone: 503-977-4314. Fax: 503-977-4887.
E-mail: jekstrom@pcc.edu.
Web site: http://www.pcc.edu.
Authorized power: 50-w. each. Antenna: 604-ft. above ground. Lat. 45° 29' 20", long. 122° 41' 40". Transmitter: 4700 S.W. Council Crest Dr. Equipment: Emcee transmitter; Andrew antenna.
Leased to American Telecasting Inc., 5575 Tech Center Dr., Suite 300, Colorado Springs, CO 80919. Phone: 719-260-5533.

Portland—WHR-746 (Channels B-1-2). Portland Community College, 12000 S.W. 49th Ave., Portland, OR 97219. Phone: 503-977-4314. Fax: 503-977-4887.
E-mail: jekstrom@pcc.edu.
Web site: http://www.pcc.edu.
Authorized power: 50-w. each. Antenna: 604-ft. above ground. Lat. 45° 29' 20", long. 122° 41' 40". Transmitter: 4700 S.W. Council Crest Dr. Equipment: Emcee transmitter; Andrew antenna.
Leased to American Telecasting Inc., 5575 Tech Center Dr., Suite 300, Colorado Springs, CO 80919. Phone: 719-260-5533.

Portland—WHR-522 (Channels C-1-4). Portland Educational Telecommunications Corp. Authorized power: 50-w. each. Antenna: 604-ft. above ground. Lat. 45° 29' 20", long. 122° 41' 40". Transmitter: 4700 S.W. Council Crest Dr. Equipment: Emcee transmitter; Andrew antenna.

Portland—WLX-681 (Channels D-1-4). Hispanic Information & Telecommunications Network Inc., 3rd Floor, 449 Broadway, New York, NY 10013. Phone: 212-966-5660. Fax: 212-966-5725.
E-mail: email@hitn.org.
Web site: http://www.hitn.org.
Authorized power: 50-w. each. Antenna: 604-ft. above ground. Lat. 45° 29' 20", long. 122° 41' 40". Transmitter: 4700 S.W. Council Crest Dr. Equipment: Emcee transmitter; Andrew antenna.
Leased to Distance Learning Service, 1155 Connecticut Ave. NW, Suite 300, Washington, DC 20036. Phone: 202-467-8500.

Portland—WHR-515 (Channels G-1-4). Network for Instructional TV Inc., Suite 110, 11490 Commerce Park Dr., Reston, VA 20191. Phone: 703-860-9200. Fax: 703-860-9237. Authorized power: 50-w. each. Antenna: 604-ft. above ground. Lat. 45° 29' 20", long. 122° 41' 40". Transmitter: 4700 S.W. Council Crest Dr. Equipment: Emcee transmitter; Andrew antenna.
Leased to American Telecasting Inc., 5575 Tech Center Dr., Suite 300, Colorado Springs, CO 80919. Phone: 719-260-5533.

Prineville—WNC-816 (Channels A-1-4). Administrative School District No. 1, 520 N.W. Wall St., Bend, OR 97701. Authorized power: 121-w. each. Antenna: 39.8-ft. above ground. Lat. 44° 26' 17", long. 120° 57' 13". Transmitter: 10.8-mi. NW of Prineville. Equipment: Comwave transmitter; Andrew antenna.

Prineville—WNC-815 (Channels D-1-4). Central Oregon Community College, 2000 N.W. College Way, Bend, OR 97701. Phone: 541-383-7569. Fax: 541-330-4388.
E-mail: jobert@cocc.edu.
Web site: http://www.cocc.edu.
Authorized power: 39.8-w. each. Antenna: 121-ft. above ground. Lat. 44° 26' 17", long. 120° 57' 13". Transmitter: Grizzly Mountain, 10.8-mi. NW of Prineville. Equipment: Comwave transmitter; Andrew antenna.

Roseburg—WHR-762 (Channel C-1). Umpqua Community College, Box 967, Roseburg, OR 97470. Phone: 503-440-4717. Fax: 503-440-4665. Authorized power: 10-w. Antenna: 30-ft. above ground. Lat. 43° 11' 14", long. 123° 23' 22". Transmitter: 1-mi. SW of Roseburg city center.

Roseburg—WHR-677 (Channel G-1). Umpqua Community College, Box 967, Roseburg, OR 97470. Phone: 503-440-4717. Fax: 503-440-4665. Lat. 43° 17' 40", long. 123° 20' 10".

Salem—WHR-771 (Channels A-1-4). Chemeketa Community College District, 4000 Lancaster Dr. NE, Salem, OR 97309. Phone: 503-399-2545. Fax: 503-399-5214.
E-mail: vins@chemek.cc.or.us.
Web site: http://www.chemek.cc.or.us.
Authorized power: 50-w. each. Antenna: 282-ft. above ground. Lat. 44° 51' 18", long. 123° 07' 14". Transmitter: Prospect Hill. Equipment: Emcee transmitter; Andrew antenna.
Leased to American Telecasting Inc., 5575 Tech Center Dr., Suite 300, Colorado Springs, CO 80919. Phone: 719-260-5533.

Salem—WNC-471 (Channels B-1-4). Oregon University System, Room 342, 1431 Johnson Lane, Eugene, OR 97403. Phone: 541-346-5705. Fax: 541-346-5790.
E-mail: john greydanus@sch.ous.edu.
Authorized power: 50-w. each. Antenna: 282-ft. above ground. Lat. 44° 51' 18", long. 123° 07' 14". Transmitter: Prospect Hill. Equipment: Emcee transmitter; Andrew antenna.
Leased to American Telecasting Inc., 5575 Tech Center Dr., Suite 300, Colorado Springs, CO 80919. Phone: 719-260-5533.

Salem—WNC-718 (Channels C-1-4). Oregon State U., Kidder Hall 109, Corvallis, OR 97331. Authorized power: 10-w. each. Antenna: 190-ft. above ground. Lat. 044° 59' 05", long. 123° 08' 30". Transmitter: Eola Hill. Equipment: ITS transmitter; Andrew antenna.

Salem—WNC-470 (Channels D-1-4). Portland State U. of Salem, 4061 Winema Place NE, Salem, OR 97305. Authorized power: 50-w. each. Antenna: 282-ft. above ground. Lat. 44° 51' 18", long. 123° 07' 14". Transmitter: Prospect Hill. Equipment: Emcee transmitter; Andrew antenna.

Salem—WNC-717 (Channels G-1-4). Western Oregon U., Administration Bldg. 305, Monmouth, OR 97361. Phone: 503-838-8958. Fax: 503-838-8474.
E-mail: heywooa@wou.edu.
Authorized power: 50-w. each. Antenna: 272-ft. above ground. Lat. 44° 51' 18", long. 123° 07' 14". Transmitter: Prospect Hill. Equipment: Emcee transmitter; Andrew antenna.
Leased to American Telecasting Inc., 5575 Tech Center Dr., Suite 300, Colorado Springs, CO 80919. Phone: 719-260-5533.

Pennsylvania

Altoona—KZC-22 (Channels G-1-4). Altoona Area School District, 1417 7th Ave., Altoona, PA 16602. Phone: 814-946-8251. Fax: 814-946-8549. Authorized power: .00013-w. each. Antenna: 70-ft. above ground. Lat. 40° 32' 16", long. 78° 25' 05". Transmitter: Penn State U., Altoona.

Bloomsburg—WHR-647 (Channel C-3). Bloomsburg U., Bloomsburg, PA 17815. Authorized power: 1-w. Antenna: 105-ft. above ground. Lat. 41° 00' 29", long. 76° 26' 51". Transmitter: Bloomsburg.

Carbondale—WHG-336 (Channels C-3-4). Northeastern Pennsylvania ETV Assn., Old Boston Rd., Pittston, PA 18640. Authorized power: 50-w. each. Antenna: 128-ft. above ground. Lat. 41° 32' 37", long. 75° 27' 44". Transmitter: Salem Mountain, 4-mi. N of Carbondale.

Hanover—KZB-21 (Channels B-1-2). Hanover Public School District, 403 Moul Ave., Hanover, PA 17331-1541. Phone: 717-637-9000. Authorized power: 1-w. each. Antenna: 39-ft. above ground. Lat. 39° 49' 07", long. 76° 58' 09". Transmitter: Hanover High School, Moul Ave. & Hollywood.

Harrisburg—WHR-650 (Channels A-1-4). WITF Inc., 1982 Locust Lane, Harrisburg, PA 17109. Phone: 717-236-6000. Fax: 717-236-4628.
E-mail: donna andrews@witf.pbs.org.
Web site: http://www.witf.org.
Authorized power: 10-w. each. Antenna: 1000-ft. above ground. Lat. 40° 20' 45", long. 76° 52' 06". Transmitter: 5-mi. N of Harrisburg on Roberts Valley Rd. Equipment: Comwave transmitter; Bogner antenna.

Harrisburg—WHR-469 (Channels D-1-4). WITF Inc., 1982 Locust Lane, Harrisburg, PA 17105. Phone: 717-236-6000. Fax: 717-236-4628. Lat. 40° 17' 21", long. 76° 51' 38".

Hazleton—WGZ-671 (Channels B-3-4). Hahnemann Medical College, 230 N. Broad St., Philadelphia, PA 19102. Authorized power: 10-w. each. Antenna: 90-ft. above ground. Lat. 40° 57' 51.1", long. 75° 58' 52". Transmitter: St. Joseph's Hospital, N. Church & 9th Sts.

Lancaster—WNC-645 (Channels A-1-4). North American Catholic Educational Programming Foundation Inc., Box 40026, Providence, RI 02940-0026. Phone: 401-729-0900. Authorized power: 10-w. each. Antenna: 196-ft. above ground. Lat. 39° 56' 38", long. 76° 08' 14". Transmitter: 500-ft. N of White Oak Rd., May. Equipment: Emcee transmitter; Andrew antenna.

Lancaster—WHR-477 (Channels B-3-4). WITF Inc., 1982 Locust Lane, Harrisburg, PA 17109. Phone: 717-236-6000. Fax: 717-236-4628.
E-mail: donna andrews@witf.pbs.org.
Web site: http://www.witf.org.
Authorized power: 10-w. each. Antenna: 262-ft. above ground. Lat. 40° 02' 17", long. 76° 18' 23". Transmitter: Griest Bldg, NW corner of Penn Square. Equipment: Comwave transmitter; Andrew antenna.

Mehoopany—WHG-335 (Channels C-1-2). Northeastern Pennsylvania ETV Assn., Old Boston Rd., Pittston, PA 18640. Authorized power: 50-w. each. Antenna: 116-ft. above ground. Lat. 41° 30' 45", long. 75° 04' 16". Transmitter: Rte. 39, 5-mi. N of Tunkhannock.

Mount Carmel—WLX-267 (Channel D-1). Mount Carmel Area School District, 600 W. 5th St., Mount Carmel, PA 17851. Phone: 717-339-1500. Fax: 717-339-0487. Authorized power: 4-w. Antenna: 31-ft. above ground. Lat. 40° 47' 30", long. 76° 25' 21". Transmitter: Mount Carmel Area School District Television Facility, Mount Carmel Area High School, 600 W. 5th St. Equipment: Comwave transmitter; Bogner antenna.

Philadelphia—WAU-29 (Channels A-1-2). Commonwealth System of Higher Education, 450 Carnell Hall, Broad St. & Montgomery Ave., Philadelphia, PA 19122. Authorized power: 81.3-w. each. Antenna: 1075-ft. above ground. Lat. 40° 02' 21", long. 75° 14' 13". Transmitter: 216 Paoli Ave. Equipment: ITS transmitter; Andrew antenna.
Leased to Popvision, 2510 Metropolitan Dr., Trevose, PA 19053. Phone: 215-396-9400.

Philadelphia—WLX-824 (Channels A-3-4). Delaware Valley Educational TV Network Inc. Authorized power: 81-w. each. Antenna: 1075-ft.

above ground. Lat. 40° 02' 21", long. 75° 14' 13". Transmitter: 216 Paoli Ave.
Leased to Popvision, 2510 Metropolitan Dr., Trevose, PA 19053. Phone: 215-396-9400.

Philadelphia—WLX-578 (Channels B-1-2). Mercer County Community College, 1200 Old Trenton Rd., Trenton, NJ 08690. Authorized power: 81.3-w. each. Antenna: 1073-ft. above ground. Lat. 40° 02' 21", long. 75° 14' 13". Transmitter: 216 Paoli Ave. Equipment: ITS transmitter; Andrew antenna.
Leased to Popvision, 2510 Metropolitan Dr., Trevose, PA 19053. Phone: 215-396-9400.

Philadelphia—WLX-566 (Channels B-3-4). New Jersey Public Broadcasting Authority, CN777, Trenton, NJ 08625. Authorized power: 81.3-w. each. Antenna: 1073-ft. above ground. Lat. 40° 02' 21", long. 75° 14' 13". Transmitter: 216 Paoli Ave. Equipment: ITS transmitter; Andrew antenna.

Philadelphia—WLX-825 (Channels C-3-4). Hispanic Information & Telecommunications Network Inc., 3rd Floor, 449 Broadway, New York, NY 10013. Phone: 212-966-5660. Fax: 212-966-5725.
Web site: http://www.hitn.org.
Authorized power: 81-w. each. Antenna: 1073-ft. above ground. Lat. 42° 02' 21", long. 75° 14' 13". Transmitter: 216 Paoli Ave. Equipment: ITS transmitter; Andrew antenna.
Leased to CAI Wireless Systems Inc., 2101 Wilson Blvd., Suite 100, Arlington, VA 22201. Phone: 703-812-8800.

Philadelphia—WHR-527 (Channels G-1-4). Instructional Telecommunications Foundation Inc., Box 6060, Boulder, CO 80306. Phone: 303-442-4180. Fax: 303-442-6472.
E-mail: ITF@fstv.org.
Authorized power: 100-w. each. Antenna: 1166-ft. above ground. Lat. 40° 02' 21", long. 75° 14' 13". Transmitter: 300 Domino Lane.

Pittsburgh—WND-296 (Channels A-1-4). Point Park College, 201 Wood St., Pittsburgh, PA 15222. Authorized power: 50-w. each. Antenna: 279-ft. above ground. Lat. 40° 26' 46", long. 79° 57' 51". Transmitter: QED tower. Equipment: ITS transmitter; Andrew antenna.

Pittsburgh—WHR-525 (Channels B-1-4). Network for Instructional TV Inc., Suite 110, 11490 Commerce Park Dr., Reston, VA 20191. Phone: 703-860-9200. Fax: 703-860-9237. Authorized power: 50-w. each. Antenna: 279-ft. above ground. Lat. 40° 26' 46", long. 79° 57' 51". Transmitter: 2850 Burtland St. Equipment: ITS transmitter; Andrew antenna.
Leased to CAI Wireless, 18 Corporate Woods Blvd, Suite 102, Albany, NY 12211. Phone: 518-462-2632.

Pittsburgh—WNC-484 (Channels C-1-4). Mon Valley Education Consortium, 336 Shaw Ave., McKeesport, PA 15132. Phone: 412-678-9215. Fax: 412-678-1698. Authorized power: 50-w. each. Antenna: 280-ft. above ground. Lat. 40° 26' 46", long. 79° 57' 51". Transmitter: 2850 Burthold St. Equipment: ITS transmitter; Andrew antenna.
Leased to American Wireless Systems, Inc., 18401 Von Karman, Suite 330, Irvine, CA 92715. Phone: 714-851-8402.

Pittsburgh—WND-297 (Channels D-1-4). La Roche College, 9000 Babcock Blvd., Pittsburgh, PA 15237. Phone: 412-536-1027.
E-mail: ritterjl@laroche.edu.
Authorized power: 50-w. each. Antenna: 279-ft. above ground. Lat. 40° 26' 46", long. 79° 57' 51". Transmitter: QED tower. Equipment: ITS transmitter; Andrew antenna.

Pittsburgh—WLX-537 (Channels G-1-4). Hispanic Information & Telecommunications Network Inc., 3rd Floor, 449 Broadway, New York, NY 10013. Phone: 212-966-5660. Fax: 212-966-5725.
E-mail: email@hitn.org.
Web site: http://www.hitn.org.
Authorized power: 50-w. each. Antenna: 279-ft. above ground. Lat. 40° 26' 46", long. 79° 57' 51". Transmitter: WQED Tower. Equipment: Emcee transmitter; Andrew antenna.
Leased to CAI Wireless Systems Inc., 2101 Wilson Blvd., Suite 100, Arlington, VA 22201. Phone: 703-812-8800.

Pittston—WHG-339 (Channels E-1-2). Northeastern Pennsylvania ETV Assn., Old Boston Rd., Pittston, PA 18640. Phone: 717-826-6144. Fax: 717-655-1180. Authorized power: 0.1-w. each. Antenna: 124-ft. above ground. Lat. 41° 17' 36", long. 75° 46' 30". Transmitter: Old Boston Rd.

Reading—WND-478 (Channels C-1-4). Oley Valley School District 17, 17 Jefferson St., Oley, PA 19547. Phone: 610-987-4134. Authorized power: 20-w. each. Antenna: 154-ft. above ground. Lat. 40° 21' 15", long. 75° 53' 56". Transmitter: Skyline Dr. between List & Spuhler Rds. Equipment: ITS transmitter; Andrew antenna.

Reading—WND-475 (Channels D-1-4). Albright College, 13th & Exeter Sts., Reading, PA 19604. Phone: 610-921-2381. Authorized power: 20-w. each. Antenna: 151-ft. above ground. Lat. 40° 21' 15", long. 75° 53' 56". Transmitter: Skyline Dr. between List & Spuhler Rds. Equipment: ITS transmitter; Andrew antenna.

South Abington Twp.—WHR-623 (Channels D-1-2). Northeastern Pennsylvania ETV Assn., Old Boston Rd., Pittston, PA 18640. Phone: 717-826-6144. Fax: 717-655-1180. Authorized power: 10-w. each. Antenna: 48-ft. above ground. Lat. 41° 28' 01", long. 75° 41' 12". Transmitter: Leach Knob, 2-mi. SSE of Clarks Summit.

State College—WNC-929 (Channels D-1-4). Rockne Educational Television, 908 Madison Ave., Albany, NY 12208. Authorized power: 100-w. each. Antenna: 157-ft. above ground. Lat. 40° 45' 08", long. 77° 45' 16". Transmitter: Little Flat, Thickhead Mountain. Equipment: Emcee transmitter; Andrew antenna.

Upper Strasburg—WLX-401 (Channels D-1-4). WITF Inc., 1982 Locust Lane, Harrisburg, PA 17105. Phone: 717-236-6000. Fax: 717-236-4628.
E-mail: donna andrews@witf.pbs.org.
Web site: http://www.witf.org.
Authorized power: 10-w. each. Lat. 40° 03' 00", long. 77° 44' 54". Transmitter: Clarks Knob, Upper Strasburg. Equipment: Comwave transmitter; Andrew antenna.

Wilkes-Barre—WHG-334 (Channels A-1-2). Northeastern Pennsylvania ETV Association, Old Boston Rd., Pittston, PA 18640. Phone: 717-826-6144. Fax: 717-655-1180. Authorized power: 50-w. each. Antenna: 243-ft. above ground. Lat. 41° 10' 57", long. 75° 52' 10". Transmitter: 200-ft. tower, Penobscot Knob, 2.5-mi. S of Wilkes-Barre.

Wilkes-Barre—WNC-326 (Channels B-1-4). Diocese of Scranton, 400 Wyoming Ave., Scranton, PA 18503. Phone: 717-346-8953. Fax: 717-346-8958. Authorized power: 10-w. each. Antenna: 454-ft. above ground. Lat. 41° 10' 58", long. 75° 52' 21". Transmitter: Penobscot Nob Electronic Heights. Equipment: Emcee transmitter; Andrew antenna.

Wilkes-Barre—WNC-539 (Channels C-1-4). Wilkes U., 170 S. Franklin St., Wilkes-Barre, PA 18766. Authorized power: 10-w. each. Antenna: 829-ft. above ground. Lat. 41° 10' 58", long. 75° 52' 21". Transmitter: Penobscot Nob Electronic Heights. Equipment: Emcee transmitter; Andrew antenna.

Wilkes-Barre—WNC-565 (Channels D-1-4). Wilkes-Barre Area School District, 730 Main St., Wilkes-Barre, PA 18711. Authorized power: 10-w. each. Antenna: 454-ft. above ground. Lat. 41° 10' 58", long. 75° 52' 21". Transmitter: Penobscot Nob Electronic Heights. Equipment: Emcee transmitter; Andrew antenna.

Wilkes-Barre—WNC-566 (Channels G-1-4). Luzerne County Community College, 1333 S. Prospect St., Nanticoke, PA 18634. Phone: 717-740-0031. Fax: 717-740-0605.
E-mail: jmonick@luzerne.edu.
Web site: http://www.luzerne.edu.
Authorized power: 10-w. each. Antenna: 829-ft. above ground. Lat. 41° 10' 58", long. 75° 52' 21". Transmitter: Penobscot Nob Electronic Heights. Equipment: Emcee transmitter; Andrew antenna.

York—WHR-651 (Channels D-1-4). WITF Inc., 1982 Locust Lane, Harrisburg, PA 17105. Phone: 717-236-6000. Fax: 717-236-4628.
E-mail: donna andrews@witf.pbs.org.
Web site: http://www.witf.org.
Authorized power: 20-w. each. Antenna: 384-ft. above ground. Lat. 39° 56' 26", long. 76° 41' 54". Equipment: Comwave transmitter; Bogner antenna.

York—WLX-647 (Channels G-1-4). North American Catholic Educational Programming Foundation Inc., Box 40026, Providence, RI 02940-0026. Phone: 401-729-0900. Authorized power: 10-w. each. Antenna: 96-ft. above ground. Lat. 39° 56' 25", long. 76° 41' 59". Transmitter: 2005 S. Queen St. Equipment: Comwave transmitter; Omni antenna.

Rhode Island

Providence—WNC-521 (Channels A-1-4). North American Catholic Educational Programming Foundation Inc., Box 40026, Providence, RI 02940-0026. Phone: 401-729-0900. Authorized power: 100-w. each. Antenna: 320-ft. above ground. Lat. 45° 35' 38", long. 71° 11' 24". Transmitter: Falmouth St. Equipment: ITS transmitter; Andrew antenna.

Providence—WLX-690 (Channels B-1-4). Hispanic Information & Telecommunications Network Inc., 3rd Floor, 449 Broadway, New York, NY 10013. Phone: 212-966-5660. Fax: 212-966-5725.
E-mail: E-mail@hitn.org.
Web site: http://www.hitn.org.
Authorized power: 100-w. each. Antenna: 873-ft. above ground. Lat. 41° 52' 14", long. 71° 17' 45". Transmitter: Neutaconkanut Hill, Ipswich Rd. Equipment: ITS transmitter; Andrew antenna.
Leased to CAI Wireless Systems Inc., 2101 Wilson Blvd., Suite 100, Arlington, VA 22201. Phone: 703-812-8800.

Providence—WHR-971 (Channels D-1-4). Brown U., Box 1913, Providence, RI 02312. Lat. 41° 49' 37", long. 71° 24' 02".

South Carolina

Aiken—WHM-935 (Channels B-1-4). South Carolina ETV Commission, Box 11000, 1101 George Rogers Blvd., Columbia, SC 29211. Phone: 803-737-3500. Fax: 803-737-3495. Authorized power: 10-w. each. Antenna: 400-ft. above ground. Lat. 33° 33' 57", long. 81° 43' 48". Transmitter: 828 Richland Ave. Equipment: Andrew antenna.

Aiken—WHR-455 (Channels G-1-4). South Carolina ETV Commission, Box 11000, 1101 George Rogers Blvd., Columbia, SC 29211. Phone: 803-737-3500. Fax: 803-737-3495. Authorized power: 10-w. each. Antenna: 400-ft. above ground. Lat. 33° 34' 05", long. 81° 43' 47". Transmitter: Aiken District One Administration Office.

Anderson—WHR-957 (Channels C-1-4). South Carolina ETV Commission, Box 11000, 1101 George Rogers Blvd., Columbia, SC 29211. Phone: 803-737-3500. Fax: 803-737-3495. Authorized power: 1-w. each. Antenna: 105-ft. above ground. Lat. 34° 29' 39", long. 82° 38' 44". Transmitter: McDuffie Vocational High School, 1225 S. McDuffie St. Equipment: Emcee transmitter; Anixter-Mark antenna.

Anderson—WHR-974 (Channels G-1-4). South Carolina ETV Commission, Box 11000, 1101 George Rogers Blvd., Columbia, SC 29211. Phone: 803-737-3500. Fax: 803-737-3495. Authorized power: 10-w. each. Antenna: 380-ft. above ground. Lat. 34° 30' 53", long. 82° 38' 15". Transmitter: Anderson College. Equipment: Emcee transmitter; Andrew antenna.

Anderson County—WHR-620 (Channels E-1-4). South Carolina ETV Commission, Box 11000, 1101 George Rogers Blvd., Columbia, SC 29211. Phone: 803-737-3500. Fax: 803-737-3495. Authorized power: 10-w. each. Antenna: 422-ft. above ground. Lat. 34° 30' 53", long. 82° 38' 15". Transmitter: Anderson College, 321 Kingsley Rd. Equipment: Emcee transmitter; Andrew antenna.

Aynor—WHN-714 (Channels E-1-4). South Carolina ETV Commission, Box 11000, 1101 George Rogers Blvd., Columbia, SC 29211. Phone: 803-737-3500. Fax: 803-737-3495. Authorized power: 10-w. each. Antenna: 842-ft. above ground. Lat. 33° 57' 05", long. 79° 06' 31". Transmitter: Rte. 2. Equipment: Emcee transmitter; Andrew antenna.

Aynor—WHM-933 (Channels G-1-4). South Carolina ETV Commission, Box 11000, 1101 George Rogers Blvd., Columbia, SC 29211. Phone: 803-737-3500. Fax: 803-737-3495. Authorized power: 10-w. each. Antenna: 600-ft. above ground. Lat. 33° 57' 05", long. 79° 06' 31". Transmitter: Rte. 2.

Barnwell—WHR-473 (Channels D-1-4). South Carolina ETV Commission, Box 11000, 1101 George Rogers Blvd., Columbia, SC 29211. Phone: 803-737-3500. Fax: 803-737-3495. Authorized power: 10-w. each. Lat. 33° 11' 12", long. 81° 23' 58". Transmitter: Rte. 3.

Bennettsville—WHR-614 (Channels E-1-4). South Carolina ETV Commission, Box 11000, 1101 George Rogers Blvd., Columbia, SC 29211. Phone: 803-737-3500. Fax: 803-737-3495. Authorized power: 10-w. each. Antenna: 395-ft. above ground. Lat. 34° 37' 11",

For a list of all cable communities included in this section, see the **Cable Community Index** located in the back of this volume.

long. 79° 39' 45". Transmitter: Marlboro Area Vocational Center.

Blackville—WHN-704 (Channels A-1-4). South Carolina ETV Commission, Box 11000, 1101 George Rogers Blvd., Columbia, SC 29211. Phone: 803-737-3500. Fax: 803-737-3495. Authorized power: 10-w. each. Antenna: 395-ft. above ground. Lat. 33° 21' 25", long. 81° 16' 11". Transmitter: Barnwell District 19 Administration Office.

Camden—WND-422 (Channels A-1-4). South Carolina ETV Commission, Box 11000, 1101 George Rogers Blvd., Columbia, SC 29201. Phone: 803-737-3500. Fax: 803-737-3495. Authorized power: 1-w. each. Antenna: 62-ft. above ground. Lat. 34° 17' 25", long. 80° 33' 42". Transmitter: Applied Technical Education Campus, 874 Vocational Lane. Equipment: Emcee transmitter; Mark antenna.

Cassatt—WHQ-396 (Channels C-1-4). South Carolina ETV Commission, Box 11000, 1101 George Rogers Blvd., Columbia, SC 29211. Phone: 803-737-3500. Fax: 803-737-3495. Authorized power: 10-w. each. Antenna: 404-ft. above ground. Lat. 34° 20' 10", long. 80° 23' 23". Transmitter: State Rd. 535. Equipment: ITS transmitter; Andrew antenna.

Charleston—WHF-220 (Channels A-1-4). South Carolina ETV Commission, Box 11000, 1101 George Rogers Blvd., Columbia, SC 29211. Phone: 803-737-3500. Fax: 803-737-3495. Authorized power: 50-w. each. Antenna: 413-ft. above ground. Lat. 32° 48' 07", long. 80° 01' 26". Transmitter: 1870 Wallace School Rd. Equipment: Comwave transmitter; Andrew antenna.

Charleston—WHR-923 (Channels B-1-4). South Carolina ETV Commission, Box 11000, 1101 George Rogers Blvd., Columbia, SC 29211. Phone: 803-737-3500. Fax: 803-737-3495. Authorized power: 1-w. each. Antenna: 400-ft. above ground. Lat. 32° 48' 01", long. 80° 01' 23". Transmitter: 1870 Wallace School Rd. Equipment: Emcee transmitter; Anixter-Mark antenna.

Charleston—WHM-931 (Channels C-1-4). South Carolina ETV Commission, Box 11000, 1101 George Rogers Blvd., Columbia, SC 27211. Phone: 803-737-3500. Fax: 803-737-3495. Authorized power: 50-w. each. Antenna: 410-ft. above ground. Lat. 32° 48' 07", long. 80° 01' 26". Transmitter: 1870 Wallace School Rd. Equipment: Comwave transmitter; Andrew antenna.

Charleston—WHF-222 (Channels G-1-4). South Carolina ETV Commission, Box 11000, 1101 George Rogers Blvd., Columbia, SC 29211. Phone: 803-737-3500. Fax: 803-737-3495. Authorized power: 0.1-w. each. Antenna: 80-ft. above ground. Lat. 32° 46' 28", long. 79° 56' 31". Transmitter: Charleston County School District Office, Chisholm St.

Chester—WHM-939 (Channels F-1-4). South Carolina ETV Commission, Box 11000, 1101 George Rogers Blvd., Columbia, SC 29211. Phone: 803-737-3500. Fax: 803-737-3495. Authorized power: 10-w. each. Antenna: 420-ft. above ground. Lat. 34° 41' 17", long. 81° 12' 10". Transmitter: Chester Area Vocational Center, 72 Bypass. Equipment: Emcee transmitter.

Chesterfield—WHR-457 (Channels B-1-4). South Carolina ETV Commission, Box 11000, 1101 George Rogers Blvd., Columbia, SC 29211. Phone: 803-737-3500. Fax: 803-737-3495. Authorized power: 10-w. each. Antenna: 300-ft. above ground. Lat. 34° 38' 46", long. 79° 56' 44". Transmitter: Chesterfield District Administration Office, 141 Main St. Equipment: Emcee transmitter; Andrew antenna.

Columbia—WHQ-258 (Channels A-1-4). South Carolina ETV Commission, Box 11000, 1101 George Rogers Blvd., Columbia, SC 29211. Phone: 803-737-3500. Fax: 803-737-3495. Authorized power: 10-w. each. Antenna: 400-ft. above ground. Lat. 34° 07' 07", long. 80° 56' 12". Transmitter: WRLK-TV transmitter site.

Columbia—WHR-674 (Channels C-1-4). South Carolina ETV Commission, Drawer L, Box 11000, 1101 George Rogers Blvd., Columbia, SC 29211. Phone: 803-737-3500. Fax: 803-737-3495. Authorized power: 1.0-w. each. Antenna: 81-ft. above ground. Lat. 34° 03' 30", long. 80° 56' 29". Transmitter: 7500 Brookfield Rd., Richland Northeast High School. Equipment: ITS transmitter; Mark antenna.

Columbia—WHR-666 (Channels D-1-4). South Carolina ETV Commission, Box 11000, 1101 George Rogers Blvd., Columbia, SC 29211. Phone: 803-737-3500. Fax: 803-737-3495. Authorized power: 0.1-w. each. Antenna: 37-ft. above ground. Lat. 34° 00' 24", long. 81° 01' 02". Transmitter: Columbia Taping Center, Oak & Lady Sts.

Columbia—WHQ-259 (Channels F-1-4). South Carolina ETV Commission, Box 11000, 1101 George Rogers Blvd., Columbia, SC 29211. Phone: 803-737-3500. Fax: 803-737-3495. Authorized power: 10-w. each. Antenna: 378-ft. above ground. Lat. 34° 00' 06", long. 81° 01' 44". Transmitter: 1111 Bull St. Equipment: ITS transmitter; Andrew antenna.

Conway—WHR-465 (Channels B-1-4). South Carolina ETV Commission, Box 11000, 1101 George Rogers Blvd., Columbia, SC 29201. Phone: 803-737-3500. Fax: 803-737-3495. Authorized power: 10-w. each. Antenna: 35-ft. above ground. Lat. 33° 50' 03", long. 79° 04' 10". Transmitter: Horry County tape center, Brown St. Equipment: Emcee transmitter.

Cottageville—WHR-456 (Channels F-1-4). South Carolina ETV Commission, Box 11000, 1101 George Rogers Blvd., Columbia, SC 29211. Phone: 803-737-3500. Fax: 803-737-3495. Authorized power: 10-w. each. Antenna: 400-ft. above ground. Lat. 32° 55' 57", long. 80° 30' 53". Transmitter: Central Elementary School, Rte. 1. Equipment: Emcee transmitter; Andrew antenna.

Florence—WHR-480 (Channels G-1-4). South Carolina ETV Commission, Box 11000, 1101 George Rogers Blvd., Columbia, SC 29211. Phone: 803-737-3500. Fax: 803-737-3495. Authorized power: 10-w. each. Antenna: 405-ft. above ground. Lat. 34° 16' 45", long. 79° 44' 36". Transmitter: WJPM-TV transmitter site, Rte. 1.

Florence County—WHQ-304 (Channels C-1-4). South Carolina ETV Commission, Box 11000, 1101 George Rogers Blvd., Columbia, SC 29211. Phone: 803-737-3500. Fax: 803-737-3495. Authorized power: 10-w. each. Antenna: 405-ft. above ground. Lat. 34° 14' 51", long. 79° 48' 41". Transmitter: Florence-Darlington Technical College, Darlington Hwy., Florence.

Gaffney—WND-462 (Channels B-1-4). Brunswick Community College, 50 College Rd. NE, Supply, NC 28462. Authorized power: 50-w. each. Antenna: 436-ft. above ground. Lat. 34° 12' 35", long. 77° 56' 53". Transmitter: Adams St. & Burnett Blvd., Wilmington, NC. Equipment: Emcee transmitter; Andrew antenna.

Gaffney—WHQ-380 (Channels G-1-4). South Carolina ETV Commission, Box 11000, 1101 George Rogers Blvd., Columbia, SC 29211. Phone: 803-737-3500. Fax: 803-737-3495. Authorized power: 10-w. each. Antenna: 968-ft. above ground. Lat. 35° 04' 03", long. 81° 40' 42". Transmitter: Twin Lakes Rd. Equipment: Emcee transmitter; Andrew antenna.

Georgetown—WGR-849 (Channels A-1-4). South Carolina ETV Commission, Box 11000, 1101 George Rogers Blvd., Columbia, SC 29211. Phone: 803-737-3500. Fax: 803-737-3495. Authorized power: 10-w. each. Antenna: 398-ft. above ground. Lat. 33° 26' 40", long. 79° 18' 15". Transmitter: County Prison Camp, State Hwy. 51N.

Georgetown—WHR-693 (Channels B-1-4). South Carolina ETV Commission, Box 11000, 1101 George Rogers Blvd., Columbia, SC 29211. Phone: 803-737-3500. Fax: 803-737-3495. Authorized power: 1-w. each. Antenna: 100-ft. above ground. Lat. 33° 22' 37", long. 79° 17' 14". Transmitter: N. Fraser St. Equipment: TTC transmitter; Anixter-Mark antenna.

Georgetown—WHR-472 (Channels D-1-4). South Carolina ETV Commission, Box 11000, 1101 George Rogers Blvd., Columbia, SC 29211. Phone: 803-737-3500. Fax: 803-737-3495. Authorized power: 10-w. each. Antenna: 395-ft. above ground. Lat. 33° 26' 41", long. 79° 18' 11". Transmitter: Georgetown ITFS tower, County Prison Farm.

Georgetown—WGR-836 (Channels G-1-4). South Carolina ETV Commission, Box 11000, 1101 George Rogers Blvd., Columbia, SC 29211. Phone: 803-737-3500. Fax: 803-737-3495. Authorized power: 0.1-w. each. Antenna: 100-ft. above ground. Lat. 33° 22' 37", long. 79° 17' 14". Transmitter: Bynum Elementary School, N. Fraser St.

Green Pond—WHR-504 (Channels B-1-4). South Carolina ETV Commission, Box 11000, 1101 George Rogers Blvd., Columbia, SC 29211. Phone: 803-737-3500. Fax: 803-737-3495. Authorized power: 10-w. each. Antenna: 1234-ft. above ground. Lat. 32° 42' 44", long. 80° 40' 49". Transmitter: WJWJ-TV transmitter site, State Rte. 1. Equipment: Emcee transmitter; Andrew antenna. Requests change to 650-ft. above ground.

Greenville—WHR-481 (Channels A-1-4). South Carolina ETV Commission, Box 11000, 1101 George Rogers Blvd., Columbia, SC 29211. Phone: 803-737-3500. Fax: 803-737-3495. Authorized power: 10-w. each. Antenna: 80-ft. above ground. Lat. 34° 56' 26", long. 82° 24' 38". Transmitter: Rte. 12, Altamont Rd.

Greenville—WHN-712 (Channels B-1-4). South Carolina ETV Commission, Box 11000, 1101 George Rogers Blvd., Columbia, SC 29211. Phone: 803-737-3500. Fax: 803-737-3495. Authorized power: 20-w. each. Antenna: 228-ft. above ground. Lat. 34° 56' 26", long. 82° 24' 38". Transmitter: Paris Mountain, 6.2-mi. N of Greenville. Equipment: ITS transmitter; Andrew antenna.

Greenville—WHR-692 (Channels B-1-4). South Carolina ETV Commission, Box 11000, 1101 George Rogers Blvd., Columbia, SC 29211. Phone: 803-737-3500. Fax: 803-737-3495. Authorized power: 1-w. each. Antenna: 100-ft. above ground. Lat. 34° 51' 40", long. 82° 25' 04". Transmitter: 1613 W. Washington Rd. Equipment: ITS transmitter; Anixter-Mark antenna.

Greenville—WHQ-305 (Channels C-1-4). South Carolina ETV Commission, Box 11000, 1101 George Rogers Blvd., Columbia, SC 29211. Phone: 803-737-3500. Fax: 803-737-3495. Authorized power: 10-w. each. Antenna: 80-ft. above ground. Lat. 34° 56' 26", long. 82° 24' 38". Transmitter: Rte. 12, Altamont Rd.

Greenville—WLX-247 (Channels D-1-4). Greenville Technical College, Box 5616, Greenville, SC 29606. Phone: 803-250-8052. Fax: 803-250-8516.

E-mail: masseyofm@gultec.edu.

Web site: http://www.gultec.edu.

Authorized power: 20-w. each. Antenna: 228-ft. above ground. Lat. 34° 56' 26", long. 82° 24' 38". Transmitter: Paris Mountain, 6.2-mi. N of Greenville. Equipment: ITS transmitter; Andrew antenna.

Greenville—WHR-720 (Channels G-1-4). South Carolina ETV Commission, Box 11000, 1101 George Rogers Blvd., Columbia, SC 29211. Phone: 803-737-3500. Fax: 803-737-3495. Authorized power: 10-w. each. Antenna: 80-ft. above ground. Lat. 34° 56' 26", long. 82° 24' 38". Transmitter: Rte. 12, Altamont Rd.

Greenwood—WHR-726 (Channels D-1-4). South Carolina ETV Commission, Box 11000, 1101 George Rogers Blvd., Columbia, SC 29211. Phone: 803-737-3500. Fax: 803-737-3495. Authorized power: 10-w. each. Antenna: 551-ft. above ground. Lat. 33° 59' 51", long. 82° 03' 07". Transmitter: County Rd. 51. Equipment: Emcee transmitter; Andrew antenna.

Greenwood—WHM-940 (Channels E-1-4). South Carolina ETV Commission, Box 11000, 1101 George Rogers Blvd., Columbia, SC 29211. Phone: 803-737-3500. Fax: 803-737-3495. Authorized power: 0.1-w. each. Antenna: 80-ft. above ground. Lat. 34° 11' 11", long. 82° 08' 57". Transmitter: Greenwood District 50 Administration Office. Equipment: Anixter-Mark antenna.

Greenwood-Ware Shoals—WHR-476 (Channels B-1-4). South Carolina ETV Commission, Box 11000, 1101 George Rogers Blvd., Columbia, SC 29211. Phone: 803-737-3500. Fax: 803-737-3495. Authorized power: 10-w. each. Antenna: 630-ft. above ground. Lat. 34° 11' 10", long. 82° 08' 57". Transmitter: Greenwood Tower, County Rd. 264, Ware Shoals. Equipment: Emcee transmitter; Andrew antenna.

Holly Hill—WHR-451 (Channels G-1-4). South Carolina Educational TV Commission, Box 11000, 1101 George Rogers Blvd., Columbia, SC 29211. Phone: 803-737-3500. Fax: 803-737-3495. Lat. 33° 19' 53", long. 80° 25' 22".

Irmo—WHR-884 (Channels D-1-4). South Carolina ETV Commission, Box 11000, 1101 George Rogers Blvd., Columbia, SC 29211. Phone: 803-737-3500. Fax: 803-737-3495. Authorized power: 1-w. each. Antenna: 255-ft. above ground. Lat. 34° 04' 06", long. 81° 10' 25". Transmitter: Irmo-Chapin Career Center. Equipment: Emcee transmitter; Andrew antenna.

Kingstree—WHQ-445 (Channels C-1-4). South Carolina ETV Commission, Box 11000, 1101 George Rogers Blvd., Columbia, SC 29211. Phone: 803-737-3500. Fax: 803-737-3495. Authorized power: 10-w. each. Antenna: 400-ft. above ground. Lat. 33° 39' 13", long. 79° 49' 22". Transmitter: Kingstree High Annex, 616 Martin Luther King Ave. Equipment: Emcee transmitter; Andrew antenna.

Lake City—KGF-20 (Channels A-1-4). South Carolina ETV Commission, Box 11000, 1101 George Rogers Blvd., Columbia, SC 29211. Phone: 803-737-3500. Fax: 803-737-3495. Authorized power: 10-w. each. Antenna: 400-ft. above ground. Lat. 33° 53' 19", long. 79° 46' 05". Transmitter: District No. 3 Occupations Career Center, Matthews Rd.

Lancaster County—WHR-609 (Channels G-1-4). South Carolina ETV Commission, Drawer L, 2712 Millwood Ave., Columbia, SC 29250. Phone: 803-737-3500. Fax: 803-737-3495. Authorized power: 10-w. each. Antenna: 395-ft. above ground. Lat. 34° 43' 43", long. 80° 46' 44". Transmitter: Lancaster County Area Vocational Center. Requests change to 1-w. each, 476-ft. above ground, lat. 34°43'40", long. 80°46'40"; transmitter to Lancaster Taping Center, Woodland & Roddey Rds.; Emcee transmitter; Mark antenna.

Lexington—WHQ-373 (Channels E-1-4). South Carolina ETV Commission, Box 11000, 1101 George Rogers Blvd., Columbia, SC 29211. Phone: 803-737-3500. Fax: 803-737-3495. Authorized power: 10-w. each. Antenna: 912-ft. above ground. Lat. 33° 58' 31", long. 81° 18' 12". Transmitter: Lexington Vocational Center, 2412 Augusta Hwy., Lexington. Equipment: Andrew antenna.

Marion County—WHR-485 (Channels B-1-4). South Carolina ETV Commission, Box 11000, 1101 George Rogers Blvd., Columbia, SC 29211. Phone: 803-737-3500. Fax: 803-737-3495. Authorized power: 10-w. each. Antenna: 395-ft. above ground. Lat. 34° 11' 08", long. 79° 20' 28". Transmitter: Marion Mullins Vocational Center.

Moncks Corner—WHR-961 (Channels B-1-4). South Carolina ETV Commission, Box 1100, 1101 George Rogers Blvd., Columbia, SC 29211. Phone: 803-737-3500. Fax: 803-737-3495. Authorized power: 10-w. each. Antenna: 354-ft. above ground. Lat. 33° 06' 53", long. 80° 01' 03". Transmitter: 2226 Old Hwy. 52. Equipment: Emcee transmitter; Andrew antenna.

Newberry County—WHN-711 (Channels C-1-4). South Carolina ETV Commission, Box 11000, 1101 George Rogers Blvd., Columbia, SC 29211. Phone: 803-737-3500. Fax: 803-737-3495. Authorized power: 10-w. each. Antenna: 317-ft. above ground. Lat. 34° 17' 04", long. 81° 34' 36". Transmitter: Newberry Vocational Center, Newberry. Equipment: Emcee transmitter; Andrew antenna.

North Charleston—WLX-206 (Channels B-1-4). Trident Technical College, Box 10367, Charleston, SC 29411. Phone: 803-569-6486. Fax: 803-820-5075. Authorized power: 10-w. each. Antenna: 410-ft. above ground. Lat. 32° 48' 07", long. 80° 01' 26". Transmitter: 1870 Wallace School Rd. Equipment: Comwave transmitter; Andrew antenna.

Leased to WLCC Management Corp., Box 62889, North Charlston, SC 29419.

North Charleston—WHR-932 (Channels G-1-4). Trident Technical College, Box 10367, Charleston, SC 29411. Phone: 803-569-6486. Fax: 803-820-5075. Authorized power: 50-w. each. Antenna: 413-ft. above ground. Lat. 32° 48' 07", long. 80° 01' 26". Transmitter: 1870 Wallace School Rd. Equipment: Comwave transmitter; Andrew antenna.

Leased to WLCC Management Corp., Box 62889, North Charleston, SC 29419.

Orangeburg—WHN-708 (Channels B-1-4). South Carolina ETV Commission, Box 11000, 1101 George Rogers Blvd., Columbia, SC 29211. Phone: 803-737-3500. Fax: 803-737-3495. Authorized power: 10-w. each. Antenna: 100-ft. above ground. Lat. 33° 31' 48", long. 80° 50' 10". Transmitter: Calhoun-Orangeburg Vocational Center.

Orangeburg—WHN-708 (Channels C-1-4). South Carolina ETV Commission, Drawer L, Columbia, SC 29250. Phone: 803-737-3500. Authorized power: 10-w. each. Antenna: 400-ft. above ground. Lat. 33° 31' 48", long. 805° 01' 0". Transmitter: Calhoun-Orangeburg county line. Equipment: Comwave transmitter; Andrew antenna.

Orangeburg—WHQ-405 (Channels F-1-2). South Carolina ETV Commission, Box 11000, 1101 George Rogers Blvd., Columbia, SC 29211. Phone: 803-737-3500. Fax: 803-737-3495. Authorized power: 10-w. each. Antenna: 400-ft. above ground. Lat. 33° 31' 47", long. 80° 50' 10". Transmitter: Calhoun-Orangeburg Vocational Center.

Pickens—WND-452 (Channels A-1-4). South Carolina ETV Commission, Box 11000, 1101 George Rogers Blvd., Columbia, SC 29211. Phone: 803-737-3500. Fax: 803-737-3495. Authorized power: 1-w. each. Antenna: 43-ft. above ground. Lat. 34° 53' 26", long. 82° 42' 21". Transmitter: Pickens County Technical Center, Ann St. & W. Jones Ave. Equipment: Emcee transmitter; Mark antenna.

Ridgeland—WHN-713 (Channels F-1-4). South Carolina ETV Commission, Box 11000, 1101 George Rogers Blvd., Columbia, SC 29211. Phone: 803-737-3500. Fax: 803-737-3495. Authorized power: 10-w. each. Antenna: 395-ft. above ground. Lat. 32° 21' 10", long. 80° 55' 16". Transmitter: Beaufort-Jasper Career Center, Rte. 1.

Rock Hill—WHM-936 (Channels C-1-4). South Carolina ETV Commission, Box 11000, 1101 George Rogers Blvd., Columbia, SC 29211. Phone: 803-737-3500. Fax: 803-737-3495. Authorized power: 10-w. each. Antenna: 88-ft. above ground. Lat. 34° 44' 11", long. 80° 47' 15". Transmitter: Rte. 2, Box 102.

Rock Hill—WHQ-397 (Channels D-1-4). South Carolina ETV Commission, Box 11000, 1101 George Rogers Blvd., Columbia, SC 29211. Phone: 803-737-3500. Fax: 803-737-3495. Authorized power: 10-w. each. Antenna: 188-ft. above ground. Lat. 34° 55' 55", long. 81° 00' 38". Transmitter: Northside Elementary School, 840 N. Annafrel St.

Seneca—WHN-702 (Channels E-1-4). South Carolina ETV Commission, Box 11000, 1101 George Rogers Blvd., Columbia, SC 29211. Phone: 803-737-3500. Fax: 803-737-3495. Authorized power: 10-w. each. Antenna: 200-ft. above ground. Lat. 34° 42' 54", long. 82° 59' 29". Transmitter: Oconee Area Vocational Center, Hwy. 188. Equipment: Emcee transmitter; Andrew antenna.

Spartanburg—WHN-705 (Channels F-1-4). South Carolina ETV Commission, Box 11000, 1101 George Rogers Blvd., Columbia, SC 29211. Phone: 803-737-3500. Fax: 803-737-3495. Authorized power: 0.1-w. each. Antenna: 76-ft. above ground. Lat. 34° 27' 26", long. 81° 53' 55". Transmitter: Spartanburg Taping Center, Du Pre Dr.

Summerville—WHR-980 (Channels B-1-4). South Carolina ETV Commission, Box 11000, 1101 George Rogers Blvd., Columbia, SC 29211. Phone: 803-737-3500. Fax: 803-737-3495. Authorized power: 10-w. each. Antenna: 405-ft. above ground. Lat. 33° 01' 56", long. 80° 14' 43". Transmitter: Old Orangeburg Rd. Equipment: Emcee transmitter; Andrew antenna. Requests change to 10-w, 125-ft. above ground, lat. 32° 59' 41", long. 80° 12' 58"; transmitter to Dorchester District 2 Administrative Offices, 105 Greenwave Blvd.

Summerville—WLX-222 (Channels D-1-4). South Carolina ETV Commission, Box 11000, 1101 George Rogers Blvd., Columbia, SC 29211. Phone: 803-737-3500. Fax: 803-737-3495. Authorized power: 10-w. each. Antenna: 405-ft. above ground. Lat. 33° 01' 56", long. 80° 14' 43". Transmitter: Old Orangeburg Rd. Equipment: Emcee transmitter; Andrew antenna.

Sumter—WHM-932 (Channels C-1-4). South Carolina ETV Commission, Box 11000, 1101 George Rogers Blvd., Columbia, SC 29211. Phone: 803-737-3500. Fax: 803-737-3495. Authorized power: 10-w. each. Antenna: 600-ft. above ground. Lat. 33° 55' 52", long. 80° 16' 14". Transmitter: WRJA-TV transmitter site.

Sumter—WHR-471 (Channels E-1-4). South Carolina ETV Commission, Box 11000, 1101 George Rogers Blvd., Columbia, SC 29211. Phone: 803-737-3500. Fax: 803-737-3495. Authorized power: 10-w. each. Lat. 33° 55' 52", long. 80° 16' 14". Transmitter: Sumter.

Sumter—WHR-470 (Channels G-1-4). South Carolina ETV Commission, Box 11000, 1101 George Rogers Blvd., Columbia, SC 29211. Phone: 803-737-3500. Fax: 803-737-3495. Authorized power: 10-w. each. Lat. 33° 55' 12", long. 80° 20' 25". Transmitter: WRJA-TV studio.

Union—WLX-244 (Channels B-1-4). South Carolina ETV Commission, Box 11000, 1101 George Rogers Blvd., Columbia, SC 29211. Phone: 803-737-3500. Fax: 803-737-3495. Authorized power: 10-w. each. Antenna: 148-ft. above ground. Lat. 34° 43' 00", long. 81° 36' 55". Transmitter: Goss St. Equipment: Emcee transmitter; Mark antenna.

Walterboro—WHR-933 (Channels C-1-4). South Carolina ETV Commission, Box 11000, 1101 George Rogers Blvd., Columbia, SC 29211. Phone: 803-737-3500. Fax: 803-737-3495. Authorized power: 1-w. each. Antenna: 90-ft. above ground. Lat. 32° 54' 12", long. 80° 40' 06". Transmitter: 807 Hampton St. Equipment: Emcee transmitter; Anixter-Mark antenna.

Ware Shoals—WHR-500 (Channels G-1-4). South Carolina ETV Commission, Box 11000, 1101 George Rogers Blvd., Columbia, SC 29211. Phone: 803-737-3500. Fax: 803-737-3495. Authorized power: 10-w. each. Lat. 34° 22' 21", long. 82° 10' 03". Transmitter: Greenwood Tower, County Rd. 30-264. Equipment: Emcee transmitter; Andrew antenna.

West Columbia School District—WHQ-446 (Channels G-1-4). South Carolina ETV Commission, Box 11000, 1101 George Rogers Blvd., Columbia, SC 29211. Phone: 803-737-3500. Fax: 803-737-3495. Authorized power: 10-w. each. Antenna: 299-ft. above ground. Lat. 33° 59' 15", long. 81° 03' 49". Transmitter: Lexington District No. 2, Administration Office, 715 9th St., West Columbia.

White Stone—WHQ-402 (Channels G-1-4). South Carolina ETV Commission, Box 11000, 1101 George Rogers Blvd., Columbia, SC 29211. Phone: 803-737-3500. Fax: 803-737-3495. Authorized power: 10-w. each. Antenna: 859-ft. above ground. Lat. 34° 53' 09", long. 81° 49' 15". Transmitter: WRET-TV transmitter site.

White Stone & Spartanburg—WHQ-447 (Channels B-1-4). South Carolina ETV Commission, Box 11000, 1101 George Rogers Blvd., Columbia, SC 29211. Phone: 803-737-3500. Fax: 803-737-3495. Authorized power: 1-w. each. Antenna: 100-ft. above ground. Lat. 34° 59' 57", long. 81° 58' 00". Transmitter: WRET-TV transmitter site. Equipment: Emcee transmitter; Anixter-Mark antenna.

Winnsboro—WND-451 (Channels A-1-4). South Carolina ETV Commission, Box 11000, 1101 George Rogers Blvd., Columbia, SC 29211. Phone: 803-737-3500. Fax: 803-737-3495. Authorized power: 1-w. each. Antenna: 105-ft. above ground. Lat. 34° 21' 27", long. 81° 05' 57". Transmitter: Fairfield Central High School, Hwy. 321 bypass. Equipment: Emcee transmitter; Mark antenna.

Winnsboro—WHM-926 (Channels D-1-4). South Carolina ETV Commission, Box 11000, 1101 George Rogers Blvd., Columbia, SC 29211. Phone: 803-737-3500. Fax: 803-737-3495. Authorized power: 10-w. each. Antenna: 395-ft. above ground. Lat. 34° 23' 57", long. 81° 05' 51". Transmitter: Winnsboro Area Vocational Center.

York—WHN-703 (Channels E-1-4). South Carolina ETV Commission, Box 11000, 1101 George Rogers Blvd., Columbia, SC 29211. Phone: 803-737-3500. Fax: 803-737-3495. Authorized power: 10-w. each. Antenna: 400-ft. above ground. Lat. 34° 59' 09", long. 81° 14' 58". Transmitter: 18 Spruce St. Equipment: ITS transmitter; HMD antenna.

York & Rock Hill—WBX-216 (Channels A-1-2). South Carolina ETV Commission, Box 11000, 1101 George Rogers Blvd., Columbia, SC 29211. Phone: 803-737-3500. Fax: 803-737-3495. Authorized power: 10-w. each. Antenna: 200-ft. above ground. Lat. 34° 55' 55", long. 81° 00' 38". Transmitter: 840 N. Annafrel St., Rock Hill.

York & Rock Hill—WBX-217 (Channels G-1-2). South Carolina ETV Commission, Box 11000, 1101 George Rogers Blvd., Columbia, SC 29211. Phone: 803-737-3500. Fax: 803-737-3495. Authorized power: 0.1-w. each. Antenna: 50-ft. above ground. Lat. 34° 55' 16", long. 81° 01' 12". Transmitter: 522 E. Main St., Rock Hill.

South Dakota

Bath—WNC-828 (Channels A-1-4). Northern State U., 1200 S. Jay St., Aberdeen, SD 57401. Authorized power: 50-w. each. Antenna: 499-ft. above ground. Lat. 45° 27' 57", long. 98° 20'

08". Transmitter: 0.5-mi. W of Bath. Equipment: Emcee transmitter; Andrew antenna.

Bath—WLX-900 (Channels B-1-4). Warner School District, 1200 2nd Ave., Warner, SD 57479. Authorized power: 50-w. each. Antenna: 1791-ft. above ground. Lat. 45° 27' 57", long. 98° 20' 12". Transmitter: 0.5-mi. W of Bath. Equipment: ITS transmitter; Bogner antenna.

Bath—WLX-288 (Channels D-1-4). Elm Valley School District, Box 6, Barnard, SD 57426. Authorized power: 50-w. each. Antenna: 1791-ft. above ground. Lat. 45° 27' 57", long. 98° 20' 12". Transmitter: 0.5-mi. W of Bath. Equipment: ITS transmitter; Andrew antenna.

Colman—WNC-780 (Channels A-1-2). Lake Central School District 39-2, 800 N.E. 9th St., Madison, SD 57042. Authorized power: 50-w. each. Antenna: 402-ft. above ground. Lat. 43° 59' 31", long. 96° 46' 10". Transmitter: 1-mi. NNW of Interstate 29 & State Rte. 34 intersection. Equipment: Emcee transmitter; Andrew antenna.

Colman—WNC-784 (Channels A-3-4). Rutland School District, Box 89, Rutland, SD 57057. Phone: 605-586-4352. Fax: 605-586-4343.

E-mail: Rutland@itc.com.

Authorized power: 50-w. each. Antenna: 402-ft. above ground. Lat. 43° 59' 31", long. 96° 46' 10". Transmitter: 1-mi. NNW of Interstate 29 & State Rte. 34 intersection. Equipment: Emcee transmitter; Andrew antenna.

Leased to Sioux Valley TV, Colman, SD 57017. Phone: 605-256-3586.

Colman—WNC-303 (Channels C-1-4). Dakota State U., Washington Ave., Madison, SD 57042. Authorized power: 50-w. each. Antenna: 404-ft. above ground. Lat. 43° 59' 31", long. 96° 46' 10". Transmitter: 1-mi. NNW of I-29 & State Rte. 34 intersection. Equipment: Emcee transmitter; Bogner antenna. Requests change to 406-ft. above ground.

Colman—WNC-783 (Channels D-1-4). Oldham-Ramona School District No. 39-5, Box 8, Ramona, SD 57054. Authorized power: 50-w. each. Antenna: 402-ft. above ground. Lat. 43° 59' 31", long. 96° 46' 10". Transmitter: 1-mi. NNW of Interstate 29 & State Rte. 34 intersection. Equipment: Emcee transmitter; Andrew antenna.

Colman—WNC-782 (Channels G-1-4). Chester Area Schools 39-1, Box 159, Chester, SD 57016. Authorized power: 50-w. each. Antenna: 402-ft. above ground. Lat. 43° 59' 31", long. 96° 46' 10". Transmitter: 1-mi. NNW of I-29 & State Rte. 34 intersection. Equipment: Emcee transmitter; Andrew antenna.

Elk Point—WNC-345 (Channels A-1-4). Dakota Valley School District No. 61-8, Box 1960, N. Sioux City, SD 57049. Phone: 605-232-3190. Fax: 605-232-3198. Authorized power: 12.6-w. each. Antenna: 348-ft. above ground. Lat. 42° 45' 35", long. 96° 44' 17". Transmitter: 2.5-mi. W of Rtes. 11 & 50 intersection, 5.9-mi. from Elk Point. Equipment: Comwave transmitter; Andrew antenna.

Elk Point—WNC-344 (Channels B-1-4). Wakonda School District No. 13-2, 2nd & Nebraska, Wakonda, SD 57033. Authorized power: 12.6-w. each. Antenna: 348-ft. above ground. Lat. 42° 45' 35", long. 96° 44' 17". Transmitter: 2.5-mi. W of Rtes. 11 & 50 intersection, 5.9-mi. from Elk Point. Equipment: Comwave transmitter; Andrew antenna.

Elk Point—WNC-343 (Channels C-1-4). Alcester Hudson District No. 61-1, 5th & Iowa, Alcester, SD 57001. Authorized power: 12.6-w. each. Antenna: 348-ft. above ground. Lat. 42° 45'35", long. 96° 44' 17". Transmitter: 2.5-mi. W of Rtes. 11 & 50 intersection, 5.9-mi. from Elk Point. Equipment: Comwave transmitter; Andrew antenna.

Elk Point—WNC-342 (Channels D-1-4). Elk Point School District No. 61-3, Box 578, Elk Point, SD 57025. Authorized power: 12.6-w. each. Antenna: 348-ft. above ground. Lat. 42° 45'35", long. 96° 44' 17". Transmitter: 2.5-mi. W of Rtes. 11 & 50 intersection, 5.9-mi. from Elk Point. Equipment: Comwave transmitter; Andrew antenna.

Elk Point—WNC-341 (Channels G-1-4). Vermillion School District No. 13-1, 17 Prospect, Vermillion, SD 57069. Authorized power: 12.6-w. each. Antenna: 348-ft. above ground. Lat. 42° 45' 35", long. 96° 44' 17". Transmitter: 2.5-mi. W of Rtes. 11 & 50 intersection, 5.9-mi. from Elk Point. Equipment: Comwave transmitter; Andrew antenna.

Kranzburg—WNC-960 (Channels B-1-4). Deuel School District, Box 770, Clear Lake, SD 57226. Authorized power: 50-w. each. Antenna: 404-ft. above ground. Lat. 44° 55' 15", long. 96° 53' 33". Transmitter: 2.25-mi N of Kranzburg. Equipment: Emcee transmitter; Bogner antenna.

Kranzburg—WNC-959 (Channels D-1-4). Waverly School District, Box 81, Waverly, SD 57202. Authorized power: 50-w. each. Antenna: 2425-ft. above ground. Lat. 44° 55' 15", long. 96° 53' 33". Transmitter: 2.25-mi. N of Kranzburg. Equipment: Emcee transmitter; Bogner antenna.

Montrose—WNC-529 (Channels D-1-4). Montrose School District No. 43-2, Box 350, Rte. 2, Montrose, SD 57048. Phone: 605-363-5025. Fax: 605-363-3513.

E-mail: ccolwill@dtgnet.com.

Authorized power: 50-w. each. Antenna: 697-ft. above ground. Lat. 43° 30' 11", long. 96° 34' 38". Transmitter: 1.7-mi. SW of Rowena. Equipment: Emcee transmitter; Andrew antenna.

Rapid City—WLX-872 (Channels B-1-4). South Dakota School of Mines & Technology, 501 E. St. Joseph St., Rapid City, SD 57701. Phone: 605-394-2371. Fax: 605-394-6131. Authorized power: 20-w. each. Antenna: 303-ft. above ground. Lat. 44° 02' 48", long. 103° 14' 46". Transmitter: 2-mi. S of Rapid City. Equipment: ITS transmitter; Bogner antenna.

Leased to American Telecasting of Rapid City Inc., 5575 Tech Center Dr., Suite 300, Colorado Springs, CO 80919. Phone: 719-260-5533.

Rapid City—WLX-863 (Channels D-1-4). Black Hills State U., Box 9500, University Station, Spearfish, SD 57799. Authorized power: 20-w. each. Antenna: 303-ft. above ground. Lat. 44° 02' 48", long. 103° 14' 46". Transmitter: 2-mi. S of Rapid City. Equipment: ITS transmitter; Bogner antenna.

Rapid City—WNC-760 (Channels G-1-4). National College, 321 Kansas City St., Rapid City, SD 57701. Authorized power: 20-w. each. Antenna: 497-ft. above ground. Lat. 44° 02' 48", long. 103° 14' 46". Transmitter: 2-mi. S of Rapid City. Equipment: ITS transmitter; Bogner antenna.

Sioux Falls—WHR-669 (Channels A-1-2). Augustana College Assn., Augusta College, 29th & Summit Ave., Sioux Falls, SD 57197. Authorized power: 50-w. each. Antenna: 623-ft. above ground. Lat. 43° 30' 11", long. 96° 34' 38". Transmitter: 1.7-mi. SW of Rowena. Equipment: Emcee transmitter; Andrew antenna.

Sioux Falls—WNC-531 (Channels A-3-4). Canistota Public School, 421 4th Ave., Canistota, SD 57012. Phone: 605-296-3458. Fax: 605-296-3158. Authorized power: 50-w. each. Antenna: 699-ft. above ground. Lat. 43° 30' 11", long. 96° 34' 38". Transmitter: 1.7-mi. SW of Rowena. Equipment: Emcee transmitter; Andrew antenna.

Sioux Falls—WNC-546 (Channels B-1-4). U. of South Dakota, 414 E. Clark, Vermillion, SD 57069. Phone: 605-677-5011. Authorized power: 50-w. each. Antenna: 623-ft. above ground. Lat. 43° 30' 11", long. 96° 34' 38". Transmitter: 1.7-mi. SW of Rowena. Equipment: Emcee transmitter; Andrew antenna.

Sioux Falls—WHR-752 (Channels C-1-4). Minnesota Public Radio, 45 E. 7th St., St. Paul, MN 55101. Phone: 651-290-1259. Fax: 651-290-1342. Authorized power: 50-w. each. Antenna: 699-ft. above ground. Lat. 43° 30' 11", long. 96° 34' 38". Transmitter: 1.7-mi SW of Rowena.

Leased to Sioux Valley Wireless, Juction Hwy. 34 & 77, Box 20, Colman, SD 57017. Phone: 605-534-3241.

Sioux Falls—WNC-547 (Channels G-1-4). Sioux Falls Catholic Schools, 3201 S. Kiwanis, Sioux Falls, SD 57105. Phone: 605-336-3644. Authorized power: 50-w. each. Antenna: 623-ft. above ground. Lat. 43° 30' 11", long. 96° 34' 38". Transmitter: 1.7-mi. SW of Rowena. Equipment: Emcee transmitter; Andrew antenna.

Willow Lake—WNC-820 (Channels B-1-4). Willow Lake School District, Box 170, Willow Lake, SD 57278. Authorized power: 50-w. each. Antenna: 492-ft. above ground. Lat. 44° 35' 24", long. 97° 40' 45". Transmitter: 2.5-mi. S & 0.5-mi. W of Willow Lake. Equipment: Emcee transmitter; Scala antenna.

Willow Lake—WNC-827 (Channels D-1-4). De Smet School District 38-2, Box K, De Smet, SD 57231. Authorized power: 50-w. each. Antenna: 492-ft. above ground. Lat. 44° 35' 24", long. 97° 40' 45". Transmitter: 2.5-mi. S & 0.5-mi. W of Willow Lake. Equipment: Emcee transmitter; Andrew antenna.

Tennessee

Chattanooga—WHR-684 (Channels B-1-4). Chattanooga State Technical Community College, 4501 Amnicola Hwy., Chattanooga, TN 37406. Phone: 423-697-4408. Fax: 423-697-4479.

Web site: http://www.cstcc.cc.tn.us.

Authorized power: 100-w. each. Antenna: 190-ft. above ground. Lat. 355° 12' 34", long. 85° 16' 39". Transmitter: 1.4-mi. N of Falling Water. Equipment: Comwave transmitter; Andrew antenna.

Leased to Wireless One, 1080 River Oaks Dr., No. A150, Jackson, MS 39208. Phone: 601-936-1515.

Clarksville—WLX-939 (Channels A-1-4). Meharry Medical College, 1005 Todd Blvd., Nashville, TN 37208. Authorized power: 10-w. each. Antenna: 152-ft. above ground. Lat. 36° 26' 00", long. 87° 25' 22". Transmitter: Clarksville area. Equipment: Comwave transmitter; Andrew antenna.

Clarksville—WNC-405 (Channels B-1-4). Immaculate Conception School, 709 Franklin St., Clarksville, TN 37040. Authorized power: 10-w. each. Antenna: 499-ft. above ground. Lat. 36° 26' 00", long. 87° 25' 22". Transmitter: Hackberry, 0.7-mi. S of Vernon Creek & Addway Rds. intersection. Equipment: Comwave transmitter; Andrew antenna.

Clarksville—WNC-918 (Channels C-1-4). Clarksville Montgomery County School, 501 Franklin St., Clarksville, TN 37041. Phone: 931-648-5600. Fax: 931-648-5612. Authorized power: 10-w. each. Antenna: 1079-ft. above ground. Lat. 36° 26' 00", long. 87° 25' 22". Transmitter: 0.7-mi. S of Vernon Creek & Addway Rds. intersection. Equipment: Comwave transmitter; Andrew antenna.

Leased to Future Vision, 316 Madison St., Clarksville, TN 37040. Phone: 931-648-8833.

Clarksville—WLX-820 (Channels D-1-4). Belmont College, 1900 Belmont Blvd., Nashville, TN 37212. Authorized power: 10-w. each. Antenna: 152-ft. above ground. Lat. 36° 26' 00", long. 87° 25' 22". Transmitter: Clarksville area. Equipment: Comwave transmitter; Andrew antenna.

Fairmont—WHR-612 (Channels D-1-4). Chattanooga State Technical Community College, 4501 Americola Hwy., Chattanooga, TN 37406. Phone: 423-697-4408. Fax: 423-697-4479.

Web site: http://www.cstcc.cc.tn.us.

Authorized power: 100-w. each. Antenna: 200-ft. above ground. Lat. 35° 12' 34", long. 85° 16' 39". Transmitter: 1.4-mi. N of Falling Water. Equipment: Comwave transmitter; Andrew antenna.

Leased to Wireless One, 1080 River Oaks Dr., No. A150, Jackson, MS 39208. Phone: 601-936-1515.

Fairmont—WNC-915 (Channels G-1-4). Walker County Board of Education, 201 S. Duke St., Lafayette, GA 30728. Authorized power: 1-w. each. Antenna: 98-ft. above ground. Lat. 35° 12' 34", long. 85° 16' 39". Transmitter: 1.4-mi. N of Falling Water. Equipment: Emcee transmitter; Bogner antenna.

Franklin—WHR-862 (Channels G-3-4). Columbia State Community College, Box 1315, Columbia, TN 38402-1315. Phone: 615-540-2791. Fax: 615-540-2565.

E-mail: ross@coscc.cc.tn.us.

Authorized power: 1-w. each. Antenna: 380-ft. above ground. Lat. 35° 55' 22", long. 86° 42' 38". Transmitter: Clovercroft Rd. Equipment: GPT-CV transmitter; Andrew antenna.

Gates—WNC-212 (Channels A-1-4). Caruthersville School District No. 8, 1711 Ward Ave., Caruthersville, TN 63830. Phone: 314-333-6100. Fax: 314-333-6108. Authorized power: 50-w. each. Antenna: 645-ft. above ground. Lat. 35° 48' 47", long. 89° 24' 23". Transmitter: 1.75-mi. S of Gates. Equipment: Comwave transmitter; Andrew antenna.

Gates—WNC-201 (Channels B-1-4). Cooter Reorganized School District R-IV, Hwy. E, Cooter, MO 63839. Phone: 573-695-4972. Fax: 573-695-3073.

E-mail: crowder.chs@cooter.k12.mo.us.

Web site: http://cooter.k12.mo.us.

Authorized power: 50-w. each. Antenna: 645-ft. above ground. Lat. 35° 48' 47", long. 89° 24' 23". Transmitter: 1.75-mi. S of Gates. Equipment: Comwave transmitter; Andrew antenna.

Nucenrix Broadband Networks, 200 Chisholm Place, Suite 200 Plano, TX 75075. Phone: 972-423-9494. Fax: 972-423-0819

Gates—WLX-617 (Channels C-1-4). Armorel School District No. 9, S. Main St., Armorel, AR 72310. Authorized power: 50-w. each. Antenna: 645-ft. above ground. Lat. 35° 48' 47", long. 89° 24' 23". Transmitter: 1.75-mi. S of Gates. Equipment: Comwave transmitter; Andrew antenna.

Gates—WLX-618 (Channels D-1-4). South Pemiscot District R-V, 611 Beasley, Steele, MO 63877. Authorized power: 50-w. each. Antenna: 645-ft. above ground. Lat. 35° 48' 47", long. 89° 24' 23". Transmitter: 1.75-mi. S of Gates. Equipment: Comwave transmitter; Andrew antenna.

Gates—WLX-621 (Channels G-1-4). Trenton Special School District, 201 W. 10th St., Trenton, TN 37074. Authorized power: 50-w. each. Antenna: 704-ft. above ground. Lat. 35° 48' 47", long. 89° 24' 23". Transmitter: 1.75-mi. S of Gates. Equipment: Comwave transmitter; Andrew antenna.

Jackson—WLX-819 (Channels A-1-4). Freed-Hardeman U., 158 E. Main St., Henderson, TN 38340. Phone: 901-989-6002. Fax: 901-989-3890. Authorized power: 20-w. each. Antenna: 300-ft. above ground. Lat. 35° 38' 46", long. 88° 49' 57". Transmitter: Hwys. 45 & 412 intersection. Equipment: ITS transmitter; Andrew antenna. Requests change to 506-ft. above ground, lat. 35° 42' 17", long. 88° 44' 45"; transmitter to 2-mi. N of I-40 I-70 intersection.

Leased to Skyview Wireless Cable Inc., 45 Executive Dr., Jackson, TN 38305. Phone: 615-645-5616.

Jackson—WLX-818 (Channels B-1-4). Lambuth College, 706 Lambuth Blvd., Jackson, TN 38301. Authorized power: 10-w. each. Antenna: 300-ft. above ground. Lat. 35° 38' 46", long. 88° 49' 57". Transmitter: Hwys. 45 & 412 intersection. Equipment: ITS transmitter; Andrew antenna. Requests change to 20-w. each; lat. 35° 42' 17", long. 88° 44' 45", transmitter to 2-mi. N of I-70 & I-40 .

Jackson—WLX-817 (Channels G-1-4). Lane College, 545 Lane Ave., Jackson, IN 38301. Authorized power: 10-w. each. Antenna: 597-ft. above ground. Lat. 35° 38' 46", long. 88° 49' 57". Transmitter: Hwys. 45 & 412 intersection. Equipment: ITS transmitter; Andrew antenna.

Johnson City area—WHR-816 (Channels A-1-4). East Tennessee State U., Box 70558, Academic Affairs, Johnson City, TN 37614-0558. Phone: 423-439-6431. Fax: 423-439-5770.

E-mail: duryc@etsu.edu.

Web site: http://www.etsu.edu.

Authorized power: 0.1-w. each. Antenna: 100-ft. above ground. Lat. 36° 18' 07", long. 82° 21' 44". Transmitter: East Tennessee State U. Telecenter. Equipment: Bogner antenna.

Johnson City area—WHR-817 (Channels D-1-4). East Tennessee State U., Box 70558, Information Resources, Johnson City, TN 37614-0558. Phone: 423-439-6431. Fax: 423-439-5770.

E-mail: duryc@etsu.edu.

Web site: http://www.etsu.edu.

Authorized power: 10-w. each. Antenna: 350-ft. above ground. Lat. 36° 16' 07", long. 82° 20' 21". Transmitter: Buffalo Mountain, approx. 2-mi. S of Johnson City. Equipment: Emcee transmitter; Bogner antenna.

Kingsport—WHR-482 (Channel B-1). Kingsport City Schools, 1800 Legion Dr., Kingsport, TN 37664. Authorized power: 10-w. Antenna: 148-ft. above ground. Lat. 36° 31' 37", long. 82° 35' 14". Equipment: Emcee transmitter; Anixter-Mark antenna.

Knoxville—WLX-223 (Channels A-1-4). Northern Arizona U. Foundation, Box 4094, Flagstaff, AZ 86011. Authorized power: 50-w. each. Antenna: 433-ft. above ground. Lat. 36° 00' 08", long. 83° 56' 41". Transmitter: 331 Sharp's Ridge Rd. Equipment: Comwave transmitter; Bogner antenna.

Leased to Cherokee Wireless of Knoxville, Box 186, Rexford, NY 12148. Phone: 518-374-0651.

Knoxville—WLX-221 (Channels B-1-4). Johnson Bible College, 7900 Johnson Dr., Knoxville, TN 37998. Authorized power: 50-w. each. Antenna: 433-ft. above ground. Lat. 36° 00' 08", long. 83° 56' 41". Transmitter: 331 Sharp's Ridge Rd. Equipment: Comwave transmitter; Bogner antenna.

Knoxville—WLX-224 (Channels D-1-4). National Conference on Citizenship, No. 504, 3550 Biscayne Blvd., Miami, FL 33143. Authorized power: 50-w. each. Antenna: 433-ft. above ground. Lat. 36° 00' 08", long. 83° 56' 41". Transmitter: 331 Sharp's Ridge Rd. Equipment: ITS transmitter; Bogner antenna.

Knoxville—WHR-732 (Channels G-1-4). Pellissippi State Technical Community College, Box 22990, Knoxville, TN 37933. Authorized power: 50-w. each. Antenna: 433-ft. above ground. Lat. 36° 00' 08", long. 83° 56' 41". Transmitter: 331 Sharp's Ridge Rd. Equipment: Emcee transmitter; Bogner antenna.

Lawrenceburg—WNC-210 (Channels A-1-4). Lawrence County Board of Education, 410 W. Gains St., Lawrenceburg, TN 38464. Authorized power: 10-w. each. Antenna: 469-ft. above ground. Lat. 35° 12' 18", long. 87° 19' 39". Transmitter: 0.5-mi. W of Hwy. 43. Equipment: ITS transmitter; Andrew antenna.

Lawrenceburg—WNC-352 (Channels B-1-4). Sacred Heart School, 307 Church St., Loretto, TN 38469. Authorized power: 10-w. each. Antenna: 469-ft. above ground. Lat. 35° 12' 18", long. 87° 19' 39". Transmitter: 0.5-mi. W of Hwy. 43. Equipment: ITS transmitter; Andrew antenna.

Lawrenceburg—WNC-211 (Channels C-1-4). Seventh Day Adventist School, 441 Crawfish Valley Rd., Lawrenceburg, TN 38464. Authorized power: 10-w. each. Antenna: 469-ft. above ground. Lat. 35° 12' 18", long. 87° 19' 39". Transmitter: 0.5-mi. W of Hwy. 43. Equipment: ITS transmitter; Andrew antenna.

Lawrenceburg—WNC-327 (Channels D-1-4). Wayne County Board of Education, 325 Hassel St., Waynesboro, TN 37221. Phone: 931-722-3548. Fax: 931-722-7579. Authorized power: 10-w. each. Antenna: 469-ft. above ground. Lat. 35° 12' 18", long. 87° 19' 39". Transmitter: Lawrence County. Equipment: ITS transmitter; Andrew antenna.

Leased to Wireless One Inc., 2506 Lakeland Dr., Suite 403, Jackson, MS 39208. Phone: 601-933-6871.

Lawrenceburg—WNC-209 (Channels G-1-4). Giles County Board of Education, 720 W. Flowers St., Pulaski, TN 38478. Authorized power: 10-w. each. Antenna: 469-ft. above ground. Lat. 35° 12' 18", long. 87° 19' 39". Transmitter: 0.5-mi. W of Hwy. 43. Equipment: ITS transmitter; Andrew antenna.

Lone Oak—WHR-613 (Channels B-1-4). Chattanooga State Technical Community College, 4501 Amnicola Hwy., Chattanooga, TN 37406. Phone: 423-697-4408. Fax: 423-697-4479.

Web site: http://www.cstcc.cc.tn.us.

Authorized power: 10-w. each. Antenna: 180-ft. above ground. Lat. 35° 14' 13", long. 85° 24' 25". Transmitter: Rte. 127, 4-mi. NW of Lone Oak.

Leased to Wireless One, 1080 River Oaks Dr., No. A150, Jackson, MS 39208. Phone: 601-936-1515.

Memphis—WHR-533 (Channels A-1-4). Mid-South Public Communications Foundation, Box 241880, Memphis, TN 38124-1880. Phone: 901-458-2521. Fax: 901-325-6505.

E-mail: wknotv@wkno.org.

Authorized power: 15-w. each. Antenna: 415-ft. above ground. Lat. 35° 06' 45", long. 89° 53' 32". Transmitter: 5100 Poplar Ave. Equipment: Comwave transmitter; Andrew antenna.

Leased to Wireless One, Baton Rouge, LA. Phone: 504-293-5000.

Memphis—WLX-907 (Channels C-1-4). Lemoyne-Owen College, 807 Walker Ave., Memphis, TN 38126. Authorized power: 15-w. each. Antenna: 415-ft. above ground. Lat. 35° 06' 45", long. 89° 53' 52". Transmitter: 5100 Poplar Ave. Equipment: ITS transmitter; Andrew antenna.

Memphis—WNC-358 (Channels D-1-4). North American Catholic Educational Programming Foundation Inc., Box 40026, Providence, RI 02940-0026. Phone: 401-709-0900. Authorized power: 10-w. each. Antenna: 295-ft. above ground. Lat. 35° 06' 47", long. 89° 53' 54". Transmitter: 5050 Poplar Ave. Equipment: Emcee transmitter; Andrew antenna.

Memphis—WNC-363 (Channels G-1-4). State Technical Institute, 5983 Macon Cove, Memphis, TN 38134-7693. Authorized power: 10-w. each. Antenna: 126-ft. above ground. Lat. 35° 06' 45", long. 89° 53' 32". Transmitter: 5100 Poplar Ave. Equipment: Comwave transmitter; Andrew antenna.

Nashville—WLX-371 (Channels A-1-2). Fisk U., 1000 17th Ave. N, Nashville, TN 37208. Authorized power: 50-w. each. Antenna: 379-ft. above ground. Lat. 35° 35' 22", long. 86° 42' 38". Transmitter: Clovercroft Rd. Equipment: Comwave transmitter; Andrew antenna.

Nashville—WLX-978 (Channels B-1-4). Shekinah Network, 14875 Powerline Rd., Atascadero, CA 93422. Phone: 805-438-3341. Authorized power: 10-w. each. Antenna: 115.8-ft. above ground. Lat. 35° 55' 22", long. 86° 42' 38". Transmitter: Clovercroft Rd. Equipment: Comwave transmitter; Andrew antenna.

Nashville—WLX-563 (Channels C-1-3). Arizona U. Foundation, Box 27130, Phoenix, AZ 85961. Authorized power: 50-w. each. Antenna: 116-ft. above ground. Lat. 35° 55' 22", long. 86° 42' 38". Transmitter: Clovercroft Rd. Equipment: Comwave transmitter; Andrew antenna.

Nashville—WLX-579 (Channel C-4). Vanderbilt U., 321 Kirkland Hall, Nashville, TN 37235. Authorized power: 10-w. Antenna: 137-ft. above ground. Lat. 36° 08' 33", long. 86° 48' 09". Transmitter: Light Hall, Vanderbilt campus. Equipment: Comwave transmitter; Andrew antenna.

Nashville—WLX-684 (Channels D-1-4). Hispanic Information & Telecommunications Network Inc., 3rd Floor, 449 Broadway, New York, NY 10013. Phone: 212-966-5660. Fax: 212-966-5725.

E-mail: E-mail@hitn.org.

Web site: http://www.hitn.org.

Authorized power: 10-w. each. Antenna: 358-ft. above ground. Lat. 36° 09' 56", long. 86° 46' 46". Transmitter: First American Center Bldg. Equipment: ITS transmitter; Andrew antenna. Requests change to 50-w. each, 373-ft. above ground, lat. 35° 55' 22", long. 86° 42' 38", transmitter to Clovercroft Rd., Nolensville.

Leased to Nashville Wireless Cable, 475 Metroplex Dr., Suite 408, Nashville, TN 37211. Phone: 615-333-9288.

Nashville—WLX-957 (Channels G-1-4). Nashville State Technical Institute, 120 Whitebridge Rd., Nashville, TN 37209. Authorized power: 10-w. each. Antenna: 530-ft. above ground. Lat. 36° 09' 49", long. 86° 46' 45". Transmitter: Davidson County. Equipment: Comwave transmitter; Andrew antenna.

Nolanville—WLX-295 (Channels A-3-4). Belmont College, 1900 Belmont Blvd., Nashville, TN 37212. Authorized power: 10-w. each. Antenna: 384-ft. above ground. Lat. 35° 55' 22", long. 86° 42' 38". Equipment: GPT transmitter; Andrew antenna. Requests change to add channels G-1-4, transmitter to Clovercroft Rd.; Comwave transmitter.

Oak Ridge—WHR-733 (Channels C-1-4). Pellissippi State Technical Community College, Box 22990, Knoxville, TN 37933. Authorized power: 50-w. each. Antenna: 437-ft. above ground. Lat. 36° 00' 08", long. 83° 56' 41". Transmitter: 331 Sharp Ridge Rd., Knoxville. Equipment: Comwave transmitter; Bogner antenna.

Pikeville—WHR-519 (Channels B-1-4). Chattanooga State Technical Community College, 4501 Amnicola Hwy., Chattanooga, TN 37406. Phone: 423-697-4408. Fax: 423-697-4479.

Web site: http://www.cstcc.cc.tn.us.

Authorized power: 10-w. each. Antenna: 200-ft. above ground. Lat. 35° 35' 53", long. 85° 08' 11". Transmitter: 0.4-mi. N of Rte. 30 at Fraley Gap, 3-mi. E of Pikeville.

Leased to Wireless One, 1080 River Oaks Dr., No. A150, Jackson, MS 39208. Phone: 601-936-1515.

Tullahoma—WNC-374 (Channels B-1-4). St. Paul the Apostle Catholic School, 306 W. Grizzard, Tullahoma, TN 37388. Authorized power: 10-w. each. Antenna: 751-ft. above ground. Lat. 35° 27' 11", long. 86° 08' 20". Transmitter: Coffee County. Equipment: ITS transmitter; Andrew antenna.

Tullahoma—WNC-564 (Channels D-1-4). Fayetteville City School System, 110-A S. Elk Ave., Fayetteville, TN 37334. Authorized power: 20-w. each. Antenna: 751-ft. above ground. Lat. 35° 27' 11", long. 86° 08' 20". Transmitter: Knox-Pearson. Equipment: ITS transmitter; Andrew antenna.

Tullahoma—WNC-563 (Channels G-1-4). Franklin County Board of Education, 902 S. Shepherd St., Winchester, TN 37398. Authorized power: 20-w. each. Antenna: 751-ft. above ground. Lat. 35° 27' 11", long. 86° 08' 20". Transmitter: Knox-Pearson. Equipment: ITS transmitter; Andrew antenna.

Texas

Abilene—WLX-368 (Channels A-1-4). Texas State Technical College, Box 18, Rte. 3, Sweetwater, TX 79556. Phone: 915-235-7300. Authorized power: 10-w. each. Antenna: 297-ft. above ground. Lat. 32° 26' 38", long. 99° 44'

04". Transmitter: 500 Chestnut St. Equipment: ITS transmitter; Andrew antenna.
Leased to Nucentrix Broadband Networks, 200 Chisholm Place, Suite 200, Plano, TX 75075. Phone: 972-423-9494. Fax: 972-423-0819.

Abilene—WLX-369 (Channels B-1-4). Roman Catholic Diocese of San Angelo, Box 1829, San Angelo, TX 76902. Authorized power: 10-w. each. Antenna: 297-ft. above ground. Lat. 32° 26' 38", ong. 99° 44' 04". Transmitter: 500 Chestnut St. Equipment: ITS transmitter; Andrew antenna.

Abilene—WLX-313 (Channels C-1-4). Abilene Christian U., Box 8000, A.C.U. Station, Abilene, TX 79699. Lat. 32° 26' 38", long. 99° 44' 04".

Abilene—WLX-311 (Channels D-1-4). Hardin-Simmons U., 2200 Hickory, Abilene, TX 79697. Phone: 915-670-1414. Fax: 915-670-1409.
E-mail: dbaergen.comm@hsutx.edu.
Web site: http://www.hsutx.edu.
Lat. 32° 26' 38", long. 99° 44' 04".
Leased to Nucentrix Broadband Networks, 200 Chisholm Place, Suite 200, Plano, TX 75075. Phone: 972-423-9494. Fax: 972-423-0819

Abilene—WLX-312 (Channels G-1-4). McMurray U., 14th & Sayles, Abilene, TX 76967. Lat. 32° 26' 38", long. 99° 44' 04".

Amarillo—WND-371 (Channels C-1-4). Catholic Diocese of Amarillo, Box 5644, Amarillo, TX 79117. Authorized power: 10-w. each. Antenna: 551-ft. above ground. Lat. 35° 20' 33", long. 101° 49' 20". Transmitter: 1.4-mi. N of Hwy. 286 & Givens Ave. intersection. Equipment: ITS transmitter; Andrew antenna.

Amarillo—WND-243 (Channels G-1-4). Lubbock Christian U., 5601 19th St., Lubbock, TX 79407. Authorized power: 10-w. each. Antenna: 551-ft. above ground. Lat. 35° 20' 33", long. 101° 49' 20". Transmitter: 1.4-mi. NNE of Hwy. 286 & Givens Ave. intersection. Equipment: Comwave transmitter; Andrew antenna.

Austin—WLX-263 (Channels B-1-4). North American Catholic Educational Programming Foundation Inc., Box 40026, Providence, RI 02940-0026. Phone: 401-729-0900. Lat. 30° 18' 18", long. 97° 50' 18".

Austin—WLX-201 (Channels C-1-4). Concordia U. at Austin, 3400 I-35 N, Austin, TX 78705. Phone: 512-486-1176. Fax: 512-302-5856.
E-mail: cde@io.com.
Authorized power: 100-w. each. Antenna: 345-ft. above ground. Lat. 30° 18' 18", long. 97° 50' 18". Transmitter: Bee Cave & St. Stephens School Rds. Equipment: ITS transmitter; Andrew antenna.
Leased to Nucentrix Broadband Networks, 200 Chisholm Place, Suite 200 Plano, TX 75075 Phone: 972-423-9494. Fax 972-423-0819.

Austin—WLX-271 (Channels D-1-4). Education Service Center Region XIII, 5701 Springdale Rd., Austin, TX 78723. Authorized power: 100-w. each. Lat. 30° 18' 18", long. 97° 50' 18". Transmitter: Bee Cave Rd. & St. Stephens School Rd. Equipment: ITS transmitter; Andrew antenna.

Austin—WLX-254 (Channels G-1-4). Huston-Tillotson College, 900 Chicon St., Austin, TX 78702-2795. Phone: 512-505-3004. Fax: 512-505-3195.
E-mail: tssmith@htc.edu.
Web site: http://www.htc.edu.
Authorized power: 10-w. each. Antenna: 349-ft. above ground. Lat. 30° 18' 18", long. 97° 50' 18". Transmitter: Bee Cave & St. Stephens Rds. Equipment: Andrew transmitter; Omni antenna.
Leased to Nucentrix Broadband Networks, 200 Chisholm Place, Suite 200, Plano, TX 75075 Phone: 972-423-9494. Fax: 972-423-0819

Benavides—WNC-354 (Channels D-1-4). Ben Bolt-Palito Blanco CISD, S. U.S. Hwy. 281/FM Rd. 131, Ben Bolt, TX 78342. Phone: 512-664-9822. Authorized power: 50-w. each. Antenna: 482-ft. above ground. Lat. 27° 15' 18", long. 98° 05' 46". Transmitter: approx. 5-mi. NE of Falfurrias. Equipment: Comwave transmitter; Andrew antenna.

Bowie—WLX-778 (Channels A-1-4). Decatur Independent School District, 309 S. Cates, Decatur, TX 76234. Authorized power: 50-w. each. Antenna: 400-ft. above ground. Lat. 33° 40' 17", long. 97° 37' 16". Transmitter: 6.5-mi. W of St. Jo. Equipment: Emcee transmitter; Andrew antenna.

Bowie—WLX-731 (Channels B-1-4). Alvord Independent School District, Box 70, Alvord, TX 76225. Phone: 817-427-5975. Authorized power: 50-w. each. Antenna: 400-ft. above ground. Lat. 33° 40' 17", long. 97° 37' 16". Transmitter: 6.5-mi. W of St. Jo. Equipment: Emcee transmitter; Andrew antenna. Requests change to 419-ft. above ground.

Bowie—WLX-752 (Channels C-3-4). Paradise Independent School District, 338 School House Rd., Paradise, TX 76073. Phone: 940-969-2501. Fax: 940-969-2908.
E-mail: seerey@pisd.net.
Web site: http://www.pisd.net.
Authorized power: 10-w. each. Antenna: 277-ft. above ground. Lat. 33° 27' 11", long. 97° 45' 33". Transmitter: Montague County. Equipment: Comwave transmitter; Andrew antenna. Requests change to 50-w each, 400-ft. above ground, lat. 33° 40' 17", long. 97° 37' 16", transmitter to 6.5-mi. W of St. Jo.; ITS transmitter.

Brady—WLX-756 (Channels C-1-4). Rochelle Independent School District, Box 167, Rochelle, TX 76872. Authorized power: 10-w. each. Antenna: 708-ft. above ground. Lat. 30° 00' 01", long. 96° 26' 15". Transmitter: 1.3-mi. NW of State Rte. 2754 & State Rte. 2502 intersection. Equipment: Emcee transmitter; Andrew antenna.

Brady—WLX-567 (Channels G-1-2). Brady Independent School District, 100 W. Main, Brady, TX 76825. Phone: 915-597-2491. Fax: 915-597-3984.
E-mail: bisdadm1@sentex.net.
Authorized power: 10-w. each. Antenna: 484-ft. above ground. Lat. 31° 15' 28", long. 99° 23' 35". Transmitter: Brady in McCulloch County. Equipment: Comwave transmitter; Andrew antenna.

Brenham—WLX-645 (Channels A-1-4). Hempstead Independent School District, Box 1007, Hempstead, TX 77445. Authorized power: 10-w. each. Antenna: 666-ft. above ground. Lat. 29° 59' 52", long. 96° 26' 14". Transmitter: S Side of State Rd. 2502, 1.3-mi. NW of intersection with State Rd. 2754. Equipment: Comwave transmitter; Andrew antenna.

Brenham—WLX-438 (Channels C-1-4). Somerville Independent School District, Box 997, Somerville, TX 77879. Phone: 409-596-2153. Authorized power: 10-w. each. Antenna: 666-ft. above ground. Lat. 29° 59' 52", long. 96° 26' 14". Transmitter: S side of State Rd. 2502, 1.3-mi. NW of intersection with State Rte. 2754. Equipment: Comwave transmitter; Andrew antenna.

Brenham—WLX-591 (Channels D-1-4). Bellville Independent School District, 404 E. Main St., Bellville, TX 77418. Authorized power: 10-w. each. Antenna: 708-ft. above ground. Lat. 30° 00' 01", long. 96° 26' 15". Transmitter: S side of State Rd. 2502, 1.3-mi. NW of intersection with State Rte. 2754. Equipment: Comwave transmitter; Andrew antenna.

Brenham—WLX-437 (Channels G-1-4). Fayetteville Independent School District, Box 129, Hwy. 159 W, Fayetteville, TX 78940-0129. Phone: 409-378-4242. Fax: 409-378-4246. Authorized power: 10-w. each. Antenna: 705-ft. above ground. Lat. 30° 00' 01", long. 96° 26' 15". Transmitter: S side of State Rte. 2502, 1.3-mi. NW of intersection with State Rte. 2754. Equipment: Comwave transmitter; Andrew antenna. Requests change to 216-ft. above ground, lat. 29° 59' 52", long. 96° 26' 14".
Leased to Wireless One of Brenham Inc., Suite 2G, 5551 Corporate Blvd., Baton Rouge, LA 70808. Phone: 504-926-7778.

Brownsville—WNC-244 (Channels A-1-4). Texas State Technical Institute, Harligen Campua, Harligen, TX 78550. Authorized power: 20-w. each. Antenna: 495-ft. above ground. Lat. 25° 57' 49", long. 97° 31' 11". Transmitter: 1-mi. N of Brownsville. Equipment: ITS transmitter; Andrew antenna.
Leased to Nucentrix Broadband Networks, 200 Chisholm Place, Suite 200, Plano, TX 75075 Phone: 972-423-9494. Fax: 972-423-0819.

Brownsville—WNC-292 (Channels B-1-4). Church Point High School, 2101 Pease, Harlingen, TX 78550. Authorized power: 20-w. each. Antenna: 495-ft. above ground. Lat. 25° 57' 49", long. 97° 31' 11". Transmitter: 1-mi. N of Brownsville. Equipment: ITS transmitter; Andrew antenna.

Brownsville—WNC-243 (Channels C-1-4). Catholic Diocese of Brownsville, 1910 E. Elizabeth St., Brownsville, TX 78520. Phone: 210-542-2501. Authorized power: 20-w. each. Antenna: 495-ft. above ground. Lat. 25° 57' 49", long. 97° 31' 11". Transmitter: 1-mi. N of Brownsville. Equipment: ITS transmitter; Andrew antenna.

Brownsville—WLX-945 (Channels D-1-4). Texas Southmost College, 80 Fort Brown, Brownsville, TX 78520. Authorized power: 20-w. each. Antenna: 495-ft. above ground. Lat. 25° 57' 49", long. 97° 31' 11". Transmitter: 1-mi. N of Brownsville. Equipment: ITS transmitter; Andrew antenna.

Brownsville—WNC-245 (Channels G-1-4). R.G.V. Educational Broadcasting Inc., Box 2147, Harlingen, TX 78551. Phone: 956-421-4111. Fax: 956-421-4150.
E-mail: rgveduca@aol.com.
Web site:
http://www.mcallen.lib.tx.us/orgs/KMBH.htm.
Authorized power: 20-w. each. Antenna: 495-ft. above ground. Lat. 025° 57' 49", long. 097° 31' 11". Transmitter: 1-mi. N of Brownsville. Equipment: ITS transmitter; Andrew antenna.
Leased to U. S. Wireless Systems Inc., 1803 West Ave., Austin, TX 78701. Phone: 512-320-8522.

Bryan—WNC-307 (Channels D-1-4). Blinn College, 1903 Texas, Bryan, TX 77802. Authorized power: 10-w. each. Antenna: 484-ft. above ground. Lat. 30° 39' 37", long. 96° 25' 01". Transmitter: 0.6-mi. E of Hwy. 21 & 28th St. intersection. Equipment: Comwave transmitter; Andrew antenna.

Burnet—WLX-589 (Channels A-1-4). Marble Falls Independent School District, 2001 Broadway St., Marble Falls, TX 78654. Authorized power: 10-w. each. Antenna: 705-ft. above ground. Lat. 30° 43' 28", long. 98° 26' 23". Transmitter: 0.92-mi. S of State Rtes. 29 & 261, 1-mi. S of Buchanan. Equipment: Comwave transmitter; Andrew antenna.

Burnet—WLX-495 (Channels B-1-4). Lampasas Independent School District, 207 W. 8th St., Lampasas, TX 76550. Phone: 512-556-6224. Fax: 512-556-8711. Authorized power: 10-w. each. Antenna: 400-ft. above ground. Lat. 30° 45' 15", long. 98° 23' 20". Transmitter: Approx. 12-mi. W of Burnet; 2-mi. E of the Buchanan Dam on Lake Buchanan. Equipment: Comwave transmitter; Andrew antenna.
Leased to Nucentrix Broadband Networks, 200 Chisholm Place, Suite 200, Plano TX 75075. Phone: 972-423-9494. Fax: 972-423-0819.

Burnet—WLX-585 (Channels C-1-4). Burnet High School, 1401 N. Main, Burnet, TX 78611. Authorized power: 10-w. each. Antenna: 400-ft. above ground. Lat. 30° 43' 28", long. 98° 26' 23". Transmitter: 0.92-mi. S of State Rtes. 28 & 261 intersection, 1-mi. S of Lake Buchanan. Equipment: Comwave transmitter; Andrew antenna.

Burnet—WND-308 (Channels D-1-3). Bertram Elementary, 308 E. Brier St., Burnet, TX 78611. Authorized power: 10-w. each. Antenna: 400-ft. above ground. Lat. 30° 45' 15", long. 98° 23' 20". Transmitter: Approx. 12-mi. W of Burnet, 1.9-mi. E of Buchanan Dam on Lake Buchanan. Equipment: Comwave transmitter; Andrew antenna.

Burnet—WLX-425 (Channels G-1-4). Cherokee Independent School District, Box 100, Hwy. 16, Cherokee, TX 76832. Phone: 915-622-4298. Fax: 915-622-4430. Authorized power: 10-w. each. Antenna: 705-ft. above ground. Lat. 30° 45' 15", long. 98° 23' 20". Transmitter: Approx. 12-mi. W of Burnet; 2-mi. E of the Buchanan Dam on Lake Buchanan. Equipment: Comwave transmitter; Andrew antenna.

Carrollton—WNC-990 (Channels C-3-4). Carrollton Farmers Branch ISD, 1445 N. Perry Rd., Carrollton, TX 75011. Authorized power: 10-w. each. Antenna: 649-ft. above ground. Lat. 32° 59' 25", long. 96° 51' 39". Transmitter: McKarny Elementary School, 3443 Briargrove. Equipment: ITS transmitter; Andrew antenna.

Chalmers—WLX-406 (Channels G-1-4). East Bernard Independent School District, 727 Fitzgerald, East Bernard, TX 77435. Lat. 29° 07' 36", long. 96° 06' 38".

Charlotte—WNC-382 (Channels B-1-4). Pearsall Independent School District, 522 E. Florida, Pearsall, TX 78061. Phone: 830-334-8001. Fax: 830-334-8007.
E-mail: jpkelly@pearsall.k12.tx.us.
Web site: http://www.pearsall.k12.tx.us.
Authorized power: 50-w. each. Antenna: 705-ft. above ground. Lat. 28° 50' 30", long. 98° 45' 29". Transmitter: Approx. 2.6-mi. W of Charlotte. Equipment: Comwave transmitter; Andrew antenna.

Charlotte—WNC-462 (Channels C-1-4). Charlotte Independent School District, Box 489, Charlotte, TX 78011. Authorized power: 50-w. each. Antenna: 705-ft. above ground. Lat. 28°

50' 30", long. 98° 45' 29". Transmitter: Approx. 2.6-mi. W of Charlotte. Equipment: Comwave transmitter; Andrew antenna.

Charlotte—WNC-461 (Channels D-1-4). Charlotte High School, Rose Blvd., Charlotte, TX 78011. Authorized power: 50-w. each. Antenna: 705-ft. above ground. Lat. 28° 50' 30", long. 98° 45' 29". Transmitter: Approx. 2.6-mi. W of Charlotte. Equipment: Comwave transmitter; Andrew antenna.

Charlotte—WNC-282 (Channels G-1-4). Pleasanton Independent School District, 831 Stadium Dr., Pleasanton, TX 78064. Authorized power: 50-w. each. Antenna: 705-ft. above ground. Lat. 28° 50' 30", long. 98° 45' 29". Transmitter: Approx. 2.6-mi. W of Charlotte. Equipment: Comwave transmitter; Andrew antenna.

Corpus Christi—WHR-958 (Channels A-1-4). Texas A & I U., Campus Box 101, Kingsville, TX 78863. Authorized power: 50-w. each. Antenna: 374-ft. above ground. Lat. 27° 47' 50", long. 97° 23' 48". Transmitter: 802 N. Carancahua. Equipment: Emcee transmitter; Andrew antenna.

Corpus Christi—WHR-995 (Channels B-1-4). Diocesan Telecommunications Corp., 1200 Lantana, Corpus Christi, TX 78407. Phone: 512-289-6437. Fax: 512-289-1420.
E-mail: mwind@goccn.org.
Web site: http://www.goccn.org.
Authorized power: 50-w. each. Antenna: 336-ft. above ground. Lat. 027° 47' 50", long. 097° 23' 48". Transmitter: 802 N. Carancahua. Equipment: Emcee transmitter; Andrew antenna.
Leased to Nucentrix Broadband Neworks, 200 Chisholm Place, Suite 200 Plano TX 75075 Phone: 972-423- 9494. Fax:972-423-0819.

Corpus Christi—WLX-220 (Channels C-1-4). Corpus Christi Independent School District, 801 Leopard St., Corpus Christi, TX 78403. Authorized power: 50-w. each. Antenna: 374-ft. above ground. Lat. 27° 47' 50", long. 97° 23' 48". Transmitter: 802 N. Carancahua St., Texas Commerce Plaza. Equipment: Emcee transmitter; Andrew antenna.

Corpus Christi—WLX-249 (Channels D-1-4). Hispanic Information & Telecommunications Network Inc., 3rd Floor, 449 Broadway ., New York, NY 10013. Phone: 212-966-5660. Fax: 212-966-5725.
E-mail: email@hitn.org.
Web site: http://www.hitn.org.
Authorized power: 50-w. each. Antenna: 333-ft. above ground. Lat. 27° 47' 50", long. 97° 23' 48". Transmitter: 802 N. Carancahua. Equipment: Emcee transmitter; Andrew antenna.
Leased to Nucentrix Broadband Networks, 200 Chisholm Place, Suite 200, Plano, TX 75075. Phone: 972-423-9494. Fax: 972-423-0819

Corpus Christi—WHR-903 (Channel G-2). Corpus Christi Jr. College District, 101 Baldwin, Corpus Christi, TX 78404. Phone: 512-886-1312. Fax: 512-886-1182.
E-mail: dtyler@delmar.edu.
Web site: http://www.delmar.edu.
Authorized power: 10-w. Antenna: 342-ft. above ground. Lat. 27° 47' 46", long. 97° 23' 47". Transmitter: 600 Building, 600 Leopard St. Equipment: ITS transmitter; Andrew antenna. Requests change to 50-w., 331-ft. above ground, lat. 27° 47' 50", long. 97° 23' 48"; transmitter to 802 N. Carancahua.
Leased to Nucentrix Broadband Networks, 200 Chisholm Place, Suite 200, Plano TX 75075. Phone: 972-423-9494. Fax: 972-423-0819.

Corsicana—WLX-545 (Channels A-1-4). Fairfield Independent School District, 615 Post Oak Rd., Fairfield, TX 75840. Phone: 903-389-2532. Fax: 903-389-7050. Authorized power: 10-w. each. Antenna: 705-ft. above ground. Lat. 32° 01' 40", long. 96° 11' 03". Transmitter: 1-mi. SW of Round Prairie. Equipment: Comwave transmitter; Andrew antenna.

Corsicana—WLX-521 (Channels B-1-4). Kerens Independent School District, Hwy. 309 S, Kerens, TX 75144. Phone: 903-396-2931. Fax: 903-396-2334. Authorized power: 10-w. each. Antenna: 705-ft. above ground. Lat. 32° 01' 40", long. 96° 11' 03". Transmitter: 1-mi. SW of Round Prairie. Equipment: Comwave transmitter; Andrew antenna.

Corsicana—WNC-685 (Channels C-1-4). Cross Roads Independent School District, Box 1265, Rte. 1, Malakoff, TX 75148. Authorized power: 10-w. each. Antenna: 705-ft. above ground. Lat. 32° 01' 40", long. 96° 11' 03". Transmitter: 1-mi. SW of Round Prairie. Equipment: Comwave transmitter; Andrew antenna.

Corsicana—WLX-552 (Channels D-1-3). Dawson Independent School District, 3rd & Gilmore, Dawson, TX 76639. Phone: 817-578-1186. Fax: 817-578-1721. Authorized power: 10-w. each. Antenna: 705-ft. above ground. Lat. 32° 01' 40", long. 96° 11' 03". Transmitter: 1-mi. SW of Round Prairie. Equipment: Comwave transmitter; Andrew antenna.

Corsicana—WLX-547 (Channels G-1-4). Rice Independent School District, Box 68, Rice, TX 75155. Authorized power: 10-w. each. Antenna: 705-ft. above ground. Lat. 32° 01' 40", long. 96° 11' 03". Transmitter: 1-mi. SW of Round Prairie. Equipment: Comwave transmitter; Andrew antenna.

Crow—WLX-850 (Channels A-1-4). All Saints Episcopal School, 2695 S. Southwest Loop 323, Tyler, TX 75701-0753. Authorized power: 50-w. each. Antenna: 495-ft. above ground. Lat. 32° 38' 01", long. 95° 18' 55". Transmitter: State Rte. 778, 0.6-mi. N of U.S. 80. Equipment: Comwave transmitter; Andrew antenna.

Crow—WLX-871 (Channels B-1-4). East Texas Christian Academy, Box 8201, Tyler, TX 75711. Phone: 903-561-8642. Authorized power: 50-w. each. Antenna: 495-ft. above ground. Lat. 32° 38' 01", long. 95° 18' 55". Transmitter: State Rte. 778, 0.6-mi. N of U.S. 80. Equipment: Comwave transmitter; Andrew antenna.

Crow—WLX-908 (Channels C-1-4). Bishop T. K. Gorman Catholic School, 1405 SE Loop 323, Tyler, TX 75701. Phone: 903-561-2424.
Web site: http://www.gower.net/btkg.
Authorized power: 50-w. each. Antenna: 500-ft. above ground. Lat. 32° 38' 01", long. 95° 18' 55". Transmitter: State Rte. 778, 0.6-mi. N of U.S. 80. Equipment: Comwave transmitter; Andrew antenna.

Dallas—WNC-582 (Channels A-1-2). Dallas County Community College District, 701 Elm St., Dallas, TX 75202. Authorized power: 50-w. each. Antenna: 889-ft. above ground. Lat. 32° 51' 57", long. 96° 48' 01". Transmitter: 6211 W. Northwest Hwy. Equipment: ITS transmitter; Andrew antenna.

Dallas—WHR-882 (Channel A-3-4). Richardson Independent School District, 9596 Walnut St., Dallas, TX 75243. Authorized power: 50-w. Antenna: 889-ft. above ground. Lat. 32° 51' 57", long. 96° 48' 01". Transmitter: 6211 W. Northwest Hwy. Equipment: ITS transmitter; Andrew antenna.

Dallas—KWU-30 (Channels C-1-4). Alliance for Higher Education, Suite 250, 17103 Preston Rd., Dallas, TX 75248-1373. Phone: 214-713-8170. Authorized power: 10-w. each. Antenna: 268-ft. above ground. Lat. 32° 59' 22", long. 96° 45' 01". Transmitter: 2400 N. Armstrong Pkwy., Richardson. Requests change to 15-w. each, 305-ft. above ground, lat. 32° 51' 57", long. 96° 48' 01", transmitter to Preston Tower, 6211 W. Northwest Hwy; Comwave transmitter, Andrew antenna

Dallas—WNC-836 (Channels C-1-4). Alliance for Higher Education, 17103 Preston Rd., Dallas TX 75248. Authorized power: 50-w. each. Antenna: 299-ft. above ground. Lat. 32° 51' 57", long. 96° 48' 01". Transmitter: 6211 W. Northwest Hwy. Equipment: ITS transmitter; Andrew antenna.

Dallas—WLX-843 (Channels D-1-4). Dallas-Fort Worth Hospital Council. Authorized power: 10-w. each. Antenna: 500-ft. above ground. Lat. 32° 46' 54", long. 96° 48' 05". Transmitter: Vicinity of 1201 Elm St. Equipment: Comwave transmitter; Andrew antenna.

Dallas—WND-242 (Channels D-1-3). Dallas-Fort Worth Hospital Council. Authorized power: 50-w. each. Antenna: 889-ft. above ground. Lat. 32° 51' 57", long. 96° 48' 01". Transmitter: 6211 W. Northwest Hwy. Equipment: ITS transmitter; Andrew antenna.

Dallas—WHR-830 (Channels G-1-3). Dallas County Community College District, LeCroy Center, Dallas, TX 75243. Authorized power: 50-w. each. Antenna: 299-ft. above ground. Lat. 32° 51' 57", long. 96° 48' 01". Transmitter: 6211 W. Northwest Hwy. Equipment: ITS transmitter; Andrew antenna.

Dallas—WHR-831 (Channel G-4). CES/Dallas Inc., 11490 Commerce Park Dr., Reston, VA 22091. Phone: 214-528-2240. Fax: 214-526-1743.
E-mail: mmcgee@cathdal.org.
Authorized power: 50-w. Antenna: 299-ft. above ground. Lat. 32° 51' 57", long. 96° 48' 01". Transmitter: Preston Tower, 6211 W. N.W. Hwy. Equipment: ITS transmitter; Andrew antenna.
Leased to CS Wireless Systems Inc., 1101 Summitt Ave., Plano, TX 75074. Phone: 972-730-3300.

Denison—WLX-587 (Channels A-1-4). Gunter Independent School District, Box 109, Gunter, TX 75058. Phone: 903-433-4750. Fax: 903-433-1053. Authorized power: 50-w. each. Antenna: 371-ft. above ground. Lat. 33° 40' 34", long. 96° 35' 04". Transmitter: E of Frisco. Equipment: Comwave transmitter; Andrew antenna.
Leased to CableMaxx, Suite 320, 6850 Austin Center Blvd., 2 Northpoint Centre, Austin, TX 78730. Phone: 512-345-1001.

Denison—WLX-508 (Channels B-1-4). Grayson County College, 6101 Grayson Dr., Denison, TX 75020. Phone: 903-463-6030. Fax: 903-463-5284.
E-mail: paikowski@grayson.edu.
Web site: http://www.grayson.edu.
Authorized power: 50-w. each. Antenna: 371-ft. above ground. Lat. 33° 40' 34", long. 96° 35' 04". Transmitter: E of Frisco. Equipment: Comwave transmitter; Andrew antenna.
Leased to Nucentrix Broadband Networks, 200 Chisholm Place, Suite 200, Plano, TX 75075. Phone: 972-423-9494. Fax: 972-423-0819.

Denison—WNC-251 (Channels C-1-4). Bells Independent School District, Box 7, Bells, TX 75414. Phone: 903-965-7721. Fax: 903-965-7036.
E-mail: whittemore@hotmail.com.
Authorized power: 50-w. each. Antenna: 371-ft. above ground. Lat. 33° 40' 34", long. 96° 35' 04". Transmitter: E of Frisco. Equipment: Comwave transmitter; Andrew antenna.

Denison—WLX-364 (Channels D-1-4). North American Catholic Educational Programming Foundation Inc., Box 40026, Providence, RI 02940-0026. Phone: 401-729-0900. Authorized power: 50-w. each. Antenna: 371-ft. above ground. Lat. 33° 40' 34", long. 96° 35' 04". Transmitter: E of Frisco. Equipment: Comwave transmitter; Andrew antenna.

Denison—WNC-709 (Channels G-1-4). Van Alstyne Independent School District, Box 518, Van Alstyne, TX 75495. Phone: 903-482-6617. Fax: 903-482-6086. Authorized power: 50-w. each. Antenna: 113-ft. above ground. Lat. 033° 42' 10", long. 096° 34' 05". Transmitter: 4816 Hwy. 75, S of Denison.

El Paso—WHR-601 (Channels A-1-4). El Paso Public Television Foundation, Box 650, El Paso, TX 79968. Authorized power: 10-w. each. Antenna: 100-ft. above ground. Lat. 31° 47' 17", long. 106° 28' 46". Transmitter: S slope of Franklin Mountain.

El Paso—WNC-583 (Channels B-1-4). Diocese of El Paso, 499 St. Matthews St., El Paso, TX 79907. Authorized power: 10-w. each. Antenna: 87-ft. above ground. Lat. 31° 47' 15", long. 106° 28' 47". Transmitter: S Slope of Commance. Equipment: Emcee transmitter; Andrew antenna.

El Paso—WHR-931 (Channels C-1-4). El Paso City Community College District, Box 20500, El Paso, TX 79998. Authorized power: 10-w. each. Antenna: 103-ft. above ground. Lat. 31° 48' 55", long. 106° 29' 20". Transmitter: Mount Franklin. Equipment: Comwave transmitter; Andrew antenna.

El Paso—WNC-587 (Channels D-1-4). Socorro Independent School District, 12300 E. Lake Dr., El Paso, TX 79927. Authorized power: 10-w. each. Antenna: 87-ft. above ground. Lat. 31° 47' 15", long. 106° 28' 47". Transmitter: S Slope of Commance. Equipment: Emcee transmitter; Andrew antenna.

El Paso—WNC-584 (Channels G-1-4). Hispanic Information & Telecommunications Network Inc., 3rd Floor, 449 Broadway, New York,

NY 10003. Phone: 212-966-5660. Fax: 212-966-5725.
E-mail: email@hitn.org.
Web site: http://www.hitn.org.
Authorized power: 10-w. each. Antenna: 84-ft. above ground. Lat. 31° 47' 15", long. 106° 28' 47". Transmitter: S Slope of Coman Mountain. Equipment: Emcee transmitter; Andrew antenna.
Leased to Nucentrix Broadband Neworks, 200 Chisholm Place, Suite 200, Plano, TX 75075. Phone: 972-423-9494. Fax: 972-423-0819.

Ennis—WHR-695 (Channels C-1-4). Education Service Center Region 10, Box 831300, 400 E. Spring Valley, Richardson, TX 75083-1300. Phone: 972-348-1342. Fax: 972-348-1343.
E-mail: canterbd@esc10.ednet10.net.
Web site: http://www.esc10.ednet10.net.
Authorized power: 10-w. each. Antenna: 451-ft. above ground. Lat. 32° 19' 21", long. 96° 33' 39". Transmitter: Hwy. 85, 4-mi. E of Ennis. Equipment: Emcee transmitter; Andrew antenna.

Falfurrias—WNC-252 (Channels G-1-4). Texas A & I U., Box 104, Station One, Kingsville, TX 78363. Authorized power: 50-w. each. Antenna: 484-ft. above ground. Lat. 27° 15' 18", long. 98° 05' 46". Transmitter: 5-mi. NE of Falfurrias. Equipment: Emcee transmitter; Andrew antenna.

Fort Worth—WHR-506 (Channels A-1-4). Tarrant County Junior College District, 1500 Houston St., Fort Worth, TX 76102. Phone: 817-531-6005. Fax: 817-531-4516. Authorized power: 50-w. each. Antenna: 581-ft. above ground. Lat. 32° 45' 01", long. 97° 20' 03". Transmitter: Burnett Plaza, 801 Cherry St. Equipment: ITS transmitter; Andrew antenna.

Fort Worth—WLX-649 (Channels B-1-4). Dallas-Fort Worth Hospital Council, 250 Decker Court, Irving, TX 75062. Phone: 972-719-4900. Fax: 972-719-4009.
E-mail: paulettes@dfwhc.org.
Web site: http://www.dfwhc.org.
Authorized power: 50-w. each. Antenna: 612-ft. above ground. Lat. 32° 45' 01", long. 97° 20' 03". Transmitter: Burnett Plaza, 801 Cherry St. Equipment: ITS transmitter; Andrew antenna.
Leased to CS Wireless Systems Inc., 1101 Summit Ave., Plano, TX 75074. Phone: 972-730-3300.

Fort Worth—WHR-883 (Channels C-1-4). Network for Instructional TV Inc., Suite 110, 11490 Commerce Park Dr., Reston, VA 22091. Phone: 703-860-9200. Fax: 703-860-9237. Authorized power: 50-w. each. Antenna: 581-ft. above ground. Lat. 32° 45' 01", long. 97° 20' 03". Transmitter: Burnett Plaza, 801 Cherry St. Equipment: ITS transmitter; Andrew antenna.
Leased to CS Wireless Systems Inc, 1101 Summit Ave., Plano, TX 75074. Phone: 972-730-3300.

Fort Worth—WHR-881 (Channels D-1-4). Richardson Independent School District, 400 S. Greenville Ave., Richardson, TX 75081. Lat. 32° 45' 01", long. 97° 20' 03".

Fort Worth—KWU-29 (Channels E-1-4). Alliance for Higher Education, Suite 250, 17103 Preston Rd., Dallas, TX 75248-1373. Phone: 214-713-8170. Authorized power: 10-w. each. Antenna: 199-ft. above ground. Lat. 32° 42' 28", long. 97° 21' 27". Transmitter: Bowie St., between Green & Waits Aves. Requests change to 15-w. each, 529-ft. above ground, lat. 32° 45' 11", kibg, 97° 19' 46", transmitter to Continental Plaza, 777 Main St.; Comwave transmitter; Andrew antenna.

Fort Worth—WNC-823 (Channels G-1-4). Alliance for Higher Education, Suite 250, 17103 Preston Rd., Dallas, TX 75248. Authorized power: 50-w. each. Antenna: 581-ft. above ground. Lat. 32° 45' 01", long. 97° 20' 03". Transmitter: Burnett Plaza, 801 Cherry St. Equipment: ITS transmitter; Andrew antenna.

Freeport—WND-219 (Channels A-1-4). Angleton Independent School District, 1900 N. Downing Rd., Angleton, TX 77515. Phone: 409-849-8594. Fax: 409-849-3041.
E-mail: jjstout@angelton.isd.tenet.edu.
Web site: http://www.angelton.isd.tenet.edu.
Authorized power: 20-w. each. Antenna: 531-ft. above ground. Lat. 29° 03' 57", long. 95° 19' 17". Transmitter: 2021 County Rd. 227. Equipment: Comwave transmitter; Andrew antenna.
Leased to Wireless One Inc., 2506 Lakeland Dr., Jackson, MS 39208. Phone: 601-936-1515.

Freeport—WND-220 (Channels B-1-4). Sweeny Independent School District, 1310 Elm St., Sweeny, TX 77480. Authorized power: 20-w. each. Antenna: 531-ft. above ground. Lat. 29° 03' 57", long. 95° 19' 17". Transmitter: 2021 County Rd. 227. Equipment: Comwave transmitter; Andrew antenna.

Freeport—WNC-457 (Channels C-1-4). Brazosport Senior High School, 300 W. Brazoswood Dr., Freeport, TX 77541. Authorized power: 10-w. each. Antenna: 496-ft. above ground. Lat. 28° 59' 23", long. 95° 14' 25". Transmitter: 0.3-mi. S of Drum Bay. Equipment: Comwave transmitter; Andrew antenna. Requests change to 20-w, 574-ft. above ground, lat. 29° 03' 57", long. 95° 19' 17"; transmitter to to 2021 County Rd. 227.

Freeport—WNC-456 (Channels D-1-4). Brazosport Senior High School, 300 W. Brazoswood Dr., Freeport, TX 77531. Authorized power: 10-w. each. Antenna: 705-ft. above ground. Lat. 28° 59' 23", long. 95° 14' 25". Transmitter: 0.3-mi. S of Drum Bay. Equipment: Comwave transmitter; Andrew antenna. Requests change to 20-w, 574-ft. above ground, lat. 29° 03' 57", long. 95° 19' 17"; transmitter to 2021 County Rd. 227.

Freeport—WLX-751 (Channels G-1-4). Danbury Independent School District, Box 378, Danbury, TX 77534. Phone: 409-922-1218. Fax: 409-922-8246. Authorized power: 10-w. each. Antenna: 499-ft. above ground. Lat. 28° 59' 23", long. 95° 14' 25". Transmitter: 0.3-mi. S of Drum Bay. Equipment: Comwave transmitter; Andrew antenna.
Leased to Wireless One, 11501 Industriplex Blvd., Baton Rouge, LA 70809. Phone: 504-293-5000.

George West—WNC-819 (Channels G-1-4). Bee County College, 3800 Charco Rd., Beeville, TX 78102. Authorized power: 50-w. each. Antenna: 620-ft. above ground. Lat. 28° 17' 37", long. 98° 13' 17". Transmitter: 7-mi. WSW of George West. Equipment: Emcee transmitter; Andrew antenna.

Goldthwaite—WLX-686 (Channels A-1-4). Priddy Independent School District, Box 40, Priddy, TX 76870. Authorized power: 10-w. each. Antenna: 410-ft. above ground. Lat. 31° 27' 21", long. 98° 33' 19". Transmitter: Near U.S. Rte. 84 & State Rte. 2005 intersection. Equipment: Emcee transmitter; Andrew antenna.

Goldthwaite—WLX-688 (Channels B-1-4). Star Independent School District, Box 838, Star, TX 77430. Phone: 915-948-3661. Fax: 915-948-3398. Authorized power: 10-w. each. Antenna: 410-ft. above ground. Lat. 31° 27' 21", long. 98° 33' 19". Transmitter: Near U.S. Rte. 84 & State Rte. 2005 intersection. Equipment: Emcee transmitter; Andrew antenna.

Goldthwaite—WLX-685 (Channels C-1-4). Mullin Independent School District, Box 128, Mullin, TX 76864. Authorized power: 10-w. each. Antenna: 410-ft. above ground. Lat. 31° 27' 21", long. 98° 33' 19". Transmitter: Near U.S. Rte. 84 & State Rte. 2005 intersection. Equipment: Emcee transmitter; Andrew antenna.

Goldthwaite—WLX-718 (Channels D-1-4). Goldthwaite Independent School District, Box 608, Goldthwaite, TX 76844. Authorized power: 10-w. each. Antenna: 410-ft. above ground. Lat. 31° 27' 21", long. 98° 33' 19". Transmitter: Near U.S. Rte. 84 & State Rte. 2005 intersection. Equipment: Emcee transmitter; Andrew antenna.

Goldthwaite—WNC-825 (Channels G-1-4). Zephyr Independent School District, Box 1, Rte. 1, Zephyr, TX 76890. Authorized power: 10-w. each. Antenna: 410-ft. above ground. Lat. 31° 27' 21", long. 98° 33' 19". Transmitter: Near U.S. Rte. 84 & State Rte. 2005 intersection. Equipment: Emcee transmitter; Andrew antenna.

Gonzales—WLX-801 (Channels A-1-4). Hallettsville Independent School District, 402 N. Ridge, Hallettsville, TX 77964. Authorized power: 50-w. each. Antenna: 390-ft. above ground. Lat. 29° 27' 14", long. 97° 14' 58". Transmitter: Hwy. 90-A, 5-mi. W of Shiner. Equipment: ITS transmitter; Andrew antenna.

Gonzales—WLX-800 (Channels B-1-4). Stockdale Independent School District, 503 S. 6th, Stockdale, TX 78160. Authorized power: 50-w. each. Antenna: 302-ft. above ground. Lat. 29° 27' 14", long. 97° 14' 58". Transmitter: Hwy. 90-A, 5-mi. W of Shiner. Equipment: ITS transmitter; Andrew antenna.

Gonzales—WLX-799 (Channels C-1-4). Yoakum Independent School District, 102 McKinnon, Yoakum, TX 77995. Authorized power: 50-w. each. Antenna: 302-ft. above ground. Lat. 29° 27' 14", long. 97° 14' 58". Transmitter: Hwy. 90-A, 5-mi. W of Shiner. Equipment: ITS transmitter; Andrew antenna.

Gonzales—WLX-798 (Channels D-1-4). Moulton Independent School District, 400 W. North St., Moulton, TX 77975. Phone: 512-596-4609. Fax: 512-596-7578. Authorized power: 50-w. each. Antenna: 302-ft. above ground. Lat. 29° 27' 14", long. 97° 14' 58". Transmitter: Hwy. 90-A, 5-mi. W of Shiner. Equipment: ITS transmitter; Andrew antenna.

Gonzales—WLX-791 (Channels G-1-4). Gonzales Independent School District, Drawer M, Gonzales, TX 78629. Authorized power: 50-w. each. Antenna: 302-ft. above ground. Lat. 29° 27' 14", long. 97° 14' 58". Transmitter: Hwy. 90-A, 5-mi. W of Shiner. Equipment: ITS transmitter; Andrew antenna.

Hamilton—WLX-399 (Channels A-1-4). Evant Independent School District, 101 Memory Lane, Evant, TX 76525. Phone: 817-471-3160. Fax: 817-471-5629. Authorized power: 10-w. each. Antenna: 709-ft. above ground. Lat. 31° 47' 57", long. 98° 08' 12". Transmitter: 6-mi. N of Hamilton. Equipment: Comwave transmitter; Andrew antenna.

Hamilton—WLX-426 (Channels B-1-4). Cranfills Gap Independent School District, 2nd St. & School Rd., Cranfills Gap, TX 76637. Phone: 817-597-2505. Fax: 817-597-0001. Authorized power: 50-w. each. Antenna: 705-ft. above ground. Lat. 31° 47' 57", long. 98° 08' 12". Transmitter: 6-mi. N of Hamilton. Equipment: Comwave transmitter; Andrew antenna.

Hamilton—WLX-727 (Channels C-1-4). Gustine Independent School District, Box 169, Gustine, TX 76455. Authorized power: 10-w. each. Antenna: 705-ft. above ground. Lat. 31° 47' 57", long. 98° 08' 12". Transmitter: 6-mi. N of Hamilton. Equipment: Comwave transmitter; Andrew antenna.

Hamilton—WLX-703 (Channels D-1-4). Hico Independent School District, Box 218, Hico, TX 76457. Phone: 817-796-2181. Fax: 817-796-2446.
E-mail: nwade@tenet.edu.
Web site: http://www.our-town.com/~hico.
Authorized power: 10-w. each. Antenna: 705-ft. above ground. Lat. 31° 47' 57", long. 98° 08' 12". Transmitter: 6-mi. N of Hamilton. Equipment: Comwave transmitter; Andrew antenna.
Leased to Nucentrix Broadband Networks, 200 Chisholm Place, Suite 200, Plano, TX 75075. Phone 972-423-9494. Fax: 972-423-0819.

Hamilton—WLX-400 (Channels G-1-4). Hamilton Independent School District, 400 S. College, Hamilton, TX 76531. Phone: 254-386-3149. Fax: 254-386-8885.
E-mail: dijones@hamilton.k12.tx.us.
Authorized power: 10-w. each. Antenna: 705-ft. above ground. Lat. 31° 47' 57", long. 98° 08' 12". Transmitter: 6-mi. N of Hamilton. Equipment: Comwave transmitter; Andrew antenna.
Leased to Nucentrix Broadband Networks, 200 Chisholm Place, Suite 200, Plano, TX 75075. Phone 972-423-9494. Fax: 972-423-0819.

Houston—WHR-492 (Channels A-1-4). Region IV Education Service Center, 7145 W. Tidwell, Houston, TX 77001. Phone: 713-744-6331. Fax: 713-744-2725.
Web site: http://www.escy.net.
Authorized power: 100-w. each. Antenna: 999-ft. above ground. Lat. 29° 45' 36", long. 95° 21' 50". Transmitter: 1000 Louisiana St.
Leased to People's Choice Television, 5301 E. Broadway Blvd., Tucson, AZ 85711. Phone: 520-519-4414.

Houston—WHQ-281 (Channels C-1-4). Region IV Education Service Center, 7145 W. Tidwell, Houston, TX 77092. Phone: 713-744-6331. Fax: 713-744-2725.
Web site: http://www.esc4.net.
Authorized power: 100-w. each. Antenna: 985-ft. above ground. Lat. 29° 45' 30", long. 95° 22' 03". Transmitter: 1000 Louisiana St. Equipment: Comwave transmitter; Bogner antenna.
Leased to People's Choice Television, 5301 E. Broadway Blvd., Tucson, AZ 85711. Phone: 520-519-4414.

Houston—KRZ-68 (Channels D-1-4). Spring Branch Independent School District, 9000 Westview Dr., Houston, TX 77055. Authorized power: 100-w. each. Antenna: 985-ft. above ground. Lat. 29° 45' 30", long. 95° 22' 03". Transmitter: 1000 Louisiana St. Equipment: Comwave transmitter; Bogner antenna.

Houston & Harris County—WAU-31 (Channels B-1-4). U. of Texas Health Science Center at Houston, UT Television, Box 157, 1100 Holcombe Blvd., Houston, TX 77030. Phone: 713-792-5017. Fax: 713-792-2984. Authorized power: 100-w. each. Antenna: 977-ft. above ground. Lat. 29° 45' 30", long. 95° 22'

03". Transmitter: 1000 Louisiana St. Equipment: Comwave transmitter; Bogner antenna.

Leased to People's Choice TV, 7272 Pinemont, Houston, TX 77040. Phone: 713-895-8373.

Huntsville—WNC-496 (Channels A-1-4). Madisonville Consolidated School District, Box 879, Madisonville, TX 77864. Authorized power: 50-w. each. Antenna: 325-ft. above ground. Lat. 30° 48' 15", long. 95° 42' 18". Transmitter: W side of U.S. 75, 11-mi. NW of Huntsville. Equipment: Comwave transmitter; Andrew antenna.

Huntsville—WNC-494 (Channels B-1-4). New Waverly Independent School District, Box 38, 355 Front St., New Waverly, TX 77358. Phone: 409-344-6751. Fax: 409-344-2438. Authorized power: 50-w. each. Antenna: 325-ft. above ground. Lat. 30° 48' 15", long. 95° 42' 18". Transmitter: W side of U.S. 75, 11-mi. NW of Huntsville. Equipment: Comwave transmitter; Andrew antenna.

Huntsville—WNC-495 (Channels C-1-4). North Zulch Independent School District, Box 158, 5th St., North Zulch, TX 77872. Authorized power: 50-w. each. Antenna: 325-ft. above ground. Lat. 30° 48' 15", long. 95° 42' 18". Transmitter: W side of U.S. 75, 11-mi. NW of Huntsville. Equipment: Comwave transmitter; Andrew antenna.

Huntsville—WNC-493 (Channels D-1-4). Anderson-Shiro Consolidated Independent School District, Box 289, Anderson, TX 77830. Authorized power: 50-w. each. Antenna: 325-ft. above ground. Lat. 30° 48' 15", long. 95° 42' 18". Transmitter: W side of U.S. 75, 11-mi. NW of Huntsville. Equipment: Comwave transmitter; Andrew antenna.

Leased to Wireless One, 2506 Lakeland Dr., Suite 403, Jackson, MS 39208. Phone: 601-933-6871.

Huntsville WNC-490 (Channels G-1-4) Iolu Independent School District, Box 159, Iolu 77861. Authorized power: 50-w. each. Antenna: 325-ft. above ground. Lat. 30° 48' 15", long. 95° 42' 18". Transmitter: W side of U.S. 75, 11-mi.NW of Huntsville. Equipment: Comwave transmitters; Andrew antenna.

Ingram—WLX-653 (Channels A-1-4). Center Point Independent School District, Box 377, Center Point, TX 78010. Phone: 830-634-2171. Fax: 830-634-2254.

E-mail: robertpayne@center-point.k12.tx.us.

Web site: http://192.168.1.22.

Authorized power: 50-w. each. Antenna: 695-ft. above ground. Lat. 30° 01' 09", long. 99° 20' 08". Transmitter: 1.6-mi. E of State Rd. 39, near Ingram. Equipment: Comwave transmitter; Andrew antenna.

Leased to Nucentrix Broadband Networks, 200 Chisholm Place, Siote 200 , Plano, TX 75075. Phone: 972-423-9494. Fax: 972-423-0819.

Ingram—WLX-654 (Channels B-1-4). Hunt Independent School District, Box 259, Hunt, TX 78024. Authorized power: 50-w. each. Antenna: 695-ft. above ground. Lat. 30° 01' 09", long. 99° 20' 08". Transmitter: 1.6-mi. E of State Rd. 39, near Ingram. Equipment: Comwave transmitter; Andrew antenna.

Ingram—WNC-217 (Channels C-1-4). Ingram Independent School District, 700 Hwy. 39, Ingram, TX 78025. Authorized power: 50-w. each. Antenna: 692-ft. above ground. Lat. 30° 01' 10", long. 99° 20' 09". Transmitter: Moore Ranch, approx. 14-mi. SE of Ingram. Equipment: Comwave transmitter; Andrew antenna.

Ingram—WLX-855 (Channels D-1-4). Comfort Independent School District, Box 398, Comfort, TX 78013. Authorized power: 50-w. each. Antenna: 692-ft. above ground. Lat. 30° 01' 10", long. 99° 20' 09". Transmitter: Moore Ranch, approx. 14-mi. SE of Ingram. Equipment: Comwave transmitter; Andrew antenna.

Leased to Nucentrix Broadband Networks, 200 Chisholm Place, Suite 200 , Plano, TX 75075. Phone: 972-423-9494. Fax: 972-423-0819.

Ingram—WLX-991 (Channels G-1-4). Fredericksburg Independent School District Authorized power: 50-w. each. Antenna: 692-ft. above ground. Lat. 30° 01' 10", long. 99° 20' 09". Transmitter: Moore Ranch, approx. 14-mi. SE of Ingram. Equipment: Comwave transmitter; Andrew antenna.

Kingsville—WHR-947 (Channels B-1-4). Texas A&M University-Kingsville, Campus Box 178, Kingsville, TX 78363. Authorized power: 10-w. each. Antenna: 100-ft. above ground. Lat. 27° 31' 24", long. 97° 52' 42". Transmitter: Communications Sciences Bldg. Tower, Texas A&M U.-Kingsville. Equipment: Crown transmitter.

Leased to Nucentrix Broadband Networks, 200 Chisholm Place, Suite 200 , Plano, TX 75075. Phone: 972-423-9494. Fax: 972-423-0819.

Knippa—WLX-976 (Channels A-1-4). Sabinal School District, Box 338, 409 W. Cullins Ave., Sabinal, TX 78881. Phone: 830-988-2472. Fax: 830-988-7151. Authorized power: 50-w. each. Antenna: 702-ft. above ground. Lat. 29° 21' 46", long. 99° 37' 14". Transmitter: Approx. 4.5-mi. N of Knippa. Equipment: Comwave transmitter; Andrew antenna.

Knippa—WNC-325 (Channels B-1-4). Hondo Independent School District, 2608 Avenue H, Hondo, TX 78861. Authorized power: 50-w. each. Antenna: 702-ft. above ground. Lat. 29° 21' 46", long. 99° 37' 14". Transmitter: Approx. 4.5-mi. N of Knippa. Equipment: Comwave transmitter; Andrew antenna.

Knippa—WLX-915 (Channels C-1-4). Knippa Independent School District, Box 99, Knippa, TX 78770. Phone: 210-934-2176. Fax: 210-934-2715.

E-mail: knippa@earthlink.net.

Authorized power: 50-w. each. Antenna: 1050-ft. above ground. Lat. 29° 21' 46", long. 99° 37' 14". Transmitter: Approx. 4.5-mi. N of Knippa. Equipment: Comwave transmitter; Andrew antenna.

Leased to Nucentrix Broadband Networks, 200 Chisholm Place, Suite 200, Plano, TX 75075. Phone: 972-423-9494. Fax: 972-423-0819.

Knippa—WLX-969 (Channels D-1-4). Uvalde Consolidated Independent School District, Box 1909, Uvalde, TX 78802. Phone: 830-278-6655. Fax: 830-591-4909.

E-mail: bskipper@uvalde-cons.k12.tx.us.

Web site: http://www.uvalde-cons.k12.tx.us.

Authorized power: 50-w. each. Antenna: 702-ft. above ground. Lat. 29° 21' 46", long. 99° 37' 14". Transmitter: Approx. 4.5-mi. N of Knippa. Equipment: Comwave transmitter; Andrew antenna.

Knippa—WLX-968 (Channels G-1-4). Utopia Consolidated Independent School District, Box 218, Utopia, TX 78884. Phone: 210-966-3339. Fax: 210-966-6162. Authorized power: 50-w. each. Antenna: 702-ft. above ground. Lat. 29° 21' 46", long. 99° 37' 14". Transmitter: Approx. 4.5-mi. N of Knippa. Equipment: Comwave transmitter; Andrew antenna.

Kossuth—WLX-544 (Channels A-1-4). Neches Independent School District, Box 310, Neches, TX 75779. Phone: 903-584-3311. Fax: 903-584-3686. Authorized power: 10-w. each. Antenna: 705-ft. above ground. Lat. 31° 43' 24", long. 95° 34' 23". Transmitter: 6-mi. W of Kossuth, 1.4-mi. SE of Palestine, near Swanson Hill Church. Equipment: ITS transmitter; Andrew antenna.

Leased to Nucentrix Broadband Networks, 200 Chishom Place, Suite 200, Plano, TX 75075 Phone: 972-423-9494. Fax: 972-423-0819.

Kossuth—WLX-520 (Channels B-1-4). Elkhart Independent School District, Bridges St. & Hwy. 294, Elkhart, TX 75839. Authorized power: 10-w. each. Antenna: 705-ft. above ground. Lat. 31° 43' 24", long. 95° 34' 23". Transmitter: 6-mi. W of Kossuth, 1.4-mi. SE of Palestine, near Swanson Hill Church. Equipment: ITS transmitter; Andrew antenna.

Kossuth—WLX-431 (Channels C-1-4). Alto Independent School District, Box 1000, Rte. One, Alto, TX 75925. Phone: 409-858-4391. Fax: 409-858-2101. Authorized power: 7.9-w. each. Antenna: 702-ft. above ground. Lat. 31° 43' 24", long. 95° 34' 23". Transmitter: 6-mi. W of Kossuth, 1.4-mi. SE of Palestine, near Swanson Hill Church. Equipment: Comwave transmitter; Bogner antenna.

Kossuth—WLX-542 (Channels D-1-4). Grapeland Independent School, 116 W. Myrtle, Grapeland, TX 75844. Authorized power: 7.9-w. each. Antenna: 702-ft. above ground. Lat. 31° 43' 24", long. 95° 34' 23". Transmitter: 6-mi. W of Kossuth, 1.4-mi. SE of Palestine, near Swanson Hill Church. Equipment: Comwave transmitter; Bogner antenna.

Leased to Nucentrix Broadband Networks, 200 Chisholm Place, Suite 200, Plano, TX 75075. Phone: 972-423-9494. Fax: 972-423-0819

Kossuth—WLX-549 (Channels G-1-4). Frankston Independent School District, 100 Perry St., Frankston, TX 75763. Phone: 903-876-2215. Fax: 903-876-4558. Authorized power: 7.9-w. each. Antenna: 702-ft. above ground. Lat. 31° 43' 24", long. 95° 34' 23". Transmitter: 6-mi. W of Kossuth, 1.4-mi. SE of Palestine, near Swanson Hill Church. Equipment: Comwave transmitter; Bogner antenna.

Laredo—WLX-755 (Channels A-1-4). Texas A & M International U., 5201 University Blvd., Laredo, TX 78041-1999. Phone: 956-326-2180. Fax: 956-326-2179.

Web site: http://www.tamiu.edu.

Authorized power: 10-w. each. Antenna: 440-ft. above ground. Lat. 27° 24' 09", long. 99° 26' 49". Transmitter: 6-mi. S of Laredo on Pinta Mangana Hein Rd. Equipment: ITS transmitter; Bogner antenna.

Leased to Nucentrix Broadband Networks, 200 Chisholm Place, Suite 200, Plano, TX 75075. Phone: 972-423-9494. Fax: 972-423-0819

Laredo—WLX-836 (Channels B-1-4). Laredo Junior College, W. end of Washington St., Laredo, TX 78040. Phone: 956-721-5323. Fax: 956-721-5456.

E-mail: gsifuentes@laredo.cc.tx.us.

Web site: http://laredo.cc.tx.us.

Authorized power: 10-w. each. Antenna: 440-ft. above ground. Lat. 27° 24' 09", long. 99° 26' 49". Transmitter: 6-mi. S of Laredo. Equipment: ITS transmitter; Andrew antenna.

Laredo—WLX-747 (Channels C-1-4). Laredo Independent School District, 1702 Houston St., Laredo, TX 78040. Phone: 210-727-4401. Fax: 210-722-6228. Authorized power: 10-w. each. Antenna: 440-ft. above ground. Lat. 27° 24' 09", long. 99° 26' 49". Transmitter: 6-mi. S of Laredo on Pinta Mangana Hein Rd. Equipment: ITS transmitter; Bogner antenna.

Laredo—WLX-743 (Channels D-1-4). Texas State Technical Institute, Harlingen Campus, Harlingen, TX 78550. Phone: 210-425-0743. Fax: 210-425-0732. Authorized power: 10-w. each. Antenna: 440-ft. above ground. Lat. 27° 24' 09", long. 99° 26' 49". Transmitter: 6-mi. S of Laredo on Pinta Mangana Hein Rd. Equipment: ITS transmitter; Bogner antenna.

Leased to Nucentrix Broadband Networks, 200 Chisholm Place, Suite 200, Plano, TX 75075. Phone: 972-423-9494. Fax: 972-423-0819

Laredo—WLX-777 (Channels G-1-4). Diocesan Telecommunications Corp., 1200 Lantana, Corpus Christi, TX 78400. Phone: 512-289-6437. Fax: 512-289-1420.

E-mail: mwind@goccn.org.

Web site: http://www.goccn.org.

Authorized power: 10-w. each. Antenna: 440-ft. above ground. Lat. 27° 24' 09", long. 99° 26' 49". Transmitter: 6-mi. S of Laredo. Equipment: ITS transmitter; Andrew antenna.

Leased to Heartland Communications, 401 W. Evergreen, Durant, OK 74701. Phone: 405-924-6220.

Lubbock—WNC-557 (Channels B-1-4). Lubbock Independent School District, 1628 19th St., Lubbock, TX 79409. Phone: 806-766-1212. Fax: 806-766-1312.

E-mail: lisd-tv@hub.ofthe.net.

Web site: http://www.lisd-tv.hub.ofthe.net.

Authorized power: 50-w. each. Antenna: 305-ft. above ground. Lat. 33° 35' 07", long. 101° 50' 49". Transmitter: Metro Tower Bldg., 1220 Broadway. Equipment: Comwave transmitter; Andrew antenna.

Leased to Nucentrix Broadband Networks, 200 Chisholm Place, Suite 200, Plano, TX 75075. Phone: 972-423-9494. Fax: 972-423-0819

Lubbock—WLX-308 (Channels C-1-4). Lubbock Christian U., 5601 19th St., Lubbock, TX 79407. Phone: 806-796-8800. Authorized power: 50-w. each. Antenna: 305-ft. above ground. Lat. 33° 35' 07", long. 101° 50' 49". Transmitter: Metro Tower Bldg., 1220 Broadway. Equipment: Comwave transmitter; Andrew antenna.

Lubbock—WLX-318 (Channels D-1-4). Catholic Diocese of Lubbock, Office of Communications, Box 98700, Lubbock, TX 79499. Phone: 806-792-3943. Fax: 806-792-8109.

E-mail: catholiclubbock.org.

Authorized power: 50-w. each. Antenna: 305-ft. above ground. Lat. 33° 35' 07", long. 101° 50' 49". Transmitter: Metro Tower Bldg., 1220 Broadway. Equipment: Comwave transmitter; Andrew antenna.

Leased to Nucentrix Broadband Networks, 200 Chisholm Place, Suite 200, Plano, TX 75075. Phone: 972-423-9494. Fax: 972-423-0819

Lubbock—WLX-689 (Channels G-1-4). Region 17 Education Service Center, 1111 W. Loop 289, Lubbock, TX 79411. Authorized power: 50-w. each. Antenna: 305-ft. above ground. Lat. 33° 35' 07", long. 101° 50' 49". Transmitter: Metro Tower Bldg., 1220 Broadway. Equipment: Comwave transmitter; Andrew antenna.

McAllen—WNC-240 (Channels A-1-4). Texas State Technical College, Harlingen Campus, Harlingen, TX 78550. Phone: 956-364-4111. Fax: 956-364-5105.

E-mail: nreynold@tstc.edu.

Web site: http://www.harlingen.tstc.edu.

Authorized power: 20-w. each. Antenna: 440-ft. above ground. Lat. 26° 15' 57", long. 98° 10' 43". Transmitter: Hwy. 281, 2-mi. S of Edinburg. Equipment: ITS transmitter; Andrew antenna.

Leased to Nucentrix Broadband Networks, 200 Chisholm Place, Suite 200, Plano, TX 75075. Phone: 972-423-9494. Fax: 972-423-0819

McAllen—WNC-349 (Channels B-1-4). Mission Consolidated Independent School District, 1201 Bryce Dr., Mission, TX 78572. Authorized power: 20-w. each. Antenna: 440-ft. above ground. Lat. 26° 15' 57", long. 98° 10' 43". Transmitter: Hwy. 281, 2-mi. S of Edinburg. Equipment: ITS transmitter; Andrew antenna.

McAllen—WNC-242 (Channels C-1-4). Edinburg Consolidated Independent School District, Drawer 900, Edinburg, TX 78540. Authorized power: 20-w. each. Antenna: 440-ft. above ground. Lat. 26° 15' 57", long. 98° 10' 43". Transmitter: Hwy. 281, 2-mi. S of Edinburg. Equipment: ITS transmitter; Andrew antenna.

McAllen—WLX-946 (Channels D-1-4). Weslaco Independent School District, Box 266, Weslaco, TX 78596. Phone: 210-969-6876. Fax: 210-969-6877. Authorized power: 20-w. each. Antenna: 440-ft. above ground. Lat. 26° 15' 57", long. 98° 10' 043". Transmitter: 2-mi. S of Edinburg on Hwy. 281. Equipment: ITS transmitter; Andrew antenna.

Leased to United States Wireless Inc., 1803 West Ave., Austin, TX 78701. Phone: 512-320-8522.

McAllen—WNC-241 (Channels G-1-4). Catholic Diocese of Brownsville, 1910 E. Elizabeth St., Brownsville, TX 78520. Phone: 210-542-2501. Authorized power: 20-w. each. Antenna: 440-ft. above ground. Lat. 26° 15' 57", long. 98° 10' 43". Transmitter: Hwy, 281, 2-mi. S of Edinburg. Equipment: ITS transmitter; Andrew antenna.

McCulloch—WLX-564 (Channels A-1-4). Lohn Independent School District, Box 277, Lohn, TX 76852. Authorized power: 10-w. each. Antenna: 484-ft. above ground. Lat. 31° 15' 28", long. 99° 23' 35". Transmitter: Brady in McCulloch County. Equipment: Comwave transmitter; Andrew antenna.

McKinney—WHR-718 (Channels G-1-4). Education Service Center Region 10, Box 831300, 400 E. Spring Valley, Richardson, TX 75083-1300. Phone: 972-348-1342. Fax: 972-348-1343.

E-mail: canterbd@esc10.ednet10.net.

Web site: http://www.esc10.ednet10.net.

Authorized power: 50-w. each. Antenna: 450-ft. above ground. Lat. 33° 22' 54", long. 96° 24' 45". Transmitter: 0.75-mi. SW of desert, approx. 0.3-mi. N of Hwy. 121. Equipment: Emcee transmitter; Andrew antenna.

Mesquite—KHS-78 (Channels D-1-4). Mesquite Independent School District, 405 E. Davis St., Mesquite, TX 75149. Phone: 972-882-7360. Fax: 972-882-7431. Authorized power: 10-w. each. Antenna: 106-ft. above ground. Lat. 32° 45' 57", long. 96° 35' 44". Equipment: Comwave transmitter; Andrew antenna.

Midland—WLX-319 (Channels A-1-4). Region 18 Education Service Center, Box 60580, 2811 La Force, Midland, TX 79711-0580. Phone: 915-567-3210. Fax: 915-567-3290.

E-mail: blabeff@esc18.tenet.edu.

Web site: http://www.esc18.tenet.edu.

Authorized power: 50-w. each. Antenna: 3524-ft. above ground. Lat. 32° 04' 05", long. 102° 31' 51". Transmitter: NW corner of Midland County. Equipment: Comwave transmitter; Andrew antenna.

Leased to Nucentrix Broadband Networks, 200 Chisholm Place, Suite 200, Plano, TX 75075. Phone: 972-423-9494. Fax: 972-423-0819

Midland—WLX-316 (Channels B-1-4). Roman Catholic Diocese of San Angelo, Box 1829, San Angelo, TX 76902. Authorized power: 50-w. each. Antenna: 3524-ft. above ground. Lat. 32° 04' 05", long. 102° 31' 51". Transmitter: NW corner of Midland County. Equipment: Comwave transmitter; Andrew antenna.

Midland—WLX-297 (Channels C-1-4). Midland College, 3600 N. Garfield, Midland, TX 79705. Authorized power: 10-w. each. Antenna: 304-ft above ground, Lat. 31° 59' 48", long. 102° 04' 41". Transmitter: 415 W. Wall St. Equipment: Comwave transmitter; Andrew antenna.

Midland—WLX-317 (Channels D-1-4). Texas State Technical College, 300 College Dr., Sweetwater, TX 79556. Phone: 915-235-7300. Authorized power: 50-w. each. Antenna: 3524-ft. above ground. Lat. 32° 04' 05", long. 102° 13' 51". Transmitter: NW corner of Midland County. Equipment: Comwave transmitter; Andrew antenna.

Leased to Nucentrix Broadband Networks, 200 Chisholm Place, Suite 200, Plano, TX 75075. Phone: 972-423-9494. Fax: 972-423-0819

Midland—WLX-338 (Channels G-1-4). Midland Physicians & Surgeons Hospital Inc. Authorized power: 50-w. each. Antenna: 3251-ft. above ground. Lat. 32° 04' 05", long. 102° 13' 51". Transmitter: NW corner of Midland County. Equipment: Comwave transmitter; Andrew antenna.

Milano—WLX-440 (Channels A-1-4). Caldwell Independent School District, 203 N. Gray St., Caldwell, TX 77836. Phone: 409-567-9559. Fax: 409-567-9876. Equipment: Andrew antenna.

Leased to RuralVision Central Inc., 124 W. Neosho Ave., Box 68, Thayer, KS 66776. Phone: 316-839-5923.

Milano—WLX-442 (Channels B-1-4). Buckholts Independent School District, 203 S. 10th, Buckholts, TX 76518. Phone: 254-593-3011. Fax: 254-593-2270. Authorized power: 50-w. each. Antenna: 695-ft. above ground. Lat. 30° 44' 15", long. 96° 50' 13". Transmitter: 2-mi. NE of Milano, 0.9-mi. E of FM 3242. Equipment: Comwave transmitter; Andrew antenna.

Leased to Wireless One, Suite 2K, Baton Rouge, LA 70808. Phone: 504-926-7778.

Milano—WLX-454 (Channels C-1-4). Rockdale Independent School District, 520 Davilla, Rockdale, TX 76567. Phone: 512-446-3403. Fax: 512-446-3460. Authorized power: 10-w. each. Lat. 30° 44' 15", long. 96° 50' 13". Equipment: Andrew antenna.

Leased to Wireless One, 5551 Corporate Blvd., Suite 2K, Baton Rouge, LA 70808. Phone: 504-926-7778.

Milano—WLX-398 (Channels D-1-4). Thorndale Independent School District, 201 E. Norris St., Thorndale, TX 76577. Lat. 30° 42' 31", long. 96° 50' 29". Equipment: ITS transmitter; Andrew antenna. Requests change to 50-w. each, 695-ft. above ground, lat. 30° 44' 14", long. 96° 50' 14"; transmitter to 2-mi. NE of Milano, 0.9-mi. E of FM 3242, Comwave transmitter.

Leased to RuralVision Central Inc., 124 W. Neosho Ave., Box 68, Thayer, KS 66776. Phone: 316-839-5923.

Milano—WLX-441 (Channels G-1-4). Mumford Independent School District, FM 50, Mumford, TX 77867. Authorized power: 50-w. each. Antenna: 695-ft. above ground. Lat. 30° 44' 15", long. 96° 50' 13". Transmitter: 2-mi. NE of Milano, 0.9-mi. E of FM 3242. Equipment: Comwave transmitter; Andrew antenna.

Leased to RuralVision Central Inc., 124 W. Neosho Ave., Box 68, Thayer, KS 66776. Phone: 316-839-5923.

Mount Pleasant—WNC-592 (Channels A-1-4). Pittsburg Independent School District, Box 621, Pittsburg, TX 75686. Authorized power: 25-w. each. Antenna: 500-ft. above ground. Lat. 33° 13' 52", long. 95° 01' 24". Transmitter: 5.8-mi. NW of Mount Pleasant. Equipment: Comwave transmitter; Andrew antenna.

Mount Pleasant—WNC-591 (Channels B-1-4). Mount Vernon Independent School District, Box 98, Mount Vernon, TX 75457. Authorized power: 25-w. each. Antenna: 500-ft. above ground. Lat. 33° 13' 52", long. 95° 01' 24". Transmitter: 5.8-mi. NW of Mount Pleasant. Equipment: Comwave transmitter; Andrew antenna.

Mount Pleasant—WNC-523 (Channels C-1-4). Mount Pleasant Independent School District, Box 1117, Mount Pleasant, TX 75456. Phone: 903-575-2000. Fax: 903-575-2014. Authorized power: 25-w. each. Antenna: 500-ft. above ground. Lat. 33° 13' 52", long. 95° 01' 24". Transmitter: 5-mi. NNE of Hwy. 271, 6-mi. NW of Mt. Pleasant. Equipment: Comwave transmitter; Andrew antenna.

Leased to Nucentrix Broadband Networks, 200 Chisholm Place, Suite 200, Plano, TX 75075. Phone: 972-423-9494. Fax: 972-423-0819

Mount Pleasant—WNC-593 (Channels D-1-4). Titus County Memorial Hospital, 2001 N. Jefferson, Mount Pleasant, TX 75455. Phone: 903-577-6190. Fax: 903-577-6284. Authorized power: 25-w. each. Antenna: 500-ft. above ground. Lat. 33° 13' 52", long. 95° 01' 24". Transmitter: Approx. 5-mi. NNE of Hwy. 271, 5.8-mi. NW of Mount Pleasant. Equipment: Emcee transmitter; Andrew antenna.

Leased to Nucentrix Broadband Networks, 200 Chisholm Place, Suite 200, Plano, TX 75075. Phone: 972-423-9494. Fax: 972-423-0819

Mount Pleasant—WNC-599 (Channels G-1-4). Northeast Texas Community College, Box 1307, Mount Pleasant, TX 75456-1307. Phone: 903-572-1911. Authorized power: 25-w. each. Antenna: 500-ft. above ground. Lat. 33° 13' 52", long. 95° 01' 24". Transmitter: Approx. 5-mi. NNE of Hwy. 271. Equipment: Comwave transmitter; Andrew antenna.

Nevada—WHR-646 (Channels C-1-4). Alliance for Higher Education, Suite 250, 17103 Preston Rd., Dallas, TX 75248-1373. Phone: 214-713-8170. Authorized power: 10-w. each. Antenna: 194-ft. above ground. Lat. 33° 00' 07", long. 96° 22' 20". Transmitter: FM 2755 & FM 1138 intersection.

Nolanville—WLX-581 (Channels A-1-4). Temple College, 2600 S. 1st St., Temple, TX 76504. Phone: 254-298-8282. Fax: 254-298-8277.

E-mail: charles.stout@templejc.edu.

Web site: http://www.templejc.edu.

Authorized power: 50-w. each. Antenna: 518-ft. above ground. Lat. 31° 05' 23", long. 97° 35' 55". Transmitter: Farm Rd. 439, 1.2-mi. NE of Nolanville. Equipment: ITS transmitter; Andrew antenna.

Leased to Nucentrix Broadband Networks, 200 Chisholm Place, Suite 200, Plano, TX 75075. Phone: 972-423-9494. Fax: 972-423-0819

Nolanville—WLX-490 (Channels B-1-4). Network for Instructional TV Inc., Suite 110, 11490 Commerce Park Dr., Reston, VA 20191. Phone: 703-860-9200. Fax: 703-860-9237. Authorized power: 50-w. each. Antenna: 518-ft. above ground. Lat. 31° 05' 23", long. 97° 35' 55". Transmitter: Farm Rd. 439, 1.24-mi. NE of Nolanville. Equipment: ITS transmitter; Andrew antenna.

Leased to Nucentrix Broadband Networks, 200 Chisholm Place, Suite 200, Plano, TX 75075. Phone: 972-423-9494. Fax: 972-423-0819

Nolanville—WLX-307 (Channels C-1-4). North American Catholic Educational Programming Foundation Inc., Box 40026, Providence, RI 02940-0026. Phone: 401-729-0900. Authorized power: 50-w. each. Antenna: 400-ft. above ground. Lat. 31° 05' 23", long. 97° 35' 55". Transmitter: Farm Rd. 439, 1.2-mi. NE of Nolanville. Equipment: ITS transmitter; Andrew antenna.

Nolanville—WLX-424 (Channels D-1-4). Central Texas College, Box 1800, Killeen, TX 76540. Authorized power: 50-w. each. Antenna: 518-ft. above ground. Lat. 31° 05' 23", long. 97° 35' 55". Transmitter: Farm Rd. 439, 1.2-mi. NE of Nolanville. Equipment: ITS transmitter; Andrew antenna.

Nolanville—WLX-352 (Channels G-1-4). Education Service Center Region 12, 2101 W. Loop 340, Waco, TX 76712. Phone: 254-666-0707. Fax: 254-666-0823.

E-mail: brascoe@tenet.edu.

Web site: http://www.esc12.tenet.edu.

Authorized power: 50-w. each. Antenna: 518-ft. above ground. Lat. 31° 05' 23", long. 97° 35' 55". Transmitter: Farm Road 439, 1.2-mi. NE of Nolanville. Equipment: ITS transmitter; Andrew antenna.

Leased to Nucentrix Broadband Networks, 200 Chisholm Place, Suite 200, Plano, TX 75075. Phone: 972-423-9494. Fax: 972-423-0819

O'Donnell—WNC-216 (Channels B-1-4). Klondike Independent School District, Box 276, RR 1, Lamesa, TX 79331. Authorized power: 50-w. each. Antenna: 709-ft. above ground. Lat. 33° 03' 52", long. 101° 52' 33". Equipment: Comwave transmitter.

O'Donnell—WLX-853 (Channels C-1-4). New Home Independent School District, 1000 Slide Rd., New Home, TX 79383. Authorized power: 50-w. each. Antenna: 705-ft. above ground. Lat. 33° 03' 52", long. 101° 52' 33". Transmitter: 3.7-mi. N of State Rte. 213. Equipment: Comwave transmitter; Andrew antenna.

O'Donnell—WLX-964 (Channels D-1-4). O'Donnell Independent School District, Box 487, 501 5th St., O'Donnell, TX 79351. Phone: 806-428-3241. Fax: 806-428-3395. Authorized power: 50-w. each. Antenna: 705-ft. above ground. Lat. 33° 03' 52", long. 101° 52' 33". Transmitter: 3.7-mi. W of U.S. 87, 3.1-mi. N of State Rte. 213. Equipment: Comwave transmitter; Andrew antenna.

Olton—WLX-428 (Channels A-1-4). Hart Independent School District, Box 490, Hart, TX 79043. Authorized power: 50-w. each. Antenna: 541-ft. above ground. Lat. 34° 16' 00", long. 102° 14' 01". Transmitter: State Rd. 1842, 9-mi. NW of Olton. Equipment: Comwave transmitter; Andrew antenna.

Leased to Nucentrix Broadband Networks, 200 Chisholm Place, Suite 200, Plano, TX 75075. Phone: 972-423-9494. Fax: 972-423-0819.

Olton—WLX-430 (Channels B-1-4). Springlake Earth Independent School District, Farm Rds. 302 & 2901, Earth, TX 79031. Phone: 806-257-3310. Fax: 806-257-3310. Authorized power: 50-w. each. Antenna: 343-ft. above ground. Lat. 34° 16' 00", long. 102° 14' 01". Transmitter: State Rd. 1842, 9-mi. NW of Olton. Equipment: Comwave transmitter; Andrew antenna.

Leased to Nucentrix Broadband Networks, 200 Chisholm Place, Suite 200, Plano, TX 75075. Phone: 972-423-9494. Fax: 972-423-0819

Olton—WLX-427 (Channels C-1-4). Spade Independent School District, Box 69, 100 S. Main, Spade, TX 73969. Phone: 806-233-2521. Fax: 806-233-2118.

E-mail: spadeschool@door.net.

Authorized power: 10-w. each. Antenna: 343-ft. above ground. Lat. 34° 16' 00", long. 102° 14' 01". Transmitter: State Rd. 1842, 9-mi. NW of Olton. Equipment: ITS transmitter; Andrew antenna.

Leased to Nucentrix Broadband Networks, 200 Chisholm Place, Suite 200, Plano, TX 75075. Phone: 972-423-9494. Fax: 972-423-0819

Olton—WLX-429 (Channels D-1-4). Cotton Center Independent School District, Box 350, Cotton Center, TX 79021. Authorized power: 50-w. each. Antenna: 343-ft. above ground. Lat. 34° 16' 00", long. 102° 14' 01". Transmitter: State Rd. 1842, 9-mi. NW of Olton. Equipment: Comwave transmitter; Andrew antenna.

Olton—WLX-407 (Channels G-1-4). Hale Center Independent School District, 410 W. 12th, Hale Center, TX 79041. Phone: 806-839-2451. Fax: 806-839-2195. Authorized power: 50-w. each. Antenna: 344-ft. above ground. Lat. 34° 16' 00", long. 102° 14' 01". Transmitter: State Rd. 1842, 9-mi. NW of Olton. Equipment: Comwave transmitter; Andrew antenna.

Leased to Nucentrix Broadband Networks, 200 Chisholm Place, Suite 200, Plano, TX 75075. Phone: 972-423-9494. Fax: 972-423-0819

Richardson—WEF-69 (Channels B-1-4). Richardson Independent School District, 400 S. Greenville Ave., Richardson, TX 75081. Authorized power: 10-w. each. Antenna: 185-ft. above ground. Lat. 32° 55' 02", long. 96° 45' 34". Transmitter: Hamilton Park School, 8221 Towns St., Dallas.

Rosston—WLX-764 (Channels C-1-4). Valley View Independent School District, Box 125, Valley View, TX 76272. Authorized power: 10-w. each. Antenna: 343-ft. above ground. Lat. 33° 28' 59", long. 97° 26' 50". Transmitter: 0.25-mi. W of Rosston. Equipment: ITS transmitter; Andrew antenna.

Rosston—WLX-802 (Channels D-1-3). Lindsay Independent School District, 625 Knight Dr., Lindsay, TX 76250. Phone: 940-668-8923. Fax: 940-668-2662. Authorized power: 10-w. each. Antenna: 343-ft. above ground. Lat. 33° 28' 59", long. 97° 26' 50". Transmitter: 0.25-mi. W of Rosston. Equipment: ITS transmitter; Andrew antenna.

Saint Jo—WLX-858 (Channels G-1-4). Turner Independent School District, Star Rte. 73, Burneyville, OK 73430. Authorized power: 50-w. each. Antenna: 305-ft. above ground. Lat. 33° 41' 27", long. 97° 31' 19". Equipment: ITS transmitter; Andrew antenna.

Leased to Rural Wireless South, Box 1378, Gainesville, TX 76241. Phone: 800-606-8278.

San Angelo—WLX-334 (Channels A-1-4). Roman Catholic Diocese of San Angelo, Box 1829, San Angelo, TX 76904. Authorized power: 10-w. each. Antenna: 195-ft. above ground. Lat. 31° 27' 43", long. 100° 26' 04". Transmitter: Hotel Cactus Bldg., 36 E. Twohig Ave. Equipment: Comwave transmitter; Andrew antenna.

San Angelo—WNC-914 (Channels B-1-4). Grape Creek/Pullian Independent School District. Authorized power: 10-w. each. Antenna: 2172-ft. above ground. Lat. 31° 25' 16", long. 100° 32' 36". Transmitter: Hwy. 67 W. Equipment: Comwave transmitter; Andrew antenna.

San Angelo—WLX-758 (Channels D-1-4). ACTS of San Angelo, 238 Edgewood Dr., San Angelo, TX 76903. Authorized power: 10-w. each. Antenna: 510-ft. above ground. Lat. 31° 25' 16", long. 100° 32' 36". Transmitter: Hwy. 67 W. Equipment: Comwave transmitter; Andrew antenna.

San Angelo—WND-265 (Channels G-1-4). Hardin-Simmons U., 2200 Hickory, Abilene, TX 79697. Phone: 915-670-1414. Fax: 915-670-1409.

E-mail: dbaergeu@hsutx.edu.

Web site: http://www.hsutx.edu.

Authorized power: 10-w. each. Antenna: 492-ft. above ground. Lat. 31° 29' 41", long. 100° 28' 36". Transmitter: 0.2-mi. S of Hwy. 87. Equipment: ITS transmitter; Andrew antenna.

Leased to Sterling Cable/C & W Enterprises, 317 N. Farr, San Angelo, TX 76902. Phone: 915-655-5795.

San Antonio—WLX-328 (Channels A-1-4). Northern Arizona U. Foundation, Babbitt Administration Bldg., Flagstaff, AZ 86011. Authorized power: 50-w. each. Antenna: 185-ft. above ground. Lat. 29° 33' 13", long. 98° 21' 15". Transmitter: 12544 Judson Rd. Equipment: ITS transmitter; Andrew antenna.

San Antonio—WHR-920 (Channels B-1-4). Education Service Center, Region 20, 1314 Hines Ave., San Antonio, TX 78208. Authorized power: 50-w. each. Antenna: 675-ft. above ground. Lat. 29° 33' 13", long. 98° 21' 15". Transmitter: 12544 Judson Rd. Equipment: ITS transmitter; Bogner antenna.

San Antonio—WLX-874 (Channels C-1-4). Network for Instructional TV Inc., Suite 110, 11490 Commerce Park Dr., Reston, VA 20191. Phone: 703-860-9200. Fax: 703-860-9237. Authorized power: 10-w. each. Antenna: 184-ft. above ground. Lat. 29° 33' 13", long. 98° 21' 15". Transmitter: 12544 Judson Rd. Equipment: ITS transmitter; Andrew antenna.

Leased to CS Wireless Systems Inc., 1101 Summit Ave., Plano, TX 75074. Phone: 972-730-3300

San Antonio—WLX-248 (Channels D-1-4). Edgewood Independent School District, 5358 W. Commerce St., San Antonio, TX 78237. Authorized power: 50-w. each. Antenna: 189-ft. above ground. Lat. 29° 33' 13", long. 98° 21' 15". Transmitter: 12544 Judson Rd. Equipment: ITS transmitter; Andrew antenna.

San Antonio—WLX-704 (Channels G-1-4). Hispanic Information & Telecommunications Network Inc., 3rd Floor, 449 Broadway, New York, NY 10013. Phone: 212-966-5660. Fax: 212-966-5725.

E-mail: email@hitn.org.

Web site: http://www.hitn.org.

Authorized power: 50-w. each. Antenna: 185-ft. above ground. Lat. 29° 33' 13", long. 98° 21' 15". Transmitter: 12544 Judson Rd., Bexar County. Equipment: ITS transmitter; Andrew antenna.

Leased to CS Wireless, 1101 Summit Ave., Plano, TX 75074. Phone: 972-730-3300.

Santa Anna—WLX-779 (Channels B-1-4). Santa Anna Independent School District, Box 99, Santa Anna, TX 76878. Phone: 915-348-3136. Fax: 915-348-3141. Authorized power: 10-w. each. Antenna: 303-ft. above ground. Lat. 31° 44' 49", long. 99° 19' 26". Transmitter: 0.5-mi. NW of State FM 1176 & U.S. Hwy. 67 intersection. Equipment: Comwave transmitter; Andrew antenna.

Santa Anna—WLX-691 (Channels D-1-4). Coleman Independent School District, Box 900, Coleman, TX 76834. Phone: 915-625-3575. Authorized power: 10-w. each. Antenna: 303-ft. above ground. Lat. 31° 44' 49", long. 99° 19' 26". Transmitter: 0.5-mi. NW of State FM 1176 & U.S. Hwy. 67 intersection. Equipment: Comwave transmitter; Andrew antenna.

Leased to Coleman County Broadcasting Systems, 801 S. Santa Fe, Santa Anna, TX 76878. Phone: 915-348-3951.

Santa Anna—WLX-576 (Channels G-3-4). Panther Creek Consolidated School District, HC73 Box 32, Valera, TX 76884. Phone: 915-357-4449. Fax: 915-357-4470.

E-mail: bhale@tenet.edu.

Authorized power: 10-w. each. Antenna: 303-ft. above ground. Lat. 31° 44' 49", long. 99° 19' 26". Transmitter: 0.5-mi. NW of State FM 1176 & U.S. Hwy. 67 intersection. Equipment: Comwave transmitter; Andrew antenna.

Seminole—WLX-993 (Channels C-1-4). Tatum Municipal School, Box 685, Tatum, NM 88267. Phone: 505-398-4455. Fax: 505-398-8220. Authorized power: 50-w. each. Antenna: 4304-ft. above ground. Lat. 32° 49' 35", long. 102° 59' 24". Transmitter: SR 212, 1.3-mi. E of Ranch Rd. 3306. Equipment: Emcee transmitter; Andrew antenna.

Leased to Leaco Rural Telephone Cooperative Inc., 1500 N. Love St., Lovington, NM 88260. Phone: 505-398-5352.

Snyder—WNC-336 (Channels A-1-4). Roby Consolidated Independent School District, Box 519, Roby, TX 79543. Phone: 915-776-2222. Fax: 915-776-2823.

E-mail: hschoolman@aol.com.

Lat. 32° 45' 53", long. 100° 53' 08". Transmitter: 2.5-mi. N of 8th & Ennis Creek. Equipment: Comwave transmitter; Andrew antenna.

Snyder—WNC-536 (Channels B-1-4). Colorado Independent School District, 534 E. 11th St., Colorado City, CO 79512. Authorized power: 10-w. each. Antenna: 407-ft. above ground. Lat. 32° 45' 53", long. 100° 53' 08". Transmitter: 2.5-mi. N of 8th & Ennis Creek. Equipment: Comwave transmitter; Andrew antenna.

Snyder—WNC-253 (Channels G-1-4). Rotan Independent School District, 100 N. McKinley Ave., Rotan, TX 79546. Authorized power: 10-w. each. Antenna: 430-ft. above ground. Lat. 32° 45' 53", long. 100° 53' 08". Transmitter: 2.5-mi. N of Ennis Creek. Equipment: Comwave transmitter; Andrew antenna.

Stowell—WLX-889 (Channels B-1-4). High Island Independent School District, Box 246, High Island, TX 77623. Authorized power: 50-w. each. Antenna: 625-ft. above ground. Lat. 29° 45' 33", long. 94° 29' 29". Transmitter: 0.5-mi. E of State Rte. 1941. Equipment: Comwave transmitter; Andrew antenna.

Stowell—WNC-423 (Channels C-1-4). Hampshire-Fannett Middle School, Box 1500, Rte. 2, Beaumont, TX 77705. Authorized power: 50-w. each. Antenna: 625-ft. above ground. Lat. 29° 45' 33", long. 94° 29' 29". Transmitter: 0.5-mi. E of State Rte. 1941, 5-mi. S of Interstate 10. Equipment: Comwave transmitter; Andrew antenna.

Stowell—WNC-427 (Channels D-1-4). Hampshire-Fannett High School, Box 1500, Rte. 2, Beaumont, TX 77705. Authorized power: 50-w. each. Antenna: 625-ft. above ground. Lat. 29° 45' 33", long. 94° 29' 29". Transmitter: 0.5-mi. E of State Rte. 1941, 5-mi. S of Interstate 10. Equipment: Comwave transmitter; Andrew antenna.

Stowell—WLX-847 (Channels G-1-4). Devers Independent School District, Box 488, Devers, TX 77538. Phone: 409-549-7135. Fax: 409-549-7595. Authorized power: 50-w. each. Antenna: 705-ft. above ground. Lat. 29° 45' 33", long. 94° 29' 29". Transmitter: 0.5-mi. E of State Rte. 1941, 5-mi. S of I-10. Equipment: Comwave transmitter; Andrew antenna.

Leased to Nucentrix Broadband Networks, 200 Chisholm Place, Suite 200, Plano, TX 75075. Phone: 972-423-0819. Fax: 972-423-0819.

Strawn—WLX-396 (Channels A-1-4). Santo Independent School District, Farm Rd. 2201, Santo, TX 76472. Phone: 817-769-2835. Fax: 817-769-3116. Authorized power: 12.6-w. each. Antenna: 1050-ft. above ground. Lat. 32° 32' 54", long. 98° 30' 47". Transmitter: 0.5-mi. W of Strawn. Equipment: Comwave transmitter; Andrew antenna.

Leased to Nucentrix Broadband Networks, 200 Chisholm Place, Suite 200, Plano, TX 75075. Phone: 972-423-9494. Fax: 972-423-0819

Strawn—WLX-395 (Channels B-1-4). Ranger Independent School District, Box 12D, Rte. 3, Ranger, TX 76470. Phone: 817-647-1187. Fax: 817-647-5215.

E-mail: risd@flash.net.

Authorized power: 12.6-w. each. Antenna: 1050-ft. above ground. Lat. 32° 32' 54", long. 98° 30' 47". Transmitter: Approx. 0.5-mi. W of Strawn. Equipment: Comwave transmitters; Andrew antenna.

Leased to Nucentrix Broadband Networks, 200 Chisholm Place, Suite 200, Plano, TX 75075. Phone: 972-423-9494. Fax: 972-423-0819

Strawn—WLX-394 (Channels C-1-4). Gordon Independent School District, 112 Rusk St., Gordon, TX 76453. Authorized power: 12.6-w. each. Antenna: 1050-ft. above ground. Lat. 32° 32' 54", long. 98° 30' 47". Transmitter: approx. 0.5-mi. W of Strawn. Equipment: Comwave transmitter; Andrew antenna.

Strawn—WLX-402 (Channels D-1-4). Morgan Mill Independent School District, Box 8, Morgan Mill, TX 76465. Authorized power: 12.6-w. each. Antenna: 1050-ft. above ground. Lat. 32° 32' 54", long. 98° 30' 47". Transmitter: approx. 0.5-mi. W of Strawn. Equipment: Comwave transmitter; Andrew antenna.

Strawn—WLX-393 (Channels G-1-4). Lingleville Independent School District, Box 134, Lingleville, TX 76461. Phone: 817-968-2596. Fax: 817-965-5821. Authorized power: 12.6-w. each. Antenna: 1050-ft. above ground. Lat. 32° 32' 54", long. 98° 30' 47". Transmitter: approx. 0.5-mi. W of Strawn. Equipment: Comwave transmitter; Andrew antenna.

Leased to Nucentrix Broadband Networks, 200 Chisholm Place, Suite 200, Plano, TX 75075. Phone: 972-423-9494. Fax: 972-423-0819

Sumner—WNC-598 (Channels A-1-2). Southeastern Oklahoma State U., Station A, Durant, OK 74701. Phone: 580-924-0121. Fax: 580-920-7475.

E-mail: kssu@sosu.

Web site: http://www.sosu.edu/al/ct/kssu.htm.

Authorized power: 50-w. each. Antenna: 609-ft. above ground. Lat. 33° 46' 33", long. 95° 37'

22". Transmitter: NW of Paris. Equipment: Comwave transmitter; Andrew antenna.

Sumner—WNC-596 (Channels A-3-4). Chisum Independent School District, 3250 Church St., Paris, TX 75460. Authorized power: 50-w. each. Antenna: 609-ft. above ground. Lat. 33° 46' 33", long. 95° 37' 22". Transmitter: 5-mi. W of U.S. 271, 8.5-mi. NW of Paris. Equipment: Comwave transmitter; Andrew antenna.

Sumner—WNC-597 (Channels B-1-2). Paris Junior College, 2400 Clarksville St., Paris, TX 75460. Phone: 713-341-3100. Authorized power: 50-w. each. Antenna: 609-ft. above ground. Lat. 33° 46' 33", long. 95° 37' 22". Transmitter: 5-mi. W of U.S. 271, 8.5-mi. NW of Paris. Equipment: Comwave transmitter; Andrew antenna.

Sumner—WNC-595 (Channels B-3-4). Prairieland Consolidated I.S.D., Box 200, Rte. 1, Pattonville, TX 75468. Phone: 903-652-6476. Fax: 903-652-3738.
E-mail: prairiland@usa.net.
Web site: http://www2.1starnet.com/prairiland.
Authorized power: 50-w. each. Antenna: 609-ft. above ground. Lat. 33° 46' 33", long. 95° 37' 22". Transmitter: 5-mi. W of U.S. 271, 8.5-mi. NW of Paris. Equipment: Comwave transmitter; Andrew antenna.
Leased to Nucentrix Broadband Networks, 200 Chisholm Place, Suite 200, Plano, TX 75075. Phone: 972-423-9494. Fax: 972-423-0819

Sumner—WNC-250 (Channels C-1-4). Paris Independent School District, Box 1159, Paris, TX 75461. Authorized power: 50-w. each. Antenna: 605-ft. above ground. Lat. 033° 46' 33", long. 095° 37' 22". Transmitter: 8.5-mi. NW of Paris. Equipment: Comwave transmitter; Andrew antenna.

Sumner—WNC-512 (Channels G-1-4). Roxton Independent School District, Box 307, Roxton, TX 75477. Phone: 903-346-3213. Fax: 903-346-3356. Authorized power: 50-w. each. Antenna: 605-ft. above ground. Lat. 33° 46' 33", long. 95° 37' 22". Transmitter: 5-mi. W of U.S. 217 & 8.5-mi. NW of Paris. Equipment: Comwave transmitter; Andrew antenna. Requests change to 609-ft. above ground.
Leased to Nucentrix Broadband Networks, 200 Chisholm Place, Suite 200, Plano, TX 75075. Phone: 972-423-9494. Fax: 972-423-0819

Terrell—WHR-836 (Channels G-1-4). Education Service Center Region 10, Box 831300, 400 E. Spring Valley, Richardson, TX 75083-1300. Authorized power: 10-w. each. Antenna: 262-ft. above ground. Lat. 32° 46' 14", long. 96° 10' 33". Transmitter: 1.5-mi. S of Hwy. 429.

Texarkana—WNC-594 (Channels A-1-4). East Texas State U., 2600 N. Robinson Rd., Texarkana, TX 75503. Phone: 903-838-6514. Fax: 903-838-8890. Authorized power: 50-w. each. Antenna: 499-ft. above ground. Lat. 33° 25' 48", long. 94° 05' 08". Transmitter: U.S. Hwy. 82 N. Equipment: Comwave transmitter; Andrew antenna.

Leased to Nucentrix Broadband Networks, 200 Chisholm Place, Suite 200, Plano, TX 75075. Phone: 972-423-9494. Fax: 972-423-0819

Texarkana—WNC-590 (Channels B-1-4). Texarkana College, 2500 N. Robinson Rd., Texarkana, TX 75501. Phone: 903-838-4541. Fax: 903-832-5030.
E-mail: smitchel@tc.cc.tx.us.
Web site: http://www.tc.cc.tx.us/ktxk.
Authorized power: 50-w. each. Antenna: 499-ft. above ground. Lat. 33° 25' 48", long. 94° 05' 08". Transmitter: U.S. Hwy. 82 N. Equipment: Comwave transmitter; Andrew antenna.

Texarkana—WNC-513 (Channels D-1-4). Texarkana Independent School District, 4241 Summerhill, Texarkana, TX 75503. Authorized power: 50-w. each. Antenna: 450-ft. above ground. Lat. 33° 25' 48", long. 94° 05' 08". Transmitter: U.S. Hwy. 82 N. Equipment: Comwave transmitter; Andrew antenna.

Texarkana—WNC-510 (Channels G-1-4). St. Michael Health Care Center, Box 1140, Texarkana, TX 75501. Authorized power: 50-w. each. Antenna: 453-ft. above ground. Lat. 33° 25' 48", long. 94° 05' 08". Transmitter: U.S. Hwy. 82 N. Equipment: Comwave transmitter; Andrew antenna.

Tyler—WNC-680 (Channels D-1-4). U. of Texas Health Center, Box 2003, Tyler, TX 75710. Phone: 903-877-7853. Authorized power: 10-w. each. Antenna: 1053-ft. above ground. Lat. 32° 19' 21", long. 95° 14' 08". Transmitter: 1-mi. W of Bascom Rd. Equipment: Comwave transmitter; Andrew antenna.
Leased to Nucentrix Broadband Networks, 200 Chisholm Place, Suite 200, Plano, TX 75075. Phone: 972-423-9494. Fax: 972-423-0819

Victoria—WNC-348 (Channels A-1-4). Texas State Technical College, 3801 Campus Dr., Waco, TX 765705. Phone: 254-867-4830. Fax: 254-867-3403.
E-mail: lynn@tstc.edu.
Web site: http://www.tstc.edu/waco.html.
Authorized power: 50-w. each. Antenna: 508-ft. above ground. Lat. 28° 49' 00", long. 97° 03' 56". Transmitter: F.M. 1685, 5-mi. W of Victoria. Equipment: ITS transmitter; Andrew antenna.
Leased to U.S. Wireless Cable, 1803 West Ave., Austin, TX 78701.

Victoria—WLX-775 (Channels B—1-4). Victoria Independent School District, 102 Profit Dr., Victoria, TX 77902. Authorized power: 50-w. each. Antenna: 505-ft. above ground. Lat. 28° 49' 00", long. 97° 03' 56". Transmitter: 5-mi. W of Victoria. Equipment: ITS transmitter; Andrew antenna.

Victoria—WNC-269 (Channels C-1-4). Edna Independent School District, Drawer D, Edna, TX 77957. Authorized power: 50-w. each. Antenna: 508-ft. above ground. Lat. 28° 49' 00", long. 97° 03' 56". Transmitter: 5-mi. W of Victoria. Equipment: ITS transmitter; Andrew antenna.

Victoria—WLX-967 (Channels D-1-4). Region 3 Education Service Center, 1905 Leary Lane, Victoria, TX 77904. Authorized power: 50-w. each. Antenna: 508-ft. above ground. Lat. 28° 49' 00", long. 97° 03' 56". Transmitter: FM 1685, 5-mi. W of Victoria. Equipment: ITS transmitter; Andrew antenna.

Victoria—WLX-896 (Channels G-1-4). Bloomington Independent School District, Box 158, Bloomington, TX 77951. Authorized power: 50-w. each. Antenna: 508-ft. above ground. Lat. 28° 49' 00", long. 97° 03' 56". Transmitter: F.M. 1685, 5-mi. W of Victoria. Equipment: ITS transmitter; Andrew antenna.

Vidor—WLX-359 (Channels A-1-4). Texas State Technical Institute, 3801 Campus Dr., Waco, TX 76705. Authorized Power: 50-w. each. Antenna: 421-ft. above ground. Lat. 30° 05' 18", long. 93° 57' 13". Transmitter: 1.5 mi. E of FM 1135.

Vidor—WLX-358 (Channels B-1-4). Nederland Independent School District, 220 N. 17th St., Nederland, TX 77627-5029. Phone: 409-724-4242. Fax: 409-724-4280.
E-mail: cworsham@nederland.k12.tx.us.
Web site: http://www.nederland.k12.tx.us.
Authorized power: 10-w. each. Antenna: 460-ft. above ground. Lat. 30° 05' 18", long. 93° 57' 12.5". Equipment: ITS transmitter; Andrews antenna.
Leased to Microlite Television, 7870 College, Beaumont, TX 77707. Phone: 409-860-9699.

Vidor—WLX-356 (Channels C-1-4). Port Arthur Independent School District, 733 5th St., Port Arthur, TX 77640. Phone: 409-989-6238. Fax: 409-989-6229.
E-mail: randazzo@tenet.edu.
Web site:
http://www.esc5.tenet.edu/paisd/main.htm//.
Authorized power: 10-w. each. Antenna: 404-ft. above ground. Lat. 30° 05' 18", long. 93° 57' 12.5". Transmitter: 1.5-mi. E of FM 1135. Equipment: ITS transmitter; Andrew antenna.

Vidor—WLX-355 (Channels D-1-4). West Orange-Cove Independent School District, Box 1107, Orange, TX 77630. Phone: 409-882-5437. Fax: 409-882-5467. Authorized power: 10-w. each. Antenna: 400-ft. above ground. Lat. 30° 05' 18", long. 93° 57' 12.5". Transmitter: 1.5-mi. E of FM 1135. Equipment: ITS transmitter; Andrew antenna.

Vidor—WLX-357 (Channels G-1-4). Education Service Center Region V, 2295 Delaware St., Beaumont, TX 77703. Authorized power: 10-w. each. Antenna: 404-ft. above ground. Lat. 30° 05' 18", long. 93° 57' 12.5". Transmitter: 1.5-mi. E of FM 1135. Equipment: ITS transmitter; Andrew antenna.

West—WLX-332 (Channels A-1-4). Central Texas College, Box 1800, Killeen, TX 76540. Authorized power: 50-w. each. Antenna: 400-ft. above ground. Lat. 31° 49' 29", long. 97° 09' 33". Transmitter: 4.3-mi. NW of West. Equipment: ITS transmitter; Andrew antenna.
Leased to Nucentrix Broadband Networks, 200 Chisholm Place, Suite 200, Plano, TX 75075. Phone: 972-423-9494. Fax: 972-423-0819

West—WLX-486 (Channels B-1-4). Network for Instructional TV Inc., Suite 110, 11490 Commerce Park Dr., Reston, VA 20191. Phone: 703-860-9200. Fax: 703-860-9237. Authorized power: 50-w. each. Antenna: 400-ft. above ground. Lat. 31° 49' 29", long. 97° 09' 33". Transmitter: 4.3-mi. NW of West. Equipment: ITS transmitter; Andrew antenna.
Leased to Nucentrix Broadband Networks, 200 Chisholm Place, Suite 200, Plano, TX 75075. Phone: 972-423-9494. Fax: 972-423-0819

West—WLX-804 (Channels C-1-4). Texas State Technical College, 3801 Campus Dr., Waco, TX 76705. Phone: 254-867-4830. Fax: 254-867-3403.
E-mail: lynn@tstc.edu.
Web site: http://www.tstc.edu/waco.html.
Authorized power: 50-w. each. Antenna: 400-ft. above ground. Lat. 31° 49' 29", long. 97° 09' 33". Transmitter: 4.3-mi. NW of West. Equipment: ITS transmitter; Andrew antenna.
Leased to Nucentrix Broadband Networks, 200 Chisholm Place, Suite 200, Plano, TX 75075. Phone: 972-423-9494. Fax: 972-423-0819

West—WLX-365 (Channels D-1-4). North American Catholic Educational Programming Foundation Inc., Box 44026, Providence, RI 02940-0026. Authorized power: 50-w. each. Antenna: 495-ft. above ground. Lat. 31° 49' 29", long. 97° 09' 33". Transmitter: 4.3-mi. NW of West. Equipment: ITS transmitter; Andrew antenna.

West—WLX-353 (Channels G-1-4). Education Service Center Region XII, 2101 W. Loop 340, Waco, TX 76712. Phone: 254-666-0707. Fax: 254-666-0823.
E-mail: brascoe@tenet.edu.
Web site: http://www.esc12.tenet.
Authorized power: 50-w. each. Antenna: 554-ft. above ground. Lat. 31° 49' 29", long. 97° 09' 33". Transmitter: 4.3-mi. NW of West. Equipment: ITS transmitter; Andrew antenna.
Leased to Nucentrix Broadband Networks, 200 Chisholm Place, Suite 200, Plano, TX 75075. Phone: 972-423-9494. Fax: 972-423-0819.

Wharton—WLX-857 (Channels B-2-4). Wharton County Junior College, 911 Boling Hwy., Wharton, TX 77488. Phone: 409-532-6402. Fax: 409-532-6526.
E-mail: bettymc@wcjc.cc.tx.us.
Web site: http://198.64.57.10/wharton/wcjc.htm.
Authorized power: 50-w. each. Antenna: 444-ft. above ground. Lat. 29° 16' 53", long. 96° 02' 27". Transmitter: 4.3-mi. SE of Wharton. Equipment: ITS transmitter; Andrew antenna.
Leased to Gulf Coast Wireless, 314 W. Texas, Box 2008, Brazoria, TX 77422.

Wharton—WLX-792 (Channels C-1-4). Bay City Independent School District, 1301 Live Oak, Bay City, TX 77414. Phone: 409-245-5766. Fax: 409-245-3175. Authorized power: 50-w. each. Antenna: 444-ft. above ground. Lat. 29° 16' 53", long. 96° 02' 27". Transmitter: 4.3-mi. SE of Wharton. Equipment: ITS transmitter; Andrew antenna.

Wharton—WLX-754 (Channels D-1-4). Region 3 Education Service Center, 1905 Leary Lane, Victoria, TX 77904. Authorized power: 50-w. each. Antenna: 444-ft. above ground. Lat. 29° 16' 53", long. 96° 02' 27". Transmitter: 4.3-mi. SE of Wharton. Equipment: ITS transmitter; Andrew antenna.

Wharton—WLX-897 (Channels G-1-4). Boling Independent School District, Box 160, Boling, TX 77420. Phone: 409-657-2770. Fax: 409-657-3265. Authorized power: 50-w. each. Antenna: 444-ft. above ground. Lat. 29° 16' 53", long. 96° 02' 27". Transmitter: 4.3-mi. SE of Wharton. Equipment: ITS transmitter; Andrew antenna.

Wichita Falls—WLX-434 (Channels A-1-4). Texas State Technical College, Box 11157, Amarillo, TX 79111. Phone: 806-335-2316. Fax: 806-335-3411. Authorized power: 10-w. each. Antenna: 445-ft. above ground. Lat. 33° 53' 00", long. 98° 36' 10". Transmitter: Wichita Falls. Equipment: ITS transmitter; Andrew antenna.

Leased to Wireless Communications, Box 1727, Durant, OK 74701. Phone: 405-924-0900.

Wichita Falls—WLX-433 (Channels B-1-4). Wichita Falls Independent School District, 1104 Broad St., Wichita Falls, TX 76307. Phone: 817-720-3160. Fax: 817-720-3176. Authorized power: 10-w. each. Antenna: 445-ft. above ground. Lat. 33° 53' 00", long. 98° 36' 10". Transmitter: Wichita Falls. Equipment: ITS transmitter; Andrew antenna.

Wichita Falls—WLX-432 (Channels C-1-4). West Wichita County Special Educational Cooperative, Box 151, Kamay, TX 76369. Phone: 817-438-2235. Fax: 817-438-2870. Authorized power: 10-w. each. Antenna: 445-ft. above ground. Lat. 33° 53' 00", long. 98° 36' 10". Transmitter: Wichita Falls. Equipment: ITS transmitter; Andrew antenna.

Wichita Falls—WLX-451 (Channels D-1-4). Midwestern State U., 3410 Taft Blvd., Wichita Falls, TX 76308. Phone: 940-397-4352. Fax: 940-397-4042.
E-mail: fbussj@nexus.mwsu.edu.
Web site: http://www.mwsu.edu.
Authorized power: 10-w. each. Antenna: 445-ft. above ground. Lat. 33° 53' 00", long. 98° 36' 10". Transmitter: Wichita Falls. Equipment: ITS transmitter; Andrew antenna.
Leased to U.S. Wireless Cable Co., Box 448, Durant, OK 74702. Phone: 405-924-0900.

Wichita Falls—WLX-452 (Channels G-1-4). Education Service Center Region IX, 301 Loop II, Wichita Falls, TX 76305. Authorized power: 10-w. each. Antenna: 445-ft. above ground. Lat. 33° 53' 00", long. 98° 36' 10". Transmitter: Wichita Falls. Equipment: ITS transmitter; Andrew antenna.

Wimberley—WNC-370 (Channels A-1-4). Johnson City Independent School District, Box 498, Johnson City, TX 78636. Phone: 210-868-7410. Authorized power: 50-w. each. Antenna: 709-ft. above ground. Lat. 29° 54' 59", long. 98° 10' 16". Transmitter: Jacobs Creek Rd. Equipment: Comwave transmitter; Andrew antenna.

Wimberley—WNC-369 (Channels B-1-4). Dripping Springs Independent School District, Hwy. 290 & Tiger Lane, Dripping Springs, TX 78620. Phone: 512-858-4905. Authorized power: 50-w. each. Antenna: 709-ft. above ground. Lat. 29° 54' 59", long. 98° 10' 16". Transmitter: Jacobs Creek Rd. Equipment: Comwave transmitter; Mark antenna.

Wimberley—WLX-937 (Channels C-1-4). Comal Independent School District, 1421 E. U.S. Hwy. 81, New Braunfels, TX 78130. Authorized power: 50-w. each. Antenna: 705-ft. above ground. Lat. 29° 54' 59", long. 98° 10' 16". Transmitter: Jacobs Creek Rd., 2.8-mi. NE of Canyon Lake Dam. Equipment: Comwave transmitter; Andrew antenna.

Wimberley—WNC-371 (Channels G-1-4). Wimberly Independent School District, Box 1809, Wimberley, TX 78676. Phone: 512-847-2414. Authorized power: 50-w. each. Antenna: 709-ft. above ground. Lat. 29° 54' 59", long. 98° 10' 16". Transmitter: Jacobs Creek Rd. Equipment: Comwave transmitter; Andrew antenna.

Utah

Magna—WLX-487 (Channels A-1-4). North American Catholic Educational Programming Foundation Inc., Box 40026, Providence, RI 02940-0026. Phone: 401-729-0900. Authorized power: 100-w. each. Antenna: 77-ft. above ground. Lat. 40° 39' 35", long. 111° 12' 50". Transmitter: Farnsworth Peak, Oquirrh Range. Equipment: Emcee transmitter; Omni antenna.

Magna—WHR-624 (Channels B-1-4). U. of Utah, 101 Wasatch Dr., Technical Services, Salt Lake City, UT 84112-1792. Phone: 801-585-3601. Fax: 801-581-3576.
E-mail: ptitus@media.utah.edu.
Authorized power: 10-w. each. Antenna: 112-ft. above ground. Lat. 40° 46' 13", long. 111° 50' 06". Transmitter: 50 N. Medical Dr., Salt Lake City. Equipment: Comwave transmitter; Andrew antenna.

Magna—WNC-988 (Channels G-1-4). Brigham Young U., C-302 HFAC, Provo, UT 84602. Authorized power: 100-w. each. Antenna: 79-ft. above ground. Lat. 40° 39' 35", long. 112° 12' 05". Transmitter: Farnsworth Peak. Equipment: ITS transmitter; Andrew antenna.

Provo—WNC-989 (Channels G-1-4). Brigham Young U., C-302 HFAC, Provo, UT 84602. Authorized power: 50-w. each. Antenna: 72-ft. above ground. Lat. 40° 05' 17", long. 111° 49' 16". Transmitter: West Mountain, NW of Provo. Equipment: ITS transmitter; Andrew antenna.

Salt Lake City—WLX-699 (Channels C-1-4). Instructional Telecommunications Foundation Inc., Box 6060, Boulder, CO 80306. Phone: 303-442-4180. Fax: 303-442-6472.
E-mail: ITF@fstv.org.
Authorized power: 10-w. each. Antenna: 77-ft. above ground. Lat. 40° 39' 35", long. 112° 12' 05". Transmitter: Farnsworth Peak. Equipment: Comwave transmitter; Bogner antenna.

Salt Lake City—WLX-667 (Channels D-1-4). Hispanic Information & Telecommunications Network Inc., 3rd Floor, 449 Broadway, New York, NY 10013. Phone: 212-966-5660. Fax: 212-966-5725.
E-mail: email@hitn.org.
Web site: http://www.hitn.org.
Authorized power: 10-w. each. Antenna: 501-ft. above ground. Lat. 40° 46' 10", long. 111° 53' 00". Transmitter: 26 S. State St. Equipment: ITS transmitter; Andrew antenna. Requests change to 100-w. each, 80-ft. above ground, lat. 40° 39' 35", long. 112° 12' 05".
Leased to People's Choice TV Corp., 5301 E. Broadway, Tucson, AZ 85711. Phone: 520-519-4400.

St. George—WNC-817 (Channels A-1-4). Tuacahn Amphitheater, 1100 Tuacahn Dr., Ivins, UT 84738. Authorized power: 50-w. each. Antenna: 49-ft. above ground. Lat. 37° 03' 49", long. 113° 34' 20". Transmitter: Webb Hill, 2.5-mi. S of St. George. Equipment: ITS transmitter; Andrew antenna.

St. George—WNC-935 (Channels B-1-4). Washington County School District, 189 West Tabernacle, St. George, UT 84770. Phone: 801-673-3553. Fax: 801-673-3216. Authorized power: 50-w. each. Antenna: 3156-ft. above ground. Lat. 37° 03' 49", long. 113° 34' 20". Transmitter: Webb Hill, 2.5-mi. S of St. George. Equipment: ITS transmitter; Andrew antenna. Requests change to 46-ft. above ground.

St. George—WNC-818 (Channels C-1-4). Dixie College, 225 South 700 East, St. George, UT 84770. Phone: 801-673-4811. Fax: 801-656-4001. Authorized power: 50-w. each. Antenna: 49-ft. above ground. Lat. 37° 03' 49", long. 113° 34' 20". Transmitter: Webb Hill, 2.5-mi. S of St. George. Equipment: ITS transmitter; Andrew antenna. Requests change to 46-ft. above ground.

St. George—WNC-746 (Channels D-1-4). Community Education Channel, 225 South 700 East, St. George, UT 84770. Authorized power: 50-w. each. Antenna: 49-ft. above ground. Lat. 37° 03' 49", long. 113° 34' 20". Transmitter: Webb Hill, 2.5-mi. S of St. George. Equipment: ITS transmitter; Andrew antenna. Requests change to 46-ft. above ground.

St. George—WNC-742 (Channels G-1-4). Utah State U., 197 East Tabernacle, St. George, UT 84770. Phone: 801-634-5706. Fax: 801-652-5870. Authorized power: 50-w. each. Antenna: 49-ft. above ground. Lat. 37° 03' 49", long. 113° 34' 20". Transmitter: Webb Hill, 2.5-mi. S of St. George. Equipment: ITS transmitter; Andrew antenna. Requests change to 46-ft. above ground.

Vermont

Brownsville—WLX-583 (Channels A-1-4). Albion Community Development Corp., 51 N. Main St., Albion, VT 14411. Authorized power: 10-w. each. Antenna: 350-ft. above ground. Lat. 43° 26' 15", long. 72° 27' 09". Equipment: ITS transmitter; Andrew antenna.

Burlington—WLX-827 (Channels A-1-4). Albion Community Development Corp., 51 N. Main St., Albion, VT 14411. Authorized power: 10-w. each. Antenna: 20-ft. above ground. Lat. 44° 31' 32", long. 72° 48' 54". Transmitter: Mount Mansfield, 20-mi. E of Burlington. Equipment: ITS transmitter; Andrew antenna.

Burlington—WNC-658 (Channels B-1-4). Vermont ETV Inc., 88 Ethan Allen, Colchester, VT 05446. Authorized power: 10-w. each. Antenna: 89-ft. above ground. Lat. 44° 31' 32", long. 72° 48' 54". Transmitter: 20-mi. E of Burlington on Mount Mansfield. Equipment: ITS transmitter; Andrew antenna.

Burlington—WNC-235 (Channels C-1-4). Counterpoint Communications Inc. Authorized power: 10-w. each. Antenna: 20-ft. above ground. Lat. 44° 31' 32", long. 72° 48' 54". Transmitter: Mount Mansfield, 20-mi. E of Burlington. Equipment: ITS transmitter; Andrew antenna.

Burlington—WLX-828 (Channels D-1-4). National Conference on Citizenship, Suite 1150 4770 Biscayne Blvd., Miami, FL 33147. Authorized power: 10-w. each. Antenna: 20-ft. above ground. Lat. 44° 31' 32", long. 72° 48' 54". Transmitter: Mount Mansfield, 20-mi. E of Burlington. Equipment: ITS transmitter; Andrew antenna.
Leased to New England Wireless, 39 Square, The Centennial Bldg., Suite 302, Bellows Falls. VT 05101. Phone: 802-643-9953.

Burlington—WLX-830 (Channels G-1-4). Rockne Educational TV, 320 Hamilton St., Albion, NY 14411. Phone: 716-589-9295. Authorized power: 10-w. each. Antenna: 20-ft. above ground. Lat. 44° 31' 32", long. 72° 48' 54". Transmitter: Mount Mansfield, 20-mi. E of Burlington. Equipment: ITS transmitter; Andrew antenna.
Leased to New England Wireless, Box 470, Ascutney, VT 05101.

Hero—WLX-609 (Channels B-1-4). Burlington College, 95 North Ave., Burlington, VT 05401. Authorized power: 1-w. each. Antenna: 104.5-ft. above ground. Lat. 44° 47' 17", long. 73° 17' 54". Transmitter: Grand Isle County. Equipment: Plessy transmitter; Andrew antenna.

Monkton—WLX-556 (Channels A-2-4). Champlain College, Box 670, 163 S. Willard St., Burlington, VT 05402. Authorized power: 10-w. each. Antenna: 159-ft. above ground. Lat. 44° 13' 24", long. 73° 07' 27". Transmitter: Addison County. Equipment: Emcee transmitter; Andrew antenna.

Monkton—WLX-608 (Channels B-1-4). Burlington College, 95 North Ave., Burlington, VT 05401. Authorized power: 1-w. each. Antenna: 140-ft. above ground. Lat. 44° 13' 24", long. 73° 07' 27". Transmitter: Addison County. Equipment: Plessy transmitter; Omni antenna.

Monkton—WLX-480 (Channels C-1-4). Norwich U., 65 S. Main, Northfield, VT 05663. Authorized power: 1-w. each. Antenna: 140-ft. above ground. Lat. 44° 13' 24", long. 73° 07' 27". Transmitter: Addison County. Equipment: Plessy transmitter; HMD antenna.

Monkton—WLX-706 (Channels D-1-4). St. Michaels College, Winooski Park, Colchester, VT 05439. Authorized power: 1-w. each. Antenna: 140-ft. above ground. Lat. 44° 13' 24", long. 73° 07' 27". Transmitter: Addison County. Equipment: Plessy transmitter; Andrew antenna.

Monkton—WLX-405 (Channels G-1-4). Trinity College of Vermont, 208 Colchester Ave., Burlington, VT 05401. Lat. 44° 13' 24", long. 73° 07' 27". Transmitter: Addison County. Equipment: Emcee transmitter; Andrew antenna. Requests change to 10-w.each, 159-ft. above ground.

North Hero—WLX-598 (Channels A-2-4). Champlain College, Box 670, 163 S. Willard St., Burlington, VT 05402. Authorized power: 10-w. each. Antenna: 129-ft. above ground. Lat. 44° 47' 17", long. 73° 17' 54". Transmitter: 0.5-mi. E, 1-mi. S of North Hero Station. Equipment: Emcee transmitter; Andrew antenna.

North Hero—WLX-459 (Channels C-1-4). Norwich U., 65 S. Main, Northfield, VT 05663. Authorized power: 1-w. each. Antenna: 104.5-ft. above ground. Lat. 44° 47' 14", long. 73° 17' 54". Transmitter: Addison County. Equipment: Emcee transmitter; Andrew antenna.

North Hero—WLX-705 (Channels D-1-4). St. Michaels College, Winooski Park, Colchester, VT 05439. Authorized power: 1-w. each. Antenna: 104.5-ft. above ground. Lat. 44° 47' 17", long. 73° 17' 54". Transmitter: Grand Isle County. Equipment: Plessy transmitter; Andrew antenna.

North Hero—WLX-660 (Channels G-1-4). Trinity College of Vermont, 208 Colchester Ave., Burlington, VT 05401. Authorized power: 1-w. each. Antenna: 104.5-ft. above ground. Lat. 44° 47' 17", long. 73° 17' 54". Transmitter: Grand Isle County. Equipment: GEC Plessy transmitter; Andrew antenna.

Northfield—WLX-722 (Channels A-1-4). Champlain College, 163 S. Willard St., Burlington, VT 05401. Phone: 802-860-2700. Authorized power: 1-w. each. Antenna: 305-ft. above ground. Lat. 44° 08' 19", long. 72° 38' 32". Transmitter: 1-mi. E of Northfield. Equipment: Plessy transmitter; Andrew antenna.

Northfield—WLX-577 (Channels C-1-4). Norwich U., 65 S. Main St., Northfield, VT 05663. Authorized power: 1-w. each. Antenna: 305-ft. above ground. Lat. 44° 08' 19", long. 72° 38' 32". Transmitter: 1-mi. E of Northfield. Equipment: Plessy transmitter; Andrew antenna.

Northfield—WLX-729 (Channels D-1-4). St. Michaels College, Winooski Park, Colchester, VT 05439. Authorized power: 1-w. each. Antenna: 305-ft. above ground. Lat. 44° 08' 19", long. 72° 38' 32". Transmitter: 1-mi. E of Northfield. Equipment: Plessy transmitter; Andrew antenna.

South Newport—WLX-638 (Channels A-1-4). Champlain College, 163 S. Willard St., Burlington, VT 05402. Authorized power: 1-w. each. Antenna: 155-ft. above ground. Lat. 44° 52' 14", long. 72° 20' 01". Transmitter: Orleans County. Equipment: Plessy transmitter; Andrew antenna.

South Newport—WLX-629 (Channels B-1-4). Burlington College, 95 North Ave., Burlington, VT 05401. Authorized power: 1-w. each. Antenna: 155-ft. above ground. Lat. 44° 52' 14", long. 72° 20' 01". Transmitter: Orleans County. Equipment: Plessy transmitter; Andrew antenna.

South Newport—WLX-635 (Channels C-1-4). Norwich U., 65 S. Main, Northfield, VT 05663. Authorized power: 1-w. each. Antenna: 155-ft. above ground. Lat. 44° 52' 14", long. 72° 20' 01". Transmitter: Orleans County. Equipment: Plessy transmitter; Andrew antenna.

South Newport—WLX-640 (Channels D-1-4). St. Michael's College, Winooski Park, Colchester, VT 05439. Authorized power: 1-w. each. Antenna: 155-ft. above ground. Lat. 44° 52' 14", long. 72° 20' 01". Transmitter: Orleans County. Equipment: Plessy transmitter; Andrew antenna.

South Newport—WLX-636 (Channels G-1-4). Trinity College of Vermont, 208 Colchester Ave., Burlington, VT 05401. Authorized power: 1-w. each. Antenna: 155-ft. above ground. Lat. 44° 52' 14", long. 72° 20' 01". Transmitter: Orleans County. Equipment: Plessy transmitter; Andrew antenna.

St. Johnsbury—WLX-786 (Channels A-1-4). Champlain College, Box 670, 163 S. Willard St., Burlington, VT 05402. Authorized power: 1-w. each. Antenna: 55-ft. above ground. Lat. 44° 34' 15", long. 71° 53' 39". Transmitter: Burke Mountain. Equipment: Plessey transmitter; Omni antenna.

St. Johnsbury—WLX-809 (Channels C-1-4). Norwich U., 65 S. Main, Northfield, VT 05663. Authorized power: 1-w. each. Antenna: 55-ft. above ground. Lat. 44° 34' 15", long. 71° 53' 39". Transmitter: Burke Mountain, 2.25-mi. SE of East Burke. Equipment: Andrew antenna.

St. Johnsbury—WLX-936 (Channels D-1-4). St. Michael's College, Winooski Park, Colchester, VT 05439. Authorized power: 1-w. each. Antenna: 55-ft. above ground. Lat. 44° 34' 15", long. 71° 53' 39". Transmitter: Burke Mountain, 2.25-mi. SE of East Burke. Equipment: Plessey transmitter.

St. Johnsbury—WLX-934 (Channels G-1-4). Trinity College of Vermont, 208 Colchester Ave., Burlington, VT 05401. Authorized power: 1-w. each. Antenna: 55-ft. above ground. Lat. 44° 34' 15", long. 71° 53' 39". Transmitter: Burke Mountain, 2.25-mi. SE of East Burke. Equipment: Plessey transmitter.

Thetford—WLX-810 (Channels C-1-4). Norwich U., 65 S. Main, Northfield, VT 05663. Authorized power: 1-w. each. Antenna: 104-ft. above ground. Lat. 43° 51' 15", long. 72° 12' 56". Transmitter: High Peak Mountain, 2.5-mi. N of Thetford. Equipment: Andrew antenna.

Thetford—WLX-933 (Channels D-1-4). St. Michael's College, Winooski Park, Colchester, VT 05439. Authorized power: 10-w. each. Antenna: 104-ft. above ground. Lat. 43° 51' 15", long. 72° 12' 56". Transmitter: 2.5-mi. N of Thetford. Equipment: Plessey transmitter; Andrew antenna.

West Enosburg—WLX-639 (Channels A-2-4). Champlain College, 163 S. Willard St., Burlington, VT 05402. Authorized power: 1-w. each. Antenna: 105-ft. above ground. Lat. 44° 51'12", long. 72° 41'11". Transmitter: 0.5-mi. W of West Hill, Franklin County. Equipment: Plessy transmitter; Andrew antenna.

West Enosburg—WLX-627 (Channels B-1-4). Burlington College, 95 North Ave., Burlington, VT 05401. Authorized power: 1-w. each. Antenna: 104.5-ft. above ground. Lat. 44° 51' 12", long. 72° 41' 11". Transmitter: Franklin County. Equipment: Plessy transmitter; Omni antenna.

West Enosburg—WLX-721 (Channels C-1-4). Norwich U., 65 S. Main, Northfield, VT 05663. Authorized power: 1-w. each. Antenna: 105-ft. above ground. Lat. 44° 51' 12", long. 72° 41' 11". Transmitter: 1-mi. S of Enosburg. Equipment: Plessy transmitter; Andrew antenna.

West Enosburg—WLX-631 (Channels D-1-4). St. Michael's College, Winooski Park, Colchester, VT 05439. Authorized power: 1-w. each. Antenna: 105-ft. above ground. Lat. 44° 51'12", long. 72° 41'11". Transmitter: 0.5-mi. W of West Hill, Franklin County. Equipment: Plessy transmitter; Andrew antenna.

West Enosburg—WLX-637 (Channels G-1-4). Trinity College of Vermont, 208 Colchester Ave., Burlington, VT 05401. Authorized power: 1-w. each. Antenna: 105-ft. above ground. Lat. 44° 51' 12", long. 72° 41' 11". Transmitter: Franklin County. Equipment: Plessy transmitter; Omni antenna.

Virginia

Buchanan—WND-387 (Channels A-3-4). R & B Communications Inc., Box 174, 1000 Roanoke Rd., Daleville, VA 24083. Authorized power: 0.2-w. each. Antenna: 174-ft. above ground. Lat. 37° 30' 57", long. 79° 40' 37". Transmitter: 0.7-mi. S of Buchanan. Equipment: ITS transmitter; Andrew antenna.

Buchanan—WND-388 (Channels B-1-4). R & B Communications Inc., Box 174, 1000 Roanoke Rd., Daleville, VA 24083. Authorized power: 0.2-w. each. Antenna: 174-ft. above ground. Lat. 37° 30' 57", long. 79° 40' 37". Transmitter: 0.7-mi. S of Buchanan. Equipment: ITS transmitter; Andrew antenna.

Buchanan—WND-391 (Channels C-1-4). R & B Communications Inc., Box 174, 1000 Roanoke Rd., Danville, VA 24083. Authorized power: 0.2-w. each. Antenna: 180-ft. above ground. Lat. 37° 30' 57", long. 79° 40' 37". Transmitter: 0.7-mi. S of Buchanan. Equipment: ITS transmitter; Andrew antenna.

Buchanan—WND-389 (Channels D-1-4). R & B Communications Inc., Box 174, 1000 Roanoke Rd., Daleville, VA 24083. Authorized power: 0.2-w. each. Antenna: 174-ft. above ground. Lat. 37° 30' 57", long. 79° 40' 37". Transmitter: 0.7-mi. S of Buchanan. Equipment: ITS transmitter; Andrew antenna.

Buchanan—WND-390 (Channels G-1-4). R & B Communications Inc., Box 174, 1000 Roanoke Rd., Daleville, VA 24083. Authorized power: 0.2-w. each. Antenna: 174-ft. above ground. Lat. 37° 30' 57", long. 79° 40' 37". Transmitter: 0.7-mi. S of Buchanan. Equipment: ITS transmitter; Andrew antenna.

Charlottesville—WLX-523 (Channels A-1-4). Charlottesville Public Schools, 1562 Dairy Rd., Charlottesville, VA 22903. Authorized power: 50-w. each. Antenna: 195-ft. above ground. Lat. 37° 58' 57", long. 78° 28' 58". Transmitter: Carter's Mountain. Equipment: ITS transmitter; Andrew antenna.

Charlottesville—WLX-519 (Channels B-1-4). County School Board of Albemarle County, 401 McIntire Rd., Charlottesville, VA 22901. Authorized power: 50-w. each. Antenna: 195-ft. above ground. Lat. 37° 58' 57", long. 78° 28' 58". Transmitter: Carter's Mountain. Equipment: ITS transmitter; Andrew antenna.

Charlottesville—WLX-518 (Channels C-1-4). Fluvanna County School Board, County Office Bldg., Palmyra, VA 22963. Authorized power: 50-w. each. Antenna: 195-ft. above ground. Lat. 37° 58' 57", long. 78° 28' 58". Transmitter: Carter's Mountain. Equipment: ITS transmitter; Andrew antenna.

Charlottesville—WLX-524 (Channels D-1-4). The Miller School of Albemarle, Miller School Rd., Charlottesville, VA 22903. Phone: 804-823-4805. Authorized power: 50-w. each. Antenna: 195-ft. above ground. Lat. 37° 58' 57", long. 78° 28' 58". Transmitter: Carter's Mountain. Equipment: ITS transmitter; Andrew antenna.

Leased to CFW Communications, 1145 River Rd., Suite 1, Charlottesville, VA 22901. Phone: 804-977-6111.

Charlottesville—WLX-517 (Channels G-1-4). Blue Ridge School, Dyke, VA 22935. Authorized power: 50-w. each. Antenna: 195-ft. above ground. Lat. 37° 58' 57", long. 78° 28' 58". Transmitter: Carter's Mountain. Equipment: ITS transmitter; Andrew antenna.

Crozet—WND-270 (Channels A-1-4). CFW Licenses Inc., 401 Spring Lane, Waynesboro, VA 22980. Authorized power: 0.0158-w. each. Antenna: 92-ft. above ground. Lat. 38° 04' 17", long. 78° 42' 17". Transmitter: Crozet. Equipment: ITS transmitter; Mark antenna.

Driver—WLX-256 (Channels B-3-4). Hampton Roads Educational Telecommunications Assn. Inc., 5200 Hampton Blvd., Norfolk, VA 23508. Phone: 757-889-9400. Fax: 757-489-0007.

E-mail: kmassie@whro.org.

Authorized power: 50-w. each. Antenna: 1027-ft. above ground. Lat. 36° 48' 56", long. 76° 28' 00". Transmitter: 1-mi. S of Driver. Equipment: Comwave transmitter; Andrew antenna.

Driver—WLX-255 (Channels C-2-3). Hampton Roads Educational Telecommunications Assn. Inc., 5200 Hampton Blvd., Norfolk, VA 23508. Phone: 757-889-9400. Fax: 757-489-0007.

E-mail: kmassie@whro.org.

Authorized power: 50-w. each. Antenna: 1029-ft. above ground. Lat. 36° 48' 56", long. 76° 28' 00". Transmitter: 2-mi. E of Driver. Equipment: Comwave transmitter; Andrew antenna.

Driver (Norfolk)—WHR-526 (Channels D-1-4). Network for Instructional TV Inc., Suite 110, 11490 Commerce Park Dr., Reston, VA 20191. Phone: 703-860-9200. Fax: 703-860-9237. Authorized power: 50-w. each. Antenna: 1029-ft. above ground. Lat. 36° 48' 56", long. 76° 28' 00". Transmitter: WTKR(TV) tower, 2-mi. E of Driver. Equipment: ITS transmitter; Bogner antenna.

Fairfax—WHB-851 (Channels E-1-4). U. of Maryland, Glen L. Martin Engineering Bldg, College Park, MD 20742. Phone: 301-405-4910. Fax: 301-314-9639.

E-mail: as20@umail.umd.edu.

Web site: http://www.glue.umd.edu/ITV/.

Authorized power: 10-w. each. Antenna: 211-ft. above ground. Lat. 38° 50' 42", long. 77° 18' 36". Transmitter: Massey Bldg., 4100 Chain Bridge Rd. Equipment: Emcee transmitter; Anixter-Mark antenna.

Franklin—WHR-940 (Channels G-1-4). Hampton Roads Educational Telecommunications Assn. Inc., 5200 Hampton Blvd., Norfolk, VA 23508. Phone: 757-899-9400. Fax: 757-489-0007.

E-mail: kmassie@whro.org.

Authorized power: 50-w. each. Antenna: 1030-ft. above ground. Lat. 36° 48' 56", long. 76° 28' 00". Transmitter: WTKR-TV Tower, 2-mi. E of Driver. Equipment: Comwave transmitter; Andrew antenna.

Hampton—WHR-737 (Channels A-1-4). Hampton Roads Educational Telecommunications Assn. Inc., 5200 Hampton Blvd., Norfolk, VA 23508. Phone: 757-889-9400. Fax: 757-489-0007.

E-mail: kmassie@whro.org.

Authorized power: 8-w. each. Antenna: 252-ft. above ground. Lat. 37° 06' 04", long. 76° 23' 22". Transmitter: NASA Langley Research Center. Equipment: Emcee transmitter; Andrew antenna.

Hanover—WNC-638 (Channels C-1-2). Hanover County Public Schools, 200 Berkley St., Ashland, VA 23005. Authorized power: 50-w. each. Antenna: 1325-ft. above ground. Lat. 37° 30' 15", long. 77° 42' 13". Transmitter: Dry Bridge Rd. Equipment: ITS transmitter; Andrew antenna.

Harrisonburg—WNC-649 (Channels A-1-4). Fishburne Military School, 225 S. Wayne Ave., Waynesboro, VA 22980. Phone: 540-946-7700. Fax: 540-946-7702.

Web site: http://www.fishburne.org.

Authorized power: 50-w. each. Antenna: 125-ft. above ground. Lat. 38° 23' 35", long. 78° 46' 12". Transmitter: Massanutten Park. Equipment: Comwave transmitter; Bogner antenna.

Harrisonburg—WNC-650 (Channels B-1-4). Waynesboro City Schools, 301 Pine Ave., Waynesboro, VA 22980. Phone: 540-946-4600. Fax: 540-946-4608. Authorized power: 50-w. each. Antenna: 38-ft. above ground. Lat. 38° 23' 36", long. 78° 46' 12". Transmitter: Massanutten Park. Equipment: Comwave transmitter; Bogner antenna.

Harrisonburg—WNC-651 (Channels C-1-4). Augusta County Schools, Rte. 1, Box 252, Fisherville, VA 22939. Authorized power: 50-w. each. Antenna: 125-ft. above ground. Lat. 38° 23' 35", long. 78° 46' 12". Transmitter: Massanutten Park. Equipment: Comwave transmitter; Bogner antenna.

Harrisonburg—WNC-652 (Channels D-1-4). Stuart Hall Inc., Box 210, Staunton, VA 22402-0210. Phone: 540-885-0356. Fax: 540-886-2275. Authorized power: 50-w. each. Antenna: 125-ft. above ground. Lat. 38° 23' 35", long. 78° 46' 12". Transmitter: Massanutten Park. Equipment: Comwave transmitter; Bogner antenna.

Harrisonburg—WNC-654 (Channels G-1-4). Bridgewater College, 402 E. College St., Florey Hall 101, Bridgewater, VA 22812. Authorized power: 50-w. each. Antenna: 98-ft. above ground. Lat. 38° 23' 34", long. 78° 46' 13". Transmitter: Massanutten Peak, Massanutten Mountain. Equipment: Comwave transmitter; Bogner antenna.

Independent Hill—WHR-972 (Channels D-1-2). Central Virginia Educational TV, 23 Sesame St., Richmond, VA 23235. Phone: 804-320-1301. Fax: 804-320-8729. Authorized power: 10-w. each. Antenna: 356-ft. above ground. Lat. 38° 37' 42", long. 77° 26' 20". Transmitter: 15100 Joplin Rd. Equipment: Emcee transmitter; Bogner antenna.

James Crossroads & surrounding Northampton County—WHG-412 (Channels G-1-4). Hampton Roads Educational Telecommunications Assn. Inc., 5200 Hampton Blvd., Norfolk, VA 23508. Phone: 757-889-9400. Fax: 757-489-0007.
E-mail: kmassie@whro.org.
Authorized power: 50-w. each. Antenna: 299-ft. above ground. Lat. 37° 21' 39", long. 75° 56' 26". Transmitter: Northampton High School, 0.68-mi. SW of Rtes. 630 & 13 intersection. Equipment: ITS transmitter; Andrew antenna.

King William—WHF-243 (Channel A-1). Hampton Roads Educational Telecommunications Assn. Inc., 5200 Hampton Blvd., Norfolk, VA 23508. Phone: 757-889-9400. Fax: 757-489-0007.
E-mail: kmassie@whro.org.
Authorized power: 50-w. Antenna: 366-ft. above ground. Lat. 37° 44' 25", long. 77° 07' 49". Transmitter: King William County High School.

Lynchburg—WHR-507 (Channels A-1-4). Liberty U. Inc., 3765 Chandlers Mountain Rd., Lynchburg, VA 24506. Authorized power: 10-w. each. Antenna: 60-ft. above ground. Lat. 37° 21' 02", long. 79° 11' 04". Transmitter: 3765 Chandlers Mountain Rd.

Lynchburg—WNC-586 (Channels C-1-4). Seven Hills School, 2001 Rivermont Ave., Lynchburg, VA 24503. Authorized power: 10-w. each. Antenna: 100-ft. above ground. Lat. 37° 33' 46", long. 79° 11' 38". Transmitter: High Peak Mountain. Equipment: ITS transmitter; Andrew antenna.

Lynchburg—WNC-585 (Channels D-1-4). Desmond T. Doss School, 130 George St., Lynchburg, VA 24502. Phone: 804-946-9386. Authorized power: 10-w. each. Antenna: 59-ft. above ground. Lat. 37° 33' 47", long. 79° 11' 38". Transmitter: High Peak Mountain. Equipment: ITS transmitter; Andrew antenna.

Mathews County—WHG-411 (Channel A-1). Hampton Roads Educational Telecommunications Assn. Inc., 5200 Hampton Blvd., Norfolk, VA 23508. Phone: 757-889-9400. Fax: 757-489-0007.
E-mail: kmassie@whro.org.
Authorized power: 50-w. Antenna: 420-ft. above ground. Lat. 37° 26' 11", long. 76° 19' 50". Transmitter: Hunter School. Equipment: ITS transmitter; Andrew antenna.

Merrifield—WHG-349 (Channels G-1-2). Central Virginia ETV Corp., 23 Sesame St., Richmond, VA 23235. Phone: 804-320-1301. Fax: 804-320-8729. Authorized power: 50-w. each. Antenna: 639-ft. above ground. Lat. 38° 57' 49", long. 77° 06' 18". Transmitter: 5202 River Rd., Bethesda, MD. Equipment: ITS transmitter; Bogner antenna.

Newport News—WHF-350 (Channels A-1-2). Hampton Roads Educational Telecommunications Assn. Inc., 5200 Hampton Blvd., Norfolk, VA 23508. Phone: 757-889-9400. Fax: 757-489-0007.
E-mail: kmassie@whro.org.
Authorized power: 50-w. each. Antenna: 2740-ft. above ground. Lat. 37° 04' 21", long. 76° 29' 51". Transmitter: 0.32-mi. NW of Hidden Blvd. & Warwick Blvd. intersection. Equipment: ITS transmitter; Andrew antenna.

Norfolk—WNC-681 (Channels B-1-2). Hispanic Information & Telecommunications Network Inc., 3rd Floor, 449 Broadway, New York, NY 10013. Phone: 212-966-5660. Fax: 212-966-5725.
E-mail: email@hitn.org.
Web site: http://www.hitn.org.
Authorized power: 50-w. each. Antenna: 820-ft. above ground. Lat. 36° 48' 56", long. 76° 28' 00". Transmitter: 1-mi. S of Driver. Equipment: Comwave transmitter; Andrew antenna.
Leased to CAI Wireless Systems Inc., 2101 Wilson Blvd., Suite 100, Arlington, VA 22201. Phone: 703-812-8800.

Northern Virginia—WHB-652 (Channels C-1-4). The George Mason U. Instructional Foundation Inc., No. 102, 4400 University Dr., Fairfax, VA 22030-4444. Phone: 703-993-3100. Fax: 703-273-2417.
E-mail: mkelley@gmu.edu.
Web site: http://www.capitolconnection.gmu.edu.
Authorized power: 50-w. each. Antenna: 636-ft. above ground. Lat. 38° 57' 49", long. 77° 06' 18". Transmitter: 5202 River Rd., Bethesda, MD. Equipment: ITS transmitter; Andrew antenna.
Leased to CAI Wireless Systems, 2101 Wilson Blvd., Arlington, VA 22201. Phone: 703-857-7685.

Onancock—WHN-710 (Channels B-1-4). Hampton Roads Educational Telecommunications Assn. Inc., 5200 Hampton Blvd., Norfolk, VA 23508. Phone: 757-889-9400. Fax: 757-489-0007.
E-mail: kmassie@whro.org.
Authorized power: 10-w. each. Antenna: 100-ft. above ground. Lat. 37° 42' 33", long. 75° 44' 56". Transmitter: Onancock High School.

Reston—WHR-687 (Channels G-1-2). Central Virginia ETV Corp., 8101-A Lee Hwy., Falls Church, VA 22042. Authorized power: 1-w. each. Antenna: 177-ft. above ground. Lat. 38° 57' 00", long. 77° 21' 18". Transmitter: Reston International Center, 11800 Sunrise Valley. Equipment: Comwave transmitter; Andrew antenna.

Richmond—WGZ-515 (Channel A-3). Richmond Public Schools, 301 N. 9th St., Richmond, VA 23219. Phone: 804-780-7816. Fax: 804-644-8120. Lat. 37° 32' 27", long. 77° 26' 00".

Richmond—WHR-719 (Channel A-4). Richmond Public Schools, 301 N. 9th St., Richmond, VA 23219. Phone: 804-780-7816. Fax: 804-644-8120. Authorized power: 0.1-w. Antenna: 50-ft. above ground. Lat. 37° 34' 25", long. 77° 27' 49". Equipment: Emcee transmitter; Andrew antenna.

Richmond—WNC-491 (Channels B-1-4). Amelia County Public Schools, 16410 Dunn St., Amelia, VA 23002. Authorized power: 50-w. each. Antenna: 01250-ft. above ground. Lat. 37° 30' 15", long. 77° 42' 13". Transmitter: 15703 Midlothian Turnpike. Equipment: ITS transmitter; Andrew antenna.

Richmond—WHQ-227 (Channels C-1-2). Center for Excellence Inc. Authorized power: 10-w. each. Antenna: 299-ft. above ground. Lat. 37° 37' 21", long. 77° 30' 03". Transmitter: 3914 Wistar Rd.

Richmond—WNC-648 (Channels C-3-4). School Board of Goochland County, Box 169, Goochland, VA 23063. Phone: 804-556-5316. Fax: 804-556-3847. Authorized power: 50-w. each. Antenna: 1007-ft. above ground. Lat. 37° 30' 15", long. 77° 42' 13". Transmitter: Dry Bridge Rd. Equipment: ITS transmitter; Andrew antenna.

Richmond—WNC-489 (Channels D-3-4). St. Christopher's School/Diocese of Virginia, 711 St. Christopher's Rd., Richmond, VA 23226. Authorized power: 50-w. each. Antenna: 1007-ft. above ground. Lat. 37° 30' 15", long. 77° 42' 13". Transmitter: 15703 Midlothian Turnpike. Equipment: Andrew transmitter; Andrew antenna.

Richmond—WHG-238 (Channels E-1-2). Central Virginia Educational TV, 23 Sesame St., Richmond, VA 23235. Phone: 804-320-1301. Fax: 804-320-8729. Authorized power: 50-w. each. Antenna: 1007-ft. above ground. Lat. 37° 30' 15", long. 77° 42' 13". Transmitter: 23 Sesame St. Equipment: ITS transmitter; Andrew antenna.

Richmond—WNC-486 (Channels G-1-2). St. Christopher's School/Diocese of Virginia, 711 St. Christopher's Rd., Richmond, VA 23226. Authorized power: 50-w. each. Antenna: 1007-ft. above ground. Lat. 37° 30' 15", long. 77° 42' 13". Transmitter: 15703 Midlothian Turnpike. Equipment: ITS transmitter; Andrew antenna.

Richmond—WNC-686 (Channels G-3-4). Central Virginia Educational Telecommunications Corp., 23 Sesame St., Richmond, VA 23235. Phone: 804-320-1301. Authorized power: 50-w. each. Antenna: 1007-ft. above ground. Lat. 037° 30' 15", long. 077° 42' 13". Transmitter: Dry Bridge Rd. Equipment: ITS transmitter; Andrew antenna.

Roanoke—WNC-983 (Channels A-1-2). Virginia Polytech Institute & State U., 134 Burruss Hall, Blacksburg, VA 24061. Authorized power: 50-w. each. Antenna: 3952-ft. above ground. Lat. 37° 11' 35", long. 80° 09' 29". Transmitter: Poor Mountain, 3-mi. NW of Bent Mountain. Equipment: Emcee transmitter; Andrew antenna.

Roanoke—WNC-984 (Channels A-3-4). School Board of the City of Roanoke, 40 Douglass Ave., Roanoke, VA 24012. Authorized power: 50-w. each. Antenna: 2362-ft. above ground. Lat. 37° 22' 26", long. 79° 55' 35". Transmitter: Tinker Mountain on Rte. 81. Equipment: Comwave transmitter; Andrew antenna.

Roanoke—WNC-207 (Channels B-1-4). Botetourt County School Board, State Rte. 681, Fincastle, VA 24090. Phone: 540-992-8263. Authorized power: 50-w. each. Antenna: 171-ft. above ground. Lat. 37° 22' 25", long. 79° 55' 36". Transmitter: Tinker Mountain on Rte. 81. Equipment: Comwave transmitter; Andrew antenna.

Roanoke—WHR-795 (Channel C-1-4). Blue Ridge Public TV Inc., Box 13246, Roanoke, VA 24032. Phone: 540-344-0991. Fax: 540-344-2148.
E-mail: bpriu@wbra.pbs.org.
Web site: http://wbra.org.
Authorized power: 10-w. Antenna: 157-ft. above ground. Lat. 37° 22' 26", long. 79° 55' 35". Transmitter: Rte. 81, Tinker Mountain. Equipment: ITS transmitter; Andrew antenna.
Leased to R & B Communications, Box 174, Daleville, VA 24083. Phone: 540-966-2230.

Roanoke—WNC-206 (Channels D-1-4). School Board of Roanoke City, 40 Douglass Ave., Roanoke, VA 94012. Phone: 540-853-2381. Authorized power: 50-w. each. Antenna: 158-ft. above ground. Lat. 37° 22' 26", long. 79° 55' 35". Transmitter: Timnker Mountain. Equipment: Comwave transmitter.

Roanoke—WNC-205 (Channels G-1-4). Salem City School Board, 19 N. College Ave., Salem, VA 24153. Phone: 540-389-0130. Authorized power: 50-w. each. Antenna: 158-ft. above ground. Lat. 37° 22' 26", long. 79° 55' 35". Transmitter: Tinker Mountain. Equipment: Comwave transmitter; Andrew antenna.

Rosslyn—WHB-836 (Channels F-1-4). George Mason U. Foundation Inc., 4400 University Dr., Fairfax, VA 22030. Phone: 703-993-3100. Fax: 703-273-2417.
E-mail: mkelley@gmu.edu.
Authorized power: 10-w. each. Antenna: 318-ft. above ground. Lat. 38° 53' 40", long. 77° 04' 13". Transmitter: 1000 Wilson Blvd., Arlington. Equipment: Comwave transmitter; Andrew antenna.

Tangier—WHR-993 (Channel D-1). Hampton Roads Educational Telecommunications Assn. Inc., 5200 Hampton Blvd., Norfolk, VA 23508. Phone: 757-889-9400. Fax: 757-489-0007.
E-mail: kmassie@whro.org.
Authorized power: 10-w. Antenna: 120-ft. above ground. Lat. 37° 49' 36", long. 75° 59' 40". Transmitter: Tower next to Tangier School. Equipment: Comwave transmitter; Anixter-Mark antenna.

Virginia Beach—WHF-232 (Channels A-1-2). Hampton Roads Educational Telecommunications Assn. Inc., 5200 Hampton Blvd., Norfolk, VA 23508. Phone: 757-889-9400. Fax: 757-489-0007.
E-mail: kmassie@whro.org.
Authorized power: 50-w. each. Antenna: 386-ft. above ground. Lat. 36° 50' 40", long. 76° 09' 40". Transmitter: Kempsville Union High School.

Virginia Beach—WHR-941 (Channels A-3-4). Hampton Roads Educational Telecommunications Assn. Inc., 5200 Hampton Blvd., Norfolk, VA 23508. Phone: 757-889-9400. Fax: 757-489-0007.
E-mail: kmassie@whro.org.
Authorized power: 10-w. each. Antenna: 350-ft. above ground. Lat. 36° 48' 54", long. 76° 12' 08". Transmitter: Woodstock Elementary School. Equipment: Comwave transmitter; Andrew antenna.

Williamsburg—WHF-231 (Channel A-1). Center for Excellence Inc. Authorized power: 0.1-w. Antenna: 150-ft. above ground. Lat. 37° 16' 24", long. 76° 44' 06". Transmitter: Ironbound Rd., behind Berkeley School.

West Point—WHF-233 (Channels A-1-2). Hampton Roads Educational Telecommunications Assn. Inc., 5200 Hampton Blvd., Norfolk, VA 23508. Phone: 757-889-9400. Fax: 757-489-0007. Authorized power: 50-w. each. Antenna: 299-ft. above ground. Lat. 37° 33' 22", long. 76° 46' 49". Transmitter: 0.1-mi. N of West Point High School.

Williamsburg—WGZ-628 (Channels A-3-4). Hampton Roads Educational Telecommunications Assn. Inc., 5200 Hampton Blvd., Norfolk, VA 23508. Phone: 757-889-9400. Fax: 757-489-0007.
E-mail: kmassie@whro.org.
Authorized power: 50-w. each. Antenna: 243-ft. above ground. Lat. 37° 16' 24", long. 76° 44' 06". Transmitter: Ironbound Rd., behind

Berkeley School, Williamsburg. Equipment: ITS transmitter; Andrew antenna.

Washington

Bellingham—WNC-848 (Channels A-1-4). Global Community Institute, 1701 Ellis St., Bellingham, WA 98225. Authorized power: 100-w. each. Antenna: 2507-ft. above ground. Lat. 48° 40' 45", long. 122° 50' 31". Equipment: Emcee transmitter; Andrew antenna.

Bellingham—WNC-847 (Channels D-1-4). City U., Suite 101, 4200 Meridian, Bellingham, WA 98226. Authorized power: 100-w. each. Antenna: 400-ft. above ground. Lat. 48° 40' 45", long. 122° 50' 31". Transmitter: Bellingham. Equipment: Emcee transmitter; Andrew antenna.

Bellingham—WNC-846 (Channels G-1-4). Skagit Valley College, 2405 E. College Way, Mount Vernon, WA 98273. Authorized power: 100-w. each. Antenna: 400-ft. above ground. Lat. 48° 40' 45", long. 122° 50' 31". Transmitter: Mount Constitution. Equipment: Emcee transmitter; Andrew antenna.

Kennewick—WNC-602 (Channels A-1-4). North American Catholic Educational Programming Foundation Inc. Authorized power: 50-w. each. Antenna: 88-ft. above ground. Lat. 46° 06' 12", long. 119° 07' 45". Transmitter: Jump Off Joe Butte. Equipment: ITS transmitter; Andrew antenna.

Kennewick—WND-367 (Channels B-1-4). Richland School District No. 400, 615 Snow Ave., Richland, WA 99352. Antenna: 82-ft. above ground. Lat. 46° 06' 12", long. 119° 07' 45". Transmitter: Jump off Joe Butte. Equipment: ITS transmitter; Andrew antenna.

Kennewick—WNC-600 (Channels C-1-4). Kennewick School District Vocational Administration for the Tri-Cities, 200 S. Dayton St., Kennewick, WA 99336. Authorized power: 10-w. each. Antenna: 80-ft. above ground. Lat. 46° 05' 15", long. 119° 07' 50". Transmitter: Jump Off Joe Butte. Equipment: Comwave transmitter; Andrew antenna.

Kennewick—WNC-916 (Channels G-1-4). Columbia School District No. 400, Maple St., Burbank, WA 99323. Authorized power: 50-w. each. Antenna: 108-ft. above ground. Lat. 46° 06' 12", long. 119° 07' 45". Transmitter: Jump off Joe Butte. Equipment: ITS transmitter; Andrew antenna.

Olympia—WNC-422 (Channels B-1-4). City U., 335 116th Ave. SE, Bellevue, WA 98004. Authorized power: 10-w. each. Antenna: 45-ft. above ground. Lat. 46° 58' 22", long. 123° 08' 17". Transmitter: Capitol Peak. Equipment: Comwave transmitter; Bogner antenna.

Seattle—WHR-528 (Channels A-1-4). KCTS Television, 401 Mercer St., Seattle, WA 98109. Phone: 206-728-6463. Fax: 206-443-6691.
E-mail: ITFS@KCTS.org.
Web site: http://WWW.KCTS.org.
Authorized power: 50-w. each. Antenna: 503-ft. above ground. Lat. 47° 36' 58", long. 122° 18' 28". Transmitter: 18th & E. Madison Sts. Equipment: ITS transmitter; Andrew antenna.
Leased to Wireless Holding.

Seattle—WHR-622 (Channels B-1-4). KCTS Television, 401 Mercer St., Seattle, WA 98109. Phone: 206-728-6463. Fax: 206-443-6691.
E-mail: itfs@kcts.org.
Web site: http://www.kcts.org.
Authorized power: 50-w. each. Antenna: 503-ft. above ground. Lat. 47° 36' 58", long. 122° 18' 28". Transmitter: 18th & E. Madison Sts. Equipment: ITS transmitter; Andrew antenna.
Leased to Wireless Holding.

Seattle—WNC-381 (Channels C-1-4). KCTS Television, 401 Mercer St., Seattle, WA 98109. Phone: 206-728-6463. Fax: 206-443-6691.
E-mail: itfs@kcts.org.
Web site: http://www.kcts.org.
Authorized power: 50-w. each. Antenna: 503-ft. above ground. Lat. 47° 36' 58", long. 122° 18' 28". Transmitter: 18th & E. Madison Sts. Equipment: ITS transmitter; Andrew antenna.

Seattle—WLX-726 (Channels D-1-4). North American Catholic Educational Programming Foundation Inc., Box 40026, Providence, RI 02940-0026. Phone: 401-729-0900. Authorized power: 10-w. each. Antenna: 955-ft. above ground. Lat. 47° 36' 17", long. 122° 19' 46". Transmitter: 701 5th Ave. Equipment: Emcee transmitter; Andrew antenna.

Seattle—WLX-546 (Channels G-1-4). Hispanic Information & Telecommunications Network Inc., 3rd Floor, 449 Broadway, New York, NY 10013. Phone: 212-966-5660. Fax: 212-966-5725.
E-mail: email@hitn.org.
Web site: http://www.hitn.org.
Authorized power: 10-w. each. Antenna: 714-ft. above ground. Lat. 47° 36' 22", long. 122° 19' 45". Transmitter: 800 5th Ave. Equipment: ITS transmitter; Andrew antenna.
Leased to Wireless Holdings Inc., 500 Clyde Ave., Mountain View, CA 94043. Phone: 650-237-9744.

Spokane—WHR-529 (Channels A-1-4). Washington State U., Pullman, WA 99164. Phone: 509-335-6511. Fax: 509-335-3772.
E-mail: nwptv@wsu.edu.
Authorized power: 50-w. each. Antenna: 194-ft. above ground. Lat. 47° 34' 58", long. 117° 17' 37". Transmitter: Krell Hill. Equipment: Comwave transmitter; Andrew antenna.
Leased to Skyline Entertainment Network, 933 E. Third Ave., Spokane, WA 99202. Phone: 509-534-7500.

Spokane—WLX-516 (Channels B-1-4). Gonzaga U. Telecom Associates, E. 502 Boone, Spokane, WA 99258. Authorized power: 50-w. each. Antenna: 194-ft. above ground. Lat. 47° 34' 52", long. 117° 17' 47". Transmitter: Krell Hill, 4-mi. SE of Spokane. Equipment: Comwave transmitter; Andrew antenna.

Spokane—WLX-276 (Channels C-1-4). North American Catholic Educational Programming Foundation Inc., Box 40026, Providence, RI 02940-0026. Phone: 401-729-0900. Authorized power: 50-w. each. Antenna: 194-ft. above ground. Lat. 47° 34' 52", long. 117° 17' 47". Equipment: Andrew antenna.

Spokane—WLX-515 (Channels D-1-4). Spokane Community College, N. 1810 Green St., Spokane, WA 99207. Phone: 509-533-7060. Fax: 509-533-8060.
E-mail: jcumming@ctc.eou.
Authorized power: 10-w. each. Antenna: 194-ft. above ground. Lat. 47° 34' 52", long. 117° 17' 47". Transmitter: Krell Hill, 4-mi. SE of Spokane. Equipment: Communications Microwave transmitter; Andrew antenna. Requests change to 50-w each.
Leased to Videowave Television, 933 E. 3rd Ave., Spokane, WA 99207. Phone: 800-563-7501.

Spokane—WLX-514 (Channels G-1-4). Spokane Falls Community College, W. 3410 Fort George Wright Dr., Spokane, WA 99204. Authorized power: 50-w. each. Antenna: 194-ft. above ground. Lat. 47° 34' 52", long. 117° 17' 47". Transmitter: Krell Hill, 4-mi. SE of Spokane. Equipment: Communications Microwave transmitter; Andrew antenna.

Wenatchee—WNC-661 (Channels A-1-4). Shekinah Network, 14875 Powerline Rd., Atascadero, CA 93422. Phone: 805-438-3341. Fax: 805-438-3341. Authorized power: 20-w. each. Antenna: 58-ft. above ground. Lat. 047° 28' 51", long. 120° 12' 46". Transmitter: Badger Mountain. Equipment: Comwave transmitter; Andrew antenna.

Wenatchee—WNC-711 (Channels C-1-4). Views on Learning Inc., 200 Kenyon Ave., Elkhart, IN 46516. Phone: 219-522-1725. Fax: 219-522-1725.
E-mail: jrueff@lsoc-vol.org.
Web site: http://www.lsoc-vol.org.
Authorized power: 20-w. each. Antenna: 17-ft. above ground. Lat. 47° 28' 51", long. 120° 12' 46". Transmitter: Badger Mountain. Equipment: Comwave transmitter; Andrew antenna.
Leased to American Telecasting Inc., 5575 Tech Center Dr., Suite 300, Colorado Springs, CO 80919. Phone: 719-260-5533.

Yakima—WLX-807 (Channels A-1-4). North American Catholic Educational Programming Foundation Inc., Box 40026, Providence, RI 02940. Authorized power: 10-w. each. Antenna: 114-ft. above ground. Lat. 46° 31' 01", long. 120° 24' 02". Transmitter: Rattlesnake Ridge. Equipment: Emcee transmitter; Andrew antenna.

West Virginia

Charles Town—WLX-888 (Channel G-3). Jefferson County Board of Education, Box 987, Charles Town, WV 25414. Authorized power: 50-w. Antenna: 194-ft. above ground. Lat. 39° 25' 16", long. 78° 05' 20". Transmitter: North Mountain. Equipment: ITS transmitter; Bogner antenna.

Shannondale—WLX-728 (Channels C-1-4). The George Mason U. Instructional Foundation Inc., 4400 University Dr., Fairfax, VA 22030. Phone: 703-993-3100. Fax: 703-993-3115.
E-mail: mkelley@gmu.edu.
Authorized power: 10-w. each. Antenna: 146-ft. above ground. Lat. 39° 12' 13", long. 77° 47' 50". Transmitter: Eagle's Nest Lane, Jefferson County. Equipment: Comwave transmitter; Andrew antenna.

Shenandoah Junction—WLX-884 (Channel G-4). Jefferson County Board of Education, Box 987, Charles Town, WV 25414. Authorized power: 50-w. Antenna: 194-ft. above ground. Lat. 39° 25' 16", long. 78° 05' 20". Transmitter: North Mountain. Equipment: ITS transmitter; Bogner antenna.

Wheeling—WNC-928 (Channels G-1-4). Wheeling Jesuit College, 316 Washington Ave., Wheeling, WV 26003. Authorized power: 10-w. each. Antenna: 75-ft. above ground. Lat. 40° 03' 41", long. 80° 45' 08". Transmitter: 0.5-mi. S of Bridgeport. Equipment: Comwave transmitter; Andrew antenna.

Wisconsin

Albertville—WLX-268 (Channels C-1-4). Chippewa Valley Technical College, 620 W. Clairmont Ave., Eau Claire, WI 54701. Phone: 715-833-6287. Fax: 715-833-6511. Lat. 44° 53' 01", long. 91° 35' 12".

Antigo—WHR-945 (Channel G-2). North Central Technical Institute, 1000 Campus Dr., Wausau, WI 54401. Authorized power: 10-w. Antenna: 299-ft. above ground. Lat. 45° 06' 50", long. 89° 08' 20". Transmitter: WATK(AM) transmitter site. Equipment: Emcee transmitter; Anixter-Mark antenna.

Appleton—WHR-786 (Channels C-1-2). Wisconsin Educational Communications Board, 3319 W. Beltline Hwy., Madison, WI 53713-4296. Phone: 608-264-9636. Fax: 608-264-9664.
E-mail: ecbweb@mail.state.wi.us.
Web site: http://www.wecb.org.
Authorized power: 10-w. each. Antenna: 70-ft. above ground. Lat. 44° 17' 00", long. 88° 27' 30". Transmitter: Fox Valley Tech. Institute, 1825 N. Bluemound Rd. Equipment: Comwave transmitter; Mark antenna.

Brighton—WLX-346 (Channels C-1-4). Wisconsin Educational Communications Board, 3319 W. Beltline Hwy., Madison, WI 53713-4296. Phone: 608-264-9636. Fax: 608-264-9664.
E-mail: ecbweb@mail.state.wi.us.
Web site: http://www.wecb.org.
Authorized power: 10-w. each. Antenna: 499-ft. above ground. Lat. 44° 49' 35", long. 90° 14' 28". Transmitter: 1.72-mi. S of County. Equipment: Comwave transmitter; Anixter antenna.

Cato—WHR-921 (Channels B-2-3). Lakeshore Technical College, 1290 North Ave., Cleveland, WI 53015. Authorized power: 50-w. each. Antenna: 1024-ft. above ground. Lat. 44° 06' 55", long. 87° 51' 27". Transmitter: Ridgeview Rd. & Morrison. Equipment: Comwave transmitter; Andrew antenna.

Center (town)—WLX-285 (Channels A-1). Wisconsin Educational Communications Board, 3319 W. Beltline Hwy., Madison, WI 53713-4296. Phone: 608-264-9636. Fax: 608-264-9664.
E-mail: ecbweb@mail.state.wi.us.
Web site: http://www.wecb.org.
Authorized power: 10-w. Antenna: 400-ft. above ground. Lat. 42° 43' 38", long. 89° 15' 02". Transmitter: Town of Magnolia, 0.5-mi. N. City Hwy. A on Coon Island Rd. Equipment: Comwave transmitter; Andrew antenna.

Chilton—WHR-591 (Channels A-1-4). Wisconsin Educational Communications Board, 3319 W. Beltline Hwy., Madison, WI 53713-4296. Phone: 608-264-9636. Fax: 608-264-9664.
E-mail: ecbweb@mail.state.wi.us.
Web site: http://www.wecb.org.
Authorized power: 10-w. each. Antenna: 455-ft. above ground. Lat. 44° 01' 42", long. 88° 17' 08". Transmitter: Tower Rd., 6-mi. W of Chilton. Equipment: Emcee transmitter; Andrew antenna.

Cleveland—WHR-922 (Channels B-1 & 4). Lakeshore Technical College, 1290 North Ave., Cleveland, WI 53015. Authorized power: 50-w. Antenna: 1024-ft. above ground. Lat. 43° 55' 30", long. 87° 45' 06". Transmitter: Ridgeview Rd. & Morrison. Equipment: Comwave transmitter; Andrew antenna.

Dover—WHR-952 (Channel G-1). North Central Technical Institute, 1000 Campus Dr., Wausau, WI 54401. Authorized power: 10-w. Antenna: 84-ft. above ground. Lat. 45° 40' 20", long. 90° 08' 42". Transmitter: 2.1-mi. E of Dover. Equipment: Emcee transmitter; Anixter-Mark antenna.

Eau Claire—WHR-648 (Channels A-1-2). Wisconsin Educational Communications Board, 3319 W. Beltline Hwy., Madison, WI 53713-4296. Phone: 608-264-9636. Fax: 608-264-9664.
E-mail: ecbweb@mail.state.wi.us.
Web site: http://www.wecb.org.
Authorized power: 10-w. each. Antenna: 439-ft. above ground. Lat. 44° 53' 04", long. 91° 35' 04". Transmitter: Starr & Longview Rds. intersection. Equipment: Emcee transmitter; Andrew antenna.

Eau Claire—WHR-849 (Channel D-1). Wisconsin Educational Communications Board, 3319 W. Beltline Hwy., Madison, WI 53713-4296. Phone: 608-264-9636. Fax: 608-264-9664.
E-mail: ecbweb@mail.state.wi.us.
Web site: http://www.wecb.org.
Authorized power: 10-w. Antenna: 45-ft. above ground. Lat. 44° 47' 39", long. 91° 30' 20". Transmitter: District 1 Technical Institute, 620 W. Clairmont Ave. Equipment: Emcee transmitter; Anixter antenna.

Eau Claire—WLX-366 (Channel D-2). Wisconsin Educational Communications Board, 3319 W. Beltline Hwy., Madison, WI 53713-4296. Phone: 608-264-9636. Fax: 608-264-9664.
E-mail: ecbweb@mail.state.wi.us.
Web site: http://www.wecb.org.
Authorized power: 4-w. Antenna: 78-ft. above ground. Lat. 44° 47' 55", long. 91° 30' 04". Transmitter: McIntyere Library Bldg., U. of Wisconsin-Eau Claire. Equipment: Comwave transmitter; Anixter-Mark antenna.

Eau Claire—WHR-979 (Channel D-4). Wisconsin Educational Communications Board, 3319 W. Beltline Hwy., Madison, WI 53713-4296. Phone: 608-264-9636. Fax: 608-264-9664.
E-mail: ecbweb@mail.state.wi.us.
Web site: http://www.wecb.org.
Authorized power: 3.0-w. Antenna: 299-ft. above ground. Lat. 44° 47' 38", long. 91° 31' 22". Transmitter: W of Clairmont Ave. & Hwy. 85 intersection. Equipment: Emcee transmitter; Anixter-Mark antenna.

Fairchild—WLX-260 (Channels B-1-4). Chippewa Valley Technical College, 620 W. Clairemont Ave., Eau Claire, WI 54701. Phone: 715-833-6287. Fax: 715-833-6511. Authorized power: 10-w. each. Antenna: 323.5-ft. above ground. Lat. 44° 32' 40", long. 90° 56' 32". Transmitter: Alma Center Rd., 3.75-mi. S of Fairchild. Equipment: ITS transmitter; Andrew antenna.

Fennimore—WHR-855 (Channel D-4). Wisconsin Educational Communications Board, 3319 W. Beltline Hwy., Madison, WI 53713-4296. Phone: 608-264-9636. Fax: 608-264-9664.
E-mail: ecbweb@mail.state.wi.us.
Web site: http://www.wecb.org.
Authorized power: 10-w. Antenna: 45-ft. above ground. Lat. 42° 58' 36", long. 90° 38' 13". Transmitter: Fennimore Technical School. Equipment: Emcee transmitter; Anixter-Mark antenna.

Fond du Lac—WND-358 (Channels B-1-4). St. Lawrence Seminary High School, 301 Church St., Mount Calvary, WI 53057. Authorized power: 10-w. each. Antenna: 226-ft. above ground. Lat. 43° 43' 53", long. 88° 17' 34". Transmitter: Pine Dr. & Circle H, 8-mi. SE of Fond du Lac. Equipment: Comwave transmitter; Andrew antenna.

Fond du Lac—WND-359 (Channels C-1-4). Oakfield School District, 330 Oak St., Oakfield, WI 53065. Authorized power: 10-w. each. Antenna: 226-ft. above ground. Lat. 43° 43' 53", long. 88° 17' 34". Transmitter: Pine Dr. & Circle H, 8-mi. SE of Fond du Lac. Equipment: Comwave transmitter; Andrew antenna.

Fond du Lac—WLX-274 (Channel G-4). Wisconsin Educational Communications Board, 3319 W. Beltline Hwy., Madison, WI 53713-4296. Phone: 608-264-9636. Fax: 608-264-9664.
E-mail: ecbweb@mail.state.wi.us.
Web site: http://www.wecb.org.
Authorized power: 2-w. Antenna: 50-ft. above ground. Lat. 43° 47' 06", long. 88° 24' 36". Equipment: Comwave transmitter; Mark Vantenna.

Granton—WLX-341 (Channel B-4). Wisconsin Educational Communications Board, 3319 W. Beltline Hwy., Madison, WI 53713. Phone: 608-264-9636. Fax: 608-264-9664.
E-mail: ecbweb@mail.state.wi.us.
Web site: http://www.wecb.org.
Authorized power: 10-w. Antenna: 199-ft. above ground. Lat. 44° 35' 36", long. 90° 27' 45". Transmitter: 217 N. Main St. Equipment: Comwave transmitter; Mark antenna.

Green Bay—WND-244 (Channels A-1-4). St. Norbert College, 100 Grant St., Depere, WI 54115. Phone: 920-403-3253. Fax: 920-403-1341.
E-mail: smitty@sncac.snc.edu.
Authorized power: 50-w. each. Antenna: 1578-ft. above ground. Lat. 44° 21' 32", long. 87° 58' 58". Equipment: Comwave transmitter; Andrew antenna.
Leased to American Telecasting, 1861 Enterprize, De Pere, WI 54115. Phone: 920-337-9441.

Green Bay—WHR-632 (Channels C-1-4). Wisconsin Educational Communications Board, 3319 W. Beltline Hwy., Madison, WI 53713-4296. Phone: 608-264-9636. Fax: 608-264-9664.
E-mail: ecbweb@mail.state.wi.us.
Web site: http://www.wecb.org.
Authorized power: 50-w. each. Antenna: 1024-ft. above ground. Lat. 44° 21' 32", long. 87° 58' 58". Transmitter: Ridgeview Rd. & Morrison intersection. Equipment: Comwave transmitter; Andrew antenna.
Leased to American Telecasting Inc., 1861 Enterprise Dr., De Pere, WI 54115. Phone: 414-337-0617.

Green Bay—WHR-938 (Channel D-1). Wisconsin Educational Communications Board, 3319 W. Beltline Hwy., Madison, WI 53713-4296. Phone: 608-264-9636. Fax: 608-264-9664.
E-mail: ecbweb@mail.state.wi.us.
Web site: http://www.wecb.org.
Authorized power: 10-w. Antenna: 48-ft. above ground. Lat. 44° 31' 07", long. 88° 05' 58". Transmitter: 1331 Packerland Dr. Equipment: Emcee transmitter; Anixter antenna.

Green Bay—WLX-208 (Channel D-2). Wisconsin Educational Communications Board, 3319 Beltline Hwy., Madison, WI 53713 4296. Phone: 608-264-9636. Fax: 608-264-9664.
E-mail: ecbweb@mail.state.wi.us.
Web site: http://www.wecb.org.
Authorized power: 10-w. Antenna: 48-ft. above ground. Lat. 44° 31' 07", long. 88° 05' 58". Transmitter: 1331 Packerland Dr. Equipment: Emcee transmitter; Anixter antenna.

Green Bay—WHR-874 (Channel D-4). Wisconsin Educational Communications Board, 3319 W. Beltline Hwy., Madison, WI 53713-4296. Phone: 608-264-9636. Fax: 608-264-9664.
E-mail: ecbweb@mail.state.wi.us.
Web site: http://www.wecb.org.
Authorized power: 10-w. Antenna: 135-ft. above ground. Lat. 44° 31' 53", long. 87° 55' 16". Transmitter: U. of Wisconsin, Green Bay Campus, Nicolet Rd. Equipment: Emcee transmitter; Anixter-Mark antenna.

Green Bay—WND-245 (Channels G-1-4). CESA 7, 1331 Packerland Dr., Green Bay, WI 54304. Phone: 920-492-2678. Fax: 920-492-2728.
E-mail: rnys@netnet.net.
Web site: http://www.cesa7.k12.wi.us.
Authorized power: 50-w. each. Antenna: 604-ft. above ground. Lat. 44° 21' 32", long. 87° 58' 58". Transmitter: Ridgeview & Morrison Rds. intersection. Equipment: Comwave transmitter; Andrew antenna.
Leased to American Telecasting Inc., 1861 Enterprise Dr., DePere, WI 54115. Phone: 920-337-9441.

Green Lake—WLX-301 (Channel G-3). Wisconsin Educational Communications Board, 3319 W. Beltline Hwy., Madison, WI 53713-4296. Phone: 608-264-9636. Fax: 608-264-9664.
E-mail: ecbweb@mail.state.wi.us.
Web site: http://www.wecb.org.
Authorized power: 10-w. Antenna: 300-ft. above ground. Lat. 43° 47' 31", long. 88° 52' 54". Transmitter: W. Fond du Lac County, 1.1-mi. S of Hwys. K, KK & Searle Rd. intersection. Equipment: Comwave transmitter; Andrew antenna.

Holcombe—WLX-641 (Channel C-4). Wisconsin Educational Communications Board, 3319 W. Beltline Hwy., Madison, WI 53713-4296. Phone: 608-264-9636. Fax: 608-264-9664. Authorized power: 2-w. Antenna: 75-ft. above ground. Lat. 45° 16' 48", long. 91° 12' 56". Transmitter: Chippewa County. Equipment: Comwave transmitter; Mark antenna.

Irma—WHR-950 (Channel G-3). North Central Technical Institute, 1000 Campus Dr., Wausau, WI 54401. Authorized power: 10-w. Antenna: 200-ft. above ground. Lat. 45° 19' 47", long. 89° 38' 48". Transmitter: Lincoln Hill School, W. 4380 Cooper Lake Rd. Equipment: Emcee transmitter; Bogner antenna.

Irma—WHR-960 (Channel G-4). North Central Technical Institute, 1000 Campus Dr., Wausau, WI 54401. Authorized power: 30-w. Antenna: 203-ft. above ground. Lat. 45° 19' 47", long. 89° 38' 48". Transmitter: Lincoln Hills School, W. 4830 Cooper Lake Rd. Equipment: Emcee transmitter; Anixter antenna.

La Crosse—WHR-576 (Channels A-1-4). Wisconsin Educational Communications Board, 3319 W. Beltline Hwy., Madison, WI 53713-4296. Phone: 608-264-9636. Fax: 608-264-9664.
E-mail: ecbweb@mail.state.wi.us.
Web site: http://www.wecb.org.
Authorized power: 10-w. each. Antenna: 213-ft. above ground. Lat. 43° 48' 44", long. 91° 11' 59". Transmitter: 93 Hixon Rd., Grandad's Bluff. Equipment: Emcee transmitter; Andrew antenna.

La Crosse—WNC-868 (Channels B-1-4). Shekinah Network, 14875 Powerline Rd., Atascadero, CA 93422. Authorized power: 11-w. each. Antenna: 1309-ft. above ground. Lat. 43° 48' 44", long. 91° 11' 59". Equipment: Comwave transmitter; Andrew antenna.

La Crosse—WNC-867 (Channels C-1-4). Morningstar Educational Network, 4012 Morningstar, Huntington Beach, CA 92649. Authorized power: 11-w. each. Antenna: 1309-ft. above ground. Lat. 43° 48' 44", long. 91° 11' 59". Transmitter: La Crosse. Equipment: Comwave transmitter; Andrew antenna.

La Crosse—WHR-936 (Channel D-4). Wisconsin Educational Communications Board, 3319 W. Beltline Hwy., Madison, WI 53713-4296. Phone: 608-264-9636. Fax: 608-264-9664.
E-mail: ecbweb@mail.state.wi.us.
Web site: http://www.wecb.org.
Authorized power: 1-w. Antenna: 85-ft. above ground. Lat. 43° 48' 11", long. 91° 13' 43". Transmitter: 6th & Pine Sts. Equipment: Emcee transmitter; Anixter-Mark antenna.

Ladysmith—WLX-233 (Channels C-3-4). Wisconsin Educational Communications Board, 3319 W. Beltline Hwy., Madison, WI 53713-4296. Phone: 608-264-9636. Fax: 608-264-9664.
E-mail: ecbweb@mail.state.wi.us.
Web site: http://www.wecb.org.
Authorized power: 2-w. each. Antenna: 83-ft. above ground. Lat. 45° 28' 19", long. 91° 04' 38". Transmitter: Ladysmith-Hawkins School District, 1700 Edgewood Ave. E. Equipment: Comwave transmitter; Mark antenna.

Long Lake—WLX-246 (Channels C-1-4). Wisconsin Educational Communications Board, 3319 W. Beltline Hwy., Madison, WI 53713-4296. Phone: 608-264-9636. Fax: 608-264-9664.
E-mail: ecbweb@mail.state.wi.us.
Web site: http://ww.wecb.org.
Authorized power: 10-w. each. Antenna: 404-ft. above ground. Lat. 45° 40' 00", long. 91° 40' 26". Transmitter: SE Washburn County, 0.8-mi. S of State Hwy. D, 3.48-mi. W of Hwy. D and State Hwy. T intersection. Equipment: Comwave transmitter; Bogner antenna.

Loyal—WLX-347 (Channel B-2). Wisconsin Educational Communications Board, 3319 W. Beltline Hwy., Madison, WI 53713-4296. Phone: 608-264-9636. Fax: 608-264-9664.
E-mail: ecbweb@mail.state.wi.us.
Web site: http://www.wecb.org.
Authorized power: 10-w. Antenna: 75-ft. above ground. Lat. 44° 44' 12", long. 90° 30' 09". Transmitter: 514 W. Central St. Equipment: Comwave transmitter; Anixter antenna.

Madison—WHR-626 (Channels B-1-4). Wisconsin Educational Communications Board, 3319 W. Beltline Hwy., Madison, WI 53713-4296. Phone: 608-264-9636. Fax: 608-264-9664.
E-mail: ecbweb@mail.state.wi.us.
Web site: http://www.wecb.org.
Authorized power: 50-w. each. Antenna: 1105-ft. above ground. Lat. 43° 03' 21", long. 89° 32' 05". Transmitter: 8559 Mineral Point Rd. Equipment: Comwave transmitter; Andrew antenna.
Leased to Skycable TV of Madison, 2520 Todd Dr., Madison, WI 53713. Phone: 608-271-6999.

Madison—WHR-907 (Channel C-3). Wisconsin Educational Communications Board, 3319 W. Beltline Hwy., Madison, WI 53713-4296. Phone: 608-264-9636. Fax: 608-264-9664.
E-mail: ecbweb@mail.state.wi.us.
Web site: http://www.wecb.org.
Authorized power: 1-w. Antenna: 188-ft. above ground. Lat. 43° 04' 35", long. 89° 25' 54".

Transmitter: 600 Highland Ave. Equipment: Emcee transmitter; Anixter antenna. Requests change to 87-ft. above ground, lat. 43° 02' 05", long. 89° 25' 59"; transmitter to 3319 Beltline Hwy., Comwave transmitter; Mark antenna.

Madison—WHR-906 (Channel C-4). Wisconsin Educational Communications Board, 3319 W. Beltline Hwy., Madison, WI 53713-4296. Phone: 608-264-9636. Fax: 608-264-9664.
E-mail: ecbweb@mail.state.wi.us.
Web site: http://www.wecb.org.
Authorized power: 1-w. Antenna: 85-ft. above ground. Lat. 43° 02' 05", long. 89° 25' 59". Transmitter: 3319 W. Beltline Hwy. Equipment: Emcee transmitter; Anixter antenna.

Madison—WHR-815 (Channels D-1-4). Madison Area Vocational & Adult Education District, 3550 Anderson St., Madison, WI 53703. Phone: 608-246-6050. Fax: 608-246-6287. Authorized power: 10-w. each. Antenna: 62-ft. above ground. Lat. 43° 07' 16", long. 89° 19' 45". Transmitter: 3550 Anderson St., Truax Campus.
Leased to Sky Cable, 171 Industrial Ave., Belleville, WI 53508. Phone: 608-271-6999.

Madison—WHR-671 (Channels G-1-4). Madison Area Vocational, Technical & Adult Education, 3550 Anderson St., Madison, WI 53704. Authorized power: 50-w. each. Antenna: 1424-ft. above ground. Lat. 43° 03' 21", long. 89° 32' 06". Transmitter: 8559 Mineral Point Rd. Equipment: Comwave transmitter; Andrew antenna.
Leased to Skyview Wireless Cable, 171 Industrial Ave., Belleville, WI 53508. Phone: 608-271-6999.

Marshfield—WNC-962 (Channel D-4). State of Wisconsin Educational Board, 3319 W. Beltline Hwy., Madison, WI 53713. Authorized power: 10-w. Antenna: 1177-ft. above ground. Lat. 44° 40' 15", long. 90° 09' 20". Transmitter: Marshfield High School, 1401 Becker Rd. Equipment: Comwave transmitter; Mark V antenna.

Medford—WHR-946 (Channel G-2). North Central Technical Institute, 1000 Campus Dr., Wausau, WI 54401. Authorized power: 10-w. Antenna: 205-ft. above ground. Lat. 45° 07' 41", long. 90° 20' 10". Transmitter: 624 E. College Ave. Equipment: Emcee transmitter; Anixter antenna.

Menomonie—WHR-990 (Channel D-3). Wisconsin Educational Communications Board, 3319 W. Beltline Hwy., Madison, WI 53713-4296. Phone: 608-264-9636. Fax: 608-264-9664.
E-mail: ecbweb@mail.state.wi.us.
Web site: http://www.wecb.org.
Authorized power: 5-w. Antenna: 132-ft. above ground. Lat. 44° 52' 33", long. 91° 55' 40". Transmitter: 800 S. Broadway. Equipment: Emcee transmitter; Anixter-Mark antenna.

Milladore—WLX-382 (Channel C-2). Wisconsin Educational Communications Board, 3319 W. Beltline Hwy., Madison, WI 53713-4296. Phone: 608-264-9636. Fax: 608-264-9664.
E-mail: ecbweb@mail.state.wi.us.
Web site: http://www.wecb.org.
Authorized power: 10-w. Antenna: 600-ft. above ground. Lat. 44° 38' 39", long. 89° 51' 12". Transmitter: 2.9-mi. N of Milladore. Equipment: Comwave transmitter; Andrew antenna.

Milwaukee—WHR-514 (Channels A-1-4). Network for Instructional TV Inc., Suite 110, 11490 Commerce Park Dr., Reston, VA 20191. Phone: 703-860-9200. Fax: 703-860-9237. Authorized power: 100-w. each. Antenna: 591-ft. above ground. Lat. 43° 02' 18", long. 87° 54' 05". Transmitter: First Wisconsin Center. Equipment: Comwave transmitter; Bogner antenna.
Leased to People's Choice TV Inc., 2 Corporate Woods Blvd., Suite 249, Shelton, CT 20191. Phone: 708-929-2800.

Milwaukee—KHF-80 (Channels B-1-4). Milwaukee Board of School Directors, 5225 W. Vliet St., Milwaukee, WI 53208. Phone: 414-475-8488. Fax: 414-475-8413. Authorized power: 10-w. each. Antenna: 443-ft. above ground. Lat. 43° 04' 42", long. 87° 52' 57". Transmitter: U. of Wisconsin-Milwaukee Campus at Sandburg Hall, 3400 N. Maryland Ave. Equipment: Emcee transmitter; Andrew antenna.

Milwaukee—WDG-56 (Channels D-1-4). Regents of U. of Wisconsin System, 1652 Van Hise Hall, Madison, WI 53706. Phone: 414-229-5470. Fax: 414-229-4777. Authorized power: 100-w. each. Antenna: 451-ft. above ground. Lat. 43° 02' 18", long. 87° 54' 05". Transmitter: First Wisconsin Center. Equipment: Comwave transmitter; Bogner antenna.

Milwaukee—WHR-810 (Channels G-1-4). Milwaukee Area Technical College District Board, 700 W. State St., Milwaukee, WI 53233. Phone: 414-271-1036. Fax: 414-297-7536.
E-mail: pritzlj@milwaukee.tec.wi.us.
Web site: http://www.mptv.org.
Authorized power: 50-w. each. Antenna: 443-ft. above ground. Lat. 43° 04' 42", long. 87° 52' 57". Transmitter: U. of Wisconsin-Milwaukee Campus at Sandburg Hall, 3400 N. Maryland Ave. Equipment: Emcee transmitter; Andrew antenna.

Milwaukee (Wood)—WAU-27 (Channels C-1-4). Milwaukee Regional Medical ITV Station Inc., 5000 W. National Ave., Milwaukee, WI 53295. Authorized power: 100-w. each. Antenna: 591-ft. above ground. Lat. 43° 02' 18", long. 87° 54' 05". Transmitter: First Wisconsin Center. Equipment: Comwave transmitter; Bogner antenna.

Oconto Falls—WLX-302 (Channels G-1-4). Wisconsin Educational Communications Board, 3319 W. Beltline Hwy., Madison, WI 53713-4296. Phone: 608-264-9636. Fax: 608-264-9664.
E-mail: ecbweb@mail.state.wi.us.
Web site: http://ww.wecb.org.
Authorized power: 10-w. each. Antenna: 263-ft. above ground. Lat. 44° 55' 49", long. 88° 13' 06". Transmitter: Hwy. K & Johnson Lane intersection. Equipment: Comwave transmitter; Andrew antenna.

Oshkosh—WLX-342 (Channel C-2). Wisconsin Educational Communications Board, 3319 W. Beltline Hwy., Madison, WI 53713-4296. Phone: 608-264-9636. Fax: 608-264-9664.
E-mail: ecbweb@mail.state.wi.us.
Web site: http://www.wecb.org.
Authorized power: 4-w. Antenna: 72-ft. above ground. Lat. 44° 01' 05", long. 88° 33' 15". Equipment: Comwave transmitter; Mark antenna.

Oshkosh—WNC-401 (Channel C-3). Wisconsin Educational Communications Board, 3319 W. Beltline Hwy., Madison, WI 53713-4296. Phone: 608-264-9636. Fax: 608-264-9664.
E-mail: ecbweb@mail.state.wi.us.
Web site: http://www.wecb.org.
Authorized power: 10-w. Antenna: 108-ft. above ground. Lat. 44° 01' 22", long. 88° 32' 55". Transmitter: 800 Algoma Blvd. Equipment: Comwave transmitter; Mark antenna.

Phillips—WHR-951 (Channel G-3). North Central Technical Institute, 100 Campus Dr., Wausau, WI 54401. Authorized power: 10-w. Antenna: 100-ft. above ground. Lat. 45° 42' 27", long. 90° 25' 07". Transmitter: 1408 Pine Ridge Rd. Equipment: Emcee transmitter; Anixter-Mark antenna.

Platteville—WHR-630 (Channels B-1-4). Wisconsin Educational Communications Board, 3319 W. Beltline Hwy., Madison, WI 53713-4296. Phone: 608-264-9636. Fax: 608-264-9664.
E-mail: ecbweb@mail.state.wi.us.
Web site: http://www.wecb.org.
Authorized power: 10-w. each. Antenna: 95-ft. above ground. Lat. 42° 45' 01", long. 90° 24' 19". Transmitter: Platte Mound, 4.7-mi. NE of Platteville. Equipment: Emcee transmitter; Bogner antenna.

Platteville—WHR-860 (Channel D-1). Wisconsin Educational Communications Board, 3319 W. Beltline Hwy., Madison, WI 53713-4296. Phone: 608-264-9636. Fax: 608-264-9664.
E-mail: ecbweb@mail.state.wi.us.
Web site: http://www.wecb.org.
Authorized power: 1-w. Antenna: 100-ft. above ground. Lat. 42° 43' 56", long. 90° 29' 09". Transmitter: 950 Jay St., Pioneer Hall. Equipment: Emcee transmitter; Anixter-Mark antenna.

Rhinelander—WHR-856 (Channels B-1-4). Wisconsin Educational Communications Board, 3319 W. Beltline Hwy., Madison, WI 53713-4296. Phone: 608-264-9636. Fax: 608-264-9664.
E-mail: ecbweb@mail.state.wi.us.
Web site: http://www.wecb.org.
Authorized power: 10-w. each. Antenna: 334-ft. above ground. Lat. 45° 37' 36", long. 89° 24' 56". Transmitter: NE corner of Nicolet College Campus. Equipment: Emcee transmitter; Bogner antenna.

Rhinelander—WHR-955 (Channel C-3). Nicolet Area Technical College, Box 158, Rhinelander, WI 54501. Phone: 715-365-4669. Fax: 715-365-4447.
E-mail: ckettner@nicolet.tec.wi.us.
Web site: http://www.nicolet.tec.wi.us.
Authorized power: 10-w. Antenna: 323-ft. above ground. Lat. 45° 36' 46", long. 89° 24' 56". Transmitter: Nicolet College. Equipment: Emcee transmitter; Andrew antenna.

Rhinelander—WHR-954 (Channel C-4). Nicolet College & Technical Institute, Box 158, Rhinelander, WI 54501. Phone: 715-365-4410. Authorized power: 10-w. Antenna: 334-ft. above ground. Lat. 45° 36' 46", long. 89° 24' 56". Transmitter: Nicolet College. Equipment: Emcee transmitter; Bogner antenna.

Rice Lake—WLX-239 (Channel C-4). Wisconsin Educational Communications Board, 3319 W. Beltline Hwy., Madison, WI 53713-4296. Phone: 608-264-9636. Fax: 608-264-9664.
E-mail: ecbweb@mail.state.wi.us.
Web site: http://www.wecb.org.
Authorized power: 4-w. Antenna: 104-ft. above ground. Lat. 45° 28' 52", long. 91° 44' 46". Transmitter: 1900 College Dr. Equipment: Comwave transmitter; Anixter antenna.

Rock Twp.—WLX-284 (Channel A-2 & 4). Wisconsin Educational Communications Board, 3319 W. Beltline Hwy., Madison, WI 53713-4296. Phone: 608-264-9636. Fax: 608-264-9664.
E-mail: ecbweb@mail.state.wi.us.
Web site: http://www.wecb.org.
Authorized power: 4-w. Antenna: 75-ft. above ground. Lat. 42° 35' 39", long. 89° 01' 01". Transmitter: 6004 Prairie Rd. Equipment: Comwave transmitter; Mark antenna.

Sheboygan—WHR-458 (Channels G-1-4). Lakeshore Technical College, 1290 North Ave., Cleveland, WI 53015. Authorized power: 10-w. each. Antenna: 100-ft. above ground. Lat. 43° 42' 12", long. 87° 45' 09". Transmitter: W78AJ tower, Sheboygan Falls.

Somers—WHR-766 (Channels A-1-4). Wisconsin Educational Communications Board, 3319 W. Beltline Hwy., Madison, WI 53713-4296. Phone: 608-264-9636. Fax: 608-264-9664.
E-mail: ecbweb@mail.state.wi.us.
Web site: http://www.wecb.org.
Authorized power: 10-w. each. Antenna: 275-ft. above ground. Lat. 42° 37' 01", long. 87° 52' 28". Transmitter: 2.3-mi. SE of Somers.

Spencer—WLX-348 (Channel B-1). Wisconsin Educational Communications Board, 3319 W. Beltline Hwy., Madision, WI 53713-4296. Phone: 608-264-9636. Fax: 608-264-9664.
E-mail: ecbweb@mail.state.wi.us.
Web site: http://www.wecb.org.
Authorized power: 10-w. Antenna: 61-ft. above ground. Lat. 44° 45' 32", long. 90° 17' 36". Transmitter: 300 School St. Equipment: ITS transmitter; Mark V antenna.

Stevens Point—WLX-373 (Channel C-1). Wisconsin Educational Communications Board, 3319 W. Beltline Hwy., Madison, WI 53713-4296. Phone: 608-264-9636. Fax: 608-264-9664.
E-mail: ecbweb@mail.state.wi.us.
Web site: http://www.wecb.org.
Authorized power: 2-w. Antenna: 124-ft. above ground. Lat. 44° 31' 36", long. 89° 34' 14". Transmitter: Stevens Point Library. Equipment: Comwave transmitter.

Stratford—WLX-349 (Channel B-3). Wisconsin Educational Communications Board, 3319 W. Beltline Hwy., Madision, WI 53713-4296. Phone: 608-264-9636. Fax: 608-264-9664.
E-mail: ecbweb@mail.state.wi.us.
Web site: http://ww.wecb.org.
Authorized power: 4-w. Antenna: 76-ft. above ground. Lat. 44° 48' 22", long. 90° 04' 29". Transmitter: 522 3rd Ave. Equipment: Comwave transmitter; Mark V antenna.

Superior—WLX-258 (Channel C-1). Wisconsin Educational Communications Board, 3319 W. Beltline Hwy., Madison, WI 53713-4296. Phone: 608-264-9636. Fax: 608-264-9664.
E-mail: ecbweb@mail.state.wi.us.
Web site: http://www.wecb.org.
Lat. 46° 43' 04", long. 92° 05' 20". Equipment: Emcee transmitter; Anixter antenna.

Wausau—WHR-580 (Channels A-1-4). Wisconsin Educational Communications Board, 3319 W. Beltline Hwy., Madison, WI 53713-4296. Phone: 608-264-9636. Fax: 608-264-9664.
E-mail: ecbweb@mail.state.wi.us.
Web site: http://www.wecb.org.
Authorized power: 10-w. each. Antenna: 300-ft. above ground. Lat. 44° 55' 14.3", long. 89° 41' 30.6". Transmitter: Rib Mountain State Park, 4-mi. SW of Wausau. Equipment: Emcee transmitter; Andrew antenna.

Wausau—WLX-799 (Channels D-1-3). Wisconsin Educational Communications Board, 3319 W. Beltline Hwy., Madison, WI 53713-4296. Phone: 608-264-9636. Fax: 608-264-9664.

E-mail: ecbweb@mail.state.wi.us.
Web site: http://www.wecb.org.
Authorized power: 2-w. each. Antenna: 55-ft. above ground. Lat. 44° 59' 11", long. 89° 38' 39". Transmitter: 1000 Campus Dr. Equipment: Comwave transmitter; Anixter antenna.

Wausau—WHR-948 (Channel G-1). North Central Technical Institute, 1000 Campus Dr., Wausau, WI 54401. Authorized power: 100-w. Antenna: 248-ft. above ground. Lat. 44° 53' 17", long. 89° 39' 07". Transmitter: Mosinee Hill. Equipment: Emcee transmitter; Bogner antenna.

Wausau—WHR-949 (Channel G-4). North Central Technical Institute, 1000 Campus Dr., Wausau, WI 54401. Authorized power: 5-w. Antenna: 55-ft. above ground. Lat. 44° 59' 11", long. 89° 38' 39". Transmitter: 1000 Campus Dr. Equipment: Emcee transmitter; Bogner antenna.

Weston—WLX-310 (Channels B-1-4). Chippewa Valley Technical College, 620 W. Clairmont Ave., Eau Claire, WI 54701. Phone: 715-833-6287. Fax: 715-833-6511. Lat. 44° 52' 04", long. 92° 04' 24".

Weyerhaeuser—WLX-232 (Channel C-2). Wisconsin Educational Communications Board, 3319 W. Beltline Hwy., Madison, WI 53713-4296. Phone: 608-264-9636. Fax: 608-264-9664.
E-mail: ecbweb@mail.state.wi.us.
Web site: http://www.wecb.org.
Authorized power: 10-w. Antenna: 404-ft. above ground. Lat. 45° 25' 32", long. 91° 25' 05". Transmitter: Weyerhaeuser Area School District, Hwy. F N. Equipment: Comwave transmitter; Bogner antenna.

Wittenberg—WNC-961 (Channels D-1-4). Northcentral Technical College, 1000 W. Campus Dr., Wausau, WI 54401. Authorized power: 20-w. each. Antenna: 315-ft. above ground. Lat. 44° 48' 57", long. 89° 09' 33". Transmitter: NW 1/4 of SW 1/4 Section 15, Twp. 27N, Range 11E. Equipment: Emcee transmitter; Andrew antenna.

Wyoming

Cheyenne—WND-249 (Channels B-1-4). U. of Wyoming, Box 3314, University Station, Laramie, WY 82071. Authorized power: 6176-w. each. Antenna: 6176-ft. above ground. Lat. 41° 09' 34", long. 104° 43' 19". Transmitter: 7100 Dell Range Blvd. Equipment: Comwave transmitter; Andrew antenna.

Cheyenne—WNC-997 (Channels C-1-4). Laramie County School District No. 1, 2810 House Ave., Cheyenne, WY 82001. Authorized power: 10-w. each. Antenna: 62-ft. above ground. Lat. 41° 09' 34", long. 104° 43' 19". Transmitter: 7100 Dell Range Blvd. Equipment: Comwave transmitter; Andrew antenna.

Gillette—WNC-619 (Channels D-1-4). Campbell City Board of Cooperative Education Services, 525 Lakeway, Gillette, WY 82718. Authorized power: 10-w. each. Antenna: 69-ft. above ground. Lat. 44° 18' 17", long. 105° 33' 53". Transmitter: 0.67-mi. N of Interstate 90, 1.71-mi. N of US Rte. 16. Equipment: Emcee transmitter; Andrew antenna.

Laramie—WND-248 (Channels B-1-4). U. of Wyoming, Box 3314, University Station, Laramie, WY 82071. Authorized power: 10-w. each. Antenna: 8931-ft. above ground. Lat. 41° 18' 36", long. 105° 27' 17". Transmitter: Pilot Knob, 2.2-mi. N of Telephone Spring. Equipment: Comwave transmitter; Andrew antenna.

Laramie—WNC-996 (Channels C-1-4). Albany County School District, 1948 Grand Ave., Laramie, WY 82070. Authorized power: 10-w. each. Antenna: 102-ft. above ground. Lat. 41° 18' 36", long. 105° 27' 17". Transmitter: Pilot Knob, 2.2-mi. N of Telephone Spring. Equipment: Comwave transmitter; Andrew antenna.

Linch—WNC-624 (Channels D-1-4). Campbell City Board of Cooperative Higher Education Services, 525 Lakeway, Gillette, WY 82718. Authorized power: 10-w. each. Antenna: 141-ft. above ground. Lat. 43° 43' 26", long. 105° 53' 02". Transmitter: Pumpkin Butte, 16-mi. NE of Linch. Equipment: Emcee transmitter; Andrew antenna.

Sheridan—WNC-426 (Channels A-1-4). Shekinah Network, 14875 Powerline Rd., Atascadero, 93422. Phone: 805-438-3341. Authorized power: 10-w. each. Antenna: 96-ft. above ground. Lat. 44° 37' 20", long. 107° 06' 57". Transmitter: Sheridan County. Equipment: Comwave transmitter; Bogner antenna.

Sheridan—WNC-796 (Channels D-1-4). Clarendon Foundation, Suite 826, 4201 S. 31st St., Arlington, VA 22206. Authorized power: 10-w. each. Antenna: 98-ft. above ground. Lat. 44° 37' 20", long. 107° 06' 57". Transmitter: Red Grade Rd. Equipment: Comwave transmitter; Bogner antenna.

Sheridan—WNC-770 (Channels G-1-4). Views on Learning Inc., 200 Kenyon Ave., Elkhart, IN 46516. Authorized power: 10-w. each. Antenna: 95-ft. above ground. Lat. 44° 37' 20", long. 107° 06' 57". Transmitter: Red Grade Rd. Equipment: Comwave transmitter; Bogner antenna.

American Samoa

Lauliifou—WNC-792 (Channels A-1-4). American Somoa Community College, Box 2609, Pago Pago, AS 96799. Authorized power: 10-w. each. Antenna: 161-ft. above ground. Lat. 14° 17' 41", long. 170° 39' 44". Transmitter: Breaker Point. Equipment: Comwave transmitter; Andrew antenna.

Lauliifou—WNC-793 (Channels B-1-4). American Samoa Community College, Box 2609, Pago Pago, AS 96799. Authorized power: 10-w. each. Antenna: 161-ft. above ground. Lat. 14° 17' 41", long. 170° 39' 44". Transmitter: Breaker Point. Equipment: Comwave transmitter; Andrew antenna.

Puerto Rico

Aguadilla—WNC-700 (Channels B-1-4). Hispanic Information & Telecommunications Network Inc., 3rd Floor, 449 Broadway, New York, NY 10013. Phone: 212-966-5660. Fax: 212-966-5725.
E-mail: email@hitn.org.
Web site: http://www.hitn.org.
Authorized power: 10-w. each. Antenna: 30-ft. above ground. Lat. 18° 19' 07", long. 67° 10' 41". Transmitter: Atayala Mountain, off Terr. Rd. 411. Equipment: Comwave transmitter; Andrew antenna.
Leased to Distance Learning Services Inc., 1155 Connecticut Ave. NW, Suite 300, Washington, DC 20036. Phone: 202-467-8500.

Aguadilla—WLX-663 (Channels C-1-4). University System of the Ana G. Mendez Educational Foundation, Apartado 21345, Rio Piedras, PR 00928. Phone: 787-766-2600. Fax: 787-250-8546. Authorized power: 20-w. each. Antenna: 200-ft. above ground. Lat. 18° 19' 06", long. 67° 10' 49". Transmitter: WIPM transmitter site, Monte Estado. Equipment: Comwave transmitter; Bogner antenna.

Aguadilla—WNC-725 (Channels D-1-4). Hispanic Information & Telecommunication Network Inc., 3rd Floor, 449 Broadway, New York, NY 10013. Phone: 212-966-5660. Fax: 212-966-5725.
E-mail: email@hitn.org.
Web site: http://www.hitn.org.
Authorized power: 10-w. each. Antenna: 30-ft. above ground. Lat. 18° 19' 07", long. 67° 10' 41". Transmitter: Atayala Mountain, Rte. 411. Equipment: Comwave transmitter; Andrew antenna.
Leased to Distance Learning Services Inc., 1155 Connecticut Ave. NW, Suite 300, Washington, DC 20036. Phone: 202-467-8500.

Aguas Buenas—WLX-323 (Channels B-1-4). American U. of Puerto Rico, Rd. No. 2, Km 14, Hato Tejas, Bayamon, PR 00621. Authorized power: 10-w. each. Antenna: 54-ft. above ground. Lat. 18° 16' 51", long. 66° 06' 38". Equipment: Emcee transmitter; Andrew antenna.

Aguas Buenas—WLX-315 (Channels C-1-4). Caribbean U., Carretera 167, Km 21.2, Bayamon, PR 06621. Authorized power: 10-w. each. Antenna: 54-ft. above ground. Lat. 18° 16' 51", long. 66° 06' 38". Transmitter: Cerro Marquesa, 1-mi. NNW of Aguas Buenas. Equipment: Emcee transmitter; Andrew antenna.

Aguas Buenas—WLX-322 (Channels D-1-4). Puerto Rico Medical Association, 1305 Fernandez Juncos Ave., Santurce, PR 00908. Authorized power: 10-w. each. Antenna: 57-ft. above ground. Lat. 18° 16' 51", long. 66° 06' 38". Transmitter: 1-mi. from Cerro Marquesa. Equipment: Emcee transmitter.

Aguas Buenas—WLX-664 (Channels G-1-4). University System of the Ana G. Mendez Educational Foundation, Apartado 21345, Rio Peidras, PR 00928. Phone: 787-766-2600. Fax: 787-250-8546. Authorized power: 10-w. each. Antenna: 148-ft. above ground. Lat. 18° 16' 54", long. 66° 06' 46". Transmitter: Cerro Marquesa. Equipment: Comwave transmitter; Andrew antenna.

Cayey—WNC-864 (Channels A-1-4). Fundacion Educativa Ana G. Mendez, Apartado 21345, Rio Piedras, PR 00928. Phone: 787-766-2600. Fax: 787-250-8546. Authorized power: 10-w. each. Antenna: 16-ft. above ground. Lat. 18° 09' 16", long. 66° 04' 50". Transmitter: Banco Popular Microwave repeater site. Equipment: Comwave transmitter; SEA antenna.

Ceiba—WNC-703 (Channels C-1-4). Fundaction Educativa Ana G. Mendez, Apartado 21345, Rio Piedras, PR 00928. Phone: 787-766-2600. Fax: 787-250-8546. Authorized power: 20-w. each. Antenna: 20-ft. above ground. Lat. 18° 16' 50", long. 65° 40' 13". Transmitter: Co-located with WNQ-772, Ceiba. Equipment: Comwave transmitter; Bogner antenna.

Gurabo—WLX-662 (Channels C-1-4). University System of the Ana G. Mendez Educational Foundation, Apartado 21345, Rio Piedras, PR 00928. Phone: 787-766-2600. Fax: 787-250-8546. Authorized power: 20-w. each. Antenna: 200-ft. above ground. Lat. 18° 16' 49", long. 65° 56' 23". Transmitter: 1-mi. N of Maria. Equipment: Comwave transmitter; Andrew antenna.

Humacao—WNC-694 (Channels G-1-4). Fundacion Educativa Ana G. Mendez, Apartado 21345, Rio Piedras, PR 00928. Phone: 787-766-2600. Fax: 787-250-8546. Authorized power: 15-w. each. Antenna: 82-ft. above ground. Lat. 18° 07' 08", long. 65° 51' 29". Transmitter: 2-mi. NNW of Comunas. Equipment: Comwave transmitter; Bogner antenna.

Jardines de Ponce—WND-492 (Channels C-1-4). Caribbean U., Box 493, Rd. 167, KM21.2 Forest Hills, Bayamon, PR 00960. Authorized power: 50-w. each. Antenna: 190-ft. above ground. Lat. 18° 03' 00", long. 66° 36' 37". Transmitter: 0.37-mi. S of Cerro El Gato. Equipment: ITS transmitter; Andrew antenna.

Jayuya—WLX-661 (Channels A-1-4). University System of the Ana G. Mendez Educational Foundation, Apartado 21345, Rio Peidras, PR 00928. Phone: 787-766-2600. Fax: 787-250-8546. Authorized power: 50-w. each. Antenna: 91-ft. above ground. Lat. 18° 10' 10", long. 66° 34' 36". Transmitter: Jayuya. Equipment: Comwave transmitter; Bogner antenna.

Maricao—WNC-693 (Channels G-1-4). Fundacion Educativa Ana G. Mendez, Apartado 21345, Rio Piedras, PR 00928. Phone: 787-766-2600. Fax: 787-250-8546. Authorized power: 20-w. each. Antenna: 98-ft. above ground. Lat. 18° 09' 00", long. 66° 59' 00". Transmitter: WIPM transmitter site, Monte Estado. Equipment: Comwave transmitter; Bogner antenna.

San Juan—WLX-321 (Channels A-1-4). Catholic Archdiocese of San Juan, 201 San Jorge St., San Juan, PR 00903. Authorized power: 10-w. each. Antenna: 54-ft. above ground. Lat. 18° 16' 51", long. 66° 06' 38". Equipment: Emcee transmitter; Andrew antenna.

Virgin Islands

Charlotte Amalie—WHR-728 (Channel A-1). College of the Virgin Islands. Authorized power: 10-w. Antenna: 60-ft. above ground. Lat. 18° 21' 16", long. 64° 58' 34". Transmitter: Hawk Hill.

Charlotte Amalie—WHR-908 (Channel C-1). College of the Virgin Islands, St. Thomas, VI 00801. Authorized power: 10-w. Antenna: 60-ft. above ground. Lat. 18° 21' 16", long. 64° 58' 34". Transmitter: Hawk Hill.

Charlotte Amalie—WNC-892 (Channels G-1-4). Shekinah Network, 14875 Powerline Rd., Atascadero, CA 93422. Authorized power: 10-w. each. Antenna: 75-ft. above ground. Lat. 18° 21' 26", long. 64° 56' 51". Transmitter: Signal Hill, 0.9-mi. NNW of Charlotte Amalie. Equipment: Emcee transmitter; Andrew antenna.

Friedenfield—WND-210 (Channels B-1-4). Shekinah Network, 14875 Powerline Rd., Atascadero, CA 93422. Authorized power: 10-w. each. Antenna: 1257-ft. above ground. Lat. 17° 45' 20", long. 64° 47' 55". Transmitter: Friedenfield. Equipment: Emcee transmitter; Andrew antenna.

MDS & MMDS Ownership

Companies with MDS or MMDS holdings are listed alphabetically by name. Each listing includes licenses, address, phone, ownership, other communications interests where available.

RON ABBOUD
3208 S. 121st
Omaha, NE 68137
Phone: 402-592-0322

Branch Offices:
Metro-Com Inc.
11111 M St.
Omaha, NE 68137
Phone: 402-592-0322

Metro-Com Inc.
109th & M St.
Omaha, NE 68137
MMDS Systems:
Nebraska: WLW992, Omaha.

WARREN F. ACHE
3206 Rustic Villa Dr.
Kingwood, TX 77345
Phone: 713-360-7365
MMDS Systems:
Texas: WLR463, Brownsville; WLR475, McAllen.

ADVANCED WIRELESS SYSTEMS INC.
No. 1
4123-A Government Blvd.
Mobile, AL 36693
MMDS Systems:
Alabama: WMX259, Mobile; WMX263, Mobile; WMX267, Mobile.

AERIE COMM INC.
4313 Sterlington Rd.
Monroe, LA 71203
Ownership: Tom Dixon, Principal.
MMDS Systems:
Louisiana: WNTI518, Monroe.

AESCO SYSTEMS INC.
14 S. Bryn Mawr Ave.
Bryn Mawr, PA 19010
MMDS Systems:
Oregon: WHT647, Portland.

AFFILIATED COMMUNICATIONS CORP.
333 Jericho Turnpike
Jericho, NY 11753
Phone: 516-822-5350
Fax: 516-433-3821
Officers:
Robert A. Rosen, Pres. & Chief Exec. Officer
Florence Rosen, Exec. V.P. & Chief Operating Officer
Peter Varous, Chief Financial Officer
Ownership: Robert A. Rosen.
Represented (legal): Fletcher, Heald & Hildreth PLC.
MMDS Systems:
Nebraska: WDU307, Lincoln.

AFFILIATED MDS CORP.
1 Financial Center
18th Floor
Boston, MA 02111
Officers:
Matthew Brown, Pres. & Chief Exec. Officer
Martin Hoffman, Secy.
Martin Hoffman, Treas. & Chief Financial Officer
Benito Gaguine, Asst. Secy.
Represented (legal): Donald E. Ward.
MMDS Systems:
Indiana: WHT673, Indianapolis.

ALASKA WIRELESS CABLE INC.
3055 Braddock St.
Fairbanks, AK 99701
Phone: 907-456-6160
MDS Systems:
Alaska: WPY44, Fairbanks.

ALCH INC.
2600 California St.
Saginaw, MI 48640
MDS Systems:
Michigan: WLW833, Saginaw.
MMDS Systems:
Michigan: WNTD763, Saginaw.

R. STANLEY ALLEN
4408 E. Conway Dr. NW
Atlanta, GA 30327-3531
MDS Systems:
Virginia: WMI910, Basye.

ALL-STAR COMMUNICATIONS
Box 487
Fajardo, PR 00648
MDS Systems:
Puerto Rico: WGX581, Fajardo.

AMERICAN COMMUNICATIONS SERVICES INC.
Box 753
Elmhurst, IL 60126-0753
MMDS Systems:
Illinois: WNEL393, Chicago.

AMERICAN TELECASTING INC.
Suite 300
5575 Tech Center Dr.
Colorado Springs, CO 80919
Phones: 719-260-5533; 800-225-1683
Fax: 719-260-5010; 719-260-5012
Officers:
Donald R. DePriest, Chmn.
Brian E. Gast, Pres. & Chief Exec. Officer
Richard F. Seney, Vice Chmn. & Secy.
Gary Jaeckel, V.P. Finance
David Sentman, Chief Financial Officer
Christopher Clark, Dir., Communications
Ownership: Charles Mauszycki, Principal.
MDS Systems:
California: WDU424, Gilroy.
Colorado: WPG39, Colorado Springs; WPW97, Colorado Springs; WMY475, Denver; WPY32, Denver.
Montana: WFY748, Billings.
Nevada: WKR65, Las Vegas.
North Dakota: WMH904, Bismarck.
Ohio: WOG60, Cincinnati.
Oregon: WHA674, Bend; WMX333, Medford.
Virginia: WMI908, Culpeper; WMI922, Wytheville.
Washington: WMI902, Seattle.
MMDS Systems:
California: WLW740, Redding; WMH681, Redding; WHT690, Sacramento; WGW280, Visalia; WMH381, Yuba City; WMH384, Yuba City.
Colorado: WHT758, Colorado Springs; WNTA854, Colorado Springs; WNTG790, Colorado Springs; WNTG791, Colorado Springs; WLK321, Denver; WNEY681, Denver; WNTH953, Denver; WNTH998, Denver.
Florida: WNTI333, Naples; WNTI465, Naples.
Hawaii: WNTH270, Kahului; WNTH288, Kahului.
Indiana: WMH360, Elkhart.
Kansas: WNTB419, Wichita; WNTU661, Wichita.
Maryland: WHT631, Baltimore.
Michigan: WMH517, Jackson.
Minnesota: WNTH394, Barnesville; WNTH396, Barnesville; WNTK426, Jeffers; WLW989, Windom; WLW990, Windom.
Montana: WFY603, Billings; WLW837, Billings; WNTA982, Billings.
Nebraska: WMH765, Geneva; WMH768, Geneva; WLW922, Grand Island.
North Dakota: WMI866, Bismarck; WLW839, Fargo.
Ohio: WHT632, Cincinnati; WHT633, Cincinnati; WMH816, Columbus; WNTJ743, Springfield; WHT742, Toledo; WMI374, Youngstown.
Oklahoma: WHT684, Oklahoma City; WNEX724, Oklahoma City; WNTM545, Oklahoma City.
Oregon: WLR492, Bend; WLW954, Bend; WNTJ728, Bend; WLK249, Medford; WLK253, Medford; WNTJ458, Medford; WHK953, Prineville; WLR496, Prineville; WMI302, Salem.
South Dakota: WMH813, Rapid City; WMH817, Rapid City; WMI825, Rapid City; WMI884, Rapid City.
Texas: WMH576, McAllen; WMI865, Waco.
Virginia: WMX240, Lexington; WMX241, Lexington; WMX242, Lexington; WNTI796, Winchester.
West Virginia: WMY290, Martinsburg; WMY291, Martinsburg.
Wisconsin: WMH660, Green Bay; WMH688, Sheboygan; WMI362, Sheboygan; WNTK964, Sheboygan.
Wyoming: WLW820, Sheridan; WLW824, Sheridan.
Other Holdings:
Cable, LPTV, ITFS, see listings.

AMERICAN WIRELESS INC.
Box 2500
845 E. Skyline Dr.
St. George, UT 84771
Phone: 801-674-0320
Fax: 801-674-7679
MDS Systems:
Utah: WMI946, St. George.
MMDS Systems:
Utah: WMI363, St. George; WMI367, St. George; WNTJ366, St. George.
Other Holdings:
Wireless Cable, see listing.

AMERICOMM INC.
568 Spyglass Lane
Thousand Oaks, CA 91360
Phone: 818-597-1837
Fax: 818-597-3221
Officers:
James R. Coburn, Chmn.
Wayne Terry, Chief Operating Officer
Ownership: James R. Coburn; Wayne Terry.
MDS Systems:
Texas: WJL88, Beaumont.
MMDS Systems:
Texas: WNTJ712, Beaumont; WNTJ737, Beaumont.

RICHARD J. AMONS JR.
Box 174
100 Roanoke Rd.
Daleville, VA 24083-0174
Phone: 540-992-2211
MMDS Systems:
Idaho: WNTJ801, Boise.

AMV COMM.
2113 Coolidge Dr.
Santa Clara, CA 95051
Phone: 408-996-5716
MDS Systems:
Texas: WMI980, Farwell.

PATRICIA A. ANDERSON
N. Lawler
Emmetsburg, IA 50536
MMDS Systems:
Minnesota: WLW783, Garfield; WLW784, Garfield.

ANTENNA VISION
4224-F Santa Fe
Oklahoma City, OK 73118-8527
Phone: 405-525-1000
MDS Systems:
Oklahoma: WJL99, Oklahoma City.

ARIZONA UNIVERSITY BOARD OF REGENTS
No. 225
Modern Languages Bldg.
Tucson, AZ 85721
Phone: 602-621-7365
Officers:
Rudy Campbell, Pres.
Kurt Davis, Secy.
George Amos, Treas.
John Platt, Asst. Treas.
MMDS Systems:
Arizona: WEH249, Tucson.
Other Holdings:
ITFS.

ARK-STAR PARTNERS-GAMMA
276 W. 20th St.
Tracy, CA 95376
Officer:
Gary F. Dobler, Pres.
Represented (legal): Hunter & Mow PC.
MMDS Systems:
Arkansas: WNTL298, Russellville.

ASHEVILLE (E) WIRELESS CABLE PARTNERSHIP
55 Auburn Rd.
Londonderry, NH 03053
MMDS Systems:
North Carolina: WMX214, Asheville.

ASHLAND PARTNERS ALPHA
8027 Northbridge Dr.
Spring, TX 77379
Phone: 713-370-7444

MMDS Systems:
Wisconsin: WMI337, Ashland.

ASHLAND PARTNERS BETA
8027 Northbridge Dr.
Spring, TX 77379
Phone: 713-370-7444
MMDS Systems:
Wisconsin: WMI341, Ashland.

ASSOCIATED INFORMATION SERVICES CORP.
200 Gateway Towers
Pittsburgh, PA 15222
MMDS Systems:
Pennsylvania: WBD240, Pittsburgh.

ATLANTA MDS CO.
Suite C-6
104 E. 68th St.
New York, NY 10021
Phone: 212-288-2356
MDS Systems:
Georgia: WGW309, Atlanta.

CAROL A. BAGLIA
7097 Brightwood Dr.
Concord, OH 44077
Phone: 216-357-5834
MMDS Systems:
Nevada: WLW721, Elko.

BAILLON MDS CORP.
1218 Pioneer Bldg.
336 N. Roberts St.
St. Paul, MN 55101
MMDS Systems:
Missouri: WMH744, Nevada.

WOODROW A. BAKER
13979 Allen Rd.
Albion, NY 14411
Phone: 716-589-9295
MMDS Systems:
Tennessee: WNTE475, Knoxville.

CINDY BARNES
Box 8909
Aspen, CO 81612
Phone: 303-927-1460
MMDS Systems:
South Carolina: WMX206, Charleston; WMX207, Charleston.

JODY BARNES
Suite 204
3628 Lynoak
Claremont, CA 91711
Phone: 909-621-1004
MMDS Systems:
Alaska: WMH736, Kenai.
Ohio: WHT741, Toledo.

BAY AREA CABLEVISION INC.
500 Clyde Ave.
Mountain View, CA 94043-2212
Phone: 415-631-9190
MDS Systems:
California: WFY976, Palo Alto; WJL36, Palo Alto; KFF81, San Francisco.
MMDS Systems:
California: WMY498, San Francisco; WMY499, San Francisco; WNEJ497, San Francisco (South); WNTM579, San Jose.

BAYPOINT TV INC.
Suite 700
919 18th St. NW
Washington, DC 20006
Phone: 202-293-0700
Fax: 202-659-5409
Officer:
William M. Barnard, Chief Exec. Officer
MMDS Systems:
Kentucky: WLW755, Paducah.
Missouri: WLK422, St. Louis.
North Carolina: WMI838, Greenville.
Oklahoma: WMH701, Enid.
Other Holdings:
Barnard is principal of Libmot Communications Partners, MDS Signal Group & Springfield One Partnership, see listings.
MMDS: 25% of Red Charleston F Partnership, 25% of Red Memphis F Partnership, see listings.

BCW SYSTEMS INC.
Drawer 377
118 N. Madison
Malden, MO 63863
Phone: 573-276-3025
MMDS Systems:
Missouri: WNTJ367, Malden.

L. M. BEAL JR.
2514 Broadmoor
Bryan, TX 77802
MMDS Systems:
Texas: WMH993, Lufkin.

BECKER BROADCASTING
Box 12641
El Paso, TX 79912
Phone: 915-585-1178
Fax: 915-585-1179
Ownership: Jed Becker.
Represented (legal): W. Randolph Young.
MDS Systems:
Texas: WMI960, Bryan.
MMDS Systems:
Texas: WLW979, Bryan; WNTG864, Bryan; WNTH514, Bryan; WLW978, Bryan-College Station; WMH288, Kerrville.

BELLSOUTH ENTERTAINMENT INC.
Suite 414
1100 Abernathy Rd. NE
500 Northpark Town Center
Atlanta, GA 30328
Phone: 770-673-2800
Fax: 770-392-4575
Officers:
Robert J. Frame, Pres.
Thompson T. Rawls II, V.P. & Gen. Counsel
Howard J. Haug, Chief Financial Officer
Ownership: BellSouth Corp.
MDS Systems:
Florida: WLK243, Daytona Beach; WLJ79, Miami.
Georgia: WQR43, Atlanta.
Kentucky: KOA86, Louisville.
MMDS Systems:
Florida: WHT762, Daytona Beach; WMX941, Daytona Beach; WNEY905, Daytona Beach; WNEZ718, Daytona Beach; WMX338, Fort Myers; WMX373, Fort Myers; WHT675, Jacksonville; WHT676, Jacksonville; WMX382, Jacksonville; WMX383, Jacksonville; WMI397, Lakeland; WMI401, Lakeland; WMY472, Lakeland; WHJ893, Miami; WNEK346, Miami; WNEY682, Orlando; WNEZ716, Orlando; WNTG591, Orlando.
Georgia: WMI284, Athens; WMI824, Athens; WNTM819, Athens; WHT663, Atlanta; WNTA434, Atlanta; WNTB872, Atlanta; WMI338, Rome.
Indiana: WNTA919, New Albany.
Kentucky: WHT725, Louisville; WNEZ577, Louisville; WNEZ666, Louisville.
Louisiana: WHT681, New Orleans; WLW963, New Orleans; WNEZ351, New Orleans; WNTB691, New Orleans.
Other Holdings:
Cable, see listing.

BELWEN INC.
7 Boyle Rd.
Scotia, NY 12302
Phone: 518-383-0550
Ownership: Wayne E. Wagner, Pres.
MMDS Systems:
Indiana: WMH997, Kokomo.
Kentucky: WLW852, Owensboro.
Massachusetts: WMI289, Pittsfield.
Michigan: WMH593, Kalamazoo.
Missouri: WMI293, St. Joseph.
North Carolina: WMI297, Wilmington.
Ohio: WLW747, Steubenville.
Pennsylvania: WMH372, Johnstown.
Puerto Rico: WMH325, Aguadilla.

CHARLES D. BENSON
4228 Barton
Lansing, MI 48917
MMDS Systems:
Michigan: WMI279, Escanaba.

DONALD E. BENSON
4755 Clydesdale Rd.
Lansing, MI 48906
MMDS Systems:
Michigan: WMI283, Cheboygan; WLW809, Manistique.

MARILYN A. BENSON
4228 Barton
Lansing, MI 48917
MMDS Systems:
Michigan: WLW797, Gaylord.

MARYLAN J. BENSON
4755 Clydesdale
Lansing, MI 48906
MMDS Systems:
Michigan: WMI317, Petoskey.

PAUL M. BENSON
5178 Griffin Lane
Vacaville, CA 95688
Phone: 209-384-7448
MDS Systems:
Washington: WMH665, Ephrata; WMH669, Ephrata.
MMDS Systems:
Washington: WMI411, Ephrata.

WILLIAM H. BENSON
Suite 600
5520 LBJ Freeway
Dallas, TX 75240-6294
MMDS Systems:
Kansas: WMY432, Griswold.

BF INVESTMENTS INC.
7521 E. Edgemont
Scottsdale, AZ 85257
Phone: 602-994-3493
MMDS Systems:
Pennsylvania: WMI365, York.

BGR WIRELESS
3526 N. California
Peoria, IL 61603
Phone: 309-686-2000
MDS Systems:
Texas: WMI973, Tyler.

WAYLAND BLAKE
716 Sunset Court
Forest City, IA 50436
MMDS Systems:
Indiana: WNTJ711, Evansville.

BLOCK & ASSOC.
3605 Frost Lane
Reno, NV 89511
Phone: 702-852-6604
MMDS Systems:
Texas: WLK305, Houston.

KELLI BOHRISCH
5178 Griffin Lane
Vacaville, CA 95688
Phone: 702-831-8335
MMDS Systems:
Colorado: WMI888, Craig.

BOLIN ENTERPRISES INC.
Box 133
Old Rte. 40 E
Casey, IL 62420
Phone: 217-932-4533
Fax: 217-932-5293
Officers:
Everett Edward Bolin Jr., Chief Exec. & Operating Officer, 2
Judy Bolin, Chief Financial Officer
Ownership: Everett E. Bolin Jr.
MDS Systems:
Illinois: WLW800, Casey; WLW804, Casey.
MMDS Systems:
Illinois: WLW821, Casey; WMI896, Casey; WNTB224, Casey; WNTB476, Jewett; WNTB577, Jewett.

JOHN H. BOND JR.
7822 Eastdale Rd.
Baltimore, MD 21224
MMDS Systems:
North Carolina: WFY686, Nags Head.

GEORGE W. BOTT
320 Hamilton St.
Albion, NY 14411-9383
Phones: 518-374-0651; 716-589-9295
Fax: 716-589-9094
Represented (legal): Fleischman & Walsh LLP.
MMDS Systems:
Tennessee: WNTF799, Knoxville.
Other Holdings:
Krisar Inc., see listing.

BPJ-TV
2603 E. Doublegate Dr.
Albany, GA 31707
Phone: 912-436-7019
MDS Systems:
Texas: WMI930, Tyler.

LAWRENCE N. BRANDT
Suite 220
3201 New Mexico Ave. NW
Washington, DC 20016
MMDS Systems:
Arkansas: WMH420, Jonesboro.
Colorado: WLW883, Pueblo.
Minnesota: WMH605, Duluth.
New York: WMH417, Elmira.
North Carolina: WLW777, Greenville.
North Dakota: WMI313, Minot.
South Carolina: WMI309, Florence.

WILLIAM A. BRANDT JR.
Suite 900
200 S. Biscayne Blvd.
Miami, FL 33134-2312
Phone: 305-374-2717
MMDS Systems:
California: WMI355, San Diego.

BRENHAM BROADCAST COMMUNICATIONS INC.
128 Redbird Trail
Georgetown, TX 78628
Phone: 512-863-3146
MDS Systems:
Texas: WLW857, Brenham.

KELLY L. BRIGGS
3100 Gold Nugget Rd.
Placerville, CA 95667
MMDS Systems:
Hawaii: WMH637, Maui.

BROADCAST DATA CORP.
1761 Fairfield Beach Rd.
Fairfield, CT 06430
Phone: 203-256-1302
Fax: 203-256-1307
Ownership: James E. Lindstrom, Pres.
Represented (legal): W. Randolph Young.
MDS Systems:
Arizona: WHB522, Phoenix.
California: WPX66, Monterey; WHT559, San Diego.
District of Columbia: WHT747, Washington.
Illinois: WHT562, Chicago.
Indiana: WLK246, Indianapolis.
Michigan: WHT594, Detroit.
Ohio: WDU606, Columbus.
Oklahoma: WFY642, Oklahoma City.
Pennsylvania: WLK231, Philadelphia.
Wisconsin: WHT566, Milwaukee.
MMDS Systems:
Florida: WHK925, Lakeland.
Indiana: WLW973, Bloomington.
Iowa: WMI281, Dubuque.
Maine: WMH221, Augusta.
Michigan: WLC270, Marquette; WMI854, Traverse City.
Minnesota: WNEY683, Minneapolis.
Mississippi: WLR618, Pascagoula.
Montana: WLW793, Butte.
Nevada: WMH709, Carson City.
New Mexico: WLW778, Farmington; WMH421, Roswell.
New York: WMI301, Glens Falls.
North Carolina: WMH693, Morganton; WMI295, Wilmington.
North Dakota: WLC269, Minot.
Pennsylvania: WLW811, Lancaster; WMI291, Sharon.
Texas: WLW760, Denison; WMX239, Lubbock.
Other Holdings:
OFS.
Phoenix MDS Co., see listing.

BURKE-DIVIDE ELECTRIC COOPERATIVE INC.
Box 6
Columbus, ND 58727
Phone: 701-939-6671
MMDS Systems:
North Dakota: WLW968, Williston.

GLENN BURKE
725 Yucca Dr.
El Centro, CA 92243
Phone: 619-353-1537
MMDS Systems:
Louisiana: WNTK965, Houma.

WALTER L. BUSH JR.
5200 Malibu Dr.
Edina, MN 55436
Phone: 612-935-7437
MMDS Systems:
Iowa: WMH676, Britt.
Minnesota: WMH329, Appleton; WMH332, Austin; WMH424, Fairmont; WMH480, Granite Falls; WMH677, Marshall; WHT607, Wadena; WMH244, Waterville; WMH680, Worthington.
Other Holdings:
LPTV, see listing.

CABLE MEDIA SYSTEMS INC.
405 N. Ave. E
Olney, TX 76374-1421
Phone: 817-564-5688
MDS Systems:
Texas: WMI972, Wellington; WMI976, Wellington.

CABLE USA INC.
Box 1448
Kearney, NE 68848-1448
Phones: 308-234-6428; 308-995-6156
Fax: 308-234-6452
Officers:
Russell G. Hilliard, Pres., Chief Exec. & Financial Officer, 3
Stuart Gilbertson, Corp. Engineer
Ownership: Russell G. Hilliard.
Represented (legal): Cole, Raywid & Braverman LLP.
MDS Systems:
Nebraska: WFY431, Kearney.
Other Holdings:
Cable, see listing.

CAGUAS/HUMACAO CABLE SYSTEMS
MDS Systems:
Puerto Rico: WFY859, Caguas.

CAI WIRELESS SYSTEMS INC.
Suite 102
12 Corporate Woods Blvd.
Albany, NY 12211
Phone: 518-462-2632
Fax: 518-462-3045
Officers:
Jared Abbruzzese, Chmn. & Chief Exec. Officer
John Prico, Pres.
George Williams, Chief Financial Officer
James Ashman, Sr. V.P., Corp. Finance & Acquisitions
Timothy Santora, Sr. V.P., Spectrum Acquisition
John Brinker, V.P., Operations

Engineering Office:
2101 Wilson Blvd.
Suite 100
Arlington, VA 22201
Phone: 703-812-8800
Fax: 703-812-8808
Ownership: MCI WorldCom, 62%.
MDS Systems:
District of Columbia: WOI93, Washington.
Maryland: WHT571, Baltimore.
Massachusetts: WSL33, Boston.
New Jersey: WCU573, New Brunswick.
New York: WHI966, Albany; WQQ79, New York; WHC998, Syracuse.
North Carolina: WFY738, Greensboro; WMH664, Winston-Salem; WMH668, Winston-Salem.
Pennsylvania: WPE97, Philadelphia; WPF48, Pittsburgh.
Rhode Island: KNV65, Providence.
MMDS Systems:
Connecticut: WHT672, Farmington; WNTG352, Farmington.
Maryland: WNEK883, Baltimore; WHJ920, Bethesda.
Massachusetts: WHJ868, Boston; WMI863, Boston; WNEK864, Boston; WNTB229, Boston; WLW859, Rehoboth; WLK226, Springfield; WMH752, Worcester; WMI893, Worcester.
New York: WHT750, Albany; WHT751, Albany; WNEZ721, Albany; WNTA389, Albany; WNTA920, Albany; WNTD891, Fairport; WNTE275, Fairport; WNTG719, Fairport; WHT665, Grand Island; WNEK802, Grand Island; WHJ897, New York; WNTQ214, New York.
Pennsylvania: WHT643, Philadelphia; WNET336, Philadelphia; WNEY590, Philadelphia; WHT645, Pittsburgh; WHT646, Pittsburgh; WNTI200, Pittsburgh.
Rhode Island: WNTI314, Tiverton.
Virginia: WNTB576, Driver.
Other Holdings:
90% of CS Wireless Systems Inc., see listing.
Wireless Cable, LPTV, see listings.

JOSEPH L. CALIBANI
1521 Mackenzie St.
San Angelo, TX 76901
Phone: 915-658-5111
MMDS Systems:
Texas: WLW827, San Angelo.

JEWEL B. CALLAHAM REVOCABLE TRUST
Box 548
Broken Bow, OK 74728
Phone: 405-584-3340
Ownership: Esta Callaham, John B. Callaham & Angela G. Wisenhunt, Trustees.
MMDS Systems:
Oklahoma: WMH376, Broken Bow/Idabel.
Other Holdings:
Cable, LPTV, see listings.
Pine Telephone Co. Inc.

C & G COMMUNICATIONS
1205 2nd St.
Moundsville, WV 26041
Phone: 304-845-7695
MDS Systems:
Kansas: WMI903, Garden City; WMI943, Garden City.

CARDIFF COMMUNICATIONS PARTNERS II
1830 E. Willow Glen Circle
Sandy, UT 84093
Phone: 801-561-9995
Officer:
Robert A. Janssen, Pres.

Branch Office:
2010 Jimmy Durante Blvd.
Suite 224
Del Mar, CA 92014
Phone: 800-444-3410
MMDS Systems:
Arizona: WLW826, Yuma; WLW829, Yuma; WNTI531, Yuma.
California: WMH781, Redding; WMH785, Redding; WMH789, Redding.

CARIBBEAN MMDS PARTNERSHIP
Box 940008
Plano, TX 75094
MMDS Systems:
Puerto Rico: WNTK992, San German.

CAROLINA MEDIA GROUP INC.
Suite 201
3012 Highwoods Blvd.
Raleigh, NC 27604
Phone: 919-876-0674
Ownership: Howard Hollar.
MDS Systems:
North Carolina: WMX524, Raleigh.

MICHAEL J. CARTER
1010 Samy Dr.
Tampa, FL 33613
Phone: 813-962-1473
MMDS Systems:
Georgia: WNTJ384, Jeffersonville; WNTJ428, Jeffersonville.
Other Holdings.
LPTV, see listing.

CASS COUNTY ELECTRIC CORP. INC.
Box 676
Kindred, ND 58051-0008
Officers:
Russell Berg, Chairman & Pres.
Michael D. Gustafson, Chief Exec. Officer
Robert Nagle, Chief Operating Officer
Duane Sullivan, Secy.-Treas.
Chad D. Sapa, Chief Financial Officer
MMDS Systems:
North Dakota: WMY312, Amenia; WMY316, Amenia; WMY320, Amenia.

CDV INC.
2414 S. Halliburton
Kirksville, MO 63501
Phone: 816-665-0300
Fax: 816-665-9121
Officers:
William C. Beykirch, Pres.
Kyle Antoine, V.P.
Represented (legal): Wilkinson, Barker, Knauer & Quinn.
MMDS Systems:
Iowa: WLW851, Batavia.
Missouri: WMH621, Kirksville; WMI895, Kirksville; WNTJ368, Kirksville.

CENTRAL DAKOTA TV INC.
Box 299
630 N. 5th St.
Carrington, ND 58421
Phone: 701-674-8122
Officer:
Gerald Eissinger, Pres.
Doug Wede, Secy.-Treas.
Keith Larson, Chief Financial Officer
Ownership: Dakota Central Telecommunications Cooperative; Tri County Electric Cooperative.
Represented (legal): Fabian Noack.
MMDS Systems:
North Dakota: WLW751, Carrington; WLW752, Carrington.
Other Holdings:
Cable, see listing.

CENTRAL IOWA TV INC.
Box 548
Bath, SD 57427
Phone: 605-229-2412
MMDS Systems:
Iowa: WLW727, Radcliffe; WNTE611, Radcliffe.

CENTRAL TEXAS TELEPHONE CO-OP INC.
Box 627
Goldthwaite, TX 76844
Phone: 915-648-2237
Officers:
Carl Grubb, Pres.
James McCoy, V.P.
L. T. Rettmann, Secy.-Treas.
Ownership: Member owned.
Represented (legal): Clyde Corbrum.
MDS Systems:
Texas: WMI987, Brady; WMI991, Goldthwaite; WMI995, Goldthwaite; WMI944, San Saba.

CENTURY MICROWAVE CORP.
51 Locust Ave.
New Canaan, CT 06840
MMDS Systems:
Indiana: WMH689, Muncie.

CFW COMMUNICATIONS
Box 1990
Waynesboro, VA 22980
Phone: 540-946-3500
Fax: 540-946-3599
Officers:
Robert S. Yeago Jr., Chmn.
James S. Quarforth, Pres. & Chief Exec. Officer
Carl A. Rosberg, Sr. V.P.
Christina S. Smith, Secy.-Treas.

Michael B. Moneymaker, Chief Financial Officer
Ownership: Publicly owned.
MDS Systems:
Virginia: WMI916, Bridgewater; WPX69, Charlottesville.
MMDS Systems:
Virginia: WMX327, Bridgewater; WMX331, Bridgewater; WLW840, Charlottesville; WMH388, Charlottesville; WNTH948, Charlottesville; WHT736, Richmond; WMX366, West Augusta; WNTI942, Wytheville.
Other Holdings:
Cellular telephone, Internet access, ITFS & paging service.
Cable, see listing.

CHAMPION INDUSTRIES INC.

300 W. Mission Dr.
Chandler, AZ 85224
Phone: 602-497-5774
Fax: 602-345-4450
Officers:
Noel C. Rudd, Pres.
Debra J. Rudd, Chief Financial Officer
Ownership: Noel C. Rudd & Debra J. Rudd, 100% jointly.
Represented (legal): Gregory E. Hinkel.
MDS Systems:
Missouri: WMH812, Fordland.
MMDS Systems:
Massachusetts: WLK212, New Bedford.
Ohio: WHT670, Columbus.
Pennsylvania: WMH737, Lancaster.

CHANEY COMMUNICATIONS INC.

MMDS Systems:
Texas: WMH697, Paris.

CHANNEL VIEW INC.

c/o Richard E. Vail
8058 Barnwood Way
Sandy, UT 84094
Phone: 801-355-7733
Fax: 801-355-7748
Officer:
Richard E. Vail, Pres.
Ownership: Via/Net Companies Inc., see listing, 50%; Richard E. Vail Family Trust, 50%. VNCI ownership: Carl B. Hilliard, see listing, 50%; Sharon E. Hilliard, 50%.
Represented (legal): Gurman, Blask & Freedman Chartered.
MDS Systems:
Utah: WGW291, Park City.

DEBRA CHAVEZ

Box 852
Morrison, CO 80465
Fax: 303-988-3019
MMDS Systems:
Colorado: WMH425, Greeley.

CHESTERFIELD COMMUNICATIONS

2401 Wisteria Lane
Muncie, IN 47302
Phone: 317-289-0683
MMDS Systems:
Wyoming: WLR472, Jackson Hole.

CMG ENTERPRISES III

1715 Hollis Rd.
Westlake, LA 70669
Phone: 318-477-1218
Ownership: Nerrel W. Guillory, Principal.
MDS Systems:
Texas: WMI994, Jasper.

CNI WIRELESS INC.

Box 373
310 W. Columbia St.
Somerset, KY 42501
Phone: 606-679-8917
Officers:
Roy Taylor, Pres. & Chief Exec. Officer
Mitchell Taylor, V.P., Operations
Louise Combs, Secy.-Treas.
Cy Waddle, Chief Financial Officer
Represented (legal): Wilkinson, Barker, Knauer & Quinn.
MDS Systems:
Kentucky: WMX332, Parkers Lake.

HAROLD COATES

MMDS Systems:
Oklahoma: WNTH362, Glencoe.

COLEMAN COUNTY TELEPHONE COOPERATIVE INC.

Box 608
215 N. Second St.
Santa Anna, CA 76878
Phone: 915-348-3124
MMDS Systems:
Texas: WMY236, Santa Anna; WMY240, Santa Anna.

COLOWAVE INC.

Box F
Shawnee, CO 80475
MMDS Systems:
Colorado: WMH700, Leadville.

COLUMBIA WIRELESS CORP.

Suite 501
1100 17th St. NW
Washington, DC 20036-4646
Phone: 202-537-1264
Fax: 202-223-4450
Officers:
W. Randolph Young, Pres. & Secy.
Richard G. Gould, V.P. & Treas.
Ownership: W. Randolph Young, Richard G. Gould & Christopher Lanning, 100% jointly. See also G & Y Communications, Springfield One Partnership & Young Communications.
Represented (legal): W. Randolph Young.
MMDS Systems:
Florida: WHK973, Fort Myers.

COMMUNICATION INNOVATIONS CORP.

Suite 401
145 Huguenot St.
New Rochelle, NY 10801
Phone: 914-576-6622
Fax: 914-576-6689
Officers:
George Ducra, Pres.
Vincent Petti, Exec. V.P.
Ownership: George Ducra & Vincent Petti, Principals.
MDS Systems:
Florida: WDU502, Pensacola; WOF43, Tampa-St. Petersburg; WGW504, West Palm Beach; WPY38, West Palm Beach.
MMDS Systems:
Utah: WMH289, Cedar City.

COMMUNICATION SECURITY ENTERPRISES

Box 2193
Bay City, TX 77414
MDS Systems:
Texas: WHT625, Bay City.

COMMUNICATIONS ENTERPRISES INC.

Box 67
Woonsocket, SD 57385
Phone: 605-796-4411
MMDS Systems:
South Dakota: WGW419, Mitchell; WHD364, Mitchell.

COMMUNICATIONS TOWERS INC. OF TEXAS

MDS Systems:
Louisiana: WFY896, Rayville.

CONSOLIDATED TELEPHONE COOPERATIVE

Box 1408
507 S. Main Ave.
Dickinson, ND 58601-1408
Phone: 701-225-6061
Fax: 701-225-0001
MMDS Systems:
North Dakota: WLW765, Killdeer; WLW766, Killdeer; WLW764, Lefor; WLW771, Lefor; WNTB636, Lefor; WNTB961, Lefor; WLW770, Scranton.
Other Holdings:
Wireless Cable, see listing.

CONTINENTAL WIRELESS CABLE TELEVISION INC.

Suite 712
7777 Alvarado Rd.
La Mesa, CA 91941
Phone: 619-668-6680
MMDS Systems:
Iowa: WLW956, Sioux City.
Tennessee: WNTE429, Nashville; WNTE741, Nashville; WNTM642, Nashville.

PLACIDO G. CORDOVA

Box 1161
Caguas, PR 00626
MMDS Systems:
Puerto Rico: WMH292, Arecibo.

EDNA CORNAGGIA

Space 345
4095 Fruit St.
LaVerne, CA 91750
Phone: 909-621-1004
Fax: 909-624-2257
MMDS Systems:
Texas: WLW875, Midland.

FRANKIE CORNELISON

1948 W. Live Oak
Durant, OK 74701
Phone: 405-924-2420
MMDS Systems:
Oklahoma: WMH336, Ada; WNTH573, Ada.

COSSA ENTERPRISE

7212 Palm Tree Circle
Bakersfield, CA 93308
Ownership: Carl Bowser.
MMDS Systems:
Indiana: WMH572, Lafayette; WNTJ438, Lafayette.

COTOPAXI COMMUNICATIONS

Phone: 202-467-8570
Officer:
Bradley T. Johnson, Pres.
Represented (legal): Evans & Sill PC.
MMDS Systems:
Virginia: WNTB262, Driver.

COX MUSIC & SOUND

Box 8083
Albuquerque, NM 87198-8083
Phone: 505-268-7700
MDS Systems:
New Mexico: WLW898, Albuquerque.

WILLIAM E. CRAFT

MMDS Systems:
Wyoming: WMY403, Pinedale.

CROSS COUNTRY NETWORK INC.

1058 W. Washington Blvd.
Chicago, IL 60607
MDS Systems:
California: WHT559, San Diego.
Illinois: WHT562, Chicago.

THOMAS CROSSFIELD

Phone: 813-822-6401
MMDS Systems:
Indiana: WNTJ744, Evansville.

CROSSFIELD WILSON BLAKE PARTNERSHIP

Phone: 813-392-1681
MMDS Systems:
Florida: WNTJ377, Panama City.

CS WIRELESS SYSTEMS INC.

1101 Summit Ave.
Plano, TX 75074
Phone: 972-398-5300
Fax: 972-398-1112
Officers:
Jared Abbruzzese, Chief Exec. Officer (Acting)
Roddy Edge, Chief Operating Officer (Acting)
Steve Moncreiff, V.P., Liscensing
Albert G. McGrath, V.P. & Gen. Counsel
Nick Nicholls, V.P., Digital Operations
John Lund, Chief Financial Officer

Branch Office:
Legal Dept.
2101 Wilson Blvd.
Arlington, VA 22201
Ownership: CAI Wireless Systems Inc., 94%.
MDS Systems:
California: WMH877, Bakersfield; WMI942, Bakersfield; WPW84, Stockton.
Kansas: WMH876, Effingham.
Minnesota: WPE99, Minneapolis.
Missouri: KOB43, Kansas City; WMX936, Maysville.
North Carolina: WGW715, Charlotte.
Ohio: WQQ66, Cleveland; WMX909, Dayton.
Texas: WJM66, Austin; WDU282, Corpus Christi; WHT564, Dallas; WQQ65, Dallas; WSL59, El Paso; WFY900, Fort Worth; WJM75, Fort Worth; WDU302, Killeen; WFY852, San Antonio; WJM80, San Antonio; WGW374, Victoria.
MMDS Systems:
California: WHT584, Bakersfield; WHT585, Bakersfield.
Minnesota: WNTJ817, Byron; WHT677, Minneapolis; WHT678, Minneapolis; WNEZ819, Minneapolis; WNTA934, Minneapolis.
Missouri: WHT790, Kansas City; WLK282, Kansas City; WMX926, Maysville; WMX927, Maysville; WMX928, Maysville.
North Carolina: WMX942, Rockingham; WMX943, Rockingham.
Ohio: WLK310, Cleveland; WHT713, Dayton; WNEX725, Dayton; WNTB420, Dayton; WNTB689, Dayton; WHJ951, Parma.
Texas: WHJ873, Dallas; WNTD967, Dallas; WHT789, Dallas/Fort Worth; WNTA693, Leon Springs; WNEY637, San Antonio.
Other Holdings:
Wireless Cable, see listing.

ARTHUR L. DALTON

Box 516
Pago Pago, AS 96799
MMDS Systems:
American Samoa: WNTK888, Pago Pago.
Arkansas: WMX222, Gurdon; WMX226, Gurdon; WMX227, Gurdon.

DANEL CO.
265 W. Broadway
Hoisington, KS 67544
MMDS Systems:
Kansas: WMH712, Hoisington.

STEVEN A. DAVIE
Suite F
3708 S. Main St.
Blacksburg, VA 24090
Phone: 540-552-6220
MMDS Systems:
Virginia: WGW371, Roanoke.

DCT LOS ANGELES LLC
229 Quaker Rd.
Chappaqua, NY 10514
Phone: 914-238-4375
Fax: 914-238-1213
Ownership: Jim Weisenberg, 29%.
MDS Systems:
California: WGX394, Anaheim; WHT573, San Bernardino.

PATRICIA M. DELOVELY
9503 Lawnsberry Terrace
Silver Spring, MD 20901
MMDS Systems:
Nevada: WMY399, Hawthorne.

DELTA BAND SERVICES LTD.
2139 Regents Blvd.
West Palm Beach, FL 33409
MMDS Systems:
Florida: WHK958, Lakeland-Winter Haven.

DENSEN ENTERPRISES INC.
710 Brundage Lane
Bakersfield, CA 93304
MDS Systems:
California: WGW348, Cummings Valley.

DES MOINES ONE PARTNERSHIP
2700 Chain Bridge Rd. NW
Washington, DC 20016
Phone: 202-659-4400
Fax: 202-237-7742
MMDS Systems:
Iowa: WMX355, Grimes; WMX356, Grimes; WMX357, Grimes.

JOHANNA DESTEFANO
3511 Rue de Fleur
Columbus, OH 43221
Phone: 614-457-7045
MMDS Systems:
Maryland: WHT630, Baltimore.
Ohio: WHT669, Columbus.

DIGITAL WIRELESS SYSTEMS INC.
Box 15065
Reading, PA 19612-5065
Phone: 610-921-9500
Fax: 610-921-0290
Officers:
David D. Schlueter, Chmn. & Chief Exec. Officer
Joseph R. Paradis, Pres. & Chief Operating Officer
MMDS Systems:
Louisiana: WHT708, Baton Rouge; WNTG414, Shreveport.
Pennsylvania: WMI314, Reading; WMI393, Reading.
Tennessee: WNTF893, Clarksville; WNTJ418, Clarksville.

DISNEY ENTERPRISES INC.
500 S. Buena Vista St.
Burbank, CA 91521
Phone: 818-560-1000
Fax: 818-566-7308
Officers:
Michael D. Eisner, Chmn. & Chief Exec. Officer
Roy E. Disney, Vice Chmn.
Sanford M. Litvack, Sr. Exec. V.P. & Chief of Corporate Operations
Lawrence P. Murphy, Exec. V.P., Strategic Planning & Development
Richard D. Namula, Sr. V.P. & Chief Financial Officer
Marsha L. Reed, V.P. & Corporate Secy.
Jack J. Garand, V.P., Planning & Control
Ownership: The Walt Disney Co.
MMDS Systems:
Tennessee: WHT720, Knoxville.
Other Holdings:
TV, see listing.

DISTINCTIVE SOUND
c/o Kevin J. Ketelsen
1205 31st St.
West Des Moines, IA 50266
Phone: 515-225-7835
Ownership: Kevin Ketelsen, Principal.
MDS Systems:
Iowa: WMH232, Des Moines.

JOHN DUDECK
11672 Harborside Circle N
Largo, FL 33773
MMDS Systems:
Alabama: WNTJ802, Montgomery.
Arkansas: WNTH815, Jonesboro.
Idaho: WNTI229, Pocatello.
Illinois: WNTI287, Rockford; WNTI343, Rockford.
Louisiana: WNTJ409, Baton Rouge.
Massachusetts: WNTI337, Deerfield.
Mississippi: WNTH472, Tupelo.
Nebraska: WNTH475, Lincoln.
New Hampshire: WNTH471, Portsmouth.
New Mexico: WNTI529, Gallup; WNTI521, Santa Fe.
Texas: WNTJ391, Wichita Falls.
Vermont: WNTH842, Burlington.
Virginia: WNTH817, Lynchburg.
Other Holdings:
Rocz Dudeck Leas Partnership, see listing.
LPTV, see listing.

LOUIS R. DU TREIL
201 Fletcher Ave.
Sarasota, FL 34237-6019
Phone: 941-329-6000
Fax: 941-329-6030
E-mail: bobsr@dlr.com
Ownership: Louis R. DuTreil
Represented (legal): William M. Barnard.
MMDS Systems:
Missouri: WHT651, St. Louis.

DYNAMIC SOUND
4910 Aircenter Circle
No. 108
Reno, NV 89502
Ownership: Donald E. Hartley & L. Bernadine Hartley.
MDS Systems:
Nevada: WFY553, Reno.

DYNASTY PARTNERS II
Phone: 702-597-9875
MMDS Systems:
North Carolina: WNTM681, Gastonia.
Tennessee: WNTM643, Mount Pleasant; WNTM644, Mount Pleasant.

EAGLE TELEVISION INC.
Box 35
Eads, CO 81036
Phone: 719-438-2221
Officers:
Vernon Koch, Pres. & Chief Financial Officer
Mike Beeson, Chief Exec. & Operating Officer, 2
MDS Systems:
Colorado: WMX339, Prowers City.
MMDS Systems:
Colorado: WLW726, Prowers City; WLW730, Prowers City; WLW734, Prowers City.

EAGLEVIEW TECHNOLOGIES INC.
Suite 6-271
5030 Champion Blvd.
Boca Raton, FL 33496
Phone: 561-274-4233
MDS Systems:
Florida: WMH805, Jacksonville; KFJ28, Pompano Beach.
Oklahoma: WPG45, Tulsa.
Tennessee: WPE83, Chattanooga.

EASTERN MICROWAVE INC.
Box 4872
Syracuse, NY 13221
Phone: 315-433-0022
Fax: 315-433-2342
Officer:
Bob Miron, Chief Exec. Officer
Ownership: Newhouse Broadcasting Corp. Newhouse Broadcasting Corp. has newspaper, publishing & cable holdings, see Advance/Newhouse Partnership.
Represented (legal): Dow, Lohnes & Albertson PLLC.
MDS Systems:
New York: KFK28, Albany.

ECHONET CORP.
Box 255
Evergreen, CO 80439
Officers:
Charles Ergen, Pres.
David M. Drucker, V.P.
Candy M. Ergen, Secy.-Treas.
Ownership: Candy M. Ergen, 40%; Charles Ergen, 40%; David M. Drucker, 20%. Drucker is Pres. of Green TV Corp., see listing in Ownership of Commercial TV Stations.
MMDS Systems:
Alaska: WHD477, Anchorage.
Colorado: WMH720, Grand Junction.
Montana: WMH729, Missoula.
Other Holdings:
TV, LPTV, see listings.

STEPHANIE ENGSTROM
Apt. 104
420 S. Catalina Ave.
Redondo Beach, CA 90277
Phone: 310-540-9867
MMDS Systems:
Florida: WMH721, Pensacola.
Texas: WMH516, Texarkana.
Washington: WMH725, Olympia; WHT784, Spokane.

EVANS MICROWAVE INC.
Box 181
Savoy, IL 61874
MDS Systems:
Illinois: WPX72, Peoria.

WILLIAM A. EVERSON
6284 Carnot Rd.
Rte. 5
Sturgeon Bay, WI 54235
MDS Systems:
Wisconsin: WHA706, Sturgeon Bay.

EVERTEK INC.
Box 270
216 N. Main St.
Everly, IA 51338
Phone: 712-834-2255
Ownership: Doug Gathman, Jack Harnes, Wayne Johnson, Willie Hartman & Ron Schoenewe, 100% jointly.
MMDS Systems:
Iowa: WLK383, Palmer; WLK386, Palmer; WNEZ929, Palmer; WNTB279, Palmer; WNTB791, Palmer; WLK267, Spencer; WLK403, Spencer; WNEZ928, Spencer; WNTB278, Spencer; WNTB792, Spencer.
Other Holdings:
Cable, see listing.

F CORP.
George Mason U. TV
Kelley Dr.
Fairfax, VA 22030
Phone: 703-993-3100
Fax: 703-273-2417
Officers:
George W. Johnson, Chmn.
Alan Merten, Pres.
Michael R. Kelley, Chief Exec. Officer
Otis D. Coston Jr., Secy.-Treas.
Roland Saldana, Chief Financial Officer
Ownership: George Mason U. Instructional Foundation Inc.
Represented (legal): Goldberg, Godles, Weiner & Wright.
MMDS Systems:
District of Columbia: WHT659, Washington.
Other Holdings:
Common Carrier: C-Band Satellite Uplink.

FAMILY ENTERTAINMENT NETWORK INC.
30 N. Harmon
Mitchell, SD 57301
MMDS Systems:
North Dakota: WMY448, Bismarck.

FAYETTEVILLE WIRELESS TV INC.
2014 Rock Creek Dr.
Arlington, TX 76010
Phone: 817-469-8687
MMDS Systems:
Arkansas: WMI881, Fayetteville.

JAMES W. FEASEL
13549 Morse Rd.
Pataskala, OH 43062
MMDS Systems:
Ohio: WMH385, Nelsonville.

FIGGIE INTERNATIONAL INC.
c/o Alfred E. Ventola
4420 Sherwin Rd.
Willoughby, OH 44094
MMDS Systems:
Michigan: WLK256, Battle Creek; WLK205, Lansing.

FMA LICENSEE SUBSIDIARY INC.
3526 E. Church St.
Fresno, CA 93725
Phone: 209-442-1977
Fax: 209-442-1745
MMDS Systems:
California: WNTM603, Visalia; WNTM668, Visalia.

FORTUNA SYSTEMS CORP.
Box 1669
819 Belleview Ave.
Crested Butte, CO 81224
Phone: 970-349-5849
Officers:
Philip C. Merrill, Pres. & Chief Exec. Officer
Richard J. Amons Jr., V.P.
Ownership: Philip C. Merrill, see Multi-Point TV Distributors Inc.
MMDS Systems:

Arizona: WNTH876, Flagstaff.
Florida: WMH513, Bradenton.
Nebraska: WNTG845, Grand Island; WNTF780, Lincoln.
North Dakota: WLW888, Grand Forks.
Pennsylvania: WLK357, Allentown.

FOUR PRO PLUS PARTNERS
3175 Callecita St.
Sacramento, CA 95815
Phone: 916-641-0556
MMDS Systems:
Nevada: WLW698, Fallon.

FRESNO MMDS ASSOCIATES
17215 Colonial Park Dr.
Monument, CO 80132
MMDS Systems:
California: WLW816, Fresno; WNTK866, Merced; WNTK983, Merced.

FRIENDLY COMMUNITY TELEVISION SERVICES
Box 632
Palmer Rd.
Cuero, TX 77954
Phone: 512-275-8332
Officers:
Earl Stewart, Chmn. & Chief Exec. Officer
Kathleen Jiles, Secy.-Treas.
Effie Stewart, Chief Financial Officer
Ownership: Earl Stewart.
MMDS Systems:
Texas: WLW927, Victoria.

G & Y COMMUNICATIONS
Suite 501
1100 17th St.
Washington, DC 20036-4646
Phone: 202-223-4449
Fax: 202-223-4450
Ownership: R. G. Gould & W. Randolph Young. See also Columbia Wireless Corp., Springfield One Partnership & Young Communications.
Represented (legal): W. Randolph Young.
MMDS Systems:
Kentucky: WNTJ752, Lexington; WNTH387, Paducah.

FREDERICK M. GANZ
15 Gallahad Lane
Nesconset, NY 11767
MMDS Systems:
Texas: WNTH938, Freeport.

JAMES D. & LAWRENCE D. GARVEY
3130 N. I-10 Service Rd. E
Metairie, LA 70002
Phone: 504-830-5400
MDS Systems:
Louisiana: WLK290, Harahan.

GATE CITY GENERAL PARTNERSHIP
7211 Dogue Forest Court
Alexandria, VA 22315
Phone: 703-922-8825
MMDS Systems:
New York: WLR464, Jamestown.

GATEWAY PARTNERS
3543 Renco St.
Castro Valley, CA 94546
MMDS Systems:
Georgia: WNTM820, Sandersville.

GEORGETOWN LOW POWER COMMUNICATIONS INC.
3412 Deer Trail
Georgetown, TX 78628

THOMAS M. GLAB
2129 San Marcos Place
Claremont, CA 91711
Phone: 714-621-1004
MMDS Systems:
Colorado: WHT756, Colorado Springs.
Connecticut: WHT671, Hartford.
Florida: WMH604, Key West.

GLENWOOD COMMUNICATIONS CORP.
Box WKPT
Kingsport, TN 37662
Phone: 423-246-9578
Fax: 423-246-6261
Officers:
William M. Boyd, Chmn. & Chief Exec. Officer
George E. DeVault Jr., Pres. & Chief Operating Officer
Joseph D. Fontana, Sr. V.P.
Janet L. Bragg, Secy.
Bette Lawson, Treas. & Chief Financial Officer
Ownership: William M. Boyd, Principal. Boyd is also principal of Cabarrus Television Corp. which holds 45% interest in Kannapolis Television Co. (see listing) & Tazewell Television Corp., applicant for Ch. 48 in Tazewell, TN.
Represented (legal): Cordon & Kelly; Wiley, Rein & Fielding.
MMDS Systems:
Virgin Islands: WMH685, St. Croix.
Other Holdings:
TV, LPTV, see listings.

GLOBAL INFORMATION TECHNOLOGIES INC.
Suite 2530, One Congress Plaza
111 Congress Ave.
Austin, TX 78701
Phone: 512-482-8111
Represented (legal): Cole, Raywid & Braverman LLP.
TV Stations (1):
Texas: KBEJ, Fredericksburg (CP).
MMDS Systems:
Texas: WMY464, Dallas.

GOLDEN BEAR COMMUNICATIONS INC.
6781 Coffee Rd.
Bakersfield, CA 93308
Phone: 805-325-8655
MMDS Systems:
California: WGW513, Modesto; WNTJ742, Modesto; WNTJ756, Modesto; WHT786, Stockton.

GARY GOLDEN
Box 161777
Austin, TX 78716-1777
MMDS Systems:
Texas: WMH477, Longview; WMI306, Longview.

ROBERT GORDON
1120 Royal Palm Beach Blvd.
Royal Palm Beach, FL 33411
Phone: 561-439-0090
MDS Systems:
Florida: WFY524, Okeechobee; WFY650, Stuart.

GOVERNMENT ENTERPRISES INC.
Suite 635
505 S. Beverly Dr.
Beverly Hills, CA 90212
Phone: 213-301-4719
MMDS Systems:
California: WMI385, Bishop; WMI389, Bishop; WNTJ493, Bishop.

GRAND MMDS ALLIANCE NEW YORK F/P PARTNERSHIP
40 Woodland St.
Hartford, CT 06105
MMDS Systems:
New York: WMY467, New York.

GRAND TELEPHONE CO. INC.
Box 308
Jay, OK 74346
MMDS Systems:
Oklahoma: WLW846, Jay, OK-Decatur, AR.

GREATER MEDIA INC.
Box 1059
2 Kennedy Blvd.
East Brunswick, NJ 08816
Phone: 732-247-6161
Fax: 732-247-0215
Officers:
Frank Kabela, Pres.
Thomas J. Milewski, Exec. V.P. & Chief Operating Officer
John Zielinski, V.P. & Chief Financial Officer
Milford K. Smith, V.P., Radio Engineering
Walter Veth, Group V.P., Cable Div.
Richard Kirsche, V.P., Engineering
Barbara Burns, V.P. & Gen. Counsel
Edward Nolan, Controller, Cable
Ownership: Peter A. Bordes Family. See Cable System Ownership.
Represented (legal): Cole, Raywid & Braverman LLP; Schwartz, Woods & Miller.
MDS Systems:
Pennsylvania: WLK231, Philadelphia.
MMDS Systems:
Tennessee: WMI898, Chattanooga.
Other Holdings:
Printing company, radio, SMATV & cable, see listing.

GREENSBORO WIRELESS INC.
MMDS Systems:
North Carolina: WMH597, Greensboro; WMH600, Greensboro.

LAUREN F. GRIFFITH
3427 Rockwood Dr.
Fort Wayne, IN 46815
Phone: 219-483-2325
MMDS Systems:
Indiana: WNTA436, Anderson.

GRISWOLD CO-OP TELEPHONE CO.
Box 640
607 Main St.
Griswold, IA 51535
Phone: 712-778-2122
MMDS Systems:
Iowa: WMY432, Griswold.
Other Holdings:
Cable, see listing.

GROUP COMMUNICATIONS INC.
1463 Oak Crest Dr.
Waterloo, IA 50701
Phones: 319-232-3696; 319-234-0921
Officer:
William Silverson, Chief Exec. Officer
MMDS Systems:
Iowa: WHK956, Waterloo-Cedar Falls.

GROUP W TELEVISON
565 5th Ave.
New York, NY 10017-2413
Phone: 212-856-8000
MMDS Systems:
Missouri: WNEK905, St. Louis.

JEFFREY D. GRUMM
Box 2982
Sierra Vista, AZ 85636
Phone: 520-459-0459
MMDS Systems:
Arizona: WNTI399, Sierra Vista.

G/S DILLON F SETTLEMENT GROUP
c/o M-Y Partnership MGP
3423 Rolston St.
Fort Wayne, IN 46805
Phone: 219-483-2741
MMDS Systems:
Montana: WMX920, Dillon; WMX921, Dillon; WMX922, Dillon.

G/S EVANSTON F SETTLEMENT GROUP
c/o Step 9 MMDS Partners MGP
11600 Pinehaven Ave.
Bakersfield, CA 93312
MDS Systems:
Wyoming: WMI408, Evanston.

G/S LEWISTOWN F SETTLEMENT GROUP
c/o Step 9 MMDS Partners
11600 Pinehaven Ave.
Bakersfield, CA 93312
Phone: 805-589-1240
MMDS Systems:
Montana: WMX916, Lewistown; WMX917, Lewistown; WMX918, Lewistown.

G/S NEWCASTLE F SETTLEMENT GROUP
c/o Step 9 MMDS Partners MGP
11600 Pinehaven Ave.
Bakersfield, CA 93312
MMDS Systems:
Wyoming: WMX919, Newcastle.

G/S RIVERTON F SETTLEMENT GROUP
c/o CMG Enterprises MGP
2120 E. Prien Lake Rd.
Lake Charles, LA 70601
Phone: 318-477-1218
MDS Systems:
Wyoming: WMI404, Riverton.
MMDS Systems:
Wyoming: WMX912, Riverton; WMX913, Riverton; WMX914, Riverton.

G/S SANDPOINT F SETTLEMENT GROUP
Box 6219
Springfield, IL 62708
MMDS Systems:
New Mexico: WMY433, Clayton.

G/S THE DALLES E SETTLEMENT GROUP
Box 6219
Springfield Park, IL 62708
Phone: 217-341-0721
Fax: 217-528-8827
MDS Systems:
Oregon: WLW746, The Dalles.
MMDS Systems:
Oregon: WMX217, The Dalles; WMX218, The Dalles; WMX221, The Dalles.

GTE MEDIA VENTURES
Suite 300
100 E. Royal Lane
Irving, TX 76051
Phone: 972-465-4125
Fax: 972-465-4972
Officers:
William D. Wilson, Pres.
James Miles, V.P., Gen. Mgr.

Gerald L. Edgar, Secy.
Larry G. Manion, Chief Financial Officer
Ownership: GTE Corp.
Represented (legal): Gerald L. Edgar.
MDS Systems:
Hawaii: WMY435, Honolulu.
MMDS Systems:
Hawaii: WHT718, Honolulu.
Other Holdings:
Cable, wireless cable, see listings.

LES GUTIERREZ
No. 300
13170-B Central SE
Albuquerque, NM 87123
Phone: 505-281-4302
MMDS Systems:
New Mexico: WNTF247, Santa Fe.

HADDONFIELD WIRELESS CO.
Box 7999
Suite 165
Mayaguez, PR 00681
Ownership: John De Celis, Pres.
MMDS Systems:
Washington: WHT783, Spokane.

HALLICRAFTERS OF FLORIDA
MDS Systems:
Texas: WPY36, Abilene.
West Virginia: WDU369, Wheeling.

ROBERT A. HART IV
Box 66436
4615 N Blvd.
Baton Rouge, LA 70896
MMDS Systems:
Texas: WNTH877, Brazoria.

PATRICK W. HAUG
Phone: 512-358-7472
MDS Systems:
Texas: WLK317, Beeville.

HD ELECTRIC
Box 1007
Clear Lake, SD 57226
Phone: 605-874-2171
MMDS Systems:
South Dakota: WLK365, Sisseton; WLK366, Sisseton; WLK327, Watertown; WLK330, Watertown; WLK319, Willow Lake; WLK323, Willow Lake.

HEARTLAND CABLE INC.
2908 S. Santa Fe St.
Chanute, KS 66720
Phone: 800-221-6788
MMDS Systems:
Kansas: WMY441, Anthony; WMY442, Anthony.

HEARTLAND WIRELESS COMMERCIAL CHANNELS INC.
Suite 200
200 Chisholm Place
Plano, TX 75075
Phone: 972-423-9494
Fax: 972-423-0819
MDS Systems:
Texas: WCZ53, Amarillo; WMH217, Corsicana.
MMDS Systems:
Oklahoma: WLW828, Lindsay.
Texas: WMI357, Decatur; WMI361, Decatur; WLW861, Pampa.

HERITAGE BROADCASTING GROUP
Box 627
Cadillac, MI 49601-0627
Phone: 616-775-3478
Fax: 616-775-3671
Officers:
Mario F. Iacobelli, Chmn., Pres. & Chief Operating Officer, 2
William E. Kring, V.P., Secy.-Treas. & Chief Financial Officer
Ownership: Mario F. Iacobelli, 98.8%; Leanne C. Schulz, 1.2%.
Represented (legal): Hogan & Hartson LLP.
MMDS Systems:
Colorado: WHK938, Denver.
Other Holdings:
TV translators, TV, see listing.

PAUL G. HERRICK
1249 Forge Rd.
Cherry Hill, NJ 08034
Phone: 609-795-2576
MMDS Systems:
Michigan: WNTM549, Lansing.

NORMAN R. HERRINGTON
144-12
159th St.
Springfield Garden, NY 11434
Phone: 718-712-3109
MMDS Systems:
Arizona: WNTI488, Sierra Vista.

CARL B. HILLIARD JR.
836 Washington St.
San Diego, CA 92103-2207
Phone: 619-481-7200
MDS Systems:
Nevada: WWZ51, Las Vegas.
Other Holdings:
Interest in Channel View Inc. & Via/Net Companies, see listings.

HINTON TELEPHONE CO. INC.
Box 100
Hinton, OK 73047
MMDS Systems:
Oklahoma: WHT683, Oklahoma City.

MANABI HIRASAKI
862 Camino Concordia
Camarillo, CA 93031
MMDS Systems:
California: WHF413, Visalia.

HISOL LP
7521 E. Edgemont
Scottsdale, AZ 85257
Phone: 602-992-3494
MMDS Systems:
Michigan: WLK200, Flint; WMI369, Saginaw.

HOBBS NM E GROUP MMDS SETTLEMENT PARTNERSHIP
MMDS Systems:
New Mexico: WMY420, Hobbs.

TERRY J. HOLMES
923 E. Edgemont Dr.
Fresno, CA 93720
MMDS Systems:
California: WNTK887, Merced.

HOLUB WAMACK PARTNERSHIP
6919 Laurel Oaks Way
Fair Oaks, CA 95628
Phone: 916-965-3895
Ownership: Frederick J. Holub, 50%; Daniel H. Wamack, 50%.
MMDS Systems:
Nevada: WMX350, Fallon; WMX352, Fallon.

HONOLULU CABLEVISION CORP.
Suite 900
1350 Connecticut Ave. NW
Washington, DC 20036
Phone: 202-296-2007
MMDS Systems:
Hawaii: WNTH954, Honolulu; WNTI201, Honolulu.

ROBERT HOSTETLER
17215 Colonial Park Dr.
Monument, CO 80132
MMDS Systems:
California: WNTA439, Fresno.

JACK G. HUBBARD
8793 Ranch Dr.
Chesterland, OH 44026
Phone: 216-729-7282
MMDS Systems:
California: WMI407, Chico.
Indiana: WMI307, South Bend.
Tennessee: WHT680, Nashville.
Washington: WMI350, Olympia; WHT656, Seattle.

JOSEPH W. HUBBARD
26573 Basswood
Rancho Palos Verdes, CA 90274
Phone: 310-373-6234
MMDS Systems:
North Dakota: WLK300, Fargo, ND-Moorhead, MN.

HUBBARD TRUST
26573 Basswood
Rancho Palos Verdes, CA 90275
Phone: 310-373-6234
Fax: 310-373-6234
Officers:
Joseph W. Hubbard, Chmn.
Warren F. Ache, Chief Exec. Officer
Marijo Ache, V.P., Finance
Alma M. Hubbard, Secy.-Treas.
Represented (legal): Donelan Cleary Wood & Maser PC.
MDS Systems:
California: KFF68, Clayton; WDU486, Oro Grande; WPX85, San Marcos.
MMDS Systems:
Idaho: WMX243, Pocatello.

ARVOL M. HYATT
Apt. 2
921 N. Broadway
Arlington, WA 98223
MMDS Systems:
Alabama: WMI379, Demopolis.

HYDRA COMMUNICATIONS
565 S. Del Puerto Ave.
Patterson, CA 95363-9310
Phone: 714-621-1004
Ownership: Thomas M. Glab, see listing.
Represented (legal): Dutton, Kappes & Overman.
MDS Systems:
California: WGW408, El Centro; WGW239, Lancaster.
Utah: WFY786, Ogden.

BOARD OF TRUSTEES OF U. OF ILLINOIS
Henry Admin. Bldg.
Room 354
506 S. Wright St.
Urbana, IL 61801
Phone: 217-333-1000
MDS Systems:
Illinois: KEW94, Urbana.

INNER CITY BROADCASTING CORP.
40th Floor
3 Park Ave
New York, NY 10016
Phone: 212-447-1000
MMDS Systems:
Georgia: WLW749, Savannah.

INTEGRATION COMMUNICATIONS INTERNATIONAL
Suite 103
6507 Ridge St.
McLean, VA 22101
Officers:
Robert L. Schmidt, Chmn. & Pres.
Richard J. Amons Jr., Chief Exec. Officer
Patricia G. Schmidt, Secy.-Treas.
Cameron V. Dunlop, Chief Financial Officer
Represented (legal): Sinderbrand & Alexander.
MMDS Systems:
California: WHT636, Grand Terrace.

THE KENNETH H. ISCOL 1990 TRUST FOR KIVA ISCOL
63 Lyndel Rd.
Pound Ridge, NY 10576
MMDS Systems:
California: WMI322, Salinas.

BARRY JAMES
Box 1010
RR 5
Coalgate, OK 74538-9530
Phone: 405-924-2301
MDS Systems:
Oklahoma: WMI932, Ada.

JB WIRELESS
7 Roundtree Dr.
Melville, NY 11747
Phone: 516-643-8349
Ownership: Phil Burkhardt, Chmn. See also listing for LC Communications.
MDS Systems:
Michigan: WLW902, Cadillac.
Oregon: WLW906, Coos Bay.

JCL ALAMOSA COLORADO F GRAND ALLIANCE
546 Sandy Hook Rd.
Treasure Island, FL 33706
Phone: 813-360-2716
Fax: 813-360-5809
MMDS Systems:
Colorado: WMY299, Alamosa.

JCL EL DORADO ARKANSAS F GRAND ALLIANCE
546 Sandy Hook Rd.
Treasure Island, FL 33706
Phone: 813-360-2716
Fax: 813-360-5809
MMDS Systems:
Arkansas: WMY298, El Dorado.

JCL LA JUNTA COLORADO E GRAND ALLIANCE
546 Sandy Hook Rd.
Treasure Island, FL 33706
Phone: 813-360-2416
Fax: 813-360-5809
MMDS Systems:
Colorado: WMX201, La Junta; WMX202, La Junta.

JCL LAMAR COLORADO E GRAND ALLIANCE
11611 Harborview Dr.
Cleveland, OH 44102
MMDS Systems:
Colorado: WMX200, Lamar; WMX203, Lamar.

JJJ PARTNERSHIP
Box 24881

GMF, GU 96921
Phone: 671-646-8886
MMDS Systems:
Guam: WMI810, Agana.

ESTATE OF CHARLES R. JONES
5588 Westside Dr.
El Paso, TX 79932
Phone: 915-584-1848
MDS Systems:
Texas: WML478, San Angelo.
MMDS Systems:
Texas: WMH612, San Angelo; WMX908, San Angelo; WNTC543, San Angelo.

JONSSON COMMUNICATIONS CORP.
233 Wilshire Blvd.
Santa Monica, CA 90401
Phone: 213-451-3230
Officers:
Keneth Jonsson, Chmn., Pres. & Chief Exec. Officer
Don McDaniel, Secy.-Treas.
James Ross, Chief Financial Officer
Represented (legal): Kaye, Scholer, Fierman, Hays & Handler LLP.
MDS Systems:
Nevada: WJL89, Carson City; WFY434, Reno.
MMDS Systems:
Nevada: WMH705, Carson City; WNTL575, Carson City; WHT781, Reno; WHT782, Reno.
Radio Stations:
California: KSAC(AM) Sacramento.

JRH/BDC PARTNERSHIP
c/o Rapid Action Mailing Service
3850 Aircraft Dr.
Anchorage, AK 99502
MMDS Systems:
Alaska: WMX529, Anchorage.

JRZ ASSOCIATES
Box 8026
3400 Tupper Dr.
Greenville, NC 27834
Phone: 919-757-0279
MMDS Systems:
Kansas: WNTM611, Wichita.
Kentucky: WNTH444, Paducah.
North Carolina: WNTM578, King.
Texas: WNTP928, Amarillo; WNTH836, Texarkana.

KA3B2 TELEVISION PARTNERSHIP
Suite 238
2219 Thousand Oaks Blvd.
Thousand Oaks, CA 91362
Phones: 818-879-2220; 800-388-7371
Fax: 818-889-8521
Ownership: Kingswood Associates M.G.P., Robert L. Button, partner.
Represented (legal): Sullivan & Worcester.
MDS Systems:
New York: WMH869, Corning.
MMDS Systems:
New York: WNTK908, Corning.

KANNEW BROADCAST TECHNOLOGIES
Box 15129
Chevy Chase, MD 20825
MMDS Systems:
Arizona: WMI320, Flagstaff.
Kansas: WMI275, Dodge City.
Kentucky: WLW995, Paducah.
Maine: WMI878, Augusta.
Mississippi: WLW835, Vicksburg.

KANSAS CITY MICROWAVE COMMUNICATIONS INC.
114 W. 11th St.
Kansas City, MO 64105
Phone: 816-556-0325
MMDS Systems:
Wisconsin: WLW871, Milwaukee.

KC CORP.
Box 206
Prince Frederick, MD 20678
Phone: 914-576-6622
MDS Systems:
District of Columbia: WHT747, Washington.
Other Holdings:
Phoenix MDS Co., see listing.

MICHAEL R. KELLEY
3623 Park Lane
Fairfax, VA 22030
Phones: 304-725-0036; 703-691-1119.
Fax: 703-691-8938
Represented (legal): Kaye, Scholer, Fierman, Hays & Handler LLP.
MMDS Systems:
West Virginia: WHT629, Martinsburg; WLK242 Martinsburg; WMY489, Martinsburg.
Other Holdings:
OFS.

GEORGE KERN
Bldg. 1, No. 11
12945 Seminole Blvd.
Largo, FL 33778
MMDS Systems:
Alabama: WNTJ725, Montgomery.

EARL S. KIM
18220 S. Broadway
Gardena, CA 90248
MDS Systems:
California: KFI79, Anaheim; KFF79, Los Angeles; WPY40, San Pedro.

PAUL M. KIMBALL
Suite A
1012 N.W. Grand Blvd.
Oklahoma City, OK 73118-6038
Phone: 405-848-1874
MMDS Systems:
New Mexico: WHT662, Albuquerque.

KLONDIKE DATA SYSTEMS
Phone: 219-471-2324
Fax: 219-471-5406.
MMDS Systems:
Ohio: WNTE288, Columbus.

RUTH I. KOLPIN
Box 696
Carthage, MO 64836
Phone: 417-358-3002
MDS Systems:
Missouri: WDU466, Carthage.
Other Holdings:
Cable, see listing.

ROSEMARIE KOSMAN
Apt. 204
1635 E. 13 Mile Rd.
Madison Heights, MI 48071
MMDS Systems:
Mississippi: WNTH936, Hattiesburg.

AGNES C. KOZEL
1434 Grant Ave.
San Francisco, CA 94133
Phone: 415-928-6871
MMDS Systems:
Kentucky: WLR488, Somerset.

EUGENE KOZEL
560 W. Franklin St.
Monterey, CA 93940
Phone: 408-375-7125
MMDS Systems:
Nebraska: WMI292, Chadron.

INA M. KOZEL
560 W. Franklin
Monterey, CA 93940
Phone: 408-375-7125
MMDS Systems:
Wisconsin: WMH248, Wausau.

RIMA KOZEL
560 W. Franklin St.
Monterey, CA 93940
Phone: 408-375-7125
MMDS Systems:
Nebraska: WMI296, Chadron.

KRAVETZ MEDIA CORP.
5130 S. Hanover
Englewood, CO 80111
MMDS Systems:
Colorado: WLW761, Grand Junction.

KRISAR INC.
320 Hamilton St.
Albion, NY 14411-9383
Phone: 716-589-9295
Fax: 716-589-9094
Ownership: George W. Bott, Chmn. & Pres.
Represented (legal): Fleischman & Walsh LLP.
MMDS Systems:
Illinois: WHI964, Bloomington-Normal.
Indiana: WMI874, Anderson; WMI877, Kokomo; WMI853, South Bend.
New York: WLK276, Binghamton.
Ohio: WLK306, Cleveland.
Pennsylvania: WMH780, Erie; WMI366, State College.
Other Holdings:
OFS.

K-TOWERS PARTNERSHIP
123 N. Easy St.
Lafayette, LA 70506
MDS Systems:
Louisiana: WPW96, Baton Rouge.

DONALD J. KUNKLE
2565 Colt Rd.
Rancho Palos Verdes, CA 90274
MMDS Systems:
Missouri: WMX953, Malden.

JOHN C. LANDY
11611 Harbour View Dr.
Cleveland, OH 44102
MMDS Systems:
Idaho: WMY426, Salmon.

LARSEN MMDS INC.
c/o David H. Larsen
2180 State Rd. 434 W
Longwood, FL 32779
MMDS Systems:
Texas: WHT693, San Antonio.

LC COMMUNICATIONS
7 Roundtree Dr.
Melville, NY 11747
Phone: 516-643-8349
Ownership: Phil Burkhardt, Chmn. See also JB Wireless.
MDS Systems:
Nevada: WLW905, Ely.
Texas: WMH397, San Angelo.
MMDS Systems:
Texas: WNTI238, Freeport.

LEE COUNTY BOARD OF COMMISSIONERS
Box 398
Fort Myers, FL 33902
Phone: 941-338-3208
MMDS Systems:
Florida: WNTH636, Fort Myers.

SUE A. LEMNA
4432 Shenandoah Circle
Fort Wayne, IN 46835
Phone: 219-486-1405
MMDS Systems:
Indiana: WNTA435, Anderson.

JONATHAN M. LEVY
Suite 2526
900 N. Stafford St.
Arlington, VA 22203-1852
Phone: 703-527-7737
Represented (legal): Brown, Nietert & Kaufman, Chartered.
MMDS Systems:
Texas: WHT705, Austin.

AUSTIN C. LEWIS
Box 740
2606 E. End Dr.
Humboldt, TN 38343
MDS Systems:
Tennessee: WFY989, Somerville.

LIBMOT COMMUNICATIONS PARTNERSHIP
2700 Chain Bridge Rd. NW
Washington, DC 20016
Phone: 202-966-2167
Fax: 202-237-7742
Ownership: William M. Barnard & T. D. Dougherty Jr. Barnard is exec. with Baypoint TV Inc. & is principal of MDS Signal Group & Springfield One Partnership, see listings.
MDS Systems:
Kentucky: WMX910, Paducah; WMX911, Paducah.
Oklahoma: WLW787, Enid.
MMDS Systems:
Alabama: WNTJ807, Birmingham.
Kentucky: WNTJ726, Lexington; WNTH681, Paducah.
Ohio: WNTH500, Youngstown.
Texas: WNTH502, Bryan; WNTI234, Texarkana.
Virginia: WNTB962, Driver; WNTH507, Roanoke.

LINE OF SITE INC.
8611 E. Santa Catalina Dr.
Scottsdale, AZ 85255
Phone: 602-995-2711
Ownership: J. Steven Rizley.
MMDS Systems:
Alabama: WMH505, Montgomery.
Arizona: WLR480, Globe; WMH512, Globe.
Florida: WHT761, Daytona Beach; WHT731, Orlando.
Illinois: WLW779, Champaign.
Louisiana: WLK223, Shreveport.
Michigan: WMH509, Muskegon.
Nebraska: WHT777, Omaha.
Nevada: WHT721, Las Vegas.
New York: WHT739, Syracuse.
Ohio: WMH228, Lima.

LIPPER COMMUNICATIONS
74 Trinity Place
New York, NY 10006
Phone: 212-393-1300
Ownership: A. Michael Lipper, 50%.
MDS Systems:
New York: WJM64, Long Island.

T.D. LITTLE SURVIVORS TRUST & V.C. LITTLE EXEMPTION TRUST
15917 E. Lincoln Rd.
Spokane, WA 99207
Phone: 509-921-9733
MMDS Systems:
Alabama: WLR564, Huntsville.

LOS ANGELES MDS CO. INC.
Suite 6-C
104 E. 68th St.
New York, NY 10021
Phone: 212-288-2356
Fax: 212-288-2312
Ownership: Hubbard Technologies, 25%.
MDS Systems:
California: WHD479, Los Angeles.

LOW POWER TECHNOLOGY INC.
c/o Jeff Nightbyrd
No. 307, 225 Congress
Austin, TX 78701
MMDS Systems:
New York: WLW939, Poughkeepsie.

MACRO DISTRIBUTION SYSTEMS INC.
Suite 660
1920 N St. NW
Washington, DC 20036
Phone: 202-887-0600
MDS Systems:
Tennessee: WMH905, Johnson City.
Utah: WMI364, Cedar City; WMI368, Cedar City.
Wisconsin: WMH884, Eau Claire; WMH885, Eau Claire; WLW742, La Crosse; WMH901, La Crosse.
MMDS Systems:
Colorado: WMX256, Alamosa; WMX525, Alamosa; WMX527, Alamosa; WMX216, Sterling; WMX934, Sterling.
Iowa: WMH468, Sioux City.
Mississippi: WMX933, Meridian.
Tennessee: WMH469, Johnson City.

MADDOX NACHMAN KERN PARTNERSHIP
10300 97th St. N
Seminole, FL 34643
Phone: 813-392-1681
MMDS Systems:
Florida: WNTJ390, Panama City.

MADDOX/NACHMAN PARTNERSHIP
Suite 201
7800 113th St. N
Seminole, FL 34642
MMDS Systems:
Tennessee: WNTJ389, Chattanooga.

MAHRLE GILDERS ROCZ PARTNERSHIP
Phone: 813-855-1718
MMDS Systems:
Louisiana: WNTJ385, Lafayette.

AUDREY MALKAN
304 Crestwood Dr.
Fort Worth, TX 76107
Phone: 817-626-0931
MMDS Systems:
Illinois: WHK999, Chicago.

MARRCO COMMUNICATIONS INC.
Suite 211
3419 Via Lido
Newport Beach, CA 92693
MMDS Systems:
Pennsylvania: WLK405, Erie.

MARS COMMUNICATIONS INC.
Suite 3300
101 E. Kennedy Blvd.
Tampa, FL 33602
Phone: 813-226-8844
Fax: 813-225-1513
Ownership: Mark D. Sena, Pres.
Represented (legal): Ross & Hardies.
MMDS Systems:
Florida: WHT699, Tampa.

MASSCOM
1023 51st St.
Moline, IL 61265
Phone: 309-764-6886
MDS Systems:
Arkansas: WKW790, Hot Springs.
Texas: WMH201, Plainview; WMH488, Plainview.
MMDS Systems:
Arkansas: WLW705, Hot Springs.

TIMOTHY A. MATHEWS
Box 181
Savoy, IL 61874
MMDS Systems:
Illinois: WNTA368, Champaign.

McDONALD GROUP
Suite 300
One Office Park Circle
Birmingham, AL 35223
Phone: 205-879-0456
Fax: 205-879-0479
Ownership: William W. McDonald, Pres.
Represented (legal): Cole, Raywid & Braverman LLP.
MMDS Systems:
California: WLW891, Santa Barbara.

MCI TELECOMMUNICATIONS CORP.
1133 19th St. NW
Washington, DC 20036
Ownership: MCI WorldCom.
MMDS Systems:
Connecticut: WMI358, New Haven.

JOHN McLAIN
7110 Jaxel Rd.
Hereford, AZ 85615
Phone: 602-378-6449
MDS Systems:
Arizona: WMY446, Sierra Vista.
MMDS Systems:
Arizona: WMI371, Sierra Vista; WMI375, Sierra Vista; WNTI467, Sierra Vista.

MDS SIGNAL GROUP
Suite 700
919 18th St. NW
Washington, DC 20006
Phone: 202-659-4400
Officer:
William M. Barnard, Chief Exec. Officer
Ownership: William M. Barnard, James K. Edmundson, John B. Kenkel, Paul Lucci & Wayne Souza. Barnard is exec. with Baypoint TV Inc. & is principal of Libmont Communications Partners & Springfield One Partnership, see listings.
MMDS Systems:
Florida: WHK974, Fort Myers.
Minnesota: WLW853, Mankato.
Nevada: WHT722, Las Vegas.
Texas: WHT766, El Paso.

MDS SYSTEMS
Box 190929
Anchorage, AK 99519-0929
Phone: 907-243-2431
Ownership: James R. Hendershot.
Represented (legal): Dow, Lohnes & Albertson PLLC.
MDS Systems:
Alaska: KFC63, Anchorage.
MMDS Systems:
Alaska: WLK270, Homer.

MEADOW MICROWAVE
Box 8909
Aspen, CO 81612
MMDS Systems:
South Carolina: WHT799, Charleston.

MEDIA BROADCASTING INC.
716 N. Westwood Ave.
Toledo, OH 43607
Phone: 419-534-2714
Ownership: Paul M. Moore, Principal.
MDS Systems:
Ohio: KFK31, Toledo.

MERRIFIELD PARTNERSHIP
1004 E. Tate
Broomfield, TX 79316
MMDS Systems:
Texas: WMH797, Pecos.

BRUCE MERRILL
6330 E. Mockingbird Lane
Paradise Valley, AZ 85253
Phone: 602-948-3776
MMDS Systems:
Nevada: WNTH881, Henderson; WNTJ881, Las Vegas.
Other Holdings:
LPTV, see listing.

MESTER'S TV
Box 300406
Brooklyn, NY 11230
Phone: 718-282-9090
Fax: 718-469-0881
Officers:
John Mester, Chmn.
Dr. Jolinda Mester-Leider, Chief Exec. Officer
Hilda Mester, Chief Financial Officer
Ownership: John Mester. Mester is also principal of Connecticut Home Theatre, see listing in LPTV ownership.
MMDS Systems:
California: WMX215, Santa Barbara; WLK217, Santa Barbara-Santa Maria-Lompoc.
Other Holdings
LPTV.

METROCALL OF NEVADA GENERAL PARTNERSHIP II
6677 Richmond Hwy.
Alexandria, VA 22306
Phone: 703-660-6677
Fax: 703-768-5407
MMDS Systems:
California: WHT637, Grand Terrace.

METROPOLITAN DADE COUNTY
5680 S.W. 87th Ave.
Miami, FL 33173
MMDS Systems:
Florida: WEF376, Miami.

BRETT MEYER
Suite 2130
1330 Ala Moana Blvd.
Honolulu, HI 96814
MMDS Systems:
Hawaii: WNTH468, Maui.

MHW ASSOCIATES
2219 California St. NW
Washington, DC 20008
Phones: 202-861-7800; 202-861-7834
Ownership: Multichannel Media Inc., see listing, 49% Abe Rosenbloom; Morton H. Wilner,
MMDS Systems:
Arizona: WHT696, Tucson.
Other Holdings:
25% of Red Charleston F Partnership & 25% of Red Memphis F Partnership, see listings.

MICKELSON MEDIA INC.
c/o Century Communications Corp.
50 Locust Ave.
New Canaan, CT 06840
MMDS Systems:
Georgia: WLW907, Brunswick.
Minnesota: WLW870, Ulm/James/Winthrop.
New Mexico: WMH296, Las Vegas; WMH297, Los Alamos.

THE MICROBAND COMPANIES INC.
Officers:
J. Patrick Dugan, Pres. & Chief Exec. Officer
William Hoffman, Sr. V.P., Secy. & Gen. Counsel
James K. Baumann, Asst. V.P. & Chief Engineer
Robert Baumann, Treas.

Branch Office:
323 Malta Ave.
Brooklyn, NY 11207
Represented (legal): Sinderbrand & Alexander.
MDS Systems:
Louisiana: WKR26, New Orleans.
Oregon: WPY39, Portland.
MMDS Systems:
Texas: WMH356, Wichita Falls.
Other Holdings:
OFS, LPTV, see listing.

MICROCOM INC.
Box 2108
Saginaw, MI 48605-2108
Phone: 517-777-8852
Fax: 517-777-8862
Officer:
David A. Bradford, Pres. & Chief Exec. Officer
Represented (legal): Pepper & Corazzini.
MDS Systems:
Michigan: WMI947, Saginaw.
Other Holdings:
Wireless Cable, see listing.

MICROWAVE BROADCAST SERVICES INC.
Suite 220
5505 South 900 East
Salt Lake City, UT 84117
Phone: 801-288-1760
MMDS Systems:
Kentucky: WMI415, Columbia; WMI419, Columbia.

MICROWAVE MOVIES INC.
Officers:
William L. Needham, Pres.
Lucille S. Needham, Secy.-Treas.
Ownership: William L. Needham & Lucille S. Needham, 60% jointly; Francis L. Guill & Caroline V. Guill, jointly, 20%; John H. Deaton, 20%.
MDS Systems:
Missouri: WOG68, Lake of the Ozarks (Osage Beach).
MMDS Systems:
Missouri: WMH257, Fulton; WLW937, Lake Ozark.

MICROWAVE SERVICE CO.
Box 163
Tupelo, MS 38802-0163
Phone: 601-842-7620
Fax: 601-844-7061

Officer:
Frank K. Spain, Pres. & Chief Exec. Officer
Mark Ledbetter, Chief Operating Officer

Branch Office:
38295 Chuperosa Lane
Cathedral City, CA 92234
Phone: 619-328-5160
Wayne C. Goff
Ownership: Frank K. Spain, see listing in TV Ownership.
Represented (legal): Haley, Bader & Potts PLC; Arent Fox Kintner Plotkin & Kahn.
MDS Systems:
California: WSL86, Palm Springs.

MID-NEBRASKA TELECOMMUNICATIONS INC.
MDS Systems:
Nebraska: WFY765, North Platte.

THARRELL D. MING
6781 Coffee Rd.
Oildale, CA 93308
Phone: 661-392-0655
MMDS Systems:
Idaho: WNTJ729, Boise; WNTJ839, Boise.

MINNEAPOLIS MDS CO.
Suite 247
189 Berdan Ave.
Wayne, NJ 07470
Phone: 201-831-7404
MDS Systems:
Minnesota: WCU552, Minneapolis.

MINORITY MDS
MMDS Systems:
Texas: WMI897, Kerrville.

MMDS INC.
Phone: 601-982-1300
MMDS Systems:
Alabama: WNTH399, Birmingham.

MMDS ORANGEBURG INC.
MMDS Systems:
South Carolina: WHT952, Orangeburg.

MOLOKA'I NETWORK CORP.
c/o Scott D. Delacourt
1776 K St. NW
Washington, DC 20006
Phone: 202-429-7000
Represented (legal): Wiley, Rein & Fielding.
MMDS Systems:
Hawaii: WMX211, Honolulu.

PAUL M. MOORE
716 N. Westwood Ave.
Toledo, OH 43607
Phone: 419-534-2714
MMDS Systems:
Arkansas: WMI816, Little Rock.

ROBERT S. MOORE
716 N. Westwood Ave.
Toledo, OH 43607
Phone: 419-531-1440
MMDS Systems:
New York: WHT688, Fairport.

RICHARD D. MORGESE
Box 14187
San Francisco, CA 94114
Phone: 415-285-1739
MDS Systems:
Texas: WMX334, Decatur; WMI852, Edgewood; WMI915, Greenville; WMI906, Mineral Wells.
MMDS Systems:
Montana: WLR476, Miles City; WMX362, Miles City; WMX364, Miles City; WMX365, Miles City.

MORRIS COMMUNICATIONS INC.
1508 W. Blue Ridge Dr.
Greenville, SC 29611
MMDS Systems:
South Carolina: WMH508, Columbia.

MOUNTRAIL-WILLIAMS ELECTRIC COOPERATIVE INC.
Box 1346
Williston, ND 58802-1346
Phone: 701-572-3765
Fax: 701-572-7307
Officers:
Dorvan Solberg, Chmn.
Dale Haugen, Chief Exec. Officer
Bill Adolf, Chief Operating Officer
Derald Hoover, Chief Financial Officer
MMDS Systems:
North Dakota: WLW968, Williston.

MRC TELECOMMUNICATIONS INC.
275 N. Corporate Dr.
Brookfield, WI 53045
Phone: 414-792-9700
Fax: 414-792-7717
Officers:
Nancy B. Carey, Pres.
Robert E. Rogers, Chief Operating Officer
Jim Dilter, Chief Financial Officer
Craig J. Stapel, V.P., Sales

Branch Offices:
Suite 890
331 S. 2nd Ave.
Minneapolis, MN 55401
Phone: 612-344-1930

3617 Oakton St.
Skokie, IL 60076
Phone: 708-674-7495
Ownership: Journal Communications. Robert A. Kahlor, Chmn.
MMDS Systems:
Wisconsin: WMH497, Eau Claire.

MULTICHANNEL DISTRIBUTION OF AMERICA INC.
Suite 300
10020 E. Girard Ave.
Denver, CO 80231
Phone: 303-751-2900
Fax: 303-751-1081
Officers:
Omar A. Duwaik, Chief Exec. Officer
Ken Roznoy, V.P. & Secy.
Geir Hauge, V.P., Engineering
Ownership: Omar Duwaik, 65%; remainder, publicly held.
Represented (legal): Fleischman & Walsh LLP.
MMDS Systems:
Illinois: WLW887, Quincy.
Oklahoma: WMH761, Woodward.

MULTI-CHANNEL MDS INC.
Box 258
Rd. 2
Elverson, PA 19520
MMDS Systems:
Alabama: WMH408, Mobile.

MULTICHANNEL MEDIA INC.
248 King George St.
Annapolis, MD 21401
Phone: 410-626-1200
Fax: 410-626-1266
Officers:
Peter A. Frank, Pres. & Chief Exec. Officer
C. J. Head, Corp. Secy.
Ownership: Peter A. Frank, 51%.
Represented (legal): Covington & Burling.
MMDS Systems:
Arizona: WHT696, Tucson.
Texas: WLW931, Beaumont; WHT766, El Paso.
Other Holdings:
MMDS: 33.3% of Red New York E Partnership; 25% of Red Charleston F Partnership; 25% of Red Memphis F Partnership, see listings.

MULTICHANNEL NETWORKS
527 Shore Acres Dr.
Mamaroneck, NY 10543-4008
Ownership: Thomas F. Delaney & John R. Loos, Principals.
MMDS Systems:
Rhode Island: WHT650, Providence.

MULTIMEDIA DEVELOPMENT CORP.
Box 878
Sandia Park, NM 87047
Phone: 505-281-4302
Fax: 505-293-2589
Officers:
Walter K. Mickelson, Chmn.
Les Gutierrez, Pres.
Ownership: Walter K. Mickelson, 74%; Les Gutierrez & Veronica Gutierrez, 24% jointly; Bill Simons & Terri Simons, 2% jointly.
Represented (legal): Rini, Coran & Lancellotta PC.
MDS Systems:
New Mexico: KFK32, Albuquerque; WJM88, Las Cruces.
MMDS Systems:
New Mexico: WNTF306, Albuquerque; WNTF451, Albuquerque; WHK961, Las Cruces; WMI332, Las Cruces; WMI336, Las Cruces; WMI340, Las Cruces.
Other Holdings:
Cable, see listing.

MULTI-MICRO INC.
Suite 120
4700 S. McClintock
Tempe, AZ 85282
Phone: 480-755-7524
Fax: 480-755-7534
Officers:
Dale E. Kipp, Chmn.
Russell H. Ritchie, Pres.
Ownership: Dale E. Kipp & Russell H. Ritchie.
Represented (legal): Wood, Maines & Brown.
MMDS Systems:
Arizona: WLW970, Flagstaff.
Indiana: WLW799, Evansville; WNTJ462, Lyford.
Ohio: WMI885, Steubenville.

MULTIPOINT INFORMATION SYSTEMS INC.
Suite 6-C
104 E. 68th St.
New York, NY 10021
Phone: 212-288-2356
Fax: 212-288-2312
Officer:
Irwin Jacobs, Pres.
MDS Systems:
District of Columbia: WHT747, Washington.
Ohio: WSL34, Canton.
Pennsylvania: WLK231, Philadelphia.

MULTI-POINT TV DISTRIBUTORS INC.
2606 E. 10th St.
Tucson, AZ 85717
Phone: 602-795-8852
Officer:
J. Michael Moeller, Pres.
Ownership: Philip C. Merrill, see Fortuna Systems Corp.
Represented (legal): Fleischman & Walsh LLP.
MMDS Systems:
Colorado: WLW762, Mancos.
Florida: WMI303, Sarasota.

MWTV INC.
3401 E. Cholla St.
Phoenix, AZ 85028
Phone: 602-996-3871
Ownership: M. Marshal Carpenter Jr., Pres.
MDS Systems:
Arizona: WMI394, Bullhead City.
MMDS Systems:
Arizona: WMH344, Casa Grande.
Iowa: WLW894, Davenport.
Louisiana: WMH361, Lafayette.
Michigan: WMH652, Kalamazoo.
Minnesota: WMI286, St. Cloud.
North Carolina: WLW938, Asheville.
Ohio: WMI899, Youngstown.

IVAN NACHMAN
11584 Harborside Circle
Largo, FL 33773-4403
Phone: 813-392-1681
MMDS Systems:
Idaho: WNTH957, Pocatello.
Louisiana: WNTH956, Lake Charles.
Massachusetts: WNTI260, Deerfield.
Mississippi: WNTJ282, Vicksburg.
New Hampshire: WNTH586, Portsmouth.
Ohio: WNTI621, Cincinnati.
Vermont: WNTI675, Burlington.
Washington: WNTJ345, Spokane; WNTJ346, Spokane; WNTJ347, Spokane; WNTJ283, Yakima.
Other Holdings:
LPTV, see listing.

NATIONAL CABLE & TELEVISION SERVICES GROUP
Suite 209
6317 Park Heights Ave.
Baltimore, MD 21215
Phone: 916-928-9320
MMDS Systems:
New Mexico: WNTL418, Las Vegas.

NATIONAL MICRO VISION SYSTEMS INC.
Fax: 714-752-1055
MMDS Systems:
Missouri: WMI405, Elmo; WMI409, Elmo.

NATIONAL TV CO.
Drawer B
Kingsville, TX 78363
Phone: 903-221-5500
Officer:
B. Waring Partridge III, Chief Exec. Officer
MMDS Systems:
Alabama: WLW709, Dothan.
Georgia: WHT664, Atlanta.
Mississippi: WLW725, Biloxi; WMH401, Pascagoula.
North Carolina: WMH601, Jacksonville.
Pennsylvania: WMI282, Williamsport.

NATIONAL WIRELESS CABLE
63 Dombey Circle
Thousand Oaks, CA 91360
MMDS Systems:
Colorado: WMH400, Fort Collins; WMH393, Pueblo.
Louisiana: WLW878, Crowley/Eunice.
Minnesota: WLW862, Mankato/Waterville.

NATIONAL WIRELESS VIDEO
24 Oak Dr.
Durham, NC 27707

Officer:
Walter E. Daniels, Pres.
MMDS Systems:
Arizona: WHT696, Tucson.
Louisiana: WMH357, Monroe.
New Mexico: WHK962, Las Cruces.
Other Holdings:
MMDS: 25% of Red Memphis F Partnership, see listing.

NBI TV PARTNERS

2570 Chateau Way
Livermore, CA 94550
Phone: 510-443-1415
MMDS Systems:
Alabama: WNTM544, Andalusia.
Arkansas: WNTM542, El Dorado.
Other Holdings:
LPTV, see listing.

NDW II INC.

Suite 200
200 Chisholm Place
Plano, TX 75075
Phone: 405-924-4638
MMDS Systems:
Oklahoma: WMH613, Lawton.
Other Holdings:
Wireless Cable, see listing.

NEBRASKA TELECOMMUNICATIONS INC.

616 Chestnut Dr.
Loveland, CO 80538
Phones: 303-663-1072; 308-285-3295
Officers:
Irvin D. Hopkins, Pres.
Donald Suda, Chief Operating Officer, 5
David Fahrenbruch, Chief Financial Officer
MMDS Systems:
Colorado: WHK935, Wray; WNEX651, Wray.
Nebraska: WLW999, Bartley; WNEX653, Bartley; WHK928, North Platte; WNEX655, North Platte; WLW997, Oshkosh; WNEX652, Oshkosh; WLW998, Wauneta; WNEX654, Wauneta.

JAMES NECAISE

2101 S. Bay St.
Georgetown, SC 29440
Phone: 803-546-1913
MMDS Systems:
South Carolina: WMX235, Georgetown.
Other Holdings:
Necaise is a principal of Southern Wireless Co. Inc., see listing.

NEW COM.

11645 Putter Way
Los Altos, CA 94024
MMDS Systems:
New York: WNTM910, Selden.

NEW ENGLAND WIRELESS INC.

Box 470
Rte. 5 S
Ascutney, VT 05030
Phone: 802-674-2206
Fax: 802-674-2751
Officers:
Alan R. Ackerman, Chmn.
Scott A. Wendel, Pres. & Chief Exec. Officer
Michael Tedesco, Chief Operating Officer
Lorry A. Lachapelle, Secy.-Treas.
Harold Doran, Chief Financial Officer

Branch Office:
Northern Region
Route 15
Box 218
Jericho, VT 05465
Phone: 802-899-1301
MDS Systems:
Vermont: WMI410, Windsor; WMI418, Windsor.
MMDS Systems:
Vermont: WLR471, Lyndonville; WLR479, Lyndonville.
Other Holdings:
Wireless Cable, LPTV, see listings.

NEW HAMPSHIRE WIRELESS

Box 168
Derry, NH 03038
Phone: 603-893-1995
MDS Systems:
Texas: WLW920, Abilene.
MMDS Systems:
Idaho: WMI391, Twin Falls.

NEW MEXICO MEDIA LTD.

Box 4816
Santa Fe, NM 87502
MMDS Systems:
New Mexico: WMH348, Gallup; WMI325, Santa Fe.

NEW YORK MDS INC.

Suite 6-C
104 E. 68th St.
New York, NY 10021
MDS Systems:
New York: WLK227, New York.

NORTH FLORIDA MMDS PARTNERS

Box 4935
Rte. 1
Williston, FL 32696
Phone: 904-528-2290
MMDS Systems:
California: WNTD875, Chico; WNTF690, Ukiah.

NORTHEAST IOWA TV INC.

Box 289
RR 1
Postville, IA 52162
Phone: 319-864-3104
MMDS Systems:
Iowa: WLW767, Postville.

NORTHEAST TELECOM INC.

Suite 155
1433 N. Jones Blvd.
Las Vegas, NV 89108
MMDS Systems:
New York: WNTM557, Watertown.

NORTHERN ELECTRIC COOPERATIVE INC.

Hwy. 12
Box 488
Bath, SD 57427
Phone: 605-225-0310
Fax: 605-229-5927
Officers:
Paul Fischbach, Pres.
Dennis W. Hagny, Chief Exec. Officer
MMDS Systems:
South Dakota: WLK408, Aberdeen; WLK409, Aberdeen; WNEX765, Aberdeen; WNEX688, Bath.
Other Holdings:
Wireless Cable, see listing.

NORTHERN RURAL CABLE TV COOPERATIVE

Box 488
Bath, SD 57427
Phone: 605-225-0310
MDS Systems:
South Dakota: WMY463, Bath.
MMDS Systems:
South Dakota: WNTI409, Aberdeen.

NORTHWEST COMMUNICATIONS COOPERATIVE

Box 38
Ray, ND 58849
Phone: 701-568-3331
Fax: 701-568-7777
Ownership: Estate of G. Russell Chambers, 33.3%; Francis E. Martin, 33.3%; Thomas E. Bird, 33.3%.
MDS Systems:
North Dakota: WMX955, Bowbells.
MMDS Systems:
North Dakota: WLW987, Bowbells; WLW748, Williston; WLW968, Williston.
Other Holdings:
Telephone, cable, see listing.

NUCENTRIX BROADBAND NETWORKS

Suite 200
200 Chisholm Place
Plano, TX 75075
Phone: 972-423-9494
Fax: 972-423-0819
Officers:
Carroll D. McHenry, Chmn., Pres., Chief Exec. & Financial Officer
Randall C. May, V.P., Operations
Wayne M. Taylor, V.P., Administration
J. Curtis Henderson, V.P., Gen. Counsel & Secy.

Branch Office:
Operations & Marketing
224 W. Evergreen
Durant, OK 74701
Phone: 405-924-6220
Ownership: David E. Webb; L. Allen Wheeler; Hunt Capital Group LLC; Jupiter Partners.
MMDS Systems:
Florida: WLW911, Ocala.
Illinois: WNTF515, McLeansboro; WNTF548, McLeansboro; WNTI571, McLeansboro; WMH200, Peoria; WMH380, Peoria; WMI327, Salem; WMI346, Salem.
Kansas: WNTG289, Erie; WNTG290, Erie; WNTG293, Erie.
Louisiana: WMH413, Monroe.
Missouri: WMH504, Columbia; WNTI251, Columbia.
New Hampshire: WLW855, Portsmouth.
Oklahoma: WMH337, Ada; WNTH577, Ada; WMI311, Colony; WMH653, Enid; WNTI252, Enid; WNTJ492, Lawton; WNTA265, Lindsay; WNTD985, Lindsay; WNTI666, Watonga; WMX577, Woodward; WMX578, Woodward; WMX579, Woodward.
Texas: WHT794, Amarillo; WNTB410, Corpus Christi; WNTB460, Corpus Christi; WNTM673, Corsicana; WNTM838, Corsicana; WNEX639, Denison; WNEZ899, Denison; WNTB287, Denison; WNTB687, El Paso; WNEY638, Lubbock; WNEZ900, Lubbock; WNTB289, Lubbock; WNEZ717, Nolanville; WNTA620, West Waco.
Other Holdings:
Formerly known as Heartland Wireless Communications Inc.
International Cable: 49% of Television Interactiva del Norte ("Telinor").
Telecommunications company: 20% of Wireless One Inc.
Wireless Cable, see listing.

NVJ COM

15071 Becky Lane
Monte Sereno, CA 95030
Phone: 408-268-3908
MMDS Systems:
Maryland: WNTK594, Salisbury.

BONNIE D. O'CONNELL

546 Sandy Hook Rd.
Treasure Island, FL 33706
Phone: 813-360-2716
Fax: 813-360-5809
MMDS Systems:
Georgia: WMY295, Swainsboro.

MAURICE P. O'CONNELL

546 Sandy Hook Rd.
Treasure Island, FL 33706
Phone: 813-360-2716
Fax: 813-360-5809
MMDS Systems:
Alaska: WMY297, Fairbanks.

OKLAHOMA WESTERN TELEPHONE CO.

Box 398
Clayton, OK 74536
Officer:
Pauline Van Horne, Pres.
MMDS Systems:
Oklahoma: WLK382, Clayton.
Other Holdings:
Wireless Cable, see listing.

OMEGA RADIOTELEPHONE

c/o David Hernandez
1601 Neptune Dr.
San Leandro, CA 94577-3162
Phone: 415-895-9500
Ownership: David Hernandez, Linda Webb & Ron Blasques.
MMDS Systems:
Arizona: WHK994, Tucson.
Kansas: WHT744, Wichita.

ORANGE COUNTY BOARD OF COMMISSIONERS

201 S. Rosalind Ave.
Orlando, FL 32801
Phone: 407-836-7300
Officer:
Mel Martinez, Chmn.
MDS Systems:
Florida: WFY742, Orlando; WGW518, Orlando.

ORION BROADCASTING SYSTEMS

Suite 208B
7231 S. Eastern Ave.
Las Vegas, NV 89119-0451
Phone: 800-356-1825
Ownership: Orionvision.
MDS Systems:
New Jersey: WMI383, Atlantic City; WMI387, Atlantic City.
MMDS Systems:
New Jersey: WHT752, Atlantic City; WMI280, Atlantic City; WNTH892, Atlantic City; WNTJ652, Atlantic City.
Other Holdings
Wireless Cable, see listing.

MATTHEW ORISTANO

5301 E. Broadway Blvd.
Tucson, AZ 85711-3710
Phone: 520-519-4400
Fax: 520-747-6830
Web site: http://www.pchoicetv.com
MDS Systems:
Arizona: WPF47, Phoenix; WMH229, Tucson; WMI956, Tucson.
Indiana: WPX33, Indianapolis.
Michigan: WJM22, Royal Oak Twp.
Missouri: WQQ64, St. Louis.
Texas: WDU206, Galveston.
Utah: KEW74, Salt Lake City.
Wisconsin: WKR27, Milwaukee.
MMDS Systems:

Arizona: WHK556, Phoenix; WHJ902, Shaw Butte; WHT685, Shaw Butte; WHT686, Shaw Butte; WNTL436, Shaw Butte.
California: WHT653, Mount San Bruno; WHJ908, San Diego; WHJ909, San Francisco.
Illinois: WMX255, Chicago; WNET334, Chicago.
Indiana: WNTG393, Anderson; WNTG394, Bloomington; WNTM675, Bloomington; WHT674, Indianapolis; WMY203, Indianapolis; WMY204, Indianapolis; WMY205, Indianapolis; WMI833, Terre Haute.
Michigan: WHJ878, Detroit; WLK238, Detroit; WNEK611, Detroit; WNTK656, Detroit; WMI843, Jackson.
Missouri: WHJ915, St. Louis.
Texas: WHJ887, Houston; WHI625, Waco.
Utah: WHT692, Magna; WLW775, Magna; WNTB421, Magna; WNTB688, Magna; WNTB690, Magna.
Other Holdings:
Oristano is Chmn. of Preferred Entertainment Inc. TV Partners, see listing in Cable System Ownership.

ORLANDO BDC-MMDS CO.
MMDS Systems:
Florida: WHT732, Orlando.

PAGING SYSTEMS INC.
Box 4249
Burlingame, CA 94011
Phone: 415-697-1000
MMDS Systems:
Kansas: WHT743, Wichita.
Other Holdings:
LPTV, see listing.

PALMER COMMUNICATIONS INC.
1801 Grand Ave.
Des Moines, IA 50309-3362
Phone: 515-242-3500
Fax: 515-242-3799
Officers:
Joseph R. Lentz, Pres. & Chief Operating Officer
Gordon A. McCollum, V.P. & Secy.-Treas.
Jerry Giesler, V.P.
Mark Halverson, V.P., Radio
Willam Katsafanas, V.P., Television
Ownership: D. D. Palmer Trust.
Represented (legal): Faegre & Benson.
MDS Systems:
California: WSL86, Palm Springs.
Florida: WFY577, Marco Island.
Radio Stations:
Florida: WNOG-AM-FM; Naples; WARO(FM), Naples-Fort
Iowa: KLYF(FM), Des Moines; WHO(AM), Des Moines.
Other Holdings:
Cellular telephone: Palmer Wireless.

STELLA A. PAPPAS
500 S. Chinowth Rd.
Visalia, CA 93277
Phone: 209-733-7800
Fax: 209-627-5363
Represented (legal): Paul, Hastings, Janofsky & Walker LLP.
MMDS Systems:
Georgia: WLW935, Columbus.

PARKERSBURG WIRELESS LLC
1025 Thomas Jefferson St. NW
Washington, DC 20007
MDS Systems:
West Virginia: WMH661, Parkersburg.
MMDS Systems:
West Virginia: WMI413, Parkersburg.

PATRICK/HYBL COMMUNICATIONS
2035 Paseo Del Oro
Colorado Springs, CO 80904-1809
Phone: 719-392-4219
MMDS Systems:
Colorado: WLW971, Vail.

PAUL COMMUNICATIONS INC.
7555 Pebble Beach Dr.
Reno, NV 89502
Officers:
Paul J. Marcille, Chief Exec. Officer
Sherry J. Marcille, Chief Financial Officer
Ownership: Paul Marcille.
MMDS Systems:
Michigan: WGW275, Saginaw.
New York: WMH804, Poughkeepsie.

PAUL JACKSON ENTERPRISES
Box 2279
Rte. 2
Chatsworth, GA 30705
MMDS Systems:
Georgia: WMY415, Chatsworth; WMY416, Chatsworth; WMY417, Chatsworth.

JERRY A. PAYNE
1840 Barron Rd.
Poplar Bluff, MO 63907
Phone: 314-785-0756
MMDS Systems:
Missouri: WMH440, Sikeston.

DONALD K. PENDLETON
Box 258
Isleboro, ME 04848
MMDS Systems:
Maine: WMH300, Camden.

PEOPLE'S CHOICE TV PARTNERS
Suite 249
2 Corporate Dr.
Shelton, CT 06484-6239
Phone: 203-929-2800
Fax: 203-929-1454
Officer:
Joel A. Strasser, Dir., Corp. Communications
MMDS Systems:
Arkansas: WMI821, Fayetteville.
Other Holdings:
Wireless Cable, see listing
Preferred Entertainment Inc., see listing in Cable System Ownership.

PHILLIP D. PERRY
2346 La Lima Way
Sacramento, CA 95833
Phone: 916-322-1572
MMDS Systems:
Hawaii: WMH484, Maui.

NANCY & TED PHILLIPS CO.
Box 431
Seminole, OK 74818
Phone: 405-382-1100
Fax: 405-382-1104
Officer:
Stu Phillips, Chief Exec. Officer
MMDS Systems:
New Mexico: WLW782, Santa Fe.

PHOENIX MDS CO.
114 Sutton Manor Rd.
New Rochelle, NY 10801
Phone: 914-235-3046
Fax: 914-235-0468
Officer:
M. Christina Selin, Managing Partner
Ownership: Broadcast Data Corp., KC Corp. & Private Networks Inc., see listings.
MDS Systems:
Arizona: WHB522, Phoenix.

RON PINGEL
8018 Simpson Dr.
Amarillo, TX 79121
Phone: 806-355-3449
MDS Systems:
Texas: WMI920, Mount Pleasant.
MMDS Systems:
Texas: WMX231, Pampa; WMX232, Pampa.

PIONEER TELEPHONE COOPERATIVE INC.
Box 539
Kingfisher, OK 73750
Phone: 405-375-4111
MDS Systems:
Oklahoma: WMY224, Guymon.

PISCES MICROCABLE PARTNERSHIP
67-755 Peineta Rd.
Palm Springs, CA 92262
Phone: 619-323-2199
MMDS Systems:
Utah: WMI395, Delta.

LOUIS F. POWELL
202 Bluffview Dr.
Belleair Bluffs, FL 34604
Phone: 813-581-1996
MMDS Systems:
Alabama: WLW737, Demopolis.

PRAIRIELAND CABLE PARTNERSHIP
MMDS Systems:
Illinois: WHI968, Bloomington-Normal.

PRESCO CORP.
c/o Lowell H. Press
4547 4th Ave. NE
Seattle, WA 98105
Phone: 206-545-0268
MMDS Systems:
Illinois: WLK292, Champaign-Urbana.
Ohio: WLK210, Mansfield.
Tennessee: WHT679, Nashville.

PRIVATE NETWORKS INC.
Box 012707
28 Old Fulton St.
Brooklyn, NY 11201
Phone: 212-777-4740
Officers:
Billy Parrott, Pres.
William Walker, V.P.
Ownership: Black Vanguard Assoc. Inc.
MDS Systems:
Arizona: WHB522, Phoenix.
California: WLK228, Mount San Bruno; WHT559, San Diego.
District of Columbia: WHT747, Washington.
Illinois: WHT562, Chicago.
Indiana: WLK246, Indianapolis.
Missouri: WHT702, St. Louis.
Pennsylvania: WLK231, Philadelphia.
Texas: WHT570, Houston.
MMDS Systems:
Alabama: WLW773, Huntsville.
Florida: WHT639, Miami.
Illinois: WHT634, Decatur.
New York: WMI301, Glens Falls; WMI294, Ithaca.
Other Holdings:
Phoenix MDS Co., see listing.

PRO-COMMUNICATIONS INC.
233 N. Garrard
Rantoul, IL 61866
Phone: 217-893-8730
MMDS Systems:
Colorado: WLW976, Greeley.

PROGRESSIVE COMMUNICATIONS INC.
Suite 214
7617 Reading Rd.
Cincinnati, OH 45237
Officers:
Henry R. Riggins, Pres.
Darlene Riggins, Secy-Treas.
Represented (legal): Brown, Nietert & Kaufman, Chartered.
MMDS Systems:
Ohio: WHT714, Dayton.

PROGRESSIVE TECHNOLOGIES CO.
MDS Systems:
Colorado: WFY716, Grand Junction.

DENNIS A. PUVALOWSKI
1910 Sand Beach Rd.
Bad Axe, MI 48413
Phone: 517-269-7709
MMDS Systems:
Michigan: WMH636, Bad Axe; WMH641, Bad Axe; WNTL898, Bad Axe.

QUADRANGLE COMMUNICATIONS INC.
Box 2090
Del Mar, CA 92014
Phone: 619-630-2129
MMDS Systems:
Florida: WNTB227, Oldsmar.

QUALICOM ELECTRONICS
c/o Marco Island MDS Co.
301 Tower Rd.
Naples, FL 33962
MDS Systems:
Florida: WFY577, Marco Island.

R & B COMMUNICATIONS
Box 174
1000 Roanoke Rd.
Daleville VA, 24083
Phone: 540-992-2211
Fax: 540-992-3094
Officers:
Ira D. Layman, Chmn.
J. Allen Layman, Pres. & Chief Exec. Officer
Robert F. Nay, V.P., Mktg.
Chris C. Foster, Chief Financial Officer
Represented (legal): Gurman, Blask & Freedman, Chartered.
MMDS Systems:
Virginia: WNTH926, Buchanan.
Other Holdings:
ITFS, wireless cable, see listing.

RED CHARLESTON F PARTNERSHIP
248 King George St.
Annapolis, MD 21401
Phone: 410-626-1200
Fax: 410-626-1266
Ownership: Baypoint TV Inc., 25%; MHW Assoc., 25%; Multichannel Media Inc., 25%; Starchannels Assoc. LP, 25%, see listings.
Represented (legal): Koteen & Naftalin.
MMDS Systems:
South Carolina: WFY743, Charleston.

RED HILL TELECOMMUNICATIONS CORP.
MDS Systems:
Illinois: WFY537, Olney.

RED MEMPHIS F PARTNERSHIP
248 King George St.
Annapolis, MD 21401

Phone: 410-626-1200
Fax: 410-626-1266
Ownership: Baypoint TV Inc., 25%; MHW Assoc., 25%; Multichannel Media Inc., 25%; National Wireless Video, 25%, see listing.
Represented (legal): Koteen & Naftalin.
MMDS Systems:
Tennessee: WHT728, Memphis.

RED NEW YORK E PARTNERSHIP
248 King George St.
Annapolis, MD 21401
Phone: 202-659-4400
Ownership: Multichannel Media Inc., 33.3%, see listing.
Represented (legal): Koteen & Naftalin.
MMDS Systems:
New York: WLR500, New York.

ROB-ART INC.
Box 85
Cody, WY 82414
Phone: 307-587-6449
Officers:
Robert K. Swanson, Pres.
Neil Swanson, V.P.
Ownership: Robert K. Swanson & Neil Swanson.
MDS Systems:
Wyoming: WHD367, Cody.

ROCZ DUDECK LEAS PARTNERSHIP
Suite 201
7800 113th St. N
Seminole, FL 34642
Phone: 813-392-1681
Ownership: John Dudeck & Ronald N. S. Rocz, Principals, see listings.
MMDS Systems:
Florida: WNTJ386, Panama City.

RONALD N.S. ROCZ
29277 Southfield
Southfield, MI 48076
Phone: 813-873-7700
MMDS Systems:
Louisiana: WNTI842, Shreveport.
Other Holdings:
Rocz Dudeck Leas Partnership, see listing.

JOSEPH L. ROFFERS
327 S. Superior St.
De Pere, WI 54115
Phone: 414-336-0947
MDS Systems:
Wisconsin: WQQ77, Green Bay.

RONALD W. BENFIELD PARTNERSHIP
702 Hartness Rd.
Statesville, NC 28677
Phone: 704-878-9004
MMDS Systems:
North Carolina: WMX320, New Bern.

MARTIN V. ROSALES
Box 211
Lordsburg, NM 88045
MMDS Systems:
New Mexico: WHT597, Deming.

SHERRY RULLMAN
2129 N. San Marcus Place
Claremont, CA 91711-1766
Phone: 714-625-2988
MMDS Systems:
Florida: WHT697, West Palm Beach.
Kansas: WMI290, Topeka.

STEPHEN RULLMAN
Box 1102
Claremont, CA 91711
Phone: 909-621-1004
MMDS Systems:
Montana: WMI851, Bozeman.

RURAL ELECTRIC COOPERATIVE INC.
Box 609
Lindsay, OK 73052
Phone: 405-756-3104
MMDS Systems:
Oklahoma: WLW983, Lindsay.

RURAL TELEVISION INC.
Box 726
Spicer, MN 56288
Phone: 320-796-7881
Officer:
Douglas J. Dietz, Chief Exec. Officer
MMDS Systems:
Minnesota: WMH540, Willmar.

RURAL TELEVISION SYSTEM INC.
6205-A Franktown Rd.
Carson City, NV 89701
MMDS Systems:
New Mexico: WHT598, Silver City.
Other Holdings:
LPTV, see listing.

SACRAMENTO WIRELESS CO.
c/o Broadcast Data Corp.
25 Rockwood Place
Englewood, NJ 07631
MDS Systems:
California: WSL88, Sacramento.

SALINA-SPAVINAW TELEPHONE CO. INC.
Box 600
109 Evanjoy Rd.
Salina, OK 74365-0600
Phone: 918-434-5392
Fax: 918-434-6960
Officers:
Janet K. Robson, Pres.
Nancy S. Cain, V.P.
Ownership: Janet K. Robson & Nancy S. Cain, Principals.
MMDS Systems:
Oklahoma: WLW874, Salina/Langley.

MARY C. SALVATO
8811 Angoff Dr.
New Port Richey, FL 34653
Phone: 813-376-9284
MMDS Systems:
Indiana: WNTM640, South Bend.

SAN JUAN MDS INC.
1725 Andres Bello Cupey
San Juan, PR 00926
Phone: 787-723-1410
Officer:
Rohel Pascual, Pres.
Represented (legal): Fleischman & Walsh LLP.
MDS Systems:
Puerto Rico: WFY444, Mayaguez; WFY440, Ponce; WPW98, San Juan-Ponce-Mayaguez.
MMDS Systems:
Puerto Rico: WMH225, Mayaguez.

SANGUINETTI INVESTMENT CORP.
168 N. Main St.
Rutland, VT 05701
Phone: 802-773-2163
MDS Systems:
Vermont: WMH868, Rutland; WMI343, Rutland.

VICKI SARDINAS
Phone: 414-233-5054
MMDS Systems:
Idaho: WLR468, Idaho Falls.

SATELLITE MICROCABLE PARTNERS
MDS Systems:
Colorado: WMY410, Trinidad.

SATELLITE SIGNALS OF NEW ENGLAND INC.
168 N. Main St.
Rutland, VT 05701
Phone: 802-775-4112
Ownership: E. Nicholas Sangrunetti.
MMDS Systems:
Massachusetts: WLK314, Hyannis.
Vermont: WLW890, Baltimore/White River Junction; WMH308, Cornwall; WMH464, East Enosburg; WLK341, Rutland; WNTI856, Rutland.
Other Holdings:
Wireless Cable, see listing.

SATELLITE VISION BROADCASTING CO.
377 Browns Bend Rd.
Alexandria, LA 71303-4138
Phone: 318-442-6714
Fax: 318-445-7231
Officers:
Charles Fine, Chmn. & Chief Financial Officer
A. R. Nolan, Pres. & Chief Operating Officer
J. E. Fryar, Chief Exec. Officer & V.P., Engineering, 6
MMDS Systems:
Louisiana: WFY645, Alexandria.

SBC MEDIA VENTURES
20 W. Gude Dr.
Rockville, MD 20850
Phone: 301-294-7633
Officers:
Edward E. Whitacre, Chmn. & Chief Exec. Officer
Jameson Scott, V.P., Mktg. & Programming, 4
Steve Dimmitt, Dir., Strategic Business Development
Ownership: SBC Communications Inc., see listing in Cable System Ownership.
Represented (legal): Fleischman & Walsh LLP.
MDS Systems:
California: WPW94, Riverside.
MMDS Systems:
California: WNET335, La Habra; WBB785, Mount Wilson; WNTD998, Riverside; WNTL542, Riverside; WNTA514, San Francisco.
Other Holdings:
Wireless cable, see listing.

THOMAS H. SCHITZIONS
Phone: 713-222-2170
MMDS Systems:
Texas: WNTB468, Corpus Christi.

JAMES H. SCHROEDER
980 Meadow Lane
Fond du Lac, WI 54935
Phone: 414-922-6130
MMDS Systems:
Colorado: WMI892, Craig.

SEA SHORE COMMUNICATIONS
1905 Spring Lake Court
Birmingham, AL 35215
Phone: 205-854-6472
MDS Systems:
Texas: WLW868, Uvalde.

SENVISTA GENERAL PARTNERSHIP
7521 E. Edgemont
Scottsdale, AZ 85257
Phones: 602-994-3493; 602-994-0919
MMDS Systems:
Florida: WNTK634, Bradenton.

SE/USA MDS CO.
Box 11
Oakway Circle, Rte. 2
Greenville, SC 29607
MMDS Systems:
South Carolina: WLW977, Myrtle Beach.

EDWARD F. SHILLING
Box 1087
Petersburg, AK 99833
Phone: 907-789-9867
MDS Systems:
Alaska: WLW792, Juneau.

JAMES A. SIMON
MDS Systems:
Indiana: WGW300, Fort Wayne; WHD358, Fort Wayne.

SIOUX VALLEY RURAL TELEVISION INC.
Box 20
Colman, SD 57017
Phone: 605-534-3241
Fax: 605-256-1691
E-mail: jbrick@svswe.com
Web site: http://www.svtv.com
Officers:
James Kiley, Chief Exec. Officer
Joel Brick, Dir., Telecommunications
Ownership: Sioux Valley Southwestern Electric.
Represented (legal): Lukas, McGowan, Nace & Gutierrez.
MMDS Systems:
South Dakota: WHI959, Colman; WNEX689, Colman; WNEX781, Colman; WNTA301, Colman; WMX344, Sioux Falls; WMX347, Sioux Falls; WMX348, Sioux Falls; WMX349, Sioux Falls; WMX358, Sioux Falls; WLK328, Yankton; WLK384, Yankton; WNTK311, Yankton.
Other Holdings:
Wireless cable, see listing.

SKYCABLE TV OF MADISON LLC
2520 Todd Dr.
Madison, WI 53713
Phone: 608-271-6999
Fax: 608-271-2256
E-mail: kegan@skycabletv.com
Web site: http://www.skycabletv.com
Officers:
Dan Lyons, Chmn.
Kim Egon, Pres.
Ownership: Dan Lyons, Principal.
MMDS Systems:
Wisconsin: WHT772, Madison; WNTJ374, Madison; WNTJ388, Madison; WNTJ432, Madison.
Other Holdings:
Wireless cable, see listing.

SKYLINE BROADCASTING
104 Stoddard Hill
Pleasant Hill, LA 71065
MMDS Systems:
Louisiana: WNTN322, Natchitoches.

SLOPE ELECTRIC COOPERATIVE INC.
Box 338
New England, ND 58647
Phone: 701-225-6061

MMDS Systems:
North Dakota: WLW769, Scranton.

SMITHCO OF FORT SMITH INC.
6609 Rogers Ave.
Fort Smith, AR 72903
MMDS Systems:
Arkansas: WLK316, Fort Smith.

SOCORRO SATELLITE SYSTEMS INC.
215 E. Manzanares Ave.
Socorro, NM 87801
Phone: 505-835-0560
MMDS Systems:
New Mexico: WMI416, Socorro; WMI417, Socorro; WNTK750, Socorro.

SOUTHEAST RURAL VISION ENTERPRISES CO.
Box 7
Kindred, ND 58051
Phone: 701-428-3292
Fax: 701-428-3044
Officers:
Bill Bertram, Chmn.
Michael D. Gustafson, Pres. & Chief Exec. Officer
John Froelich, Secy.-Treas.
Chad T. Sapa, Chief Financial Officer
Ownership: Cass County Electric Cooperative Inc.
MMDS Systems:
North Dakota: WMI875, Fort Ransom; WMI879, Fort Ransom; WNTK290, Fort Ransom.

SOUTHERN WIRELESS CABLE PARTNERS
605 Lake Shore Dr.
Maitland, FL 32751
Phone: 407-647-3952
MMDS Systems:
Georgia: WMX932, Carrollton.

SOUTHERN WIRELESS CO. INC.
2101 S. Bay St.
Georgetown, SC 29440
Phones: 803-546-1913; 803-546-0400
Officers:
Ron Charlton Sr., Chmn. & Chief Exec. Officer
James Necaise, Pres.
Robert Adkison, Secy.-Treas.
Keith Harpen, Chief Financial Officer
Ownership: James Necaise, see listing & Ron Charlton Sr. Charlton & Adkison are execs. of Southern Cable Communications, see listing in Cable System Ownership.
Represented (legal): Pepper & Corazzini.
MMDS Systems:
South Carolina: WMH616, Georgetown; WMX234, Georgetown.

SOUTHWEST CABLE INC.
1108 Bayshope
Allen, TX 75002
Phone: 405-924-8065
MDS Systems:
Texas: WMI929, Longview; WMI933, Longview.

SOUTHWEST INDIANA PUBLIC BROADCASTING INC.
405 Carpenter St.
Evansville, IN 47708-1027
Phone: 812-423-2973
Fax: 812-428-7548
Officers:
Robert Stayman, Chmn.
John Stanley, Vice Chmn.
David L. Dial, Pres. & Chief Operating Officer
Gail K. Williams, V.P. Marketing
Al Perry, Treas.
Dorlis Johnson, Chief Financial Officer
Represented (legal): David L. Dial.
TV Stations (1):
Indiana: WNIN, Evansville-Henderson-Owensboro, KY.
MMDS Systems:
Indiana: WMI378, Evansville.
Radio Stations:
Indiana: WNIN-FM, Evansville-Henderson-Owensboro.

SOUTHWEST TELECOMMUNICATIONS CO-OP ASSN. INC.
Box 309
Palisade, NE 69040
Phone: 308-285-3880
Fax: 308-285-3811
Officer:
David Fahrenbruch, Chief Financial Officer
Represented (legal): Burger & Bennet.
MMDS Systems:
Colorado: WHK934, Wray; WNEX782, Wray.
Nebraska: WHK929, Bartley; WNEX783, Bartley; WHK923, North Platte; WNEX785, North Platte; WLW964, Oshkosh; WNEZ240, Oshkosh; WHK926, Wauneta; WNEX784, Wauneta.
Other Holdings:
Wireless cable, see listing.

SPECCHIO DEVELOPERS LTD.
Box 846
233 N. Garrard
Rantoul, IL 61866
MDS Systems:
Illinois: WLW763, Champaign.
MMDS Systems:
Illinois: WNTA575, Champaign.
Other Holdings:
LPTV, see listing

SPRINGFIELD ONE PARTNERSHIP
Suite 501
1100 17th St. NW
Washington, DC 20036
Phone: 202-223-4449
Fax: 202-223-4450
Ownership: William M. Barnard, Thomas Dougherty, Richard Gould, W. Randolph Young & Lawrence Behr, 100% jointly. See also Baypoint TV Inc., Columbia Wireless Corp., G & Y Communications, Libmot Communications Partnership, MDS Signal Group & Young Communications.
Represented (legal): Evans & Sill PC.
MMDS Systems:
Illinois: WMY460, Springfield.
Missouri: WMX370, Springfield; WMX371, Springfield; WMX372, Springfield.

JOSEPH W. ST. CLAIR
35 Kutz Rd.
Temple, PA 19560-9762
MMDS Systems:
Nevada: WMY400, Hawthorne.

CITY OF ST. LOUIS METROPOLITAN POLICE DEPT.
1200 Clark
St. Louis, MO 63103
Phone: 314-444-5993
MMDS Systems:
Missouri: WBF80, St. Louis.

STARCHANNELS ASSOCIATES LP
Suite 212
100 Jericho Quadrangle
Jericho, NY 11753
MMDS Systems:
Mississippi: WMI886, Biloxi.
New Hampshire: WMH548, Manchester.
Texas: WHT712, Corpus Christi; WHT766, El Paso.
Other Holdings:
25% of Red Charleston F Partnership, see listing.

STARCOM INC.
1986 Julep Rd.
St. Cloud, MN 56301
Phone: 320-253-9600
Fax: 320-255-5276
Officers:
Dennis Carpenter, Pres. & Chief Exec. Officer
Bart Ward, Secy.-Treas.
MDS Systems:
Minnesota: WMI359, Fairmont.
MMDS Systems:
Minnesota: WLW724, Fairmont; WLW728, Fairmont; WLW732, Fairmont; WLW834, Fairmont.
Other Holdings:
LPTV, see listing.

STEPHEN COMMUNICATIONS INC.
1127 Alpine Place
Salt Lake City, UT 84105-1501
Phone: 801-582-0381
Fax: 801-582-4601
Officers:
Stephen A. Merrill, Chief Exec. Officer
J. Colette Merrill, Secy.-Treas.
Ownership: Stephen A. Merrill.
Represented (legal): Rini, Coran & Lancellotta PC.
MMDS Systems:
Arkansas: WHT723, Little Rock.
Other Holdings:
LPTV, see listing.

BOB C. STORY
Box 1307
Durant, OK 74701
Phone: 405-920-0788
MMDS Systems:
Oklahoma: WNTH576, Ada.

SUN MULTI-CHANNEL MDS INC.
Suite 500
3200 Cherry Creek S Dr.
Denver, CO 80209
MMDS Systems:
South Carolina: WMH501, Columbia.

SUNAMERICA INC.
1 SunAmerica Center
Century City
Los Angeles, CA 90067-6002
Phone: 310-772-6000
MMDS Systems:
Michigan: WMH808, Lansing.

SUNBELT ENTERTAINMENT CORP.
Oakland-Alameda Coliseum
7000 Coliseum Way
Oakland, CA 94621
Phone: 510-638-6300
MMDS Systems:
Georgia: WHT561, Augusta.

SUPER COMM
738 Intrepid Way
Davidsonville, MD 21035
Phone: 301-261-4766
Officer:
Redge Mahaffey, Managing Partner
MDS Systems:
Wyoming: WLW901, Cheyenne.
MMDS Systems:
Hawaii: WMH745, Koloa.

SUPER WIRELESS TV
214 Broadway
Millbrae, CA 94030
MMDS Systems:
Montana: WMY423, Lewistown.

SUPERIOR COMMUNICATIONS SYSTEMS
4140 Elkhorn Dr.
Cedar Rapids, IA 52411
Phone: 319-393-0094
Ownership: James R. Maccani, Principal.
Represented (legal): Joel L. Massie.
MDS Systems:
Michigan: WHT576, Ironwood.
MMDS Systems:
Michigan: WGW502, Ironwood.

TAFT BROADCASTING CO.
4808 San Felipe Rd.
Houston, TX 77056
Phone: 713-622-1015
Fax: 713-622-9314
Officers:
Paul E. Taft, Pres. & Chief Exec. Officer
Philip D. Taft, Chief Operating Officer
Jerry G. Bridges, Exec. V.P. & Chief Financial Officer
Ownership: Paul E. Taft, 65%; Phillip D. Taft, 21%; Jerry G. Bridges, 14%.
MDS Systems:
Texas: WOF76, Houston.
Other Holdings:

TC COMMUNICATIONS INC.
2323 Country Aire Estates
Aberdeen, SD 57401
Phone: 605-229-3854
MMDS Systems:
Iowa: WLW731, Radcliffe.

TCI ACQUISITION CORP.
500 Clyde Ave.
Mountain View, CA 94043-2212
MMDS Systems:
South Carolina: WLW738, Greenville.

TEEWINOT LICENSING INC.
Box 1550
Port Orchard, WA 98366
Phone: 360-871-5981
Officers:
Willis E. Twiner, Pres.
Patrick J. Carey, Chief Exec. Officer
Thomas Carey, Chief Operating Officer
Sheryll Curtis, Secy.-Treas. & Chief Financial Officer
MDS Systems:
Idaho: WKR64, Twin Falls.
MMDS Systems:
Idaho: WMX247, Idaho Falls; WLW965, Twin Falls.
Other Holdings:
Wireless cable, see listing.

TEL-COM WIRELESS CABLE TV CORP.
1506 N.E. 162nd St.
North Miami Beach, FL 33162
Phone: 305-947-3010
E-mail: info@telcom.net
Web site: http://www.tel_com.net
Ownership: Melvin Rosen & Samuel Simkin.
MMDS Systems:
Wisconsin: WMH472, La Crosse; WMH473, La Crosse; WNTI731, La Crosse.

TELE-ACQUISITIONS LLC
225 Portsmouth Court
Roswell, GA 30076
Phone: 770-754-6212
Officer:

Christopher Blair, Pres.
MMDS Systems:
Minnesota: WNTG603, Mankato; WNTH457, Mankato; WNTH575, Mankato; WNTG601, Mankato/ Gaylord.

TELECOMMUNICATIONS SYSTEMS INC.

Box 7222
Menlo Park, CA 94026
Phone: 415-324-4811
Ownership: Fisher Medical Publications.
MDS Systems:
Washington: WDU571, Bellingham.

TELECRAFTER SERVICES CORP.

Box 11
Hardin, MT 59034
Represented (legal): Gardner, Carton & Douglas.
MDS Systems:
Montana: WHC973, Glasgow.

TELE-VIEW INC.

Box 186
Roma, TX 78584
Phone: 512-849-1470
Officer:
J. C. Guerra, Pres.
MMDS Systems:
Texas: WLW940, Roma.

TEL MASTER

MDS Systems:
New Mexico: WHD499, Deming; WGW313, Pinos Altos-Silver City.

TEL-RADIO COMMUNICATIONS PROPERTIES INC.

301 S. Westfield Rd.
Madison, WI 53705
Phone: 608-845-4000
Officers:
Donald L. Porter, Pres.
Donald R. Brown, V.P.
David M. Wilson, Secy.
Terry M. Busse, Dir.
Ownership: Telephone & Data Systems Inc., see listing in Cable System Ownership.
Represented (legal): Koteen & Naftalin.
MDS Systems:
Maine: KNJ27, Augusta-Belgrade.
Wisconsin: WFY430, Janesville-Beloit; WPY30, Madison.

ROBERT E. TERRES

2430 Norwood Ave.
Pennsauken, NJ 08109
MMDS Systems:
Illinois: WNTA478, Champaign.

TEX-STAR WIRELESS COMMUNICATIONS ALPHA/BETA/GAMMA

Box 940008
Plano, TX 75094-0008
Phone: 214-424-1661
Represented (legal): Fletcher, Heald & Hildreth PLC.
MMDS Systems:
Texas: WMI373, Snyder; WMI377, Snyder; WNTK882, Snyder.

THOMAS ALEXANDER & ASSOCIATES

MMDS Systems:
North Carolina: WMH536, Raleigh.

THREE SIXTY CORP.

120 Floral Ave.
New Providence, NJ 07974
Phone: 908-665-0094
Fax: 908-665-0343
Officers:
Robert Bilodeau, Pres.
Salvatore LaMarca, V.P. & Chief Operating Officer
Ronald Rizzo, Chief Financial Officer
Roy Tartaglia, V.P.
Robert Greenwood, Secy. & Legal Counsel
Ownership: Robert Bilodeau, Burr Egan Delage Co. & Robert Greenwood, Principals.
MMDS Systems:
Texas: WHT711, Corpus Christi.
Other Holdings:
SMATV, cable, see listing.

TIDE MICROCABLE PARTNERSHIP

67-755 Peineta Rd.
Palm Springs, CA 92262
MMDS Systems:
Texas: WMY445, Fort Stockton.

TIMPVIEW WIRELESS INC.

845 Skyline Dr.
St. George, UT 84770
Officers:
Mical J. Terry, Pres. & Chief Exec. Officer
James C. Hoskins, V.P.
Patti Goodman, Secy.-Treas.
MMDS Systems:
Utah: WMH776, Provo-Orem.

TMT PARTNERSHIP

25 Alexander Ave.
Carlisle, PA 17013
Phone: 717-243-7893
Ownership: Marian L. Marsh, 33.33%; Shirley A. Thomas, 33.33%; Vera M. Thomas, 33.33%.
MMDS Systems:
South Dakota: WMX353, Pierre; WMX354, Pierre.

TODD COMMUNICATIONS INC.

6545 Cecilia Circle
Minneapolis, MN 55435
Ownership: B. J. Klindworth.
MMDS Systems:
Illinois: WMH557, Galesburg; WMH577, Ladd/ Streator; WMH256, Mount Sterling; WMH565, Witt.
Iowa: WMH553, Britt.
Minnesota: WMH313, Appleton; WMH316, Austin; WMH317, Brainerd; WMH481, Granite Falls; WMH549, Marshall; WMH533, St. James.

TOKEN PARTNERSHIP

1023 51st St.
Moline, IL 61265
Phone: 309-764-6886
MDS Systems:
Utah: WLW932, Logan.
MMDS Systems:
California: WNTD890, Chico.
Georgia: WNTC450, Albany.
Kansas: WLW885, Salina.

VICTOR J. TOTH

2719 Soapstone Dr.
Reston, VA 22091
Phone: 703-476-5515
MDS Systems:
Guam: WLW921, Barigada.
MMDS Systems:
Guam: WMI814, Agana.

TOUCH TEL CORP.

Box 4008
Burlingame, CA 94011
Phone: 415-697-1000
MMDS Systems:
Montana: WNTA626, Billings.

TRIBUNE BROADCASTING CO.

No. 1800
435 N. Michigan Ave.
Chicago, IL 60611
Phone: 312-222-3333
Fax: 312-321-0446
Officers:
John W. Madigan, Chmn., Pres. & Chief Exec. Officer, Tribune Co.
Dick Askin, Pres. & Chief Exec. Officer, Tribune Entertainment
Dennis J. FitzSimons, Pres., Tribune Broadcasting Co.
Jeff Scherb, Sr. V.P., Technology, Tribune Co.
James C. Dowdle, Exec. V.P., Media Operations, Tribune Co.
Donald Grenesko, Sr. V.P. & Chief Financial Officer, Tribune Co.
David Hiller, Sr. V.P., Development, Tribune Co.
Gerald Agema, V.P., Admin. & Chief Financial Officer, Tribune
James L. Ellis, V.P., Creative Services, Tribune Broadcasting Co.
Ira Goldstone, V.P., Engineering, Tribune Broadcasting Co.
Marc Schacher, V.P., Programming, Tribune Broadcasting Co.
Shaun Sheehan, V.P., Washington, Tribune Co.
Crane Kenney, V.P., Gen. Counsel & Secy., Tribune Bstg. Co. & Tribune
Ownership: Tribune Co., publicly held.
Represented (legal): Sidley & Austin.
MDS Systems:
Illinois: WOF49, Chicago; WGW344, Waukegan.
Other Holdings:
Newspapers, radio, TV, see listing.

TRI-COUNTY COMMUNICATIONS INC. (TX)

Box 1065
Weslaco, TX 78596
Phone: 210-565-6129
Fax: 210-969-0110
Officers:
R. A. McAllen, Chmn. & Pres.
Jon Schill, Chief Exec. & Operating Officer, 2
Tony Brunneman, Chief Operating Officer
Jesse R. Russell, Secy.-Treas.
Ownership: R. A. McAllen, Chmn. & J. R. Russel.
Represented (legal): Pepper & Corazzini; Atlas-Hall.
MDS Systems:
Texas: WDU443, McAllen.

TV COMMUNICATIONS NETWORK INC.

Suite 300
10020 E. Girard Ave.
Denver, CO 80231
Phone: 303-751-2900
Fax: 303-751-1081
Officers:
Omar A. Duwaik, Pres. & Chief Exec. Officer
Geir Hauge, V.P., Engineering
Ken Roznoy, V.P., Business Development & Secy.
Ownership: Omar Duwaik, 90%; remainder publicly held.
Represented (legal): Fleischman & Walsh LLP.
MMDS Systems:
Alabama: WHT773, Mobile.
California: WGW606, San Luis Obispo.
Kansas: WHT621, Hays; WHT623, Salina.
Other Holdings:
Wireless cable, see listing.

TV2S

1811 D. Roache Harbor Rd.
Friday Harbor, WA 98250
MDS Systems:
Idaho: WGW349, Payette.
MMDS Systems:
Washington: WLW741, Bellingham.

ALICE TWEDT

701 Park St.
Harvard, IL 60033
MMDS Systems:
Illinois: WNTI207, Rockford.

BLAKE TWEDT

5102 Rosegreen Court
Tampa, FL 33624
Phone: 727-587-9959
MDS Systems:
New Mexico: WMY449, Hobbs.
MMDS Systems:
Arkansas: WNTH889, Jonesboro.
Georgia: WMX233, Augusta; WNTJ424, Jeffersonville; WMX340, Savannah; WMX341, Savannah.
Idaho: WNTH960, Pocatello.
Kansas: WNTH894, Dover.
Kentucky: WNTJ710, Lexington.
Louisiana: WNTJ395, Baton Rouge; WNTJ425, Lafayette; WNTH843, Lake Charles; WNTH893, Monroe.
Massachusetts: WNTH970, Deerfield.
Nebraska: WNTH745, Lincoln.
New Hampshire: WNTH747, Portsmouth.
New Mexico: WMX359, Albuquerque; WNTI462, Roswell; WNTI583, Santa Fe.
Ohio: WNTH748, Oregon.
South Carolina: WMY462, Augusta Road.
Tennessee: WNTJ382, Fairmont.
Texas: WNTV757, Brownsville; WNTJ394, Wichita Falls.
Vermont: WNTI680, Burlington.
Virginia: WNTJ713, Richmond; WNTJ739, Richmond.
Other Holdings:
LPTV, see listing.

LYNN TWEDT

701 Grant St.
Harvard, IL 60033
Phone: 815-943-4760
MMDS Systems:
Florida: WNTJ809, Jacksonville.

216 PAOLI AVE. CORP.

300 Domino Lane
Philadelphia, PA 19128
Represented (legal): Schwartz, Woods & Miller.
MDS Systems:
New Jersey: KHH87, Trenton.

ULTRA VISION OF TEXAS

Box 1538
100 E. Kleberg
Kingsville, TX 78363
Phone: 512-851-8588
MDS Systems:
Texas: WMH433, Dilley; WLW936, Falfurrias; WMI392, George West; WMI396, Karnes City.
MMDS Systems:
Texas: WLW892, Falfurrias; WLW896, Falfurrias; WLW735, George West; WLW739, George West; WLW743, George West; WLW900, George West; WLW904, George West.

ULTRACOM CABLEVISION

700 7th St. SW
Washington, DC 20024
Phone: 202-479-4658
MMDS Systems:
American Samoa: WMH584, Pago Pago.

UNION CITY MICROVISION

Box 709

1200 Bishop St.
Union City, TN 38261
Phone: 901-885-3341
Officers:
Joseph H. Harpole Sr., Chmn.
James W. Thompson, Chief Financial Officer
Ownership: Joseph H. Harpole Sr.
MDS Systems:
Tennessee: WGW505, Union City.
MMDS Systems:
Tennessee: WGW628, Union City; WNTK889, Union City.
Other Holdings:
SMATV.

UNITED COMMUNICATIONS LTD.
Phone: 214-929-4002
MMDS Systems:
New York: WMI820, Middleville; WNTJ461, Middleville.

UNITED STATES WIRELESS SYSTEMS INC.
1803 West Ave.
Austin, TX 78701
Phone: 512-320-8522
Officers:
Robert T. Davis, Chmn.
Paul Zukowski, Pres.
MMDS Systems:
Texas: WLK284, Brownsville-Harlingen; WNTH388, Victoria; WNTH481, Victoria; WNTJ758, Victoria.

UNITED TELEPHONE MUTUAL AID CORP.
Box 729
411 7th Ave.
Langdon, ND 58259
Phone: 701-256-5156
Fax: 701-256-5150
E-mail: utc@utma.com
Web site: http://www.utma.com
Officer:
Kenneth Carlson, Pres.
Ownership: Community cooperative.
Represented (legal): Scott R. Stewart.
MDS Systems:
North Dakota: WMY208, Cando; WMY447, Langdon.
MMDS Systems:
North Dakota: WLW982, Cando; WLW986, Cando; WNTA471, Egeland; WNTA554, Egeland; WNTC634, Egeland; WLW984, Langdon; WLW985, Langdon; WNTC624, Lefor; WNEZ907, Milton; WNEZ913, Milton; WNTC633, Milton.
Other Holdings.
Cable, see listing.

UNITY CABLE PARTNERS
Phone: 619-944-9217
MMDS Systems:
Wyoming: WMI333, Worland.

UNIVERSAL WIRELESS TELEVISION CORP.
331 Sea Ridge Dr.
La Jolla, CA 92037
Phone: 303-349-5849
MMDS Systems:
Indiana: WLW814, Lafayette.

U.S. SATELLITE CORP.
935 W. Bullion St.
Murray, UT 84123
Phone: 801-263-0519
Fax: 801-263-0796
Officer:
M. G. Worthington, Sr. V.P. & Chief Operating Officer, 1
Ownership: American Stores Co.
Represented (legal): Kaye, Scholer, Fierman, Hays & Handler LLP.
MMDS Systems:
California: WMH541, San Diego.
Other Holdings:
Teleport.

VIA/NET COMPANIES
836 E. Washington St.
San Diego, CA 92103
Phone: 619-260-0110
Officers:
Carl B. Hilliard, Pres. & Chief Exec. Officer
Sharon E. Hilliard, V.P.
Ownership: Carl B. Hilliard, see listing, 50%; Sharon E. Hilliard, 50%. See also listing for Video Communications Systems.
Represented (legal): Fletcher, Heald & Hildreth PLC.
MDS Systems:
California: WFY435, San Diego.
MMDS Systems:
California: WHT715, Fresno; WNEZ574, Fresno; WNTB228, Sacramento; WNTB230, San Francisco.
Florida: WHJ947, Oldsmar.
Georgia: WHJ940, Atlanta.
Indiana: WHT768, Fort Wayne.
Nevada: WNTH951, Henderson.
Other Holdings:
OFS.

VIDEO COMMUNICATIONS SYSTEMS
2100 Electronics Lane
Fort Myers, FL 33912
Phone: 813-936-2153
Ownership: James S. Dwyer, 50%; Carl B. Hilliard, see listing, 50%. See also listing for Via/Net Companies Inc.
Represented (legal): O'Connor & Hannan LLP.

VIDEO/MULTIPOINT INC.
Suite A
2809 Pine St.
San Francisco, CA 94115-2501
Phone: 415-775-9552
Fax: 415-775-9536
Ownership: William M. Saura, Pres.
MMDS Systems:
California: WMH640, El Centro; WMI278, Salinas.
Kentucky: WLR484, Lexington.
Louisiana: WMI870, Alexandria.

VIDEOTRON (BAY AREA) INC.
975-H Industrial Rd.
San Carlos, CA 94070
Phone: 813-530-1812
MMDS Systems:
Florida: WHT700, Oldsmar.

VIDICOM INC.
Box 206
494 Main St.
Prince Frederick, MD 20678
Phone: 301-535-3400
Officer:
Boyd King, Pres.
Ownership: Boyd King.
MDS Systems:
District of Columbia: WHT747, Washington.

VIKING VISION
Suite 101
901 Hwy. 29 N
Alexandria, MN 56308
Phone: 320-763-4122
MMDS Systems:
Minnesota: WMH352, Willmar.
Other Holdings:
Wireless cable, see listing.

VIRGINIA COMMUNICATIONS INC.
6330 E. Mockingbird Lane
Scottsdale, AZ 85253
Phone: 602-948-3776
Fax: 602-991-6797
Ownership: Virginia Merrill, Pres.
Represented (legal): Pepper & Corazzini.
MDS Systems:
Iowa: WFY595, Davenport.
West Virginia: WMH656, Huntington.
MMDS Systems:
Arizona: WMI839, Casa Grande; WMH800, Prescott; WNTJ440, Prescott; WMI827, Verde Valley; WMI864, Verde Valley.
Arkansas: WLK312, Fort Smith.
Iowa: WMI345, Cedar Rapids; WNTJ376, Davenport; WNTJ387, Davenport; WNTJ392, Davenport; WHT588, Davenport,IA-Rock Island-Moline, IL; WNTH585, Marion; WNTI403, Marion.
Louisiana: WMI831, Houma.
Massachusetts: WLK255, Springfield.
Mississippi: WLK203, Vicksburg.
Pennsylvania: WLK302, Altoona.
Tennessee: WLW966, Clarksville; WLW969, Clarksville; WNTF896, Clarksville.
Other Holdings:
Wireless cable, see listing.

VISIONAIRE INC.
63 Lyndel Rd.
Pound Ridge, NY 10576
Ownership: The Kenneth H. Iscol 1990 Trust for Kiva Iscol, see listing.
MMDS Systems:
North Carolina: WHK991, Burlington.
Pennsylvania: WLK221, Scranton.
Texas: WMI835, Nolanville; WMH396, Texarkana.

ROBERT J. WALSER
Box 366236
San Juan, PR 00936
Phone: 787-722-0111
MMDS Systems:
Puerto Rico: WLW576, San German.

WALTER COMMUNICATIONS INC.
Suite 120
4700 S. McClintock
Tempe, AZ 85282
Phone: 602-755-7524
Fax: 602-755-7534
Ownership: Walter Merrill, Chmn. & Pres.
MMDS Systems:
Indiana: WMH569, Anderson.
Other Holdings:
LPTV, see listing.

RONALD D. WARD
10010 Crazy Horse Dr.
Juneau, AK 99801
Phone: 907-789-9867
MDS Systems:
Alaska: WLW796, Juneau.

JOHN F. WARMATH
Box 408
Humboldt, TN 38343
Phone: 901-784-5000
Fax: 901-784-2533
MDS Systems:
Tennessee: WFY989, Somerville.
Cable Holdings:
John Warmath is a principal of Warmath Communications Inc., see Cable System Ownership.

AUDREY B. WARWICK
8140 W. Linvale Place
Denver, CO 80231
MMDS Systems:
Wyoming: WMY404, Pinedale.

W.A.T.C.H. TV CO.
3225 W. Elm St.
Lima, OH 45805
Phone: 419-999-2824
Fax: 419-999-2140
Officers:
Thomas N. Knippen V.P. & Gen. Mgr.
Kim Horne, Secy.-Treas.
Ownership: Benton Ridge Telephone Co., see listing in Cable System Ownership.
MDS Systems:
Ohio: WMI386, Lima; WMI390, Lima.
MMDS Systems:
Ohio: WMH528, Lima; WNTH924, Lima.
Other Holdings:
LPTV, see listing.

WAYNE STATE U.
70 W. Palmer
Detroit, WI 48202
MMDS Systems:
Michigan: WLK367, Detroit.

WBSS AMERICA LLC
Suite 325
9250 E. Costilla Ave.
Englewood, CO 80112
MDS Systems:
Washington: WKR57, Yakima.

WC WIRELESS
Phone: 941-352-7849
MDS Systems:
Hawaii: WMY434, Honolulu.

WCSC INC.
Box 160005
Charleston, SC 29416-6005
MMDS Systems:
Alabama: WLW867, Montgomery.

WCTV PARTNERS
1616 Parkins Mill Rd.
Greenville, SC 29607
Phone: 803-288-0930
MDS Systems:
Tennessee: WMI904, Johnson City.
MMDS Systems:
Georgia: WNTC449, Albany.

DAVID WEICHMAN
8929 Etiwanda Ave:
Northridge, CA 91325
MMDS Systems:
Kentucky: WMH573, Lexington.

WEST RIVER TELECOMMUNICATIONS COOPERATIVE
Box 467
Hazen, ND 58545
Phone: 701-748-2211
Officer:
Albert Grosz, Pres.
MMDS Systems:
North Dakota: WLR504, Hazen; WLR508, Hazen.

WHITCOM PARTNERS
Room 4310
110 W. 51st St.
New York, NY 10020
Phone: 212-582-2300
Fax: 212-582-2310
Officers:
Edward L. Barlow, Chmn.

Robert S. Blank, Chief Operating Officer
Edward B. Cohen, Chief Financial Officer
MMDS Systems:
Maine: WLW836, Bangor.

STEPHEN L. & SUSAN W. WHITMAN
206 Grove St.
Westwood, MA 02090
Phone: 617-329-2004
MMDS Systems:
Missouri: WNTM561, Appleton City.
Other Holdings:
LPTV, see listing.

WHTV BROADCASTING CORP.
Box 8437
Fernandez Juncos Station
San Juan, PR 00910-8437
Phone: 787-722-7815
Officers:
Dr. Luis F. Sala, Chmn. & Chief Exec. Officer
Abelardo Le Compte, Chief Operating Officer
Jorge P. Sala, Chief Financial Officer
Ownership: Sala Business Corp., 80%; Ponce Broadcasting Corp., 20%.
MMDS Systems:
Puerto Rico: WHT655, San Juan; WNTB423, San Juan; WNTB467, San Juan; WNTF632, San Juan.
Other Holdings:
Wireless cable, see listing.

WICHITA BUSINESS MUSIC CO.
4724 Jacksboro Hwy.
Wichita Falls, TX 76302
MMDS Systems:
Texas: WMI807, Lufkin.

WILD RICE ELECTRIC CO-OP INC.
Box 438
Mahnomen, MN 56557
Phone: 218-935-2517
MMDS Systems:
Minnesota: WMH373, Bagley; WMH989, Erskine.

JOHN HOBART WILSON ESTATE
5th Floor
1201 Pennsylvania Ave. NW
Washington, DC 20037
Phone: 202-626-6290
Ownership: Charles H. Wilson, Sally K. Bang & Benito Gaguine, Personal Representatives.
MMDS Systems:
Wisconsin: WHT641, Milwaukee.

MELISSA S. WILSON
701 Grant St.
Harvard, IL 60033
Phone: 815-943-4760
MMDS Systems:
Alabama: WNTJ773, Montgomery.

WIRELESS 2000 PARTNERSHIP
1440 Chattahoochee Run Dr.
Suwanee, GA 30174
MMDS Systems:
Florida: WMY476, Key West.

WIRELESS ADVANTAGE INC.
2155 Main St.
Sarasota, FL 34237
MMDS Systems:
Louisiana: WHT707, Baton Rouge.

WIRELESS BROADCASTING SYSTEMS OF AMERICA INC.
Suite 325
9250 E. Costilla Ave.
Englewood, CO 80112
Phone: 303-649-1195
Fax: 303-649-1196
Officers:
William Kingery, Chief Exec. Officer
Sharan Wilson, Chief Operating Officer
Chris Scurto, V.P., Mktg.
Peer Pedersen, Secy.-Treas.
Jeb Dickey, Chief Financial Officer
Ownership: WBS America LLC.
MDS Systems:
California: WGW352, Sacramento.
Idaho: WMH801, Boise.
MMDS Systems:
California: WHT689, Sacramento; WNET337, Sacramento.
Florida: WLW758, Fort Pierce; WMI887, Melbourne; WMI891, Melbourne; WNTJ436, Melbourne; WNTM547, Melbourne; WMI841, West Palm Beach.
Idaho: WHT797, Boise; WLW924, Boise.
Michigan: WMH389, Muskegon.
Other Holdings:
Wireless cable, LPTV, see listings.

WIRELESS CABLE INTERNATIONAL INC.
67-A Mountain Blvd. Ext.
Warren, NJ 07060
MMDS Systems:
Florida: WNEY710, Tampa.

WIRELESS CABLE SYSTEMS INC.
Phone: 212-268-2828
Fax: 212-268-5675
MMDS Systems:
Illinois: WMH333, Rockford; WMI326, Rockford.
Other Holdings:
Wireless cable, see listing.

WIRELESS ENTERTAINMENT SYSTEMS INC.
Suite B
2530 E. Broadway Blvd.
Tuscon, AZ 85716-5334
Phone: 602-497-5778
MMDS Systems:
Indiana: WHT767, Fort Wayne.

WIRELESS ONE INC.
Suite 400
2506 Lakeland Dr.
Jackson, MS 39208
Phones: 504-926-7778; 601-933-6879
Fax: 504-926-7583
Officers:
Hans Sternberg, Chmn.
Henry Burkhalter, Vice Chmn. & Pres.
Sean Reilly, Chief Exec. Officer
Alton C. Rye, Exec. V.P., Operations
Henry Schopfer, Exec. V.P. & Chief Financial Officer

Branch Offices:
2019 Parkerson Ave.
Suite B
Crowley, LA

1106 Richmond Rd.
Wharton, TX 77488

580 A. Graham Rd.
College Station, TX 77845

8804 B. Grow Rd.
Pensacola, FL 32514
Represented (legal): Pepper & Corazzini.
MDS Systems:
Georgia: WLW877, Valdosta.
MMDS Systems:
Alabama: WMH568, Auburn; WMH985, Auburn; WHT710, Birmingham; WNTH963, Dothan; WNTF818, Huntsville; WNTG242, Huntsville; WNTG248, Huntsville.
Florida: WNTJ383, Fort Walton Beach; WNTJ426, Fort Walton Beach; WNTJ427, Fort Walton Beach; WGW515, Gainesville; WMH620, Gainesville; WMI847, Pensacola.
Georgia: WMH545, Jeffersonville; WMI857, Jeffersonville; WLW848, Valdosta; WLW881, Valdosta.
Louisiana: WLW801, Lake Charles; WMH708, Lake Charles; WNTJ459, Lake Charles.
Mississippi: WNTG905, Clarksdale; WNTJ746, Clarksdale; WNTJ875, Clarksdale.
North Carolina: WHT667, Charlotte; WHT734, Raleigh; WNTA867, Raleigh; WNTK909, Rockingham.
Tennessee: WMI855, Fairmont; WMI883, Memphis; WNTH952, Memphis; WNTI565, Memphis.
Texas: WMX228, Wharton; WMX229, Wharton.
Other Holdings:
Cable, see listing.

WIRELESS PROPERTIES EAST INC.
Suite 500
1555 King St.
Alexandria, VA 22314
Phone: 703-683-8726
Fax: 703-683-6329
MMDS Systems:
Florida: WMX338, Fort Myers.

WIRELESS SUPERVISION TV INC.
Box 1789
921 Carroll St.
Perry, GA 31069
Phone: 912-987-7055
MMDS Systems:
Alaska: WMI316, Fairbanks.

WJB-TV FORT PIERCE INC.
8423 U.S. Rte. 1
Port St. Lucie, FL 34952
Phone: 407-871-1688
MMDS Systems:
Florida: WLK308, Fort Pierce; WNTI841, Fort Pierce; WNTJ380, Fort Pierce.

WKBN BROADCASTING CORP.
3930 Sunset Blvd.
Youngstown, OH 44512
Phone: 216-782-1144
Fax: 216-782-3504
Officers:
W. P. Williamson Jr., Chmn.
W. P. Williamson III, Vice Chmn.
J. D. Williamson II, Pres.
Doris J. Saloom, V.P. & Secy.
Lowry A. Stewart, Treas.
Ownership: W. P. Williamson Family.
Represented (legal): Bryan Cave LLP.
MDS Systems:
Ohio: WDU693, Youngstown.
Youngstown: 273490.
Other Holdings:
TV, see listing.

LAURENCE E. WOLFF
Box 787
Gillette, WY 82717
MMDS Systems:
Colorado: WMY396, Burlington.

YATES ENTERPRISES INC.
Box 111
Harrodsburg, KY 40330-0111
Phone: 606-734-5063
Officer:
Donald Yates Jr., Pres.
MDS Systems:
Kentucky: WFY837, Harrodsburg.

YOUNG COMMUNICATIONS
2715 Jenifer St. NW
Washington, DC 20015
Phone: 202-537-1264
Ownership: W. Randolph Young. See also Columbia Wireless Corp., G & Y Communications & Springfield One Partnership.
Represented (legal): W. Randolph Young.
MMDS Systems:
Nebraska: WNTF452, Omaha.

MICHELE ZAHN
1023 9th Ave. NE
Aberdeen, SD 57401
MMDS Systems:
Minnesota: WNTH469, Mankato.

ESTIMATED GROWTH OF THE CABLE INDUSTRY
(as of January 1 of each year)

Note: Figures do not include wireless cable systems.

Year	Operating Systems	Total Subscribers
1952	70	14,000
1953	150	30,000
1954	300	65,000
1955	400	150,000
1956	450	300,000
1957	500	350,000
1958	525	450,000
1959	560	550,000
1960	640	650,000
1961	700	725,000
1962	800	850,000
1963	1,000	950,000
1964	1,200	1,085,000
1965	1,325	1,275,000
1966	1,570	1,575,000
1967	1,770	2,100,000
1968	2,000	2,800,000
1969	2,260	3,600,000
1970	2,490	4,500,000
1971	2,639	5,300,000
1972	2,841	6,000,000
1973	2,991	7,300,000
1974	3,158	8,700,000
1975	3,506	9,800,000
1976	3,681	10,800,000
1977	3,832	11,900,000
1978	3,875	13,000,000
1979	4,150	14,100,000
1980	4,225	16,000,000
1981	4,375	18,300,000
1982	4,825	21,000,000
1983	5,600	25,000,000
1984	6,200	29,000,000
1985	6,600	32,000,000
1986	7,500	37,500,000
1987	7,900	41,000,000
1988	8,500	44,000,000
1989	9,050	47,500,000
1990	9,575	50,000,000
1991	10,704	51,000,000
1992	11,035	53,000,000
1993	11,108	54,200,000
1994	11,214	55,300,000
1995	11,218	56,500,000
1996	11,119	60,280,000
1997	10,950	64,050,000
1998	10,845	64,170,000
1999	10,700	65,500,000
2000	10,400	66,500,000

Note: The change in the number of systems operating each year is determined by three factors: (1) New systems which began operation during the year. (2) Older systems coming to the attention of Television & Cable Factbook for the first time and therefore included in the total for the first time. (3) The splitting or combining of systems by operators.

U.S. CABLE SYSTEMS BY SUBSCRIBER SIZE

(As of October 1999)

Note: Figures do not include wireless cable systems.

Size by Subscribers	Systems	% of Total	Subscribers	% of Total
50,000 & over	279	2.67%	33,600,099	50.868%
20,000 - 49,999	442	4.22%	13,976,190	21.159%
10,000 - 19,999	481	4.60%	6,981,822	10.570%
5,000 - 9,999	651	6.22%	4,515,744	6.836%
3,500 - 4,999	394	3.76%	1,739,537	2.634%
1,000 - 3,499	1,842	17.60%	3,468,754	5.251%
500 - 999	1,324	12.65%	955,975	1.447%
250 - 499	1,290	12.33%	463,097	0.701%
249 & under	3,051	29.15%	352,486	0.534%
Not available	363	3.35%	—	—
TOTAL	**10,466**	**100%**	**62,053,704**	**100%**

CHANNEL CAPACITY OF EXISTING CABLE SYSTEMS

(As of October 1999)

Note: Figures do not include wireless cable systems.

Channel Capacity	Systems	% of Total	Subscribers	% of Total
125 & over	8	0.08%	199,844	0.303%
91 - 124	71	0.68%	2,839,391	4.299%
54 - 90	2,085	19.92%	37,993,220	57.519%
30 - 53	6,072	58.02%	21,997,890	33.303%
20 - 29	833	7.96%	739,934	1.120%
13 - 19	254	2.43%	69,804	0.106%
6 - 12	309	2.95%	76,941	0.116%
5 only	7	0.07%	1,024	0.002%
Sub-5	5	0.05%	3,865	0.006%
Not available	822	7.85%	2,131,791	3.227%
TOTAL	**10,466**	**100%**	**62,053,704**	**100%**

U.S. CABLE PENETRATION STATE BY STATE

(As of October 1999)

Note: Figures reflect information supplied by system operators and do not include wireless cable systems.

State	Systems	Basic Subscribers	Expanded Basic Subscribers	Pay Units	Miles of Plant	Homes Passed
ALABAMA	224	1,041,636	510,254	429,256	29,298	1,202,564
ALASKA	43	116,521	72,063	63,952	2,528	172,041
ARIZONA	93	1,041,299	123,355	384,780	19,994	1,770,673
ARKANSAS	267	571,233	252,245	209,604	16,995	635,069
CALIFORNIA	348	7,995,746	3,033,092	3,598,065	97,984	11,117,682
COLORADO	171	882,680	362,459	229,826	16,210	1,410,397
CONNECTICUT	24	1,042,783	583,856	424,856	22,527	1,440,259
DC	3	108,116	92,151	168,927	1,128	258,832
DELAWARE	6	255,424	156,027	159,132	5,424	319,034
FLORIDA	272	4,925,374	1,835,770	1,941,637	75,779	5,744,471
GEORGIA	250	2,106,846	704,239	847,516	41,590	2,410,962
HAWAII	11	395,538	33,733	229,354	4,952	410,195
IDAHO	81	219,593	172,377	113,615	4,990	326,970
ILLINOIS	581	2,607,272	1,288,378	2,024,298	51,646	4,550,965
INDIANA	317	1,336,176	464,536	541,855	28,336	1,847,176
IOWA	513	597,930	400,704	409,805	13,080	940,766
KANSAS	402	604,497	293,027	312,320	11,810	874,509
KENTUCKY	239	927,778	860,433	436,903	24,890	1,142,713
LOUISIANA	186	1,018,006	371,087	603,511	21,293	1,241,829
MAINE	105	322,292	247,065	126,521	11,452	437,572
MARYLAND	39	1,252,989	659,684	1,054,425	19,972	1,892,576
MASSACHUSETTS	84	1,695,200	819,554	1,275,704	24,796	2,092,520
MICHIGAN	379	2,286,491	897,779	1,134,039	50,369	3,210,416
MINNESOTA	354	863,866	501,112	447,315	21,415	1,482,804
MISSISSIPPI	177	517,940	191,379	201,521	12,746	569,483
MISSOURI	419	989,324	490,373	673,483	24,666	1,612,169
MONTANA	119	170,567	138,738	130,167	3,494	219,166
NEBRASKA	305	423,304	442,717	250,720	6,454	598,957
NEVADA	50	440,684	369,345	346,964	7,990	669,653
NEW HAMPSHIRE	55	350,733	161,636	160,583	9,607	397,468
NEW JERSEY	47	2,403,445	1,155,532	1,482,570	35,700	3,718,899
NEW MEXICO	86	342,881	220,849	134,215	7,996	497,037
NEW YORK	225	4,451,822	2,054,082	2,577,594	59,007	6,259,564
NORTH CAROLINA	208	1,708,633	979,930	735,051	54,295	2,058,220
NORTH DAKOTA	206	149,650	121,159	67,432	2,622	208,216
OHIO	389	2,871,138	1,035,561	1,570,202	57,402	4,052,964
OKLAHOMA	355	712,074	537,743	304,143	18,307	1,151,826
OREGON	141	743,997	515,317	341,683	18,623	1,133,031
PENNSYLVANIA	367	3,591,723	2,180,288	1,543,565	67,912	3,959,958
RHODE ISLAND	8	272,266	153,219	255,446	3,614	253,297
SOUTH CAROLINA	128	850,512	511,590	328,562	27,443	1,230,871
SOUTH DAKOTA	191	150,349	32,174	66,376	3,804	200,346
TENNESSEE	143	1,272,257	671,249	677,642	32,545	1,655,834
TEXAS	791	3,574,093	2,465,619	1,744,547	85,128	6,766,542
UTAH	79	266,636	170,632	210,932	8,399	390,553
VERMONT	76	136,576	112,426	35,025	4,659	152,321
VIRGINIA	156	1,837,172	647,710	959,779	36,478	1,954,970
WASHINGTON	182	1,264,767	856,214	677,545	24,665	1,806,762
WEST VIRGINIA	224	521,157	315,238	186,781	14,326	640,789
WISCONSIN	269	1,361,491	468,991	376,988	20,779	1,596,358
WYOMING	60	118,793	78,957	72,570	2,765	146,019
CUBA	1	1,504	0	2,918	40	3,000
GUAM	1	29,485	0	0	806	53,043
PUERTO RICO	13	278,592	152,049	98,439	6,594	737,928
MARIANAS ISLANDS	1	6,580	0	0	110	10,000
VIRGIN ISLANDS	2	28,273	22,354	18,906	840	61,591
TOTAL	**10,466**	**66,053,704**	**31,988,051**	**33,399,565**	**1,278,274**	**91,699,830**

LARGEST U.S. CABLE SYSTEMS

(Those with 20,000 & more basic subscribers as of October 1999)

Note: Figures do not include wireless cable systems.

SYSTEM	BASIC SUBSCRIBERS	PAY UNITS
NEW YORK, NY	1,148,000	149,740
ATLANTA, GA	859,943	266,000
HOUSTON, TX	642,502	378,479
PHOENIX, AZ	604,994	202,200
ORLANDO, FL	571,868	112,414
EL CAJON, CA	498,052	221,704
WOODBURY, NY	460,000	706,051
DENVER, CO	450,000	—
HAMPTON ROADS, VA	391,706	167,271
ELMHURST, IL	388,686	437,022
MILWAUKEE, WI	377,416	—
CINCINNATI, OH	330,000	184,592
LAS VEGAS, NV	301,262	230,022
SAN ANTONIO, TX	300,715	199,425
PINELLAS COUNTY, FL	292,000	50,900
SEATTLE, WA	283,460	153,257
UNION, NJ	266,547	225,100
JACKSONVILLE, FL	258,636	159,009
AKRON, OH	255,000	54,897
SACRAMENTO, CA	252,000	214,343
HONOLULU, HI	248,161	176,000
PLANT CITY (Portions), FL	245,000	201,000
BRONX, NY	241,000	—
FAIRFAX COUNTY, VA	237,000	192,310
MONTGOMERY COUNTY, MD	227,376	110,176
MEMPHIS, TN	227,000	153,000
OAKLAND, NJ	220,000	159,247
ORANGE COUNTY, CA (Cox Communications)	218,999	79,032
CHERRY HILL, NJ	212,117	135,325
AUSTIN, TX	212,000	116,000
ROCHESTER, NY	205,800	108,753
TOWSON, MD	205,000	130,771
KANSAS CITY, MO	204,000	157,115
LOUISVILLE, KY	203,097	106,016
SAN JOSE, CA	195,000	135,384
COLUMBUS, OH (Time Warner Communications)	189,000	118,708
SAN FRANCISCO, CA	186,500	—
SAN DIEGO, CA	185,040	74,815
CHARLOTTE, NC	181,541	91,356
POMPANO BEACH, FL	175,108	115,270
PHILADELPHIA (Area 4), PA	173,200	—
OMAHA, NE	171,116	133,160
BUFFALO (Suburbs), NY	168,000	68,700
PISCATAWAY, NJ	163,618	165,200
SUFFOLK COUNTY, NY	161,096	286,088
BOSTON, MA	157,102	120,600
DALLAS, TX	157,000	162,242
LOS ANGELES, CA (MediaOne)	156,979	—
LOS ANGELES, CA (Century Southwest Cable)	153,960	119,100
TULSA, OK	153,703	—
INDIANAPOLIS, IN	150,000	—
WILMINGTON, DE	149,433	116,558
TACOMA, WA	149,350	—
WILLOW GROVE, PA	148,039	—
APPLETON, WI	142,000	48,000
HARTFORD, CT	141,661	54,393
RICHMOND, VA	140,176	37,210
NASHVILLE, TN	140,146	137,106
CHICAGO (Areas 2 & 3), IL	140,000	155,323
AUBURN, WA	137,426	153,119
MEDFORD, MA	134,065	88,600
MONMOUTH COUNTY, NJ	133,818	150,795
ORANGE COUNTY, CA (Time Warner Communications)	133,091	—
JEFFERSON PARISH, LA	131,047	119,505
ROSEVILLE, MN	130,640	74,511
STERLING HEIGHTS, MI	129,820	—
PORTLAND, OR (TCI Cable)	128,900	43,798
TOLEDO, OH	128,603	60,115
DETROIT, MI	128,146	226,773
WORCESTER, MA	126,000	93,286
GRAND RAPIDS, MI	125,721	54,439
OSSINING, NY	125,000	—
SAN JUAN, PR	125,000	—
WALLINGFORD, PA	123,598	95,700
NAPLES, FL	122,069	21,862
WEST SAN FERNANDO VALLEY, CA	121,824	64,284
OKLAHOMA CITY, OK	121,000	75,900
PLEASANT HILL, CA	120,000	37,198
EL PASO, TX	118,000	34,593
DOVER, NJ	116,214	37,069
ALHAMBRA, CA	115,869	104,861
ALBUQUERQUE, NM	115,000	52,100
MELBOURNE, FL	113,301	—
WICHITA, KS	112,356	48,151
BALTIMORE, MD	112,000	122,947
WEST PALM BEACH, FL	110,700	—
NORWALK, CT	109,809	95,300
COLUMBIA, SC	109,800	40,075
HARRISBURG, PA	108,529	40,901
KNOXVILLE, TN	107,334	63,951
PLEASANTVILLE, NJ	106,981	54,210
WASHINGTON, DC	106,240	168,927
STATEN ISLAND, NY	106,000	119,763
FRESNO, CA	105,543	108,484
NORTH MIAMI, FL	105,000	59,036
PITTSBURGH, PA	103,902	111,983
NEWPORT & LINCOLN, RI	102,593	58,273
COLORADO SPRINGS, CO	102,075	39,829
TUCSON, AZ	101,960	83,610
PALM BEACH GARDENS, FL	101,785	31,787
SALT LAKE CITY, UT	101,016	107,367
FORT WORTH, TX	100,428	—
PROVIDENCE, RI	99,399	66,704
BERKELEY TWP., NJ	98,682	—
ONTARIO, CA	98,000	—
BATON ROUGE, LA	97,186	62,500
AUGUSTA, GA	97,000	47,344
KENOSHA, WI	97,000	22,000
HIALEAH, FL	96,000	37,631
NEW ORLEANS, LA	95,230	96,824
OVERLAND PARK, KS	95,000	70,427
HENRICO COUNTY, VA	94,301	60,288
FORT LAUDERDALE, FL	94,046	43,300
BRIDGEPORT, CT	94,000	—
SOUTH BEND, IN	94,000	23,597
SPOKANE, WA	93,405	45,224
BURTON, MI	93,195	—
WINSTON-SALEM, NC	92,759	50,567
LEHIGH VALLEY, PA	91,396	25,875
STOCKTON, CA	91,000	55,127
CHATTANOOGA, TN	90,178	42,583
BROOKLYN PARK, MN	90,000	28,659
EAST SAN FERNANDO VALLEY, CA	90,000	137,057
STUART, FL	89,914	26,668
PRINCE GEORGE'S COUNTY, MD	89,614	72,336
REDLANDS, CA	89,000	65,006
YORK, PA	89,000	32,150
GLENDALE, CA	86,500	18,566
COLUMBUS, OH (Insight Communications)	86,041	68,049
MADISON, WI	85,105	62,048
SYRACUSE, NY (Time Warner Cable)	84,051	59,256
PORTLAND, OR (TCI Cablevision of Oregon)	84,000	81,900
CLEVELAND HEIGHTS, OH	83,979	83,394
BRADENTON, FL	83,712	19,822
MAMARONECK, NY	83,324	91,528
NORTHAMPTON, PA	83,274	17,340

SYSTEM	BASIC SUBSCRIBERS	PAY UNITS
LANCASTER, PA	83,039	15,597
DES MOINES, IA	82,986	103,012
CANTON, OH	82,500	28,234
BUFFALO, NY	81,900	99,213
CHARLESTON, SC	81,362	—
CLEVELAND, OH	81,142	112,047
FORT WAYNE, IN	80,627	—
BEAVERTON, OR	80,528	—
PRINCE GEORGE'S COUNTY, MD	79,307	138,201
MIAMI, FL (Adelphia Cable-South Dade)	78,705	30,245
PHILADELPHIA (Area 1), PA	78,126	67,549
MINNEAPOLIS, MN	78,000	46,400
RALEIGH, NC	78,000	45,448
ST. PAUL, MN	78,000	68,000
MONTGOMERY, AL	77,500	29,866
BAKERSFIELD, CA (Time Warner Cable)	77,447	29,658
LINCOLN, NE	77,039	28,431
LEXINGTON, KY	76,176	71,747
BIRMINGHAM, AL	76,000	41,900
COMPTON, CA	75,840	93,183
JACKSON, MS	75,000	42,836
TRI-VALLEY, CA	75,000	—
EATONTOWN, NJ	74,800	55,273
CHICAGO (Area 5), IL	74,000	115,669
READING, PA	73,983	40,059
PENSACOLA, FL	73,551	41,555
FAYETTEVILLE, NC	73,464	46,150
FORT WALTON BEACH, FL	73,000	15,701
MACON, GA	72,586	38,445
WOODSTOCK, GA	72,575	36,457
MONTEREY, CA	71,271	32,884
CHICAGO (Area 1), IL	71,020	79,475
OAKLAND, CA	70,669	57,381
COVINGTON, KY	70,400	40,824
INDIANAPOLIS (Portions), IN	70,294	82,550
BROOKHAVEN, NY	70,000	67,393
NEW HAVEN, CT	70,000	30,793
ROMEOVILLE, IL	69,898	52,418
MERRILLVILLE, IN	69,653	—
RASNOW, CA	69,375	—
GREENVILLE, SC	69,136	—
TORRANCE, CA	69,109	53,370
TAYLOR, MI	69,100	34,927
ANN ARBOR, MI	69,000	36,623
INDEPENDENCE, MO	68,774	54,320
PALMDALE, CA	68,000	39,300
LONG BEACH, CA	67,375	49,970
ROYAL OAK, MI	67,373	78,031
NEW BEDFORD, MA	67,115	22,712
MOBILE, AL	67,056	3,916
SANTA BARBARA, CA	67,000	30,000
ANCHORAGE, AK	66,862	39,088
FOXBOROUGH, MA	66,731	46,300
SAVANNAH, GA	66,350	39,135
PLANO, TX	66,250	—
ROCKFORD, IL	66,000	8,115
CHESTERFIELD COUNTY, VA	65,983	—
ALBANY, NY	65,494	—
MANCHESTER, CT	65,000	23,499
MIAMI BEACH, FL	65,000	30,565
PORT RICHEY, FL	64,784	34,871
DELRAY BEACH, FL	64,296	19,465
ORO VALLEY, AZ	63,727	23,870
PORTSMOUTH, NH	63,672	35,075
LANSING, MI	63,574	29,764
MOLINE, IL	63,570	33,300
WAUKEGAN, IL	63,315	—
BEVERLY, MA	62,992	16,800
BROWARD COUNTY, FL	62,684	38,100

SYSTEM	BASIC SUBSCRIBERS	PAY UNITS
MARIN COUNTY (Southeastern portion), CA	62,650	—
BRANFORD, CT	62,219	29,322
MIAMI, FL (Miami Tele-Communications Inc.)	62,000	38,294
BINGHAMTON, NY	61,882	28,793
HAYWARD, CA	61,507	—
CHESTER COUNTY, PA	60,304	26,298
ALCOA, TN	60,206	32,231
KENDALL, FL	60,000	40,444
NEW HAVEN, MI	60,000	15,412
PARMA, OH	60,000	40,000
PHILADELPHIA (Area 2), PA	60,000	74,685
PORTLAND, ME	59,980	23,479
ARLINGTON, VA	59,578	36,557
WILMINGTON, NC	59,358	—
CARLSBAD, CA	59,230	28,841
EUGENE, OR	59,000	59,000
ARLINGTON, TX	58,500	—
SHREVEPORT, LA	58,225	38,000
JAMISON, PA	58,142	26,255
SCRANTON, PA	58,060	24,821
GREENSBORO, NC	58,000	31,767
TALLAHASSEE, FL	57,703	—
MODESTO & OAKDALE, CA	57,500	23,690
ROANOKE, VA	57,488	30,306
HEMET, CA	57,050	26,453
HILLSBOROUGH, NJ	56,733	—
PEORIA, IL	56,694	34,500
GREENFIELD, WI	56,466	—
NEWTOWN, CT	56,310	24,633
ST. LOUIS, MO	56,252	111,400
PALOS HILLS, IL	56,000	65,621
VANCOUVER, WA	56,000	35,447
BERGENFIELD, NJ	55,200	—
CHICAGO (Area 4), IL	55,000	87,192
MOUNT PROSPECT, IL	54,921	78,983
EAST WINDSOR, NJ	54,830	—
PALISADES PARK, NJ	54,631	47,712
SARASOTA, FL	54,419	34,785
LAFAYETTE, LA	54,397	27,057
SAN MATEO, CA	54,363	51,826
MIDDLETOWN, NY	54,343	40,300
LEESBURG, FL	54,178	16,063
ABERDEEN, MD	54,000	44,880
ROSS TWP., PA	53,719	36,154
ROLLING MEADOWS, IL	53,121	58,703
MECKLENBURG, NC	53,000	—
GAINESVILLE, FL	52,663	28,050
FREDERICK, MD	52,648	31,530
HOBOKEN, NJ	52,504	29,059
SPRINGFIELD, MO	52,500	—
CHARLESTON, WV	52,412	22,584
DE LAND, FL	52,400	10,741
WESTFIELD, MA	52,324	38,389
ROCKLAND, NY	52,000	62,338
YONKERS, NY	52,000	73,409
WOBURN, MA	51,952	39,387
POTTSTOWN, PA	51,658	17,240
GREENSBURG, PA	51,623	39,695
MILLERSVILLE, MD	51,623	56,452
SALEM, OR	51,620	19,532
RIVERSIDE, CA	51,534	40,024
LITTLE ROCK, AR	51,300	33,067
IRVINE, CA	51,149	20,916
EVANSVILLE, IN	50,924	24,543
PALM DESERT, CA	50,924	13,302
TROY, NY	50,702	42,043
ANNE ARUNDEL COUNTY, MD	50,347	41,776
WAUWATOSA, WI	50,000	—
SOUTH YARMOUTH, MA	49,538	10,274

Note: Pay unit counts include expanded basic subscribers.

SYSTEM	BASIC SUBSCRIBERS	PAY UNITS
PHARR, TX	49,456	16,123
KALAMAZOO, MI	49,400	—
LANSDALE, PA	49,218	42,283
BOISE, ID	49,166	29,745
NEWARK, NJ	49,000	59,563
SANTA ROSA, CA	49,000	23,000
DURHAM, NC	48,500	32,090
CORPUS CHRISTI, TX	48,387	64,283
CEDAR RAPIDS, IA	48,000	40,598
ROHNERT PARK, CA	48,000	22,039
RIVERHEAD, NY	47,978	35,485
GENEVA, NY	47,970	23,880
SANTA CRUZ, CA	47,885	—
BENSALEM TWP., PA	47,854	31,820
SANTA ANA, CA	47,800	—
UTICA, NY	47,758	14,464
SPRINGFIELD, IL	47,461	—
RICHMOND, CA	47,393	35,139
ELLICOTT CITY, MD	46,845	71,053
MANCHESTER, NH	46,789	19,016
AMARILLO, TX	46,778	38,339
LOS ANGELES, CA (MediaOne)	46,742	68,716
WATERBURY, CT	46,500	15,700
ST. CHARLES, MO	46,400	42,254
NEWPORT NEWS, VA	46,367	57,500
DAYTON, OH	46,000	—
LUBBOCK, TX	45,627	44,927
SPRINGFIELD, MA	45,575	48,322
BUENA PARK, CA	45,400	15,273
WACO, TX	45,300	30,342
WEST CHICAGO, IL	44,958	26,704
RUSTON, WA	44,357	62,602
CHICOPEE, MA	44,335	30,757
WARREN, OH	44,233	31,347
LOWELL, MA	44,077	30,645
DAYTONA BEACH, FL	44,000	25,949
STROUDSBURG, PA	44,000	8,500
WILLIAMSTON, MI	44,000	283
QUINCY, MA	43,747	42,030
TAMPA BAY, FL	43,541	48,852
SEYMOUR, CT	43,525	30,131
SAN LUIS OBISPO, CA	43,500	19,600
VENICE, FL	43,500	12,714
JERSEY CITY, NJ	43,147	43,580
MOREHEAD CITY, NC	43,100	22,960
TARENTUM BOROUGH, PA	42,996	—
TRENTON, NJ	42,937	18,993
SPARTANBURG, SC	42,821	—
ST. TAMMANY PARISH, LA	42,529	24,949
LEVITTOWN, PA	42,526	20,765
BONITA SPRINGS, FL	42,499	8,965
ALTOONA, PA	42,153	14,622
CONCORD, CA	42,099	18,106
ANAHEIM, CA	42,000	35,852
DEARBORN HEIGHTS, MI	41,884	44,412
TOPEKA, KS	41,803	26,820
LANCASTER (Town), NY	41,800	14,200
OLYMPIA, WA	41,775	30,061
IRVING, TX	41,141	22,948
VINELAND, NJ	41,048	16,386
PITTSBURG, CA	41,000	33,200
KETTERING, OH	40,778	100,941
MUSKEGON, MI	40,600	22,600
MENTOR, OH	40,456	26,796
LAFAYETTE, IN	40,174	13,854
CHAMBERSBURG, PA	40,043	7,455
MERIDEN, CT	40,000	16,631
NEW LONDON, CT	40,000	20,771
SELLERSVILLE, PA	39,954	12,873
CRANSTON, RI	39,615	32,731
SYRACUSE, NY (Time Warner Cable)	39,600	26,456
URBANA, IL	39,500	—
UNIONTOWN, PA	39,479	11,474
TURNERSVILLE, NJ	39,393	30,516

SYSTEM	BASIC SUBSCRIBERS	PAY UNITS
KILLEEN, TX	39,318	24,591
WILDWOOD, NJ	39,232	12,629
GARLAND, TX	39,219	—
DUNMORE, PA	39,199	11,649
BAY HEAD, NJ	39,161	21,380
KANNAPOLIS, NC	39,000	—
SPARTA, NJ	39,000	17,000
HAMILTON, OH	38,597	24,029
WILLINGBORO, NJ	38,439	18,056
ALEXANDRIA, VA	38,400	30,730
GWINNETT COUNTY, GA	38,225	24,245
FREMONT, CA	38,124	46,968
MARYVILLE, IL	38,084	19,416
WESTFORD, MA	38,000	—
FORT SMITH, AR	37,892	34,015
HAMPTON, VA	37,092	32,322
FORT MYERS, FL	37,018	23,308
DANBURY, CT	37,000	—
HARBORCREEK TWP., PA	37,000	26,414
OXNARD, CA	37,000	—
TRAVERSE CITY, MI	36,956	4,681
TUSCALOOSA, AL	36,800	—
WOODBURY, NJ	36,520	25,323
HAGERSTOWN, MD	36,500	20,180
HICKORY, NC	36,500	17,000
WEST MONROE, LA	36,200	—
CORVALLIS, OR	36,057	7,997
SAN BERNARDINO, CA	36,051	17,451
KENNEWICK, WA	36,007	19,583
ALBANY, GA	36,000	22,737
ANNISTON, AL	36,000	17,400
ELYRIA, OH	35,989	—
BROCKTON, MA	35,953	36,644
WARREN, MI	35,733	—
SIOUX FALLS, SD	35,727	19,454
HOOVER, AL	35,439	25,697
SAGINAW, MI	35,430	15,583
HUNTSVILLE, AL (Knowledgy)	35,315	23,682
NEWTON, MA	35,306	33,829
PETALUMA, CA	35,300	17,900
ENFIELD, CT	35,200	29,340
NORRISTOWN, PA	35,160	9,502
CAPE CORAL, FL	35,000	11,618
DECATUR, IL	35,000	20,284
FLORENCE, SC	35,000	18,493
PICO RIVERA, CA	35,000	48,500
VERO BEACH, FL	35,000	14,330
WILLIAMSPORT, PA	35,000	—
MEDFORD, OR	34,877	24,379
RENO, NV	34,757	44,188
AURORA, IL	34,554	29,784
VANDALIA, OH	34,498	—
ASHEVILLE, NC	34,461	17,984
CARPENTERSVILLE, IL	34,341	20,744
CASTLE SHANNON, PA	34,330	23,543
PACIFICA, CA	34,327	18,779
NORTH LITTLE ROCK, AR	34,200	15,236
ROCHESTER, MN	34,061	21,019
REDDING, CA	34,019	—
ATHENS, TN	34,015	4,573
HOLLYWOOD, FL	34,000	28,130
LOUDOUN COUNTY, VA	34,000	52,364
ALLENDALE, MI	33,747	1,253
BILOXI, MS	33,732	14,303
ORANGE COUNTY (Portions), FL	33,440	—
FORT COLLINS, CO	33,425	8,164
HUNTSVILLE, AL (Comcast Cablevision of Huntsville)	33,388	16,979
CORAL SPRINGS, FL	33,374	23,905
LEBANON, PA	33,365	13,262
CAMBRIDGE, MA	33,360	30,746
BRYAN, TX	33,000	—
CHAMBLEE, GA	33,000	26,388
HOMOSASSA, FL	33,000	8,381
ZELIENOPLE, PA	33,000	14,958

SYSTEM	BASIC SUBSCRIBERS	PAY UNITS
GULFPORT/LONG BEACH, MS	32,700	3,330
PONTIAC, MI	32,413	—
PLYMOUTH, MI	32,411	20,421
SCHENECTADY, NY	32,364	29,869
SOUTHFIELD, MI	32,293	38,050
ASHFORD, CT	32,259	7,638
FLORENCE, AL	32,233	—
MYRTLE BEACH, SC	32,207	18,887
SUNBURY, PA	32,200	8,912
SPOTSYLVANIA, VA	32,160	11,500
ABILENE, TX	32,144	25,144
BELLEVILLE, IL	32,137	35,195
LA PORTE, IN	32,076	21,864
VICTORVILLE, CA	32,000	8,701
MANSFIELD, OH	31,843	1,920
CARLSTADT BOROUGH, NJ	31,833	—
JACKSON, TN	31,782	—
FARMINGTON, MI	31,758	28,456
MONROEVILLE, PA	31,675	17,530
BROWNSVILLE, TX	31,640	13,295
MUNCIE, IN	31,600	7,000
HAMILTON TWP., NJ	31,508	23,298
YUBA CITY, CA	31,411	20,335
COLUMBUS, GA	31,378	40,275
PEMBROKE, MA	31,350	19,700
EUREKA, CA	31,180	13,000
KINGSPORT, TN	31,162	10,543
LAWRENCE, KS	30,807	7,420
MORGANTOWN, WV	30,800	—
MASSILLON, OH	30,787	12,480
JOHNSTOWN, PA	30,750	7,383
LOS ANGELES, CA (MediaOne)	30,606	14,025
BLOOMINGTON, IL	30,603	—
AMHERST, MA	30,600	—
GARDENDALE, AL	30,417	13,134
ERIE, PA	30,400	14,735
MIDLAND, TX	30,376	16,872
BANGOR, ME	30,313	16,845
PALOS VERDES PENINSULA, CA	30,300	11,000
PALM SPRINGS, CA	30,100	11,212
OAK LAWN, IL	30,063	29,781
NOBLESVILLE, IN	30,033	12,727
BOCA RATON, FL	30,000	22,825
CHICO, CA	30,000	—
EPHRATA, PA	30,000	8,091
NIAGARA FALLS, NY	30,000	14,850
SIMI VALLEY, CA	30,000	—
PANAMA CITY, FL	29,995	22,960
MALVERN, PA	29,797	16,803
MAUI ISLAND, HI	29,762	16,558
TYLER, TX	29,753	20,851
TURLOCK, CA	29,700	5,553
AGANA, GU	29,485	—
GLENDALE HEIGHTS, IL	29,436	33,486
LIVONIA, MI	29,337	21,265
LIMA, OH	29,283	13,057
MARGATE, FL	29,100	41,044
CLINTON TWP., MI	29,086	—
CONCORD, NH	28,986	15,488
PORT ARTHUR, TX	28,824	35,013
EAU CLAIRE, WI	28,816	8,200
MURFREESBORO, TN	28,806	11,036
PRESCOTT, AZ	28,800	7,435
CARMEL, NY	28,764	—
KIRKWOOD, MO	28,613	17,779
NAPERVILLE, IL	28,606	15,275
SANDY, UT	28,549	21,585
LAKE CHARLES, LA	28,434	24,067
PALO ALTO, CA	28,432	17,226
STAFFORD, NY	28,400	23,800
SANTA CLARITA, CA	28,363	15,394
BEAUMONT, TX	28,253	32,248
PINEVILLE, LA	28,240	—
PUEBLO, CO	28,127	26,025
MAYAGUEZ, PR	28,100	8,419
NASHUA, NH	28,093	12,250
JAMESTOWN, NY	28,000	—
LITCHFIELD, CT	28,000	14,900
WATERLOO, IA	28,000	21,500
WILKES-BARRE, PA	28,000	8,200
MANASSAS, VA	27,986	23,385
PALMERTON, PA	27,946	—
LAWRENCE, MA	27,830	23,021
GROTON, CT	27,800	12,725
KOKOMO, IN	27,799	13,392
ODESSA, TX	27,600	14,577
LAREDO, TX	27,502	20,800
OVIEDO, FL	27,320	14,508
PORT CHARLOTTE, FL	27,319	—
ANDERSON, IN	27,296	19,795
BLAIRSVILLE, PA	27,244	7,135
CHARLES TOWN, WV	27,210	7,817
INWOOD, WV	27,210	7,817
OCALA, FL	27,089	12,526
EAST HILLS, PA	27,081	27,273
NEWARK, OH	27,072	16,509
MERCEDITA, PR	27,067	23,024
ONEIDA, NY	27,024	4,990
BURLINGTON, VT	27,000	—
GRAND JUNCTION, CO	27,000	15,750
HARRINGTON, DE	27,000	13,500
OCEAN CITY, MD	26,976	20,455
ST. JOSEPH, MO	26,940	8,796
TERRE HAUTE, IN	26,893	13,000
FITCHBURG, MA	26,835	27,597
FAIRFIELD, CA	26,823	15,154
SMYRNA, GA	26,700	16,500
NEWBURGH, NY	26,664	22,300
GAINESVILLE, GA	26,600	16,883
DULUTH, MN	26,551	20,658
JEFFERSONVILLE, IN	26,500	6,096
HUSTISFORD, WI	26,444	10,948
PROVO, UT	26,434	7,057
SIOUX CITY, IA	26,342	13,150
DANVILLE, VA	26,328	13,481
ELMIRA, NY	26,323	—
LAKE ELSINORE, CA	26,300	12,750
VALLEJO, CA	26,288	11,117
STOCKBRIDGE, GA	26,271	811
DUNEDIN, FL	26,242	25,459
KANKAKEE, IL	26,050	12,182
BURLINGTON, NC	26,000	13,400
DAGSBORO, DE	26,000	15,620
TULARE, CA	26,000	21,162
PARKERSBURG, WV	25,958	18,475
SARATOGA SPRINGS, NY	25,939	16,030
ELKHART, IN	25,928	19,348
GRAY COURT, SC	25,909	11,729
BAY CITY, MI	25,906	11,122
ORANGE PARK, FL	25,859	24,227
CLARKSVILLE, TN	25,681	11,148
ROME, GA	25,674	9,980
DEARBORN, MI	25,620	16,663
MIDDLETOWN, OH	25,544	26,997
FARGO, ND	25,529	9,520
ATHENS, GA	25,526	14,219
OROVILLE, CA	25,483	—
STAUNTON, VA	25,412	8,424
BATTLE CREEK, MI	25,391	20,502
BILLINGS, MT	25,343	19,436
CHARLOTTESVILLE, VA	25,325	11,900
GLENDORA, CA	25,319	44,545
PADUCAH, KY	25,298	11,000
PORT ORCHARD, WA	25,251	8,718
HOMEWOOD, SC	25,206	5,160
YORKTOWN, NY	25,200	2,625
WINTER HAVEN, FL	25,098	11,714
CARROLL COUNTY, MD	25,064	10,652

SYSTEM	BASIC SUBSCRIBERS	PAY UNITS
LAS CRUCES, NM	25,032	11,443
CARY, NC	25,000	8,900
FORT PIERCE, FL	25,000	14,683
ITHACA, NY	25,000	9,000
LAWTON, OK	25,000	—
SAN ANGELO, TX	25,000	3,395
LONGVIEW, TX	24,930	11,784
ST. CLAIR SHORES, MI	24,899	—
BOARDMAN, OH	24,810	13,338
HAMMOND, IN	24,800	—
WICHITA FALLS, TX	24,689	—
PORT MURRAY, NJ	24,637	—
MIDDLETOWN, CT	24,622	—
IOWA CITY, IA	24,500	14,012
NAPA, CA	24,500	11,300
WEST SACRAMENTO, CA	24,500	14,296
FARMINGTON, UT	24,405	26,145
BISMARCK, ND	24,390	10,095
HARLINGEN, TX	24,340	7,519
BUTLER, PA	24,325	10,972
NORMAN, OK	24,238	13,909
RENSSELAER, NY	24,223	13,119
SUNNYVALE, CA	24,151	27,059
ALTON, IL	24,135	18,464
SOUTHAVEN, MS	24,125	—
WALDORF, MD	24,115	22,931
MATTESON, IL	24,058	—
HAMMOND, LA	24,000	7,000
SUMTER, SC	24,000	—
CUMBERLAND, MD	23,897	23,708
ST. AUGUSTINE, FL	23,848	6,421
YAKIMA, WA	23,840	17,679
BIRMINGHAM, MI	23,804	12,477
ANNAPOLIS, MD	23,688	14,111
HOT SPRINGS, AR	23,615	7,192
COMMERCE TWP., MI	23,556	16,948
YUMA, AZ	23,500	10,241
PATERSON, NJ	23,496	18,162
MERCED, CA	23,482	16,503
ROSEMOUNT, MN	23,469	14,426
STATE COLLEGE, PA	23,408	16,587
GREELEY, CO	23,384	12,444
WINCHESTER, VA	23,350	4,305
LEWISTON, ME	23,050	9,581
CHEYENNE, WY	23,000	20,454
COLUMBIA, MO	23,000	34,200
COSTA MESA, CA	23,000	16,725
NORTH ATTLEBORO, MA	23,000	—
TEXARKANA, TX	22,879	12,000
LAKE ZURICH, IL	22,856	—
CLINTON, CT	22,848	8,463
BLOOMINGTON, IN	22,814	15,640
MARTIN, KY	22,800	840
AIKEN, SC	22,787	12,654
SCITUATE, MA	22,768	20,856
JANESVILLE, WI	22,746	14,308
ANDOVER, MA	22,549	23,410
SALISBURY, MD	22,542	—
EAST LANSING, MI	22,516	8,400
ELIZABETH, NJ	22,504	20,651
BAKERSFIELD, CA (Cox Communications)	22,503	14,415
AUBURN, AL	22,500	13,408
ROCK HILL, SC	22,475	16,165
PEARL, MS	22,472	11,299
FREEHOLD, NJ	22,461	9,226
YOUNGSTOWN, OH	22,458	17,817
REHOBOTH BEACH, DE	22,456	10,063
FRANKLINVILLE, NJ	22,455	9,860
BRUNSWICK, GA	22,432	13,000
JOHNSON CITY, TN	22,293	7,087
VERNON, CT	22,245	—
LAFOURCHE PARISH, LA	22,209	12,327
ELIZABETHTOWN, PA	22,196	7,152
AGUADILLA, PR	22,074	3,313
HOUMA, LA	22,071	20,049
GOLDEN GATE, FL	22,059	5,770
WAUSAU, WI	22,025	14,170
CARBONDALE, PA	22,000	2,850
SURFSIDE BEACH, SC	22,000	16,116
VACAVILLE, CA	22,000	19,710
GADSDEN, AL	21,914	5,431
HERSHEY, PA	21,684	4,467
BELLINGHAM, WA	21,655	15,557
POMONA, CA	21,638	28,791
LYNCHBURG, VA	21,631	8,361
SHELBY, NC	21,617	—
HAZLETON, PA	21,576	6,594
ELGIN, IL	21,575	—
NEW PHILADELPHIA, OH	21,527	8,056
HUNTINGTON, WV	21,504	5,633
CARNEGIE, PA	21,494	13,553
DUBUQUE, IA	21,453	10,107
WILMINGTON, CA	21,440	24,419
PASCAGOULA, MS	21,378	13,170
IDAHO FALLS, ID	21,349	19,932
MCKEESPORT, PA	21,331	17,266
AUGUSTA, ME	21,282	9,821
MON VALLEY, PA	21,247	14,050
BOSSIER CITY, LA	21,214	26,521
JACKSONVILLE, NC	21,200	—
MARTINSVILLE, VA	21,172	7,271
BEDFORD, TX	21,160	—
WARWICK, NY	21,150	13,631
GRAY, TN	21,101	8,983
CONNELLSVILLE, PA	21,000	9,479
EDMONDS, WA	21,000	—
HIGH POINT, NC	21,000	13,100
LONGVIEW, WA	21,000	—
QUEENSBURY, NY	21,000	5,705
GREENVILLE, NC	20,913	14,810
DALTON, GA	20,876	7,001
ROSCOE, IL	20,871	9,244
HERNANDO COUNTY, FL	20,849	5,623
SHELBY TWP., MI	20,750	—
GOLDSBORO, NC	20,746	11,098
SANDUSKY, OH	20,728	7,600
CHINO, CA	20,725	—
CANYON COUNTRY, CA	20,700	—
LACONIA, NH	20,651	—
GILROY, CA	20,643	6,474
OWENSBORO, KY	20,520	2,575
MORTON GROVE, IL	20,515	20,927
BOONE, NC	20,500	2,593
SHARON, PA	20,500	7,800
NORTH PLAINFIELD, NJ	20,491	20,620
SHERMAN, TX	20,454	15,494
BELOIT, WI	20,438	10,321
OLATHE, KS	20,412	12,595
ROCKY MOUNT, NC	20,364	12,115
FAYETTEVILLE, AR	20,300	4,954
WALNUT CREEK, CA	20,300	8,968
BOWLING GREEN, KY	20,222	11,281
CLINTON, IA	20,200	23,420
DIAMOND BAR, CA	20,066	13,228
HERMOSA BEACH, CA	20,000	14,917
WOODHAVEN, MI	20,000	15,000

U.S. CABLE SYSTEM TOTALS STATE BY STATE

(As of October 1999)

Note: Figures reflect information supplied by system operators and do not include wireless cable systems.

State	Systems	Communities Served	Franchises Not Yet Operating	Applications Pending	Communities with Applications	Total Basic Units
ALABAMA	224	683	0	0	0	1,041,636
ALASKA	43	69	0	0	0	116,521
ARIZONA	93	252	0	0	0	1,041,299
ARKANSAS	267	599	0	0	0	571,233
CALIFORNIA	348	1,368	1	0	0	7,995,746
COLORADO	171	395	0	0	0	882,680
CONNECTICUT	24	197	0	0	0	1,042,783
DC	3	3	0	0	0	108,116
DELAWARE	6	114	0	0	0	255,424
FLORIDA	272	960	0	0	0	4,925,374
GEORGIA	250	819	1	0	0	2,106,846
HAWAII	11	129	0	0	0	395,538
IDAHO	81	213	0	0	0	219,593
ILLINOIS	581	1,479	5	0	0	2,607,272
INDIANA	317	930	0	0	0	1,336,176
IOWA	513	824	0	0	0	597,930
KANSAS	402	567	0	0	0	604,497
KENTUCKY	239	1,085	0	0	0	927,778
LOUISIANA	186	511	0	0	0	1,018,006
MAINE	105	399	2	0	0	322,292
MARYLAND	39	363	0	0	0	1,252,989
MASSACHUSETTS	84	372	0	0	0	1,695,200
MICHIGAN	379	1,758	2	0	0	2,286,491
MINNESOTA	354	915	0	0	0	863,866
MISSISSIPPI	177	414	0	0	0	517,940
MISSOURI	419	891	0	0	0	989,324
MONTANA	119	179	0	0	0	170,567
NEBRASKA	305	437	0	0	0	423,304
NEVADA	50	122	0	0	0	440,684
NEW HAMPSHIRE	55	256	1	0	0	350,733
NEW JERSEY	47	646	0	0	0	2,403,445
NEW MEXICO	86	181	0	0	0	342,881
NEW YORK	225	1,777	1	0	0	4,451,822
NORTH CAROLINA	208	913	0	0	0	1,708,633
NORTH DAKOTA	206	227	0	0	0	149,650
OHIO	389	2,244	7	0	0	2,871,138
OKLAHOMA	355	528	0	0	0	712,074
OREGON	141	411	0	0	0	743,997
PENNSYLVANIA	367	3,284	0	0	0	3,591,723
RHODE ISLAND	8	54	0	0	0	272,266
SOUTH CAROLINA	128	461	0	0	0	850,512
SOUTH DAKOTA	191	268	0	0	0	150,349
TENNESSEE	143	574	0	0	0	1,272,257
TEXAS	791	1,716	0	0	0	3,574,093
UTAH	79	223	0	0	0	266,636
VERMONT	76	258	34	0	0	136,576
VIRGINIA	156	609	0	0	0	1,837,172
WASHINGTON	182	532	1	0	0	1,264,767
WEST VIRGINIA	224	1,016	0	0	0	521,157
WISCONSIN	269	998	1	0	0	1,361,491
WYOMING	60	124	0	0	0	118,793
CUBA	1	1	0	0	0	1,504
GUAM	1	1	0	0	0	29,485
MARIANAS ISLANDS	1	2	0	0	0	6,580
PUERTO RICO	13	73	0	0	0	278,592
VIRGIN ISLANDS	2	3	0	0	0	28,273
TOTAL	**10,466**	**34,427**	**56**	**0**	**0**	**66,053,704**

A. C. Nielsen Co. Cable TV Household Estimates

Alphabetically by State

STATE	CABLE TV % RANK [1]	TV HOUSEHOLDS (Jan. 1998)	CABLE TV (Sept. 1997)	CABLE TV % OF TV HOUSEHOLDS
ALABAMA	14	1,613,550	1,111,850	69
ALASKA [2]	46	151,870	83,280	55
ARIZONA	42	1,692,280	1,000,360	59
ARKANSAS	30	953,340	607,320	64
CALIFORNIA	23	10,894,220	7,312,740	67
COLORADO	33	1,504,320	940,960	63
CONNECTICUT	2	1,222,970	1,052,860	86
DELAWARE	3	273,280	222,860	82
DISTRICT OF COLUMBIA	46	218,720	120,670	55
FLORIDA	9	5,788,730	4,321,330	75
GEORGIA	20	2,727,260	1,842,290	68
HAWAII	1	380,380	333,470	88
IDAHO	46	432,180	237,750	55
ILLINOIS	33	4,324,040	2,714,620	63
INDIANA	37	2,199,100	1,372,330	62
IOWA	33	1,095,570	693,620	63
KANSAS	14	976,410	678,290	69
KENTUCKY	23	1,457,720	982,480	67
LOUISIANA	11	1,546,080	1,113,580	72
MAINE	14	474,150	328,800	69
MARYLAND	23	1,861,390	1,251,270	67
MASSACHUSETTS	6	2,282,450	1,788,600	78
MICHIGAN	28	3,562,290	2,317,770	65
MINNESOTA	51	1,757,740	944,720	54
MISSISSIPPI	39	961,180	588,350	61
MISSOURI	46	2,050,640	1,137,770	55
MONTANA	45	333,610	187,860	56
NEBRASKA	14	632,310	438,110	69
NEVADA	20	656,680	446,410	68
NEW HAMPSHIRE	4	435,650	347,780	80
NEW JERSEY	4	2,868,740	2,298,960	80
NEW MEXICO	41	606,820	366,160	60
NEW YORK	14	6,535,450	4,515,620	69
NORTH CAROLINA	28	2,837,230	1,837,330	65
NORTH DAKOTA	26	246,490	163,780	66
OHIO	20	4,215,080	2,860,910	68
OKLAHOMA	33	1,253,690	791,300	63
OREGON	30	1,238,440	788,640	64
PENNSYLVANIA	7	4,537,300	3,441,210	76
RHODE ISLAND	7	367,740	279,770	76
SOUTH CAROLINA	37	1,364,030	849,930	62
SOUTH DAKOTA	30	270,720	173,670	64
TENNESSEE	26	2,043,430	1,349,000	66
TEXAS	42	6,813,840	4,019,220	59
UTAH	46	634,110	348,720	55
VERMONT	39	221,390	135,430	61
VIRGINIA	12	2,492,580	1,741,850	70
WASHINGTON	12	2,110,600	1,469,320	70
WEST VIRGINIA	10	702,620	523,200	74
WISCONSIN	44	1,933,690	1,130,430	58
WYOMING	14	179,530	123,350	69

[1] Ranked by cable TV penetration, i.e., cable TV households as % of TV households.
[2] Anchorage and Fairbanks DMAs only.

A. C. Nielsen Co. Cable TV Household Estimates

Alphabetically by Designated Market Area

U.S. TV HOUSEHOLD ESTIMATES
CABLE TV BY DESIGNATED MARKET AREA (DMA)

DESIGNATED MARKET AREA	CABLE TV % RANK [1]	TV HSHLDS (Jan. 1998)	CABLE TV HSHLDS (Sept. 1997)	CABLE TV % OF TV HSHLDS
Abilene-Sweetwater, TX	62	111,400	78,590	71
Albany, GA	139	137,750	86,890	63
Albany-Schenectady-Troy, NY	38	508,730	375,880	74
Albuquerque-Santa Fe, NM	179	560,130	332,260	59
Alexandria, LA	72	80,880	56,960	70
Alpena, MI	117	16,520	10,680	65
Amarillo, TX	99	187,640	126,560	67
Anchorage, AK	179	122,190	72,320	59
Anniston, AL	4	43,150	36,160	84
Atlanta, GA	88	1,674,700	1,144,080	68
Augusta, GA	163	226,170	137,780	61
Austin, TX	109	452,430	299,280	66
Bakersfield, CA	43	176,090	128,730	73
Baltimore, MD	117	988,040	641,250	65
Bangor, ME	204	127,440	66,500	52
Baton Rouge, LA	32	267,630	201,560	75
Beaumont-Port Arthur, TX	62	161,280	113,960	71
Bend, OR	62	39,240	27,770	71
Billings, MT	190	94,650	53,480	57
Biloxi-Gulfport, MS	9	113,900	92,060	81
Binghamton, NY	32	130,130	97,300	75
Birmingham, AL	109	546,620	363,430	66
Bluefield-Beckley-Oak Hill, WV	17	137,570	108,640	79
Boise, ID	204	188,440	97,230	52
Boston, MA	20	2,174,300	1,694,410	78
Bowling Green, KY	196	74,740	41,230	55
Bristol, VA-Kingsport-Johnson City, TN: Tri Cities	38	288,150	213,880	74
Buffalo, NY	32	629,970	474,740	75
Burlington, VT-Plattsburgh, NY	139	292,300	183,140	63
Butte-Bozeman, MT	196	54,190	29,710	55
Casper-Riverton, WY	129	47,820	30,790	64
Cedar Rapids-Waterloo-Dubuque, IA	129	308,170	197,570	64
Champaign-Springfield-Decatur, IL	32	330,820	249,490	75
Charleston, SC	117	215,430	139,840	65
Charleston-Huntington, WV	43	480,160	352,850	73
Charlotte, NC	99	840,290	561,420	67
Charlottesville, VA	129	50,710	32,380	64
Chattanooga, TN	72	310,040	216,730	70
Cheyenne, WY-Scottsbluff, NE-Sterling, CO	53	49,940	35,890	72
Chicago, IL	153	3,140,460	1,949,910	62
Chico-Redding, CA	171	177,020	105,830	60
Cincinnati, OH	153	797,230	490,310	62
Clarksburg-Weston, WV	72	105,240	73,590	70
Cleveland, OH	72	1,469,010	1,026,140	70
Colorado Springs-Pueblo, CO	88	275,430	188,240	68
Columbia-Jefferson City, MO	171	147,850	89,020	60
Columbia, SC	171	303,700	182,340	60
Columbus, GA	53	182,840	131,620	72
Columbus-Tupelo-West Point, MS	186	171,050	99,300	58
Columbus, OH	129	739,440	473,100	64
Corpus Christi, TX	99	184,700	124,390	67
Dallas-Fort Worth, TX	204	1,899,330	989,090	52
Davenport, IA-Rock Island-Moline, IL	99	301,800	201,520	67
Dayton, OH	72	502,590	351,000	70
Denver, CO	153	1,198,580	741,290	62
Des Moines-Ames, IA	163	383,460	232,660	61
Detroit, MI	99	1,781,710	1,191,410	67
Dothan, AL	88	86,390	58,500	68
Duluth, MN-Superior, WI	208	169,270	85,150	50
El Paso, TX	163	264,210	159,980	61
Elmira, NY	43	92,550	67,100	73
Erie, PA	99	153,100	101,920	67
Eugene, OR	109	209,730	137,630	66
Eureka, CA	25	56,450	42,760	76
Evansville, IN	163	274,320	167,900	61
Fairbanks, AK	211	29,680	10,960	37
Fargo-Valley City, ND	139	221,050	139,230	63
Flint-Saginaw-Bay City, MI	109	442,380	291,980	66
Florence-Myrtle Beach, SC	88	221,280	151,160	68
Fort Myers-Naples, FL	17	319,960	252,940	79
Fort Smith, AR	117	216,360	141,010	65
Fort Wayne, IN	190	243,910	137,860	57
Fresno-Visalia, CA	199	495,550	263,250	53
Gainesville, FL	79	99,580	69,090	69
Glendive, MT	88	4,030	2,730	68
Grand Junction-Montrose, CO	129	55,780	35,730	64
Grand Rapids-Kalamazoo-Battle Creek, MI	153	659,340	411,670	62
Great Falls, MT	179	62,830	36,820	59
Green Bay-Appleton, WI	179	381,100	225,820	59
Greensboro-High Point-Winston Salem, NC	129	577,070	366,510	64
Greenville-New Bern-Washington, NC	117	234,490	152,120	65
Greenville-Spartanburg, SC-Asheville, NC	171	717,510	428,740	60
Greenwood-Greenville, MS	62	76,830	54,650	71
Harlingen-Weslaco-Brownsville, TX	210	240,670	109,610	46
Harrisburg-Lancaster-Lebanon-York, PA	25	588,310	449,080	76
Harrisonburg, VA	38	81,120	59,970	74
Hartford-New Haven, CT	3	915,770	791,980	86
Hattiesburg-Laurel, MS	186	95,150	54,860	58
Helena, MT	88	21,000	14,240	68
Honolulu, HI	2	380,380	333,470	88
Houston, TX	192	1,624,340	917,710	56
Huntsville-Decatur-Florence, AL	62	330,560	234,500	71
Idaho Falls-Pocatello, ID	196	94,540	51,760	55
Indianapolis, IN	117	957,050	618,080	65
Jackson, MS	171	296,820	177,470	60
Jackson, TN	153	62,080	38,590	62
Jacksonville, FL-Brunswick, GA	32	502,370	375,580	75
Johnstown-Altoona, PA	13	288,350	229,590	80
Jonesboro, AR	72	76,030	52,930	70
Joplin, MO-Pittsburg, KS	192	145,510	81,880	56
Kansas City, MO	117	791,800	517,950	65
Knoxville, TN	88	440,720	298,800	68
La Crosse-Eau Claire, WI	171	179,050	106,720	60
Lafayette, IN	7	48,800	39,930	82
Lafayette, LA	72	205,190	143,050	70
Lake Charles, LA	53	78,210	56,690	72
Lansing, MI	99	236,150	157,280	67
Laredo, TX	79	49,440	34,040	69
Las Vegas, NV	99	450,170	302,350	67
Lexington, KY	79	402,610	276,900	69
Lima, OH	9	38,020	30,970	81
Lincoln-Hastings-Kearney, NE	79	253,040	174,620	69
Little Rock-Pine Bluff, AR	139	481,270	300,850	63
Los Angeles, CA	139	5,009,230	3,132,980	63
Louisville, KY	117	554,240	361,360	65

DESIGNATED MARKET AREA	CABLE TV % RANK [1]	TV HSHLDS (Jan. 1998)	CABLE TV HSHLDS (Sept. 1997)	CABLE TV % OF TV HSHLDS
Lubbock, TX	129	140,500	89,400	64
Macon, GA	109	203,850	134,500	66
Madison, WI	139	316,370	198,280	63
Mankato, MN	62	58,420	41,470	71
Marquette, MI	43	84,590	61,510	73
Medford-Klamath Falls, OR	139	153,620	96,540	63
Memphis, TN	129	614,050	390,430	64
Meridian, MS	199	67,303	35,220	53
Miami-Fort Lauderdale, FL	53	1,385,940	992,860	72
Milwaukee, WI	171	790,660	477,410	60
Minneapolis-St. Paul, MN	204	1,448,100	745,960	52
Minot-Bismarck-Dickinson, ND	139	133,430	83,830	63
Missoula, MT	199	91,240	48,490	53
Mobile, AL-Pensacola, FL	53	449,950	323,840	72
Monroe, LA-El Dorado, AR	139	171,470	107,360	63
Monterey-Salinas, CA	20	206,250	159,910	78
Montgomery, AL	79	219,210	152,190	69
Nashville, TN	139	789,220	496,280	63
New Orleans, LA	43	622,760	454,630	73
New York, NY	62	6,755,510	4,824,730	71
Norfolk-Portsmouth-Newport News, VA	32	635,810	473,830	75
North Platte, NE	117	14,570	9,430	65
Odessa-Midland, TX	43	133,740	98,270	73
Oklahoma City, OK	139	593,040	374,410	63
Omaha, NE	79	370,560	255,900	69
Orlando-Daytona Beach-Melbourne, FL	25	1,041,380	796,270	76
Ottumwa, IA-Kirksville, MO	163	48,480	29,470	61
Paducah, KY-Cape Girardeau, MO-Harrisburg, IL	171	354,850	213,380	60
Palm Springs, CA	1	111,860	101,680	91
Panama City, FL	88	117,220	79,130	68
Parkersburg, WV	22	61,730	47,690	77
Peoria-Bloomington, IL	62	225,370	158,910	71
Philadelphia, PA	25	2,659,260	2,032,740	76
Phoenix, AZ	179	1,289,210	755,480	59
Pittsburgh, PA	17	1,140,330	899,280	79
Portland-Auburn, ME	25	349,560	265,880	76
Portland, OR	139	976,190	611,440	63
Presque Isle, ME	43	26,000	19,090	73
Providence, RI-New Bedford, MA	22	559,080	433,180	77
Quincy, IL-Hannibal, MO-Keokuk, IA	163	111,400	68,450	61
Raleigh-Durham, NC	153	826,010	512,210	62
Rapid City, SD	186	87,640	51,070	58
Reno, NV	53	215,380	154,250	72
Richmond-Petersburg, VA	139	457,980	288,670	63
Roanoke-Lynchburg, VA	109	401,550	263,230	66
Rochester, MN-Mason City, IA-Austin, MN	139	130,280	82,010	63
Rochester, NY	43	366,930	267,380	73
Rockford, IL	79	166,510	114,910	69
Sacramento-Stockton-Modesto, CA	129	1,126,990	726,490	64
St. Joseph, MO	88	52,820	35,840	68
St. Louis, MO	199	1,108,930	585,170	53
Salisbury, MD	25	106,120	80,330	76
Salt Lake City, UT	192	690,310	386,930	56
San Angelo, TX	13	49,730	39,860	80
San Antonio, TX	117	648,550	422,290	65
San Diego, CA	7	924,190	762,450	82
San Francisco-Oakland-San Jose, CA	62	2,297,880	1,639,830	71
Santa Barbara-Santa Maria-San Luis Obispo, CA	4	216,820	182,570	84
Savannah, GA	88	259,650	175,580	68
Seattle-Tacoma, WA	43	1,513,900	1,103,580	73
Sherman, TX-Ada, OK	153	110,790	68,730	62
Shreveport, LA	179	366,100	217,300	59
Sioux City, IA	117	154,570	100,200	65
Sioux Falls-Mitchell, SD	117	229,590	148,530	65
South Bend-Elkhart, IN	179	312,840	185,180	59
Spokane, WA	153	374,920	232,570	62
Springfield-Holyoke, MA	9	243,020	197,260	81
Springfield, MO	209	361,660	179,000	49
Syracuse, NY	38	378,390	279,480	74
Tallahassee, FL-Thomasville, GA	99	221,080	147,180	67
Tampa-St. Petersburg-Sarasota, FL	43	1,435,520	1,042,950	73
Terre Haute, IN	153	156,660	97,220	62
Toledo, OH	99	407,980	274,320	67
Topeka, KS	62	156,800	111,810	71
Traverse City-Cadillac, MI	192	213,440	120,160	56
Tucson-Nogales, AZ	163	355,680	215,220	61
Tulsa, OK	129	468,000	298,520	64
Tuscaloosa, AL	13	59,390	47,570	80
Twin Falls, ID	186	55,830	32,300	58
Tyler-Longview, TX	153	229,730	142,660	62
Utica, NY	9	93,770	75,980	81
Victoria, TX	53	28,370	20,370	72
Waco-Temple-Bryan, TX	109	274,260	180,370	66
Washington, DC	83	1,928,290	1,330,770	69
Watertown, NY	38	85,550	63,110	74
Wausau-Rhinelander, WI	199	162,820	85,810	53
West Palm Beach-Fort Pierce, FL	4	593,480	495,860	84
Wheeling, WV-Steubenville, OH	22	157,770	122,080	77
Wichita Falls, TX-Lawton, OK	79	152,400	105,600	69
Wichita-Hutchinson, KS	88	426,290	290,400	68
Wilkes Barre-Scranton, PA	13	566,270	452,210	80
Wilmington, NC	53	131,130	93,900	72
Yakima, WA	163	198,890	121,690	61
Youngstown, OH	53	273,960	196,260	72
Yuma, AZ-El Centro, CA	109	82,550	54,420	66
Zanesville, OH	25	31,930	24,350	76

[1] Ranked by cable TV penetration, i.e., cable TV households as % of TV households.

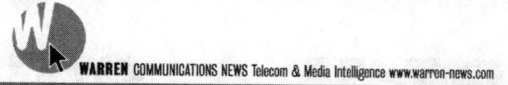

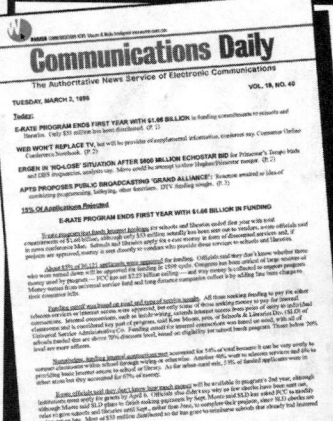

Cable Community Index

This is an index of all communities served by cable systems in the Icarus database. The following symbols indicate the type of service. A delta (▲) indicates an operating cable system. An asterisk (*) indicates a cable franchise awarded but not yet operating. A dagger (†) indicates a cable system application has been made. Cross references in all capital letter (e.g. **LAWSON**) indicate communities served by an operating cable system. Cross references with an initial capital letter (e.g. **Williams**) indicate planned service by operating cable systems. An index of Wireless Cable Systems follows this index.

ALABAMA

▲ **ABBEVILLE**—Galaxy Cablevision

ABERFOIL—See UNION SPRINGS, AL

▲ **ABERNANT**—Twin County Cable TV Inc.

ADAMSBURG—See FORT PAYNE, AL

ADAMSVILLE—See GARDENDALE, AL

▲ **ADDISON**—Addison Cablevision

▲ **AKRON**—Torrence Cable

ALABASTER—See MONTEVALLO, AL

▲ **ALBERTVILLE**—Charter Communications Inc.

▲ **ALEXANDER CITY**—Charter Communications Inc.

▲ **ALICEVILLE**—Northland Communications Corp.

ALLEN'S CROSSROADS—See MORGAN CITY, AL

▲ **ALLGOOD**—SouthTel Communications LP

ALLIANCE—See MAYTOWN, AL

▲ **ALTOONA**—Falcon Cablevision

▲ **ANDALUSIA**—TV Cable Co. of Andalusia Inc.

ANDERSON—See ELGIN, AL

▲ **ANNISTON**—Cable One

ANNISTON ARMY DEPOT—See ANNISTON, AL

▲ **APPLETON**—Torrence Cablevision USA Inc.

▲ **ARAB**—Charter Communications Inc.

▲ **ARDMORE**—Mediacom

ARITON—See CLIO, AL

▲ **ARLEY**—Galaxy Cablevision

▲ **ASHFORD**—Galaxy Cablevision

▲ **ASHLAND**—Communicom Services

▲ **ASHVILLE**—A. D. Cable

▲ **ATHENS**—Falcon First Inc.

▲ **ATHENS**—P.C.L. Cable

ATHENS—See also ARDMORE, AL

▲ **ATMORE**—Mediacom

▲ **ATTALLA**—Falcon Cablevision

▲ **AUBURN**—TCI of Lee County Inc.

AUTAUGA COUNTY—See MONTGOMERY, AL (AT&T Cable Services)

▲ **AUTAUGAVILLE**—Com-Link Inc.

AVON—See ASHFORD, AL

BABBIE—See HEATH, AL

▲ **BAILEYTON**—Charter Communications

▲ **BALDWIN COUNTY (northwestern portion)**—Baldwin County Cable

▲ **BALDWIN COUNTY (portions)**—Cable Options Inc.

▲ **BALDWIN COUNTY (unincorporated areas)**—Brister's Cable TV

BALDWIN COUNTY (portions)—See also FAIRHOPE, AL

BALDWIN COUNTY (portions)—See also GULF SHORES, AL

BALDWIN COUNTY (portions)—See also SPANISH COVE, AL

BARBOUR COUNTY (unincorporated areas)—See EUFAULA, AL

BARTON—See CHEROKEE, AL

▲ **BAY MINETTE**—AT&T Cable Services

BAYOU LA BATRE—See MOBILE COUNTY, AL (Mediacom)

BAYVIEW—See MAYTOWN, AL

BEAR CREEK—See HALEYVILLE, AL

▲ **BEATRICE**—B & L Communications

BEL FOREST—See BALDWIN COUNTY (unincorporated areas), AL

BELK—See FAYETTE, AL

▲ **BELLAMY**—Sky Cablevision

BELLWOOD—See CHANCELLOR, AL

▲ **BERRY**—Charter Communications Inc.

BESSEMER (portions)—See BIRMINGHAM, AL

BESSEMER (rural areas)—See also MONTEVALLO, AL

▲ **BEULAH**—Charter Communications Inc.

BIBB COUNTY (portions)—See CENTREVILLE, AL

BIBB COUNTY (portions)—See also WEST BLOCTON, AL

▲ **BIG COVE**—Mediacom

▲ **BIRMINGHAM**—Time Warner Cable

BLOUNT COUNTY (northwestern portion)—See BLOUNTSVILLE, AL

BLOUNT COUNTY (southwestern portion)—See HAYDEN, AL

▲ **BLOUNTSVILLE**—Century Cullman Corp.

BLUFF PARK—See HOOVER, AL

BOAZ—See ALBERTVILLE, AL

▲ **BOLIGEE**—Sky Cablevision

BON AIR—See CHILDERSBURG, AL

BON SECOUR—See FOLEY, AL

▲ **BRADFORD**—Charter Communications Inc.

BRANCHVILLE—See ODENVILLE, AL

BRANTLEY—See LUVERNE, AL

BRENT—See CENTREVILLE, AL

▲ **BREWTON**—Mediacom

BRIDGEPORT—See JASPER, TN

BRIGHTON—See BIRMINGHAM, AL

BRILLIANT—See WINFIELD, AL

BROMLEY—See BALDWIN COUNTY (northwestern portion), AL

BROMPTON—See ODENVILLE, AL

BROOKSIDE—See GARDENDALE, AL

▲ **BROOKWOOD**—Charter Communications Inc.

BROWNVILLE—See BIRMINGHAM, AL

BRUNDIDGE—See TROY, AL (AT&T Cable Services)

BUCKSVILLE—See ABERNANT, AL

BUHL—See TUSCALOOSA COUNTY, AL

▲ **BUTLER**—Galaxy Cablevision

BUTLER COUNTY (portions)—See GREENVILLE, AL

CAHABA VALLEY—See MONTEVALLO, AL

CALERA—See MONTEVALLO, AL

CALHOUN COUNTY (unincorporated areas)—See ANNISTON, AL

▲ **CAMDEN**—Mediacom

CAPSHAW—See ARDMORE, AL

▲ **CARBON HILL**—Charter Communications Inc.

CARROLLTON—See ALICEVILLE, AL

▲ **CASTLEBERRY**—B & L Communications

▲ **CEDAR BLUFF**—Falcon First Inc.

CEDAR GROVE—See JASPER, TN

▲ **CENTER POINT**—TCI Media Services

CENTER STAR—See ELGIN, AL

▲ **CENTRE**—Falcon Cable TV

▲ **CENTREVILLE**—Charter Communications Inc.

CHAMBERS COUNTY—See AUBURN, AL

CHAMBERS COUNTY—See also WEST POINT, GA

▲ **CHANCELLOR**—Americable International Florida Inc.

▲ **CHATOM**—Torrence Cable

▲ **CHEROKEE**—Falcon First Inc.

CHEROKEE COUNTY—See CENTRE, AL

▲ **PELL CITY**—Coosa Cable Co.

▲ **PENCE**—Charter Communications

▲ **PENNINGTON**—Galaxy Cablevision

▲ **PERDIDO BEACH**—Blackstone Cable

PERRY COUNTY—See UNIONTOWN, AL

PERRY COUNTY (unincorporated areas)—See also MARION, AL

PETERSON—See BROOKWOOD, AL

▲ **PHENIX CITY**—Phenix City Cable

▲ **PHIL CAMPBELL**—Tri-County Cable

PICKENS COUNTY (northern portion)—See REFORM, AL

PICKENS COUNTY (southern portion)—See ALICEVILLE, AL

PICKENSVILLE—See ALICEVILLE, AL

▲ **PIEDMONT**—Falcon Cable TV

PIKE COUNTY—See TROY, AL (AT&T Cable Services)

PINCKARD—See DALEVILLE, AL (Paragon Cable)

▲ **PINE HILL**—Galaxy Cablevision

PINE RIDGE—See FORT PAYNE, AL

PINSON—See GARDENDALE, AL

PISGAH—See HENAGAR, AL

PLANTATION HILLS—See BALDWIN COUNTY (unincorporated areas), AL

PLEASANT GROVE—See FAIRFIELD, AL

POINT CLEAR—See FAIRHOPE, AL

▲ **POLLARD**—Torrence Cablevision USA Inc.

POWELL—See RAINSVILLE, AL

PRATTVILLE—See MONTGOMERY, AL (AT&T Cable Services)

PRICEVILLE (portions)—See DECATUR, AL

PRICEVILLE (portions)—See also HARTSELLE, AL

PRICHARD—See MOBILE, AL

PRICHARD—See also MOBILE COUNTY, AL (Enstar IX)

▲ **PROVIDENCE**—Sky Cablevision

▲ **RAGLAND**—Ragland Telephone Co.

RAINBOW CITY—See GADSDEN, AL

▲ **RAINSVILLE**—Falcon First Inc.

▲ **RANBURNE**—Galaxy Cablevision

RANDOLPH COUNTY—See ROANOKE, AL

▲ **RED BAY**—Galaxy Cablevision

▲ **RED LEVEL**—B & L Communications

REDSTONE ARSENAL—See HUNTSVILLE, AL (Knowledgy)

REECE CITY—See ATTALLA, AL

▲ **REFORM**—Northland Communications Corp.

REFORM—See also ALICEVILLE, AL

REHOBETH—See DALEVILLE, AL (Paragon Cable)

REPTON—See MONROEVILLE, AL

RESCUE—See MORGAN CITY, AL

RIDGEVILLE—See ATTALLA, AL

RIPLEY—See LIMESTONE COUNTY (western portion), AL

RIVER FALLS—See HEATH, AL

RIVER VIEW—See WEST POINT, GA

RIVERCHASE—See HOOVER, AL

RIVERSIDE—See PELL CITY, AL

▲ **ROANOKE**—Communicom Services

▲ **ROBERTSDALE**—Mediacom

ROCK MILLS—See ROANOKE, AL

ROCKFORD—See ALEXANDER CITY, AL

ROCKY RIDGE—See HOOVER, AL

ROGERSVILLE—See ELGIN, AL

ROMAR BEACH—See GULF SHORES, AL

ROOSEVELT CITY—See BIRMINGHAM, AL

RUSSELL COUNTY—See PHENIX CITY, AL

▲ **RUSSELLVILLE**—Charter Communications Inc.

RUTH—See BAILEYTON, AL

RUTLEDGE—See LUVERNE, AL

SALEM—See PHENIX CITY, AL

▲ **SAMSON**—TCI TKR of the Gulf Plains Inc.

SANFORD—See HEATH, AL

SARALAND—See MOBILE, AL

SARALAND—See also MOBILE COUNTY, AL (Enstar IX)

SARDIS CITY—See ALBERTVILLE, AL

▲ **SATSUMA**—Mediacom

▲ **SCOTTSBORO**—Falcon First Inc.

SCOTTSBORO—See also GUNTERSVILLE, AL

SEALE—See HATCHECHUBBEE, AL

SECTION—See RAINSVILLE, AL

▲ **SELBROOK**—B & L Communications

▲ **SELMA**—TCI of Selma Inc.

SEMMES—See MOBILE COUNTY, AL (Mediacom)

SHADES MOUNTAIN—See HOOVER, AL

SHADY LAKE TRAILER PARK—See SELBROOK, AL

SHAWMUT—See WEST POINT, GA

SHEFFIELD—See FLORENCE, AL

▲ **SHELBY COUNTY (northern portion)**—Charter Communications Inc.

SHELBY COUNTY—See also HARPERSVILLE, AL

SHELBY COUNTY—See also HOOVER, AL

SHELBY COUNTY—See also MOUNTAIN BROOK, AL

SHELBY COUNTY (portions)—See also COLUMBIANA, AL

SHELBY COUNTY (portions)—See also MONTEVALLO, AL

SHELBY COUNTY (southern portion)—See also SHELBY LAKE, AL

▲ **SHELBY LAKE**—Charter Communications Inc.

SHILOH—See RAINSVILLE, AL

SILVER HILL—See ROBERTSDALE, AL

SIPSEY—See SUMITON, AL

▲ **SKYLINE**—Helicon Cable Communications

▲ **SLOCOMB**—TCI TKR of the Gulf Plains Inc.

SMITHS—See PHENIX CITY, AL

▲ **SOUTHSIDE**—Charter Communications Inc.

▲ **SPANISH COVE**—Mediacom

SPANISH FORT—See FAIRHOPE, AL

SPEAKE—See HARTSELLE, AL

SPRING VALLEY—See LEIGHTON, AL

SPRINGVILLE—See ASHVILLE, AL

ST. CLAIR COUNTY (portions)—See ASHVILLE, AL

ST. CLAIR COUNTY (portions)—See also GARDENDALE, AL

ST. CLAIR COUNTY (portions)—See also PELL CITY, AL

▲ **ST. ELMO**—Torrence Cablevision USA Inc.

ST. FLORIAN—See FLORENCE, AL

▲ **STAPLETON**—Blackstone Cable

STEELE—See ASHVILLE, AL

STEVENSON—See JASPER, TN

▲ **SULLIGENT**—Tri-County Cable

▲ **SUMITON**—Charter Communications Inc.

SUMMERDALE—See FOLEY, AL

▲ **SWEET WATER**—Sky Cablevision

SYCAMORE—See SYLACAUGA, AL

▲ **SYLACAUGA**—TCI of Alabama

SYLVAN SPRINGS—See MAYTOWN, AL

SYLVANIA—See HENAGAR, AL

▲ **TALLADEGA**—Charter Communications Inc.

TALLADEGA COUNTY (portions)—See SYLACAUGA, AL

TALLADEGA COUNTY (portions)—See also TALLADEGA, AL

TALLADEGA COUNTY (southern portion)—See also ALEXANDER CITY, AL

TALLADEGA COUNTY (unincorporated areas)—See also ANNISTON, AL

TALLADEGA COUNTY (western portion)—See also CHILDERSBURG, AL

TALLAPOOSA COUNTY—See ALEXANDER CITY, AL

TALLAPOOSA COUNTY (portions)—See also LAKE MARTIN RESORT, AL

TALLAPOOSA COUNTY (southern portion)—See also WETUMPKA, AL

TALLASSEE—See WETUMPKA, AL

TARRANT CITY—See CENTER POINT, AL

ALASKA

▲ **THORNE BAY**—Thorne Bay Community TV Inc.

▲ **TOGIAK**—Frontier Cable Inc.

▲ **TOKSOOK BAY**—Frontier Cable Inc.

▲ **TUNUNAK**—Frontier Cable Inc.

▲ **UNALAKLEET**—Frontier Cable Inc.

▲ **UNALASKA**—Eyecom Inc.

▲ **VALDEZ**—GCI Cable Inc.

WASILLA—See PALMER, AK

▲ **WHITTIER**—Supervision Cable TV

▲ **WRANGELL**—GCI Cable Inc.

ARIZONA

AHWATUKEE—See PHOENIX, AZ

▲ **AJO**—Mediacom LLC

▲ **ALPINE**—Eagle West Cable

AMADA—See NOGALES, AZ

APACHE COUNTRY CLUB—See PHOENIX, AZ

APACHE COUNTY (southern portion)—See ST. JOHNS, AZ

▲ **APACHE JUNCTION**—Triax Cablevision

APACHE WELLS—See PHOENIX, AZ

ARIVACA—See NOGALES, AZ

▲ **ARIZONA CITY**—Wander Cable Communications

ARIZONA SUNSITES—See WILLCOX, AZ

ASH CANYON (unincorporated area)—See SIERRA VISTA, AZ

▲ **AVONDALE**—Cox Communications

AVRA VALLEY (portions)—See ORO VALLEY, AZ

▲ **BAGDAD**—Eagle West Cable

▲ **BEAR FLATS**—Eagle West Cable

BENSON—See WILLCOX, AZ

▲ **BISBEE**—CableOne

▲ **BISBEE JUNCTION**—M.A.S. Co.

▲ **BLACK CANYON CITY**—Eagle West Cable

BUCKEYE—See PHOENIX, AZ

▲ **BULLHEAD CITY**—Cablevision

BUSHMAN ACRES—See WINSLOW, AZ

BYLAS—See SAN CARLOS, AZ

CAMP VERDE—See SEDONA, AZ

▲ **CAREFREE**—Cox Communications

CARR CANYON (unincorporated area)—See SIERRA VISTA, AZ

▲ **CASA GRANDE**—Cox Cable

▲ **CASA GRANDE (northern portion)**—Eagle West Cable

CASHION—See LUKE AFB, AZ

CATALINA (portions)—See ORO VALLEY, AZ

▲ **CAVE CREEK**—Wander Cable Television

CAVE CREEK—See also CAREFREE, AZ

CHANDLER—See PHOENIX, AZ

▲ **CHINLE**—N.C.C.S.I.

CHINO VALLEY—See PRESCOTT, AZ

CHRISTOPHER CREEK—See SADDLE MOUNTAIN, AZ

CLAYPOOL—See GLOBE-MIAMI, AZ

▲ **CLIFTON**—CableOne

COCHISE COUNTY—See BISBEE, AZ

COCONINO COUNTY—See FLAGSTAFF, AZ

COCONINO COUNTY—See also PAGE, AZ

COCONINO COUNTY—See also WILLIAMS, AZ

COLORADO RIVER INDIAN TRIBE—See PARKER, AZ

▲ **CONCHO VALLEY**—Eagle West Cable

▲ **COOLIDGE**—Cable America Corp.

▲ **CORDES LAKES**—Americable International Arizona Inc.

▲ **CORNVILLE**—Cable One

COTTONWOOD (portions)—See SEDONA, AZ

CRYSTAL BEACH—See LAKE HAVASU CITY, AZ

DAVIS-MONTHAN AFB—See TUCSON, AZ

DESERT HILLS—See LAKE HAVASU CITY, AZ

DEWEY—See SEDONA, AZ

▲ **DOLAN SPRINGS**—Wander Cable Communications

▲ **DOUGLAS**—Robin Cable Systems of Tucson

▲ **DUDLEYVILLE**—Wander Cable Communications

▲ **EAGAR**—Eagle West Cable

▲ **EAST MESA**—Eagle West Cable

EAST MESA—See also PHOENIX, AZ

EHRENBERG—See BLYTHE, CA

EL MIRAGE—See LUKE AFB, AZ

▲ **ELOY**—Wander Cable Communications

▲ **FLAGSTAFF**—NPG Cable of Arizona

▲ **FLORENCE (northern portion)**—Eagle West Cable

FLORENCE—See also COOLIDGE, AZ

FLORENCE GARDEN MHP—See FLORENCE (northern portion), AZ

FOOTHILLS—See TUCSON, AZ

FOREST HIGHLANDS—See FLAGSTAFF, AZ

FORT DEFIANCE—See NAVAJO, NM

FORT HUACHUCA—See DOUGLAS, AZ

▲ **FORT MOHAVE MESA**—Americable International Arizona Inc.

FOUNTAIN HILLS—See PHOENIX, AZ

▲ **FREDONIA**—TCI Cablevision of Arizona Inc.

GANADO—See NAVAJO, NM

▲ **GILA BEND**—Cable America

GILA COUNTY—See GLOBE-MIAMI, AZ

▲ **GILBERT**—Cox Communications

▲ **GISELA**—Indevideo Co. Inc.

GLENDALE—See PHOENIX, AZ

▲ **GLOBE-MIAMI**—Cable One

GOLD CANYON—See APACHE JUNCTION, AZ

GOLDEN HILLS—See PHOENIX, AZ

▲ **GOLDEN SHORES**—Americable International Arizona Inc.

▲ **GOLDEN VALLEY**—Americable International Arizona Inc.

GOODYEAR—See PHOENIX, AZ

GRAHAM COUNTY—See SAFFORD, AZ

▲ **GRAND CANYON**—Indevideo Co. Inc.

▲ **GRAND MISSOURI MOBILE HOME PARK**—Sun Valley Cable Inc.

▲ **GREEN VALLEY**—Robin Cable Systems of Tucson

GREENLEE COUNTY—See CLIFTON, AZ

GUADALUPE—See PHOENIX, AZ

HAYDEN—See DUDLEYVILLE, AZ

▲ **HEBER**—Wander Cable Communications

▲ **HEREFORD**—M.A.S. Co.

▲ **HOLBROOK**—Cable One

HORIZAN SIX—See LAKE HAVASU CITY, AZ

HUACHUCA CITY—See SIERRA VISTA, AZ

HUMBOLDT—See SEDONA, AZ

ICE HOUSE CANYON—See GLOBE-MIAMI, AZ

INDIAN HILLS—See DUDLEYVILLE, AZ

JOSEPH CITY—See HOLBROOK, AZ

KACHINA—See FLAGSTAFF, AZ

▲ **KAYENTA**—N.C.C.S.I.

▲ **KEAMS CANYON**—Indevideo Co. Inc.

▲ **KEARNY**—Wander Cable Communications

▲ **KINGMAN**—Cablevision

KOHL'S RANCH—See SADDLE MOUNTAIN, AZ

LA PAZ COUNTY—See PARKER, AZ

▲ **LAKE HAVASU CITY**—Cablevision of Lake Havasu

LAKE MONTEZUMA—See SEDONA, AZ

LAKESIDE—See SHOW LOW, AZ

LEISURE WORLD—See PHOENIX, AZ

▲ **LEUPP**—Indevideo Co. Inc.

LITCHFIELD PARK—See PHOENIX, AZ

▲ **LUKE AFB**—Cox Communications

▲ **MAMMOTH**—Wander Cable Communications

MANY FARMS—See CHINLE, AZ

MARANA—See ORO VALLEY, AZ

MARICOPA COUNTY (eastern portion)—See MESA, AZ

MARICOPA COUNTY (portions)—See also LUKE AFB, AZ

MARICOPA COUNTY (portions)—See also PHOENIX, AZ

MARINE CORPS AIR STATION—See YUMA, AZ

MAYER—See SEDONA, AZ

▲ **MESA**—Cable America Corp.

MESA—See also PHOENIX, AZ

MESA (portions)—See also EAST MESA, AZ

MESA DEL CABALLO—See PAYSON, AZ

MILLER CANYON (unincorporated area)—See SIERRA VISTA, AZ

MIRACLE VALLEY—See HEREFORD, AZ

MOHAVE COUNTY—See KINGMAN, AZ

MOHAVE COUNTY—See also LAKE HAVASU CITY, AZ

MOHAVE COUNTY—See also MESQUITE, NV

MOHAVE COUNTY (portions)—See also BULLHEAD CITY, AZ

MOHAVE VALLEY—See BULLHEAD CITY, AZ

MORENCI—See CLIFTON, AZ

▲ **MOSON ROAD**—M.A.S. Co.

MOUNTAINAIRE—See FLAGSTAFF, AZ

▲ **MUNDS PARK**—NPG Cable

NACO—See BISBEE, AZ

NAVAJO COUNTY—See HOLBROOK, AZ

NAVAJO COUNTY—See also WINSLOW, AZ

NAVAJO COUNTY (portions)—See also SHOW LOW, AZ

NICKSVILLE—See SIERRA VISTA, AZ

▲ **NOGALES**—Mediacom LLC

OAK CREEK (village)—See SEDONA, AZ

▲ **ORACLE**—Wander Cable Communications

▲ **ORO VALLEY**—Jones Intercable

OVERGAARD—See HEBER, AZ

OXBOW ESTATES—See PAYSON, AZ

▲ **PAGE**—Cable One

Page Springs—See CORNVILLE, AZ

PALOMINAS—See HEREFORD, AZ

PARADISE VALLEY—See PHOENIX, AZ

▲ **PARKER**—Cablevision of Parker

PARKER DAM—See PARKER, AZ

▲ **PATAGONIA**—Robin Cable Systems of Tucson

▲ **PAYSON**—NPG Cable of Arizona Inc.

▲ **PEACH SPRINGS**—Wander Cable Television

PEORIA—See PHOENIX, AZ

PERIDOT—See SAN CARLOS, AZ

▲ **PERRYVILLE**—Wander Cable Television

▲ **PHOENIX**—Cox Communications

PHOENIX (northwestern portion)—See also PHOENIX, AZ

PHOENIX (western portion)—See also LUKE AFB, AZ

PIMA—See SAFFORD, AZ

PIMA COUNTY—See TUCSON, AZ

PINAL COUNTY—See CASA GRANDE, AZ

PINAL COUNTY (portions)—See also APACHE JUNCTION, AZ

PINAL COUNTY (portions)—See also KEARNY, AZ

▲ **PINE**—NPG Cable of Arizona Inc.

PINEDALE—See FLAGSTAFF, AZ

PINETOP—See SHOW LOW, AZ

PINEVIEW—See SHOW LOW, AZ

PINEWOOD—See MUNDS PARK, AZ

PINEWOOD—See also SEDONA, AZ

▲ **PRESCOTT**—CableOne

PRESCOTT VALLEY—See PRESCOTT, AZ

▲ **QUARTZSITE (unincorporated areas)**—Americable International Arizona Inc.

QUEEN CREEK—See MESA, AZ

▲ **QUEEN VALLEY**—Triax Cablevision

RAMSEY CANYON (unincorporated area)—See SIERRA VISTA, AZ

▲ **RIO RICO**—Mediacom LLC

▲ **RIO VERDE**—Cox Communications

RITA RANCH—See TUCSON, AZ

ROCK SHADOWS—See APACHE JUNCTION, AZ

ROUND VALLEY—See PAYSON, AZ

▲ **SADDLE MOUNTAIN**—Eagle West Cable

▲ **SAFFORD**—CableOne

SAHUARITA—See GREEN VALLEY, AZ

▲ **SAN CARLOS**—Apache Cablevision

SAN LUIS—See YUMA, AZ

▲ **SAN MANUEL**—Wander Cable Communications

SAND BANKS—See APACHE JUNCTION, AZ

SANTA CRUZ COUNTY (portions)—See NOGALES, AZ

▲ **SANTA RITA BEL AIRE**—AT&T Cable Services

SANTO TOMAS—See GREEN VALLEY, AZ

SCOTTSDALE—See PHOENIX, AZ

▲ **SEDONA**—Sedona Cablevision

▲ **SELLS**—Western Cablevision Inc.

▲ **SHONTO**—Indevideo Co. Inc.

▲ **SHOW LOW**—CableOne

▲ **SIERRA VISTA**—Cox Communications

SIX SHOOTER CANYON—See GLOBE-MIAMI, AZ

SNOWFLAKE—See SHOW LOW, AZ

SOLOMON—See SAFFORD, AZ

SOMERTON—See YUMA, AZ

SONOITA—See PATAGONIA, AZ

SOUTH TUCSON—See TUCSON, AZ

SPRINGERVILLE—See EAGAR, AZ

ST. DAVID—See WILLCOX, AZ

▲ **ST. JOHNS**—Eagle West Cable

STAR VALLEY—See PAYSON, AZ

STRAWBERRY—See PINE, AZ

STUMP CANYON (unincorporated area)—See SIERRA VISTA, AZ

SUN CITY—See PHOENIX, AZ

SUN CITY WEST—See PHOENIX, AZ

SUN LAKES—See PHOENIX, AZ

▲ **SUPERIOR**—Wander Cable Communications

SURPRISE—See PHOENIX, AZ

SWIFT TRAIL—See SAFFORD, AZ

TAYLOR—See SHOW LOW, AZ

TEMPE—See PHOENIX, AZ

THATCHER—See SAFFORD, AZ

THOMPSON DRAW—See SADDLE MOUNTAIN, AZ

TOLLESON—See LUKE AFB, AZ

TOLTEC CITY—See ARIZONA CITY, AZ

TOMBSTONE—See SIERRA VISTA, AZ

TONTO VILLAGE—See SADDLE MOUNTAIN, AZ

▲ **TSAILE**—N.C.C.S.I.

▲ **TUBA CITY**—Indevideo Co. Inc.

▲ **TUCSON**—Cox Communications

TUCSON (unincorporated areas)—See also ORO VALLEY, AZ

▲ **TUCSON ESTATES**—Western Cablevision Inc.

▲ **TUSAYAN**—Indevideo Co. Inc.

VERDE VILLAGE—See SEDONA, AZ

VISTA GRANDE—See SIERRA VISTA, AZ

WAGON WHEEL—See SHOW LOW, AZ

▲ **WELLTON**—Western Cablevision Inc.

WHEATFIELDS—See GLOBE-MIAMI, AZ

WHITE MOUNTAIN LAKE—See SHOW LOW, AZ

WICKENBURG—See MESA, AZ

▲ **WILLCOX**—Robin Cable Systems of Sierra Vista LP

▲ **WILLIAMS**—Eagle West Cable

WILLOW VALLEY ESTATES—See BULLHEAD CITY, AZ

WINDOW ROCK—See NAVAJO, NM

WINKELMAN—See DUDLEYVILLE, AZ

▲ **WINSLOW**—Cable One

▲ **YARNELL**—Eagle West Cable

YAVAPAI COUNTY—See PRESCOTT, AZ

YAVAPAI COUNTY—See also SEDONA, AZ

YAVAPAI COUNTY (portions)—See also CORNVILLE, AZ

YOUNGTOWN—See PHOENIX, AZ

▲ **YUMA**—Century Communications

YUMA COUNTY—See YUMA, AZ

YUMA PROVING GROUND—See YUMA, AZ

ARKANSAS

ALBION—See PANGBURN, AR

ALEXANDER—See SHANNON HILLS, AR

ALLPORT—See HUMNOKE, AR

ALMA—See RUDY/HIGHWAY 71, AR

ALMA—See also VAN BUREN, AR

▲ **ALMYRA**—Friendship Cable of Arkansas Inc.

▲ **ALPENA**—Inco Cable TV

▲ **ALTHEIMER**—Friendship Cable of Arkansas Inc.

ALTUS—See OZARK, AR

▲ **AMITY**—Cablevision

ANTOINE—See DELIGHT, AR

▲ **ARKADELPHIA**—TCA Cable TV

▲ **ARKANSAS CITY**—Cablevision

ARKOLA—See MIDLAND, AR

▲ **ASH FLAT**—Cablevision Communications

▲ **ASHDOWN**—Enstar XI

▲ **ATKINS**—Friendship Cable of Arkansas Inc.

▲ **AUBREY**—Community Communications Co.

▲ **AUGUSTA**—Augusta Video Inc.

AUSTIN—See CABOT, AR

▲ **BALD KNOB**—Wehco Video Inc.

BARLING—See FORT SMITH, AR

BASSETT—See OSCEOLA, AR

▲ **BATESVILLE**—TCA Cable Partners

BAUXITE—See SHANNON HILLS, AR

▲ **BAXTER COUNTY (unincorporated areas)**—Friendship Cable of Arkansas Inc.

BAXTER COUNTY (portions)—See also MOUNTAIN HOME, AR

BAY—See JONESBORO, AR

▲ **BEARDEN**—Friendship Cable of Arkansas Inc.

▲ **BEAVER LAKE**—Peak Cablevision

BEAVER SHORES—See BEAVER LAKE, AR

BEAVERAMA—See SONORA, AR

▲ **BEEBE**—Falcon Cable Media

▲ **BEEN RIDGE**—Quality Entertainment Corp.

▲ **BELLA VISTA**—TCA Cable Partners

BELLEFONTE—See HARRISON, AR

BELLEVILLE—See DANVILLE, AR

BENTON—See SHANNON HILLS, AR

▲ **BENTON COUNTY**—Peak Cablevision

BENTON COUNTY—See also BEAVER LAKE, AR

BENTON COUNTY—See also BENTONVILLE, AR

BENTON COUNTY—See also SILOAM SPRINGS, AR

▲ **BENTONVILLE**—TCA Cable TV

BERGMAN—See HARRISON, AR

▲ **BERRYVILLE**—TCA Cable TV

BETHEL HEIGHTS TWP.—See SPRINGDALE, AR

▲ **BIGGERS**—Cablevision Communications

▲ **BISCOE**—Friendship Cable of Arkansas Inc.

▲ **BISMARCK**—Community Communications Co.

BLACK OAK—See MANILA, AR

▲ **BLACK ROCK**—Inco Cable TV

BLEVINS—See McCASKILL, AR

BLOOMER—See LAVACA, AR

BLUE EYE—See LAMPE, MO

BLUE MOUNTAIN—See MAGAZINE, AR

BLUE SPRINGS—See SONORA, AR

▲ **BLYTHEVILLE**—Blytheville TV Cable Co.

BONANZA—See FORT SMITH, AR

▲ **BONO**—Friendship Cable of Arkansas Inc.

BOONE COUNTY—See HARRISON, AR

▲ **BOONEVILLE**—TCA Cable TV

▲ **BOONEVILLE HUMAN DEVELOPMENT CENTER**—Quality Entertainment

▲ **BRADFORD**—Inco Cable TV

▲ **BRADLEY**—Friendship Cable of Arkansas Inc.

BRADLEY COUNTY—See WARREN, AR

BRANCH—See RATCLIFF, AR

▲ **BRIARCLIFF**—Cablevision Communications

▲ **BRINKLEY**—East Arkansas Video Inc.

BROOKLAND—See LAKE CITY, AR

BRYANT—See LITTLE ROCK, AR

BUCKNER—See LEWISVILLE, AR

BULL SHOALS—See MOUNTAIN HOME, AR

▲ **CABOT**—Friendship Cable of Arkansas Inc.

CADDO VALLEY—See ARKADELPHIA, AR

▲ **CALDWELL**—Inco Cable TV

▲ **CALICO ROCK**—Inco Cable TV

CALION—See SMACKOVER, AR

▲ **CAMDEN**—Cam-Tel Co.

CAMMACK VILLAGE—See LITTLE ROCK, AR

CAMPBELL STATION—See TUCKERMAN, AR

CARAWAY—See MANILA, AR

CARBON CITY—See RATCLIFF, AR

CARLISLE—See HAZEN, AR

▲ **CARPENTER DAM**—Community Communications Co.

CARROLL COUNTY (portions)—See BERRYVILLE, AR

▲ **CARTHAGE**—Friendship Cable of Arkansas Inc.

▲ **CASA**—Quality Entertainment Corp.

CASH—See HARRISBURG, AR

CAULKSVILLE—See RATCLIFF, AR

▲ **CAVE CITY**—Inco Cable TV

CAVE SPRINGS—See TONTITOWN, AR

▲ **CEDARVILLE**—Peak Cablevision

CENTER POINT—See DIERKS, AR

CENTERTON—See BENTON COUNTY, AR

CENTRAL—See FRIENDSHIP, AR

CENTRAL CITY—See LAVACA, AR

▲ **CHARLESTON**—Classic Cable

CHEROKEE VILLAGE—See HARDY, AR

CHERRY VALLEY—See HARRISBURG, AR

CHESTER—See RUDY/HIGHWAY 71, AR

▲ **CHIDESTER**—Friendship Cable of Arkansas Inc.

▲ **CLARENDON**—Friendship Cable of Arkansas Inc.

▲ **CLARKSVILLE**—TCA Cable TV

CLAY COUNTY (portions)—See PIGGOTT, AR

CLEBURNE COUNTY—See GREERS FERRY, AR

CLEBURNE COUNTY (portions)—See also FAIRFIELD BAY, AR

▲ **CLINTON**—Clinton Cablevision

▲ **COAL HILL**—Friendship Cable of Arkansas Inc.

COLLEGE CITY—See WALNUT RIDGE, AR

COLT—See CALDWELL, AR

COLUMBIA COUNTY—See MAGNOLIA, AR

COLUMBIA COUNTY (portions)—See also TAYLOR, AR

▲ **CONWAY**—Conway Corp. C.T.S.

▲ **CONWAY (eastern portion)**—Friendship Cable of Arkansas Inc.

CONWAY COUNTY (portions)—See MORRILTON, AR

▲ **CORNING**—TCA Cable Partners

COTTER—See MOUNTAIN HOME, AR

COVE—See HATFIELD, AR

CRAIGHEAD COUNTY (northwestern portion)—See BONO, AR

CRAIGHEAD COUNTY (portions)—See also LAKE CITY, AR

CRAWFORD COUNTY—See VAN BUREN, AR

CRAWFORD COUNTY (unincorporated areas)—See also CEDARVILLE, AR

▲ **CRAWFORDSVILLE**—Friendship Cable of Arkansas Inc.

CRITTENDEN COUNTY—See PARKIN, AR

CRITTENDEN COUNTY—See also WEST MEMPHIS, AR

CRITTENDEN COUNTY (portions)—See also HUGHES, AR

CROSS COUNTY (portions)—See HARRISBURG, AR

▲ **CROSSETT**—American Cable Entertainment

▲ **HOT SPRINGS**—Resort TV Cable Co. Inc.

▲ **HOT SPRINGS VILLAGE**—TCA Cable Partners

HOXIE—See WALNUT RIDGE, AR

▲ **HUGHES**—Friendship Cable of Arkansas Inc.

▲ **HUMNOKE**—Friendship Cable of Arkansas Inc.

▲ **HUMPHREY**—Friendship Cable of Arkansas Inc.

▲ **HUNTINGTON**—Peak Cablevision

▲ **HUNTSVILLE**—Inco Cable TV

▲ **HUTTIG**—Bayou Cable TV

IDA—See TUMBLING SHOALS, AR

IMBODEN—See RAVENDEN, AR

INDEPENDENCE COUNTY—See MOOREFIELD, AR

INDEPENDENCE COUNTY—See also WEAVERS CHAPEL, AR

INDEPENDENCE COUNTY (portions)—See also BATESVILLE, AR

INDEPENDENCE COUNTY (unincorporated areas)—See also PLEASANT PLAINS, AR

IZARD COUNTY—See HORSESHOE BEND, AR

JACKSON COUNTY—See NEWPORT, AR

JACKSONPORT—See NEWPORT, AR

JACKSONVILLE—See NORTH LITTLE ROCK, AR

▲ **JASPER**—Friendship Cable of Arkansas Inc.

JEFFERSON COUNTY (portions)—See PINE BLUFF, AR

JEFFERSON COUNTY (portions)—See also PINE BLUFF (southern portion), AR

JEFFERSON COUNTY (portions)—See also PINEBERGEN, AR

JEFFERSON COUNTY (portions)—See also WHITEHALL, AR

JENNY LIND—See FORT SMITH, AR

JOHNSON—See SPRINGDALE, AR

JOHNSON COUNTY (southwestern portion)—See COAL HILL, AR

JOINER—See OSCEOLA, AR

▲ **JONES MILL**—Community Communications Co.

▲ **JONESBORO**—TCA Cable TV

JUDSONIA—See SEARCY, AR

▲ **JUNCTION CITY**—Friendship Cable of Arkansas Inc.

KEISER—See OSCEOLA, AR

KENSETT—See SEARCY, AR

▲ **KEO**—Community Communications Co.

KIBLER—See VAN BUREN, AR

KIRBY—See DAISY, AR

KNOB HILL—See SONORA, AR

▲ **KNOBEL**—Friendship Cable of Arkansas Inc.

▲ **KNOXVILLE**—Quality Entertainment Corp.

LAFAYETTE COUNTY (portions)—See LAKE ERLING, AR

LAFE—See MARMADUKE, AR

▲ **LAKE CITY**—Friendship Cable of Arkansas Inc.

▲ **LAKE ERLING**—Friendship Cable of Arkansas Inc.

LAKE FAIRCREST—See EL DORADO, AR

LAKE POINSETT—See HARRISBURG, AR

▲ **LAKE VIEW**—Cable Entertainment Co.

▲ **LAKE VILLAGE**—TCA Cable Partners

LAKEVIEW—See MOUNTAIN HOME, AR

LAMAR—See RUSSELLVILLE, AR

▲ **LAVACA**—TCA Cable TV

LAWRENCE COUNTY—See WALNUT RIDGE, AR

LAWSON—See EL DORADO, AR

LEACHVILLE—See MANILA, AR

LEAD HILL—See DIAMOND CITY, AR

LEE COUNTY (portions)—See MARIANNA, AR

▲ **LEOLA**—Friendship Cable of Arkansas Inc.

LEPANTO—See MARKED TREE, AR

▲ **LESLIE**—Friendship Cable of Arkansas Inc.

LETONA—See PANGBURN, AR

▲ **LEWISVILLE**—Friendship Cable of Arkansas Inc.

LEXA—See HELENA, AR

LINCOLN—See PRAIRIE GROVE, AR

LINCOLN COUNTY—See STAR CITY, AR

LITTLE FLOCK—See BENTON COUNTY, AR

LITTLE RED RIVER—See HEBER SPRINGS, AR

LITTLE RIVER COUNTY (portions)—See ASHDOWN, AR

▲ **LITTLE ROCK**—Comcast Cablevision of Little Rock Inc.

LITTLE ROCK AFB—See CABOT, AR

▲ **LOCKESBURG**—Lockesburg Cablevision

▲ **LOCUST BAYOU**—Friendship Cable of Arkansas Inc.

LOGAN COUNTY (northwestern portion)—See RATCLIFF, AR

LOGAN COUNTY (unincorporated areas)—See also MAGAZINE, AR

▲ **LONDON**—Friendship Cable of Arkansas Inc.

▲ **LONOKE**—Classic Cable

LONOKE COUNTY (portions)—See CABOT, AR

LOUANN—See SMACKOVER, AR

LOWELL—See SPRINGDALE, AR

LUXORA—See OSCEOLA, AR

▲ **LYNN**—Friendship Cable of Arkansas

MACON—See CABOT, AR

MADISON—See HUGHES, AR

▲ **MAGAZINE**—Friendship Cable of Arkansas Inc.

▲ **MAGIC SPRINGS**—Community Communications Co.

MAGNESS—See NEWARK, AR

▲ **MAGNOLIA**—TCA Cable TV

▲ **MALVERN**—TCA Cable Partners

MAMMOTH SPRING—See THAYER, MO

MANDEVILLE—See FOUKE, AR

▲ **MANILA**—Friendship Cable of Arkansas Inc.

▲ **MANSFIELD**—Peak Cablevision

▲ **MARIANNA**—East Arkansas Video Inc.

MARION—See WEST MEMPHIS, AR

MARION COUNTY—See YELLVILLE, AR

MARION COUNTY (portions)—See also MOUNTAIN HOME, AR

▲ **MARKED TREE**—Friendship Cable of Arkansas Inc.

▲ **MARMADUKE**—Cablevision Communications

▲ **MARSHALL**—Treece TV Cable Service

▲ **MARVELL**—TCA Cable Partners

▲ **MAUMELLE**—Falcon Cable Media

MAYFIELD—See SONORA, AR

▲ **MAYFLOWER**—Friendship Cable of Arkansas Inc.

▲ **MAYNARD**—Cablevision Communications

▲ **McALMONT**—Falcon Cable Media

▲ **McCASKILL**—Peak Cablevision

▲ **McCRORY**—TCA Cable Partners

▲ **McDOUGAL**—Friendship Cable of Arkansas Inc.

▲ **McGEHEE**—TCA Cable TV

▲ **McNEIL**—Electronic Vision

McRAE—See HIGGINSON, AR

▲ **MELBOURNE**—Inco Cable TV

▲ **MENA**—TCA Cable Partners

MENIFEE—See PLUMERVILLE, AR

▲ **MIDLAND**—Peak Cablevision

MIDWAY—See MOUNTAIN HOME, AR

MILLER COUNTY (unincorporated areas)—See FOUKE, AR

▲ **MINERAL SPRINGS**—Peak Cablevision

MISSISSIPPI COUNTY (portions)—See BLYTHEVILLE, AR

MISSISSIPPI COUNTY (portions)—See also MANILA, AR

MISSISSIPPI COUNTY (portions)—See also OSCEOLA, AR

MITCHELLVILLE—See McGEHEE, AR

MONETTE—See MANILA, AR

MONTE NE—See BEAVER LAKE, AR

MONTGOMERY COUNTY (unincorporated areas)—See MOUNT IDA, AR

▲ **MONTICELLO**—Community Communications Co.

Montrose—See WILMOT, AR

▲ **MOOREFIELD**—TCA Cable Partners

▲ **MORO**—Inco Cable TV

▲ **MORRILTON**—TCA Cable Partners

▲ **MOUNT IDA**—Friendship Cable of Arkansas Inc.

▲ **MOUNT PLEASANT**—Inco Cable TV

MOUNTAIN HARBOR RESORT—See MOUNT IDA, AR

▲ **MOUNTAIN HOME**—TCA Cable Partners

MOUNTAIN PINE—See HOT SPRINGS, AR

▲ **MOUNTAIN VIEW**—Inco Cable TV

MOUNTAINBURG—See RUDY/HIGHWAY 71, AR

▲ **MULBERRY**—Peak Cablevision

▲ **MURFREESBORO**—Peak Cablevision

▲ **NASHVILLE**—Friendship Cable of Arkansas Inc.

▲ **NEWARK**—Inco Cable TV

NEWHOPE—See DAISY, AR

▲ **NEWPORT**—TCA Cable Partners

NORFORK—See BRIARCLIFF, AR

▲ **NORMAN**—Community Communications Co.

NORPHLET—See SMACKOVER, AR

NORRISTOWN—See RUSSELLVILLE, AR

NORTH CROSSETT—See CROSSETT, AR

▲ **NORTH LITTLE ROCK**—Comcast Cablevision of Arkansas Inc.

NORTH LITTLE ROCK—See also MAUMELLE, AR

▲ **O'KEAN**—Friendship Cable of Arkansas Inc.

OAK GROVE—See LAMPE, MO

▲ **OAK GROVE HEIGHTS**—Oak Grove Heights Cable Co.

▲ **OIL TROUGH**—Inco Cable TV

OLA—See PLAINVIEW, AR (Friendship Cable of Arkansas Inc.)

OLD JENNY LIND—See FORT SMITH, AR

OLD UNION—See EL DORADO, AR

OPPELO—See GREENBRIER, AR

▲ **OSCEOLA**—Friendship Cable of Arkansas Inc.

OUACHITA COUNTY (portions)—See CHIDESTER, AR

OUACHITA COUNTY (portions)—See also EAST CAMDEN, AR

OUACHITA COUNTY (portions)—See also SMACKOVER, AR

▲ **OXFORD**—Cablevision Communications

▲ **OZARK**—Cable Time

▲ **OZARK ACRES**—Friendship Cable of Arkansas Inc.

▲ **PALESTINE**—Friendship Cable of Arkansas Inc.

▲ **PANGBURN**—Inco Cable TV

▲ **PARAGOULD**—Paragould City Light & Water Commission

▲ **PARIS**—TCA Cable TV

PARKDALE—See WILMOT, AR

▲ **PARKIN**—Time Warner

PATTERSON—See McCRORY, AR

PEA RIDGE—See BENTON COUNTY, AR

▲ **PEARCY**—Cablevision

▲ **PENCIL BLUFF/ODEN**—Quality Entertainment Corp.

PERLA—See MALVERN, AR

PERRY—See GREENBRIER, AR

PERRYTOWN—See HOPE, AR

PERRYVILLE—See GREENBRIER, AR

PFEIFFER—See WEAVERS CHAPEL, AR

PHILLIPS COUNTY—See HELENA, AR

▲ **PIGGOTT**—Cablevision Communications

PIKE COUNTY (unincorporated areas)—See MURFREESBORO, AR

▲ **PINE BLUFF**—Pine Bluff Cable TV Co. Inc.

▲ **PINE BLUFF (southern portion)**—Friendship Cable of Arkansas Inc.

PINE BLUFF ARSENAL—See WHITEHALL, AR

▲ **PINEBERGEN**—Friendship Cable of Arkansas Inc.

PINEVILLE—See CALICO ROCK, AR

▲ **PLAINVIEW**—Friendship Cable of Arkansas Inc.

▲ **PLAINVIEW**—Inco Cable TV

▲ **PLEASANT PLAINS**—Inco Cable TV

PLEASURE HEIGHTS—See HICKORY CREEK, AR

▲ **PLUMERVILLE**—Cable Entertainment Co.

▲ **POCAHONTAS**—TCA Cable Partners

POINSETT COUNTY (portions)—See HARRISBURG, AR

POLK COUNTY (western portion)—See HATFIELD, AR

POLLARD—See PIGGOTT, AR

POPE COUNTY (portions)—See ATKINS, AR

Pope County (portions)—See also RUSSELLVILLE, AR

POPE COUNTY (unincorporated areas)—See also DOVER, AR

POPLAR GROVE—See HELENA, AR

PORTIA—See BLACK ROCK, AR

PORTLAND—See WILMOT, AR

Pottsville—See RUSSELLVILLE, AR

POYEN—See SHERIDAN, AR

PRAIRIE COUNTY (portions)—See BISCOE, AR

PRAIRIE COUNTY (portions)—See also DES ARC, AR

PRAIRIE COUNTY (unincorporated areas)—See also HAZEN, AR

PRAIRIE CREEK—See BEAVER LAKE, AR

▲ **PRAIRIE GROVE**—Peak Cablevision

PRATTSVILLE—See SHERIDAN, AR

▲ **PRESCOTT**—Prescott Video Inc.

PULASKI COUNTY—See CABOT, AR

PULASKI COUNTY—See also NORTH LITTLE ROCK, AR

PULASKI COUNTY (eastern portion)—See also McALMONT, AR

PULASKI COUNTY (portions)—See also LITTLE ROCK, AR

QUAIL VALLEY—See MOOREFIELD, AR

▲ **RATCLIFF**—Quality Entertainment Corp.

▲ **RAVENDEN**—TCA Cable

▲ **RAVENDEN SPRINGS**—Friendship Cable of Arkansas Inc.

▲ **RECTOR**—Cablevision Communications

REDFIELD—See WHITEHALL, AR

▲ **REED**—Community Communications Co.

REYNO—See BIGGERS, AR

▲ **RISON**—Cablevision

RIVERCLIFF—See BEAVER LAKE, AR

ROCHELL—See SONORA, AR

ROCK HILL—See LOCKESBURG, AR

ROCKPORT—See MALVERN, AR

▲ **ROGERS**—Peak Cablevision

▲ **RONDO**—Community Communications Co.

▲ **ROSSTON**—Community Communications Co.

▲ **ROYAL**—Community Communications Co.

▲ **RUDY/HIGHWAY 71**—Peak Cablevision

▲ **RUSSELL**—Inco Cable TV

▲ **RUSSELLVILLE**—TCA Cable TV

▲ **SALEM**—Peak Cablevision

SALESVILLE—See BRIARCLIFF, AR

▲ **SALINE COUNTY (unincorporated areas)**—Cablevision

SALINE COUNTY—See also HOT SPRINGS VILLAGE, AR

SALINE COUNTY (eastern portion)—See also SHANNON HILLS, AR

SARATOGA—See FULTON, AR

▲ **SCRANTON**—Quality Entertainment Corp.

▲ **SEARCY**—White County Video Inc.

SEBASTIAN COUNTY (eastern portion)—See LAVACA, AR

SEBASTIAN COUNTY (southern portion)—See also MANSFIELD, AR

SEBASTIAN COUNTY (southern portion)—See also MIDLAND, AR

SEBASTIAN LAKES—See FORT SMITH, AR

▲ **SEDGWICK**—Friendship Cable of Arkansas Inc.

SEVIER COUNTY—See DE QUEEN, AR

SEVIER COUNTY (portions)—See also DIERKS, AR

▲ **SHANNON HILLS**—Falcon Cable Media

SHARP COUNTY (portions)—See HARDY, AR

▲ **SHERIDAN**—Friendship Cable of Arkansas Inc.

SHERWOOD—See McALMONT, AR

SHERWOOD—See also NORTH LITTLE ROCK, AR

SHIRLEY—See FAIRFIELD BAY, AR

▲ **SILOAM SPRINGS**—TCA Cable TV

▲ **SMACKOVER**—Friendship Cable of Arkansas Inc.

▲ **SONORA**—TCA Cable Partners

SOUTH BEND—See CABOT, AR

SOUTH SIDE—See BATESVILLE, AR

▲ **SPRINGDALE**—TCA Cable TV

ST. FRANCIS—See PIGGOTT, AR

ST. FRANCIS COUNTY—See CALDWELL, AR

STAMPS—See LEWISVILLE, AR

▲ **STAR CITY**—Community Communications Co.

▲ **STEPHENS**—Friendship Cable of Arkansas Inc.

STRAWBERRY—See LYNN, AR

▲ **STRONG**—Bayou Cable TV

▲ **STUTTGART**—Classic Cable

▲ **SUBIACO**—Quality Entertainment Corp.

SUCCESS—See BIGGERS, AR

SUGARLOAF LAKE—See MIDLAND, AR

SULPHUR ROCK—See MOOREFIELD, AR

SULPHUR SPRINGS—See NOEL, MO

SULPHUR SPRINGS—See also PINEBERGEN, AR

SUMMIT—See YELLVILLE, AR

SUNSET—See WEST MEMPHIS, AR

SWIFTON—See HARRISBURG, AR

▲ **TAYLOR**—Buford Television Inc.

TEXARKANA—See TEXARKANA, TX

▲ **THORNTON**—Friendship Cable of Arkansas Inc.

TILLAR—See REED, AR

TOLETTE—See FULTON, AR

▲ **TONTITOWN**—TCA Cable Partners

▲ **TRASKWOOD**—Friendship Cable of Arkansas Inc.

▲ **TRUMANN**—Friendship Cable of Arkansas Inc.

▲ **TUCKERMAN**—TCA Cable Partners

TULL—See SHANNON HILLS, AR

▲ **TUMBLING SHOALS**—Inco Cable TV

▲ **TUPELO**—Inco Cable TV

▲ **TURRELL**—Friendship Cable of Arkansas Inc.

TYRONZA—See MARKED TREE, AR

UNION COUNTY (portions)—See SMACKOVER, AR

URBANA—See EL DORADO, AR

VALLEY SPRINGS—See HARRISON, AR

▲ **VAN BUREN**—TCA Cable TV

VAN BUREN COUNTY—See CLINTON, AR

VAN BUREN COUNTY (portions)—See also GREERS FERRY, AR

VANDERVOORT—See HATFIELD, AR

VILLAGE ESTATES—See SONORA, AR

▲ **VILONIA**—Falcon Cable Media

▲ **VIOLA**—Cablevision Communications

WABBASEKA—See ALTHEIMER, AR

WALDO—See MAGNOLIA, AR

▲ **WALDRON**—Classic Cable

▲ **WALNUT RIDGE**—Cable Time

WARD—See CABOT, AR

WAREAGLE—See SONORA, AR

WAREAGLE COVE—See SONORA, AR

▲ **WARREN**—Cablevision

WASHINGTON COUNTY—See FAYETTEVILLE, AR

▲ **WATSON**—Community Communications Co.

▲ **WEAVERS CHAPEL**—Inco Cable TV

Wedington—See TONTITOWN, AR

WEINER—See HARRISBURG, AR

WEST CROSSETT—See CROSSETT, AR

▲ **WEST FORK**—Peak Cablevision

WEST HELENA—See HELENA, AR

▲ **WEST MEMPHIS**—Time Warner

WEST POINT—See HIGGINSON, AR

▲ **WEST PULASKI**—Falcon Cable Media

▲ **WESTERN GROVE**—Friendship Cable of Arkansas Inc.

▲ **WHEATLEY**—Friendship Cable of Arkansas Inc.

WHITE COUNTY (portions)—See HIGGINSON, AR

▲ **WHITEHALL**—Friendship Cable of Arkansas Inc.

WICKES—See HATFIELD, AR

WIDENER—See HUGHES, AR

▲ **WILMAR**—Friendship Cable of Arkansas Inc.

WILMAR—See also MONTICELLO, AR

▲ **WILMOT**—Dean Hill Cable

WILSON—See OSCEOLA, AR

WILTON—See ASHDOWN, AR

▲ **WINSLOW**—Peak Cablevision

▲ **WITCHERVILLE**—Quality Entertainment Corp.

WITCHERVILLE—See also MIDLAND, AR

WOOSTER—See GREENBRIER, AR

WRIGHTSVILLE—See SHANNON HILLS, AR

▲ **WYNNE**—East Arkansas Video Inc.

YELL COUNTY (eastern portion)—See DANVILLE, AR

YELL COUNTY (eastern portion)—See also PLAINVIEW, AR (Friendship Cable of Arkansas Inc.)

▲ **YELLVILLE**—Inco Cable TV

YORKTOWN—See STAR CITY, AR

CALIFORNIA

ACAMPO—See LODI, CA

▲ **ADELANTO**—Falcon Cable Systems Co.

▲ **ADOBE WELLS MOBILE HOME PARK**—TCI Cablevision

AEGEAN HILLS—See ORANGE COUNTY, CA

AGATE BAY—See NORTH STAR, CA

AGOURA (portions)—See CALABASAS, CA

▲ **AGOURA HILLS**—Falcon Cablevision

AGOURA HILLS—See also THOUSAND OAKS, CA (TCI)

AHWAHNEE—See OAKHURST, CA

▲ **ALABAMA HILLS**—Lone Pine TV Inc.

▲ **ALAMEDA**—TCI Cablevision of California

ALAMEDA COUNTY—See ALAMEDA, CA

ALAMEDA COUNTY—See also HAYWARD, CA

ALAMEDA COUNTY—See also TRI-VALLEY, CA

ALAMEDA NAVAL AIR STATION—See ALAMEDA, CA

ALBANY—See SAN PABLO, CA

ALBION—See UKIAH, CA

▲ **ALDERCROFT HEIGHTS**—Matrix Cablevision Inc.

▲ **ALHAMBRA**—Charter Communications

ALISO VIEJO—See ORANGE COUNTY, CA

ALPINE MEADOWS—See TRUCKEE, CA

ALTA LOMA—See LOS ANGELES, CA (Century Southwest Cable)

ALTA LOMA—See also ONTARIO, CA

ALTA LOMA—See also SAN BERNARDINO, CA (Charter Cable)

ALTA SIERRA—See LAKE OF THE PINES, CA

Alta Sierra Estates—See LAKE OF THE PINES, CA

ALTADENA—See ALHAMBRA, CA

ALTADENA—See also PASADENA, CA

ALTO—See MARIN COUNTY (southeastern portion), CA

▲ **ALTURAS**—TCI Cablevision of California Inc.

AMADOR COUNTY—See PINE GROVE, CA

American Canyon—See NAPA, CA

▲ **ANAHEIM**—Century Communications

ANAHEIM (portions)—See also ORANGE COUNTY (western portion), CA

ANAHEIM HILLS—See YORBA LINDA, CA

ANCHOR BAY—See THE SEA RANCH, CA

ANDERSON—See PALO CEDRO, CA

ANDERSON—See also REDDING, CA

ANGELS CAMP—See SAN ANDREAS, CA

LA CRESCENTA—See GLENDALE, CA

LA HABRA—See BREA, CA

LA HABRA HEIGHTS—See BREA, CA

LA HABRA HEIGHTS—See also HACIENDA HEIGHTS, CA

LA HONDA—See HALF MOON BAY, CA

LA JOLLA—See SAN DIEGO, CA

LA MESA—See EL CAJON, CA

LA MESA NAVAL BASE—See GILROY (2), CA

LA MIRADA—See DOWNEY, CA

LA PALMA—See CYPRESS, CA

LA PUENTE—See PICO RIVERA, CA

LA QUINTA—See PALM DESERT, CA

LA SELVA BEACH—See SANTA CRUZ, CA

LA VERNE—See GLENDORA, CA

LADERA—See PALO ALTO, CA

LADERA HEIGHTS—See LOS ANGELES (western portion), CA

LAFAYETTE—See PLEASANT HILL, CA

LAGUNA BEACH—See ORANGE COUNTY, CA

LAGUNA HILLS—See ORANGE COUNTY, CA

LAGUNA NIGUEL—See ORANGE COUNTY, CA

LAGUNA SECA—See GILROY (2), CA

LAGUNITAS—See MARIN COUNTY (southeastern portion), CA

LAKE ALMANOR—See DIRE MOUNTAIN, CA

▲ **LAKE ARROWHEAD**—Falcon Cablevision

LAKE COUNTY—See CLEARLAKE OAKS, CA

▲ **LAKE ELSINORE**—MediaOne

LAKE FOREST—See NORTH STAR, CA

LAKE FOREST—See also ORANGE COUNTY, CA

▲ **LAKE HUGHES**—Lake Hughes Cable TV Service

LAKE ISABELLA—See KERN RIVER VALLEY, CA

▲ **LAKE OF THE PINES**—USA Media Group LLC

LAKE SAN MARCOS—See CARLSBAD, CA

LAKE TAHOE—See TRUCKEE, CA

LAKE TAMARISK—See DESERT CENTER, CA

▲ **LAKE WILDWOOD**—TCI Cablevision of California Inc.

LAKELAND VILLAGE—See LAKE ELSINORE, CA

LAKEPORT—See CLEARLAKE OAKS, CA

LAKESIDE PARK—See WEST SAN FERNANDO VALLEY, CA

LAKEVIEW—See PERRIS, CA

LAKEVIEW TERRACE—See LOS ANGELES, CA (MediaOne)

▲ **LAKEWOOD**—MediaOne

LAMONT—See TEHACHAPI, CA

LANCASTER—See PALMDALE, CA

LARKSPUR—See MARIN COUNTY (southeastern portion), CA

LAS LOMAS—See GILROY (2), CA

LASSEN COUNTY—See SUSANVILLE, CA

LATHROP—See STOCKTON, CA

LATON—See HANFORD, CA

LAWNDALE—See TORRANCE, CA

▲ **LE GRAND**—Northland Cable TV

LEAVITT LAKE—See SUSANVILLE, CA

▲ **LEE VINING**—USA Media Group LLC

LEMON GROVE—See EL CAJON, CA

LEMOORE—See HANFORD, CA

LEMOORE NAVAL AIR STATION—See HANFORD, CA

LEONA VALLEY—See PALMDALE, CA

LEUCADIA—See EL CAJON, CA

▲ **LEWISTON**—Mark's Cablevision

LINCOLN—See PLACER COUNTY (southwestern portion), CA

LINCOLN HEIGHTS—See LOS ANGELES, CA (Century Southwest Cable)

LINDA—See YUBA CITY, CA

LINDA VISTA—See SAN DIEGO, CA

LINDEN—See STOCKTON, CA

LINDSAY—See PORTERVILLE, CA

LITTLERIVER—See UKIAH, CA

LITTLEROCK—See PALMDALE, CA

LIVE OAK—See SANTA CRUZ, CA

LIVE OAK—See also YUBA CITY, CA

LIVERMORE—See TRI-VALLEY, CA

▲ **LIVINGSTON**—Charter Communications

LOCKEFORD—See LODI, CA

▲ **LODI**—MediaOne

LOMA LINDA—See REDLANDS, CA

LOMA LINDA—See also SAN BERNARDINO, CA (Comcast Cablevision of San Bernardino Inc.)

LOMITA—See WILMINGTON, CA

LOMPICO—See SANTA CRUZ, CA

▲ **LOMPOC**—Comcast Cablevision of Lompoc Inc.

▲ **LONE PINE**—Lone Pine TV Inc.

▲ **LONG BARN**—Meyerhoff Cable Systems

▲ **LONG BEACH**—Charter Communications

▲ **LONG BEACH NAVAL BASE**—Americable International

LOOMIS—See PLACER COUNTY (southwestern portion), CA

LOS ALAMITOS—See LONG BEACH NAVAL BASE, CA

LOS ALAMITOS—See also ORANGE COUNTY (western portion), CA

▲ **LOS ALAMOS**—Falcon Cable Systems Co.

LOS ALTOS—See SAN JOSE, CA

▲ **LOS ALTOS HILLS**—Sun Country Cable

▲ **LOS ANGELES**—Buena Vision Telecommunications

▲ **LOS ANGELES**—Century Southwest Cable

▲ **LOS ANGELES**—MediaOne

▲ **LOS ANGELES (south central portion)**—MediaOne

▲ **LOS ANGELES (western portion)**—MediaOne

LOS ANGELES (unincorporated areas)—See MALIBU, CA

▲ **LOS ANGELES (Hollywood-Wilshire)**—MediaOne

LOS ANGELES COUNTY—See ALHAMBRA, CA

LOS ANGELES COUNTY—See also BREA, CA

LOS ANGELES COUNTY—See also CANYON COUNTRY, CA

LOS ANGELES COUNTY—See also LOS ANGELES, CA (Century Southwest Cable)

LOS ANGELES COUNTY—See also LOS ANGELES, CA (MediaOne)

LOS ANGELES COUNTY—See also PALMDALE, CA

LOS ANGELES COUNTY—See also WILMINGTON, CA

LOS ANGELES COUNTY (eastern portion)—See also CLAREMONT, CA

LOS ANGELES COUNTY (portions)—See also BOX CANYON, CA

LOS ANGELES COUNTY (portions)—See also COVINA, CA

LOS ANGELES COUNTY (portions)—See also LOS ANGELES, CA (Buena Vision Telecommunications)

LOS ANGELES COUNTY (portions)—See also MALIBU 2, CA

LOS ANGELES COUNTY (portions)—See also PALOS VERDES PENINSULA, CA

LOS BANOS—See NEWMAN, CA

▲ **LOS GATOS**—TCI

LOS GATOS (portions)—See also SAN JOSE, CA

LOS MOLINOS—See TEHAMA, CA

LOS OSOS—See SAN LUIS OBISPO COUNTY, CA

* **LOS TRANCOS WOODS**—TCI Cablevision

▲ **LOST HILLS**—Falcon Cablevision

LOWER LAKE—See CLEARLAKE OAKS, CA

LOYALTON—See PORTOLA, CA

LUCERNE—See CLEARLAKE OAKS, CA

▲ **LUSHMEADOWS**—Northland Cable TV

LYNWOOD—See DOWNEY, CA

LYTLE CREEK—See SAN BERNARDINO, CA (Comcast Cablevision of San Bernardino Inc.)

MADERA—See FRESNO, CA

MADERA COUNTY (southern portion)—See FRESNO, CA

MADERA COUNTY (southwestern portion)—See also CHOWCHILLA, CA

SAN JOAQUIN COUNTY—See STOCKTON, CA

SAN JOAQUIN COUNTY—See also TRACY, CA

SAN JOAQUIN COUNTY (portions)—See also RIVERBANK, CA

▲ **SAN JOSE**—AT&T Broadband & Internet Services

SAN JUAN BAUTISTA (portions)—See GILROY, CA

SAN JUAN BAUTISTA (portions)—See also GILROY (2), CA

SAN JUAN CAPISTRANO—See ORANGE COUNTY, CA

SAN LEANDRO—See HAYWARD, CA

SAN LORENZO—See HAYWARD, CA

▲ **SAN LUIS OBISPO**—Charter Communications

▲ **SAN LUIS OBISPO COUNTY**—Falcon Cable Systems Co.

SAN MARCOS—See EL CAJON, CA

SAN MARCOS (portions)—See also CARLSBAD, CA

▲ **SAN MARINO**—American Cablevision of San Marino

SAN MARINO—See also SOUTH PASADENA, CA

SAN MARTIN—See GILROY, CA

▲ **SAN MATEO**—TCI Cablevision of California

SAN MATEO COUNTY—See BURLINGAME, CA

SAN MATEO COUNTY—See also SOUTH SAN FRANCISCO, CA

SAN MATEO COUNTY (portions)—See also PALO ALTO, CA

SAN MIGUEL—See SAN LUIS OBISPO, CA

SAN ONOFRE—See ORANGE COUNTY, CA

▲ **SAN PABLO**—Century Cable of Northern California

SAN PABLO—See also RICHMOND, CA

SAN PEDRO—See PALOS VERDES PENINSULA, CA

SAN PEDRO—See also WILMINGTON, CA

SAN QUENTIN—See MARIN COUNTY (southeastern portion), CA

SAN RAFAEL—See MARIN COUNTY (southeastern portion), CA

SAN RAMON—See TRI-VALLEY, CA

▲ **SAN SIMEON ACRES**—San Simeon Community Cable Inc.

SAND CITY—See MONTEREY, CA

▲ **SANGER**—MediaOne

▲ **SANTA ANA**—Comcast Cablevision of Santa Ana Inc.

SANTA ANA (portions)—See also ORANGE COUNTY (western portion), CA

SANTA ANA (unincorporated areas)—See also TUSTIN, CA

▲ **SANTA BARBARA**—Cox Communications Santa Barbara

SANTA BARBARA COUNTY—See LOMPOC, CA

SANTA BARBARA COUNTY (portions)—See also SANTA BARBARA, CA

SANTA BARBARA SOUTH—See SANTA MARIA, CA

▲ **SANTA CLARA**—TCI

SANTA CLARA COUNTY—See LOS GATOS, CA

SANTA CLARA COUNTY—See also SAN JOSE, CA

SANTA CLARA COUNTY—See also SANTA CLARA, CA

SANTA CLARA COUNTY—See also SUNNYVALE, CA

SANTA CLARA COUNTY (portions)—See also SARATOGA, CA

▲ **SANTA CLARITA**—MediaOne

SANTA CLARITA—See also CANYON COUNTRY, CA

▲ **SANTA CRUZ**—TCI Cablevision

SANTA CRUZ—See also WATSONVILLE, CA

SANTA CRUZ COUNTY (portions)—See WATSONVILLE, CA

SANTA CRUZ COUNTY (unincorporated areas)—See also SANTA CRUZ, CA

SANTA FE SPRINGS—See DOWNEY, CA

SANTA MARGARITA—See SAN LUIS OBISPO COUNTY, CA

▲ **SANTA MARIA**—Comcast Cablevision of Santa Maria Inc.

SANTA MONICA—See LOS ANGELES, CA (Century Southwest Cable)

SANTA PAULA—See RASNOW, CA

▲ **SANTA ROSA**—Cable One

SANTA VENETIA—See MARIN COUNTY (southeastern portion), CA

SANTA YNEZ—See SANTA MARIA, CA

SANTEE—See EL CAJON, CA

▲ **SARATOGA**—TCI

SAUGUS—See SANTA CLARITA, CA

SAUGUS (portions)—See also CANYON COUNTRY, CA

SAUSALITO—See MARIN COUNTY (southeastern portion), CA

SCOTIA—See EUREKA, CA

SCOTTS VALLEY—See SANTA CRUZ, CA

SCRIPPS RANCH—See SAN DIEGO, CA

▲ **SEAL BEACH**—Comcast Cablevision of Seal Beach Inc.

SEARLES VALLEY—See RIDGECREST, CA

SEASIDE—See MONTEREY, CA

SEBASTOPOL—See ROHNERT PARK, CA

SEDCO HILLS—See LAKE ELSINORE, CA

▲ **SELMA**—MediaOne

SEPULVEDA—See WEST SAN FERNANDO VALLEY, CA

SERENE LAKES—See TRUCKEE, CA

SERRA MESA—See SAN DIEGO, CA

SHADOW RIDGE CREEK—See THOUSAND PALMS, CA

SHAFTER—See BAKERSFIELD, CA (Time Warner Cable)

SHASTA COUNTY—See REDDING, CA

SHASTA COUNTY (portions)—See also PALO CEDRO, CA

▲ **SHAVER LAKE**—USA Media Group LLC

SHERMAN OAKS—See EAST SAN FERNANDO VALLEY, CA

SHERMAN OAKS—See also LOS ANGELES, CA (Century Southwest Cable)

SHINGLE SPRINGS—See PLACERVILLE, CA

SIERRA COUNTY (portions)—See PORTOLA, CA

▲ **SIERRA DAWN ESTATES**—Sierra Dawn Cablevision

▲ **SIERRA MADRE**—TCI Cablevision

SIERRA MEADOWS—See TRUCKEE, CA

SIERRA VILLAGE—See TWAIN HARTE, CA

SIGNAL HILL—See LONG BEACH, CA

SILVER LAKES—See ADELANTO, CA

SILVERADO—See ORANGE COUNTY, CA

▲ **SIMI VALLEY**—Comcast Cablevision of Simi Valley

SISKIYOU COUNTY—See FORT JONES, CA

SISKIYOU COUNTY—See also MOUNT SHASTA, CA

SISKIYOU COUNTY—See also YREKA, CA

SODA BAY—See CLEARLAKE OAKS, CA

SODA SPRINGS—See TRUCKEE, CA

SOLANA BEACH—See CARLSBAD, CA

SOLANA BEACH—See also EL CAJON, CA

SOLANO COUNTY—See FAIRFIELD, CA

SOLANO COUNTY—See also VALLEJO, CA

SOLANO COUNTY (western portion)—See also VACAVILLE, CA

▲ **SOLEDAD**—Falcon Cable Systems Co.

SONOMA—See PETALUMA, CA

SONOMA COUNTY (portions)—See ROHNERT PARK, CA

SONOMA COUNTY (portions)—See also SANTA ROSA, CA

▲ **SONORA**—TCI Cablevision

SOQUEL—See SANTA CRUZ, CA

SOULSBYVILLE—See TWAIN HARTE, CA

SOUTH EL MONTE—See DOWNEY, CA

SOUTH GATE—See EL MONTE, CA

SOUTH LAGUNA—See ORANGE COUNTY, CA

SOUTH LAKE—See KERN RIVER VALLEY, CA

▲ **SOUTH LAKE TAHOE**—TCI Cablevision of California Inc.

▲ **SOUTH PASADENA**—American Cablevision of South Pasadena

▲ **SOUTH SAN FRANCISCO**—TCI Cablevision of California

SOUTH SAN GABRIEL—See ALHAMBRA, CA

SOUTH TAFT—See TAFT, CA

SOUTH WHITTIER—See PICO RIVERA, CA

▲ **SPANISH RANCH MOBILE HOME PARK**—TCI Cablevision

SPRING VALLEY—See EL CAJON, CA

SPRING VALLEY LAKE—See VICTORVILLE, CA

SPRINGVILLE—See PORTERVILLE, CA

SQUAW VALLEY—See TRUCKEE, CA

ST. HELENA—See ROHNERT PARK, CA

STANDARD (portions of Tuolmne County)—See TWAIN HARTE, CA

STANFORD—See PALO ALTO, CA

STANISLAUS COUNTY—See MODESTO & OAKDALE, CA

STANISLAUS COUNTY—See also TURLOCK, CA

STANISLAUS COUNTY (portions)—See also NEWMAN, CA

STANISLAUS COUNTY (portions)—See also RIVERBANK, CA

STANTON—See ORANGE COUNTY (western portion), CA

STINSON BEACH—See HAMILTON AFB, CA

▲ **STOCKTON**—MediaOne

STRATFORD—See HANFORD, CA

STRATHMORE—See PORTERVILLE, CA

▲ **STRAWBERRY**—MediaOne

STRAWBERRY—See also MARIN COUNTY (southeastern portion), CA

STRAWBERRY—See also PINECREST, CA

SUGAR BOWL—See TRUCKEE, CA

SUGAR PINE—See TWAIN HARTE, CA

SUISIN CITY—See FAIRFIELD, CA

▲ **SUN CITY**—Mediacom

SUN VALLEY—See LOS ANGELES, CA (MediaOne)

SUNLAND—See LOS ANGELES, CA (MediaOne)

SUNNYSLOPE—See RIVERSIDE, CA

▲ **SUNNYVALE**—TCI Cablevision of California Inc.

SUNOL—See TRI-VALLEY, CA

SUNSET BEACH—See SEAL BEACH, CA

▲ **SUSANVILLE**—Century Communications

SUTTER COUNTY (portions)—See YUBA CITY, CA

SYLMAR—See LOS ANGELES, CA (MediaOne)

▲ **TAFT**—Time Warner Cable

TAFT HEIGHTS—See TAFT, CA

TAHOE CITY—See NORTH STAR, CA

TAHOE CITY (southeastern portion)—See TRUCKEE, CA

TAHOE DONNER—See TRUCKEE, CA

TAHOE PARADISE—See MEYERS, CA

TAHOE PARK—See NORTH STAR, CA

TAHOE VISTA—See NORTH STAR, CA

TALMAGE—See UKIAH, CA

TAMALPAIS—See MARIN COUNTY (southeastern portion), CA

TARZANA—See WEST SAN FERNANDO VALLEY, CA

▲ **TASSAJARA VALLEY**—Ponderosa Cable Systems Ltd.

▲ **TEHACHAPI**—Time Warner Cable

▲ **TEHAMA**—Mark's Cablevision

TEHAMA COUNTY—See REDDING, CA

TEMECULA—See HEMET, CA

TEMELAC—See ROHNERT PARK, CA

TEMESCAL CANYON—See LAKE ELSINORE, CA

TEMPLE CITY—See ALHAMBRA, CA

TEMPLETON—See SAN LUIS OBISPO COUNTY, CA

TERRA BELLA—See PORTERVILLE, CA

TERWER VALLEY—See KLAMATH, CA

THE FARM—See LAKE ELSINORE, CA

▲ **THE SEA RANCH**—Wander Cable Television

▲ **THOUSAND OAKS**—Falcon Cablevision

▲ **THOUSAND OAKS**—GTE Americast

▲ **THOUSAND OAKS**—TCI

▲ **THOUSAND PALMS**—CalaVision

THREE RIVERS—See PORTERVILLE, CA

TIBURON—See MARIN COUNTY (southeastern portion), CA

TIERRASANTA—See SAN DIEGO, CA

TIPTON—See PORTERVILLE, CA

Todd Valley—See FORESTHILL, CA

▲ **TOPANGA CANYON**—Falcon Cablevision

▲ **TORRANCE**—Time Warner Communications

TRABUCO CANYON—See ORANGE COUNTY, CA

▲ **TRACY**—UACC Midwest Inc.

▲ **TRAVIS AFB**—TCI Cablevision of California Inc.

TREASURE ISLAND NAVAL STATION—See OAKLAND, CA

▲ **TRI-PALM ESTATES**—Tri-Palm Estates Division of Great Western Properties

TRI-PALM ESTATES—See also THOUSAND PALMS, CA

▲ **TRI-VALLEY**—AT&T Broadband & Internet Services

TRINIDAD—See EUREKA, CA

▲ **TRINITY CENTER**—Blackstone Cable LLC

TRONA—See RIDGECREST, CA

TROUT CLUB—See PARADISE PARK, CA

▲ **TRUCKEE**—USA Media Group LLC

TUJUNGA—See LOS ANGELES, CA (MediaOne)

▲ **TULARE**—MediaOne

TULARE COUNTY—See TULARE, CA

TULARE COUNTY (northeastern portion)—See PORTERVILLE, CA

▲ **TULELAKE**—Blackstone Cable

TUOLUMNE CITY (portions of Tuolumne County)—See TWAIN HARTE, CA

TUOLUMNE COUNTY—See SONORA, CA

▲ **TURLOCK**—Charter Communications Inc.

▲ **TUSTIN**—MediaOne

TUSTIN—See also IRVINE, CA

TUSTIN (portions)—See ORANGE COUNTY, CA

▲ **TWAIN HARTE**—TCI

TWENTYNINE PALMS—See YUCCA VALLEY, CA

TWENTYNINE PALMS MARINE CORPS BASE—See YUCCA VALLEY, CA

TWIN BRIDGES—See STRAWBERRY, CA

TWIN LAKES—See SANTA CRUZ, CA

▲ **UKIAH**—Century Communications

▲ **UNION CITY**—TCI

UNIVERSITY CITY—See SAN DIEGO, CA

UPLAND—See ONTARIO, CA

UPPER LAKE—See CLEARLAKE OAKS, CA

▲ **VACAVILLE**—TCI Cablevision of California

VALENCIA—See SANTA CLARITA, CA

VALINDA—See PICO RIVERA, CA

VALLECITO—See SAN ANDREAS, CA

▲ **VALLEJO**—TCI Cablevision

▲ **VALLEY CENTER**—Mediacom LLC

VALLEY SPRINGS—See SAN ANDREAS, CA

VAN NUYS—See LOS ANGELES, CA (Century Southwest Cable)

VAN NUYS—See also WEST SAN FERNANDO VALLEY, CA

▲ **VANDENBERG AFB**—Americable International

VANDENBURG VILLAGE—See LOMPOC, CA

VENICE—See LOS ANGELES (western portion), CA

▲ **VENTURA**—Avenue TV Cable Service Inc.

▲ **VENTURA**—Century Cable of Northern California Inc.

VENTURA COUNTY—See SANTA BARBARA, CA

VENTURA COUNTY—See also VENTURA, CA (Century Cable of Northern California Inc.)

VENTURA COUNTY (portions)—See BOX CANYON, CA

VENTURA COUNTY (portions)—See also MALIBU 2, CA

VENTURA COUNTY (portions)—See also SIMI VALLEY, CA

VENTURA COUNTY (Rincon area)—See VENTURA, CA (Avenue TV Cable Service Inc.)

VICTOR—See LODI, CA

▲ **VICTORVILLE**—Charter Cable

VILLA PARK—See ANAHEIM, CA

VINE HILL—See PLEASANT HILL, CA

VISALIA—See TULARE, CA

COLORADO

▲ **CALHAN**—Big Sandy Telecommunications

CAMPION—See BERTHOUD, CO

▲ **CANON CITY**—AT&T Cable Services

▲ **CANTERBURY PARK**—Cable USA

▲ **CARBONDALE**—AT&T Cable Services

CASCADE—See COLORADO SPRINGS, CO

CASTLE PINES—See DENVER (suburbs), CO

▲ **CASTLE ROCK**—TCI of Colorado Inc.

CEDAREDGE—See HOTCHKISS, CO

▲ **CENTER**—Town of Center Municipal Cable

CENTRAL CITY—See BLACK HAWK, CO

CHAFFEE COUNTY—See BUENA VISTA, CO

CHAFFEE COUNTY—See also SALIDA, CO

CHAMA—See SAN LUIS, CO

CHAPPERAL SUBDIVISION—See DENVER (suburbs), CO

CHERRY HILLS VILLAGE—See DENVER (suburbs), CO

▲ **CHEYENNE MOUNTAIN ESTATES**—Tri-Lakes Cable

▲ **CHEYENNE WELLS**—Galaxy Cablevision

CHIPITA PARK—See COLORADO SPRINGS, CO

CIMARRON HILLS—See MONUMENT, CO

CLEAR CREEK COUNTY—See IDAHO SPRINGS, CO

CLEAR CREEK COUNTY (eastern portion)—See CONIFER, CO

COAL CREEK—See CANON CITY, CO

▲ **COAL CREEK CANYON**—Galaxy Cable

▲ **COLLBRAN**—Mountain Cable

▲ **COLORADO CITY**—Heritage Cablevision of Colorado Inc.

▲ **COLORADO SPRINGS**—Century Communications

COLUMBINE—See HIGHLANDS RANCH, CO

COLUMBINE LAKE MOBILE HOME PARK—See COLUMBINE VALLEY, CO

▲ **COLUMBINE VALLEY**—TCI

COMMERCE CITY—See DENVER (suburbs), CO

▲ **CONIFER**—US Cable of Colorado

▲ **CONSTITUTION HILLS MOBILE HOME PARK**—Cable USA

▲ **COPPER MOUNTAIN**—Copper Mountain Consolidated Metropolitan District

▲ **CORTEZ**—Scott Cable Communications Inc.

COTTONWOOD—See DENVER (suburbs), CO

▲ **CRAIG**—AT&T Cable Services

CRAWFORD—See HOTCHKISS, CO

▲ **CREEDE**—Pagosa Vision Inc.

CRESTED BUTTE—See GUNNISON, CO

▲ **CRIPPLE CREEK**—US Cable of Colorado

▲ **CUCHARA VALLEY**—Lee's Cable

DACONO—See FREDERICK, CO

DEER CREEK (unincorporated areas)—See BAILEY, CO

▲ **DEER TRAIL**—Galaxy Cablevision

▲ **DEL NORTE**—TCI Cablevision of Colorado Inc.

▲ **DELTA**—TCI Cablevision of Colorado Inc.

DELTA COUNTY—See DELTA, CO

DELTA COUNTY—See also PAONIA, CO

▲ **DENVER**—TCI of Colorado Inc.

▲ **DENVER (suburbs)**—AT&T Cable Services

▲ **DILLON**—AT&T Cable Services

▲ **DOLORES**—AT&T Cable Services

DOUGLAS COUNTY—See DENVER (suburbs), CO

▲ **DOVE CREEK**—AT&T Cable Services

DOWD JUNCTION—See AVON, CO

DOWNIEVILLE—See EMPIRE, CO

DUMONT—See EMPIRE, CO

▲ **DURANGO**—AT&T Cable Services

▲ **DURANGO WEST**—AT&T Cable Services

▲ **EADS**—Galaxy Cablevision

▲ **EAGLE**—Com-Link Inc.

EAGLE COUNTY—See BASALT, CO

EAGLE VAIL—See AVON, CO

▲ **EATON**—US Cable of Colorado

ECKERT—See HOTCHKISS, CO

EDGEWATER—See LAKEWOOD, CO

EDWARDS—See AVON, CO

EL PASO COUNTY—See COLORADO SPRINGS, CO

ELBERT COUNTY—See BENNETT, CO

ELIZABETH—See BENNETT, CO

▲ **EMPIRE**—TCI Cable

ENGLEWOOD—See DENVER (suburbs), CO

▲ **ERIE**—Comcast Cablevision

▲ **ESTES PARK**—Cable Systems Inc.

EVANS—See GREELEY, CO

EVANSTON—See FREDERICK, CO

▲ **EVERGREEN**—TCI of Colorado

▲ **EVERGREEN**—US Cable of Colorado

▲ **FAIRPLAY**—Classic Cable

FEDERAL HEIGHTS—See DENVER (suburbs), CO

FIRESTONE—See FREDERICK, CO

FITZSIMMONS ARMY BASE—See DENVER (suburbs), CO

▲ **FLAGLER**—Galaxy Cablevision

▲ **FLEMING**—Cable USA

FLORENCE—See CANON CITY, CO

▲ **FORT CARSON**—Charter Communications

▲ **FORT COLLINS**—AT&T Cabel Services

FORT COLLINS (Poudre Valley Mobile Home Park)—See LAPORTE, CO

FORT GARLAND—See BLANCA, CO

▲ **FORT LUPTON**—Comcast Cablevision

▲ **FORT MORGAN**—TCI Cablevision of Colorado Inc.

FOUNTAIN—See COLORADO SPRINGS, CO

▲ **FOWLER**—Heritage Cablevision of Colorado Inc.

FOX RIDGE MOBILE HOME PARK—See BENNETT, CO

FRANKTOWN—See CASTLE ROCK, CO

FRASER—See WINTER PARK, CO

▲ **FREDERICK**—TCI Cablevision of Colorado Inc.

FREMONT COUNTY—See CANON CITY, CO

FRISCO—See DILLON, CO

FRUITA—See GRAND JUNCTION, CO

GARDEN CITY—See GREELEY, CO

GARFIELD COUNTY—See BASALT, CO

GARFIELD COUNTY—See also NEW CASTLE, CO

GARFIELD COUNTY—See also RIFLE, CO

GARFIELD COUNTY (southeastern portion)—See CARBONDALE, CO

Garfield County (unincorporated areas)—See GLENWOOD SPRINGS, CO

▲ **GENESEE**—TCI

GEORGETOWN—See EMPIRE, CO

▲ **GILCREST**—US Cable of Colorado

GILPIN COUNTY (portions)—See COAL CREEK CANYON, CO

GLENDALE—See DENVER, CO

GLENEAGLE—See MONUMENT, CO

▲ **GLENWOOD SPRINGS**—AT&T Cable Services

GOLDEN—See DENVER (suburbs), CO

GOLDEN—See also LAKEWOOD, CO

▲ **GRANADA**—Galaxy Cablevision

▲ **GRANBY**—Heritage Cablevision of Colorado Inc.

GRAND COUNTY—See GRANBY, CO

GRAND COUNTY (unincorporated areas)—See KREMMLING, CO

▲ **GRAND JUNCTION**—AT&T Cable Services

GRAND LAKE—See GRANBY, CO

▲ **GREELEY**—AT&T Broadband & Internet Services

GREEN MOUNTAIN FALLS—See COLORADO SPRINGS, CO

GREENWOOD VILLAGE—See DENVER (suburbs), CO

▲ **GUNNISON**—Gunnison Cablevision

GUNNISON COUNTY—See GUNNISON, CO

HAPPY CANYON—See DENVER (suburbs), CO

HAXTUN—See HOLYOKE, CO

▲ **HAYDEN**—TCI Cablevision of Colorado Inc.

▲ **HERMOSA**—Hermosa Cablevision Inc.

▲ **HIGHLANDS RANCH**—AT&T Cable Services

HIWAN HILLS—See GENESEE, CO

▲ **HOLLY**—Galaxy Cablevision

▲ **HOLYOKE**—Cable USA

HOT SULPHUR SPRINGS—See GRANBY, CO

▲ **HOTCHKISS**—Rapid Cable

▲ **HUDSON**—US Cable of Colorado

HUERFANO—See WALSENBURG, CO

▲ **HUGO**—Galaxy Cablevision

HYGIENE—See LONGMONT, CO

▲ **IDAHO SPRINGS**—TCI of Colorado

IDLEDALE—See EVERGREEN, CO (TCI of Colorado)

▲ **IGNACIO**—Rural Route Video

INDIAN HILLS—See EVERGREEN, CO (TCI of Colorado)

JANSEN—See TRINIDAD, CO

JEFFERSON COUNTY (portions)—See HIGHLANDS RANCH, CO

JEFFERSON COUNTY (portions)—See also LAKEWOOD, CO

JEFFERSON COUNTY (southern portion)—See CONIFER, CO

JOHNSON VILLAGE—See BUENA VISTA, CO

▲ **JOHNSTOWN**—US Cable of Colorado

▲ **JULESBURG**—Cable USA

KEENESBERG—See HUDSON, CO

KEN CARYL—See HIGHLANDS RANCH, CO

▲ **KERSEY**—US Cable of Colorado

KEYSTONE INTERNATIONAL DEVELOPMENT—See DILLON, CO

KIOWA—See BENNETT, CO

▲ **KIT CARSON**—B & C Cablevision Inc.

KITTREDGE—See EVERGREEN, CO (TCI of Colorado)

▲ **KREMMLING**—Heritage Cablevision of Colorado Inc.

LA JARA—See MANASSA, CO

▲ **LA JUNTA**—Heritage Cablevision of Colorado Inc.

LA PLATA COUNTY—See DURANGO, CO

LA SALLE—See GREELEY, CO

▲ **LA VETA**—Lee's Cable

▲ **LAFAYETTE**—Comcast Cablevision

▲ **LAKE CITY**—Century Telephone

LAKE COUNTY—See LEADVILLE, CO

▲ **LAKEWOOD**—TCI of Colorado Inc.

LAKEWOOD—See also DENVER (suburbs), CO

▲ **LAMAR**—Heritage Cablevision of Colorado Inc.

▲ **LAPORTE**—US Cable of Colorado

LARIMER COUNTY—See ESTES PARK, CO

LARIMER COUNTY—See also LOVELAND, CO

LARIMER COUNTY (portions)—See FORT COLLINS, CO

LARIMER COUNTY (portions)—See also LAPORTE, CO

▲ **LAS ANIMAS**—Cable Systems Inc.

LAS ANIMAS COUNTY (portions)—See TRINIDAD, CO

LAWSON—See EMPIRE, CO

▲ **LEADVILLE**—AT&T Cable Services

LEADVILLE NORTH—See LEADVILLE, CO

▲ **LIMON**—Galaxy Cablevision

LITTLETON—See HIGHLANDS RANCH, CO

LOCHBUIE—See BRIGHTON, CO

LOG LANE VILLAGE—See FORT MORGAN, CO

LOGAN COUNTY—See STERLING, CO

LONE TREE—See CASTLE ROCK, CO

▲ **LONGMONT**—Comcast Cablevision

LOOKOUT MOUNTAIN—See GENESEE, CO

▲ **LOUISVILLE**—Comcast Cablevision

LOUVIERS—See CASTLE ROCK, CO

▲ **LOVELAND**—Comcast Cablevision

▲ **LOVELAND (Columbine Mobile Home Park)**—US Cable of Colorado

LOWRY AFB—See DENVER, CO

▲ **LYONS**—Galaxy Cablevision

MADRID—See VALDEZ, CO

▲ **MANASSA**—TCI Cablevision of Colorado Inc.

▲ **MANCOS**—AT&T Cable Services

MANITOU SPRINGS—See COLORADO SPRINGS, CO

▲ **MANZANOLA**—Heritage Cablevision of Colorado Inc.

▲ **MARSHDALE**—US Cable of Colorado

▲ **MEAD**—MEI Cable Inc.

MEDINA PLAZA—See VALDEZ, CO

▲ **MEEKER**—TCI Cablevision of Colorado Inc.

▲ **MERINO**—B & C Cablevision Inc.

MESA COUNTY—See GRAND JUNCTION, CO

MILLIKEN—See JOHNSTOWN, CO

MINTURN—See AVON, CO

MOFFAT COUNTY—See CRAIG, CO

▲ **MONTE VISTA**—TCI Cablevision of Colorado Inc.

▲ **MONTROSE**—TCI Cablevision of Colorado Inc.

MONTROSE COUNTY—See MONTROSE, CO

▲ **MONUMENT**—Tri-Lakes Cable

MORGAN COUNTY—See FORT MORGAN, CO

MORRISON—See HIGHLANDS RANCH, CO

MOUNT CRESTED BUTTE—See GUNNISON, CO

MOUNTAIN RANGE SHADOWS—See LOVELAND (Columbine Mobile Home Park), CO

MOUNTAIN SHADOW SUBDIVISION—See NEW CASTLE, CO

NATURITA—See NUCLA, CO

▲ **NEDERLAND**—Pagosa Vision Inc.

▲ **NEW CASTLE**—TCI Cablevision of Colorado Inc.

NORTHCOAST—See CONSTITUTION HILLS MOBILE HOME PARK, CO

NORTHGLENN—See HIGHLANDS RANCH, CO

▲ **NORWOOD**—B & C Cable

▲ **NUCLA**—TCI Cablevision of Colorado Inc.

▲ **OAK CREEK**—Total Local Communications

Oak Meadows—See GLENWOOD SPRINGS, CO

▲ **OLATHE**—Illini Cablevision Inc.

▲ **OLNEY SPRINGS**—Total Local Communications Inc.

ORCHARD CITY—See HOTCHKISS, CO

▲ **ORDWAY**—Galaxy Cablevision

OTERO COUNTY—See ROCKY FORD, CO

OTERO COUNTY (northern portion)—See MANZANOLA, CO

OTERO COUNTY (unincorporated areas)—See LA JUNTA, CO

OTERO COUNTY (western portion)—See FOWLER, CO

▲ **OTIS**—CommuniComm Services

OVID—See JULESBURG, CO

▲ **PAGOSA SPRINGS**—Pagosa Vision Inc.

PALISADE—See GRAND JUNCTION, CO

PALMER LAKE—See MONUMENT, CO

▲ **PAONIA**—TCI Cablevision of Colorado Inc.

▲ **PARACHUTE**—Comcast Cablevision

PARK COUNTY (northwestern portion)—See CONIFER, CO

PARKER—See CASTLE ROCK, CO

▲ **PENROSE (unincorporated areas)**—TCI Cablevision of Colorado Inc.

PERRY PARK—See CASTLE ROCK, CO

▲ **PETERSON AFB**—Americable International Colorado Inc.

PIERCE—See EATON, CO

PINE—See BAILEY, CO

PINE JUNCTION—See BAILEY, CO

PINETOP-DURANGO WEST—See DURANGO WEST, CO

PITKIN COUNTY—See ASPEN, CO

PITKIN COUNTY—See also BASALT, CO

Platteville—See GILCREST, CO

PLEASANT VIEW—See COLORADO SPRINGS, CO

PONCHA SPRINGS—See SALIDA, CO

PONDEROSA HILLS—See DENVER (suburbs), CO

CONNECTICUT

COLUMBIA—See ASHFORD, CT

CORNWALL—See LITCHFIELD, CT

COVENTRY—See ASHFORD, CT

CROMWELL—See MIDDLETOWN, CT

▲ **DANBURY**—Comcast Cablevision of Danbury Inc.

DARIEN—See NORWALK, CT

DEEP RIVER—See CLINTON, CT

DERBY—See SEYMOUR, CT

DURHAM—See CLINTON, CT

EAST GLASTONBURY—See MANCHESTER, CT

EAST GRANBY—See ENFIELD, CT

EAST HADDAM—See OLD LYME, CT

EAST HAMPTON—See MIDDLETOWN, CT

EAST HARTFORD—See HARTFORD, CT

EAST HAVEN—See BRANFORD, CT

EAST LYME—See NEW LONDON, CT

EAST WINDSOR—See ENFIELD, CT

EASTFORD—See ASHFORD, CT

EASTON—See NORWALK, CT

ELLINGTON—See HARTFORD, CT

▲ **ENFIELD**—Cox Communications Inc.

ESSEX—See CLINTON, CT

FAIRFIELD—See NORWALK, CT

FAIRFIELD COUNTY—See NORWALK, CT

FALLS VILLAGE—See SHARON, CT

FARMINGTON—See HARTFORD, CT

FRANKLIN—See NORWICH, CT

GLASTONBURY—See MANCHESTER, CT

GOSHEN—See LITCHFIELD, CT

GOSHEN—See also WINSTED, CT

GRANBY—See ENFIELD, CT

GREENWICH—See NORWALK, CT

GRISWOLD—See NEW LONDON, CT

▲ **GROTON**—Comcast Cablevision of Groton Inc.

GUILFORD—See BRANFORD, CT

HADDAM—See CLINTON, CT

Haddam (portions)—See OLD LYME, CT

Haddam (town)—See OLD LYME, CT

Haddam Neck—See OLD LYME, CT

HAMDEN—See NEW HAVEN, CT

HAMPTON—See ASHFORD, CT

▲ **HARTFORD**—TCI Cablevision of Central Connecticut

HARTFORD—See also UNIONVILLE, CT

HARTLAND—See ENFIELD, CT

HARWINTON—See WINSTED, CT

HEBRON—See HARTFORD, CT

HIGGANUM—See CLINTON, CT

HUNTINGTON—See SEYMOUR, CT

IVORYTON—See CLINTON, CT

JEWETT CITY—See NEW LONDON, CT

KENT—See NEWTOWN, CT

KILLINGLY—See NEW LONDON, CT

KILLINGWORTH—See CLINTON, CT

LAKEVILLE—See SHARON, CT

LEBANON—See ASHFORD, CT

LEDYARD—See GROTON, CT

LISBON—See NORWICH, CT

▲ **LITCHFIELD**—Cablevision

Lyme (portions)—See OLD LYME, CT

MADISON—See BRANFORD, CT

▲ **MANCHESTER**—Cox Cable Greater Hartford Inc.

MANSFIELD—See ASHFORD, CT

MARLBOROUGH—See HARTFORD, CT

▲ **MERIDEN**—Cox Cable

MIDDLEBURY—See WATERBURY, CT

MIDDLEFIELD—See MIDDLETOWN, CT

▲ **MIDDLETOWN**—Comcast Cablevision of Middletown Inc.

MILFORD—See BRIDGEPORT, CT

MONROE—See NEWTOWN, CT

MONTVILLE—See NEW LONDON, CT

MORRIS—See LITCHFIELD, CT

NAUGATUCK—See SEYMOUR, CT

NEW BRITAIN—See HARTFORD, CT

NEW CANAAN—See NORWALK, CT

NEW FAIRFIELD—See NEWTOWN, CT

NEW HARTFORD—See WINSTED, CT

▲ **NEW HAVEN**—Comcast Cablevision of New Haven Inc.

NEW HAVEN—See also UNIONVILLE, CT

▲ **NEW LONDON**—Eastern Connecticut Cable TV Inc.

NEW LONDON SUBMARINE BASE—See GROTON, CT

NEW MILFORD—See NEWTOWN, CT

NEWINGTON—See MANCHESTER, CT

▲ **NEWTOWN**—Charter Communications

NORFOLK—See SHARON, CT

NORTH BRANFORD—See BRANFORD, CT

NORTH CANAAN—See SHARON, CT

NORTH HAVEN—See BRANFORD, CT

NORTH STONINGTON—See GROTON, CT

NORTHFIELD—See LITCHFIELD, CT

NORTHFORD—See BRANFORD, CT

▲ **NORWALK**—Cablevision of Connecticut LP

▲ **NORWICH**—Century Norwich Corp.

OAKVILLE—See LITCHFIELD, CT

▲ **OLD LYME**—Century Cable Management Corp.

OLD SAYBROOK—See CLINTON, CT

ORANGE—See BRIDGEPORT, CT

OXFORD—See SEYMOUR, CT

PLAINFIELD—See NEW LONDON, CT

PLAINVILLE—See HARTFORD, CT

PLYMOUTH—See WATERBURY, CT

POMFRET—See ASHFORD, CT

PORTLAND—See MIDDLETOWN, CT

PRESTON—See NORWICH, CT

PROSPECT—See WATERBURY, CT

PUTNAM—See NEW LONDON, CT

REDDING—See NORWALK, CT

RIDGEFIELD—See DANBURY, CT

ROCKY HILL—See MANCHESTER, CT

ROXBURY—See NEWTOWN, CT

Salem (town)—See OLD LYME, CT

SALISBURY—See SHARON, CT

SALISBURY TWP.—See SHARON, CT

SCOTLAND—See ASHFORD, CT

▲ **SEYMOUR**—Tele-Media Co. of Western Connecticut

▲ **SHARON**—TCI Cablevision of Northwestern Connecticut

SHELTON—See SEYMOUR, CT

SHERMAN—See NEWTOWN, CT

SIMSBURY—See HARTFORD, CT

SOMERS—See ENFIELD, CT

SOUTH GLASTONBURY—See MANCHESTER, CT

South Lyme—See OLD LYME, CT

SOUTH WINDSOR—See MANCHESTER, CT

SOUTHBURY—See NEWTOWN, CT

SOUTHINGTON—See MERIDEN, CT

SPRAGUE—See NORWICH, CT

STAFFORD—See ENFIELD, CT

STAMFORD—See NORWALK, CT

STERLING—See NEW LONDON, CT

STONINGTON—See GROTON, CT

STRATFORD—See BRIDGEPORT, CT

SUFFIELD—See ENFIELD, CT

TERRYVILLE—See WATERBURY, CT

THOMASTON—See LITCHFIELD, CT

THOMPSON—See ASHFORD, CT

TOLLAND—See HARTFORD, CT

TORRINGTON—See LITCHFIELD, CT

TRUMBULL—See NEWTOWN, CT

UNION—See ENFIELD, CT

▲ **UNIONVILLE**—SNET Americast

▲ **VERNON**—TCI Cablevision of Central Connecticut

VOLUNTOWN—See GROTON, CT

WALLINGFORD—See BRANFORD, CT

WARREN—See LITCHFIELD, CT

WASHINGTON—See NEWTOWN, CT

▲ **WATERBURY**—Tele-Media Corp.

WATERBURY—See also UNIONVILLE, CT

WATERFORD—See NEW LONDON, CT

WATERTOWN—See LITCHFIELD, CT

WEST CORNWALL—See SHARON, CT

WEST HARTFORD—See HARTFORD, CT

WEST HARTLAND—See WINSTED, CT

WEST HAVEN—See NEW HAVEN, CT

WESTBROOK—See CLINTON, CT

WESTON—See NORWALK, CT

WESTPORT—See NORWALK, CT

WETHERSFIELD—See MANCHESTER, CT

WILLIMANTIC—See ASHFORD, CT

WILLINGTON—See ASHFORD, CT

WILTON—See NORWALK, CT

WINCHESTER—See WINSTED, CT

WINDHAM—See ASHFORD, CT

WINDSOR—See HARTFORD, CT

WINDSOR LOCKS—See ENFIELD, CT

▲ **WINSTED**—Avalon Cable

WINTHROP—See CLINTON, CT

WOLCOTT—See WATERBURY, CT

WOODBRIDGE—See BRIDGEPORT, CT

WOODBURY—See NEWTOWN, CT

WOODSTOCK—See ASHFORD, CT

DISTRICT OF COLUMBIA

▲ **BOLLING AFB**—Mid-Atlantic Communications

▲ **U.S. SOLDIERS' & AIRMEN'S HOME**—Chesapeake Cable Partners

▲ **WASHINGTON**—District Cablevision LP

DELAWARE

ARDEN—See WILMINGTON, DE

ARDENCROFT—See WILMINGTON, DE

ARDENTOWN—See WILMINGTON, DE

BELLEFONTE—See WILMINGTON, DE

BETHANY BEACH—See DAGSBORO, DE

BETHEL—See REHOBOTH BEACH, DE

BLADES—See REHOBOTH BEACH, DE

BOWERS BEACH—See HARRINGTON, DE

BRIDGEVILLE—See HARRINGTON, DE

BROADKILL (town)—See HARRINGTON, DE

BROADKILL BEACH—See HARRINGTON, DE

CAMDEN—See DOVER, DE

CANNON (town)—See HARRINGTON, DE

CHESWOLD—See DOVER, DE

CLARKSVILLE—See DAGSBORO, DE

CLAYTON—See DOVER, DE

▲ **DAGSBORO**—Mediacom of Lower Delaware/Maryland

DELAWARE CITY—See MIDDLETOWN, DE

DELMAR—See SALISBURY, MD

DEWEY BEACH—See REHOBOTH BEACH, DE

▲ **DOVER**—Comcast Cablevision of Delmarva Inc.

DOVER AFB—See DOVER, DE

ELLENDALE—See HARRINGTON, DE

ELSMERE—See WILMINGTON, DE

FARMINGTON—See HARRINGTON, DE

FELTON—See HARRINGTON, DE

FENWICK ISLAND—See OCEAN CITY, MD

FRANKFORD—See DAGSBORO, DE

FREDERICA—See HARRINGTON, DE

GEORGETOWN—See REHOBOTH BEACH, DE

GREENWOOD—See HARRINGTON, DE

▲ **HARRINGTON**—Comcast Cablevision

HARTLY—See HARRINGTON, DE

HENLOPEN ACRES—See REHOBOTH BEACH, DE

HOUSTON—See HARRINGTON, DE

KENT COUNTY—See DOVER, DE

KENT COUNTY (portions)—See HARRINGTON, DE

KENT COUNTY (unincorporated areas)—See REHOBOTH BEACH, DE

KENTON—See HARRINGTON, DE

LAUREL—See REHOBOTH BEACH, DE

LEIPSIC—See DOVER, DE

LEWES—See REHOBOTH BEACH, DE

LINCOLN—See HARRINGTON, DE

LITTLE CREEK—See DOVER, DE

LITTLE CREEK—See also HARRINGTON, DE

MAGNOLIA—See HARRINGTON, DE

▲ **MIDDLETOWN**—Tri-State CableComm

MILFORD—See REHOBOTH BEACH, DE

MILLSBORO—See DAGSBORO, DE

MILLVILLE—See DAGSBORO, DE

MILTON—See HARRINGTON, DE

NEW CASTLE—See WILMINGTON, DE

NEW CASTLE COUNTY—See MIDDLETOWN, DE

NEW CASTLE COUNTY—See also WILMINGTON, DE

NEW CASTLE COUNTY (southern portion)—See DOVER, DE

NEWARK—See WILMINGTON, DE

NEWPORT—See WILMINGTON, DE

OCEAN VIEW—See DAGSBORO, DE

ODESSA—See MIDDLETOWN, DE

▲ **REHOBOTH BEACH**—Comcast Cablevision of Delmarva Inc.

ROXANA—See DAGSBORO, DE

SEAFORD—See REHOBOTH BEACH, DE

SELBYVILLE—See DAGSBORO, DE

SLAUGHTER BEACH—See DAGSBORO, DE

SLAUGHTER BEACH—See also HARRINGTON, DE

SMYRNA—See DOVER, DE

SOUTH BETHANY—See DAGSBORO, DE

ST. GEORGES—See MIDDLETOWN, DE

SUSSEX COUNTY—See DAGSBORO, DE

SUSSEX COUNTY—See also HARRINGTON, DE

SUSSEX COUNTY—See also OCEAN CITY, MD

SUSSEX COUNTY—See also SALISBURY, MD

SUSSEX COUNTY (portions)—See REHOBOTH BEACH, DE

TOWNSEND—See MIDDLETOWN, DE

VIOLA—See HARRINGTON, DE

▲ **WILMINGTON**—Suburban Cable TV Co. Inc.

WOODSIDE—See DOVER, DE

WYOMING—See DOVER, DE

FLORIDA

▲ **ADVENT CHRISTIAN VILLAGE**—Advent Christian Village Cable TV

ADVENTURA—See FORT LAUDERDALE, FL

▲ **ALACHUA**—Cable Florida

ALACHUA COUNTY—See ALACHUA, FL

ALACHUA COUNTY (portions)—See GAINESVILLE, FL

▲ **ALFORD**—Comcast Cablevision of Marianna Inc.

▲ **ALLIGATOR POINT**—Mediacom

▲ **ALTAMONTE SPRINGS**—Time Warner Cable

ALTHA—See MARIANNA, FL

ALTOONA—See ASTOR, FL

▲ **ALVA**—Cablevision Industries Inc.

AMELIA ISLAND—See FERNANDINA BEACH, FL

ANNA MARIA—See BRADENTON, FL

▲ **ANTHONY**—Galaxy Cablevision

▲ **APALACHICOLA**—Mediacom

▲ **APOLLO BEACH**—Time Warner Cable

APOPKA—See ORLANDO, FL

▲ **ARCADIA**—Comcast Cable

▲ **ARCHER**—Century Cable

ASTATULA—See ASTOR, FL

▲ **ASTOR**—Florida Cable

ATLANTIC BEACH—See JACKSONVILLE BEACH, FL

ATLANTIS—See PALM BEACH COUNTY, FL

AUBURNDALE—See WINTER HAVEN, FL

AVENTURA—See MIAMI BEACH, FL

AVON PARK—See SEBRING, FL

CINCO BAYOU—See FORT WALTON BEACH, FL

▲ **CITRA**—Galaxy Cablevision

CITRUS COUNTY—See DUNNELLON, FL

CITRUS COUNTY—See also HOMOSASSA, FL

CITRUS HILLS—See HOMOSASSA, FL

CITRUS SPRINGS—See HOMOSASSA, FL

CLAY COUNTY—See KEYSTONE HEIGHTS, FL

CLAY COUNTY (portions)—See ORANGE PARK, FL

CLAY HILL—See MIDDLEBURG, FL

CLEARVIEW ESTATES—See HOMOSASSA, FL

CLEARWATER—See PINELLAS COUNTY, FL

CLEARWATER—See also TAMPA BAY, FL

CLERMONT—See WINTER GARDEN, FL

▲ **CLEWISTON**—Time Warner Cable

CLOUD LAKE—See WEST PALM BEACH, FL

▲ **CLOVERLEAF MOBILE HOME PARK**—Time Warner Cable

COCOA—See MELBOURNE, FL

COCOA BEACH—See MELBOURNE, FL

COCOA WOOD LAKES—See DELRAY BEACH, FL

COCONUT CREEK—See MARGATE, FL

COLLIER COUNTY—See BONITA SPRINGS, FL

COLLIER COUNTY—See also NAPLES, FL

COLUMBIA COUNTY—See LAKE CITY, FL

COMPASS LAKE—See ALFORD, FL

CONCH KEY—See KEY COLONY BEACH, FL

COOPER CITY—See BROWARD COUNTY, FL

CORAL GABLES—See HIALEAH, FL

▲ **CORAL SPRINGS**—Advanced Cable Communications

Cottage Hills—See CANTONMENT, FL

COTTONDALE—See GREENWOOD, FL

COUNTRY CLUB ESTATES—See DUNNELLON, FL

▲ **CRAWFORDVILLE**—Comcast Cablevision

CRESCENT BEACH—See ST. AUGUSTINE, FL

▲ **CRESCENT CITY**—MediaOne

▲ **CRESTVIEW**—Cox Communications

▲ **CROSS CITY**—Cable Florida

CRYSTAL POINTE—See PALM BEACH COUNTY (southeastern portion), FL

CRYSTAL RIVER—See HOMOSASSA, FL

CUTLER RIDGE—See MIAMI, FL (Adelphia Cable-South Dade)

CYPRESS—See MARIANNA, FL

CYPRESS LAKE—See FORT MYERS, FL

DADE CITY—See PASCO COUNTY (central & eastern portions), FL

DADE COUNTY—See NORTH MIAMI, FL

DADE COUNTY (portions)—See HIALEAH, FL

DADE COUNTY (portions)—See also MIAMI BEACH, FL

DADE COUNTY (southern portion)—See KENDALL, FL

DADE COUNTY (southern portion)—See also SOUTH MIAMI, FL

DADE COUNTY (unincorporated areas)—See MIAMI, FL (Adelphia Cable-South Dade)

DANIA—See BROWARD COUNTY, FL

DAVENPORT—See LAKELAND, FL

DAVENPORT—See also THREE WORLD RECREATIONAL VEHICLE PARK, FL

DAVIE—See BROWARD COUNTY, FL

▲ **DAYTONA BEACH**—Time Warner Cable

DAYTONA BEACH SHORES—See DAYTONA BEACH, FL

▲ **DE BARY**—Comcast Communications

DE BARY—See also LEESBURG, FL

▲ **DE FUNIAK SPRINGS**—Time Warner Cable

▲ **DE LAND**—Time Warner Cable

DE LAND (portions)—See PAISLEY, FL

DE LEON SPRINGS—See DE LAND, FL

▲ **DEER CREEK GOLF RV RESORT**—Time Warner Communications

DEER CREEK MOBILE HOME PARK—See ENGLEWOOD, FL

DEERFIELD BEACH—See POMPANO BEACH, FL

DEKLE BEACH—See KEATON BEAD, FL

DELRAY—See PALM BEACH COUNTY, FL

DELRAY—See also PALM BEACH COUNTY (southeastern portion), FL

▲ **DELRAY BEACH**—Adelphia Cable

DELRAY DUNES—See GOLF VILLAGE, FL

DELTONA—See DE LAND, FL

▲ **DESTIN**—Cox Communications

DESTIN—See also WALTON COUNTY (southern portion), FL

DISTRICT FIVE—See DAYTONA BEACH, FL

DISTRICT FOUR—See DAYTONA BEACH, FL

DIXIE COUNTY—See CROSS CITY, FL

DUCK KEY—See KEY COLONY BEACH, FL

DUNDEE—See LAKELAND, FL

DUNE ALLEN—See WALTON COUNTY (southern portion), FL

▲ **DUNEDIN**—Time Warner Communications

DUNEDIN—See also PINELLAS COUNTY, FL

DUNEDIN—See also TAMPA BAY, FL

▲ **DUNNELLON**—Century Cable

EAGLE LAKE—See WINTER HAVEN, FL

EAST ARCADIA—See ARCADIA, FL

EAST FORT MYERS—See FORT MYERS, FL

EAST LAKE WOODLANDS—See PINELLAS COUNTY, FL

EAST NAPLES—See GOLDEN GATE, FL

EAST NAPLES—See also NAPLES, FL

EAST PALATKA—See PALATKA, FL

EAST POINTE—See PALM BEACH GARDENS, FL

▲ **EASTPOINT**—Mediacom

EASTRIDGE ESTATES—See STUART, FL

EATONVILLE—See ORLANDO, FL

EDGEWATER—See DE LAND, FL

EDGEWOOD—See ORLANDO, FL

▲ **EGLIN AIR FORCE BASE**—Cox Communications

EL PORTAL—See NORTH MIAMI, FL

ELFERS—See PORT RICHEY, FL

ELLENTON—See BRADENTON, FL

▲ **ENGLEWOOD**—Comcast Cablevision of West Florida Inc.

ESCAMBIA COUNTY—See CANTONMENT, FL

ESCAMBIA COUNTY—See also PENSACOLA, FL

ESCAMBIA COUNTY (portions)—See GULF BREEZE, FL

ESTERO—See BONITA SPRINGS, FL

ESTERO—See also GOLDEN GATE, FL

▲ **ESTO**—Galaxy Cablevision

EUREKA—See FORT MCCOY, FL

EUSTIS—See ASTOR, FL

EUSTIS—See also LEESBURG, FL

▲ **EVERGLADES CITY**—MediaOne

FAIRVIEW ESTATES—See HOMOSASSA, FL

FELLSMERE—See SEBASTIAN, FL

▲ **FERNANDINA BEACH**—MediaOne

FLAGER COUNTY—See PALM COAST, FL

▲ **FLAGLER BEACH**—Time Warner Cable

FLAGLER BY THE SEA—See BEVERLY BEACH, FL

FLAGLER COUNTY—See FLAGLER BEACH, FL

FLAGLER COUNTY (southern portion)—See ORMOND BEACH, FL

▲ **FLORAHOME**—P.D.Q. Cable TV Inc.

FLORIDA CITY—See MIAMI, FL (Adelphia Cable-South Dade)

▲ **FLORIDA HIGHLANDS**—Highlands Cablevision

▲ **FOREST GLEN**—Southeast Florida Cable Inc.

FOREST LAKE—See HOMOSASSA, FL

FOREST LAKES—See FOREST GLEN, FL

▲ **FORT LAUDERDALE**—Comcast Communications Inc.

▲ **FORT McCOY**—Time Warner Cable

FORT MEADE—See BARTOW, FL

▲ **FORT MYERS**—Jones Intercable

FORT MYERS BEACH—See BONITA SPRINGS, FL

FORT MYERS SHORES—See FORT MYERS, FL

FORT OGDEN—See ARCADIA, FL

▲ **FORT PIERCE**—TCI

FORT PIERCE (portions)—See GATOR TRACE, FL

FORT PIERCE (portions)—See also MOON RIVER, FL

▲ **FORT WALTON BEACH**—Cox Communications

FRANCIS—See PALATKA, FL

FRANKLIN COUNTY (portions)—See APALACHICOLA, FL

FREEPORT—See FORT WALTON BEACH, FL

FRENCHMANS CREEK—See PALM BEACH COUNTY (southeastern portion), FL

FROSTPROOF—See LAKE WALES, FL

FRUIT COVE—See JACKSONVILLE, FL

FRUITLAND—See WELAKA, FL

FRUITLAND PARK—See LEESBURG, FL

GADSDEN COUNTY—See QUINCY, FL

GADSDEN COUNTY (portions)—See CHATTAHOOCHEE, FL

GADSDEN COUNTY (unincorporated areas)—See HAVANA, FL

▲ **GAINESVILLE**—Cox Cable-Gainesville/Ocala Inc.

GARDENS OF GULF COVE—See ENGLEWOOD, FL

▲ **GATOR TRACE**—Southeast Florida Cable Inc.

▲ **GENEVA**—Time Warner Cable

GEORGETOWN—See WELAKA, FL

GIBSONTON—See APOLLO BEACH, FL

GLADES COUNTY—See MOORE HAVEN, FL

GLADES COUNTY—See also OKEECHOBEE, FL

GLADES COUNTY (southern portion)—See LA BELLE, FL

GLEN RIDGE—See WEST PALM BEACH, FL

GLEN ST. MARY—See MACCLENNY, FL

GOLDEN BEACH—See MIAMI BEACH, FL

▲ **GOLDEN GATE**—Time Warner Cable

▲ **GOLF VILLAGE**—Adelphia Communications

GOLFVIEW—See WEST PALM BEACH, FL

GOULDS—See MIAMI, FL (Adelphia Cable-South Dade)

GRACEVILLE—See CHIPLEY, FL

GRAND ISLAND—See LEESBURG, FL

GRAND RIDGE—See SEMINOLE COUNTY, GA

GRANDIN—See FLORAHOME, FL

GRASSY KEY—See KEY COLONY BEACH, FL

GRAYTON BEACH—See WALTON COUNTY (southern portion), FL

GREEN COVE SPRINGS—See ORANGE PARK, FL

▲ **GREENACRES CITY**—Adelphia Communications

▲ **GREENSBORO**—Mediacom

▲ **GREENVILLE**—Galaxy Cablevision

▲ **GREENWOOD**—Galaxy Cablevision

GREENWOOD MANOR—See MELBOURNE, FL

GREENWOOD VILLAGE—See MELBOURNE, FL

▲ **GRETNA**—Mediacom

GROVELAND—See WINTER GARDEN, FL

▲ **GULF BREEZE**—Mediacom

GULF COUNTY (portions)—See MEXICO BEACH, FL

GULF COUNTY (portions)—See also PORT ST. JOE, FL

GULF STREAM—See DELRAY BEACH, FL

GULFPORT—See PINELLAS COUNTY, FL

HAINES CITY—See LAKELAND, FL

▲ **HALLANDALE**—Comcast Cablevision of Hallandale Inc.

▲ **HAMPTON**—Galaxy Cablevision

HAMPTON HILLS—See HOMOSASSA, FL

HARDEE COUNTY (portions)—See WAUCHULA, FL

HARLEM—See CLEWISTON, FL

▲ **HASTINGS**—MediaOne

▲ **HAVANA**—Mediacom

HAVERHILL—See WEST PALM BEACH, FL

▲ **HAWTHORNE**—Cable Florida

HAWTHORNE—See also MELROSE, FL

HENDRY COUNTY—See CLEWISTON, FL

HENDRY COUNTY (portions)—See LA BELLE, FL

HERACALA ACRES—See HOMOSASSA, FL

HERITAGE RIDGE—See STUART, FL

HERNANDO—See HOMOSASSA, FL

HERNANDO (portions)—See INVERNESS, FL

▲ **HERNANDO COUNTY**—Time Warner

HERNANDO COUNTY (northeastern portion)—See NOBLETON, FL

▲ **HIALEAH**—MediaOne

HIALEAH GARDENS—See HIALEAH, FL

▲ **HICKORY LAKES ESTATES**—Comcast Cable Communications Inc.

▲ **HIDDEN ACRES**—Comcast Cable Communications Inc.

HIDE AWAY MOBILE HOME PARK—See ANTHONY, FL

▲ **HIGH SPRINGS**—Cable Florida

▲ **HIGHLAND BEACH**—Southeast Florida Cable Inc.

HIGHLANDS COUNTY (portions)—See LAKE PLACID, FL

HIGHLANDS COUNTY (portions)—See also SEBRING, FL

HILAND PARK—See SPRINGFIELD, FL

▲ **HILLIARD**—MediaOne

HILLSBORO BEACH—See POMPANO BEACH, FL

HILLSBOROUGH COUNTY (southern portion)—See APOLLO BEACH, FL

HOBE SOUND—See STUART, FL

HOLIDAY—See PORT RICHEY, FL

HOLIDAY LAKES—See ENGLEWOOD, FL

HOLIDAY MOBILE ESTATES—See VENICE, FL (Comcast Cablevision of West Florida Inc.)

HOLLEY (portions)—See GULF BREEZE, FL

HOLLISTER—See PALATKA, FL

HOLLY HILL—See ORMOND BEACH, FL

▲ **HOLLYWOOD**—TCI TKR of Hollywood Inc.

HOLLYWOOD SEMINOLE RESERVE—See BROWARD COUNTY, FL

HOLMES BEACH—See BRADENTON, FL

HOLMES COUNTY (portions)—See ESTO, FL

▲ **HOLOPAW**—P.D.Q. Cable TV Inc.

HOLT—See BAKER, FL

HOMELAND—See BARTOW, FL

HOMESTEAD—See MIAMI, FL (Adelphia Cable-South Dade)

▲ **HOMOSASSA**—Time Warner Cable

HOMOSASSA SPRINGS—See HOMOSASSA, FL

HOOKER POINT—See CLEWISTON, FL

▲ **HOSFORD**—Southeast Cable TV Inc.

HOWEY-IN-THE-HILLS—See LEESBURG, FL

HUDSON—See PORT RICHEY, FL

▲ **HUNTERS CREEK**—Hunters Creek Communications

HUNTERS RUN—See WEST PALM BEACH, FL

HUNTINGTON LAKES—See DELRAY BEACH, FL

HURLBURT FIELD—See FORT WALTON BEACH, FL

HUTCHINSON—See STUART, FL

HUTCHINSON ISLAND SOUTH—See STUART, FL

HYPOLUXO—See WEST PALM BEACH, FL

▲ **IMMOKALEE**—Time Warner Cable

IMMOKALEE SEMINOLE INDIAN RESERVATION—See BROWARD COUNTY, FL

INDIATLANTIC—See MELBOURNE, FL

INDIAN HARBOR BEACH—See MELBOURNE, FL

INDIAN LAKE ESTATES—See RIVER RANCH, FL

INDIAN RIVER—See SEBASTIAN, FL

INDIAN RIVER COUNTY—See SEBASTIAN, FL

INDIAN RIVER COUNTY—See also VERO BEACH, FL

▲ **ORANGE LAKE**—Cable Florida

▲ **ORANGE PARK**—MediaOne

▲ **ORANGE SPRINGS**—P.D.Q. Cable TV Inc.

ORANGEDALE—See JACKSONVILLE, FL

ORCHID—See VERO BEACH, FL

▲ **ORLANDO**—Time Warner

▲ **ORMOND BEACH**—Time Warner Communications

▲ **ORMOND BEACH (western portion)**—Tomoka Cable TV

ORMAND BEACH—See also PALM COAST, FL

ORMOND BY THE SEA—See ORMOND BEACH, FL

▲ **ORTONA**—Time Warner Cable

▲ **OSCEOLA COUNTY (unincorporated areas)**—Adelphia Communications Corp.

OSCEOLA COUNTY—See also POINCIANA, FL

OSCEOLA COUNTY—See also WINTER GARDEN, FL

OSCEOLA COUNTY (northern portion)—See also KISSIMMEE, FL

OSTEEN—See DE LAND, FL

▲ **OVIEDO**—Time Warner Cable

▲ **OZELLO**—Highlands Cablevision

PAHOKEE—See BELLE GLADE, FL

▲ **PAISLEY**—Galaxy Cablevision

▲ **PALATKA**—Time Warner Cable

PALATKA—See also WELAKA, FL

PALM AIRE—See POMPANO BEACH, FL

▲ **PALM BAY**—Falcon Cable Media

PALM BAY—See also MELBOURNE, FL

PALM BEACH—See WEST PALM BEACH, FL

PALM BEACH CITY—See PALM BEACH GARDENS, FL

▲ **PALM BEACH COUNTY**—Adelphia Cable

▲ **PALM BEACH COUNTY (southeastern portion)**—Adelphia Cable

PALM BEACH COUNTY—See also BOCA RATON, FL (Comcast Cablevision of Boca Raton Inc.)

PALM BEACH COUNTY—See also DELRAY BEACH, FL

PALM BEACH COUNTY—See also GREENACRES CITY, FL

PALM BEACH COUNTY—See also WEST PALM BEACH, FL

PALM BEACH COUNTY (portions)—See also BELLE GLADE, FL

▲ **PALM BEACH GARDENS**—Adelphia Communications

PALM BEACH GARDENS—See also PALM BEACH COUNTY, FL

PALM BEACH SHORES—See PALM BEACH GARDENS, FL

▲ **PALM CAY**—Palm Cay Cablevision

▲ **PALM CHASE**—Southeast Florida Cable Inc.

PALM CITY—See STUART, FL

▲ **PALM COAST**—Palm Coast Cablevision Ltd.

PALM HARBOR—See DUNEDIN, FL

PALM HARBOR—See also PINELLAS COUNTY, FL

PALM RIVER ESTATES—See BONITA SPRINGS, FL

PALM SHORES—See MELBOURNE, FL

▲ **PALM SPRINGS**—Adelphia Communications Corp.

PALM SPRINGS—See also WEST PALM BEACH, FL

PALMETTO—See BRADENTON, FL

PALMLAND—See GOLF VILLAGE, FL

▲ **PANAMA CITY**—Comcast Cable of Panama City

▲ **PANAMA CITY BEACH**—Jones Spacelink

▲ **PANAMA CITY BEACH**—Knowledgy

PARK SOUTH—See ORLANDO, FL

PARKER—See PANAMA CITY, FL

PARKLAND—See MARGATE, FL

PARRISH—See BRADENTON, FL

▲ **PASCO COUNTY (central & eastern portions)**—Florida Satellite Network Inc.

PASCO COUNTY (southern portion)—See PLANT CITY (portions), FL

PASCO COUNTY (western portion)—See APOLLO BEACH, FL

PASCO COUNTY (western portion)—See also PORT RICHEY, FL

PATRICK AFB—See MELBOURNE, FL

PAXTON—See FLORALA, AL

PEMBROKE PARK—See NORTH MIAMI, FL

PEMBROKE PINES—See NORTH MIAMI, FL

PENNBROOK—See WILDWOOD, FL

▲ **PENSACOLA**—Cox Cable TV of Pensacola

PENSACOLA BEACH—See GULF BREEZE, FL

PENSACOLA NAVAL AIR STATION—See GULF BREEZE, FL

PERRINE—See MIAMI, FL (Adelphia Cable-South Dade)

▲ **PERRY**—Comcast Cablevision of Perry Inc.

PIERSON—See ASTOR, FL

▲ **PINE ISLAND**—MediaOne

PINECREST—See KENDALL, FL

PINELAND—See PINE ISLAND, FL

▲ **PINELLAS COUNTY**—Time Warner Communications

PINELLAS COUNTY—See also DUNEDIN, FL

PINELLAS COUNTY—See also TAMPA BAY, FL

PINELLAS COUNTY (portions)—See also MADEIRA BEACH, FL

PINELLAS COUNTY (unincorporated areas)—See also PINELLAS COUNTY, FL

PINELLAS PARK—See PINELLAS COUNTY, FL

PINES OF DELRAY—See PALM BEACH COUNTY (southeastern portion), FL

▲ **PLANT CITY (portions)**—Time Warner Communications

PLANT CITY (portions)—See also BRANDON (portions), FL

▲ **PLANTATION**—MediaOne

▲ **POINCIANA**—American Cablevision Services Inc.

POINCIANA PLACE—See PALM BEACH COUNTY, FL

POLK CITY—See WINTER HAVEN, FL

POLK COUNTY—See LAKELAND, FL

POLK COUNTY—See also POINCIANA, FL

POLK COUNTY (northern portion)—See also KISSIMMEE, FL

POLK COUNTY (portions)—See also LAKE WALES, FL

POLK COUNTY (portions)—See also RIVER RANCH, FL

POLK COUNTY (portions)—See also WINTER HAVEN, FL

POLO'S OF KISSIMMEE—See ORLANDO, FL

POMONA PARK—See CRESCENT CITY, FL

POMPANO—See POMPANO BEACH, FL

▲ **POMPANO BEACH**—MediaOne

PONCE DE LEON—See WESTVILLE, FL

PONCE INLET—See DAYTONA BEACH, FL

▲ **PONTE VEDRA BEACH**—MediaOne

▲ **PORT CHARLOTTE**—Comcast Cable

PORT ORANGE—See DAYTONA BEACH, FL

▲ **PORT RICHEY**—Time Warner Cable

PORT SALERNO—See STUART, FL

▲ **PORT ST. JOE**—Gulf Cable TV

PORT ST. LUCIE—See STUART, FL

PUNTA GORDA—See CAPE CORAL, FL

PUNTA GORDA—See also PORT CHARLOTTE, FL

PUTNAM COUNTY—See CRESCENT CITY, FL

▲ **QUINCY**—Comcast Cablevision of Quincy Inc.

RAIFORD—See LAWTEY, FL

RAINBOW LAKES—See DUNNELLON, FL

▲ **RAINBOW PARK**—Time Warner Cable

RAINBOW SPRINGS—See DUNNELLON, FL

RAINBOWS END—See DUNNELLON, FL

REDDICK—See ORANGE LAKE, FL

REDINGTON BEACH—See MADEIRA BEACH, FL

REDINGTON SHORES—See MADEIRA BEACH, FL

RIDGEWAY—See STUART, FL

▲ **RIMA RIDGE**—Interactive Cable Systems

RIO VISTA—See DUNNELLON, FL

RIVER GARDENS—See DUNNELLON, FL

▲ **RIVER RANCH**—Americable International Florida Inc.

RIVERVIEW—See APOLLO BEACH, FL

RIVIERA BEACH—See PALM BEACH GARDENS, FL

RIVIERA BEACH—See also WEST PALM BEACH, FL

ROCKLEDGE—See MELBOURNE, FL

ROCKY CREEK—See MARIANNA, FL

ROLLING GREENS—See SILVER SPRINGS SHORES, FL

ROSELAND—See SEBASTIAN, FL

ROTONDA—See ENGLEWOOD, FL

ROUND LAKE—See ALFORD, FL

ROYAL PALM BEACH—See PALM BEACH COUNTY, FL

RUSKIN—See APOLLO BEACH, FL

SAFETY HARBOR—See DUNEDIN, FL

SAFETY HARBOR—See also TAMPA BAY, FL

▲ **SALT SPRINGS**—Time Warner Cable

▲ **SAMSULA**—Consolidated Cablevision

SAN ANTONIO—See PASCO COUNTY (central & eastern portions), FL

SAN CARLOS ISLAND—See BONITA SPRINGS, FL

SAN MATEO—See PALATKA, FL

▲ **SAND-N-SEA**—Southeast Florida Cable Inc.

SANDCLIFF—See WALTON COUNTY (southern portion), FL

▲ **SANDESTIN BEACH RESORT**—Mediacom

SANDY CREEK—See PANAMA CITY, FL

SANFORD—See GENEVA, FL

SANFORD—See also ORLANDO, FL

▲ **SANIBEL ISLAND**—MediaOne

SANTA ROSA BEACH—See WALTON COUNTY (southern portion), FL

SANTA ROSA COUNTY—See MILTON, FL

SANTA ROSA COUNTY (northern portion)—See CENTURY, FL

SANTA ROSA COUNTY (portions)—See GULF BREEZE, FL

▲ **SARALAKE ESTATES**—Saralake Estates Mobile Home Park

▲ **SARASOTA**—Comcast Cablevision of West Florida Inc.

SARASOTA COUNTY—See SARASOTA, FL

SARASOTA COUNTY—See also VENICE, FL (Comcast Cablevision of West Florida Inc.)

SARASOTA COUNTY (portions)—See ENGLEWOOD, FL

SATELLITE BEACH—See MELBOURNE, FL

SATSUMA—See PALATKA, FL

SEA RANCH LAKES—See FORT LAUDERDALE, FL

SEAGROVE BEACH—See WALTON COUNTY (southern portion), FL

SEASIDE—See WALTON COUNTY (southern portion), FL

▲ **SEBASTIAN**—Falcon Cable Media

▲ **SEBRING**—Comcast Cablevision of West Florida Inc.

SEMINOLE—See PINELLAS COUNTY, FL

SEMINOLE COUNTY—See ALTAMONTE SPRINGS, FL

SEMINOLE COUNTY—See also ORLANDO, FL

SEMINOLE COUNTY (portions)—See OVIEDO, FL

SEWALL'S POINT—See STUART, FL

SHAKER VILLAGE—See POMPANO BEACH, FL

SHALIMAR—See FORT WALTON BEACH, FL

SHELL POINT—See CRAWFORDVILLE, FL

▲ **SILVER SPRINGS**—Time Warner Cable

SILVER SPRINGS—See also SILVER SPRINGS, FL

▲ **SILVER SPRINGS SHORES**—Comcast Communications

SILVER SPRINGS SHORES—See also LEESBURG, FL

SINGER ISLAND—See WEST PALM BEACH, FL

SKYLAND MEADOWS—See HOMOSASSA, FL

SNEADS—See SEMINOLE COUNTY, GA

SNUG HARBOR VILLAGE—See BAREFOOT BAY, FL

SOPCHOPPY—See TALLAHASSEE, FL

SORRENTO—See ASTOR, FL

SORRENTO—See also LEESBURG, FL

SOUTH BAY—See BELLE GLADE, FL

SOUTH DAYTONA—See DAYTONA BEACH, FL

SOUTH DUNNELLON—See DUNNELLON, FL

SOUTH FORT MYERS—See FORT MYERS, FL

▲ **SOUTH MIAMI**—Cable Satellite of South Miami Inc.

SOUTH MIAMI HEIGHTS—See MIAMI, FL (Adelphia Cable-South Dade)

SOUTH PALM BEACH—See WEST PALM BEACH, FL

SOUTH PASADENA—See PINELLAS COUNTY, FL

SOUTH ST. PETERSBURG—See ISLA DEL SOL, FL

▲ **SOUTHGATE**—Time Warner Cable

▲ **SOUTHPORT**—Mediacom

SPARR—See CITRA, FL

SPRING HILL—See HERNANDO COUNTY, FL

▲ **SPRING LAKE**—Comcast Cable Communications Inc.

▲ **SPRINGFIELD**—Springfield Cablevision

SPRINGFIELD—See also PANAMA CITY, FL

SPRUCE CREEK—See DAYTONA BEACH, FL

▲ **ST. AUGUSTINE**—Time Warner Cable

ST. AUGUSTINE BEACH—See ST. AUGUSTINE, FL

ST. AUGUSTINE SHORES—See ST. AUGUSTINE, FL

ST. CLOUD—See WINTER GARDEN, FL

▲ **ST. GEORGES ISLAND**—Mediacom

ST. JAMES CITY—See PINE ISLAND, FL

ST. JOE BEACH—See MEXICO BEACH, FL

ST. JOHNS COUNTY—See HASTINGS, FL

ST. JOHNS COUNTY (northern portion)—See JACKSONVILLE, FL

ST. JOHNS COUNTY (unincorporated areas)—See ST. AUGUSTINE, FL

ST. LEO—See PASCO COUNTY (central & eastern portions), FL

ST. LUCIE COUNTY—See FORT PIERCE, FL

ST. LUCIE COUNTY—See also STUART, FL

ST. LUCIE VILLAGE—See FORT PIERCE, FL

▲ **ST. LUCIE WEST**—St. Lucie West Cablevision

ST. PETERSBURG—See PINELLAS COUNTY, FL

ST. PETERSBURG—See also TAMPA BAY, FL

ST. PETERSBURG BEACH—See PINELLAS COUNTY, FL

STARKE—See ORANGE PARK, FL

▲ **STEINHATCHEE**—Cable Florida

▲ **STUART**—Adelphia Cable Communications

STUART—See also PALM BEACH COUNTY, FL

SUMMIT PINES—See FOREST GLEN, FL

SUMTER COUNTY (portions)—See WILDWOOD, FL

SUMTER COUNTY (southwestern portion)—See NOBLETON, FL

SUN CITY CENTER—See APOLLO BEACH, FL

SUN LAKE ESTATES—See LEESBURG, FL

▲ **SUNNY HILLS**—Americable International Florida Inc.

SUNNY ISLES—See MIAMI BEACH, FL

SUNRISE—See POMPANO BEACH, FL

SURFSIDE—See MIAMI BEACH, FL

SURFSIDE ESTATES—See BEVERLY BEACH, FL

SUWANNEE COUNTY—See BRANFORD, FL

SUWANNEE COUNTY (portions)—See LIVE OAK, FL

SWEETWATER—See HIALEAH, FL

▲ **SWEETWATER GOLF & TENNIS CLUB EAST**—Sweetwater Golf & Tennis Club East Inc.

SWITZERLAND—See JACKSONVILLE, FL

TAFT—See ORLANDO, FL

▲ **TALLAHASSEE**—Comcast Cablevision of Tallahassee Inc.

TAMARAC—See POMPANO BEACH, FL

TAMARAC GARDENS—See POMPANO BEACH, FL

TAMPA—See PLANT CITY (portions), FL

▲ **TAMPA BAY**—GTE Media Ventures

TARPON SPRINGS—See DUNEDIN, FL

TARPON SPRINGS—See also TAMPA BAY, FL

TAVARES—See LEESBURG, FL

TAYLOR COUNTY—See PERRY, FL

TEMPLE TERRACE—See PLANT CITY (portions), FL

▲ **TEQUESTA**—Adelphia Communications Corp.

TERRA CEIA—See BRADENTON, FL

THE POLO CLUB—See PALM BEACH COUNTY (southeastern portion), FL

THE RESERVE—See STUART, FL

THE VILLAGES—See LEESBURG, FL

THIRTY A—See WALTON COUNTY (southern portion), FL

▲ **THREE WORLD RECREATIONAL VEHICLE PARK**—Comcast Cable Communications Inc.

TIERRA VERDE—See ISLA DEL SOL, FL

TIERRA VERDE—See also PINELLAS COUNTY, FL

TITUSVILLE—See MELBOURNE, FL

TOPSIL—See FORT WALTON BEACH, FL

TREASURE ISLAND—See PINELLAS COUNTY, FL

▲ **TRENTON**—Century Cable

▲ **TYNDALL AFB**—Mediacom

UMATILLA—See LEESBURG, FL

UNION COUNTY—See LAKE BUTLER, FL

▲ **UNIVERSITY OF WEST FLORIDA**—Cox Communications

Useppa Island—See PINE ISLAND, FL

VACA KEY—See KEY COLONY BEACH, FL

▲ **VALPARAISO**—City of Valparaiso

VALRICO (southern portion)—See APOLLO BEACH, FL

VANDERBILT BEACH—See BONITA SPRINGS, FL

▲ **VENICE**—Comcast Cablevision of West Florida Inc.

▲ **VENICE**—Time Warner Cable

▲ **VERNON**—Mediacom

▲ **VERO BEACH**—TCI

VICTORIA WOODS—See FOREST GLEN, FL

VILLAGE CLUB—See FOREST GLEN, FL

VIRGINIA GARDENS—See HIALEAH, FL

VOLUSIA—See ASTOR, FL

VOLUSIA COUNTY—See ORMOND BEACH, FL

VOLUSIA COUNTY—See also PALM COAST, FL

VOLUSIA COUNTY (portions)—See DE BARY, FL

VOLUSIA COUNTY (unincorporated areas)—See ASTOR, FL

VOLUSIA COUNTY (western portion)—See DE LAND, FL

WABASSO—See SEBASTIAN, FL

▲ **WALDO**—MediaOne

▲ **WALTON COUNTY (southern portion)**—Mediacom

Walton County—See also DE FUNIAK SPRINGS, FL

WALTON COUNTY (portions)—See also FORT WALTON BEACH, FL

WARD RIDGE—See PORT ST. JOE, FL

WASHINGTON COUNTY—See CHIPLEY, FL

▲ **WAUCHULA**—Comcast Cablevision of Tallahassee Inc.

WAUSAU—See SUNNY HILLS, FL

WEEKI WACHEE—See HERNANDO COUNTY, FL

▲ **WELAKA**—MediaOne

WELLINGTON—See PALM BEACH COUNTY, FL

WESLEY CHAPEL—See PASCO COUNTY (central & eastern portions), FL

WEST DELRAY BEACH—See DELRAY BEACH, FL

WEST MELBOURNE—See MELBOURNE, FL

WEST MIAMI—See HIALEAH, FL

▲ **WEST PALM BEACH**—Comcast Cablevision

WEST PALM BEACH—See also GREENACRES CITY, FL

▲ **WESTON**—Advanced Cable Communications

▲ **WESTVILLE**—Americable International Florida Inc.

▲ **WEWAHITCHKA**—Mediacom

WHISPER WALK—See PALM BEACH COUNTY (southeastern portion), FL

▲ **WHITE SPRINGS**—Southeast Cable TV Inc.

WHITING FIELD NAVAL AIR STATION—See MILTON, FL

▲ **WILDWOOD**—Time Warner Cable

▲ **WILLISTON**—Century Cable

WILTON MANORS—See POMPANO BEACH, FL

WIMAUMA—See APOLLO BEACH, FL

WINDERMERE—See ORLANDO, FL

WINDMILL VILLAGE—See PORT CHARLOTTE, FL

WINTER BEACH—See SEBASTIAN, FL

▲ **WINTER GARDEN**—Time Warner Cable

▲ **WINTER HAVEN**—Time Warner Cable

WINTER HAVEN OAKS MOBILE HOME PARK—See WINTER HAVEN, FL

WINTER PARK—See ORLANDO, FL

WINTER SPRINGS—See ORLANDO, FL

▲ **WOODFIELD**—Adelphia Communications Corp.

WOODLANDS—See FOREST GLEN, FL

WORTHINGTON SPRINGS—See BROOKER, FL

▲ **YANKEETOWN**—Century Cable

YOUNGSTOWN—See PANAMA CITY, FL

▲ **YULEE**—Century Cable

▲ **ZELLWOOD**—Constel Communications

ZEPHYRHILLS—See PASCO COUNTY (central & eastern portions), FL

▲ **ZOLFO SPRINGS**—Comcast Cable Communications Inc.

GEORGIA

▲ **ABBEVILLE**—Blackstone Cable LLC

ACWORTH—See ATLANTA, GA

ADAIRSVILLE—See CARTERSVILLE, GA

ADEL—See NASHVILLE, GA

▲ **ADRIAN**—Comcast Cablevision of the South

AILEY—See MOUNT VERNON, GA

ALAMO—See MOUNT VERNON, GA

ALAPAHA—See ENIGMA, GA

▲ **ALBANY**—TCI of Georgia

ALDORA—See STOCKBRIDGE, GA

ALLENHURST—See HINESVILLE, GA

ALLENTOWN—See DANVILLE, GA

▲ **ALMA**—Alma Telephone Co.

ALPHARETTA—See ATLANTA, GA

ALTO—See CORNELIA, GA

▲ **AMBROSE**—Charter Communications

▲ **AMERICUS**—TCI of Georgia Inc.

APPLING COUNTY (unincorporated areas)—See SURRENCY, GA

▲ **ARABI**—Phoenix Cable Inc.

ARAGON—See ROCKMART, GA

ARCADE—See JEFFERSON, GA

ARGYLE (portions)—See HOMERVILLE, GA

ARLINGTON—See CUTHBERT, GA

▲ **ARNOLDSVILLE**—Galaxy Cablevision

▲ **ASHBURN**—TCI of Georgia Inc.

▲ **ATHENS**—InterMedia

▲ **ATLANTA**—MediaOne

ATLANTA (portions)—See FAIRBURN, GA

▲ **ATTAPULGUS**—Galaxy Cablevision

▲ **AUGUSTA**—Jones Intercable

AUSTELL—See ATLANTA, GA

▲ **AVALON**—Galaxy Cablevision

▲ **AVERA**—National Cable Inc.

AVONDALE ESTATES—See ATLANTA, GA

▲ **BAINBRIDGE**—TCI of Georgia Inc.

▲ **NAHUNTA**—MediaOne

▲ **NASHVILLE**—TCI of Georgia Inc.

▲ **NEWNAN**—Charter Communications

NEWTON COUNTY—See ATLANTA, GA

NEWTON COUNTY—See also COVINGTON, GA

NICHOLLS—See DOUGLAS, GA

NICHOLSON—See COMMERCE, GA

NORCROSS—See ATLANTA, GA

▲ **NORMAN PARK**—Wainwright Cable

NORTH DRUID HILLS—See CHAMBLEE, GA (Comcast Cablevision of the South)

NORTH HIGH SHOALS—See BISHOP, GA

▲ **OAK PARK**—Rigel Communications Inc., c/o Phoenix Cable

OAKWOOD—See GAINESVILLE, GA

▲ **OCHLOCKNEE**—Southeast Cable TV Inc.

OCILLA—See FITZGERALD, GA

▲ **OCONEE**—National Cable Inc.

OCONEE COUNTY—See ATHENS, GA

OCONEE COUNTY (portions)—See WATKINSVILLE, GA

ODUM—See JESUP, GA

OFFERMAN—See PATTERSON, GA

OGLETHORPE—See MONTEZUMA, GA

OGLETHORPE COUNTY (unincorporated areas)—See ARNOLDSVILLE, GA

OMEGA—See TIFTON, GA

ORCHARD HILL—See GRIFFIN, GA

OXFORD—See COVINGTON, GA

PALMETTO—See FAIRBURN, GA

▲ **PATTERSON**—Patterson Cable TV

PAULDING COUNTY—See DALLAS, GA

▲ **PAVO**—Southeast Cable TV Inc.

PAYNE CITY—See MACON, GA

PEACH COUNTY—See FORT VALLEY, GA

PEACH COUNTY (portions)—See MACON, GA

▲ **PEACHTREE CITY**—InterMedia

Peachtree City—See also ATLANTA, GA

▲ **PEARSON**—TCI Cablevision of Georgia Inc.

PELHAM—See CAMILLA, GA

▲ **PEMBROKE**—Cablevision of Pembroke

PENDERGRASS—See JACKSON COUNTY, GA

▲ **PERRY**—Peach State Cable

PICKENS COUNTY (portions)—See BIG CANOE, GA

PIKE COUNTY (unincorporated areas)—See STOCKBRIDGE, GA

PINE GLEN—See ALBANY, GA

PINE LAKE—See ATLANTA, GA

▲ **PINE MOUNTAIN**—Charter Communications Inc.

▲ **PINEHURST**—Communicomm

▲ **PINEVIEW**—Galaxy Cablevision

▲ **PITTS**—Galaxy Cablevision

▲ **PLAINS**—Blackstone Cable

PLAINVILLE—See CALHOUN, GA

POLK COUNTY—See CEDARTOWN, GA

POLK COUNTY (eastern portion)—See ROCKMART, GA

POLK COUNTY (portions)—See CARTERSVILLE, GA

POOLER—See SAVANNAH, GA

PORT WENTWORTH—See SAVANNAH, GA

▲ **PORT WENTWORTH (portions)**—Rigel Communications Inc.

PORT WENTWORTH (portions)—See also GUYTON, GA

▲ **PORTAL**—Blackstone Cable, c/o Phoenix Cable Inc.

PORTERDALE—See COVINGTON, GA

POULAN—See SYLVESTER, GA

▲ **POWDER SPRINGS**—InterMedia

POWDER SPRINGS—See also ATLANTA, GA

▲ **PRESTON**—Southern Cablevision Inc.

PULASKI COUNTY (portions)—See HAWKINSVILLE, GA

PULASKI COUNTY (southern portion)—See PINEVIEW, GA

PUTNAM COUNTY—See EATONTON, GA

PUTNAM COUNTY (southern portion)—See BALDWIN COUNTY (northern portion), GA

PUTNAM COUNTY (unincorporated areas)—See GREENE COUNTY (unincorporated areas), GA

PUTNEY—See ALBANY, GA

▲ **QUITMAN**—Comcast Cablevision of the South

QUITMAN COUNTY—See EUFAULA, AL

RANDOLPH COUNTY—See CUTHBERT, GA

▲ **RANGER**—3D Cable Inc.

RAY CITY—See LAKELAND, GA

▲ **REBECCA**—Galaxy Cablevision

▲ **REIDSVILLE**—Kennedy Cablevision Inc.

REMERTON—See VALDOSTA, GA (TCI Cablevision of Georgia Inc.)

RENTZ—See LAURENS COUNTY (eastern portion), GA

RESACA—See CALHOUN, GA

REST HAVEN—See GWINNETT COUNTY (portions), GA

▲ **REYNOLDS**—Flint Cable TV

▲ **RHINE**—Rigel Communications Inc.

RICEBORO—See HINESVILLE, GA

RICHLAND—See CUTHBERT, GA

RICHMOND COUNTY—See AUGUSTA, GA

RICHMOND HILL—See HINESVILLE, GA

RINCON—See GUYTON, GA

RINCON—See also SAVANNAH, GA

▲ **RINGGOLD**—Falcon First Inc.

RISING FAWN—See TRENTON, GA

RIVER NORTH COMMUNITY—See MACON, GA

RIVERDALE—See ATLANTA, GA

▲ **ROBERTA**—Flint Cable TV

ROBINS AFB—See ATLANTA, GA

ROBINS AFB—See also MACON, GA

▲ **ROCHELLE**—Rigel Communications Inc.

ROCK SPRING—See LA FAYETTE, GA

ROCKDALE COUNTY (portions)—See ATLANTA, GA

ROCKDALE COUNTY (unincorporated areas)—See STOCKBRIDGE, GA

▲ **ROCKMART**—Falcon Community Ventures I

▲ **ROME**—Comcast Cable of NW Georgia

▲ **ROSSVILLE**—Comcast Cablevision of the South

▲ **ROSWELL**—Cablevision Communications

ROSWELL—See also ATLANTA, GA

ROSWELL (portions)—See WOODSTOCK, GA

▲ **ROYSTON**—Northland Cable TV

RUTLEDGE—See EATONTON, GA

▲ **SANDERSVILLE**—InterMedia

SANDY SPRINGS—See ATLANTA, GA

▲ **SANFORD**—Galaxy Cablevision

SANTA CLAUS—See VIDALIA, GA

SAPELO GARDENS—See EULONIA, GA

▲ **SARDIS**—Blackstone Cable

▲ **SASSER**—Southern Cablevision Inc.

▲ **SAVANNAH**—Jones Communications

SCHLEY COUNTY (portions)—See AMERICUS, GA

SCREVEN—See JESUP, GA

SCREVEN COUNTY (portions)—See SYLVANIA, GA

▲ **SEMINOLE COUNTY**—Galaxy Cablevision

SEMINOLE COUNTY (portions)—See DONALSONVILLE, GA

SEMINOLE COUNTY (portions)—See also IRON CITY, GA

SENOIA—See GRANTVILLE, GA

SEVILLE—See PITTS, GA

SHARPSBURG—See NEWNAN, GA

SHELLMAN—See CUTHBERT, GA

SHELLMAN BLUFF—See EULONIA, GA

▲ **SKIDAWAY ISLAND**—US Cable Coastal Properties

SKY VALLEY—See CLAYTON, GA

▲ **SMITHVILLE**—Blackstone Cable

▲ **SMYRNA**—Smyrna Cable TV

SNELLVILLE—See ATLANTA, GA

SOCIAL CIRCLE—See WALTON COUNTY, GA

▲ **SOPERTON**—Comcast Cablevision of the South

▲ **SOUTHBRIDGE**—Savannah Quarters Cable TV

SPALDING COUNTY—See GRIFFIN, GA

SPARKS—See NASHVILLE, GA

▲ **SPARTA**—Rigel Communications Inc.

SPRING CREEK—See ATLANTA, GA

SPRING PLACE—See CHATSWORTH, GA

SPRINGFIELD—See GUYTON, GA

SPRINGFIELD—See also SAVANNAH, GA

▲ **ST. MARYS**—US Cable Coastal Properties

▲ **STAPLETON**—Rigel Communications Ltd.

STATENVILLE—See LAKE PARK, GA

▲ **STATESBORO**—Northland Cable TV

▲ **STATHAM**—Benchmark Communications

STEPHENS COUNTY—See TOCCOA, GA

STEPHENS COUNTY (southern portion)—See AVALON, GA

▲ **STILLMORE**—Rigel Communications Inc.

▲ **STOCKBRIDGE**—Charter Communications Inc.

STONE MOUNTAIN—See ATLANTA, GA

SUGAR HILL—See GWINNETT COUNTY (portions), GA

▲ **SUMMERVILLE**—Helicon Communications

SUMTER—See PLAINS, GA

SUMTER COUNTY (portions)—See AMERICUS, GA

SUMTER COUNTY (portions)—See also LESLIE, GA

SUNNY SIDE—See GRIFFIN, GA

▲ **SURRENCY**—Blackstone Cable

SUWANEE—See GWINNETT COUNTY (portions), GA

▲ **SWAINSBORO**—Northland Cable

SYCAMORE—See ASHBURN, GA

▲ **SYLVANIA**—Comcast Cablevision of the South

▲ **SYLVESTER**—TCI of Georgia Inc.

TALBOTTON—See LA GRANGE, GA

TALBOTTON—See also MANCHESTER, GA

▲ **TALLAPOOSA**—Comcast Cablevision of Northwest Georgia

TALMO—See JACKSON COUNTY, GA

TATTNALL COUNTY (portions)—See COLLINS, GA

TAYLORSVILLE—See CARTERSVILLE, GA

TELFAIR COUNTY (portions)—See MCRAE, GA

TEMPLE—See VILLA RICA, GA

TENNILLE—See SANDERSVILLE, GA

TERRELL COUNTY (portions)—See DAWSON, GA

THOMAS COUNTY—See THOMASVILLE, GA

▲ **THOMASTON**—Charter Communications

▲ **THOMASVILLE**—TCI Cablevision of Georgia Inc.

THOMSON—See AUGUSTA, GA

THUNDERBOLT—See SAVANNAH, GA

TIFT COUNTY—See ENIGMA, GA

▲ **TIFTON**—TCI of Georgia Inc.

TIGER—See CLAYTON, GA

▲ **TIGNALL**—Premiere Cable

▲ **TOCCOA**—Northland Cable TV

TOCCOA FALLS—See TOCCOA, GA

TOOMBS COUNTY—See VIDALIA, GA

TOOMBS COUNTY (portions)—See UVALDA, GA

▲ **TOOMSBORO**—Rigel Communications Inc.

TOWNS COUNTY—See HIAWASSEE, GA

▲ **TOWNSEND (unincorporated areas)**—Worth Cable

TOWNSEND—See also EULONIA, GA

▲ **TRENTON**—Helicon Cable Communications

TRION—See SUMMERVILLE, GA

TROUP COUNTY—See LA GRANGE, GA

TROUP COUNTY—See also PINE MOUNTAIN, GA

TROUP COUNTY—See also WEST POINT, GA

TUNNEL HILL—See DALTON, GA

TURIN—See NEWNAN, GA

TURNER COUNTY (portions)—See ASHBURN, GA

TWIGGS COUNTY (eastern portion)—See DANVILLE, GA

TWIGGS COUNTY (northern portion)—See DRY BRANCH, GA

TWIGGS COUNTY (portions)—See JEFFERSONVILLE, GA

▲ **TWIN CITY**—Comcast Cablevision of the South

TY TY—See TIFTON, GA

▲ **TYBEE ISLAND**—US Cable Coastal Properties

TYRONE—See ATLANTA, GA

U.S. MARINE LOGISTICS BASE (Government Reserve)—See ALBANY, GA

▲ **UNADILLA**—Communicomm

UNION CITY—See FAIRBURN, GA

UNION COUNTY—See BLAIRSVILLE, GA

UNION POINT—See EATONTON, GA

UPSON COUNTY (northeastern portion)—See ROBERTA, GA

UPSON COUNTY (unincorporated areas)—See THOMASTON, GA

▲ **UVALDA**—Rigel Communications Inc.

▲ **VALDOSTA**—Falcon Cable TV

▲ **VALDOSTA**—TCI Cablevision of Georgia Inc.

VANCEVILLE—See ENIGMA, GA

VARNELL—See DALTON, GA

VERNONBURG—See SAVANNAH, GA

▲ **VIDALIA**—Northland Cable

VIENNA—See CORDELE, GA

▲ **VILLA RICA**—Enstar Income/Growth Program Six-B

VININGS—See ATLANTA, GA

WADLEY—See LOUISVILLE, GA

WALKER—See LA FAYETTE, GA

WALKER COUNTY (portions)—See ROSSVILLE, GA

WALNUT GROVE—See WALTON COUNTY, GA

WALTHOURVILLE—See HINESVILLE, GA

▲ **WALTON COUNTY**—Comcast Cablevision of the South

WARE COUNTY (eastern portion)—See WAYCROSS, GA

WARM SPRINGS—See MANCHESTER, GA

WARNER ROBINS—See MACON, GA

WARREN COUNTY (portions)—See WARRENTON, GA

▲ **WARRENTON**—Comcast Cablevision of the South

▲ **WARWICK**—Galaxy Cablevision

▲ **WASHINGTON**—Comcast Cablevision of the South

WASHINGTON COUNTY (portions)—See SANDERSVILLE, GA

▲ **WATKINSVILLE**—InterMedia

WATKINSVILLE—See also BISHOP, GA

▲ **WAVERLY HALL**—Charter Communications Inc.

▲ **WAYCROSS**—Waycross Cable Co. Inc.

WAYNE COUNTY (unincorporated areas)—See JESUP, GA

▲ **WAYNESBORO**—Comcast Cablevision of the South

▲ **WAYNESVILLE**—Jones Communications

WEST GEORGIA COLLEGE—See CARROLLTON, GA

▲ **WEST POINT**—Charter Communications Inc.

WHEELER COUNTY (portions)—See MOUNT VERNON, GA

▲ **WHIGHAM**—Lexander Cablevision Inc.

WHITE—See CARTERSVILLE, GA

WHITE COUNTY (portions)—See HELEN, GA

WHITEMARSH ISLAND—See SAVANNAH, GA

▲ **WHITESBURG**—Comcast Communications of the South

WHITFIELD COUNTY—See DALTON, GA

WILCOX COUNTY (northern portion)—See PINEVIEW, GA

WILKES COUNTY (portions)—See WASHINGTON, GA

WILKINSON COUNTY—See GORDON, GA

HAWAII

IDAHO

▲ **MONTPELIER**—Blackstone Cable LLC

MORELAND—See BLACKFOOT, ID

▲ **MOSCOW**—Century Communications Corp.

▲ **MOUNTAIN HOME**—Century Communications

MOUNTAIN HOME AFB—See MOUNTAIN HOME, ID

▲ **MULLAN**—Mullan TV Co.

NAMPA—See CALDWELL, ID

▲ **NEW MEADOWS**—Falcon Video Communications

NEW PLYMOUTH—See PAYETTE, ID

NEZ PERCE COUNTY (portions)—See LEWISTON, ID

NEZPERCE—See OROFINO, ID

NOTUS—See PAYETTE, ID

▲ **OAKLEY**—MediaOne

OLDTOWN—See NEWPORT, WA

OLDTOWN—See also PRIEST RIVER, ID

ONAWAY—See MOSCOW, ID

▲ **OROFINO**—USA Media

▲ **OSBURN**—USA Media

PAGE—See OSBURN, ID

▲ **PARIS**—Blackstone Cable LLC

PARMA—See PAYETTE, ID

PAUL—See BURLEY, ID

▲ **PAYETTE**—Chambers Cable of Payette Inc.

PECK—See OROFINO, ID

PIERCE—See OROFINO, ID

PINEHURST—See OSBURN, ID

PLUMMER—See WORLEY, ID

▲ **POCATELLO**—AT&T Cable Services

POLLOCK—See RIGGINS, ID

PONDERAY—See SANDPOINT, ID

POST FALLS—See COEUR D'ALENE, ID

POTLATCH—See MOSCOW, ID

▲ **PRESTON**—AT&T Cable Services

▲ **PRICHARD**—Telesystems Inc.

▲ **PRIEST RIVER**—Northland Cable TV

PRIEST RIVER—See also NEWPORT, WA

PURPLE SAGE—See PAYETTE, ID

RATHDRUM—See COEUR D'ALENE, ID

REXBURG—See IDAHO FALLS, ID

▲ **RICHFIELD**—Millennium Digital Media

RIGBY—See IDAHO FALLS, ID

▲ **RIGGINS**—USA Media

RIRIE—See IDAHO FALLS, ID

RIVERSIDE—See BLACKFOOT, ID

ROSS RANCH—See CATALDO, ID

RUPERT—See BURLEY, ID

SAGLE—See SANDPOINT, ID

▲ **SALMON**—Upper Valley Telecable Co. Inc.

▲ **SANDPOINT**—Northland Cable TV

SANDPOINT (unincorporated areas)—See SANDPOINT, ID

SHELLEY—See IDAHO FALLS, ID

▲ **SHOSHONE**—Millennium Digital Media

SILVERTON—See OSBURN, ID

SMELTERVILLE—See OSBURN, ID

▲ **SODA SPRINGS**—Blackstone Cable LLC

▲ **SPIRIT LAKE**—USA Media

▲ **ST. ANTHONY**—Upper Valley Telecable Co. Inc.

ST. CHARLES—See FISH HAVEN, ID

▲ **ST. MARIES**—USA Media

STAR—See PAYETTE, ID

SUGAR CITY—See IDAHO FALLS, ID

SUN VALLEY—See KETCHUM, ID

TETON—See ST. ANTHONY, ID

▲ **TROY**—Troy Television Co. Inc.

TWIN FALLS—See FILER, ID

TWIN FALLS COUNTY (portions)—See FILER, ID

▲ **TWIN LAKES**—Century Communications

▲ **TWIN LAKES**—USA Media

UCON—See IDAHO FALLS, ID

▲ **VICTOR**—Blackstone Cable LLC

WALLACE—See OSBURN, ID

WARDNER—See OSBURN, ID

WEIPPE—See OROFINO, ID

▲ **WEISER**—Falcon Telecable

WENDELL—See FILER, ID

WILDER—See PAYETTE, ID

WINCHESTER—See OROFINO, ID

WOODLAND PARK—See OSBURN, ID

▲ **WORLEY**—Northwest Cable LP

ILLINOIS

▲ **ABINGDON**—Triax Cablevision

▲ **ADAIR (unincorporated areas)**—New Path Communications LC

ADAMS COUNTY—See QUINCY, IL

▲ **ADDIEVILLE**—Westcom

ADDISON—See GLENDALE HEIGHTS, IL (TCI)

ADDISON—See also WEST CHICAGO, IL

ALBANY—See CLINTON, IA

ALBERS—See SCOTT AFB, IL

▲ **ALBION**—Falcon/Capital Cable Partners

ALEDO—See COAL VALLEY, IL

▲ **ALEXANDER COUNTY**—Galaxy Cablevision

▲ **ALEXIS**—Triax Cablevision

ALGONQUIN—See CARPENTERSVILLE, IL

▲ **ALHAMBRA**—Charter Communications Inc.

▲ **ALLENDALE**—Galaxy Cablevision

ALMA—See KINMUNDY, IL

ALORTON—See EAST ST. LOUIS, IL

▲ **ALPHA**—Diverse Communications Inc.

▲ **ALSEY TWP.**—Westcom LC

ALSIP—See OAK LAWN, IL

▲ **ALTAMONT**—Warner Cable

ALTO PASS—See COBDEN, IL

▲ **ALTON**—TCI of Illinois Inc.

▲ **ALTONA**—Triax Cablevision

ALVIN—See CISSNA PARK (village), IL

AMBOY—See OREGON, IL

ANDALUSIA—See COAL VALLEY, IL

ANDALUSIA TWP.—See COAL VALLEY, IL

▲ **ANDOVER**—Triax Cablevision

▲ **ANNA**—Falcon Cable TV

ANNAWAN—See MINERAL, IL

ANTIOCH—See WAUKEGAN, IL

▲ **APOLLO ACRES**—Triax Cablevision

APPLE RIVER—See WARREN, IL

ARCOLA—See TUSCOLA, IL

▲ **ARENZVILLE**—Triax Cablevision

▲ **ARGENTA**—Cablevision Communications

▲ **ARLINGTON HEIGHTS**—Americast

▲ **ARLINGTON HEIGHTS**—Telenois Inc.

▲ **ARMINGTON (village)**—Heartland Cable Inc.

AROMA PARK—See KANKAKEE, IL

AROMA TWP.—See KANKAKEE, IL

▲ **ARROWSMITH (village)**—Galaxy Cablevision

ARTHUR—See TUSCOLA, IL

ASHKUM—See KANKAKEE, IL

ASHLAND—See VIRGINIA, IL

ASHLEY—See WOODLAWN, IL

ASHMORE—See CHARLESTON, IL

ASHTON—See OREGON, IL

ASSUMPTION—See MOWEAQUA, IL

▲ **ASTORIA**—Triax Cablevision

▲ **ATHENS**—Greene County Partners Inc.

ATKINSON—See MINERAL, IL

▲ **ATLANTA**—Triax Cablevision

ATWOOD—See TUSCOLA, IL

AUBURN—See GIRARD, IL

▲ **AUGUSTA**—Cablevision Communications

▲ **AURORA**—TCI

▲ **AVA**—Galaxy Cablevision

AVISTON—See SCOTT AFB, IL

▲ **AVON**—Triax Cablevision

CARTHAGE—See also KEOKUK, IA

CARY—See CARPENTERSVILLE, IL

▲ **CASEY**—TCI Cable

CASEYVILLE—See MARYVILLE, IL

CASEYVILLE TWP.—See BELLEVILLE, IL

CATLIN—See WESTVILLE, IL

CEDAR LAKE TRAILER PARK—See CARBONDALE, IL

▲ **CEDAR POINT**—McNabb Cablevision

CEDARVILLE—See FREEPORT, IL

CENTRAL CITY—See CENTRALIA, IL

▲ **CENTRALIA**—Cablevision of Illinois

CENTREVILLE—See EAST ST. LOUIS, IL

CENTREVILLE TWP.—See BELLEVILLE, IL

▲ **CERRO GORDO**—Illinet Communications

CHADWICK—See MOUNT CARROLL, IL

CHAMPAIGN—See URBANA, IL

CHAMPAIGN COUNTY—See HOMER, IL

CHAMPAIGN COUNTY—See also MAHOMET, IL

CHAMPAIGN COUNTY—See also URBANA, IL

CHANDLERVILLE—See VIRGINIA, IL

CHANNAHON—See MINOOKA, IL

▲ **CHAPIN**—Triax Cablevision

▲ **CHARLESTON**—TCI of Illinois Inc.

▲ **CHATHAM**—Cass Cable TV Inc.

▲ **CHATSWORTH**—Triax Cablevision

CHEBANSE—See KANKAKEE, IL

▲ **CHEMUNG**—Mid American Cable Systems

CHENOA—See FAIRBURY, IL

CHERRY—See LADD, IL

CHERRY VALLEY—See ROCKFORD, IL

▲ **CHESTER**—Cablevision Communications

▲ **CHESTERFIELD (village)**—Westcom

▲ **CHESTNUT**—Galaxy Cablevision

▲ **CHICAGO (area 1)**—AT & T Cable Services

▲ **CHICAGO (areas 2 & 3)**—Prime Cable of Chicago

▲ **CHICAGO (area 4)**—Chicago Cable TV

▲ **CHICAGO (area 5)**—Chicago Cable TV

▲ **CHICAGO HEIGHTS**—TCI Great Lakes

CHICAGO RIDGE—See OAK LAWN, IL

▲ **CHILLICOTHE**—Triax Cablevision

CHRISMAN—See RIDGE FARM, IL

CHRISTIAN COUNTY (portions)—See PANA, IL

CHRISTIAN COUNTY (portions)—See also TAYLORVILLE, IL

CHRISTOPHER—See BENTON, IL

CICERO—See ELMHURST, IL

▲ **CISCO (village)**—New Path Communications LC

▲ **CISNE**—Falcon Cable

▲ **CISSNA PARK (village)**—Galaxy Cablevision

▲ **CLAREMONT**—Galaxy Cablevision

CLARENDON HILLS—See ELMHURST, IL

CLARK COUNTY—See MARTINSVILLE, IL

CLAY CITY—See LOUISVILLE, IL

CLAY COUNTY (portions)—See FLORA, IL

CLAYTON—See CAMP POINT, IL

CLEAR LAKE (village)—See RIVER OAKS (village), IL

CLEAR LAKE TWP.—See RIVER OAKS (village), IL

CLEVELAND—See COAL VALLEY, IL

CLIFTON—See KANKAKEE, IL

▲ **CLINTON**—Triax Telecommunications

Clinton County—See BREESE, IL

CLINTON COUNTY—See also CENTRALIA, IL

CLINTON COUNTY—See also SCOTT AFB, IL

COAL CITY—See WILMINGTON, IL

▲ **COAL VALLEY**—TCI of Illinois Inc.

COALTON—See NOKOMIS, IL

COATSBURG—See GOLDEN, IL

▲ **COBDEN**—Mediacom

COELLO/NORTH CITY—See BENTON, IL

▲ **COFFEEN**—Triax Cablevision

COLCHESTER—See MACOMB, IL

COLES COUNTY—See MATTOON, IL

▲ **COLFAX**—Triax Cablevision

COLLINSVILLE—See MARYVILLE, IL

COLOMA TWP.—See STERLING, IL

COLONA—See COAL VALLEY, IL

COLP (village)—See HERRIN, IL

COLUMBIA—See WATERLOO, IL

▲ **COMPTON**—Compton Cable TV Co.

▲ **CONGERVILLE**—Tel-Star Cablevision Inc.

COOK COUNTY—See OAK LAWN, IL

COOK COUNTY—See also SCHAUMBURG, IL (Telenois Inc.)

COOK COUNTY (northern portion)—See MORTON GROVE, IL

COOK COUNTY (unincorporated areas)—See DOLTON, IL

COOK COUNTY (unincorporated areas)—See also ELMHURST, IL

COOK COUNTY (unincorporated areas)—See also HIGHLAND PARK, IL

COOK COUNTY (unincorporated areas)—See also ORLAND PARK, IL

COOK COUNTY (unincorporated areas)—See also ROLLING MEADOWS, IL

COOK COUNTY (unincorporated areas)—See also ROMEOVILLE, IL

COOK COUNTY (unincorporated areas)—See also MERRILLVILLE, IN

CORDOVA—See RAPIDS CITY, IL

▲ **CORNELL**—Triax Cablevision

▲ **CORTLAND (village)**—Mid American Cable Systems

COTTAGE HILLS—See ALTON, IL

▲ **COULTERVILLE**—Mediacom

COUNTRY CLUB HILLS—See ELMHURST, IL

COUNTRYSIDE—See ELMHURST, IL

COUNTRYSIDE—See also WESTERN SPRINGS, IL

COUNTRYSIDE ESTATES—See MILLINGTON, IL

▲ **COWDEN**—Galaxy Cablevision

CRAINVILLE—See HERRIN, IL

CRAWFORD COUNTY—See ROBINSON, IL

▲ **CREAL SPRINGS**—Galaxy Cablevision

CRESCENT CITY—See WATSEKA, IL (Triax Cablevision)

CREST HILL—See ROMEOVILLE, IL

CRESTON—See DE KALB, IL

CRESTWOOD—See PALOS HILLS, IL

CRETE—See MATTESON, IL

CREVE COEUR—See PEORIA, IL

▲ **CROSSVILLE**—Capital Cable Partners

CRYSTAL LAKE—See CARPENTERSVILLE, IL

CUBA—See LEWISTOWN, IL

▲ **CULLOM**—Triax Cablevision

CURRAN—See SANGAMON COUNTY, IL

CURRAN TWP.—See SPRINGFIELD, IL

▲ **CUSTER PARK**—TCI of Illinois Inc.

CUTLER—See AVA, IL

▲ **CYPRESS (village)**—Westcom

▲ **DAHLGREN**—Galaxy Cablevision

DAKOTA—See DURAND, IL

▲ **DALLAS CITY**—Triax Cablevision

DALTON CITY—See BETHANY, IL

DALZELL—See LADD, IL

DAMIANSVILLE—See SCOTT AFB, IL

DANFORTH—See ONARGA, IL

▲ **DANVERS**—Triax Cablevision

▲ **DANVILLE**—TCI Cable

DANVILLE (portions)—See WESTVILLE, IL

DARIEN—See ELMHURST, IL

DAVIS—See DURAND, IL

DAWSON—See BUFFALO, IL

DAYTON TWP.—See OTTAWA, IL

▲ **DE KALB**—TCI Cable

DE LAND—See WELDON, IL

DE SOTO—See CARBONDALE, IL

DE WITT COUNTY (portions)—See WARRENSBURG, IL

▲ **DECATUR**—TCI Cablevision of Decatur

DECATUR—See also ARGENTA, IL

▲ **DEER CREEK**—Triax Cablevision

DEER PARK—See LAKE ZURICH, IL

DEERFIELD—See HIGHLAND PARK, IL

▲ **DELAVAN**—Triax Cablevision

DEPUE—See LADD, IL

* **DES PLAINES**—Americast

DES PLAINES—See also MORTON GROVE, IL

DES PLAINES—See also MOUNT PROSPECT, IL

DIAMOND—See WILMINGTON, IL

▲ **DIETERICH**—DMS Cable.

DIVERNON—See CHATHAM, IL

▲ **DIX**—Riley Cable TV

DIXMOOR—See ELMHURST, IL

▲ **DIXON**—TCI of Illinois Inc.

▲ **DOLTON**—MediaOne

▲ **DONGOLA**—Galaxy Cablevision

DONNELLSON—See PANAMA, IL

▲ **DONOVAN TWP.**—New Path Communications LC

DOUGLAS COUNTY—See NEWMAN, IL

DOUGLAS COUNTY (unincorporated areas)—See TUSCOLA, IL

DOWELL—See ZEIGLER, IL

DOWNERS GROVE—See ELMHURST, IL

▲ **DOWNS**—Triax Cablevision

DU PAGE COUNTY—See LISLE, IL

DU PAGE COUNTY—See also NAPERVILLE, IL (TCI)

DU PAGE COUNTY—See also VILLA PARK, IL

DU PAGE COUNTY (portions)—See GLENDALE HEIGHTS, IL (TCI)

DU PAGE COUNTY (unincorporated areas)—See ELMHURST, IL

DU PAGE COUNTY (unincorporated areas)—See also WEST CHICAGO, IL

▲ **DU QUOIN**—SBC Cable Co. of Du Quoin

▲ **DUBOIS (village)**—Westcom

▲ **DUNLAP**—Triax Cablevision

DUPO—See MARYVILLE, IL

▲ **DURAND**—Triax Cablevision

▲ **DWIGHT**—Triax Cablevision

EAGLE TWP.—See STREATOR, IL

EARLVILLE—See LELAND, IL

EAST ALTON—See ALTON, IL

EAST BROOKLYN (village)—See SOUTH WILMINGTON (village), IL

EAST CAPE GIRARDEAU—See ALEXANDER COUNTY, IL

▲ **EAST CARONDELET (town)**—Westcom

▲ **EAST DUBUQUE**—TCI of Illinois Inc.

EAST DUNDEE—See CARPENTERSVILLE, IL

EAST GALESBURG—See GALESBURG, IL

EAST HAZEL CREST—See ELMHURST, IL

EAST MOLINE—See MOLINE, IL

EAST MOLINE—See also RAPIDS CITY, IL

EAST PEORIA—See PEORIA, IL

▲ **EAST ST. LOUIS**—TCI of Illinois Inc.

▲ **EASTON**—Cass Cable TV Inc.

ECHO LAKE—See LAKE ZURICH, IL

▲ **EDGEWOOD**—Galaxy Cablevision

EDINBURG—See KINCAID, IL

▲ **EDWARDS**—Tel-Star Cablevision Inc.

EDWARDSVILLE—See MARYVILLE, IL

▲ **EFFINGHAM**—United Cable Television of Southern Illinois Inc.

EFFINGHAM (portions)—See EFFINGHAM COUNTY, IL

▲ **EFFINGHAM COUNTY**—Falcon/Capital Cable Partners LP

EFFINGHAM COUNTY (unincorporated areas)—See EFFINGHAM, IL

EFFINGHAM WATER AUTHORITY—See EFFINGHAM, IL

EILEEN—See WILMINGTON, IL

EL PASO—See ROANOKE, IL

ELBURN—See SUGAR GROVE, IL

ELDORADO—See HARRISBURG, IL

▲ **ELDRED**—Westcom

▲ **ELGIN**—Americast

▲ **ELGIN**—TCI

▲ **ELIZABETH**—Triax Cablevision

ELIZABETHTOWN—See ROSICLARE, IL

ELK GROVE (village)—See ROLLING MEADOWS, IL

▲ **ELKHART TWP.**—Triax Cablevision

ELKVILLE—See ZEIGLER, IL

ELLIOTT—See SIBLEY (village), IL

▲ **ELLIS GROVE**—Westcom

ELLSWORTH—See SIBLEY (village), IL

▲ **ELMHURST**—MediaOne

▲ **ELMWOOD**—Triax Cablevision

ELMWOOD PARK—See ELMHURST, IL

EMDEN—See DELAVAN, IL

ENERGY—See HERRIN, IL

▲ **ENFIELD**—Capital Cable Partners

EQUALITY—See SHAWNEETOWN, IL

ERIE—See CLINTON, IA

ESSEX (village)—See SOUTH WILMINGTON (village), IL

EUREKA—See ROANOKE, IL

EVANSTON—See ELMHURST, IL

▲ **EVANSVILLE**—Cablevision Communications

EVERGREEN PARK—See OAK LAWN, IL

EWING—See BENTON, IL

▲ **FAIRBURY**—Triax Telecommunications

▲ **FAIRFIELD**—Falcon Cable

FAIRMONT CITY—See WASHINGTON PARK, IL

FAIRMOUNT—See DANVILLE, IL

▲ **FAIRVIEW**—Triax Cablevision

FAIRVIEW HEIGHTS—See BELLEVILLE, IL

FAR HILLS—See ROANOKE, IL

FARINA—See LOUISVILLE, IL

▲ **FARMER CITY**—Triax Telecommunications

▲ **FARMERSVILLE**—Falcon Cable

▲ **FARMINGTON**—Triax Cablevision

▲ **FAYETTEVILLE**—Westcom

FIATT—See WEE-MA-TUK HILLS, IL

▲ **FIELDON**—Westcom

▲ **FILLMORE**—Westcom

▲ **FINDLAY**—Cablevision Communications

FISHER—See MAHOMET, IL

FITHIAN—See DANVILLE, IL

▲ **FLANAGAN**—Heartland Cable Inc.

▲ **FLAT ROCK**—Galaxy Cablevision

▲ **FLORA**—Falcon Cable

FLOSSMOOR—See MATTESON, IL

FORD HEIGHTS—See MERRILLVILLE, IN

FOREST CITY—See MANITO, IL

FOREST HOMES—See ALTON, IL

FOREST PARK—See ELMHURST, IL

FOREST VIEW—See ELMHURST, IL

FORREST—See CHATSWORTH, IL

FORRESTON—See OREGON, IL

FORSYTH—See DECATUR, IL

FORT SHERIDAN—See HIGHLAND PARK, IL

FOUR LAKES—See LISLE, IL

FOWLER—See GOLDEN, IL

FOX CREEK—See EDWARDS, IL

FOX LAKE—See WAUKEGAN, IL

FOX RIVER GROVE—See CARPENTERSVILLE, IL

FOX RIVER VALLEY GARDENS—See McHENRY, IL

FRANKFORT—See ROMEOVILLE, IL

FRANKLIN—See WAVERLY, IL

FRANKLIN COUNTY—See HERRIN, IL

FRANKLIN COUNTY—See also ZEIGLER, IL

FRANKLIN GROVE—See OREGON, IL

FRANKLIN PARK—See ELMHURST, IL

FREEBURG—See SCOTT AFB, IL

▲ **FREEMAN SPUR**—Galaxy Cablevision

▲ **FREEPORT**—MediaOne

FULTON—See CLINTON, IA

FULTON COUNTY—See LEWISTOWN, IL

FYRE LAKE—See VIOLA, IL

▲ **GALATIA**—Galaxy Cablevision

▲ **GALENA**—Rapid Cable

▲ **GALENA**—TCI of Illinois Inc.

▲ **GALESBURG**—Northwest Illinois TV Cable Co.

▲ **GALVA**—Triax Cablevision

GANEER TWP.—See KANKAKEE, IL

▲ **GARDEN PRAIRIE**—Mid American Cable Systems

▲ **GARDNER**—Gardner Cable TV Co.

GARDNER—See also SANGAMON COUNTY, IL

GARDNER TWP.—See SPRINGFIELD, IL

GARRETT—See TUSCOLA, IL

▲ **GAYS (village)**—New Path Communications LC

GEFF—See FAIRFIELD, IL

▲ **GEM SUBURBAN MOBILE HOME PARK**—Gem Court Cable

▲ **GENESEO**—Tri-Com Cable

GENEVA—See WEST CHICAGO, IL

▲ **GENOA**—Charter Communications Inc.

GEORGETOWN—See WESTVILLE, IL

▲ **GERMAN VALLEY**—Dowden Cable

GERMANTOWN—See BREESE, IL

GERMANTOWN HILLS—See ROANOKE, IL

▲ **GIBSON CITY**—Triax Telecommunications

GIFFORD (village)—See RANTOUL, IL

▲ **GILBERTS**—Triax Cablevision

▲ **GILLESPIE**—Falcon Cable

GILMAN—See ONARGA, IL

▲ **GINGER RIDGE**—Universal Cable Inc.

▲ **GIRARD**—Falcon Cable

▲ **GLADSTONE**—Nova Cablevision Inc.

▲ **GLASFORD**—Triax Cablevision

GLEN CARBON—See MARYVILLE, IL

▲ **GLEN ELLYN**—Americast

GLEN ELLYN—See also GLENDALE HEIGHTS, IL (TCI)

GLEN ELLYN—See also WEST CHICAGO, IL

GLENARM—See CHATHAM, IL

GLENCOE—See HIGHLAND PARK, IL

▲ **GLENDALE HEIGHTS**—Americast

▲ **GLENDALE HEIGHTS**—TCI

▲ **GLENVIEW**—TCI of Illinois

GLENVIEW—See also MORTON GROVE, IL

GLENVIEW NAVAL AIR STATION—See GLENVIEW, IL

GLENWOOD—See MERRILLVILLE, IN

GODFREY TWP.—See ALTON, IL

GODLEY (village)—See SOUTH WILMINGTON (village), IL

▲ **GOLCONDA**—Galaxy Cablevision

▲ **GOLDEN**—Adams Telcom Inc.

GOLDEN—See also CAMP POINT, IL

GOLF—See MOUNT PROSPECT, IL

▲ **GOOD HOPE**—Triax Cablevision

GOODFIELD—See DEER CREEK, IL

GOOFY RIDGE—See HAVANA, IL

GOOSE LAKE TWP.—See CUSTER PARK, IL

▲ **GOREVILLE**—Galaxy Cablevision

▲ **GORHAM TWP.**—Westcom

▲ **GRAFTON**—Cablevision Communications

▲ **GRAND CHAIN (town)**—Westcom

▲ **GRAND DETOUR**—Mid American Cable Systems

▲ **GRAND RIDGE**—Grand Ridge Cable Co. Inc.

▲ **GRAND TOWER (village)**—Westcom

GRANDVIEW—See SPRINGFIELD, IL

GRANITE CITY—See MARYVILLE, IL

GRANITE CITY DEPOT—See MARYVILLE, IL

▲ **GRANT PARK (village)**—Mid American Cable Systems

▲ **GRANTFORK (village)**—A-G Cable TV

GRANVILLE—See STANDARD, IL

GRAYSLAKE—See LIBERTYVILLE, IL

▲ **GRAYVILLE**—Cablevision Communications

▲ **GREAT LAKES NAVAL TRAINING CENTER**—TCI of Illinois Inc.

GREEN OAKS—See WAUKEGAN, IL

GREEN ROCK—See COAL VALLEY, IL

GREEN VALLEY—See DELAVAN, IL

GREEN VALLEY—See also ELMHURST, IL

▲ **GREENFIELD**—Cablevision Communications

▲ **GREENUP**—TCI Cable

▲ **GREENVIEW**—Triax Cablevision

▲ **GREENVILLE**—Greene County Cable TV

▲ **GRIDLEY**—Gridley Cable Inc.

▲ **GRIGGSVILLE**—Cablevision Communications

GROVELAND—See PEKIN, IL

GRUNDY COUNTY—See MORRIS, IL

GRUNDY COUNTY (unincorporated areas)—See CUSTER PARK, IL

GURNEE TWP.—See WAUKEGAN, IL

HAINESVILLE—See McHENRY, IL

▲ **HAMEL**—Charter Communications Inc.

HAMILTON—See KEOKUK, IA

HAMMOND—See TUSCOLA, IL

▲ **HAMPSHIRE**—Triax Cablevision

HAMPTON—See MOLINE, IL

HANNA CITY—See GLASFORD, IL

▲ **HANOVER**—TCI of Illinois Inc.

HANOVER PARK—See MOUNT PROSPECT, IL

▲ **HARDIN**—Cablevision Communications

HARDIN COUNTY—See ROSICLARE, IL

HARLEM TWP.—See ROSCOE, IL

▲ **HARRISBURG**—TCI of Illinois Inc.

HARRISTOWN—See NIANTIC, IL

HARTFORD—See ALTON, IL

▲ **HARTSBURG**—Triax Cablevision

▲ **HARVARD**—TCI Cablevision of Illinois Inc.

▲ **HARVEL**—Triax Cablevision

▲ **HARVEY**—TCI of Illinois

HARWOOD HEIGHTS—See PALOS HILLS, IL

▲ **HAVANA**—Cass Cable TV Inc.

HAWTHORNE WOODS—See LAKE ZURICH, IL

HAZEL CREST—See MATTESON, IL

HEARTVILLE—See EFFINGHAM COUNTY, IL

HEARTVILLE—See also WATSON, IL

▲ **HEBRON (village)**—Mid American Cable Systems

HECKER—See RED BUD, IL

HEGELER—See WESTVILLE, IL

HENDERSON—See WATAGA, IL

HENNEPIN—See STANDARD, IL

▲ **HENNING (village)**—New Path Communications LC

HENRY—See CHILLICOTHE, IL

HENRY COUNTY—See KEWANEE, IL

HENRY COUNTY (portions)—See GENESEO, IL

HENRY COUNTY (unincorporated areas)—See COAL VALLEY, IL

▲ **HERITAGE LAKE**—Tel-Star Cablevision Inc.

▲ **HERRICK**—Triax Cablevision

▲ **HERRIN**—TCI of Illinois Inc.

▲ **HERSCHER**—Illinois Communications Cablevision Inc.

HERSMAN—See MOUNT STERLING, IL

▲ **HETTICK (village)**—Westcom

HEWITTVILLE—See TAYLORVILLE, IL

▲ **HEYWORTH**—Triax Cablevision

HICKORY HILLS—See PALOS HILLS, IL

HIGHLAND—See MARYVILLE, IL

▲ **HIGHLAND PARK**—Tele-Communications Inc.

HIGHWOOD—See HIGHLAND PARK, IL

HILLCREST—See DE KALB, IL

▲ **HILLSBORO**—Falcon Cable

HILLSDALE—See RAPIDS CITY, IL

HILLSIDE—See ELMHURST, IL

HINCKLEY—See WATERMAN, IL

HINDSBORO—See TUSCOLA, IL

HINES V.A. HOSPITAL—See ELMHURST, IL

HINSDALE—See ELMHURST, IL

HODGKINS—See ELMHURST, IL

▲ **HOFFMAN**—Westcom

HOFFMAN ESTATES—See ROLLING MEADOWS, IL

HOLIDAY ESTATES—See MILLINGTON, IL

HOLIDAY HILLS—See McHENRY, IL

HOLLIS TWP.—See PEORIA, IL

HOLLYWOOD HEIGHTS—See MARYVILLE, IL

HOME GARDENS—See WESTVILLE, IL

▲ **HOMER**—TCI Cable

HOMER—See also ROMEOVILLE, IL

HOMETOWN—See OAK LAWN, IL

HOMEWOOD—See ELMHURST, IL

HONEY SCHOOL LOOKOUT—See ALEXANDER COUNTY, IL

▲ **HOOPESTON**—Hoopeston Cable TV Co.

▲ **HOOPPOLE**—Mid American Cable Systems

HOPEDALE—See MINIER, IL

HOPKINS TWP.—See STERLING, IL

▲ **HOYLETON**—Westcom

▲ **HUDSON**—Triax Cablevision

HULL—See KINDERHOOK, IL

HUMBOLDT—See TUSCOLA, IL

▲ **HUME (village)**—Illinet

HUNTLEY—See CARPENTERSVILLE, IL

HURST—See ZEIGLER, IL

HUTSONVILLE—See ROBINSON, IL

ILLIOPOLIS—See NIANTIC, IL

▲ **INA**—Galaxy Cablevision

INDIAN CREEK—See LAKE ZURICH, IL

INDIAN HEAD PARK—See WESTERN SPRINGS, IL

INDIANOLA—See DANVILLE, IL

▲ **INDUSTRY**—Triax Cablevision

INVERNESS—See ROLLING MEADOWS, IL

INVERNESS (village)—See BARRINGTON HILLS, IL

▲ **IPAVA**—Triax Cablevision

▲ **IROQUOIS (village)**—New Path Communications LC

▲ **IRVING**—Triax Cablevision

▲ **IRVINGTON**—Galaxy Cablevision

ISLAND LAKE—See McHENRY, IL

ITASCA—See GLENDALE HEIGHTS, IL (TCI)

▲ **IUKA**—Advanced Technologies & Technical Resources Inc.

IVESDALE—See TUSCOLA, IL

▲ **JACKSON COUNTY**—Galaxy Cablevision

JACKSON COUNTY (portions)—See ZEIGLER, IL

▲ **JACKSONVILLE**—Triax Cablevision

JASPER COUNTY (southern portion)—See OLNEY, IL

JEFFERSON COUNTY—See MOUNT VERNON, IL

JEISYVILLE—See KINCAID, IL

JEROME—See SPRINGFIELD, IL

JERSEY COUNTY (portions)—See JERSEYVILLE, IL

▲ **JERSEYVILLE**—Falcon Cable

JO DAVIESS COUNTY—See EAST DUBUQUE, IL

JO DAVIESS COUNTY (portions)—See GALENA, IL (Rapid Cable)

JOHNSON COUNTY (northern portion)—See GOREVILLE, IL

JOHNSTON CITY—See HERRIN, IL

JOLIET—See ROMEOVILLE, IL

JONESBORO—See ANNA, IL

▲ **JOPPA**—Westcom

▲ **JOY**—New Path Communications LC

JUNCTION—See SHAWNEETOWN, IL

JUNCTION CITY—See SALEM, IL

JUSTICE—See ELMHURST, IL

▲ **KAMPSVILLE (village)**—Cass Cable TV Inc.

KANE COUNTY—See AURORA, IL

KANE COUNTY—See also BATAVIA, IL

KANE COUNTY—See also ELGIN, IL (TCI)

KANE COUNTY—See also SUGAR GROVE, IL

KANE COUNTY—See also WEST CHICAGO, IL

KANE COUNTY (unincorporated areas)—See CARPENTERSVILLE, IL

KANGLEY—See STREATOR, IL

▲ **KANKAKEE**—TCI of Illinois Inc.

KANKAKEE (portions)—See MOMENCE, IL

KANKAKEE COUNTY—See ROSELAWN, IN

KANKAKEE TWP.—See KANKAKEE, IL

KANSAS—See CHARLESTON, IL

▲ **KARNAK**—Galaxy Cablevision

KEENEYVILLE—See GLENDALE HEIGHTS, IL (TCI)

▲ **KEENSBURG**—Galaxy Cablevision

▲ **KEITHSBURG**—New Path Communications LC

KELL—See DIX, IL

KENDALL COUNTY—See AURORA, IL

KENILWORTH (village)—See HIGHLAND PARK, IL

▲ **KENNEY**—Heartland Cable Inc.

▲ **KEWANEE**—MediaOne

▲ **KEYESPORT**—Galaxy Cablevision

▲ **KICKAPOO**—McNabb Cablevision

KICKAPOO TWP.—See PEORIA, IL

KILBOURNE (village)—See OAKFORD (village), IL

KILDEER—See LAKE ZURICH, IL

▲ **KINCAID**—Triax Cablevision

▲ **KINDERHOOK**—Cablevision Communications

▲ **KINGSTON**—Kingston Cable TV Co.

KINGSTON (village)—See COMPTON, IL

▲ **KINGSTON MINES**—KMHC Inc.

▲ **KINMUNDY**—Capital Cable Partners

▲ **KIRKLAND**—Triax Cablevision

▲ **KIRKWOOD**—New Path Communications LC

KNOXVILLE—See GALESBURG, IL

LA GRANGE—See WESTERN SPRINGS, IL

LA GRANGE PARK—See WESTERN SPRINGS, IL

▲ **LA HARPE**—TCI of Illinois Inc.

▲ **LA MOILLE (village)**—Mid American Cable Systems

▲ **LA PLACE**—New Path Communications LC

▲ **LA ROSE**—Tel-Star Cablevision Inc.

LA SALLE—See PERU, IL

LA SALLE TWP.—See OTTAWA, IL

▲ **LACON**—Triax Cablevison

▲ **LADD**—TCI Cable

LAKE BARRINGTON—See LAKE ZURICH, IL

LAKE BLUFF—See WAUKEGAN, IL

▲ **LAKE BRACKEN**—Rio Cablevision

▲ **LAKE CAMELOT**—Galaxy Cablevision

LAKE COUNTY—See HIGHLAND PARK, IL

LAKE COUNTY—See also McHENRY, IL

LAKE COUNTY (portions)—See LAKE ZURICH, IL

LAKE COUNTY (portions)—See also LIBERTYVILLE, IL

LAKE COUNTY (unincorporated areas)—See WAUKEGAN, IL

LAKE FOREST—See WAUKEGAN, IL

▲ **LAKE HOLIDAY**—TCI Cable

LAKE IN THE HILLS—See CARPENTERSVILLE, IL

LAKE OF EGYPT—See GOREVILLE, IL

LAKE OF THE WOODS—See MAHOMET, IL

Lake Petersburg—See PETERSBURG, IL

LAKE SARA—See EFFINGHAM, IL

LAKE SOMMERSET—See DURAND, IL

LAKE VILLA—See WAUKEGAN, IL

LAKE VILLA TWP.—See WAUKEGAN, IL

LAKE WINDERMERE—See HERITAGE LAKE, IL

▲ **LAKE ZURICH**—TCI

LAKEMOOR (Lake County)—See CARPENTERSVILLE, IL

LAKEMOOR (McHenry County)—See McHENRY, IL

LAKEWOOD VILLAGE—See CARPENTERSVILLE, IL

LAMPLIGHTER—See TOWANDA, IL

LANARK—See MOUNT CARROLL, IL

▲ **LANSING**—TCI

LATHAM—See WARRENSBURG, IL

LAWRENCE COUNTY (portions)—See LAWRENCEVILLE, IL

▲**LAWRENCEVILLE**—Cablevision Communications

▲ **LE ROY**—Triax Telecommunications

▲ **LEAF RIVER**—Grand River Cablevision

LEBANON—See SCOTT AFB, IL

▲ **LEE (village)**—Mid American Cable Systems

LEE COUNTY—See OREGON, IL

LEE COUNTY (western portion)—See DIXON, IL

▲ **LELAND**—Triax Cablevision

LELAND GROVE—See SPRINGFIELD, IL

LEMONT—See ROMEOVILLE, IL

▲ **LENA**—Triax Cablevision

▲ **LENZBURG**—Cablevision Communications

▲ **LERNA**—New Path Communications LC

▲ **LEWISTOWN**—TCI of Illinois Inc.

▲ **LEXINGTON**—Triax Cablevision

LEYDEN TWP.—See ELMHURST, IL

▲ **LIBERTY**—Cablevision Communications

▲ **LIBERTYVILLE**—TCI

LIMA—See GOLDEN, IL

LIMESTONE TWP. (Kankakee County)—See KANKAKEE, IL

LIMESTONE TWP. (Peoria County)—See PEORIA, IL

▲ **LINCOLN**—MediaOne

LINCOLNSHIRE—See HIGHLAND PARK, IL

LINCOLNWOOD—See ELMHURST, IL

LINDENHURST—See WAUKEGAN, IL

▲ **LISLE**—TCI

▲ **LITCHFIELD**—Enstar Cable TV

▲ **LITTLE YORK**—Nova Cablevision Inc.

LIVINGSTON—See STAUNTON, IL

▲ **LOAMI**—Triax Cablevision

LOCKPORT—See ROMEOVILLE, IL

LOCKPORT TWP. (portions)—See ROMEOVILLE, IL

LODA—See PAXTON, IL

▲ **LOGAN (village)**—Westcom

LOGAN COUNTY—See LINCOLN, IL

LOMAX—See DALLAS CITY, IL

LOMBARD—See ELMHURST, IL

▲ **LONDON MILLS**—Triax Cablevision

LONG CREEK—See DECATUR, IL

LONG GROVE—See LAKE ZURICH, IL

▲ **LONG POINT (village)**—Mid American Cable Systems

▲ **LONGVIEW**—Danville Radio & TV

LORAINE—See GOLDEN, IL

▲ **LOUISVILLE**—United Cable Television of Southern Illinois

LOVES PARK—See ROCKFORD, IL

▲ **LOVINGTON**—Moultrie Telecommunications

▲ **LOWPOINT**—Tel-Star Cablevision Inc.

LUDLOW (village)—See RANTOUL, IL

LYNDON—See CLINTON, IA

LYNWOOD—See MERRILLVILLE, IN

LYONS—See ELMHURST, IL

MACHESNEY PARK—See ROCKFORD, IL

MACKINAW—See MINIER, IL

▲ **MACOMB**—TCI of Illinois Inc.

MACON—See MOWEAQUA, IL

MACON COUNTY—See DECATUR, IL

MACON COUNTY (portions)—See WARRENSBURG, IL

MACOUPIN COUNTY (portions)—See GILLESPIE, IL

MADISON—See MARYVILLE, IL

MADISON COUNTY—See ALTON, IL

MADISON COUNTY—See also MARYVILLE, IL

MADISON COUNTY—See also WASHINGTON PARK, IL

▲ **MAGNOLIA (village)**—Mid American Cable Systems

▲ **MAHOMET**—Triax Cablevision

MAKANDA—See CARBONDALE, IL

▲ **MALDEN**—McNabb Cablevision

MALIBU TRAILER PARK—See CARBONDALE, IL

▲ **MALTA**—Triax Cablevision

▲ **MANCHESTER (village)**—Westcom

▲ **MANHATTAN**—Manhattan Cable TV

▲ **MANITO**—Cass Cable TV Inc.

▲ **MANLIUS (village)**—Dowden Cable

▲ **MANSFIELD**—Triax Cablevision

MANTENO—See PEOTONE, IL

MAPLE PARK (village)—See CORTLAND (village), IL

▲ **MAPLETON**—Tel-Star Cablevision Inc.

MAPLETON—See also CHESTNUT, IL

▲ **MAQUON**—Triax Cablevision

MARCELLINE—See GOLDEN, IL

▲ **MARENGO**—Charter Communications Inc.

▲ **MARINE**—Charter Communications Inc.

▲ **MARION**—TCI of Illinois Inc.

MARION COUNTY—See CENTRALIA, IL

MARION COUNTY (portions)—See SALEM, IL

MARISSA—See LENZBURG, IL

MARK—See STANDARD, IL

MARKHAM—See OAK FOREST, IL

▲ **MAROA**—Cablevision Communications

MARQUETTE HEIGHTS—See PEKIN, IL

MARSEILLES—See OTTAWA, IL

MARSHALL—See CASEY, IL

▲ **MARTINSVILLE**—TCI Cable

▲ **MARTINTON (village)**—New Path Communicatons LC

▲ **MARYVILLE**—Charter Communications Inc.

MASCOUTAH—See SCOTT AFB, IL

▲ **MASON**—South Shore Cable TV Inc.

MASON—See also EDGEWOOD, IL

▲ **MASON CITY**—Greene County Partners Inc.

MASSAC COUNTY—See PADUCAH, KY

MATHERVILLE—See VIOLA, IL

▲ **MATTESON**—TCI

▲ **MATTOON**—TCI of Illinois Inc.

▲ **MAYWOOD**—TCI of Illinois Inc.

▲ **MAZON (village)**—Mid American Cable Systems

McCLURE—See ALEXANDER COUNTY, IL

McCONNELL—See WINSLOW, IL

McCOOK—See ELMHURST, IL

McCULLOM LAKE—See McHENRY, IL

McDONOUGH COUNTY—See MACOMB, IL

▲ **McHENRY**—TCI of Illinois Inc.

McHENRY (unincorporated areas)—See HARVARD, IL

McHENRY COUNTY—See CARPENTERSVILLE, IL

McHENRY COUNTY—See also McHENRY, IL

McHENRY SHORES—See McHENRY, IL

McLEAN—See ATLANTA, IL

McLEAN COUNTY—See BLOOMINGTON, IL

▲ **McLEANSBORO**—Cablevision Communications

▲ **McNABB**—McNabb Cablevision

MECHANICSBURG—See BUFFALO, IL

MEDINA TWP.—See PEORIA, IL

MEDINAH—See GLENDALE HEIGHTS, IL (TCI)

▲ **MEDORA**—Westcom

MELROSE PARK—See PALOS HILLS, IL

▲ **MELVIN**—Triax Cablevision

MENARD COUNTY—See PETERSBURG, IL

MENDON—See GOLDEN, IL

▲ **MENDOTA**—TCI Cable

MEREDOSIA—See BLUFFS, IL

MERRIONETTE PARK—See ELMHURST, IL

METAMORA—See ROANOKE, IL

METCALF (village)—See HUME (village), IL

METROPOLIS—See PADUCAH, KY

▲ **MIDDLETOWN**—Triax Cablevision

MIDLOTHIAN—See PALOS HILLS, IL

MILAN—See ROCK ISLAND, IL

MILFORD—See HOOPESTON, IL

▲ **MILL SHOALS**—Galaxy Cablevision

MILLEDGEVILLE—See MOUNT CARROLL, IL

▲ **MILLINGTON**—TCI Cable

MILLSTADT (portions)—See MARYVILLE, IL

▲ **MILTON**—Cass Cable TV Inc.

▲ **MINERAL**—Triax Cablevision

▲ **MINIER**—Triax Cablevision

MINONK—See ROANOKE, IL

▲ **MINOOKA**—TCI of Illinois Inc.

MOBET—See RAPIDS CITY, IL

MODESTO—See PALMYRA, IL

MOKENA—See ROMEOVILLE, IL

▲ **MOLINE**—TCI

▲ **MOMENCE**—Triax Cablevision

MONEE—See PEOTONE, IL

▲ **MONMOUTH**—Northwest Illinois TV Cable Co.

Monroe Center—See GRAND DETOUR, IL

MONTGOMERY—See AURORA, IL

MONTGOMERY COUNTY (central portion)—See CHESTERFIELD (village), IL

MONTGOMERY COUNTY (portions)—See LITCHFIELD, IL

▲ **MONTICELLO**—Illinet Communications

MONTMORENCY TWP.—See STERLING, IL

▲ **MONTROSE**—DMS Cable Systems Inc.

MORO TWP.—See ALTON, IL

▲ **MORRIS**—TCI of Illinois Inc.

MORRISON—See CLINTON, IA

▲ **MORRISONVILLE**—Triax Cablevision

▲ **MORTON**—MediaOne

▲ **MORTON GROVE**—MediaOne

MOUND CITY—See MOUNDS, IL

▲ **MOUNDS**—Mediacom

▲ **MOUNT AUBURN**—Triax Cablevision

▲ **MOUNT CARMEL**—Falcon Cable

▲ **MOUNT CARROLL**—Triax Cablevision

MOUNT CLARE—See STAUNTON, IL

MOUNT MORRIS—See OREGON, IL

MOUNT MORRIS ESTATES—See OREGON, IL

MOUNT OLIVE—See STAUNTON, IL

▲ **MOUNT PROSPECT**—AT & T Cable Services

▲ **MOUNT PULASKI**—UACC Midwest Inc.

▲ **MOUNT STERLING**—Cass Cable TV Inc.

▲ **MOUNT VERNON**—Cablevision Communications

MOUNT ZION—See DECATUR, IL

▲ **MOWEAQUA**—Cablevision Communications

▲ **MULBERRY GROVE**—Galaxy Cablevision

MUNCIE—See DANVILLE, IL

MUNDELEIN—See LIBERTYVILLE, IL

MURPHYSBORO—See CARBONDALE, IL

▲ **MURRAYVILLE**—Cablevision Communications

▲ **NAPERVILLE**—Americast

▲ **NAPERVILLE**—TCI

NAPLATE—See OTTAWA, IL

▲ **NASHVILLE**—Cablevision Communications

NASHVILLE (unincorporated areas)—See NEW MINDEN, IL

▲ **NAUVOO**—Triax Cablevision

NEBO—See PLEASANT HILL, IL

▲ **NEOGA**—TCI Cable

NEPONSET—See MINERAL, IL

NEW ATHENS—See LENZBURG, IL

NEW BADEN—See SCOTT AFB, IL

▲ **NEW BERLIN**—Triax Cablevision

▲ **NEW BOSTON**—New Path Communications LC

▲ **NEW BURNSIDE**—Westcom

NEW CANTON—See KINDERHOOK, IL

▲ **NEW DOUGLAS**—Charter Communications Inc.

▲ **NEW HAVEN** (village)—Westcom

▲ **NEW HOLLAND**—Triax Cablevision

NEW LENOX—See ROMEOVILLE, IL

NEW MILFORD—See ROCKFORD, IL

▲ **NEW MINDEN**—Westcom

NEW TRIER TWP.—See MORTON GROVE, IL

NEW WINDSOR—See ALPHA, IL

NEWARK—See MILLINGTON, IL

▲ **NEWMAN**—TCI Cable

▲ **NEWTON**—Capital Cable Partners

▲ **NIANTIC**—UACC Midwest Inc.

NILES—See ELMHURST, IL

NILWOOD—See GIRARD, IL

▲ **NOBLE**—Falcon Cable

▲ **NOKOMIS**—Falcon Cable

NORMAL—See BLOOMINGTON, IL

NORRIDGE—See PALOS HILLS, IL

▲ **NORRIS**—Nova Cablevision Inc.

▲ **NORRIS CITY**—Capital Cable Partners

NORTH AURORA—See AURORA, IL

NORTH BARRINGTON (village)—See BARRINGTON HILLS, IL

NORTH CHICAGO—See WAUKEGAN, IL

NORTH HENDERSON—See RIO, IL

NORTH PEKIN—See PEKIN, IL

NORTH RIVERSIDE—See ELMHURST, IL

▲ **NORTH UTICA**—TCI of Illinois Inc.

NORTHBROOK—See MOUNT PROSPECT, IL

NORTHFIELD—See MORTON GROVE, IL

NORTHLAKE—See PALOS HILLS, IL

NORWOOD—See PEORIA, IL

O'FALLON—See BELLEVILLE, IL

OAK BROOK—See ELMHURST, IL

▲ **OAK FOREST**—TCI of Illinois

OAK GROVE—See ROCK ISLAND, IL

▲ **OAK LAWN**—TCI

OAK PARK—See ELMHURST, IL

OAK PARK ESTATES—See STANDARD, IL

OAKBROOK TERRACE—See ELMHURST, IL

▲ **OAKFORD (village)**—Cass Cable TV Inc.

OAKLAND—See TUSCOLA, IL

OAKWOOD—See DANVILLE, IL

OAKWOOD HILLS—See CARPENTERSVILLE, IL

OBLONG—See ROBINSON, IL

▲ **OCONEE**—Triax Cablevision

▲ **ODELL**—Triax Cablevision

ODIN—See SALEM, IL

OGDEN—See HOMER, IL

OGLE COUNTY—See OREGON, IL

OGLESBY—See PERU, IL

▲ **OHIO**—Mid American Cable Systems

▲ **OKAWVILLE**—Cablevision Communcations

OLD SHAWNEE TOWN—See SHAWNEETOWN, IL

OLIVE BRANCH—See ALEXANDER COUNTY, IL

OLIVET—See DANVILLE, IL

▲ **OLMSTED**—Galaxy Cablevision

▲ **OLNEY**—SBC Cable Co.

OLYMPIA FIELDS—See MATTESON, IL

▲ **OMAHA**—Westcom

▲ **ONARGA**—TCI of Illinois Inc.

▲ **ONEIDA**—Oneida Cablevision Inc.

▲ **OQUAWKA**—Triax Cablevision

ORANGEVILLE—See WINSLOW, IL

OREANA—See ARGENTA, IL

▲ **OREGON**—TCI of Illinois Inc.

ORION—See COAL VALLEY, IL

ORLAND HILLS—See PALOS HILLS, IL

▲ **ORLAND PARK**—TCI

OSWEGO—See AURORA, IL

▲ **OTTAWA**—Triax Cablevision

OTTER CREEK TWP.—See STREATOR, IL

OTTO—See KANKAKEE, IL

OWANECO—See TAYLORVILLE, IL

PALATINE—See ROLLING MEADOWS, IL

PALESTINE—See ROBINSON, IL

▲ **PALMER**—Triax Cablevision

▲ **PALMYRA**—Cablevision Communications

PALOMA—See GOLDEN, IL

PALOS HEIGHTS—See ELMHURST, IL

▲ **PALOS HILLS**—TCI

▲ **PALOS PARK**—Optel Cable

▲ **PANA**—Falcon Cable

▲ **PANAMA**—Becks Cable Systems

PANKEYVILLE—See ALEXANDER COUNTY, IL

▲ **PARIS**—Cardinal Telecable Corp.

PARK CITY—See WAUKEGAN, IL

▲ **PARK FOREST**—TCI

PARK RIDGE—See MORTON GROVE, IL

PARK RIDGE—See also MOUNT PROSPECT, IL

▲ **PARKERSBURG**—Galaxy Cablevision

▲ **PATOKA**—Capital Cable Partners

PAWNEE—See CHATHAM, IL

▲ **PAWPAW (village)**—Mid American Cable Systems

▲ **PAXTON**—Triax Cablevision

▲ **PAYSON**—Cablevision Communications

▲ **PEARL CITY** (village)—Dowden Cable

▲ **PECATONICA**—Triax Cablevision

▲ **PEKIN**—MediaOne

▲ **PENFIELD**—New Path Communications LC

▲ **PEORIA**—TCI Cablevision of Central Illinois

PEORIA COUNTY—See CHILLICOTHE, IL

PEORIA COUNTY (portions)—See KICKAPOO, IL

PEORIA HEIGHTS—See PEORIA, IL

▲ **PEOTONE**—MediaOne

PERCY—See STEELEVILLE, IL

PERRY COUNTY—See ZEIGLER, IL

PERRY TWP.—See GRIGGSVILLE, IL

▲ **PERU**—TCI Cable

PESOTUM—See TOLONO, IL

▲ **PETERSBURG**—Greene County Partners Inc.

PHILO—See HOMER, IL

PHOENIX—See HARVEY, IL

PIATT COUNTY (eastern portion)—See SEYMOUR (village), IL

▲ **PIERRON**—Westcom LC

PIERSON—See TUSCOLA, IL

▲ **PINCKNEYVILLE**—SBC Cable

PINGREE GROVE—See ELGIN, IL (TCI)

PINKSTAFF—See FLAT ROCK, IL

▲ **PIPER CITY**—TCI of Illinois Inc.

▲ **PITTSBURG**—Galaxy Cablevision

▲ **PITTSFIELD**—Cass Cable TV Corp.

▲ **PLAINFIELD**—Western Cable Communications

PLAINFIELD—See also ROMEOVILLE, IL

PLAINFIELD TWP.—See ROMEOVILLE, IL

PLAINVILLE—See PAYSON, IL

▲ **PLANO**—TCI

PLATO TWP.—See CAMPTON TWP., IL

▲ **PLEASANT HILL**—Cablevision Communications

PLEASANT PLAINS—See VIRGINIA, IL

PLYMOUTH—See GOLDEN, IL

▲ **POCAHONTAS**—Galaxy Cablevision

POCAHONTAS (unincorporated areas)—See PIERRON, IL

POLO—See OREGON, IL

▲ **PONTIAC**—Triax Cablevision

PONTOON BEACH—See MARYVILLE, IL

PONTOOSUC—See DALLAS CITY, IL

▲ **POPLAR GROVE**—Triax Cablevision

PORT BYRON—See RAPIDS CITY, IL

POSEN—See PALOS HILLS, IL

▲ **POTOMAC (village)**—Park TV & Electronics Inc.

▲ **PRAIRIE CITY**—New Path Communications LC

PRAIRIE DU ROCHER—See EVANSVILLE, IL

PREEMPTION—See VIOLA, IL

▲ **PRINCETON**—TCI Cablevision of Princeton

▲ **PRINCEVILLE**—Triax Cablevision

PROPHETSTOWN—See CLINTON, IA

* **PROSPECT HEIGHTS**—Americast

PROSPECT HEIGHTS—See also MOUNT PROSPECT, IL

PULASKI—See ALEXANDER COUNTY, IL

PULASKI COUNTY—See ALEXANDER COUNTY, IL

PULASKI COUNTY (portions)—See MOUNDS, IL

▲ **QUINCY**—MediaOne of Illinois Inc.

QUIVER TWP.—See HAVANA, IL

RALEIGH—See GALATIA, IL

▲ **RAMSEY**—Capital Cable Partners

▲ **RANKIN (village)**—Park TV & Electronics Inc.

RANSOM—See GRAND RIDGE, IL

▲ **RANTOUL**—Triax Cablevision

RANTOUL (village)—See RANTOUL, IL

▲ **RAPIDS CITY**—Triax Cablevision

▲ **RAYMOND**—Falcon Cable

READING TWP.—See STREATOR, IL

▲ **RED BUD**—Mediacom

▲ **REDMON**—New Path Communications LC

REYNOLDS—See VIOLA, IL

RICHMOND—See GENOA CITY, WI

RICHTON PARK—See MATTESON, IL

▲ **RICHVIEW**—Galaxy Cablevision

RICHWOODS TWP.—See PEORIA, IL

▲ **RIDGE FARM**—TCI Cable

RIDGWAY—See SHAWNEETOWN, IL

RIDOTT TWP.—See GERMAN VALLEY, IL

▲ **RINGWOOD**—Mid American Cable Systems

▲ **RIO**—Rio Cablevision

RITCHIE—See CUSTER PARK, IL

RIVER FOREST—See ELMHURST, IL

RIVER GROVE—See ELMHURST, IL

▲ **RIVER OAKS (village)**—Triax Cablevision

RIVERDALE—See DOLTON, IL

RIVERSIDE—See WESTERN SPRINGS, IL

▲ **RIVERTON**—Greene County Partners Inc.

RIVERWOODS (village)—See HIGHLAND PARK, IL

▲ **ROANOKE**—Triax Cablevision

▲ **ROBBINS**—TCI Lake Area

ROBBINS (village)—See CHICAGO HEIGHTS, IL

▲ **ROBINSON**—Triax Cablevision

ROCHELLE—See DE KALB, IL

ROCHESTER—See SPRINGFIELD, IL

ROCK CITY—See DURAND, IL

ROCK FALLS—See STERLING, IL

▲ **ROCK ISLAND**—TCI of Illinois Inc.

ROCK ISLAND ARSENAL—See MOLINE, IL

ROCK ISLAND COUNTY—See MOLINE, IL

ROCK ISLAND COUNTY (portions)—See COAL VALLEY, IL

ROCK ISLAND COUNTY (western portion)—See ROCK ISLAND, IL

ROCKDALE—See ROMEOVILLE, IL

▲ **ROCKFORD**—Insight Communications

ROCKTON—See ROSCOE, IL

ROCKTON (village)—See BELOIT, WI

ROCKTON TWP.—See BELOIT, WI

▲ **ROLLING MEADOWS**—MediaOne

▲ **ROMEOVILLE**—MediaOne

ROMEOVILLE—See also PLAINFIELD, IL

▲ **SUGAR GROVE**—Triax Cablevision

▲ **SULLIVAN**—Triax Cablevision

SUMMERFIELD—See SCOTT AFB, IL

SUMMIT—See ELMHURST, IL

▲ **SUMNER**—Capital Cable Partners

SUN RIVER TERRACE—See KANKAKEE, IL

SUNNYSIDE—See McHENRY, IL

SUNSET LAKE—See GIRARD, IL

SWANSEA—See BELLEVILLE, IL

SYCAMORE—See DE KALB, IL

SYLVAN LAKE—See LAKE ZURICH, IL

▲ **TABLE GROVE**—New Path Communications LC

TALBOT ADDITION—See MANITO, IL

TALLULA—See VIRGINIA, IL

▲ **TAMAROA**—Galaxy Cablevision

▲ **TAMMS**—Cablevision Communications

▲ **TAMPICO**—Triax Cablevision

TANTARA MOBILE HOME PARK—See JACKSON COUNTY, IL

▲ **TAYLOR RIDGE**—Rio Cablevision

TAYLOR SPRINGS—See HILLSBORO, IL

▲ **TAYLORVILLE**—Falcon Cable

TAZEWELL COUNTY (portions)—See CHESTNUT, IL

TAZEWELL COUNTY (portions)—See also MORTON, IL

TAZEWELL COUNTY (portions)—See also PEKIN, IL

TAZEWELL TWP.—See PEORIA, IL

TEUTOPOLIS—See EFFINGHAM, IL

▲ **THAWVILLE**—New Path Communications LC

THAYER—See GIRARD, IL

THEBES—See ALEXANDER COUNTY, IL

THIRD LAKE—See WAUKEGAN, IL

THOMASBORO—See RANTOUL, IL

THOMSON—See CLINTON, IA

THORNTON—See LANSING, IL

TILDEN—See COULTERVILLE, IL

TILTON—See WESTVILLE, IL

TIMBER CREEK TRAILER PARK—See McHENRY, IL

TIMBER RIDGE—See LEXINGTON, IL

TINLEY PARK—See PALOS HILLS, IL

TISKILWA—See PRINCETON, IL

TOLEDO—See GREENUP, IL

▲ **TOLONO**—Illinet Communications

TOLUCA—See ROANOKE, IL

TOULON—See WYOMING, IL

TOVEY—See KINCAID, IL

▲ **TOWANDA**—Triax Cablevision

▲ **TOWER HILL**—Triax Cablevision

TOWER LAKES—See BARRINGTON HILLS, IL

TOWN & COUNTRY TRAILER PARK—See CARBONDALE, IL

TREMONT—See PEKIN, IL

TRENTON—See SCOTT AFB, IL

▲ **TRIANGLE MOBILE HOME PARK**—Galaxy Cablevision

▲ **TRIVOLI**—Nova Cablevision Inc.

TROY—See MARYVILLE, IL

▲ **TROY GROVE (village)**—Mid American Cable Systems

TROY TWP.—See ROMEOVILLE, IL

▲ **TUSCOLA**—Illini Cablevision of Central Illinois Inc.

ULLIN—See ALEXANDER COUNTY, IL

▲ **UNION**—Optel Cable

UNION COUNTY (portions)—See ANNA, IL

UNIVERSITY PARK—See MATTESON, IL

▲ **URBANA**—TCI Cable

URSA—See GOLDEN, IL

UTICA TWP.—See NORTH UTICA, IL

VALIER—See SESSER, IL

* **VALMEYER**—WestCom

▲ **VANDALIA**—Capital Cable Partners

▲ **VARNA**—Triax Cablevision

VENICE—See MARYVILLE, IL

VERA—See VANDALIA, IL

▲ **VERGENNES**—Galaxy American Communications

VERMILION GROVE—See DANVILLE, IL

▲ **VERMILLION (village)**—New Path Communications LC

▲ **VERMONT**—Triax Cablevision

VERNON—See PATOKA, IL

VERNON HILLS—See LAKE ZURICH, IL

* **VERNON HILLS**—Americast

▲ **VERSAILLES**—Cass Cable TV Inc.

▲ **VICTORIA**—Triax Cablevision

▲ **VIENNA**—Galaxy Cablevision

VILLA GROVE—See TUSCOLA, IL

▲ **VILLA PARK**—TCI

▲ **VIOLA**—Triax Cablevision

VIRDEN—See GIRARD, IL

▲ **VIRGINIA**—Cass Cable TV Inc.

WABASH COUNTY (portions)—See MOUNT CARMEL, IL

WADSWORTH—See WAUKEGAN, IL

▲ **WALNUT**—Triax Cablevision

▲ **WALTONVILLE**—Westcom

WAMAC—See CENTRALIA, IL

WAPELLA—See HEYWORTH, IL

▲ **WARREN**—Triax Cablevision

WARREN COUNTY—See MONMOUTH, IL

WARREN TWP.—See WAUKEGAN, IL

▲ **WARRENSBURG**—Cablevision Communications

WARRENVILLE—See WEST CHICAGO, IL

WARSAW—See KEOKUK, IA

WASHBURN—See ROANOKE, IL

WASHINGTON—See PEORIA, IL

WASHINGTON COUNTY—See NASHVILLE, IL

▲ **WASHINGTON PARK**—Triax Cablevision

▲ **WATAGA**—Triax Cablevision

▲ **WATERLOO**—Charter Communications Inc.

▲ **WATERMAN**—Triax Cablevision

▲ **WATSEKA**—Galaxy Cablevision

▲ **WATSEKA**—Triax Cablevision

▲ **WATSON**—Capital Cable Partners

WAUCONDA—See CARPENTERSVILLE, IL

WAUCONDA—See also LIBERTYVILLE, IL

▲ **WAUKEGAN**—AT&T Cable Services

WAUKEGAN TWP.—See WAUKEGAN, IL

▲ **WAVERLY**—Cablevision Communications

▲ **WAYNE CITY**—Cablevision Communicatons

WAYNE COUNTY (portions)—See FAIRFIELD, IL

WAYNESVILLE—See ATLANTA, IL

▲ **WEE-MA-TUK HILLS**—Rio Cablevision

▲ **WELDON**—Triax Cablevision

WELLINGTON—See HOOPESTON, IL

WENONA—See ROANOKE, IL

WEST BROOKLYN—See COMPTON, IL

WEST BROOKLYN (village)—See COMPTON, IL

▲ **WEST CHICAGO**—TCI

WEST CHICAGO—See also GLENDALE HEIGHTS, IL (TCI)

WEST CITY—See BENTON, IL

WEST DUNDEE—See CARPENTERSVILLE, IL

WEST FRANKFORT—See HERRIN, IL

WEST LIBERTY—See OLNEY, IL

WEST PEORIA TWP.—See PEORIA, IL

▲ **WEST SALEM**—Galaxy Cablevision

▲ **WEST UNION**—New Path Communications LC

WEST YORK—See WEST UNION, IL

WESTCHESTER—See ELMHURST, IL

▲ **WESTERN SPRINGS**—TCI

WESTFIELD—See CHARLESTON, IL

WESTHAVEN—See GLENDALE HEIGHTS, IL (TCI)

WESTMONT—See ELMHURST, IL

▲ **WESTVILLE**—See-More TV Corp.

WHEATLAND—See ROMEOVILLE, IL

INDIANA

BROWNSBURG—See HENDRICKS COUNTY, IN

BROWNSBURG (town)—See INDIANAPOLIS, IN

▲ **BROWNSTOWN**—Insight Communications

BRUCE LAKE—See WINAMAC, IN

BRUCEVILLE—See BICKNELL, IN

BRYANT—See PORTLAND, IN

BUCK CREEK—See LAFAYETTE, IN

BUFFALO—See MONTICELLO, IN

BUNKER HILL—See PERU, IN

BURKET—See WARSAW, IN

BURLINGTON—See MONTICELLO, IN

BURNETTSVILLE—See MONTICELLO, IN

BURNS HARBOR—See PORTAGE, IN

▲ **BUTLER**—Triax Cablevision

BUTLERVILLE—See NORTH VERNON, IN

CADIZ—See MOUNT SUMMIT, IN

CAMBRIDGE CITY—See DUBLIN, IN

CAMDEN—See MONTICELLO, IN

▲ **CAMPBELLSBURG**—EQC Cable Inc.

CANNELBURG—See MONTGOMERY, IN

CANNELTON—See TELL CITY, IN

CANTERBURY GREEN—See FORT WAYNE, IN

CARBON—See BRAZIL, IN

▲ **CARLISLE**—CableVision Communications

▲ **CARMEL**—Time Warner Cable

CARROLL COUNTY—See MONTICELLO, IN

CARTHAGE—See KNIGHTSTOWN, IN

CASS COUNTY—See KOKOMO, IN

CASS COUNTY—See also LOGANSPORT, IN

▲ **CATARACT LAKE**—New Path Communications LC

CAYUGA—See DANVILLE, IL

CEDAR LAKE—See MERRILLVILLE, IN

CEDARVILLE—See HARLAN, IN

▲ **CENTER POINT**—New Path Communications LC

CENTERVILLE—See RICHMOND, IN

CEYLON—See PORTLAND, IN

CHALMERS—See MONTICELLO, IN

CHANDLER—See NEWBURGH, IN

CHARLESTOWN—See JEFFERSONVILLE, IN

CHESTERFIELD—See ANDERSON, IN

CHESTERTON—See LA PORTE, IN

▲ **CHRISNEY**—New Path Communications LC

CHRISNEY—See also SANTA CLAUS, IN

CHRISTMAS LAKE VILLAGE—See SANTA CLAUS, IN

▲ **CHURUBUSCO**—Triax Cablevision

CICERO—See NOBLESVILLE, IN

CIRCLEVILLE—See RUSHVILLE, IN

CLARK COUNTY (portions)—See JEFFERSONVILLE, IN

CLARKS HILL—See THORNTOWN, IN

CLARKSVILLE—See JEFFERSONVILLE, IN

▲ **CLAY CITY**—CableVision Communications

CLAY COUNTY (north central portion)—See BRAZIL, IN

CLAY TWP.—See CARMEL, IN

▲ **CLAYPOOL**—Mid American Cable Systems

CLAYTON—See HENDRICKS COUNTY (southern portion), IN

CLEAR CREEK—See BLOOMINGTON, IN

▲ **CLEAR LAKE**—Mid American Cable Systems

CLERMONT—See INDIANAPOLIS, IN

CLIFFORD—See COLUMBUS, IN

▲ **CLINTON**—Clinton Cable TV Co. Inc.

CLINTON COUNTY—See FRANKFORT, IN

CLINTON COUNTY (northwestern portion)—See LAFAYETTE, IN

▲ **CLOVERDALE**—New Path Communications LC

▲ **COAL CITY**—New Path Communications LC

COALMONT—See JASONVILLE, IN

COATESVILLE—See HENDRICKS COUNTY (southern portion), IN

COLFAX—See LINDEN, IN

COLLEGE CORNER—See OXFORD, OH

▲ **COLUMBIA CITY**—Triax Cablevision

COLUMBIA CITY—See also LOON LAKE, IN

▲ **COLUMBUS**—Charter Communications Inc.

▲ **CONNERSVILLE**—Charter Communications Inc.

CONVERSE—See SWEETSER, IN

CORDRY LAKE—See CORDRY/SWEETWATER CONSERVANCY DISTRICT, IN

▲ **CORDRY/SWEETWATER CONSERVANCY DISTRICT**—Omega Cable TV of Brown County

▲ **CORUNNA**—New Path Communications LC

CORYDON—See NEW ALBANY, IN

COUNTRY MANOR—See BROOKLYN, IN

▲ **COVINGTON**—Charter Communications Inc.

COWAN—See MUNCIE, IN

CRAIGVILLE—See BLUFFTON, IN

▲ **CRANE**—New Path Communications LC

CRAWFORD—See NORTH VERNON, IN

▲ **CRAWFORD COUNTY**—Cablecomm

▲ **CRAWFORDSVILLE**—Charter Communications Inc.

CROMWELL—See NORTH WEBSTER, IN

CROMWELL (unincorporated areas)—See KIMMEL, IN

CROWN POINT—See MERRILLVILLE, IN

CROWS NEST—See INDIANAPOLIS, IN

▲ **CULVER**—Triax Cablevision

CULVER—See also MARSHALL COUNTY, IN

CUMBERLAND—See INDIANAPOLIS, IN

▲ **CYNTHIANA**—CableVision Communications

DALE—See SANTA CLAUS, IN

DALEVILLE—See MUNCIE, IN

▲ **DANA**—New Path Communications LC

DANVILLE—See HENDRICKS COUNTY, IN

DANVILLE (town)—See INDIANAPOLIS, IN

▲ **DARLINGTON**—Phoenix Concept Cablevision of Indiana

DARMSTADT—See EVANSVILLE, IN

Daviess County—See WASHINGTON, IN

DAVIESS COUNTY (eastern portion)—See LOOGOOTEE, IN

DAVIESS COUNTY (portions)—See ODON, IN

DAYTON—See LAFAYETTE, IN

DE KALB COUNTY—See HARLAN, IN

▲ **DE SOTO**—Century Communications

DEARBORN COUNTY—See MILAN, IN

DEARBORN COUNTY (unincorporated areas)—See DILLSBORO, IN

DEARBORN COUNTY (unincorporated areas)—See also LAWRENCEBURG, IN

DECATUR—See BLUFFTON, IN

DECATUR COUNTY (portions)—See GREENSBURG, IN

▲ **DECKER**—New Path Communications LC

DELAWARE COUNTY—See HARTFORD CITY, IN

DELAWARE COUNTY—See also MUNCIE, IN

DELAWARE COUNTY (northeastern portion)—See DE SOTO, IN

DELPHI—See MONTICELLO, IN

DEMOTTE—See ROSELAWN, IN

DENVER—See PERU, IN

DEWARTE LAKE—See NORTH WEBSTER, IN

▲ **DILLSBORO**—Fairbanks Cable

DONALDSON—See MARSHALL COUNTY, IN

▲ **DUBLIN**—Insight Communications

▲ **DUBOIS COUNTY**—New Path Communications LC

DUBOIS COUNTY—See also JASPER, IN

▲ **DUGGER**—CableVision Communications

Dune Acres—See LA PORTE, IN

DUNELAND BEACH—See MICHIGAN CITY, IN

DUNKIRK—See PORTLAND, IN

DUNREITH—See KNIGHTSTOWN, IN

HENDRICKS COUNTY (portions)—See JAMESTOWN, IN

Hendricks County (portions)—See also MONROVIA, IN

HENRY COUNTY—See NEW CASTLE, IN

HENRY COUNTY (portions)—See KNIGHTSTOWN, IN

HERBST—See SWAYZEE, IN

▲ **HERITAGE LAKE**—Heritage Lake Cable

Hidden Valley Lake—See LAWRENCEBURG, IN

HIGHLAND—See HILLSDALE, IN

HIGHLAND—See also MERRILLVILLE, IN

▲ **HILL LAKE RESORTS**—New Path Communications LC

▲ **HILLSBORO**—Mid American Cable Systems

▲ **HILLSDALE**—New Path Communications LC

▲ **HOAGLAND**—Mid American Cable Systems

HOBART—See MERRILLVILLE, IN

▲ **HOLLAND**—New Path Communications LC

▲ **HOLTON**—New Path Communications LC

HOMECROFT—See INDIANAPOLIS, IN

▲ **HOMER**—New Path Communications LC

HOPE—See SHELBYVILLE, IN

HOWARD COUNTY—See KOKOMO, IN

HOWE—See LAGRANGE, IN

HUDSON—See ASHLEY, IN

HUNTERTOWN—See FORT WAYNE, IN

HUNTERTOWN—See also HARLAN, IN

HUNTINGBURG—See JASPER, IN

▲ **HUNTINGTON**—Huntington CATV Inc.

HUNTINGTON COUNTY—See HUNTINGTON, IN

HUNTINGTON COUNTY (portions)—See FORT WAYNE, IN

HUNTSVILLE—See ANDERSON, IN

HYMERA—See JASONVILLE, IN

IDAVILLE—See MONTICELLO, IN

▲ **INDIANAPOLIS**—Comcast Cablevision of Indianapolis Inc.

▲ **INDIANAPOLIS (portions)**—Time Warner Cable

INGALLS—See FORTVILLE, IN

ISREAL LAKE—See PAINT MILL LAKE, IN

JACKSON COUNTY—See SEYMOUR, IN

JALAPA—See SWEETSER, IN

▲ **JAMESTOWN**—Phoenix Concept Cablevision of Indiana

▲ **JASONVILLE**—CableVision Communications

▲ **JASPER**—Insight Communications

JASPER COUNTY—See MONTICELLO, IN

JASPER COUNTY (western portion)—See ROSELAWN, IN

JAY COUNTY—See PORTLAND, IN

JEFFERSON—See FRANKFORT, IN

JEFFERSON COUNTY (portions)—See MADISON, IN

▲ **JEFFERSON TWP. (Elkhart County)**—Heritage Cablevision Assoc.

▲ **JEFFERSONVILLE**—Insight Communications

JENNINGS COUNTY—See NORTH VERNON, IN

JOHNSON COUNTY—See GREENWOOD, IN

JOHNSON COUNTY (portions)—See FRANKLIN, IN

JONESBORO—See MARION, IN

JONESVILLE—See COLUMBUS, IN

▲ **KEMPTON**—Country Cablevision

▲ **KENDALLVILLE**—Triax Cablevision

KENNARD—See WILKINSON, IN

▲ **KENTLAND**—Triax Cablevision

▲ **KEWANNA**—Mid American Cable Systems

▲ **KIMMEL**—New Path Communications LC

▲ **KINGMAN**—Mid American Cable Systems

KINGSBURY—See LA PORTE, IN

KINGSFORD HEIGHTS—See LA PORTE, IN

KINGSLAND—See BLUFFTON, IN

KIRKLIN—See SHERIDAN, IN

▲ **KNAPP LAKE**—New Path Communications LC

▲ **KNIGHTSTOWN**—CableVision Communications

KNIGHTSVILLE—See BRAZIL, IN

▲ **KNOX**—Triax Cablevision

KNOX COUNTY—See VINCENNES, IN

KNOX COUNTY (eastern portion)—See MONROE CITY, IN

KNOX COUNTY (portions)—See ODON, IN

▲ **KOKOMO**—Insight Communications

KOONTZ LAKE—See WALKERTON, IN

KOSCIUSKO COUNTY—See NORTH WEBSTER, IN

KOSCIUSKO COUNTY—See also WARSAW, IN

KOSCIUSKO COUNTY (unincorporated areas)—See SILVER LAKE, IN

▲ **KOUTS**—Mid American Cable Systems

LA CROSSE—See KOUTS, IN

▲ **LA FONTAINE**—Mid American Cable Systems

▲ **LA PORTE**—TCI

LA PORTE COUNTY—See LA PORTE, IN

LA PORTE COUNTY (portions)—See THREE OAKS, MI

LA PORTE COUNTY (unincorporated areas)—See MICHIGAN CITY, IN

▲ **LA PORTE MOBILE HOME PARK**—North American Cablevision

▲ **LAFAYETTE**—Insight Communications

▲ **LAGRANGE**—Triax Cablevision

LAGRANGE COUNTY—See THREE RIVERS, MI

▲ **LAGRO**—Mid American Cable Systems

▲ **LAKE CICOTT**—Charter Communications Inc.

LAKE COUNTY (southern portion)—See ROSELAWN, IN

LAKE COUNTY (unincorporated areas)—See MERRILLVILLE, IN

LAKE GAGE—See ANGOLA, IN

LAKE HART (town)—See INDIANAPOLIS, IN

LAKE HOLIDAY—See ROSELAWN, IN

▲ **LAKE OF THE FOUR SEASONS**—TCI Lake Area

▲ **LAKE SANTEE**—New Path Communications LC

LAKE STATION—See MERRILLVILLE, IN

LAKE VILLAGE—See ROSELAWN, IN

LAKETON—See NORTH MANCHESTER, IN

▲ **LAKEVILLE**—Triax Cablevision

LANESVILLE—See NEW ALBANY, IN

LAOTTO—See AUBURN, IN

LAPAZ—See LAKEVILLE, IN

▲ **LAPEL**—Phoenix Concept Cablevision of Indiana

▲ **LARWILL**—New Path Communications LC

▲ **LAUREL TWP.**—New Path Communications LC

LAWRENCE—See INDIANAPOLIS, IN

LAWRENCE COUNTY (northern portion)—See MONROE COUNTY (southern portion), IN

LAWRENCE COUNTY (portions)—See BEDFORD, IN

LAWRENCE COUNTY (southern portion)—See MONROE COUNTY (portions), IN

LAWRENCE COUNTY (unincorporated areas)—See MITCHELL, IN

▲ **LAWRENCEBURG**—Fairbanks Cable

▲ **LEAVENWORTH**—New Path Communications LC

▲ **LEBANON**—Insight Communications

LEESBURG—See NORTH WEBSTER, IN

▲ **LEITERS FORD**—New Path Communications LC

LEO—See HARLAN, IN

LEWISVILLE—See KNIGHTSTOWN, IN

▲ **LIBERTY**—Charter Communications Inc.

LIBERTY CENTER—See BLUFFTON, IN

▲ **LIBERTY MILLS**—New Path Communications LC

LIBERTY TWP.—See MUNCIE, IN

▲ **LIGONIER**—Triax Cablevision

▲ **LINDEN**—Tri-County Communications Corp.

▲ **LINTON**—Insight Communications

LIZTON—See HENDRICKS COUNTY, IN

LODI—See DANVILLE, IL

▲ **LOGANSPORT**—Charter Communications Inc.

LONG BEACH—See MICHIGAN CITY, IN

▲ **LOOGOOTEE**—Cablecomm

▲ **LOON LAKE**—New Path Communications LC

LOSANTVILLE—See MOUNT SUMMIT, IN

LOST CREEK TWP. (northeastern portion)—See BRAZIL, IN

LOWELL—See MERRILLVILLE, IN

▲ **LYNN**—Insight Communications

▲ **LYNNVILLE**—Cablecomm

▲ **LYONS**—CableVision Communications

MACKEY—See FRANCISCO, IN

MACY—See FULTON, IN

▲ **MADISON**—FrontierVision

MADISON COUNTY (portions)—See ALEXANDRIA, IN

MADISON COUNTY (portions)—See also ANDERSON, IN

MADISON COUNTY (portions)—See also ELWOOD, IN

MADISON COUNTY (portions)—See also FRANKTON, IN

MAGLEY—See BLUFFTON, IN

▲ **MALDEN**—Mid American Cable Systems

MANILLA—See HOMER, IN

MARENGO—See CRAWFORD COUNTY, IN

MARIAH HILL—See SANTA CLAUS, IN

▲ **MARION**—Time Warner Cable

MARION COUNTY—See INDIANAPOLIS, IN

MARION TWP.—See FORT WAYNE, IN

▲ **MARKLE**—Mid American Cable Systems

MARKLEVILLE—See ANDERSON, IN

MARSHALL—See ROCKVILLE, IN

▲ **MARSHALL COUNTY**—Cablecomm

MARSHALL COUNTY—See also LAKEVILLE, IN

MARSHALL COUNTY—See also SOUTH BEND, IN

MARTIN COUNTY (portions)—See SHOALS, IN

▲ **MARTINSVILLE**—Insight Communications

▲ **MATTHEWS**—Mid American Cable Systems

McCORDSVILLE—See FORTVILLE, IN

McCORDSVILLE—See also NOBLESVILLE, IN

MECCA—See ROCKVILLE, IN

▲ **MEDARYVILLE**—Mid American Cable Systems

▲ **MEDORA**—Medora Cable TV

▲ **MELLOT**—Mid American Cable Systems

▲ **MENTONE**—Mid American Cable Systems

MERIDIAN HILLS—See INDIANAPOLIS, IN

▲ **MEROM**—New Path Communications LC

▲ **MERRILLVILLE**—TCI Lake Area

▲ **METAMORA**—New Path Communications LC

MEXICO—See PERU, IN

▲ **MIAMI**—New Path Communications LC

MIAMI COUNTY—See KOKOMO, IN

MICHIANA SHORES—See MICHIGAN CITY, IN

▲ **MICHIGAN CITY**—TCI Lake Area

▲ **MICHIGANTOWN**—Country Cablevision

▲ **MIDDLEBURY**—Heritage Cablevision Assoc.

▲ **MIDDLETOWN**—CableVision Communications

MIDDLETOWN—See also ANDERSON, IN

▲ **MILAN**—Fairbanks Cable

MILFORD—See SYRACUSE, IN

MILLERSBURG—See NEW PARIS, IN

MILLERSBURG—See also TOPEKA, IN

▲ **MILROY**—New Path Communications LC

MILTON—See DUBLIN, IN

MISHAWAKA—See SOUTH BEND, IN

▲ **MITCHELL**—Hoosier Hills Cable Co.

MODOC—See MOUNT SUMMIT, IN

▲ **MONGO**—New Path Communications LC

MONON—See MONTICELLO, IN

MONROE—See BLUFFTON, IN

▲ **MONROE CITY**—Cablevision Communications

▲ **MONROE COUNTY (portions)**—TCI of Indiana Inc.

MONROE COUNTY (portions)—See also BLOOMINGTON, IN

▲ **MONROE COUNTY (southern portion)**—Insight Communications

MONROE TWP.—See MUNCIE, IN

▲ **MONROEVILLE (town)**—Comcast Cablevision of Fort Wayne LP

▲ **MONROVIA**—Comcast Cable

▲ **MONTEREY**—New Path Communications LC

▲ **MONTEZUMA**—Phoenix Concept Cablevision of Indiana

▲ **MONTGOMERY**—New Path Communications LC

MONTGOMERY COUNTY (portions)—See CRAWFORDSVILLE, IN

MONTGOMERY COUNTY (portions)—See also NEW MARKET, IN

▲ **MONTICELLO**—Charter Communications Inc.

MONTPELIER—See PERU, IN

MOONVILLE—See ANDERSON, IN

MOORELAND—See MOUNT SUMMIT, IN

MOORES HILL—See MILAN, IN

MOORESVILLE—See INDIANAPOLIS, IN

MORGAN COUNTY—See INDIANAPOLIS, IN

MORGAN COUNTY—See also MARTINSVILLE, IN

MORGAN COUNTY (northern portion)—See HENDRICKS COUNTY (southern portion), IN

Morgan County (portions)—See MONROVIA, IN

▲ **MOROCCO**—TV Cable of Rensselaer Inc.

MORRIS—See BATESVILLE, IN

▲ **MORRISTOWN**—New Path Communications LC

MOUNT AUBURN—See DUBLIN, IN

MOUNT PLEASANT TWP.—See MUNCIE, IN

▲ **MOUNT SUMMIT**—CableVision Communications

▲ **MOUNT VERNON**—Insight Communications

MULBERRY—See LAFAYETTE, IN

▲ **MUNCIE**—Century Communications

MUNSTER—See MERRILLVILLE, IN

MURRAY—See BLUFFTON, IN

NAPOLEON—See SUNMAN, IN

NAPPANEE—See BREMEN, IN

NASHVILLE—See CORDRY/SWEETWATER CONSERVANCY DISTRICT, IN

▲ **NEW ALBANY**—Charter Communications Inc.

NEW CARLISLE—See THREE OAKS, MI

▲ **NEW CASTLE**—Insight Communications

NEW CHICAGO—See MERRILLVILLE, IN

NEW DURHAM TWP.—See WESTVILLE, IN

▲ **NEW HARMONY**—Capital Cable

NEW HAVEN—See FORT WAYNE, IN

▲ **NEW MARKET**—Phoenix Concept Cablevision of Indiana

NEW PALESTINE—See NOBLESVILLE, IN

▲ **NEW PARIS**—New Paris Telephone Quality Cablevision

▲ **NEW POINT**—Sunman Telecommunications Inc.

NEW RICHMOND—See LINDEN, IN

NEW ROSS—See JAMESTOWN, IN

NEW WASHINGTON—See JEFFERSONVILLE, IN

NEW WAVERLY—See PERU, IN

NEW WHITELAND—See GREENWOOD, IN

NEWBERN—See COLUMBUS, IN

NEWBERRY—See ODON, IN

▲ **NEWBURGH**—Century Cable

▲ **NEWPORT**—New Path Communications LC

NEWTON COUNTY (northern portion)—See ROSELAWN, IN

NEWTOWN—See HILLSBORO, IN

NINEVEH—See PRINCE'S LAKES, IN

▲ **WAKARUSA**—Heritage Cablevision Assoc.

▲ **WALDRON**—New Path Communications LC

WALESBORO—See COLUMBUS, IN

▲ **WALKERTON**—Triax Cablevision

WALKERTON—See also MARSHALL COUNTY, IN

▲ **WALTON**—Mid American Cable Systems

WANATAH—See WESTVILLE, IN

▲ **WARREN**—Warren Cable

WARREN COUNTY—See ATTICA, IN

WARREN PARK—See INDIANAPOLIS, IN

WARRICK COUNTY—See BOONVILLE, IN

WARRICK COUNTY—See also NEWBURGH, IN

▲ **WARSAW**—Charter Communications Inc.

▲ **WASHINGTON**—Cablevision Communications

WASHINGTON TWP.—See CAMPBELLSBURG, IN

WATERLOO—See AUBURN, IN

▲ **WAVELAND**—Mid American Cable Systems

WAYNE COUNTY—See RICHMOND, IN

WAYNE COUNTY (portions)—See MOUNT SUMMIT, IN

WAYNE TWP.—See FORT WAYNE, IN

WAYNESVILLE—See COLUMBUS, IN

▲ **WAYNETOWN**—Phoenix Concept Cablevision of Indiana

WELLS COUNTY—See FORT WAYNE, IN

WELLS COUNTY (western portion)—See BLUFFTON, IN

WEST BADEN SPRINGS—See FRENCH LICK, IN

WEST LAFAYETTE—See LAFAYETTE, IN

▲ **WEST LEBANON**—New Path Communications LC

WEST TERRE HAUTE—See TERRE HAUTE, IN

WESTBROOK MOBILE HOME PARK—See EVANSVILLE, IN

WESTFIELD—See NOBLESVILLE, IN

▲ **WESTPOINT**—New Path Communications LC

▲ **WESTPORT**—Charter Communications Inc.

▲ **WESTVILLE**—Mid American Cable Systems

▲ **WHEATFIELD**—Mid American Cable Systems

WHEATLAND—See MONROE CITY, IN

WHITE COUNTY—See MONTICELLO, IN

WHITELAND—See GREENWOOD, IN

▲ **WHITESTOWN**—Phoenix Concept Cablevision of Indiana

WHITING—See MERRILLVILLE, IN

WHITLEY COUNTY (portions)—See FORT WAYNE, IN

WILFRED—See SHELBURN, IN

▲ **WILKINSON**—CableVision Communications

WILLIAMS CREEK—See INDIANAPOLIS, IN

▲ **WILLIAMSBURG**—Galaxy American Communications

▲ **WILLIAMSBURG**—Time Warner Cable

WILLIAMSPORT—See ATTICA, IN

▲ **WINAMAC**—TV Cable of Winamac Inc.

▲ **WINCHESTER**—Insight Communications

WINDFALL—See KOKOMO, IN

WINGATE—See LINDEN, IN

WINONA LAKE—See WARSAW, IN

WINSLOW—See PETERSBURG, IN

WOLCOTT—See MONTICELLO, IN

WOLCOTTVILLE—See ROME CITY, IN

WOLCOTTVILLE (unincorporated areas)—See OLIVER LAKE, IN

WOODBURN—See FORT WAYNE, IN

▲ **WORTHINGTON**—Phoenix Concept Cablevision of Indiana

WYNNEDALE—See INDIANAPOLIS, IN

▲ **YANKEETOWN**—New Path Communications LC

YEOMAN—See MONTICELLO, IN

▲ **YODER**—Mid American Cable Systems

YORKTOWN—See MUNCIE, IN

▲ **YOUNG AMERICA**—New Path Communications LC

▲ **ZANESVILLE**—Mid American Cable Systems

▲ **ZIONSVILLE**—Time Warner Cable

IOWA

▲ **ACKLEY**—TCI Cablevision

ACKWORTH—See INDIANOLA, IA

▲ **ADAIR**—New Path Communications LC

▲ **ADEL**—Cablevision V Inc.

▲ **AFTON**—New Path Communications LC

AGENCY—See OTTUMWA, IA

▲ **AKRON**—Vernon Communications & TV Inc.

▲ **ALBERT CITY**—Albert City Communications Inc.

▲ **ALBIA**—TCI of Southern Iowa

▲ **ALBION**—Mid American Cable Systems

ALBURNETT—See SHELLSBURG, IA

▲ **ALDEN**—Latimer/Coulter Cablevision

▲ **ALEXANDER**—New Path Communications LC

▲ **ALGONA**—TCI

▲ **ALLEMAN**—Walnut Creek Communications Inc.

▲ **ALLERTON**—Falcon/Capital Cable Partners

ALLISON—See GREENE, IA

ALTA—See STORM LAKE, IA

▲ **ALTA VISTA (town)**—Mid American Cable Systems

ALTON—See ORANGE CITY, IA

ALTOONA—See DES MOINES, IA

▲ **AMANA**—Triax Cablevision

▲ **AMES**—TCI of Central Iowa

▲ **ANAMOSA**—Triax Cablevision

▲ **ANDREW**—Andrew Telephone Co. Inc.

▲ **ANITA**—West Iowa Telephone Co.

ANKENY—See DES MOINES, IA

▲ **ANTHON**—Comserv Ltd.

APLINGTON—See PARKERSBURG, IA

APPANOOSE COUNTY—See CENTERVILLE, IA

ARCADIA—See WESTSIDE, IA

ARION—See DOW CITY, IA

▲ **ARLINGTON**—Alpine Communications LC

▲ **ARMSTRONG**—Triax Cablevision

ARNOLDS PARK—See SPIRIT LAKE, IA

▲ **ARTHUR**—Sac County Mutual Telco

▲ **ASBURY**—TCI of Iowa Inc.

▲ **ASHTON**—Vernon Communications & TV Inc.

▲ **ATALISSA**—Mississippi Cablevision

▲ **ATKINS**—Atkins Cablevision Inc.

▲ **ATLANTIC**—TCI

ATTICA—See KNOXVILLE, IA

▲ **AUDUBON**—TCI

▲ **AURELIA**—Peoples Cable TV

▲ **AURORA**—Alpine Communications LC

▲ **AVOCA**—Heritage Cablevision Inc.

▲ **AYRSHIRE**—ATC Cablevision

▲ **BADGER**—Goldfield Communication Services Corp.

▲ **BAGLEY**—Panora Cooperative Cablevision Assn. Inc.

▲ **BANCROFT**—Triax Cablevision

BARNES CITY—See DEEP RIVER, IA

BARNUM—See CLARE, IA

▲ **BATAVIA**—New Path Communications LC

Batavia—See also OTTUMWA, IA

▲ **BATTLE CREEK**—Sac County Mutual Telco

BAXTER—See GILMAN, IA

▲ **BAYARD**—Tele-Services Ltd.

BEACON—See OSKALOOSA, IA

BEAMAN—See GLADBROOK, IA

▲ **BEDFORD**—Heritage Cablevision Inc.

▲ **BELLE PLAINE**—TCI Cablevision

▲ **BELLEVUE**—Bellevue Municipal Cable

BELMOND—See CLARION, IA

▲ **BENNETT**—F & B Cablevision

BERTRAM—See CEDAR RAPIDS, IA

BETTENDORF—See MOLINE, IL

▲ **BIRMINGHAM**—Starwest Inc.

BIRMINGHAM—See also KEOSAUQUA, IA

BLACK HAWK COUNTY (portions)—See WATERLOO, IA

▲ **BLAIRSBURG**—Cable Systems Management of Iowa Inc.

▲ **BLAIRSTOWN**—Coon Creek Telephone & Cablevision

▲ **BLAKESBURG**—Mississippi Cablevision

▲ **BLENCOE**—Sky Scan Cable Co.

▲ **BLOCKTON**—Deans Cablevision Inc.

▲ **BLOOMFIELD**—Televents Group Joint Venture

▲ **BLUE GRASS**—Triax Cablevision

▲ **BODE**—Video Services Ltd.

▲ **BONAPARTE**—Triax Cablevision

Bonaparte—See also KEOSAUQUA, IA

BONDURANT—See DES MOINES, IA

▲ **BOONE**—TCI of Central Iowa

BOONE COUNTY (eastern portion)—See AMES, IA

BOONE COUNTY (southern portion)—See MADRID, IA

BOONEVILLE—See ADEL, IA

▲ **BOYDEN**—Vernon Communications & TV Inc.

BRAYTON—See ELK HORN, IA

▲ **BREDA**—Tele-Services Ltd.

▲ **BRIDGEWATER**—New Path Communications LC

▲ **BRIGHTON**—Starwest Inc.

▲ **BRISTOW**—Dumont Cablevision

BRITT—See GARNER, IA

▲ **BRONSON**—New Path Communications LC

▲ **BROOKLYN**—Inter-County Cable Co.

BUENA VISTA COUNTY—See STORM LAKE, IA

BUFFALO—See BLUE GRASS, IA

▲ **BUFFALO CENTER**—Triax Cablevision

BUFFALO CENTER—See also THOMPSON, IA

▲ **BURLINGTON**—Televents Group Joint Venture

▲ **BURT**—Triax Cablevision

▲ **BUSSEY**—Mississippi Cablevision

CALAMUS—See WHEATLAND, IA

CALLENDER—See LEHIGH, IA

▲ **CALMAR**—Triax Cablevision

CALUMET—See SUTHERLAND, IA

CAMANCHE—See CLINTON, IA

▲ **CAMBRIDGE**—Walnut Creek Communications Inc.

CANTRIL—See MILTON, IA

CARLISLE—See DES MOINES, IA

▲ **CARROLL**—Televents Group Joint Venture

▲ **CARSON**—Interstate Cablevision Inc.

CARTER LAKE—See OMAHA, NE

▲ **CASCADE**—TCI of Iowa Inc.

▲ **CASEY**—Casey Cable Co.

▲ **CEDAR FALLS**—Cedar Falls Municipal Communications Utility

▲ **CEDAR RAPIDS**—TCI of Iowa

▲ **CENTER JUNCTION**—Center Junction Telephone Co.

CENTER POINT—See SHELLSBURG, IA

▲ **CENTERVILLE**—Televents Group Joint Venture

▲ **CENTRAL CITY**—Shellsburg Cablevision Inc.

CENTRAL CITY—See also SHELLSBURG, IA

CERRO GORDO—See MASON CITY, IA

▲ **CHARITON**—TCI of Southern Iowa

▲ **CHARLES CITY**—WestMarc Cable Holding Inc.

CHARLOTTE—See PRESTON, IA

▲ **CHARTER OAK**—Tip Top Communication

▲ **CHEROKEE**—TCI

▲ **CHESTER**—New Path Communications LC

▲ **CINCINNATI**—Falcon/Capital Cable Partners

▲ **CLARE**—Cablevision VI Inc.

▲ **CLARENCE**—Clarence Telephone Co. Inc.

▲ **CLARINDA**—Heritage Cablevision Inc.

▲ **CLARION**—TCI of Northern Iowa

▲ **CLARKSVILLE**—Triax Cablevision

▲ **CLAYTON**—Triax Cablevision

CLEAR LAKE—See MASON CITY, IA

▲ **CLEARFIELD**—Deans Cablevision Inc.

▲ **CLEGHORN**—Cleghorn Cable TV

CLEMONS—See ZEARING, IA

▲ **CLERMONT**—Alpine Communications LC

▲ **CLINTON**—TCI of Eastern Iowa

CLINTON COUNTY—See PRESTON, IA

CLIVE—See DES MOINES, IA

▲ **CLUTIER**—Farmers Cooperative Telephone Co.

COALVILLE—See FORT DODGE, IA

▲ **COGGON**—Shellsburg Cablevision Inc.

▲ **COLESBURG**—Alpine Communications LC

▲ **COLFAX**—TCI of Southern Iowa

▲ **COLLINS**—Walnut Creek Communications Inc.

▲ **COLO**—Walnut Creek Communications Inc.

COLUMBUS CITY—See COLUMBUS JUNCTION, IA

▲ **COLUMBUS JUNCTION**—Cablevision VII Inc.

▲ **CONESVILLE**—Mississippi Cablevision

CONRAD—See GLADBROOK, IA

▲ **COON RAPIDS**—Coon Rapids Municipal Cable System

CORALVILLE—See IOWA CITY, IA

CORNELIA—See CLARION, IA

▲ **CORNING**—Heritage Cablevision Inc.

▲ **CORRECTIONVILLE**—Comserv Inc.

▲ **CORWITH**—Wesley Cable Co.

▲ **CORYDON**—TCI of Southern Iowa

▲ **COULTER**—Latimer/Coulter Cablevision

COUNCIL BLUFFS—See OMAHA, NE

COVINGTON—See CEDAR RAPIDS, IA

CRAWFORD COUNTY—See DENISON, IA

▲ **CRAWFORDSVILLE**—New Path Communications LC

▲ **CRESCENT**—New Path Communications LC

▲ **CRESCO**—Triax Cablevision

▲ **CRESTON**—Heritage Cablevision Inc.

CRYSTAL LAKE—See WODEN, IA

▲ **CUMBERLAND**—New Path Communications LC

▲ **CUSHING**—Comserv Ltd.

▲ **CYLINDER**—ATC Cablevision

DAKOTA CITY—See HUMBOLDT, IA

DALLAS—See MELCHER, IA

DALLAS CENTER—See ADEL, IA

DALLAS COUNTY (eastern portion)—See GRANGER, IA

DALLAS COUNTY (northern portion)—See MADRID, IA

▲ **DANBURY**—New Path Communications LC

DANVILLE—See BURLINGTON, IA

DAVENPORT—See MOLINE, IL

▲ **DAVIS CITY**—Mississippi Cablevision

▲ **DAYTON**—Dayton Cable TV

DE WITT—See CLINTON, IA

▲ **DECATUR**—Mississippi Cablevision

DECATUR COUNTY (rural portion)—See DAVIS CITY, IA

▲ **DECORAH**—Telnet of Decorah LC

▲ **DEDHAM**—Templeton Telephone Co.

▲ **DEEP RIVER**—Deep River Telephone Co.

▲ **DEFIANCE**—Defiance Telephone Co.

▲ **DELHI**—Shellsburg Cablevision Inc.

▲ **DELMAR**—F & B Cablevision

▲ **DELOIT**—Tip Top Communication

▲ **DELTA**—Mississippi Cablevision

▲ **DENISON**—TCI of the Heartlands

▲ **DENMARK**—Mississippi Cablevision

DENVER—See WAVERLY, IA

▲ **DES MOINES**—TCI Cablevision

DESOTO—See ADEL, IA

▲ **DEXTER**—Heritage Cablevision Inc.

▲ **DIAGONAL**—Deans Cablevision Inc.

▲ **DICKENS**—Vernon Communications & TV Inc.

DIKE—See NEW HARTFORD, IA

▲ **DIXON**—Dixon Telephone Co.

▲ **DONAHUE**—Dixon Telephone Co.

▲ **DONNELLSON**—New Path Communications LC

▲ **DOON**—Premier Communications Inc.

▲ **DOW CITY**—Tip Top Communication

▲ **DOWS**—Dows Cablevision

▲ **DRAKESVILLE**—Mississippi Cablevision

▲ **DUBUQUE**—TCI of Iowa Inc.

DUBUQUE COUNTY—See DUBUQUE, IA

▲ **DUMONT**—Dumont Cablevision

DUNCAN—See GARNER, IA

DUNCOMBE—See LEHIGH, IA

▲ **DUNKERTON**—Dunkerton Telephone Cooperative

▲ **DUNLAP**—Tip Top Communication

DURANT—See WILTON, IA

▲ **DYERSVILLE**—TCI of Iowa Inc.

DYSART—See TRAER, IA

▲ **EAGLE GROVE**—Triax Cablevision

EARLHAM—See DEXTER, IA

▲ **EARLING**—Farmers Mutual Cooperative Telephone Co.

▲ **EARLVILLE**—Alpine Communications LC

EARLY—See CLEGHORN, IA

▲ **EDDYVILLE**—TCI

▲ **EDGEWOOD**—Triax Cablevision

ELBERON—See KEYSTONE, IA

▲ **ELDON**—TCI

▲ **ELDORA**—TCI Cablevision

ELDRIDGE—See MOLINE, IL

▲ **ELGIN**—Triax Cablevision

▲ **ELK HORN**—Marne & Elk Horn Telephone Co.

ELK RUN HEIGHTS—See WATERLOO, IA

ELKADER—See PRAIRIE DU CHIEN, WI

ELKHART—See ALLEMAN, IA

ELKPORT—See GARBER, IA

▲ **ELLIOTT**—Elliott Cable TV

ELLSWORTH—See JEWELL, IA

▲ **ELMA**—Triax Cablevision

ELWOOD—See LOST NATION, IA

▲ **ELY**—Mid American Cable Systems

▲ **EMERSON**—Interstate Cablevision Inc.

▲ **EMMETSBURG**—Triax Cablevision

EPWORTH—See DYERSVILLE, IA

ESSEX—See SHENANDOAH, IA

▲ **ESTHERVILLE**—Triax Cablevision

EVANSDALE—See WATERLOO, IA

▲ **EVERLY**—Evertek Inc.

▲ **EXIRA**—Marne & Elk Horn Telephone Co.

▲ **FAIRBANK**—Triax Cablevision

▲ **FAIRFAX**—Starwest Inc.

FAIRFAX—See also CEDAR RAPIDS, IA

▲ **FAIRFIELD**—TCI

FAIRVIEW—See MARTELLE, IA

FARLEY—See DYERSVILLE, IA

FARMERSBURG—See MONONA, IA

▲ **FARMINGTON**—Starwest Inc.

▲ **FARRAGUT**—Tele-Services Ltd.

▲ **FAYETTE**—Triax Cablevision

▲ **FENTON**—Fenton Cablevision

FLOYD—See CHARLES CITY, IA

▲ **FONDA**—New Path Communications LC

▲ **FONTANELLE**—Visioncom

▲ **FOREST CITY**—TCI of Northern Iowa

FOREST CITY—See also THOMPSON, IA

FORT ATKINSON—See CALMAR, IA

▲ **FORT DODGE**—Cablevision VI Inc.

▲ **FORT MADISON**—TCI Cablevision

FOSTORIA—See MILFORD, IA

FRANKLIN—See DONNELLSON, IA

FRANKLIN COUNTY (eastern portion)—See ACKLEY, IA

▲ **FREDERICKSBURG**—Triax Cablevision

FREDERIKA—See TRIPOLI, IA

FREDONIA—See COLUMBUS JUNCTION, IA

▲ **FREMONT**—Starwest Inc.

FRUITLAND—See MUSCATINE, IA

GALVA—See CLEGHORN, IA

▲ **GARBER**—Alpine Communications LC

▲ **GARDEN GROVE**—Falcon/Capital Cable Partners

▲ **GARNAVILLO**—Triax Cablevision

▲ **GARNER**—TCI of Northern Iowa

GARRISON—See KEYSTONE, IA

GARWIN—See GLADBROOK, IA

▲ **GENEVA**—Dumont Cablevision

▲ **GEORGE**—Siebring Cable TV

▲ **GILBERT**—Complete Communications

GILBERTVILLE—See WATERLOO, IA

▲ **GILLETT GROVE**—ATC Cablevision Inc.

▲ **GILMAN**—Mid-Iowa Communications

▲ **GILMORE CITY**—Cable Systems Management of Iowa Inc.

▲ **GLADBROOK**—Triax Cablevision

▲ **GLENWOOD**—Heritage Cablevision Inc.

GLIDDEN—See CARROLL, IA

▲ **GOLDFIELD**—Goldfield Communication Services Corp.

▲ **GOODELL (village)**—New Path Communications LC

GOOSE LAKE—See PRESTON, IA

▲ **GOWRIE**—Gowrie Cablevision

GRAETTINGER—See ESTHERVILLE, IA

▲ **GRAND JUNCTION**—Tele-Services Ltd.

▲ **GRAND MOUND**—Grand Mound Cooperative Telephone Assn.

GRAND MOUND—See also CLINTON, IA

▲ **GRAND RIVER**—Deans Cablevision Inc.

▲ **GRANDVIEW**—New Path Communications LC

▲ **GRANGER**—TCI of Central Iowa

GRANT—See GRISWOLD, IA

▲ **GRAVITY**—New Path Communications LC

▲ **GREELEY**—Alpine Communications LC

GREEN MOUNTAIN—See MARSHALLTOWN, IA

▲ **GREENE**—Triax Cablevision

GREENE COUNTY—See JEFFERSON, IA

▲ **GREENFIELD**—Heritage Cablevision Inc.

GRIMES—See DES MOINES, IA

▲ **GRINNELL**—TCI of Southern Iowa

▲ **GRISWOLD**—Griswold Cable TV

▲ **GRUNDY CENTER**—TCI Cablevision

▲ **GUTHRIE CENTER**—Cablevision VI Inc.

GUTTENBERG—See PRAIRIE DU CHIEN, WI

▲ **HAMBURG**—Tele-Services Ltd.

HAMILTON—See BUSSEY, IA

HAMILTON COUNTY—See WEBSTER CITY, IA

▲ **HAMPTON**—TCI of Northern Iowa

HANCOCK—See EARLING, IA

HARCOURT—See LEHIGH, IA

HARDIN COUNTY—See ELDORA, IA

HARDIN COUNTY—See also IOWA FALLS, IA

▲ **HARLAN**—Heritage Cablevision Inc.

HARPERS FERRY—See PRAIRIE DU CHIEN, WI

HARRIS—See LAKE PARK, IA

HARRISON COUNTY (unincorporated areas)—See MISSOURI VALLEY, IA

▲ **HARTFORD**—Walnut Creek Communications Inc.

▲ **HARTLEY**—Hartley Municipal Cable TV

▲ **HASTINGS**—New Path Communications LC

▲ **HAVELOCK**—Northwest Communications Inc.

▲ **HAWARDEN**—City of Hawarden

▲ **HAWARDEN**—TCI

▲ **HAWKEYE**—Hawkeye TV Co.

HAZLETON—See OELWEIN, IA

▲ **HEDRICK**—Starwest Inc.

▲ **HENDERSON**—New Path Communications LC

HENRY COUNTY (portions)—See MOUNT PLEASANT, IA

HIAWATHA—See CEDAR RAPIDS, IA

▲ **HILLS**—Mississippi Cablevision

HILLSBORO—See SALEM, IA

▲ **HINTON**—Vernon Communications & TV Inc.

▲ **HOLLAND**—New Path Communications LC

▲ **HOLSTEIN**—Comserv Ltd.

HOLY CROSS—See LUXEMBURG, IA

▲ **HOPKINTON**—Shellsburg Cablevision Inc.

▲ **HORNICK**—New Path Communications LC

▲ **HOSPERS**—HTC Cablecom

▲ **HUBBARD**—Hubbard Co-op Cable

▲ **HUDSON**—Triax Cablevision

HULL—See SIOUX CENTER, IA

▲ **HUMBOLDT**—TCI

▲ **HUMESTON**—Falcon/Capital Cable Partners

HUXLEY—See SHELDAHL, IA

▲ **IDA GROVE**—Comserv Ltd.

▲ **INDEPENDENCE**—TCI

▲ **INDIANOLA**—TCI Cablevision

▲ **INWOOD**—Dakota Telecom Inc.

▲ **IONIA**—Mid American Cable Systems

IOWA ARMY MUNITIONS PLANT—See BURLINGTON, IA

▲ **IOWA CITY**—TCI of Eastern Iowa

▲ **IOWA FALLS**—WestMarc Cable Holding Inc.

▲ **IRETON**—Vernon Communication & TV Inc.

IRWIN—See EARLING, IA

JACKSON COUNTY—See PRESTON, IA

▲ **JAMAICA**—Panora Cooperative Cablevision Assn. Inc.

JANESVILLE—See WAVERLY, IA

JASPER COUNTY (central portion)—See NEWTON, IA

JASPER COUNTY (southwestern portion)—See also COLFAX, IA

▲ **JEFFERSON**—Heritage Cablevision Inc.

JEFFERSON COUNTY (portions)—See FAIRFIELD, IA

▲ **JESUP**—Jesup Farmer's Mutual Telephone

▲ **JEWELL**—Complete Communications

JOHNSON COUNTY—See IOWA CITY, IA

JOHNSON COUNTY (rural portion)—See NORTH LIBERTY, IA

JOHNSON COUNTY (rural portion)—See also SOLON, IA

JOHNSTON—See DES MOINES, IA

▲ **JOICE (village)**—New Path Communications LC

▲ **KALONA**—Triax Cablevision

KAMRAR (village)—See STRATFORD, IA

▲ **KANAWHA**—Norway Cablevision Inc.

▲ **KELLERTON**—Mississippi Cablevision

▲ **KELLEY**—Walnut Creek Communications Inc.

KELLOGG—See GILMAN, IA

KENSETT—See NORTHWOOD, IA

▲ **KEOKUK**—TCI of Eastern Iowa

▲ **KEOSAUQUA**—Starwest Inc.

▲ **KEOTA**—Triax Cablevision

▲ **KESWICK**—Mississippi Cablevision

▲ **KEYSTONE**—South Benton Cablevision Inc.

KIMBALLTON—See ELK HORN, IA

▲ **KINGSLEY**—Comserv

KIRKMAN—See EARLING, IA

▲ **KIRON**—Comserv Ltd.

▲ **KLEMME**—Norway Cablevision Inc.

▲ **KNOXVILLE**—TCI Cablevision

▲ **LA PORTE CITY**—Triax Cablevision

▲ **LACONA**—Walnut Creek Communications Inc.

LADORA—See BROOKLYN, IA

LAKE CITY—See LAVINIA, IA

LAKE MILLS—See THOMPSON, IA

LAKE PANORAMA—See PANORA, IA

▲ **LAKE PARK**—Cable Systems Management of Iowa Inc.

▲ **LAKE VIEW**—Comserv Ltd.

LAKESIDE—See STORM LAKE, IA

LAKEWOOD—See DES MOINES, IA

▲ **LAKOTA**—Heck's TV & Cable Co.

LAMBS GROVE—See NEWTON, IA

▲ **LAMONI**—Mississippi Cablevision

▲ **LAMONT**—Alpine Communications LC

▲ **LANSING**—InterMedia Partners

LANSING—See also PRAIRIE DU CHIEN, WI

▲ **LARCHWOOD**—Dakota Telecom Inc.

▲ **LATIMER**—Latimer/Coulter Cablevision

LAUREL—See GILMAN, IA

▲ **LAURENS**—Televents Group Joint Venture

▲ **LAVINIA**—Heritage Communications Inc.

▲ **LAWLER**—Alpine Communications LC

▲ **LAWTON**—New Path Communications LC

LE CLAIRE—See CLINTON, IA

LE GRAND—See MARSHALLTOWN, IA

▲ **LE MARS**—Cablevision VI Inc.

▲ **LEDYARD (village)**—New Path Communications LC

LEE COUNTY (northern portion)—See FORT MADISON, IA

▲ **LEHIGH**—Lehigh Services Inc.

LELAND—See FOREST CITY, IA

▲ **LENOX**—Lenox Municipal Cablevision

▲ **LEON**—Heritage Cablevision Inc.

▲ **LETTS**—New Path Communications LC

LEWIS—See GRISWOLD, IA

▲ **LIME SPRINGS**—Triax Cablevision

▲ **LINCOLN**—New Path Communications LC

LINDEN—See PANORA, IA

▲ **LINEVILLE**—Falcon/Capital Cable Partners

LINN COUNTY (unincorporated areas)—See CEDAR RAPIDS, IA

▲ **LISBON**—TCI

▲ **LITTLE ROCK**—Vernon Communications & TV Inc.

▲ **LITTLE SIOUX**—New Path Communications LC

▲ **LITTLETON**—Farmers Mutual

▲ **LIVERMORE**—Livermore Cable Inc.

▲ **LOGAN**—New Path Communications LC

▲ **LOHRVILLE**—Tele-Services Ltd.

▲ **LONE TREE**—Triax Cablevision

LONG GROVE—See MOLINE, IL

▲ **LOST NATION**—LN Satellite Communications Co.

LOUISA COUNTY—See MUSCATINE, IA

LOUISA COUNTY—See also WAPELLO, IA

LOVILIA—See BUSSEY, IA

LOW MOOR—See CLINTON, IA

▲ **LOWDEN**—F & B Cablevision

▲ **LOWDEN**—Triax Cablevision

▲ **LU VERNE**—Video Services Ltd.

LUANA—See MONONA, IA

▲ **LUXEMBURG**—Shellsburg Cablevision Inc.

LYNNVILLE—See SULLY, IA

▲ **LYTTON**—New Path Communications LC

M & W MOBILE HOME PARK—See MUSCATINE COUNTY, IA

MACEDONIA—See CARSON, IA

▲ **MADRID**—Heritage Communications Inc.

MAGNOLIA—See LOGAN, IA

MALCOM—See BROOKLYN, IA

MALLARD—See HAVELOCK, IA

▲ **MALVERN**—Tele-Services Ltd.

▲ **MANCHESTER**—Triax Cablevision

▲ **MANILLA**—Manilla Municipal Cable

▲ **MANLY**—Triax Cablevision

▲ **MANNING**—Manning Municipal Cable TV

MANSON—See LAVINIA, IA

▲ **MAPLETON**—Mapleton Municipal CATV

▲ **MAQUOKETA**—TCI of Iowa Inc.

MARATHON—See CLEGHORN, IA

▲ **MARBLE ROCK**—Farmer's Mutual Telephone Co.

▲ **MARCUS**—Cable Systems Management of Iowa Inc.

▲ **MARENGO**—TCI Cablevision

MARION—See CEDAR RAPIDS, IA

MARION COUNTY—See KNOXVILLE, IA

MARION COUNTY—See also PELLA, IA

MARNE—See ELK HORN, IA

MARQUETTE—See PRAIRIE DU CHIEN, WI

MARSHALL COUNTY—See MARSHALLTOWN, IA

▲ **MARSHALLTOWN**—TCI Cablevision

▲ **MARTELLE**—Martelle Cooperative Telephone Assn.

▲ **MARTENSDALE**—Interstate Cablevision Inc.

▲ **MASON CITY**—TCI of Northern Iowa

▲ **MASSENA**—New Path Communications LC

▲ **MAURICE**—Vernon Communications & TV Inc.

▲ **MAXWELL**—Walnut Creek Communications Inc.

▲ **MAYNARD**—Triax Cablevision

▲ **MAYSVILLE**—Dixon Telephone Co.

McCAUSLAND—See CLINTON, IA

McGREGOR—See PRAIRIE DU CHIEN, WI

▲ **MECHANICSVILLE**—Mechanicsville Telephone Co.

▲ **MEDIAPOLIS**—Mediapolis Cablevision

MELBOURNE—See GILMAN, IA

▲ **MELCHER**—Mississippi Cablevision

▲ **MELVIN**—Vernon Communications & TV Inc.

▲ **MENLO**—Coon Valley Cablevision

MENLO—See also CASEY, IA

MERIDEN—See CLEGHORN, IA

▲ **MERRILL**—Vernon Communications & TV Inc.

▲ **MESERVEY**—Northland Communications Inc.

MIDDLETOWN—See BURLINGTON, IA

MIDWAY—See CEDAR RAPIDS, IA

MILES—See PRESTON, IA

▲ **MILFORD**—Milford Cable TV

MILLS COUNTY—See GLENWOOD, IA

▲ **MILO**—Walnut Creek Communications Inc.

▲ **MILTON**—New Path Communications LC

▲ **MINBURN**—Minburn Cablevision Inc.

▲ **MINDEN**—Minden Cablevision

▲ **MISSOURI VALLEY**—Cable USA

MITCHELLVILLE—See COLFAX, IA

▲ **MONDAMIN**—New Path Communications LC

▲ **MONONA**—Northeast Iowa Telephone Co.

▲ **MONROE**—Mississippi Cablevision

▲ **MONTEZUMA**—Triax Cablevision

▲ **MONTICELLO**—Triax Cablevision

MONTOUR—See GILMAN, IA

▲ **MONTROSE**—Triax Cablevision

▲ **MOORHEAD**—Soldier Valley Telephone

MOORLAND—See FORT DODGE, IA

▲ **MORAVIA**—Capital Cable

MORLEY—See MARTELLE, IA

▲ **MORNING SUN**—Cablevision VII Inc.

▲ **MOULTON**—Mississippi Cablevision

▲ **MOUNT AYR**—Heritage Cablevision Inc.

MOUNT JOY—See MOLINE, IL

▲ **MOUNT PLEASANT**—TCI Cablevision

MOUNT VERNON—See LISBON, IA

▲ **MOVILLE**—Comserv Ltd.

▲ **MURRAY**—Interstate Cablevision Inc.

▲ **MUSCATINE**—TCI of Eastern Iowa

▲ **MUSCATINE COUNTY**—New Path Communications LC

MUSCATINE COUNTY—See also MUSCATINE, IA

▲ **MYSTIC**—Capital Cable

▲ **NASHUA**—Triax Cablevision

▲ **NEOLA**—Tele-Services Ltd.

NEVADA—See AMES, IA

▲ **NEW ALBIN**—Triax Cablevision

▲ **NEW HAMPTON**—Triax Cablevision

▲ **NEW HARTFORD**—Triax Cable TV

▲ **NEW LIBERTY**—Dixon Telephone Co.

NEW LONDON—See MOUNT PLEASANT, IA

▲ **NEW MARKET**—Farmers Mutual Telephone Co. of Stanton Inc.

▲ **NEW SHARON**—Triax Cablevision

NEW VIENNA—See LUXEMBURG, IA

▲ **NEW VIRGINIA**—Interstate Cablevision Inc.

▲ **NEWELL**—New Path Communications LC

▲ **NEWHALL**—Triax Cablevision

▲ **NEWTON**—TCI Cablevision

▲ **NICHOLS**—PEC Cablevision

NORA SPRINGS—See GREENE, IA

▲ **NORTH ENGLISH**—Triax Cablevision

▲ **NORTH LIBERTY**—Mississippi Cablevision

▲ **NORTHWOOD**—TCI of Northern Iowa

NORWALK—See DES MOINES, IA

▲ **OAKLAND**—Tele-Services Ltd.

OAKLAND ACRES—See GILMAN, IA

▲ **OAKVILLE**—New Path Communications LC

▲ **OCHEYEDAN**—Vernon Communications & TV Inc.

▲ **ODEBOLT**—Comserv Ltd.

▲ **OELWEIN**—TCI

▲ **OGDEN**—Ogden Telephone & Cable Co.

OKOBOJI—See SPIRIT LAKE, IA

OLDS—See WAYLAND, IA

OLIN—See CLARENCE, IA

OLIN—See also STANWOOD, IA

▲ **ONAWA**—Metro Cable Inc.

▲ **ONSLOW**—Onslow Cooperative Telephone Assn.

▲ **ORANGE CITY**—Orange City/Alton Cable

▲ **ORIENT**—New Path Communications LC

ORLEANS—See SPIRIT LAKE, IA

ORTONVILLE—See ADEL, IA

▲ **OSAGE**—TCI of Northern Iowa

▲ **OSCEOLA**—TCI Cablevision

▲ **OSKALOOSA**—Televents Group Joint Venture

OSSIAN—See CALMAR, IA

OTHO—See STRATFORD, IA

OTO—See SMITHLAND, IA

▲ **OTTUMWA**—Ottumwa Cablevision Inc.

▲ **OXFORD**—Mississippi Cablevision

▲ **OXFORD JUNCTION**—Triax Cablevision

OXFORD JUNCTION—See also LOST NATION, IA

OYENS—See LE MARS, IA

▲ **PACIFIC JUNCTION**—New Path Communications LC

▲ **PALMER**—Palmer Mutual Telephone Co.

▲ **PALO**—Palo Cooperative Telephone Assn.

PANAMA—See DEFIANCE, IA

▲ **PANORA**—Panora Cooperative Cablevision Assn. Inc.

PANORAMA PARK—See MOLINE, IL

▲ **PARKERSBURG**—TCI of Northern Iowa

PARKVIEW—See MOLINE, IL

▲ **PATON**—Gowrie Cablevision

▲ **PAULINA**—Cable Systems Management of Iowa Inc.

▲ **PELLA**—TCI Cablevision

▲ **PERRY**—TCI of Central Iowa

PERSHING—See KNOXVILLE, IA

▲ **PETERSON**—Cable Systems Management of Iowa Inc.

PIERSON—See CLEGHORN, IA

▲ **PISGAH**—New Path Communications LC

PLAINFIELD—See TRIPOLI, IA

PLEASANT HILL—See DES MOINES, IA

PLEASANT VALLEY—See MOLINE, IL

▲**PLEASANTVILLE**—Mississippi Cablevision

PLOVER—See HAVELOCK, IA

▲ **PLYMOUTH**—Farmers Mutual Telephone Co.

PLYMOUTH—See also MARBLE ROCK, IA

PLYMOUTH COUNTY—See LE MARS, IA

▲ **POCAHONTAS**—Televents Group Joint Venture

POLK—See DES MOINES, IA

POLK CITY—See SHELDAHL, IA

POLK COUNTY (western portion)—See SHELDAHL, IA

▲ **POMEROY**—Telepartners

▲ **POSTVILLE**—Postville Telephone Co.

PRAIRIE CITY—See COLFAX, IA

▲ **PRESCOTT**—New Path Communications LC

▲ **PRESTON**—Telnet of Preston

PRIMGHAR—See SANBORN, IA

PRINCETON—See CLINTON, IA

▲ **PROTIVIN**—Protivin Cablevision

▲ **PULASKI**—Mississippi Cablevision

QUASQUETON—See WINTHROP, IA

▲ **RADCLIFFE**—Radcliffe Cablevision

▲ **RAKE (village)**—New Path Communications LC

RANDALL—See STORY CITY, IA

▲ **RANDOLPH**—New Path Communications LC

RAYMOND—See WATERLOO, IA

▲ **READLYN**—Readlyn Telephone Co.

▲ **RED OAK**—Heritage Cablevision Inc.

REDFIELD—See DEXTER, IA

▲ **REINBECK**—WestMarc Cable Holding Inc.

REMBRANDT—See CLEGHORN, IA

REMSEN—See LE MARS, IA

▲ **RENWICK**—Heck's TV & Cable Co.

RHODES—See GILMAN, IA

▲ **RICEVILLE**—Triax Cablevision

▲ **RICHLAND**—Starwest Inc.

RICKETTS—See CHARTER OAK, IA

▲ **RINGSTED**—Ringsted Cablevision Ltd.

RIPLEYS MOBILE HOME PARK—See MUSCATINE COUNTY, IA

RIVERDALE—See MOLINE, IL

▲ **RIVERSIDE**—Triax Cablevision

ROBINS—See SHELLSBURG, IA

▲ **ROCK RAPIDS**—Modern Communications

ROCK VALLEY—See SIOUX CENTER, IA

ROCKFORD—See GREENE, IA

ROCKWELL—See SHEFFIELD, IA

ROCKWELL CITY—See LAVINIA, IA

RODNEY—See SMITHLAND, IA

▲ **ROLAND**—Complete Communications

ROLFE—See HAVELOCK, IA

ROLLING GREEN ESTATES—See DIXON, IA

▲ **ROWAN (village)**—New Path Communications LC

▲ **ROWLEY (village)**—New Path Communications LC

▲ **ROYAL**—Royal Telephone Co.

▲ **RUDD**—Farmers Mutual Telephone Co.

RUDD—See also MARBLE ROCK, IA

▲ **RUNNELLS**—Walnut Creek Communications Inc.

▲ **RUSSELL**—Capital Cable

RUTHVEN—See TERRIL, IA

▲ **RYAN**—Shellsburg Cablevision Inc.

SABULA—See CLINTON, IA

SAC CITY—See LAVINIA, IA

SAGEVILLE—See DUBUQUE, IA

▲ **SALEM**—New Path Communications LC

▲ **SALIX**—Northwest Iowa Telephone Co.

▲ **SANBORN**—Community Cable TV Corp.

SAYLORVILLE—See DES MOINES, IA

▲ **SCHALLER**—Comserv Ltd.

▲ **SCHLESWIG**—Tip Top Communication

SCOTT COUNTY (northern portion)—See CLINTON, IA

SCOTT COUNTY (portions)—See also MOLINE, IL

▲ **SCRANTON**—Scranton Community Antenna Television

SERGEANT BLUFF—See SIOUX CITY, IA

▲ **SEYMOUR**—Capital Cable

▲ **SHEFFIELD**—Triax Cablevision

▲ **SHELBY**—Marne & Elk Horn Telephone & CATV Co.

SHELBY—See also NEOLA, IA

▲ **SHELDAHL**—TCI Cablevision

▲ **SHELDON**—HTC Cablecom

SHELL ROCK—See WAVERLY, IA

▲ **SHELLSBURG**—Shellsburg Cablevision Inc.

▲ **SHENANDOAH**—TCI Cablevision

▲ **SHERRILL**—Alpine Communications LC

SHUEYVILLE—See SWISHER, IA

▲ **SIBLEY**—HTC Cablecom

▲ **SIDNEY**—Tele-Services Ltd.

▲ **SIGOURNEY**—Triax Cablevision

▲ **SILVER CITY**—Interstate Cablevision Co.

▲ **SIOUX CENTER**—Premier Communications Inc.

▲ **SIOUX CITY**—Cable One

SIOUX COUNTY—See HAWARDEN, IA (TCI)

▲ **SIOUX RAPIDS**—Cable Systems Management of Iowa Inc.

SLATER—See SHELDAHL, IA

SLOAN—See SALIX, IA

▲ **SMITHLAND**—New Path Communications LC

▲ **SOLDIER**—Soldier Valley Telephone

▲ **SOLON**—Mississippi Cablevision

▲ **SPENCER**—Triax Cablevision

SPILLVILLE—See CALMAR, IA

▲ **SPIRIT LAKE**—Spirit Lake Cable TV

▲ **SPRINGVILLE**—Springville Cable Co.

▲ **ST. ANSGAR**—Triax Cablevision

ST. ANTHONY—See ZEARING, IA

▲ **ST. CHARLES**—Interstate Cablevision Inc.

▲ **ST. LUCAS**—Alpine Communications LC

ST. OLAF—See MONONA, IA

▲ **STACYVILLE**—Triax Cablevision

STANHOPE—See STRATFORD, IA

▲ **STANTON**—Farmers Mutual Telephone Co. of Stanton Inc.

▲ **STANWOOD**—Triax Cablevision

▲ **STATE CENTER**—Complete Communications

▲ **STEAMBOAT ROCK**—Steamboat Rock Cablevision

STOCKPORT—See BIRMINGHAM, IA

STONE CITY—See MARTELLE, IA

▲ **STORM LAKE**—Heritage Cablevision Inc.

▲ **STORY CITY**—TCI Cablevision

STORY COUNTY—See AMES, IA

STORY COUNTY (southwestern portion)—See also SHELDAHL, IA

▲ **STRATFORD**—Complete Communications Service (CCS)

▲ **STRAWBERRY POINT**—Triax Cablevision

STUART—See DEXTER, IA

▲ **SULLY**—Triax Cablevision

SUMMERSET—See INDIANOLA, IA

▲ **SUMNER**—Triax Cablevision

▲ **SUN VALLEY LAKE**—Interstate Cablevision Co.

▲ **SUTHERLAND**—Cable Systems Management of Iowa Inc.

▲ **SWALEDALE (village)**—New Path Communications LC

▲ **SWEA CITY**—Triax Cablevision

▲ **SWISHER**—Mississippi Cablevision

▲ **TABOR**—Tele-Services Ltd.

TAMA—See TOLEDO, IA

▲ **TEMPLETON**—Templeton Telephone Co.

▲ **TERRIL**—Terril Cable Systems

▲ **THOMPSON**—Winnebago Cooperative Telephone Assn.

▲ **THOR**—Cable Systems Management of Iowa Inc.

▲ **THORNTON**—Northland Communications Inc.

▲ **THURMAN**—Tele-Services Ltd.

TIFFIN—See OXFORD, IA

▲ **TIPTON**—Triax Cablevision

▲ **TITONKA**—Titonka Telephone Co.

TODDVILLE—See CEDAR RAPIDS, IA

▲ **TOLEDO**—TCI Cablevision

▲ **TRAER**—TCI Cablevision

▲ **TREYNOR**—Tele-Services Ltd.

▲ **TRIPOLI**—Butler-Bremer Mutual Telephone Co.

▲ **TRURO**—Interstate Cablevision Inc.

▲ **UNDERWOOD**—New Path Communications LC

▲ **UNION**—Mid American Cable Systems

UNIVERSITY HEIGHTS—See IOWA CITY, IA

UNIVERSITY PARK—See OSKALOOSA, IA

URBANA—See SHELLSBURG, IA

URBANDALE—See DES MOINES, IA

▲ **UTE**—Soldier Valley Telephone

▲ **VAIL**—Tip Top Communication

Van Buren County—See KEOSAUQUA, IA

▲ **VAN HORNE**—Van Horne Telephone Co.

VAN METER—See ADEL, IA

▲ **VAN WERT**—Deans Cablevision Inc.

VENTURA—See MASON CITY, IA

VICTOR—See BROOKLYN, IA

▲ **VILLISCA**—Heritage Cablevision Inc.

VINCENT—See THOR, IA

▲ **VINTON**—WestMarc Cable Holding Inc.

▲ **VOLGA**—Alpine Communications LC

▲ **WADENA (village)**—Alpine Communications LC

WAHPETON—See SPIRIT LAKE, IA

WALCOTT—See BLUE GRASS, IA

▲ **WALFORD (town)**—Mid American Cable Systems

WALKER—See ELY, IA

▲ **WALL LAKE**—Wall Lake Cable TV System

WALLINGFORD—See ESTHERVILLE, IA

▲ **WALNUT**—Walnut Telephone Co.

▲ **WAPELLO**—TCI of Eastern Iowa

WAPELLO COUNTY—See OTTUMWA, IA

WARREN COUNTY (portions)—See DES MOINES, IA

WARREN COUNTY (portions)—See also INDIANOLA, IA

WASHBURN—See WATERLOO, IA

▲ **WASHINGTON**—Ottumwa Cablevision

WASHTA—See CLEGHORN, IA

▲ **WATERLOO**—TCI of Northern Iowa

WAUKEE—See ADEL, IA

WAUKEE (eastern portion)—See also DES MOINES, IA

▲ **WAUKON**—InterMedia Partners

WAUKON JUNCTION—See PRAIRIE DU CHIEN, WI

▲ **WAVERLY**—Heritage Cablevision

▲ **WAYLAND**—Wayland Cable TV

▲ **WEBB**—Vernon Communications & TV Inc.

▲ **WEBSTER CITY**—TCI Cablevision

WEBSTER COUNTY—See FORT DODGE, IA

WELDON—See VAN WERT, IA

WELLMAN—See KALONA, IA

▲ **WELLSBURG**—Union Cablevision

▲ **WESLEY**—Wesley Cable Co.

WEST BEND—See HAVELOCK, IA

▲ **WEST BRANCH**—TCI

WEST BURLINGTON—See BURLINGTON, IA

WEST DES MOINES—See DES MOINES, IA

WEST LIBERTY—See ATALISSA, IA

WEST OKOBOJI—See SPIRIT LAKE, IA

WEST POINT—See FORT MADISON, IA

▲ **WEST UNION**—Triax Cablevision

▲ **WESTGATE (village)**—Alpine Communications LC

WESTPHALIA—See EARLING, IA

▲ **WESTSIDE**—Tele-Services Ltd.

▲ **WHAT CHEER**—Triax Cablevision

▲ **WHEATLAND**—F & B Cablevision

▲ **WHITING**—New Path Communications LC

▲ **WHITTEMORE**—ATC Cablevision Co.

▲ **WILLIAMS**—Williams Cablevision

▲ **WILLIAMSBURG**—Triax Cablevision

▲ **WILTON**—Cablevision VII Inc.

WINDSOR HEIGHTS—See DES MOINES, IA

▲ **WINFIELD**—New Path Communications LC

▲ **WINTERSET**—TCI Cablevision

▲ **WINTHROP**—East Buchanan Telephone Cooperative

▲ **WODEN**—Heck's TV & Cable

▲ **WOODBINE**—New Path Communications LC

WOODBURY COUNTY—See SIOUX CITY, IA

WOODWARD—See MADRID, IA

▲ **WOOLSTOCK**—Goldfield Communication Services Corp.

▲ **WORTHINGTON**—Shellsburg Cablevision Inc.

WRIGHT COUNTY (central portion)—See CLARION, IA

WYOMING—See OXFORD JUNCTION, IA

YALE—See PANORA, IA

▲ **ZEARING**—Minerva Valley Cablevision

KANSAS

▲ **ABBYVILLE**—Five Star Cable TV

▲ **ABILENE**—Classic Cable

▲ **ADMIRE**—Galaxy Cablevision

AGRA—See KENSINGTON, KS

ALBERT—See McCRACKEN, KS

▲ **ALMA**—Galaxy Cablevision

▲ **ALMENA**—Classic Cable

▲ **ALTA VISTA**—Galaxy Cablevision

▲ **ALTAMONT**—Altamont Cable TV

ALTON—See WOODSTON, KS

▲ **ALTOONA**—Mediacom

▲ **AMERICUS**—Galaxy Cablevision

▲ **ANDALE**—Classic Cable

▲ **ANDOVER**—Multimedia Cablevision Inc.

▲ **ANTHONY**—Classic Cable

AQUARIAN ACRES—See TECUMSEH, KS

▲ **ARCADIA**—National Cable Inc.

▲ **ARGONIA**—Classic Cable

▲ **ARKANSAS CITY**—Multimedia Cablevision Inc.

▲ **ARLINGTON**—Classic Cable

▲ **ARMA**—TCI of Pittsburg

▲ **ASHLAND**—Classic Cable

▲ **ASSARIA**—Galva Cable Co.

▲ **ATCHISON**—Atchison Cablecomm

ATCHISON COUNTY (portions)—See ATCHISON, KS

▲ **ATLANTA**—Southern Kansas Telephone Co.

▲ **ATTICA**—Classic Cable

▲ **ATWOOD**—Atwood Cable Systems Inc.

▲ **AUBURN**—Multimedia Cablevision

▲ **AUGUSTA**—Multimedia Cablevision Inc.

▲ **AXTELL**—C.L.R. Video LLC

▲ **BAILEYVILLE**—Carson Communications LLC

▲ **BALDWIN CITY**—Mediacom

BARBER COUNTY—See SHARON, KS

▲ **BARNARD**—Twin Valley Communications

▲ **BARNES**—Galaxy Cablevision

BARTON COUNTY—See GREAT BEND, KS

▲ **BASEHOR**—Galaxy Cablevision

▲ **BAXTER SPRINGS**—City of Baxter Springs

▲ **BAZINE**—Classic Cable

▲ **BEATTIE**—Beatrice Cable TV Co.

BEL AIRE—See WICHITA, KS

▲ **BELLE PLAINE**—Clearwater CableVision Inc.

▲ **BELLEVILLE**—Belleville Community Antenna Systems Inc.

▲ **BELOIT**—Black Creek Communications

▲ **BELVUE**—C.L.R. Video LLC

▲ **BENNINGTON**—Twin Valley Communications

▲ **BENTLEY**—Westcom

▲ **BENTON**—Galaxy Cablevision

▲ **BERN**—Carson Communications LLC

BERRYTON—See TECUMSEH, KS

▲ **BEVERLY**—Twin Valley Communications

BIRD CITY—See McDONALD, KS (Classic Cable)

BISON—See RUSH CENTER, KS

▲ **BLUE MOUND**—National Cable Inc.

▲ **BLUE RAPIDS**—Galaxy Cablevision

BOGUE—See HILL CITY, KS

BONNER SPRINGS—See KANSAS CITY, MO

BOURBON COUNTY (unincorporated areas)—See FORT SCOTT, KS

▲ **BREWSTER**—S & T Communications of Northwest Kansas

▲ **BRONSON**—Galaxy Cablevision

▲ **BROOKVILLE**—Westcom

▲ **BUCKLIN**—Classic Cable

▲ **BUFFALO**—National Cable Inc.

▲ **BUHLER**—Multimedia Cablevision Inc.

▲ **BURDEN**—Clearwater CableVision Inc.

BURDETT—See RUSH CENTER, KS

BURLINGAME—See OSAGE CITY, KS

▲ **BURLINGTON**—Mediacom

▲ **BURNS**—Westcom

▲ **BURR OAK**—Vision Plus

▲ **BURRTON**—Classic Cable

BUSHTON—See HOLYROOD, KS

BUTLER COUNTY—See AUGUSTA, KS

BUTLER COUNTY—See also EL DORADO, KS

BUTLER COUNTY (portions)—See also WICHITA, KS

BUTLER COUNTY (southwestern portion)—See also ROSE HILL, KS

▲ **CALDWELL**—Classic Cable

▲ **CANEY**—TCI

▲ **CANTON**—Five Star Cable TV

CARBONDALE—See OSAGE CITY, KS

▲ **CAWKER CITY**—City of Cawker City

▲ **CEDAR VALE**—Southern Kansas Telephone Co.

▲ **CENTRALIA**—C.L.R. Video LLC

▲ **CHANUTE**—Time Warner Cable

▲ **CHAPMAN**—Galaxy Cablevision

CHASE—See HOLYROOD, KS

▲ **CHENEY**—Multimedia Cablevision Inc.

CHEROKEE—See WEIR, KS

▲ **CHERRYVALE**—TCI

▲ **CHETOPA**—TCI

CHICOPEE—See PITTSBURG, KS

▲ **CIMARRON**—United Communications Assn. Inc.

CIRCLEVILLE—See HOLTON, KS

CLAFLIN—See HOLYROOD, KS

▲ **CLAY CENTER**—Classic Cable

CLAY COUNTY (portions)—See CLAY CENTER, KS

▲ **CLEARWATER**—Clearwater CableVision Inc.

CLEARWATER (unincorporated areas)—See also SEDGWICK COUNTY (portions), KS

▲ **CLIFTON**—Galaxy Cablevision

CLOUD COUNTY (portions)—See CONCORDIA, KS

CLYDE—See CLIFTON, KS

▲ **COFFEYVILLE**—Multimedia Cablevision Inc.

▲ **COLBY**—Cablevision Industries

▲ **COLDWATER**—Classic Cable

▲ **COLONY**—Galaxy Cablevision

▲ **COLUMBUS**—Columbus Cablevision

▲ **COLWICH**—Classic Cable

▲ **CONCORDIA**—Classic Cable

▲ **CONWAY SPRINGS**—Capital Cable

▲ **COPELAND**—United Communications Assn. Inc.

COTTONWOOD FALLS—See STRONG CITY, KS

▲ **COUNCIL GROVE**—Community Antenna Systems Inc.

COUNTRYSIDE—See OVERLAND PARK, KS

▲ **COURTLAND**—Courtland Cable TV

Crawford County—See FRONTENAC, KS

▲ **CUBA**—Galaxy Cablevision

▲ **CUNNINGHAM**—Five Star Cable TV

DAMAR—See HILL CITY, KS

DE SOTO—See KANSAS CITY, MO

▲ **DEARING**—Southern Kansas Telephone Co.

▲ **DEERFIELD**—Pioneer Communications

▲ **DELPHOS**—Cunningham Telephone & Cable Co.

▲ **DENISON**—Carson Communications LLC

DERBY—See WICHITA, KS

DETROIT—See CHAPMAN, KS

▲ **DEXTER**—Southern Kansas Telephone Co.

DICKINSON COUNTY—See ABILENE, KS

DICKINSON COUNTY—See also HERINGTON, KS

▲ **DIGHTON**—Classic Cable

▲ **DODGE CITY**—Multimedia Cablevision

DORRANCE—See HOLYROOD, KS

DOUGLAS COUNTY (unincorporated areas)—See LAWRENCE, KS

▲ **DOUGLASS**—Capital Cable

▲ **DOWNS**—Classic Cable

▲ **DURHAM**—Galaxy Cablevision

▲ **DWIGHT**—Galaxy Cablevision

EASTBOROUGH—See WICHITA, KS

▲ **EASTON**—C.L.R. Video LLC

EDGERTON—See BALDWIN CITY, KS

▲ **EDMOND**—Vision Plus Inc.

▲ **EDNA**—Craw-Kan Telephone Co.

EDWARDSVILLE—See KANSAS CITY, MO

EDWARDSVILLE PARK—See KANSAS CITY, MO

▲ **EFFINGHAM**—C.L.R. Video LLC

▲ **EL DORADO**—Multimedia Cablevision Inc.

▲ **ELK CITY**—Southern Kansas Telephone Co.

ELK COUNTY—See HOWARD, KS

▲ **ELKHART**—Elkhart TV Cable Co.

▲ **ELLINWOOD**—Cable Comm

ELLIS—See HAYS, KS

▲ **ELLSWORTH**—Classic Cable

ELWOOD—See WATHENA, KS

▲ **EMMETT**—Carson Communications LLC

▲ **EMPORIA**—Time Warner Cable

▲ **ENSIGN**—United Communications Assn. Inc.

ENTERPRISE—See CHAPMAN, KS

▲ **ERIE**—TCI

ESBON—See LEBANON, KS

▲ **ESKRIDGE**—Galaxy Cablevision

EUDORA—See LAWRENCE, KS

▲ **EUREKA**—Mediacom

EVEREST—See HORTON, KS

▲ **FAIRVIEW**—Carson Communications LLC

FAIRWAY—See OVERLAND PARK, KS

FINNEY COUNTY—See GARDEN CITY, KS

▲ **FLORENCE**—Galaxy Cablevision

▲ **FONTANA**—Murray Radio & TV Service

▲ **FORD**—United Communications Assn. Inc.

FORD COUNTY—See DODGE CITY, KS

▲ **FORMOSO**—Cunningham Telephone & Cable Co.

FORT LEAVENWORTH—See KANSAS CITY, MO

▲ **FORT RILEY**—Charter Communications Inc.

▲ **FORT SCOTT**—Classic Cable

▲ **FOWLER**—Cable Systems Inc.

▲ **FRANKFORT**—C.L.R. Video LLC

FRANKLIN—See ARMA, KS

▲ **FREDONIA**—TCI

▲ **FRONTENAC**—Classic Cable

▲ **GALENA**—Mediacom

▲ **GALVA**—Galva Cable Co.

▲ **GARDEN CITY**—Multimedia Cablevision Inc.

▲ **GARDEN PLAIN**—Classic Cable

GARDNER—See KANSAS CITY, MO

GARFIELD—See RUSH CENTER, KS

▲ **GARNETT**—TCI

GAS—See IOLA, KS

GAYLORD—See WOODSTON, KS

▲ **GENESEO**—Classic Cable

▲ **GIRARD**—Classic Cable

▲ **GLASCO**—Cunningham Telephone & Cable Co.

▲ **GLEN ELDER**—Cunningham Telephone & Cable Co.

▲ **GODDARD**—Multimedia Cablevision Inc.

GODDARD—See also WICHITA, KS

GODDARD (unincorporated areas)—See also SEDGWICK COUNTY (portions), KS

▲ **GOESSEL**—Mid-Kansas Cable Services Inc.

▲ **GOFF**—Carson Communications LLC

▲ **GOODLAND**—Goodland Cable TV Co.

▲ **GORHAM**—Vision Plus

▲ **GRAINFIELD**—Vision Plus

GRANDVIEW PLAZA—See JUNCTION CITY, KS

▲ **GRANTVILLE**—SCI Cable Inc.

▲ **GREAT BEND**—Multimedia Cablevision Inc.

▲ **GREELEY**—Murray Radio & TV Service

▲ **GREENLEAF**—Beatrice Cable TV Co.

▲ **GREENSBURG**—Cable Systems Inc.

▲ **GRENOLA**—Southern Kansas Telephone Co.

GRIDLEY—See BURLINGTON, KS

▲ **GRINNELL**—S & T Communications of Northwest Kansas

▲ **GYPSUM**—Galva Cable Co.

▲ **HADDAM**—Westcom

HALSTEAD—See NEWTON, KS

▲ **HAMILTON**—Mediacom

▲ **HANOVER**—Beatrice Cable TV Co.

▲ **HANSTON**—United Communications Assn. Inc.

HARDTNER—See KIOWA, KS

▲ **HARPER**—Multimedia Cablevision Inc.

▲ **HARTFORD**—Galaxy Cablevision

HARVEY COUNTY (unincorporated areas)—See NEWTON, KS

▲ **HARVEYVILLE**—Galaxy Cablevision

▲ **HAVEN**—Multimedia Cablevision Inc.

HAVENSVILLE—See ONAGA, KS

▲ **HAVILAND**—Haviland Cable-Vision

▲ **HAYS**—Hays Cable TV Co.

HAYSVILLE—See WICHITA, KS

▲ **HEALY**—S & T Communications of Northwest Kansas

▲ **HERINGTON**—Multimedia Cablevision Inc.

▲ **HERNDON**—Vision Plus Inc.

HESSTON—See NEWTON, KS

▲ **HIAWATHA**—Carson Communications LLC

▲ **HIGHLAND**—Carson Communications LLC

▲ **HILL CITY**—Vision Plus Inc.

▲ **HILLSBORO**—Galaxy Cablevision

HOISINGTON—See GREAT BEND, KS

▲ **HOLCOMB**—Pioneer Communications

▲ **HOLTON**—C.L.R. Video LLC

▲ **HOLYROOD**—H & B Cable Service Inc.

▲ **HOME**—Diode Cable Co.

▲ **HOPE**—Galaxy Cablevision

▲ **HORTON**—C.L.R. Video LLC

▲ **HOWARD**—Southern Kansas Telephone Co.

▲ **HOXIE**—Hoxie Cable TV Co.

▲ **HOYT**—C.L.R. Video LLC

▲ **HUGOTON**—Pioneer Communications

▲ **HUMBOLDT**—TCI of Kansas Inc.

▲ **HUTCHINSON**—Multimedia Cablevision Inc.

▲ **INDEPENDENCE**—Cablevision of Independence

▲ **INGALLS**—United Communications Assn. Inc.

▲ **INMAN**—Multimedia Cablevision Inc.

▲ **IOLA**—Multimedia Cablevision Inc.

▲ **IUKA**—Five Star Cable TV

▲ **JAMESTOWN**—Cunningham Telephone & Cable Co.

JEFFERSON COUNTY (unincorporated areas)—See SHAWNEE COUNTY (northern portion), KS

JENNINGS—See EDMOND, KS

▲ **JETMORE**—Classic Cable

▲ **JEWELL**—Cunningham Telephone & Cable Co.

▲ **JOHNSON**—Pioneer Communications

JOHNSON COUNTY—See OLATHE, KS

JOHNSON COUNTY (northeastern portion)—See also OVERLAND PARK, KS

JOHNSON COUNTY (southern portion)—See also SPRING HILL, KS

▲ **JUNCTION CITY**—Multimedia Cablevision Inc.

KANOPOLIS—See ELLSWORTH, KS

▲ **KANORADO**—S & T Communications of Northwest Kansas

▲ **KANSAS CITY (portions)**—Capital Cable

KANSAS CITY (south of Kaw River)—See also KANSAS CITY, MO

KANSAS STATE UNIVERSITY—See MANHATTAN, KS

KECHI—See WICHITA, KS

▲ **KENSINGTON**—Classic Cable

▲ **KINGMAN**—Multimedia Cablevision Inc.

▲ **KINSLEY**—Communications Services Inc.

▲ **KIOWA**—Classic Cable

▲ **KIRWIN**—Vision Plus Inc.

▲ **KISMET**—Cable Systems Inc.

▲ **LA CROSSE**—Multimedia Cablevision

▲ **LA CYGNE**—Classic Cable

▲ **LA HARPE**—Capital Cable

▲ **LAKE DABINAWA**—Carson Communications LLC

▲ **LAKE OF THE FOREST**—Capital Cable

▲ **LAKE WABAUNSEE**—Galaxy Cablevision

LAKEWOOD HILLS—See LAKE DABINAWA, KS

▲ **LAKIN**—Pioneer Communications

LANCASTER—See ATCHISON, KS

▲ **LANE**—National Cable Inc.

LANSING—See KANSAS CITY, MO

LARNED—See GREAT BEND, KS

▲ **LAWRENCE**—Sunflower Cablevision

LE ROY—See BURLINGTON, KS

LEAVENWORTH—See KANSAS CITY, MO

LEAVENWORTH COUNTY (portions)—See KANSAS CITY, MO

LEAWOOD—See OVERLAND PARK, KS

▲ **LEBANON**—Vision Plus

LEBO—See OSAGE CITY, KS

LECOMPTON—See PERRY, KS

LENEXA—See OVERLAND PARK, KS

LENORA—See EDMOND, KS

▲ **LEON**—Clearwater CableVision Inc.

▲ **LEONARDVILLE**—C.L.R. Video LLC

▲ **LEOTI**—Classic Cable

▲ **LEWIS**—Kline's Cable TV

▲ **LIBERAL**—Century Communications

LIEBENTHAL—See SCHOENCHEN, KS

▲ **LINCOLN**—Classic Cable

▲ **LINCOLNVILLE**—Galaxy Cablevision

▲ **LINDSBORG**—Classic Cable

▲ **LINN**—Beatrice Cable TV Co.

▲ **LITTLE RIVER**—Home Town Cable

LOGAN—See EDMOND, KS

▲ **LONGTON**—Southern Kansas Telephone Co.

LORRAINE—See HOLYROOD, KS

▲ **LOUISBURG**—Classic Cable

LOUISVILLE—See WAMEGO, KS

▲ **LOWELL**—Riverton-Lowell Cablevision

▲ **LUCAS**—Lucas Cable TV Inc.

▲ **LURAY**—Classic Cable

LYNDON—See OSAGE CITY, KS

LYON COUNTY—See EMPORIA, KS

▲ **LYONS**—Multimedia Cablevision Inc.

▲ **MACKSVILLE**—Classic Cable

▲ **MADISON**—Mediacom

▲ **MAHASKA**—Westcom

MAIZE—See WICHITA, KS

▲ **MANHATTAN**—Multimedia Cablevision

MANHATTAN (portions)—See ST. GEORGE, KS

▲ **MANKATO**—Mankato Cable TV Inc.

MANTER—See JOHNSON, KS

▲ **MAPLE HILL**—TCI of Kansas Inc.

▲ **MARION**—Galaxy Cablevision

▲ **MARQUETTE**—Five Star Cable TV

MARSHALL COUNTY (portions)—See MARYSVILLE, KS

▲ **MARYSVILLE**—Beatrice Cable TV Co.

▲ **MAYETTA**—C.L.R. Video LLC

McCONNELL AFB—See WICHITA, KS

▲ **McCRACKEN**—G & K Communications

▲ **McCUNE**—Craw-Kan Telephone Co.

▲ **McDONALD**—Classic Cable

▲ **McDONALD**—Vision Plus Inc.

▲ **McFARLAND**—Galaxy Cablevision

▲ **McLOUTH**—C.L.R. Video LLC

▲ **McPHERSON**—Multimedia Cablevision Inc.

McPHERSON COUNTY (portions)—See McPHERSON, KS

▲ **MEADE**—Cable Systems Inc.

▲ **MEDICINE LODGE**—Multimedia Cablevision Inc.

▲ **MELVERN**—Galaxy Cablevision

▲ **MERIDEN**—Galaxy Cablevision

MERIDEN (portions)—See also GRANTVILLE, KS

MERRIAM—See OVERLAND PARK, KS

MIAMI COUNTY (unincorporated areas)—See PAOLA, KS

▲ **MILFORD**—Galaxy Cablevision

▲ **MILTONVALE**—Twin Valley Communications

▲ **MINNEAPOLIS**—Galaxy Cablevision

▲ **MINNEOLA**—Cable Systems Inc.

MISSION—See OVERLAND PARK, KS

MISSION HILLS—See KANSAS CITY, MO

MISSION WOODS—See KANSAS CITY, MO

MITCHELL COUNTY—See BELOIT, KS

▲ **MOLINE**—Southern Kansas Telephone Co.

MONTARA—See PAULINE, KS

▲ **MONTEZUMA**—United Communications Assn. Inc.

MONTGOMERY COUNTY (portions)—See INDEPENDENCE, KS

▲ **MORAN**—Galaxy Cablevision

▲ **MORGANVILLE**—Galaxy Cablevision

MORLAND—See HILL CITY, KS

▲ **MORRILL**—Carson Communications LLC

MORRIS COUNTY (portions)—See COUNCIL GROVE, KS

▲ **MORROWVILLE**—Diode Cable Co.

MOSCOW—See SUBLETTE, KS

MOUND CITY—See PLEASANTON, KS

▲ **MOUND VALLEY**—National Cable Inc.

▲ **MOUNDRIDGE**—Mid-Kansas Cable Services Inc.

▲ **MOUNT HOPE**—Classic Cable

MULBERRY—See LIBERAL, MO

▲ **MULLINVILLE**—Mullinville Cable TV

▲ **MULVANE**—Westcom

▲ **MULVANE (unincorporated areas)**—Westcom

MULVANE—See also WICHITA, KS

▲ **MUNDEN**—Westcom

▲ **MUNJOR**—GBT Communications

▲ **MUSCOTAH**—Carson Communications LLC

NARKA—See MAHASKA, KS

▲ **NATOMA**—Classic Cable

▲ **NEODESHA**—Cablevision of Neodesha

NEOSHO COUNTY (portions)—See ERIE, KS

▲ **NEOSHO RAPIDS**—Galaxy Cablevision

▲ **NESS CITY**—Classic Cable

▲ **NEW CAMBRIA**—Twin Valley Communications

NEW STRAWN—See BURLINGTON, KS

▲ **NEWTON**—Multimedia Cablevision of Newton

▲ **NICKERSON**—Multimedia Cablevision Inc.

▲ **NORCATUR**—Vision Plus Inc.

NORTH NEWTON—See NEWTON, KS

▲ **NORTON**—Classic Cable

▲ **NORTONVILLE**—C.L.R. Video LLC

▲ **NORWICH**—Classic Cable

▲ **OAKLEY**—Cablevision Industries

▲ **OBERLIN**—Classic Cable

▲ **OFFERLE**—Kline's Cable TV

OGDEN—See JUNCTION CITY, KS

▲ **OKETO**—Diode Cable Co.

▲ **OLATHE**—Jones Intercable

▲ **OLPE**—Galaxy Cablevision

▲ **OLSBURG**—C.L.R. Video LLC

▲ **ONAGA**—Galaxy Cablevision

▲ **OSAGE CITY**—Mediacom

▲ **OSAWATOMIE**—Classic Cable

OSBORNE—See WOODSTON, KS

▲ **OSKALOOSA**—C.L.R. Video LLC

▲ **OSWEGO**—Mediacom

OTIS—See RUSH CENTER, KS

▲ **OTTAWA**—Multimedia Cablevision

▲ **OVERBROOK**—Galaxy Cablevision

▲ **OVERLAND PARK**—Time Warner Cable of Johnson County

▲ **OXFORD**—Capital Cable

▲ **OZAWKIE**—C.L.R. Video LLC

PALCO—See HILL CITY, KS

▲ **PAOLA**—Classic Cable

PARK—See GRAINFIELD, KS

PARK CITY—See WICHITA, KS

▲ **PARKER**—National Cable Inc.

▲ **PARSONS**—Cablevision of Parsons

▲ **PARTRIDGE**—Westcom

▲ **PAULINE**—Multimedia Cablevision

▲ **PAWNEE ROCK**—GBT Communications

▲ **PAXICO**—Galaxy Cablevision

▲ **PEABODY**—Multimedia Cablevision of Peabody

▲ **PERRY**—Perry Cablevision

▲ **PHILLIPSBURG**—Classic Cable

▲ **PITTSBURG**—Multimedia Cablevision Inc.

▲ **PLAINS**—Cable Systems Inc.

▲ **PLAINVILLE**—Classic Cable

▲ **PLEASANTON**—Classic Cable

PLEVNA—See ABBYVILLE, KS

▲ **POMONA**—Galaxy Cablevision

POTTAWATOMIE COUNTY (portions)—See ST. MARYS, KS

POTTAWATOMIE COUNTY (portions)—See also WAMEGO, KS

▲ **POTWIN**—Galaxy Cablevision

PRAIRIE VILLAGE—See OVERLAND PARK, KS

▲ **PRATT**—Multimedia Cablevision Inc.

▲ **PRESCOTT**—National Cable Inc.

PRESTON—See TURON, KS

▲ **PRETTY PRAIRIE**—Classic Cable

▲ **PRINCETON**—Westcom

▲ **PROTECTION**—Classic Cable

▲ **QUENEMO**—Galaxy Cablevision

▲ **QUINTER**—Quinter Cable Co.

▲ **RANDALL**—Cunningham Telephone & Cable Co.

▲ **RANDOLPH**—Carson Communications LLC

RANSOM—See McCRACKEN, KS

▲ **RANTOUL**—Murray Radio & TV Service Inc.

▲ **READING**—Galaxy Cablevision

▲ **RED BUD LAKE**—Twin Valley Communications

RENO COUNTY (portions)—See HUTCHINSON, KS

▲ **REPUBLIC**—Diode Cable Co.

▲ **RESERVE**—Carson Communications LLC

RICE COUNTY—See LYONS, KS

▲ **RICHMOND**—Galaxy Cablevision

▲ **RILEY**—Galaxy Cablevision

RIVERTON—See LOWELL, KS

ROBINSON—See HORTON, KS

ROELAND PARK—See OVERLAND PARK, KS

ROLLA—See ELKHART, KS

▲ **ROSALIA**—Westcom

▲ **ROSE HILL**—Multimedia Cablevision Inc.

▲ **ROSSVILLE**—Galaxy Cablevision

ROZEL—See RUSH CENTER, KS

▲ **RUSH CENTER**—GBT Communications Inc.

▲ **RUSSELL**—Russell Cable TV Co.

▲ **SABETHA**—Galaxy Cablevision

▲ **SALINA**—Multimedia Cablevision

▲ **SATANTA**—Pioneer Communications

Scammon—See WEIR, KS

▲ **SCANDIA**—Cunningham Telephone & Cable Co.

▲ **SCHOENCHEN**—GBT Communications

SCHULTE—See SEDGWICK COUNTY (portions), KS

▲ **SCOTT CITY**—Cable Systems Inc.

SCRANTON—See OSAGE CITY, KS

▲ **SEDAN**—Cablecomm

SEDGWICK—See WICHITA, KS

▲ **SEDGWICK COUNTY (portions)**—Westcom

SEDGWICK COUNTY (portions)—See also GODDARD, KS

SEDGWICK COUNTY (portions)—See also NEWTON, KS

SEDGWICK COUNTY (southeastern portion)—See also ROSE HILL, KS

SELDEN—See EDMOND, KS

▲ **SENECA**—Galaxy Cablevision

▲ **SEVERY**—Southern Kansas Telephone Co.

SEWARD COUNTY (portions)—See KISMET, KS

▲ **SHARON**—Multimedia Cablevision Inc.

▲ **SHARON SPRINGS**—Classic Cable

SHAWNEE—See OVERLAND PARK, KS

▲ **SHAWNEE COUNTY (northern portion)**—Multimedia Cablevision

SHAWNEE COUNTY—See also TOPEKA, KS

SHAWNEE COUNTY (southwestern portion)—See also AUBURN, KS

SHAWNEE HILLS TRAILER PARK—See PAULINE, KS

SILVER LAKE—See ROSSVILLE, KS

▲ **SMITH CENTER**—Classic Cable

▲ **SMOLAN**—Galva Cable Co.

▲ **SOLOMON**—Galaxy Cablevision

▲ **SOUTH HAVEN**—Classic Cable

SOUTH HUTCHINSON—See HUTCHINSON, KS

▲ **SPEARVILLE**—United Communications Assn. Inc.

▲ **SPRING HILL**—Classic Cable

▲ **ST. FRANCIS**—Classic Cable

▲ **ST. GEORGE**—SCI Cable Inc.

▲ **ST. JOHN**—Classic Cable

▲ **ST. MARYS**—Wamego Cablevision

▲ **ST. PAUL**—Cable TV of St. Paul

STAFFORD—See ELLINWOOD, KS

▲ **STERLING**—Classic Cable

▲ **STOCKTON**—Classic Cable

▲ **STRONG CITY**—Galaxy Cablevision

▲ **SUBLETTE**—Pioneer Communications

▲ **SUMMERFIELD**—Carson Communications LLC

▲ **SYLVAN GROVE**—Classic Cable

▲ **SYLVIA**—Five Star Cable TV

▲ **SYRACUSE**—Pioneer Communications

▲ **TALMAGE**—Twin Valley Communications

▲ **TAMPA**—Galaxy Cablevision

▲ **TECUMSEH**—Multimedia Cablevision

▲ **TESCOTT**—Twin Valley Communications Inc.

▲ **THAYER**—Mediacom

TIMKEN—See RUSH CENTER, KS

▲ **TIPTON**—Classic Cable

▲ **TONGANOXIE**—Galaxy Cablevision

▲ **TOPEKA**—Multimedia Cablevision

TOPEKA (portions)—See also AUBURN, KS

▲ **TORONTO**—Mediacom

TOWANDA—See EL DORADO, KS

TREECE—See PICHER, OK

▲ **TRIBUNE**—Classic Cable

▲ **TROY**—Carson Communications LLC

▲ **TURON**—Five Star Cable TV

▲ **UDALL**—Wheat State Telecable Inc.

▲ **ULYSSES**—Pioneer Communications

▲ **UNIONTOWN**—National Cable Inc.

▲ **UTICA**—GBT Communications

VALLEY CENTER—See WICHITA, KS

▲ **VALLEY FALLS**—C.L.R. Video LLC

▲ **VASSAR**—Galaxy Cablevision

VASSAR LAKE (portions)—See VASSAR, KS

▲ **VERMILLION**—Carson Communications LLC

▲ **VICTORIA**—Classic Cable

VINING—See CLIFTON, KS

▲ **VIOLA**—Southern Kansas Telephone Co.

VIOLA—See also SEDGWICK COUNTY (portions), KS

▲ **WAKEENEY**—Wakeeney Cable TV Co.

▲ **WAKEFIELD**—Galaxy Cablevision

▲ **WALNUT**—National Cable Inc.

▲ **WALTON**—Galaxy Cablevision

▲ **WAMEGO**—Wamego Cable

▲ **WASHINGTON**—Washington Cable TV Inc.

▲ **WATERVILLE**—Waterville Cable TV

WATERVILLE—See also BLUE RAPIDS, KS

▲ **WATHENA**—Carson Communications LLC

▲ **WAVERLY**—Galaxy Cablevision

▲ **WEIR**—WSC Cablevision

▲ **WELLINGTON**—Wellington Cable TV Co.

WELLSVILLE—See BALDWIN CITY, KS

▲ **WESTMORELAND**—C.L.R. Video LLC

WESTWOOD—See KANSAS CITY, MO

WESTWOOD HILLS—See KANSAS CITY, MO

▲ **WETMORE**—C.L.R. Video LLC

▲ **WHITE CITY**—Galaxy Cablevision

▲ **WHITE CLOUD**—Carson Communications LLC

▲ **WHITEWATER**—Galaxy Cablevision

▲ **WHITING**—Carson Communications LLC

▲ **WICHITA**—Multimedia Cablevision

WICHITA (portions)—See also SEDGWICK COUNTY (portions), KS

▲ **WILLIAMSBURG**—Galaxy Cablevision

WILLOWBROOK—See HUTCHINSON, KS

▲ **WILSEY**—Westcom

▲ **WILSON**—Wilson Cable Co.

WILSON COUNTY—See FREDONIA, KS

▲ **WINCHESTER**—C.L.R. Video LLC

▲ **WINFIELD**—Multimedia Cablevision Inc.

▲ **WINONA**—S & T Communications of Northwest Kansas

▲ **WOODBINE**—Galaxy Cablevision

▲ **WOODSTON**—Vision Plus Inc.

WYANDOTTE COUNTY (portions)—See KANSAS CITY, MO

KENTUCKY

▲ **BULLSKIN CREEK**—Bullskin Cable TV

BURDINE—See JENKINS, KY

BURGIN—See HARRODSBURG, KY

▲ **BURKESVILLE**—Mediacom

BURLINGTON—See COVINGTON, KY

▲ **BURNAUGH**—FrontierVision

▲ **BURNING SPRINGS**—C & W Cable

▲ **BURNSIDE**—Falcon Cable TV

BURNWELL—See WILLIAMSON, WV

BURTONVILLE—See TOLLESBORO, KY

BUSKIRK—See MARTIN, KY

BUSY—See HINDMAN, KY

BUTLER—See FALMOUTH, KY

BUTTONSBERRY—See ISLAND, KY

▲ **CADIZ**—Mediacom

CALDWELL COUNTY—See DAWSON SPRINGS, KY

CALDWELL COUNTY—See also PRINCETON, KY

CALF CREEK—See INEZ, KY

CALHOUN—See LIVERMORE, KY

CALLOWAY COUNTY—See MURRAY, KY

CALLOWAY COUNTY (unincorporated areas)—See also GILBERTSVILLE, KY

▲ **CALVERT CITY**—Falcon Cable TV

CALVIN—See BELL COUNTY, KY

CAMARGO—See MOUNT STERLING, KY

CAMBRIDGE—See LOUISVILLE, KY

CAMP NO. 1—See STURGIS, KY

CAMP SPRINGS—See COVINGTON, KY

CAMPBELL COUNTY—See COVINGTON, KY

CAMPBELLSBURG—See LOUISVILLE, KY

▲ **CAMPBELLSVILLE**—Comcast Cablevision of the South

▲ **CAMPTON**—FrontierVision

CANADA—See MARTIN, KY

CANEY—See LENORE, WV

CANEY—See also MARTIN, KY

CANEY—See also WEST LIBERTY, KY

▲ **CANEYVILLE**—Rapid Cable

CANNEL CITY—See WEST LIBERTY, KY

CANNON—See GRAY, KY

CANNONSBURG—See BOYD COUNTY, KY

CANTEES—See WILLIAMSON, WV

▲ **CARLISLE**—FrontierVision

CARLISLE COUNTY (portions)—See ARLINGTON, KY

CARLISLE COUNTY (portions)—See also BARDWELL, KY

CARLISLE COUNTY (portions)—See also GRAVES COUNTY, KY

▲ **CARROLLTON**—FrontierVision

CARTER COUNTY—See GRAYSON, KY

CARTER COUNTY (southwestern portion)—See OLIVE HILL, KY

▲ **CASEY COUNTY (southwestern portion)**—Rapid Cable

CASEY COUNTY—See also LIBERTY, KY

CASEY COUNTY (southern portion)—See also RUSSELL COUNTY (unincorporated areas), KY

CATHRON'S CREEK—See HARLAN, KY

CATLETTSBURG—See BURNAUGH,KY

CATLETTSBURG—See also SOUTH POINT, OH

CAVE CITY—See HORSE CAVE, KY

CAWOOD—See BLACK MOUNTAIN, KY

CENTERTOWN—See HARTFORD, KY

CENTRAL CITY—See GREENVILLE, KY

CENTRAL CITY (unincorporated areas)—See also NELSON, KY

CHAPLIN—See NEW HAVEN, KY

CHAPMAN—See LAWRENCE COUNTY (southern portion), KY

CHAVIES—See HINDMAN, KY

CHENOA—See FRAKES, KY

CHERRYVILLE—See LAWRENCE COUNTY (southern portion), KY

CHERRYWOOD VILLAGE—See LOUISVILLE, KY

CHEVROLET—See BLACK MOUNTAIN, KY

CHRISTIAN COUNTY—See NORTONVILLE, KY

CHRISTIAN COUNTY—See also PEMBROKE, KY

CHRISTOPHER—See HINDMAN, KY

CLARK COUNTY—See WINCHESTER, KY

CLARKSON—See LEITCHFIELD, KY

CLARYVILLE—See COVINGTON, KY

▲ **CLAY**—Century Communications

CLAY CITY—See MOUNT STERLING, KY

CLAY COUNTY—See BURNING SPRINGS, KY

CLAYHOLE—See ALTRO, KY

CLEAR CREEK—See PINEVILLE, KY

CLEATON—See GREENVILLE, KY

CLIFFORD—See GLENHAYES, WV

▲ **CLINTON**—Galaxy Cablevision

▲ **CLINTON COUNTY**—South Kentucky Services

CLOSPLINT—See BLACK MOUNTAIN, KY

▲ **CLOVER BOTTOM**—McKee TV Enterprises Inc.

▲ **CLOVERPORT**—Tele-Media Co. of Green River

COAL RUN—See MARTIN, KY

COALGOOD—See BLACK MOUNTAIN, KY

COLD SPRING—See COVINGTON, KY

COLDIRON—See WALLINS, KY

COLDWATER CREEK—See INEZ, KY

COLLIER CREEK—See EOLIA, KY

COLONY—See LONDON, KY

COLSON—See HINDMAN, KY

▲ **COLUMBIA**—Falcon Cable TV

CONGLETON—See BEATTYVILLE, KY

CONKLING—See ISLAND CITY, KY

CONSTANCE—See COVINGTON, KY

▲ **CORBIN**—Falcon Cable TV

▲ **CORINTH**—New Path Communications LC

▲ **CORYDON**—Century Communications

CORYDON—See also HENDERSON (southern portion), KY

▲ **COVINGTON**—InterMedia

COWAN—See FLEMINGSBURG, KY

COWAN CREEK—See HINDMAN, KY

COWPEN—See MARTIN, KY

▲ **CRAB ORCHARD**—Wilcop Cable TV

CRANE—See BULLSKIN CREEK, KY

CRANE—See also GARRARD, KY

CRANKS—See BLACK MOUNTAIN, KY

CREECH—See WALLINS, KY

CREEKSIDE—See LOUISVILLE, KY

CRESCENT PARK—See COVINGTON, KY

CRESCENT SPRINGS—See COVINGTON, KY

CRESTVIEW HILLS—See COVINGTON, KY

▲ **CRITTENDEN**—Telesat Cable TV

CRITTENDEN—See also COVINGTON, KY

CRITTENDEN COUNTY—See MARION, KY

CROFTON—See NORTONVILLE, KY

CROMONA—See HINDMAN, KY

▲ **CROMWELL**—New Path Communications LC

CROSSGATE—See LOUISVILLE, KY

CRUMMIES—See BLACK MOUNTAIN, KY

CUBAGE—See BELL COUNTY, KY

▲ **CUMBERLAND**—Falcon Cable TV

CUMBERLAND COUNTY (portions)—See BURKESVILLE, KY

CUNNINGHAM—See GRAVES COUNTY, KY

▲ **CUTSHIN**—Craft Cable Service

▲ **CYNTHIANA**—FrontierVision

▲ **DANVILLE**—InterMedia

DARFORK—See BULAN, KY

DARTMONT—See BLACK MOUNTAIN, KY

DAVELLA—See INEZ, KY

DAVID—See MARTIN, KY

DAVIESS—See WHITESVILLE, KY

DAVIESS COUNTY—See OWENSBORO, KY

DAVIESS COUNTY (eastern portion)—See UPTON, KY

DAVISBURG—See FRAKES, KY

▲ **DAWSON SPRINGS**—Insight Communications

DAYHOIT—See WALLINS, KY

DE WITT—See FLAT LICK, KY

DEANE—See JENKINS, KY

DEBORD—See INEZ, KY

DENVER—See VAN LEAR, KY

DEPOY—See GREENVILLE, KY

DEVONDALE—See LOUISVILLE, KY

DEXTER—See GILBERTSVILLE, KY

DIONE—See BLACK MOUNTAIN, KY

▲ **DIXON**—Century Communiciations

DIZNEY—See BLACK MOUNTAIN, KY

DOE VALLEY—See BRANDENBURG, KY

DORTON—See MARTIN, KY

DOUGLASS HILLS—See LOUISVILLE, KY

DRAKESBORO—See GREENVILLE, KY

DRUID HILLS—See LOUISVILLE, KY

DRY FORK—See HINDMAN, KY

DRY RIDGE—See CRITTENDEN, KY

▲ **DUNMOR**—Paxton Cable TV

DUNNVILLE—See LIBERTY, KY

DWALE—See MARTIN, KY

EARLINGTON—See MADISONVILLE, KY

EAST BERNSTADT—See LONDON, KY

EAST PINEVILLE—See PINEVILLE, KY

EAST POINT—See VAN LEAR, KY

EASTERN—See MARTIN, KY

▲ **EDDYVILLE**—Galaxy Cablevision

EDGEWOOD—See COVINGTON, KY

EDMONSON COUNTY—See BROWNSVILLE, KY

▲ **EDMONTON**—Mediacom

▲ **ELIZABETHTOWN**—Comcast Cablevision of the South

ELIZAVILLE—See FLEMINGSBURG, KY

ELK CREEK—See LENORE, WV

▲ **ELKHORN CITY**—Tele-Media Co. of KWV

ELKHORN CREEK—See ELKHORN CITY, KY

ELKHORN CREEK—See also MARTIN, KY

▲ **ELKTON**—Mediacom

ELSMERE—See COVINGTON, KY

▲ **EMINENCE**—Cencom of Kentucky

EMLYN—See JELLICO, TN

EMMA—See MARTIN, KY

ENTERPRISE—See SOLDIER, KY

▲ **EOLIA**—CableVision Communications

EPWORTH—See TOLLESBORO, KY

ERLANGER—See COVINGTON, KY

ERMINE—See HINDMAN, KY

ESTILL—See HINDMAN, KY

ESTILL COUNTY—See IRVINE, KY

▲ **EUBANK**—Falcon Cable TV

▲ **EVARTS**—Evarts TV Inc.

EVERSOLE—See EOLIA, KY

EWING—See FLEMINGSBURG, KY

EZEL—See FRENCHBURG, KY

FAIRMEADE—See LOUISVILLE, KY

FAIRVIEW—See COVINGTON, KY

FAIRVIEW—See also FLEMINGSBURG, KY

FAIRVIEW—See also WILLIAMSON, WV

FALCON—See SALYERSVILLE, KY

▲ **FALLSBURG**—CableVision Communications

▲ **FALMOUTH**—FrontierVision

FANCY FARM—See GRAVES COUNTY, KY

FAYETTE COUNTY—See LEXINGTON, KY

▲ **FEDSCREEK**—Fuller's TV

FERGUSON—See BURNSIDE, KY

FERNDALE—See PINEVILLE, KY

FINCASTLE—See LOUISVILLE, KY

FISTY—See BULAN, KY

FITCH—See SOLDIER, KY

FIVE FORKS—See LAWRENCE COUNTY (southern portion), KY

▲ **FIVE STAR**—InterMedia

▲ **FLAT LICK**—Mountain View Cablecom

FLATWOODS—See ASHLAND, KY

FLEMING—See JENKINS, KY

FLEMING COUNTY—See FLEMINGSBURG, KY

▲**FLEMINGSBURG**—FrontierVision

FLORENCE—See COVINGTON, KY

FLOYD COUNTY—See MARTIN, KY

▲ **FOGERTOWN**—Mountain View Cablecom

FORDSVILLE—See WHITESVILLE, KY

FOREST HILLS—See LOUISVILLE, KY

FORSTERS CREEK—See WALLINS, KY

▲ **FORT CAMPBELL**—InterMedia Partners

FORT KNOX—See RADCLIFF, KY

FORT MITCHELL—See COVINGTON, KY

FORT THOMAS—See COVINGTON, KY

FORT WRIGHT—See COVINGTON, KY

FOXPORT—See FLEMINGSBURG, KY

▲ **FRAKES**—Tele-Media Co. of Cumberland Gap

▲ **FRANKFORT**—Frankfort Plant Board Cable Service

FRANKFORT (unincorporated areas)—See also STONEWALL ESTATES, KY

▲ **FRANKLIN**—Tele-Media of Franklin

FRANKLIN COUNTY (portions)—See LAWRENCEBURG, KY

FREDONIA—See MARION, KY

FREEBURN—See MARTIN, KY

▲**FRENCHBURG**—FrontierVision

FRESH MEADOWS—See WALLINS, KY

▲ **FULTON**—Falcon Cable TV

GALVESTON—See MARTIN, KY

GAMALIEL—See TOMPKINSVILLE, KY

▲ **GARRARD**—Mountain View Cablecom

GARRETT—See MARTIN, KY

▲ **GARRISON**—Century Communications

▲**GEORGETOWN**—FrontierVision

GERMANTOWN—See BROOKSVILLE, KY

GHENT—See CARROLLTON, KY

GIBBO—See EOLIA, KY

▲ **GILBERTSVILLE**—Mediacom

GIRDLER—See GRAY, KY

▲ **GLASGOW**—Comcast Cablevision of the South

▲ **GLASGOW**—Glasgow Electric Plant Board-CATV Division

GLENVIEW HILLS—See LOUISVILLE, KY

GLENVIEW MANOR—See LOUISVILLE, KY

GLOBE—See SOLDIER, KY

GOOSE CREEK—See LOUISVILLE, KY

GRAEFENBURG—See FRANKFORT, KY

GRAHAM—See GREENVILLE, KY

GRAND RIVERS—See EDDYVILLE, KY

GRANGERTOWN—See STURGIS, KY

GRANT COUNTY—See CRITTENDEN, KY

GRASSY CREEK—See WEST LIBERTY, KY

▲ **GRAVES COUNTY**—Galaxy Cablevision

GRAVES COUNTY—See also PADUCAH, KY

▲ **GRAY**—Eastern Cable Corp.

GRAY HAWK—See McKEE, KY

GRAYMOOR—See LOUISVILLE, KY

GRAYS KNOB—See HARLAN, KY

▲ **GRAYSON**—Thompson Cable

GRAYSON COUNTY (portions)—See CANEYVILLE, KY

GRAYSON COUNTY (portions)—See also UPTON, KY

▲ **GREASY CREEK**—Tele-Media Co. of Cumberland Gap

GREEN COUNTY—See GREENSBURG, KY

GREEN COUNTY (northern portion)—See also SUMMERSVILLE, KY

GREEN MEADOWS—See BURNSIDE, KY

GREEN SPRING—See LOUISVILLE, KY

GREEN VALLEY—See VANCEBURG, KY

▲ **GREENSBURG**—Falcon Cable TV

▲ **GREENUP**—Armstrong Cable Services

▲ **GREENUP**—CableVision Communications

GREENUP COUNTY—See GREENUP, KY (Armstrong Cable Services)

GREENUP COUNTY—See also PORTSMOUTH, OH

GREENUP COUNTY (portions)—See also ASHLAND, KY

GREENUP COUNTY (unincorporated areas)—See also MALONETON, KY

▲ **GREENVILLE**—Comcast Cablevision of the South

GRETHEL—See MARTIN, KY

GULSTON—See HARLAN, KY

GUTHRIE—See PEMBROKE, KY

HADDIX—See ALTRO, KY

HAGERHILL—See VAN LEAR, KY

HAGINSVILLE—See JACKSON, KY

HALDEMAN—See SOLDIER, KY

HANSON—See MADISONVILLE, KY

HAPPY CIRCLE—See BURNSIDE, KY

HAPPY TOP—See WALLINS, KY

HARDBURLY—See BULAN, KY

▲ **HARDIN**—Mediacom

Hardin County (northern portion)—See RADCLIFF, KY

HARDIN COUNTY (southeastern portion)—See UPTON, KY

▲ **HARDINSBURG**—Tele-Media Co. of Green River

HARDSHELL—See BULAN, KY

HARDY—See MARTIN, KY

HARDY—See also WILLIAMSON, WV

▲ **HARLAN**—Harlan Community TV Inc.

HARLAN COUNTY—See CUMBERLAND, KY

HARLAN COUNTY—See also HARLAN, KY

HARLAN COUNTY (unincorporated areas)—See also EVARTS, KY

HAROLD—See MARTIN, KY

▲ **HARRODSBURG**—TCI of North Central Kentucky

HART COUNTY—See MUNFORDVILLE, KY

▲ **HARTFORD**—Ohio County Cablevision

HARVEYTON—See BONNYMAN, KY

HATFIELD—See LENORE, WV

HATFIELD—See also MARTIN, KY

HATTON CREEK—See STANTON, KY

▲ **HAWESVILLE**—Tele-Media Co. of Green River

HAYMOND—See HINDMAN, KY

HAYWARD—See SOLDIER, KY

▲ **HAZARD**—Hazard TV Cable Co. Inc.

▲ **HAZEL**—Galaxy Cablevision

HAZEL GREEN—See CAMPTON, KY

HEBBERDSVILLE—See HENDERSON (town), KY

HEBRON—See COVINGTON, KY

HEIDELBERG—See BEATTYVILLE, KY

HEIDRICK—See BARBOURVILLE, KY

HELTON—See MOZELLE, KY

▲ **HENDERSON**—Insight Communications

▲ **HENDERSON (southern portion)**—Rapid Cable

▲ **HENDERSON (town)**—Century Communications

Henderson County (portions)—See CORYDON, KY

HENDERSON COUNTY (portions)—See also OWENSBORO, KY

HENDERSON COUNTY (unincorporated areas)—See HENDERSON, KY

HENRY COUNTY—See SHELBYVILLE, KY

HI HAT—See MARTIN, KY

▲ **HICKMAN**—Galaxy Cablevision

HICKORY—See GRAVES COUNTY, KY

HICKORY HILL—See LOUISVILLE, KY

HIGHLAND HEIGHTS—See COVINGTON, KY

HIGHSPLINT—See BLACK MOUNTAIN, KY

HILLS AND DALES—See LOUISVILLE, KY

HILLSBORO—See PINE HILL, KY

HILLVIEW—See BULLITT, KY

HIMYAR—See FLAT LICK, KY

▲ **HINDMAN**—TV Service Inc.

HINKLE MILLS—See FLAT LICK, KY

HIPPO—See MARTIN, KY

HIRAM—See CUMBERLAND, KY

HISEVILLE—See HORSE CAVE, KY

HITCHINS—See GRAYSON, KY

HITE—See MARTIN, KY

HODE—See KERMIT, WV

▲ **HODGENVILLE**—Comcast Cablevision of the South

HOLLOW CREEK—See LOUISVILLE, KY

HOLLYVILLA—See LOUISVILLE, KY

HOLMES MILL—See BLACK MOUNTAIN, KY

HOPKINS COUNTY—See DAWSON SPRINGS, KY

HOPKINS COUNTY—See also NEBO, KY

HOPKINS COUNTY (portions)—See also NORTONVILLE, KY

HOPKINS COUNTY (portions)—See also WHITE PLAINS, KY

▲ **HOPKINSVILLE**—Cencom of Hopkinsville

▲ **HORSE CAVE**—Comcast Cablevision of the South

HOUSTON ACRES—See LOUISVILLE, KY

HUDDY—See WILLIAMSON, WV

HUEYSVILLE—See MARTIN, KY

HULEN—See PINEVILLE, KY

HUNTER—See MARTIN, KY

HUNTERS HOLLOW—See BULLITT, KY

HURRICANE CREEK—See MARTIN, KY

HURTSBOURNE ACRES—See LOUISVILLE, KY

▲ **HUSTONVILLE**—Falcon Cable TV

HYATTSVILLE—See PAINT LICK, KY

▲ **HYDEN**—Bowling Corp.

HYDEN—See also LESLIE COUNTY (northern portion), KY

INDEPENDENCE—See COVINGTON, KY

INDIAN HILLS—See BURNSIDE, KY

INDIAN HILLS—See also LOUISVILLE, KY

INDIAN HILLS-CHEROKEE—See LOUISVILLE, KY

▲ **INEZ**—CableVision Communications

INGRAM—See GREASY CREEK, KY

IRONVILLE—See BOYD COUNTY, KY

▲ **IRVINE**—Irvine Community TV Inc.

▲ **IRVINGTON**—Tele-Media Co. of Green River

IRVINGTON (village)—See IRVINGTON, KY

▲ **ISLAND**—New Path Communications LC

▲ **ISLAND CITY**—City TV Cable

ISLAND CREEK—See MARTIN, KY

ISOM—See HINDMAN, KY

IVEL—See MARTIN, KY

IVYTON—See SALYERSVILLE, KY

JACKHORN—See JENKINS, KY

▲ **JACKSON**—FrontierVision

JACKSON COUNTY—See McKEE, KY

JACKSON COUNTY (portions)—See also BURNING SPRINGS, KY

JAMESTOWN—See RUSSELL COUNTY (unincorporated areas), KY

JAMESTOWN—See also RUSSELL SPRINGS, KY

JARVIS—See GRAY, KY

JEFF—See HINDMAN, KY

JEFFERSON COUNTY—See LOUISVILLE, KY

JEFFERSONTOWN—See LOUISVILLE, KY

JEFFERSONVILLE—See MOUNT STERLING, KY

▲ **JENKINS**—CableVision Communications

JEREMIAH—See HINDMAN, KY

JESSAMINE COUNTY—See NICHOLASVILLE, KY

Jessamine County (northern portion)—See LEXINGTON, KY

JOB—See INEZ, KY

JOHNNY YOUNG BRANCH—See VARNEY, KY

JOHNS CREEK—See MARTIN, KY

JOHNSON COUNTY—See MARTIN, KY

JOHNSON COUNTY—See also PAINTSVILLE, KY

JUNCTION CITY—See DANVILLE, KY

KAYJAY—See GREASY CREEK, KY

KEAVY—See LONDON, KY

KEENELAND—See LOUISVILLE, KY

KEITH—See HARLAN, KY

KEITH—See also WALLINS, KY

MEADS BRANCH—See LAWRENCE COUNTY (southern portion), KY

MEALLY—See VAN LEAR, KY

MEANS—See FRENCHBURG, KY

MELBER—See GRAVES COUNTY, KY

MELBOURNE—See COVINGTON, KY

MELVIN—See MARTIN, KY

MENIFEE COUNTY (unincorporated areas)—See CAMPTON, KY

MERCER COUNTY—See HARRODSBURG, KY

META—See MARTIN, KY

MIDDLEBURG—See LIBERTY, KY

▲ **MIDDLESBORO**—Charter Communications Inc.

MIDDLETOWN—See LOUISVILLE, KY

▲ **MIDWAY**—FrontierVision

MILLERSBURG—See CARLISLE, KY

MILLSTONE—See HINDMAN, KY

▲ **MILLVILLE**—Chumley's Antenna Systems Inc.

MILLVILLE—See also FRANKFORT, KY

MILLWOOD—See CANEYVILLE, KY

MILO—See INEZ, KY

MINOR LANE HEIGHTS—See LOUISVILLE, KY

MIRACLE—See BELL COUNTY, KY

MISLAND—See EDDYVILLE, KY

MITCHELLSBURG—See PARKSVILLE, KY

MIZE—See WEST LIBERTY, KY

MOCKINGBIRD VALLEY—See LOUISVILLE, KY

MONTGOMERY COUNTY—See MOUNT STERLING, KY

▲ **MONTICELLO**—Falcon Cable TV

MOORLAND—See LOUISVILLE, KY

▲ **MOREHEAD**—FrontierVision

MOREHEAD—See also PINE HILL, KY

▲ **MOREHEAD STATE UNIVERSITY**—Morehead State University, Dept. of Communication

MORELAND—See HUSTONVILLE, KY

MORGAN COUNTY—See CAMPTON, KY

MORGANFIELD—See STURGIS, KY

▲ **MORGANTOWN**—Tele-Media Southwest Kentucky

MORNING VIEW—See COVINGTON, KY

MORRELL—See CLOVER BOTTOM, KY

MORRIS CREEK—See STANTON, KY

MORTONS GAP—See MADISONVILLE, KY

MOUNT CARMEL—See FLEMINGSBURG, KY

▲ **MOUNT OLIVET**—Bracken Cable Vision Inc.

▲ **MOUNT TERLING**—FrontierVision

▲ **MOUNT VERNON**—Falcon Cable TV

MOUNT WASHINGTON—See BULLITT, KY

▲ **MOZELLE**—FrontierVision

MUD LICK—See TOLLESBORO, KY

MUHLENBERG COUNTY (southern portion)—See DUNMOR, KY

MULDRAUGH—See RADCLIFF, KY

▲ **MUNFORDVILLE**—Mediacom

▲ **MURRAY**—Murray Cablevision

MYRA—See MARTIN, KY

NANCY—See SOMERSET, KY

NAVAL ORDNANCE STATION (Government Reserve)—See LOUISVILLE, KY

▲ **NEBO**—Mediacom

NED—See ALTRO, KY

▲ **NELSON**—New Path Communications LC

NELSON COUNTY—See BARDSTOWN, KY

NELSON COUNTY—See also NEW HAVEN, KY

NEON—See JENKINS, KY

NEPTON—See FLEMINGSBURG, KY

NEW CAMP—See WILLIAMSON, WV

NEW CASTLE—See EMINENCE, KY

▲ **NEW HAVEN**—FrontierVision

NEW HOPE (Clay County)—See BULLSKIN CREEK, KY

NEWFOUNDLAND—See SANDY HOOK, KY

▲ **NEWPORT**—InterMedia

NICHOLAS COUNTY—See CARLISLE, KY

▲**NICHOLASVILLE**—FrontierVision

NOCTOR (portions)—See JACKSON, KY

NOLANSBURG—See BLACK MOUNTAIN, KY

NORBOURNE ESTATES—See LOUISVILLE, KY

▲ **NORTH MIDDLETOWN**—FrontierVision

NORTHFIELD—See LOUISVILLE, KY

▲ **NORTONVILLE**—Mediacom

NORWOOD—See LOUISVILLE, KY

▲ **OAK GROVE**—Mediacom

OAKLAND—See BOWLING GREEN, KY

OHIO COUNTY—See HARTFORD, KY

OHIO COUNTY (northern portion)—See also UPTON, KY

OLD BROWNSBORO PLACE—See LOUISVILLE, KY

▲ **OLIVE HILL**—FrontierVision

OLIVE HILL—See also SOLDIER, KY

ONEIDA—See GARRARD, KY

OPPY—See LENORE, WV

OVEN FORK—See EOLIA, KY

▲ **OWENSBORO**—Century Communications

▲**OWINGSVILLE**—FrontierVision

OWSLEY FORK—See CLOVER BOTTOM, KY

PACTOLUS—See GRAYSON, KY

▲ **PADUCAH**—Comcast Cablevision of Paducah Inc.

PAGE—See PINEVILLE, KY

PAINT CREEK—See STANTON, KY

▲ **PAINT LICK**—Falcon Cable TV

▲ **PAINTSVILLE**—Cablecomm

PANCO—See BULLSKIN CREEK, KY

▲ **PARIS**—FrontierVision

PARK CITY—See BROWNSVILLE, KY

PARK HILLS—See COVINGTON, KY

▲ **PARKSVILLE**—Falcon Cable TV

PARKWAY VILLAGE—See LOUISVILLE, KY

PARTRIDGE—See EOLIA, KY

▲ **PATHFORK**—Tele-Media Co. of Cumberland Gap

PAYNE GAP—See JENKINS, KY

▲ **PEMBROKE**—Mediacom

PEOPLES—See BOND, KY

▲ **PERRYVILLE**—TCI of North Central Kentucky Inc.

PETER FORK—See MARTIN, KY

PEWEE VALLEY—See LOUISVILLE, KY

PHELPS—See MARTIN, KY

PHILPOT—See PLEASANT RIDGE, KY

PHYLLIS—See MARTIN, KY

PIKE COUNTY—See MARTIN, KY

PIKE COUNTY—See also RAGLAND, WV

PIKE COUNTY (portions)—See also ELKHORN CITY, KY

PIKE COUNTY (unincorporated areas)—See also WILLIAMSON, WV

▲ **PIKEVILLE**—Tele-Media Co. of KWV

PIKEVILLE—See also ELKHORN CITY, KY

PIKEVILLE—See also MARTIN, KY

PILGRIM—See KERMIT, WV

PILOT KNOB—See CLOVER BOTTOM, KY

▲ **PINE HILL**—FrontierVision

PINE KNOT—See WHITLEY CITY, KY

▲ **PINEVILLE**—TMC of Pineville

PINEVILLE—See also BELL COUNTY, KY

PINSONFORK—See MARTIN, KY

PIONEER VILLAGE—See BULLITT, KY

PIPPA PASSES—See HINDMAN, KY

PLANTATION—See LOUISVILLE, KY

PLATTS FORK—See WALLINS, KY

PLEASANT HILL—See SALYERSVILLE, KY

▲ **PLEASANT RIDGE**—New Path Communications LC

PLEASUREVILLE—See EMINENCE, KY

PLEASUREVILLE—See also FLEMINGSBURG, KY

PLUM SPRINGS—See BOWLING GREEN, KY

PLYMOUTH VILLAGE—See LOUISVILLE, KY

POND CREEK—See WILLIAMSON, WV

POPLAR GROVE—See TOLLESBORO, KY

POWDERLY—See GREENVILLE, KY

POWELL COUNTY (unincorporated areas)—See STANTON, KY

PRATER CREEK—See MARTIN, KY

PRATER FORK—See MARTIN, KY

▲ **PRESTONSBURG**—CableVision of Prestonsburg

PRESTONSBURG—See also MARTIN, KY

PRIMROSE—See BEATTYVILLE, KY

▲ **PRINCETON**—Mediacom

PRINTER—See MARTIN, KY

PROCTOR—See BEATTYVILLE, KY

PROSPECT—See LOUISVILLE, KY

▲ **PROVIDENCE**—Insight Communications

PULASKI COUNTY—See EUBANK, KY

PULASKI COUNTY—See also SOMERSET, KY

PULASKI COUNTY (portions)—See also BURNSIDE, KY

PUTNEY—See BLACK MOUNTAIN, KY

PYRAMID—See MARTIN, KY

QUICKSAND—See JACKSON, KY

QUINCY—See GARRISON, KY

RACELAND—See ASHLAND, KY

RACELAND—See also GREENUP, KY (Armstrong Cable Services)

▲ **RADCLIFF**—InterMedia

RADCLIFF—See also ELIZABETHTOWN, KY

RADO HOLLOW—See EOLIA, KY

RANSOM—See MARTIN, KY

RATFORD—See BELL COUNTY, KY

RAVEN—See HINDMAN, KY

RAVENNA—See IRVINE, KY

REDBUD—See BLACK MOUNTAIN, KY

REDFOX—See HINDMAN, KY

REDWINE—See SANDY HOOK, KY

REED—See HENDERSON (town), KY

RENFRO VALLEY—See MOUNT VERNON, KY

REVELO—See WHITLEY CITY, KY

RHEA—See BLACK MOUNTAIN, KY

RIBOLT—See TOLLESBORO, KY

RICHLAWN—See LOUISVILLE, KY

▲ **RICHMOND**—FrontierVision

RIDGEVIEW HEIGHTS—See COVINGTON, KY

RINGOS MILLS—See PINE HILL, KY

RISNER—See MARTIN, KY

RIVER BLUFF—See LOUISVILLE, KY

RIVERWOOD—See LOUISVILLE, KY

ROBERTS BRANCH—See EOLIA, KY

ROBINETTE KNOB—See VARNEY, KY

ROBINSON CREEK—See MARTIN, KY

ROBINSWOOD—See LOUISVILLE, KY

▲ **ROCHESTER**—New Path Communications LC

ROCKCASTLE COUNTY—See MOUNT VERNON, KY

ROCKCASTLE COUNTY (western portion)—See also LINCOLN COUNTY (eastern portion), KY

ROCKDALE—See BOYD COUNTY, KY

ROCKHOLDS—See WHITLEY COUNTY (unincorporated areas), KY

ROCKHOUSE—See VARNEY, KY

ROCKHOUSE CREEK—See HYDEN, KY

ROCKPORT—See HARTFORD, KY

ROLLING FIELDS—See LOUISVILLE, KY

ROLLING HILLS—See LOUISVILLE, KY

ROSSPOINT—See BLACK MOUNTAIN, KY

▲ **ROUGH RIVER DAM**—Rapid Cable

ROWAN COUNTY—See MOREHEAD, KY

ROWAN COUNTY (portions)—See also PINE HILL, KY

ROWDY—See BULAN, KY

RUMSEY—See LIVERMORE, KY

RUSSELL—See ASHLAND, KY

▲ **RUSSELL COUNTY (unincorporated areas)**—Rapid Cable

RUSSELL COUNTY—See also RUSSELL SPRINGS, KY

▲ **RUSSELL SPRINGS**—Falcon Cable TV

▲ **RUSSELLVILLE**—TMC of Logan County

RYLAND HEIGHTS—See COVINGTON, KY

SACRAMENTO—See BREMEN, KY

SALDEE—See ALTRO, KY

SALEM—See MARION, KY

SALT GUM—See FLAT LICK, KY

SALT LICK—See MOREHEAD, KY

SALT LICK—See also TOLLESBORO, KY

▲ **SALYERSVILLE**—Frank Howard's TV Cable

SANDGAP—See CLOVER BOTTOM, KY

▲ **SANDY HOOK**—FrontierVision

SASSAFRAS—See HINDMAN, KY

SAWBIAR TOWN—See WALLINS, KY

SCALF—See FLAT LICK, KY

SCHULTZ CREEK—See MALONETON, KY

SCIENCE HILL—See SOMERSET, KY

SCOTT COUNTY—See GEORGETOWN, KY

▲ **SCOTTSVILLE**—Tele-Media Co. of Southwest Kentucky

▲ **SEBREE**—Falcon/Capital Cable Partners

SECO—See HINDMAN, KY

SECOND CREEK—See BULAN, KY

SEDALIA—See GRAVES COUNTY, KY

SENECA GARDENS—See LOUISVILLE, KY

SEXTONS CREEK—See ISLAND CITY, KY

SHARKEY—See PINE HILL, KY

▲ **SHARPSBURG**—FrontierVision

SHELBY—See MARTIN, KY

SHELBY COUNTY—See FRANKFORT, KY

SHELBY COUNTY—See also SHELBYVILLE, KY

▲ **SHELBYVILLE**—Charter Communications

SHEPHERDSVILLE—See BULLITT, KY

SHIVELY—See LOUISVILLE, KY

SILER—See WHITLEY COUNTY (unincorporated areas), KY

SILICA—See SOLDIER, KY

SILVER GROVE—See COVINGTON, KY

SIMPSON COUNTY—See FRANKLIN, KY

SIMPSONVILLE—See SHELBYVILLE, KY

SIZEROCK—See BULLSKIN CREEK, KY

SLATER'S BRANCH—See CHATTAROY, WV

▲ **SLAUGHTERS**—New Path Communications LC

SLOANS VALLEY—See BURNSIDE, KY

SMILAX—See CUTSHIN, KY

SMITH—See MARTINS FORK, KY

SMITH MILLS BOROUGH—See CORYDON, KY

SMITHLAND—See EDDYVILLE, KY

SMITHS GROVE—See BOWLING GREEN, KY

▲ **SOLDIER**—FrontierVision

▲ **SOMERSET**—Falcon Cable TV

SONORA—See UPTON, KY

SOUTH BEATTYVILLE—See BEATTYVILLE, KY

SOUTH CARROLLTON—See GREENVILLE, KY

SOUTH PARK VIEW—See LOUISVILLE, KY

SOUTH PIKEVILLE—See ELKHORN CITY, KY

SOUTH PORTSMOUTH—See PORTSMOUTH, OH

SOUTH SHORE—See MALONETON, KY

SOUTH SHORE—See also PORTSMOUTH, OH

SOUTH WILLIAMSON—See WILLIAMSON, WV

SOUTHFORK—See ISLAND CITY, KY

SOUTHGATE—See COVINGTON, KY

SPENCER COUNTY (central portion)—See TAYLORSVILLE, KY

SPENCER COUNTY (western portion)—See FIVE STAR, KY

SPLINT—See BLACK MOUNTAIN, KY

SPOTTSVILLE—See HENDERSON (town), KY

SPRINGFIELD—See LEBANON, KY

SPRINGLEE—See LOUISVILLE, KY

ST. CHARLES—See DAWSON SPRINGS, KY

ST. HELENS—See BEATTYVILLE, KY

ST. MATTHEWS—See LOUISVILLE, KY

ST. PAUL—See BIG CLIFTY, KY

LOUISIANA

▲ **DENHAM SPRINGS**—Communications Services Inc.

DENHAM SPRINGS—See also WALKER, LA

DESTREHAN—See ST. CHARLES PARISH, LA

▲ **DIXIE INN**—Falcon Telecable

▲ **DODSON**—Friendship Cable

▲ **DONALDSONVILLE**—TCI of Louisiana

DONALDSONVILLE—See also LAFOURCHE PARISH, LA

DOYLINE—See SIBLEY, LA

▲ **DRY PRONG**—Friendship Cable of Texas Inc.

DUBACH—See BERNICE, LA

DUBBERLY—See SIBLEY, LA

DULAC—See TERREBONNE PARISH, LA

DULARGE—See TERREBONNE PARISH, LA

DUPLESSIS—See GONZALES, LA

DUSON—See LAFAYETTE, LA

EAST BATON ROUGE PARISH—See BATON ROUGE, LA

EAST HODGE—See JONESBORO, LA

ECHO—See MOREAUVILLE, LA

▲ **EFFIE**—Friendship Cable of Texas Inc.

▲ **EGAN**—Torrence Cablevision

ELIZABETH—See BUNKIE, LA

ELTON—See KINDER, LA

▲ **EMPIRE**—Plaquemines Cablevision Inc.

ENGLAND AUTHORITY—See PINEVILLE, LA

ERATH—See ABBEVILLE, LA

ERATH—See also LYDIA, LA

▲ **ERWINVILLE**—TCI of Louisiana

▲ **ESTHERWOOD**—Bayouvision

▲ **ETHEL**—Torrence Cablevision

EUNICE—See ST. LANDRY PARISH, LA

EVANGELINE PARISH—See VILLE PLATTE, LA

EVANGELINE PARISH (portions)—See also TURKEY CREEK, LA

EVERGREEN—See BUNKIE, LA

▲ **FARMERVILLE**—Broadband Cablevision Inc.

FERRIDAY—See BUNKIE, LA

FILLMORE—See BOSSIER CITY, LA

FISHER—See MANY, LA

FLORIEN—See MANY, LA

▲ **FOLSOM**—Charter Communications Inc.

FORDOCHE—See MARINGOUIN, LA

FOREST HILL—See LECOMPTE, LA

▲ **FORKED ISLAND**—Torrence Cablevision

▲ **FORT POLK**—Star Cable

▲ **FOUR CORNERS**—Torrence Cablevision

FOURCHON—See GOLDEN MEADOW, LA

▲ **FRANKLIN**—TCA Cable TV of Franklin

FRANKLINTON—See BOGALUSA, LA

FRENCH SETTLEMENT—See HAMMOND, LA

FROST—See HAMMOND, LA

GALION—See COLLINSTON, LA

GALLIANO—See GOLDEN MEADOW, LA

GARDEN CITY—See FRANKLIN, LA

GARYVILLE—See LA PLACE, LA

▲ **GEORGETOWN**—Friendship Cable of Texas, Inc.

GHEENS—See GOLDEN MEADOW, LA

▲ **GIBSLAND**—Friendship Cable of Arkansas Inc.

GIBSON—See TERREBONNE PARISH, LA

GILBERT—See WISNER, LA

GILLIAM—See HOSSTON, LA

GLENMORA—See LECOMPTE, LA

▲ **GOLDEN MEADOW**—Callais Cablevision Inc.

▲ **GONZALES**—TCI of Louisiana

GOODPINE—See JENA, LA

GRAMBLING—See RUSTON, LA

▲ **GRAMERCY**—TCI of Louisiana

GRAND CAILLOU—See TERREBONNE PARISH, LA

▲ **GRAND CHENIER**—Torrence Cablevision

▲ **GRAND COTEAU**—Allen's TV Cable Service Inc.

GRAND ISLE—See GOLDEN MEADOW, LA

▲ **GRAND LAKE**—Torrence Cablevision

GRANT PARISH—See PINEVILLE, LA

GRANT PARISH (portions)—See also DRY PRONG, LA

GRANT PARISH (portions)—See also GEORGETOWN, LA

GRAY—See HOUMA, LA

GRAYSON—See COLUMBIA, LA

▲ **GREENSBURG**—Falcon Telecable

GREENWOOD—See SHREVEPORT, LA

GRETNA—See JEFFERSON PARISH, LA

GROSSE TETE—See ROSEDALE, LA

▲ **HACKBERRY**—Delta Cablecomm

HAHNVILLE—See ST. CHARLES PARISH, LA

▲ **HALL SUMMIT**—Cable TV

▲ **HAMMOND**—Charter Communications Inc.

HARAHAN—See JEFFERSON PARISH, LA

▲ **HAUGHTON**—Friendship Cable of Arkansas

HAUGHTON—See also BOSSIER CITY, LA

HAYES—See IOWA, LA

▲ **HAYNESVILLE**—Claiborne Cable TV Inc.

HEFLIN—See SIBLEY, LA

HENDERSON—See ST. MARTINVILLE, LA

▲ **HENRY**—Torrence Cablevision

HESSMER—See MARKSVILLE, LA (Scott Cable Communications Inc.)

HODGE—See JONESBORO, LA

HOLDEN—See HAMMOND, LA

▲ **HOMER**—Claiborne Cable TV

HORNBECK—See MANY, LA

▲ **HOSSTON**—Cablevision of Shreveport

HOTWELLS—See BOYCE, LA

▲ **HOUMA**—Time Warner Cable

HOUMA—See also TERREBONNE PARISH, LA

IBERIA PARISH—See NEW IBERIA, LA

IBERIA PARISH (portions)—See also LYDIA, LA

IBERVILLE—See ST. GABRIEL, LA

IBERVILLE PARISH (northern portion)—See WHITE CASTLE, LA

IBERVILLE PARISH (portions)—See MARINGOUIN, LA

IBERVILLE PARISH (western portion)—See PLAQUEMINE, LA

IDA—See RODESSA, LA

INDEPENDENCE—See HAMMOND, LA

▲ **INNIS**—Spillway Cablevision Inc.

▲ **IOTA**—Delta Cablecomm

▲ **IOWA**—Delta Cablecomm

JACKSON—See CLINTON, LA

JACKSON PARISH (portions)—See JONESBORO, LA

JEAN LAFITTE—See JEFFERSON PARISH, LA

JEANERETTE—See NEW IBERIA, LA

▲ **JEFFERSON PARISH**—Cox Cable Jefferson Parish

▲ **JENA**—Scott Cable Communications Inc.

JENNINGS—See ST. LANDRY PARISH, LA

▲ **JONESBORO**—Jonesboro-Hodge Cable TV

JONESVILLE—See BUNKIE, LA

JOYCE—See WINNFIELD, LA

JUNCTION CITY—See JUNCTION CITY, AR

KAPLAN—See ABBEVILLE, LA

KENNER—See JEFFERSON PARISH, LA

▲ **KENTWOOD**—Galaxy Cablevision

▲ **KILBOURNE**—Kilbourne Cablevision

KILLIAN—See HAMMOND, LA

▲ **KINDER**—Communicom

KOLIN—See LECOMPTE, LA

▲ **KROTZ SPRINGS**—Friendship Cable of Texas Inc.

▲ **LA PLACE**—Time Warner Cable

LA SALLE PARISH—See JENA, LA

LACASSINE—See IOWA, LA

LACOMBE—See ST. TAMMANY PARISH, LA

▲ **LAFAYETTE**—Lafayette Cable TV

LAFAYETTE PARISH—See LAFAYETTE, LA

▲ **LAFOURCHE PARISH**—Charter Communications Inc.

LAFOURCHE PARISH—See also GOLDEN MEADOW, LA

LAFOURCHE PARISH—See also HOUMA, LA

LAFOURCHE PARISH (western portion)—See also LAFOURCHE PARISH, LA

▲ **LAKE ARTHUR**—Communicom

LAKE BISTINEAU—See SIBLEY, LA

LAKE BRUIN—See ST. JOSEPH, LA

▲ **LAKE CHARLES**—TCA Cable TV

▲ **LAKE CLAIBORNE**—Friendship Cable of Arkansas Inc.

LAKE COTILE—See BOYCE, LA

▲ **LAKE PROVIDENCE**—Delta Cablevision

▲ **LAKE ST. JOHN**—Friendship Cable of Texas Inc.

LAKESHORE—See WEST MONROE, LA

LAROSE—See GOLDEN MEADOW, LA

LE BLEU—See IOWA, LA

▲ **LEBEAU**—Torrence Cablevision

▲ **LECOMPTE**—Friendship Cable of Texas Inc.

▲ **LEESVILLE**—Galaxy Cablevision

LEEVILLE—See GOLDEN MEADOW, LA

LEONVILLE—See ST. LANDRY PARISH, LA

LIBUSE (portions)—See PINEVILLE, LA

LINCOLN PARISH—See RUSTON, LA

LINCOLN PARISH (portions)—See also BERNICE, LA

▲ **LIVINGSTON**—Gulf South Cable Inc.

LIVINGSTON—See also HAMMOND, LA

LIVINGSTON PARISH (portions)—See HAMMOND, LA

LIVONIA—See MARINGOUIN, LA

LOCKHART—See WALKER, LA

LOCKPORT—See GOLDEN MEADOW, LA

▲ **LOGANSPORT**—Mansfield Cablevision

LOREAUVILLE—See NEW IBERIA, LA

LUBADIEVILLE—See LAFOURCHE PARISH, LA

LULING—See ST. CHARLES PARISH, LA

LUTCHER—See GRAMERCY, LA

▲ **LYDIA**—Star Cable

MADISON PARISH—See TALLULAH, LA

MADISONVILLE—See ST. TAMMANY PARISH, LA

MAMOU—See VILLE PLATTE, LA

MANDEVILLE—See ST. TAMMANY PARISH, LA

▲ **MANGHAM**—Falcon Telecable

▲ **MANSFIELD**—Mansfield Cablevision

MANSURA—See MARKSVILLE, LA (Scott Cable Communications Inc.)

▲ **MANY**—Star Cable

▲ **MARINGOUIN**—Spillway Cablevision Inc.

▲ **MARION**—Bayou Cable TV

▲ **MARKSVILLE**—Friendship Cable of Texas Inc.

▲ **MARKSVILLE**—Scott Cable Communications Inc.

MATHEWS—See GOLDEN MEADOW, LA

MAURICE—See LAFAYETTE, LA

▲McINTYRE—Friendship Cable of Arkansas

McNARY—See LECOMPTE, LA

▲ **MELVILLE**—Friendship Cable of Texas Inc.

MER ROUGE—See BASTROP, LA

MERAUX—See ST. BERNARD PARISH, LA

MERMENTAU—See ESTHERWOOD, LA

▲ **MERRYVILLE**—Delta Cablecomm

MIDWAY—See JENA, LA

MILTON—See LAFAYETTE, LA

▲ **MINDEN**—Minden Cable TV

▲ **MIRE**—Torrence Cablevision

MONROE—See WEST MONROE, LA

MONTEGUT—See TERREBONNE PARISH, LA

▲ **MONTEREY**—Friendship Cable of Texas Inc.

▲ **MONTGOMERY**—Friendship Cable of Texas Inc.

MONTZ—See ST. CHARLES PARISH, LA

▲ **MOORINGSPORT**—Macco Communications Inc.

▲ **MOREAUVILLE**—Friendship Cable of Texas Inc.

MOREHOUSE PARISH (portions)—See BASTROP, LA

MOREHOUSE PARISH (unincorporated areas)—See also COLLINSTON, LA

▲ **MORGAN CITY**—Allen's TV Cable Service Inc.

MORGANZA—See POINTE COUPEE, LA

MORSE—See ESTHERWOOD, LA

MOSS BLUFF—See WESTLAKE, LA

MOSSVILLE—See SULPHUR, LA

NAPOLEONVILLE—See LAFOURCHE PARISH, LA

▲ **NATCHEZ**—Friendship Cable of Texas Inc.

▲**NATCHITOCHES**—Natchitoches Cable TV

▲ **NATCHITOCHES (portions)**—Cane River Cable Co.

NATCHITOCHES PARISH—See NATCHITOCHES, LA

NATCHITOCHES PARISH (portions)—See also ROBELINE, LA

▲ **NEW IBERIA**—New Iberia Cable TV

NEW IBERIA—See also LYDIA, LA

▲ **NEW ORLEANS**—Cox Louisiana

NEW ROADS—See POINTE COUPEE, LA

▲ **NEWELLTON**—Friendship Cable of Texas Inc.

NEWLLANO—See LEESVILLE, LA

NORCO—See ST. CHARLES PARISH, LA

NORTH HODGE—See JONESBORO, LA

▲ **NORTH MONROE**—Southwest Cablevision

▲ **NORWOOD**—Torrence Cablevision

▲ **OAK GROVE**—Delta Cablevision

▲ **OAK RIDGE**—Falcon Telecable

OAKDALE—See BUNKIE, LA

OBERLIN—See KINDER, LA

OIL CITY—See BLANCHARD, LA

OLLA—See JENA, LA

OPELOUSAS—See ST. LANDRY PARISH, LA

ORLEANS PARISH—See NEW ORLEANS, LA

OUACHITA PARISH (northern portion)—See WEST MONROE, LA

OUACHITA PARISH (portions)—See CALHOUN, LA (Louisiana Cablevision)

▲ **PALMETTO**—Village Cable Co.

PARKS—See ST. MARTINVILLE, LA

▲ **PATTERSON**—Patterson Cable TV

PAULINA—See LAFOURCHE PARISH, LA

PEARL RIVER—See ST. TAMMANY PARISH, LA

▲ **PECANIERE**—Torrence Cablevision

▲ **PIERRE PART**—Allen's TV Cable Service Inc.

▲ **PINE PRAIRIE**—Delta Cablecomm

▲ **PINEVILLE**—TCA Cable TV Inc.

▲ **PLAIN DEALING**—Falcon Telecable

▲**PLAQUEMINE**—Telecommunications Cable Systems Inc.

PLAQUEMINES PARISH—See JEFFERSON PARISH, LA

PLAUCHEVILLE—See MOREAUVILLE, LA

▲ **POINTE A LA HACHE**—Plaquemines Cablevision Inc.

▲ **POINTE COUPEE**—Charter Communications Inc.

POINTE COUPEE PARISH—See MARINGOUIN, LA

POINTE COUPEE PARISH—See also POINTE COUPEE, LA

POINTE PLACE—See NATCHEZ, LA

POLLOCK—See PINEVILLE, LA

PONCHATOULA—See HAMMOND, LA

▲ **PORT ALLEN**—TCI of Louisiana

▲ **PORT BARRE**—Allen's TV Cable Service Inc.

PORT SULPHUR—See EMPIRE, LA

PORT VINCENT—See HAMMOND, LA

PORTERVILLE—See SPRINGHILL, LA

PRINCETON—See BOSSIER CITY, LA

QUITMAN—See JONESBORO, LA

RACELAND—See GOLDEN MEADOW, LA

MAINE

MARYLAND

WASHINGTON COUNTY (unincorporated areas)—See also FREDERICK, MD

WASHINGTON GROVE—See MONTGOMERY COUNTY, MD

WEST BETHESDA—See MONTGOMERY COUNTY, MD

WEST FRIENDSHIP—See HOWARD COUNTY, MD

WESTERNPORT—See KEYSER, WV

WESTMINSTER—See CARROLL COUNTY, MD

WHALEYSVILLE—See DAGSBORO, DE

WHEATON—See MONTGOMERY COUNTY, MD

WHITE PLAINS—See WALDORF, MD

WHITEHALL—See BEL AIR, MD

WICOMICO COUNTY—See SALISBURY, MD

WICOMICO COUNTY (portions)—See also HARRINGTON, DE

WICOMICO COUNTY (southwestern portion)—See also CAMBRIDGE, MD

WILLARDS—See DAGSBORO, DE

WILLIAMSPORT—See HAGERSTOWN, MD

WILSON LANDING MOBILE HOME PARK—See SALISBURY, MD

WOODBINE—See HOWARD COUNTY, MD

WOODLAND—See KEYSER, WV

WOODLAWN—See TOWSON, MD

WOODSBORO—See FREDERICK, MD

WORCESTER COUNTY—See OCEAN CITY, MD

WORCESTER COUNTY—See also POCOMOKE, MD

WORCESTER COUNTY—See also SALISBURY, MD

ZIHLMAN—See KEYSER, WV

MASSACHUSETTS

ABINGTON—See PEMBROKE, MA

ACTON—See MAYNARD, MA

ACUSHNET—See FAIRHAVEN, MA

ADAMS—See NORTH ADAMS, MA

AGAWAM—See WESTFIELD, MA

ALLSTON—See BOSTON, MA

▲ **AMESBURY**—New England Cablevision of Massachusetts Inc.

▲ **AMHERST**—MediaOne

▲ **ANDOVER**—MediaOne

ARLINGTON—See CAMBRIDGE, MA

ARLINGTON (town)—See CAMBRIDGE, MA

ASHBURNHAM—See WESTFORD, MA

ASHBY (town)—See WESTFORD, MA

ASHLAND—See FOXBOROUGH, MA

ATHOL—See ORANGE, MA

▲ **ATTLEBORO**—MediaOne

AUBURN—See WORCESTER, MA

AVON—See STOUGHTON, MA

AYER—See WESTFORD, MA

BACK BAY—See BOSTON, MA

BARNSTABLE—See SOUTH YARMOUTH, MA

BARRE—See RUTLAND (town), MA

BARRE (town)—See RUTLAND (town), MA

BEACON HILL—See BOSTON, MA

BEDFORD—See LEXINGTON, MA

▲ **BELCHERTOWN**—Amrac Clear View

BELLINGHAM—See FOXBOROUGH, MA

BELMONT—See WESTFORD, MA

BERKLEY—See MIDDLEBOROUGH, MA

BERLIN—See PEPPERELL, MA

▲ **BERNARDSTON**—MediaOne

▲ **BEVERLY**—MediaOne

BILLERICA—See WOBURN, MA

BLACKSTONE—See NEWPORT & LINCOLN, RI

BOLTON—See STERLING, MA

BOLTON (town)—See STERLING, MA

BONDSVILLE—See AMHERST, MA

▲ **BOSTON**—Cablevision of Boston LP

BOURNE—See PEMBROKE, MA

BOXBOROUGH—See WESTFORD, MA

BOXFORD (town)—See BEVERLY, MA

BOYLSTON—See WORCESTER, MA

▲ **BRAINTREE**—Cablevision Systems Corp.

BREWSTER—See ORLEANS, MA

BRIDGEWATER—See FOXBOROUGH, MA

BRIGHTON—See BOSTON, MA

BRIMFIELD—See WALES, MA

▲ **BROCKTON**—MediaOne

BROOKFIELD—See CHARLTON, MA

BROOKLINE—See BOSTON, MA

BUCKLAND—See AMHERST, MA

BURLINGTON—See WOBURN, MA

▲ **CAMBRIDGE**—MediaOne

CANTON—See FOXBOROUGH, MA

CARLISLE (town)—See WESTFORD, MA

CARVER—See PEMBROKE, MA

CENTERVILLE—See SOUTH YARMOUTH, MA

▲ **CHARLEMONT**—Charlemont Cable Inc.

CHARLESTOWN—See BOSTON, MA

▲ **CHARLTON**—Pegasus Cable Television

CHATHAM—See SOUTH YARMOUTH, MA

CHATHAM (town)—See SOUTH YARMOUTH, MA

CHELMSFORD—See LOWELL, MA

CHELSEA—See MEDFORD, MA

CHESHIRE—See NORTH ADAMS, MA

▲ **CHESTER**—MediaOne

▲ **CHICOPEE**—Charter Communications

CHILMARK—See MARTHA'S VINEYARD, MA

CHINATOWN—See BOSTON, MA

CLARKSBURG—See NORTH ADAMS, MA

CLINTON—See STERLING, MA

COHASSET—See SCITUATE, MA

CONCORD—See WESTFORD, MA

▲ **CONWAY**—MediaOne

COTUIT—See SOUTH YARMOUTH, MA

DALTON—See PITTSFIELD, MA

▲ **DANVERS**—Cablevision of Nashoba

DARTMOUTH—See NEW BEDFORD, MA

▲ **DEDHAM**—MediaOne

DEERFIELD—See CONWAY, MA

DENNIS—See SOUTH YARMOUTH, MA

DENNIS PORT—See SOUTH YARMOUTH, MA

DIGHTON—See MIDDLEBOROUGH, MA

DORCHESTER—See BOSTON, MA

DOUGLAS—See UXBRIDGE, MA

DOUGLAS (town)—See UXBRIDGE, MA

DOVER—See FOXBOROUGH, MA

DOVER (town)—See FOXBOROUGH, MA

DRACUT—See ANDOVER, MA

DUDLEY—See WORCESTER, MA

DUNSTABLE—See PEPPERELL, MA

DUXBURY—See MARSHFIELD, MA

EAST BOSTON—See BOSTON, MA

EAST BRIDGEWATER—See BROCKTON, MA

EAST BROOKFIELD (town)—See CHARLTON, MA

EAST DENNIS—See SOUTH YARMOUTH, MA

EAST FALMOUTH—See FALMOUTH, MA

EAST HARWICH—See SOUTH YARMOUTH, MA

EAST LONGMEADOW—See CHICOPEE, MA

EASTHAM—See ORLEANS, MA

EASTHAMPTON—See CHICOPEE, MA

EASTON—See STOUGHTON, MA

EDGARTOWN—See MARTHA'S VINEYARD, MA

ERVING—See AMHERST, MA

ESSEX—See GLOUCESTER, MA

EVERETT—See MEDFORD, MA

▲ **FAIRHAVEN**—MediaOne

FALL RIVER—See NEW BEDFORD, MA

▲ **FALMOUTH**—Adelphia Cable

FENWAY—See BOSTON, MA

▲ **FITCHBURG**—A-R Cable Services Inc.

▲ **FORT DEVENS**—Americable International

FOXBORO—See FOXBOROUGH, MA

▲ **FOXBOROUGH**—MediaOne

RANDOLPH—See QUINCY, MA

RAYNHAM—See STOUGHTON, MA

READING—See WOBURN, MA

REHOBOTH—See ATTLEBORO, MA

REVERE—See SAUGUS, MA

RICHMOND—See PITTSFIELD, MA

ROCHESTER—See MARION, MA

ROCKLAND—See PEMBROKE, MA

ROCKPORT—See GLOUCESTER, MA

ROSLINDALE—See BOSTON, MA

ROWLEY—See NEWBURYPORT, MA

ROXBURY—See BOSTON, MA

▲ **RUSSELL**—Russell Municipal Cable TV

▲ **RUTLAND (town)**—Charter Communications

SALEM—See MEDFORD, MA

SALISBURY—See AMESBURY, MA

SANDWICH—See PEMBROKE, MA

▲ **SAUGUS**—MediaOne

▲ **SCITUATE**—MediaOne

SEEKONK—See FOXBOROUGH, MA

SHARON—See FOXBOROUGH, MA

SHEFFIELD (town)—See GREAT BARRINGTON, MA

SHELBURNE—See AMHERST, MA

SHELBURNE FALLS—See AMHERST, MA

SHERBORN—See NATICK, MA

SHIRLEY (town)—See WESTFORD, MA

▲ **SHREWSBURY**—Shrewsbury's Community Cablevision

SIASCONSET—See NANTUCKET, MA

SOMERSET—See NEWPORT & LINCOLN, RI

SOMERVILLE—See MEDFORD, MA

SOUTH BOSTON—See BOSTON, MA

SOUTH CHATHAM—See SOUTH YARMOUTH, MA

SOUTH DEERFIELD—See CONWAY, MA

SOUTH DENNIS—See SOUTH YARMOUTH, MA

SOUTH END—See BOSTON, MA

SOUTH HADLEY—See WESTFIELD, MA

SOUTH HARWICH—See SOUTH YARMOUTH, MA

▲ **SOUTH YARMOUTH**—MediaOne

SOUTHAMPTON—See CHICOPEE, MA

SOUTHBOROUGH—See WORCESTER, MA

SOUTHBRIDGE—See WORCESTER, MA

SOUTHWICK—See WESTFIELD, MA

SPENCER—See WORCESTER, MA

▲ **SPRINGFIELD**—MediaOne

▲ **STERLING**—MediaOne

STERLING (town)—See STERLING, MA

STOCKBRIDGE—See GREAT BARRINGTON, MA

STONEHAM—See WOBURN, MA

▲ **STOUGHTON**—MediaOne

STOW—See MAYNARD, MA

STURBRIDGE—See WORCESTER, MA

SUDBURY—See MAYNARD, MA

SUNDERLAND—See CONWAY, MA

SUTTON—See UXBRIDGE, MA

SWAMPSCOTT—See MEDFORD, MA

SWANSEA—See NEWPORT & LINCOLN, RI

▲ **TAUNTON**—MediaOne

TEMPLETON—See FITCHBURG, MA

TEWKSBURY—See LOWELL, MA

THORNDIKE—See AMHERST, MA

THREE RIVERS—See AMHERST, MA

TISBURY—See MARTHA'S VINEYARD, MA

TOPSFIELD—See BEVERLY, MA

TOWNSEND (town)—See WESTFORD, MA

TRURO—See ORLEANS, MA

TURNERS FALLS—See AMHERST, MA

TYNGSBOROUGH—See WESTFORD, MA

UPTON—See MILFORD, MA

UPTON—See also WORCESTER, MA

UPTON (town)—See MILFORD, MA

▲ **UXBRIDGE**—Charter Communications

VINEYARD HAVEN—See MARTHA'S VINEYARD, MA

WAKEFIELD—See MEDFORD, MA

▲ **WALES**—Charter Communications

WALPOLE—See FOXBOROUGH, MA

▲ **WALTHAM**—MediaOne

Waquoit—See FALMOUTH, MA

WARE—See AMHERST, MA

WAREHAM—See MARION, MA

WARREN—See AMHERST, MA

Washington—See WEST STOCKBRIDGE, MA

Washington (town)—See WEST STOCKBRIDGE, MA

▲ **WATERTOWN**—MediaOne

WAYLAND—See NEWTON, MA

WEBSTER—See WORCESTER, MA

WELLESLEY—See NEWTON, MA

WELLFLEET—See ORLEANS, MA

WENHAM—See BEVERLY, MA

WEST BARNSTABLE—See SOUTH YARMOUTH, MA

WEST BOYLSTON—See WORCESTER, MA

WEST BRIDGEWATER—See BROCKTON, MA

WEST BROOKFIELD—See WORCESTER, MA

WEST CHATHAM—See SOUTH YARMOUTH, MA

WEST DENNIS—See SOUTH YARMOUTH, MA

WEST HARWICH—See SOUTH YARMOUTH, MA

WEST NEWBURY—See NEWBURYPORT, MA

WEST ROXBURY—See BOSTON, MA

WEST SPRINGFIELD—See WESTFIELD, MA

▲ **WEST STOCKBRIDGE**—Pegasus Cable Television

WEST TISBURY—See MARTHA'S VINEYARD, MA

WEST YARMOUTH—See SOUTH YARMOUTH, MA

WESTBOROUGH—See WORCESTER, MA

▲ **WESTFIELD**—MediaOne

▲ **WESTFORD**—A-R Cable Partners

WESTHAMPTON—See CHESTER, MA

Westminster—See FITCHBURG, MA

WESTON—See NEWTON, MA

▲ **WESTPORT**—Charter Communications

WESTWOOD—See NORWOOD, MA

▲ **WEYMOUTH**—MediaOne

WHATELY—See CHESTER, MA

WHITMAN—See BROCKTON, MA

WILBRAHAM—See CHICOPEE, MA

WILLIAMSTOWN—See NORTH ADAMS, MA

WILMINGTON—See WOBURN, MA

▲ **WINCHENDON**—MediaOne

WINCHESTER—See WOBURN, MA

WINTHROP—See MEDFORD, MA

▲ **WOBURN**—MediaOne

▲ **WORCESTER**—Greater Media Cable

WRENTHAM—See FOXBOROUGH, MA

YARMOUTH—See SOUTH YARMOUTH, MA

YARMOUTH (town)—See SOUTH YARMOUTH, MA

YARMOUTH PORT—See SOUTH YARMOUTH, MA

MICHIGAN

ACME TWP.—See TRAVERSE CITY, MI

ACME TWP. (northern portion)—See also TRAVERSE CITY, MI

ADA—See GRAND RAPIDS, MI

ADAMS TWP. (Hillsdale County)—See HILLSDALE, MI

ADAMS TWP. (Houghton County)—See HOUGHTON, MI

ADDISON—See DEVILS LAKE, MI

ADDISON TWP.—See OXFORD, MI

▲ **ADRIAN**—TCI Cable

ADRIAN TWP.—See ADRIAN, MI

AETNA TWP. (Mecosta County)—See HOWARD CITY, MI

AGATE HARBOR—See EAGLE HARBOR TWP., MI

AKRON (village)—See AKRON/FAIRGROVE, MI

CAMBRIA TWP.—See also HILLSDALE, MI

CAMBRIDGE TWP.—See BROOKLYN (irish hills), MI

▲ **CAMDEN TWP.**—New Path Communications LC

CAMPBELL TWP.—See CLARKSVILLE, MI

CANADA CREEK RANCH—See ONAWAY, MI

▲ **CANADIAN LAKES**—Bresnan Communications

CANNON—See ROCKFORD, MI

CANNON TWP.—See GRAND RAPIDS, MI

▲ **CANTON TWP.**—Americast

CANTON TWP.—See also PLYMOUTH, MI (MediaOne)

▲ **CAPAC**—Harron Cable

CARLETON (village)—See MONROE, MI (River Raisin Cablevision Inc.)

CARLTON TWP.—See FREEPORT, MI

CARMEL TWP.—See CHARLOTTE, MI

CARNEY—See POWERS, MI

▲ **CARO**—Cable Michigan

CARP LAKE—See LEVERING, MI

CARP LAKE—See also ONTONAGON, MI

CARROLLTON—See SAGINAW, MI

▲ **CARSON CITY**—Cable Michigan

CARSONVILLE—See DECKERVILLE, MI

CASCADE—See GRAND RAPIDS, MI

CASCADE TWP.—See MIDDLEVILLE/CALEDONIA, MI

CASCO TWP. (Allegan County)—See SOUTH HAVEN, MI

CASCO TWP. (St. Clair County)—See NEW HAVEN, MI

▲ **CASEVILLE**—Harron Cable

CASEVILLE (village)—See CASEVILLE, MI

CASEVILLE TWP.—See CASEVILLE, MI

CASNOVIA (village)—See GRANT, MI

CASNOVIA TWP.—See GRANT, MI

▲ **CASPIAN**—Caspian Community TV Corp.

▲ **CASS CITY**—Cable Michigan

CASS COUNTY—See EDWARDSBURG, MI

▲ **CASSOPOLIS**—TCI Cablevision

CATO TWP.—See LAKEVIEW, MI

CEDAR CREEK TWP. (Muskegon County)—See MUSKEGON, MI

CEDAR CREEK TWP. (Muskegon County)—See also TWIN LAKE, MI

CEDAR CREEK TWP. (Wexford County)—See MANTON, MI

CEDAR SPRINGS—See ROCKFORD, MI

Cedar Twp.—See BIG RAPIDS, MI

CEDARVILLE—See CLARK TWP., MI

CEMENT CITY (village)—See BROOKLYN (irish hills), MI

CENTER LINE—See EAST DETROIT, MI

CENTRAL LAKE—See MANCELONA, MI

CENTRAL LAKE TWP.—See MANCELONA, MI

CENTREVILLE—See THREE RIVERS, MI

CERESCO—See BATTLE CREEK, MI

▲ **CHAMPION TWP.**—Upper Peninsula Communications

CHARLESTON TWP.—See CLIMAX TWP., MI

CHARLESTON TWP.—See also KALAMAZOO, MI (Adelphia Cable)

▲ **CHARLEVOIX**—Bresnan Communications

CHARLEVOIX TWP.—See CHARLEVOIX, MI

▲ **CHARLOTTE**—Millennium Digital Media

CHASSELL TWP.—See HOUGHTON, MI

CHATHAM—See MARQUETTE, MI

▲ **CHEBOYGAN**—Bresnan Communications

CHELSEA—See SALINE, MI

CHERRY GROVE TWP.—See CADILLAC, MI

▲ **CHESANING**—TCI Cablevision

CHESANING (village)—See CHESANING, MI

CHESANING TWP.—See CHESANING, MI

CHESHIRE TWP.—See BLOOMINGDALE, MI

CHESTER TWP. (Otsego County)—See GAYLORD, MI

▲ **CHESTER TWP. (Ottawa County)**—Cable Michigan

CHESTERFIELD—See NEW HAVEN, MI

CHESTERFIELD TWP.—See NEW HAVEN, MI

CHESTONIA TWP.—See ALBA, MI

CHIKAMING TWP.—See THREE OAKS, MI

CHINA TWP.—See NEW HAVEN, MI

CHIPPEWA TWP.—See MOUNT PLEASANT, MI

▲ **CHIPPEWA TWP. (Isabella County)**—Bresnan Communications

CHIPPEWA TWP. (Mecosta County)—See CANADIAN LAKES, MI

CHOCOLAY TWP.—See MARQUETTE, MI

CHRISTMAS—See MARQUETTE, MI

CHURCHILL TWP.—See SKIDWAY LAKE, MI

CLAM LAKE TWP.—See CADILLAC, MI

CLARE—See MOUNT PLEASANT, MI

CLARENCE TWP.—See SPRINGPORT TWP., MI

▲ **CLARK TWP.**—Northwoods Cable Inc.

▲ **CLARKSTON**—Tribune United Cable Communications

▲ **CLARKSVILLE**—Millennium Digital Media

▲ **CLAWSON**—Americast

CLAWSON—See also ROYAL OAK, MI (TCI Cablevision of Oakland County Inc.)

CLAY TWP.—See NEW HAVEN, MI

CLAYTON TWP. (Genesee County)—See DURAND, MI

CLEARWATER TWP.—See TRAVERSE CITY, MI

CLEMENT TWP.—See BUTMAN TWP., MI

CLEVELAND TWP.—See TRAVERSE CITY, MI

CLIFFORD—See KINGSTON TWP., MI

▲ **CLIMAX TWP.**—Climax Telephone Co.

▲ **CLINTON**—Americast

CLINTON—See also SALINE, MI

CLINTON COUNTY—See LANSING, MI

▲ **CLINTON TWP. (Macomb County)**—Comcast Cablevision of Clinton/Mount Clemens Inc.

CLIO—See THETFORD TWP., MI

CLIO—See also BURTON, MI

CLYDE TWP. (Allegan County)—See FENNVILLE, MI

CLYDE TWP. (St. Clair County)—See PORT HURON, MI

COE TWP.—See MOUNT PLEASANT, MI

COLD SPRINGS TWP.—See MANCELONA, MI

▲ **COLDWATER**—Coldwater Cablevision Inc.

COLDWATER (unincorporated areas)—See also KINDERHOOK TWP., MI

COLDWATER TWP. (Branch County)—See COLDWATER, MI

▲ **COLEMAN**—Falcon Telecable

COLFAX TWP. (Huron County)—See BAD AXE, MI

COLFAX TWP. (Huron County)—See also BIG RAPIDS, MI

COLOMA—See WATERVLIET, MI

COLOMA TWP.—See WATERVLIET, MI

COLON—See COLDWATER, MI

COLUMBIA TWP.—See BROOKLYN (irish hills), MI

COLUMBIA TWP. (Van Buren County)—See BLOOMINGDALE, MI

COLUMBIAVILLE—See LAPEER, MI

COLUMBUS TWP. (St. Clair County)—See NEW HAVEN, MI

COMINS TWP.—See ROSE CITY, MI

▲ **COMMERCE TWP.**—Community Cable Television

COMSTOCK—See KALAMAZOO, MI (Cablevision of Michigan Inc.)

COMSTOCK TWP.—See CLIMAX TWP., MI

COMSTOCK TWP. (portions)—See also KALAMAZOO, MI (Adelphia Cable)

▲ **CONCORD**—Millennium Digital Media

CONCORD TWP.—See CONCORD, MI

CONRIS TWP.—See OLIVET, MI

CONSTANTINE—See THREE RIVERS, MI

CONSTANTINE TWP.—See THREE RIVERS, MI

CONWAY—See PETOSKEY, MI

COOPER TWP.—See ALLEGAN, MI

EMPIRE TWP.—See TRAVERSE CITY, MI

▲ **ENGADINE**—Upper Peninsula Communications

ENSLEY—See GRANT, MI

ENSLEY TWP.—See HOWARD CITY, MI

ERIE TWP.—See MONROE, MI (River Raisin Cablevision Inc.)

ERIE TWP.—See also TOLEDO, OH

ERWIN TWP.—See IRONWOOD, MI

▲ **ESCANABA**—Bresnan Communications Co.

ESCANABA TWP.—See ESCANABA, MI

ESSEXVILLE—See BAY CITY, MI

ESTRAL BEACH—See MONROE, MI (River Raisin Cablevision Inc.)

EUREKA TWP.—See GREENVILLE, MI

EVANGELINE TWP.—See EAST JORDAN, MI

▲ **EVART**—Cable Michigan

EVART TWP.—See EVART, MI

EVELINE TWP.—See EAST JORDAN, MI

EVERETT—See FREMONT, MI

EVERETT TWP.—See GRANT, MI

EVERGREEN TWP. (Montcalm County)—See STANTON, MI

▲ **EWEN**—Bresnan Communications Co.

EXCELSIOR TWP.—See MANCELONA, MI

EXETER TWP.—See MONROE, MI (River Raisin Cablevision Inc.)

FABIUS—See THREE RIVERS, MI

FAIRFIELD—See ADRIAN, MI

FAIRGROVE (village)—See AKRON/FAIRGROVE, MI

FAIRGROVE TWP.—See AKRON/FAIRGROVE, MI

FAIRHAVEN TWP.—See PIGEON, MI

FAIRHAVEN TWP.—See also SEBEWAING, MI

FAIRVIEW—See MIO, MI

▲ **FARMINGTON**—Time Warner Cable

FARMINGTON HILLS—See FARMINGTON, MI

FAWN RIVER TWP.—See COLDWATER, MI

FAYETTE TWP.—See HILLSDALE, MI

▲ **FENNVILLE**—TCI Cablevision

▲ **FENTON**—Mid Lakes CableComm

FENTON TWP.—See FENTON, MI

▲ **FERNDALE**—Americast

FERNDALE—See also ROYAL OAK, MI (TCI Cablevision of Oakland County Inc.)

FERRYSBURG—See MUSKEGON, MI

▲ **FIFE LAKE**—Cable Michigan

FIFE LAKE TWP.—See FIFE LAKE, MI

FILER TWP.—See MANISTEE, MI

FILLMORE—See ALLEGAN, MI

FILLMORE TWP. (portions)—See ALLENDALE, MI

FILLMORE TWP. (portions)—See also COUNTRY ACRES, MI

▲ **FINE LAKE**—Avalon Cable

FLAT ROCK—See TAYLOR, MI

FLINT—See BURTON, MI

FLINT TWP.—See BURTON, MI

FLOWERFIELD—See THREE RIVERS, MI

FLUSHING—See BURTON, MI

FLUSHING TWP.—See BURTON, MI

FORD RIVER TWP.—See ESCANABA, MI

FOREST HOME TWP.—See MANCELONA, MI

FOREST TWP. (Genesee County)—See DAVISON, MI

FOREST TWP. (Missaukee County)—See MANTON, MI

▲ **FORESTER TWP.**—Mid Lakes CableComm

▲ **FORESTVILLE**—Mid Lakes CableComm

FORSYTH TWP.—See MARQUETTE, MI

FORT GRATIOT TWP.—See PORT HURON, MI

FOUNTAIN—See CUSTER, MI

▲ **FOWLER**—Cable Michigan

FOWLERVILLE—See WILLIAMSTON, MI

FRANKENLUST TWP.—See BAY CITY, MI

FRANKENMUTH—See BRIDGEPORT TWP., MI

FRANKENMUTH TWP.—See BRIDGEPORT TWP., MI

FRANKFORT—See TRAVERSE CITY, MI

FRANKLIN—See BIRMINGHAM, MI

FRANKLIN TWP. (Houghton County)—See HOUGHTON, MI

FRANKLIN TWP. (Lenawee County)—See BROOKLYN (irish hills), MI

▲ **FRASER**—Americast

FRASER—See also ST. CLAIR SHORES, MI (Comcast Cable Investors Inc.)

FRASER TWP.—See BEAVER TWP. (Bay County), MI

FRASER TWP.—See also LINWOOD, MI

▲ **FREDERIC TWP.**—Village Cable

FREDONIA TWP.—See COLDWATER, MI

FREDONIA TWP.—See also MARSHALL, MI

▲ **FREE SOIL**—Westcom LC

FREELAND—See THOMAS TWP., MI

FREEMAN TWP.—See LAKE GEORGE, MI

FREEMONT TWP.—See MAYVILLE, MI

▲ **FREEPORT**—North Star Cable

FREEPORT CITY—See FREEPORT, MI

▲ **FREMONT**—TCI Cablevision of Greater Michigan

FRENCHTOWN TWP.—See MONROE, MI (Monroe Cablevision Inc.)

FRENCHTOWN TWP.—See also MONROE, MI (River Raisin Cablevision Inc.)

FRONTIER—See CAMBRIA TWP., MI

▲ **FROST TWP.**—Mid Lakes CableComm

FRUITLAND—See WHITEHALL, MI

FRUITLAND TWP.—See MUSKEGON, MI

FRUITPORT CHARTER TWP.—See ALLENDALE, MI

FRUITPORT CHARTER TWP.—See also MUSKEGON, MI

FRUITPORT VILLAGE—See ALLENDALE, MI

GAASTRA—See CASPIAN, MI

▲ **GAGETOWN**—Bresnan Communications

GAINES—See DURAND, MI

GAINES TWP. (Genesee County)—See DURAND, MI

GAINES TWP. (Kent County)—See GRAND RAPIDS, MI

GAINES TWP. (Kent County)—See also MIDDLEVILLE/CALEDONIA, MI

GALESBURG—See KALAMAZOO, MI (Adelphia Cable)

GALIEN—See MARSHALL COUNTY, IN

GALIEN TWP.—See MARSHALL COUNTY, IN

GANGES TWP.—See FENNVILLE, MI

▲ **GARDEN CITY**—Americast

GARDEN CITY—See also TAYLOR, MI

▲ **GARDEN TWP.**—Upper Peninsula Communications Inc.

GARFIELD TWP. (Bay County)—See BEAVER TWP. (Bay County), MI

GARFIELD TWP. (Bay County)—See also HOPE TWP. (Midland County), MI

▲ **GARFIELD TWP. (Clare County)**—Avalon Cable

GARFIELD TWP. (Grand Traverse County)—See TRAVERSE CITY, MI

GARFIELD TWP. (Newaygo County)—See FREMONT, MI

GARFIELD TWP. (Newaygo County)—See also GRANT, MI

▲ **GAYLORD**—Bresnan Communications

GENESEE TWP.—See BURTON, MI

GENEVA TWP. (Midland County)—See CHIPPEWA TWP. (Isabella County), MI

GENEVA TWP. (Van Buren County)—See SOUTH HAVEN, MI

GENOA TWP.—See BRIGHTON, MI

GEORGETOWN TWP.—See GRAND RAPIDS, MI

▲ **GERMFASK**—Upper Peninsula Communications

GERRISH TWP. (portions)—See HIGGINS LAKE, MI

GERRISH TWP. (portions)—See also ROSCOMMON, MI

GIBRALTAR—See WOODHAVEN, MI

▲ **GILEAD**—New Path Communications LC

GILMORE TWP. (Benzie County)—See TRAVERSE CITY, MI

▲ **GILMORE TWP. (Isabella County)**—Avalon Cable

LARKIN TWP. (portions)—See also MIDLAND (portions), MI

LATHRUP VILLAGE—See SOUTHFIELD, MI

LAURIUM—See HOUGHTON, MI

LAWRENCE—See LAWTON, MI

LAWRENCE—See also SOUTH HAVEN, MI

LAWRENCE TWP.—See LAWTON, MI

LAWRENCE TWP.—See also SOUTH HAVEN, MI

▲ **LAWTON**—Adelphia Cable

LAWTON (village)—See LAWTON, MI

Lee Twp. (Allegan County)—See BLOOMINGDALE, MI

LEE TWP. (Midland County)—See SANFORD, MI

LEELANAU TWP.—See TRAVERSE CITY, MI

LEIGHTON TWP.—See MIDDLEVILLE/CALEDONIA, MI

LELAND TWP.—See TRAVERSE CITY, MI

LENNON—See DURAND, MI

LENOX TWP.—See NEW HAVEN, MI

LEONARD—See OXFORD, MI

LEONI TWP.—See SUMMIT-LEONI, MI

▲ **LEROY (village)**—Pine River Cable Co.

LEROY TWP. (Calhoun County)—See BATTLE CREEK, MI

LEROY TWP. (Ingham County)—See WILLIAMSTON, MI

▲ **LESLIE**—Millennium Digital Media

LESLIE TWP.—See LESLIE, MI

▲ **LEVERING**—Bresnan Communications

▲ **LEWISTON**—North Star Cable

LEXINGTON—See CROSWELL, MI

LEXINGTON TWP.—See CROSWELL, MI

LIBERTY TWP. (Jackson County)—See CONCORD, MI

LIBERTY TWP. (Jackson County)—See also SUMMIT-LEONI, MI

LIBERTY TWP. (Wexford County)—See MANTON, MI

▲ **LILLEY TWP.**—Westcom

LIMA TWP.—See SALINE, MI

LINCOLN—See OSCODA, MI

▲ **LINCOLN PARK**—Americast

LINCOLN PARK—See also WOODHAVEN, MI

LINCOLN TWP.—See PORT AUSTIN, MI

LINCOLN TWP. (Arenac County)—See STANDISH, MI

LINCOLN TWP. (Berrien County)—See ST. JOSEPH TWP., MI

LINCOLN TWP. (Clare County)—See LAKE GEORGE, MI

LINCOLN TWP. (Isabella County)—See MOUNT PLEASANT, MI

LINCOLN TWP. (Midland County)—See SANFORD, MI

LINCOLN TWP. (Osceola County)—See MOUNT PLEASANT, MI

LINDEN—See FENTON, MI

▲ **LINWOOD**—Falcon Telecable

LITCHFIELD—See COLDWATER, MI

LITTLE LAKE—See MARQUETTE, MI

LITTLE TRAVERSE TWP.—See PETOSKEY, MI

LITTLEFIELD TWP.—See INDIAN RIVER, MI

LITTLEFIELD TWP.—See also PETOSKEY, MI

LIVINGSTON TWP.—See GAYLORD, MI

▲ **LIVONIA**—Time Warner Cable

LOCKPORT—See THREE RIVERS, MI

LODI TWP.—See SALINE, MI

LOGAN TWP.—See SKIDWAY LAKE, MI

LONDON TWP.—See MONROE, MI (River Raisin Cablevision Inc.)

LONG LAKE—See OSCODA, MI

LONG LAKE TWP.—See TRAVERSE CITY, MI

LONG RAPIDS TWP.—See ALPENA, MI

LOST LAKE WOODS (village)—See OSCODA, MI

LOST PENINSULA—See TOLEDO, OH

▲ **LOWELL**—Lowell Cable TV

LOWELL TWP.—See GRAND RAPIDS, MI

LOWELL TWP.—See also LOWELL, MI

LOWELL TWP.—See also MIDDLEVILLE/CALEDONIA, MI

▲ **LUDINGTON**—Bresnan Communications Co.

LUNA PIER—See MONROE, MI (River Raisin Cablevision Inc.)

LUPTON—See ROSE CITY, MI

LUTHER (village)—See LEROY (village), MI

▲ **LUZERNE**—Westcom

LYON TWP. (Oakland County)—See COMMERCE TWP., MI

LYON TWP. (Roscommon County)—See HIGGINS LAKE, MI

LYONS TWP.—See IONIA, MI

LYONS TWP.—See also PEWAMO, MI

LYONS VILLAGE—See IONIA, MI

▲ **MACKINAC ISLAND**—Bresnan Communications Co.

▲ **MACKINAW CITY**—Bresnan Communications

MACKINAW TWP.—See MACKINAW CITY, MI

MACOMB TWP.—See CLINTON TWP. (Macomb County), MI

MACOMB TWP.—See also SHELBY TWP. (Macomb County), MI

▲ **MADISON HEIGHTS**—Americast

▲ **MADISON HEIGHTS**—MediaOne

MADISON TWP.—See ADRIAN, MI

▲ **MANCELONA**—Cable Michigan

MANCELONA (village)—See MANCELONA, MI

MANCELONA TWP.—See ALBA, MI

MANCHESTER—See SALINE, MI

▲ **MANISTEE**—Cable Michigan

MANISTEE TWP. (portions)—See BEAR LAKE, MI

MANISTEE TWP. (portions)—See also MANISTEE, MI

▲ **MANISTIQUE**—Bresnan Communications Co.

MANISTIQUE—See also ESCANABA, MI

MANISTIQUE TWP.—See ESCANABA, MI

MANISTIQUE TWP.—See also MANISTIQUE, MI

MANITOU BEACH—See ADRIAN, MI

MANLIUS—See ALLEGAN, MI

MANLIUS TWP.—See FENNVILLE, MI

▲ **MANTON**—Cable Michigan

MAPLE GROVE TWP. (Manistee County)—See KALEVA (village), MI

MAPLE GROVE TWP. (Saginaw County)—See BURT, MI

▲ **MAPLE RAPIDS**—Avalon Cable

MAPLE RIDGE TWP. (Alpena County)—See ALPENA, MI

MAPLE VALLEY TWP. (Montcalm County)—See HOWARD CITY, MI

MAPLEVIEW ESTATES TRAILER PARK—See CHIPPEWA TWP. (Isabella County), MI

MARATHON TWP.—See LAPEER, MI

MARATHON TWP.—See also MAYVILLE, MI

▲ **MARCELLUS**—Triax Cablevision

MARENGO—See MARSHALL, MI

▲ **MARENISCO TWP.**—Upper Peninsula Communications Inc.

MARINE CITY—See NEW HAVEN, MI

▲ **MARION**—Cable Michigan

MARION TWP. (Charlevoix County)—See CHARLEVOIX, MI

MARION TWP. (Livingston County)—See HAMBURG TWP., MI

MARION TWP. (Osceola County)—See MARION, MI

MARION TWP. (Sanilac County)—See YALE, MI

MARKEY TWP.—See HIGGINS LAKE, MI

MARKEY TWP.—See also HOUGHTON LAKE, MI

▲ **MARLETTE**—Harron Cable

▲ **MARQUETTE**—Bresnan Communications Co.

MARQUETTE TWP. (Marquette County)—See MARQUETTE, MI

▲ **MARSHALL**—Millennium Digital Media

MARSHALL—See also BATTLE CREEK, MI

MARSHALL TWP.—See MARSHALL, MI

MARTIN (village)—See ALLEGAN, MI

MARTIN TWP.—See ALLEGAN, MI

NEWBERG TWP.—See DOWAGIAC, MI

▲ **NEWBERRY**—Bresnan Communications

NEWTON TWP.—See BATTLE CREEK, MI

▲ **NILES**—TCI Cablevision

NILES TWP.—See NILES, MI

NORTH ADAMS VILLAGE—See HILLSDALE, MI

▲ **NORTH BRANCH**—Mid Lakes CableComm

NORTH BRANCH TWP.—See NORTH BRANCH, MI

NORTH LAKE (Marquette County)—See MARQUETTE, MI

NORTH MUSKEGON—See MUSKEGON, MI

NORTH PLAINS TWP.—See PEWAMO, MI

NORTH STAR TWP.—See ALMA, MI

NORTHFIELD TWP.—See HAMBURG TWP., MI

NORTHPORT—See TRAVERSE CITY, MI

▲ **NORTHVILLE**—Americast

NORTHVILLE—See also PLYMOUTH, MI (MediaOne)

▲ **NORTHVILLE TWP.**—Americast

NORTHVILLE TWP.—See also PLYMOUTH, MI (MediaOne)

NORTON SHORES—See MUSKEGON, MI

NORVELL TWP.—See BROOKLYN (irish hills), MI

▲ **NORWAY**—City of Norway CATV

NORWAY TWP.—See NORWAY, MI

NORWAY TWP. (western portion)—See IRON MOUNTAIN, MI (Bresnan Communications Co.)

NORWOOD—See CHARLEVOIX, MI

NOTTAWA TWP. (Isabella County)—See WEIDMAN, MI

NOTTAWA TWP. (St. Joseph County)—See THREE RIVERS, MI

NOVESTA TWP.—See CASS CITY, MI

NOVESTA TWP.—See also KINGSTON TWP., MI

NOVI—See FARMINGTON, MI

OAK PARK—See SOUTHFIELD, MI

OAKFIELD TWP.—See GRAND RAPIDS, MI

OAKFIELD TWP.—See also GREENVILLE, MI

OAKLAND TWP.—See ROYAL OAK, MI (TCI Cablevision of Oakland County Inc.)

OAKLEY (village)—See CHESANING, MI

OCEOLA TWP.—See BRIGHTON, MI

ODEN—See PETOSKEY, MI

ODESSA TWP.—See LAKE ODESSA, MI

OGEMAW COUNTY (unincorporated areas)—See HALE, MI

OGEMAW TWP.—See WEST BRANCH, MI

OKEMOS—See EAST LANSING, MI

▲ **OLIVE TWP. (Ottawa County)**—Bresnan Communications Co.

OLIVE TWP. (Ottawa County)—See also ALLENDALE, MI

OLIVER TWP.—See PIGEON, MI

▲ **OLIVET**—Millennium Digital Media

▲ **OMER**—Bresnan Communications

▲ **ONAWAY**—Northwoods Cable Inc.

ONEIDA CHARTER TWP.—See POTTERVILLE, MI

ONEIDA TWP.—See LANSING, MI

ONEKAMA—See BEAR LAKE, MI

ONEKAMA (village)—See BEAR LAKE, MI

ONEKAMA TWP.—See BEAR LAKE, MI

ONONDAGA TWP.—See LESLIE, MI

ONSTED (village)—See BROOKLYN (irish hills), MI

▲ **ONTONAGON**—Bresnan Communications Co.

ONTONAGON TWP.—See ONTONAGON, MI

ONTWA TWP.—See EDWARDSBURG, MI

ORANGE TWP. (Kalkaska County)—See BOARDMAN TWP., MI

ORANGEVILLE TWP.—See MIDDLEVILLE/CALEDONIA, MI

ORCHARD LAKE—See WEST BLOOMFIELD TWP., MI

OREGON TWP.—See DAVISON, MI

OREGON TWP.—See also LAPEER, MI

ORID TWP.—See COLDWATER, MI

ORION TWP.—See LAKE ORION, MI

ORLEANS TWP. (portions)—See GREENVILLE, MI

ORLEANS TWP. (portions)—See also IONIA, MI

ORONOKO TWP.—See ST. JOSEPH TWP., MI

ORTONVILLE—See OXFORD, MI

OSCEOLA—See HOUGHTON, MI

OSCEOLA TWP. (Houghton County)—See HOUGHTON, MI

OSCEOLA TWP. (Osceola County)—See EVART, MI

▲ **OSCODA**—Mid Lakes CableComm

OSCODA TWP.—See OSCODA, MI

OSHTEMO—See KALAMAZOO, MI (Adelphia Cable)

OSHTEMO—See also KALAMAZOO, MI (Cablevision of Michigan Inc.)

OSHTEMO—See also MATTAWAN, MI

OSHTEMO TWP.—See PIONEER, MI

OSSINEKE—See ALPENA, MI

OSSINEKE TWP.—See OSCODA, MI

OTISCO TWP.—See GREENVILLE, MI

OTISVILLE—See DAVISON, MI

OTSEGO CITY—See ALLEGAN, MI

OTSEGO LAKE—See GAYLORD, MI

OTSEGO LAKE TWP.—See ALLEGAN, MI

OTTER LAKE—See MAYVILLE, MI

OVERISEL—See ALLEGAN, MI

OVID VILLAGE—See ELSIE, MI

OWENDALE—See GAGETOWN, MI

▲ **OWOSSO**—Bresnan Communications Co.

OWOSSO TWP.—See OWOSSO, MI

▲ **OXFORD**—Mid Lakes CableComm

OXFORD (village)—See OXFORD, MI

OXFORD TWP.—See OXFORD, MI

PALMER—See MARQUETTE, MI

PALMYRA—See ADRIAN, MI

PALMYRA TWP.—See MONROE, MI (River Raisin Cablevision Inc.)

PARADISE TWP.—See TRAVERSE CITY, MI

PARCHMENT—See KALAMAZOO, MI (Cablevision of Michigan Inc.)

PARIS—See BIG RAPIDS, MI

PARK—See THREE RIVERS, MI

PARK TWP. (Ottawa County)—See ALLENDALE, MI

PARMA—See CONCORD, MI

PARMA TWP.—See CONCORD, MI

Parma Twp.—See also SPRINGPORT TWP., MI

PAVILION—See KALAMAZOO, MI (Cablevision of Michigan Inc.)

PAVILION TWP.—See CLIMAX TWP., MI

PAVILION TWP.—See also THREE RIVERS, MI

PAW PAW (village)—See LAWTON, MI

PAW PAW TWP.—See LAWTON, MI

PECK—See YALE, MI

▲ **PELLSTON**—Cable Michigan

PENINSULA TWP.—See TRAVERSE CITY, MI

PENN—See CASSOPOLIS, MI

PENN TWP.—See DOWAGIAC, MI

PENNFIELD TWP.—See BATTLE CREEK, MI

PENTLAND TWP.—See NEWBERRY, MI

▲ **PENTWATER**—Cable Michigan

PENTWATER TWP.—See PENTWATER, MI

▲ **PERRINTON**—Avalon Cable

PERRY—See WILLIAMSTON, MI

PERRY TWP.—See WILLIAMSTON, MI

PETERSBURG—See MONROE, MI (River Raisin Cablevision Inc.)

▲ **PETOSKEY**—Bresnan Communications Co.

▲ **PEWAMO**—Millennium Digital Media

▲ **PICKFORD TWP.**—Bresnan Communications Co.

PIERSON (village)—See HOWARD CITY, MI

PIERSON TWP.—See HOWARD CITY, MI

▲ **PIGEON**—Harron Cable

PINCKNEY—See HAMBURG TWP., MI

PINCONNING—See STANDISH, MI

PINCONNING TWP.—See STANDISH, MI

PINE GROVE TWP.—See ALLEGAN, MI

PINE RIVER TWP.—See ALMA, MI

PINE TWP.—See HOWARD CITY, MI

PINE TWP.—See also STANTON, MI

PINEWOOD CREEK—See NEW HAVEN, MI

▲ **PIONEER**—Adelphia Cable

PIPESTONE TWP.—See WATERVLIET, MI

PITTSFIELD TWP.—See ANN ARBOR, MI

PITTSFORD TWP.—See HILLSDALE, MI

PLAINFIELD TWP. (Iosco County)—See OSCODA, MI

PLAINFIELD TWP. (Kent County)—See GRAND RAPIDS, MI

PLAINFIELD TWP. (Kent County)—See also ROCKFORD, MI

PLAINWELL CITY—See ALLEGAN, MI

PLEASANT LAKE—See LESLIE, MI

▲ **PLEASANT RIDGE**—Americast

PLEASANT RIDGE—See also ROYAL OAK, MI (TCI Cablevision of Oakland County Inc.)

PLEASANT VIEW TWP.—See PETOSKEY, MI

PLEASANTON TWP.—See BEAR LAKE, MI

▲ **PLYMOUTH**—Americast

▲ **PLYMOUTH**—MediaOne

▲ **PLYMOUTH TWP.**—Ameritech New Media

PLYMOUTH TWP.—See also PLYMOUTH, MI (MediaOne)

POINTE AUX BARQUES TWP.—See PORT AUSTIN, MI

POKAGON TWP. (portions)—See DOWAGIAC, MI

POLKTON TWP.—See ALLENDALE, MI

▲ **PONTIAC**—Comcast Cable Investors Inc.

PONTIAC TWP.—See ROYAL OAK, MI (TCI Cablevision of Oakland County Inc.)

▲ **PORT AUSTIN**—Harron Cable

PORT AUSTIN TWP.—See PORT AUSTIN, MI

▲ **PORT HOPE**—Harron Cable

▲ **PORT HURON**—Harron Communications

PORT HURON TWP.—See PORT HURON, MI

PORT SANILAC—See DECKERVILLE, MI

PORT SHELDON TWP.—See OLIVE TWP. (Ottawa County), MI

PORTAGE (northeastern portion)—See KALAMAZOO, MI (Cablevision of Michigan Inc.)

PORTAGE (portions)—See PIONEER, MI

PORTAGE (southern portion)—See THREE RIVERS, MI

▲ **PORTAGE TWP.**—Upper Peninsula Communications Inc.

PORTAGE TWP. (Houghton County)—See HOUGHTON, MI

PORTER TWP. (Cass County)—See DOWAGIAC, MI

PORTER TWP. (Van Buren County)—See LAWTON, MI

▲ **PORTLAND**—Millennium Digital Media

PORTLAND TWP.—See PORTLAND, MI

PORTSMOUTH TWP.—See BAY CITY, MI

▲ **POSEN**—Cable Michigan

▲ **POTTERVILLE**—Millennium Digital Media

▲ **POWERS**—Upper Peninsula Communications Inc.

PRAIRIE RONDE—See WATERVLIET, MI

PRAIRIEVILLE TWP.—See ALLEGAN, MI

PRAIRIEVILLE TWP.—See also DELTON, MI

PRAIRIEVILLE TWP.—See also KALAMAZOO, MI (Adelphia Cable)

▲ **PRESCOTT (village)**—Westcom

PRESQUE ISLE TWP.—See GRAND LAKE, MI

PRINCETON—See MARQUETTE, MI

PULASKI—See CONCORD, MI

Pulaski Twp.—See POSEN, MI

PULAWSKI TWP.—See GRAND LAKE, MI

PUTNAM TWP.—See HAMBURG TWP., MI

QUAIL RUN—See NEW HAVEN, MI

QUANICASSEE—See WISNER (village), MI

QUINCY—See COLDWATER, MI

QUINCY TWP. (Branch County)—See COLDWATER, MI

QUINCY TWP. (Houghton County)—See HOUGHTON, MI

RAISIN TWP.—See ADRIAN, MI

RAISINVILLE TWP.—See MONROE, MI (River Raisin Cablevision Inc.)

RAPID RIVER—See ESCANABA, MI

RAPID RIVER TWP.—See MANCELONA, MI

RAVENNA—See CHESTER TWP. (Ottawa County), MI

RAVENNA TWP.—See CHESTER TWP. (Ottawa County), MI

RAY TWP.—See CLINTON TWP. (Macomb County), MI

RAY TWP.—See also NEW HAVEN, MI

RAY TWP.—See also SHELBY TWP. (Macomb County), MI

READING—See COLDWATER, MI

▲ **REDFORD**—Time Warner Cable

▲ **REED CITY**—Cable Michigan

REEDER TWP.—See MANTON, MI

▲ **REESE**—Bresnan Communications

▲ **REMUS**—Avalon Cable

▲ **REPUBLIC TWP.**—Grove Cable Co.

RESORT TWP.—See PETOSKEY, MI

REYNOLDS TWP.—See HOWARD CITY, MI

RICHFIELD TWP. (Genesee County)—See DAVISON, MI

RICHFIELD TWP. (Roscommon County)—See ST. HELEN, MI

RICHLAND TWP. (Kalamazoo County)—See KALAMAZOO, MI (Adelphia Cable)

RICHLAND TWP. (Montcalm County)—See RIVERDALE, MI

RICHLAND TWP. (Saginaw County)—See THOMAS TWP., MI

RICHLAND VILLAGE—See KALAMAZOO, MI (Adelphia Cable)

RICHMOND—See NEW HAVEN, MI

RICHMOND TWP. (Macomb County)—See NEW HAVEN, MI

RICHMOND TWP. (Marquette County)—See MARQUETTE, MI

RICHMOND TWP. (Osceola County)—See REED CITY, MI

RIDGEWAY—See ADRIAN, MI

RIGA TWP.—See MONROE, MI (River Raisin Cablevision Inc.)

RILEY TWP.—See NEW HAVEN, MI

RIPLEY—See HOUGHTON, MI

RIVER ROUGE—See TAYLOR, MI

▲ **RIVERDALE**—Cable Michigan

RIVERSIDE TWP.—See MCBAIN, MI

▲ ***RIVERVIEW**—Americast

RIVERVIEW—See also WOODHAVEN, MI

▲ **RIVES JUNCTION**—Mid Lakes CableComm

RIVES TWP.—See JACKSON, MI

ROBINSON TWP.—See ALLENDALE, MI

ROCHESTER—See ROYAL OAK, MI (TCI Cablevision of Oakland County Inc.)

ROCHESTER HILLS—See ROYAL OAK, MI (TCI Cablevision of Oakland County Inc.)

ROCK RIVER TWP.—See MARQUETTE, MI

▲ **ROCKFORD**—Cable Michigan

ROCKFORD—See also LILLEY TWP., MI

ROCKLAND TWP.—See MASS CITY, MI

ROCKWOOD—See TAYLOR, MI

▲ **ROGERS CITY**—Cable Michigan

ROGERS HEIGHTS—See BIG RAPIDS, MI

ROGERS TWP.—See ROGERS CITY, MI

ROLLIN—See DEVILS LAKE, MI

ROMEO—See NEW HAVEN, MI

▲ **ROMULUS**—MediaOne

RONALD TWP.—See IONIA, MI

ROOSEVELT PARK—See MUSKEGON, MI

▲ **ROSCOMMON**—Cable Michigan

ROSCOMMON (village)—See ROSCOMMON, MI

ROSCOMMON TWP.—See HIGGINS LAKE, MI

ROSCOMMON TWP.—See also HOUGHTON LAKE, MI

▲ **ROSE CITY**—Mid Lakes CableComm

ROSE TWP. (Oakland County)—See BURTON, MI

WAKEFIELD TWP.—See IRONWOOD, MI

WALDRON VILLAGE—See HILLSDALE, MI

WALKER—See GRAND RAPIDS, MI

WALLED LAKE—See COMMERCE TWP., MI

WALTON TWP.—See OLIVET, MI

▲ **WARREN**—Americast

▲ **WARREN**—Comcast Cablevision of Warren

WARREN—See also CLINTON TWP. (Macomb County), MI

WARREN TWP.—See COLEMAN, MI

WASHINGTON—See EDWARDSBURG, MI

WASHINGTON TWP. (Macomb County)—See NEW HAVEN, MI

WATERFORD TWP.—See PONTIAC, MI

WATERLOO TWP.—See LESLIE, MI

▲ **WATERSMEET**—Bresnan Communications Co.

▲ **WATERTOWN TWP. (Clinton County)**—Millennium Digital Media

WATERTOWN TWP. (Clinton County)—See also LANSING, MI

WATERTOWN TWP. (Sanilac County)—See SANDUSKY, MI

WATERTOWN TWP. (Tuscola County)—See MAYVILLE, MI

▲ **WATERVLIET**—Jones Intercable

WATERVLIET TWP.—See WATERVLIET, MI

WATSON TWP.—See ALLEGAN, MI

WAUCEDAH TWP.—See IRON MOUNTAIN, MI (Bresnan Communications Co.)

WAVERLY TWP. (Van Buren County)—See BLOOMINGDALE, MI

WAVERLY TWP. (Van Buren County)—See also LAWTON, MI

WAWATAM TWP.—See MACKINAW CITY, MI

WAYLAND—See MIDDLEVILLE/CALEDONIA, MI

WAYLAND TWP.—See MIDDLEVILLE/CALEDONIA, MI

▲ **WAYNE**—Americast

▲ **WAYNE**—MediaOne

WAYNE TWP.—See DOWAGIAC, MI

WEBBERVILLE—See WILLIAMSTON, MI

WEBSTER TWP.—See ANN ARBOR, MI

WEBSTER TWP.—See also HAMBURG TWP., MI

WEESAW—See THREE OAKS, MI

▲ **WEIDMAN**—Avalon Cable

WELLS—See ESCANABA, MI

▲ **WELLSTON**—Westcom

▲ **WEST BLOOMFIELD TWP.**—MediaOne

▲ **WEST BRANCH**—Cable Michigan

WEST BRANCH TWP. (Ogemaw County)—See WEST BRANCH, MI

WEST TRAVERSE TWP.—See PETOSKEY, MI

▲ **WESTLAND**—Americast

WESTLAND—See also DEARBORN HEIGHTS, MI

WESTPHALIA—See PEWAMO, MI

WETMORE—See MARQUETTE, MI

WHEATFIELD TWP.—See EAST LANSING, MI

WHEATFIELD TWP.—See also WILLIAMSTON, MI

WHEATLAND TWP. (Mecosta County)—See REMUS, MI

WHEELER—See ALMA, MI

WHEELER TWP.—See ALMA, MI

WHITE BIRCH TRAILER PARK—See BEAVER TWP. (Bay County), MI

WHITE LAKE—See COMMERCE TWP., MI

WHITE PIGEON—See THREE RIVERS, MI

WHITE PIGEON TWP. (eastern portion)—See COLDWATER, MI

WHITE PINE—See ONTONAGON, MI

WHITE RIVER TWP.—See WHITEHALL, MI

Whiteford—See BEDFORD TWP. (Monroe County), MI

▲ **WHITEHALL**—Cable Michigan

WHITEHALL TWP. (Oceana County)—See WHITEHALL, MI

WHITEWATER TWP.—See TRAVERSE CITY, MI

WHITNEY TWP.—See AU GRES, MI

▲ **WHITTEMORE**—Bresnan Communications

WILBER TWP.—See OSCODA, MI

WILLIAMS TWP. (eastern portion)—See BAY CITY, MI

WILLIAMS TWP. (western portion)—See MIDLAND (portions), MI

WILLIAMSPORT—See LAKE ODESSA, MI

▲ **WILLIAMSTON**—Millennium Digital Media

WILLIAMSTON TWP.—See WILLIAMSTON, MI

WILSON TWP. (Alpena County)—See ALPENA, MI

WILSON TWP. (Charlevoix County)—See EAST JORDAN, MI

WINDSOR—See POTTERVILLE, MI

WINDSOR CHARTER TWP.—See LANSING, MI

WINFIELD TWP.—See HOWARD CITY, MI

WINSOR TWP.—See PIGEON, MI

▲ **WISNER (village)**—Mid Lakes CableComm

WIXOM—See COMMERCE TWP., MI

▲ **WOLVERINE (village)**—Upper Peninsula Communications

WOLVERINE LAKE—See COMMERCE TWP., MI

WOLVERINE LAKE VILLAGE—See COMMERCE TWP., MI

WOODCREEK MANOR—See DURAND, MI

▲ **WOODHAVEN**—TCI Cablevision of Woodhaven

WOODHULL TWP.—See BATH, MI

WOODHULL TWP.—See also WILLIAMSTON, MI

WOODLAND—See LAKE ODESSA, MI

▲ **WOODLAND (village)**—Avalon Cable

WOODSTOCK TWP.—See DEVILS LAKE, MI

WORTH TWP.—See CROSWELL, MI

WRIGHT TWP. (Ottawa County)—See ALLENDALE, MI

WRIGHT TWP. (Ottawa County)—See also GRAND RAPIDS, MI

▲ **WYANDOTTE**—Wyandotte Municipal Services

WYOMING—See GRAND RAPIDS, MI

▲ **YALE**—Harron Cable

YANKEE SPRINGS TWP.—See MIDDLEVILLE/CALEDONIA, MI

▲ **YORK TWP.**—Televista Communications

YPSILANTI—See ANN ARBOR, MI

YPSILANTI TWP.—See ANN ARBOR, MI

ZEELAND TWP.—See ALLENDALE, MI

ZEELAND TWP.—See also OLIVE TWP. (Ottawa County), MI

ZILWAUKEE—See SAGINAW, MI

MINNESOTA

▲ **ADA**—Loretel Cablevision

▲ **ADAMS**—Triax Cablevision

▲ **ADRIAN**—Dakota Telecom Inc.

AFTON—See ST. CROIX, MN

▲ **AITKIN**—WestMarc Cable Holding Inc.

AKELEY—See WALKER, MN

AKELEY TWP.—See WALKER, MN

▲ **ALBANY**—WestMarc Communications of Minnesota Inc.

▲ **ALBERT LEA**—Bresnan Communications Co.

ALBERTVILLE—See BUFFALO, MN

▲ **ALDEN**—US Cable of Minnesota

▲ **ALEXANDRIA**—Bresnan Communications Co.

ALEXANDRIA TWP.—See ALEXANDRIA, MN

ALTURA—See ROLLINGSTONE, MN

ALTURA—See also STOCKTON, MN

▲ **ALVARADO**—Stephen Cable TV Inc.

AMBOY—See GOOD THUNDER, MN

AMOR TWP.—See PERHAM, MN

ANDOVER—See ROSEVILLE, MN

▲ **ANNANDALE**—Heart of the Lakes Cable System Inc.

ANOKA—See ROSEVILLE, MN

APPLE VALLEY—See ROSEMOUNT, MN

▲ **APPLETON**—Triax Cablevision

ARDEN HILLS—See ROSEVILLE, MN

COKATO—See BUFFALO, MN

COKATO TWP.—See BUFFALO, MN

COLD SPRING—See AVON, MN

▲ **COLERAINE**—Coleraine Cable Communications System

COLERAINE—See also BOVEY, MN

▲ **COLOGNE**—North American Communications

COLUMBIA HEIGHTS—See ROSEVILLE, MN

COLUMBUS TWP.—See FOREST LAKE, MN

▲ **COMFREY**—Comfrey Cable TV

▲ **CONCORD**—Triax Cablevision

▲ **COOK**—Triax Cablevision

COON RAPIDS—See ROSEVILLE, MN

CORCORAN—See BROOKLYN PARK, MN

CORINNA TWP.—See ANNANDALE, MN

CORLISS TWP.—See PERHAM, MN

CORMORANT LAKE (eastern portion)—See PELICAN LAKE, MN

CORMORANT TWP.—See PELICAN LAKE, MN

▲ **COSMOS**—Triax Cablevision

COTTAGE GROVE—See ST. CROIX, MN

▲ **COTTONWOOD**—Harmon Cable Communications

▲ **COURTLAND**—Courtland Cable TV

CREDIT RIVER—See PRIOR LAKE, MN

CROOKED LAKE—See EMILY, MN

▲ **CROOKSTON**—TCI Cablevision of Minnesota

CROSBY—See BRAINERD, MN

▲ **CROSSLAKE**—Crosslake Cablevision Co.

CROW WING COUNTY (northern portion)—See PEQUOT LAKES, MN

CROW WING COUNTY (unincorporated areas)—See BRAINERD, MN

▲ **CROWN**—US Cable of Minnesota

CRYSTAL—See BROOKLYN PARK, MN

▲ **CURRIE**—Dakota Telecom Inc.

CUYUNA—See BRAINERD, MN

CYRUS—See BARRETT, MN

▲ **DAKOTA**—Triax Cablevision

DAKOTA COUNTY (northern portion)—See ST. PAUL, MN

DALTON—See PERHAM, MN

DANE PRAIRIE TWP.—See FERGUS FALLS, MN

DANE PRAIRIE TWP.—See also WALL LAKE, MN

DANUBE—See OLIVIA, MN

DASSEL—See BUFFALO, MN

▲ **DAWSON**—Triax Cablevision

DAYTON—See BUFFALO, MN

DEAD LAKE TWP.—See PERHAM, MN

DEEPHAVEN—See LAKE MINNETONKA, MN

DEER CREEK—See PERHAM, MN

▲ **DEER RIVER**—Paul Bunyon Telephone

DEER RIVER TWP.—See DEER RIVER, MN

DEERWOOD—See BRAINERD, MN

DEERWOOD TWP.—See BRAINERD, MN

DEERWOOD TWP.—See also KARLSTAD, MN

DELANO—See BUFFALO, MN

▲ **DELAVAN**—North American Communications Corp.

DELLWOOD—See ROSEVILLE, MN

DENMARK TWP.—See ST. CROIX, MN

DENT—See PERHAM, MN

DETROIT LAKES—See PERHAM, MN

▲ **DEXTER**—North American Communications Corp.

▲ **DILWORTH**—Loreltel Cablevision

▲ **DODGE CENTER**—Triax Cablevision

DONNELLY—See BARRETT, MN

DOVER—See CHATFIELD, MN

DOVER TWP.—See CHATFIELD, MN

DOVER TWP.—See also WILLMAR, MN

DRESBACH—See DAKOTA, MN

▲ **DULUTH**—Bresnan Communications Co.

DULUTH (unincorporated areas)—See CANOSIA TWP., MN

DUNDAS—See NORTHFIELD, MN

▲ **DUNDEE**—American Telecasting of Minnesota Inc.

DUNN TWP.—See PELICAN LAKE, MN

▲ **DUNNELL**—US Cable of Minnesota

EAGAN—See ROSEVILLE, MN

EAGLE BEND—See PARKERS PRAIRIE, MN

EAGLE LAKE—See MANKATO, MN

EAST BETHEL—See CROWN, MN

EAST GRAND FORKS—See GRAND FORKS, ND

▲ **EAST GULL LAKE**—Savage Communications

▲ **EASTON**—North American Communications Corp.

▲ **ECHO**—Echo Cable TV

EDEN PRAIRIE—See MINNEAPOLIS, MN

EDEN VALLEY—See AVON, MN

▲ **EDGERTON**—Dakota Telecom Inc.

EDINA—See MINNEAPOLIS, MN

EDNA TWP.—See PERHAM, MN

▲ **EITZEN**—North American Communications Corp.

▲ **ELBOW LAKE**—Runestone Cable TV

ELBOW LAKE—See also BARRETT, MN

ELGIN—See PLAINVIEW, MN

ELIZABETH—See PERHAM, MN

ELIZABETH TWP.—See WALL LAKE, MN

ELK RIVER—See BUFFALO, MN

▲ **ELKO**—Tri-Cable Inc.

ELLENDALE—See ALDEN, MN

▲ **ELLSWORTH**—Dakota Telecom Inc.

ELMORE—See BLUE EARTH, MN

ELMWOOD TWP.—See SABIN, MN

▲ **ELY**—WestMarc Cable Holding Inc.

ELYSIAN—See ALDEN, MN

▲ **EMILY**—Emily Cooperative Telephone Co. CATV Division

▲ **EMMONS**—Heck's TV & Cable

EMPIRE (town)—See ROSEMOUNT, MN

ERHARD—See WALL LAKE, MN

ERHARDS GROVE TWP.—See WALL LAKE, MN

▲ **ERSKINE**—Garden Valley Telephone Co.

ESKO—See CLOQUET, MN

EVANSVILLE—See BARRETT, MN

▲ **EVELETH**—Triax Cablevision

EVERTS TWP.—See WALL LAKE, MN

EXCELSIOR—See LAKE MINNETONKA, MN

EYOTA—See ROCHESTER, MN

FAIRFAX—See REDWOOD FALLS, MN

▲ **FAIRMONT**—Fairmont Cable TV

FAIRVIEW TWP.—See PEQUOT LAKES, MN

FALCON HEIGHTS—See ROSEVILLE, MN

▲ **FARIBAULT**—Bresnan Communications Co.

FARMINGTON—See ROSEMOUNT, MN

FAYAL TWP.—See EVELETH, MN

FELTON—See ADA, MN

▲ **FERGUS FALLS**—Bresnan Communications Co.

FERGUS FALLS TWP.—See WALL LAKE, MN

▲ **FERTILE**—Loretel Cablevision

FIFTY LAKES—See EMILY, MN

▲ **FINLAND**—Cable Systems Management of Iowa Inc.

FISHER—See ADA, MN

▲ **FLOODWOOD**—Savage Communications Inc.

FLORENCE TWP.—See LAKE CITY, MN

FOLEY—See AVON, MN

▲ **FOREST LAKE**—US Cable of Minnesota

▲ **FOSSTON**—City of Fosston Cable TV

▲ **FOUNTAIN**—North American Communications Corp.

FRANKFORT TWP.—See BUFFALO, MN

FRANKLIN—See REDWOOD FALLS, MN

FRANKLIN TWP.—See BUFFALO, MN

FRANZEE—See PERHAM, MN

FREEBORN—See ALDEN, MN

FREEPORT—See AVON, MN

▲ **FRENCH RIVER TWP.**—Cable Systems Management of Iowa Inc.

▲ **FRIDLEY**—Paragon Cable

FRONTENAC—See LAKE CITY, MN

FROST—See BRICELYN, MN

▲ **FULDA**—Triax Cablevision

▲ **GARDEN CITY**—North American Communications Corp.

▲ **GARY**—Loretel Cablevision

▲ **GAYLORD**—Triax Cablevision

GEM LAKE—See ROSEVILLE, MN

GENEVA—See ALDEN, MN

GHENT—See MINNEOTA, MN

GIBBON—See GAYLORD, MN

GILBERT—See EVELETH, MN

GIRARD TWP.—See PERHAM, MN

▲ **GLENCOE**—Bresnan Communications Co.

▲ **GLENVILLE**—US Cable of Minnesota

▲ **GLENWOOD**—WestMarc Communications of Minnesota Inc.

GLENWOOD (village)—See GLENWOOD, MN

GLYNDON—See DILWORTH, MN

GODFREY—See ERSKINE, MN

GODFREY TWP.—See ERSKINE, MN

GOLDEN VALLEY—See BROOKLYN PARK, MN

GONVICK—See CLEARBROOK, MN

▲ **GOOD THUNDER**—Woodstock LLC

▲ **GOODHUE**—Sleepy Eye Telephone Co.

GOODVIEW—See WINONA, MN

GORMAN TWP.—See PERHAM, MN

▲ **GRACEVILLE**—Triax Cablevision

▲ **GRANADA**—US Cable of Minnesota

▲ **GRAND MARAIS**—Triax Cablevision

▲ **GRAND MEADOW**—Southern Cablevision Inc.

GRAND PRAIRIE—See GRAND RAPIDS, MN

▲ **GRAND RAPIDS**—Triax Cablevision

GRAND RAPIDS TWP.—See GRAND RAPIDS, MN

▲ **GRANITE FALLS**—Triax Cablevision

GRANT TWP.—See ROSEVILLE, MN

▲ **GREEN ISLE**—North American Communications Corp.

GREEN LAKE TWP.—See WILLMAR, MN

GREEN PRAIRIE TWP.—See LITTLE FALLS, MN

▲ **GREENBUSH**—Sjoberg's Cable TV

GREENWOOD—See LAKE MINNETONKA, MN

▲ **GREY EAGLE**—Upsala Cooperative Telephone Assn.

▲ **GROVE CITY**—Triax Cablevision

GROVE PARK—See ERSKINE, MN

GROVE PARK TWP.—See ERSKINE, MN

▲ **GRYGLA**—Garden Valley Telephone Co.

GULDRID—See BAUDETTE, MN

▲ **HACKENSACK**—Interlake CableVision

▲ **HALLOCK**—Midcontinent Cable Co.

HALSTAD—See ADA, MN

HAM LAKE—See ROSEVILLE, MN

HAMBURG—See NORWOOD, MN

▲ **HAMPTON**—Dakota Cable TV

▲ **HANCOCK**—Triax Cablevision

▲ **HANLEY FALLS**—Project Services Inc.

HANOVER—See BROOKLYN PARK, MN

▲ **HANSKA**—Hanska Cable TV

▲ **HARMONY**—Harmony Cable Inc.

HARRIS—See CAMBRIDGE, MN

HARRIS TWP.—See GRAND RAPIDS, MN

HARRISON TWP.—See WILLMAR, MN

HASSAN TWP.—See BUFFALO, MN

HASTINGS—See ST. CROIX, MN

HAUGEN TWP.—See ROUND LAKE TWP., MN

HAVEN—See ST. CLOUD, MN

HAVERHILL TWP.—See ROCHESTER, MN

▲ **HAWLEY**—Loreltel Cablevision

▲ **HAYFIELD**—Tri-Cable Inc.

▲ **HAYWARD**—North American Communications Corp.

▲ **HECTOR**—Triax Cablevision

HENDERSON—See LE SUEUR, MN

▲ **HENDRICKS**—US Cable of Minnesota

HENDRUM—See ADA, MN

HENNING—See PERHAM, MN

HENNING TWP.—See PERHAM, MN

HENRIETTA TWP.—See WALKER, MN

HEREIM TWP.—See GREENBUSH, MN

HERMAN—See BARRETT, MN

HERMANTOWN—See PROCTOR, MN

▲ **HERON LAKE**—US Cable of Minnesota

▲ **HIBBING**—Range TV Cable Co. Inc.

HIDDEN VALLEY—See STOCKTON, MN

▲ **HILL CITY**—Savage Communications Systems Inc.

HILL RIVER TWP.—See ERSKINE, MN

▲ **HILLS**—Dakota Telecom Inc.

HILLTOP—See ROSEVILLE, MN

HINCKLEY—See SANDSTONE, MN

HIRAM TWP.—See HACKENSACK, MN

HITTERDAL—See ULEN, MN

HOFFMAN—See BARRETT, MN

▲ **HOKAH**—Triax Cablevision

HOLDINGFORD—See AVON, MN

HOLLAND—See RUTHTON, MN

HOMER—See WINONA, MN

HOPE TWP.—See IVANHOE, MN

HOPKINS—See MINNEAPOLIS, MN

▲ **HOUSTON**—Triax Cablevision

▲ **HOWARD LAKE**—US Cable of Minnesota

▲ **HOYT LAKES**—Charter Communications Inc.

HUDSON—See ALEXANDRIA, MN

HUGO—See ROSEVILLE, MN

▲ **HUTCHINSON**—Triax Cablevision

IDEAL CORNERS—See PEQUOT LAKES, MN

▲ **INTERNATIONAL FALLS**—Bresnan Communications Co.

INVER GROVE HEIGHTS—See ST. PAUL, MN

▲ **IONA**—American Telecasting of Minnesota Inc.

IRONDALE—See BRAINERD, MN

IRONTON—See BRAINERD, MN

IRVING—See WILLMAR, MN

ISANTI—See CAMBRIDGE, MN

ISANTI ESTATES MOBILE HOME PARK—See CAMBRIDGE, MN

▲ **ISLE**—Savage Communications Inc.

ISLE HARBOR—See ISLE, MN

▲ **IVANHOE**—Triax Cablevision

▲ **JACKSON**—Jackson Municipal TV System

JAMESON—See INTERNATIONAL FALLS, MN

▲ **JANESVILLE**—Triax Cablevision

▲ **JASPER**—Dakota Telecom Inc.

▲ **JEFFERS**—New Ulm Telecom

JENKINS—See PEQUOT LAKES, MN

▲ **JORDAN**—Paragon Cable

KANDIYOHI—See WILLMAR, MN

▲ **KARLSTAD**—Sjoberg's Cablevision Inc.

KASOTA—See ST. PETER, MN

KASOTA—See also WASHINGTON TWP., MN

KASSON—See ROCHESTER, MN

▲ **KEEWATIN**—Triax Cablevision

KEGO—See WALKER, MN

▲ **KELLIHER**—North American Communications Corp.

KELLOGG—See WABASHA, MN

▲ **KENNEDY**—Stephen Cable TV Inc.

KENSINGTON—See BARRETT, MN

▲ **KENYON**—Triax Cablevision

▲ **KERKHOVEN**—TCI of Central Minnesota

KIESTER—See BRICELYN, MN

KIMBALL—See AVON, MN

KING TWP.—See ERSKINE, MN

KINNEY—See CHISHOLM, MN

▲ **KNIFE LAKE TWP.**—Cable Systems Management of Iowa Inc.

▲ **KNIFE RIVER**—Cable Systems Management of Iowa Inc.

KNUTE TWP.—See ERSKINE, MN

KOOCHICHING COUNTY—See INTERNATIONAL FALLS, MN

LA CRESCENT—See LA CROSSE, WI

LA GRANDE—See ALEXANDRIA, MN

LA PRAIRIE TWP.—See GRAND RAPIDS, MN

▲ **LAFAYETTE**—Triax Cablevision

LAKE BENTON—See IVANHOE, MN

LAKE BENTON TWP.—See IVANHOE, MN

▲ **LAKE BRONSON**—Lake Bronson Cable TV

▲ **LAKE CITY**—Triax Cablevision

Lake County—See TWO HARBORS, MN

LAKE COUNTY (western portion)—See HOYT LAKES, MN

▲ **LAKE CRYSTAL**—Triax Cablevision

LAKE EDWARDS TWP.—See PEQUOT LAKES, MN

LAKE ELMO—See ROSEVILLE, MN

LAKE LIDA—See PELICAN LAKE, MN

▲ **LAKE LILLIAN**—Project Services Inc.

▲ **LAKE MINNETONKA**—Triax Cablevision

LAKE PARK—See PERHAM, MN

LAKE ST. CROIX BEACH—See ST. CROIX, MN

LAKE TWP.—See LAKE CITY, MN

LAKE TWP.—See also WARROAD, MN

LAKE VALLEY—See WHEATON, MN

▲ **LAKE WILSON**—Dakota Telecom

▲ **LAKEFIELD**—Lakefield Cable TV

LAKELAND—See ST. CROIX, MN

LAKELAND SHORES—See ST. CROIX, MN

LAKEVIEW TWP.—See PERHAM, MN

LAKEVILLE—See ROSEMOUNT, MN

▲ **LAMBERTON**—Lamberton TV Cable Co.

▲ **LANCASTER**—Stephen Cable TV Inc.

LANDFALL—See ROSEVILLE, MN

▲ **LANESBORO**—Triax Cablevision

LANGOLA (portions)—See RICE, MN

LANSING—See MAPLEVIEW, MN

LAUDERDALE—See ROSEVILLE, MN

LE CENTER—See ALDEN, MN

▲ **LE ROY**—Triax Cablevision

▲ **LE SUEUR**—Triax Cablevision

LEECH LAKE TWP.—See WALKER, MN

LENT—See STACY, MN

LEONARD (portions)—See CLEARBROOK, MN

▲ **LEOTA**—American Telecasting of Minnesota Inc.

LESAUK TWP.—See ST. CLOUD, MN

LESSOR TWP.—See ERSKINE, MN

▲ **LESTER PRAIRIE**—Triax Cablevision

LEWISTON—See STOCKTON, MN

▲ **LEWISVILLE**—North American Communications Corp.

LEXINGTON—See ROSEVILLE, MN

LILYDALE—See ST. PAUL, MN

LIME TWP.—See MANKATO, MN

LINDSTROM—See CHISAGO CITY, MN

LINO LAKES—See ROSEVILLE, MN

LINWOOD—See STACY, MN

▲ **LISMORE**—K-Communications Inc.

▲ **LITCHFIELD**—Triax Cablevision

LITTLE CANADA—See ROSEVILLE, MN

▲ **LITTLE FALLS**—WestMarc Cable Holding Inc.

LITTLE FALLS TWP.—See LITTLE FALLS, MN

▲ **LITTLEFORK**—WestMarc Cable Holding Inc.

▲ **LIVONIA**—US Cable of Minnesota

LONG BEACH—See GLENWOOD, MN

▲ **LONG LAKE**—Cable Systems Management of Iowa Inc.

LONG LAKE—See also LAKE MINNETONKA, MN

▲ **LONG PRAIRIE**—TCI

LONGVILLE—See WALKER, MN

LONSDALE—See ALDEN, MN

LOON LAKE TWP.—See PEQUOT LAKES, MN

LORETTO—See LAKE MINNETONKA, MN

LOWER SIOUX—See REDWOOD FALLS, MN

▲ **LOWRY**—Nordly's Telecom Inc.

▲ **LUVERNE**—Luverne Cable TV

▲ **LYLE**—Triax Cablevision

▲ **MABEL**—Triax Cablevision

▲ **MADELIA**—Paragon Cable

▲ **MADISON**—Triax Cablevision

▲ **MADISON LAKE**—North American Communications

▲ **MAGNOLIA**—American Telecasting of Minnesota Inc.

▲ **MAHNOMEN**—Loreltel Cablevision

MAHTOMEDI—See ROSEVILLE, MN

MAINE—See PERHAM, MN

MANHATTAN BEACH—See CROSSLAKE, MN

▲ **MANKATO**—Bresnan Communications Co.

MANKATO TWP.—See MANKATO, MN

MANTORVILLE—See DODGE CENTER, MN

MANTRAP TWP.—See WALKER, MN

MAPLE GROVE—See BROOKLYN PARK, MN

MAPLE LAKE—See BUFFALO, MN

MAPLE PLAIN—See LAKE MINNETONKA, MN

MAPLETON—See ALDEN, MN

▲ **MAPLEVIEW**—North American Communications Corp.

MAPLEWOOD—See ROSEVILLE, MN

▲ **MARBLE**—Marble Cable TV Systems

MARINE ON ST. CROIX—See FOREST LAKE, MN

MARION TWP.—See ROCHESTER, MN

▲ **MARSHALL**—Bresnan Communications Co.

MARSHAN TWP.—See ST. CROIX, MN

▲ **MAYER**—North American Communications Corp.

MAYNARD—See CLARA CITY, MN

▲ **MAZEPPA**—US Cable of Minnesota

▲ **McGREGOR**—Savage Communications Inc.

McGREGOR (unincorporated areas)—See ROUND LAKE TWP., MN

McINTOSH—See ERSKINE, MN

MEDFORD—See ALDEN, MN

MEDICINE LAKE—See BROOKLYN PARK, MN

MEDINA—See LAKE MINNETONKA, MN

▲ **MELROSE**—WestMarc Communications of Minnesota Inc.

▲ **MENAHGA**—United DataVision

MENDOTA—See ST. PAUL, MN

MENDOTA HEIGHTS—See ST. PAUL, MN

MENTOR—See ERSKINE, MN

▲ **MIDDLE RIVER**—Sjoberg's Cable TV Inc.

MIDDLE RIVER—See also ARGYLE, MN

MIDWAY TWP.—See PROCTOR, MN

MILACA—See CAMBRIDGE, MN

MILAN—See WATSON, MN

MILTONA—See PARKERS PRAIRIE, MN

MINDEN TWP.—See ST. CLOUD, MN

▲ **MINNEAPOLIS**—Paragon Cable

▲ **MINNEOTA**—US Cable of Minnesota

MINNESOTA CITY—See WINONA, MN

▲ **MINNESOTA LAKE**—Lake Cablevision Inc.

MINNETONKA—See MINNEAPOLIS, MN

MINNETONKA BEACH—See LAKE MINNETONKA, MN

MINNETRISTA—See LAKE MINNETONKA, MN

MISSION TWP.—See CROSSLAKE, MN

▲ **MONTEVIDEO**—Bresnan Communications Co.

▲ **MONTGOMERY**—Tri-Cable Inc.

MONTICELLO—See BUFFALO, MN

MONTICELLO TWP.—See BUFFALO, MN

▲ **MONTROSE**—Paragon Cable

▲ **MOORHEAD**—Cable One Inc.

▲ **MOOSE LAKE**—Triax Cablevision

Moose Lake Twp.—See MOOSE LAKE, MN

MORA—See CAMBRIDGE, MN

▲ **ROLLINGSTONE**—TCI of the Blufflands Inc.

ROLLINGSTONE—See also STOCKTON, MN

▲ **ROSE CREEK**—North American Communications Corp.

▲ **ROSEAU**—Sjoberg's Cable TV Inc.

▲ **ROSEMOUNT**—Charter Communications Inc.

▲ **ROSEVILLE**—Meredith Cable Inc.

ROTHSAY—See PERHAM, MN

▲ **ROUND LAKE**—US Cable of Minnesota

▲ **ROUND LAKE TWP.**—Cable Systems Management of Iowa Inc.

ROYALTON—See AVON, MN

RUSH CITY—See CAMBRIDGE, MN

RUSH LAKE—See CAMBRIDGE, MN

RUSH LAKE TWP.—See PERHAM, MN

RUSHFORD—See CHATFIELD, MN

RUSHFORD VILLAGE (eastern portion)—See CHATFIELD, MN

▲**RUSHMORE**—K-Communications Inc.

▲ **RUTHTON**—K-Communications Inc.

▲ **RUTLEDGE (village)**—Cable Systems Management of Iowa Inc.

▲ **SABIN**—Midcontinent Cable Co.

SABIN—See also RENVILLE, MN

SAGINAW—See CANOSIA TWP., MN

▲ **SANBORN**—New Ulm Telecom

▲ **SANDSTONE**—Savage Communications Inc.

SARTELL—See ST. CLOUD, MN

▲ **SAUK CENTRE**—WestMarc Communications of Minnesota Inc.

SAUK CENTRE TWP.—See SAUK CENTRE, MN

SAUK RAPIDS—See ST. CLOUD, MN

SAUK RAPIDS (portions)—See RICE, MN

SAVAGE—See PRIOR LAKE, MN

SCAMBLER TWP.—See PELICAN LAKE, MN

SCANLON—See CLOQUET, MN

SEBEKA—See MENAHGA, MN

SHAFER—See TAYLORS FALLS, MN

▲ **SHAKOPEE**—Paragon Cable

SHELLY—See ADA, MN

▲ **SHERBURN**—Fairmont Cable TV

▲ **SHEVLIN**—Garden Valley Telephone Co.

SHINGOBEE TWP.—See WALKER, MN

SHOREVIEW—See ROSEVILLE, MN

SHOREWOOD—See LAKE MINNETONKA, MN

▲ **SHULTZ LAKE TWP.**—Cable Systems Management of Iowa Inc.

▲ **SILVER BAY**—Triax Cablevision

SILVER BAY (unincorporated areas)—See FINLAND, MN

Silver Creek Twp.—See TWO HARBORS, MN

SILVER LAKE—See LESTER PRAIRIE, MN

SKYLINE VILLAGE—See MANKATO, MN

▲ **SLAYTON**—Triax Cablevision

SLEEPY EYE—See SPRINGFIELD, MN

SLETTEN TWP.—See ERSKINE, MN

SOUDAN—See TOWER, MN

SOUTH BEND TWP.—See MANKATO, MN

SOUTH HARBOR—See ISLE, MN

SOUTH INTERNATIONAL FALLS—See INTERNATIONAL FALLS, MN

SOUTH ST. PAUL—See ST. PAUL, MN

SPICER—See WILLMAR, MN

SPOONER—See BAUDETTE, MN

▲ **SPRING GROVE**—Triax CableVision

SPRING LAKE PARK—See ROSEVILLE, MN

SPRING LAKE TWP.—See PRIOR LAKE, MN

SPRING PARK—See LAKE MINNETONKA, MN

SPRING VALLEY—See CHATFIELD, MN

SPRING VALLEY TWP.—See CHATFIELD, MN

▲ **SPRINGFIELD**—Triax Cablevision

SPRUCE VALLEY TWP.—See MIDDLE RIVER, MN

ST. ANTHONY—See ROSEVILLE, MN

ST. BONIFACIUS—See LAKE MINNETONKA, MN

ST. CHARLES—See CHATFIELD, MN

ST. CLAIR—See ALDEN, MN

▲ **ST. CLOUD**—Bresnan Communications Co.

ST. CLOUD TWP.—See ST. CLOUD, MN

▲ **ST. CROIX**—King Videocable Co.

▲ **ST. FRANCIS**—US Cable of Minnesota

▲ **ST. HILAIRE**—Garden Valley Telephone Co.

▲ **ST. JAMES**—Triax Cablevision

ST. JOHNS—See WILLMAR, MN

▲ **ST. JOSEPH**—North Star Communications

ST. JOSEPH—See also AVON, MN

▲ **ST. LOUIS PARK**—Paragon Cable

ST. MARYS POINT—See ST. CROIX, MN

ST. MICHAEL—See BUFFALO, MN

▲ **ST. PAUL**—MediaOne

ST. PAUL PARK—See ST. CROIX, MN

▲ **ST. PETER**—Triax Cablevision

ST. STEPHEN—See AVON, MN

ST. VINCENT—See PEMBINA, ND

▲ **STACY**—Savage Communications Inc.

▲ **STAPLES**—TCI

▲ **STARBUCK**—Triax Cablevision

▲ **STEPHEN**—Stephen Cable TV Inc.

STEWART—See BROWNTON, MN

STEWARTVILLE—See ROCHESTER, MN

STILLWATER—See ST. CROIX, MN

▲ **STOCKTON**—Charter Communications Inc.

▲ **STORDEN**—US Cable of Minnesota

SUNFISH LAKE—See ST. PAUL, MN

SUNRISE VILLA—See CANNON FALLS, MN

SVERDRUP TWP.—See PERHAM, MN

▲ **SWANVILLE**—Upsala Cooperative Telephone Association

▲ **TACONITE**—City of Taconite Cable TV

TAUNTON—See MINNEOTA, MN

▲ **TAYLORS FALLS**—Savage Communications Inc.

▲ **THIEF RIVER FALLS**—Sjoberg's Cable TV

THOMPSON—See CLOQUET, MN

TINTAH—See BARRETT, MN

TONKA BAY—See LAKE MINNETONKA, MN

▲ **TOWER**—WestMarc Cable Holding Inc.

▲ **TRACY**—Harmon Cable Communications

▲ **TRIMONT**—Terril Cable Systems

▲ **TRUMAN**—Terril Cable Systems

TURTLE LAKE TWP.—See WALKER, MN

▲ **TWIN VALLEY**—Tekstar Cablevision Inc.

▲ **TWO HARBORS**—Triax Cablevision

TWO HARBORS (unincorporated areas)—See KNIFE RIVER, MN

TYLER—See IVANHOE, MN

▲ **ULEN**—Loretel Cablevision

UNDERWOOD—See PERHAM, MN

URBANK—See PARKERS PRAIRIE, MN

VADNAIS HEIGHTS—See ROSEVILLE, MN

▲ **VERMILLION**—Dakota Cable TV

▲ **VERNDALE**—Savage Communications Inc.

▲ **VERNON CENTER**—North American Communications Corp.

VICTORIA—See LAKE MINNETONKA, MN

VINING (village)—See PERHAM, MN

VIRGINIA—See EVELETH, MN

WABANICA—See BAUDETTE, MN

▲ **WABASHA**—US Cable of Minnesota

▲ **WABASSO**—New Ulm Telecom

WABEDO TWP.—See WALKER, MN

WACONIA—See LAKE MINNETONKA, MN

▲ **WADENA**—Bresnan Communications Co.

WAHKON—See ISLE, MN

WAITE PARK—See ST. CLOUD, MN

WAKEFIELD TWP.—See AVON, MN

WALCOTT TWP.—See FARIBAULT, MN

WALDEN TWP.—See PEQUOT LAKES, MN

▲ **WALDORF**—Dynax Communications Inc.

▲ **WALKER**—Tekstar Cablevision Inc.

▲ **WALL LAKE**—Tekstar Cablevision Inc.

▲ **WALNUT GROVE**—Walnut Grove Cable TV

WALTHAM—See HAYFIELD, MN

▲ **WANAMINGO**—US Cable of Minnesota

▲ **WARREN**—Sjoberg's Cablevision Inc.

▲ **WARROAD**—Sjoberg's Cablevision Inc.

▲ **WARSAW**—North American Communications Corp.

WARSAW—See also MORRISTOWN, MN

▲ **WASECA**—Triax Cablevision

WASHINGTON COUNTY (portions)—See ROSEVILLE, MN

▲ **WASHINGTON TWP.**—North American Communications Corp.

WATAB TWP.—See RICE, MN

WATAB TWP.—See also ST. CLOUD, MN

WATERTOWN—See BUFFALO, MN

WATERVILLE—See ALDEN, MN

WATKINS—See AVON, MN

▲ **WATSON**—Project Services Inc.

WAUBUN—See TWIN VALLEY, MN

WAVERLY—See MONTROSE, MN

WAYZATA—See LAKE MINNETONKA, MN

WEBSTER TWP.—See ELKO, MN

▲ **WELCOME**—Terril Cable Systems

▲ **WELLS**—Triax Cablevision

WELLS—See also WARSAW, MN

WELLS TWP.—See FARIBAULT, MN

WENDELL—See BARRETT, MN

WEST ST. PAUL—See ST. PAUL, MN

▲ **WESTBROOK**—US Cable of Minnesota

WESTLAKELAND—See ST. CROIX, MN

▲ **WHEATON**—Triax Cablevision

WHEELER—See BAUDETTE, MN

WHITE BEAR LAKE—See ROSEVILLE, MN

WHITE BEAR TWP.—See ROSEVILLE, MN

WHYTE TWP.—See HOYT LAKES, MN

WILLERNIE—See ROSEVILLE, MN

▲ **WILLMAR**—Bresnan Communications Co.

▲ **WILLOW RIVER**—Cable Systems Management of Iowa Inc.

▲ **WILMONT**—K-Communications Inc.

WILSON TWP.—See PEQUOT LAKES, MN

WILSON TWP.—See also WINONA, MN

Windermere Twp.—See MOOSE LAKE, MN

▲ **WINDOM**—Windom Cable Communications

WINGER—See ERSKINE, MN

▲ **WINNEBAGO**—Triax Cablevision

▲ **WINONA**—Bresnan Communications Co.

WINONA TWP.—See WINONA, MN

WINSTED—See LESTER PRAIRIE, MN

WINTHROP—See GAYLORD, MN

WINTON—See ELY, MN

WOLFORD—See BRAINERD, MN

▲ **WOOD LAKE**—Wood Lake Cable TV

WOODBURY—See ST. CROIX, MN

WOODLAND—See LAKE MINNETONKA, MN

WOODSIDE—See ERSKINE, MN

WOODSIDE TWP.—See ERSKINE, MN

WOODSTOCK—See RUTHTON, MN

▲ **WORTHINGTON**—Worthington Cable TV

▲ **WRENSHALL**—Cable Systems Management of Iowa Inc.

▲ **WYKOFF**—North American Communications Corp.

WYOMING—See FOREST LAKE, MN

YOUNG AMERICA—See NORWOOD, MN

ZEMPLE—See DEER RIVER, MN

ZIMMERMAN—See CROWN, MN

ZUMBROTA—See ROCHESTER, MN

MISSISSIPPI

ABBEVILLE—See OXFORD, MS

▲ **ABERDEEN**—Galaxy Cablevision

▲ **ACKERMAN-WEIR**—Telapex

ADAMS COUNTY—See NATCHEZ, MS

ALCORN COUNTY—See CORINTH, MS

ALCORN COUNTY (portions)—See KOSSUTH, MS

▲ **AMORY**—Galaxy Cablevision

▲ **ANGUILLA**—Cable Video Communications

▲ **ARCOLA**—Cable Video Communications

▲ **ARTESIA**—Magnolia Cable Co.

▲ **ASHLAND**—Galaxy Cablevision

ATTALA COUNTY (unincorporated areas)—See KOSCIUSKO, MS

▲ **BALDWYN**—Galaxy Cablevision

▲ **BASSFIELD**—Galaxy Cablevision

▲ **BATESVILLE**—Cable One Inc.

▲ **BAY SPRINGS**—Video Inc.

▲ **BAY ST. LOUIS**—Torrence Cablevision

BAY ST. LOUIS—See also WAVELAND, MS

▲ **BEAUMONT**—Mediacom

BECKER—See AMORY, MS

BELDEN—See TUPELO, MS

▲ **BELMONT**—Falcon First Inc.

▲ **BELZONI**—Cable TV of Belzoni Inc.

▲ **BENOIT**—AMW Cable Winslow Communication

▲ **BENTONIA**—Galaxy Cablevision

▲ **BEULAH**—Torrence Cablevision

BIGGERSVILLE—See KOSSUTH, MS

▲ **BILOXI**—Cable One Inc.

BISSELL—See TUPELO, MS

BLUE MOUNTAIN—See RIPLEY, MS

BOLIVAR COUNTY (unincorporated areas)—See BENOIT, MS

▲ **BOLTON**—Capitol Cablevision

▲ **BOONEVILLE**—Galaxy Cablevision

BOYLE—See CLEVELAND, MS

BRANDON—See PEARL, MS

▲ **BROOKHAVEN**—Cable One Inc.

BROOKSVILLE—See MACON, MS

▲ **BROWNFIELD**—Cablevision of West Tennessee

▲ **BRUCE**—Cable One

BUCKATUNNA—See WAYNESBORO, MS

▲ **BURNSVILLE**—Falcon Cable TV

BYHALIA—See SOUTHAVEN, MS

▲ **CALEDONIA**—Cable One

CALHOUN—See LAUREL, MS

▲ **CALHOUN CITY**—Galaxy Cablevision

CALHOUN COUNTY—See CALHOUN CITY, MS

CALHOUN COUNTY (portions)—See BRUCE, MS

▲ **CANTON**—Galaxy Cablevision

▲ **CARRIERRE**—Torrence Cablevision

CARROLLTON—See WINONA, MS

▲ **CARTHAGE**—Northland Cable TV

▲ **CARY**—AMW Cable Winslow Communication

▲ **CENTREVILLE**—Torrence Cablevision

▲ **CHARLESTON**—Galaxy Cablevision

CHICKASAW—See TUPELO, MS

CHOCTAW INDIAN RESERVATION—See PHILADELPHIA, MS

▲ **CHUNKY**—Galaxy Cablevision

▲ **CLARKSDALE**—Cable One

CLAY COUNTY—See TUPELO, MS

CLEARY HEIGHTS—See JACKSON, MS

▲ **CLEVELAND**—Cable One Inc.

CLINTON—See JACKSON, MS

COAHOMA COUNTY—See CLARKSDALE, MS

▲ **COFFEEVILLE**—Galaxy Cablevision

COLDWATER—See SOUTHAVEN, MS

▲ **COLES POINT**—Foster Communications Inc.

▲ **COLLINS**—Collins Communications

▲ **COLUMBIA**—Pearl River Cablecomm

▲ **COLUMBUS**—Cable One

COLUMBUS AFB—See COLUMBUS, MS

COMO—See SOUTHAVEN, MS

COPIAH COUNTY—See HAZLEHURST, MS

▲ **CORINTH**—Comcast Cable Investors Inc.

COUNTRY CLUB LAKE ESTATES—See HATTIESBURG, MS

COURTLAND—See BATESVILLE, MS

COVINGTON COUNTY (portions)—See COLLINS, MS

▲ **CRAWFORD**—Magnolia Cablevision

CRENSHAW—See SOUTHAVEN, MS

▲ **CROSBY**—Telapex

▲ **CROWDER**—Cable Entertainment Company

▲ **CRUGER**—Torrence Cablevision

▲ **CRYSTAL SPRINGS**—Bailey Cable TV Inc.

d'IBERVILLE—See BILOXI, MS

d'LO—See MENDENHALL, MS

DALEWOOD—See LAUDERDALE, MS

▲ **DE KALB**—Galaxy Cablevision

DE LISLE—See DIAMONDHEAD, MS

DE SOTO COUNTY—See MEMPHIS, TN

▲ **DECATUR**—Mediacom

DEERFIELD—See JACKSON, MS

DENNIS—See BELMONT, MS

DERMA—See CALHOUN CITY, MS

▲ **DIAMONDHEAD**—Diamondhead Cable TV

DIXIE—See MCLAURIN, MS

DREW—See CLEVELAND, MS

DUCK HILL—See WINONA, MS

DUNCAN—See CLARKSDALE, MS

▲ **DURANT**—Galaxy Cablevision

ECRU—See NEW ALBANY, MS

▲ **EDWARDS**—Capitol Cablevision

ELIZABETH—See LELAND, MS

ELLISVILLE—See LAUREL, MS

ENTERPRISE—See QUITMAN, MS

ESCATAWPA—See PASCAGOULA, MS

▲ **EUPORA**—Galaxy Cablevision

▲ **EVERGREEN**—SouthTel Communications LP

FALKNER—See RIPLEY, MS

FANNIN—See PEARL, MS

▲ **FAYETTE**—Laribay Cablecom

FERNWOOD—See McCOMB, MS

▲ **FLORA**—T.A.T. Cablevision

FLORENCE—See JACKSON, MS

FLOWOOD—See PEARL, MS

▲ **FOREST**—Northland Cable TV

FORREST COUNTY—See HATTIESBURG, MS

▲ **FRANKLIN CREEK**—Torrence Cablevision

▲ **FRIARS POINT**—Cable Entertainment Company

▲ **FULTON**—Comcast Cablevision

GAUTIER—See PASCAGOULA, MS

GEORGE COUNTY—See LUCEDALE, MS (Mediacom)

GLEN—See KOSSUTH, MS

▲ **GLEN ALLAN**—Torrence Cablevision

GLOSTER—See CENTREVILLE, MS

GOLDEN—See BELMONT, MS

GOODMAN—See PICKENS, MS

▲ **GREENVILLE**—TCA Cable TV

▲ **GREENWOOD**—Century Mississippi Corp.

▲ **GRENADA**—Cable One

GRENADA COUNTY—See GRENADA, MS

▲ **GULFPORT/LONG BEACH**—Cable One

▲ **GUNNISON**—AMW Cable Winslow Communication

GUNTOWN—See BALDWYN, MS

▲ **HAMILTON**—Cable One

HANCOCK COUNTY (portions)—See DIAMONDHEAD, MS

HANCOCK COUNTY (portions)—See also WAVELAND, MS

▲ **HARMONTOWN**—Foster Communications Inc.

HARRISON COUNTY—See BILOXI, MS

HARRISON COUNTY (portions)—See DIAMONDHEAD, MS

HATLEY—See AMORY, MS

▲ **HATTIESBURG**—Comcast Cable

▲ **HAZLEHURST**—Bailey Cable TV Inc.

HEIDELBERG—See SANDERSVILLE, MS

HERNANDO—See SOUTHAVEN, MS

HICKORY—See CHUNKY, MS

▲ **HICKORY FLAT**—Galaxy Cablevision

HINDS COUNTY—See JACKSON, MS

HINDS COUNTY (portions)—See BOLTON, MS

▲ **HOLLANDALE**—Broadband Cablevision Inc.

▲ **HOLLY SPRINGS**—Galaxy Cablevision

HORN LAKE—See SOUTHAVEN, MS

HOULKA—See RIENZI, MS

▲ **HOUSTON**—Mediacom

HUMPHREYS COUNTY—See ISOLA-INVERNESS, MS

HURLEY—See PASCAGOULA, MS

INDIAN SPRINGS—See LAUREL, MS

▲ **INDIANOLA**—Century Mississippi Corp.

INGOMAR—See NEW ALBANY, MS

▲ **ISOLA-INVERNESS**—Telapex

ISSAQUENA COUNTY (unincorporated areas)—See MAYERSVILLE, MS

▲ **ITTA BENA**—Galaxy Cablevision

▲ **IUKA**—Galaxy Cablevision

▲ **JACKSON**—Capitol Cablevision

JACKSON COUNTY—See BILOXI, MS

JACKSON COUNTY—See also PASCAGOULA, MS

JASPER COUNTY (unincorporated areas)—See SANDERSVILLE, MS

JOHNS—See PEARL, MS

JOHNS—See also PUCKETT, MS

JONES COUNTY—See LAUREL, MS

JONES COUNTY (portions)—See SANDERSVILLE, MS

▲ **JONESTOWN**—Cable Entertainment Company

JORDAN RIVER SHORES—See WAVELAND, MS

▲ **JUMPERTOWN**—Galaxy Cablevision

KEESLER AFB—See BILOXI, MS

KILMICHAEL—See WINONA, MS

▲ **KILN**—Torrence Cablevision

KILN—See also DIAMONDHEAD, MS

▲ **KOSCIUSKO**—Northland Cable TV

▲ **KOSSUTH**—Benchmark Communications

LACKEY—See HAMILTON, MS

LAFAYETTE COUNTY—See OXFORD, MS

▲ **LAKE**—Galaxy Cablevision

LAKE RIGELEA—See JACKSON, MS

LAKE SERENE—See HATTIESBURG, MS

LAMAR COUNTY—See HATTIESBURG, MS

▲ **LAMBERT**—Cable One Inc.

▲ **LAUDERDALE**—Galaxy Cablevision

LAUDERDALE COUNTY—See MERIDIAN, MS

▲ **LAUREL**—Comcast Cablevision of Laurel Inc.

▲ **LEAKESVILLE**—Galaxy Cablevision

LEAKESVILLE—See also HATTIESBURG, MS

LEE COUNTY—See BALDWYN, MS

LEE COUNTY—See also TUPELO, MS

LEE COUNTY (portions)—See also MOOREVILLE, MS (SouthTel Communications LP)

LEE COUNTY (portions)—See also NETTLETON, MS

LEFLORE COUNTY—See GREENWOOD, MS

LEFLORE COUNTY—See also ITTA BENA, MS

▲ **LELAND**—Broadband Cablevision Inc.

▲ **LEXINGTON**—Galaxy Cablevision

LIBERTY—See CENTREVILLE, MS

LINCOLN COUNTY (portions)—See BROOKHAVEN, MS

▲ **LOUISE**—Telapex

▲ **LOUISVILLE**—Mediacom

LOWNDES COUNTY—See COLUMBUS, MS

▲ **LUCEDALE**—Mediacom

▲ **LUCEDALE**—Torrence Cablevision

▲ **LULA**—Cable Entertainment Company

▲ **LUMBERTON**—Galaxy Cablevision

LYON—See CLARKSDALE, MS

▲ **MABEN**—Northland Cable TV

▲ **MACEDONIA**—Galaxy Cablevision

▲ **MACON**—Galaxy Cablevision

MADISON—See JACKSON, MS

MADISON COUNTY—See CANTON, MS

MADISON COUNTY—See also JACKSON, MS

▲ **MAGEE**—Bailey Cable TV Inc.

MAGNOLIA—See McCOMB, MS

MANATACHIE—See FULTON, MS

MARIETTA—See FULTON, MS

MARION—See MERIDIAN, MS

MARION COUNTY (portions)—See COLUMBIA, MS

MARKS—See LAMBERT, MS

MARSHALL COUNTY (unincorporated areas)—See VICTORIA, MS

MATHISTON—See MABEN, MS

▲ **MAYERSVILLE**—AMW Cable Winslow Communication

MAYWOOD—See MEMPHIS, TN

▲ **McADAMS**—Torrence Cablevision

McADAMS—See also KOSCIUSKO, MS

▲ **McCOMB**—Cable One

▲ **McLAURIN**—Home Cable Entertainment

McNEIL—See CARRIERRE, MS

▲ **MEADVILLE-BUDE**—Telapex

▲ **MENDENHALL**—Bailey Cable TV Inc.

▲ **MERIDIAN**—Comcast Cablevision of Meridian Inc.

MERIGOLD—See MOUND BAYOU, MS

METCALFE—See GREENVILLE, MS

MISSISSIPPI STATE UNIVERSITY—See STARKVILLE, MS

MONROE—See MEADVILLE-BUDE, MS

MONTGOMERY COUNTY (portions)—See WINONA, MS

▲ **MONTICELLO**—Galaxy Cablevision

MOON LAKE—See LULA, MS

▲ **MOOREVILLE**—Foster Communications Inc.

▲ **MOOREVILLE**—SouthTel Communications LP

MOOREVILLE—See also FULTON, MS

MOORHEAD—See INDIANOLA, MS

▲ **MORGANTOWN**—Torrence Cablevision

MORTON—See FOREST, MS

▲ **MOSELLE**—Galaxy Cablevision

MOSS POINT—See PASCAGOULA, MS

▲ **MOUND BAYOU**—Galaxy Cablevision

MOUNT OLIVE—See MAGEE, MS

MYRTLE—See NEW ALBANY, MS

▲ **NATCHEZ**—Cable One

NESHOBA COUNTY (unincorporated areas)—See PHILADELPHIA, MS

▲ **NETTLETON**—Galaxy Cablevision

▲ **NEW ALBANY**—Galaxy Cablevision

▲ **NEW AUGUSTA**—Telapex

▲ **NEW HEBRON**—Telapex

NEW HOPE—See COLUMBUS, MS

NEW SIGHT—See BROOKHAVEN, MS

▲ **NEWTON**—Mediacom

NEWTON COUNTY (portions)—See CHUNKY, MS

NEWTON COUNTY (portions)—See also LAKE, MS

NORTH CARROLLTON—See WINONA, MS

NOXAPATER—See LOUISVILLE, MS

OAK GROVE—See HATTIESBURG, MS

▲ **OAKLAND**—AMW Cable Winslow Communication

OCEAN SPRINGS—See BILOXI, MS

OKOLONA—See TUPELO, MS

OKTIBBEHA COUNTY—See STARKVILLE, MS

OLIVE BRANCH—See SOUTHAVEN, MS

▲ **OSYKA**—Parish Cablevision Inc.

▲ **OXFORD**—Galaxy Cablevision

▲ **PACE**—AMW Cable Winslow Communication

▲ **PACHUTA**—Galaxy Cablevision

▲ **PASCAGOULA**—Cable One

PASS CHRISTIAN—See DIAMONDHEAD, MS

PASS CHRISTIAN—See also GULFPORT/LONG BEACH, MS

▲ **PEARL**—Rankin County CableVision

PEARL RIVER COUNTY—See PICAYUNE, MS (Charter Communications Inc.)

PEARL RIVER VALLEY WATER SUPPLY DISTRICT—See JACKSON, MS

▲ **PEARLINGTON**—Mediacom

PELAHATCHIE—See PEARL, MS

PENDORFF—See LAUREL, MS

PETAL—See HATTIESBURG, MS

▲ **PHILADELPHIA**—Northland Cable TV

▲ **PICAYUNE**—Charter Communications Inc.

▲ **PICAYUNE**—Torrence Cablevision

▲ **PICKENS**—Galaxy Cablevision

PIKE COUNTY—See McCOMB, MS

PINE GROVE—See RIPLEY, MS

PITTSBORO—See BRUCE, MS

PLANTERSVILLE—See TUPELO, MS

▲ **PONTOTOC**—Benchmark Communications

▲ **PONTOTOC**—Mediacom

PONTOTOC COUNTY (portions)—See TUPELO, MS

POPE—See BATESVILLE, MS

▲ **POPLARVILLE**—Galaxy Cablevision

POTTS CAMP—See HICKORY FLAT, MS

▲ **PRENTISS**—Galaxy Cablevision

PRENTISS COUNTY—See BOONEVILLE, MS

▲ **PROJECT ROAD**—Torrence Cablevision

▲ **PUCKETT**—Rankin County Cablevision

PURVIS—See HATTIESBURG, MS

▲ **QUITMAN**—Twin County Cablevision

▲ **RALEIGH**—Northland Cable TV

RANKIN COUNTY—See JACKSON, MS

RAWLS SPRINGS—See HATTIESBURG, MS

▲ **RAYMOND**—Capitol Cablevision

RED BANKS—See VICTORIA, MS

RENOVA—See CLEVELAND, MS

RICHLAND—See JACKSON, MS

RICHMOND—See EVERGREEN, MS

▲ **RICHTON**—Galaxy Cablevision

RICHTON—See also HATTIESBURG, MS

RIDGELAND—See JACKSON, MS

▲ **RIENZI**—Mid-South Cablevision Co.

▲ **RIPLEY**—Ripley Video Cable Co. Inc.

ROBINSONVILLE—See SOUTHAVEN, MS

▲ **ROLLING FORK**—Yazoo Answer Call Inc. of Rolling Fork

▲ **ROSEDALE**—Cablevision of Rosedale

▲ **ROXIE**—Telapex

RULEVILLE—See CLEVELAND, MS

RUNNELSTOWN—See MACEDONIA, MS

RURAL HILL—See COLUMBUS, MS

RUSSELL—See LAUDERDALE, MS

SALTILLO—See BALDWYN, MS

SALTILLO—See also TUPELO, MS

▲ **SANDERSVILLE**—Northland Cable TV

▲ **SANFORD**—Home Cable Entertainment

SARDIS—See SOUTHAVEN, MS

SARDIS LAKE—See SOUTHAVEN, MS

SAUCIER—See GULFPORT/LONG BEACH, MS

▲ **SCHLATER**—Torrence Cablevision

SCOTT COUNTY (portions)—See LAKE, MS

SCOTT COUNTY (unincorporated areas)—See FOREST, MS

▲ **SEMINARY**—Home Cable Entertainment

SENATOBIA—See SOUTHAVEN, MS

SHADY GROVE (portions)—See LAUREL, MS

SHADY GROVE (portions)—See also SEMINARY, MS

SHANNON—See NETTLETON, MS

SHARKEY COUNTY (unincorporated areas)—See CARY, MS

SHARON—See LAUREL, MS

SHAW—See ROSEDALE, MS

▲ **SHELBY**—Galaxy Cablevision

SHERMAN—See TUPELO, MS

▲ **SHUBUTA**—Galaxy Cablevision

SHUQUALAK—See MACON, MS

SIDON—See GREENWOOD, MS

SILVER CREEK—See PRENTISS, MS

SIMPSON COUNTY—See MENDENHALL, MS

SLEDGE—See SOUTHAVEN, MS

SMITHVILLE—See AMORY, MS

SNOW LAKE SHORES—See ASHLAND, MS

SOSO—See BAY SPRINGS, MS

▲ **SOUTHAVEN**—Time Warner Communications

▲ **ST. ANDREWS**—Mediacom

▲ **STARKVILLE**—Northland Cable TV

▲ **STATE LINE**—Galaxy Cablevision

STEENS—See COLUMBUS, MS

STONE COUNTY (portions)—See WIGGINS, MS

STONEWALL—See QUITMAN, MS

STRICKLAND—See KOSSUTH, MS

SUMMIT—See McCOMB, MS

▲ **SUMNER**—Galaxy Cablevision

▲ **SUMRALL**—Galaxy Cablevision

SUMRALL—See also HATTIESBURG, MS

▲ **SUNFLOWER**—Sledge Cable Co. Inc.

SUNFLOWER COUNTY—See INDIANOLA, MS

▲ **SUNRISE**—Home Cable Entertainment

SWIFTWATER—See GREENVILLE, MS

SYMONDS—See PACE, MS

TALLAHATCHIE COUNTY (eastern portion)—See CHARLESTON, MS

TALLAHATCHIE COUNTY (western portion)—See SUMNER, MS

▲ **TAYLORSVILLE**—Galaxy Cablevision

▲ **TCHULA**—Galaxy Cablevision

Terry—See CRYSTAL SPRINGS, MS

THEO—See KOSSUTH, MS

TISHOMINGO—See BELMONT, MS

TISHOMINGO—See also IUKA, MS

TOOMSUBA—See LAUDERDALE, MS

TREMONT—See FULTON, MS

TUNICA—See SOUTHAVEN, MS

▲ **TUPELO**—Comcast Cablevision of Tupelo Inc.

TUTWILER—See SUMNER, MS

▲ **TYLERTOWN**—Galaxy Cablevision

▲ **UNION**—Mediacom

UNION COUNTY—See NEW ALBANY, MS

UNION COUNTY (portions)—See TUPELO, MS

UNIVERSITY OF MISSISSIPPI—See OXFORD, MS

VAIDEN—See WINONA, MS

VAN CLEAVE—See BILOXI, MS

VARDAMAN—See CALHOUN CITY, MS

VERONA—See TUPELO, MS

▲ **VICKSBURG**—Vicksburg Video Inc.

▲ **VICTORIA**—Galaxy Cablevision

WADE—See PASCAGOULA, MS

WALLS—See SOUTHAVEN, MS

WALNUT—See MIDDLETON, TN

▲ **WALNUT GROVE**—Galaxy Cablevision

▲ **WATER VALLEY**—Mediacom

▲ **WAVELAND**—Mediacom

WAYNE COUNTY—See WAYNESBORO, MS

▲ **WAYNESBORO**—Twin County Cablevision

WAYSIDE—See GREENVILLE, MS

WEBB—See SUMNER, MS

WEBSTER COUNTY—See EUPORA, MS

▲ **WEST**—Torrence Cablevision

WEST POINT—See TUPELO, MS

▲ **WIGGINS**—Mediacom

▲ **WINONA**—Galaxy Cablevision

▲ **WINSTONVILLE**—AMW Cable Winslow Communication

WOODVILLE—See CENTREVILLE, MS

YALOBUSHA COUNTY—See COFFEEVILLE, MS

▲ **YAZOO CITY**—Cable One Inc.

MISSOURI

ADAIR COUNTY—See KIRKSVILLE, MO

▲ **ADRIAN**—Galaxy Cablevision

▲ **ADVANCE**—Cablevision Communications

AGENCY—See ST. JOSEPH, MO

AIRPORT DRIVE VILLAGE—See CARL JUNCTION, MO

▲ **ALBA**—Mediacom

▲ **ALBANY**—Mediacom

▲ **ALMA**—Galaxy Cablevision

▲ **ALTON**—Falcon Cable

▲ **AMAZONIA**—Westcom

▲ **AMSTERDAM**—Galaxy American Communications

▲ **ANDERSON**—Mediacom

▲ **ANNAPOLIS**—Falcon Telecable

▲ **ANNISTON**—Semo Communications Inc.

▲ **APPLETON CITY**—Mediacom

ARBYRD—See MANILA, AR

ARCADIA—See IRONTON, MO

▲ **ARCHIE**—Mediacom

▲ **ARGYLE**—First Cable of Missouri Inc.

▲ **ARMSTRONG**—Classic Cable

▲ **ARNOLD**—TCI Cablevision of Missouri

ASH GROVE—See EVERTON, MO

ASHLAND—See BOONE COUNTY, MO

ATCHISON COUNTY—See TARKIO, MO

▲ **ATLANTA**—Galaxy Cablevision

AUDRAIN COUNTY—See MEXICO, MO

AULVILLE—See HIGGINSVILLE, MO

AUNT'S CREEK—See HIGHWAY DD, MO

AURORA—See MONETT, MO

AUXVASSE—See FULTON, MO

▲ **AVA**—Mediacom

AVONDALE—See KANSAS CITY, MO

BAGNELL—See OSAGE BEACH, MO

BALDWIN PARK—See INDEPENDENCE, MO

BALLWIN—See CHESTERFIELD, MO

BALLWIN—See also KIRKWOOD, MO

▲ **BARING**—Galaxy Cablevision

▲ **BARNARD**—New Path Communications LC

▲ **BARNHART**—Charter Communications

BATES CITY—See INDEPENDENCE, MO

BATTLEFIELD—See SPRINGFIELD, MO

BEL-NOR—See FERGUSON, MO

BEL-RIDGE—See FERGUSON, MO

▲ **BELL CITY**—Falcon Telecable

BELLA VISTA—See CHESTERFIELD, MO

▲ **BELLE**—Capital Cable

BELLEFONTAINE NEIGHBORS—See ST. LOUIS COUNTY, MO

BELLERIVE—See FERGUSON, MO

BELLFLOWER—See MONTGOMERY CITY, MO

BELTON—See KANSAS CITY, MO

▲ **BENTON**—Falcon Telecable

BERKELEY—See FERGUSON, MO

▲ **BERNIE**—CableVision Communications

BERTRAND—See SIKESTON, MO

▲ **BETHANY**—Mediacom

BEVERLY HILLS—See FERGUSON, MO

▲ **BEVIER**—Chariton Valley Communication Corp.

▲ **BILLINGS**—Mediacom

▲ **BIRCH TREE**—Cablevision Communications

▲ **BISMARCK**—Farmington Cablevision Inc.

BLACK JACK—See CHESTERFIELD, MO

▲ **BLACKBURN**—Galaxy Cablevision

▲ **BLACKWATER**—Galaxy Cablevision

BLAND—See BELLE, MO

BLODGETT—See MORLEY, MO

BLOOMFIELD—See DEXTER, MO

BLOOMSDALE—See STE. GENEVIEVE, MO (Westcom)

BLUE EYE—See LAMPE, MO

BLUE SPRINGS—See INDEPENDENCE, MO

BLYTHEDALE—See EAGLEVILLE, MO

▲ **BOGARD**—Galaxy Cablevision

▲ **BOLCKOW**—New Path Communications LC

▲ **BOLIVAR**—Alltel Corp.

BONNE TERRE—See FLAT RIVER, MO

▲ **BOONE COUNTY**—Capital Cable

BOONE COUNTY—See also COLUMBIA, MO

BOONE COUNTY (western portion)—See HARRISBURG, MO

▲ **BOONVILLE**—Classic Cable

▲ **BOSWORTH**—Galaxy Cablevision

BOURBON—See SULLIVAN, MO

▲ **BOWLING GREEN**—Charter Communications

BRANCH—See MACKS CREEK, MO

▲ **BRANSON**—Rapid Cable

BRANSON VIEW ESTATES—See ROCKAWAY BEACH, MO

BRANSON WEST—See HIGHWAY DD, MO

▲ **BRASHEAR**—Mark Twain Communications

▲ **BRAYMER**—Capital Cable

▲ **BRECKENRIDGE**—Capital Cable

BRECKENRIDGE HILLS—See ST. LOUIS COUNTY, MO

BRENTWOOD—See ST. LOUIS COUNTY, MO

BRIDGETON—See KIRKWOOD, MO

BRIDGETON TERRACE—See KIRKWOOD, MO

▲ **BROOKFIELD**—Classic Cable

▲ **BROOKING PARK**—Galaxy Cablevision

BROOKLINE (portions)—See SPRINGFIELD, MO

BROOKLYN HEIGHTS—See CARTHAGE, MO

▲ **BROWNING**—Galaxy Cablevision

▲ **BRUNSWICK**—Mediacom

BUCHANAN COUNTY—See ATCHISON, KS

▲ **BUCKLIN**—Chariton Valley Communication Corp.

BUCKNER—See INDEPENDENCE, MO

▲ **BUFFALO**—Galaxy Cablevision

BULL CREEK—See ROCKAWAY BEACH, MO

▲ **BUNCETON**—Mid-Missouri Telephone Co.

▲ **BUNKER**—CableVision Communications

▲ **BURLINGTON JUNCTION**—New Path Communications LC

▲ **BUTLER**—Mediacom

▲ **BUTLER COUNTY**—Boycom Cablevision Inc.

BUTLER COUNTY (portions)—See POPLAR BLUFF, MO

BYRNES MILLS—See BARNHART, MO

▲ **CABOOL**—Mediacom

▲ **CAINSVILLE**—Capital Cable

▲ **CAIRO**—Capital Cable

▲ **CALHOUN**—Galaxy Cablevision

▲ **CALIFORNIA**—Falcon Cable

CALLAO—See BEVIER, MO

CALLAWAY COUNTY—See HOLTS SUMMIT, MO

CALLAWAY COUNTY (portions)—See FULTON, MO

CALVERTON PARK—See FERGUSON, MO

CAMDEN COUNTY—See OSAGE BEACH, MO

▲ **CAMDEN POINT**—Atchison Cablecomm

CAMDENTON—See OSAGE BEACH, MO

▲ **CAMERON**—Mediacom

CAMPBELL—See MALDEN, MO

CANALOU—See MATTHEWS, MO

▲ **CANTON**—Charter Communications

▲ **CAPE GIRARDEAU**—Falcon Cable TV

CARDWELL—See MANILA, AR

▲ **CARL JUNCTION**—Mediacom

▲ **CARROLLTON**—Mediacom

CARTERVILLE—See JOPLIN, MO

▲ **CARTHAGE**—Southwest Missouri Cable

▲ **CARUTHERSVILLE**—Mediacom

▲ **CASS COUNTY (northwestern portion)**—Midwest Cable Inc.

▲ **CASSVILLE**—Mediacom

CEDAR HILL—See BARNHART, MO

CEDAR HILL LAKES—See BARNHART, MO

CENTERTOWN—See COLE COUNTY (portions), MO

▲ **CENTERVIEW**—Galaxy American Communications

CENTERVILLE—See LESTERVILLE, MO

▲ **CENTRALIA**—TCI Cablevision of Missouri Inc.

▲ **CHAFFEE**—Falcon Telecable

▲ **CHAMOIS**—Capital Cable

CHARLACK—See KIRKWOOD, MO

▲ **CHARLESTON**—Falcon Telecable

▲ **CHESTERFIELD**—Charter Communications

CHESTERFIELD—See also ST. LOUIS COUNTY, MO

▲ **CHILHOWEE**—National Cable Inc.

▲ **CHILLICOTHE**—Chillicothe Cable TV

CHRISTIAN COUNTY—See OZARK, MO

▲ **CHULA**—Galaxy Cablevision

▲ **CLARENCE**—Capital Cable

▲ **CLARK**—Galaxy Cablevision

▲ **CLARKSBURG**—First Cable of Missouri Inc.

▲ **CLARKSDALE**—New Path Communications LC

CLARKSON VALLEY—See CHESTERFIELD, MO

▲ **CLARKSVILLE**—First Cable of Missouri Inc.

▲ **CLARKTON**—CableVision Communications

CLAYCOMO—See KANSAS CITY, MO

CLAYTON—See ST. LOUIS COUNTY, MO

▲ **CLEVER**—Friendship Cable of Missouri

CLIFF VILLAGE—See JOPLIN, MO

▲ **CLINTON**—Falcon Cable TV

CLYDE—See CONCEPTION JUNCTION, MO

COBALT VILLAGE—See FREDERICKTOWN, MO

▲ **COFFMAN BEND**—Friendship Cable of Missouri

▲ **COLE CAMP**—Galaxy Cablevision

▲ **COLE COUNTY (portions)**—Classic Cable

COLE COUNTY (portions)—See also JEFFERSON CITY, MO

▲ **COLUMBIA**—TCI Cablevision of Missouri

COLUMBIA—See also BOONE COUNTY, MO

COMPTON RIDGE—See INDIAN POINT, MO

CONCEPTION—See CONCEPTION JUNCTION, MO

▲ **CONCEPTION JUNCTION**—Deans Cablevision Inc.

▲ **CONCORDIA**—Galaxy Cablevision

▲ **CONWAY**—Friendship Cable of Missouri

COOL VALLEY—See FERGUSON, MO

COOPER COUNTY—See BOONVILLE, MO

CORDER—See HIGGINSVILLE, MO

COTTLEVILLE—See ST. CHARLES, MO

COUNTRY CLUB HILLS—See ST. LOUIS COUNTY, MO

COUNTRY CLUB VILLAGE—See ST. JOSEPH, MO

COUNTRY LIFE ACRES—See CHESTERFIELD, MO

▲ **COWGILL**—Green Hills Communications Inc.

▲ **CRAIG**—Westcom

▲ **CRANE**—Mediacom

CRAWFORD COUNTY—See CUBA, MO

▲ **CREIGHTON**—Galaxy Cablevision

CRESTWOOD—See CHESTERFIELD, MO

CREVE COEUR—See CHESTERFIELD, MO

CREVE COEUR—See also ST. LOUIS COUNTY, MO

▲ **CROCKER**—Galaxy Cablevision

CRYSTAL CITY—See ARNOLD, MO

CRYSTAL LAKE PARK—See CHESTERFIELD, MO

CRYSTAL LAKES—See EXCELSIOR SPRINGS, MO

▲ **CUBA**—Capital Cable

▲ **CURRYVILLE**—First Cable of Missouri Inc.

DARDENNE PRAIRIE—See LAKE ST. LOUIS, MO

DARDENNE PRAIRIE—See also ST. CHARLES, MO

▲ **DE KALB**—New Path Communications LC

DE SOTO—See ARNOLD, MO

DE SOTO—See also BARNHART, MO

DEARBORN—See CAMDEN POINT, MO

DEFIANCE—See LAKE SHERWOOD, MO

DELLWOOD—See FERGUSON, MO

▲ **DELTA**—Semo Communications Inc.

DENT COUNTY—See SALEM, MO

DES PERES—See CHESTERFIELD, MO

DESLOGE—See FLAT RIVER, MO

▲ **DEXTER**—Falcon Cable

▲ **DIAMOND**—Mediacom

▲ **DIXON**—Cable America Corp.

▲ **DONIPHAN**—CableVision Communications

▲ **DOOLITTLE**—Cable America Corp.

▲ **DOWNING**—Galaxy Cablevision

▲ **DREXEL**—Classic Cable

▲ **DUDLEY**—CableVision Communications

DUENWEG—See DUQUESNE, MO

DUNKLIN COUNTY—See CLARKTON, MO

DUNKLIN COUNTY—See also KENNETT, MO

DUNKLIN COUNTY (portions)—See MALDEN, MO

▲ **DUQUESNE**—Mediacom

▲ **DURHAM**—Galaxy Cablevision

▲ **EAGLEVILLE**—Capital Cable

EAST BONNE TERRE—See FLAT RIVER, MO

▲ **EAST LYNNE**—Galaxy Cablevision

EAST PRAIRIE—See CHARLESTON, MO

▲ **EASTON**—Green Hills Communications Inc.

EDGERTON—See CAMDEN POINT, MO

▲ **EDINA**—US Cable of Missouri

EDMUNDSON—See ST. LOUIS COUNTY, MO

▲ **EL DORADO SPRINGS**—Falcon Cablevision

▲ **ELDON**—Falcon Cable TV

▲ **ELLINGTON**—CableVision Communications

ELLISVILLE—See KIRKWOOD, MO

▲ **ELLSINORE**—CableVision Communications

▲ **ELSBERRY**—Capital Cable

ELVINS—See FLAT RIVER, MO

▲ **EMINENCE**—CableVision Communications

▲ **EMMA**—Galaxy Cablevision

▲ **EOLIA**—First Cable of Missouri Inc.

▲ **ESSEX**—CableVision Communications

ESTHER—See FLAT RIVER, MO

▲ **EUGENE**—First Cable of Missouri Inc.

EUREKA—See CHESTERFIELD, MO

▲ **EVERTON**—Mediacom

▲ **EWING**—Galaxy Cablevision

EXCELSIOR ESTATES—See EXCELSIOR SPRINGS, MO

▲ **EXCELSIOR SPRINGS**—Mediacom

EXETER—See CASSVILLE, MO

▲ **FAIR GROVE**—Classic Cable

▲ **FAIR PLAY**—Friendship Cable of Missouri

FAIRFAX—See TARKIO, MO

▲ **FARBER**—US Cable of Missouri

▲ **FARMINGTON**—Farmington Cablevision Co.

FARMINGTON—See also FLAT RIVER, MO

▲ **FAUCETT**—New Path Communications LC

▲ **FAYETTE**—Classic Cable

FENTON—See CHESTERFIELD, MO

▲ **FERGUSON**—American Cablevision of St. Louis

▲ **FERRELVIEW**—Galaxy Cablevision

FESTUS—See ARNOLD, MO

▲ **FISK**—Falcon Cable

▲ **FLAT RIVER**—Charter Cablevision

FLINT HILL—See LAKE ST. LOUIS, MO

FLORDELL HILLS—See ST. LOUIS COUNTY, MO

FLORISSANT—See CHESTERFIELD, MO

FOLEY—See WINFIELD, MO

▲ **FORDLAND**—Friendship Cable of Missouri

FOREST CITY—See OREGON, MO

▲ **FORSYTH**—Mediacom

FORT LEONARD WOOD—See ST. ROBERT, MO

FRANKCLAY—See FLAT RIVER, MO

▲ **FRANKFORD**—Charter Communications

FRANKLIN—See NEW FRANKLIN, MO

FRANKLIN COUNTY (northeastern portion)—See PACIFIC, MO

FRANKLIN COUNTY (southern portion)—See ST. CLAIR, MO

FRANKLIN COUNTY (western portion)—See WASHINGTON, MO

▲ **FREDERICKTOWN**—Falcon Telecable

▲ **FREEBURG**—Galaxy Cablevision

▲ **FREMONT**—CableVision Communications

FRISBEE—See CLARKTON, MO

FRONTENAC—See CHESTERFIELD, MO

FRUITLAND—See POCAHONTAS, MO

▲ **FULTON**—CableVision Communications

▲ **GAINESVILLE**—Friendship Cable of Arkansas

▲ **GALENA**—Friendship Cable of Missouri

▲ **GALLATIN**—Galaxy Cablevision

▲ **GALT**—Galaxy Cablevision

▲ **GARDEN CITY**—Galaxy Cablevision

▲ **GASCONADE**—First Cable of Missouri Inc.

▲ **GERALD**—Capital Cable

GIBSON—See CLARKTON, MO

GIDEON—See CLARKTON, MO

▲ **GILLIAM**—Galaxy Cablevision

▲ **GILMAN CITY**—Capital Cable

GLADSTONE—See KANSAS CITY, MO

▲ **GLASGOW**—Classic Cable

GLEN ECHO PARK—See FERGUSON, MO

GLENAIRE—See KANSAS CITY, MO

GLENALLEN—See MARBLE HILL, MO

GLENDALE—See KIRKWOOD, MO

GLENWOOD—See LANCASTER, MO

GOLDEN CITY—See EVERTON, MO

▲ **GOODMAN**—Mediacom

▲ **GORIN**—Galaxy Cablevision

▲ **GOWER**—Falcon Cable TV

GRAIN VALLEY—See INDEPENDENCE, MO

▲ **GRANBY**—Mediacom

GRANDIN—See ELLSINORE, MO

GRANDVIEW—See KANSAS CITY, MO

▲ **GRANT CITY**—New Path Communications LC

GRANTWOOD VILLAGE—See CHESTERFIELD, MO

▲ **GRAVOIS MILLS**—Friendship Cable of Missouri

GRAY SUMMIT—See PACIFIC, MO

▲ **GREEN CASTLE**—Galaxy Cablevision

GREEN CITY—See GREEN CASTLE, MO

▲ **GREEN RIDGE**—Galaxy Cablevision

GREENDALE—See FERGUSON, MO

GREENE COUNTY (portions)—See FAIR GROVE, MO

GREENE COUNTY (portions)—See also SPRINGFIELD, MO

GREENE COUNTY (southwestern portion)—See REPUBLIC, MO

GREENE COUNTY (unincorporated areas)—See EVERTON, MO

GREENFIELD—See EVERTON, MO

▲ **GREENTOP**—Galaxy Cablevision

GREENVIEW (unincorporated areas)—See PORTER MILL, MO

▲ **GREENVILLE**—CableVision Communications

GREENWOOD—See INDEPENDENCE, MO

GRUNDY COUNTY—See TRENTON, MO

▲ **HALE**—Galaxy Cablevision

HALFWAY—See BOLIVAR, MO

▲ **HALLSVILLE**—Galaxy Cablevision

▲ **HAMILTON**—Capital Cable

HANLEY HILLS—See KIRKWOOD, MO

▲ **HANNIBAL**—TCI Cablevision of Missouri

▲ **HARDIN**—Capital Cable

▲ **HARRISBURG**—First Cable of Missouri Inc.

▲ **HARRISONVILLE**—Falcon Cablevision

▲ **HARTVILLE**—Friendship Cable of Missouri

HARVESTER—See ST. CHARLES, MO

▲ **HAWK POINT**—First Cable of Missouri Inc.

HAYTI—See CARUTHERSVILLE, MO

HAYTI HEIGHTS—See CARUTHERSVILLE, MO

HAYWOOD CITY—See MORLEY, MO

HAZELWOOD—See ST. LOUIS COUNTY, MO

HENRIETTA—See RICHMOND, MO

HENRY COUNTY—See CLINTON, MO

HERCULANEUM—See ARNOLD, MO

▲ **HERMANN**—TCI Cablevision of Missouri Inc.

HERMITAGE—See POMME DE TERRE, MO

HICKORY COUNTY—See POMME DE TERRE, MO

HICKORY HILLS—See KNOB NOSTER, MO

▲ **HIGBEE**—Galaxy Cablevision

▲ **HIGGINSVILLE**—Galaxy Cablevision

HIGH RIDGE—See ARNOLD, MO

HIGH RIDGE—See also BARNHART, MO

HIGHLANDVILLE—See OZARK, MO

▲ **HIGHWAY DD**—Friendship Cable of Missouri

HILLSBORO—See ARNOLD, MO

HILLSDALE—See FERGUSON, MO

HOLCOMB—See CLARKTON, MO

▲ **HOLDEN**—Falcon Cablevision

▲ **HOLLISTER**—Rapid Cable

HOLLISTER—See also BRANSON, MO

▲ **HOLT**—New Path Communications LC

▲ **HOLTS SUMMIT**—TCI Cablevision of Missouri Inc.

HOMESTEAD VILLAGE—See EXCELSIOR SPRINGS, MO

HOMESTOWN—See WARDELL, MO

▲ **HOPKINS**—New Path Communications LC

▲ **HORNERSVILLE**—Base Cablevision

HORSESHOE BEND—See OSAGE BEACH, MO

HOUSE SPRINGS—See BARNHART, MO

▲ **HOUSTON**—Houston Cable Inc.

HOUSTON LAKE—See KANSAS CITY, MO

▲ **HOUSTONIA**—Galaxy Cablevision

HOWARDVILLE—See NEW MADRID, MO

HOWELL COUNTY—See ALTON, MO

HOWELL COUNTY—See also WEST PLAINS, MO

HUMANSVILLE—See POMME DE TERRE, MO

▲ **HUME**—Midwest Cable Inc.

HUNTER—See ELLSINORE, MO

HUNTLEIGH ACRES—See CHESTERFIELD, MO

HUNTSVILLE—See MOBERLY, MO

▲ **HURDLAND**—Galaxy Cablevision

Hurricane Deck—See OSAGE BEACH, MO

▲ **IBERIA**—Galaxy Cablevision

ILLMO—See SCOTT CITY, MO

IMPERIAL—See BARNHART, MO

▲ **INDEPENDENCE**—Jones Intercable

INDEPENDENCE—See also KANSAS CITY, MO

INDIAN HILLS LAKE—See CUBA, MO

▲ **INDIAN POINT**—Rapid Cable

IRON COUNTY—See IRONTON, MO

IRON MOUNTAIN LAKE—See IRONTON, MO

▲ **IRONTON**—Falcon Telecable

▲ **IVY BEND**—Friendship Cable of Missouri

JACKSON—See CAPE GIRARDEAU, MO

JACKSON COUNTY—See INDEPENDENCE, MO

▲ **JACKSONVILLE**—First Cable of Missouri Inc.

▲ **JAMESPORT**—Galaxy Cablevision

▲ **JAMESTOWN**—Galaxy Cablevision

▲ **JASPER**—Mediacom

JASPER COUNTY—See DUQUESNE, MO

▲ **JEFFERSON CITY**—TCI Cablevision of Missouri Inc.

JEFFERSON COUNTY—See ARNOLD, MO

JEFFERSON COUNTY (unincorporated areas)—See BARNHART, MO

▲ **JEFFERSON PARK**—Galaxy Cablevision

JENNINGS—See ST. LOUIS COUNTY, MO

JOE BALD—See HIGHWAY DD, MO

JOHN KNOX VILLAGE—See KANSAS CITY, MO

JOHNSON COUNTY (portions)—See WARRENSBURG, MO

▲ **JONESBURG**—US Cable

▲ **JOPLIN**—Cable One

▲ **JOPLIN (northwest)**—Friendship Cable of Missouri

▲ **JOPLIN (southwest)**—Friendship Cable of Missouri

JUNCTION CITY—See FREDERICKTOWN, MO

▲ **KAHOKA**—Kahoka Communications Cable Co.

▲ **KANSAS CITY**—Time Warner Cable

KANSAS CITY (portions)—See INDEPENDENCE, MO

KEARNEY—See KANSAS CITY, MO

KELSO—See SCOTT CITY, MO

▲ **KENNETT**—Kennett Cablevision

▲ **KEYTESVILLE**—Galaxy Cablevision

▲ **KIMBERLING CITY**—Mediacom

KIMBERLING CITY (unincorporated areas)—See HIGHWAY DD, MO

▲ **KING CITY**—New Path Communications LC

KINGDOM CITY—See FULTON, MO

▲ **KINGSTON**—Green Hills Communications Inc.

▲ **KINLOCH**—Visioncomm Inc.

▲ **KIRKSVILLE**—Cable One

▲ **KIRKWOOD**—Charter Communications

▲ **KNOB NOSTER**—Falcon Cable TV

▲ **KNOX CITY**—Galaxy Cablevision

▲ **LA BELLE**—Charter Communications

LA GRANGE—See CANTON, MO

▲ **LA MONTE**—Galaxy Cablevision

▲ **LA PLATA**—Capital Cable

▲ **LACLEDE**—Galaxy Cablevision

LACLEDE COUNTY—See LEBANON, MO

LADDONIA—See FARBER, MO

LADUE—See CHESTERFIELD, MO

LAKE LOTAWANO—See INDEPENDENCE, MO

LAKE MYKEE TOWN—See NEW BLOOMFIELD, MO

LAKE OZARK—See OSAGE BEACH, MO

▲ **LAKE SHERWOOD**—Heartland Cable TV Inc.

▲ **LAKE ST. LOUIS**—TCI Cablevision

LAKE TAPAWINGO—See INDEPENDENCE, MO

▲ **LAKE VIKING**—Green Hills Communications Inc.

LAKE WAUKOMIS—See KANSAS CITY, MO

LAKE WINNEBAGO—See INDEPENDENCE, MO

LAKELAND—See OSAGE BEACH, MO

LAKESHIRE—See CHESTERFIELD, MO

LAKESIDE—See OSAGE BEACH, MO

LAKEVIEW—See HIGHWAY DD, MO

LAKEVIEW—See also OSAGE BEACH, MO

▲ **LAMAR**—Southwest Missouri Cable

LAMAR HEIGHTS—See LAMAR, MO

▲ **LAMPE**—Friendship Cable of Missouri

LANAGAN—See NOEL, MO

▲ **LANCASTER**—Galaxy Cablevision

▲ **LAREDO**—Capital Cable

▲ **LATHROP**—Capital Cable

LAURIE—See OSAGE BEACH, MO

LAWSON—See EXCELSIOR SPRINGS, MO

LEADINGTON—See FLAT RIVER, MO

Leadwood—See FLAT RIVER, MO

LEAWOOD—See JOPLIN, MO

▲ **LEBANON**—Classic Cable

LEEPER—See PIEDMONT, MO

LEES SUMMIT—See INDEPENDENCE, MO

LEES SUMMIT—See also KANSAS CITY, MO

▲ **LEETON**—Galaxy Cablevision

▲ **LESTERVILLE**—Falcon Telecable

LEWIS & CLARK VILLAGE—See ATCHISON, KS

LEWISTOWN—See CANTON, MO

▲ **LEXINGTON**—Classic Cable

▲ **LIBERAL**—Mediacom

LIBERTY—See KANSAS CITY, MO

▲ **LICKING**—Licking Cable Inc.

LILBOURN—See NEW MADRID, MO

▲ **LINCOLN**—Galaxy Cablevision

LINCOLN COUNTY—See TROY, MO

LINCOLN COUNTY (southeastern portion)—See WINFIELD, MO

▲ **LINN**—Capital Cable

LINN COUNTY—See BROOKFIELD, MO

LINN CREEK—See OSAGE BEACH, MO

▲ **LINNEUS**—Capital Cable

LIVINGSTON COUNTY (portions)—See CHILLICOTHE, MO

LOCKWOOD—See EVERTON, MO

LOHMAN—See COLE COUNTY (portions), MO

▲ **LOOSE CREEK**—First Cable of Missouri Inc.

▲ **LOUISIANA**—TCI Cablevision of Missouri Inc.

▲ **LOWRY CITY**—Mediacom

LUTESVILLE—See MARBLE HILL, MO

MACKENZIE—See CHESTERFIELD, MO

▲ **MACKS CREEK**—Friendship Cable of Missouri

▲ **MACON**—Macon Cablevision Inc.

▲ **MADISON**—US Cable of Missouri

▲ **MAITLAND**—N.W. Telephone

▲ **MALDEN**—Falcon Cable

MALDEN—See also CLARKTON, MO

MANCHESTER—See KIRKWOOD, MO

▲ **MANSFIELD**—Mediacom

MAPLEWOOD—See ST. LOUIS COUNTY, MO

▲ **MARBLE HILL**—Falcon Telecable

▲ **MARCELINE**—Mediacom

MARIONVILLE—See MONETT, MO

MARLBOROUGH—See CHESTERFIELD, MO

▲ **MARSHALL**—Marshall Cable TV

▲ **MARSHFIELD**—Mediacom

MARSTON—See NEW MADRID, MO

MARTHASVILLE—See LAKE SHERWOOD, MO

MARTINSBURG—See MONTGOMERY CITY, MO

▲ **MARYLAND HEIGHTS**—Cable America Corp.

MARYLAND HEIGHTS—See also ST. LOUIS COUNTY, MO

▲ **MARYVILLE**—Classic Cable

▲ **MATTHEWS**—Semo Communications Inc.

▲ **MAYSVILLE**—Falcon Cablevision

▲ **MAYVIEW**—Galaxy Cablevision

MAYWOOD—See DURHAM, MO

McCORD BEND—See GALENA, MO

McDONALD COUNTY—See NOEL, MO

▲ **MEADVILLE**—Galaxy Cablevision

▲ **MEMPHIS**—Galaxy Cablevision

▲ **MERCER**—Galaxy Cablevision

MERRIAM WOODS—See ROCKAWAY BEACH, MO

▲ **META**—Galaxy Cablevision

▲ **MEXICO**—TCI Cablevision of Missouri

MIDDLEBROOK—See IRONTON, MO

▲ **MIDDLETOWN**—First Cable of Missouri Inc.

▲ **MILAN**—Capital Cable

MILL SPRING—See PIEDMONT, MO

MILLER—See EVERTON, MO

MILLER COUNTY (portions)—See ELDON, MO

MILLER COUNTY (portions)—See also OSAGE BEACH, MO

▲ **MINDENMINES**—Friendship Cable of Missouri

MINER—See SIKESTON, MO

▲ **MISSIONARY**—Friendship Cable of Missouri

MISSISSIPPI COUNTY (central portion)—See CHARLESTON, MO

▲ **MOBERLY**—TCI Cablevision of Missouri

▲ **MOKANE**—First Cable of Missouri Inc.

MOLINE ACRES—See ST. LOUIS COUNTY, MO

▲ **MONETT**—Southwest Missouri Cable TV Inc. of Monett

MONITEAU COUNTY (portions)—See CALIFORNIA, MO

▲ **MONROE CITY**—TCI Cablevision of Missouri Inc.

▲ **MONTGOMERY CITY**—US Cable of Missouri

▲ **MONTICELLO**—Galaxy Cablevision

MOORESVILLE—See UTICA, MO

MOREHOUSE—See SIKESTON, MO

MOREHOUSE COLONY—See MATTHEWS, MO

MORGAN COUNTY (portions)—See OSAGE BEACH, MO

▲ **MORLEY**—Semo Communications Inc.

MOSCOW MILLS—See TROY, MO

▲ **MOUND CITY**—New Path Communications LC

MOUNT VERNON—See EVERTON, MO

▲ **MOUNTAIN GROVE**—Cable America Corp.

▲ **MOUNTAIN VIEW**—CableVision Communications

NAPOLEON—See LEXINGTON, MO

▲ **NAYLOR**—CableVision Communications

NECK CITY—See ALBA, MO

NEELYVILLE—See NAYLOR, MO

▲ **NEOSHO**—Classic Cable

▲ **NEVADA**—Falcon Cable TV

▲ **NEW BLOOMFIELD**—Galaxy Cablevision

▲ **NEW CAMBRIA**—Chariton Valley Communication Corp.

NEW FLORENCE—See MONTGOMERY CITY, MO

▲ **NEW FRANKLIN**—Galaxy Cablevision

NEW HAMBURG—See BENTON, MO

▲ **NEW HAMPTON**—Capital Cable

▲ **NEW HAVEN**—Capital Cable

NEW LONDON—See CANTON, MO

▲ **NEW MADRID**—Falcon Telecable

NEW MADRID COUNTY—See NEW MADRID, MO

NEW MADRID COUNTY—See also PORTAGEVILLE, MO

NEW MELLE—See LAKE SHERWOOD, MO

▲ **NEWBURG**—Newburg Cable TV System

▲ **NEWTON**—Midwest Cable Inc.

NEWTON COUNTY—See NEOSHO, MO

▲ **NIANGUA**—Friendship Cable of Missouri

▲ **NIANGUA BRIDGE**—Friendship Cable of Missouri

NIXA—See OZARK, MO

NODAWAY COUNTY—See MARYVILLE, MO

▲ **NOEL**—Classic Cable

▲ **NORBORNE**—Mediacom

NORMANDY—See FERGUSON, MO

NORTH KANSAS CITY—See KANSAS CITY, MO

NORTH LILBOURN—See NEW MADRID, MO

NORTH SHORE—See OSAGE BEACH, MO

NORTH WARDELL—See WARDELL, MO

NORTHMOOR—See KANSAS CITY, MO

▲ **NORTHSHORE**—Friendship Cable of Missouri

NORTHWOODS OVERLAND—See ST. LOUIS COUNTY, MO

▲ **NORWOOD**—Friendship Cable of Missouri

NORWOOD COURT—See FERGUSON, MO

▲ **NOVINGER**—Galaxy Cablevision

O'FALLON—See LAKE ST. LOUIS, MO

O'FALLON—See also ST. CHARLES, MO

OAK GROVE—See INDEPENDENCE, MO

OAKLAND—See KIRKWOOD, MO

OAKLAND PARK—See JOPLIN, MO

OAKVIEW—See KANSAS CITY, MO

OAKWOOD—See KANSAS CITY, MO

OAKWOOD PARK—See KANSAS CITY, MO

ODESSA—See INDEPENDENCE, MO

OLD MONROE—See WINFIELD, MO

OLIVETTE—See CHESTERFIELD, MO

OLYMPIAN VILLAGE—See BARNHART, MO

ORAN—See CHAFFEE, MO

▲ **OREGON**—South Holt Cablevision Inc.

ORONOGO—See CARL JUNCTION, MO

▲ **ORRICK**—Capital Cable

▲ **OSAGE BEACH**—Falcon Cable

OSAGE COUNTY (northwestern portion)—See LOOSE CREEK, MO

▲ **OSBORN**—New Path Communications LC

▲ **OSCEOLA**—Mediacom

▲ **OTTERVILLE**—Galaxy Cablevision

OWENSVILLE—See BELLE, MO

▲ **OZARK**—Classic Cable

OZARK BEACH (portions)—See FORSYTH, MO

▲ **PACIFIC**—Falcon Telecable

PAGEDALE—See FERGUSON, MO

▲ **PALMYRA**—Cass Cable TV Inc.

▲ **PARIS**—US Cable of Missouri

PARKVILLE—See KANSAS CITY, MO

PARKWAY—See ST. CLAIR, MO

▲ **PARMA**—CableVision Communications

▲ **PARNELL**—Deans Cablevision Inc.

PASADENA HILLS—See FERGUSON, MO

PASADENA PARK—See FERGUSON, MO

PECULIAR—See INDEPENDENCE, MO

PEMISCOT COUNTY—See PORTAGEVILLE, MO

PEMISCOT COUNTY—See also STEELE, MO

▲ **PERRY**—US Cable of Missouri

PERRY COUNTY (portions)—See PERRYVILLE, MO

▲ **PERRYVILLE**—Falcon Telecable

PERSIMMON HOLLOW—See LAMPE, MO

PETTIS COUNTY—See SEDALIA, MO

PEVELY—See ARNOLD, MO

PEVELY—See also BARNHART, MO

PHELPS COUNTY (portions)—See ST. JAMES, MO

PHILLIPSBURG—See LEBANON, MO

▲ **PIEDMONT**—CableVision Communications

PIERCE CITY—See MONETT, MO

▲ **PILOT GROVE**—Mid-Missouri Telephone Co.

PILOT KNOB—See IRONTON, MO

PINE LAWN—See ST. LOUIS COUNTY, MO

PINEVILLE—See NOEL, MO

PLATTE CITY—See KANSAS CITY, MO

PLATTE COUNTY—See ATCHISON, KS

PLATTE COUNTY (portions)—See KANSAS CITY, MO

PLATTE WOODS—See KANSAS CITY, MO

▲ **PLATTSBURG**—Falcon Cablevision

PLEASANT HILL—See INDEPENDENCE, MO

▲ **PLEASANT HOPE**—Friendship Cable of Missouri

PLEASANT VALLEY—See KANSAS CITY, MO

▲ **POCAHONTAS**—Semo Communications Corp.

POLK COUNTY—See BOLIVAR, MO

▲ **POLO**—Capital Cable

▲ **POMME DE TERRE**—Enstar Cable Cumberland Valley

▲ **POPLAR BLUFF**—Falcon Cable

▲ **PORTAGE DES SIOUX**—Heartland Cable TV Inc.

▲ **PORTAGEVILLE**—CableVision Communications

▲ **PORTER MILL**—Friendship Cable of Missouri

▲ **POTOSI**—Falcon Telecable

▲ **POWERSITE**—Friendship Cable of Missouri

▲ **PRINCETON**—Galaxy Cablevision

PULASKI COUNTY (northern portion)—See DIXON, MO

PULASKI COUNTY (portions)—See ST. ROBERT, MO

PURCELL—See ALBA, MO

PURDIN—See LINNEUS, MO

▲ **PURDY**—Mediacom

▲ **PUXICO**—CableVision Communications

QUEEN CITY—See GREENTOP, MO

▲ **QULIN**—Falcon Cable

RANDOLPH COUNTY—See MOBERLY, MO

▲ **RAVENWOOD**—Deans Cablevision Inc.

RAYMORE—See INDEPENDENCE, MO

RAYTOWN—See INDEPENDENCE, MO

REDINGS MILL—See JOPLIN, MO

REEDS SPRING—See HIGHWAY DD, MO

▲ **RENICK**—Capital Cable

▲ **REPUBLIC**—Cable America Corp.

REYNOLDS COUNTY—See ELLINGTON, MO

▲ **RICH HILL**—KLM Telephone Co.

RICHARDS-GEBAUR AFB—See KANSAS CITY, MO

▲ **RICHLAND**—Cable America Corp.

▲ **RICHMOND**—Mediacom

RICHMOND HEIGHTS—See CHESTERFIELD, MO

▲ **RIDGEWAY**—Capital Cable

RISCO—See PARMA, MO

RIVERMINES—See FLAT RIVER, MO

RIVERSIDE—See KANSAS CITY, MO

RIVERVIEW—See ST. LOUIS COUNTY, MO

ROCHEPORT—See BOONE COUNTY, MO

ROCK HILL—See KIRKWOOD, MO

▲ **ROCKAWAY BEACH**—Rapid Cable

▲ **ROCKPORT**—Rockport Cablevision

▲ **ROCKVILLE**—KLM Telephone Co.

▲ **ROCKWOOD POINT**—Falcon Cable

▲ **ROGERSVILLE**—Mediacom

▲ **ROLLA**—Fidelity Cablevision

▲ **ROLLA**—Phelps County Cable

ROSEBUD—See GERALD, MO

RUSHVILLE—See ATCHISON, KS

▲ **RUSSELLVILLE**—Galaxy Cablevision

SAGINAW—See JOPLIN, MO

▲ **SALEM**—CableVision Communications

▲ **SALISBURY**—Mediacom

▲ **SARCOXIE**—Mediacom

SAVANNAH—See ST. JOSEPH, MO

▲ **SCOTT CITY**—Falcon Telecable

SCOTT COUNTY (northern portion)—See SCOTT CITY, MO

SCOTT COUNTY (northwestern portion)—See CHAFFEE, MO

SCOTT COUNTY (southwestern portion)—See SIKESTON, MO

▲ **SEDALIA**—Falcon Cablevision

▲ **SELIGMAN**—Peak Cablevision

SENATH—See KENNETT, MO

▲ **SENECA**—Classic Cable

▲ **SEYMOUR**—Mediacom

SHAWNEE BEND—See OSAGE BEACH, MO

▲ **SHELBINA**—US Cable of Missouri

SHELBYVILLE—See SHELBINA, MO

▲ **SHELDON**—Friendship Cable of Missouri Inc.

▲ **SHERIDAN**—Deans Cablevision Inc.

SHOAL CREEK DRIVE—See JOPLIN, MO

SHREWSBURY—See KIRKWOOD, MO

SIBLEY—See INDEPENDENCE, MO

▲ **SIKESTON**—Falcon Telecable

▲ **SILEX**—First Cable of Missouri Inc.

SILVER CREEK—See JOPLIN, MO

▲ **SKIDMORE**—N.W. Telephone

▲ **SLATER**—Galaxy Cablevision

▲ **SMITHTON**—Galaxy Cablevision

SMITHVILLE—See KANSAS CITY, MO

SOUTH GREENFIELD—See EVERTON, MO

SOUTH LINEVILLE—See LINEVILLE, IA

SOUTH WEST CITY—See NOEL, MO

▲ **SPARTA**—Friendship Cable of Missouri

▲ **SPICKARD**—Capital Cable

▲ **SPRINGFIELD**—TCI of Springfield

ST. ANN—See ST. LOUIS COUNTY, MO

▲ **ST. CHARLES**—TCI Cablevision of Missouri

ST. CHARLES COUNTY—See LAKE SHERWOOD, MO

ST. CHARLES COUNTY—See also LAKE ST. LOUIS, MO

ST. CHARLES COUNTY—See also ST. CHARLES, MO

ST. CHARLES COUNTY (unincorporated areas)—See PORTAGE DES SIOUX, MO

▲ **ST. CLAIR**—Falcon Telecable

ST. GEORGE—See CHESTERFIELD, MO

▲ **ST. JAMES**—Falcon Telecable

ST. JOHN—See KIRKWOOD, MO

▲ **ST. JOSEPH**—St. Joseph Cablevision

▲ **ST. LOUIS**—St. Louis Tele-Communications Inc.

▲ **ST. LOUIS COUNTY**—TCI Cablevision

ST. LOUIS COUNTY—See also CHESTERFIELD, MO

ST. MARTINS—See COLE COUNTY (portions), MO

ST. PAUL—See LAKE ST. LOUIS, MO

ST. PETERS—See ST. CHARLES, MO

▲ **ST. ROBERT**—Cable America Corp.

▲ **ST. THOMAS**—First Cable of Missouri Inc.

▲ **STANBERRY**—New Path Communications LC

▲ **STE. GENEVIEVE**—Falcon Telecable

▲ **STE. GENEVIEVE**—Westcom

▲ **STEELE**—CableVision Communications

▲ **STEELVILLE**—Falcon Telecable

▲ **STEWARTSVILLE**—Capital Cable

▲ **STOCKTON**—Alltel Corp.

STODDARD COUNTY (portions)—See BERNIE, MO

STODDARD COUNTY (portions)—See also DEXTER, MO

▲ **STOTTS CITY**—Friendship Cable of Missouri

▲ **STOVER**—Galaxy Cablevision

▲ **STRAFFORD**—Mediacom

STURGEON—See CLARK, MO

SUGAR CREEK—See INDEPENDENCE, MO

▲ **SULLIVAN**—Falcon Telecable

▲ **SUMMERSVILLE**—CableVision Communications

SUNRISE BEACH—See OSAGE BEACH, MO

SUNSET HILLS—See CHESTERFIELD, MO

▲ **SWEET SPRINGS**—Galaxy Cablevision

SYCAMORE HILLS—See KIRKWOOD, MO

▲ **SYRACUSE**—First Cable of Missouri Inc.

TABLE ROCK—See HIGHWAY DD, MO

TALLAPOOSA—See PARMA, MO

TANEY COUNTY—See HOLLISTER, MO

TANEY COUNTY (portions)—See POWERSITE, MO

TANEY COUNTY (portions)—See also ROCKAWAY BEACH, MO

TANEYVILLE—See POWERSITE, MO

▲ **TAOS**—Galaxy Cablevision

▲ **TARKIO**—Cablevision VI Inc.

▲ **TERRE DU LAC**—Charter Communications

▲ **THAYER**—Falcon Telecable

TIMES BEACH—See CHESTERFIELD, MO

▲ **TINA**—Green Hills Communications Inc.

▲ **TIPTON**—Falcon Cablevision

TOWN & COUNTRY—See CHESTERFIELD, MO

TRACY—See KANSAS CITY, MO

▲ **TRENTON**—Classic Cable

▲ **TRIMBLE**—New Path Communications LC

▲ **TROY**—Charter Communications

TRUESDALE—See WARRENTON, MO

TURKEY BEND—See OSAGE BEACH, MO

TWIN OAKS—See CHESTERFIELD, MO

UNION—See WASHINGTON, MO

UNION STAR—See ST. JOSEPH, MO

▲ **UNIONVILLE**—Unionville Missouri CATV

UNITY VILLAGE—See KANSAS CITY, MO

UNIVERSITY CITY—See ST. LOUIS COUNTY, MO

UPLANDS PARK—See FERGUSON, MO

▲ **URBANA**—Friendship Cable of Missouri

▲ **URICH**—Galaxy Cablevision

▲ **UTICA**—Green Hills Communications Inc.

VALLEY PARK—See CHESTERFIELD, MO

▲ **VAN BUREN**—CableVision Communications

▲ **VANDALIA**—Capital Cable

VANDIVER—See MEXICO, MO

VANDUSER—See MORLEY, MO

VELDA CITY—See FERGUSON, MO

VELDA VILLAGE HILLS—See FERGUSON, MO

VENICE ON THE LAKE—See ROCKAWAY BEACH, MO

VERONA—See MONETT, MO

▲ **VERSAILLES**—Falcon Cable

▲ **VIBURNUM**—Capital Cable

▲ **VIENNA**—Galaxy Cablevision

▲ **VILLA RIDGE**—Charter Communications

VILLAGE OF FOUR SEASONS—See OSAGE BEACH, MO

VILLAGE OF THE OAKS—See KANSAS CITY, MO

VINITA PARK—See KIRKWOOD, MO

VINITA TERRACE—See FERGUSON, MO

WALNUT GROVE—See EVERTON, MO

WALNUT HILLS—See SEDALIA, MO

▲ **WAPPAPELLO**—Falcon Cable

▲ **WARDELL**—CableVision Communications

WARDSVILLE—See COLE COUNTY (portions), MO

WARREN COUNTY—See LAKE SHERWOOD, MO

▲ **WARRENSBURG**—Falcon Cablevision

▲ **WARRENTON**—Charter Communications

▲ **WARSAW**—Falcon Cablevision

WARSON WOODS—See KIRKWOOD, MO

WASHBURN—See SELIGMAN, MO

▲ **WASHINGTON**—Falcon Telecable

▲ **WAVERLY**—Galaxy Cablevision

WAYNE COUNTY (portions)—See PIEDMONT, MO

WAYNESVILLE—See ST. ROBERT, MO

WEATHERBY LAKE—See KANSAS CITY, MO

WEAUBLEAU—See POMME DE TERRE, MO

WEBB CITY—See JOPLIN, MO

WEBSTER GROVES—See KIRKWOOD, MO

WELDON SPRING—See LAKE ST. LOUIS, MO

WELDON SPRING—See also ST. CHARLES, MO

WELDON SPRING HEIGHTS—See LAKE ST. LOUIS, MO

▲ **WELLINGTON**—Classic Cable

▲ **WELLSTON**—Visioncomm Inc.

WELLSVILLE—See MONTGOMERY CITY, MO

WENTZVILLE—See LAKE ST. LOUIS, MO

▲ **WEST PLAINS**—Falcon Cable

▲ **WESTBORO**—New Path Communications LC

WESTON—See KANSAS CITY, MO

▲ **WESTPHALIA**—Galaxy Cablevision

WESTWOOD—See CHESTERFIELD, MO

WHEATLAND—See POMME DE TERRE, MO

▲ **WHEELING**—Galaxy Cablevision

WHERING HOUSING BASE—See ST. LOUIS COUNTY, MO

WHITE BRANCH—See WARSAW, MO

WHITEMAN AFB—See KNOB NOSTER, MO

WILBUR PARK—See CHESTERFIELD, MO

WILLARD—See EVERTON, MO

▲**WILLIAMSVILLE**—CableVision Communications

▲ **WILLOW SPRINGS**—Falcon Cable

▲ **WILSON BEND**—Friendship Cable of Missouri

WILSON CITY—See WYATT, MO

WINCHESTER—See KIRKWOOD, MO

▲ **WINDSOR**—Falcon Cablevision

▲ **WINFIELD**—US Cable of Missouri

▲ **WINONA**—CableVision Communications

WOODS HEIGHTS—See EXCELSIOR SPRINGS, MO

WOODSON TERRACE—See KIRKWOOD, MO

WRIGHT CITY—See WARRENTON, MO

▲ **WYACONDA**—Galaxy Cablevision

▲ **WYATT**—Semo Communications Inc.

MONTANA

▲ **ABSAROKEE**—Fibervision Inc.

▲ **ALBERTON**—Charter Communications

ALHAMBRA—See MONTANA CITY, MT

▲ **ANACONDA**—TCI Cablevision of Montana

▲ **ARLEE**—Charter Communications

▲ **ASHLAND**—Ashland Entertainment Inc.

▲ **BAKER**—Baker Cable TV

BEAVERHEAD COUNTY (portions)—See DILLON, MT

▲ **BELFRY**—Belfry Cable TV

BELGRADE—See BOZEMAN, MT

▲ **BELT**—Blackstone Cable LLC

▲ **BIG FLAT**—Charter Communications

▲ **BIG SANDY**—Triangle Communication System Inc.

▲ **BIG SKY**—Big Sky Community TV Inc.

▲ **BIG TIMBER**—Fibervision Inc.

BIGFORK—See KALISPELL, MT

▲ **BILLINGS**—Billings TCI

▲ **BILLINGS (western portion)**—Blackstone Cable

BLACK EAGLE—See GREAT FALLS, MT

BLACKFOOT CANYON—See MILLTOWN, MT

BLAINE COUNTY (northern portion)—See CHINOOK, MT

BONNER—See MILLTOWN, MT

▲ **BOULDER**—TCI Cablevision of Montana Inc.

▲ **BOZEMAN**—TCI Cablevision of Montana Inc.

▲ **BROADUS**—Ashland Entertainment Inc.

BROADWATER COUNTY—See TOWNSEND, MT

▲ **BUTTE**—TCI Cablevision of Montana

▲ **CASCADE**—TCI Cablevision of Montana Inc.

CASCADE COUNTY—See GREAT FALLS, MT

▲ **CHARLO**—High Mountain

▲ **CHESTER**—Blackstone Cable LLC

▲ **CHINOOK**—TCI Cablevision of Montana Inc.

▲ **CHOTEAU**—TCI Cablevision of Montana Inc.

▲ **CIRCLE**—Mid Rivers Cable TV

CLANCY—See MONTANA CITY, MT

CLINTON—See MILLTOWN, MT

▲ **COLSTRIP**—Colstrip Cable TV Co. Inc.

COLUMBIA FALLS—See KALISPELL, MT

▲ **COLUMBUS**—Fibervision Inc.

▲ **CONRAD**—TCI Cablevision of Montana Inc.

▲ **CROW AGENCY**—Crow Cable TV

CROW INDIAN RESERVATION—See CROW AGENCY, MT

▲ **CULBERTSON**—Blackstone Cable LLC

CUSTER COUNTY—See MILES CITY, MT

▲ **CUT BANK**—TCI Cablevision of Great Falls Inc.

▲ **DARBY**—High Mountain

DAWSON COUNTY—See GLENDIVE, MT

▲ **DEER LODGE**—TCI Cablevision of Montana Inc.

DEER LODGE COUNTY—See ANACONDA, MT

DENTON—See STANFORD, MT

▲ **DILLON**—TCI Cablevision of Montana Inc.

▲ **DRUMMOND**—Drummond Cable TV

▲ **DUTTON**—Blackstone Cable LLC

EAST HELENA—See HELENA, MT

▲ **EKALAKA**—Mid Rivers Cable TV

▲ **ENNIS**—High Mountain

▲ **EUREKA**—Tobacco Valley Communications

EVERGREEN—See KALISPELL, MT

▲ **FAIRFIELD**—TCI Cablevision of Montana Inc.

▲ **FAIRVIEW**—Midcontinent Cable Co.

FERGUS COUNTY—See LEWISTOWN, MT

FLATHEAD COUNTY—See KALISPELL, MT

FLORENCE—See LOLO, MT

▲ **FORSYTH**—Fibervision Inc.

▲ **FORT BENTON**—TCI Cablevision of Montana Inc.

▲ **FOUR CORNERS**—Northwestern Communications

FRENCHTOWN—See NINE MILE, MT

▲ **FROMBERG**—Blackstone Cable LLC

GALLATIN COUNTY—See BOZEMAN, MT

▲ **GARDINER**—North Yellowstone Cable TV

GLACIER COUNTY—See CUT BANK, MT

▲ **GLASGOW**—TCI Cablevision of Montana Inc.

▲ **GLENDIVE**—TCI Cablevision of Montana Inc.

▲ **GRANT CREEK**—Charter Communications

▲ **GREAT FALLS**—TCI Cablevision of Great Falls

▲ **HAMILTON**—TCI Cablevision of Montana Inc.

▲ **HARDIN**—Fibervision Inc.

▲ **HARLEM**—TCI Cablevision of Montana Inc.

▲ **HARLOWTON**—Cable TV of Harlo

▲ **HAVRE**—TCI Cablevision of Montana Inc.

▲ **HELENA**—TCI Cablevision of Montana

HELENA VALLEY—See HELENA, MT

HILL COUNTY—See HAVRE, MT

▲ **HOT SPRINGS**—High Mountain

HUSON—See NINE MILE, MT

▲ **HYSHAM**—Blackstone Cable LLC

JEFFERSON COUNTY (unincorporated areas)—See MONTANA CITY, MT

▲ **JOLIET**—Blackstone Cable LLC

▲ **JORDAN**—Mid Rivers Cable TV

▲ **KALISPELL**—TCI Cablevision of Montana Inc.

LAKE COUNTY—See POLSON, MT (AT&T Cable Services)

LAKE WEST—See POLSON, MT (Charter Communications)

▲ **LAME DEER**—Eagle Cablevision

▲ **LAUREL**—Fibervision Inc.

▲ **LAVINA**—ABC Cable TV

LEWIS & CLARK COUNTY—See HELENA, MT

▲ **LEWISTOWN**—TCI Cablevision of Montana Inc.

▲ **LIBBY**—Kootenai Cable Inc.

▲ **LINCOLN**—Lincoln Cable TV

LINCOLN COUNTY—See LIBBY, MT

▲ **LIVINGSTON**—TCI Cablevision of Montana

LOCKWOOD—See BILLINGS, MT

▲ **LODGE GRASS**—Eagle Cablevision

▲ **LOLO**—Charter Communications

MADISON COUNTY (portions)—See ENNIS, MT

▲ **MALMSTROM AFB**—TCI Cablevision of Great Falls

▲ **MALTA**—TCI Cablevision of Montana Inc.

▲ **MANHATTAN**—TCI Cablevision of Montana Inc.

▲ **MARION**—High Mountain Communications, Inc.

▲ **MELSTONE**—Mel-View Cable TV

▲ **MILES CITY**—TCI Cablevision of Montana Inc.

▲ **MILLTOWN**—Charter Communications

▲ **MISSOULA**—Fibervision Inc.

▲ **MISSOULA**—TCI Cablevision of Montana

MISSOULA COUNTY—See MILLTOWN, MT

MISSOULA COUNTY—See also MISSOULA, MT (TCI Cablevision of Montana)

MISSOULA SOUTH—See MISSOULA, MT (TCI Cablevision of Montana)

▲ **MONTANA CITY**—TCI Cablevision of Montana Inc.

▲ **NINE MILE**—Charter Cable Communications

▲ **OPPORTUNITY**—TCI Cable

ORCHARD HOMES (portions)—See MISSOULA, MT (TCI Cablevision of Montana)

PABLO—See RONAN, MT

▲ **PARADISE**—High Mountain

▲ **PARK CITY**—Fibervision Inc.

PARK COUNTY—See LIVINGSTON, MT

▲ **PHILIPSBURG**—Eagle Cablevision

▲ **PLAINS**—High Mountain

▲ **PLENTYWOOD**—Plentywood Cable TV Co.

▲ **POLSON**—AT&T Cable Services

▲ **POLSON**—Charter Communications

PONDERA COUNTY—See CONRAD, MT

▲ **POPLAR**—Blackstone Cable LLC

POWELL COUNTY—See DEER LODGE, MT

RATTLESNAKE—See MISSOULA, MT (Fibervision Inc.)

RATTLESNAKE VALLEY—See MISSOULA, MT (Fibervision Inc.)

RAVALLI COUNTY—See HAMILTON, MT

RAVALLI COUNTY—See also STEVENSVILLE, MT

▲ **RED LODGE**—Fibervision Inc.

▲ **RICHEY**—Mid Rivers Cable TV

▲ **RIVERSIDE GREENS**—Northwestern Communications Corp.

▲ **RONAN**—Premiere Cable Communications

ROOSEVELT COUNTY—See WOLF POINT, MT

▲ **ROUNDUP**—Roundup Cable Inc.

▲ **RYEGATE**—Ryegate Cable TV

▲ **SAVAGE**—Savage Cable TV

▲ **SCOBEY**—Blackstone Cable LLC

▲ **SEELEY LAKE**—Charter Communications

▲ **SHELBY**—TCI Cablevision of Great Falls Inc.

▲ **SHERIDAN**—Ruby Valley Cable Co. Inc.

▲ **SIDNEY**—AT&T Cable Services

SILVER BOW COUNTY—See BUTTE, MT

▲ **ST. IGNATIUS**—High Mountain

▲ **ST. MARIE**—Charter Communications

▲ **ST. REGIS**—High Mountain

▲ **STANFORD**—B.E.K. Inc.

▲ **STEVENSVILLE**—TCI Cablevision of Montana Inc.

STEVENSVILLE—See also LOLO, MT

▲ **SUN PRAIRIE**—Blackstone Cable LLC

▲ **SUPERIOR**—Charter Communications

▲ **TERRY**—TCI Cablevision of Montana Inc.

TETON COUNTY—See CHOTEAU, MT

▲ **THOMPSON FALLS**—TCI Cablevision of Montana Inc.

TOOLE COUNTY—See CUT BANK, MT

▲ **TOWNSEND**—TCI Cablevision of Montana Inc.

TROY—See LIBBY, MT

TURAH—See MILLTOWN, MT

▲ **TWIN BRIDGES**—Twin Bridges Cable TV Inc.

▲ **VALIER**—Blackstone Cable LLC

VALLEY COUNTY—See GLASGOW, MT

VAUGHN—See SUN PRAIRIE, MT

▲ **VICTOR**—Charter Communications

WALKERVILLE—See BUTTE, MT

▲ **WEST YELLOWSTONE**—High Mountain

▲ **WHITE SULPHUR SPRINGS**—Eagle Cablevision

WHITEFISH—See KALISPELL, MT

▲ **WHITEHALL**—Whitehall Cable TV

▲ **WIBAUX**—Mid Rivers Cable TV

▲ **WOLF POINT**—TCI Cablevision of Montana Inc.

YELLOWSTONE COUNTY—See BILLINGS, MT

NEBRASKA

▲ **ADAMS**—Beatrice Cable TV Co.

ADAMS COUNTY—See HASTINGS, NE

▲ **AINSWORTH**—Ainsworth Cable TV

▲ **ALBION**—Galaxy Cablevision

ALDA—See GRAND ISLAND, NE

▲ **ALEXANDRIA**—Diode Cable Co.

▲ **ALLEN**—Sky Scan Cable Co.

▲ **ALLIANCE**—Bresnan Communications Co.

▲ **ALMA**—Classic Cable

▲ **AMHERST**—Cable USA

▲ **ANSELMO**—Consolidated Cable Inc.

▲ **ANSLEY**—Cable USA

▲ **ARAPAHOE**—Arapahoe Cable TV Inc.

▲ **ARCADIA**—Galaxy Cablevision

▲ **ARLINGTON**—Arlington Cablevision

▲ **ARNOLD**—Galaxy Cablevision

▲ **ASHLAND**—Harmon Cable Communications

▲ **ASHTON**—Consolidated Cable Inc.

▲ **ATKINSON**—Cable TV Assoc. (Atkinson)

▲ **AUBURN**—Time Warner Cable

▲ **AURORA**—Mid-State Community TV Inc.

▲ **AVOCA**—Westcom

▲ **AXTELL**—Cable USA Inc.

▲ **BANCROFT**—Great Plains Communications Inc.

BARTLEY—See CAMBRIDGE, NE

▲ **BASSETT**—Rock County Telephone Co.

BATTLE CREEK—See NORFOLK, NE

▲ **BAYARD**—TCI Cablevision of Nebraska Inc.

▲ **BEATRICE**—Bresnan Communications Co.

▲ **BEAVER CITY**—Classic Cable

▲ **BEAVER CROSSING**—Galaxy Cablevision

▲ **BEAVER LAKE**—Tele-Services Ltd.

▲ **BEE (village)**—Cable USA

▲ **BEEMER**—TelePartners

BELDEN—See CARROLL, NE

BELLEVUE—See OMAHA, NE

▲ **BELLWOOD**—Galaxy Cablevision

▲ **BENEDICT**—Galaxy Cablevision

▲ **BENKELMAN**—Cable TV Co. Inc.

BENNET—See SYRACUSE, NE

▲ **BENNINGTON**—Cable USA

▲ **BERTRAND**—Cable USA Inc.

▲ **BIG SPRINGS**—Consolidated Cable Inc.

BLADEN—See BLUE HILL, NE

▲ **BLAIR**—Cable USA

▲ **BLOOMFIELD**—Great Plains Cable TV

▲ **BLUE HILL**—Glenwood Telecommunications

BLUE SPRINGS—See WYMORE, NE

BOELUS—See BLAIR, NE

BOX BUTTE COUNTY (portions)—See ALLIANCE, NE

▲ **BRADSHAW**—Galaxy Cablevision

▲ **BRADY**—Eustis Telephone Exchange

▲ **BRAINARD**—Galaxy Cablevision

▲ **BRIDGEPORT**—TCI Cablevision of Nebraska Inc.

▲ **BRISTOW TWP.**—Sky Scan Cable

▲ **BROCK**—Westcom

▲ **BROKEN BOW**—TCI Cablevision of Nebraska Inc.

BROWNVILLE—See BROCK, NE

▲ **BRULE**—Post Cablevision

BRUNING—See GENEVA, NE

▲ **BRUNSWICK**—Sky Scan Cable Co.

BURT—See CRAIG, NE

▲ **BURWELL**—Galaxy Cablevision

▲ **BUTTE**—Vision Electronics

▲ **BYRON**—Galaxy Cablevision

▲ **CAIRO**—Cable USA

▲ **CALLAWAY**—Galaxy Cablevision

▲ **CAMBRIDGE**—Cambridge Cable TV

CAMPBELL—See BLUE HILL, NE

CAPITAL HEIGHTS—See GRAND ISLAND, NE

▲ **CARROLL**—Carroll CableVision

CASS COUNTY—See PLATTSMOUTH, NE

▲ **CEDAR BLUFFS**—Cable USA

CEDAR COUNTY—See NORFOLK, NE

▲ **CEDAR CREEK**—Hillcom Communications Inc.

▲ **CEDAR RAPIDS**—Galaxy Cablevision

CENTER—See BLOOMFIELD, NE

▲ **CENTRAL CITY**—Galaxy Cablevision

▲ **CERESCO**—Galaxy Cablevision

▲ **CHADRON**—Scott Cable Communications Inc.

▲ **CHAMBERS**—Sky Scan Cable Co.

▲ **CHAPMAN**—Great Plains Cable TV

▲ **CHAPPELL**—Cable USA

CHASE COUNTY—See WAUNETA, NE

▲ **CHESTER**—Galaxy Cablevision

CHEYENNE COUNTY—See SIDNEY, NE

▲ **CLARKS**—Clarks Cable TV

▲ **CLARKSON**—Vision Electronics

CLATONIA—See WILBER, NE

▲ **CLAY CENTER**—Galaxy Cablevision

▲ **CLEARWATER**—Cencom Inc.

▲ **CODY**—Midcontinent Cable Co.

▲ **COLERIDGE**—Cencom Inc.

▲ **COLUMBUS**—Columbus Cable TV

▲ **COLUMBUS (portions)**—Sky Scan Cable Co.

▲ **COMSTOCK**—Consolidated Cable Inc.

▲ **COOK**—Hillcom Communications Inc.

▲ **CORTLAND**—Beatrice Cable TV Co.

COUNTRY CLUB—See SCOTTSBLUFF, NE

▲ **COZAD**—Cable USA

▲ **CRAIG**—TelePartners

▲ **CRAWFORD**—Scott Cable Communications Inc.

▲ **CREIGHTON**—Great Plains Cable TV

▲ **CRESTON**—Sky-Scan Cable Co.

CRETE—See LINCOLN, NE

CROFTON—See BLOOMFIELD, NE

▲ **CULBERTSON**—Classic Cable

CUMING COUNTY—See NORFOLK, NE

▲ **CURTIS**—Curtis Cable TV Co. Inc.

DAKOTA CITY—See SOUTH SIOUX CITY, NE

DAKOTA COUNTY (portions)—See SOUTH SIOUX CITY, NE

▲ **DALTON**—Dalton Cable Television Inc.

▲ **DANNEBROG**—Cable USA

▲ **DAVENPORT**—Hillcom Communications Inc.

▲ **DAVEY (village)**—Cable USA

▲ **DAWSON**—Westcom

DAWSON COUNTY (portions)—See LEXINGTON, NE

▲ **DAYKIN**—Comstar Cable TV Inc.

DE WITT—See WILBER, NE

▲ **DECATUR**—Vision Electronics

DENTON—See LINCOLN, NE

▲ **DESHLER**—Galaxy Cablevision

DILL ADDITION—See SCOTTSBLUFF, NE

▲ **DILLER**—Diode Cable Co.

▲ **DIX**—Dalton Cable Television Inc.

▲ **DODGE**—TelePartners

DODGE COUNTY—See FREMONT, NE

DODGE COUNTY (portions)—See LAKE VENTURA, NE

▲ **DONIPHAN**—Mid-State Community TV Ltd.

DORCHESTER—See WILBER, NE

DOUGLAS COUNTY—See BENNINGTON, NE

DOUGLAS COUNTY—See also OMAHA, NE

DOUGLAS COUNTY (portions)—See GRETNA, NE

▲ **DUBOIS**—Westcom

▲ **DUNCAN**—Galaxy Cablevision

DUNNING—See ANSELMO, NE

▲ **DWIGHT (village)**—Cable USA

EAGLE—See SYRACUSE, NE

EDGAR—See CLAY CENTER, NE

▲ **ELBA**—Cable USA

▲ **ELGIN**—Scope CATV of Nebraska Co.

ELKHORN—See GRETNA 4023623698, NE

ELKHORN—See also OMAHA, NE

▲ **ELM CREEK**—Cable USA

ELMWOOD—See SYRACUSE, NE

▲ **ELSIE**—Consolidated Cable Inc.

▲ **ELWOOD**—Arapahoe Cable TV Inc.

▲ **EMERSON**—TelePartners

▲ **ENDICOTT**—Westcom

▲ **EUSTIS**—Eustis Telephone Exchange

▲ **EWING**—Vision Electronics

EXETER—See GENEVA, NE

▲ **FAIRBURY**—Time Warner Cable

FAIRFIELD—See CLAY CENTER, NE

FAIRMONT—See GENEVA, NE

▲ **FALLS CITY**—Falls City Cable TV

▲ **FARNAM**—Consolidated Cable Inc.

▲ **FILLEY**—Comstar Cable TV Inc.

▲ **FIRTH**—Beatrice Cable TV Co.

▲ **FORT CALHOUN**—Cable USA

▲ **FRANKLIN**—Classic Cable

FRANKLIN COUNTY (unincorporated areas)—See FRANKLIN, NE

▲ **FREMONT**—Time Warner Cable

FRIEND—See WILBER, NE

▲ **FULLERTON**—Galaxy Cablevision

▲ **FUNK**—Glenwood Telecommunications

▲ **GARLAND**—Galaxy Cablevision

▲ **GENEVA**—Galaxy Cablevision

▲ **GENOA**—Galaxy Cablevision

GERING—See SCOTTSBLUFF, NE

GIBBON—See SHELTON, NE

▲ **GILTNER**—Mid-State Community TV Inc.

▲ **GLENVIL**—Galaxy Cablevision

▲ **GOEHNER (village)**—Cable USA

▲ **GORDON**—Scott Cable Communications Inc.

▲ **GOTHENBURG**—Cable USA

▲ **GRAND ISLAND**—Bresnan Communications Co.

▲ **GRAND ISLAND (southern portion)**—Galaxy Cablevision

▲ **GRANT**—Grant Cable TV

▲ **GREELEY**—Center Cable TV

▲ **GREENWOOD**—Harmon Cable Communications

▲ **GRESHAM**—Galaxy Cablevision

▲ **GRETNA 4023623698**—Galaxy Cablevision

▲ **GUIDE ROCK**—Glenwood Telecommunications

▲ **GURLEY**—Dalton Cable Television Inc.

▲ **HADAR**—Sky Scan Cable Co.

▲ **HAIGLER**—Cable TV Co.

HALL COUNTY—See GRAND ISLAND, NE

HALLAM—See WILBER, NE

HALSEY—See ANSELMO, NE

HAMPTON—See AURORA, NE

▲ **HARDY**—Diode Cable Co.

HARRISON—See LYMAN, NE

▲ **HARTINGTON**—CedarVision Inc.

HARVARD—See CLAY CENTER, NE

▲ **HASTINGS**—Bresnan Communications Co.

HASTINGS AFB—See HASTINGS, NE

▲ **HAY SPRINGS**—Galaxy Cablevision

▲ **HAYES CENTER**—Great Plains Cable TV

▲ **HEBRON**—Hebron Cable TV

HEMINGFORD—See CRAWFORD, NE

▲ **HENDERSON**—Henderson Co-op Telephone Co.

▲ **HERMAN (village)**—Cable USA Inc.

▲ **HERSHEY**—Scope CATV of Nebraska Co.

HICKMAN—See WILBER, NE

▲ **HILDRETH**—Cable USA Inc.

▲ **HOLBROOK**—Arapahoe Cable TV Inc.

▲ **HOLDREGE**—Cable USA

HOLSTEIN—See BLUE HILL, NE

HOMER—See SOUTH SIOUX CITY, NE

▲ **HOOPER**—Hooper Telephone Co.

▲ **HORDVILLE**—Mid-State Community TV

HOSKINS—See HADAR, NE

▲ **HUMBOLDT**—Time Warner Cable

HUMBOLDT—See also AUBURN, NE

▲ **HUMPHREY**—Galaxy Cablevision

HUNTS ACRES—See SCOTTSBLUFF, NE

▲ **IMPERIAL**—Great Plains Cable TV

INDIAN HILLS—See LAKE MALONEY, NE

▲ **INDIANOLA**—Classic Cable

INGLEWOOD—See FREMONT, NE

INMAN—See PAGE (village), NE

▲ **JANSEN**—Diode Cable Co.

JEFFERSON COUNTY (southeastern portion)—See DILLER, NE

▲ **JOHNSON**—Hillcom Communications Inc.

▲ **JOHNSON LAKE**—Cable USA

▲ **JUNIATA**—Cable USA

▲ **KEARNEY**—Cable USA

KEITH COUNTY—See OGALLALA, NE

▲ **KENNARD**—Cable USA Inc.

▲ **KIMBALL**—TCI Cablevision of Nebraska Inc.

KIMBALL COUNTY—See KIMBALL, NE

▲ **KUESTERS LAKE**—Kuesters Lake TV

LA VISTA—See OMAHA, NE

▲ **LAKE CUNNINGHAM**—Cable USA

▲ **LAKE MALONEY**—Cable USA

▲ **LAKE VENTURA**—Harmon Cable Communications

▲ **LAKE WACONDA**—Hillcom Communications Inc.

LANCASTER COUNTY—See LINCOLN, NE

▲ **LAUREL**—TelePartners

LAWRENCE—See BLUE HILL, NE

▲ **LEWELLEN**—Consolidated Cable Inc.

▲ **LEXINGTON**—TCI Cablevision of Nebraska

▲ **LINCOLN**—Time Warner Cable

LINCOLN COUNTY—See NORTH PLATTE, NE

▲ **LITCHFIELD**—Patriot Cable

LOCHLAND—See BLUE HILL, NE

▲ **LODGEPOLE**—Dalton Cable Television Inc.

▲ **LONG PINE**—Long Pine Cable TV

▲ **LOOMIS**—Cable USA Inc.

▲ **LOUISVILLE**—Harmon Cable Communications

▲ **LOUP CITY**—Cable USA

▲ **LYMAN**—Windbreak Cable TV

▲ **LYONS**—TelePartners

MADISON—See NORFOLK, NE

MADISON COUNTY—See NORFOLK, NE

▲ **MADRID**—Consolidated Cable Inc.

▲ **MALCOLM**—Galaxy Cablevision

▲ **MARQUETTE**—Mid-State Community TV

▲ **MASON CITY**—Cable USA

▲ **MAXWELL**—Eustis Telephone Exchange

MAYWOOD—See CURTIS, NE

▲ **McCOOK**—TCI Cablevision of Nebraska Inc.

McCOOL JUNCTION—See GENEVA, NE

▲ **MEAD**—Cable USA

▲ **MEADOW GROVE**—Galaxy Cablevision

MEADOWBROOK TRAILER PARK—See LAKE VENTURA, NE

MELBETA—See MINATARE, NE

▲ **MERNA**—Consolidated Cable Inc.

MILFORD—See WILBER, NE

MILLIGAN—See GENEVA, NE

▲ **MINATARE**—TCI Cablevision of Nebraska Inc.

▲ **MINDEN**—Cable USA

▲ **MITCHELL**—TCI Cablevision of Nebraska Inc.

▲ **MORRILL**—TCI Cablevision of Nebraska Inc.

MORSE BLUFF—See NORTH BEND, NE

▲ **MULLEN**—Galaxy Cablevision

MURDOCK—See SYRACUSE, NE

▲ **MURRAY**—Hillcom Communications Inc.

▲ **NAPER**—Midcontinent Cable TV

NEBRASKA CITY—See AUBURN, NE

▲ **NEHAWKA**—Hillcom Communications Inc.

▲ **NELIGH**—Great Plains Cable TV

▲ **NELSON**—Galaxy Cablevision

NEMAHA—See BROCK, NE

▲ **NEWCASTLE**—Cencom Inc.

▲ **NEWMAN GROVE**—Galaxy Cablevision

▲ **NIOBRARA**—Great Plains Cable TV

▲ **NORFOLK**—Cable One

▲ **NORTH BEND**—Scope Cable TV of Nebraska

▲ **NORTH LOUP**—Galaxy Cablevision

▲ **NORTH PLATTE**—Bresnan Communications Co.

▲ **O'NEILL**—Midcontinent Cable Co.

▲ **OAKDALE**—Great Plains Cable TV

▲ **OAKLAND**—Cable USA

▲ **OCONTO**—Patriot Cable TV Inc.

ODELL—See DILLER, NE

▲ **OGALLALA**—Bresnan Communications Co.

▲ **OMAHA**—Cox Communications Omaha Inc.

▲ **ORD**—Cable USA Inc.

▲ **ORLEANS**—Classic Cable

▲ **OSCEOLA**—Galaxy Cablevision

▲ **OSHKOSH**—Cable USA

▲ **OSMOND**—Osmond CableVision

▲ **OTOE**—Westcom

▲ **OVERTON**—Cable USA Inc.

▲ **OXFORD**—Classic Cable

▲ **PAGE (village)**—Sky Scan Cable

▲ **PALISADE**—Scope CATV of Nebraska Co.

▲ **PALMER**—Sky Scan Cable Co.

PALMYRA—See SYRACUSE, NE

PAPILLION—See OMAHA, NE

▲ **PAXTON**—Peregrine Communications

▲ **PENDER**—TelePartners

▲ **PERU**—Galaxy Cablevision

▲ **PHILLIPS**—Cable USA

▲ **PICKRELL**—Comstar Cable TV Inc.

PIERCE—See NORFOLK, NE

PIERCE COUNTY—See NORFOLK, NE

▲ **PILGER**—Sky Scan Cable Co.

▲ **PLAINVIEW**—Great Plains Cable TV

▲ **PLATTSMOUTH**—Harmon Cable Communications

PLEASANT DALE—See WILBER, NE

▲ **PLEASANTON**—Cable USA

PLYMOUTH—See WILBER, NE

▲ **POLK**—Galaxy Cablevision

▲ **PONCA**—Great Plains Communications Inc.

▲ **POTTER**—Dalton Cable Television Inc.

▲ **PRAGUE**—Westcom

RANDOLPH—See NORFOLK, NE

▲ **RAVENNA**—Cable USA

▲ **RAYMOND**—Galaxy Cablevision

▲ **RED CLOUD**—Classic Cable

RED WILLOW COUNTY—See McCOOK, NE

▲ **REPUBLICAN CITY**—Vision Plus Inc.

RICHLAND—See COLUMBUS (portions), NE

RIVERDALE (village)—See KEARNEY, NE

ROCK COUNTY—See BASSETT, NE

ROSELAND—See BLUE HILL, NE

▲ **RULO**—Westcom

RUSHVILLE—See GORDON, NE

▲ **RUSKIN**—Diode Cable Co.

▲ **SALEM**—Westcom

▲ **SARGENT**—Galaxy Cablevision

SARPY COUNTY (portions)—See GRETNA, NE

SARPY COUNTY (unincorporated areas)—See OMAHA, NE

▲ **SCHUYLER**—Galaxy Cablevision

▲ **SCOTIA**—Galaxy Cablevision

SCOTTS BLUFF COUNTY—See SCOTTSBLUFF, NE

▲ **SCOTTSBLUFF**—Bresnan Communications Co.

▲ **SCRIBNER**—Scope CATV of Nebraska Co.

SEWARD—See YORK, NE

SEWARD COUNTY—See YORK, NE

▲ **SHELBY**—Galaxy Cablevision

▲ **SHELTON**—TCI Cablevision of Nebraska Inc.

SHICKLEY—See GENEVA, NE

▲ **SHUBERT**—Westcom

▲ **SIDNEY**—Bresnan Communications Co.

▲ **SILVER CREEK**—Galaxy Cablevision

▲ **SOUTH SIOUX CITY**—Jones Intercable Inc.

▲ **SPALDING**—Sky Scan Cable Co.

▲ **SPENCER**—Vision Electronics

▲ **SPRINGFIELD**—Harmon Cable Communications

▲ **SPRINGVIEW**—Springview Cable TV

▲ **ST. EDWARD**—Galaxy Cablevision

▲ **ST. LIBORY**—Cable USA

▲ **ST. PAUL**—TCI Cablevision of Nebraska Inc.

▲ **STAMFORD**—Vision Plus Inc.

▲ **STANTON**—Cable TV of Stanton

STANTON COUNTY—See NORFOLK, NE

▲ **STAPLEHURST**—Galaxy Cablevision

▲ **STAPLETON**—Great Plains Cable TV

STEINAUR—See DUBOIS, NE

▲ **STELLA**—StellaVision

STERLING—See SYRACUSE, NE

▲ **STRATTON**—Peregrine Communications

▲ **STROMSBURG**—Galaxy Cablevision

▲ **STUART**—Vision Electronics

▲ **SUMNER**—Cable USA

SUPERIOR—See FAIRBURY, NE

▲ **SUTHERLAND**—Scope CATV of Nebraska Co.

SUTTON—See CLAY CENTER, NE

▲ **SWANTON**—Comstar Cable TV Inc.

▲ **SYRACUSE**—Galaxy Cablevision

▲ **TALMAGE**—Beatrice Cable TV Co.

▲ **TAYLOR**—Galaxy Cablevision

▲ **TEKAMAH**—Cable USA

TERRYTOWN—See SCOTTSBLUFF, NE

TILDEN—See NORFOLK, NE

▲ **TOBIAS**—Westcom

▲ **TRENTON**—Community CATV/Time Warner

▲ **TRUMBULL**—Mid-State Community TV

▲ **UEHLING**—Sky Scan Cable Co.

▲ **ULYSSES**—Galaxy Cablevision

▲ **UNADILLA**—Hillcom Communications Inc.

▲ **UNION**—Hillcom Communications Inc.

UPLAND—See BLUE HILL, NE

▲ **UTICA**—Galaxy Cablevision

▲ **VALENTINE**—Valentine Cable TV Service

VALLEY—See GRETNA, NE

▲ **VALPARAISO**—Galaxy Cablevision

▲ **VENANGO**—Great Plains Cable TV

▲ **VERDIGRE**—Vision Electronics

▲ **VERDON**—Westcom

VIRGINIA—See DILLER, NE

▲ **WACO**—Galaxy Cablevision

▲ **WAHOO**—Harmon Cable Communications

▲ **WAKEFIELD**—TelePartners

▲ **WALLACE**—Consolidated Cable Inc.

WALTHILL—See SOUTH SIOUX CITY, NE

▲ **WASHINGTON (village)**—Cable USA

WASHINGTON COUNTY—See BLAIR, NE

WASHINGTON COUNTY—See also FORT CALHOUN, NE

WATERLOO—See GRETNA 4023623698, NE

▲ **WAUNETA**—Cable TV Co. Inc.

▲ **WAUSA**—Vision Electronics

▲ **WAVERLY**—Harmon Cable Communications

WAYNE—See SOUTH SIOUX CITY, NE

WEEPING WATER—See SYRACUSE, NE

WEST POINT—See NORFOLK, NE

▲ **WESTERN**—Galaxy Cablevision

▲ **WESTON**—Westcom

▲ **WILBER**—Galaxy Cablevision

▲ **WILCOX**—Cable USA Inc.

WINNETOON—See BLOOMFIELD, NE

▲ **WINSIDE**—Sky Scan Cable Co.

WISNER—See NORFOLK, NE

▲ **WOLBACH**—Great Plains Cable TV

WOOD RIVER—See SHELTON, NE

▲ **WYMORE**—Galaxy Cablevision

▲ **WYNOT**—Cencom Inc.

▲ **YORK**—Cablevision

▲ **YUTAN**—Cable USA

NEVADA

▲ **ALAMO**—Rainbow Cable

ALPINE VIEW—See GARDNERVILLE, NV

AUTUMN HILLS—See GARDNERVILLE, NV

BABBITT ARMY BASE—See HAWTHORNE, NV

▲ **BATTLE MOUNTAIN**—TCI Cablevision of Nevada Inc.

▲ **BEATTY**—Wander Communications of Nevada LLC

▲ **BLUE DIAMOND**—Wander Communications of Nevada LLC

BOULDER BEACH—See BOULDER CITY (northern portion), NV

▲ **BOULDER CITY (northern portion)**—Wander Communications of Nevada LLC

BOULDER CITY—See also LAS VEGAS, NV

BUNKERVILLE—See MESQUITE, NV

▲ **CAL-NEV-ARI**—Wander Communications of Nevada LLC

▲ **CALIENTE**—Rainbow Cable

▲ **CALLVILLE BAY**—Wander Communications of Nevada LLC

▲ **CARLIN**—TCI Cablevision of Nevada Inc.

▲ **CARSON CITY**—TCI Cablevision of Nevada Inc.

CARSON VALLEY—See GARDNERVILLE, NV

CENTERVILLE—See GARDNERVILLE, NV

CHURCHILL COUNTY—See FALLON, NV

CLARK COUNTY—See LAS VEGAS, NV

COLD SPRINGS—See WASHOE COUNTY, NV

▲ **CRYSTAL BAY**—TCI Cable of North Lake Tahoe

▲ **DAYTON**—TCI Cable of Carson City

DOUGLAS COUNTY—See SOUTH LAKE TAHOE, CA

EAST LAS VEGAS—See LAS VEGAS, NV

▲ **ELKO**—TCI Cablevision of Nevada Inc.

ELKO COUNTY (portions)—See ELKO, NV

▲ **ELY**—Peak Cablevision

▲ **EMPIRE**—United States Gypsum Co.

ENTERPRISE—See LAS VEGAS, NV

ESMERALDA COUNTY (portions)—See TONOPAH, NV

▲ **EUREKA**—Peak Cablevision

▲ **FALLON**—TCI Cablevision of Nevada Inc.

FALLON STATION—See FALLON, NV

▲ **FERNLEY**—TCI Cablevision of Nevada Inc.

FISH SPRING—See GARDNERVILLE, NV

▲ **GABBS**—Wander Communications of Nevada LLC

▲ **GARDNERVILLE**—TCI Cablevision of Nevada Inc.

GARDNERVILLE TWP.—See GARDNERVILLE, NV

GENOA—See GARDNERVILLE, NV

GOLD HILL—See VIRGINIA CITY, NV

GOLDEN VALLEY—See WASHOE COUNTY, NV

▲ **GOLDFIELD**—Wander Communications of Nevada LLC

GREEN VALLEY (portions)—See LAS VEGAS, NV

▲ **HADLEY**—Wander Communications of Nevada LLC

▲ **HAWTHORNE**—TCI Cablevision of Nevada Inc.

HEMENWAY—See BOULDER CITY (northern portion), NV

HENDERSON—See LAS VEGAS, NV

HIDDEN VALLEY—See RENO, NV

HOLBROOK JUNCTION—See TOPAZ LAKE, NV

INCLINE VILLAGE—See NORTH STAR, CA

INDIAN HILLS—See GARDNERVILLE, NV

▲ **INDIAN SPRINGS**—United Cable Management

▲ **INDIAN SPRINGS AFB**—United Cable Management

JACK VALLEY—See GARDNERVILLE, NV

▲ **JACKPOT**—Jackpot Antenna-Vision Inc.

JOHNSON LANE—See GARDNERVILLE, NV

JOHNSON VALLEY—See GARDNERVILLE, NV

LAKE MEAD BASE—See BOULDER CITY (northern portion), NV

LAKEVIEW—See BOULDER CITY (northern portion), NV

▲ **LAS VEGAS**—Cox Communications

▲ **LAUGHLIN**—Clark Cablevision Inc.

LEMMON VALLEY—See WASHOE COUNTY, NV

▲ **LOCKWOOD**—TCI Cablevision of Nevada Inc.

LOGANDALE—See OVERTON, NV

▲ **LOVELOCK**—Lovelock Cable TV

LYON COUNTY—See DAYTON, NV

LYON COUNTY (northern portion)—See also FERNLEY, NV

MARK TWAIN—See DAYTON, NV

▲ **McGILL**—Peak Cablevision

▲ **MESQUITE**—Falcon Telecable

MINDEN—See GARDNERVILLE, NV

MOGUL—See RENO, NV

▲ **NELLIS AFB**—Nellis AFB Cable TV

NELLIS AFB—See also LAS VEGAS, NV

NORTH LAS VEGAS—See LAS VEGAS, NV

▲ **OVERTON**—Falcon Telecable

▲ **PAHRUMP**—Wander Cable Communications

▲ **PANACA**—Rainbow Cable

PANTHER VALLEY—See WASHOE COUNTY, NV

PARADISE—See LAS VEGAS, NV

▲ **PIOCHE**—Rainbow Cable

PYRAMID LAKE—See FERNLEY, NV

RANCHOS SUBDIVISION UNITS—See GARDNERVILLE, NV

RED ROCK—See WASHOE COUNTY, NV

▲ **RENO**—AT&T Cable Services

RENO CASCADE—See RENO, NV

ROUND MOUNTAIN—See TONOPAH, NV

▲ **RUTH**—Peak Cablevision

SEARCHLIGHT—See LAUGHLIN, NV

SHERIDAN ACRES—See GARDNERVILLE, NV

SIERRA ROYAL—See RENO, NV

▲ **SILVER SPRINGS**—TCI Cablevision of Nevada Inc.

▲ **SILVERPEAK**—Wander Communications of Nevada LLC

SPANISH SPRINGS—See WASHOE COUNTY, NV

SPARKS—See SPARKS CITY, NV

▲ **SPARKS CITY**—TCI Cablevision of Nevada Inc.

▲ **SPRING CREEK**—TCI Cablevision of Nevada Inc.

SPRING VALLEY—See LAS VEGAS, NV

STAGECOACH—See SILVER SPRINGS, NV

STATELINE—See SOUTH LAKE TAHOE, CA

STEAMBOAT—See RENO, NV

STOREY COUNTY (portions)—See DAYTON, NV

SUN VALLEY—See RENO, NV

SUN VALLEY—See also WASHOE COUNTY, NV

SUNRISE MANOR—See LAS VEGAS, NV

▲ **TONOPAH**—Wander Communications of Nevada LLC

▲ **TOPAZ LAKE**—HFU TV

TOPAZ RANCH ESTATES—See TOPAZ LAKE, NV

VERDI—See RENO, NV

▲ **VIRGINIA CITY**—Comstock Community TV Inc.

WADSWORTH—See FERNLEY, NV

▲ **WASHOE COUNTY**—TCI Cablevision of Nevada

WASHOE COUNTY—See also CRYSTAL BAY, NV

WASHOE COUNTY (southern portion)—See also NORTH STAR, CA

▲ **WELLS**—TCI Cablevision of Nevada Inc.

▲ **WENDOVER**—Peak Cablevision

WEST WENDOVER—See WENDOVER, UT

WINCHESTER—See LAS VEGAS, NV

▲ **WINNEMUCCA**—SunTel Cable

YERINGTON—See FALLON, NV

NEW HAMPSHIRE

ALBANY—See CONWAY, NH

ALEXANDRIA—See CONCORD, NH

ALLENSTOWN—See CONCORD, NH

▲ **ALSTEAD**—Adelphia

ALSTEAD (town-eastern portion)—See ALSTEAD, NH

ALSTEAD CENTER—See ALSTEAD, NH

▲ **ALTON**—MetroCast Cablevision

AMHERST—See MERRIMACK, NH

▲ **ANDOVER (town)**—First Carolina TV

ANTRIM—See CONCORD, NH

ASHLAND—See PLYMOUTH, NH

ASHUELOT—See HINSDALE, NH

ATKINSON—See LONDONDERRY, NH

AUBURN—See MANCHESTER, NH

BARNSTEAD—See PITTSFIELD, NH

BARRINGTON—See ROCHESTER, NH

BARTLETT—See CONWAY, NH

BATH—See ST. JOHNSBURY, VT

▲ **BATH (village)**—FrontierVision Partners LP

BEDFORD—See MANCHESTER, NH

BELMONT—See LACONIA, NH

BENNINGTON—See PETERBOROUGH, NH

▲ **BERLIN**—Warner Cable of Berlin

BETHLEHEM (town)—See LITTLETON, NH

BOSCAWEN—See CONCORD, NH

BOW—See CONCORD, NH

BRADFORD—See WARNER TWP., NH

BRENTWOOD—See PORTSMOUTH, NH

BRIDGEWATER—See CONCORD, NH

BRISTOL—See CONCORD, NH

BROOKFIELD (town)—See WAKEFIELD (town), NH

BROOKLINE—See PEPPERELL, MA

▲ **CAMPTON**—Adelphia Cable

CANAAN (town)—See LEBANON, NH

CANDIA—See MANCHESTER, NH

CANTERBURY—See CONCORD, NH

▲ **CARROLL**—FrontierVision Partners LP

CENTER HARBOR—See LACONIA, NH

CENTER OSSIPEE—See MOULTONBOROUGH (town), NH

CHARLESTOWN—See CORNISH, NH

CHESTER—See LONDONDERRY, NH

CHESTER (town)—See LONDONDERRY, NH

CHESTERFIELD—See SPOFFORD, NH

CHESTERFIELD—See also BRATTLEBORO, VT

CHICHESTER (town)—See CONCORD, NH

▲ **CLAREMONT**—Adelphia Cable

COLEBROOK—See WEST STEWARTSTOWN, NH

COLUMBIA—See WEST STEWARTSTOWN, NH

▲ **CONCORD**—MediaOne

▲ **CONWAY**—FrontierVision

▲ **CORNISH**—Adelphia

CORNISH—See also CLAREMONT, NH

CORNISH—See also PLAINFIELD (town), NH

CORNISH (town)—See PLAINFIELD (town), NH

CORNISH FLAT—See CORNISH, NH

DALTON—See BERLIN, NH

DANBURY (town)—See ANDOVER (town), NH

DANVILLE—See LONDONDERRY, NH

▲ **DEERFIELD**—MetroCast Cablevision

DEERING—See CONCORD, NH

▲ **DERRY**—MediaOne

DORCHESTER (town)—See WENTWORTH (town), NH

DOVER—See PORTSMOUTH, NH

DREWSVILLE—See ALSTEAD, NH

DUNBARTON—See NEW BOSTON, NH

DUNBARTON (town)—See NEW BOSTON, NH

DURHAM—See PORTSMOUTH, NH

EAST KINGSTON—See PORTSMOUTH, NH

EAST ROCHESTER—See ROCHESTER, NH

EAST WESTMORELAND—See SPOFFORD, NH

EATON (town)—See MADISON (town), NH

EFFINGHAM—See FREEDOM (town), NH

ENFIELD—See LEBANON, NH

ENFIELD—See also PLAINFIELD (town), NH

EPPING—See PORTSMOUTH, NH

EPSOM—See PITTSFIELD, NH

ETNA—See LEBANON, NH

EXETER—See PORTSMOUTH, NH

FARMINGTON—See ROCHESTER, NH

FITZWILLIAM—See TROY, NH

FRANCESTOWN—See NEW BOSTON, NH

FRANCONIA—See LITTLETON, NH

▲ **FRANKLIN**—MetroCast Cablevision

▲ **FREEDOM (town)**—FrontierVision

FREMONT—See PORTSMOUTH, NH

FREMONT (town)—See PORTSMOUTH, NH

GILFORD—See LACONIA, NH

GILSUM—See ALSTEAD, NH

GLEN—See CONWAY, NH

GOFFSTOWN—See MANCHESTER, NH

GONIC—See ROCHESTER, NH

GORHAM—See BERLIN, NH

▲ **GRANTHAM**—Adelphia

GREENLAND—See PORTSMOUTH, NH

▲ **GREENVILLE**—Adelphia Cable

GROTON (town)—See WENTWORTH (town), NH

▲ **GROVETON**—Warner Cable Communications

GROVETON—See also STRATFORD (town), NH

▲ **HAMPSTEAD**—MediaOne

HAMPTON—See PORTSMOUTH, NH

HAMPTON FALLS—See PORTSMOUTH, NH

HANCOCK—See PETERBOROUGH, NH

HANOVER—See LEBANON, NH

HARRISVILLE (town)—See NELSON (town), NH

HAVERHILL—See ST. JOHNSBURY, VT

HEBRON—See CONCORD, NH

HENNIKER—See CONCORD, NH

HILL—See HILL (town), NH

▲ **HILL (town)**—FrontierVision Partners LP

HILL (town)—See also ANDOVER (town), NH

HILLSBORO—See CONCORD, NH

HILLSBOROUGH COUNTY—See MANCHESTER, NH

▲ **HINSDALE**—Adelphia

HOLDERNESS (portions)—See CAMPTON, NH

HOLLIS—See PEPPERELL, MA

HOOKSETT—See MANCHESTER, NH

HOPKINTON—See CONCORD, NH

HUDSON—See MERRIMACK, NH

JACKSON—See CONWAY, NH

JAFFREY—See PETERBOROUGH, NH

Jefferson—See JEFFERSON (town), NH

* **JEFFERSON (town)**—FrontierVision Partners LP

KEARSARGE—See CONWAY, NH

▲ **KEENE**—Paragon Cable

KENSINGTON—See PORTSMOUTH, NH

KINGSTON—See LONDONDERRY, NH

▲ **LACONIA**—MetroCast Cablevision

LANCASTER—See BERLIN, NH

LANGDON—See ALSTEAD, NH

▲ **LEBANON**—FrontierVision

LEE—See PORTSMOUTH, NH

▲ **LINCOLN**—FrontierVision

LISBON—See LITTLETON, NH

LITCHFIELD—See MERRIMACK, NH

▲ **LITTLETON**—FrontierVision

▲ **LONDONDERRY**—Harron Cablevision

LOUDON (town)—See CONCORD, NH

MADBURY—See PORTSMOUTH, NH

▲ **MADISON (town)**—FrontierVision Partners LP

▲ **MANCHESTER**—MediaOne

MARLBOROUGH—See KEENE, NH

MARLOW—See STODDARD, NH

MEREDITH—See LACONIA, NH

▲ **MERRIMACK**—Harron Communications

MERRIMACK—See also MANCHESTER, NH

MIDDLETON (town)—See WAKEFIELD (town), NH

▲ **MILAN (town)**—Adelphia

MILFORD—See MERRIMACK, NH

MILTON—See ROCHESTER, NH

MILTON MILLS—See ROCHESTER, NH

▲ **MONROE (town)**—FrontierVision Partners LP

▲ **MOULTONBOROUGH (town)**—FrontierVision

▲ **NASHUA**—MediaOne

▲ **NELSON (town)**—Pine Tree Cablevision

▲ **NEW BOSTON**—Harron Communications

NEW BOSTON (town)—See NEW BOSTON, NH

NEW CASTLE—See PORTSMOUTH, NH

NEW DURHAM—See ALTON, NH

NEW HAMPTON—See CONCORD, NH

NEW IPSWICH—See PETERBOROUGH, NH

▲ **NEW LONDON**—FrontierVision

NEWBURY—See WARNER TWP., NH

NEWFIELDS—See PORTSMOUTH, NH

NEWINGTON (town)—See PORTSMOUTH, NH

NEWMARKET—See PORTSMOUTH, NH

▲ **NEWPORT**—FrontierVision

NEWTON—See LONDONDERRY, NH

NORTH CONWAY—See CONWAY, NH

NORTH HAMPTON—See PORTSMOUTH, NH

NORTH HAVERHILL—See ST. JOHNSBURY, VT

NORTH HUDSON—See MERRIMACK, NH

NORTH WALPOLE—See BELLOWS FALLS, VT

NORTH WOODSTOCK—See LINCOLN, NH

NORTHFIELD—See FRANKLIN, NH

NORTHFIELD (town)—See LACONIA, NH

NORTHUMBERLAND (town)—See BERLIN, NH

NORTHWOOD—See PITTSFIELD, NH

NOTTINGHAM—See PORTSMOUTH, NH

NOTTINGHAM (town)—See PORTSMOUTH, NH

OSSIPEE (town)—See MOULTONBOROUGH (town), NH

PELHAM—See LONDONDERRY, NH

PEMBROKE—See CONCORD, NH

▲ **PETERBOROUGH**—Adelphia

PIERMONT—See ST. JOHNSBURY, VT

PIKE—See ST. JOHNSBURY, VT

PITTSBURG—See WEST STEWARTSTOWN, NH

▲ **PITTSFIELD**—MetroCast Cablevision

NEW JERSEY

RAMSEY—See OAKLAND, NJ

RANDOLPH TWP.—See DOVER, NJ

RARITAN—See PISCATAWAY, NJ

RARITAN TWP.—See HILLSBOROUGH, NJ

READINGTON—See HILLSBOROUGH, NJ

RED BANK—See EATONTOWN, NJ

RIDGEFIELD—See PALISADES PARK, NJ

RIDGEFIELD PARK—See PALISADES PARK, NJ

RIDGEWOOD—See OAKLAND, NJ

RINGWOOD—See OAKLAND, NJ

RIVER EDGE—See OAKLAND, NJ

RIVER VALE TWP.—See BERGENFIELD, NJ

RIVERDALE—See OAKLAND, NJ

RIVERSIDE—See WILLINGBORO, NJ

RIVERTON—See WILLINGBORO, NJ

ROBBINSVILLE—See MILLSTONE TWP., NJ

ROCHELLE PARK—See OAKLAND, NJ

ROCKAWAY—See DOVER, NJ

ROCKAWAY TWP.—See DOVER, NJ

ROCKLEIGH—See BERGENFIELD, NJ

ROCKY HILL—See HILLSBOROUGH, NJ

ROOSEVELT—See EAST WINDSOR, NJ

ROSELAND—See UNION, NJ

ROSELLE—See UNION, NJ

ROSELLE PARK—See UNION, NJ

ROXBURY TWP.—See DOVER, NJ

RUMSON—See EATONTOWN, NJ

RUNNEMEDE—See CHERRY HILL, NJ

RUTHERFORD BOROUGH—See CARLSTADT BOROUGH, NJ

SADDLE BROOK—See OAKLAND, NJ

SADDLE RIVER—See BERGENFIELD, NJ

▲ **SALEM**—Suburban Cable

SANDYSTON TWP.—See MONTAGUE TWP., NJ

SANDYSTON TWP.—See also SPARTA, NJ

SAYREVILLE—See PISCATAWAY, NJ

SCOTCH PLAINS TWP.—See UNION, NJ

SEA BRIGHT—See EATONTOWN, NJ

SEA GIRT—See MONMOUTH COUNTY, NJ

SEA ISLE CITY—See AVALON, NJ

SEASIDE HEIGHTS—See MONMOUTH COUNTY, NJ

SEASIDE PARK—See MONMOUTH COUNTY, NJ

SECAUCUS TWP.—See UNION, NJ

SHAMONG TWP.—See CHERRY HILL, NJ

SHILOH—See VINELAND, NJ

SHIP BOTTOM—See LONG BEACH TWP., NJ

SHORT HILLS—See UNION, NJ

SHREWSBURY—See EATONTOWN, NJ

SHREWSBURY TWP.—See EATONTOWN, NJ

SKILLMAN—See HILLSBOROUGH, NJ

SOMERDALE—See CHERRY HILL, NJ

SOMERS POINT—See PLEASANTVILLE, NJ

SOMERSET—See HILLSBOROUGH, NJ

SOMERVILLE—See PISCATAWAY, NJ

SOUTH AMBOY—See PISCATAWAY, NJ

SOUTH BELMAR—See MONMOUTH COUNTY, NJ

SOUTH BOUND BROOK—See PISCATAWAY, NJ

SOUTH BRANCH—See HILLSBOROUGH, NJ

SOUTH BRUNSWICK—See EAST WINDSOR, NJ

SOUTH HACKENSACK TWP.—See OAKLAND, NJ

SOUTH HARRISON TWP.—See FRANKLINVILLE, NJ

SOUTH ORANGE—See NEWARK, NJ

SOUTH PLAINFIELD—See NORTH PLAINFIELD, NJ

SOUTH RIVER—See UNION, NJ

SOUTH SEASIDE PARK—See MONMOUTH COUNTY, NJ

SOUTH TOMS RIVER—See BERKELEY TWP., NJ

SOUTHAMPTON TWP.—See CHERRY HILL, NJ

▲ **SPARTA**—Service Electric Cable TV of New Jersey Inc.

SPARTA TWP.—See SPARTA, NJ

SPOTSWOOD—See EAST WINDSOR, NJ

SPRING LAKE—See MONMOUTH COUNTY, NJ

SPRING LAKE HEIGHTS—See MONMOUTH COUNTY, NJ

SPRINGFIELD—See UNION, NJ

SPRINGFIELD TWP.—See CHERRY HILL, NJ

STAFFORD TWP.—See BERKELEY TWP., NJ

STANHOPE—See DOVER, NJ

STEWARTSVILLE—See PHILLIPSBURG, NJ

STILLWATER TWP.—See SPARTA, NJ

STIRLING—See LONG HILL TWP., NJ

STOCKTON—See LAMBERTVILLE, NJ

STONE HARBOR—See AVALON, NJ

STONE HARBOR MANOR—See AVALON, NJ

STRATFORD—See CHERRY HILL, NJ

STRATHMERE—See AVALON, NJ

SUMMIT—See UNION, NJ

SURF CITY—See LONG BEACH TWP., NJ

SUSSEX—See SPARTA, NJ

SWAINTON—See AVALON, NJ

SWEDESBORO—See FRANKLINVILLE, NJ

TABERNACLE TWP.—See CHERRY HILL, NJ

TAVISTOCK—See CHERRY HILL, NJ

TEANECK—See OAKLAND, NJ

TENAFLY—See BERGENFIELD, NJ

TETERBORO—See PALISADES PARK, NJ

TEWKSBURY—See LONG HILL TWP., NJ

TEWKSBURY TWP.—See LONG HILL TWP., NJ

THREE BRIDGES—See HILLSBOROUGH, NJ

TINTON FALLS—See EATONTOWN, NJ

TITUSVILLE—See LAMBERTVILLE, NJ

TOMS RIVER—See BERKELEY TWP., NJ

TOTOWA—See OAKLAND, NJ

▲ **TRENTON**—Comcast Cablevision of Mercer County Inc.

TUCKERTON—See BERKELEY TWP., NJ

▲ **TURNERSVILLE**—Suburban Cable

▲ **UNION**—Comcast Cablevision of New Jersey

UNION BEACH—See PISCATAWAY, NJ

UNION CITY—See HOBOKEN, NJ

UNION GAP—See HILLSBOROUGH, NJ

UNION TWP.—See HILLSBOROUGH, NJ

UNION TWP.—See also UNION, NJ

UPPER DEERFIELD TWP.—See FRANKLINVILLE, NJ

UPPER DEERFIELD TWP.—See also VINELAND, NJ

UPPER FREEHOLD TWP.—See MILLSTONE TWP., NJ

UPPER PITTSGROVE TWP.—See FRANKLINVILLE, NJ

UPPER SADDLE RIVER—See OAKLAND, NJ

UPPER TWP.—See PLEASANTVILLE, NJ

VENTNOR CITY—See PLEASANTVILLE, NJ

VERNON TWP.—See SPARTA, NJ

VERONA—See UNION, NJ

VICTORY GARDENS—See DOVER, NJ

VILLAS—See WILDWOOD, NJ

▲ **VINELAND**—Suburban Cable TV

VOORHEES TWP.—See CHERRY HILL, NJ

WALDWICK—See OAKLAND, NJ

WALL—See MONMOUTH COUNTY, NJ

WALL TWP.—See MONMOUTH COUNTY, NJ

WALLINGTON BOROUGH—See CARLSTADT BOROUGH, NJ

WANAQUE—See OAKLAND, NJ

WANTAGE TWP.—See SPARTA, NJ

WARETOWN—See BERKELEY TWP., NJ

WARREN—See PISCATAWAY, NJ

WARREN TWP.—See PISCATAWAY, NJ

WASHINGTON—See PORT MURRAY, NJ

WASHINGTON TWP. (Bergen County)—See also OAKLAND, NJ

WASHINGTON TWP. (Gloucester County)—See TURNERSVILLE, NJ

WASHINGTON TWP. (Mercer County)—See HAMILTON TWP. (Mercer County), NJ

WASHINGTON TWP. (Morris County)—See PORT MURRAY, NJ

WASHINGTON TWP. (Warren County)—See PORT MURRAY, NJ

WATCHUNG—See PISCATAWAY, NJ

WATERFORD TWP.—See TURNERSVILLE, NJ

WAYNE—See OAKLAND, NJ

WEEHAWKEN—See HOBOKEN, NJ

WENONAH—See WOODBURY, NJ

WEST AMWELL TWP.—See LAMBERTVILLE, NJ

WEST BERLIN TWP.—See CHERRY HILL, NJ

WEST CALDWELL—See UNION, NJ

WEST CAPE MAY—See WILDWOOD, NJ

WEST DEPTFORD—See WOODBURY, NJ

WEST LONG BRANCH—See EATONTOWN, NJ

WEST MILFORD—See WARWICK, NY

WEST NEW YORK—See HOBOKEN, NJ

WEST ORANGE—See UNION, NJ

WEST PATERSON—See OAKLAND, NJ

WEST TRENTON—See LAMBERTVILLE, NJ

WEST WILDWOOD—See WILDWOOD, NJ

WEST WINDSOR TWP.—See EAST WINDSOR, NJ

WESTAMPTON—See WILLINGBORO, NJ

WESTFIELD—See UNION, NJ

WESTHAMPTON TWP.—See CHERRY HILL, NJ

WESTVILLE—See WOODBURY, NJ

WESTWOOD—See OAKLAND, NJ

WEYMOUTH TWP. (Atlantic County)—See PLEASANTVILLE, NJ

WHARTON—See DOVER, NJ

WHITE HOUSE STATION—See HILLSBOROUGH, NJ

WHITE TWP.—See PORT MURRAY, NJ

▲ **WILDWOOD**—TCI

WILDWOOD CREST—See WILDWOOD, NJ

▲ **WILLINGBORO**—Comcast Cable Communications

WINFIELD PARK—See UNION, NJ

WINSLOW TWP.—See TURNERSVILLE, NJ

WOOD-RIDGE—See OAKLAND, NJ

WOODBINE—See PLEASANTVILLE, NJ

WOODBRIDGE—See UNION, NJ

▲ **WOODBURY**—Comcast Cable Communications

WOODBURY HEIGHTS—See WOODBURY, NJ

WOODCLIFF LAKE—See BERGENFIELD, NJ

WOODLAND TWP.—See CHERRY HILL, NJ

WOODLYNNE—See CHERRY HILL, NJ

WOODSTOWN—See FRANKLINVILLE, NJ

WOOLWICH TWP.—See FRANKLINVILLE, NJ

WRIGHTSTOWN—See CHERRY HILL, NJ

WYCKOFF—See OAKLAND, NJ

NEW MEXICO

▲ **ALAMOGORDO**—Scott Cable Communications Inc.

▲ **ALBUQUERQUE**—Jones Intercable

ALTO—See RUIDOSO, NM

ANACONDA—See GRANTS, NM

▲ **ANGEL FIRE**—Century Communications

ANTHONY—See EL PASO, TX

ARENAS VALLEY—See SILVER CITY, NM

▲ **ARTESIA**—US Cable of New Mexico

AZTEC—See FARMINGTON, NM

BAYARD—See SILVER CITY, NM

▲ **BELEN**—Valencia County Cable TV

BERNALILLO—See ALBUQUERQUE, NM

BERNALILLO COUNTY (portions)—See EDGEWOOD, NM

BLOOMFIELD—See FARMINGTON, NM

BLUEWATER—See GRANTS, NM

BOLES ACRES—See ALAMOGORDO, NM

BOSQUE FARMS—See ALBUQUERQUE, NM

▲ **BRAZOS**—US Cable of New Mexico

CANNON AFB—See CLOVIS, NM

CANON—See TAOS, NM

CAPITAN—See RUIDOSO, NM

▲ **CARLSBAD**—US Cable of New Mexico

▲ **CARRIZOZO**—Scott Cable Communications Inc.

CATRON COUNTY (unincorporated areas)—See RESERVE, NM

CENTRAL—See SILVER CITY, NM

CERRO—See QUESTA, NM

▲ **CHAMA**—US Cable of New Mexico

CHAVES COUNTY—See ROSWELL, NM

▲ **CIMARRON**—TCI Cablevision of New Mexico Inc.

▲ **CLAYTON**—CSI-Cablecomm

▲ **CLOUDCROFT**—Cloudcroft Cable TV

▲ **CLOVIS**—TCA Cable TV

CORRALES—See ALBUQUERQUE, NM

▲ **CROWNPOINT**—Crownpoint Cable TV Inc.

▲ **CUBA**—Sun Valley Cable Inc.

DEL CERRO ESTATES—See EL PASO, TX

▲ **DEMING**—Century Communications

DEXTER—See SEMINOLE, TX

▲ **DIXON**—US Cable of New Mexico

DONA ANA—See LAS CRUCES, NM

DONA ANA COUNTY (portions)—See MOONGATE, NM

Dona Ana County (portions)—See also WHITE SANDS, NM

DONA ANA COUNTY (portions)—See also EL PASO, TX

EDDY COUNTY—See CARLSBAD, NM

EDDY COUNTY (portions)—See ARTESIA, NM

▲ **EDGEWOOD**—Jones Intercable

EL CERRO MISSION—See BELEN, NM

EL PRADO—See TAOS, NM

▲ **ELDORADO**—Eldorado Cable TV Inc.

▲ **ELEPHANT BUTTE**—Butte Cable TV

ENSENADA—See TIERRA AMARILLA, NM

▲ **ESPANOLA**—US Cable of New Mexico

▲ **ESTANCIA**—Sierra Cablevision

▲ **EUNICE**—TCI Cablevision of New Mexico Inc.

▲ **FARMINGTON**—TCI Cablevision of New Mexico Inc.

▲ **FORT SUMNER**—Classic Cable

▲ **FORT WINGATE**—Indevideo Co. Inc.

▲ **FOUR HILLS**—JRC Telecommunications

▲ **GALLUP**—AT&T Cable Services

GAMERCO—See GALLUP, NM

▲ **GLENWOOD**—Eagle West Cable

GRANT COUNTY (portions)—See SILVER CITY, NM

▲ **GRANTS**—Jones Spacelink

HAGERMAN—See SEMINOLE, TX

▲ **HATCH**—Century Communications

▲ **HIGH ROLLS MOUNTAIN PARK**—Scott Cable Communications Inc.

▲ **HOBBS**—US Cable of New Mexico

HOLLOMAN AFB—See ALAMOGORDO, NM

HURLEY—See SILVER CITY, NM

▲ **ISLETA**—Jones Intercable

▲ **JAL**—TCI Cablevision of New Mexico Inc.

JEMEZ SPRINGS—See LOS ALAMOS, NM

KIRTLAND—See FARMINGTON, NM

KIRTLAND AFB—See ALBUQUERQUE, NM

LA LUZ—See ALAMOGORDO, NM

LA MESA—See EL PASO, TX

▲ **LAS CRUCES**—TCI Cablevision of New Mexico Inc.

▲ **LAS VEGAS**—Century Communications

LEA COUNTY—See HOBBS, NM

LEA COUNTY—See also LOVINGTON, NM

LLANO—See TAOS, NM

▲ **LOGAN**—CSI-Cablecomm

▲ **LORDSBURG**—City TV Cable Service

▲ **LOS ALAMOS**—Century Communications

LOS ALAMOS COUNTY—See LOS ALAMOS, NM

LOS CHAVEZ—See BELEN, NM

LOS LUNAS—See BELEN, NM

▲ **LOS OJOS**—US Cable of New Mexico

LOS RANCHOS DE ALBUQUERQUE—See ALBUQUERQUE, NM

LOVING—See CARLSBAD, NM

▲ **LOVINGTON**—Century New Mexico Cable TV

▲ **MAXWELL**—Rocky Mountain Cable Systems

McKINLEY COUNTY (portions)—See THOREAU, NM

McKINLEY COUNTY (south central portion)—See also GRANTS, NM

MEADOW LAKE—See BELEN, NM

▲ **MELROSE**—Classic Cable

MESCALERO APACHE INDIAN RESERVATION (portions)—See RUIDOSO, NM

MESILLA—See LAS CRUCES, NM

▲ **MESILLA VALLEY**—Mesilla Valley Cable Co.

MESQUITE—See EL PASO, TX

MILAN—See GRANTS, NM

MISSION PARK—See BELEN, NM

▲ **MOONGATE**—Mesilla Valley Cable Co.

▲ **MORA**—Rocky Mountain Cable Systems

▲ **MORIARTY**—Jones Intercable

MOUNT TAYLOR—See GRANTS, NM

▲ **MOUNTAINAIR**—Sierra Cablevision

NAMBE PUEBLO—See LOS ALAMOS, NM

▲ **NAVAJO**—Navajo Communications

NORTH VALLEY—See ALBUQUERQUE, NM

PARADISE HILLS—See ALBUQUERQUE, NM

PARK VIEW—See TIERRA AMARILLA, NM

▲ **PECOS**—Century Communications

PERALTA—See ALBUQUERQUE, NM

▲ **PLACITAS**—Jones Intercable

PLACITAS—See also HATCH, NM

▲ **PLAYAS**—Playas CATV

POJOAQUE—See LOS ALAMOS, NM

POJOAQUE PUEBLO—See LOS ALAMOS, NM

▲ **PORTALES**—Century Communications

QUAY COUNTY—See TUCUMCARI, NM

▲ **QUESTA**—Century Communications

▲ **RAMAH**—Navajo Communications

▲ **RANCHO GRANDE ESTATES**—Eagle West Cable

RANCHOS DE TAOS—See TAOS, NM

▲ **RATON**—TCI Cablevision of New Mexico Inc.

▲ **RED RIVER**—TCI Cablevision of New Mexico Inc.

▲ **RESERVE**—Eagle West Cable

RIO ARRIBA COUNTY—See CHAMA, NM

RIO ARRIBA COUNTY (southeastern portion)—See also SANTA CLARA INDIAN RESERVATION, NM

RIO COMMUNITIES—See BELEN, NM

▲ **RIO RANCHO**—Cable One

RODEY—See HATCH, NM

ROOSEVELT COUNTY—See PORTALES, NM

▲ **ROSWELL**—Cable One

▲ **RUIDOSO**—Lincoln Cablevision

RUIDOSO DOWNS—See RUIDOSO, NM

▲ **SAN ANTONIO**—Sun Valley Cable Inc.

SAN IDLEFONSO PUEBLO—See LOS ALAMOS, NM

SAN JUAN PUEBLO—See SANTA CLARA INDIAN RESERVATION, NM

SAN MIGUEL—See EL PASO, TX

SAN MIGUEL COUNTY—See LAS VEGAS, NM

SAN RAFAEL—See GRANTS, NM

SANDIA KNOLLS—See EDGEWOOD, NM

SANDOVAL COUNTY (portions)—See PLACITAS, NM

▲ **SANTA BARBARA**—JRC Telecommunications

▲ **SANTA CLARA INDIAN RESERVATION**—US Cable of New Mexico

▲ **SANTA FE**—TCI Cablevision of Santa Fe

SANTA FE—See also LOS ALAMOS, NM

SANTA FE COUNTY—See EDGEWOOD, NM

SANTE FE COUNTY—See also LOS ALAMOS, NM

SANTA FE COUNTY—See also SANTA FE, NM

SANTA FE COUNTY (northern portion)—See also SANTA CLARA INDIAN RESERVATION, NM

▲ **SANTA ROSA**—Classic Cable

SANTA TERESA—See EL PASO, TX

▲ **SHIPROCK**—Navajo Communications

SIERRA COUNTY (unincorporated areas)—See TRUTH OR CONSEQUENCES, NM

▲ **SILVER CITY**—Century New Mexico Cable TV Corp.

▲ **SOCORRO**—Jones Spacelink Ltd.

SOUTH VALLEY—See ALBUQUERQUE, NM

▲ **SPRINGER**—TCI Cablevision of New Mexico Inc.

SUNLAND PARK—See EL PASO, TX

SUNLAND PARK II—See EL PASO, TX

TALPA—See TAOS, NM

▲ **TAOS**—Century Communications

TAOS COUNTY (portions)—See RED RIVER, NM

▲ **TATUM**—Classic Cable

TAYLOR RANCH—See ALBUQUERQUE, NM

TESUQUE—See LOS ALAMOS, NM

TESUQUE PUEBLO—See LOS ALAMOS, NM

TEXICO—See CLOVIS, NM

▲ **THOREAU**—Jones Spacelink

▲ **TIERRA AMARILLA**—US Cable of New Mexico

▲ **TIJERAS**—Jones Intercable

▲ **TOHATCHI**—Navajo Communications

▲ **TRUTH OR CONSEQUENCES**—Scott Cable Communications Inc.

▲ **TUCUMCARI**—Century New Mexico Cable TV Corp.

TULAROSA—See ALAMOGORDO, NM

▲ **TWIN FORKS**—Twin Forks Cable TV

TYRONE—See SILVER CITY, NM

VADO—See EL PASO, TX

VALENCIA COUNTY (portions)—See BELEN, NM

VALENCIA COUNTY (portions)—See also GRANTS, NM

▲ **VAUGHN**—Classic Cable

▲ **WAGON MOUND**—Rocky Mountain Cable Systems

WHITE ROCK—See LOS ALAMOS, NM

▲ **WHITE SANDS**—Mesilla Valley Cable Co.

WILLIAMSBURG—See TRUTH OR CONSEQUENCES, NM

▲ **YAH-TA-HEY**—NCC Systems Inc.

▲ **ZUNI**—Navajo Communications

NEW YORK

ADAMS—See ADAMS (town), NY

▲ **ADAMS (town)**—Time Warner Cable

ADAMS (village)—See ADAMS (town), NY

ADAMS CENTER—See ADAMS (town), NY

ADDISON (town)—See CORNING, NY

ADDISON (village)—See CORNING, NY

AFTON—See BAINBRIDGE, NY

AFTON (southwestern portion)—See also WINDSOR (town), NY

AFTON (town)—See BAINBRIDGE, NY

AIRMONT (village)—See ROCKLAND, NY

AKRON (village)—See ALDEN, NY

ALABAMA (town)—See STAFFORD, NY

▲ **ALBANY**—Time Warner Entertainment Co.

▲ **ALBION**—Time Warner Cable

ALBION (village)—See ALBION, NY

▲ **ALDEN**—Time Warner Cable

ALEXANDER (town)—See STAFFORD, NY

ALEXANDER (village)—See STAFFORD, NY

ALEXANDRIA (town)—See ALEXANDRIA BAY, NY

ALEXANDRIA (town)—See also CHAUMONT, NY

▲ **ALEXANDRIA BAY**—Castle Cable TV

▲ **ALFRED**—Alfred Cable System Inc.

ALLEGANY (town)—See OLEAN, NY

ALLEGANY (village)—See OLEAN, NY

▲ **ALLENTOWN**—TW Fanch 2

ALMA—See ALLENTOWN, NY

ALMOND (town)—See ALFRED, NY

▲ **ALPINE**—Haefele TV Inc.

ALPLAUS—See SARATOGA SPRINGS, NY

ALTAMONT—See ALBANY, NY

ALTAMONT (town)—See SARANAC LAKE (resort), NY

ALTONA—See CHAMPLAIN, NY

AMAGANSETT—See EAST HAMPTON, NY

AMENIA (town)—See DOVER PLAINS, NY

AMHERST—See BUFFALO (suburbs), NY

AMITY (town)—See WELLSVILLE, NY

AMITYVILLE—See WOODBURY (Nassau County), NY

▲ **AMSTERDAM**—Time Warner Cable

ANCRAM (town)—See CHATHAM, NY

▲ **ANDES**—MTC Cable

ANDOVER (town)—See WELLSVILLE, NY

ANDOVER (village)—See WELLSVILLE, NY

▲ **ANGELICA**—TW Fanch 2

ANGOLA—See EVANS (town), NY

ANNSVILLE—See ROME, NY

ANTWERP (town)—See CARTHAGE, NY

ANTWERP (village)—See CARTHAGE, NY

APALACHIN—See BINGHAMTON, NY

APULIA STATION—See CUYLER, NY

AQUEBOGUE—See RIVERHEAD, NY

ARCADE (town)—See SPRINGVILLE (village), NY

ARCADE (village)—See SPRINGVILLE (village), NY

ARCADIA (town)—See GENEVA, NY

ARDSLEY—See MAMARONECK, NY

▲ **ARGYLE**—Harron Communications

ARKPORT—See HORNELL, NY

ARKVILLE—See MARGARETVILLE, NY

ARKWRIGHT—See DUNKIRK, NY

ARMONK—See MOUNT KISCO, NY

ASHAROKEN—See WOODBURY (Nassau County), NY

ASHLAND (town-Chemung County)—See ELMIRA, NY

ASHLAND (town-Greene County)—See CATSKILL, NY

ASTORIA—See NEW YORK, NY

ATHENS (town)—See CATSKILL, NY

ATHENS (village)—See CATSKILL, NY

ATLANTIC BEACH—See WOODBURY (Nassau County), NY

ATTICA (town)—See STAFFORD, NY

ATTICA (village)—See STAFFORD, NY

AU SABLE (town)—See PLATTSBURGH (town), NY

▲ **AUBURN**—Auburn Cablevision Inc.

AUBURNDALE—See NEW YORK, NY

▲ **AUGUSTA**—Phoenix Cablevision

AURELIUS (town)—See GENEVA, NY

AURORA (Cayuga County)—See GENEVA, NY

AURORA TWP.—See BUFFALO (suburbs), NY

AUSTERLITZ (town)—See CHATHAM, NY

AVERILL PARK—See RENSSELAER, NY

▲ **AVOCA**—TW Fanch 2

AVON (town)—See STAFFORD, NY

AVON (village)—See STAFFORD, NY

BABYLON (village)—See ISLIP, NY

BABYLON TWP.—See WOODBURY (Nassau County), NY

▲ **BAINBRIDGE**—Time Warner Cable

▲ **BALDWINSVILLE**—Time Warner Cable

BALLSTON—See SARATOGA SPRINGS, NY

BALLSTON LAKE—See SARATOGA SPRINGS, NY

BALLSTON SPA (portions)—See SARATOGA SPRINGS, NY

BANGOR—See MALONE, NY

BARKER—See LANCASTER (town), NY

BARNEVELD (village)—See UTICA, NY

BARRINGTON—See HAMMONDSPORT, NY

BARRYVILLE—See TUSTEN, NY

BARTON (town)—See TIOGA, NY

BARTON (town)—See also SAYRE, PA

BATAVIA—See STAFFORD, NY

BATAVIA (town)—See STAFFORD, NY

▲ **BATH**—Bath TV Service Corp.

BATH (town)—See BATH, NY

BATH (village)—See BATH, NY

▲ **BATTENKILL**—Time Warner Cable

BAXTER ESTATES—See WOODBURY (Nassau County), NY

BAY POINT—See RIVERHEAD, NY

BAY RIDGE—See NEW YORK, NY

BAYSIDE—See NEW YORK, NY

BAYVILLE—See WOODBURY (Nassau County), NY

BEACON—See OSSINING, NY

BEDFORD—See MOUNT KISCO, NY

BEDFORD—See also OSSINING, NY

BEDFORD HILLS—See MOUNT KISCO, NY

BEECHHURST—See NEW YORK, NY

BEEKMAN—See CARMEL, NY

BEEKMAN (town)—See CARMEL, NY

▲ **BEEKMANTOWN**—Falcon First Inc.

BELFAST—See ANGELICA, NY

BELLE TERRE—See SUFFOLK COUNTY, NY

BELLEROSE (Nassau County)—See WOODBURY (Nassau County), NY

BELLEROSE (Queens County)—See NEW YORK, NY

BELLEVILLE—See ADAMS (town), NY

BELLPORT (village)—See BROOKHAVEN, NY

BELMONT (village)—See WELLSVILLE, NY

BEMUS POINT (village)—See JAMESTOWN, NY

BENNINGTON—See ALBION, NY

BENTON—See PENN YAN, NY

BERGEN (town)—See STAFFORD, NY

BERGEN (village)—See STAFFORD, NY

▲ **BERKSHIRE**—Haefele TV Inc.

BERKSHIRE (town)—See BERKSHIRE, NY

▲ **BERLIN (town)**—Hometown TV

BERNE (town)—See ALBANY, NY

Bethany (town)—See STAFFORD, NY

BETHEL (town)—See SULLIVAN COUNTY, NY

BETHLEHEM—See RENSSELAER, NY

BETHLEHEM (town)—See CATSKILL, NY

BIG FLATS—See ELMIRA, NY

Big Indian—See PINE HILL, NY

▲ **BINGHAMTON**—Time Warner Cable

BINGHAMTON (town)—See BINGHAMTON, NY

BLACK BROOK (town)—See JAY, NY

BLACK RIVER (village)—See WATERTOWN, NY

BLASDELL—See BUFFALO (suburbs), NY

BLOOMING GROVE (town)—See WASHINGTONVILLE, NY

BLOOMINGBURG (village)—See MIDDLETOWN (Orange County), NY

BLOOMINGDALE—See SARANAC LAKE (resort), NY

BLOOMINGTON—See ROSENDALE, NY

▲ **BLOOMVILLE**—Bloomville Cable

BLUE MOUNTAIN LAKE—See INDIAN LAKE (town), NY

BLUE POINT—See BROOKHAVEN, NY

BOERUM HILL—See NEW YORK, NY

BOICEVILLE—See OLIVE, NY

▲ **BOLIVAR**—Cablecomm

BOLTON—See GLENS FALLS, NY

BOMBAY—See MALONE, NY

BOMBAY (town)—See MALONE, NY

BOONVILLE—See LEYDEN, NY

BOSTON—See BUFFALO (suburbs), NY

BOWNE PARK—See NEW YORK, NY

BRADFORD (town)—See ORANGE (town), NY

▲ **BRANCHPORT**—Adelphia Cable

BRANT—See EVANS (town), NY

BRANT (town)—See EVANS (town), NY

BRASHER—See MASSENA, NY

BREWSTER—See CARMEL, NY

BRIARCLIFF MANOR—See OSSINING, NY

BRIDGEHAMPTON—See RIVERHEAD, NY

KINDERHOOK (village)—See RENSSELAER, NY

KINGS POINT—See WOODBURY (Nassau County), NY

KINGSBURY (town)—See QUEENSBURY, NY

▲ **KINGSTON**—Time Warner

KINGSTON (town)—See KINGSTON, NY

KIRKLAND (town)—See UTICA, NY

KIRKWOOD—See BINGHAMTON, NY

KIRKWOOD (portions)—See also WINDSOR (town), NY

KNOX (town)—See ALBANY, NY

KNOXBORO—See AUGUSTA, NY

KORTRIGHT—See BLOOMVILLE, NY

KORTRIGHT—See also STAMFORD, NY

LA FAYETTE—See SYRACUSE, NY (Time Warner Cable)

LA GRANGE—See OSSINING, NY

LA GRANGE (town)—See POUGHKEEPSIE, NY

LACKAWANNA—See BUFFALO (suburbs), NY

LACONA—See MEXICO (village), NY

LAKE GEORGE (town)—See GLENS FALLS, NY

LAKE GEORGE (village)—See GLENS FALLS, NY

LAKE GROVE (village)—See BROOKHAVEN, NY

LAKE LUZERNE (town)—See QUEENSBURY, NY

LAKE PLACID—See SARANAC LAKE (resort), NY

LAKE PLEASANT—See WELLS, NY

LAKE SUCCESS (village)—See WOODBURY (Nassau County), NY

LAKEWOOD (village)—See JAMESTOWN, NY

▲ **LANCASTER (town)**—Adelphia Cable

LANCASTER (village)—See LANCASTER (town), NY

LANSING (town)—See ITHACA, NY

LANSING (village)—See ITHACA, NY

LARCHMONT (village)—See MAMARONECK, NY

LATTINGTOWN—See WOODBURY (Nassau County), NY

LAUREL—See RIVERHEAD, NY

LAUREL HOLLOW—See WOODBURY (Nassau County), NY

LAURELTON—See NEW YORK, NY

LAURENS (town)—See ONEONTA, NY

LAURENS (village)—See ONEONTA, NY

LAVA—See TUSTEN, NY

LAWRENCE—See MASSENA, NY

LAWRENCE (village)—See LYNBROOK, NY

LAWTON (town)—See SPRINGVILLE (village), NY

LAZY POINT—See EAST HAMPTON, NY

LE RAY (town)—See CARTHAGE, NY

LE RAY TWP.—See WATERTOWN, NY

LE ROY (town)—See STAFFORD, NY

LE ROY (village)—See STAFFORD, NY

LEBANON—See ILION, NY

LEDYARD—See GENEVA, NY

LEE—See ROME, NY

LEICESTER (town)—See STAFFORD, NY

LEICESTER (village)—See STAFFORD, NY

LENOX (town)—See ONEIDA, NY

LEONARDSVILLE—See BROOKFIELD, NY

LEWIS—See WESTPORT (village), NY

LEWISBORO—See NORTH SALEM, NY

LEWISTON (town)—See NIAGARA FALLS, NY

LEWISTON (village)—See NIAGARA FALLS, NY

LEXINGTON—See HUNTER (village), NY

▲ **LEYDEN**—TCI of New York Inc.

LIBERTY (town)—See SULLIVAN COUNTY, NY

LIBERTY (village)—See SULLIVAN COUNTY, NY

LIMA (town)—See STAFFORD, NY

LIMA (village)—See STAFFORD, NY

▲ **LIMESTONE**—El Mar Communications

LINCOLN (town)—See ONEIDA, NY

LINDEN HILL—See NEW YORK, NY

LINDENHURST—See WOODBURY (Nassau County), NY

▲ **LINDLEY (town)**—TW Fanch 2

LISBON—See OGDENSBURG, NY

LISLE (town)—See WHITNEY POINT (village), NY

LISLE (village)—See WHITNEY POINT (village), NY

LITCHFIELD (town)—See ILION, NY

LITTLE FALLS—See ILION, NY

LITTLE FALLS (town)—See ILION, NY

LITTLE GENESEE—See BOLIVAR, NY

LITTLE NECK—See NEW YORK, NY

LITTLE VALLEY (town)—See SALAMANCA, NY

LITTLE VALLEY (village)—See SALAMANCA, NY

LIVERPOOL—See SYRACUSE, NY (Time Warner Cable)

LIVINGSTON (town)—See CATSKILL, NY

LIVINGSTON MANOR (town)—See SULLIVAN COUNTY, NY

LIVONIA (town)—See STAFFORD, NY

LIVONIA (village)—See STAFFORD, NY

LLOYD—See OSSINING, NY

LLOYD HARBOR—See WOODBURY (Nassau County), NY

LOCKE TWP.—See MORAVIA, NY

LOCKPORT—See LANCASTER (town), NY

LOCKPORT (town)—See LANCASTER (town), NY

LODI (town)—See GENEVA, NY

LODI (village)—See GENEVA, NY

LONG BEACH—See WOODBURY (Nassau County), NY

LONG ISLAND CITY—See NEW YORK, NY

▲ **LONG LAKE**—Falcon First Inc.

LOUISVILLE—See MASSENA, NY

▲ **LOWVILLE**—TCI of New York Inc.

LUMBERLAND—See SULLIVAN COUNTY, NY

LYME (town)—See CHAUMONT, NY

▲ **LYNBROOK**—A-R Cable Services-NY Inc.

LYNDONVILLE—See ALBION, NY

LYONS (town)—See GENEVA, NY

LYONS (village)—See GENEVA, NY

LYONS FALLS—See LEYDEN, NY

LYONSDALE—See LEYDEN, NY

LYSANDER (town)—See BALDWINSVILLE, NY

LYSANDER (town)—See also SYRACUSE, NY (Time Warner Cable)

MACEDON (town)—See GENEVA, NY

MACEDON (village)—See GENEVA, NY

MACHIAS (town)—See SPRINGVILLE (village), NY

MADISON—See ILION, NY

MADISON (village)—See ORISKANY FALLS, NY

MADISON TWP.—See ORISKANY FALLS, NY

MADRID (town)—See POTSDAM, NY

MAHOPAC—See CARMEL, NY

MAINE—See BINGHAMTON, NY

MALBA—See NEW YORK, NY

▲ **MALONE**—Time Warner Cable

MALONE (town)—See MALONE, NY

MALONE (village)—See MALONE, NY

MALTA—See SARATOGA SPRINGS, NY

MALVERNE—See WOODBURY (Nassau County), NY

MAMAKATING—See ELLENVILLE, NY

MAMAKATING—See also SULLIVAN COUNTY, NY

MAMAKATING (town)—See MIDDLETOWN (Orange County), NY

▲ **MAMARONECK**—Cablevision

MAMARONECK (town)—See MAMARONECK, NY

MAMARONECK (village)—See MAMARONECK, NY

MANCHESTER (town)—See GENEVA, NY

MANCHESTER (village)—See GENEVA, NY

Mandana—See AUBURN, NY

MANHATTAN—See NEW YORK, NY

MANLIUS—See SYRACUSE, NY (Time Warner Cable)

MANNSVILLE—See ADAMS (town), NY

MANORHAVEN—See WOODBURY (Nassau County), NY

MANORVILLE—See BROOKHAVEN, NY

MANSFIELD (town)—See SPRINGVILLE (village), NY

MAPLE SPRINGS—See JAMESTOWN, NY

MARATHON (town)—See WHITNEY POINT (village), NY

MARATHON (village)—See WHITNEY POINT (village), NY

MARBLETOWN (Ulster County)—See KINGSTON, NY

MARBLETOWN (Ulster County)—See also ROSENDALE, NY

MARCELLUS—See SYRACUSE, NY (Time Warner Cable)

MARCY—See ROME, NY

MARCY (town)—See UTICA, NY

▲ **MARGARETVILLE**—MTC Cable

MARIAVILLE—See PRINCETOWN (town), NY

MARILLA (town)—See ALDEN, NY

MARION (town)—See GENEVA, NY

MARLBORO—See NEWBURGH, NY

MARLBORO—See also OSSINING, NY

MARSHALL TWP.—See ORISKANY FALLS, NY

MARTINSBURG—See GREIG, NY

MARYLAND—See ONEONTA, NY

MASONVILLE—See SIDNEY, NY

MASPETH—See NEW YORK, NY

MASSAPEQUA PARK—See WOODBURY (Nassau County), NY

▲ **MASSENA**—Time Warner Cable

MASSENA (town)—See MASSENA, NY

MASSENA (village)—See MASSENA, NY

MASTIC—See BROOKHAVEN, NY

MASTIC BEACH—See BROOKHAVEN, NY

MATINECOCK—See WOODBURY (Nassau County), NY

MATTITUCK—See RIVERHEAD, NY

MAYBROOK (village)—See WALDEN, NY

MAYFIELD—See AMSTERDAM, NY

MAYFIELD (town)—See JOHNSTOWN (city), NY

MAYFIELD (village)—See JOHNSTOWN (city), NY

MAYVILLE—See WESTFIELD, NY

▲ **McDONOUGH**—Haefele TV Inc.

McGRAW—See CORTLAND, NY

MECHANICVILLE—See TROY, NY

MECKLENBURG—See ENFIELD, NY

MEDFORD—See BROOKHAVEN, NY

MEDINA (village)—See ALBION, NY

MEDUSA—See DURHAM, NY

MELVILLE—See WOODBURY (Nassau County), NY

MENANDS—See ALBANY, NY

MENDON (town)—See STAFFORD, NY

MENTZ (town)—See SYRACUSE, NY (Time Warner Cable)

MEREDITH—See DELHI, NY

MERIDIAN—See SYRACUSE, NY (Time Warner Cable)

MERRICK (southern portion)—See WOODBURY (Nassau County), NY

MEXICO (town)—See MEXICO (village), NY

▲ **MEXICO (village)**—Time Warner Cable

MIDDLE GRANVILLE—See GRANVILLE, NY

MIDDLE VILLAGE—See NEW YORK, NY

MIDDLEBURGH (town)—See COBLESKILL (town), NY

MIDDLEBURGH (village)—See COBLESKILL (town), NY

MIDDLEBURY—See STAFFORD, NY

MIDDLEFIELD—See COOPERSTOWN, NY

MIDDLEPORT (village)—See STAFFORD, NY

MIDDLESEX—See GORHAM, NY

MIDDLETOWN (Delaware County)—See PINE HILL, NY

▲ **MIDDLETOWN (Orange County)**—Time Warner Cable

MIDDLEVILLE (village)—See UTICA, NY

MILFORD (town)—See ONEONTA, NY

MILFORD (village)—See ONEONTA, NY

MILL NECK—See WOODBURY (Nassau County), NY

MILLBROOK—See DOVER PLAINS, NY

MILLERTON—See DOVER PLAINS, NY

MILLPORT—See ELMIRA, NY

MILO—See PENN YAN, NY

MILTON—See SARATOGA SPRINGS, NY

MINA—See CLYMER, NY

MINDEN (town)—See CANAJOHARIE, NY

MINEOLA—See WOODBURY (Nassau County), NY

MINERVA—See MINERVA (town), NY

▲ **MINERVA (town)**—Chain Lakes Cablevision

MINETTO—See OSWEGO, NY

▲ **MINISINK**—Cable TV of Tri-State Inc.

MINISINK FORD—See TUSTEN, NY

MINOA—See SYRACUSE, NY (Time Warner Cable)

MOHAWK—See ILION, NY

MOHAWK (town)—See AMSTERDAM, NY

MOIRA—See MALONE, NY

MONROE (town)—See OSSINING, NY

MONROE (village)—See OSSINING, NY

MONTAUK—See EAST HAMPTON, NY

MONTEBELLO—See ROCKLAND, NY

MONTGOMERY (town)—See WALDEN, NY

MONTGOMERY (village)—See WALDEN, NY

MONTICELLO (village)—See SULLIVAN COUNTY, NY

MONTOUR—See GENEVA, NY

MONTOUR (town)—See CORNING, NY

MONTOUR FALLS—See GENEVA, NY

MONTOUR FALLS (village)—See CORNING, NY

MONTOUR FALLS (village)—See also GENEVA, NY

MOOERS—See CHAMPLAIN, NY

MOOERS (village)—See CHAMPLAIN, NY

▲ **MORAVIA**—Southern Cayuga County Cablevision

MORAVIA (village)—See MORAVIA, NY

MOREAU (town)—See QUEENSBURY, NY

MORIAH (town)—See PORT HENRY (village), NY

MORICHES—See BROOKHAVEN, NY

▲ **MORRIS**—Time Warner Cable

MORRIS (town)—See MORRIS, NY

MORRIS (town)—See also ONEONTA, NY

MORRIS (village)—See ONEONTA, NY

MORRISTOWN (town)—See OGDENSBURG, NY

MORRISTOWN (village)—See OGDENSBURG, NY

MORRISVILLE—See ILION, NY

MOUNT HOPE (town)—See MIDDLETOWN (Orange County), NY

▲ **MOUNT KISCO**—A-R Cable Services-NY Inc.

MOUNT MORRIS (town)—See STAFFORD, NY

MOUNT MORRIS (village)—See STAFFORD, NY

MOUNT PLEASANT (Ulster County)—See PHOENICIA, NY

MOUNT PLEASANT (Westchester County)—See OSSINING, NY

▲ **MOUNT TREMPER**—Time Warner Cable

MOUNT UPTON—See GUILFORD (town), NY

▲ **MOUNT VERNON**—Paragon Cable

MUNNSVILLE (village)—See ONEIDA, NY

MUNSEY PARK (village)—See WOODBURY (Nassau County), NY

MURRAY (town)—See ROCHESTER, NY

MURRAY HILL—See NEW YORK, NY

MUTTONTOWN—See WOODBURY (Nassau County), NY

NANTICOKE—See BINGHAMTON, NY

NAPANOCH—See ELLENVILLE, NY

NAPEAQUE—See EAST HAMPTON, NY

▲ **NAPLES**—TW Fanch 2

NARROWSBURG—See TUSTEN, NY

NASSAU (town)—See RENSSELAER, NY

NASSAU (village)—See RENSSELAER, NY

NASSAU SHORES—See LYNBROOK, NY

NELLISTON—See CANAJOHARIE, NY

NELSONVILLE—See OSSINING, NY

NEVERSINK (town)—See SULLIVAN COUNTY, NY

NEW ALBION (town)—See SPRINGVILLE (village), NY

NEW BALTIMORE—See CATSKILL, NY

▲ **NEW BERLIN**—Time Warner Cable

NEW BERLIN (village)—See NEW BERLIN, NY

NEW BREMEN—See CARTHAGE, NY

NEW CASTLE—See OSSINING, NY

NEW HARTFORD (town)—See UTICA, NY

NEW HARTFORD (village)—See UTICA, NY

NEW HAVEN—See FULTON, NY

NEW HEMPSTEAD—See ROCKLAND, NY

NEW HYDE PARK—See WOODBURY (Nassau County), NY

NEW LEBANON (town)—See CHATHAM, NY

NEW LISBON—See BURLINGTON (town), NY

▲ **NEW PALTZ**—Time Warner Cable

NEW PALTZ (village)—See NEW PALTZ, NY

NEW ROCHELLE—See MAMARONECK, NY

NEW SCOTLAND—See RENSSELAER, NY

NEW WINDSOR—See NEWBURGH, NY

▲ **NEW YORK**—Time Warner Cable of New York City/QUICS

NEW YORK MILLS (village)—See UTICA, NY

NEWARK (village)—See GENEVA, NY

NEWARK VALLEY—See BINGHAMTON, NY

▲ **NEWARK VALLEY (town)**—Time Warner Binghamton

NEWARK VALLEY (town)—See also BERKSHIRE, NY

NEWARK VALLEY (village)—See NEWARK VALLEY (town), NY

▲ **NEWBURGH**—Time Warner Cable

NEWBURGH (town)—See NEWBURGH, NY

NEWBURGH (town)—See also WALDEN, NY

▲ **NEWCOMB**—Chain Lakes Cablevision

NEWFANE (town)—See LANCASTER (town), NY

NEWFIELD—See ITHACA, NY

NEWPORT (town)—See UTICA, NY

NEWPORT (village)—See UTICA, NY

NEWSTEAD (town)—See ALDEN, NY

NIAGARA (town)—See NIAGARA FALLS, NY

▲ **NIAGARA FALLS**—Adelphia

NICHOLS (town)—See SAYRE, PA

NISKAYUNA—See SCHENECTADY, NY

NISSEQUOGUE—See SUFFOLK COUNTY, NY

NORFOLK—See POTSDAM, NY

NORFOLK (northeastern portion)—See also MASSENA, NY

NORTH BRANCH—See SULLIVAN COUNTY, NY

NORTH CASTLE—See MAMARONECK, NY

NORTH CASTLE—See also MOUNT KISCO, NY

NORTH CLYMER—See CLYMER, NY

NORTH COLLINS (town)—See SPRINGVILLE (village), NY

NORTH COLLINS (village)—See SPRINGVILLE (village), NY

NORTH CREEK—See JOHNSBURG (town), NY

NORTH EAST (town)—See DOVER PLAINS, NY

NORTH ELBA—See SARANAC LAKE (resort), NY

NORTH GRANVILLE—See GRANVILLE, NY

NORTH GREENBUSH—See RENSSELAER, NY

NORTH HARMONY (town)—See JAMESTOWN, NY

NORTH HARMONY (town)—See also WESTFIELD, NY

NORTH HAVEN—See RIVERHEAD, NY

NORTH HEMPSTEAD—See WOODBURY (Nassau County), NY

NORTH HILLS (village)—See WOODBURY (Nassau County), NY

NORTH HOOSICK—See BENNINGTON, VT

NORTH HORNELL—See HORNELL, NY

NORTH NORWICH—See NORWICH, NY

NORTH PITCHER—See OTSELIC, NY

▲ **NORTH SALEM**—Cablevision Systems Corp.

NORTH SYRACUSE—See SYRACUSE, NY (Time Warner Cable)

NORTH TARRYTOWN—See OSSINING, NY

NORTH TONAWANDA—See BUFFALO (suburbs), NY

NORTHAMPTON (Fulton County)—See NORTHVILLE, NY

NORTHAMPTON (Suffolk County)—See RIVERHEAD, NY

NORTHPORT—See WOODBURY (Nassau County), NY

NORTHUMBERLAND (town)—See BATTENKILL, NY

▲ **NORTHVILLE**—Gateway Cablevision Corp.

▲ **NORWICH**—Century Communications

NORWICH (village)—See NORWICH, NY

NORWOOD—See POTSDAM, NY

NOYAC—See RIVERHEAD, NY

NUNDA (town)—See STAFFORD, NY

NUNDA (village)—See STAFFORD, NY

NYACK—See ROCKLAND, NY

OAK HILL—See DURHAM, NY

OAKFIELD (town)—See STAFFORD, NY

OAKFIELD (village)—See STAFFORD, NY

OAKLAND GARDENS—See NEW YORK, NY

ODESSA (village)—See CORNING, NY

ODESSA (village)—See also GENEVA, NY

OGDEN (town)—See ROCHESTER, NY

▲ **OGDENSBURG**—Time Warner Cable

OLD BROOKVILLE—See WOODBURY (Nassau County), NY

OLD FIELD—See SUFFOLK COUNTY, NY

▲ **OLD FORGE**—Harron Communications

OLD WESTBURY—See WOODBURY (Nassau County), NY

▲ **OLEAN**—Adelphia Cable

OLEAN (town)—See OLEAN, NY

▲ **OLIVE**—Time Warner Cable

OLIVEBRIDGE—See OLIVE, NY

Oliverea—See PINE HILL, NY

▲ **ONEIDA**—Time Warner Cable

ONEIDA CASTLE (village)—See ONEIDA, NY

▲ **ONEONTA**—Time Warner Cable

ONEONTA (town)—See ONEONTA, NY

ONONDAGA—See SYRACUSE, NY (Time Warner Cable)

ONTARIO (town)—See GENEVA, NY

▲ **ORANGE (town)**—Haefele TV Inc.

ORANGETOWN (town)—See ROCKLAND, NY

ORANGEVILLE (town)—See ALDEN, NY

ORCHARD PARK (town)—See LANCASTER (town), NY

ORCHARD PARK (village)—See LANCASTER (town), NY

ORIENT—See RIVERHEAD, NY

ORISKANY—See UTICA, NY

▲ **ORISKANY FALLS**—NU View TV Inc.

ORLEANS—See CHAUMONT, NY

▲ **OSSINING**—MediaOne

OSSINING (town)—See OSSINING, NY

OSSINING (village)—See OSSINING, NY

OSWEGATCHIE—See OGDENSBURG, NY

▲ **OSWEGO**—Time Warner Cable

OSWEGO (town)—See OSWEGO, NY

OTEGO (town)—See ONEONTA, NY

OTEGO (village)—See ONEONTA, NY

OTISCO (town)—See SYRACUSE, NY (Time Warner Cable)

OTISVILLE (village)—See MIDDLETOWN (Orange County), NY

OTSEGO—See COOPERSTOWN, NY

▲ **OTSELIC**—Milestone Communications LP

OTSELIC (town)—See OTSELIC, NY

OVID (town)—See GENEVA, NY

OVID (village)—See GENEVA, NY

TILLSON—See ROSENDALE, NY

▲ **TIOGA**—Haefele TV Inc.

TIOGA—See also OWEGO (village), NY

TIOGA (town)—See TIOGA, NY

TIVOLI—See RHINEBECK (town), NY

TIVOLI (village)—See KINGSTON, NY

TOMPKINS (town)—See HANCOCK, NY

TONAWANDA—See BUFFALO (suburbs), NY

TONAWANDA (town)—See BUFFALO (suburbs), NY

TRENTON (town)—See UTICA, NY

Triangle—See WHITNEY POINT (village), NY

TRIANGLE (town)—See WHITNEY POINT (village), NY

▲ **TROUPSBURG**—TW Fanch 2

▲ **TROY**—Time Warner Cable

TRUMANSBURG (village)—See ITHACA, NY

TRUXTON (town)—See CUYLER, NY

TUCKAHOE—See MAMARONECK, NY

TULLY—See SYRACUSE, NY (Time Warner Cable)

TULLY (town)—See CUYLER, NY

TUPPER LAKE—See SARANAC LAKE (resort), NY

▲ **TURIN (town)**—Turin Cable TV

TUSCARORA (town)—See ELMIRA, NY

▲ **TUSTEN**—Time Warner Cable

TUXEDO—See RAMAPO, NY

Tuxedo Park—See RAMAPO, NY

TYRONE—See HAMMONDSPORT, NY

ULSTER (town)—See KINGSTON, NY

ULYSSES (town)—See ITHACA, NY

UNADILLA (town)—See SIDNEY, NY

UNADILLA (village)—See SIDNEY, NY

UNION—See BINGHAMTON, NY

UNION SPRINGS—See GENEVA, NY

UNION VALE (town)—See DOVER PLAINS, NY

UNIONVILLE—See MINISINK, NY

UPPER BROOKVILLE—See WOODBURY (Nassau County), NY

UPPER NYACK—See ROCKLAND, NY

URBANA—See HAMMONDSPORT, NY

▲ **UTICA**—Harron Cable Television

UTOPIA—See NEW YORK, NY

VALATIE—See RENSSELAER, NY

VALLEY FALLS (village)—See TROY, NY

VALLEY STREAM—See WOODBURY (Nassau County), NY

VALOIS—See BURDETT, NY

VAN BUREN—See SYRACUSE, NY (Time Warner Cable)

VAN BUREN (town)—See BALDWINSVILLE, NY

VAN ETTEN (village)—See SPENCER, NY

VARICK (town)—See GENEVA, NY

VERMONTVILLE—See SARANAC LAKE (resort), NY

VERNON (town)—See ONEIDA, NY

VERNON (village)—See ONEIDA, NY

VERONA (town)—See ONEIDA, NY

VESTAL—See BINGHAMTON, NY

VETERAN (Chemung County)—See ELMIRA, NY

VICTOR (town)—See GENEVA, NY

VICTOR (village)—See GENEVA, NY

VICTORY MILLS (village)—See BATTENKILL, NY

VIENNA—See CAMDEN, NY

VILLAGE OF THE BRANCH—See SUFFOLK COUNTY, NY

Villenova (town)—See SOUTH DAYTON (village), NY

VIRGIL (town)—See BERKSHIRE, NY

VOLNEY—See FULTON, NY

VOORHEESVILLE—See RENSSELAER, NY

WADDINGTON (town)—See OGDENSBURG, NY

WADDINGTON (village)—See OGDENSBURG, NY

WADHAMS—See WESTPORT (village), NY

WADING RIVER—See RIVERHEAD, NY

WAINSCOT—See EAST HAMPTON, NY

▲ **WALDEN**—Time Warner Cable

WALDEN (village)—See WALDEN, NY

WALES—See BUFFALO (suburbs), NY

▲ **WALLACE**—TW Fanch 2

WALLKILL—See MIDDLETOWN (Orange County), NY

WALLKILL (town)—See MIDDLETOWN (Orange County), NY

WALTON (town)—See WALTON (village), NY

▲ **WALTON (village)**—Time Warner Cable

WALWORTH (town)—See GENEVA, NY

WAMPSVILLE (village)—See ONEIDA, NY

WAPPINGER (town)—See OSSINING, NY

WAPPINGERS FALLS—See OSSINING, NY

WARRENSBURG (town)—See GLENS FALLS, NY

WARSAW (town)—See WARSAW (village), NY

▲ **WARSAW (village)**—Warsaw Television Cable Corp.

▲ **WARWICK**—Cablevision of Warwick

WARWICK (village)—See WARWICK, NY

WARWICK TWP.—See WARWICK, NY

WASHINGTON (town)—See DOVER PLAINS, NY

▲ **WASHINGTONVILLE**—Time Warner Cable

WASHINGTONVILLE (village)—See WASHINGTONVILLE, NY

WATER MILL—See RIVERHEAD, NY

WATERFORD (town)—See TROY, NY

WATERFORD (village)—See TROY, NY

WATERLOO (town)—See GENEVA, NY

WATERLOO (village)—See GENEVA, NY

▲ **WATERTOWN**—Time Warner Cable

WATERTOWN TWP.—See WATERTOWN, NY

WATERVILLE—See ORISKANY FALLS, NY

WATERVLIET—See ALBANY, NY

WATKINS GLEN—See GENEVA, NY

WATKINS GLEN (village)—See CORNING, NY

WATSON—See GREIG, NY

WAVERLY (village)—See SAYRE, PA

WAWARSING—See ELLENVILLE, NY

WAWAYANDA (town)—See MIDDLETOWN (Orange County), NY

WAYLAND—See DANSVILLE, NY

WAYNE—See HAMMONDSPORT, NY

WEBSTER (town)—See ROCHESTER, NY

WEBSTER (village)—See ROCHESTER, NY

WEEDSPORT—See SYRACUSE, NY (Time Warner Cable)

▲ **WELLS**—Hamilton County Cable TV Inc.

WELLSBURG—See ELMIRA, NY

▲ **WELLSVILLE**—Adelphia

WELLSVILLE (town)—See WELLSVILLE, NY

WELLSVILLE (village)—See WELLSVILLE, NY

WESLEY HILLS—See ROCKLAND, NY

WEST BLOOMFIELD (town)—See STAFFORD, NY

WEST CARTHAGE—See CARTHAGE, NY

West Chazy—See CHAMPLAIN, NY

WEST CORNERS—See BINGHAMTON, NY

WEST HARRISON—See PORT CHESTER, NY

WEST HAVERSTRAW—See OSSINING, NY

WEST HURLEY—See WOODSTOCK (town), NY

WEST HURLEY—See also KINGSTON, NY

WEST LEYDEN—See LEYDEN, NY

WEST MONROE (town)—See CONSTANTIA (town), NY

WEST NYACK—See ROCKLAND, NY

WEST POINT—See HIGHLAND FALLS (village), NY

WEST POINT MILITARY ACADEMY—See HIGHLAND FALLS (village), NY

WEST SENECA—See BUFFALO (suburbs), NY

WEST SHOKAN—See OLIVE, NY

WEST SPARTA (town)—See DANSVILLE, NY

WEST TIANA—See RIVERHEAD, NY

WEST TURIN—See LEYDEN, NY

WEST VALLEY—See FRIENDSHIP, NY

WEST WINFIELD—See ILION, NY

WESTBROOKVILLE (village)—See PORT JERVIS, NY

WESTBURY—See WOODBURY (Nassau County), NY

WESTERLO—See CATSKILL, NY

WESTERN—See ROME, NY

▲ **WESTFIELD**—Adelphia Cable

WESTHAMPTON—See RIVERHEAD, NY

WESTHAMPTON BEACH—See RIVERHEAD, NY

WESTMORELAND—See UTICA, NY

WESTMORELAND—See also ROME, NY

WESTPORT (town)—See WESTPORT (village), NY

▲ **WESTPORT (village)**—Falcon First Inc.

WESTVILLE—See MALONE, NY

WHEATFIELD—See BUFFALO (suburbs), NY

WHEATLAND (town)—See STAFFORD, NY

WHEELER—See HAMMONDSPORT, NY

WHITE PLAINS—See MAMARONECK, NY

▲ **WHITEHALL (town)**—Time Warner Cable

WHITEHALL (village)—See WHITEHALL (town), NY

WHITESBORO (village)—See UTICA, NY

WHITESTONE—See NEW YORK, NY

WHITESTOWN—See UTICA, NY

WHITESTOWN—See also ROME, NY

▲ **WHITESVILLE**—Fitzpatrick Cable TV

▲ **WHITNEY POINT (village)**—Time Warner Cable

WILLIAMSBURG—See NEW YORK, NY

WILLIAMSON (town)—See GENEVA, NY

WILLIAMSVILLE—See BUFFALO (suburbs), NY

WILLING—See WELLSVILLE, NY

WILLISTON PARK—See WOODBURY (Nassau County), NY

WILLSBORO—See WILLSBORO (town), NY

▲ **WILLSBORO (town)**—Cable Communications of Willsboro

WILLSBORO BAY—See WILLSBORO (town), NY

WILLSBORO POINT—See WILLSBORO (town), NY

WILMINGTON (town)—See JAY, NY

WILNA—See CARTHAGE, NY

WILSON (town)—See NIAGARA FALLS, NY

WILSON (village)—See NIAGARA FALLS, NY

WILTON—See SARATOGA SPRINGS, NY

WINDHAM (town)—See CATSKILL, NY

WINDSOR (Broome County)—See CARBONDALE, PA

▲ **WINDSOR (town)**—Adams Cable

WINDSOR (village)—See WINDSOR (town), NY

WINDSOR TERRACE—See NEW YORK, NY

WINFIELD—See ILION, NY

WITTENBERG—See KINGSTON, NY

WOLCOTT (town)—See GENEVA, NY

WOLCOTT (village)—See GENEVA, NY

▲ **WOODBURY (Nassau County)**—Cablevision Systems Corp.

WOODBURY—See also OSSINING, NY

▲ **WOODHULL**—TW Fanch 2

Woodland—See PINE HILL, NY

▲ **WOODRIDGE**—Time Warner Cable

WOODSBURGH—See WOODBURY (Nassau County), NY

WOODSIDE—See NEW YORK, NY

▲ **WOODSTOCK (town)**—Time Warner

WORCESTER—See ONEONTA, NY

WURTSBORO—See SULLIVAN COUNTY, NY

WURTSBORO (village)—See MIDDLETOWN (Orange County), NY

WYOMING—See STAFFORD, NY

YAPHANK—See BROOKHAVEN, NY

YATES (town)—See ALBION, NY

▲ **YONKERS**—Cablevision of Westchester

YORK (town)—See STAFFORD, NY

YORKSHIRE (town)—See SPRINGVILLE (village), NY

▲ **YORKTOWN**—Cablevision of Yorktown

YORKVILLE (village)—See UTICA, NY

YOUNGSTOWN (village)—See NIAGARA FALLS, NY

YULAN—See TUSTEN, NY

NORTH CAROLINA

ABERDEEN—See SOUTHERN PINES, NC

ACME—See RURAL, NC

ADVANCE—See MOCKSVILLE, NC

▲ **AHOSKIE**—Adelphia Cable

ALAMANCE (village)—See BURLINGTON, NC

ALAMANCE COUNTY—See BURLINGTON, NC

ALAMANCE COUNTY (eastern portion)—See MEBANE, NC

▲ **ALBEMARLE**—Time Warner Cable

ALEXANDER COUNTY—See LINCOLNTON, NC

ALEXANDER MILLS—See FOREST CITY, NC

ALLEGHANY COUNTY (unincorporated areas)—See NORTH WILKESBORO, NC

ALLIANCE—See BAYBORO, NC

▲ **ANDERSON CREEK**—Charter Communications

▲ **ANDREWS**—Cable TV of Andrews

ANGIER—See BUIES CREEK, NC

ANSON COUNTY—See WADESBORO, NC

ANSON COUNTY (unincorporated areas)—See MORVEN, NC

APEX—See CARY, NC

ARCADIA—See DAVIDSON COUNTY, NC

▲ **ARCHDALE**—Time Warner Cable

ARLINGTON—See ELKIN, NC

ARMOUR—See RURAL, NC

▲ **ARROWHEAD BEACH**—Mediacom

ASH—See SHALLOTTE, NC

ASHE COUNTY—See WEST JEFFERSON, NC

ASHE COUNTY—See also BOONE, NC

ASHE COUNTY (unincorporated areas)—See ROAN FORK, NC

▲ **ASHEBORO**—Time Warner

▲ **ASHEVILLE**—InterMedia

ATLANTIC—See MOREHEAD CITY, NC

▲ **ATLANTIC BEACH**—Cablevision Industries Inc.

ATLANTIC BEACH—See also MOREHEAD CITY, NC

▲ **AULANDER**—FrontierVision

▲ **AURORA**—Time Warner Cable

AUTRYVILLE—See FAYETTEVILLE, NC

AVERY COUNTY—See BOONE, NC

AVON—See BUXTON, NC

AYDEN—See GREENVILLE, NC

AYDLETT—See CURRITUCK COUNTY (southern portion), NC

▲ **BAILEY**—FrontierVision

BAKERSVILLE—See SPRUCE PINE, NC

▲ **BALD HEAD ISLAND**—Southern Cable Communications

BANNER ELK—See BOONE, NC

BANNERTOWN—See DOBSON, NC

BARNARDSVILLE—See MARSHALL, NC

BAT CAVE—See FAIRFIELD MOUNTAIN, NC

▲ **BATH**—Red's TV Cable Inc.

BATTLEBORO—See ROCKY MOUNT, NC

▲ **BAYBORO**—Time Warner Cable

BEACON RIDGE COUNTRY CLUB—See PINEHURST, NC

BEARGRASS—See PARMELE, NC

BEARGRASS—See also PARMELE, NC

BEAUFORT—See MOREHEAD CITY, NC

BEAUFORT COUNTY—See WASHINGTON, NC

BEAUFORT COUNTY (portions)—See AURORA, NC

BEAUFORT COUNTY (unincorporated areas)—See BATH, NC

BEAVER CREEK—See WEST JEFFERSON, NC

BEECH MOUNTAIN—See BOONE, NC

▲ **BELHAVEN**—Belhaven Cable TV

BELHAVEN—See also SIDNEY, NC

▲ **BELMONT**—Time Warner Cable

BELWOOD—See SHELBY, NC

▲ **BENSON**—Charter Communications

BERMUDA RUN—See WINSTON-SALEM, NC

BERTIE COUNTY (central portion)—See WINDSOR, NC

BERTIE COUNTY (northern portion)—See AULANDER, NC

BERTIE COUNTY (portions)—See PLYMOUTH, NC

BERTIE COUNTY (portions)—See also RICH SQUARE, NC

BESSEMER CITY—See GASTONIA, NC

BETHANIA—See KING, NC

BETHEL—See PARMELE, NC

BETHLEHEM—See LINCOLNTON, NC

BEULAVILLE—See CHINQUAPIN, NC

BILTMORE FOREST—See ASHEVILLE, NC

BISCOE—See ASHEBORO, NC

BLACK CREEK—See WILSON, NC

▲ **BLACK MOUNTAIN**—Charter Communications Inc.

BLADEN COUNTY (portions)—See BLADENBORO, NC

BLADEN COUNTY (portions)—See also RURAL, NC

▲ **BLADENBORO**—Time Warner Cable

BLOWING ROCK—See BOONE, NC

BOILING SPRINGS—See SHELBY, NC

BOLIVIA—See SHALLOTTE, NC

BOLTON—See RURAL, NC

▲ **BOONE**—Helicon Cable Communications

BOONVILLE—See DOBSON, NC

BOSTIC—See ELLENBORO, NC

▲ **BREVARD**—Sylvan Valley CATV Co.

BRICKS—See WHITAKERS, NC

BRIDGETON—See NEW BERN, NC

BROADWAY—See SANFORD, NC

BROOKFORD—See HICKORY, NC

BRUNSWICK—See WHITEVILLE, NC

BRUNSWICK COUNTY (portions)—See RURAL, NC

BRUNSWICK COUNTY (unincorporated areas)—See SHALLOTTE, NC

▲ **BRYSON CITY**—Bryson City Cablevision Assoc. LP

BUCKHEAD—See RURAL, NC

▲ **BUIES CREEK**—Charter Communications

▲ **BUNN**—FrontierVision

▲ **BUNNLEVEL**—Carolina Cable Partners

BURGAW—See WILMINGTON, NC

▲ **BURKE COUNTY**—Falcon Cable TV

BURKE COUNTY—See also HICKORY, NC

▲ **BURLINGTON**—Time Warner Cable of Alamance County

▲ **BURNSVILLE**—Country Cablevision Inc.

▲ **BURNSVILLE**—Charter Communications

BUTNER—See CREEDMOOR, NC

▲ **BUXTON**—Falcon Cable TV

Bynum—See CHAPEL HILL, NC

CABARRUS—See CHARLOTTE, NC

CABARRUS COUNTY—See KANNAPOLIS, NC

Cajah Mountain—See LENOIR, NC

CALABASH—See SHALLOTTE, NC

CALDWELL COUNTY—See BOONE, NC

CALDWELL COUNTY—See also LENOIR, NC

CALYPSO—See FAISON, NC

▲ **CAMDEN COUNTY**—Mediacom

CAMERON—See VASS, NC

▲ **CAMP LEJEUNE**—Charter Communications

▲ **CAMP WESLEY**—Benchmark Communications

CANDLER—See MARSHALL, NC

CANDOR—See ASHEBORO, NC

CANTON—See WAYNESVILLE, NC (Charter Communications Inc.)

CAPE CARTERET—See MOREHEAD CITY, NC

▲ **CAROLINA BEACH**—Falcon Cable TV

▲ **CARRBORO**—Time Warner Cable

CARRBORO—See also CHAPEL HILL, NC

CARTERET COUNTY—See MOREHEAD CITY, NC

▲ **CARTHAGE**—Time Warner

▲ **CARY**—Time Warner Cable

CASAR—See SHELBY, NC

CASHIERS—See SAPPHIRE, NC

CASTALIA—See DORTCHES, NC

CASTLE HAYNE—See WILMINGTON, NC

CASWELL COUNTY (portions)—See DANVILLE, VA

CASWELL COUNTY (portions)—See also ROXBORO, NC

CATAWBA (northern portion)—See LENOIR, NC

CATAWBA COUNTY—See HICKORY, NC

CEDAR CREEK RESORTS—See SAPPHIRE, NC

CEDAR POINT—See MOREHEAD CITY, NC

CHADBOURN—See WHITEVILLE, NC

CHAPEL GROVE TWP.—See KINGS MOUNTAIN, NC

▲ **CHAPEL HILL**—Time Warner Cable

▲ **CHARLOTTE**—Time Warner Cable

CHARLOTTE (portions)—See MECKLENBURG, NC

CHATHAM COUNTY—See CHAPEL HILL, NC

CHATHAM COUNTY (portions)—See GOLDSTON, NC

CHATHAM COUNTY (unincorporated areas)—See SANFORD, NC

CHEROKEE COUNTY—See MURPHY, NC

CHEROKEE COUNTY (portions)—See RANGER, NC

▲ **CHEROKEE INDIAN RESERVATION**—Cherokee Cablevision

▲ **CHERRY POINT**—Time Warner Cable of Cherry Point

CHERRYVILLE—See KINGS MOUNTAIN, NC

CHIMNEY ROCK—See FAIRFIELD MOUNTAIN, NC

CHIMNEY ROCK—See also FOREST CITY, NC

CHINA GROVE—See KANNAPOLIS, NC

▲ **CHINQUAPIN**—Falcon Cable TV

CHOCOWINITY—See WASHINGTON, NC

CHOWAN BEACH—See ARROWHEAD BEACH, NC

CHOWAN COUNTY—See EDENTON, NC

CHURCH'S ISLAND—See CURRITUCK COUNTY (southern portion), NC

CHURCHLAND—See REEDS CROSS ROADS, NC

CLAREMONT—See HICKORY, NC

CLARKTON—See BLADENBORO, NC

CLAY COUNTY—See HIAWASSEE, GA

CLAYTON—See GARNER, NC

CLEMMONS—See WINSTON-SALEM, NC

CLEVELAND—See SALISBURY, NC

CLEVELAND COUNTY—See SHELBY, NC

CLIFFSIDE—See ELLENBORO, NC

▲ **CLINTON**—Clinton Cable TV

CLYDE—See WAYNESVILLE, NC (Charter Communications Inc.)

COATS—See BUIES CREEK, NC

COFIELD—See AHOSKIE, NC

COINJOCK—See CURRITUCK COUNTY (southern portion), NC

COLERAIN—See POWELLSVILLE, NC

COLERIDGE—See ASHEBORO, NC

COLFAX—See GREENSBORO, NC

COLINGTON—See MANTEO, NC

▲ **COLUMBIA**—Mediacom

COLUMBUS—See LYNN, NC

▲ **COLUMBUS COUNTY (central portion)**—Carolina Cable Partners

COLUMBUS COUNTY (portions)—See LAKE WACCAMAW, NC

COLUMBUS COUNTY (portions)—See also RURAL, NC

COLUMBUS COUNTY (unincorporated areas)—See TABOR CITY, NC

CONCORD—See KANNAPOLIS, NC

CONETOE—See TARBORO, NC

CONNELLY SPRINGS—See BURKE COUNTY, NC

CONOVER—See HICKORY, NC

▲ **CONWAY**—Mediacom

COOLEEMEE—See MOCKSVILLE, NC

CORNELIUS—See MOORESVILLE, NC

▲ **COROLLA**—Falcon Cable TV

COURTNEY—See DOBSON, NC

▲ **CRAMERTON**—Time Warner Cable

▲ **CRAVEN**—Benchmark Communications

CRAVEN COUNTY—See MOREHEAD CITY, NC

CRAVEN COUNTY—See also NEW BERN, NC

▲ **CREEDMOOR**—Durham Cablevision

▲ **CRESTON (southern portion)**—Helicon Cable

CRESWELL—See COLUMBIA, NC

CRISP—See MACCRIPINES, NC

CROSS CREEK—See DOBSON, NC

CROSSNORE—See BOONE, NC

CROUSE—See LINCOLNTON, NC

CROWDERS MOUNTAIN TWP.—See KINGS MOUNTAIN, NC

▲ **CRUSO**—Haywood Cablevision Inc.

CULLOWHEE—See SYLVA, NC

CUMBERLAND COUNTY—See FAYETTEVILLE, NC

▲ **CURRITUCK COUNTY (southern portion)**—Mediacom

CURRITUCK COUNTY (northern portion)—See HAMPTON ROADS, VA

DALLAS—See LINCOLNTON, NC

DANA—See HENDERSONVILLE, NC

DANBURY—See WALNUT COVE, NC

DARE COUNTY (portions)—See MANTEO, NC

DAVIDSON—See MOORESVILLE, NC

▲ **DAVIDSON COUNTY**—Time Warner

DAVIDSON COUNTY (western portion)—See REEDS CROSS ROADS, NC

DAVIE COUNTY (portions)—See MOCKSVILLE, NC

DEEP GAP—See BOONE, NC

DELCO—See RURAL, NC

▲ **DENTON**—Time Warner

DENTON—See also DAVIDSON COUNTY, NC

DENVER—See LINCOLNTON, NC

DILLSBORO—See SYLVA, NC

DOBBINS HEIGHTS—See ROCKINGHAM, NC

▲ **DOBSON**—Time Warner Cable

▲ **DORTCHES**—FrontierVision

DOUGLAS CROSSROADS—See SIDNEY, NC

▲ **DOVER**—Johnston County Cable LP

DREXEL—See ASHEVILLE, NC

DREXEL—See also BURKE COUNTY, NC

DUBLIN—See BLADENBORO, NC

DUCK—See MANTEO, NC

▲ **DUNCAN**—Carolina Cable Partners

DUNN—See FAYETTEVILLE, NC

DUPLIN COUNTY—See CHINQUAPIN, NC

▲ **DURHAM**—Time Warner Cable

DURHAM COUNTY—See CHAPEL HILL, NC

DURHAM COUNTY—See also DURHAM, NC

EARL—See SHELBY, NC

EAST ARCADIA—See RURAL, NC

EAST BEND—See DOBSON, NC

EAST FLAT ROCK—See HENDERSONVILLE, NC

EAST JEFFERSON—See WEST JEFFERSON, NC

EAST LAURINBURG—See LAURINBURG, NC

EAST SPENCER—See SALISBURY, NC

▲ **EDEN**—Time Warner

▲ **EDENTON**—Mediacom

EDGECOMBE COUNTY (eastern portion)—See ROCKY MOUNT, NC

EDGECOMBE COUNTY (portions)—See WHITAKERS, NC

EDGECOMBE COUNTY (portions)—See also DORTCHES, NC

EDGECOMBE COUNTY (portions)—See also MID LAKES TRAILER PARK, NC

EDGECOMBE COUNTY (portions)—See also OAK CITY, NC

▲ **ELIZABETH CITY**—Adelphia Cable

ELIZABETHTOWN—See BLADENBORO, NC

ELK PARK—See BOONE, NC

▲ **ELKIN**—InterMedia Partners

▲ **ELLENBORO**—Mountains Cablevision

ELLERBE—See ROCKINGHAM, NC

ELM CITY—See WILSON, NC

ELON COLLEGE—See BURLINGTON, NC

EMERALD ISLE—See MOREHEAD CITY, NC

EMMA—See MARSHALL, NC

▲ **ENFIELD**—Tar River Cable TV

Engelhard—See BELHAVEN, NC

ENKA—See MARSHALL, NC

ERWIN—See BUIES CREEK, NC

ERWIN—See also FAYETTEVILLE, NC

EUREKA—See WAYNE COUNTY (northern portion), NC

EVERETTS—See PARMELE, NC

▲ **FAIR BLUFF**—MIM Cable

FAIRFIELD—See BELHAVEN, NC

▲ **FAIRFIELD MOUNTAIN**—Mountains Cablevision

FAIRMONT—See RED SPRINGS, NC

▲ **FAISON**—Falcon Cable TV

FAITH—See SALISBURY, NC

FALCON—See FAYETTEVILLE, NC

FALLSTON—See SHELBY, NC

▲ **FARMVILLE**—Time Warner Cable

▲ **FAYETTEVILLE**—Time Warner Cable

FAYETTEVILLE—See also RAEFORD, NC

FLAT ROCK—See HENDERSONVILLE, NC

FLETCHER—See ASHEVILLE, NC

FLETCHER—See also HENDERSONVILLE, NC

▲ **FOREST CITY**—Northland Cable TV

FORSYTH COUNTY—See WINSTON-SALEM, NC

FORT BRAGG—See FAYETTEVILLE, NC

FORT FISHER AFB—See CAROLINA BEACH, NC

FOSCOE—See BOONE, NC

▲ **FOUNTAIN**—FrontierVision

FOUR OAKS—See SELMA, NC

FOXFIRE VILLAGE—See SOUTHERN PINES, NC

FRANCISCO—See WALNUT COVE, NC

▲ **FRANKLIN**—Mediacom

FRANKLIN COUNTY—See FRANKLINTON, NC

FRANKLIN COUNTY (portions)—See YOUNGSVILLE, NC

FRANKLIN COUNTY (portions)—See also LOUISBURG, NC

▲ **FRANKLINTON**—Cablevision of Raleigh Division

FRANKLINVILLE—See ASHEBORO, NC

FREMONT—See GOLDSBORO, NC

FRISCO—See BUXTON, NC

FUQUAY-VARINA—See CARY, NC

GAMEWELL—See LENOIR, NC

▲ **GARLAND**—StarVision

▲ **GARNER**—Alert Cable TV of North Carolina Inc.

GARYSBURG—See ROANOKE RAPIDS, NC

GASTON—See ROANOKE RAPIDS, NC

GASTON COUNTY—See CLOVER, SC

GASTON COUNTY—See also LINCOLNTON, NC

GASTON COUNTY (eastern portion)—See BELMONT, NC

GASTON COUNTY (portions)—See CRAMERTON, NC

GASTON COUNTY (unincorporated areas)—See KINGS MOUNTAIN, NC

▲ **GASTONIA**—Time Warner Cable

▲ **GATES COUNTY**—Falcon Cable TV

GATESVILLE—See GATES COUNTY, NC

GERMANTON—See WALNUT COVE, NC

GERTON—See FAIRFIELD MOUNTAIN, NC

GIBSON—See LAURINBURG, NC

GIBSONVILLE—See BURLINGTON, NC

GLEN ALPINE—See BURKE COUNTY, NC

GODWIN—See FAYETTEVILLE, NC

▲ **GOLD HILL**—Benchmark Communications

GOLD POINT—See OAK CITY, NC

▲ **GOLDSBORO**—Time Warner Cable

▲ **GOLDSTON**—Goldston CATV

GRAHAM—See BURLINGTON, NC

GRAHAM COUNTY (central portion)—See ROBBINSVILLE, NC

GRAHAM COUNTY (eastern portion)—See BRYSON CITY, NC

GRANDFATHER MOUNTAIN—See BOONE, NC

GRANDY—See CURRITUCK COUNTY (southern portion), NC

GRANITE FALLS—See HICKORY, NC

GRANITE QUARRY—See SALISBURY, NC

GRANNY SQUIRRELL—See ANDREWS, NC

GRANVILLE COUNTY (portions)—See OXFORD, NC

GREENE COUNTY (portions)—See SNOW HILL, NC

▲ **GREENSBORO**—Time Warner of Greensboro

▲ **GREENVILLE**—Multimedia Cablevision

GRIFTON—See SNOW HILL, NC

GRIMESLAND—See SIMPSON, NC

GROVER—See SHELBY, NC

▲ **HALIFAX**—FrontierVision

HALIFAX COUNTY—See ROANOKE RAPIDS, NC

HALIFAX COUNTY (portions)—See OAK CITY, NC

HALIFAX COUNTY (western portion)—See HOLLISTER, NC

HALLSBORO—See LAKE WACCAMAW, NC

HAMILTON—See OAK CITY, NC

HAMLET—See ROCKINGHAM, NC

HARBINGER—See CURRITUCK COUNTY (southern portion), NC

HARKERS ISLAND—See MOREHEAD CITY, NC

HARRISBURG—See KANNAPOLIS, NC

HEARTSEASE—See DORTCHES, NC

HASSEL—See OAK CITY, NC

HATTERAS—See BUXTON, NC

HAVELOCK—See MOREHEAD CITY, NC

HAW RIVER—See BURLINGTON, NC

HAYESVILLE—See HIAWASSEE, GA

HAYWOOD COUNTY—See WAYNESVILLE, NC (Charter Communications Inc.)

HAYWOOD COUNTY (unincorporated areas)—See CRUSO, NC

HAZELWOOD—See WAYNESVILLE, NC (Charter Communications Inc.)

HEMPSTEAD—See OLDE POINT, NC

▲ **HENDERSON**—Time Warner Cable

HENDERSON COUNTY—See HENDERSONVILLE, NC

HENDERSON COUNTY (northeastern portion)—See FAIRFIELD MOUNTAIN, NC

▲ **HENDERSONVILLE**—Mediacom

HENRICO—See LAKE GASTON, NC

HERTFORD—See EDENTON, NC

HERTFORD COUNTY—See AHOSKIE, NC

HERTFORD COUNTY—See also MURFREESBORO, NC

HERTFORD COUNTY (southern portion)—See AULANDER, NC

▲ **HICKORY**—Charter Communications

HIDDENITE—See LINCOLNTON, NC

▲ **HIGH POINT**—Time Warner Cable

HIGH SHOALS—See LINCOLNTON, NC

▲ **HIGHLANDS**—Northland Cable TV

HIGHT POINT—See GREENSBORO, NC

HILDEBRAN—See HICKORY, NC

HILLSBOROUGH—See CARRBORO, NC

HOBGOOD—See OAK CITY, NC

HOFFMAN—See ROCKINGHAM, NC

HOKE COUNTY—See RED SPRINGS, NC

▲ **HOLDEN BEACH**—Time Warner Cable

▲ **HOLLISTER**—FrontierVision

HOLLY RIDGE—See SURF CITY, NC

HOLLY SPRINGS—See CARY, NC

HOLLY SPRINGS—See also DOBSON, NC

HOOKERTON—See SNOW HILL, NC

HOPE MILLS—See FAYETTEVILLE, NC

HOUND EARS—See BOONE, NC

HUBERT—See JACKSONVILLE, NC

HUDSON—See LENOIR, NC

HUNTERSVILLE—See CHARLOTTE, NC

HUNTERSVILLE—See also MOORESVILLE, NC

HUNTERSVILLE (portions)—See MECKLENBURG, NC

HYDE COUNTY (portions)—See SIDNEY, NC

INDIAN BEACH—See MOREHEAD CITY, NC

INDIAN TRAIL—See MONROE, NC

IREDELL COUNTY—See STATESVILLE, NC

IREDELL COUNTY (portions)—See LAKE NORMAN, NC

▲ **IRONDUFF**—Haywood Cable TV

JACKSON—See CONWAY, NC

JACKSON COUNTY (portions)—See HIGHLANDS, NC

JACKSON COUNTY (unincorporated areas)—See SYLVA, NC

▲ **JACKSONVILLE**—Time Warner Cable

JAMESTOWN—See HIGH POINT, NC

JAMESVILLE—See PLYMOUTH, NC

JARVISBURG—See CURRITUCK COUNTY (southern portion), NC

JEFFERSON—See WEST JEFFERSON, NC

JOHNSONVILLE—See ANDERSON CREEK, NC

JOHNSTON COUNTY—See GARNER, NC

Johnston County—See also PRINCETON, NC

JOHNSTON COUNTY—See also SELMA, NC

Jonathan Creek—See IRONDUFF, NC

JONES COUNTY (portions)—See JACKSONVILLE, NC

JONESVILLE—See ELKIN, NC

JULLAN—See GREENSBORO, NC

JUPITER—See MARSHALL, NC

▲ **KANNAPOLIS**—Time Warner Cable

KELFORD—See RICH SQUARE, NC

KEMERSVILLE—See GREENSBORO, NC

KENANSVILLE—See CHINQUAPIN, NC

▲ **KENLY**—Southern Cablevision

KERNERSVILLE—See WINSTON-SALEM, NC

KILL DEVIL HILLS—See MANTEO, NC

▲ **KING**—Benchmark Communications

KINGS CREEK—See LENOIR, NC

▲ **KINGS MOUNTAIN**—Time Warner Cable

KINGSTOWN—See SHELBY, NC

▲ **KINSTON**—Kinston Cable TV

KIPLING—See DUNCAN, NC

KITTRELL—See HENDERSON, NC

KITTY HAWK—See MANTEO, NC

KNIGHTDALE—See ZEBULON, NC

KURE BEACH—See CAROLINA BEACH, NC

LA GRANGE—See KINSTON, NC

LA GRANGE—See also KINSTON, NC

▲ **LAKE GASTON**—FrontierVision

LAKE JUNALUSKA—See WAYNESVILLE, NC (Charter Communications Inc.)

LAKE LURE—See FAIRFIELD MOUNTAIN, NC

▲ **LAKE NORMAN**—Prestige Cable TV Inc.

LAKE NORMAN—See also LINCOLNTON, NC

▲ **LAKE TOXAWAY**—Sylvan Valley CATV Co.

▲ **LAKE WACCAMAW**—Benchmark Communications

LANCASTER—See CHARLOTTE, NC

LAND HARBOR—See BOONE, NC

LANDIS—See KANNAPOLIS, NC

LANDRAN—See LYNN, NC

▲ **LANSING**—Mediacom

LATTIMORE—See SHELBY, NC

LAUREL PARK—See HENDERSONVILLE, NC

▲ **LAURINBURG**—Century Communications

LAWNDALE—See SHELBY, NC

LEE COUNTY—See SANFORD, NC

LEICESTER—See MARSHALL, NC

LELAND—See WILMINGTON, NC

▲ **LENOIR**—Charter Communications

LENOIR COUNTY (portions)—See SNOW HILL, NC

LEWISTON—See RICH SQUARE, NC

LEWISVILLE—See WINSTON-SALEM, NC

LEXINGTON—See DAVIDSON COUNTY, NC

▲ **LIBERTY**—Time Warner

LIBERTY—See also ASHEBORO, NC

LILESVILLE—See WADESBORO, NC

LILLINGTON—See BUIES CREEK, NC

LINCOLN COUNTY—See LINCOLNTON, NC

▲ **LINCOLNTON**—Charter Communications

LINVILLE RIDGE—See BOONE, NC

LITTLE SWITZERLAND—See BURNSVILLE, NC (Country Cablevision Inc.)

▲ **LITTLETON**—FrontierVision

LOCUST—See ALBEMARLE, NC

LONE HICKORY—See DOBSON, NC

LONGVIEW—See HICKORY, NC

LONGWOOD—See SHALLOTTE, NC

▲ **LOUISBURG**—Time Warner Cable

LOVELADY—See LENOIR, NC

LOWELL—See CRAMERTON, NC

LUCAMA—See KENLY, NC

LUMBER BRIDGE—See RAEFORD, NC

LUMBER BRIDGE—See also RED SPRINGS, NC

LUMBER BRIDGE (town)—See RED SPRINGS, NC

▲ **LUMBERTON**—Time Warner Cable

▲ **LYNN**—Charter Communications

MACCLESFIELD—See MACCRIPINES, NC

▲**MACCRIPINES**—FrontierVision

MACON—See OXFORD, NC

MACON COUNTY—See FRANKLIN, NC

MACON COUNTY (eastern portion)—See HIGHLANDS, NC

▲ **MADISON**—Time Warner

MADISON COUNTY—See BURNSVILLE, NC (Country Cablevision Inc.)

MAGGIE VALLEY—See WAYNESVILLE, NC (Charter Communications Inc.)

MAGNOLIA—See CHINQUAPIN, NC

MAIDEN—See HICKORY, NC

MAMERS—See BUIES CREEK, NC

MAMIE—See CURRITUCK COUNTY (southern portion), NC

MANNS HARBOR—See MANTEO, NC

▲ **MANTEO**—Falcon Cable TV

MARBLE—See ANDREWS, NC

▲ **MARION**—InterMedia Partners

MARS HILL—See MARSHALL, NC

▲ **MARSHALL**—Charter Communications

MARSHVILLE—See MONROE, NC

MARSTON—See ROCKINGHAM, NC

MARTIN COUNTY (central portion)—See PARMELE, NC

MARTIN COUNTY (portions)—See PARMELE, NC

MARTIN COUNTY (portions)—See also PLYMOUTH, NC

MARTIN COUNTY (unincorporated areas)—See OAK CITY, NC

MARTIN CREEK—See MURPHY, NC

MATTHEWS—See CHARLOTTE, NC

MATTHEWS (portions)—See MECKLENBURG, NC

MAURY—See SNOW HILL, NC

MAXTON—See LAURINBURG, NC

MAYODAN—See MADISON, NC

McADENVILLE—See CRAMERTON, NC

McDOWELL COUNTY (central portion)—See MARION, NC

▲ **MEAT CAMP**—FrontierVision

▲ **MEBANE**—Time Warner

▲ **MECKLENBURG**—Time Warner Cable

Mecklenburg County—See MOORESVILLE, NC

MECKLENBURG COUNTY (unincorporated areas)—See CHARLOTTE, NC

MICAVILLE—See BURNSVILLE, NC (Charter Communications)

MICRO—See KENLY, NC

▲ **MID LAKES TRAILER PARK**—FrontierVision

MIDDLEBURG—See HENDERSON, NC

Middlesex—See BAILEY, NC

MIDLAND—See KANNAPOLIS, NC

MIDWAY PARK—See JACKSONVILLE, NC

MILDRED—See TARBORO, NC

MILLS RIVER—See HENDERSONVILLE, NC

MINT HILL—See CHARLOTTE, NC

MINT HILL—See also MECKLENBURG, NC

MITCHELL COUNTY—See SPRUCE PINE, NC

MITCHELL COUNTY—See also BURNSVILLE, NC (Country Cablevision Inc.)

▲ **MOCKSVILLE**—Benchmark Communications

MOMEYER—See SPRING HOPE, NC

▲ **MONROE**—Cablevision of Monroe

MONTREAT—See BLACK MOUNTAIN, NC

MOORE COUNTY—See SOUTHERN PINES, NC

MOORE COUNTY—See also SANFORD, NC

MOORE COUNTY (portions)—See SEVEN LAKES, NC

MOORE COUNTY (unincorporated areas)—See VASS, NC

MOORESBORO—See SHELBY, NC

▲ **MOORESVILLE**—Prestige Cable

▲ **MOREHEAD CITY**—Time Warner Cable

▲ **MORGANTON**—Compas Cable City of Morganton Public Antenna

MORRISVILLE—See CARY, NC

▲ **MORVEN**—WFL Cable Television Associates Inc.

▲ **MOUNT AIRY**—InterMedia Partners

MOUNT GILEAD—See ALBEMARLE, NC

MOUNT HOLLY—See BELMONT, NC

MOUNT OLIVE—See GOLDSBORO, NC

MOUNT PILOT (eastern portion)—See DOBSON, NC

MOUNT PILOT (western portion)—See DOBSON, NC

MOUNT PLEASANT—See KANNAPOLIS, NC

▲ **MURFREESBORO**—Adelphia Cable

▲ **MURPHY**—Cable TV of Murphy

NAGS HEAD—See MANTEO, NC

NASH COUNTY—See ROCKY MOUNT, NC

NASH COUNTY (portions)—See WHITAKERS, NC

NASH COUNTY (southwestern portion)—See BAILEY, NC

NASHVILLE—See ROCKY MOUNT, NC

▲ **NEBO**—Mediacom

Nebraska—See BELHAVEN, NC

▲ **NEW BERN**—New Bern Cable TV Inc.

NEW HANOVER COUNTY—See WILMINGTON, NC

NEW HANOVER COUNTY (unincorporated areas)—See CAROLINA BEACH, NC

NEW LONDON—See ALBEMARLE, NC

NEWLAND—See BOONE, NC

NEWPORT—See MOREHEAD CITY, NC

NEWTON—See HICKORY, NC

▲ **NEWTON GROVE**—Charter Cable

NORLINA—See OXFORD, NC

NORTH LAKE—See LENOIR, NC

NORTH TOPSAIL BEACH—See SURF CITY, NC

NORTH WEST—See RURAL, NC

▲ **NORTH WILKESBORO**—Falcon Cable TV

NORTHAMPTON COUNTY—See CONWAY, NC

NORTHAMPTON COUNTY—See also RICH SQUARE, NC

NORTHAMPTON COUNTY—See also ROANOKE RAPIDS, NC

NORTHAMPTON COUNTY (portions)—See LAKE GASTON, NC

NORWOOD—See ALBEMARLE, NC

▲ **OAK CITY**—FrontierVision

OAK RIDGE—See GREENSBORO, NC

OAKBORO—See ALBEMARLE, NC

OCRACOKE ISLAND—See BELHAVEN, NC

OLD FORT—See MARION, NC

▲ **OLDE POINT**—Falcon Cable TV

OLDS—See CURRITUCK COUNTY (southern portion), NC

ONSLOW COUNTY—See SURF CITY, NC

ORANGE COUNTY—See CARRBORO, NC

ORANGE COUNTY—See also CHAPEL HILL, NC

ORIENTAL—See BAYBORO, NC

▲ **ORRUM**—Carolina Cable Partners

▲ **OXFORD**—Time Warner Cable

PAMLICO BEACH—See SIDNEY, NC

PANTEGO—See BELHAVEN, NC

PARKTON—See FAYETTEVILLE, NC

▲ **PARMELE**—Greenville Cable TV Inc.

PASQUOTANK COUNTY—See ELIZABETH CITY, NC

PATTERSON—See LENOIR, NC

PATTERSON SPRINGS—See SHELBY, NC

PEACHLAND—See MORVEN, NC

PEACHTREE—See MURPHY, NC

PEMBROKE—See RED SPRINGS, NC

PENDER COUNTY—See WILMINGTON, NC

PENDER COUNTY (portions)—See SURF CITY, NC

PENSACOLA—See BURNSVILLE, NC (Charter Communications)

PERQUIMANS COUNTY—See EDENTON, NC

PERSON COUNTY—See ROXBORO, NC

PFAFFTOWN—See KING, NC

PIKE ROAD—See SIDNEY, NC

PIKEVILLE—See GOLDSBORO, NC

PILOT—See BUNN, NC

PILOT MOUNTAIN EAST—See DOBSON, NC

PINE HALL—See WALNUT COVE, NC

PINE KNOLL SHORES—See MOREHEAD CITY, NC

PINE LEVEL—See SELMA, NC

PINEBLUFF—See SOUTHERN PINES, NC

▲ **PINEHURST**—Time Warner Cable

PINEHURST—See also SOUTHERN PINES, NC

PINETOPS—See MACCRIPINES, NC

PINETOWN—See SIDNEY, NC

PINEVILLE (portions)—See CHARLOTTE, NC

PINEVILLE (portions)—See also MECKLENBURG, NC

PINEWILD COUNTRY CLUB—See PINEHURST, NC

▲ **PINK HILL**—FrontierVision

PINNACLE—See KING, NC

PITT COUNTY—See FARMVILLE, NC

PITT COUNTY—See also GREENVILLE, NC

PITT COUNTY (portions)—See SIMPSON, NC

PITT COUNTY (portions)—See also SNOW HILL, NC

PITTSBORO—See CHAPEL HILL, NC

PLAINVIEW—See NEWTON GROVE, NC

PLEASANT GARDEN—See GREENSBORO, NC

▲ **PLYMOUTH**—Mediacom

POINT HARBOR—See CURRITUCK COUNTY (southern portion), NC

POLK COUNTY (northern portion)—See FAIRFIELD MOUNTAIN, NC

POLKTON—See MORVEN, NC

POLKVILLE—See SHELBY, NC

POPE AFB—See FAYETTEVILLE, NC

POPLAR BRANCH—See CURRITUCK COUNTY (southern portion), NC

POWELLS POINT—See CURRITUCK COUNTY (southern portion), NC

▲ **POWELLSVILLE**—Mediacom

▲ **PRINCETON**—Southern Cablevision

PRINCEVILLE—See TARBORO, NC

PROCTORVILLE—See ORRUM, NC

QUALLA—See CHEROKEE INDIAN RESERVATION, NC

▲ **RAEFORD**—Benchmark Communications

RAEFORD—See also RED SPRINGS, NC

▲ **RALEIGH**—Time Warner Cable

RAMSEUR—See ASHEBORO, NC

RANDLEMAN—See ASHEBORO, NC

RANDLEMAN—See also GREENSBORO, NC

▲ **RANGER**—Kudzu Cable TV Inc.

RANLO—See CRAMERTON, NC

RED OAK—See DORTCHES, NC

▲ **RED SPRINGS**—Time Warner Cable

RED SPRINGS—See also RAEFORD, NC

▲ **REEDS CROSS ROADS**—Piedmont Telephone-Cable

▲ **REIDSVILLE**—CVI

RENNERT—See RED SPRINGS, NC

RHODHISS—See HICKORY, NC

▲ **RICH SQUARE**—Mediacom

RICHFIELD—See ALBEMARLE, NC

RICHLANDS—See CHINQUAPIN, NC

RICHMOND COUNTY—See ROCKINGHAM, NC

RIEGELWOOD—See RURAL, NC

RIVER BEND—See NEW BERN, NC

▲ **ROAN FORK**—FrontierVision

▲ **ROANOKE RAPIDS**—Helicon Cable Communications

▲ **ROARING GAP**—Falcon Cable TV

ROARING RIVER—See NORTH WILKESBORO, NC

▲ **ROBBINS**—CMA Winston-Salem Cablevision Associates

▲ **ROBBINSVILLE**—Bryson City Cablevision Assoc. LP

ROBERSONVILLE—See OAK CITY, NC

ROBERSONVILLE—See also PARMELE, NC

▲ **ROBESON COUNTY (western portion)**—Carolina Cable Partners

ROBESON COUNTY—See also LAURINBURG, NC

ROBESON COUNTY—See also LUMBERTON, NC

ROBESON COUNTY—See also RED SPRINGS, NC

ROCKFISH—See RAEFORD, NC

▲ **ROCKINGHAM**—Cablevision of Rockingham-Hamlet

ROCKINGHAM COUNTY—See EDEN, NC

ROCKINGHAM COUNTY—See also REIDSVILLE, NC

ROCKINGHAM COUNTY (portions)—See STONEVILLE, NC

ROCKINGHAM COUNTY (portions)—See also GREENSBORO, NC

ROCKINGHAM COUNTY (portions)—See also MADISON, NC

ROCKWELL—See SALISBURY, NC

▲ **ROCKY MOUNT**—Multimedia Cablevision

ROCKY MOUNT (portions)—See DORTCHES, NC

RODANTHE—See BUXTON, NC

ROLESVILLE—See WAKE FOREST, NC

RONDA—See NORTH WILKESBORO, NC

ROPER—See PLYMOUTH, NC

ROSE HILL—See CHINQUAPIN, NC

▲ **ROSEBORO**—StarVision

ROWAN COUNTY—See KANNAPOLIS, NC

ROWAN COUNTY—See also SALISBURY, NC

ROWAN COUNTY (eastern portion)—See CRAVEN, NC

ROWAN COUNTY (portions)—See GOLD HILL, NC

ROWAN COUNTY (portions)—See also LAKE NORMAN, NC

ROWAN COUNTY (southwestern portion)—See CAMP WESLEY, NC

▲ **ROWLAND**—Benchmark Communications

▲ **ROXBORO**—Helicon Cable Communications

ROXOBEL—See RICH SQUARE, NC

▲ **RURAL**—Benchmark Communications

RURAL HALL—See WINSTON-SALEM, NC

RURAL HALL—See also KING, NC

RUTH—See FOREST CITY, NC

RUTHERFORD COLLEGE—See BURKE COUNTY, NC

Rutherford College—See also LENOIR, NC

RUTHERFORD COUNTY—See ELLENBORO, NC

RUTHERFORD COUNTY (portions)—See also FAIRFIELD MOUNTAIN, NC

RUTHERFORD COUNTY (unincorporated areas)—See FOREST CITY, NC

RUTHERFORDTON—See FOREST CITY, NC

SALEMBURG—See ROSEBORO, NC

▲ **SALISBURY**—Time Warner Cable

SALUDA—See LYNN, NC

SALVO—See BUXTON, NC

SAMPSON COUNTY—See CLINTON, NC

SAMPSON COUNTY (portions)—See ROSEBORO, NC

SANDY CREEK—See RURAL, NC

SANDY MUSH—See FOREST CITY, NC

SANDY RIDGE—See DOBSON, NC

▲ **SANFORD**—Charter Communications

SANTEETLAH—See ROBBINSVILLE, NC

▲ **SANTREE MOBILE HOME PARK**—FrontierVision

▲ **SAPPHIRE**—Mountains Cablevision-Sapphire Valley

SAPPHIRE VALLEY—See SAPPHIRE, NC

SARATOGA—See WILSON, NC

SAURATOWN TWP.—See WALNUT COVE, NC

Sawmills—See LENOIR, NC

SCOTLAND COUNTY—See LAURINBURG, NC

▲ **SCOTLAND NECK**—Tar River Cable TV Inc.

SEABOARD—See CONWAY, NC

SEAGROVE—See ASHEBORO, NC

▲ **SELMA**—Time Warner Cable

SEVEN DEVILS—See BOONE, NC

▲ **SEVEN LAKES**—Time Warner Cable

SEVERN—See CONWAY, NC

SEYMOUR JOHNSON AFB—See GOLDSBORO, NC

▲ **SHALLOTTE**—Atlantic Telephone Membership Corp.

SHANNON—See RAEFORD, NC

SHARPSBURG—See ROCKY MOUNT, NC

▲ **SHELBY**—Time Warner Cable

▲ **SIDNEY**—Tri-County Communications Inc.

SILER CITY—See SANFORD, NC

▲ **SIMPSON**—FrontierVision

SIMS—See BAILEY, NC

SIX POINTS—See ELLENBORO, NC

▲ **SMITHFIELD**—Johnston County Cable LP

SMITHFIELD—See also SELMA, NC

SNEADS FERRY—See SURF CITY, NC

▲ **SNOW HILL**—Enstar Cable TV

▲ **SOUTHERN PINES**—Sandhill Cablevision

SOUTHERN SHORES—See MANTEO, NC

SOUTHMONT—See DAVIDSON COUNTY, NC

SOUTHPORT—See WILMINGTON, NC

▲ **SPARTA**—Mediacom

▲ **SPARTA**—Alleghany Cablevision Inc.

SPENCER—See SALISBURY, NC

SPENCER MOUNTAIN—See CRAMERTON, NC

SPINDALE—See FOREST CITY, NC

SPIVEY'S CORNER—See NEWTON GROVE, NC

▲ **SPRING HOPE**—FrontierVision

SPRING LAKE—See FAYETTEVILLE, NC

▲ **SPRUCE PINE**—Charter Communications

SPRUCE PINE—See also BURNSVILLE, NC (Country Cablevision Inc.)

ST. PAULS—See RED SPRINGS, NC

STALLINGS—See MONROE, NC

STANFIELD—See ALBEMARLE, NC

STANLEY—See CRAMERTON, NC

STANLY COUNTY—See ALBEMARLE, NC

STANTONSBURG—See WILSON, NC

STAR—See ASHEBORO, NC

▲ **STATESVILLE**—Prestige Cable TV of North Carolina Inc.

STEDMAN—See FAYETTEVILLE, NC

STEM—See CREEDMOOR, NC

STOKES COUNTY (portions)—See WINSTON-SALEM, NC

STOKES COUNTY (portions)—See also DOBSON, NC

STOKES COUNTY (southern portion)—See WALNUT COVE, NC

STOKESDALE—See GREENSBORO, NC

▲ **STONEVILLE**—CVI

STONEWALL—See BAYBORO, NC

STONY POINT—See LINCOLNTON, NC

STOVALL—See OXFORD, NC

STUMPY POINT—See MANTEO, NC

SUGAR GROVE—See ZIONVILLE, NC

SUGAR MOUNTAIN—See BOONE, NC

SUMMERFIELD—See GREENSBORO, NC

SUNSET BEACH—See SHALLOTTE, NC

SUPPLY—See SHALLOTTE, NC

▲ **SURF CITY**—Falcon Cable TV

SURRY COUNTY—See DOBSON, NC

SURRY COUNTY (northern portion)—See MOUNT AIRY, NC

SURRY COUNTY (southern portion)—See ELKIN, NC

SWAIN COUNTY—See BRYSON CITY, NC

SWAN CREEK—See DOBSON, NC

Swan Quarter—See BELHAVEN, NC

SWANNANOA—See BLACK MOUNTAIN, NC

SWANSBORO—See MOREHEAD CITY, NC

▲ **SYLVA**—Mediacom

▲ **TABOR CITY**—Benchmark Communications

▲ **TARBORO**—Multimedia Cablevision

TAYLORSVILLE—See LINCOLNTON, NC

TAYLORTOWN—See SOUTHERN PINES, NC

TEACHEY—See CHINQUAPIN, NC

THOMASVILLE—See DAVIDSON COUNTY, NC

THURMOND—See ROARING GAP, NC

TOAST—See MOUNT AIRY, NC

TOBACCOVILLE—See KING, NC

TOMOTLA—See MURPHY, NC

TOPSAIL BEACH—See SURF CITY, NC

TOPTON—See ANDREWS, NC

TOWNSVILLE—See HENDERSON, NC

TRANSYLVANIA COUNTY—See BREVARD, NC

TRANSYLVANIA COUNTY (portions)—See LAKE TOXAWAY, NC

TRAPHILL—See NORTH WILKESBORO, NC

TRAVIS—See COLUMBIA, NC

TRENT WOODS—See NEW BERN, NC

TRINITY—See ARCHDALE, NC

TROUTMAN—See STATESVILLE, NC

TROY—See SANFORD, NC

TRYON—See LYNN, NC

TWIN LAKES—See SPARTA, NC (Mediacom)

TYRO—See REEDS CROSS ROADS, NC

TYRRELL COUNTY (portions)—See COLUMBIA, NC

UNION COUNTY—See MONROE, NC

VALDESE—See BURKE COUNTY, NC

VALLE CRUCIS—See BOONE, NC

VANCE COUNTY—See HENDERSON, NC

VANCEBORO—See NEW BERN, NC

▲ **VASS**—Carolina Cable Partners

VENGENCE CREEK—See ANDREWS, NC

VILAS—See ZIONVILLE, NC

WACO—See SHELBY, NC

WADE—See FAYETTEVILLE, NC

▲ **WADESBORO**—Time Warner

▲ **WAGRAM**—Riverton Cable TV Inc.

WAKE COUNTY—See WAKE FOREST, NC

WAKE COUNTY—See also CARY, NC

WAKE COUNTY—See also GARNER, NC

WAKE COUNTY—See also RALEIGH, NC

▲ **WAKE FOREST**—Time Warner Cable

WALKERTOWN—See WINSTON-SALEM, NC

WALLACE—See CHINQUAPIN, NC

WALLBURG—See DAVIDSON COUNTY, NC

▲ **WALNUT COVE**—Time Warner Cable

WALNUT CREEK—See KINSTON, NC

WALNUT CREEK—See also KINSTON, NC

WALNUT ISLAND—See CURRITUCK COUNTY (southern portion), NC

WALSTONBURG—See SNOW HILL, NC

WANCHESE—See MANTEO, NC

NORTH DAKOTA

▲ **DRAYTON**—Midcontinent Cable Systems Co. of North Dakota

▲ **DUNN CENTER**—Eagle Cablevision

▲ **DUNSEITH**—Midcontinent Cable Systems Co. of North Dakota

▲ **EDGELEY**—The Community Development Corp.

▲ **EDINBURG**—Viking Electronics Inc.

▲ **EDMORE**—Midcontinent Cable Systems Co. of North Dakota

▲ **ELGIN**—Western Dakota Cable Inc.

▲ **ELLENDALE**—Cable Services Inc.

EMERADO—See GRAND FORKS AFB, ND

▲ **ESMOND**—Midcontinent Cable Systems Co. of North Dakota

▲ **FAIRMOUNT**—Midcontinent Cable Systems Co. of North Dakota

▲ **FARGO**—Cable One

▲ **FESSENDEN**—Midcontinent Cable Systems Co. of North Dakota

▲ **FINLEY**—Loreltel Cablevision

▲ **FLASHER**—Flasher Cablevision Inc.

▲ **FORDVILLE**—Viking Electronics Inc.

▲ **FOREST RIVER**—TCI of North Dakota Inc.

▲ **FORMAN**—Dickey Rural Services Inc.

FRONTIER—See FARGO, ND

▲ **GACKLE**—Midcontinent Cable Systems Co. of North Dakota

▲ **GALESBURG**—Midcontinent Cable Systems Co. of North Dakota

▲ **GARRISON**—Midcontinent Cable Systems Co. of North Dakota

▲ **GILBY**—TCI of North Dakota Inc.

▲ **GLADSTONE**—Midcontinent Cable Systems Co. of North Dakota

▲ **GLEN ULLIN**—Midcontinent Cable Systems Co. of North Dakota

▲ **GLENBURN**—Midcontinent Cable Systems Co. of North Dakota

▲ **GLENFIELD Glenfield**—Dakota Central Rural Telephone

▲ **GOLDEN VALLEY**—Midcontinent Cable Systems Co. of North Dakota

▲ **GOODRICH**—Midcontinent Cable Systems Co. of North Dakota

▲ **GRAFTON**—Midcontinent Cable Systems Co. of North Dakota

▲ **GRAND FORKS**—TCI of North Dakota Inc.

▲ **GRAND FORKS AFB**—TCI of North Dakota Inc.

▲ **GRANDIN**—Midcontinent Cable Systems Co. of North Dakota

▲ **GRANVILLE**—Souris River Telecommunications

▲ **GRENORA**—Northwest Communications

▲ **GWINNER**—Dickey Rural Services Inc.

▲ **HALLIDAY**—Midcontinent Cable Systems Co. of North Dakota

▲ **HANKINSON**—Midcontinent Cable Systems Co. of North Dakota

▲ **HANNAFORD**—Midcontinent Cable Systems Co. of North Dakota

▲ **HARVEY**—Midcontinent Cable Systems Co. of North Dakota

▲ **HARWOOD**—Midcontinent Cable Systems Co. of North Dakota

▲ **HATTON**—Midcontinent Cable Systems Co. of North Dakota

▲ **HAZELTON**—BEK Communications Cooperative

▲ **HAZEN**—Midcontinent Cable Systems Co. of North Dakota

▲ **HEBRON**—Midcontinent Cable Systems Co. of North Dakota

▲ **HETTINGER**—Midcontinent Cable Systems Co. of North Dakota

▲ **HILLSBORO**—Midcontinent Cable Systems Co. of North Dakota

▲ **HOOPLE**—Viking Electronics Inc.

▲ **HOPE**—Midcontinent Cable Systems Co. of North Dakota

▲ **HORACE**—Midcontinent Cable Systems Co. of North Dakota

▲ **HUNTER**—Midcontinent Cable Systems Co. of North Dakota

▲ **JAMESTOWN**—Cable Services Inc.

▲ **KARLSRUHE**—Souris River Telecommunications

▲ **KENMARE**—Midcontinent Cable Systems Co. of North Dakota

▲ **KENSAL**—Midcontinent Cable Systems Co. of North Dakota

▲ **KILLDEER**—Midcontinent Cable Systems Co. of North Dakota

▲ **KULM**—Cable Services Inc.

▲ **LA MOURE**—Midcontinent Cable Systems Co. of North Dakota

▲ **LAKOTA**—TCI of North Dakota Inc.

▲ **LANGDON**—Midcontinent Cable Systems Co. of North Dakota

▲ **LANSFORD**—Midcontinent Cable Systems Co. of North Dakota

▲ **LARIMORE**—TCI of North Dakota Inc.

▲ **LEEDS**—Midcontinent Cable Systems Co. of North Dakota

▲ **LEHR**—Midcontinent Cable Systems Co. of North Dakota

▲ **LEONARD**—Midcontinent Cable Systems Co. of North Dakota

▲ **LIDGERWOOD**—Midcontinent Cable Systems Co. of North Dakota

▲ **LIGNITE**—Midcontinent Cable Systems Co. of North Dakota

LINCOLN—See BISMARCK, ND

▲ **LINTON**—Midcontinent Cable Systems Co. of North Dakota

▲ **LISBON**—Cable Services Inc.

▲ **LITCHVILLE**—Dickey Rural Services Inc.

▲ **MADDOCK**—Maddock Cable TV

MAKOTI—See PARSHALL, ND

MANDAN—See BISMARCK, ND

▲ **MANVEL**—TCI of North Dakota Inc.

▲ **MAPLETON**—Midcontinent Cable Systems Co. of North Dakota

▲ **MARION**—Dickey Rural Services Inc.

▲ **MAX**—Midcontinent Cable Systems Co. of North Dakota

▲ **MAXBASS**—Souris River Telecommunications

▲ **MAYVILLE**—Midcontinent Cable Systems Co. of North Dakota

▲ **McCLUSKY**—Midcontinent Cable Systems Co. of North Dakota

McHENRY COUNTY—See DRAKE, ND

▲ **MEDINA**—Cable Services Medina

▲ **METIGOSHE**—Souris River Telecommunications

▲ **MICHIGAN**—Viking Electronics Inc.

▲ **MILNOR**—Dickey Rural Services Inc.

▲ **MINNEWAUKAN**—Midcontinent Cable Systems Co. of North Dakota

▲ **MINOT**—TCI of North Dakota Inc.

▲ **MINOT**—ProVision

▲ **MINOT AFB**—Midcontinent Cable Systems Co. of North Dakota

▲ **MINTO**—TCI of North Dakota Inc.

▲ **MOHALL**—Midcontinent Cable Systems Co. of North Dakota

▲ **MOTT**—Midcontinent Cable Systems Co. of North Dakota

▲ **MUNICH**—United Telephone Mutual Aid Corp.

▲ **NAPOLEON**—Midcontinent Cable Systems Co. of North Dakota

▲ **NECHE**—Viking Electronics Inc.

▲ **NEW ENGLAND**—New England Cablevision Inc.

▲ **NEW LEIPZIG**—Western Dakota Cable Inc.

▲ **NEW ROCKFORD**—Midcontinent Cable Systems Co. of North Dakota

▲ **NEW SALEM**—Midcontinent Cable Systems Co. of North Dakota

NEW TOWN—See PARSHALL, ND

▲ **NEWBURG**—RAE Cable

▲ **OAKES**—Cable Services Inc.

▲ **OSNABROCK**—Viking Electronics Inc.

▲ **PAGE**—Midcontinent Cable Systems Co. of North Dakota

▲ **PARK RIVER**—Viking Electronics Inc.

▲ **PARSHALL**—Reservation Telephone Cooperative

▲ **PEMBINA**—Pembina Cable TV Inc.

▲ **PETERSBURG**—Viking Electronics Inc.

▲ **PICK CITY**—Midcontinent Cable Systems Co. of North Dakota

PLAZA—See PARSHALL, ND

▲ **PORTLAND**—Midcontinent Cable Systems Co. of North Dakota

▲ **POWERS LAKE**—Northwest Communications Cooperative

PRAIRIE ROSE—See FARGO, ND

▲ **RAY**—Northwest Communications Cooperative

REED—See OAKPORT, MN

▲ **REEDER**—Midcontinent Cable Systems Co. of North Dakota

▲ **REGENT**—Consolidated Telephone Cooperative

▲ **REYNOLDS**—Midcontinent Cable Systems Co. of North Dakota

▲ **RHAME**—Midcontinent Cable Systems Co. of North Dakota

▲ **RICHARDTON**—Midcontinent Cable Systems Co. of North Dakota

▲ **RIVERDALE**—Midcontinent Cable Systems Co. of North Dakota

RIVERSIDE—See WEST FARGO, ND

▲ **ROBINSON**—BEK Communications Cooperative

ROCK LAKE—See MUNICH, ND

▲ **ROLETTE**—Midcontinent Cable Systems Co. of North Dakota

▲ **ROLLA**—Midcontinent Cable Systems Co. of North Dakota

▲ **RUGBY**—Midcontinent Cable Systems Co. of North Dakota

▲ **RUTHVILLE**—Midcontinent Cable Systems Co. of North Dakota

RYDER—See PARSHALL, ND

▲ **SANBORN**—Cable Services Inc.

▲ **SAWYER**—Sawyer CATV

▲ **SCRANTON**—Midcontinent Cable Systems Co. of North Dakota

▲ **SELFRIDGE**—Midcontinent Cable Systems Co. of North Dakota

▲ **SHERWOOD**—Souris River Telecommunications

▲ **SHEYENNE**—Sheyenne Cable TV

▲ **SOLEN**—Midcontinent Cable Systems Co. of North Dakota

▲ **SOURIS**—RAE Cable

▲ **SOUTH HEART**—Midcontinent Cable Systems Co. of North Dakota

▲ **ST. JOHN**—Midcontinent Cable Systems Co. of North Dakota

▲ **ST. THOMAS**—Viking Electronics Inc.

▲ **STANLEY**—Stanley Cablevision Inc.

▲ **STANTON**—Midcontinent Cable Systems Co. of North Dakota

▲ **STARKWEATHER**—Midcontinent Cable Systems Co. of North Dakota

▲ **STRASBURG**—BEK Communications Cooperative

▲ **STREETER**—Midcontinent Cable Systems Co. of North Dakota

▲ **SURREY**—Midcontinent Cable Systems Co. of North Dakota

▲ **SYKESTON**—Dakota Central Rural Telephone

▲ **TAPPEN**—BEK Communications Cooperative

▲ **TAYLOR**—Eagle Cablevision

▲ **THOMPSON**—Midcontinent Cable Systems Co. of North Dakota

▲ **TIOGA**—Midcontinent Cable Systems Co. of North Dakota

▲ **TOWNER**—Midcontinent Cable Systems Co. of North Dakota

▲ **TURTLE LAKE**—Midcontinent Cable Systems Co. of North Dakota

▲ **TUTTLE**—BEK Communications Cooperative

▲ **UNDERWOOD**—Midcontinent Cable Systems Co. of North Dakota

▲ **UPHAM**—RAE Cable

▲ **VALLEY CITY**—Cable Services Inc.

▲ **VELVA**—Star City Cable TV

▲ **WAHPETON**—TCI of the Valley

▲ **WALHALLA**—Midcontinent Cable Systems Co. of North Dakota

WARD COUNTY (Portions)—See MINOT, ND (TCI of North Dakota Inc.)

▲ **WASHBURN**—Midcontinent Cable Systems Co. of North Dakota

▲ **WATFORD CITY**—Midcontinent Cable Systems Co. of North Dakota

▲ **WEST FARGO**—Harmon Cable Investments Inc.

▲ **WESTHOPE**—Souris River Telecommunications

▲ **WILDROSE**—Northwest Communications Cooperative

▲ **WILLISTON**—TCI of North Dakota Inc.

WILLISTON TWP. (portions)—See WILLISTON, ND

▲ **WILLOW CITY**—Midcontinent Cable Systems Co. of North Dakota

▲ **WILTON**—Midcontinent Cable Systems Co. of North Dakota

▲ **WIMBLEDON**—Midcontinent Cable Systems Co. of North Dakota

▲ **WING**—BEK Communications Cooperative

▲ **WISHEK**—Midcontinent Cable Systems Co. of North Dakota

▲ **WOODWORTH**—Dakota Central Rural Telephone

▲ **WYNDMERE**—Dickey Rural Services Inc.

▲ **YPSILANTI**—Dakota Central Rural Telephone

▲ **ZAP**—Midcontinent Cable Systems Co. of North Dakota

▲ **ZEELAND**—Midcontinent Cable Systems Co. of North Dakota

OHIO

ABERDEEN—See RIPLEY (Brown County), OH

▲ **ADA**—FrontierVision

ADAMS COUNTY (portions)—See WEST UNION, OH

ADAMS TWP. (Champaign County)—See PIQUA, OH

ADAMS TWP. (Clinton County)—See WILMINGTON, OH

ADAMS TWP. (Darke County)—See GREENVILLE, OH

ADAMS TWP. (Guernsey County)—See CAMBRIDGE, OH

ADAMS TWP. (Seneca County)—See BELLEVUE, OH

ADAMS TWP. (Washington County)—See WATERTOWN, OH

ADAMSVILLE—See NORWICH, OH

ADDYSTON—See DELHI TWP., OH

ADELPHI—See KINGSTON, OH

▲ **ADENA**—TCI Cablevision of Ohio Inc.

ADRIAN—See SYCAMORE, OH

▲ **AKRON**—Time Warner Cable

▲ **ALBANY**—FrontierVision

ALEXANDER TWP.—See ATHENS, OH

ALEXANDRIA—See KIRKERSVILLE, OH

ALGER—See ADA, OH

ALLEN COUNTY (portions)—See FORT SHAWNEE, OH

▲ **ALLEN TWP. (Ottawa County)**—FrontierVision

ALLEN TWP. (Darke County)—See GREENVILLE, OH

ALLEN TWP. (Hancock County)—See FINDLAY, OH

ALLEN TWP. (Union County)—See RICHWOOD, OH

ALLIANCE—See CANTON, OH

ALTON—See LONDON, OH

AMANDA—See OAKLAND, OH

AMANDA TWP.—See FINDLAY, OH

AMANDA TWP. (Allen County)—See LIMA, OH

AMANDA TWP. (Fairfield County)—See CHILLICOTHE, OH

AMBERLEY—See CINCINNATI, OH

AMBOY TWP.—See FULTON TWP., OH

AMBOY TWP.—See also METAMORA, OH

▲ **AMELIA**—Coaxial Communications of Southern Ohio Inc.

AMERICAN TWP. (Allen County)—See LIMA, OH

▲ **AMESVILLE**—Riley Video Services

▲ **AMHERST**—MediaOne

AMHERST TWP.—See AMHERST, OH

AMLIN—See HAYDEN HEIGHTS, OH

▲ **AMSTERDAM**—TCI Cablevision of Ohio Inc.

ANDERSON TWP. (Hamilton County)—See CINCINNATI, OH

▲ **ANDOVER**—CableVision Communications

ANDOVER BORO—See ANDOVER, OH

ANDOVER TWP. (Ashtabula County)—See VERNON, OH

ANDOVER TWP. (Ashtabula County)—See also ANDOVER, OH

ANDOVER VILLAGE—See ANDOVER, OH

▲ **COLUMBUS GROVE (village)**—Quality One Technologies Inc.

▲ **COMMERCIAL POINT**—FrontierVision

▲ **CONCORD TWP. (Lake County)**—Adelphia

CONCORD TWP. (Delaware County)—See COLUMBUS, OH (Time Warner Communications)

CONCORD TWP. (Miami County)—See TIPP CITY, OH

CONCORD TWP. (Miami County)—See also TROY, OH

CONCORDIA—See WATERVILLE, OH

CONESVILLE—See COSHOCTON, OH

▲ **CONGRESS**—Time Warner Cable

CONGRESS TWP. (Wayne County)—See LODI, OH

▲ **CONNEAUT**—Adelphia

CONNORVILLE—See MOUNT PLEASANT TWP. (Jefferson County), OH

CONTINENTAL—See LEIPSIC, OH

CONVOY—See FORT WAYNE, IN

COOLVILLE—See PORTERFIELD, OH

COPLEY TWP.—See BATH TWP. (Summit County), OH

CORDOBA—See NORTHWOOD, OH

▲ **CORNING**—Cablevision Communications

CORTLAND—See WARREN, OH

CORWIN VILLAGE—See KETTERING, OH

CORYVILLE—See IRONTON, OH

▲ **COSHOCTON**—FrontierVision

COSTONIA—See TORONTO, OH

COVENTRY TWP. (Summit County)—See GREEN TWP. (Summit County), OH

COVINGTON—See PIQUA, OH

▲ **CRAIG BEACH**—Time Warner Cable

CRAIG BEACH—See also NEWTON FALLS, OH

CRANBERRY PRAIRIE—See CELINA, OH

CRANBERRY TWP.—See ATTICA, OH

CRANE TWP.—See UPPER SANDUSKY, OH

CRANE TWP. (Paulding County)—See VAN WERT, OH

CRESCENT—See BARTON, OH

CRESTLINE—See GALION, OH

CRESTON—See LODI, OH

CRIDERSVILLE—See FORT SHAWNEE, OH

▲ **CROOKSVILLE**—Cablecomm

CROSBY TWP. (Hamilton County)—See CINCINNATI, OH

CROSBY TWP. (Hamilton County)—See also ROSS TWP. (Butler County), OH

CROSS CREEK TWP. (Jefferson County)—See STEUBENVILLE, OH

CROTON—See JOHNSTOWN, OH

▲ **CROWN CITY**—FrontierVision

▲ **CUMBERLAND**—Cablevision Communications

CURTICE—See ALLEN TWP. (Ottawa County), OH

CUSTAR (village)—See BOWLING GREEN, OH

CUYAHOGA FALLS—See AKRON, OH

CUYAHOGA FALLS—See also BATH TWP. (Summit County), OH

CUYAHOGA HEIGHTS—See GARFIELD HEIGHTS, OH

CYGNET—See NORTH BALTIMORE, OH

DADSVILLE—See LEWISBURG, OH

DALTON—See ORRVILLE, OH

Danbury Twp. (Ottawa County)—See ALLEN TWP. (Ottawa County), OH

DANBURY TWP. (Ottawa County)—See also PORT CLINTON, OH

▲ **DANVILLE**—Time Warner Cable

DARBY TWP. (Madison & Union Counties)—See MARYSVILLE, OH

DARBY TWP. (Madison County)—See CANAAN TWP. (Madison County), OH

DARBY TWP. (Pickaway County)—See COLUMBUS, OH (Time Warner Entertainment Co. LP)

DARBYDALE—See COLUMBUS, OH (Time Warner Entertainment Co. LP)

DARBYVILLE—See COMMERCIAL POINT, OH

DARRTOWN—See COLLINSVILLE, OH

▲ **DAYTON**—Time Warner Cable

DE GRAFF—See ANNA, OH

DECATUR TWP. (Lawrence County)—See PEDRO, OH

DEER CREEK TWP. (Madison County)—See LONDON, OH

DEER CREEK TWP. (Pickaway County)—See NEW HOLLAND, OH

DEER PARK—See CINCINNATI, OH

DEERFIELD TWP. (Portage County)—See ATWATER TWP., OH

DEERFIELD TWP. (Warren County)—See CINCINNATI, OH

DEERFIELD TWP. (Warren County)—See also MORROW, OH

DEERING—See IRONTON, OH

▲ **DEFIANCE**—FrontierVision

DEFIANCE COUNTY (portions)—See DEFIANCE, OH

DELAWARE TWP.—See FINDLAY, OH

DELAWARE TWP. (Delaware County)—See COLUMBUS, OH (Insight Communications)

DELHI—See CINCINNATI, OH

▲ **DELHI TWP.**—FrontierVision

▲ **DELLROY**—FrontierVision

▲ **DELPHOS**—Warner Cable Communications Inc.

DELTA—See SWANTON, OH

▲ **DENMARK TWP.**—Star Cable

DENNISON—See NEW PHILADELPHIA, OH

DERBY—See COLUMBUS, OH (Time Warner Entertainment Co. LP)

DERWENT—See SENECAVILLE, OH

▲ **DESHLER**—FrontierVision

DEXTER CITY—See WARNER, OH

DILLONVALE—See ADENA, OH

DINSMORE TWP.—See ANNA, OH

DODSON TWP.—See HILLSBORO, OH

DONNELSVILLE—See KETTERING, OH

DORSET TWP.—See DENMARK TWP., OH

DOVER—See NEW PHILADELPHIA, OH

DOVER TWP.—See ATHENS, OH

DOVER TWP. (Fulton County)—See also DEFIANCE, OH

DOVER TWP. (Union County)—See MARYSVILLE, OH

DOYLESTOWN—See AKRON, OH

▲ **DRESDEN**—Cablecomm

DUBLIN—See COLUMBUS, OH (Time Warner Communications)

* **DUBLIN**—Americast

DUCHOQUET TWP. (southern portion)—See WAPAKONETA, OH

DUDLEY—See WARNER, OH

DUFFY—See HANNIBAL, OH

DUNBRIDGE—See BOWLING GREEN, OH

DUNCAN FALLS—See PHILO (portions), OH

DUNCAN FALLS (portions)—See MUSKINGUM COUNTY (portions), OH

▲ **DUNKIRK**—FrontierVision

EAGLE TWP. (Hancock County)—See FINDLAY, OH

EAST CANTON—See CANTON, OH

▲ **EAST CLEVELAND**—East Cleveland Cable TV & Communications LLC

EAST FULTONHAM—See ZANESVILLE, OH

EAST LIBERTY—See WEST MANSFIELD, OH

▲ **EAST LIVERPOOL**—TCI Cablevision of Ohio Inc.

▲ **EAST PALESTINE**—TCI Cablevision of Ohio Inc.

EAST SPARTA—See CANTON, OH

EAST UNION TWP. (Wayne County)—See WOOSTER, OH

EASTLAKE—See MENTOR, OH

EASTPOINT—See NORTHWOOD, OH

EATON—See LEWISBURG, OH

EATON TWP. (Lorain County)—See GRAFTON, OH

EDEN TWP.—See UPPER SANDUSKY, OH

EDEN TWP. (Seneca County)—See FOSTORIA, OH

EDGERTON—See BRYAN, OH

EDINBURGH TWP.—See ATWATER TWP., OH

EDISON—See MOUNT GILEAD, OH

▲ **EDON**—FrontierVision

GETTYSBURG—See GREENVILLE, OH

GETTYSBURG (village)—See GREENVILLE, OH

GIBSONBURG—See ALLEN TWP. (Ottawa County), OH

GILBOA—See LEIPSIC, OH

GILEAD TWP.—See MOUNT GILEAD, OH

GIRARD—See WARREN, OH

GLANDORF (village)—See OTTAWA, OH

GLEN ROBBINS—See MARTINS FERRY, OH

GLEN ROY—See JACKSON, OH

▲ **GLENCOE**—TCI Cablevision of Ohio Inc.

GLENDALE—See CINCINNATI, OH

▲ **GLENMONT**—FrontierVision

GLENWILLOW (village)—See SOLON, OH

GLORIA GLEN VILLAGE—See LODI, OH

GLOUSTER—See NELSONVILLE, OH

GNADENHUTTON—See NEW PHILADELPHIA, OH

▲ **GOLF MANOR**—TCI Cablevision of Ohio Inc.

GOLF MANOR—See also CINCINNATI, OH

GOMER—See LIMA, OH

GOOD HOPE TWP.—See ENTERPRISE, OH

GORDON—See LEWISBURG, OH

GOSHEN (Clermont County)—See CINCINNATI, OH

GOSHEN (Mahoning County) (portions)—See SALEM, OH

▲ **GOSHEN TWP. (Clermont County)**—Time Warner Cable

GOSHEN TWP. (Belmont County)—See BELLAIRE, OH

GOSHEN TWP. (Mahoning County)—See BERLIN TWP. (Mahoning County), OH

GOSHEN TWP. (Mahoning County)—See also SEBRING, OH

▲ **GRAFTON**—Grafton Cable Communications

GRAFTON TWP.—See GRAFTON, OH

GRAND PRAIRIE TWP.—See MARION, OH

GRAND RAPIDS—See WATERVILLE, OH

GRAND RIVER—See MENTOR, OH

GRANDVIEW HEIGHTS—See COLUMBUS, OH (Time Warner Communications)

GRANGER—See BATH TWP. (Summit County), OH

GRANVILLE (portions)—See LICKING COUNTY (northwestern portion), OH

GRANVILLE (village)—See NEWARK, OH

GRANVILLE TWP. (Licking County)—See NEWARK, OH

GRANVILLE TWP. (Mercer County)—See CELINA, OH

GRATIOT (Muskingum County)—See MOUNT STERLING (Muskingum County), OH

GRATIS—See LEWISBURG, OH

GRAYTOWN—See OAK HARBOR, OH

GREEN ACRES—See LICK TWP. (Jackson County), OH

GREEN CAMP—See RICHWOOD, OH

▲ **GREEN COVE CONDOMINIUMS**—Time Warner Entertainment Co. LP

GREEN CREEK TWP. (Sandusky County)—See BELLEVUE, OH

▲ **GREEN MEADOWS**—Time Warner Entertainment Co. LP

GREEN SPRINGS—See BELLEVUE, OH

GREEN TWP. (Brown County)—See AMELIA, OH

GREEN TWP. (Brown County)—See also OWENSVILLE, OH

GREEN TWP. (Clark County)—See KETTERING, OH

GREEN TWP. (Clark County)—See also YELLOW SPRINGS, OH

▲ **GREEN TWP. (Hamilton County)**—Time Warner Cable

GREEN TWP. (Hamilton County)—See also CINCINNATI, OH

GREEN TWP. (Mahoning County)—See BERLIN TWP. (Mahoning County), OH

GREEN TWP. (Scioto County)—See FRANKLIN FURNACE, OH

▲ **GREEN TWP. (Summit County)**—Cable One

GREEN TWP. (Wayne County)—See ORRVILLE, OH

GREEN TWP. (Wayne County)—See also WOOSTER, OH

GREEN VILLAGE (Summit County)—See GREEN TWP. (Summit County), OH

GREENBURG TWP.—See KALIDA, OH

▲ **GREENFIELD**—Cox Communications

▲ **GREENFIELD ESTATES**—The Greenfield Co.

GREENFIELD TWP. (Fairfield County)—See LANCASTER, OH

GREENFIELD TWP. (Huron County)—See WILLARD, OH

GREENHILLS—See CINCINNATI, OH

▲ **GREENVILLE**—Time Warner Cable

GREENVILLE TWP. (Darke County)—See GREENVILLE, OH

GREENWICH—See WILLARD, OH

GREENWICH VILLAGE—See WILLARD, OH

▲ **GREENWOOD (village)**—Adelphia Cable Communications

GROTON TWP. (Erie County)—See SANDUSKY, OH

GROVE CITY (Franklin County)—See COLUMBUS, OH (Time Warner Communications)

GROVE CITY (Franklin County)—See also COLUMBUS, OH (Time Warner Entertainment Co. LP)

GROVEPORT—See COLUMBUS, OH (Time Warner Communications)

GROVERHILL—See OTTOVILLE, OH

▲ **GUERNSEY COUNTY (portions)**—FrontierVision

▲ **GUILFORD LAKE**—Time Warner Cable

GUILFORD TWP.—See LODI, OH

▲ **GUYSVILLE**—FrontierVision

HALE TWP.—See RICHWOOD, OH

HALLSVILLE—See KINGSTON, OH

HAMBDEN TWP. (Geauga County)—See THOMPSON TWP. (Geauga County), OH

HAMBDEN TWP. (Geauga County)—See also CHARDON, OH

HAMDEN—See JACKSON, OH

HAMER TWP.—See HILLSBORO, OH

HAMERSVILLE—See AMELIA, OH

▲ **HAMILTON**—Time Warner Cable

HAMILTON TWP. (Franklin County)—See COLUMBUS, OH (Time Warner Communications)

HAMILTON TWP. (Franklin County)—See also COLUMBUS, OH (Insight Communications)

HAMILTON TWP. (Warren County)—See CINCINNATI, OH

HAMILTON TWP. (Warren County)—See also MORROW, OH

HAMLER—See DESHLER, OH

HAMMONDSVILLE—See IRONDALE, OH

HANGING ROCK—See FRANKLIN FURNACE, OH

▲ **HANNIBAL**—FrontierVision

HANOVER (portions)—See NEWARK, OH

▲ **HANOVER (Licking County) village)**—FrontierVision

HANOVER TWP. (Butler County South)—See HAMILTON, OH

HANOVER TWP. (Butler County North)—See also MIDDLETOWN, OH

HANOVER TWP. (Butler County)—See also ROSS TWP. (Butler County), OH

HANOVER TWP. (Columbiana County)—See GUILFORD LAKE, OH

HANOVERTON—See GUILFORD LAKE, OH

HARBOR HILLS—See THORNVILLE, OH

HARBOR VIEW—See TOLEDO, OH

HARDIN—See ANNA, OH

HARDIN COUNTY—See KENTON, OH

HARDING TWP.—See SWANTON, OH

HARLAN TWP.—See MORROW, OH

HARLEM TWP. (Delaware County)—See COLUMBUS, OH (Insight Communications)

HARLEM TWP. (Delaware County)—See also MANSFIELD, OH

HARMONY TWP. (Clark County)—See KETTERING, OH

HARMONY TWP. (Morrow County)—See MARENGO, OH

HARPERSFIELD TWP. (Ashtabula County)—See GENEVA, OH

HARPSTER—See UPPER SANDUSKY, OH

HARRIS TWP. (Ottawa County)—See ALLEN TWP. (Ottawa County), OH

JACKSON TWP. (Stark County)—See CANTON, OH

JACKSON TWP. (Stark County)—See also MASSILLON, OH

JACKSON TWP. (Van Wert County)—See OTTOVILLE, OH

JACKSONBURG (village)—See COLLINSVILLE, OH

JACKSONTOWN—See THORNVILLE, OH

JACKSONVILLE—See NELSONVILLE, OH

JAMESTOWN (village)—See KETTERING, OH

JASPER VILLAGE—See CHILLICOTHE, OH

JASPER TWP.—See WASHINGTON COURT HOUSE, OH

JEFFERSON—See PLYMOUTH TWP. (Ashtabula County), OH

JEFFERSON TWP. (Ashtabula County)—See DENMARK TWP., OH

JEFFERSON TWP. (Ashtabula County)—See also PLYMOUTH TWP. (Ashtabula County), OH

JEFFERSON TWP. (Brown County)—See OWENSVILLE, OH

JEFFERSON TWP. (Coshocton County)—See COSHOCTON, OH

JEFFERSON TWP. (Crawford County)—See GALION, OH

JEFFERSON TWP. (Fayette County)—See WASHINGTON COURT HOUSE, OH

JEFFERSON TWP. (Franklin County)—See COLUMBUS, OH (Insight Communications)

JEFFERSON TWP. (Greene County)—See PORT WILLIAM, OH

JEFFERSON TWP. (Logan County)—See BELLEFONTAINE, OH

JEFFERSON TWP. (Madison County)—See CANAAN TWP. (Madison County), OH

JEFFERSON TWP. (Madison County)—See also LONDON, OH

JEFFERSON TWP. (Montgomery County)—See GERMANTOWN, OH

JEFFERSON TWP. (Ross County)—See RICHMOND DALE, OH

JEFFERSON TWP. (Scioto County)—See LUCASVILLE, OH

JEFFERSON TWP. (Williams County)—See BRYAN, OH

JEFFERSONVILLE—See WASHINGTON COURT HOUSE, OH

JENERA—See ADA, OH

JENNINGS TWP. (Putnam County)—See OTTOVILLE, OH

JEROME TWP. (Union County)—See CANAAN TWP. (Madison County), OH

JEROME TWP. (Union County)—See also MARYSVILLE, OH

▲ **JEROMESVILLE**—Time Warner Cable

JERSEY TWP.—See COLUMBUS, OH (Insight Communications)

JERUSALEM—See MALAGA TWP., OH

JERUSALEM TWP. (Lucas County)—See OAK HARBOR, OH

JERUSALEM TWP. (Lucas County)—See ALLEN TWP. (Ottawa County), OH

▲ **JEWETT**—TCI Cablevision of Ohio Inc.

JOHNSON TWP. (Champaign County)—See ST. PARIS, OH

JOHNSON TWP. (Champaign County)—See also PIQUA, OH

JOHNSTON TWP. (Trumbull County)—See BAZETTA TWP., OH

▲ **JOHNSTOWN**—Time Warner Cable

JOHNSTOWN (portions)—See LICKING COUNTY (northwestern portion), OH

JOHNSVILLE—See MANSFIELD, OH

JUNCTION CITY—See NEW LEXINGTON (Perry County), OH

▲ **KALIDA**—Kalida Telephone Co.

KEENE TWP.—See COSHOCTON, OH

▲ **KENT**—Time Warner Cable

▲ **KENTON**—Time Warner Cable

▲ **KETTERING**—Time Warner Cable

KETTLERSVILLE—See MINSTER, OH

KILLBUCK—See MILLERSBURG, OH

KIMBOLTON—See GUERNSEY COUNTY (portions), OH

KING MINES—See SENECAVILLE, OH

▲ **KINGSTON**—FrontierVision

KINGSTON TWP.—See MANSFIELD, OH

KINGSVILLE—See CONNEAUT, OH

▲ **KINSMAN**—CableVision Communications

KINSMAN (Trumbull County)—See also VERNON, OH

KINSMAN TWP.—See VERNON, OH

KINSMAN TWP.—See KINSMAN, OH

KIPLING—See SENECAVILLE, OH

KIPTON (village)—See WELLINGTON, OH

Kirby—See MARSEILLES, OH

▲ **KIRKERSVILLE**—Time Warner Cable

KIRTLAND—See CONCORD TWP. (Lake County), OH

KIRTLAND HILLS—See CONCORD TWP. (Lake County), OH

KITTS HILL—See IRONTON, OH

KNOX COUNTY (portions)—See HOWARD, OH

KNOX TWP. (Columbiana County)—See SEBRING, OH

KNOX TWP. (Jefferson County)—See KNOXVILLE, OH

▲ **KNOXVILLE**—Star Cable

▲ **LA RUE**—Time Warner Cable

LACARNE—See OAK HARBOR, OH

LAFAYETTE—See LIMA, OH

LAFAYETTE TWP. (Coshocton County)—See WEST LAFAYETTE, OH

LAFAYETTE TWP. (Medina County)—See LODI, OH

LAFFERTY—See ST. CLAIRSVILLE, OH

LAGRANGE—See GRAFTON, OH

LAGRANGE (village)—See GRAFTON, OH

LAGRANGE TWP.—See GRAFTON, OH

LAKE BUCKHORN—See MILLERSBURG, OH

▲ **LAKE MOHAWK MOBILE HOME PARK**—Warner Cable Communications

LAKE TWP. (Logan County)—See BELLEFONTAINE, OH

LAKE TWP. (Stark County)—See CANTON, OH

LAKE TWP. (Stark County)—See also GREEN TWP. (Summit County), OH

LAKE TWP. (Wood County)—See WATERVILLE, OH

LAKE TWP. (Wood County)—See also ALLEN TWP. (Ottawa County), OH

LAKE TWP. (Wood County)—See also LUCKEY, OH

LAKE TWP. (Wood County)—See also NORTHWOOD, OH

LAKE WHITE—See WAVERLY, OH

LAKELINE—See MENTOR, OH

LAKEMORE—See AKRON, OH

LAKESIDE—See PORT CLINTON, OH

LAKEVIEW (Logan County)—See WAYNESFIELD, OH

LAKEVIEW (Logan County)—See also BELLEFONTAINE, OH

LAKEVILLE—See SHREVE, OH

LAKEWOOD (Cuyahoga County)—See BROOK PARK, OH

LAKEWOOD (Cuyahoga County)—See also PARMA, OH

▲ **LANCASTER**—Time Warner Cable

LANSING VALLEY—See MARTINS FERRY, OH

LATTY TWP.—See OTTOVILLE, OH

LAURA—See TIPP CITY, OH

LAUREL TWP.—See ENTERPRISE, OH

LAURELVILLE—See KINGSTON, OH

LAWRENCE TWP. (Stark County)—See MASSILLON, OH

LAWRENCE TWP. (Tuscarawas County)—See BOLIVAR, OH

LAWRENCEVILLE—See YELLOW SPRINGS, OH

LE SOURDSVILLE MOBILE HOME PARK—See LIBERTY TWP. (Butler County), OH (Coaxial Communications)

LEAVITTSBURG—See NEWTON FALLS, OH

▲ **LEBANON**—Coaxial Communications

LEBANON—See also CINCINNATI, OH

▲ **LEESBURG**—Time Warner Cable

▲ **LEESVILLE**—TCI Cable Television

LEESVILLE—See also GALION, OH

LEETONIA—See EAST PALESTINE, OH

LEHMKUHL LANDING—See ANNA, OH

▲ **LEIPSIC**—Orwell Cable TV Co.

LEMON TWP. (Butler County)—See MIDDLETOWN, OH

LEMOYNE—See LUCKEY, OH

▲ **MALAGA TWP.**—Richards Cable Inc.

MALINTA—See NAPOLEON, OH

MALTA—See MCCONNELSVILLE, OH

MALVERN—See MINERVA, OH

MALVERN (village)—See CANTON, OH

▲**MANCHESTER**—FrontierVision

▲ **MANSFIELD**—Time Warner Cable

▲ **MANTUA**—Adelphia Cable Communications

MANTUA—See also KENT, OH

MANTUA TWP.—See MANTUA, OH

MAPLE HEIGHTS—See CLEVELAND HEIGHTS, OH

MAPLEWOOD—See ANNA, OH

MARBLE CLIFF—See COLUMBUS, OH (Time Warner Communications)

MARBLEHEAD—See PORT CLINTON, OH

▲ **MARENGO**—Time Warner Cable

▲ **MARGARETTA TWP.**—FrontierVision

MARGARETTA TWP.—See also SANDUSKY, OH

MARIEMONT—See CINCINNATI, OH

▲ **MARIETTA**—TCI Cablevision of Ohio Inc.

▲ **MARION**—Frontiervision

MARION—See also HIDE-A-WAY HILLS, OH

MARION COUNTY—See MARION, OH

MARION TWP. (Allen County)—See LIMA, OH

MARION TWP. (Clinton County)—See WILMINGTON, OH

MARION TWP. (Hancock County)—See FINDLAY, OH

MARION TWP. (Henry County)—See DESHLER, OH

MARION TWP. (Marion County)—See LA RUE, OH

MARION TWP. (Marion County)—See also MARION, OH

MARLBORO TWP.—See ATWATER TWP., OH

MARLBORO TWP. (Stark County)—See CANTON, OH

* **MARSEILLES**—Paxton Cable

Marseilles Twp.—See MARSEILLES, OH

MARSHALL TWP.—See HILLSBORO, OH

MARSHALLVILLE—See ORRVILLE, OH

▲ **MARTINS FERRY**—TCI Cablevision of Ohio Inc.

▲ **MARTINSBURG**—National Cable Inc.

MARTINSVILLE—See OWENSVILLE, OH

▲ **MARYSVILLE**—Time Warner Cable

MASON—See CINCINNATI, OH

▲ **MASSILLON**—Massillon Cable TV Inc.

MASURY—See SHARON, PA

MAUMEE—See TOLEDO, OH

MAYFIELD HEIGHTS—See CLEVELAND HEIGHTS, OH

MAYFIELD VILLAGE—See CLEVELAND HEIGHTS, OH

▲ **MAYNARD**—Powhaton Point Cable Co.

McARTHUR—See JACKSON, OH

McCARTYVILLE—See ANNA, OH

McCLURE—See BOWLING GREEN, OH

McCLURE (village)—See BOWLING GREEN, OH

McCOMB—See FINDLAY, OH

▲ **McCONNELSVILLE**—FrontierVision

McCUTCHENVILLE—See SYCAMORE, OH

McDONALD—See AUSTINTOWN TWP., OH

McGUFFEY—See ADA, OH

MEAD TWP.—See BRIDGEPORT, OH

MECCA TWP. (Trumbull County)—See BAZETTA TWP., OH

MECHANICSBURG—See URBANA, OH

▲ **MEDINA**—Armstrong Cable Services

MEDINA TWP.—See MEDINA, OH

MEIGS TWP. (Adams County)—See PEEBLES, OH

MELMORE—See SYCAMORE, OH

MELROSE—See LEIPSIC, OH

MELROSE MOBILE HOME PARK—See WOOSTER, OH

MENDON—See ROCKFORD, OH

▲ **MENTOR**—MediaOne

MENTOR-ON-THE-LAKE—See CONCORD TWP. (Lake County), OH

MERCER (portions)—See ROCKFORD, OH

MESOPOTAMIA—See NELSON TWP., OH

MESOPOTAMIA TWP.—See NELSON TWP., OH

▲ **METAMORA**—FrontierVision

MEYERS LAKE—See CANTON, OH

MIAMI TWP. (Clark County)—See KETTERING, OH

MIAMI TWP. (Clermont County)—See CINCINNATI, OH

MIAMI TWP. (Greene County)—See YELLOW SPRINGS, OH

MIAMI TWP. (Greene County)—See also KETTERING, OH

MIAMI TWP. (Hamilton County)—See CINCINNATI, OH

MIAMI TWP. (Hamilton County)—See also DELHI TWP., OH

MIAMI TWP. (Logan County)—See BELLE CENTER, OH

MIAMI TWP. (Montgomery County)—See KETTERING, OH

MIAMI TWP. (Montgomery County)—See also MIDDLETOWN, OH

MIAMISBURG—See KETTERING, OH

▲ **MIDDLEBURG (Noble County)**—CableVision Communications

MIDDLEBURG (Logan County)—See WEST MANSFIELD, OH

MIDDLEBURG HEIGHTS—See STRONGSVILLE, OH

MIDDLEFIELD—See CHARDON, OH

MIDDLEFIELD TWP.—See NELSON TWP., OH

MIDDLEPORT—See POINT PLEASANT, WV

MIDDLETON TWP.—See TOLEDO, OH

MIDDLETON TWP. (Columbiana County)—See EAST PALESTINE, OH

MIDDLETON TWP. (Lucas County)—See WATERVILLE, OH

MIDDLETON TWP. (Wood County)—See WATERVILLE, OH

▲ **MIDDLETOWN**—Time Warner Cable

MIDLAND—See OWENSVILLE, OH

MIDVALE—See NEW PHILADELPHIA, OH

MIDWAY—See CANAAN TWP. (Madison County), OH

MIFFLIN—See MANSFIELD, OH

▲ **MIFFLIN TWP.**—Americast

MIFFLIN TWP. (Ashland & Richland Counties)—See MANSFIELD, OH

MIFFLIN TWP. (Ashland County)—See ASHLAND, OH

MIFFLIN TWP. (Franklin County)—See COLUMBUS, OH (Insight Communications)

MIFFLIN TWP. (Franklin County)—See also COLUMBUS, OH (Time Warner Communications)

MIFFLIN TWP. (Pike County)—See CHILLICOTHE, OH

MILAN—See WAKEMAN, OH

MILAN—See also NORWALK, OH

MILAN TWP. (Erie County)—See NORWALK, OH

MILAN TWP. (Erie County)—See also SANDUSKY, OH

MILFORD—See CINCINNATI, OH

MILFORD CENTER—See MARYSVILLE, OH

MILFORD TWP. (Butler County)—See COLLINSVILLE, OH

MILL CREEK TWP.—See CANAAN TWP. (Madison County), OH

MILLBURY—See ALLEN TWP. (Ottawa County), OH

MILLEDGEVILLE—See WASHINGTON COURT HOUSE, OH

MILLER CITY—See LEIPSIC, OH

▲**MILLERSBURG**—FrontierVision

MILLERSPORT—See BALTIMORE, OH

MILLERSPORT—See also CIRCLEVILLE, OH

MILLFIELD—See NELSONVILLE, OH

MILLVILLE—See HAMILTON, OH

MILLWOOD—See GAMBIER, OH

MILLWOOD TWP.—See SENECAVILLE, OH

MILTON CENTER (village)—See BOWLING GREEN, OH

MILTON TWP. (Ashland County)—See ASHLAND, OH

MILTON TWP. (Mahoning County)—See BERLIN TWP. (Mahoning County), OH

MILTON TWP. (Mahoning County)—See also CRAIG BEACH, OH

MINERAL CITY—See CANTON, OH

MINERAL RIDGE—See AUSTINTOWN TWP., OH

▲ **MINERVA**—TCI Cablevision of Ohio Inc.

MINERVA PARK—See COLUMBUS, OH (Time Warner Communications)

MINFORD TWP. (Scioto County)—See LUCASVILLE, OH

MINGO JUNCTION—See STEUBENVILLE, OH

▲ **MINSTER**—FrontierVision

MINSTER—See also NEW KNOXVILLE, OH

MOGADORE—See AKRON, OH

MONCLOVA—See WATERVILLE, OH

MONCLOVA TWP. (Lucas County)—See TOLEDO, OH

MONROE—See DELLROY, OH

MONROE—See also MIDDLETOWN, OH

MONROE TWP. (Allen County)—See LIMA, OH

MONROE TWP. (Ashtabula County)—See DENMARK TWP., OH

MONROE TWP. (Clermont County)—See AMELIA, OH

MONROE TWP. (Knox County)—See THORNVILLE, OH

MONROE TWP. (Licking County)—See COLUMBUS, OH (Insight Communications)

MONROE TWP. (Licking County)—See also JOHNSTOWN, OH

MONROE TWP. (Logan County)—See URBANA, OH

MONROE TWP. (Madison County)—See CANAAN TWP. (Madison County), OH

MONROE TWP. (Perry County)—See CORNING, OH

MONROE TWP. (Richland County)—See MANSFIELD, OH

MONROEVILLE—See NORWALK, OH

MONTEREY TWP. (Putnam County)—See OTTOVILLE, OH

MONTEZUMA—See CELINA, OH

MONTGOMERY—See CINCINNATI, OH

MONTGOMERY TWP. (Ashland County)—See ASHLAND, OH

MONTGOMERY TWP. (Wood County)—See ALLEN TWP. (Ottawa County), OH

MONTPELIER—See BRYAN, OH

MONTRA—See ANNA, OH

MONTVILLE—See THOMPSON TWP. (Geauga County), OH

MONTVILLE TWP.—See MEDINA, OH

MONTVILLE TWP. (Medina County)—See LODI, OH

MOOREFIELD TWP. (Clark County)—See YELLOW SPRINGS, OH

MOOREFIELD TWP. (Clark County)—See also KETTERING, OH

MORAINE—See KETTERING, OH

MORELAND HILLS—See CLEVELAND HEIGHTS, OH

MORGAN COUNTY—See CROOKSVILLE, OH

MORGAN TWP. (Butler County)—See ROSS TWP. (Butler County), OH

MORGAN TWP. (Scioto County)—See LUCASVILLE, OH

▲ **MORRAL**—Paxton Cable

MORRIS TWP. (Knox County)—See THORNVILLE, OH

▲ **MORROW**—Coaxial Communications of Southern Ohio Inc.

MORROW COUNTY—See MOUNT GILEAD, OH

MOSCOW—See AMELIA, OH

MOULTON TWP.—See WAPAKONETA, OH

MOUNT BLANCHARD—See FINDLAY, OH

MOUNT CORY—See FINDLAY, OH

▲ **MOUNT EATON**—National Cable Inc.

▲ **MOUNT GILEAD**—Time Warner Cable

MOUNT HEALTHY—See CINCINNATI, OH

▲ **MOUNT ORAB**—Thompson Cable

MOUNT PLEASANT—See MOUNT PLEASANT TWP. (Jefferson County), OH

▲ **MOUNT PLEASANT TWP. (Jefferson County)**—Community TV Systems Cable Co.

MOUNT PLEASANT TWP. (Jefferson County)—See ADENA, OH

▲ **MOUNT STERLING (Muskingum County)**—Time Warner Cable

MOUNT STERLING (Madison County)—See COLUMBUS, OH (Time Warner Entertainment Co. LP)

▲ **MOUNT VERNON**—Time Warner Cable

MOUNT VICTORY (village)—See RICHWOOD, OH

▲ **MOWRYSTOWN**—FrontierVision

MOXAHALA—See CORNING, OH

MUHLENBERG TWP.—See COMMERCIAL POINT, OH

MUNROE FALLS—See AKRON, OH

MUNSON TWP. (Geauga County)—See CHARDON, OH

MUNSON TWP. (Geauga County)—See also CONCORD TWP. (Lake County), OH

▲ **MURRAY CITY**—FrontierVision

MUSKINGUM COUNTY—See ZANESVILLE, OH

▲ **MUSKINGUM COUNTY (portions)**—FrontierVision

MUSKINGUM COUNTY (southern portion)—See PHILO (portions), OH

MUSKINGUM TWP. (Muskingum County)—See HANOVER (village)(Licking County), OH

MUSKINGUM TWP. (Muskingum County)—See also NASHPORT, OH

MUTUAL—See URBANA, OH

NANKIN—See ASHLAND, OH

▲ **NAPOLEON**—FrontierVision

▲ **NASHPORT**—Cablecomm

NASHPORT—See also HANOVER (village) (Licking County), OH

NASHVILLE—See SHREVE, OH

NASHVILLE (village)—See SHREVE, OH

NAVARRE—See MASSILLON, OH

NEAPOLIS—See SWANTON, OH

NEAVE TWP. (Darke County)—See GREENVILLE, OH

NEFFS—See BELLAIRE, OH

NEGLEY—See EAST PALESTINE, OH

NELSON—See NEWTON FALLS, OH

▲ **NELSON MOBILE HOME PARK**—Warner Cable Communications

▲ **NELSON TWP.**—Star Cable

▲ **NELSONVILLE**—Nelsonville TV Cable

NEVADA—See UPPER SANDUSKY, OH

NEW ALBANY—See COLUMBUS, OH (Insight Communications)

NEW ALEXANDRIA—See STEUBENVILLE, OH

▲ **NEW ATHENS**—Richards & Sons Communications Co.

NEW BLOOMINGTON—See LA RUE, OH

NEW BOSTON—See PORTSMOUTH, OH

NEW BREMEN—See MINSTER, OH

NEW BREMEN—See also NEW KNOXVILLE, OH

NEW CARLISLE—See KETTERING, OH

▲ **NEW CONCORD**—Cablecomm

NEW CONCORD—See also NORWICH, OH

NEW CUMBERLAND—See DELLROY, OH

NEW GARDEN—See GUILFORD LAKE, OH

NEW HAMPSHIRE—See WAYNESFIELD, OH

NEW HAVEN—See WILLARD, OH

▲ **NEW HOLLAND**—FrontierVision

NEW JASPER TWP. (Greene County)—See KETTERING, OH

▲ **NEW KNOXVILLE**—New Knoxville Cable Systems

NEW LEBANON—See LEWISBURG, OH

▲ **NEW LEXINGTON (Perry County)**—Time Warner Cable

NEW LEXINGTON (Perry County)—See CORNING, OH

NEW LEXINGTON (Preble County)—See LEWISBURG, OH

▲ **NEW LONDON**—Time Warner Cable

NEW LYME TWP. (Ashtabula County)—See PLYMOUTH TWP. (Ashtabula County), OH

NEW MADISON—See GREENVILLE, OH

NEW MADISON (village)—See GREENVILLE, OH

NEW MARKET TWP.—See HILLSBORO, OH

NEW MARSHFIELD—See ALBANY, OH

▲ **NEW MATAMORAS**—FrontierVision

NEW MIAMI—See HAMILTON, OH

NEW MIDDLETOWN—See SPRINGFIELD TWP. (Mahoning County), OH

NEW PARIS—See LEWISBURG, OH

▲ **NEW PHILADELPHIA**—FrontierVision

NEW RICHMOND—See AMELIA, OH

NEW RIEGEL—See SYCAMORE, OH

* **NEW ROME**—Americast

NEW SALEM—See THORNVILLE, OH

NEW SPRINGFIELD (portions)—See BOARDMAN, OH

NEW STRAITSVILLE—See CORNING, OH

NEW VIENNA—See LEESBURG, OH

NEW WASHINGTON—See ATTICA, OH

NEW WATERFORD—See EAST PALESTINE, OH

NEW WESTON—See GREENVILLE, OH

▲ **NEWARK**—FrontierVision

NEWARK (portions)—See LICKING COUNTY (northeastern portion), OH

NEWARK TWP. (Licking County)—See THORNVILLE, OH

NEWARK TWP. (Licking County)—See also NEWARK, OH

NEWBERRY TWP.—See TROY, OH

NEWBERRY TWP.—See also PIQUA, OH

NEWBURGH HEIGHTS—See GARFIELD HEIGHTS, OH

NEWBURY (Geauga County)—See AUBURN TWP., OH

NEWBURY (Geauga County)—See also CHARDON, OH

NEWBURY TWP. (Geauga County)—See AUBURN TWP., OH

NEWBURY TWP. (Geauga County)—See also CHARDON, OH

NEWCOMERSTOWN—See NEW PHILADELPHIA, OH

▲ **NEWPORT**—FrontierVision

▲ **NEWTON FALLS**—TCI Cablevision of Ohio Inc.

▲ **NEWTON TWP.**—Star Cable

NEWTON TWP. (Miami County)—See TIPP CITY, OH

NEWTON TWP. (Miami County)—See also PIQUA, OH

NEWTON TWP. (Muskingum County)—See ZANESVILLE, OH

NEWTON TWP. (Pike County)—See CHILLICOTHE, OH

NEWTONSVILLE—See OWENSVILLE, OH

NEWTOWN—See CINCINNATI, OH

NEY—See DEFIANCE, OH

NILE TWP.—See FRIENDSHIP, OH

NILES—See WARREN, OH

NIMISHILLEN—See CANTON, OH

NIMISHILLEN TWP. (Stark County)—See CANTON, OH

NOBLE COUNTY—See CAMBRIDGE, OH

NOBLE TWP. (Auglaize County)—See WAPAKONETA, OH

NOBLE TWP. (Noble County)—See CAMBRIDGE, OH

▲ **NORTH BALTIMORE**—Americable USA Inc.

NORTH BEND—See DELHI TWP., OH

NORTH BLOOMFIELD TWP.—See GALION, OH

NORTH BLOOMFIELD TWP.—See also ORWELL, OH

NORTH CANTON—See CANTON, OH

NORTH COLLEGE HILL—See CINCINNATI, OH

NORTH FAIRFIELD—See WILLARD, OH

NORTH HAMPTON—See YELLOW SPRINGS, OH

NORTH JACKSON—See BAZETTA TWP., OH

NORTH KINGSVILLE—See CONNEAUT, OH

NORTH LEWISBURG VILLAGE—See MARYSVILLE, OH

NORTH LIMA—See BOARDMAN, OH

▲ **NORTH OLMSTED**—Cablevision of Ohio

▲ **NORTH OLMSTED**—Americast

NORTH PERRY (village)—See CONCORD TWP. (Lake County), OH

NORTH RANDALL—See CLEVELAND HEIGHTS, OH

NORTH RIDGEVILLE—See AMHERST, OH

NORTH ROBINSON—See GALION, OH

NORTH ROYALTON—See NORTH OLMSTED, OH (Cablevision of Ohio)

NORTH STAR—See VERSAILLES, OH

NORTHAMPTON TWP. (Summit County)—See BATH TWP. (Summit County), OH

NORTHFIELD (village)—See SOLON, OH

NORTHFIELD CENTER TWP. (Summit County)—See MACEDONIA, OH

▲ **NORTHWOOD**—FrontierVision

NORTON—See AKRON, OH

▲ **NORWALK**—Time Warner Cable

NORWALK TWP. (Huron County)—See NORWALK, OH

▲ **NORWICH**—Time Warner Cable

▲ **NORWICH TWP.**—Americast

NORWICH TWP. (Franklin County)—See CANAAN TWP. (Madison County), OH

NORWICH TWP. (Franklin County)—See also COLUMBUS, OH (Time Warner Communications)

NORWICH TWP. (Huron County)—See WILLARD, OH

NORWOOD—See CINCINNATI, OH

▲ **OAK HARBOR**—FrontierVision

Oak Harbor—See also ALLEN TWP. (Ottawa County), OH

▲ **OAK HILL**—FrontierVision

OAKFIELD—See CORNING, OH

▲ **OAKLAND**—FrontierVision

OAKLEAF—See WATERVILLE, OH

OAKWOOD (Montgomery County)—See KETTERING, OH

OAKWOOD (Paulding County)—See LEIPSIC, OH

OAKWOOD (village)—See SOLON, OH

▲ **OBERLIN**—Cable Co-op Inc.

OBETZ—See COLUMBUS, OH (Time Warner Communications)

OCTA—See WASHINGTON COURT HOUSE, OH

OHIO CITY—See VAN WERT, OH

OHIO TWP.—See AMELIA, OH

OLD FORT—See BETTSVILLE, OH

OLD WASHINGTON—See SENECAVILLE, OH

OLIVE TWP. (Meigs County)—See PORTERFIELD, OH

OLIVE TWP. (Noble County)—See WARNER, OH

OLIVE TWP. (Noble County)—See also CAMBRIDGE, OH

OLIVESBURG—See ASHLAND, OH

OLMSTED FALLS—See PARMA, OH

▲ **OLMSTED TWP.**—Olmsted Cable Co. Corp.

OLMSTED TWP.—See also PARMA, OH

ONTARIO—See MANSFIELD, OH

ORANGE—See CLEVELAND HEIGHTS, OH

ORANGE TWP. (Ashland County)—See ASHLAND, OH

ORANGE TWP. (Delaware County)—See COLUMBUS, OH (Insight Communications)

ORANGE TWP. (Meigs County)—See PORTERFIELD, OH

ORANGE TWP. (Shelby County)—See SIDNEY, OH

ORANGEVILLE—See SHARON, PA

OREGON—See TOLEDO, OH

ORIENT—See COLUMBUS, OH (Time Warner Entertainment Co. LP)

▲ **ORRVILLE**—Armstrong Cable Services

▲ **ORWELL**—Orwell Cable TV

OSGOOD—See VERSAILLES, OH

OSNABURG TWP. (Stark County)—See CANTON, OH

OSTRANDER (village)—See ST. PARIS, OH

▲ **OTTAWA**—Warner Cable Communications Inc.

OTTAWA HILLS—See TOLEDO, OH

OTTAWA TWP. (Putnam County)—See OTTAWA, OH

▲ **OTTOVILLE**—OTEC Communications Co.

OUTVILLE—See KIRKERSVILLE, OH

▲ **OWENSVILLE**—Time Warner Cable

▲ **OXFORD**—Warner Cable Communications Inc.

OXFORD TWP. (Butler County)—See COLLINSVILLE, OH

PLEASANTVILLE—See BALTIMORE, OH

PLYMOUTH—See NORWALK, OH

PLYMOUTH (Ashtabula County)—See PLYMOUTH TWP. (Ashtabula County), OH

▲ **PLYMOUTH TWP. (Ashtabula County)**—Adelphia

PLYMOUTH TWP. (Ashtabula County)—See DENMARK TWP., OH

PLYMOUTH TWP. (Richland County)—See SHELBY, OH

POLAND—See BOARDMAN, OH

POLAND TWP. (Mahoning County)—See STRUTHERS, OH

POLAND TWP. (Mahoning County)—See also BOARDMAN, OH

▲ **POLK**—Time Warner Cable

POLK TWP.—See GALION, OH

POMEROY—See POINT PLEASANT, WV

POMEROY—See also PORTERFIELD, OH

▲ **PORT CLINTON**—FrontierVision

PORT JEFFERSON—See SIDNEY, OH

PORT WASHINGTON—See NEW PHILADELPHIA, OH

▲ **PORT WILLIAM**—TCI Cablevision of Ohio Inc.

PORTAGE—See BOWLING GREEN, OH

PORTAGE TWP. (Ottawa County)—See PORT CLINTON, OH

PORTAGE TWP. (Sandusky County)—See OAK HARBOR, OH

PORTER TWP. (Delaware County)—See JOHNSTOWN, OH

PORTER TWP. (Scioto County)—See PORTSMOUTH, OH

▲**PORTERFIELD**—FrontierVision

▲ **PORTSMOUTH**—Century Ohio Cable Television

POTSDAM—See TIPP CITY, OH

POTTERY ADDITION—See TORONTO, OH

POWELL (village)—See COLUMBUS, OH (Time Warner Communications)

▲ **POWHATON POINT**—Powhaton Point Cable Co.

* **PRAIRIE TWP.**—Americast

PRAIRIE TWP. (Franklin County)—See COLUMBUS, OH (Time Warner Communications)

PRAIRIE TWP. (Franklin County)—See also LONDON, OH

▲ **PROCTORVILLE**—Green Tree Cable TV Inc.

PROCTORVILLE—See also SOUTH POINT, OH

PROSPECT—See RICHWOOD, OH

PROSPECT TWP. (Marion County)—See MARION, OH

PROSPECT TWP. (Marion County)—See also RICHWOOD, OH

PROVIDENCE—See SWANTON, OH

PROVIDENT—See ST. CLAIRSVILLE, OH

PULASKI—See BRYAN, OH

PULASKI TWP. (Williams County)—See BRYAN, OH

PULTNEY TWP.—See BRIDGEPORT, OH

PUNDERSON LAKE—See AUBURN TWP., OH

▲**PUT-IN-BAY**—FrontierVision

PYMATUNING STATE PARK—See VERNON, OH

QUAKER CITY—See SENECAVILLE, OH

QUINCY—See ANNA, OH

RADNOR (town)—See MARYSVILLE, OH

RANDOLPH—See KENT, OH

RANDOLPH TWP. (Montgomery County)—See KETTERING, OH

RANDOLPH TWP. (Portage County)—See ATWATER TWP., OH

RANGE TWP.—See CANAAN TWP. (Madison County), OH

RAVENNA—See KENT, OH

RAVENNA TWP. (Portage County)—See KENT, OH

RAWSON—See FINDLAY, OH

RAYLAND—See MARTINS FERRY, OH

READING—See CINCINNATI, OH

READING TWP. (Perry County)—See THORNVILLE, OH

REED TWP.—See ATTICA, OH

REEDSVILLE—See PORTERFIELD, OH

REESE STATION—See COLUMBUS, OH (Time Warner Communications)

REILY TWP.—See COLLINSVILLE, OH

REMINDERVILLE—See MACEDONIA, OH

RENDVILLE—See CORNING, OH

RENO—See MARIETTA, OH

REPUBLIC—See SYCAMORE, OH

REYNOLDSBURG—See COLUMBUS, OH (Insight Communications)

RICE TWP.—See OAK HARBOR, OH

RICHFIELD (village)—See BATH TWP. (Summit County), OH

RICHFIELD TWP. (Lucas County)—See FULTON TWP., OH

RICHFIELD TWP. (Summit County)—See BATH TWP. (Summit County), OH

RICHLAND—See ST. CLAIRSVILLE, OH

RICHLAND COUNTY—See MANSFIELD, OH

RICHLAND TWP. (Allen County)—See LIMA, OH

RICHLAND TWP. (Clinton County)—See WASHINGTON COURT HOUSE, OH

RICHLAND TWP. (Fairfield County)—See THORNVILLE, OH

RICHLAND TWP. (Guernsey County)—See SENECAVILLE, OH

RICHLAND TWP. (Holmes County)—See GLENMONT, OH

RICHLAND TWP. (Marion County)—See RICHWOOD, OH

RICHMOND—See STEUBENVILLE, OH

▲ **RICHMOND DALE**—FrontierVision

RICHMOND HEIGHTS—See CLEVELAND HEIGHTS, OH

RICHMOND TWP.—See WILLARD, OH

RICHVILLE—See MASSILLON, OH

▲ **RICHWOOD**—Time Warner Cable

RIDGE TWP. (Van Wert County)—See VAN WERT, OH

RIDGEFIELD TWP. (Huron County)—See NORWALK, OH

▲ **RIDGEVILLE TWP.**—Ridgeville Telephone Co.

RIDGEWAY (village)—See RICHWOOD, OH

RILEY TWP. (Sandusky County)—See BELLEVUE, OH

RILEY TWP. (Sandusky County)—See also OAK HARBOR, OH

▲ **RIO GRANDE**—FrontierVision

▲ **RIPLEY (Brown County)**—FrontierVision

RIPLEY TWP. (portions)—See WILLARD, OH

▲ **RISING SUN**—Time Warner Entertainment Co. LP

RISING SUN—See also ALLEN TWP. (Ottawa County), OH

RITTMAN—See LODI, OH

▲ **RIVERLEA**—Americast

RIVERLEA—See also COLUMBUS, OH (Time Warner Communications)

RIVERSIDE (Licking County)—See NEWARK, OH

RIVERSIDE (Montgomery County)—See DAYTON, OH

▲ **ROBBINS MOBILE HOME PARK**—Warner Cable Communications

ROCHESTER (village)—See WELLINGTON, OH

ROCHESTER TWP.—See WELLINGTON, OH

▲ **ROCK CREEK**—Star Cable

ROCKBRIDGE—See ENTERPRISE, OH

▲ **ROCKFORD**—Time Warner Cable

ROCKY RIDGE TWP.—See OAK HARBOR, OH

ROCKY RIVER—See PARMA, OH

ROGERS—See NEWTON TWP., OH

ROME TWP.—See ORWELL, OH

ROME TWP. (Athens County)—See GUYSVILLE, OH

ROME TWP. (Lawrence County)—See SOUTH POINT, OH

ROOTSTOWN TWP. (Portage County)—See KENT, OH

ROSEVILLE—See CROOKSVILLE, OH

ROSEWOOD (village)—See PIQUA, OH

ROSS—See AMELIA, OH

ROSS COUNTY (portions)—See CHILLICOTHE, OH

▲ **ROSS TWP. (Butler County)**—Coaxial Communications of Southern Ohio Inc.

ROSS TWP. (Butler County)—See also HAMILTON, OH

ROSS TWP. (Jefferson County)—See BLOOMINGDALE, OH

ROSSBURG—See GREENVILLE, OH

ROSSFORD—See TOLEDO, OH

ROSWELL—See NEW PHILADELPHIA, OH

ROUNDHEAD—See WAYNESFIELD, OH

ROWSBURG—See JEROMESVILLE, OH

ROYALTON—See METAMORA, OH

RUSH CREEK—See HIDE-A-WAY HILLS, OH

RUSH CREEK TWP. (Fairfield County)—See LANCASTER, OH

▲ **RUSH RUN**—Jefferson County Cable Inc.

RUSH TWP. (Champaign County)—See MARYSVILLE, OH

RUSH TWP. (Scioto County)—See LUCASVILLE, OH

RUSHSYLVANIA—See BELLE CENTER, OH

RUSHVILLE—See SOMERSET, OH

RUSSELL TWP. (Geauga County)—See BAINBRIDGE TWP. (Geauga County), OH

RUSSELLS POINT—See BELLEFONTAINE, OH

RUSSELLVILLE—See RIPLEY (Brown County), OH

RUSSIA—See VERSAILLES, OH

RUSSIA TWP.—See AMHERST, OH

RUSSIA TWP.—See also WELLINGTON, OH

RUSTIC ARMS—See ST. CLAIRSVILLE, OH

RUSTIC PINES—See THOMPSON TWP. (Geauga County), OH

SABINA—See WASHINGTON COURT HOUSE, OH

SAGAMORE HILLS TWP. (Summit County)—See MACEDONIA, OH

▲ **SALEM**—Time Warner Cable

SALEM—See also EAST PALESTINE, OH

SALEM TWP. (Columbiana County)—See SALEM, OH

SALEM TWP. (Jefferson County)—See BLOOMINGDALE, OH

SALEM TWP. (Ottawa County)—See OAK HARBOR, OH

SALEM TWP. (Shelby County)—See SIDNEY, OH

SALEM TWP. (Warren County)—See MORROW, OH

SALEM TWP. (Washington County)—See WARNER, OH

SALESVILLE—See SENECAVILLE, OH

SALINE TWP.—See KNOXVILLE, OH

▲ **SALINEVILLE**—TCI Cablevision of Ohio Inc.

SALISBURY TWP.—See SCIPIO TWP. (Meigs County), OH

SALT CREEK TWP. (Pickaway County)—See CHILLICOTHE, OH

SALT CREEK TWP. (Pickaway County)—See also KINGSTON, OH

SALT LICK TWP.—See CORNING, OH

▲ **SANDUSKY**—Erie County Cablevision Inc.

SANDUSKY—See also MARGARETTA TWP., OH

SANDUSKY TWP. (Richland County)—See GALION, OH

SANDUSKY TWP. (Richland County)—See also MANSFIELD, OH

SANDUSKY TWP. (Sandusky County)—See BELLEVUE, OH

SANDUSKY TWP. (Sandusky County)—See also FREMONT, OH

SANDUSKY TWP. (Sandusky County)—See also OAK HARBOR, OH

SANDY TWP. (Stark County)—See CANTON, OH

SANDY TWP. (Tuscarawas County)—See CANTON, OH

▲ **SARAHSVILLE**—CableVision Communications

SARDINIA—See MOWRYSTOWN, OH

SARDIS—See HANNIBAL, OH

SAVANNAH—See NEW LONDON, OH

SAYBROOK TWP. (Ashtabula County)—See GENEVA, OH

SAYBROOK TWP. (Ashtabula County)—See also PLYMOUTH TWP. (Ashtabula County), OH

▲ **SCIO**—TCI Cablevision of Ohio Inc.

SCIOTO COUNTY—See LUCASVILLE, OH

SCIOTO TWP. (Delaware County)—See ST. PARIS, OH

SCIOTO TWP. (Pickaway County)—See COMMERCIAL POINT, OH

SCIOTO TWP. (Scioto County)—See PORTSMOUTH, OH

SCIOTOVILLE—See PORTSMOUTH, OH

▲ **SCIPIO TWP. (Meigs County)**—FrontierVision

SCIPIO TWP. (Seneca County)—See SYCAMORE, OH

▲ **SCOTT (village)**—New Path Communications LC

SEAL TWP. (Pike County)—See PIKETON, OH

▲ **SEAMAN**—Time Warner Cable

▲ **SEBRING**—TCI Cablevision of Ohio Inc.

SENECA TWP.—See SYCAMORE, OH

▲ **SENECAVILLE**—CableVision Communications

SEVEN HILLS—See PARMA, OH

SEVEN MILE—See HAMILTON, OH

SEVILLE—See LODI, OH

▲ **SHADYSIDE**—TCI Cablevision of Ohio Inc.

SHAKER HEIGHTS—See CLEVELAND HEIGHTS, OH

SHALERSVILLE—See KENT, OH

SHALERSVILLE—See also MANTUA, OH

▲ **SHARON TWP.**—Americast

SHARON TWP. (Franklin County)—See COLUMBUS, OH (Time Warner Entertainment Co. LP)

SHARON TWP. (Medina County)—See BATH TWP. (Summit County), OH

SHARON TWP. (Richland County)—See SHELBY, OH

SHARONVILLE—See CINCINNATI, OH

SHAWNEE—See CORNING, OH

SHAWNEE HILLS—See COLUMBUS, OH (Time Warner Communications)

SHAWNEE TWP. (Allen County)—See LIMA, OH

SHEFFIELD (village)—See SHEFFIELD LAKE, OH

▲ **SHEFFIELD LAKE**—Cablevision of Ohio

SHEFFIELD TWP. (Ashtabula County)—See DENMARK TWP., OH

SHEFFIELD TWP. (Ashtabula County)—See also GENEVA, OH

SHEFFIELD TWP. (Lorain County)—See LORAIN, OH

▲ **SHELBY**—Time Warner Cable

SHERIDAN—See SOUTH POINT, OH

SHERRODSVILLE—See DELLROY, OH

▲ **SHERWOOD**—Shertel Cable Inc.

SHILOH—See WILLARD, OH

SHORT CREEK—See ADENA, OH

▲ **SHREVE**—Time Warner Cable

SIAM—See ATTICA, OH

▲ **SIDNEY**—Time Warner Entertainment Co. LP

SIDNEY—See also ANNA, OH

SILVER CREEK TWP. (Greene County)—See KETTERING, OH

SILVER LAKE—See AKRON, OH

SILVERTON—See CINCINNATI, OH

SMITH TWP. (portions)—See ATWATER TWP., OH

SMITH TWP. (Belmont County)—See BRIDGEPORT, OH

SMITH TWP. (Mahoning County)—See SEBRING, OH

SMITH TWP. (Mahoning County) (portions)—See also BERLIN TWP. (Mahoning County), OH

SMITHFIELD—See TORONTO, OH

SMITHFIELD TWP. (Jefferson County)—See ADENA, OH

SMITHVILLE—See WOOSTER, OH

▲ **SOLON**—Cablevision of Ohio

▲ **SOMERSET**—Time Warner Cable

SONORA—See NORWICH, OH

SOUTH AMHERST—See AMHERST, OH

SOUTH BLOOMFIELD—See CIRCLEVILLE, OH

SOUTH CANTON—See CANTON, OH

SOUTH CHARLESTON—See SPRINGFIELD, OH

SOUTH DRIVE—See WARNER, OH

TIFFIN—See FOSTORIA, OH

TILTONSVILLE—See MARTINS FERRY, OH

TIMBERLAKE—See MENTOR, OH

▲ **TIPP CITY**—Time Warner Cable

TIRO—See SHELBY, OH

TOBOSO—See HANOVER (village)(Licking County), OH

▲ **TOLEDO**—Buckeye Cablevision Inc.

TONTOGANY—See WATERVILLE, OH

TORCH—See PORTERFIELD, OH

▲ **TORONTO**—Jefferson County Cable Inc.

TOWNSEND TWP.—See BELLEVUE, OH

TOWNSEND TWP.—See also SANDUSKY, OH

TREMONT CITY—See YELLOW SPRINGS, OH

TRENTON—See HAMILTON, OH

TRENTON TWP.—See JOHNSTOWN, OH

TRIMBLE—See NELSONVILLE, OH

TRINWAY—See DRESDEN, OH

TROTWOOD—See VANDALIA, OH

▲ **TROY**—Warner Cable Communications Inc.

TROY TWP. (Ashland County)—See ASHLAND, OH

TROY TWP. (Athens County)—See PORTERFIELD, OH

TROY TWP. (Richland County)—See MANSFIELD, OH

TROY TWP. (Wood County)—See LUCKEY, OH

TROY TWP. (Wood County)—See also NORTHWOOD, OH

TRUMBULL COUNTY—See AUSTINTOWN TWP., OH

TRUMBULL TWP.—See THOMPSON TWP. (Geauga County), OH

TUPPERS PLAINS—See PORTERFIELD, OH

TURTLE CREEK TWP. (Warren County)—See CINCINNATI, OH

TURTLE CREEK TWP. (Warren County)—See also LEBANON, OH

TURTLE CREEK TWP. (Warren County)—See also MIDDLETOWN, OH

TUSCARAWAS—See NEW PHILADELPHIA, OH

TUSCARAWAS TWP. (Stark County)—See MASSILLON, OH

TWIN TWP. (Ross County)—See BAINBRIDGE, OH

TWINSBURG—See MACEDONIA, OH

TWINSBURG TWP. (Summit County)—See MACEDONIA, OH

TYMOCHTEE TWP.—See SYCAMORE, OH

UHRICHSVILLE—See NEW PHILADELPHIA, OH

UNION—See VANDALIA, OH

UNION CITY—See UNION CITY, IN

UNION FURNACE—See NELSONVILLE, OH

UNION TWP. (Auglaize County)—See WAPAKONETA, OH

UNION TWP. (Butler County)—See CINCINNATI, OH

UNION TWP. (Butler County)—See also LIBERTY TWP. (Butler County), OH (Coaxial Communications)

UNION TWP. (Clermont County)—See AMELIA, OH

UNION TWP. (Clermont County)—See also CINCINNATI, OH

UNION TWP. (Clinton County)—See WILMINGTON, OH

UNION TWP. (Fayette County)—See WASHINGTON COURT HOUSE, OH

UNION TWP. (Hancock County)—See BENTON RIDGE, OH

UNION TWP. (Hancock County)—See also FINDLAY, OH

UNION TWP. (Highland County)—See HILLSBORO, OH

UNION TWP. (Knox County)—See THORNVILLE, OH

UNION TWP. (Lawrence County)—See SOUTH POINT, OH

UNION TWP. (Licking County)—See NEWARK, OH

UNION TWP. (Logan County)—See BELLEFONTAINE, OH

UNION TWP. (Madison County)—See LONDON, OH

UNION TWP. (Miami County)—See TIPP CITY, OH

UNION TWP. (Muskingum County)—See NORWICH, OH

UNION TWP. (Putnam County)—See KALIDA, OH

UNION TWP. (Union County)—See MARYSVILLE, OH

UNION TWP. (Van Wert County)—See VAN WERT, OH

UNION TWP. (Warren County)—See MORROW, OH

UNIONVILLE CENTER—See ST. PARIS, OH

UNIOPOLIS—See WAYNESFIELD, OH

UNITY—See EAST PALESTINE, OH

UNITY TWP.—See EAST PALESTINE, OH

UNIVERSITY HEIGHTS—See CLEVELAND HEIGHTS, OH

▲ **UPPER ARLINGTON**—Americast

UPPER ARLINGTON—See also COLUMBUS, OH (Time Warner Communications)

▲ **UPPER SANDUSKY**—Time Warner Cable

▲ **URBANA**—Time Warner Entertainment Co. LP

URBANCREST—See COLUMBUS, OH (Time Warner Communications)

▲ **UTICA**—Time Warner Cable

VALLEY HI—See WEST MANSFIELD, OH

VALLEY TWP. (Guernsey County)—See SENECAVILLE, OH

VALLEY TWP. (Scioto County)—See LUCASVILLE, OH

VALLEY TWP. (Scioto County)—See also PORTSMOUTH, OH

VALLEY VIEW—See GARFIELD HEIGHTS, OH

▲ **VALLEYVIEW**—Americast

VALLEYVIEW—See also COLUMBUS, OH (Time Warner Communications)

VAN BUREN—See FINDLAY, OH

VAN BUREN TWP.—See ANNA, OH

▲ **VAN WERT**—FrontierVision

VAN WERT TWP. (Van Wert County)—See VAN WERT, OH

▲ **VANDALIA**—MediaOne

VANLUE—See FINDLAY, OH

VAUGHNSVILLE—See LIMA, OH

VENICE TWP.—See ATTICA, OH

▲ **VERMILION**—Adelphia Cable

VERMILION TWP.—See VERMILION, OH

▲ **VERNON**—Star Cable

VERNON TWP. (Crawford County)—See SHELBY, OH

VERNON TWP. (Trumbull County)—See VERNON, OH

VERONA—See LEWISBURG, OH

▲ **VERSAILLES**—FrontierVision

VETO—See WATERTOWN, OH

VETO LAKE—See WATERTOWN, OH

VICKERY—See BELLEVUE, OH

VICKERY—See also MARGARETTA TWP., OH

VIENNA AIR FORCE BASE—See BAZETTA TWP., OH

VIENNA TWP.—See WARREN, OH

VINCENT—See WATERTOWN, OH

VIOLET TWP.—See COLUMBUS, OH (Insight Communications)

WADSWORTH (Medina County)—See AKRON, OH

WADSWORTH TWP. (Medina County)—See AKRON, OH

WAINWRIGHT—See NEW PHILADELPHIA, OH

WAITE HILL—See CONCORD TWP. (Lake County), OH

▲ **WAKEMAN**—FrontierVision

WALBRIDGE—See ALLEN TWP. (Ottawa County), OH

WALBRIDGE—See also NORTHWOOD, OH

WALDO—See RICHWOOD, OH

WALNUT CREEK—See WINESBURG, OH

WALNUT CREEK TWP.—See MILLERSBURG, OH

WALNUT TWP. (Fairfield County)—See CIRCLEVILLE, OH

WALNUT TWP. (Pickaway County)—See CIRCLEVILLE, OH

WALTON HILLS—See GARFIELD HEIGHTS, OH

▲ **WAPAKONETA**—Time Warner Cable

WARD TWP.—See MURRAY CITY, OH

▲ **WARNER**—CableVision Communications

WHITEWATER TWP. (Hamilton County)—See DELHI TWP., OH

WICKLIFFE—See MENTOR, OH

WILBERFORCE—See KETTERING, OH

WILKSHIRE HILLS—See BOLIVAR, OH

▲ **WILLARD**—Time Warner Cable

WILLIAMSBURG—See AMELIA, OH

WILLIAMSFIELD—See VERNON, OH

WILLIAMSPORT—See NEW HOLLAND, OH

WILLISTON—See ALLEN TWP. (Ottawa County), OH

WILLOUGHBY—See MENTOR, OH

WILLOUGHBY HILLS—See MENTOR, OH

WILLOWICK—See CLEVELAND HEIGHTS, OH

▲ **WILLOWS MOBILE HOME PARK**—Warner Cable Communications

WILLS TWP.—See SENECAVILLE, OH

WILLSHIRE—See ROCKFORD, OH

▲ **WILMINGTON**—TCI Cablevision of Ohio Inc.

WILMOT—See BOLIVAR, OH

WILSON—See MALAGA TWP., OH

WINCHESTER—See SEAMAN, OH

WINDHAM (Portage County)—See NELSON TWP., OH

WINDHAM (Portage County)—See also NEWTON FALLS, OH

WINDHAM TWP.—See NELSON TWP., OH

WINDSOR—See ORWELL, OH

WINDSOR—See also THOMPSON TWP. (Geauga County), OH

▲ **WINESBURG**—National Cable Inc.

WINONA—See GUILFORD LAKE, OH

WINTERSVILLE—See STEUBENVILLE, OH

WOOD VALLEY—See CALEDONIA, OH

WOODINGTON—See GREENVILLE, OH

WOODLAND—See WATERVILLE, OH

WOODLAWN—See CINCINNATI, OH

WOODMERE—See CLEVELAND HEIGHTS, OH

▲ **WOODSFIELD**—CableVision Communications

WOODSTOCK—See ST. PARIS, OH

WOODVILLE—See ALLEN TWP. (Ottawa County), OH

▲ **WOOSTER**—Clear Picture Inc.

WOOSTER TWP. (Wayne County)—See WOOSTER, OH

▲ **WORTHINGTON**—Americast

WORTHINGTON—See also COLUMBUS, OH (Time Warner Communications)

▲ **WORTHINGTON ARMS**—Time Warner Entertainment Co. LP

WREN—See ROCKFORD, OH

WYOMING—See CINCINNATI, OH

XENIA—See FAIRBORN, OH

XENIA TWP. (Greene County)—See KETTERING, OH

YANKEE LAKE—See SHARON, PA

YELLOW CREEK—See EAST LIVERPOOL, OH

▲ **YELLOW SPRINGS**—Warner Cable Communications Inc.

YORK—See CROOKSVILLE, OH

YORK TWP.—See MEDINA, OH

YORK TWP. (Fulton County)—See SWANTON, OH

YORK TWP. (Morgan County)—See CROOKSVILLE, OH

YORK TWP. (Sandusky County)—See BELLEVUE, OH

YORKSHIRE—See VERSAILLES, OH

YORKVILLE—See MARTINS FERRY, OH

▲ **YOUNGSTOWN**—Time Warner Cable

ZANESFIELD (village)—See BELLEFONTAINE, OH

▲ **ZANESVILLE**—Cablecomm

ZANESVILLE—See also MOUNT STERLING (Muskingum County), OH

ZANESVILLE—See also NORWICH, OH

ZANESVILLE (northern portion)—See also HANOVER (village)(Licking County), OH

ZANESVILLE (portions)—See also MUSKINGUM COUNTY (portions), OH

ZOAR—See BOLIVAR, OH

OKLAHOMA

▲ **ACHILLE**—CommuniComm Services

▲ **ADA**—Cable One

▲ **ADAIR**—Oklahoma Cablecomm

▲ **AFTON**—Oklahoma Cablecomm

▲ **AGRA**—Oklahoma Cablecomm

ALDERSON—See McALESTER, OK

▲ **ALEX**—Southwestern CATV Inc.

▲ **ALLEN**—Peak Cablevision

ALMA—See VELMA, OK

▲ **ALTUS**—Cable One

ALTUS AFB—See ALTUS, OK

▲ **ALVA**—Peak Cablevision

▲ **AMES**—Classic Cable

▲ **ANADARKO**—Classic Cable

▲ **ANTLERS**—Peak Cablevision

▲ **APACHE**—Southwestern CATV Inc.

▲ **ARAPAHO**—Classic Cable

▲ **ARDMORE**—Cable One

ARKOMA—See FORT SMITH, AR

ARMSTRONG—See DURANT, OK

▲ **ARNETT**—Classic Cable

ARPELAR—See STUART, OK

▲ **ASHER**—Westcom

▲ **ATOKA**—CommuniComm Services

▲ **AVANT**—Community Cablevision

▲ **BARNSDALL**—Community Cablevision

▲ **BARTLESVILLE**—Cable One

▲ **BEAVER**—Classic Cable

▲ **BEGGS**—Oklahoma Cablecomm

▲ **BENNINGTON**—Peak Cablevision

▲ **BERNICE**—Classic Cable

▲ **BESSIE**—Classic Cable

▲ **BETHANY**—Cablevision of Bethany

▲ **BILLINGS**—Classic Cable

▲ **BINGER**—Classic Cable

▲ **BIXBY**—TCI Cable of Kansas

▲ **BLACKWELL**—TCA Cable Partners

▲ **BLAIR**—Rapid Cable

▲ **BLANCHARD**—Classic Cable

▲ **BOISE CITY**—Classic Cable

BOKCHITO—See COLBERT, OK

▲ **BOKOSHE**—Classic Cable

▲ **BOSWELL**—Peak Cablevision

▲ **BOYNTON**—Oklahoma Cablecomm

▲ **BRAGGS**—Peak Cablevision

▲ **BRECKENRIDGE**—Classic Cable

BRIDGEPORT—See HINTON, OK

▲ **BRISTOW**—Peak Cablevision

BROKEN ARROW—See TULSA, OK

▲ **BROKEN BOW**—Broken Bow TV Cable Co. Inc.

BROOKEN—See LONGTOWN, OK

BRYAN COUNTY—See DURANT, OK

▲ **BUFFALO**—Classic Cable

BUNCOMBE CREEK—See COLBERT, OK

BURLINGTON—See KIOWA, KS

▲ **BURNS FLAT**—Classic Cable

▲ **BUTLER**—Rapid Cable

▲ **BYARS**—Classic Cable

BYNG—See ADA, OK

▲ **CACHE**—Classic Cable

CADDO—See COLBERT, OK

CALERA—See DURANT, OK

▲ **CALUMET**—Classic Cable

▲ **CALVIN**—Peak Cablevision

▲ **CAMARGO**—Classic Cable

▲ **CAMERON**—Oklahoma Cablecomm

▲ **CANADIAN**—Lakeland Cable TV Inc.

CANDLESTICK BEACH—See TULSA COUNTY (western portion), OK

▲ **CANEY**—Peak Cablevision

CANEY CREEK RESORT—See KINGSTON, OK

▲ **CANTON**—Rapid Cable

▲ **CANUTE**—Classic Cable

CARDIN—See PICHER, OK

▲ **CARMEN**—Classic Cable

▲ **CARNEGIE**—SMS Cable Co.

▲ **CARNEY**—Oklahoma Cablecomm

▲ **CARTER**—Rapid Cable

CARTER COUNTY—See ARDMORE, OK

CARTWRIGHT—See DURANT, OK

▲ **CASHION**—Classic Cable

▲ **CATOOSA**—Blackstone Cable

CATOOSA—See also TULSA, OK

CEDAR LAKE—See HINTON, OK

▲ **CEMENT**—Southwestern CATV

▲ **CHANDLER**—Peak Cablevision

▲ **CHATTANOOGA**—Rapid Cable

CHECOTAH—See EUFAULA, OK

▲ **CHELSEA**—Oklahoma Cablecomm

▲ **CHEROKEE**—Classic Cable

CHEROKEE HEIGHTS—See PRYOR (unincorporated areas), OK

▲ **CHEYENNE**—James Mogg TV

▲ **CHICKASHA**—Multimedia Cablevision of Chickasha

▲ **CHICKEN CREEK**—Quality Entertainment

▲ **CHOCTAW**—Multimedia Cablevision

CHOCTAW COUNTY (portions)—See HUGO, OK

CHOCTAW COUNTY (unincorporated areas)—See also BOSWELL, OK

▲ **CHOUTEAU**—Oklahoma Cablecomm

▲ **CLAREMORE**—Tulsa Cable Television Inc.

CLAREMORE—See also ROGERS COUNTY (northern portion), OK

▲ **CLAYTON**—Peak Cablevision

▲ **CLEO SPRINGS**—Rapid Cable

▲ **CLEVELAND**—Cim Tel Cable Inc.

▲ **CLINTON**—Cable One

▲ **COALGATE**—CommuniComm Services

▲ **COLBERT**—CommuniComm Services

▲ **COLCORD**—Oklahoma Cablecomm

▲ **COLLINSVILLE**—Community Cablevision

COLONY—See EAKLY, OK

▲ **COMANCHE**—Classic Cable

COMANCHE—See also MERIDIAN, OK

COMANCHE COUNTY—See LAWTON, OK

COMMERCE—See MIAMI, OK

▲ **COOKSON**—Quality Entertainment Corp.

▲ **COPAN**—Community Cablevision Co.

▲ **CORDELL**—Cable One

▲ **CORN**—Classic Cable

CORNISH—See HEALDTON, OK

COTTONWOOD—See ATOKA, OK

COUNTYLINE—See VELMA, OK

▲ **COVINGTON**—Classic Cable

▲ **COWETA**—Peak Cable

COYLE—See LANGSTON, OK

CRAIG COUNTY—See VINITA, OK

CREEK COUNTY (portions)—See TULSA, OK

CREEK COUNTY (portions)—See also TULSA COUNTY (western portion), OK

▲ **CRESCENT**—Multimedia Cablevision Inc.

▲ **CROMWELL**—Oklahoma Cablecomm

CROWDER—See CANADIAN, OK

▲ **CUMBERLAND**—Quality Entertainment Corp.

CUMBERLAND COVE—See CUMBERLAND, OK

▲ **CUSHING**—Peak Cablevision

▲ **CUSTER CITY**—Classic Cable

▲ **CYRIL**—Classic Cable

CYRIL—See also ELGIN, OK

▲ **DACOMA**—Classic Cable

DALE—See SHAWNEE, OK

▲ **DAVENPORT**—Vi-Tel Inc.

▲ **DAVIDSON**—Rapid Cable

DAVIS—See SULPHUR, OK

▲ **DEER CREEK**—Westcom

▲ **DEL CITY**—Cablevision of Del City

▲ **DELAWARE**—Oklahoma Cablecomm

DELAWARE COUNTY (northern portion)—See GROVE, OK (Peak Cablevision)

▲ **DEPEW**—Oklahoma Cablecomm

DEWAR—See HENRYETTA, OK

DEWEY—See BARTLESVILLE, OK

DICKSON—See ARDMORE, OK

▲ **DILL CITY**—Classic Cable

▲ **DISNEY**—Omni III Cable TV Inc.

▲ **DOVER**—Classic Cable

▲ **DRUMMOND**—Classic Cable

▲ **DRUMRIGHT**—Peak Cablevision

▲ **DUKE**—Rapid Cable

▲ **DUNCAN**—Cable One

▲ **DURANT**—CommuniComm Services

▲ **DUSTIN**—Oklahoma Cablecomm

EAGLETOWN—See BROKEN BOW, OK

▲ **EAKLY**—Hinton CATV Co.

▲ **EARLSBORO**—Falcon Cable Media

▲ **EDMOND**—Edmond Cablevision

▲ **EL RENO**—El Reno Cablevision Inc.

▲ **ELDORADO**—Rapid Cable

▲ **ELGIN**—Classic Cable

▲ **ELK CITY**—Cable One

▲ **ELK CREEK**—Quality Entertainment Corp.

▲ **ELMORE CITY**—Harmon Cable Communications

▲ **ENID**—Peak Cablevision

ENTERPRISE—See LONGTOWN, OK

▲ **ERICK**—Classic Cable

ERIN SPRINGS—See LINDSAY, OK

▲ **EUFAULA**—Classic Cable

▲ **FAIRFAX**—Cim Tel Cable Inc.

FAIRLAND—See AFTON, OK

▲ **FAIRVIEW**—Classic Cable

▲ **FARGO**—Classic Cable

FLETCHER—See ELGIN, OK

FOREST PARK—See OKLAHOMA CITY, OK

FORGAN—See BEAVER, OK

▲ **FORT COBB**—Rapid Cable

▲ **FORT GIBSON**—Oklahoma Cablecomm

▲ **FORT SILL**—Classic Cable

▲ **FORT SUPPLY**—Rapid Cable

FOX—See VELMA, OK

FRANCIS—See ADA, OK

▲ **FREDERICK**—Cable One

▲ **FREEDOM**—Classic Cable

GAGE—See SHATTUCK, OK

▲ **GANS**—Oklahoma Cablecomm

▲ **GARBER**—Rapid Cable

GARFIELD COUNTY—See ENID, OK

GARVIN COUNTY (unincorporated areas)—See PAULS VALLEY, OK

▲ **GEARY**—Classic Cable

▲ **GERONIMO**—Rapid Cable

▲ **GLENCOE**—Oklahoma Cablecomm

GLENPOOL—See TULSA, OK

▲ **GOLTRY**—Classic Cable

▲ **GOODWELL**—Classic Cable

▲ **GORE**—Oklahoma Cablecomm

▲ **GOTEBO**—Rapid Cable

GOULD—See HOLLIS, OK

▲ **GRACEMONT**—Rapid Cable

GRADY COUNTY (portions)—See CHICKASHA, OK

▲ **GRAND LAKE-MONKEY ISLAND**—Oklahoma Cablecomm

▲ **GRANDFIELD**—Southwestern CATV Inc.

▲ **GRANITE**—Rapid Cable

GRANITE—See also LONE WOLF, OK

GREER COUNTY—See MANGUM, OK

▲ **GROVE**—Oklahoma Cablecomm

▲ **GROVE**—Peak Cablevision

▲ **GUTHRIE**—Cablevision of Guthrie

▲ **GUYMON**—TCA Cable Partners

HAILEYVILLE—See HARTSHORNE, OK

HALL PARK—See NORMAN, OK

▲ **HAMMON**—Classic Cable

▲ **HARDESTY**—Classic Cable

HARRAH—See CHOCTAW, OK

▲ **HARTSHORNE**—Oklahoma Cablecomm

▲ **HASKELL**—Peak Cablevision

HASKELL COUNTY—See STIGLER, OK

HAWORTH—See BROKEN BOW, OK

HAYWOOD—See STUART, OK

▲ **HEALDTON**—Classic Cable

▲ **HEAVENER**—Classic Cable

▲ **HECTORVILLE**—Quality Cablevision of Oklahoma Inc.

▲ **HELENA**—Classic Cable

▲ **HENNESSEY**—Classic Cable

▲ **HENRYETTA**—Peak Cablevision

▲ **HINTON**—Hinton CATV Co.

▲ **HOBART**—Cable One

HOCHATOWA—See BROKEN BOW, OK

▲ **HOLDENVILLE**—Peak Cablevision

▲ **HOLLIS**—Classic Cable

▲ **HOMINY**—Community Cablevision

▲ **HOOKER**—Classic Cable

▲ **HOWE**—Peak Cablevision

▲ **HUGO**—Classic Cable

▲ **HULBERT**—Oklahoma Cablecomm

▲ **HUNTER**—Classic Cable

HYDRO—See WEATHERFORD, OK

▲ **IDABEL**—Cable One

IDABEL (Shultz Community)—See BROKEN BOW, OK

INDIAHOMA—See CACHE, OK

INDIANOLA—See CANADIAN, OK

▲ **INOLA**—Oklahoma Cablecomm

JACKSON COUNTY—See ALTUS, OK

JAY—See DISNEY, OK

JENKS—See TULSA, OK

▲ **JENNINGS**—Cim Tel Cable Inc.

▲ **JET**—Classic Cable

JOHNSTON COUNTY (portions)—See TISHOMINGO, OK

▲ **JONES**—Classic Cable

▲ **KANSAS**—Oklahoma Cablecomm

▲ **KAW CITY**—Community Cablevision Co.

KAY COUNTY (portions)—See PONCA CITY, OK

▲ **KELLYVILLE**—Oklahoma Cablecomm

▲ **KEOTA**—Oklahoma Cablecomm

▲ **KETCHUM**—Oklahoma Cablecomm

KEYES—See ELKHART, KS

KIEFER—See TULSA, OK

▲ **KINGFISHER**—Classic Cable

▲ **KINGSTON**—CommuniComm Services

KINTA—See QUINTON, OK

KIOWA—See SAVANNA, OK

KIOWA COUNTY (portions)—See HOBART, OK

▲ **KONAWA**—Peak Cablevision

KREBS—See McALESTER, OK

▲ **KREMLIN**—Classic Cable

▲ **LAHOMA**—Classic Cable

▲ **LAKE TENKILLER**—Peak Cablevision

▲ **LAMONT**—Rapid Cable

LANGLEY—See KETCHUM, OK

▲ **LANGSTON**—Oklahoma Cablecomm

▲ **LAVERNE**—Classic Cable

▲ **LAWTON**—Lawton Cablevision Inc.

LE FLORE COUNTY (unincorporated areas)—See PANAMA, OK

LE FLORE COUNTY (unincorporated areas)—See also POCOLA, OK

▲ **LEEDEY**—Classic Cable

LENAPAH—See DELAWARE, OK

LEXINGTON—See PURCELL, OK

▲ **LINDSAY**—Multimedia Cablevision

LITTLE CITY—See CUMBERLAND, OK

LOCUST GROVE—See SALINA, OK

LONE GROVE—See ARDMORE, OK

▲ **LONE WOLF**—Rapid Cable

LONE WOLF—See also GRANITE, OK

▲ **LONGDALE**—Rapid Cable

▲ **LONGTOWN**—Oklahoma Cablecomm

LOOKEBA—See HINTON, OK

LUKFATA—See BROKEN BOW, OK

▲ **LUTHER**—Oklahoma Cablecomm

▲ **MADILL**—Cable One

▲ **MANGUM**—Cable One

▲ **MANNFORD**—Cim Tel Cable Inc.

▲ **MARIETTA**—Cable One

▲ **MARLAND**—Oklahoma Cablecomm

MARLOW—See DUNCAN, OK

▲ **MARSHALL**—Classic Cable

MARSHALL COUNTY (northern portion)—See MADILL, OK

MARSHALL COUNTY (portions)—See also KINGSTON, OK

▲ **MARTHA**—Rapid Cable

▲ **MAUD**—Peak Cablevision

MAYES COUNTY (portions)—See PRYOR, OK

MAYES COUNTY (western portion)—See also ROGERS COUNTY (northern portion), OK

▲ **MAYSVILLE**—Classic Cable

▲ **McALESTER**—Peak Cablevision

McALESTER ARMY AMMUNITION PLANT—See SAVANNA, OK

McCLAIN COUNTY—See PURCELL, OK

▲ **McCURTAIN**—Peak Cablevision

McCURTAIN COUNTY (portions)—See BROKEN BOW, OK

McINTOSH COUNTY—See EUFAULA, OK

McLOUD—See SHAWNEE, OK

MEDFORD—See LAMONT, OK

▲ **MEDICINE PARK**—Classic Cable

▲ **MEEKER**—Falcon Cable Media

▲ **MENO**—Westcom

▲ **MERIDIAN**—Classic Cable

▲ **MIAMI**—Cable One

▲ **MIDWEST CITY**—Multimedia Cablevision Inc.

▲ **MILBURN**—Oklahoma Cablecomm

MINCO—See TUTTLE, OK

▲ **MOORE**—Multimedia Cablevision

MOORELAND—See WOODWARD, OK

▲ **MORRIS**—Oklahoma Cablecomm

▲ **MORRISON**—Oklahoma Cablecomm

▲ **MOUNDS**—Oklahoma Cablecomm

▲ **MOUNTAIN PARK**—Rapid Cable

▲ **MOUNTAIN VIEW**—Mountain View Cable TV

MT. PARK—See SNYDER, OK

MULDROW—See FORT SMITH, AR

MULHALL—See ORLANDO, OK

▲ **MUSKOGEE**—Peak Cablevision

MUSKOGEE COUNTY—See MUSKOGEE, OK

▲ **MUSTANG**—Multimedia Cablevision

▲ **NASH**—Classic Cable

▲ **NEWCASTLE**—Classic Cable

▲ **NEWKIRK**—Multimedia Cablevision Inc.

▲ **NICHOLS HILLS**—Cablevision of Nichols Hills

NICOMA PARK—See CHOCTAW, OK

▲ **NINNEKAH**—Rapid Cable

▲ **NOBLE**—Classic Cable

NOBLE COUNTY (portions)—See PERRY, OK

▲ **NORMAN**—Multimedia Cablevision

NORTH ENID—See ENID, OK

NORTH MIAMI—See MIAMI, OK

▲ **NOWATA**—Cable One

NOWATA COUNTY—See NOWATA, OK

OAK HILL—See BROKEN BOW, OK

OAKLAND—See MADILL, OK

▲ **OCHELATA**—Community Cablevision Co.

▲ **OILTON**—Community Cablevision

▲ **OKARCHE**—Classic Cable

▲ **OKAY**—Oklahoma Cablecomm

▲ **OKEENE**—Classic Cable

▲ **OKEMAH**—Peak Cablevision

▲ **OKLAHOMA CITY**—Cox Communications

▲ **OKMULGEE**—Peak Cablevision

OKMULGEE COUNTY (central portion)—See OKMULGEE, OK

▲ **OLUSTEE**—Rapid Cable

▲ **OOLOGAH**—Oklahoma Cablecomm

▲ **ORLANDO**—Westcom

▲ **OSAGE**—Cim Tel Cable Inc.

OSAGE COUNTY (portions)—See PONCA CITY, OK

OSAGE COUNTY (portions)—See also TULSA, OK

OSAGE COUNTY (portions)—See also TULSA COUNTY (western portion), OK

OTTAWA COUNTY—See MIAMI, OK

OWASSO—See TULSA, OK

▲ **PANAMA**—Peak Cablevision

▲ **PAOLI**—Classic Cable

▲ **PARADISE HILL**—Quality Entertainment Corp.

▲ **PARK HILL**—Quality Entertainment Corp.

▲ **PAULS VALLEY**—Multimedia Cablevision of Pauls Valley

▲ **PAWHUSKA**—Peak Cablevision

▲ **PAWNEE**—Cim Tel Cable Inc.

PERKINS—See STILLWATER, OK

▲ **PERRY**—Peak Cablevision

▲ **PICHER**—Mediacom

▲ **PIEDMONT**—Classic Cable

PLATTER—See DURANT, OK

▲ **POCASSET**—Rapid Cable

▲ **POCOLA**—TCA Cable TV Inc.

▲ **PONCA CITY**—Cable One

▲ **POND CREEK**—Classic Cable

PONTOTOC COUNTY—See ADA, OK

▲ **PORTER**—Oklahoma Cablecomm

▲ **PORUM**—Oklahoma Cablecomm

▲ **PORUM LANDING**—Peak Cablevision

▲ **POTEAU**—Classic Cable

▲ **PRAGUE**—Falcon Cable Media

▲ **PRESTON**—Quality Cablevision of Oklahoma Inc.

PRETTY WATER—See TULSA COUNTY (western portion), OK

PRUITT CITY—See VELMA, OK

▲ **PRYOR**—Peak Cablevision

▲ **PRYOR (unincorporated areas)**—Peak Cablevision

▲ **PURCELL**—Classic Cable

QUAPAW—See PICHER, OK

▲ **QUINTON**—Oklahoma Cablecomm

▲ **RALSTON**—Oklahoma Cablecomm

▲ **RAMONA**—Community Cablevision Co.

▲ **RANDLETT**—Cable Television Inc.

RATLIFF CITY—See VELMA, OK

▲ **RATTAN**—Peak Cablevision

RAVIA—See TISHOMINGO, OK

RED OAK—See WILBURTON, OK

▲ **RED ROCK**—Westcom

RINGLING—See HEALDTON, OK

▲ **RINGWOOD**—Classic Cable

▲ **RIPLEY**—Westcom

▲ **ROCKY**—Rapid Cable

ROCKY POINT—See WHITE HORN COVE, OK

ROFF—See SULPHUR, OK

▲ **ROGERS COUNTY (northern portion)**—Benchmark Communications

ROGERS COUNTY (portions)—See also CATOOSA, OK

ROGERS COUNTY (portions)—See also TULSA, OK

ROLAND—See FORT SMITH, AR

ROLLING HILLS—See TULSA, OK

▲ **ROOSEVELT**—Classic Cable

▲ **RUSH SPRINGS**—Classic Cable

▲ **RYAN**—Classic Cable

▲ **SALINA**—Oklahoma Cablecomm

▲ **SALLISAW**—Classic Cable

SAND SPRINGS—See TULSA, OK

▲ **SANDPOINT**—CommuniComm Services

SAPULPA—See TULSA, OK

▲ **SAVANNA**—Oklahoma Cablecomm

▲ **SAYRE**—Cable One

▲ **SCHULTER**—Oklahoma Cablecomm

▲ **SEILING**—Classic Cable

▲ **SEMINOLE**—Peak Cablevision

SEMINOLE COUNTY (southern portion)—See KONAWA, OK

▲ **SENTINEL**—Rapid Cable

SEQUOYAH COUNTY (southern portion)—See FORT SMITH, AR

SEQUOYAH COUNTY (unincorporated areas)—See also GANS, OK

SHADY POINT—See PANAMA, OK

▲ **SHATTUCK**—Classic Cable

▲ **SHAWNEE**—Falcon Cable Media

SICKLES—See HINTON, OK

▲ **SKIATOOK**—Community Cablevision

▲ **SNYDER**—Rapid Cable

▲ **SOPER**—Soper Cable TV

SOUTH COFFEYVILLE—See COFFEYVILLE, KS

▲ **SPAVINAW**—Oklahoma Cablecomm

SPENCER—See MIDWEST CITY, OK

SPERRY—See SKIATOOK, OK

▲ **SPIRO**—Classic Cable

SPORTSMEN ACRES—See PRYOR (unincorporated areas), OK

▲ **STERLING**—Southwestern CATV Inc.

▲ **STIGLER**—Peak Cablevision

▲ **STILLWATER**—Peak Cablevision

▲ **STILWELL**—Oklahoma Cablecomm

▲ **STONEWALL**—CommuniComm Services

▲ **STRANG**—Oklahoma Cablecomm

▲ **STRATFORD**—Falcon Cable Media

▲ **STRINGTOWN**—CommuniComm Services

▲ **STROUD**—Peak Cablevision

▲ **STUART**—Peak Cablevision

▲ **SULPHUR**—Harmon Cable Communications

▲ **TAHLEQUAH**—Tahlequah Cable TV Inc.

▲ **TALALA**—Quality Cablevision of Oklahoma Inc.

▲ **TALIHINA**—Peak Cablevision

▲ **TALOGA**—Taloga Cable TV

TECUMSEH—See SHAWNEE, OK

TEMPLE—See WALTERS, OK

▲ **TERRAL**—Classic Cable

TEXHOMA—See TEXHOMA, TX

THE VILLAGE—See NICHOLS HILLS, OK

▲ **THOMAS**—Classic Cable

TILLMAN COUNTY—See FREDERICK, OK

TINKER AFB—See DEL CITY, OK

▲ **TIPTON**—Rapid Cable

▲ **TISHOMINGO**—CommuniComm Services

TONKAWA—See BLACKWELL, OK

TONKAWA—See also PONCA CITY, OK

▲ **TRYON**—Oklahoma Cablecomm

▲ **TULSA**—TCI Cable Television Inc.

TULSA (northwestern portion)—See also ROGERS COUNTY (northern portion), OK

▲ **TULSA COUNTY (western portion)**—Blackstone Cable

TUPELO—See STONEWALL, OK

▲ **TURPIN**—Cable Systems Inc.

TUSHKA—See ATOKA, OK

▲ **TUTTLE**—Southwestern CATV Inc.

▲ **TYRONE**—Cablecomm

▲ **UNION CITY**—Classic Cable

VALLEY BROOK—See DEL CITY, OK

▲ **VALLIANT**—Peak Cablevision

VANCE AFB—See ENID, OK

▲ **VELMA**—Classic Cable

▲ **VERDEN**—Rapid Cable

▲ **VERDIGRIS**—Oklahoma Cablecomm

▲ **VIAN**—Oklahoma Cablecomm

OREGON

DETROIT—See IDANHA, OR

DEXTER—See BEAR MOUNTAIN, OR

DILLARD—See MYRTLE CREEK, OR

DONALD—See CANBY, OR

DOUGLAS COUNTY (northern portion)—See DRAIN, OR

DOUGLAS COUNTY (portions)—See also ROSEBURG, OR

DOUGLAS COUNTY (portions)—See also SUTHERLIN, OR

DOUGLAS COUNTY (unincorporated areas)—See also GLENDALE, OR

▲ **DRAIN**—Falcon Cable Systems Co.

▲ **DUFUR**—Northstate Cablevision

DUNDEE—See NEWBERG, OR

DUNES CITY—See FLORENCE, OR

DUNTHORPE—See PORTLAND, OR

DURHAM—See BEAVERTON, OR

EAGLE CREEK—See PORTLAND (eastern portion), OR

EAGLE POINT—See MEDFORD, OR

ECHO—See HERMISTON, OR

▲ **ELGIN**—Elgin TV Assn. Inc.

▲ **ELKTON**—Interstate Cable Inc.

ELMIRA—See VENETA, OR

▲ **ENTERPRISE**—Crestview Cable TV

▲ **ESTACADA**—Cascade Cable TV Inc.

▲ **EUGENE**—TCI Cablevision of Oregon Inc.

FAIRVIEW—See PORTLAND (eastern portion), OR

FALCON COVE—See NEHALEM, OR

FALLS CITY—See DALLAS, OR

▲ **FLORENCE**—Falcon Cable Systems Co.

FOREST GROVE—See BEAVERTON, OR

▲ **FOSSIL**—Fossil Community TV Inc.

GARDINER—See REEDSPORT, OR

GARIBALDI—See NEHALEM, OR

GASTON—See BEAVERTON, OR

GATES—See SUBLIMITY, OR

GEARHART—See ASTORIA, OR

GERVAIS—See WOODBURN, OR

▲ **GILCHRIST**—Country Cablevision Ltd.

GLADSTONE—See PORTLAND, OR

▲ **GLENDALE**—Phoenix Cablevision of Oregon Inc.

GLENEDEN BEACH—See DEPOE BAY, OR

GLENWOOD—See EUGENE, OR

▲ **GLIDE**—Glide Cablevision

▲ **GOLD BEACH**—Falcon Telecable

GOLD HILL—See MEDFORD, OR

▲ **GOVERNMENT CAMP**—CharlieVision

GRAND RONDE—See SHERIDAN, OR

▲ **GRANTS PASS**—Falcon Cable TV

GREEN—See MYRTLE CREEK, OR

▲ **GREENACRES**—Greenacres TV Cable

GRESHAM—See PORTLAND (eastern portion), OR

▲ **HAINES**—Blackstone Cable LLC

▲ **HALFWAY**—Falcon Video Communications

▲ **HALSEY**—RTI Cable Television

HAMMOND—See ASTORIA, OR

HAPPY VALLEY—See PORTLAND (eastern portion), OR

HARNEY COUNTY (portions)—See BURNS, OR

HARRISBURG—See EUGENE, OR

▲ **HAUSER**—Falcon Cable Systems Co.

HAYDEN ISLAND—See VANCOUVER, WA

HEBO—See TILLAMOOK COUNTY (southwestern portion), OR

▲ **HELIX**—Helix Communications

▲ **HEPPNER**—Heppner TV Inc.

▲ **HERMISTON**—TCI Cablevision of Northeastern Oregon

HERMISTON—See also UMATILLA, OR

HILLSBORO—See BEAVERTON, OR

HINES—See BURNS, OR

▲ **HOOD RIVER**—Falcon Cablevision

HOOD RIVER COUNTY—See HOOD RIVER, OR

HUBBARD—See CANBY, OR

HUBBARD—See also WOODBURN, OR

▲ **HUNTINGTON**—Chambers Cable of Oregon Inc.

▲ **IDANHA**—North Santiam Communications

IDLEYLD PARK—See GLIDE, OR

▲ **IMBLER**—Blackstone Cable LLC

INDEPENDENCE—See DALLAS, OR

▲ **IONE**—Ione City TV Co-op

IRRIGON—See UMATILLA, OR

ISLAND CITY—See LA GRANDE, OR

JACKSON COUNTY—See MEDFORD, OR

JACKSONVILLE—See MEDFORD, OR

JASPER—See BEAR MOUNTAIN, OR

JEFFERSON—See DALLAS, OR

JOHN DAY—See MOUNT VERNON, OR

JOSEPH—See ENTERPRISE, OR

JOSEPHINE COUNTY—See GRANTS PASS, OR

JOSEPHINE COUNTY (portions)—See also CAVE JUNCTION, OR

JUNCTION CITY—See EUGENE, OR

KEIZER—See SALEM, OR

KENO—See KLAMATH FALLS, OR

KERBY—See CAVE JUNCTION, OR

KERNVILLE—See DEPOE BAY, OR

KING CITY—See BEAVERTON, OR

KLAMATH COUNTY (unincorporated areas)—See KLAMATH FALLS, OR

▲ **KLAMATH FALLS**—Falcon Cable TV

▲ **KNAPPA**—Pacific Sun Cable Partners LP

▲ **LA GRANDE**—Falcon Cable TV

▲ **LA PINE**—Crestview Cable TV

▲ **LACOMB**—CVF Cablevision

LAFAYETTE—See NEWBERG, OR

LAKE COUNTY (portions)—See LAKEVIEW, OR

LAKE LABISH—See BROOKS, OR

LAKE OSWEGO—See BEAVERTON, OR

LAKESIDE—See REEDSPORT, OR

▲ **LAKEVIEW**—TCI Cablevision of Oregon Inc.

LANE COUNTY—See EUGENE, OR

LANE COUNTY (portions)—See also BEAR MOUNTAIN, OR

LANE COUNTY (portions)—See also FLORENCE, OR

LEABURG—See BEAR MOUNTAIN, OR

▲ **LEBANON**—TCI Cablevision of Oregon Inc.

LEWIS & CLARK—See ASTORIA, OR

LINCOLN BEACH—See DEPOE BAY, OR

▲ **LINCOLN CITY**—Falcon Telecable

LINCOLN COUNTY (northern portion)—See DEPOE BAY, OR

LINCOLN COUNTY (portions)—See also LINCOLN CITY, OR

LINCOLN COUNTY (portions)—See also NEWPORT, OR

LINCOLN COUNTY (portions)—See also SOUTHBEACH, OR

LINCOLN COUNTY (portions)—See also WALDPORT, OR

LINCOLN COUNTY (southern portion)—See also YACHATS, OR

LINN COUNTY (western portion)—See LEBANON, OR

LINNTON—See PORTLAND (eastern portion), OR

▲ **LOOKINGGLASS**—Interstate Cable Inc.

LOSTINE—See ENTERPRISE, OR

LOWELL—See BEAR MOUNTAIN, OR

LYONS—See SUBLIMITY, OR

▲ **MACLEAY**—Country Cablevision Ltd.

▲ **MADRAS**—Crestview Cable TV

▲ **MALIN**—Blackstone Cable LLC

MANZANITA—See NEHALEM, OR

▲ **MAPLETON**—Falcon Cable Systems Co.

MARCOLA—See BEAR MOUNTAIN, OR

MARION—See MACLEAY, OR

MARION COUNTY (northern portion)—See BROOKS, OR

MARION COUNTY (northwestern portion)—See also CANBY, OR

MARION COUNTY (portions)—See also MACLEAY, OR

MARION COUNTY (portions)—See also SALEM, OR

MARION COUNTY (portions)—See also SILVERTON, OR

MARION COUNTY (portions)—See also SOUTH SALEM, OR

MARION COUNTY (portions)—See also WOODBURN, OR

MARION COUNTY (southwestern portion)—See also DALLAS, OR

MAYWOOD PARK—See PORTLAND (eastern portion), OR

McKENZIE—See BEAR MOUNTAIN, OR

McMINNVILLE—See NEWBERG, OR

▲ **MEDFORD**—Falcon Cable

MEHAMA—See SUBLIMITY, OR

▲ **MERRILL**—Blackstone Cable LLC

METOLIUS—See MADRAS, OR

MIDLAND—See KLAMATH FALLS, OR

MILL CITY—See SUBLIMITY, OR

MILLERSBURG—See CORVALLIS, OR

▲ **MILTON-FREEWATER**—TCI Cablevision of Oregon Inc.

▲ **MILWAUKIE**—TCI of Milwaukie

MOHAWK—See BEAR MOUNTAIN, OR

MOLALLA—See CANBY, OR

MONMOUTH—See DALLAS, OR

▲ **MONROE**—Monroe Area Communications Inc.

▲ **MORO**—Moro TV Club

MOUNT ANGEL—See SILVERTON, OR

MOUNT HOOD—See PARKDALE, OR

▲ **MOUNT VERNON**—Blue Mountain TV Cable Co.

MULINO—See BEAVERCREEK, OR

MULINO—See also CANBY, OR

MULTNOMAH COUNTY (portions)—See PORTLAND, OR

MULTNOMAH COUNTY (unincorporated areas)—See also PORTLAND (eastern portion), OR

▲ **MYRTLE CREEK**—Falcon Cable

▲ **MYRTLE POINT**—Falcon Cable Systems Co.

NEEDY—See CANBY, OR

▲ **NEHALEM**—Falcon Telecable

NESKOWIN—See TILLAMOOK COUNTY (southwestern portion), OR

▲ **NETARTS**—Falcon Telecable

▲ **NEWBERG**—TCI Cablevision of Oregon Inc.

▲ **NEWPORT**—Falcon Cable TV

NORTH ALBANY—See CORVALLIS, OR

NORTH BEND—See COOS BAY, OR

NORTH PLAINS—See BEAVERTON, OR

▲ **NORTH POWDER**—Blackstone Cable LLC

NORTH SMITH RIVER—See CRESCENT CITY, CA

NOTI—See VENETA, OR

NYSSA—See ONTARIO, OR

OAKLAND—See SUTHERLIN, OR

OAKRIDGE—See BEAR MOUNTAIN, OR

OAKVILLE—See LEBANON, OR

OCEANSIDE—See NETARTS, OR

▲ **ODELL**—Valley TV Co-op Inc.

▲ **ONTARIO**—Chambers Cable of Oregon Inc.

OREGON CITY—See PORTLAND, OR

OREGON CITY (portions)—See also CANBY, OR

ORIENT—See PORTLAND (eastern portion), OR

OTIS—See ROSE LODGE, OR

OTTER ROCK—See NEWPORT, OR

PACIFIC CITY—See TILLAMOOK COUNTY (southwestern portion), OR

▲ **PARKDALE**—Valley TV Co-op Inc.

▲ **PENDLETON**—Falcon Cable TV

PHILOMATH—See CORVALLIS, OR

PHOENIX—See MEDFORD, OR

PILOT ROCK—See PENDLETON, OR

▲ **PIONEER MOBILE HOME PARK**—Interstate Cable Inc.

PLEASANT HILL—See BEAR MOUNTAIN, OR

PLEASANT VALLEY—See BORING, OR

POLK COUNTY (portions)—See DALLAS, OR

POLK COUNTY (portions)—See also SALEM, OR

PORT ORFORD—See COOS BAY, OR

▲ **PORTLAND**—TCI Cablevision of Oregon Inc.

▲ **PORTLAND (eastern portion)**—TCI Cable

▲ **POWERS 89**—Falcon Cable Systems Co.

▲ **PRAIRIE CITY**—Blue Mountain TV Cable Co.

▲ **PRINEVILLE**—Crestview Cable TV

▲ **PROSPECT**—Phoenix Cablevision of Oregon Inc.

▲ **RAINIER**—Pacific Sun Cable Partners LP

▲ **REDMOND**—Bend Cable Communications LLC

▲ **REEDSPORT**—Falcon Cable Systems Co.

REEDVILLE—See BEAVERTON, OR

▲ **RICHLAND**—Eagle Valley Communications

RIDDLE—See MYRTLE CREEK, OR

RIETH—See PENDLETON, OR

RIVERDALE—See PORTLAND, OR

RIVERGROVE—See BEAVERTON, OR

ROCKAWAY BEACH—See NEHALEM, OR

ROGUE RIVER—See GRANTS PASS, OR

▲ **ROSE LODGE**—Millennium Digital Media

▲ **ROSEBURG**—Falcon Cable TV

▲ **RUCH**—Sunnyside Cable TV Co.

▲ **SALEM**—TCI

▲ **SALEM (southeastern portion)**—Mill Creek Cable TV Inc.

SALMON RIVER—See ROSE LODGE, OR

SAND LAKE—See TILLAMOOK COUNTY (southwestern portion), OR

▲ **SANDY**—Falcon Cablevision

SANTA CLARA—See EUGENE, OR

SCAPPOOSE—See ST. HELENS, OR

▲ **SCIO**—Scio Cablevision Inc.

SEAL ROCK—See SOUTHBEACH, OR

SEAL ROCK—See also YACHATS, OR

SEASIDE—See ASTORIA, OR

▲ **SENECA**—Blue Mountain TV Cable Co.

▲ **SHADY COVE**—Phoenix Cablevision of Oregon Inc.

SHAW—See MACLEAY, OR

▲ **SHERIDAN**—Stuck Electric Inc.

SHERWOOD—See BEAVERTON, OR

▲ **SILETZ**—Millennium Digital Media

SILETZ RIVER—See DEPOE BAY, OR

▲ **SILVERTON**—Falcon Cable Systems Co.

SISTERS—See BEND, OR

SODAVILLE—See CORVALLIS, OR

▲ **SOUTH SALEM**—Country Cablevision Ltd.

▲ **SOUTHBEACH**—Millennium Digital Media

SPRING RIVER—See SUNRIVER, OR

SPRINGDALE—See PORTLAND (eastern portion), OR

SPRINGFIELD—See EUGENE, OR

▲ **ST. HELENS**—TCI Cablevision of Oregon Inc.

▲ **ST. PAUL (town)**—Interstate Cable Inc.

STANFIELD—See HERMISTON, OR

STAYTON—See SUBLIMITY, OR

▲ **SUBLIMITY**—North Santiam Communications

▲ **SUMPTER**—Blackstone Cable LLC

▲ **SUNRIVER**—Chambers Cable of Sunriver Inc.

▲ **SUTHERLIN**—Falcon Cable Systems Co.

SVENSEN—See KNAPPA, OR

▲ **SWEET HOME**—TCI Cablevision of Oregon Inc.

SYLVAN—See PORTLAND, OR

TALENT—See MEDFORD, OR

TANGENT—See LEBANON, OR

▲ **TENMILE**—Interstate Cable Inc.

▲ **THE DALLES**—Falcon Community Ventures I

TIGARD—See BEAVERTON, OR

▲ **TILLAMOOK**—Falcon Telecable

▲ **TILLAMOOK COUNTY (southwestern portion)**—Falcon Telecable

TILLAMOOK COUNTY (portions)—See also NEHALEM, OR

TOLEDO—See NEWPORT, OR

TRAIL—See SHADY COVE, OR

TRI-CITY—See MYRTLE CREEK, OR

TROUTDALE—See PORTLAND (eastern portion), OR

TUALATIN—See BEAVERTON, OR

TUMALO—See BEND, OR

TURNER—See SUBLIMITY, OR

▲ **TYGH VALLEY**—Cascade Cable Systems

▲ **UMATILLA**—Columbia Basin Cable

UMATILLA COUNTY—See HERMISTON, OR

UMATILLA COUNTY (portions)—See also PENDLETON, OR

UMATILLA COUNTY (unincorporated areas)—See also MILTON-FREEWATER, OR

UMATILLA COUNTY (unincorporated areas)—See also UMATILLA, OR

UMATILLA INDIAN RESERVATION—See PENDLETON, OR

▲ **UNION**—TCI Cablevision of Oregon Inc.

UNION COUNTY—See LA GRANDE, OR

VALE—See ONTARIO, OR

▲ **VENETA**—Falcon Cable Systems Co.

▲ **VERNONIA**—Vernonia CATV Inc.

▲ **WALDPORT**—Alsea River Cable Co.

WALDPORT—See also YACHATS, OR

WALLOWA—See ENTERPRISE, OR

WALLOWA LAKE—See ENTERPRISE, OR

WALLUSKI LOOP—See ASTORIA, OR

WALTERVILLE—See BEAR MOUNTAIN, OR

▲ **WARM SPRINGS**—American Telecasting

WARREN—See ST. HELENS, OR

WARRENTON—See ASTORIA, OR

▲ **WASCO**—J & N Cable Systems

WASCO COUNTY—See THE DALLES, OR

WASHINGTON COUNTY—See BEAVERTON, OR

WASHINGTON COUNTY—See also PORTLAND, OR

WATERLOO—See CORVALLIS, OR

WEMME—See SANDY, OR

WEST FIR—See BEAR MOUNTAIN, OR

WEST LINN—See PORTLAND, OR

WEST STAYTON—See MACLEAY, OR

▲ **WESTON**—TCI Cablevision of Oregon Inc.

▲ **WESTPORT**—Sun Country Cable

WHEELER—See NEHALEM, OR

WHITE CITY—See MEDFORD, OR

WHITEWATER—See BEAR MOUNTAIN, OR

WILLAMINA—See SHERIDAN, OR

WILSON RIVER—See NEHALEM, OR

WILSONVILLE—See BEAVERTON, OR

WINCHESTER BAY—See REEDSPORT, OR

WINSTON—See MYRTLE CREEK, OR

WOCUS—See KLAMATH FALLS, OR

WOOD VILLAGE—See PORTLAND (eastern portion), OR

▲ **WOODBURN**—Northland Cable TV

WOODBURN—See also CANBY, OR

▲ **YACHATS**—TCI Cablevision of Oregon Inc.

YAMHILL—See NEWBERG, OR

YONCALLA—See DRAIN, OR

PENNSYLVANIA

AARONSBURG—See MILLHEIM, PA

ABBOTTSTOWN—See YORK, PA

ABINGTON TWP. (Lackawanna County)—See DUNMORE, PA

ABINGTON TWP. (Montgomery County)—See WILLOW GROVE, PA

ACOSTA—See SOMERSET, PA

ACRE LAKE—See LOOMIS LAKE, PA

ADAMS TWP. (Butler County)—See ZELIENOPLE, PA

▲ **ADAMS TWP. (Cambria County)**—Adelphia

ADAMSBURG—See GREENSBURG, PA

ADAMSTOWN—See EPHRATA, PA

ADDISON—See ADDISON TWP. (southern portion), PA

▲ **ADDISON TWP. (southern portion)**—Somerfield Cable TV Co.

ADDISON TWP.—See also MARKLEYSBURG, PA

AHRENSVILLE—See PLUMER, PA

AKRON—See EPHRATA, PA

ALBA—See CANTON, PA

ALBANY TWP.—See MESHOPPEN, PA

ALBION—See HARBORCREEK TWP., PA

ALBRIGHTSVILLE—See LANSFORD, PA

ALBURTIS—See LEHIGH VALLEY, PA

ALCOA VILLAGE—See NEW BETHLEHEM, PA

ALDAN—See WALLINGFORD, PA

ALDENVILLE—See CARBONDALE, PA

ALEPPO—See BADEN, PA

ALEXANDRIA—See HUNTINGDON, PA

▲ **ALIQUIPPA**—AT&T Cable Services

ALLANVALE—See SOMERSET, PA

ALLEGHENY TWP. (Blair County)—See ALTOONA, PA

ALLEGHENY TWP. (Cambria County)—See GALLITZIN TWP., PA

ALLEGHENY TWP. (Somerset County)—See NEW BALTIMORE, PA

ALLEGHENY TWP. (Westmoreland County)—See KISKIMINETAS TWP., PA

ALLEN TWP.—See LEHIGH VALLEY, PA

ALLEN TWP.—See also NORTHAMPTON, PA

ALLENPORT—See CALIFORNIA, PA

▲ **ALLENSVILLE**—Valley Cable Systems

ALLENTOWN—See LEHIGH VALLEY, PA

ALLENTOWN—See also NORTHAMPTON, PA

ALLENWOOD—See CLINTON TWP. (Lycoming County), PA

ALLISON I—See UNIONTOWN, PA

ALLISON II—See UNIONTOWN, PA

ALLISON TWP.—See LOCK HAVEN, PA

ALPINE HEIGHTS—See SOMERSET, PA

ALSACE TWP.—See READING, PA

ALTHOM—See TIDIOUTE, PA

▲ **ALTOONA**—CableCom

ALTOONA—See also CANOE CREEK, PA

ALUM BANK—See BEDFORD, PA

ALVERDA—See GREEN TWP. (Indiana County), PA

AMBLER—See MONTGOMERY, PA

AMBRIDGE—See BADEN, PA

AMITY TWP. (Berks County)—See BIRDSBORO, PA

AMWELL TWP.—See BENTLEYVILLE, PA

AMWELL TWP.—See also WASHINGTON, PA

ANNIN TWP.—See COUDERSPORT, PA

ANNVILLE TWP.—See LEBANON, PA

▲ **ANTHONY TWP.**—Commuter Cable Television-East

ANTIS TWP.—See ALTOONA, PA

ANTRIM TWP.—See CARLISLE, PA

APOLLO—See KISKIMINETAS TWP., PA

APPLEWOLD—See KITTANNING, PA

ARARAT TWP.—See THOMPSON TWP., PA

ARCHBALD—See CARBONDALE, PA

ARCHBALD—See also DUNMORE, PA

ARENDTSVILLE—See GETTYSBURG, PA

ARISTES—See SUNBURY, PA

ARMAGH—See WEST WHEATFIELD TWP. (Indiana County), PA

ARMAGH TWP.—See ELIZABETHTOWN, PA

ARMAGH TWP.—See also REEDSVILLE, PA

ARMSTRONG TWP. (Indiana County)—See BLAIRSVILLE, PA

ARMSTRONG TWP. (Indiana County)—See also ELDERTON BOROUGH, PA

ARMSTRONG TWP. (Lycoming County)—See WILLIAMSPORT, PA

ARNOLD—See TARENTUM BOROUGH, PA

▲ **ARNOT**—Blue Ridge Cable TV Inc.

ARONA—See GREENSBURG, PA

ASHLAND—See MAHANOY CITY, PA

ASHLAND TWP.—See NINEVAH, PA

ASHLEY—See WILKES-BARRE, PA

ASHVILLE—See GALLITZIN TWP., PA

ASPINWALL—See ROSS TWP. (Allegheny County), PA

ASTON—See WALLINGFORD, PA

ASTON TWP.—See WALLINGFORD, PA

ASYLUM TWP.—See TOWANDA, PA

ATGLEN (Chester County)—See CHESTER COUNTY, PA

ATHENS (borough)—See SAYRE, PA

ATHENS TWP.—See SAYRE, PA

ATLASBURG—See BURGETTSTOWN, PA

▲ **AULTMAN**—Adelphia Cable

AUSTIN BOROUGH—See COUDERSPORT, PA

AUSTINVILLE TWP.—See TROY, PA

AVALON—See ROSS TWP. (Allegheny County), PA

▲ **AVELLA**—Jefferson County Cable Inc.

▲ **AVIS**—Susquehanna Communications

AVOCA—See SCRANTON, PA

AVONDALE—See KENNETT SQUARE, PA

AVONMORE—See SALTSBURG, PA

AYR TWP.—See McCONNELLSBURG, PA

▲ **BADEN**—AT&T Cable Services

BAKERSVILLE—See SOMERSET, PA

BALA CYNWYD—See LOWER MERION TWP., PA

BALD EAGLE TWP. (Clinton County)—See LOCK HAVEN, PA

BALD EAGLE TWP. (Clinton County)—See also MILL HALL, PA

BALDWIN—See CASTLE SHANNON, PA

BALDWIN TWP.—See CASTLE SHANNON, PA

BALLY—See POTTSTOWN, PA

BANGOR (Northampton County)—See NORTHAMPTON, PA

BANGOR BORO—See LEHIGH VALLEY, PA

BANKS TWP. (Carbon County)—See HAZLETON, PA

▲ **BARBOURS**—Ralph Herr TV

BAREVILLE—See LANCASTER, PA

BARIONVILLE—See SOMERSET, PA

BARKEYVILLE—See CLINTONVILLE, PA

BARNESBORO—See CARROLLTOWN BOROUGH, PA

BARR TWP.—See CARROLLTOWN BOROUGH, PA

BARRETT TWP.—See STROUDSBURG, PA

BARRY TWP.—See MAHANOY CITY, PA

BART TWP.—See LANCASTER, PA

▲ **BASTRESS TWP.**—Bastress TV Cable

BATH—See NORTHAMPTON, PA

BATH BORO—See LEHIGH VALLEY, PA

BAXTER—See SUMMERVILLE, PA

BEACH HAVEN TWP.—See BERWICK, PA

▲ **BEACH LAKE**—Blue Ridge Cable TV

BEALLSVILLE—See UNIONTOWN, PA

BEAR CREEK—See POCONO, PA

BEAR CREEK TWP.—See WILKES-BARRE, PA

BEAVER—See ROCHESTER, PA

▲ **BEAVER FALLS**—TCI of Pennsylvania

BEAVER MEADOWS—See HAZLETON, PA

▲ **BEAVER SPRINGS**—Beaver Springs Mutual TV Assn.

BEAVER TWP. (Clarion County)—See NINEVAH, PA

BEAVER TWP. (Jefferson County)—See SUMMERVILLE, PA

BEAVER TWP. (Snyder County)—See SUNBURY, PA

▲ **BEAVER VALLEY**—Adelphia

BEAVERDALE—See ADAMS TWP. (Cambria County), PA

▲ **BEAVERTOWN**—Community TV

BEAVERTOWN BOROUGH—See SUNBURY, PA

BECCARIA—See BIGLER TWP., PA

BECCARIA TWP.—See COALPORT, PA

BECHTELSVILLE—See POTTSTOWN, PA

▲ **BEDFORD**—TCI of Pennsylvania Inc.

BEDFORD BOROUGH—See BEDFORD, PA

BEDFORD TWP.—See BEDFORD, PA

BEDMINSTER TWP.—See SELLERSVILLE, PA

BEECH CREEK BOROUGH—See MILL HALL, PA

BEECH CREEK TWP.—See MILL HALL, PA

BELL ACRES—See BADEN, PA

BELL TWP. (Clearfield County)—See MAHAFFEY, PA

BELL TWP. (Jefferson County)—See PUNXSUTAWNEY, PA

BELL TWP. (Westmoreland County)—See SALTSBURG, PA

BELLE VERNON—See MON VALLEY, PA

BELLEFONTE—See STATE COLLEGE, PA

▲ **BELLEVILLE**—Belleville Area CATV System

BELLEVUE—See ROSS TWP. (Allegheny County), PA

BELLS LANDING—See GRAMPIAN, PA

BELLWOOD—See ALTOONA, PA

BEN AVON—See ROSS TWP. (Allegheny County), PA

BEN AVON HEIGHTS—See ROSS TWP. (Allegheny County), PA

BENDERSVILLE—See GETTYSBURG, PA

BENNER TWP.—See STATE COLLEGE, PA

▲ **BENSALEM TWP.**—Suburban Cable

BENSON—See JOHNSTOWN, PA

▲ **BENTLEY CREEK**—Mastervision

▲ **BENTLEYVILLE**—Bentleyville Telephone CATV

BENTLEYVILLE—See also UNIONTOWN, PA

BENTON BOROUGH—See BERWICK, PA

BENTON TWP. (Columbia County)—See BERWICK, PA

BENTON TWP. (Lackawanna County)—See DUNMORE, PA

BENZINGER TWP.—See ST. MARYS, PA

▲ **BERLIN BOROUGH**—TCI of Pennsylvania Inc.

BERLIN TWP. (Wayne County)—See BEACH LAKE, PA

BERLIN TWP. (Wayne County)—See also HONESDALE, PA

BERN TWP. (Berks County)—See HAMBURG, PA

BERN TWP. (Berks County)—See also READING, PA

BERNVILLE—See READING, PA

BERRYSBURG—See LYKENS, PA

▲ **BERWICK**—Cable TV Inc.

BERWICK TWP.—See YORK, PA

BESCO—See UNIONTOWN, PA

BESSEMER—See SPRINGFIELD TWP. (Mahoning County), OH

BETHANY—See HONESDALE, PA

▲ **BETHEL**—TCI

▲ **BETHEL PARK**—Adelphia Cable Communications

BETHEL TWP. (Armstrong County)—See BETHEL, PA

BETHEL TWP. (Berks County)—See LEBANON, PA

BETHEL TWP. (Delaware County)—See WALLINGFORD, PA

BETHEL TWP. (Lebanon County)—See LEBANON, PA

BETHLEHEM—See LEHIGH VALLEY, PA

BETHLEHEM (Northampton County)—See NORTHAMPTON, PA

BETHLEHEM TWP.—See LEHIGH VALLEY, PA

BETHLEHEM TWP. (Northampton County)—See EASTON, PA

BETHLEHEM TWP. (Northampton County)—See also NORTHAMPTON, PA

BIG BASS (Clifton Twp.)—See POCONO, PA

BIG BEAVER (Beaver County)—See DARLINGTON TWP. (Beaver County), PA

BIG BEAVER (Beaver County)—See also ELLWOOD CITY, PA

▲ **BIG POND**—Barrett's TV Cable System

BIG RUN—See PUNXSUTAWNEY, PA

BIG SOLDIER—See PUNXSUTAWNEY, PA

▲ **BIGLER TWP.**—TCI of Pennsylvania Inc.

BIGLERVILLE—See GETTYSBURG, PA

▲ **BIRDSBORO**—Service Electric Cablevision

BIRMINGHAM BOROUGH—See WARRIORS MARK, PA

BIRMINGHAM TWP. (Chester County)—See CHESTER COUNTY, PA

BIRMINGHAM TWP. (Chester County)—See also KENNETT SQUARE, PA

BLACK CREEK TWP.—See BERWICK, PA

BLACK LICK TWP.—See BLAIRSVILLE, PA

BLACK TWP.—See ROCKWOOD, PA

BLACKLICK TWP.—See NANTY GLO, PA

BLAIR TWP. (Blair County)—See ALTOONA, PA

BLAIRS MILLS—See DOYLESBURG, PA

▲ **BLAIRSVILLE**—Adelphia

BLAKELY—See DUNMORE, PA

BLAKESLEE—See POCONO, PA

BLAWNOX BOROUGH—See TARENTUM BOROUGH, PA

BLOOM TWP.—See GRAMPIAN, PA

BLOOMFIELD TWP.—See ALTOONA, PA

BLOOMING VALLEY—See MEADVILLE, PA

BLOOMINGTON—See GLEN RICHEY, PA

▲ **BLOOMSBURG**—Service Electric Cablevision Inc.

▲ **BLOSSBURG**—Williamson Road TV Co. Inc.

BLUE BALL—See LANCASTER, PA

BLUE RIDGE SUMMIT—See CARLISLE, PA

BLYTHE TWP.—See BERWICK, PA

BOBTOWN—See UNIONTOWN, PA

▲ **BODINES**—Ralph Herr TV

BOGGS TWP. (Centre County)—See CURTIN TWP., PA

BOGGS TWP. (Centre County)—See also STATE COLLEGE, PA

BOGGS TWP. (Clearfield County)—See CLEARFIELD, PA

BOGGS TWP. (Clearfield County)—See also GRAHAM TWP., PA

BOGGS TWP. (Clearfield County)—See also PHILIPSBURG BOROUGH, PA

BOILING SPRINGS—See CARLISLE, PA

BOLIVAR—See BLAIRSVILLE, PA

BONNEAUVILLE—See GETTYSBURG, PA

BOSWELL—See SOMERSET, PA

BOSWELL—See also SOMERSET BOROUGH, PA

BOWMANSTOWN—See PALMERTON, PA

▲ **BOYERS**—CableVision Communications

BOYERTOWN BOROUGH—See POTTSTOWN, PA

BOYNTON—See GRANTSVILLE, MD

BRACKENRIDGE BOROUGH—See TARENTUM BOROUGH, PA

BRADDOCK—See MONROEVILLE, PA

BRADDOCK HILLS—See EAST HILLS, PA

BRADEN PLAN—See UNIONTOWN, PA

▲ **BRADFORD**—Cablecomm

BRADFORD COUNTY—See BENTLEY CREEK, PA

BRADFORD TWP. (Clearfield County)—See CLEARFIELD, PA

BRADFORD TWP. (McKean County)—See BRADFORD, PA

BRADFORD WOODS—See ZELIENOPLE, PA

BRADY TWP. (Butler County)—See GROVE CITY, PA

BRADY TWP. (Clearfield County)—See DU BOIS, PA

BRADY TWP. (Huntingdon County)—See MILL CREEK, PA

BRADY TWP. (Lycoming County)—See CLINTON TWP. (Lycoming County), PA

BRADYS BEND TWP.—See CHICORA, PA

BRAINTRIM TWP.—See MESHOPPEN, PA

BRANCH TWP.—See POTTSVILLE, PA (AT&T Cable Services)

BRANCH TWP.—See also PRIMROSE, PA

BRANDONVILLE—See SHENANDOAH, PA

▲ **BRAVE**—CableVision Communications

BRAZNELL—See UNIONTOWN, PA

BRECKNOCK TWP. (Berks County)—See BIRDSBORO, PA

BRECKNOCK TWP. (Lancaster County)—See EPHRATA, PA

BRECKNOCK TWP. (Lancaster County)—See also READING, PA

BREEZEWOOD—See BEDFORD, PA

BRENIZER—See BLAIRSVILLE, PA

BRENTWOOD—See CASTLE SHANNON, PA

BRIAR CREEK BOROUGH—See BERWICK, PA

BRIAR CREEK TWP.—See BERWICK, PA

BRIDGEPORT—See NORRISTOWN, PA

BRIDGETON TWP.—See LEHIGH VALLEY, PA

BRIDGEVILLE—See CARNEGIE, PA

BRIDGEWATER—See ROCHESTER, PA

BRIDGEWATER TWP.—See MONTROSE, PA

BRIGHTON TWP.—See MIDLAND, PA

BRISBIN—See BIGLER TWP., PA

BRISTOL—See LEVITTOWN, PA

BRISTOL TWP.—See LEVITTOWN, PA

▲ **BROAD TOP CITY**—Broad Top Mountain Cable

BROCKPORT—See RIDGWAY BOROUGH, PA

BROCKTON—See BERWICK, PA

▲ **BROCKWAY**—Brockway TV Inc.

BROKENSTRAW TWP.—See YOUNGSVILLE, PA

BROKENSTRAW TWP. (portions)—See also TIDIOUTE, PA

BROOKHAVEN—See WALLINGFORD, PA

BROOKLYN TWP.—See LOOMIS LAKE, PA

▲ **BROOKSIDE**—Ralph Herr TV

BROOKVILLE—See ROSE TWP., PA

BROOMALL—See LANSDALE, PA

BROTHERSVALLEY TWP.—See BERLIN BOROUGH, PA

BROWN TWP. (Mifflin County)—See ELIZABETHTOWN, PA

BROWN TWP. (Mifflin County)—See also REEDSVILLE, PA

BROWNDALE—See FOREST CITY, PA

BROWNSTOWN (Cambria County)—See JOHNSTOWN, PA

BROWNSVILLE—See UNIONTOWN, PA

BROWNSVILLE TWP. (Fayette County)—See UNIONTOWN, PA

BRUIN—See CHICORA, PA

▲ **BRUSH VALLEY TWP.**—TCI of Pennsylvania Inc.

BRYN ATHYN BOROUGH—See WILLOW GROVE, PA

BUCK HILL FALLS—See STROUDSBURG, PA

BUCK TWP.—See WILKES-BARRE, PA

BUCKINGHAM—See JAMISON, PA

BUCKINGHAM TWP. (Bucks County)—See JAMISON, PA

BUFFALO TWP. (Butler County)—See BUTLER, PA

BUFFALO TWP. (Butler County)—See also TARENTUM BOROUGH, PA

BUFFALO TWP. (Union County)—See DANVILLE, PA

BUFFALO TWP. (Union County)—See also MIFFLINBURG, PA

BUFFALO TWP. (Washington County)—See WASHINGTON, PA

BUFFINGTON—See BRUSH VALLEY TWP., PA

BULGER—See BURGETTSTOWN, PA

BULLSKIN TWP.—See CONNELLSVILLE, PA

▲ **BURGETTSTOWN**—Jefferson County Cable Inc.

BURLINGTON—See TROY, PA

BURLINGTON BOROUGH—See TROY, PA

BURNHAM—See LEWISTOWN, PA (TCI of Pennsylvania Inc.)

BURNSIDE TWP. (Cambria County)—See CARROLLTOWN BOROUGH, PA

BURNSIDE TWP. (Centre County)—See SNOW SHOE, PA

BURNT CABINS—See FANNETTSBURG, PA (Fannettsburg Cable TV Co.)

BURRELL TWP. (Indiana County)—See BLAIRSVILLE, PA

BURSON PLAN—See UNIONTOWN, PA

BUSHKILL—See STROUDSBURG, PA

BUSHKILL TWP.—See LEHIGH VALLEY, PA

BUSHKILL TWP. (Northampton County)—See NORTHAMPTON, PA

CHESTER—See WALLINGFORD, PA

▲ **CHESTER COUNTY**—Suburban Cable

CHESTER HEIGHTS—See WALLINGFORD, PA

CHESTER HILL—See PHILIPSBURG BOROUGH, PA

CHESTER TWP. (Delaware County)—See WALLINGFORD, PA

CHESTNUT HILL TWP.—See STROUDSBURG, PA

CHESWICK—See TARENTUM BOROUGH, PA

CHICKENTOWN—See SOMERSET, PA

▲ **CHICORA**—CableVision Communications

CHINCHILLA—See DUNMORE, PA

CHIPPEWA TWP.—See BEAVER FALLS, PA

CHRISTIANA (Lancaster County)—See LANCASTER, PA

CHRISTIANA BOROUGH—See LANCASTER, PA

CHURCHILL—See MONROEVILLE, PA

CLAIRTON—See CASTLE SHANNON, PA

CLARENCE—See SNOW SHOE, PA

▲ **CLARENDON**—Clarendon TV Association

CLARENDON HEIGHTS—See CLARENDON, PA

CLARION—See CLARION BOROUGH, PA

CLARION—See also LIMESTONE, PA

▲ **CLARION BOROUGH**—TCI of Pennsylvania Inc.

CLARION TWP.—See CLARION BOROUGH, PA

CLARK—See SHARON, PA

CLARKS GREEN—See DUNMORE, PA

CLARKS SUMMIT—See DUNMORE, PA

CLARKSBURG—See AULTMAN, PA

CLARKSVILLE—See UNIONTOWN, PA

CLAY TWP. (Butler County)—See BUTLER, PA

CLAY TWP. (Huntingdon County)—See THREE SPRINGS, PA

CLAY TWP. (Lancaster County)—See EPHRATA, PA

CLAYSBURG—See ALTOONA, PA

▲ **CLAYSVILLE**—Jefferson County Cable Inc.

▲ **CLEARFIELD**—Cablecomm

CLEARFIELD COUNTY—See DU BOIS, PA

CLEARFIELD COUNTY—See also GALLITZIN TWP., PA

CLEARFIELD TWP. (Butler County)—See BUTLER, PA

CLEARFIELD TWP. (Cambria County)—See CARROLLTOWN BOROUGH, PA

CLEARFIELD TWP. (Cambria County)—See also COALPORT, PA

CLEONA—See LEBANON, PA

CLEVELAND TWP.—See BLOOMSBURG, PA

CLIFFORD TWP. (Susquehanna County)—See CARBONDALE, PA

CLIFTON HEIGHTS—See WALLINGFORD, PA

CLIFTON TWP.—See POCONO, PA

CLINTON TWP.—See TARENTUM BOROUGH, PA

CLINTON TWP. (Butler County)—See ZELIENOPLE, PA

▲ **CLINTON TWP. (Lycoming County)**—TCI of Pennsylvania Inc.

CLINTON TWP. (Venango County)—See CLINTONVILLE, PA

CLINTON TWP. (Wayne County)—See CARBONDALE, PA

CLINTON TWP. (Wyoming County)—See DUNMORE, PA

▲ **CLINTONVILLE**—Multi-Tech Communications

CLOE—See PUNXSUTAWNEY, PA

CLOVER TWP.—See SUMMERVILLE, PA

CLYMER—See BLAIRSVILLE, PA

COAL—See SUNBURY, PA

COAL CENTER—See CALIFORNIA, PA

COAL HILL—See ROCKMERE, PA

COAL RUN (Indiana County)—See AULTMAN, PA

COAL RUN (Somerset County)—See GRANTSVILLE, MD

COAL TWP. (Northumberland County)—See SUNBURY, PA

COALDALE—See LANSFORD, PA

COALMONT—See BROAD TOP CITY, PA

▲ **COALPORT**—Cooney Cable

COATESVILLE—See CHESTER COUNTY, PA

COBURN—See MILLHEIM, PA

COCHRANTON—See MEADVILLE, PA

CODORUS—See GLEN ROCK, PA

CODORUS TWP.—See GETTYSBURG, PA

▲ **COGAN STATION**—Retel TV Cable Co.

COKEBURG—See UNIONTOWN, PA

COLEBROOK TWP.—See LOCK HAVEN, PA

COLEBROOKDALE TWP.—See POTTSTOWN, PA

COLERAIN TWP. (Bedford County)—See BEDFORD, PA

COLLEGE TWP. (Centre County)—See STATE COLLEGE, PA

COLLEGEVILLE—See KING OF PRUSSIA, PA

COLLEY TWP. (Sullivan County)—See DUSHORE, PA

COLLIER—See CARNEGIE, PA

COLLIER TWP.—See CARNEGIE, PA

COLLINGDALE—See WALLINGFORD, PA

COLONIAL IV—See UNIONTOWN, PA

COLUMBIA—See LANCASTER, PA

COLUMBIA BOROUGH—See LANCASTER, PA

COLUMBIA CROSSROADS—See TROY, PA

COLUMBIA CROSSROADS TWP.—See TROY, PA

COLUMBIA TWP. (Bradford County)—See TROY, PA

COLUMBUS TWP. (Warren County)—See CORRY, PA

COLWYN—See WALLINGFORD, PA

COMMODORE (Indiana County)—See BLAIRSVILLE, PA

COMMODORE (Indiana County)—See also GREEN TWP. (Indiana County), PA

CONCORD—See WALLINGFORD, PA

CONCORD TWP. (Butler County)—See GROVE CITY, PA

CONCORD TWP. (Delaware County)—See WALLINGFORD, PA

CONCORD TWP. (Erie County)—See CORRY, PA

CONEMAUGH TWP. (Cambria County)—See JOHNSTOWN, PA

CONEMAUGH TWP. (Indiana County)—See AULTMAN, PA

CONEMAUGH TWP. (Indiana County)—See also SALTSBURG, PA

CONEMAUGH TWP. (Somerset County)—See JOHNSTOWN, PA

CONESTOGA—See LANCASTER, PA

CONEWAGO TWP. (Adams County)—See YORK, PA

CONEWAGO TWP. (Dauphin County)—See HERSHEY, PA

CONEWAGO TWP. (York County)—See YORK, PA

CONEWANGO TWP. (Warren County)—See WARREN, PA

CONFLUENCE—See MARKLEYSBURG, PA

CONNEAT TWP.—See HARBORCREEK TWP., PA

CONNEAUT LAKE—See MEADVILLE, PA

CONNEAUTVILLE—See SPRING TWP. (Crawford County), PA

▲ **CONNELLSVILLE**—Armstrong Communications Inc.

CONNELLSVILLE TWP. (Fayette County)—See CONNELLSVILLE, PA

CONNOQUENESSING TWP. (Butler County)—See BUTLER, PA

CONOY TWP.—See ELIZABETHTOWN, PA

CONSHOHOCKEN—See NORRISTOWN, PA

CONWAY—See BADEN, PA

CONWAY HEIGHTS—See BADEN, PA

CONYNGHAM BOROUGH—See HAZLETON, PA

CONYNGHAM TWP. (Columbia County)—See BERWICK, PA

CONYNGHAM TWP. (Columbia County)—See also SUNBURY, PA

COOK TWP.—See INDIAN CREEK, PA

COOLBAUGH TWP.—See POCONO, PA

COOLBAUGH TWP.—See also STROUDSBURG, PA

COOLSPRING TWP. (portions)—See GROVE CITY, PA

INDEPENDENCE TWP.—See BEAVER VALLEY, PA

INDEPENDENT LAKE—See THOMPSON TWP., PA

INDIAN COUNTY CAMPSITE—See POCONO, PA

▲ **INDIAN CREEK**—Laurel Highland TV Co.

INDIAN HEAD—See INDIAN CREEK, PA

INDIAN LAKE—See CENTRAL CITY BOROUGH, PA

INDIAN ORCHARD—See HONESDALE, PA

INDIANA—See BLAIRSVILLE, PA

INDIANA TWP. (Allegheny County)—See BLAIRSVILLE, PA

INDIANA TWP. (Allegheny County)—See also TARENTUM BOROUGH, PA

INDUSTRY—See MIDLAND, PA

INGRAM—See CARNEGIE, PA

IRVINE—See TIDIOUTE, PA

IRVONA—See COALPORT, PA

IRWIN—See GREENSBURG, PA

IRWIN TWP. (Venango County)—See CLINTONVILLE, PA

ISABELLA (portions)—See UNIONTOWN, PA

ISELIN—See AULTMAN, PA

IVYLAND (portions)—See HOLLAND, PA

IVYLAND (portions)—See also JAMISON, PA

JACKSON CENTER—See SANDY LAKE, PA

JACKSON CENTER BOROUGH—See SANDY LAKE, PA

JACKSON TWP. (Butler County)—See GROVE CITY, PA

JACKSON TWP. (Butler County)—See also ZELIENOPLE, PA

JACKSON TWP. (Cambria County)—See JOHNSTOWN, PA

JACKSON TWP. (Cambria County)—See also NANTY GLO, PA

JACKSON TWP. (Columbia County)—See BERWICK, PA

JACKSON TWP. (Dauphin County)—See MILLERSBURG, PA

JACKSON TWP. (Lebanon County)—See LEBANON, PA

JACKSON TWP. (Monroe County)—See STROUDSBURG, PA

JACKSON TWP. (Northumberland County)—See SUNBURY, PA

JACKSON TWP. (Snyder County)—See SUNBURY, PA

JACKSON TWP. (Susquehanna County)—See THOMPSON TWP., PA

JACKSON TWP. (Venango County)—See COOPERSTOWN, PA

JACKSON TWP. (York County)—See YORK, PA

JACKSONVILLE (Centre County)—See CURTIN TWP., PA

JACKSONVILLE (Centre County)—See also WALKER TWP. (Centre County), PA

JACKSONVILLE (Indiana County)—See AULTMAN, PA

JACOBUS—See YORK, PA

JAMES CITY—See KANE, PA

▲ **JAMESTOWN**—CableVision Communications

▲ **JAMISON**—Suburban Cable TV

JAY TWP.—See CALEDONIA, PA

JAY TWP.—See also WEEDVILLE, PA

JEANNETTE—See GREENSBURG, PA

JEDDO—See HAZLETON, PA

JEFFERSON (Allegheny County)—See CASTLE SHANNON, PA

JEFFERSON (Greene County)—See UNIONTOWN, PA

JEFFERSON (Washington County)—See CALIFORNIA, PA

JEFFERSON (York County)—See GLEN ROCK, PA

JEFFERSON COUNTY—See DU BOIS, PA

JEFFERSON TWP. (Berks County)—See LEBANON, PA

JEFFERSON TWP. (Berks County)—See also READING, PA

JEFFERSON TWP. (Butler County)—See BUTLER, PA

JEFFERSON TWP. (Dauphin County)—See MILLERSBURG, PA

JEFFERSON TWP. (Fayette County)—See UNIONTOWN, PA

JEFFERSON TWP. (Lackawanna County)—See CARBONDALE, PA

JEFFERSON TWP. (Lackawanna County)—See also DUNMORE, PA

JEFFERSON TWP. (Somerset County)—See SOMERSET, PA

JENKINS TWP. (Luzerne County)—See DUNMORE, PA

JENKINTOWN BOROUGH—See WILLOW GROVE, PA

JENKS TWP.—See MARIENVILLE, PA

JENNER TWP. (Somerset County)—See JOHNSTOWN, PA

JENNER TWP. (Somerset County)—See also SOMERSET, PA

JENNERS—See SOMERSET BOROUGH, PA

JENNERSTOWN (Somerset County)—See SOMERSET, PA

JENNERSTOWN (Somerset County)—See also SOMERSET BOROUGH, PA

JERMYN—See CARBONDALE, PA

JEROME—See JOHNSTOWN, PA

JERSEY MILLS—See WATERVILLE, PA

JERSEY SHORE—See AVIS, PA

JESSUP—See DUNMORE, PA

JIM THORPE—See LANSFORD, PA

JIM THORPE—See also PALMERTON, PA

JOFFRE—See BURGETTSTOWN, PA

▲ **JOHNSONBURG**—Johnsonburg Community TV Co.

▲ **JOHNSTOWN**—Cablecomm

JONESTOWN (Columbia County)—See DUSHORE, PA

JONESTOWN (Lebanon County)—See LEBANON, PA

JORDAN—See SUNBURY, PA

JULIAN—See UNION TWP. (Centre County), PA

JUNIATA TERRACE—See LEWISTOWN, PA (TCI of Pennsylvania Inc.)

JUNIATA TWP. (Blair County)—See ALTOONA, PA

JUNIATA TWP. (Huntingdon County)—See HUNTINGDON, PA

JUNIATA TWP. (Perry County)—See ELIZABETHTOWN, PA

KAHLES CORNERS—See ROCKMERE, PA

▲ **KANE**—TCI of Pennsylvania Inc.

KANEVILLE—See TITUSVILLE, PA

KARNS CITY—See CHICORA, PA

▲ **KARTHAUS**—CableVision Communications

KARTHAUS TWP.—See SNOW SHOE, PA

KASKA—See BERWICK, PA

KAYLOR—See CHICORA, PA

KEATING TWP. (McKean County)—See SMETHPORT, PA

KEATING TWP. (Potter County)—See COUDERSPORT, PA

KEISTERVILLE—See UNIONTOWN, PA

▲ **KELLETTVILLE**—CableVision Communications

KELLY TWP. (Union County)—See DANVILLE, PA

KELLY TWP. (Union County)—See also LEWISBURG, PA

KENHORST—See READING, PA

KENNEDY TWP.—See McKEES ROCKS, PA

KENNEDYVILLE—See WELLSBORO, PA

KENNERDELL—See CLINTONVILLE, PA

▲ **KENNETT SQUARE**—Harron Communications

KENT—See AULTMAN, PA

KERSEY—See ST. MARYS, PA

KIDDER TWP. (Carbon County)—See PALMERTON, PA

KIDDER TWP. (Luzerne County)—See POCONO, PA

KILBUCK—See ROSS TWP. (Allegheny County), PA

KIMMELL TWP.—See ALTOONA, PA

▲ **KING OF PRUSSIA**—Suburban Cable

KING TWP.—See WOODBURY, PA

KINGSLEY—See LOOMIS LAKE, PA

KINGSLEY TWP.—See TIDIOUTE, PA

KINGSTON (Luzerne County)—See WILKES-BARRE, PA

KINGSTON TWP.—See DALLAS, PA

KINGWOOD—See SOMERSET, PA

KINZERS—See LANCASTER, PA

▲ **KISKIMINETAS TWP.**—AT&T Cable Services

KISKIMINETAS TWP.—See also BETHEL, PA

KISTLER—See SHIRLEY TWP., PA

▲ **KITTANNING**—Adelphia

KLINE TWP.—See HAZLETON, PA

KNOX—See PAINT TWP. (Clarion County), PA

KNOX TWP. (Clarion County)—See NORTH CLARION, PA

KNOX TWP. (Jefferson County)—See ROSE TWP., PA

KNOX TWP. (Jefferson County)—See also TIMBLIN BOROUGH, PA

KNOXVILLE (Fayette County)—See UNIONTOWN, PA

KOPPEL—See ELLWOOD CITY, PA

KREAMER—See SUNBURY, PA

KULPMONT (Northumberland County)—See SUNBURY, PA

KUNKLE—See NOXEN, PA

▲ **KUTZTOWN**—Service Electric Cablevision

LA BELLE—See UNIONTOWN, PA

LA PLUME—See DUNMORE, PA

LACEYVILLE—See MESHOPPEN, PA

LACKAWAXEN TWP.—See MILFORD, PA

LACONTES MILLS—See KARTHAUS, PA

LAFLIN BOROUGH—See DUNMORE, PA

▲ **LAIRDSVILLE**—Ralph Herr TV

LAKE ARIEL—See CARBONDALE, PA

LAKE CAREY—See MESHOPPEN, PA

LAKE CITY—See HARBORCREEK TWP., PA

LAKE COMO (village)—See LAKEWOOD, PA

LAKE HARMONY—See POCONO, PA

LAKE LATONKA BOROUGH—See GROVE CITY, PA

LAKE LORAIN—See THOMPSON TWP., PA

LAKE LUCY—See NORTH CLARION, PA

LAKE TWP. (Mercer County)—See SANDY LAKE, PA

LAKE TWP. (Wayne County)—See CARBONDALE, PA

LAKE WINOLA—See MESHOPPEN, PA

LAKEVILLE—See CARBONDALE, PA

▲ **LAKEWOOD**—Lakewood Cable Co.

LAMAR TWP. (Clinton County)—See MILL HALL, PA

LAMBS CREEK—See MANSFIELD, PA

▲ **LANCASTER**—Suburban Cable

LANCASTER TWP. (Butler County)—See ZELIENOPLE, PA

LANCASTER TWP. (Lancaster County)—See LANCASTER, PA

LANDINGVILLE—See POTTSVILLE, PA (AT&T Cable Services)

LANESBORO—See THOMPSON TWP., PA

LANGELOTH—See BURGETTSTOWN, PA

LANGHORNE—See LEVITTOWN, PA

LANGHORNE MANOR—See LEVITTOWN, PA

▲ **LANSDALE**—Adelphia Cable

LANSDOWNE—See WALLINGFORD, PA

▲ **LANSFORD**—Blue Ridge Cable TV Inc.

▲ **LAPORTE BOROUGH**—Eagles Mere/Laporte Cablevision Inc.

LAPORTE TWP. (Sullivan County)—See LAPORTE BOROUGH, PA

LARKSVILLE—See BERWICK, PA

LATHROP TWP.—See LOOMIS LAKE, PA

LATIMORE TWP.—See DILLSBURG, PA

LATIMORE TWP.—See also GETTYSBURG, PA

LATROBE—See BLAIRSVILLE, PA

LAUREL MOUNTAIN—See BLAIRSVILLE, PA

LAUREL RUN—See WILKES-BARRE, PA

LAURELDALE—See READING, PA

LAURELTON—See MIFFLINBURG, PA

LAUSANNE TWP.—See BERWICK, PA

LAVEROCK—See MONTGOMERY, PA

LAWRENCE COUNTY—See ELLWOOD CITY, PA

LAWRENCE PARK—See HARBORCREEK TWP., PA

LAWRENCE TWP. (Clearfield County)—See CLEARFIELD, PA

LAWRENCE TWP. (Tioga County)—See ELKLAND, PA

▲ **LAWRENCEVILLE**—Cablecomm

LE RAYSVILLE—See ROME, PA

LE RAYSVILLE BOROUGH—See ROME, PA

LEACOCK—See LANCASTER, PA

LEACOCK TWP. (Lancaster County)—See LANCASTER, PA

▲ **LEBANON**—AT&T Cable Services

LEECHBURG—See KISKIMINETAS TWP., PA

LEEPER—See NORTH CLARION, PA

LEESPORT—See HAMBURG, PA

LEET TWP. (Allegheny County)—See BADEN, PA

LEETSDALE—See BADEN, PA

LEHIGH TWP. (Carbon County)—See BERWICK, PA

LEHIGH TWP. (Northampton County)—See NORTHAMPTON, PA

LEHIGH TWP. (Northampton County)—See also PALMERTON, PA

LEHIGH TWP. (Wayne County)—See POCONO, PA

▲ **LEHIGH VALLEY**—Service Electric Cable TV Inc.

LEHIGHTON—See PALMERTON, PA

LEHMAN TWP. (Luzerne County)—See DALLAS, PA

LEHMAN TWP. (Pike County)—See STROUDSBURG, PA

LEMON TWP.—See MESHOPPEN, PA

LEMOYNE—See HARRISBURG, PA

LENHARTSVILLE—See HAMBURG, PA

LENOX TWP. (Susquehanna County)—See CARBONDALE, PA

LEOLA—See LANCASTER, PA

▲ **LEROY TWP.**—Blue Ridge Cable Technologies Inc.

LETTERKENNY TWP. (Franklin County)—See CHAMBERSBURG, PA

LETTERKENNY TWP. (Franklin County)—See also ORRSTOWN, PA

LEVANSVILLE—See SOMERSET, PA

▲ **LEVITTOWN**—TCI

LEVITTOWN—See also BENSALEM TWP., PA

LEWIS RUN—See BRADFORD, PA

LEWIS TWP. (Northumberland County)—See ANTHONY TWP., PA

LEWIS TWP. (Northumberland County)—See also DANVILLE, PA

LEWIS TWP. (Union County)—See MIFFLINBURG, PA

LEWISBERRY—See NEWBERRY TWP., PA

▲ **LEWISBURG**—Lewisburg CATV

LEWISBURG—See also DANVILLE, PA

▲ **LEWISTOWN**—Cablecomm

▲ **LEWISTOWN**—TCI of Pennsylvania Inc.

LIBERTY—See COUDERSPORT, PA

LIBERTY—See also GLASSPORT, PA

LIBERTY TWP.—See GETTYSBURG, PA

LIBERTY TWP.—See also HUNTINGDON, PA

LIBERTY TWP. (Centre County)—See MILL HALL, PA

LIBERTY TWP. (Mercer County)—See GROVE CITY, PA

LIBERTY TWP. (Montour County)—See DANVILLE, PA

LICKING TWP. (Clarion County)—See NORTH CLARION, PA

LICKINGVILLE—See NORTH CLARION, PA

LIGONIER—See BLAIRSVILLE, PA

LIGONIER TWP.—See BLAIRSVILLE, PA

LILLY—See GALLITZIN TWP., PA

LIMERICK TWP.—See POTTSTOWN, PA

▲ **LIMESTONE**—Multi-Tech Communications

LIMESTONE TWP. (Clarion County)—See SUMMERVILLE, PA

▲ **LIMESTONE TWP. (Lycoming County)**—TCI of Pennsylvania Inc.

LIMESTONE TWP. (Montour County)—See ANTHONY TWP., PA

LIMESTONE TWP. (Montour County)—See also DANVILLE, PA

LIMESTONE TWP. (Union County)—See MIFFLINBURG, PA

LIMESTONE TWP. (Union County)—See also SUNBURY, PA

PATTERSON TWP.—See BEAVER FALLS, PA

PATTON—See CARROLLTOWN BOROUGH, PA

PATTON TWP. (Centre County)—See STATE COLLEGE, PA

PATTONVILLE—See KITTANNING, PA

PAUPACK TWP. (Wayne County)—See CARBONDALE, PA

PAUPACK TWP. (Wayne County)—See also HAWLEY, PA

PAVIA TWP.—See ALTOONA, PA

PAXINOS—See SUNBURY, PA

PAXTANG—See HARRISBURG, PA

PAXTONVILLE—See SUNBURY, PA

PAYNE—See BLAIRSVILLE, PA

PEACH BOTTOM TWP. (York County)—See FAWN GROVE, PA

PECKVILLE—See DUNMORE, PA

PEN ARGYL—See NORTHAMPTON, PA

PEN ARGYL BORO—See LEHIGH VALLEY, PA

PENBROOK—See HARRISBURG, PA

PENFIELD—See SABULA, PA

PENLLYN—See MONTGOMERY, PA

PENN—See GREENSBURG, PA

PENN FOREST TWP. (Carbon County)—See PALMERTON, PA

PENN HILLS TWP.—See EAST HILLS, PA

PENN LAKE BOROUGH—See POCONO, PA

PENN TWP.—See YORK, PA

PENN TWP. (Berks County)—See READING, PA

PENN TWP. (Butler County)—See BUTLER, PA

PENN TWP. (Chester County)—See KENNETT SQUARE, PA

PENN TWP. (Clearfield County)—See GRAMPIAN, PA

PENN TWP. (Cumberland County)—See CARLISLE, PA

PENN TWP. (Cumberland County)—See also WALNUT BOTTOM, PA

PENN TWP. (Huntingdon County)—See HUNTINGDON, PA

PENN TWP. (Lancaster County)—See EPHRATA, PA

PENN TWP. (Lycoming County)—See MUNCY, PA

PENN TWP. (Snyder County)—See SUNBURY, PA

PENN TWP. (Westmoreland County)—See GREENSBURG, PA

PENN TWP. (Westmoreland County)—See also MURRYSVILLE, PA

PENNDEL—See LEVITTOWN, PA

PENNS CREEK—See SUNBURY, PA

PENNS PARK—See NEWTOWN, PA

PENNSBURG—See POTTSTOWN, PA

PENNSBURY TWP. (Chester County)—See KENNETT SQUARE, PA

PENNSBURY VILLAGE—See CARNEGIE, PA

PEQUEA TWP. (Lancaster County)—See LANCASTER, PA

PERKASIE—See SELLERSVILLE, PA

PERKIOMEN—See KING OF PRUSSIA, PA

PERRY TWP. (Berks County)—See HAMBURG, PA

PERRY TWP. (Clarion County)—See MONTEREY, PA

PERRY TWP. (Clarion County)—See also NORTH CLARION, PA

PERRY TWP. (Clarion County)—See also ST. PETERSBURG, PA

PERRY TWP. (Fayette County)—See UNIONTOWN, PA

PERRY TWP. (Greene County)—See MOUNT MORRIS, PA

PERRY TWP. (Indiana County)—See PUNXSUTAWNEY, PA

PERRY TWP. (Lawrence County)—See ELLWOOD CITY, PA

PERRY TWP. (Mercer County)—See MEADVILLE, PA

PERRYOPOLIS—See UNIONTOWN, PA

PERRYVILLE—See COGAN STATION, PA

PETERS TWP.—See BETHEL PARK, PA

PETERS TWP.—See also CARLISLE, PA

PETERS TWP.—See also FORT LOUDON, PA

PETERSBURG—See HUNTINGDON, PA

PETERSBURG—See also McALEVYS FORT, PA

PETROLIA—See CHICORA, PA

▲ **PHILADELPHIA (area 1)**—Greater Media Cable

▲ **PHILADELPHIA (area 2)**—Wade Cable

▲ **PHILADELPHIA (area 3)**—Comcast Cablevision of Philadelphia

▲ **PHILADELPHIA (area 4)**—Comcast Cablevision of Philadelphia

PHILIPSBURG—See PHILIPSBURG BOROUGH, PA

▲ **PHILIPSBURG BOROUGH**—TCI of Pennsylvania Inc.

PHOENIXVILLE—See POTTSTOWN, PA

PIATT TWP. (Lycoming County)—See AVIS, PA

PIATT TWP. (Lycoming County)—See also WILLIAMSPORT, PA

PICTURE ROCKS—See MUNCY, PA

PIKE MINE—See UNIONTOWN, PA

PIKE TWP. (Clearfield County)—See CLEARFIELD, PA

PIKE TWP. (Potter County)—See GAINES, PA

PIKE TWP. (Potter County)—See also GALETON, PA

PILLOW—See LYKENS, PA

PINE CREEK TWP. (Lycoming County)—See AVIS, PA

PINE GROVE (Schuylkill County)—See POTTSVILLE, PA (AT&T Cable Services)

PINE GROVE TWP. (Schuylkill County)—See POTTSVILLE, PA (AT&T Cable Services)

PINE GROVE TWP. (Warren County)—See WARREN, PA

PINE RIDGE—See STROUDSBURG, PA

PINE TWP.—See BETHEL, PA

PINE TWP. (Allegheny County)—See ZELIENOPLE, PA

PINE TWP. (Butler County)—See ZELIENOPLE, PA

PINE TWP. (Columbia County)—See BERWICK, PA

PINE TWP. (Crawford County)—See LINESVILLE, PA

PINE TWP. (Indiana County)—See GREEN TWP. (Indiana County), PA

PINE TWP. (Indiana County)—See also NANTY GLO, PA

PINE TWP. (Mercer County)—See CLINTONVILLE, PA

PINE TWP. (Mercer County)—See also GROVE CITY, PA

PINECREEK—See HAZEN, PA

PINECREEK TWP. (Jefferson County)—See ROSE TWP., PA

PINEGROVE TWP. (Venango County)—See PINOAK, PA

PINEGROVE TWP. (Venango County)—See also ROCKMERE, PA

PINEVILLE—See NEWTOWN, PA

PINEY—See LIMESTONE, PA

PINEY TWP.—See TOBY TWP., PA

▲ **PINOAK**—CableVision Communications

PINOAK VILLAGE—See PINOAK, PA

PIONEER PARK CAMP GROUND—See SOMERSET, PA

PIPERSVILLE—See NEWTOWN, PA

▲ **PITCAIRN**—Pitcairn Community Cable

PITT GAS—See UNIONTOWN, PA

▲ **PITTSBURGH**—AT&T Cable Services

PITTSBURGH AFB—See CORAOPOLIS, PA

PITTSFIELD—See YOUNGSVILLE, PA

PITTSTON—See DUNMORE, PA

PITTSTON TWP.—See DUNMORE, PA

PLAIN GROVE TWP.—See NEW CASTLE, PA

PLAINFIELD TWP.—See LEHIGH VALLEY, PA

PLAINFIELD TWP. (Northampton County)—See EASTON, PA

PLAINFIELD TWP. (Northampton County)—See also NORTHAMPTON, PA

PLAINS TWP. (Luzerne County)—See SCRANTON, PA

PLATEA BORO—See HARBORCREEK TWP., PA

PLEASANT HILLS—See WEST MIFFLIN, PA

PLEASANT MOUNT—See CARBONDALE, PA

PLEASANT TWP. (Warren County)—See TIDIOUTE, PA

PLEASANT TWP. (Warren County)—See also WARREN, PA

PLEASANTVILLE—See TITUSVILLE, PA

PLUM—See MURRYSVILLE, PA

PLUM TWP.—See TITUSVILLE, PA

PLUMCREEK TWP.—See ELDERTON BOROUGH, PA

▲ PLUMER—CableVision Communications

PLUMVILLE—See RURAL VALLEY, PA

PLYMOUTH—See SCRANTON, PA

PLYMOUTH TWP. (Luzerne County)—See BERWICK, PA

PLYMOUTH TWP. (Montgomery County)—See MONTGOMERY, PA

▲ POCONO—Pocono CATV Inc.

POCONO LAKE—See STROUDSBURG, PA

POCONO MOBILE MANOR—See POCONO, PA

POCONO RANCHETTES—See POCONO, PA

POCONO SPRINGS—See POCONO, PA

POCONO TWP.—See STROUDSBURG, PA

POCOPSON—See KENNETT SQUARE, PA

POCOPSON TWP.—See CHESTER COUNTY, PA

POCOPSON TWP.—See also KENNETT SQUARE, PA

POINT MARION—See UNIONTOWN, PA

POINT TWP. (Montour County)—See SUNBURY, PA

POINT TWP. (Northumberland County)—See DANVILLE, PA

POLK—See FRANKLIN (Venango County), PA

POLK CENTER—See FRANKLIN (Venango County), PA

POLK TWP. (Jefferson County)—See HAZEN, PA

POLK TWP. (Monroe County)—See STROUDSBURG, PA

PORT ALLEGANY—See COUDERSPORT, PA

PORT CARBON—See POTTSVILLE, PA (Wire Tele-View Corp.)

PORT CLINTON—See HAMBURG, PA

PORT MATILDA—See STATE COLLEGE, PA

▲ PORT ROYAL—Nittany Media Inc.

PORT TREVORTON—See MOUNT PLEASANT MILLS, PA

PORT VUE—See GLASSPORT, PA

▲ PORTAGE—Adelphia

PORTAGE (borough)—See PORTAGE, PA

PORTAGE TWP. (Cambria County)—See PORTAGE, PA

PORTAGE TWP. (Cameron County)—See COUDERSPORT, PA

PORTER TWP. (Clarion County)—See LIMESTONE, PA

PORTER TWP. (Clarion County)—See also NEW BETHLEHEM, PA

PORTER TWP. (Clinton County)—See AVIS, PA

PORTER TWP. (Clinton County)—See also MILL HALL, PA

PORTER TWP. (Huntingdon County)—See HUNTINGDON, PA

PORTER TWP. (Lycoming County)—See AVIS, PA

PORTER TWP. (Schuylkill County)—See LYKENS, PA

PORTERSVILLE—See ZELIENOPLE, PA

PORTLAND—See NORTHAMPTON, PA

PORTLAND BORO—See LEHIGH VALLEY, PA

POSEY CORNERS—See SOMERSET, PA

POTTER (unincorporated areas)—See COUDERSPORT, PA

POTTER TWP. (Beaver County)—See BEAVER VALLEY, PA

POTTER TWP. (Centre County)—See STATE COLLEGE, PA

POTTERVILLE—See ROME, PA

▲ POTTSTOWN—Suburban Cable

▲ POTTSVILLE—AT&T Cable Services

▲ POTTSVILLE—Wire Tele-View Corp.

POVERTY HOLLOW—See SOMERSET, PA

POWELL—See TROY, PA

POWELL TWP.—See TROY, PA

POYNTELLE—See THOMPSON TWP., PA

PRESIDENT TWP.—See NORTH CLARION, PA

PRESTON PARK (village)—See LAKEWOOD, PA

PRESTON TWP.—See THOMPSON TWP., PA

PRICE TWP. (Monroe County)—See STROUDSBURG, PA

▲ PRIMROSE—J. B. Cable

PRINGLE—See WILKES-BARRE, PA

PROMPTON—See CARBONDALE, PA

PROSPECT—See BUTLER, PA

PROSPECT PARK—See WALLINGFORD, PA

PROVIDENCE TWP. (Lancaster County)—See LANCASTER, PA

▲ PULASKI—Ward Communications

PULASKI TWP. (Beaver County)—See BEAVER FALLS, PA

PULASKI TWP. (Lawrence County)—See PULASKI, PA

▲PUNXSUTAWNEY—Punxsutawney TV Cable Co.

PUTNAM TWP.—See MANSFIELD, PA

PYMATUNING TWP.—See SHARON, PA

QUAKER HILL—See ELDRED TWP. (Lycoming County), PA

QUAKERTOWN—See SELLERSVILLE, PA

QUARRYVILLE—See LANCASTER, PA

QUECREEK—See SOMERSET, PA

QUEMAHONING (Somerset County)—See SOMERSET BOROUGH, PA

QUEMAHONING TWP. (Somerset County)—See CENTRAL CITY BOROUGH, PA

QUEMAHONING TWP. (Somerset County)—See also JOHNSTOWN, PA

QUEMAHONING TWP. (Somerset County)—See also SOMERSET, PA

QUIGGLEVILLE—See COGAN STATION, PA

QUINCY TWP.—See CARLISLE, PA

RACCOON TWP. (southern portion)—See BEAVER VALLEY, PA

RADNOR TWP. (Delaware County)—See LANSDALE, PA

RAHNS—See KING OF PRUSSIA, PA

RAILROAD—See GLEN ROCK, PA

RAINSBURG—See BEDFORD, PA

RALPHO TWP.—See SUNBURY, PA

▲ RALSTON—Retel TV Cable Co. Inc.

RAMEY—See BIGLER TWP., PA

RANDOLPH TWP. (Crawford County)—See MEADVILLE, PA

RANKIN—See MONROEVILLE, PA

RAPHO TWP. (Lancaster County)—See ELIZABETHTOWN, PA

RAPHO TWP. (Lancaster County)—See also EPHRATA, PA

RAPHO TWP. (Lebanon County)—See LEBANON, PA

RATHMEL—See PUNXSUTAWNEY, PA

RAUCHTOWN—See AVIS, PA

▲ RAYNE TWP.—Satterlee Leasing Inc.

RAYNE TWP. (portions)—See also BLAIRSVILLE, PA

READE TWP. (Cambria County)—See COALPORT, PA

▲ READING—TCI

READING TWP.—See GETTYSBURG, PA

RED HILL—See POTTSTOWN, PA

RED LION—See YORK, PA

REDBANK TWP. (Clarion County)—See LIMESTONE, PA

REDBANK TWP. (Clarion County)—See also NEW BETHLEHEM, PA

REDBANK TWP. (Clarion County)—See also SUMMERVILLE, PA

REDSTONE TWP. (Fayette County)—See UNIONTOWN, PA

REED TWP. (Dauphin County)—See MILLERSBURG, PA

REED TWP. (Perry County)—See DUNCANNON, PA

▲ REEDSVILLE—Warner Cable of Reedsville

REILLY TWP.—See PRIMROSE, PA

▲ RENO—Reno Cable Co.

RENOVO—See AVIS, PA

REPUBLIC—See UNIONTOWN, PA

RESERVE TWP. (Allegheny County)—See ROSS TWP. (Allegheny County), PA

▲ RETREAT CORRECTIONAL INSTITUTION—Cosmic Cable TV

REYNOLDS—See PALMERTON, PA

REYNOLDSVILLE—See PUNXSUTAWNEY, PA

RICE—See BERWICK, PA

RICE TWP.—See WILKES-BARRE, PA

RICES LANDING—See UNIONTOWN, PA

RICHBORO—See HOLLAND, PA

RICHBORO—See also JAMISON, PA

▲ RICHFIELD—R. J. Shelley CATV

RICHHILL TWP.—See WIND RIDGE, PA

RICHLAND (Lebanon County)—See LEBANON, PA

RICHLAND TWP.—See LEHIGH VALLEY, PA

RICHLAND TWP. (Allegheny County)—See TARENTUM BOROUGH, PA

RICHLAND TWP. (Allegheny County)—See also ZELIENOPLE, PA

RICHLAND TWP. (Bucks County)—See SELLERSVILLE, PA

RICHLAND TWP. (Cambria County)—See JOHNSTOWN, PA

RICHLAND TWP. (Clarion County)—See NINEVAH, PA

RICHLAND TWP. (Clarion County)—See also ST. PETERSBURG, PA

RICHLAND TWP. (Venango County)—See TOBY TWP., PA

RICHLANDTOWN—See SELLERSVILLE, PA

RICHMOND TWP. (Berks County)—See FLEETWOOD, PA

RICHMOND TWP. (Berks County)—See also KUTZTOWN, PA

RICHMOND TWP. (Crawford County)—See EDINBORO, PA

RICHMOND TWP. (Tioga County)—See MANSFIELD, PA

RICHMONDALE VILLAGE—See FOREST CITY, PA

RIDGWAY—See RIDGWAY BOROUGH, PA

▲ RIDGWAY BOROUGH—TCI of Pennsylvania Inc.

RIDGWAY TWP. (Elk County)—See RIDGWAY BOROUGH, PA

RIDLEY PARK (Delaware County)—See WALLINGFORD, PA

RIDLEY TWP.—See WALLINGFORD, PA

RIEGELSVILLE BORO—See LEHIGH VALLEY, PA

RIMERSBURG—See TOBY TWP., PA

RINGGOLD TWP.—See TIMBLIN BOROUGH, PA

RINGTOWN—See MAHANOY CITY, PA

RIVERSIDE (Northumberland County)—See DANVILLE, PA

RIXFORD—See SMETHPORT, PA

ROARING BRANCH—See RALSTON, PA

ROARING BROOK TWP.—See DUNMORE, PA

ROARING CREEK TWP.—See BLOOMSBURG, PA

ROARING SPRING—See ALTOONA, PA

ROBERTSDALE—See BROAD TOP CITY, PA

ROBESON TWP.—See BIRDSBORO, PA

ROBESONIA—See LEBANON, PA

▲ ROBINSON TWP. (Allegheny County)—Adelphia Cable

ROBINSON TWP. (Allegheny County)—See also McDONALD, PA

ROBINSON TWP. (Washington County)—See MIDWAY, PA

▲ ROCHESTER—Adelphia Communications Corp.

ROCHESTER BOROUGH—See ROCHESTER, PA

ROCHESTER TWP.—See ROCHESTER, PA

ROCKDALE TWP. (Crawford County)—See EDINBORO, PA

ROCKEFELLER TWP.—See SUNBURY, PA

ROCKLAND—See NINEVAH, PA

ROCKLAND TWP. (Berks County)—See KUTZTOWN, PA

ROCKLAND TWP. (Venango County)—See CLINTONVILLE, PA

ROCKLEDGE BOROUGH—See WILLOW GROVE, PA

▲ ROCKMERE—CableVision Communications

▲ ROCKWOOD—FrontierVision

ROCKWOOD BOROUGH—See SOMERSET, PA

▲ ROGERSVILLE—DuCom Cable TV

▲ ROME—Beaver Valley Cable Co.

ROME BOROUGH—See ROME, PA

ROME TWP.—See TITUSVILLE, PA

ROSCOE—See CALIFORNIA, PA

▲ ROSE TWP.—TCI of Pennsylvania Inc.

ROSE TWP.—See also TIMBLIN BOROUGH, PA

ROSE VALLEY—See WALLINGFORD, PA

ROSES—See MARIENVILLE, PA

ROSETO—See NORTHAMPTON, PA

ROSETO BORO—See LEHIGH VALLEY, PA

ROSEVILLE—See CHICORA, PA

▲ ROSS TWP. (Allegheny County)—AT&T Cable Services

ROSS TWP. (Monroe County)—See STROUDSBURG, PA

ROSSITER—See PUNXSUTAWNEY, PA

ROSSLYN FARMS—See CARNEGIE, PA

ROSSTON—See KITTANNING, PA

ROSTRAVER (Westmoreland County)—See UNIONTOWN, PA

ROSTRAVER (Westmoreland County)—See also WEST NEWTON, PA

ROSTRAVER TWP.—See MON VALLEY, PA

ROULETTE TWP.—See COUDERSPORT, PA

ROUSEVILLE—See OIL CITY, PA

ROUZERVILLE—See CARLISLE, PA

ROWES RUN—See UNIONTOWN, PA

ROWLAND—See MILFORD, PA

ROYALTON—See HARRISBURG, PA

ROYERSFORD—See POTTSTOWN, PA

ROYTOWN—See SOMERSET, PA

▲ RURAL VALLEY—AT&T Cable Services

RUSCOMBMANOR TWP. (Berks County)—See FLEETWOOD, PA

RUSCOMBMANOR TWP. (Berks County)—See also KUTZTOWN, PA

RUSCOMBMANOR TWP. (Berks County)—See also READING, PA

RUSH TWP. (Clearfield County)—See PHILIPSBURG BOROUGH, PA

RUSH TWP. (Dauphin County)—See LYKENS, PA

RUSH TWP. (Schuylkill County)—See LANSFORD, PA

RUSH TWP. (Schuylkill County)—See also MAHANOY CITY, PA

RUTLEDGE (Delaware County)—See WALLINGFORD, PA

RYAN TWP.—See MAHANOY CITY, PA

RYE TWP.—See DUNCANNON, PA

RYND FARM—See TITUSVILLE, PA

▲ SABULA—DuCom Communications Inc.

SADSBURY TWP. (Chester County)—See CHESTER COUNTY, PA

SADSBURY TWP. (Crawford County)—See MEADVILLE, PA

SADSBURY TWP. (Lancaster County)—See LANCASTER, PA

SAEGERTOWN—See MEADVILLE, PA

SALEM TWP. (Clarion County)—See NINEVAH, PA

SALEM TWP. (Luzerne County)—See BERWICK, PA

SALEM TWP. (Wayne County)—See CARBONDALE, PA

SALEM TWP. (Westmoreland County)—See GREENSBURG, PA

SALEM TWP. (Westmoreland County)—See also MURRYSVILLE, PA

SALFORD—See SELLERSVILLE, PA

SALISBURY—See GRANTSVILLE, MD

SALISBURY TWP.—See LEHIGH VALLEY, PA

SALISBURY TWP. (Lancaster County)—See LANCASTER, PA

SALISBURY TWP. (Lehigh County)—See EMMAUS, PA

SALISBURY TWP. (Lehigh County)—See also NORTHAMPTON, PA

SALIX—See ADAMS TWP. (Cambria County), PA

SALLADASBURG—See AVIS, PA

▲ SALTILLO—Saltillo TV Cable Corp.

SALTLICK TWP. (Fayette County)—See INDIAN CREEK, PA

SALTLICK TWP. (Fayette County)—See also SOMERSET, PA

▲ SALTSBURG—AT&T Cable Services

SANDY CREEK TWP. (Mercer County)—See MEADVILLE, PA

THROOP—See SCRANTON, PA

▲ **TIDIOUTE**—CableVision Communications

TILDEN TWP.—See HAMBURG, PA

▲ **TIMBLIN BOROUGH**—Commuter Cable Television-West

TIMOTHY LAKE—See STROUDSBURG, PA

TINGLEY LAKE—See LOOMIS LAKE, PA

TINICUM TWP.—See LEHIGH VALLEY, PA

TINICUM TWP. (Bucks County)—See JAMISON, PA

TINICUM TWP. (Delaware County)—See WALLINGFORD, PA

▲ **TIOGA**—Cablecomm

TIOGA TWP.—See ELKLAND, PA

TIONESTA—See NORTH CLARION, PA

TIONESTA TWP.—See NORTH CLARION, PA

TIPPERY—See ROCKMERE, PA

TIRE HILL—See JOHNSTOWN, PA

▲ **TITUSVILLE**—CableVision Communications

TOBY—See ST. MARYS, PA

▲ **TOBY TWP.**—TCI of Pennsylvania Inc.

TOBYHANNA TWP. (Monroe County)—See POCONO, PA

TOBYHANNA TWP. (Monroe County)—See also STROUDSBURG, PA

TODD—See UNION TWP. (Huntingdon County), PA

TODD TWP. (Fulton County)—See MCCONNELLSBURG, PA

TODD TWP. (Huntingdon County)—See UNION TWP. (Huntingdon County), PA

TOPTON—See KUTZTOWN, PA

TOWAMENCIN—See LANSDALE, PA

TOWAMENSING TWP.—See PALMERTON, PA

▲ **TOWANDA**—TCI of Pennsylvania Inc.

TOWANDA TWP.—See TOWANDA, PA

TOWER CITY—See LYKENS, PA

▲ **TOWNVILLE**—CableVision Communications

TOWNVILLE—See also EDINBORO, PA

TRAFFORD—See MONROEVILLE, PA

TRAINER—See WALLINGFORD, PA

TRAPPE—See KING OF PRUSSIA, PA

TREDYFFRIN TWP.—See MALVERN, PA

TREESDALE—See ZELIENOPLE, PA

▲ **TREMONT**—Wire Tele-View Corp.

TREMONT TWP.—See POTTSVILLE, PA (AT&T Cable Services)

TRENT—See SOMERSET, PA

TROUT RUN—See COGAN STATION, PA

TROUTVILLE—See DU BOIS, PA

▲ **TROY**—Blue Ridge Cable TV Inc.

TROY TWP.—See TROY, PA

TRUMBAUERSVILLE—See SELLERSVILLE, PA

TULLYTOWN—See BENSALEM TWP., PA

TULPEHOCKEN TWP.—See LEBANON, PA

TUNKHANNOCK BOROUGH—See MESHOPPEN, PA

TUNKHANNOCK TWP. (Monroe County)—See POCONO, PA

TUNKHANNOCK TWP. (Wyoming County)—See MESHOPPEN, PA

TUNNELHILL—See GALLITZIN TWP., PA

TURBETT TWP.—See OLD PORT, PA

TURBOT TWP. (Northumberland County)—See ANTHONY TWP., PA

TURBOT TWP. (Northumberland County)—See also DANVILLE, PA

TURBOTVILLE—See DANVILLE, PA

TURTLE CREEK—See MONROEVILLE, PA

TUSCARORA—See BERWICK, PA

TUSCARORA TWP. (Bradford County)—See MESHOPPEN, PA

TUSCARORA TWP. (Perry County)—See ELIZABETHTOWN, PA

TWILIGHT—See MON VALLEY, PA

TWIN ROCKS—See NANTY GLO, PA

TYLERSBURG—See NORTH CLARION, PA

▲ **TYLERSVILLE**—Community TV

▲ **TYRONE**—TCI of Pennsylvania Inc.

TYRONE—See also WARRIORS MARK, PA

TYRONE TWP.—See GETTYSBURG, PA

TYRONE TWP. (Blair County)—See ALTOONA, PA

▲ **ULSTER**—Beaver Valley Cable Co.

ULSTER (town)—See SAYRE, PA

▲ **ULYSSES**—Cablecomm

UNION CITY—See CORRY, PA

UNION COUNTY—See MIFFLINBURG, PA

UNION TWP.—See GETTYSBURG, PA

UNION TWP.—See also YORK, PA

UNION TWP. (Berks County)—See BIRDSBORO, PA

▲ **UNION TWP. (Centre County)**—Country Cable

UNION TWP. (Crawford County)—See MEADVILLE, PA

UNION TWP. (Erie County)—See CORRY, PA

▲ **UNION TWP. (Huntingdon County)**—Calvin Cable System Inc.

UNION TWP. (Jefferson County)—See DU BOIS, PA

UNION TWP. (Jefferson County)—See also ROSE TWP., PA

UNION TWP. (Lawrence County)—See NEW CASTLE, PA

UNION TWP. (Lebanon County)—See FORT INDIANTOWN GAP, PA

UNION TWP. (Lebanon County)—See also LEBANON, PA

UNION TWP. (Luzerne County)—See BERWICK, PA

UNION TWP. (Luzerne County)—See also SWEET VALLEY, PA

UNION TWP. (Schuylkill County)—See MAHANOY CITY, PA

UNION TWP. (Schuylkill County)—See also SHENANDOAH, PA

UNION TWP. (Union County)—See SUNBURY, PA

UNION TWP. (Union County)—See also DANVILLE, PA

UNION TWP. (Washington County)—See BETHEL PARK, PA

UNIONDALE—See CARBONDALE, PA

▲ **UNIONTOWN**—Helicon Cablevision

UNITY TWP. (Westmoreland County)—See BLAIRSVILLE, PA

UNITY TWP. (Westmoreland County)—See also GREENSBURG, PA

UPLAND—See WALLINGFORD, PA

UPPER ALLEN TWP.—See HARRISBURG, PA

UPPER AUGUSTA TWP.—See SUNBURY, PA

UPPER BURRELL TWP.—See MURRYSVILLE, PA

UPPER CHICHESTER TWP.—See WALLINGFORD, PA

UPPER DARBY—See WALLINGFORD, PA

UPPER DARBY TWP.—See WALLINGFORD, PA

UPPER DUBLIN TWP.—See LANSDALE, PA

UPPER FREDERICK TWP.—See SELLERSVILLE, PA

UPPER GWYNEDD TWP.—See LANSDALE, PA

UPPER HANOVER TWP.—See POTTSTOWN, PA

UPPER LEACOCK TWP.—See LANCASTER, PA

UPPER MACUNGIE TWP.—See LEHIGH VALLEY, PA

UPPER MACUNGIE TWP. (Lehigh County)—See NORTHAMPTON, PA

UPPER MAHANOY TWP.—See SUNBURY, PA

UPPER MAHANTANGO TWP.—See LYKENS, PA

UPPER MAKEFIELD TWP.—See NEWTOWN, PA

UPPER MERION TWP.—See KING OF PRUSSIA, PA

UPPER MILFORD TWP.—See EMMAUS, PA

UPPER MORELAND TWP.—See WILLOW GROVE, PA

UPPER MOUNT BETHEL—See NORTHAMPTON, PA

UPPER MOUNT BETHEL TWP.—See LEHIGH VALLEY, PA

UPPER NAZARETH TWP.—See LEHIGH VALLEY, PA

UPPER NAZARETH TWP. (Northampton County)—See NORTHAMPTON, PA

UPPER OXFORD TWP.—See KENNETT SQUARE, PA

▲ **WATTSBURG**—CableVision Communications

WAYMART—See CARBONDALE, PA

WAYNE—See KING OF PRUSSIA, PA

WAYNE HEIGHTS—See CARLISLE, PA

WAYNE TWP. (Clinton County)—See AVIS, PA

WAYNE TWP. (Crawford County)—See MEADVILLE, PA

WAYNE TWP. (Dauphin County)—See MILLERSBURG, PA

WAYNE TWP. (Erie County)—See CORRY, PA

WAYNE TWP. (Greene County)—See WAYNESBURG, PA

WAYNE TWP. (Lawrence County)—See ELLWOOD CITY, PA

WAYNE TWP. (Lawrence County)—See also NEW CASTLE, PA

WAYNE TWP. (Mifflin County)—See SHIRLEY TWP., PA

WAYNE TWP. (Schuylkill County)—See POTTSVILLE, PA (AT&T Cable Services)

WAYNESBORO—See CHAMBERSBURG, PA

WAYNESBORO—See also STAUNTON, VA

▲ **WAYNESBURG**—AT&T Cable Services

WEATHERLY—See BERWICK, PA

▲ **WEEDVILLE**—DuCom Inc.

WEIKERT—See MIFFLINBURG, PA

WEISENBERG TWP.—See LEHIGH VALLEY, PA

WEISENBERG TWP. (Lehigh County)—See NORTHAMPTON, PA

WEISSPORT—See PALMERTON, PA

WELLS TANNERY—See WATERFALL, PA

▲ **WELLSBORO**—Blue Ridge Cable TV Inc.

WELLSVILLE—See NEWBERRY TWP., PA

WERNERSVILLE—See READING, PA

WESLEYVILLE—See HARBORCREEK TWP., PA

▲ **WEST ALEXANDER**—Community TV Systems Cable Co.

WEST BRADFORD TWP.—See CHESTER COUNTY, PA

WEST BRANCH TWP. (Potter County)—See GALETON, PA

WEST BRANDYWINE TWP.—See CHESTER COUNTY, PA

WEST BROWNSVILLE—See CALIFORNIA, PA

WEST BRUNSWICK TWP.—See POTTSVILLE, PA (AT&T Cable Services)

WEST BUFFALO TWP. (portions)—See MIFFLINBURG, PA

▲ **WEST BURLINGTON TWP.**—Barrett's TV Cable System

WEST CALN TWP.—See CHESTER COUNTY, PA

WEST CAMERON TWP.—See SUNBURY, PA

WEST CARROLL TWP. (Cambria County)—See CARROLLTOWN BOROUGH, PA

WEST CHESTER—See CHESTER COUNTY, PA

WEST CHILLISQUAQUE TWP. (portions)—See DANVILLE, PA

WEST COCALICO TWP.—See EPHRATA, PA

WEST CONSHOHOCKEN—See NORRISTOWN, PA

WEST CORNWALL TWP.—See LEBANON, PA

WEST DEER TWP.—See TARENTUM BOROUGH, PA

WEST DEER TWP. (portions)—See also ZELIENOPLE, PA

WEST DONEGAL TWP.—See ELIZABETHTOWN, PA

WEST EARL TWP.—See LANCASTER, PA

WEST EARL TWP. (northern portion)—See also EPHRATA, PA

WEST EASTON—See EASTON, PA

WEST EASTON—See also NORTHAMPTON, PA

WEST ELIZABETH—See CASTLE SHANNON, PA

WEST FAIRVIEW—See HARRISBURG, PA

WEST FALLOWFIELD TWP.—See JAMESTOWN, PA

WEST FALLOWFIELD TWP.—See also MEADVILLE, PA

WEST FALLOWFIELD TWP.—See also OXFORD, PA

WEST FREEDOM—See CALLENSBURG, PA

WEST GOSHEN—See CHESTER COUNTY, PA

WEST GROVE—See KENNETT SQUARE, PA

WEST HANOVER TWP. (Dauphin County)—See HARRISBURG, PA

WEST HAZLETON BOROUGH—See HAZLETON, PA

WEST HEMLOCK TWP.—See DANVILLE, PA

WEST HEMPFIELD TWP. (Lancaster County)—See ELIZABETHTOWN, PA

WEST HEMPFIELD TWP. (Lancaster County)—See also LANCASTER, PA

WEST HICKORY—See TIDIOUTE, PA

WEST HOMESTEAD—See WEST MIFFLIN, PA

WEST KITTANNING—See KITTANNING, PA

WEST LAMPETER TWP.—See LANCASTER, PA

WEST LAWN—See READING, PA

WEST LEBANON TWP.—See LEBANON, PA

WEST LEECHBURG—See KISKIMINETAS TWP., PA

WEST MAHANOY—See MAHANOY CITY, PA

WEST MAHANOY TWP.—See SHENANDOAH, PA

WEST MANCHESTER TWP.—See YORK, PA

WEST MANHEIM TWP.—See GETTYSBURG, PA

WEST MANHEIM TWP.—See also YORK, PA

WEST MAYFIELD—See BEAVER FALLS, PA

WEST MEAD TWP.—See MEADVILLE, PA

WEST MIDDLESEX—See SHARON, PA

▲ **WEST MIFFLIN**—Adelphia Cable Communications

WEST NANTICOKE—See BERWICK, PA

WEST NANTMEAL—See CHESTER COUNTY, PA

▲ **WEST NEWTON**—Adelphia Communications Corp.

WEST NORRITON TWP.—See NORRISTOWN, PA

WEST NOTTINGHAM TWP.—See OXFORD, PA

WEST PENN TWP. (northwestern portion)—See MAHANOY CITY, PA

WEST PENN TWP. (southeastern portion)—See PALMERTON, PA

WEST PENNSBORO TWP. (Cumberland County)—See CARLISLE, PA

WEST PENNSBORO TWP. (Cumberland County)—See also CHAMBERSBURG, PA

WEST PERRY TWP.—See RICHFIELD, PA

WEST PIKE RUN TWP.—See CALIFORNIA, PA

WEST PIKELAND TWP. (portions)—See CHESTER COUNTY, PA

WEST PITTSTON—See DUNMORE, PA

WEST POTTSGROVE TWP.—See POTTSTOWN, PA

WEST PROVIDENCE TWP.—See BEDFORD, PA

WEST READING—See READING, PA

WEST ROCKHILL TWP.—See SELLERSVILLE, PA

WEST SADSBURY TWP. (Chester County)—See CHESTER COUNTY, PA

WEST SALEM TWP.—See GREENVILLE, PA

WEST SALISBURY—See GRANTSVILLE, MD

West Shenango Twp.—See JAMESTOWN, PA

WEST ST. CLAIR—See BEDFORD, PA

WEST SUNBURY—See GROVE CITY, PA

WEST TAYLOR TWP.—See JOHNSTOWN, PA

WEST VIEW—See ROSS TWP. (Allegheny County), PA

WEST VINCENT TWP.—See CHESTER COUNTY, PA

▲ **WEST WHEATFIELD TWP. (Indiana County)**—TCI of Pennsylvania Inc.

WEST WHEATFIELD TWP. (Indiana County)—See also BLAIRSVILLE, PA

WEST WHITEHEAD TWP. (Chester County)—See CHESTER COUNTY, PA

WEST WHITELAND TWP. (Chester County)—See MALVERN, PA

WEST WYOMING—See SCRANTON, PA

WEST YORK—See YORK, PA

WESTFALL—See MATAMORAS, PA

WESTFALL TWP. (portions)—See MATAMORAS, PA

RHODE ISLAND

SOUTH CAROLINA

CENTRAL PACOLET—See SPARTANBURG, SC

CHAMBERT FOREST—See IVA, SC

CHAPIN—See COLUMBIA, SC

▲ **CHARLESTON**—Comcast Cable of Carolina Inc.

CHARLESTON AIR FORCE BASE—See CHARLESTON, SC

CHARLESTON COUNTY (northern portion)—See CHARLESTON, SC

CHARLESTON COUNTY (unincorporated areas)—See also McCLELLANVILLE, SC

CHARLESTON NAVAL BASE—See CHARLESTON, SC

▲ **CHERAW**—Century Communications

CHEROKEE COUNTY (unincorporated areas)—See GAFFNEY, SC

CHEROKEE COUNTY (western portion)—See also SPARTANBURG, SC

CHESNEE—See SPARTANBURG, SC

▲ **CHESTER**—Charter Communications

CHESTER COUNTY—See GREAT FALLS, SC

CHESTER COUNTY (unincorporated areas)—See also CHESTER, SC

CHESTER COUNTY (unincorporated areas)—See also LOCKHART, SC

CHESTER COUNTY (unincorporated areas)—See also ROCK HILL, SC

▲ **CHESTERFIELD**—Enstar Cable TV

CHESTERFIELD COUNTY—See CHERAW, SC

CHESTERFIELD COUNTY (portions)—See also CHESTERFIELD, SC

CHOPPEE—See BROWNS FERRY, SC

CITY VIEW—See GREENVILLE, SC

CLARENDON COUNTY—See MANNING, SC

CLEMSON (unincorporated areas)—See SENECA, SC

CLINTON—See GRAY COURT, SC

CLIO—See BENNETTSVILLE, SC

▲ **CLOVER**—Time Warner Cable

COLLETON COUNTY—See COTTAGEVILLE, SC

COLLETON COUNTY—See also WALTERBORO, SC

▲ **COLUMBIA**—Time Warner Cable

CONWAY—See MYRTLE BEACH, SC

CONWAY (rural portions)—See also HOMEWOOD, SC

CORDOVA (southwestern portion)—See ORANGEBURG, SC

▲ **COTTAGEVILLE**—Pine Tree Cablevision

▲ **COWARD**—Galaxy Cablevision

COWPENS—See SPARTANBURG, SC

▲ **CROSS**—Pine Tree Cablevision

▲ **CROSS HILL**—Galaxy Cablevision

CYPRESS POINT—See DUNES WEST, SC

DALZELL—See SUMTER, SC

DARLINGTON—See FLORENCE, SC

DARLINGTON COUNTY—See FLORENCE, SC

DARLINGTON COUNTY (unincorporated areas)—See also HARTSVILLE, SC

DARLINGTON COUNTY (unincorporated areas)—See also SOCIETY HILL, SC

DATAW ISLAND—See LADY'S ISLAND, SC

▲ **DAUFUSKIE ISLAND**—Falcon Cable TV

DAVIS STATION—See SUMMERTON, SC

▲ **DEBORDIEU COLONY**—Benchmark Communications

DENMARK—See BARNWELL, SC

DENTSVILLE—See COLUMBIA, SC

▲ **DILLON**—Century Communications

DILLON COUNTY—See DILLON, SC

DONALDS—See DUE WEST, SC

DORCHESTER COUNTY (portions)—See SUMMERVILLE, SC

DORCHESTER COUNTY (unincorporated areas)—See also ST. GEORGE, SC

▲ **DOVESVILLE**—Galaxy Cablevision

▲ **DUE WEST**—Due West Cablevision

DUNBAR—See BROWNS FERRY, SC

DUNCAN—See SPARTANBURG, SC

▲ **DUNES WEST**—Southern Cable Communications

EASLEY—See GREENVILLE, SC

EASTOVER—See COLUMBIA, SC

EASTOVER—See also HOPKINS, SC

EBENEZER—See SALEM, SC

▲ **EDGEFIELD**—Aiken Cablevision Inc.

EDGEFIELD COUNTY—See EDGEFIELD, SC

▲ **EDISTO BEACH**—US Cable Coastal Properties

ELGIN—See COLUMBIA, SC

ELKO—See BARNWELL, SC

▲ **ELLOREE**—Pine Tree Cablevision

ENOREE—See GRAY COURT, SC

▲ **ESTILL**—Hargray CATV Co. Inc.

EUTAWVILLE—See HOLLY HILL, SC

FAIRFAX—See BARNWELL, SC

FAIRFIELD—See SALEM, SC

FAIRFIELD COUNTY (portions)—See GREAT FALLS, SC

FAIRFIELD COUNTY (portions)—See also WINNSBORO, SC

▲ **FIVE POINTS**—Galaxy Cablevision

▲ **FLORENCE**—Time Warner Cable

FLORENCE COUNTY—See FLORENCE, SC

FLORENCE COUNTY—See also JOHNSONVILLE, SC

FLORENCE COUNTY—See also LAKE CITY, SC

FLORENCE COUNTY (portions)—See also COWARD, SC

▲ **FOLLY BEACH**—US Cable Coastal Properties

FOREST ACRES—See COLUMBIA, SC

FORESTBROOK—See MYRTLE BEACH, SC

FORT JACKSON—See COLUMBIA, SC

FORT LAWN—See LANCASTER, SC

▲ **FORT MILL**—Palmetto Cable TV

FOUNTAIN INN—See GRAY COURT, SC

▲ **FRIPP ISLAND**—US Cable

GADSDEN—See HOPKINS, SC

▲ **GAFFNEY**—Charter Communications

GARDEN CITY BEACH—See SURFSIDE BEACH, SC

▲ **GASTON**—Pine Tree Cablevision

▲ **GEORGETOWN**—Alert Cable TV of South Carolina Inc.

GEORGETOWN COUNTY—See GEORGETOWN, SC

GEORGETOWN COUNTY—See also MYRTLE BEACH, SC

GEORGETOWN COUNTY—See also SURFSIDE BEACH, SC

GEORGETOWN COUNTY (eastern portion)—See also PAWLEYS ISLAND, SC

▲ **GILBERT**—Pond Branch Cable

GOAT ISLAND—See SUMMERTON, SC

GOOSE CREEK—See CHARLESTON, SC

▲ **GRAY COURT**—Charter Communications

▲ **GREAT FALLS**—Great Falls Cable TV

▲ **GREENVILLE**—InterMedia

GREENVILLE COUNTY—See GRAY COURT, SC

GREENVILLE COUNTY—See also GREENVILLE, SC

GREENVILLE COUNTY—See also GREER, SC

GREENVILLE COUNTY—See also SPARTANBURG, SC

GREENVILLE COUNTY—See also TRAVELERS REST, SC

GREENVILLE COUNTY—See also WEST PELZER, SC

GREENVILLE COUNTY (southeastern portion)—See also WARE PLACE, SC

▲ **GREENWOOD**—Northland Cable TV

GREENWOOD COUNTY—See GREENWOOD, SC

GREENWOOD COUNTY—See also WARE SHOALS, SC

▲ **GREER**—Charter Communications

GREER—See also SPARTANBURG, SC

▲ **HAMPTON**—Jones Communications

HAMPTON COUNTY (portions)—See HAMPTON, SC

HANAHAN—See CHARLESTON, SC

HARBISON—See COLUMBIA, SC

HARBOUR ISLAND—See FRIPP ISLAND, SC

▲ **HARDEEVILLE**—Hargray CATV Co. Inc.

HARLEYVILLE—See MONCKS CORNER, SC

▲ **HARTSVILLE**—Century Cable

▲ **HARTWELL VILLAS**—Charter Communications

HEATH SPRINGS—See KERSHAW, SC

HEMINGWAY—See JOHNSONVILLE, SC

HICKORY GROVE—See YORK, SC

▲ **HILDA**—Galaxy Cablevision

▲ **HILTON HEAD ISLAND**—Adelphia Cable

HODGES—See WARE SHOALS, SC

▲ **HOLLY HILL**—Phoenix Cable

▲ **HOLLYWOOD**—US Cable Coastal Properties

▲ **HOMEWOOD**—Horry Telephone Cablevision

HONEA PATH—See BELTON, SC

▲ **HOPKINS**—Pine Tree Cablevision

HORRY COUNTY—See MYRTLE BEACH, SC

HORRY COUNTY—See also SURFSIDE BEACH, SC

HORRY COUNTY (eastern portion)—See also BRIARCLIFF ACRES, SC

HUNLEY PARK—See CHARLESTON, SC

HUNTING TOWN—See FRIPP ISLAND, SC

INMAN—See SPARTANBURG, SC

IRMO—See COLUMBIA, SC

ISLE OF PALMS—See CHARLESTON, SC

▲ **IVA**—Charter Communications

JACKSON—See AIKEN, SC

JAMES ISLAND—See CHARLESTON, SC

▲ **JEFFERSON**—Pine Tree Cablevision

JOANNA—See LAURENS, SC

▲ **JOHNS ISLAND**—US Cable Coastal Properties

▲ **JOHNSONVILLE**—Time Warner Cable

JOHNSTON—See EDGEFIELD, SC

JONESVILLE—See SPARTANBURG, SC

KELLYTOWN—See HARTSVILLE, SC

KEOWEE KEY—See SALEM, SC

▲ **KERSHAW**—Enstar Cable TV

KERSHAW COUNTY—See CAMDEN, SC

KERSHAW COUNTY (western portion)—See also PINE GROVE, SC

KIAWAH ISLAND—See JOHNS ISLAND, SC

▲ **KINGSTREE**—Time Warner Cable

LA FRANCE—See ANCHOR POINT, SC

▲ **LADY'S ISLAND**—US Cable Coastal Properties

▲ **LAKE CITY**—Time Warner Cable

LAKE MURRAY—See GILBERT, SC

LAKE MURRY—See COLUMBIA, SC

▲ **LAKE VIEW**—Southern Cable

LAKE WYLIE—See CRAMERTON, NC

LAKE WYLIE (north central portion)—See also CLOVER, SC

LAKE WYLIE WOODS—See RIVER HILLS, SC

▲ **LAMAR**—Pine Tree Cablevision

LAMBERTOWN—See SAMPIT, SC

▲ **LANCASTER**—Lancaster Cable TV

LANCASTER COUNTY—See LANCASTER, SC

LANCASTER COUNTY (portions)—See also FORT MILL, SC

LANCASTER COUNTY (portions)—See also KERSHAW, SC

LANCASTER COUNTY (portions)—See also MECKLENBURG, NC

LANDRUM—See SPARTANBURG, SC

▲ **LANE**—Time Warner Cable

LATTA—See DILLON, SC

LAUREL BAY—See CHARLESTON, SC

▲ **LAURENS**—Charter Communications

LAURENS COUNTY—See GRAY COURT, SC

LAURENS COUNTY—See also LAURENS, SC

LAURENS COUNTY—See also WARE SHOALS, SC

LAURENS COUNTY (northwestern portion)—See also WARE PLACE, SC

LAURENS COUNTY (portions)—See also CROSS HILL, SC

LAURENS COUNTY (portions)—See also GREENWOOD, SC

LEE COUNTY—See BISHOPVILLE, SC

LEE COUNTY (portions)—See also LYNCHBURG, SC

LEESVILLE—See BATESBURG, SC

LEXINGTON—See COLUMBIA, SC

LEXINGTON COUNTY—See BATESBURG, SC

LEXINGTON COUNTY—See also COLUMBIA, SC

LEXINGTON COUNTY (northwestern portion)—See also GILBERT, SC

LEXINGTON COUNTY (unincorporated areas)—See also GASTON, SC

▲ **LIBERTY**—Northland Cable TV

LITCHFIELD—See PAWLEYS ISLAND, SC

LITCHFIELD BEACH—See BRIARCLIFF ACRES, SC

LITTLE MOUNTAIN—See COLUMBIA, SC

▲ **LITTLE RIVER**—Savannah River Cable

LITTLE RIVER—See also MYRTLE BEACH, SC

▲ **LOCKHART**—Charter Communications

LONGS—See HOMEWOOD, SC

LORIS—See HOMEWOOD, SC

LOST CREEK—See COLUMBIA, SC

LUGOFF—See CAMDEN, SC

LUGOFF—See also PINE GROVE, SC

LYMAN—See SPARTANBURG, SC

▲ **LYNCHBURG**—Galaxy Cablevision

MACEDONIA—See ST. STEPHEN, SC

▲ **MANNING**—Time Warner Cable

MANNING—See also SUMMERTON, SC

MARIETTA—See GREER, SC

MARION—See MULLINS, SC

MARION COUNTY (northern portion)—See LAKE VIEW, SC

MARION COUNTY (portions)—See also MULLINS, SC

MARLBORO COUNTY—See BENNETTSVILLE, SC

MARLBORO COUNTY (unincorporated areas)—See also WALLACE, SC

MAULDIN—See GRAY COURT, SC

MAYESVILLE—See SUMTER, SC

▲ **McCLELLANVILLE**—Benchmark Communications

McCOLL—See BENNETTSVILLE, SC

▲ **McCORMICK**—Robin Cable Systems LP

McCORMICK COUNTY (portions)—See McCORMICK, SC

McCORMICK COUNTY (portions)—See also PLUM BRANCH, SC

▲ **MONCKS CORNER**—Berkeley Cable TV

MOUNT PLEASANT—See CHARLESTON, SC

MOUNT PLEASANT—See also DUNES WEST, SC

▲ **MULLINS**—Century Communications

MURRELLS INLET—See HOMEWOOD, SC

MURRELLS INLET—See also SURFSIDE BEACH, SC

▲ **MYRTLE BEACH**—Time Warner Cable

MYRTLE BEACH (portions)—See also SURFSIDE BEACH, SC

NEW ELLENTON—See AIKEN, SC

▲ **NEWBERRY**—Comcast Cablevision of the South

NEWBERRY—See also COLUMBIA, SC

NEWBERRY COUNTY—See NEWBERRY, SC

NEWBERRY COUNTY (unincorporated areas)—See also WHITMIRE, SC

NICHOLS—See LAKE VIEW, SC

NINETY-SIX—See GREENWOOD, SC

NORRIS—See LIBERTY, SC

▲ **NORTH**—Pine Tree Cablevision

NORTH AUGUSTA—See AUGUSTA, GA

NORTH CHARLESTON—See CHARLESTON, SC

NORTH CHARLESTON (western portion)—See also SUMMERVILLE, SC

NORTH MYRTLE BEACH—See HOMEWOOD, SC

NORTH MYRTLE BEACH—See also MYRTLE BEACH, SC

NORTH SANTEE—See SAMPIT, SC

NORTH STONE—See SAMPIT, SC

OCONEE COUNTY (portions)—See FIVE POINTS, SC

OCONEE COUNTY (unincorporated areas)—See also SALEM, SC

OCONEE COUNTY (unincorporated areas)—See also SENECA, SC

OLANTA—See TURBEVILLE, SC

OLAR—See HILDA, SC

▲ **ORANGEBURG**—Time Warner Cable

ORANGEBURG COUNTY—See ORANGEBURG, SC

ORANGEBURG COUNTY (unincorporated areas)—See also HOLLY HILL, SC

OWINGS—See GRAY COURT, SC

PACOLET—See SPARTANBURG, SC

PACOLET MILLS—See SPARTANBURG, SC

▲ **PAGELAND**—Enstar Cable TV

PAMPLICO—See FLORENCE, SC

PARKSVILLE—See PLUM BRANCH, SC

PARRIS ISLAND—See BEAUFORT, SC

▲ **PAWLEYS ISLAND**—Jones Intercable Inc.

PAWLEYS ISLAND—See also SURFSIDE BEACH, SC

PELION—See COLUMBIA, SC

PELZER—See WEST PELZER, SC

PENDLETON—See SENECA, SC

▲ **PICKENS**—Charter Communications

PICKENS—See also GREENVILLE, SC

PICKENS—See also LIBERTY, SC

PICKENS COUNTY—See LIBERTY, SC

PICKENS COUNTY—See also WEST PELZER, SC

PICKENS COUNTY (portions)—See also PICKENS, SC

PICKETT POST—See SALEM, SC

PIERCETOWN—See WEST PELZER, SC

▲ **PINE GROVE**—Galaxy Cablevision

PINERIDGE—See COLUMBIA, SC

PINERIDGE—See also HARTSVILLE, SC

PINEVILLE—See ST. STEPHEN, SC

PINEWOOD—See SUMTER, SC

▲ **PLUM BRANCH**—Galaxy Cablevision

PORT ROYAL—See BEAUFORT, SC

PORTMAN MARINA—See ANCHOR POINT, SC

POTATO CREEK—See SUMMERTON, SC

Prosperity—See NEWBERRY, SC

QUINBY—See FLORENCE, SC

RAVENEL—See HOLLYWOOD, SC

RAVENWWOD—See COLUMBIA, SC

REEVESVILLE—See ST. GEORGE, SC

▲ **REGENT PARK**—Palmetto Cable

RICHBURG—See ROCK HILL, SC

RICHLAND COUNTY—See COLUMBIA, SC

RIDGE SPRING—See GILBERT, SC

▲ **RIDGELAND**—Hargray CATV Co. Inc.

▲ **RIDGEVILLE**—Time Warner Cable

RIDGEWAY—See WINNSBORO, SC

▲ **RIVER HILLS**—Enstar Cable TV

RIVERHILL—See COLUMBIA, SC

▲ **ROCK HILL**—Rock Hill Cable TV

RUBY—See CHESTERFIELD, SC

RUSSELLVILLE—See ST. STEPHEN, SC

▲ **SALEM**—Charter Communications

▲ **SALUDA**—Robin Cable Systems LP

SALUDA COUNTY—See BATESBURG, SC

SALUDA COUNTY—See also SALUDA, SC

SALUDA COUNTY (eastern portion)—See also GILBERT, SC

▲ **SAMPIT**—Benchmark Communications

SANDY SPRINGS—See ANCHOR POINT, SC

▲ **SANTEE**—Blackstone Cable LLC

SCRANTON—See LAKE CITY, SC

SEABROOK ISLAND—See JOHNS ISLAND, SC

▲ **SENECA**—Northland Cable Television

SHARON—See YORK, SC

SHAW AFB—See SUMTER, SC

SIMPSONVILLE—See GRAY COURT, SC

SIX MILE—See LIBERTY, SC

SNELLING—See BARNWELL, SC

SOCASTEE—See HOMEWOOD, SC

SOCASTEE—See also SURFSIDE BEACH, SC

▲ **SOCIETY HILL**—Galaxy Cablevision

SOUTH CONGAREE—See COLUMBIA, SC

SOUTH SANTEE—See MCCLELLANVILLE, SC

▲ **SPARTANBURG**—InterMedia of Spartanburg

SPARTANBURG COUNTY—See GREER, SC

SPARTANBURG COUNTY—See also SPARTANBURG, SC

SPARTANBURG COUNTY (unincorporated areas)—See also GREENVILLE, SC

SPRINGDALE—See COLUMBIA, SC

▲ **ST. GEORGE**—Phoenix Concept Cablevision of Indiana

ST. HELENA ISLAND—See LADY'S ISLAND, SC

ST. MATHEWS—See ORANGEBURG, SC

▲ **ST. MATTHEWS**—Alert Cable TV of South Carolina Inc.

▲ **ST. STEPHEN**—Pine Tree Cablevision

STARR—See IVA, SC

SULLIVAN'S ISLAND—See CHARLESTON, SC

▲ **SUMMERTON**—Blackstone Cable LLC

SUMMERTON—See also MANNING, SC

▲ **SUMMERVILLE**—Time Warner Cable

SUMMERVILLE—See also CHARLESTON, SC

SUMMIT—See GILBERT, SC

▲ **SUMTER**—Time Warner Cable

SUMTER COUNTY—See SUMTER, SC

▲ **SURFSIDE BEACH**—Jones Intercable

▲ **SWANSEA**—Pine Tree Cablevision

TATUM—See BENNETTSVILLE, SC

TAW CAW—See SUMMERTON, SC

TEGA CAY—See FORT MILL, SC

▲ **THE SUMMIT**—Benchmark Communications

TIMMONSVILLE—See FLORENCE, SC

TOWNVILLE—See ANCHOR POINT, SC

▲ **TRAVELERS REST**—Charter Communications

TRENTON—See AUGUSTA, GA

▲ **TURBEVILLE**—Farmers Telephone Co-op Inc.

▲ **UNION**—Charter Communications

UNION COUNTY—See SPARTANBURG, SC

UNION COUNTY (portions)—See also UNION, SC

UNION COUNTY (unincorporated areas)—See also LOCKHART, SC

UNION COUNTY (unincorporated areas)—See also WHITMIRE, SC

VANCE—See SANTEE, SC

VARNVILLE—See HAMPTON, SC

WACCAMAWNECK—See PAWLEYS ISLAND, SC

WADMALAW ISLAND—See JOHNS ISLAND, SC

▲ **WAGENER**—Pine Tree Cablevision

WALHALLA—See SENECA, SC

▲ **WALLACE**—Galaxy Cablevision

▲ **WALTERBORO**—Comcast Cablevision of Carolina Inc.

WAMPEE—See HOMEWOOD, SC

▲ **WARE PLACE**—Galaxy Cablevision

▲ **WARE SHOALS**—Ware Shoals Cablevision

WATERFORD—See COLUMBIA, SC

WELLFORD—See SPARTANBURG, SC

WEST COLUMBIA—See COLUMBIA, SC

▲ **WEST PELZER**—Charter Communications

WEST UNION—See SENECA, SC

WESTMINSTER—See SENECA, SC

▲ **WHITMIRE**—Charter Communications

▲ **WILD DUNES**—TriTek Communications

WILLIAMSBURG COUNTY—See JOHNSONVILLE, SC

WILLIAMSBURG COUNTY—See also KINGSTREE, SC

WILLIAMSBURG COUNTY—See also MYRTLE BEACH, SC

▲ **WILLIAMSTON**—Charter Communications

WILLISTON—See BARNWELL, SC

▲**WINNSBORO**—Winnsboro/Ridgeway Cable TV

WOODRUFF—See GRAY COURT, SC

▲ **YORK**—York Cable TV

YORK COUNTY—See KINGS MOUNTAIN, NC

YORK COUNTY—See also ROCK HILL, SC

YORK COUNTY (portions)—See also CLOVER, SC

YORK COUNTY (portions)—See also FORT MILL, SC

YORK COUNTY (portions)—See also RIVER HILLS, SC

YORK COUNTY (unincorporated areas)—See also YORK, SC

SOUTH DAKOTA

▲ **ABERDEEN**—Midcontinent Cable Co.

▲ **ALCESTER**—Telecom Inc.

▲ **ALEXANDRIA**—Central Cableland TV

ALPENA—See WOONSOCKET, SD

ANDOVER—See GROTON, SD

ARLINGTON—See BROOKINGS, SD

▲ **ARMOUR**—Cable TV Services

ARTESIAN—See WOONSOCKET, SD

▲ **ASHTON**—Satellite Cable Services Inc.

▲ **ASTORIA**—Satellite Cable Services Inc.

AURORA—See BROOKINGS, SD

▲ **AVON**—Village Cable Inc.

BALTIC—See SIOUX FALLS, SD

▲ **BATH**—Midcontinent Cable Systems of South Dakota

Beadle County—See HURON, SD

▲ **BELLE FOURCHE**—TCI Cablevision

▲ **BERESFORD**—Beresford Cablevision Inc.

BIG STONE CITY—See ORTONVILLE, MN

▲ **BISON**—West River CATV

▲ **BLACK HAWK**—TCI Cablevision

▲ **BLUNT**—Sully Buttes Telephone Cooperative Inc.

BONESTEEL—See FAIRFAX, SD

▲ **BOULDER CANYON**—Galaxy Cablevision

▲ **BOWDLE**—Midcontinent Cable Systems Co. of South Dakota

BOX ELDER—See RAPID CITY, SD

BRANDON—See GARRETSON, SD

BRIDGEWATER—See FREEMAN, SD

▲ **BRISTOL**—Midcontinent Cable Systems Co. of South Dakota

▲ **BRITTON**—Britton Community Cable TV

▲ **BROOKINGS**—Brookings Cablevision

BROWN COUNTY—See ABERDEEN, SD

▲ **BRUCE**—Satellite Cable Services Inc.

▲ **BRYANT**—Satellite Cable Services Inc.

▲ **BUFFALO**—Midcontinent Cable Systems Co. of South Dakota

▲ **BUFFALO GAP**—Golden West Cablevision

▲ **BURKE**—Rosebud Community Cable TV

CANISTOTA—See FREEMAN, SD

▲ **CANOVA**—Communications Enterprises Inc.

▲ **CANTON**—Midcontinent Communications

CANTON (portions)—See also VIBORG, SD

▲ **CARTHAGE**—Satellite Cable Services Inc.

▲ **CASTLEWOOD**—Satellite Cable Services Inc.

▲ **CAVOUR**—Satellite Cable Services Inc.

CENTERVILLE—See VIBORG, SD

CENTRAL CITY—See DEADWOOD, SD

▲ **CHAMBERLAIN**—Satellite Cable Services Inc.

CHANCELLOR—See VIBORG, SD

▲ **CHERRY CREEK**—Cheyenne River Sioux Tribe Telephone Cable

▲ **CHESTER**—Satellite Cable Services Inc.

CLAREMONT—See GROTON, SD

▲ **CLARK**—Clark Community Cable TV

▲ **CLEAR LAKE**—Village Cable

CODINGTON COUNTY (portions)—See WATERTOWN, SD

▲ **COLMAN**—Satellite Cable Services Inc.

COLMAN—See also BROOKINGS, SD

COLOME—See WINNER, SD

▲ **COLTON**—Telecom Inc.

COLUMBIA—See GROTON, SD

▲ **CONDE**—Satellite Cable Services Inc.

▲ **CORSICA**—Ollig Cablevision

CORSON—See GARRETSON, SD

▲ **COUNTRY VILLAGE/PRAIRIE ACRES MOBILE HOME PARK**—Galaxy Cablevision

▲ **COUNTRYSIDE MOBILE HOME PARK**—Galaxy Cablevision

CRESBARD—See MELLETTE, SD

CROOKS—See SIOUX FALLS, SD

▲ **CUSTER**—TCI Cablevision

CUSTER COUNTY (unincorporated areas)—See CUSTER, SD

DAKOTA DUNES—See SIOUX CITY, IA

DE SMET—See BROOKINGS, SD

▲ **DEADWOOD**—TCI Cablevision

▲ **DELL RAPIDS**—Valley Cablevision

DELMONT—See MITCHELL, SD (Communications Enterprises Inc.)

▲ **DOLAND**—Midcontinent Cable

DUPREE—See EAGLE BUTTE, SD

▲ **EAGLE BUTTE**—Cheyenne River Sioux Tribe Telephone Cable

▲ **EDEN**—Satellite Cable Services Inc.

▲ **EDGEMONT**—Wy-Dak Inc.

EGAN—See BROOKINGS, SD

▲ **ELK POINT**—TelePartners

ELKTON—See BROOKINGS, SD

ELLSWORTH AFB—See RAPID CITY, SD

▲ **EMERY**—Emery Cable Vision Inc.

▲ **ESTELLINE**—Satellite Cable Services Inc.

▲ **ETHAN**—Communications Enterprises Inc.

▲ **EUREKA**—Village Cable Inc.

▲ **EVERGREEN HOUSING**—Golden West Cablevision

▲ **FAIRFAX**—Sky Scan Cable Co. Inc.

▲ **FAITH**—Midcontinent Cable Systems Co. of South Dakota

FALL RIVER COUNTY—See HOT SPRINGS, SD

▲ **FAULKTON**—Faulkton Cable TV

FLANDREAU—See BROOKINGS, SD

▲ **FLORENCE**—Satellite Cable Services Inc.

▲ **FORT PIERRE**—Midcontinent Cable Systems Co. of South Dakota

▲ **FRANKFORT**—Village Cable

▲ **FREDERICK**—Midcontinent Cable Systems Co. of South Dakota

▲ **FREEMAN**—Satellite Cable Services Inc.

▲ **GARRETSON**—Splitrock Telecom Cooperative Inc.

▲ **GARY**—Satellite Cable Services Inc.

GAYVILLE—See VIBORG, SD

▲ **GEDDES**—Sky Scan Cable Co. Inc.

▲ **GETTYSBURG**—Midcontinent Cable Systems Co. of South Dakota

▲ **GLENHAM**—Valley Telecommunication

GRANT COUNTY—See MILBANK, SD

▲ **GREGORY**—Rosebud Community Cable TV

▲ **GROTON**—James Valley Cooperative Telephone Co.

HARRISBURG—See VIBORG, SD

▲ **HARROLD**—Sully Buttes Telephone Cooperative Inc.

▲ **HARTFORD**—WMW Cable TV

▲ **HAYTI**—Satellite Cable Services Inc.

HECLA—See GROTON, SD

▲ **HENRY**—Satellite Cable Services Inc.

▲ **HERREID**—Valley Telco

▲ **HIGHMORE**—Sully Buttes Telephone Cooperative

▲ **HILL CITY**—Galaxy Cablevision

▲ **HITCHCOCK**—Sully Buttes Telephone Cooperative

HORSE CREEK HOUSING—See WHITE RIVER, SD

▲ **HOSMER**—Valley Telco Cooperative Assn. Inc.

▲ **HOT SPRINGS**—TCI Cablevision

▲ **HOVEN**—Sully Buttes Telephone Cooperative

▲ **HOWARD**—Satellite Cable Services Inc.

▲ **HUDSON**—American Telecasting Inc.

▲ **HUMBOLDT**—Telecom Inc.

HURLEY—See VIBORG, SD

▲ **HURON**—Midcontinent Cable Systems Co. of South Dakota

▲ **IPSWICH**—Midcontinent Cable Systems

IRENE—See VIBORG, SD

▲ **IROQUOIS**—Satellite Cable Services Inc.

▲ **JAVA**—Midcontinent Cable Systems of South Dakota

▲ **JEFFERSON**—Jefferson Satellite Telecommunications Inc.

▲ **KADOKA**—Golden West Cablevision

▲ **KENNEBEC**—Kennebec CATV Co.

▲ **KIMBALL**—WCENet Inc.

▲ **KYLE**—Golden West Cablevision

▲ **LAKE ANDES**—Village Cable

▲ **LAKE NORDEN**—Satellite Cable Services Inc.

LAKE PRESTON—See BROOKINGS, SD

LAKE WAGGONER—See PHILIP, SD

LANE—See MITCHELL, SD (Communications Enterprises Inc.)

▲ **LANGFORD**—Sully Buttes Telephone Cooperative Inc.

LAWRENCE COUNTY—See DEADWOOD, SD

LEAD—See DEADWOOD, SD

▲ **LEMMON**—Midcontinent Cable Systems of South Dakota

LENNOX—See VIBORG, SD

▲ **LEOLA**—Valley Telco

▲ **LESTERVILLE**—American Telecasting Inc.

LETCHER—See WOONSOCKET, SD

▲ **MADISON**—TCI Cablevision

▲ **MANDERSON-WHITE HORSE CREEK**—Golden West Cablevision

MARION—See FREEMAN, SD

▲ **MARTIN**—Golden West Cablevision

▲ **McINTOSH**—Midcontinent Cable Systems Co. of South Dakota

▲ **McLAUGHLIN**—Midcontinent Cable Systems of South Dakota

MEADE COUNTY (portions)—See RAPID CITY, SD

MEADE COUNTY (portions)—See also STURGIS, SD

▲ **MELLETTE**—Village Cable

MENNO—See FREEMAN, SD

▲ **MIDLAND**—Golden West Cablevision

▲ **MILBANK**—TCI Cablevision of South Dakota

▲ **MILLER**—Midcontinent Cable Systems of South Dakota

MILLER—See also HURON, SD

▲ **MINA**—Midcontinent Cable Systems of South Dakota

MINNEHAHA COUNTY—See DELL RAPIDS, SD

MINNEHAHA COUNTY (southern portion)—See also HARTFORD, SD

▲ **MISSION**—Savage Communications

▲ **MITCHELL**—Communications Enterprises Inc.

▲ **MITCHELL**—Mitchell Cable Television

▲ **MOBRIDGE**—TCI Cablevision

▲ **MONROE**—Dakota Telecommunications Inc.

▲ **MONTROSE**—Ollig Cablevision

▲ **MOUNT VERNON**—Communications Enterprises Inc.

▲ **MURDO**—WCENet Inc.

▲ **NEW EFFINGTON**—Satellite Cable Services Inc.

▲ **NEW UNDERWOOD**—Golden West Cablevision

▲ **NEWELL**—Galaxy Cablevision

NORTH SIOUX CITY—See SIOUX CITY, IA

▲ **OACOMA**—WCENet Inc.

▲ **OELRICHS**—Golden West Cablevision

▲ **OLDHAM**—Satellite Cable Services Inc.

OLIVET—See FREEMAN, SD

▲ **ONAKA**—Sully Buttes Telephone Cooperative Inc.

▲ **ONIDA**—Onida Cable TV

PARKER—See VIBORG, SD

PARKSTON—See FREEMAN, SD

PENNINGTON COUNTY—See RAPID CITY, SD

PENNINGTON COUNTY (portions)—See also BLACK HAWK, SD

▲ **PHILIP**—Golden West Cablevision

▲ **PICKSTOWN**—Sky Scan Cable Co.

PIEDMONT—See BLACK HAWK, SD

▲ **PIERPONT**—Satellite Cable Services Inc.

▲ **PIERRE**—Midcontinent Cable Systems of South Dakota

▲ **PINE RIDGE**—Pine Ridge Cable TV

▲ **PLATTE**—Platte Community Cable TV

▲ **POLLOCK**—Valley Telco Cooperative Assn. Inc.

▲ **PRAIRIEWOOD VILLAGE**—Satellite Cable Services Inc.

▲ **PRESHO**—WCENet Inc.

▲ **PUKWANA**—Satellite Cable Services Inc.

▲ **RAMONA**—Satellite Cable Services Inc.

▲ **RAPID CITY**—TCI Cablevision of South Dakota

RAPID CITY (portions)—See also COUNTRYSIDE MOBILE HOME PARK, SD

RAPID CITY (portions)—See also RIMROCK, SD

▲ **RAYMOND**—Satellite Cable Services Inc.

▲ **REDFIELD**—Midcontinent Cable Systems of South Dakota

▲ **REE HEIGHTS**—Sully Buttes Telephone Cooperative Inc.

▲ **RELIANCE**—WCENet Inc.

RENNER—See SIOUX FALLS, SD

▲ **REVILLO**—Satellite Cable Services Inc.

RHODE ADDITION—See PHILIP, SD

▲ **RIMROCK**—Galaxy Cablevision

▲ **ROSCOE**—Midcontinent Cable Systems of South Dakota

▲ **ROSEBUD**—Savage Communications

▲ **ROSHOLT**—TCI Cablevision of South Dakota

▲ **ROSLYN**—Midcontinent Cable Systems of South Dakota

SALEM—See FREEMAN, SD

SCOTLAND—See FREEMAN, SD

▲ **SELBY**—Midcontinent Cable Systems Co. of South Dakota

▲ **SENECA**—Sully Buttes Telephone Cooperative Inc.

SHERMAN—See GARRETSON, SD

▲ **SIOUX FALLS**—Sioux Falls Cable

▲ **SISSETON**—TCI Cablevision of South Dakota

▲ **SOUTH SHORE**—Satellite Cable Services Inc.

▲ **SPEARFISH**—TCI Cablevision

▲ **SPENCER**—Central Cableland TV

▲ **SPRINGFIELD**—Springfield Cable Inc.

▲ **ST. FRANCIS**—Savage Communications

▲ **ST. LAWRENCE**—Midcontinent Cable Systems

ST. LAWRENCE—See also HURON, SD

STICKNEY—See MITCHELL, SD (Communications Enterprises Inc.)

STRATFORD—See GROTON, SD

▲ **STURGIS**—TCI Cablevision

▲ **SUMMIT**—Satellite Cable Services Inc.

▲ **TABOR**—Telecom Inc.

▲ **TAKINI**—Cheyenne River Sioux Tribe Telephone Authority

TEA—See VIBORG, SD

▲ **TIMBER LAKE**—Midcontinent Cable Systems of South Dakota

▲ **TOLSTOY**—Sully Buttes Telephone Cooperative Inc.

▲ **TORONTO**—Satellite Cable Services Inc.

▲ **TRENT**—Satellite Cable Services Inc.

▲ **TRIPP**—Village Cable Inc.

▲ **TULARE**—Sully Buttes Telephone Cooperative Inc.

TURTON—See GROTON, SD

▲ **TYNDALL**—Village Cable Inc.

UNION COUNTY—See SIOUX CITY, IA

▲ **VALLEY SPRINGS**—Telecom Inc.

▲ **VERMILLION**—Vermillion Cable TV Ltd.

▲ **VIBORG**—Dakota Telecom Inc.

VOLGA—See BROOKINGS, SD

▲ **VOLIN**—Dakota Telecommunications Inc.

▲ **WAGNER**—Village Cable Inc.

WAKONDA—See VIBORG, SD

▲ **WALL**—Golden West Cablevision

WALWORTH COUNTY—See MOBRIDGE, SD

▲ **WANBLEE**—Golden West Cablevision

▲ **WARNER**—Midcontinent Cable Systems of South Dakota

▲ **WATERTOWN**—TCI of Watertown Inc.

▲ **WAUBAY**—Midcontinent Cable Systems of South Dakota

▲ **WEBSTER**—Midcontinent Cable Systems of South Dakota

▲ **WENTWORTH**—Satellite Cable Services Inc.

▲ **WESSINGTON**—Sully Buttes Telephone Cooperative Inc.

▲ **WESSINGTON SPRINGS**—Satellite Cable Services Inc.

▲ **WEST WHITLOCK**—Village Cable

▲ **WHITE**—Satellite Cable Services Inc.

▲ **WHITE LAKE**—Satellite Cable Services Inc.

▲ **WHITE RIVER**—Golden West Cablevision

▲ **WHITEWOOD**—Galaxy Cablevision

▲ **WILLOW LAKE**—Satellite Cable Services Inc.

▲ **WILMOT**—TCI Cablevision of South Dakota

▲ **WINNER**—Midcontinent Cable Systems of South Dakota

▲ **WOLSEY**—Midcontinent Cable Systems of South Dakota

WOLSEY—See also HURON, SD

▲ **WOONSOCKET**—Communications Enterprises Inc.

WORTHING—See VIBORG, SD

▲ **YALE**—Satellite Cable Services Inc.

▲ **YANKTON**—Yankton Cable TV Ltd.

TENNESSEE

ADAMSVILLE—See SELMER, TN

AFTON—See GREENEVILLE, TN

▲ **ALAMO**—Time Warner Cable

▲ **ALCOA**—InterMedia

▲ **ALEXANDRIA**—Alexandria Cablevision

ALGOOD—See COOKEVILLE, TN

▲ **ALTAMONT**—HDC Cable

ANDERSON COUNTY (portions)—See HARRIMAN, TN

ANDERSON COUNTY (portions)—See also OAK RIDGE, TN

▲ **ANTHONY HILL**—Charter Communications

ARDMORE—See ARDMORE, AL

ARTHUR—See NEW TAZEWELL, TN

▲ **ASHLAND CITY**—Charter Communications

▲ **ATHENS**—Comcast Cablevision of the South

ATOKA—See MILLINGTON, TN

ATWOOD—See McKENZIE, TN

BAGGETTSVILLE—See GREENBRIER, TN

BAILEYTON—See GREENEVILLE, TN

BANEBERRY—See MORRISTOWN, TN

BARTLETT—See MEMPHIS, TN

BAXTER—See COOKEVILLE, TN

▲ **BEAN STATION**—FrontierVision

BEDFORD COUNTY (portions)—See LEWISBURG, TN

BEDFORD COUNTY (unincorporated areas)—See also CHAPEL HILL, TN

BEERSHEBA SPRINGS—See ALTAMONT, TN

BELL BUCKLE—See SHELBYVILLE, TN

BELLEVUE—See NASHVILLE, TN

BELLS—See ALAMO, TN

BEMIS—See JACKSON, TN

▲ **BENTON**—Comcast Cablevision of the South

BETHEL SPRINGS—See SELMER, TN

BLAINE—See MAYNARDVILLE, TN

BLEDSOE COUNTY (central portion)—See PIKEVILLE, TN

BLOUNT COUNTY (portions)—See ALCOA, TN

BLOUNT COUNTY (portions)—See also KNOXVILLE, TN

BLOUNT COUNTY (portions)—See also WALDEN CREEK, TN

BLOUNTVILLE—See BRISTOL, TN

BLUFF CITY—See PINEY FLATS, TN

▲ **BOLIVAR**—Enstar Cable TV

BON AQUA—See NASHVILLE, TN

▲ **BRADEN**—Time Warner Communications

▲ **BRADFORD**—Enstar Cable TV

Bradley County—See CALHOUN, TN

BRADLEY COUNTY—See also CLEVELAND, TN

BRADYVILLE—See WOODBURY, TN

BRAEMAR—See GRAY, TN

BRENTWOOD—See NASHVILLE, TN

BRENTWOOD POINTE I—See NASHVILLE, TN

BRENTWOOD PINTE II—See NASHVILLE, TN

BRENTWOOD TWO—See NASHVILLE, TN

BRIGHTON—See COVINGTON, TN

▲ **BRISTOL**—Charter Communications Inc.

▲ **BROWNSVILLE**—Enstar Cable TV

BRUCETON—See McKENZIE, TN

BUCHANAN—See KENTUCKY LAKE, TN

BULLS GAP—See WHITESBURG, TN

BURLISON—See COVINGTON, TN

BURNS—See DICKSON, TN

BURRVILLE—See WARTBURG, TN

▲ **BYRDSTOWN**—CommuniComm Cable

▲ **CALHOUN**—Helicon Cable

▲ **CAMDEN**—Time Warner Cable

CAMPBELL COUNTY—See LA FOLLETTE, TN

CANNON COUNTY—See WOODBURY, TN

CARTER COUNTY—See BOONE, NC

CARTER COUNTY—See also GRAY, TN

CARTER COUNTY (portions)—See also PINEY FLATS, TN

▲ **CARTHAGE**—Intermedia

CARTWRIGHT—See DUNLAP, TN

CARYVILLE—See LA FOLLETTE, TN

▲ **CELINA**—Mid South Cable TV Inc.

CENTERTOWN—See McMINNVILLE, TN

CENTERVILLE—See HOHENWALD, TN

CENTERVILLE TWO—See HOHENWALD, TN

▲ **CHAPEL HILL**—Small Town Cable

CHARLESTON—See CALHOUN, TN

CHARLESTON—See also CLEVELAND, TN

CHARLOTTE—See DICKSON, TN

▲ **CHATTANOOGA**—Comcast Communications

CHEAP HILL—See MONTGOMERY COUNTY, TN

Cheatham County—See ASHLAND CITY, TN

CHEATHAM COUNTY (portions)—See also DICKSON, TN

CHESTER COUNTY—See HENDERSON, TN

CHESTNUT GROVE—See GREENBRIER, TN

CHESTNUT ORCHARD—See GREENBRIER, TN

CHUCKEY—See GREENEVILLE, TN

CHURCH HILL—See KINGSPORT, TN

CLAIBORNE COUNTY (portions)—See FRAKES, KY

CLAIRFIELD—See FRAKES, KY

CLARKSBURG—See McKENZIE, TN

▲ **CLARKSVILLE**—Charter Communications

CLAXTON—See OAK RIDGE, TN

CLAY COUNTY (unincorporated areas)—See CELINA, TN

▲ **CLEVELAND**—InterMedia

▲ **CLIFTON**—InterMedia Partners

CLINTON—See OAK RIDGE, TN

COALFIELD—See WARTBURG, TN

COALMONT—See McMINNVILLE, TN

COBBLY NOB—See WALDEN CREEK, TN

COCKE COUNTY—See MORRISTOWN, TN

COFFEE COUNTY (portions)—See MANCHESTER, TN

COFFEE COUNTY (portions)—See also TULLAHOMA, TN

COLLEGE GROVE—See HOHENWALD, TN

COLLEGEDALE—See CHATTANOOGA, TN

COLLIERVILLE—See MEMPHIS, TN

COLLINWOOD—See WAYNESBORO, TN

COLONIAL HEIGHTS—See KINGSPORT, TN

▲ **COLUMBIA**—Columbia Cablevision

CONCORD—See LOUDON, TN

▲ **COOKEVILLE**—Cookeville Cablevision

COOPERTOWN—See GREENBRIER, TN

COPPERHILL—See BLUE RIDGE, GA

▲ **CORNERSVILLE**—Small Town Cable

COSBY—See WALDEN CREEK, TN

▲ **COUNCE**—Pickwick Cablevision

▲ **COVINGTON**—Enstar Cable TV

COWAN—See WINCHESTER, TN

CRAB ORCHARD—See PLEASANT HILL, TN

CROCKETT COUNTY (portions)—See ALAMO, TN

CROSS PLAINS—See WHITE HOUSE, TN

▲ **CROSSVILLE**—InterMedia

CROSSVILLE—See also PLEASANT HILL, TN

CROSSVILLE (unincorporated areas)—See also FAIRFIELD GLADE, TN

CRUMP—See SAVANNAH, TN

CUMBERLAND COUNTY—See CROSSVILLE, TN

CUMBERLAND COUNTY (central portion)—See also PLEASANT HILL, TN

CUMBERLAND COUNTY (portions)—See also FAIRFIELD GLADE, TN

CUMBERLAND COUNTY (portions)—See also HARRIMAN, TN

CUMBERLAND COUNTY (portions)—See also ROCKWOOD, TN

CUMBERLAND GAP—See NEW TAZEWELL, TN

CUNNINGHAM—See MONTGOMERY COUNTY, TN

DANDRIDGE—See MORRISTOWN, TN

DAVIDSON COUNTY—See NASHVILLE, TN

DAVIDSON COUNTY (western portion)—See also DICKSON, TN

▲ **DAYTON**—Helicon Communications

▲ **DECATUR**—Helicon Communications

DECATUR COUNTY—See PARSONS, TN

DECATURVILLE—See PARSONS, TN

DECHERD—See WINCHESTER, TN

DEER LODGE—See WARTBURG, TN

DEKALB COUNTY—See SMITHVILLE, TN

DELANO—See ATHENS, TN

▲ **DICKSON**—InterMedia Partners

DICKSON COUNTY—See DICKSON, TN

▲ **DOVER**—Mediacom

DOWELLTOWN—See ALEXANDRIA, TN

DOWELLTOWN—See also SMITHVILLE, TN

DOYLE—See McMINNVILLE, TN

▲ **DRESDEN**—Dresden Cable Inc.

DRUMMONDS—See MILLINGTON, TN

DUCKTOWN—See BLUE RIDGE, GA

▲ **DUNLAP**—Bledsoe Telephone Co-op/CATV

DUNN—See LAWRENCEBURG, TN

▲ **DYER**—Enstar Cable TV

DYER COUNTY—See DYERSBURG, TN

▲ **DYERSBURG**—Cable One

▲ **EAGLEVILLE**—Mid South Cable TV Inc.

EAST RIDGE—See CHATTANOOGA, TN

EL BETHEL—See CHAPEL HILL, TN

ELIZABETHTON—See JOHNSON CITY, TN

ELKTON—See ARDMORE, AL

ELMWOOD—See CARTHAGE, TN

ENGLEWOOD—See ATHENS, TN

ERIN—See TENNESSEE RIDGE, TN

ERWIN—See GRAY, TN

ESTILL SPRINGS—See WINCHESTER, TN

ETHRIDGE—See SUMMERTOWN, TN

ETOWAH—See ATHENS, TN

▲ **FAIRFIELD GLADE**—Phoenix Cable

FALL BRANCH—See GRAY, TN

FARMINGTON—See HOHENWALD, TN

FARRAGUT—See LOUDON, TN

▲ **FAYETTEVILLE**—Cablevision Communications

FAYETTEVILLE—See also PULASKI, TN

FAIRVIEW—See NASHVILLE, TN

FINLEY—See DYERSBURG, TN

FRANKLIN—See NASHVILLE, TN

FRANKLIN COUNTY—See WINCHESTER, TN

FRANKLIN COUNTY (portions)—See TULLAHOMA, TN

FRIENDSHIP—See DYERSBURG, TN

▲ **FRIENDSVILLE**—FrontierVision

▲ **GALLATIN**—InterMedia Partners

GARLAND—See COVINGTON, TN

GATES—See RIPLEY, TN

▲ **GATLINBURG**—InterMedia

GERMANTOWN—See MEMPHIS, TN

GIBSON—See McKENZIE, TN

GIBSON COUNTY—See DYER, TN

GIBSON COUNTY—See also McKENZIE, TN

GILES COUNTY—See ARDMORE, AL

GILES COUNTY (portions)—See PULASKI, TN

GILES COUNTY (unincorporated areas)—See ANTHONY HILL, TN

GILES COUNTY (unincorporated areas)—See also LYNNVILLE, TN

GILT EDGE—See COVINGTON, TN

GLADEVILLE—See MOUNT JULIET, TN

GLEASON—See McKENZIE, TN

GOODLETTSVILLE—See NASHVILLE, TN

GORDONSVILLE—See ALEXANDRIA, TN

GRAINGER COUNTY (northeastern portion)—See BEAN STATION, TN

▲ **GRAND JUNCTION**—Time Warner Communications

▲ **GRAY**—Comcast Communciations

GREENBACK—See FRIENDSVILLE, TN

▲ **GREENBRIER**—Tennessee Valley CableVision

GREENE COUNTY—See GREENEVILLE, TN

▲ **GREENEVILLE**—FrontierVision

GREENFIELD—See McKENZIE, TN

GRUETLI-LAAGER—See McMINNVILLE, TN

GRUNDY COUNTY (portions)—See McMINNVILLE, TN

GRUNDY COUNTY (unincorporated areas)—See ALTAMONT, TN

GUYS—See CORINTH, MS

HALETOWN-LADDS—See JASPER, TN

HALLS—See KNOXVILLE, TN

HALLS—See also RIPLEY, TN

HAMBLEN COUNTY—See MORRISTOWN, TN

HAMBLEN COUNTY—See also WHITESBURG, TN

HAMILTON COUNTY—See CHATTANOOGA, TN

HAMLIN TOWN—See FRAKES, KY

HAMPTON—See GRAY, TN

HAMPTON—See also SIMMERLY CREEK, TN

HARDEMAN COUNTY (portions)—See BOLIVAR, TN

HARDIN COUNTY—See SAVANNAH, TN

HARDIN COUNTY (portions)—See COUNCE, TN

HARMONY—See GRAY, TN

▲ **HARRIMAN**—Comcast Cablevision of the South

HARROGATE—See NEW TAZEWELL, TN

▲ **HARTSVILLE**—InterMedia Partners

HAWKINS COUNTY—See KINGSPORT, TN

HAWKINS COUNTY—See also WHITESBURG, TN

HAWKINS COUNTY (central portion)—See ROGERSVILLE, TN

HAYWOOD COUNTY (portions)—See BROWNSVILLE, TN

▲ **HENDERSON**—InterMedia Partners

HENDERSON COUNTY—See LEXINGTON, TN

▲ **HENDERSONVILLE**—InterMedia Partners

HENNING—See RIPLEY, TN

HENRIETTA—See MONTGOMERY COUNTY, TN

▲ **HENRY**—Peoples CATV Inc.

MORGAN COUNTY—See WARTBURG, TN

MORRISON—See McMINNVILLE, TN

▲ **MORRISTOWN**—Charter Communications Inc.

MOSHEIM—See GREENEVILLE, TN

MOUNT CARMEL—See KINGSPORT, TN

▲ **MOUNT JULIET**—Central Tennessee Cablevision

MOUNT PLEASANT—See COLUMBIA, TN

MOUNT PLEASANT—See also HOHENWALD, TN

▲ **MOUNTAIN CITY**—Cablevision Communications

MOUNTAIN CITY—See also GRAY, TN

MUNFORD—See MILLINGTON, TN

▲ **MURFREESBORO**—InterMedia Partners

▲ **NASHVILLE**—InterMedia

NEW DEAL—See WHITE HOUSE, TN

NEW HOPE—See JASPER, TN

NEW MARKET—See MORRISTOWN, TN

▲ **NEW TAZEWELL**—Fannon Cable TV

▲ **NEWBERN**—Tennessee Cablevision Inc.

NEWCOMB—See JELLICO, TN

NEWPORT—See MORRISTOWN, TN

NEWPORT—See also WALDEN CREEK, TN

▲ **NIOTA**—Rapid Cable

NOLENSVILLE—See NASHVILLE, TN

▲ **NORRIS**—Comcast Cablevision of the South

NORTHAVEN—See MILLINGTON, TN

OAK PLAINS—See MONTGOMERY COUNTY, TN

▲ **OAK RIDGE**—Tennessee Cablevision Inc.

OAKDALE—See WARTBURG, TN

OAKPLAIN—See MONTGOMERY COUNTY, TN

OBION—See NEWBERN, TN

OBION COUNTY—See DYER, TN

OBION COUNTY—See also FULTON, KY

OBION COUNTY (unincorporated areas)—See NEWBERN, TN

OCOEE—See BENTON, TN

OLD HICKORY—See MOUNT JULIET, TN

OLDFORT—See BENTON, TN

OLIVER SPRINGS—See OAK RIDGE, TN

ONEIDA—See WARTBURG, TN

ORLINDA—See WHITE HOUSE, TN

OSWEGO—See JELLICO, TN

OVERTON COUNTY (portions)—See LIVINGSTON, TN (Overton County Cable TV)

OWENS—See GREENBRIER, TN

PALMER—See McMINNVILLE, TN

▲ **PARIS**—Paris Cablevision

PARK CITY—See ARDMORE, AL

▲ **PARSONS**—InterMedia Partners

PEGRAM—See DICKSON, TN

PETROS—See WARTBURG, TN

PHILADELPHIA—See LOUDON, TN

PICKETT COUNTY—See BYRDSTOWN, TN

PICKWICK—See COUNCE, TN

PIGEON FORGE—See GATLINBURG, TN

PIGEON FORGE—See also WALDEN CREEK, TN

▲ **PIKEVILLE**—Bledsoe Telephone Co-op/CATV

▲ **PINEY FLATS**—Hickory Hill Cablevision

▲ **PLEASANT HILL**—Mid South Cable TV Inc.

POLK COUNTY (portions)—See ATHENS, TN

POLK COUNTY (portions)—See also BENTON, TN

▲ **PORTLAND**—InterMedia Partners

POWELL—See KNOXVILLE, TN

POWELLS CROSSROADS—See JASPER, TN

PROSPECT—See ARDMORE, AL

▲ **PULASKI**—Cablevision Communications

Puryear—See HAZEL, KY

PUTNAM COUNTY—See MONTEREY, TN

PUTNAM COUNTY (portions)—See COOKEVILLE, TN

RED BANK—See CHATTANOOGA, TN

▲ **RED BOILING SPRINGS**—InterMedia Partners

RHEA COUNTY—See SPRING CITY, TN

RHEATOWN—See GREENEVILLE, TN

RICEVILLE—See ATHENS, TN

RIDGELY—See TIPTONVILLE, TN

RIDGESIDE—See CHATTANOOGA, TN

RIDGETOP—See GREENBRIER, TN

▲ **RIPLEY**—Enstar Cable TV

RIVES—See MARTIN, TN

ROAN MOUNTAIN—See BOONE, NC

ROAN MOUNTAIN—See also SIMMERLY CREEK, TN

ROANE COUNTY—See HARRIMAN, TN

ROANE COUNTY—See also OAK RIDGE, TN

ROBERTSON COUNTY—See WHITE HOUSE, TN

ROBERTSON COUNTY (portions)—See GREENBRIER, TN

ROCK CITY—See CARTHAGE, TN

ROCK SPRINGS—See PINEY FLATS, TN

ROCKFORD—See ALCOA, TN

ROCKFORD—See also KNOXVILLE, TN

▲ **ROCKWOOD**—Comcast Cablevision of the South

ROELLEN—See DYERSBURG, TN

ROGERS DOCK—See LA FOLLETTE, TN

▲ **ROGERSVILLE**—Small Town Cable

ROME—See CARTHAGE, TN

ROSSVILLE—See MEMPHIS, TN

ROUND POND—See MONTGOMERY COUNTY, TN

ROVER—See CHAPEL HILL, TN

RUSSELLVILLE—See WHITESBURG, TN

RUSSWOOD SHORES—See KENTUCKY LAKE, TN

RUTHERFORD—See DYER, TN

RUTHERFORD COUNTY—See MURFREESBORO, TN

RUTHERFORD COUNTY—See also SMYRNA, TN

RUTLEDGE—See BEAN STATION, TN

RUTLEDGE—See also MORRISTOWN, TN

SALEM—See MONTGOMERY COUNTY, TN

SALTILLO—See SAVANNAH, TN

SAMBURG—See TIPTONVILLE, TN

SAULSBURY—See GRAND JUNCTION, TN

▲ **SAVANNAH**—InterMedia Partners

▲ **SCOTTS HILL**—Pat's Cable TV

▲ **SELMER**—Tennessee Cablevision Inc.

SEQUATCHIE—See JASPER, TN

SEQUATCHIE COUNTY (central portion)—See DUNLAP, TN

SEQUATCHIE COUNTY (unincorporated areas)—See CHATTANOOGA, TN

SEVIER COUNTY—See SEYMOUR, TN

SEVIERVILLE—See GATLINBURG, TN

SEVIERVILLE—See also WALDEN CREEK, TN

SEWANEE—See McMINNVILLE, TN

▲ **SEYMOUR**—InterMedia

SHADY GROVE—See MONTGOMERY COUNTY, TN

SHARON—See McKENZIE, TN

SHAWANEE—See NEW TAZEWELL, TN

SHELBY COUNTY—See MEMPHIS, TN

▲ **SHELBYVILLE**—Cablevision of Shelbyville

SIGNAL MOUNTAIN—See CHATTANOOGA, TN

SILOAM—See WESTMORELAND, TN

▲ **SIMMERLY CREEK**—FrontierVision

SMITH COUNTY—See CARTHAGE, TN

SMITH COUNTY (unincorporated areas)—See ALEXANDRIA, TN

▲ **SMITHVILLE**—Central Tennessee Cablevision

▲ **SMYRNA**—Tennessee Valley CableVision

▲ **SNEEDVILLE**—Charter Communications Inc.

SODDY DAISY—See CHATTANOOGA, TN

▲ **SOMERVILLE**—Time Warner Communications

SOUTH CARTHAGE—See CARTHAGE, TN

SOUTH CLINTON—See OAK RIDGE, TN

TEXAS

ANGELINA COUNTY—See CORRIGAN, TX

ANGELINA COUNTY (portions)—See ZAVALLA, TX

▲ **ANGLETON**—CMA Cablevision

▲ **ANNA**—Friendship Cable of Texas Inc.

ANNETTA—See WILLOW PARK, TX

ANNETTA NORTH—See WILLOW PARK, TX

ANNETTA SOUTH—See WILLOW PARK, TX

ANNONA—See CLARKSVILLE, TX

▲ **ANSON**—Friendship Cable of Texas Inc.

ANTHONY—See EL PASO, TX

▲ **ANTON**—Classic Cable

▲ **APPLEHEAD**—Horseshoe Bay-Applehead Cablevision

APRIL SOUND SUBDIVISION—See WALDEN, TX

▲ **AQUA VISTA**—Classic Cable

▲ **ARANSAS PASS**—Cable One

ARBOR VINEYARD—See HOUSTON, TX (Warner Cable Communications)

▲ **ARCHER CITY**—Vista Cablevision

▲ **ARCOLA**—Star Cable

▲ **ARGYLE**—SouthTel Communications LP

▲ **ARLINGTON**—TCI of Arlington Inc.

ARMY RESIDENCE COMMUNITY—See SAN ANTONIO, TX

▲ **ARP**—Friendship Cable of Texas Inc.

▲ **ARROWHEAD ADDITION**—National Cable Inc.

▲ **ASHERTON**—Time Warner Communications

ASHFORD PARK—See HOUSTON, TX (Warner Cable Communications)

▲ **ASPERMONT**—Cablecomm

▲ **ATASCOSA**—Friendship Cable of Texas Inc.

ATASCOSA COUNTY—See CHARLOTTE, TX

ATASCOSA COUNTY—See also POTEET, TX

ATASCOSA COUNTY—See also SOMERSET, TX

▲ **ATHENS**—TCA Cable TV

▲ **ATLANTA**—Falcon Cable TV

AUBREY—See PILOT POINT, TX

AURORA—See BOYD, TX

▲ **AUSTIN**—Time Warner Cable

AUTUMN RUN—See HOUSTON, TX (Warner Cable Communications)

AVERY—See CLARKSVILLE, TX

▲ **AVINGER**—Friendship Cable of Texas Inc.

▲ **AZLE**—North Texas Cablecomm

▲ **AZTEC**—Friendship Cable of Texas Inc.

BACLIFF—See HOUSTON, TX (Warner Cable Communications)

▲ **BAILEY**—Torrence Cablevision

BAILEY'S PRAIRIE—See ANGLETON, TX

▲ **BAIRD**—Brownwood TV Cable Service Inc.

BALCH SPRINGS—See TERRELL, TX

BALCONES HEIGHTS—See SAN ANTONIO, TX

BALD HILL—See HOMER, TX

▲ **BALLINGER**—TCA Cable TV

▲ **BALMORHEA**—Balmorhea TV Cable

BAMMEL OAKS—See HOUSTON, TX (Warner Cable Communications)

▲ **BANDERA**—Time Warner Communications

BANGS—See BROWNWOOD, TX

BARKER'S LANDING—See HOUSTON, TX (Warner Cable Communications)

BARRETT STATION—See HOUSTON, TX (Warner Cable Communications)

▲ **BARSTOW**—Classic Cable

▲ **BARTLETT**—Time Warner Cable

BARTONVILLE (portions)—See ARGYLE, TX

▲ **BASTROP**—Time Warner Communications

▲ **BATESVILLE**—Falcon Cable TV

BATSON—See HULL, TX

▲ **BAY CITY**—Northland Cable TV

BAYOU VISTA—See HOUSTON, TX (Warner Cable Communications)

BAYTOWN—See HOUSTON, TX (Warner Cable Communications)

BAYTOWN—See also MONT BELVIEU, TX

▲ **BEACH CITY**—Friendship Cable of Texas Inc.

BEAR CREEK FARMS—See HOUSTON, TX (Warner Cable Communications)

BEASLEY—See PLEAK, TX

▲ **BEAUMONT**—Time Warner Communications

BEAUMONT (portions)—See SOUR LAKE, TX

▲ **BEAUMONT COLONY**—Friendship Cable of Texas Inc.

BEAUXART GARDENS—See PORT ARTHUR, TX

BECKVILLE—See LAKE CHEROKEE, TX

▲ **BEDFORD**—TCI TKR of the Metroplex Inc.

▲ **BEDIAS**—Mission Cable

▲ **BEEVILLE**—Communications Services Inc.

BELL COUNTY—See KILLEEN, TX

BELLAIRE—See HOUSTON, TX (Warner Cable Communications)

▲ **BELLEVUE**—Classic Cable

BELLMEAD—See WACO, TX

BELLS—See WHITEWRIGHT, TX

▲ **BELLVILLE**—CMA Cablevision

BELTON—See TEMPLE, TX (Time Warner Cable)

▲ **BEN BOLT**—National Cable Inc.

▲ **BEN WHEELER**—Friendship Cable of Texas Inc.

▲ **BENAVIDES**—TCI Cablevision of Texas Inc.

BENBROOK—See FORT WORTH, TX

▲ **BENJAMIN**—Jayroc Cablevision

▲ **BENTSEN GROVE**—Rapid Cable

▲ **BERCLAIR**—Torrence Cablevision

BERMUDA BEACH—See HOUSTON, TX (Warner Cable Communications)

▲ **BERRYVILLE**—Northland Cable TV

▲ **BERTRAM**—Time Warner Cable

BEVERLY HILLS—See WACO, TX

BEVIL OAKS—See SOUR LAKE, TX

BEXAR COUNTY—See BOERNE, TX

BEXAR COUNTY—See also SAN ANTONIO, TX

BEXAR COUNTY (unincorporated areas)—See SOMERSET, TX

BIG EDDY—See LAKE PALESTINE, TX

▲ **BIG LAKE**—Western Community TV Cable

BIG SANDY—See HAWKINS, TX

▲ **BIG SPRING**—TCA Cable TV

▲ **BIG WELLS**—Falcon Cable TV

BIGGS AIRFIELD—See EL PASO, TX

▲ **BIRCH CREEK**—BRDC Cablevision

▲ **BISHOP**—TCI Cablevision of Texas

▲ **BLACKWELL**—Big Country Cablevision

BLANCO—See SAN ANTONIO, TX

▲ **BLANKET**—Cab-Tel Corp.

▲ **BLESSING**—Mid Coast Cable TV Inc.

BLOOMING GROVE—See FROST, TX

▲ **BLOOMINGTON**—Classic Cable

BLOSSOM—See CLARKSVILLE, TX

BLUE BELL—See HOUSTON, TX (Warner Cable Communications)

BLUE MOUND—See FORT WORTH, TX

▲ **BLUE RIDGE**—Torrence Cablevision

BLUEBONNET HILLS—See CHAPPELL HILL, TX

▲ **BLUFF DALE**—Torrence Cablevision

▲ **BOERNE**—Guadalupe Valley Communication Systems Inc.

BOGATA—See CLARKSVILLE, TX

▲ **BOLING**—Star Cable

▲ **BONHAM**—Cable One

▲ **BOOKER**—Classic Cable

▲ **BORGER**—Charter Communications Inc.

BOVINA—See FRIONA, TX

▲ **BOWIE**—Southwest Cablevision

BOWIE COUNTY—See DE KALB, TX

BOWIE COUNTY—See also HOOKS, TX

BOWIE COUNTY—See also MAUD, TX

BOWIE COUNTY—See also TEXARKANA, TX

BOWIE COUNTY (northern portion)—See NEW BOSTON, TX

▲ **BOYD**—South Tel

▲ **BRACKETTVILLE**—Falcon Cable TV

▲ **BRADY**—Classic Cable

▲ **BRAZORIA**—Star Cable

BRAZORIA COUNTY—See BRAZORIA, TX

BRAZORIA COUNTY—See also HOUSTON, TX (Warner Cable Communications)

BRAZOS COUNTY (unincorporated areas)—See BRYAN, TX

▲ **BRECKENRIDGE**—Friendship Cable of Texas Inc.

▲ **BREMOND**—Galaxy Cablevision

▲ **BRENHAM**—Northland Cable TV

BREWSTER COUNTY—See SEMINOLE, TX

BRIAR—See PELICAN BAY, TX

BRIAR CREEK—See HOUSTON, TX (Warner Cable Communications)

BRIAR HILLS—See HOUSTON, TX (Warner Cable Communications)

BRIARCLIFF—See LAKEWAY, TX

BRIAROAKS—See BURLESON, TX

▲ **BRIDGE CITY**—Warner Cable

BRIDGEPORT—See DECATUR, TX

BRINWOOD SHORES—See QUINLAN, TX

BROKEN BAYOU—See HOUSTON, TX (Warner Cable Communications)

▲ **BRONTE**—West Texas Cablevision

BROOK HOLLOW WEST—See HOUSTON, TX (Warner Cable Communications)

▲ **BROOKELAND**—Friendship Cable of Texas Inc.

BROOKS AFB—See SAN ANTONIO, TX

▲ **BROOKSHIRE**—Northland Cable

BROOKSIDE VILLAGE—See HOUSTON, TX (Warner Cable Communications)

BROWNDELL—See BROOKELAND, TX

▲ **BROWNFIELD**—Cablecomm

BROWNSBORO—See BEN WHEELER, TX

▲ **BROWNSVILLE**—Time Warner Communications

▲ **BROWNWOOD**—Brownwood TV Cable Service Inc.

BRUCEVILLE-EDDY—See LORENA, TX

▲ **BRUNI**—TCI Cablevision of Texas Inc.

▲ **BRYAN**—TCA Cable TV

BRYSON—See JACKSBORO, TX

BUCHANAN—See REDWATER, TX

▲ **BUCHANAN DAM**—Northland Cable

▲ **BUCKHOLTS**—National Cable Inc.

BUDA—See GRANADA HILLS, TX

▲ **BUFFALO**—Northland Cable

▲ **BUFFALO GAP**—Big Country Cablevision Inc.

▲ **BUFFALO SPRINGS LAKE**—Classic Cable

BULLARD—See FLINT, TX

BUNA—See SILSBEE, TX

BUNKER HILL—See HOUSTON, TX (Warner Cable Communications)

BURGER ESTATES—See HOUSTON, TX (Warner Cable Communications)

▲ **BURKBURNETT**—Friendship Cable of Texas Inc.

BURKE—See CORRIGAN, TX

BURKEVILLE—See TOLEDO VILLAGE, TX

▲ **BURLESON**—Mallard Cablevision

BURLESON—See also FORT WORTH, TX

BURLESON CITY—See JOSHUA, TX

▲ **BURNET**—Northland Cable TV

BURNET COUNTY—See KINGSLAND, TX

▲ **BURTON**—BRDC Cablevision

▲ **BYERS**—Byers-Petrolia Cable TV

▲ **CACTUS**—High Plains Cablevision Inc.

CADDO MILLS—See QUINLAN, TX

▲ **CADDO PEAK**—Friendship Cable of Texas Inc.

▲ **CALDWELL**—Classic Cable

CALENDAR LAKE—See BEN WHEELER, TX

CALHOUN COUNTY—See PORT LAVACA, TX

▲ **CALVERT**—Galaxy Cablevision

▲ **CAMERON**—Galaxy Cablevision

CAMERON—See also PORT ISABEL, TX

CAMERON COUNTY—See LOS FRESNOS, TX

CAMERON COUNTY (portions)—See BROWNSVILLE, TX

CAMERON COUNTY (western portion)—See HARLINGEN, TX

CAMP COUNTY (portions)—See PITTSBURG, TX

▲ **CAMP WOOD**—Classic Cable

▲ **CAMPBELL**—Torrence Cablevision

▲ **CAMPBELLTON**—Torrence Cablevision

▲ **CAMPO ALTO**—Torrence Cablevision

▲ **CANADIAN**—Classic Cable

CANEY CITY—See MALAKOFF, TX

▲ **CANTON**—East Texas Cable Co.

CANUTILLO—See EL PASO, TX

▲ **CANYON**—TCA Cable of Amarillo Inc.

▲ **CANYON LAKE**—Guadalupe Valley Communication Systems Inc.

▲ **CAPISALLO PARK**—Torrence Cablevision

▲ **CARLSBAD**—Classic Cable

CARLTON—See WAXAHACHIE, TX

▲ **CARMINE**—BRDC Cablevision

▲ **CAROLINA COVE**—World Wide Systems Inc.

CARRIZO SPRINGS—See CRYSTAL CITY, TX

▲ **CARROLLTON**—Charter Communications Inc.

▲ **CARROLLTON**—TCI TKR of the Metroplex Inc.

CARSWELL AFB—See RIVER OAKS (Tarrant County), TX

▲ **CARTHAGE**—Falcon Cable TV

CASH—See QUINLAN, TX

CASON—See DAINGERFIELD, TX

CASS COUNTY (portions)—See ATLANTA, TX

CASS COUNTY (portions)—See also AVINGER, TX

CASS COUNTY (portions)—See also RODESSA, LA

CASTLE HILLS—See SAN ANTONIO, TX

▲ **CASTROVILLE**—Falcon Cable TV

▲ **CEDAR CREEK**—Torrence Cablevision

▲ **CEDAR CREEK LAKE**—Torrence Cablevision

CEDAR HILL—See DE SOTO, TX

CEDAR PARK—See AUSTIN, TX

▲ **CEDAR SPRINGS**—Friendship Cable of Texas Inc.

CEDAR VALLEY—See GRANADA HILLS, TX

CELESTE—See LEONARD, TX

CELINA—See PILOT POINT, TX

▲ **CENTER**—Friendship Cable of Texas Inc.

▲ **CENTER POINT**—Classic Cable

▲ **CENTERVILLE**—Mission Cable

▲ **CENTRAL**—Friendship Cable of Texas Inc.

CENTRAL GARDENS—See PORT ARTHUR, TX

CHAMBERS COUNTY (western portion)—See HOUSTON, TX (Warner Cable Communications)

CHAMBERS COUNTY (western portion)—See also MONT BELVIEU, TX

▲ **CHANDLER**—Northland Cable TV

CHANNELVIEW—See HOUSTON, TX (Warner Cable Communications)

▲ **CHANNING**—High Plains Cablevision Inc.

▲ **CHAPPELL HILL**—BRDC Cablevision

▲ **CHARLOTTE**—Time Warner Communications

CHASE FIELD NAVAL AIR STATION—See BEEVILLE, TX

▲ **CHEEK**—Friendship Cable of Texas Inc.

CHEROKEE COUNTY—See JACKSONVILLE, TX

CHEROKEE COUNTY—See also RUSK, TX

▲ **CHESTER**—Friendship Cable of Texas Inc.

CHICO—See DECATUR, TX

▲ **CHILDRESS**—Classic Cable

CHILDRESS COUNTY—See CHILDRESS, TX

▲ **CHILLICOTHE**—Classic Cable

▲ **CHILTON**—Galaxy Cablevision

CHIMNEY HILL—See HOUSTON, TX (Warner Cable Communications)

▲ **CHINA**—Timberlake Cablevision Inc.

CHINA GROVE—See SAN ANTONIO, TX

▲ **CHRISTOVAL**—Classic Cable

CIBOLO—See SAN ANTONIO, TX

CIBOLO CREEK—See SAN ANTONIO, TX

CIRCLE C—See AUSTIN, TX

CISCO—See EASTLAND, TX

CITY BY THE SEA—See ARANSAS PASS, TX

▲ **CLARENDON**—Classic Cable

▲ **CLARKSVILLE**—Friendship Cable of Texas Inc.

CLARKSVILLE CITY—See GLADEWATER, TX

▲ **CLAUDE**—Classic Cable

CLAWSON—See CENTRAL, TX

CLEAR LAKE SHORES—See HOUSTON, TX (Warner Cable Communications)

CLEARWATER COVE—See WALDEN, TX

▲ **CLEBURNE**—Charter Communications Inc.

▲ **CLEVELAND**—Crown Cable

▲ **CLIFTON**—Friendship Cable of Texas Inc.

CLINT—See EL PASO, TX

CLUTE—See HOUSTON, TX (Warner Cable Communications)

CLYDE—See BAIRD, TX

COAHOMA—See BIG SPRING, TX

COCKRELL HILL—See GRAND PRAIRIE, TX

COLDSPRING—See SHEPHERD, TX

▲ **COLEMAN**—North Texas Cablecomm

▲ **COLETO CREEK**—National Cable Inc.

COLFAX—See BEN WHEELER, TX

COLLEGE STATION—See BRYAN, TX

COLLEYVILLE—See BEDFORD, TX

COLLIN COUNTY (portions)—See JOSEPHINE, TX

COLLINGSWORTH COUNTY—See WELLINGTON, TX

▲ **COLLINSVILLE**—North Texas Communications Co.

▲ **COLMESNEIL**—Friendship Cable of Texas Inc.

COLONIES—See HOUSTON, TX (Warner Cable Communications)

▲ **COLORADO CITY**—Cablecomm

COLUMBIA LAKES—See WEST COLUMBIA, TX

▲ **COLUMBUS**—Time Warner Communications

COMAL COUNTY—See GARDEN RIDGE, TX

COMAL COUNTY—See also SAN ANTONIO, TX

COMAL COUNTY (portions)—See CANYON LAKE, TX

COMAL COUNTY (portions)—See also NEW BRAUNFELS, TX

▲ **COMANCHE**—Falcon Cable TV

COMBES—See HARLINGEN, TX

▲ **COMBINE**—Charter Communications Inc.

▲ **COMFORT**—Classic Cable

▲ **COMMERCE**—Paragon Cable

COMSTOCK—See SEMINOLE, TX

CONCORD COLONY—See HOUSTON, TX (Warner Cable Communications)

▲ **CONROE**—Conroe Cable TV

▲ **CONROE WEST**—Lakewood Cablevision

CONVERSE—See SAN ANTONIO, TX

COOKE COUNTY—See GAINESVILLE, TX

COOKE COUNTY (portions)—See LAKE KIOWA, TX

▲ **COOLIDGE**—Northland Cable

COOPER—See COMMERCE, TX

COPEVILLE—See JOSEPHINE, TX

▲ **COPPELL**—Paragon Cable

COPPERAS COVE—See KILLEEN, TX

COPPERAS COVE (unincorporated areas)—See KEMPNER, TX

COPPERFIELD—See HOUSTON, TX (Warner Cable Communications)

CORINTH—See DENTON, TX

CORNERSTONE VILLAGE NORTH—See HOUSTON, TX (Warner Cable Communications)

▲ **CORPUS CHRISTI**—TCI Cablevision of Texas Inc.

CORPUS CHRISTI NAVAL AIR STATION—See CORPUS CHRISTI, TX

▲ **CORRIGAN**—TCA Cable

▲ **CORSICANA**—Northland Cable TV

COTTONWOOD—See HOUSTON, TX (Warner Cable Communications)

COTTONWOOD SHORES—See HORSESHOE BAY, TX

▲ **COTULLA**—Time Warner Communications

▲ **COUNTRY CLUB SHORES**—Torrence Cablevision

▲ **COUNTRY HAVEN**—Classic Cable

COVE—See BEACH CITY, TX

▲ **CRANDALL**—Charter Communications Inc.

▲ **CRANE**—Classic Cable

CRANE COUNTY (unincorporated areas)—See CRANE, TX

▲ **CRANFILLS GAP**—National Cable Inc.

▲ **CRAWFORD**—Galaxy Cablevision

CREEDMOOR—See MUSTANG RIDGE, TX

▲ **CRESSON**—Torrence Cablevision

▲ **CROCKETT**—Northland Cable TV LP

CROSBY—See HOUSTON, TX (Warner Cable Communications)

▲ **CROSBYTON**—Classic Cable

CROSS PLAINS—See RISING STAR, TX

▲ **CROWELL**—Classic Cable

CROWLEY—See FORT WORTH, TX

▲ **CRYSTAL BEACH**—Star Cable

▲ **CRYSTAL CITY**—Time Warner Communications

▲ **CUERO**—Time Warner Communications

▲ **CUMBY**—Friendship Cable of Texas Inc.

▲ **CUSHING**—Friendship Cable of Texas Inc.

▲ **CUT AND SHOOT**—Northland Cable

▲ **CYPRESS**—Friendship Cable of Texas Inc.

CYPRESS TRAILS—See HOUSTON, TX (Warner Cable Communications)

▲ **DAINGERFIELD**—Star Cable Assoc.

DAISETTA—See HULL, TX

▲ **DALHART**—TCA Cable TV of Dalhart

DALLAM COUNTY—See DALHART, TX

▲ **DALLAS**—TCI Cablevision of Dallas Inc.

DALLAS COUNTY—See GARLAND, TX

DALLAS COUNTY (portions)—See TERRELL, TX

DALWORTHINGTON GARDENS—See ARLINGTON, TX

DAMON—See GUY, TX

DANBURY—See ANGLETON, TX

▲ **DARROUZETT**—Classic Cable

DAWSON—See HUBBARD, TX

DAWSON COUNTY (unincorporated areas)—See LAMESA, TX

DAYTON—See LIBERTY, TX

▲ **DE KALB**—TCA Cable TV

▲ **DE LEON**—Friendship Cable of Texas Inc.

▲ **DE SOTO**—TCI TKR of the Metroplex Inc.

▲ **DECATUR**—Southwest Cablevision

DEER PARK—See HOUSTON, TX (Warner Cable Communications)

DEERFIELD VILLAGE—See HOUSTON, TX (Warner Cable Communications)

▲ **DEL RIO**—Time Warner Communications

DENISON—See SHERMAN, TX

▲ **DENTON**—Charter Communications Inc.

DENTON COUNTY (portions)—See LAKE KIOWA, TX

DENVER CITY—See SEMINOLE, TX

DEPORT—See CLARKSVILLE, TX

DETROIT—See CLARKSVILLE, TX

DEVERS—See RAYWOOD, TX

▲ **DEVINE**—Falcon Cable TV

DEWEYVILLE—See MAURICEVILLE, TX

DEWITT COUNTY—See CUERO, TX

▲ **DIANA**—Friendship Cable of Texas Inc.

DIBOLL—See CORRIGAN, TX

▲ **DICKENS**—Classic Cable

DICKINSON—See HOUSTON, TX (Warner Cable Communications)

▲ **DILLEY**—Time Warner Communications

▲ **DIME BOX**—BRDC Cablevision

FULTON—See ROCKPORT, TX

▲ **GAINESVILLE**—TCA Cable TV

GALENA PARK—See HOUSTON, TX (Warner Cable Communications)

GALVESTON—See HOUSTON, TX (Warner Cable Communications)

GALVESTON COUNTY—See HOUSTON, TX (Warner Cable Communications)

▲ **GANADO**—Cablevision Ltd.

GARCENO—See ROMA, TX

GARCIASVILLE—See LA GRULLA, TX

▲ **GARDEN CITY**—Torrence Cablevision

▲ **GARDEN RIDGE**—Time Warner Cable

▲ **GARDENDALE**—Classic Cable

▲ **GARFIELD**—Mission Cable

▲ **GARLAND**—TCI Cablevision of the Metroplex Inc.

GARRETT—See ENNIS, TX

▲ **GARRISON**—Friendship Cable of Texas Inc.

▲ **GARWOOD**—National Cable Inc.

▲ **GARY**—Friendship Cable of Texas Inc.

▲ **GATESVILLE**—Gatesville Cable TV

▲ **GAUSE**—National Cable Inc.

▲ **GEORGE WEST**—TCI Cablevision of Texas

▲ **GEORGETOWN**—Williamson County Cablevision

GERONIMO—See SAN ANTONIO, TX

GIDDINGS—See LA GRANGE, TX

GILLESPIE COUNTY—See FREDERICKSBURG, TX

▲ **GILMER**—Gilmer Cable TV Co.

▲ **GLADEWATER**—TCA Cable TV

GLADEWATER—See also HAWKINS, TX

▲ **GLEN ROSE**—Glen Rose Cablevision

GLEN ROSE—See also GRANBURY, TX

GLENEAGLES—See SPRING, TX

GLENN HEIGHTS—See WAXAHACHIE, TX

GLENWOOD—See EAST MOUNTAIN, TX

GLENWOOD ACRES—See EAST MOUNTAIN, TX

▲ **GOAT CREEK**—Classic Cable

▲ **GODLEY**—Charter Communications Inc.

▲ **GOLDEN**—Friendship Cable of Texas Inc.

▲ **GOLDSMITH**—Classic Cable

▲ **GOLDTHWAITE**—Post Cablevision of Texas Ltd.

▲ **GOLIAD**—Falcon Cable TV

▲ **GOLINDA**—National Cable Inc.

▲ **GONZALES**—Time Warner Communications

GOODFELLOW AFB—See SAN ANGELO, TX

▲ **GOODRICH**—Star Cable

▲ **GORDON**—Mallard Cablevision

GORDONVILLE—See SHERWOOD SHORES, TX

▲ **GOREE**—Goree Cablevision

▲ **GORMAN**—Friendship Cable of Taxas Inc.

GRAFORD—See JACKSBORO, TX

▲ **GRAHAM**—Paragon Cable

GRANADA—See HOUSTON, TX (Warner Cable Communications)

▲ **GRANADA HILLS**—Time Warner Cable

▲ **GRANBURY**—North Texas Cablecomm

▲ **GRAND PRAIRIE**—TCI Cablevision of the Metroplex Inc.

GRAND SALINE—See MINEOLA, TX

▲ **GRANDFALLS**—Classic Cable

GRANDVIEW—See ALVARADO, TX

GRANGER—See BARTLETT, TX

GRANGERLAND—See NEW CANEY, TX

GRANITE SHOALS—See KINGSLAND, TX

▲ **GRAPE CREEK**—West Texas Cablevision Inc.

▲ **GRAPELAND**—Friendship Cable of Texas Inc.

▲ **GRAPEVINE**—Paragon Cable

GRAYSON COUNTY (northern portion)—See SHERMAN, TX

▲ **GREEN ACRES/ZION HILL**—National Cable Inc.

▲ **GREENVILLE**—Time Warner Cable

GREGORY—See ARANSAS PASS, TX

GRESHAM—See FLINT, TX

GREY FOREST—See SAN ANTONIO, TX

GROESBECK—See MEXIA, TX

▲ **GROOM**—Classic Cable

GROVES—See PORT ARTHUR, TX

▲ **GROVETON**—Friendship Cable of Texas Inc.

▲ **GRUVER**—Gruver Cablevision Inc.

GUADALUPE COUNTY—See SAN ANTONIO, TX

GUADALUPE COUNTY (portions)—See NEW BRAUNFELS, TX

GUADALUPE COUNTY (portions)—See also SEGUIN, TX

▲ **GUN BARREL CITY**—Northland Cable TV

GUNTER—See PILOT POINT, TX

▲ **GUSTINE**—Cable Ventures Ltd.

▲ **GUTHRIE**—6666 Supply House

▲ **GUY**—Star Cable

▲ **HALE CENTER**—Classic Cable

HALE COUNTY—See PLAINVIEW, TX

HALL COUNTY (portions)—See MEMPHIS, TX

HALLETTSVILLE—See LA GRANGE, TX

▲ **HALLSVILLE**—Falcon Cable TV

HALTOM CITY—See FORT WORTH, TX

▲ **HAMILTON**—Hamilton TV Cable Co.

▲ **HAMLIN**—Friendship Cable of Texas Inc.

HAMPTON—See MAURICEVILLE, TX

HAMSHIRE—See FANNETT, TX

HAMSHIRE—See also WINNIE, TX

HANKAMER—See ANAHUAC, TX

▲ **HAPPY**—Classic Cable

HAPPY COUNTRY HOMES—See TERRELL, TX

▲ **HARBOR POINT**—Torrence Cablevision

HARDIN—See HULL, TX

HARKER HEIGHTS—See KILLEEN, TX

▲ **HARLINGEN**—Time Warner Communications

▲ **HARPER**—Cableview Co.

▲ **HARRIS COUNTY (northern portion)**—Scott Cable Communications Inc.

HARRIS COUNTY—See also HOUSTON, TX (Warner Cable Communications)

HARRIS COUNTY (portions)—See CUT AND SHOOT, TX

HARRIS COUNTY (southeastern portion)—See MONT BELVIEU, TX

HARRISON COUNTY (portions)—See MARSHALL, TX

▲ **HART**—Classic Cable

HARVEST ACRES—See SAN ANGELO, TX

▲ **HASKELL**—Harmon Cable Communications

HASLET—See TROPHY CLUB, TX

▲ **HASSE**—Cable Ventures Ltd.

▲ **HAWKINS**—Friendship Cable of Texas Inc.

▲ **HAWLEY**—Jayroc Cablevision

HAYS—See GRANADA HILLS, TX

HAYS COUNTY—See KYLE, TX

▲ **HEARNE**—TCA Cable TV Inc.

HEARTHSTONE—See HOUSTON, TX (Warner Cable Communications)

HEARTHSTONE GREEN—See HOUSTON, TX (Warner Cable Communications)

HEATH—See TERRELL, TX

HEATHERGLEN—See HOUSTON, TX (Warner Cable Communications)

▲ **HEBBRONVILLE**—TCI Cablevision of Texas Inc.

HEBRON—See CARROLLTON, TX (TCI TKR of the Metroplex Inc.)

▲ **HEDLEY**—Classic Cable

HEDWIG—See HOUSTON, TX (Warner Cable Communications)

HEIDELBERG—See CAPISALLO PARK, TX

▲ **HEIGHTS**—Star Cable Co.

HELOTES—See SAN ANTONIO, TX

▲ **HEMPHILL**—Star Cable

▲ **HEMPSTEAD**—CMA Cablevision

HEMPSTEAD—See also BELLVILLE, TX

▲ **HENDERSON**—TCA Cable TV

HENDERSON COUNTY—See ATHENS, TX

HENDERSON COUNTY (portions)—See BEN WHEELER, TX

HENDERSON COUNTY (portions)—See also EUSTACE, TX

▲ **HENRIETTA**—Friendship Cable of Texas Inc.

▲ **HEREFORD**—Hereford Cablevision Co.

HERITAGE PARK—See HOUSTON, TX (Warner Cable Communications)

HERMLEIGH—See SNYDER, TX

HICKORY CREEK—See DENTON, TX

▲ **HICO**—Northland Cable TV

▲ **HIDALGO**—Time Warner Communications

HIDALGO COUNTY—See EDCOUCH, TX

HIDALGO COUNTY—See also WESLACO, TX

HIDALGO COUNTY (portions)—See BENTSEN GROVE, TX

▲ **HIGGINS**—Classic Cable

HIGH ISLAND—See CRYSTAL BEACH, TX

HIGHLAND PARK—See UNIVERSITY PARK, TX

▲ **HIGHLAND RANGE**—Highland Cable

HIGHLAND VILLAGE—See FLOWER MOUND, TX

HIGHLANDS—See HOUSTON, TX (Warner Cable Communications)

HILL COUNTRY VILLAGE—See SAN ANTONIO, TX

HILLCREST VILLAGE—See HOUSTON, TX (Warner Cable Communications)

HILLEBRANDT—See FANNETT, TX

HILLISTER—See WOODVILLE, TX

▲ **HILLSBORO**—Northland Cable

HILLSHIRE—See HOUSTON, TX (Warner Cable Communications)

HITCHCOCK—See HOUSTON, TX (Warner Cable Communications)

HOCKLEY—See MAGNOLIA, TX

HOCKLEY COUNTY—See LEVELLAND, TX

HOLIDAY BEACH—See ROCKPORT, TX

▲ **HOLIDAY LAKES**—Star Cable

HOLLAND—See BARTLETT, TX

▲ **HOLLIDAY**—Vista Cablevision

HOLLYWOOD PARK—See SAN ANTONIO, TX

▲ **HOMER**—Friendship Cable of Texas Inc.

HOMESTEADS—See BURLESON, TX

▲ **HONDO**—Falcon Cable TV

▲ **HONEY GROVE**—TCA Cable TV

HONEY GROVE—See also COMMERCE, TX

HOOD COUNTY—See GRANBURY, TX

▲ **HOOKS**—TCA Cable TV

HOPKINS COUNTY—See SULPHUR SPRINGS, TX

HORIZON CITY—See EL PASO, TX

▲ **HORSESHOE BAY**—Northland Cable TV

▲ **HOUSTON**—Phonoscope Ltd.

▲ **HOUSTON**—Warner Cable Communications

HOUSTON (eastern & western suburbs)—See HOUSTON, TX

HOWARD COUNTY—See BIG SPRING, TX

▲ **HOWARDWICK**—Classic Cable

HOWE—See WHITEWRIGHT, TX

▲ **HUBBARD**—Charter Communications Inc.

▲ **HUDSON**—TCA Cable

HUDSON OAKS—See WILLOW PARK, TX

▲ **HUFFMAN**—Northland Cable

HUGHES SPRINGS—See DAINGERFIELD, TX

▲ **HULL**—Friendship Cable of Texas Inc.

HUMBLE—See HOUSTON, TX (Warner Cable Communications)

HUNGERFORD—See PLEAK, TX

HUNT—See INGRAM, TX

HUNT COUNTY (portions)—See QUINLAN, TX

HUNTER CREEK—See HOUSTON, TX (Warner Cable Communications)

▲ **HUNTINGTON**—Communicom

▲ **HUNTSVILLE**—TCA/Huntsville Cable TV

HURST—See FORT WORTH, TX

HUTCHINS—See LANCASTER, TX

HUTTO—See GRANADA HILLS, TX

▲ **IDALOU**—Classic Cable

▲ **IMPERIAL**—Classic Cable

INDIAN LAKE—See LOS FRESNOS, TX

▲ **INDIAN LAKE/LAKE THUNDERBIRD**—BRDC Cablevision

INDIAN SHORES—See HUFFMAN, TX

▲ **INDIAN SPRINGS**—Star Cable

INGLESIDE—See ARANSAS PASS, TX

INGLESIDE ON THE BAY—See ARANSAS PASS, TX

▲ **INGRAM**—Classic Cable

INKS LAKE—See BUCHANAN DAM, TX

▲ **IOLA**—National Cable Inc.

IOWA COLONY—See ARCOLA, TX

▲ **IOWA PARK**—Friendship Cable of Texas Inc.

IOWA PARK—See also PLEASANT VALLEY, TX

IRAAN—See SEMINOLE, TX

▲ **IRVING**—Paragon Cable

ITALY—See WAXAHACHIE, TX

ITASCA—See ALVARADO, TX

IVANHOE ESTATES—See WOODVILLE, TX

JACINTO CITY—See HOUSTON, TX (Warner Cable Communications)

▲ **JACKSBORO**—Southwest Cablevision

▲ **JACKSON'S LANDING**—Northland Cable TV

▲ **JACKSONVILLE**—TCA Cable TV

JAMAICA BEACH—See HOUSTON, TX (Warner Cable Communications)

JAMESTOWN COLONY—See HOUSTON, TX (Warner Cable Communications)

▲ **JARRELL**—Williamson County Cablevision Co.

▲ **JASPER**—Tri-City Cablevision

JASPER COUNTY (portions)—See BROOKELAND, TX

▲ **JAYTON**—Jayroc Cablevision

▲ **JEFFERSON**—Falcon Cable TV

JERSEY VILLAGE—See HOUSTON, TX (Warner Cable Communications)

▲ **JEWETT**—Northland Cable

▲ **JOAQUIN**—Mansfield Cablevision

▲ **JOHNSON CITY**—Post Cablevision of Texas Ltd.

JOHNSON COUNTY (portions)—See JOSHUA, TX

JONES COUNTY (portions)—See ANSON, TX

JONES COUNTY (portions)—See also HAMLIN, TX

JONES CREEK—See BRAZORIA, TX

JONESTOWN—See LAKEWAY, TX

▲ **JOSEPHINE**—Friendship Cable of Texas Inc.

▲ **JOSHUA**—North Texas Cablevision

JOSHUA—See also CADDO PEAK, TX

JOURDANTON—See POTEET, TX

▲ **JUNCTION**—Classic Cable

JUSTIN—See PONDER, TX

KARNES CITY—See KENEDY, TX

KATY—See HOUSTON, TX (Warner Cable Communications)

▲ **KATY (southern portion)**—Friendship Cable of Texas Inc.

▲ **KAUFMAN**—Northland Cable

KAUFMAN COUNTY—See TERRELL, TX

KEEGANS GLEN—See HOUSTON, TX (Warner Cable Communications)

KEENE—See ALVARADO, TX

KELLER—See FORT WORTH, TX

KELLY AFB—See SAN ANTONIO, TX

KEMAH—See HOUSTON, TX (Warner Cable Communications)

KEMP (unincorporated areas)—See COUNTRY CLUB SHORES, TX

▲ **KEMPNER**—National Cable Inc.

KENDALL COUNTY—See BOERNE, TX

KENDLETON—See PLEAK, TX

▲ **KENEDY**—Classic Cable

▲ **KENEFICK**—Friendship Cable of Texas Inc.

▲ **KENNEDALE**—Charter Communications Inc.

KENNEDALE—See also FORT WORTH, TX

▲ **KERENS**—Northland Cable TV

▲ **KERMIT**—Classic Cable

KERR COUNTY—See KERRVILLE, TX

▲ **KERRVILLE**—Time Warner Communications

▲ **KILGORE**—Friendship Cable of Texas Inc.

▲ **KILGORE**—Kilgore Cable TV Co.

▲ **KILLEEN**—Time Warner Cable

KINGS COURT RV PARK—See EMORY, TX

▲ **KINGSLAND**—Northland Cable TV

▲ **KINGSVILLE**—CMA Cablevision

KINGSVILLE (unincorporated areas)—See RICARDO, TX

▲ **KINGWOOD**—Kingwood Cablevision Inc.

KIRBY—See SAN ANTONIO, TX

▲ **KIRBYVILLE**—Communicom

KIRKLAND DOCKS—See THUNDERBIRD BAY, TX

KLIENBROOK—See HOUSTON, TX (Warner Cable Communications)

▲ **KNIPPA**—Torrence Cablevision

KNOLLWOOD—See SHERMAN, TX

▲ **KNOX CITY**—Classic Cable

▲ **KOSSE**—Mission Cable

▲ **KOUNTZE**—Time Warner Cable

▲ **KRESS**—Classic Cable

KRUGERVILLE—See PILOT POINT, TX

▲ **KRUM**—Friendship Cable of Texas Inc.

▲ **KYLE**—Time Warner Entertainment/Advance-Newhouse

LA BLANCA—See SAN CARLOS, TX

▲ **LA COSTE**—TCI Cablevision of Texas

LA FERIA—See HARLINGEN, TX

▲ **LA GRANGE**—CMA Cablevision

▲ **LA GRULLA**—Time Warner Communications

LA JOYA—See SULLIVAN CITY, TX

LA MARQUE—See HOUSTON, TX (Warner Cable Communications)

LA PORTE—See HOUSTON, TX (Warner Cable Communications)

▲ **LA PRYOR**—Falcon Cable TV

LA SALLE COUNTY (portions)—See COTULLA, TX

LA SALLE COUNTY (southern portion)—See ENCINAL, TX

LA VILLA—See EDCOUCH, TX

LABELLE—See FANNETT, TX

LACKLAND AFB—See SAN ANTONIO, TX

LACY-LAKEVIEW—See WACO, TX

LADONIA—See WOLFE CITY, TX

LAGO VISTA—See GRANADA HILLS, TX

LAGUNA HEIGHTS—See PORT ISABEL, TX

LAGUNA VISTA—See PORT ISABEL, TX

LAJITAS—See SEMINOLE, TX

▲ **LAKE ARROWHEAD**—Vista Cablevision

LAKE BRIDGEPORT—See DECATUR, TX

▲ **LAKE BROWNWOOD**—National Cable Inc.

▲ **LAKE CHEROKEE**—Friendship Cable of Texas Inc.

LAKE CITY—See MATHIS, TX

LAKE COLORADO CITY—See COLORADO CITY, TX

LAKE CONROE EAST—See WALDEN, TX

LAKE COUNTRY ESTATES—See AZLE, TX

LAKE DALLAS—See DENTON, TX

LAKE GRAHAM—See THROCKMORTON, TX

LAKE JACKSON—See HOUSTON, TX (Warner Cable Communications)

▲ **LAKE KIOWA**—North Texas Communications Co.

LAKE L. B. JOHNSON—See KINGSLAND, TX

LAKE LIVINGSTON—See CAROLINA COVE, TX

LAKE MEXIA—See MEXIA, TX

LAKE MURVAUL—See GARY, TX

▲ **LAKE PALESTINE**—Northland Cable TV

LAKE TANGLEWOOD—See ROCKWELL, TX

LAKE TAWAKONI—See QUINLAN, TX

▲ **LAKE THUNDERBIRD ESTATES**—BRDC Cablevision

LAKE TRAVIS—See LAKEWAY, TX

LAKE TYLER—See NEW CHAPEL HILL, TX

LAKE WHITNEY—See WHITNEY, TX

LAKE WORTH—See FORT WORTH, TX

▲ **LAKEHILLS**—TCI Cablevision of Texas

LAKEPORT—See LAKE CHEROKEE, TX

LAKESIDE—See AZLE, TX

LAKESIDE—See also MATHIS, TX

LAKESIDE CITY—See WICHITA FALLS, TX

▲ **LAKEWAY**—Cablevision of Lake Travis

LAKEWOOD—See OKLAHOMA, TX

LAKEWOOD VILLAGE—See PILOT POINT, TX

LAMAR COUNTY (unincorporated areas)—See PARIS, TX

▲ **LAMESA**—Northland Cable TV

▲ **LAMPASAS**—Classic Cable

LAMPASAS COUNTY—See LAMPASAS, TX

▲ **LANCASTER**—TCI TKR of the Metroplex Inc.

▲ **LANEVILLE**—Friendship Cable of Texas Inc.

LANGHAM COLONY—See HOUSTON, TX (Warner Cable Communications)

▲ **LANSING**—Friendship Cable of Texas Inc.

▲ **LAREDO**—Paragon Cable

LAS COLINAS—See IRVING, TX

▲ **LAS GALLINAS**—Friendship Cable of Texas Inc.

LAS MILPAS—See HIDALGO, TX

▲ **LASARA**—Torrence Cablevision

LATEXO—See GRAPELAND, TX

LAUGHLIN AFB—See DEL RIO, TX

▲ **LAVERNIA**—Comfort Cable Co.

LAVON—See JOSEPHINE, TX

▲ **LAWN**—Big Country Cablevision

LEAGUE CITY—See HOUSTON, TX (Warner Cable Communications)

▲ **LEANDER**—Cablevision of Leander

LEARY—See REDWATER, TX

▲ **LEFORS**—Classic Cable

▲ **LEON SPRINGS**—TCI Cablevision of Central Texas

LEON VALLEY—See SAN ANTONIO, TX

▲ **LEONA**—Mission Cable

▲ **LEONARD**—Friendship Cable of Texas Inc.

▲ **LEVELLAND**—CableComm

▲ **LEWISVILLE**—Paragon Cable

▲ **LEXINGTON**—Cable-Vision Ltd.

▲ **LIBERTY**—Time Warner Communications

LIBERTY CITY—See GLADEWATER, TX

LIBERTY COUNTY (portions)—See KENEFICK, TX

LIBERTY COUNTY (portions)—See also MOSS BLUFF, TX

LIBERTY COUNTY (portions)—See also PLUM GROVE, TX

LIBERTY COUNTY (southeastern portion)—See MONT BELVIEU, TX

▲ **LIBERTY HILL**—Time Warner Cable

LINDALE—See MINEOLA, TX

▲ **LINDEN**—Star Cable

LINDSAY—See MUENSTER, TX

LITTLE ELM—See PILOT POINT, TX

LITTLE FLOCK—See HOMER, TX

▲ **LITTLE RIVER-ACADEMY**—Centrovision Inc.

▲ **LITTLEFIELD**—Cablecomm

LIVE OAK—See SAN ANTONIO, TX

▲ **LIVERPOOL**—Star Cable

▲ **LIVINGSTON**—Cable One

LLANO COUNTY (portions)—See KINGSLAND, TX

▲ **LOCKHART**—Time Warner Entertainment/Advance-Newhouse

▲ **LOCKNEY**—Classic Cable

LOG CABIN ESTATES—See MALAKOFF, TX

▲ **LOLITA**—Koch Cable TV

▲ **LOMETA**—Post Cablevision of Texas Ltd.

LONE OAK—See QUINLAN, TX

LONE STAR—See DAINGERFIELD, TX

LONG MOUNTAIN ESTATES—See BUCHANAN DAM, TX

▲ **LONGVIEW**—Longview Cable Television

▲ **LOOP**—Torrence Cablevision

LOPEZVILLE—See PHARR, TX

▲ **LORAINE**—Cablecomm

▲ **LORENA**—Galaxy Cablevision

LORENA—See also GOLINDA, TX

▲ **LORENZO**—Classic Cable

LOS BARRERAS—See ROMA, TX

▲ **LOS FRESNOS**—Time Warner Communications

LOS MORENOS—See ROMA, TX

▲ **LOST PINES**—Friendship Cable of Texas Inc.

▲ **LOTT**—Galaxy Cablevision

▲ **LOUISE**—Mid Coast Cable TV

▲ **LOVELADY**—Friendship Cable of Texas Inc.

▲ **LOWRY CROSSING**—Friendship Cable of Texas Inc.

▲ **LUBBOCK**—Classic Cable

▲ **LUBBOCK**—Cox Communications

▲ **LUBBOCK COUNTY (southeastern portion)**—Classic Cable

LUBBOCK COUNTY (portions)—See WOODROW, TX

▲ **LUCAS**—Friendship Cable of Texas Inc.

▲ **LUEDERS**—Jayroc Cablevision

LUFKIN—See CORRIGAN, TX

▲ **LULING**—Time Warner Cable

LUMBERTON—See SILSBEE, TX

LYFORD—See RAYMONDVILLE, TX

▲ **LYONS**—Classic Cable

LYTLE—See DEVINE, TX

MABANK—See GUN BARREL CITY, TX

MADISON COUNTY—See MADISONVILLE, TX

▲ **MADISONVILLE**—Northland Cable

▲ **MAGNOLIA**—Friendship Cable of Texas

MAGNOLIA—See also HOUSTON, TX (Warner Cable Communications)

▲ **MALAKOFF**—Northland Cable TV

▲ **MALONE**—Torrence Cable Inc.

▲ **MANOR**—Mission Cable

▲ **MANSFIELD**—Charter Communications Inc.

MANVEL—See HEIGHTS, TX

MAPLE LEAF GARDENS—See HOUSTON, TX (Warner Cable Communications)

▲ **MARATHON**—Marathon TV Cable

▲ **MARBLE FALLS**—Northland Cable TV

▲ **MARFA**—Marfa TV Cable Co. Inc.

MARION—See SAN ANTONIO, TX

MARION COUNTY—See JEFFERSON, TX

MARKHAM—See BAY CITY, TX

▲ **MARLIN**—Northland Cable

▲ **MARSHALL**—Falcon Cable TV

MARSHALL CREEK—See TROPHY CLUB, TX

▲ **MART**—Friendship Cable of Texas Inc.

MARTINDALE—See SAN MARCOS, TX

▲ **MASON**—Classic Cable

MASON COUNTY—See MASON, TX

▲ **MATADOR**—Classic Cable

▲ **MATAGORDA**—Northland Cable TV

MATAGORDA COUNTY—See BAY CITY, TX

MATAGORDA COUNTY (portions)—See BLESSING, TX

▲ **MATHIS**—TCI Cablevision of Texas

▲ **MAUD**—TCA Cable TV

▲ **MAURICEVILLE**—Friendship Cable of Texas Inc.

MAVERICK COUNTY—See EAGLE PASS, TX

▲ **MAXWELL**—Torrence Cablevision

▲ **MAY**—Cable Ventures Inc.

MAYPEARL—See ALVARADO, TX

McALLEN—See PHARR, TX

McCAMEY—See SEMINOLE, TX

McCLENDON-CHISOLM—See TERRELL, TX

McGREGOR—See WACO, TX

▲ **McKINNEY**—TCI Cablevision of Texas Inc.

▲ **McLEAN**—Charter Communications Inc.

McLENNAN COUNTY—See LORENA, TX

McLENNAN COUNTY (portions)—See WACO, TX

MEADOW—See LUBBOCK, TX (Classic Cable)

MEADOW LAKE HEIGHTS—See GARFIELD, TX

MEADOWLAKES—See MARBLE FALLS, TX

▲ **MEDINA**—Advanced Cable

MEDINA COUNTY—See DEVINE, TX

MEDINA COUNTY—See also LA COSTE, TX

MELISSA—See ANNA, TX

MEMORIAL POINT—See SHEPHERD, TX

MEMORIAL THICKET—See HOUSTON, TX (Warner Cable Communications)

▲ **MEMPHIS**—Classic Cable

▲ **MENARD**—Classic Cable

MERCEDES—See WESLACO, TX

▲ **MERIDIAN**—Mission Cable

▲ **MERKEL**—Big Country Cablevision Inc.

▲ **MERTZON**—Classic Cable

▲ **MESQUITE**—TCI Cablevision of Dallas Inc.

▲ **MEXIA**—Northland Cable TV

▲ **MIAMI**—High Plains Cablevision

▲ **MIDLAND**—Cox Cable

MIDLAND COUNTY (portions)—See MIDLAND, TX

MIDLOTHIAN—See WAXAHACHIE, TX

▲ **MIDWAY**—Mission Cable

MILAM COUNTY (portions)—See CAMERON, TX

▲ **MILES**—TCA Cable TV

MILFORD—See WAXAHACHIE, TX

MILLS WALK—See HOUSTON, TX (Warner Cable Communications)

▲ **MILLSAP**—Mallard Cablevision

▲ **MINEOLA**—TCA Cable TV

▲ **MINERAL WELLS**—TCA Cable TV

MIRANDO CITY—See OILTON, TX

MISSION—See ALTON, TX

MISSION BEND—See HOUSTON, TX (Warner Cable Communications)

MISSION DORADO—See ODESSA, TX

MISSOURI CITY—See HOUSTON, TX (Warner Cable Communications)

MITCHELL COUNTY—See COLORADO CITY, TX

MOBILE CITY—See ROYSE CITY, TX

MODOT VILLAGE—See HOUSTON, TX (Warner Cable Communications)

▲ **MONAHANS**—Classic Cable

▲ **MONT BELVIEU**—Star Cable

▲ **MONTAGUE**—Classic Cable

▲ **MONTE ALTO**—Torrence Cablevision

▲ **MONTGOMERY**—Intermedia Cable

MONTGOMERY—See also WALDEN, TX

MONTGOMERY (unincorporated areas)—See CONROE WEST, TX

MONTGOMERY COUNTY—See CONROE, TX

MONTGOMERY COUNTY—See also HOUSTON, TX (Warner Cable Communications)

MONTGOMERY COUNTY—See also WALDEN, TX

MONTGOMERY COUNTY (portions)—See HOUSTON, TX (Phonoscope Ltd.)

▲ **MOODY**—Centrovision Inc.

MOON CITY—See EL PASO, TX

▲ **MORAN**—Double D Cable

▲ **MORGAN'S POINT RESORT**—Centrovision Inc.

MORGANS POINT—See HOUSTON, TX (Warner Cable Communications)

MORRIS COUNTY—See DAINGERFIELD, TX

▲ **MORTON**—Cablecomm

▲ **MOSS BLUFF**—Friendship Cable of Texas Inc.

▲ **MOULTON**—National Cable

▲ **MOUND**—National Cable Inc.

▲ **MOUNT ENTERPRISE**—Friendship Cable of Texas Inc.

▲ **MOUNT PLEASANT**—TCA Cable TV

▲ **MOUNT VERNON**—TCA Cable TV

MOUNTAIN CITY—See KYLE, TX

▲ **MUENSTER**—North Texas Communications Co.

▲ **MULESHOE**—Classic Cable

▲ **MUNDAY**—Harmon Cable Communications

MURCHISON—See BEN WHEELER, TX

MURPHY—See PLANO, TX

▲ **MUSTANG RIDGE**—Mission Cable

▲ **MYRTLE SPRINGS**—Friendship Cable of Texas Inc.

▲ **NACOGDOCHES**—Nacogdoches Cable TV

NACOGDOCHES COUNTY—See NACOGDOCHES, TX

NACOGDOCHES COUNTY (portions)—See WODEN, TX

NADA—See GARWOOD, TX

▲ **NAPLES**—Star Cable Co.

NASH—See TEXARKANA, TX

NASSAU BAY—See HOUSTON, TX (Warner Cable Communications)

NATALIA—See DEVINE, TX

▲ **NAVASOTA**—Northland Cable TV

▲ **NAZARETH**—High Plains Cablevision Inc.

NEDERLAND—See PORT ARTHUR, TX

NEEDVILLE—See HOUSTON, TX (Warner Cable Communications)

NEVADA—See JOSEPHINE, TX

▲ **NEW BOSTON**—TCA Cable TV

▲ **NEW BRAUNFELS**—Time Warner Cable

▲ **NEW CANEY**—Northland Cable TV

▲ **NEW CHAPEL HILL**—Northland Cable TV

NEW DEAL—See LUBBOCK, TX (Classic Cable)

NEW HOPE—See LOWRY CROSSING, TX

NEW LONDON—See ARP, TX

▲ **NEW SUMMERFIELD**—Friendship Cable of Texas Inc.

▲ **NEW ULM**—National Cable Inc.

NEWARK—See BOYD, TX

NEWCASTLE—See THROCKMORTON, TX

NEWTON—See KIRBYVILLE, TX

NEWTON COUNTY (portions)—See BROOKELAND, TX

▲ **NIXON**—Classic Cable

▲ **NOCONA**—Friendship Cable

NOLAN COUNTY (northern portion)—See SWEETWATER, TX

NOLANVILLE—See KILLEEN, TX

▲ **NOME**—Friendship Cable of Texas Inc.

NOONDAY—See FLINT, TX

NOONDAY—See also LAKE PALESTINE, TX

▲ **NORDHEIM**—National Cable Inc.

▲ **NORMANGEE**—Mission Cable

NORTH CLIFFE MANOR—See HOUSTON, TX (Warner Cable Communications)

NORTH PINES RANCHETTS—See HOUSTON, TX (Warner Cable Communications)

NORTH RICHLAND HILLS—See FORT WORTH, TX

▲ **NORTH SILSBEE**—Friendship Cable of Texas

NORTH VIDOR—See MAURICEVILLE, TX

▲ **NORTH ZULCH**—Mission Cable

NORTHCLIFFE—See GARDEN RIDGE, TX

NORTHCREST—See WACO, TX

▲ **NORTHEAST HAYS**—Time Warner Cable

NORTHWEST GREEN—See HOUSTON, TX

NORTHWEST PARK—See HOUSTON, TX

NUECES COUNTY—See CORPUS CHRISTI, TX

▲ **NURSERY**—National Cable Inc.

O'BRIEN—See KNOX CITY, TX

▲ **O'DONNELL**—Cablecomm

▲ **OAK GROVE**—Northland Cable

OAK LEAF—See WAXAHACHIE, TX

OAK POINT—See PILOT POINT, TX

OAK RIDGE—See TERRELL, TX

OAK RIDGE—See also GAINESVILLE, TX

OAK RIDGE—See also HORSESHOE BAY, TX

OAK RIDGE NORTH—See SPRING, TX

OAK TERRACE—See QUINLAN, TX

OAKLAND VILLAGE—See HOUSTON, TX

▲ **OAKWOOD**—Mission Cable

ODEM—See SAN PATRICIO, TX

▲ **ODESSA (western portion)**—US Cable of West Texas

▲ **ODESSA**—Cable One

▲ **OGLESBY**—Torrence Cablevision

▲ **OILTON**—TCI Cablevision of Texas Inc.

▲ **OKLAHOMA**—Friendship Cable of Texas Inc.

OLD RIVER-WINFREE—See MONT BELVIEU, TX

OLMITO—See BROWNSVILLE, TX

OLMOS PARK—See SAN ANTONIO, TX

▲ **OLNEY**—Friendship Cable of Texas Inc.

OLSON GREEN ACRES—See WILLOW PARK, TX

▲ **OLTON**—Classic Cable

OMAHA—See NAPLES, TX

OMEGA BAY—See HOUSTON, TX

ONALASKA—See SHEPHERD, TX

▲ **ORANGE**—Time Warner Communications

▲ **ORANGE GROVE**—TCI Cablevision of Texas

ORANGE GROVE—See also SAN CARLOS, TX

ORANGE GROVE (portions)—See ARROWHEAD ADDITION, TX

ORANGEFIELD—See MAURICEVILLE, TX

ORCHARD—See WALLIS, TX

▲ **ORE CITY**—Star Cable

OVERTON—See ARP, TX

OVILLA—See WAXAHACHIE, TX

OWENTOWN—See HAWKINS, TX

▲ **OYSTER CREEK**—Star Cable

▲ **OZONA**—Circle Bar Cable TV Inc.

PADDOCK—See HOUSTON, TX (created just for also serves)

▲ **PADUCAH**—Classic Cable

▲ **PALACIOS**—Falcon Cable TV

▲ **PALESTINE**—Paragon Cable

PALM HARBOR—See ARANSAS PASS, TX

PALM VALLEY—See HARLINGEN, TX

PALMER—See WAXAHACHIE, TX

PALMHURST—See ALTON, TX

PALMVIEW—See ALTON, TX

▲ **PALO PINTO**—Mallard Cablevision

PALO PINTO COUNTY—See MINERAL WELLS, TX

▲ **PAMPA**—Charter Communications Inc.

PANARAMA ESTATES—See QUINLAN, TX

PANHANDLE—See PAMPA, TX

PANORAMA VILLAGE—See CONROE, TX

PANTEGO—See ARLINGTON, TX

▲ **PARADISE**—Torrence Cablevision

▲ **PARIS**—TCA Cable TV

PARKER—See PLANO, TX

PARKER COUNTY—See AZLE, TX

PARKER COUNTY—See also WILLOW PARK, TX

PARKER COUNTY (portions)—See RENO (Parker County), TX

▲ **PARKWAY VILLAGE**—Warner Cable

PASADENA—See HOUSTON, TX

PATTON VILLAGE—See NEW CANEY, TX

PAYNE SPRINGS—See GUN BARREL CITY, TX

PEARLAND—See HEIGHTS, TX

PEARLAND—See also HOUSTON, TX

▲ **PEARSALL**—Time Warner Communications

▲ **PECAN GAP**—Torrence Cablevision

PECAN HILL—See WAXAHACHIE, TX

▲ **PECOS**—Classic Cable

▲ **PELICAN BAY**—SouthTel Communications LP

PENELOPE—See MALONE, TX

PENITAS—See SULLIVAN CITY, TX

▲ **PERRIN**—Mallard Cablevision

▲ **PERRYTON**—TCA Cable of Perryton

▲ **PETERSBURG**—Classic Cable

PETROLIA—See BYERS, TX

▲ **PETTUS**—Torrence Cablevision

▲ **PFLUGERVILLE**—Cablevision of Pflugerville Inc.

▲ **PHARR**—Time Warner Communications

PHILLIPS—See BORGER, TX

▲ **PILOT POINT**—Friendship Cable of Texas Inc.

PINE FOREST—See VIDOR, TX

PINEDALE—See HOUSTON, TX

PINEHURST—See MAGNOLIA, TX

PINEHURST—See also ORANGE, TX

▲ **PINELAND**—Star Cable

PINEY POINT—See HOUSTON, TX (Warner Cable Communications)

PIRATE BEACH—See HOUSTON, TX

PIRATE COVE—See HOUSTON, TX

▲ **PITTSBURG**—TCA Cable TV

▲ **PLACEDO**—Torrence Cablevision

▲ **PLAINS**—Classic Cable

▲ **PLAINVIEW**—TCA Cable TV

▲ **PLANO**—TCI of Plano Inc.

▲ **PLEAK**—Star Cable

▲ **PLEASANT VALLEY**—Rapid Cable

▲ **PLEASANTON**—Falcon Cable TV

▲ **PLUM GROVE**—Friendship Cable of Texas Inc.

POINT—See EMORY, TX

POINT BLANK—See SHEPHERD, TX

POINT COMFORT—See PORT LAVACA, TX

POINT ENTERPRISE—See MEXIA, TX

POLK COUNTY (portions)—See CORRIGAN, TX

POLK COUNTY (portions)—See also LIVINGSTON, TX

▲ **PONDER**—SouthTel Communications LP

PORT ACRES—See PORT ARTHUR, TX

▲ **PORT ARANSAS**—Falcon Cable TV

▲ **PORT ARANSAS**—Falcon Telecable

▲ **PORT ARTHUR**—Time Warner Communications

PORT BOLIVAR—See CRYSTAL BEACH, TX

▲ **PORT ISABEL**—Time Warner Communications

▲ **PORT LAVACA**—Cable One

PORT NECHES—See PORT ARTHUR, TX

▲ **PORT O'CONNOR**—TCI Cablevision of Texas

▲ **PORTER**—Friendship Cable of Texas Inc.

PORTER—See also KINGWOOD, TX

PORTER HEIGHTS—See NEW CANEY, TX

▲ **PORTLAND**—Falcon Cable TV

POSSUM KINGDOM LAKE—See JACKSBORO, TX

▲ **POST**—Classic Cable

▲ **POTEET**—Time Warner Communications

POTH—See FLORESVILLE, TX

▲ **POTOSI**—Jayroc Cablevision

▲ **POTTSBORO**—Friendship Cable of Texas Inc.

▲ **POWDERLY**—Friendship Cable of Texas Inc.

PRAIRIE LEA—See FENTRESS, TX

PRAIRIE VIEW—See WALLER, TX

▲ **PREMONT**—Heritage Cablevision of Texas Inc.

▲ **PRESIDIO**—Presidio TV Cable

▲ **PRESTON PENINSULA**—Mission Cable

▲ **PRICE**—Friendship Cable of Texas Inc.

PRIMERA—See HARLINGEN, TX

PRIMROSE—See SOMERSET, TX

PRINCETON—See WYLIE, TX

▲ **PROGRESO**—Rapid Cable

PROSPER—See PILOT POINT, TX

▲ **QUANAH**—Classic Cable

QUEEN CITY—See ATLANTA, TX

Queen City—See also LINDEN, TX

▲ **QUEMADO**—Time Warner Communications

▲ **QUINLAN**—Friendship Cable of Texas Inc.

▲ **QUITAQUE**—Classic Cable

QUITMAN—See MINEOLA, TX

RAINS COUNTY—See EMORY, TX

RAINS COUNTY (portions)—See QUINLAN, TX

▲ **RALLS**—Classic Cable

RANCHO VIEJO—See BROWNSVILLE, TX

▲ **RANDOLPH**—Torrence Cablevision

RANDOLPH AFB—See SAN ANTONIO, TX

RANGER—See EASTLAND, TX

RANKIN—See SEMINOLE, TX

RAYFORD FOREST—See SPRING, TX

▲ **RAYMONDVILLE**—Time Warner Communications

▲ **RAYWOOD**—Friendship Cable of Texas Inc.

▲ **REALITOS**—National Cable Inc.

▲ **RED ACKERS**—Northland Cable TV

RED OAK—See WAXAHACHIE, TX

RED RIVER ARMY DEPOT—See HOOKS, TX

REDLAND—See CENTRAL, TX

▲ **REDWATER**—Friendship Cable of Arkansas Inc.

REEVES COUNTY (portions)—See PECOS, TX

▲ **REFUGIO**—TCI Cablevision of Texas

REID ESTATES—See HOUSTON, TX

▲ **REKLAW**—Friendship Cable of Texas Inc.

RENDON—See BURLESON, TX

RENO (Lamar County)—See CLARKSVILLE, TX

RENO (Lamar County)—See also PARIS, TX

▲ **RENO (Parker** County)—Friendship Cable of Texas Inc.

RHOME—See BOYD, TX

▲ **RICARDO**—Ricardo Cable TV

▲ **RICE**—Northland Cable

▲ **RICHARDS**—Torrence Cablevision

RICHARDSON—See PLANO, TX

RICHLAND HILLS—See FORT WORTH, TX

▲ **RICHLAND SPRINGS**—Post Cablevision of Texas Ltd.

RICHMOND—See HOUSTON, TX

RICHWOOD—See HOUSTON, TX

▲ **RIESEL**—Cabletex Systems Inc.

RIO BRAVO—See LAREDO, TX

RIO DEL SOL—See BROWNSVILLE, TX

▲ **RIO GRANDE CITY**—Time Warner Communications

RIO HONDO—See HARLINGEN, TX

▲ **RIO VISTA**—National Cable Inc.

▲ **RISING STAR**—Brownwood TV Cable Service Inc.

▲ **RIVER OAKS (Tarrant County)**—Mallard Cablevision

▲ **RIVERSIDE**—Friendship Cable of Texas Inc.

▲ **RIVIERA**—Riviera Cable TV

ROANOKE—See TROPHY CLUB, TX

▲ **ROARING SPRINGS**—Classic Cable

▲ **ROBERT LEE**—West Texas Cablevision

ROBINSON—See WACO, TX

ROBSTOWN—See CORPUS CHRISTI, TX

▲ **ROBY**—Classic Cable

▲ **ROCHESTER**—Rochester Cablevision

ROCHESTER—See also PADUCAH, TX

▲ **ROCK SPRINGS**—Classic Cable

▲ **ROCKDALE**—Classic Cable

ROCKETT—See WAXAHACHIE, TX

▲ **ROCKPORT**—Falcon Cable TV

▲ **ROCKWALL**—Mission Cable

ROCKWALL COUNTY (portions)—See ROYSE CITY, TX

▲ **ROCKWELL**—TCA Cable of Amarillo

▲ **ROGERS**—Centrovision Inc.

ROLLING FORK—See HOUSTON, TX

ROLLING HILLS—See AMARILLO, TX

ROLLING OAKS—See QUINLAN, TX

ROLLINGWOOD—See AUSTIN, TX

▲ **ROMA**—Time Warner Communications

ROMAN FOREST—See NEW CANEY, TX

ROPESVILLE—See LUBBOCK, TX (Classic Cable)

▲ **ROSCOE**—Big Country Cablevision Inc.

▲ **ROSE CITY**—Friendship Cable of Texas

ROSE HILL—See CYPRESS, TX

▲ **ROSEBUD**—Rosebud Cable TV

ROSENBERG—See HOUSTON, TX

ROSITA—See ROMA, TX

▲ **ROTAN**—Friendship Cable of Texas Inc.

ROUND ROCK—See GRANADA HILLS, TX

ROWLETT—See GARLAND, TX

▲ **ROXTON**—TCA Cable

▲ **ROYSE CITY**—Friendship Cable Ltd.

RULE—See HASKELL, TX

RUNAWAY BAY—See DECATUR, TX

▲ **RUNGE**—Classic Cable

▲ **RUSK**—Friendship Cable of Texas Inc.

RUSK COUNTY—See HENDERSON, TX

▲ **SABINAL**—Falcon Cable TV

SABINE PASS—See PORT ARTHUR, TX

SACHSE—See WYLIE, TX

SADLER—See WHITESBORO, TX

SAGINAW—See FORT WORTH, TX

▲ **SALADO**—Centrovision Inc.

▲ **SAN ANGELO**—TCA of San Angelo

SAN ANGELO—See also GRAPE CREEK, TX

▲ **SAN ANTONIO**—Paragon Cable

▲ **SAN AUGUSTINE**—Friendship Cable of Texas Inc.

SAN BENITO—See HARLINGEN, TX

▲ **SAN CARLOS**—Rapid Cable

SAN DIEGO—See ALICE, TX

SAN JACINTO COUNTY (portions)—See WATERWOOD, TX

SAN JUAN (Hidalgo County)—See PHARR, TX

SAN LEANNA—See AUSTIN, TX

▲ **SAN LEON**—Star Cable

▲ **SAN MARCOS**—Time Warner Communications

▲ **SAN PATRICIO**—TCI Cablevision of Texas

▲ **SAN SABA**—Classic Cable

▲ **SAN YGNACIO**—TCI Cablevision of Texas Inc.

SANDERSON—See SEMINOLE, TX

▲ **SANDIA**—National Cable Inc.

SANGER—See PILOT POINT, TX

SANSOM PARK—See RIVER OAKS (Tarrant County), TX

▲ **SANTA ANNA**—Brownwood TV Cable Service Inc.

SANTA CRUZ—See LA GRULLA, TX

▲ **SANTA FE**—Star Cable

SANTA FE—See also HOUSTON, TX

▲ **SANTA MARIA/BLUETOWN**—Torrence Cablevision

SANTA ROSA—See HARLINGEN, TX

▲ **SANTO**—Mallard Cablevision

▲ **SARGENT**—Star Cable

SAVOY—See WHITEWRIGHT, TX

SCENIC OAKS—See SAN ANTONIO, TX

SCHERTZ—See SAN ANTONIO, TX

SCHULENBURG—See LA GRANGE, TX

SCURRY COUNTY—See SNYDER, TX

SEABROOK—See HOUSTON, TX

▲ **SEADRIFT**—TCI Cablevision of Texas

SEAGOVILLE—See TERRELL, TX

SEAGRAVES—See SEMINOLE, TX

SEALY—See BELLVILLE, TX

▲ **SEBASTIAN**—Rapid Cable

▲ **SEGUIN**—Communications Services Inc.

SELMA—See SAN ANTONIO, TX

▲ **SEMINOLE**—US Cable of West Texas

SEPCO PARK—See HOUSTON, TX

SETTLERS VILLAGE—See HOUSTON, TX

▲ **SEVEN POINTS**—Torrence Cablevision

SEVEN POINTS—See also GUN BARREL CITY, TX

▲ **SEYMOUR**—Friendship Cable of Texas Inc.

SHALLIMAR—See SOMERSET, TX

SHALLOWATER (unincorporated areas)—See LUBBOCK, TX (Classic Cable)

▲ **SHAMROCK**—Classic Cable

SHAVANO PARK—See SAN ANTONIO, TX

▲ **SHEFFIELD**—Sheffield TV Cable

SHENANDOAH—See SPRING, TX

SHENANDOAH (unincorporated areas)—See HOUSTON, TX

▲ **SHEPHERD**—Lakewood Cablevision

SHEPPARD AFB—See WICHITA FALLS, TX

▲ **SHERIDAN**—National Cable Inc.

▲ **SHERMAN**—Cable One

SHERWOOD—See MERTZON, TX

▲ **SHERWOOD SHORES**—Friendship Cable of Texas Inc.

SHILOH—See MEXIA, TX

▲ **SHINER**—Falcon Cable TV

SHOREACRES—See HOUSTON, TX

▲ **SIERRA BLANCA**—Sierra Cable TV

▲ **SILSBEE**—Cable Texas Inc.

▲ **SILVERTON**—Classic Cable

▲ **SINTON**—Falcon Cable TV

▲ **SKELLYTOWN**—Classic Cable

▲ **SLATON**—Cablecomm

SLEEPY HOLLOW—See ELMO, TX

▲ **SMILEY**—National Cable Inc.

SMITH COUNTY—See MINEOLA, TX

SMITH COUNTY—See also TYLER, TX

SMITH COUNTY (unincorporated areas)—See DIXIE, TX

SMITH COUNTY (unincorporated areas)—See also NEW CHAPEL HILL, TX

SMITHVILLE—See GRANADA HILLS, TX

SMYER—See LUBBOCK, TX (Classic Cable)

▲ **SNOOK**—National Cable Inc.

▲ **SNYDER**—TCA Cable TV

SOCORRO—See EL PASO, TX

▲ **SOMERSET**—TCI Cablevision of Texas Inc.

SOMERVELL—See GRANBURY, TX

SOMERVILLE—See LYONS, TX

SOMMERALL—See HOUSTON, TX

▲ **SONORA**—Classic Cable

▲ **SOUR LAKE**—Timberlake Cablevision Inc.

SOUTH CREEK—See HOUSTON, TX

SOUTH HOUSTON—See HOUSTON, TX

▲ **SOUTH PADRE ISLAND**—Time Warner Communications

▲ **SOUTH SHORES**—Cable Ventures

▲ **SOUTH SILSBEE**—Friendship Cable of Texas Inc.

SOUTH TAWAKONI—See QUINLAN, TX

▲ **SOUTH WEATHERFORD**—Charter Communications Inc.

SOUTHLAKE—See FORT WORTH, TX

SOUTHLAKE—See also TROPHY CLUB, TX

▲ **SPEARMAN**—Classic Cable

▲ **SPICEWOOD BEACH**—Post Cablevision of Texas Ltd.

▲ **SPLENDORA**—Friendship Cable of Texas Inc.

SPLENDORA—See also NEW CANEY, TX

▲ **SPRING**—Cablevision Communications

SPRING FOREST—See SPRING, TX

SPRING HILLS—See SPRING, TX

SPRING OAKS—See SPRING, TX

SPRING VALLEY—See HOUSTON, TX (Warner Cable Communications)

SPRING VALLEY CREEK—See HOUSTON, TX

▲ **SPRINGTOWN**—Southwest Cablevision

▲ **SPUR**—Classic Cable

SPURGER—See WOODVILLE, TX

▲ **ST. FRANCIS VILLAGE**—Torrence Cablevision

▲ **ST. JO**—Classic Cable

ST. PAUL—See WYLIE, TX

STAFFORD—See HOUSTON, TX (Warner Cable Communications)

▲ **STAMFORD**—Harmon Cable Communications

▲ **STANTON**—Cablecomm

STAR HARBOR—See MALAKOFF, TX

STARR COUNTY—See ROMA, TX

▲ **STEPHENVILLE**—Northland Cable TV

▲ **STERLING CITY**—Classic Cable

STINNETT—See BORGER, TX

▲ **STOCKDALE**—TCI Cablevision of Texas Inc.

STONE CREEK—See HOUSTON, TX

▲ **STONEBRIDGE RANCH**—TCI Cablevision of Texas Inc.

STONEHENGE—See HOUSTON, TX

STONY POINT—See GARFIELD, TX

▲ **STRATFORD**—Classic Cable

▲ **STRAWN**—Strawn TV Cable Inc.

SUDAN—See MULESHOE, TX

SUFFOLK CHASE—See HOUSTON, TX

SUGAR LAND—See HOUSTON, TX

▲ **SULLIVAN CITY**—Time Warner Communications

▲ **SULPHUR SPRINGS**—TCA Cable TV

▲ **SUNDOWN**—Classic Cable

SUNDOWN—See also HOUSTON, TX

SUNNYVALE—See GARLAND, TX

SUNRAY—See DUMAS, TX

SUNRISE BEACH—See KINGSLAND, TX

SUNSET VALLEY—See AUSTIN, TX

SURFSIDE BEACH—See OYSTER CREEK, TX

▲ **SWEENY**—Falcon Cable TV

▲ **SWEETWATER**—TCA Cable TV

SWISS ALPINE VILLAGE—See GARFIELD, TX

TAFT—See ARANSAS PASS, TX

▲ **TAHOKA**—Cablecomm

TALCO—See CLARKSVILLE, TX

TALLOWOOD—See HOUSTON, TX

TARRANT COUNTY—See AZLE, TX

TARRANT COUNTY (portions)—See BURLESON, TX

TATUM—See LAKE CHEROKEE, TX

▲ **TAYLOR**—Cablevision of Taylor

TAYLOR—See also GRANADA HILLS, TX

TAYLOR COUNTY (northern portion)—See ABILENE, TX

TAYLOR LAKE VILLAGE—See HOUSTON, TX

TEAGUE—See FAIRFIELD, TX

TEHUACANA—See MEXIA, TX

▲ **TEMPLE**—Centrovision Inc.

▲ **TEMPLE**—Time Warner Cable

▲ **TENAHA**—Friendship Cable of Texas Inc.

▲ **TERRELL**—Friendship Cable Ltd.

TERRELL HILLS—See SAN ANTONIO, TX

TERRY COUNTY—See BROWNFIELD, TX

▲ **TEXARKANA**—Cable One

TEXAS CITY—See HOUSTON, TX

▲ **TEXHOMA**—Texhoma Cable TV

▲ **TEXLINE**—Fanch Communications

▲ **THE COLONY**—TCI Cablevision of Texas Inc.

THE MEADOWS—See HOUSTON, TX (Warner Cable Communications)

THE WOODLANDS—See HOUSTON, TX

▲ **THE WOODS**—Classic Cable

▲ **THORNDALE**—Time Warner Cable

THORNHILL APARTMENTS—See HOUSTON, TX

▲ **THORNTON**—Thornton Cable TV

THORNTONVILLE—See MONAHANS, TX

THRALL—See THORNDALE, TX

▲ **THREE RIVERS**—Falcon Cable TV

▲ **THROCKMORTON**—Friendship Cable

▲ **THUNDERBIRD BAY**—Cable Ventures Ltd.

TIKI ISLAND—See HOUSTON, TX

▲ **TILDEN**—Falcon Cable TV

TIMBER RIDGE—See SPRING, TX

TIMBERWOOD PARK—See SAN ANTONIO, TX

▲ **TIMPSON**—Friendship Cable of Texas Inc.

TIOGA—See PILOT POINT, TX

TITUS COUNTY (portions)—See MOUNT PLEASANT, TX

TOLAR—See GRANBURY, TX

▲ **TOLEDO VILLAGE**—Friendship Cable of Texas Inc.

TOM BEAN—See WHITEWRIGHT, TX

TOM GREEN COUNTY—See ROBERT LEE, TX

TOMBALL—See HOUSTON, TX

TOMBALL—See also MAGNOLIA, TX

TOOL—See GUN BARREL CITY, TX

▲ **TRENT**—Jayroc Cablevision

▲ **TRENTON**—Northland Cable TV

TRI-LAKE ESTATES—See WALDEN, TX

TRINIDAD—See MALAKOFF, TX

▲ **TRINITY**—Friendship Cable of Texas Inc.

▲ **TROPHY CLUB**—Charter Communications Inc.

TROUP—See ARP, TX

▲ **TROY**—Centrovision Inc.

▲ **TRUMBULL**—Time Warner Cable

▲ **TULETA**—National Cable Inc.

▲ **TULIA**—Classic Cable

▲ **TURKEY**—High Plains Cablevision Inc.

TURNERTOWN—See ARP, TX

TURTLE COVE—See OYSTER CREEK, TX

TURTLE LAKE—See HOUSTON, TX

▲ **TUSCOLA**—Big Country Cablevision Inc.

TWIN VALLEY—See SOMERSET, TX

TYE—See ABILENE, TX

▲ **TYLER**—TCA Cable TV

UNION GROVE—See GLADEWATER, TX

UNIVERSAL CITY—See SAN ANTONIO, TX

▲ **UNIVERSITY PARK**—Charter Communications Inc.

▲ **UVALDE**—Time Warner Communications

UVALDE COUNTY (portions)—See UVALDE, TX

▲ **VALENTINE**—Valentine TV Cable

▲ **VALLEY MILLS**—Mission Cable

▲ **VALLEY VIEW**—North Texas Communications Co.

VAN—See BEN WHEELER, TX

VAN ALSTYNE—See WHITEWRIGHT, TX

VAN HORN—See SEMINOLE, TX

VAN VLECK—See BAY CITY, TX

VAN ZANDT COUNTY—See MINEOLA, TX

VAN ZANDT COUNTY (portions)—See BEN WHEELER, TX

VANDERBILT—See LOLITA, TX

▲ **VEGA**—Gruver Cablevision Inc.

VENUS—See ALVARADO, TX

▲ **VERNON**—Friendship Cable of Texas Inc.

VICKSBURG—See SPRING, TX

▲ **VICTORIA**—TCA Cable TV

VICTORIA COUNTY (unincorporated areas)—See VICTORIA, TX

▲ **VIDOR**—Warner Cable

▲ **VIDOR (southern portion)**—Friendship Cable of Texas

▲ **WACO**—Time Warner Cable

▲ **WAELDER**—National Cable

WAKE VILLAGE—See TEXARKANA, TX

▲ **WALDEN**—Lakewood Cablevision

WALKER COUNTY—See HUNTSVILLE, TX

▲ **WALLER**—Northland Cable

WALLER COUNTY—See HOUSTON, TX

▲ **WALLIS**—Star Cable

▲ **WALNUT SPRINGS**—National Cable Inc.

WARD COUNTY—See MONAHANS, TX

WARREN—See WOODVILLE, TX

WARREN CITY—See GLADEWATER, TX

WASHINGTON COUNTY (portions)—See BRENHAM, TX

WASKOM—See SHREVEPORT, LA

WATAUGA—See FORT WORTH, TX

▲ **WATERWOOD**—Northland Cable

▲ **WAXAHACHIE**—Charter Communications Inc.

▲ **WEATHERFORD**—Charter Communications Inc.

WEATHERFORD (unincorporated areas)—See GREEN ACRES/ZION HILL, TX

WEBB COUNTY—See LAREDO, TX

UTAH

▲ **ENOCH**—Blackstone Cable LLC

▲ **ENTERPRISE**—Blackstone Cable LLC

▲ **EPHRAIM**—Peak Cablevision

▲ **ESCALANTE**—B & L Cable

▲ **EUREKA**—Blackstone Cable LLC

FAIRVIEW—See MOUNT PLEASANT, UT

▲ **FARMINGTON**—AT&T Cable Services

FARR WEST—See HOOPER, UT

▲ **FERRON**—Peak Cablevision

▲ **FIELDING**—AT&T Cable Services

▲ **FILLMORE**—Peak Cablevision

FOUNTAIN GREEN—See MORONI, UT

FRANCIS—See KAMAS, UT

▲ **FRUIT HEIGHTS**—AT&T Cable Services

FRUIT HEIGHTS—See also FARMINGTON, UT

GARDEN CITY—See FISH HAVEN, ID

GARLAND—See TREMONTON, UT

▲ **GLENWOOD**—Blackstone Cable LLC

▲ **GOSHEN**—Blackstone Cable LLC

GRAND COUNTY—See MOAB, UT

▲ **GRANTSVILLE**—TCI Cablevision of Utah Inc.

▲ **GREEN RIVER**—Falcon Telecable

▲ **GUNNISON**—Peak Cablevision

HARRISBURG JUNCTION—See LEEDS, UT

HARRISVILLE—See RIVERDALE, UT

▲ **HEBER CITY**—TCI Cablevision of Utah Inc.

HELPER—See PRICE, UT

HERRIMAN—See SALT LAKE CITY, UT

HIGHLAND—See SANDY, UT

HILL AFB—See FARMINGTON, UT

HONEYVILLE—See BEAR RIVER CITY, UT

▲ **HOOPER**—AT&T Cable Services

HOYTSVILLE—See COALVILLE, UT

HUNTINGTON—See CASTLE DALE, UT

▲ **HUNTSVILLE**—Colonial Cablevision

▲ **HURRICANE**—Falcon Telecable

HYDE PARK—See LOGAN, UT

HYRUM—See LOGAN, UT

▲ **IVINS**—Enstar Cable TV

JEREMY RANCH—See PARK CITY, UT

▲ **KAMAS**—All West Inc.

▲ **KANAB**—Peak Cablevision

▲ **KANARRAVILLE**—Blackstone Cable LLC

KAYSVILLE—See FARMINGTON, UT

KEARNS—See WEST VALLEY CITY, UT

LA VERKIN—See HURRICANE, UT

LAYTON—See FARMINGTON, UT

LAYTON—See also HOOPER, UT

▲ **LEEDS**—Falcon Cablevision

LEHI—See SANDY, UT

▲ **LEWISTON**—TCI Cablevision of Utah Inc.

LINDON—See SANDY, UT

LOA—See LYMAN, UT

▲ **LOGAN**—Charter Communications

▲ **LYMAN**—Blackstone Cable LLC

MAGNA—See WEST VALLEY CITY, UT

▲ **MANILA**—Myvocom Inc.

MANTI—See EPHRAIM, UT

MAPLETON—See SANDY, UT

MARION—See KAMAS, UT

MENDON—See LOGAN, UT

MIDVALE—See SALT LAKE CITY, UT

MIDVALE (western portion)—See SANDY, UT

MIDWAY—See HEBER CITY, UT

▲ **MILFORD**—Peak Cablevision

MILLVILLE—See LOGAN, UT

▲ **MINERSVILLE**—Peak Cablevision

▲ **MOAB**—Peak Cablevision

▲ **MONA**—Blackstone Cable LLC

▲ **MONROE**—Blackstone Cable LLC

▲ **MONTICELLO**—Peak Cablevision

▲ **MORGAN CITY**—AT&T Cable Services

▲ **MORGAN COUNTY**—TCI Cablevision of Utah Inc.

▲ **MORONI**—Peak Cablevision

▲ **MOUNT PLEASANT**—Peak Cablevision

MURRAY—See SALT LAKE CITY, UT

NAPLES—See VERNAL, UT

▲ **NEPHI**—TCI Cablevision of Utah Inc.

▲ **NEW HARMONY**—Blackstone Cable LLC

NEWTON—See LOGAN, UT

NIBLEY—See LOGAN, UT

NORTH LOGAN—See LOGAN, UT

NORTH OGDEN—See RIVERDALE, UT

NORTH SALT LAKE—See FARMINGTON, UT

OAKLEY—See KAMAS, UT

OGDEN—See HOOPER, UT

OGDEN—See also RIVERDALE, UT

OGDEN CANYON—See RIVERDALE, UT

ORANGEVILLE—See CASTLE DALE, UT

OREM—See SANDY, UT

▲ **PANGUITCH**—Blackstone Cable LLC

PARADISE—See LOGAN, UT

▲ **PARAGONAH**—Blackstone Cable LLC

▲ **PARK CITY**—TCI Cablevision of Utah Inc.

▲ **PAROWAN**—Blackstone Cable LLC

PAYSON—See SALEM, UT

PEOA—See KAMAS, UT

PERRY—See BRIGHAM CITY, UT

PLAIN CITY—See HOOPER, UT

PLEASANT GROVE—See SANDY, UT

PLEASANT VIEW—See HOOPER, UT

PLYMOUTH—See FIELDING, UT

▲ **PRICE**—Peak Cablevision

PROVIDENCE—See LOGAN, UT

▲ **PROVO**—TCI Cablevision of Utah Inc.

▲ **RANDOLPH**—All West Inc.

REDMOND—See SALINA, UT

▲ **RICHFIELD**—Peak Cablevision

▲ **RICHMOND**—TCI Cablevision of Utah Inc.

RIVER HEIGHTS—See LOGAN, UT

▲ **RIVERDALE**—AT&T Cable Services

Riverside—See FIELDING, UT

RIVERTON—See SALT LAKE CITY, UT

▲ **ROCKVILLE**—Falcon Telecable

RON CLAIR—See RIVERDALE, UT

▲ **ROOSEVELT**—Peak Cablevision

ROY—See RIVERDALE, UT

▲ **SALEM**—TCI Cablevision of Utah Inc.

▲ **SALINA**—Peak Cablevision

▲ **SALT LAKE CITY**—TCI Cablevision of Utah Inc.

SALT LAKE COUNTY—See SALT LAKE CITY, UT

SALT LAKE COUNTY (portions)—See WEST VALLEY CITY, UT

▲ **SANDY**—TCI Cablevision

SANDY (eastern portion)—See SALT LAKE CITY, UT

SANPETE COUNTY—See MOUNT PLEASANT, UT

SANTA CLARA—See ST. GEORGE, UT

▲ **SANTAQUIN**—Blackstone Cable LLC

SEVIER COUNTY—See SALINA, UT

SMITHFIELD—See RICHMOND, UT

SOMERSET CONDOMINIUMS—See FARMINGTON, UT

SOUTH JORDAN—See SALT LAKE CITY, UT

SOUTH OGDEN—See RIVERDALE, UT

SOUTH SALT LAKE CITY—See SALT LAKE CITY, UT

SOUTH WEBER—See RIVERDALE, UT

SPANISH FORK—See PROVO, UT

SPANISH FORK CITY—See SALEM, UT

SPRING CITY—See MOUNT PLEASANT, UT

SPRING LAKE—See SALEM, UT

SPRINGDALE—See ROCKVILLE, UT

SPRINGVILLE—See SANDY, UT

▲ **ST. GEORGE**—Falcon Telecable

▲ **STANSBURY PARK**—TCI Cablevision of Utah Inc.

SUMMIT COUNTY—See PARK CITY, UT

SUMMIT COUNTY (portions)—See COALVILLE, UT

SUNNYSIDE—See EAST CARBON, UT

SUNSET—See FARMINGTON, UT

SYRACUSE—See HOOPER, UT

TAYLORSVILLE—See WEST VALLEY CITY, UT

▲ **TOOELE**—TCI Cablevision of Utah Inc.

TOOELE ARMY DEPOT—See TOOELE, UT

TOOELE COUNTY—See GRANTSVILLE, UT

TOOELE COUNTY—See also TOOELE, UT

TOQUERVILLE—See HURRICANE, UT

▲ **TREMONTON**—AT&T Cable Services

UINTAH CITY—See RIVERDALE, UT

UTAH COUNTY—See SALEM, UT

UTAH COUNTY (portions)—See PROVO, UT

UTAH COUNTY (unincorporated areas)—See SANDY, UT

▲ **VERNAL**—Peak Cablevision

WASATCH COUNTY—See HEBER CITY, UT

WASHINGTON—See ST. GEORGE, UT

WASHINGTON COUNTY (unincorporated areas)—See NEW HARMONY, UT

WASHINGTON TERRACE—See RIVERDALE, UT

WEBER COUNTY (portions)—See HOOPER, UT

WEBER COUNTY (portions)—See also RIVERDALE, UT

WELLINGTON—See PRICE, UT

WELLSVILLE—See LOGAN, UT

▲ **WENDOVER**—TCI Cablevision of Utah Inc.

WENDOVER—See also WENDOVER, NV

WEST BOUNTIFUL—See FARMINGTON, UT

WEST HAVEN—See HOOPER, UT

WEST JORDAN—See SANDY, UT

WEST OGDEN—See RIVERDALE, UT

WEST POINT—See HOOPER, UT

▲ **WEST VALLEY CITY**—TCI Cablevision of Utah Inc.

▲ **WILLARD**—AT&T Cable Services

WOODRUFF—See RANDOLPH, UT

WOODS CROSS—See FARMINGTON, UT

VERMONT

* **ALBANY TWP.**—FrontierVision Partners LP

* **ALBURG TWP.**—FrontierVision Partners LP

ARLINGTON—See MANCHESTER, VT

ASCUTNEY—See CLAREMONT, NH

ATHENS—See GRAFTON, VT

* **BAKERSFIELD TWP.**—FrontierVision Partners LP

* **BARNARD TWP.**—FrontierVision Partners LP

BARNET—See ST. JOHNSBURY, VT

* **BARNET TWP.**—FrontierVision Partners LP

▲ **BARRE**—Helicon Cable Communications

BARRE (town)—See BARRE, VT

BARTON—See NEWPORT, VT

BEEBE PLAIN—See NEWPORT, VT

▲ **BELLOWS FALLS**—Adelphia Cable

▲ **BENNINGTON**—Better TV Inc. of Bennington

BERKSHIRE—See ENOSBURG FALLS, VT

BERLIN—See BARRE, VT

BERLIN—See also MONTPELIER, VT

BETHEL—See MONTPELIER, VT

BIRCH HILL—See MANCHESTER, VT

* **BLOOMFIELD TWP.**—FrontierVision Partners LP

BOMOSEEN—See FAIR HAVEN, VT

BONDVILLE—See MANCHESTER, VT

▲ **BRADFORD**—Helicon Cablevision

BRADFORD TWP.—See ST. JOHNSBURY, VT

▲ **BRAINTREE**—Adelphia Communications Corp.

BRANDON TWP.—See RUTLAND, VT

▲ **BRATTLEBORO**—Adelphia Cable

BRIDGEWATER—See MOUNT ASCUTNEY, VT

BRISTOL—See SHELBURNE, VT

BRISTOL VILLAGE—See SHELBURNE, VT

BURKE—See ST. JOHNSBURY, VT

BURKE HOLLOW—See ST. JOHNSBURY, VT

▲ **BURLINGTON**—Adelphia Cable

Cabot—See MONTPELIER, VT

* **CABOT TWP.**—FrontierVision Partners LP

Calais—See MONTPELIER, VT

CAMBRIDGE—See JEFFERSONVILLE, VT

CAMBRIDGE (town)—See JEFFERSONVILLE, VT

CAMBRIDGE JUNCTION—See JEFFERSONVILLE, VT

CAMBRIDGEPORT—See GRAFTON, VT

CANAAN—See WEST STEWARTSTOWN, NH

CASTLETON—See FAIR HAVEN, VT

CASTLETON CORNERS—See FAIR HAVEN, VT

CAVENDISH—See MOUNT ASCUTNEY, VT

* **CHARLESTON TWP.**—FrontierVision Partners LP

CHARLOTTE—See SHELBURNE, VT

▲ **CHELSEA**—Helicon Cablevision

CHELSEA TWP.—See BARRE, VT

CHESTER—See MOUNT ASCUTNEY, VT

CHESTER DEPOT (village)—See MOUNT ASCUTNEY, VT

CHITTENDEN—See PITTSFORD, VT

CLARENDON TWP.—See RUTLAND, VT

COLCHESTER—See MILTON, VT

COLCHESTER (portions)—See BURLINGTON, VT

CONCORD—See ST. JOHNSBURY, VT

* **COVENTRY TWP.**—FrontierVision Partners LP

DANBY—See RUTLAND, VT

DANVILLE (town)—See ST. JOHNSBURY, VT

DERBY CENTER—See NEWPORT, VT

DERBY LINE—See NEWPORT, VT

DORSET—See MANCHESTER, VT

DUXBURY—See MONTPELIER, VT

DUXBURY TWP.—See MONTPELIER, VT

EAST ARLINGTON—See MANCHESTER, VT

EAST BARRE—See BARRE, VT

EAST BURKE—See ST. JOHNSBURY, VT

▲ **EAST CORINTH**—Olsen TV

EAST DORSET—See MANCHESTER, VT

EAST HARDWICK—See HARDWICK, VT

EAST MIDDLEBURY—See BURLINGTON, VT

EAST MONTPELIER—See MONTPELIER, VT

* **EAST MONTPELIER TWP.**—FrontierVision Partners LP

EAST POULTNEY—See FAIR HAVEN, VT

EAST RYEGATE—See ST. JOHNSBURY, VT

EAST ST. JOHNSBURY—See ST. JOHNSBURY, VT

ENOSBURG—See ENOSBURG FALLS, VT

▲ **ENOSBURG FALLS**—North Country Cablevision Inc.

ESSEX—See BURLINGTON, VT

ESSEX JUNCTION—See BURLINGTON, VT

▲ **FAIR HAVEN**—Adelphia Communications Corp.

* **FAIRFAX TWP.**—FrontierVision Partners LP

* **FAIRLEE TWP.**—FrontierVision Partners LP

FAYSTON—See WAITSFIELD, VT

FERRISBURG—See SHELBURNE, VT

* **FLETCHER TWP.**—FrontierVision Partners LP

FOREST DALE—See RUTLAND, VT

GEORGIA—See MILTON, VT

GLOVER—See NEWPORT, VT

▲ **GRAFTON**—Adelphia Cable

* **GRAND ISLE TWP.**—FrontierVision Parners LP

GRANITEVILLE—See BARRE, VT

GROTON—See ST. JOHNSBURY, VT

* **GUILFORD TWP.**—FrontierVision Partners LP

▲ **HARDWICK**—FrontierVision

HARTFORD—See LEBANON, NH

HARTLAND (portions)—See LEBANON, NH

* **HARTLAND TWP.**—FrontierVision Partners LP

HUNTINGTON TWP.—See SHELBURNE, VT

HYDE PARK—See MORRISVILLE, VT

HYDEVILLE—See FAIR HAVEN, VT

* **IRASBURG TWP.**—FrontierVision Partners LP

ISLAND POND—See NEWPORT, VT

▲ **JACKSONVILLE**—Area Telecable

* **JAMAICA TWP.**—FrontierVision Partners LP

▲**JEFFERSONVILLE**—Jeffersonville Cable TV Corp.

JERICHO—See RICHMOND, VT

JOHNSON—See MORRISVILLE, VT

▲ **KILLINGTON**—Adelphia Communications Corp.

KIRBY—See ST. JOHNSBURY, VT

LEMINGTON—See WEST STEWARTSTOWN, NH

* **LONDONDERRY TWP.**—FrontierVision Partners LP

LONDONDERRY TWP.—See also WESTON, VT

LUDLOW—See MOUNT ASCUTNEY, VT

* **LUNENBURG TWP.**—FrontierVision Partners LP

LYNDON—See ST. JOHNSBURY, VT

LYNDON CENTER—See ST. JOHNSBURY, VT

LYNDON CORNERS—See ST. JOHNSBURY, VT

LYNDONVILLE—See ST. JOHNSBURY, VT

▲ **MANCHESTER**—Adelphia Communications Corp.

MARSHFIELD TWP.—See BARRE, VT

Marshfield Twp.—See also MONTPELIER, VT

McINDOES—See ST. JOHNSBURY, VT

MENDON (portions)—See KILLINGTON, VT

MENDON TWP.—See RUTLAND, VT

▲ **MIDDLEBURY**—Mountain Cable Co.

MIDDLESEX—See MONTPELIER, VT

* **MIDDLETOWN SPRINGS TWP.**—FrontierVision Partners LP

▲ **MILTON**—Adelphia Cable

▲ **MONTPELIER**—Adelphia Cable Communications

MORETOWN—See WAITSFIELD, VT

MORETOWN—See also MONTPELIER, VT

MORETOWN TWP.—See MONTPELIER, VT

MORRISTOWN—See MORRISVILLE, VT

▲**MORRISVILLE**—FrontierVision

▲ **MOUNT ASCUTNEY**—Adelphia Cable

MOUNT TABOR—See RUTLAND, VT

MOUNTAIN LAKES—See ST. JOHNSBURY, VT

NEWBURY—See ST. JOHNSBURY, VT

▲ **NEWFANE**—Southern Vermont Cable Co.

NEWFANE HILL—See NEWFANE, VT

▲ **NEWPORT**—Adelphia Cable

NEWPORT CENTER—See NEWPORT, VT

* **NEWPORT TWP.**—FrontierVision Partners LP

NORTH BENNINGTON—See BENNINGTON, VT

NORTH DANVILLE—See ST. JOHNSBURY, VT

NORTH HYDE PARK—See MORRISVILLE, VT

North Troy—See NEWPORT, VT

NORTH WESTMINSTER—See BELLOWS FALLS, VT

NORTHFIELD (town)—See NORTHFIELD (village), VT

▲ **NORTHFIELD (village)**—Trans-Video Inc.

NORWICH—See LEBANON, NH

OLD BENNINGTON—See BENNINGTON, VT

ORANGE—See BARRE, VT

ORANGE (town)—See BARRE, VT

ORLEANS—See NEWPORT, VT

* **ORWELL TWP.**—FrontierVision Partners LP

PASSUMPSIC—See ST. JOHNSBURY, VT

▲ **PAWLET**—Adelphia Communications Corp.

PEACHAM—See ST. JOHNSBURY, VT

* **PEACHAM TWP.**—FrontierVision Partners LP

PERKINSVILLE—See MOUNT ASCUTNEY, VT

PERU TWP.—See MANCHESTER, VT

▲ **PITTSFORD**—Adelphia Communications Corp.

PITTSFORD (village)—See PITTSFORD, VT

PLAINFIELD TWP.—See BARRE, VT

Plainfield Twp.—See also MONTPELIER, VT

PLYMOUTH—See MOUNT ASCUTNEY, VT

POULTNEY—See FAIR HAVEN, VT

POWNAL—See BENNINGTON, VT

PROCTOR TWP.—See RUTLAND, VT

PROCTORSVILLE—See MOUNT ASCUTNEY, VT

▲ **PUTNEY**—Southern Vermont Cable Co.

QUECHEE—See LEBANON, NH

RANDOLPH—See BRAINTREE, VT

RANDOLPH—See also MONTPELIER, VT

▲ **READING**—Adelphia Communications Corp.

READSBORO—See CHARLEMONT, MA

RICHFORD—See ENOSBURG FALLS, VT

▲ **RICHMOND**—Adelphia Cable

RIVERTON—See NORTHFIELD (village), VT

▲ **ROCHESTER**—Mountain Cable Co.

ROCKINGHAM—See BELLOWS FALLS, VT

* **RUPERT TWP.**—FrontierVision Partners LP

▲ **RUTLAND**—Adelphia Cable

RUTLAND (city)—See RUTLAND, VT

RUTLAND COUNTY—See GRANVILLE, NY

RUTLAND TWP.—See RUTLAND, VT

RYEGATE—See ST. JOHNSBURY, VT

* **RYEGATE TWP.**—FrontierVision Partners LP

SANDGATE—See MANCHESTER, VT

SAXTONS RIVER—See GRAFTON, VT

SHAFTSBURY—See BENNINGTON, VT

SHEFFIELD—See ST. JOHNSBURY, VT

▲ **SHELBURNE**—Adelphia Cable

SHERBURNE (town)—See KILLINGTON, VT

SOUTH BURLINGTON—See BURLINGTON, VT

SOUTH DORSET—See MANCHESTER, VT

SOUTH LONDONDERRY—See WESTON, VT

SOUTH NEWFANE—See NEWFANE, VT

SOUTH ROYALTON—See BARRE, VT

SOUTH RYEGATE—See ST. JOHNSBURY, VT

SPRINGFIELD—See MOUNT ASCUTNEY, VT

▲ **ST. ALBANS (city)**—FrontierVision

ST. ALBANS TWP.—See ST. ALBANS (city), VT

ST. GEORGE (town)—See BURLINGTON, VT

▲ **ST. JOHNSBURY**—Helicon Cable Communications

ST. JOHNSBURY CENTER—See ST. JOHNSBURY, VT

* **STAMFORD TWP.**—FrontierVision Partners LP

STARKSBORO TWP.—See SHELBURNE, VT

▲ **STOWE**—Stowe Cablevision

STRATTON—See MANCHESTER, VT

STRATTON MOUNTAIN—See MANCHESTER, VT

SUNDERLAND—See MANCHESTER, VT

SUNRISE—See MOUNT ASCUTNEY, VT

SUTTON—See ST. JOHNSBURY, VT

SWANTON (village)—See ST. ALBANS (city), VT

SWANTON TWP.—See ST. ALBANS (city), VT

TAFTSVILLE—See MOUNT ASCUTNEY, VT

* **THETFORD TWP.**—FrontierVision Partners LP

* **TOWNSHEND TWP.**—FrontierVision Partners LP

* **TROY TWP.**—FrontierVision Partners LP

TUNBRIDGE TWP.—See BARRE, VT

TYSON—See MOUNT ASCUTNEY, VT

UNDERHILL (town)—See RICHMOND, VT

VERGENNES—See SHELBURNE, VT

▲ **WAITSFIELD**—Waitsfield Cable Co.

WALLINGFORD TWP.—See RUTLAND, VT

* **WARDSBORO TWP.**—FrontierVision Partners LP

WARREN—See WAITSFIELD, VT

WASHINGTON—See BARRE, VT

WASHINGTON (town)—See BARRE, VT

WASHINGTON COUNTY (portions)—See WAITSFIELD, VT

WATERBURY—See MONTPELIER, VT

WATERFORD—See ST. JOHNSBURY, VT

WEBSTERVILLE—See BARRE, VT

WELLS—See GRANVILLE, NY

WELLS RIVER—See ST. JOHNSBURY, VT

WEST ARLINGTON (portions)—See MANCHESTER, VT

WEST BRIDGEWATER—See KILLINGTON, VT

WEST BURKE—See ST. JOHNSBURY, VT

▲ **WEST DOVER**—Area Telecable

WEST PAWLET—See PAWLET, VT

WEST RUTLAND TWP.—See RUTLAND, VT

* **WESTFORD TWP.**—FrontierVision Partners LP

* **WESTMINSTER TWP.**—FrontierVision Partners LP

▲ **WESTON**—Adelphia Communications Corp.

WEYBRIDGE (portions)—See MIDDLEBURY, VT

WHEELOCK—See ST. JOHNSBURY, VT

WHITE RIVER JUNCTION—See LEBANON, NH

▲ **WHITINGHAM**—Area Telecable

WILDER—See LEBANON, NH

WILLIAMSTOWN—See BARRE, VT

▲ **WILLIAMSTOWN (portions)**—North Valley Cable Systems Inc.

WILLIAMSVILLE—See NEWFANE, VT

WILLISTON—See BURLINGTON, VT

▲ **WILMINGTON**—Duncan Cable TV Service

* **WINDHAM TWP.**—FrontierVision Partners LP

WINDSOR—See MOUNT ASCUTNEY, VT

WINHALL—See MANCHESTER, VT

WINOOSKI—See BURLINGTON, VT

Woodbury—See MONTPELIER, VT

WOODFORD—See BENNINGTON, VT

WOODSTOCK—See MOUNT ASCUTNEY, VT

Worcester—See MONTPELIER, VT

VIRGINIA

ABINGDON—See GLADE SPRING, VA

ABINGDON (portions)—See BRISTOL, VA

▲ **ACCOMAC**—Falcon Cable TV

ACCOMACK COUNTY—See ACCOMAC, VA

ADRIA—See TAZEWELL, VA

ALBEMARLE COUNTY—See CHARLOTTESVILLE, VA

ALBEMARLE COUNTY—See also CROZET, VA

ALBEMARLE COUNTY (portions)—See SCOTTSVILLE, VA

▲ **ALEXANDRIA**—Jones Intercable

ALEXANDRIA (portions)—See FAIRFAX COUNTY, VA

ALLEGHANY COUNTY—See COVINGTON, VA

ALLEGHANY SPRINGS—See BLACKSBURG, VA

ALTA VISTA—See TIMBERLAKE, VA

▲ **ALTAVISTA**—Adelphia Cablevision

▲ **AMELIA COUNTY (portions)**—FrontierVision

AMHERST—See AMHERST COUNTY (southern portion), VA

▲ **AMHERST COUNTY (southern portion)**—Adelphia Cable TV

AMONATE—See WAR, WV

ANNANDALE—See FAIRFAX COUNTY, VA

APPALACHIA—See NORTON, VA

▲ **APPOMATTOX**—Nesbe Cable TV

▲ **ARLINGTON**—Cable TV Arlington

ASHLAND—See HENRICO COUNTY, VA

ATKINS—See MARION, VA

AUGUSTA—See STAUNTON, VA

AUGUSTA COUNTY (portions)—See STAUNTON, VA

AUGUSTA COUNTY (portions)—See also WINTERGREEN, VA

AUGUSTA SPRINGS—See CRAIGSVILLE, VA

AUSTINVILLE—See FORT CHISWELL, VA

AXTON—See MARTINSVILLE, VA

AYLETT—See KING WILLIAM (portions), VA

BACHELOR'S HALL—See BROSVILLE, VA

BACOVA—See HOT SPRINGS, VA

BALLSVILLE—See POWHATAN, VA

BANDY—See TAZEWELL, VA

BANNER—See COEBURN, VA

BAPTIST VALLEY—See TAZEWELL, VA

BASSETT—See MARTINSVILLE, VA

▲ **BASTIAN**—Cooney Cable Assoc. Inc.

BATH COUNTY—See HOT SPRINGS, VA

BEALTON—See WARRENTON, VA

▲ **BEDFORD**—Cablevision Communications

BEDFORD—See also TROUTVILLE, VA

▲ **BEDFORD COUNTY (southwestern portion)**—Blue Ridge Cablecomm

Bedford County—See also BEDFORD, VA

BEDFORD COUNTY (northern portion)—See TIMBERLAKE, VA

BEDFORD COUNTY (portions)—See LYNCHBURG, VA

BELFAST MILLS—See ROSEDALE, VA

▲ **BELLE HAVEN**—Falcon Cable TV

▲ **BEN HUR**—Century Virginia Corp.

BENTONVILLE—See FRONT ROYAL, VA

BERRYVILLE—See WINCHESTER, VA

BIG ROCK—See GRUNDY, VA

BIG STONE GAP—See NORTON, VA

▲ **BIRCHLEAF**—Cooney Cable Assoc. of Bastian LP

▲ **BISHOP**—Bishop TV Club Inc.

▲ **BLACKSBURG**—Adelphia Cable

▲ **BLACKSTONE**—Nesbe Cable TV

BLAND COUNTY—See BASTIAN, VA

BLAND COUNTY (portions)—See BLUEFIELD, WV

BLOXOM—See ACCOMAC, VA

BLUE GRASS—See MONTEREY, VA

BLUE RIDGE—See TROUTVILLE, VA

BOLD CAMP—See NORTON, VA

BONDTOWN—See COEBURN, VA

BOONES MILL—See FRANKLIN COUNTY, VA

▲ **BOWLING GREEN**—Tri-State Cablecomm

BOWLING GREEN—See also KING GEORGE, VA

BOYCE—See WINCHESTER, VA

BOYDTON—See CHASE CITY, VA

BOYKINS—See FRANKLIN, VA

BRACEY—See LAKE GASTON, VA

BRANCHVILLE—See FRANKLIN, VA

BRIDGEWATER—See HARRISONBURG, VA

▲ **BRISTOL**—FrontierVision

BROADWAY—See HARRISONBURG, VA

▲ **BROOKNEAL**—Adelphia Cable

▲ **BROSVILLE**—Chatmoss Cablevision

BRUNSWICK COUNTY—See LAWRENCEVILLE, VA

BRUNSWICK COUNTY (portions)—See LAKE GASTON, VA

BRUSHY—See GRUNDY, VA

▲ **BUCHANAN**—Buchanan CableVision

BUCHANAN COUNTY—See MARTIN, KY

BUCKINGHAM COUNTY (portions)—See DILLWYN, VA

BUCKINGHAM COUNTY (portions)—See also SCOTTSVILLE, VA

▲ **BUENA VISTA**—Adelphia Cable Communications

BURKE—See FAIRFAX COUNTY, VA

BURSON PLACE—See BRISTOL, VA

▲ **CALLAGHAN**—Callaghan Cable TV

CAMPBELL COUNTY—See LYNCHBURG, VA

CAROLINE COUNTY—See BOWLING GREEN, VA

CAROLINE COUNTY (unincorporated areas)—See KING GEORGE, VA

CARROLL COUNTY (portions)—See DOBSON, NC

CARROLL COUNTY (portions)—See also FORT CHISWELL, VA

CARROLL COUNTY (portions)—See also GALAX, VA

CARROLLTON—See FRANKLIN, VA

CASCADE—See BROSVILLE, VA

CASTLETON—See FRONT ROYAL, VA

CASTLEWOOD—See LEBANON, VA (CableVision)

CASTLEWOOD—See also LEBANON (portions), VA (Cooney Cable Assoc. of Bastian LP)

CATLETT—See WARRENTON, VA

CEDAR BLUFF—See RICHLANDS, VA

CENTRAL GARAGE—See KING WILLIAM (portions), VA

CENTREVILLE—See FAIRFAX COUNTY, VA

CHAMBLISSBURG—See TROUTVILLE, VA

CHANTILLY—See FAIRFAX COUNTY, VA

▲ **CHARLES CITY COUNTY (portions)**—FrontierVision

CHARLOTTE COUNTY (eastern portion)—See KEYSVILLE, VA

CHARLOTTE COUNTY (portions)—See DRAKES BRANCH, VA

CHARLOTTE COURT HOUSE—See KEYSVILLE, VA

▲**CHARLOTTESVILLE**—Multi-Channel TV Cable Co.

▲ **CHASE CITY**—Tele-Media Co. of Southern Virginia

CHATHAM—See DANVILLE, VA

CHERITON—See ACCOMAC, VA

▲ **CHESAPEAKE**—Rapid Cable

CHESAPEAKE—See also HAMPTON ROADS, VA

CHESTER GAP—See FRONT ROYAL, VA

▲ **CHESTERFIELD COUNTY**—Comcast Cablevision of Chesterfield Inc.

CHILHOWIE—See GLADE SPRING, VA

▲ **CHINCOTEAGUE**—Falcon Cable TV

CHRISTIANSBURG—See BLACKSBURG, VA

CHRISTIANSBURG—See also RADFORD, VA

CHURCHVILLE—See STAUNTON, VA

CLARION—See TIMBERLAKE, VA

CLARKE COUNTY—See WINCHESTER, VA

▲ **CLARKSVILLE**—Tri-State Cablecomm

CLAY POOL HILL—See RICHLANDS, VA

CLEVELAND—See LEBANON (portions), VA

CLIFFIELD—See TAZEWELL, VA

CLIFTON—See FAIRFAX COUNTY, VA

CLIFTON FORGE—See COVINGTON, VA

CLINCHCO—See CLINTWOOD, VA

CLINCHPORT (portions)—See DUFFIELD, VA

▲ **CLINTWOOD**—Century Mountain Corp.

CLOVERDALE—See TROUTVILLE, VA

▲ **COEBURN**—Century Communications Corp.

COEBURN—See also WISE, VA

COLLINSVILLE—See MARTINSVILLE, VA

▲ **COLONIAL BEACH**—Tri-State Cablecomm

COLONIAL HEIGHTS—See PETERSBURG, VA

CONCORD—See TIMBERLAKE, VA

COURTLAND—See FRANKLIN, VA

▲ **COVINGTON**—CFW Cable of Virginia Inc.

CRAB ORCHARD—See COEBURN, VA

CRAIG COUNTY (portions)—See NEWCASTLE, VA

▲**CRAIGSVILLE**—Multi-Channel TV Cable Co. of Virginia

▲ **CRAWFORD MANOR**—Tel-Con Systems

▲ **CREWE**—Nesbe Cable TV

CRIMORA—See STAUNTON, VA

CROCKETT—See SPEEDWELL, VA

CROCKETTS COVE—See BISHOP, VA

▲ **CROZET**—Multi-Channel TV Cable Co. of Virginia

▲ **CULPEPER**—TCI of Virginia Inc.

▲ **CULPEPER COUNTY**—GS Communications Inc.

CULPEPER COUNTY—See also CULPEPER, VA

CUMBERLAND COUNTY (southwestern portion)—See FARMVILLE, VA

CURLEY'S TRAILER PARK—See COLONIAL BEACH, VA

DAHLGREN—See KING GEORGE, VA

DALE CITY—See MANASSAS, VA

DALEVILLE—See TROUTVILLE, VA

▲ **DAMASCUS**—CableVision

DANIEL BOONE—See WEBER CITY, VA

DANTE—See LEBANON, VA

▲ **DANVILLE**—Adelphia Cable

DAYTON—See HARRISONBURG, VA

DEEL—See GRUNDY, VA

DELTAVILLE—See MIDDLESEX COUNTY, VA

DESKINS—See GRUNDY, VA

DICKENSON COUNTY—See CLINTWOOD, VA

DICKENSON COUNTY (portions)—See HAYSI, VA

▲ **DILLWYN**—FrontierVision

▲ **DINWIDDIE**—Adelphia Cable

DORAN—See RICHLANDS, VA

▲ **DRAKES BRANCH**—Cable Comm

DRY FORK—See BROSVILLE, VA

DUBLIN—See PULASKI, VA

▲ **DUFFIELD**—Century Cable TV

DUMFRIES—See MANASSAS, VA

EASTVILLE—See ACCOMAC, VA

▲ **EDINBURG**—Shenandoah Cable TV Co.

ELKTON—See SHENANDOAH, VA

ELLISTON—See BLACKSBURG, VA

ELTHAM—See NEW KENT, VA

▲ **EMPORIA**—SVHH Cable Acquisition LP

ESSERVILLE—See NORTON, VA

ESSEX COUNTY (portions)—See TAPPAHANNOCK, VA

EVINGTON—See TIMBERLAKE, VA

▲ **EWING**—Tele-Media Co. of Cumberland Gap

EXMORE—See BELLE HAVEN, VA

FAIRFAX—See FAIRFAX COUNTY, VA

▲ **FAIRFAX COUNTY**—Media General Cable of Fairfax Inc.

FAIRFAX STATION—See FAIRFAX COUNTY, VA

FAIRLAWN—See RADFORD, VA

FALLS CHURCH—See FAIRFAX COUNTY, VA

▲ **FARMVILLE**—Cable Comm

FERRUM—See FRANKLIN COUNTY, VA

FIELDALE—See MARTINSVILLE, VA

FINCASTLE—See TROUTVILLE, VA

FLAT ROCK—See POWHATAN, VA

▲ **FLOYD**—Time Warner Cable

FLOYD COUNTY—See FLOYD, VA

FLUVANNA COUNTY (portions)—See SCOTTSVILLE, VA

FOREST—See TIMBERLAKE, VA

FORT BELVOIR—See MANASSAS, VA

▲ **FORT BELVOIR ARMY BASE**—Jones Communications

▲ **FORT CHISWELL**—Time Warner Cable

FORT EUSTIS ARMY BASE—See NEWPORT NEWS, VA

FORT LEE—See PETERSBURG, VA

FORT MONROE—See HAMPTON, VA

FORT MYER MILITARY BASE—See ALEXANDRIA, VA

FORT STORY—See HAMPTON ROADS, VA

▲ **FRANKLIN**—Falcon Cable TV

▲ **FRANKLIN COUNTY**—CableVision Communications

FREDERICK COUNTY—See WINCHESTER, VA

▲ **FREDERICKSBURG**—Media General Cable of Fredericksburg Inc.

FRIES—See GALAX, VA

▲ **FRONT ROYAL**—Central Virginia Cable Inc.

GAINESVILLE—See WARRENTON, VA

▲ **GALAX**—Southwest Virginia Cable

WASHINGTON

ADAMS COUNTY—See OTHELLO, WA

AGATE—See UNION, WA

AIRWAY HEIGHTS—See FAIRCHILD AFB, WA

ALBION—See MOSCOW, ID

ALGONA—See AUBURN, WA

ALLYN (portions)—See PORT ORCHARD, WA

▲ **ALMIRA**—Sun Country Cable

AMES LAKE—See DUVALL, WA

▲ **ANACORTES**—TCI Cablevision of Washington Inc.

▲ **ANDERSON ISLAND**—Millennium Digital Media

ARDEN—See COLVILLE, WA

▲ **ARLINGTON**—TCI Cablevision of Washington Inc.

ASOTIN—See LEWISTON, ID

ASOTIN COUNTY—See LEWISTON, ID

▲ **AUBURN**—TCI Cablevision Inc.

BABY ISLAND—See ANACORTES, WA

▲ **BAINBRIDGE ISLAND**—Northland Cable TV

BANGOR SUBMARINE BASE—See PORT ORCHARD, WA

BATTLE GROUND—See VANCOUVER, WA

▲ **BAYVIEW**—Northland Cable TV

BEAUX ARTS VILLAGE—See REDMOND, WA

BEAVER—See FORKS, WA

BELFAIR—See PORT ORCHARD, WA

BELLEVUE—See REDMOND, WA

▲ **BELLINGHAM**—TCI Cablevision of Washington Inc.

BELLS BEACH—See ANACORTES, WA

BELVIDERE—See GRAND COULEE, WA

▲ **BENTON CITY**—Columbia Basin Cable

BENTON COUNTY—See BENTON CITY, WA

BENTON COUNTY—See also KENNEWICK, WA

▲ **BIG LAKE**—Cedar Communications

BINGEN—See HOOD RIVER, OR

BLACK DIAMOND—See AUBURN, WA

▲ **BLAINE**—TCI Cablevision of Washington Inc.

BONNEY LAKE—See TACOMA, WA (TCI Cablevision Inc.)

BOTHELL—See SEATTLE, WA

▲ **BREMERTON**—TCI Cablevision of Washington Inc.

BREMERTON—See also PORT ORCHARD, WA

▲ **BREWSTER**—Millennium Digital Media

BRIDGEHAVEN—See HOOD CANAL, WA

BRIDGEPORT—See BREWSTER, WA

BRIDGEPORT BAR—See BREWSTER, WA

BRIER—See SEATTLE, WA

BRINNON—See PORT TOWNSEND, WA

BRYANT—See LAKE GOODWIN, WA

BUCKLEY—See TACOMA, WA (TCI Cablevision Inc.)

▲ **BUCODA**—Millennium Digital Media

BURBANK—See KENNEWICK, WA

▲ **BURLINGTON**—TCI Cablevision of Washington Inc.

BURLINGTON (rural areas)—See BAYVIEW, WA

▲ **CAMANO ISLAND**—Northland Cable

CAMAS—See VANCOUVER, WA

CARBONADO—See TACOMA, WA (TCI Cablevision Inc.)

CARNATION—See DUVALL, WA

CARNATION—See also REDMOND, WA

CARROLLS—See LONGVIEW, WA

▲ **CARSON**—Millennium Digital Media

CASHMERE—See WENATCHEE, WA

CASTLE ROCK—See LONGVIEW, WA

▲ **CATHLAMET**—Falcon Communications Ventures I

CENTRAL PARK—See ABERDEEN, WA

▲ **CENTRALIA-CHEHALIS**—TCI Cablevision

▲ **CHATTAROY**—Phoenix Cable

Chattaroy—See also DEER PARK, WA

▲ **CHELAN**—Millennium Digital Media

CHELAN COUNTY—See LEAVENWORTH, WA

CHELAN COUNTY—See also WENATCHEE, WA

CHELAN FALLS—See CHELAN, WA

▲ **CHENEY**—Cheney TV Cable

CHEWELAH—See LOON LAKE, WA

▲ **CHINOOK**—Chinook Progressive Club TV

▲ **CHINOOK PASS**—Columbia Basin Cable TV

▲ **CLALLAM BAY**—Northland Cable TV

CLALLAM COUNTY (northwestern portion)—See PORT ANGELES, WA

CLALLAM COUNTY (southeastern portion)—See FORKS, WA

CLALLAM COUNTY (unincorporated areas)—See SEQUIM, WA

CLARK COUNTY (unincorporated areas)—See VANCOUVER, WA

CLARK COUNTY (urban areas)—See VANCOUVER, WA

CLARKSTON—See LEWISTON, ID

▲ **CLE ELUM**—TCI Cablevision of Southwest Washington Inc.

CLEAR LAKE—See BIG LAKE, WA

CLIFFDELL—See CHINOOK PASS, WA

▲ **CLINTON**—TCI Cablevision of Washington Inc.

▲ **CLYDE HILL**—Telepro Communications

▲ **COLFAX**—Colfax Highline Cable Co.

COLLEGE PLACE—See WALLA WALLA, WA

Colony Surf—See UNION, WA

COLTON—See MOSCOW, ID

▲ **COLVILLE**—Falcon Telecable

COLVILLE INDIAN AGENCY—See NESPELEM, WA

▲ **CONCRETE**—Millennium Digital Media

▲ **CONNELL**—Community Cable Service

CONWAY—See BAYVIEW, WA

COPALIS BEACH—See OCEAN SHORES, WA

COPALIS CROSSING—See OCEAN SHORES, WA

COSMOPOLIS—See ABERDEEN, WA

▲ **COULEE CITY**—Sun Country Cable

▲ **COULEE DAM**—TV Assn. of Coulee Dam

▲ **COUPEVILLE**—TCI Cablevision of Washington Inc.

COUPEVILLE—See also WHIDBEY ISLAND (c), WA

COWICHE—See NACHES, WA

COWLITZ COUNTY—See LONGVIEW, WA

CRESCENT BAR—See QUINCY, WA

▲ **CRESTON**—Cable Plus

DALLESPORT—See THE DALLES, OR

▲ **DARRINGTON**—Millennium Digital Media

▲ **DAVENPORT**—Sun Country Cable

▲ **DAYTON**—Touchet Valley TV Inc.

▲ **DEER PARK**—Sun Country Cable

DEERLAKE—See LOON LAKE, WA

DEMING—See MAPLE FALLS, WA

DES MOINES—See AUBURN, WA

DESERT AIRE—See MATTAWA, WA

▲ **DIAMOND LAKE**—Phoenix Cable

DIAMOND LAKE—See also CHATTAROY, WA

▲ **DIXIE**—TCI Cablevision of Yakima Inc.

DOTY—See PE ELL, WA

DOUGLAS COUNTY—See WENATCHEE, WA

DRYAD—See PE ELL, WA

DRYDEN—See LEAVENWORTH, WA

DU PONT—See TACOMA, WA (TCI Cablevision Inc.)

▲ **DUVALL**—Millennium Digital Media

EAST WENATCHEE—See WENATCHEE, WA

▲ **EASTON**—Cable Plus

EATONVILLE—See TACOMA, WA (TCI Cablevision Inc.)

EDGEWOOD—See TACOMA, WA (TCI Cablevision Inc.)

▲ **EDMONDS**—Chambers Cable of Edmonds

ELECTRIC CITY—See GRAND COULEE, WA

▲ **ELLENSBURG**—Falcon Cable TV

ELMA—See MONTESANO, WA

▲ **ELMER**—TCI Cablevision of Washington Inc.

ELMER CITY—See ELMER, WA

ENDICOTT—See ST. JOHN, WA

▲ **ENTIAT**—Millennium Digital Media

ENUMCLAW—See AUBURN, WA

▲ **EPHRATA**—Northland Cable TV

EVERETT—See SEATTLE, WA

EVERETT NAVAL STATION—See SEATTLE, WA

Evergreen Mobile Home Park—See SUNNYSIDE, WA

EVERSON—See LYNDEN, WA

▲ **FAIRCHILD AFB**—Fibervision Inc.

▲ **FAIRFIELD**—Northwest Cable LP

FALL CITY—See REDMOND, WA

FEDERAL WAY—See AUBURN, WA

▲ **FERNDALE**—TCI Cablevision of Washington Inc.

FIFE—See TACOMA, WA (TCI Cablevision Inc.)

FINLEY—See KENNEWICK, WA

FIRCREST—See TACOMA, WA (TCI Cablevision Inc.)

▲ **FORKS**—Millennium Digital Media

FORT LEWIS—See TACOMA, WA (TCI Cablevision Inc.)

FOX ISLAND—See TACOMA, WA (TCI Cablevision Inc.)

FOX SPIT—See ANACORTES, WA

FRANKLIN COUNTY—See KENNEWICK, WA

▲ **FREELAND**—TCI Cablevision of Washington Inc.

▲ **FRIDAY HARBOR**—Century Communications

GAMBLEWOOD—See KINGSTON, WA

▲ **GARFIELD**—Northwest Cable LP

GEORGE—See QUINCY, WA

GIG HARBOR—See TACOMA, WA (TCI Cablevision Inc.)

GIG HARBOR PENINSULA—See TACOMA, WA (TCI Cablevision Inc.)

GLEED—See NACHES, WA

GLEN MOBILE HOME PARK—See MAPLE FALLS, WA

▲ **GLENOMA**—Millennium Digital Media

GOLD BAR—See SEATTLE, WA

▲ **GOLDENDALE**—Columbia Basin Cable

GRAHAM—See TACOMA, WA (TCI Cablevision Inc.)

▲ **GRAND COULEE**—TCI Cablevision of Washington Inc.

▲ **GRANDVIEW**—TCI Cablevision of Yakima Valley Inc.

GRANGER—See TOPPENISH, WA

GRANITE FALLS—See SEATTLE, WA

GRANT COUNTY—See EPHRATA, WA

GRANT COUNTY—See also MOSES LAKE, WA

GRAYLAND—See WESTPORT, WA

GRAYS HARBOR—See ROCHESTER, WA

GRAYS HARBOR COUNTY—See ABERDEEN, WA

GRAYS HARBOR COUNTY—See also MONTESANO, WA

GRAYS HARBOR COUNTY—See also OCEAN SHORES, WA

GRAYS HARBOR COUNTY—See also WESTPORT, WA

▲ **GREENBANK**—Cable Services

GREENBANK—See also WHIDBEY ISLAND (c), WA

▲ **GUEMES ISLAND**—Index Cable TV Inc.

HAMILTON—See CONCRETE, WA

▲ **HANSVILLE**—North Star Cable Inc.

▲ **HARRINGTON**—Northwest Cable LP

HERRON ISLAND—See ANDERSON ISLAND, WA

HOGAN'S CORNER—See OCEAN SHORES, WA

▲ **HOLLY**—Falcon Video Communications

▲ **HOOD CANAL**—Interstate Cable Inc.

HOODSPORT—See UNION, WA

HOQUIAM—See ABERDEEN, WA

HORSESHOE BEND—See CHINOOK PASS, WA

HUNTS POINT—See REDMOND, WA

ILWACO—See LONG BEACH, WA

▲ **INDEX**—Index Cable TV Inc.

Indian Beach—See CAMANO ISLAND, WA

INDIANOLA—See BAINBRIDGE ISLAND, WA

▲ **IONE**—Community Cable Service

ISLAND COUNTY—See ANACORTES, WA

ISLAND COUNTY—See also COUPEVILLE, WA

ISLAND COUNTY—See also FREELAND, WA

ISLAND COUNTY—See also SEATTLE, WA

ISSAQUAH—See REDMOND, WA

JACKSON PARK—See PORT ORCHARD, WA

▲ **KAHLOTUS**—Community Cable Service

▲ **KALA POINT**—Millennium Digital Media

KALAMA—See LONGVIEW, WA

KELSO—See LONGVIEW, WA

▲ **KENNEWICK**—Falcon Cable TV

KENT—See AUBURN, WA

KETTLE FALLS—See COLVILLE, WA

KEY PENINSULA—See ANDERSON ISLAND, WA

KEYPORT—See PORT ORCHARD, WA

KEYPORT NAVAL BASE—See PORT ORCHARD, WA

KING COUNTY—See AUBURN, WA

KING COUNTY—See also REDMOND, WA

KING COUNTY—See also SEATTLE, WA

▲ **KINGSTON**—NorthStar Cable Inc.

KIRKLAND—See SEATTLE, WA

KITSAP COUNTY—See BREMERTON, WA

KITSAP COUNTY (northern portion)—See POULSBO, WA

KITSAP LAKE—See PORT ORCHARD, WA

KITTITAS—See ELLENSBURG, WA

KITTITAS COUNTY—See CLE ELUM, WA

KITTITAS COUNTY—See also ELLENSBURG, WA

KITTITAS COUNTY (portions)—See EASTON, WA

KLICKITAT—See HOOD RIVER, OR

KLICKITAT COUNTY—See HOOD RIVER, OR

KLICKITAT COUNTY (portions)—See THE DALLES, OR

KOONTZVILLE—See GRAND COULEE, WA

LA CENTER—See VANCOUVER, WA

▲ **LA CONNER**—Northland Cable

LACEY—See OLYMPIA, WA

LACROSSE—See ST. JOHN, WA

▲ **LAKE BAY**—Millennium Digital Media

LAKE CLE ELUM—See ROSLYN, WA

LAKE CREEK—See FORKS, WA

LAKE CUSHMAN—See UNION, WA

LAKE FOREST PARK—See SEATTLE, WA

▲ **LAKE GOODWIN**—Lake TV Cable

LAKE HOLLIDAY—See TACOMA, WA (TCI Cablevision Inc.)

LAKE MINTERWOOD—See TACOMA, WA (TCI Cablevision Inc.)

LAKE OF THE WOODS—See TACOMA, WA (TCI Cablevision Inc.)

LAKE STEVENS—See SEATTLE, WA

LAKE SYMINGTON—See PORT ORCHARD, WA

LAKE TAHUYA—See PORT ORCHARD, WA

LAKEBAY—See TACOMA, WA (TCI Cablevision Inc.)

LAKEWOOD—See BIG LAKE, WA

LAKEWOOD CENTER—See TACOMA, WA (TCI Cablevision Inc.)

LANGLEY—See CLINTON, WA

LARSON AFB—See MOSES LAKE, WA

▲ **LEAVENWORTH**—TCI Cablevision of Washington Inc.

LEWIS COUNTY—See CENTRALIA-CHEHALIS, WA

LEWIS COUNTY—See also MORTON, WA

LEWIS COUNTY—See also MOSSYROCK, WA

▲ **LIBERTY LAKE**—Community Cable Service

Lilliwaup Falls—See UNION, WA

▲ **LIND**—Community Cable Service

LITTLE BOSTON—See KINGSTON, WA

LOFALL—See POULSBO, WA

LONE PINE—See COULEE DAM, WA

▲ **LONG BEACH**—Falcon Community Ventures I

LONG POINT—See COUPEVILLE, WA

▲ **LONGVIEW**—Cowlitz Cablevision Inc.

▲ **LOOMIS**—JKA Cable Systems Inc.

▲ **LOON LAKE**—Falcon Telecable

Lost Lake—See CAMANO ISLAND, WA

LOWER HOOD CANAL—See UNION, WA

▲ **LUMMI INDIAN RESERVATION**—San Juan Cable & Construction

LUMMI INDIAN RESERVATION—See also FERNDALE, WA

▲ **LYLE**—Cascade Cable Systems

LYMAN—See CONCRETE, WA

▲ **LYNDEN**—TCI Cablevision of Washington Inc.

LYNNWOOD—See SEATTLE, WA

MABTON—See SUNNYSIDE, WA

MADRONA—See COUPEVILLE, WA

Madrona Beach—See CAMANO ISLAND, WA

MADRONA POINT—See TACOMA, WA (TCI Cablevision Inc.)

▲ **MALAGA**—Sun Country Cable

▲ **MALTBY**—Cable Plus

MANCHESTER—See PORT ORCHARD, WA

▲ **MANSFIELD**—Sun Cable TV

▲ **MANSON**—Sun Cable TV

▲ **MAPLE FALLS**—TCI Cablevision of Washington Inc.

MAPLE VALLEY—See AUBURN, WA

MAPLETON—See PROSSER, WA

▲ **MARBLEMOUNT**—Millennium Digital Media

MARYSVILLE—See SEATTLE, WA

MASON COUNTY—See PORT ORCHARD, WA

MASON COUNTY (southwestern portion)—See SHELTON, WA

▲ **MATTAWA**—Sun Country Cable

▲ **MAXWELTON**—Pioneer Cable Contractors

MAYFIELD LAKE—See MOSSYROCK, WA

▲ **McCHORD AIR FORCE BASE**—TCI of Tacoma Inc.

McCLEARY—See MONTESANO, WA

McKENNA—See TACOMA, WA (TCI Cablevision Inc.)

▲ **MEDICAL LAKE**—Cheney/Medical Lake TV Cable

MEDINA—See REDMOND, WA

MERCER ISLAND—See REDMOND, WA

METALINE—See METALINE FALLS, WA

▲ **METALINE FALLS**—Community Cable Service

MILL CREEK—See SEATTLE, WA

MILLER BAY ESTATES—See BAINBRIDGE ISLAND, WA

MILLWOOD—See SPOKANE, WA

MILTON—See TACOMA, WA (TCI Cablevision Inc.)

▲ **MINERAL**—TCI Cablevision of Southwest Washington Inc.

MIRRORMONT—See REDMOND, WA

MONROE—See SEATTLE, WA

▲ **MONTESANO**—TCI Cablevision of Washington Inc.

▲ **MORTON**—Mike's TV Inc.

▲ **MOSES LAKE**—Northland Cable

▲ **MOSSYROCK**—TCI Cablevision of Southwest Washington Inc.

MOUNT VERNON—See BURLINGTON, WA

MOUNTLAKE TERRACE—See SEATTLE, WA

MOXEE CITY—See YAKIMA, WA

MUKILTEO—See SEATTLE, WA

MURDOCK—See THE DALLES, OR

MUTINY BAY—See FREELAND, WA

▲ **NACHES**—Columbia Basin Cable

NAHCOTTA—See LONG BEACH, WA

▲ **NAPAVINE**—Millennium Digital Media

▲ **NASELLE**—Falcon Community Ventures I

▲ **NESPELEM**—JKA Cable Systems Inc.

NEWCASTLE—See REDMOND, WA

▲ **NEWPORT**—Concept Cable

NEWPORT—See also PRIEST RIVER, ID

NOOKSACK—See LYNDEN, WA

NORMANDY PARK—See AUBURN, WA

▲ **NORTH BONNEVILLE**—North Bonneville Community Cable TV System

NORTH SHORE—See PORT ORCHARD, WA

▲ **NORTHPORT**—Falcon Telecable

OAK HARBOR—See SEATTLE, WA

▲ **OAKESDALE**—Northwest Cable LP

OAKVILLE—See ROCHESTER, WA

OCEAN CITY—See OCEAN SHORES, WA

OCEAN PARK—See LONG BEACH, WA

▲ **OCEAN SHORES**—Coast Communications Co. Inc.

▲ **ODESSA**—Community Cable Service

OKANOGAN COUNTY (unincorporated areas)—See OMAK, WA

OKANOGAN COUNTY (unincorporated areas)—See also OROVILLE, WA

OKANOGAN COUNTY (unincorporated areas)—See also TONASKET, WA

OLALLA—See PORT ORCHARD, WA

▲ **OLYMPIA**—TCI Cablevision of Washington Inc.

▲ **OMAK**—TCI Cablevision of Okanogan Valley Inc.

▲ **ORCAS ISLAND**—Sun Country Cable

▲ **OROVILLE**—TCI Cablevision of Okanogan Valley Inc.

ORTING—See TACOMA, WA (TCI Cablevision Inc.)

▲ **OTHELLO**—Northland Cable TV

PACIFIC—See AUBURN, WA

PACIFIC BEACH—See OCEAN SHORES, WA

PACIFIC COUNTY—See ASTORIA, OR

PACIFIC COUNTY—See also LONG BEACH, WA

PACIFIC COUNTY—See also RAYMOND, WA

PACIFIC COUNTY—See also WESTPORT, WA

▲ **PACKWOOD**—Millennium Digital Media

PALOUSE—See MOSCOW, ID

PARK PLACE MOBILE HOME PARK—See TACOMA, WA (TCI Cablevision Inc.)

PASCO—See KENNEWICK, WA

PATEROS—See BREWSTER, WA

▲ **PE ELL**—Millennium Digital Media

PEND OREILLE COUNTY—See NEWPORT, WA

PENINSULA—See TACOMA, WA (TCI Cablevision Inc.)

PESHASTIN—See LEAVENWORTH, WA

PHILLIPS LAKE—See UNION, WA

PICKERING—See UNION, WA

▲ **POINT ROBERTS**—Delta CableVision

POMEROY—See LEWISTON, ID

▲ **PORT ANGELES**—Northland Cable TV

PORT HADLOCK—See PORT TOWNSEND, WA

PORT LUDLOW—See PORT TOWNSEND, WA

▲ **PORT ORCHARD**—Falcon Video Communications

▲ **PORT TOWNSEND**—Millennium Digital Media

▲ **POULSBO**—TCI Cablevision of Washington Inc.

▲ **PRESCOTT**—TCI Cablevision of Yakima Inc.

PRESTON—See REDMOND, WA

PRINCETON—See MOSCOW, ID

▲ **PROSSER**—Falcon Cable

PUGET SOUND NAVAL SHIPYARD—See PORT ORCHARD, WA

PULLMAN—See MOSCOW, ID

PUYALLUP—See TACOMA, WA (TCI Cablevision Inc.)

QUILCENE—See PORT TOWNSEND, WA

▲ **QUINCY**—Sun Country Cable

RAINIER—See TACOMA, WA (TCI Cablevision Inc.)

RANDLE—See GLENOMA, WA

RANDLE—See also PACKWOOD, WA

▲ **RAYMOND**—TCI Cablevision of Washington Inc.

▲ **REARDAN**—Northwest Cable LP

▲ **REDMOND**—TCI Cablevision Inc.

REDMOND—See also DUVALL, WA

RENTON—See AUBURN, WA

▲ **REPUBLIC**—Television Assn. of Republic

RICHLAND—See KENNEWICK, WA

WEST VIRGINIA

▲ **BRANDYWINE**—Brandywine Cablevision

BRANHAM HEIGHTS—See WHITESVILLE, WV

BRAXTON COUNTY—See GASSAWAY, WV (Cablecomm)

BRAXTON COUNTY—See also GASSAWAY, WV (Paxton Cable)

BREEDEN—See DINGESS, WV

BRENTON—See PINEVILLE, WV

BRETZ—See KINGWOOD, WV

BRIAR CREEK—See FANROCK, WV

BRIARWOOD ESTATES—See MARIETTA, OH

BRIDGEPORT—See CLARKSBURG, WV (Time Warner Cable)

BRISTOL—See SALEM, WV

▲ **BROAD RUN**—Basco Electronics Inc.

BROOKE COUNTY—See STEUBENVILLE, OH

BROOKE COUNTY—See also WEIRTON, WV

BROOKE COUNTY—See also WELLSBURG, WV

BROOKE COUNTY (portions)—See BETHANY, WV

▲ **BROOKHAVEN**—Century Huntington Co.

BROOKLYN—See OAK HILL, WV

BROWNSVILLE—See CHELYAN, WV

BROWNTON—See FLEMINGTON, WV

BRUCETON MILLS—See MARKLEYSBURG, PA

▲ **BRUNO**—Cooney Cable Assoc.

BRUSH CREEK—See CHELYAN, WV

BUCKEYE—See MARLINTON, WV

▲ **BUCKHANNON**—CableVision Communications

▲ **BUD**—Bud-Alpoca TV Cable Club Inc.

BUD (portions)—See MULLENS, WV

BUFFALO—See RED HOUSE, WV

BULL CREEK—See PANTHER, WV (CableVision Communications)

▲ **BURNSVILLE**—Helicon Cablevision

BURTON—See LITTLETON, WV

CABELL COUNTY—See MILTON, WV

CABELL COUNTY (unincorporated areas)—See APPLE GROVE, WV

CABELL COUNTY (unincorporated areas)—See also SALT ROCK, WV

CABIN CREEK—See CHELYAN, WV

▲ **CAIRO**—CableVision Communications

CALDWELL—See LEWISBURG, WV

CALF CREEK—See KERMIT, WV

▲ **CAMDEN ON GAULEY**—Helicon Group Ltd.

▲ **CAMERON**—CableVision Communications

CAMERON—See also GLEN DALE, WV

CAMP CREEK—See CHELYAN, WV

CAMPBELLS CREEK—See CHELYAN, WV

CAMPBELLTOWN—See MARLINTON, WV

CANAAN VALLEY (portions)—See DAVIS, WV

CANE FORK—See LOUDENDALE, WV

CANEBRAKE—See WAR, WV

▲ **CANVAS**—Econoco Inc.

CAPELS—See WELCH, WV

▲ **CAPON BRIDGE**—Valley Cable

CARBON—See CHELYAN, WV

CARETTA—See WAR, WV

CARPENDALE—See CUMBERLAND, MD

▲ **CASS**—Milestone Communications of New York LP

CASSVILLE—See ARNETTSVILLE, WV

CEDAR GROVE—See CHELYAN, WV

▲**CENTERVILLE**—FrontierVision

CEREDO—See SOUTH POINT, OH

CHAPMANVILLE—See LOGAN, WV

CHAPMANVILLE—See also WAYNE, WV

▲ **CHARLES TOWN**—GS Communications

▲ **CHARLESTON**—Capitol CableComm

CHARLTON HEIGHTS—See CHELYAN, WV

CHARMCO—See RUPERT, WV

▲ **CHATTAROY**—Capital Cablecomm

▲ **CHELYAN**—Capital Cablecomm

CHESAPEAKE—See CHELYAN, WV

▲ **CHESTER**—TCI of West Virginia Inc.

CINCO—See CHELYAN, WV

▲ **CLARKSBURG**—Century Huntington Co.

▲ **CLARKSBURG**—Time Warner Cable

▲ **CLARKSBURG**—West Virginia Country Cable

▲ **CLAY**—Thompson Cablevision Co. Inc.

CLAY COUNTY (portions)—See INDORE, WV

CLAY COUNTY (unincorporated areas)—See BIRCH RIVER, WV

CLEAR FORK—See OCEANA, WV

CLEARVIEW—See WHEELING, WV

CLENDENIN—See ELKVIEW, WV

CLOVER DRIVE—See CHELYAN, WV

COAL CITY—See BECKLEY, WV

COAL FORK—See CHELYAN, WV

▲ **COALTON**—West Virginia Country Cable

▲ **COLFAX**—Century Huntington Co.

▲ **COLLIERS**—Jefferson County Cable Inc.

COLUMBIA—See CHELYAN, WV

COMFORT—See CHELYAN, WV

CONKINTOWN—See NORTHFORK, WV

COONSKIN DRIVE—See CHELYAN, WV

COOPERTOWN—See CHELYAN, WV

CORE—See ARNETTSVILLE, WV

CORE GAP—See WAYNE, WV

CORINNE—See MULLENS, WV

CORINNE—See also OAK HILL, WV

CORINTH—See KINGWOOD, WV

COSTA—See CHELYAN, WV

▲ **COTTAGEVILLE**—Community Antenna Service

COTTLE—See CRAIGSVILLE, WV

COVEL—See HERNDON, WV

COW CREEK—See OMAR, WV

▲ **COWEN**—Cablecomm

CRABTREE—See WAYNE, WV

▲ **CRAIGSVILLE**—Nesbe Cable

CRAWFORD—See IRELAND, WV

▲ **CRAWLEY CREEK ROAD**—Bowen Cablevision

CREDE—See ELKVIEW, WV

CRICHTON—See RUPERT, WV

CROOKED RUN—See CLARKSBURG, WV (West Virginia Country Cable)

CROSS LANES—See NITRO, WV

▲ **CROSSROADS**—Crossroads TV Cable

CROWN—See ARNETTSVILLE, WV

CROWN HILL—See CHELYAN, WV

CRUM—See KERMIT, WV

CRUMPLER—See NORTHFORK, WV

CRYSTAL SPRINGS—See BEVERLY, WV

CUB CREEK JUNCTION—See PINEVILLE, WV

CUCUMBER—See WAR, WV

CULLODEN—See MILTON, WV

CUNARD—See OAK HILL, WV

▲ **CURTIN**—Cablecomm

CYCLONE—See LOGAN, WV

CYCLONE—See also OCEANA, WV

▲ **CYRUS**—FrontierVision

DALLISON—See MURPHYTOWN, WV

DAMERON—See CHELYAN, WV

DANESE—See MEADOW BRIDGE, WV

DANVILLE—See MADISON, WV

▲ **DAVIS**—Cablecomm

DAVIS CREEK—See LOUDENDALE, WV

DAVISVILLE—See MURPHYTOWN, WV

▲ **DAVY**—Hurley Cablevision

DAWES—See CHELYAN, WV

DAYBROOK—See BRAVE, PA

DEANSVILLE—See BUCKHANNON, WV

DECOTA—See CHELYAN, WV

DEEPWATER—See CHELYAN, WV

▲ **DELBARTON**—Cooney Cable Assoc.

DENVER—See TUNNELTON, WV

DIAMOND—See CHELYAN, WV

▲ **DIANA**—West Virginia Country Cable

HARPERS FERRY—See CHARLES TOWN, WV

HARRISON COUNTY—See SALEM, WV

HARRISON COUNTY (rural areas)—See CLARKSBURG, WV (Time Warner Cable)

▲ **HARRISVILLE**—Helicon Cablevision

HARTFORD—See POINT PLEASANT, WV

HARTS—See WAYNE, WV

HARTWELL—See WAR, WV

HASTINGS—See PINE GROVE, WV

HATFIELD BOTTOM—See MARTIN, KY

HAVACO—See WELCH, WV

HAYWOOD—See SHINNSTON, WV

HEDGESVILLE—See HANCOCK, MD

HEDGESVILLE—See also INWOOD, WV

HELEN—See OAK HILL, WV

HEMPHILL—See WELCH, WV

HENDERSON—See POINT PLEASANT, WV

HENDRICKS—See PARSONS, WV

HEPZIBAH—See SHINNSTON, WV

▲ **HERNDON**—Wyoming Cable TV Inc.

HERNSHAW—See CHELYAN, WV

HILLSBORO—See LEWISBURG, WV

HINES—See RUPERT, WV

▲ **HINTON**—Helicon Cablevision

HINTON—See also SUMMERS COUNTY (portions), WV

HODGESVILLE—See BUCKHANNON, WV

HOLCOMB—See RICHWOOD, WV

HOLLY—See CHELYAN, WV

HOLLY LAWN—See CHELYAN, WV

HOMETOWN—See RED HOUSE, WV

▲ **HOTCHKISS**—Wyoming Cable TV Inc.

HOTCHKISS—See also MULLENS, WV

HUBBALL—See WAYNE, WV

HUFF CREEK—See OCEANA, WV

HUGHESTON—See CHELYAN, WV

HUNDRED—See LITTLETON, WV

HUNTER ROAD—See CHELYAN, WV

▲ **HUNTINGTON**—Century Huntington Co.

HURRICANE—See MILTON, WV

HURRICANE—See also RED HOUSE, WV

▲ **HUTCHINSON**—Century Huntington Co.

HUTTONSVILLE—See BEVERLY, WV

▲ **IAEGER**—TMC of KWV

IDAMAY—See FARMINGTON, WV

INDEPENDENCE—See KINGWOOD, WV

▲ **INDEPENDENT MOUNTAIN**—Capital Cablecomm

INDIAN CREEK—See FANROCK, WV

▲ **INDORE**—Capital Cablecomm

INDUSTRIAL—See SALEM, WV

INGLESIDE—See OAKVALE, WV

INGRAM BRANCH—See SCARBRO, WV

INSTITUTE—See CHARLESTON, WV

▲ **INWOOD**—GS Communications Inc. West Virginia Division

▲ **IRELAND**—Basco Electronics Inc.

ISAACS CREEK—See CLARKSBURG, WV (West Virginia Country Cable)

ISABAN—See PANTHER, WV (CableVision Communications)

ITMANN—See MULLENS, WV

JACKSONBURG—See PINE GROVE, WV

JANE LEW—See WESTON, WV

JANIE—See WHITESVILLE, WV

JEFFERSON COUNTY—See CHARLES TOWN, WV

▲ **JENKINJONES**—Obey's TV Cable

JENNIES CREEK—See KERMIT, WV

JESSE—See PINEVILLE, WV

▲ **JODIE**—Capital Cablecomm

JOHNSON BRANCH—See SCARBRO, WV

JOHNSON RUN—See PETERSBURG, WV

▲ **JULIAN**—Capital Cablecomm

JUMBO—See DIANA, WV

JUMPING BRANCH—See HINTON, WV

JUNIOR—See BELINGTON, WV

JUSTICE—See GILBERT, WV

KANAWHA COUNTY—See CHELYAN, WV

KANAWHA DRIVE—See TANNER, WV

KANAWHA FALLS—See CHELYAN, WV

KATY LICK—See CLARKSBURG, WV (West Virginia Country Cable)

KAYFORD—See CHELYAN, WV

KEARNEYSVILLE—See CHARLES TOWN, WV

KEITH—See WHITESVILLE, WV

KELLYSVILLE—See OAKVALE, WV

KENNA—See GOLDTOWN, WV

KENOVA—See SOUTH POINT, OH

▲ **KERMIT**—CableVision Communications

KESLING MILL—See BUCKHANNON, WV

▲ **KEYROCK**—Holly TV Cable

▲ **KEYSER**—Tele-Media Co.

KEYSTONE—See NORTHFORK, WV

▲ **KIMBALL**—Comcast Cable

KIMBERLY—See CHELYAN, WV

▲ **KINGWOOD**—CableVision Communications

KINGWOOD—See also TUNNELTON, WV

KITCHEN—See WAYNE, WV

KNOWLWOOD—See CHELYAN, WV

KOPPERSTON—See OCEANA, WV

KYLE—See NORTHFORK, WV

LA FRANK—See RICHWOOD, WV

LAING—See CHELYAN, WV

LAKE FLOYD—See SALEM, WV

LAKE RIDGE—See FLEMINGTON, WV

LANDRAFF—See KIMBALL, WV

LANSING—See SCARBRO, WV

LAUREL CREEK—See LENORE, WV

LAUREL FORK—See POND GAP, WV

LAUREL POINT—See ARNETTSVILLE, WV

LAVALETTE—See WAYNE, WV

LAWRENCEVILLE—See CHESTER, WV

LAYLAND—See MEADOW BRIDGE, WV

LECKIE—See NORTHFORK, WV

LEEVALE—See WHITESVILLE, WV

LEEWOOD—See CHELYAN, WV

▲ **LEFT HAND**—Econoco Inc.

▲ **LEIVASY**—Paxton Cable

▲ **LENORE**—CableVision Communications

LERONA—See PIPESTEM, WV

LESAGE—See APPLE GROVE, WV

LESAGE—See also HUNTINGTON, WV

LESLIE—See RUPERT, WV

LESTER—See BECKLEY, WV

LEWIS COUNTY—See WESTON, WV

LEWIS COUNTY (northern portion)—See BUCKHANNON, WV

▲ **LEWISBURG**—Capital Cablecomm

LICK CREEK—See CHELYAN, WV

LIMESTONE—See GLEN DALE, WV

LINDSEY LANE—See FORK RIDGE, WV

LINN—See ALUM BRIDGE, WV

LITTLE BIRCH—See BIRCH RIVER, WV

LITTLE GRAVE CREEK—See MOUNDSVILLE, WV

▲ **LITTLE OTTER**—R & R Cable Co.

LITTLE SANDY—See ELKVIEW, WV

▲ **LITTLETON**—CableVision Communications

LOBATA—See WILLIAMSON, WV

LOCHGELLY—See OAK HILL, WV

LOCKWOOD—See SCARBRO, WV

▲ **LOGAN**—Cablecomm

LOGAN COUNTY—See LOGAN, WV

LONDON—See CHELYAN, WV

LORENTZ—See BUCKHANNON, WV

LOST CREEK—See WEST MILFORD, WV

▲ **LOUDENDALE**—Capital Cablecomm

LUBECK—See PARKERSBURG, WV

LUMBERPORT—See SHINNSTON, WV

▲ **LYBURN**—Bowen Cablevision

LYNN—See MARTIN, KY

LYNN SIDE—See PEARISBURG, VA

NEWHALL—See WAR, WV

NEWTON—See LEFT HAND, WV

NEWTOWN—See MARTIN, KY

NICHOLAS COUNTY—See SUMMERSVILLE, WV

NIMITZ—See HINTON, WV

▲ **NITRO**—Harmon Cable Communications

NITRO (portions)—See RED HOUSE, WV

NOAMA—See WHITESVILLE, WV

NOLAN—See LENORE, WV

NORTH FORK—See PETERSBURG, WV

NORTH HILLS—See PARKERSBURG, WV

NORTH MATEWAN—See MARTIN, KY

NORTH MATEWAN—See also MATEWAN, WV

NORTH PAGE—See SCARBRO, WV

NORTH RIVER MILLS—See AUGUSTA, WV

NORTH WELCH—See WELCH, WV

▲ **NORTHFORK**—TMC of Northfork

NUTTER FORT—See CLARKSBURG, WV (Time Warner Cable)

▲ **OAK HILL**—CableVision Communications

OAK RIDGE—See OAK HILL, WV

▲ **OAKVALE**—Nesbe Cable

OAKWOOD ESTATES—See MARIETTA, OH

▲ **OCEANA**—Wyoming TV Cable Co.

OHIO COUNTY—See WHEELING, WV

OHIO COUNTY (unincorporated areas)—See WEST LIBERTY, WV

OHLEY—See CHELYAN, WV

▲ **OMAR**—Colane Cable TV Inc.

ONA—See MILTON, WV

ORGAS—See WHITESVILLE, WV

ORIENT HILL—See RUPERT, WV

OSAGE—See MORGANTOWN, WV

OTSEGO—See MULLENS, WV

OTTAWA—See LOGAN, WV

OWINGS—See SHINNSTON, WV

PACK BRANCH—See WHITESVILLE, WV

PACKSVILLE—See WHITESVILLE, WV

PADEN CITY—See NEW MARTINSVILLE, WV

▲ **PAGE**—Helicon Cablevision

PAGETON—See NORTHFORK, WV

PAINT CREEK (portions)—See CHELYAN, WV

▲ **PANTHER**—CableVision Communications

▲ **PANTHER**—Hurley Cablevision

▲ **PARKERSBURG**—Cablecomm

PARKERSTOWN—See MARIETTA, OH

PARKVIEW—See GRAFTON, WV

▲ **PARSONS**—TCI of West Virginia Inc.

▲ **PAW PAW**—Cablecomm

▲ **PAX**—Capital Cablecomm

PAYTONA—See CHELYAN, WV

PEA RIDGE—See OAK HILL, WV

PENDLETON COUNTY—See FRANKLIN, WV

▲ **PENNSBORO**—CableVision Communications

PENTRESS—See BRAVE, PA

PEORA—See WYATT, WV

▲ **PETERSBURG**—CableVision Communications

▲ **PETERSTOWN**—CableVision Communications

PETTUS—See WHITESVILLE, WV

▲ **PHILIPPI**—Philippi Communications System

PIEDMONT—See KEYSER, WV

PIERPOINT—See MULLENS, WV

PINCH—See ELKVIEW, WV

PINE BLUFF—See WYATT, WV

▲ **PINE GROVE**—CableVision Communications

PINEGROVE—See DURBIN, WV

▲ **PINEVILLE**—Wyoming Cable TV Inc.

▲ **PIPESTEM**—Helicon Cablevision

PLEASANT VALLEY—See COLFAX, WV

PLEASANT VIEW (Lincoln County)—See HAMLIN, WV

PLEASANT VIEW (Monongalia County)—See ARNETTSVILLE, WV

PLEASANTS COUNTY (portions)—See ST. MARYS, WV

POCA—See NITRO, WV

POCA—See also RED HOUSE, WV

POCAHONTAS COUNTY (portions)—See LEWISBURG, WV

▲ **POCATALICO**—Thompson Cable

POINT LICK—See CHELYAN, WV

▲ **POINT PLEASANT**—Rifkin Communications Partners

▲ **POND GAP**—Capital Cablecomm

PORT AMHERST—See CHELYAN, WV

PORTERWOOD—See PARSONS, WV

POSEY—See CHELYAN, WV

POWELLTON—See CHELYAN, WV

POWER—See WARWOOD, WV

POWHATAN—See NORTHFORK, WV

PRATT—See CHELYAN, WV

PRENTER—See CHELYAN, WV

PRENTER ROAD—See CHELYAN, WV

PRESTON COUNTY (portions)—See MORGANTOWN, WV

▲ **PRICETOWN**—CableVision Communications

PRICHARD—See CENTERVILLE, WV

▲ **PRINCETON**—Cablecomm

PROCIOUS—See MAYSEL, WV

PROCTOR—See NEW MARTINSVILLE, WV

PRUNTYTOWN—See GRAFTON, WV

▲ **PULLMAN**—CableVision Communications

PURSGLOVE—See ARNETTSVILLE, WV

PUTNAM COUNTY—See MILTON, WV

QUARRIER—See CHELYAN, WV

QUINCY—See CHELYAN, WV

QUINLAND—See MADISON, WV

QUINWOOD—See RUPERT, WV

RACHEL—See MANNINGTON, WV

RACINE—See CHELYAN, WV

▲ **RAGLAND**—FrontierVision

RAIN TREE ACRES—See FLEMINGTON, WV

RAINELLE—See RUPERT, WV

RALEIGH COUNTY (portions)—See BECKLEY, WV

RALEIGH COUNTY (portions)—See also OAK HILL, WV

RAMEY—See FANROCK, WV

RAND—See CHELYAN, WV

RANDOLPH COUNTY (unincorporated areas)—See ELLAMORE, WV

RANGER—See WAYNE, WV

RANSON—See CHARLES TOWN, WV

▲ **RAVENCLIFF**—Nesbe Cable

RAVENSWOOD—See POINT PLEASANT, WV

RAWL—See WILLIAMSON, WV

RD NO. 1 TRAILER COURTS—See WARWOOD, WV

READER—See PINE GROVE, WV

▲ **RED HOUSE**—Century Communications

RED JACKET—See MARTIN, KY

RED JACKET—See also MATEWAN, WV

REEDSVILLE—See KINGWOOD, WV

REGER—See BUCKHANNON, WV

RENSFORD—See CHELYAN, WV

RHODELL—See OAK HILL, WV

RICH CREEK—See JODIE, WV

RICH CREEK—See also PEARISBURG, VA

RICHARD—See BROOKHAVEN, WV

▲ **RICHWOOD**—CableVision Communications

RIDER—See WEST MILFORD, WV

RIDGE FARMS—See ARNETTSVILLE, WV

RIDGELEY—See CUMBERLAND, MD

RIDGEVIEW—See CHELYAN, WV

▲ **RIG**—C T & R Cable

RIPLEY—See POINT PLEASANT, WV

RIPPLEMEAD—See PEARISBURG, VA

RIPPON—See CHARLES TOWN, WV

RIVERSIDE—See CHELYAN, WV

VALLS CREEK—See WAR, WV

▲ **VARNEY**—Cooney Cable Assoc.

▲ **VAUGHAN**—Capital Cablecomm

VIENNA—See PARKERSBURG, WV

VINSON STREET—See WILLIAMSON, WV

VIVIAN—See KIMBALL, WV

WADESTOWN—See BRAVE, PA

WALKER—See MURPHYTOWN, WV

WALKERSVILLE—See IRELAND, WV

WALLACE—See FOLSOM, WV

WALLBACK—See MAYSEL, WV

WANA—See BRAVE, PA

▲ **WAR**—Thompson Cablevision Co.

▲ **WARDENSVILLE**—Valley Cable

▲ **WARWOOD**—Centre TV Cable

WARWOOD—See also WINDSOR HEIGHTS, WV

▲ **WASHINGTON**—Community Antenna Service

WASHINGTON LANDS—See MOUNDSVILLE, WV

WAVERLY—See MARIETTA, OH

▲ **WAYNE**—CableVision Communications

WAYNE COUNTY—See DUNLOW, WV

WAYNE COUNTY (northern portion)—See SOUTH POINT, OH

WAYNE COUNTY (northwestern portion)—See HUNTINGTON, WV

WAYNE COUNTY (portions)—See RAGLAND, WV

WAYNE COUNTY (unincorporated areas)—See CENTERVILLE, WV

WEBB—See GLENHAYES, WV

WEBSTER COUNTY (central portion)—See WEBSTER SPRINGS, WV

WEBSTER COUNTY (portions)—See CAMDEN ON GAULEY, WV

WEBSTER COUNTY (portions)—See also COWEN, WV

WEBSTER COUNTY (unincorporated areas)—See DIANA, WV

▲ **WEBSTER SPRINGS**—Cablecomm

▲ **WEIRTON**—TCI

▲ **WELCH**—Thompson Cablevision Co. Inc.

▲ **WELLSBURG**—TCI of West Virginia Inc.

WEST BELLE—See CHELYAN, WV

WEST HAMLIN—See HAMLIN, WV

▲ **WEST LIBERTY**—Marshall County Cable

WEST LOGAN—See LOGAN, WV

▲ **WEST MILFORD**—CableVision Communications

WEST PEA RIDGE—See HUNTINGTON, WV

▲ **WEST UNION**—CableVision Communications

▲ **WESTON**—Cablecomm

▲ **WESTOVER**—Century Huntington Co.

WETZEL COUNTY—See PINE GROVE, WV

WETZEL COUNTY (portions)—See NEW MARTINSVILLE, WV

WEVACO—See CHELYAN, WV

WHARNECLIFFE—See BENS CREEK, WV

▲ **WHEELING**—TCI of West Virginia Inc.

WHEELING—See also GLEN DALE, WV

WHEELING—See also WEST LIBERTY, WV

▲ **WHITE SULPHUR SPRINGS**—Cablevision

▲ **WHITEHALL**—Century Huntington Co.

▲ **WHITESVILLE**—Capital Cablecomm

WIDEN—See BIRCH RIVER, WV

WILEY FORD—See CUMBERLAND, MD

▲ **WILEYVILLE**—CableVision Communications

▲ **WILLIAMSON**—CableVision Communications

WILLIAMSTOWN—See MARIETTA, OH

WILLOWTON—See OAKVALE, WV

▲ **WINDSOR HEIGHTS**—Centre TV Cable

WINDSOR HEIGHTS—See also WEST LIBERTY, WV

WINFIELD—See RED HOUSE, WV

WINIFREDE—See CHELYAN, WV

WITCHER—See CHELYAN, WV

WOOD COUNTY—See PARKERSBURG, WV

WOODVILLE—See ALKOL, WV

WORTH—See NORTHFORK, WV

▲ **WORTHINGTON**—Century Huntington Co.

WORTHINGTON—See also SHINNSTON, WV

WRISTON—See SCARBRO, WV

▲ **WYATT**—West Virginia Country Cable

WYATT—See also SHINNSTON, WV

WYCO—See OAK HILL, WV

WYOMING COUNTY—See HANOVER, WV

WYOMING COUNTY (portions)—See LOGAN, WV

WYOMING COUNTY (portions)—See also OAK HILL, WV

YOLYN—See LOGAN, WV

YOUNGS BOTTOM—See ELKVIEW, WV

WISCONSIN

ABBOTSFORD—See SPENCER, WI

▲ **ADAMS**—Charter Communications Inc.

ADAMS—See also BLACK RIVER FALLS, WI

ADAMS (town)—See ADAMS, WI

ADDISON (town)—See WEST BEND, WI

ADELL—See PLYMOUTH, WI

AFTON—See JANESVILLE, WI

▲ **ALBANY**—Triax Cablevision

ALBANY TWP.—See ALBANY, WI

ALBION—See JANESVILLE, WI

▲ **ALGOMA**—Charter Communications Inc.

▲ **ALGOMA TWP.**—Charter Communications Inc.

ALLENTON—See WEST BEND, WI

ALLOUEZ—See APPLETON, WI

▲ **ALMA**—US Cable

ALMA CENTER—See INDEPENDENCE, WI

ALMENA—See DALLAS, WI

▲ **ALMOND**—Cable Systems Management of Iowa Inc.

ALTOONA—See EAU CLAIRE, WI

▲ **AMERY**—Amery Telephone Co.

▲ **AMHERST (village)**—Tomorrow Valley Cable TV Co.

AMHERST JUNCTION—See AMHERST (village), WI

AMHERST TWP. (western portion)—See AMHERST (village), WI

ANGELO—See SPARTA, WI

ANIWA—See WAUSAU, WI

ANIWA (village)—See WAUSAU, WI

▲ **ANSON TWP.**—S & K TV Systems

▲ **ANTIGO**—Charter Communications Inc.

ANTIGO (town)—See ANTIGO, WI

▲ **APPLETON**—Time Warner Cable

ARBOR VITAE—See MINOCQUA, WI

ARCADIA—See INDEPENDENCE, WI

▲ **ARENA**—Spring Green CableComm

ARENA (town)—See ARENA, WI

ARGONNE—See RHINELANDER, WI

▲ **ARGYLE**—Triax Cablevision

ARKANSAW—See DURAND, WI

ARLINGTON—See MADISON, WI

ARLINGTON (village)—See also POYNETTE, WI

ARPIN (village)—See VESPER, WI

ASHFORD—See FOND DU LAC, WI

ASHIPPUN—See OCONOMOWOC LAKE, WI

▲ **ASHLAND**—Charter Communications Inc.

ASHWAUBENON—See APPLETON, WI

ATHENS—See SPENCER, WI

▲ **AUBURNDALE**—HLM Cable Corp.

▲ **AUGUSTA**—KRM Cablevision Inc.

AURORA—See IRON MOUNTAIN, MI (Bresnan Communications Co.)

AURORA (town)—See BERLIN, WI

▲ **AVOCA**—Spring Green CableComm

AZTALAN—See JANESVILLE, WI

▲ **BAGLEY (village)**—Dairyland Cable Systems Inc.

▲ **BALDWIN (village)**—Baldwin Telecom Inc.

BALSAM LAKE—See LUCK, WI

▲ **BANCROFT**—Cable Systems Management of Iowa Inc.

BANGOR—See ONALASKA, WI

▲ **BARABOO**—Bresnan Communications Co.

BARKSDALE (town)—See ASHLAND, WI

BARNEVELD—See RIDGEWAY, WI

BARRE—See ONALASKA, WI

▲ **BARRON**—Chibardun Telephone Cooperative

BARRON—See also RICE LAKE, WI

BARRON (town)—See RICE LAKE, WI

BARTON (town)—See WEST BEND, WI

▲ **BAY CITY**—Delta Cablevision I LP

▲ **BAYFIELD**—Hadland Communications Inc.

BAYFIELD—See also ASHLAND, WI

BAYFIELD (town)—See ASHLAND, WI

BAYSIDE—See GREENFIELD (Milwaukee County), WI

▲ **BEAR CREEK**—Northern Lakes Cable TV

BEAR LAKE—See MANAWA, WI

BEAVER DAM—See HUSTISFORD, WI

BEAVER DAM (town)—See HUSTISFORD, WI

BELGIUM—See RANDOM LAKE, WI

▲ **BELL CENTER**—Richland Grant Telephone Co-op Inc.

BELLE PLAIN—See CLINTONVILLE, WI

▲ **BELLEVILLE**—Belleville CATV Inc.

BELLEVUE—See APPLETON, WI

BELMONT—See PLATTEVILLE, WI (Triax Cablevision)

▲ **BELOIT**—Charter Communications Inc.

BELOIT TWP.—See BELOIT, WI

BENTON—See PLATTEVILLE, WI (Triax Cablevision)

BERGEN TWP.—See WAUSAU, WI

▲ **BERLIN**—Charter Communications Inc.

BERLIN (town)—See BERLIN, WI

BERRY—See MADISON, WI

BEVENT—See WITTENBERG, WI

BIG BEND—See MUSKEGO, WI

BIRNAMWOOD—See WAUSAU, WI

BIRON—See WISCONSIN RAPIDS, WI

▲ **BLACK CREEK**—Charter Communications Inc.

BLACK CREEK (town)—See BLACK CREEK, WI

BLACK EARTH—See MAZOMANIE, WI

▲ **BLACK RIVER FALLS**—Charter Communications Inc.

BLACK WOLF—See ALGOMA TWP., WI

BLAIR—See INDEPENDENCE, WI

▲ **BLANCHARDVILLE**—Triax Cablevision

▲ **BLOOMER**—Charter Communications Inc.

BLOOMFIELD—See KENOSHA, WI

BLOOMFIELD (town)—See GENOA CITY, WI

BLOOMFIELD (town)—See also TUSTIN, WI

BLOOMING GROVE—See MADISON, WI

▲ **BLOOMINGDALE**—Midwest Cable

Blue Mounds—See RIDGEWAY, WI

▲ **BLUE RIVER (village)**—Dairyland Cable Systems Inc.

▲ **BLUFFVIEW**—HLM Cable Corp.

▲ **BOAZ**—Village of Boaz

▲ **BONDUEL**—Bonduel Cable TV

BOSCOBEL—See PRAIRIE DU CHIEN, WI

▲ **BOULDER JUNCTION**—Karban TV Systems Inc.

BOVINA—See BLACK CREEK, WI

BOWLER—See WAUSAU, WI

BOWLER (village)—See WAUSAU, WI

▲ **BOYCEVILLE**—Star Satellite TV & Cable

▲ **BOYD/CADOTT**—Charter Communications Inc.

BRADFORD—See JANESVILLE, WI

BRADLEY—See RHINELANDER, WI

BRADLEY (town)—See RHINELANDER, WI

▲ **BRANDON**—Charter Communications Inc.

BRIDGEPORT (town)—See PRAIRIE DU CHIEN, WI

▲ **BRIGGSVILLE**—Cable Systems Management of Iowa Inc.

▲ **BRILLION**—Charter Communications Inc.

BRISTOL—See KENOSHA, WI

BROCKWAY—See BLACK RIVER FALLS, WI

▲ **BRODHEAD**—Charter Communications

BROKAW—See WAUSAU, WI

▲ **BROOKFIELD**—Time Warner Cable

BROOKFIELD (town)—See WAUWATOSA, WI

BROOKLYN—See GREEN LAKE, WI

BROOKLYN (town)—See GREEN LAKE, WI

BROOKVIEW TRAILER COURT—See VIROQUA, WI

BROWN DEER—See GREENFIELD (Milwaukee County), WI

▲ **BROWNSVILLE**—Dodge County Cablevision

BROWNTOWN—See WINSLOW, IL

BRUCE—See LADYSMITH, WI

BRUNSWICK TWP.—See EAU CLAIRE, WI

BUCHANAN (town)—See APPLETON, WI

BUFFALO—See ALMA, WI

BURKE—See MADISON, WI

▲ **BURLINGTON**—Time Warner Cable

BURLINGTON—See also KENOSHA, WI

BURLINGTON (town)—See BURLINGTON, WI

BUTLER (village)—See WAUWATOSA, WI

BUTTE DES MORTS—See OMRO, WI

▲ **BUTTERNUT**—KRM Cablevision

▲ **CABLE**—S & K TV Systems

CALAMUS TWP.—See HUSTISFORD, WI

CALEDONIA—See KENOSHA, WI

CALEDONIA (town)—See MERRIMAC, WI

CAMBRIA—See RANDOLPH, WI

CAMBRIDGE—See MADISON, WI

CAMERON—See DALLAS, WI

CAMERON (town)—See MARSHFIELD, WI

CAMP DOUGLAS—See MAUSTON, WI

CAMPBELL—See ONALASKA, WI

CAMPBELLSPORT—See FOND DU LAC, WI

CARLTON (town)—See MISHICOT, WI

CARLTON TWP.—See MISHICOT, WI

CAROLINE—See CLINTONVILLE, WI

CASCADE—See PLYMOUTH, WI

▲ **CASCO**—Century Televideo

CASCO (town)—See CASCO, WI

CASCO (village)—See CASCO, WI

CASHTON—See VIROQUA, WI

▲ **CASSVILLE**—Spring Green CableComm

CATO—See MANITOWOC, WI

▲ **CAZENOVIA**—Community Antenna System Inc.

CEDAR GROVE—See RANDOM LAKE, WI

▲ **CEDARBURG**—Time Warner Cable

CEDARBURG—See also MEQUON, WI

CENTER—See APPLETON, WI

CENTURIA—See LUCK, WI

CHARLESTON—See CHILTON, WI

▲ **CHASEBURG**—Triax Cablevision

CHENEQUA—See OCONOMOWOC LAKE, WI

CHESTER—See HUSTISFORD, WI

CHETEK—See RICE LAKE, WI

CHETEK (town)—See RICE LAKE, WI

▲ **CHILTON**—Charter Communications Inc.

CHILTON (town)—See CHILTON, WI

CHIPPEWA FALLS—See EAU CLAIRE, WI

CHRISTIANA—See MADISON, WI

CLARNO (town)—See MONROE, WI

CLAYTON (Polk County)—See AMERY, WI

CLAYTON (Winnebago County)—See APPLETON, WI

CLEAR LAKE—See AMERY, WI

CLEVELAND—See HOWARDS GROVE, WI

CLINTON—See JANESVILLE, WI

CLINTON (village)—See JANESVILLE, WI

▲ **CLINTONVILLE**—Charter Communications Inc.

CLOVERLEAF LAKES—See CLINTONVILLE, WI

CLYMAN—See HUSTISFORD, WI

COBB—See MONTFORT, WI

▲ **LA CROSSE**—Bresnan Communications Co.

LA CROSSE—See also ONALASKA, WI

LA CROSSE—See also VIROQUA, WI

LA FARGE—See VIROQUA, WI

LA GRANGE—See BURLINGTON, WI

LA GRANGE (town)—See TOMAH, WI

▲ **LA VALLE**—Spring Green CableComm

LA VALLE (town)—See LA VALLE, WI

▲ **LAC DU FLAMBEAU**—Gauthier Cablevision

▲ **LADYSMITH**—Charter Communications Inc.

▲ **LAFAYETTE**—Charter Communications Inc.

LAFAYETTE—See also BURLINGTON, WI

LAKE—See PARK FALLS, WI

LAKE DELTON—See BARABOO, WI

LAKE GENEVA—See KENOSHA, WI

▲ **LAKE HOLCOMBE**—S & K TV Systems

LAKE MILLS—See HUSTISFORD, WI

LAKE MILLS (town)—See HUSTISFORD, WI

▲ **LAKE NEBAGAMON**—Bresnan Communications Co.

LAKE REDSTONE—See LA VALLE, WI

LAKE WISSOTA—See LAFAYETTE, WI

▲ **LANCASTER**—Spring Green CableComm

▲ **LAND O'LAKES**—Karban TV Systems Inc.

LANNON—See MENOMONEE FALLS, WI

▲ **LAONA**—Northern Lakes Cable TV

LARRABEE (town)—See CLINTONVILLE, WI

LAWRENCE (town)—See APPLETON, WI

LEBANON—See NEW LONDON, WI

LEDGEVIEW (town)—See APPLETON, WI

▲ **LENA**—Charter Communications Inc.

LEON—See SPARTA, WI

LEROY—See BROWNSVILLE, WI

LIBERY (town)—See NEW LONDON, WI

LIBERTY GROVE—See SISTER BAY, WI

LIMA—See PLYMOUTH, WI

LIMA (town)—See SHEBOYGAN, WI

LINCOLN—See EAGLE RIVER, WI

LINCOLN—See also RHINELANDER, WI

LINCOLN TWP.—See INDEPENDENCE, WI

LIND (town)—See WAUPACA, WI

LINDEN (town)—See MONTFORT, WI

LINDEN (village)—See MONTFORT, WI

LINN—See KENOSHA, WI

LINN (town)—See HARVARD, IL

LINWOOD—See STEVENS POINT, WI

LISBON—See HUSTISFORD, WI

LITTLE CHUTE—See APPLETON, WI

LITTLE SUAMICO—See APPLETON, WI

LITTLE WOLF—See MANAWA, WI

LIVINGSTON—See MONTFORT, WI

LODI—See DANE, WI

LODI (town)—See DANE, WI

▲ **LOGANVILLE (village)**—Dairyland Cable Systems Inc.

LOHRVILLE—See WAUTOMA, WI

LOMIRA—See FOND DU LAC, WI

LONE ROCK—See SPRING GREEN, WI

LONG LAKE—See RICE LAKE, WI

LOWELL—See REESEVILLE, WI

LOWVILLE TWP.—See RANDOLPH, WI

LOYAL—See SPENCER, WI

▲ **LUCK**—Vision Communications

LUXEMBURG—See CASCO, WI

LUXEMBURG (town)—See CASCO, WI

LYNXVILLE (unincorporated areas)—See SENECA (village), WI

LYONS—See KENOSHA, WI

LYONS (town)—See BURLINGTON, WI

▲ **MADISON**—Bresnan Communications Co.

MADISON (town)—See MADISON, WI

MADISON UNIVERSITY—See MADISON, WI

MAINE TWP.—See WAUSAU, WI

▲ **MANAWA**—Manawa Telecom Cable TV

▲ **MANITOWOC**—Jones Intercable

MANITOWOC (town)—See MANITOWOC, WI

MANITOWOC RAPIDS—See MANITOWOC, WI

MAPLE BLUFF—See MADISON, WI

MAPLE CREEK (town)—See NEW LONDON, WI

MARATHON CITY—See SPENCER, WI

MARCELLON—See RANDOLPH, WI

MARIBEL—See MISHICOT, WI

MARIBEL VILLAGE—See MISHICOT, WI

▲ **MARINETTE**—Time Warner Cable

MARINETTE—See also APPLETON, WI

MARION—See CLINTONVILLE, WI

MARION (town)—See WAUTOMA, WI

▲ **MARKESAN**—Charter Communications Inc.

▲ **MARQUETTE**—Cable Systems Management of Iowa Inc.

MARSHALL—See MADISON, WI

▲ **MARSHFIELD**—Charter Communications Inc.

MARSHFIELD (portions)—See AUBURNDALE, WI

MARSHFIELD TWP.—See FOND DU LAC, WI

MARTINTOWN—See WINSLOW, IL

MATTESON (town)—See CLINTONVILLE, WI

MATTOON—See WAUSAU, WI

MATTOON (village)—See WAUSAU, WI

▲ **MAUSTON**—Triax Cablevision

MAYVILLE—See HUSTISFORD, WI

▲ **MAZOMANIE**—Charter Communications Inc.

McFARLAND (village)—See MADISON, WI

McMILLAN (town)—See MARSHFIELD, WI

MEDARY—See ONALASKA, WI

▲ **MEDFORD**—Charter Communications Inc.

MEDINA—See APPLETON, WI

MEDINA (town)—See MADISON, WI

▲ **MELLEN**—KRM Cablevision

▲ **MELROSE**—Charter Communications Inc.

▲ **MELVINA**—Midwest Cable

MENASHA (town-northern portion)—See APPLETON, WI

MENOMINEE (town)—See MARINETTE, WI

▲ **MENOMONEE FALLS**—Time Warner Cable

▲ **MENOMONIE**—Charter Communications Inc.

MENOMONIE (town)—See MENOMONIE, WI

▲ **MEQUON**—Time Warner Cable

MEQUON—See also WAUWATOSA, WI

▲ **MERCER**—Karban TV Systems Inc.

MERILLAN—See INDEPENDENCE, WI

▲ **MERRILL**—Warner Cable of Merrill

▲ **MERRIMAC**—Merrimac Area Cable

MERRIMAC (town)—See MERRIMAC, WI

MERTON (town)—See OCONOMOWOC LAKE, WI

MERTON (town)—See also WAUWATOSA, WI

MIDDLETON—See MADISON, WI

MIDDLETON (town)—See MADISON, WI

▲ **MIKANA**—S & K TV Systems

MILFORD—See HUSTISFORD, WI

▲ **MILLADORE (town)**—Cable Systems Management of Iowa Inc.

MILLTOWN—See LUCK, WI

MILTON—See JANESVILLE, WI

MILTON (town)—See JANESVILLE, WI

▲ **MILWAUKEE**—Time Warner Entertainment Co. LP

▲ **MINDORO**—Charter Communications Inc.

MINERAL POINT—See DODGEVILLE, WI

▲ **MINOCQUA**—Charter Communications Inc.

▲ **MINONG**—S & K TV Systems

▲ **MISHICOT**—Charter Communications Inc.

MISHICOT (town)—See MISHICOT, WI

MISHICOT (village)—See MISHICOT, WI

MISHICOT TWP.—See MISHICOT, WI

▲ **MONDOVI**—Durand Cable Co. Inc.

MONICO—See RHINELANDER, WI

MONONA—See MADISON, WI

▲ **MONROE**—Charter Communications Inc.

▲ **MONTELLO**—Charter Communications Inc.

▲ **MONTFORT**—Spring Green CableComm

▲ **MONTICELLO**—Triax Cablevision

MONTREAL—See IRONWOOD, MI

MONVAE (town)—See MONROE, WI

MOSINEE—See WAUSAU, WI

MOSINEE (town)—See WAUSAU, WI

MOUNT CALVARY—See FOND DU LAC, WI

▲ **MOUNT HOREB**—Charter Communications Inc.

MOUNT PLEASANT—See KENOSHA, WI

MOUNT STERLING (unincorporated areas)—See SENECA (village), WI

MUKWA—See NEW LONDON, WI

MUKWONAGO (town)—See NORTH PRAIRIE, WI

MUKWONAGO (village)—See WAUWATOSA, WI

MUSCODA—See PLATTEVILLE, WI (Triax Cablevision)

▲ **MUSKEGO**—Time Warner Cable

NASAWAPI—See STURGEON BAY, WI

NASHOTA (town)—See OCONOMOWOC LAKE, WI

NECEDAH—See MAUSTON, WI

NEENAH (town)—See APPLETON, WI

NEILLSVILLE—See SPENCER, WI

NEKIMI—See ALGOMA TWP., WI

NEKOOSA—See WISCONSIN RAPIDS, WI

NELSONVILLE—See AMHERST (village), WI

NEOSHO—See HUSTISFORD, WI

NESHKORO—See WAUTOMA, WI

▲ **NEW AUBURN**—S & K TV Systems

▲ **NEW BERLIN**—Time Warner Cable

▲ **NEW FRANKEN**—PTI TeleVideo

▲ **NEW GLARUS**—Charter Communications Inc.

▲ **NEW HOLSTEIN**—Charter Communications Inc.

NEW LISBON—See MAUSTON, WI

▲ **NEW LONDON**—Charter Communications Inc.

▲ **NEW RICHMOND**—Frontier Cable

NEWBOLD—See RHINELANDER, WI

▲ **NEWBURG**—Time Warner Cable

NEWTON (town)—See MANITOWOC, WI

▲ **NIAGARA**—Niagara Community TV Co-op

NIAGARA (town)—See NIAGARA, WI

NOKOMIS—See RHINELANDER, WI

NORTH BAY—See KENOSHA, WI

NORTH FOND DU LAC—See FOND DU LAC, WI

NORTH HUDSON—See ST. CROIX, MN

▲ **NORTH PRAIRIE**—Time Warner Cable Communications Inc.

NORTHFIELD—See INDEPENDENCE, WI

NORTHPORT (village)—See NEW LONDON, WI

▲ **NORWALK**—Triax Cablevision

NORWAY—See MUSKEGO, WI

NORWAY (town)—See KENOSHA, WI

OAK CREEK—See GREENFIELD (Milwaukee County), WI

OAKDALE—See WARRENS, WI

▲ **OAKFIELD**—Charter Communications Inc.

OAKLAND (town)—See MADISON, WI

OCONOMOWOC—See HUSTISFORD, WI

OCONOMOWOC (town)—See OCONOMOWOC LAKE, WI

▲ **OCONOMOWOC LAKE**—Warner Cable Communications

▲ **OCONTO**—Charter Communications Inc.

▲ **OCONTO FALLS**—Oconto Falls Cable TV

▲ **OMRO**—Charter Communications Inc.

OMRO (town)—See ALGOMA TWP., WI

▲ **ONALASKA**—Charter Communications Inc.

ONALASKA (town)—See ONALASKA, WI

ONEIDA—See APPLETON, WI

▲ **ONTARIO**—Triax Cablevision

OOSTBURG—See RANDOM LAKE, WI

OREGON (village)—See MADISON, WI

OREGON TWP.—See MADISON, WI

▲ **ORFORDVILLE**—Triax Cablevision

OSCEOLA—See DRESSER, WI

OSHKOSH—See APPLETON, WI

OSHKOSH (town)—See APPLETON, WI

OSHKOSH (town)—See also OMRO, WI

OSSEO—See INDEPENDENCE, WI

OTSEGO—See RANDOLPH, WI

OTTAWA (town)—See NORTH PRAIRIE, WI

OWEN—See SPENCER, WI

▲ **OXFORD**—Cable Systems Management of Iowa Inc.

PACIFIC TWP.—See RANDOLPH, WI

▲ **PACKWAUKEE**—Cable Systems Management of Iowa Inc.

PADDOCK LAKE—See KENOSHA, WI

PALMYRA (town)—See WHITEWATER, WI

PALMYRA (village)—See WHITEWATER, WI

PARDEEVILLE—See RANDOLPH, WI

▲ **PARK FALLS**—Charter Communications Inc.

PARK RIDGE (village)—See STEVENS POINT, WI

PELICAN—See RHINELANDER, WI

PELL LAKE—See GENOA CITY, WI

PENCE—See IRONWOOD, MI

▲ **PEPIN**—US Cable

PESHTIGO—See MARINETTE, WI

PESHTIGO (town)—See MARINETTE, WI

PEWAUKEE (town)—See WAUWATOSA, WI

PEWAUKEE (village)—See WAUWATOSA, WI

▲ **PHELPS**—Upper Peninsula Communications

▲ **PHILLIPS**—Price County Telephone Co.

PIERCE—See ALGOMA, WI

PIGEON—See INDEPENDENCE, WI

PIGEON FALLS—See INDEPENDENCE, WI

PINE LAKE—See RHINELANDER, WI

PITTSFIELD—See APPLETON, WI

▲ **PITTSVILLE**—HLM Cable Corp.

▲ **PLAIN**—Spring Green CableComm

PLAINFIELD—See WAUTOMA, WI

▲ **PLATTEVILLE**—CenturyTel TeleVideo

▲ **PLATTEVILLE**—Triax Cablevision

PLATTEVILLE TWP. (eastern portion)—See PLATTEVILLE, WI (CenturyTel TeleVideo)

PLEASANT PRAIRIE—See KENOSHA, WI

PLEASANT SPRINGS (town)—See MADISON, WI

PLEASANT VALLEY—See EAU CLAIRE, WI

PLOVER—See STEVENS POINT, WI

PLOVER (village)—See STEVENS POINT, WI

▲ **PLUM CITY**—Durand Cable Co. Inc.

▲ **PLYMOUTH**—Warner Cable

POLK—See HUSTISFORD, WI

POLK (town)—See WEST BEND, WI

POLK COUNTY (portions)—See AMERY, WI

PORT EDWARDS—See WISCONSIN RAPIDS, WI

PORT EDWARDS (village)—See WISCONSIN RAPIDS, WI

PORT WASHINGTON—See WAUWATOSA, WI

▲ **PORTAGE**—Bresnan Communications Inc.

PORTLAND—See HUSTISFORD, WI

PORTLAND (town)—See HUSTISFORD, WI

POTOSI—See PLATTEVILLE, WI (Triax Cablevision)

POTTER—See BRILLION, WI

POUND—See COLEMAN, WI

POY SIPPI—See APPLETON, WI

▲ **POYNETTE**—Charter Communications Inc.

▲ **PRAIRIE DU CHIEN**—Triax Cablevision

PRAIRIE DU CHIEN (town)—See PRAIRIE DU CHIEN, WI

▲ **PRAIRIE DU SAC**—Charter Communications Inc.

PRAIRIE DU SAC (town)—See PRAIRIE DU SAC, WI

PRAIRIE DU SAC (village)—See PRAIRIE DU SAC, WI

PRAIRIE FARM—See DALLAS, WI

▲ **PRENTICE**—KRM Cablevision

PRESCOTT—See ST. CROIX, MN

PRESTON—See ADAMS, WI

PRINCETON—See GREEN LAKE, WI

PRINCETON (town)—See GREEN LAKE, WI

▲ **PULASKI**—Net Cable Inc.

PULCIFER—See GILLETT, WI

RACINE—See KENOSHA, WI

RANDALL—See KENOSHA, WI

RANDALL (town-Racine County)—See KENOSHA, WI

RANDALL TWP.—See GENOA CITY, WI

▲ **RANDOLPH**—Peoples Broadband Communications Systems Inc.

▲ **RANDOM LAKE**—Warner Cable

RAYMOND (town)—See KENOSHA, WI

READSTOWN—See VIROQUA, WI

RED CEDAR (town)—See MENOMONIE, WI

REDGRANITE—See WAUTOMA, WI

REEDSBURG—See BARABOO, WI

REEDSVILLE—See APPLETON, WI

▲ **REESEVILLE**—Warner Cable Communications

REMYS—See STURGEON BAY, WI

RHINE—See PLYMOUTH, WI

▲ **RHINELANDER**—Rhinelander Cable TV

▲ **RIB LAKE**—Rib Lake Telecom Inc.

RIB MOUNTAIN—See WAUSAU, WI

▲ **RICE LAKE**—Charter Communications Inc.

RICE LAKE (town)—See RICE LAKE, WI

▲ **RICHFIELD**—Charter Communications Inc.

▲ **RICHLAND CENTER**—Bresnan Communications Co.

RICHMOND—See NEW RICHMOND, WI

RICHMOND—See also SHAWANO, WI

RIDGELAND—See DALLAS, WI

▲ **RIDGEWAY**—Spring Green CableComm

RINGLE (town)—See WAUSAU, WI

RIO—See RANDOLPH, WI

RIVER FALLS—See ST. CROIX, MN

RIVER HILLS—See GREENFIELD (Milwaukee County), WI

▲ **ROBERTS**—Vision Communications

ROCHESTER—See BURLINGTON, WI

ROCHESTER—See also KENOSHA, WI

ROCHESTER (village)—See BURLINGTON, WI

ROCK TWP.—See JANESVILLE, WI

ROLLING—See ANTIGO, WI

ROLLING (town)—See ANTIGO, WI

▲ **ROME TWP.**—SCA Cable Inc.

▲ **ROSENDALE**—Charter Communications Inc.

▲ **ROSHOLT**—Cable Systems Management of Iowa Inc.

ROTHSCHILD—See WAUSAU, WI

ROXBURY—See PRAIRIE DU SAC, WI

ROYALTON—See NEW LONDON, WI

ROYALTON TWP.—See MANAWA, WI

ROYALTON TWP.—See also WAUPACA, WI

▲ **ROZELLVILLE**—Cable Systems Management of Iowa Inc.

▲ **RUDOLPH**—HLM Cable Corp.

RUDOLPH (town)—See WISCONSIN RAPIDS, WI

SALEM—See KENOSHA, WI

SAND CREEK—See DALLAS, WI

SAND LAKE—See HAYWARD, WI

SARATOGA—See WISCONSIN RAPIDS, WI

▲ **SAUK CITY**—Bresnan Communications Inc.

SAUKVILLE (village)—See WAUWATOSA, WI

▲ **SAXEVILLE**—Cable Systems Management of Iowa Inc.

* **SAYNER**—Northern Lights Cable Corp.

SCANDINAVIA—See IOLA, WI

SCHOFIELD—See WAUSAU, WI

SENECA—See WISCONSIN RAPIDS, WI

▲ **SENECA (village)**—Dairyland Cable Systems Inc.

SEVASTAPOL—See STURGEON BAY, WI

▲ **SEXTONVILLE**—Spring Green CableComm

SEYMOUR TWP.—See EAU CLAIRE, WI

▲ **SHARON**—TCI Cablevision of Wisconsin Inc.

SHARON (town)—See STEVENS POINT, WI

▲ **SHAWANO**—Charter Communications Inc.

▲ **SHEBOYGAN**—Charter Communications Inc.

SHEBOYGAN (town)—See SHEBOYGAN, WI

SHEBOYGAN FALLS—See SHEBOYGAN, WI

SHEBOYGAN FALLS (town)—See SHEBOYGAN, WI

SHELBY—See LA CROSSE, WI

SHELBY—See also VIROQUA, WI

SHELL LAKE—See SPOONER, WI

SHERMAN TWP.—See RANDOM LAKE, WI

SHERWOOD (village)—See APPLETON, WI

SHIOCTON—See BLACK CREEK, WI

SHOREWOOD—See GREENFIELD (Milwaukee County), WI

SHOREWOOD HILLS—See MADISON, WI

SHULLSBURG—See PLATTEVILLE, WI (Triax Cablevision)

SILVER LAKE—See KENOSHA, WI

▲ **SIREN**—Vision Communications

▲ **SISTER BAY**—Charter Communications Inc.

SLINGER—See HUSTISFORD, WI

SOLDIER'S GROVE—See VIROQUA, WI

▲ **SOLON SPRINGS**—Vision Communications

SOMERS—See KENOSHA, WI

▲ **SOMERSET**—Somerset Communications

SOUTH BYRON—See BROWNSVILLE, WI

SOUTH MILWAUKEE—See GREENFIELD (Milwaukee County), WI

SOUTH MISHICOT—See MISHICOT, WI

SOUTH WAYNE—See WINSLOW, IL

SPACIOUS ACRES TRAILER COURT—See HUSTISFORD, WI

▲ **SPARTA**—Charter Communications Inc.

SPARTA (city)—See SPARTA, WI

SPARTA (town)—See SPARTA, WI

▲ **SPENCER**—Charter Communications Inc.

SPENCER (village)—See SPENCER, WI

▲ **SPOONER**—Charter Communications Inc.

SPREAD EAGLE—See IRON MOUNTAIN, MI (Bresnan Communications Co.)

▲ **SPRING GREEN**—Spring Green CableComm

SPRING GREEN (town)—See SPRING GREEN, WI

SPRING GREEN RESORT—See SPRING GREEN, WI

SPRING PRAIRIE—See KENOSHA, WI

▲ **SPRING VALLEY**—DeMarce TV & Cable

SPRINGFIELD—See DANE, WI

ST. CLOUD—See FOND DU LAC, WI

ST. CROIX FALLS—See DRESSER, WI

ST. FRANCIS—See WAUWATOSA, WI

▲ **ST. JOSEPH**—Charter Communications Inc.

▲ **ST. JOSEPH TWP.**—Tele-Communications Cable Co.

ST. NAZIANZ—See APPLETON, WI

▲ **STANLEY**—Charter Communications Inc.

STANTON—See NEW RICHMOND, WI

STAR PRAIRIE (town)—See NEW RICHMOND, WI

STAR PRAIRIE (village)—See NEW RICHMOND, WI

STELLA—See RHINELANDER, WI

▲ **STETSONVILLE**—KRM Cablevision

STETTIN—See WAUSAU, WI

WISCONSIN DELLS—See BARABOO, WI

▲ **WISCONSIN RAPIDS**—Charter Communications Inc.

WITHEE—See SPENCER, WI

▲ **WITTENBERG**—Wittenberg Cable TV

▲ **WOLF RIVER**—Cable Systems Management of Iowa Inc.

▲ **WONEWOC**—Spring Green CableComm

▲ **WOODMAN**—Woodman TV Cable System

WOODRUFF—See MINOCQUA, WI

WOODVILLE (town)—See APPLETON, WI

WOODVILLE (village)—See BALDWIN (village), WI

WRIGHTSTOWN—See APPLETON, WI

WYOCENA TWP.—See RANDOLPH, WI

YORKVILLE—See BURLINGTON, WI

YORKVILLE—See also KENOSHA, WI

WYOMING

▲ **AFTON**—Blackstone Cable LLC

ALBANY COUNTY—See LARAMIE, WY

BAR NUNN—See CASPER, WY

BASIN—See GREYBULL, WY

BIG HORN COUNTY—See GREYBULL, WY

▲ **BIG PINEY**—Blackstone Cable LLC

BRIDGER VALLEY—See LYMAN, WY

▲ **BUFFALO**—TCI Cablevision of Wyoming Inc.

▲ **BURNS**—B & C Cablevision Inc.

CAMPBELL COUNTY—See GILLETTE, WY

CARBON COUNTY (portions)—See SARATOGA, WY

▲ **CASPER**—TCI Cablevision of Casper

▲ **CHEYENNE**—TCI Cablevision of Wyoming

▲ **CODY**—TCI Cablevision of Wyoming

▲ **COKEVILLE**—All West Inc.

▲ **COWLEY**—Cowley Telecable Inc.

DAYTON—See RANCHESTER, WY

DIAMONDVILLE—See KEMMERER, WY

▲ **DOUGLAS**—CommuniComm Services

▲ **DUBOIS**—Blackstone Cable LLC

EAST THERMOPOLIS—See THERMOPOLIS, WY

▲ **EDGERTON**—Tongue River Cable TV

ELK MOUNTAIN—See SARATOGA, WY

ELMO—See SARATOGA, WY

ENCAMPMENT—See SARATOGA, WY

▲ **EVANSTON**—Century Communications

EVANSVILLE—See CASPER, WY

FORT BRIDGER—See LYMAN, WY

FORT LARAMIE—See GUERNSEY, WY

FOX FARM COLLEGE—See CHEYENNE, WY

FREMONT COUNTY—See LANDER, WY

FREMONT COUNTY—See also RIVERTON, WY

FRONTIER—See KEMMERER, WY

▲ **GARDENS NORTH**—Galaxy Cablevision

▲ **GILLETTE**—AT&T Cable Services

▲ **GLENDO**—CommuniComm Services

▲ **GLENROCK**—CommuniComm Services

GOSHEN COUNTY (unincorporated areas)—See TORRINGTON, WY

▲ **GRANGER**—Union Cable Co.

▲ **GREEN RIVER**—Green River Cable TV Co.

▲ **GREYBULL**—TCI Cablevision of Wyoming Inc.

▲ **GUERNSEY**—Guernsey Community TV System

HANNA—See SARATOGA, WY

HARTVILLE—See GUERNSEY, WY

HOT SPRINGS COUNTY—See THERMOPOLIS, WY

HUDSON—See SHOSHONI, WY

▲ **HULETT**—Tongue River Cable TV Inc.

▲ **JACKSON**—AT&T Cable Services

JAMES TOWN—See GREEN RIVER, WY

JOHNSON COUNTY—See BUFFALO, WY

▲ **KEMMERER**—Blackstone Cable LLC

▲ **LA BARGE**—Blackstone Cable LLC

▲ **LANDER**—TCI Cablevision of Wyoming Inc.

▲ **LARAMIE**—TCI Cablevision of Wyoming

LARAMIE COUNTY—See CHEYENNE, WY

LINGLE—See TORRINGTON, WY

▲ **LOVELL**—Lovell Cable TV Co.

▲ **LUSK**—CommuniComm Services

▲ **LYMAN**—Blackstone Cable LLC

▲ **MAMMOTH HOT SPRINGS**—North Yellowstone Cable TV

MARBLETON—See BIG PINEY, WY

▲ **MEDICINE BOW**—Blackstone Cable LLC

▲ **MEETEETSE**—Blackstone Cable LLC

MIDWEST—See EDGERTON, WY

MILLS—See CASPER, WY

▲ **MOORCROFT**—TCI Cablevision of Wyoming Inc.

MOUNTAIN VIEW (Natrona County)—See CASPER, WY

▲ **MOUNTAIN VIEW (Uinta County)**—Union Cable Co.

NATRONA COUNTY—See CASPER, WY

▲ **NEWCASTLE**—TCI Cablevision of Wyoming Inc.

NORTH ROCK SPRINGS—See ROCK SPRINGS, WY

OAKLEY—See KEMMERER, WY

OLD BALDY—See SARATOGA, WY

▲ **OPAL**—Union Cable Co.

▲ **OSAGE**—Tongue River Cable TV Inc.

PARADISE VALLEY—See CASPER, WY

PARK COUNTY—See CODY, WY

▲ **PINE BLUFFS**—Pine Bluffs Community TV System

▲ **PINE HAVEN**—Tongue River Cable TV Inc.

▲ **PINEDALE**—Blackstone Cable LLC

PLATTE COUNTY (unincorporated areas)—See WHEATLAND, WY

▲ **POWELL**—TCI Cablevision of Wyoming Inc.

RAFTER J RANCH—See JACKSON, WY

▲ **RANCHESTER**—Tongue River Cable TV Inc.

▲ **RAWLINS**—TCI Cablevision of Wyoming Inc.

RELIANCE—See ROCK SPRINGS, WY

▲ **RENO JUNCTION**—TCI Cablevision of Wyoming Inc.

RIVERSIDE—See SARATOGA, WY

▲ **RIVERTON**—TCI Cablevision of Wyoming Inc.

RIVERTON—See also GARDENS NORTH, WY

▲ **ROCK SPRINGS**—Sweetwater Cable TV Co. Inc.

ROLLING HILLS—See GLENROCK, WY

▲ **SARATOGA**—CommuniComm Services

▲ **SHERIDAN**—AT&T Cable Services

SHERIDAN COUNTY—See SHERIDAN, WY

▲ **SHOSHONI**—Winhill Corp.

SINCLAIR—See RAWLINS, WY

SLEEPY HOLLOW—See GILLETTE, WY

SOUTH GREELEY—See CHEYENNE, WY

SOUTH PARK—See JACKSON, WY

SOUTH TORRINGTON—See TORRINGTON, WY

▲ **STORY**—Tongue River Cable TV Inc.

SUBLETTE COUNTY—See PINEDALE, WY

▲ **SUNDANCE**—Sundance Cable TV Inc.

SWEETWATER COUNTY—See GREEN RIVER, WY

SWEETWATER COUNTY (unincorporated areas)—See ROCK SPRINGS, WY

▲ **TEN SLEEP**—Ten Sleep Cablevision

TETON COUNTY—See JACKSON, WY

TETON VILLAGE—See JACKSON, WY

▲ **THERMOPOLIS**—TCI Cablevision of Wyoming Inc.

▲ **TORRINGTON**—James Cable Partners

UINTA COUNTY—See LYMAN, WY

UINTA COUNTY (portions)—See EVANSTON, WY

▲ **UPTON**—TCI Cablevision of Wyoming Inc.

URIE—See LYMAN, WY

▲ **WAMSUTTER**—Sweetwater Cable TV Co. Inc.

WARREN AFB—See CHEYENNE, WY

WASHAKIE COUNTY—See WORLAND, WY

WESTON COUNTY—See NEWCASTLE, WY

▲ **WHEATLAND**—CommuniComm Services

WILSON—See JACKSON, WY

▲ **WORLAND**—TCI Cablevision of Wyoming Inc.

WRIGHT—See RENO JUNCTION, WY

▲ **WYODAK**—Tongue River Cable TV Inc.

PUERTO RICO

ADJUNTAS—See MERCEDITA, PR

AGUADA—See AGUADILLA, PR

▲ **AGUADILLA**—Pegasus Cable Television

AGUAS BUENAS—See CAGUAS, PR

AIBONITO—See CAYEY, PR

ANASCO—See MAYAGUEZ, PR

▲ **ARECIBO**—TCI Cablevision of Puerto Rico

ARROYO—See MERCEDITA, PR

BARCELONETA—See ARECIBO, PR

▲ **BARRANQUITAS**—BuenaVision

BAYAMON—See SAN JUAN, PR

CABA ROJO—See MAYAGUEZ, PR

▲ **CAGUAS**—BuenaVision

CAMUY—See ARECIBO, PR

CANOVANAS—See LUQUILLO, PR

CAROLINA—See SAN JUAN, PR

CATANO—See LEVITTOWN, PR

▲ **CAYEY**—BuenaVision

CEIBA—See LUQUILLO, PR

▲ **CEIBA NAVAL BASE**—Americable International Roosevelt Roads Inc.

CIDRA—See CAGUAS, PR

COAMO—See MERCEDITA, PR

COMERIO—See BARRANQUITAS, PR

DORADO—See VEGA BAJA, PR

FAJARDO—See LUQUILLO, PR

GUANICA—See MAYAGUEZ, PR

GUAYAMA—See MERCEDITA, PR

GUAYANILLA—See MERCEDITA, PR

GUAYNABO—See SAN JUAN, PR

GURABO—See CAGUAS, PR

HATILLO—See ARECIBO, PR

HORMIGUEROS—See MAYAGUEZ, PR

▲ **HUMACAO**—BuenaVision

ISABELA—See AGUADILLA, PR

JAYUYA—See MERCEDITA, PR

JUANA DIAZ—See MERCEDITA, PR

JUNCOS—See CAGUAS, PR

LAJAS—See MAYAGUEZ, PR

LAS MARIAS—See MAYAGUEZ, PR

LAS PIEDRAS—See HUMACAO, PR

▲ **LEVITTOWN**—Community Cablevision of Puerto Rico

LOIZA—See LUQUILLO, PR

▲ **LUQUILLO**—TCI Cablevision of Puerto Rico

MANATI—See VEGA BAJA, PR

MARICAO—See MAYAGUEZ, PR

MAUNABO—See MERCEDITA, PR

▲ **MAYAGUEZ**—Pegasus Communications of Puerto Rico

▲ **MERCEDITA**—Teleponce Cable TV Inc.

MOCA—See AGUADILLA, PR

NAGUABO—See LUQUILLO, PR

NARANJITO—See BARRANQUITAS, PR

PATILLAS—See MERCEDITA, PR

PENUELAS—See MERCEDITA, PR

PLAYA DE PONCE—See MERCEDITA, PR

PONCE—See MERCEDITA, PR

QUEBRADILLAS—See AGUADILLA, PR

RINCON—See MAYAGUEZ, PR

RIO GRANDE—See LUQUILLO, PR

SABANNA GRANDE—See MAYAGUEZ, PR

SALINAS—See MERCEDITA, PR

SAN GERMAN—See MAYAGUEZ, PR

▲ **SAN JUAN**—Cable TV of Greater San Juan

SAN LORENZO—See CAGUAS, PR

SANTA ISABEL—See MERCEDITA, PR

TALLABOA—See MERCEDITA, PR

TOA ALTA—See LEVITTOWN, PR

TOA BAJA—See LEVITTOWN, PR

TRUJILLO ALTO—See SAN JUAN, PR

VEGA ALTA—See VEGA BAJA, PR

▲ **VEGA BAJA**—TCI Cablevision of Puerto Rico

VILLALBA—See MERCEDITA, PR

YABUCOA—See HUMACAO, PR

YAUCO—See MERCEDITA, PR

CUBA

▲ **GUANTANAMO BAY**—Antilles Cable

GUAM

▲ **AGANA**—Guam Cable TV

MARIANA ISLAND

▲ **SAIPAN**—Saipan Cable TV

TINIAN—See SAIPAN

VIRGIN ISLANDS

▲ **ST. CROIX**—St. Croix Cable TV

ST. JOHN—See ST. THOMAS, VI

▲ **ST. THOMAS**—Caribbean Communications Corp.

Wireless Cable Community Index

This is an index of all communities served by cable systems in the icarus database. The followings ymbols indicate the type of service. A delta indicates an operating cable system. An asterisk indicates a cable franchise awarded but not yet operating. Crossreferences in all capital letter (e.g.**LAWSON**) indicate communities served by an operating cable system. Cross references with an initial captial letter (e.g. **Williams**) indicate service planned by operating cable systems.

ALABAMA

▲ **ATHENS**—Madison Communications Inc.

ATHENS—See also HUNTSVILLE, AL

BALDWIN COUNTY (portions)—See BUCKS, AL

BAY MINETTE—See BUCKS, AL

▲ **BUCKS**—Wireless One of Bucks

CITRONELLE—See BUCKS, AL

DAPHNE—See BUCKS, AL

▲ **DEMOPOLIS**—Wireless One of Demopolis

▲ **DOTHAN**—Wireless One of Dothan

FAIRHOPE—See BUCKS, AL

▲ **FLORENCE**—Wireless One of Florence

▲ **GADSDEN**—Wireless One of Gadsden

GRAND BAY—See BUCKS, AL

GRAND BAY—See also MOBILE, AL

▲ **HUNTSVILLE**—Wireless One of Huntsville

IRVINGTON—See MOBILE, AL

LOXLEY—See BUCKS, AL

MADISON—See HUNTSVILLE, AL

▲ **MOBILE**—Mobile Wireless TV

MOBILE—See also BUCKS, AL

MOBILE COUNTY—See BUCKS, AL

MOBILE COUNTY—See also MOBILE, AL

PERDIDO—See BUCKS, AL

SARALAND—See BUCKS, AL

SATSUMA—See BUCKS, AL

SEMMES—See BUCKS, AL

SILVERHILL—See BUCKS, AL

THEODORE—See BUCKS, AL

▲ **TUSCALOOSA**—Wireless One of Tuscaloosa

WASHINGTON COUNTY (portions)—See BUCKS, AL

WILMER—See BUCKS, AL

ALASKA

▲ **ANCHORAGE**—Alaskan Choice Television

▲ **ANCHORAGE**—American Telecasting of Anchorage Inc.

▲ **FAIRBANKS**—Alaskan Choice Television

WASILLA—See ANCHORAGE, AK (Alaskan Choice Television)

ARIZONA

▲ **FLAGSTAFF**—Microwave Communication Services

▲ **PHOENIX**—People's Choice TV

▲ **TUCSON**—People's Choice TV

▲ **VERDE VALLEY**—Virginia Communications Inc.

▲ **YUMA**—Microlink Television

ARKANSAS

BONO—See PARAGOULD, AR

▲ **FORT SMITH**—Nucentrix Broadband Networks Inc.

JONESBORO—See PARAGOULD, AR

▲ **LITTLE ROCK**—American Telecasting of Little Rock Inc.

MARMADUKE—See PARAGOULD, AR

▲ **PARAGOULD**—Nucentrix Broadband Networks Inc.

RECTOR—See PARAGOULD, AR

TRUMANN—See PARAGOULD, AR

CALIFORNIA

ANDERSON—See REDDING, CA

▲ **BAKERSFIELD**—CS Wireless Systems Inc.

CARUTHERS—See FRESNO, CA

EASTON—See FRESNO, CA

EL DORADO COUNTY (portions)—See SACRAMENTO, CA

▲ **FRESNO**—Choice TV

KESWICK—See REDDING, CA

▲ **MERCED**—Choice TV

▲ **MONTEREY**—American Telecasting of Monterey Bay Inc.

OLINDA—See REDDING, CA

PLACER COUNTY (portions)—See SACRAMENTO, CA

RED BLUFF—See REDDING, CA

▲ **REDDING**—American Telecasting of Redding Inc.

▲ **RIVERSIDE & SAN BERNARDINO**—Cross Country Wireless Cable

ROUND MOUNTAIN—See REDDING, CA

▲ **SACRAMENTO**—Pacific West Cable TV

▲ * **SAN FRANCISCO**—Videowave Television

▲ **SAN JOSE**—Pacific Bell Video Services

▲ * **SAN JOSE**—Videowave Television

▲ **SAN LUIS OBISPO**—TVCN

SHINGLETOWN—See REDDING, CA

▲ * **STOCKTON**—CAI Wireless Systems Inc.

▲ **VISALIA**—Choice TV

YOLO COUNTY (portions)—See SACRAMENTO, CA

▲ **YUBA CITY**—American Telecasting of Yuba City Inc.

COLORADO

AVONDALE—See COLORADO SPRINGS, CO

CALHAN—See COLORADO SPRINGS, CO

▲ **COLORADO SPRINGS**—American Telecasting of Colorado Springs Inc.

▲ **DENVER**—American Telecasting of Denver Inc.

ELLICOTT—See COLORADO SPRINGS, CO

▲ **FORT COLLINS**—American Telecasting of Fort Collins Inc.

FOUNTAIN—See COLORADO SPRINGS, CO

FOWLER—See COLORADO SPRINGS, CO

MONUMENT—See COLORADO SPRINGS, CO

ORDWAY—See COLORADO SPRINGS, CO

PENROSE—See COLORADO SPRINGS, CO

PUEBLO—See COLORADO SPRINGS, CO

ROCKY FORD—See COLORADO SPRINGS, CO

RUSH—See COLORADO SPRINGS, CO

▲ **WRAY**—Southwest Telecommunications

YODER—See COLORADO SPRINGS, CO

YUMA COUNTY—See WRAY, CO

CONNECTICUT

▲ ***HARTFORD**—Connecticut Choice Television Inc.

DISTRICT OF COLUMBIA

▲ **WASHINGTON**—Washington Choice

WASHINGTON—See also FAIRFAX, VA

FLORIDA

ALACHUA COUNTY—See GAINESVILLE, FL

BAKER COUNTY (portions)—See GAINESVILLE, FL

BAY COUNTY—See PANAMA CITY, FL

▲ ***BRADENTON**—American Telecasting Inc.

BRADFORD COUNTY—See GAINESVILLE, FL

BREVARD COUNTY—See MELBOURNE, FL

BRONSON—See GAINESVILLE, FL

CALHOUN COUNTY (portions)—See PANAMA CITY, FL

CHIPLEY—See PANAMA CITY, FL

CITRA—See GAINESVILLE, FL

COCOA—See MELBOURNE, FL

COLUMBIA COUNTY (portions)—See GAINESVILLE, FL

▲ **DAYTONA BEACH**—American Telecasting of Daytona Beach

EBRO—See PANAMA CITY, FL

ESCAMBIA COUNTY—See PENSACOLA, FL

▲ FORT MYERS—Superview of Fort Myers

▲ FORT PIERCE—Wireless Broadcasting of Fort Pierce

▲ FORT WALTON BEACH—Wireless One of Fort Walton Beach

FORT WHITE—See GAINESVILLE, FL

FOUNTAIN—See PANAMA CITY, FL

▲ GAINESVILLE—Wireless One of Gainesville

GULF BREEZE—See PENSACOLA, FL

GULF COUNTY (portions)—See PANAMA CITY, FL

HAMPTON—See GAINESVILLE, FL

HAWTHORNE—See GAINESVILLE, FL

HIGH SPRINGS—See GAINESVILLE, FL

HILLSBOROUGH COUNTY—See TAMPA, FL

▲ JACKSONVILLE—American Telecasting of Jacksonville Inc.

JAY—See PENSACOLA, FL

LAKE BUTLER—See GAINESVILLE, FL

▲ LAKELAND—American Telecasting of Lakeland Inc.

LAWTEY—See GAINESVILLE, FL

LEVY COUNTY (portions)—See GAINESVILLE, FL

LYNN HAVEN—See PANAMA CITY, FL

MARTIN COUNTY—See FORT PIERCE, FL

McDAVID—See PENSACOLA, FL

▲ MELBOURNE—Wireless Broadcasting of Melbourne

MELROSE—See GAINESVILLE, FL

MERRITT ISLAND—See MELBOURNE, FL

NEWBERRY—See GAINESVILLE, FL

▲ ORLANDO—American Telecasting of Central Florida Inc.

PALM BAY—See MELBOURNE, FL

▲ PANAMA CITY—Wireless One of Panama City

PASCO COUNTY—See TAMPA, FL

▲ PENSACOLA—Wireless One of Pensacola

PINELLAS COUNTY—See TAMPA, FL

▲ POLK COUNTY—People's Wireless Cable

PUTNAM COUNTY (portions)—See GAINESVILLE, FL

REDDICK—See GAINESVILLE, FL

ROCKLEDGE—See MELBOURNE, FL

SANTA ROSA (portions)—See PENSACOLA, FL

ST. LUCIE COUNTY—See FORT PIERCE, FL

STARKE—See GAINESVILLE, FL

▲ TALLAHASSEE—Wireless One of Tallahassee

▲ TAMPA—Video Wave Television

UNION COUNTY—See GAINESVILLE, FL

VERNON—See PANAMA CITY, FL

WALDO—See GAINESVILLE, FL

WALTON COUNTY (portions)—See PANAMA CITY, FL

WASHINGTON COUNTY (portions)—See PANAMA CITY, FL

WILLISTON—See GAINESVILLE, FL

YOUNGSTOWN—See PANAMA CITY, FL

GEORGIA

▲ ALBANY—Wireless One of Albany

▲ ATLANTA—Bell South Entertainment

BALDWIN COUNTY—See JEFFERSONVILLE, GA

BIBB COUNTY—See JEFFERSONVILLE, GA

BUTTS COUNTY (portions)—See JEFFERSONVILLE, GA

BYRON—See JEFFERSONVILLE, GA

▲ CHARING—Wireless One of Charing

DANVILLE—See JEFFERSONVILLE, GA

FORSYTH—See JEFFERSONVILLE, GA

GORDON—See JEFFERSONVILLE, GA

JASPER COUNTY—See JEFFERSONVILLE, GA

▲ JEFFERSONVILLE—Wireless One of Jeffersonville

JONES COUNTY—See JEFFERSONVILLE, GA

LIZELLA—See JEFFERSONVILLE, GA

MACON—See JEFFERSONVILLE, GA

MILLEDGEVILLE—See JEFFERSONVILLE, GA

MONROE COUNTY—See JEFFERSONVILLE, GA

MONTICELLO—See JEFFERSONVILLE, GA

PERRY—See JEFFERSONVILLE, GA

TOOMSBORO—See JEFFERSONVILLE, GA

TWIGGS COUNTY—See JEFFERSONVILLE, GA

WARNER ROBINS—See JEFFERSONVILLE, GA

WILKINSON COUNTY—See JEFFERSONVILLE, GA

HAWAII

▲ HONOLULU—GTE Media Ventures

▲ MAUI—Maui Cablevision Corp.

IDAHO

▲ BOISE—Wireless Broadcasting Systems

CALDWELL—See BOISE, ID

COEUR D'ALENE—See SPOKANE, WA

EMMETT—See BOISE, ID

KUNA—See BOISE, ID

MERIDIAN—See BOISE, ID

NAMPA—See BOISE, ID

PAYETTE—See BOISE, ID

POST FALLS—See SPOKANE, WA

▲ TWIN FALLS—Teton Wireless Television

ILLINOIS

▲ BLOOMINGTON—Microwave Cable Corp.

▲ CHAMPAIGN & URBANA—Nucentrix Broadband Networks Inc.

▲ CHICAGO—Preferred Entertainment of Chicago

▲ FREEPORT—Nucentrix Broadband Networks Inc.

▲ JACKSONVILLE—Nucentrix Broadband Networks Inc.

▲ MACOMB—Nucentrix Broadband Networks Inc.

MADISON COUNTY—See ST. LOUIS, MO

▲ McLEANSBORO—Nucentrix Broadband Networks Inc.

MONROE COUNTY—See ST. LOUIS, MO

NORMAL—See BLOOMINGTON, IL

▲ OLNEY—Nucentrix Broadband Networks Inc.

▲ *PEORIA—Nucentrix Broadband Networks Inc.

▲ ROCKFORD—Wireless Cable Systems Inc.

ST. CLAIR COUNTY—See ST. LOUIS, MO

▲ TAYLORVILLE—Nucentrix Broadband Networks Inc.

▲ VANDALIA—Nucentrix Broadband Networks Inc.

INDIANA

ADAMS COUNTY—See FORT WAYNE, IN

ALLEN COUNTY—See FORT WAYNE, IN

▲ *ANDERSON—Broadcast Cable Inc.

AUSTIN—See SCOTTSBURG, IN

CLARK COUNTY (northern portion)—See HENRYVILLE, IN

CLARK COUNTY (portions)—See SCOTTSBURG, IN

CROTHERSVILLE—See SCOTTSBURG, IN

DE KALB COUNTY—See FORT WAYNE, IN

ELKHART COUNTY—See MICHIANA, IN

▲ EVANSVILLE—Ohio Valley Wireless Ltd.

▲ FORT WAYNE—Choice TV of Fort Wayne

▲ HENRYVILLE—Insight Communications

HUNTINGTON COUNTY—See FORT WAYNE, IN

▲ INDIANAPOLIS—People's Choice TV

KOSCIUSKO COUNTY—See MICHIANA, IN

LA PORTE COUNTY—See MICHIANA, IN

LEXINGTON—See SCOTTSBURG, IN

LITTLE YORK—See SCOTTSBURG, IN

MARSHALL COUNTY—See MICHIANA, IN

▲ MICHIANA—American Telecasting of Michiana Inc.

Monroe—See HENRYVILLE, IN

NOBLE COUNTY—See FORT WAYNE, IN

▲ SALEM—Insight Communications

SCOTT COUNTY (portions)—See SCOTTSBURG, IN

▲ SCOTTSBURG—Insight Communications

▲ SOUTH BEND—Choice TV

ST. JOSEPH COUNTY—See MICHIANA, IN

UNDERWOOD—See SCOTTSBURG, IN

VIENNA—See SCOTTSBURG, IN

WASHINGTON COUNTY—See SALEM, IN

WELLS COUNTY—See FORT WAYNE, IN

WHITLEY COUNTY—See FORT WAYNE, IN

IOWA

AGENCY—See BATAVIA, IA

▲ **BATAVIA**—Iowa Rural TV Inc.

BLOOMFIELD—See BATAVIA, IA

▲ **CEDAR FALLS**—TCI of Northern Iowa

DICKINSON COUNTY—See RUTHVEN, IA

DOUDS—See BATAVIA, IA

ELDON—See BATAVIA, IA

EMMET COUNTY—See RUTHVEN, IA

▲ **EVERLY**—Evertek

FAIRFIELD—See BATAVIA, IA

FLORIS—See BATAVIA, IA

KOSSUTH COUNTY—See RUTHVEN, IA

LIBERTYVILLE—See BATAVIA, IA

OTTUMWA—See BATAVIA, IA

PACKWOOD—See BATAVIA, IA

PALO ALTO COUNTY—See RUTHVEN, IA

PULASKI—See BATAVIA, IA

▲ **RUTHVEN**—Terril Cable Systems

▲ **STORY CITY**—Nucentrix Broadband Networks Inc.

TROY—See BATAVIA, IA

▲ **WATERLOO**—Wireless Cable TV of Waterloo

KANSAS

▲ **BELOIT**—Nucentrix Broadband Networks Inc.

▲ **CHANUTE**—Nucentrix Broadband Networks Inc.

CHANUTE—See also SHAW, KS

ERIE—See SHAW, KS

INDEPENDENCE—See SHAW, KS

IOLA—See SHAW, KS

▲ **MANHATTAN**—Nucentrix Broadband Networks Inc.

▲ **MARION**—Nucentrix Broadband Networks Inc.

▲ **MEDICINE LODGE**—Nucentrix Broadband Networks Inc.

PARSONS—See SHAW, KS

▲ **RICE COUNTY**—Nucentrix Broadband Network Inc.

▲ **SALINA**—TVCN

▲ **SHAW**—Nucentrix Broadband Networks Inc.

ST. PAUL—See SHAW, KS

▲ **WICHITA**—American Telecasting of Wichita Inc.

KENTUCKY

▲ **LEXINGTON**—Wireless Associates LP

▲ **LOUISVILLE**—Superview of Louisville

▲ **PADUCAH**—NDW II Inc.

LOUISIANA

ACADIA PARISH (portions)—See LAFAYETTE, LA

▲ **ALEXANDRIA**—Wireless One of Alexandria

ALEXANDRIA—See also BUNKIE, LA

ALLEN PARISH (portions)—See BUNKIE, LA

ALLEN PARISH (portions)—See also LAKE CHARLES, LA

AVOYELLES PARISH—See BUNKIE, LA

BASTROP—See MONROE, LA

BEAUREGARD PARISH (portions)—See LAKE CHARLES, LA

BONITA—See MONROE, LA

BROUSSARD—See LAFAYETTE, LA

▲ **BUNKIE**—Wireless One of Bunkie

CALCASIEU PARISH—See LAKE CHARLES, LA

CAMERON PARISH (portions)—See LAKE CHARLES, LA

CHENEYVILLE—See BUNKIE, LA

CHOUDRANT—See MONROE, LA

COLLINSTON—See MONROE, LA

COTTONPORT—See BUNKIE, LA

CROWLEY—See LAFAYETTE, LA

DOWNSVILLE—See MONROE, LA

ELTON—See LAKE CHARLES, LA

EROS—See MONROE, LA

EVANGELINE PARISH—See BUNKIE, LA

FARMERVILLE—See MONROE, LA

GLENMORA—See BUNKIE, LA

HESSMER—See BUNKIE, LA

▲ **HOUMA**—Wireless One of Houma

IBERIA—See LAFAYETTE, LA

IOWA—See LAKE CHARLES, LA

JACKSON PARISH (portions)—See MONROE, LA

JEFFERSON DAVIS PARISH—See LAKE CHARLES, LA

KINDER—See LAKE CHARLES, LA

▲ **LAFAYETTE**—Wireless One of Lafayette

LAFAYETTE PARISH—See LAFAYETTE, LA

▲ **LAKE CHARLES**—Wireless One of Lake Charles

LECOMPTE—See BUNKIE, LA

LINCOLN PARISH (portions)—See MONROE, LA

LONGVILLE—See LAKE CHARLES, LA

LOREAUVILLE—See LAFAYETTE, LA

MAMOU—See BUNKIE, LA

MAUGHAM—See MONROE, LA

MARION—See MONROE, LA

MARKSVILLE—See BUNKIE, LA

MER ROUGE—See MONROE, LA

MITTIE—See LAKE CHARLES, LA

▲ **MONROE**—Wireless One of Monroe

MOREHOUSE PARISH—See MONROE, LA

MORROW—See BUNKIE, LA

NEW IBERIA PARISH—See LAFAYETTE, LA

OAK RIDGE—See MONROE, LA

OPELOUSAS—See BUNKIE, LA

OPELOUSAS—See also LAFAYETTE, LA

OUACHITA PARISH—See MONROE, LA

PALMETTO—See BUNKIE, LA

PINEVILLE—See BUNKIE, LA

RAGLEY—See LAKE CHARLES, LA

RAPIDES PARISH (portions)—See BUNKIE, LA

RAYNE—See LAFAYETTE, LA

▲ **RAYVILLE**—Cotton Country Cable

RAYVILLE—See also MONROE, LA

RICHLAND PARISH—See MONROE, LA

ROANOKE—See LAKE CHARLES, LA

RUSTON—See MONROE, LA

SIMMESPORT—See BUNKIE, LA

SINGER—See LAKE CHARLES, LA

ST. LANDRY—See BUNKIE, LA

ST. LANDRY PARISH (portions)—See BUNKIE, LA

ST. LANDRY PARISH (portions)—See also LAFAYETTE, LA

ST. MARTIN PARISH—See LAFAYETTE, LA

STARKS—See LAKE CHARLES, LA

SULPHUR—See LAKE CHARLES, LA

UNION PARISH—See MONROE, LA

VERMILION PARISH (portions)—See LAFAYETTE, LA

VICK—See BUNKIE, LA

VINTON—See LAKE CHARLES, LA

WASHINGTON—See BUNKIE, LA

WELSH—See LAKE CHARLES, LA

WEST CARROLL PARISH (portions)—See MONROE, LA

WEST MONROE—See MONROE, LA

YOUNGSVILLE—See LAFAYETTE, LA

MARYLAND

▲ **BALTIMORE**—People's Choice TV

MONTGOMERY COUNTY (portions)—See FAIRFAX, VA

PRINCE GEORGE'S COUNTY (portions)—See FAIRFAX, VA

MICHIGAN

▲ **BAY CITY &**

SAGINAW—Microcom

BERRIEN COUNTY—See MICHIANA, IN

CASS COUNTY—See MICHIANA, IN

DEARBORN—See DETROIT, MI

▲ **DETROIT**—People's Choice TV

GROSSE POINTE—See DETROIT, MI

▲ **JACKSON**—Wireless Cable Systems Inc.

▲ **LANSING**—American Telecasting of Lansing Inc.

▲ **MIDLAND**—Microcom

MONROE—See TOLEDO, OH

SOUTHFIELD—See DETROIT, MI

MINNESOTA

▲ **ALEXANDRIA**—Viking Vision

▲ **BARNESVILLE**—American Telecasting Inc.

BLUE EARTH COUNTY—See RUTHVEN, IA

▲ **CLARKFIELD**—US Cable of Minnesota

FARIBAULT COUNTY—See RUTHVEN, IA

LYND—See CLARKFIELD, MN

MARTIN COUNTY—See RUTHVEN, IA

MILROY—See CLARKFIELD, MN

▲ **MINNEAPOLIS/ST. PAUL**—OmniVision

PIPESTONE COUNTY (portions)—See COLMAN, SD

RUSSELL—See CLARKFIELD, MN

ST. JAMES—See WINDOM, MN

▲ **WINDOM**—American Telecasting of Minnesota Inc.

MISSISSIPPI

COLUMBUS—See STARKVILLE, MS

DELTA—See NATCHEZ, MS

GEORGE COUNTY (portions)—See BUCKS, AL

GREENE COUNTY (portions)—See BUCKS, AL

▲ **GULF COAST AREA**—Wireless One of Gulf Coast

▲ **HATTIESBURG**—Wireless One of Hattiesburg

INDIANOLA—See NATCHEZ, MS

▲ **INVERNESS**—Wireless One of Inverness

▲ **JACKSON**—Wireless One of Jackson

▲ **MERIDIAN**—Wireless One of Meridian

▲ **NATCHEZ**—Wireless One of Natchez

▲ **OXFORD**—Wireless One of Oxford

▲ **STARKVILLE**—Wireless One of Starkville

▲ **TUPELO**—Wireless One of Tupelo

MISSOURI

EAST PRAIRIE—See SIKESTON, MO

JEFFERSON COUNTY—See ST. LOUIS, MO

▲ **KANSAS CITY**—People's Choice TV

▲ **MALDEN**—Broadcast Cablevision

MALDEN—See also SIKESTON, MO

MINER—See SIKESTON, MO

▲ **MONROE CITY**—Nucentrix Broadband Networks Inc.

▲ **MONTGOMERY CITY**—Nucentrix Broadband Networks Inc.

PORTAGEVILLE—See SIKESTON, MO

▲ **SIKESTON**—Nucentrix Broadband Networks Inc.

ST. CHARLES COUNTY—See ST. LOUIS, MO

▲ **ST. LOUIS**—People's Choice TV of St. Louis

ST. LOUIS COUNTY—See ST. LOUIS, MO

MONTANA

▲ **BILLINGS**—American Telecasting of Billings Inc.

CARBON COUNTY (portions)—See BILLINGS, MT

YELLOWSTONE COUNTY (portions)—See BILLINGS, MT

NEBRASKA

▲ **BARTLEY**—Southwest Telecommunications

CHASE COUNTY—See WAUNETA, NE

FRONTIER COUNTY—See BARTLEY, NE

▲ **GENEVA**—American Telecasting of Grand Island/Geneva/Omaha

▲ **GRAND ISLAND**—American Telecasting of Grand Island/Geneva/Omaha

▲ **HUMBOLDT**—Time Warner Cable

▲ **KEARNEY**—Cable USA

▲ **LINCOLN**—American Telecasting of Nebraska Inc.

▲ **NORTH PLATTE**—Southwest Telecommunications

▲ **OMAHA**—Digital Broadcast Corp.

▲ **OSHKOSH**—Southwest Telecommunications

PAWNEE CITY—See HUMBOLDT, NE

TABLE ROCK—See HUMBOLDT, NE

TECUMSEH—See HUMBOLDT, NE

▲ **WAUNETA**—Southwest Telecommmunications

NEVADA

▲ **CARSON CITY**—Quadravision

▲ **LAS VEGAS**—Superchannels of Las Vegas

▲ **RENO**—Quadravision

NEW JERSEY

▲ **ATLANTIC CITY**—OrionVision

ATLANTIC COUNTY—See ATLANTIC CITY, NJ

CAPE MAY COUNTY—See ATLANTIC CITY, NJ

CUMBERLAND COUNTY—See ATLANTIC CITY, NJ

NEW MEXICO

▲ **ALBUQUERQUE**—Multimedia Development Corp.

▲ **LAS CRUCES**—Santa Fe Wireless Cable TV

▲ **ROSWELL**—Microwave Communication Services

▲ **SANTA FE**—Santa Fe Wireless Cable TV

NEW YORK

▲ **ALBANY**—Capital Choice Television Inc.

▲ **BROOKLYN**—CellularVision of New York

▲ **CAZENOVIA**—Selectavision of Cazenovia & Nelson Inc.

CAZENOVIA (village)—See CAZENOVIA, NY

FARMINGTON (town)—See ROCHESTER, NY

MONROE COUNTY (portions)—See ROCHESTER, NY

NELSON (town)—See CAZENOVIA, NY

▲ **NEW YORK**—Wireless Cable of New York

ONTARIO COUNTY (portions)—See ROCHESTER, NY

▲ **ROCHESTER**—Rochester Choice TV

WAYNE COUNTY (portions)—See ROCHESTER, NY

NORTH CAROLINA

▲ **CHARLOTTE**—CAI Wireless Systems Inc.

▲ **WILMINGTON**—Microwave Communication Services

NORTH DAKOTA

▲ **BOWBELLS**—Northwest Communications Cooperative

▲ **CARRINGTON**—Central Dakota TV Inc.

CAVALIER COUNTY—See LANGDON, ND

▲ **EPPING**—Northwest Communications Cooperative

▲ **FARGO**—American Telecasting of Barnesville

▲ **GRAND FORKS**—Microwave Communication Services

▲ **KILLDEER**—Consolidated Telephone Cooperative

▲ **LANGDON**—United Telephone Mutual Aid Corp.

▲ **LEFOR**—Consolidated Telephone Cooperative

▲ **MINOT**—Microwave Communication Services

PEMBINA COUNTY—See LANGDON, ND

RAMSEY COUNTY—See LANGDON, ND

ROLETT COUNTY—See LANGDON, ND

TOWNER COUNTY—See LANGDON, ND

WALSH COUNTY—See LANGDON, ND

OHIO

BOWLING GREEN—See TOLEDO, OH

BROOK PARK—See CLEVELAND, OH

BROOKLYN—See CLEVELAND, OH

BROOKLYN HEIGHTS—See CLEVELAND, OH

▲ **BUCYRUS**—Nucentrix Broadband Network Inc.

BUCYRUS—See also LYKENS, OH

CALEDONIA—See LYKENS, OH

▲ **CLEVELAND**—Popvision

COLUMBIANA COUNTY (portions)—See YOUNGSTOWN, OH

▲ **COLUMBUS**—American Telecasting of Columbus Inc.

▲ **DAYTON**—CS Wireless Systems Inc.

DEFIANCE COUNTY—See FORT WAYNE, IN

▲ **LIMA**—W.A.T.C.H. TV

▲ **LYKENS**—Nucentrix Broadband Networks Inc.

MAHONING COUNTY (portions)—See YOUNGSTOWN, OH

MAUMEE—See TOLEDO, OH

MIAMISBURG—See DAYTON, OH

▲ **MONROE TWP. (Miami County)**—Time Warner Cable

NEW WASHINGTON—See LYKENS, OH

NEWBURGH HEIGHTS—See CLEVELAND, OH

PAULDING COUNTY—See FORT WAYNE, IN

PERRYSBURG—See TOLEDO, OH

▲ **TOLEDO**—American Telecasting of Toledo

TRUMBULL COUNTY (portions)—See YOUNGSTOWN, OH

UPPER SANDUSKY—See LYKENS, OH

VAN WERT COUNTY—See FORT WAYNE, IN

▲ **YOUNGSTOWN**—American Telecasting of Youngstown Inc.

OKLAHOMA

▲ **ADA**—Nucentrix Broadband Networks Inc.

▲ **ARDMORE**—Nucentrix Broadband Networks Inc.

ARNETT—See WOODWARD, OK

▲ **CLAYTON**—Star Search Rural TV Inc.

DURANT—See TEXOMA, TX

▲ **ENID**—Nucentrix Broadband Networks Inc.

FORT SUPPLY—See WOODWARD, OK

GAGE—See WOODWARD, OK

▲ **KINGFISHER**—Nucentrix Broadband Networks

▲ **LAWTON**—Nucentrix Broadband Networks Inc.

▲ **LINDSAY**—Nucentrix Broadband Networks Inc.

MOORELAND—See WOODWARD, OK

▲ **MUSKOGEE**—Nucentrix Broadband Networks Inc.

MUTUAL—See WOODWARD, OK

▲ **OKLAHOMA CITY**—American Telecasting of Oklahoma City Inc.

SEILING—See WOODWARD, OK

SHARON—See WOODWARD, OK

SHATTUCK—See WOODWARD, OK

▲ **STILLWATER**—Nucentrix Broadband Networks Inc.

▲ **TULSA**—Nucentrix Broadband Networks Inc.

VICI—See WOODWARD, OK

▲ **WEATHERFORD**—Nucentrix Broadband Networks Inc.

▲ **WOODWARD**—Nucentrix Broadband Networks Inc.

OREGON

▲ **BEND**—American Telecasting of Bend

▲ **PRINEVILLE**—Central Vision

▲ **REDMOND**—Central Vision

PENNSYLVANIA

▲ **GREENVILLE**—Nucentrix Broadband Networks Inc.

MERCER COUNTY (portions)—See YOUNGSTOWN, OH

▲ **PHILADELPHIA**—Popvision

▲ **READING**—Digital Wireless Systems

SOUTH DAKOTA

▲ **ABERDEEN & BATH**—Northern Rural Cable TV Cooperative Inc.

AMHERST—See ABERDEEN & BATH, SD

ANDOVER—See ABERDEEN & BATH, SD

ASHTON—See ABERDEEN & BATH, SD

ATHOL—See ABERDEEN & BATH, SD

BARNARD—See ABERDEEN & BATH, SD

BROOKINGS COUNTY (portions)—See COLMAN, SD

BROWN COUNTY—See ABERDEEN & BATH, SD

CHELSEA—See ABERDEEN & BATH, SD

CLAREMONT—See ABERDEEN & BATH, SD

▲ **CLEAR LAKE**—HD Electric Cooperative

▲ **COLMAN**—Sioux Valley Wireless

COLUMBIA—See ABERDEEN & BATH, SD

CONDE—See ABERDEEN & BATH, SD

CRESBARD—See ABERDEEN & BATH, SD

DAY COUNTY (portions)—See ABERDEEN & BATH, SD

▲ **DE SMET**—Kingsbury Electric

EDMUNDS COUNTY (portions)—See ABERDEEN & BATH, SD

FAULK COUNTY (portions)—See ABERDEEN & BATH, SD

FERNEY—See ABERDEEN & BATH, SD

GROTON—See ABERDEEN & BATH, SD

HECLA—See ABERDEEN & BATH, SD

HOUGHTON—See ABERDEEN & BATH, SD

▲ **HURON**—Northeast TV Cooperative

IPSWICH—See ABERDEEN & BATH, SD

LAKE COUNTY (portions)—See COLMAN, SD

LANGFORD—See ABERDEEN & BATH, SD

LEOLA—See ABERDEEN & BATH, SD

LINCOLN COUNTY (portions)—See ROWENA, SD

MANSFIELD—See ABERDEEN & BATH, SD

MARSHALL COUNTY (portions)—See ABERDEEN & BATH, SD

McPHERSON COUNTY (portions)—See ABERDEEN & BATH, SD

MINA—See ABERDEEN & BATH, SD

MINNEHAHA COUNTY (portions)—See ROWENA, SD

MOODY COUNTY (portions)—See COLMAN, SD

PIERPOINT—See ABERDEEN & BATH, SD

PUTNEY—See ABERDEEN & BATH, SD

▲ **RAPID CITY**—American Telecasting

▲ **REDFIELD**—Spink Electric

▲ **ROWENA**—Sioux Valley Wireless

▲ **SISSETON**—Northeast TV Cooperative

SPINK COUNTY (portions)—See ABERDEEN & BATH, SD

STRATFORD—See ABERDEEN & BATH, SD

TURTON—See ABERDEEN & BATH, SD

VERDON—See ABERDEEN & BATH, SD

WARNER—See ABERDEEN & BATH, SD

▲ **WATERTOWN**—Northeast TV Cooperative

▲ **WEBSTER**—Lake Region Electric

WESTPORT—See ABERDEEN & BATH, SD

WETONKA—See ABERDEEN & BATH, SD

▲ **WILLOW LAKE**—Northeast TV Cooperative

▲ **YANKTON**—Sioux Valley Wireless

TENNESSEE

BEDFORD COUNTY—See TULLAHOMA, TN

BEERSHEBA SPRINGS—See TULLAHOMA, TN

BELL BUCKLE—See TULLAHOMA, TN

BLOUNT—See KNOXVILLE, TN

CANNON COUNTY—See TULLAHOMA, TN

▲ **CLARKSVILLE**—Digital Wireless Systems

COFFEE COUNTY—See TULLAHOMA, TN

DECHERD—See TULLAHOMA, TN

ESTILL SPRINGS—See TULLAHOMA, TN

FRANKLIN COUNTY—See TULLAHOMA, TN

GRUNDY COUNTY—See TULLAHOMA, TN

JEFFERSON—See KNOXVILLE, TN

KNOX—See KNOXVILLE, TN

▲ **KNOXVILLE**—Tennessee Wireless Inc.

▲ **LAWRENCEBURG**—Wireless One of Lawrenceburg

LOUDON—See KNOXVILLE, TN

LYNCHBURG—See TULLAHOMA, TN

MANCHESTER—See TULLAHOMA, TN

MARION COUNTY (portions)—See TULLAHOMA, TN

MONTEAGLE—See TULLAHOMA, TN

MORRISON—See TULLAHOMA, TN

▲ **NASHVILLE**—Nashville Wireless Associates

ROCKVALE—See TULLAHOMA, TN

RUTHERFORD COUNTY—See TULLAHOMA, TN

SHELBYVILLE—See TULLAHOMA, TN

SUMNER COUNTY—See NASHVILLE, TN

TRACY CITY—See TULLAHOMA, TN

▲ **TULLAHOMA**—Wireless One of Tullahoma

▲ **UNION CITY**—MetroVision

UNIONVILLE—See TULLAHOMA, TN

WARREN COUNTY—See TULLAHOMA, TN

WILLIAMSON COUNTY—See NASHVILLE, TN

WILSON COUNTY—See NASHVILLE, TN

WINCHESTER—See TULLAHOMA, TN

WOODBURY—See TULLAHOMA, TN

TEXAS

▲ **ABILENE**—Nucentrix Broadband Networks Inc.

▲ **AUSTIN**—Heartland Wireless Communications

AUSTIN COUNTY (portions)—See BRENHAM, TX

BELL COUNTY (portions)—See MILANO, TX

▲ **BIG COUNTRY**—Nucentrix Broadband Networks Inc.

BOWIE COUNTY—See TEXARKANA, TX

BRAZORIA COUNTY (portions)—See WHARTON, TX

BRAZOS COUNTY (portions)—See BRENHAM, TX

BRAZOS COUNTY (portions)—See also BRYAN, TX

▲ **BRENHAM**—Wireless One

▲ **BRYAN**—Wireless One of Bryan

BURLESON COUNTY (portions)—See BRENHAM, TX

BURLESON COUNTY (portions)—See also BRYAN, TX

BURLESON COUNTY (portions)—See also MILANO, TX

CAMERON—See MILANO, TX

CASS COUNTY—See TEXARKANA, TX

COLLEGE STATION—See BRYAN, TX

COLORADO CITY—See SNYDER, TX

COLORADO COUNTY (portions)—See BRENHAM, TX

COLORADO COUNTY (portions)—See also WHARTON, TX

▲ **CORPUS CHRISTI**—Nucentrix Broadband Networks Inc.

▲ **CORSICANA**—Nucentrix Broadband Networks Inc.

▲ **DALLAS**—Nucentrix Broadband Networks Inc.

EAGLE LAKE—See WHARTON, TX

EL CAMPO—See WHARTON, TX

FAYETTE COUNTY (portions)—See BRENHAM, TX

▲ **FORT WORTH**—CS Wireless Systems Inc.

▲ **FREEPORT**—Wireless One of Freeport

GAIL—See SNYDER, TX

▲ **GAINESVILLE**—Nucentrix Broadband Networks Inc.

GALVESTON (portions)—See HOUSTON, TX

▲ **GEORGE WEST**—Nucentrix Broadband Networks Inc.

GIDDINGS—See MILANO, TX

▲ **GOLDTHWAITE**—Central Texas Wireless

GRIMES COUNTY (portions)—See BRENHAM, TX

GRIMES COUNTY (portions)—See also BRYAN, TX

▲ **HAMILTON**—Nucentrix Broadband Networks Inc.

HEARNE—See MILANO, TX

HERMLEIGH—See SNYDER, TX

▲ **HOUSTON**—People's Choice TV of Houston

IRA—See SNYDER, TX

▲ **JOURDANTON**—Nucentrix Broadband Networks Inc.

▲ **KERRVILLE**—Nucentrix Broadband Networks Inc.

▲ **KINGSVILLE**—Nucentrix Broadband Networks Inc.

▲ **LAREDO**—Nucentrix Broadband Networks Inc.

LEE COUNTY—See MILANO, TX

LORAINE—See SNYDER, TX

▲ **LUBBOCK**—Nucentrix Broadband Networks Inc.

MADISON COUNTY (portions)—See BRYAN, TX

MATAGORDA COUNTY (portions)—See WHARTON, TX

▲ **MIDLAND**—Nucentrix Broadband Networks Inc.

MILAM COUNTY—See MILANO, TX

MILAM COUNTY (portions)—See BRYAN, TX

▲ **MILANO**—Wireless One of Milano

▲ **MOUNT PLEASANT**—Nucentrix Broadband Networks Inc.

NAVASOTA—See BRENHAM, TX

O'DONNEL—See LUBBOCK, TX

▲ **OLTON**—Nucentrix Broadband Networks Inc.

OLTON—See also LUBBOCK, TX

▲ **PARIS**—Nucentrix Broadband Networks Inc.

RICHMOND—See WHARTON, TX

ROBERTSON COUNTY (portions)—See BRYAN, TX

ROBERTSON COUNTY (portions)—See also MILANO, TX

ROBY—See SNYDER, TX

ROCKDALE—See MILANO, TX

ROSCOE—See SNYDER, TX

ROSENBERG—See WHARTON, TX

ROTAN—See SNYDER, TX

▲ **SAN ANGELO**—Sterling Wireless Cable

▲ **SAN ANTONIO**—CS Wireless Systems Inc.

SEALY—See WHARTON, TX

▲ **SNYDER**—Snyder Microwave Communications LC

SWEETWATER—See SNYDER, TX

▲ **TEMPLE**—Nucentrix Broadband Networks Inc.

▲ **TEXARKANA**—Nucentrix Broadband Networks Inc.

▲ **TEXOMA**—Nucentrix Broadband Networks Inc.

▲ **UVALDE**—Nucentrix Broadband Networks Inc.

▲ **WACO**—Nucentrix Broadband Networks Inc.

WALLER COUNTY (portions)—See BRENHAM, TX

WASHINGTON COUNTY (portions)—See BRENHAM, TX

WASHINGTON COUNTY (portions)—See also BRYAN, TX

WEST COLUMBIA—See WHARTON, TX

WESTBROOK—See SNYDER, TX

▲ **WHARTON**—Wireless One of Wharton

WHARTON COUNTY—See WHARTON, TX

▲ **WICHITA FALLS**—Nucentrix Broadband Networks Inc.

WILLIAMSON COUNTY (portions)—See MILANO, TX

UTAH

▲ **SALT LAKE CITY**—TechniVision Inc.

▲ **ST. GEORGE**—Sky-View Technologies

VERMONT

▲ **MOUNT ASCUTNEY**—New England Wireless Inc.

▲ **RUTLAND**—Satellite Signals of New England

VIRGINIA

ALBEMARLE COUNTY—See CHARLOTTESVILLE, VA

ALEXANDRIA—See FAIRFAX, VA

AMELIA COUNTY—See RICHMOND, VA

ARLINGTON COUNTY—See FAIRFAX, VA

AUGUSTA COUNTY—See HARRISONBURG, VA

BOTETOURT COUNTY—See ROANOKE, VA

BUCKINGHAM COUNTY—See CHARLOTTESVILLE, VA

CAROLINE COUNTY—See RICHMOND, VA

▲ **CHARLOTTESVILLE**—CFW Communications

CHESTERFIELD COUNTY—See RICHMOND, VA

DINWIDDIE COUNTY—See RICHMOND, VA

▲ **FAIRFAX**—Capitol Connection

FAIRFAX COUNTY—See FAIRFAX, VA

FLUVANNA COUNTY—See CHARLOTTESVILLE, VA

FRANKLIN COUNTY—See ROANOKE, VA

GOOCHLAND COUNTY (portions)—See CHARLOTTESVILLE, VA

GREENE COUNTY—See CHARLOTTESVILLE, VA

HANOVER COUNTY—See RICHMOND, VA

▲ **HARRISONBURG**—CFW Communications

KING WILLIAM COUNTY—See RICHMOND, VA

LOUISA COUNTY—See CHARLOTTESVILLE, VA

MONTGOMERY COUNTY—See ROANOKE, VA

NELSON COUNTY (portions)—See CHARLOTTESVILLE, VA

▲ **NORFOLK & VIRGINIA BEACH**—Hampton Roads Wireless

NOTTOWAY COUNTY—See RICHMOND, VA

ORANGE COUNTY—See CHARLOTTESVILLE, VA

PAGE COUNTY—See HARRISONBURG, VA

POWHATAN COUNTY—See RICHMOND, VA

PRINCE GEORGE COUNTY—See RICHMOND, VA

▲ **RICHMOND**—CFW Communications

▲ **ROANOKE**—R & B Cable

ROANOKE COUNTY—See ROANOKE, VA

ROCKINGHAM COUNTY—See HARRISONBURG, VA

WASHINGTON

▲ ***SEATTLE**—American Telecasting Inc.

▲ **SPOKANE**—Video Wave Television

▲ **YAKIMA**—Wireless Broadcasting Systems of Yakima Inc.

WISCONSIN

▲ **GREEN BAY**—American Telecasting of Green Bay

▲ **JANESVILLE**—Wireless Cable Systems Inc.

▲ **MADISON**—Skycable TV of Madison

WYOMING

▲ **SHERIDAN**—American Telecasting of Sheridan

PUERTO RICO

▲ **SAN JUAN**—WHTV Broadcasting Corp.

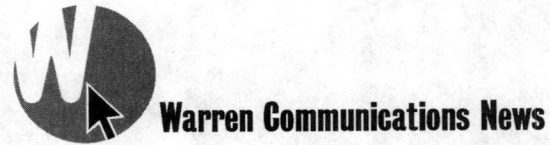